S0-AKM-101

Pratt's Guide to Private Equity & Venture Capital Sources

2011 Edition

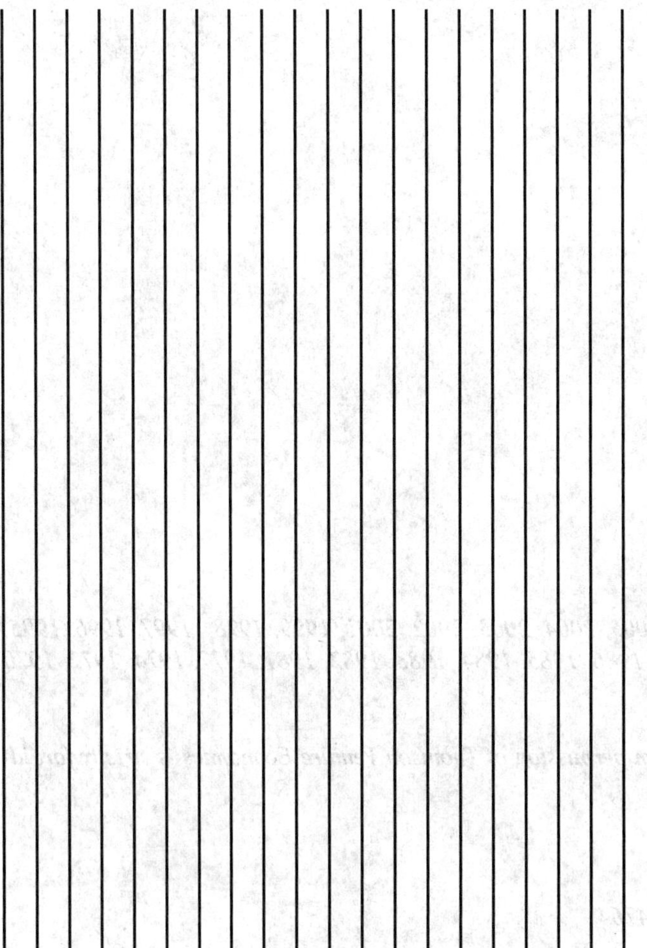

Pratt's

Guide to Private Equity & Venture Capital Sources

2011 Edition

Thomson Reuters
3 Times Square, 18th Floor
New York, NY 10036
Fax: 646-223-4470

For book orders call 800-455-5844
For access to Pratt's Guide Online
call greg Winterton at 646-223-6787
or email greg.winterton@thomsonreuters.com

Customer Service 1-646-223-6783

Eamon Beltran ....Research Editor
David Cooke ....Senior Art Director
Greg Winterton ....Manager, Subscription Sales
David Toll ....Editor
Jim Beecher................Publisher
Elizabeth Benson ......VP, Head of Private Equity and Desktop Products

2011 Edition

Printed in the United States of America
ISSN13 978-0-9796278-6-6
ISBN 0-9796278-6-9
Library of Congress Catalog Card Number 85-644764
Thomson Reuters

Preface

Worldwide, private equity has by definition thrived on principles of entrepreneurship and individual and collective risk-taking. In myriad ways, its development has sprung from the willingness to assume the risks involved in new business development. The imagination, boldness, and energy of entrepreneurs and small-business owners combined with the involvement and persistence of experienced private equity investors have helped create new industries and new technologies, which in turn have significantly increased the productivity of many economies and the workers involved in them.

This publication is dedicated both to the men and women who are willing to take on the challenges of building new businesses and also to those private equity investors with the skills, fortitude, and foresight to identify and participate in new business development. The contributions of the world's entrepreneurs are as important as ever as we seek to create new jobs and broaden our economic activities. With globalization increasing, this has become even more significant.

An important element in a successful private equity financing is a good relationship between the entrepreneur and the investor. Understanding this partnership is a necessary initial step for the prospective entrepreneur. The entrepreneur brings fresh ideas, management skills, and personal commitment to this relationship, while the private equity investor adds financial backing and valuable new business development experience. Although the entrepreneur and the management team are usually the most crucial elements in the relationship (especially since private equity investors cannot perform their roles without entrepreneurs), the collaboration of entrepreneurial management and private equity investors usually enables a developing business to achieve its objectives faster and more efficiently. In today's dynamic and competitive marketplace such an investor/management partnership is often vital to the survival and success of new business development.

Private equity has acted as a catalyst for economies worldwide by igniting the flames of expansion.

The amount of private equity raised internationally remains a fraction of the asset base of entities such as commercial banks and insurance companies. In the United States, certain state pension funds control more money than the entire domestic private equity industry.

As a result, the private equity process involves a personal relationship, which can either grow and endure or end in frustration and disappointment.

In the future, companies that have received private equity financing will require continued financial support to fuel their growth. These follow-on investments, which constitute a large part of current private equity activity, as well as the commitments to new investment opportunities, will absorb the capital currently available in the industry, including any "dry powder", or capital raised, but not yet invested. As these commitments are made, the demand for private equity will intensify. This book was conceived and has grown over the last 34 years by helping to increase the entrepreneur's chances of success in receiving funding. It provides the most thorough analysis of what each private equity firm can and will provide to fledgling businesses. It is our hope that by organizing and simplifying this process, we can help you get the right financing for your business idea.

Table of Contents

Introduction

This is the 35th edition of *Pratt's Guide to Private Equity & Venture Capital Sources*, a directory long considered to be the industry benchmark. The goal of this publication is to incorporate the most current information on individual private equity and venture capital firms as well as the private equity investment process.

This current edition contains over 5,500 listings, including firms from around the world. Our collection of data has continued to increase with the inclusion of the research efforts of PricewaterhouseCoopers, with which in 2002 one of Thomson Reuters predecessors, Thomson Financial, together with the National Venture Capital Association jointly conducted the quarterly MoneyTree™ data collection report.

Pratt's Guide was created as a practical tool to help entrepreneurs and small-business managers understand the process of raising capital and locating compatible private equity investors.

Both information on the industry and guidelines for companies seeking financing are provided in the articles written by professional private equity investors who discuss important aspects of private equity financing and describe criteria for investments. The text is divided into four sections: "Background on Private Equity," "How to Raise Private Equity," "Sources of Business Development Financing," and "Perspectives."

"Background on Private Equity" is designed to help prospective entrepreneurs understand the private equity investment process. The nature of a private equity investor's involvement is described as well as the characteristics of successful entrepreneurial management teams.

This section includes "Characteristics of a Successful Entrepreneurial Management Team" by Alexander L.M. Dingee, Brian Haslett, and Leonard E. Smollen and also contains articles on value creation and acquiring distressed entities.

The articles in "How to Raise Private Equity" are written by industry professionals whose goal is to expedite the investing process for the investor as well as the entrepreneur by clearly laying out realistic expectations and standard procedures for approaching a private equity investor.

The information in "Sources of Business Development Financing" describes private- and public-sector financing opportunities. Private equity sources include private partnerships and corporations, publicly held venture firms, venture capital funds formed by banks and bank holding companies, LBO firms, divisions of major corporations, affiliates of investment banking firms, venture leasing companies and direct private equity investment activity by insurance companies, pension funds or investment advisory firms.

The articles in "Perspectives" provide insight into the characteristics private equity investors look for in their clients, as well as an entrepreneur's view of the private equity process. Understanding the different facets of the private equity development process will increase the chances of establishing a productive working relationship with a private equity investor, which can be critical to a company's success or failure.

The venture capital segment of private equity financing was traditionally regarded as early-stage financing for relatively small, rapidly growing companies. Today, more than ever, venture investment activity encompasses an entire spectrum of interests including virtually all phases of business growth, including those of more mature companies. In addition to early-stage funding, private equity investors provide expansion financing for companies that have overcome initial hurdles and require additional capital for growth, but that do not yet have access to public or credit-oriented institutional funding. Lines have been blurred as venture capitalists, together with entrepreneurs and the management of companies, also finance leveraged buyouts, which may involve purchasing ailing corporate divisions or absentee-owned private businesses with the objective of revitalizing them.

The listings of names following the articles contain detailed information on private equity companies on a global basis.

Since various terms are mentioned throughout the text and in the directories, it is important that these terms are clearly defined.

Early-Stage Financing

• *Seed Financing* is generally a relatively small amount of capital provided to an inventor or entrepreneur to prove a concept and to qualify for start-up capital. This may involve product development and market research as well as building a management team and developing a business plan, if the initial steps are successful.

• *Research and Development Financing* is a taxadvantaged partnership set up to finance product development for start-ups as well as more mature companies. Investors secure tax write-offs for the investments as well as a later share of the profits if the product development is successful.

• *Start-up Financing* is provided to companies completing product development and initial marketing. Companies may be in the process of organizing or they may already be in business for one year or less, but have not sold their product commercially. Usually such firms will have made market studies, assembled the key management, developed a business plan and are ready to do business.

• *First-Stage Financing* is provided to companies that have expended their initial capital (often in developing and market testing a prototype), and require funds to initiate full-scale manufacturing and sales.

Expansion Financing

• *Second-Stage Financing* is working capital for the initial expansion of a company that is producing and shipping, and has growing accounts receivable and inventories. Although the company has made progress, it may not yet be showing a profit.

• *Third-Stage or Mezzanine Financing* is provided for major expansion of a company whose sales volume is increasing and that is breaking even or profitable. These funds are used for further plant expansion, marketing, working capital, or development of an improved product.

• *Bridge Financing* is needed at times when a company plans to go public within six months to a year. Often bridge financing is structured so that it can be repaid from the proceeds of a public underwriting. It can also involve restructuring of major stockholder positions through secondary transactions. Restructuring is undertaken if there are early investors who want to reduce or liquidate their positions, or if management has changed and the stockholdings of the former management, their relatives and associates are being bought out to relieve a potential oversupply of stock when public.

• *Balanced* is a venture strategy in which a variety of venture stages of development are invested in or there is no stated venture focus.

Acquisition/Buyout Financing

• Acquisition Financing provides funds to finance an acquisition of another company.

• *Management/Leveraged Buyout* funds enable an operating management group to acquire a product line or business (which may be at any stage of development) from either a public or private company; often these companies are closely held or family owned.

Management/leveraged buyouts usually involve revitalizing an operation, with entrepreneurial management acquiring a significant equity interest.

• *Industry Rollups* are financings that are involved in acquiring companies within the same industry category.

• *Control-block Purchases* are investments in which at least 50% of company's outstanding shares are acquired.

Other Financings

• *Generalist PE* refers to either a stated focus of investing in all stages of private equity investment (not just venture) or a fund considered to be a generalist by its investment record when it has no one investment focus.

• *Fund of funds* have direct investments that consist of investments in other private equity funds.

• *Recapitalization*s consist of financing provided for turnaround situations, particularly for distressed companies.

• *Special Situations* is a catchall category consisting of financings that do not apply to more specific categories.

• *Private Placement* financings consist of acquiring shares of publicly traded companies in privately placed issuances, as opposed to acquiring them on the open market.

• *Public Companies* are financings of publicly traded companies that occur in the open market.

• *Distressed Debt* financings consist of investing in the debt of companies that have either filed for bankruptcy or are likely to do so in the future.

• *Turnaround* financings involve investing in companies at a time of operational or financial difficulty with the intention of improving the company's performance.

Each company seeking financing and its advisors must determine the type of private equity firm best suited for their specific investment situation. Each private equity firm has particular preferences, methods of investing and selecting investments, and its own type of legal investment agreements. Since no two private equity firms operate exactly in the same way, it is essential that entrepreneurs and business managers analyze their needs and attempt to match these requirements with the skills and interests of an appropriate private equity firm.

While the private equity firms included in *Pratt's Guide* have been selected because they are devoted primarily to private equity financing, there is no assurance that a specific group will be receptive to an approach or will have immediately available funds. At present, however, most private equity investors are actively seeking new investment opportunities. Even with the current availability of investment capital, the majority of new investment proposals are not financed. Convincing private equity investors that a potential development is an important investment opportunity is truly a new company's first major sale. Further, a good working relationship must be established and maintained to optimize the benefits of a private equity investment.

The private equity firms in this directory have different capacities for servicing client companies and it is critical for the entrepreneur or business management to understand these capabilities. Some firms can provide a range of financial and managerial services, while others may have specialized talents that would be valuable to some new businesses, but less important to others.

Both the nature and extent of active involvement private equity investors put into their investments vary. For the most part, the most successful investors nee to be actively involved in the companies they finance. While the directories in Pratt's Guide attempt to delineate preferences as well as levels of activity and involvement, the entrepreneur and management team must develop a means of evaluating the ongoing role of the private equity investor.

Generally, private equity firms are not interested in reviewing situations that are clearly not going to meet their stated preferences. Consequently, a careful review of the information in the text and in the directories should help capital seekers begin to develop a productive investment relationship with the firms.

Background of Private Equity

Previously, private equity was considered a private industry with a low profile. Although the national media gave increased attention to LBO transactions in the midto late-1980s and to the venture capital process during the 1980s and early-1990s, misconceptions about the industry continue to proliferate even today, particularly with the reaction of the stock market to technology stocks in 2000 and the subsequent downturn for the next couple of years. One of the objectives of this publication is to provide a realistic view of what the entrepreneur can expect from venture financing, what the business management and ownership can expect from LBO financing, and what can be expected from a long-term relationship with professional private equity investors.

The qualities of entrepreneurs are examined in "Characteristics of an Entrepreneurial Management Team," which outlines the characteristics needed to create and grow a new venture. Also included are criteria that can be used to judge a new venture's viability and its potential risks.

"Acquiring a Financially Troubled Company in Financially Troubled Times" provides insight into the special considerations that must be taken into account using buyout financing to acquire distressed companies. This field provides unique opportunities that require unique methodologies.

Understanding the operations of the private equity industry and the process of new business development, as well as the individual roles involved, is critical to anyone seeking private equity financing.

Characteristics of a Successful Entrepreneurial Management Team

Alexander L. M. Dingee, Brian Haslett and Leonard E. Smollen

Alexander L. M. Dingee *is the Chairman of the M.I.T. Venture Mentoring Service, which supports innovation and entrepreneurial activity throughout the M.I.T. community by matching prospective entrepreneurs with volunteer mentors. Mr. Dingee is also the Chairman and a founder of Kortec, Inc. Previously he served as a Founder, Director and Treasurer of Nexabit Networks, Inc. Mr. Dingee has also been the founding CEO of Venture Founders Corporation, Geodyne Corporation, and Massey Dickinson, Inc. He is a co-author of the textbook New Venture Creation.*

Brian Haslett *was a cofounder of Venture Founders Corporation and played a lead role in establishing its U.K. subsidiary and in helping many American and British entrepreneurs create and finance their new enterprises. He subsequently was a contributor to Venture Capital Journal. Mr. Haslett died in 1985.*

Leonard E. Smollen *was executive vice president and a cofounder of Venture Founders Corporation, a private company that manages venture capital funds. Currently, Mr. Smollen provides consulting services to new ventures and venture capital partnerships.*

What are the personal characteristics required to be a successful entrepreneur? Before making the personal sacrifices required to start and build a major enterprise, would-be entrepreneurs should engage in serious soul-searching to be sure they have what it takes to thrive in the toughest jungle of the business world.

To assist in this introspection, the following guidelines have been prepared by principals of Venture Founders Corporation (VFC).

Venture capitalists say they prefer a grade A entrepreneur with a grade B business idea to a grade B entrepreneur with a grade A idea. And it is generally a strong management team not a lone entrepreneur that they back.

With that in mind, there are some initial questions that would-be entrepreneurs must consider: Do I have adequate commitment, motivation and skills to start and build a major business—to be a successful entrepreneur? Does my management team have the necessary skills to enable us to succeed in building a particular venture? And finally, do I have a viable idea?

If these questions can be answered affirmatively, then it may be wise to consider developing a business plan and beginning a search for venture capital. This, however, is only the first step of the entrepreneurial self-examination process.

Am I an Entrepreneur?

A good way to answer this question is by objectively comparing yourself to a successful entrepreneur. Begin by studying the following characteristics that successful entrepreneurs, venture capitalists and behavioral scientists say are important for success.

Drive and energy level: A successful entrepreneur must have the ability to work long hours for sustained periods with less than the normal amount of sleep.

Self-confidence: A belief in yourself and your ability to achieve your goals and a sense that events in your life are self-determined is essential.

Setting challenging but realistic goals: The ability to set clear goals and objectives that are challenging, yet realistic and attainable.

Long-term involvement: A commitment to projects that will reach completion in four to seven years and to work towards distant goals. This means total dedication to the business and to attaining these goals.

Using money as a performance measure: Money, in the form of salary, profits, or capital gains, should be viewed more as a measure of how the company is doing rather than as an end in itself.

Persistent problem solving: You must have an intense and determined desire to solve problems toward the completion of tasks.

Taking moderate risks: Entrepreneurial success is generally the result of calculated risk-taking that provides a reasonable and challenging chance of success.

Learning from failure: Understanding your role in a failure can be instrumental in avoiding similar problems in the future. A failure may be disappointing, but should not be discouraging.

Using criticism: You need to be able to seek and use criticism of the style and substance of your performance.

Taking initiative and seeking personal responsibility: You need to seize opportunities and put yourself in situations where you are personally responsible for success or failure. You should be able to take the initiative to solve problems or fill leadership vacuums. You should enjoy being involved in situations where your impact on a problem can be measured.

Making good use of resources: Can you identify and use expertise and assistance that is relevant to the accomplishment of your goals? You should not be so involved in the achievement of your goals and in independent accomplishment that you will not let anyone help you.

Competing against self-imposed standards: Do you tend to establish your own standard of performance, which is high yet realistic, and then compete with yourself?

No one individual possesses all these attributes. Weaknesses can be compensated for through other members of your management team. Do remember, though, you are the most critical risk. Rate yourself on each of these key characteristics "strong," "average," or "weak" compared with others you know and respect. Be as honest and accurate as you can. If you think you are average or weak on most of them, then do yourself, your family, and your would-be business associates a favor—do not start a business.

If you rate yourself high on most traits, this may be unrealistic and therefore you should review these ratings with people who know you well. Spouses, teachers, peers, and professional advisors are all likely to view you differently, both in terms of your past accomplishments and your potential. Take time with each reviewer to explain why you rate yourself as you do. Be prepared to alter your ratings in light of their opinions. If people you know tell you that you are likely to fail as an entrepreneur, they may be right. But both of you should be aware that making such an evaluation realistically is no quick-and-dirty task.

Once you believe you have an adequate assessment of yourself, think back on personal experiences that demanded entrepreneurial strengths. Reflect on these incidences and see if you acted in a manner consistent with your rating.

If you are convinced that you have the entrepreneurial wherewithal to start and build a business, you must now evaluate your management skills to determine your abilities and those that your management team must have. To this end, you should systematically audit your managerial experience and accomplishments in marketing and sales; operations; research, development, and engineering; finance and accounting; general management and administration; personnel; and the legal and tax aspects of business. To rate yourself, we suggest the following standards.

Strong	=	Know thoroughly and have proven ability
Average	=	Have limited knowledge and accomplishments and will need backup perhaps part-time
Weak	=	Unfamiliar and need someone's full-time skills

The different nature of each element makes it unlikely for individuals to be equally strong in all elements of these seven functions. For example, a powerful direct salesperson probably will not show equal strength in market research and evaluation.

Before giving yourself an overall rating on each of these functions, we suggest that you break them down to the principal elements and rate yourself on each element. Note that the critical elements of any function may vary with each venture: the marketing and sales function includes market research and evaluation and marketing planning as well as sales management and merchandising, direct selling, service, and distribution. The latter will not be critical if you market through distributors.

A listing and brief description of representative elements of all seven functions is presented at the end of this article.

For a more objective evaluation, you may want to review your management skills with former and current supervisors, peers and subordinates, who may all see a different side of you. After thoroughly evaluating your entrepreneurial traits and your management skills, you should be able to determine the personal risks you will run if you try to create a business.

If your dream is to build a multimillion-dollar business, it might also be wise to check your evaluation with one or more of the professionals who are active and respected in the fields of career counseling and entrepreneurial behavior. A man with a weak heart may only ask his wife about taking a gentle stroll up a small grassy hill, but he would be wise to consult a doctor before trying to climb a mountain.[1]

Does My Team Have the Necessary Complementary Skills?

Research into successful ventures shows that teams perform better than one individual. Knowing this, venture capitalists always look for a balanced team. So your next task is to analyze the business you are contemplating and determine what abilities and skills are critical to its success in the first two to three years. Then set about building a management team that includes people who are strong where you are weak.

In a new company, you may not need or be able to afford full-time staff to perform all functions. It is, however, important to choose part-time people carefully, since you may want some of them to come on board later. Avoid teaming up with a school friend whom you only know in casual situations or a colleague in the lab or office whose skills match your own. Although these collaborations are tempting, they rarely work out, and venture capitalists may be put off by a team that is made up of all engineers, salespeople or relatives.[2]

Do I Have a Viable Idea?

Imagine yourself a venture capitalist who has just analyzed the few hundred business proposals examined last year. Your analysis shows that you handled the various proposals in these ways.

1. Sixty percent were rejected after a 20-to-30 minute scanning.
2. Another quarter were discarded after a lengthier review.
3. About 15% were investigated in depth and two-thirds of those were dismissed because of serious flaws in the management team or the business plan that could not be easily resolved.
4. Of the 5% that were viable investment opportunities, terms acceptable to the entrepreneur(s) and other existing stock holders were negotiated in only 3%.

The 15% that were investigated in depth were presented by strong, well-balanced management teams who were able to show you relevant accomplishments in marketing, finance and operations and had developed (perhaps with some prodding by you) a comprehensive business plan.

As an entrepreneur, think what that venture capitalist's analysis means to you: there is a three-in-one-hundred chance of securing capital from any one source on terms acceptable to you and the investor and only a 15% chance of being considered seriously for investment, and a comprehensive business plan is usually required to qualify for such consideration.

So if you are really serious about going into business for yourself, you should start to develop a comprehensive business plan. If the plan is done properly and completely, it will probably take you 150 to 300 hours of intense work. Even when it is done, there is no guarantee that you will raise enough investment capital.

Is there any way to avoid going to all this effort only to have your plan rejected after a 20-minute perusal? Try seeing your business idea through the objective, critical eyes of a venture capitalist.

Before developing a business plan, it is important to

---

1. For a discussion and appraisal of such evaluation, see "Business Leadership training:
2. For further discussion, see "The Entrepreneurial Team: Formation and Development" by Jeffrey A. Timmons, D.B.A., a competitive paper presented at the annual Academy of Management meeting in 1973.

answer the questions that venture capitalists may have on their minds when they review a plan to determine if it is worth studying and calling a meeting to discuss. The first question: What exactly will be sold to whom? Other key market questions are:

- Why will the customer buy your product?
- Who are the ultimate users and what influences on their purchasing habits are beyond your control?
- Who is the competition? Are they profitable now? Why do you think you can successfully compete with them?
- Is the market large and growing? Does it offer a multimillion-dollar potential for your company?
- Are you or will you be in a recognized growth industry?

You should then answer several questions about the other major aspects of the business you contemplate, questions about your team, your financial needs and the risks you are running. Such questions may include:

- What is the maximum amount of dollars and length of time that will be needed before your product is ready for market?
- What is the depth of your team's knowledge and extent of their reputations in the types of markets, technologies and operations in which you will be active?
- What are your team's management skills in the three key areas of marketing, finance and operations?
- How many unproven marketing, technical and manufacturing approaches do you contemplate?
- What are the strengths, weaknesses and major risks of your venture?

Careful thought about these areas should enable you to take a reasonable first look at your own venture ideas and to evaluate the potential for success as well as the major risks. The risks in any entrepreneurial venture are you, the entrepreneur, your team and any fundamental flaws in your venture idea. You should then be able to put together a business plan and avoid many of the early errors (for example, team inadequacies; underpricing; weak cash management) that so often cripple new ventures. You should also be able to improve your chances of securing financing and launching a successful venture.

Representative Elements of Seven Management Functions

1. Marketing and sales

a. *Market research and evaluation:* Ability to design and conduct market research studies and to analyze and interpret study results; familiarity with questionnaire design and sampling techniques.

b. *Strategic sales:* Experience in developing marketing strategies and establishing forces and then planning appropriate sales, advertising and promotional programs and setting up an effective network distributor or sales representative organization.

c. *Sales management and merchandising:* Ability in organizing, supervising, motivating and providing merchandising support to a direct sales force; analyzing territory and sales potential; and managing a sales force to obtain a target share of the market.

d. *Direct sales:* Experience in identifying, meeting and developing new customers, demonstrated success in closing sales.

e. *Service:* Experience in identifying service needs of particular products and in determining service and spare parts requirements, handling customer complaints, and managing a service organization.

f. *Distribution management:* Ability to organize and manage the flow of the product from manufacturing through distribution channels to the ultimate customer, including familiarity with shipping costs, scheduling techniques, carriers, etc.

g. *Overall marketing skills:* Give yourself a combined rating reflecting your skill level across all of the above marketing areas.

2. Operations

a. Manufacturing management: Knowledge of the production processes, machines, manpower, and space requirements to produce the product; experience in managing production to produce products within time, cost, and quality constraints.

b. *Inventory control:* Familiarity with techniques of controlling inprocess and finished goods inventories of materials.

c. *Quality control:* Ability to set up inspection systems and standards for effective control of quality in incoming, in-process and finished materials.

d. *Purchasing:* Ability to identify appropriate sources of supply, the amount of material in inventory, familiarity with economical order quantities and discount advantage.

e. *Overall operations skills:* Give yourself a combined rating reflecting your skill level across all of the above operations areas.

3. Research, development and engineering

a. *Direction and management of applied research:* Ability to distinguish and keep a prudent balance between long-range projects at the frontiers of your technology, which attract the most creative individuals, and shorter range research in support of current product development activity.

b. *Management of development:* Ability to plan and direct work of development engineers and to use time and cost budgets so that perfectionists do not ruin you and yet product performance, appearance, and production engineering needs can be met; ability to distinguish between bread-board, field and pre-production prototype programs.

c. *Management of engineering:* Ability to plan and direct engineers in the final design of a new product for manufacture and in the engineering and testing of the production process to manufacture that new product.

d. *Technical know-how:* Ability to contribute personally to research, development, and/or engineering because of up-to-date in-depth knowledge of the technologies in which your company is involved.

e. *Overall research, development, and engineering skills:* Give yourself a combined rating reflecting your skill level across the above areas.

4. Financial management

a. *Raising capital:* Ability to decide how best to acquire funds for start-up and growth; ability to forecast the need for funds and to prepare budgets; familiarity with sources and vehicles of short- and long-term financing.

b. *Money management:* Ability to design, install, maintain, use financial controls; familiarity with accounting and control systems needed to manage; ability to set up a project cost control system, analyze overhead/contribution/absorption, prepare profit and loss and balance sheets, and manage a bookkeeper.

c. *Specific skills:* Cash flow analysis; break-even analysis; contribution analysis; budgeting and profit-planning techniques; profit and loss, balance sheet, and present value analysis of return on investment and payback.

d. *Overall financial skills:* Give yourself a combined rating reflecting your skill level across all of the above financial areas.

5. General management and administration

a. *Strategic planning and carryout:* Ability to see the big picture complete with a carryout strategy and believably carry this vision to cofounders, staff and employees, customers, financiers, media and pundits.

b. *Problem solving:* Ability to anticipate potential problems and plan to avoid them; ability to gather facts about problems, analyze them for real causes, and plan effective action to solve problems; thoroughness in dealing with the details of particular problems and in follow-through.

c. *Communications:* Ability to communicate effectively and clearly, both in speech and in writing, to the media, the public, customers, peers, and subordinates.

d. *Planning:* Ability to set realistic and attainable goals, identify obstacles to achieving the goals and develop detailed action plans to achieve those goals; ability to schedule own time very systematically.

e. *Decision making:* Ability to make decisions on your best analysis of incomplete data.

f. *Project management:* Skill in organizing project teams, setting project goals, defining project tasks, and monitoring task completion in the face of problems and cost/quality constraints.

g. *Negotiating:* Ability to work effectively in a negotiating situation; ability to quickly balance value given and value received.

h. *Personnel administration:* Ability to set up payroll, hiring, compensation, and training functions.

i. *Overall administrative skills:* Give yourself a combined rating reflecting your skill level across all of the above administrative areas.

6. Personnel management

a. *Leadership:* Ability to understand the relationships between tasks, the leader, and the followers; ability to lead in situations where it is appropriate; willingness to manage actively, supervise, and control activities of others through directions, suggestions, inspiration, and other techniques.

b. *Listening:* Ability to listen to and understand without interrupting or mentally preparing your own rebuttal at the expense of hearing the message.

c. *Helping:* Ability to ask for and provide help and to determine situations where assistance is warranted.

d. *Criticism:* Ability to provide performance and interpersonal criticism to others that they find useful; ability to receive feedback from others without becoming defensive or argumentative.

e. *Conflict resolution:* Ability to confront differences openly and to deal with them until resolution is obtained.

f. *Teamwork:* Ability to work well with others in pursuing common goals.

g. *Selecting and developing subordinates:* Ability to select and delegate responsibility to subordinates and to coach them in the development of their managerial capabilities.

h. *Climate building:* Ability to create, by the way you manage, a climate and spirit conducive to high performance; ability to press for higher performance while rewarding work well done.

i. *Overall interpersonal skills:* Give yourself a combined rating reflecting your skill level across all of the above personnel management areas.

7. Legal and tax aspects

a. *Corporate law:* Familiarity with legal issues relating to stock issues, incorporation, distribution agreements, leases, etc.

b. *Contract law:* Familiarity with contract procedures and requirements (government and commercial), including default, warranty, and incentive provisions; fee structures; overhead, general and administrative expenses allowable, and so forth.

c. *Patent law:* Experience with preparation and revision of patent applications; ability to recognize a strong patent; familiarity with claim requirements. Familiarity with copyright and trade secret law.

d. *Tax law:* Familiarity with general state and federal reporting requirements for businesses and with special provisions concerning Subchapter S corporations, tax shelters, fringe benefits, etc.

e. *Overall legal and tax skills:* Give yourself a combined rating reflecting your skill level across all of the above legal and tax areas.

Acquiring a Financially Troubled Company in Financially Troubled Times

James M. Hill, Ira C. Kaplan and William I. Kohn

James M. Hill, Ira C. Kaplan and William I. Kohn *are partners with the law firm of Benesch Friedlander Coplan & Aronoff LLP. Mr. Hill and Mr. Kaplan are members of the firm's Corporate and Securities Practice Group. Mr. Kohn is the Chair of the firm's Business Reorganization Practice Group. All are resident in the firm's Cleveland office.*

In today's near-recession landscape, finding financially troubled companies doesn't take binoculars or a kaleidoscope. Many manufacturers of consumer durables, including suppliers to the automotive industry, construction (direct and indirect, i.e., appliances) and major service providers from international banks, insurance companies and investment houses are all in play as cash flows become trickles, supplier and customer bases shrink and there are no sources of succor on the horizon.

Today's market may create a terrible time to sell ? but it may be one of the best times to buy. As a purchaser, you will not get the best price on an umbrella in a rainstorm, but you may get a bargain if you buy while the sun is shining.

Why Seek a Transaction

Opportunistic owners can view the current unsettled market as the perfect chance to build market share or enter a new market at the potentially lowest cost and strategically place themselves to greatly capitalize on their bargain acquisitions as the economic cycle turns.

So why should a company poised to ride out the current downturn look to acquire?

Strategic assets may not be available for sale in the market in better times;

Strategic assets will certainly not be available at current pricing if investment money becomes more available, the appetite for commercial lending returns and, in such an improved environment, additional competitors are drawn to the same targets.

Special Considerations in Acquiring a Distressed Business

The acquisition of a distressed business has its own unique difficulties: a prospective suitor needs to conduct careful due diligence to ascertain the motivation of the seller (lack of liquidity or is the product about to become obsolete?), key elements of the business (sole source supplier about to be liquidated or major customer just developed a new replacement technology?) or another target is the real dominant player in the sector. Also key for the due diligence effort is to confirm the sources creating the financial difficulty of the target, are they incurable such as those suggested above, or is it a matter that a different operating model under new leadership which the potential acquiring company is confident it can provide, will cure?

When considering the purchase of a distressed company, however, there is a critical competing element to the extensive due diligence of a potential transaction ? TIME.

If the target if financially distressed, time may quickly dissipate the target's ability to be salvaged ? customers will flee, key personnel will obtain alternate employment and the goal of the acquisition may not be realized.

Moving to a Deal

The move to acquisition of a financially troubled business requires several deliberate but prompt actions:

Assemble an Acquisition Team. The purchasing company will want to team with professionals who will work seamlessly with company representatives and have transactional experience with the special issues arising in a situation where the target may be (or just as risky ? determined later to be) an insolvent company. The Team will, therefore, be comprised of the company's experienced management to evaluate the quality of the target's management and operational systems and to determine "real" not "logical" cost savings from potential "synergies." The legal aspect of the Team must include seasoned transactional attorneys who can bring focus on the material aspects of a time-sensitive due diligence effort and experienced creditors' and debtors' rights counsel to help guide the parties to a prompt closing.

In determining the purchase price the appropriate legal payment priorities recognizing the rights of creditors must be considered.

A company cannot transfer its property free and clear of liens unless the secured creditor agrees to release its liens upon receiving a discounted payment. Similarly, shareholders cannot receive payment for transferring their interests if general creditors are going to remain unpaid. These principals require that most acquisitions of financially troubled companies are "asset purchases" rather than a "stock purchase" transaction.

As part of the due diligence process, understanding who is determining the urgency of a transaction can be quite telling. If the major working capital lender is forcing the sale because of a default in the target's working capital line, the company may be under threat of closure and the seller's anticipated sale price will be greatly discounted to avoid the threat of liquidation.

The price may also reflect if the prospective purchaser is a financial buyer who is looking to enter an industry and needs to buy the target fairly much intact with both supplier sources and customer groups being satisfied at closing that there will be an appropriate distribution to suppliers and a recognition of warranties and other customer obligations to maintain market share.

The Acquisition Team should, early in the process, structure a "liquidation analysis" of the target company. This analysis reasonably estimates a closed company's value with regard to the sale of its facilities (discounted by holding costs such as taxes, security, insurance and sales commission), the orderly liquidation value in place of the equipment (discounted by auction costs), the value of inventory (little for raw and work in progress) and receivable collections (less discounting for warranty loss and perhaps other contractual rights such as advertising allowances).

Once the asset side of the ledger has been estimated, then potential distributions to creditors starting with those with liens on some or all of the liquidating assets will be subtracted leading to a percentage payment, if any, to the general creditors of the troubled company.

Practical issues which must also be considered is the existence of personal guarantees of any of the target's principals for any segment of the company's indebtedness, the nature of pending suits and the status of the company's tax liabilities (which may, depending on the nature of the unpaid tax, be a lien on some or all of the company's assets or create personal liabilities for some of the company's officers).

Other aspects impacting price consideration, and even whether or not to buy, include analysis of the target's standing within its market and its reputation with its customers. Interviews with key customers are important as is understanding existing and likely competitors and their financial strength.

In addition to the market study, a careful analysis of operations must also be undertaken. Most financially troubled companies cut maintenance and delay capital improvements. Remaining useful life of equipment may be an issue as well as whether the company has maintained the state of the art technology for its production which will determine if the sale prices of the target's products will be competitive in the marketplace.

For most companies, their most valuable assets are their employees, including knowledgeable and loyal middle management and an experienced line crew who know the product and how to produce efficiently. Most employee claims are protected under both state and federal law and any plan premised on significant labor savings, particularly wage cuts, must realistically consider the effect on productivity and turnover. Maintaining key personnel may also become conditions to a final transaction and must be considered as an economic item in the purchase negotiations.

Legal due diligence is particularly critical in a financially troubled financial situation. Warranties given by the selling company as part of the transaction documents will turn out, in many cases, to not be enforceable so any underlying risk must be reflected in a discounted offering price by the buying company.

Legal review of non-competition agreements of key employees, the status of existing liens and the property subject to liens, the risk of subsequent liens, such as mechanics' liens that become fixed later but dating back to a prior time, are all critical issues to be reviewed. Key supplier contracts, their duration and assignability and alternate supply sources are part of this critical review as are the customer relationships, whether sole source, price-sensitivity, and the history of warranty claims.

Information is only as good as the accuracy of input and the target's existing informational technology system, in practice and not as proposed, must be verified.

Finally, how a transaction is to close is a final critical element for the buyer in setting the price.

In the mid- to late 1990s, most states dropped their Bulk Sales statutes (Article 6 of the Uniform Commercial Code) as being ineffective and no longer needed to protect general creditors with the passage by all states of the Uniform Fraudulent Transfer Act.

That statute permits any partially paid or unpaid general creditor of a company which sells its asset to sue either its account-debtor (selling company) or the buying company on the grounds that the price paid was not "fair value" for the assets purchased. Unfortunately this analysis will be determined by a court after the fact with many unpaid suppliers before the court claiming that their materials were transferred to the buying company for less than fair recompense. At best, the buyer is faced with the cost of litigation; at worst, it may be required to return the goods (although subject to a lien in favor of the buyer for the price paid). Obtaining fairness opinions from a responsible investment banking house alleviates some of the risk if there is the time to obtain such evidence of fair value.

Many times a condition to close is the requirement for releases from the general creditors in exchange for some partial payment (remember the liquidation analysis) plus, perhaps, an agreement to continue to buy from existing suppliers as long as pricing remains competitive. Most transactions will have 80% of the general debt of the target held by less than 20% of the number of creditors of the target, allowing the buyer to settle with a relatively small number of creditors to allow the transaction to close and perhaps assume the balance of known payables, with a credit against the sale price.

Another solution to the unpaid creditor issue is to consider a "Section 363" bankruptcy sale for larger transactions. The benefit is that the ultimate sale will be approved by a federal court and binding on all creditors, assuring good title to the purchaser. However, the moderate delay (average 45 to 90 days), the interim operating costs, and the costs of a bankruptcy filing made this tool more practical for larger transactions.

A sale in bankruptcy requires an auction-like process which may let competitive bidders emerge and there is an entire strategy involving "stalking-horse bidding" and alternate strategies of reorganization with outside funding which are beyond the scope of this article.

With all this complexity and risk, why engage in seeking to acquire the business of a financially troubled company? As in any market, the pricing of the transaction must justify the effort and for those companies that grow strategically in a down market, the profits to be realized as the business cycle turns will more than amply reward the risk takers.

How to Raise Private Equity

For this section, we detail steps that can be taken to help entrepreneurs obtain private equity financing. Each article was written by experienced industry participants and explores the practical considerations for dealing with the private equity process. Especially helpful is an outline of a detailed business plan that will facilitate a private equity investor's investment decision. This information offers entrepreneurs and business owners guidance in approaching the private equity investors and presenting the business plan, anticipating the pricing and structure of the financing, and understanding the legal requirements. Also examined are the goals of private equity investors, their expectations from the entrepreneurs and business owners, the process of making an investment decision, and the situations they would prefer to avoid. Examining the private equity investors' objectives and decision-making processes should help the entrepreneur and business owner locate the appropriate investor and establish a productive investment relationship.

Some of the articles in this section include "Preparing a Business Plan", a helpful guide for entrepreneurs seeking financing, and two articles on taking the next step in the process, "How to Choose and Approach a Venture Capitalist" and "How to Choose and Approach a Buyout Firm". In addition, "Venture Capital: More Than Money?" presents a case study on the value-added benefits that venture capitalists can provide in addition to capital.

Structuring Venture Capital Investments

Jonathan E. Cole, Esq. and Albert L. Sokol, Esq.

Jonathan Cole *is a partner in Edwards and Angell's Private Equity and Venture Capital Group and has been involved in venture capital practice since 1971, first in the Firm's Providence, RI office, and since 1981, in the Firm's Florida offices. He has written and spoken extensively on the venture capital process.*

Albert Sokol *is a partner in the Private Equity, Venture Capital and Technology Groups and resides in the Boston office of Edwards and Angell. Since beginning his venture practice in 1977, he has represented foreign and U.S. venture capital funds as well as venture-backed foreign and U.S. life sciences and IT/software technology companies. He has been designated a "Recommended Counsel" for Corporate and for M&A matters in the Global 3000 Report for several years, and has written and spoken extensively to both U.S. and foreign groups on venture capital, corporate and technology topics.*

An entrepreneur raising capital faces a daunting challenge. Regardless of whether the company is in the US, Europe or Asia, or whether it is in the life sciences, or IT/software, or some other arena, the challenge is to keep the R&D, marketing, sales, etc. "show on the road", and yet still find time and energy to obtain sufficient capital to fund these activities.

After running the gauntlet of visiting one venture capitalist (VC) after another in order to find sophisticated VCs who like the company and who also can be a "value-added" addition to the stockholder group, the entrepreneur's next challenge is to deal with the VCs potentially complex investment structures.

Such structures can be perceived as confusing, and perhaps overbearing, and involving too much "control" for the VCs and too little appreciation of the sacrifices and contributions of the entrepreneurs. An entrepreneur receiving such a proposal might feel that the structure of the VC's proposed investment sets back the founders' relationship with the VC.

And yet, the VC fund's key objectives and the realities of financial markets usually drive the VC to employ the same basic structure for all investments. This article seeks to help entrepreneurs understand the link between VC deal structure and VC objectives.

The discussion below focuses on the structures used most frequently by the institutional venture capital community, meaning primarily the professionally managed pools of capital listed in Pratt's Guide to Venture Capital Sources. In venture capital, as elsewhere, the "golden rule" generally applies ("He who has the Gold makes the Rules"), and a VC's objectives will influence the structure of its investment.

We have not discussed investment structures utilized by so-called "angel investors" (typically private individuals, such as friends and family, wealthy individuals, suppliers or customers, or other industry contacts), or by so-called "strategic partners" (typically operating companies in the same or allied industry or marketplace, including non-U.S. firms). Those types of structures tend to be more diverse and again, are often driven by different objectives than those which drive VCs.

Pre-Investment Considerations

Before approaching VCs, an entrepreneur should prepare his company's legal and organizational structure so that the company is ready to attract and receive institutional financing. Examples of pre-investment considerations are the following:

Business Plan: Management must have developed a coherent, fairly complete and readable Business Plan with a clear statement of business strategy and a relatively complete picture of the resources required (including people, plant, intellectual property and money).

The Business Plan not only describes the business opportunity, but also constitutes preliminary evidence of the management team's ability to plan for and organize a successful business venture. For structural purposes, however, the Business Plan is important both because its predicted results (including milestones) directly affect valuation and thus how much of the pie each party will own, and also because it forms the basis for key portions of the deal, such as conditions to the release of deferred investment commitments, the vesting of management equity or control of the Board of Directors. The relationship between the Business Plan and the investment structure is discussed further below.

Intellectual Property Rights: The Company's value is considerably enhanced if its patents and other intellectual property form a barrier-to-entry against its competitors. Particularly in the life sciences, patent rights are crown jewels. Due diligence is required so that the company's rights to its primary intellectual property (patents, copyrights, trade secrets or other rights) is clear and protected. Most importantly, the company must be prepared to provide detailed analysis of patentability (eg, evaluating prior art) and of the company's "freedom to operate" (i.e., to be able to sell its products free of infringement claims by third parties).

Other mechanics include ensuring that inventors have signed proper assignments to the company of all patents, inventions or other rights. Most VCs will refuse to invest in a company if the founders insist on retaining ownership of the principal intellectual property that the company needs for its business.

Similarly, the company should require its key employees to sign non-disclosure and invention assignments agreements, and where appropriate, to sign reasonably designed non-competition agreements. The company should also evaluate and clear up any possible entangling relationships between its key employees and their prior employers regarding company's intellectual property.

Prior History of the Company: The legal entity to be used as the vehicle for the investment and the conduct of the business should have no unusual prior history. For example, the company should not have been engaged in a prior business that was closed or sold. In particular, the company must not be a "public shell", with the attendant diverse and unrelated stockholder group. These situations present too many opportunities for unknown risks or unasserted claims. In most cases, the equity interests should be held by the entrepreneur and the key management team, and a small group of people who have made investments in the company to support the early development of the business described in its Business Plan.

The company's organizational documents (charter, bylaws and director and shareholder minutes) should be clear, complete and up-to-date, with no unusual provisions granting special rights to any group of stockholders or others. Provisions giving the stockholders, or a particular group of them, "preemptive" rights to acquire a pro rata share of new equity issues can be problematical, and in some cases such rights can be implied by law unless specifically denied in the charter documents. If possible, these should be removed.

All prior issuances of equity interests (including not only common or preferred stock, but also options or warrants to acquire stock, or if applicable, partnership interests or limited liability company member interests) must be properly documented and reviewed for compliance with applicable securities laws. In particular, there should be no "exclusive dealing" arrangements with finders, brokers or other financial intermediaries, including arrangements providing for equity interests, options or warrants in the event of a successful financing. These arrangements not only restrict the company's ability to raise capital in the future, but also dilute the ownership percentage of the existing stockholder group and potentially the VC investors.

In most cases, the equity interests held by minority stockholders, including key employees, should be subject to vesting arrangements and to restrictions on transfer and rights of first refusal in favor of the company, as well as rights for the company to acquire the stock held by the employees upon termination of their employment.

Finally, there should be no litigation of any material nature involving the company.

Regulatory Matters: All regulatory filings required by the company should be up-to-date and well documented. Any regulatory or governmental restrictions on the transfer of ownership interests should be analyzed and the impact of a substantial equity financing should be anticipated.

Tax Matters: The impact of federal and state tax on the probable investment structure should be analyzed and understood. For the moment, the institutional VC community appears to continue to favor the "C" corporation as the preferred legal entity for the investee company. "C" corporations present the simplest and perhaps most easily under-stood legal and capital structures and are the preferred vehicle (in fact, practically the exclusive vehicle) for an initial public offering. Because of the prevalence of the "C" corporation as the investment vehicle for most VC funds, these are the focus of the discussion below.

C corporations can present tricky structuring issues where a substantial net operating loss ("NOL") has been generated from prior operations. While NOLs can be used to "shelter" future profits, such sheltering will be severely restricted if there is a "change of ownership" under the tax regulations in any three year period. Accordingly, the past and predicted future changes in stock ownership must be considered by the company's tax advisors.

"S" corporations are often used by entrepreneurs during the start-up phase and can provide tax deferral opportunities for the initial, individual investors. However, "S" corporations should plan to convert to "C" corporation status and to manage the tax impact of such conversion. In fact, this conversion will happen automatically if equity interests are issued to non-qualifying investors, such as VC funds. Other structures, principally limited partnerships and limited liability companies, are sometimes utilized. For liability reasons, general partnerships are almost never used.

Of course, all tax returns and other tax filings must be current and well documented.

Cross-border Considerations: For many entrepreneurs and companies, cross-border considerations are significant for at least two reasons.

First, as markets and competition for most products are increasingly global, VCs generally expect every company's business plan to evaluate and discuss how the company will deal with international opportunities and threats. Is there a potential competitor with superior technology in another country? How will the company distribute its products outside its home market? Is it necessary to have different versions of the product to account for regional/geographic variances in markets?

Second, in appropriate cases, a company's global strategy might include arranging that the VCs which invest in the company include one or two VCs from another country. Advantages to be gained for the company include validation of the "international" part of the business plan by the foreign VC, and assistance in certain cross-border matters (for example, access to the foreign VC's business network and to the VC's financial, business and legal expertise in foreign countries). The strategy of arranging a cross-border VC syndicate is not without its problems, however, as some VCs will not do a deal that is more than two hours distance from their home base. Also, such deals do involve some extra planning to account for the cross-border effect of various countries' tax and other laws on VC investments.

Proper attention to these pre-investment structure considerations, as well as to any other unusual aspects of the company or its history, will ease the investment process for VC funds. However, inattention may well make it difficult to attract VC interest.

Typical Documentation for a VC Investment

Term Sheet: Typically, the basic terms of the investment structure will be set forth in a Term Sheet prepared by the VC fund and submitted to the entrepreneur and the company, sometimes stand-alone and sometimes as a part of a Letter of Intent. The Letter of Intent and Term Sheet generally are not intended to be binding on the parties, with the exception of certain provisions for the payment of expenses (whether or not the transaction closes) or exclusive dealing ("no shop") rights, which may be included as legally binding agreements. The Term Sheet can be, and often is, negotiated in detail, since it sets forth the fundamental terms of the investment structure as well as the financial terms upon which the investment is proposed to be made.

VC funds sometimes prepare the Term Sheet and/or Letter of Intent without using outside counsel, and expect that the business people in the proposed deal will discuss and negotiate it without the active participation of counsel on either side. However, because the Term Sheet becomes the "road map" for the preparation of the definitive investment documentation, and since the Term Sheet is only a summary of the principal contractual terms of the investment, the entrepreneur should consult with experienced counsel and other financial advisors while the Term Sheet is being negotiated. Such advisors can give the entrepreneur a more complete explanation of the ramifications of the Term Sheet and can suggest negotiating positions that can move the parties toward an agreement relatively quickly and smoothly. Often, this process can minimize the likelihood of unpleasant surprises arising later from the negotiation of the full-blown investment documentation.

Once the Term Sheet has been negotiated and the Letter of Intent (if any) executed by the parties, counsel for the VC fund will prepare and circulate drafts of the principal investment documents, based upon the provisions agreed to in the Term Sheet, but set forth in more complete detail, and including other "standard" provisions. This set of documents, including not only agreements among or between the company, some or all of its existing stockholders and, where relevant, its employees, as well as the VC investors, also includes provisions to be included in the company's charter and bylaws. A typical set of investment documents is described further below.

"Standard" Investment Documentation

General: The investment documentation describes the contract and legal rights of the parties governing their future relations. While some of the documentation, or at least certain provisions, will be peculiar to each transaction, depending upon the circumstances involved, the venture capital industry has developed a relatively standard set of documentation that the entrepreneur should expect to see.

Since the documentation is prepared by the VC fund in connection with its investment, it is designed largely to protect the rights of the investors. Again, the terms are largely negotiable, although negotiating positions that vary materially from the principal terms set forth in the Term Sheet will typically not be accepted, absent unusual circumstances, and may result in a breakdown of the investment process. Accordingly, the entrepreneur should address the principal terms when the Letter of Intent is executed, even though it may not be legally binding.

The most common "standard" investment documentation typically includes the following:

- **Securities Purchase Agreement** (also called a Preferred Stock Purchase Agreement or Note and Warrant Purchase Agreement, or similar designation, depending upon the structure of the investment).
- **An amended certificate of incorporation or other document describing the Investment Security** (including typically the Preferred Stock terms, or the forms of Note and Warrant).
- **Registration Rights Agreement.**
- **Stockholders Agreement.**
- **Employee Agreements, such as:**
- **Employment Agreement.**
- **Option and/or Restricted Stock Agreement.**
- **Non-Compete Agreement.**
- **Inventions and Confidentiality Agreement.**

This set of documentation, taken together, governs the legal rights of the parties relating to the investment and the legal aspects of the company's operations after the investment. The principal terms of these documents are described below.

Securities Purchase Agreement: The Securities Purchase Agreement (or Preferred Stock Purchase Agreement or Note and Warrant Purchase Agreement or similar designation) typically contains the following principal terms:

(i) The financial commitment of the investors to purchase the newly issued securities of the company, which may be common stock, preferred stock, promissory notes (including convertible notes) and stock purchase warrants, or some combination of these securities, which may be purchased in whole at the initial closing, or which may be purchased over time, depending upon the achievement of certain milestones;

(ii) The representations and warranties of the company as to the material facts relating to its organization and business, requiring relatively complete disclosure of any material arrangements;

(iii) The representations and warranties of investors as purchasers of the company's securities;

(iv) Affirmative and negative covenants of the company (the breach of which may give rise to contractual claims for damages, or which may result in other consequences, such as changes in the composition of the Board of Directors, or a default on outstanding indebtedness, or the like), including limitations on debt, mergers and acquisitions, changing the business focus, transactions with affiliates and changes in compensation for the key managers, as well as provision for certain information rights (financial statements, board participation, inspection rights, etc.);

(v) Conditions to the obligations of the VC investors to fund the investment (which will typically include the execution and delivery of the other agreements included in the standard investment documentation);

(vi) Special provisions (covering any special

arrangements between the parties); and

(vii) Miscellaneous provisions (often called "legal boilerplate").

Sometimes provisions governing future agreements and operations (such as the affirmative and negative covenants, Board participation rights, and the like) are not part of the Securities Purchase Agreement, but instead appear in a separate Investor Rights Agreement.

Form of Investment Security: The investment security will be either an equity security (i.e., common stock or preferred stock in the case of corporate issuers), or some sort of debt instrument (i.e., promissory notes or debentures, which may be convertible into an equity security), or rights to acquire an equity security (i.e., stock purchase warrants which may cover either preferred or common stock). The principal terms of the security will be contained in the company's certificate of incorporation for common or preferred stock and in the terms of the instrument itself for promissory notes, debentures or warrants. The terms of equity securities typically cover voting rights, dividends (including preferential and cumulative dividends), liquidation preferences, conversion or exchange rights, redemption or "put" rights (usually in favor of the investors), and special provisions relating to the Board of Directors, including rights to assume control. The terms of debt instruments will include provisions for the payment of interest and principal, default provisions, provision for collateral or guarantees (which will be more completely set forth in separate documents) and, if applicable, conversion or exchange rights.

Special affirmative or negative covenants may also be included in the terms of the equity or debt securities as well as in the Securities Purchase Agreement, Stockholders Agreement or Investor Rights Agreement.

Convertible securities (e.g., convertible preferred stock or convertible or exchangeable notes) or warrants will also typically contain "anti-dilution" protection, usually giving the investors the right to obtain more common stock, without additional aggregate consideration, in the event the company subsequently issues new common stock (or common stock equivalents) at a price below the effective "as converted" common stock price paid by the investors. The anti-dilution provisions can be quite complex and typically will be based on either the so-called "full ratchet" or "weighted average" formula.

Registration Rights Agreement: The Registration Rights Agreement sets forth the rights of the investors to SEC registration of their equity securities, which will typically include "demand" registration rights and "piggyback" registration rights, as well as related agreements governing the procedures and understandings of the parties as to the implementation of such rights (e.g., so-called "cutback" provisions and indemnity agreements).

Stockholders Agreement: The Stockholders Agreement, which will be entered into among the company, the investors and the principal management stockholders of the company, will often contain provisions that are peculiar to each investment transaction or company, but will typically include restrictions on transfer (e.g., no transfers for a period of time or without the approval of the Board of Directors), rights of first refusal on proposed transfers, voting agreements with respect to the Board of Directors or other matters, and "co-sale" rights (sometimes referred to as "tag-along" or "drag-along" rights). The co-sale rights set forth the rights of the investors and/or others to participate in certain sales of stock by the entrepreneur or other key management stockholders (the "tag-along" right) and the right of the investors to require the management to participate in a sale of stock by the investors (the "drag-along" right). The Stockholders Agreement (or in some cases, the Restricted Stock Agreement with each key stockholder employee) may also include provision for the purchase of the stock held by the entrepreneur or other key management personnel in the event of death or termination of employment (including a "call" in favor of the company, or a "put" in favor of the stockholder or his or her estate, or both), with provision for differing valuations applicable to the purchase, depending upon the circumstances.

Exit Rights or Investor Rights Agreement: Sometimes, there is an Exit Rights Agreement or an Investor Rights Agreement, which may supplement or replace the Registration Rights Agreement or Stockholders Agreement or both. It may set forth affirmative and negative covenants applicable to future operations, Board seat rights, information delivery requirements and the like, and may contain the registration rights of the investors as well as any redemption or "put" rights as to common stock or warrants and any "co-sale" rights, all of which provide opportunities for the investors to obtain liquidity for, or "exit", the investment.

Employee Agreements: Typically the investors will want the employment arrangement of the entrepreneur and other key management personnel to be set forth in written agreements, which will provide for duties and responsibilities, compensation (including participation in bonus or other profit sharing or incentive compensation plans or stock option arrangements) and the rights of the company to terminate the employment arrangements, including severance benefits that may be available. Often the VC investors will require that some or all of the common stock or options held by the key management team, or issued to them pursuant to equity incentive plans, be subject to "vesting" of the rights to the stock or options over a period of three to five years, with restrictions on transfer and "call" or buyback rights in favor of the company at death or other termination of employment at a price depending on the circumstances of such termination.

Non-Compete Agreement: The investors will typically want the key employees, including the entrepreneur, to enter into non-compete agreements in the event of termination of employment, the duration of which may be related to the availability of severance benefits.

Inventions and Confidentiality Agreement: The investors may require the key employees to enter into inventions and confidentiality agreements confirming the rights of the company to any intellectual property developed by the key employees, as well as setting forth the obligation of the key employees to maintain confidentiality as to the company's proprietary information and trade secrets.

Achieving Goals through Investment Structure

Four key considerations motivate a VC's investment structure:

- Maximizing financial returns;
- Priority protection against loss;
- Participation in control of the company, and
- "Exit" or liquidity rights.

It can be complex to implement these simple objectives. For example, although using common stock as the investment instrument will often permit the VC to maximize potential financial returns, common stock will not provide priority protection against loss or supply the control features that VCs usually require, and may provide only limited "exit" (or rights to obtain liquidity) opportunities.

Entrepreneurs who understand how his or her prospective investors' key objectives are reflected in the documentation will be better able to deal with VCs on an efficient, pragmatic and realistic basis.

Financial Returns: The VC achieves its financial returns primarily in the form of capital appreciation of the equity securities, and occasionally in a current return (i.e., dividends on equity securities or interest on debt securities). In most early stage investments, there will be no current return, since the company's cash flow (if any) will most often be dedicated toward funding future growth of the business. Even in these investments, however, the structure may provide for a "cumulative" dividend on a convertible preferred stock, which will become part of the "liquidation preference" upon sale or redemption. This has the effect of providing a minimum rate of return to the investors on a priority basis before the common stock held by the entrepreneur and others will receive anything.

In later stage and expansion financings, where the company's projected cash flow is strong enough to provide some sort of current return, the structure will often include a so-called "current pay" dividend on preferred stock or current interest payments on debt instruments. Even in those situations, however, the principal financial objective of the VC investors will be capital appreciation of the equity securities associated with the investment.

Standard debt instruments (such as straight promissory notes) or conventional preferred stock provide only for the return of capital through repayment of the principal of the notes or redemption of the preferred stock at its liquidation preference (typically the purchase price plus unpaid cumulative dividends). As a standard debt instrument does not participate in the capital appreciation represented by the company's increase in value, most VC investors will want to obtain their financial return through an equity security that will participate with the common stock in the increased value of the company upon achievement of its business plan.

The most common investment structures that permit the VC investors to participate in the appreciation of common stock value are (a) convertible preferred stock, which is convertible into common stock at the option of the investors and, perhaps, mandatorily upon the occurrence of certain events, such as a public offering; (b) a convertible note, which provides for conversion of the principal amount of the note into common stock at the option of the VC investors or mandatorily upon the occurrence of certain events; (c) stock purchase warrants (usually issued in conjunction with promissory notes), giving the investors the right to purchase common stock at a fixed price at some future date; and (d) common stock purchased directly at the time of the initial investment, usually in conjunction with the purchase of non-convertible preferred stock or debt instruments.

A key VC consideration is the percentage of the company that the investors will hold on a common stock equivalent basis. Typically, investors will base their investment decision upon an analysis of the risk-adjusted projected value of the company, assuming it achieves its business plan, at a fixed time in the future, such that the VC investors will receive an appropriate percentage of the projected value of the company at that time to provide them with their required rates of return on invested capital. This analysis will take into account the projected dilution of the percentage ownership of the VC investors that will arise from anticipated follow-on equity investments, and the investment documentation will typically include both preemptive rights to participate in future equity financings as well as the "anti-dilution" provisions described earlier.

Protection against Loss: VC investors typically expect that their invested capital will be protected against loss to a greater degree than the capital interests of the founders or other earlier stage stockholders. The investment structure is designed to provide this protection in a number of ways. Of course, with respect to debt securities, the investors have a right to the return of the invested capital through repayment of the debt. This right may be secured through collateral interests in the company's assets or guarantees of others.

The principal "downside" protection for investments in equity securities is typically achieved through the use of preferred stock, which gives the investors the right to receive the liquidation preference (typically, the invested capital plus perhaps a guaranteed return through unpaid cumulative dividends) on a priority basis before any distributions can be made on the common stock or junior preferred stock held by the entrepreneur and other stockholders.

And, perhaps the most common type of preferred stock is the so-called "participating convertible preferred" stock, which combines the foregoing downside protection with the additional upside right to participate with the common stockholders in the general distribution of assets that follows the priority distribution of the foregoing liquidation preference. Interestingly, although the downside protection features (often labeled as a "liquidation preference") do apply to classic liquidations and winding-ups, they also typically apply in good-news situations such as mergers. In this latter sense, these features are also a "liquidity preference".

Finally, as most companies receive multiple rounds of VC investment, each time a new round is negotiated it will be necessary to determine the relative priority of each round's series of preferred stock or notes. It is not uncommon for there to be four or five such rounds, each with its own investment security, each ranked junior or senior to the other rounds' securities.

VC investors also seek protection against loss through rights to control or liquidate the company in the event the Business Plan is not achieved or other material defaults arise. In the event of such a default, these rights are intended to permit maximum flexibility for the VC investors to determine the advisability and timing of a sale or liquidation or other material development affecting the company, or a change in management. It is possible that the course of action decided upon may substantially impair the value of the equity securities held by the entrepreneur and other stockholders. Such default or "change of control" provisions for equity investments are typically included in the Securities Purchase Agreement or in the preferred stock terms, or both.

In some situations, the investors will invest their funds in installments, depending upon the company's achievement of certain business milestones. This aspect of the structure is intended to reduce the capital commitment of the investors in the event that the company's business does not proceed as anticipated or other developments arise. The installment mechanism is also sometimes used to address possible disagreements on valuation between management and the VCs – for example, as the company is not as valuable if it cannot reach a particular milestone, then VCs might feel that they should not be required to invest the next installment at the same price per share as applied to the first installment.

Participation in Management and Control: While most VC investors expect that the entrepreneur and management team will control and operate the business on a day to day basis without interference from the investors, the investment structure will typically provide for the investors to participate in the management and operation of the company (a) through representation on the Board of Directors, (b) through the restrictions and limitations imposed by the affirmative and negative covenants in the Securities Purchase Agreement or terms of the equity or debt securities, and (c) through stock transfer restrictions on the equity interests held by the management team imposed under the Stockholders Agreement. In addition, the investors will typically insist that the Employee Agreements provide for termination of the employment of the key management upon relatively short notice without cause, but subject to severance and buy-back rights.

However, if the company materially fails to achieve its business plan or certain specific milestones, or if the company violates any of the affirmative and negative covenants contained in the Securities Purchase Agreement or the terms of its equity or debt securities, the VC investors may expect the right to either take control of the Board of Directors of the company (including the right to remove existing management), and/or the right to require the company to purchase the equity securities held by the VC investors (sometimes called "put" or "redemption" rights), as well as to pay off any debt owed to the VCs. These draconian measures are often hotly negotiated. Rights to control the company are typically reserved to situations where the VC investors have acquired a majority ownership position, while the "put" rights are typically reserved for those situations where VC investors hold a minority ownership position. In any event, the incidence of the actual exercise of such rights appears to be fairly low, but the availability of such rights in the investment documentation is a useful negotiating tool in the hands of the VC investors in discussions with management in those situations where serious problems have arisen.

"Exit" Rights: As VCs' primary goal is return-on-investment, they favor a structure that provides a means to liquidity (i.e., realization of the return through sale of the investment or sale of the company). VCs use the term "exits" to refer to these paths to liquidity, and a typical structure will provide at least one and often two or more exit mechanisms.

VC funds generally have a limited life (usually 10 years, with a possible extension of up to 2 years). Therefore, VCs will favor structures that provide for an agreed upon exit opportunity within 5 to 7 years, so that an investment made in the third or fourth year of the fund's life will be turned into cash or marketable securities prior to the time when the fund winds up and the fruits of the fund's investments are to be distributed fully to the VC fund's investors. Such timing is important to the VCs not only for such obvious reasons, but also because the VCs need to accumulate attractive returns near the end of each fund's life so that such returns can be employed as evidence of the VC's investment management capabilities – for when they raise their next fund. It is not uncommon for successful VCs to raise a series of funds, one after another, each built, to some extent, on the successful record of their previous funds.

Entrepreneurs seeking capital from institutional VC funds should be aware of these constraints and be prepared to accommodate them. (In this connection, it is advisable for the entrepreneur to inquire about the "age" and investment horizon of the particular investor funds involved so that there are no surprises about the desired timing of an exit.)

The primary paths to liquidity for ventured-backed companies have historically been the public offering, or the sale of the company (by merger or otherwise) to another firm, typically an operating company in the same or an allied industry. IPOs and mergers tend to produce the highest valuations and accordingly the highest returns to the investors (although an IPO may have a markedly different effect on the management team than a merger). A secondary path to the investors' liquidity for financially successful companies has been to redeem or repurchase the VCs' investment, usually in connection with a refinancing or recapitalization of the company.

In the case of IPOs, the Registration Rights Agreement permits the investors to use their "demand" registration rights to compel the company to go public, and also to participate in company-initiated IPOs though their "piggyback" registration rights. Since most entrepreneurs share the investors' view of the desirability of going public — the management stays in control and also obtains liquidity opportunities at a high initial valuation, while the company receives substantial capital to fund future growth — registration rights are typically willingly accepted.

One of the ways that investors' try influence exits other than through the public market is through a "put", or option to sell, in favor of the investors as to equity securities (generally referred to as a redemption right in the case of preferred stock), usually exercisable after a period of time (five to seven years) if no other liquidity event has occurred (such as a public offering).

The critical issue in the "put" or redemption structure is the pricing formula. Typically the investors will be looking for (a) no less than the minimum return provided for in the liquidation preference of a preferred stock investment (original purchase price plus unpaid cumulative dividends) and (b) if higher, the common stock equivalent value of the investment (e.g., the "as converted value" of the preferred stock as if it had been converted to common stock as shared in the value of the company's common equity on a pro rata basis). Some "put" or redemption pricing formulas determine common stock equivalent value by reference to "fair market value" (FMV), usually fixed by appraisal, while others determine such value by reference to a multiple of earnings (usually EBITDA, or earnings before interest, taxes, depreciation and amortization). In some cases, the "put" or redemption price may be the highest of all three of liquidation preference, FMV, or EBITDA formula value. Other, more exotic, pricing formulas are also used in appropriate cases.

Whatever the pricing mechanism, however, the ultimate structure will likely contain some form of exit right involving thc right of the investors to require the company to "take them out", and entrepreneurs should be prepared to deal with these issues in the Term Sheet and definitive investment documentation.

On a practical basis, however, the "put" may not give the investors the ability to receive cash upon exercise, since many growing companies, especially ones that have experienced bumps in the road to success, will likely not be able to finance a buyout of a significant equity partner. Rather, a "put" gives the VCs the power to force the management to find a practical solution to the exit requirements of the investors, the absence of which will give the investors the right to cause the liquidation and forced sale of the company. Also, the failure of the company to meet a redemption or "put" exercise will likely give rise to a potential shift in control of the Board under the preferred stock terms or Put Agreement or Stockholders' Agreement. The "put" rights set the negotiating table far in advance of the exit date and give a strong incentive to management to plan for a liquidity event for the investors in a timely manner.

Other exit rights that appear in typical investment structures are "tag along" rights, which give the investors the right to join (to "tag along") in any sales of equity securities by management. In cases where the investors control a majority of the company on a common stock equivalent basis, it is not uncommon for the structure to contain "drag- along" rights in favor of the investors. These give the investors the right to require management and other stockholders to sell (to be "dragged along") in the sale of all or substantially all of the company's stock to a third party, providing yet another full exit opportunity to the investors.

With respect to debt oriented investments, of course the repayment of the principal with interest is the primary means to liquidity, but since VC debt investments are typically paired with a convertibility feature or warrants as means of providing for the "upside" financial return, the structure will typically provide for a "put" of the debt or warrants on a formula basis that is the functional equivalent of the redemption pricing structure discussed above.

Conclusion

Entrepreneurs who are new to fundraising efforts may consider VC investment structures to be unduly complex and at times overbearing. However, while the details may vary from one VC fund or deal to another, the investment structures used by the VC community tend to fit common patterns and are designed to achieve a few basic objectives.

If entrepreneurs can understand the objectives of the investors, then the entrepreneurs can avoid early breakdowns in what might otherwise be fruitful discussions and negotiations. Entrepreneurs who wish to be successful in dealing with VCs should spend the time and effort to understand the objectives of their potential investors and to expect proposed investment structures that accommodate those objectives. At that point the entrepreneurs, together with knowledgeable and experienced counsel and other advisors, should be in a better position to negotiate a fair and rational investment structure which can provide the opportunity for all parties to profit from the arrangement.

Preparing a Business Plan*

Brian Haslett and Leonard E. Smollen

See previous background descriptions.

Developing a business plan that will attract professional venture investors' interest as well as their financial commitment is a challenge in itself, and it can be more daunting if it is being done for the first time.

Even those with advanced degrees in business may not have learned how to put together a comprehensive business plan.

Many successful venture capitalists were interviewed and numerous venture proposals were analyzed in order to help the entrepreneur comprehend the scope and the detail required in a business plan. Though entrepreneurs often find the process of building their teams and preparing their plans more arduous than they anticipated, those who complete the course are generally able to raise the capital they need and proceed to successfully move their businesses ahead.

Using These Guidelines

When raising equity capital, a business plan is a vital sales tool. Before committing their funds for what will probably be at least five years, most venture capital investors will want to be certain the plan has been carefully thought through and that management has the appropriate skills and experience in its chosen business area to be able to manage effectively, seize opportunities, solve problems, and make profits. These prospective backers will—or should—insist on reviewing the proposal before considering any investment seriously. Some will not meet with an entrepreneur without first seeing the business plan. For this reason, the plan must be well-prepared and very persuasive in conveying the company's potential. It should cover all major issues but not be so detailed that it puts the investor-reader off. Fifty pages should suffice for most businesses.

When starting up or expanding a business in a particular industry or market there are certain current critical issues that should be addressed. In the chemical industry, for instance, significant issues may include the following:

- Reduced availability of raw materials and resultant bartering and allocation
- Increasingly strict government regulations covering the use of chemical products and the operation of chemical processes
- Diminishing viability of the high capital cost of special-purpose chemical processing plants that serve narrow markets

Make whatever investigations are needed to develop a list of special issues that are significant to the particular business.

Because these guidelines contain a list of potentially relevant issues and are meant to cover a wide variety of manufacturing and service businesses, they will help tailor a list. But it is up to the entrepreneur, while preparing the plan, to determine which issues are significant to future business development.

Professional venture capitalists are not the only people who find business plans invaluable. For the entrepreneur, careful preparation of a plan can be an opportunity to think through all facets of a business expansion or start-up, to examine the consequences of different marketing, operations and financing strategies, and to determine what human, physical and financial resources are required. Much of this can be done effectively on paper without the crippling expense of trial-and-error operation.

In one venture, the discipline of writing the business plan caused the entrepreneur to realize that the major market for his biomedical product was in nursing homes, not in hospital emergency rooms as he had originally thought. He changed the focus of his marketing effort accordingly.

Another successful entrepreneur found that besides using his plan to help raise $650,000 in start-up capital, it helped him monitor his company's performance during its first 18 months. Then, when he needed to increase his company's credit lines and to secure long-term financing for building and equipment, he was able to update his plan in two or three days. Without a

**Originally published and copyrighted (1972) by The Institute for New Enterprise Development (INED). Revised for this book by the author.*

plan, it would have taken two to three weeks.

Summary of the Plan

Many investors prefer to read a one- to three-page summary of a business plan that highlights its important features and opportunities to decide about reviewing the entire plan. The summary should be written after the plan is completed. As each section is drafted, it might be a good idea to circle a few sentences that are important enough to include in the summary.

The summary should be thoughtfully put together since it is probably the first thing about the business that a would-be investor is going to read. Unless it is appealing and convincing, it may also be the last!

The summary should contain very brief statements about

1. the company's origins, activities, management and performance
2. any distinguishing features of the product or service
3. the attractiveness of the market
4. a summary of the financial projections
5. the amount of money being sought, in what form (equity or debt or both) and for what purpose

Several people who are not involved in the venture should review the summary while it is still in draft form. Their reactions should be evaluated. Did they quickly grasp the essence of proposal? Were they excited by what they read? This feedback should provide useful indications of how the professional venture capital investor is likely to react.

Description of the Business and Its Industry

This section is an introduction to subsequent sections on the product/service, the market opportunity and the people and plans that will be involved in the venture. The product or service should be described briefly as well as the nature and current condition of the industry to show where and how the product will fit in it.

The Company

The business as well as the product or service should be described along with potential customers and regions of operation.

The company's history should also be detailed: when it was formed, how its products/services were chosen and developed, and what role management has played in bringing the business to where it is today.

If the company is already trading and is now seeking further development or expansion financing, the entrepreneur must review its market penetration and its financial performance (sales, profits, return on equity).

If the company has had early setbacks and incurred losses, these need to be described, as well as methods to avoid recurrences. Omission of any reference to past problems can make the proposal appear too good to be true.

The Industry

This section should include the entrepreneur's view of the nature, current status and prospects for the industry in which the business operates; the industry's principal participants and how they are performing; the growth in sales and profits and any published forecasts for the current year; companies that have recently entered or left these markets and why; and what major economic, social, technological, or regulatory trends are affecting your business.

This section should not go into too much detail. That is done later. Each topic should be covered summarily in two or three sentences.

Features and Advantages of Products or Services

The potential investor wants to know the entrepreneur's plan: what is going to be sold, what kind of special know-how and protection management has and what its advantages and drawbacks are.

• *Description.* This section should contain detailed information on the products or services and what needs they satisfy. Diagrams and sketches may be used to improve understanding and heighten interest. The product's or service's distinctive features should be emphasized by highlighting the differences between what competitors currently have on the market and what will be offered. Each feature's advantage or disadvantage should be stated candidly.

• *Proprietary Position.* Any patents, trade secrets, or other proprietary features should be discussed as well as any advantage that would achieve a favored or entrenched position in the industry.

• *Potential.* Any opportunities for the logical extension of the existing product line or the development of related products or services should be discussed as well. Investors like to know what entrepreneurs are planning for an encore.

Market Research and Analysis

In this section, the entrepreneur should present enough facts to convince the investor that the market for the product or service is such that sales targets can be met despite competition.

This is probably the most difficult section for entrepreneurs to do well. And because choice of marketing strategies, size of operating work force and facilities and requirements for inventory and receivables financing are all derived from sales forecasts, it is also the most crucial. For these reasons, this section of the business plan should be prepared first and with the greatest care.

Customers

Markets should be clearly defined: who are the major purchasers, where are they, and why they buy. The significance of price, quality, service, personal contacts, and political pressures should be detailed in rank order along with the purchasers buying habits and the significance of seasonality—when the buying is done, and how it affects the offering.

List some actual or potential customers who have purchased or expressed an interest in the product or service and indicate why. List any actual or potential customers who have dropped or are uninterested in the product or service, and explain why this was so. The means for counteracting negative customer reaction should also be explained. The absence of frank discussion about the negatives of the offering may precipitate concern about the plan's thoroughness.

Market Size and Trends

The size of the current total market should be described. Discussing the market with potential distributors, dealers, sales representatives, customers and, to some extent, reviewing published data will help define the market. Published information should not be relied on solely since it is often inadequate. The size of the total market in both units and dollars should be provided with care to include only the market that will affect the product. If regional markets are going to be targeted, their sizes should be shown as well.

The potential annual growth of the total market for the product or service must be discussed and market projections should be made for at least three future years. The ways in which major factors such as industry trends, new technical developments, new or changing customer needs are affecting market growth should be thoroughly detailed and previous market trends should be reviewed. Any differences between past and projected future growth rates should be explained. Reasons for the presumed continuation of market trends should be explained. Entrepreneurs tend to overestimate the size of their market. If potential investors become dubious about the market size and growth estimates, they may lose interest in the rest of the proposal.

Competition

Make a realistic assessment of the strengths and weaknesses of competitive products and services and name the companies that supply them. State the data sources used to determine which products are competitive and the strengths of the competition.

The potential products or services should be compared with the competitors' on the basis of price, performance, service, warranties and other pertinent features. A table can be an effective way of presenting these data.

Review competitors' managerial and financial strengths and weaknesses, assessing each competitor's capability in marketing, operations, and finance, and their recent trends in sales, market share, and profitability. If they are not doing well, successful market and sales strategies should be explained.

Entrepreneurs often know less about their competition than they should. Professional investors are very wary of proposals in which competition is treated lightly. Therefore this section should conclude with an explanation of why customers buy from three or four key competitors. Then, if growth is planned by capturing a share of the competitors' business, the reasons why this is feasible should be explained.

Estimated Market Share and Sales

Identify any major customers who have made or are

willing to make purchase commitments. Indicate the extent of these commitments.

Estimate the share of the market and the sales in units and dollars that you think that you can achieve. Base this estimate on your assessment of your customers and their acceptance of your product or service, your market size and trends, and the competition, their offerings and their share of sales in prior year. The growth of your sales and your estimated market share should be related to the growth of your industry and customers and the strengths and weaknesses of your competitors. The data should be presented in tabular form, as shown below. If yours is an existing business, also indicate the total market, your market share, and sales for two prior years.

Marketing Plan

Your marketing plan should describe how you will achieve your sales target. The marketing plan should include a description of your sales and service policies and pricing, distribution and advertising strategies that you will use to achieve your goal. The marketing plan should make clear what is to be done, how it will be done, and who will do it.

Marketing Strategy

A description of your marketing strategy should include a discussion of the kinds of customers who will be targeted for initial heavy selling effort, customers who will be sought for later selling efforts, method of identifying specific potential customers and of contacting them, and the features of the product or service (quality, price, delivery, warranty) that will be emphasized to generate sales.

If the sales of your product or service are seasonal, discuss this and indicate any ideas you have for obtaining out-of-season sales.

Pricing

Many entrepreneurs, after convincing the investors that they have a superior product, then say they intend to sell it for less than their competitors. This makes a bad impression for two reasons. First, if their product is as good as they say it is, the entrepreneurs can be judged as poor sales people if they have to offer their product at a lower price than the competition. Second, costs do tend to be underestimated. If you start out with low prices, there is little room to maneuver if costs run over budget. Price hikes are tougher to make stick than price cuts.

Your pricing policy is one of the more important decisions you make. Your "price must be right" to penetrate your market, maintain your market position, and produce the profits you project. Devote enough time to considering a number of pricing strategies and convincingly present the one you select.

Discuss the prices to be charged for your product and service and compare your pricing policy with those of your major competitors. Explain how the price you set will enable you to:

- secure/increase acceptance of your offering,
- maintain and desirably increase your market share in the face of competition, and
- produce profits.

Justify any price increases over competitive items on the basis of newness, quality, warranty, and service. If your product is to be priced lower than your competitors' products, explain how you will do this and maintain profitability.

Sales Tactics

Describe how you will sell and distribute your product or service. Do you or will you use your own sales force, sales representatives, and distributors? Are there ready-made manufacturers' sales organizations already selling related products that you already use or can use? If distributors or sales representatives are used, describe how they have been or will be selected, and the areas they will cover. Discuss the margins to be given to retailers, wholesalers, and your commissions to sales representatives, and compare them to those given your competition. Describe any special policies regarding such items as discounts and exclusive distribution rights.

If a direct sales force is being introduced, indicate how it will be organized and at what rate it will be built up. Show the sales expected per salesman per year and what commission incentive and/or salary they will receive. Explain how these figures compare to those of your competition.

Service and Warranty Policies

If your company will offer a product that will require

service and warranties, indicate the importance of these to the customer's purchasing decision and discuss your method of handling service problems.

Advertising, Public Relations, and Promotion

Describe the program you will use to bring your product to the attention of prospective customers. Indicate your plans for public relations, trade show participation, trade magazine advertisements, direct mailings, and the preparation of product sheets and promotional literature. If advertising will be a significant part of company expenses, details of how and when these costs will be incurred should be presented.

Design and Development Plans

If any of your products or services require design and development before they are ready to be placed on the market, the nature and extent of this work should be fully discussed. The costs and time required to achieve a marketable product or service should be indicated.

Such design and development might be the engineering work necessary to convert a laboratory prototype to a finished product, the design of special tooling, the work of an industrial designer to make a product more attractive and salable, or the identification and organization of manpower, equipment, and special techniques or to implement a service business, for example, the equipment, new computer software, and skills required for computerized credit checking.

Development Status and Tasks

Describe the current status of the product or service and explain what remains to be done to make it marketable. Describe briefly the competence or expertise that your company has or will acquire to complete this development. Indicate the type and extent of technical assistance that will be required, and state who will supervise this activity within your organization, and give his or her experience in related development work.

Difficulties and Risks

Identify any major anticipated design and development problems and approaches to their solution. Discuss their possible impact on the timing of the market introduction of your product or service and the cost of design and development.

Costs

Present and discuss a design and development budget. The costs should include labor, materials, consulting fees, etc. Design and development costs are often underestimated. This can seriously impact cash flow projections. Accordingly, consider and perhaps show a 10% to 20% cost contingency. These cost data will become an integral part of the financial plan.

Operations Plan

The operations plan should describe the kind of facilities, space requirements, capital equipment, and labor force (part and full time) that are required to deliver the forecast quantities of the company's product or service. For a manufacturing business, discuss your policies regarding purchasing, "make or buy decisions" (which parts of the product will be purchased and which operations will be performed by your work force), inventory control, and production control. A service business should describe the appropriateness of location, and lease of required equipment, and competitive productivity from a skilled or trained labor force.

The discussion guidelines given below are general enough to cover both product and service businesses. Only those that are relevant to your venture—be it product or service—should be used in preparing the business plan.

Geographic Location

Describe the location of the business and discuss any advantages or disadvantages of the site in terms of wage rates, labor unions, labor availability, closeness to customers or suppliers, access to transportation, state and local taxes, state and local laws, utilities, and zoning. For a service business, proximity to customers is generally "a must."

Facilities and Improvements

If yours is an existing business, describe the facilities currently used to conduct the company's business. This should include plant and office space, storage and land areas, machinery, special tooling, and other capital equipment.

If your venture is a start-up, describe how and when the necessary facilities to start production will be acquired. Discuss whether equipment and space will be leased or acquired (new or used), and indicate the costs and timing of such actions. Indicate how much of the proposed financings will be devoted to plant and equipment. These cost data will become part of the plan.

Discuss how and when plant space and equipment will be expanded to the capacities required for future sales projections. Discuss any plans to improve or add to existing plant space or to move the facility. Explain future equipment needs and indicate the timing and cost of any acquisitions. A three-year planning period should be used for these projections.

Strategy and Plans

Describe the manufacturing processes involved in your product's production and any decisions with respect to subcontracting component parts rather than manufacturing them in house. The "make or buy" strategy adopted should consider inventory financing, available labor skills and other nontechnical questions as well as purely production, cost, and capability issues. Justify your proposed "make or buy" policy. Discuss any surveys you have completed of potential subcontractors and suppliers and who these are.

Present a production plan that shows cost-volume information at various sales levels of operation with breakdowns of applicable material, labor, purchased components, and factory overhead. Discuss the inventory required at various sales levels. These data will be incorporated into cash flow projections. Explain how any seasonal production loads will be handled without severe dislocation, for example, by building to inventory, using part-time help, or subcontracting the work.

Briefly, describe your approach to quality control, production control, and inventory control. Explain what quality control and inspection procedures the company will use to minimize service problems and associated customer dissatisfaction.

Discuss how you will organize and operate your purchasing function to insure that adequate materials are on hand for production, that the best price and payment terms have been obtained, and that raw materials and in-process inventory, and, hence, working capital have been minimized.

Labor Force

Explain, exclusive of management functions (discussed later), to what extent local labor force has the necessary skills in sufficient quantity and quality (lack of absenteeism, productivity) to manufacture the product or supply the services of your company to whatever quality, time and cost standards you have established. If the skills of the labor force are inadequate for the needs of your company, describe the kinds of training that you will use to upgrade their skills. Discuss how your business can provide and pay for such training and still offer a competitive product both in the short term (first year) and long term (two to five years).

Management Team

The management team is the key to a successful business. Investors look for a committed management team with a balance in marketing operations and financial skills and experience in doing what is proposed.

Accordingly, this section of the business plan will be of primary interest to potential investors and will significantly influence their investment decisions. It should include a description of the key members of the management team and their primary duties, the organizational structure, and the board of directors.

Organization

In a table, present the key management roles in the company and name the person for each position.

Discuss any current or past situations in which the key management people have worked together that indicate how their skills and personalities complement each other and result in an effective management team. If any key individuals will not be on hand at the start of the venture, indicate when they will join the company or what you are doing to locate and secure commitments from such individuals.

In a new business, it may not be possible to fill each executive role with a full-time person without excessively burdening the overhead of the venture. One solution is to use part-time specialists or consultants to perform some functions. If this is your plan, discuss it and indicate who will be used and when they will be replaced by a full-time staff member.

If the company is established and of sufficient size, an organization chart can be appended as an exhibit.

Key Management Personnel

Describe the exact duties and responsibilities of

each of the key members of the management team. Include a brief (three or four sentence) statement of the career highlights of each individual to focus on accomplishments that demonstrate ability to perform the assigned role.

Complete resumes for each key management member should be included here or as an exhibit to the business plan. These resumes should stress education, training, experience, and accomplishments of each person in performing functions similar to that person's role in the venture. Accomplishments should be discussed in such concrete terms as profit and sales improvement, labor productivity gains, reduced operating costs, improved product performance, and ability to meet budgets and schedules. When possible, it should be noted who can attest to accomplishments and recognition or rewards received, such as pay increases and promotions.

Management Compensation and Ownership

The likelihood of obtaining financing for a start-up is small when the founding management team is not prepared to accept modest initial salaries. If the founders demand substantial salaries in excess of what they received at their prior employment, the potential investor will conclude that their psychological commitment to the venture is a good deal less than it should be.

State the salary that is to be paid to each key person and compare it with the salary received at his last independent job. Set forth the stock ownership planned for the key management team members, the amount of their equity investment (if any), and any performance-dependent stock option or bonus plans that are contemplated. Mention any loans made to the company by management, indicating on what terms they were made and under what circumstances they can be converted to equity.

Board of Directors

Identify board members and include a one or two sentence statement of the member's background to show how he or she can benefit the company and what investment (if any) has been made.

Management Assistance and Training Needs

Describe candidly the strengths and weaknesses of your management team and board of directors. Discuss the kind, extent, and timing of any management training that will be required to overcome any weaknesses.

Supporting Professional Services

State the legal (including patent-counsel), accounting, public relations, advertising, banking, and other service organizations that you have selected for your venture. Supporting service organizations that are reputable and capable (remember reputations often live on after capability diminishes) not only provide professional assistance, but can also add significantly to the credibility of your business. In addition, properly selected professional organizations can help you establish good contacts in the business community, identify potential investors, and help you secure financing.

Overall Schedule

A schedule that shows the timing and interrelationship of the major events necessary to launch the venture and realize its objectives is an essential part of a business plan. In addition to being a planning aid and showing deadlines critical to a venture's success, a well-prepared schedule can be an extremely effective sales tool in raising money from potential investors. A well-prepared and realistic schedule demonstrates the ability of the management team to plan for venture growth in a way that recognizes obstacles and minimizes risk.

Prepare, as a part of this section, a month-by-month schedule that shows the timing of activities such as product development, market planning, sales programs, and operations. Sufficient detail should be included to show the timing of the primary tasks required to accomplish each major goal.

Show on the schedule the deadlines or milestones critical to the venture's success. This should include events as follows:

- Incorporation of the venture (for a new business).
- Completion of prototypes. This is a key date. Its achievement is a tangible measure of the company's ability to perform.
- When sales representatives are obtained.
- Dates of displays at trade shows.
- When distributors and dealers are signed up.

- Order of materials in sufficient quantities for full-time operation.
- Start of operation. This is another key date because it is related to the production of income.
- Receipt of first orders.
- First sales and deliveries. This is a date of maximum interest because it relates directly to the company's credibility and need for capital.
- Payment of first accounts receivable (cash in).

The schedule should also show the following and their relation to the development of the business.

- Number of management personnel
- Number of operations personnel
- Additions to plant or equipment

Discuss in a general way the activities most likely to cause a schedule slippage and what steps you would take to correct such slippages. Discuss the impact of schedule slippages on the venture's operation, especially on its potential viability and capital needs. Keep in mind that the time to do things tends to be underestimated—even more than financing requirements. So be realistic about your schedule.

Critical Risks and Problems

The development of a business has risks and problems, and the business plan invariably contains some implicit assumptions about them. The discovery of any unstated negative factors by potential investors can seriously undermine the credibility of the entrepreneur and his venture and endanger its financing.

On the other hand, identifying and discussing the risks in your venture demonstrates your skill as a manager and in creases your credibility with a venture capital investor. Taking the initiative to identify and discuss risks helps you demonstrate to the investor that you have thought about them and can handle them. Risks then tend not to loom as large black clouds in the investor's thinking about your venture.

Accordingly, identify and discuss the major problems and risks that you think you will have to deal with to develop your venture. This should include a description of the risks relating to your industry, your company and its personnel, your product's market appeal, and the timing and financing of your start-up. Among the risks that might require discussion are the following.

- Price cutting by competitors
- Any potentially unfavorable industry-wide trends
- Design or operating costs significantly in excess of estimates
- Development schedule not met
- Sales projections not achieved by target date
- Difficulties or long lead times encountered in the procurement of parts or raw materials
- Difficulties encountered in obtaining needed bank Background of Venture Capital credit line because of tight money
- Larger than expected innovation and development costs to stay competitive
- Lack of availability of trained labor

This list is not meant to be in any way comprehensive but only indicative of the kinds of risks and assumptions involved.

Indicate which business plan assumptions or potential problems are most critical to the success of the venture. Describe your plans for minimizing the impact of unfavorable developments in each risk area on the success of your venture.

The Financial Plan

The financial plan is basic to any investor's evaluation of your business and should represent your best estimates of future operations. Its purpose is to indicate the financial potential of your venture and its capital needs. The financial plan should also serve as an operating plan for financial management of your business.

In developing your financial plan, three basic exhibits must be prepared.

- Profit and loss forecasts for three years
- Cash flow projections for three years
- Pro forma balance sheets at start-up, semi-annually in the first year, and at the end of each of the first three years of operation.

In the case of an existing business seeking expansion capital, balance sheets and income statements for the current and two prior years should be presented in addition to these financial projections.

After you have completed the preparation of the financial exhibits, briefly highlight in writing the important conclusions that can be drawn. This might include such items as the maximum cash requirement, the amount to be supplied by equity and debt, the level of profits as a percent of sales, and how fast any debts are repaid.

Profit and Loss Forecast

The preparation of your business' projected income statements is the planning-for-profit part of your financial plan. Crucial to the earnings forecasts, as well as other projections, is the sales forecast. The methods for developing sales forecasts have already been described in these guidelines, and the sales forecasts made there should be used here.

The following list is a group of headings that can be used in drawing up your profit and loss (P&L) forecast for prospective investors. Italics indicate items that should be included in the figures for that heading but not listed separately in the statement.

Sales
Less: Discounts
Less: Bad debt provision
Less: Material used
  Direct labor
  Manufacturing overhead
    includes rent, utilities, fringe benefits, telephone.
  Other manufacturing expense
    leased equipment, etc.
  Depreciation
Total cost of goods sold
Gross profit (or loss)
Less: Sales expense
  Engineering expense
  General and administrative expense
    office supplies, accounting and legal services, management, etc.
Operating profit (or loss)
Less: Other expense
    (e.g., interest)
Profit (or loss) before taxes
Income tax provision
Profit (or loss) after taxes

Figures should be projected for three years. The first year should show a breakdown by month for each item. The second and third years should project quarterly figures. Figures for all three years should appear on a single sheet of ruled paper-make sure the paper you use is large enough. Tape two pages together, if necessary.

Once the sales forecasts are in hand, production costs, or operations costs for a service business, should be budgeted. The level of production or operation that is required to meet the sales forecasts and also to fulfill inventory requirements must be determined. The material, labor, service, and manufacturing overhead requirements must be developed and translated into cost data.

Sales expense should include the costs of selling and distribution, storage, discounts, and advertising and promotion. General and administrative expense should include management salaries, secretarial costs, and legal and accounting expenses. Manufacturing or operations overhead includes such items as rent, utilities, fringe benefits, and telephone.

If these earning projections are to be useful, they must represent your realistic and best estimate of probable operating results.

Discussion of Assumptions

Because of the importance of profit and loss projections, you should explain any assumptions that you made in their preparation. Such assumptions could include the amount allowed for bad debts and discounts and sales expenses or general and administrative costs as a fixed percentage of costs or sales.

Cash Flow Forecast

For a new business, the cash flow forecast can be more important than the forecasts of profits because it details the amount and timing of expected cash inflows and outflows. Usually the level of profits, particularly during the start-up years of a venture, will not be sufficient to finance operating cash needs. Moreover, cash inflows do not match the outflows on a short-term basis. The cash flow forecast will indicate these conditions.

The following headings can be used in preparing the pro forma cash flow analysis. Like the income statement, the cash flow analysis should cover three years, with the first year broken down into 12 monthly figures and the second and third year projected by quarters. Again, this analysis should be made on a single large sheet of ruled paper.

Cash balance: Opening
Add: Cash receipts
Collection of accounts receivable
Miscellaneous receipts
Bank loan proceeds
Sale of stock
Total receipts

Less: Disbursements
Trade payables
Direct labor
Manufacturing overhead
Leased equipment
Sales expense
Warranty expense
General and administrative expense
Fixed asset additions
Income tax
Loan interest @ ________%
Loan repayments
Other payments
Total Disbursements

Cash increase (or decrease)
Cash balance: Closing

Given a level of projected sales and capital expenditures over a specific period, the cash flow forecast will highlight the need for and timing of additional financing and show you your peak requirements of working capital. You must decide how this additional financing is to be obtained, on what terms, and how it is to be repaid. Part of the needed financing will be supplied by the professional venture capitalists, part by bank loans for one of five years, and the balance by short-term lines of credit from banks. This information becomes part of the final cash flow forecasts.

If the venture is in a seasonal or cyclical industry, in an industry in which suppliers require a new firm to pay cash, or if an inventory buildup occurs before the product can be sold and produce revenues, the cash flow forecast is crucial to the continuing operation of your business. A detailed cash flow forecast that you understand can enable you to direct your attention to operating problems without the distractions caused by periodic cash crises that you should have anticipated.

Discussion of Assumptions

This should include assumptions made on the timing of collection of receivables, trade discounts given, terms of payments to your suppliers, planned salary and wage increases, anticipated increases in any operating expenses, seasonality characteristics of the business as they affect inventory requirements, and capital equipment purchases. Thinking about such assumptions when planning the operation of your business is useful for identifying issues that may later require attention if they are not to become significant problems.

Balance Sheet Forecasts

The balance sheets are used to show the assets required in the operation of your business and, through liabilities, how these assets are to be financed. Investors and bankers look to the projected balance sheets for such information as debt to equity ratios, working capital, current ratios, and inventory turnover. The investor will relate them to the acceptable limits required to justify future financings that are projected for the venture.

The following headings may be used to prepare the balance sheet forecasts.

Assets
Current assets
Cash
Marketable securities
Inventories
Raw materials and supplies
Work in process
Finished goods
Total inventory

Prepaid items
Total current assets

Plant and equipment
Less: Accumulated depreciation
Net plant and equipment

Deferred charges
Other assets (identify)
Total assets

Liabilities and Stockholder's Equity
Current liabilities
Note payable to banks
Accounts payable
Accruals
Federal and state taxes accrued
Other
Total current liabilities
Long-term notes
Other liabilities
Common stock
Capital surplus
Retained earnings
Total liabilities and stockholder's equity

Forecasted balance sheets should be prepared at start-up, semi-annually for the first year, and at the end of each of the first three years of operation.

Cost and Cash Flow Control

Your ability to meet your income and cash flow projections will depend critically on your ability to secure timely reports on, and effectively control, your operating costs. For this reason, investors will want to know what kind of cost and cash control systems you have or will use in your business. The financial plan should included a brief description of how you will design, install, and maintain systems for controlling costs and cash flows appropriate to the nature and size of your business, who will be responsible for getting cost data, how often cost data will be obtained, and how you will take actions to reduce costs that are running higher than you expected.

Proposed Company Offering

The purpose of this section of the plan is to indicate the amount of capital that is being sought and to briefly describe the uses that will be made of the funds raised. The discussion and guidelines given on this page should help you do this.

Desired Financing

Summarize from your cash flow projections how much money you will need over the next three years to carry out the development and expansion of your business that have been described. Indicate how much of this money you expect to obtain now from the sale of stock and how much you think you can borrow from the bank. Describe the kind (common stock, convertible debenture, etc.), unit price, and total amount of securities to be sold in this offering. Also show the percentage of the company that the investors of this offering will hold after the offering is completed or after any exercise of stock conversion or purchase rights.

Capitalization

Show in a table the names of your current shareholders and the number of shares each holds. Also indicate how many shares of your company's common stock will remain authorized but unissued after the offering.

Use of Funds

Investors like to know how their money is going to be spent. Provide a brief description of how the capital raised will be used. Summarize as specifically as possible what amount will be used for such things as product development, capital equipment, marketing, and general working capital needs.

Writing a Business Plan for a Leveraged Buyout

T. James Herrmann

T. James Herrmann *is president of Pacific Coast Capital, a Larkspur, California, investment banking firm that specializes in private placement of capital for acquisitions and corporate expansion and also performs acquisition search programs. In its leveraged buyout business, Pacific Coast Capital focuses on companies with sales in the range of $20 million to $70 million. Mr. Herrmann previously was associated with the Lawrence Corporate Finance Group in San Francisco and has been president of two middle-market companies. He has a B.S. in Metallurgical Engineering from Michigan State University and an M.B.A. from Harvard Business School.*

Despite the many recent articles and books published on the writing of business plans, we frequently see business plans for leveraged buyouts that are improperly prepared. One reason may be that most available business plan guides are oriented toward start-up or early-stage financings, in which the emphasis is placed on the product or the technology of the new venture. While these are not inconsequential items in a leveraged buyout, they are far less important than other aspects of a proposed transaction, such as the target company's historical financial performance, the management team's experience and the structure of the balance sheet that will result from the transaction.

An investor in an early-stage company looks to sales and earnings growth to achieve a return on investment. A buyout investor, on the other hand, looks initially to the use of financial leverage to achieve a satisfactory return. That return is then enhanced by the improved performance of the company. Lenders in a buyout, meanwhile, are equally concerned with both the quality of the assets and the company's cash flow.

This article provides a detailed outline for writing a buyout business plan. It differs from a business plan for an early-stage company primarily in that it emphasizes those factors that will be of most concern to investors and lenders in the marketplace for middle-sized leveraged buyouts. Let's go through the outline item by item.

First Section: Summary and Financing Request

Summary

This section should be viewed as an executive summary of the deal. It should contain the complete essence of the transaction, the information that would be communicated in a three-to-five minute oral presentation. Remember, this is like the beginning of any

Sources and Use of Funds at Closing ($ thousands)

Sources	Advance	Available
Cash in Company	349	340
Accounts Receivable Line	1,120	1,660
Inventory Line	570	570
Equipment Loan	2,850	2,850
Mezzanine Investor	2,000	2,000
Note to Seller	1,000	1,000
Founders' Investment	500	500
Total Sources	**8,380**	**8,920**
Uses		
Cash to Seller	7,130	
Note to Seller	1,000	
Transaction Fees	250	
Total Uses	**8,380**	

Collateral and Loan Values ($ thousands)

	Book Value	Fair Market Value	Loan Value	Advance Rate	Available Loan Amount
Accounts Receivable	2,060	2,060	1,950	85%	1,660
Inventories	1,610	1,610	1,040	55%	570
Equipment	1,880	3,565	3,565	80%	2,850
Total	**5,550**	**7,235**	**6,555**		**5,080**

book. If the reader's interest isn't whetted at the beginning, he won't make it to the end. The summary should include the following topics:

The Company. Summarize its history and the significant events or major milestones in terms of the business ownership, management, products, customers and markets. Include a summary of the past five years of sales, gross profits and EBIT (earnings before interest and taxes).

Operations. This might better be called the summary of planned changes in operations. Briefly mention the planned changes and the impact they will have on financial performance. Include a summary of a five-year forecast of sales, EBIT and net income.

Management. A brief description of the management, which is a most important aspect of a buyout, deserves a place in the summary. Include a description of the backgrounds of the management team, and supplement this later, in the second section, with either a detailed paragraph or a resume of each individual. If the founders/buyers will be different from the manager currently running the business, describe the new roles and relationships.

Risks and Opportunities. A properly written business plan will present the company in a factual and objective fashion. This section can be used to overcome, or at least address, some of the obvious objections to the proposed transaction.

For example, if the company's plant is in a remote location, the lender will see a risk in using it for collateral. Should the company fail, liquidating the plant probably would be difficult. Such an objection might be overcome by including data about recent sales of nearby facilities, or about local companies that are expanding and in need of space. Another approach might be to point out benefits and opportunities the business enjoys because of its isolated location, such as reasonable labor costs or low worker turnover.

Obvious questions about the deal should be addressed in this section, even if there isn't an easy answer. Most lenders and investors know that they must take some risks and they want those risks to be identified.

Financing Request

Tied together with the summary above, the financing request quickly completes the picture of the proposed deal for the reader. It includes:

Structure of the Deal . This must include the price of the company, the terms of the transaction (whether it will involve, for example, cash, notes, preferred stock, royalty payments, etc.) and the amounts to be raised from all sources, including common stock, preferred stock, subordinated debentures, term debt and lines of credit.

Sources and Uses of Funds at Closing. Include a table describing all sources and uses of funds available for the closing. An example of a sources and uses table from an actual transaction appears with this article.

The "Sources" portion of the table includes two columns of figures, one indicating the total amounts available for the closing and showing the advance actually needed for the closing. The senior lender, based on the company's eligible accounts receivable and the lender's advance rate, made $1.660 million available for an accounts receivable line, but only $1.120 million was funded at closing, leaving a cushion for future working capital needs.

The uses portion of the table includes a line for "Transaction Fees". These are the fees and expenses such as legal, broker, accounting, appraisal, etc.

incurred in putting the buyout together.

Collateral and Loan Values. For the secured lender, prepare a summary table of all collateral available at the closing. The table should include the loan values, advance rates and loan amounts.

An example of a table of collateral and loan values appears in this article. The accounts receivable loan is a revolving credit based on the actual amount of outstanding invoices. The inventory loan is a revolving credit that generally excludes work-in-process inventory. The equipment loan is a term loan based on the appraised orderly liquidation value (OLV), not the fair market value. However, the land and building loan is a term loan which is based on the appraised fair market value.

Second Section: The Company

Industry

Start with an overview of the industry and the nature of the company's business. This helps the reader understand the business context in which the company operates.

Markets. Distinguish between the overall, general marketplace and the segment the company serves, whether it is a niche market or a regional market. When the general market has received negative publicity (as is often the case in mature industries, which offer some of the best candidates for leveraged buyouts), be sure to define the served market clearly. Identify both the positive and negative factors that influence the served market to provide a sense of the market's dynamics.

Market Trends. This is an extension of the discussion of markets. It should describe how the served market is changing in terms of its growth rate, pricing trends, product quality considerations, competition, cyclicality, obsolescence rates, etc. The business plan should relate these trends to the company's position in the marketplace.

Competition. This is one of the most important — and, surprisingly, one of the most frequently neglected — subjects in the presentation. One paragraph should be devoted to each direct competitor. The information should be concise, yet so detailed that each paragraph becomes, in effect, a "mini" business plan of that particular company. Each profile should cover the competitor's size, location, pricing strategy, market share, product quality, financial strength, etc.

It would be helpful to include here a matrix showing the candidate company and its competitors along one axis and the key elements that drive the business — such as sales volume, pricing points, quality levels, location, financial strength, sales strategies, etc. — along the other. In one glance, this would give a reader an overview of the industry and the buyout candidate's position within it. The matrix should be included here within the competition section, not in the exhibits.

Company History

This section should relate the history of the company's ownership, management, products, customers and markets. In general, the early history of an older business should be mentioned briefly, with more details added as the summary draws closer to the present.

Products

Describe products and services in terms of how they differ from what the competition offers. What are the price points? What are the benefits to the customer? Don't get too technical here; reserve technical information for an appendix. Include separate charts that show sales and gross margins by product line, both before and after the proposed buyout. This will demonstrate how planned changes in the product mix would affect performance.

Operations and Facilities

Include a general description of the company's plants and their locations, its equipment and its sales offices. Save the detailed descriptions of equipment, plants, land and buildings for the Description of Assets section below.

Operating, Selling and Marketing Plan

This may be broken into its separate subject areas, but, essentially, this section should describe the new owners' plans for the operations of the company. It should explain all planned changes, as well as aspects of the operation that will remain unchanged and why. The changes should be described in terms of their financial impact and related to the financial projections contained in the third section. A company break-even chart — showing sales volume on one axis and costs on the other — would be helpful to the reader here.

Management

This section may expand upon the relationships between the new owners and the former management. Include an organization chart and a paragraph or detailed resume on each of the key members of management. The resumes should be formatted in reverse chronological order, showing dates of employment, company, position and accomplishments in each job. Use a track-record approach that relates previous experience to the task at hand.

Description of Assets A secured lender will want to know a lot about the assets being purchased, with particular emphasis on their value in a liquidation. This section should describe the following assets in detail:

Accounts Receivable. Include a summary of the receivables aging; a more detailed description can be provided as an appendix or upon request. Also, this section should cover terms, customers (include a list of major accounts), concentration of accounts, bad-debt experience, any receivables that have been dated, repurchase agreements, etc.

Inventory. This should include a description of inventories by the categories of finished goods, work-in-process and raw materials. It should describe their marketability in a distress sale.

Machinery and Equipment. A forced liquidation and an orderly liquidation appraisal is essential, but wait for a recommendation from the lender before paying for one. In the meantime, use management's estimates of the value.

Land and Buildings. It will be necessary to have both market value and liquidation value appraisals of these assets. It should also be obtained from an appraiser that your lender recommends, or one who has the general acceptance of many lenders. Put summaries of appraisals in the narrative; enclose the actual appraisals in an appendix.

Liabilities

Where appropriate, describe liabilities that the buyout group would assume, such as payables, debt, contingent liabilities, product liability claims, etc.

Price of the Company

It is generally advisable to explain how the price of the company was determined. It may be based on other recent transactions, on price-to-free-cash-flow or other ratios, or on rules-of-thumb used to value companies in the industry. If payment terms are used, they should be translated into their present value using the discounted cash flow method, or their cash-equivalent value, taking into account the lower value that notes, preferred stock and royalties will have coming from a leveraged company.

Third Section: Financial Review

Historical Financial Statements

The financial statements should include audited or reviewed annual income statements, balance sheets and cash flow statements for the last three to five years. Also include the most recent year-to-date statements. If the company's business is seasonal, a one-year cash flow statement should be included and should be broken out by month.

Forecasted Financial Performance

The forecasted financials should spell out in detail all assumptions that are built into them. Many of these assumptions will be based on the planned changes in operations described in the operating, selling and marketing plan contained in the second section.

These forecasted financials should include spreadsheets with income statements, balance sheets, and cash flow statements. There should be at least two sets of spreadsheets: One by month for one or two years, and one by year for five years.

Cash Flow Formats

Financial sources require realistic cash flow statements to help them decide whether they want to do the transaction. The best cash flow format for this purpose, therefore, is one showing receipts and disbursements, sometimes called the "checkbook" format. A format that shows sources and applications, including changes in balance sheet items, is acceptable but sometimes not as useful.

Sensitivity Analysis

Investors are bombarded by stacks of spreadsheet

analyses filled with pie-in-the-sky numbers. Nevertheless, a leveraged buyout can lend itself to a reasonable and objective use of alternative scenarios. The business plan might include several runs (summaries only). Additional scenarios could be provided to specific lenders or investors upon request. Include a sensitivity matrix that along one axis shows critical assumptions, such as sales levels, interest rates, or the gross margin and along the other axis shows their impact on key financial results, such as profitability, cash flow, reduction of debt or coverage ratios.

Exhibits

Wherever possible, tables, graphs and other exhibits should be incorporated into the text. This way, the reader doesn't have to thumb back and forth between the text and an exhibits section at the back of the document. However, some exhibits don't lend themselves to such treatment and need to be placed in an exhibits section. Examples would be copies of the letter of intent, the secured debt proposal, appraisals and product literature.

Appendix

Prepare a separate appendix that financial sources with a strong interest in the project might use as reference material for a due diligence undertaking. This booklet might include a receivable aging, inventory listings, historical financial statements, patents, products or technical literature, market studies, magazine articles and annual reports of industry participants.

General Comments

In developing the business plan, remember the 80/20 rule and be sure that 80% of the plan addresses the 20% of the issues that are of the greatest concern to the financial sources. Don't follow a long check list. Omit unimportant items.

Envision the plan as though it were a resume for a job search. Just as a good resume doesn't guarantee a job but might open the door for an interview, a business plan is, in effect, the preparation and script that might clear the way for a personal presentation that can raise the capital. Make your oral presentation parallel your plan.

When structuring your deal, keep in mind the issues created by laws governing fraudulent conveyance, equitable subordination, and environmental protection. Because of recent court decisions, lenders and investors are increasingly concerned about potential liabilities that could result from violations of these laws.

Bear in mind that, regardless of how well the plan is prepared, the most important element in any buyout is its proper structuring. This includes the purchase terms and the various layers of financing. Get help from an advisor with experience in leveraged buyouts.

Put plenty of equity and/or subordinated capital in the deal. Leveraging a healthy company puts it in trouble on day one. If it needs more capital for growth, the company takes a double whammy, and if the business requires seasonal lines, it takes a triple whammy. Equity and sub debt allow the business to operate with leverage and weather some storms.

How to Choose and Approach a Venture Capitalist

Jack Tankersley

Jack Tankersley *has spent 30 years in the venture capital industry. He is founder of Meritage Private Equity Funds, a Colorado-based VC firm with $480 million of capital under management.*

In the aftermath of the dot com and telecom meltdown, venture capital firms ("VCs") are very cautious about whom they back and what they fund. While significant amounts of money are available for investment, the venture capital industry is only cautiously putting money to work. It is therefore essential for entrepreneurs to select the right VCs to approach, obtain a credible introduction and be properly prepared for the VC meeting in order to succeed in the fundraising process.

Choosing the Right Venture Capital Firm

Identifying the most appropriate group of venture capitalists to approach is critical. It is surprising how little research many entrepreneurs conduct before they begin the time-consuming task of raising capital. Two problems can result from approaching venture capitalists unprepared. First, once an investment opportunity is rejected, it is very difficult to get it reconsidered, even with a proper introduction. Second, if an investment opportunity is rejected by a number of firms, it may get an "over-shopped" reputation. Venture capitalists frequently share investment information and a turndown by one firm may influence others.

Gathering preliminary information to narrow the field of potential VC firms is key. The internet makes collecting background information on venture firms quite easy. Information on a VC's website is a good starting place. Specifically, an entrepreneur should set out to gather information on VCs based on five factors: geographical location, stage of development preference, investment level parameters, industry focus and whether the firm prefers to lead investments. This information is important as it provides five ways for choosing venture capital firms that are most likely to respond to your business plan.

The first filter you should apply is geography. If you are based in an area well served by venture capital, a "local lead" investor is critical. If you cannot attract a local lead, you will have a more difficult time raising capital elsewhere. Although there are many firms investing nationwide, the closer the venture capitalist is to the investment, the easier it is to add value and to monitor the investment, especially in early-stage companies. Today, virtually every region of the country is home to experienced venture capitalists.

Secondly, many venture capitalists have a stage of development bias. There are some who prefer the seed capital arena while others are interested only in later-stage investing. Make certain your company's stage of development matches the stage preferred by the venture firm you are approaching. One word of caution: many in the venture capital industry invest in "startups," but definitions vary between firms. A start-up for one firm can actually be a later-stage investment for another. So beware of inconsistent uses of stage of development terms.

The third criterion is amount of capital needed. There are many firms that have an upper and lower limit to the size of an investment. If your project falls far outside a firm's range, it is better not to approach them. Also, it is unwise to inflate the amount of capital you need to meet their minimum. Some venture capitalists shy away from large dollar syndications and prefer to invest smaller amounts to give them a meaningful position in an emerging company. These firms may be more appropriate for your initial requirements.

The venture capital industry is witnessing greater industry specialization than ever before. This is the fourth filter to apply to your search. There are venture capital firms and individual venture capitalists that specialize in medical technology, communications, consumer products and distribution, for instance. Clearly, if a venture capital firm has a stated investment preference in your industry, not only is it more likely to understand your opportunity, but it will also be in a position to add value to your company. This industry expertise is often acknowledged and respected by other VCs that may provide additional funding. In addition, a number of venture capital firms have excluded certain investment categories such as real estate or oil and gas.

Finally, in every successful venture capital financing, there is a need for venture capital leadership. There are a number of funds that are active investors and are willing to lead a financing, while others serve as passive investors. In order to complete a syndication, you will need venture capital leadership. It is unwise to approach passive investors until after a lead investor is identified. Therefore, identify venture capitalists that take early leadership roles in syndications similar to your opportunity.

Using these five criteria as a basis, prepare a target group of venture capitalists. Make certain that this target group is a reasonable size. No one likes to receive a business plan that is number 128, knowing it has been sent to a broad audience. A simple matrix may assist this effort. For example, subjectively rate a venture firm's investment orientation as it relates to your firm's needs. Let two (2) represent a good match, one (1) represent an acceptable match and zero (0) represent a poor match. The VCs with the highest ratings should be the initial targets. Obvious trade-offs occur. Be prepared to make fine discriminations between the relative importance of these key factors.

By applying this method, you can successfully narrow your VC targets. However, before you approach a targeted venture capital firm, research it thoroughly. Learn as much as possible about the people who lead the firm and the companies it has funded. In addition to websites, most firms publish brochures which offer more information. A phone call can usually result in obtaining a copy of the brochure. This information has been thoughtfully prepared to generate investment opportunities that fit the firm's interests and to discourage opportunities that do not.

This background information will further qualify the types of investments the VC has made. Venture capitalists' past successes can offer insight to their areas of personal interest and expertise.

Once the target group has been identified and the firms have been researched, it is now time to approach the venture capitalist.

How to Approach the Venture Capitalist

The best way to approach a venture capitalist is through a quality introduction, because venture capitalists are more likely to turn down an unsolicited business plan. This introduction may be through a banker, a lawyer, an accountant, another entrepreneur or even another venture capitalist. If your banker, lawyer or accountant appears unwilling to provide an introduction, their hesitancy may indicate doubts about the financeability of you and/or your product. If your contact does not know venture capitalists, you may have the wrong banker, lawyer or accountant.

If you are well known by a successful entrepreneur who has received funding from a specific venture capitalist, this is often the best introduction as venture capitalists pay particular attention to such relationships. Be careful with venture capital references, however. If one venture capitalist you ask for an introduction has turned you down, others will want to know why. If a venture capitalist whom you ask is a passive investor, but introduces you to an active investor with the comment "if you invest, we want to do it with you," this can be very positive. (The same holds true even if a venture firm is fully invested and is not currently making new commitments.)

Be sure to prepare the person making an introduction. Provide them with an executive summary that clearly highlights the opportunity. Remember, they are selling on your behalf – help them be successful.

Finally, if you use someone's name as a means of introduction to a venture capitalist, make sure you have permission to do so. Most venture capitalists will call your reference before meeting with you – if they aren't a supporter of you and your idea, you will lose significant credibility.

The Purpose of the Initial Contact

The initial contact following the introduction should be by telephone or e-mail. The purpose of this contact is to convince the venture capitalist to request your business plan and to have that business plan read upon receipt. There are a number of articles and books on writing a business plan and a number of service organizations -including accounting firms, consultants and investment bankers – specializing in business plan preparation. It is important to understand that the sole purpose of sending the business plan to a venture capitalist is to get a meeting. Let the significance of a meeting be clear. The majority of business plans received by a venture capitalist are turned down after the initial reading. In a typical scenario, a VC may receive hundreds if not thousands of plans in a year, and meet with only 60 teams and fund 3 to 5 ideas. Firms that invest in more companies per year will have a corresponding increase in business plan submissions.

The business plan should be concise, well written and include a summary that covers the following five essential points:

1 What is the market and growth opportunity? Different risk profiles exist for business plans in established markets versus ideas aimed at creating a new market. An entrepreneur must be able to clearly articulate the existing market dynamics and why strong growth can be expected over the next five years.

2 Who are the people on the management team and why are they qualified to succeed in the endeavor? Many venture capitalists state that they invest in people before products or markets. Therefore, to build a credible case, the people who are responsible for making it happen must be highlighted.

3 How well has the business succeeded to date? Any business, even a seed capital entity, has a history. Detail this history and describe what has been accomplished with the time and resources to date. In today's market, many venture capitalists are leery of investing in conceptual business ideas. Entrepreneurs are being rewarded for well developed ideas which include a completed product and beta customers.

4 What is the company's unique competitive advantage? The era of "first mover advantage" has lost its appeal to most venture capitalists. While "me too" investments are no longer funded, it is still essential to demonstrate a solid value proposition for your target customers and a clear advantage over other product solutions and competitors.

5 How well do you expect it to do? Most businesses do not meet a venture capitalist's expectations because of the size or scope of the potential business. As a rule of thumb, a company should have the potential to return multiples of the initial investment within three to five years to be of interest.

Unfortunately, in the initial review venture capitalists generally look for reasons to turn down an investment rather than search for reasons to invite you for a meeting. For example, typographical errors, incomplete or erroneous market information and ill-conceived organizational structures are all negatives.

Finally, many business plans don't "sell" the idea. Too often business plans lead investors to conclusions that are inaccurate. It is helpful to include an investment highlights page at the beginning of the plan which clearly articulates the business, market, product, management and other success indicators. Make it easy for the venture capitalist to understand your business.

Meeting the Venture Capitalist

If a meeting has been set up, be prepared to make a formal presentation. Bring a PowerPoint presentation, which has been tailored to address questions that arose during your initial telephone calls. However, be prepared to deviate from this agenda if necessary. Never answer a question with "we will be getting to that later in the presentation." Demonstrate that you can be agile. The venture capitalist is using the meeting to learn about the product and market but is primarily focusing on evaluating you and your team. Remember, you may have limited time to make a positive impression and to leave the venture capitalist enthusiastic about your company.

The entrepreneur should also use the meeting to size up the venture capitalist. Do not hesitate to ask a prospective investor for references, especially names of other portfolio entrepreneurs. Call them and find out how well they have worked together, from the entrepreneurs' perspectives.

Deepening the Relationship with the Venture Capitalist

Once you have met with a venture capitalist, you will have to work hard to keep their attention. Always have a reason to contact the venture capitalist, rather than simply asking about the status of your business plan. Offer "good news" updates on the progress of your business. Make their learning process about your market and product as easy as possible. If they have questions or concerns, follow up with relevant research or information that addresses their issues. Suggest that the venture capitalist call customers (or beta customers), as this is always useful information. In addition, if you have industry experts on your advisory board, suggest that you arrange a call. If you think your product or service would be particularly useful to one of the VC's existing portfolio companies, suggest that the VC introduce you to the company so they can evaluate your product. This is one of the most credible means for a VC to secure validation of your product. Ultimately, it is your responsibility to keep the VC's attention and push your plan through the due diligence process. Don't let your plan stand idle in the stack of other plans.

In today's venture capital marketplace you must be well prepared to successfully compete for VC dollars. It is the task of the entrepreneur to prudently select and approach the venture capitalist. If this is done wisely and systematically, you will improve your odds of putting together an appropriate venture capital syndicate.

How to Choose and Approach a Buyout Firm

Keith R. Larson

Keith R. Larson *is a corporate business development manager with Intel Corporation, the world's largest manufacturer of microprocessors, where he pursues strategic investments related to the networking industry. Before joining Intel, he operated a consulting practice focused on M&A and investment banking advisory services. He is a co-founder and former general partner of InterVen II, L.P., a growth buyout and venture capital fund. Mr. Larson is a CPA, and also served as CFO of the buyout and venture capital subsidiary of a large bank holding company.*

Before a management team mails a business plan or places a phone call to set up a meeting with a buyout fund, the management group must decide which buyout funds it will approach for financing. An important first step is to realize how buyout firms differ from traditional venture capital funds. Buyout funds are interested in more mature companies and are much less specialized than most venture capital funds in the industries in which they invest. While venture funds may be restrictive in their focus, buyout funds have a focus that is much more general, sometimes encompassing an entire industry, such as manufacturing or service-related businesses.

Management should contact an adequate number of prospective financial partners, so that even if a few decline the opportunity, there are still enough interested firms to fund the investment. The exact number is difficult to pin down, but many people feel more comfortable initially selecting a small group of prospective partners - maybe six to ten - and then approaching additional firms if any of the initial prospects declines the opportunity. Don't flood the market with business plans, however. My former fund received countless plans from management teams that didn't bother to follow up with phone calls or other communications. Whenever this happens, I suspect there are so many copies of the business plan floating around that management isn't in control of the fund-raising process.

Criteria for Selecting a Financial Partner

The most important and easiest criterion in targeting potential financial partners is the size of the buyout opportunity. It is unlikely that a $1 billion fund will be interested in committing its time and resources to a buyout requiring only $10 million of equity financing. When judging a buyout firm's appetite and capability for pursuing a certain buyout size, management must also consider whether the fund will be the sole investor or participate with other funds. The size of the buyout also will determine fees. Legal, accounting, and investment banking fees can run into hundreds of thousands, even millions, of dollars, and management should inquire as to the buyout firm's willingness to cover these up-front costs.

The strategic direction of a buyout the type of transaction it represents and how it will be managed is as important as its size in deciding which funds to target. Some buyout funds won't consider investing in a growth buyout because of the added financial risk inherent in aggressively growing the business. Similarly, many funds won't invest in turnaround situations in which the target company lacks a solid earnings history. A buyout fund's investment horizon also should be evaluated. If the management team is interested in quickly flipping the buyout, it probably won't attract a fund that has a long-term outlook. The key point here is finding a buyout fund whose goals are coincident with management's.

Management must also ascertain the buyout firm's ability to help attract bank or mezzanine financing. To the extent the buyout firm can help overcome financing hurdles, it increases the probability that the deal will close. Some buyout funds have established special relationships with particular lenders. They refer the majority of their deals to these lenders, which, because they are familiar with a particular buyout firm's standard, will render a decision quickly. Other buyout funds have bank or insurance companies as limited partners, and these institutions frequently look to the firm as a source of deals. Some banks are fully integrated and provide all the layers of financing (i.e., bank debt, mezzanine financing and equity financing) that are needed to complete a buyout.

The final consideration is geographical. A local buyout firm may already be familiar with the buyout candidate. It can also do the legwork needed to attract more distant partners if additional funds are required.

The Buyout Financing Process

Approaching a buyout firm is just one part of putting a leveraged acquisition together. The buyout financing process begins when a management team identifies a company to buy, as this flow chart illustrates. The team next has a decision to make: Whether to engage an investment banker to help line up financing. With or without an investment bank, the next few steps are similar. In consultation with its advisors, the management team prices and structures the proposed buyout, writes a business plan and identifies financing sources to approach with the deal. The financing sources will include an equity partner and a debt provider at minimum and, depending on how the deal is structured, perhaps a provider of mezzanine financing as well. It is useful to approach different types of financing sources simultaneously to get an indication of which types of financing will be most difficult to obtain. A financing source that is seriously interested will proceed to the due diligence step. Any financing source that agrees to fund the buyout should provide a commitment letter, which can be used to revisit uncommitted financing sources and to maintain momentum. Once financing is completely arranged, lawyers draft the necessary documents, while accountants and others perform preclosing "testwork," such as a physical inventory of property and equipment. Once all conditions have been satisfied, the buyout moves to its closing.

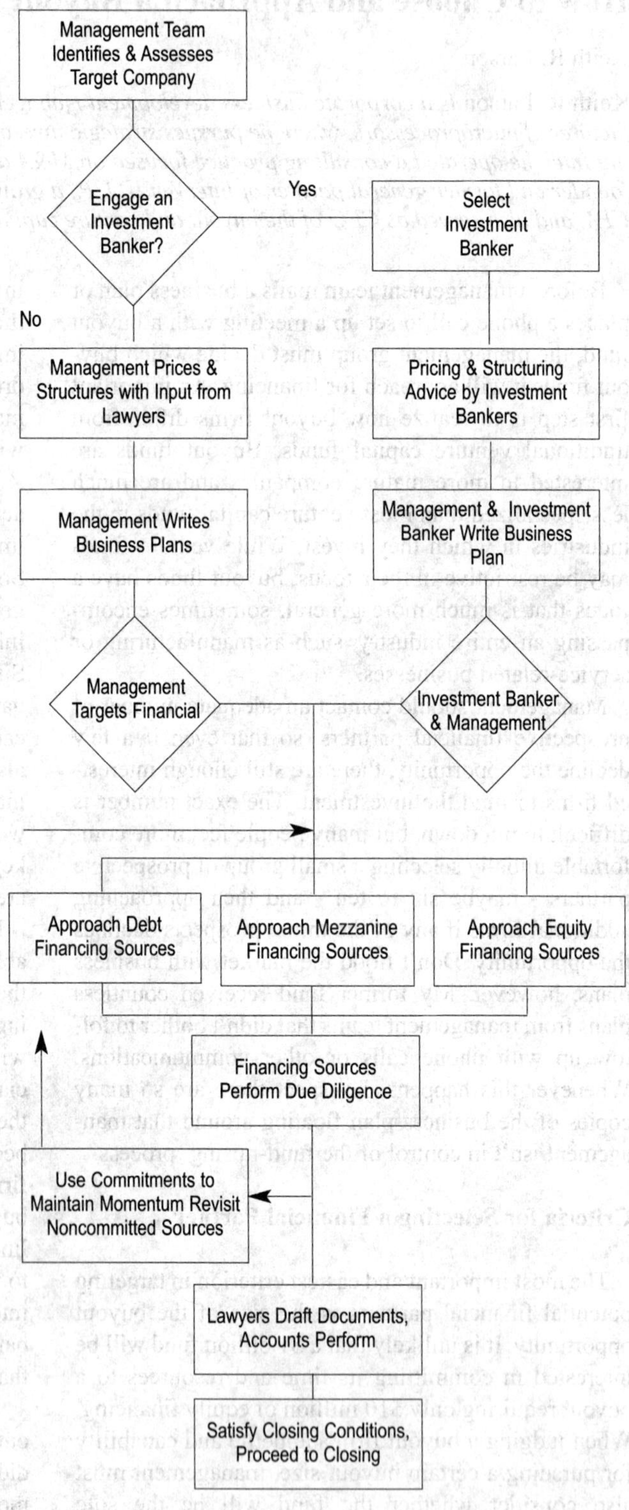

Location can also be a factor in the early stages of a buyout as the firm visits plants and completes its due diligence. Even so, the geographic location of a financing source is not as important a consideration in a buyout as it is in a venture capital transaction. In addition to the national presence many buyout candidates already have, they also generally require less-intensive management after the investment is made than does an early-stage company with venture capital backing.

Management might want to consider using an investment banker to help it target financial partners. Investment bankers know whom to contact and how to make introductions. It is rare, however, for an investment banker to actually raise the equity. Management is the key to successfully operating the buyout, and most funds want to interact directly with the management team. This doesn't necessarily diminish the value of investment bankers. They can help structure the transaction and assemble collateral financial and market data. They also can play a significant role in placing the mezzanine financing with institutional investors, since their contacts in that area are usually well developed.

Credibility and Communication

How do you approach a buyout firm? Contrary to popular belief, you don't sneak up on them. Just as management will gravitate towards more reputable firms in its investigation of potential partners, the buyout firm is going to be interested in a management group with credibility. A buyout firm will find most credible a management group that it has worked with before (successfully, of course). If management has received favorable attention in the industry, this, too will give it credibility with the buyout firm.

Since those situations are relatively rare, most managers will have to rely on the next best alternative: An introduction. The key to the introduction is that it should be made by someone the buyout firm respects. Candidates for the introduction include lawyers, accountants, bankers, consultants, friends and relatives. If management has elected to hire an investment banker, this will be one of his principal duties.

Credibility alone, however, doesn't make a buyout investment attractive. Creating an opportunity and communicating it to the buyout firm is crucial. The management team usually identifies and champions a buyout opportunity, and a buyout fund wants to see management's confidence in the potential of its proposed transaction. Management must demonstrate its commitment to success. It must prove it has the stamina and drive needed to complete the financing process and the willingness to "get down into the trenches" to fight. Management also must be ready to invest a meaningful amount of its net worth. This does not mean, however, that the buyout fund will want its manager/partners spending sleepless nights worrying that they have invested their last dime into the company. The fact is that more buyouts fail to get financed due to lack of drive and planning than due to a lack of management's finances.

Management should be careful not to sell itself short when presenting an opportunity to a buyout firm. As buyouts become more competitive, prices paid get stretched to the upper boundaries of reasonability. As this happens, management and marketing considerations begin to take on increased importance relative to historical financial analysis. In describing the buyout opportunity, many managements tend to let numerical analysis overshadow their own accomplishments. Buyout firms know that a business won't be successful without people of talent and quality. Part of describing the attractiveness of the buyout is demonstrating how the management team's background has prepared its members for achieving their goals and objectives.

A very important element in describing the opportunity is establishing management's command of the specific tactics required to reach the stated goals and objectives. This is critical in growth and turnaround buyouts. It simply isn't enough to say management plans to grow the ABC Division 20% per year or to cut expenses 30%. Management's description of and support for specific plans paint the picture of opportunity for the buyout firm.

The best medium for communicating all of this, of course, is the business plan, especially the executive summary. Every new business plan competes for a buyout firm's attention with other business plans, pending due diligence work and the needs of investments already in the fund's portfolio. A strong, concise executive summary grabs the attention of the buyout firm and directs it to the body of the plan, where the nuts and bolts of an opportunity are described.

Price and Structure

The primary question management must ask is, Will the buyout fund see this situation as an attractive opportunity? Price and structure directly affect the buyout firm's answer. Management should establish specific parameters regarding prices at which it will find the opportunity attractive. The purchase price must be an amount that will, after proper structuring, yield an attractive rate of return to the buyout fund. The rate of return required will depend on the type of buyout targeted. For example, growth or turnaround buyouts have higher perceived risks and generally command higher returns than a standard leveraged buyout.

Another consideration is the stage of the transaction at which pricing occurs. Depending on the type of buyout and the specific situation of the target company, the price may be established early in the process. In other instances, a final price may not be determined until well into the financing process. Up-front price commitments are frequently seen in friendly corporate spin-offs. In hostile buyouts or auction situations, a firm price may not be established until later in the negotiations.

The structure of the transaction must take into account the rates of return required by equity and mezzanine providers, the operations of the company, such as peak working capital needs, and any special terms negotiated in the purchase price. Some structuring issues, such as whether to buy stock or assets and what the tax effect will be, may require outside advisors. But management should have a clear idea of the price and structure needed to yield a self-sustaining opportunity that won't require additional investment in the near term.

Initially, it is useful to approach different types of financing sources simultaneously. This allows management to evaluate and anticipate the sources that are going to be the most difficult to close. For example, the ease with which the buyout can be bank-financed may determine whether mezzanine financing will be required. Any positive answers, such as a firm commitment, should be passed on to all noncommitted sources to maintain the momentum.

Meeting with the Buyout Firm

The management team must have a clear idea of what it wants to convey in its initial meeting with the buyout firm, and it will need a well polished presentation to achieve those goals. Buyout firms will judge the transaction on management's ability to communicate its plan for achieving success. Management should anticipate tough questions. A team approach to the presentation is best, because it gives the buyout firm a chance to evaluate individual managers as well as the team as a whole. The team approach also insures that the meeting will cover all key business areas, such as marketing, finance, sales and operations.

The goal of the initial meeting is to leave the buyout firm with and interest in pursuing the investment. Ask what the next step is in the firm's selection process. Don't expect to leave with a commitment after the first, second or even third meeting. If the buyout firm remains interested in pursuing the deal, it will proceed to the next step: Due diligence.

Facing Up to Due Diligence

What should management expect from a buyout firm's due diligence? In a word, thoroughness. My former fund has seen everything from simple exaggeration to non-disclosed criminal records. Management should assume that the buyout firm will ferret out all the negatives. If management explains the negatives at the beginning of the due diligence process, at least it will control how the negatives are presented to the buyout firm. Any information management can prepare in advance will expedite the process.

When tangible assets significantly affect the price of a buyout, a condition to closing may be a physical inventory inspection by an independent accountant. Depending on how the terms of the buyout were structured, this type of inventory test work may provide price protection for the seller, the buyer, or both. Physical inventorying of property, plant and equipment also is fairly common. Other "cutoff" work may be performed to assure that transactions are recorded in the proper period.

Obtaining Commitments and Negotiating Terms

When a financing source finally agrees to fund the buyout, management should get a commitment letter. My former partners and current associates like to refer to these letters as "Swiss cheese" because they are full of holes. Although these holes may allow the financing source to get out of its commitment, the letters are considered to represent a good-faith obligation to perform. These commitments are used to maintain and gain momentum in the financing process. It is amazing how much interest can be generated with other financing sources after one firm legitimizes the opportunity with a commitment. A commitment not only attracts additional financing sources; it substantially reduces the risk to the other sources that the transaction will fail to be financed.

A "term sheet" should be drafted for the buyout. The timing of this will depend on the nature of the buyout. In friendly buyouts, terms often are negotiated early in the process. The more details that are ironed out in the terms sheet, the easier it will be to complete the final documents. When it appears likely that all necessary financial commitments will be obtained, the lawyers should begin drafting documents. During the entire process, management may want to consider using separate legal counsel to represent its own interests.

Closing the deal is the fun part of the process. But it isn't the time to relax. Management must be attentive to avoid letting unexpected little problems derail the closing. Press the lawyers, accountants, financial partners and everyone else to get the documents signed.

Summary

When preparing to solicit buyout firms for financing, use a rifle not a shotgun approach. In all prospective financial partners, look for that quintessential element: The desire and will to make the deal come together. Throughout the financing process, sell yourselves and the opportunity in the same manner and with the same intensity as you would sell to your most valued customer. If you are not firmly convinced of the opportunity, the buyout firm won't be either.

Meeting with the Venture Capitalist

Wayne B. Kingsley

Wayne B. Kingsley *is a general partner of InterVen Partners, Inc., a venture capital firm with offices in Portland, OR, and Los Angeles. He has 18 years of venture capital experience. Prior to joining InterVen in 1983, Mr. Kingsley was a vice president of Norwest Venture Capital Management, Inc., a Minneapolis-based small business investment company. From 1972 to 1976, he was chief operating officer of Cascade Capital Corporation, which was acquired by Norwest in 1976. Mr. Kingsley is a graduate of Miami University of Ohio and has an M.B.A. from the Darden School at the University of Virginia.*

Obtaining financing for your firm is no different than any other selling task. Every step is important. One of the more critical steps is the first meeting with your customer—the venture capitalist. The impressions formed during this meeting will be the basis for his or her subsequent regard for you and your proposal. Your initial objective is to convince the venture capitalist that your proposal merits further investigation. Your task in this meeting is to present the essence of your plan in a clear, concise manner.

Hopefully, the venture capitalist has studied your plan before meeting with you, but the chances are it was just skimmed. Even worse, the only knowledge of the proposal may be from your telephone conversation or the two page summary you sent. So assume that very little is remembered about your business and that other partners or junior associates totally unfamiliar with your proposal will attend this meeting and will be there to render advice or do subsequent investigation work.

In preparation, you should plan and rehearse a half-hour explanation of your proposal that describes the company's business, the market and external environment in which it operates, the strengths of the management team and similarities to other successful ventures. The presentation should emphasize your proposal's strengths. Weak points as well as remedies for them should also be addressed, to illustrate your recognition of them. You should also state why this will be a profitable investment for the venture capitalist. To do this you have to state your objectives for the company, and how you will attain them. Be reasonable. Even if you firmly believe you will achieve $200 million in sales your first year, revise your projections to something more conservative and consistent with the average, successful venture-backed company.

What image should you convey? First, you should be natural. If you and the venture capitalist want to continue discussions, this will be the first of many meetings. You are going to see each other at the best and worst moments. So a good starting point is the "real you." Beyond this, be confident. You are offering the investor an opportunity to invest in a very promising company, one in which you have decided to risk a part of your life and assets. The venture capitalist may become your partner, so you want to demonstrate your potential as a good partner. Always use reason rather than argument.

When you have concluded your presentation, you want your listeners to have a clear and concise understanding of your business, what is unique about it and how you will achieve your projections. Something they could easily explain to others.

It is most important they understand what is unique about the proposal, if it is not the product then the management team or the location or something else. Very few venture capitalists will invest in something which is a "me-too" product going against established competition.

Using visual aids for your presentation is strictly a matter of preference. Remember, one reason for the meeting is to establish rapport. Overhead projections, slides and videotapes diminish contact and may minimize the interchange of a head-on presentation. Many venture capitalists' offices, however, have equipment to accommodate visual presentations, so do what you think is necessary to present yourself in the best light.

Handling Questions

During and after your presentation, you should be prepared for questions. You may assume the venture capitalist knows something about your business and will ask some obvious questions and some that are more penetrating. Your assumptions may also be challenged. Some of the questions may be blunt and some may expose preconceptions with which you disagree.

You may not be questioned at all in these areas. In other words, prepare for any response.

How do you handle this? If you have done your homework and know your business, you should be able to answer most questions in a brief and concise manner. If you do not know the answer or have to prepare an answer, this is an ideal opportunity to arrange another meeting to deliver the necessary information. If you disagree with a statement the venture capitalist makes, explain your reasons and offer to provide additional information on the subject. Do not get sidetracked from your objective by arguing a small point. In the case of an obvious objection which was not raised, you may want to bring it up for discussion so that it does not become a problem if the venture capitalist thinks of it after you have gone.

Even if the person you are talking to is a technological whiz kid in your field, try to keep the meeting focused on the big picture and not get off on details of a technology that he may not be able to fully comprehend in a brief first meeting. Discuss the quality of the management team's technological capabilities and the accomplishments of the technologists. To assess technology, most venture capitalists will hire consultants and check the reputations of the technical people in your company, rather than rely on their own knowledge of the technology. They will probably be more concerned in this first meeting with your ability to demonstrate your overall business acumen.

Maintaining Momentum

If the venture capitalist seems interested, find out what the next step in the process will be. Even the best intentioned people can become involved with a new proposal or with the many flash fires which occur in any portfolio. What you want to do is get a tentative schedule set up with dates and milestones that will hopefully lead to an investment. Once scheduled, you and the prospective investor should keep to these dates religiously. If the venture capitalist starts to fall seriously behind schedule or becomes too distant, this might indicate disinterest in your proposal. If this happens, you will probably have to find a replacement investor who will be more active. Do not be surprised, however, if the first venture capitalist becomes very interested and active again when a deal starts to go together.

Entrepreneurs are always trying to develop a magic money raising strategy. If investors cannot be convinced of the merits of the investment, no amount of intrigue or cosmetics will improve your chances for funding. However, how you present and market your proposal can influence the value investors place on it, as well as their degree of comfort with you and the other members of the management team.

Camp Followers

One common strategy question is whether or not to involve "camp followers" in the project. Camp followers may be of two types. The first is a series of smaller investors who "seed" the deal to establish price and credibility and the second type is the well-known person who becomes an advisor or a director, primarily to establish credibility. This type may also make a small investment to confirm faith in the project.

Do not add camp followers to your project if there is no operational benefit from doing so. Small, unsophisticated investors can complicate a larger venture financing by making compliance with securities laws more difficult, by balking at the seemingly onerous terms of the professional financing, by "helping" negotiate the terms and by presenting an unstated but always present risk of suit in the future. New and growing companies often go from crisis to crisis before achieving success. These crises are usually better met by the professionals who deal with them daily. On the other hand, a number of companies start and grow successfully with only the help of smaller investors. If small investors are essential to your company, by all means embrace them. If you plan an institutional venture financing, prepare them for this event.

A number of successful companies have included well-known business people on their boards of directors. Sometimes these people are sought out as advisors or merely passive investors. Far too often these people are included only for cosmetic purposes, similar to an athlete endorsing a brand of running shoe. These people usually add nothing to the company and occasionally they can be detrimental, if they try to become too involved and do not really understand small businesses. On the other hand, a talented person, with proven ability who has worked, and intends to continue working with a business can be an invaluable asset. This decision should be based on whether or not the person will actually take time to work with the company and has the specific talents required to add value.

A few additional helpful hints:

Requiring signed secrecy agreements can be an impediment to obtaining financing. Before you decide to ask for these, make sure that the secret is really worth all the effort. It should also be an easily definable entity—like the formula for Coca-cola.

Investors generally want some rights and information that may not initially appear reasonable. It is perfectly proper to negotiate, but not on every point. Fight only for the issues that seem most important to you. If the investor does the same thing, the chances are neither of you will be left with many substantive areas of disagreement.

Do not become discouraged. Every venture capitalist is different. Sometimes the same proposal will appeal to a number of them. Often one will be interested in funding a proposal that is of no interest to others. Keep looking until you find the person who likes your company.

The investor will usually negotiate price and terms after the proposal has been investigated. In the beginning, you should talk about price only to ensure the investor's expectations are in a reasonable range. At the end of the process, you and the investor will have considerable time and money invested in each other and will have incentive to strike a deal you each can accept. If you try to negotiate price in the beginning of the relationship, it is much easier to walk away from each other.

For the venture capital relationship to be successful, it has to be built on trust and mutual respect. When negotiating price the relationship is adversarial, when working through problems and facing a competitive world, it must be supportive. If either party suspects such a relationship cannot be perfected, it should be abandoned. Be open and honest with your current and prospective investors and demand the same from them.

Venture Capital: More Than Money?

Dr. Jeffry A. Timmons and Dr. Harry J. Sapienza

Dr. Jeffry A. Timmons *is nationally and internationally recognized for his work in entrepreneurship, new ventures, and venture capital. He is currently the Franklin W. Olin Distinguished Professor at Babson College. In 1989, Dr. Timmons became the first to hold a joint appointment at the Harvard Business School, as the first MBA Class of 1954 Professor of New Ventures, and at Babson College as the Frederic C. Hamilton Professor of Free Enterprise Development. He has authored or co-authored ten books including New Venture Creation, 5th ed., (McGraw Hill, Irwin, 1999) and Venture Capital at the Crossroad (Harvard Business School Press, 1992), and six articles in Harvard Business Review on these topics. He was co-founder and director of Boston Communications Group, owners of cellular and telecommunications related ventures, is an advisor to venture funds, and is a Special Advisor to the Board of the Center for Entrepreneurial Leadership at the Ewing Marion Kauffman Foundation, where he created and is dean of the Kauffman Fellows Program.*

Dr. Harry J. Sapienza *is currently the Carlson Chair in Entrepreneurship and co-director of the Center for Entrepreneurial Studies in the Carlson School of Management at the University of Minnesota. Dr. Sapienza is nationally and internationally known for his work in venture capitalist-entrepreneur relationships and his work on the internationalization of new high potential ventures. His work has three times won best paper awards in the Entrepreneurship Division of the Academy of Management. His dissertation, "Variations in Venture Capitalist-Entrepreneur Relations: Antecedents and Consequences," conducted with the cooperation of Venture Economics, Inc. won awards as the outstanding dissertation in the entrepreneurship divisions of both the Academy of Management and the Institute of Management Sciences. Dr. Sapienza continues to conduct studies into both private and corporate venture capital.*

You've survived the start-up-thanks to your own sweat equity, help from some friends, your wits, guts and a lot of dedication. Your aspirations and the responses from the marketplace are agreeing more and more: your business can become a substantial one. Your ambitious expansion plans indicate a voracious appetite for cash, and today venture capital is a prime source.

If this is the first time you have sought venture capital, you wonder if it is worth it. You know it can take weeks, months, sometimes a year or more to secure financing, while diverting scarce management's resources away from building and running your fledgling firm. And besides, you wonder if you really want outsiders involved in your company. You ponder a vital question: What real value will the venture capital infuse in your venture beyond money?

To gain some insights into this question, we examined one company in depth, conducted over forty interviews with entrepreneurs and venture capitalists, and surveyed the CEO and the lead investor in 51 venture-backed companies across the U.S.

The extensive interviewing and the survey help validate much of what is observed in the case study and highlight the roles of venture capitalist in launching and building businesses. As you will see, excellent personal chemistry developed between the venture capitalist and the management team. The interviews and survey results indicate the importance of this relationship.

Case Study: NBI, Inc.

For our case study, we spoke to the management team of NBI, Inc. (Boulder, Colorado), one of the most successful and rapidly growing firms in the word-processing and office-automation industry. The company was launched in 1973 and in the first year NBI's president, Tom Kavanagh, and his two partners joined the venture, the firm reached sales of $167,000. By 1982, NBI sales had exceeded $100 million, its rapid growth fueled by venture capital and subsequent public offerings. For NBI, the lead investor's main contributions were recruiting management and acting as a sounding board and financier for the long haul. Additionally, the lead investor provided industry expertise, helped foster the necessary entrepreneurial climate, and was a voice of calm and rationality during difficult times.

Tom Kavanagh certainly found significant "added value" in his venture capital partners. Enough so that he succinctly expressed what we call Kavanagh's

Law: "It is far more important whose money you get than how much you get or how much you pay for it." The following narrative demonstrates many of the ways a lead investor made contributions the NBI management team deemed to be of great value.

Early Stages: Vital Contributions in Recruiting Key Management

The experience of Kavanagh and his top three vice presidents shows that having the right venture capital partner during the start-up and fragile early stages make a tremendous difference in the odds favoring survival and success. In their minds, there is no doubt that recruiting the top management team was "probably the most indispensable value added" by their venture capital partners. Despite NBI's ambitious and impressive plans, it was very difficult to entice a high-performing executive away from a top-notch company to join the launching of a new venture. The lead investor who played an invaluable role in recruiting two of the three top people was Burton J. McMurtry, then a general partner of Institutional Venture Associates and now of Technology Venture Investors. McMurtry helped bring in Mark Stevenson as vice president of marketing, and David Klein as vice president of new business development; their contribution was central to NBI's explosive growth.

Venture capitalists have developed a specialized network of thousands of contacts, leads and reliable sources of intelligence and verification on personnel. But you can have all that and still wind up with gaps in top management. Locating the right team members is truly an art. McMurtry was always available to assist in searching for and researching top people. The trick, according to Kavanagh, is the ability to convince truly top-notch candidates to give up all they have to take the plunge with you.

Perhaps you're in a situation similar to Tom Kavanagh's in 1975. Your business plan has been well-received by the venture capitalists who have taken the time to get to know you and to review your plan carefully. Further, they have expressed a sincere interest in your venture. But there is one hitch: without an outstanding marketing person with an impressive track record-someone who knows your business inside and out-the investors simply decline to act. You have been pursuing your number-one candidate for over two months, and you hope to celebrate Thanksgiving with the acceptance of your offer.

The call comes; the message is clear: "I like you, your prospective backers, your company, your product and your philosophy. But we've moved eight or nine times, and I'm very happy in what I'm doing. I believe I can achieve income, position, and personal financial goals while becoming a driving force in the industry right where I am." Now what? You cannot bootstrap it forever. Once your prospective backers find out, and word gets around the industry that your top prospect said "no," well . . .

After hearing Kavanagh's story, McMurtry was convinced that Mark Stevenson-the prime candidate for the marketing position-had "not thought it through completely, particularly the financial consequences," and had thus declined for the wrong reasons. The next day the McMurtry and Kavanagh were on a plane from San Francisco to Dallas to meet with Stevenson. The eyeball-to-eyeball meeting ex tended well into the night. The next day, Stevenson quit his job at Xerox to join NBI.

What had happened? According to Stevenson, "There is no question that without Burt, I would not have done it. His very professional, straightforward manner convinced me. He said that he and Tom wanted to sit down with me and my wife and my two children to talk over the reasons why we should reconsider. He had the sensitivity to know that if my wife also understood the reasons why we might want to change our minds, it would make all the difference. The offer was really not different in terms of salary and stock. What he was able to do was enable me to see the decision in a different context: what it could mean to be in control of my own destiny, while also achieving those other personal goals." Several months later, David Klein, a close colleague from Stevenson's prior job also decided to join NBI, even though he had originally advised Stevenson against moving.

"I would not have joined if it were not for Burt," Klein said. "His understanding of what had to happen to make it a good deal for both of us was key. He was able to convey in a very professional and credible way that he could not get rich unless we did." The advantages of having a top-flight venture capital partner extend far beyond recruiting. Hundreds of times

McMurtry played a vital role at NBI, closing with numerous prospective suppliers, dealers and customers.

A Sounding Board

According to Kavanagh, playing devil's advocate was the second major way his lead investor added value to building the venture. Having someone to discuss and critique your plans and ideas before you are firmly committed can help avoid costly mistakes. Ironically, a savvy outsider can provide that insight to a management team. Venture teams come to work together so closely and intimately that they begin to think alike. New product ideas, strategies and directions, can emerge as if out of one mind. The dangers of this tendency are obvious, and the outside investor, because of a reasonably removed and objective view, can better assess the rationale of plans, ideas and initiatives.

At NBI, according to Klein, it was tough to get "tests of reasonableness." In contrast, he found that at an IBM or Xerox you're forced to do so; the "implementors" challenge your innovative decisions. But at NBI, as in most smaller ventures, each member of the top management team has their area of accountability, and they are pretty much on their own. What McMurtry did, was to talk with the individuals of the team, often several times a week. According to the group at NBI, it was extremely valuable to have someone vitally concerned asking constructive questions. One of McMurtry's favorite questions was, "What decisions did you make last week that you were most uncomfortable with?"

Still another example of the kind of immersion NBI experienced centered on the need for longer-range planning, initiating some strategic thinking, even though the immediate pressures of the start-up or expansion seem to be overwhelming. Kavanagh stresses that it was McMurtry who "gets lots of credit for getting us to do it first. He got the process on track and going a good two years earlier than we would have without his prodding, and you never do it soon enough."

In for the Long Haul

For a company with potential and aspirations that are compelling enough to initially attract venture capital investors, it is almost a given that subsequent rounds of financing will be necessary as the venture progresses. Unlike many other sources of finance, professional venture capitalists must possess both the patience and bravery for the longer haul. If you have found the right investors for your company, then you can expect them to be 100% behind you to arrange for subsequent rounds of financing. In doing so, such investors will look out for the best interests of your company, rather than what is most advantageous for the venture capital firm.

In NBI's case, McMurtry was the vital link in attracting two other highly regarded venture capitalists to participate in the later rounds: William Hambrecht, of Hambrecht & Quist, and David Dullum, of Frontenac Venture Capital. According to Kavanagh, Dullum served the company very effectively as a director and member of the audit committee. As an investor and member of NBI's board, Hambrecht served a critical role when it came to determining the most suitable structure and timing of subsequent public offerings. Their contributions complemented McMurtry's and were considered invaluable by the leaders of NBI. They were involved where they could make the greatest contribution.

Other Key Contributions

Securing key customers and accounts is an area where immense help can be contributed. Again, in the fragile start-up period and early stages, every customer can be crucial. Venture capitalists can often articulate the company's case in a more objective manner than the founders. What they add is a sufficient comfort level to enable big-company buyers to cast their fate as customers of a new or small firm. Venture investors can outline by phone why they invested in the venture and the reasons for their confidence. A sense of professional objectivity can shift doubt to confidence. According to the NBI team, McMurtry spent untold hours doing just that. The carefully documented letter he prepared explaining the rationale for investing in NBI was a source of considerable comfort to buyers and vendors alike. AT NBI, "100 times or more" McMurtry played an important role in closing with suppliers, dealers and customers.

Another area that had a lot to do with NBI's success was a sense of clarity about what it takes to create and perpetuate an "entrepreneurial climate and commitment." Kavanagh credits McMurtry's ability in helping create such a climate to his extensive experience working with similar start-up and early-stage ventures. The soul of this spirit appeared to be an incentive system encouraging teamwork rather than only rewarding individual success. "Getting promoted simply did not matter since we did not pay ourselves much anyway," said one NBI vice president. "All the payoffs were based on what was good for NBI." The key executives were convinced that they could all achieve their financial goals, if they could drive NBI to accomplish its business objectives. This spirit continues to permeate the company today.

Roaring cannons are inevitable for most fledgling firms that grow as rapidly as NBI. There are crises, periods of doubt, even some desperation; it's never simple. The fragile process of launching and building such an enterprise requires the qualities of an investor rather than the shirt-sleeve perseverance and uncanny degree of ingenuity of an entrepreneur. Beyond an investor's objectivity and insight, another vital contribution emerged for NBI-support with patience and fortitude.

When a situation takes an unexpected turn-some missed deadlines, a lost key account, a sudden resignation, and the inevitable cash and confidence crisis-nothing is more disturbing than a backer with a weak heart and a weaker pocketbook. "No matter how bad things got at NBI, there was a calmness in Burt. Never once," according to Stevenson, "did he step on your hands when you were lying flat on your back." In short, that kind of professional behavior meant there were no "I told you so's" or threats to withhold future financial backing, or a panicky haste to start changing management, strategies or product. The message was one of concern accompanied by complete confidence in the team and how they were going about the business. For NBI, the involvement was described as "complete immersion, but never any meddling."

The contributions of McMurtry and other venture capitalists in the development of NBI extended well beyond these few examples. Industry savvy, mentoring, strategic insights, and comradery-all these and more played a part in nurturing and building the company.

Our investigation extended across the country to see how the experience here matched those of other entrepreneurs and other venture capitalists. During 1987 through 1988, our research included both questionnaires and in-depth personal interviews to gain a better understanding of the process.

Letters from Our Field Study

We conducted research on over 120 entrepreneurs and venture capitalists on their view of the importance and effectiveness of the lead investor's involvement in developing their current businesses. For each venture, we obtained the view of both the CEO-entrepreneur and the lead venture capital investor. Their perceptions were startlingly similar! While each venture's problems, challenges, and strengths differ from those at NBI, many common themes, however, did emerge-and a few differences were revealed as well.

Our surveys and in-depth interviews revealed the following generalizations: 1) the most intense involvement does indeed occur at the tender early stages of the business; 2) openness of communications and personal chemistry are crucial; 3) venture capitalists add value in a variety of ways, especially through strategic and supportive roles; 4) most of the venture capitalist's key roles become increasingly important as the venture develops.

Lead Investor Importance and Effectiveness: Survey Results

Each entrepreneur-lead investor pair rated the importance and effectiveness of the lead investor's involvement in the venture in eight separate roles. The results of this research is shown on the next page, broken into ratings from early-stage and later-stage ventures.

These ratings show that both entrepreneurs and venture capitalists believe that lead investors make important and effective contributions in a wide variety of value-added roles beyond merely providing capital and sources of additional financing.

The experience of NBI demonstrated how at one company a lead investor could be absolutely crucial to attracting top managers to help launch the new business; at NBI, McMurtry was also viewed as a key strategic adviser who was immersed even in the operating decisions of the venture. Our research indicates that after the initial launching of the business, networking and management recruiting roles are not typically as important as the strategic and supportive roles.

Extent of Involvement

Entrepreneurs often express concern over the extent to which a venture capitalist is involved in the company. The key consideration, of course, is the bottom line effect of such involvement-whether the additional effort and support, in fact, achieves recognized value.

We found a wide fluctuation in terms of the intensity and extent of involvement on the part of venture capitalists. For the most part, however, the quality of the relationship is key. Said one entrepreneur, "Think of it as you would marriage. You don't want to go into it lightly. Think about what it would be like to work with these people day in and day out." Echoing this sentiment, a general partner in a top Boston venture capital firm said, "its like getting married. You've got to ask yourself, 'Can I live with this person when things get really tough?'"

One venture capitalist expressed the value and importance of personal chemistry: "One of the evaluations we make is 'Can you work with this person?' not 'Is this person good?'" For their part, entrepreneurs seem to favor lead investors who are active, involved and interested: "What I like best

Ratings for Late-Stage Ventures

V.C. Roles	Importance (5 pt. scale) entre	Importance (5 pt. scale) v.c.	Effectiveness (10 pt. scale) entre	Effectiveness (10 pt. scale) v.c.
Strategic Roles				
Sounding Board	4.29	4.67	8.15	8.13
Business Consultant	3.96	4.42	6.90	7.58
Financier	3.46	2.96	7.22	6.73
Social/Supportive Roles				
Coach/Mentor	3.54	4.08	6.95	7.29
Friend/Confidant	3.25	3.52	6.80	6.50
Networking Roles				
Management Recruiter	2.42	2.33	3.38	3.06
Professor Contact	2.42	2.46	4.94	5.32
Industry Contact	2.04	1.87	2.61	2.55
Overall effectiveness ratings			7.70	7.22

Ratings for Entire Set of Ventures

V.C. Roles	Importance (5 pt. scale) entre	Importance (5 pt. scale) v.c.	Effectiveness (10 pt. scale) entre	Effectiveness (10 pt. scale) v.c.
Strategic Roles				
Sounding Board	4.27	4.49	8.18	7.96
Business Consultant	4.12	4.41	7.67	7.75
Financier	3.78	3.67	7.73	7.63
Social/Supportive Roles				
Coach/Mentor	3.57	3.94	6.95	7.06
Friend/Confidant	3.37	3.35	6.91	6.55
Networking Roles				
Management Recruiter	2.82	3.04	4.67	4.81
Professor Contact	2.82	2.92	6.17	6.20
Industry Contact	2.26	2.67	4.18	3.96
Overall effectiveness ratings			7.88	7.35

Ratings for Early-Stage Ventures

V.C. Roles	Importance (5 pt. scale) entre	Importance (5 pt. scale) v.c.	Effectiveness (10 pt. scale) entre	Effectiveness (10 pt. scale) v.c.
Strategic Roles				
Sounding Board	4.25	4.37	8.05	7.67
Business Consultant	4.17	4.46	8.14	7.83
Financier	4.17	4.42	8.05	8.41
Social/Supportive Roles				
Coach/Mentor	3.63	3.75	6.86	6.79
Friend/Confidant	3.46	3.33	6.71	6.39
Networking Roles				
Management Recruiter	3.17	3.75	5.36	6.17
Professor Contact	3.18	3.33	6.90	6.83
Industry Contact	2.58	3.46	5.52	5.33
Overall effectiveness ratings			8.04	7.39

Summary Ratings

V.C. Roles	Importance Avg. Rating (5 pt. scale)	Effectiveness Avg. Rating (10 pt. scale)
Strategic Roles		
Sounding Board	4.38	8.07
Business Consultant	4.27	7.71
Financier	3.73	7.78
Social/Supportive Roles		
Coach/Mentor	3.76	7.00
Friend/Confidant	2.93	6.73
Networking Roles		
Management Recruiter	2.93	4.74
Professor Contact	2.88	6.17
Industry Contact	2.47	4.07

about Jim's involvement is his enthusiasm for the investment. He really cares, and he's really interested in what we're doing. He is always very positive, helpful and supportive. That's something that, perhaps more than any of the other things, we need most." Another entrepreneur expressed this idea differently: "Experienced venture capitalists are good at listening above and between the lines. They listen real hard."

When things work well, entrepreneurs find themselves seeking a much higher level of involvement than they ever imagined wanting. The CEO of a fast-growing high technology firm said this about his relationship with the lead investor: "It's much more than a professional relationship. We're personal friends . . . I wouldn't change anything-I just wish we had the opportunity to interact more."

Two Sides of the Coin

Needless to say, there are those relationships that fail to develop the special chemistry needed to catapult the venture to bigger and better things. Some venture capitalists are less adept at turning around such situations. As in most relationships, a common complaint when this occurs is the failure to communicate effectively. One entrepreneur complained, "What I can't stand is his unwillingness to listen. He has preconceived ideas about a particular topic . . . he just doesn't want to hear the details."

While it has bandied about in the popular press that venture capitalists can be hard-nosed, cutthroat negotiators aiming to take advantage of aspiring entrepreneurs, our interview and survey data paint a much different picture. Every profession will have some who are uncivilized and unscrupulous. An effective venture capitalist, however, generally must have a high level of integrity and interpersonal skills. As one entrepreneur said, "It takes a rare combination of abilities and attributes to make a good venture capitalist. They must have the ability to manage people and to analyze a wide set of diverse information." Our survey ratings show that a surprisingly high percentage of venture capitalists fit the bill.

In Summary

The successful development of a business can be critically impacted by the interaction of the management team and the involved venture capitalists. If a peer relationship can be established, the value-added synergy can be a powerful stimulant for success.

Not all venture capitalists are exactly like those NBI was able to attract, nor will every founder-investor partnership evolve as that one did. Yet many aspiring founders overlook some of the very large "value-added" contributions that professional venture capital investors are accustomed to making and erroneously opt for a "better deal," or a debt backer.

If you have progressed far enough to gain the serious interest of professional venture investors, they will welcome as thorough an examination of their credentials and track record as they will conduct on you, your team and venture. By taking the time to talk to entrepreneurs they have backed, you are likely to discover many of the exceptional qualities that NBI found in their backers. Having just such resources on your team can be the difference in making visions become reality for both the investors and the entrepreneurs.

Structuring the Financing

Stanley C. Golder

Prior to his passing, Stanley C. Golder was a general partner and consultant in the firm of GTCR Golder Rauner, LLC in Chicago. Founded in 1980, the company currently manages over $6.0 billion in equity and mezzanine funds. For nine years, Mr. Golder was president of the Equity Group of First Chicago Corp., one of the largest and most successful bank holding company business development investment affiliates. He was a past chairman of both the National Association of Small Business Investment Companies and the National Venture Capital Association. GTCR Golder Rauner, LLC is an active investor in consolidating fragmented industries.

The structure of venture capital investments follows no set formula nor does it fit into a perfect structure: the objective is to reconcile the differing needs and concerns of the venture capitalist and the entrepreneur in a way that is satisfactory to both parties. Since each situation is different, structures vary widely.

One issue that relates to the process of formalizing a venture investment is the financial structure; in other words, the form of securities instruments used. These securities instruments have certain advantages and disadvantages and can be used to provide a fair and equitable structure.

Needs and Concerns

The needs of the venture firm and the company will vary based on the company's stage of development, the risk and the ultimate potential as well as the requirements and the philosophy of the individual venture firm. However, there are a number of factors for venture capitalists and entrepreneurs to consider when creating any investment.

Primary considerations for the venture capitalist include:

- Reasonable reward given the level of risk.
- Sufficient influence on the development of the company, usually through board representation.
- Management's relative contribution to capital. (This assures that managers have more at stake than just their egos.)
- Minimization of taxes resulting from the various types of cash flows to investors (dividends versus interest, versus capital gains).
- Future liquidity in the event that the company is successful or stagnates.
- Voting control, which is particularly desirable if performance is substantially below expectations and the management team must be replaced.
- Protection from having any remaining investor dollars split with entrepreneur in the event that the company is unsuccessful and dissolves.
- Current yield in the case of an SBIC (Small Business Investment Company), which has debt to service.

Primary considerations for the typical entrepreneur include:

- Ability to lead the creation of the business that they have conceptualized (operating and strategic control).
- Financial rewards for creating the business.
- Adequate resources needed to achieve their goal.
- Minimization of tax exposure for buying cheap stock.
- Value of substantive contribution from board members.

Common considerations for both sides include:

- Flexibility of structure that will allow room to enable additional investments later, incentives for future management and retention of stock if management leaves.
- Balance sheet attractiveness to suppliers and debt financiers.
- Retention of key employees through adequate equity participation.

The structuring process includes laying out the needs and concerns of both parties; evaluating all the alternatives; and choosing and negotiating a structure that is consistent with the company's financial needs and capabilities and that will provide liquidity and, in extenuating circumstances, control for the investors.

Securities Instruments Commonly Used

The structure of a venture capital financing uses a range of securities instruments, from straight debt to debt with equity features (convertible debt to debt with warrants) to common stock. The following is a summary of the securities that are often used in combination with one another:

- Senior Debt—Generally used for long-term financing for low-risk companies or for mezzanine (later stage) financings.

- Subordinated Debenture—This is a type of debt that is subordinated to financing from other financial institutions such as banks and may be unsecured. It is usually convertible to common stock or accompanied by warrants to purchase common shares. Senior lenders accept this as equity and therefore allow increased debt from other sources.

- Preferred Stock—Generally convertible to common stock, preferred stock gives the venture capitalists "preference" over common shareholders and some rights while from the entrepreneur's perspective it improves the company's debt-to-equity ratio. One disadvantage is that if dividends are attached, they are not tax deductible.

- Common Stock—Generally the most expensive in terms of ownership given to the venture capitalist because it has the most risk. But from the venture capitalist's view it is also the least flexible. It affords no protection, allows the least amount of control over management and since there is generally no dividend, provides no return until the stock is sold.

Choosing the "Right" Instruments

The advantage to debt instruments from the venture capitalist's perspective is that they can be designed to provide (1) preference in case of liquidation, (2) some current income and (3) remedies in case of default. An SBIC that has used its leverage and thus has debt to service will prefer an income bearing security. For the company, however, excessive debt can strain its credit standing and make future long-term financing difficult and, in case of default, places the venture capitalist in a position of control. On the other hand, common stock or (as it is often termed) straight equity provides no protection for the venture capitalist and as a result will ultimately be very costly for the entrepreneur in terms of equity give-up.

Entrepreneurs, venture capitalists and their respective attorneys can be creative in modifying traditional securities to meet the needs of a particular situation. Most venture capital financing structures are a combination of debt and equity that satisfies both parties. The often used preferred stock structure is a compromise between common stock and note structures for several reasons. First, preferred stock has more protection than common stock, but less than subordinated notes.

Second, preferred stock usually carries a dividend, but it can only be paid if the company is profitable. Also, preferred stock is a separate class of stock, and accordingly, has certain rights established in the articles of incorporation which are stronger than the rights of common shareholders, but usually not as strong as noteholders. Finally, preferred stock may be redeemable, which would allow investors to obtain a return of principal, assuming that sufficient capital is available for redemption.

Other combinations and unique hybrid structures can often provide preference in sale, liquidation or merger; and current income plus capital gain for the venture capitalist without weighing the balance sheet with too much debt.

A no-load convertible preferred, for example, has no dividend attached; has liquidation preference; converts to common at the option of the holder and automatically at a public offering; votes as if common stock; is considered equity; and requires a board seat, monthly reports, registration rights and a right of first refusal for future financings. This is typically used for start-up and early-stage financings and is attractive to the entrepreneur because there is no dividend obligation.

Common stock may be used in a larger successful

company while senior debt with warrants may be more appropriate in a turnaround situation.

Flexibility of Structure

The structure adopted initially affects the ability to take actions subsequently and therefore should be as flexible as possible. Firstly, the rights of initial investors to participate in subsequent financing rounds should be established so as to provide as little obstacle as possible to their being completed. Secondly, there needs to be provision made for providing stock that can motivate key management brought in subsequent to the financing. Thirdly, if management members leave, some or all of their stock should be retained by the company. These last two issues can be dealt with by having a class of stock for management differing from that issued to investors. Reserves can be established for additions to management and stock issued can be escrowed. Care needs to be paid to the tax implications so that members of management are not faced with unexpected liabilities in connection with their holding this stock.

Another point on structure of transactions, which seems obvious, but is often ignored, is that an investor in an early-stage company who puts in considerably more dollars than the entrepreneur should generally not lose money on their investment, while an entrepreneur makes money. This, again, mitigates toward using a senior instrument so as to protect the investor's position.

Obviously, it is in the best interest of both the investor and the entrepreneur that the instruments used be considered equity and be leverageable as the company grows. Preferred stocks should cause no problems as they are clearly equity, even though they may have redemption requirements. These are easily handled by senior lenders if and when the company is capable of acquiring debt. Subordinated debt can be accommodated to this need, but has a few more problems vis-a-vis senior lenders as the company grows. In either case, however, these instruments should be equity as far as any senior creditors are concerned, so that appropriate leverage can be obtained when necessary.

Many venture capitalists prefer not to make outright purchases of common stock except in cases where the majority ownership is in the hands of an investor group. Even then, there are many arguments for preferred stocks. Before taking a common equity position, there can be a waiting period to determine if the company performs as expected and to see if management's objectives are similar to those of the investors and will protect the investors' interest.

The question of ultimate liquidity is also very significant. While there are differences in various parts of the country, an ultimate maturity on investments is preferred, which either provides liquidity or the ability to negotiate toward liquidity when the company has not reached its objectives, but is viable.

In most cases, investments are thought of only in terms of success or failure, but it is very possible that a company will move relatively sideward (sometimes called the living dead) or plateau in its growth and therefore be unable to achieve a public market. Even if companies go public, the market will not usually accept a large amount of stock from inside investors, unless the company makes major progress. The only way out for the venture capitalist is the company's sale or merger. At this point, the goals of the entrepreneurs or managers of the company may differ from the investors' objectives. Consequently, contractual arrangements to achieve liquidity become most important and can be best achieved at the inception of the investment.

Control

Another problem that is handled by appropriate structuring is the very serious aspect of control. Businesspeople approach venture capitalists with the idea that they should control their own business, but history has shown that many entrepreneurs do not have the desire, may not have the ability and certainly do not have the experience to run a business as it grows. Most venture capitalists do not want to run companies, but they feel that it is their basic responsibility to see that the companies in which they invest are well run and if management changes are appropriate, they can be achieved.

Various types of senior instruments can give investors the opportunity to have their interests protected as these types of problems develop. This is not a means to financially disadvantage the equity interest of the entrepreneur. In fact, it is designed to help that interest and to enable a board of directors to make changes in management if they deem appropriate.

There are major differences between investors and not all of the companies in the industry have the same philosophies. Having been involved with many successful companies and having heard many successful entrepreneurs speak who have been backed by venture capitalists, I think entrepreneurs will find that control may be an issue with inexperienced investors and entrepreneurs but not with those who have been successful. De facto day-to-day control needs to be distinguished from voting control.

Keep in mind, appropriate structuring of a transaction cannot make a bad investment good; it can, however, influence the results of investments that are not meeting the initial expectations.

In making every investment, the parties presume a high level of success. Over the years, the record proves that only a small percentage are truly successful. Therefore, achieving liquidity and/or return of capital and the possible remedies available by using instruments other than common stock can be helpful to the investment process and beneficial to both the entrepreneur and venture capitalists.

Avoid inflexible structures. More often than not, an inflexible structure will exaggerate a strategic problem rather than provide a simple solution. For example, there have been situations where an inflexible deal structure enabled one very small player to obstruct an entire round of badly needed financing. Therefore, the best advice for both the entrepreneur and venture capitalist is to keep the structure simple and flexible and to be sure to understand the terms so that they have a good, constructive relationship.

Preliminary Legal Considerations in Forming a New Enterprise

Michael P. Ridley, Esq.

Michael P. Ridley *is a principal of the law firm of Good, Wildman, Hegness & Walley in Newport Beach, California. He and his firm represent numerous venture capital funds and small business investment companies and a large number of companies that have been financed by venture capital sources. Mr. Ridley is a graduate of Stanford University and Yale Law School.*

The following article is a summary of the key legal concerns of the entrepreneur in the planning stages and start-up of a business.

Form of Enterprise

Prior to the Tax Reform Act of 1986, the normal form of business entity would be a corporation. With the repeal of General Utilities, founders should consult with counsel to determine whether S Corp. status, partnership, limited partnership, proprietorship, or a limited liability company may be appropriate during the pre-venture capital period of the entity's existence. If founders operate as a limited partnership or limited liability company, care must be taken to follow statutory formalities to avoid personal liabilities on behalf of limited partners, or to avoid classification as a corporation if a limited liability company is chosen. Unfortunately, S Corp. status, which would be ideal from a liability standpoint and a pass through of income and losses at individual rates without tax at the corporate level, will not be available if venture capital investors are other than individuals or certain trusts (most venture capital funds are limited partnerships) or if there is more than one class of security (most venture capital funds would take preferred stock or convertible debt). In order to minimize out-of-pocket expenses, founders should determine name availability before purchasing stationery, directory listings, brochures, etc.

Relations with Prior Employers

Venture capitalists typically invest in enterprises headed by superior managers with prior track records. It is therefore likely that founders and key employees in a new business will have recently left or are considering leaving their present employment. As such, it will be important during the formation process to ensure that the founders and key employees do not misappropriate the trade secrets of prior employers or otherwise engage in unfair competition with the prior employer.

Trade Secrets

Although employees are free to leave employment and start a competing enterprise, they are not free to utilize their employer's trade secrets or compete while still employed. Most litigation involving the improper use by a departing employee of an employer's trade secrets will center on whether the information used by a departing employee is in fact a trade secret. Definitions of what constitutes a trade secret will vary from state to state. As a general rule, a trade secret means "information, including a formula, pattern, computation, program, device, method, technique or process that (1) derives independent economic value, actual or potential, from not being generally known to the public or to other persons who can obtain economic value from its disclosure or use; and (2) is the subject of efforts that are reasonable under the circumstances to maintain its secrecy." Uniform Trade Secret Act.

It will be important for the new enterprise to avoid situations in which it is involved in the misappropriation of trade secrets of prior employers for several reasons: (a) certain jurisdictions make it a criminal offense to misappropriate trade secrets, e.g., California Penal Code Section 499(c) makes it a misdemeanor punishable by up to one year in prison and up to $5,000 in fines to steal, copy or use without authorization trade secrets; (b) the prior employer has legal recourse to enjoin the new enterprise's use of the employer's trade secrets and to seek damages, including royalties and, where appropriate, punitive damages, which recourse could very well mean the termination of the start-up's activities and, at a minimum, the incurrence in a very short period of time of substantial legal fees and management time diverted from the enterprise; and, last, but not least, (c) venture capitalists, depending upon their respective involvement in formulating the start-up and whether they knew or should have known that the start-up they were financing had misappropriated trade secrets, may themselves be liable for damages to the prior employer.

Although one can never obtain complete assurance that a start-up or a departing employee will not be sued by a prior employer, the departing employees should follow certain steps:

1. Review all nondisclosure and assignment of invention agreements executed by founders and new employees, particularly those sections relating to prior discoveries. Certain jurisdictions provide that inventions developed on an employee's own time not relating to the employer's business constitute the property of the employee. Any work on technology to be utilized by a start-up should be done on the employee's time with the employee's own resources. Employment agreements should be reviewed to determine the existence of and enforceability of covenants not to compete.

2. Prepare the business plan on the employee's individual time.

3. Do not use the prior employer's premises or equipment in preparing the business plan or doing preparatory work in setting up the new venture. Calls to future suppliers, employees and funding sources should be done at home or during the employee's free time. Utilizing E-mail at the employer will leave a trail that is readily discoverable as "deleted".

4. Turn in all customer lists, product specifications, marketing plans, etc. Do not bring copies of proprietary information to the start-up.

5. A problem area will exist where the founder is not merely an employee but rather an officer or director of the former employer. The fiduciary relationship to the former employer may be breached by failing to offer the opportunity to the employer. Corporate opportunity problems may be solved by having the prior employer decline to pursue the opportunity or invention which the start-up is formed to pursue.

6. The safest course of action is for the employee to depart from the employer prior to competing with the employer and to disclose preparations to compete if such failure to disclose preparation would be harmful to the employer. Departing employees should inform the prior employer of plans rather than have the prior employer learn of plans from reference checks of venture capitalists or in a newspaper.

Solicitation of Fellow Employees

The general rule is that, absent unfair or deceptive means, the public interest of the mobility of employees enables the start-up to hire employees, after departure, of former employer. A problem arises if the solicitation occurs while the founders are still employed by the former employer or if the employees are hired not for their skills but rather to obtain the prior employer's trade secrets.

Solicitation of Business of Former Employer

The general rule is that, absent a valid noncompetition agreement, employees may solicit customers of former employers after departing unless proprietary customer lists or confidential information, such as pricing, is used. A problem area is the difficulty of defining what constitutes customer lists. To the extent that the identity of customers, purchasing agents, required terms a vendor must meet, etc., are known to the public, the more likely a customer list will not be found.

Ownership and Protection of Technology

If technology will be important to the success of the start-up, steps should be implemented on formation to acquire and protect the technology. To the extent that technology or intellectual property is being contributed to prior to the raising of funds. There are several alternatives to follow in protecting technology—trade secrets, patents and copyrights. The best method to be used is dependent on the type of technology involved.

Trade Secrets

The general rule is that a trade secret is lost if it is disclosed to the general public or competitors or if the person seeking to protect a trade secret does not take reasonable steps under the circumstances to ensure its confidentiality. A start-up should require that all employees and founders, prior to and as a condition of employment, execute nondisclosure and assignment of invention agreements that (a) set forth recognition of employee of the nature of the importance of trade secrets to the company and contain an agreement to keep all such information in confidence; (b) set forth the prior inventions that are being brought by the employee to the company; (c) represent that no trade secrets of prior employers are being brought to the new enterprise and require that the employee will not disclose to the company trade secrets which may have been obtained as a result of prior employment; and (d) assign all inventions to be used by the company or which are developed during the course of employment, except those inventions which are developed entirely on an employee's own time and do not relate either to the business of the employer or to the employer's actual or anticipated research or development or do not result from any work performed by the employee for the employer; and (e) require such individual to execute and deliver any and all documents necessary to perfect company's ownership rights in and to such intellectual property.

The company should seek a proper balance between the cost to implement certain procedures designed to restrict the flow of information to protect the confidentiality of trade secrets and the necessity for information to flow within the enterprise. At minimum, the company should consider the following:

1. Sensitive areas should be under lock and key with only specified employees having access and that access should be logged. Access to computer files should similarly be controlled. Visitors to the facility should not be shown sensitive areas containing trade secret information, such as a manufacturing process or computer programs. Visitors, consultants or possible purchasers, suppliers or providers of capital should sign nondisclosure and confidentiality agreements. Confidential documents should not be left in open view or unattended in areas in which employees or other persons not authorized to have access to the information would have access. Courts are often impressed with a lock box for blue prints or source and object codes.

2. Proprietary information stored on magnetic or paper media is subject to recovery from such discarded media. Trash should not be an inadvertent conduit of trade secrets to third parties.

3. Proprietary documents and information should be legended as such with restrictions on copying or disseminating the same. Trade secrets and privileged or confidential commercial or financial information disclosed to the federal government should be marked as such to prevent disclosure under the Freedom of Information Act.

4. Departing employees should be interviewed to determine identity of future employer or plans, to ensure no trade secrets are being withdrawn or in the possession of the departing employee and to reiterate the company's claim of trade secrets. Caution should be used in the form of any communications to a departing employee's new employer concerning trade secrets.

5. Employees must be made aware of the fact that they are dealing with trade secrets, that such trade secrets are the property of the employer and are of vital importance to that employer, and that the company will prevent the improper use of the company's trade secrets.

6. To the extent that the company contracts with the federal government and delivers trade secrets such as computer software agreements, it should comply with applicable Federal Acquisition Regulations; Federal Procurement Regulations System, or Defense Federal Acquisition Regulations to limit use.

Patent

A 20-year monopoly created by statute for "new and useful process, machine, manufacture or composition of matter, or any new and useful improvement thereof." The invention must be "new" to be patentable. 35 U.S.C. 102(b) prevents issuance of patent if the invention has been in public use for over a year or if the invention has been described in a publication that has been published for over a year prior to the application. It is important for the company to see patent counsel early to determine patentability, particularly on the issues of (i) when public use has occurred, (ii) whether a patent would be the most appropriate method of protection, (iii) the scope of the license to be granted by the inventor and (iv) whether federal research or contract funds have been utilized in conjunction with the proposed invention. Patent protection extends only to jurisdictions in which it is filed. Major disadvantages relate to the fact that the invention must be disclosed after issued or denied, patent litigation is expensive, and, until recently, most inventors were not successful in patent claims. Patent protection is afforded only in the jurisdiction in which it is issued. In today's global economy advice should be procured with respect to the advisability of filing for patent protection in foreign jurisdictions.

Copyright

A limited monopoly is granted for the term of the individual author's life plus 50 years for an original work of authorship, including computer software, but not ideas, principles, concepts or discoveries. Difficulties will arise in the area of whether "non-employees" are creating copyrightable material and are developing "work for hire" which would grant authorship and copyright protection to the company. New regulations provide that to perfect, an author must deposit a copy of the work with the Library of Congress and the Copyright Office. An author may deposit the first and last 10 or 25 pages of a computer program depending on presence of trade secrets with ability to block out trade secret portions which may prevent disclosure of integral workings of the program. Material must be marked to indicate copyright protection.

Trademark

The company should, at a very early stage after determining its name and the names of its proposed products, conduct name and a trademark availability search. It makes no sense to incur significant advertising, printing and marketing costs only to find that a desired name has been registered by a third party as a trademark. As of November 16, 1989, it is now possible to register a federal trademark prior to consummating a sale in interstate commerce. Evidence of sale must be filed thereafter within six months subject to extensions up to 30 months and affidavits of use must be filed subsequently. Federal registration gives right of holder of trademark to seek damages, including treble damages, for infringement of trademark. Pending registration, a company should not indicate the existence of a trademark on its products. Trademark needs to be renewed every 10 years.

Securities Issues

Shares Issued for Compensation

It will be critical to reduce to writing the proposed ownership split of company by founders. Founders, hopefully, should receive shares in the start-up at a fraction of what the venture capitalists are paying. As such, the company should be organized and shares issued as soon as possible during the formation process. The founders should avoid situations in which the founders are incorporating the enterprise on day one at a low valuation, and capitalists are being issued shares at a much higher valuation.

If shares are issued for services and will be subject to a risk of forfeiture, regardless of whether the founder is paying fair market value, employees and founders should file 83(b) elections with the Internal Revenue Service within 30 days of issuance of such shares to elect to have the value of the securities in excess of the cost to the employee (which should be zero) treated as income in year of issuance. Failure to file will mean that when the risk of forfeiture lapses, the employee will be taxed at the difference between what was paid for the shares and their value at the date the restrictions lapse. If the company is successful, the effect will be disastrous to the founders and employees, since the shares may not then be marketable but may have great value.

An emerging area of the law is wrongful termination of employment. All stock purchase or option agreements should provide that no employment agreement is intended and that the company has the right to terminate employment and repurchase any nonvested shares. Similarly, technology transfer agreements should be independent of ability of company to terminate employee.

Shareholder Agreements

The founders should execute rights of first refusal giving the company and the other founders rights of first refusal in the event of any transfer to a third party. Founders should also consider (i) granting to company and founders rights to purchase in event of founder's death, disability or dissolution of marriage, (ii) imposing restrictions upon transfer by any of the founders during the first years of the enterprise of any significant percentage of shares and (iii) vesting of shares based on length of service with the company and granting to the company of a right to repurchase unvested shares at cost. Venture capitalists will typically insist upon such restrictions and a vesting requirement; it is far better to obtain them while the only value of the company is as perceived in the business plan or in an untested prototype as opposed to after the financing is in place and value is more apparent. Although the founding team, at the onset, may appear quite compatible, as the enterprise grows it is entirely possible that certain elements of that team will not be up to the task and, as such, a portion of those shares should be made available to bring in new people. If the initial funding is from friends and families and includes notes, such persons should be made aware of venture capitalists' typical demands that such notes either should be contributed to capital at closing or subject to deferred pay-out. As such, the founders should ensure that amendments to such notes be made by other than unanimous consent of the note holders. As such, the founders should avoid granting preemptive rights or antidilution rights to such initial funding sources.

Regulatory Compliance

Securities issued to the founders and pre-venture capital sources of funds should be issued in compliance with applicable state blue sky laws and the Securities Act of 1933. Failure to do so gives rights of rescission and may delay and/or hinder a subsequent public offering. The general rule for state purposes is that no securities may be issued without a permit unless an exemption is otherwise available. Exemptions will vary from state to state but will be predicated on the type of security, the qualifications of the purchaser and/or the amount of financing or number of purchasers. Even if an exemption is available for the issuance of securities to sophisticated individuals, the company may wish to issue shares or options to all employees, regardless of their sophistication. In such case, very early in the formation process the company should implement a restricted stock purchase plan or nonqualified or qualified incentive stock option plan (recent tax law changes make qualified incentive stock option plans less desirable for the company) and obtain permit for the same. Promises to new employees for securities should not be made in absence of permit or exemption.

Under the Securities Act of 1933, securities may not be issued unless registered or unless an exemption from registration is available. The typical exemption would be Regulation D adopted by the SEC on April 15, 1982 which sets forth a means wherein an issuer may issue securities without the need for registering the same.

Rule 504: $1 million limit in 12 months preceding issue, no requirement of disclosure (caveat: fraud rules still applicable), no advertising, restrictions on resale.

Rule 505: $5,000,000 limit in 12 months preceding issue, no more than 35 unaccredited purchasers, no requirement of disclosure to accredited investors but if to nonaccredited investors, Part II of Form 1-A and financial statement information required under Item 310 of SB-2 (only balance sheet) if less than $2 million and the financial information required in Form SB-2 Part 1 of 5-18 if less than $5 million, no advertising, restrictions on resale.

Rule 506: No limit as to dollar size, no more than 35 nonaccredited investors (nonaccredited investor must be able to evaluate merits and risks), no requirement of disclosure to accredited investors but disclosure of information on Part 1 of form SB-2 if nonaccredited and less than $7,500,000 and financial statement as required in a registration statement if over $7,500,000, no advertising, restrictions on resale. The issuer must complete and file Form D with SEC with 15 days of first sale.

Rule 701: Securities issued to employees, directors, consultants or advisers pursuant to written compensatory plan or agreement, shall not exceed in 12 months the greater of $500,000 or 15% of total assets or outstanding securities.

Employment Relationships

Due Diligence

Venture capitalists can be expected to perform extensive reference checks on key people in the company. Misleading or fraudulent resumes may be sufficient grounds for withdrawing a proposed funding. Nondisclosed criminal convictions or existing SEC consent decrees may be disastrous to the company in the future. The chief executive officer should investigate backgrounds of key personnel consistent with statutory and constitutional prohibitions on invasion of privacy.

Wrongful Termination

Ability of employer to terminate at will without "cause" is being eroded in many jurisdictions. Employment agreements, employer handbooks and manuals, personnel files and interview notes should all indicate absence of any implied or oral understanding of continual employment, particularly in cases where new employees are being asked to terminate existing employment and relocate.

Miscellaneous

Insurance: Have in force necessary general liability, casualty, workers' compensation. If certain individuals are key to success of the venture, company should acquire key man life insurance which is usually inexpensive. Venture capitalists will also want it in place.

Permits: Nature of critical governmental permits required to operate business will depend on nature of business and jurisdictions; examples are resale certificate to avoid sales tax on sales, permits to discharge hazardous waste, permits to possess goods, export licenses needed to export high technology products. Company should apply early and have in force prior to obtaining venture capital. Failure to obtain could delay funding or result in fines, penalties or shut down of business.

Conclusion

These are just a few of the potential problem areas to consider prior to commencing a new business and seeking capital. It is wise to consult with an attorney experienced in new company formations very early in the planning process to avoid future difficulties.

Sources of Business Development Financing

This particular section describes a variety of sources of capital for potential entrepreneurs. As most entrepreneurs are bewildered by the various financing sources available to developing businesses, the articles in this segment are written to shed light on where to best access capital.

The private equity industry has widespread investment interests that run through the entire life of a company and it has the resources to work with entrepreneurs at any point along the way.

Major corporations also are providing significant amounts of financing to independent business development.

"Dealing with the Corporate Strategic Investor", examines the unique problems and opportunities afforded to entrepreneurial companies by venture programs affiliated with major corporations.

Another article, "Non-Traditional Financing Sources", takes a look at sources of entrepreneurial capital outside the venture capital industry.

Corporate Strategic Partnerships

Mark L. Radtke and George W. McKinney

Mark Radtke *was a vice president with Advent International Corp., a Boston-based venture capital firm. At Advent, Mr. Radtke managed strategic investment programs for 12 major industrial corporations. Prior to Advent, he was a strategic partnering consultant to large and small corporations. Mr. Radtke died in 1994.*

George McKinney, *currently retired, was vice chairman and chief operating officer of Integra LifeSciences Corporation, a medical technology firm in Plainsboro, NJ. He has acted as founding president for several venture-backed firms, including American Superconductor. Dr. McKinney has also been director of planning for Corning and managing partner of ARD, the venture capital firm.*

Industrial corporations have been supporting the development of entrepreneurial companies far longer than the organized venture capital industry has been in existence. Over 70 years ago, DuPont provided funding for a fledgling General Motors Corp. In more recent years, DuPont has formed partnerships with more than 20 young companies.

Today, corporate investors usually fund and support small firms either through a corporate venture capital relationship, in which an individual corporation purchases minority equity positions in smaller firms, or through a strategic partnering relationship.

Strategic partnering, corporate partnering, and strategic alliances all refer to the establishment of long-term collaborative relationships between major corporations and smaller entrepreneurial companies, an activity that has become increasingly popular in recent years. The relationship is initially based on a strategic business agreement—such as a joint technology development program, marketing, or manufacturing agreement—and it may include an equity investment the large company makes in the smaller partner.

Strategic partnerships focus on the business agreement, not the equity position; the long-term relationship; and the fit with the larger corporation's strategic direction. While the business agreement is usually contractual in nature, the relationship differs from a typical contract, since it is expected to be a long-term association, extending beyond the immediate project goals and commitments.

An equity or other financial investment is often part of a strategic partnering relationship because it may be necessary to allow the small company to commit the resources necessary to fulfill the contractual agreement; it may foster a closer working relationship and a more open flow of information; and because the large company may want to share in the increased valuation of the smaller partner resulting from the collaboration.

If an equity investment is part of the relationship, it is usually a minority position of 5% to 20%. The expectation is that the large company will eventually sell out its position when the relationship has run its course. Other typical monetary and non-monetary support for the small company partner includes loans; guaranteed credit lines from suppliers; loans of equipment, facilities, and personnel; market research studies; and beta site testing of new products.

Basic Partnering Strategy for the Small Company

In thinking about strategic planning, the small company should first analyze its business to determine where a corporate relationship can provide the most leverage. The most common partnering relationships center on marketing and product development agreements. If the small company is strong in product development and manufacturing but needs help bringing the new product to market, then a partnership with an established company with a strong market presence makes sense.

The most important strategic partnerships for smaller firms often occur when the smaller firm's technology is broadly "enabling," with a variety of specific market applications. A company developing a new advanced material used in the electronics, medical, aerospace and construction industries, is one example. Here, the small company might be better off forming relationships with larger corporations established in those industries and knowledgeable about product requirements and customer needs, rather than attempting to develop and market a specific product for each industry independently. By giving larger partners the right to pursue the application in a specific market, the smaller company can be funded to develop the basic technology or business concept on a broader basis.

It is important, however, to recognize that large corporations primarily are interested in products, not technologies, and that it is incumbent on the small corporation to define the opportunity for the large company in product terms. If the small company can see product sales within a 24-30 month time frame, then the large corporation becomes a valid partner in managing the product definition and product adoption process. If the small company really needs research or technology development funding, then partnerships are valid only when the opportunity is of major scale and importance to the large corporation.

How to Find Strategic Partners

Successful partnerships almost always involve two elements: direct personal contact with a key executive within the large firm, and a strong fit between the small company's area of product development and the strategic direction of the larger firm. Therefore, in finding large-company partners, a good starting point is developing a list of all the "suspects" : companies that could be reasonably expected to be interested in what you are doing. Think "laterally," some of the best partners can come from industries on the periphery. Many strategic partners of young biotechnology companies, for example, are chemical companies as well as the more obvious pharmaceutical firms.

After preparing the suspect list, run it through two filters: Where do I know a senior executive? (or can get to one through a close friend of the company); and which companies have stated that my technology/market area is one of strategic importance to them? The latter can be determined through annual reports, magazine and newspaper articles and security analyst reports. Compare the list of companies where you have a contact with those that have a strategic interest to yield your best initial list of prospects for partnering.

Strategic partnerships are most likely with a medium-sized corporation ($100-$500M in sales) which has a single technology/market focus or a larger corporation where the partnership is with a division with similar focus. Look for larger corporations where the stated strategy and the smaller company's capabilities are a good match. Experience suggests a need to be realistic in examining the larger corporation's actual strategy rather than its logical strategy.

Corporations with a captive venture capital program are also good initial contacts. The people managing those programs are accustomed to dealing with smaller companies and can usually respond quickly as to whether the parent corporation might have an interest in partnering. In cases where you know that a corporation is interested in your field but you have no contact, ask to speak to someone in the following offices:

- corporate development
- new business development
- mergers and acquisitions
- new ventures
- technology planning/acquisition
- corporate/strategic planning
- licensing

If a company is involved in partnering, these are usually the offices that handle these relationships.

Approaching Potential Corporate Partners

Become an expert on the company before making contact with potential partners. Get their annual report, 10Ks and 10Qs. Use library resources to research their strategy, customers, key executives, etc. Lay out a compelling argument to justify their interest in your company and your interest in them. This should be based on your understanding of their strategic direction, and how the work you are doing helps them achieve their objectives. When explaining your interest in them, do not (repeat, do not!) begin by expressing your desperation for money. While this may be the case, emphasize first that strategically, it is logical (based, for example, on mutual marketing, manufacturing, or technology interests) to work together and that some form of investment might also be considered part of a relationship. This message should be incorporated into a document that includes the following:

- an overview of your company and the business opportunity
- why you are seeking a partner
- your products/technology (do not go into extensive/proprietary details)
- the market you are addressing
- your basic concept for a partnering structure

During your initial meetings with a potential partner, try to meet people from the technical as well as the "business" side of the corporation. Your goal is to try to find a "champion" who sees the strategic logic for working with you and who is willing to put some career capital on the line in selling your cause. That person could come from either the technical or business side of the larger firm, and you should try to expose your company to both. Almost all partnerships require two- or three-tier selling. (In fact, the whole process is like large account selling!) This means you should ideally have a technical sponsor, a line business sponsor and a corporate staff or senior executive sponsor.

Negotiating the Agreement

Beyond the basic decision of whether there is a strategic logic for working with you, the next major decision for the representatives of the large company to make is whether they want to work with you as people and whether they feel you can develop a trusting and open relationship. A recommended approach is to be straightforward about what you can realistically deliver and what your "must haves" may be in the following areas:

- technology/market control
- financial support (equity/non-equity)
- long-term independence

Similarly, try to get the large company to clearly articulate the contribution they will make to the relationship and their "must haves." Based on both sides' objectives and "must haves," design an agreement that meets all the key issues. A common issue for negotiation, for example, is marketing rights to new products developed under the agreement. The large corporation might be willing to co-market or not market the products at all in certain markets if they can have exclusive rights to certain other markets that may be less important to you. The key to arriving at a mutually satisfying and beneficial agreement is frank communication between the two companies and a willingness to explore alternative approaches.

After a proposed agreement is reached, you may still have to help sell the agreement within the large corporation, where the board of directors may have to make the final approval. If your "champion" is high enough in the company, that person can often expedite the process. A good rule of thumb, however, is to expect the process to take as much as two to three times longer than you originally thought. As a consequence, planning for a strategic partner should begin well in advance of the time you will actually need one. One of the most common mistakes seen is a small company deciding to seek a corporate partner when they have only three or four months of cash remaining. Not only does it take longer than that, but large corporations are noticeably reluctant to seriously consider companies, even some very good companies, when they are on the brink of running out of money. Therefore, plan your attack on potential corporate partners 9 to 12 months ahead of your cash needs, perhaps just after a venture financing round.

After the Agreement

Most of the work in making partner relationships successful begins after closing the original agreement. Some advice on making the relationship work includes the following:

- communicate openly and frequently with the partner
- head off problems early and do not let them become a "surprise"
- perform to plan
- be willing to alter the agreement as objectives or circumstances change
- continually "sell" the strategic logic and value of the relationship within the large company partner—remember, you usually need them

more than they need you
- make sure both sides are deriving benefits from the partnership, otherwise they become unstable

Strategic partnering has become an important element of corporate business development and should be part of the strategic thinking of both large and small firms. It takes time and effort, both before and after a deal is struck. As a small company executive, you should consider strategic partnering to be perhaps your highest leverage development tool and should plan for it and make initial approaches to potential partners early in your company's development.

Dealing with the Corporate Strategic Investor

Kenneth W. Rind

Dr. Rind *has been both a practitioner and a long-time objective observer of corporate strategic investing's ebbs and flows. In addition, he has been a founder/partner in eight venture capital funds, whose L.P.'s included over 25 different corporate strategic investors, with funding from their pension funds as well as from corporate monies. Recently, he co-founded PEI Corporate Investors to extend the activities of corporate programs by purchasing their no-longer-strategic investments in portfolio companies and/or funds, and he has become a Senior Advisor to Caris & Company.*

Corporate strategic investing (the preferred term to "corporate venturing") generally differs from conventional venture investing because motivations beyond strictly financial rewards are present. Typically, a corporation's goals are to: enhance internal innovation; gain early exposure to new markets and technologies; generate new products faster and less expensively; identify and assess acquisition candidates; assure a stable source of supply or create a competitor to a monopoly supplier; assist a valued customer; and/or provide access to cooperative, knowledgeable individuals who are then more willing to help it in various ways. Corporations may also use venture capital approaches to initiate new ventures internally, or to spin off businesses that are not appropriately kept in-house. Although corporate strategic investors represent only a small part of the venture capital community, their contribution has been considerable, and their dollars invested, particularly in healthcare companies, have been disproportionate to their number. However, once again 80% of the corporations that had active strategic investing programs in 2000 have terminated them, in some cases abandoning their portfolio companies, thereby doing damage to all parties.

Defining Corporate Strategic Investing

Corporate strategic investments are sometimes called strategic alliances or corporate partnerships. However, it is more usual to allow corporate alliances to be the blanket term encompassing joint ventures and outside business arrangements (e.g. technology exchanges, teaming, licensing, etc.), as well as corporate strategic investing.

Typically, strategic investments are cooperative business arrangements coupled with the provision of financing in the form of: an equity purchase; a loan; a lease/credit guarantee; advance payments; R&D funding; license fees; pre-paid royalties; development contracts; beta- site payments; asset transfers; free advertising; etc.

These arrangements typically fall into one of three categories:

"Corporate strategic partnering"—a relationship with a less than 24-month time frame, usually to obtain access to a product in order to strengthen the core business. This is most often driven by an operating unit for tactical reasons. An example is a computer manufacturer providing funding to a software company with the proviso that the software will be ported to the investor's platforms.

"Strategically directed venturing"—characterized by a two-to-seven year time horizon, and used strategically by a corporate development staff that sees a longer-term market opportunity. An example would be a medical device manufacturer that finances the development of a new piece of equipment with the expectation that it will later add it to its product line.

"Corporate venturing"—a long-term (up to 20 year) program driven by a desire to prevent being blindsided by developments from outside. It may be driven by corporate visionaries or others with a desire for a "window" on new technologies, such as nanotechnology. However, the program must also provide financial returns, or it will be terminated prematurely. Many examples exist in the pharmaceutical industry.

Numerous corporations have also invested in venture capital partnerships to assist their other programs. Venture capitalists have facilitated this approach by organizing partnerships having just a single corporate

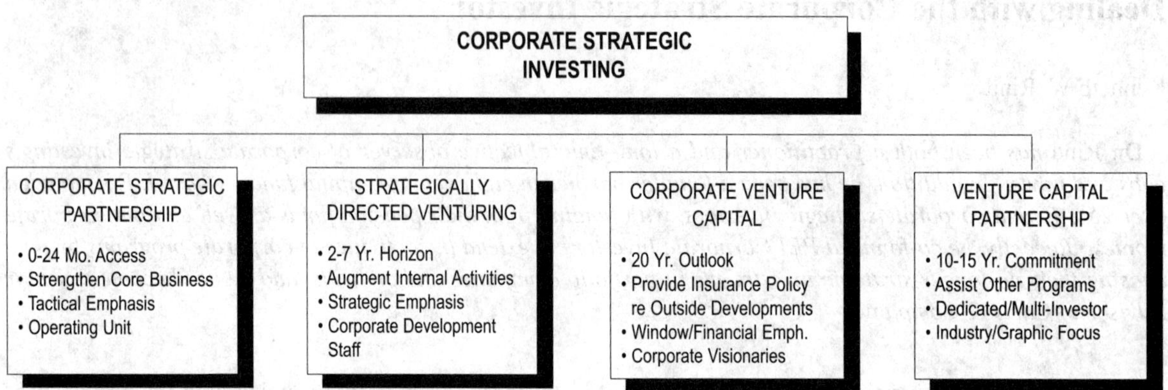

strategic investor (a "dedicated fund") and also by forming multi-investor partnerships focusing on a particular industry and/or geographic area, including a few partnerships having primarily foreign corporations from a single country.

No matter what form a corporate strategic investment program takes, there are many problems, as well as benefits, of which an entrepreneur must be cognizant when dealing with strategic funds.

History of Corporate Strategic Investing

Probably the first corporate strategic investor was DuPont. When one of its important new customers ran out of funds in 1919, it purchased a 38% equity interest and brought in a new president, Alfred Sloan. General Motors has grown substantially since that investment.

After World War I, AT&T, General Electric and Westinghouse bought out British Marconi's holdings of American Marconi. They subsequently changed the name of their venture to Radio Corporation of America. Thus GE, in purchasing RCA, acquired a venture it originally helped finance.

Soon after World War II ended, a small company, Haloid Corporation, funded the commercialization of a new technology developed by Chester Carlson and the Battelle Memorial Institute. Haloid later changed its name to Xerox Corporation, whose venture capital subsidiary helped launch Apple, and thereby Windows, as well as: Ethernet, packet switching, use of wireless to bypass the local telephone companies, voice recognition, and omnifont optical character recognition.

Another corporate strategic investor probably became interested in the activity because its largest stockholder was the son of the venture capitalist behind the formation of IBM. (IBM itself has embraced investing in venture funds to build quality relationships around the world.)

Fairchild Camera and Instrument financed a group of eight technologists who left Shockley Transistor in 1957. They later acquired this venture, Fairchild Semiconductor, the grandparent of many of the companies now populating Silicon Valley, including, of course, Intel. The latter is currently the most active corporate strategic investor, with a world-wide direct program, two dedicated programs that incorporate funding from others, and even an outside fund investment.

Many corporations became "strategic" investors in the 1960's, seeking a "window on technology". However, the lack of profit orientation and the decline of the stock market in 1970, followed by its near collapse in 1974 and 1975, brought about the exit of most of them.

Another cycle took place beginning in 1982, with corporations primarily investing in venture funds for strategic reasons. However, having learned from these relatively safer investments, and usually investing alongside their investee partnerships, corporations began to expand their direct investment programs. Some even formed their own partnerships and leveraged internal monies with institutional capital despite the evident conflicts.

But, the stock market crash of 1986 took its toll, with a decline in the number of corporate strategic investors from 125 to 30 by 1993. In the next decade, hypnotized by the dot.com bubble, almost 500 companies, including numerous foreign corporations, made "strategic investments" totaling $30B. These included: the five largest U.S electronics companies, the 10 largest pharmaceutical companies, most of the major telecom service providers, and many media companies. Unfortunately, fewer than 100 are still actively investing in new opportunities, and many declined to invest further in their portfolios. On the other hand, many of the large pharmaceutical companies have stepped up their investments in biotechnology firms.

Problems of the Corporate Strategic Investor

Corporate funds that have been run by experienced professionals, even if not primarily for maximum return, have performed well, with reported compound annual returns of as high as 100% over a cycle. Nonetheless, some of the best ones have closed down, usually due to one of the following problems:

Lack of appropriately skilled people. Venture capitalists must be entrepreneurially motivated, patient, realistically optimistic, good at negotiation, persuasive and

able to evaluate people as well as businesses. They must also be more than superficially familiar with accounting principles, tax regulations, corporate finance structures, securities analysis and securities law. Good internal people are generally unwilling to leave a company's mainstream activities, especially if they possess the appropriate skills. Experienced people from the outside are hard to attract and retain without compensation packages that are tricky to structure and maintain.

Contradictory rationales. A corporate strategic investor may find it difficult to act in the best interests of both the investee company and the parent. For example: if the goal of the corporation is to acquire, then equity financing by others is undesirable; if the rationale is an exclusive marketing arrangement or a preferred supplier role, then the investee's operations may be unduly limited. The parent's desire to have continuous profit increases is also incompatible with the normal results of a venture program. The entire problem can be exacerbated by an inappropriate reporting structure. For example: if the investment group reports to the vice president of finance, its focus may shift to profitability; if reporting to the vice president of R&D, the focus may be on technology; and if reporting to the vice president of corporate planning, then market information may be the main emphasis.

Legal problems. A corporate investor must be extremely careful to organize its activities so that it will not run afoul of conflict of interest problems, including "fiduciary responsibility" and "corporate opportunity" doctrines. However, several corporations have left the field because they believed, erroneously, that legal constraints would inhibit them from obtaining any desired benefits.

Inadequate time horizon. A new strategic investment program usually shows its losses and problems early, with success taking more time to develop than anticipated. Unless a corporation's commitment is at least seven to 10 years, its activities will generally be terminated before any pearls can be harvested.

Selecting a Corporate Partner

In order to assure the viability of a long-term relationship and to avoid the common problems that arise in corporate investment programs, the following points should be considered:

Compatibility of goals. As previously noted, corporations make investments for diverse reasons, including: tactical, strategic, insurance, and for obtaining a financial return. The business interests of both parties may reinforce the possibility of success or lead to future conflicts.

Longevity. Many corporate groups have been terminated due to a lack of early success, an inability to set clear objectives or a shift in corporate strategy. Support will probably wane at a time in the economic cycle when raising funds from others is most difficult. A true long-term commitment to the concept must be present.

People. If the corporate group is not managed by dedicated venture capitalists, unnecessary conflicts may develop. Staff people want to return to a career path inside the corporation, thereby requiring continual efforts at educating new people. The near and long-term goals of the corporate managers should be considered.

Adequate financing. The corporation must provide appropriate financial resources to enable building and maintaining an independent operation, including adequate rewards to the mangers. The likelihood of obtaining capital in later rounds and in the IPO from the strategic investor must be understood.

Flexibility. The route necessary for decision-making may be uncomplicated or tortuous. It is essential that the investment group have appropriate autonomy so that crises can be confronted expeditiously. Major corporations often measure performance against a yearly plan, whereas entrepreneurs must have the flexibility to react and restructure plans to overcome unexpected problems.

Interference. Unless the relationship is well-structured, the corporation may attempt to require burdensome reporting and staff policies. Curiosity visits may also become an annoyance.

Time Pressures. Not all corporate personnel realize the length of time that is usually necessary to bring a new business to profitability. If they do not react rationally to unforeseen slippage, then substantial unnecessary difficulties will be created.

Style. Corporate strategic investment groups, like their noncorporate counterparts, differ in attitudes, approaches and interests. A harmonious relationship, which should have developed before the investment, is helpful to a successful alliance and must be fostered in the aftermath.

The most important indicator of likely compatibility is the manner in which the program is being managed. If investments are being made by the corporate development/corporate planning staff on a part-time, un-incentivized basis, the situation is fraught with danger of early termination, since the group will not do well financially. Also, several incentivized captive (wholly internal) strategic investing groups have been closed down because their people did too well, and "compensation envy" became an issue. The maximum longevity has been achieved when the corporation outsourced the activity to a new, dedicated fund in which it was the sole investor, and which was managed by people who had been in the corporation teamed with experienced, professional venture capitalists kept on a loose leash by the head of corporate/business development.

Considerations for the Transaction

Before entering into serious discussions, it is important to understand what benefits are being sought by the corporate strategic investor. It may be seeking: an acquisition option or right of first refusal; the sole use of your product/service; a modified product; exclusive technology/manufacturing/ territorial marketing rights; most favored customer status; first deliveries; and/or certain information flows. Some of these requests may be non-negotiable and will make completing a contract problematic.

There are many other issues that need to be addressed at the beginning of a transaction: decision-making and controls; confidentiality; rights to the technology; creation of a potential competitor; ability to work with competing corporations; responses to changes in the corporate partner's executive strategies or policies; post-development collaboration; reporting; milestone or performance measurement; and winding down if the arrangement is unsuccessful. Additional details that must be negotiated when relevant include: front-end payments; reimbursement; sharing and payment of economic benefits; quality; quantity; price; delivery terms; other charges; royalties; future product or enhancement rights/procedures; field maintenance; warranty exposure; remedies on default; and rights of first negotiation/refusal.

Corporate Investors Do Bring Benefits

Despite the problems cited, many corporations believe they should be preferred investors. In addition to the financial and strategic assistance offered by most venture capitalists, corporate investors can offer many other benefits.

• Assistance in almost all facets of corporate endeavor, such as: setting up financial systems; qualifying suppliers; meeting government regulations; and adding needed technological/clinical/regulatory skills;

• Credibility with customers, banks and other investors, both from a technical and financial standpoint;

• Relief, if desired, from some normal start-up activities—for instance, the corporate investor may take on manufacturing and/or marketing responsibilities;

- Immediate income from an R&D or consulting contract;
- An investor with an infinite lifetime, although the time horizon for profitability will be shorter;
- A merger partner, if and when appropriate;

A more flexible or lower-cost financing package, since return on investment may not be the only criterion used.

Also, the corporate investor may:

- Act as a second source;
- Provide a distribution channel;
- Add patents to strengthen an exiting portfolio;
- Offer a friendly customer interface.

A recent study reported that companies with multiple corporate strategic investors alongside independent venture funds were more likely to be able to consummate an IPO, and were valued more highly in the offering.

Thus, corporate strategic investors can be good partners. However, corporations are very sensitive to down markets and, even in the best of times, several strategic investors have terminated their activities despite excellent returns. In fact, with few exceptions, no strategically-oriented corporate venture capital group has succeeded in retaining its key personnel for more than seven years.

Therefore, it is incumbent upon the entrepreneurial team to exercise the same thoroughness in choosing a potential corporate investor as a venture group does in choosing its investments. Indeed, it is likely that several of the most active corporations today will exit the business within the next few years, wreaking havoc as they go, despite the option of selling their holdup to sophisticated secondary purchasers that can protect their good reputation.

Perspectives

Companies that have received private equity such as Dell Computer, VeriSign, Amgen, and Starbucks have achieved noteworthy success as industry leaders and innovators and in the process have created new industry sectors. The role of private equity investors can be vital to the success of new business development and the character of private equity-backed companies and their founders.

In addition, the relationship between the entrepreneur and the private equity investor is often a critical factor in the success of a new business. To develop a productive, cohesive working relationship, all parties involved need to recognize the biases, prejudices, and pressure points that have emerged from the experiences of both private equity investors and entrepreneurs.

Before making an investment, private equity investors need to carefully examine the management team and look for appropriate skills and disciplines that they believe will lead to a successful relationship. But they also need to look for chemistry, a "gut feeling" that gives them the internal go-ahead to invest in the team. This section examines the techniques used by several industry professionals in evaluating management teams and offers some valuable advice for the entrepreneur on early relationships with the private equity investor.

One of the articles, "An Entrepreneur's Guide to Financing the High Technology Company", provides a unique perspective as it reflects the views of Thomas Bruggere, an entrepreneur. Mr. Bruggere has worked with and won the respect of a number of private equity investors. His insights are valuable as a guide, and they place the entrepreneur-private equity investor relationship and the money-raising process in a new perspective.

An Entrepreneur's Guide to Financing the High Technology Company

Thomas H. Bruggere

Thomas H. Bruggere *is founder and former chairman/CEO of Mentor Graphics Corporation, Wilsonville, Oregon. He founded the company in 1981 to manufacture products for the electronics portion of the computer-aided design industry. Mr. Bruggere has extensive management experience including software engineering and product management and development with Tektronix, Inc. from 1977 to 1981, and with Burroughs Corporation from 1972 to 1977. He obtained a B.S. in mathematics from the University of California at Santa Barbara, an M.S. in computer science from the University of Wisconsin, and an M.B.A. from Pepperdine University.*

Raising money for a start-up firm is like getting your first date—it seems like an impossible task, it's hard to take the first step and it's the beginning of an effort you must continue for the rest of your (company's) life in order to be successful. Like that first date, your attitudes, strategies and personal abilities will be instrumental in determining your ultimate degree of success.

The financial guidance a new high technology company may receive will be imprecise and inconsistent. Some successful companies have financed themselves in every imaginable way. Certain details should be attended to in order to maximize a company's chance for success. What follows is one entrepreneur's reflections on where to look for the problems and the opportunities. So let us start at the beginning.

Getting Up the Nerve

Most would-be entrepreneurs worry about one question: what product should I build? The question of raising money is usually not addressed until after the decision is made to strike out on one's own. Because of the entrepreneur's optimism and confidence, it is often assumed that financing will be available.

At this stage, the main concern is leaving the nest of their existing company. A great deal of energy is put into the product technology because, after all, that is the key to success. And, therefore, that is what will bring the financial world to the door, right?

Not necessarily. A good product is certainly important, but it is not the most important detail to consider when starting a company. People are the most important ingredient at this or any other stage. Investors put their money into people first, and then product and market matches. The right people will make a mediocre product successful, while the wrong people for a project will fall short even with a superior product.

Remember, if you really do have a good product idea, you are going to have competition; the bigger the market potential, the tougher the competition. Also, regardless of your experience or success, you will face difficult problems. Your ability to successfully meet the competition and to overcome these problems will depend upon the quality of your people.

So, good people are what will make the company successful, and investors know this. If you want to make it easier to finance the company, pay attention to its people from the beginning. If you are having trouble raising money initially, take a long, introspective look at the people in the company. You may need to make some changes.

Asking the Question

Now that you have your product idea refined and the best people committed, you are almost ready to ask for the money. First, however, you must decide what to ask for, and whom to ask.

What to Ask For

A business plan will be needed that will include pro forma financial statements indicating how much money you will need to make the company profitable. You must decide how much of that money you want to raise now, and how much you are willing to raise later, hopefully at a higher price. A typical financial plan calls for $50 million in sales in five years with 10% after tax earnings.

The general financial stages of a start-up company are prototype development, product development, successful marketing and expansion. Obviously, the farther along your company is, the less business risk an investor is taking, and the greater the price you can charge for your stock. Most high technology companies raise enough money in their initial financing to take them through the product development stage. This strategy allows the company to prove that the product can be built and that someone will buy it.

It is not uncommon for a company to run out of money before the product development is completed. For this reason, you should try to get investors in the first financing who can and will put up more money if things do not go as planned. You should also raise more money than you think you need in order to give yourself a buffer. A good rule is to take 50% more money than you think you need to achieve your plan.

Whom to Ask

The sources of money for the start-up company are almost everywhere. Personal finances, relatives, banks, individuals, investment banks, venture capitalists and many other sources may be available to you if you just know where to look. But, all money is not created equal, so you must know what to look for.

Any time you bring an investor or group of investors into your company, you should ask yourself (and them), "what will they add to the company?" The answer may be guidance, prestige, contacts, high valuation, etc.

Make certain that there is a good match between what your company needs and what the investors bring. And always get the highest quality investors possible. Top quality investors will attract other investors to your company and provide a smooth financing plan.

How can you tell a quality investor? There are some simple tests, and they all attempt to determine how the investors will help you. Ask about their other investments. If they have had a successful track record of investing, they probably can help you be successful too. Find out how well-known they are; the financial community is very close knit, and reputations are often well deserved.

Determine how long they stay invested in a company; you want early investors with "deep pockets" who can continue investing in subsequent financings. You don't, however, want someone with short arms who will not reach down into those pockets to help you in rough times. Finally, ask how they have helped other companies. This will give you some idea how they might help your company.

Next, you should try to match the type of investor to the needs of your company. For example, a start-up company usually requires different types of support from the consultive help of a venture capitalist to adequate lines of credit at the bank. The following priority ranking of what a company needs is broken down by its financial stage.

Prototype/Product Development

Company Need: Active participation in guidance, product strategy, recruiting contacts, management team development

Best Investors: Venture capitalists, knowledgeable individuals

Successful Marketing

Company Need: Customer contacts, prestige, sales strategy, sales recruitment, less price sensitivity

Best Investors: Venture capitalists, investment bankers, large funds

Market Expansion

Company Need: Low price sensitivity, customer contacts, prestige, credibility

Best Investors: Large funds, general public

Venture capital investors are the most popular source of initial capital. Good ones will help nurture a company by providing counseling, insights gained from previous investments, access to potential employees, prestige and often customer contacts. They are, however, often the most price sensitive: a typical initial funding is $1 million to $5 million for 30% to 60% of your company.

Beware of inexperienced venture capitalists. A number of venture capital funds are managed by people who are either inexperienced in helping a company or spread too thin to provide adequate help. Always ask what the venture capitalists will bring to your company besides money, and what other companies they have been involved with—both as investors and as board members.

Investment banking firms can provide a limited private or public offering for your company. This can be an easy way to raise money by selling stock to relatively sophisticated institutional or individual investors who will probably not take an active role in the company. This group of investors will generally pay a higher price than a venture capitalist but will usually contribute minimal operating experience to the company.

For a company's initial financings, this method of financing is less attractive than venture capital, unless the company already has significant operating experience. As with venture capitalists, investment bankers span a wide range of capability, prestige and experience. Always ask about their most recent offerings and be concerned about the type of investors with whom they will try to place your stock. Unsophisticated or impatient investors may not be very supportive if your company stumbles.

Banks will loan you money if you pledge assets as collateral. If the company has assets (inventory, accounts receivable, for example), bank debt is an excellent way to generate cash. If, however, you are just getting started, your only assets may be items like your house. While many companies have gotten started this way, banks are not venture investors (they currently cannot even own stock), and may not be patient when things don't go as planned. In general, it is best not to use banks to finance your start-up, other than traditional leases and debt. It is important, however, to develop a close, supportive relationship with a good bank from the beginning.

Family, friends and personal finances have started many high technology companies. You certainly should plan on a personal investment, however small. If you do finance your company this way, remember two things: growing the company too slowly because of inadequate capital may cost market share and ultimately the long-term viability of your company, and friends and relatives probably won't bring operating experience or accountability to the company. You must, then, get these elsewhere.

One Example

Mentor Graphics is a public company in the fast growing electronic design automation (EDA) industry. It was initially funded in 1981 by three venture capital firms: Venrock Associates, Greylock Management and Sutter Hill Ventures. It received three private rounds of financing totaling $10 million before raising $52 million in a public offering in January 1984. The figure below shows the stages of funding for Mentor Graphics, including the price paid per share by the investors and the total dollars raised.

Building the Relationship

Plan on an ongoing effort to raise money. If your company is successful, you will need capital for expansion. If it is not, you may need it for survival. In any event, you should have a long term financing plan. And don't hesitate to raise money just to have a reserve. These "war chests" have helped many companies to survive rough times while their under capitalized competition has failed.

Also, because financing your company is an ongoing process, you should always be working at it. Don't wait until you need money to go out and tell your company's story. The more investors are informed about what you do, the better able you may be to raise money. (And besides, the best time to raise money is usually when you don't need it.)

For example, there are numerous financing semi-

Mentor Graphics' Financing History

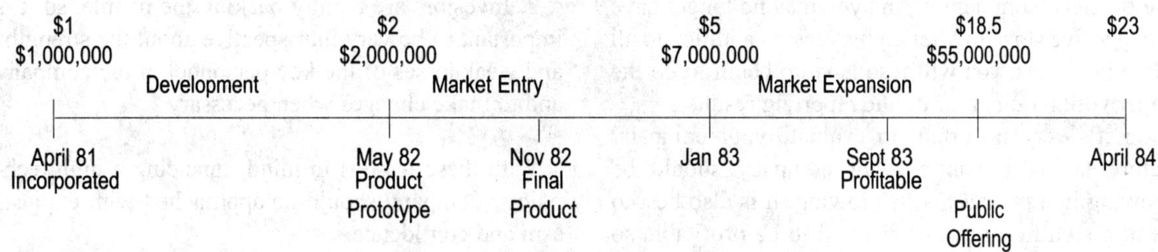

nars you can participate in whether your company is public or private. And because information on the financial "grapevine" travels quickly, a little exposure goes a long way. Also, always keep in mind that the better you tell your story (form and substance), the more attractive your company may be to an investor.

If the goal is to go public, you should plan your investor strategy accordingly. All else being equal, the strongest initial public offerings will come to companies with the most prestigious backers. (Of course, a strong sales and earnings story will always attract attention in an initial public offering [IPO].)

With either strategy, pay attention to your investors, (especially bankers). Keep them regularly informed of progress (at least quarterly), and treat them as an asset of the company. Their support in subsequent financings will be important to you.

The Marriage

The climax of your financing efforts may be either going public or being acquired. Investors will look for these goals in your plan because that is the way they will get their investment back. This is when it is most important to have a good investment banker and a supportive group of previous investors.

There are a variety of reasons why a company should go public. A public offering will provide a significant source of lower-cost capital for the company. It may also enhance the credibility and prestige of your company in the eyes of customers and employees. And it will give early investors and employees some potential liquidity. Besides, the "war chest" of money you raise may give you an important edge over competitors.

On the other hand, being a public company will place new stresses on the company. It will focus you on managing for quarter to quarter increases in earnings, often for the sake of long-term strategy. There will be a significant draw on management's time to deal with the financial community. And you may no longer have inexpensive stock to offer employees. In addition to all these problems, you will also have to begin to do the paperwork required for public reporting results.

So it's very important to evaluate your company before taking it public. Your company should be growing in a market that is growing. It is also best to be at a significant sales level and to be profitable so you will be taken seriously by investors, always try to do an offering when the stock market is strong or you may be in for some disappointments. Most important, be certain you have the infrastructure within your company to manage a public company.

The amount of money you raise during an offering will depend largely on your company's need for cash. You will also want to consider your competitors' resources, since they will probably be trying to outpace you. Also, the price of the stock will be a factor since it will determine the overall dilution of the offering. Finally, listen to your investment bankers since they will have a good measure of what is possible in a given stock market.

If you have done everything right, many of your existing investors, especially the later-stage investors, will show their support by increasing their investment at the public offering. The worst thing you can have is existing investors selling most of their stock at the initial public offering. Potential investors will be unsettled if they see the people who know the most about the company selling out. However, if you have had good investors all along, you will be in good shape at the public offering.

The process of going public may seem so confusing and expensive as to be formidable. But with the right investors, it can be the rewarding pinnacle for your company.

Summary

In summary, there are two lessons that most successful high technology companies have learned about financings:

1. A continuing supply of funds will be needed, so it is important to have a planned investment strategy that brings in investors who will continue to support the company through good and bad times.

2. Investors are mainly backing the people, so it is important to be very introspective about the strengths and weaknesses of the key personnel in the company and to make changes when necessary.

With these lessons in mind, financing a high technology company should be approached with enthusiasm and confidence.

Managing Problem Deals

Claes E. Larsson

Claes E. Larsson *is the founder and president of Point Ledge Associates, which advises venture capital and private equity investors. The firm offers support to improve returns on particular portfolio investments through active, part-time involvement of up to nine months, or more. On behalf of financial owners of smaller companies, Mr. Larsson also acts as a principal, at times taking on active directorships. Prior to establishing this business in 1985, Mr. Larsson was a banking officer with J.P. Morgan and was part of two private equity funds, all in New York. He received his undergraduate degree from Stockholm School of Economics and his MBA from Harvard Business School.*

Few venture capital investments are realized without encountering problems that require action on the part of the board or other outsiders. Even good companies have problems and perform poorly at times. In the following article, we will explore issues that may arise and need to be addressed subsequent to the initial investment in a portfolio company.

Poorly performing portfolio companies are very common, but little has been written about how to deal with them. Rapid growth leading to increasing complexity, as well as changes in the competitive environment, requires management to make changes. Sometimes they need to be initiated by the board. Changing the CEO is an obvious, but many times, poor solution. In a small, dynamic environment, the information available to management can easily become inadequate. The financial presentation to the directors may not permit the board to identify the causes for the poor performance or give little direction how it could be improved.

Fundamental problems many times require basic solutions. However, what has worked with other companies, rarely fits the problem "deal" at hand. To tackle problem investments, a new perspective will need to be developed together with management. A great deal of time is required to find the right course of action and to make sure it is properly implemented. With significantly more capital raised by venture capital funds in recent years, venture capitalists' time is increasingly committed to choosing among a finite number of high-potential investment opportunities. Even at a critical juncture for a particular investment, it can prove difficult to find a board member with enough time to address the issues without outside assistance.

Increasingly, the money invested by venture funds goes into well-established companies. We will focus on problems with portfolio companies that have reached at least a few million dollars in sales and where value created over the time of the investment is an important part of generating a superior return.

Underperformance Is the Norm

Less than 10 percent of venture backed portfolio companies reach even the relatively modest target of 25 percent return on investment, according to a study performed for this article with the help of Thomson Venture Economics. The study, which includes more than 3,500 venture portfolio companies, shows that in recent years, more than half, in fact, have negative returns five years after investment. This is true regardless of investment stage. Nevertheless, the same portfolios returned five times the investment due to a few run away successes. Though all the investments passed venture firms' usually rigorous due diligence process, the data show that well over half of the investments that proved viable have not even generated a return to the investors that could have been obtained on a bank CD!

Little Is Written About Problem Investments

A recent review of the literature and research on underperforming portfolio companies showed that this prevalent phenomenon, which has a significant bearing on venture capital returns, is hardly covered at all. How can this be? Two principal reasons come to mind.

The terminology used gives us the first hint.

Portfolio companies are commonly referred to by venture capitalists as "deals" or "investments". These terms primarily are used to describe transactions in the investment banking field or in the management of portfolios of public stocks. Critical aspects of managing a private equity/venture capital fund are also transaction oriented, such as fund raising and the acquisition and divestiture of portfolio companies. But just as critical is the management of portfolio companies, and, as the terminology suggests, this aspect of a venture capitalist's job can get short shrift. This is particularly true for the many venture capitalists who have a transactions background. Many entrepreneurs find unexpectedly that few of their venture backers have any real operating experience.

The second reason is more obvious. Talking about the great successes in one's portfolio is more rewarding than discussing the problem "deals." Specifics about portfolio returns remain a well-kept secret in the industry. This article is thus based on practical experience gained over more than 15 years working with venture capitalists on specific underperforming portfolio companies. It hopes to shed some light on how problems are identified and on the types of problems most often encountered. Managements' need to change and adapt over time to new challenges within their organization and marketplace is being dealt with here. We will also discuss how problems can be addressed. Special emphasis will be given to the role of the board of directors of portfolio companies in solving problem "deals".

Avoiding Problems

Missed projections, operating losses or negative cash flow might indicate problems, but they do not identify the reasons causing them. In some cases, in particular where an operation never gets off the ground because it is not able to deliver a product that can be sold economically, the problem might be obvious. In other cases, especially with more mature companies, the investment could have some fundamental problem that the placement memorandum and the due diligence conducted prior to investment did not reveal. Needless to say, even what appears to be a most exciting investment opportunity warrants careful scrutiny. It should be remembered that the owner willing to sell and the management of the target company know much more about the business than what can be determined in due diligence. Some things can only be found out once on the inside.

A more thorough investigation up front, especially at the operating level, could sometimes have uncovered issues that later became significant problems. An extra effort on due diligence is well spent to avoid having to attempt to turn a "frog into a princess". In addition, not uncovering an existing or potential problem, the investors are likely to have overpaid, further hurting the potential return.

Identifying Problems

What primarily concerns us here are the underperforming "deals" that were good initial investments, but for some reason, maybe a year or two later, are no longer meeting expectations. Portfolio companies that are well established with sales typically in the $5-50 million range are our focus. The company is beyond the "burn rate" associated with the start-up phase. There is no longer a question of the fundamentals (product, market and maybe not even management). However, the board repeatedly is disappointed by shortfalls in sales, margin or cash flow but is unclear as to the real cause. The IPO planned down the line seems ever more distant.

The immediate reaction to this situation from most directors with whom I have worked is that the CEO needs to be replaced. An excellent management team and CEO are almost always the most important factors to getting superior results from a venture investment. However, poor results far less often reflect poor management. In addition, many times the CEO of a company at this stage of its development might have product or market knowledge that is very difficult to replace.

With a good management team and experienced directors on the board, inadequate information is, in my experience, the most common deterrent to identifying the problem. When an operation is small, the CEO is in frequent personal contact with all aspects of the enterprise. As it grows and becomes more complex, the information systems become outmoded. It is not unusual to find a rapidly growing $15 MM company with management systems that barely could support a $5 MM operation. A national rollout of an initially proven successful concept is prone to this type of failure.

Most board packages for small to mid sized companies, at least with financially oriented owners, do not reveal the effect on profitability and cash flow from changes in the customer structure or product mix. In many cases, if the management or the board had a better appreciation for the product and market dynamics and had more timely access to the right information, they would have started to address some of the issues confronting the company with disappointing performance.

A related problem area is the management and board reporting of cost structures. I worked with one investment where, unfortunately, I had to inform the Board that what management reported and what had been accepted by the investors from the time of their investment as fixed costs, in fact, were variable with growth. In other words, with sales increasing, things for this company were not going to get better!

As a venture grows, more emphasis needs to be given to where the margin is generated and less to sales growth. Margin reporting by product or district is something any well-established company takes for granted but something a start-up is not born with. Unless stronger systems are implemented in time, a good investment can become a problem "deal" along the way.

Fundamental problems sometimes cannot be fixed without fundamental changes. As a company develops, management's information needs change. If this is addressed, potential problems often can be identified before the problems become serious. If the company has been subject to a major shift in its circumstances, it might require in-depth work, which is time consuming, just to identify the relationship to the symptoms - weak sales or margins or cost overruns.

Management and the investors might be rutted in an established way of approaching their business, sometimes only relying on information generated by accountants for fiscal reasons. This makes the identification of problems and solutions more difficult. There might be suspicions as to what needs to be changed. The raw data from which the problem can be identified generally are available to management, if not to the board. However, the information needs to be put together in different ways for management to see that they need to redirect their efforts.

Some of the causes of problem deals seem basic in hindsight, so much so that one wonders how they could elude sophisticated, venture-dominated boards. Often, a solution that seems obvious in retrospect, once a new focus has been given to the situation, was very difficult to uncover and has required significant effort to implement.

The Causes of Problem "Deals"

The incidence of the problems I have mentioned so far, in my experience, seems to increase with less industry specialization of the fund and greater geographical distance from the lead investor(s) to the portfolio company. Another issue contributing to problems is a lack of commitment from a particular investor. For example, when there are multiple minority investors or when owners no longer are working with a common objective, problem "deals" seem to appear more often.

Many companies reach $5 or $10 MM in sales on the strength of a superior or novel product offering. The problem initially has been to produce it consistently at an attractive enough cost. It is often at this stage that the venture investors come in, inheriting the management and the sometimes rudimentary organizations and systems the entrepreneur has relied on. I have been surprised to find that companies even beyond this size, as competition has entered for the first time, have to be persuaded to develop something as basic as a sales force and all that comes with it.

For example, a medical service firm had developed a new elective procedure for an indication that previously had not been successfully addressed. It was of great benefit to a major market segment. Business grew rapidly based on patient demand, and the company went public to finance a rollout of its operations nationally. The procedure became well accepted. Then, many physicians started to enter the field providing competition, and the initially pent-up demand was dwindling. The company faced major losses, and the stock price tumbled. The market had fundamentally changed, but the company was too involved in addressing other issues to see it. While the company was marketing directly to consumers, referring physicians were now directing their patients to treatment with specialist colleagues. To address this major change in the marketplace, marketing based on direct sales to referring physicians needed to be developed in place of the previous consumer-oriented efforts. The new customer definition also had major repercussions in terms of the product offering and how the company had to be organized. In the year following the implementation of the new strategy, the stock recovered to more than three times its low.

It is not only the customer definition that can get off track. Once a small company gets the product or service to work well technically, there could be a brief spurt of growing sales that level off later. Based on an intimate understanding of how the market accepts it, the product definition might need to be revamped. The technically skilled entrepreneur sometimes needs support to structure the pricing differently or to aim the product for a different use before sales can successfully take off again.

In some situations, founders have proven unable to learn to manage through delegation, a necessity caused by growth. Others are unable to deal in a more leveraged environment resulting from being bought. Still others chafe at sharing control with new investors. Often, these kinds of problems, one type of which we might call hurdle problems, can be solved by supplementing or temporarily supporting the CEO to get over the hurdle.

There seems always to be the suggestion that more money from the investors will solve the shortfall to expectations. From companies that have gotten beyond the startup phase, a request for more money without a plan for change is more often a sign that there is a problem than an indication of the real cause of it. Buying time rarely makes problems go away. On the other hand, few new game plans can be implemented without the support of additional funds.

How are the Problems Best Addressed?

The best solutions come from management. They know the business. They implement changes and live with them. The issue becomes to get management to accept that often painful change is required and get it focused on addressing it.

Working through a new business plan could be what is called for. To gain perspective, time away from an intense office environment could be productive if thoroughly prepared for beforehand with the help of a neutral outsider. Replacement or addition of certain key management functions, maybe only on a temporary basis, might be a solution. A significant legal problem or real estate-related issues could, for example, become a major distraction for an excellent management team. Relieving management from dealing directly with such issues could be another way a hurdle could be overcome. Finally, while the management team generally is growing with the greater challenge, certain members of it might not be. It is very difficult to realize that this is the case and to take the necessary steps of letting one of the original members of the team go. The board has a big role here as it is, of course, unusual for CEOs to admit their own or their team's shortcomings and ask for help.

Firm Statistics Report

Firm Statistics Reported
Ranked Firms (capital under management)
Buyout Firms
Data as of: 06/30/2010

Rank	Firm Name	Capital under Management (USD Mil)	Pct. of Total	Number of Funds	Avg. Fund Size (USD Mil)
1	TPG Capital	49,939.2	3.8	10.0	4,993.9
2	Carlyle Group, The	45,205.0	3.4	16.0	2,825.3
3	Blackstone Group, L.P.	44,453.0	3.4	9.0	4,939.2
4	Kohlberg, Kravis, Roberts & Company, L.P.	42,692.7	3.2	6.0	7,115.4
5	Apollo Management	39,751.9	3.0	6.0	6,625.3
6	Goldman, Sachs & Co.	34,050.0	2.6	4.0	8,512.5
7	Bain Capital	32,280.3	2.4	7.0	4,611.5
8	CVC Capital Partners, Ltd.	30,944.7	2.3	4.0	7,736.2
9	Apax Partners Worldwide, Ltd.	28,301.3	2.1	5.0	5,660.3
10	Hellman & Friedman LLC	22,900.0	1.7	4.0	5,725.0
11	Advent International	21,767.0	1.7	11.0	1,978.8
12	Permira Advisers LLP	21,315.4	1.6	3.0	7,105.1
13	Providence Equity Partners LLC	20,101.0	1.5	5.0	4,020.2
14	Thomas H. Lee Partners	16,200.0	1.2	3.0	5,400.0
15	Warburg Pincus LLC	15,000.0	1.1	1.0	15,000.0
16	Madison Dearborn Partners LLC	14,636.0	1.1	3.0	4,878.7
17	Silver Lake Sumeru	14,000.0	1.1	3.0	4,666.7
18	Bridgepoint Capital, Ltd.	13,527.5	1.0	11.0	1,229.8
19	Charterhouse Capital Partners LLP	13,475.2	1.0	3.0	4,491.7
20	Cinven, Ltd.	12,626.5	1.0	2.0	6,313.2
21	EQT Funds management Limited	12,576.5	1.0	7.0	1,796.6
22	Welsh, Carson, Anderson & Stowe	12,265.4	0.9	4.0	3,066.4
23	Candover Investments PLC	10,798.1	0.8	3.0	3,599.4
24	BC Partners, Ltd.	10,751.4	0.8	3.0	3,583.8
25	Lindsay Goldberg LLC (FKA: Lindsay Goldberg & Bessemer GP)	9,800.0	0.7	3.0	3,266.7
26	Terra Firma Capital Partners, Ltd.	9,744.9	0.7	2.0	4,872.5
27	Sun Capital Partners, Inc.	9,435.0	0.7	5.0	1,887.0
28	Onex Corporation	9,354.0	0.7	3.0	3,118.0
29	PAI Partners SAS	9,307.6	0.7	3.0	3,102.5
30	Clayton, Dubilier & Rice, Inc.	9,054.1	0.7	2.0	4,527.0
31	Nordic Capital	8,697.7	0.7	4.0	2,174.4
32	DLJ Merchant Banking Partners	7,679.9	0.6	3.0	2,560.0
33	New Mountain Capital LLC	7,602.8	0.6	4.0	1,900.7
34	Lone Star Funds	7,500.0	0.6	1.0	7,500.0
35	Fortress Investment Group LLC	7,451.0	0.6	5.0	1,490.2
36	Kelso & Company	7,200.0	0.5	2.0	3,600.0
37	Leonard Green & Partners	7,150.0	0.5	2.0	3,575.0
38	CVC Asia Pacific, Ltd.	6,940.3	0.5	3.0	2,313.4
39	Barclays Private Equity, Ltd.	6,720.1	0.5	3.0	2,240.0
40	Francisco Partners	6,700.3	0.5	4.0	1,675.1
41	GTCR Golder Rauner LLC	6,586.7	0.5	4.0	1,646.7
42	Doughty Hanson & Co., Ltd.	6,357.8	0.5	4.0	1,589.4
43	Oak Hill Capital Management, Inc.	6,300.0	0.5	2.0	3,150.0
44	J.C. Flowers & Co. LLC	6,134.7	0.5	3.0	2,044.9

Rank	Firm Name	Capital under Management (USD Mil)	Pct. of Total	Number of Funds	Avg. Fund Size (USD Mil))
45	TA Associates, Inc.	6,050.0	0.5	3.0	2,016.7
46	Court Square Capital Partners	5,666.6	0.4	2.0	2,833.3
47	TowerBrook Capital Partners L.P.	5,250.0	0.4	4.0	1,312.5
48	Pacific Equity Partners	5,247.0	0.4	4.0	1,311.8
49	AIG Capital Partners	5,198.4	0.4	3.0	1,732.8
50	Altor Equity Partners AB	5,115.1	0.4	3.0	1,705.0
51	Jordan Company, The	5,100.0	0.4	2.0	2,550.0
52	AXA Private Equity SA	4,947.4	0.4	9.0	549.7
53	Montagu Private Equity, Ltd.	4,925.1	0.4	6.0	820.9
54	Berkshire Partners LLC	4,805.4	0.4	2.0	2,402.7
55	Lehman Brothers, Inc.	4,508.1	0.3	3.0	1,502.7
56	Irving Place Capital	4,200.0	0.3	2.0	2,100.0
57	H.I.G. Capital LLC	4,200.0	0.3	3.0	1,400.0
58	Abraaj Capital Limited	4,148.6	0.3	7.0	592.7
59	American Securities Capital Partners LLC	3,977.9	0.3	4.0	994.5
60	Global Innovation Partners LLC	3,826.7	0.3	3.0	1,275.6
61	Avista Capital Holdings, L.P.	3,800.0	0.3	2.0	1,900.0
62	Vestar Capital Partners, Inc.	3,700.0	0.3	1.0	3,700.0
63	Riverside Company	3,613.6	0.3	9.0	401.5
64	Affinity Equity Partners	3,500.0	0.3	2.0	1,750.0
65	3i Group PLC	3,488.4	0.3	4.0	872.1
66	IK Investment Partners, Ltd.	3,451.9	0.3	2.0	1,725.9
67	Platinum Equity LLC	3,450.0	0.3	2.0	1,725.0
68	CCMP Capital Advisors LLC	3,400.0	0.3	1.0	3,400.0
69	Stone Point Capital LLC	3,316.0	0.3	2.0	1,658.0
70	Blum Capital Partners, LP	3,250.0	0.2	3.0	1,083.3
71	Centerbridge Partners	3,200.0	0.2	1.0	3,200.0
72	MBK Partners	3,160.0	0.2	2.0	1,580.0
73	KRG Capital Partners LLC	3,125.0	0.2	3.0	1,041.7
74	Charlesbank Capital Partners LLC	3,107.5	0.2	4.0	776.9
75	Quadrangle Group LLC	3,083.5	0.2	2.0	1,541.8
76	ABRY Partners LLC	3,026.1	0.2	3.0	1,008.7
77	JLL Partners (FKA: Joseph, Littlejohn & Levy, Inc.)	3,000.0	0.2	3.0	1,000.0
78	Mid Europa Partners	2,925.4	0.2	2.0	1,462.7
79	Kohlberg & Company LLC	2,876.0	0.2	3.0	958.7
80	Duke Street Capital	2,804.5	0.2	2.0	1,402.2
81	TDR Capital LLP	2,793.0	0.2	3.0	931.0
82	Gores Group LLC, The	2,739.3	0.2	3.0	913.1
83	AEA Investors LP	2,728.8	0.2	4.0	682.2
84	Forstmann Little & Company	2,717.9	0.2	2.0	1,358.9
85	Littlejohn & Company LLC	2,690.0	0.2	3.0	896.7
86	Navis Investment Partners (Asia), Ltd.	2,680.5	0.2	4.0	670.1
87	Southern Cross Group (AKA: SCG)	2,648.1	0.2	3.0	882.7
88	CDH China Management Co., Ltd.	2,600.0	0.2	2.0	1,300.0
89	HM Capital Partners LLC	2,555.0	0.2	4.0	638.8
90	Golden Gate Capital	2,500.0	0.2	2.0	1,250.0
91	Mount Kellett Capital Management	2,500.0	0.2	1.0	2,500.0
92	Hopu Investment Management Co., Ltd.	2,500.0	0.2	1.0	2,500.0
93	Triton Partners	2,422.1	0.2	3.0	807.4

Rank	Firm Name	Capital under Management (USD Mil)	Pct. of Total	Number of Funds	Avg. Fund Size (USD Mil)
94	Cognetas LLP	2,416.4	0.2	2.0	1,208.2
95	Morgan Stanley Private Equity	2,366.0	0.2	4.0	591.5
96	Investindustrial Partners, Ltd.	2,363.5	0.2	3.0	787.8
97	SPO Partners & Co	2,340.0	0.2	1.0	2,340.0
98	Clessidra Capital	2,337.4	0.2	2.0	1,168.7
99	Exponent Private Equity LLP (FKA: Square Capital Management)	2,317.7	0.2	2.0	1,158.8
100	Olympus Advisory Partners, Inc.	2,287.5	0.2	2.0	1,143.8
101	Friedman, Fleischer & Lowe, LLC	2,250.0	0.2	2.0	1,125.0
102	Odyssey Investment Partners, LLC	2,250.0	0.2	2.0	1,125.0
103	Genstar Capital LLC	2,246.0	0.2	3.0	748.7
104	Gilde Buy Out Partners	2,238.6	0.2	3.0	746.2
105	Macquarie Capital Funds (Europe) Ltd.	2,201.0	0.2	1.0	2,201.0
106	Englefield Capital	2,179.6	0.2	2.0	1,089.8
107	HSBC Pte Equity (Asia), Ltd. (FKA: HSBC Private Equity Mgt.)	2,171.0	0.2	2.0	1,085.5
108	Ripplewood Holdings LLC	2,155.7	0.2	2.0	1,077.8
109	Unison Capital, Inc.	2,155.6	0.2	2.0	1,077.8
110	Thoma Bravo LLC	2,141.7	0.2	3.0	713.9
111	Hony Capital Ltd.	2,134.0	0.2	4.0	533.5
112	Freeman Spogli & Co.	2,131.2	0.2	3.0	710.4
113	Wind Point Partners	2,106.0	0.2	3.0	702.0
114	Advantage Partners LLP	2,097.2	0.2	3.0	699.1
115	Summit Partners	2,085.0	0.2	1.0	2,085.0
116	HgCapital	2,060.8	0.2	2.0	1,030.4
117	Tailwind Capital Partners	2,050.0	0.2	2.0	1,025.0
118	Yucaipa Companies LLC, The	2,027.1	0.2	5.0	405.4
119	Centre Partners Management LLC	2,020.0	0.2	3.0	673.3
120	Norwest Equity Partners	2,000.0	0.2	2.0	1,000.0
121	CapMan Plc	1,973.0	0.1	10.0	197.3
122	Castle Harlan, Inc.	1,963.0	0.1	2.0	981.5
123	Waterland Private Equity Investments B.V.	1,957.8	0.1	3.0	652.6
124	Catterton Partners	1,950.0	0.1	3.0	650.0
125	Wellspring Capital Management LLC	1,935.0	0.1	2.0	967.5
126	Nautic Partners LLC	1,882.7	0.1	2.0	941.3
127	Trimaran Capital Partners, LLC	1,867.1	0.1	2.0	933.5
128	Sterling Partners	1,846.3	0.1	3.0	615.4
129	Diamond Castle Holdings LLC	1,825.0	0.1	1.0	1,825.0
130	Pamplona Capital Management LLP	1,807.6	0.1	1.0	1,807.6
131	Elevation Associates LLC	1,800.0	0.1	1.0	1,800.0
132	Willis Stein & Partners	1,800.0	0.1	1.0	1,800.0
133	CITIC Capital Partners, Ltd.	1,796.2	0.1	6.0	299.4
134	Vista Equity Partners	1,794.7	0.1	3.0	598.2
135	CHAMP Private Equity Pty Ltd.	1,790.8	0.1	3.0	596.9
136	J.W. Childs Associates	1,750.0	0.1	1.0	1,750.0
137	BPEP International	1,727.9	0.1	5.0	345.6
138	Archer Capital	1,713.3	0.1	4.0	428.3
139	Levine Leichtman Capital Partners, Inc.	1,707.0	0.1	3.0	569.0
140	Audax Group	1,700.0	0.1	2.0	850.0
141	Greenbriar Equity Group LLC	1,697.7	0.1	2.0	848.8
142	Alpha Group	1,685.6	0.1	3.0	561.9

Rank	Firm Name	Capital under Management (USD Mil)	Pct. of Total	Number of Funds	Avg. Fund Size (USD Mil)
143	GCP Capital Partners	1,684.1	0.1	3.0	561.4
144	Quad-C Management, Inc.	1,622.0	0.1	3.0	540.7
145	Calera Capital (FKA: Fremont Partners)	1,619.2	0.1	2.0	809.6
146	Lightyear Capital LLC	1,609.0	0.1	2.0	804.5
147	CBPE Capital, LLP (AKA: Close Brothers Private Equity, Ltd.)	1,596.8	0.1	3.0	532.3
148	Unitas Capital Pte, Ltd.	1,590.0	0.1	1.0	1,590.0
149	American Capital, Ltd.	1,585.0	0.1	2.0	792.5
150	Aquiline Capital Partners	1,575.6	0.1	2.0	787.8
151	GIMV N.V.	1,568.6	0.1	4.0	392.1
152	Segulah Advisor AB	1,557.6	0.1	3.0	519.2
153	LGV Capital, Ltd. (FKA: Legal & General Ventures, Ltd.)	1,548.7	0.1	6.0	258.1
154	BS Private Equity SpA (FKA: B&S Private Equity Group)	1,546.0	0.1	4.0	386.5
155	Graphite Capital (FKA: F&C Ventures, Ltd.)	1,540.3	0.1	3.0	513.4
156	Veritas Capital	1,528.0	0.1	3.0	509.3
157	Newbridge Capital, Ltd.	1,500.0	0.1	1.0	1,500.0
158	Baring Vostok Capital Partners	1,500.0	0.1	2.0	750.0
159	RoundTable Health Care Partners	1,500.0	0.1	3.0	500.0
160	Alchemy Partners LLP	1,483.9	0.1	3.0	494.6
161	Resource Capital Funds, The	1,471.1	0.1	3.0	490.4
162	Mercapital Servicios Financieros	1,464.3	0.1	3.0	488.1
163	Odewald & Compagnie GmbH	1,452.7	0.1	3.0	484.2
164	Parthenon Capital LLC	1,450.0	0.1	2.0	725.0
165	Pine Brook Road Partners LLC	1,430.0	0.1	1.0	1,430.0
166	Roark Capital Group	1,426.6	0.1	3.0	475.5
167	Birch Hill Equity Partners Management, Inc.	1,426.0	0.1	2.0	713.0
168	Behrman Capital	1,413.5	0.1	2.0	706.8
169	Capvis Equity Partners AG	1,403.3	0.1	3.0	467.8
170	Sterling Group, L.P., The (FKA: The Sterling Group, Inc.)	1,403.0	0.1	3.0	467.7
171	Corsair Capital LLC	1,398.2	0.1	2.0	699.1
172	LBO France SAS	1,398.0	0.1	1.0	1,398.0
173	Monitor Clipper Partners LLC	1,391.8	0.1	3.0	463.9
174	Vitruvian Partners LLP	1,388.9	0.1	1.0	1,388.9
175	Accel-KKR LLC	1,375.0	0.1	4.0	343.8
176	TSG Consumer Partners	1,375.0	0.1	2.0	687.5
177	Harvest Partners LLC	1,373.0	0.1	2.0	686.5
178	Blue Ridge Capital	1,345.8	0.1	1.0	1,345.8
179	New Silk Route Partners LLC	1,343.1	0.1	1.0	1,343.1
180	Patron Capital, Ltd.	1,331.5	0.1	2.0	665.8
181	Thoma Cressey Bravo	1,327.7	0.1	3.0	442.6
182	CITIC Private Equity Funds Management Co., Ltd.	1,318.3	0.1	1.0	1,318.3
183	MidOcean Partners	1,310.1	0.1	2.0	655.0
184	EdgeStone Capital Partners, Inc.	1,304.5	0.1	4.0	326.1
185	Lake Capital Partners, Inc.	1,300.0	0.1	2.0	650.0
186	Code, Hennessy & Simmons LLC	1,300.0	0.1	1.0	1,300.0
187	Veronis Suhler Stevenson (FKA: Veronis, Suhler & Associates)	1,300.0	0.1	1.0	1,300.0
188	India Value Fund Advisors Private Ltd. (FKA: GW Capital)	1,275.0	0.1	3.0	425.0
189	SAIF Partners	1,250.0	0.1	1.0	1,250.0
190	Lincolnshire Management, Inc.	1,250.0	0.1	2.0	625.0
191	Heartland Industrial Partners	1,233.0	0.1	1.0	1,233.0

Rank	Firm Name	Capital under Management (USD Mil)	Pct. of Total	Number of Funds	Avg. Fund Size (USD Mil)
192	Egeria B.V.	1,226.4	0.1	2.0	613.2
193	Markstone Capital	1,210.9	0.1	1.0	1,210.9
194	Spectrum Equity Investors	1,200.0	0.1	1.0	1,200.0
195	Phoenix Equity Partners (FKA: DLJ European Private Equity)	1,185.0	0.1	3.0	395.0
196	Paine & Partners LLC	1,182.9	0.1	1.0	1,182.9
197	Investitori Associati SpA	1,180.6	0.1	2.0	590.3
198	AnaCap Financial Partners LLP	1,176.9	0.1	2.0	588.5
199	Tinicum Capital Partners	1,164.9	0.1	1.0	1,164.9
200	Vision Capital LLP	1,162.5	0.1	2.0	581.2
201	Clarity Partners	1,159.5	0.1	3.0	386.5
202	Jefferies Group, Inc.	1,158.9	0.1	3.0	386.3
203	Ironbridge Capital Pty., Ltd.	1,143.7	0.1	2.0	571.8
204	BV Investment Partners	1,134.0	0.1	2.0	567.0
205	Great Hill Equity Partners LLC	1,116.6	0.1	1.0	1,116.6
206	Brockway Moran & Partners, Inc.	1,110.0	0.1	2.0	555.0
207	Angelo, Gordon & Company	1,106.8	0.1	3.0	368.9
208	Huntsman Gay Global Capital LLC	1,104.2	0.1	2.0	552.1
209	Brazos Private Equity Partners LLC	1,100.0	0.1	2.0	550.0
210	Lee Equity Partners	1,094.0	0.1	2.0	547.0
211	Sentinel Capital Partners	1,084.0	0.1	2.0	542.0
212	Bridgepoint Development Capital	1,065.3	0.1	2.0	532.7
213	Chequers Capital SA	1,055.0	0.1	2.0	527.5
214	Global Investment House	1,050.0	0.1	2.0	525.0
215	Cartesian Capital Group, LLC	1,050.0	0.1	1.0	1,050.0
216	Richardson Capital Limited	1,045.0	0.1	2.0	522.5
217	Gresham LLP	1,039.2	0.1	3.0	346.4
218	Hudson Capital Management, L.P.	1,024.0	0.1	1.0	1,024.0
219	Marlin Equity Partners, LLC	1,024.0	0.1	3.0	341.3
220	J.H. Whitney & Co. LLC	1,022.0	0.1	2.0	511.0
221	STAR Capital Partners, Ltd.	1,022.0	0.1	1.0	1,022.0
222	Water Street Healthcare Partners	1,020.0	0.1	2.0	510.0
223	Flexpoint Ford (FKA: Flexpoint Partners LLC)	1,015.0	0.1	2.0	507.5
224	capiton AG	1,003.2	0.1	3.0	334.4
225	Brysam Global Partners	1,000.0	0.1	1.0	1,000.0
226	Fox Paine & Company LLC	1,000.0	0.1	1.0	1,000.0
227	KSL Capital Partners	1,000.0	0.1	1.0	1,000.0
228	Symphony Technology Group LLC	1,000.0	0.1	1.0	1,000.0
229	Bencis Capital Partners	993.8	0.1	3.0	331.3
230	Wexford Capital, LLC (AKA: Wexford Management, LLC)	982.5	0.1	3.0	327.5
231	Black Diamond Capital Management, LLC	982.0	0.1	1.0	982.0
232	Banc Funds, The	973.9	0.1	3.0	324.6
233	FriedbergMilstein, LLC	966.0	0.1	2.0	483.0
234	Inflexion PLC	961.1	0.1	3.0	320.4
235	HealthpointCapital LLC	956.7	0.1	3.0	318.9
236	N+1	954.8	0.1	1.0	954.8
237	Herkules Capital AS	953.7	0.1	2.0	476.9
238	Graham Partners, Inc.	952.5	0.1	2.0	476.2
239	FountainVest Partners (Asia), Ltd.	950.0	0.1	1.0	950.0
240	New York Life Capital Partners (AKA: NYLCAP)	950.0	0.1	3.0	316.7

Rank	Firm Name	Capital under Management (USD Mil)	Pct. of Total	Number of Funds	Avg. Fund Size (USD Mil)
241	Leeds Equity Partners	950.0	0.1	2.0	475.0
242	CIVC Partners LP (FKA: Continental Illinois Venture Corp.)	937.5	0.1	2.0	468.8
243	Palladium Equity Partners LLC	936.3	0.1	2.0	468.1
244	Quadriga Capital	935.6	0.1	3.0	311.9
245	21 Centrale Partners	928.8	0.1	3.0	309.6
246	Snow Phipps Group LLC	928.0	0.1	2.0	464.0
247	Eos Partners, L.P.	925.0	0.1	3.0	308.3
248	Clearwater Capital Partners, LLC	914.6	0.1	2.0	457.3
249	Deutsche Beteiligungs AG	909.2	0.1	2.0	454.6
250	Chicago Growth Partners (William Blair Capital Partners)	902.8	0.1	3.0	300.9

Source: Thomson Reuters

Firm Statistics Reported
Ranked Firms (capital under management)
Venture Capital Firms
Data as of: 06/30/2010

Rank	Firm Name	Capital under Management (USD Mil)	Pct. of Total	Number of Funds	Avg. Fund Size (USD Mil)
1	New Enterprise Associates, Inc.	8,441.8	1.5	4.0	2,110.4
2	Summit Partners	6,857.9	1.2	9.0	762.0
3	Panorama Capital	6,540.0	1.1	2.0	3,270.0
4	Oak Investment Partners	6,455.0	1.1	4.0	1,613.8
5	PAI Partners SAS	6,400.6	1.1	1.0	6,400.6
6	Sequoia Capital	5,722.5	1.0	14.0	408.8
7	Technology Crossover Ventures	5,300.0	0.9	3.0	1,766.7
8	Accel Partners	3,974.2	0.7	9.0	441.6
9	Carlyle Group, The	3,784.0	0.7	7.0	540.6
10	Kleiner Perkins Caufield & Byers	3,612.2	0.6	8.0	451.5
11	JAFCO Co., Ltd. (FKA: Japan Associated Finance Co. Ltd.)	3,474.8	0.6	12.0	289.6
12	VantagePoint Venture Partners	3,294.8	0.6	6.0	549.1
13	Babcock & Brown Capital Management Pty., Ltd.	3,172.1	0.6	1.0	3,172.1
14	Shenzhen Capital Group Co., Ltd.	3,021.8	0.5	6.0	503.6
15	Benchmark Capital	3,006.1	0.5	8.0	375.8
16	Polaris Venture Partners	2,984.4	0.5	4.0	746.1
17	Battery Ventures, L.P.	2,842.0	0.5	5.0	568.4
18	U.S. Venture Partners	2,841.0	0.5	4.0	710.2
19	Highland Capital Partners LLC	2,824.6	0.5	5.0	564.9
20	Greylock Partners	2,820.0	0.5	6.0	470.0
21	Menlo Ventures	2,715.2	0.5	2.0	1,357.6
22	Terra Firma Capital Partners, Ltd.	2,685.5	0.5	1.0	2,685.5
23	Matrix Partners	2,679.0	0.5	5.0	535.8
24	Warburg Pincus LLC	2,670.0	0.5	2.0	1,335.0
25	Draper Fisher Jurvetson	2,481.1	0.4	7.0	354.4
26	Columbia Capital LLC	2,427.3	0.4	5.0	485.5
27	SAIF Partners	2,411.2	0.4	5.0	482.2
28	North Bridge Venture Partners	2,399.3	0.4	4.0	599.8
29	Weston Presidio (FKA: Weston Presidio Capital Management)	2,374.2	0.4	2.0	1,187.1
30	Canaan Partners	2,300.0	0.4	4.0	575.0
31	Foundation Capital	2,295.0	0.4	5.0	459.0
32	Morgenthaler Ventures	2,288.9	0.4	4.0	572.2
33	Austin Ventures, L.P.	2,255.0	0.4	3.0	751.7
34	Norwest Venture Partners	2,250.0	0.4	3.0	750.0
35	IDG Technology Venture Investment, Inc.	2,221.1	0.4	6.0	370.2
36	Domain Associates LLC	2,196.2	0.4	8.0	274.5
37	MPM Capital	2,190.0	0.4	4.0	547.5
38	Essex Woodlands Health Ventures	2,180.5	0.4	4.0	545.1
39	Index Ventures	2,177.5	0.4	5.0	435.5
40	ChrysCapital Management Company	2,176.7	0.4	4.0	544.2
41	Lightspeed Venture Partners	2,100.0	0.4	3.0	700.0
42	J.H. Whitney & Co. LLC	2,084.8	0.4	4.0	521.2
43	Venrock Associates	2,052.1	0.4	5.0	410.4
44	Bessemer Venture Partners	2,048.0	0.4	7.0	292.6

Rank	Firm Name	Capital under Management (USD Mil)	Pct. of Total	Number of Funds	Avg. Fund Size (USD Mil)
45	InterWest Partners	2,033.5	0.4	5.0	406.7
46	Apax Partners Worldwide, Ltd.	2,001.2	0.3	3.0	667.1
47	TA Associates, Inc.	2,000.1	0.3	1.0	2,000.1
48	Dubai International Capital LLC	2,000.0	0.3	1.0	2,000.0
49	Atlas Venture, Ltd.	1,972.3	0.3	4.0	493.1
50	Spectrum Equity Investors	1,955.0	0.3	1.0	1,955.0
51	Henderson Equity Partners (AKA: Henderson Private Capital)	1,942.7	0.3	4.0	485.7
52	Sagard SAS	1,921.7	0.3	2.0	960.8
53	Redpoint Ventures	1,903.3	0.3	6.0	317.2
54	Institutional Venture Partners	1,875.0	0.3	4.0	468.8
55	OrbiMed Advisors LLC	1,855.0	0.3	5.0	371.0
56	Mayfield Fund	1,807.3	0.3	6.0	301.2
57	DCM	1,771.9	0.3	5.0	354.4
58	AXA Private Equity SA	1,769.9	0.3	10.0	177.0
59	Sequoia Capital India (FKA: WestBridge Capital Partners)	1,744.5	0.3	5.0	348.9
60	Park Square Capital, LLP	1,681.9	0.3	1.0	1,681.9
61	BPEP International	1,679.0	0.3	9.0	186.6
62	Rho Capital Partners, Inc.	1,658.8	0.3	5.0	331.8
63	Aisling Capital	1,648.8	0.3	3.0	549.6
64	Frazier Healthcare and Technology Ventures	1,628.7	0.3	5.0	325.7
65	August Capital Management	1,618.7	0.3	3.0	539.6
66	ICICI Venture Funds Management Co., Pvt. Ltd. (FKA: TDICI)	1,604.4	0.3	11.0	145.9
67	Mohr Davidow Ventures	1,602.6	0.3	3.0	534.2
68	Sigma Partners	1,599.0	0.3	3.0	533.0
69	Siguler Guff & Company	1,541.8	0.3	4.0	385.5
70	Bain Capital Ventures	1,525.0	0.3	4.0	381.2
71	General Catalyst Partners (FKA: General Catalyst Group LLC)	1,506.0	0.3	5.0	301.2
72	SV Life Sciences Advisers	1,497.0	0.3	3.0	499.0
73	SBI Investment Company, Ltd. (FKA:Softbank Investment Corp)	1,481.6	0.3	7.0	211.7
74	Alta Partners	1,426.5	0.2	5.0	285.3
75	Advanced Technology Ventures	1,425.0	0.2	3.0	475.0
76	Intel Capital	1,400.0	0.2	6.0	233.3
77	New Horizon Capital	1,396.0	0.2	3.0	465.3
78	Sierra Ventures	1,395.2	0.2	3.0	465.1
79	GP Investimentos	1,371.6	0.2	2.0	685.8
80	J.P. Morgan Capital Corporation	1,333.9	0.2	2.0	667.0
81	Crosslink Capital	1,326.0	0.2	5.0	265.2
82	Pamodzi Investment Holdings	1,300.0	0.2	1.0	1,300.0
83	Versant Ventures	1,300.0	0.2	3.0	433.3
84	Charles River Ventures	1,292.0	0.2	4.0	323.0
85	Scale Venture Partners	1,291.0	0.2	4.0	322.8
86	Fondo Italiano d'Investimento SGR SpA	1,282.9	0.2	1.0	1,282.9
87	Paul Capital Partners	1,260.0	0.2	3.0	420.0
88	Mobius Venture Capital, Inc.	1,250.0	0.2	1.0	1,250.0
89	Ignition Partners (FKA: Ignition Corporation)	1,229.7	0.2	4.0	307.4
90	Walden International	1,228.7	0.2	8.0	153.6
91	Abingworth Management, Ltd.	1,215.9	0.2	4.0	304.0
92	Khosla Ventures	1,213.2	0.2	4.0	303.3
93	Great Hill Equity Partners LLC	1,210.0	0.2	2.0	605.0

Rank	Firm Name	Capital under Management (USD Mil)	Pct. of Total	Number of Funds	Avg. Fund Size (USD Mil)
94	FirstMark Capital LLC	1,202.3	0.2	5.0	240.5
95	Pitango Venture Capital (FKA:Polaris Venture Capital Israel)	1,177.4	0.2	4.0	294.4
96	Bio*One Capital	1,175.5	0.2	3.0	391.8
97	Globespan Capital Partners	1,172.8	0.2	4.0	293.2
98	Clarus Ventures	1,160.0	0.2	2.0	580.0
99	Sofinnova Partners	1,159.2	0.2	3.0	386.4
100	ABS Capital Partners	1,154.8	0.2	3.0	384.9
101	ARCH Venture Partners	1,151.3	0.2	5.0	230.3
102	Meritech Capital Partners	1,138.7	0.2	2.0	569.3
103	Trident Capital	1,129.7	0.2	4.0	282.4
104	Baker Capital Corp.	1,124.7	0.2	1.0	1,124.7
105	CLSA Capital Partners (AKA: Credit Lyonnais Securities Asia)	1,121.0	0.2	6.0	186.8
106	M/C Venture Partners	1,110.5	0.2	2.0	555.2
107	Bay City Capital LLC	1,100.0	0.2	3.0	366.7
108	HealthCare Ventures LLC	1,085.3	0.2	4.0	271.3
109	BlueRun Ventures	1,055.0	0.2	3.0	351.7
110	TVM Capital GmbH	1,044.5	0.2	4.0	261.1
111	Partech International	1,044.1	0.2	6.0	174.0
112	Olympus Capital Holdings Asia	1,022.1	0.2	3.0	340.7
113	Prospect Venture Partners (FKA: Prospect Management LLC)	1,012.0	0.2	3.0	337.3
114	Kaupthing Bank hf.	1,007.0	0.2	3.0	335.7
115	Prism VentureWorks	1,006.5	0.2	4.0	251.6
116	Sino-African Development Fund Ltd.	1,000.0	0.2	1.0	1,000.0
117	Accenture Technology Ventures	1,000.0	0.2	1.0	1,000.0
118	Alta Communications	987.2	0.2	3.0	329.1
119	GGV Capital	985.0	0.2	3.0	328.3
120	B-Business partners BV	965.0	0.2	1.0	965.0
121	Actis Capital LLP	959.0	0.2	6.0	159.8
122	Partners Group AG	951.6	0.2	2.0	475.8
123	DT Capital Partners	945.4	0.2	5.0	189.1
124	Sunstone Capital A/S	939.3	0.2	8.0	117.4
125	China Renaissance Capital Investment	937.8	0.2	2.0	468.9
126	FTV Capital	935.5	0.2	2.0	467.8
127	Duff Ackerman & Goodrich LLC	933.1	0.2	4.0	233.3
128	DB Venture Partners	915.6	0.2	1.0	915.6
129	Trinity Ventures	905.1	0.2	3.0	301.7
130	Sevin Rosen Funds	905.0	0.2	2.0	452.5
131	Alloy Ventures	898.0	0.2	3.0	299.3
132	Wellington Partners GmbH	883.3	0.2	4.0	220.8
133	Brait Capital Partners	880.0	0.2	1.0	880.0
134	Western Technology Investment	880.0	0.2	3.0	293.3
135	Lehman Brothers, Inc.	878.2	0.2	2.0	439.1
136	STIC Investments, Inc.	872.0	0.2	20.0	43.6
137	CMEA Capital	862.0	0.2	3.0	287.3
138	Lighthouse Capital Partners	858.7	0.2	3.0	286.2
139	Sofinnova Ventures	855.7	0.1	3.0	285.2
140	Fuse Capital	850.0	0.1	2.0	425.0
141	Delphi Ventures	847.0	0.1	4.0	211.8
142	DFJ Esprit	842.0	0.1	4.0	210.5

Rank	Firm Name	Capital under Management (USD Mil)	Pct. of Total	Number of Funds	Avg. Fund Size (USD Mil)
143	Invesco Private Capital	841.8	0.1	3.0	280.6
144	Rockport Capital Partners	839.8	0.1	3.0	279.9
145	Cabot Square Capital, Ltd.	826.6	0.1	2.0	413.3
146	BOC International Holdings, Ltd.	806.0	0.1	1.0	806.0
147	Sanderling Ventures	805.8	0.1	3.0	268.6
148	LGT Capital Partners AG	805.6	0.1	1.0	805.6
149	Third Rock Ventures LLC	804.0	0.1	2.0	402.0
150	Acartha Technology Partners, L.P.	800.0	0.1	1.0	800.0
151	Three Arch Partners	784.8	0.1	5.0	157.0
152	ProQuest Investments	783.3	0.1	4.0	195.8
153	Paladin Capital Management LLC	783.0	0.1	3.0	261.0
154	HgCapital	773.9	0.1	1.0	773.9
155	Enterprise Ireland	772.0	0.1	1.0	772.0
156	Element Partners	770.0	0.1	2.0	385.0
157	CDH China Management Co., Ltd.	768.0	0.1	4.0	192.0
158	Macquarie Capital Alliance Management Ltd.	764.1	0.1	1.0	764.1
159	SGAM Private Equity	760.2	0.1	18.0	42.2
160	New Leaf Venture Partners LLC	760.0	0.1	2.0	380.0
161	Edmond de Rothschild Investment Partners	756.0	0.1	12.0	63.0
162	Flagship Ventures	753.9	0.1	6.0	125.7
163	Ant Capital Partners Co., Ltd.	747.8	0.1	8.0	93.5
164	TL Ventures	745.6	0.1	2.0	372.8
165	BOC Investment Zheshang Industry Fund Management Co., Ltd.	737.9	0.1	1.0	737.9
166	inventages venture capital S.A.	734.5	0.1	2.0	367.2
167	Advent Venture Partners LLP	734.0	0.1	2.0	367.0
168	Sinovo Growth Capital Management Co., Ltd.	732.4	0.1	1.0	732.4
169	Draper Fisher Jurvetson ePlanet Ventures, L.P.	726.8	0.1	4.0	181.7
170	Skyline Ventures	724.8	0.1	4.0	181.2
171	Focus Ventures	720.7	0.1	4.0	180.2
172	SOFTBANK Corp.	720.0	0.1	5.0	144.0
173	Maveron LLC	717.7	0.1	3.0	239.2
174	CCB International (Holdings), Ltd.	704.7	0.1	2.0	352.4
175	Quaker BioVentures, Inc.	701.0	0.1	5.0	140.2
176	Swicorp Capital Partners	700.0	0.1	2.0	350.0
177	Amadeus Capital Partners, Ltd.	698.5	0.1	5.0	139.7
178	Odlander, Fredrikson & Co. AB	693.4	0.1	3.0	231.1
179	CID Group, The	684.0	0.1	3.0	228.0
180	Generation Investment Management LLP	683.0	0.1	1.0	683.0
181	IBM Corporation	680.0	0.1	2.0	340.0
182	Carmel Ventures	677.0	0.1	4.0	169.2
183	GSR Ventures	675.9	0.1	6.0	112.7
184	BankInvest Group A/S	675.2	0.1	7.0	96.5
185	St. Paul Venture Capital, Inc.	675.0	0.1	1.0	675.0
186	ONSET Ventures	669.4	0.1	3.0	223.1
187	Bay Partners	669.0	0.1	3.0	223.0
188	Tenaya Capital (FKA: Lehman Brothers Venture Partners)	665.0	0.1	2.0	332.5
189	Kotak Investment Advisors, Ltd. (AKA: KPEG)	665.0	0.1	3.0	221.7
190	Life Sciences Partners BV	658.5	0.1	6.0	109.8
191	Intersouth Partners	655.3	0.1	3.0	218.4

Rank	Firm Name	Capital under Management (USD Mil)	Pct. of Total	Number of Funds	Avg. Fund Size (USD Mil)
192	Golden Gate Capital	655.2	0.1	2.0	327.6
193	Sun Microsystems, Inc.	650.0	0.1	2.0	325.0
194	Fidelity Ventures	650.0	0.1	2.0	325.0
195	CDTI-Centro Para El Desar.Tecn.Ind.	649.5	0.1	1.0	649.5
196	Crescendo Venture Management LLC	646.0	0.1	2.0	323.0
197	VPSA (FKA: Viventures Partners)	640.0	0.1	1.0	640.0
198	Granite Ventures LLC	635.0	0.1	4.0	158.8
199	Amerindo Investment Advisors, Inc.	633.7	0.1	1.0	633.7
200	Hummer Winblad Venture Partners	632.8	0.1	3.0	210.9
201	IDFC Private Equity	632.0	0.1	2.0	316.0
202	Albion Ventures LLP (FKA: Close Venture Management)	626.2	0.1	5.0	125.2
203	Spark Capital	624.0	0.1	3.0	208.0
204	Mercapital Servicios Financieros	623.9	0.1	1.0	623.9
205	HBM BioVentures AG	622.1	0.1	2.0	311.0
206	Reiten & Co Strategic Investments AS	612.5	0.1	6.0	102.1
207	Vivo Ventures	610.1	0.1	6.0	101.7
208	Kodiak Venture Partners	606.4	0.1	2.0	303.2
209	Worldview Technology Partners	605.4	0.1	2.0	302.7
210	Oxford Bioscience Partners	604.3	0.1	3.0	201.4
211	Hamilton Lane Advisors, Inc.	604.3	0.1	1.0	604.3
212	Orchid Asia Group Management, Ltd.	601.0	0.1	2.0	300.5
213	Legend Capital	600.0	0.1	5.0	120.0
214	3i (US)	600.0	0.1	1.0	600.0
215	Olympus Real Estate Partners	600.0	0.1	1.0	600.0
216	Prologis	600.0	0.1	1.0	600.0
217	TeleSoft Partners	599.9	0.1	2.0	300.0
218	Thomas, McNerney & Partners	591.0	0.1	2.0	295.5
219	Bridgepoint Capital, Ltd.	588.5	0.1	1.0	588.5
220	Tudor Ventures	587.3	0.1	2.0	293.6
221	GRP Partners	585.0	0.1	2.0	292.5
222	Capital Today	580.0	0.1	2.0	290.0
223	Split Rock Partners LLC	575.0	0.1	2.0	287.5
224	TPG Growth	570.0	0.1	3.0	190.0
225	Acon Bastion Capital (FKA: ACON Investments)	570.0	0.1	1.0	570.0
226	De Novo Ventures	566.5	0.1	3.0	188.8
227	Primus Capital Funds	560.0	0.1	2.0	280.0
228	Qualcomm Ventures	560.0	0.1	2.0	280.0
229	Flybridge Capital Partners	560.0	0.1	3.0	186.7
230	Constellation Ventures (AKA: Constellation Growth Capital)	558.0	0.1	2.0	279.0
231	Qiming Venture Partners	556.6	0.1	3.0	185.5
232	Celtic House Venture Partners	555.0	0.1	3.0	185.0
233	Inversiones Ibersuizas S.A.	551.1	0.1	2.0	275.5
234	Gemini Israel Funds, Ltd.	550.6	0.1	3.0	183.5
235	H.I.G. Capital LLC	550.0	0.1	2.0	275.0
236	Technology Partners	545.0	0.1	2.0	272.5
237	Azure Capital Partners	540.0	0.1	1.0	540.0
238	CBC Capital	534.0	0.1	3.0	178.0
239	Adams Capital Management, Inc.	533.8	0.1	2.0	266.9
240	Japan Asia Investment Company, Ltd. (AKA: JAIC)	533.4	0.1	25.0	21.3

Rank	Firm Name	Capital under Management (USD Mil)	Pct. of Total	Number of Funds	Avg. Fund Size (USD Mil)
241	QuestMark Partners, L.P.	533.0	0.1	2.0	266.5
242	Kennet Venture Partners, Ltd. (FKA: Kennet Capital, Ltd.)	530.0	0.1	2.0	265.0
243	Svarog Capital Advisors	529.8	0.1	3.0	176.6
244	Iris Capital Management SAS	528.1	0.1	3.0	176.0
245	Care Capital, LLC	527.5	0.1	3.0	175.8
246	JVP	526.8	0.1	3.0	175.6
247	RRE Ventures LLC	525.0	0.1	2.0	262.5
248	JK&B Capital	521.5	0.1	3.0	173.8
249	Founders Fund, The	520.0	0.1	3.0	173.3
250	Genesis Partners	519.2	0.1	3.0	173.1

Source: Thomson Reuters

Firm Statistics Reported
Ranked Firms (capital under management)
Mezzanine Firms
Data as of: 06/30/2010

Rank	Firm Name	Capital under Management (USD Mil)	Pct. of Total	Number of Funds	Avg. Fund Size (USD Mil)
1	Goldman, Sachs & Co.	27,649.6	20.8	5.0	5,529.9
2	Intermediate Capital Group Plc	10,736.4	8.1	14.0	766.9
3	Trust Company of the West (AKA: TCW/Crescent)	5,121.8	3.9	4.0	1,280.4
4	Lone Star Funds	4,200.0	3.2	1.0	4,200.0
5	Oaktree Capital Management LLC	3,010.8	2.3	3.0	1,003.6
6	Babson Capital Management LLC	2,840.8	2.1	3.0	946.9
7	Summit Partners	2,611.0	2.0	6.0	435.2
8	Tennenbaum Capital Partners LLC	2,511.5	1.9	2.0	1,255.8
9	Prudential Capital Group	2,359.0	1.8	3.0	786.3
10	Euromezzanine Conseil (AKA: Euromezzanine Gestion)	2,218.2	1.7	3.0	739.4
11	Golub Capital	2,210.6	1.7	6.0	368.4
12	GSC Partners (FKA: Greenwich Street Capital Partners)	2,066.5	1.6	2.0	1,033.2
13	Lehman Brothers, Inc.	1,908.0	1.4	2.0	954.0
14	ABRY Partners LLC	1,907.5	1.4	3.0	635.8
15	Audax Group	1,840.0	1.4	3.0	613.3
16	TA Associates, Inc.	1,797.5	1.4	3.0	599.2
17	Partners Group AG	1,700.4	1.3	3.0	566.8
18	TCW Capital	1,644.1	1.2	2.0	822.0
19	CapVest, Ltd	1,639.3	1.2	2.0	819.7
20	DLJ Merchant Banking Partners	1,530.0	1.2	1.0	1,530.0
21	Falcon Investment Advisors LLC	1,392.0	1.0	3.0	464.0
22	New York Life Capital Partners (AKA: NYLCAP)	1,376.4	1.0	3.0	458.8
23	Park Square Capital, LLP	1,373.4	1.0	1.0	1,373.4
24	Indigo Capital, Ltd.	1,169.3	0.9	2.0	584.7
25	Norwest Mezzanine Partners	1,150.0	0.9	3.0	383.3
26	Merrill Lynch Capital Partners	1,100.0	0.8	1.0	1,100.0
27	Babson Capital Europe	1,073.8	0.8	2.0	536.9
28	Blackstone Group, L.P.	1,060.0	0.8	1.0	1,060.0
29	CT Investment Management Co. (AKA: Capital Trust)	1,045.1	0.8	2.0	522.5
30	MML Capital Partners	1,039.5	0.8	4.0	259.9
31	Merit Capital Partners (FKA:William Blair Mezzanine)	1,017.5	0.8	2.0	508.8
32	Barclays Private Equity, Ltd.	1,000.0	0.8	1.0	1,000.0
33	DB Capital Partners	1,000.0	0.8	2.0	500.0
34	Global Investment House	1,000.0	0.8	1.0	1,000.0
35	Peninsula Capital Partners LLC	994.7	0.7	3.0	331.6
36	Carlyle Group, The	989.3	0.7	2.0	494.6
37	Caltius Mezzanine	980.0	0.7	4.0	245.0
38	York Street Capital Partners LLC	950.0	0.7	2.0	475.0
39	Hutton Collins & Company Limited	934.7	0.7	2.0	467.4
40	Bain Capital	900.0	0.7	1.0	900.0
41	Northstar Capital, LLC (FKA: Seidler Capital, Ltd.)	898.8	0.7	3.0	299.6
42	Gleacher & Co.	779.0	0.6	2.0	389.5
43	Prairie Capital	720.0	0.5	4.0	180.0
44	Nordic Mezzanine Advisers Ltd	711.8	0.5	3.0	237.3
45	Citigroup Private Equity	680.0	0.5	1.0	680.0

Rank	Firm Name	Capital under Management (USD Mil)	Pct. of Total	Number of Funds	Avg. Fund Size (USD Mil)
46	Darby Overseas Investments, Ltd.	666.0	0.5	3.0	222.0
47	Prospect Street Ventures	642.0	0.5	1.0	642.0
48	EdgeStone Capital Partners, Inc.	591.0	0.4	2.0	295.5
49	Key Principal Partners LLC (AKA: KPP)	578.0	0.4	2.0	289.0
50	Kayne Anderson Capital Advisors, L.P.	576.0	0.4	1.0	576.0
51	CapMan Plc	534.0	0.4	5.0	106.8
52	First Israel Mezzanine Investors, Ltd. (AKA: FIMI)	530.0	0.4	1.0	530.0
53	AEA Investors LP	478.4	0.4	2.0	239.2
54	Florida Mezzanine Fund, The	450.0	0.3	1.0	450.0
55	Veronis Suhler Stevenson (FKA: Veronis, Suhler & Associates)	434.5	0.3	2.0	217.2
56	IFE Mezzanine	432.0	0.3	1.0	432.0
57	Hancock Capital Management LLC	430.9	0.3	2.0	215.4
58	Desai Capital Management Inc.	409.7	0.3	1.0	409.7
59	EP Power Finance, L.L.C.	400.0	0.3	1.0	400.0
60	TD Capital Group, Ltd.	383.3	0.3	2.0	191.6
61	Brown Brothers Harriman & Company (AKA: BBH)	377.0	0.3	1.0	377.0
62	Newstone Capital Partners	374.0	0.3	1.0	374.0
63	CapitalSouth Partners, L.L.C.	366.9	0.3	2.0	183.4
64	Syntaxis Capital Unternehmens- und Finanzierungsberatung	363.3	0.3	2.0	181.6
65	Kohlberg, Kravis, Roberts & Company, L.P.	350.0	0.3	1.0	350.0
66	PNC Equity Management Corp.	350.0	0.3	1.0	350.0
67	Smith Whiley & Company	343.0	0.3	4.0	85.8
68	GarMark Partners	330.4	0.2	1.0	330.4
69	Penfund Partners, Inc.	327.9	0.2	3.0	109.3
70	Providence Equity Partners LLC	320.0	0.2	1.0	320.0
71	Greyrock Capital Group	312.0	0.2	2.0	156.0
72	TriplePoint Capital	310.0	0.2	1.0	310.0
73	Midwest Mezzanine Funds	310.0	0.2	2.0	155.0
74	Asia Mezzanine Capital Advisers, Ltd.	300.0	0.2	1.0	300.0
75	Western Technology Investment	294.0	0.2	1.0	294.0
76	BIA Digital Partners, L.P.	283.0	0.2	2.0	141.5
77	Ironwood Capital (AKA: Ironwood Capital Advisors LLC)	263.0	0.2	2.0	131.5
78	C3 Capital LLC	260.0	0.2	2.0	130.0
79	Fifth Street Capital LLC	257.0	0.2	2.0	128.5
80	Darby Asia Investors, Ltd.	254.0	0.2	1.0	254.0
81	MVC Capital (FKA: meVC)	253.0	0.2	1.0	253.0
82	Bush O'Donnell Capital Partners	245.0	0.2	2.0	122.5
83	Capzanine	244.6	0.2	1.0	244.6
84	Needham Asset Management	240.0	0.2	2.0	120.0
85	Kendall Court Capital Partners, Ltd.	240.0	0.2	2.0	120.0
86	Nomura International PLC	235.1	0.2	1.0	235.1
87	AXA Private Equity SA	230.3	0.2	1.0	230.3
88	CIT Group Inc.	225.0	0.2	1.0	225.0
89	Churchill Equity, Inc.	222.6	0.2	1.0	222.6
90	McKenna Gale Capital Inc.	221.8	0.2	1.0	221.8
91	AAC Capital Partners	217.2	0.2	1.0	217.2
92	Apollo Real Estate Advisors	214.0	0.2	1.0	214.0
93	Maranon Capital, L.P.	210.1	0.2	2.0	105.1
94	Stonehenge Capital Company	200.0	0.2	1.0	200.0

Rank	Firm Name	Capital under Management (USD Mil)	Pct. of Total	Number of Funds	Avg. Fund Size (USD Mil)
95	Brooks, Houghton & Company, Inc.	200.0	0.2	1.0	200.0
96	Armada Mezzanine Capital Oy	199.1	0.1	2.0	99.6
97	GMB Mezzanine Capital, L.P.	198.0	0.1	1.0	198.0
98	Northwestern Mutual Capital	192.5	0.1	1.0	192.5
99	Stratus Banco de Negocios	185.0	0.1	1.0	185.0
100	Credit Agricole Private Equity SA	183.1	0.1	1.0	183.1
101	Knorr Capital Partner AG	179.0	0.1	1.0	179.0
102	IK Investmentbank AG	177.3	0.1	3.0	59.1
103	Wellington Financial LP	176.5	0.1	3.0	58.8
104	Centerfield Capital Partners	176.0	0.1	2.0	88.0
105	Praesidian Capital, LLC	176.0	0.1	2.0	88.0
106	Capital Resource Partners	166.2	0.1	2.0	83.1
107	Natixis Private Equity SA	164.8	0.1	1.0	164.8
108	Harbert Management Corporation	164.7	0.1	1.0	164.7
109	Mezz. Management Finanz- und Unternehmensberatungs GmbH	154.1	0.1	1.0	154.1
110	Webster Capital Mezzanine	150.0	0.1	1.0	150.0
111	BB&T Capital Partners, LLC	150.0	0.1	1.0	150.0
112	CIT Mezzanine Partners of Canada (FKA CCFL)	150.0	0.1	1.0	150.0
113	NBK Capital, Ltd.	150.0	0.1	1.0	150.0
114	Crown Capital Partners Inc.	150.0	0.1	1.0	150.0
115	Patriot Capital Funding, Inc.	150.0	0.1	1.0	150.0
116	Chatham Capital	150.0	0.1	2.0	75.0
117	Prism Capital	140.0	0.1	1.0	140.0
118	Eastward Capital	138.1	0.1	2.0	69.1
119	RBC Capital Partners	135.0	0.1	1.0	135.0
120	Kelso & Company	132.0	0.1	1.0	132.0
121	Cerea Gestion SAS	130.9	0.1	1.0	130.9
122	Bank of New York	129.7	0.1	1.0	129.7
123	BanyanTree Finance Pvt., Ltd.	125.0	0.1	1.0	125.0
124	St. Cloud Capital, LLC	125.0	0.1	1.0	125.0
125	Capital Trust, Ltd.	120.0	0.1	1.0	120.0
126	Growth Capital Partners, L.P.	115.3	0.1	2.0	57.7
127	Merion Investment Partners, L.P.	115.0	0.1	1.0	115.0
128	Endeavour Capital	115.0	0.1	1.0	115.0
129	Insight Equity Holdings LLC	111.1	0.1	1.0	111.1
130	True North Partners LLC	110.0	0.1	1.0	110.0
131	Calvert Street Capital Partners, Inc. (FKA: Legg Mason)	110.0	0.1	1.0	110.0
132	Mezzanove Capital	104.0	0.1	1.0	104.0
133	BM H Beteiligungs- Managementgesellschaft Hessen mbH	102.2	0.1	1.0	102.2
134	Main Street Capital Corporation	100.0	0.1	1.0	100.0
135	Validus Partners, LLC	100.0	0.1	1.0	100.0
136	3A Investment Partners Private, Ltd.	100.0	0.1	1.0	100.0
137	CDIB Venture Management	100.0	0.1	1.0	100.0
138	Search Asian Mezzanine Capital	100.0	0.1	1.0	100.0
139	White Rose GP I, LLC	100.0	0.1	1.0	100.0
140	Tenth Street Capital Partners, LLC	96.7	0.1	2.0	48.3
141	NewSpring Capital	90.0	0.1	1.0	90.0
142	Triangle Capital Corporation	80.0	0.1	1.0	80.0

Source: Thomson Reuters

Rank	Firm Name	Capital under Management (USD Mil)	Pct. of Total	Number of Funds	Avg. Fund Size (USD Mil)
143	Sand Hill Capital	80.0	0.1	2.0	40.0
144	Development Principles Group, Ltd.	80.0	0.1	1.0	80.0
145	Huntington Capital	78.0	0.1	1.0	78.0
146	Fidus Capital	78.0	0.1	1.0	78.0
147	Marquette Capital Partners	78.0	0.1	1.0	78.0
148	Salem Capital Partners, LP (FKA: Venture Capital Solutions)	75.2	0.1	2.0	37.6
149	Seacoast Capital	75.0	0.1	1.0	75.0
150	Growth Capital Partners	71.2	0.1	1.0	71.2

Directory of Private Equity & Venture Capital Firms

Private Equity & Venture Capital Firms

Pratt's Guide to Private Equity & Venture Capital Sources 2011 Edition contains information on thousands of firms. Although most of the firms listed are U.S.-based an increasing number of firms listed are outside the U.S. Because this information has been compiled on the basis of data received from these companies with additional follow-up, we believe that the data accurately represents the interests and structure of these firms.

Names of the managers for the independent private equity firms are included, but only appropriate officers are listed for investment banking operations, commercial banks, insurance companies, and operating companies with private equity activities. Each company has indicated the appropriate people to contact about new financing proposals.

Private equity firms have been categorized by type of organization. For instance, if the company is a private private equity firm, SBIC, or a subsidiary of an operating company. Differences between these categories are described in the text. "Affiliation" refers to the existence of a parent firm or an involved partner or organization. Describing the private equity activities of investment banking firms and specialized consultants is complicated because some firms listed will act as intermediaries to assist in raising capital and will also invest in projects with their own capital or that of selected clients. In most cases, such investment will be made only when the individual firm is instrumental in handling private placement activity.

Membership in a national private equity trade association is indicated. These associations include the National Venture Capital Association (NVCA); the National Association of Investment Companies (NAIC); the National Association of Small Business Investment Companies (NASBIC); Mid-Atlantic Venture Association (MAVA); and the Western Association of Venture Capitalists (WAVC). The emergence of these organizations as been a significant development since it has fostered cooperation within a previously individualistic industry. Membership in these associations is generally open to private equity organizations and individual private equity investors who invest private capital in young companies on a professional basis. In addition, there are many local private equity associations, too numerous to list.

Entries in the directory show project preferences and each firm's usual extent of involvement. Most firms indicated their minimum and preferred sizes of investment, although when acting as lead investor, many of the firms will often assist in raising money for larger projects. While specific project financings may total $10 million to $15 million, an individual private equity firm may invest only $250,000 to $1,000,000. Investment bankers and consultants, however, generally described the minimum and preferred size of the total private placement-not the amount the investment banking or consulting firm is interested in investing. In some cases, both of these amounts are indicated.

While many firms have expressed an interest in all types of financing, some prefer to finance either early-stage projects (seed, start-up, and first-stage financing) or expansion financing (second- and third-stage financing) or buyout or acquisition financings. Firms that only focus on buyout or acquisition financing usually are interested in situations where the investment group assumes a controlling position in the project. For a detailed description of the types of financing, please see the Introduction. A financing stage preference index is provided at the end of the book.

The private equity companies have also indicated their criteria for minimum operating standards of new financing proposals. This information is designed to indicate the range of interests of the private equity firms, but the minimum does not mean that all of a private equity investor's will be this size. This information only indicates that the private equity firm will primarily consider projects that meet these minimum standards, except when firms are exclusively oriented to startups or first-stage projects.

Although companies' geographic preferences are included, this does not necessarily indicate strict adherence to these areas; investment opportunities outside these areas may be considered as well. Many times, private equity investors may participate in financing a geographically distant company if a local private equity investor also participates. They may, in fact, attempt to interest a private equity investor located near the company being considered.

In the portfolio breakdown section, each listee was asked to list the specific industries the preferred to invest in. The investment preferences section contains the percentages of the listee's actual investments when that information was available.

The portfolio breakdown should be used in combination with the industry preferences section, where firms indicate in greater detail the areas they would consider for investment, regardless of whether they have invested in them before. Together, the sections give directory users a sense of where private equity firms have investment experience and where they expect to make future investments. An index of industry preferences can be found at the end of the book. While this data should serve as a guide, most companies will range outside these expressed interests if they find a project particularly appealing. These descriptions should not, therefore, be taken as the sole interests of a private equity firm. The industries listed in the questionnaire were as follows:

Communications
Commercial Communications
CATV & Pay TV Systems
Radio & TV Broadcasting
Telecommunications
Data Communications
Satellite Microwave Communications
Other Communications Products
Wireless Communications
Entertainment
Publishing
Media and Entertainment
Communications and Media

Computer Hardware
Mainframes & Scientific Computers
Mini & Personal/Desktop Computers
Computer Graphics & Digital Imaging
Integrated Turnkey System
Terminals
Disk Related Memory Device
Computer Services
Computers

Computer Software
Software
Systems Software
Applications Software
Artificial Intelligence
Data Processing
Computer Services

Internet Specific
Internet Related
Internet
Ecommerce
Ecommerce Technology
Web Aggregation/Portal/Exchanges

Computer Other
Computer Related
Computer Stores

Semiconductor/Electronics
Electronics
Electronic Components
Semiconductor
Micro-Processing
Controllers and Sensors
Sensors
Circuit Boards
Component Testing Equipment
Laser Related
Fiber Optics
Analytical & Scientific
Optoelectronics

Biotechnology
Biotechnology
Human Biotechnology
Agricultural/Animal Biotechnology
Industrial Biotechnology
Biosensors
Biotech Related Research Equipment
Biotech Related Research Services
Genetic Engineering

Medical/Health
Medical Diagnostics
Diagnostic Services
Diagnostic Test Products
Medical Therapeutics
Drug Delivery & Other Equipment
Medical Products
Disposable Medical Products
Health Services
Hospitals/Clinics/Primary Care
Hospital & Other Institute
Pharmaceuticals
Medical/Health
Other Therapeutic

Consumer Related
Entertainment
Entertainment and Leisure
Casino/Gambling
Consumer
Consumer Products
Consumer Services
Sports
Retail
Franchises
Food/Beverage
Hotels and Resorts
Education Related
Other Restaurants
Publishing-Retail

Business Services
Distribution
Consulting Services
Services
Media

Industrial/Energy
Alternative Energy
Energy Conservation
Robotics
Coal Related
Energy
Factory Automation
Process Control
Industrial Products
Machinery
Advanced Materials
Superconductivity
Environment Related
Oil & Gas Drilling, Exploration
Oil and Gas Exploration
Materials

Transportation
Transportation
Aerospace

Financial Services
Financial Services
Insurance
Real Estate

Manufacturing
Manufacturing
Office Automation Equipment
Publishing

Agriculture/Forestry/Fishing
Agriculture Related
Agribusiness
Mining and Minerals

Other
Socially Responsible
Environmentally Responsible
Women/Minority-Owned Businesses

Utilities
Utilities

Firms Listings

- A -

@CAPITAL-ENTERPRISES

3510 Rue de la Montage
Bureau 84
Montreal, Canada H3G1A6
Phone: 514-213-3025

Type of Firm

Private Equity Firm

Additional Information

Year Founded: 1998
Current Activity Level: Actively seeking new investments

@VENTURES

187 Ballardvale Street
Suite A260
Wilmington, MA USA 01887
Phone: 978-658-8980
Fax: 978-658-8981
E-mail: bizplans@ventures.com
Website: www.ventures.com

Other Offices

800 Menlo Avenue
Suite 120
Portola Valley, CA USA 94028
Phone: 650-322-3246

Management and Staff

Marc Poirier, General Partner
Matt Horton, Principal
Peter Mills, Managing Partner
Rob Day, Principal

Type of Firm

Corporate PE/Venture

Association Membership

National Venture Capital Association - USA (NVCA)

Project Preferences

Role in Financing:
Will function either as deal originator or investor in deals created by others

Type of Financing Preferred:
Early Stage
Expansion
Generalist PE
Later Stage
Industry Rollups
Special Situation
Recapitalizations

Size of Investments Considered:
Min Size of Investment Considered (000s): $1,000
Max Size of Investment Considered (000s): $20,000

Geographical Preferences

United States Preferences:
All U.S.

Canadian Preferences:
All Canada

Industry Preferences

In Internet Specific prefer:
Internet

Additional Information

Year Founded: 1995
Capital Under Management: $700,000,000
Current Activity Level : Actively seeking new investments
Method of Compensation: Return on investment is of primary concern, do not charge fees

A PLUS FINANCE

8 rue Bellini
Paris, France 75116
Phone: 33-1-4008-0340
Fax: 33-1-4008-0350
E-mail: infos@aplusfinance.com
Website: www.aplusfinance.com

Type of Firm

Private Equity Firm

Association Membership

French Venture Capital Association (AFIC)

Project Preferences

Type of Financing Preferred:
Fund of Funds
Early Stage
Expansion
Balanced

Geographical Preferences

International Preferences:
Europe
France

Industry Preferences

In Communications prefer:
Telecommunications

In Industrial/Energy prefer:
Environmental Related

Additional Information

Year Founded: 2001
Capital Under Management: $226,500,000
Current Activity Level: Actively seeking new investments

AAC CAPITAL PARTNERS (FKA: ABN AMRO CAPITAL)

ITO Tower, 21st and 22nd Floor
Gustav Mahlerplein 106
Amsterdam, Netherlands 1082
Phone: 31-20-383-1808
Fax: 31-20-383-9703
E-mail: info@aaccapitalpartners.com
Website: www.aaccapitalpartners.com

Other Offices

1 Carey Lane
London, United Kingdom EC2V 8AE
Phone: 44-20-7678-8000
Fax: 44-20-7678-2050

c/Jose Ortega y Gasset, 29
5th Floor
Madrid, Spain 28006
Phone: 34-91-423-6963
Fax: 34-91-423-6953

Birger Jarlsgatan 12, 1st Floor
P.O. Box 26124
Stockholm, Sweden SE-10041
Phone: 46-8-407-4440

corso Magenta 10
Milano, Italy 20123
Phone: 39-02-802-9181
Fax: 39-02-8029-1845

Management and Staff

Antonio Corbani, Partner
Bert Mol, Partner
Bob Kramer, Managing Director
Francesco Panfilo, Partner
Gabe Marino, Partner
Herve Claquin, Managing Partner
Johan Bjurstrom, Managing Partner
Marc Staal, Managing Partner
Paul Southwell, Managing Partner
Roger Marshall, Managing Director

Type of Firm

Private Equity Firm

Association Membership

Italian Venture Capital Association (AIFI)
British Venture Capital Association (BVCA)
Hong Kong Venture Capital Association (HKVCA)
Hungarian Venture Capital Association (HVCA)
German Venture Capital Association (BVK)
European Private Equity and Venture Capital Assoc.
Dutch Venture Capital Associaton (NVP)
Indian Venture Capital Association (IVCA)

Project Preferences

Role in Financing:
Prefer role as deal originator

Type of Financing Preferred:
Second Stage Financing
Leveraged Buyout
Early Stage
Expansion
Mezzanine
Research and Development
Generalist PE
Start-up Financing
Balanced
Turnaround
Management Buyouts
Recapitalizations

Size of Investments Considered:
Min Size of Investment Considered (000s): $4,708
Max Size of Investment Considered (000s): $94,160

Geographical Preferences

International Preferences:
Hungary
Europe
Netherlands
Switzerland
Central Europe
Austria
Brazil
Croatia
Eastern Europe
Australia
Belgium
Germany
Asia
France
All International

Industry Focus

(% based on actual investment)

Consumer Related	28.0%
Industrial/Energy	21.4%
Other Products	15.4%
Biotechnology	12.0%
Semiconductors/Other Elect.	7.2%
Medical/Health	4.5%
Communications and Media	4.4%
Internet Specific	3.3%
Computer Software and Services	2.1%
Computer Hardware	1.8%

Additional Information
Year Founded: 1980
Capital Under Management: $2,900,000
Current Activity Level: Actively seeking new investments
Method of Compensation: Return on investment is of primary concern, do not charge fees

---

AAVIN EQUITY ADVISORS LLC

118 Third Avenue South East
Suite 630
Cedar Rapids, IA USA 52401
Phone: 319-247-1072
Fax: 319-363-9519
E-mail: inquiries@aavin.com
Website: www.aavin.com

Other Offices
2500 Rand Tower
527 Marquette Avenue South
Minneapolis, MN USA 55402
Phone: 612-375-9866
Fax: 319-363-9519

Management and Staff
James Thorp, Managing Partner
Thies Kolln, Partner

Type of Firm
Private Equity Firm

Association Membership
National Venture Capital Association - USA (NVCA)
Natl Assoc of Small Bus. Inv. Co (NASBIC)

Project Preferences

Role in Financing:
Prefer role as deal originator but will also invest in deals created by others

Type of Financing Preferred:
Second Stage Financing
Leveraged Buyout
Expansion
Turnaround
Later Stage
Management Buyouts
First Stage Financing
Acquisition
Startup
Recapitalizations

Size of Investments Considered:
Min Size of Investment Considered (000s): $500
Max Size of Investment Considered (000s): $3,000

Geographical Preferences

United States Preferences:
Midwest

Industry Preferences

In Communications prefer:
Communications and Media
Telecommunications

In Computer Hardware prefer:
Computers

In Computer Software prefer:
Software

In Semiconductor/Electr prefer:
Electronics

In Medical/Health prefer:
Medical/Health
Medical Products
Health Services

In Consumer Related prefer:
Consumer
Entertainment and Leisure
Sports
Retail
Franchises(NEC)
Hotels and Resorts
Education Related

In Industrial/Energy prefer:
Energy
Industrial Products
Superconductivity
Factory Automation
Process Control
Robotics
Machinery

In Transportation prefer:
Transportation
Aerospace

In Financial Services prefer:
Financial Services

In Business Serv. prefer:
Services
Distribution
Consulting Services
Media

In Manufact. prefer:
Manufacturing

In Agr/Forestr/Fish prefer:
Agriculture related

In Utilities prefer:
Utilities

In Other prefer:
Socially Responsible
Environment Responsible
Women/Minority-Owned Bus.

Additional Information
Name of Most Recent Fund: Aavin Equity Partners I, LP
Most Recent Fund Was Raised: 01/20/2000
Year Founded: 1999
Capital Under Management: $47,000,000
Current Activity Level: Actively seeking new investments
Method of Compensation: Return on invest. most important, but chg. closing fees, service fees, etc.

AAVISHKAAR VENTURE MANAGEMENT SERVICES PVT, LTD.

512, 5th Floor, Palm Spring
Link Road, Malad (West)
Mumbai, India 400064
Phone: 91-22-3253-5292
Fax: 91-22-2877-8255
E-mail: info@aavishkaar.org
Website: www.aavishkaar.org

Other Offices
57, Grange Road
Suite 16-02, Lucky Tower
Singapore, Singapore 249569

125 Bay Street, Suite Eight
San Francisco, CA USA 94133
Phone: 650-207-0880

Management and Staff
Jennifer Meehan, Founder

Type of Firm
Private Equity Firm

Association Membership
Indian Venture Capital Association (IVCA)

Project Preferences

Type of Financing Preferred:
Early Stage
Expansion
Startup

Size of Investments Considered:
Min Size of Investment Considered (000s): $20
Max Size of Investment Considered (000s): $2,000

Geographical Preferences

International Preferences:
India

Industry Preferences

In Medical/Health prefer:
Medical/Health

In Industrial/Energy prefer:
Energy

In Agr/Forestr/Fish prefer:
Agriculture related

Additional Information
Year Founded: 2002
Capital Under Management: $6,000,000
Current Activity Level: Actively seeking new investments

AB CAPITAL & INVESTMENT CORPORATION
8th Floor, Phinma Plaza
39 Plaza Drive, Rockwell Ctr.
Makati City, Philippines 1200
Phone: 632-898-7555
Fax: 632-898-7597
Website: www.abcapitalonline.com

Management and Staff
Ericson Wee, Vice President
Lamberto Santos, President
Ramon Del Rosario, Chairman & CEO

Type of Firm
Bank Affiliated

Project Preferences

Type of Financing Preferred:
Leveraged Buyout
Early Stage
Expansion
Mezzanine
Startup

Size of Investments Considered:
Min Size of Investment Considered (000s): $579
Max Size of Investment Considered (000s): $3,589

Geographical Preferences

International Preferences:
Philippines

Industry Preferences

In Communications prefer:
Communications and Media

In Computer Other prefer:
Computer Related

In Semiconductor/Electr prefer:
Electronics

In Consumer Related prefer:
Consumer

In Industrial/Energy prefer:
Energy
Industrial Products

In Transportation prefer:
Transportation

In Financial Services prefer:
Financial Services

In Business Serv. prefer:
Services

In Manufact. prefer:
Manufacturing

Additional Information
Year Founded: 1980
Current Activity Level: Actively seeking new investments

AB CHALMERSINVEST
Stena Center 1A
Goteborg, Sweden 412 92
Phone: 46-31-772-4030
Fax: 46-31-772-4033
Website: www.chalmersinvest.se

Management and Staff
Ingvar Andersson, Managing Director

Type of Firm
Private Equity Firm

Association Membership
Swedish Venture Capital Association (SVCA)

Project Preferences

Role in Financing:
Prefer role as deal originator but will also invest in deals created by others

Type of Financing Preferred:
Seed

Size of Investments Considered:
Min Size of Investment Considered (000s): $72
Max Size of Investment Considered (000s): $290

Geographical Preferences

International Preferences:
Sweden

Industry Preferences

In Communications prefer:
Communications and Media

In Computer Other prefer:
Computer Related

In Biotechnology prefer:
Biotechnology

In Medical/Health prefer:
Medical/Health

In Consumer Related prefer:
Consumer

In Industrial/Energy prefer:
Energy

Additional Information
Name of Most Recent Fund: AB Chalmersinvest
Most Recent Fund Was Raised: 02/28/1998
Year Founded: 1998
Capital Under Management: $7,200,000
Current Activity Level: Actively seeking new investments

AB POSSESSOR
Stora Nygatan 25
Malmo, Sweden 211 37
Phone: 46-40-713-75
Fax: 46-40-97-42-66

Type of Firm
Private Equity Firm

Additional Information
Current Activity Level: Actively seeking new investments

AB TRACTION (AKA: TRACTION KONSULT AB)
Saltmatargatan 7
P.O. Box 3314
Stockholm, Sweden 103 66
Phone: 46-8-5062-8900
Fax: 46-8-5062-8930

E-mail: post@traction.se
Website: www.traction.se

Management and Staff

Bengt Stillstrom, President
Lars Olof Larson, Chief Financial Officer

Type of Firm

Private Equity Firm

Association Membership

Swedish Venture Capital Association (SVCA)

Project Preferences

Type of Financing Preferred:
Leveraged Buyout
Expansion
Seed
Startup

Size of Investments Considered:
Min Size of Investment Considered (000s): $11
Max Size of Investment Considered (000s): $10,620

Geographical Preferences

International Preferences:
Sweden
United Kingdom
Scandanavia/Nordic Region

Additional Information

Year Founded: 1999
Capital Under Management: $74,300,000
Current Activity Level: Actively seeking new investments

ABACUS INVEST S.C.A. SICAR

207, route d'Arlon
Luxembourg, Luxembourg 1150
Website: www.abacus.com

Management and Staff

Daniele Monarca, Founder
Paolo Vacchino, Founder

Type of Firm

Private Equity Firm

Project Preferences

Type of Financing Preferred:
Leveraged Buyout

Geographical Preferences

International Preferences:
Italy

Additional Information

Year Founded: 2006
Capital Under Management: $52,600,000
Current Activity Level: Actively seeking new investments

ABACUS PRIVATE EQUITY (ASA: ABACUS CAPITAL CORPORATION)

161 Bay Street
Suite 2430
Toronto, Canada M5J 2S1
Phone: 416-861-8711
Fax: 416-861-9979
E-mail: info_toronto@abacuscapitalcorp.com
Website: www.abacuspe.com

Other Offices

1095 West Pender Street
Suiet 1305
Vancouver, Canada V6E 2M6
Phone: 604-696-9995
Fax: 604-696-9935

Rene Levesque Boulevard West
Suite 2200
Montreal, Canada H3B 4W8
Phone: 514-841-1315
Fax: 514-841-1318

140 Oxford Street
Suite 203
London, Canada N6A 5R9
Phone: 519-679-0880
Fax: 519-679-6556

Management and Staff

Cooper Seeman, Managing Director
Gene Gomes, Managing Director
Michael Donner, Managing Director
Oliver Ness, Vice President
Russell Negus, President

Type of Firm

Private Equity Firm

Project Preferences

Type of Financing Preferred:
Leveraged Buyout
Balanced
Acquisition

Geographical Preferences

Canadian Preferences:
All Canada

Industry Preferences

In Biotechnology prefer:
Agricultural/Animal Bio.

In Industrial/Energy prefer:
Energy
Oil and Gas Exploration
Industrial Products
Machinery

In Financial Services prefer:
Real Estate

In Agr/Forestr/Fish prefer:
Agriculture related

Additional Information

Year Founded: 1996
Current Activity Level: Actively seeking new investments

ABBEY ROAD VENTURE LTD

10 Noble Street
5th Floor, Alder Castle
London, United Kingdom EC2V 7QJ

Management and Staff

Paul Harvey, Partner

Type of Firm

Private Equity Firm

Project Preferences

Type of Financing Preferred:
Balanced

Geographical Preferences

International Preferences:
United Kingdom
Europe

Additional Information

Year Founded: 2004
Current Activity Level: Actively seeking new investments

ABENEX CAPITAL (FKA: ABN AMRO CAPITAL FRANCE)

9 Avenue Matignon
Paris, France 75008
Phone: 33-1-5393-6900
Fax: 33-1-5393-6925
E-mail: contact@abnamrocapital.fr
Website: www.abnamrocapital.fr

Management and Staff

Bruno Houette, Partner
Herve Claquin, Chief Executive Officer
Olivier Moatti, Partner
Patrice Verrier, Partner

Type of Firm

Private Equity Firm

Association Membership

French Venture Capital Association (AFIC)

Project Preferences

Type of Financing Preferred:
Leveraged Buyout

Expansion
Management Buyouts
Acquisition

Geographical Preferences

International Preferences:
France

Additional Information
Year Founded: 1995
Capital Under Management: $300,400,000
Current Activity Level: Actively seeking new investments

ABERDARE VENTURES
One Embarcadero Center
Suite 4000
San Francisco, CA USA 94111
Phone: 415-392-7442
Fax: 415-392-4264
Website: www.aberdare.com

Management and Staff
Daniel Kisner, Partner
Naheed Ismaili Misfeldt, Partner
Paul Klingenstein, Managing Partner
Sami Hamade, Partner
Terry Spraker, Venture Partner
Y.Vincent Kim, Partner

Type of Firm
Private Equity Firm

Association Membership
National Venture Capital Association - USA (NVCA)

Project Preferences

Role in Financing:
Will function either as deal originator or investor in deals created by others

Type of Financing Preferred:
Second Stage Financing
Early Stage
Expansion
First Stage Financing
Startup

Size of Investments Considered:
Min Size of Investment Considered (000s): $4,000
Max Size of Investment Considered (000s): $7,000

Industry Preferences

In Biotechnology prefer:
Human Biotechnology

In Medical/Health prefer:
Medical/Health
Medical Therapeutics

Additional Information
Name of Most Recent Fund: Aberdare Ventures IV, L.P.
Most Recent Fund Was Raised: 04/09/2008
Year Founded: 1999
Capital Under Management: $100,000,000
Current Activity Level: Actively seeking new investments
Method of Compensation: Return on investment is of primary concern, do not charge fees

ABERDEEN ASSET MANAGERS GROWTH CAPITAL
Sutherland House
149 St. Vincent Street
Glasgow, United Kingdom G2 5NW
Phone: 44-141-306-7400
Website: www.aberdeen-asset.com/aam.nsf/privateequity

Other Offices
3 The Embankment
Sovereign Street
Leeds, United Kingdom LS1 4BJ
Phone: 44-113-242-2644

10 Queens Terrace
United Kingdom AB10 1YG
Phone: 44-1224-631-999

St James's House
7 Charlotte Street
Manchester, United Kingdom M1 4DZ
Phone: 44-161-233-3500

1 Cornwall Street
Birmingham, United Kingdom B3 2JN
Phone: 44-121-236-1222

Ballantyne House
84 Academy Street
Inverness, United Kingdom IV1 1LU
Phone: 44-1463-717-214

One Bow Churchyard
London, United Kingdom EC4M 9HH
Phone: 44-20-7463-6136
Fax: 44-20-7463-6452

Management and Staff
Hugh Little, Managing Director

Type of Firm
Bank Affiliated

Project Preferences

Type of Financing Preferred:
Balanced

Geographical Preferences

International Preferences:
United Kingdom

Additional Information
Name of Most Recent Fund: Aberdeen Income and Growth VCT PLC (FKA: Murray VCT 4)
Most Recent Fund Was Raised: 08/13/1999
Year Founded: 1981
Capital Under Management: $471,400,000
Current Activity Level: Actively seeking new investments

ABERDEEN GOULD
55 Street Claire Avenue West
Suite 401
Toronto, Canada M4V2Y7
Phone: 416-488-2887
Fax: 416-488-1233
E-mail: info@aberdeengould.com
Website: www.aberdeengould.com

Management and Staff
Roger Rosmus, Principal

Type of Firm
Private Equity Firm

Additional Information
Year Founded: 2009
Current Activity Level: Actively seeking new investments

ABERLYN CAPITAL MANAGEMENT CO., INC.
701 Mohican Court
Morganville, NJ USA 07751
Phone: 732-332-1170
Fax: 732-332-1172

Other Offices
18 Winter Place
Matawan, NJ USA 07747
Phone: 908-583-5108
Fax: 908-583-8499

Type of Firm
Bank Affiliated

Project Preferences

Role in Financing:
Prefer role as deal originator

Type of Financing Preferred:
Second Stage Financing
Leveraged Buyout
Start-up Financing
First Stage Financing
Special Situation

Size of Investments Considered:
Min Size of Investment Considered (000s): $25,000
Max Size of Investment Considered: No Limit

Industry Preferences

In Computer Software prefer:
Systems Software
Applications Software
Artificial Intelligence

In Semiconductor/Electr prefer:
Laser Related
Fiber Optics

In Biotechnology prefer:
Industrial Biotechnology
Biotech Related Research

In Medical/Health prefer:
Medical/Health
Medical Diagnostics
Medical Therapeutics
Medical Products

In Consumer Related prefer:
Food/Beverage

Additional Information
Year Founded: 1992
Capital Under Management: $90,000,000
Current Activity Level: Actively seeking new investments
Method of Compensation: Return on invest. most important, but chg. closing fees, service fees, etc.

ABINGWORTH MANAGEMENT, LTD.

5th Floor, Princes House
38 Jermyn Street
London, United Kingdom SW1Y 6DN
Phone: 44-20-7534-1500
Fax: 44-20-7287-0480
E-mail: info@abingworth.com
Website: www.abingworth.com

Other Offices
890 Winter Street
Waltham, MA USA 02451
Phone: 781-466-8800
Fax: 781-466-8813

Wellington House
East Road
Cambridge, United Kingdom CB1 1BH
Phone: 44-1223-451-032
Fax: 44-1223-451-032

3000 Sand Hill Road
Building Four, Suite 135
Menlo Park, CA USA 94025
Phone: 650-926-0600
Fax: 650-926-9782

Management and Staff
Andrew Sandham, Venture Partner
Andrew Sinclair, Principal
David Kirkpatrick, Principal
David Leathers, Partner
David Mayer, Partner
Genghis Lloyd-Harris, Partner
James Abell, Chief Financial Officer
Joe Anderson, Partner
John Shields, Principal
Jonathan MacQuitty, Partner
Ken Haas, Venture Partner
Kristin Woolley, Principal
Michael Bigham, Partner
Michelle Doig, Principal
Sarah Shackelton, Principal
Stephen Bunting, Managing Partner
Timothy Haines, Partner
Victoria Stewart, Principal
Vincent Miles, Venture Partner

Type of Firm
Private Equity Firm

Association Membership
British Venture Capital Association (BVCA)

Project Preferences

Role in Financing:
Prefer role as deal originator but will also invest in deals created by others

Type of Financing Preferred:
Early Stage
Expansion
Balanced
Seed
Startup

Size of Investments Considered:
Min Size of Investment Considered (000s): $1,000
Max Size of Investment Considered (000s): $20,000

Geographical Preferences

United States Preferences:
All U.S.

International Preferences:
United Kingdom
Europe
Western Europe
Bermuda
Germany
France

Industry Focus
(% based on actual investment)

Biotechnology	59.5%
Medical/Health	25.8%
Computer Software and Services	5.8%
Computer Hardware	2.5%
Communications and Media	2.3%
Other Products	1.8%
Industrial/Energy	0.9%
Semiconductors/Other Elect.	0.9%
Consumer Related	0.5%

Additional Information
Name of Most Recent Fund: Abingworth Bioequities Fund Limited
Most Recent Fund Was Raised: 07/18/2005
Year Founded: 1973
Capital Under Management: $700,000,000
Current Activity Level: Actively seeking new investments
Method of Compensation: Return on investment is of primary concern, do not charge fees

ABOA VENTURE MANAGEMENT OY

Aurakatu 12 A
6th Floor
Turku, Finland FIN-20100
Phone: 358-2-752-8010
Fax: 358-2-752-8011
E-mail: info@aboaventure.fi
Website: www.aboaventure.fi

Other Offices
Mikonkatu 4 D
Pori, Finland 28100
Phone: 358-2-641-6433
Fax: 358-2-641-6434

Type of Firm
Private Equity Firm

Association Membership
Finnish Venture Capital Association (FVCA)
European Private Equity and Venture Capital Assoc.

Project Preferences

Type of Financing Preferred:
Leveraged Buyout
Expansion
Later Stage
Seed
Management Buyouts
Acquisition
Startup
Recapitalizations

Size of Investments Considered:
Min Size of Investment Considered (000s): $126
Max Size of Investment Considered (000s): $1,255

Geographical Preferences

International Preferences:
Finland

Industry Focus
(% based on actual investment)

Biotechnology	42.5%
Industrial/Energy	21.2%
Other Products	14.1%
Computer Software and Services	12.4%
Internet Specific	5.1%
Medical/Health	4.7%

Additional Information
Year Founded: 1994
Capital Under Management: $15,900,000
Current Activity Level: Actively seeking new investments

ABRAAJ CAPITAL

Dubai International Financial
Gate Village 8, 3rd Floor
Dubai, Utd. Arab Em.

Phone: 971-4-506-4400
Fax: 971-4-506-4600
E-mail: info@abraaj.com
Website: www.abraaj.com

Management and Staff

Ashok Aram, Managing Director
Mustafa Abdel-Wadood, Managing Director
Waqar Hassan Siddique, Chief Executive Officer

Type of Firm

Private Equity Firm

Project Preferences

Type of Financing Preferred:

Leveraged Buyout
Unknown
Balanced
Acquisition
Private Placement

Geographical Preferences

International Preferences:

India
Pakistan
Middle East
Asia
Africa
All International

Industry Preferences

In Communications prefer:

Communications and Media

In Medical/Health prefer:

Medical/Health

In Consumer Related prefer:

Retail
Education Related

In Industrial/Energy prefer:

Energy
Oil and Gas Exploration
Industrial Products

In Transportation prefer:

Transportation

In Financial Services prefer:

Financial Services
Real Estate

In Manufact. prefer:

Manufacturing

In Agr/Forestr/Fish prefer:

Mining and Minerals

In Utilities prefer:

Utilities

Additional Information

Year Founded: 2003
Capital Under Management: $4,000,000,000
Current Activity Level: Actively seeking new investments

ABRIS CAPITAL PARTNERS

ul. Grzybowska 5a
Warsaw, Poland 00-132
Phone: 48-22-564-5858
Fax: 48-22-564-5859
Website: www.abris-capital.com

Other Offices

24-26 Polona Street
Bucharest, Romania 010503
Phone: 40-21-312-1622
Fax: 40-21-312-1644

Management and Staff

George Swirski, Managing Partner
Neil Milne, Managing Partner
Pawel Gierynski, Partner
Roberta Brzezinski, Partner

Type of Firm

Private Equity Firm

Project Preferences

Type of Financing Preferred:

Leveraged Buyout
Expansion
Generalist PE
Management Buyouts

Geographical Preferences

International Preferences:

Central Europe
Eastern Europe

Industry Preferences

In Communications prefer:

Telecommunications

In Medical/Health prefer:

Medical/Health
Health Services

In Consumer Related prefer:

Retail
Education Related

In Industrial/Energy prefer:

Alternative Energy
Environmental Related

In Financial Services prefer:

Financial Services

In Business Serv. prefer:

Media

In Manufact. prefer:

Manufacturing

Additional Information

Year Founded: 2008
Capital Under Management: $407,300,000
Current Activity Level: Actively seeking new investments

ABRT VENTURE FUND

9, Bolotnaya emb.
Golden Island
Moscow, Russia 119072
Phone: 7-812-335-5545
Website: www.abrtfund.com

Other Offices

15/3 Kondratyevsky
"Kondratyevsky" Business Centre
Saint- Petersburg, Russia 195197
Phone: 7-812-335-5545
Fax: 7-812-335-5546

Management and Staff

Andrei Baronav, Partner
Nikolay Mitushin, Partner
Ratmir Timashev, President

Type of Firm

Private Equity Firm

Project Preferences

Type of Financing Preferred:

Early Stage
Expansion
Seed
Startup

Geographical Preferences

United States Preferences:

All U.S.

International Preferences:

Europe
Russia

Industry Preferences

In Computer Software prefer:

Software
Systems Software
Applications Software

In Internet Specific prefer:

Internet

Additional Information

Year Founded: 2005
Current Activity Level: Actively seeking new investments

ABRUZZO CAPITAL SPA

Via Silvio Pellico 28/1
Pescara, Italy 65123
Phone: 39-85-421-7674
Fax: 39-85-422-1186

Type of Firm

Private Equity Firm

Association Membership

European Private Equity and Venture Capital Assoc.

Project Preferences

Type of Financing Preferred:
Early Stage
Expansion
Seed
Startup

Geographical Preferences

International Preferences:
Italy

Additional Information
Year Founded: 2000
Capital Under Management: $3,300,000
Current Activity Level: Actively seeking new investments

ABRY PARTNERS LLC
111 Huntington Avenue
Boston, MA USA 02199
Phone: 617-859-2959
Fax: 617-859-8797
E-mail: information@abry.com
Website: www.abry.com

Management and Staff
Azra Kanji, Vice President
Blake Battaglia, Principal
Brent Stone, Principal
Brian St. Jean, Principal
C.J. Brucato, Partner
Debbie Johnson, Chief Financial Officer
Erik Brooks, Partner
Hilary Grove, Principal
Jay Grossman, Managing Partner
John Hunt, Partner
John Connor, Partner
Peggy Koenig, Partner
Peni Garber, Partner
Robert MacInnis, Partner
Roger Marrero, Principal
Timothy Nickel, Vice President

Type of Firm
Private Equity Firm

Association Membership
Natl Assoc of Investment Cos. (NAIC)
Natl Assoc of Small Bus. Inv. Co (NASBIC)
European Private Equity and Venture Capital Assoc.

Project Preferences

Type of Financing Preferred:
Leveraged Buyout
Mezzanine
Distressed Debt

Geographical Preferences

United States Preferences:
All U.S.

Industry Focus
(% based on actual investment)

Communications and Media	37.5%
Internet Specific	24.0%
Computer Hardware	17.5%
Consumer Related	8.9%
Other Products	6.4%
Semiconductors/Other Elect.	3.5%
Computer Software and Services	2.2%

Additional Information
Name of Most Recent Fund: ABRY Senior Equity II, L.P.
Most Recent Fund Was Raised: 04/27/2006
Year Founded: 1989
Capital Under Management: $1,700,000,000
Current Activity Level: Actively seeking new investments

ABS CAPITAL PARTNERS
400 East Pratt Street
Suite 910
Baltimore, MD USA 21202
Phone: 410-246-5600
Fax: 410-246-5606
E-mail: abscapital@abscapital.com
Website: www.abscapital.com

Other Offices
1700 Montgomery Street
Suite 440
San Francisco, CA USA 94111
Phone: 415-989-5100
Fax: 415-989-5105

1050 Winter Street
Suite 1000
Waltham, MA USA 02451
Phone: 781-839-7136
Fax: 781-839-7137

Management and Staff
Ashoke Goswami, General Partner
Calbraith Wheaton, General Partner
Deric Emry, General Partner
James Stevenson, Chief Financial Officer
John Stobo, Managing General Partner
Laura Witt, General Partner
Mark Anderson, General Partner
Paul Mariani, Principal
Phillip Clough, Managing General Partner
Ralph Terkowitz, General Partner
Rob Tobin, Vice President
Robyn Lehman, Principal
Timothy Weglicki, Founding Partner

Type of Firm
Private Equity Firm

Association Membership
Mid-Atlantic Venture Association
Western Association of Venture Capitalists (WAVC)
National Venture Capital Association - USA (NVCA)

Project Preferences

Role in Financing:
Prefer role as deal originator but will also invest in deals created by others

Type of Financing Preferred:
Expansion
Later Stage
Management Buyouts
Industry Rollups
Recapitalizations

Size of Investments Considered:
Min Size of Investment Considered (000s): $10,000
Max Size of Investment Considered (000s): $40,000

Industry Focus
(% based on actual investment)

Internet Specific	27.1%
Computer Software and Services	25.8%
Medical/Health	18.7%
Other Products	15.1%
Communications and Media	5.6%
Industrial/Energy	2.7%
Computer Hardware	2.2%
Biotechnology	2.1%
Consumer Related	0.8%

Additional Information
Name of Most Recent Fund: ABS Capital Partners VI, L.P.
Most Recent Fund Was Raised: 07/28/2008
Year Founded: 1990
Capital Under Management: $1,894,000,000
Current Activity Level: Actively seeking new investments
Method of Compensation: Return on invest. most important, but chg. closing fees, service fees, etc.

ABS VENTURES
950 Winter Street
Suite 2600
Waltham, MA USA 02451
Phone: 781-250-0400
Fax: 781-250-0345
E-mail: abs@absventures.com
Website: www.absventures.com

Other Offices
One Market Plaza, Steuart Tower
Suite 2400
San Francisco, CA USA 94105
Phone: 415-217-4260
Fax: 415-217-4266

31 West 52nd Street
14th Floor
New York, NY USA 10019
Phone: 212-469-0063
Fax: 646-324-7075

1650 Tyson's Boulevard
Suite 900
Vienna, VA USA 22180

Phone: 703-903-1860
Fax: 703-903-1865

Management and Staff

Bill Burgess, Managing Partner
Bruns Grayson, Managing Partner
Jim Sanger, General Partner
Scott Yaphe, General Partner
Susan Adams, Chief Financial Officer
Thayer Swartwood, Principal

Type of Firm

Private Equity Firm

Association Membership

Mid-Atlantic Venture Association
National Venture Capital Association - USA (NVCA)

Project Preferences

Role in Financing:

Will function either as deal originator or investor in deals created by others

Type of Financing Preferred:

Expansion
Balanced
Later Stage
Fund of Funds of Second

Size of Investments Considered:

Min Size of Investment Considered (000s): $3,000
Max Size of Investment Considered (000s): $15,000

Industry Focus

(% based on actual investment)

Computer Software and Services	23.2%
Medical/Health	19.9%
Internet Specific	19.0%
Communications and Media	15.5%
Computer Hardware	11.4%
Biotechnology	3.5%
Other Products	2.4%
Industrial/Energy	2.3%
Consumer Related	1.5%
Semiconductors/Other Elect.	1.3%

Additional Information

Year Founded: 1982
Capital Under Management: $500,000,000
Current Activity Level: Making few, if any, new investments
Method of Compensation: Return on investment is of primary concern, do not charge fees

---

ABSA CAPITAL PRIVATE EQUITY (PTY) LTD.

15 Alice Lane
Sandton
Gauteng, South Africa 2146
Phone: 27-11-895-6896
Fax: 27-11-895-7812
E-mail: privateequity@absacapital.com
Website: www.absacapitalprivateequity.com

Management and Staff

Andrew Dewar, Principal
Brett Clark, Principal
Ekow Duker, Principal
Gareth Druce, Principal
Gert Van der Merwe, Principal
Marlene Jennigs, Principal
Norman Basthdaw, Principal
Peter Van den Heever, Principal
Steve Booysen, Chief Executive Officer
Tony Brewitt, Principal

Type of Firm

Private Equity Firm

Association Membership

South African Venture Capital Association (SAVCA)

Project Preferences

Type of Financing Preferred:

Leveraged Buyout
Expansion
Generalist PE
Acquisition

Geographical Preferences

International Preferences:

South Africa

Additional Information

Year Founded: 1999
Capital Under Management: $28,000,000
Current Activity Level: Actively seeking new investments

ABU DHABI INVESTMENT HOUSE

P.O. Box 106699
Abu Dhabi, Utd. Arab Em.
Phone: 971-2-681-1233
Fax: 971-2-681-1844
E-mail: info@adih.ae
Website: www.adih.ae

Management and Staff

Rashad Yusuf Janahi, Chief Executive Officer

Type of Firm

Private Equity Firm

Project Preferences

Type of Financing Preferred:

Expansion
Mezzanine
Balanced

Geographical Preferences

International Preferences:

Middle East

Additional Information

Year Founded: 2005
Capital Under Management: $75,000,000
Current Activity Level: Actively seeking new investments

ABUNDANCE VENTURE CAPITAL

9, Jalan 12/21A
Petailing Jaya
Selangor, Malaysia 46200
Phone: 91-6037956-2151
E-mail: infor@abundancevc.com
Website: www.abundancevc.com

Management and Staff

Gurmit Sidhu, Managing Director

Type of Firm

Private Equity Firm

Association Membership

Indian Venture Capital Association (IVCA)

Project Preferences

Type of Financing Preferred:

Expansion
Balanced

Size of Investments Considered:

Min Size of Investment Considered (000s): $250
Max Size of Investment Considered (000s): $5,000

Geographical Preferences

International Preferences:

India
Australia
Singapore
Asia
Malaysia

Industry Preferences

In Computer Software prefer:

Software

In Internet Specific prefer:

Internet

In Biotechnology prefer:

Biotechnology

In Medical/Health prefer:

Health Services

In Industrial/Energy prefer:

Energy
Alternative Energy
Environmental Related

Additional Information

Year Founded: 1993
Current Activity Level: Actively seeking new investments

AC CAPITAL INC.

4F, Akabishi II
4-1-30 Akasaka, Minato-ku
Tokyo, Japan 107-0052
Phone: 81-3-3560-6710
Fax: 81-3-3560-6730
E-mail: questionablly@ac-capital.co.jp
Website: www.ac-capital.co.jp

Management and Staff

Daisuke Ozawa, Chief Financial Officer
Fumitoshi Fujiwara, CEO & Managing Director
Kosaku Tokiwa, Chief Operating Officer

Type of Firm

Service Provider

Project Preferences

Role in Financing:
Unknown

Type of Financing Preferred:
Leveraged Buyout
Management Buyouts
Acquisition

Geographical Preferences

International Preferences:
China
Japan

Industry Preferences

In Consumer Related prefer:
Entertainment and Leisure
Food/Beverage
Consumer Products

Additional Information

Year Founded: 2002
Capital Under Management: $900,000
Current Activity Level: Actively seeking new investments

AC DESARROLLO SGECR SA (AKA: AHORRO CORPORACION)

Paseo de la Catellana 89
5 planta
Madrid, Spain 28046
Phone: 34-91-586-4242
Fax: 34-91-555-8525
E-mail: acdesarrollo@ahorro.com
Website: www.acdesarrollo.com

Other Offices

C/ Balbino Marron, s/n Portal A
Edificio Viapol, 5 planta Modulo 13-14
Sevilla, Spain 41018
Phone: 33-954-63-28-00
Fax: 33-954-63-38-06

Avenida de las Americas n 3
5 F Edificio America
Malaga, Spain 29006
Phone: 34-952-60-04-77
Fax: 34-952-22-37-46

Avenida de Aragon, 30
Edificio Europa, pl.12 C
Valencia, Spain 46021
Phone: 34-96-369-92-49
Fax: 34-96-369-05-45

C/Maria de Molina n 3, 2 B
Valladolid, Spain 47001
Phone: 34-983-363-544
Fax: 34-983-363-869

Management and Staff

Antonio Fernandez Lopez, Chief Executive Officer
Rafael Perez Benayas, Managing Director

Type of Firm

Private Equity Firm

Association Membership

Spanish Venture Capital Association (ASCRI)

Project Preferences

Type of Financing Preferred:
Leveraged Buyout
Early Stage
Expansion
Generalist PE
Management Buyouts
Startup
Acquisition

Geographical Preferences

International Preferences:
Portugal
Spain

Additional Information

Year Founded: 1999
Capital Under Management: $430,700,000
Current Activity Level: Actively seeking new investments

AC INVEST AB (AKA: ACKRA INVEST)

Expolaris Center
Skelleftea, Sweden 93178
Phone: 46-910-770-885
Fax: 46-910-770-887
Website: www.ac-invest.se

Management and Staff

Nils-Gunnar Larsson, Managing Director

Type of Firm

Private Equity Firm

Association Membership

Swedish Venture Capital Association (SVCA)

Project Preferences

Type of Financing Preferred:
Expansion

Geographical Preferences

International Preferences:
Sweden

Additional Information

Year Founded: 1999
Capital Under Management: $4,500,000
Current Activity Level: Actively seeking new investments

AC VENTURES CO., LTD.

2F ACOMShinbashi Rengadori Blg
2-14-4 Shinbashi, MInato-ku
Tokyo, Japan 105-0004
Phone: 81-3-3597-8222
Fax: 81-3-3597-8266
Website: www.ac-v.co.jp

Type of Firm

Bank Affiliated

Geographical Preferences

International Preferences:
Japan

Industry Preferences

In Biotechnology prefer:
Biotechnology

In Business Serv. prefer:
Distribution
Media

In Manufact. prefer:
Manufacturing

Additional Information

Year Founded: 1996
Capital Under Management: $100,000
Current Activity Level: Actively seeking new investments

ACA EQUITY-PARTNERS GMBH

Freiherr-vom-Stein Str. 63
Frankfurt, Germany 60323
Phone: 49-69-7191-420
Fax: 49-69-7191-4229
E-mail: info@aca-ep.com
Website: www.aca-equity-partners.com

Management and Staff

Christoph Benner, Managing Partner

Hans-Dieter Klein, Managing Partner
Martina Neske, Partner
Oliver Schnatz, Managing Partner

Type of Firm

Private Equity Firm

Project Preferences

Type of Financing Preferred:
Leveraged Buyout
Early Stage
Expansion
Later Stage

Geographical Preferences

International Preferences:
Germany

Additional Information

Year Founded: 2002
Current Activity Level: Actively seeking new investments

ACACIA CAPITAL PARTNERS

7 Cavendish Square
London, United Kingdom W1G 0PE
Phone: 44-20-7299-7399
Fax: 44-20-7299-7390
E-mail: info@acaciacp.com
Website: www.acaciacp.com

Management and Staff

Ajay Chowdhury, General Partner
Christopher Smart, General Partner
Hitesh Mehta, General Partner

Type of Firm

Private Equity Firm

Association Membership

British Venture Capital Association (BVCA)

Project Preferences

Type of Financing Preferred:
Balanced

Size of Investments Considered:
Min Size of Investment Considered (000s): $5
Max Size of Investment Considered (000s): $8

Geographical Preferences

International Preferences:
Europe

Additional Information

Name of Most Recent Fund: Acacia I LP (FKA: IDG Ventures Europe (IDGVE))
Most Recent Fund Was Raised: 11/08/2000
Year Founded: 2006
Current Activity Level: Actively seeking new investments

ACACIA CAPITAL, INC.

48 Wall Street
11th Floor
New York, NY USA 10005
Phone: 212-918-4935
Fax: 212-918-4936
Website: www.acacia.com

Management and Staff

Dean Christiansen, Principal

Type of Firm

Bank Affiliated

Project Preferences

Role in Financing:
Prefer role as deal originator but will also invest in deals created by others

Type of Financing Preferred:
Leveraged Buyout
Generalist PE
Management Buyouts
Strategic Alliances
Acquisition
Private Placement
Industry Rollups
Special Situation
Recapitalizations

Geographical Preferences

United States Preferences:
All U.S.

International Preferences:
Australia
South Africa

Industry Focus

(% based on actual investment)

Semiconductors/Other Elect.	96.5%
Internet Specific	3.5%

Additional Information

Year Founded: 1990
Current Activity Level: Actively seeking new investments
Method of Compensation: Return on investment is of primary concern, do not charge fees

ACACIA VENTURE PARTNERS

235 Montgomery Street
Suite 967
San Francisco, CA USA 94104
Phone: 415-433-4200
Fax: 415-433-4250
E-mail: info@acaciavp.com
Website: www.acaciavp.com

Management and Staff

C. Sage Givens, Managing Director
David Heer, Managing Director
Pete Patterson, Chief Financial Officer

Type of Firm

Private Equity Firm

Association Membership

Western Association of Venture Capitalists (WAVC)
National Venture Capital Association - USA (NVCA)

Project Preferences

Role in Financing:
Prefer role as deal originator

Type of Financing Preferred:
Second Stage Financing
Leveraged Buyout
Mezzanine
Start-up Financing
Seed
First Stage Financing

Size of Investments Considered:
Min Size of Investment Considered (000s): $500
Max Size of Investment Considered (000s): $8,000

Geographical Preferences

United States Preferences:
All U.S.

Industry Focus

(% based on actual investment)

Internet Specific	44.4%
Medical/Health	30.7%
Computer Software and Services	13.0%
Consumer Related	8.7%
Industrial/Energy	2.2%
Communications and Media	1.0%

Additional Information

Year Founded: 1995
Capital Under Management: $200,000,000
Current Activity Level: Actively seeking new investments
Method of Compensation: Return on investment is of primary concern, do not charge fees

ACADEMY FUNDS

633 Davis Drive
Suite 500
Durham, NC USA 27713
Phone: 919-991-5420
Fax: 919-991-5421
E-mail: info@academyfunds.com
Website: www.academyfunds.com

Other Offices

111 North Chestnut Street
Suite 105
Winston Salem, NC USA 27101
Phone: 336-748-9991
Fax: 336-748-9909

11540 North Community
House Road, Suite 150
Charlotte, NC USA 28277
Phone: 704-540-9379
Fax: 704-540-9868

Management and Staff

Brad Walters, Partner
Gregory Johnson, Partner
John Ciannamea, Managing Partner

Type of Firm

Private Equity Firm

Project Preferences

Role in Financing:

Prefer role as deal originator but will also invest in deals created by others

Type of Financing Preferred:

Early Stage
Research and Development
Seed
First Stage Financing
Startup

Geographical Preferences

United States Preferences:

Southeast
North Carolina

Industry Preferences

In Communications prefer:

Commercial Communications
Telecommunications
Wireless Communications
Data Communications
Satellite Microwave Comm.
Other Communication Prod.

In Computer Hardware prefer:

Computer Graphics and Dig
Disk Relat. Memory Device

In Computer Software prefer:

Software
Systems Software
Applications Software
Artificial Intelligence

In Internet Specific prefer:

E-Commerce Technology
Internet
Web Aggregration/Portals

In Semiconductor/Electr prefer:

Electronics
Semiconductor

In Biotechnology prefer:

Biotechnology
Human Biotechnology
Agricultural/Animal Bio.
Industrial Biotechnology
Biosensors
Biotech Related Research

In Medical/Health prefer:

Medical Diagnostics
Diagnostic Services
Diagnostic Test Products
Medical Therapeutics
Drug/Equipmt Delivery
Medical Products
Disposable Med. Products
Pharmaceuticals

In Consumer Related prefer:

Education Related

In Industrial/Energy prefer:

Energy
Superconductivity
Factory Automation
Process Control
Robotics

In Transportation prefer:

Aerospace

Additional Information

Name of Most Recent Fund: Academy Venture Fund II
Most Recent Fund Was Raised: 12/01/1999
Year Founded: 1998
Capital Under Management: $36,000,000
Current Activity Level: Actively seeking new investments
Method of Compensation: Return on investment is of primary concern, do not charge fees

---

ACCEDE CAPITAL

Level 11
1 Chifley Square
Sydney, Australia 2000
Phone: 612-8233-0030
Fax: 612-8233-0031
E-mail: info@accedecapital.com
Website: www.accedecapital.com

Management and Staff

Chris Beare, General Partner
David Shields, General Partner
Mark Richards, General Partner
Matthew Koertge, General Partner
Nicholas McDonagh, General Partner

Type of Firm

Private Equity Firm

Project Preferences

Role in Financing:

Prefer role as deal originator but will also invest in deals created by others

Type of Financing Preferred:

Early Stage
Expansion
Seed
First Stage Financing

Size of Investments Considered:

Min Size of Investment Considered (000s): $85
Max Size of Investment Considered (000s): $12,738

Geographical Preferences

International Preferences:

Australia
New Zealand

Industry Preferences

In Communications prefer:

Communications and Media
Telecommunications
Wireless Communications

In Computer Software prefer:

Software

In Internet Specific prefer:

E-Commerce Technology

In Semiconductor/Electr prefer:

Semiconductor
Fiber Optics

Additional Information

Year Founded: 2006
Capital Under Management: $72,200,000
Current Activity Level: Actively seeking new investments
Method of Compensation: Return on investment is of primary concern, do not charge fees

---

ACCEL INDIA VENTURE FUND (FKA: ERASMIC VENTURE FUND PVT)

#21/1-1, Nawab Towers
Cunningham Road
Bangalore, India 560-052
Phone: 91-80-4123-2551
Fax: 91-80-4123-8853
E-mail: india@accel.com
Website: www.accel.com

Other Offices

#21/1-1, Nawab Towers
Cunningham Road
Bangalore, India 560 052
Phone: 91-80-4123-2551
Fax: 91-80-4123-8853

Type of Firm

Private Equity Firm

Project Preferences

Type of Financing Preferred:

Early Stage
Seed

Geographical Preferences

International Preferences:

India

Industry Preferences

In Communications prefer:

Wireless Communications

Additional Information

Year Founded: 2007
Capital Under Management: $123,900,000
Current Activity Level: Actively seeking new investments

ACCEL PARTNERS

428 University Avenue
Palo Alto, CA USA 94301
Phone: 650-614-4800
Fax: 650-614-4880
E-mail: siliconvalley@accel.com
Website: www.accel.com

Other Offices

16 St. James's Street
London, United Kingdom SW1A 1ER
Phone: 44-20-7170-1000
Fax: 44-20-7170-1099

Room 616 Tower A, COFCO Plaza
8 Jianguomen nei Daije
Beijing, China 100005
Phone: 86-10-6526-2400
Fax: 86-10-6526-0700

Number 21/1-1, Nawab Towers
Cunningham Road
Bangalore, India 560 052
Phone: 91-80-4123-2551
Fax: 91-80-4123-8853

Room 1105, Aetna Tower
Number 107 Zunyi Road
Shanghai, China 200051
Phone: 86-21-6237-5899
Fax: 86-21-6237-5899

Management and Staff

Arthur Patterson, Founding Partner
Bruce Golden, Partner
Carl Everett, Partner
James Breyer, Managing Partner
James Swartz, General Partner
Kaj-Erik Relander, Partner
Kevin Efrusy, General Partner
Kevin Comolli, Managing Partner
Neeraj Bharadwaj, Managing Director
Peter Wagner, Managing Partner
Richard Wong, Partner
Ryan Sweeney, Partner
Sameer Gandhi, Partner
Sonali De Rycker, Partner
Theresia Ranzetta, General Partner

Type of Firm

Private Equity Firm

Association Membership

Western Association of Venture Capitalists (WAVC)
National Venture Capital Association - USA (NVCA)
European Private Equity and Venture Capital Assoc.

Project Preferences

Role in Financing:

Will function either as deal originator or investor in deals created by others

Type of Financing Preferred:

Early Stage
Expansion
Seed
Startup

Size of Investments Considered:

Min Size of Investment Considered (000s): $1,000
Max Size of Investment Considered: No Limit

Geographical Preferences

United States Preferences:

All U.S.

International Preferences:

Italy
United Kingdom
India
Luxembourg
Netherlands
Europe
Belgium
Germany
Israel
France
All International

Industry Focus

(% based on actual investment)

Internet Specific	36.7%
Communications and Media	23.5%
Computer Software and Services	23.5%
Semiconductors/Other Elect.	4.5%
Computer Hardware	4.2%
Other Products	2.5%
Medical/Health	2.4%
Biotechnology	2.0%
Industrial/Energy	0.4%
Consumer Related	0.1%

Additional Information

Name of Most Recent Fund: Accel Growth Fund, L.P.
Most Recent Fund Was Raised: 12/11/2008
Year Founded: 1983
Capital Under Management: $3,000,000,000
Current Activity Level: Actively seeking new investments
Method of Compensation: Return on investment is of primary concern, do not charge fees

---

ACCEL-KKR LLC

2500 Sand Hill Road
Suite 300
Menlo Park, CA USA 94025
Phone: 650-289-2460
Fax: 650-289-2461
E-mail: inquiries@accel-kkr.com
Website: www.accel-kkr.com

Other Offices

3500 Lenox Road
Suite 1500
Atlanta, GA USA 30326
Phone: 404-419-2444
Fax: 404-419-2447

4300 Paces Ferry Road
Suite 610
Atlanta, GA USA 30339.
Phone: 770-436-1643
Fax: 770-436-1653

Management and Staff

Ben Bisconti, Managing Director
David Crisp, Vice President
Dean Jacobson, Vice President
Greg Williams, Managing Director
Jason Klein, Managing Director
Joe Savig, Vice President
Rob Palumbo, Managing Director
Thomas Barnds, Managing Director

Type of Firm

Private Equity Firm

Project Preferences

Role in Financing:

Prefer role as deal originator

Type of Financing Preferred:

Leveraged Buyout
Later Stage
Acquisition
Recapitalizations

Size of Investments Considered:

Min Size of Investment Considered (000s): $10,000
Max Size of Investment Considered (000s): $250,000

Geographical Preferences

United States Preferences:

All U.S.

Canadian Preferences:

All Canada

International Preferences:

Europe
Australia

Industry Preferences

In Communications prefer:

CATV & Pay TV Systems
Radio & TV Broadcasting
Telecommunications
Wireless Communications
Data Communications
Other Communication Prod.

In Computer Software prefer:

Software

In Internet Specific prefer:

Internet
Ecommerce

In Computer Other prefer:
Computer Related

In Semiconductor/Electr prefer:
Electronic Components
Semiconductor
Analytic/Scientific

In Business Serv. prefer:
Services

Additional Information
Name of Most Recent Fund: Accel-KKR Capital Partners II, L.P.
Most Recent Fund Was Raised: 11/20/2006
Year Founded: 2000
Capital Under Management: $1,100,000,000
Current Activity Level: Actively seeking new investments
Method of Compensation: Return on investment is of primary concern, do not charge fees

---

ACCELERATOR MEDIA (UK) LTD
30 St. James' Square
London, United Kingdom SW1Y 4AL
Phone: 44 20 7968 4288
Fax: 44 20 7968 4298
E-mail: proposals@acceleratormedia.com
Website: www.accelerator-media.com

Management and Staff
Philip McDanell, Chief Executive Officer

Type of Firm
Bank Affiliated

Project Preferences

Type of Financing Preferred:
Early Stage

Geographical Preferences

International Preferences:
United Kingdom

Industry Preferences

In Communications prefer:
Communications and Media

In Internet Specific prefer:
Internet

In Computer Other prefer:
Computer Related

In Semiconductor/Electr prefer:
Electronics

In Business Serv. prefer:
Media

Additional Information
Name of Most Recent Fund: Accelerator Media Fund
Most Recent Fund Was Raised: 09/30/2000
Year Founded: 2004
Capital Under Management: $52,400,000
Current Activity Level: Actively seeking new investments

ACCELERATOR VENTURES
300 Beale Street
Suite 603
San Francisco, CA USA 94105
Phone: 415-596-5932
Fax: 415-869-2802
E-mail: info@acceleratorventures.com
Website: www.acceleratorventures.com

Management and Staff
Alexander Lloyd, Managing Partner

Type of Firm
Private Equity Firm

Project Preferences

Type of Financing Preferred:
Early Stage
Seed
Startup

Industry Preferences

In Consumer Related prefer:
Consumer

Additional Information
Year Founded: 2008
Capital Under Management: $5,800,000
Current Activity Level: Actively seeking new investments

ACCENT CAPITAL
5300 Bee Caves Road
Building One, Suite 240
Austin, TX USA 78746
Phone: 512-306-9967
Fax: 512-306-9383
E-mail: info@accentcap.com
Website: www.accentcap.com

Management and Staff
Cliff Mountain, Vice President
Gil Burciaga, Vice President
Lee Urbina, Chief Financial Officer

Type of Firm
Private Equity Firm

Project Preferences

Type of Financing Preferred:
Second Stage Financing
Expansion
Early Stage
Mezzanine
Balanced
Later Stage
Management Buyouts
Acquisition

Size of Investments Considered:
Min Size of Investment Considered (000s): $500
Max Size of Investment Considered (000s): $3,000

Geographical Preferences

United States Preferences:
All U.S.

Industry Preferences

In Communications prefer:
Telecommunications

In Computer Hardware prefer:
Mini and Personal/Desktop

In Computer Software prefer:
Computer Services
Software
Systems Software
Applications Software

In Internet Specific prefer:
E-Commerce Technology
Internet
Ecommerce
Web Aggregration/Portals

In Semiconductor/Electr prefer:
Electronic Components

In Medical/Health prefer:
Medical Diagnostics
Disposable Med. Products
Health Services

In Consumer Related prefer:
Entertainment and Leisure
Sports

In Industrial/Energy prefer:
Energy

In Business Serv. prefer:
Services

In Manufact. prefer:
Manufacturing

Additional Information
Name of Most Recent Fund: Accent Texas Fund II, L.P.
Most Recent Fund Was Raised: 01/31/2008
Year Founded: 2005
Capital Under Management: $37,400,000
Current Activity Level: Actively seeking new investments

ACCENT EQUITY PARTNERS (FKA: EUROVENTURES AB / NORDICO)
Engelbrektsgatan 5
P.O. Box 5784
Stockholm, Sweden SE-11487

Phone: 46-8-5450-7300
Fax: 46-8-5450-7329
E-mail: info@accentequity.se
Website: www.accentequity.se

Management and Staff

Hannu Santasalo, Partner
Jan Ohlsson, Chief Executive Officer
Roland Nilsson, Partner

Type of Firm

Private Equity Firm

Association Membership

Finnish Venture Capital Association (FVCA)
Swedish Venture Capital Association (SVCA)
European Private Equity and Venture Capital Assoc.

Project Preferences

Type of Financing Preferred:
Leveraged Buyout
Early Stage
Expansion
Turnaround
Later Stage
Management Buyouts

Size of Investments Considered:
Min Size of Investment Considered (000s): $3,800
Max Size of Investment Considered (000s): $10,000

Geographical Preferences

International Preferences:
Sweden
Europe
Scandanavia/Nordic Region
Finland
Norway
Denmark

Industry Preferences

In Communications prefer:
Communications and Media

In Semiconductor/Electr prefer:
Electronics

In Medical/Health prefer:
Medical/Health

In Industrial/Energy prefer:
Industrial Products

In Financial Services prefer:
Financial Services

In Manufact. prefer:
Manufacturing

Additional Information

Name of Most Recent Fund: Accent Equity 2003
Most Recent Fund Was Raised: 08/29/2003
Year Founded: 2003
Capital Under Management: $380,700,000
Current Activity Level: Actively seeking new investments

ACCERA VENTURE PARTNERS AG

11/12 Kunststrasse
Mannheim, Germany 68181
Phone: 49-621-181-5370
Fax: 49-621-181-3799
E-mail: info@accera.de
Website: www.accera.de

Management and Staff

Christofer Dittmar, Managing Director
Marcus Rist, Managing Director
Matthias Helfrich, Managing Director

Type of Firm

Bank Affiliated

Project Preferences

Type of Financing Preferred:
Early Stage
Balanced

Geographical Preferences

International Preferences:
Europe
Germany
All International

Industry Preferences

In Communications prefer:
Telecommunications

In Internet Specific prefer:
Internet

In Industrial/Energy prefer:
Energy
Environmental Related

Additional Information

Name of Most Recent Fund: ENERGY Innovations Portfolio AG
Most Recent Fund Was Raised: 08/15/2005
Year Founded: 2001
Capital Under Management: $10,000,000
Current Activity Level: Actively seeking new investments

ACCERES BETEILIGUNGS-MANAGEMENT GMBH & CO KG

Sachsen-Anhalt
Bundesrepublik
Magdeburg, Germany 39104
Phone: 49-391-532-8140
Fax: 49-391-532-8159

Management and Staff

Dinnies Von der Osten, Chief Executive Officer

Type of Firm

Private Equity Firm

Project Preferences

Type of Financing Preferred:
Early Stage
Expansion

Geographical Preferences

International Preferences:
Germany

Additional Information

Year Founded: 2007
Current Activity Level: Actively seeking new investments

ACCES CAPITAL QUEBEC

1000 Route de L'eglise
Sainte-Foy, Canada G1V3V9
Phone: 418-650-9199
Fax: 418-650-7666
E-mail: info@acces-capital.ca
Website: www.acces-capital.ca

Management and Staff

Lise Lapierre, General Partner
Pierre Olivier, General Partner
Serge Olivier, General Partner

Type of Firm

Private Equity Firm

Additional Information

Year Founded: 1997
Current Activity Level: Actively seeking new investments

ACCESS CAPITAL PARTNERS

121 avenue des Champs Elysees
Paris, France 75008
Phone: 33-1-5643-6100
Fax: 33-1-5643-6101
E-mail: acp@accesscp.com
Website: www.access-capital-partners.com

Other Offices

P.O. Box 431 13-15 Victoria Road
St Peter Port Guernsey
Channel Islands, United Kingdom GY1 3ZD
Phone: 44-1481-713-843

Management and Staff

Agnes Nahum, Managing Partner
Alexandre Delos, Partner
Bernard De la Brosse, Chief Financial Officer
Dominique Peninon, Managing Partner
Philippe Poggioli, Managing Partner

Type of Firm
Private Equity Advisor or Fund of Funds

Association Membership
French Venture Capital Association (AFIC)
European Private Equity and Venture Capital Assoc.

Project Preferences

Type of Financing Preferred:
Fund of Funds
Leveraged Buyout
Early Stage
Later Stage
Management Buyouts

Size of Investments Considered:
Min Size of Investment Considered (000s): $4,708
Max Size of Investment Considered (000s): $23,540

Geographical Preferences

International Preferences:
Europe
Western Europe
France

Industry Focus
(% based on actual investment)

Other Products	99.8%
Computer Software and Services	0.2%

Additional Information
Year Founded: 1999
Capital Under Management: $2,179,200,000
Current Activity Level: Actively seeking new investments

ACCESS MICROFINANCE HOLDING AG
Linienstrasse 126
Berlin, Germany 10115
Phone: 49-3030-87470
E-mail: info@accessholding.com
Website: www.accessholding.com

Type of Firm
Investment Management Firm

Project Preferences

Type of Financing Preferred:
Early Stage
Expansion
Seed
Startup

Geographical Preferences

International Preferences:
All International

Additional Information
Year Founded: 2006
Capital Under Management: $28,700,000
Current Activity Level: Actively seeking new investments

ACCESS VENTURE PARTNERS
8787 Turnpike Drive
Suite 260
Westminster, CO USA 80031
Phone: 303-426-8899
Fax: 303-426-8828
Website: www.accessventurepartners.com

Other Offices
12112 Technology Boulevard
Suite 100
Austin, TX USA 78727
Phone: 512-236-0450
Fax: 512-249-3452

Management and Staff
Brian Wallace, Managing Director
Jay Campion, Managing Director
V. Frank Mendicino II, Managing Director
V. Frank Mendicino III, Managing Director

Type of Firm
Private Equity Firm

Project Preferences

Role in Financing:
Will function either as deal originator or investor in deals created by others

Type of Financing Preferred:
Early Stage
Seed

Size of Investments Considered:
Min Size of Investment Considered (000s): $250
Max Size of Investment Considered (000s): $2,000

Geographical Preferences

United States Preferences:
Northern California
Rocky Mountain
Southwest

Industry Focus
(% based on actual investment)

Computer Software and Services	26.4%
Communications and Media	18.2%
Semiconductors/Other Elect.	16.9%
Biotechnology	13.9%
Other Products	7.5%
Internet Specific	7.3%
Computer Hardware	6.6%
Industrial/Energy	3.1%

Additional Information
Name of Most Recent Fund: Access Venture Partners II, L.P.
Most Recent Fund Was Raised: 10/30/2006
Year Founded: 1999
Capital Under Management: $33,400,000
Current Activity Level: Actively seeking new investments
Method of Compensation: Return on investment is of primary concern, do not charge fees

---

ACCESSTURKEY PRIVATE EQUITY
Ataturk Cad. No. 72
Kozyatagi
Istanbul, Turkey 34736
Phone: 90-216-468-1015
Fax: 90-216-302-8682
E-mail: info@accessturkey.com
Website: www.accessturkey.com

Management and Staff
Mustafa Erhan Say, Founder

Type of Firm
Private Equity Firm

Project Preferences

Type of Financing Preferred:
Leveraged Buyout
Management Buyouts
Acquisition

Industry Preferences

In Communications prefer:
Communications and Media

In Financial Services prefer:
Financial Services

In Business Serv. prefer:
Distribution

In Manufact. prefer:
Manufacturing

Additional Information
Year Founded: 1999
Current Activity Level: Actively seeking new investments

ACCOLADE CAPITAL MANAGEMENT (FKA: ACCOLADE PARTNERS, L.P.)
1717 Rhode Island Avenue, NW
Suite 610
Washington, DC USA 20036
Phone: 202-775-5595
Fax: 202-775-5599
E-mail: info@accoladepartners.com
Website: www.accoladepartners.com

Management and Staff
Joelle Kayden, Managing Partner

Type of Firm
Private Equity Advisor or Fund of Funds

Project Preferences

Type of Financing Preferred:
Fund of Funds

Additional Information

Year Founded: 2000
Capital Under Management: $323,000,000
Current Activity Level: Actively seeking new investments

ACCORD CAPITAL INVESTORS PTY., LTD.

Level 5
60 Pitt Street
Sydney, Australia 2000
Phone: 612-9241-2496
Fax: 612-9241-2750

Management and Staff

Glenn Goodacre, Managing Director

Type of Firm

Private Equity Firm

Project Preferences

Type of Financing Preferred:
Leveraged Buyout

Geographical Preferences

International Preferences:
Pacific

Additional Information

Year Founded: 1993
Current Activity Level: Actively seeking new investments

ACCRETION INVESTMENT MANAGEMENT PTY, LTD.

Level 46, Gov. Phillip Tower
1 Farrer Place
Sydney, Australia 2000
Phone: 612-9947-9792
Fax: 612-9947-9774
Website: www.accretion.com.au

Management and Staff

Peter Chapman, Chief Executive Officer

Type of Firm

Private Equity Firm

Association Membership

Australian Venture Capital Association (AVCAL)

Project Preferences

Role in Financing:
Prefer role as deal originator but will also invest in deals created by others

Type of Financing Preferred:
Generalist PE
Expansion
Balanced
Later Stage
Management Buyouts
Fund of Funds of Second

Size of Investments Considered:
Min Size of Investment Considered (000s): $837
Max Size of Investment Considered (000s): $8,370

Geographical Preferences

International Preferences:
Asia
New Zealand
Australia

Industry Preferences

In Computer Software prefer:
Software

In Business Serv. prefer:
Services

In Manufact. prefer:
Manufacturing

Additional Information

Name of Most Recent Fund: Accretion IV Fund
Most Recent Fund Was Raised: 07/31/2006
Year Founded: 2002
Capital Under Management: $19,500,000
Current Activity Level: Actively seeking new investments
Method of Compensation: Return on investment is of primary concern, do not charge fees

---

ACCRETIVE EXIT CAPITAL PARTNERS LLC

225 Franklin Street
26th Floor
Boston, MA USA 02110
Phone: 617-217-2771
Fax: 617-217-2001
Website: www.accretiveexit.com

Management and Staff

Andrew Reilly, Managing Director
Edwin Wang, Senior Managing Director
Theodore Tedeschi, Managing Director

Type of Firm

Private Equity Firm

Project Preferences

Type of Financing Preferred:
Leveraged Buyout

Additional Information

Year Founded: 2007
Capital Under Management: $225,000,000
Current Activity Level: Actively seeking new investments

ACCRETIVE LLC (FKA: ACCRETIVE TECHNOLOGY PARTNERS LLC)

51 Madison Avenue
31st Floor
New York, NY USA 10010
Phone: 646-282-1920
Fax: 646-282-3138
E-mail: info@accretivellc.com
Website: www.accretivetechnology.com

Management and Staff

Adam Boehler, Principal
Alan Cline, General Partner
Edgar Bronfman, General Partner
J. Michael Cline, Managing Partner
Jeffrey Rodek, General Partner
Jim Madden, General Partner
John Tam, Principal
Madhu Tadikonda, General Partner
Martin Muoto, Principal
Scott Werner, General Partner

Type of Firm

Private Equity Firm

Project Preferences

Type of Financing Preferred:
Balanced

Industry Preferences

In Computer Software prefer:
Software

Additional Information

Year Founded: 2000
Current Activity Level: Actively seeking new investments

ACCRUE SPORTS AND ENTERTAINMENT PARTNERS LLC

1350 Broadway
Suite 602
New York, NY USA 10018
Phone: 646-214-0625
Website: www.accruesev.com

Other Offices

210 Bear Hill Road
Suite 300
Waltham, MA USA 02451
Phone: 781-314-0129

Management and Staff

Doug Perlman, Managing Partner
Paul Levy, Managing Director
Steve Solomon, Managing Partner

Type of Firm
Private Equity Firm

Project Preferences

Type of Financing Preferred:
Early Stage

Geographical Preferences

United States Preferences:
All U.S.

Industry Preferences

In Consumer Related prefer:
Entertainment and Leisure

In Business Serv. prefer:
Media

Additional Information
Year Founded: 2008
Current Activity Level: Actively seeking new investments

ACCUITIVE MEDICAL VENTURES
2750 Premiere Parkway
Suite 200
Duluth, GA USA 30097
Phone: 678-812-1101
Fax: 678-417-7325
E-mail: info@amvpartners.com
Website: www.amvpartners.com

Other Offices
3652 Hermann Court North East
Rochester, MN USA 55906
Phone: 507-529-4003
Fax: 507-529-4004

5542 First Coast Highway
Suite 400
Fernandina Beach, FL USA 32034
Phone: 904-261-9690
Fax: 678-812-1144

Management and Staff
Barak Azmon, Venture Partner
Charles Larsen, Managing Director
Gerard van Hamel Platerink, Managing Director
Gordon Wyatt, Chief Financial Officer
John Deedrick, Managing Director
Steven Waite, Managing Director
Thomas Weldon, Chairman & Managing Director

Type of Firm
Private Equity Firm

Association Membership
National Venture Capital Association - USA (NVCA)

Project Preferences

Role in Financing:
Will function either as deal originator or investor in deals created by others

Type of Financing Preferred:
Early Stage
Expansion
Seed
Startup

Size of Investments Considered:
Min Size of Investment Considered (000s): $1,500
Max Size of Investment Considered (000s): $8,000

Geographical Preferences

United States Preferences:
All U.S.

Industry Preferences

In Medical/Health prefer:
Medical Products

Additional Information
Name of Most Recent Fund: AMV Partners II, L.P.
Most Recent Fund Was Raised: 02/15/2006
Year Founded: 2004
Capital Under Management: $230,000,000
Current Activity Level: Actively seeking new investments

ACE MANAGEMENT
48 rue de Lisbonne
Paris, France 75008
Phone: 33-1-5856-2562
Fax: 33-1-5856-2563
E-mail: ace@acemanagement.fr
Website: www.acemanagement.fr

Other Offices
Financiere de Brienne
2 place Rio de Janeiro
Paris Cedex 08, France 75362
Phone: 33-1-4495-2960
Fax: 33-1-4495-2969

Management and Staff
Alain Pechon, Venture Partner
Didier Picot, Venture Partner

Type of Firm
Private Equity Firm

Association Membership
French Venture Capital Association (AFIC)

Project Preferences

Type of Financing Preferred:
Leveraged Buyout
Early Stage
Expansion
Balanced
Seed
Startup

Geographical Preferences

International Preferences:
Switzerland
Europe
Germany
France

Industry Preferences

In Internet Specific prefer:
Internet

In Semiconductor/Electr prefer:
Electronics

In Transportation prefer:
Aerospace

Additional Information
Year Founded: 2000
Capital Under Management: $73,500,000
Current Activity Level: Actively seeking new investments

ACE VENTURE CAPITAL
Av. das Americas 700
Bloco 3 - Sala 121
Rio de Janeiro, Brazil
Phone: 55-21-2132-7510
Fax: 55-21-2132-7510
E-mail: contato@acecapital.com.br
Website: www.acecapital.com.br

Type of Firm
Private Equity Firm

Association Membership
Brazilian Venture Capital Association (ABCR)

Project Preferences

Type of Financing Preferred:
Balanced

Geographical Preferences

International Preferences:
Brazil

Industry Preferences

In Communications prefer:
Communications and Media
Media and Entertainment

In Internet Specific prefer:
Internet

In Consumer Related prefer:
Consumer Products

In Agr/Forestr/Fish prefer:
Agribusiness
Mining and Minerals

Additional Information

Year Founded: 2006
Current Activity Level: Actively seeking new investments

ACG PRIVATE EQUITY (FKA: ALTIUM CAPITAL GESTION)

84 avenue d'Iena
Paris, France 75016
Phone: 33-1-5689-5900
Fax: 33-1-5689-5915
Website: www.acg-pe.fr

Other Offices

C/ Velazquez, 10 - 3° Izq.
Madrid, Spain 28001
Phone: 34-91-761-8800
Fax: 34-91-761-8820

Via Della Spiga 26
Milan, Italy 20121
Phone: 39-2-7601-7340
Fax: 39-2-7602-0155

Possartstrasse 13
Munich, Germany 81679
Phone: 49-89-4131-20
Fax: 49-89-4131-2513

7 Stratigi Street
154 51 Neo Psychiko
Athens, Greece
Phone: 30-210-677-2281
Fax: 30-210-672-8624

Dufourstrasse 60
Zollikon
Zurich, Switzerland CH-8702
Phone: 41-43-499-4343
Fax: 41-43-499-4344

30 St James's Square
London, United Kingdom SW1Y 4AL
Phone: 44-20-7484-4040
Fax: 44-20-7484-4010

5 Ralli Courts
West Riverside
Manchester, United Kingdom M3 5FT
Phone: 44-161-831-9133
Fax: 44-161-831-9144

Conference House
152 Morrison Street
Edinburgh, United Kingdom EH3 8EB
Phone: 44-131-200-6054
Fax: 44-131-200-6200

Management and Staff

Eric Malahieude, Chief Financial Officer
Gilles Michat, Managing Director
Lorenzo Lorenzotti, Managing Director
Wladimir Mollof, President

Type of Firm

Bank Affiliated

Association Membership

French Venture Capital Association (AFIC)
European Private Equity and Venture Capital Assoc.

Project Preferences

Type of Financing Preferred:
Fund of Funds

Geographical Preferences

International Preferences:
Italy
United Kingdom
Central Europe
Europe
Western Europe
Spain
Scandanavia/Nordic Region
Germany
France

Additional Information

Year Founded: 1998
Capital Under Management: $270,300,000
Current Activity Level: Actively seeking new investments

ACI CAPITAL CO., LLC

666 Third Avenue
29th Floor
New York, NY USA 10017
Phone: 212-634-3333
Fax: 212-634-3330
Website: www.acicapital.com

Management and Staff

Gregory Nolff, Chief Financial Officer
Hunter Reisner, Managing Director
Ian Haft, Vice President
Kevin Penn, Managing Director
Matthew Bronfman, Managing Director
Thomas Auth, Vice President

Type of Firm

Private Equity Firm

Project Preferences

Type of Financing Preferred:
Leveraged Buyout
Special Situation
Recapitalizations

Geographical Preferences

United States Preferences:
All U.S.

Additional Information

Year Founded: 1995
Capital Under Management: $335,000,000
Current Activity Level: Actively seeking new investments

ACKERLEY PARTNERS, LLC

601 Union Street
Suite 3003
Seattle, WA USA 98101
Phone: 206-624-2888
Fax: 206-623-7853
E-mail: info@ackerleypartners.com
Website: www.ackerley.com

Management and Staff

Christopher Ackerley, Co-Founder
Kevin Hylton, Chief Financial Officer
Kim Ackerley Cleworth, Co-Founder
Ted Ackerley, Co-Founder

Type of Firm

Private Equity Firm

Project Preferences

Type of Financing Preferred:
Second Stage Financing
Later Stage

Geographical Preferences

United States Preferences:
All U.S.

Industry Preferences

In Communications prefer:
Wireless Communications
Media and Entertainment

Additional Information

Year Founded: 2002
Current Activity Level: Actively seeking new investments

ACOFI GESTION

31-33 rue de La Baume
Paris, France 75008
Phone: 33-1-5376-9999
Fax: 33-1-5376-9998
E-mail: contact@acofi.com
Website: www.acofi.com

Management and Staff

Francois Delavenne, President

Type of Firm

Private Equity Firm

Association Membership

French Venture Capital Association (AFIC)

Project Preferences

Type of Financing Preferred:

Generalist PE
Balanced

Geographical Preferences

International Preferences:

Europe
France

Additional Information

Year Founded: 1997
Capital Under Management: $14,200,000
Current Activity Level: Actively seeking new investments

ACORN (NETHERLANDS) Z B.V.

Weena 340
Rotterdam, Netherlands 3012
Phone: 31-104-047-644

Type of Firm

Private Equity Firm

Project Preferences

Type of Financing Preferred:

Balanced

Geographical Preferences

International Preferences:

Europe

Additional Information

Year Founded: 2007
Current Activity Level: Actively seeking new investments

ACORN CAMPUS VENTURES

Three Results Way
Cupertino, CA USA 95014
Phone: 408-777-8090
Fax: 408-777-8091
E-mail: info@acorncampus.com
Website: www.acorncampus.com

Management and Staff

Chester Wang, Managing Director
David Tsang, Managing Director
Hsing Kung, Managing Director
Rueiming Jamp, Venture Partner
Tien-Lai Hwang, Managing Director
Wu-fu Chen, Managing Director

Type of Firm

Private Equity Firm

Project Preferences

Role in Financing:

Prefer role as deal originator but will also invest in deals created by others

Type of Financing Preferred:

Early Stage
Seed
Startup

Size of Investments Considered:

Min Size of Investment Considered (000s): $250
Max Size of Investment Considered (000s): $5,000

Geographical Preferences

United States Preferences:

Northern California

International Preferences:

Asia

Industry Preferences

In Communications prefer:

Commercial Communications
Telecommunications
Wireless Communications
Data Communications

In Computer Software prefer:

Software
Applications Software

In Semiconductor/Electr prefer:

Semiconductor
Controllers and Sensors
Sensors
Fiber Optics

In Biotechnology prefer:

Biotechnology
Human Biotechnology
Agricultural/Animal Bio.
Industrial Biotechnology

In Medical/Health prefer:

Medical Diagnostics

Additional Information

Name of Most Recent Fund: Acorn Campus Venture Fund III, LLC
Most Recent Fund Was Raised: 05/30/2006
Year Founded: 2000
Capital Under Management: $78,000,000
Current Activity Level: Actively seeking new investments
Method of Compensation: Return on investment is of primary concern, do not charge fees

---

ACORN CAPITAL PARTNERS

Bollin House
Riverside Park
Wilmslow, United Kingdom SK9 1DP
Phone: 44-870-122-5420
Fax: 44-870-122-5421
E-mail: mail@acorncapital.co.uk
Website: www.acorncapital.co.uk

Management and Staff

Ian Templeton, Chief Executive Officer

Type of Firm

Private Equity Firm

Association Membership

British Venture Capital Association (BVCA)

Project Preferences

Type of Financing Preferred:

Second Stage Financing
Leveraged Buyout
Early Stage
Expansion
Balanced
Turnaround
Startup

Size of Investments Considered:

Min Size of Investment Considered (000s): $157
Max Size of Investment Considered (000s): $3,129

Geographical Preferences

International Preferences:
Ireland
United Kingdom

Industry Preferences

In Communications prefer:

Commercial Communications

In Computer Software prefer:

Computer Services
Software

In Internet Specific prefer:

Internet

In Biotechnology prefer:

Biotechnology

In Medical/Health prefer:

Medical/Health

In Business Serv. prefer:

Media

In Manufact. prefer:

Manufacturing

Additional Information

Year Founded: 2000
Capital Under Management: $59,500,000
Current Activity Level: Actively seeking new investments

ACORN GROWTH COMPANIES

2701 Liberty Parkway
Suite 311
Midwest City, OK USA 73110
Phone: 405-737-2676
Fax: 405-732-4141
Website: www.acorngrowthcompanies.com
Other Offices
113 Quay Street
Alexandria, VA USA 22314

Management and Staff

Jeff Davis, Partner
Rick Nagel, Partner
Warren Thomas, Partner

Type of Firm

Private Equity Firm

Project Preferences

Type of Financing Preferred:
Leveraged Buyout

Industry Preferences

In Communications prefer:

Communications and Media

In Industrial/Energy prefer:

Environmental Related

In Transportation prefer:

Aerospace

Additional Information

Name of Most Recent Fund: Acorn Growth Capital Fund III LLC
Most Recent Fund Was Raised: 08/31/2007
Year Founded: 2007
Capital Under Management: $4,800,000
Current Activity Level: Actively seeking new investments

ACORN VENTURES, INC.

268 Bush Street
Suite 2829
San Francisco, CA USA 94104
Phone: 650-994-7801
Fax: 925-249-1748
E-mail: Partners@acorn-ventures.com
Website: www.acornventures.com

Management and Staff

Cliff Girard, Chief Executive Officer

Type of Firm

Private Equity Firm

Association Membership

Natl Assoc of Small Bus. Inv. Co (NASBIC)

Project Preferences

Role in Financing:

Will function either as deal originator or investor in deals created by others

Type of Financing Preferred:

Fund of Funds
Second Stage Financing
Leveraged Buyout
Early Stage
Turnaround
Later Stage
Seed
First Stage Financing
Acquisition

Size of Investments Considered:

Min Size of Investment Considered (000s): $3,000
Max Size of Investment Considered (000s): $10,000
Geographical Preferences

United States Preferences:

West Coast

Industry Focus

(% based on actual investment)

Communications and Media	29.3%
Computer Software and Services	25.0%
Internet Specific	13.7%
Semiconductors/Other Elect.	12.1%
Industrial/Energy	10.9%
Biotechnology	3.6%
Medical/Health	2.3%
Other Products	2.2%
Computer Hardware	0.7%
Consumer Related	0.3%

Additional Information

Name of Most Recent Fund: Acorn Ventures VI
Most Recent Fund Was Raised: 06/01/2003
Year Founded: 1986
Capital Under Management: $1,375,000,000
Current Activity Level: Reducing investment activity
Method of Compensation: Return on investment is of primary concern, do not charge fees

ACP CAPITAL, LTD.

MacMillan House
96 Kensington High Street
London, United Kingdom W8 4SG
Phone: 44-20-7082-3922
Fax: 44-80-8208-3437
E-mail: info@acpcapital.com
Website: www.acpcapital.com

Management and Staff

Derek Vago, Chief Executive Officer
Eric Youngblood, Chief Financial Officer
Nikolaj Larsen, Managing Director

Type of Firm

Private Equity Firm

Project Preferences

Type of Financing Preferred:

Mezzanine
Generalist PE
Balanced

Geographical Preferences

International Preferences:

Europe
Germany

Industry Preferences

In Consumer Related prefer:

Retail
Food/Beverage

Additional Information

Year Founded: 2006
Capital Under Management: $173,200,000
Current Activity Level: Actively seeking new investments

ACQUISITION SEARCH CORP., THE

5555 Glenridge Connector
Suite 200
Atlanta, GA USA 30342
Phone: 404-459-2777
E-mail: info@acquisitionsearch.com
Website: www.acquisitionsearch.com

Type of Firm

Service Provider

Project Preferences

Role in Financing:

Prefer role as deal originator

Type of Financing Preferred:

Second Stage Financing
Leveraged Buyout
Control-block Purchases
First Stage Financing
Special Situation

Size of Investments Considered:

Min Size of Investment Considered (000s): $1,000
Max Size of Investment Considered: No Limit

Additional Information

Year Founded: 1992
Current Activity Level: Actively seeking new investments
Method of Compensation: Function primarily in service area, receive contingent fee in cash or equity

ACROSS PRIVATE EQUITY - HEALTH CARE

Apollo Business Centrum
Mlynske nivy 45
Bratislava, Slovakia 821 09

Phone: 421-2-58240300
Fax: 421-2-58240311
Website: www.across.sk

Type of Firm

Private Equity Firm

Project Preferences

Type of Financing Preferred:
Balanced

Geographical Preferences

International Preferences:
Central Europe
Eastern Europe

Additional Information

Year Founded: 2005
Current Activity Level: Actively seeking new investments

ACT VENTURE CAPITAL, LTD.

Richview Office Park
Clonskeagh
Dublin 14, Ireland
Phone: 353-1-260-0966
Fax: 353-1-260-0538
E-mail: info@actvc.ie
Website: www.actventure.com

Management and Staff

Charlie Glass, Partner
Dan Maher, Partner
Debbie Rennick, Partner
John Flynn, Partner
John O'Sullivan, Partner
Kieron Branagan, Partner
Niall Carroll, Managing Partner
Owen Murphy, Partner
Walter Hobbs, Partner

Type of Firm

Private Equity Firm

Association Membership

Irish Venture Capital Association
British Venture Capital Association (BVCA)
European Private Equity and Venture Capital Assoc.

Project Preferences

Role in Financing:
Prefer role as deal originator but will also invest in deals created by others

Type of Financing Preferred:
Second Stage Financing
Leveraged Buyout
Early Stage
Expansion
Balanced
Startup
Recapitalizations

Size of Investments Considered:
Min Size of Investment Considered (000s): $900
Max Size of Investment Considered (000s): $18,000

Geographical Preferences

International Preferences:
Ireland
Europe
Western Europe

Industry Focus

(% based on actual investment)	
Semiconductors/Other Elect.	29.5%
Computer Software and Services	20.4%
Internet Specific	18.9%
Medical/Health	8.7%
Computer Hardware	6.9%
Consumer Related	6.0%
Communications and Media	4.8%
Other Products	2.9%
Industrial/Energy	2.0%

Additional Information

Name of Most Recent Fund: ACT 2001
Most Recent Fund Was Raised: 10/26/2001
Year Founded: 1994
Capital Under Management: $455,100,000
Current Activity Level: Actively seeking new investments

ACTEM PARTNERS (FKA: SPEF LBO)

5-7, rue de Monttessuy
Paris Cedex 07, France 75340
Phone: 33-1-5819-2250
Fax: 33-1-5819-2260
E-mail: contact@actem-partners.com
Website: www.actem-partners.com

Management and Staff

Arnaud Leclercq, Managing Director
Cyril Miller, Managing Partner
Laurent Allegot, Managing Director

Type of Firm

Bank Affiliated

Association Membership

French Venture Capital Association (AFIC)

Project Preferences

Type of Financing Preferred:
Leveraged Buyout
Balanced
Management Buyouts

Geographical Preferences

International Preferences:
Europe
France

Additional Information

Year Founded: 1996
Capital Under Management: $54,600,000
Current Activity Level: Actively seeking new investments

ACTERA GROUP

Stratejik Yonetim Hizmetleri
Kizilserce Sokak No 30
Istanbul, Turkey 34810
Phone: 90-216516-0100
Fax: 90-216516-0101
E-mail: info@acteragroup.com
Website: www.acteragroup.com

Management and Staff

Isak Antika, Managing Director
Murat Cavusoglu, Managing Director

Type of Firm

Endowment, Foundation or Pension Fund

Project Preferences

Type of Financing Preferred:
Leveraged Buyout
Expansion
Generalist PE

Geographical Preferences

International Preferences:
Turkey

Additional Information

Name of Most Recent Fund: Actera Partners
Most Recent Fund Was Raised: 02/06/2007
Year Founded: 2007
Capital Under Management: $475,000,000
Current Activity Level: Actively seeking new investments

ACTIDEV

74 rue de Bonnel
Lyon Cedex 03, France 69428
Phone: 33-4-7860-5871
Fax: 33-4-7871-0571
E-mail: actidev@wanadoo.fr

Management and Staff

Pierre Collet, President

Type of Firm

Private Equity Firm

Project Preferences

Type of Financing Preferred:
Leveraged Buyout
Expansion

Geographical Preferences

International Preferences:

France

Additional Information

Year Founded: 1992
Capital Under Management: $4,000,000
Current Activity Level: Actively seeking new investments

ACTIS CAPITAL LLP

2 More London Riverside
London, United Kingdom SE1 2JT
Phone: 44-20-7234-5000
Fax: 44-20-7234-5010
E-mail: info@act.is
Website: www.act.is

Other Offices

Ground Floor, 1 Gabalya Street
Zamalek
Cairo, Egypt 11211
Phone: 20-2-736-1628
Fax: 20-2-736-1634

First Floor, Bahria Complex II
MT Khan Road
Karachi, Pakistan 74000
Phone: 92-21-561-0091
Fax: 92-21-561-1891

Norfolk Towers, 1st Floor
Kijabe Street
Nairobi, Kenya 43233-0010
Phone: 254-20-219-952
Fax: 254-20-219-744

712 China World Tower 2
No. 1 Jian Guo Men Wai Street
Beijing, China 100004
Phone: 86-10-6535-4800
Fax: 86-10-6505-8111

311 Calle 22
Miramar
Havana, Cuba
Phone: 537-204-4468
Fax: 537-204-4460

Maersk House, PO Box 51906
121 Louis Solomon Close, Victoria Island
Lagos, Nigeria
Phone: 234-1-262-6475-67
Fax: 234-1-262-6479

World Trade Centre, Level 16
Jalan Jenderal Sudirman kav 29-31
Jakarta, Indonesia 12920
Phone: 62-21-525-4993
Fax: 62-21-525-4902

704, 7th Floor, Dalamai House
Jamnalal Bajaj Road, Nariman Point
Mumbai, India 400 021
Phone: 91-22-2281-6430
Fax: 91-22-2282-0737

15 Rest House
Cresent
Bangalore, India 560001
Phone: 91-80-2555-0651
Fax: 91-80-2555-0592

NBCC Place, 1/F East Tower
Bhisham Pitamah Marg, Pragati Vihar
New Delhi, India 110 003
Phone: 91-11-4366-7000
Fax: 91-11-4366-7070

3rd Floor, 50 Mirambo Street
PO Box 8020
Dar es Salaam, Tanzania
Phone: 255-22-211-2926
Fax: 255-22-211-3645

Cocody Danga, 2, rue de la Canebiere
Immeuble Canebiere, 1er etage, Porte 5
Abidjan , Ivory Coast 04 BP 161
Phone: 225-22-48-7759
Fax: 225-22-48-7759

55 Market Street
#11-02
Singapore, Singapore 048941
Phone: 65-6416-6400
Fax: 65-6227-1004

Suite 6.1, Level 6
Menara IMC, Jalan Sultan Ismail
Kuala Lumpur, Malaysia
Phone: 603-2031-4088
Fax: 603-2032-1162

1st Floor, Cradock Heights
21 Cradock Avenue, Rosebank
Johannesburg, South Africa 2132
Phone: 27-11-778-5900
Fax: 27-11-327-7407

Torre Cainco, Floor 13th
Av. Las Americas Esq. Gral Saavedra
Santa Cruz de la Sierra, Bolivia POBox 7100
Phone: 591-3-333-3133
Fax: 591-3-333-1980

Management and Staff

Alistair Mackintosh, Managing Partner
Alun Branigan, Partner
Andrew Reicher, Managing Partner
Bay Chong Chin, Managing Partner
Donald Peck, Managing Partner
G Rathinam, Partner
Gillian Arthur, Managing Partner
Hywel Rees-Jones, Partner
J.M. Trivedi, Partner
Jiansheng Wang, Partner
John Van Wyk, Partner
Jonathon Bond, Managing Partner
Mark Pay, Partner
Meb Soman, Managing Director
Meng Ann Lim, Partner
Michael Till, Managing Partner
Michael Turner, Partner
Murray Grant, Partner
Nkosana Moyo, Managing Partner
Patrick Helson, Chief Operating Officer
Paul Owers, Partner
Rick Phillips, Partner
Steven Enderby, Partner
Subba Rao Telidevara, Partner
Tony Halligan, Chief Financial Officer

Type of Firm

Private Equity Firm

Association Membership

South African Venture Capital Association (SAVCA)
Indian Venture Capital Association (IVCA)
African Venture Capital Association (AVCA)

Project Preferences

Type of Financing Preferred:

Leveraged Buyout
Expansion
Mezzanine
Generalist PE
Balanced
Public Companies
Later Stage
Management Buyouts
Recapitalizations

Size of Investments Considered:

Min Size of Investment Considered (000s): $10,000
Max Size of Investment Considered (000s): $100,000

Geographical Preferences

International Preferences:

Vietnam
Bangladesh
Indonesia
India
Pakistan
United Kingdom
Latin America
China
Iran
Thailand
Philippines
Sri Lanka
Asia
Singapore
Malaysia
Africa

Industry Preferences

In Communications prefer:

Telecommunications

In Medical/Health prefer:

Medical/Health
Pharmaceuticals

In Consumer Related prefer:
Consumer

In Industrial/Energy prefer:
Energy
Oil and Gas Exploration

In Transportation prefer:
Transportation

In Financial Services prefer:
Financial Services

In Business Serv. prefer:
Services

In Manufact. prefer:
Manufacturing

In Agr/Forestr/Fish prefer:
Agriculture related
Mining and Minerals

Additional Information
Year Founded: 2004
Capital Under Management: $3,400,000,000
Current Activity Level: Actively seeking new investments

ACTIVA CAPITAL SAS
203 rue du Faubourg
Saint-Honore
Paris, France 75008
Phone: 33-1-4312-5012
Fax: 33-1-4312-5013
E-mail: infos@activacapital.com
Website: www.activacapital.com

Management and Staff
Charles Diehl, Partner
Christophe Parier, Partner
Jean-Hugues Verdu, Chief Operating Officer
Jean-Louis De Bernardy, Partner
Michael Diehl, Partner
Philippe Latorre, Partner
Thierry Celestin, Partner

Type of Firm
Private Equity Firm

Association Membership
French Venture Capital Association (AFIC)
European Private Equity and Venture Capital Assoc.

Project Preferences

Type of Financing Preferred:
Leveraged Buyout
Expansion
Open Market
Management Buyouts
Acquisition

Size of Investments Considered:
Min Size of Investment Considered (000s): $18,608
Max Size of Investment Considered (000s): $93,041

Geographical Preferences

International Preferences:
France

Industry Preferences

In Medical/Health prefer:
Medical/Health

In Consumer Related prefer:
Consumer
Food/Beverage
Consumer Services

In Industrial/Energy prefer:
Industrial Products

In Business Serv. prefer:
Services
Media

Additional Information
Year Founded: 2000
Capital Under Management: $53,500,000
Current Activity Level: Actively seeking new investments

ACTIVE CAPITAL ASIA, LTD.
105 Cecil Street
#06-01 The Octagon
Singapore, Singapore 069534
Phone: 65-6827-9667
Fax: 65-6836-0521
E-mail: info@activecapitalasia.com
Website: www.activecapitalasia.com

Management and Staff
Dominique Pommier, Managing Director

Type of Firm
Private Equity Advisor or Fund of Funds

Association Membership
Singapore Venture Capital Association (SVCA)

Project Preferences

Type of Financing Preferred:
Balanced
Seed
Startup
Special Situation

Geographical Preferences

International Preferences:
India
Australia
Singapore
Asia

Industry Preferences

In Communications prefer:
Wireless Communications

In Internet Specific prefer:
E-Commerce Technology

In Financial Services prefer:
Financial Services

Additional Information
Year Founded: 2000
Current Activity Level: Actively seeking new investments

ACTIVE CAPITAL PARTNERS S.L.
Paseo de Gracia 76, 1 1a
Barcelona, Spain 8008
Phone: 34-93-487-6666
Fax: 34-93-488-1461
E-mail: info@acpvc.com
Website: www.acpvc.com

Management and Staff
Christopher Pommerening, Managing Partner
Joaquin Molins Gil, Partner
Philipp Schroeder, Managing Partner
Ricard Soderberg, Managing Partner

Type of Firm
Private Equity Firm

Association Membership
European Private Equity and Venture Capital Assoc.

Project Preferences

Type of Financing Preferred:
Early Stage
Seed
Startup

Size of Investments Considered:
Min Size of Investment Considered (000s): $600
Max Size of Investment Considered (000s): $1,200

Geographical Preferences

International Preferences:
Europe
Spain

Industry Preferences

In Communications prefer:
Commercial Communications
Media and Entertainment

In Manufact. prefer:
Manufacturing

Additional Information
Name of Most Recent Fund: Molins Capital Inversion S.C.R. S.A.
Most Recent Fund Was Raised: 09/23/2004
Year Founded: 2004
Capital Under Management: $13,400,000
Current Activity Level: Actively seeking new investments

ACTIVE PRIVATE EQUITY ADVISORY LLP

6 Chesterfield Gardens
5th Floor
London, United Kingdom W1J 5BQ
Phone: 44-207-016-6480
Fax: 44-207-016-6490
Website: www.apeq.co.uk

Management and Staff

Bryan Vaniman, Partner
Gavyn Davies, Founding Partner
Spencer Skinner, Founding Partner
Tom Hopkins, Chief Operating Officer

Type of Firm

Private Equity Firm

Association Membership

British Venture Capital Association (BVCA)

Project Preferences

Type of Financing Preferred:

Leveraged Buyout
Management Buyouts
Acquisition

Size of Investments Considered:

Min Size of Investment Considered (000s): $994
Max Size of Investment Considered (000s): $29,829

Geographical Preferences

International Preferences:

United Kingdom

Industry Preferences

In Communications prefer:

Media and Entertainment

In Internet Specific prefer:

E-Commerce Technology

In Consumer Related prefer:

Entertainment and Leisure
Food/Beverage
Consumer Products
Consumer Services

In Business Serv. prefer:

Media

Additional Information

Year Founded: 2004
Current Activity Level: Actively seeking new investments

ACTON CAPITAL PARTNERS GMBH

Widenmayerstr, 29
Munich, Germany D-80538
Phone: 49-89-2421-8870
Fax: 49-89242-188759
E-mail: info@actoncapital.de
Website: www.actoncapital.de

Management and Staff

Christoph Braun, Managing Partner
Frank Seehaus, Managing Partner
Jan-Gisbert Schultze, Managing Partner
Paul-Bernhard Kallen, Managing Partner

Type of Firm

Private Equity Firm

Project Preferences

Type of Financing Preferred:

Expansion
Balanced
Later Stage
Acquisition

Additional Information

Year Founded: 2008
Current Activity Level: Actively seeking new investments

ACTUATE CORPORATION

701 Gateway Boulevard
South San Francisco, CA USA 94080
Phone: 650-837-2000
Fax: 650-827-1560
E-mail: Info@actuate.com
Website: www.actuate.com

Type of Firm

Private Equity Firm

Additional Information

Year Founded: 2009
Current Activity Level: Actively seeking new investments

ACUITY CAPITAL LLP (FKA: ELECTRA PARTNERS LLP)

Paternoster House, 1st Floor
65 St Paul's Chruchyard
London, United Kingdom EC4M8AB
Phone: 44-20-7214-4200
Fax: 44-20-7214-4201
E-mail: info@electrapartners.com
Website: www.electrapartners.com

Management and Staff

David Symondson, Managing Partner
Hugh Mumford, Managing Partner
Philip Dyke, Partner
Rhian Davies, Partner
Stephen Ozin, Partner
Tim Syder, Managing Partner

Type of Firm

Private Equity Firm

Association Membership

British Venture Capital Association (BVCA)

Project Preferences

Type of Financing Preferred:

Leveraged Buyout
Expansion
Public Companies
Turnaround
Other
Management Buyouts

Size of Investments Considered:

Min Size of Investment Considered (000s): $18,000
Max Size of Investment Considered (000s): $58,000

Geographical Preferences

International Preferences:

United Kingdom
Europe

Additional Information

Name of Most Recent Fund: Acuity VCT 2 (FKA: Electra Kingsway VCT 2)
Most Recent Fund Was Raised: 12/31/2004
Year Founded: 1975
Capital Under Management: $1,410,200,000
Current Activity Level: Actively seeking new investments

ACUITY VENTURES

1960 The Alameda
Suite 200
San Jose, CA USA 95126-1493
Phone: 408-261-4286
Fax: 408-557-6555
Website: www.acuityventures.com

Other Offices

600 Hansen Way
Suite 200
Palo Alto, CA USA 94304
Phone: 650-843-8766
Fax: 650-843-8768

Type of Firm

Private Equity Firm

Project Preferences

Type of Financing Preferred:

Early Stage

Additional Information

Name of Most Recent Fund: Acuity Ventures III, L.P.
Most Recent Fund Was Raised: 02/09/2006
Year Founded: 1999
Capital Under Management: $11,700,000
Current Activity Level: Actively seeking new investments

ACUMEN CAPITAL FINANCE PARTNERS LTD.

513-Eight Avenue South West
Suite 200
Calgary, Canada T2P1G3
Phone: 403-571-0300
Fax: 403-571-0310
E-mail: info@acumencapital.com
Website: www.acumencapital.com

Management and Staff

Lynn Wittiger, Chief Financial Officer

Type of Firm

Private Equity Firm

Additional Information

Year Founded: 2009
Current Activity Level: Actively seeking new investments

ACUTE

117, quai de Valmy
Paris, France 75010
Phone: 33-155-26-7373
Fax: 33-155-26-7363
E-mail: info@acute.fr
Website: www.acute.fr

Type of Firm

Private Equity Firm

Project Preferences

Type of Financing Preferred:
Early Stage
Seed
Startup

Geographical Preferences

International Preferences:
Europe
France

Industry Preferences

In Business Serv. prefer:
Services

Additional Information

Year Founded: 1999
Current Activity Level: Actively seeking new investments

ADAMASTOR CAPITAL - SGPS, SA

R. Dom Luis I, n 19, 4
Lisbon, Portugal 1200-149
Phone: 351-21-392-1200
Fax: 351-21-392-1299

Type of Firm

Bank Affiliated

Additional Information

Year Founded: 2003
Current Activity Level: Actively seeking new investments

ADAMS AND REESE LLP

450 Laurel Street
Suite 1900
Baton Rouge, LA USA 70801
Phone: 225-336-5200
Website: www.adamsandreese.com

Management and Staff

Joseph Lovett, Managing Director

Type of Firm

Service Provider

Project Preferences

Type of Financing Preferred:
Early Stage
Seed

Geographical Preferences

United States Preferences:
Louisiana

Industry Preferences

In Computer Software prefer:
Software

In Medical/Health prefer:
Medical Products

Additional Information

Name of Most Recent Fund: Louisiana Fund I, L.P.
Most Recent Fund Was Raised: 12/09/2004
Year Founded: 2004
Capital Under Management: $16,900,000
Current Activity Level: Actively seeking new investments

ADAMS CAPITAL MANAGEMENT, INC.

500 Blackburn Avenue
Sewickley, PA USA 15143
Phone: 412-749-9454
Fax: 412-749-9459
E-mail: info@acm.com
Website: www.acm.com

Other Offices

211 Ranch Road 620 South
Suite 140
Austin, TX USA 78734
Phone: 512-697-0900
Fax: 512-697-0888

245 First Street
18th Floor
Cambridge, MA USA 021412
Phone: 617-444-8620

525 University Avenue
Suite 230
Palo Alto, CA USA 94301
Phone: 650-473-0700

Management and Staff

Andrea Stephenson, Partner
Anthony Warren, Venture Partner
Jerry Sullivan, General Partner
Joel Adams, General Partner
Joseph Raffa, Venture Partner
Martin Neath, General Partner
N.George Ugras, General Partner
William Frezza, General Partner

Type of Firm

Private Equity Firm

Association Membership

National Venture Capital Association - USA (NVCA)

Project Preferences

Role in Financing:
Prefer role as deal originator but will also invest in deals created by others

Type of Financing Preferred:
Second Stage Financing
Early Stage
First Stage Financing

Size of Investments Considered:
Min Size of Investment Considered (000s): $5,000
Max Size of Investment Considered (000s): $30,000

Geographical Preferences

United States Preferences:
All U.S.

Industry Focus

(% based on actual investment)

Semiconductors/Other Elect.	31.3%
Internet Specific	30.2%
Computer Software and Services	17.1%
Communications and Media	9.2%
Medical/Health	6.1%
Industrial/Energy	3.6%
Computer Hardware	2.2%
Other Products	0.2%

Additional Information

Name of Most Recent Fund: Adams Capital Management IV, L.P.
Most Recent Fund Was Raised: 03/09/2009
Year Founded: 1994
Capital Under Management: $700,000,000
Current Activity Level: Actively seeking new investments
Method of Compensation: Return on investment is of primary concern, do not charge fees

ADAMS STREET PARTNERS LLC

One North Wacker Drive
Suite 2200
Chicago, IL USA 60606
Phone: 312-553-7890
Fax: 312-553-7891
E-mail: info@adamsstreetpartners.com
Website: www.adamsstreetpartners.com

Other Offices

20 Grosvenor Place
London, United Kingdom SW1X 7HN
Phone: 44-20-7823-0640
Fax: 44-20-7823-0659

2500 Sand Hill Road
Suite 100
Menlo Park, CA USA 94025
Phone: 650-331-4860
Fax: 650-331-4861

250 North Bridge Road
#14-02, Raffles City Tower
Singapore, Singapore 179101
Phone: 65-6303-8730
Fax: 65-6303-8740

Management and Staff

Arnaud de Cremiers, Partner
Craig Waslin, Partner
David Welsh, Partner
David Brett, Partner
David Timson, Partner
Dongbai Wang, Principal
Greg Holden, Partner
Gregory Garrett, Partner
James Korczak, Partner
Jamie Floersch, Principal
Jason Gull, Partner
Jeffery Burgis, Partner
Jeffrey Diehl, Partner
Jeffrey Akers, Partner
Katherine Wanner, Partner
Kelly Meldrum, Partner
Kevin Callahan, Chief Operating Officer
Michael Lynn, Partner
Piau Voon Wang, Partner
Robin Murray, Partner
Sara Cushing, Partner
Sergey Sheshuryak, Partner
Sunil Mishra, Principal
T. Bondurant French, Chief Executive Officer
Thomas Gladden, Partner
Thomas Berman, Partner
Timothy Kelly, Partner
Troy Barnett, Partner
William Hupp, Chief Financial Officer

Type of Firm

Private Equity Advisor or Fund of Funds

Association Membership

British Venture Capital Association (BVCA)
National Venture Capital Association - USA (NVCA)
European Private Equity and Venture Capital Assoc.

Project Preferences

Role in Financing:

Prefer role as deal originator but will also invest in deals created by others

Type of Financing Preferred:

Fund of Funds
Leveraged Buyout
Early Stage
Expansion
Mezzanine
Generalist PE
Balanced
Later Stage
Acquisition
Special Situation
Distressed Debt
Fund of Funds of Second

Size of Investments Considered:

Min Size of Investment Considered (000s): $5,000
Max Size of Investment Considered (000s): $25,000

Geographical Preferences

United States Preferences:

All U.S.

International Preferences:

Italy
India
United Kingdom
Netherlands
China
Hong Kong
Australia
New Zealand
Germany
All International
France

Industry Focus

(% based on actual investment)

Other Products	82.0%
Medical/Health	4.3%
Computer Software and Services	3.5%
Internet Specific	3.3%
Communications and Media	2.1%
Consumer Related	1.8%
Biotechnology	1.3%
Semiconductors/Other Elect.	1.0%
Computer Hardware	0.6%
Industrial/Energy	0.1%

Additional Information

Name of Most Recent Fund: Adams Street Co-Investment Fund, L.P.
Most Recent Fund Was Raised: 02/02/2006
Year Founded: 2001
Capital Under Management: $19,900,000,000
Current Activity Level: Actively seeking new investments
Method of Compensation: Return on investment is of primary concern, do not charge fees

ADARA VENTURE PARTNERS

Calle Jose Abascal 58
Madrid, Spain 28003
Phone: 34-91-451-7070
Fax: 34-91-451-7090
E-mail: info@adaravp.com
Website: www.adaravp.com

Management and Staff

Alberto Gomez, Managing Partner
Nicolas Goulet, Managing Partner
Roberto De Saint-Malo, Managing Partner

Type of Firm

Private Equity Firm

Project Preferences

Type of Financing Preferred:

Startup

Geographical Preferences

International Preferences:

Portugal
Spain

Additional Information

Year Founded: 2002
Capital Under Management: $78,800,000
Current Activity Level: Actively seeking new investments

ADCAPITAL AG (FKA: BERLINER ELEKTRO HOLDING AG)

Gutenbergstrasse 13
Leinfelden-Echterdingen, Germany 70771
Phone: 49-711-389-4000
Fax: 49-711-38940020
E-mail: investment@adcapital.de
Website: www.adcapital.de

Management and Staff

Christoph Schug, Chief Executive Officer

Type of Firm

Private Equity Firm

Association Membership

German Venture Capital Association (BVK)

Project Preferences

Type of Financing Preferred:

Early Stage
Expansion
Balanced
Management Buyouts
Startup
Recapitalizations

Size of Investments Considered:
Min Size of Investment Considered (000s): $433
Max Size of Investment Considered (000s): $119,800

Geographical Preferences

International Preferences:
Europe
Germany

Industry Preferences

In Communications prefer:
Communications and Media

In Internet Specific prefer:
Internet

In Semiconductor/Electr prefer:
Electronics

In Financial Services prefer:
Financial Services

In Business Serv. prefer:
Media

Additional Information
Year Founded: 1979
Capital Under Management: $292,700,000
Current Activity Level: Actively seeking new investments

ADCURAM GROUP AG (FKA: ADCURAM INDUSTRIEKAPITAL AG)
Theatinerstrasse 7
Arco Palais
Munich, Germany 80333
Phone: 49-89-2020-9590
Fax: 49-89-2020-9599
Website: www.adcuram.de

Management and Staff
Florian Meise, Co-Founder

Type of Firm
Private Equity Firm

Project Preferences

Type of Financing Preferred:
Leveraged Buyout

Geographical Preferences

International Preferences:
Europe

Additional Information
Year Founded: 2007
Current Activity Level: Actively seeking new investments

ADD PARTNERS, LTD.
53 Davies Street
Mayfair
London, United Kingdom W1K 5JH
Phone: 44-20-7152-6902
Fax: 44-20-7152-6903
Website: www.addpartners.com

Management and Staff
Jean Appleyard, Chief Financial Officer
Jim Martin, Managing Partner
Maisy Ng, Managing Partner
Martin Mackay, Venture Partner
Sebastien de Lafond, Managing Partner

Type of Firm
Private Equity Firm

Association Membership
European Private Equity and Venture Capital Assoc.

Project Preferences

Role in Financing:
Prefer role as deal originator but will also invest in deals created by others

Type of Financing Preferred:
Early Stage
Expansion
Later Stage
Startup

Size of Investments Considered:
Min Size of Investment Considered (000s): $500
Max Size of Investment Considered (000s): $500,000

Geographical Preferences

International Preferences:
United Kingdom
Europe

Industry Preferences

In Communications prefer:
Communications and Media
Commercial Communications
Telecommunications
Data Communications

Additional Information
Year Founded: 2000
Capital Under Management: $237,000,000
Current Activity Level: Actively seeking new investments

ADDISON CLARK CAPITAL, LLC
2960 Post Road
Suite 200
Southport, CT USA 06890
Phone: 203-254-8700

Type of Firm
Private Equity Firm

Additional Information
Year Founded: 2002
Capital Under Management: $3,200,000
Current Activity Level: Actively seeking new investments

ADELPHIA COMMUNICATIONS
One North Main Street
Coudersport, PA USA 16915
Phone: 303-268-6424
Website: www.adelphia.net

Management and Staff
Ron Cooper, Chief Operating Officer
William Schleyer, Chief Executive Officer

Type of Firm
Private Equity Firm

Additional Information
Year Founded: 2004
Current Activity Level: Actively seeking new investments

ADENA VENTURES
20 East Circle Drive
Athens, OH USA 45701
Phone: 740-597-1470
Fax: 740-597-1399
E-mail: info@adenaventures.com
Website: www.adenaventures.com

Other Offices
2300 MaeCorkle Avenue SE
Charleston, WV USA 25302
Phone: 304-340-3736

70 East Lake Street
Suite 1700
Chicago, IL USA 60601
Phone: 312-855-8500
Fax: 312-855-0488

Management and Staff
David Wilhelm, General Partner
Jakki Haussler, General Partner
Jeff Doose, General Partner
Lynn Gellermann, President
Thomas Parkinson, General Partner

Type of Firm
Private Equity Firm

Association Membership
Community Development Venture Capital Alliance
National Venture Capital Association - USA (NVCA)

Project Preferences

Role in Financing:
Will function either as deal originator or investor in deals created by others

Type of Financing Preferred:
Balanced

Size of Investments Considered:
Min Size of Investment Considered (000s): $200
Max Size of Investment Considered (000s): $2,000

Geographical Preferences

United States Preferences:
Mid Atlantic
Midwest
Maryland
Ohio
Kentucky
West Virginia

Industry Preferences

In Computer Software prefer:
Software

In Biotechnology prefer:
Human Biotechnology
Agricultural/Animal Bio.

In Medical/Health prefer:
Health Services

In Consumer Related prefer:
Sports
Food/Beverage

In Industrial/Energy prefer:
Energy

In Business Serv. prefer:
Media

In Manufact. prefer:
Manufacturing

Additional Information
Name of Most Recent Fund: Adena Ventures, L.P.
Most Recent Fund Was Raised: 04/24/2002
Year Founded: 2002
Capital Under Management: $34,000,000
Current Activity Level: Actively seeking new investments
Method of Compensation: Return on investment is of primary concern, do not charge fees

---

ADINVEST AG

Rigistrasse 25
Zumikon, Switzerland 8126
Phone: 41-1-202-2155
Fax: 41-1-202-1942

Other Offices
Lavaterstrasse 45
Zurich, Switzerland CH-8027
Phone: 41-1-202-2155
Fax: 41-1-202-1942

Type of Firm
Private Equity Firm

Association Membership
Swiss Venture Capital Association (SECA)

Project Preferences

Type of Financing Preferred:
Leveraged Buyout
Early Stage
Expansion
Turnaround
Balanced
Later Stage
Management Buyouts
Recapitalizations

Geographical Preferences

International Preferences:
Switzerland
Europe
Australia
Asia
All International

Additional Information
Year Founded: 1987
Current Activity Level: Actively seeking new investments

ADIRONDACK VENTURE FUND, THE

2038 Saranac Avenue
P.O. Box 1071
Lake Placid, NY USA 12946
Phone: 518-523-0043
E-mail: invest@adirondackventurefund.com
Website: www.adirondackventurefund.com

Management and Staff
Edward Roetman, Partner
John Hopkinson, Partner
Patrick Wheeler, Partner
Paul Evans, Partner

Type of Firm
Private Equity Firm

Project Preferences

Type of Financing Preferred:
Early Stage
Expansion
Startup

Geographical Preferences

United States Preferences:
Northeast
New York

Canadian Preferences:
Quebec

Industry Preferences

In Communications prefer:
Telecommunications

In Biotechnology prefer:
Biotechnology

In Industrial/Energy prefer:
Alternative Energy
Advanced Materials

In Manufact. prefer:
Manufacturing

In Other prefer:
Socially Responsible
Environment Responsible

Additional Information
Year Founded: 2002
Capital Under Management: $500,000
Current Activity Level: Actively seeking new investments

ADITYA BIRLA CAPITAL ADVISORS PVT., LTD.

18th Flr., 1 India BullsCentre
841, Senapati Bapat Marg
Mumbai, India 400 013
Phone: 91-22-4356-7400
Fax: 91-22-4356-7444
E-mail: abg.pe@adityabirla.com
Website: www.adityabirla-pe.com

Management and Staff
Bharat Banka, CEO & Managing Director
Mehul Maroo, Principal
Sandeep Bhat, Chief Financial Officer
Shamik Moitra, Principal

Type of Firm
Investment Management Firm

Project Preferences

Type of Financing Preferred:
Leveraged Buyout
Early Stage
Acquisition

Geographical Preferences

International Preferences:
India

Industry Preferences

In Communications prefer:
Media and Entertainment

In Medical/Health prefer:
Medical/Health

In Consumer Related prefer:
Consumer
Retail

In Financial Services prefer:
Financial Services

In Business Serv. prefer:
Services

In Manufact. prefer:
Manufacturing

Additional Information

Year Founded: 2008
Capital Under Management: $250,000,000
Current Activity Level: Actively seeking new investments

ADLER & CO.

342 Madison Avenue
Suite 807
New York, NY USA 10173
Phone: 212-599-2535
Fax: 212-599-2526

Other Offices

100 First Stamford Place
Third Floor
Stamford, CT USA 06902
Phone: 203-359-9595
Fax: 203-359-0880

222 Lakeview Avenue
Suite 160-286
West Palm Beach, FL USA 33401
Phone: 407-837-2220
Fax: 407-837-1010

690 Market Street
Suite 702
San Francisco, CA USA 94104
Phone: 415-398-6352
Fax: 415-398-6355

1122 Kenilworth Drive
Suite 301
Baltimore, MD USA 21204
Phone: 410-828-6497

Management and Staff

Frederick Adler, General Partner
Jay Nickse, Chief Financial Officer
Mark Beaudoin, General Partner

Type of Firm

Private Equity Firm

Project Preferences

Role in Financing:
Prefer role as deal originator but will also invest in deals created by others

Type of Financing Preferred:
Second Stage Financing
Leveraged Buyout
Control-block Purchases
Start-up Financing
First Stage Financing

Size of Investments Considered:
Min Size of Investment Considered (000s): $1,000
Max Size of Investment Considered: No Limit

Geographical Preferences

United States Preferences:
All U.S.

Industry Focus

(% based on actual investment)	
Computer Software and Services	21.9%
Semiconductors/Other Elect.	19.4%
Computer Hardware	17.5%
Communications and Media	9.7%
Medical/Health	9.1%
Biotechnology	5.9%
Other Products	5.5%
Industrial/Energy	4.5%
Consumer Related	4.3%
Internet Specific	2.4%

Additional Information

Name of Most Recent Fund: Venad IV
Most Recent Fund Was Raised: 04/01/1984
Year Founded: 1965
Capital Under Management: $200,000,000
Current Activity Level: Reducing investment activity
Method of Compensation: Return on invest. most important, but chg. closing fees, service fees, etc.

ADLEVO CAPITAL MANAGERS LLC

84 Ozumba Mbadiwe Street
Victoria Island
Lagos, Nigeria
Phone: 234-1-462-7600
Fax: 234-1-462-7601
E-mail: info@adlevocapital.com
Website: www.adlevocapital.com

Other Offices

Innovation Centre, Office M39
Mark Shuttleworth Street, Persequor
Pretoria, South Africa
Phone: 27-11-844-0031
Fax: 27-11-844-0034

Management and Staff

Folabi Esan, Partner
Greg Voigt, Partner
Yemi Lalude, Managing Partner

Type of Firm

Private Equity Firm

Project Preferences

Type of Financing Preferred:
Leveraged Buyout
Expansion
Acquisition

Additional Information

Year Founded: 2008
Capital Under Management: $20,000,000
Current Activity Level: Actively seeking new investments

ADMIRAL CAPITAL GROUP

240 Central Park South
Suite 41
New York, NY USA 10019
Phone: 646-405-4808
E-mail: info@admiralcapitalgroup.com
Website: www.admiralcapitalgroup.com

Other Offices

24165 IH-10 West
Suite 217-628
San Antonio, TX USA 78257
Phone: 646-405-4808

Management and Staff

Daniel Bassichis, Founder
David Robinson, Founder

Type of Firm

Private Equity Firm

Project Preferences

Type of Financing Preferred:
Leveraged Buyout
Acquisition

Industry Preferences

In Financial Services prefer:
Real Estate

Additional Information

Year Founded: 2008
Current Activity Level: Actively seeking new investments

ADVANCE ASSET MANAGEMENT, LTD.

Level 5
182 George Street
Sydney, Australia 2000
Phone: 618-9415-5655
Fax: 618-9481-4318
E-mail: investorservices@advance.com.au
Website: www.advance.com.au

Management and Staff

Kate Mulligan, Managing Director

Type of Firm

Bank Affiliated

Project Preferences

Type of Financing Preferred:
Second Stage Financing
First Stage Financing
Startup

Size of Investments Considered:
Min Size of Investment Considered (000s): $37,000
Max Size of Investment Considered (000s): $154,000

Geographical Preferences

International Preferences:
Australia

Additional Information
Year Founded: 1983
Capital Under Management: $537,000,000
Current Activity Level: Actively seeking new investments

ADVANCED CAPITAL
Via Brera 5
Milano, Italy 20121
Phone: 39-02-799-555
E-mail: segretaria@advancedcapital.com
Website: www.advancedcapital.com

Other Offices
14 Dover Street - 2nd piano
London, United Kingdom W1S 4LW
Phone: 44-207-499-4342

Via Magatti 3
Lugano, Switzerland 6900
Phone: 41-91-924-9240

6, Rue Guillaume Schneider
Luxembourg, Luxembourg L-2522
Phone: 352-26948-601
Fax: 352-26948-620

Management and Staff
Fabio Brambilla, General Partner

Type of Firm
Private Equity Firm

Project Preferences

Type of Financing Preferred:
Fund of Funds
Balanced

Geographical Preferences

International Preferences:
Italy
All International

Additional Information
Year Founded: 2000
Current Activity Level: Actively seeking new investments

ADVANCED EQUITIES CAPITAL PARTNERS LLC
311 South Wacker Drive
Suite 1650
Chicago, IL USA 60606
Phone: 312-377-5300
Fax: 312-377-5314
Website: www.advancedequities.com

Management and Staff
Adam Antoniades, President
Gregg Glaser, Chief Financial Officer
Joel Marks, Chief Operating Officer

Type of Firm
Private Equity Firm

Project Preferences

Type of Financing Preferred:
Early Stage
Expansion
Later Stage

Geographical Preferences

United States Preferences:
All U.S.

Industry Preferences

In Communications prefer:
Telecommunications

In Biotechnology prefer:
Biotechnology

In Medical/Health prefer:
Medical/Health

In Consumer Related prefer:
Education Related

Additional Information
Name of Most Recent Fund: AEI 2008 Venture Investments I, LLC
Most Recent Fund Was Raised: 06/02/2008
Year Founded: 1999
Capital Under Management: $2,000,000
Current Activity Level: Actively seeking new investments

ADVANCED FINANCE & INVESTMENT GROUP LLC (AKA: AFIG)
c/o Multiconsult, Ltd.
Rogers House 5
Port-Louis, Mauritius
Phone: 230-405-2000
Fax: 230-212-5265
E-mail: info@afigfunds.com
Website: www.afigfunds.com

Other Offices
2nd Floor-West Tower
Nelson Mandela Square
Sandton, South Africa 2196
Phone: 27-11-881-5685
Fax: 27-11-881-5611

83, Boulevard de la Republique
Immeuble Horizons
Dakar, Senegal
Phone: 221-33-869-8082
Fax: 221-33-864-6555

1776 I Street North West
Ninth Floor
Washington, DC USA 20006
Phone: 202-756-4782
Fax: 202-318-2276

Management and Staff
Papa Madiaw Ndiaye, Chief Executive Officer
Patrice Backer, Chief Operating Officer

Type of Firm
Private Equity Firm

Project Preferences

Type of Financing Preferred:
Expansion
Balanced

Geographical Preferences

International Preferences:
Angola
Nigeria
Senegal
Gabon
Ghana
Cameroon
Morocco
Congo, Dem Rep
Africa

Industry Preferences

In Communications prefer:
Telecommunications

In Industrial/Energy prefer:
Industrial Products

In Transportation prefer:
Transportation

In Financial Services prefer:
Financial Services

In Agr/Forestr/Fish prefer:
Mining and Minerals

Additional Information
Year Founded: 2005
Capital Under Management: $90,000,000
Current Activity Level: Actively seeking new investments

ADVANCED SCIENCE AND TECHNOLOGY ENTERPRISE CORPORATION
Suite 242 Shin-Otemachi Bldg.
2-2-1 Otemachi, Chiyoda-ku
Tokyo, Japan 100-0004

Phone: 81-3-3243-0870
Fax: 81-3-3243-0875
Website: www.ut-astec.com

Management and Staff

Hiroaki Nakai, General Partner
Hiroyuki Hashimoto, General Partner
Takuro Wakabayashi, General Partner

Type of Firm

Private Equity Firm

Project Preferences

Type of Financing Preferred:

Seed
Startup

Geographical Preferences

International Preferences:

Japan

Industry Preferences

In Communications prefer:

Telecommunications

In Computer Software prefer:

Software

In Semiconductor/Electr prefer:

Electronics

Additional Information

Year Founded: 2001
Capital Under Management: $100,000
Current Activity Level: Actively seeking new investments

ADVANCED TECHNOLOGY DEVELOPMENT CENTER

75 Fifth Street Northwest
Suite 202
Atlanta, GA USA 30308
Phone: 404-894-3575
Fax: 404-894-4545
Website: www.atdc.org

Other Offices

311 Ferst Street
Atlanta, GA USA 30308
Phone: 404-894-3575
Fax: 404-894-4545
3100 Gentian Boulevard
Suite 114
Columbus, GA USA 31907
Phone: 706-562-8339

151 Osigian Boulevard
Warner Robins, GA USA 31088
Phone: 478-953-3155
Fax: 478-953-3169

Jimmy Deloach Parkway
Savannah, GA USA 31322
Phone: 912-963-2525

Type of Firm

Government Affiliated Program

Project Preferences

Type of Financing Preferred:

Early Stage
Seed

Size of Investments Considered:

Min Size of Investment Considered (000s): $50
Max Size of Investment Considered (000s): $1,000

Geographical Preferences

United States Preferences:

Southeast
Georgia
All U.S.

Industry Preferences

In Communications prefer:

Communications and Media

In Computer Hardware prefer:

Computers

In Semiconductor/Electr prefer:

Electronics

In Biotechnology prefer:

Biotechnology

In Medical/Health prefer:

Medical/Health

Additional Information

Year Founded: 1987
Capital Under Management: $13,000,000
Current Activity Level: Actively seeking new investments
Method of Compensation: Return on investment is of primary concern, do not charge fees

---

ADVANCED TECHNOLOGY VENTURES

Bay Colony Corporate Center
1000 Winter Street, Suite 3700
Waltham, MA USA 02451
Phone: 781-290-0707
Fax: 781-684-0045
E-mail: info@atvcapital.com
Website: www.atvcapital.com

Other Offices

485 Ramona Street
Palo Alto, CA USA 94301
Phone: 650-321-8601
Fax: 650-321-0934

Management and Staff

Adam Berger, Chief Financial Officer
Andrew Friendly, Principal
Christian Cortis, Principal
Edward Frank, Partner
Edward Birss, Venture Partner
Jean George, General Partner
Michael Carusi, General Partner
Robert Finocchio, Venture Partner
Robert Hower, General Partner
Steve Baloff, General Partner
Todd Kimmel, Principal
Tom Rodgers, Partner
Wes Raffel, General Partner
William Wiberg, General Partner

Type of Firm

Private Equity Firm

Association Membership

Western Association of Venture Capitalists (WAVC)
National Venture Capital Association - USA (NVCA)

Project Preferences

Role in Financing:

Prefer role as deal originator but will also invest in deals created by others

Type of Financing Preferred:

Second Stage Financing
Early Stage
Balanced
Later Stage
Seed
First Stage Financing

Size of Investments Considered:

Min Size of Investment Considered (000s): $5,000
Max Size of Investment Considered (000s): $50,000

Geographical Preferences

United States Preferences:

All U.S.

Industry Focus

(% based on actual investment)

Computer Software and Services	19.6%
Internet Specific	16.6%
Communications and Media	16.4%
Medical/Health	16.4%
Semiconductors/Other Elect.	9.7%
Biotechnology	8.7%
Industrial/Energy	6.7%
Computer Hardware	4.8%
Other Products	0.9%

Additional Information

Name of Most Recent Fund: Advanced Technology Ventures VIII, L.P.
Most Recent Fund Was Raised: 07/09/2007
Year Founded: 1979
Capital Under Management: $1,400,000,000
Current Activity Level: Actively seeking new investments
Method of Compensation: Return on investment is of primary concern, do not charge fees

ADVANS S.A., SICAR (FKA: LA FAYETTE INVESTISSEMENT)

69, route d'Esch
Luxembourg, Luxembourg L-2953
Phone: 33-1-5332-7575
Fax: 33-1-5332-7576
E-mail: contact@advansgroup.com
Website: www.advansgroup.com

Type of Firm

Bank Affiliated

Project Preferences

Type of Financing Preferred:
Early Stage
Startup

Geographical Preferences

International Preferences:
Asia
Africa

Industry Preferences

In Financial Services prefer:
Financial Services

Additional Information

Year Founded: 2005
Capital Under Management: $25,500,000
Current Activity Level: Actively seeking new investments

ADVANTAGE CAPITAL LIMITED

37 Harley Street
London, United Kingdom W1G 8QG
Phone: 44-20-7436-6022
Fax: 44-20-7636-7890
E-mail: firstname@advantagecapital.co.uk
Website: www.advantagecapital.co.uk

Management and Staff

Martin Bodenham, Co-Founder
Trevor Jones, Co-Founder

Type of Firm

Private Equity Firm

Association Membership

British Venture Capital Association (BVCA)

Project Preferences

Role in Financing:
Prefer role as deal originator

Type of Financing Preferred:
Leveraged Buyout
Management Buyouts

Geographical Preferences

International Preferences:
United Kingdom
Europe

Industry Preferences

In Financial Services prefer:
Financial Services

Additional Information

Year Founded: 2000
Current Activity Level: Actively seeking new investments
Method of Compensation: Return on invest. most important, but chg. closing fees, service fees, etc.

ADVANTAGE CAPITAL PARTNERS

909 Poydras Street
Suite 2230
New Orleans, LA USA 70112
Phone: 504-522-4850
Fax: 504-522-4950
E-mail: information@advantagecap.com
Website: www.advantagecap.com

Other Offices

16750 Gulf Boulevard
Suite 416
Saint Petersburg, FL USA 33708
Phone: 727-319-6649
Fax: 727-319-6649

7733 Forsyth Boulevard
Suite 1850
St. Louis, MO USA 63105
Phone: 314-725-0800
Fax: 314-725-4265

1911 Elmore Avenue
Downers Grove, IL USA 60515
Phone: 630-241-1848
Fax: 630-241-1836

Five Warren Street
Suite 204
Glens Falls, NY USA 12801
Phone: 518-743-0060
Fax: 518-743-1787

3128 M Street Northwest
Suite 310
Washington, DC USA 20007
Phone: 202-337-0034
Fax: 202-337-0036
c/o Venture Investors
505 South Rosa Road., Suite 100
Madison, WI USA 53719
Phone: 608-441-2700
Fax: 608-441-2700

c/o Wolf Ventures
1600 Stout Street, Suite 1500
Denver, CO USA 80202
Phone: 303-321-4800
Fax: 303-321-4848

Building One, 6300 Bridgepoint
Suite 220
Austin, TX USA 78730
Phone: 512-380-1168
Fax: 512-241-1186

c/o Southeastern Technology Fund
207 East Side Square
Huntsville, AL USA 35801
Phone: 256-883-8711
Fax: 256-883-8558

Management and Staff

Crichton Brown, Managing Director
Damon Rawie, Managing Director
Deborah Dubin, Vice President
Doug Beekman, Principal
Jeffrey Craver, Vice President
Louis Dubuque, Managing Director
Mark Lewis, Principal
Maurice Doyle, Managing Director
Michael Johnson, Managing Director
Ryan Brennan, Principal
Scott Zajac, Senior Managing Director
Scott Murphy, Managing Director
Steven Stull, President
Thomas Lavin, Managing Director
Timothy Cockshutt, Managing Director
W. Anthony Toups, Vice President

Type of Firm

Private Equity Firm

Association Membership

Natl Assoc of Investment Cos. (NAIC)
Natl Assoc of Small Bus. Inv. Co (NASBIC)
National Venture Capital Association - USA (NVCA)

Project Preferences

Role in Financing:
Will function either as deal originator or investor in deals created by others

Type of Financing Preferred:
Mezzanine
Balanced
Later Stage
Other

Size of Investments Considered:
Min Size of Investment Considered (000s): $500
Max Size of Investment Considered (000s): $10,000

Geographical Preferences

United States Preferences:
Illinois
Midwest
Southeast
Hawaii
Northeast

Rocky Mountain
D. of Columbia
Texas

Industry Focus

(% based on actual investment)

Other Products	24.3%
Industrial/Energy	13.3%
Communications and Media	12.0%
Medical/Health	11.2%
Internet Specific	10.0%
Computer Software and Services	6.9%
Consumer Related	6.1%
Computer Hardware	6.1%
Semiconductors/Other Elect.	5.6%
Biotechnology	4.5%

Additional Information

Name of Most Recent Fund: Advantage Capital Alabama Partners I, L.P.
Most Recent Fund Was Raised: 01/10/2004
Year Founded: 1992
Capital Under Management: $650,000,000
Current Activity Level: Actively seeking new investments
Method of Compensation: Return on invest. most important, but chg. closing fees, service fees, etc.

ADVANTAGE PARTNERS LLP

17/F Toranomon Towers
4-1-28 Toranomon, Minato-ku
Tokyo, Japan 105-0001
Phone: 81-3-5425-8202
Fax: 81-3-5425-8205
E-mail: master@advantagegroup.co.jp
Website: www.advantagegroup.co.jp

Management and Staff

Akira Iwamoto, Principal
Emmett Thomas, Partner
Hideo Nagatsuyu, Partner
Hironobu Nakano, Partner
Katsuya Baba, Principal
Koichi Ashida, Principal
Richard Folsom, Founding Partner
Taisuke Sasanuma, Founding Partner
Yuji Takei, Principal

Type of Firm

Private Equity Firm

Project Preferences

Type of Financing Preferred:
Leveraged Buyout
Expansion
Research and Development
Turnaround
Later Stage
Management Buyouts
Acquisition

Geographical Preferences

International Preferences:
Japan

Industry Focus

(% based on actual investment)

Consumer Related	55.6%
Other Products	31.8%
Computer Software and Services	11.8%
Internet Specific	0.9%

Additional Information

Year Founded: 1992
Capital Under Management: $2,014,300,000
Current Activity Level: Actively seeking new investments

ADVANTUS CAPITAL MANAGEMENT, INC.

400 Robert Street North
Saint Paul, MN USA 55101
Website: www.advantuscapital.com

Management and Staff

Robert Senkler, President

Type of Firm

Insurance Firm Affiliate

Project Preferences

Type of Financing Preferred:
Fund of Funds

Additional Information

Current Activity Level: Actively seeking new investments

ADVENT CAPITAL AND FINANCE CORPORATION

6/F SSHG Law Center
105 Paseo de Roxas
Makati City, Philippines 1200
Phone: 632-813-01-88
Fax: 632-817-1728
Website: www.allasiacapital.com.ph

Type of Firm

Private Equity Firm

Project Preferences

Type of Financing Preferred:
Balanced

Geographical Preferences

International Preferences:
Philippines

Additional Information

Year Founded: 2000
Current Activity Level: Actively seeking new investments

ADVENT INTERNATIONAL

75 State Street
29th Floor
Boston, MA USA 02109
Phone: 617-951-9400
Fax: 617-951-0566
E-mail: info@adventinternational.com
Website: www.adventinternational.com

Other Offices

22 Shovkovychna Street
Kiev, Ukraine 01024
Phone: 38-044-501-0189

Av. Del Libertador 498 Floor 13 N
Buenos Aires, Argentina C1001ABR
Phone: 54-11-5077-8900
Fax: 54-11-5077-8910

Atrium, 4th Floor
Strawinskylaan 3145
Amsterdam, Netherlands 1077 ZX
Phone: 31-20-301-2530
Fax: 31-20-301-2539

Edificio Omega
Campos Eliseos 345-7 piso
Col Polanco, Mexico 11560
Phone: 52-55-5281-0303
Fax: 52-55-5281-0999

Velazquez, 140 - 2 Izda
Madrid, Spain 28006
Phone: 34-91-745-4860
Fax: 34-91-745-4861

Warsaw Financial Center
ul. Emilii Plater 53
Warsaw, Poland 00-113
Phone: 48-22-627-5141
Fax: 48-22-627-5140

Na Porici 3a
Prague, Czech Republic 110 00
Phone: 420-234-749-750
Fax: 420-234-749-759

Av. Brig. Faria Lima 3311
Sao Paulo, Brazil 04538-132
Phone: 55-11-3014-6800
Fax: 55-11-3014-6820

7 Maresal Pilsudski Street
Sector 1
Bucharest, Romania
Phone: 40-21-211-1602

9-7-1, Akasaka, Minato-ku
Midtown Tower 23 Floor
Tokyo, Japan 107-6223

Phone: 81-3-6406-4800
Fax: 81-3-6406-4848

8-10 rue Lamennais
Paris, France 75008
Phone: 33-1-5537-2900
Fax: 33-1-5537-2929

Westhafenplatz 1
Frankfurt am Main, Germany 60327
Phone: 49-69-955-2700
Fax: 49-69-9552-7020

111 Buckingham Palace Road
London, United Kingdom SW1W 0SR
Phone: 44-20-7333-0800
Fax: 44-20-7333-0801

Via Marina, 6
Milan, Italy 20121
Phone: 39-2-771-2981
Fax: 39-2-7712-9888

Management and Staff

Alfredo Alfaro, Managing Partner
Avnish Mehra, Principal
Beverly Berman, Partner
Bruce Barclay, Managing Director
Chris Egan, Principal
Chris Mruck, Managing Partner
Christopher Pike, Managing Director
David McKenna, Managing Partner
David Mussafer, Managing Partner
Derrick Lee, Managing Director
Diego Serebrisky, Managing Director
Emma Popa-Radu, Managing Director
Eric Adjoubel, Managing Director
Ernest Bachrach, Chief Executive Officer
Filippo De Vecchi, Managing Director
Francesco De Giglio, Managing Director
Fred Wakeman, Managing Partner
Frederico Brito e Abreu, Principal
Gabriel Gomez, Principal
Guillaume Darbon, Managing Director
Hiroshi Matsumoto, Managing Director
Holger Schnoes, Managing Partner
Humphrey Battcock, Managing Partner
Istvan Szoke, Managing Director
James Brocklebank, Managing Director
Janet Hennessy, Managing Director & CFO
Jeff Case, Principal
Jenny Ming, Venture Partner
Joanna James, Managing Partner
John Maldonado, Principal
John Singer, Managing Partner
Juan Torres, Managing Director
Juan Diaz-Laviada, Managing Director
Juan Pablo Zucchini, Managing Director
Khai Tan, Chief Executive Officer
Luis Solorzano, Principal
Luiz Antonio Alves, Managing Partner
Mohammed Anjarwala, Principal
Monika Morali-Efinowicz, Managing Director
Nicolas Sujoy, Principal
Pascal Stefani, Managing Director
Patrice Etlin, Managing Partner
Peter Rutland, Principal
Ranjen Sen, Managing Director
Robert Taylor, Managing Partner
Ronald Sheldon, Managing Director
Ronald Ayles, Managing Director
Rory Pope, Managing Director
Santiago Castillo, Principal
Stephen Hoffmeister, Managing Director
Steven Tadler, Managing Partner
Steven Collins, Managing Director
Timothy Franks, Managing Director
Tom Lauer, Chief Operating Officer
Will Schmidt, Managing Partner
Wilson Rosa, Principal
Wilson Louren da Rosa, Principal

Type of Firm

Private Equity Firm

Association Membership

Brazilian Venture Capital Association (ABCR)
British Venture Capital Association (BVCA)
Hong Kong Venture Capital Association (HKVCA)
French Venture Capital Association (AFIC)
Hungarian Venture Capital Association (HVCA)
Western Association of Venture Capitalists (WAVC)
Polish Venture Capital Association (PSIC/PPEA)
European Private Equity and Venture Capital Assoc.

Project Preferences

Role in Financing:

Prefer role as deal originator but will also invest in deals created by others

Type of Financing Preferred:

Leveraged Buyout
Control-block Purchases
Expansion
Generalist PE
Public Companies
Later Stage
Industry Rollups
Special Situation
Recapitalizations

Size of Investments Considered:

Min Size of Investment Considered (000s): $20,000
Max Size of Investment Considered (000s): $60,000

Geographical Preferences

United States Preferences:

All U.S.

Canadian Preferences:

All Canada

International Preferences:

Latin America
Central Europe
Europe
Argentina
Mexico
Brazil
Eastern Europe
Asia
Japan
All International

Industry Focus

(% based on actual investment)

Other Products	33.3%
Consumer Related	23.7%
Medical/Health	8.3%
Communications and Media	7.9%
Computer Software and Services	7.5%
Industrial/Energy	6.4%
Internet Specific	5.5%
Biotechnology	2.8%
Semiconductors/Other Elect.	2.6%
Computer Hardware	2.0%

Additional Information

Name of Most Recent Fund: Advent International GPE VI, L.P.
Most Recent Fund Was Raised: 03/12/2008
Year Founded: 1984
Capital Under Management: $10,000,000,000
Current Activity Level: Actively seeking new investments
Method of Compensation: Return on investment is of primary concern, do not charge fees

---

ADVENT PRIVATE CAPITAL

Level 17, HWT Tower
40 City Road
Southbank, Australia 3006
Phone: 613-9690-9566
Fax: 613-9690-9466
E-mail: enquiry@adventgroup.com.au
Website: www.adventprivatecapital.com.au

Management and Staff

Brian Ball, Managing Director
Rupert Harrington, Managing Director

Type of Firm

Bank Affiliated

Association Membership

Australian Venture Capital Association (AVCAL)

Project Preferences

Role in Financing:

Prefer role as deal originator but will also invest in deals created by others

Type of Financing Preferred:

Leveraged Buyout
Expansion
Generalist PE
Mezzanine
Turnaround
Later Stage
Management Buyouts

Size of Investments Considered:

Min Size of Investment Considered (000s): $4,029
Max Size of Investment Considered (000s): $48,348

Geographical Preferences

International Preferences:

New Zealand
Australia

Industry Preferences

In Communications prefer:
Communications and Media
Wireless Communications
Media and Entertainment

In Internet Specific prefer:
Internet

In Semiconductor/Electr prefer:
Sensors

In Medical/Health prefer:
Medical/Health
Health Services

In Consumer Related prefer:
Entertainment and Leisure
Retail
Hotels and Resorts

In Transportation prefer:
Transportation

In Business Serv. prefer:
Services

In Manufact. prefer:
Manufacturing

Additional Information

Name of Most Recent Fund: Advent V Trust A&B
Most Recent Fund Was Raised: 09/21/2006
Year Founded: 1984
Capital Under Management: $388,100,000
Current Activity Level: Actively seeking new investments
Method of Compensation: Return on investment is of primary concern, do not charge fees

---

ADVENT VENTURE PARTNERS LLP

25 Buckingham Gate
London, United Kingdom SW1E 6LD
Phone: 44-20-7932-2100
Fax: 44-20-7828-1474
E-mail: info@adventventures.com
Website: www.adventventures.com

Management and Staff

David Cheesman, General Partner
Donald Drakeman, Venture Partner
Frederic Court, Partner
Jerry Benjamin, General Partner
Martin McNair, General Partner
Mike Chalfen, General Partner
Neil Pearce, General Partner
Nick Teasdale, General Partner
Patrick Lee, General Partner
Peter Baines, General Partner
Raj Parekh, General Partner
Rudi Pauwels, Venture Partner
Shahzad Malik, General Partner

Type of Firm

Private Equity Firm

Association Membership

British Venture Capital Association (BVCA)
European Private Equity and Venture Capital Assoc.

Project Preferences

Role in Financing:
Prefer role as deal originator but will also invest in deals created by others

Type of Financing Preferred:
Early Stage
Expansion
Balanced
Later Stage
Management Buyouts
Startup

Size of Investments Considered:
Min Size of Investment Considered (000s): $2,046
Max Size of Investment Considered (000s): $16,370

Geographical Preferences

International Preferences:
United Kingdom
Europe
Western Europe

Industry Focus

(% based on actual investment)	
Medical/Health	27.2%
Biotechnology	22.7%
Computer Software and Services	16.1%
Internet Specific	10.1%
Communications and Media	9.0%
Semiconductors/Other Elect.	7.0%
Computer Hardware	2.6%
Other Products	2.3%
Industrial/Energy	1.8%
Consumer Related	1.2%

Additional Information

Name of Most Recent Fund: Advent Private Equity Fund IV (APEF IV)
Most Recent Fund Was Raised: 12/16/2004
Year Founded: 1981
Capital Under Management: $940,600,000
Current Activity Level: Actively seeking new investments

ADVENT-MORRO EQUITY PARTNERS

Banco Popular Building
206 Tetuan Street Suite 903
Viejo San Juan, PR USA 00902
Phone: 787-725-5285
Fax: 787-721-1735
Website: www.adventmorro.com

Management and Staff

Cyril Meduna, President

Type of Firm

Private Equity Advisor or Fund of Funds

Project Preferences

Role in Financing:
Will function either as deal originator or investor in deals created by others

Type of Financing Preferred:
Second Stage Financing
Leveraged Buyout
Early Stage
Expansion
Generalist PE
Turnaround
Later Stage
Management Buyouts
First Stage Financing
Acquisition
Recapitalizations

Size of Investments Considered:
Min Size of Investment Considered (000s): $500
Max Size of Investment Considered (000s): $3,000

Geographical Preferences

International Preferences:
Puerto Rico

Industry Preferences

In Communications prefer:
Commercial Communications
Telecommunications
Wireless Communications
Data Communications

In Computer Hardware prefer:
Integrated Turnkey System

In Computer Software prefer:
Computer Services
Systems Software
Applications Software

In Internet Specific prefer:
E-Commerce Technology
Internet
Web Aggregration/Portals

In Medical/Health prefer:
Health Services

In Consumer Related prefer:
Consumer
Retail
Food/Beverage
Hotels and Resorts
Education Related

In Financial Services prefer:
Financial Services

In Business Serv. prefer:
Distribution

In Manufact. prefer:
Manufacturing

Additional Information

Name of Most Recent Fund: Guayacon Private Equity Fund L.P. II-A
Most Recent Fund Was Raised: 05/02/2007
Year Founded: 1989

Capital Under Management: $52,000,000
Current Activity Level: Actively seeking new investments
Method of Compensation: Return on invest. most important, but chg. closing fees, service fees, etc.

ADVENTURE FUNDS LLC

P.O. Box 820114
Portland, OR USA 97282
Phone: 503-546-5589
E-mail: inquiries@adventurefunds.com
Website: www.adventurefunds.com

Management and Staff

Tal Johnson, Managing Partner

Type of Firm

Private Equity Firm

Project Preferences

Type of Financing Preferred:
Expansion
Management Buyouts
Recapitalizations

Geographical Preferences

United States Preferences:
Oregon
West Coast

Industry Preferences

In Consumer Related prefer:
Retail
Food/Beverage
Education Related

In Business Serv. prefer:
Distribution

In Manufact. prefer:
Manufacturing

Additional Information

Year Founded: 2007
Capital Under Management: $15,000,000
Current Activity Level: Actively seeking new investments

ADVEQ MANAGEMENT AG (FKA: ADVISERS ON PRIVATE EQUITY AG)

Affolternstrasse 56
Zurich, Switzerland 8050
Phone: 41-43-288-3200
Fax: 41-43-288-3210
E-mail: info@adveq.com
Website: www.adveq.com

Other Offices

12th Floor, Beijing Excel Centre
6 Wudinghou Street, Xicheng District
Beijing, China 100032
Phone: 86-10-8800-3758
Fax: 86-10-880037583868

100 Park Avenue
Suite 2800
New York, NY USA 10017
Phone: 212-488-5330
Fax: 212-297-1743

An der Welle 4
Frankfurt am Main, Germany D-60322
Phone: 49-69-7593-8586
Fax: 49-69-7593-8319

Management and Staff

Alison Wheeler Kennedy, Vice President
Amand Sunderji, Vice President
Andre Jaeggi, Managing Director
Berry Polmann, Vice President
Bruno Raschle, Managing Director
Lee Gardella, Managing Director
Markus Emberger, Vice President
Nils Rode, Managing Director
Peter Laib, Managing Director
Philippe Bucher, Managing Director
Rainer Ender, Managing Director
Steven Yang, Vice President

Type of Firm

Private Equity Advisor or Fund of Funds

Association Membership

European Private Equity and Venture Capital Assoc.

Project Preferences

Type of Financing Preferred:
Fund of Funds

Geographical Preferences

United States Preferences:
All U.S.

International Preferences:
Europe
Asia

Additional Information

Year Founded: 1997
Capital Under Management: $4,000,000,000
Current Activity Level: Actively seeking new investments

AEA INVESTORS LLC

55 East 52nd Street
New York, NY USA 10055
Phone: 212-644-5900
Fax: 212-888-1459
E-mail: info@aeainvestors.com
Website: www.aeainvestors.com

Other Offices

78 Brook Street
London, United Kingdom W1K 5EF
Phone: 44-20-7659-7800
Fax: 44-20-7491-2155

200 First Stamford Place
Stamford, CT USA 06902
Phone: 203-564-2660
Fax: 203-564-2661

15 Queen's Road
Suite 3001, 30th floor
Central, Hong Kong
Phone: 852-3556-8888
Fax: 852-3356-8808

Management and Staff

Alan Wilkinson, Partner
Brian Hoesterey, Partner
Christopher Mahan, Partner
Damon Ball, Partner
David Ryan, Partner
Frankie Ko, Partner
Gary Cappeline, Partner
Glenn Fischer, Partner
John Cozzi, Partner
John Kenney, Partner
Joseph Carrabino, Partner
Martin Eltrich, Partner
Richard Woolworth, Partner
Scott Zoellner, Partner
Shivanandan Dalvie, Partner
Susan Shui-Shien Lin, Managing Director
Thomas Groves, Partner
Thomas Pryma, Partner
William Owens, Partner

Type of Firm

Private Equity Firm

Project Preferences

Type of Financing Preferred:
Leveraged Buyout
Mezzanine
Management Buyouts

Geographical Preferences

United States Preferences:
All U.S.

International Preferences:
Europe
Asia

Industry Focus

(% based on actual investment)

Industrial/Energy	32.4%
Communications and Media	27.1%
Consumer Related	23.3%
Other Products	8.8%
Medical/Health	4.9%
Biotechnology	3.4%

Additional Information

Name of Most Recent Fund: AEA Small Business Fund, LP
Most Recent Fund Was Raised: 03/25/2005
Year Founded: 1969

Capital Under Management: $2,400,000,000
Current Activity Level: Actively seeking new investments

AEA INVESTORS, INC.

55 East 52nd Street
New York, NY USA 10055
Phone: 212-644-5900
Fax: 212-888-1459

Type of Firm

Private Equity Firm

Project Preferences

Type of Financing Preferred:
Leveraged Buyout

Geographical Preferences

International Preferences:
Europe

Additional Information

Name of Most Recent Fund: American European Associates
Most Recent Fund Was Raised: 01/01/1973
Year Founded: 1974
Current Activity Level: Actively seeking new investments

AEGIS CAPITAL GROUP LLC

1325 Avenue of the Americas
27th Floor
New York, NY USA 10019
Phone: 212-786-6321
Fax: 800-804-4278
Website: www.aegiscapitalgroup.com

Other Offices

11000 Richmond
Suite 550
Houston, TX USA 77042
Phone: 713-339-1903
Fax: 800-804-4278

107 Frankfurt Circle
Birmingham, AL USA 35211
Phone: 205-443-3455
Fax: 800-804-4278

446 Jack Martin Boulevard
Brick, NJ USA 08724
Phone: 212-731-2275
Fax: 800-804-4218

16633 Dallas Parkway
Hanover Park Center, Suite 600
Addison, TX USA 75001
Phone: 972-588-1803
Fax: 800-804-4278

Management and Staff

Aruna Viswanathan, Vice President
Brett Hickey, President, Founder
Clete Walker, Chief Operating Officer
Kevin Dragan, Managing Director & CFO
Kyle Hickey, Vice President
Neil McPherson, Managing Director
Stephen Dondero, Managing Director

Type of Firm

Private Equity Firm

Project Preferences

Type of Financing Preferred:
Expansion
Mezzanine
Early Stage
Seed
Acquisition
Recapitalizations

Size of Investments Considered:
Min Size of Investment Considered (000s): $500
Max Size of Investment Considered (000s): $5,000

Geographical Preferences

United States Preferences:
Northeast
New York
All U.S.
Texas

Industry Preferences

In Communications prefer:
Communications and Media
Telecommunications
Entertainment

In Computer Software prefer:
Software

In Internet Specific prefer:
Ecommerce

In Biotechnology prefer:
Biotechnology

In Consumer Related prefer:
Consumer
Retail

In Industrial/Energy prefer:
Oil and Gas Exploration

In Financial Services prefer:
Financial Services

In Business Serv. prefer:
Services

Additional Information

Year Founded: 2005
Capital Under Management: $6,300,000
Current Activity Level: Actively seeking new investments

AEQUITAS CAPITAL MANAGEMENT, INC.

5300 Meadows Road
Suite 400
Lake Oswego, OR USA 97035
Phone: 503-419-3500
Fax: 419-419-3530
E-mail: info@aequitascapital.com
Website: www.aequitascapital.com

Other Offices

Bellevue Way Center
800 Bellevue Way Northeast, Suite 400
Bellevue, WA USA 98004
Phone: 425-462-4041
Fax: 425-462-4046

Management and Staff

Brian Oliver, Senior Managing Director
Charles Mautz, Managing Director
Robert Jesenik, Chief Executive Officer
Robert Noack, Managing Director
Steven Wright, Managing Director

Type of Firm

Investment Management Firm

Project Preferences

Type of Financing Preferred:
Leveraged Buyout
Acquisition

Geographical Preferences

United States Preferences:
All U.S.

Industry Preferences

In Medical/Health prefer:
Medical/Health

In Industrial/Energy prefer:
Alternative Energy

In Business Serv. prefer:
Distribution

In Manufact. prefer:
Manufacturing

Additional Information

Year Founded: 1993
Current Activity Level: Actively seeking new investments

AESCAP VENTURE

Strawinskylaan 629
Amsterdam, Netherlands 1077 XX
Phone: 31-20-570-2940
Fax: 31-20-673-7846
Website: www.aescap.com

Type of Firm

Private Equity Firm

Association Membership

European Private Equity and Venture Capital Assoc.

Project Preferences

Type of Financing Preferred:

Early Stage
Expansion
Balanced
Seed
Startup

Geographical Preferences

International Preferences:

Europe

Industry Preferences

In Medical/Health prefer:

Medical/Health

Additional Information

Year Founded: 2006
Capital Under Management: $6,600,000
Current Activity Level: Actively seeking new investments

AETOS CAPITAL LLC

875 Third Avenue
New York, NY USA 10022
Phone: 212-201-2500
Fax: 212-201-2525
E-mail: info@aetoscapital.com
Website: www.aetoscapital.com

Other Offices

Atago Green Hills MORI Tower
24th Floor 5-1 Atago 2-chome, Minato-ku
Tokyo, Japan 105-6224
Phone: 81-3-6402-6880
Fax: 81-3-6402-6881

2180 Sand Hill Road
Menlo Park, CA USA 94025
Phone: 650-234-1860
Fax: 650-234-1888

30/F, Gloucester Tower
The Landmark, 15 Queen's Road Central
Central, Hong Kong
Phone: 852-3556-8888
Fax: 852-3556-8808

Management and Staff

Andrea Bollyky, Managing Director
Anne Casscells, Managing Director
Daniel Klebes, Managing Director
David Cheung, Managing Director
James Allwin, President
James Gibbons, Managing Director
Kenneth DeRegt, Managing Director
Kenny Tse, Managing Director
Mayree Clark, Partner
Michael Klein, Managing Director
Reid Conway, Vice President
Sean Sullivan, Managing Director
Willaim Owens, Partner

Type of Firm

Private Equity Firm

Project Preferences

Type of Financing Preferred:

Balanced
Other

Geographical Preferences

International Preferences:

Asia
Japan
All International

Industry Preferences

In Financial Services prefer:

Real Estate

Additional Information

Year Founded: 2000
Capital Under Management: $2,430,000,000
Current Activity Level: Actively seeking new investments

AFFARSSTRATEGERNA AB

Artillerigatan 6
Stockholm, Sweden 114 51
Phone: 46-8-662-4030
Fax: 46-8-660-8319
E-mail: info@astrateg.se
Website: www.astrateg.se

Management and Staff

Lennart Ekberg, Chief Financial Officer

Type of Firm

Private Equity Firm

Association Membership

Swedish Venture Capital Association (SVCA)
European Private Equity and Venture Capital Assoc.

Project Preferences

Type of Financing Preferred:

Early Stage

Size of Investments Considered:

Min Size of Investment Considered (000s): $100
Max Size of Investment Considered (000s): $100,000

Geographical Preferences

International Preferences:

Sweden
Europe

Industry Preferences

In Communications prefer:

Telecommunications

In Biotechnology prefer:

Biotechnology

Additional Information

Year Founded: 1988
Capital Under Management: $20,700,000
Current Activity Level: Actively seeking new investments

AFFENTRANGER ASSOCIATES (FKA: ULTREIA CAPITAL, LTD.)

Rue du Rhone 100
Geneva, Switzerland 1204
Phone: 41-228-180-180
Fax: 41-223-102-729
E-mail: info@aasa.com
Website: www.affentrangerassociates.com

Management and Staff

Anton Affentranger, Chairman & CEO
Christoph Schwegler, Partner
Claudio Mohr, Partner
Ernst Messmer, Partner

Type of Firm

Private Equity Advisor or Fund of Funds

Project Preferences

Type of Financing Preferred:

Leveraged Buyout
Early Stage
Expansion
Public Companies
First Stage Financing

Geographical Preferences

United States Preferences:

All U.S.

International Preferences:

Switzerland
Europe
Western Europe

Industry Preferences

In Biotechnology prefer:

Biotechnology

In Medical/Health prefer:

Medical/Health

Additional Information

Year Founded: 1992
Capital Under Management: $200,000,000
Current Activity Level: Actively seeking new investments

AFFINITY CAPITAL MANAGEMENT

901 Marquette Avenue
Suite 2820
Minneapolis, MN USA 55402
Phone: 612-252-9900
Fax: 612-252-9911
Website: www.affinitycapital.net

Management and Staff

B. Kristine Johnson, Managing Partner
Edson Spencer, Managing Partner
Robin Dowdle, Chief Financial Officer
Serafin Samson, Venture Partner

Type of Firm

Private Equity Firm

Association Membership

Natl Assoc of Small Bus. Inv. Co (NASBIC)
National Venture Capital Association - USA (NVCA)

Project Preferences

Role in Financing:
Will function either as deal originator or investor in deals created by others

Type of Financing Preferred:
Second Stage Financing
Early Stage
Start-up Financing
Balanced
Seed
First Stage Financing

Geographical Preferences

United States Preferences:
Midwest

Industry Focus

(% based on actual investment)

Medical/Health	57.0%
Internet Specific	13.4%
Biotechnology	11.2%
Computer Hardware	10.8%
Computer Software and Services	7.4%
Semiconductors/Other Elect.	0.1%

Additional Information

Name of Most Recent Fund: Affinity Ventures V, L.P.
Most Recent Fund Was Raised: 03/31/2008
Year Founded: 1991
Capital Under Management: $74,900,000
Current Activity Level: Actively seeking new investments
Method of Compensation: Return on investment is of primary concern, do not charge fees

AFFINITY EQUITY PARTNERS

8 Connaught Place
One Exchange Square, 40/F
Central, Hong Kong
Phone: 852-3102-8329
Fax: 852-3102-8321
Website: www.affinityequity.com

Other Offices

9 Temasek Boulevard
#27-03 Suntec Tower Two
Singapore, Singapore 038989
Phone: 65-6238-2260
Fax: 65-6238-7765

16/F Young Poong Bldg.
33 Seorin-Dong, Chongro-ku
Seoul, South Korea 110-752
Phone: 82-2-399-7773
Fax: 82-2-399-7771

Level 7
61 York St.
Sydney, Australia 2000
Phone: 612-9299-0889
Fax: 612-9299-0809

Management and Staff

Chul-Joo Lee, Partner
James Fung, Partner
Lak-Chuan Ng, Partner
Sam Johnson, Vice President
Sanghyun Lee, Partner
Weng-Sun Mok, Partner
Young-Taeg Park, Managing Partner

Type of Firm

Private Equity Firm

Association Membership

Australian Venture Capital Association (AVCAL)

Project Preferences

Role in Financing:
Prefer role as deal originator but will also invest in deals created by others

Type of Financing Preferred:
Leveraged Buyout
Management Buyouts

Size of Investments Considered:
Min Size of Investment Considered (000s): $75,000
Max Size of Investment Considered (000s): $500,000

Geographical Preferences

International Preferences:
Taiwan
China
Hong Kong
Pacific
Australia
Singapore
Korea, South
Asia
New Zealand
Japan

Industry Preferences

In Communications prefer:
Telecommunications
Entertainment

In Computer Other prefer:
Computer Related

In Semiconductor/Electr prefer:
Electronics

In Medical/Health prefer:
Medical/Health
Health Services

In Consumer Related prefer:
Retail
Food/Beverage
Consumer Products
Consumer Services

In Industrial/Energy prefer:
Industrial Products

In Transportation prefer:
Transportation

In Financial Services prefer:
Insurance
Financial Services

In Business Serv. prefer:
Services

In Manufact. prefer:
Manufacturing

Additional Information

Year Founded: 2004
Capital Under Management: $700,000,000
Current Activity Level: Actively seeking new investments
Method of Compensation: Return on invest. most important, but chg. closing fees, service fees, etc.

AFFYMETRIX, INC.

3420 Central Expressway
Santa Clara, CA USA 95051
Phone: 408-731-5000
Fax: 408-731-5380
E-mail: investor@affymetrix.com
Website: www.affymetrix.com

Other Offices

Mita NN Bldg. 16F
4-1-23 Shiba Minato-ku
Tokyo , Japan 108-0014
Phone: 81-3-5730-8200
Fax: 81-3-5730-8201

6550 Vallejo St
Suite 100

Emeryville, CA USA 94608
Phone: 510-428-8500
Fax: 510-428-8585

890 Embarcadero Dr
West Sacramento, CA USA 95605
Phone: 916-376-1000
Fax: 916-376-1111

Voyager, Mercury Park
Wycombe Lane, Wooburn Green
High Wycombe , United Kingdom HP10 0HH
Phone: 44-1628-552-550
Fax: 44-1628-552585

3380 Central Expressway
Santa Clara, CA USA 95051
Phone: 408-731-5000
Fax: 408-481-0422

3450 Central Expressway
Santa Clara, CA USA 95051
Phone: 408-731-5000
Fax: 408-481-0435

428 Oakmead Parkway
Sunnyvale, CA USA 94086
Phone: 408-731-5000
Fax: 408-481-0516

434 W. Dussel Drive
Maumee, OH USA 43537
Phone: 419-891-3030
Fax: 419-891-3037

6519 Dumbarton Circle
Fremont, CA USA 94555
Phone: 510-818-2660
Fax: 510-818-2610

26111 Miles Road
Cleveland, OH USA 44128
Phone: 419-891-3030
Fax: 419-891-3037

Management and Staff

Stephen Fodor, Chairman & CEO
Susan Siegel, President

Type of Firm

Corporate PE/Venture

Additional Information

Year Founded: 1999
Current Activity Level: Actively seeking new investments

AFINUM MANAGEMENT GMBH

Theatinerstrasse 7
Munich, Germany D-80333
Phone: 49-89-255-43301
Fax: 49-89-255-43399
E-mail: info@afinum.de
Website: www.afinum.de

Other Offices

Seefeldstrasse 69
Zurich, Switzerland 8008
Phone: 41-43-4-883-658
Fax: 41-43-4-883-530

Management and Staff

Gernot Eisinger, Managing Partner
Robert Greitl, Chief Financial Officer
Thomas Buhler, Managing Partner

Type of Firm

Private Equity Firm

Association Membership

Swiss Venture Capital Association (SECA)

Project Preferences

Type of Financing Preferred:
Leveraged Buyout
Expansion

Geographical Preferences

International Preferences:
Europe
Germany

Additional Information

Year Founded: 2001
Capital Under Management: $64,700,000
Current Activity Level: Actively seeking new investments

AFRICAN AGRICULTURAL CAPITAL LTD

Plot 2, Serunkuma Road,
P.O.Box 71782
Kampala, Uganda
Phone: 256 312264980
Fax: 256 312264985
E-mail: info@aac.co.ke
Website: www.aac.co.ke

Management and Staff

Tom Adlam, Managing Director

Type of Firm

Incubator/Development Program

Association Membership

African Venture Capital Association (AVCA)

Project Preferences

Type of Financing Preferred:
Early Stage
Balanced

Geographical Preferences

International Preferences:
Uganda
Tanzania
Africa

Industry Preferences

In Agr/Forestr/Fish prefer:
Agribusiness
Agriculture related

Additional Information

Year Founded: 2005
Capital Under Management: $7,000,000
Current Activity Level: Actively seeking new investments

AFRICAN ALLIANCE PRIVATE EQUITY

African Alliance House
Fairgrounds Office Park
Gaborone, Botswana
Phone: 267-318-8958
Fax: 267-318-8956
E-mail: privateequity@africanalliance.bw
Website: www.africanalliance.com

Other Offices

2nd Floor, Nedbank Centre
Cnr Sishayi and Sozisa Roads
Mbabane, Swaziland
Phone: 268-404-8394
Fax: 268-404-8391

Ground Floor, Kenya Re Towers
Upper Hill
Nairobi, Kenya
Phone: 254-20-273-5154
Fax: 254-20-273-1162

4th Floor, Kenya Re Towers
Upper Hill
Nairobi, Kenya
Phone: 254-20-271-0978
Fax: 254-20-271-0247

6th Floor, Workers House
1 Pilkington Road
Kampala, Uganda
Phone: 256-41-235-577
Fax: 256-41-235-575

Type of Firm

Bank Affiliated

Project Preferences

Type of Financing Preferred:
Generalist PE
Expansion
Mezzanine
Management Buyouts
Acquisition

Geographical Preferences

International Preferences:

Uganda
Africa

Industry Preferences

In Business Serv. prefer:

Services

In Manufact. prefer:

Manufacturing

Additional Information

Year Founded: 2009
Current Activity Level: Actively seeking new investments

AFRICAN CAPITAL ALLIANCE (AKA: CAPITAL ALLIANCE NIGERIA)

C&C Towers, Sanusi Fafunwa St.
Victoria Island
Lagos, Nigeria
Phone: 234-1-270-6909
Fax: 234-1-270-6908
Website: www.aca-web.com

Other Offices

320, Park Avenue
28th Floor
New York, NY USA 10022
Phone: 212-508-9400
Fax: 212-508-9494

Management and Staff

Arnold Ekpe, Partner
Chief Ernest Shonekan, Partner
Mohammed Hayatu-Deen, Partner
Pascal Dozie, Partner
Rotimi Oyekanmi, Partner
Sam Oniovosa, Chief Financial Officer
Thomas Barry, Partner

Type of Firm

Private Equity Firm

Association Membership

Emerging Markets Private Equity Association
Nigerian Venture Capital Association
African Venture Capital Association (AVCA)

Project Preferences

Type of Financing Preferred:

Early Stage
Expansion
Balanced

Size of Investments Considered:

Min Size of Investment Considered (000s): $2,000
Max Size of Investment Considered (000s): $7,000

Geographical Preferences

International Preferences:

Nigeria
Africa

Industry Preferences

In Communications prefer:

Communications and Media
Telecommunications

In Internet Specific prefer:

Internet

In Medical/Health prefer:

Medical/Health

In Industrial/Energy prefer:

Energy
Oil and Gas Exploration

In Transportation prefer:

Transportation

In Financial Services prefer:

Financial Services

In Manufact. prefer:

Manufacturing

Additional Information

Year Founded: 1997
Capital Under Management: $83,400,000
Current Activity Level: Actively seeking new investments

AFRICAN LION MANAGEMENT LTD (AKA: AFL MANAGEMENT LTD)

Level 4
15 Queen Street
Melbourne, Australia 3000
Phone: 613-9614-8008
Fax: 613-9614-8009
Website: www.afl.co.za

Type of Firm

Bank Affiliated

Association Membership

African Venture Capital Association (AVCA)

Project Preferences

Type of Financing Preferred:

Early Stage
Balanced

Geographical Preferences

International Preferences:

Africa

Industry Preferences

In Industrial/Energy prefer:

Coal Related

In Agr/Forestr/Fish prefer:

Mining and Minerals

Additional Information

Year Founded: 1999
Capital Under Management: $27,000,000
Current Activity Level: Actively seeking new investments

AFRICAP MICROFINANCE INVESTMENT COMPANY

12th Floor, The Forum Building
2 Maude Street, Sandton
Johannesburg, South Africa 2146
Phone: 27-11-784-0815
Fax: 27-11-784-3101
E-mail: information@africapfund.com
Website: www.africapfund.com

Other Offices

TM Building,
Pope Hennessy Street
Port Louis, Mauritius
Phone: 230-211-9300
Fax: 230-211-4457

Management and Staff

Wagane Diouf, Managing Director

Type of Firm

Bank Affiliated

Association Membership

African Venture Capital Association (AVCA)
Project Preferences

Type of Financing Preferred:

Expansion
Acquisition

Size of Investments Considered:

Min Size of Investment Considered (000s): $300
Max Size of Investment Considered (000s): $1,500

Geographical Preferences

International Preferences:

Africa

Industry Preferences

In Financial Services prefer:

Financial Services

Additional Information

Year Founded: 2001
Current Activity Level: Actively seeking new investments

AFTVIN-NUPROUNARSJOOUR SUOURLANDS

Austurvegi 56
Selfoss, Iceland 800
Phone: 354-482-2419
Fax: 354-482-2921

Type of Firm
Private Equity Firm

Association Membership
European Private Equity and Venture Capital Assoc.

Project Preferences

Type of Financing Preferred:
Balanced

Geographical Preferences

International Preferences:
Europe
Iceland

Additional Information
Year Founded: 2004
Current Activity Level: Actively seeking new investments

AG-WEST BIOTECH, INC./ICAST

111 Research Drive
Suite 101
Saskatoon, Canada S7N3R2
Phone: 306-975-1939
Fax: 306-975-1966
Website: www.agwest.sk.ca

Type of Firm
Government Affiliated Program

Project Preferences

Type of Financing Preferred:
Startup

Additional Information
Year Founded: 1989
Current Activity Level: Actively seeking new investments

AGAVE CAPITAL

11910 FM2769
Suite Two
Austin, TX USA 78726
Phone: 512-258-1724
Fax: 512-258-1369
E-mail: info@agavecapital.com
Website: www.agavecapital.com

Management and Staff
Bob Locklear, General Partner

Type of Firm
Private Equity Firm

Project Preferences

Type of Financing Preferred:
Seed
Startup

Geographical Preferences

United States Preferences:
Texas

Industry Preferences

In Communications prefer:
Telecommunications

In Computer Software prefer:
Software

In Internet Specific prefer:
Internet

In Semiconductor/Electr prefer:
Semiconductor

Additional Information
Name of Most Recent Fund: Agave Capital II
Most Recent Fund Was Raised: 01/15/2001
Year Founded: 1999
Capital Under Management: $10,900,000
Current Activity Level: Actively seeking new investments

AGENCIA DE INNOVACION Y DESARROLLO DE ANDALUCIA (AKA: IDEA)

Calle Torneo 26
Seville, Spain 41002
Phone: 34-95-503-0700
Fax: 34-95-503-0780
E-mail: informacion@central.ifa.es
Website: www.agenciaidea.es

Other Offices

C/ Cister, 5
Malaga, Spain
Phone: 34-951-042-902

C/angel, 3
Granada, Spain
Phone: 34-958-002-500

Carrera De Jesus, 9, bajo
Jaen, Spain
Phone: 34-951-042-902

Plaza Cardenal Toldeo, 6
Bajo
Cordoba, Spain
Phone: 34-957-005-000

Avda. Alemania, 3
Huelva, Spain
Phone: 34-959-011-200

C/Adriano del Valle, 7
Local 1
Sevilla, Spain
Phone: 34-95-503-0900

Avda. Pablo Iglesias, 24
Almeria, Spain
Phone: 34-950-006-808

Alameda Apodaca, 20
Cadiz, Spain
Phone: 34-956-009-510

Type of Firm
Private Equity Firm

Association Membership
Spanish Venture Capital Association (ASCRI)

Project Preferences

Type of Financing Preferred:
Balanced

Geographical Preferences

International Preferences:
Europe
Spain

Additional Information
Year Founded: 1987
Current Activity Level: Actively seeking new investments

AGF PRIVATE EQUITY

3, boulevard des Italiens
Paris Cedex 02, France 75113
Phone: 33-1-5818-5656
Fax: 33-1-5818-5689
E-mail: contact1@agfpe.com
Website: www.agfpe.com

Management and Staff
Benoist Grossmann, Managing Director
Christophe Baviere, Chairman & CEO
Guillaume Lautour, Partner
Jean Plamondon, Partner
Jean-Francois Gallouin, Venture Partner
Laure Ory-Lavollee, Venture Partner
Luc Maruenda, Partner
Matthieu Baret, Partner
Nicolas Chaudron, Partner
Sylvianne Guyonnet, Chief Financial Officer
Thierry Laugel, Partner

Type of Firm
Insurance Firm Affiliate

Association Membership
French Venture Capital Association (AFIC)
European Private Equity and Venture Capital Assoc.

Project Preferences

Type of Financing Preferred:
Fund of Funds
Leveraged Buyout
Early Stage
Expansion
Balanced
Turnaround
Management Buyouts

Size of Investments Considered:
Min Size of Investment Considered (000s): $1,955
Max Size of Investment Considered (000s): $7,820

Geographical Preferences

United States Preferences:
All U.S.

International Preferences:
Europe
Asia
France
All International

Industry Preferences

In Communications prefer:
Telecommunications

In Computer Software prefer:
Software

In Internet Specific prefer:
Internet

In Semiconductor/Electr prefer:
Electronics

In Biotechnology prefer:
Biotechnology

In Medical/Health prefer:
Medical/Health

In Other prefer:
Environment Responsible

Additional Information
Year Founded: 1999
Capital Under Management: $1,684,900,000
Current Activity Level: Actively seeking new investments

AGILENT VENTURES
5301 Stevens Creek Boulevard
MS 54U-GT
Santa Clara, CA USA 95051-7201
Phone: 408-553-7200
Fax: 408-553-3817
E-mail: agilent_ventures@agilent.com
Website: www.agilentventures.com

Type of Firm
Corporate PE/Venture

Project Preferences

Role in Financing:
Prefer role in deals created by others

Type of Financing Preferred:
Second Stage Financing
Early Stage
First Stage Financing
Startup

Size of Investments Considered:
Min Size of Investment Considered (000s): $500
Max Size of Investment Considered (000s): $10,000

Geographical Preferences

Canadian Preferences:
All Canada

International Preferences:
Italy
Sweden
United Kingdom
Netherlands
China
Scandanavia/Nordic Region
Israel
Germany
France

Industry Preferences

In Communications prefer:
Telecommunications
Wireless Communications
Data Communications

In Semiconductor/Electr prefer:
Semiconductor
Controllers and Sensors
Component Testing Equipmt
Laser Related
Fiber Optics
Analytic/Scientific

In Biotechnology prefer:
Biotechnology
Human Biotechnology
Biosensors
Biotech Related Research

In Medical/Health prefer:
Diagnostic Test Products

In Industrial/Energy prefer:
Advanced Materials

Additional Information
Year Founded: 2000
Capital Under Management: $100,000,000
Current Activity Level: Actively seeking new investments
Method of Compensation: Return on investment is of primary concern, do not charge fees

---

AGILITY CAPITAL LLC
226 East Canon Perdido Street
Suite F
Santa Barbara, CA USA 93101
Phone: 805-568-0424
Fax: 805-568-0427
E-mail: info@agilitycap.com
Website: www.agilitycap.com

Other Offices
1512 W. 35th Street Cutoff
Suite 310
Austin, TX USA 78731
Phone: 512-472-3600
Fax: 512-472-1548

Management and Staff
John Winsauer, General Partner
Kam Pasha, General Partner
Kenneth Rand, General Partner
Robert Skinner, Chief Executive Officer
Tom Blinten, President

Type of Firm
Private Equity Firm

Project Preferences

Type of Financing Preferred:
Early Stage
Balanced

Geographical Preferences

United States Preferences:
East Coast
Southwest

Industry Preferences

In Communications prefer:
Communications and Media

In Computer Software prefer:
Applications Software

In Internet Specific prefer:
Internet

In Business Serv. prefer:
Media

Additional Information
Name of Most Recent Fund: Agility Capital
Most Recent Fund Was Raised: 07/01/2000
Year Founded: 2000
Capital Under Management: $33,000,000
Current Activity Level: Actively seeking new investments

AGORA INVESTMENT MANAGEMENT, LTD.
8/F, No 52 Lan-Kang Rd.
Section 3
Taipei, Taiwan 104
Phone: 886-2-2782-8929
Fax: 886-2-2785-9673

Type of Firm
Private Equity Firm

Association Membership
Taiwan Venture Capital Association(TVCA)

Project Preferences
Type of Financing Preferred:
Balanced

Geographical Preferences
International Preferences:
Taiwan

Industry Preferences
In Communications prefer:
Telecommunications

In Computer Software prefer:
Software

In Internet Specific prefer:
Internet

In Semiconductor/Electr prefer:
Electronics

In Biotechnology prefer:
Biotechnology

In Business Serv. prefer:
Services

Additional Information
Name of Most Recent Fund: Comtel Technology Venture Fund
Most Recent Fund Was Raised: 10/20/1999
Year Founded: 1999
Capital Under Management: $60,300,000
Current Activity Level: Actively seeking new investments

AGRIVEST CAPITAL CORPORATION
Box 6115
High River, Canada T1V1P7
Phone: 403-601-0296
Fax: 403-652-7051
Website: www.agrivestcapital.com

Type of Firm
Private Equity Firm

Project Preferences
Type of Financing Preferred:
Other
Seed
Acquisition

Geographical Preferences
United States Preferences:
All U.S.

Canadian Preferences:
All Canada

Additional Information
Year Founded: 1996
Current Activity Level: Actively seeking new investments

AGRO INVEST
12 Avenue George V
Paris, France 75008
Management and Staff
Jean Louis Ruatti, President

Type of Firm
Private Equity Firm

Association Membership
French Venture Capital Association (AFIC)

Project Preferences
Type of Financing Preferred:
Leveraged Buyout
Expansion

Geographical Preferences
International Preferences:
France

Industry Preferences
In Biotechnology prefer:
Agricultural/Animal Bio.

In Agr/Forestr/Fish prefer:
Agribusiness
Agriculture related

Additional Information
Name of Most Recent Fund: Agro Invest
Most Recent Fund Was Raised: 05/29/2007
Year Founded: 2007
Capital Under Management: $108,200,000
Current Activity Level: Actively seeking new investments

AH SMAFORETAGSINVEST AB
Vasagatan 11, 11tr
Stockholm, Sweden 111 20
Phone: 46-8-5879-1970
Fax: 46-8-5879-1975
E-mail: info@smafi.se
Website: www.smafi.se

Other Offices
Jarntorget 12 C
P.O. Box 105
Arboga, Sweden 732 22
Phone: 46-589-611-417
Fax: 46-589-611-422

Type of Firm
Bank Affiliated

Association Membership
Swedish Venture Capital Association (SVCA)

Project Preferences
Type of Financing Preferred:
Expansion
Balanced
Management Buyouts

Geographical Preferences
International Preferences:
Scandanavia/Nordic Region

Additional Information
Year Founded: 1999
Capital Under Management: $9,400,000
Current Activity Level: Actively seeking new investments

AH VENTURES (AKA: ADAMS HARKNESS & HILL TECHNOLOGY VENTURES)
99 High Street
Boston, MA USA 02110
Phone: 617-788-1670
Fax: 617-788-1663
E-mail: info@ahventures.com
Website: www.ahventures.com

Other Offices
One Liberty Square
Boston, MA USA 02109
Phone: 617-423-6688
Fax: 617-426-8399

Management and Staff
Jay Corscadden, General Partner
Thomas Palmer, General Partner

Type of Firm
Bank Affiliated

Project Preferences
Role in Financing:
Prefer role as deal originator

Type of Financing Preferred:
Second Stage Financing
Expansion
Later Stage

Size of Investments Considered:
Min Size of Investment Considered (000s): $500
Max Size of Investment Considered (000s): $2,000

Industry Preferences
In Computer Hardware prefer:
Computer Graphics and Dig

In Computer Software prefer:
Computer Services
Software

Systems Software
Applications Software
Artificial Intelligence

In Internet Specific prefer:
Internet
Ecommerce
Web Aggregration/Portals

In Semiconductor/Electr prefer:
Electronic Components
Semiconductor
Micro-Processing
Controllers and Sensors
Sensors
Circuit Boards
Component Testing Equipmt
Laser Related
Optoelectronics

Additional Information

Year Founded: 1969
Capital Under Management: $18,000,000
Current Activity Level: Actively seeking new investments
Method of Compensation: Return on investment is of primary concern, do not charge fees

---

AHEIM CAPITAL GMBH (FKA: BUCHANAN CAPITAL PARTNERS GMBH)

Schlossbergstrasse 1
Starnberg, Germany 82319
Phone: 49-815-655-980
Fax: 49-815-959-6670
E-mail: info@aheim.com
Website: www.aheim.com

Management and Staff

Frank Henkelmann, Managing Director
Herbert Seggewiss, Managing Director
Peter Blumenwitz, Managing Director

Type of Firm

Bank Affiliated

Project Preferences

Type of Financing Preferred:
Balanced

Geographical Preferences

International Preferences:
Liechtenstein
Luxembourg
Switzerland
Austria
Germany

Industry Preferences

In Industrial/Energy prefer:
Advanced Materials

Additional Information

Year Founded: 2005
Capital Under Management: $227,000,000
Current Activity Level: Actively seeking new investments

AHLSTROM & PARTNERS

Montorsgatan 7
Halmstad, Sweden 302 60
Phone: 46-35-173-570
Fax: 46-35-173-572
Website: www.ahlstrompartners.se

Type of Firm

Investment Management Firm

Association Membership

Swedish Venture Capital Association (SVCA)

Project Preferences

Type of Financing Preferred:
Leveraged Buyout
Expansion
Seed
Startup

Geographical Preferences

International Preferences:
Sweden

Additional Information

Year Founded: 1999
Capital Under Management: $3,800,000
Current Activity Level: Actively seeking new investments

AHLSTROM CAPITAL OY

Etelaesplanadi 14
P.O. Box 329
Helsinki, Finland 00101
Phone: 358-10-88-818
Fax: 358-10-888-4769
E-mail: info@ahlstromcapital.com
Website: www.ahlstromcapital.com

Type of Firm

Private Equity Firm

Association Membership

Finnish Venture Capital Association (FVCA)
European Private Equity and Venture Capital Assoc.

Project Preferences

Type of Financing Preferred:
Leveraged Buyout
Expansion
Turnaround

Geographical Preferences

International Preferences:
Europe
Scandanavia/Nordic Region
Finland

Industry Focus

(% based on actual investment)

Semiconductors/Other Elect.	52.5%
Other Products	32.7%
Industrial/Energy	10.0%
Computer Hardware	4.8%

Additional Information

Year Founded: 2001
Capital Under Management: $169,400,000
Current Activity Level: Actively seeking new investments

AIB EQUITY

AIB International Centre
IFSC
Dublin , Ireland 1
Phone: 353-1-641-7993
Fax: 353-1-641-7993
Website: www.aibequity.com

Type of Firm

Bank Affiliated

Association Membership

Irish Venture Capital Association

Project Preferences

Type of Financing Preferred:
Early Stage

Geographical Preferences

International Preferences:
Ireland

Additional Information

Year Founded: 2000
Capital Under Management: $22,000,000
Current Activity Level: Making few, if any, new investments

AICEP CAPITAL GLOBAL - SOCIEDADE DE CAPITAL DE RISCO, S.A.

Av. da Liberdade 258, 5 andar
Lisboa, Portugal 1250-149
Phone: 351-217-802-080
Fax: 351-217-950-027
E-mail: capitalglobal@capitalglobal.pt
Website: www.capitalglobal.pt

Other Offices

Edificio Peninsula
Praca do Bom Sucesso 127/131, Sala 507

Porto, Portugal 4150-146
Phone: 351-226-055-320
Fax: 351-226-062-519

Management and Staff

Abel Cubal De Almeida, Chief Executive Officer

Type of Firm

Government Affiliated Program

Association Membership

Portuguese Venture Capital Association (APCRI)
European Private Equity and Venture Capital Assoc.

Project Preferences

Type of Financing Preferred:

Early Stage
Expansion
Balanced

Geographical Preferences

International Preferences:

Italy
Portugal
Europe

Industry Preferences

In Communications prefer:

Communications and Media

In Computer Other prefer:

Computer Related

In Consumer Related prefer:

Consumer

In Industrial/Energy prefer:

Energy
Industrial Products

Additional Information

Name of Most Recent Fund: FIQ API Capital Grandes Projectos de Investimento
Most Recent Fund Was Raised: 07/31/2004
Year Founded: 2003
Capital Under Management: $222,700,000
Current Activity Level: Actively seeking new investments

AIF CAPITAL PVT, LTD.

Suite 3401, Jardine House
1 Connaught Place
Central, Hong Kong
Phone: 852-2912-7888
Fax: 852-2845-0786
E-mail: info@aifcapital.com
Website: www.aifcapital.com

Other Offices

Regus Business Centre
Augusta Point, DLF Golf Course Road
Gurgaon, India 122001
Phone: 91-124-414-7888
Fax: 91-124-414-7898

Management and Staff

Daniel Hui, Managing Director
Doris Ng, Managing Director
Peter Amour, Chief Executive Officer
Rajeev Kalra, Managing Director

Type of Firm

Private Equity Firm

Project Preferences

Type of Financing Preferred:

Leveraged Buyout
Early Stage
Expansion
Generalist PE
Balanced
Turnaround
Special Situation
Recapitalizations

Size of Investments Considered:

Min Size of Investment Considered (000s): $3,000
Max Size of Investment Considered (000s): $75,000

Geographical Preferences

International Preferences:

Vietnam
Bangladesh
Indonesia
India
Pakistan
Taiwan
China
Hong Kong
Thailand
Philippines
Singapore
Korea, South
Sri Lanka
Asia
Malaysia

Industry Preferences

In Communications prefer:

Telecommunications

In Medical/Health prefer:

Health Services

In Consumer Related prefer:

Retail
Consumer Products

In Industrial/Energy prefer:

Energy

In Transportation prefer:

Transportation

In Financial Services prefer:

Financial Services

In Business Serv. prefer:

Media

In Manufact. prefer:

Manufacturing

In Other prefer:

Environment Responsible

Additional Information

Year Founded: 1994
Capital Under Management: $1,000,000,000
Current Activity Level: Actively seeking new investments
Method of Compensation: Professional fee required whether or not deal closes

---

AIFG

3-38-10, Sendagaya
Shibuya, Tokyo, Japan

Type of Firm

Private Equity Firm

Project Preferences

Type of Financing Preferred:

Balanced

Geographical Preferences

International Preferences:

Asia

Additional Information

Year Founded: 2005
Current Activity Level: Actively seeking new investments

AIG CAPITAL INVESTMENTS DO BRASIL S.A.

Av. Eng. Luiz Carlos Berrini
550, Conj. 132
Sao Paulo, Brazil 04571-000
Phone: 5511-2184-7474
Fax: 5511-5505-0313
Website: www.aig.com

Management and Staff

Marcos Rechtman, Chief Executive Officer

Type of Firm

Bank Affiliated

Association Membership

Brazilian Venture Capital Association (ABCR)

Project Preferences

Type of Financing Preferred:

Expansion

Geographical Preferences

International Preferences:

Brazil

Additional Information

Name of Most Recent Fund: AIG Brazil Special

Situations Fund
Most Recent Fund Was Raised: 02/01/2000
Year Founded: 2000
Capital Under Management: $215,000,000
Current Activity Level: Actively seeking new investments

AIG CAPITAL PARTNERS

175 Water Street
23rd Floor
New York, NY USA 10038
Phone: 212-458-2000
Fax: 212-458-2200
Website: www.aig.com

Other Offices

1209 Taj Mahal Hotel
Apollo Bunder
Mumbai, India 400 001
Phone: 9122-284-3932
Fax: 9122-288-5584

Shanghai Center Suite 519
Nanjing Shanghai, China 1376
Phone: 8621-6279-7222

Illica 16 Street
Zagreb, Croatia 1000
Phone: 385-1-483-8377
Fax: 385-1-481-4392

ul. Skorupki 5, 5th floor
Warsaw, Poland 00-546
Phone: 48-22-583-7000
Fax: 48-22-583-6969

Rm 1401 14/F AIA Building
1 Stubbs Road
Central, Hong Kong
Phone: 852-2832-1800
Fax: 852-2234-0637

AIG Building, 1-3
Marunouchi 1-chome
Chiyoda-Ku, Tokyo , Japan 100-0005
Phone: 813-5208-5800
Fax: 813-5208-9080

145 Wellington St. West
9th Floor
Toronto, Canada M5J1H8
Phone: 416-596-4111
Fax: 416-596-4191

AIG Private Equity (Bermuda) Ltd.
29 Richmond Road
Pembroke, Bermuda HM 08

AIG Centre
North Wall Quay
Dublin, Ireland 1
Phone: 353-1-672-0222
Fax: 353-1-672-0233

Baarerstrasse 8
Postfach 244
Zug, Switzerland 6301
Phone: 41-41-710-7060
Fax: 41-41-710-7064

Stern Palace, H-1061
10 Andreassy Ut
Budapest, Hungary
Phone: 36-1428-4060
Fax: 36-411-1271

2929 Allen Parkway
A37
Houston, TX USA 77019
Phone: 713-831-5233
Fax: 713-620-3920

55 Bryanston Street,
17th Floor, Marble Arch Tower
London, United Kingdom EC3M 4AB
Phone: 44-207-954-8162
Fax: 44-207-954-8062

Agustinas 640, 15th Fl
Santiago, Chile
Phone: 562-630-3000
Fax: 562-630-3980

Nan Shan Life Building
144 Min Chuan East Road Section 2
Taipei, Taiwan
Phone: 886-2-2500-8778
Fax: 886-2-2516-5383

Birchin Court
20 Birchin Lane
London, United Kingdom EC3B 9HV
Phone: 44-207-335-8100
Fax: 44-207-337-0000

Nad Ondrejovem 24
Praha 4
Prague, Czech Republic CZ-140 00
Phone: 420-2-6121-6367
Fax: 420-2-6121-0405

Str. Gen. Berthelot 57
Bucharest, Romania 70747
Phone: 40-1-311-0571
Fax: 40-1-311-3352

Tte. Gral. J.D. Peron 646
3rd FLoor
Buenos Aires, Brazil C1038AAN
Phone: 541-14-340-35621
Fax: 541-14-340-3560

Level 24, Menara AIA
99 Jalan Ampang
Kuala Lumpur, Malaysia 50450
Phone: 603-2056-1111
Fax: 603-2056-3392

9/F. Hanil Building Ste. 910
64-5 Chungmu-Ro 2-Ga
Chung-Ku Seoul, South Korea
Phone: 822-752-3876
Fax: 822-752-3877

1 Robinson Road
#12-00 AIA Tower
Singapore, Singapore 048542
Phone: 65-2918-000
Fax: 65-538-5602

Management and Staff

Boris Evseev, Vice President
Christopher Liu, Vice President
David Pinkerton, Managing Director
John Casale, Managing Director
Klaus Hermann, Partner
Marc Kasher, Vice President
Patrick McGinnis, Vice President
Pierre Francois Mellinger, Partner
Rocco Sgobbo, Managing Director
Scott Foushee, Managing Director
Serkan Elden, Managing Director
Steven Costabile, Partner
Thomas Farley, Vice President
Val Ionescu, Partner
Win Neuger, Chairman & CEO

Type of Firm

Private Equity Firm

Association Membership

European Private Equity and Venture Capital Assoc.

Project Preferences

Type of Financing Preferred:

Fund of Funds
Leveraged Buyout
Early Stage
Expansion
Mezzanine
Generalist PE
Balanced
Other
Management Buyouts
Special Situation
Recapitalizations

Geographical Preferences

International Preferences:

Latin America
India
Europe
China
Israel
Asia
Korea, South
France
Africa
Japan

Industry Focus

(% based on actual investment)

Consumer Related	29.5%
Communications and Media	19.9%
Other Products	11.9%

Medical/Health	11.5%
Internet Specific	9.8%
Computer Software and Services	5.8%
Semiconductors/Other Elect.	3.6%
Computer Hardware	3.2%
Biotechnology	2.6%
Industrial/Energy	2.3%

Additional Information

Name of Most Recent Fund: AIG Highstar Capital III Prism Fund I-A, L.P.
Most Recent Fund Was Raised: 06/15/2007
Year Founded: 1996
Capital Under Management: $8,814,300,000
Current Activity Level: Actively seeking new investments

AIG GLOBAL INVESTMENT GROUP

70 Pine Street
16th Floor
New York, NY USA 10270
Phone: 212-770-7000
Fax: 212-770-9491
Website: www.aiginvestments.com

Other Offices

Peninsula Corp. Park
FCH House, Ground Floor, GT Marg
Mumbai, India 400 013
Phone: 91-22-4093-0002

Stern Palace, H-1061
10 Andreassy ut
Budapest, Hungary
Phone: 361-428-4060

Management and Staff

Ada Tse, Managing Director
Brian McLoone, Senior Managing Director
Christopher Lee, Managing Director
David Yeung, Managing Director
F.T Chong, Managing Director
Hans Danielsson, Senior Managing Director
Jack Boyce, Managing Director
Larry Mellinger, Senior Managing Director
Nick Brown, Managing Director
Richard Scott, Senior Managing Director
Robert Thompson, Senior Managing Director
Saurabh Srivastava, Chief Executive Officer
Steven Costabile, Managing Director
Steven Guterman, Senior Managing Director
Stewart Homler, Managing Director
Thomas Belthoff, Managing Director
Win Neuger, Chairman & CEO

Type of Firm

Insurance Firm Affiliate

Project Preferences

Type of Financing Preferred:

Fund of Funds
Mezzanine
Generalist PE
Balanced
Fund of Funds of Second

Geographical Preferences

United States Preferences:

All U.S.

International Preferences:

Europe
All International

Additional Information

Name of Most Recent Fund: AIG PEP IV Non-U.S., L.P.
Most Recent Fund Was Raised: 08/18/2006
Year Founded: 1990
Capital Under Management: $12,700,000,000
Current Activity Level: Actively seeking new investments

AIG INVESTMENT CORPORATION, (ASIA) LTD.

16/F AIG Tower
1 Connaught Road Central
Central, Hong Kong
Phone: 852-2832-1800
E-mail: aiggic@aig.com
Website: www.aiggig.com

Other Offices

7&8 Jl. Jend
Sudirman Senayan
Jakarta, Indonesia 10270

12/F Al Tower
181 Suraqongse Road
Bangkok, Thailand 10500

Suite 542, Shanghai Center
1376 Nanjing Xi Lu
Shanghai, China 200040

9th Floor, Hanil Building Suite 910
64-5 Chungmuro 2ga, Chung-Ku
Seoul, South Korea 100012
Phone: 822-6353-7400
Fax: 822-6353-7444

7th Floor, 168 Jhuangjing Road
Taipei, Taiwan
Phone: 886-2-758-9520
Fax: 886-2-8786-7377

23/F Philamlife Building
Paseo de Roxas, Makati City
Manila, Philippines
Phone: 632-885-8877
Fax: 632-885-8882

FCH House, G/F, Peninsula Corporate Park
G.K. Marg, Lower Parel
Mumbai, India 400 013
Phone: 91-22-4093-0001

Level 24, Menara AIA
99 Jalan Ampang
Kuala Lumpur, Malaysia 50450

AIA Tower #12-00
1 Robinson Road
Singapore, Singapore 048542

AIG Building, 1-3, Marunouchi
1-chome, Chiyoda-Ku
Tokyo, Japan 100-0005

Management and Staff

Ada Tse, Managing Director
Anil Gudibande, Vice President
Apichat Nataslipa, Vice President
Ashish Kumar, Vice President
David Yeung, Managing Director
Jo Tang, Vice President
Ronald Seah, Vice President
Santosh Senapati, Managing Director
Stewart Homler, Managing Director
Stewart Thong, Vice President
Terry Loh, Vice President
Timothy Kim, Vice President
Vivian Zheng, Managing Director

Type of Firm

Insurance Firm Affiliate

Association Membership

Hong Kong Venture Capital Association (HKVCA)

Project Preferences

Type of Financing Preferred:

Fund of Funds
Leveraged Buyout
Early Stage
Expansion
Mezzanine
Acquisition

Size of Investments Considered:

Min Size of Investment Considered (000s): $5,000
Max Size of Investment Considered: No Limit

Geographical Preferences

United States Preferences:

All U.S.

International Preferences:

Western Europe
Asia
Japan

Industry Preferences

In Medical/Health prefer:

Health Services

In Industrial/Energy prefer:

Energy

In Transportation prefer:

Transportation

In Business Serv. prefer:

Services

In Manufact. prefer:
Manufacturing

In Agr/Forestr/Fish prefer:
Mining and Minerals

Additional Information
Year Founded: 1987
Capital Under Management: $5,000,000,000
Current Activity Level: Actively seeking new investments

AIG JAPAN PARTNERS INC.

1-1-3 Marunouchi
8/F AIG Bldg., Chiyoda-ku
Tokyo, Japan 130-8234
Phone: 81-3-3218-5951
Fax: 81-3-3217-3680
Website: www.aig.co.jp

Type of Firm
Bank Affiliated

Project Preferences

Type of Financing Preferred:
Leveraged Buyout
Expansion
Turnaround
Later Stage
Management Buyouts

Geographical Preferences

International Preferences:
Japan

Industry Preferences

In Consumer Related prefer:
Consumer Products
Consumer Services

In Transportation prefer:
Transportation

In Manufact. prefer:
Manufacturing

Additional Information
Year Founded: 2000
Capital Under Management: $65,700,000
Current Activity Level: Actively seeking new investments

AIR PRODUCTS AND CHEMICALS, INC.

7201 Hamilton Boulevard
Allentown, PA USA 18195
Phone: 610-481-4911
Fax: 610-481-5900
E-mail: info@airproducts.com
Website: www.airproducts.com

Other Offices
2880 Lakeside Drive
Suite 150
Santa Clara, CA USA 95054
Phone: 408-492-9080

Kanaalweg 15, Box 3193
3502 GD
Utrecht, Netherlands
Phone: 31-30-2857100
Fax: 31-30-2857111

9901 Valley Ranch Parkway E.
Ste 1040
Irving, TX USA 75063
Phone: 214-574-1401
Fax: 214-574-1430

Hersham Place, Molesey Road
Hersham, Walton-on-Thames
Surrey, United Kingdom KT12 4RZ
Phone: 44-1932-249200
Fax: 44-1932-249565

5508 Highway 290 West
Suite 150
Austin, TX USA 78735
Phone: 512-892-7772

36637 Highway 30
Geismar, LA USA 70734
Phone: 225-677-7007

Suite 196
12600 Northborough Dr.
Houston, TX USA 77067
Phone: 281-873-5151

1969 Palomar Oaks Way
Carlsbad, CA USA 92009
Phone: 760-931-9555

2415, 2441, and 2507 West Erie Drive
Tempe, AZ USA 85282
Phone: 602 453-9229

Nine Temasek Boulevard
Suite 08-02 Suntec Tower Two
Singapore 038989
Phone: 65-6332-1610
Fax: 65-6332-1600

Suite 6505-7, Central Plaza
18 Harbour Road
Hong Kong
Phone: 852-2527-1922
Fax: 852-2527-1827

17330 Brookhurst St
Suite 260
Fountain Valley, CA USA 92708
Phone: 714-968-5133

Type of Firm
Corporate PE/Venture

Association Membership
National Venture Capital Association - USA (NVCA)

Project Preferences

Role in Financing:
Prefer role in deals created by others

Type of Financing Preferred:
Second Stage Financing
Expansion
Later Stage
Strategic Alliances
Acquisition
Private Placement

Size of Investments Considered:
Min Size of Investment Considered (000s): $500
Max Size of Investment Considered (000s): $3,000

Geographical Preferences

United States Preferences:
All U.S.

Canadian Preferences:
All Canada

International Preferences:
United Kingdom
Spain
Germany
France

Industry Preferences

In Communications prefer:
Data Communications

In Computer Software prefer:
Data Processing
Systems Software

In Semiconductor/Electr prefer:
Semiconductor
Fiber Optics
Optoelectronics

In Biotechnology prefer:
Biosensors

In Medical/Health prefer:
Health Services

In Consumer Related prefer:
Food/Beverage

In Industrial/Energy prefer:
Energy
Industrial Products
Environmental Related

In Transportation prefer:
Transportation

In Manufact. prefer:
Manufacturing

Additional Information
Name of Most Recent Fund: Air Products and Chemicals
Most Recent Fund Was Raised: 10/10/2000
Year Founded: 1940
Capital Under Management: $45,800,000

Current Activity Level: Actively seeking new investments
Method of Compensation: Return on investment is of primary concern, do not charge fees

AISLING CAPITAL (FKA: PERSEUS-SOROS MANAGEMENT COMPANY)

888 Seventh Avenue
30th Floor
New York, NY USA 10106
Phone: 212-651-6380
Fax: 212-651-6379
Website: www.aislingcapital.com

Management and Staff

Andrew Schiff, Managing Director
Anthony Sun, Principal
Brett I.W. Zbar, Principal
Dennis Purcell, Senior Managing Director
Dov Goldstein, Principal
Lloyd Appel, Chief Financial Officer
Steven Elms, Managing Director

Type of Firm

Private Equity Firm

Project Preferences

Role in Financing:
Prefer role as deal originator but will also invest in deals created by others

Type of Financing Preferred:
Balanced
Public Companies

Size of Investments Considered:
Min Size of Investment Considered (000s): $15,000
Max Size of Investment Considered (000s): $30,000

Industry Preferences

In Biotechnology prefer:
Biotechnology

In Medical/Health prefer:
Pharmaceuticals

Additional Information

Name of Most Recent Fund: Aisling Capital III, L.P.
Most Recent Fund Was Raised: 09/02/2008
Year Founded: 2000
Capital Under Management: $1,600,000,000
Current Activity Level: Actively seeking new investments

AITEC, SGPS, SA

Av. Duque de Avila, 23
Lisboa, Portugal 1000-138
Phone: 351-21-310-0013
Fax: 351-21-352-6314
E-mail: info@aitec.pt
Website: www.aitec.pt

Type of Firm

Private Equity Firm

Project Preferences

Type of Financing Preferred:
Balanced

Additional Information

Year Founded: 2007
Current Activity Level: Actively seeking new investments

AJU IB INVESMENT CO., LTD. (FKA: KIBO TECHNOLOGY) (FKA: KTAC)

20th Floor, Glass Tower Bldg.
946-1, Taechi-Dong, Kangnam-Gu
Seoul, South Korea 135-839
Phone: 822-3451-9200
Fax: 82-02-3452-9805
Website: www.ajuib.co.kr

Management and Staff

Kwang-sun Yang, Managing Director
Nam-Chun Cho, Managing Director
Sang-Sun Park, Managing Director
Sei-yong Oh, Managing Director

Type of Firm

Private Equity Firm

Association Membership

Korean Venture Capital Association (KVCA)

Project Preferences

Type of Financing Preferred:
Fund of Funds
Early Stage
Mezzanine
Balanced
Seed
Startup

Geographical Preferences

International Preferences:
Korea, South

Industry Preferences

In Communications prefer:
Communications and Media

In Semiconductor/Electr prefer:
Electronics

In Biotechnology prefer:
Biotechnology

In Business Serv. prefer:
Media

In Manufact. prefer:
Manufacturing

Additional Information

Year Founded: 1974
Capital Under Management: $142,100,000
Current Activity Level: Actively seeking new investments

AKARA, LTD. (DBA: IDG VENTURES EUROPE)

2 Cavendish Square
London, United Kingdom W1G 0PD
Phone: 44-207-299-7399
Fax: 44-207-299-7390
E-mail: info@idgve.com
Website: www.idgve.com

Management and Staff

Ajay Chowdhury, General Partner
Anil Hansjee, Principal
Christopher Smart, General Partner
Hitesh Mehta, General Partner
Patrick Kenealy, Partner
Patrick McGovern, Partner

Type of Firm

Private Equity Advisor or Fund of Funds

Association Membership

British Venture Capital Association (BVCA)

Project Preferences

Type of Financing Preferred:
Fund of Funds
Startup

Geographical Preferences

International Preferences:
Europe
Israel

Industry Preferences

In Communications prefer:
Communications and Media
Wireless Communications

In Computer Software prefer:
Software

In Internet Specific prefer:
Internet

In Computer Other prefer:
Computer Related

Additional Information

Year Founded: 2005
Capital Under Management: $100,000,000
Current Activity Level: Actively seeking new investments

AKJ INVESTMENTS SA

ul. Wilcza 46
Warsaw, Poland 00-679
Phone: 48-22-622-4470
Fax: 48-22-622-4482

Management and Staff

Kazimierz Waga, Chief Executive Officer

Type of Firm

Private Equity Firm

Project Preferences

Type of Financing Preferred:
Balanced

Geographical Preferences

International Preferences:
Europe
Poland

Additional Information

Year Founded: 2005
Current Activity Level: Actively seeking new investments

AKSIA GROUP SPA

Piazza del Liberty, 2
Milan, Italy 20121
Phone: 39-02-890-4631
Fax: 39-02-890-4635
E-mail: info@aksiagroup.com
Website: www.aksia.it

Other Offices

Via des Am,brois, 3
Turin, Italy 10123
Phone: 39-11-812-9611
Fax: 39-11-569-0840

Management and Staff

Nicola Emanuele, Managing Director
Roberto Borsa, Managing Director
Stefano Guidotti, Managing Director

Type of Firm

Private Equity Firm

Association Membership

Italian Venture Capital Association (AIFI)

Project Preferences

Type of Financing Preferred:
Leveraged Buyout
Early Stage
Expansion
Balanced

Size of Investments Considered:
Min Size of Investment Considered (000s): $863
Max Size of Investment Considered (000s): $5,179

Geographical Preferences

International Preferences:
Italy

Industry Preferences

In Communications prefer:
Telecommunications

In Consumer Related prefer:
Consumer Products

In Industrial/Energy prefer:
Industrial Products

In Business Serv. prefer:
Media

In Manufact. prefer:
Manufacturing

Additional Information

Year Founded: 2001
Capital Under Management: $25,900,000
Current Activity Level: Actively seeking new investments

AKTIVA INVEST JAMTLAND & HARJEDALEN AB

Prastgatan 31 B
Ostersund, Sweden 831 31
Phone: 46-63-132-040
E-mail: info@aktivainvest.se
Website: www.aktivainvest.se

Type of Firm

Private Equity Firm

Association Membership

European Private Equity and Venture Capital Assoc.

Additional Information

Year Founded: 2006
Capital Under Management: $5,600,000
Current Activity Level: Actively seeking new investments

AL ANWAR HOLDINGS SAOG

Villa No. 897
Way No. 3013
Shati Al Qurum, Oman
Phone: 968-2469-2503
Fax: 968-2469-2507
E-mail: aaitco@omantel.net.om
Website: www.alanwarholdings.com

Management and Staff

Krishna Kumar Gupta, Chief Executive Officer

Type of Firm

Private Equity Firm

Project Preferences

Type of Financing Preferred:
Acquisition

Geographical Preferences

International Preferences:
Oman
Utd. Arab Em.

Industry Preferences

In Consumer Related prefer:
Consumer Products

In Industrial/Energy prefer:
Energy
Oil and Gas Exploration
Industrial Products

In Financial Services prefer:
Financial Services
Insurance

In Business Serv. prefer:
Services

Additional Information

Year Founded: 1994
Current Activity Level: Actively seeking new investments

AL MAL CAPITAL

302, Burj Dubai Square 4
Sheikh Zayed Road
Dubai, Utd. Arab Em.
Phone: 971-4-360-1111
Fax: 971-4-360-1122
Website: www.almalcapital.com

Management and Staff

Blair Look, Managing Director
Khalid Madi, Managing Director
Narendra Gajria, Chief Operating Officer

Type of Firm

Bank Affiliated

Project Preferences

Type of Financing Preferred:
Balanced
Later Stage
Recapitalizations

Geographical Preferences

International Preferences:
Middle East
Africa

Industry Preferences

In Communications prefer:
Communications and Media
Telecommunications
Media and Entertainment

In Consumer Related prefer:
Consumer Services

In Financial Services prefer:
Financial Services
Real Estate
Financial Services

Additional Information

Year Founded: 2007
Capital Under Management: $48,000,000
Current Activity Level: Actively seeking new investments

ALACON VENTURES LLC

101 California Street
Suite 2940
San Francisco, CA USA 94111
Phone: 415-392-9020
Fax: 415-392-9026
Website: www.alaconventures.com

Management and Staff

David Williams, Managing Partner

Type of Firm

Private Equity Firm

Association Membership

National Venture Capital Association - USA (NVCA)

Project Preferences

Type of Financing Preferred:
Early Stage
Expansion
Later Stage

Geographical Preferences

United States Preferences:
All U.S.

International Preferences:
China

Industry Preferences

In Communications prefer:
Communications and Media

In Internet Specific prefer:
Internet

In Consumer Related prefer:
Consumer Services

Additional Information

Year Founded: 2007
Capital Under Management: $100,000,000
Current Activity Level: Actively seeking new investments

ALAFI CAPITAL CO.

P.O. Box 7338
Berkeley, CA USA 94707
Phone: 510-653-7425
Fax: 510-653-6231
Website: www.alafi.com

Management and Staff

Christopher Alafi, General Partner
Moshe Alafi, General Partner

Type of Firm

Private Equity Firm

Association Membership

Western Association of Venture Capitalists (WAVC)

Project Preferences

Role in Financing:
Will function either as deal originator or investor in deals created by others

Type of Financing Preferred:
Early Stage
Research and Development
Start-up Financing
Seed
First Stage Financing

Size of Investments Considered:
Min Size of Investment Considered (000s): $500
Max Size of Investment Considered (000s): $2,000

Industry Preferences

In Semiconductor/Electr prefer:
Analytic/Scientific

In Biotechnology prefer:
Biotechnology
Genetic Engineering

In Medical/Health prefer:
Diagnostic Services
Drug/Equipmt Delivery

Additional Information

Name of Most Recent Fund: Alafi Capital Company
Most Recent Fund Was Raised: 01/01/1984
Year Founded: 1984
Capital Under Management: $60,000,000
Current Activity Level: Reducing investment activity
Method of Compensation: Return on investment is of primary concern, do not charge fees

ALAMEDA CAPITAL LLC

5424 Sunol Boulevard
Building Ten, Suite 225
Pleasanton, CA USA 94566
Phone: 925-251-1200
Fax: 925-484-2566
E-mail: ihaveaquestion@alamedavc.com
Website: www.alamedavc.com

Management and Staff

Alex Krem, Managing Director
Mark Klopp, Venture Partner
Norm Wu, Venture Partner
Po Chi Wu, Managing Director
Richard Helfrich, Managing Director

Type of Firm

Private Equity Firm

Project Preferences

Role in Financing:
Prefer role as deal originator but will also invest in deals created by others

Type of Financing Preferred:
Expansion
Early Stage
First Stage Financing

Size of Investments Considered:
Min Size of Investment Considered (000s): $500
Max Size of Investment Considered (000s): $2,000

Geographical Preferences

United States Preferences:
Arizona
Oregon
California
Washington
Texas

Industry Preferences

In Semiconductor/Electr prefer:
Electronics
Semiconductor
Sensors

In Biotechnology prefer:
Biosensors

In Medical/Health prefer:
Medical Diagnostics

In Industrial/Energy prefer:
Alternative Energy
Advanced Materials

Additional Information

Year Founded: 2003
Capital Under Management: $1,000,000
Current Activity Level: Actively seeking new investments
Method of Compensation: Return on invest. most important, but chg. closing fees, service fees, etc.

ALBANY VENTURE MANAGERS, LTD.

Forth House
28 Rutland Square
Edinburgh, United Kingdom EH1 2BW
Phone: 44-131-221-6510
Fax: 44-131-221-6511
E-mail: info@albanyventures.co.uk
Website: www.albanyventures.co.uk

Management and Staff
Raymond Abbott, Managing Director

Type of Firm
Private Equity Advisor or Fund of Funds

Project Preferences
Type of Financing Preferred:
Early Stage

Geographical Preferences
International Preferences:
United Kingdom
Europe

Industry Preferences
In Computer Software prefer:
Software

In Medical/Health prefer:
Medical/Health

Additional Information
Year Founded: 2000
Capital Under Management: $31,800,000
Current Activity Level: Actively seeking new investments

ALBATROS INVESTMENTS
Wilhelminaplantsoen 7d
Bussum, Netherlands 1404 JA
Phone: 31-355-315-080
Fax: 31-356-245-606
E-mail: info@albatrosinvestments.nl
Website: www.albatrosinvestments.nl

Management and Staff
Willem Van Waveren, Managing Partner

Type of Firm
Private Equity Firm

Additional Information
Current Activity Level: Actively seeking new investments

ALBATROSS INVESTMENT CAPITAL CO., LTD.
107-111 Nogosan-Dong, Mapo-Gu
4/F Mihwa Building
Seoul, South Korea 121-807
Phone: 822-703-0231
Fax: 822-705-7968

Management and Staff
Young Min Lee, Chief Executive Officer

Type of Firm
Private Equity Firm

Project Preferences
Type of Financing Preferred:
Balanced

Additional Information
Year Founded: 2008
Capital Under Management: $8,300,000
Current Activity Level: Actively seeking new investments

ALBATROZ PARTICIPACOES
Av. das Americas 4200
Bl. 8 Ed. Geneve, Cob. 301a
Rio de Janeiro, Brazil 22640-102
Phone: 55-21-3150-2522
Fax: 55-21-3385-4139
E-mail: comercial@albatroznet.com.br
Website: www.albatroznet.com.br

Management and Staff
Alexandre Icaza, Partner
Gabriella Icaza, Partner

Type of Firm
Private Equity Firm

Project Preferences
Type of Financing Preferred:
Balanced

Geographical Preferences
International Preferences:
Brazil

Additional Information
Year Founded: 2002
Current Activity Level: Actively seeking new investments

ALBERTA REVENUE
331 Terrace Building
9515-107 Street
Edmonton, Canada T5K2C3
Phone: 780-422-5620
Fax: 780-422-0257
Website: www.finance.gov.ab.ca

Type of Firm
Government Affiliated Program

Project Preferences
Type of Financing Preferred:
Leveraged Buyout

Additional Information
Year Founded: 2009
Current Activity Level: Actively seeking new investments

ALBION INVESTORS, LLC (FKA: ALBION ALLIANCE, LLC)
75 Rockefeller Plaza
15th Floor
New York, NY USA 10019
Phone: 212-277-7520
Website: www.albioninvestors.com

Management and Staff
Alastair Tedford, Chief Executive Officer
Mark Arnold, Chief Executive Officer

Type of Firm
Bank Affiliated

Additional Information
Name of Most Recent Fund: Albion Alliance Mezzanine Fund II
Most Recent Fund Was Raised: 10/12/1999
Year Founded: 1998
Current Activity Level: Actively seeking new investments

ALBION VENTURES LLP (FKA: CLOSE VENTURE MANAGEMENT)
10 Crown Place
London, United Kingdom EC2A 4FT
Phone: 44-20-7422-7830
Fax: 44-20-7422-7849
E-mail: info@closeinvestments.com
Website: www.closeventures.co.uk

Management and Staff
Patrick Reeve, Managing Director

Type of Firm
Bank Affiliated

Project Preferences
Type of Financing Preferred:
Early Stage
Expansion
Balanced
Start-up Financing
Management Buyouts

Size of Investments Considered:
Min Size of Investment Considered (000s): $1,370
Max Size of Investment Considered (000s): $13,697

Geographical Preferences
International Preferences:
United Kingdom
Europe

Industry Preferences

In Consumer Related prefer:

Entertainment and Leisure
Other Restaurants
Hotels and Resorts

Additional Information

Year Founded: 1996
Capital Under Management: $178,600,000
Current Activity Level: Actively seeking new investments

ALCATEL CANADA INC.

600 March Road
P.O. Box 13600
Ottawa, Canada K2K2E6
Phone: 613-591-3600
Fax: 613-599-3626
Website: www.alcatel.ca

Type of Firm

Private Equity Firm

Additional Information

Year Founded: 2009
Current Activity Level: Actively seeking new investments

ALCATEL-LUCENT VENTURES (FKA: LUCENT VENTURE PARTNERS, INC.)

600-700 Mountain Avenue
Murray Hill, NJ USA 07974
Phone: 908-508-8080
Fax: 908-582-6069
Website: www.alcatel-lucent.com/ventures

Management and Staff

Bob Slater, Vice President
Jill DiRoma, Chief Financial Officer

Type of Firm

Corporate PE/Venture

Project Preferences

Role in Financing:

Will function either as deal originator or investor in deals created by others

Type of Financing Preferred:

Early Stage

Size of Investments Considered:

Min Size of Investment Considered (000s): $500
Max Size of Investment Considered (000s): $5,000

Geographical Preferences

International Preferences:

Europe
Middle East

Industry Focus

(% based on actual investment)

Communications and Media	28.3%
Semiconductors/Other Elect.	25.7%
Computer Software and Services	20.0%
Internet Specific	19.8%
Computer Hardware	6.3%

Additional Information

Name of Most Recent Fund: Lucent Venture Partners III
Most Recent Fund Was Raised: 06/20/2001
Year Founded: 1998
Capital Under Management: $300,000,000
Current Activity Level: Making few, if any, new investments
Method of Compensation: Return on investment is of primary concern, do not charge fees

---

ALCEDO SGR S.P.A.

Vicolo XX Settembre, 11
Treviso, Italy 31100
Phone: 39-422-559-111
Fax: 39-422-580-000
E-mail: info@alcedo.it
Website: www.alcedo.it

Management and Staff

Giovanni Gajo, President
Maurizio Masetti, Managing Director

Type of Firm

Private Equity Firm

Project Preferences

Type of Financing Preferred:

Leveraged Buyout
Management Buyouts
Acquisition

Geographical Preferences

International Preferences:

Italy
Europe

Additional Information

Year Founded: 2001
Capital Under Management: $257,000,000
Current Activity Level: Actively seeking new investments

ALCHEMY PARTNERS LLP

25 Bedford Street
Covent Garden
London, United Kingdom WC2E 9ES
Phone: 44-20-7240-9596
Fax: 44-20-7240-9594
E-mail: info@alchemypartners.com
Website: www.alchemypartners.co.uk

Management and Staff

Dominic Slade, Managing Partner
Frits Prakke, Managing Director
Gavin Loughrey, Partner
Ian Cash, Managing Director
John Martin, Partner
Paul Bridges, Partner
Simon Oakland, Partner

Type of Firm

Private Equity Firm

Association Membership

British Venture Capital Association (BVCA)
European Private Equity and Venture Capital Assoc.

Project Preferences

Role in Financing:

Prefer role as deal originator

Type of Financing Preferred:

Leveraged Buyout
Generalist PE
Balanced
Turnaround
Management Buyouts
Special Situation
Acquisition
Distressed Debt

Size of Investments Considered:

Min Size of Investment Considered (000s): $51,155
Max Size of Investment Considered (000s): $327,392

Geographical Preferences

International Preferences:

United Kingdom
Switzerland
Europe
Austria
Australia
Germany
Asia
All International

Industry Focus

(% based on actual investment)

Consumer Related	39.1%
Other Products	22.8%
Industrial/Energy	10.1%
Communications and Media	9.1%
Computer Hardware	9.0%
Computer Software and Services	7.7%
Medical/Health	2.0%
Internet Specific	0.4%

Additional Information

Year Founded: 1997
Capital Under Management: $1,328,700,000
Current Activity Level: Actively seeking new investments
Method of Compensation: Return on invest. most important, but chg. closing fees, service fees, etc.

ALCUIN CAPITAL

5th Floor, 140 Brompton Road
London, United Kingdom SW3 1HY
Phone: 44-207-808-0220
Fax: 44-207-584-7933
E-mail: info@alcuincapital.com
Website: www.alcuincapital.com

Management and Staff

Mark Storey, Managing Director

Type of Firm

Private Equity Firm

Project Preferences

Type of Financing Preferred:
Leveraged Buyout
Expansion
Management Buyouts
Recapitalizations

Size of Investments Considered:
Min Size of Investment Considered (000s): $1,679
Max Size of Investment Considered (000s): $6,716

Geographical Preferences

International Preferences:
United Kingdom
Europe

Additional Information

Year Founded: 2003
Current Activity Level: Actively seeking new investments

ALDANO AB

Vasagatan 11
11 tr
Stockholm, Sweden 111 20
Phone: 46-8-587-91-970
Fax: 46-8-587-91-975
E-mail: info@aldano.se
Website: www.aldano.se

Management and Staff

Eric Martin, Partner

Type of Firm

Corporate PE/Venture

Association Membership

Swedish Venture Capital Association (SVCA)
European Private Equity and Venture Capital Assoc.

Project Preferences

Type of Financing Preferred:
Leveraged Buyout
Expansion
Turnaround

Size of Investments Considered:
Min Size of Investment Considered (000s): $400
Max Size of Investment Considered (000s): $400,000

Geographical Preferences

International Preferences:
Sweden

Additional Information

Year Founded: 2000
Capital Under Management: $13,400,000
Current Activity Level: Actively seeking new investments

ALERION CAPITAL GROUP, LLC

7702 East Doubletree Ranch Rd.
Suite 350
Scottsdale, AZ USA 85258
Phone: 480-367-0900
Fax: 480-367-0936
Website: www.alerion.com

Management and Staff

James Unruh, Principal
Jeffrey Unruh, Managing Director
Ricardo DeAvila, Managing Director

Type of Firm

Bank Affiliated

Project Preferences

Type of Financing Preferred:
Leveraged Buyout
Later Stage
Management Buyouts
Recapitalizations

Geographical Preferences

United States Preferences:
Rocky Mountain
Southwest

Industry Preferences

In Semiconductor/Electr prefer:
Electronics

In Industrial/Energy prefer:
Industrial Products

In Business Serv. prefer:
Distribution

Additional Information

Year Founded: 1999
Capital Under Management: $1,000,000
Current Activity Level: Actively seeking new investments

ALERION PARTNERS

105 Rowayton Avenue
Rowayton, CT USA 06853
Phone: 203-838-6700
Fax: 203-838-6712
E-mail: info@alerionpartners.com
Website: www.alerionpartners.com

Management and Staff

Bruce Failing, Partner
Michael Persky, Partner
Norman Tsang, Partner
Robert Cioffi, Venture Partner

Type of Firm

Private Equity Firm

Project Preferences

Type of Financing Preferred:
Early Stage
Balanced
Recapitalizations

Size of Investments Considered:
Min Size of Investment Considered (000s): $3,000
Max Size of Investment Considered (000s): $7,000

Geographical Preferences

United States Preferences:
All U.S.

Industry Preferences

In Communications prefer:
Communications and Media

In Consumer Related prefer:
Consumer Services

In Business Serv. prefer:
Services

Additional Information

Year Founded: 2004
Capital Under Management: $40,000,000
Current Activity Level: Actively seeking new investments

ALETHEIA PARTNERS LTD

37 Upper Grosvenor Street
London, United Kingdom W1K 2NE
Phone: 44-207-663-6666
E-mail: info@aletheiapartners.com
Website: www.aletheiapartners.com

Type of Firm

Private Equity Firm

Project Preferences

Type of Financing Preferred:
Leveraged Buyout

Geographical Preferences

International Preferences:
United Kingdom
Germany
France

Additional Information
Year Founded: 2002
Current Activity Level: Actively seeking new investments

ALETTI MERCHANT BANK
Piazza Missori 3
Milan, Italy 20122
Phone: 39-02-72108524
Fax: 39-02-72108555

Type of Firm
Bank Affiliated

Geographical Preferences
International Preferences:
Italy

Additional Information
Year Founded: 2003
Current Activity Level: Actively seeking new investments

ALETTI PRIVATE EQUITY SGR
Via Giulini, 3
Milan, Italy 20123
Phone: 39-2-854-6421
Website: www.alettiprivateequity.it

Management and Staff
Massimo Spisni, President

Type of Firm
Private Equity Firm

Project Preferences
Type of Financing Preferred:
Expansion

Geographical Preferences
International Preferences:
Italy
Europe

Additional Information
Year Founded: 2001
Current Activity Level: Actively seeking new investments

ALEUTIAN CAPITAL PARTNERS LLC
350 Fifth Avenue
Suite 6720, Empire State Bldg.
New York, NY USA 10118
Phone: 212-652-4000
Fax: 212-652-4030
E-mail: info@aleutiancapital.com
Website: www.aleutiancapital.com

Management and Staff
Eyal Zadik, Vice President
Louis Black, Managing Director
O. James Sterling, Managing Director

Type of Firm
Private Equity Firm

Project Preferences
Type of Financing Preferred:
Leveraged Buyout
Management Buyouts
Acquisition

Geographical Preferences
United States preferences:
All U.S.

Industry Preferences
In Computer Software prefer:
Software
In Business Serv. prefer:
Services
Distribution
In Manufact. prefer:
Manufacturing

Additional Information
Year Founded: 2007
Current Activity Level: Actively seeking new investments

ALEXANDER HUTTON VENTURE PARTNERS
999 Third Avenue
Suite 3700
Seattle, WA USA 98104
Phone: 206-341-9800
Fax: 206-341-9810
E-mail: ahvp@ahvp.com
Website: www.ahvp.com

Other Offices
2626 North Pearl
Tacoma, WA USA 98407
Phone: 253-752-3612
Fax: 253-752-3676

Management and Staff
James Thompson, Principal
Jerry Keppler, Managing Director
Kent Johnson, Managing Director
Mark Klebanoff, Managing Director
Tom Johnston, Managing Director

Type of Firm
Private Equity Firm

Association Membership
National Venture Capital Association - USA (NVCA)

Project Preferences
Role in Financing:
Will function either as deal originator or investor in deals created by others
Type of Financing Preferred:
Early Stage
Expansion
Mezzanine
Balanced
Seed
Private Placement
Size of Investments Considered:
Min Size of Investment Considered (000s): $500
Max Size of Investment Considered (000s): $5,000

Geographical Preferences
United States Preferences:
Oregon
Washington
Canadian Preferences:
British Columbia

Industry Preferences
In Internet Specific prefer:
Internet

Additional Information
Name of Most Recent Fund: Alexander Hutton Venture Partners, LP
Most Recent Fund Was Raised: 12/31/1999
Year Founded: 1999
Capital Under Management: $95,000,000
Current Activity Level: Actively seeking new investments
Method of Compensation: Return on investment is of primary concern, do not charge fees

ALEXANDRIA REAL ESTATE EQUITIES, LLC
135 North Los Robles
Suite 250
Pasadena, CA USA 91101
Phone: 626-578-9693
Fax: 626-578-0896
E-mail: corporateinformation@labspace.com
Website: www.labspace.com

Management and Staff
Etsuko Mason, Vice President
Joel Marcus, Chief Executive Officer

Type of Firm
Corporate PE/Venture

Association Membership
National Venture Capital Association - USA (NVCA)

Additional Information

Year Founded: 2000
Current Activity Level: Actively seeking new investments

ALF YAD, LTD.

c/o Daman Investments PCS
P.O. Box 9436
Dubai, Utd. Arab Em.
Phone: 971-4-408-0422
Fax: 971-4-332-4164
E-mail: alfyad@daman.ae
Website: www.alfyad.ae

Type of Firm

Investment Management Firm

Project Preferences

Type of Financing Preferred:
Balanced

Geographical Preferences

International Preferences:
Utd. Arab Em.
Middle East

Additional Information

Year Founded: 2005
Current Activity Level: Actively seeking new investments

ALFA CAPITAL PARTNERS

32/1 Sadovaya-Kudrinskaya St.
Moscow, Russia 123001
Phone: 7-495-775-1828
Fax: 7-495-775-1827
E-mail: info@alfacp.ru
Website: www.alfacp.ru

Management and Staff

Bill Lane, Managing Director
Daniel Wolfe, Senior Managing Director
Mark Lang, Managing Director
Richard Sobel, Chief Executive Officer
Slava Sinadski, Managing Director
Vladislav Mamoulkine, Managing Director

Type of Firm

Private Equity Firm

Project Preferences

Type of Financing Preferred:
Leveraged Buyout
Expansion
Early Stage
Balanced
Other
Management Buyouts

Geographical Preferences

International Preferences:
Armenia
Belarus
Kazakhstan
Europe
Kyrgyzstan
Tajikistan
Turkmenistan
Eastern Europe
Azerbaijan
Moldova
Ukraine
Uzbekistan
Russia

Industry Preferences

In Communications prefer:
Communications and Media
Telecommunications

In Medical/Health prefer:
Medical/Health
Health Services
Pharmaceuticals

In Consumer Related prefer:
Entertainment and Leisure
Retail
Consumer Products
Consumer Services

In Business Serv. prefer:
Media

In Manufact. prefer:
Publishing

In Agr/Forestr/Fish prefer:
Agribusiness

Additional Information

Year Founded: 2003
Capital Under Management: $626,000,000
Current Activity Level: Actively seeking new investments

ALGEBRA CAPITAL

DIFC, Building 3, 7th Floor
P.O. Box 506558
Dubai, Utd. Arab Em.
Phone: 971-4-425-0999
Fax: 971-4-425-0998
E-mail: info@algebra-capital.com
Website: www.algebra-capital.com

Management and Staff

Alain Antoniades, Chief Operating Officer
Daniel Smaller, Managing Director
Jacques Visser, Managing Director
Joe Kawkabani, Managing Director
Mohieddine Kronfol, Managing Director

Type of Firm

Private Equity Firm

Project Preferences

Type of Financing Preferred:
Balanced

Geographical Preferences

International Preferences:
Middle East
Asia
Africa

Additional Information

Year Founded: 2006
Current Activity Level: Actively seeking new investments

ALICE VENTURES SRL

Piazzale F. Baracca 1
Milan, Italy 20123
Phone: 39-02-499-8171
Fax: 39-02-4851-7583
E-mail: info@aliceventures.it
Website: www.aliceventures.it

Other Offices

11 Galgaley Haplada St.
Entrance C. 3rd Floor
Herzliya, Israel 46733
Phone: 972-9-956-1370
Fax: 972-9-956-1361

Management and Staff

Edoardo Lecaldano, Partner
Ilaria Rajevich, Chief Financial Officer
John Gonzalez, Partner

Type of Firm

Private Equity Firm

Association Membership

Italian Venture Capital Association (AIFI)
European Private Equity and Venture Capital Assoc.

Project Preferences

Type of Financing Preferred:
Early Stage
Balanced
Seed
Startup

Size of Investments Considered:
Min Size of Investment Considered (000s): $900
Max Size of Investment Considered: No Limit

Geographical Preferences

International Preferences:
Europe
Israel

Industry Preferences

In Communications prefer:
Communications and Media
Telecommunications

In Internet Specific prefer:
Internet

In Business Serv. prefer:
Media

Additional Information

Name of Most Recent Fund: MB Venture Capital Fund I
Most Recent Fund Was Raised: 06/18/1999
Year Founded: 1999
Capital Under Management: $143,500,000
Current Activity Level: Actively seeking new investments

ALLBA INVEST AB

Banvaktsvagen 20
Solna, Sweden 17148
Phone: 46-8-735-3660
Fax: 46-8-730-0700
Website: www.allbainvest.se

Management and Staff

Jonny E Jensen, Founder

Type of Firm

Private Equity Firm

Association Membership

Swedish Venture Capital Association (SVCA)

Project Preferences

Type of Financing Preferred:
Early Stage
Seed
Startup

Geographical Preferences

International Preferences:
Sweden

Industry Preferences

In Semiconductor/Electr prefer:
Electronics

In Biotechnology prefer:
Biotechnology

In Medical/Health prefer:
Medical/Health

In Industrial/Energy prefer:
Environmental Related

Additional Information

Year Founded: 2006
Current Activity Level: Actively seeking new investments

ALLCO EQUITY PARTNERS MANAGEMENT PTY LTD.

Level 35
101 Collins Street
Melbourne, Australia 3000
Phone: 613-8626-9800
Fax: 613-8626-9811
E-mail: enquiries@allcoequitypartners.com.au
Website: www.allcoequitypartners.com.au

Other Offices

Level 24 Gateway
1 Macquarie Place
Sydney, Australia 2000
Phone: 612-9255-4100
Fax: 612-9241-4900

Management and Staff

Peter Yates, Managing Director
Robert Moran, Managing Director

Type of Firm

Bank Affiliated

Project Preferences

Type of Financing Preferred:
Leveraged Buyout
Mezzanine
Turnaround
Management Buyouts
Acquisition
Recapitalizations

Geographical Preferences

International Preferences:
Australia

Industry Preferences

In Communications prefer:
Media and Entertainment

In Medical/Health prefer:
Health Services

In Consumer Related prefer:
Casino/Gambling

In Financial Services prefer:
Financial Services

Additional Information

Year Founded: 2004
Capital Under Management: $332,700,000
Current Activity Level: Actively seeking new investments

ALLEGIS CAPITAL (AKA: MEDIA TECHNOLOGY VENTURES)

130 Lytton Avenue
Suite 210
Palo Alto, CA USA 94301
Phone: 650-687-0500
Fax: 650-687-0234
E-mail: vc@allegiscapital.com
Website: www.allegiscapital.com

Other Offices

345 Spear Street
Suite 505
San Francisco, CA USA 94105
Phone: 415-348-8868
Fax: 415-278-9794

100 Wilshire Boulevard
Suite 1770
Santa Monica, CA USA 90401
Phone: 310-319-3880
Fax: 310-319-3881

Management and Staff

Barry Weinman, Managing Director
Frank Fanzilli, Venture Partner
Gordon Radley, Venture Partner
Herbert Schorr, Venture Partner
J. Michael Giles, Venture Partner
Jean-Louis Gassee, Partner
Jim Friedlich, Venture Partner
Jonathan Funk, Managing Director
Lara Druyan, General Partner
Leo Hindery, Venture Partner
Pete Bodine, General Partner
Philip Monego, Venture Partner
Purvi Gandhi, Chief Financial Officer
Robert Ackerman, Managing Director
Spencer Tall, General Partner

Type of Firm

Private Equity Firm

Association Membership

Western Association of Venture Capitalists (WAVC)
National Venture Capital Association - USA (NVCA)

Project Preferences

Type of Financing Preferred:
Early Stage
Research and Development
Seed
Startup

Size of Investments Considered:
Min Size of Investment Considered (000s): $3,000
Max Size of Investment Considered (000s): $7,000

Geographical Preferences

United States Preferences:
West Coast

International Preferences:
India
Singapore
All International

Industry Focus

(% based on actual investment)

Internet Specific	49.5%
Communications and Media	20.5%

Computer Software and Services	16.4%
Computer Hardware	5.1%
Semiconductors/Other Elect.	4.5%
Consumer Related	2.2%
Other Products	1.7%

Additional Information

Year Founded: 1996
Capital Under Management: $500,000,000
Current Activity Level: Actively seeking new investments
Method of Compensation: Return on investment is of primary concern, do not charge fees

---

ALLEGRA CAPITAL GMBH

Pachmayrplatz 11
Munich, Germany D-81927
Phone: 49-89-9240-1646
Fax: 49-89-9209-1518
Website: www.allegracapital.de

Management and Staff

Bruno Gross, Partner
Dimitrij Saldanha, Partner
Hendrik Heinze, Chief Executive Officer
Jurgen Konig, Partner
Klaus Pieger, Partner
Matthias Dammig, Partner

Type of Firm

Private Equity Firm

Project Preferences

Type of Financing Preferred:

Leveraged Buyout
Acquisition

Geographical Preferences

International Preferences:

Europe

Industry Preferences

In Business Serv. prefer:

Services

In Manufact. prefer:

Manufacturing

Additional Information

Year Founded: 2004
Current Activity Level: Actively seeking new investments

ALLEGRA PARTNERS (FKA: LAWRENCE, SMITH & HOREY)

320 Park Avenue
18th Floor
New York, NY USA 10022
Phone: 212-277-1526
Fax: 212-277-1533
E-mail: info@allegrapartners.com
Website: www.allegrapartners.com

Management and Staff

Larry Lawrence, General Partner
Richard Defieux, General Partner
Richard Lefebvre, General Partner
Richard Smith, General Partner

Type of Firm

Private Equity Firm

Project Preferences

Role in Financing:

Will function either as deal originator or investor in deals created by others

Type of Financing Preferred:

Early Stage
Expansion
Later Stage

Size of Investments Considered:

Min Size of Investment Considered (000s): $5,000
Max Size of Investment Considered: No Limit

Geographical Preferences

United States Preferences:

All U.S.

Industry Focus

(% based on actual investment)

Computer Software and Services	46.9%
Communications and Media	31.9%
Internet Specific	10.4%
Other Products	7.3%
Consumer Related	3.5%

Additional Information

Name of Most Recent Fund: Allegra Capital Partners IV, L.P.
Most Recent Fund Was Raised: 12/20/1999
Year Founded: 1981
Capital Under Management: $135,000,000
Current Activity Level: Actively seeking new investments
Method of Compensation: Return on investment is of primary concern, do not charge fees

---

ALLEGRO INVESTMENT FUND N.V. (AKA: AIF)

Research Park Haasrode
Romeinse straat 18
Heverlee, Belgium B-3001
Phone: 32-485-664-654
E-mail: geert.everaert@axilius.be
Website: www.allegroinvestmentfund.com

Type of Firm

Private Equity Firm

Project Preferences

Type of Financing Preferred:

Seed

Size of Investments Considered:

Min Size of Investment Considered (000s): $135
Max Size of Investment Considered (000s): $677

Geographical Preferences

International Preferences:

Europe
Belgium

Additional Information

Year Founded: 2007
Current Activity Level: Actively seeking new investments

ALLEGRO PRIVATE EQUITY PTY, LTD.

210 George Street
Level 11
Sydney, Australia 2000
Phone: 612-8228-8700
Fax: 612-9251-8028
E-mail: enquiries@allegrofunds.com.au
Website: www.allegrofunds.com.au

Management and Staff

Adrian Loader, Managing Director
Chester Moynihan, Managing Director

Type of Firm

Private Equity Firm

Association Membership

Australian Venture Capital Association (AVCAL)

Project Preferences

Type of Financing Preferred:

Leveraged Buyout
Expansion
Generalist PE
Public Companies
Turnaround
Later Stage
Management Buyouts
Special Situation
Private Placement
Fund of Funds of Second
Recapitalizations

Size of Investments Considered:

Min Size of Investment Considered (000s): $8,058
Max Size of Investment Considered (000s): $80,580

Geographical Preferences

International Preferences:

Australia
New Zealand

Additional Information

Name of Most Recent Fund: Allegro Private Equity Fund I
Most Recent Fund Was Raised: 03/31/2006
Year Founded: 2008
Capital Under Management: $248,600,000
Current Activity Level: Actively seeking new investments

ALLEN & BUCKERIDGE PTY, LTD.

18 Bulletin Place
Sydney, Australia 2000
Phone: 612-9252-3600
Fax: 612-9251-9808
E-mail: contact@a-b.com.au
Website: www.a-b.com.au

Management and Staff

David Landers, General Partner
Helen Liu, Chief Financial Officer
Ian Maxwell, Venture Partner
Roger Buckeridge, General Partner
Roger Allen, General Partner
Shane Allan, General Partner
Tom Freed, General Partner

Type of Firm

Private Equity Firm

Association Membership

Australian Venture Capital Association (AVCAL)

Project Preferences

Role in Financing:

Prefer role as deal originator but will also invest in deals created by others

Type of Financing Preferred:

Early Stage
Expansion
Balanced
Seed
Startup

Size of Investments Considered:

Min Size of Investment Considered (000s): $161
Max Size of Investment Considered (000s): $12,087

Geographical Preferences

International Preferences:

Pacific
All International

Industry Focus

(% based on actual investment)

Internet Specific	35.2%
Computer Software and Services	18.2%
Semiconductors/Other Elect.	17.6%
Communications and Media	14.2%
Computer Hardware	8.6%
Other Products	2.8%
Industrial/Energy	2.6%
Medical/Health	0.4%
Consumer Related	0.4%

Additional Information

Name of Most Recent Fund: Allen & Buckeridge Emerging Technologies Fund
Most Recent Fund Was Raised: 03/31/2003
Year Founded: 1996
Capital Under Management: $202,000,000
Current Activity Level: Actively seeking new investments
Method of Compensation: Return on invest. most important, but chg. closing fees, service fees, etc.

ALLEN & COMPANY

711 Fifth Avenue
Ninth Floor
New York, NY USA 10022
Phone: 212-832-8000
Fax: 212-832-8023
Website: www.alleninvestments.com

Management and Staff

Enrique Senior, Managing Director
Eugene Protash, Vice President
Harold Wit, Managing Director
John Schneiorr, Managing Director
Kim Wieland, Managing Director & CFO
Paul Gould, Managing Director
Philip Scaturro, Managing Director
Robert Coseriff, Managing Director
Stanley Shuman, Managing Director
Walter O Hara, Managing Director
William Bradley, Managing Director

Type of Firm

Bank Affiliated

Industry Focus

(% based on actual investment)

Internet Specific	39.0%
Communications and Media	20.2%
Medical/Health	10.4%
Biotechnology	8.2%
Computer Software and Services	6.0%
Other Products	5.7%
Industrial/Energy	5.4%
Computer Hardware	3.0%
Consumer Related	1.2%
Semiconductors/Other Elect.	1.0%

Additional Information

Name of Most Recent Fund: Allen Value Partners, L.P.
Most Recent Fund Was Raised: 11/01/1988
Year Founded: 1988
Current Activity Level: Actively seeking new investments

ALLEN CAPITAL PARTNERS LLC

55 Old Field Point Road
Greenwich, CT USA 06830
Phone: 203-422-5150
Fax: 203-422-2481
E-mail: inquiries@acptrs.com
Website: www.allencapitalpartners.com

Type of Firm

Bank Affiliated

Project Preferences

Type of Financing Preferred:

Special Situation
Distressed Debt
Fund of Funds of Second

Additional Information

Year Founded: 2002
Current Activity Level: Actively seeking new investments

ALLIANCE ENTREPRENDRE

53, Avenue Victor Hugo
Paris, France 75116
Phone: 33-1-5364-8750
Fax: 33-1-5364-8765
Website: www.allianceentreprendre.com

Type of Firm

Bank Affiliated

Association Membership

French Venture Capital Association (AFIC)

Project Preferences

Type of Financing Preferred:

Leveraged Buyout
Expansion
Generalist PE
Balanced

Size of Investments Considered:

Min Size of Investment Considered (000s): $274
Max Size of Investment Considered (000s): $2,058

Geographical Preferences

International Preferences:

Europe
France

Additional Information

Year Founded: 1995
Capital Under Management: $40,000,000
Current Activity Level: Actively seeking new investments

ALLIANCE FUND MANAGERS, LTD.

5th Floor, Cunard Building
Pier Head
Liverpool, United Kingdom L3 1DS
Phone: 44-151-236-4040
Fax: 44-151-236-3060
E-mail: enquiry@msif.co.uk
Website: www.msif.co.uk

Management and Staff

Mark Fuller, Managing Director

Type of Firm

Bank Affiliated

Association Membership

British Venture Capital Association (BVCA)

Project Preferences

Type of Financing Preferred:
Second Stage Financing
Leveraged Buyout
Early Stage
Expansion
Mezzanine
Turnaround
Seed
Management Buyouts
Startup

Geographical Preferences

International Preferences:
United Kingdom
Europe

Additional Information

Year Founded: 1996
Capital Under Management: $104,400,000
Current Activity Level: Actively seeking new investments

ALLIANCE MEZZANINE INVESTORS, L.P.

96 Pompton Avenue
Verona, NJ USA 07044
Phone: 973-239-8900
Fax: 973-239-8909
Website: www.mezcap.com

Management and Staff

Bob Eberhardt, Partner
Doug Smith, Partner

Type of Firm

Private Equity Firm

Project Preferences

Role in Financing:
Will function either as deal originator or investor in deals created by others

Type of Financing Preferred:
Leveraged Buyout
Mezzanine
Later Stage
Management Buyouts
Acquisition

Size of Investments Considered:
Min Size of Investment Considered (000s): $1,500
Max Size of Investment Considered (000s): $2,500

Geographical Preferences

United States Preferences:
Mid Atlantic
Pennsylvania
Connecticut
New Jersey
New York

Industry Preferences

In Business Serv. prefer:
Services
Distribution

In Manufact. prefer:
Manufacturing

Additional Information

Year Founded: 1999
Capital Under Management: $11,500,000
Current Activity Level: Actively seeking new investments

ALLIANCE TECHNOLOGY VENTURES

1990 Main Street
Suite 750
Sarasota, FL USA 34236
Phone: 678-336-2000
Fax: 678-336-2001
Website: www.alliancetechventures.com

Management and Staff

Connor Seabrook, General Partner
Michael Slawson, General Partner
Michael Henos, General Partner
Nicholas Papantonis, Venture Partner
Robert Curry, Venture Partner

Type of Firm

Private Equity Firm

Project Preferences

Role in Financing:
Will function either as deal originator or investor in deals created by others

Type of Financing Preferred:
Seed
First Stage Financing

Size of Investments Considered:
Min Size of Investment Considered (000s): $500
Max Size of Investment Considered (000s): $5,000

Geographical Preferences

United States Preferences:
All U.S.

Industry Focus

(% based on actual investment)

Biotechnology	26.5%
Medical/Health	18.7%
Communications and Media	16.2%
Internet Specific	15.2%
Semiconductors/Other Elect.	15.0%
Computer Software and Services	5.2%
Computer Hardware	3.1%

Additional Information

Year Founded: 1993
Capital Under Management: $255,000,000
Current Activity Level: Actively seeking new investments
Method of Compensation: Return on investment is of primary concern, do not charge fees

ALLIANCE TRUST EQUITY PARTNERS

Forth House
28 Rutland Square
Edinburgh, United Kingdom EH1 2BW
Phone: 44-131-221-6510
Fax: 44-131-221-6511
E-mail: contact@atep.co.uk
Website: www.atep.co.uk

Management and Staff

Raymond Abbott, Managing Director

Type of Firm

Bank Affiliated

Association Membership

British Venture Capital Association (BVCA)

Project Preferences

Type of Financing Preferred:
Expansion
Early Stage

Geographical Preferences

International Preferences:
United Kingdom
Europe

Industry Preferences

In Computer Software prefer:
Software

In Biotechnology prefer:
Biotechnology

In Medical/Health prefer:
Health Services

Additional Information

Year Founded: 2007
Current Activity Level: Actively seeking new investments

ALLIANCE VENTURE AS

Stranden 57
Aker Brygge
Oslo, Norway 0250
Phone: 47-22-944-020
Fax: 47-22-471-221
E-mail: info@allianceventure.com
Website: www.allianceventure.com

Other Offices

2100 Geng Road
Suite 200
Palo Alto, CA USA 94303
Phone: 650-494-7400

Management and Staff

Arne Tonning, Partner
Bjorn Christensen, Partner
Erling Maartman-Moe, Partner
Jan-Erik Hareid, Managing Partner
Morten Monrad, Partner

Type of Firm

Private Equity Firm

Association Membership

Norwegian Venture Capital Association

Project Preferences

Type of Financing Preferred:
Early Stage
Balanced

Geographical Preferences

International Preferences:
Scandanavia/Nordic Region
Norway

Industry Preferences

In Communications prefer:
Commercial Communications
Wireless Communications

In Computer Software prefer:
Software

In Internet Specific prefer:
Internet

In Industrial/Energy prefer:
Energy

Additional Information

Year Founded: 2001
Capital Under Management: $54,500,000
Current Activity Level: Actively seeking new investments

ALLIANCEBERNSTEIN L.P. (FKA: ALLIANCE CAPITAL MANAGEMENT)

1345 Avenue of the Americas
New York, NY USA 10105
Phone: 212-969-1000
E-mail: ir@alliancebernstein.com
Website: www.alliancebernstein.com

Management and Staff

John Carifa, President & COO
Lewis Sanders, Chief Executive Officer
Matt Pedley, Vice President

Type of Firm

Insurance Firm Affiliate

Project Preferences

Type of Financing Preferred:
Balanced

Industry Focus

(% based on actual investment)

Other Products	39.8%
Consumer Related	24.9%
Communications and Media	7.0%
Biotechnology	5.7%
Computer Hardware	5.5%
Industrial/Energy	5.0%
Internet Specific	4.1%
Semiconductors/Other Elect.	3.4%
Medical/Health	2.9%
Computer Software and Services	1.7%

Additional Information

Year Founded: 1973
Current Activity Level: Actively seeking new investments

ALLIANZ PRIVATE EQUITY PARTNERS

Giselastrasse 4
Munich, Germany 80802
Phone: 49-89-380019900
Fax: 49-89-380019436
E-mail: munich@apep.com
Website: www.apep.com

Other Offices

1114 Avenue of the Americas
31st floor
New York, NY USA 10036-7703
Phone: 212-938-0630
Fax: 212-938-0660

Management and Staff

Adam Lichtenstein, Partner
Andress Goh, Partner
Christian Mayert, Managing Director
Claus Zellner, Chief Financial Officer
Elliot Royce, Managing Director
James Kester, Managing Director

Type of Firm

Insurance Firm Affiliate

Association Membership

German Venture Capital Association (BVK)
European Private Equity and Venture Capital Assoc.

Project Preferences

Type of Financing Preferred:
Fund of Funds
Leveraged Buyout
Expansion
Mezzanine

Geographical Preferences

International Preferences:
Europe
Germany
All International

Industry Focus

(% based on actual investment)

Computer Software and Services	53.3%
Other Products	22.1%
Internet Specific	13.4%
Industrial/Energy	4.8%
Communications and Media	3.2%
Biotechnology	2.5%
Computer Hardware	0.6%
Medical/Health	0.1%

Additional Information

Year Founded: 1996
Capital Under Management: $4,200,000,000
Current Activity Level: Actively seeking new investments

ALLIED CAPITAL CORPORATION

1919 Pennsylvania Avenue, NW
Third Floor
Washington, DC USA 20006-3434
Phone: 202-721-6100
Fax: 202-721-6101
E-mail: info@alliedcapital.com
Website: www.alliedcapital.com

Other Offices

321 North Clark Street
Suite 1425
Chicago, IL USA 60654
Phone: 312-846-5128
Fax: 312-846-5134

11601 Wilshire Boulevard
Suite 500
Los Angeles, CA USA 90025
Phone: 310-689-2817
Fax: 310-689-2818

520 Madison Avenue
27th Floor
New York, NY USA 10022
Phone: 212-822-7800
Fax: 212-822-7801

Management and Staff

Benton Cummings, Managing Director
Bruce Kelleher, Managing Director
Christina DelDonna, Managing Director
Daniel Russell, Managing Director
Eric Groberg, Managing Director
Frank Izzo, Managing Director
Frederick Hill, Managing Director
George Ferris, Managing Director
Jeri Harman, Managing Director
Joan Sweeney, Managing Director
John Scheurer, Managing Director
John Fruehwirth, Managing Director
John Shulman, Managing Director
Joseph Taylor, Managing Director
Justin Maccarone, Managing Director
Michael Miller, Managing Director
Michael Grisius, Managing Director
Paul Tanen, Managing Director
Penni Roll, Chief Financial Officer
Robert Monk, Managing Director
Robert Hicks, Managing Director
Robert Long, Managing Director
Scott Binder, Managing Director
Shelley Huechel, Vice President
Susan Mayer, Managing Director
Thomas Lauer, Managing Director
Thomas Turpin, Managing Director
William Walton, President, CEO, Chairman

Type of Firm

Private Equity Firm

Association Membership

Mid-Atlantic Venture Association
Illinois Venture Capital Association
Natl Assoc of Small Bus. Inv. Co (NASBIC)

Project Preferences

Role in Financing:

Will function either as deal originator or investor in deals created by others

Type of Financing Preferred:

Leveraged Buyout
Expansion
Mezzanine
Management Buyouts
Private Placement
Acquisition
Recapitalizations

Size of Investments Considered:

Min Size of Investment Considered (000s): $10,000
Max Size of Investment Considered (000s): $99,999

Geographical Preferences

United States Preferences:

All U.S.

Industry Focus

(% based on actual investment)

Other Products	43.3%
Industrial/Energy	24.4%
Consumer Related	18.3%
Communications and Media	4.1%
Computer Software and Services	4.0%
Medical/Health	2.8%
Internet Specific	2.1%
Biotechnology	0.8%
Computer Hardware	0.3%

Additional Information

Year Founded: 1958
Capital Under Management: $4,471,000,000
Current Activity Level: Actively seeking new investments
Method of Compensation: Return on invest. most important, but chg. closing fees, service fees, etc.

ALLIED IRISH INVESTMENT (AKA: AIB BANK) (AKA: AIB GROUP)

Bankcentre
Ballsbridge
Dublin, Ireland 4
Phone: 353-1-660-0311
Fax: 353-1-660-4715
Website: www.aibgroup.com

Other Offices

PO Box 11258
Church Street Station
New York, NY USA 10286-1258
Phone: 1-888-269-2377

Type of Firm

Bank Affiliated

Project Preferences

Type of Financing Preferred:

Generalist PE

Geographical Preferences

International Preferences:

Ireland
Europe

Additional Information

Year Founded: 2002
Current Activity Level: Actively seeking new investments

ALLOY VENTURES

400 Hamilton Avenue
Fourth Floor
Palo Alto, CA USA 94301
Phone: 650-687-5000
Fax: 650-687-5010
E-mail: info@alloyventures.com
Website: www.alloyventures.com

Management and Staff

Ammar Hanafi, General Partner
Craig Taylor, General Partner
Daniel Rubin, Venture Partner
David Ezequelle, Venture Partner
Douglas Kelly, General Partner
J. Leighton Read, General Partner
John Shoch, General Partner
Michael Hunkapiller, General Partner
Tony Di Bona, Chief Financial Officer

Type of Firm

Private Equity Firm

Association Membership

National Venture Capital Association - USA (NVCA)

Project Preferences

Type of Financing Preferred:

Early Stage
Seed
Startup

Geographical Preferences

United States Preferences:

All U.S.

Industry Focus

(% based on actual investment)

Internet Specific	21.0%
Computer Software and Services	19.5%
Medical/Health	15.7%
Biotechnology	15.6%
Communications and Media	12.2%
Semiconductors/Other Elect.	6.9%
Industrial/Energy	6.3%
Computer Hardware	2.7%

Additional Information

Name of Most Recent Fund: Alloy Ventures 2005, L.P.
Most Recent Fund Was Raised: 06/28/2005
Year Founded: 1996
Capital Under Management: $726,000,000
Current Activity Level: Actively seeking new investments

ALMASA CAPITAL

4445 Calgary Trail South
888 Terrace Plaza Alberta
Edmonton, Canada T6H 5R7
Phone: 780-438-3535
Fax: 780-438-3129
E-mail: almasa@telusplanet.net

Management and Staff

Michael Welsh, General Partner
Robert Mee, Vice President

Type of Firm

Private Equity Firm

Geographical Preferences

Canadian Preferences:

Western Canada

Additional Information

Year Founded: 1998
Capital Under Management: $33,000,000
Current Activity Level: Actively seeking new investments

ALOE PRIVATE EQUITY

34 Boulevard Malesherbes
Paris, France 75008
Phone: 33-1-5573-2158
Fax: 33-1-5573-2200
E-mail: aloe@aloe-group.com
Website: www.aloe-group.com

Other Offices

Huan Teng Edifice
Room 4002, Chaoyang District
Beijing, China 100021

8 High Street
Twyford, United Kingdom RG10 9AE

Kornhamstorg 53
Stockholm, Sweden 103 12

128 Jolly Makers Chamber II
Nariman Point
Mumbai, India 400-021

Rosedale House, Rosedale Road
Richmond Surrey TW9 2SZ
London, United Kingdom W1K 1QT

Number 1071, Road Number 44
Jubilee Hills
Hyderabad, India 500 038

Management and Staff

Ludovic Edward Both, Chief Financial Officer

Type of Firm

Private Equity Firm

Association Membership

French Venture Capital Association (AFIC)

Project Preferences

Type of Financing Preferred:

Early Stage
Generalist PE
Balanced

Size of Investments Considered:

Min Size of Investment Considered (000s): $7,315
Max Size of Investment Considered (000s): $36,576

Geographical Preferences

International Preferences:

India
Europe
China
Asia

Industry Preferences

In Communications prefer:

Communications and Media
Media and Entertainment

In Computer Software prefer:

Software

In Consumer Related prefer:

Retail

In Industrial/Energy prefer:

Energy Conservation Relat
Environmental Related

In Other prefer:

Environment Responsible

Additional Information

Name of Most Recent Fund: Aloe Environment Fund II
Most Recent Fund Was Raised: 08/15/2007
Year Founded: 2004
Capital Under Management: $244,700,000
Current Activity Level: Actively seeking new investments

ALOTHON GROUP LLC

400 Madison Avenue
18th Floor
New York, NY USA 10017
Phone: 212-810-2727
E-mail: info@alothon.com
Website: www.alothon.com

Management and Staff

Ettore Biagioni, Managing Director

Type of Firm

Private Equity Firm

Project Preferences

Type of Financing Preferred:

Leveraged Buyout
Expansion

Geographical Preferences

International Preferences:

Argentina
Mexico
Brazil

Additional Information

Year Founded: 2008
Capital Under Management: $54,900,000
Current Activity Level: Actively seeking new investments

ALP CAPITAL

9 Rue Daru
Paris, France 75008
Phone: 33-1-7118-1850
Website: www.alpcapital.com

Management and Staff

Nicolas Guyon, Principal

Type of Firm

Private Equity Firm

Association Membership

French Venture Capital Association (AFIC)

Project Preferences

Type of Financing Preferred:

Generalist PE
Expansion
Acquisition

Additional Information

Year Founded: 2007
Current Activity Level: Actively seeking new investments

ALPHA ASSOCIATES AG

Talstrasse 80
P.O. Box 2038
Zurich, Switzerland 8022
Phone: 41-43-244-3000
Fax: 41-43-244-3001
E-mail: info@alpha-associates.ch
Website: www.alpha-associates.ch

Management and Staff

Christoph Huber, Chief Financial Officer
Daniela Hauenstein, Partner
Guy Myint-Maung, Partner
Henry Potter, Partner
Peter Derendinger, Chief Executive Officer
Petra Salesny, Chief Operating Officer
Richard Seewald, Partner

Type of Firm

Private Equity Advisor or Fund of Funds

Project Preferences

Type of Financing Preferred:

Fund of Funds
Leveraged Buyout
Expansion

Geographical Preferences

International Preferences:

Armenia
Belarus
Central Europe
Europe
Kazakhstan
Turkey

Eastern Europe
Kyrgyzstan
Tajikistan
Azerbaijan
Moldova
Uzbekistan
Georgia
Russia

Additional Information

Name of Most Recent Fund: 5E Holding (Excellence in Eastern Emerging Equity)
Most Recent Fund Was Raised: 02/10/1998
Year Founded: 1997
Capital Under Management: $923,900,000
Current Activity Level: Actively seeking new investments

ALPHA CAPITAL PARTNERS, LTD.

122 South Michigan Avenue
Suite 1700
Chicago, IL USA 60603
Phone: 312-322-9800
Fax: 312-322-9808
E-mail: kalnow@alphacapital.com
Website: www.alphacapital.com

Other Offices

3155 Research Boulevard
Dayton, OH USA 45402
Phone: 937-252-9580
Fax: 937-253-2634

2083 Bedford Road
Columbus, OH USA 43212
Phone: 614-487-8780

2593 Walnut Road
Ann Arbor, MI USA 48103
Phone: 734-994-1003
Fax: 734-994-0044

Management and Staff

Andrew Kalnow, President
David DeVore, Partner
Gary Stark, Managing Director
John Rose, Principal
Richard Goff, Partner

Type of Firm

Private Equity Firm

Association Membership

Natl Assoc of Small Bus. Inv. Co (NASBIC)

Project Preferences

Role in Financing:

Prefer role as deal originator but will also invest in deals created by others

Type of Financing Preferred:

Second Stage Financing
Leveraged Buyout
Expansion
Later Stage
First Stage Financing
Special Situation

Size of Investments Considered:

Min Size of Investment Considered (000s): $750
Max Size of Investment Considered (000s): $5,000

Geographical Preferences

United States Preferences:

Midwest

Industry Focus

(% based on actual investment)	
Computer Software and Services	33.5%
Other Products	25.5%
Consumer Related	16.6%
Communications and Media	7.6%
Industrial/Energy	5.5%
Medical/Health	5.4%
Biotechnology	2.6%
Semiconductors/Other Elect.	1.9%
Internet Specific	1.2%
Computer Hardware	0.2%

Additional Information

Name of Most Recent Fund: Alpha Capital Fund III, L.P.
Most Recent Fund Was Raised: 01/11/2001
Year Founded: 1984
Capital Under Management: $135,000,000
Current Activity Level: Actively seeking new investments
Method of Compensation: Return on investment is of primary concern, do not charge fees

---

ALPHA GROUP (FKA: ALPHA ASSOCIATES MANAGEMENT, LTD.)

22 Grenville Street
Saint Helier
Jersey, Channel Islands JE4 8PX
Phone: 44-1534-609-000
Fax: 44-1534-609-333
E-mail: info@alphape.com
Website: www.groupealpha.com

Other Offices

916, Gildo Pastor Center
7 rue du Gabian
Monaco, Monaco 98000
Phone: 377-9350-4727
Fax: 377-9350-4730

Via Monte di Pieta, 15
Milan, Italy 20121
Phone: 39-2-0064-0064
Fax: 39-2-0064-0090

Niedenau 68
Frankfurt-am-Main, Germany D-60325
Phone: 49-69-9714-9411
Fax: 49-69-9714-9490

49 Avenue Hoche
Paris, France F - 75008
Phone: 33-1-5660-2020
Fax: 33-1-5660-1022

Management and Staff

Alain Blanc-Brude, Managing General Partner
Florence Fesneau, General Partner
Harald Ronn, General Partner
Herve Hautin, Chief Financial Officer
Nicolas Ver Hulst, Managing Director
Olaf Kordes, Principal

Type of Firm

Private Equity Firm

Association Membership

European Private Equity and Venture Capital Assoc.

Project Preferences

Role in Financing:

Prefer role as deal originator but will also invest in deals created by others

Type of Financing Preferred:

Leveraged Buyout
Expansion

Size of Investments Considered:

Min Size of Investment Considered (000s): $14,275
Max Size of Investment Considered (000s): $185,582

Geographical Preferences

International Preferences:

Italy
United Kingdom
Luxembourg
Netherlands
Switzerland
Europe
Austria
Belgium
Germany
France

Industry Focus

(% based on actual investment)	
Other Products	45.9%
Communications and Media	19.6%
Semiconductors/Other Elect.	9.6%
Internet Specific	7.2%
Consumer Related	5.6%
Medical/Health	5.5%
Computer Software and Services	3.3%
Biotechnology	2.7%
Industrial/Energy	0.7%

Additional Information

Name of Most Recent Fund: Alpha Private Equity Fund 5 (AKA: APEF 5)
Most Recent Fund Was Raised: 02/17/2006
Year Founded: 1985

Capital Under Management: $2,426,800,000
Current Activity Level: Actively seeking new investments
Method of Compensation: Return on investment is of primary concern, do not charge fees

ALPHA VENTURES SA

45 Panepistimiou Street
Athens, Greece 105 64
Phone: 30-210-326-2700
Fax: 30-210-326-2709
E-mail: mail@alphavc.gr
Website: www.alpha.gr

Management and Staff

Demetrios P. Mantzounis, Managing Director

Type of Firm

Private Equity Firm

Additional Information

Name of Most Recent Fund: Alpha Ventures
Most Recent Fund Was Raised: 01/01/1991
Year Founded: 1990
Current Activity Level: Actively seeking new investments

ALPINE INVESTORS, L.P.

Three Embarcadero Center
Suite 2330
San Francisco, CA USA 94111
Phone: 415-392-9100
Fax: 415-392-9101
Website: www.alpine-investors.com

Management and Staff

Billy Maguy, Partner
Chris Santa Maria, Chief Financial Officer
Dan Sanner, Partner
Graham Weaver, Managing Partner
Mike Duran, Partner
Ned Weaver, Partner
Will Adams, Partner

Type of Firm

Private Equity Firm

Project Preferences

Type of Financing Preferred:

Leveraged Buyout

Size of Investments Considered:

Min Size of Investment Considered (000s): $5,000
Max Size of Investment Considered (000s): $50,000

Geographical Preferences

United States Preferences:

All U.S.

Additional Information

Year Founded: 2001
Capital Under Management: $247,000,000
Current Activity Level: Actively seeking new investments

ALPINE TECHNOLOGY INVESTMENT CO., LTD.

7/F, 779-10, Daelim 3 dong
Youngdeungpo-ku
Seoul, South Korea 150-073
Phone: 822-836-2053
Fax: 822-836-2087

Management and Staff

Jinwoo Nam, President

Type of Firm

Corporate PE/Venture

Association Membership

Korean Venture Capital Association (KVCA)

Project Preferences

Type of Financing Preferred:

Balanced
Later Stage
Seed

Geographical Preferences

International Preferences:

Korea, South

Additional Information

Year Founded: 1999
Capital Under Management: $12,100,000
Current Activity Level: Actively seeking new investments

ALPINVEST PARTNERS N.V. (FKA: NIB CAPITAL PRIVATE EQUITY NV)

Jachthavenweg 118
Amsterdam, Netherlands 1081 KJ
Phone: 31-20-540-7575
Fax: 31-20-540-7500
E-mail: info@alpinvest.com
Website: www.alpinvest.com

Other Offices

630 Fifth Avenue, 28th Floor
New York, NY USA 10111
Phone: 212-332-6240
Fax: 212-332-6241

Uitbreidingstraat 10-16
Antwerp, Belgium 2600
Phone: 32-3-286-9930
Fax: 32-3-286-9939

701 Citibank Tower
3 Garden Road
Hong Kong, Hong Kong
Phone: 852-2878-7099
Fax: 852-2878-7009

Friedrich-Ebert-Anlage 54
Frankfurt am Main, Germany 60325
Phone: 49-69-972-0830
Fax: 49-69-9720-8320

Management and Staff

Alexander Van Wassenaer, Partner
Christian M. Bachle, Partner
Christopher Perriello, Principal
Elliot Royce, Partner
Eric Bosman, Partner
Erik Thyssen, Managing Partner
Ernest Lambers, Principal
George Westerkamp, Partner
Harald Graf, Principal
Helen Lais, Partner
Henry Robin, Partner
Hilde Famaey, Principal
Iain Leigh, Managing Partner
Johan Buyle, Principal
Joris De Meester, Principal
Maarten Vervoort, Partner
Paul Lamers, Partner
Paul De Klerk, Chief Financial Officer
Sander Van Maanen, Principal
Theo Bot, Principal
Tjarko Hektor, Partner
Volkert Doeksen, Chief Executive Officer
Wouter Moerel, Partner

Type of Firm

Private Equity Firm

Association Membership

European Private Equity and Venture Capital Assoc.

Project Preferences

Role in Financing:

Prefer role as deal originator but will also invest in deals created by others

Type of Financing Preferred:

Second Stage Financing
Leveraged Buyout
Mezzanine
Balanced

Size of Investments Considered:

Min Size of Investment Considered (000s): $5,000
Max Size of Investment Considered: No Limit

Geographical Preferences

International Preferences:

Italy
United Kingdom
Bermuda
Spain
Germany
France

Industry Focus

(% based on actual investment)

Consumer Related	26.4%
Other Products	20.4%
Computer Hardware	17.0%
Industrial/Energy	12.1%
Medical/Health	11.7%
Computer Software and Services	7.5%
Biotechnology	3.4%
Communications and Media	0.9%
Internet Specific	0.7%
Semiconductors/Other Elect.	0.1%

Additional Information

Year Founded: 1999
Capital Under Management: $750,000,000
Current Activity Level: Actively seeking new investments
Method of Compensation: Return on invest. most important, but chg. closing fees, service fees, etc.

ALPS INVESTMENT RESEARCH

3553 North First Street
San Jose, CA USA 95134
Phone: 408-432-6000

Type of Firm

Corporate PE/Venture

Additional Information

Year Founded: 2002
Current Activity Level: Actively seeking new investments

ALSOP LOUIE PARTNERS

1255 Battery Street
Suite 400
San Francisco, CA USA 94111
Phone: 415-596-0981
Fax: 415-956-1506
Website: www.alsop-louie.com

Management and Staff

Gilman Louie, Founder
Nancy Lee, Chief Financial Officer
Stewart Alsop, General Partner

Type of Firm

Private Equity Firm

Association Membership

National Venture Capital Association - USA (NVCA)

Project Preferences

Type of Financing Preferred:

Early Stage

Additional Information

Year Founded: 2006
Capital Under Management: $75,000,000
Current Activity Level: Actively seeking new investments

ALTA BERKELEY VENTURE PARTNERS

42 Berkeley Square
London, United Kingdom W1J 5AW
Phone: 44-207-409-5012
Fax: 44-207-226-6401
E-mail: info@altaberkeley.com
Website: www.altaberkeley.com

Other Offices

17A rue de la Croix d'Or
Geneva, Switzerland 1204
Phone: 41-22-311-5533
Fax: 41-22-311-5536

Management and Staff

Barun Dutta, Partner
Bryan Wood, Founder
Hugh Smith, Chief Operating Officer
Kevin Fielding, Partner
Peter Magowan, Partner
Pini Lozowick, Partner
Tim Brown, General Partner

Type of Firm

Private Equity Firm

Association Membership

Swedish Venture Capital Association (SVCA)
European Private Equity and Venture Capital Assoc.

Project Preferences

Role in Financing:

Prefer role as deal originator but will also invest in deals created by others

Type of Financing Preferred:

Early Stage
Balanced

Size of Investments Considered:

Min Size of Investment Considered (000s): $2,000
Max Size of Investment Considered: No Limit

Geographical Preferences

International Preferences:

United Kingdom
Europe
Israel

Industry Focus

(% based on actual investment)

Communications and Media	29.2%
Biotechnology	19.5%
Semiconductors/Other Elect.	13.4%
Computer Hardware	11.0%
Medical/Health	10.8%
Computer Software and Services	5.8%
Other Products	5.2%
Internet Specific	3.2%
Industrial/Energy	1.7%
Consumer Related	0.3%

Additional Information

Year Founded: 1982
Capital Under Management: $178,300,000
Current Activity Level: Actively seeking new investments
Method of Compensation: Return on investment is of primary concern, do not charge fees

---

ALTA CAPITAL

K. Ulmana gatve 119
Second Floor
Marupe, Latvia LV 2167
Phone: 371-6716-1400
Fax: 371-6716-1410
E-mail: info@altacapital.ee
Website: www.altacapital.ee

Other Offices

Tartu mnt 2
Talinn, Estonia 10145
Phone: 372-681-8050
Fax: 372-681-8055

Savanoriu pr.1
Fifth floor
Vilnius, Lithuania 03116
Phone: 370-5205-8600
Fax: 370-5205-8601

Management and Staff

Andres Ratsepp, Partner
Indrek Rahumaa, Managing Partner
Jaak Raid, Partner
Marius Binkevicius, Partner
Priit Poldoja, Partner

Type of Firm

Private Equity Firm

Project Preferences

Type of Financing Preferred:

Leveraged Buyout
Generalist PE

Geographical Preferences

International Preferences:

Scandanavia/Nordic Region

Additional Information

Year Founded: 2001
Current Activity Level: Actively seeking new investments

ALTA COMMUNICATIONS

200 Clarendon Street
51st Floor
Boston, MA USA 02116
Phone: 617-262-7770

Fax: 617-262-9779
E-mail: info@altacomm.com
Website: www.altacomm.com

Other Offices

One Embarcadero Center
Suite 4050
San Francisco, CA USA 94111
Phone: 415-362-4022
Fax: 415-362-6178

Management and Staff

Andrew Mulderry, General Partner
Brian McNeill, Managing General Partner
Eileen McCarthy, Chief Financial Officer
Lane MacDonald, General Partner
Matthew Blodgett, Vice President
Patrick Brubaker, General Partner
Philip Thompson, General Partner
Robert Benbow, General Partner
Timothy Dibble, Managing General Partner
Wayne Mack, Vice President
William Egan, General Partner

Type of Firm

Private Equity Firm

Association Membership

National Venture Capital Association - USA (NVCA)

Project Preferences

Role in Financing:
Prefer role as deal originator but will also invest in deals created by others

Type of Financing Preferred:
Second Stage Financing
Leveraged Buyout
Early Stage
Expansion
Mezzanine
Turnaround
Balanced
Later Stage
Seed
First Stage Financing
Acquisition
Special Situation
Startup
Recapitalizations

Size of Investments Considered:
Min Size of Investment Considered (000s): $5,000
Max Size of Investment Considered (000s): $75,000

Geographical Preferences

Canadian Preferences:
All Canada

International Preferences:
All International

Industry Focus

(% based on actual investment)

Communications and Media	58.0%
Internet Specific	16.4%
Other Products	12.9%
Computer Software and Services	3.3%
Consumer Related	3.2%
Semiconductors/Other Elect.	2.2%
Computer Hardware	1.8%
Biotechnology	1.4%
Medical/Health	0.6%

Additional Information

Year Founded: 1996
Capital Under Management: $1,518,900,000
Current Activity Level: Actively seeking new investments
Method of Compensation: Return on investment is of primary concern, do not charge fees

ALTA GROWTH CAPITAL

Homero 440 - 9th floor
Mexico, Mexico DF 11560
Phone: 52-55-5254-3280
E-mail: info@agcmexico.com
Website: www.agcmexico.com

Management and Staff

Erik Carlberg, Managing Director
Rafael Payro, Managing Director
Scott McDonough, Managing Director

Type of Firm

Private Equity Firm

Project Preferences

Type of Financing Preferred:
Expansion

Geographical Preferences

International Preferences:
Mexico

Industry Preferences

In Communications prefer:
Entertainment

In Medical/Health prefer:
Medical/Health
Health Services

In Consumer Related prefer:
Entertainment and Leisure
Consumer Products
Consumer Services
Education Related

In Financial Services prefer:
Financial Services

In Manufact. prefer:
Manufacturing

Additional Information

Year Founded: 2008
Current Activity Level: Actively seeking new investments

ALTA PARTNERS

One Embarcadero Center
37th Floor
San Francisco, CA USA 94111
Phone: 415-362-4022
Fax: 415-362-6178
E-mail: alta@altapartners.com
Website: www.altapartners.com

Management and Staff

Daniel Janney, Managing Director
Ekaterina Smirnyagina, Venture Partner
Farah Champsi, Managing Director
Guy Nohra, Managing Director
Hilary Strain, Chief Financial Officer
Jean Deleage, Founding Partner

Type of Firm

Private Equity Firm

Association Membership

Western Association of Venture Capitalists (WAVC)
National Venture Capital Association - USA (NVCA)

Project Preferences

Role in Financing:
Prefer role as deal originator but will also invest in deals created by others

Type of Financing Preferred:
Second Stage Financing
Early Stage
Expansion
Mezzanine
Start-up Financing
Turnaround
Later Stage
Seed
First Stage Financing

Size of Investments Considered:
Min Size of Investment Considered (000s): $2,000
Max Size of Investment Considered (000s): $15,000

Geographical Preferences

United States Preferences:
West Coast

International Preferences:
Europe

Industry Focus

(% based on actual investment)

Biotechnology	40.0%
Medical/Health	31.5%
Communications and Media	7.5%
Internet Specific	6.3%
Semiconductors/Other Elect.	6.3%
Computer Software and Services	3.5%
Computer Hardware	2.6%
Other Products	1.0%
Industrial/Energy	0.8%
Consumer Related	0.4%

Additional Information

Name of Most Recent Fund: Alta Partners VIII. L.P.
Most Recent Fund Was Raised: 03/31/2006
Year Founded: 1996
Capital Under Management: $1,871,000,000
Current Activity Level: Actively seeking new investments

ALTA PARTNERS CAPITAL (FKA: ACTIVA VENTURES SGECR SA)

Avda. Diagonal 399 Pral 2A
Barcelona, Spain 08008
Phone: 34-93-238-4341
Fax: 34-93-238-6226
Website: www.altapartners.es

Management and Staff

Rafael Sunol, President
Roberto Gili, Partner

Type of Firm

Private Equity Firm

Association Membership

Spanish Venture Capital Association (ASCRI)

Project Preferences

Type of Financing Preferred:
Leveraged Buyout
Expansion

Size of Investments Considered:
Min Size of Investment Considered (000s): $2,825
Max Size of Investment Considered (000s): $22,598

Geographical Preferences

International Preferences:
Europe
Spain

Additional Information

Name of Most Recent Fund: Fons d'Inversio en Innovacio a Catalunya, FCR (Invernova)
Most Recent Fund Was Raised: 07/11/2003
Year Founded: 2000
Capital Under Management: $9,000,000
Current Activity Level: Actively seeking new investments

ALTAMAR PRIVATE EQUITY

Paseo de la Castellana, 31
Madrid, Spain 28046
Phone: 34-91-310-7230
Fax: 34-91-310-7231
E-mail: altamar@altamarcapital.com
Website: www.altamarprivateequity.com

Management and Staff

Claudio Aguirre, Managing Director
Jose Luis Molina, Managing Director
Mariano Olaso-Yohn, Managing Director

Type of Firm

Private Equity Firm

Association Membership

Spanish Venture Capital Association (ASCRI)

Project Preferences

Type of Financing Preferred:
Fund of Funds

Size of Investments Considered:
Min Size of Investment Considered (000s): $5,921
Max Size of Investment Considered (000s): $35,523

Geographical Preferences

International Preferences:
Europe
Spain

Additional Information

Year Founded: 2004
Capital Under Management: $1,000,000,000
Current Activity Level: Actively seeking new investments

ALTARIA AS

Drammensveien 123
Oslo, Norway 0277
Phone: 47-22-556-400
Fax: 47-22-556-401
Website: www.altaria.no

Management and Staff

Nigel Wilson, Managing Partner

Type of Firm

Private Equity Firm

Association Membership

Norwegian Venture Capital Association

Geographical Preferences

International Preferences:
Scandanavia/Nordic Region

Additional Information

Year Founded: 2006
Capital Under Management: $90,500,000
Current Activity Level: Actively seeking new investments

ALTARIS CAPITAL PARTNERS LLC

600 Lexington Avenue
Eleventh Floor
New York, NY USA 10022
Phone: 212-931-0250
Fax: 212-931-0236
E-mail: info@altariscap.com
Website: www.altarishp.com

Management and Staff

Daniel Tully, Managing Director
George Aitken-Davies, Managing Director
Michael Kluger, Managing Director
Young Chang, Vice President

Type of Firm

Private Equity Firm

Project Preferences

Type of Financing Preferred:
Leveraged Buyout
Expansion
Recapitalizations

Size of Investments Considered:
Min Size of Investment Considered (000s): $15,000
Max Size of Investment Considered (000s): $50,000

Industry Preferences

In Medical/Health prefer:
Medical/Health
Medical Products
Health Services
Pharmaceuticals

Additional Information

Name of Most Recent Fund: AIG Altaris Health Partners II, L.P.
Most Recent Fund Was Raised: 05/11/2007
Year Founded: 2003
Capital Under Management: $500,000,000
Current Activity Level: Actively seeking new investments

ALTERNATIVE INVESTMENT CAPITAL LTD.

10F Marunouchi Chuo Bldg.
1-9-1 Marunouchi, Chiyoda-ku
Tokyo, Japan 100-0005
Phone: 81-3-5218-5230
Fax: 81-3-5218-5254
E-mail: info@aicapital.co.jp
Website: www.aicapital.co.jp

Type of Firm

Corporate PE/Venture

Project Preferences

Type of Financing Preferred:
Fund of Funds

Geographical Preferences

International Preferences:
Asia
Japan

Additional Information

Year Founded: 2002
Capital Under Management: $160,000,000
Current Activity Level: Actively seeking new investments

ALTERNATIVE VENTURES

23 rue Lalande
Paris, France 75014
Phone: 33-1-4471-3588
Website: www.altvent.com/index.html

Type of Firm

Private Equity Firm

Project Preferences

Type of Financing Preferred:

Early Stage

Geographical Preferences

International Preferences:

France

Industry Preferences

In Other prefer:

Socially Responsible
Environment Responsible

Additional Information

Year Founded: 2001
Current Activity Level: Actively seeking new investments

ALTHERA CAPITAL

20 rue de la Banque
Paris, France 75002
Phone: 33-1-4296-0686
Fax: 33-8-2519-8088
E-mail: contact@althera.com
Website: www.altheracapital.fr

Management and Staff

Alain Vaury, Partner
Philippe Venditelli, Partner
Pierre Schmidt, Partner

Type of Firm

Private Equity Firm

Project Preferences

Type of Financing Preferred:

Balanced

Size of Investments Considered:

Min Size of Investment Considered (000s): $328
Max Size of Investment Considered (000s): $1,314

Additional Information

Year Founded: 2009
Current Activity Level: Actively seeking new investments

ALTIEN VENTURES LLC

1331 Northwest Lovejoy Street
Suite 850
Portland, OR USA 97209
Phone: 503-226-8642

Management and Staff

John Miner, Co-Founder

Type of Firm

Private Equity Firm

Project Preferences

Type of Financing Preferred:

Start-up Financing
Startup

Geographical Preferences

United States Preferences:

Oregon

Industry Preferences

In Computer Software prefer:

Software

In Semiconductor/Electr prefer:

Semiconductor

Additional Information

Name of Most Recent Fund: Altien Investors I LLC
Most Recent Fund Was Raised: 08/30/2007
Year Founded: 2007
Capital Under Management: $2,100,000
Current Activity Level: Actively seeking new investments

ALTIRA GROUP LLC

1675 Broadway
Suite 2400
Denver, CO USA 80202
Phone: 303-592-5500
Fax: 303-592-5519
E-mail: info@altiragroup.com
Website: www.altiragroup.com

Management and Staff

Dirk McDermott, Managing Partner
Jan Boyer, Partner
Jim Newell, Partner

Type of Firm

Private Equity Firm

Association Membership

National Venture Capital Association - USA (NVCA)

Project Preferences

Role in Financing:

Prefer role as deal originator but will also invest in deals created by others

Type of Financing Preferred:

Early Stage
Expansion
Later Stage
First Stage Financing

Size of Investments Considered:

Min Size of Investment Considered (000s): $3,000
Max Size of Investment Considered (000s): $30,000

Geographical Preferences

United States Preferences:

All U.S.

Canadian Preferences:

All Canada

Industry Preferences

In Industrial/Energy prefer:

Energy
Oil and Gas Exploration
Alternative Energy
Coal Related
Energy Conservation Relat

In Other prefer:

Environment Responsible

Additional Information

Name of Most Recent Fund: Altira Technology Fund V, L.P.
Most Recent Fund Was Raised: 06/19/2006
Year Founded: 1996
Capital Under Management: $275,000,000
Current Activity Level: Actively seeking new investments
Method of Compensation: Return on investment is of primary concern, do not charge fees

---

ALTITUDE CAPITAL PARTNERS

485 Madison Avenue
New York, NY USA 10022
Phone: 212-584-2184
Fax: 212-826-0826
E-mail: info@altitudecp.com
Website: www.altitudecp.com

Management and Staff

Robert Kramer, Managing Partner

Type of Firm

Private Equity Firm

Project Preferences

Type of Financing Preferred:

Early Stage

Geographical Preferences

United States Preferences:

All U.S.

Industry Preferences

In Communications prefer:
Wireless Communications
Data Communications

In Computer Hardware prefer:
Mini and Personal/Desktop
Computer Graphics and Dig

In Computer Software prefer:
Systems Software

In Internet Specific prefer:
E-Commerce Technology
Internet

In Medical/Health prefer:
Medical Products

Additional Information
Year Founded: 2006
Current Activity Level: Actively seeking new investments

ALTITUDE LIFE SCIENCE MANAGEMENT, LLC
14933 Highway 172
P.O. Box 367
Ignacio, CO USA 81137
Phone: 970-563-5000

Management and Staff
David Maki, General Partner
Steven Johnson, General Partner

Type of Firm
Private Equity Firm

Project Preferences

Type of Financing Preferred:
Balanced

Additional Information
Year Founded: 2005
Capital Under Management: $24,000,000
Current Activity Level: Actively seeking new investments

ALTO INVEST
6 avenue Charles de Gaulle
Hall B
Le Chesnay, France 78150
Phone: 33-1-3954-3567
Fax: 33-1-3954-5376
E-mail: contact@altoinvest.fr
Website: www.altoinvest.fr

Management and Staff
Antoine Valdes, President, Founder
Gerard Hontebeyrie, Venture Partner
Helene Gans, Venture Partner
Jacques Loux, Venture Partner
Jea-Paul Beti, Venture Partner
Jean-Francois Paumelle, Managing Director
Patrice Furia, Venture Partner

Type of Firm
Private Equity Firm

Association Membership
French Venture Capital Association (AFIC)

Project Preferences

Type of Financing Preferred:
Fund of Funds
Expansion
Early Stage
Startup

Geographical Preferences

International Preferences:
Europe
Western Europe
France

Industry Preferences

In Computer Software prefer:
Software

In Consumer Related prefer:
Consumer Products
Consumer Services

In Industrial/Energy prefer:
Environmental Related

In Business Serv. prefer:
Distribution

Additional Information
Year Founded: 2001
Current Activity Level: Actively seeking new investments

ALTOR EQUITY PARTNERS
Birger Jarlsgatan 14
Stockholm, Sweden 114 34
Phone: 46-8-678-9100
Fax: 46-8-678-9101
E-mail: info@altor.com
Website: www.altor.com

Other Offices
Bredgade 29 III
Copenhagen, Denmark 1260
Phone: 45-33-367-300
Fax: 45-33-367-301

Karenslyst Alle 4
Oslo, Norway N-0278
Phone: 47-22-128-383
Fax: 47-22-128-384

erottajankatu 5
Helsinki, Finland 00130
Phone: 358-9-682-947-50

Management and Staff
Denis Viet-Jacobsen, Partner
Fredrik Stromholm, Partner
Harald Mix, Partner
Hugo Maurstad, Partner
Jaakko Kivinen, Partner
Jesper Eliasson, Chief Financial Officer
Johan Cervin, Partner
Reynir Indahl, Partner
Stefan Linder, Partner

Type of Firm
Private Equity Firm

Association Membership
European Private Equity and Venture Capital Assoc.

Project Preferences

Type of Financing Preferred:
Leveraged Buyout
Turnaround
Management Buyouts

Geographical Preferences

International Preferences:
Europe
Scandanavia/Nordic Region

Additional Information
Name of Most Recent Fund: Altor 2006 Fund (AKA: Altor Fund II)
Most Recent Fund Was Raised: 02/22/2006
Year Founded: 2003
Capital Under Management: $834,000,000
Current Activity Level: Actively seeking new investments

ALTOS VENTURES
2882 Sand Hill Road
Suite 100
Menlo Park, CA USA 94025
Phone: 650-234-9771
Fax: 650-233-9821
E-mail: info@altosvc.com
Website: www.altosvc.com

Management and Staff
Alan Beringsmith, Chief Financial Officer
Anthony Lee, General Partner
Brendon Kim, General Partner
Han Kim, General Partner
Hodong Nam, General Partner

Type of Firm
Private Equity Firm

Association Membership
Western Association of Venture Capitalists (WAVC)
National Venture Capital Association - USA (NVCA)

Project Preferences

Type of Financing Preferred:
Second Stage Financing

Early Stage
Start-up Financing
Later Stage
Seed
First Stage Financing

Size of Investments Considered:

Min Size of Investment Considered (000s): $1,000
Max Size of Investment Considered (000s): $5,000

Geographical Preferences

United States Preferences:

Northern California
West Coast
California

Industry Focus

(% based on actual investment)

Internet Specific	51.5%
Computer Software and Services	35.6%
Communications and Media	8.9%
Consumer Related	1.1%
Other Products	1.1%
Medical/Health	0.7%
Computer Hardware	0.6%
Semiconductors/Other Elect.	0.5%

Additional Information

Year Founded: 1996
Capital Under Management: $220,000,000
Current Activity Level: Actively seeking new investments

ALTOTECH VENTURES

One Lagoon Drive
Suite 100
Redwood City, CA USA 94065
Phone: 650-631-8080
Fax: 650-631-8081
E-mail: info@altotechventures.com
Website: www.altotechventures.com

Management and Staff

Gloria Wahl, General Partner
Walter Lee, General Partner

Type of Firm

Private Equity Firm

Association Membership

Western Association of Venture Capitalists (WAVC)
Natl Assoc of Small Bus. Inv. Co (NASBIC)
National Venture Capital Association - USA (NVCA)

Project Preferences

Type of Financing Preferred:

Early Stage

Industry Preferences

In Communications prefer:

Telecommunications
Wireless Communications
Data Communications

In Computer Software prefer:

Computer Services
Data Processing
Software
Systems Software
Applications Software

In Internet Specific prefer:

E-Commerce Technology
Internet
Ecommerce

In Semiconductor/Electr prefer:

Semiconductor
Laser Related
Fiber Optics

In Biotechnology prefer:

Industrial Biotechnology

Additional Information

Year Founded: 2000
Capital Under Management: $51,000,000
Current Activity Level: Actively seeking new investments

ALTRA INVESTMENTS

Carrera 7, No. 71-52
Torre A, Oficina 901
Bogota, Colombia
Phone: 57-1-325-2440
Fax: 57-1-312-0540
E-mail: info@altrainvestments.com
Website: www.altrainvestments.com

Type of Firm

Private Equity Firm

Project Preferences

Type of Financing Preferred:

Leveraged Buyout
Acquisition

Size of Investments Considered:

Min Size of Investment Considered (000s): $15,000
Max Size of Investment Considered (000s): $30,000

Geographical Preferences

International Preferences:

Latin America

Additional Information

Year Founded: 2005
Capital Under Management: $80,000,000
Current Activity Level: Actively seeking new investments

ALTUS CAPITAL PARTNERS

10 Wright Street
Suite 110
Westport, CT USA 06880
Phone: 203-429-2000
Fax: 203-429-2010
Website: www.altuscapitalpartners.com

Other Offices

250 Parkway Drive
Suite 120
Lincolnshire, IL USA 60069
Phone: 847-229-0770
Fax: 847-229-9271

Management and Staff

Elizabeth Burgess, Partner
Gregory Greenberg, Partner
Russell Greenberg, Managing Partner

Type of Firm

Private Equity Firm

Project Preferences

Role in Financing:

Will function either as deal originator or investor in deals created by others

Type of Financing Preferred:

Leveraged Buyout
Management Buyouts
Recapitalizations

Size of Investments Considered:

Min Size of Investment Considered (000s): $3,000
Max Size of Investment Considered (000s): $10,000

Geographical Preferences

United States Preferences:

Midwest
Southeast
East Coast

Industry Preferences

In Manufact. prefer:

Manufacturing

Additional Information

Year Founded: 2003
Capital Under Management: $79,700,000
Current Activity Level: Actively seeking new investments
Method of Compensation: Return on invest. most important, but chg. closing fees, service fees, etc.

ALTUS VENTURES, LLC

120 West Broadway
Altus, OK USA 73521
Phone: 580-480-1319
Fax: 580-477-2983
Website: www.altusventuresok.com

Type of Firm

Bank Affiliated

Project Preferences

Type of Financing Preferred:

Early Stage

Expansion
Startup

Geographical Preferences

United States Preferences:
Oklahoma

Additional Information

Name of Most Recent Fund: Altus Venture Capital Fund V, LLC
Most Recent Fund Was Raised: 05/15/2006
Year Founded: 2002
Capital Under Management: $14,400,000
Current Activity Level: Actively seeking new investments

ALUMNI CAPITAL NETWORK

51 East 42nd Street
Suite 1100
New York, NY USA 10017
Phone: 212-792-5510
Fax: 212-922-0522
Website: www.alumnicapitalnetwork.com

Management and Staff

A. William Kapler, Managing Director
Daniel Minerva, Managing Director
Daniel Vantucci, Managing Director
Denise Kelly, Managing Director
Jeffrey Miller, Managing Director
Kevin Jones, Managing Director
Michael Petrushka, Managing Director
Michael Bozarth, Managing Director
Paul Detlefs, Managing Director
Richard Golden, Managing Director
Thomas Fox, Managing Director
Thomas Donahue, Managing Director
V. Charles Pisciotta, Managing Director
Walter Nollmann, Managing Director

Type of Firm

Private Equity Firm

Industry Preferences

In Consumer Related prefer:
Consumer

In Industrial/Energy prefer:
Industrial Products

In Financial Services prefer:
Financial Services

In Business Serv. prefer:
Services

Additional Information

Year Founded: 2007
Capital Under Management: $37,000,000
Current Activity Level: Actively seeking new investments

ALVEN CAPITAL

1, place Andre Malraux
Paris, France 75001
Phone: 33-1-5534-3838
Fax: 33-1-5534-3839
E-mail: contact@alvencapital.com
Website: www.alvencapital.com

Management and Staff

Charles Letourneur, Managing Partner
Guillaume Aubin, Managing Partner
Julie Barchilon, Chief Financial Officer
Nicolas Celier, Partner

Type of Firm

Private Equity Firm

Association Membership

French Venture Capital Association (AFIC)

Project Preferences

Type of Financing Preferred:
Early Stage
Balanced
Startup

Size of Investments Considered:
Min Size of Investment Considered (000s): $286
Max Size of Investment Considered (000s): $7,153

Geographical Preferences

International Preferences:
France

Industry Preferences

In Communications prefer:
Media and Entertainment

In Internet Specific prefer:
Internet

In Business Serv. prefer:
Services

Additional Information

Year Founded: 2000
Capital Under Management: $13,700,000
Current Activity Level: Actively seeking new investments

AMADEUS CAPITAL PARTNERS, LTD.

Mount Pleasant House
2 Mount Pleasant
Cambridge, United Kingdom CB3 0RN
Phone: 44-1223-707-000
Fax: 44-1223-707-070
E-mail: info@amadeuscapital.com
Website: www.amadeuscapital.com

Other Offices

16 St. James's Street
London, United Kingdom SW1A 1ER
Phone: 44-20-7024-6900
Fax: 44-20-7024-6999

Management and Staff

Alastair Breward, Chief Operating Officer
Andrea Traversone, Partner
Barak Maoz, Partner
Hermann Hauser, Co-Founder
Jeppe Zink, Partner
Laurence John, Chief Executive Officer
Peter Wynn, Co-Founder
Richard Anton, Partner
Roy Merritt, Partner
Shantanu Bhagwat, Partner
Simon Cornwell, Partner

Type of Firm

Private Equity Firm

Association Membership

British Venture Capital Association (BVCA)
European Private Equity and Venture Capital Assoc.

Project Preferences

Role in Financing:
Prefer role as deal originator but will also invest in deals created by others

Type of Financing Preferred:
Second Stage Financing
Early Stage
Research and Development
Balanced
Start-up Financing
Later Stage
Seed
First Stage Financing
Startup

Size of Investments Considered:
Min Size of Investment Considered (000s): $700
Max Size of Investment Considered: No Limit

Geographical Preferences

International Preferences:
Ireland
United Kingdom
Europe
Western Europe

Industry Focus

(% based on actual investment)

Semiconductors/Other Elect.	30.2%
Computer Software and Services	19.9%
Internet Specific	19.1%
Communications and Media	15.5%
Computer Hardware	7.9%
Biotechnology	5.7%
Consumer Related	1.5%
Medical/Health	0.2%

Additional Information

Name of Most Recent Fund: Amadeus III Affiliates Fund LP
Most Recent Fund Was Raised: 05/23/2006

Year Founded: 1997
Capital Under Management: $757,400,000
Current Activity Level: Actively seeking new investments
Method of Compensation: Return on investment is of primary concern, do not charge fees

AMANDA CAPITAL PLC (FKA: FINVEST OYJ)

Aleksanterinkatu 15 A
6th Floor
Helsinki, Finland 00101
Phone: 358-9-6829-600
Fax: 358-9-6829-6020
E-mail: amandainfo@amandacapital.fi
Website: www.amandacapital.fi

Management and Staff

Martin Paasi, Chief Executive Officer
Petter Hoffstroem, Chief Financial Officer

Type of Firm

Private Equity Advisor or Fund of Funds

Association Membership

Finnish Venture Capital Association (FVCA)
European Private Equity and Venture Capital Assoc.

Project Preferences

Type of Financing Preferred:

Fund of Funds
Leveraged Buyout
Fund of Funds of Second

Geographical Preferences

International Preferences:

Western Europe
Eastern Europe
Scandanavia/Nordic Region
Ukraine
Russia

Additional Information

Year Founded: 2000
Capital Under Management: $3,263,100,000
Current Activity Level: Actively seeking new investments

AMANSA CAPITAL PTE., LTD.

90 Amoy Street
Singapore, Singapore 069909
Phone: 65-6327-8120
Fax: 65-6327-4315
Website: www.amansacapital.com

Management and Staff

Akash Prakash, Chief Executive Officer
Krupesh Patel, Chief Operating Officer

Type of Firm

Private Equity Advisor or Fund of Funds

Project Preferences

Type of Financing Preferred:

Balanced

Geographical Preferences

International Preferences:

India

Additional Information

Year Founded: 2006
Current Activity Level: Actively seeking new investments

AMB PRIVATE EQUITY PARTNERS LIMITED (AKA: AMB PARTNERS)

18 Fricker Road
Illovo, South Africa
Phone: 27-11-215-2099
Fax: 27-11-268-6889
E-mail: queries@amb.co.za
Website: www.ambpartners.co.za

Type of Firm

Private Equity Firm

Association Membership

South African Venture Capital Association (SAVCA)

Project Preferences

Type of Financing Preferred:

Leveraged Buyout
Early Stage
Expansion
Seed
Acquisition
Startup

Geographical Preferences

International Preferences:

South Africa

Additional Information

Year Founded: 1999
Current Activity Level: Actively seeking new investments

AMBERTANK

Sveavagen 17
Stockholm, Sweden SE-111 57
Phone: 46-707-443-307
E-mail: info@ambertank.com
Website: www.ambertank.com

Type of Firm

Private Equity Firm

Project Preferences

Type of Financing Preferred:

Leveraged Buyout
Balanced
Management Buyouts
Acquisition

Industry Preferences

In Medical/Health prefer:

Medical/Health
Health Services

Additional Information

Year Founded: 2008
Current Activity Level: Actively seeking new investments

AMBIENTA SGR S.P.A.

Via Larga 2
Milano, Italy 20122
Phone: 39-2-7217-461
Fax: 39-2-7217-4646
E-mail: info@ambientasgr.com
Website: www.ambientasgr.com

Management and Staff

Jonathan Gibson, Partner
Mauro Roversi, Partner
Nino Tronchetti Provera, Chief Executive Officer
Rivolta Rivolta, Partner

Type of Firm

Private Equity Firm

Project Preferences

Type of Financing Preferred:

Leveraged Buyout
Later Stage

Geographical Preferences

International Preferences:

Europe

Industry Preferences

In Industrial/Energy prefer:

Energy
Energy Conservation Relat

In Other prefer:

Environment Responsible

Additional Information

Year Founded: 2007
Capital Under Management: $321,700,000
Current Activity Level: Actively seeking new investments

AME VENTURES

9, Via Camperio
Milan, Italy 20123
Phone: 39-02-637862140

E-mail: info@ameventures.it
Website: www.ameventures.it

Type of Firm

Private Equity Firm

Project Preferences

Type of Financing Preferred:

Early Stage
Expansion

Size of Investments Considered:

Min Size of Investment Considered (000s): $121
Max Size of Investment Considered (000s): $1,817

Geographical Preferences

International Preferences:

Italy
Europe

Industry Preferences

In Consumer Related prefer:

Entertainment and Leisure
Retail

In Industrial/Energy prefer:

Energy

In Financial Services prefer:

Financial Services

In Business Serv. prefer:

Services

In Utilities prefer:

Utilities

Additional Information

Year Founded: 2005
Current Activity Level: Actively seeking new investments

AMERICAN BEACON ADVISORS, INC. (FKA:AMR INVESTMENT SERVICES)

4151 Amon Carter Boulevard
MD 2450
Fort Worth, TX USA 76155
Phone: 817-967-3509
Fax: 817-931-4331
E-mail: American AAdvantage.Funds@aa.com
Website: www.aafunds.com

Management and Staff

Nancy Eckl, Vice President

Type of Firm

Bank Affiliated

Project Preferences

Type of Financing Preferred:

Fund of Funds
Leveraged Buyout

Additional Information

Name of Most Recent Fund: American Private Equity Partners II, L.P.
Most Recent Fund Was Raised: 06/09/2005
Year Founded: 2001
Capital Under Management: $117,400,000
Current Activity Level: Actively seeking new investments

AMERICAN CAPITAL, LTD.

Two Bethesda Metro Center
14th Floor
Bethesda, MD USA 20814
Phone: 301-951-6122
Fax: 301-654-6714
E-mail: Info@AmericanCapital.com
Website: www.american-capital.com

Other Offices

525 University Avenue
Suite 500
Palo Alto, CA USA 94301
Phone: 650-289-4560
Fax: 650-289-4570

Velazquez, 47, 7
Madrid, Spain 28001
Phone: 34-91-423-2760

76 Westminster Street
Suite 1400
Providence, RI USA 02903
Phone: 401-456-1530
Fax: 401-456-1543

29th Floor Gloucester Tower
The Landmark, 15 Queens Road C
Central, Hong Kong
Phone: 852-3476-9238
Fax: 852-3015-9354

11755 Wilshire Boulevard
Suite 2400
Los Angeles, CA USA 90025
Phone: 310-806-6280
Fax: 310-806-6299

c/o European Capital
25 Bedford Street
London, Uganda WC2E 9ES
Phone: 44-20-7539-7000
Fax: 44-20-7539-7001

2200 Ross Avenue
Suite 4500W
Dallas, TX USA 75201
Phone: 214-273-6630
Fax: 214-273-6635

161 Worcester Road
Suite 606
Framingham, MA USA 01701
Phone: 508-598-1100
Fax: 508-598-1101

5425 Wisconsin Avenue
Sixth Floor
Chevy Chase, MD USA 20815
Phone: 301-968-9200

c/o European Capital
112 avenue Kleber
Paris, France 75784
Phone: 33-1-4068-0666
Fax: 33-1-4068-0688

225 Franklin Street
26th Floor
Boston, MA USA 02110
Phone: 617-217-2075

505 Fifth Avenue
26th Floor
New York, NY USA 10017
Phone: 212-213-2009
Fax: 212-213-2060

29/F Gloucester Tower
15 Queens Road C
Hong Kong, Hong Kong
Phone: 852-3476-9238
Fax: 852-3015-9354

Management and Staff

Adam Stern, Vice President
Adam Spence, Managing Director
Alex Grau, Vice President
Allison Young, Vice President
Alvin Tan, Vice President
Andrew Bonanno, Vice President
Bill Bujake, Vice President
Bob Sharp, Principal
Bowen Diehl, Managing Director
Bradley Nii, Principal
Brady Busch, Vice President
Brendan Gallaher, Managing Director
Bret Bero, Vice President
Brett Donelan, Vice President
Brian Martin, Vice President
Brian Graff, Managing Director
Chong Moua, Vice President
Chris McCormack, Vice President
Chris Carey, Principal
Christian Toro, Vice President
Christopher Jackson, Vice President
Colin Cropper, Vice President
Craig Moore, Managing Director
Cydonii Fairfax, Vice President
Dan Cohn-Sfetcu, Vice President
Dana Dratch, Vice President
Darin Winn, Managing Director
David Gessel, Vice President
David McReynolds, Principal
David Steinglass, Managing Director
David Zhang, Vice President
Dean Anderson, Managing Director
Dennis Kirby, Vice President
Derek Walton, Vice President
Diana Stewart, Vice President
Diane Prier, Principal
Didiere Lefevre, Principal

Douglas Cooper, Managing Director
Dustin Smith, Principal
Eric Heith, Vice President
Erik Van Duijvenvoorde, Vice President
Erin Soule, Vice President
Eugene Krichevsky, Principal
Evan Kurtz, Vice President
Fernando Ruiz, Vice President
Frank Do, Managing Director
Gordon O'Brien, Managing Director
Gregg Newmark, Managing Director
Griffith Lee, Vice President
Harry Davoody, Principal
Heather French, Vice President
Helen Yang, Principal
James Shevlin, Principal
James Lau, Principal
Jason Campbell, Vice President
Jay Squiers, Principal
Jay Heirshberg, Vice President
Jean Eichenlaub, Managing Director
Jeffrey Anapolsky, Vice President
Jeffrey MacDowell, Managing Director
Jennifer Vaughn, Principal
Joel Houck, Managing Director
John Neis, Principal
John Drennan, Principal
John Weinhardt, Principal
John Capperella, Managing Director
John Rhoades, Vice President
John Hooker, Vice President
Jon Isaacson, Managing Director
Jonathan Leiman, Principal
Joseph Romic, Principal
Juan Miguel Estela, Vice President
Justin Cressall, Vice President
Justin DuFour, Vice President
Kacy Moutray Ellis, Vice President
Ken Halperin, Vice President
Kenneth Pollack, Vice President
Kenneth Jones, Principal
Kevin Kuykendall, Managing Director
Kevin McAllister, Vice President
Kimberley Robinson-Corbin, Vice President
Kimberly Reed, Principal
Kyle Bradford, Principal
Lee Robinson, Vice President
Luis Felipe Castellanos, Managing Director
Lynn JangJan, Vice President
Malon Wilkus, President, CEO, Chairman
Mark Fikse, Principal
Mark Pelletier, Managing Director
Mathew Frankel, Vice President
Matthew Bigge, Vice President
Michael Cerullo, Principal
Michael Meretta, Vice President
Michael Thompson, Vice President
Michael Shin, Principal
Michael Messersmith, Vice President
Michael Sarner, Vice President
Michael Ho, Vice President
Michael Jordan, Vice President
Michael Schmitz, Vice President
Mike Michienzi, Principal
Miles Arnone, Managing Director
Myung Yi, Managing Director
Natasha Volyanskaya, Principal
Natasha Fox, Principal
Nathalie Faure Beaulieu, Managing Director
Nathan Horvath, Vice President
Pankaj Gupta, Principal
Patrick White, Vice President
Peter Dahms, Vice President
Peter Reijula, Principal
Rick Richert, Principal
Rob Carraway, Vice President
Robert Grunewald, Managing Director
Robert Klein, Managing Director
Robert Neighoff, Principal
Robert Von Finckenstein, Managing Director
Robert Brooks, Vice President
Rodd Macklin, Vice President
Roland Cline, Managing Director
Ross Fuller, Vice President
Rustey Emmet, Vice President
Ryan Brauns, Vice President
Scott Pinsonnault, Vice President
Sean Eagle, Principal
Steve Gord, Vice President
Steven Devloo, Vice President
Steven Stubitz, Principal
Steven Price, Managing Director
Thomas Szczurek, Principal
Thomas Evans, Vice President
Thomas Nathanson, Principal
Timothy Robinson, Principal
Todd Redmon, Vice President
Todd Friant, Vice President
Todd Wilson, Principal
Virginia Turezyn, Managing Director
Walter Munnich, Managing Director
William Rudat, Vice President
William Dyer, Principal

Type of Firm

Private Equity Firm

Association Membership

Illinois Venture Capital Association

Project Preferences

Role in Financing:

Will function either as deal originator or investor in deals created by others

Type of Financing Preferred:

Leveraged Buyout
Generalist PE
Management Buyouts
Acquisition
Recapitalizations

Size of Investments Considered:

Min Size of Investment Considered (000s): $5,000
Max Size of Investment Considered (000s): $50,000

Geographical Preferences

United States Preferences:

All U.S.

International Preferences:

Europe

Industry Preferences

In Medical/Health prefer:

Health Services

In Consumer Related prefer:

Consumer
Retail
Food/Beverage
Education Related

In Industrial/Energy prefer:

Industrial Products
Factory Automation
Machinery

In Transportation prefer:

Transportation
Aerospace

In Business Serv. prefer:

Services

In Manufact. prefer:

Manufacturing

In Other prefer:

Women/Minority-Owned Bus.

Additional Information

Year Founded: 1986
Capital Under Management: $20,000,000,000
Current Activity Level: Actively seeking new investments
Method of Compensation: Return on invest. most important, but chg. closing fees, service fees, etc.

AMERICAN INDUSTRIAL PARTNERS

535 Fifth Avenue
32nd Floor
New York, NY USA 10017
Phone: 212-627-2360
Fax: 212-627-2372
Website: www.aipartners.com

Management and Staff

Derek Leck, Partner
Dino Cusumano, Partner
Eric Baroyan, Partner
Graham Sullivan, Partner
John Becker, Partner
Kenneth Dabrowski, Partner
Kim Marvin, Partner
Ryan Hodgson, Partner

Type of Firm

Private Equity Firm

Project Preferences

Type of Financing Preferred:

Leveraged Buyout

Geographical Preferences

United States Preferences:

All U.S.

Industry Focus

(% based on actual investment)

Industrial/Energy	73.0%
Other Products	27.0%

Additional Information

Name of Most Recent Fund: American Industrial Partners Capital Fund IV, L.P.
Most Recent Fund Was Raised: 02/09/2007
Year Founded: 1989
Capital Under Management: $405,500,000
Current Activity Level: Actively seeking new investments

AMERICAN INTERNATIONAL GROUP, INC.

70 Pine Street
34th Floor
New York, NY USA 10270
Phone: 212-770-7000
Fax: 212-509-9705
E-mail: info@aig.com
Website: www.aig.com

Type of Firm

Insurance Firm Affiliate

Project Preferences

Type of Financing Preferred:

Expansion
Balanced

Geographical Preferences

International Preferences:

China
All International

Industry Preferences

In Consumer Related prefer:

Retail

Additional Information

Year Founded: 1958
Current Activity Level: Actively seeking new investments

AMERICAN RIVER VENTURES

2270 Douglas Boulevard
Suite 212
Roseville, CA USA 95661
Phone: 916-780-2828
Fax: 916-780-5443
E-mail: info@arventures.com
Website: www.arventures.com

Management and Staff

Barbara Grant, Managing Director
Cheryl Beninga, Managing Director
F.Ray Nunez, Chief Financial Officer
Harry Laswell, Managing Director
John Kunhart, Managing Director

Type of Firm

SBIC

Association Membership

Western Association of Venture Capitalists (WAVC)
National Venture Capital Association - USA (NVCA)
Natl Assoc of Small Bus. Inv. Co (NASBIC)

Project Preferences

Role in Financing:

Prefer role as deal originator but will also invest in deals created by others

Type of Financing Preferred:

Second Stage Financing
Early Stage
Seed
First Stage Financing
Startup

Size of Investments Considered:

Min Size of Investment Considered (000s): $500
Max Size of Investment Considered (000s): $6,700

Geographical Preferences

United States Preferences:

New Mexico
Nevada
Arizona
Oregon
West Coast
California
Colorado
Idaho
Utah
Washington

Industry Preferences

In Computer Software prefer:

Software

In Semiconductor/Electr prefer:

Electronics
Electronic Components
Semiconductor

In Industrial/Energy prefer:

Energy
Energy Conservation Relat

Additional Information

Name of Most Recent Fund: American River Ventures Fund I
Most Recent Fund Was Raised: 11/28/2001
Year Founded: 2001
Capital Under Management: $100,000,000
Current Activity Level: Actively seeking new investments
Method of Compensation: Return on investment is of primary concern, do not charge fees

AMERICAN SECURITIES CAPITAL PARTNERS LLC

Chrysler Center
666 Third Avenue, 29th Floor
New York, NY USA 10017
Phone: 212-476-8000
Fax: 212-697-5524
E-mail: info@american-securities.com
Website: www.american-securities.com

Management and Staff

Charles Klein, Managing Director
Connie Ma, Vice President
David Horing, Managing Director
Glenn Kaufman, Managing Director
Marc Saiontz, Managing Director
Matthew LeBaron, Managing Director
Matthew Levine, Vice President
Paul Rossetti, Managing Director

Type of Firm

Bank Affiliated

Project Preferences

Role in Financing:

Prefer role as deal originator but will also invest in deals created by others

Type of Financing Preferred:

Second Stage Financing
Leveraged Buyout
Control-block Purchases
Industry Rollups
Special Situation

Size of Investments Considered:

Min Size of Investment Considered (000s): $25,000
Max Size of Investment Considered: No Limit

Geographical Preferences

United States Preferences:

All U.S.

Canadian Preferences:

All Canada

International Preferences:

China

Industry Focus

(% based on actual investment)

Industrial/Energy	34.4%
Other Products	28.1%
Consumer Related	26.1%
Computer Hardware	6.2%
Communications and Media	2.9%
Internet Specific	2.3%

Additional Information

Name of Most Recent Fund: American Securities Partners IV, L.P.
Most Recent Fund Was Raised: 10/26/2004
Year Founded: 1947
Capital Under Management: $21,000,000,000
Current Activity Level: Actively seeking new investments

Method of Compensation: Return on invest. most important, but chg. closing fees, service fees, etc.

AMERIMARK CAPITAL GROUP

511 East John Carpenter Freewa
Suite 220
Irving, TX USA 75062
Phone: 214-638-7878
Fax: 214-638-7612
E-mail: amerimark@amcapital.com
Website: www.amcapital.com

Management and Staff

Charles Martin, Chief Executive Officer

Type of Firm

Bank Affiliated

Project Preferences

Role in Financing:

Prefer role as deal originator

Type of Financing Preferred:

Second Stage Financing
Leveraged Buyout
Mezzanine

Size of Investments Considered:

Min Size of Investment Considered (000s): $500
Max Size of Investment Considered: No Limit

Geographical Preferences

United States Preferences:

All U.S.

Industry Preferences

In Communications prefer:

Radio & TV Broadcasting
Telecommunications
Data Communications

In Computer Hardware prefer:

Integrated Turnkey System

In Internet Specific prefer:

Internet

In Consumer Related prefer:

Entertainment and Leisure
Retail
Food/Beverage
Consumer Products
Consumer Services

In Industrial/Energy prefer:

Materials
Machinery
Environmental Related

In Financial Services prefer:

Financial Services

In Business Serv. prefer:

Distribution
Consulting Services

Additional Information

Year Founded: 1989
Capital Under Management: $32,000,000
Current Activity Level: Actively seeking new investments
Method of Compensation: Return on invest. most important, but chg. closing fees, service fees, etc.

AMGEN, INC.

One Amgen Center Drive
Thousand Oaks, CA USA 91320
Phone: 805-447-1000
Fax: 805-447-1010
Website: www.amgen.com

Management and Staff

Kevin Sharer, Chief Executive Officer

Type of Firm

Corporate PE/Venture

Project Preferences

Type of Financing Preferred:

Early Stage
Geographical Preferences

United States Preferences:

All U.S.

Industry Preferences

In Biotechnology prefer:

Biotechnology

Additional Information

Name of Most Recent Fund: Amgen Ventures
Most Recent Fund Was Raised: 11/11/2004
Year Founded: 1980
Capital Under Management: $100,000,000
Current Activity Level: Actively seeking new investments

AMICUS CAPITAL, LLC

1045 Sansome Street
Suite 326
San Francisco, CA USA 94111
Phone: 415-646-0120
Fax: 415-276-4755
Website: www.amicuscapital.com

Management and Staff

Bob Zipp, Partner

Type of Firm

Private Equity Firm

Additional Information

Year Founded: 1998
Current Activity Level: Actively seeking new investments

AMIDZAD, LLC

353 University Avenue
Palo Alto, CA USA 94301
Phone: 650-323-4777
Fax: 650-323-4044
E-mail: info@amidzad.com
Website: www.amidzad.com

Management and Staff

Pejman Nozad, General Partner
Rahim Amidi, General Partner
Saeed Amidi, General Partner

Type of Firm

Private Equity Firm

Project Preferences

Type of Financing Preferred:

Balanced
Start-up Financing

Additional Information

Year Founded: 2000
Capital Under Management: $3,000,000
Current Activity Level: Actively seeking new investments

AMMER!PARTNERS

Chilehaus A
Fischertwiete 2
Hamburg, Germany 20095
Website: www.ammerfriends.net

Management and Staff

Dieter Ammer, Founder

Type of Firm

Private Equity Firm

Additional Information

Year Founded: 2007
Current Activity Level: Actively seeking new investments

AMORCAGE RHONE-ALPES

10 rue du Chateau d'Eau
Champagne au mont d'or, France 69410
Phone: 33-4-7252-3952
Fax: 33-4-7252-3930
E-mail: info@a-r-a.fr
Website: www.a-r-a.fr

Type of Firm

Private Equity Firm

Additional Information

Year Founded: 2002
Current Activity Level: Actively seeking new investments

AMP CAPITAL INVESTORS (AKA: AMP ASSET MNGMT LTD.)

50 Bridge Street
Level 13
Sydney, Australia 2000
Phone: 612-9257-5000
Fax: 612-9257-1234
E-mail: AMPCI_Investment_Research@amp.com.au
Website: www.ampcapital.com.au

Other Offices

Level 31
10 Eagle Street
Brisbane, Australia 4000
Phone: 61-7-3226-1234
Fax: 61-7-3226-1958

Level 5 City Tower
95 Customhouse Quay
Wellington, New Zealand
Phone: 644-494-2200
Fax: 644-494-2100

Level 6, AMP Square
535 Bourke Street
Melbourne, Australia 3000
Phone: 61-3-9622-6000
Fax: 61-3-9622-6439

Level 2
1260 Hay Street
West Perth, Australia 6005
Phone: 61-8-9483-4700
Fax: 61-8-9483-4711

Level 2
191 Fullarton Road
Dulwich, Australia 5001
Phone: 61-8-8333-8200
Fax: 61-8-8333-8224

Management and Staff

Henry Capra, Chief Financial Officer
Stephen Dunne, Managing Director

Type of Firm

Bank Affiliated

Association Membership

Australian Venture Capital Association (AVCAL)

Project Preferences

Role in Financing:

Prefer role as deal originator

Type of Financing Preferred:

Leveraged Buyout
Generalist PE
Expansion
Balanced
Later Stage
Management Buyouts

Size of Investments Considered:

Min Size of Investment Considered (000s): $8,058
Max Size of Investment Considered (000s): $24,174

Geographical Preferences

International Preferences:

Australia
New Zealand

Industry Focus

(% based on actual investment)

Other Products	60.9%
Consumer Related	17.3%
Industrial/Energy	8.4%
Medical/Health	7.0%
Internet Specific	4.6%
Computer Software and Services	1.7%

Additional Information

Name of Most Recent Fund: Private Equity Fund III
Most Recent Fund Was Raised: 01/04/2005
Year Founded: 1993
Capital Under Management: $212,000,000
Current Activity Level: Actively seeking new investments
Method of Compensation: Return on invest. most important, but chg. closing fees, service fees, etc.

AMPERSAND VENTURES

55 William Street
Suite 240
Wellesley, MA USA 02481
Phone: 781-239-0700
Fax: 781-239-0824
E-mail: info@ampersandventures.com
Website: www.ampersandventures.com

Other Offices

12555 High Bluff Drive
Suite 380
San Diego, CA USA 92130
Phone: 858-259-4664
Fax: 858-259-8384

Management and Staff

Charles Yie, General Partner
David Parker, Venture Partner
Douglas Rohall, Venture Partner
Herbert Hooper, Managing General Partner
Jared Bartok, Principal
Laurence McCarthy, Venture Partner
Marc Dulude, General Partner
Peter Glick, General Partner
Richard Charpie, Managing General Partner
Stuart Auerbach, General Partner
Suzanne MacCormack, Partner
Timothy Tuff, Venture Partner
Todd Rainville, Partner

Type of Firm

Private Equity Firm

Association Membership

National Venture Capital Association - USA (NVCA)

Project Preferences

Role in Financing:

Prefer role as deal originator but will also invest in deals created by others

Type of Financing Preferred:

Second Stage Financing
Early Stage
Expansion
Mezzanine
Generalist PE
Turnaround
Balanced
Later Stage
Seed
Management Buyouts
First Stage Financing
Private Placement
Industry Rollups
Special Situation
Recapitalizations

Size of Investments Considered:

Min Size of Investment Considered (000s): $5,000
Max Size of Investment Considered (000s): $10,000

Industry Focus

(% based on actual investment)

Medical/Health	19.8%
Biotechnology	15.1%
Semiconductors/Other Elect.	13.4%
Other Products	12.3%
Computer Software and Services	10.5%
Internet Specific	9.4%
Industrial/Energy	6.2%
Communications and Media	5.6%
Consumer Related	4.0%
Computer Hardware	3.6%

Additional Information

Year Founded: 1988
Capital Under Management: $600,000,000
Current Activity Level: Actively seeking new investments
Method of Compensation: Return on invest. most important, but chg. closing fees, service fees, etc.

AMPHION CAPITAL MANAGEMENT, LLC (FKA: WOLFENSOHN ASSOCIATES)

350 Madison Avenue
New York, NY USA 10022
Phone: 212-210-6200
Fax: 212-210-6271
Management and Staff
Richard Morgan, Managing Partner
Robert Bertoldi, Managing Partner

Type of Firm
Private Equity Firm

Project Preferences

Role in Financing:
Prefer role as deal originator but will also invest in deals created by others

Type of Financing Preferred:
Second Stage Financing
Leveraged Buyout
First Stage Financing
Acquisition
Startup

Size of Investments Considered:
Min Size of Investment Considered (000s): $3,000
Max Size of Investment Considered (000s): $20,000

Industry Preferences

In Communications prefer:
Communications and Media

In Computer Other prefer:
Computer Related

In Semiconductor/Electr prefer:
Electronics

In Medical/Health prefer:
Medical/Health

Additional Information
Name of Most Recent Fund: Wolfensohn Associates LP
Most Recent Fund Was Raised: 01/01/1984
Year Founded: 1984
Capital Under Management: $100,000,000
Current Activity Level: Reducing investment activity
Method of Compensation: Return on investment is of primary concern, do not charge fees

---

AMPHION INNOVATIONS PLC
15-19 Athol Street
Douglas
Isle of Man, United Kingdom IM1 1LB
E-mail: info@amphionplc.com
Website: www.amphionplc.com

Other Offices
One Berkeley Street
London, United Kingdom W1J 8DJ
Phone: 44-20-7016-8821
Fax: 44-20-7016-9100

330 Madison Avenue
New York, NY USA 10017

Type of Firm
Private Equity Firm

Additional Information
Year Founded: 2006
Current Activity Level: Actively seeking new investments

AMPLICO KAPITAL AB
Vastra Hamngatan 12
Goteborg, Sweden 403 17
Phone: 46-31-105-463
Fax: 46-31-711-1003
E-mail: info@amplico.se
Website: www.amplico.se

Management and Staff
Hakan Hansen, Partner
Mats Lindahl, Managing Partner
Mikael Olsson, Partner

Type of Firm
Private Equity Firm

Association Membership
Swedish Venture Capital Association (SVCA)

Project Preferences

Type of Financing Preferred:
Leveraged Buyout
Expansion
Seed
Special Situation
Startup

Size of Investments Considered:
Min Size of Investment Considered (000s): $531
Max Size of Investment Considered (000s): $5,310

Geographical Preferences

International Preferences:
Scandanavia/Nordic Region

Industry Preferences

In Consumer Related prefer:
Consumer Products

In Industrial/Energy prefer:
Energy
Industrial Products
Machinery

In Other prefer:
Environment Responsible

Additional Information
Year Founded: 2000
Capital Under Management: $59,300,000
Current Activity Level: Actively seeking new investments

AMPLIFIER VENTURE PARTNERS
7901 Jones Branch Drive
Suite 130
McLean, VA USA 22102
Phone: 703-635-2655
Fax: 703-991-7581
E-mail: info@amplifierventures.com
Website: www.amplifierventures.com

Management and Staff
Jonathan Aberman, Managing Director

Type of Firm
Private Equity Firm

Association Membership
Mid-Atlantic Venture Association

Project Preferences

Type of Financing Preferred:
Early Stage
Seed
First Stage Financing
Special Situation
Startup

Size of Investments Considered:
Min Size of Investment Considered (000s): $500
Max Size of Investment Considered (000s): $1,000

Geographical Preferences

United States Preferences:
Mid Atlantic
Maryland
Virginia
All U.S.

Industry Preferences

In Communications prefer:
Communications and Media
Telecommunications
Media and Entertainment

In Computer Software prefer:
Software
Systems Software
Applications Software
Artificial Intelligence

In Internet Specific prefer:
E-Commerce Technology
Internet
Ecommerce
Web Aggregration/Portals

In Consumer Related prefer:
Entertainment and Leisure
Education Related

In Industrial/Energy prefer:
Alternative Energy

Additional Information
Year Founded: 2005
Capital Under Management: $15,000,000
Current Activity Level: Actively seeking new investments

AMWAL ALKHALEEJ
P.O. Box 59115
Riyadh, Saudi Arabia
Phone: 966-1216-4666
Fax: 966-1216-4777
E-mail: Riyadh@amwalalkhaleej.com
Website: www.amwalalkhaleej.com

Type of Firm
Private Equity Firm

Project Preferences

Type of Financing Preferred:
Balanced

Geographical Preferences

International Preferences:
Middle East

Additional Information
Year Founded: 2005
Capital Under Management: $266,700,000
Current Activity Level: Actively seeking new investments

AMWIN MANAGEMENT PTY., LTD.

Level 4 Customs House
31 Alfred Street
Sydney, Australia 2000
Phone: 612-9251-9655
Fax: 612-9251-7655
E-mail: partners@amwin.com.au
Website: www.amwin.com.au

Management and Staff
Stuart Wardman-Browne, Chief Operating Officer

Type of Firm
Private Equity Firm

Project Preferences

Type of Financing Preferred:
Early Stage
Seed
Startup

Size of Investments Considered:
Min Size of Investment Considered (000s): $564
Max Size of Investment Considered (000s): $2,254

Geographical Preferences

International Preferences:
Pacific

Additional Information
Year Founded: 1998
Capital Under Management: $16,200,000
Current Activity Level: Actively seeking new investments

ANACACIA CAPITAL

4-10 Bay Street
Level 2, Double Bay
Sydney, Australia 2028
Phone: 612-9363-1222
Fax: 612-8580-4600
E-mail: contact@anacacia.com.au
Website: www.anacacia.com.au

Management and Staff
Jeremy Samuel, Managing Director

Type of Firm
Private Equity Firm

Association Membership
Australian Venture Capital Association (AVCAL)
Project Preferences

Role in Financing:
Prefer role as deal originator but will also invest in deals created by others

Type of Financing Preferred:
Leveraged Buyout
Acquisition

Geographical Preferences

International Preferences:
Australia
New Zealand

Additional Information
Year Founded: 2007
Capital Under Management: $42,500,000
Current Activity Level: Actively seeking new investments

ANACAP FINANCIAL PARTNERS LLP

Stanford House
27a Floral Street
London, United Kingdom WC2E 9EZ
Phone: 44-20-7070-5250
Fax: 44-20-7070-5290
E-mail: contact@anacapfp.com
Website: www.anacapfp.com

Management and Staff
Chris Patrick, Principal
Finlay McFadyen, Principal
Justin Sulger, Managing Director
Michael Edwards, Chief Operating Officer
Peter Cartwright, Principal

Type of Firm
Private Equity Firm

Project Preferences

Type of Financing Preferred:
Expansion
Generalist PE
Balanced
Turnaround
Startup

Geographical Preferences

International Preferences:
United Kingdom
Europe

Industry Preferences

In Medical/Health prefer:
Medical/Health

In Consumer Related prefer:
Consumer

In Financial Services prefer:
Financial Services
Insurance

Additional Information
Name of Most Recent Fund: AnaCap Financial Partners, L.P.
Most Recent Fund Was Raised: 04/10/2006
Year Founded: 2005
Capital Under Management: $428,300,000
Current Activity Level: Actively seeking new investments

ANCHORAGE CAPITAL PARTNERS

Six Bridge Street
Level Four
Sydney, Australia 2000
Phone: 612-8259-7777
Fax: 612-8259-7778
E-mail: anchorage@anchoragecapital.com.au
Website: www.anchoragecapital.com.au

Management and Staff
Dani Sher, Chief Financial Officer
Daniel Wong, Partner
Mark Bayliss, Partner
Michael Briggs, Partner
Philip Cave, Partner

Type of Firm
Private Equity Firm

Association Membership
Australian Venture Capital Association (AVCAL)

Project Preferences

Role in Financing:
Will function either as deal originator or investor in deals created by others

Type of Financing Preferred:
Leveraged Buyout
Special Situation
Recapitalizations

Size of Investments Considered:
Min Size of Investment Considered (000s): $40,850
Max Size of Investment Considered (000s): $122,550

Geographical Preferences

International Preferences:
Australia
New Zealand
Asia

Industry Preferences

In Business Serv. prefer:
Services

In Manufact. prefer:
Manufacturing

Additional Information

Year Founded: 2007
Capital Under Management: $8,600,000
Current Activity Level: Actively seeking new investments

ANCOR CAPITAL PARTNERS

Two City Place
100 Throckmorton, Suite 1600
Fort Worth, TX USA 76102
Phone: 817-877-4458
Fax: 817-877-4909
Website: www.ancorcapital.com

Management and Staff

Brook Smith, Managing Director
Craig Porter, Managing Director
J. Randall Keene, Managing Director
Michael Evans, Managing Director
Mitchell Green, Chief Financial Officer
Raymond Kingsbury, Managing Director
Timothy McKibben, Managing Director

Type of Firm

Private Equity Firm

Project Preferences

Type of Financing Preferred:
Leveraged Buyout
Acquisition
Recapitalizations

Geographical Preferences

United States Preferences:
All U.S.

Industry Preferences

In Medical/Health prefer:
Medical/Health

In Consumer Related prefer:
Consumer Products
Consumer Services

In Business Serv. prefer:
Distribution

In Manufact. prefer:
Manufacturing

Additional Information

Year Founded: 1994
Current Activity Level: Actively seeking new investments

ANDLINGER & COMPANY, INC.

520 White Plains Road
Suite 500
Tarrytown, NY USA 10591
Phone: 914-332-4900
Fax: 914-332-4977
E-mail: info@andlinger.net
Website: www.andlinger.com

Other Offices

4445 North AIA
Suite 235
Vero Beach, FL USA 32963
Phone: 772-234-4998
Fax: 772-234-4952

Sieveringer Strasse 36/9
Vienna, Austria 1190
Phone: 43-1-328-7145
Fax: 43-1-328-7145-20

Avenue Louise 326
Brussels, Belgium 1050
Phone: 32-2-647-8070
Fax: 32-2-648-2105

Management and Staff

Anthony Crupi, Managing Director
Charles Ball, Managing Director
Ernst Reichmayr, Managing Director
George Doomany, Managing Director
Gerhard Unterganschnigg, Managing Director
Hermann Lutzenberger, Managing Director
Ivar Mitchell, Managing Director
Mark Callaghan, Managing Director
Merrick Andlinger, Chief Executive Officer
Robert Castello, Managing Director
Stefan Krieglstein, Managing Director
Stephen Magida, Managing Director

Type of Firm

Private Equity Firm

Project Preferences

Type of Financing Preferred:
Balanced
Turnaround
Acquisition
Special Situation

Size of Investments Considered:
Min Size of Investment Considered (000s): $5,000
Max Size of Investment Considered (000s): $25,000

Geographical Preferences

Canadian Preferences:
All Canada

International Preferences:
Europe
Canal Zone

Industry Preferences

In Communications prefer:
Telecommunications

In Computer Software prefer:
Software

In Medical/Health prefer:
Medical Products
Pharmaceuticals

In Industrial/Energy prefer:
Industrial Products

In Manufact. prefer:
Manufacturing

Additional Information

Year Founded: 1976
Current Activity Level: Actively seeking new investments

ANDREESSEN HOROWITZ

2875 Sand Hill Road
Menlo Park, CA USA 94025
Phone: 650-321-2400

Management and Staff

Benjamin Horowitz, Founder
Marc Andreessen, Founder
Scott Kupor, Chief Operating Officer

Type of Firm

Private Equity Firm

Project Preferences

Type of Financing Preferred:
Early Stage
Expansion
Seed
Startup

Industry Preferences

In Communications prefer:
Wireless Communications

In Internet Specific prefer:
Internet

Additional Information

Year Founded: 2009
Capital Under Management: $300,000,000
Current Activity Level: Actively seeking new investments

ANDREW W. BYRD & CO. LLC

201 Fourth Avenue North
Suite 1250
Nashville, TN USA 37219
Phone: 615-256-8061
Fax: 615-256-7057

E-mail: information@awbyrdco.com
Website: www.awbyrdco.com

Management and Staff

Andrew Byrd, President
Charles Sell, Principal
Jay Binkley, Principal
Rick Reisner, Principal

Type of Firm

Private Equity Firm
Project Preferences

Role in Financing:

Prefer role as deal originator

Type of Financing Preferred:

Leveraged Buyout
Control-block Purchases
Generalist PE
Later Stage
Management Buyouts
Recapitalizations

Size of Investments Considered:

Min Size of Investment Considered (000s): $1,000
Max Size of Investment Considered (000s): $5,000

Geographical Preferences

United States Preferences:

Midwest
Southeast

Additional Information

Name of Most Recent Fund: Tennessee Valley Ventures II, L.P.
Most Recent Fund Was Raised: 02/11/2003
Year Founded: 1994
Capital Under Management: $35,000,000
Current Activity Level: Actively seeking new investments
Method of Compensation: Return on invest. most important, but chg. closing fees, service fees, etc.

ANGEL CAPITAL NETWORK

One Harbor Drive
Suite 205
Sausalito, CA USA 94965
Phone: 415-289-8701
Fax: 415-331-3978
Website: www.angelcapitalnetwork.com

Management and Staff

Jim Matthew, Chief Financial Officer
Osamu Tagaya, Chief Executive Officer

Type of Firm

Bank Affiliated

Project Preferences

Type of Financing Preferred:

Early Stage

Industry Preferences

In Biotechnology prefer:

Biotechnology

Additional Information

Year Founded: 1999
Current Activity Level: Actively seeking new investments

ANGEL INVESTORS, LP

817 Orange Blossom Way
Danville, CA USA 94526
Phone: 650-814-7075
Fax: 208-975-8550
E-mail: webmaster@svangel.com
Website: www.svangel.com

Management and Staff

Bob Bozeman, General Partner
J. Casey McGlynn, General Partner
Ronald Conway, General Partner

Type of Firm

Private Equity Firm

Project Preferences

Type of Financing Preferred:

Early Stage

Geographical Preferences

United States Preferences:

Northern California
California

Industry Focus

(% based on actual investment)

Internet Specific	56.4%
Computer Software and Services	30.2%
Other Products	5.0%
Communications and Media	4.2%
Computer Hardware	2.7%
Consumer Related	1.5%

Additional Information

Year Founded: 1998
Capital Under Management: $150,000,000
Current Activity Level: Making few, if any, new investments

ANGEL SECURITIES INC.

1-1-3-1000, Umeda, Kita-ku
Osaka City
Osaka, Japan
Phone: 816-6456-3600
Fax: 816-6456-3600
Website: www.angelsec.co.jp

Management and Staff

Masnao Hosokawa, Managing Director

Type of Firm

Private Equity Firm

Project Preferences

Type of Financing Preferred:

Balanced

Geographical Preferences

International Preferences:

Japan

Additional Information

Year Founded: 2000
Current Activity Level: Actively seeking new investments

ANGELENO GROUP, LLC

2029 Century Park East
Suite 2980
Los Angeles, CA USA 90067
Phone: 310-552-2790
Fax: 310-552-2727
E-mail: info@angelenogroup.com
Website: www.angelenogroup.com

Management and Staff

Daniel Weiss, Managing Partner
Yaniv Tepper, Managing Partner
Zeb Rice, Managing Partner

Type of Firm

Private Equity Firm

Project Preferences

Type of Financing Preferred:

Balanced

Geographical Preferences

United States Preferences:

All U.S.

Industry Preferences

In Semiconductor/Electr prefer:

Electronics
Electronic Components

In Industrial/Energy prefer:

Energy
Alternative Energy
Energy Conservation Relat
Environmental Related

In Transportation prefer:

Transportation

Additional Information

Name of Most Recent Fund: Angeleno Investors II, L.P.
Most Recent Fund Was Raised: 03/18/2006
Year Founded: 2005
Capital Under Management: $139,300,000
Current Activity Level: Actively seeking new investments

ANGELO, GORDON & COMPANY

245 Park Avenue
New York, NY USA 10167
Phone: 212-692-2000
Fax: 212-867-9328
E-mail: information@angelogordon.com
Website: www.angelogordon.com

Other Offices

25 Hanover Square
London, United Kingdom W1S 1JF
Phone: 44-207-758-5300
Fax: 44-207-758-5420

700 Commerce Drive
Suite 500
Oak Brook, IL USA 60523
Phone: 630-288-4990
Fax: 630-288-4991

One Exchange Square
Suite 1604
Central, Hong Kong
Phone: 852-3416-7300
Fax: 852-3416-7500

9440 Santa Monica Boulevard
Suite 708
Beverly Hills, CA USA 90210
Phone: 310-777-5440
Fax: 310-246-0796

9th Floor, Youngpoong Building
33 Seorin-Dong, Chongno-Gu
Seoul, South Korea 110-752
Phone: 822-733-9200
Fax: 822-733-9339

Management and Staff

David Roberts, Senior Managing Director
Joe Wekselblatt, Chief Financial Officer
John Angelo, Chief Executive Officer
Keith Barket, Senior Managing Director
Marsha Roth, Managing Director
Michael Gordon, Chief Operating Officer
Thomas Fuller, Senior Managing Director

Type of Firm

Private Equity Firm

Project Preferences

Type of Financing Preferred:

Leveraged Buyout
Expansion
Turnaround
Distressed Debt

Geographical Preferences

United States Preferences:

All U.S.

Industry Focus

(% based on actual investment)

Internet Specific	35.5%
Computer Hardware	24.0%
Consumer Related	20.3%
Computer Software and Services	20.3%

Additional Information

Year Founded: 1988
Capital Under Management: $7,237,400,000
Current Activity Level: Actively seeking new investments

ANGELS FORUM & THE HALO FUND

2458 Embarcadero Way
Palo Alto, CA USA 94303
Phone: 650-857-0700
Fax: 650-857-0773
E-mail: inquiries@AngelsForum.com
Website: www.angelsforum.com

Management and Staff

Leif Langensand, Chief Financial Officer

Type of Firm

Angel Group

Association Membership

National Venture Capital Association - USA (NVCA)

Project Preferences

Role in Financing:

Will function either as deal originator or investor in deals created by others

Type of Financing Preferred:

Second Stage Financing
Early Stage
Expansion
Balanced
Seed
First Stage Financing
Startup

Size of Investments Considered:

Min Size of Investment Considered (000s): $100
Max Size of Investment Considered (000s): $750

Geographical Preferences

United States Preferences:

Northern California
California
All U.S.

Industry Preferences

In Communications prefer:

Telecommunications
Wireless Communications
Data Communications

In Computer Software prefer:

Software
Systems Software
Applications Software
Artificial Intelligence

In Internet Specific prefer:

Internet
Ecommerce

In Computer Other prefer:

Computer Related

In Semiconductor/Electr prefer:

Electronic Components
Semiconductor
Micro-Processing
Controllers and Sensors
Sensors
Component Testing Equipmt
Laser Related
Analytic/Scientific

In Biotechnology prefer:

Biotechnology
Human Biotechnology
Agricultural/Animal Bio.
Industrial Biotechnology
Biosensors
Biotech Related Research

In Medical/Health prefer:

Medical/Health
Medical Diagnostics
Diagnostic Services
Diagnostic Test Products
Medical Therapeutics
Drug/Equipmt Delivery
Other Therapeutic
Medical Products
Disposable Med. Products
Health Services
Pharmaceuticals

In Consumer Related prefer:

Consumer
Entertainment and Leisure
Retail

In Industrial/Energy prefer:

Energy
Alternative Energy
Industrial Products
Superconductivity
Factory Automation
Process Control

In Transportation prefer:

Transportation

In Financial Services prefer:

Financial Services

In Business Serv. prefer:

Services

In Manufact. prefer:

Manufacturing

In Other prefer:

Socially Responsible
Environment Responsible
Women/Minority-Owned Bus.

Additional Information

Name of Most Recent Fund: Halo Fund III, L.P., The Most Recent Fund Was Raised: 03/18/2008
Year Founded: 1997
Capital Under Management: $58,000,000
Current Activity Level: Actively seeking new investments
Method of Compensation: Return on investment is of primary concern, do not charge fees

ANGLER CAPITAL MANAGEMENT LLC

630 Fifth Avenue
Suite 2950
New York, NY USA 10111
Phone: 646-234-7745
Website: www.anglercap.com

Type of Firm

Private Equity Firm

Project Preferences

Type of Financing Preferred:

Leveraged Buyout
Expansion
Acquisition
Recapitalizations

Industry Preferences

In Consumer Related prefer:

Consumer Products

In Industrial/Energy prefer:

Energy
Industrial Products
Environmental Related

In Financial Services prefer:

Financial Services

In Business Serv. prefer:

Consulting Services
Media

Additional Information

Year Founded: 2008
Current Activity Level: Actively seeking new investments

ANGLO IRISH CAPITAL PARTNERS LIMITED

18/21 St. Stephens Green
Stephen Court
Dublin, Ireland
Phone: 353-1-616-2000
Fax: 353-1-616-2488
E-mail: enquiries@angloirishbank.ie
Website: www.angloirishbank.ie

Management and Staff

Matt Moran, Chief Financial Officer

Type of Firm

Bank Affiliated

Association Membership

Irish Venture Capital Association
European Private Equity and Venture Capital Assoc.

Project Preferences

Type of Financing Preferred:

Leveraged Buyout
Expansion

Geographical Preferences

International Preferences:

Ireland
United Kingdom
Europe

Additional Information

Year Founded: 2004
Current Activity Level: Actively seeking new investments

ANGOLA CAPITAL PARTNERS

Vernon Building
Avenida de Portugal 18,6th Flr
Luanda, Angola
Phone: 244-22-269-3800
E-mail: contacto@angolacapitalpartners.com
Website: www.angolacapitalpartners.com

Management and Staff

Tiago Laranjeiro, Managing Director

Type of Firm

Bank Affiliated

Project Preferences

Type of Financing Preferred:

Expansion
Early Stage
Generalist PE
Management Buyouts
Private Placement
Startup

Size of Investments Considered:

Min Size of Investment Considered (000s): $500
Max Size of Investment Considered (000s): $10,000

Geographical Preferences

International Preferences:

Africa

Additional Information

Year Founded: 2009
Current Activity Level: Actively seeking new investments

ANGRA PARTNERS

Rua Lauro Muller 116 Sala 4102
Ed Torre Rio Sul
Rio de Janeiro, Brazil 22290-160
Phone: 55-21-2196-7200
Fax: 55-21-2196-7201
Website: www.angrapartners.com.br

Other Offices

Av. Brigadeiro Faria Lima
2055 - 15 andar
Sao Paulo, Brazil 01452-001
Phone: 55-11-3039-5720
Fax: 55-21-2196-7201

Type of Firm

Private Equity Firm

Association Membership

Brazilian Venture Capital Association (ABCR)

Project Preferences

Type of Financing Preferred:

Balanced

Geographical Preferences

International Preferences:

Brazil

Industry Preferences

In Communications prefer:

Telecommunications

In Industrial/Energy prefer:

Oil & Gas Drilling,Explor

In Transportation prefer:

Transportation

In Utilities prefer:

Utilities

Additional Information

Year Founded: 2003
Current Activity Level: Actively seeking new investments

ANKAR CAPITAL MANAGEMENT LLC

41 West 57th Street
New York, NY USA 10019
Phone: 212-688-6410
Fax: 212-688-6497
Website: www.ankarcapital.com

Type of Firm

Private Equity Advisor or Fund of Funds

Geographical Preferences

International Preferences:

Asia

Additional Information

Year Founded: 1999
Current Activity Level: Actively seeking new investments

ANN ARBOR SPARK

201 South Division
Suite 430
Ann Arbor, MI USA 48104
Phone: 734-821-0072
Fax: 734-761-9062
Website: www.annarborusa.org

Management and Staff

Mike Finney, Chief Executive Officer

Type of Firm

Government Affiliated Program

Project Preferences

Role in Financing:

Will function either as deal originator or investor in deals created by others

Type of Financing Preferred:

Seed
Startup

Size of Investments Considered:

Min Size of Investment Considered (000s): $50
Max Size of Investment Considered (000s): $250

Geographical Preferences

United States Preferences:

Michigan

Industry Preferences

In Industrial/Energy prefer:

Alternative Energy
Advanced Materials

In Transportation prefer:

Transportation

In Manufact. prefer:

Manufacturing

Additional Information

Year Founded: 2007
Capital Under Management: $16,300,000
Current Activity Level: Actively seeking new investments
Method of Compensation: Other

ANNEX VENTURE MANAGEMENT, LLC

2370 Watsom Court
Suite 210
Palo Alto, CA USA 94303
Website: www.annexventures.com
Management and Staff
Mark Pearson, Managing Director
Ven Reddy, Managing Director

Type of Firm

Private Equity Firm

Industry Preferences

In Biotechnology prefer:

Biotechnology

Additional Information

Year Founded: 2004
Current Activity Level: Actively seeking new investments

ANT CAPITAL PARTNERS CO., LTD. (FKA: NIKKO ANTFACTORY K.K.)

1-2-1 Marunouchi, Chiyoda-ku
5/F Tokio Marine Nichido Bldg.
Tokyo, Japan 100-0005
Phone: 81-3-3284-1711
Fax: 81-3-3284-1885
Website: www.antcapital.jp

Management and Staff

Ataru Onuma, Managing Partner
Ayako Tani, Managing Partner
Kazunori Ozaki, Chairman & CEO
Kenichi Ueda, Managing Partner
Mikio Sato, Managing Partner
Reijiro Samura, Managing Partner
Ryosuke Iinuma, Managing Partner
Shinzo Ono, President
Shuji Yoshioka, Managing Partner
Shunsa Hayashi, Managing Partner
Tadashi Takashina, Managing Partner
Tomoyuki Imaizumi, Managing Partner
Toru Tanimoto, Managing Partner
Xu Ping, Managing Partner

Type of Firm

Private Equity Firm

Project Preferences

Type of Financing Preferred:

Leveraged Buyout
Early Stage
Expansion
Balanced
Turnaround
Later Stage

Geographical Preferences

International Preferences:

China
Asia
Japan

Industry Preferences

In Communications prefer:

Media and Entertainment

In Computer Software prefer:

Software

In Semiconductor/Electr prefer:

Electronics
Semiconductor

In Medical/Health prefer:

Health Services

In Consumer Related prefer:

Sports

In Industrial/Energy prefer:

Environmental Related

In Transportation prefer:

Transportation

In Financial Services prefer:

Financial Services

In Business Serv. prefer:

Services

Additional Information

Year Founded: 2000
Capital Under Management: $33,000,000
Current Activity Level: Actively seeking new investments

ANTARES CAPITAL CORPORATION (FKA: HARBOR VENTURES CORP.)

9999 NorthEast Second Avenue
Suite 306
Miami, FL USA 33138-2346
Phone: 305-894-2888
Fax: 305-894-3227
Website: www.antarescapital.com

Other Offices

P.O. Box 410730
Melbourne, FL USA 32941
Phone: 321-777-4884
Fax: 321-777-5884

Management and Staff

Jonathan Kislak, General Partner
Randall Poliner, General Partner

Type of Firm

Private Equity Firm

Association Membership

National Venture Capital Association - USA (NVCA)

Project Preferences

Role in Financing:

Prefer role as deal originator but will also invest in deals created by others

Type of Financing Preferred:
Second Stage Financing
Expansion
Later Stage
Management Buyouts
Special Situation

Size of Investments Considered:
Min Size of Investment Considered (000s): $500
Max Size of Investment Considered (000s): $5,000

Geographical Preferences

United States Preferences:
Southeast
Texas

Industry Focus

(% based on actual investment)

Other Products	28.9%
Consumer Related	24.0%
Medical/Health	22.7%
Internet Specific	7.7%
Computer Software and Services	7.3%
Semiconductors/Other Elect.	5.4%
Communications and Media	2.2%
Industrial/Energy	1.8%
Computer Hardware	0.1%

Additional Information

Name of Most Recent Fund: Antares Capital Fund IV, L.P.
Most Recent Fund Was Raised: 06/21/2007
Year Founded: 1993
Capital Under Management: $20,000,000
Current Activity Level: Actively seeking new investments
Method of Compensation: Return on investment is of primary concern, do not charge fees

---

ANTEA PARTICIPATIES MANAGEMENT BV

Lange Vijverberg 9 b
Postbus 11665
Den Haag, Netherlands 2502 AR
Phone: 31-70-311-5959
Fax: 31-70-311-5950
E-mail: info@antea.nl
Website: www.antea.nl

Type of Firm

Private Equity Firm

Association Membership

Dutch Venture Capital Associaton (NVP)
European Private Equity and Venture Capital Assoc.

Project Preferences

Type of Financing Preferred:
Expansion
Turnaround
Balanced
Later Stage
Management Buyouts

Geographical Preferences

International Preferences:
Netherlands
Europe

Industry Focus

(% based on actual investment)

Other Products	35.7%
Computer Software and Services	25.9%
Internet Specific	22.2%
Consumer Related	16.1%

Additional Information

Year Founded: 1993
Capital Under Management: $33,000,000
Current Activity Level: Actively seeking new investments

ANTHEM CAPITAL MANAGEMENT

1414 Key Highway
Suite 300
Baltimore, MD USA 21230
Phone: 410-625-1510
Fax: 410-625-1735
E-mail: info@anthemcapital.com
Website: www.anthemcapital.com

Other Offices

Radnor Court, 259 Radnor-Chester Road
Suite 210
Radnor, PA USA 19087
Phone: 610-687-9773
Fax: 610-971-2154

Management and Staff

Edward Spiva, General Partner
Gerald Schaafsma, General Partner
William Gust, Managing Partner
Xander Perry, General Partner

Type of Firm

Private Equity Firm

Association Membership

Natl Assoc of Investment Cos. (NAIC)
Mid-Atlantic Venture Association
Natl Assoc of Small Bus. Inv. Co (NASBIC)
National Venture Capital Association - USA (NVCA)

Project Preferences

Role in Financing:
Prefer role as deal originator

Type of Financing Preferred:
Early Stage
Seed
First Stage Financing

Size of Investments Considered:
Min Size of Investment Considered (000s): $1,000
Max Size of Investment Considered (000s): $5,000

Geographical Preferences

United States Preferences:
Mid Atlantic

Industry Focus

(% based on actual investment)

Computer Software and Services	32.5%
Biotechnology	31.5%
Internet Specific	22.9%
Medical/Health	11.9%
Other Products	0.7%
Industrial/Energy	0.5%

Additional Information

Name of Most Recent Fund: Anthem Capital II, L.P.
Most Recent Fund Was Raised: 09/30/2002
Year Founded: 1997
Capital Under Management: $100,000,000
Current Activity Level: Actively seeking new investments
Method of Compensation: Return on investment is of primary concern, do not charge fees

---

ANTHEM VENTURE PARTNERS

225 Arizona Avenue
Suite 200
Santa Monica, CA USA 90401
Phone: 310-899-6225
Fax: 310-899-6234
E-mail: info@anthemvp.com
Website: www.anthemvp.com

Management and Staff

Brian Mesic, Partner
Samit Varma, Partner
Todd Jerry, Partner
William Woodward, Managing Director

Type of Firm

Private Equity Firm

Project Preferences

Role in Financing:
Prefer role as deal originator but will also invest in deals created by others

Type of Financing Preferred:
Early Stage
Seed
Startup

Size of Investments Considered:
Min Size of Investment Considered (000s): $500
Max Size of Investment Considered (000s): $5,000

Industry Preferences

In Computer Software prefer:
Software

In Internet Specific prefer:
Internet

In Semiconductor/Electr prefer:
Semiconductor

In Business Serv. prefer:
Media

Additional Information

Year Founded: 2000
Capital Under Management: $170,000,000
Current Activity Level: Actively seeking new investments

ANU CONNECT VENTURES PTY., LTD.

15 London Circuit
Suite 1, Level 8
Canberra, Australia 2600
Phone: 612-6247-7000
Fax: 612-6248-8000
Website: www.anuconnectventures.com.au

Management and Staff

Tim Hirst, Chief Executive Officer

Type of Firm

University Program

Association Membership

Australian Venture Capital Association (AVCAL)

Project Preferences

Type of Financing Preferred:
Early Stage
Seed

Size of Investments Considered:
Min Size of Investment Considered (000s): $47,910
Max Size of Investment Considered (000s): $500,000

Geographical Preferences

International Preferences:
Australia

Industry Preferences

In Biotechnology prefer:
Biotechnology

In Medical/Health prefer:
Health Services

In Industrial/Energy prefer:
Energy
Advanced Materials

In Transportation prefer:
Aerospace

Additional Information

Year Founded: 2005
Capital Under Management: $30,200,000
Current Activity Level: Actively seeking new investments

AOZORA INVESTMENT CO,. LTD.

1-3 Kudan-minami
1-chome, Chiyoda-ku
Tokyo, Japan 102-8660
Phone: 81-3-3261-6061
Fax: 81-3-3261-7550
E-mail: info@aozora-invest.co.jp
Website: www.aozora-invest.co.jp

Management and Staff

Takashi Matsumoto, Managing Director

Type of Firm

Bank Affiliated

Association Membership

Japan Venture Capital Association

Project Preferences

Type of Financing Preferred:
Leveraged Buyout
Balanced
Later Stage
Startup

Geographical Preferences

International Preferences:
Japan

Industry Preferences

In Communications prefer:
Communications and Media

In Biotechnology prefer:
Biotechnology

In Consumer Related prefer:
Food/Beverage
Consumer Services

n Industrial/Energy prefer:
Machinery

In Business Serv. prefer:
Services

Additional Information

Year Founded: 1991
Current Activity Level: Actively seeking new investments

AP CAPITAL PARTNERS

6000 Metrowest Boulevard
Suite 208
Orlando, FL USA 32835
Phone: 407-472-1892
Fax: 407-472-1896
Website: www.apcpartners.com

Management and Staff

Frantz Alphonse, Managing Partner
Richard Powell, Managing Partner

Type of Firm

Private Equity Firm

Project Preferences

Type of Financing Preferred:
Leveraged Buyout
Acquisition

Geographical Preferences

United States Preferences:
Southeast
Southwest
All U.S.

Additional Information

Year Founded: 2008
Current Activity Level: Actively seeking new investments

APAX PARTNERS WORLDWIDE

33 Jermyn Street
London, United Kingdom SW1Y 6DN
Phone: 44-20-7872-6300
Fax: 44-20-7666-6441
Website: www.apax.com

Other Offices

Est2004 Advisors AB
Birger Jarlsgatan 5
Stockholm, Sweden SE-111 45
Phone: 46-8-5450-7400
Fax: 46-8-5450-7401

16th Floor, Nexxus Building
41 Connaught Road
Central, Hong Kong
Phone: 852-2297-2313
Fax: 852-2297-2320

153 East 53rd Street
53rd Floor
New York, NY USA 10022
Phone: 212-753-6300
Fax: 212-319-6155

Possartstrasse 11
Kopernikusstrasse
Munich, Germany 81679
Phone: 49-89-998-9090
Fax: 49-89-9989-0933

Velazquez 10-5
Madrid , Spain 28001
Phone: 34-91-423-1000
Fax: 34-91-423-1010

Museum Tower
4 Berkowitz Street
Tel Aviv , Israel 64238
Phone: 972-3-777-4400
Fax: 972-3-777-4411

Palazzo Gallarati Scotti
Via A. Manzoni, 30
Milan , Italy 20121
Phone: 39-2-762-1191
Fax: 39-2-7621-19222

Hilton Towers
Rooms 1433-35, Nariman Point
Mumbai, India 400 021
Phone: 91-22-6630-8715
Fax: 91-22-2285-6300

Management and Staff

Adele Oliva, Partner
Bill Sullivan, Partner
Buddy Gumina, Partner
David Kim, Partner
Giancarlo Aliberti, Partner
Hetty Wang, Principal
Ian Jones, Partner
Jacqueline Reses, Partner
Jason Wright, Partner
John McMonigall, Partner
Martin Halusa, Partner
Michael Phillips, Partner
Michael Prahl, Principal
Paul Fitzsimons, Partner
Peter Englander, Partner
Peter Skinner, Partner
Ralf Gruss, Partner
Richard Wilson, Partner
Ronald Weissman, Venture Partner
Stephen Green, Partner
Timothy Armstrong, Partner
William Logan, Principal

Type of Firm

Private Equity Firm

Association Membership

British Venture Capital Association (BVCA)
French Venture Capital Association (AFIC)
Western Association of Venture Capitalists (WAVC)
European Private Equity and Venture Capital Assoc.
Private Equity Council (PEC)

Project Preferences

Type of Financing Preferred:

Second Stage Financing
Leveraged Buyout
Expansion
Generalist PE
Early Stage
Turnaround
Balanced
Later Stage
Startup

Size of Investments Considered:

Min Size of Investment Considered (000s): $4,000
Max Size of Investment Considered (000s): $151,100

Geographical Preferences

United States Preferences:

All U.S.

International Preferences:

United Kingdom
India
Luxembourg
Switzerland
Europe
Central Europe
Belgium
Asia
France

Industry Focus

(% based on actual investment)

Consumer Related	30.9%
Other Products	21.6%
Internet Specific	13.5%
Computer Software and Services	9.1%
Communications and Media	8.5%
Industrial/Energy	5.4%
Medical/Health	5.0%
Biotechnology	2.8%
Semiconductors/Other Elect.	2.0%
Computer Hardware	1.3%

Additional Information

Name of Most Recent Fund: Apax Europe VII-I, LP
Most Recent Fund Was Raised: 05/22/2007
Year Founded: 1969
Capital Under Management: $35,000,000,000
Current Activity Level: Actively seeking new investments

APECTEC, INC.

3911 Trasimene Cres. S.W.
Calgary, Canada T3E 7J6
Phone: 403-685-1888
Fax: 403-685-1880
Website: www.apectec.com

Management and Staff

Barclay Hambrook, President
Dave Curtis, Principal
Larry Delf, Principal
Nasir Bukhari, Co-Founder
Rod Wittig, Principal

Type of Firm

Private Equity Firm

Project Preferences

ype of Financing Preferred:

Start-up Financing

Geographical Preferences

International Preferences:

Europe

Additional Information

Year Founded: 2009
Current Activity Level: Actively seeking new investments

APERTURE VENTURE PARTNERS, LLC

645 Madison Avenue
20th Floor
New York, NY USA 10022
Phone: 212-758-7325
Fax: 212-319-8779
Website: www.aperturevp.com

Management and Staff

Eric Sillman, General Partner
Matthew Tierney, General Partner
Paul Tierney, General Partner
Thomas Cooper, General Partner

Type of Firm

Private Equity Firm

Association Membership

National Venture Capital Association - USA (NVCA)

Project Preferences

Role in Financing:

Will function either as deal originator or investor in deals created by others

Type of Financing Preferred:

Second Stage Financing
Early Stage
Balanced
First Stage Financing

Size of Investments Considered:

Min Size of Investment Considered (000s): $1,000
Max Size of Investment Considered (000s): $5,000

Geographical Preferences

United States Preferences:

Northeast
West Coast
All U.S.

Industry Preferences

In Biotechnology prefer:

Biotechnology
Human Biotechnology

In Medical/Health prefer:

Medical/Health
Medical Diagnostics
Medical Therapeutics
Drug/Equipmt Delivery
Medical Products
Health Services

In Consumer Related prefer:

Consumer

In Business Serv. prefer:

Services

Additional Information

Name of Most Recent Fund: Aperture Capital II, L.P.
Most Recent Fund Was Raised: 11/14/2005
Year Founded: 2002

Capital Under Management: $3,800,000
Current Activity Level: Actively seeking new investments
Method of Compensation: Return on investment is of primary concern, do not charge fees

APEX CAPITAL MANAGEMENT

701 Robley Drive
Suite 200
Lafayette, LA USA 70503
Phone: 337-984-7010
Fax: 337-981-6001
Website: www.apexcapitalmanagement.com

Management and Staff

Christopher Arsement, Partner
John Redd, Partner
Kimberly Gardner, Partner
Robert Morella, Managing Partner
Stephen Arsement, Partner

Type of Firm

Private Equity Firm

Additional Information

Year Founded: 2009
Current Activity Level: Actively seeking new investments

APEX VENTURE PARTNERS

225 West Washington Street
Suite 1500
Chicago, IL USA 60606
Phone: 312-857-2800
Fax: 312-857-1800
E-mail: apex@apexvc.com
Website: www.apexvc.com

Management and Staff

Armando Pauker, General Partner
Babu Ranganathan, General Partner
George Middlemas, General Partner
James Johnson, General Partner
Lon Chow, General Partner
Wayne Boulais, General Partner

Type of Firm

Private Equity Firm

Association Membership

Illinois Venture Capital Association

Project Preferences

Role in Financing:
Prefer role as deal originator but will also invest in deals created by others

Type of Financing Preferred:
Early Stage
Seed
First Stage Financing
Startup

Size of Investments Considered:
Min Size of Investment Considered (000s): $5,000
Max Size of Investment Considered (000s): $15,000

Geographical Preferences

United States Preferences:
All U.S.

Canadian Preferences:
All Canada

Industry Focus

(% based on actual investment)

Computer Software and Services	28.2%
Internet Specific	22.6%
Other Products	12.7%
Communications and Media	9.9%
Industrial/Energy	8.7%
Semiconductors/Other Elect.	8.2%
Computer Hardware	6.0%
Consumer Related	2.4%
Medical/Health	1.0%
Biotechnology	0.2%

Additional Information

Name of Most Recent Fund: Apex Investment Fund VI, L.P.
Most Recent Fund Was Raised: 06/30/2006
Year Founded: 1987
Capital Under Management: $620,000,000
Current Activity Level: Actively seeking new investments
Method of Compensation: Return on investment is of primary concern, do not charge fees

APHELION CAPITAL, LLC

One Ferry Building
Suite 255
San Francisco, CA USA 94111
Phone: 415-677-5320
Website: www.aphelioncapital.net

Management and Staff

Ned Scheetz, Founder

Type of Firm

Private Equity Firm

Project Preferences

Type of Financing Preferred:
Early Stage
Public Companies

Geographical Preferences

United States Preferences:
All U.S.

Industry Preferences

In Medical/Health prefer:
Medical/Health
Medical Therapeutics

Additional Information

Year Founded: 2005
Current Activity Level: Actively seeking new investments

APJOHN VENTURES, LLC

259 East Michigan Avenue
Kalamazoo, MI USA 49007
Phone: 269-349-8999
Fax: 269-349-8993
Website: www.apjohnventures.com

Management and Staff

Mina Sooch, General Partner

Type of Firm

Private Equity Firm

Project Preferences

Type of Financing Preferred:
Balanced

Additional Information

Year Founded: 2002
Capital Under Management: $1,500,000
Current Activity Level: Actively seeking new investments

APOLLO CAPITAL PARTNERS

Maximilianstrase 12-14
Munich, Germany 80539
Phone: 49-89-599886-0
Fax: 49-89-599886-25
E-mail: info@apollopartners.de
Website: www.apollocp.de

Type of Firm

Private Equity Firm

Additional Information

Year Founded: 1999
Capital Under Management: $153,800,000
Current Activity Level: Actively seeking new investments

APOLLO MANAGEMENT (FKA: APOLLO ADVISORS L.P.)

Two Manhattanville Road
Purchase, NY USA 10577
Phone: 914-694-8000

Fax: 914-694-8067
Website: www.apolloic.com

Management and Staff

Cheryl Krongard, Partner
Henry Silverman, Chief Operating Officer
James Zelter, Managing Partner
Jordan Zaken, Principal
Marc Rowan, Partner
Scott Kleinman, Partner
Steven Martinez, Partner
Tony Tortorelli, Chief Financial Officer

Type of Firm

Bank Affiliated

Association Membership

French Venture Capital Association (AFIC)
Private Equity Council (PEC)

Project Preferences

Type of Financing Preferred:

Leveraged Buyout
Distressed Debt

Geographical Preferences

International Preferences:

Asia

Industry Focus

(% based on actual investment)

Other Products	36.4%
Industrial/Energy	28.3%
Consumer Related	25.7%
Communications and Media	3.7%
Computer Software and Services	3.6%
Medical/Health	1.3%
Internet Specific	1.0%

Additional Information

Name of Most Recent Fund: Apollo Investment Fund VI, L.P.
Most Recent Fund Was Raised: 09/09/2005
Year Founded: 1990
Capital Under Management: $37,796,900,000
Current Activity Level: Actively seeking new investments

APOLLO REAL ESTATE ADVISORS

60 Columbus Circle
20th Floor
New York, NY USA 10023
Phone: 212-515-3400
Fax: 212-515-3283
Website: www.apollo-re.com

Other Offices

Two Manhattanville Road
Second Floor
Purchase, NY USA 10577
Phone: 914-694-8000
Fax: 914-694-6380

Liscartan House
127 Sloane Street
London , United Kingdom SW1X 9BA
Phone: 44-207-881-4240
Fax: 44-207-881-4242

444 North Michigan Avenue
Suite 2900
Chicago, IL USA 60611
Phone: 312-245-0707
Fax: 312-245-0831

10250 Constellation Boulevard
Suite 2900
Los Angeles, CA USA 90067
Phone: 310-843-1900
Fax: 310-843-1989

Management and Staff

Andrew Cohen, Principal
Anthony Scandariato, Vice President
Bill Benjamin, Principal
Bradford Wildauer, Principal
Chris Schiermbock, Vice President
David Glickman, Principal
John Jacobsson, Principal
Julie Bierman, Vice President
Kenneth Picache, Vice President
Michael Weiner, Principal
Mike Pashley, Chief Financial Officer
Nitin Karnani, Vice President
Richard Mack, Principal
Richard Ackerman, Principal
Rick Koenigsberger, Principal
Stuart Koenig, Chief Financial Officer
William Scully, Principal

Type of Firm

Corporate PE/Venture

Project Preferences

Type of Financing Preferred:

Mezzanine
Other

Size of Investments Considered:

Min Size of Investment Considered (000s): $300
Max Size of Investment Considered (000s): $150,000

Geographical Preferences

United States Preferences:

All U.S.

International Preferences:

Europe
Japan

Industry Focus

(% based on actual investment)

Consumer Related	82.6%
Other Products	9.4%
Communications and Media	4.7%
Internet Specific	2.9%
Computer Software and Services	0.4%

Additional Information

Name of Most Recent Fund: Apollo-GMAC Real Estate Mezzanine Fund, L.P.
Most Recent Fund Was Raised: 03/01/2003
Year Founded: 1993
Capital Under Management: $4,108,000,000
Current Activity Level: Actively seeking new investments

APPIAN VENTURES

1512 Larimer Street
Suite 200
Denver, CO USA 80202
Phone: 303-830-2450
Fax: 303-830-2449
E-mail: admin@appianvc.com
Website: www.appianvc.com

Management and Staff

Chris Onan, Managing Director
Donald Parsons, Managing Director
Mark Soane, Managing Director
Stacey McKittrick, Managing Director

Type of Firm

SBIC

Association Membership

National Venture Capital Association - USA (NVCA)

Project Preferences

Role in Financing:

Prefer role as deal originator

Type of Financing Preferred:

Early Stage
Later Stage
Seed

Size of Investments Considered:

Min Size of Investment Considered (000s): $500
Max Size of Investment Considered (000s): $5,000

Geographical Preferences

United States Preferences:

Midwest
Rocky Mountain
West Coast
Colorado
Southwest

Industry Preferences

In Communications prefer:

Data Communications

In Computer Software prefer:

Software

Additional Information

Year Founded: 2002
Capital Under Management: $80,000,000
Current Activity Level: Actively seeking new investments

APPLIED VENTURES, LLC

3050 Bowers Avenue
P.O. Box 58039
Santa Clara, CA USA 95054
Phone: 408-727-5555
Fax: 408-748-9943
Website: www.appliedventures.com

Other Offices

974 East Arques Avenue
Sunnyvale, CA USA 94085
Phone: 408-727-5555

Management and Staff

Ray Sun, Managing Director

Type of Firm

Corporate PE/Venture

Association Membership

National Venture Capital Association - USA (NVCA)

Project Preferences

Type of Financing Preferred:
Early Stage
Seed

Size of Investments Considered:
Min Size of Investment Considered (000s): $250
Max Size of Investment Considered (000s): $3,000

Geographical Preferences

United States Preferences:
All U.S.

Industry Preferences

In Semiconductor/Electr prefer:
Optoelectronics

In Industrial/Energy prefer:
Energy

Additional Information

Year Founded: 2000
Capital Under Management: $26,900,000
Current Activity Level: Actively seeking new investments

APPOSITE CAPITAL LLP

Bracken House
One Friday Street
London, United Kingdom EC4M 9JA
Phone: 44-20-7090-6190
Fax: 44-20-7090-6022
E-mail: enquiry@apposite-capital.com
Website: www.apposite-capital.com

Management and Staff

Allan Marchington, Partner
Christopher Hollowood, Principal
David Porter, Managing Partner
Sam Gray, Principal
Steve Adkin, Partner

Type of Firm

Private Equity Firm

Association Membership

British Venture Capital Association (BVCA)

Project Preferences

Type of Financing Preferred:
Leveraged Buyout
Early Stage
Expansion
Generalist PE
Public Companies
Balanced
Management Buyouts
Startup

Size of Investments Considered:
Min Size of Investment Considered (000s): $5,000
Max Size of Investment Considered (000s): $30,000

Geographical Preferences

Canadian Preferences:
All Canada

International Preferences:
United Kingdom
Western Europe
All International

Industry Preferences

In Biotechnology prefer:
Biotechnology

In Medical/Health prefer:
Medical/Health
Medical Therapeutics

Additional Information

Name of Most Recent Fund: Apposite Healthcare Fund, L.P.
Most Recent Fund Was Raised: 04/14/2006
Year Founded: 2006
Capital Under Management: $200,000,000
Current Activity Level: Actively seeking new investments

AQUA ALTA NV/SA

Lombardstraat 47
rue du Lombard
Brussels, Belgium 1000
Phone: 32-2-790-3499
Fax: 32-2-790-3488

Management and Staff

Brent Wilkey, Managing Director

Type of Firm

Private Equity Firm

Association Membership

Belgium Venturing Association
European Private Equity and Venture Capital Assoc.

Project Preferences

Type of Financing Preferred:
Early Stage
Expansion
Start-up Financing
Seed

Geographical Preferences

United States Preferences:
All U.S.

International Preferences:
Europe

Industry Preferences

In Communications prefer:
Media and Entertainment

In Medical/Health prefer:
Medical/Health

In Industrial/Energy prefer:
Industrial Products

Additional Information

Year Founded: 2004
Capital Under Management: $2,100,000
Current Activity Level: Actively seeking new investments

AQUA INTERNATIONAL PARTNERS, LP

345 California Street
Suite 1770
San Francisco, CA USA 94104
Phone: 415-743-1505
Fax: 415-743-1504

Other Offices

201 Main Street
Suite 2420
Fort Worth, TX USA 76102
Phone: 817-871-4000

Management and Staff

John Sylvia, Managing Director

Type of Firm

Private Equity Firm

Project Preferences

Role in Financing:
Will function either as deal originator or investor in deals created by others

Type of Financing Preferred:
Leveraged Buyout

Industry Focus

(% based on actual investment)

Consumer Related	54.7%
Other Products	27.3%
Industrial/Energy	18.0%

Additional Information

Year Founded: 1997
Capital Under Management: $300,000,000
Current Activity Level: Actively seeking new investments
Method of Compensation: Professional fee required whether or not deal closes

AQUARIUS EQUITY PARTNERS, LTD.

74 Gartside Street
Spinningfields
Manchester, United Kingdom M3 3EL
Phone: 44-161-837-6200
Fax: 44-161-837-6201
E-mail: info@aquariusequity.com
Website: www.aquariusequity.com

Management and Staff

Alan Aubrey, Co-Founder

Type of Firm

Private Equity Firm

Project Preferences

Type of Financing Preferred:
Expansion
Early Stage

Geographical Preferences

International Preferences:
United Kingdom

Additional Information

Year Founded: 2005
Capital Under Management: $28,000,000
Current Activity Level: Actively seeking new investments

AQUARIUS INVESTMENT ADVISORS PTE., LTD.

5 Shenton Way
35-05 Uic Building
Singapore, Singapore 068808
Phone: 65-6324-4960
Fax: 65-6324-4961
E-mail: sing@aquarius.com.sg
Website: www.aquarius.com.sg

Other Offices

4th Floor, Trident Towers
278/23, 10th Main, Jayanagar 2nd Block
Bangalore, India 560 011
Phone: 91-80-4112-4880
Fax: 91-80-4112-3077

302 Samarpan
Chakala New Link Road
Mumbai, India 400 099
Phone: 91-22-6692-2203
Fax: 91-22-2830-0979

Management and Staff

AST Rajan, Senior Managing Director
SN Subramanya, Managing Director

Type of Firm

Private Equity Firm

Project Preferences

Type of Financing Preferred:
Leveraged Buyout

Geographical Preferences

International Preferences:
Asia

Additional Information

Year Founded: 1995
Current Activity Level: Actively seeking new investments

AQUASOURCA SOCIETE D INVESTISSEMENT

Le Premium - 131
Bd Stalingrad
Villeurbanne Cedex, France 69624
Phone: 33-4-7269-0890
Fax: 33-4-7269-0895
E-mail: invest@aquasourca.com
Website: www.aquasourca.com

Other Offices

1, Rue du Fort Rheinsheim
Luxembourg L-2419
Phone: 352-26-258-251
Fax: 352-26-458-235

Management and Staff

Sophie Defforey-Crepet, Chief Executive Officer

Type of Firm

Private Equity Firm

Association Membership

French Venture Capital Association (AFIC)

Project Preferences

Type of Financing Preferred:
Balanced

Size of Investments Considered:
Min Size of Investment Considered (000s): $2,889
Max Size of Investment Considered (000s): $14,445

Geographical Preferences

United States Preferences:
All U.S.

International Preferences:
Tunisia
Czech Republic
Cambodia
Germany
France

Additional Information

Year Founded: 2007
Current Activity Level: Actively seeking new investments

AQUILINE CAPITAL PARTNERS

535 Madison Avenue
24th Floor
New York, NY USA 10022
Phone: 212-624-9500
Fax: 212-624-9510
E-mail: contact@aquiline-llc.com
Website: www.aquiline-llc.com

Management and Staff

Bruce MacFarlane, Principal
Christopher Watson, Principal
Geoffrey Kalish, Principal
Ian Smith, Principal
Jeffrey Greenberg, Chief Executive Officer
Laurent Bouyoux, Principal
Matthew Grayson, Principal

Type of Firm

Private Equity Firm

Project Preferences

Type of Financing Preferred:
Leveraged Buyout

Industry Preferences

In Financial Services prefer:
Financial Services

Additional Information

Name of Most Recent Fund: Aquiline Financial Services Fund, L.P.
Most Recent Fund Was Raised: 12/13/2005
Year Founded: 2005
Capital Under Management: $143,200,000
Current Activity Level: Actively seeking new investments

AQUITAINE CREATION INNOVATION

162, avenue du Dr Schweitzer
Centre Condorcet
Pessac, France 33600
Phone: 33-556-15-1190
Fax: 33-556-15-1197
E-mail: contact@aquitaine-creation.com
Website: www.aquitaine-creation.com

Type of Firm

Private Equity Firm

Project Preferences

Type of Financing Preferred:
Early Stage
Seed
Startup

Geographical Preferences

International Preferences:
France

Additional Information

Year Founded: 1998
Current Activity Level: Actively seeking new investments

AQUITAINE INVESTMENT ADVISORS, LTD.

308 Des Voeux Road Central
Suite 1905, ING Tower
Central, Hong Kong
Phone: 852-2528-1600
Fax: 852-2528-1900
E-mail: info@aquitaine.com.hk
Website: www.aquitaine.com.hk

Other Offices

5/F Izumi Shibkoen Building
1-6-8 Shiba Koen, Minato-ku
Tokyo, Japan 105-0011
Phone: 813-5401-3002
Fax: 813-5401-3004

Management and Staff

Arthur Yama, Managing Director
Marlene Wittman, Managing Director

Type of Firm

Private Equity Advisor or Fund of Funds

Project Preferences

Type of Financing Preferred:
Early Stage
Expansion
Later Stage

Geographical Preferences

International Preferences:
Taiwan
China
Hong Kong
Thailand
Philippines
Singapore
Asia
Japan
Malaysia

Industry Preferences

In Medical/Health prefer:
Medical/Health
Pharmaceuticals

In Consumer Related prefer:
Entertainment and Leisure

In Financial Services prefer:
Financial Services

Additional Information

Year Founded: 1999
Current Activity Level: Actively seeking new investments

ARAGON VENTURES, INC.

1455 Adams Drive
Menlo Park, CA USA 94025
Phone: 650-566-8000
Fax: 650-566-1251
E-mail: info@aragonvc.biz
Website: www.aragonventures.com

Management and Staff

Dave Hanabusa, Partner
Harold Johnson, Partner
Michael Ballard, Partner

Type of Firm

Private Equity Firm

Project Preferences

Role in Financing:
Prefer role as deal originator but will also invest in deals created by others

Type of Financing Preferred:
Early Stage
Expansion
Mezzanine
Later Stage
Seed
Startup

Size of Investments Considered:
Min Size of Investment Considered (000s): $200
Max Size of Investment Considered (000s): $10,000

Geographical Preferences

United States Preferences:
Northern California
California

Industry Preferences

In Computer Software prefer:
Software

In Internet Specific prefer:
Internet

In Medical/Health prefer:
Medical Products

Additional Information

Year Founded: 1998
Capital Under Management: $35,000,000
Current Activity Level: Actively seeking new investments

ARALON AG

Churer Strasse 135
Pfaffikon, Switzerland 8808
Phone: 41-55-416-2630
Fax: 41-55-416-2633
Website: www.aralon.ch

Management and Staff

Werner Schwendimann, Chief Financial Officer

Type of Firm

Private Equity Firm

Association Membership

European Private Equity and Venture Capital Assoc.

Project Preferences

Type of Financing Preferred:
Leveraged Buyout
Early Stage
Expansion
Mezzanine
Balanced
Seed
Startup
Recapitalizations

Geographical Preferences

International Preferences:
Croatia
Bulgaria
Moldova
Ukraine
Bosnia
Romania
Russia

Additional Information

Year Founded: 2005
Current Activity Level: Actively seeking new investments

ARAVIS SA (FKA: VENTURE ASSOCIATES AG)

Hauptstrasse 16
Muttenz, Switzerland CH-4132
Phone: 41-61-466-1000
Fax: 41-61-466-1001
E-mail: info@aravis.ch
Website: www.aravis.ch

Other Offices

Lehfrauenweg 10
Zurich, Switzerland CH-8053
Phone: 41-43-499-2000
Fax: 41-43-499-2001

Management and Staff

Fatt-Kah Foo, Venture Partner

Jacques Essinger, Venture Partner
Johanna Holldack, Venture Partner
Oliver Thalmann, Chief Financial Officer
Rolf Zinkernagel, Venture Partner
Simon Nebel, Managing Partner

Type of Firm

Private Equity Firm

Association Membership

European Private Equity and Venture Capital Assoc.

Project Preferences

Role in Financing:

Prefer role as deal originator

Type of Financing Preferred:

Early Stage
Turnaround
Seed
Startup
Special Situation

Geographical Preferences

International Preferences:

Switzerland
Europe
Singapore

Industry Preferences

In Biotechnology prefer:

Biotechnology

In Medical/Health prefer:

Medical/Health

Additional Information

Name of Most Recent Fund: Aravis Venture II, L.P.
Most Recent Fund Was Raised: 07/12/2007
Year Founded: 2002
Capital Under Management: $122,500,000
Current Activity Level: Actively seeking new investments

ARBA SEED INVESTMENT GROUP

600 Harrison Street
Suite 100
San Francisco, CA USA 94107
Fax: 415-227-0120
Website: www.arbagroup.com

Type of Firm

Angel Group

Additional Information

Year Founded: 1995
Current Activity Level: Actively seeking new investments

ARBAH GLOBAL

c/o Arbah Capital
P. O. Box 8807
Dammam , Saudi Arabia 31492
E-mail: info@arbahcapital.com
Website: www.arbahcapital.com

Management and Staff

Dhafer Alqahtani, Chief Executive Officer

Type of Firm

Private Equity Firm

Project Preferences

Type of Financing Preferred:

Balanced

Geographical Preferences

International Preferences:

Middle East
Saudi Arabia
Asia
Africa

Industry Preferences

In Biotechnology prefer:

Biotechnology

Additional Information

Year Founded: 2008
Current Activity Level: Actively seeking new investments

ARBOR PARTNERS LLC

130 South First Street
2nd Floor
Ann Arbor, MI USA 48104
Phone: 734-668-9000
Fax: 734-669-4195
E-mail: info@arborpartners.com
Website: www.arborpartners.com

Management and Staff

Donald Walker, Managing Director
John Bolg, Chief Financial Officer
Joshua Beebe, Principal
Richard Crandall, Founding Partner
Richard Eidswick, Founding Partner

Type of Firm

Private Equity Firm

Project Preferences

Role in Financing:

Will function either as deal originator or investor in deals created by others

Type of Financing Preferred:

Early Stage
Expansion

Size of Investments Considered:

Min Size of Investment Considered (000s): $500
Max Size of Investment Considered (000s): $2,000

Geographical Preferences

United States Preferences:

Midwest
Michigan

Industry Focus

(% based on actual investment)

Internet Specific	44.4%
Computer Software and Services	42.0%
Computer Hardware	7.1%
Consumer Related	3.9%
Communications and Media	2.5%

Additional Information

Name of Most Recent Fund: Arbor Venture Partners II LLC ("the eFund")
Most Recent Fund Was Raised: 10/29/1999
Year Founded: 1996
Capital Under Management: $38,200,000
Current Activity Level: Actively seeking new investments
Method of Compensation: Return on investment is of primary concern, do not charge fees

---

ARBOR PRIVATE INVESTMENT COMPANY, LLC

676 North Michigan Avenue
Suite 3410
Chicago, IL USA 60611
Phone: 312-981-3770
Fax: 312-981-3771
Website: www.arborpic.com

Other Offices

5135 Riverlake Drive
Duluth, GA USA 30097

Management and Staff

Gregory Purcell, Managing Partner
J. David Foster, Chief Financial Officer
Joseph Campolo, Partner
Kimberly Harrod, Vice President

Type of Firm

Private Equity Firm

Project Preferences

Role in Financing:

Prefer role as deal originator

Type of Financing Preferred:

Leveraged Buyout
Management Buyouts
Acquisition
Recapitalizations

Size of Investments Considered:

Min Size of Investment Considered (000s): $10,000
Max Size of Investment Considered (000s): $75,000

Geographical Preferences

United States Preferences:
All U.S.

Canadian Preferences:
All Canada

Additional Information
Name of Most Recent Fund: Arbor Private Investment Company Fund
Most Recent Fund Was Raised: 06/01/2001
Year Founded: 1999
Capital Under Management: $58,000,000
Current Activity Level: Actively seeking new investments
Method of Compensation: Return on invest. most important, but chg. closing fees, service fees, etc.

ARBORETUM VENTURES

303 Detroit Street, Suite 301
Market Place Building
Ann Arbor, MI USA 48104
Phone: 734-998-3688
Fax: 734-988-3689
E-mail: info@arboretumvc.com
Website: www.arboretumvc.com

Other Offices
11000 Cedar Avenue
Suite 100
Cleveland, OH USA 44106
Phone: 216-658-3989
Fax: 216-658-3998

Management and Staff
Jan Garfinkle, Managing Director
Jon Snyder, Venture Partner
Timothy Petersen, Managing Director

Type of Firm
Private Equity Firm

Association Membership
National Venture Capital Association - USA (NVCA)

Project Preferences

Role in Financing:
Will function either as deal originator or investor in deals created by others

Type of Financing Preferred:
Early Stage
Later Stage

Size of Investments Considered:
Min Size of Investment Considered (000s): $1,000
Max Size of Investment Considered (000s): $3,000

Geographical Preferences

United States Preferences:
All U.S.

Industry Preferences

In Medical/Health prefer:
Medical Diagnostics
Diagnostic Services
Diagnostic Test Products
Medical Therapeutics
Drug/Equipmt Delivery
Medical Products
Disposable Med. Products
Health Services
Hospitals/Clinics/Primary
Hospital/Other Instit.

Additional Information
Year Founded: 2002
Capital Under Management: $98,000,000
Current Activity Level: Actively seeking new investments
Method of Compensation: Return on investment is of primary concern, do not charge fees

---

ARC CAPITAL PARTNERS, LTD. (AKA: ARC CAPITAL)

Suite 1905 City Center
Tower A, 100 Zunyi Road
Shanghai, China 200051
Phone: 86-21-6237-1202
Fax: 85-2-3544-7699
E-mail: info@arccapitalchina.com
Website: www.arch-fund.com

Other Offices
33 Garden Road
13th Floor St. John's Building
Central, Hong Kong
Phone: 852-3115-0243
Fax: 852-3544-7699

Management and Staff
Clement Kwong, Managing Director
Rachel Chiang, Managing Director

Type of Firm
Investment Management Firm

Project Preferences

Type of Financing Preferred:
Expansion
Later Stage

Geographical Preferences

International Preferences:
China
Asia

Industry Preferences

In Consumer Related prefer:
Consumer
Retail

In Business Serv. prefer:
Services

Additional Information
Year Founded: 2006
Capital Under Management: $134,000,000
Current Activity Level: Actively seeking new investments

ARC FINANCIAL CORPORATION

400 - 3rd Avenue SouthWest
Suite 4300
Calgary, Canada T2P 4H2
Phone: 403-292-0680
Fax: 403-292-0693
E-mail: genfeedback@arcfinancial.com
Website: www.arcfinancial.com

Management and Staff
Bill Slavin, Managing Director
Douglas Freel, Vice President
Jeff Pearson, Vice President
Kevin Brown, Chief Executive Officer
Lauchlan Currie, President
Malcolm Adams, Vice President
Nancy Smith, Managing Director
Nancy Lever, Managing Director
Tanya Causgrove, Chief Financial Officer

Type of Firm
Investment Management Firm

Association Membership
Canadian Venture Capital Association

Project Preferences

Role in Financing:
Will function either as deal originator or investor in deals created by others

Type of Financing Preferred:
Early Stage
Other
Startup

Size of Investments Considered:
Min Size of Investment Considered (000s): $20,415
Max Size of Investment Considered (000s): $61,244

Geographical Preferences

Canadian Preferences:
All Canada

International Preferences:
All International

Industry Focus
(% based on actual investment)

Other Products	50.9%
Computer Hardware	20.0%
Industrial/Energy	16.9%
Communications and Media	12.3%

Additional Information
Name of Most Recent Fund: ARC Energy Fund 5
Most Recent Fund Was Raised: 02/28/2006

Year Founded: 1989
Capital Under Management: $1,859,000,000
Current Activity Level: Actively seeking new investments
Method of Compensation: Return on invest. most important, but chg. closing fees, service fees, etc.

ARC INVESTMENT PARTNERS LLC

9440 Little Santa Monica Blvd.
Suite 401
Beverly Hills, CA USA 90210
Phone: 310-402-5901
Fax: 310-402-5931
E-mail: info@arcinvestmentpartners.com
Website: www.arcinvestmentpartners.com

Other Offices

The Bank Of China Building, 14/F Bund 23
23 Zhongshan East No. 1 Road
Shanghai, China 200002
Phone: 86-21-6323-1717

590 Madison Avenue
26th Floor
New York, NY USA 10022
Phone: 212-375-6258

Management and Staff

Adam Roseman, Chief Executive Officer
Michael Kurdziel, Managing Director
Steven Magami, Partner

Type of Firm

Private Equity Firm

Project Preferences

Type of Financing Preferred:
Later Stage

Geographical Preferences

United States Preferences:
All U.S.

Industry Preferences

In Internet Specific prefer:
Internet

In Biotechnology prefer:
Biotechnology

In Consumer Related prefer:
Retail

In Industrial/Energy prefer:
Energy
Alternative Energy

Additional Information

Year Founded: 2005
Current Activity Level: Actively seeking new investments

ARCA CAPITAL

Bratislava Business Center V
Plynarenska 7/A
Bratislava, Slovakia 82109
Phone: 421-2-5825-3510
Fax: 421-2-5825-3511
E-mail: info@arcacapital.sk
Website: www.arcacapital.com

Other Offices

3 Tenterden Street, Hanover square
4th Floor
London, United Kingdom W1S1TD
Phone: 44-20-8371-2365
Fax: 44-20-8371-2360

Palac Myslbek
Ovocny trh 8
Prague, Czech Republic 11719
Phone: 420-224-231-813
Fax: 420-224-231-818

34, Vasilkovskaya Street
Kiev, Ukraine 03022
Phone: 38-44-492-9413
Fax: 38-44-492-9414

Type of Firm

Private Equity Firm

Project Preferences

Type of Financing Preferred:
Expansion
Seed
Startup

Geographical Preferences

International Preferences:
Slovak Repub.
United Kingdom
Czech Republic
Ukraine

Additional Information

Year Founded: 2003
Current Activity Level: Actively seeking new investments

ARCADIA BETEILIGUNGEN

Kehrwieder 12
Hamburg, Germany D-20457
Phone: 49-40-307097-0
Fax: 49-40-307097-55
E-mail: info@arcadia-beteiligungen.de
Website: www.arcadia-beteiligungen.de

Management and Staff

Christoph Tiefenbacher, Partner
Fredrik Elmberg, Partner
Mathias Turwitt, Partner
Wolfgang Bensel, Partner

Type of Firm

Private Equity Firm

Association Membership

German Venture Capital Association (BVK)

Project Preferences

Type of Financing Preferred:
Leveraged Buyout
Recapitalizations

Geographical Preferences

International Preferences:
Switzerland
Austria
Germany

Industry Focus

(% based on actual investment)

Computer Software and Services	100.0%

Additional Information

Year Founded: 2000
Capital Under Management: $185,900,000
Current Activity Level: Actively seeking new investments

ARCADIA MANAGEMENT, LLC (AKA: ARCADIA PARTNERS)

One Washington Mall
Eighth Floor
Boston, MA USA 02108
Phone: 617-226-2600
Fax: 617-351-0101
Website: www.arcadiapartners.com

Management and Staff

Andrew Hallowell, Founding Partner
Jane Swift, Partner
Joseph O'Neill, Chief Financial Officer
Liam Donohue, Founding Partner

Type of Firm

Private Equity Firm

Project Preferences

Role in Financing:
Will function either as deal originator or investor in deals created by others

Type of Financing Preferred:
Second Stage Financing
Early Stage
Expansion
Generalist PE
Start-up Financing
Later Stage
Seed
First Stage Financing

Size of Investments Considered:
Min Size of Investment Considered (000s): $100
Max Size of Investment Considered (000s): $5,000

Geographical Preferences

Canadian Preferences:
All Canada

Industry Preferences

In Consumer Related prefer:
Education Related

Additional Information
Name of Most Recent Fund: DHM Arcadia Partners, L.P.
Most Recent Fund Was Raised: 10/01/1999
Year Founded: 1998
Capital Under Management: $50,000,000
Current Activity Level: Actively seeking new investments

ARCANO CAPITAL
Almagro 31, 3 planta
Madrid, Spain 28010
Phone: 34-91-700-3880

Management and Staff
Alvaro De Remedios, Partner
Constantino Gomez, Partner
Ignacio Sarria, Partner
Jaime Carvajal, Partner
Juan Jose Nieto, Partner
Lorenzo Madridejos, Partner

Type of Firm
Private Equity Advisor or Fund of Funds

Project Preferences

Type of Financing Preferred:
Fund of Funds

Geographical Preferences

United States Preferences:
All U.S.

Canadian Preferences:
All Canada

International Preferences:
Europe
Spain
Asia
Australia

Additional Information
Year Founded: 2006
Current Activity Level: Actively seeking new investments

ARCAPITA, INC.
75 Fourteenth Street
24th Floor
Atlanta, GA USA 30309
Phone: 404-920-9000
Fax: 404-920-9001
E-mail: info@arcapita.com
Website: www.arcapita.com

Other Offices
North Tower, Level 25
One Raffles
Quay, Singapore 048583
Phone: 65-6622-5390
Fax: 65-6622-5391

P.O. Box 1406
Manama, Bahrain
Phone: 973-17-218333
Fax: 973-17-217555

9 Raffles Place
Level 44 Republic Plaza
Singapore , Singapore 048619
Phone: 65-6499-9888
Fax: 65-6499-9800

15 Sloane Square
2nd Floor
London, United Kingdom SW1W 8ER
Phone: 44-20-7824-5600
Fax: 44-20-7824-5601

Management and Staff
Andrea Malik, Principal
Bill Lundstrom, Principal
David Innes, Principal
James J. W. Ransom, Principal
Manuel Barbieux, Principal
Ranjeev Bhatia, Principal
Scott Buschmann, Principal
William Miller, Principal

Type of Firm
Bank Affiliated

Association Membership
British Venture Capital Association (BVCA)
National Venture Capital Association - USA (NVCA)

Project Preferences

Type of Financing Preferred:
Leveraged Buyout
Expansion

Size of Investments Considered:
Min Size of Investment Considered (000s): $50,000
Max Size of Investment Considered (000s): $400,000

Geographical Preferences

International Preferences:
United Kingdom
Europe
Middle East

Industry Focus
(% based on actual investment)

Industrial/Energy	49.5%
Consumer Related	28.3%
Other Products	9.2%
Computer Software and Services	6.9%
Communications and Media	5.1%
Medical/Health	0.9%
Internet Specific	0.1%

Additional Information
Year Founded: 1997
Capital Under Management: $1,000,000,000
Current Activity Level: Actively seeking new investments

ARCH DEVELOPMENT PARTNERS LLC
20 North Wacker
Suite 2000
Chicago, IL USA 60606
Phone: 312-442-4400
Fax: 312-263-0724
Website: www.archdp.com

Other Offices
241 Falcon Court
West Lafayette, IN USA 47906

346 West Michigan Avenue
Kalamazoo, MI USA 49007

Management and Staff
Elizabeth Long, Chief Financial Officer
Thomas Churchwell, Managing Partner

Type of Firm
University Program

Association Membership
National Venture Capital Association - USA (NVCA)
Illinois Venture Capital Association

Project Preferences

Type of Financing Preferred:
Early Stage
Seed
Startup

Size of Investments Considered:
Min Size of Investment Considered (000s): $300
Max Size of Investment Considered (000s): $2,000

Geographical Preferences

United States Preferences:
Midwest
Illinois
Michigan
Ohio
Indiana

Industry Preferences

In Computer Software prefer:
Software

In Biotechnology prefer:
Biotechnology

In Consumer Related prefer:
Education Related

Additional Information

Name of Most Recent Fund: ARCH Development Fund I (ADF I)
Most Recent Fund Was Raised: 12/31/2002
Year Founded: 2001
Capital Under Management: $31,500,000
Current Activity Level: Actively seeking new investments

ARCH VENTURE PARTNERS

8725 West Higgins Road
Suite 290
Chicago, IL USA 60631
Phone: 773-380-6600
Fax: 773-380-6606
E-mail: info@archventure.com
Website: www.archventure.com

Other Offices

6300 Bridgepoint Parkway
Building One, Suite 500
Austin, TX USA 78730
Phone: 512-795-5830
Fax: 512-795-5849

1000 Second Avenue
Suite 3700
Seattle, WA USA 98104
Phone: 206-674-3028
Fax: 206-674-3026

1700 Owens Street
Suite 535
San Francisco, CA USA 94158
Phone: 415-565-7103
Fax: 415-565-7107

Management and Staff

Ajit Medhekar, Venture Partner
Clinton Bybee, Managing Director
Keith Crandell, Managing Director
Kristina Burow, Partner
Paul Thurk, Partner
Robert Nelsen, Managing Director
Scott Minick, Managing Director
Steven Lazarus, Managing Director
Steven Gillis, Managing Director

Type of Firm

Private Equity Firm

Association Membership

Illinois Venture Capital Association
National Venture Capital Association - USA (NVCA)

Project Preferences

Role in Financing:
Prefer role as deal originator but will also invest in deals created by others

Type of Financing Preferred:
Early Stage
Start-up Financing
Seed
Special Situation
Startup

Size of Investments Considered:
Min Size of Investment Considered (000s): $500
Max Size of Investment Considered (000s): $10,000

Geographical Preferences

United States Preferences:
Mid Atlantic
Midwest
Northwest
Southern California
Northern California
Northeast
Rocky Mountain
West Coast
All U.S.
Southwest

Industry Focus

(% based on actual investment)

Biotechnology	28.5%
Semiconductors/Other Elect.	20.1%
Medical/Health	18.6%
Internet Specific	13.0%
Industrial/Energy	7.2%
Computer Software and Services	6.2%
Communications and Media	3.5%
Computer Hardware	2.6%
Other Products	0.2%
Consumer Related	0.1%

Additional Information

Year Founded: 1986
Capital Under Management: $999,000,000
Current Activity Level: Actively seeking new investments
Method of Compensation: Return on investment is of primary concern, do not charge fees

---

ARCHANGEL INFORMAL INVESTMENTS LIMITED

20 Rutland Square
Edinburgh, United Kingdom EH1 2BB
Phone: 44-131-221-9876
Fax: 44-131-229-1956
Website: www.archangelsonline.com

Management and Staff

John Waddell, Chief Executive Officer

Type of Firm

Angel Group

Project Preferences

Type of Financing Preferred:
Seed
Startup

Geographical Preferences

International Preferences:
United Kingdom

Industry Preferences

In Biotechnology prefer:
Biotechnology

In Medical/Health prefer:
Medical/Health

Additional Information

Year Founded: 1992
Current Activity Level: Actively seeking new investments

ARCHBROOK CAPITAL MANAGEMENT LLC

100 Front Street
Suite 1410
West Conshohocken, PA USA 19428
Phone: 610-684-4900
Fax: 610-684-4901
E-mail: info@archbrook.com
Website: www.archbrook.com

Other Offices

500 Fifth Avenue
Suite 1940
New York, NY USA 10115
Phone: 212-421-6710
Fax: 646-417-5747

1003 East 31st Street
La Grange Park, IL USA 60526
Phone: 708-354-0078
Fax: 708-579-2177

Management and Staff

David Apple, Founding Partner
John McGlinn, Founding Partner
Timothy O'Connell, Partner

Type of Firm

Private Equity Firm

Project Preferences

Type of Financing Preferred:
Leveraged Buyout
Mezzanine
Expansion
Later Stage
Acquisition
Distressed Debt

Geographical Preferences

United States Preferences:
East Coast

Additional Information

Year Founded: 2002
Current Activity Level: Actively seeking new investments

ARCHER CAPITAL (FKA: GS PRIVATE EQUITY PTY LTD.)

13 Hickson Road
Suite 7, Pier 2/3, Dawes Point
Sydney, Australia 2000
Phone: 612-8243-3333
Fax: 612-9241-3151
Website: www.archercapital.com.au

Management and Staff

Andrew Gray, Partner
Craig Cartner, Partner
David Bull, Chief Financial Officer
Greg Minton, Managing Partner
James Carnegie, Partner
Justin Punch, Partner
Peter Wiggs, Managing Partner
Peter Gold, Partner
Scott Greck, Partner
Tim Spencer, Partner

Type of Firm

Private Equity Firm

Association Membership

Australian Venture Capital Association (AVCAL)

Project Preferences

Role in Financing:
Prefer role as deal originator

Type of Financing Preferred:
Leveraged Buyout
Generalist PE
Balanced
Public Companies
Open Market
Management Buyouts
Acquisition
Industry Rollups

Size of Investments Considered:
Min Size of Investment Considered (000s): $9,582
Max Size of Investment Considered (000s): $258,714

Geographical Preferences

International Preferences:
Pacific
New Zealand
Australia

Industry Focus

(% based on actual investment)

Consumer Related	27.2%
Computer Software and Services	21.5%
Other Products	14.5%
Medical/Health	14.2%
Industrial/Energy	11.7%
Internet Specific	5.4%
Computer Hardware	3.3%
Semiconductors/Other Elect.	2.3%

Additional Information

Name of Most Recent Fund: Archer Capital Fund 4
Most Recent Fund Was Raised: 06/30/2007
Year Founded: 1996
Capital Under Management: $2,000,000,000
Current Activity Level: Actively seeking new investments
Method of Compensation: Return on investment is of primary concern, do not charge fees

---

ARCIS FINANCE SA

30 rue Galilee
Paris, France 75116
Phone: 33-1-4723-8862
Fax: 33-1-4723-8855
E-mail: mail@arcisgroup.com
Website: www.arcisgroup.com

Other Offices

509 Madison Avenue
Suite 1400
New York, NY USA 10022
Phone: 212-838-5577
Fax: 212-838-8858

2 Savile Row
London, United Kingdom W1S 3PA
Phone: 44-20-7494-2110
Fax: 44-20-7494-2105

Management and Staff

Anne Rousseau, Partner
Arnaud Isnard, Co-Founder
Henri Isnard, Co-Founder
Mark Burch, Managing Partner

Type of Firm

Private Equity Firm

Association Membership

British Venture Capital Association (BVCA)
French Venture Capital Association (AFIC)
European Private Equity and Venture Capital Assoc.

Project Preferences

Type of Financing Preferred:
Fund of Funds
Fund of Funds of Second
Recapitalizations

Geographical Preferences

International Preferences:
Switzerland
Western Europe
Norway
Japan

Additional Information

Name of Most Recent Fund: Pan-European Secondary Development Fund
Most Recent Fund Was Raised: 10/06/1999
Year Founded: 1993
Capital Under Management: $356,600,000
Current Activity Level: Actively seeking new investments

ARCLIGHT CAPITAL

200 Clarendon Street
55th Floor
Boston, MA USA 02117
Phone: 617-531-6300
Fax: 617-867-4698
E-mail: info@arclightcapital.com
Website: www.arclightcapital.com

Other Offices

152 West 57th Street
53rd Floor
New York, NY USA 10019
Phone: 212-901-1500
Fax: 212-888-9275

Management and Staff

Carter Ward, Managing Director
Christopher Picotte, Managing Director
Daniel Revers, Managing Partner
Eric Lammers, Principal
Jake Erhard, Principal
Kevin Crosby, Principal
Mark Tarini, Managing Director
Matthew Runkle, Vice President
Matthew LeBlanc, Principal
Michael Christopher, Vice President
Thomas Kilgore, Managing Director

Type of Firm

Private Equity Firm

Project Preferences

Type of Financing Preferred:
Balanced

Geographical Preferences

United States Preferences:
All U.S.

International Preferences:
Eastern Europe

Industry Preferences

In Industrial/Energy prefer:
Energy

Additional Information

Name of Most Recent Fund: ArcLight Energy Partners Fund III, LP
Most Recent Fund Was Raised: 02/07/2006
Year Founded: 2001
Capital Under Management: $4,685,000,000
Current Activity Level: Actively seeking new investments

ARCTURUS CAPITAL

350 West Colorado Boulevard
Suite 215
Pasadena, CA USA 91105
Phone: 626-578-5700
Fax: 626-578-5710
E-mail: info@arcturusvc.com
Website: www.arcturusvc.com

Other Offices

19700 Fairchild Road
Suite 290
Irvine, CA USA 92612
Phone: 949-635-0705
Fax: 949-635-0706

Management and Staff

Amnon Yariv, Venture Partner
Donald Hall, Managing Director
Edwin Moss, Venture Partner
John Baldeschwieler, Venture Partner
Stephen Watkins, Managing Director
Stevan Birnbaum, Managing Director

Type of Firm

Private Equity Firm

Association Membership

National Venture Capital Association - USA (NVCA)

Project Preferences

Role in Financing:

Will function either as deal originator or investor in deals created by others

Type of Financing Preferred:

Second Stage Financing
Early Stage
Expansion
Start-up Financing
Later Stage
Seed
First Stage Financing

Size of Investments Considered:

Min Size of Investment Considered (000s): $250
Max Size of Investment Considered (000s): $3,000

Geographical Preferences

United States Preferences:

Southern California

Industry Preferences

In Communications prefer:

Commercial Communications
Wireless Communications
Data Communications
Satellite Microwave Comm.
Other Communication Prod.

In Computer Software prefer:

Software
Systems Software
Applications Software
Artificial Intelligence

In Internet Specific prefer:

E-Commerce Technology
Internet
Ecommerce
Web Aggregration/Portals

In Semiconductor/Electr prefer:

Electronic Components
Semiconductor
Micro-Processing
Controllers and Sensors
Sensors
Component Testing Equipmt
Laser Related
Fiber Optics
Analytic/Scientific
Optoelectronics

In Biotechnology prefer:

Human Biotechnology
Genetic Engineering
Industrial Biotechnology
Biosensors
Biotech Related Research

In Medical/Health prefer:

Medical Diagnostics
Diagnostic Test Products
Medical Therapeutics
Drug/Equipmt Delivery
Medical Products
Disposable Med. Products

In Industrial/Energy prefer:

Energy
Factory Automation
Robotics

Additional Information

Name of Most Recent Fund: Arcturus Capital Venture Fund, L.P.
Most Recent Fund Was Raised: 10/12/2004
Year Founded: 2000
Capital Under Management: $31,700,000
Current Activity Level: Actively seeking new investments
Method of Compensation: Return on invest. most important, but chg. closing fees, service fees, etc.

ARCUS VENTURES MANAGEMENT LLC

55 Broad Street
Suite 1840
New York, NY USA 10004
Phone: 212-785-2236
Fax: 212-785-2237
Website: www.arcusventures.com

Management and Staff

James Dougherty, General Partner
Steven Soignet, General Partner

Type of Firm

Private Equity Firm

Project Preferences

Type of Financing Preferred:

Balanced

Industry Preferences

In Medical/Health prefer:

Medical Diagnostics
Diagnostic Services
Diagnostic Test Products
Medical Therapeutics
Drug/Equipmt Delivery
Health Services

Additional Information

Name of Most Recent Fund: Arcus Ventures Fund, L.P.
Most Recent Fund Was Raised: 10/17/2007
Year Founded: 2007
Capital Under Management: $25,500,000
Current Activity Level: Actively seeking new investments

ARDENS & ASSOCIES SAS

28, Rue Boissy d'Anglas
Paris, France 75008
Phone: 33-1-4742-4426
Fax: 33-1-4742-4423
Website: www.ardens.fr

Type of Firm

Private Equity Firm

Association Membership

French Venture Capital Association (AFIC)

Project Preferences

Type of Financing Preferred:

Leveraged Buyout

Geographical Preferences

International Preferences:

Europe
France

Additional Information
Year Founded: 2003
Capital Under Management: $74,000,000
Current Activity Level: Actively seeking new investments

ARDESTA (FKA: MEMS TECH)
201 South Main Street
Tenth Floor
Ann Arbor, MI USA 48104
Phone: 734-994-7000
Fax: 734-994-4302
E-mail: info@ardesta.com
Website: www.ardesta.com

Other Offices
15 East Birchwood Avenue
Hinsdale, IL USA 60521
Phone: 630-321-0960
Fax: 734-994-4302

Type of Firm
Private Equity Firm

Project Preferences
Role in Financing:
Will function either as deal originator or investor in deals created by others

Type of Financing Preferred:
Early Stage
First Stage Financing
Startup

Size of Investments Considered:
Min Size of Investment Considered (000s): $200
Max Size of Investment Considered (000s): $3,000

Industry Preferences
In Communications prefer:
Telecommunications
Wireless Communications

In Semiconductor/Electr prefer:
Sensors
Laser Related
Fiber Optics

In Biotechnology prefer:
Human Biotechnology
Industrial Biotechnology
Biosensors

Additional Information
Name of Most Recent Fund: Ardesta Fund I
Most Recent Fund Was Raised: 10/20/2000
Year Founded: 2000
Capital Under Management: $100,000,000
Current Activity Level: Actively seeking new investments
Method of Compensation: Return on investment is of primary concern, do not charge fees

ARES MANAGEMENT, INC.
2000 Avenue of the Stars
12th Floor
Los Angeles, CA USA 90067
Phone: 310-201-4100
Fax: 310-201-4170
Website: www.aresmgmt.com

Other Offices
One Finsbury Square
London, United Kingdom EC2A 1AE
Phone: 44-20-7153-4600
Fax: 44-20-7153-4601

280 Park Avenue
22nd Floor East
New York, NY USA 10017
Phone: 212-750-7300
Fax: 212-750-1777

Management and Staff
Daniel Nguyen, Chief Financial Officer
Daniel Katz, Vice President
Eric Beckman, Managing Director
Kipp DeVeer, Managing Director
Michael Arougheti, Managing Director
Michael Smith, Managing Director
Mitchell Goldstein, Managing Director

Type of Firm
Bank Affiliated

Project Preferences
Type of Financing Preferred:
Mezzanine
Distressed Debt

Geographical Preferences
United States Preferences:
All U.S.

Additional Information
Year Founded: 1997
Capital Under Management: $205,000,000
Current Activity Level: Actively seeking new investments

ARETE CORPORATION
P.O. Box 1299
Center Harbor, NH USA 03226
Phone: 603-253-9797
Fax: 603-253-9799
E-mail: aretecorp@adelphia.net
Website: www.arete-microgen.com

Management and Staff
Robert Shaw, President

Type of Firm
Private Equity Firm

Association Membership
National Venture Capital Association - USA (NVCA)

Project Preferences
Role in Financing:
Prefer role as deal originator but will also invest in deals created by others

Type of Financing Preferred:
Early Stage
Research and Development
Start-up Financing
Seed
First Stage Financing

Size of Investments Considered:
Min Size of Investment Considered (000s): $500
Max Size of Investment Considered (000s): $3,000

Geographical Preferences
United States Preferences:
All U.S.

Canadian Preferences:
All Canada

International Preferences:
United Kingdom
Australia
France

Industry Preferences
In Industrial/Energy prefer:
Energy
Alternative Energy
Environmental Related

Additional Information
Name of Most Recent Fund: Micro-Generation Technology Fund
Most Recent Fund Was Raised: 09/15/1997
Year Founded: 1985
Capital Under Management: $20,000,000
Current Activity Level: Actively seeking new investments

ARGAN CAPITAL (FKA: BA CAPITAL PARTNERS EUROPE, BACPE)
Monopolis House
9 South Street
London, United Kingdom W1K 2XA
Phone: 44-20-7647-6970
Fax: 44-20-76476999
Website: www.argancapital.com

Other Offices
Al Szucha 13/15
Lokal Nr. 6
Warsaw, Poland 02-670
Phone: 48-226-271-272
Fax: 48-226-271-274

Via degli Omenoni 2
Milan, Italy 20121
Phone: 39-2-720-2571
Fax: 39-2-7202-5780

8-10 rue Lamnnais
Paris, France 75008
Phone: 33-1-4562-4646
Fax: 33-1-4562-4649

Biblioteksgatan 6
Stockholm, Sweden SE-111 46

Management and Staff

Carlo Mammola, Managing Partner
Lloyd Perry, Managing Director
Paul Jeremy, Chief Financial Officer
Wojciech Goc, Managing Director

Type of Firm

Private Equity Firm

Project Preferences

Type of Financing Preferred:
Leveraged Buyout
Balanced

Geographical Preferences

International Preferences:
United Kingdom
Europe
Western Europe
France

Industry Preferences

In Communications prefer:
Communications and Media

Additional Information

Year Founded: 1996
Capital Under Management: $504,000,000
Current Activity Level: Actively seeking new investments

ARGANTIS GMBH

Konrad-Adenauer-Ufer 11
koln, Germany 50668
Phone: 49-221-280-6424
Fax: 49-221-280-6410
E-mail: Info@argantis.de
Website: www.argantis.net

Management and Staff

Fritz Graf von der Schulenburg, Managing Director
Michael Hildisch, Managing Director
Robert Stein, Managing Director

Type of Firm

Private Equity Firm

Project Preferences

Type of Financing Preferred:
Leveraged Buyout
Open Market
Management Buyouts
Acquisition

Geographical Preferences

International Preferences:
Switzerland
Europe
Austria
Germany

Additional Information

Year Founded: 2004
Capital Under Management: $124,400,000
Current Activity Level: Actively seeking new investments

ARGENTUM

Bygdoy Alle 2
Hydrobygget
Oslo, Norway 0257
Phone: 47-55-547-000
Fax: 47-55-547-001
E-mail: post@argentum.no
Website: www.argentum.no

Management and Staff

Joachim Hoegh-Krohn, CEO & Managing Director
Trude Husevag, Chief Financial Officer

Type of Firm

Private Equity Advisor or Fund of Funds

Association Membership

Norwegian Venture Capital Association
European Private Equity and Venture Capital Assoc.

Project Preferences

Type of Financing Preferred:
Fund of Funds

Geographical Preferences

International Preferences:
Norway

Industry Preferences

In Communications prefer:
Telecommunications

In Biotechnology prefer:
Biotechnology

In Industrial/Energy prefer:
Energy
Environmental Related

In Transportation prefer:
Transportation

Additional Information

Year Founded: 2001
Capital Under Management: $340,100,000
Current Activity Level: Actively seeking new investments

ARGIL VENTURE CAPITAL (PTY) LTD

Wanderers Office Park
52 Corlett Drive
Illovo, South Africa 2128
Phone: 27-11-783-7219
Fax: 27-11-783-7355
Website: www.argil.co.za

Type of Firm

Private Equity Firm

Association Membership

South African Venture Capital Association (SAVCA)

Project Preferences

Type of Financing Preferred:
Second Stage Financing
Expansion

Geographical Preferences

International Preferences:
Africa

Additional Information

Year Founded: 2000
Capital Under Management: $6,200,000
Current Activity Level: Actively seeking new investments

ARGO INVESTORS L.L.C.

200 Concord Plaza
Suite 700
San Antonio, TX USA 78216
Phone: 210-828-1700

Type of Firm

Private Equity Firm

Additional Information

Year Founded: 2002
Capital Under Management: $12,700,000
Current Activity Level: Actively seeking new investments

ARGON VENTURE PARTNERS

303 Twin Dolphin Drive
Sixth Floor
Redwood City, CA USA 94065
E-mail: info@argoncap.com
Website: www.argoncap.com

Other Offices

3553 31 Street NorthWest
Calgary, Canada T2L2K7

Management and Staff

Jason Bross, General Partner
Juan-Antonio Carballo, General Partner
Randy Stewart Thompson, General Partner

Type of Firm

Private Equity Firm

Project Preferences

Type of Financing Preferred:
Early Stage

Geographical Preferences

Canadian Preferences:
All Canada

Additional Information

Year Founded: 2007
Current Activity Level: Actively seeking new investments

ARGONAUT PARTNERS, LLC

155 Bodwell Street
Avon, MA USA 02322
Phone: 508-584-2224
Fax: 508-559-9046
Website: www.argollc.com

Type of Firm

Private Equity Firm

Project Preferences

Type of Financing Preferred:
Acquisition

Geographical Preferences

United States Preferences:
All U.S.

Industry Preferences

In Consumer Related prefer:
Publishing-Retail

Additional Information

Year Founded: 1998
Current Activity Level: Actively seeking new investments

ARGONAUT PRIVATE EQUITY

6733 South Yale
Tulsa, OK USA 74136
Phone: 918-491-4504

Management and Staff

Anil Khatod, Managing Director
Gagan Kapur, Vice President
Jason Martin, Managing Director
Steven Mitchell, Managing Director

Type of Firm

Private Equity Firm

Project Preferences

Type of Financing Preferred:
Leveraged Buyout
Generalist PE
Balanced

Size of Investments Considered:
Min Size of Investment Considered (000s): $1,000
Max Size of Investment Considered (000s): $200,000

Geographical Preferences

United States Preferences:
All U.S.

Industry Preferences

In Communications prefer:
Telecommunications

In Semiconductor/Electr prefer:
Electronics

In Biotechnology prefer:
Biotech Related Research

In Medical/Health prefer:
Drug/Equipmt Delivery
Medical Products
Health Services
Pharmaceuticals

In Industrial/Energy prefer:
Advanced Materials

In Transportation prefer:
Aerospace

In Financial Services prefer:
Financial Services

In Manufact. prefer:
Manufacturing

Additional Information

Year Founded: 2002
Current Activity Level: Actively seeking new investments

ARGOS SODITIC SA

118 Rue de Rhone
Geneva, Switzerland CH-1204
Phone: 41-22-849-6633
Fax: 41-22-849-6627
Website: www.argos-soditic.com

Other Offices

14 Rue de Bassano
Paris Cedex 16, France 75783
Phone: 33-1-5367-2050
Fax: 33-1-5367-2055

5 Piazza Diaz
Milano, Italy 20123
Phone: 39-02-0066-0700
Fax: 39-02-0066-0799

Management and Staff

Cedric Bruix, Partner
Gilles Mougenot, Partner
Gilles Lorang, Partner
Guy Semmens, Partner
Jean-Pierre Di Benedetto, Partner
Louis Godron, Partner
Matteo Carlotti, Partner
Mirco Dilda, Partner
Raymond Totah, Partner

Type of Firm

Private Equity Firm

Association Membership

Italian Venture Capital Association (AIFI)
Swiss Venture Capital Association (SECA)
French Venture Capital Association (AFIC)
European Private Equity and Venture Capital Assoc.

Project Preferences

Role in Financing:
Prefer role as deal originator but will also invest in deals created by others

Type of Financing Preferred:
Second Stage Financing
Leveraged Buyout
Early Stage
Expansion
Mezzanine
Balanced
Turnaround
Later Stage
Management Buyouts
Special Situation
Recapitalizations

Size of Investments Considered:
Min Size of Investment Considered (000s): $6,000
Max Size of Investment Considered (000s): $60,000

Geographical Preferences

International Preferences:
Italy
Luxembourg
Portugal
Switzerland
Europe
Western Europe
Spain
France

Industry Focus

(% based on actual investment)

Consumer Related	43.9%
Industrial/Energy	19.4%

Other Products	18.8%
Medical/Health	11.5%
Internet Specific	4.8%
Communications and Media	1.7%

Additional Information

Year Founded: 1989
Capital Under Management: $555,900,000
Current Activity Level: Actively seeking new investments
Method of Compensation: Return on invest. most important, but chg. closing fees, service fees, etc.

ARGOSY PARTNERS

141 Adelaide Street West
Suite 760
Toronto, Canada M5H 3L5
Phone: 416-367-3617
Fax: 416-367-3896
E-mail: info@shotgunfund.com
Website: www.shotgunfund.com

Type of Firm

Corporate PE/Venture

Project Preferences

Type of Financing Preferred:
Management Buyouts

Geographical Preferences

Canadian Preferences:
All Canada

Industry Preferences

In Computer Software prefer:
Software

In Internet Specific prefer:
Internet

Additional Information

Year Founded: 1995
Current Activity Level: Actively seeking new investments
Method of Compensation: Return on invest. most important, but chg. closing fees, service fees, etc.

ARGOSY PARTNERS (FKA: ODYSSEY CAPITAL GROUP)

950 West Valley Road
Suite 2900
Wayne, PA USA 19087
Phone: 610-971-9685
Fax: 610-964-9524
Website: www.argosycapital.com

Management and Staff

Jack Nugent, Principal
John Kirwin, Partner
Keven Shanahan, Principal
Kirk Griswold, Partner
Knute Albrecht, Partner
Michael Bailey, Partner

Type of Firm

Private Equity Firm

Association Membership

Natl Assoc of Small Bus. Inv. Co (NASBIC)

Project Preferences

Role in Financing:
Will function either as deal originator or investor in deals created by others

Type of Financing Preferred:
Leveraged Buyout
Mezzanine
Expansion
Later Stage
Management Buyouts
Acquisition
Recapitalizations

Size of Investments Considered:
Min Size of Investment Considered (000s): $3,000
Max Size of Investment Considered (000s): $15,000

Geographical Preferences

United States Preferences:
Mid Atlantic
Midwest
Southeast
Northeast

Canadian Preferences:
Ontario

Industry Preferences

In Consumer Related prefer:
Franchises(NEC)

In Business Serv. prefer:
Services

In Manufact. prefer:
Manufacturing

Additional Information

Name of Most Recent Fund: Argosy Investment Partners II, L.P.
Most Recent Fund Was Raised: 02/22/2001
Year Founded: 1989
Capital Under Management: $250,000,000
Current Activity Level: Actively seeking new investments
Method of Compensation: Return on investment is of primary concern, do not charge fees

---

ARGUS CAPITAL GROUP

Academy House
36 Poland Street
London, United Kingdom W1F 7LU
Phone: 44-20-7439-0088
Fax: 44-20-7439-0092
Website: www.arguscapitalgroup.com

Other Offices

Nagy Jeno u. 12
Hu-1126
Budapest, Hungary 1118
Phone: 36-1-309-0090
Fax: 36-1-391-0091

Krakovska 9
Prague, Czech Republic 110 00
Phone: 420-2-9637-0270
Fax: 420-2-9637-0271

Warsaw Corporate Center
ul. Emilii Plater 28
Warsaw, Poland 00-688
Phone: 48-22-630-3031
Fax: 48-22-630-3033

Management and Staff

Ali Artunkal, Managing Director
Mallindi Baldassarro, Chief Financial Officer

Type of Firm

Private Equity Firm

Association Membership

Czech Venture Capital Association (CVCA)
Polish Venture Capital Association (PSIC/PPEA)
European Private Equity and Venture Capital Assoc.

Project Preferences

Type of Financing Preferred:
Leveraged Buyout
Expansion
Balanced
Turnaround
Management Buyouts
Joint Ventures
Industry Rollups
Recapitalizations

Size of Investments Considered:
Min Size of Investment Considered (000s): $5,000
Max Size of Investment Considered (000s): $25,000

Geographical Preferences

International Preferences:
Hungary
Slovenia
Slovak Repub.
Czech Republic
Turkey
Central Europe
Europe
Poland
Croatia
Eastern Europe
Bulgaria
Estonia
Romania
Latvia
Lithuania

Additional Information

Name of Most Recent Fund: Argus Capital Partners Fund II
Most Recent Fund Was Raised: 12/31/2005
Year Founded: 1998
Capital Under Management: $172,000,000
Current Activity Level: Actively seeking new investments

ARGY VENTURE CAPITAL

72, Corso di Porta Romana
Milan, Italy 20122
Phone: 39-2-5843-0900
Fax: 39-2-5843-0489
Website: www.argyventurecapital.it

Type of Firm

Private Equity Firm

Project Preferences

Type of Financing Preferred:

Early Stage
Expansion
Balanced

Geographical Preferences

International Preferences:

Europe

Additional Information

Year Founded: 2004
Current Activity Level: Actively seeking new investments

ARIADNE CAPITAL, LTD.

9 Devonshire Square
London, United Kingdom EC2M 4YF
Phone: 44-20-3356-9690
Fax: 44-20-3356-9690
E-mail: info@ariadnecapital.com
Website: www.ariadnecapital.com

Type of Firm

Private Equity Advisor or Fund of Funds

Project Preferences

Role in Financing:

Will function either as deal originator or investor in deals created by others

Type of Financing Preferred:

Early Stage
Later Stage
Seed
Startup

Geographical Preferences

International Preferences:

United Kingdom
Europe

Industry Preferences

In Communications prefer:

Communications and Media
Wireless Communications
Satellite Microwave Comm.
Media and Entertainment

In Computer Software prefer:

Software

In Internet Specific prefer:

Internet

In Financial Services prefer:

Financial Services

Additional Information

Year Founded: 2000
Capital Under Management: $1,400,000
Current Activity Level: Actively seeking new investments
Method of Compensation: Return on invest. most important, but chg. closing fees, service fees, etc.

ARISAIG PARTNERS (ASIA) PTE., LTD.

7A Lorong Telok
Singapore, Singapore 049019
Phone: 65-6532-3378
Fax: 65-6532-6618
E-mail: limpris@arisaig.com.sg
Website: www.arisaig.com.sg

Type of Firm

Investment Management Firm

Project Preferences

Type of Financing Preferred:

Balanced

Geographical Preferences

International Preferences:

Vietnam
Indonesia
Philippines
Singapore
Asia
Malaysia

Industry Preferences

In Medical/Health prefer:

Pharmaceuticals

In Consumer Related prefer:

Consumer
Retail
Food/Beverage

In Financial Services prefer:

Real Estate
Financial Services

In Business Serv. prefer:

Services
Media

In Manufact. prefer:

Manufacturing

Additional Information

Year Founded: 1996
Current Activity Level: Actively seeking new investments

ARISE CAPITAL PARTNERS, INC.

2F Tosenkandasudacho Bldg
1-28 Kandasudacho, Chiyoda-ku
Tokyo, Japan 101-0041
Phone: 81-3-5297-6121
Fax: 81-3-5297-0505
E-mail: info@arise-cp.co.jp
Website: www.arise-cp.co.jp

Management and Staff

Daisuke Atsuumi, Managing Director
Kazunori Miyamoto, Managing Director
Kei Wada, Managing Director
Koichi Fujikawa, Managing Director
Masahiro Mine, Managing Director
Shin Kato, Managing Director
Shinya Takahashi, President

Type of Firm

Bank Affiliated

Project Preferences

Type of Financing Preferred:

Leveraged Buyout
Management Buyouts

Geographical Preferences

International Preferences:

Japan

Additional Information

Year Founded: 2005
Capital Under Management: $96,100,000
Current Activity Level: Actively seeking new investments

ARIYA CAPITAL GROUP, LTD.

Berkeley Square House
Berkeley Square
London, United Kingdom W1J 6BD
Phone: 44-207-887-1550
E-mail: info@ariyacapital.com
Website: www.ariyacapital.com

Management and Staff

Bryan Lemar, Partner
Stuart Spence, Partner

Type of Firm

Private Equity Firm

Project Preferences

Type of Financing Preferred:
Early Stage
Balanced

Geographical Preferences

International Preferences:
Zambia
Botswana
Mozambique

Industry Preferences

In Communications prefer:
Telecommunications

In Industrial/Energy prefer:
Alternative Energy
Energy Conservation Relat

In Financial Services prefer:
Financial Services

Additional Information
Year Founded: 2009
Current Activity Level: Actively seeking new investments

ARLINGTON CAPITAL PARTNERS

600 New Hampshire Avenue NW
Suite 660
Washington, DC USA 20037
Phone: 202-337-7500
Fax: 202-337-7525
E-mail: requestinfo@arlingtoncap.com
Website: www.arlingtoncap.com

Management and Staff
Edward Weklar, Vice President
Jeffrey Freed, Partner
Jesse Liu, Vice President
John Bates, Principal
Matthew Buckley, Chief Financial Officer
Matthew Altman, Principal
Michael Lustbader, Principal
Paul Stern, Partner
Perry Steiner, Partner
Peter Manos, Partner
Raymond Smith, Partner
Robert Knibb, Partner

Type of Firm
Bank Affiliated

Project Preferences

Role in Financing:
Prefer role as deal originator but will also invest in deals created by others

Type of Financing Preferred:
Leveraged Buyout
Public Companies
Turnaround
Later Stage
Management Buyouts
Acquisition
Industry Rollups
Special Situation
Recapitalizations

Size of Investments Considered:
Min Size of Investment Considered (000s): $15,000
Max Size of Investment Considered (000s): $500,000

Geographical Preferences

United States Preferences:
All U.S.

Industry Focus
(% based on actual investment)

Internet Specific	41.2%
Other Products	24.8%
Communications and Media	22.5%
Computer Software and Services	11.5%

Additional Information
Name of Most Recent Fund: Arlington Capital Partners II, L.P.
Most Recent Fund Was Raised: 07/13/2005
Year Founded: 1999
Capital Under Management: $585,000,000
Current Activity Level: Actively seeking new investments
Method of Compensation: Return on invest. most important, but chg. closing fees, service fees, etc.

ARMADA VENTURE GROUP LLC

Seestrasse 39
Suite 450
Kusnacht, Switzerland CH-8700
Phone: 41-44-914-9000
Fax: 41-44-914-9001
E-mail: office@armada.com
Website: www.armada.com

Management and Staff
Benedict Gotte, Principal
Harry Marshall, General Partner
I. Sigmund Mosley, Venture Partner
Joseph Velk, General Partner
Timothy Mann, Venture Partner

Type of Firm
Private Equity Firm

Project Preferences

Role in Financing:
Will function either as deal originator or investor in deals created by others

Type of Financing Preferred:
Early Stage
Later Stage

Size of Investments Considered:
Min Size of Investment Considered (000s): $750
Max Size of Investment Considered (000s): $10,000

Geographical Preferences

United States Preferences:
Southeast

International Preferences:
United Kingdom
Germany
All International

Industry Preferences

In Communications prefer:
Commercial Communications
Telecommunications
Wireless Communications
Data Communications

In Computer Hardware prefer:
Mini and Personal/Desktop
Computer Graphics and Dig
Disk Relat. Memory Device

In Computer Software prefer:
Computer Services
Software
Systems Software
Applications Software
Artificial Intelligence

In Internet Specific prefer:
Internet
Ecommerce
Web Aggregration/Portals

In Semiconductor/Electr prefer:
Electronic Components
Semiconductor
Micro-Processing
Controllers and Sensors
Sensors
Circuit Boards
Component Testing Equipmt
Laser Related
Fiber Optics
Analytic/Scientific

In Medical/Health prefer:
Medical Diagnostics
Medical Therapeutics
Medical Products
Disposable Med. Products

In Industrial/Energy prefer:
Factory Automation
Process Control
Robotics

In Business Serv. prefer:
Services

Additional Information
Year Founded: 2000
Capital Under Management: $120,000,000
Current Activity Level: Actively seeking new investments
Method of Compensation: Return on investment is of primary concern, do not charge fees

AROWANA CAPITAL PTY, LTD.

100 Mount Street
Level 3, Suite 303
Sydney, Australia 2060
Phone: 612-8083-9800
Fax: 612-8083-9804
E-mail: info@arowanacapital.com
Website: www.arowanacapital.com

Management and Staff

Kevin Chin, Managing Director

Type of Firm

Private Equity Firm

Association Membership

Australian Venture Capital Association (AVCAL)

Project Preferences

Type of Financing Preferred:

Leveraged Buyout
Expansion
Balanced

Size of Investments Considered:

Min Size of Investment Considered (000s): $806
Max Size of Investment Considered (000s): $80,580

Geographical Preferences

International Preferences:

Hong Kong
Australia
Singapore
New Zealand

Industry Preferences

In Internet Specific prefer:

Internet

In Consumer Related prefer:

Retail
Consumer Products

In Industrial/Energy prefer:

Energy

In Financial Services prefer:

Financial Services

In Business Serv. prefer:

Media

In Utilities prefer:

Utilities

Additional Information

Name of Most Recent Fund: AC Australasian Micro-Cap Private Equity Partnership 1, L.P.
Most Recent Fund Was Raised: 06/08/2007
Year Founded: 2007
Capital Under Management: $32,200,000
Current Activity Level: Actively seeking new investments

ARROWPATH VENTURE CAPITAL (FKA: E*TRADE GROUP, INC.)

303 Twin Dolphin Drive
Sixth Floor
Redwood City, CA USA 94065
Phone: 650-551-6460
Fax: 650-551-6468
E-mail: vc@arrowpathvc.com
Website: www.arrowpathvc.com

Other Offices

1230 Avenue of the Americas
Seventh Floor
New York, NY USA 10020
Phone: 917-639-4152
Fax: 917-639-4005

Management and Staff

F.Morgan Rodd, Managing Partner
Robert McIntosh, Partner
Teresa McDaniel, Chief Financial Officer

Type of Firm

Private Equity Firm

Project Preferences

Role in Financing:

Will function either as deal originator or investor in deals created by others

Type of Financing Preferred:

Second Stage Financing
Early Stage
Expansion
Balanced
First Stage Financing
Startup

Size of Investments Considered:

Min Size of Investment Considered (000s): $1,000
Max Size of Investment Considered (000s): $10,000

Industry Preferences

In Communications prefer:

Wireless Communications
Data Communications

In Computer Software prefer:

Data Processing
Software
Systems Software
Applications Software
Artificial Intelligence

In Internet Specific prefer:

E-Commerce Technology
Internet
Ecommerce
Web Aggregration/Portals

In Financial Services prefer:

Financial Services

Additional Information

Name of Most Recent Fund: ArrowPath Fund II, L.P.
Most Recent Fund Was Raised: 06/30/2000
Year Founded: 1997
Capital Under Management: $400,000,000
Current Activity Level: Actively seeking new investments
Method of Compensation: Return on investment is of primary concern, do not charge fees

ARSENAL CAPITAL PARTNERS

320 Park Avenue
30th Floor
New York, NY USA 10022
Phone: 212-771-1717
Fax: 212-771-1718
Website: www.arsenalcapital.com

Other Offices

Room 1805 Kerry Center
Number 1515 Nanjing West Road
Shanghai, China 200040
Phone: 86-21-5298-5858
Fax: 86-21-5298-5878

Management and Staff

Aaron Davenport, Principal
Carty Chock, Principal
Cenzig Selman, Managing Director
Chee We Ng, Vice President
Christopher Johnson, Vice President
Jeffrey Kovach, Managing Director
Joelle Marquis, Principal
John Televantos, Principal
Pilar Lorente, Chief Financial Officer
Steve (XiaoHu) Li, Principal
Terrence Mullen, Managing Director

Type of Firm

Private Equity Firm

Project Preferences

Type of Financing Preferred:

Leveraged Buyout
Recapitalizations

Industry Preferences

In Semiconductor/Electr prefer:

Electronics

In Medical/Health prefer:

Health Services
Pharmaceuticals

In Industrial/Energy prefer:

Industrial Products
Materials

In Transportation prefer:

Aerospace

In Financial Services prefer:

Financial Services

In Business Serv. prefer:
Services
Distribution

In Manufact. prefer:
Manufacturing

Additional Information

Name of Most Recent Fund: Arsenal Capital Partners II, L.P.
Most Recent Fund Was Raised: 11/14/2006
Year Founded: 2001
Capital Under Management: $300,000,000
Current Activity Level: Actively seeking new investments

ARSENAL VENTURE PARTNERS

250 Park Avenue South
Suite 360
Winter Park, FL USA 32789
Phone: 407-838-1439
Website: www.arsenalvp.com

Other Offices

385 Homer Avenue
Palo Alto, CA USA 94301
Phone: 650-838-9200

Management and Staff

Christopher Fountas, General Partner
David Odom, Principal
Denny Behm, Principal
Henry Huey, Principal
Jason Rottenberg, General Partner
John Trbovich, General Partner

Type of Firm

Private Equity Firm

Project Preferences

Type of Financing Preferred:
Seed

Industry Preferences

In Communications prefer:
Communications and Media

In Computer Software prefer:
Software

In Industrial/Energy prefer:
Energy

Additional Information

Year Founded: 1997
Current Activity Level: Actively seeking new investments

ARTA CAPITAL, S.A.

Marques de Salamanca
10- 4 Dcha.
Madrid, Spain 28006
Phone: 34-91-781-7882
Fax: 34-91-781-9329

Type of Firm

Private Equity Advisor or Fund of Funds

Project Preferences

Role in Financing:
Prefer role as deal originator

Type of Financing Preferred:
Expansion
Balanced

Size of Investments Considered:
Min Size of Investment Considered (000s): $35,083
Max Size of Investment Considered (000s): $91,215

Geographical Preferences

International Preferences:
Portugal
Spain

Industry Preferences

In Consumer Related prefer:
Consumer

In Industrial/Energy prefer:
Energy

Additional Information

Name of Most Recent Fund: Deya Capital
Most Recent Fund Was Raised: 07/31/2008
Year Founded: 2007
Capital Under Management: $561,300,000
Current Activity Level: Actively seeking new investments

ARTEMIS INVESTMENT MANAGEMENT INC.

77 Bloor Street West
Suite 1401
Toronto, Canada M5S1M2
Phone: 416-934-7455
Fax: 416-925-5100
E-mail: info@artemisfunds.ca
Website: www.artemisfunds.ca

Type of Firm

Private Equity Firm

Additional Information

Year Founded: 2009
Current Activity Level: Actively seeking new investments

ARTHUR VENTURES

51 Broadway
Suite 502
Fargo, ND USA 58102
Phone: 701-232-3521
Fax: 701-232-3530
E-mail: info@arthurventures.com
Website: www.arthurventures.com

Management and Staff

James Burgum, Co-Founder

Type of Firm

Private Equity Firm

Project Preferences

Type of Financing Preferred:
Balanced

Additional Information

Year Founded: 2008
Capital Under Management: $13,200,000
Current Activity Level: Actively seeking new investments

ARTICON-INTEGRALIS AG

Gutenbergstrasse 1
Ismaning, Germany D-85737
Phone: 49-89-94573-000
Fax: 49-89-94573-199
E-mail: info@integralis.de
Website: www.integralis.de

Type of Firm

Private Equity Firm

Additional Information

Year Founded: 2009
Current Activity Level: Actively seeking new investments

ARTIMAN VENTURES

2000 University Avenue
Suite 602
East Palo Alto, CA USA 94303
Phone: 650-845-2020
Fax: 650-845-2019
E-mail: info@artimanventures.com
Website: www.artiman.com

Other Offices

No. 15 Rest House
Crescent Road
Bangalore, India 560 001
Phone: 91-80-2509-1454
Fax: 91-80-2509-1453

Management and Staff

Amit Shah, Founding Partner
MJ Aravind, Partner
Saurabh Srivastava, Partner
Yatin Mundkur, Partner

Type of Firm

Private Equity Firm

Project Preferences

Role in Financing:
Will function either as deal originator or investor in deals created by others

Type of Financing Preferred:
Early Stage
Balanced
Later Stage

Size of Investments Considered:
Min Size of Investment Considered (000s): $250
Max Size of Investment Considered (000s): $4,000

Geographical Preferences

United States Preferences:
All U.S.

Industry Preferences

In Computer Software prefer:
Software

In Internet Specific prefer:
E-Commerce Technology
Internet

n Semiconductor/Electr prefer:
Semiconductor
Sensors

Additional Information
Year Founded: 2000
Capital Under Management: $285,000,000
Current Activity Level: Actively seeking new investments

ARTS ALLIANCE ADVISORS
5 Young Street
London, United Kingdom W8 5EH
Phone: 44-20-7361-7720
Fax: 44-20-7361-7766
E-mail: info@artsalliance.co.uk
Website: www.artsalliance.com

Management and Staff
Adam Valkin, Partner
Joshua Green, Principal
Laurent Laffy, Managing Partner
Thomas Hoegh, Managing Partner

Type of Firm
Private Equity Firm

Project Preferences

Type of Financing Preferred:
Early Stage
Balanced
Startup

Size of Investments Considered:
Min Size of Investment Considered (000s): $500
Max Size of Investment Considered (000s): $5,000

Geographical Preferences

United States Preferences:
All U.S.

International Preferences:
Europe
Western Europe

Industry Focus
(% based on actual investment)

Internet Specific	43.4%
Consumer Related	23.4%
Computer Software and Services	18.5%
Communications and Media	7.8%
Other Products	7.0%

Additional Information
Name of Most Recent Fund: Digital Venture III
Most Recent Fund Was Raised: 03/06/2001
Year Founded: 1996
Capital Under Management: $80,200,000
Current Activity Level: Actively seeking new investments

ARX EQUITY PARTNERS (FKA: DBG EASTERN EUROPE S.R.O.)
Al. Jana Pawla II 12
8th Floor
Warsaw, Poland 00-124
Phone: 48-22-850-9960
Fax: 48-22-850-9961
Website: www.arxequity.com

Other Offices
Szabadsag ter 7
Bank Center, Granit torony (6. em.)
Budapest, Hungary 1054
Phone: 36-1-302-9270
Fax: 36-1-302-9273

Kronberg Building
Senovazne namesti 8
Prague, Czech Republic 110 00
Phone: 420-22-423-5399
Fax: 420-22-423-9424

Romniceanu Grigore de. 3A
Bucharest, Romania 050574
Phone: 40-21-410-0123
Fax: 40-21-410-5284

Management and Staff
Brian Wardrop, Managing Partner
David Marek, Partner
Jacek Korpala, Managing Partner
Jaroslav Horak, Managing Partner
Meda Micsunescu, Managing Partner

Type of Firm
Private Equity Firm

Association Membership
Czech Venture Capital Association (CVCA)
Polish Venture Capital Association (PSIC/PPEA)
European Private Equity and Venture Capital Assoc.

Project Preferences

Role in Financing:
Prefer role as deal originator

Type of Financing Preferred:
Second Stage Financing
Leveraged Buyout
Expansion
Balanced
Later Stage
Management Buyouts

Size of Investments Considered:
Min Size of Investment Considered (000s): $4,237
Max Size of Investment Considered (000s): $16,947

Geographical Preferences

International Preferences:
Hungary
Slovak Repub.
Europe
Czech Republic
Central Europe
Poland
Croatia
Eastern Europe

Industry Preferences

In Consumer Related prefer:
Consumer
Entertainment and Leisure
Retail
Food/Beverage
Consumer Products
Consumer Services

Additional Information
Year Founded: 1997
Capital Under Management: $259,700,000
Current Activity Level: Actively seeking new investments

AS MTVP (AKA: MARTINSON TRIGON VENTURE PARTNERS)
Tartu Road 2
Tallinn, Estonia 10145
Phone: 372-2-666-0235
Fax: 372-2-666-0236
E-mail: mtvp@mtvp.eu
Website: www.mtvp.ee

Management and Staff
Allan Martinson, Managing Partner
Joakim Helenius, Chairman & CEO

Type of Firm
Investment Management Firm

Association Membership
European Private Equity and Venture Capital Assoc.

Project Preferences

Role in Financing:
Prefer role as deal originator but will also invest in deals created by others

Type of Financing Preferred:
Leveraged Buyout
Early Stage
Expansion
Balanced
Seed

Size of Investments Considered:
Min Size of Investment Considered (000s): $700
Max Size of Investment Considered (000s): $7,000

Geographical Preferences

International Preferences:
Ukraine
Estonia
Finland
Latvia
Lithuania

Industry Preferences

In Communications prefer:
Communications and Media
Telecommunications

In Computer Other prefer:
Computer Related

In Business Serv. prefer:
Media

Additional Information
Year Founded: 2005
Capital Under Management: $26,800,000
Current Activity Level: Actively seeking new investments

ASCEND TECHNOLOGY VENTURES
14A Achimeir Street
Ramat Gan, Israel 52587
Phone: 972-3-751-3707
Fax: 972-3-751-3706
E-mail: office@ascendvc.com
Website: www.ascendvc.com

Management and Staff
Avner Shelem, Principal
Liora Lev, General Partner
Moshe Bar-Niv, Principal

Type of Firm
Private Equity Firm

Project Preferences

Type of Financing Preferred:
Early Stage
Seed
Startup

Geographical Preferences

International Preferences:
Israel

Industry Preferences

In Communications prefer:
Communications and Media

In Medical/Health prefer:
Medical/Health

Additional Information
Year Founded: 1999
Capital Under Management: $100,000,000
Current Activity Level: Actively seeking new investments

ASCEND VENTURE GROUP LLC
1500 Broadway
14th Floor
New York, NY USA 10036
Phone: 212-324-2222
Fax: 212-324-2230
E-mail: info@ascendventures.com
Website: www.ascendventures.com

Management and Staff
Charles Crockett, Partner
Darryl Wash, Managing Partner
David Bowen, Partner
Kylie A.D. Sachs, Partner
Ralph Clark, Venture Partner
Roszell Mack, Partner

Type of Firm
Private Equity Firm

Association Membership
Natl Assoc of Investment Cos. (NAIC)

Project Preferences

Role in Financing:
Will function either as deal originator or investor in deals created by others

Type of Financing Preferred:
Early Stage
Expansion

Size of Investments Considered:
Min Size of Investment Considered (000s): $1,000
Max Size of Investment Considered (000s): $5,000

Geographical Preferences

United States Preferences:
Mid Atlantic
Midwest
Northern California
Northeast
West Coast
California
New York
All U.S.

Industry Preferences

In Computer Hardware prefer:
Disk Relat. Memory Device

In Computer Software prefer:
Data Processing
Software
Systems Software
Applications Software

In Internet Specific prefer:
Internet
Ecommerce
Web Aggregration/Portals

In Consumer Related prefer:
Education Related

In Other prefer:
Women/Minority-Owned Bus.

Additional Information
Year Founded: 2000
Capital Under Management: $148,000,000
Current Activity Level: Actively seeking new investments
Method of Compensation: Return on invest. most important, but chg. closing fees, service fees, etc.

ASCEND VENTURE PARTNERS
Room 1218 , Bldg.16 Huamao Ctr
JianHuan Rd., #89, Chaoyang
Beijing, China 100025
Phone: 8610-6530-5661
Fax: 8610-6530-5653
E-mail: hello@ascendvp.com.cn
Website: www.ascendvp.com.cn

Other Offices
Room 1903, Fortress Tower
250 King's Road
North Point, Hong Kong
Phone: 852-2312-0966
Fax: 852-2369-8484

276 Fifth Avenue
Suite 703
New York, NY USA 10001
Phone: 212-447-6538
Fax: 212-447-0292

Management and Staff

Monita Mo-Co, Managing Partner

Type of Firm

Bank Affiliated

Project Preferences

Type of Financing Preferred:

Expansion
Balanced

Geographical Preferences

International Preferences:

China

Additional Information

Year Founded: 1999
Current Activity Level: Actively seeking new investments

ASCENSION HEALTH VENTURES LLC

11775 Borman Drive
Suite 310
Saint Louis, MO USA 63146
Phone: 314-733-8100
Fax: 314-733-8678
E-mail: ahv@ascensionhealth.org.
Website: www.ascensionhealthventures.org

Management and Staff

Matthew Hermann, Managing Director

Type of Firm

Private Equity Firm

Association Membership

National Venture Capital Association - USA (NVCA)

Project Preferences

Role in Financing:

Prefer role as deal originator but will also invest in deals created by others

Type of Financing Preferred:

Fund of Funds
Expansion
Later Stage

Size of Investments Considered:

Min Size of Investment Considered (000s): $7,500
Max Size of Investment Considered (000s): $10,000

Geographical Preferences

United States Preferences:

All U.S.

Industry Preferences

In Biotechnology prefer:

Biotechnology

In Medical/Health prefer:

Medical/Health
Medical Products
Health Services

In Other prefer:

Socially Responsible

Additional Information

Name of Most Recent Fund: CHV II, L.P.
Most Recent Fund Was Raised: 07/20/2007
Year Founded: 2001
Capital Under Management: $325,000,000
Current Activity Level: Actively seeking new investments
Method of Compensation: Return on investment is of primary concern, do not charge fees

---

ASCENT BIOMEDICAL VENTURES

41 West 57th Street
6th Floor
New York, NY USA 10019
Phone: 212-303-1680
Fax: 212-752-3633
Website: www.abvlp.com

Management and Staff

Arthur Tinkelenberg, Principal
Avi Kometz, Principal
Geoffrey Smith, Managing Partner
Jon Edelson, Venture Partner
Steve Hochberg, Managing Partner

Type of Firm

Private Equity Firm

Project Preferences

Type of Financing Preferred:

Early Stage
Balanced
Seed

Geographical Preferences

United States Preferences:

All U.S.

Industry Preferences

In Biotechnology prefer:

Biotechnology

In Medical/Health prefer:

Medical/Health

Additional Information

Year Founded: 2005
Capital Under Management: $53,200,000
Current Activity Level: Actively seeking new investments

ASCENT EQUITY CAPITAL (FKA: PINNACLE EQUITY CAPITAL)

875 North Michigan Avenue
31st Floor, John Hancock Tower
Chicago, IL USA 60611
Phone: 312-265-6706
Fax: 312-277-1967
Website: www.ascentequitycapital.com

Management and Staff

Chad Mollman, General Partner

Type of Firm

Private Equity Firm

Project Preferences

Type of Financing Preferred:

Leveraged Buyout
Acquisition

Industry Preferences

In Financial Services prefer:

Financial Services

Additional Information

Year Founded: 2002
Capital Under Management: $5,000,000
Current Activity Level: Actively seeking new investments

ASCENT VENTURE PARTNERS

255 State Street
Fifth Floor
Boston, MA USA 02109
Phone: 617-720-9400
Fax: 617-720-9401
E-mail: info@ascentvp.com
Website: www.ascentvp.com

Management and Staff

Christopher Lynch, Managing Director
Christopher Walter Dick, Managing Director
Geoffrey Oblak, Partner
Matt Fates, Principal

Type of Firm

Private Equity Firm

Association Membership

Natl Assoc of Small Bus. Inv. Co (NASBIC)
National Venture Capital Association - USA (NVCA)

Project Preferences

Role in Financing:

Prefer role as deal originator but will also invest in deals created by others

Type of Financing Preferred:
Balanced

Size of Investments Considered:
Min Size of Investment Considered (000s): $2,000
Max Size of Investment Considered (000s): $6,000

Geographical Preferences

United States Preferences:
Mid Atlantic
Northeast
East Coast

Industry Focus

(% based on actual investment)

Computer Software and Services	30.7%
Internet Specific	25.2%
Communications and Media	14.2%
Computer Hardware	7.1%
Medical/Health	7.1%
Other Products	6.9%
Industrial/Energy	4.5%
Consumer Related	3.2%
Semiconductors/Other Elect.	1.1%

Additional Information

Name of Most Recent Fund: Ascent Venture Partners V, L.P.
Most Recent Fund Was Raised: 08/27/2008
Year Founded: 1981
Capital Under Management: $380,000,000
Current Activity Level: Actively seeking new investments
Method of Compensation: Return on investment is of primary concern, do not charge fees

---

ASCET INVESTIMENTOS

Rua Taques Alvim, 172
Cidade Jardim
Sao Paulo, Brazil 05671-030
Phone: 55-11-3038-1308
Fax: 55-11-3038-1318
Website: www.ascet.com.br

Type of Firm
Private Equity Firm

Association Membership
Brazilian Venture Capital Association (ABCR)

Project Preferences

Type of Financing Preferred:
Balanced

Geographical Preferences

International Preferences:
Brazil

Industry Preferences

In Communications prefer:
Communications and Media
Commercial Communications

In Business Serv. prefer:
Media

Additional Information

Year Founded: 2006
Current Activity Level: Actively seeking new investments

ASER CAPITAL SCR

Calle Urgell
Barcelona, Spain
Management and Staff
Daniel Gomez Garcia, President

Type of Firm
Private Equity Firm

Project Preferences

Type of Financing Preferred:
Balanced

Geographical Preferences

International Preferences:
Spain

Additional Information

Year Founded: 2008
Current Activity Level: Actively seeking new investments

ASHBY POINT CAPITAL

1240 Ashby Court
Arnold, MD USA 21012
Phone: 410-544-6250
Fax: 410-544-3264
Website: www.ashbypointcapital.com

Management and Staff
James Leroux, Partner
William Westervelt, Partner

Type of Firm
Private Equity Advisor or Fund of Funds

Project Preferences

Type of Financing Preferred:
Early Stage
Balanced
Later Stage

Additional Information

Year Founded: 2009
Current Activity Level: Actively seeking new investments

ASHMORE INVESTMENT MANAGEMENT, LTD.

61 Aldwych
London, United Kingdom WC2B 4AE
Phone: 44-20-3077-6000
Fax: 44-20-3077-6001
E-mail: corporate@ashmoregroup.com
Website: www.ashmoregroup.com

Type of Firm
Private Equity Firm

Project Preferences

Type of Financing Preferred:
Leveraged Buyout
Turnaround
Special Situation
Distressed Debt

Geographical Preferences

International Preferences:
India
Europe
Guernsey

Additional Information

Year Founded: 1992
Capital Under Management: $2,400,000,000
Current Activity Level: Actively seeking new investments

ASIA ALTERNATIVES MANAGEMENT LLC

Ste 412-416, 4F, Jardine House
One Connaught Place
Central, Hong Kong
Phone: 852-2971-0707
Fax: 852-2971-0700
E-mail: info@asiaalt.com
Website: www.asiaalternatives.com

Other Offices

Office P5, 3F North Tower
Beijing Kerry Center, One Guang Hua Road
Beijing, China 100022
Phone: 86-10-8523-3039
Fax: 86-10-8523-3001

One Maritime Plaza
Suite 1000
San Francisco, CA USA 94111
Phone: 415-723-8100
Fax: 415-399-1713

Management and Staff
Laure Wang, Managing Director
Melissa Ma, Managing Director
Rebecca Xu, Managing Director
William LaFayette, Chief Financial Officer

Type of Firm
Private Equity Advisor or Fund of Funds

Project Preferences

Type of Financing Preferred:
Fund of Funds
Leveraged Buyout
Expansion
Special Situation

Geographical Preferences

International Preferences:
India
Taiwan
China
Hong Kong
Pacific
Australia
New Zealand
Korea, South
Asia
Japan

Additional Information
Year Founded: 2006
Capital Under Management: $1,985,900,000
Current Activity Level: Actively seeking new investments

ASIA CAPITAL MANAGEMENT (ACM) LIMITED (AKA: ACL ASIA LTD)
17/F, China Hong Kong Tower
8-12 Hennessy Road
Wanchai, Hong Kong
Phone: 852-2525-8151
Fax: 852-2810-5590
E-mail: info@acmhk.com
Website: www.acmhk.com

Other Offices
16/F New Century Trade Center
No. 50 Hu Qiu Road
Shanghai, China
Phone: 86-21-6329-8979
Fax: 86-21-6323-5366

1100 Louisiana
Suite 5005
Houston, TX USA 77002
Phone: 713-655-8500
Fax: 713-655-8503

Longbao Mansion, Suite 312
36 Maizidian Jie, Chaoyang Qu
Beijing, China 100026
Phone: 86-10-6591-6491
Fax: 86-10-6591-6460

5th Floor PTC Building
105 Aguirre Street, Legazpi Village
Makati City, Philippines
Phone: 63-2-840-3020
Fax: 63-2-813-1278

2nd Industrial Zone
Yulu Gong Ming Town, Baoan County
Shenzhen City, China
Phone: 86-755-717-2931
Fax: 86-755-717-2930

Management and Staff
Louis Bowen, Managing Director

Type of Firm
Private Equity Firm

Association Membership
Hong Kong Venture Capital Association (HKVCA)

Project Preferences

Role in Financing:
Prefer role as deal originator but will also invest in deals created by others

Type of Financing Preferred:
Early Stage
Expansion
Mezzanine

Size of Investments Considered:
Min Size of Investment Considered (000s): $1,000
Max Size of Investment Considered (000s): $5,000

Geographical Preferences

International Preferences:
Taiwan
China
Hong Kong
Philippines

Industry Preferences

In Communications prefer:
Communications and Media
Data Communications

In Computer Software prefer:
Computer Services

In Semiconductor/Electr prefer:
Electronics

In Biotechnology prefer:
Biotechnology

In Medical/Health prefer:
Medical/Health
Medical Diagnostics
Diagnostic Services
Diagnostic Test Products
Medical Therapeutics
Drug/Equipmt Delivery
Disposable Med. Products
Hospitals/Clinics/Primary
Hospital/Other Instit.
Pharmaceuticals

In Consumer Related prefer:
Retail
Food/Beverage
Consumer Products
Consumer Services
Other Restaurants

In Industrial/Energy prefer:
Energy
Alternative Energy
Industrial Products
Robotics
Machinery

In Financial Services prefer:
Financial Services
Insurance
Real Estate

In Business Serv. prefer:
Services
Distribution

Additional Information
Year Founded: 1981
Capital Under Management: $198,000,000
Current Activity Level: Actively seeking new investments
Method of Compensation: Return on investment is of primary concern, do not charge fees

---

ASIA CULTURE TECHNOLOGY INVESTMENT CO., LTD.
Second Floor, Kijung Bldg.
703-7 Yeonsan-dong, Yeonjae-ku
Busan, South Korea 611-080
Phone: 82-51-868-9333
Fax: 82-51-868-9332

Other Offices
2F, Hwanyoong Building
52-1, Nonheon-Dong, Gangnam-Gu
Seoul, South Korea 121-839

Management and Staff
Intack Yu, President

Type of Firm
Bank Affiliated

Project Preferences

Type of Financing Preferred:
Balanced

Geographical Preferences

International Preferences:
Korea, South

Industry Preferences

In Business Serv. prefer:
Media

Additional Information
Year Founded: 2007
Capital Under Management: $31,400,000
Current Activity Level: Actively seeking new investments

ASIA MEZZANINE CAPITAL ADVISERS, LTD.

3205 Alexandra House
16-20 Chater Road
Central, Hong Kong
Phone: 852-3104-2570
Fax: 852-3104-2915
Website: www.asiamezzanine.com

Management and Staff

David Bussman, Partner
Jon Robinson, Partner
Joseph Ferrigno, Managing Partner
Patrick Chovanec, Vice President
Stephen Yeung, Vice President
Stephen Temple, Partner

Type of Firm

Private Equity Firm

Project Preferences

Type of Financing Preferred:
Leveraged Buyout
Mezzanine
Expansion
Management Buyouts
Acquisition
Recapitalizations

Size of Investments Considered:
Min Size of Investment Considered (000s): $20,000
Max Size of Investment Considered (000s): $50,000

Geographical Preferences

International Preferences:
Vietnam
India
China
Thailand
Philippines
Asia
Korea, South
Japan
Malaysia

Additional Information

Year Founded: 2003
Capital Under Management: $40,000,000
Current Activity Level: Actively seeking new investments

ASIA PACIFIC INVESTMENT PARTNERS

4-R Khoroo, 1-40 Myangat
Sukhbaatar District
Ulaanbaatar, Mongolia
Phone: 976-11-324-545
Fax: 976-11-311-558
E-mail: info@apipcorp.com
Website: www.apipcorp.com

Other Offices

11th Floor
New York, NY USA 10005
Phone: 212-724-0150

4&5 Golden Cross Walk
Oxford, United Kingdom OX1 3EU
Phone: 44-77-6610-3778
Fax: 44-18-6572-7672

Suite 503, St. Georges Building
2 Ice House Street
Central, Hong Kong
Phone: 852-2868-0696
Fax: 852-2868-0696

Management and Staff

Lee Cashell, Managing Partner

Type of Firm

Private Equity Firm

Project Preferences

Type of Financing Preferred:
Balanced

Geographical Preferences

International Preferences:
Asia

Industry Preferences

In Consumer Related prefer:
Consumer Products

In Financial Services prefer:
Financial Services
Real Estate

In Agr/Forestr/Fish prefer:
Mining and Minerals

Additional Information

Year Founded: 2001
Current Activity Level: Actively seeking new investments

ASIA PACIFIC VENTURES

2370 Watson Court
Suite 200
Palo Alto, CA USA 94303-3226
Phone: 650-354-3250
Fax: 650-813-1244
Website: www.apvco.com

Management and Staff

David Duimich, President
David McQuilkin, Managing Director
Mitchell Nelson, Vice President

Type of Firm

Private Equity Firm

Project Preferences

Type of Financing Preferred:
Expansion

Additional Information

Year Founded: 2009
Current Activity Level: Actively seeking new investments

ASIA PRIVATE EQUITY CAPITAL (FKA: MEDIBIC ALLIANCE)

Daido Kasumigaseki Bldg. 8F
Kasumigaseki, Chiyoda-ku
Tokyo, Japan 100-0013
Phone: 81-3-5251-2700
Fax: 81-3-5510-2312
Website: www.asia-pe.com

Other Offices

Metro Center Tower, 950 Tower Lane
Suite 1775
Foster City, CA USA 94404
Phone: 650-240-4900
Fax: 650-240-4999

49F, 268 XiZang, Middle Rd.
Raffles City Office Tower
Shanghai, China 200001

Management and Staff

Akiyoshi Uchiyama, Partner
Ali Zareh, Partner
Mayumi Kanai, Managing Director
Tomohiko Asahara, Partner
Yasuhiro Hashimoto, Partner

Type of Firm

Bank Affiliated

Association Membership

National Venture Capital Association - USA (NVCA)

Project Preferences

Type of Financing Preferred:
Early Stage
Balanced
Later Stage

Geographical Preferences

United States Preferences:
All U.S.

International Preferences:
China
Asia
Korea, South
Japan
Africa

Industry Preferences

In Biotechnology prefer:
Biotechnology

In Medical/Health prefer:
Medical/Health
Pharmaceuticals

Additional Information

Year Founded: 2004
Capital Under Management: $30,000,000
Current Activity Level: Actively seeking new investments

ASIA WEST, LLC

One East Weaver Street
Greenwich, CT USA 06831
Phone: 203-983-6300
Website: www.asiawestfunds.com

Management and Staff

Sanford Selman, Managing Director

Type of Firm

Private Equity Firm

Project Preferences

Type of Financing Preferred:
Later Stage

Geographical Preferences

United States Preferences:
All U.S.

International Preferences:
China
All International

Industry Preferences

In Other prefer:
Environment Responsible

Additional Information

Year Founded: 2002
Current Activity Level: Actively seeking new investments

ASIAN DEVELOPMENT BANK

Six ADB Avenue
Mandaluyong City, Philippines 1550
Phone: 632-632-4444
Fax: 632-636-2444
Website: www.adb.org

Type of Firm

Bank Affiliated

Project Preferences

Type of Financing Preferred:
Balanced

Geographical Preferences

International Preferences:
China
Asia

Industry Preferences

In Industrial/Energy prefer:
Environmental Related

Additional Information

Year Founded: 1966
Current Activity Level: Actively seeking new investments

ASIAN TIGER CAPITAL PARTNERS, LTD. (AKA: AT CAPITAL)

UTC Building, Level 16
8 Panthapath
Dhaka, Bangladesh 1215
Phone: 880-2-815-5144
Fax: 880-2-911-8582
E-mail: info@at-capital.com
Website: www.at-capital.com

Management and Staff

Syeed Khan, Founding Partner

Type of Firm

Private Equity Firm

Project Preferences

Type of Financing Preferred:
Leveraged Buyout
Early Stage
Expansion
Generalist PE
Acquisition

Geographical Preferences

International Preferences:
Asia
Industry Preferences

In Medical/Health prefer:
Pharmaceuticals

In Consumer Related prefer:
Consumer
Retail
Consumer Products

In Industrial/Energy prefer:
Energy
Industrial Products

In Financial Services prefer:
Financial Services
Real Estate

In Business Serv. prefer:
Services

In Manufact. prefer:
Manufacturing

In Agr/Forestr/Fish prefer:
Agribusiness

Additional Information

Year Founded: 2008
Current Activity Level: Actively seeking new investments

ASIATECH INTERNET GROUP

535 Cowper Street
Second Floor
Palo Alto, CA USA 94301
Phone: 650-321-0688
Fax: 650-321-6188
E-mail: jyao@asiatechV.com
Website: www.asiatechv.com

Type of Firm

Private Equity Firm

Additional Information

Year Founded: 2002
Current Activity Level: Actively seeking new investments

ASIATECH INTERNET GROUP (ATIG) (FKA: ASIATECH VENTURES)

39F. One Exchange Square
8 Connaught Place
Central, Hong Kong
Phone: 852-2116-6868
Fax: 852-2116-0000
E-mail: info@asiatechgroup.com
Website: www.asiatechgroup.com

Other Offices

4F, No. 261, Sec. 3
Nan-King East Road,
Taipei, Taiwan
Phone: 886-2-8712-1010
Fax: 886-2-8712-2020

1830, 18F China Merchants Tower
118, Jian Guo Rd., Chao Yang Dist.
Beijing, China 100004
Phone: 86-10-6567-2299
Fax: 86-10-6566-2732

2F, 65 Club Street
Singapore, Singapore 069439
Phone: 65-6327-1800
Fax: 65-6327-1877

Level 21 HSBC Tower
101 Yin Cheng East, Pudong
Shanghai, China
Phone: 86-21-2890-3433
Fax: 86-21-2890-3434

20660 Stevens Creed Blvd.
Suite 188
Cupertino, CA USA 95014
Phone: 650-321-0688
Fax: 650-321-6188

535 Cowper Street
2nd Floor
Palo Alto, CA USA 94301
Phone: 1650-321-0688
Fax: 1650-321-6188

Management and Staff

Anthony Fan, Managing Partner
Derek Kwik, Vice President
Hanson Cheah, Managing Partner
James Yao, Managing Partner
Jun Wang, Managing Partner
Peter Chu, Managing Partner
Phillip Wong, Managing Partner
Stephanie Choy, Vice President
Teresa Woo, Vice President

Type of Firm

Private Equity Firm

Association Membership

Venture Capital Association of Beijing (VCAB)
Hong Kong Venture Capital Association (HKVCA)

Project Preferences

Type of Financing Preferred:

Early Stage
Expansion
Balanced
Seed

Geographical Preferences

United States Preferences:

Southern California

International Preferences:

Taiwan
China
Hong Kong
Singapore
Asia
Malaysia

Industry Focus

(% based on actual investment)

Internet Specific	65.7%
Computer Software and Services	13.0%
Computer Hardware	10.2%
Communications and Media	6.4%
Semiconductors/Other Elect.	4.8%

Additional Information

Year Founded: 1997
Capital Under Management: $96,800,000
Current Activity Level: Actively seeking new investments

ASIATECH MANAGEMENT LLC

20450 Stevens Creek Boulevard
Suite 200
Santa Clara, CA USA 95054
Phone: 408-330-9366
Fax: 408-330-9365
E-mail: info@asiatechventure.com
Website: www.asiatechventure.com

Other Offices

Rm. 0106, Bldg. C, Dragon Century Plaza
No. 3, Hangda Road
Hangzhou, China 31007
Phone: 86-571-2893-5296
Fax: 56-571-2893-5295

Rm. 1606, International Trade Bldg.
333 Keelung Road., Sec 1
Taipei, Taiwan 110
Phone: 886-2-2758-5828
Fax: 886-2-2758-1607

Management and Staff

Elise Huang, Principal
Katherine Jen, Managing Director
Louie Liu, Partner

Type of Firm

Private Equity Firm

Project Preferences

Type of Financing Preferred:

Balanced

Geographical Preferences

International Preferences:

Asia
All International

Additional Information

Year Founded: 1998
Capital Under Management: $60,000,000
Current Activity Level: Actively seeking new investments

ASIAVEST PARTNERS, TCW/YFY LTD. (FKA: TCW/YFY INVESTMENT)

11/F, 318 Ruie Guang Road
Nei Hu District
Taipei, Taiwan 114
Phone: 886-2-2797-2989
Fax: 886-2-2797-8289
E-mail: info@asiavest.com
Website: www.asiavest.com

Other Offices

25/F, West Tower Twin Towers
B-12, Jianguomenwai Avenue, Chaoyang
Beijing, China 100022
Phone: 86-10-6568-6428
Fax: 86-10-6568-7458

28F,Citigroup Tower,Hua Yuan Shi Qiao Rd
Lu Jia Zui Finance and Trade Area
Shanghai, China 200120
Phone: 86-21-5840-3179
Fax: 86-21-5840-3169

Management and Staff

Chris Ni, Vice President
Darren Huang, Managing Director
Don D.C. Yeh, Partner
Franny Lee, Partner
Janet C.C. Tai, Partner
Kevin Chen, Vice President
Roland Chang, Partner
Tsong-Jen Huang, Managing Partner

Type of Firm

Private Equity Firm

Association Membership

Singapore Venture Capital Association (SVCA)

Project Preferences

Type of Financing Preferred:

Early Stage
Mezzanine
Balanced
Startup

Size of Investments Considered:

Min Size of Investment Considered (000s): $2,000
Max Size of Investment Considered (000s): $20,000

Geographical Preferences

United States Preferences:

All U.S.

International Preferences:

Taiwan
China
Hong Kong
Singapore

Industry Preferences

In Communications prefer:

Communications and Media

In Computer Software prefer:

Software

In Semiconductor/Electr prefer:

Semiconductor

In Manufact. prefer:

Manufacturing

Additional Information

Year Founded: 1995
Capital Under Management: $800,000,000
Current Activity Level: Actively seeking new investments

ASK GROUP

Bandbox House, 1/F, 254 - D
Dr. Annie Besant Road, Worli
Mumbai, India 400 025
Phone: 91-22-6652-0000
Website: www.askfinancials.com

Type of Firm

Bank Affiliated

Project Preferences

Type of Financing Preferred:

Balanced

Geographical Preferences

International Preferences:

India

Industry Preferences

In Financial Services prefer:

Real Estate

Additional Information

Year Founded: 1983
Current Activity Level: Actively seeking new investments

ASKEMBLA ASSET MANAGEMENT AB

Strandvagen 5b
Stockholm, Sweden 114 51
Phone: 46-8-678-0610
Fax: 46-8-678-0680
E-mail: info@askembla.se
Website: www.askembla.se

Other Offices

Akas iela 5/7
Riga, Latvia LV-1011
Phone: 371-784-49-74

Jogailos g.4
Vilnius, Lithuania LT-01116
Phone: 370-526-90-702

Liivalaia 14
Tallinn, Estonia ES-101 18
Phone: 372-646-11-72

Management and Staff

Christoffer Kurpatow, Founding Partner
Hanno Riismaa, Partner
Sarunas Siugzda, Partner
Stefan Kaiser, Chief Financial Officer

Type of Firm

Private Equity Advisor or Fund of Funds

Association Membership

European Private Equity and Venture Capital Assoc.

Project Preferences

Type of Financing Preferred:

Leveraged Buyout

Size of Investments Considered:

Min Size of Investment Considered (000s): $1,781
Max Size of Investment Considered (000s): $8,905

Geographical Preferences

International Preferences:

Central Europe
Poland
Eastern Europe
Scandanavia/Nordic Region

Additional Information

Year Founded: 1994
Capital Under Management: $102,600,000
Current Activity Level: Actively seeking new investments

ASML VENTURES

77 Danbury Road
Wilton, CT USA 06897
Phone: 203-761-4000
Fax: 646-822-6072
Website: www.asml.com

Type of Firm

Corporate PE/Venture

Project Preferences

Type of Financing Preferred:

Early Stage
Research and Development

Industry Preferences

In Semiconductor/Electr prefer:

Semiconductor

Additional Information

Year Founded: 2007
Current Activity Level: Actively seeking new investments

ASPEN GROVE VENTURES

2825 E. Cottonwood Parkway
Suite 500
Salt Lake City, UT USA 84121
Phone: 801-990-1220
Fax: 866-206-1508
Website: www.aspengroveventures.com

Other Offices

4128 North Boulder Canyon
Mesa, AZ USA 85207
Phone: 480-981-2060
Fax: 480-981-2061

Management and Staff

Brian Cropper, Partner
Evan Hill, Partner
Russell Sewell, Managing Partner

Type of Firm

Private Equity Firm

Project Preferences

Type of Financing Preferred:

Expansion

Size of Investments Considered:

Min Size of Investment Considered (000s): $2,000
Max Size of Investment Considered (000s): $4,000

Geographical Preferences

United States Preferences:

Rocky Mountain

Industry Preferences

In Communications prefer:

Communications and Media
Wireless Communications

In Computer Software prefer:

Software

In Internet Specific prefer:

Internet

In Semiconductor/Electr prefer:

Semiconductor

Additional Information

Year Founded: 2000
Capital Under Management: $9,000,000
Current Activity Level: Actively seeking new investments

ASPEN VENTURES

1000 Fremont Avenue
Suite 200
Los Altos, CA USA 94024
Phone: 650-917-5670
Fax: 650-917-5677
Website: www.aspenventures.com

Other Offices

1198 Jefferson Way
Laguna Beach, CA USA 92651
Phone: 949-494-2707
Fax: 949-497-3753

Management and Staff

Alexander Cilento, General Partner
Debra Schilling, Chief Financial Officer
E. David Crockett, General Partner

Type of Firm
SBIC

Association Membership
Western Association of Venture Capitalists (WAVC)
Natl Assoc of Small Bus. Inv. Co (NASBIC)

Project Preferences

Role in Financing:
Prefer role as deal originator but will also invest in deals created by others

Type of Financing Preferred:
Second Stage Financing
Early Stage
Seed
First Stage Financing

Size of Investments Considered:
Min Size of Investment Considered (000s): $300
Max Size of Investment Considered (000s): $500

Geographical Preferences

United States Preferences:
West Coast

Industry Focus
(% based on actual investment)

Computer Software and Services	52.3%
Medical/Health	10.9%
Internet Specific	10.7%
Communications and Media	6.7%
Biotechnology	6.2%
Semiconductors/Other Elect.	4.4%
Computer Hardware	4.1%
Industrial/Energy	3.8%
Consumer Related	0.9%

Additional Information
Name of Most Recent Fund: Aspen Ventures III, L.P.
Most Recent Fund Was Raised: 10/31/1998
Year Founded: 1991
Capital Under Management: $140,000,000
Current Activity Level: Actively seeking new investments
Method of Compensation: Return on investment is of primary concern, do not charge fees

---

ASSET MANAGEMENT COMPANY VENTURE CAPITAL
2100 Geng Road
Suite 200
Palo Alto, CA USA 94303
Phone: 650-494-7400
Fax: 650-856-1826
E-mail: info@assetman.com
Website: www.assetman.com

Management and Staff
Bennett Dubin, Managing Partner
Evgeny Zaytsev, Partner
Franklin Johnson, Founding Partner
Graham Crooke, Managing Partner
Richard Simoni, Partner
Skip Fleshman, Partner

Type of Firm
Private Equity Firm

Association Membership
Western Association of Venture Capitalists (WAVC)
National Venture Capital Association - USA (NVCA)

Project Preferences

Role in Financing:
Prefer role as deal originator but will also invest in deals created by others

Type of Financing Preferred:
Early Stage
Start-up Financing
Seed
First Stage Financing
Startup

Size of Investments Considered:
Min Size of Investment Considered (000s): $100
Max Size of Investment Considered (000s): $2,000

Geographical Preferences

United States Preferences:
West Coast

Industry Focus
(% based on actual investment)

Biotechnology	24.6%
Computer Software and Services	19.0%
Medical/Health	17.9%
Semiconductors/Other Elect.	9.7%
Internet Specific	9.3%
Computer Hardware	9.0%
Communications and Media	6.6%
Consumer Related	1.8%
Industrial/Energy	1.0%
Other Products	1.0%

Additional Information
Year Founded: 1965
Capital Under Management: $180,000,000
Current Activity Level: Actively seeking new investments
Method of Compensation: Return on investment is of primary concern, do not charge fees

---

ASSET MANAGERS HOLDING COMPANY, LTD.
17F Imperial Tower
1-1-1 Uchisaiwaicho,Chiyodaku
Tokyo, Japan
Phone: 81-3-3502-4800
Website: www.assetmanagers.co.jp

Other Offices
Room 1108-09, Bank of America Tower
12 Harcourt Road
Central, Hong Kong
Phone: 852-2521-8222
Fax: 852-2521-9100

Management and Staff
Eric Yip, Chief Executive Officer
Kazuya Sahashi, Chief Financial Officer
Kenji Iwasaki, President
Kenji Shibasaki, Managing Director
Ryoji Furukawa, Founder
Savio Cheung, Vice President

Type of Firm
Bank Affiliated

Project Preferences

Role in Financing:
Prefer role as deal originator but will also invest in deals created by others

Type of Financing Preferred:
Expansion

Geographical Preferences

International Preferences:
Japan

Industry Preferences

In Financial Services prefer:
Real Estate

Additional Information
Year Founded: 2000
Capital Under Management: $160,300,000
Current Activity Level: Actively seeking new investments

ASTELLAS VENTURE CAPITAL (FKA: YAMANOUCHI VENTURE CAPITAL)
2180 Sand Hill Road
Suite 460
Menlo Park, CA USA 94025
Phone: 650-926-0731
Fax: 650-926-0740
E-mail: yvc@yamanouchiventure.com
Website: www.astellasventure.com

Management and Staff
Steve Knowles, Chief Financial Officer

Type of Firm
Corporate PE/Venture

Project Preferences

Role in Financing:
Prefer role in deals created by others

Type of Financing Preferred:
Early Stage
Later Stage

Size of Investments Considered:
Min Size of Investment Considered (000s): $500

Max Size of Investment Considered (000s): $3,000

Geographical Preferences

International Preferences:

Western Europe
All International

Industry Preferences

In Biotechnology prefer:

Biotechnology
Human Biotechnology

In Medical/Health prefer:

Medical Therapeutics
Pharmaceuticals

Additional Information

Year Founded: 2000
Capital Under Management: $60,000,000
Current Activity Level: Actively seeking new investments
Method of Compensation: Other

ASTOR PARTICIPATIES BV

Bezuidenhoutseweg 161
Den Haag, Netherlands 2594 AG
Phone: 31-70-427-8001
Fax: 31-70-365-7155
E-mail: info@astorparticipaties.nl
Website: www.astorparticipaties.nl

Type of Firm

Private Equity Firm

Project Preferences

Role in Financing:

Will function either as deal originator or investor in deals created by others

Type of Financing Preferred:

Generalist PE
Early Stage
Expansion
Management Buyouts

Geographical Preferences

International Preferences:

Netherlands
Europe

Industry Preferences

In Medical/Health prefer:

Medical/Health

In Consumer Related prefer:

Consumer

In Industrial/Energy prefer:

Industrial Products

Additional Information

Year Founded: 2003
Capital Under Management: $26,400,000
Current Activity Level: Actively seeking new investments

Method of Compensation: Unknown

ASTORG PARTNERS SAS (FKA: SUEZ CAPITAL PARTENAIRES)

68 rue du Faubourg St. Honore
Paris, France 75008
Phone: 33-1-5305-4050
Fax: 33-1-5305-4057
E-mail: info@astorg-partners.com
Website: www.astorg-partners.com

Management and Staff

Catherine Couet, Chief Financial Officer
Christian Couturier, Partner
Joel Lacourte, Managing Partner
Thierry Timsit, Managing Partner

Type of Firm

Private Equity Firm

Association Membership

French Venture Capital Association (AFIC)
European Private Equity and Venture Capital Assoc.

Project Preferences

Role in Financing:

Will function either as deal originator or investor in deals created by others

Type of Financing Preferred:

Leveraged Buyout
Expansion
Generalist PE
Turnaround
Balanced
Recapitalizations

Size of Investments Considered:

Min Size of Investment Considered (000s): $2,700
Max Size of Investment Considered: No Limit

Geographical Preferences

International Preferences:

Europe
Germany
Asia
France

Industry Focus

(% based on actual investment)	
Semiconductors/Other Elect.	58.7%
Internet Specific	11.1%
Consumer Related	10.1%
Industrial/Energy	9.2%
Other Products	8.7%
Biotechnology	2.1%

Additional Information

Year Founded: 1998
Capital Under Management: $680,600,000
Current Activity Level: Actively seeking new investments

ASTROLABE VENTURES (FKA: RED PLANET CAPITAL)

100 Hamilton Avenue
Suite 250
Palo Alto, CA USA 94301
Phone: 650-462-9800
Fax: 650-462-9826
E-mail: info@redplanetcapital.com
Website: www.astrolabeventures.com

Management and Staff

Graham Burnette, General Partner
Jacques Vallee, General Partner
Peter Banks, General Partner

Type of Firm

Private Equity Firm

Association Membership

National Venture Capital Association - USA (NVCA)

Project Preferences

Type of Financing Preferred:

Early Stage
Seed

Size of Investments Considered:

Min Size of Investment Considered (000s): $3,000
Max Size of Investment Considered (000s): $5,000

Geographical Preferences

International Preferences:

All International

Industry Preferences

In Communications prefer:

Commercial Communications

In Medical/Health prefer:

Medical/Health

In Industrial/Energy prefer:

Energy
Advanced Materials
Environmental Related

In Manufact. prefer:

Manufacturing

Additional Information

Name of Most Recent Fund: Red Planet Capital Partners, L.P.
Most Recent Fund Was Raised: 10/10/2006
Year Founded: 2006
Capital Under Management: $75,000,000
Current Activity Level: Actively seeking new investments

ASTUTIA VENTURES GMBH

Bruderstr. 12
Munich, Germany 80538
Phone: 49-700-24926435
E-mail: info@atutia-ventures.de
Website: www.astutia-ventures.de

Management and Staff

Benedict Rodenstock, Chief Executive Officer

Type of Firm

Private Equity Firm

Project Preferences

Type of Financing Preferred:
Early Stage
Seed
Startup

Geographical Preferences

International Preferences:
Netherlands
Germany

Additional Information

Year Founded: 2006
Current Activity Level: Actively seeking new investments

ATA VENTURES

203 Redwood Shores Parkway
Suite 550
Redwood City, CA USA 94065
Phone: 650-594-0189
Fax: 650-594-0220
E-mail: info@ataventures.com
Website: www.ataventures.com

Management and Staff

Hatch Graham, Managing Director
Michael Hodges, Venture Partner
Michio Fujimura, Managing Director
Nancy McCroskey, Chief Financial Officer
T. Peter Thomas, Managing Director

Type of Firm

Private Equity Firm

Association Membership

National Venture Capital Association - USA (NVCA)

Project Preferences

Type of Financing Preferred:
Early Stage
Start-up Financing
Seed

Size of Investments Considered:
Min Size of Investment Considered (000s): $2,000
Max Size of Investment Considered (000s): $8,000

Geographical Preferences

United States Preferences:
All U.S.

Industry Preferences

In Communications prefer:
Telecommunications

Additional Information

Year Founded: 2004
Capital Under Management: $350,000,000
Current Activity Level: Actively seeking new investments

ATEL VENTURES, INC.

600 California Street
Sixth Floor
San Francisco, CA USA 94104
Phone: 415-616-3436
Fax: 415-989-3796
Website: www.atel.com/ventures

Management and Staff

Steven Rea, Vice President

Type of Firm

Corporate PE/Venture

Association Membership

National Venture Capital Association - USA (NVCA)

Project Preferences

Type of Financing Preferred:
Early Stage
Startup

Industry Preferences

In Computer Other prefer:
Computer Related

In Manufact. prefer:
Manufacturing

Additional Information

Year Founded: 2002
Current Activity Level: Actively seeking new investments

ATHENA CAPITAL PARTNERS LLC

8840 Wilshire Boulevard
Second Floor
Beverly Hills, CA USA 90211
Phone: 310-652-5900
Fax: 310-358-3285
Website: www.athenacapital.net

Type of Firm

Private Equity Firm

Project Preferences

Role in Financing:
Will function either as deal originator or investor in deals created by others

Type of Financing Preferred:
Acquisition
Special Situation
Startup

Geographical Preferences

United States Preferences:
Southern California

Additional Information

Year Founded: 2000
Current Activity Level: Actively seeking new investments

ATHENA HIGH TECHNOLOGY INCUBATOR, LTD.

3 Poseidon Street
Emergo House
Nicosia, Cyprus 1507
Phone: 357-22-819-381
Fax: 357-22-819-382
Website: www.athenatech.com.cy

Type of Firm

Private Equity Firm

Association Membership

European Private Equity and Venture Capital Assoc.

Project Preferences

Type of Financing Preferred:
Balanced
Startup

Size of Investments Considered:
Min Size of Investment Considered (000s): $300
Max Size of Investment Considered (000s): $1,000

Geographical Preferences

International Preferences:
Greece
Albania
Jordan
Turkey
Egypt
Iran
Lebanon
Macedonia
Croatia
Bulgaria
Bosnia
Israel
Romania
Cyprus

Industry Preferences

In Biotechnology prefer:
Biotechnology

Additional Information

Year Founded: 2001
Current Activity Level: Actively seeking new investments

ATHENIAN VENTURES (FKA: OHIO VALLEY VENTURE FUND)

20 East Circle Drive
Suite 37146
Athens, OH USA 45701
Phone: 614-360-1155
Fax: 740-593-9311
E-mail: info@athenianvp.com
Website: www.athenianvp.com

Management and Staff

Daniel Kosoy, Partner
Karl Elderkin, Managing Partner
Mitchell Rosich, Partner
William Tanner, Chief Financial Officer

Type of Firm

Private Equity Firm

Project Preferences

Type of Financing Preferred:
Early Stage

Size of Investments Considered:
Min Size of Investment Considered (000s): $1,000
Max Size of Investment Considered (000s): $10,000

Industry Preferences

In Communications prefer:
Communications and Media

Additional Information

Name of Most Recent Fund: Athenian III, Ltd.
Most Recent Fund Was Raised: 12/22/2004
Year Founded: 1997
Capital Under Management: $31,000,000
Current Activity Level: Actively seeking new investments

ATHERTON VENTURE PARTNERS, LLC

1010 El Camino Real
Suite 300
Menlo Park, CA USA 94025
Phone: 650-323-8357
Fax: 650-323-8350
E-mail: info@athertonventures.com
Website: www.athertonventures.com

Management and Staff

David Neubauer, Managing Partner
Wally Buch, Principal

Type of Firm

Private Equity Firm

Project Preferences

Type of Financing Preferred:
Seed

Industry Preferences

In Computer Software prefer:
Software

In Internet Specific prefer:
Internet

In Medical/Health prefer:
Diagnostic Test Products
Medical Products
Health Services

Additional Information

Year Founded: 1997
Current Activity Level: Actively seeking new investments

ATHLONE GLOBAL SECURITY, INC.

Chesapeake Innovation Center
175 Admiral Cochrane Drive
Annapolis, MD USA 21401
Phone: 202-657-5909
E-mail: info@athloneglobalsecurity.com
Website: www.athloneglobalsecurity.com

Other Offices

1 Hamada Street
Rehovot, Israel 76703

Management and Staff

Arik Nir, Managing Director
George Faught, Chief Financial Officer

Type of Firm

Private Equity Firm

Project Preferences

Type of Financing Preferred:
Early Stage

Geographical Preferences

United States Preferences:
All U.S.

International Preferences:
Europe
Israel

Additional Information

Year Founded: 2006
Current Activity Level: Actively seeking new investments

ATHLONE INTERNATIONAL, LTD

200 Brook Drive
Green Park
Reading, United Kingdom RG2 6UB
Phone: 44-870-351-9312
Fax: 44-870-351-9313
E-mail: info@athloneinternational.com
Website: www.athlonegroup.co.uk

Management and Staff

Alex Miller, Chief Operating Officer
Jojar Singh Dhinsa, Chief Executive Officer

Type of Firm

Service Provider

Project Preferences

Type of Financing Preferred:
Public Companies
Turnaround

Geographical Preferences

International Preferences:
United Kingdom

Industry Preferences

In Communications prefer:
Telecommunications

In Business Serv. prefer:
Media

Additional Information

Year Founded: 2002
Current Activity Level: Actively seeking new investments

ATILA VENTURES

3rd Floor, Par la Ville Place
14, Par-la-Ville Road
Hamilton, Bermuda HM JX
Phone: 441-295-6081
Fax: 441-295-5704
Website: www.atilaventures.com

Other Offices

The Old Church
Quicks Road, Wimbledon
London, United Kingdom SW19 1EX
Phone: 44-208-545-2675
Fax: 44-208-545-2604

Mariahilferstrasse
1/Getreidemarkt 17
Vienna, Austria 1060
Phone: 43-1-581-8390210
Fax: 43-1-581-7611

Rue du Grand-Pont 12
Lausanne, Switzerland CH-1003

Phone: 44-21-317-5700
Fax: 41-21-317-5701

2006-8 Hopewell Center
183 Queens Road East, Central
Hong Kong, Hong Kong
Phone: 852-3107-6932
Fax: 852-3107-0911

Pilotystrasse 4
Munich, Germany D-80538
Phone: 49-89-413-1370
Fax: 49-89-413-137-11

Management and Staff

Stephen Rees, Founding Partner

Type of Firm

Private Equity Firm

Association Membership

European Private Equity and Venture Capital Assoc.

Project Preferences

Type of Financing Preferred:

Leveraged Buyout
Early Stage
Expansion
Mezzanine
Seed
Startup

Geographical Preferences

International Preferences:

Italy
Switzerland
Europe
Austria
Germany

Industry Preferences

In Communications prefer:

Telecommunications

In Internet Specific prefer:

Internet

In Semiconductor/Electr prefer:

Electronics

Additional Information

Year Founded: 1999
Capital Under Management: $176,200,000
Current Activity Level: Actively seeking new investments

ATLANTA CAPITAL PARTNERS LLC

3390 Peachtree Road
Suite 1000
Atlanta, GA USA 30326
Phone: 404-467-0800
E-mail: info@atlcp.com
Website: www.atlcp.com

Type of Firm

Private Equity Firm

Project Preferences

Type of Financing Preferred:

Leveraged Buyout
Mezzanine
Management Buyouts
Acquisition
Recapitalizations

Additional Information

Year Founded: 2007
Capital Under Management: $53,000,000
Current Activity Level: Actively seeking new investments

ATLANTA EQUITY INVESTORS LLC

191 Peachtree Street Northeast
Suite 4050
Atlanta, GA USA 30303
Phone: 404-478-6770
Fax: 404-478-6771
Website: www.atlantaeq.com

Management and Staff

David Crosland, Managing Partner
Gerald Benjamin, Managing Partner
Greg Cohn, Principal
Robert Annas, Partner

Type of Firm

Private Equity Firm

Project Preferences

Type of Financing Preferred:

Leveraged Buyout
Expansion

Geographical Preferences

United States Preferences:

Southeast

Additional Information

Year Founded: 2007
Capital Under Management: $103,600,000
Current Activity Level: Actively seeking new investments

ATLANTA TECHNOLOGY ANGELS (AKA: ATA)

75 Fifth Street, NW
Suite 311
Atlanta, GA USA 30308
Phone: 404-526-6039
Fax: 404-526-6035
E-mail: director@angelatlanta.com
Website: www.angelatlanta.com

Type of Firm

Angel Group

Project Preferences

Type of Financing Preferred:

Early Stage
Seed

Size of Investments Considered:

Min Size of Investment Considered (000s): $250
Max Size of Investment Considered (000s): $1,000

Industry Preferences

In Communications prefer:

Communications and Media

In Computer Software prefer:

Applications Software

In Internet Specific prefer:

E-Commerce Technology

In Computer Other prefer:

Computer Related

In Semiconductor/Electr prefer:

Controllers and Sensors

Additional Information

Year Founded: 1999
Capital Under Management: $20,000,000
Current Activity Level: Actively seeking new investments

ATLANTIC ASSET MANAGEMENT, L.L.C.

Clearwater House
2187 Atlantic Street
Stamford, CT USA 06902
Phone: 203-351-2800
Fax: 203-363-5110
E-mail: pdenver@atlanticasset.com
Website: www.atlanticasset.com

Other Offices

10801 Mastin Boulevard
Suite 218
Overland Park, KS USA 66210
Phone: 913-345-1114

Type of Firm

Private Equity Firm

Additional Information

Year Founded: 2001
Capital Under Management: $122,500,000
Current Activity Level: Actively seeking new investments

ATLANTIC BRIDGE VENTURES

31 Kildare Street
Dublin, Ireland
Phone: 353-1603-4450
Fax: 353-1642-5661
Website: www.abven.com

Other Offices

33 St. James Square
London, United Kingdom SW1 4JS
Phone: 44-207-661-9304
Fax: 44-207-661-9594

Management and Staff

Brian Long, Partner
Elaine Coughlan, Partner
Gerry Maguire, Venture Partner
John Hartnett, Venture Partner
Kevin Dillon, Partner
Larry Quinn, Venture Partner
Mark Horgan, Venture Partner
Paul Harvey, Partner
Peter McManamon, Venture Partner

Type of Firm

Private Equity Firm

Project Preferences

Type of Financing Preferred:
Early Stage
Expansion
Start-up Financing

Geographical Preferences

International Preferences:
Europe

Industry Preferences

In Communications prefer:
Wireless Communications

In Computer Software prefer:
Software

In Semiconductor/Electr prefer:
Semiconductor

Additional Information

Year Founded: 2005
Capital Under Management: $65,000,000
Current Activity Level: Actively seeking new investments

ATLANTIC CANADA OPPORTUNITY AGENCY

644 Main Street
Blue Cross Centre, Third Floor
Moncton, Canada E1C9J8
Phone: 506-851-2271
Fax: 506-851-7403
Website: www.acoa.ca

Management and Staff

Monique Colette, President

Type of Firm

Government Affiliated Program

Additional Information

Year Founded: 2009
Current Activity Level: Actively seeking new investments

ATLANTIC CAPITAL BV

Takkebijsters 37B
Breda, Netherlands 4817 BL
Phone: 31-76-578-0066
Fax: 31-76-578-0065
Website: www.atlanticcapital.nl

Type of Firm

Private Equity Firm

Association Membership

European Private Equity and Venture Capital Assoc.

Project Preferences

Type of Financing Preferred:
Balanced

Geographical Preferences

International Preferences:
Netherlands

Additional Information

Year Founded: 2004
Capital Under Management: $3,200,000
Current Activity Level: Actively seeking new investments

ATLANTIC STREET CAPITAL MANAGEMENT, LLC

300 Atlantic Street
Suite 1103
Stamford, CT USA 06901
Phone: 203-428-3150
Website: www.atlanticstreetcapital.com

Management and Staff

Andrew Wilkins, Partner
Peter Shabecoff, Managing Partner
Timothy Lewis, Partner

Type of Firm

Private Equity Firm

Project Preferences

Type of Financing Preferred:
Leveraged Buyout
Turnaround
Special Situation
Acquisition
Recapitalizations

Geographical Preferences

United States Preferences:
All U.S.

Industry Preferences

In Medical/Health prefer:
Medical/Health

In Consumer Related prefer:
Retail
Consumer Products
Consumer Services
Other Restaurants

In Business Serv. prefer:
Distribution

In Manufact. prefer:
Manufacturing

Additional Information

Year Founded: 2007
Capital Under Management: $35,000,000
Current Activity Level: Actively seeking new investments

ATLANTIC-PACIFIC CAPITAL, INC.

102 Greenwich Avenue
Second Floor
Greenwich, CT USA 06830
Phone: 203-862-9182
Fax: 203-622-0125
E-mail: info@apcap.com
Website: www.apcap.com

Other Offices

40th Floor
118 Connaught Road West
Hong Kong, Hong Kong
Phone: 852-3579-2205
Fax: 852-3579-2691

123 North Wacker Drive
Suite 800
Chicago, IL USA 60606
Phone: 312-922-9450
Fax: 312-922-9468

800 Riverview Square
Suite 101
Brielle, NJ USA 08730
Phone: 732-292-0363
Fax: 732-292-0365

50 California Street
Suite 920
San Francisco, CA USA 94111
Phone: 415-291-8199
Fax: 415-291-8198

2100 McKinney Avenue
Suite 700
Dallas, TX USA 75201
Phone: 214-661-8390
Fax: 214-661-8395

52 Jermyn Street
6th Floor
London, United Kingdom SW1Y 6LX
Phone: 44-20-7290-3080
Fax: 44-20-7290-3089

Management and Staff

Alexander Leykikh, Vice President
Anthony Bosson, Chief Financial Officer
Brad Barsily, Principal
Brendan Edmonds, Vice President
Brian Bode, Managing Director
Brian Levine, Principal
Daniel Prendergast, Principal
Donna Toth, Chief Financial Officer
Edward Chestnut, Partner
Geoffrey Berger, Principal
Hugh Bingham, Principal
James Manley, Chairman & CEO
James Weidner, Vice President
Jennifer Tedesko, Vice President
John Chase, Vice President
Joseph Herman, President
Kevin Newman, President & COO
Lawrence Thuet, Principal
Magnus Christensson, Partner
Michael Sotirhos, Partner
Michael Hewett, Principal
Michael Moreno, Principal
Paul Arena, Principal
Peter Zidlicky, Managing Director
Robert Bibow, Partner
Robin Latour, Vice President
Scott Richter, Principal
Sean Keene, Principal
Stephen Salyer, Vice President
Tanguy Cotton, Partner
Terry Wetterman, Vice President
Thomas Roberts, Principal
Victor Manuel, Vice President

Type of Firm

Service Provider

Project Preferences

Type of Financing Preferred:
Private Placement

Geographical Preferences

Canadian Preferences:
All Canada

International Preferences:
Latin America
Europe
Middle East
Pacific
Asia
Africa
All International

Additional Information

Year Founded: 1995
Current Activity Level: Actively seeking new investments
Method of Compensation: Function primarily in service area, receive contingent fee in cash or equity

---

ATLANTIS CAPITAL SPECIAL SITUATIONS SPA

22 Foro Buonaparte
Milan, Italy 20121
Phone: 39-024547-5210
Fax: 39-024547-5206
E-mail: info@atlantispartners.it
Website: www.atlantispartners.it

Type of Firm

Private Equity Firm

Association Membership

Italian Venture Capital Association (AIFI)

Project Preferences

Type of Financing Preferred:
Generalist PE
Turnaround

Size of Investments Considered:
Min Size of Investment Considered (000s): $1,270
Max Size of Investment Considered (000s): $38,106

Geographical Preferences

International Preferences:
Italy

Additional Information

Year Founded: 2005
Capital Under Management: $79,300,000
Current Activity Level: Actively seeking new investments

ATLANTIS GROUP LLC, THE

2530 Meridian Parkway
Third Floor
Durham, NC USA 27713
Phone: 919-806-4340
Fax: 919-806-4739
E-mail: info@theatlantisgroup.net
Website: www.theatlantisgroup.net

Type of Firm

Private Equity Firm

Project Preferences

Type of Financing Preferred:
Early Stage

Size of Investments Considered:
Min Size of Investment Considered (000s): $36
Max Size of Investment Considered (000s): $305

Geographical Preferences

United States Preferences:
North Carolina

Additional Information

Year Founded: 2000
Capital Under Management: $5,400,000
Current Activity Level: Actively seeking new investments

ATLAS CAPITAL CLOSE BROTHERS (FKA: ATLAS CAPITAL INVESTMENT)

Calle Montalban 9
Madrid, Spain 28014
Phone: 34-91-524-1123
Fax: 34-91-524-5160
E-mail: info@atlascapital.es
Website: www.atlascapital.es

Other Offices

Paseo de Gracia 60
Barcelona, Spain 08007
Phone: 34-93-467-7047
Fax: 34-93-467-7048

Management and Staff

Laura Martinez, Chief Executive Officer
Leon Benelbas, Managing Director
Moises Israel, Managing Director

Type of Firm

Bank Affiliated

Project Preferences

Type of Financing Preferred:
Leveraged Buyout
Generalist PE
Public Companies
Seed
Acquisition
Private Placement
Recapitalizations

Size of Investments Considered:
Min Size of Investment Considered (000s): $6,990
Max Size of Investment Considered (000s): $27,960

Geographical Preferences

International Preferences:
Spain
All International

Industry Preferences

In Communications prefer:
Communications and Media
Telecommunications

In Consumer Related prefer:
Food/Beverage
Hotels and Resorts

In Industrial/Energy prefer:
Energy

In Transportation prefer:
Transportation

In Financial Services prefer:
Financial Services
Real Estate

In Business Serv. prefer:
Services
Distribution

Additional Information
Year Founded: 2000
Capital Under Management: $116,200,000
Current Activity Level: Actively seeking new investments

ATLAS CAPITAL GROUP, INC., THE

1800 Century Park East
Suite 600
Los Angeles, CA USA 90067
Phone: 310-868-2944
Fax: 310-861-5148
E-mail: vc@atlascp.com
Website: www.atlascp.com

Other Offices
141 Tun Hua North Road
7F
Taipei, Taiwan
Phone: 886-2-2545-3758
Fax: 886-2-2545-3610

Management and Staff
Bill Hoffman, Vice President
Conrad Huang, Managing Director
Jennifer Lin, Managing Director
Katherine Lin, Managing Director

Type of Firm
Bank Affiliated

Project Preferences

Type of Financing Preferred:
Early Stage

Geographical Preferences

International Preferences:
Portugal
Spain

Industry Preferences

In Communications prefer:
Communications and Media
Wireless Communications

In Computer Software prefer:
Software

In Internet Specific prefer:
Internet
Ecommerce

Additional Information
Year Founded: 1998
Capital Under Management: $133,800,000
Current Activity Level: Actively seeking new investments

ATLAS HOLDINGS FRM LLC

One Sound Shore Drive
Suite 203
Greenwich, CT USA 06830
Phone: 203-622-9138
Fax: 203-622-0151
Website: www.atlasholdingsllc.com

Management and Staff
Andrew Bursky, Managing Partner
Daniel Cromie, Principal
Edward Fletcher, Principal
Jacob Hudson, Vice President
Philip Schuch, Chief Financial Officer
Timothy Fazio, Managing Partner
Zachary Sufrin, Vice President

Type of Firm

Private Equity Firm
Project Preferences

Type of Financing Preferred:
Leveraged Buyout
Turnaround
Distressed Debt
Recapitalizations

Industry Preferences

In Biotechnology prefer:
Industrial Biotechnology

In Industrial/Energy prefer:
Industrial Products

In Financial Services prefer:
Financial Services

In Agr/Forestr/Fish prefer:
Agribusiness

Additional Information
Year Founded: 2009
Current Activity Level: Actively seeking new investments

ATLAS VENTURE, LTD.

890 Winter Street
Suite 320
Waltham, MA USA 02451
Phone: 781-622-1700
Fax: 781-622-1701
E-mail: boston@atlasventure.com
Website: www.atlasventure.com

Other Offices
55 Grosvenor Street
London, United Kingdom W1K 3BW
Phone: 44-207-529-4444
Fax: 44-207-529-4455

Management and Staff
Axel Bichara, Partner
Barry Fidelman, Partner
Bruce Booth, Principal
Christopher Spray, Partner
Fred Destin, Partner
Gerard Montanus, Partner
Grace Zhang, Principal
Graham O'Keeffe, Partner
Jean-Francois Formela, Partner
Jeffrey Fagnan, Partner
Jeffrey Andrews, Partner
Karl Naegler, Principal
Kristen Laguerre, Chief Financial Officer
Maximilian Niederhofer, Principal
Peter Barrett, Partner
Timothy Wilson, Principal

Type of Firm
Private Equity Firm

Association Membership
British Venture Capital Association (BVCA)
National Venture Capital Association - USA (NVCA)
European Private Equity and Venture Capital Assoc.

Project Preferences

Role in Financing:
Will function either as deal originator or investor in deals created by others

Type of Financing Preferred:
Second Stage Financing
Early Stage
Mezzanine
Research and Development
Start-up Financing
Later Stage
Seed
First Stage Financing

Size of Investments Considered:
Min Size of Investment Considered (000s): $5,000
Max Size of Investment Considered (000s): $25,000

Geographical Preferences

United States Preferences:
Massachusetts
West Coast
East Coast

International Preferences:
Latin America
United Kingdom
Luxembourg
Netherlands
Switzerland
Western Europe
China
Eastern Europe

Belgium
Germany
France

Industry Focus

(% based on actual investment)

Internet Specific	26.2%
Biotechnology	19.5%
Computer Software and Services	19.4%
Medical/Health	11.9%
Communications and Media	8.7%
Semiconductors/Other Elect.	8.3%
Computer Hardware	4.3%
Other Products	0.8%
Industrial/Energy	0.7%
Consumer Related	0.1%

Additional Information

Year Founded: 1980
Capital Under Management: $2,426,000,000
Current Activity Level: Actively seeking new investments
Method of Compensation: Return on investment is of primary concern, do not charge fees

---

ATP PRIVATE EQUITY PARTNERS

Sjaeleboderne 2
1st Floor
Copenhagen k, Denmark DK - 1122
Phone: 45-33-193-070
Fax: 45-33-193-071
E-mail: info@atp-pep.com
Website: www.atp-pep.com

Other Offices

410 Park Avenue
Suite 540
New York, NY USA 10022
Phone: 212-644-5020
Fax: 212-644-1458

Management and Staff

Anette Moller Beck, Chief Financial Officer
Klaus Ruehne, Partner
Susanne Forsingdal, Partner
Torben Vangstrup, Partner

Type of Firm

Private Equity Advisor or Fund of Funds

Association Membership

Danish Venture Capital Association (DVCA)
European Private Equity and Venture Capital Assoc.

Project Preferences

Role in Financing:

Other

Type of Financing Preferred:

Fund of Funds
Leveraged Buyout
Early Stage
Expansion
Mezzanine
Balanced
Seed

Size of Investments Considered:

Min Size of Investment Considered (000s): $4,732
Max Size of Investment Considered (000s): $141,971

Geographical Preferences

United States Preferences:

All U.S.

International Preferences:

Europe
Scandanavia/Nordic Region
Pacific
Asia
All International

Industry Focus

(% based on actual investment)

Internet Specific	67.9%
Other Products	22.6%
Biotechnology	9.5%

Additional Information

Year Founded: 2001
Capital Under Management: $8,026,400,000
Current Activity Level: Actively seeking new investments

ATRIA CAPITAL PARTENAIRES

61, rue de Monceau
Paris, France 75008
Phone: 33-1-4526-6016
Fax: 33-1-4526-6024
E-mail: atria@atria-partenaires.com
Website: www.atria-partenaires.com

Management and Staff

Edouard Thomazeau, Managing Partner
Fabien Sultan, Founding Partner
Francois Poupee, Managing Partner
Louis-Eric Michel-Weltert, Managing Partner
Thibaut De Chassey, Managing Partner

Type of Firm

Private Equity Firm

Association Membership

French Venture Capital Association (AFIC)
European Private Equity and Venture Capital Assoc.

Project Preferences

Type of Financing Preferred:

Leveraged Buyout
Early Stage
Expansion
Management Buyouts
Startup

Size of Investments Considered:

Min Size of Investment Considered (000s): $2,825
Max Size of Investment Considered (000s): $11,299

Geographical Preferences

International Preferences:

Europe
France

Additional Information

Year Founded: 1999
Capital Under Management: $783,400,000
Current Activity Level: Actively seeking new investments

ATRIUM CAPITAL

3000 Sand Hill Road
Building 2, Suite 240
Menlo Park, CA USA 94025
Phone: 650-233-7878
Fax: 650-233-6944
E-mail: info@atriumcapital.com
Website: www.atriumcapital.com

Management and Staff

Barton Faber, Managing Director
Chris Heivly, Venture Partner
George Petracek, Managing Director
James Hornthal, Venture Partner
Jonathan Rattner, Chief Operating Officer
Russell Pyne, Managing Director

Type of Firm

Private Equity Firm

Project Preferences

Role in Financing:

Will function either as deal originator or investor in deals created by others

Type of Financing Preferred:

Early Stage

Geographical Preferences

International Preferences:

All International

Industry Focus

(% based on actual investment)

Computer Software and Services	48.5%
Internet Specific	36.6%
Other Products	8.1%
Semiconductors/Other Elect.	5.7%
Industrial/Energy	1.0%

Additional Information

Name of Most Recent Fund: HSV Technology Fund LLC
Most Recent Fund Was Raised: 11/01/2004
Year Founded: 1991
Capital Under Management: $75,000,000
Current Activity Level: Actively seeking new investments

ATTICA VENTURES

8 Mavromichali Street
Athens, Greece 10679
Phone: 30-210-363-7663
Fax: 30-210-363-7859
E-mail: contact@attica-ventures.gr
Website: www.attica-ventures.com

Management and Staff

Giannis Papadopoulus, Chief Executive Officer

Type of Firm

Bank Affiliated

Project Preferences

Type of Financing Preferred:
Early Stage
Expansion
Seed
Startup

Geographical Preferences

International Preferences:
Greece
Industry Preferences

In Communications prefer:
Telecommunications

In Internet Specific prefer:
E-Commerce Technology

In Biotechnology prefer:
Biotechnology

In Industrial/Energy prefer:
Energy
Advanced Materials

Additional Information

Year Founded: 2003
Capital Under Management: $41,000,000
Current Activity Level: Actively seeking new investments

ATVENTURES, INC. (FKA: AUGUST TIGER VENTURES, INC.)

1707 Pantheon Regency 27
Jungja-Dong Bundang-Gu
Kyeonggi-Do, South Korea
Phone: 82-31-785-7190
Fax: 82-31-785-7196

Management and Staff

Joong Suk Lee, President

Type of Firm

Insurance Firm Affiliate

Project Preferences

Type of Financing Preferred:
Balanced

Geographical Preferences

International Preferences:
Korea, South

Additional Information

Year Founded: 2001
Current Activity Level: Actively seeking new investments

AUCTUS MANAGEMENT GMBH & CO. KG

Brienner Strasse 7
Munich, Germany 80333
Phone: 49-891590-70000
Fax: 49-891590-70049
E-mail: info@auctus.com
Website: www.auctus.com

Management and Staff

Ingo Krocke, Managing Director
Nicolas Himmelmann, Partner
Steven Murray, Partner

Type of Firm

Private Equity Firm

Association Membership

German Venture Capital Association (BVK)
European Private Equity and Venture Capital Assoc.

Project Preferences

Type of Financing Preferred:
Balanced

Geographical Preferences

International Preferences:
Europe
Germany

Additional Information

Year Founded: 2001
Capital Under Management: $111,200,000
Current Activity Level: Actively seeking new investments

AUDA PRIVATE EQUITY LLC

888 Seventh Avenue
41st Floor
New York, NY USA 10106
Phone: 212-863-2300
Fax: 212-593-2974
E-mail: info@auda.com
Website: www.auda.net

Other Offices

Kungsgatan 5
6th Floor
Stockholm, Sweden 111 43
Phone: 46-8-5452-9060
Fax: 46-8-5452-9069

Harald Quandt Haus
Am Pilgerrain 17
Bad Homburg, Germany 61352
Phone: 49-6172-402-801
Fax: 49-6172-402-809

2 Eaton Gate
Belgravia
London, United Kingdom SW1W 9BJ
Phone: 44-20-3043-0222
Fax: 44-20-3043-0221

One Exchange Square, Suite 1602
8 Connaught Place
Hong Kong, Hong Kong
Phone: 852-2869-2219
Fax: 852-2869-2237

Management and Staff

Andrew Levy, Managing Director
David Andryc, Managing Director
Gordon Murphy, Vice President
Lawrence Wong, Vice President
Marc Lohser, Vice President
Pak-Seng Lai, Managing Director
Philippe Roesch, Managing Director
Ricky Li, Vice President
Stephen Wesson, Managing Director
Timothy Brody, Managing Director

Type of Firm

Private Equity Advisor or Fund of Funds

Project Preferences

Type of Financing Preferred:
Fund of Funds
Fund of Funds of Second

Geographical Preferences

International Preferences:
India
China
Hong Kong
All International

Additional Information

Name of Most Recent Fund: Auda Capital IV Co-Investment Fund L.P.
Most Recent Fund Was Raised: 07/13/2006
Year Founded: 1989
Capital Under Management: $1,800,000,000
Current Activity Level: Actively seeking new investments

AUDAX GROUP

101 Huntington Avenue
24th Floor
Boston, MA USA 02199
Phone: 617-859-1500
Fax: 617-859-1600
E-mail: inquiries@audaxgroup.com
Website: www.audaxgroup.com

Other Offices

280 Park Avenue
20th Floor
New York, NY USA 10017
Phone: 212-703-2700
Fax: 212-703-2799

Management and Staff

Adam Abramson, Managing Director
Donald Bramley, Managing Director
Edgar Soule, Managing Director
Edward Feuerstein, Principal
Franklin Foster, Vice President
Hiren Mankodi, Principal
Jay Jester, Managing Director
Joel Russ, Principal
John Mitchell, Vice President
Keith Palumbo, Managing Director
Kevin Magid, Managing Director
Michael McGonigle, Managing Director
Oliver Ewald, Managing Director
Pamela Martin, Vice President
Peter Gummeson, Managing Director
Richard Joseph, Chief Operating Officer
Steven Loose, Managing Director
Young Lee, Managing Director

Type of Firm

Private Equity Firm

Project Preferences

Role in Financing:
Prefer role as deal originator

Type of Financing Preferred:
Leveraged Buyout
Mezzanine
Generalist PE
Later Stage
Other
Management Buyouts
Acquisition
Special Situation

Size of Investments Considered:
Min Size of Investment Considered (000s): $25,000
Max Size of Investment Considered (000s): $400,000

Geographical Preferences

United States Preferences:
All U.S.

International Preferences:
United Kingdom

Industry Focus

(% based on actual investment)

Other Products	34.4%
Computer Software and Services	21.9%
Consumer Related	15.7%
Medical/Health	8.6%
Internet Specific	6.6%
Biotechnology	5.0%
Industrial/Energy	4.5%
Semiconductors/Other Elect.	1.8%
Communications and Media	1.5%

Additional Information

Year Founded: 1999
Capital Under Management: $3,400,000,000
Current Activity Level: Actively seeking new investments

AUDIOLUX

6, rue Albert Borschette
Luxembourg, Luxembourg 1246
Phone: 352-420-947
Fax: 352-425-462
E-mail: contact@audiolux.lu
Website: www.audiolux.lu

Type of Firm

Private Equity Firm

Project Preferences

Type of Financing Preferred:
Balanced

Geographical Preferences

International Preferences:
Luxembourg

Industry Preferences

In Communications prefer:
Communications and Media

Additional Information

Year Founded: 1987
Current Activity Level: Actively seeking new investments

AUDUR CAPITAL

Laugavegur 182
Reykjavik, Iceland 105
Phone: 354-585-6500
Fax: 354-585-6515
E-mail: audur@audur.is
Website: www.audur.is

Management and Staff

Halla Tomasdottir, Founder

Type of Firm

Investment Management Firm

Project Preferences

Type of Financing Preferred:
Early Stage
Seed
Startup

Geographical Preferences

International Preferences:
Iceland

Additional Information

Year Founded: 2008
Capital Under Management: $800,000
Current Activity Level: Actively seeking new investments

AUGMENTA VENTURE PARTNERS AB

Zinkgatan 2
Lomma, Sweden 234 21
Phone: 46-8-267-330
Fax: 46-8-5643-4055
E-mail: info@avp.se
Website: www.avp.se

Type of Firm

Private Equity Firm

Additional Information

Year Founded: 2003
Current Activity Level: Actively seeking new investments

AUGUR CAPITAL GROUP

Gruneburgweg 101
Frankfurt am Main, Germany 60323
Phone: 49-69-7167-990
Fax: 49-69-7167-9910
E-mail: info@augurcapital.com
Website: www.augurcapital.com

Other Offices

2, rue Heine
Luxembourg, Luxembourg L-1720
Phone: 352-451-314-524
Fax: 352-451-3145

Management and Staff

Gunther Skrzypek, Managing Partner
Thomas Schmitt, Managing Partner

Type of Firm

Private Equity Firm

Project Preferences

Type of Financing Preferred:
Leveraged Buyout
Balanced
Management Buyouts

Size of Investments Considered:
Min Size of Investment Considered (000s): $21,608
Max Size of Investment Considered (000s): $288,101

Geographical Preferences

International Preferences:
Europe
Central Europe
Western Europe

Industry Preferences

In Financial Services prefer:
Financial Services

Additional Information
Year Founded: 2007
Capital Under Management: $144,000,000
Current Activity Level: Actively seeking new investments

AUGUST CAPITAL MANAGEMENT

2480 Sand Hill Road
Suite 101
Menlo Park, CA USA 94025
Phone: 650-234-9900
Fax: 650-234-9910
Website: www.augustcap.com

Management and Staff
Andrew Rappaport, General Partner
David Marquardt, General Partner
Howard Hartenbaum, Partner
John Johnston, General Partner
Mark Wilson, General Partner
Vivek Mehra, General Partner

Type of Firm
Private Equity Firm

Association Membership
Western Association of Venture Capitalists (WAVC)
National Venture Capital Association - USA (NVCA)

Project Preferences

Role in Financing:
Prefer role as deal originator but will also invest in deals created by others

Type of Financing Preferred:
Early Stage
Start-up Financing
Balanced
Public Companies
Seed
Later Stage
First Stage Financing
Management Buyouts
Special Situation
Startup

Geographical Preferences

United States Preferences:
Northwest
Rocky Mountain
West Coast
Southwest

Industry Focus
(% based on actual investment)

Internet Specific	37.5%
Semiconductors/Other Elect.	22.6%
Computer Software and Services	19.7%
Communications and Media	14.1%
Computer Hardware	3.6%
Other Products	1.4%
Biotechnology	1.1%

Additional Information
Year Founded: 1995
Capital Under Management: $1,212,800,000
Current Activity Level: Actively seeking new investments
Method of Compensation: Return on investment is of primary concern, do not charge fees

---

AUGUST EQUITY LLP (FKA: KLEINWORT CAPITAL LIMITED)

10 Bedford Street
London, United Kingdom WC2E 9HE
Phone: 44-20-7632-8200
Fax: 44-20-7632-8201
Website: www.augustequity.com

Management and Staff
Ian Grant, Partner
Philip Rattle, Partner
Richard Green, Managing Partner
Sam Watkinson, Partner
Tim Clarke, Partner

Type of Firm
Bank Affiliated

Association Membership
British Venture Capital Association (BVCA)
European Private Equity and Venture Capital Assoc.

Project Preferences

Role in Financing:
Prefer role as deal originator but will also invest in deals created by others

Type of Financing Preferred:
Leveraged Buyout
Expansion
Generalist PE
Turnaround
Management Buyouts

Size of Investments Considered:
Min Size of Investment Considered (000s): $19,648
Max Size of Investment Considered (000s): $98,240

Geographical Preferences

International Preferences:
Ireland
United Kingdom
Europe

Industry Focus
(% based on actual investment)

Other Products	33.5%
Internet Specific	17.2%
Consumer Related	16.5%
Computer Hardware	8.6%
Computer Software and Services	7.6%
Biotechnology	7.5%
Medical/Health	5.8%
Industrial/Energy	1.9%
Communications and Media	1.1%
Semiconductors/Other Elect.	0.3%

Additional Information
Name of Most Recent Fund: August Equity Partners IV, L.P. (FKA: Kleinwort Capital IV)
Most Recent Fund Was Raised: 11/01/2001
Year Founded: 2001
Capital Under Management: $424,100,000
Current Activity Level: Actively seeking new investments

AURA CAPITAL OY

Lantinen Rantakatu 27 A 4
Turku, Finland FI-20100
Phone: 358-2-6516-6600
Fax: 358-2-6516-6601
Website: www.auracapital.com

Other Offices
Kluuvikatu 5
Helsinski, Finland FI-00100
Phone: 358-10-830-0600
Fax: 358-10-830-0601
Management and Staff
Ari Siponmaa, Managing Partner
Petri Salonen, Partner

Type of Firm
Private Equity Firm

Association Membership
Finnish Venture Capital Association (FVCA)

Project Preferences

Type of Financing Preferred:
Fund of Funds
Early Stage
Expansion
Mezzanine
Turnaround
Seed
Management Buyouts
Startup

Size of Investments Considered:
Min Size of Investment Considered (000s): $200
Max Size of Investment Considered (000s): $1,000

Geographical Preferences

International Preferences:
Western Europe
Finland

Industry Preferences

In Communications prefer:
Commercial Communications
Wireless Communications

In Computer Software prefer:
Software

In Internet Specific prefer:
Internet

In Biotechnology prefer:
Biotechnology

In Industrial/Energy prefer:
Industrial Products

Additional Information
Year Founded: 1997
Capital Under Management: $9,400,000
Current Activity Level: Actively seeking new investments

AURELIA PRIVATE EQUITY GMBH
Kurhessenstrasse 1-3
Frankfurt, Germany 60431
Phone: 49-69-8090-0
Fax: 49-69-8090-109
E-mail: info@aurelia-pe.de
Website: www.aurelia-pe.de

Management and Staff
J. Wolfgang Posselt, Managing Partner
Jurgen Leschke, Managing Partner
Tobias Hasenjager, Managing Partner

Type of Firm
Private Equity Firm

Project Preferences

Type of Financing Preferred:
Early Stage
Expansion
Seed
Startup

Geographical Preferences

International Preferences:
Europe
Israel
Germany

Industry Preferences

In Communications prefer:
Communications and Media
Telecommunications

In Computer Other prefer:
Computer Related

In Biotechnology prefer:
Biotechnology

In Medical/Health prefer:
Medical/Health

Additional Information
Name of Most Recent Fund: Aurelia Technology Funds I
Most Recent Fund Was Raised: 12/31/2001
Year Founded: 2001
Capital Under Management: $42,500,000
Current Activity Level: Actively seeking new investments

AUREOS CAPITAL, LTD.
4th Floor
24 Old Bond Street
London, United Kingdom W1S 4AN
Phone: 44-20-7647-6800
Fax: 44-20-7647-6801
E-mail: mail@aureos.com
Website: www.aureos.com

Other Offices
1st Floor, Norfolk Towers
Kijabi Street
Nairobi, Kenya
Phone: 254-20-228-870
Fax: 254-20-310-355

Regimanuel Gray Headquarters
No. 2 La By Pass
Accra, Ghana
Phone: 233-21-770-212
Fax: 233-21-765-118

Rue 3 X C, Point E - 1er etage
Ponty
Dakar, Senegal 23717
Phone: 221-338-697-807
Fax: 221-338-248-099

Chase Plaza, 2nd Floor Podium
Jl. Jend Sudirman Kav 21
Jakarta, Indonesia 12920
Phone: 62-21-520-8380
Fax: 62-21-520-8318

Ghandi Mall, N 9, 3eme Etage
Porte N 9, Boulevard Ghandi
Casablanca, Morocco 20100
Phone: 212-522-774-042
Fax: 212-522-774-018

193/104, 25/f, Lake Rajada Bldg.
New Rajadapisek Road, Klongtoey
Bangkok, Thailand 10110
Phone: 66-2-661-8899
Fax: 66-2-661-9894

2/F Fountain Chambers, Sandown Village
corner Maude & Gwen Street, Sandton
Johannesburg, South Africa 2146
Phone: 27-11-884-2066
Fax: 27-11-884-2067

Room 501, Wanchai Commercial Centre
Johnston Road
Wanchai, Hong Kong 194-204
Phone: 852-2529-2866
Fax: 852-2529-1991

Unit T3-6, Level 3
8 First Avenue, Bandar Utama
Petaling Java, Malaysia 47800
Phone: 603-7710-0388
Fax: 603-7710-6268

Office 14, Nurly Tau Building 4A
7, Al Farabi Avenue
Almaty, Kazakhstan
Phone: 7-727-311-0287
Fax: 7-727-311-0288

Level 2, Level 24, AMP Place
10 Eagle Street
Brisbane, Australia 4000
Phone: 617-3303-0894
Fax: 617-3303-0895

Bandra-Kurla Complex
303 Vaibhav Chambers, Bandra East
Mumbai, India 400051
Phone: 91-22-3068-5500
Fax: 91-22-3068-5504

Plot 3a, Frajend Close, Via Udi Street
Osborne Foreshore Estate, Ikoyi
Lagos, Nigeria
Phone: 234-1-269-6150
Fax: 234-1-269-6225

3rd Floor
50 Mirambo Street
Dar es Salaam, Tanzania
Phone: 255-22-211-4277
Fax: 255-22-211-3645

Room 1601, Site A, Yihe Int'l Bldg.
10 Hong Kong Middle Rd., Qingdao
Shandong, China 266071
Phone: 86-532-6677-7161
Fax: 86-532-6677-7160

Cr. 7 # 74-56
Oficina 806
Bogota, Colombia
Phone: 57-1-313-1737
Fax: 57-1-313-1737-104

8th Floor, Newton Tower
Sir William Newton Street
Port Louis, Mauritius
Phone: 230-211-4949
Fax: 230-211-9393

Somerset Chancellor Court, 1st Floor
21-23 Nguyen Thi Minh Khai St., Dist. 1
Ho Chi Minh, Vietnam
Phone: 84-8-8230-326
Fax: 84-8-8230-329

Calle Monte Rosa 255
Piso 4, Oficina 405
Chacarrilla, Peru
Phone: 51-1-717-2341
Fax: 51-1-717-1846

1st Floor, Parkway Building
48/1/1, Park Street, Colombo-02
Sri Lanka, Sri Lanka
Phone: 94-11-451-9720
Fax: 94-11-451-9583

A-707, Carlton Towers
Airport Road
Bangalore, India 560008
Phone: 91-80-4115-1260
Fax: 91-80-4115-1261

Monte Caucaso 915-604
Lomas de Chapultepec
Mexico, Mexico 11000
Phone: 52-5-591-789-010
Fax: 52-5-589-178-9021

Unit 1210, Prestige Tower
F. Ortigas Jr. Road, Ortigas Center
Pasig City, Philippines 1605
Phone: 63-2-637-4000
Fax: 63-2-637-4001

5th Floor, Mpile Office Park
74 Independence Avenue
Lusaka, Zambia
Phone: 260-1-256-502
Fax: 260-1-250-306

200 Metros al Sur de la Esquina
Edificio Terraforte, Piso 4 , Escazu
San Jose, Costa Rica 1260
Phone: 506-201-9191
Fax: 506-201-5033

Edifcio Gran Plaza, Piso 5, Suite 502
Boulevard Del Hipodromo
San Salvador, El Salvador
Phone: 503-2298-4748
Fax: 503-2279-1687

Unit 2, 2/F, Bangunan Suria
Kampong Kiulap
Seri Begawan, Brunei BE1518
Phone: 673-2232-400
Fax: 673-2232-404

Management and Staff

Ainadin Cader, Partner
Anusorn Buranakanonda, Partner
Balaji Srinivas, Managing Partner
Basil Nundwe, Partner
Chanaka Wickramasuriya, Partner
Cheryl Ranasinghe, Partner
Davinder Sikand, Managing Partner
Erik Peterson, Managing Partner
Gerardo Aguilar, Partner
Hanjaya Umanto, Partner
Hanjaya Limanto, Managing Partner
Jacob Kholi, Managing Partner
Jose Ulate, Partner
Liam Cully, Managing Partner
Nilesh Mehta, Managing Partner
Nissanka Weerasekera, Managing Partner
Peter Grant, Partner
Raj Morjaria, Partner
Ricardo Ariz, Partner
Ron Den Besten, Managing Partner
Samuel Occena, Partner
Sandeep Khanna, Partner
Sangeeta Modi, Principal
Satyam Ramnauth, Partner
Sivendran Vettivetpillai, Managing Director
Sivendran Vettivetpillai, Chief Executive Officer
Steve Wu, Managing Partner
Talgat Kukenov, Managing Partner
Tokunboh Ishmael, Partner

Type of Firm

Private Equity Firm

Association Membership

South African Venture Capital Association (SAVCA)
Emerging Markets Private Equity Association
Nigerian Venture Capital Association
African Venture Capital Association (AVCA)
Project Preferences

Type of Financing Preferred:

Leveraged Buyout
Early Stage
Expansion
Generalist PE
Balanced
Turnaround
Later Stage
Management Buyouts
Acquisition
Startup

Size of Investments Considered:

Min Size of Investment Considered (000s): $2,000
Max Size of Investment Considered (000s): $10,000

Geographical Preferences

International Preferences:

Laos
Vietnam
Ethiopia
Angola
Fiji
Indonesia
India
Rwanda
Latin America
Bangladesh
Kiribati
Kazakhstan
Micronesia
Marshall Islands
Mauritius
Nigeria
Senegal
Uganda
Vanuatu
Zambia
Cook Islands
Papua N Guinea
Somoa
Tanzania
Bolivia
China
Peru
Botswana
El Salvador
Ghana
Kenya
Nauru
Panama
Thailand
Tonga
Belize
Pacific Rim
Kyrgyzstan
Tajikistan
Turkmenistan
Mexico
Dominican Rep.
Azerbaijan
Cambodia
Costa Rica
Nicaragua
Namibia
Philippines
Congo
Dominica
Mozambique
South Africa
Sri Lanka
Solomon Isl.
Uzbekistan
Zimbabwe
Asia
Colombia
Guatemala
Africa
Burundi
Malaysia
Georgia
Honduras

Industry Preferences

In Communications prefer:

Telecommunications

In Biotechnology prefer:

Agricultural/Animal Bio.

In Medical/Health prefer:

Medical/Health
Medical Diagnostics
Diagnostic Services
Pharmaceuticals

In Consumer Related prefer:

Entertainment and Leisure
Retail
Food/Beverage

Consumer Products
Hotels and Resorts
Education Related

In Industrial/Energy prefer:
Energy
Oil and Gas Exploration
Materials

In Transportation prefer:
Transportation

In Financial Services prefer:
Real Estate
Financial Services

In Business Serv. prefer:
Services
Distribution

In Manufact. prefer:
Manufacturing

In Agr/Forestr/Fish prefer:
Agribusiness
Agriculture related
Mining and Minerals

Additional Information

Year Founded: 2001
Capital Under Management: $600,000,000
Current Activity Level: Actively seeking new investments

AURIGA PARTNERS S.A.

18 avenue Matignon
Paris, France 75008
Phone: 33-1-5330-0707
Fax: 33-1-5330-0700
E-mail: auriga@aurigapartners.com
Website: www.auriga-ventures.com

Management and Staff

Franck Lescure, Partner
Francois Lainee, Partner
Jacques Mallet, Partner
Philippe Granger, Partner
Philippe Peltier, Partner
Sebastien Descarpentries, Partner

Type of Firm

Private Equity Firm

Association Membership

French Venture Capital Association (AFIC)
European Private Equity and Venture Capital Assoc.

Project Preferences

Type of Financing Preferred:
Early Stage
Seed
Startup

Size of Investments Considered:
Min Size of Investment Considered (000s): $471
Max Size of Investment Considered (000s): $4,708

Geographical Preferences

United States Preferences:
All U.S.

International Preferences:
Europe
Israel
France

Industry Preferences

In Communications prefer:
Communications and Media

In Computer Software prefer:
Software
Systems Software

In Computer Other prefer:
Computer Related

In Biotechnology prefer:
Biotechnology

In Medical/Health prefer:
Medical/Health

In Industrial/Energy prefer:
Factory Automation

Additional Information

Year Founded: 1998
Capital Under Management: $115,900,000
Current Activity Level: Actively seeking new investments

AURINVEST SAS

11bis rue Portalis
Paris, France 75008
Phone: 33-1-4490-7320
Fax: 33-1-4490-7324
E-mail: contact@aurinvest.com
Website: www.aurinvest.com

Management and Staff

Michel Demont, President

Type of Firm

Private Equity Firm

Association Membership

French Venture Capital Association (AFIC)

Project Preferences

Type of Financing Preferred:
Early Stage
Balanced

Geographical Preferences

International Preferences:
Europe
France

Industry Preferences

In Computer Software prefer:
Software

In Computer Other prefer:
Computer Related

Additional Information

Year Founded: 2001
Capital Under Management: $25,100,000
Current Activity Level: Actively seeking new investments

AURORA CAPITAL GROUP (FKA: AURORA CAPITAL PARTNERS)

10877 Wilshire Boulevard
Suite 2100
Westwood, CA USA 90024
Phone: 310-551-0101
Fax: 310-277-5591
Website: www.auroracap.com

Management and Staff

David Alpern, Vice President
Gerald Parsky, Partner
J. Doyl Burkett, Vice President
John Mapes, Partner
Josh Klinefelter, Vice President
Mark Hardy, Partner
Mark Rosenbaum, Partner
Richard Roeder, Partner
Richard Crowell, Partner
William Coughlin, Partner

Type of Firm

Private Equity Firm

Project Preferences

Role in Financing:
Prefer role as deal originator

Type of Financing Preferred:
Leveraged Buyout
Management Buyouts
Distressed Debt

Industry Preferences

In Computer Other prefer:
Computer Related

In Medical/Health prefer:
Medical/Health

In Consumer Related prefer:
Publishing-Retail

In Industrial/Energy prefer:
Materials

In Transportation prefer:
Transportation
Aerospace

In Financial Services prefer:
Financial Services

In Manufact. prefer:
Manufacturing

Additional Information

Name of Most Recent Fund: Aurora Equity Partners III L.P.
Most Recent Fund Was Raised: 10/28/2004
Year Founded: 1991
Capital Under Management: $2,000,000,000
Current Activity Level: Actively seeking new investments

AURORA FUNDS, INC.

2525 Meridian Parkway
Suite 220
Durham, NC USA 27713
Phone: 919-484-0400
Fax: 919-484-0444
E-mail: afinfo@aurorafunds.com
Website: www.aurorafunds.com

Management and Staff

Adrian Wilson, Venture Partner
B. Jefferson Clark, Managing General Partner
Christopher Kroeger, Partner
Douglas Gooding, Venture Partner
Jan Bouten, Venture Partner
M. Scott Albert, Managing General Partner
Mike Gorman, Chief Financial Officer
Richard Holcomb, Venture Partner

Type of Firm

Private Equity Firm

Association Membership

Mid-Atlantic Venture Association
National Venture Capital Association - USA (NVCA)

Project Preferences

Role in Financing:
Will function either as deal originator or investor in deals created by others

Type of Financing Preferred:
Early Stage
Seed
Startup

Size of Investments Considered:
Min Size of Investment Considered (000s): $100
Max Size of Investment Considered (000s): $2,000

Geographical Preferences

United States Preferences:
Mid Atlantic
Southeast

Industry Focus

(% based on actual investment)

Medical/Health	24.6%
Computer Software and Services	21.6%
Biotechnology	19.4%
Internet Specific	16.3%
Semiconductors/Other Elect.	8.6%
Communications and Media	5.0%
Other Products	3.4%
Consumer Related	0.9%
Industrial/Energy	0.1%

Additional Information

Name of Most Recent Fund: Aurora Ventures V, LP
Most Recent Fund Was Raised: 08/26/2005
Year Founded: 1994
Capital Under Management: $234,000,000
Current Activity Level: Actively seeking new investments
Method of Compensation: Return on investment is of primary concern, do not charge fees

AURORA INVESTMENT ADVISORS, LTD.

Trafalgar Court
Admiral Park
St. Peter Port, Channel Islands GY1 2JA
Website: www.aurorarussia.com

Other Offices

Business Centre Sheremetyevsky
10, Nikolskaya Street, 6th Floor
Moscow, Russia 103012
Phone: 7-495-644-1662
Fax: 7-495-644-1663

Management and Staff

James Cook, Co-Founder
John McRoberts, Co-Founder

Type of Firm

Private Equity Firm

Project Preferences

Type of Financing Preferred:
Expansion
Early Stage
Balanced

Geographical Preferences

International Preferences:
Europe
Russia

Industry Preferences

In Consumer Related prefer:
Consumer
Consumer Services

In Financial Services prefer:
Financial Services

Additional Information

Year Founded: 2006
Capital Under Management: $130,700,000
Current Activity Level: Actively seeking new investments

AURORA RESURGENCE MANAGEMENT PARTNERS LLC

10877 Wilshire Boulevard
21st Floor
Westwood, CA USA 90024
Phone: 310-551-0101
Fax: 310-277-5591
Website: www.aurorares.com

Management and Staff

Anthony DiSimone, Managing Partner
Joshua Phillips, Principal
Peter Leibman, Vice President
Ryan McCarthy, Vice President
Steven Martinez, Managing Director

Type of Firm

Private Equity Firm

Project Preferences

Type of Financing Preferred:
Generalist PE
Special Situation
Distressed Debt

Industry Preferences

In Consumer Related prefer:
Consumer Services

In Business Serv. prefer:
Services

In Manufact. prefer:
Manufacturing

Additional Information

Year Founded: 2007
Capital Under Management: $232,700,000
Current Activity Level: Actively seeking new investments

AURORA VENTURES

One Riverchase Pkwy, So
Birmingham, AL USA 35244
Phone: 205-987-5582

Type of Firm

Private Equity Firm

Additional Information

Year Founded: 1994
Current Activity Level: Actively seeking new investments

AUSTIN VENTURES, L.P.

300 West Sixth Street
Suite 2300
Austin, TX USA 78701

Phone: 512-485-1900
Fax: 512-651-8500
E-mail: moreinfo@ausven.com
Website: www.austinventures.com

Management and Staff

Ben Scott, Venture Partner
Bill Razzouk, Chief Executive Officer
Blaine Wesner, General Partner
Bob Stull, Chief Executive Officer
Brian Sharples, Chief Executive Officer
C. Thomas Ball, Partner
Christopher Pacitti, General Partner
Clark Jernigan, Venture Partner
Craig Milius, General Partner
David Lack, Partner
Dean Wiltse, Chief Executive Officer
Elisabeth DeMarse, Chief Executive Officer
James Clardy, Venture Partner
Jeffrey Dachis, Chief Executive Officer
Jim Casella, Chief Executive Officer
John Thornton, General Partner
John Dirvin, Chief Operating Officer
Joseph Aragona, General Partner
Joseph Marengi, Venture Partner
Kari-Pekka Wilska, Venture Partner
Kenneth DeAngelis, General Partner
Kevin Kunz, Chief Financial Officer
Krishna Srinivasan, Partner
Michael Rovner, Partner
Mike Dodd, Venture Partner
Phillip Siegel, General Partner
Ronald Sorrow, Chief Executive Officer
Sherman Atkinson, Chief Executive Officer
Venu Shamapant, General Partner

Type of Firm

Private Equity Firm

Association Membership

National Venture Capital Association - USA (NVCA)

Project Preferences

Role in Financing:

Prefer role as deal originator but will also invest in deals created by others

Type of Financing Preferred:

Second Stage Financing
Leveraged Buyout
Early Stage
Expansion
Balanced
Start-up Financing
Later Stage
Seed
Management Buyouts
First Stage Financing
Special Situation

Size of Investments Considered:

Min Size of Investment Considered (000s): $100
Max Size of Investment Considered (000s): $50,000

Geographical Preferences

United States Preferences:

Southwest
Texas
All U.S.

Industry Focus

(% based on actual investment)

Internet Specific	23.9%
Computer Software and Services	22.7%
Other Products	13.5%
Communications and Media	12.6%
Semiconductors/Other Elect.	11.6%
Computer Hardware	7.2%
Medical/Health	3.8%
Consumer Related	3.3%
Industrial/Energy	1.5%

Additional Information

Year Founded: 1979
Capital Under Management: $2,413,000,000
Current Activity Level: Actively seeking new investments
Method of Compensation: Return on investment is of primary concern, do not charge fees

---

AUSTRALIAN CAPITAL VENTURES, LTD.

71 Constitution Avenue
Campbell, Australia 2612
Phone: 612-6247-4999
Fax: 612-6248-0751
E-mail: info@hindmarsh.com.au
Website: www.hindmarsh.com.au

Other Offices

Level 22
25 Bligh Street
Sydney, Australia 2000
Phone: 612-9274-1100
Fax: 612-9233-3886

57 Wyatt Street
Adelaide, Australia
Phone: 618-8228-4188
Fax: 618-8228-4199

No. 18 Huangyang Road
Room 3021, Block 4
Shanghai, China
Phone: 86-21-1640-1001
Fax: 86-21-5033-3004

Level 1
9/10 Hudson Road
Albion, Australia 4010
Phone: 617-3259-2000
Fax: 617-3259-2099

GPO Box 3945
Darwin, Australia 0801
Phone: 618-8941-7124
Fax: 618-8941-7164

Management and Staff

Stephen Hardy, Chief Executive Officer

Type of Firm

Corporate PE/Venture

Project Preferences

Type of Financing Preferred:

Early Stage
Seed

Geographical Preferences

International Preferences:

Australia

Industry Preferences

In Communications prefer:

Communications and Media
Wireless Communications
Data Communications

In Biotechnology prefer:

Biotechnology

In Transportation prefer:

Transportation

In Manufact. prefer:

Manufacturing

Additional Information

Year Founded: 2000
Capital Under Management: $7,100,000
Current Activity Level: Actively seeking new investments

AUSTRALIAN DISTRIBUTED INCUBATOR PTY, LTD. (AKA: ADI)

Level Three
51-57 Holt Street Surry Hills
Sydney, Australia 2010
Phone: 612-9212-5505
Fax: 612-9212-5545
E-mail: info@bsi.com.au
Website: www.bsi.com.au

Other Offices

Level 1, Innovation Building
1010 La Trobe Street
Melbourne, Australia 3008
Phone: 613-9605-9300
Fax: 613-9605-9301

Management and Staff

Mat McDonald, Chief Executive Officer

Type of Firm

Incubator/Development Program

Project Preferences

Type of Financing Preferred:
Seed
Startup

Size of Investments Considered:
Min Size of Investment Considered (000s): $780
Max Size of Investment Considered (000s): $3,903

Geographical Preferences

International Preferences:
Australia

Industry Preferences

In Communications prefer:
Communications and Media

Additional Information

Year Founded: 2000
Capital Under Management: $10,400,000
Current Activity Level: Actively seeking new investments

AUSTRIA WIRTSCHAFTSSERVICE GESELLSCHAFT MBH

Ungargasse 37
Vienna, Austria 1030
Phone: 43-1-5017-50
Fax: 43-1-5017-5900
E-mail: office@awsg.at
Website: www.awsg.at

Management and Staff

Horst Bednar, Managing Director
Karl Schiller, Partner
Peter Takacs, Managing Director

Type of Firm

Government Affiliated Program

Association Membership

European Private Equity and Venture Capital Assoc.

Project Preferences

Role in Financing:
Prefer role as deal originator

Type of Financing Preferred:
Early Stage
Expansion
Seed
Startup

Geographical Preferences

International Preferences:
Austria

Industry Preferences

In Communications prefer:
Commercial Communications

In Computer Other prefer:
Computer Related

In Semiconductor/Electr prefer:
Electronics

In Biotechnology prefer:
Biotechnology

In Medical/Health prefer:
Medical/Health

In Industrial/Energy prefer:
Materials
Factory Automation
Environmental Related

Additional Information

Year Founded: 1989
Capital Under Management: $48,200,000
Current Activity Level: Actively seeking new investments

AUTHOSIS VENTURES

No. 2101 21/F Westland Centre
20 Westlands Road
Hong Kong, Hong Kong
Phone: 852-2960-4611
Fax: 852-2960-0185
E-mail: info@authosisvc.com
Website: www.authosisvc.com

Management and Staff

Danny Lui, Chairman & CEO

Type of Firm

Private Equity Firm

Association Membership

Hong Kong Venture Capital Association (HKVCA)

Project Preferences

Type of Financing Preferred:
Second Stage Financing
Early Stage
Balanced
Seed
First Stage Financing

Geographical Preferences

United States Preferences:
All U.S.

International Preferences:
China

Industry Preferences

In Communications prefer:
Commercial Communications
Wireless Communications

In Computer Software prefer:
Software

In Internet Specific prefer:
Internet
Ecommerce

Additional Information

Year Founded: 2000
Current Activity Level: Actively seeking new investments

AUTONOMIE ET SOLIDARITE

81 bis, Rue Gantois
Lille, France 59000
Phone: 33-320-14-3062
Fax: 33-320-54-6842
E-mail: contact@autonomieetsolidarite.fr
Website: www.autonomieetsolidarite.fr

Management and Staff

Jean-Marie Didier, Managing Director

Type of Firm

Private Equity Firm

Project Preferences

Type of Financing Preferred:
Balanced

Geographical Preferences

International Preferences:
France

Additional Information

Year Founded: 2000
Current Activity Level: Actively seeking new investments

AUTOVISION GMBH

Major-Hirst-Strasse 11
Wolfsburg, United Kingdom 38442
E-mail: info.ventures@autovision-gmbh.com
Website: www.autovision-gmbh.com

Management and Staff

Dirk Coers, Managing Director
Joerg Blecker, Managing Director

Type of Firm

Corporate PE/Venture

Project Preferences

Type of Financing Preferred:
Balanced

Additional Information

Year Founded: 2001
Current Activity Level: Actively seeking new investments

AUXITEX

24, rue du 4 Septembre
Paris, France 75002
Phone: 33-1-5364-9639
Fax: 33-1-5364-9630

Management and Staff

Bertrand Roux, President

Type of Firm

Private Equity Firm

Association Membership

French Venture Capital Association (AFIC)

Project Preferences

Type of Financing Preferred:
Balanced

Geographical Preferences

International Preferences:
France

Additional Information

Year Founded: 2005
Current Activity Level: Actively seeking new investments

AV LABS

300 West Sixth Street
Suite 2300
Austin, TX USA 78701
Phone: 512-485-1900
Fax: 512-476-3952
E-mail: info@avlabs.com
Website: www.austinventures.com

Management and Staff

Kevin Kunz, Chief Financial Officer

Type of Firm

Private Equity Firm

Project Preferences

Role in Financing:
Prefer role as deal originator but will also invest in deals created by others

Type of Financing Preferred:
Early Stage
Seed
First Stage Financing

Size of Investments Considered:
Min Size of Investment Considered (000s): $500
Max Size of Investment Considered (000s): $5,000

Geographical Preferences

United States Preferences:
Texas

Industry Focus

(% based on actual investment)

Computer Software and Services	60.7%
Internet Specific	22.0%
Communications and Media	13.9%
Other Products	1.7%
Computer Hardware	1.7%

Additional Information

Name of Most Recent Fund: AV Labs II
Most Recent Fund Was Raised: 03/26/2001
Year Founded: 1999
Capital Under Management: $65,000,000
Current Activity Level: Actively seeking new investments

AVALLON SP. Z O.O.

Al. Kosciuszki 17
Lodz, Poland 90-418
Phone: 42-6309-771
Fax: 42-6309-775
E-mail: avallon@avallon.pl
Website: www.avallon.pl

Management and Staff

Michal Zawisza, Partner
Piotr Miller, Partner
Robert Wieclawski, Partner
Tomasz Stamirowski, Partner

Type of Firm

Private Equity Firm

Association Membership

Polish Venture Capital Association (PSIC/PPEA)

Project Preferences

Role in Financing:
Prefer role as deal originator

Type of Financing Preferred:
Leveraged Buyout
Management Buyouts
Acquisition

Geographical Preferences

International Preferences:
Central Europe
Eastern Europe

Additional Information

Year Founded: 2001
Current Activity Level: Actively seeking new investments

AVALON VENTURES

888 Prospect Street
Suite 320
La Jolla, CA USA 92037
Phone: 858-348-2180
Fax: 858-348-2183
E-mail: Info@Avalon-Ventures.com
Website: www.Avalon-Ventures.com

Management and Staff

Kevin Kinsella, Managing Director
Richard Levandov, Managing Director
Stephen Tomlin, Managing Director

Type of Firm

Private Equity Firm

Association Membership

National Venture Capital Association - USA (NVCA)

Project Preferences

Role in Financing:
Prefer role as deal originator

Type of Financing Preferred:
Second Stage Financing
Early Stage
Balanced
Seed
Startup

Size of Investments Considered:
Min Size of Investment Considered (000s): $250
Max Size of Investment Considered (000s): $5,000

Geographical Preferences

United States Preferences:
Southern California
West Coast
California
All U.S.

Industry Preferences

In Communications prefer:
Wireless Communications

In Biotechnology prefer:
Biotechnology
Human Biotechnology

Additional Information

Name of Most Recent Fund: Avalon Ventures VIII, L.P.
Most Recent Fund Was Raised: 11/20/2007
Year Founded: 1983
Capital Under Management: $100,000,000
Current Activity Level: Actively seeking new investments
Method of Compensation: Return on invest. most important, but chg. closing fees, service fees, etc.

AVANSIS VENTURES, LLC

12010 Sunset Hills Road
Suite 900
Herndon, VA USA 20190
Phone: 703-796-0222
Fax: 703-735-0574
E-mail: plans@avansis.com
Website: www.avansis.com

Management and Staff

Brownell Chalstrom, Venture Partner
Christine Hughes, Venture Partner
Laura Lukaczyk, Managing General Partner
Mark Modica, General Partner

Type of Firm

Private Equity Firm

Association Membership

Mid-Atlantic Venture Association

Project Preferences

Role in Financing:

Prefer role as deal originator but will also invest in deals created by others

Type of Financing Preferred:

Seed
First Stage Financing

Size of Investments Considered:

Min Size of Investment Considered (000s): $100
Max Size of Investment Considered (000s): $1,000

Geographical Preferences

United States Preferences:

Mid Atlantic

Industry Preferences

In Communications prefer:

Telecommunications
Wireless Communications
Data Communications
Other Communication Prod.

In Internet Specific prefer:

Internet

Additional Information

Year Founded: 2000
Capital Under Management: $10,000,000
Current Activity Level: Actively seeking new investments
Method of Compensation: Return on invest. most important, but chg. closing fees, service fees, etc.

AVANTA INVESTMENT (INTERNATIONAL)

Unit 1001, Tower Two
Lippo Centre 89 Queensway
Central, Hong Kong
Phone: 852-2160-2880
Fax: 852-2801-7485

Type of Firm

Private Equity Firm

Project Preferences

Type of Financing Preferred:

Balanced

Geographical Preferences

International Preferences:

Hong Kong

Additional Information

Year Founded: 2005
Current Activity Level: Actively seeking new investments

AVANTE CAPITAL PARTNERS

10th Floor, The Octagon
13A, A.J. Marinho Drive
Victoria Island, Lagos, Nigeria
Phone: 234-1461-6223
Fax: 234-1461-6221
E-mail: info@avantecp.com
Website: www.avantecp.com

Type of Firm

Private Equity Firm

Association Membership

African Venture Capital Association (AVCA)

Project Preferences

Type of Financing Preferred:

Leveraged Buyout
Expansion
Recapitalizations

Geographical Preferences

International Preferences:

Nigeria
Africa

Industry Preferences

In Financial Services prefer:

Financial Services
Real Estate

Additional Information

Year Founded: 2002
Capital Under Management: $100,000,000
Current Activity Level: Actively seeking new investments

AVC VENTURE CAPITAL S.A.

24 Kifissias Avenue
Maroussi, Greece 15125
Phone: 30-210-817-0000
Fax: 30-210-817-1969

Type of Firm

Bank Affiliated

Project Preferences

Type of Financing Preferred:

Expansion
Balanced

Geographical Preferences

International Preferences:

Greece

Industry Preferences

In Communications prefer:

Telecommunications

In Industrial/Energy prefer:

Energy

Additional Information

Year Founded: 2007
Current Activity Level: Actively seeking new investments

AVENDIS CAPITAL S.A.

50, rue du Rhone
Geneva, Switzerland 1204
Phone: 41-22-855-1212
Fax: 41-22-855-1210
E-mail: info@avendis-capital.com
Website: www.avendis-capital.com

Type of Firm

Private Equity Firm

Project Preferences

Type of Financing Preferred:

Turnaround

Geographical Preferences

International Preferences:

Europe

Additional Information

Year Founded: 2005
Current Activity Level: Actively seeking new investments

AVENIR ENTREPRISES SA

137 Rue de l'Universite
Paris, France 75007
Phone: 33-1-5383-7430
Fax: 33-1-5383-7457
E-mail: prenom.nom@avenir-entreprises.fr
Website: www.avenir-entreprises.fr

Other Offices

22-28 Rue Joubert
Paris, France 75009
Phone: 33-1-5389-7701
Fax: 33-1-5389-7746

Technopole de Nancy Brabois
10, route de l?Aviation
Villers les Nancy cedex, France 54602
Phone: 33-3-8367-2013
Fax: 33-3-8367-2015

Immeuble Le 6eme Sens
186, avenue Thiers
Lyon cedex 06, France 69465
Phone: 33-4-7260-5759
Fax: 33-4-7260-5490

63 quai Magellan
BP 42304
Nantes, France 44023
Phone: 33-2-5172-9951
Fax: 33-2-4035-1899

Arche Jacques Coeur
222, place Ernest Granier
Montpellier cedex 2, France 34967
Phone: 33-4-6769-7611
Fax: 33-4-6769-7632

Immeuble Axe Europe
213 bd de Turin
Lille, France 59777
Phone: 33-3-2081-9448
Fax: 33-3-2081-9456

Type of Firm
Private Equity Firm

Association Membership
French Venture Capital Association (AFIC)

Project Preferences

Type of Financing Preferred:
Leveraged Buyout
Mezzanine
Early Stage
Expansion
Seed

Size of Investments Considered:
Min Size of Investment Considered (000s): $137
Max Size of Investment Considered (000s): $1,372

Geographical Preferences

International Preferences:
France

Additional Information
Year Founded: 1984
Capital Under Management: $65,600,000
Current Activity Level: Actively seeking new investments

AVENIR FINANCE GESTION SAS

51 Rue de Saint Cyr
Lyon, France 69009
Phone: 33-4-2770-5400
Fax: 33-4-2770-5401
E-mail: info@avenirfinancegestion.fr
Website: www.avenirfinancegestion.fr

Other Offices
57 rue de Saint Cyr
Lyon, France 69009
Phone: 33-4-7864-6060
Fax: 33-4-7847-1172

Type of Firm
Bank Affiliated

Association Membership
French Venture Capital Association (AFIC)

Project Preferences

Type of Financing Preferred:
Early Stage
Expansion
Balanced

Geographical Preferences

International Preferences:
Europe
France

Industry Preferences

In Communications prefer:
Communications and Media

In Semiconductor/Electr prefer:
Electronics

In Biotechnology prefer:
Biotechnology

In Medical/Health prefer:
Medical/Health

In Consumer Related prefer:
Consumer

In Industrial/Energy prefer:
Industrial Products

In Business Serv. prefer:
Distribution

Additional Information
Name of Most Recent Fund: Avenir Capital Croissance FCPI
Most Recent Fund Was Raised: 06/30/2004
Year Founded: 2000
Capital Under Management: $50,300,000
Current Activity Level: Actively seeking new investments

AVENIR TOURISME

23 Avenue Franklin Roosevelt
Paris, France 75008
Phone: 33-1-5383-7438
Fax: 33-1-5383-7457

Type of Firm
Private Equity Firm

Project Preferences

Type of Financing Preferred:
Balanced

Geographical Preferences

International Preferences:
Europe

Additional Information
Year Founded: 1986
Current Activity Level: Actively seeking new investments

AVENTURES

16/15 Vyborzka Street
Kiev, Ukraine 03056
Phone: 380-444618882
Fax: 380-444618883
E-mail: info@aventures.biz
Website: www.aventures.biz

Management and Staff
Andriy Kolodyuk, President
Svitlana Bezprozvanna, Chief Financial Officer

Type of Firm
Private Equity Firm

Project Preferences

Type of Financing Preferred:
Early Stage

Geographical Preferences

International Preferences:
Europe
Ukraine

Industry Preferences

In Communications prefer:
Communications and Media
Telecommunications
Wireless Communications
Media and Entertainment

In Computer Software prefer:
Software

In Internet Specific prefer:
Internet

Additional Information
Year Founded: 2003
Current Activity Level: Actively seeking new investments

AVENUE CAPITAL GROUP (AKA: AVENUE ADVISORS, L.L.C.)

535 Madison Avenue
15th Floor
New York, NY USA 10022
Phone: 212-878-3500
Fax: 212-878-3559
Website: www.avenuecapital.com

Management and Staff

Alexander Wolfman, Managing Director
Amy Heneghan, Managing Director
Campbell Korff, Managing Director
Eric Ross, Managing Director
Ira Balsam, Chief Financial Officer
Jennifer Tang, Managing Director
Joseph Peters, Chief Financial Officer
Julie Baumann, Managing Director
Mark Harris, Senior Managing Director
Robert Ollwerther, Chief Operating Officer
Stuart Sarnoff, Managing Director
Todd Greenbarg, Managing Director

Type of Firm

Private Equity Firm

Project Preferences

Type of Financing Preferred:
Special Situation
Distressed Debt

Geographical Preferences

International Preferences:
Asia

Industry Focus

(% based on actual investment)

Other Products	74.8%
Industrial/Energy	25.2%

Additional Information

Name of Most Recent Fund: Avenue Special Situation Fund V, L.P.
Most Recent Fund Was Raised: 05/18/2007
Year Founded: 1995
Capital Under Management: $12,246,500,000
Current Activity Level: Actively seeking new investments

AVERROES FINANCE

6 allees Turcat-Mery
Marseille, France 13008
Phone: 33-158-50-182
Fax: 33-158-500-777

Type of Firm

Private Equity Advisor or Fund of Funds

Project Preferences

Type of Financing Preferred:
Fund of Funds

Geographical Preferences

International Preferences:
Africa

Additional Information

Year Founded: 2003
Capital Under Management: $35,500,000
Current Activity Level: Actively seeking new investments

AVERY BUSINESS DEVELOPMENT SERVICES

2506 St. Michel Court
Ponte Vedra, FL USA 32082
Phone: 904-285-6033
Fax: 904-280-8840

Management and Staff

Henry Avery, President

Type of Firm

Angel Group

Project Preferences

Role in Financing:
Will function either as deal originator or investor in deals created by others

Type of Financing Preferred:
Second Stage Financing
Early Stage
Expansion
Turnaround
Later Stage
Management Buyouts
First Stage Financing
Acquisition
Joint Ventures
Special Situation
Startup

Size of Investments Considered:
Min Size of Investment Considered (000s): $50
Max Size of Investment Considered (000s): $5,000

Geographical Preferences

United States Preferences:
Southeast

Industry Preferences

In Communications prefer:
Radio & TV Broadcasting

In Computer Software prefer:
Artificial Intelligence

In Biotechnology prefer:
Industrial Biotechnology
Biosensors
Biotech Related Research

In Medical/Health prefer:
Drug/Equipmt Delivery
Medical Products
Pharmaceuticals

In Consumer Related prefer:
Retail
Franchises(NEC)

In Industrial/Energy prefer:
Oil and Gas Exploration
Oil & Gas Drilling,Explor
Alternative Energy
Coal Related
Industrial Products
Materials
Robotics
Environmental Related

In Business Serv. prefer:
Consulting Services

In Agr/Forestr/Fish prefer:
Mining and Minerals

Additional Information

Year Founded: 1981
Current Activity Level: Actively seeking new investments
Method of Compensation: Function primarily in service area, receive contingent fee in cash or equity

AVESTA

Five rue de Logelbach
Paris, France 75017
Phone: 33-1-4440-3082
Fax: 33-1-4440-2048

Other Offices

10 place du General Catroux
France 75017
Phone: 33-14-440-3082

Management and Staff

Herve Marion, President

Type of Firm

Private Equity Firm

Project Preferences

Type of Financing Preferred:
Expansion

Geographical Preferences

International Preferences:
Europe
France

Additional Information

Year Founded: 2002
Current Activity Level: Actively seeking new investments

AVIGO CAPITAL PARTNERS

404/ 407, Mercantile House
15, Kasturba Gandhi Marg
New Delhi, India 100 001
Phone: 91-11-4153-1230
Fax: 91-11-4153-1235
Website: www.avigocorp.com

Other Offices

355, Barkly Wharf
Le Caudan Waterfront
Port Loius, Mauritius
Phone: 230-210-7275
Fax: 230-210-7285

LOB 15, Suite # 410, P.O. Box 18264
Jebel Ali Free Zone
Dubai, Utd. Arab Em.
Phone: 9714-881-4681
Fax: 9714-881-1297

Management and Staff

Achal Ghai, Managing General Partner
Vivek Subramanian, General Partner

Type of Firm

Private Equity Firm

Project Preferences

Type of Financing Preferred:
Leveraged Buyout
Expansion
Generalist PE
Balanced
Management Buyouts
Acquisition

Size of Investments Considered:
Min Size of Investment Considered (000s): $3,000
Max Size of Investment Considered (000s): $10,000

Geographical Preferences

International Preferences:
India

Industry Preferences

In Semiconductor/Electr prefer:
Electronics

In Medical/Health prefer:
Health Services
Pharmaceuticals

In Consumer Related prefer:
Consumer Products

In Industrial/Energy prefer:
Energy

In Business Serv. prefer:
Services

In Manufact. prefer:
Manufacturing

Additional Information

Year Founded: 2003
Capital Under Management: $275,000,000
Current Activity Level: Actively seeking new investments

AVISTA CAPITAL HOLDINGS, LP

65 East 55th Street
18th Floor
New York, NY USA 10022
Phone: 212-593-6900
Fax: 212-593-6901
E-mail: info@avistacap.com
Website: www.avistacap.com

Other Offices

1000 Louisiana Street
Suite 1200
Houston, TX USA 77002
Phone: 713-328-1099
Fax: 713-328-1097

Management and Staff

Ben Silbert, Principal
Bevin O'Neil, Principal
Brendan Scollans, Principal
David Durkin, Partner
David Burgstahler, Partner
Greg Evans, Vice President
James Finkelstein, Partner
Jeff Gunst, Principal
Larry Pickering, Partner
OhSang Kwon, Partner
Robert Cabes, Principal
Sriram Venkataraman, Principal

Type of Firm

Private Equity Firm

Project Preferences

Role in Financing:
Prefer role as deal originator

Type of Financing Preferred:
Leveraged Buyout
Expansion
Generalist PE

Size of Investments Considered:
Min Size of Investment Considered (000s): $80,000
Max Size of Investment Considered (000s): $380,000

Geographical Preferences

United States Preferences:
All U.S.

Canadian Preferences:
All Canada

International Preferences:
Europe

Industry Preferences

In Communications prefer:
Communications and Media

In Medical/Health prefer:
Medical/Health

In Industrial/Energy prefer:
Energy

Additional Information

Name of Most Recent Fund: Avista Capital Partners, L.P.
Most Recent Fund Was Raised: 01/08/2007
Year Founded: 2005
Capital Under Management: $2,000,000,000
Current Activity Level: Actively seeking new investments

AVIV VENTURE CAPITAL (FKA: FANTINE GROUP, THE)

36 Shacham Street, Ram Bldg.
Fifth Floor
Petach Tikva, Israel 49517
Phone: 972-3-976-1111
Fax: 972-3-919-9300
E-mail: info@avivvc.com
Website: www.avivvc.com

Management and Staff

Arie Guez, Co-Founder
Daniel Barnea, Venture Partner
Gideon Ben-Zvi, Venture Partner
Roy Ramati, Co-Founder
Yoav Chelouche, Managing Partner

Type of Firm

Private Equity Firm

Project Preferences

Type of Financing Preferred:
Early Stage
Expansion
Later Stage

Geographical Preferences

International Preferences:
Western Europe
Israel

Industry Preferences

In Communications prefer:
Communications and Media

In Computer Software prefer:
Software

In Internet Specific prefer:
Internet

Additional Information

Year Founded: 1997

Capital Under Management: $20,000,000
Current Activity Level: Actively seeking new investments

AVLAR BIOVENTURES, LTD.

Highfield Court, Church Lane
Madingley
Cambs, United Kingdom CB23 8AG
Phone: 44-1954-211-515
Fax: 44-1954-211-516
E-mail: info@avlar.com
Website: www.avlar.com

Management and Staff

Alan Goodman, Chief Executive Officer

Type of Firm

Private Equity Firm

Association Membership

British Venture Capital Association (BVCA)

Project Preferences

Type of Financing Preferred:
Early Stage
Seed
Startup

Size of Investments Considered:
Min Size of Investment Considered (000s): $37
Max Size of Investment Considered (000s): $2,985

Geographical Preferences

International Preferences:
United Kingdom
Europe

Industry Preferences

In Biotechnology prefer:
Biotechnology

Additional Information

Year Founded: 1998
Capital Under Management: $110,200,000
Current Activity Level: Actively seeking new investments

AVM ITALIA

Via dei Bossi, 6
Milan, Italy 20121
Phone: 39-02-8690033
Fax: 39-02-89012321

Type of Firm

Private Equity Firm

Additional Information

Year Founded: 2003
Current Activity Level: Actively seeking new investments

AVRIO VENTURES MANAGEMENT CORP.

Scotia Centre, Suite 3820
700 2nd Street South West
Calgary, Canada T2P 2W2
Phone: 403-215-5490
Fax: 403-215-5495
Website: www.avrioventures.com

Other Offices

205-1075 North Service Road W
Oakville
Toronto, Canada L6M 2G2
Phone: 905-465-0885

840 des Oeillets
Saint-Charles-de-Drummond
Montreal, Canada J2C 7T8
Phone: 819-472-1818

Management and Staff

Aki Georgacacos, Partner
Jim Taylor, Partner
John Kennedy, Vice President
W.B. Kirchner, Partner

Type of Firm

Private Equity Firm

Project Preferences

Type of Financing Preferred:
Second Stage Financing
Early Stage
Expansion
Later Stage
First Stage Financing

Geographical Preferences

Canadian Preferences:
All Canada

Industry Preferences

In Biotechnology prefer:
Industrial Biotechnology

Additional Information

Name of Most Recent Fund: Avrio Ventures, L.P.
Most Recent Fund Was Raised: 11/02/2006
Year Founded: 2006
Capital Under Management: $46,800,000
Current Activity Level: Actively seeking new investments

AVW MANAGMENT BETEILIGUNGS AG

Hauptstrasse 118
Krumpendorf, Austria 9201
Phone: 43 4229 36 21
Fax: 44 4229 23 86
E-mail: geldanlage@avw.at
Website: www.avw.at

Type of Firm

Private Equity Firm

Project Preferences

Type of Financing Preferred:
Balanced

Additional Information

Year Founded: 2007
Current Activity Level: Actively seeking new investments

AWEIDA CAPITAL MANAGEMENT LLP

500 Discovery Parkway
Suite 300
Superior, CO USA 80027
Phone: 303-664-9520
Fax: 303-664-9530
E-mail: info@aweida.com
Website: www.aweida.com

Management and Staff

Daniel Aweida, Managing Partner
Harry Ross, Managing Partner
Jesse Aweida, Managing Partner

Type of Firm

Private Equity Firm

Project Preferences

Role in Financing:
Prefer role as deal originator but will also invest in deals created by others

Type of Financing Preferred:
Early Stage
Seed
Startup

Size of Investments Considered:
Min Size of Investment Considered (000s): $500
Max Size of Investment Considered (000s): $10,000

Geographical Preferences

United States Preferences:
Rocky Mountain

International Preferences:
China
Hong Kong

Industry Preferences

In Computer Hardware prefer:
Disk Relat. Memory Device

In Computer Software prefer:
Software

In Internet Specific prefer:
Internet

In Biotechnology prefer:
Human Biotechnology
Biosensors

In Medical/Health prefer:
Medical Diagnostics

Additional Information
Year Founded: 1988
Capital Under Management: $100,000,000
Current Activity Level: Actively seeking new investments
Method of Compensation: Return on invest. most important, but chg. closing fees, service fees, etc.

AXA INVESTMENT MANAGERS
One Fawcett Place
Greenwich, CT USA 06830
Phone: 203-863-8973
Fax: 203-861-4112
Website: www.axa-im.com

Other Offices
Corso di Porta Romana, 68
Milan, Italy 20122
Phone: 39-02-582-990-23
Fax: 39-02-582-990-60

P.O. Box 22415, 15th Floor
Ministry of Economy & Commerce building
DOHA, Qatar
Phone: 974-496-7200
Fax: 974-496-7205

Paseo de la Castellana, 79
1 Planta
Madrid, Spain 28046
Phone: 34-91-538-5555
Fax: 34-91-555-5030

7 Newgate Street
London, United Kingdom ECIA7NY
Phone: 44-20-7003-123
Fax: 44-20-7003-231

Pr Marques de Pombal 14
2/F
Lisbon, Portugal 1250
Phone: 351-21-350-6220
Fax: 351-21-356-6164

Boulevard du Souverain 36
Brussels, Belgium 1170
Phone: 32-2-679-6372
Fax: 32-2-679-6399

Bleichstrasse 2-4
Frankfurt, Germany 60313
Phone: 49-69-900-250
Fax: 49-69-900-251-5990

Management and Staff
Barry Miller, Chief Financial Officer
Laurent Clamagirand, Chief Operating Officer
Mikifumi Watanabe, Chief Executive Officer
Robert Kypriano, Chief Executive Officer

Type of Firm
Private Equity Advisor or Fund of Funds

Project Preferences

Role in Financing:
Prefer role as deal originator

Type of Financing Preferred:
Fund of Funds

Geographical Preferences

International Preferences:
Latin America
Western Europe
Eastern Europe
Asia

Additional Information
Name of Most Recent Fund: Europe Select Private Equity Partners II
Most Recent Fund Was Raised: 12/31/2000
Year Founded: 1998
Capital Under Management: $855,000,000
Current Activity Level: Actively seeking new investments
Method of Compensation: Return on investment is of primary concern, do not charge fees

AXA PRIVATE EQUITY
20 Place Vendome
Paris, France 75001
Phone: 33-1-4445-9200
Fax: 33-1-4445-9299
Website: www.axaprivateequity.com

Other Offices
68 Corso di Porta Romana
Milan, Italy 20122
Phone: 39-2-5844-2421
Fax: 39-2-5844-2450

1370 Avenue of the Americas
New York, NY USA 10019
Phone: 212-641-8604
Fax: 212-641-8616

55 Grosvenor Street
London, United Kingdom W1K 3HY
Phone: 44-20-7003-1350
Fax: 44-20-7575-8309

1 Temasek Avenue
Unit 20-02A Millenia Tower
Singapore, Singapore 039192
Phone: 65-6513-3410
Fax: 65-6513-3426

Affolternstrasse 42
P.O. Box 6961
Zurich, Switzerland 8050
Phone: 41-43-299-1199
Fax: 41-43-299-1175

An der Welle 4
Frankfurt, Germany D-60322
Phone: 49-69-5050-41500
Fax: 49-69-5050-41550

Karntner Ring 5-7
Vienna, Austria 1010
Phone: 43-1-20511-601069

Management and Staff
Beatrice Beitmann, Managing Director
Bruno Ladriere, Managing Director
Cecile Mayer-Levi, Managing Director
Christof Namenyi, Managing Director
Christophe Florin, Managing Director
Dominique Senequier, Chairman & CEO
Dominique Gaillard, Managing Director
Eric Neuplanche, Managing Director
Franck Nguyen, Managing Director
Frederic Collard, Managing Director
Laurent Grimaldi, Managing Director
Lise Fauconnier, Managing Director
Olivier Berment, Managing Director
Olivier Decanniere, Managing Director
Philippe Poletti, Managing Director
Stephan Illenberger, Managing Director
Thomas Wilfing, Managing Director
Vincent Gombault, Managing Director
Wolfgang Pietzsch, Managing Director

Type of Firm
Private Equity Firm

Association Membership
French Venture Capital Association (AFIC)
European Private Equity and Venture Capital Assoc.

Project Preferences

Type of Financing Preferred:
Fund of Funds
Leveraged Buyout
Early Stage
Expansion
Generalist PE
Mezzanine
Balanced
Start-up Financing
Turnaround
Later Stage
Other
Fund of Funds of Second
Recapitalizations

Size of Investments Considered:
Min Size of Investment Considered (000s): $900
Max Size of Investment Considered (000s): $13,437

Geographical Preferences

United States Preferences:
All U.S.

International Preferences:
Italy

India
Europe
China
Western Europe
Australia
Korea, South
Germany
Asia
France
Japan
All International

Industry Preferences

In Communications prefer:
Communications and Media
Telecommunications

In Computer Hardware prefer:
Computers

In Semiconductor/Electr prefer:
Electronics
Semiconductor

In Biotechnology prefer:
Biotechnology

Additional Information

Name of Most Recent Fund: AXA France Investissement FCPR
Most Recent Fund Was Raised: 06/30/2009
Year Founded: 1995
Capital Under Management: $3,008,700,000
Current Activity Level: Actively seeking new investments

AXCEL INDUSTRIINVESTOR AS

Sankt Annae Plads 10
Copenhagen , Denmark DK-1250
Phone: 45-3336-6999
Fax: 45-3336-6998
E-mail: axcel@axcel.dk
Website: www.axcel.dk

Other Offices

Strandvagen 5B, 5tr
Stockholm, Sweden S - 114 51
Phone: 46-8-442-5390

Management and Staff

Christian Frigast, Managing Partner
Jacob Thygesen, Partner
Lars Thomassen, Chief Financial Officer
Nikolaj Vejlsgaard, Partner
Per Christensen, Partner
Soren Lindberg, Partner
Vilhelm Sundstrom, Managing Partner
Vilhelm Hahn-Petersen, Partner

Type of Firm

Private Equity Firm

Association Membership

Danish Venture Capital Association (DVCA)

Project Preferences

Role in Financing:
Prefer role as deal originator

Type of Financing Preferred:
Leveraged Buyout
Turnaround
Acquisition
Recapitalizations

Size of Investments Considered:
Min Size of Investment Considered (000s): $45,399
Max Size of Investment Considered (000s): $635,579

Geographical Preferences

International Preferences:
Sweden
Scandanavia/Nordic Region
Denmark

Industry Preferences

In Consumer Related prefer:
Retail

In Industrial/Energy prefer:
Industrial Products

In Business Serv. prefer:
Services

Additional Information

Year Founded: 1994
Capital Under Management: $1,066,500,000
Current Activity Level: Actively seeking new investments

AXE INVESTMENTS

Noorderlaan 139
Antwerp, Belgium 2030
Phone: 32-3543-7311
Fax: 32-3541-9110
Website: www.axe-investments.com

Type of Firm

Bank Affiliated

Project Preferences

Type of Financing Preferred:
Fund of Funds
Early Stage
Later Stage

Geographical Preferences

International Preferences:
Belgium
Singapore
Germany

Industry Preferences

In Communications prefer:
Communications and Media
Telecommunications

In Internet Specific prefer:
Internet

Additional Information

Year Founded: 2001
Capital Under Management: $22,600,000
Current Activity Level: Actively seeking new investments

AXIA CAPITAL

Landmark 1, 1 Van de Graaff Dr
Suite 104
Burlington, MA USA 01803
Phone: 781-273-6065
Fax: 781-240-6050
E-mail: phunter@axia-partners.com
Website: www.axia-partners.com

Management and Staff

James Pelusi, Managing Director
Peter Hunter, Managing Director

Type of Firm

Private Equity Firm

Association Membership

National Venture Capital Association - USA (NVCA)

Project Preferences

Role in Financing:
Will function either as deal originator or investor in deals created by others

Type of Financing Preferred:
Leveraged Buyout
Expansion
Later Stage
Management Buyouts
Acquisition
Recapitalizations

Size of Investments Considered:
Min Size of Investment Considered (000s): $500
Max Size of Investment Considered (000s): $1,500

Geographical Preferences

United States Preferences:
Mid Atlantic
Midwest
Northeast

Canadian Preferences:
Eastern Canada

Industry Preferences

In Semiconductor/Electr prefer:
Electronic Components
Semiconductor
Controllers and Sensors
Sensors
Component Testing Equipmt
Laser Related
Fiber Optics
Analytic/Scientific
Optoelectronics

In Biotechnology prefer:
Biotech Related Research

In Medical/Health prefer:
Diagnostic Test Products
Drug/Equipmt Delivery

In Industrial/Energy prefer:
Industrial Products
Factory Automation
Robotics

In Manufact. prefer:
Manufacturing

Additional Information
Year Founded: 2003
Capital Under Management: $8,000,000
Current Activity Level: Actively seeking new investments
Method of Compensation: Return on invest. most important, but chg. closing fees, service fees, etc.

AXIOM ASIA PRIVATE CAPITAL ASSOCIATES, LTD.
250 North Bridge Road
11-02 Raffles City Tower
Singapore, Singapore 179101
Phone: 65-6336-8886
Fax: 65-6336-8868
E-mail: info@axiomasia.com
Website: www.axiomasia.com

Management and Staff
Chih-Tsung Lam, Managing Director
Edmond Chi-Man Ng, Managing Director
Yewhong Goh, Managing Director

Type of Firm
Private Equity Advisor or Fund of Funds

Project Preferences

Type of Financing Preferred:
Fund of Funds
Mezzanine
Distressed Debt

Geographical Preferences

International Preferences:
Vietnam
Laos
Indonesia
China
Brunei
Thailand
Philippines
Cambodia
Korea, South
Australia
Asia
Singapore
Japan
Malaysia

Additional Information
Year Founded: 2006
Capital Under Management: $955,300,000
Current Activity Level: Actively seeking new investments

AXIOM EQUITY PARTNERS
8000 East Maplewood Avenue
Suite 125
Englewood, CO USA 80111
Phone: 303-643-5500
E-mail: AEPInfo@axiomequity.com
Website: www.axiomequity.com

Management and Staff
Frank Saya, Partner
Greg Lauric, Partner
Larry Nealy, Partner
Michael Vollman, Partner
Richard Akright, Managing Director & CFO
Roger Heaston, Partner
Royce Palazzo, Partner
Sandy Hamilton, Managing Director

Type of Firm
Private Equity Firm

Project Preferences

Type of Financing Preferred:
Management Buyouts
Acquisition
Industry Rollups
Recapitalizations

Geographical Preferences

United States Preferences:
All U.S.

Industry Preferences

In Industrial/Energy prefer:
Alternative Energy

In Business Serv. prefer:
Services
Distribution

In Manufact. prefer:
Manufacturing

Additional Information
Year Founded: 2006
Current Activity Level: Actively seeking new investments

AXIOM VENTURE PARTNERS, L.P.
CityPlace II - 17th Floor
185 Asylum Street
Hartford, CT USA 06103
Phone: 860-548-7799
Fax: 860-548-7797
E-mail: info@axiomventures.com
Website: www.axiomventures.com

Other Offices
One Post Street
Suite 2525
San Francisco, CA USA 94104
Phone: 415-284-1400
Fax: 415-284-1401

Management and Staff
Alan Mendelson, General Partner
Barry Bronfin, General Partner
John Wieczorek, Chief Financial Officer
Samuel McKay, General Partner
William Wilcoxson, General Partner

Type of Firm
Private Equity Firm

Project Preferences

Role in Financing:
Will function either as deal originator or investor in deals created by others

Type of Financing Preferred:
Early Stage
Later Stage

Size of Investments Considered:
Min Size of Investment Considered (000s): $1,000
Max Size of Investment Considered (000s): $5,000

Geographical Preferences

Canadian Preferences:
All Canada

Industry Focus
(% based on actual investment)

Medical/Health	23.8%
Communications and Media	23.7%
Biotechnology	15.2%
Computer Software and Services	13.9%
Internet Specific	7.3%
Semiconductors/Other Elect.	6.9%
Industrial/Energy	3.1%
Computer Hardware	2.9%
Other Products	1.7%
Consumer Related	1.5%

Additional Information
Year Founded: 1994
Capital Under Management: $205,000,000
Current Activity Level: Actively seeking new investments
Method of Compensation: Return on investment is of primary concern, do not charge fees

AXIS CAPITAL CORPORATION (FKA: STARTINGSTARTUPS, L.P.)

105 Murray Street
Ottawa, Canada K1N 5M5
Phone: 613-236-6006
Fax: 613-236-6336
E-mail: info@axisfunds.com
Website: www.axisfunds.com

Management and Staff

Doug Hewson, Managing Partner
Kevin Goheen, Partner
Peter Low, Managing Partner

Type of Firm

Private Equity Firm

Association Membership

Canadian Venture Capital Association

Project Preferences

Role in Financing:
Prefer role as deal originator

Type of Financing Preferred:
Expansion
Early Stage
Balanced
Seed
First Stage Financing
Startup

Size of Investments Considered:
Min Size of Investment Considered (000s): $500
Max Size of Investment Considered (000s): $1,000

Geographical Preferences

Canadian Preferences:
All Canada
Ontario

Industry Preferences

In Communications prefer:
Telecommunications
Wireless Communications

In Internet Specific prefer:
Internet

Additional Information

Year Founded: 2000
Current Activity Level: Actively seeking new investments

AXIS HOLDINGS PVT, LTD.

3rd Floor, Arth Vishwas
5th Lane, Koregaon Park
Pune, India 411 001
Phone: 91-20-3052-3460
Fax: 91-20-3052-3461
E-mail: info@axisholdings.in
Website: www.axisholdings.in

Other Offices

112, Highway Commerce Center
I.B. Patel Road, Goregaon (East)
Mumbai, India 400 063
Phone: 91-22-2686-6210
Fax: 91-22-2686-6211

Management and Staff

Manish Jain, Managing Director

Type of Firm

Investment Management Firm

Project Preferences

Type of Financing Preferred:
Expansion
Later Stage
Private Placement

Geographical Preferences

International Preferences:
India

Industry Preferences

In Semiconductor/Electr prefer:
Electronics

In Industrial/Energy prefer:
Industrial Products

Additional Information

Year Founded: 2008
Capital Under Management: $47,000,000
Current Activity Level: Actively seeking new investments

AXIS PARTICIPACIONES EMPRESARIALES SGECR SA

C/ Prim, 19-3
Madrid, Spain 28004
Phone: 34-91-523-1654
Fax: 34-91-532-1933
E-mail: axis@axispart.com
Website: www.axispart.com

Management and Staff

Javier Rodriguez Segovia, Partner
Rosario Nistal Murillo, Partner

Type of Firm

Private Equity Advisor or Fund of Funds

Association Membership

European Private Equity and Venture Capital Assoc.

Project Preferences

Type of Financing Preferred:
Second Stage Financing
Early Stage
Expansion
Startup

Size of Investments Considered:
Min Size of Investment Considered (000s): $600
Max Size of Investment Considered: No Limit

Geographical Preferences

International Preferences:
Europe
Spain

Additional Information

Year Founded: 1993
Capital Under Management: $85,500,000
Current Activity Level: Actively seeking new investments

AXIS PRIVATE EQUITY, LTD.

131 Maker Tower - F
Cuffe Parade, Colaba
Mumbai, India 400 005
Phone: 91-22-6707-4407
Fax: 91-22-2218-1429
E-mail: axbmbd@axisbank.com
Website: www.axisbank.com

Management and Staff

Alok Gupta, CEO & Managing Director

Type of Firm

Bank Affiliated

Project Preferences

Type of Financing Preferred:
Balanced
Other

Geographical Preferences

International Preferences:
India

Industry Preferences

In Communications prefer:
Communications and Media

In Medical/Health prefer:
Pharmaceuticals

In Consumer Related prefer:
Consumer
Consumer Products
Consumer Services

In Industrial/Energy prefer:
Energy
Industrial Products

In Financial Services prefer:
Financial Services
Real Estate

In Business Serv. prefer:
Media

Additional Information

Year Founded: 2007
Capital Under Management: $150,000,000
Current Activity Level: Actively seeking new investments

AXM VENTURE CAPITAL, LTD.

Dilke House
1 Malet Street
London, United Kingdom WC1E 7JN
Phone: 44-870-909-6333
Fax: 44-870-133-6872
E-mail: info@ccfund.co.uk
Website: www.ccfund.co.uk

Management and Staff

Fred Mendelsohn, Managing Director

Type of Firm

Private Equity Firm

Project Preferences

Type of Financing Preferred:
Early Stage
Balanced
Seed
Startup

Size of Investments Considered:
Min Size of Investment Considered (000s): $99
Max Size of Investment Considered (000s): $994

Geographical Preferences

International Preferences:
United Kingdom
Europe

Industry Preferences

In Communications prefer:
Communications and Media

Additional Information

Year Founded: 2005
Capital Under Management: $9,100,000
Current Activity Level: Actively seeking new investments

AXON CAPITAL

Plaza del Marques de Salamanca
Number 11
Madrid, Spain 28006
E-mail: businesscontact@axon-capital.com
Website: www.axon-capital.com

Management and Staff

Brent Segal, Venture Partner
Francisco Velazquez, Chief Executive Officer
Gonzalo Leon, Vice President
Gregg Hershenson, Venture Partner
Juan Mulet, President
Pierluigi Paracchi, Venture Partner
Stefano Peroncini, Venture Partner

Type of Firm

Private Equity Firm

Project Preferences

Type of Financing Preferred:
Leveraged Buyout
Expansion
Early Stage

Size of Investments Considered:
Min Size of Investment Considered (000s): $445
Max Size of Investment Considered (000s): $7,413

Geographical Preferences

International Preferences:
Spain

Industry Preferences

In Communications prefer:
Telecommunications

In Semiconductor/Electr prefer:
Electronics

In Medical/Health prefer:
Medical/Health

In Industrial/Energy prefer:
Energy
Materials

In Business Serv. prefer:
Media

Additional Information

Year Founded: 2007
Current Activity Level: Actively seeking new investments

AXXESS CAPITAL PARTNERS S.A. (FKA: ENTERPRISE CAPITAL)

33 Aviatorilor Boulevard
Bucharest, Romania 011853
Phone: 40-21-207-7100
Fax: 40-21-222-8503
Website: www.axxesscapital.net

Other Offices

36 Oborishte Strasse
Sofia 1504
Sofia, Bulgaria
Phone: 359-2-819-4570
Fax: 359-2-944-1475

545 Fifth Avenue
Suite 300
New York, NY USA 10017
Phone: 212-697-5766
Fax: 212-818-0445

Management and Staff

Bistra Kirova, Partner
Cristina Mogoroase, Partner
Daniela Toader, Chief Financial Officer
Neculai Sandu, Partner
Thomas Higgins, Managing Partner

Type of Firm

Government Affiliated Program

Project Preferences

Type of Financing Preferred:
Generalist PE
Expansion
Mezzanine

Size of Investments Considered:
Min Size of Investment Considered (000s): $3,810
Max Size of Investment Considered (000s): $8,891

Geographical Preferences

International Preferences:
Albania
Turkey
Bulgaria
Moldova
Ukraine
Romania

Industry Preferences

In Communications prefer:
Communications and Media
Commercial Communications
Telecommunications

In Medical/Health prefer:
Medical/Health

In Consumer Related prefer:
Consumer
Retail
Consumer Products
Consumer Services

In Industrial/Energy prefer:
Energy
Industrial Products
Materials

In Transportation prefer:
Transportation

In Financial Services prefer:
Financial Services

In Business Serv. prefer:
Distribution

Additional Information

Name of Most Recent Fund: Balkan Accession Fund (AKA: BAF)
Most Recent Fund Was Raised: 01/10/2005
Year Founded: 1995
Capital Under Management: $265,000,000
Current Activity Level: Actively seeking new investments

AXXON GROUP

Ladeira de Nossa Senhora, 311
Gloria
Rio de Janeiro, Brazil 22211-100
Phone: 55-21-2245-8087
Fax: 55-21-2245-8048
E-mail: axxon@axxongroup.com.br
Website: www.axxongroup.com.br

Other Offices

Avenida del Libertador, 7400
1st Floor
Buenos Aires, Argentina C1429BMT
Phone: 5411-4703-1112
Fax: 5411-4703-1112

Avenida Paulista, 37
7th Floor, Suite 72
Sao Paulo, Brazil 01311-902
Phone: 55-11-3253-3733
Fax: 55-11-3253-2918

Management and Staff

Fabio Maranhao, Partner
Jose Augusto De Carvalho, Partner
Juan Carlos Apostolo, Partner
Nicholas Wollak, Founder
Paulo Mordehachvili, Partner
Peter Davenport, CEO & Managing Director

Type of Firm

Private Equity Firm

Association Membership

Brazilian Venture Capital Association (ABCR)

Project Preferences

Type of Financing Preferred:
Expansion
Balanced

Geographical Preferences

International Preferences:
Brazil

Industry Preferences

In Consumer Related prefer:
Retail

In Transportation prefer:
Transportation

Additional Information

Year Founded: 1993
Capital Under Management: $250,000,000
Current Activity Level: Actively seeking new investments

AZALEA CAPITAL LLC

55 Beattie Place
Suite 1500
Greenville, SC USA 29601
Phone: 864-235-0201
Fax: 864-235-1155
Website: www.azaleacapital.com

Management and Staff

Ben Wallace, Vice President
Benny LaRussa, Partner
Marshall Cole, Chief Financial Officer
Patrick Duncan, Managing Partner
Porter Rose, Managing Partner
R.Patrick Weston, Managing Partner

Type of Firm

Private Equity Firm

Project Preferences

Type of Financing Preferred:
Leveraged Buyout
Later Stage
Acquisition
Recapitalizations

Geographical Preferences

United States Preferences:
Southeast

Industry Preferences

In Medical/Health prefer:
Health Services

In Consumer Related prefer:
Consumer Products

In Business Serv. prefer:
Distribution

In Manufact. prefer:
Manufacturing

Additional Information

Year Founded: 1995
Capital Under Management: $45,300,000
Current Activity Level: Actively seeking new investments

AZTEC EQUITY PARTNERS, LLC

One Gateway Center
Suite 2600
Newark, NJ USA 07102
Phone: 888-774-2983
E-mail: info@aztecpartners.com
Website: www.aztecpartners.com

Management and Staff

Alex Garcia, Managing Director
Alex Luis Pupo, Chief Financial Officer
Ali Akansu, Managing Director

Type of Firm

Private Equity Firm

Project Preferences

Type of Financing Preferred:
Early Stage
Generalist PE

Size of Investments Considered:
Min Size of Investment Considered (000s): $10
Max Size of Investment Considered (000s): $1,000

Industry Preferences

In Industrial/Energy prefer:
Environmental Related

Additional Information

Year Founded: 2005
Current Activity Level: Actively seeking new investments

AZULIS CAPITAL (FKA:BANEXI CAPITAL PARTENAIRES)

21 Boulevard de la Madeleine
Paris, France 75001
Phone: 33-1-4298-7020
Fax: 33-1-4298-7021
E-mail: info@azuliscapital.fr
Website: www.azuliscapital.fr

Management and Staff

Andre Belard, Partner
Bruno Lavolle, Partner
Christine Mariette, Partner
Donatien Noyelle, Chief Financial Officer
Franck Boget, Managing Partner
Gilles Perony, Partner
Michel Rowan, Managing Partner
Nicolas Cosson, Partner
Pierre Jourdain, Partner
Yann Collignon, Partner

Type of Firm

Bank Affiliated

Association Membership

French Venture Capital Association (AFIC)
European Private Equity and Venture Capital Assoc.

Project Preferences

Type of Financing Preferred:
Leveraged Buyout
Expansion

Size of Investments Considered:
Min Size of Investment Considered (000s): $6,366
Max Size of Investment Considered (000s): $25,465

Geographical Preferences

International Preferences:
Europe
France

Industry Preferences

In Medical/Health prefer:
Medical/Health

In Consumer Related prefer:
Consumer
Food/Beverage

In Industrial/Energy prefer:
Energy
Industrial Products
Materials

In Business Serv. prefer:
Services

In Manufact. prefer:
Manufacturing

Additional Information

Name of Most Recent Fund: Middle Market Fund III
Most Recent Fund Was Raised: 04/21/2004
Year Founded: 2000
Capital Under Management: $890,700,000
Current Activity Level: Actively seeking new investments

AZURE CAPITAL PARTNERS

650 California Street
Eleventh Floor
San Francisco, CA USA 94108
Phone: 415-276-5500
Fax: 415-276-5590
E-mail: info@azurecap.com
Website: www.azurecap.com

Other Offices

3500 Alameda de Las Pulgas
Menlo Park, CA USA 94025

Management and Staff

Cameron Lester, General Partner
Hans Roderich, General Partner
Larry Augustin, Venture Partner
Martin Brusco, Chief Financial Officer
Michael Kwatinetz, General Partner
Paul Ferris, General Partner
Paul Weinstein, General Partner
Ray Carey, General Partner

Type of Firm

Private Equity Firm

Project Preferences

Role in Financing:
Prefer role as deal originator but will also invest in deals created by others

Type of Financing Preferred:
Second Stage Financing
Early Stage
First Stage Financing
Startup

Size of Investments Considered:
Min Size of Investment Considered (000s): $250
Max Size of Investment Considered (000s): $25,000

Geographical Preferences

United States Preferences:
All U.S.

Canadian Preferences:
All Canada

Industry Preferences

In Communications prefer:
Telecommunications
Wireless Communications
Data Communications

In Computer Software prefer:
Software
Systems Software
Applications Software

In Internet Specific prefer:
Ecommerce

In Semiconductor/Electr prefer:
Electronic Components
Semiconductor
Controllers and Sensors
Fiber Optics

Additional Information

Year Founded: 2000
Capital Under Management: $540,000,000
Current Activity Level: Actively seeking new investments
Method of Compensation: Return on investment is of primary concern, do not charge fees

- B -

B.P. MARSH & PARTNERS, LTD.

Granville House
132-135 Sloane Street
London, United Kingdom SW1X 9AX
Phone: 44-20-7730-2626
Fax: 44-20-7823-5225
Website: www.bpmarsh.co.uk

Management and Staff

Rupert Marsh, Chief Executive Officer

Type of Firm

Private Equity Firm

Project Preferences

Type of Financing Preferred:
Balanced

Additional Information

Year Founded: 2007
Current Activity Level: Actively seeking new investments

B12 CAPITAL PARTNERS LLC

4900 Main Street
Suite 950
Kansas City, MO USA 64112
Phone: 816-994-8631
Fax: 816-994-8633
Website: www.b12capitalpartners.com

Management and Staff

Gregory Gaeddert, Managing Partner
Michael Wedel, Managing Partner

Type of Firm

Private Equity Firm

Project Preferences

Type of Financing Preferred:
Expansion
Generalist PE
Management Buyouts
Acquisition
Recapitalizations

Geographical Preferences

United States Preferences:
Midwest
Southeast

Industry Preferences

Semiconductor/Electr prefer:
Analytic/Scientific

In Medical/Health prefer:
Medical Products

In Consumer Related prefer:
Entertainment and Leisure
Food/Beverage
Consumer Products
Consumer Services
Education Related

In Industrial/Energy prefer:
Energy
Environmental Related

In Transportation prefer:
Aerospace

In Business Serv. prefer:
Services
Distribution

Manufact. prefer:
Publishing

Additional Information

Year Founded: 2007
Capital Under Management: $16,000,000
Current Activity Level: Actively seeking new investments

B4 VENTURES

15851 North Dallas Parkway
Suite 180
Addison, TX USA 75001
Phone: 972-233-2270
Fax: 972-233-4403
Website: www.b4ventures.com

Management and Staff

Carl Karnes, Principal
Scott Pollock, Principal

Type of Firm

Private Equity Firm

Project Preferences

Role in Financing:
Prefer role as deal originator but will also invest in deals created by others

Type of Financing Preferred:
Expansion
Startup

Size of Investments Considered:
Min Size of Investment Considered (000s): $250
Max Size of Investment Considered (000s): $5,000

Additional Information

Year Founded: 2002
Current Activity Level: Actively seeking new investments

BA PRIVATE EQUITY GMBH

Operngasse 6
Vienna, Austria A-1010
Phone: 43-15-1322-0181
Fax: 43-15-1322-0125
E-mail: office@privateequity.at
Website: www.privateequity.at

Management and Staff

Klaus Haberzettl, Managing Director

Type of Firm

Private Equity Firm

Association Membership

Austrian PE and Venture Capital Association (AVCO)

Project Preferences

Type of Financing Preferred:
Early Stage
Mezzanine

Geographical Preferences

International Preferences:
Europe

Additional Information

Year Founded: 2001
Current Activity Level: Actively seeking new investments

BABEG KARNTNER BETRIEBSANSIEDLUNGS- UND BETEILIGUNGS-GES.M.B.

Heuplatz 2
Klagenfurt, Austria 9020
Phone: 43-463-558-000
Fax: 43-463-558-0022
E-mail: office@kwf.at
Website: www.kwf.at

Type of Firm

Incubator/Development Program

Association Membership

European Private Equity and Venture Capital Assoc.

Project Preferences

Type of Financing Preferred:
Early Stage
Expansion
Management Buyouts
Startup

Size of Investments Considered:
Min Size of Investment Considered (000s): $100
Max Size of Investment Considered (000s): $100,000

Geographical Preferences

International Preferences:
Austria

Industry Preferences

In Semiconductor/Electr prefer:
Electronics

In Industrial/Energy prefer:
Energy

In Other prefer:
Environment Responsible

Additional Information

Year Founded: 1981
Capital Under Management: $17,000,000
Current Activity Level: Actively seeking new investments

BABSON CAPITAL EUROPE

61 Aldwych
London, United Kingdom WC2B 4AE
Phone: 4420-3206-4500
Fax: 4420-3206-4591
Website: www.babsoncapitaleurope.com

Other Offices

1500 Main Street
Springfield, MA USA 01115
Phone: 413-226-1000

340 Madison Avenue
18th Floor
New York, NY USA 10017
Phone: 917-542-8300

Suite 2400
Charlotte, NC USA 28244
Phone: 704-805-7200

Independence Wharf
470 Atlantic Avenue
Boston, MA USA 02210
Phone: 617-225-3800

Management and Staff

Adam Eifion-Jones, Managing Director
David Wilmot, Managing Director
Ian Hazelton, Chief Executive Officer
Oliver Burgel, Managing Director
Zak Summerscale, Managing Director

Type of Firm

Bank Affiliated

Project Preferences

Type of Financing Preferred:
Mezzanine

Geographical Preferences

International Preferences:
Europe

Additional Information

Year Founded: 2000
Capital Under Management: $1,023,800,000
Current Activity Level: Actively seeking new investments

BABSON CAPITAL MANAGEMENT LLC

1500 Main Street
PO Box 15189
Springfield, MA USA 01115
Phone: 413-226-1000
Website: www.babsoncapital.com

Other Offices

2029 Century Park East
Suite 1130
Los Angeles, CA USA 90067
Phone: 310-407-2900

Independence Wharf
470 Atlantic Avenue
Boston, MA USA 02210
Phone: 617-225-3800

340 Madison Avenue
18th Floor
New York, NY USA 10017
Phone: 917-542-8300

201 South College Street
Suite 2400
Charlotte, NC USA 28244
Phone: 704-805-7200

Management and Staff

Benjamin Silver, Managing Director
Michael Hermsen, Managing Director
Michael Ross, Managing Director

Type of Firm

Bank Affiliated

Project Preferences

Type of Financing Preferred:
Mezzanine
Generalist PE

Additional Information

Year Founded: 1992
Capital Under Management: $260,800,000
Current Activity Level: Actively seeking new investments

BACCHUS CAPITAL MANAGEMENT LLC

5000 Hopyard Road
Suite 318
Pleasanton, CA USA 94588
Phone: 925-469-0202
Fax: 925-469-6373
Website: www.bacchuswinefund.com

Management and Staff

Henry Owsley, Managing Partner
Mike Jaeger, President
Peter Kaufman, Managing Partner
Quinton Jay, Managing Director
Samuel Bronfman, Managing Partner

Type of Firm

Private Equity Firm

Project Preferences

Type of Financing Preferred:
Mezzanine

Geographical Preferences

United States Preferences:
West Coast

Industry Preferences

In Consumer Related prefer:
Food/Beverage

Additional Information

Year Founded: 2007
Capital Under Management: $35,800,000
Current Activity Level: Actively seeking new investments

BADER YOUNG ENTREPRENEURS PROGRAM

Berytech Building, Damascus Rd
National Museum area
Beirut, Lebanon
Phone: 961-3-198-989
Fax: 961-1-611-005
E-mail: info@baderlebanon.com
Website: www.baderlebanon.com

Type of Firm

Incubator/Development Program

Project Preferences

Type of Financing Preferred:
Balanced

Geographical Preferences

International Preferences:
Lebanon

Industry Preferences

In Business Serv. prefer:
Services

Additional Information

Year Founded: 2007
Capital Under Management: $17,000,000
Current Activity Level: Actively seeking new investments

BAER CAPITAL PARTNERS, LTD.

Building No.3, Level 5
The Dubai Int'l Finance Center
Dubai, Utd. Arab Em.
Phone: 971-4-428-3100
Fax: 971-4-425-0230
E-mail: info@baercapital.com
Website: www.baercapital.com

Other Offices

11 Upper Grosvenor Street
London, United Kingdom W1K 2ND
Phone: 44-207-491-9039
Fax: 44-207-491-9070

Third Floor
4/6 Siri Fort Institutional Area
New Delhi, India 110 049
Phone: 91-11-4175-1997
Fax: 91-11-4175-1994

11-B Nirmal Building
Nariman Point
Mumbai, India 400 021
Phone: 91-22-6618-0000
Fax: 91-22-6618-0001

Seefeldstrasse. 215
Zurich, Switzerland 8008
Phone: 41-44-388-2040
Fax: 41-44-388-2049

Management and Staff

Alok Sama, President, Founder
Deepak Shahdadpuri, Managing Director

Type of Firm

Investment Management Firm

Project Preferences

Type of Financing Preferred:
Expansion
Balanced

Geographical Preferences

International Preferences:
India
Middle East
Industry Preferences

In Consumer Related prefer:
Consumer

Additional Information
Year Founded: 2006
Capital Under Management: $200,000,000
Current Activity Level: Actively seeking new investments

BAHAMAS ENTREPRENEURIAL VENTURE FUND, LTD.
The Deanery
28 Cumberland Hill Street
Nassau, Bahamas
Phone: 242-356-4114
Fax: 242-356-4125
E-mail: info@bahamasventurefund.com
Website: www.bahamasventurefund.com

Type of Firm
Private Equity Firm

Project Preferences

Type of Financing Preferred:
Expansion
Startup

Geographical Preferences

International Preferences:
Bahamas

Additional Information
Year Founded: 2005
Capital Under Management: $3,000,000
Current Activity Level: Actively seeking new investments

BAHRAIN DEVELOPMENT BANK
P. O. Box 20501
Manama, Bahrain
Phone: 97-31-751-1111
Fax: 97-31-7534005
E-mail: info@bdb-bh.com
Website: www.bdb-bh.com

Type of Firm
Bank Affiliated

Project Preferences

Type of Financing Preferred:
Balanced

Geographical Preferences

International Preferences:
Bahrain
Asia

Additional Information
Year Founded: 2006
Capital Under Management: $10,000,000
Current Activity Level: Actively seeking new investments

BAIGO CAPITAL GMBH
Bockenheimer Anlage 4
Frankfurt, Germany 60322
Phone: 49-69-1739-2600
Fax: 49-69-1739-2619
E-mail: info@baigo-capital.com
Website: www.baigo-capital.com

Management and Staff
Dariusch Mani, Founding Partner
Frank Duffner, Founding Partner
Marcus Bracklo, Founding Partner
Markus Solibieda, Founding Partner

Type of Firm
Private Equity Firm

Project Preferences

Type of Financing Preferred:
Leveraged Buyout
Expansion
Management Buyouts
Acquisition

Geographical Preferences

International Preferences:
Europe

Industry Preferences

In Medical/Health prefer:
Medical Diagnostics
Diagnostic Test Products
Drug/Equipmt Delivery
Medical Products
Health Services
Hospitals/Clinics/Primary
Hospital/Other Instit.
Pharmaceuticals

Additional Information
Year Founded: 2007
Capital Under Management: $146,700,000
Current Activity Level: Actively seeking new investments

BAIN CAPITAL
111 Huntington Avenue
Boston, MA USA 02199
Phone: 617-516-2000
Fax: 617-516-2010
E-mail: info@baincapital.com
Website: www.baincapital.com

Other Offices
1603 Orrington Avenue
Suite 815
Evanston, IL USA 60201
Phone: 847-563-5330
Fax: 847-563-5331

47/F Cheung Kong Center
2 Queen's Road
Central, Hong Kong
Phone: 852-3656-6800
Fax: 852-3656-6801

2nd Floor, Free Press House
Nariman Point
Mumbai, India 400 021
Phone: 91-22-6752-8000
Fax: 91-22-6752-8010

Maximilianstrasse 11
Munich, Germany 80539
Phone: 49-89-2444-1070
Fax: 49-89-244-410-731

6th Floor, Devonshire House
Mayfair Place
London, United Kingdom W1J 8AJ
Phone: 44-20-7514-5252
Fax: 44-20-7514-5250

42nd Floor
590 Madison Avenue
New York, NY USA 10022
Phone: 212-326-9420
Fax: 212-421-2225

Room 2306 Jin Mao Tower
88 Century Boulevard
Shanghai, China 200121
Phone: 86-21-6163-2000
Fax: 86-21-6163-2088

8F Kishimmoto Building
2-2-1 Marunouchi, Chiyoda-ku
Tokyo, Japan 100-0005
Phone: 813-6212-7070
Fax: 813-6212-7071

Management and Staff
Ajay Agarwal, Managing Director
Alice Limakakeng, Principal
Alykhan Nathoo, Principal
Amit Chandra, Managing Director
Anand More, Managing Director
Andrew Balson, Managing Director
Benjamin Nye, Managing Director
Bob Gay, Managing Director
Chris Gordon, Principal
David Gross-Loh, Principal
Dewey Awad, Managing Director
Diane Exter, Managing Director
Domenic Ferrante, Managing Director
Doug Rudisch, Managing Director
Douglas Schreiber, Principal
Dwight Poler, Managing Director
Ed Brakeman, Managing Director

Edward Conard, Managing Director
Ferdinando Grimaldi Quartieri, Managing Director
Fernando Vigil, Principal
Hans Freudenberg, Principal
Ian Loring, Managing Director
Ian Blasco, Principal
Ian Andrew Reynolds, Principal
James Nahirny, Managing Director
Jamie Kellogg, Managing Director
Jeff Crisan, Principal
Jeffrey Schwartz, Managing Director
Jeffrey Glass, Partner
Jingsheng Huang, Managing Director
Johannes Wendt, Principal
John Tudor, Principal
John Connaughton, Managing Director
Jonathan Goodman, Principal
Jonathan Lavine, Managing Director
Jordan Hitch, Managing Director
Joseph Pretlow, Managing Director
Joshua Bekenstein, Managing Director
Kim Harris, Vice President
Kristin Mugford, Managing Director
Mark Nunnelly, Managing Director
Marlene Wojcik, Chief Financial Officer
Marshall Haines, Principal
Matthew McPherron, Managing Director
Matthew Levin, Managing Director
Melissa Bethell, Principal
Michael Bevacqua, Managing Director
Michael Ward, Managing Director
Michael Colato, Chief Financial Officer
Michael Krupka, Managing Director
Michael Siefke, Principal
Michael Goss, Managing Director & CFO
Michel Plantevin, Managing Director
Paul Edgerley, Managing Director
Pete Riehl, Managing Director
Phil Carter, Managing Director
Philip Loughlin, Principal
Robert White, Managing Director
Stephen Zide, Managing Director
Stephen Pagliuca, Managing Director
Steve Petrow, Managing Director
Steven Barnes, Managing Director
Stuart Davies, Managing Director
Ted Pappendick, Managing Director
Ted Berk, Principal
Todd MacLean, Principal
Todd Cook, Principal
Ulrich Biffar, Managing Director
Vincent Jachet, Principal
Walid Sarkis, Managing Director
William Lovejoy, Principal
Yoo Jin Kim, Principal

Type of Firm

Private Equity Firm
Association Membership
British Venture Capital Association (BVCA)
Private Equity Council (PEC)

Project Preferences

Type of Financing Preferred:

Leveraged Buyout
Early Stage
Expansion
Mezzanine
Generalist PE
Start-up Financing
Balanced
First Stage Financing
Distressed Debt

Geographical Preferences

United States Preferences:

All U.S.

Canadian Preferences:

All Canada

International Preferences:

Europe
China
Pacific
Japan
All International

Industry Focus

(% based on actual investment)	
Consumer Related	33.6%
Other Products	23.9%
Medical/Health	10.4%
Semiconductors/Other Elect.	9.7%
Computer Software and Services	6.0%
Internet Specific	5.9%
Communications and Media	4.7%
Computer Hardware	3.8%
Industrial/Energy	2.1%

Additional Information

Name of Most Recent Fund: Sankaty Credit Opportunities (Offshore) III, L.P.
Most Recent Fund Was Raised: 02/28/2007
Year Founded: 1983
Capital Under Management: $27,000,000,000
Current Activity Level: Actively seeking new investments

BAIN CAPITAL VENTURES

111 Huntington Avenue
Boston, MA USA 02199
Phone: 617-516-2000
Fax: 617-516-2010
Website: www.baincapitalventures.com

Management and Staff

Ajay Agarwal, Managing Director
Ben Holzman, Principal
Daniel Allen, Principal
Fernando Vigil, Principal
J. Benjamin Nye, Managing Director
James Nahirny, Managing Director
Jeffrey Glass, Venture Partner
Jeffrey Schwartz, Managing Director
Justin Caldbeck, Principal
Michael Krupka, Managing Director
Michelle Lam, Principal
Paul Zurlo, Venture Partner
Scott Friend, Venture Partner

Type of Firm

Bank Affiliated

Project Preferences

Type of Financing Preferred:

Leveraged Buyout
Expansion
Balanced
Seed
Later Stage

Industry Preferences

In Communications prefer:

Wireless Communications

In Computer Software prefer:

Software

In Computer Other prefer:

Computer Related

In Semiconductor/Electr prefer:

Semiconductor

In Medical/Health prefer:

Health Services

In Consumer Related prefer:

Consumer
Retail

In Business Serv. prefer:

Services

Additional Information

Year Founded: 2001
Capital Under Management: $1,000,000,000
Current Activity Level: Actively seeking new investments

BAIRD CAPITAL PARTNERS

777 East Wisconsin Avenue
28th Floor
Milwaukee, WI USA 53202
Phone: 414-765-3500
Fax: 414-298-7490
E-mail: bcp@rwbaird.com
Website: www.bairdcapitalpartners.com

Other Offices

Steinhoft 5-7
Haus am Hafen
Hamburg, Germany 204959
Phone: 49-40-37-480-210

510 Charmany Drive
Suite 172
Madison, WI USA 53719
Phone: 608-441-2900
Fax: 608-441-2901

No. 50-1 Wangjing Xi Road
Unit 1006-A Qaunshitiandi, Chaoyang
Beijing, China 100102
Phone: 86-1-6479-5151

18 Harbour Road
Suite 3202 Central Plaza
Wanchai, Hong Kong
Phone: 852-2827-8822

175 Strafford Avenue
Wayne, PA USA 19087
Phone: 610-975-0929
Fax: 610-975-0922

No. 1000 Lujiazui Ring Road
Room 42-022 HSBC Tower
Shanghai, China 200120
Phone: 86-21-6182-0980

227 West Monroe Street
Suite 2200
Chicago, IL USA 60606
Phone: 800-799-5770

Management and Staff

C. Andrew Brickman, Partner
David Pelisek, Partner
Gordon Pan, Partner
Paul Carbone, Managing Partner
Randall Mehl, Partner
Rob Ospalik, Vice President

Type of Firm

Bank Affiliated

Project Preferences

Role in Financing:
Prefer role as deal originator but will also invest in deals created by others

Type of Financing Preferred:
Leveraged Buyout
Expansion
Management Buyouts
Acquisition
Recapitalizations

Size of Investments Considered:
Min Size of Investment Considered (000s): $15,000
Max Size of Investment Considered (000s): $35,000

Geographical Preferences

United States Preferences:
Midwest
Southeast

International Preferences:
China

Industry Focus

(% based on actual investment)

Other Products	29.1%
Industrial/Energy	21.5%
Consumer Related	18.9%
Computer Software and Services	18.2%
Medical/Health	5.6%
Computer Hardware	5.5%
Biotechnology	0.7%
Semiconductors/Other Elect.	0.5%

Additional Information

Name of Most Recent Fund: Baird Asia Partners I, Limited Partnership
Most Recent Fund Was Raised: 12/21/2004
Year Founded: 1989
Capital Under Management: $300,000,000
Current Activity Level: Actively seeking new investments
Method of Compensation: Return on invest. most important, but chg. closing fees, service fees, etc.

BAIRD CAPITAL PARTNERS ASIA

Room 42-022, 42/F, HSBC Tower
No. 1000 Lujiazui Ring Road
Shanghai, China 200120
Phone: 86-21-6182-0980
Website: www.bairdprivateequity.com

Other Offices

18 Harbour Road, Central Plaza
Suite 3202, Wanchai
Hong Kong, Hong Kong
Phone: 852-2827-8822

Unit 1006, Quanshitiandi Tower A
Wangjing Xilu, Chaoyang District
Beijing, China 100102
Phone: 86-10-6479-5151

Management and Staff

Brett Tucker, Partner
Hock Goh, Partner
Huaming Gu, Partner

Type of Firm

Bank Affiliated

Project Preferences

Size of Investments Considered:
Min Size of Investment Considered (000s): $8,000
Max Size of Investment Considered (000s): $15,000

Geographical Preferences

International Preferences:
China
Asia

Industry Preferences

In Medical/Health prefer:
Medical/Health
Medical Products

In Consumer Related prefer:
Consumer

In Industrial/Energy prefer:
Industrial Products

In Financial Services prefer:
Financial Services

In Manufact. prefer:
Manufacturing

Additional Information

Year Founded: 2003
Capital Under Management: $47,100,000
Current Activity Level: Actively seeking new investments

BAIRD CAPITAL PARTNERS EUROPE

77 Mansell Street
Mint House
London, United Kingdom E1 8AF
Phone: 44-20-7667-8400
Fax: 44-20-7667-8481
Website: www.bcpe.co.uk

Other Offices

Aintree House
1 York Place
Leeds, United Kingdom LS1 2DR
Phone: 44-113-280-3500
Fax: 44-113-280-3501

16 Avenue Hoche
Paris, France 75008
Phone: 33-140-76-0401
Fax: 33-140-76-0402

Robert W. Baird & Co.
777 East Wisconsin Avenue
Milwaukee, WI USA 53202
Phone: 414-765-3758

Castle Chambers
Fourth Floor
Liverpool, United Kingdom LS1 9SH
Phone: 44-51-258-1859
Fax: 44-51-258-1860

Brazennose House West
Brazennose Street
Manchester, United Kingdom M2 5BP
Phone: 44-161-236-6600
Fax: 44-161-236-6650

Kaiserkai 69
Granville Baird Am
Hamburg, Germany 20457
Phone: 49-40-3748-0210
Fax: 49-40-3748-0223

Palais Liechtenstein
Alserbachstrasse 14-16
Vienna, Austria 1090
Phone: 43-1-310-5730
Fax: 43-1-310-5733

Management and Staff

Andrew Ferguson, Managing Director
Gary Solomon, Chief Executive Officer
Jacques Paquin, Partner
Matthias Zillmer, Partner
Moritz Freiherr Schenck, Partner
Simon Havers, Managing Director

Type of Firm
Private Equity Firm

Association Membership
British Venture Capital Association (BVCA)
German Venture Capital Association (BVK)
European Private Equity and Venture Capital Assoc.
Spanish Venture Capital Association (ASCRI)

Project Preferences

Role in Financing:
Prefer role as deal originator but will also invest in deals created by others

Type of Financing Preferred:
Leveraged Buyout
Early Stage
Expansion
Balanced
Turnaround
Management Buyouts
Recapitalizations

Size of Investments Considered:
Min Size of Investment Considered (000s): $8,000
Max Size of Investment Considered: No Limit

Geographical Preferences

International Preferences:
Italy
United Kingdom
Europe
Spain
Germany
France

Industry Focus
(% based on actual investment)

Other Products	43.1%
Computer Software and Services	15.0%
Internet Specific	14.2%
Industrial/Energy	13.0%
Medical/Health	10.4%
Computer Hardware	2.1%
Consumer Related	1.1%
Biotechnology	0.8%
Communications and Media	0.5%

Additional Information
Year Founded: 1973
Capital Under Management: $649,000,000
Current Activity Level: Actively seeking new investments
Method of Compensation: Return on invest. most important, but chg. closing fees, service fees, etc.

BAIRD VENTURE PARTNERS
227 West Monroe
Suite 1900
Chicago, IL USA 60606
Phone: 312-609-4700
Fax: 312-609-4700
E-mail: bvp@rwbaird.com
Website: www.bairdventurepartners.com

Other Offices
510 Charmany Drive
Suite 172
Madison, WI USA 53719
Phone: 608-441-2900
Fax: 608-441-2901

227 West Monroe Street
Suite 2200
Chicago, IL USA 60606
Phone: 312-609-4700
Fax: 312-609-4707

175 Strafford Avenue
Wayne, PA USA 19087
Phone: 610-975-0929
Fax: 610-975-0922

Management and Staff
Benedict Rocchio, Principal
Devin Mathews, Managing Partner
Jim Pavlik, Principal
Michael Liang, Principal
Paul Carbone, Partner
Peter Shagory, Partner
William Filip, Partner

Type of Firm
Bank Affiliated

Association Membership
National Venture Capital Association - USA (NVCA)
Illinois Venture Capital Association

Project Preferences

Role in Financing:
Prefer role as deal originator but will also invest in deals created by others

Type of Financing Preferred:
Second Stage Financing
Early Stage
Expansion
Balanced
Later Stage
First Stage Financing

Size of Investments Considered:
Min Size of Investment Considered (000s): $2,000
Max Size of Investment Considered (000s): $10,000

Industry Preferences

In Computer Software prefer:
Computer Services
Data Processing
Software
Systems Software
Applications Software

In Semiconductor/Electr prefer:
Analytic/Scientific

In Biotechnology prefer:
Human Biotechnology
Biotech Related Research

In Medical/Health prefer:
Medical/Health
Medical Diagnostics
Diagnostic Services
Diagnostic Test Products
Medical Therapeutics
Drug/Equipmt Delivery
Medical Products
Disposable Med. Products
Health Services

In Business Serv. prefer:
Services
Consulting Services

Additional Information
Year Founded: 2000
Capital Under Management: $171,000,000
Current Activity Level: Actively seeking new investments
Method of Compensation: Return on investment is of primary concern, do not charge fees

---

BAKER BROS. ADVISORS, LLC
667 Madison Avenue
New York, NY USA 10065
Phone: 212-524-4400

Management and Staff
Felix Baker, Managing Director
Julian Baker, Managing Director

Type of Firm
Private Equity Firm

Additional Information
Year Founded: 2000
Capital Under Management: $252,000,000
Current Activity Level: Actively seeking new investments

BAKER CAPITAL CORP.
540 Madison Avenue
29th Floor
New York, NY USA 10022
Phone: 212-848-2000
Fax: 212-486-0660
Website: www.bakercapital.com

Management and Staff
Faisal Nisar, Partner
Henry Baker, Founding Partner
John Baker, Co-Founder
Jonathan Grabel, Partner
Joseph Saviano, Chief Financial Officer
Robert Manning, General Partner

Type of Firm
Private Equity Firm

Association Membership

National Venture Capital Association - USA (NVCA)

Project Preferences

Type of Financing Preferred:

Leveraged Buyout
Early Stage
Generalist PE
Later Stage
Acquisition

Geographical Preferences

United States Preferences:

All U.S.

International Preferences:

Western Europe

Industry Focus

(% based on actual investment)	
Computer Software and Services	33.2%
Communications and Media	27.6%
Internet Specific	23.0%
Computer Hardware	6.8%
Semiconductors/Other Elect.	6.5%
Consumer Related	3.0%

Additional Information

Name of Most Recent Fund: Baker Communications Fund II
Most Recent Fund Was Raised: 06/30/2000
Year Founded: 1995
Current Activity Level: Actively seeking new investments

BALATON GROUP INC.

152 King Street East
Suite 400
Toronto, Canada M5A1J3
Phone: 416-366-5702
Fax: 416-366-8273
Website: www.balatongroupinc.com

Type of Firm

Private Equity Firm

Additional Information

Year Founded: 2009
Current Activity Level: Actively seeking new investments

BALDERTON CAPITAL (FKA: BENCHMARK CAPITAL EUROPE)

20 Balderton Street
London, United Kingdom W1K 6TL
Phone: 44-20-7016-6800
Fax: 44-20-7016-6810
E-mail: information@balderton.com
Website: www.balderton.com

Management and Staff

Barry Maloney, Partner
Bernard Liataud, General Partner
Dharmash Mistry, Partner
Jerome Misso, Partner
Johan Brenner, Partner
Klaus Hommels, Venture Partner
Mark Evans, Partner
Roberto Bonanzinga, Partner
Tim Bunting, Partner

Type of Firm

Private Equity Firm

Project Preferences

Type of Financing Preferred:

Early Stage
Expansion
Later Stage

Size of Investments Considered:

Min Size of Investment Considered (000s): $100
Max Size of Investment Considered (000s): $50,000

Geographical Preferences

United States Preferences:

All U.S.

International Preferences:

Europe
Asia

Industry Preferences

In Communications prefer:

Communications and Media
Wireless Communications

In Computer Software prefer:

Software

In Internet Specific prefer:

Internet

In Semiconductor/Electr prefer:

Semiconductor

In Consumer Related prefer:

Consumer Services

In Financial Services prefer:

Financial Services

In Business Serv. prefer:

Media

Additional Information

Year Founded: 2000
Capital Under Management: $1,500,000,000
Current Activity Level: Actively seeking new investments

BALLAST POINT VENTURE PARTNERS

880 Carillon Parkway
Saint Petersburg, FL USA 33716
Phone: 727-567-1500
Fax: 727-567-1515
E-mail: info@ballastpointventures.com
Website: www.ballastpointventures.com

Management and Staff

Donald Burton, Venture Partner
Drew Graham, Managing Partner
O. Gene Gabbard, Venture Partner
Paul Johan, Partner
Richard Brandewie, Managing Partner

Type of Firm

Private Equity Firm

Project Preferences

Role in Financing:

Prefer role as deal originator but will also invest in deals created by others

Type of Financing Preferred:

Expansion
Other
Management Buyouts
Acquisition
Recapitalizations

Size of Investments Considered:

Min Size of Investment Considered (000s): $2,000
Max Size of Investment Considered (000s): $10,000

Geographical Preferences

United States Preferences:

Southeast
Florida
Texas

Industry Preferences

In Communications prefer:

Communications and Media

In Computer Software prefer:

Software

In Internet Specific prefer:

Internet

In Medical/Health prefer:

Medical/Health
Medical Products
Health Services

In Consumer Related prefer:

Retail
Consumer Products

In Financial Services prefer:

Financial Services

In Business Serv. prefer:

Services

In Manufact. prefer:

Manufacturing

Additional Information

Name of Most Recent Fund: Ballast Point Ventures II, L.P.
Most Recent Fund Was Raised: 12/21/2007
Year Founded: 2002
Capital Under Management: $175,000,000

Current Activity Level: Actively seeking new investments

BALMORAL CAPITAL

Cassini House
57-59 St James's Street
London, United Kingdom SW1A 1LD
Phone: 44-20-7647-0020
Fax: 44-20-7647-0021
E-mail: contact@balmoralcapital.com
Website: www.balmoralcapital.com

Management and Staff

Agostino Ascani, Partner
Alec D Janoeff, Partner
Bruno Mathieu, Partner
Eric Delangle, Principal
Julie Harper, Partner
Richard Winckles, Managing Partner

Type of Firm

Private Equity Firm

Project Preferences

Type of Financing Preferred:
Leveraged Buyout
Public Companies
Turnaround
Acquisition

Geographical Preferences

International Preferences:
United Kingdom
Europe

Additional Information

Year Founded: 2004
Current Activity Level: Actively seeking new investments

BALMORAL PARTNERS LTD.

165 University Avenue
Suite 200
Toronto, Canada
Phone: 416-350-3741
Fax: 416-366-0257

Type of Firm

Private Equity Firm

Additional Information

Year Founded: 1994
Current Activity Level: Actively seeking new investments

BALTIK AG FUR KAPITAL-BETEILIGUNGEN

Katharinenstrasse 31.
Lubeck, Germany 23554
Phone: 49-451-4707-0
Fax: 49-451-4707-290
E-mail: info@baltik-ag.de
Website: www.baltik-ag.de

Type of Firm

Private Equity Firm

Project Preferences

Type of Financing Preferred:
Balanced

Geographical Preferences

International Preferences:
Germany

Additional Information

Year Founded: 2005
Current Activity Level: Actively seeking new investments

BALYASNY ASSET MANAGEMENT LP (AKA: BAM)

181 West Madison Street
Suite 3600
Chicago, IL USA 60602
Phone: 312-499-2999
Fax: 312-499-2998
E-mail: investorrelations@bamfunds.com
Website: www.bam-us.com

Other Offices

135 East 57th Street, 27th Floor
New York, NY USA 10022
Phone: 212-808-2300
Fax: 212-808-2301

73 Arch Street
Greenwich, CT USA 06830
Phone: 203-863-5400
Fax: 203-863-5433

28 King Street, Third Floor
London, United Kingdom SW1Y 6SL
Phone: 44-207-149-0000
Fax: 44-207-149-0002

1007, Embassy Center
Nariman Point
Mumbai, India 400021

Type of Firm

Private Equity Firm

Project Preferences

Type of Financing Preferred:
Balanced

Geographical Preferences

International Preferences:
All International

Industry Preferences

In Financial Services prefer:
Investment Groups
Financial Services

Additional Information

Year Founded: 2001
Current Activity Level: Actively seeking new investments

BANC OF AMERICA CAPITAL INVESTORS (FKA:NATIONSBANC CAPITAL)

100 North Tryon Street
25th Floor
Charlotte, NC USA 28255
Phone: 704-386-4710
Fax: 704-386-6432
E-mail: CapitalInvestors@BankofAmerica.com
Website: www.bacapitalinvestors.com

Management and Staff

Ann Hayes Browning, Partner
Craig Elson, Partner
Donny Harrison, Partner
Edward Balogh, Chief Financial Officer
George Morgan, Partner
John Shimp, Partner
Peter Stoneberg, Partner
Rob Edwards, Partner
Scott Poole, Partner
Travis Hain, Partner
Trey Sheridan, Partner
Walker Poole, Partner

Type of Firm

Bank Affiliated

Association Membership

Natl Assoc of Small Bus. Inv. Co (NASBIC)

Project Preferences

Role in Financing:
Will function either as deal originator or investor in deals created by others

Type of Financing Preferred:
Leveraged Buyout
Mezzanine
Later Stage
Management Buyouts
Recapitalizations

Size of Investments Considered:
Min Size of Investment Considered (000s): $10,000
Max Size of Investment Considered (000s): $75,000

Geographical Preferences

United States Preferences:
All U.S.

Industry Focus
(% based on actual investment)

Communications and Media	32.2%
Other Products	17.9%
Industrial/Energy	13.5%
Consumer Related	12.3%
Internet Specific	8.9%
Computer Software and Services	6.6%
Medical/Health	4.9%
Semiconductors/Other Elect.	3.7%

Additional Information
Year Founded: 1993
Capital Under Management: $2,220,000,000
Current Activity Level: Actively seeking new investments
Method of Compensation: Return on invest. most important, but chg. closing fees, service fees, etc.

BANC OF AMERICA EQUITY PARTNERS ASIA
Country Office, Express Towers
16th Floor,Nariman Point
Mumbai, India 400021
Phone: 91-22-6632-3000
Fax: 91-22-2287-0981
Website: www.bankofamerica.com

Other Offices
5th Flr J K Millennium Centre
Block B, 46D Jawaharlal Nehru Road
Kolkata, India 700 071
Phone: 91-33-2288-3388
Fax: 91-33-2288-4488

17/F, Devin House
979 King's Road
Central, Hong Kong
Phone: 852-2597-3310
Fax: 852-2597-3311

907/908 Prestige Meridian 1
29 M.G Road
Bangalore, India 560 001
Phone: 91-80-2532-6030
Fax: 91-80-2532-6025

748 Anna Salai
Chennai, India 600 002
Phone: 91-44-2852-3856
Fax: 91-44-2852-2550

78 Shenton Way
Suite 07-01 A
Singapore, Singapore 079120
Phone: 65-6320-2902
Fax: 65-6320-2920

1st Floor, DLF Centre
Sansad Marg
Delhi, India 110 001
Phone: 91-11-2340-2000
Fax: 91-11-2371-4042

Management and Staff
David Kurczek, Principal
Dharma Bajpai, Managing Director
Kayu Mehta, Managing Director
Namit Arora, Principal

Type of Firm
Bank Affiliated

Project Preferences

Role in Financing:
Prefer role in deals created by others

Type of Financing Preferred:
Leveraged Buyout
Mezzanine
Early Stage
Expansion
Turnaround
Later Stage
Management Buyouts

Size of Investments Considered:
Min Size of Investment Considered (000s): $1,000
Max Size of Investment Considered (000s): $25,000

Geographical Preferences

International Preferences:
India
Asia

Industry Preferences

In Communications prefer:
Communications and Media
Telecommunications

In Computer Software prefer:
Software

In Semiconductor/Electr prefer:
Electronics
Semiconductor

In Biotechnology prefer:
Biotechnology

In Medical/Health prefer:
Medical/Health
Pharmaceuticals

In Consumer Related prefer:
Consumer
Retail

In Business Serv. prefer:
Services
Distribution

Additional Information
Year Founded: 1997
Capital Under Management: $500,000,000
Current Activity Level: Actively seeking new investments

BANC OF AMERICA SECURITIES LLC
9 West 57th Street
New York, NY USA 10019
Phone: 212-583-8000
Fax: 212-847-6994
Website: www.bofasecurities.com

Other Offices
100 North Tryon Street
Charlotte, NC USA 28255
Phone: 704-386-5000

600 Montgomery Street
San Francisco, CA USA 94111
Phone: 800-227-4786

Management and Staff
Carter McClelland, President
Filip Rensky, Managing Director
Frank Ryan, Chief Financial Officer
Joan Solotar, Managing Director
Teresa Teague, Managing Director

Type of Firm
Bank Affiliated

Project Preferences

Type of Financing Preferred:
Fund of Funds

Geographical Preferences

International Preferences:
Europe

Additional Information
Year Founded: 2001
Current Activity Level: Actively seeking new investments

BANC ONE MEZZANINE CORPORATION
120 South LaSalle Street
6th Floor, IL1-1472
Chicago, IL USA 60603
Phone: 312-661-9713
Fax: 312-661-6936
Website: www.bankone.com

Other Offices
1717 Main Street
TX1-2448
Dallas, TX USA 75201
Fax: 214-290-2336

100 East Broad Street
7th Floor, OH 1-0170
Columbus, OH USA 43215
Fax: 614-248-5518

Management and Staff

Cheryl Turnbull, Managing Director
Jay Turner, Managing Director
Michael Revord, Managing Director

Type of Firm

Bank Affiliated

Project Preferences

Role in Financing:

Prefer role as deal originator but will also invest in deals created by others

Type of Financing Preferred:

Mezzanine

Size of Investments Considered:

Min Size of Investment Considered (000s): $5,000
Max Size of Investment Considered (000s): $30,000

Industry Focus

(% based on actual investment)

Medical/Health	75.3%
Other Products	24.7%

Additional Information

Name of Most Recent Fund: Banc One Mezzanine Corporation
Most Recent Fund Was Raised: 01/01/1989
Year Founded: 1994
Capital Under Management: $225,000,000
Current Activity Level: Actively seeking new investments
Method of Compensation: Return on investment is of primary concern, do not charge fees

---

BANCA INTESA SPA - DIREZIONE PRIVATE EQUITY

Via Monte di Pieta 8
Milan, Italy 20121
Phone: 39-02-879-11
Fax: 39-02-8794-2220
E-mail: info@bancaintesa.it
Website: www.bancaintesa.it

Management and Staff

Corrado Passera, CEO & Managing Director

Type of Firm

Bank Affiliated

Association Membership

Italian Venture Capital Association (AIFI)
European Private Equity and Venture Capital Assoc.

Project Preferences

Type of Financing Preferred:

Leveraged Buyout
Expansion
Turnaround
Startup

Geographical Preferences

International Preferences:

Italy

Additional Information

Year Founded: 1998
Capital Under Management: $744,000,000
Current Activity Level: Actively seeking new investments

BANCA POPOLARE COMMERCIO E INDUSTRIA (AKA: GROUP BPCI)

40/1, Via della Moscova
Milan, Italy 20121
Phone: 39-02-6275-5344
Fax: 39-02-6275-2041
E-mail: merchantbanking@bpci.it
Website: www.bpci.it

Type of Firm

Bank Affiliated

Association Membership

Italian Venture Capital Association (AIFI)

Project Preferences

Type of Financing Preferred:

Leveraged Buyout
Early Stage
Expansion
Turnaround
Management Buyouts

Geographical Preferences

International Preferences:

Italy
Europe

Additional Information

Year Founded: 1994
Current Activity Level: Actively seeking new investments

BANCA POPOLARE DI MILANO SPA (AKA: BPM PRIVATE EQUITY SGR)

Piazza F. Meda 4
Milan, Italy 20121
Phone: 39-02-7700-2007
Fax: 39-02-7700-2612

Type of Firm

Private Equity Firm

Additional Information

Year Founded: 2003
Current Activity Level: Actively seeking new investments

BANCA PROFILO (FONDO SPINNAKER)

Corso Italia 49
Milan, Italy 20122
Phone: 39-02-584081
Fax: 39-02-58316057
E-mail: info@bancaprofilo.it
Website: www.bancaprofilo.it

Type of Firm

Bank Affiliated

Additional Information

Year Founded: 2003
Current Activity Level: Actively seeking new investments

BANCBOSTON CAPITAL/BANCBOSTON VENTURES

175 Federal Street
10th Floor
Boston, MA USA 02110
Phone: 617-434-2509
Fax: 617-434-1153
Website: www.bankofamerica.com

Other Offices

Rua Pedroso Alvarenga
1221-7th Floor
Sao Paulo, SP, Brazil 04531-012
Phone: 55-11-3167-4611
Fax: 55-11-3167-5545

33/F Jardine House
1 Connaught Place
HongKong, Hong Kong
Phone: 852-2867-7687
Fax: 852-2521-0798

Bank of Boston House
39 Victoria Street
Westminster, London, United Kingdom SW1H OED
Phone: 44-207-932-9053
Fax: 44-207-932-9117

Bouchard 547
Piso 14
Buenos Aires, Argentina C1106ABG
Phone: 54-11-4315-4545
Fax: 54-11-4315-4816

435 Tasso Street
Suite 250
Palo Alto, CA USA 94305
Phone: 650-470-4184
Fax: 650-853-1425

Type of Firm

Bank Affiliated

Association Membership

British Venture Capital Association (BVCA)
Hong Kong Venture Capital Association (HKVCA)
Natl Assoc of Small Bus. Inv. Co (NASBIC)
National Venture Capital Association - USA (NVCA)
European Private Equity and Venture Capital Assoc.

Project Preferences

Role in Financing:

Prefer role as deal originator but will also invest in deals created by others

Type of Financing Preferred:

Fund of Funds
Early Stage
Expansion
Mezzanine
Generalist PE
Later Stage
Seed
Management Buyouts
Acquisition
Recapitalizations

Size of Investments Considered:

Min Size of Investment Considered (000s): $1,000
Max Size of Investment Considered (000s): $15,000

Geographical Preferences

United States Preferences:

All U.S.

Canadian Preferences:

Eastern Canada

International Preferences:

Italy
United Kingdom
China
Bermuda
Mexico
Middle East
Spain
Australia
South Africa
Germany
France

Industry Focus

(% based on actual investment)

Other Products	21.1%
Communications and Media	18.0%
Internet Specific	14.8%
Consumer Related	14.2%
Computer Software and Services	12.9%
Industrial/Energy	6.5%
Semiconductors/Other Elect.	5.2%
Medical/Health	3.5%
Biotechnology	2.4%
Computer Hardware	1.3%

Additional Information

Name of Most Recent Fund: Private Equity Portfolio Fund III, L.L.C.
Most Recent Fund Was Raised: 03/14/2002
Year Founded: 1959
Capital Under Management: $2,996,000,000
Current Activity Level: Actively seeking new investments
Method of Compensation: Return on invest. most important, but chg. closing fees, service fees, etc.

BANCO EFISA SA

Av. Antonio Augusto Aguiar 132
Lisbon, Portugal 1050-020
Phone: 351-21-311-7800
Fax: 351-21-311-7915
E-mail: pequity@bancoefisa.pt
Website: www.bancoefisa.pt

Other Offices

11 Carlos Place
London, United Kingdom W1Y 5AF
Phone: 44-20-7533-1600
Fax: 44-20-7533-5316

Rua da Imprensa n. 264, 30. Esq.
Maputo, Mozambique
Phone: 258-130-7706
Fax: 258-130-7707

Type of Firm

Bank Affiliated

Association Membership

European Private Equity and Venture Capital Assoc.

Project Preferences

Type of Financing Preferred:

Early Stage
Expansion
Balanced
Management Buyouts
Startup

Geographical Preferences

International Preferences:

Portugal
Europe

Additional Information

Name of Most Recent Fund: Fundo de Capital de Risco - Dinamizacao e Competitivdade Emp
Most Recent Fund Was Raised: 06/06/2003
Year Founded: 1994
Capital Under Management: $36,000,000
Current Activity Level: Actively seeking new investments

BANCO ESPANOL DE CREDITO SA (AKA: BANESTO)

Avda Gran Via de Hortaleza no3
Madrid, Spain 28033
Phone: 34-91-767-9046
E-mail: correo@banesto.es
Website: www.banesto.es

Type of Firm

Bank Affiliated

Project Preferences

Type of Financing Preferred:

Balanced

Geographical Preferences

International Preferences:

Spain

Additional Information

Year Founded: 1982
Capital Under Management: $47,800,000
Current Activity Level: Actively seeking new investments

BANCO NACIONAL DE DESENVOLVIMENTO ECONOMICO E SOCIAL - BNDES

Av. Republica do Chile, 100
Protocolo - Terreo
Rio de Janeiro, Brazil 20031-917
Website: www.bndes.gov.br

Type of Firm

Bank Affiliated

Project Preferences

Type of Financing Preferred:

Unknown

Geographical Preferences

International Preferences:

Brazil

Industry Preferences

In Communications prefer:

Communications and Media
Telecommunications

In Consumer Related prefer:

Consumer
Retail
Food/Beverage

In Transportation prefer:

Aerospace

Additional Information

Year Founded: 2002
Current Activity Level: Actively seeking new investments

BANCO SABADELL CAPITAL DEVELOPMENT

Pl. Sant Roc, 20
Sabadell
Barcelona, Spain 08201
Phone: 34-902-323-555
E-mail: Info@bancsabadell.com
Website: www.bancsabadell.com

Type of Firm

Bank Affiliated

Project Preferences

Type of Financing Preferred:
Leveraged Buyout
Expansion
Generalist PE
Acquisition

Geographical Preferences

International Preferences:
Europe
Spain

Additional Information

Name of Most Recent Fund: Aurica XXI SCR SA
Most Recent Fund Was Raised: 09/30/2000
Year Founded: 2000
Capital Under Management: $149,700,000
Current Activity Level: Actively seeking new investments

BANCO SANTANDER SA (FKA: BANCO SANTANDER CENTRAL HISPANO)

Plaza De Canalejas, 1
Madrid, Spain 28014
Phone: 34-91-558-1571
Fax: 34-91-521-3387
Website: www.gruposantander.com/es

Type of Firm

Bank Affiliated

Project Preferences

Type of Financing Preferred:
Balanced
Geographical Preferences

International Preferences:
Europe
Spain

Industry Preferences

In Industrial/Energy prefer:
Alternative Energy
Environmental Related

In Other prefer:
Environment Responsible

Additional Information

Year Founded: 2001
Capital Under Management: $23,400,000
Current Activity Level: Actively seeking new investments

BANCROFT CAPITAL, LLC

1112 Ocean Drive
Suite 300
Manhattan Beach, CA USA 90266
Phone: 310-318-9120
Fax: 310-318-9611

Type of Firm

Private Equity Firm

Industry Preferences

In Financial Services prefer:
Real Estate

Additional Information

Year Founded: 2002
Capital Under Management: $6,000,000
Current Activity Level: Actively seeking new investments

BANCROFT GROUP

195 Brompton Road
London, United Kingdom SW3 1NE
Phone: 44-20-7823-9222
Fax: 44-20-7589-3442
E-mail: theoffice@bancroftgroup.com
Website: www.bancroftgroup.com

Other Offices

Parizska 22
Prague, Czech Republic 110 00
Phone: 420-224-238-505
Fax: 420-224-238-506

Csorszu. 45
Budapest , Hungary 1123
Phone: 36-1-487-6210
Fax: 36-1-487-6205

607 Fourteenth Street N.W.
Suite 800
Washington, DC USA 20005
Phone: 1-202-654-1780
Fax: 1-202-654-9680

Management and Staff

Alain Patry, Chief Financial Officer

Type of Firm

Private Equity Firm

Project Preferences

Type of Financing Preferred:
Later Stage

Geographical Preferences

International Preferences:
Hungary
Greece
United Kingdom
Central Europe
Czech Republic
Turkey
Eastern Europe
Croatia

Industry Preferences

In Communications prefer:
Telecommunications

In Business Serv. prefer:
Media

In Manufact. prefer:
Manufacturing

Additional Information

Name of Most Recent Fund: Bancroft II
Most Recent Fund Was Raised: 11/30/2002
Year Founded: 1989
Capital Under Management: $100,000,000
Current Activity Level: Actively seeking new investments

BAND OF ANGELS

535 Middlefield Road
Suite 190
Menlo Park, CA USA 94025
Phone: 650-321-0854
Fax: 650-321-1968
E-mail: info@bandangels.com
Website: www.bandangels.com

Management and Staff

Ed Canty, Chief Financial Officer
Ian Sobieski, Managing Director
Tim Massey, Principal

Type of Firm

Angel Group

Association Membership

Western Association of Venture Capitalists (WAVC)

Project Preferences

Type of Financing Preferred:
Early Stage
Balanced
Seed

Size of Investments Considered:
Min Size of Investment Considered (000s): $300
Max Size of Investment Considered (000s): $2,000

Geographical Preferences

United States Preferences:
Northern California
California

Industry Preferences

In Communications prefer:
Telecommunications

In Computer Software prefer:
Software

In Semiconductor/Electr prefer:
Semiconductor

In Biotechnology prefer:
Biotechnology

In Industrial/Energy prefer:
Industrial Products

Additional Information
Name of Most Recent Fund: Band of Angels Fund, L.P.
Most Recent Fund Was Raised: 07/01/1999
Year Founded: 1994
Capital Under Management: $50,000,000
Current Activity Level: Actively seeking new investments

BANEXI VENTURES PARTNERS
13-15 rue Taitbout
Paris, France 75009
Phone: 33-1-7302-8969
Fax: 33-1-4014-9896
Website: www.banexiventures.com

Management and Staff
Anne-Valerie Bach, Partner
Marie-Laure Berthie, Partner
Michel Dahan, General Partner
Philippe Mere, General Partner
Sophie Pierrin-Lepinard, General Partner

Type of Firm
Private Equity Firm

Association Membership
French Venture Capital Association (AFIC)
European Private Equity and Venture Capital Assoc.

Project Preferences

Role in Financing:
Prefer role as deal originator but will also invest in deals created by others

Type of Financing Preferred:
Early Stage
Balanced
Startup

Size of Investments Considered:
Min Size of Investment Considered (000s): $700
Max Size of Investment Considered (000s): $3,700

Geographical Preferences

International Preferences:
Europe

Industry Preferences

In Semiconductor/Electr prefer:
Electronics
Semiconductor

In Biotechnology prefer:
Biotech Related Research

In Medical/Health prefer:
Medical/Health

Additional Information
Name of Most Recent Fund: Banexi Ventures 4
Most Recent Fund Was Raised: 04/18/2005
Year Founded: 1983
Capital Under Management: $94,200,000
Current Activity Level: Actively seeking new investments
Method of Compensation: Return on investment is of primary concern, do not charge fees

---

BANFIELD CAPITAL
2200 Yonge St.
Suite 605
Toronto, Canada M4S 2C6
Phone: 416-322-7607
Fax: 416-322-7610
Website: www.banfieldcapital.com

Management and Staff
Jeff Banfield, Chief Executive Officer

Type of Firm
Investment Management Firm

Additional Information
Year Founded: 1996
Current Activity Level: Actively seeking new investments

BANGERT DAWES READE DAVIS & THOM
605 Third Avenue
Suite 424
New York, NY USA 10158
Phone: 212-573-6716

Other Offices
One Madison Avenue
New York, NY USA 10010
Phone: 212-689-7404

Management and Staff
K. Deane Reade, President

Type of Firm
Private Equity Firm

Project Preferences

Role in Financing:
Prefer role as deal originator but will also invest in deals created by others

Type of Financing Preferred:
Other

Size of Investments Considered:
Min Size of Investment Considered (000s): $200
Max Size of Investment Considered (000s): $1,500

Geographical Preferences

International Preferences:
Europe

Industry Preferences

In Medical/Health prefer:
Medical Products
Disposable Med. Products

Additional Information
Year Founded: 1975
Capital Under Management: $100,000,000
Current Activity Level: Actively seeking new investments
Method of Compensation: Return on invest. most important, but chg. closing fees, service fees, etc.

BANIF - BANCO DE INVESTIMENTOS SA
Rua Tierno Galvan
Torre 3, 14. Piso
Lisbon, Portugal 1070-274
Phone: 351-21-380-5414
Fax: 351-21-381-6201
E-mail: banif.investimento@banifinvestimento.pt
Website: www.banifinvestimento.pt

Type of Firm
Bank Affiliated

Association Membership
European Private Equity and Venture Capital Assoc.

Project Preferences

Type of Financing Preferred:
Balanced

Geographical Preferences

International Preferences:
Portugal

Additional Information
Year Founded: 2004
Capital Under Management: $21,700,000

Current Activity Level: Actively seeking new investments

BANK OF AMERICA CAPITAL ADVISORS (BACA)

100 Federal Street
Boston, MA USA 02110
Phone: 888-786-9977

Management and Staff

Lawrence Morgenthal, President

Type of Firm

Bank Affiliated

Association Membership

Illinois Venture Capital Association

Additional Information

Year Founded: 2006
Current Activity Level: Actively seeking new investments

BANK OF AMERICA COMMERCIAL FINANCE

10220 NW Executive Hills Blvd
Kansas City, MO USA 64153
Phone: 816-891-7400

Type of Firm

Bank Affiliated

Additional Information

Year Founded: 2002
Current Activity Level: Actively seeking new investments

BANK OF SCOTLAND CORPORATE

New Uberior House
11 Earl Grey Street
Edinburgh, United Kingdom EH3 9BN
Website: www.bankofscotland.co.uk

Other Offices

155 Bishopsgate
London, United Kingdom EC2M 3YB
Phone: 44-207-012-9404

Management and Staff

George Mitchell, Chief Executive Officer
Graeme Shankland, Managing Director

Type of Firm

Bank Affiliated

Project Preferences

Type of Financing Preferred:
Second Stage Financing
Leveraged Buyout
Expansion
Mezzanine
Generalist PE
Balanced
Management Buyouts
Acquisition

Geographical Preferences

International Preferences:
United Kingdom
Central Europe
Europe
Western Europe
Eastern Europe

Industry Preferences

In Communications prefer:
Communications and Media

In Computer Other prefer:
Computer Related

In Semiconductor/Electr prefer:
Electronics

In Medical/Health prefer:
Medical/Health

In Consumer Related prefer:
Consumer

In Industrial/Energy prefer:
Energy
Industrial Products

Additional Information

Name of Most Recent Fund: Uberior Equity, Ltd.
Most Recent Fund Was Raised: 08/01/2000
Year Founded: 1988
Capital Under Management: $4,000,000
Current Activity Level: Actively seeking new investments

BANK OF SCOTLAND VENTURE CAPITAL (FKA: ICC VENTURE CAPITAL)

Bank of Scotland House
124 -127 St Stephens Green
Dublin, Ireland
Phone: 353-1-267-4000
Fax: 353-1-267-4010
E-mail: ventcap@icc.ie
Website: www.iccvc.ie

Management and Staff

Anne Bannon, Partner
David Fassbender, Managing Director
Martin O'Brian, Partner
Maurice McHenry, Partner
Pat McGrath, Partner
Prisca Grady, Partner
Tom Kirwan, Partner

Type of Firm

Bank Affiliated

Association Membership

Irish Venture Capital Association
European Private Equity and Venture Capital Assoc.

Project Preferences

Role in Financing:
Prefer role as deal originator

Type of Financing Preferred:
Second Stage Financing
Leveraged Buyout
Expansion
Mezzanine
Balanced
Recapitalizations

Size of Investments Considered:
Min Size of Investment Considered (000s): $700
Max Size of Investment Considered: No Limit

Geographical Preferences

International Preferences:
Ireland
Europe
Western Europe

Industry Focus

(% based on actual investment)	
Computer Software and Services	36.3%
Consumer Related	19.0%
Communications and Media	11.3%
Other Products	9.0%
Industrial/Energy	6.5%
Semiconductors/Other Elect.	6.2%
Internet Specific	4.9%
Biotechnology	4.2%
Medical/Health	2.5%

Additional Information

Year Founded: 1987
Capital Under Management: $245,000,000
Current Activity Level: Actively seeking new investments
Method of Compensation: Return on invest. most important, but chg. closing fees, service fees, etc.

BANK VONTOBEL AG

Dreikoenigstrasse 37
Zurich, Switzerland 8022
Phone: 41-1-283-7021
Fax: 41-1-283-5130
Website: www.vontobel.ch/privateequity

Type of Firm

Bank Affiliated

Association Membership

European Private Equity and Venture Capital Assoc.

Project Preferences

Type of Financing Preferred:
Fund of Funds
Early Stage
Expansion
Mezzanine
Later Stage

Geographical Preferences

United States Preferences:
All U.S.

International Preferences:
Central Europe
Europe
Western Europe
Eastern Europe
Israel

Industry Preferences

In Internet Specific prefer:
Internet

In Computer Other prefer:
Computer Related

In Semiconductor/Electr prefer:
Electronics

In Biotechnology prefer:
Biotechnology

In Consumer Related prefer:
Consumer

In Industrial/Energy prefer:
Industrial Products

Additional Information

Year Founded: 2000
Capital Under Management: $47,080,000,000
Current Activity Level: Actively seeking new investments

BANKCAP PARTNERS

2100 McKinney
Suite 1460
Dallas, TX USA 75201
Phone: 214-740-6100
Website: www.bankcap.com

Management and Staff

Brian Jones, Principal
Scott Reed, Principal

Type of Firm

Private Equity Firm

Project Preferences

Type of Financing Preferred:
Balanced

Size of Investments Considered:
Min Size of Investment Considered (000s): $15,000
Max Size of Investment Considered (000s): $50,000

Geographical Preferences

United States Preferences:
Texas

Industry Preferences

In Financial Services prefer:
Financial Services

Additional Information

Name of Most Recent Fund: BankCap Partners Fund I, L.P.
Most Recent Fund Was Raised: 06/14/2006
Year Founded: 2005
Capital Under Management: $109,500,000
Current Activity Level: Reducing investment activity

BANKINVEST

Sundkrogsgade 7
P.O. Box 2672
Copenhagen , Denmark 2100
Phone: 45-7730-9000
Fax: 45-3341-9100
E-mail: info@bankinvest.dk
Website: www.biventure.com

Other Offices

Avenue de la Gare 8 -10
Luxembourg, Luxembourg L-1610
Phone: 352-248-388

BankInvest Group
P.O. Box 360
Sevenoaks, United Kingdom TN13 9GH

Ludwigshohe 1
Strasslach, Germany D-82064

Management and Staff

Bjorn Dellgren, Partner
Jan Honore, Partner
Jens W. Kindtler, Partner
Jesper Zeuthen, Managing Director
Linda Sjostrom, Partner
Niels Thuesen, CEO & Managing Director

Type of Firm

Private Equity Firm

Association Membership

Danish Venture Capital Association (DVCA)
European Private Equity and Venture Capital Assoc.

Project Preferences

Type of Financing Preferred:
Second Stage Financing
Leveraged Buyout
Early Stage
Expansion
Balanced
Management Buyouts
Startup

Size of Investments Considered:
Min Size of Investment Considered (000s): $1,387
Max Size of Investment Considered (000s): $13,870

Geographical Preferences

United States Preferences:
All U.S.

International Preferences:
Vietnam
Ireland
Sweden
United Kingdom
Luxembourg
Netherlands
Switzerland
Europe
Egypt
Scandanavia/Nordic Region
South Africa
Belgium
Germany
Asia
Denmark
Africa

Industry Preferences

In Computer Software prefer:
Software

In Internet Specific prefer:
Internet

In Biotechnology prefer:
Biotechnology

In Medical/Health prefer:
Health Services
Pharmaceuticals

In Consumer Related prefer:
Consumer Products

In Industrial/Energy prefer:
Alternative Energy
Materials

In Financial Services prefer:
Financial Services

In Agr/Forestr/Fish prefer:
Agribusiness

In Other prefer:
Environment Responsible

Additional Information

Name of Most Recent Fund: P/S BI New Energy Solutions
Most Recent Fund Was Raised: 06/05/2002
Year Founded: 1969
Capital Under Management: $329,200,000
Current Activity Level: Actively seeking new investments

BANQUE DE VIZILLE

Espace Cordeliers
2 rue President Carnot
Lyon, France 69293

Phone: 33-4-7256-9100
Fax: 33-4-7277-5855
E-mail: contact@banquedevizille.fr
Website: www.banquedevizille.fr

Management and Staff

Antoine Jarmak, President

Type of Firm

Bank Affiliated

Association Membership

French Venture Capital Association (AFIC)

Project Preferences

Role in Financing:

Prefer role as deal originator but will also invest in deals created by others

Type of Financing Preferred:

Second Stage Financing
Leveraged Buyout

Geographical Preferences

International Preferences:

France

Industry Preferences

In Biotechnology prefer:

Industrial Biotechnology

In Medical/Health prefer:

Diagnostic Services

In Consumer Related prefer:

Food/Beverage
Consumer Products
Consumer Services

In Industrial/Energy prefer:

Industrial Products
Materials
Factory Automation
Machinery

In Transportation prefer:

Transportation

In Financial Services prefer:

Financial Services

Additional Information

Year Founded: 1988
Capital Under Management: $170,000,000
Current Activity Level: Actively seeking new investments
Method of Compensation: Return on invest. most important, but chg. closing fees, service fees, etc.

BANYAN CAPITAL ADVISORS LLC

150 Southeast 2nd Avenue
Suite 712
Miami, FL USA 33131
Phone: 305-250-4681
Fax: 305-371-3422
E-mail: info@banyanadvisors.com
Website: www.banyanadvisors.com

Management and Staff

James Davidson, Managing Director
John Miller, Managing Director
Richard Starke, Managing Director
Stephen Smith, Managing Director

Type of Firm

Private Equity Firm

Project Preferences

Type of Financing Preferred:

Mezzanine
Management Buyouts
Acquisition
Recapitalizations

Size of Investments Considered:

Min Size of Investment Considered (000s): $1,000
Max Size of Investment Considered (000s): $5,000

Geographical Preferences

United States Preferences:

Southeast
Alabama
South Carolina
Florida
Georgia

Additional Information

Year Founded: 2003
Capital Under Management: $9,900,000
Current Activity Level: Actively seeking new investments

BANYAN CAPITAL PARTNERS

1111 West Georgia Street
Suite 2150
Vancouver, Canada V6E 4M3
Phone: 604-643-2089
Fax: 604-653-2011
E-mail: info@banyancp.com
Website: www.banyancapitalpartners.com

Other Offices

800 5th Avenue
Suite 101-503
Seattle, WA USA 98104
Phone: 206-621-1623

350 7th Avenue S.W.
Suite 2800
Calgary, Canada T2P 3N9
Phone: 403-537-6713

Management and Staff

David Stitt, Managing Director
David Eisler, Managing Director
Frank Stack, Managing Director
George Clute, Managing Director

Type of Firm

Bank Affiliated

Project Preferences

Type of Financing Preferred:

Leveraged Buyout
Expansion
Management Buyouts
Acquisition
Recapitalizations

Geographical Preferences

United States Preferences:

Northwest
Oregon
Washington

Canadian Preferences:

Alberta
British Columbia
Western Canada

Industry Focus

(% based on actual investment)

Industrial/Energy	27.5%
Other Products	24.2%
Computer Software and Services	15.9%
Semiconductors/Other Elect.	14.9%
Medical/Health	13.2%
Internet Specific	4.4%

Additional Information

Year Founded: 1999
Capital Under Management: $82,400,000
Current Activity Level: Actively seeking new investments

BANYAN VENTURES SDN BHD

Suite 13-17, Plaza Mont Kiara
Two Jalan 1/70C, Mont Kiara
Kuala Lumpur, Malaysia
Phone: 603-6203-4205
Fax: 603-6203-4204
E-mail: tzekai@pd.jaring.my
Website: www.banyanvc.com

Management and Staff

Tze Kai Wong, Principal

Type of Firm

Bank Affiliated

Project Preferences

Type of Financing Preferred:

Mezzanine
Balanced
Seed
Startup

Geographical Preferences

International Preferences:
Asia
Malaysia

Industry Preferences

In Communications prefer:
Communications and Media
Telecommunications

In Internet Specific prefer:
Internet

In Computer Other prefer:
Computer Related

In Consumer Related prefer:
Entertainment and Leisure
Education Related

In Business Serv. prefer:
Media

Additional Information
Year Founded: 2001
Capital Under Management: $4,500,000
Current Activity Level: Actively seeking new investments

BANYANTREE FINANCE PVT. LTD.
1418, Maker Chambers V
Nariman Point
Mumbai, India 400021
Phone: 91-22-6623-5555
Website: www.banyantreefinance.com

Management and Staff
Arvind Jain, Vice President
Mitin Jain, Vice President
Sanjiv Singhal, Managing Director

Type of Firm
Private Equity Firm

Project Preferences

Type of Financing Preferred:
Mezzanine

Geographical Preferences

International Preferences:
India

Additional Information
Year Founded: 2009
Capital Under Management: $125,000,000
Current Activity Level: Actively seeking new investments

BARAKA AFRICA FUND, LTD.
P.O. Box 44223
Nairobi, Kenya 00100
Phone: 254-20-210-178
Fax: 254-20-210-500

Management and Staff
Kibuga Karitihi, Chief Executive Officer

Type of Firm
Private Equity Firm

Association Membership
African Venture Capital Association (AVCA)

Project Preferences

Type of Financing Preferred:
Early Stage
Generalist PE

Size of Investments Considered:
Min Size of Investment Considered (000s): $7
Max Size of Investment Considered (000s): $138

Geographical Preferences

International Preferences:
Kenya

Industry Preferences

In Financial Services prefer:
Real Estate

In Business Serv. prefer:
Media

In Agr/Forestr/Fish prefer:
Agribusiness

Additional Information
Year Founded: 2005
Capital Under Management: $600,000
Current Activity Level: Actively seeking new investments

BARCLAYS PRIVATE EQUITY, LTD.
4th Floor, Condor House
St. Paul's Churchyard
London, United Kingdom EC4M 8AL
Phone: 44-20-7512-9900
Fax: 44-20-7653-5350
Website: www.bpe.com

Other Offices
4th Floor, Apex Plaza
Forbury Road
Reading, United Kingdom RG1 1AX
Phone: 44-118-939-4796
Fax: 44-118-939-4695

1st Floor, Bank House
8 Cherry Street
Birmingham, United Kingdom B2 5AL
Phone: 44-121-631-4220
Fax: 44-121-631-1071

Platzl 4
Munich, Germany 80331
Phone: 49-89-242-0640
Fax: 49-89-242-06433

6th Floor
55 King Street
Manchester, United Kingdom M2 4LQ
Phone: 44-161-214-0800
Fax: 44-161-214-0805

General Guisan Quai 34
Zurich, Switzerland CH-8002
Phone: 41-44-289-8090
Fax: 41-44-289-8091

Foro Bounaparte 51
Milan, Italy 20121
Phone: 39-02-8029-051
Fax: 39-02-8029-0535

Centre d'affaires Paris-Trocadero
112 Avenue Kleber
Paris, France 75116
Phone: 33-1-5669-4343
Fax: 33-1-5669-4344

Management and Staff
Andrew Pars, Chief Operating Officer
Emanuele Cairo, Managing Director
Guillaume Jacqueau, Managing Director
Michael Bork, Managing Director
Owen Clarke, Managing Director
Paul Goodson, Managing Director
Stephen Koehler, Chief Operating Officer

Type of Firm
Bank Affiliated

Association Membership
Italian Venture Capital Association (AIFI)
British Venture Capital Association (BVCA)
French Venture Capital Association (AFIC)
European Private Equity and Venture Capital Assoc.

Project Preferences

Type of Financing Preferred:
Leveraged Buyout
Expansion
Mezzanine
Balanced
Turnaround
Other
Recapitalizations

Geographical Preferences

United States Preferences:
All U.S.

International Preferences:
Italy
United Kingdom
Switzerland
Europe
Germany
France

Industry Focus
(% based on actual investment)

Other Products	60.5%
Consumer Related	29.7%
Computer Software and Services	4.0%
Semiconductors/Other Elect.	2.1%
Internet Specific	1.7%
Industrial/Energy	1.4%
Medical/Health	0.4%
Communications and Media	0.3%

Additional Information
Year Founded: 1979
Capital Under Management: $6,613,500,000
Current Activity Level: Actively seeking new investments

BARCLAYS VENTURES
7th Floor, UK House
180 Oxford Street
London, United Kingdom Q1D 1EA
Phone: 44-20-7599-4538
Fax: 44-20-7599-4691
E-mail: barclays.ventures@barclays.co.uk
Website: www.barclaysventures.com

Other Offices
6th Floor
55 King Street
Manchester, United Kingdom M2 4LQ
Phone: 44-161-214-0818
Fax: 44-161-214-0805

15 Colmore Row
P.O. Box 12796
Birmingham, United Kingdom B2 2DH
Phone: 44-121-480-5435
Fax: 44-121-480-5450

Management and Staff
Kip Kapur, Managing Director

Type of Firm
Bank Affiliated

Association Membership
British Venture Capital Association (BVCA)

Project Preferences

Type of Financing Preferred:
Leveraged Buyout
Expansion
Management Buyouts
Recapitalizations

Size of Investments Considered:
Min Size of Investment Considered (000s): $3,764
Max Size of Investment Considered (000s): $18,818

Geographical Preferences

International Preferences:
United Kingdom

Industry Focus
(% based on actual investment)

Industrial/Energy	29.0%
Other Products	24.6%
Consumer Related	21.0%
Internet Specific	11.7%
Computer Software and Services	6.2%
Computer Hardware	4.1%
Communications and Media	3.4%

Additional Information
Year Founded: 1997
Capital Under Management: $65,300,000
Current Activity Level: Actively seeking new investments

BARD CAPITAL GROUP, LLC
535 16th Street
Suite 800
Denver, CO USA 80202
Phone: 303-985-8543
Fax: 303-985-1706
E-mail: info@bardcapital.com
Website: www.bardcapital.com

Management and Staff
Michael Carrazza, Managing Director
Richard Bard, Chairman & CEO

Type of Firm
Private Equity Firm

Project Preferences

Type of Financing Preferred:
Leveraged Buyout
Acquisition

Size of Investments Considered:
Min Size of Investment Considered (000s): $10,000
Max Size of Investment Considered (000s): $100,000

Geographical Preferences

United States Preferences:
All U.S.

Industry Preferences

In Communications prefer:
Media and Entertainment

In Medical/Health prefer:
Medical/Health

In Consumer Related prefer:
Consumer Products

In Transportation prefer:
Transportation

In Financial Services prefer:
Financial Services

In Business Serv. prefer:
Services
Distribution

In Manufact. prefer:
Manufacturing

Additional Information
Year Founded: 2003
Current Activity Level: Actively seeking new investments

BARING VOSTOK CAPITAL PARTNERS
Gasheka str. 7, Building 1
Ducat Place II, Suite 750
Moscow, Russia 123056
Phone: 7-95-967-1307
Fax: 7-501-967-1308
E-mail: info@bvcp.ru
Website: www.bvcp.ru

Management and Staff
Alexander Tyapin, Partner
Alexander Drozdkov, Partner
Alexei Kalinin, Managing Partner
Anna Kozina, Partner
David Bernstein, Chief Financial Officer
Elena Ivashentseva, Partner
Jean Michel Broun, Partner
Michael Lomtadze, Partner
Mike Calvey, Managing Partner
Paul Roberts, Chief Operating Officer
Philippe Der Megreditchian, Partner
Sergey Abramov, Partner

Type of Firm
Bank Affiliated

Association Membership
Russian Venture Capital Association (RVCA)

Project Preferences

Type of Financing Preferred:
Leveraged Buyout
Expansion
Generalist PE
Balanced
Turnaround
Acquisition

Geographical Preferences

International Preferences:
Central Europe
Europe
Turkmenistan

Eastern Europe
Ukraine
Georgia
Russia

Industry Preferences

In Communications prefer:
Telecommunications
Media and Entertainment

In Medical/Health prefer:
Pharmaceuticals

In Consumer Related prefer:
Consumer

In Industrial/Energy prefer:
Energy

In Transportation prefer:
Transportation

Additional Information

Name of Most Recent Fund: Baring Vostok IV Supplemental Fund, L.P.
Most Recent Fund Was Raised: 06/26/2007
Year Founded: 1994
Capital Under Management: $765,000,000
Current Activity Level: Actively seeking new investments

BARISH FUND, THE

55 Fifth Avenue
15th Floor
New York, NY USA 10013
Phone: 212-741-3200
Website: www.barishfund.com

Other Offices

65 Lafayette
Suite 302
North Hampton, NH USA 03862
Phone: 603-964-8313
Fax: 603-964-8317

60 William Street
Suite 130
Wellesley, MA USA 02481
Phone: 781-237-1300
Fax: 781-237-0311

Management and Staff

Andrew Fligor, Managing Partner
Keith Barish, Partner

Type of Firm

Private Equity Firm

Project Preferences

Type of Financing Preferred:
Leveraged Buyout
Early Stage
Management Buyouts
Acquisition
Startup

Geographical Preferences

United States Preferences:
All U.S.

Industry Preferences

In Business Serv. prefer:
Services

In Manufact. prefer:
Manufacturing

Additional Information

Year Founded: 2005
Current Activity Level: Actively seeking new investments

BARNARD ASSOCIATES, INC.

20 North Meridian Street
Guaranty Building, Suite 801
Indianapolis, IN USA 46204
Phone: 317-684-9106
Fax: 317-684-9195
E-mail: info@barnardassociates.com
Website: www.barnardassociates.com

Management and Staff

John Barnard, Founder
Timothy Tichenor, Managing Director

Type of Firm

Private Equity Advisor or Fund of Funds

Project Preferences

Type of Financing Preferred:
Balanced

Geographical Preferences

United States Preferences:
All U.S.

Additional Information

Name of Most Recent Fund: Pearl Street Venture Fund, L.P.
Most Recent Fund Was Raised: 05/28/2004
Year Founded: 1994
Capital Under Management: $15,000,000
Current Activity Level: Actively seeking new investments

BARODA VENTURES LLC

245 South Beverly Drive
Suite 2151
Beverly Hills, CA USA 90212
Phone: 310-276-0005
Fax: 310-276-0007
E-mail: info@barodaventures.com
Website: www.barodaventures.com

Management and Staff

David Bohnett, Founder
Peter Lee, Partner

Type of Firm

Private Equity Firm

Project Preferences

Type of Financing Preferred:
Balanced

Industry Preferences

In Internet Specific prefer:
E-Commerce Technology
Internet

Additional Information

Year Founded: 1998
Current Activity Level: Actively seeking new investments

BASECAMP VENTURES

One Executive Drive
Suite 8
Moorestown, NJ USA 08057
Phone: 856-813-1100
Fax: 856-813-1148
Website: www.basecampventures.com

Management and Staff

Mel Baiada, Managing Director
Tom Drury, Partner

Type of Firm

Private Equity Firm

Association Membership

Mid-Atlantic Venture Association

Project Preferences

Role in Financing:
Prefer role as deal originator but will also invest in deals created by others

Type of Financing Preferred:
Early Stage
First Stage Financing

Geographical Preferences

United States Preferences:
Mid Atlantic

Industry Preferences

In Communications prefer:
Telecommunications
Data Communications

In Computer Software prefer:
Computer Services
Software
Systems Software
Applications Software

In Internet Specific prefer:
E-Commerce Technology
Internet

Additional Information
Name of Most Recent Fund: BaseCamp Ventures Fund
Most Recent Fund Was Raised: 11/01/2000
Year Founded: 2000
Capital Under Management: $5,000,000
Current Activity Level: Actively seeking new investments
Method of Compensation: Return on investment is of primary concern, do not charge fees

---

BASF FUTURE BUSINESS GMBH
Investor Relations - D 100
Ludwigshafen, Germany D-67056
Phone: 49-621-600
Fax: 49-621-60-42525
E-mail: investorrelations@basf-ag.de
Website: www.basf.com

Management and Staff
Karl-Rudolf Kurtz, Managing Director

Type of Firm
Bank Affiliated

Project Preferences
Type of Financing Preferred:
Seed

Geographical Preferences
International Preferences:
Europe

Industry Preferences
In Semiconductor/Electr prefer:
Analytic/Scientific

In Industrial/Energy prefer:
Materials

Additional Information
Year Founded: 2001
Current Activity Level: Actively seeking new investments

BASF VENTURE CAPITAL GMBH
4 Gartenweg
Gebaude Z 025
Ludwigshafen, Germany 67063
Phone: 49-621-607-6801
Fax: 49-621-607-6819
E-mail: info@basf-vc.de
Website: www.basf-vc.de

Other Offices
46820 Fremont Boulevard
Fremont, CA USA 94538
Phone: 650-440-1924

45th Floor, Jardine House
No. 1 Connaught Place
Central, Hong Kong
Phone: 852-2731-3755

Management and Staff
Dirk Nachtigal, Chief Financial Officer

Type of Firm
Corporate PE/Venture

Project Preferences
Type of Financing Preferred:
Early Stage
Mezzanine
Balanced
Seed
Startup

Geographical Preferences
International Preferences:
Europe
Asia

Industry Preferences
In Semiconductor/Electr prefer:
Analytic/Scientific

In Biotechnology prefer:
Biotechnology

In Medical/Health prefer:
Medical/Health

In Industrial/Energy prefer:
Energy
Materials

In Other prefer:
Environment Responsible

Additional Information
Year Founded: 2001
Capital Under Management: $100,700,000
Current Activity Level: Actively seeking new investments

BASIC ELEMENT (AKA: BAZOVY ELEMENT; FKA: SIBIRSKY ALUMINIUM)
30, Rochdelskaya Street
Moscow, Russia 123022
Phone: 7-495-720-50-25
Fax: 7-495-720-53-95
E-mail: info@basel.ru
Website: www.basel.ru

Type of Firm
Private Equity Firm

Project Preferences
Type of Financing Preferred:
Generalist PE

Geographical Preferences
International Preferences:
Russia

Industry Preferences
In Industrial/Energy prefer:
Energy
Materials
Machinery

In Financial Services prefer:
Real Estate
Financial Services

In Agr/Forestr/Fish prefer:
Mining and Minerals

Additional Information
Year Founded: 1997
Current Activity Level: Actively seeking new investments

BATANAI CAPITAL FINANCE
3 Lawson Avenue, Milton Park
P.O. Box A1480, Avondale
Harare, Zimbabwe
Website: www.africaonline.co.zw/bcf

Management and Staff
Ndaba Mpofu, Managing Director
Nkosana Moyo, Founder

Type of Firm
Private Equity Firm

Additional Information
Year Founded: 1998
Current Activity Level: Actively seeking new investments

BATTELLE MEMORIAL INSTITUTE
505 King Avenue
Columbus, OH USA 43201
Phone: 614-424-6424
Website: www.battelle.org

Management and Staff
Jim Millar, General Partner
Kef Kasdin, General Partner
Morton Collins, General Partner
Ronald Hahn, General Partner

Type of Firm

Private Equity Firm

Additional Information

Year Founded: 2009
Current Activity Level: Actively seeking new investments

BATTELLE VENTURES

103 Carnegie Center
Suite 100
Princeton, NJ USA 08540
Phone: 609-921-1456
Fax: 609-921-8703
E-mail: partners@battelleventures.com
Website: www.battelleventures.com

Management and Staff

Glenn Kline, General Partner
James Millar, General Partner
Kef Kasdin, General Partner
Morton Colins, General Partner
Ralph Taylor-Smith, General Partner
Ronald Hahn, General Partner
Tammi Jantzen, Chief Financial Officer
Tracy Warren, General Partner

Type of Firm

Private Equity Firm

Association Membership

National Venture Capital Association - USA (NVCA)

Project Preferences

Role in Financing:

Prefer role as deal originator but will also invest in deals created by others

Type of Financing Preferred:

Second Stage Financing
Early Stage
Start-up Financing
Seed
First Stage Financing

Size of Investments Considered:

Min Size of Investment Considered (000s): $500
Max Size of Investment Considered (000s): $1,000

Geographical Preferences

United States Preferences:

All U.S.

Industry Preferences

In Semiconductor/Electr prefer:

Sensors

In Industrial/Energy prefer:

Advanced Materials
Environmental Related

Additional Information

Name of Most Recent Fund: Innovation Valley Partners
Most Recent Fund Was Raised: 08/19/2005
Year Founded: 2003
Capital Under Management: $220,000,000
Current Activity Level: Actively seeking new investments
Method of Compensation: Return on investment is of primary concern, do not charge fees

BATTERSON VENTURE PARTNERS (AKA: BVP)

303 West Madison Street
Suite 1625
Chicago, IL USA 60606
Phone: 312-269-0300
Fax: 312-269-0021
E-mail: bvp@battersonvp.com
Website: www.battersonvp.com

Management and Staff

Leonard Batterson, Chairman & CEO

Type of Firm

Private Equity Firm

Project Preferences

Role in Financing:

Will function either as deal originator or investor in deals created by others

Type of Financing Preferred:

Early Stage
Later Stage
Seed
Startup

Size of Investments Considered:

Min Size of Investment Considered (000s): $500
Max Size of Investment Considered (000s): $3,000

Industry Focus

(% based on actual investment)

Computer Software and Services	36.2%
Medical/Health	20.2%
Internet Specific	17.4%
Communications and Media	7.6%
Biotechnology	4.6%
Industrial/Energy	3.9%
Computer Hardware	3.6%
Other Products	3.3%
Semiconductors/Other Elect.	2.4%
Consumer Related	0.8%

Additional Information

Year Founded: 1988
Capital Under Management: $72,000,000
Current Activity Level: Actively seeking new investments
Method of Compensation: Return on invest. most important, but chg. closing fees, service fees, etc.

BATTERY VENTURES, L.P.

Reservoir Woods
930 Winter Street, Suite 2500
Waltham, MA USA 02451
Phone: 781-478-6600
Fax: 781-478-6601
Website: www.battery.com

Other Offices

Trident Nariman Point
Suite 1134, 11th Floor
Mumbai, India 400021
Phone: 91-22-6632-4351
Fax: 91-22-6632-4355

2884 Sand Hill Road
Suite 101
Menlo Park, CA USA 94025
Phone: 650-372-3939
Fax: 650-372-3930

85 Medinat Hayehudim Street
9th Floor, P.O. Box 4075
Herzilya, Israel 46140
Phone: 972-9-9541004
Fax: 972-9-955-4898

Management and Staff

Alexander Benik, Principal
Avi Domoshevizki, Venture Partner
Brian Lieber, Principal
Brian O'Malley, Principal
Chris Hanson, Chief Operating Officer
Chris Schiavo, Chief Financial Officer
Cornel Faucher, Partner
David Tabors, General Partner
David Dreesen, Partner
Jason Matlof, Partner
Jesse Feldman, Principal
Kenneth Lawler, General Partner
Mark Sherman, General Partner
Matthew Niehaus, Partner
Michael Brown, General Partner
Morgan Jones, General Partner
Neeraj Agrawal, General Partner
Oliver Curme, General Partner
Ramneek Gupta, Partner
Richard Frisbie, General Partner
Roger Lee, General Partner
Satya Patel, Principal
Scott Tobin, General Partner
Sunil Dhaliwal, General Partner
Thomas Crotty, General Partner

Type of Firm

Private Equity Firm

Association Membership

Israel Venture Association
Western Association of Venture Capitalists (WAVC)
National Venture Capital Association - USA (NVCA)

Project Preferences

Role in Financing:
Prefer role as deal originator but will also invest in deals created by others

Type of Financing Preferred:
Leveraged Buyout
Mezzanine
Balanced
Start-up Financing
Seed
First Stage Financing
Industry Rollups
Special Situation

Size of Investments Considered:
Min Size of Investment Considered (000s): $100
Max Size of Investment Considered (000s): $50,000

Geographical Preferences

United States Preferences:
All U.S.

Canadian Preferences:
All Canada

International Preferences:
India
United Kingdom
China
Israel
All International

Industry Focus

(% based on actual investment)

Computer Software and Services	27.2%
Internet Specific	24.8%
Communications and Media	19.5%
Semiconductors/Other Elect.	14.6%
Other Products	6.7%
Computer Hardware	5.0%
Industrial/Energy	1.7%
Medical/Health	0.4%
Consumer Related	0.2%

Additional Information

Name of Most Recent Fund: Battery Ventures VIII, L.P.
Most Recent Fund Was Raised: 07/11/2007
Year Founded: 1983
Capital Under Management: $2,900,000,000
Current Activity Level: Actively seeking new investments
Method of Compensation: Return on invest. most important, but chg. closing fees, service fees, etc.

BAUGUR-ID

Tungotu 6
Reykjavik, Iceland 101
Phone: 354-530-7810
Fax: 354-530-7811
Website: www.baugur-id.com

Management and Staff

Jon Thorsteinsson, Managing Director
Skarphedinn Steinarsson, Managing Director

Type of Firm

Corporate PE/Venture

Project Preferences

Type of Financing Preferred:
Leveraged Buyout
Early Stage
Expansion
Mezzanine
Public Companies
Management Buyouts

Geographical Preferences

International Preferences:
United Kingdom
Europe
Iceland
Faroe Islands

Industry Preferences

In Consumer Related prefer:
Retail
Food/Beverage
Consumer Products

Additional Information

Year Founded: 2002
Current Activity Level: Actively seeking new investments

BAX CAPITAL ADVISORS AG

Lindenstrasse 41
Zurich, Switzerland 8008
Phone: 41-43-268-4950
Fax: 41-43-268-4954
Website: www.baxcapital.com

Management and Staff

Alexander Pfeifer, Founder
Felix Ruebel, Founder
Robert Naville, Founder

Type of Firm

Private Equity Firm

Project Preferences

Type of Financing Preferred:
Balanced
Special Situation

Geographical Preferences

International Preferences:
Switzerland
Austria
Germany

Additional Information

Year Founded: 2006
Current Activity Level: Actively seeking new investments

BAY CAPITAL ADVISORS, LLC

One Turks Head Place
Suite 1492
Providence, RI USA 02903
Phone: 401-228-3834
Fax: 401-228-3835
Website: www.baycapllc.com

Management and Staff

Gregory Mulligan, Managing Director

Type of Firm

Bank Affiliated

Project Preferences

Type of Financing Preferred:
Mezzanine

Size of Investments Considered:
Min Size of Investment Considered (000s): $1,000
Max Size of Investment Considered (000s): $10,000

Geographical Preferences

United States Preferences:
East Coast

Additional Information

Year Founded: 2006
Capital Under Management: $30,000,000
Current Activity Level: Actively seeking new investments

BAY CITY CAPITAL LLC

750 Battery Street
Suite 400
San Francisco, CA USA 94111
Phone: 415-676-3830
Fax: 415-837-0996
Website: www.baycitycapital.com

Management and Staff

Carl Goldfischer, Managing Director
David Milligan, Principal
Frederick Craves, Managing Director
Judy Koh, Chief Financial Officer
Manuel Lopez-Figueroa, Vice President
Min Cui, Principal

Type of Firm

Private Equity Firm

Association Membership

National Venture Capital Association - USA (NVCA)

Project Preferences

Role in Financing:
Prefer role as deal originator

Type of Financing Preferred:
Balanced

Size of Investments Considered:
Min Size of Investment Considered (000s): $1,000
Max Size of Investment Considered (000s): $50,000

Geographical Preferences

United States Preferences:
All U.S.

Industry Focus

(% based on actual investment)

Medical/Health	57.8%
Biotechnology	33.2%
Computer Software and Services	3.0%
Internet Specific	2.9%
Consumer Related	1.6%
Computer Hardware	1.5%

Additional Information

Name of Most Recent Fund: Bay City Capital Fund V, L.P.
Most Recent Fund Was Raised: 05/24/2007
Year Founded: 1997
Capital Under Management: $1,500,000,000
Current Activity Level: Actively seeking new investments

BAY HILLS CAPITAL (FKA: MANSBRIDGE CAPITAL MANAGEMENT)

101 California Street
Suite 1725
San Francisco, CA USA 94111
Phone: 415-391-4240
Fax: 415-391-4210
Website: www.bayhillscapital.com

Management and Staff

Albert Chiang, Partner
David Smith, Partner
Jeff Mansukhani, Partner
Joseph Zanone, Chief Financial Officer
Lance Mansbridge, Managing Partner

Type of Firm

Private Equity Advisor or Fund of Funds

Project Preferences

Type of Financing Preferred:
Fund of Funds
Leveraged Buyout
Fund of Funds of Second

Geographical Preferences

United States Preferences:
All U.S.

Additional Information

Year Founded: 2006
Capital Under Management: $30,000,000
Current Activity Level: Actively seeking new investments

BAY PARTNERS

490 South California Avenue
Suite 200
Palo Alto, CA USA 94306
Phone: 650-854-1500
Fax: 650-854-1515
E-mail: partners@baypartners.com
Website: www.baypartners.com

Management and Staff

Atul Kapadia, Managing General Partner
Eric Chin, Partner
Neal Dempsey, Managing General Partner
Neil Sadaranganey, General Partner
Salil Deshpande, Partner
Sandesh Patnam, General Partner

Type of Firm

Private Equity Firm

Association Membership

Western Association of Venture Capitalists (WAVC)
Natl Assoc of Small Bus. Inv. Co (NASBIC)
National Venture Capital Association - USA (NVCA)

Project Preferences

Role in Financing:
Will function either as deal originator or investor in deals created by others

Type of Financing Preferred:
Early Stage
Seed

Size of Investments Considered:
Min Size of Investment Considered (000s): $1,000
Max Size of Investment Considered (000s): $10,000

Geographical Preferences

United States Preferences:
West Coast

Canadian Preferences:
All Canada

Industry Focus

(% based on actual investment)

Computer Software and Services	38.8%
Communications and Media	21.0%
Internet Specific	19.3%
Semiconductors/Other Elect.	11.4%
Computer Hardware	3.9%
Industrial/Energy	2.1%
Biotechnology	1.4%
Other Products	1.2%
Consumer Related	0.8%
Medical/Health	0.2%

Additional Information

Name of Most Recent Fund: Bay Partners XI Parallel Fund, L.P.
Most Recent Fund Was Raised: 10/31/2005
Year Founded: 1976
Capital Under Management: $1,180,000,000
Current Activity Level: Actively seeking new investments
Method of Compensation: Return on investment is of primary concern, do not charge fees

BAY VENTURES, LLC

21 Willow Road
Suite 36
Menlo Park, CA USA 94025
Phone: 650-815-8399
Fax: 650-566-1268
Website: www.bayventuresllc.com

Management and Staff

Donovan Jones, Managing Partner

Type of Firm

Private Equity Firm

Project Preferences

Type of Financing Preferred:
Early Stage
Seed
First Stage Financing

Size of Investments Considered:
Min Size of Investment Considered (000s): $25
Max Size of Investment Considered (000s): $25

Geographical Preferences

United States Preferences:
All U.S.

Industry Preferences

In Semiconductor/Electr prefer:
Sensors

In Medical/Health prefer:
Medical/Health

In Business Serv. prefer:
Media

Additional Information

Year Founded: 2005
Capital Under Management: $6,000,000
Current Activity Level: Actively seeking new investments

BAYARD GROUP (AKA: LANDIS+GYR HOLDINGS)

60 O'Riordan Street
Alexandria
Sydney, Australia 2015
Phone: 61-2-9210-0800
Fax: 61-2-9221-4333
Website: www.landisgyr.com

Management and Staff

Andreas Umbach, President & COO

Andreas Spreiter, Chief Financial Officer
Cameron O'Reilly, CEO & Managing Director

Type of Firm

Private Equity Firm

Project Preferences

Type of Financing Preferred:

Expansion
Acquisition

Geographical Preferences

International Preferences:

Western Europe
Australia

Industry Preferences

In Industrial/Energy prefer:

Energy

Additional Information

Year Founded: 2003
Capital Under Management: $100,000,000
Current Activity Level: Actively seeking new investments

BAYBG BAYERISCHE BETEILIGUNGSGESELLSCHAFT MBH

Koeniginstrasse 23
Munich, Germany D-80539
Phone: 49-89-122280100
Fax: 49-89-122280101
E-mail: info@baybg.de
Website: www.baybg.de

Other Offices

Gewerbemuseumsplatz 2
Nuernberg, Germany 90403
Phone: 49-112-358-605

Type of Firm

Bank Affiliated

Association Membership

German Venture Capital Association (BVK)

Project Preferences

Role in Financing:

Prefer role as deal originator

Type of Financing Preferred:

Early Stage
Expansion
Turnaround
Balanced
Later Stage
Management Buyouts
Startup

Geographical Preferences

International Preferences:

Germany

Industry Preferences

In Consumer Related prefer:

Retail
Consumer Services

Additional Information

Year Founded: 1994
Capital Under Management: $375,500,000
Current Activity Level: Actively seeking new investments

BAYERN KAPITAL GMBH

Laendgasse 135 a
Landshut, Germany 84028
Phone: 49 871 92325-0
Fax: 49 871 92325-55
E-mail: info@bayernkapital.de
Website: www.bayernkapital.de

Management and Staff

Alexander Garnreiter, Partner
Boris Mannhardt, Chief Financial Officer
Brigitte Linseis, Partner
Georg Reid, Partner
Heinz Michael Meier, Managing Director
Joseph Martin Schuster, Managing Director
Klaus Loschner, Partner
Markus Mrachacz, Partner
Markus Baumgartner, Partner
Monika Steger, Partner
Stefan Gotz, Partner

Type of Firm

Bank Affiliated

Association Membership

German Venture Capital Association (BVK)

Project Preferences

Type of Financing Preferred:

Early Stage
Expansion
Later Stage
Seed
Startup

Size of Investments Considered:

Min Size of Investment Considered (000s): $1,000
Max Size of Investment Considered: No Limit

Geographical Preferences

International Preferences:

Germany

Industry Preferences

In Communications prefer:

Communications and Media

In Semiconductor/Electr prefer:

Electronics

In Biotechnology prefer:

Biotechnology

In Industrial/Energy prefer:

Environmental Related

In Other prefer:

Environment Responsible

Additional Information

Year Founded: 1995
Capital Under Management: $95,000,000
Current Activity Level: Actively seeking new investments

BAYERN LB PRIVATE EQUITY (FKA: BLB EQUITY MANAGEMENT GMBH)

Promenadeplatz 1
Munich, Germany 80333
Phone: 49-8955-2563-0
Fax: 49-8955-2563-90
E-mail: info@blb-equity.de
Website: www.blb-equity.de

Type of Firm

Private Equity Firm

Association Membership

German Venture Capital Association (BVK)

Project Preferences

Type of Financing Preferred:

Leveraged Buyout
Expansion
Other
Recapitalizations

Geographical Preferences

International Preferences:

Europe
Germany

Additional Information

Year Founded: 2001
Current Activity Level: Actively seeking new investments

BAYSHORE CAPITAL CORPORATION

181 Bay Street
Suite 2810
Toronto, Canada M5J 2T3
Phone: 416-214-1991
Fax: 416-214-9895

Type of Firm

Private Equity Firm

Additional Information

Year Founded: 1989
Current Activity Level: Actively seeking new investments

BAYTECH VENTURE CAPITAL BERATUNGS GMBH

Theatinerstrasse 7
Munich, Germany D-80333
Phone: 49-89-287-009-0
Fax: 49-89-287009-11
E-mail: info@baytechventure.com
Website: www.baytechventure.com

Management and Staff

Andreas Demleitner, Partner
Bernard Wobker, Venture Partner
Jude Ngu Ewodo, Partner
Rolf Schneider-Gunther, Managing Director

Type of Firm

Bank Affiliated

Association Membership

German Venture Capital Association (BVK)
European Private Equity and Venture Capital Assoc.

Project Preferences

Type of Financing Preferred:

Early Stage
Expansion
Seed
Startup

Size of Investments Considered:

Min Size of Investment Considered (000s): $440
Max Size of Investment Considered (000s): $8,803

Geographical Preferences

United States Preferences:

All U.S.

International Preferences:

Europe
Western Europe
Germany
France

Industry Preferences

In Communications prefer:

Commercial Communications
Telecommunications

In Computer Software prefer:

Systems Software
Applications Software

In Internet Specific prefer:

Internet
Ecommerce

In Computer Other prefer:

Computer Related

In Semiconductor/Electr prefer:

Electronics
Semiconductor

In Biotechnology prefer:

Biotechnology

In Medical/Health prefer:

Medical/Health

In Industrial/Energy prefer:

Advanced Materials

In Other prefer:

Environment Responsible

Additional Information

Year Founded: 2000
Capital Under Management: $89,100,000
Current Activity Level: Actively seeking new investments

BB&T CAPITAL MARKETS | WINDSOR GROUP

12010 Sunset Hills Road
Suite 700
Reston, VA USA 20190
Phone: 703-471-8500
Fax: 703-471-3888
E-mail: windsorinfo@bbandtcm.com
Website: www.windsorgroupllc.com

Management and Staff

Gregory Van Beuren, Managing Director
Gregory Woodford, Managing Director
Gregory Nossaman, Vice President
Norman Bishop, Vice President
Samuel Maness, Vice President

Type of Firm

Bank Affiliated

Project Preferences

Type of Financing Preferred:

Acquisition

Size of Investments Considered:

Min Size of Investment Considered (000s): $10,000
Max Size of Investment Considered: No Limit

Industry Preferences

In Transportation prefer:

Aerospace

In Business Serv. prefer:

Services

Additional Information

Year Founded: 2002
Current Activity Level: Actively seeking new investments

BBE BUSINESS DEVELOPMENT AB

Smalandsgatan 2
Stockholm, Sweden
Phone: 46-8-5180-0010
Fax: 46-8-5180-0013
E-mail: info@bbe.se
Website: www.bbe.se

Management and Staff

Lars Blomberg, Founding Partner

Type of Firm

Private Equity Firm

Association Membership

European Private Equity and Venture Capital Assoc.

Project Preferences

Type of Financing Preferred:

Balanced

Geographical Preferences

International Preferences:

Sweden
Norway
Denmark

Additional Information

Year Founded: 2006
Capital Under Management: $5,900,000
Current Activity Level: Actively seeking new investments

BBI CAPITAL SA

ul. E. Plater 28
Warszawa, Poland
Phone: 48-22-630-3399
Fax: 48-22-630-3370
Website: www.bbicapital.pl

Type of Firm

Private Equity Firm

Project Preferences

Type of Financing Preferred:

Early Stage
Balanced
Seed
First Stage Financing

Geographical Preferences

International Preferences:

Europe

Additional Information

Year Founded: 2008
Current Activity Level: Actively seeking new investments

BBIG VENTURE CAPITAL

Neathouse Place
Victoria
london, United Kingdom SW1V1BH
Phone: 44-207-807-4000
Fax: 44-207-802-4111
Website: www.bhpbilliton.com

Type of Firm

Private Equity Firm

Additional Information

Year Founded: 2001
Current Activity Level: Actively seeking new investments

BC ADVANTAGE FUNDS (VCC), LTD. (FKA: LIONS CAPITAL CORP.)

885 West Georgia Street
Suite 1280
Vancouver, Canada V6C 3E8
Phone: 604-688-6877
Fax: 604-688-6166
E-mail: info@lionscapital.com
Website: www.bcadvantagefunds.com

Management and Staff

Frank Holler, Chief Executive Officer

Type of Firm

Private Equity Firm

Project Preferences

Type of Financing Preferred:

Early Stage
Expansion
Seed
Startup

Geographical Preferences

Canadian Preferences:

Alberta
British Columbia

Industry Preferences

In Computer Hardware prefer:

Computers

In Computer Software prefer:

Software

In Internet Specific prefer:

Internet

In Semiconductor/Electr prefer:

Electronics

In Biotechnology prefer:

Biotechnology

In Medical/Health prefer:

Health Services
Pharmaceuticals

In Industrial/Energy prefer:

Energy

In Other prefer:

Environment Responsible

Additional Information

Year Founded: 2004
Capital Under Management: $74,600,000
Current Activity Level: Actively seeking new investments

BC BRANDENBURG CAPITAL GMBH

Steinstrasse 104-106
Potsdam, Germany 14480
Phone: 49-331-660-1698
Fax: 49-331-660-1699
E-mail: info@bc-capital.de
Website: www.bc-capital.de

Other Offices

Im Technologiepark 1
Frankfurt, Germany 15236
Phone: 49-335-5571690

Management and Staff

Michael Gross, Managing Director
Michael Tones, Managing Director

Type of Firm

Bank Affiliated

Association Membership

German Venture Capital Association (BVK)

Project Preferences

Type of Financing Preferred:

Early Stage
Expansion
Turnaround
Later Stage
Seed
Management Buyouts
Startup
Recapitalizations

Size of Investments Considered:

Min Size of Investment Considered (000s): $241
Max Size of Investment Considered (000s): $4,814

Geographical Preferences

International Preferences:

Germany

Industry Focus

(% based on actual investment)	
Medical/Health	63.2%
Computer Software and Services	17.0%
Biotechnology	11.0%
Semiconductors/Other Elect.	5.4%
Industrial/Energy	3.4%

Additional Information

Year Founded: 1996
Capital Under Management: $33,000,000
Current Activity Level: Actively seeking new investments

BC PARTNERS

43-45 Portman Square
London, United Kingdom W1H 6DA
Phone: 44-20-7009-4800
Fax: 44-20-7009-4899
E-mail: london@bcpartners.com
Website: www.bcpartners.com

Other Offices

667 Madison Avenue
New York, NY USA 10065
Phone: 212-891-2880
Fax: 212-891-2899

7 Quai du Mont Blanc
Geneva, Switzerland 1201
Phone: 41-22-757-8000
Fax: 41-22-757-8080

Neuer Wall 55
Hamburg, Germany 20354
Phone: 49-40-889-1770
Fax: 49-40-8891-7710

Via Brera 3
Milan, Italy 20121
Phone: 39-02-881-231
Fax: 39-02-8812-3290

54 Avenue Marceau
Paris, France 75008
Phone: 33-1-5357-6000
Fax: 33-1-5357-6006

Management and Staff

Charles Bott, Managing Director
Kevin O'Donohue, Partner
Simon Palley, Partner

Type of Firm

Private Equity Firm

Association Membership

Italian Venture Capital Association (AIFI)
British Venture Capital Association (BVCA)
French Venture Capital Association (AFIC)
Swiss Venture Capital Association (SECA)
European Private Equity and Venture Capital Assoc.

Project Preferences

Role in Financing:

Prefer role as deal originator but will also invest in deals created by others

Type of Financing Preferred:
Leveraged Buyout
Expansion

Size of Investments Considered:
Min Size of Investment Considered (000s): $150,000
Max Size of Investment Considered: No Limit

Geographical Preferences

International Preferences:
Italy
United Kingdom
Europe
Germany
France

Industry Focus
(% based on actual investment)

Medical/Health	41.5%
Consumer Related	29.1%
Other Products	20.0%
Communications and Media	7.7%
Industrial/Energy	1.8%

Additional Information
Year Founded: 1986
Capital Under Management: $14,951,900,000
Current Activity Level: Actively seeking new investments
Method of Compensation: Return on invest. most important, but chg. closing fees, service fees, etc.

BCC PRIVATE EQUITY SGR (FKA: BCC CAPITAL)
Via San Vittore al Teatro, 3
Milan, Italy 20123
Phone: 39-02-45495600
Fax: 39-02-45495504
E-mail: info@bcc-privatequity.it
Website: www.bcc-capital.it

Other Offices
Via G. Savelli, 24
Padua, Italy 35129
Phone: 39-049-7800333
Fax: 39-049-7929120

Management and Staff
Enrico Duranti, Managing Director

Type of Firm
Bank Affiliated

Project Preferences

Type of Financing Preferred:
Balanced

Geographical Preferences

International Preferences:
Europe

Additional Information
Year Founded: 2004
Current Activity Level: Actively seeking new investments

BCM TECHNOLOGIES, INC.
1709 Dryden Road
Suite 1790
Houston, TX USA 77030
Phone: 713-795-0105
Fax: 713-795-4602
E-mail: lbell@bcmtechnologies.com
Website: www.bcmtechnologies.com

Management and Staff
Caroline Popper, President

Type of Firm
Corporate PE/Venture

Association Membership
National Venture Capital Association - USA (NVCA)

Project Preferences

Role in Financing:
Prefer role as deal originator

Type of Financing Preferred:
Early Stage
Seed

Size of Investments Considered:
Min Size of Investment Considered (000s): $100
Max Size of Investment Considered (000s): $5,000

Geographical Preferences

United States Preferences:
Texas

Industry Preferences

In Biotechnology prefer:
Biotechnology
Human Biotechnology

In Medical/Health prefer:
Medical/Health
Medical Diagnostics
Medical Therapeutics
Drug/Equipmt Delivery
Other Therapeutic
Medical Products
Pharmaceuticals

Additional Information
Year Founded: 1983
Capital Under Management: $25,000,000
Current Activity Level: Actively seeking new investments
Method of Compensation: Return on investment is of primary concern, do not charge fees

---

BCP CAPITAL SA
Av. Jose Malhoa, 1686
Lisboa, Portugal 1070-157
Phone: 351-21-113-2117
Fax: 351-21-006-7143

Type of Firm
Private Equity Firm

Association Membership
Portuguese Venture Capital Association (APCRI)
European Private Equity and Venture Capital Assoc.

Project Preferences

Type of Financing Preferred:
Second Stage Financing
Expansion

Size of Investments Considered:
Min Size of Investment Considered (000s): $445
Max Size of Investment Considered (000s): $4,453

Geographical Preferences

International Preferences:
Portugal
Europe

Industry Preferences

In Semiconductor/Electr prefer:
Electronics

In Consumer Related prefer:
Consumer

In Industrial/Energy prefer:
Industrial Products

Additional Information
Name of Most Recent Fund: M Inovacao - Fundo de Capital de Risco BCP Capital
Most Recent Fund Was Raised: 10/31/1997
Year Founded: 1987
Capital Under Management: $45,700,000
Current Activity Level: Actively seeking new investments

BD VENTURES (AKA: BECTON, DICKINSON & CO.)
One Becton Drive
Franklin Lakes, NJ USA 07417
Phone: 201-847-6711
Fax: 201-847-4874
E-mail: BDVentures@bd.com
Website: www.bd.com

Other Offices
2350 Qume Drive
San Jose, CA USA 95131

Management and Staff
Peter Origenes, President

Type of Firm
Corporate PE/Venture

Project Preferences

Role in Financing:
Will function either as deal originator or investor in deals created by others

Type of Financing Preferred:
Second Stage Financing
Early Stage
Balanced
Later Stage

Size of Investments Considered:
Min Size of Investment Considered (000s): $250
Max Size of Investment Considered (000s): $5,000

Geographical Preferences

International Preferences:
Europe
Asia

Industry Preferences

In Biotechnology prefer:
Biotechnology

In Medical/Health prefer:
Medical/Health
Medical Diagnostics
Medical Therapeutics
Medical Products

Additional Information
Year Founded: 1998
Capital Under Management: $140,000,000
Current Activity Level: Actively seeking new investments

BDC CAPITAL (AKA: MASSACHUSETTS BUSINESS DEVELOPMENT CORP.)
500 Edgewater Drive
Suite 555
Wakefield, MA USA 01880
Phone: 781-928-1100
Fax: 781-928-1101
Website: www.mass-business.com

Other Offices
20 Church Street
Suite 1740
Hartford, CT USA 06103
Phone: 860-218-2912
Fax: 860-218-2913

120 Exchange Street
Suite 205
Portland, ME USA 04101
Phone: 207-773-3104

Management and Staff
John Hackett, Chief Financial Officer
Karen Michalski, Vice President

Type of Firm
Incubator/Development Program

Project Preferences

Type of Financing Preferred:
Fund of Funds
Early Stage
Mezzanine
Balanced

Size of Investments Considered:
Min Size of Investment Considered (000s): $500
Max Size of Investment Considered (000s): $5,000

Geographical Preferences

United States Preferences:
Northeast
Massachusetts

Additional Information
Year Founded: 1979
Capital Under Management: $27,500,000
Current Activity Level: Actively seeking new investments

BEA SYSTEMS
2315 North First Street
San Jose, CA USA 95131
Phone: 408-570-8000
Fax: 408-570-8901
Website: www.bea.com

Type of Firm
Corporate PE/Venture

Additional Information
Year Founded: 1999
Current Activity Level: Actively seeking new investments

BEACON PARTNERS, INC.
40 Powell Place
Stamford, CT USA 06902
Phone: 203-348-8858
Fax: 203-323-3188
E-mail: information@beaconpartnersinc.com
Website: www.beaconpartnersinc.com

Management and Staff
Eric Vignola, Managing Director
Jim Nixon, Managing Director
Leonard Vignola, Founding Partner

Type of Firm
Private Equity Firm

Association Membership
Natl Assoc of Small Bus. Inv. Co (NASBIC)

Project Preferences

Role in Financing:
Prefer role as deal originator

Type of Financing Preferred:
Second Stage Financing
Leveraged Buyout
Mezzanine
Turnaround
Recapitalizations

Size of Investments Considered:
Min Size of Investment Considered (000s): $300
Max Size of Investment Considered (000s): $1,000

Geographical Preferences

United States Preferences:
Northeast

Industry Focus
(% based on actual investment)

Consumer Related	39.6%
Industrial/Energy	20.5%
Other Products	16.1%
Internet Specific	10.5%
Medical/Health	4.9%
Computer Software and Services	3.4%
Communications and Media	3.4%
Semiconductors/Other Elect.	1.5%

Additional Information
Name of Most Recent Fund: Beacon Group Energy Investment Fund II
Most Recent Fund Was Raised: 03/17/1998
Year Founded: 1976
Capital Under Management: $1,000,000
Current Activity Level: Actively seeking new investments

BEAR GROWTH CAPITAL PARTNERS
383 Madison Avenue
40th Floor
New York, NY USA 10179
Phone: 212-272-2000
Fax: 212-272-7425
Website: www.bsmb.com

Management and Staff
Joseph Scharfenberger, Vice President
Paul Lattanzio, Senior Managing Director

Type of Firm
Bank Affiliated

Project Preferences

Role in Financing:
Prefer role as deal originator but will also invest in deals created by others

Type of Financing Preferred:
Leveraged Buyout
Expansion
Generalist PE
Management Buyouts
Acquisition
Recapitalizations

Size of Investments Considered:
Min Size of Investment Considered (000s): $3,000
Max Size of Investment Considered (000s): $20,000

Additional Information
Year Founded: 2003
Capital Under Management: $150,000,000
Current Activity Level: Actively seeking new investments
Method of Compensation: Return on invest. most important, but chg. closing fees, service fees, etc.

BEAR STEARN VENTURE PARTNERS LLC
575 Lexington Avenue
New York, NY USA 10022
Phone: 212-272-5565

Management and Staff
Earl Hedin, Managing Director

Type of Firm
Bank Affiliated

Project Preferences

Type of Financing Preferred:
Fund of Funds

Additional Information
Year Founded: 1999
Capital Under Management: $153,700,000
Current Activity Level: Actively seeking new investments

BEAR STEARNS HEALTH INNOVENTURES, LLC
237 Park Avenue
Seventh Floor
New York, NY USA 10017
Phone: 212-272-2253
Fax: 917-849-3091
Website: www.healthinnoventures.com

Management and Staff
Elizabeth Czerepak, Managing Partner
Fritz Buhler, Managing Partner
Jurgen Drews, Managing Partner
Stefan Ryser, Managing Partner
Ted Slocomb, Principal

Type of Firm
Bank Affiliated

Project Preferences

Role in Financing:
Prefer role as deal originator but will also invest in deals created by others

Type of Financing Preferred:
Early Stage
Later Stage

Size of Investments Considered:
Min Size of Investment Considered (000s): $5,000
Max Size of Investment Considered (000s): $10,000

Geographical Preferences

United States Preferences:
Mid Atlantic
Northeast
West Coast

International Preferences:
Germany

Industry Preferences

In Biotechnology prefer:
Biotechnology
Human Biotechnology

Additional Information
Year Founded: 2001
Capital Under Management: $212,500,000
Current Activity Level: Actively seeking new investments
Method of Compensation: Return on investment is of primary concern, do not charge fees

---

BEAUFORT CAPITAL GMBH
Alsterarkaden 9
Hamburg, Germany 20354
Phone: 49-40-349-9996
Fax: 49-40-3499-9977
E-mail: info@bo4.de
Website: www.bo4.de

Management and Staff
Anja Moje, Founding Partner
Johann David Herstatt, Founding Partner
Stefan Friese, Partner

Type of Firm
Private Equity Firm

Project Preferences

Type of Financing Preferred:
Leveraged Buyout
Expansion
Balanced

Geographical Preferences

International Preferences:
Europe
Switzerland
Austria
Germany

Additional Information
Year Founded: 2000
Current Activity Level: Actively seeking new investments

BEDFORD CAPITAL
130 Adelaide St. West
Suite 2900
Toronto, Canada
Phone: 416-947-1492
Fax: 416-947-9673
E-mail: info@bedfordcapital.ca
Website: www.bedfordcapital.ca

Management and Staff
Elliott Knox, Managing Director
Tim Bowman, Managing Director

Type of Firm
Private Equity Firm

Association Membership
Canadian Venture Capital Association

Project Preferences

Type of Financing Preferred:
Leveraged Buyout
Management Buyouts
Acquisition
Recapitalizations

Size of Investments Considered:
Min Size of Investment Considered (000s): $100
Max Size of Investment Considered (000s): $300

Geographical Preferences

Canadian Preferences:
All Canada

Additional Information
Year Founded: 1982
Current Activity Level: Actively seeking new investments
Method of Compensation: Return on invest. most important, but chg. closing fees, service fees, etc.

BEDMINSTER CAPITAL LLC
350 Main Street
Suite 5
Bedminster, NJ USA 07921
Phone: 908-234-1063
Fax: 908-234-0664

Management and Staff
David Mathewson, Managing Director

Type of Firm
Other

Project Preferences

Type of Financing Preferred:
Generalist PE

Geographical Preferences

International Preferences:
Eastern Europe
Bulgaria
Romania

Additional Information
Year Founded: 2006
Capital Under Management: $50,000,000
Current Activity Level: Actively seeking new investments

BEECKEN, PETTY & COMPANY LLC
131 South Dearborn Street
Suite 2800
Chicago, IL USA 60603
Phone: 312-435-0300
Fax: 312-435-0371
E-mail: partners@bpoc.com
Website: www.bpoc.com

Other Offices
901 Warrenville Road
Suite 205
Lisle, IL USA 60532
Phone: 630-435-0300
Fax: 630-435-0370

Management and Staff
Brian Chambers, Vice President
Dave Beecken, Partner
David Cooney, Partner
Grant Patrick, Vice President
Greg Moerschel, Partner
John Kneen, Partner
Kenneth O'Keefe, Partner
Pete Magas, Vice President
Thomas Schlesinger, Partner
Troy Philips, Vice President
William Petty, Partner

Type of Firm
Private Equity Firm

Association Membership
National Venture Capital Association - USA (NVCA)
Illinois Venture Capital Association

Project Preferences

Role in Financing:
Will function either as deal originator or investor in deals created by others

Type of Financing Preferred:
Leveraged Buyout
Expansion
Later Stage
Management Buyouts
Recapitalizations

Size of Investments Considered:
Min Size of Investment Considered (000s): $5,000
Max Size of Investment Considered (000s): $50,000

Geographical Preferences

United States Preferences:
All U.S.

Canadian Preferences:
All Canada

Industry Focus
(% based on actual investment)

Medical/Health	66.3%
Computer Software and Services	24.0%
Internet Specific	7.7%
Communications and Media	1.9%

Additional Information
Year Founded: 1996
Capital Under Management: $475,000,000
Current Activity Level: Actively seeking new investments
Method of Compensation: Return on invest. most important, but chg. closing fees, service fees, etc.

BEEKMAN GROUP LLC, THE
708 Third Avenue
Suite 2500
New York, NY USA 10017
Phone: 646-502-3300
Fax: 646-502-3333
E-mail: info@thebeekmangroup.com
Website: www.thebeekmangroup.com

Management and Staff
Andrew Marolda, Managing Director
John Troiano, Chief Executive Officer
Lex Wolf, Vice President
Marc Aronstein, Managing Director
Vikram Sithian, Vice President

Type of Firm
Private Equity Firm

Project Preferences

Type of Financing Preferred:
Mezzanine
Expansion
Management Buyouts
Special Situation
Recapitalizations

Geographical Preferences

United States Preferences:
All U.S.

Industry Preferences

In Medical/Health prefer:
Health Services

In Consumer Related prefer:
Consumer Products
Consumer Services
Education Related

In Industrial/Energy prefer:
Energy

In Transportation prefer:
Transportation

In Financial Services prefer:
Financial Services

Additional Information
Year Founded: 2004
Capital Under Management: $100,000,000
Current Activity Level: Actively seeking new investments

BEFORE SA
140 Rue Faubourg-saint-honore
Paris, France 75008

Type of Firm
Private Equity Firm

Project Preferences

Type of Financing Preferred:
Balanced

Geographical Preferences

International Preferences:
Europe
France

Additional Information
Year Founded: 2000
Current Activity Level: Actively seeking new investments

BEHRMAN CAPITAL
126 East 56th Street
27th Floor
New York, NY USA 10022
Phone: 212-980-6500
Fax: 212-980-7024
E-mail: info@behrmancap.com
Website: www.behrmancap.com

Other Offices
Four Embarcadero Center
Suite 3640
San Francisco, CA USA 94111
Phone: 415-434-7300
Fax: 415-434-7310

Management and Staff

Abhaya Shrestha, Vice President
Gary Dieber, Chief Financial Officer
Grant Behrman, Managing Partner
Gregory Chiate, Principal
Jeff Wu, Vice President
Joshua Batchelor, Vice President
Mark Visser, Partner
Mark Grimes, Vice President
Matthew Lozow, Vice President
Milan Mandaric, Partner
Pradyut Shah, Vice President
Rodney Cohen, Partner
Simon Lonergan, Partner
Tom Perlmutter, Partner
William Matthes, Managing Partner

Type of Firm

Private Equity Firm

Project Preferences

Role in Financing:
Prefer role as deal originator but will also invest in deals created by others

Type of Financing Preferred:
Leveraged Buyout
Expansion
Management Buyouts
Recapitalizations

Size of Investments Considered:
Min Size of Investment Considered (000s): $25,000
Max Size of Investment Considered (000s): $100,000

Geographical Preferences

United States Preferences:
All U.S.

Canadian Preferences:
All Canada

Industry Focus

(% based on actual investment)

Semiconductors/Other Elect.	40.8%
Other Products	25.2%
Industrial/Energy	15.5%
Internet Specific	7.0%
Medical/Health	6.1%
Computer Hardware	2.2%
Computer Software and Services	1.6%
Communications and Media	1.5%

Additional Information

Name of Most Recent Fund: Behrman Capital III, L.P.
Most Recent Fund Was Raised: 04/14/2000
Year Founded: 1992
Capital Under Management: $1,802,000,000
Current Activity Level: Actively seeking new investments
Method of Compensation: Return on invest. most important, but chg. closing fees, service fees, etc.

BEIJING AN CAI TECHNOLOGY VENTURE CAPITAL COMPANY, LTD.

No.11 Baishiqiao
Haidian District
Beijing, China
Phone: 86-10-6846-7066
Fax: 86-10-6846-7061

Type of Firm

Private Equity Firm

Association Membership

Venture Capital Association of Beijing (VCAB)

Project Preferences

Type of Financing Preferred:
Expansion
Startup

Geographical Preferences

International Preferences:
China

Industry Preferences

In Communications prefer:
Telecommunications

In Computer Software prefer:
Software

In Biotechnology prefer:
Biotechnology

In Medical/Health prefer:
Medical/Health

In Industrial/Energy prefer:
Materials

In Manufact. prefer:
Manufacturing

In Other prefer:
Environment Responsible

Additional Information

Year Founded: 2000
Current Activity Level: Actively seeking new investments

BEIJING COLLEGE VENTURE CAPITAL COMPANY, LTD.

Industry Exploit Miyun County
Beijing, China
Phone: 86-10-8909-9027
Fax: 86-10-8909-9523

Type of Firm

University Program

Association Membership

Venture Capital Association of Beijing (VCAB)

Project Preferences

Type of Financing Preferred:
Startup

Geographical Preferences

International Preferences:
China

Industry Preferences

In Industrial/Energy prefer:
Materials

In Other prefer:
Environment Responsible

Additional Information

Year Founded: 2000
Current Activity Level: Actively seeking new investments

BEIJING ELECTRICITY INVESTMENT COMPANY, LTD.

No.2A Tianyin Mansion
FuXinMeng South Street
Beijing, China
Phone: 86-10-6641-1571
Fax: 86-10-6641-1104

Type of Firm

Private Equity Firm

Association Membership

Venture Capital Association of Beijing (VCAB)

Project Preferences

Type of Financing Preferred:
Balanced

Geographical Preferences

International Preferences:
China

Additional Information

Year Founded: 1993
Current Activity Level: Actively seeking new investments

BEIJING GEM I&CC COMPANY, LTD.

21/F, 3 Huaaozhongxin Apt.
31 Zhizhuyuan Haidian District
Beijing, China
Phone: 86-10-6872-8858
Fax: 86-10-6841-0981

Type of Firm
Private Equity Firm

Association Membership
Venture Capital Association of Beijing (VCAB)

Project Preferences
Type of Financing Preferred:
Balanced

Geographical Preferences
International Preferences:
China

Additional Information
Year Founded: 1999
Current Activity Level: Actively seeking new investments

BEIJING GUI GU INDUSTRY INVESTMENT COMPANY, LTD.
Room 109 Xueyan Mansion A
Tsinghua University
Beijing, China
Phone: 86-10-6277-0583
Fax: 86-10-6279-9779

Type of Firm
Private Equity Firm

Association Membership
Venture Capital Association of Beijing (VCAB)

Project Preferences
Type of Financing Preferred:
Startup

Geographical Preferences
International Preferences:
China

Industry Preferences
In Computer Software prefer:
Software

In Semiconductor/Electr prefer:
Electronics

In Medical/Health prefer:
Medical/Health

In Industrial/Energy prefer:
Materials

In Other prefer:
Environment Responsible

Additional Information
Year Founded: 2000
Current Activity Level: Actively seeking new investments

BEIJING GUO HENG TECHNOLOGY GROUP COMPANY, LTD.
Room 40419 Comity Hotel
Beijing, China
Phone: 86-10-8841-7748
Fax: 86-10-6871-1242

Type of Firm
Private Equity Firm

Association Membership
Venture Capital Association of Beijing (VCAB)

Project Preferences
Type of Financing Preferred:
Expansion
Startup

Geographical Preferences
International Preferences:
China

Industry Preferences
In Communications prefer:
Telecommunications

In Computer Software prefer:
Software

In Biotechnology prefer:
Biotechnology

In Medical/Health prefer:
Medical/Health

Additional Information
Year Founded: 1994
Current Activity Level: Actively seeking new investments

BEIJING GUO KE NEW ECONOMY INVESTMENT COMPANY, LTD.
Rm.1505 Jingyu Mansion
100 Xisanhuan North Street
Beijing, China
Phone: 86-10-6842-9358
Fax: 86-10-6872-8868

Type of Firm
Private Equity Firm

Association Membership
Venture Capital Association of Beijing (VCAB)

Project Preferences
Type of Financing Preferred:
Expansion

Geographical Preferences
International Preferences:
China

Industry Preferences
In Communications prefer:
Telecommunications

In Semiconductor/Electr prefer:
Electronics

In Industrial/Energy prefer:
Energy

Additional Information
Year Founded: 2000
Current Activity Level: Actively seeking new investments

BEIJING JI FENG INDUSTRY INVESTMENT & MANAGEMENT COMPANY
6-01/E CITIC Building 19
JianGuomen Wai Street
Beijing, China 100004
Phone: 86-10-8526-2728
Fax: 86-10-6500-7699
E-mail: services@mschina.com
Website: www.mcschina.com

Other Offices
13th Floor, Room 8
150 Fu Hsin North Road
Taipei, Taiwan
Phone: 886-2-2713-4321
Fax: 886-2-2716-3731

No. 79 An Qing Road
He Fei
An Hui, China 230001
Phone: 86-551-267-8222
Fax: 86-551-267-7799

Unit 1106-7, Lippo Sun Plaza
28 Canton Road, Tsimshatsui
Kowloon, Hong Kong
Phone: 852-2375-0085
Fax: 852-2375-1601

20th Floor, Shartex Plaza
88 Zun Yi Road South
Shanghai, China 200336
Phone: 86-21-6219-6908
Fax: 86-21-6208-9355

Type of Firm
Bank Affiliated

Association Membership
Venture Capital Association of Beijing (VCAB)

Project Preferences

Type of Financing Preferred:
Balanced

Geographical Preferences

International Preferences:
China

Industry Preferences

In Communications prefer:
Telecommunications

In Medical/Health prefer:
Medical/Health

Additional Information

Year Founded: 2000
Current Activity Level: Actively seeking new investments

BEIJING JIN CHANG INVESTMENT & CONSULTATION COMPANY, LTD.

17 Fuhua Mansion
8 Chaoyangmeng North Street
Beijing, China
Phone: 86-10-6554-1306
Fax: 86-10-6554-1678

Type of Firm

Private Equity Firm

Association Membership

Venture Capital Association of Beijing (VCAB)

Project Preferences

Type of Financing Preferred:
Startup

Geographical Preferences

International Preferences:
China

Industry Preferences

In Communications prefer:
Telecommunications

In Computer Software prefer:
Software

In Medical/Health prefer:
Medical/Health

Additional Information

Year Founded: 1999
Current Activity Level: Actively seeking new investments

BEIJING JIN GANG VENTURE CAPITAL COMPANY, LTD.

Room 204 Taihua Commerce
13 Huayuan Street
Beijing, China
Phone: 86-10-6207-3380
Fax: 86-10-6207-3381

Type of Firm

Private Equity Firm

Association Membership

Venture Capital Association of Beijing (VCAB)

Project Preferences

Type of Financing Preferred:
Expansion
Startup

Geographical Preferences

International Preferences:
China

Industry Preferences

In Medical/Health prefer:
Medical/Health

In Industrial/Energy prefer:
Materials

Additional Information

Year Founded: 2000
Current Activity Level: Actively seeking new investments

BEIJING JIN GUAN INVESTMENT COMPANY, LTD.

No.801 Unit 3 Meihui Mansion
58 Dongzhong Street
Beijing, China
Phone: 86-10-6554-2710
Fax: 86-10-6554-2711

Type of Firm

Private Equity Firm

Association Membership

Venture Capital Association of Beijing (VCAB)

Project Preferences

Type of Financing Preferred:
Expansion

Geographical Preferences

International Preferences:
China

Industry Preferences

In Communications prefer:
Telecommunications

In Computer Software prefer:
Software

In Semiconductor/Electr prefer:
Electronics

In Biotechnology prefer:
Biotechnology

In Medical/Health prefer:
Medical/Health

Additional Information

Year Founded: 2000
Current Activity Level: Actively seeking new investments

BEIJING SME VENTURE CAPITAL FUND OF FUNDS

c/o Invest Beijing Int'l
No. 2 Fuxingmen South Street
Beijing, China 100031
Phone: 86-10-6641-7900

Type of Firm

Government Affiliated Program

Project Preferences

Type of Financing Preferred:
Fund of Funds
Early Stage
Seed

Geographical Preferences

International Preferences:
China

Industry Preferences

In Industrial/Energy prefer:
Environmental Related

In Manufact. prefer:
Manufacturing

Additional Information

Year Founded: 2008
Capital Under Management: $116,500,000
Current Activity Level: Actively seeking new investments

BEIJING TECHNOLOGY YUAN PORTFOLIO VALUATION COMPANY, LTD.

No.9 Sanyimao
Haidian District
Beijing, China
Phone: 86-10-8269-0424
Fax: 86-10-8269-0506

Type of Firm
Government Affiliated Program

Association Membership
Venture Capital Association of Beijing (VCAB)

Project Preferences

Type of Financing Preferred:
Expansion
Seed

Geographical Preferences

International Preferences:
China

Industry Preferences

In Communications prefer:
Telecommunications

In Semiconductor/Electr prefer:
Electronics
Semiconductor

In Biotechnology prefer:
Biotechnology

In Medical/Health prefer:
Medical/Health

In Industrial/Energy prefer:
Energy
Materials

In Other prefer:
Environment Responsible

Additional Information
Year Founded: 1999
Current Activity Level: Actively seeking new investments

BEIJING TORCH CHENG XIN INVESTMENT & CONSULTATION

Beijing Changchun Bridge 5
New Beginnings Bldgs. 4 2003
Beijing, China 100-089
Phone: 86-10-8256-2615
Fax: 86-10-8256-2616
E-mail: vci@vci.com.cn
Website: www.vci.com.cn

Type of Firm
Private Equity Firm

Association Membership
Venture Capital Association of Beijing (VCAB)

Project Preferences

Type of Financing Preferred:
Expansion
Seed
Startup

Geographical Preferences

International Preferences:
China

Industry Preferences

In Communications prefer:
Telecommunications

In Computer Software prefer:
Software

In Biotechnology prefer:
Biotechnology

In Medical/Health prefer:
Medical/Health

In Industrial/Energy prefer:
Materials

Additional Information
Year Founded: 1997
Current Activity Level: Actively seeking new investments

BEIJING ZHENGRUN INVESTMENT CO., LTD. (AKA: PROPE)

No. 1 Zhongguancun East Road
Room 302 Tower C
Beijing, China 100084
Phone: 86-1-8215-8686
Fax: 86-1-8215-8669
Website: www.prope.com.cn

Management and Staff
Chunwei Lu, President

Type of Firm
Private Equity Firm

Project Preferences

Type of Financing Preferred:
Balanced

Industry Preferences

In Biotechnology prefer:
Biotechnology

In Medical/Health prefer:
Medical/Health

In Consumer Related prefer:
Education Related

In Industrial/Energy prefer:
Energy
Environmental Related

In Business Serv. prefer:
Media

Additional Information
Year Founded: 2007
Current Activity Level: Actively seeking new investments

BELLEVUE ASSET MANAGEMENT AG

Seestrasse 16
Kusnacht/Zurich, Switzerland 8700
Phone: 41-44-267-6700
Fax: 41-44-267-6701
Website: www.bbbiotechventures.com

Other Offices
111 Huntington Avenue
Suite 510
Boston, MA USA 02199-7610

Management and Staff
Anders Hove, Chief Executive Officer
Juerg Eckhardt, Partner
Klaus Breiner, Partner
Martin Muenchbach, Partner

Type of Firm
Investment Management Firm

Project Preferences

Type of Financing Preferred:
Balanced

Geographical Preferences

Canadian Preferences:
All Canada

International Preferences:
Europe
All International

Industry Preferences

In Communications prefer:
Communications and Media
Telecommunications
Wireless Communications

In Computer Software prefer:
Software

In Semiconductor/Electr prefer:
Semiconductor

In Biotechnology prefer:
Biotechnology

In Medical/Health prefer:
Medical/Health
Medical Products
Health Services

Additional Information
Year Founded: 1993
Capital Under Management: $123,000,000
Current Activity Level: Actively seeking new investments

BELTONE PRIVATE EQUITY

Isis Building, Osiris Street
8th and 9th Flr., Garden City
Cairo, Egypt 11451
Phone: 20-2-2792-6610
Fax: 20-2-2792-6852
E-mail: info.privateequity@beltonefinancial.com
Website: www.beltonefinancial.com

Management and Staff

Aladdin Saba, Co-Founder

Type of Firm

Bank Affiliated

Project Preferences

Role in Financing:
Will function either as deal originator or investor in deals created by others

Type of Financing Preferred:
Leveraged Buyout
Acquisition
Recapitalizations

Size of Investments Considered:
Min Size of Investment Considered (000s): $4,443
Max Size of Investment Considered (000s): $177,718

Geographical Preferences

International Preferences:
Egypt
Middle East
Africa

Industry Preferences

In Manufact. prefer:
Manufacturing

In Agr/Forestr/Fish prefer:
Agribusiness
Agriculture related

Additional Information

Year Founded: 2006
Current Activity Level: Actively seeking new investments

BELUGA NV

Assesteenweg 65
Ternat, Belgium 1740
Phone: 32-2-462-6115
Fax: 32-2-462-6141
E-mail: info@belugainvest.com
Website: www.belugainvest.com

Type of Firm

Private Equity Firm

Association Membership

Belgium Venturing Association
European Private Equity and Venture Capital Assoc.

Project Preferences

Type of Financing Preferred:
Balanced

Geographical Preferences

International Preferences:
Belgium

Additional Information

Year Founded: 1998
Current Activity Level: Actively seeking new investments

BELVEDERE CAPITAL PARTNERS LLC

One Maritime Plaza
Suite 825
San Francisco, CA USA 94111
Phone: 415-434-1236
Fax: 415-434-9918
E-mail: contactus@belvederecapital.com
Website: www.belvederecapital.com

Management and Staff

Anthony Frank, Co-Founder
J. Thomas Byrom, Chief Financial Officer
Ronald Bachli, President

Type of Firm

Investment Management Firm

Project Preferences

Role in Financing:
Prefer role as deal originator

Type of Financing Preferred:
Leveraged Buyout
Acquisition

Size of Investments Considered:
Min Size of Investment Considered (000s): $5,000
Max Size of Investment Considered (000s): $100,000

Geographical Preferences

United States Preferences:
West Coast

Industry Focus

(% based on actual investment)

Other Products	99.5%
Computer Software and Services	0.5%

Additional Information

Year Founded: 1998
Capital Under Management: $168,400,000
Current Activity Level: Actively seeking new investments
Method of Compensation: Return on invest. most important, but chg. closing fees, service fees, etc.

BEN FRANKLIN TECHNOLOGY PARTNERS OF CENTRAL AND NORTHERN PA

115 Technology Center
University Park, PA USA 16802
Phone: 814-863-4558
E-mail: info@cnp.benfranklin.org
Website: www.cnp.benfranklin.org

Type of Firm

Government Affiliated Program

Project Preferences

Type of Financing Preferred:
Seed

Additional Information

Year Founded: 1997
Current Activity Level: Actively seeking new investments

BEN FRANKLIN TECHNOLOGY PARTNERS OF NORTHEASTERN PA

125 Goodman Drive
Bethlehem, PA USA 18015
Phone: 610-758-5200
Fax: 800-445-9515
E-mail: info@nep.benfranklin.org
Website: www.nep.benfranklin.org

Other Offices

Berks County Chamber of Commerce
Suite 101, 601 Penn Street
Reading, PA USA 19601
Phone: 610-376-6766
Fax: 610-376-4135

115 Farley Circle
Suite 106
Lewisburg, PA USA 17837
Phone: 570-522-9222
Fax: 570-522-9225

Phoenix Plaza, Suite 200
22 E. Union Street
Wilkes-Barre, PA USA 18701
Phone: 570-819-4002
Fax: 570-819-8931

115 Research Drive
Bethlehem, PA USA 18015
Phone: 610-758-5261
Fax: 610-861-8247

Management and Staff

R. Chadwick Paul, Chief Executive Officer

Type of Firm

Government Affiliated Program

Project Preferences

Type of Financing Preferred:
Early Stage

Geographical Preferences

United States Preferences:
Pennsylvania

Industry Preferences

In Manufact. prefer:
Manufacturing

Additional Information

Year Founded: 1983
Current Activity Level: Actively seeking new investments

BEN FRANKLIN TECHNOLOGY PARTNERS SOUTHEASTERN PA

4801 S. Broad Street-Suite 200
The Navy Yard
Philadelphia, PA USA 19112
Phone: 215-972-6700
Fax: 215-972-5588
E-mail: info@sep.benfranklin.org
Website: www.benfranklin.org

Other Offices

115 Technology Center
University Park, PA USA 16802
Phone: 814-863-4558

2000 Technology Drive
Suite 250
Pittsburgh, PA USA 15219
Phone: 412-681-1520

200 North Third Street
Suite 400
Harrisburg, PA USA 17101
Phone: 717-234-1748

125 Goodman Drive
Bethlehem, PA USA 18015
Phone: 610-758-5200

Management and Staff

Terrence Hicks, Vice President

Type of Firm

Government Affiliated Program

Association Membership

National Venture Capital Association - USA (NVCA)

Project Preferences

Role in Financing:
Will function either as deal originator or investor in deals created by others

Type of Financing Preferred:
Early Stage
Seed

Size of Investments Considered:
Min Size of Investment Considered (000s): $100
Max Size of Investment Considered (000s): $500

Geographical Preferences

United States Preferences:
Pennsylvania

Industry Focus

(% based on actual investment)

Biotechnology	43.9%
Medical/Health	20.1%
Computer Software and Services	8.9%
Internet Specific	8.9%
Other Products	5.0%
Industrial/Energy	3.9%
Computer Hardware	3.1%
Consumer Related	2.5%
Communications and Media	2.5%
Semiconductors/Other Elect.	1.2%

Additional Information

Year Founded: 1983
Capital Under Management: $26,000,000
Current Activity Level: Actively seeking new investments

BENAROYA CAPITAL COMPANY

1100 Olive Way
Suite 1700
Seattle, WA USA 98101
Phone: 206-343-4750
Fax: 206-447-9384
E-mail: general@benaroya.com
Website: www.benaroya.com

Type of Firm

Private Equity Firm

Project Preferences

Role in Financing:
Will function either as deal originator or investor in deals created by others

Type of Financing Preferred:
Second Stage Financing
Balanced
First Stage Financing

Size of Investments Considered:
Min Size of Investment Considered (000s): $500
Max Size of Investment Considered (000s): $3,000

Geographical Preferences

United States Preferences:
Northwest

Industry Preferences

In Communications prefer:
Telecommunications
Wireless Communications
Data Communications

In Semiconductor/Electr prefer:
Semiconductor

Additional Information

Year Founded: 1995
Capital Under Management: $35,000,000
Current Activity Level: Actively seeking new investments
Method of Compensation: Return on investment is of primary concern, do not charge fees

---

BENCHMARK CAPITAL

2480 Sand Hill Road
Suite 200
Menlo Park, CA USA 94025
Phone: 650-854-8180
Fax: 650-854-8183
E-mail: informationUS@benchmark.com
Website: www.benchmark.com

Other Offices

9 Hamanofim Street
Herzliya Pituach, Israel 46725
Phone: 972-9-961-7600
Fax: 972-9-961-7601

Management and Staff

Alexandre Balkanski, General Partner
Andy Rachleff, Partner
Bill Gurley, General Partner
Bruce Dunlevie, General Partner
David Beirne, Partner
Kevin Harvey, General Partner
Matt Cohler, General Partner
Mitchell Lasky, General Partner
Peter Fenton, General Partner
Richard Barton, Venture Partner
Robert Kagle, General Partner
Steve Spurlock, General Partner

Type of Firm

Private Equity Firm

Association Membership

Western Association of Venture Capitalists (WAVC)
National Venture Capital Association - USA (NVCA)
European Private Equity and Venture Capital Assoc.

Project Preferences

Role in Financing:
Prefer role as deal originator but will also invest in deals created by others

Type of Financing Preferred:
Second Stage Financing
Leveraged Buyout
Early Stage
Expansion

Research and Development
Start-up Financing
Seed
First Stage Financing
Special Situation

Size of Investments Considered:
Min Size of Investment Considered (000s): $100
Max Size of Investment Considered (000s): $15,000

Geographical Preferences

United States Preferences:
West Coast
Southwest

International Preferences:
Europe
Israel

Industry Focus
(% based on actual investment)

Internet Specific	39.3%
Computer Software and Services	17.6%
Communications and Media	11.8%
Semiconductors/Other Elect.	11.4%
Other Products	7.8%
Computer Hardware	6.1%
Consumer Related	4.1%
Industrial/Energy	1.6%
Medical/Health	0.4%

Additional Information
Year Founded: 1995
Capital Under Management: $2,500,000,000
Current Activity Level: Actively seeking new investments
Method of Compensation: Return on invest. most important, but chg. closing fees, service fees, etc.

BENCIS CAPITAL PARTNERS

Tower H, Ninth Floor
Zuidplein 76
Amsterdam, Netherlands 1077 XV
Phone: 31-20-5400-940
Fax: 31-20-5400-941
E-mail: info@bencis.nl
Website: www.bencis.nl

Other Offices
Parklane
Culliganlaan 2C
Diegem, Belgium 1831
Phone: 32-2-610-0300
Fax: 32-2-610-0301

Management and Staff
Benoit Graulich, Partner
Bert Godefroid, Partner
Filip Leflot, Partner
Jeroen Pit, Partner
Lesley Van Zutphen, Partner
Zoran Van Gessel, Partner

Type of Firm
Private Equity Firm

Project Preferences

Type of Financing Preferred:
Leveraged Buyout

Geographical Preferences

International Preferences:
Luxembourg
Netherlands
Belgium

Industry Preferences

In Consumer Related prefer:
Consumer

In Industrial/Energy prefer:
Industrial Products

In Transportation prefer:
Transportation

In Financial Services prefer:
Financial Services

In Manufact. prefer:
Manufacturing

Additional Information
Year Founded: 2000
Capital Under Management: $822,700,000
Current Activity Level: Actively seeking new investments

BENEX INVESTMENT, INC.

18/F, 63 Building
60 Yoido-dong, Yongdeungpo-ku
Seoul, South Korea 150-763
Phone: 822-786-6622
Fax: 822-786-3993

Management and Staff
Bum Seok Suh, Chief Executive Officer
Jun Hong Kim, Chief Executive Officer

Type of Firm
Private Equity Firm

Project Preferences

Type of Financing Preferred:
Balanced

Geographical Preferences

International Preferences:
Asia

Industry Preferences

In Communications prefer:
Communications and Media
Commercial Communications
Telecommunications
Wireless Communications
Media and Entertainment

In Consumer Related prefer:
Entertainment and Leisure

In Industrial/Energy prefer:
Environmental Related

In Business Serv. prefer:
Media

Additional Information
Year Founded: 2006
Capital Under Management: $255,400,000
Current Activity Level: Actively seeking new investments

BENFORD CAPITAL PARTNERS LLC

30 North LaSalle Street
Suite 3924
Chicago, IL USA 60602
Phone: 312-932-0200
Fax: 312-932-0220
Website: www.benfordcapital.com

Management and Staff
Benjamin Riefe, Vice President
Edward Benford, Founder

Type of Firm
Private Equity Firm

Project Preferences

Type of Financing Preferred:
Leveraged Buyout
Mezzanine
Recapitalizations

Geographical Preferences

United States Preferences:
All U.S.

Canadian Preferences:
All Canada

Industry Preferences

In Computer Software prefer:
Software

In Biotechnology prefer:
Biotechnology

In Consumer Related prefer:
Retail
Consumer Products
Consumer Services
Other Restaurants

In Financial Services prefer:
Real Estate

Additional Information
Year Founded: 2004
Current Activity Level: Actively seeking new investments

BENNETT JONES

Suite 3400
First Canadian Place
Toronto, Canada M5X1A4
Phone: 416-863-1200
Fax: 416-863-1716
E-mail: firmwatch@bennetjones.ca
Website: www.bennettjones.ca

Management and Staff

Barry Reiter, Partner
Gary Solway, Partner

Type of Firm

Private Equity Firm

Additional Information

Year Founded: 2009
Current Activity Level: Actively seeking new investments

BENSON OAK CAPITAL

Dykova 20
Prague, Czech Republic 101 00
Phone: 420-222-512-422
Fax: 420-222-520-334
Website: www.bensonoak.com

Type of Firm

Private Equity Firm

Project Preferences

Type of Financing Preferred:

Leveraged Buyout

Geographical Preferences

International Preferences:

Czech Republic

Additional Information

Year Founded: 1991
Current Activity Level: Actively seeking new investments

BERENS CAPITAL MANAGEMENT LLC

One Rockefeller Plaza
23rd Floor
New York, NY USA 10020
Phone: 212-698-2030
Fax: 212-698-2021
E-mail: info@berenscapital.com
Website: www.berenscapital.com

Management and Staff

James Dannis, Partner

Type of Firm

Private Equity Firm

Project Preferences

Type of Financing Preferred:

Distressed Debt

Additional Information

Year Founded: 2002
Capital Under Management: $29,300,000
Current Activity Level: Actively seeking new investments

BERGEN VENTURE AS

Skanselien 14
Bergen, Norway 5031
Phone: 47-5531-1328
Fax: 47-5521-4055

Type of Firm

Private Equity Firm

Association Membership

European Private Equity and Venture Capital Assoc.

Project Preferences

Type of Financing Preferred:

Second Stage Financing
Early Stage
Expansion
Turnaround
Seed
Startup

Size of Investments Considered:

Min Size of Investment Considered (000s): $100
Max Size of Investment Considered (000s): $100,000

Geographical Preferences

International Preferences:

Norway

Industry Preferences

In Communications prefer:

Communications and Media
Telecommunications

In Computer Software prefer:

Software

In Internet Specific prefer:

Internet

In Computer Other prefer:

Computer Related

In Semiconductor/Electr prefer:

Electronics

In Biotechnology prefer:

Biotechnology

In Medical/Health prefer:

Medical/Health

In Industrial/Energy prefer:

Factory Automation

Additional Information

Year Founded: 1986
Capital Under Management: $8,200,000
Current Activity Level: Actively seeking new investments

BERINGEA LLC

32330 West Twelve Mile Road
Farmington Hills, MI USA 48334
Phone: 248-489-9000
Fax: 248-489-8819
E-mail: info@beringea.com
Website: www.beringea.com

Other Offices

39 Earlham Street
London, United Kingdom WC2H 9LT
Phone: 44-20-7845-7820
Fax: 44-20-7845-7821

528 Laoshan East Road
Room B5 24th Floor
Shanghai , China 200122

11400 West Olympic Boulevard
Suite 200
Cheviot Hills, CA USA 90064
Phone: 310-445-8859

Management and Staff

Alexander Spiro, Senior Managing Director
Charles Rothstein, Senior Managing Director
David Eberly, Senior Managing Director
Malcolm Moss, Senior Managing Director
Michael Gross, Managing Director
Stuart Veale, Managing Director

Type of Firm

SBIC

Association Membership

British Venture Capital Association (BVCA)
Natl Assoc of Small Bus. Inv. Co (NASBIC)
National Venture Capital Association - USA (NVCA)

Project Preferences

Role in Financing:

Will function either as deal originator or investor in deals created by others

Type of Financing Preferred:

Fund of Funds
Expansion
Balanced
Later Stage

Size of Investments Considered:

Min Size of Investment Considered (000s): $1,000
Max Size of Investment Considered (000s): $5,000

Geographical Preferences

International Preferences:

United Kingdom

Industry Preferences

In Medical/Health prefer:
Medical Diagnostics
Diagnostic Services
Diagnostic Test Products
Drug/Equipmt Delivery
Medical Products
Health Services

In Consumer Related prefer:
Entertainment and Leisure

In Business Serv. prefer:
Media

Additional Information
Year Founded: 1984
Capital Under Management: $225,000,000
Current Activity Level: Actively seeking new investments
Method of Compensation: Return on invest. most important, but chg. closing fees, service fees, etc.

BERK MANAGEMENT B.V.

Marathon 9 F
Hilversum, Netherlands 1213 PE
Phone: 31-35-646-0510
Fax: 31-35-646-0511
E-mail: info@berkpartners.nl
Website: www.berkpartners.nl

Type of Firm
Private Equity Firm

Project Preferences

Type of Financing Preferred:
Leveraged Buyout
Expansion
Balanced

Geographical Preferences

International Preferences:
Netherlands

Additional Information
Year Founded: 1992
Current Activity Level: Actively seeking new investments

BERKELEY MINERAL RESOURCES PLC (FKA: TECTEON PLC)

Second Floor
19/20, Grosvenor Street
London, United Kingdom W1K 4QH
Phone: 44-20-7408-1181
Fax: 44-20-7408-1711
E-mail: info@tecteon.com
Website: www.tecteon.com

Management and Staff
Masoud Ahmadi, Managing Director
Ziv Navoh, Founder

Type of Firm
Corporate PE/Venture

Project Preferences

Type of Financing Preferred:
Startup

Geographical Preferences

International Preferences:
Europe
Israel

Industry Preferences

In Internet Specific prefer:
Internet

Additional Information
Year Founded: 1999
Current Activity Level: Actively seeking new investments

BERKSHIRE PARTNERS LLC

200 Clarendon Street
35th Floor
Boston, MA USA 02116
Phone: 617-227-0050
Fax: 617-227-6105
Website: www.berkshirepartners.com

Management and Staff
Brad Turner, Vice President
Bradley Bloom, Managing Director
Carl Ferenbach, Managing Director
Christopher Hadley, Managing Director
D. Randolph Peeler, Managing Director
David Bordeau, Principal
Edward Whelan, Principal
Elizabeth Hoffman, Principal
Gary Giordano, Vice President
Jane Brock-Wilson, Managing Director
Jay Makadia, Principal
Joshua Lutzker, Principal
Kenneth Bring, Chief Financial Officer
Kevin Callaghan, Managing Director
Lawrence Hamelsky, Managing Director
Marni Payne, Principal
Michael Ascione, Managing Director
Raleigh Shoemaker, Principal
Richard Lubin, Managing Director
Robert Small, Managing Director
Ross Jones, Managing Director
Roy Rosas, Vice President
Vishnu Srinivasan, Principal

Type of Firm
Private Equity Firm

Project Preferences

Role in Financing:
Prefer role as deal originator but will also invest in deals created by others

Type of Financing Preferred:
Leveraged Buyout
Expansion
Recapitalizations

Size of Investments Considered:
Min Size of Investment Considered (000s): $50,000
Max Size of Investment Considered (000s): $500,000

Geographical Preferences

Canadian Preferences:
All Canada

International Preferences:
Europe

Industry Focus

(% based on actual investment)

Consumer Related	29.9%
Other Products	26.3%
Internet Specific	16.6%
Medical/Health	9.6%
Industrial/Energy	7.6%
Communications and Media	5.7%
Semiconductors/Other Elect.	3.7%
Computer Software and Services	0.7%

Additional Information
Year Founded: 1984
Capital Under Management: $6,500,000,000
Current Activity Level: Actively seeking new investments
Method of Compensation: Return on invest. most important, but chg. closing fees, service fees, etc.

BERKSHIRES CAPITAL INVESTORS

430 Main Street
Suite 4
Williamstown, MA USA 01267
Phone: 413-458-9683
Fax: 413-458-5603
E-mail: info@berkshirescap.com
Website: www.berkshirescap.com

Management and Staff
Bradley Svrluga, Partner
Matthew Harris, Managing Partner
Peter Willmott, Managing Partner
Russell Howard, Managing Director

Type of Firm
Bank Affiliated

Project Preferences

Role in Financing:
Will function either as deal originator or investor in deals created by others

Type of Financing Preferred:
Early Stage
Seed

Size of Investments Considered:
Min Size of Investment Considered (000s): $250
Max Size of Investment Considered (000s): $1,500

Geographical Preferences

United States Preferences:
Massachusetts
New York

Industry Preferences

In Communications prefer:
Wireless Communications

In Computer Software prefer:
Software

In Internet Specific prefer:
Internet

In Business Serv. prefer:
Services

Additional Information
Year Founded: 1997
Capital Under Management: $20,700,000
Current Activity Level: Actively seeking new investments

BERTRAM CAPITAL
1117 California Avenue
Palo Alto, CA USA 94304
Phone: 650-543-9300
Fax: 650-543-9329
Website: www.bertramcapital.com

Management and Staff
Ingrid Swenson, Chief Financial Officer
Jared Ruger, Vice President
Jeffrey Drazan, Managing Director
Joseph Tou, Vice President
Kenneth Drazan, Managing Director
Kevin Yamashita, Vice President
Michael Chang, Vice President
Ryan Craig, Vice President
Stephanie Ho, Vice President

Type of Firm
Private Equity Firm

Project Preferences

Type of Financing Preferred:
Public Companies
Management Buyouts
Acquisition

Size of Investments Considered:
Min Size of Investment Considered (000s): $10,000
Max Size of Investment Considered (000s): $50,000

Industry Preferences

In Medical/Health prefer:
Health Services

In Industrial/Energy prefer:
Environmental Related

In Transportation prefer:
Aerospace

In Financial Services prefer:
Financial Services

In Business Serv. prefer:
Services

In Manufact. prefer:
Manufacturing

Additional Information
Year Founded: 2006
Capital Under Management: $35,000,000
Current Activity Level: Actively seeking new investments

BES.COM, SGPS SA
R. Alexandre Herculano, 38-4
Lisboa, Portugal 1250-011
Phone: 351-21-351-5060
Fax: 351-21-351-5079
Website: www.bes.pt

Type of Firm
Bank Affiliated

Additional Information
Current Activity Level: Actively seeking new investments

BESSEMER TRUST CO. FUNDS OF FUNDS GROUP
630 Fifth Avenue
New York, NY USA 10111
Phone: 212-708-9100

Type of Firm
Private Equity Advisor or Fund of Funds

Project Preferences

Type of Financing Preferred:
Fund of Funds

Geographical Preferences

United States Preferences:
All U.S.

Additional Information
Year Founded: 1999
Capital Under Management: $377,000,000
Current Activity Level: Actively seeking new investments

BESSEMER VENTURE PARTNERS
1865 Palmer Avenue
Suite 104
Larchmont, NY USA 10538
Phone: 914-833-9100
Fax: 914-833-9200
E-mail: businessplan@bvp.com
Website: www.bessemervp.com

Other Offices
10 Abba Eban Boulevard
Ackerstein Tower C, 4th Floor
Herzliya Piitauch, Israel 46725
Phone: 972-9-972-1200
Fax: 972-9-972-1220

333 Huai Hai Central Road
Suite 1606 B
Shanghai, China 200021
Phone: 86-21-6120-8860
Fax: 86-21-6120-8835

83 Walnut Street
Wellesley Hills, MA USA 02481
Phone: 781-237-6050
Fax: 781-237-7576

Level Two, Prestige Omega
No. 104, EPIP Zone, Whitefield
Bangalore, India 560 066
Phone: 91-80-4060-0669
Fax: 91-80-4060-0700

535 Middlefield Road
Suite 245
Menlo Park, CA USA 94025
Phone: 650-853-7000
Fax: 650-853-7001

Suite 71 Free Press House
Journal Road, 216 Nariman Point
Mumbai, India 400021
Phone: 91-22-6616-2000
Fax: 91-22-6616-2001

Management and Staff
Adam Fisher, Partner
Alex Ferrara, Vice President
Anil Sarin, Managing Director
Byron Deeter, Partner
Christopher Farmer, Vice President
David Cowan, Managing Partner
Derrick Lee, Vice President
Devesh Garg, Managing Director
J. Edmund Colloton, Managing Partner
James Cham, Vice President
Jeremy Levine, Partner
Justin Label, Partner
Li Gong, Partner
Nancy Straface, Vice President
Rob Chandra, Managing Partner
Robert Stavis, Managing Partner
Robert Goodman, Managing Partner

S.V. Subramanya, Vice President
Sandy Grippo, Chief Financial Officer
Sara Byrne, Vice President
Stephen Kraus, Vice President

Type of Firm

Private Equity Firm

Association Membership

Western Association of Venture Capitalists (WAVC)
National Venture Capital Association - USA (NVCA)

Project Preferences

Role in Financing:
Will function either as deal originator or investor in deals created by others

Type of Financing Preferred:
Second Stage Financing
Leveraged Buyout
Control-block Purchases
Early Stage
Expansion
Research and Development
Balanced
Start-up Financing
Seed
First Stage Financing
Special Situation

Size of Investments Considered:
Min Size of Investment Considered (000s): $1,000
Max Size of Investment Considered (000s): $50,000

Geographical Preferences

United States Preferences:
All U.S.

International Preferences:
India
Sweden
United Kingdom
Europe
China
Iran
Africa

Industry Focus

(% based on actual investment)

Internet Specific	24.6%
Computer Software and Services	18.6%
Communications and Media	16.7%
Semiconductors/Other Elect.	10.4%
Other Products	8.2%
Computer Hardware	5.0%
Consumer Related	4.9%
Medical/Health	4.3%
Industrial/Energy	4.0%
Biotechnology	3.4%

Additional Information

Year Founded: 1911
Capital Under Management: $2,000,000,000
Current Activity Level: Actively seeking new investments
Method of Compensation: Return on investment is of primary concern, do not charge fees

BEST, PATTERSON, CROTHERS & YEOHAM, LTD. (AKA: BPCY)

2200 Ross Avenue
Suite 3838
Dallas, TX USA 75201
Phone: 214-978-3800
Fax: 214-978-3899
Website: www.bpcy.com

Type of Firm

Private Equity Firm

Project Preferences

Type of Financing Preferred:
Recapitalizations

Additional Information

Year Founded: 1990
Current Activity Level: Actively seeking new investments

BETA, SOCIEDADE CAPITAL DE RISCO, SA

Rua Eng. Frederico Ulrich
N 2650
Moreira da Maia, Portugal 4470-605
Phone: 351-220-913-520
Fax: 351-229-428-508
E-mail: info@betascr.com
Website: www.betascr.com

Type of Firm

Private Equity Firm

Association Membership

European Private Equity and Venture Capital Assoc.

Project Preferences

Type of Financing Preferred:
Early Stage
Balanced

Geographical Preferences

International Preferences:
Portugal

Industry Preferences

In Communications prefer:
Communications and Media

In Computer Other prefer:
Computer Related

In Biotechnology prefer:
Biotechnology

In Medical/Health prefer:
Medical/Health

In Consumer Related prefer:
Consumer Services

In Industrial/Energy prefer:
Energy

Additional Information

Year Founded: 2003
Capital Under Management: $7,200,000
Current Activity Level: Actively seeking new investments

BETEILIGUNGSGE-SELLSCHAFT FUR DIE DEUTSCHE WIRTSCHAFT GMBH

Bleichstrasse 2-4
Frankfurt am Main, Germany D-60313
Phone: 49-69-2730-090
Fax: 49-69-273009190
E-mail: info@bdw-gmbh.de

Management and Staff

Berthold Bonanni, Partner
Friedrich Wagener, Partner
Hans E Damisch, Managing Director

Type of Firm

Bank Affiliated

Association Membership

German Venture Capital Association (BVK)
European Private Equity and Venture Capital Assoc.

Project Preferences

Type of Financing Preferred:
Leveraged Buyout
Early Stage
Expansion
Mezzanine
Recapitalizations

Geographical Preferences

International Preferences:
Switzerland
Austria
Germany

Industry Focus

(% based on actual investment)

Biotechnology	75.0%
Other Products	25.0%

Additional Information

Year Founded: 2001
Capital Under Management: $298,500,000
Current Activity Level: Actively seeking new investments

BETWIN INVESTMENTS, INC.

Box 23110
Sault Ste. Marie, Canada P6A 6W6
Phone: 705-253-0744
Fax: 705-253-0744

Management and Staff

D.B.Stinson
Whom to Contact
D.B. Stinson

Type of Firm

Service Provider

Project Preferences

Role in Financing:
Prefer role as deal originator but will also invest in deals created by others

Type of Financing Preferred:
Second Stage Financing

Size of Investments Considered:
Min Size of Investment Considered (000s): $500
Max Size of Investment Considered (000s): $1,000

Geographical Preferences

United States Preferences:
All U.S.

Canadian Preferences:
All Canada

International Preferences:
United Kingdom

Industry Preferences

In Computer Other prefer:
Computer Related

In Semiconductor/Electr prefer:
Electronic Components
Circuit Boards
Fiber Optics

In Medical/Health prefer:
Hospitals/Clinics/Primary
Pharmaceuticals

In Consumer Related prefer:
Food/Beverage
Hotels and Resorts
Education Related

In Industrial/Energy prefer:
Oil and Gas Exploration
Oil & Gas Drilling,Explor
Industrial Products
Machinery
Environmental Related

In Financial Services prefer:
Real Estate

Additional Information

Year Founded: 1983
Capital Under Management: $2,000,000,000
Current Activity Level: Actively seeking new investments
Method of Compensation: Function primarily in service area, receive contingent fee in cash or equity

BEV CAPITAL (FKA: BRAND EQUITY VENTURES)

263 Tresser Boulevard
One Stamford Plaza, Suite 1600
Stamford, CT USA 06901
Phone: 203-724-1100
Fax: 203-724-1155
E-mail: info@bevcapital.com
Website: www.bevcapital.com

Management and Staff

Christopher Kirchen, Managing General Partner
David Yarnell, Managing General Partner
Marc Singer, General Partner
Michael Majors, Vice President
William Meurer, General Partner

Type of Firm

Private Equity Firm

Project Preferences

Role in Financing:
Will function either as deal originator or investor in deals created by others

Type of Financing Preferred:
Second Stage Financing
Early Stage
Expansion
Balanced
Later Stage
Private Placement

Size of Investments Considered:
Min Size of Investment Considered (000s): $1,000
Max Size of Investment Considered (000s): $5,000

Geographical Preferences

United States Preferences:
Mid Atlantic
Northeast

Industry Focus

(% based on actual investment)	
Internet Specific	56.7%
Consumer Related	21.5%
Computer Software and Services	8.7%
Semiconductors/Other Elect.	5.0%
Industrial/Energy	4.4%
Other Products	3.7%

Additional Information

Name of Most Recent Fund: Brand Equity Ventures II, L.P.
Most Recent Fund Was Raised: 03/31/2000
Year Founded: 1997
Capital Under Management: $207,700,000
Current Activity Level: Actively seeking new investments
Method of Compensation: Return on investment is of primary concern, do not charge fees

BEZOS EXPEDITIONS

505 5th Avenue South
Seattle, WA USA 98104
Phone: 206-812-8773
Fax: 206-812-8767
Website: www.bezosexpeditions.com

Type of Firm

Private Equity Firm

Project Preferences

Type of Financing Preferred:
Balanced

Geographical Preferences

United States Preferences:
All U.S.

Additional Information

Year Founded: 2003
Current Activity Level: Actively seeking new investments

BGM BETEILIGUNGSGESELLSCHAFT KS RAVENSBURG

Kreissparkasse Ravensburg
Meersburger Strasse 1
Ravensburg, Germany 88213
Phone: 49-751-84-1301
Fax: 49-751-84-1475
E-mail: andreas.mittelberg@ksk-rv.de
Website: www.kreissparkasse-ravensburg.de

Management and Staff

Andreas Mittelberg, Chief Executive Officer

Type of Firm

Bank Affiliated

Project Preferences

Type of Financing Preferred:
Leveraged Buyout
Early Stage
Expansion

Geographical Preferences

International Preferences:
Germany

Additional Information

Year Founded: 2006
Current Activity Level: Actively seeking new investments

BHF-BANK

Bockenheimer Landstrasse 10
Frankfurt, Germany 60323
Phone: 49-697-180
Fax: 49-69-718-2296
E-mail: corp-comm@bhf-bank.com
Website: www.bhf-bank.com

Type of Firm

Bank Affiliated

Project Preferences

Type of Financing Preferred:
Expansion

Additional Information

Year Founded: 2000
Current Activity Level: Actively seeking new investments

BIA DIGITAL PARTNERS, L.P.

15120 Enterprise Court
Suite 200
Chantilly, VA USA 20151
Phone: 703-227-9600
Fax: 703-227-9645
E-mail: contactdp@bia.com
Website: www.biadigitalpartners.com

Management and Staff

Amy Seibel, Chief Financial Officer
Charles Wiebe, Principal
Damien Dovi, Vice President
Mike Andres, Managing Director
Scott Chappell, Principal
Thomas Buono, Principal

Type of Firm

Bank Affiliated

Project Preferences

Type of Financing Preferred:
Mezzanine

Size of Investments Considered:
Min Size of Investment Considered (000s): $2,000
Max Size of Investment Considered (000s): $25,000

Industry Focus

(% based on actual investment)

Communications and Media	47.0%
Internet Specific	28.8%
Other Products	22.9%
Medical/Health	1.4%

Additional Information

Name of Most Recent Fund: BIA Digital Partners II, L.P.
Most Recent Fund Was Raised: 02/16/2006
Year Founded: 2001
Capital Under Management: $88,000,000
Current Activity Level: Actively seeking new investments

BIBB CO. (FKA: NTC GROUP, THE)

Three Pickwick Plaza
Suite 200
Greenwich, CT USA 06830
Phone: 203-862-2800
Fax: 203-622-6538
Website: www.ntcgroupinc.com

Type of Firm

Private Equity Firm

Project Preferences

Role in Financing:
Prefer role as deal originator but will also invest in deals created by others

Type of Financing Preferred:
Leveraged Buyout
Control-block Purchases
Seed
First Stage Financing

Size of Investments Considered:
Min Size of Investment Considered (000s): $1,000
Max Size of Investment Considered: No Limit

Geographical Preferences

United States Preferences:
All U.S.

Industry Preferences

In Semiconductor/Electr prefer:
Electronic Components
Sensors

In Industrial/Energy prefer:
Factory Automation
Machinery

Additional Information

Year Founded: 1985
Capital Under Management: $150,000,000
Current Activity Level: Actively seeking new investments
Method of Compensation: Return on investment is of primary concern, do not charge fees

BIDV VIETNAM PARTNERS INVESTMENT MANAGEMENT CO. (AKA: BVIM)

Suite 501, 5th Floor
Hoan Kiem
Hanoi, Vietnam
Phone: 84-4-936-6767
Fax: 84-4-936-6768
Website: www.vietnampartnersllc.com

Other Offices

1025 Vermont Avenue North West
Suite 730
Washington, DC USA 20005
Phone: 202-263-5620
Fax: 202-263-5622

16D Phung Khac Khoan Street
District 1
Ho Chi Minh , Vietnam
Phone: 84-8-822-6216
Fax: 84-8-822-6339

52 Vanderbilt Avenue
17th Floor New York
New York, NY USA 10017
Phone: 212-418-4781
Fax: 212-317-8666

Management and Staff

Le T. T. Vu, Principal
Phong Vo, Partner
Virginia Foote, Partner

Type of Firm

Bank Affiliated

Geographical Preferences

International Preferences:
Vietnam

Additional Information

Year Founded: 2006
Capital Under Management: $70,000,000
Current Activity Level: Actively seeking new investments

BIG BANG VENTURES CVA

Hangar 26
Rijnkaai 98
Antwerpen, Belgium B-2000
Phone: 32-3-292-3710
Fax: 32-3-303-5291
E-mail: info@bbv.be
Website: www.bbvc.eu

Management and Staff

Barend Van den Brande, Partner
Frank Maene, Partner
Herman DeLatte, Partner
Patrick De Smedt, Venture Partner

Type of Firm

Incubator/Development Program

Association Membership

European Private Equity and Venture Capital Assoc.

Project Preferences

Role in Financing:
Will function either as deal originator or investor in deals created by others

Type of Financing Preferred:
Early Stage
Expansion
Seed
Startup

Size of Investments Considered:
Min Size of Investment Considered (000s): $428
Max Size of Investment Considered (000s): $2,141

Geographical Preferences

International Preferences:
Luxembourg
Netherlands
Europe
Belgium
Germany
France

Industry Preferences

In Communications prefer:
Telecommunications

In Computer Software prefer:
Computer Services
Software

In Internet Specific prefer:
Internet

In Business Serv. prefer:
Services

Additional Information

Name of Most Recent Fund: Big Bang Ventures II
Most Recent Fund Was Raised: 03/30/2006
Year Founded: 2000
Capital Under Management: $64,600,000
Current Activity Level: Actively seeking new investments

BIG CAPITAL, SA

Praca Duque de Saldanha 1-8
Edificio Atrium Saldanha
Lisbon, Portugal 1050-094
Phone: 351-21-330-5318
Fax: 351-21-330-5519
Website: www.bigonline.pt

Other Offices

Rua Pedro Homem de Melo 55 - 6
Edificio Aviz 4
Porto, Portugal
Phone: 351-22-156-700
Fax: 351-226-169-859

Management and Staff

Nicholas Racich, Chief Operating Officer
Pedro Lameira, Chief Financial Officer

Type of Firm

Private Equity Firm

Association Membership

European Private Equity and Venture Capital Assoc.

Project Preferences

Type of Financing Preferred:
Leveraged Buyout

Geographical Preferences

International Preferences:
Portugal
Europe
Spain

Additional Information

Name of Most Recent Fund: Lead Capital - Fundo de Capital Risco para Investidores Q
Most Recent Fund Was Raised: 06/29/2004
Year Founded: 1999
Capital Under Management: $21,800,000
Current Activity Level: Actively seeking new investments

BIG SKY PARTNERS

One Gate Six Road
Suite 203, Building B
Sausalito, CA USA 94965
Phone: 415-289-1141
Fax: 415-289-1149
Website: www.bigskyvc.com

Management and Staff

Michael Schwab, Managing Director

Type of Firm

Private Equity Firm

Project Preferences

Role in Financing:
Will function either as deal originator or investor in deals created by others

Type of Financing Preferred:
Early Stage
Mezzanine
Seed

Size of Investments Considered:
Min Size of Investment Considered (000s): $100
Max Size of Investment Considered (000s): $1,500

Geographical Preferences

United States Preferences:
All U.S.

Industry Preferences

In Computer Software prefer:
Software

In Industrial/Energy prefer:
Alternative Energy
Energy Conservation Relat
Advanced Materials

Additional Information

Year Founded: 1999
Capital Under Management: $27,000,000
Current Activity Level: Actively seeking new investments
Method of Compensation: Return on investment is of primary concern, do not charge fees

---

BILTMORE VENTURES, L.P.

4828 East Hashknife Road
Phoenix, AZ USA 85054
Phone: 480-585-2535
Fax: 480-585-2546
Website: www.biltmoreventures.com

Management and Staff

Adam Bruss, Managing Director
Howard Lindzon, Managing Director
Morris Callahan, Managing Director

Type of Firm

Private Equity Firm

Project Preferences

Type of Financing Preferred:
Seed

Geographical Preferences

United States Preferences:
All U.S.

Industry Preferences

In Internet Specific prefer:
Internet

Additional Information

Year Founded: 2006
Capital Under Management: $20,000,000
Current Activity Level: Actively seeking new investments

BINEXT CAPITAL (FKA: INSIGHT VENTURE COMPANY, LTD.)

6th Floor, Dongdeok Building
151-8 Gwanhun Dong, Jongno-Gu
Seoul, South Korea 110-300
Phone: 822-3700-1800
Fax: 822-3700-1890
Website: www.binext.com

Management and Staff

David Younghoon Kim, Chairman & CEO
Haksoo Suh, Chief Executive Officer

Type of Firm

Corporate PE/Venture

Association Membership

Korean Venture Capital Association (KVCA)

Project Preferences

Type of Financing Preferred:
Expansion
Balanced
Seed
Startup

Geographical Preferences

International Preferences:
Korea, South

Industry Preferences

In Communications prefer:
Telecommunications

In Computer Software prefer:
Software

In Semiconductor/Electr prefer:
Semiconductor

In Biotechnology prefer:
Biotechnology

In Consumer Related prefer:
Entertainment and Leisure
Food/Beverage

In Industrial/Energy prefer:
Energy
Industrial Products

In Business Serv. prefer:
Distribution

Additional Information

Year Founded: 1987
Capital Under Management: $62,900,000
Current Activity Level: Actively seeking new investments

BIO (BELGIAN INVESTMENT COMPANY FOR DEVELOPING COUNTRIES)

Avenue De Tervuren, 188A
Brussels, Belgium B-1150
Phone: 32-277-89999
Fax: 32-277-89990
Website: www.b-i-o.be

Type of Firm

Government Affiliated Program

Association Membership

African Venture Capital Association (AVCA)

Project Preferences

Type of Financing Preferred:
Fund of Funds

Size of Investments Considered:
Min Size of Investment Considered (000s): $350
Max Size of Investment Considered (000s): $7,000

Geographical Preferences

International Preferences:
Latin America
Middle East
Asia
Africa

Additional Information

Year Founded: 2001
Current Activity Level: Actively seeking new investments

BIO EQUITY RISK MANAGEMENT LLC

75 Arlington Street
Suite 500
Boston, MA USA 02116
Phone: 857-241-3681
E-mail: admin@bioequityrisk.com
Website: www.bioequityrisk.com

Management and Staff

Joseph Siletto, Managing Partner

Type of Firm

Private Equity Firm

Project Preferences

Type of Financing Preferred:
Special Situation

Industry Preferences

In Medical/Health prefer:
Medical/Health

Additional Information

Year Founded: 2009
Current Activity Level: Actively seeking new investments

BIO FUND MANAGEMENT OY

Aleksanterinkatu 17
Helsinki, Finland FI-00100
Phone: 358-9-251-4460
Fax: 358-9-2514-4620
E-mail: biofund@biofund.fi
Website: www.biofund.fi

Other Offices

Store Kongensgade 81A
1st floor
Copenhagen, Denmark DK-1264
Phone: 45-2964-7727

Management and Staff

Eric Leire, Partner
Erkki Pekkarinen, Partner
Juhana Rauramo, Partner
Kalevi Kurkijarvi, Founding Partner
Matts Andersson, Partner
Morten Bro Nielsen, Managing Partner
Pasi Jankala, Partner
Seppo Makinen, Managing Partner

Type of Firm

Private Equity Firm

Association Membership

Finnish Venture Capital Association (FVCA)
European Private Equity and Venture Capital Assoc.

Project Preferences

Type of Financing Preferred:
Leveraged Buyout
Early Stage
Expansion
Balanced
Start-up Financing
Turnaround
Startup

Size of Investments Considered:
Min Size of Investment Considered (000s): $500
Max Size of Investment Considered (000s): $500,000

Geographical Preferences

International Preferences:
Europe
Scandanavia/Nordic Region

Industry Focus

(% based on actual investment)

Medical/Health	50.6%
Biotechnology	42.6%
Computer Software and Services	6.1%
Industrial/Energy	0.7%

Additional Information

Year Founded: 1997
Capital Under Management: $203,700,000
Current Activity Level: Actively seeking new investments

BIO*ONE CAPITAL

20 Biopolis Way
#09-01 Centros
Singapore, Singapore 138668
Phone: 65-6395-7700
Fax: 65-6395-7796
E-mail: infohq@bio1capital.com
Website: www.bio1capital.com

Management and Staff

Lily Chan, Managing Director
Swee-Yeok Chu, Chief Executive Officer

Type of Firm

Government Affiliated Program

Project Preferences

Type of Financing Preferred:
Early Stage
Expansion
Balanced
Seed
Startup

Geographical Preferences

United States Preferences:
All U.S.

International Preferences:
Singapore
All International

Industry Preferences

In Biotechnology prefer:
Biotechnology

In Medical/Health prefer:
Medical/Health
Health Services
Pharmaceuticals

Additional Information

Year Founded: 1990
Capital Under Management: $733,200,000
Current Activity Level: Actively seeking new investments

BIOADVANCE

3701 Market Street
Philadelphia, PA USA 19104
Phone: 215-966-6214
Fax: 215-966-6215
E-mail: info@bioadvance.com
Website: www.bioadvance.com

Other Offices

259 Radnor-Chester Road
Suite 220
Radnor, PA USA 19087
Phone: 610-230-0544
Fax: 610-230-0646

Management and Staff

Barbara Schilberg, CEO & Managing Director
Christopher Damm, Venture Partner

Type of Firm

Government Affiliated Program

Association Membership

Mid-Atlantic Venture Association
National Venture Capital Association - USA (NVCA)

Project Preferences

Role in Financing:
Prefer role as deal originator

Type of Financing Preferred:
Early Stage
Seed
First Stage Financing
Startup

Geographical Preferences

United States Preferences:
Pennsylvania

Industry Preferences

In Biotechnology prefer:
Human Biotechnology
Genetic Engineering
Biosensors
Biotech Related Research

In Medical/Health prefer:
Medical Diagnostics
Diagnostic Test Products
Medical Therapeutics
Drug/Equipmt Delivery
Pharmaceuticals

Additional Information

Year Founded: 2002
Capital Under Management: $20,300,000
Current Activity Level: Actively seeking new investments
Method of Compensation: Return on investment is of primary concern, do not charge fees

---

BIOCATALYST YORKTON, INC.

160 eglinton Aveneu East
Suite 600
Toronto, Canada M4P3B5
Phone: 416-484-4666
Fax: 416-484-6490
E-mail: info@biocatalyst.com

Type of Firm

Private Equity Firm

Project Preferences

Type of Financing Preferred:
Early Stage
Startup

Geographical Preferences

Canadian Preferences:
All Canada

Additional Information

Year Founded: 1996
Current Activity Level: Actively seeking new investments

BIOCROSSROADS, INC.

300 North Meridian Street
Suite 950
Indianapolis, IN USA 46204
Phone: 317-238-2450
Fax: 317-238-2451
Website: www.biocrossroads.com

Management and Staff

Anne Shane, Vice President
Nora Doherty, Chief Financial Officer

Type of Firm

Private Equity Firm

Project Preferences

Type of Financing Preferred:
Balanced
Seed

Geographical Preferences

United States Preferences:
Indiana

Industry Preferences

In Biotechnology prefer:
Human Biotechnology
Biosensors

Additional Information

Year Founded: 2002
Capital Under Management: $6,000,000
Current Activity Level: Actively seeking new investments

BIOENTERPRISE

11000 Cedar Avenue
Suite 100
Cleveland, OH USA 44106
Phone: 216-658-3999
Fax: 216-658-3998
E-mail: info@bioenterprise.com
Website: www.bioenterprise.com

Management and Staff

Baiju Shah, Vice President

Type of Firm

Private Equity Firm

Geographical Preferences

United States Preferences:
Ohio

Industry Preferences

In Biotechnology prefer:
Biotechnology

Additional Information

Year Founded: 2000
Current Activity Level: Actively seeking new investments

BIOFRONTIER PARTNERS, INC.

3F Daiya Yaesuguchi Building
2-2-1 Yaesu Chuo-ku
Tokyo, Japan 104-0028
Phone: 813-5204-7007
Fax: 813-5204-7009
E-mail: info@biofrontier.co.jp
Website: www.biofrontier.co.jp

Other Offices

200 Harbor Drive
Suite 2801,
San Diego, CA USA 92101
Phone: 1-619-531-1100
Fax: 1-619-531-1177

Management and Staff

Hinako Schroeter, Partner
Hiroshi Gushima, Partner
Hiroshi Kawano, Managing Director
Hisanori Ezoe, Partner
Kazuo Kobayashi, Partner
Masami Yamada, Partner
Mitsuo Fujinami, Partner

Type of Firm

Private Equity Firm

Project Preferences

Type of Financing Preferred:
Early Stage
Mezzanine
Balanced

Size of Investments Considered:
Min Size of Investment Considered (000s): $500
Max Size of Investment Considered (000s): $300,000

Geographical Preferences

Canadian Preferences:
All Canada

International Preferences:
Europe
Australia
Japan
All International

Industry Preferences

In Biotechnology prefer:
Biotechnology

In Medical/Health prefer:
Medical Diagnostics
Drug/Equipmt Delivery
Pharmaceuticals

Additional Information

Year Founded: 1999
Capital Under Management: $100,000,000
Current Activity Level: Actively seeking new investments

BIOGENERATION VENTURES

Gooimeer 2-35
Naarden
Leiden, Netherlands 1411 DC
Phone: 31-35-699-3000
Fax: 31-35-699-3001
E-mail: info@biogenerationventures.com
Website: www.biogenerationventures.com

Management and Staff

Edward Van Wezel, Managing Partner
Wil Hazenberg, Partner

Type of Firm

Private Equity Firm

Project Preferences

Type of Financing Preferred:
Early Stage
Startup

Geographical Preferences

International Preferences:
Netherlands

Industry Preferences

In Biotechnology prefer:
Agricultural/Animal Bio.
Industrial Biotechnology

In Medical/Health prefer:
Pharmaceuticals

In Consumer Related prefer:
Food/Beverage

Additional Information

Year Founded: 2006
Capital Under Management: $16,700,000
Current Activity Level: Actively seeking new investments

BIOGESTION S.A. (AKA: BIOAM GESTION - FONDS BIOAM)

12 rue de la Boetie
Paris, France 75008
Phone: 33-1-5818-6070
Fax: 33-1-5818-6078
E-mail: contact@bioam.fr
Website: www.bioam.fr

Management and Staff

Philippe Boucheron, Managing Partner

Type of Firm

Government Affiliated Program

Association Membership

French Venture Capital Association (AFIC)
European Private Equity and Venture Capital Assoc.

Project Preferences

Type of Financing Preferred:
Early Stage
Seed

Size of Investments Considered:
Min Size of Investment Considered (000s): $669
Max Size of Investment Considered (000s): $2,674

Geographical Preferences

International Preferences:
Europe
France

Industry Preferences

In Biotechnology prefer:
Biotechnology

In Medical/Health prefer:
Medical/Health

In Industrial/Energy prefer:
Environmental Related

Additional Information

Year Founded: 2000
Capital Under Management: $75,900,000
Current Activity Level: Actively seeking new investments

BIOLIN MEDICAL AB

Cylindervagen 12
Nacka Strand, Sweden 131 26
Phone: 46-8-4101-8170
Fax: 46-8-4101-8179
E-mail: info@biolin.se
Website: www.biolin.se

Other Offices

Goteborgsv. 74
Savedalen, Sweden S-433 63
Phone: 46-31-340-8642
Fax: 46-31-41-3115

Management and Staff

Per Spangberg, Chief Executive Officer

Type of Firm

Private Equity Firm

Association Membership

Swedish Venture Capital Association (SVCA)

Project Preferences

Type of Financing Preferred:
Early Stage
Expansion
Seed
Startup

Size of Investments Considered:
Min Size of Investment Considered (000s): $106
Max Size of Investment Considered (000s): $531

Geographical Preferences

International Preferences:
Sweden

Industry Preferences

In Biotechnology prefer:
Biotechnology

In Medical/Health prefer:
Medical Products

Additional Information

Year Founded: 1997
Capital Under Management: $6,400,000
Current Activity Level: Actively seeking new investments

BIOM AG

Klopferspitz 19
Haus Nr 7 3 Stock
Munich, Germany D-82152
Phone: 49-89-89-9679-0
Fax: 49-89-89-967979
E-mail: info@bio-m.de
Website: www.bio-m.de

Management and Staff

Enno Spillner, Chief Financial Officer
Horst Domdey, Chief Executive Officer

Type of Firm

Corporate PE/Venture

Project Preferences

Type of Financing Preferred:
Expansion
Seed
Startup

Geographical Preferences

International Preferences:
Germany

Industry Preferences

In Biotechnology prefer:
Biotechnology

Additional Information

Year Founded: 1997
Current Activity Level: Actively seeking new investments

BIOMEDICAL INNOVATIONS, LTD.

Bleicherweg 45
Zurich, Switzerland 8002
Phone: 41-43-344-5707
Fax: 41-43-344-5709
E-mail: info@bmivc.com
Website: www.biomedicalinnovations.com

Other Offices

467 Powers Drive
El Dorado Hills, CA USA 95762
Phone: 916-941-0150
Fax: 916-941-0155

Management and Staff

Andreas Vogler, Managing General Partner
Mikael Von Euw, Managing General Partner
Rafael Andujar, Managing General Partner
Stephen Fry, Managing General Partner
Urs Wettstein, General Partner

Type of Firm

Private Equity Firm

Project Preferences

Type of Financing Preferred:
Expansion
Early Stage
Start-up Financing
Seed
Later Stage

Geographical Preferences

International Preferences:
Europe
Israel

Industry Preferences

In Biotechnology prefer:
Biotechnology

In Medical/Health prefer:
Medical Diagnostics
Drug/Equipmt Delivery
Medical Products
Pharmaceuticals

Additional Information

Year Founded: 2000
Current Activity Level: Actively seeking new investments

BIOMEDPARTNERS

Elisabethenstrasse 23
Basel, Switzerland 4051
Phone: 41-61-270-3535
Fax: 41-61-270-3500
E-mail: info@biomedvc.com
Website: www.biomedvc.com

Other Offices

Bahnhofshasse 10
Zug, Switzerland 6301
Phone: 41-61-270-3567
Fax: 41-61-270-3500

Management and Staff

Andreas Schulze, Partner
Andres Huber, Venture Partner
Bert Van Toor, Partner
Erwin Locher, Venture Partner
Frances Wildhaber, Partner
Gerhard Ries, General Partner
Hans-Reinhard Zerkowski, Venture Partner
Helmut Fanner, Venture Partner
Henri Meier, Founding Partner
Markus Hosang, General Partner
Patrick Burgermeister, Principal
Thomas Moeller, General Partner
Urs Meyer, Venture Partner

Type of Firm

Private Equity Firm

Project Preferences

Role in Financing:
Will function either as deal originator or investor in deals created by others

Type of Financing Preferred:
Early Stage
Start-up Financing
First Stage Financing

Size of Investments Considered:
Min Size of Investment Considered (000s): $360
Max Size of Investment Considered (000s): $3,600

Geographical Preferences

International Preferences:
Switzerland
Central Europe
Europe

Industry Preferences

In Biotechnology prefer:
Biotechnology
Biotech Related Research

In Medical/Health prefer:
Medical/Health
Medical Therapeutics
Health Services

Additional Information

Year Founded: 2002
Capital Under Management: $168,400,000
Current Activity Level: Actively seeking new investments

BIOSTAR VENTURES

560 West Mitchell Street
Suite 480
Petoskey, MI USA 49770

Phone: 213-487-9186
Fax: 213-487-9183
E-mail: info@biostarfund.com
Website: www.biostarfund.com

Management and Staff

Chris Miller, Chief Financial Officer

Type of Firm

Private Equity Firm

Project Preferences

Role in Financing:
Prefer role as deal originator but will also invest in deals created by others

Type of Financing Preferred:
Early Stage
First Stage Financing

Size of Investments Considered:
Min Size of Investment Considered (000s): $250
Max Size of Investment Considered (000s): $1,000

Industry Preferences

In Medical/Health prefer:
Medical/Health
Medical Products

Additional Information

Name of Most Recent Fund: BioStar Ventures II, L.P.
Most Recent Fund Was Raised: 03/11/2008
Year Founded: 2003
Capital Under Management: $10,100,000
Current Activity Level: Actively seeking new investments

BIOTECH TURNAROUND FUND B.V.

Kenaupark 3
Haarlem, Netherlands 2011 MP
Phone: 31-23-553-3988
Fax: 31-23-553-3980
E-mail: info@btf-bv.com
Website: www.btf.eu

Management and Staff

Jan Mellegers, Chief Executive Officer

Type of Firm

Private Equity Firm

Project Preferences

Type of Financing Preferred:
Later Stage

Geographical Preferences

United States Preferences:
All U.S.

International Preferences:
Europe

Industry Preferences

In Biotechnology prefer:
Biotechnology

Additional Information

Year Founded: 2008
Current Activity Level: Actively seeking new investments

BIOTECHONOMY VENTURES, LLC

800 Boylston Street
Suite 1585
Boston, MA USA 02199
Phone: 617-421-5299
Fax: 617-450-9749
E-mail: info@biotechonomy.com
Website: www.biotechonomy.com

Management and Staff

Caleb Winder, Principal
Juan Enriquez, Chairman & CEO

Type of Firm

Private Equity Firm

Project Preferences

Role in Financing:
Will function either as deal originator or investor in deals created by others

Type of Financing Preferred:
Mezzanine
Early Stage
Expansion
Start-up Financing
Later Stage
First Stage Financing

Industry Preferences

In Biotechnology prefer:
Biotechnology

In Industrial/Energy prefer:
Alternative Energy

Additional Information

Name of Most Recent Fund: Biotechonomy SG Entrepreneur Fund I, L.P.
Most Recent Fund Was Raised: 10/07/2005
Year Founded: 2005
Capital Under Management: $5,900,000
Current Activity Level: Actively seeking new investments

BIOTECHVEST

570 Seventh Avenue
New York, NY USA 10018
Phone: 212-262-4646
Fax: 212-462-4360

Management and Staff

Michael Ehrenreich, President

Type of Firm

Private Equity Firm

Additional Information

Year Founded: 2009
Current Activity Level: Actively seeking new investments

BIOTEK PARTENAIRES

41 quai Fulchiron
Lyon, France 69005
Phone: 33-4-7240-2731
Fax: 33-4-7842-3424
E-mail: mdubois@ambis.fr

Management and Staff

Michel Dubois, President

Type of Firm

Private Equity Firm

Project Preferences

Type of Financing Preferred:
Early Stage
Seed
Startup

Geographical Preferences

International Preferences:
France

Industry Preferences

In Biotechnology prefer:
Biotechnology

In Medical/Health prefer:
Medical Therapeutics

Additional Information

Year Founded: 1996
Current Activity Level: Actively seeking new investments

BIOVEDA CAPITAL PRIVATE, LTD.

50 Cuscaden Road
#07-02 HPL House
Singapore, Singapore 249724
Phone: 65-6238-9200
Fax: 65-6733-383
E-mail: info@biovedacapital.com
Website: www.biovedacapital.com

Other Offices

Three Lagoon Drive
Suite 190
Redwood City, CA USA 94065

Phone: 650-508-1388
Fax: 650-508-1188

Management and Staff

Carolynn Gandolfo, General Partner
Celine Chen, Principal
Damien Lim, General Partner
Fredrik Nyberg, General Partner
Juanita Fu, Partner
Kho Choon Joo, Venture Partner
Leon Chen, Partner
Sunny Tan, Venture Partner
Zhi Yang, General Partner

Type of Firm

Private Equity Firm

Association Membership

Singapore Venture Capital Association (SVCA)

Project Preferences

Type of Financing Preferred:
Early Stage
Expansion
Mezzanine
Balanced
Public Companies
Startup

Size of Investments Considered:
Min Size of Investment Considered (000s): $1,000
Max Size of Investment Considered (000s): $5,000

Geographical Preferences

International Preferences:
China
Singapore
Asia

Industry Preferences

In Biotechnology prefer:
Biotechnology

In Medical/Health prefer:
Health Services

Additional Information

Year Founded: 2000
Capital Under Management: $32,000,000
Current Activity Level: Actively seeking new investments

BIOVENTURES (AKA: BIOTECH VENTURE PARTNERS)

45 Roeland Square
Roeland Street
Capetown, South Africa 2024
Phone: 27-21-462-2152
Fax: 27-21-462-2096
E-mail: info@bioventures.co.za
Website: www.bioventures.co.za

Type of Firm

Bank Affiliated

Association Membership

South African Venture Capital Association (SAVCA)

Project Preferences

Type of Financing Preferred:
Early Stage
Startup

Geographical Preferences

International Preferences:
South Africa

Industry Preferences

In Biotechnology prefer:
Biotechnology

Additional Information

Year Founded: 2001
Capital Under Management: $5,000,000
Current Activity Level: Actively seeking new investments

BIOVENTURES INVESTORS

101 Main Street
Suite 1750
Cambridge, MA USA 02142
Phone: 617-252-3443
Fax: 617-621-7993
E-mail: info@bioventuresinvestors.com
Website: www.bioventuresinvestors.com

Management and Staff

Anthony Coia, Principal
Marc Goldberg, General Partner
Peter Feinstein, General Partner
Walter Gilbert, General Partner

Type of Firm

Private Equity Firm

Association Membership

National Venture Capital Association - USA (NVCA)

Project Preferences

Role in Financing:
Will function either as deal originator or investor in deals created by others

Type of Financing Preferred:
Second Stage Financing
Early Stage
Balanced
Seed
First Stage Financing
Private Placement

Size of Investments Considered:
Min Size of Investment Considered (000s): $500
Max Size of Investment Considered (000s): $7,500

Geographical Preferences

United States Preferences:
East Coast
All U.S.

Canadian Preferences:
All Canada

Industry Preferences

In Biotechnology prefer:
Human Biotechnology

In Medical/Health prefer:
Medical Therapeutics
Drug/Equipmt Delivery
Medical Products
Health Services
Pharmaceuticals

Additional Information

Name of Most Recent Fund: BioVentures Investors III, L.P.
Most Recent Fund Was Raised: 12/27/2005
Year Founded: 1997
Capital Under Management: $133,400,000
Current Activity Level: Actively seeking new investments
Method of Compensation: Return on investment is of primary concern, do not charge fees

---

BIP INVESTMENT PARTNERS SA (FKA: BGL INVESTMENT PARTNERS)

Rue des Coquelicots 1
Luxembourg, Luxembourg L-1356
Phone: 352-26-002-61
Fax: 352-26-002-650
E-mail: info@bip.lu
Website: www.bip.lu

Type of Firm

Bank Affiliated

Association Membership

European Private Equity and Venture Capital Assoc.

Project Preferences

Type of Financing Preferred:
Fund of Funds
Leveraged Buyout
Early Stage
Expansion

Size of Investments Considered:
Min Size of Investment Considered (000s): $1,823
Max Size of Investment Considered (000s): $4,558

Geographical Preferences

International Preferences:
Luxembourg
Belgium

Germany
France

Industry Focus

(% based on actual investment)

Biotechnology	38.9%
Other Products	27.3%
Computer Hardware	24.9%
Computer Software and Services	8.9%

Additional Information

Year Founded: 2000
Current Activity Level: Actively seeking new investments

BIRC CORPORATION

1055 West Hastings Street
Suite 1400
Vancouver, Canada V6E 2E9
Phone: 604-214-9415
Fax: 604-214-9416
Website: www.birc.net

Other Offices

1055 West Hastings Street
Suite 1400
Vancouver, Canada V6E 2E9
Phone: 604-214-9415
Fax: 604-214-9416

Management and Staff

John Jeffries, Managing Director

Type of Firm

Private Equity Firm

Additional Information

Year Founded: 1997
Current Activity Level: Actively seeking new investments

BIRCH HILL EQUITY PARTNERS MANAGEMENT INC.

100 Wellington Street West
CP Tower; Suite 230
Toronto, Canada M5K 1A1
Phone: 416-775-3815
Fax: 416-360-1688
E-mail: info@birchhillequity.com
Website: www.birchhillequity.com

Management and Staff

David McCann, Partner
David Samuel, Partner
John MacIntyre, Managing Director
John Loh, Principal
Joseph Wiley, Managing Director
Kevin Godwin, Managing Director
Linda Dougherty, Managing Director
Michael Mazan, Partner
Michael Salamon, Partner
Paul Henry, Partner
Peter Zissis, Chief Financial Officer
Pierre Schuurmans, Partner
Steve Dent, Managing Director
Thecla Sweeney, Principal
Tom Savage, Partner
William Stevens, Principal

Type of Firm

Private Equity Firm

Association Membership

Canadian Venture Capital Association

Project Preferences

Type of Financing Preferred:

Leveraged Buyout
Turnaround
Acquisition

Geographical Preferences

Canadian Preferences:

All Canada

Additional Information

Year Founded: 1995
Capital Under Management: $730,900,000
Current Activity Level: Actively seeking new investments

BIRCH VENTURE CAPITAL, INC.

No. 135 Jianguo North Road
3/F Sec. 2
Taipei, Taiwan 10484
Phone: 886-2-2503-1190
Fax: 886-2-2503-1506
Website: www.birchvc.com

Management and Staff

Terry Huang, Vice President

Type of Firm

Private Equity Firm

Project Preferences

Type of Financing Preferred:

Balanced

Geographical Preferences

United States Preferences:

California

International Preferences:

Taiwan
China

Industry Preferences

In Communications prefer:

Communications and Media
Wireless Communications

In Computer Software prefer:

Software

In Internet Specific prefer:

Internet

In Computer Other prefer:

Computer Related

In Semiconductor/Electr prefer:

Electronics
Semiconductor

In Industrial/Energy prefer:

Environmental Related

Additional Information

Year Founded: 2007
Current Activity Level: Actively seeking new investments

BIRCHMERE VENTURES

One North Shore Center
12 Federal Street, Suite 201
Pittsburgh, PA USA 15212
Phone: 412-322-3300
Fax: 412-322-3226
E-mail: info@birchmerevc.com
Website: www.birchmerevc.com

Management and Staff

Gary Glausser, Founding Partner
Jeanne Cunicelli, Partner
Ned Renzi, Founding Partner
Sean Sebastian, Founding Partner

Type of Firm

Private Equity Firm

Association Membership

Mid-Atlantic Venture Association

Project Preferences

Role in Financing:

Prefer role as deal originator but will also invest in deals created by others

Type of Financing Preferred:

Second Stage Financing
Early Stage
Expansion
Balanced
Later Stage
First Stage Financing
Startup

Size of Investments Considered:

Min Size of Investment Considered (000s): $2,000
Max Size of Investment Considered (000s): $5,000

Geographical Preferences

United States Preferences:

Mid Atlantic

Industry Focus

(% based on actual investment)

Medical/Health	44.5%
Computer Software and Services	14.5%
Industrial/Energy	9.2%
Biotechnology	9.1%
Internet Specific	8.0%
Semiconductors/Other Elect.	6.6%
Communications and Media	4.3%
Computer Hardware	3.8%

Additional Information

Name of Most Recent Fund: Birchmere Ventures III, L.P.
Most Recent Fund Was Raised: 02/11/2005
Year Founded: 1996
Capital Under Management: $160,000,000
Current Activity Level: Actively seeking new investments
Method of Compensation: Return on investment is of primary concern, do not charge fees

---

BIRMINGHAM TECHNOLOGY (VENTURE CAPITAL) LTD

Faraday Wharf
Holt Street
Birmingham, United Kingdom B7 4BB
Phone: 44-121-260-6000
Fax: 44-121-250-3567
E-mail: info@astonsciencepark.co.uk
Website: www.astonsciencepark.co.uk

Management and Staff

Derek Harris, Chief Executive Officer

Type of Firm

Private Equity Firm

Project Preferences

Role in Financing:

Prefer role as deal originator but will also invest in deals created by others

Type of Financing Preferred:

Early Stage
Expansion
Startup

Geographical Preferences

International Preferences:

United Kingdom
Central Europe
Western Europe
Eastern Europe
All International

Industry Preferences

In Computer Other prefer:

Computer Related

In Medical/Health prefer:

Medical/Health

Additional Information

Year Founded: 1999
Capital Under Management: $3,000,000
Current Activity Level: Actively seeking new investments

BISON CAPITAL ASSET MANAGEMENT LLC

10877 Wilshire Boulevard
Suite 1520
Westwood, CA USA 90024
Phone: 310-260-6570
Fax: 310-260-6576
Website: www.bisoncapital.com

Other Offices

401 North Tryon Street
Tenth Floor
Charlotte, NC USA 28202
Phone: 704-333-4899
Fax: 704-998-5770

Management and Staff

Douglas Trussler, President
Jason Strife, Principal
Lou Caballero, Principal
Louis Bissette, Partner
Yee-Ping Chu, Partner

Type of Firm

Private Equity Firm

Project Preferences

Type of Financing Preferred:

Leveraged Buyout
Expansion
Management Buyouts
Acquisition
Recapitalizations

Size of Investments Considered:

Min Size of Investment Considered (000s): $5,000
Max Size of Investment Considered (000s): $30,000

Geographical Preferences

United States Preferences:

Northwest
West Coast
Southwest

Industry Preferences

In Business Serv. prefer:

Distribution

In Manufact. prefer:

Manufacturing

Additional Information

Name of Most Recent Fund: Bison Capital Structured Equity Partners, L.P.
Most Recent Fund Was Raised: 02/01/2003
Year Founded: 2001
Capital Under Management: $110,000,000
Current Activity Level: Actively seeking new investments

BLACK CANYON CAPITAL

2000 Avenue of the Stars
Eleventh Floor
Los Angeles, CA USA 90067
Phone: 310-272-1800
Fax: 310-272-1801
Website: www.blackcanyoncapital.com

Management and Staff

Bradley Spencer, Chief Financial Officer
Cameron Reilly, Principal
Desmond Henry, Principal
Mark Lanigan, Managing Director
Michael Hooks, Managing Director
Paras Mehta, Principal
Tom Barber, Principal
Wayne Wilson, Vice President

Type of Firm

Private Equity Firm

Project Preferences

Type of Financing Preferred:

Mezzanine
Management Buyouts
Acquisition
Recapitalizations

Geographical Preferences

United States Preferences:

All U.S.

Industry Preferences

In Medical/Health prefer:

Health Services

In Consumer Related prefer:

Consumer
Retail
Other Restaurants

In Industrial/Energy prefer:

Industrial Products

In Financial Services prefer:

Financial Services

In Business Serv. prefer:

Media

In Manufact. prefer:

Manufacturing

Additional Information

Year Founded: 2004
Capital Under Management: $500,000,000
Current Activity Level: Actively seeking new investments

BLACK CORAL CAPITAL

60 East 42nd Street
Suite 2514
New York, NY USA 10165
Phone: 514-585-7606
E-mail: info@blackcoralcapital.com
Website: www.blackcoralcapital.com

Other Offices

55 Union Street
Third Floor
Boston, MA USA 02108

2000 McGill College
Suite 500
Montreal, Canada H3A 3H3

Management and Staff

Christian Zabbal, Managing Director
Rob Day, Partner

Type of Firm

Private Equity Firm

Project Preferences

Type of Financing Preferred:
Balanced

Industry Preferences

In Industrial/Energy prefer:
Alternative Energy
Environmental Related

Additional Information

Year Founded: 2008
Current Activity Level: Actively seeking new investments

BLACK DIAMOND CAPITAL MANAGEMENT, LLC

One Conway Park
100 Field Drive, Suite 140
Lake Forest, IL USA 60045
Phone: 847-615-9000

Management and Staff

James Zenni, President, Founder
Mounir Nahas, Senior Managing Director
Stephen Deckoff, Founder

Type of Firm

Private Equity Firm

Project Preferences

Type of Financing Preferred:
Leveraged Buyout
Special Situation
Distressed Debt

Industry Preferences

In Industrial/Energy prefer:
Materials

Additional Information

Year Founded: 2002
Capital Under Management: $982,000,000
Current Activity Level: Actively seeking new investments

BLACKEAGLE PARTNERS (FKA: CENTURION CAPITAL PARTNERS)

6905 Telegraph Road
Suite 205
Bloomfield Hills, MI USA 48301
Phone: 313-647-5348
Website: www.blackeaglepartners.com

Other Offices

1285 Avenue of the Americas
35th Floor
New York, NY USA 10019
Phone: 212-554-4600

Management and Staff

Garrett Kanehann, Founding Partner
J.W.Henry Watson, Founding Partner
Jason Runco, Founding Partner

Type of Firm

Private Equity Firm

Project Preferences

Type of Financing Preferred:
Leveraged Buyout

Size of Investments Considered:
Min Size of Investment Considered (000s): $10,000
Max Size of Investment Considered (000s): $40,000

Geographical Preferences

United States Preferences:
All U.S.

Industry Preferences

In Industrial/Energy prefer:
Energy

In Transportation prefer:
Transportation

In Business Serv. prefer:
Services

In Manufact. prefer:
Manufacturing

Additional Information

Year Founded: 2005
Capital Under Management: $200,000,000
Current Activity Level: Actively seeking new investments

BLACKROCK ALTERNATIVE ADVISORS

800 Scudders Mill Road
Section 3B
Plainsboro, NJ USA 08536
Phone: 609-282-6970
Fax: 609-282-0761
Website: www.blackrock.com

Other Offices

One Financial Centre
Boston, MA USA 02111
Phone: 617-342-1666

55 East 52nd Street
New York, NY USA 10055

33 King William Street
London, United Kingdom EC4R 9AS
Phone: 44-20-7743-3000
Fax: 44-20-7743-1126

Management and Staff

Elliot Asarnow, Managing Director
Jay Park, Managing Director
Joe Sutka, Managing Partner
Laurence Fink, Chairman & CEO
Lynn Baranski, Managing Director
Russ Steenberg, Managing Director
Sallie Shuping Russell, Managing Director
Stephen Kelly, Vice President

Type of Firm

Private Equity Advisor or Fund of Funds

Association Membership

British Venture Capital Association (BVCA)
National Venture Capital Association - USA (NVCA)
European Private Equity and Venture Capital Assoc.

Project Preferences

Role in Financing:
Prefer role in deals created by others

Type of Financing Preferred:
Fund of Funds
Second Stage Financing
Leveraged Buyout
Early Stage
Expansion
Mezzanine
Generalist PE
Turnaround
Other
Later Stage
Open Market
Special Situation
Distressed Debt
Fund of Funds of Second

Size of Investments Considered:
Min Size of Investment Considered (000s): $10,000
Max Size of Investment Considered (000s): $100,000

Geographical Preferences

United States Preferences:
All U.S.

International Preferences:
All International

Industry Focus

(% based on actual investment)

Communications and Media	44.5%
Other Products	31.1%
Medical/Health	14.5%
Industrial/Energy	6.9%
Computer Software and Services	2.2%
Biotechnology	0.9%

Additional Information

Year Founded: 1999
Capital Under Management: $6,100,000,000
Current Activity Level: Actively seeking new investments
Method of Compensation: Return on invest. most important, but chg. closing fees, service fees, etc.

BLACKSMITH CAPITAL

220 Halleck Street
Suite 220
San Francisco, CA USA 94129
Phone: 415-561-3350
E-mail: info@blacksmithcapital.com
Website: www.blacksmithcapital.com

Management and Staff

Philip Black, Senior Managing Director

Type of Firm

Private Equity Firm

Project Preferences

Type of Financing Preferred:
Early Stage

Geographical Preferences

United States Preferences:
All U.S.

Additional Information

Name of Most Recent Fund: Blacksmith Ventures 1-A, L.P.
Most Recent Fund Was Raised: 07/13/2003
Year Founded: 2003
Capital Under Management: $5,000,000
Current Activity Level: Actively seeking new investments

BLACKSTONE GROUP, L.P.

345 Park Avenue
31st Floor
New York, NY USA 10154
Phone: 212-583-5000
Fax: 212-583-5712
E-mail: info@blackstone.com
Website: www.blackstone.com

Other Offices

4401 Northside Parkway
Third Floor, Suite 375
Atlanta, GA USA 30327
Phone: 404-460-2321
Fax: 404-460-2337

40 Berkeley Square
London, United Kingdom W1J 5AL
Phone: 44-20-7451-4000
Fax: 44-20-7451-4001

11-13 Avenue de Friedland
Paris, France 75008
Phone: 33-1-5669-1630
Fax: 33-1-5669-1631

Exchange Place
53 State, 30th Floor
Boston, MA USA 02109
Phone: 617-646-2900
Fax: 617-646-2905

11F AIG Building
1-1-3 Marunouchi, Chiyoda-ku
Tokyo, Japan 100-0005
Phone: 81-3-4577-8400
Fax: 81-3-4577-8401

2494 Sand Hill Road
Suite 200
Menlo Park, CA USA 94025
Phone: 650-798-3800
Fax: 650-798-3801

Express Towers, 5th Floor
Nariman Point
Mumbai, India 400-021
Phone: 91-22-6752-8500
Fax: 91-22-6752-8531

1299 Ocean Avenue
Suite 320
Santa Monica, CA USA 90401
Phone: 310-310-6949
Fax: 310-310-6998

8 Finance Street, Suite 901, 9th Floor
Two International Finance Centre
Central, Hong Kong
Phone: 852-3656-8600
Fax: 852-3656-8601

Winland International Finance Center
Unit F817-18, No. 7, Finance Street
Beijing, China
Phone: 86-10-6649-7300
Fax: 86-10-6649-7301

Management and Staff

Akhil Gupta, Chief Executive Officer
Alan Miyasaki, Managing Director
Alexandra Hill, Principal
Amit Dixit, Managing Director
Andrea Valeri, Principal
Andrew Lax, Principal
Andrew Kuo, Senior Managing Director
Anjan Mukherjee, Managing Director
Anthony Myers, Managing Director
Anthony Steains, Senior Managing Director
Anthony Leung, Senior Managing Director
Arthur Newman, Senior Managing Director
Avi Abergel, Managing Director
Ben Jenkins, Senior Managing Director
Ben Hakim, Managing Director
Bennett Goodman, Senior Managing Director
Brian Gavin, Senior Managing Director
Carolyn Aitchison, Managing Director
Chad Pike, Senior Managing Director
Charles Purse, Senior Managing Director
Chinh Chu, Senior Managing Director
Chris Pasko, Senior Managing Director
Chris Sullivan, Managing Director
Christopher Chee, Principal
Daniel Prendergast, Senior Managing Director
Daniel McMullen, Managing Director
Daniel Fujii, Managing Director
Daniel Smith, Senior Managing Director
Darren Richman, Managing Director
David Bradley, Senior Managing Director
David Riddell, Managing Director
David Blitzer, Senior Managing Director
David Clayton, Managing Director
David Foley, Senior Managing Director
David Hirsh, Managing Director
David Tolley, Senior Managing Director
David Posnick, Senior Managing Director
Dean Criares, Senior Managing Director
Debra Anderson, Managing Director
Dennis McDonagh, Managing Director
Dennis Walsh, Managing Director
Dominik Brambring, Managing Director
Donald Scott, Senior Managing Director
Douglas Ostrover, Senior Managing Director
Douglas Paolilo, Managing Director
Douglas Kirkman, Managing Director
Edwin Conway, Senior Managing Director
Elliot Eisenberger, Managing Director
Fabian Godbersen, Principal
Flip Huffard, Senior Managing Director
Francisco Rey, Senior Managing Director
Frank Cohen, Principal
Frank Schmitz, Senior Managing Director
Frank Forster, Principal
Gabriel Petersen, Principal
Garrett Moran, Senior Managing Director
Garrett Goldberg, Chief Financial Officer
Gary Sumers, Senior Managing Director
George Fan, Managing Director
Gerry Murphy, Senior Managing Director
Gideon Berger, Senior Managing Director
Glenn Alba, Vice President
Greg Hewett, Senior Managing Director
Gregory Leong, Principal
Gregory Miller, Principal
Halbert Lindguist, Senior Managing Director
Hamilton James, President & COO
Harry Moseley, Managing Director

Henry Hsu, Managing Director
Ivan Brockman, Senior Managing Director
J. Albert Smith, Senior Managing Director
James Kiggen, Senior Managing Director
James Didden, Senior Managing Director
James Quella, Senior Managing Director
James Lee, Managing Director
James Christopher, Managing Director
Jan Nielsen, Principal
Jane Lee, Managing Director
Jason New, Senior Managing Director
Jean-Manuel Richier, Senior Managing Director
Jean-Michel Steg, Senior Managing Director
Jeremy Wee, Principal
Jerry DeVito, Managing Director
Jesse Selnick, Managing Director
Jianping Zheng, Senior Managing Director
Jill Greenthal, Senior Managing Director
Joan Solotar, Senior Managing Director
Johan Van Jaarsveld, Managing Director
John Magliano, Managing Director
John Dionne, Senior Managing Director
John Lee, Managing Director
John Hodge, Senior Managing Director
John Studzinski, Senior Managing Director
Jonathan Koplovitz, Senior Managing Director
Jonathan Gray, Senior Managing Director
Joonyong Song, Managing Director
Joseph Baratta, Senior Managing Director
Joseph Russick, Managing Director
Joseph Herman, Senior Managing Director
Joshua Rovine, Managing Director
Julia Kahr, Principal
Kallan Resnick, Principal
Karen Sprogis, Managing Director
Katherine Chung, Principal
Kearnon O Molony, Principal
Keigo Kuroda, Principal
Kenneth Caplan, Senior Managing Director
Kenneth Whitney, Senior Managing Director
Kent Moser, Principal
Khaled Kudsi, Principal
Larry Nath, Senior Managing Director
Laura Waitz, Managing Director
Lawrence Thuet, Senior Managing Director
Lawrence Guffey, Senior Managing Director
Lee Shairman, Managing Director
Lionel Yves Assant, Principal
Louis Salvatore, Senior Managing Director
Louis Pomponio, Managing Director
Luzile Manigbas, Managing Director
Marc Baliotti, Managing Director
Maria Singer, Managing Director
Marisa Beeney, Managing Director
Mark Bandak, Managing Director
Mark Buschmann, Managing Director
Martin Kandrac, Managing Director
Martin Brand, Principal
Martin Schimmler, Principal
Martin Alderson-Smith, Senior Managing Director
Martin Gudgeon, Senior Managing Director
Mary Anne Citrino, Senior Managing Director
Maryfrances Metrick, Principal
Mathew Tooth, Managing Director
Matthew Cyriac, Managing Director
Matthew Quigley, Senior Managing Director
Michael Chae, Senior Managing Director
Michael Dalbello, Managing Director
Michael Whitman, Senior Managing Director
Michael Stark, Senior Managing Director
Michael Puglisi, Senior Managing Director
Michael Dorrell, Senior Managing Director
Michael Genereux, Senior Managing Director
Michael Nash, Senior Managing Director
Miguel Ramos-Fuentenebro, Managing Director
Mike Casey, Managing Director
Neil Simpkins, Senior Managing Director
Nicholas Leone, Senior Managing Director
Nick Lyle, Principal
Nitin Karnani, Managing Director
Pamela Zilly, Senior Managing Director
Patrick Ochs, Managing Director
Patrick Schumacher, Managing Director
Patty Lynett, Managing Director
Paul Schlaack, Managing Director
Paul Schorr, Senior Managing Director
Peter Laurinaitis, Managing Director
Peter Rose, Managing Director
Peter Koffler, Managing Director
Peter Wallace, Managing Director
Peter Stoll, Managing Director
Peter Sotoloff, Principal
Philip Anker, Managing Director
Philip Levinson, Managing Director
Pilar Junco, Chief Operating Officer
Prakash Melwani, Senior Managing Director
Punita Kumar-Sinha, Senior Managing Director
Raffiq Nathoo, Senior Managing Director
Rafic Said, Principal
Richard Troyer, Principal
Rob Harper, Principal
Robert McMullan, Managing Director
Robert Petrini, Managing Director
Robert Friedman, Senior Managing Director
Robert Reid, Managing Director
Robert Barrack, Managing Director
Robert Yang, Principal
Robert Schoder, Principal
Robert Lester, Principal
Sean Klimczak, Principal
Sean Keene, Senior Managing Director
Shan Fu, Managing Director
Shervin Korangy, Managing Director
Shiong Tan, Principal
Simon Davies, Managing Director
Stefan Feuerabendt, Senior Managing Director
Stephen Skrenta, Managing Director
Stephens Sullens, Senior Managing Director
Steve Zelin, Senior Managing Director
Stuart Grant, Vice President
Susannah Lindenfield, Managing Director
Sylvia Moss, Senior Managing Director
Ted Coons, Principal
Thomas Stoddard, Senior Managing Director
Thomas Kelly, Managing Director
Thomas Roberts, Senior Managing Director
Thomas Middleton, Senior Managing Director
Timothy White, Senior Managing Director
Tom Scibetta, Principal
Tuhin Parikh, Managing Director
Tyler Henritze, Principal
Vikrant Sawhney, Senior Managing Director
Vincent Lu, Managing Director
Viral Parikh, Principal
William Tice, Principal
William Oglesby, Senior Managing Director
William Stein, Managing Director
Xiaowen Jing, Managing Director
Xuming Bao, Principal
Zachary Stassi, Principal
Zheng Jianping, Senior Managing Director

Type of Firm

Bank Affiliated

Association Membership

Private Equity Council (PEC)

Project Preferences

Type of Financing Preferred:

Leveraged Buyout
Mezzanine
Generalist PE
Other
Strategic Alliances
Distressed Debt

Size of Investments Considered:

Min Size of Investment Considered (000s): $100,000
Max Size of Investment Considered (000s): $400,000

Geographical Preferences

United States Preferences:

All U.S.

International Preferences:

Latin America
Europe
China
Western Europe
All International

Industry Focus

(% based on actual investment)

Other Products	36.2%
Consumer Related	36.0%
Industrial/Energy	8.6%
Communications and Media	6.3%
Semiconductors/Other Elect.	5.3%
Medical/Health	4.5%
Computer Hardware	2.1%
Internet Specific	0.5%
Computer Software and Services	0.5%
Biotechnology	0.1%

Additional Information

Name of Most Recent Fund: Blackstone Real Estate Partners VI.TE.2, L.P.
Most Recent Fund Was Raised: 02/22/2007
Year Founded: 1985
Capital Under Management: $62,141,100,000
Current Activity Level: Actively seeking new investments

BLACKSTREET CAPITAL MANAGEMENT (FKA: MMP CAPITAL ADVISORS)

4800 Montgomery Lane
Suite 940
Bethesda, MD USA 20814
Phone: 240-223-1330
Fax: 240-223-1331
E-mail: info@blackstreetcapital.com
Website: www.blackstreetcapital.com

Other Offices

2nd Floor, Room 204
222 Calea Victoriei
Sector 1, Bucharest , Romania 71104
Phone: 40-21-314-8206
Fax: 40-21-314-0703

1007 Raheja Centre
Free Press Journal Marg
Nariman Point, Bombay , India 400 021
Phone: 91-22-282-3047
Fax: 91-22-281-8156

One Southeast Third Avenue
Suite 2920
Miami, FL USA 33131
Phone: 305-579-2001

51 JFK Parkway
1st Floor, West
Short Hills, NJ USA 07078
Phone: 866-367-3002
Fax: 973-833-0249

Management and Staff

Aldus Chapin II, Managing Director
Lawrence Berger, Principal
Murry Gunty, Managing Director
Steven Quamme, Managing Director

Type of Firm

Bank Affiliated

Project Preferences

Type of Financing Preferred:

Leveraged Buyout
Balanced
Turnaround

Geographical Preferences

United States Preferences:

Mid Atlantic
Midwest
Southeast

International Preferences:

Eastern Europe
Asia

Industry Preferences

In Medical/Health prefer:

Medical/Health

In Consumer Related prefer:

Retail
Education Related

In Financial Services prefer:

Real Estate
Financial Services

In Business Serv. prefer:

Services
Distribution

In Manufact. prefer:

Manufacturing

Additional Information

Name of Most Recent Fund: Black Street Capital Partners I, L.P. (AKA: BRP, FKA: MMP I)
Most Recent Fund Was Raised: 03/03/2003
Year Founded: 2002
Capital Under Management: $88,000,000
Current Activity Level: Actively seeking new investments

BLADE VENTURES

27762 Antonio Parkway
Suite L1-426
Ladera Ranch, CA USA 92694
Phone: 949-298-4577
Fax: 949-554-0181
E-mail: admin@bladeventures.com
Website: www.bladeventures.com

Management and Staff

Brian Flucht, Principal
Craig Gunther, Managing Director
Rajeev Varshneya, Venture Partner

Type of Firm

Private Equity Firm

Project Preferences

Role in Financing:

Prefer role as deal originator but will also invest in deals created by others

Type of Financing Preferred:

Second Stage Financing
Early Stage
Balanced
Seed
First Stage Financing
Startup
Special Situation
Recapitalizations

Size of Investments Considered:

Min Size of Investment Considered (000s): $200
Max Size of Investment Considered (000s): $2,000

Geographical Preferences

United States Preferences:

All U.S.

Industry Preferences

In Communications prefer:

Commercial Communications
CATV & Pay TV Systems
Telecommunications
Wireless Communications
Data Communications
Satellite Microwave Comm.
Other Communication Prod.

In Computer Software prefer:

Software
Systems Software
Applications Software

In Internet Specific prefer:

E-Commerce Technology
Internet
Ecommerce

In Semiconductor/Electr prefer:

Electronic Components
Semiconductor
Micro-Processing
Controllers and Sensors
Sensors
Laser Related
Fiber Optics
Optoelectronics

In Biotechnology prefer:

Biosensors

In Medical/Health prefer:

Medical Diagnostics
Medical Therapeutics
Medical Products
Disposable Med. Products
Health Services

Additional Information

Year Founded: 2005
Current Activity Level: Actively seeking new investments
Method of Compensation: Return on investment is of primary concern, do not charge fees

BLS VENTURE CAPITAL GMBH

Wilhelmstrasse 140
Berlin, Germany 10963
Phone: 49-30-790-1800
Fax: 49-30-790-18020
E-mail: info@bls-venture.de
Website: www.bls-venture.de

Management and Staff

Bernhard Bohm, Chief Executive Officer

Type of Firm

Private Equity Firm

Project Preferences

Type of Financing Preferred:

Balanced

Geographical Preferences

International Preferences:
Germany

Additional Information

Year Founded: 1997
Current Activity Level: Actively seeking new investments

BLUE CHIP VENTURE COMPANY

1100 Chiquita Center
250 East Fifth Street
Cincinnati, OH USA 45202
Phone: 513-723-2300
Fax: 513-723-2306
E-mail: info@bcvc.com
Website: www.bcvc.com

Other Offices

11611 North Meridian Street
Suite 310
Carmel, IN USA 46032
Phone: 317-275-6800
Fax: 317-275-1100

130 South First Street
Suite 310
Ann Arbor, MI USA 48104
Phone: 734-668-9000
Fax: 734-669-4195

1177 Summer Street
Third Floor
Stamford, CT USA 06905
Phone: 203-961-9688
Fax: 203-961-1198

Management and Staff

Christopher McCleary, Venture Partner
Don Aquilano, Managing Director
Donald Walker, Managing Director
Gregory Taylor, Venture Partner
John McIlwraith, Managing Director
John Wyant, Managing Director
Joshua Beebe, Venture Partner
Mark Wright, Managing Director
Richard Kiley, Venture Partner
Susan Schieman, Chief Financial Officer

Type of Firm

Private Equity Firm

Association Membership

Natl Assoc of Investment Cos. (NAIC)
National Venture Capital Association - USA (NVCA)

Project Preferences

Role in Financing:
Prefer role as deal originator

Type of Financing Preferred:
Early Stage
Seed
First Stage Financing
Startup

Size of Investments Considered:
Min Size of Investment Considered (000s): $50
Max Size of Investment Considered (000s): $10,000

Geographical Preferences

United States Preferences:
Midwest
Northeast
All U.S.

Canadian Preferences:
All Canada

Industry Focus

(% based on actual investment)

Internet Specific	35.8%
Computer Software and Services	20.0%
Medical/Health	17.5%
Communications and Media	6.7%
Consumer Related	4.6%
Semiconductors/Other Elect.	4.0%
Other Products	3.4%
Computer Hardware	3.3%
Biotechnology	2.6%
Industrial/Energy	2.1%

Additional Information

Name of Most Recent Fund: Blue Chip V, L.P.
Most Recent Fund Was Raised: 09/23/2008
Year Founded: 1991
Capital Under Management: $600,000,000
Current Activity Level: Actively seeking new investments
Method of Compensation: Return on investment is of primary concern, do not charge fees

---

BLUE EQUITY, LLC

333 East Main Street
Suite 200
Louisville, KY USA 40202
Phone: 502-589-8181
Fax: 502-588-7150
E-mail: info@blueequity.com
Website: www.blueequity.com

Management and Staff

Jonathan Blue, Chairman & Managing Director
Juan Reffreger, Vice President

Type of Firm

Private Equity Firm

Project Preferences

Type of Financing Preferred:
Leveraged Buyout

Geographical Preferences

United States Preferences:
All U.S.

Industry Preferences

In Consumer Related prefer:
Entertainment and Leisure
Sports

In Financial Services prefer:
Financial Services
Real Estate

In Business Serv. prefer:
Media

In Manufact. prefer:
Publishing

Additional Information

Year Founded: 2004
Current Activity Level: Actively seeking new investments

BLUE HILL PARTNERS LLC

40 West Evergreen Avenue
Philadelphia, PA USA 19118
Phone: 215-247-2400
Fax: 215-248-2381
Website: www.bluehillpartners.com

Management and Staff

Alan Grant, Managing Partner
Gary Weiss, Partner
Joyce Ferris, Managing Partner
Peter Williams, Principal

Type of Firm

Private Equity Firm

Project Preferences

Type of Financing Preferred:
Early Stage
Expansion

Geographical Preferences

United States Preferences:
Pennsylvania
All U.S.

International Preferences:
All International

Industry Preferences

In Industrial/Energy prefer:
Energy
Energy Conservation Relat
Process Control
Environmental Related

In Agr/Forestr/Fish prefer:
Agribusiness

Additional Information

Year Founded: 2002
Capital Under Management: $5,000,000
Current Activity Level: Actively seeking new investments

BLUE HORIZON EQUITY

615 Battery Street
Fourth Floor
San Francisco, CA USA 94111
Phone: 415-493-5190
Fax: 415-352-4060
Website: www.bluehorizonequity.com

Management and Staff

Alan Nichols, Managing Director
John Hommeyer, Managing Director
Scott Wu, Managing Director

Type of Firm

Private Equity Firm

Project Preferences

Type of Financing Preferred:
Leveraged Buyout
Expansion

Industry Preferences

In Medical/Health prefer:
Medical/Health
Health Services

In Consumer Related prefer:
Entertainment and Leisure
Consumer Products

In Industrial/Energy prefer:
Environmental Related

In Business Serv. prefer:
Media

In Other prefer:
Environment Responsible

Additional Information

Year Founded: 2008
Current Activity Level: Actively seeking new investments

BLUE POINT CAPITAL PARTNERS (FKA: KEY EQUITY CAPITAL)

127 Public Square
Suite 5100
Cleveland, OH USA 44114
Phone: 216-535-4700
Fax: 216-535-4701
E-mail: info@bluepointcapital.com
Website: www.bluepointcapital.com

Other Offices

1201 Third Avenue
Suite 3090
Seattle, WA USA 98101
Phone: 206-332-9200
Fax: 206-332-9209

201 South Tryon Street
Suite 850
Charlotte, NC USA 28202
Phone: 704-347-1111
Fax: 704-347-1107

1233 Lujiazui Ring Road
Suite 1507, Azia Center
Shanghai, China 200120
Phone: 86-21-5047-4700

Management and Staff

Bill Lehr, Vice President
Chip Chaikin, Partner
Dave DiFranco, Principal
David Given, Managing Partner
John Kirby, Managing Partner
John LeMay, Partner
Julianne Marley, Partner
Mark Morris, Partner
Paul Neundorfer, Vice President
Sean Ward, Partner

Type of Firm

Private Equity Firm

Project Preferences

Type of Financing Preferred:
Leveraged Buyout
Expansion
Management Buyouts
Acquisition
Recapitalizations

Size of Investments Considered:
Min Size of Investment Considered (000s): $15,000
Max Size of Investment Considered (000s): $50,000

Geographical Preferences

United States Preferences:
All U.S.

Industry Focus

(% based on actual investment)

Other Products	100.0%

Additional Information

Name of Most Recent Fund: Blue Point Capital Partners
Most Recent Fund Was Raised: 02/01/2001
Year Founded: 1990
Capital Under Management: $415,000,000
Current Activity Level: Actively seeking new investments

BLUE RIDGE CAPITAL

660 Madison Avenue
20th Floor
New York, NY USA 10021
Phone: 212-446-6200
Fax: 212-446-6201

Management and Staff

Richard Bello, Managing Director

Type of Firm

Private Equity Firm

Project Preferences

Type of Financing Preferred:
Generalist PE
Balanced

Geographical Preferences

International Preferences:
Macau
Taiwan
Hong Kong
China

Industry Preferences

In Consumer Related prefer:
Retail
Consumer Products

In Industrial/Energy prefer:
Energy

In Financial Services prefer:
Real Estate

Additional Information

Name of Most Recent Fund: Blue Ridge China Partners II, L.P.
Most Recent Fund Was Raised: 02/05/2008
Year Founded: 2001
Capital Under Management: $440,900,000
Current Activity Level: Actively seeking new investments

BLUE RIVER CAPITAL ADVISORS (INDIA) PVT. LTD.

20th Floor, Express Towers
Nariman Point
Mumbai, India 400 021
Phone: 91-22-4019-4800
Fax: 91-22-4019-4832
E-mail: Indiainfo@blueriverCapital.com
Website: www.blueriverCapital.com

Other Offices

c/o International Financial Services
IFS Court, TwentyEight, Cybercity
Ebene, Mauritius
Phone: 230-467-3000
Fax: 230-467-4000

Management and Staff

Muneesh Chawla, Managing Director
Rahul Mehta, Vice President
Shujaat Khan, Managing Director

Type of Firm

Private Equity Firm

Project Preferences

Type of Financing Preferred:
Generalist PE
Management Buyouts

Size of Investments Considered:
Min Size of Investment Considered (000s): $4,740
Max Size of Investment Considered (000s): $10,000

Geographical Preferences

International Preferences:
India

Industry Preferences

In Medical/Health prefer:
Health Services
Pharmaceuticals

In Consumer Related prefer:
Consumer Products

In Financial Services prefer:
Financial Services

In Manufact. prefer:
Manufacturing

Additional Information
Year Founded: 2005
Capital Under Management: $135,000,000
Current Activity Level: Actively seeking new investments

BLUE ROCK CAPITAL
P.O. Box 4513
Wilmington, DE USA 19807
Phone: 302-426-0981
Fax: 302-426-0982
Website: www.bluerockcapital.com

Other Offices
230 Lackawanna Drive
Andover, NJ USA 07821
Phone: 973-426-1767
Fax: 973-426-0224

18004 Calico Circle
Olney, MD USA 20832
Management and Staff
James Zucco, Partner
Terry Collison, General Partner
Virginia Bonker, General Partner

Type of Firm
SBIC
Association Membership
Mid-Atlantic Venture Association

Project Preferences

Role in Financing:
Prefer role as deal originator but will also invest in deals created by others

Type of Financing Preferred:
Start-up Financing
Seed
First Stage Financing

Geographical Preferences

United States Preferences:
Mid Atlantic
Northeast

Industry Focus
(% based on actual investment)

Internet Specific	45.2%
Semiconductors/Other Elect.	23.2%
Computer Software and Services	12.3%
Communications and Media	11.6%
Consumer Related	6.1%
Other Products	1.5%

Additional Information
Name of Most Recent Fund: Blue Rock Capital
Most Recent Fund Was Raised: 08/09/1995
Year Founded: 1995
Capital Under Management: $51,000,000
Current Activity Level: Actively seeking new investments
Method of Compensation: Return on investment is of primary concern, do not charge fees

---

BLUE SAGE CAPITAL, L.P.
114 West 7th Street
Suite 820
Austin, TX USA 78701
Phone: 512-536-1900
Fax: 512-236-9215
E-mail: contact@bluesage.com
Website: www.bluesage.com

Other Offices
1155 University Boulevard SE
Albuquerque, NM USA 87106
Phone: 505-843-4267
Fax: 505-843-4246

Management and Staff
Emily Boon, Vice President
Jack Cardwell, Partner
James McBride, General Partner
Pat Baskin, General Partner
Peter Huff, Managing Partner

Type of Firm
Private Equity Firm

Project Preferences

Role in Financing:
Prefer role as deal originator but will also invest in deals created by others

Type of Financing Preferred:
Second Stage Financing
Leveraged Buyout
Control-block Purchases
Expansion
Mezzanine
Generalist PE
Later Stage
Management Buyouts
Acquisition
Industry Rollups
Recapitalizations

Size of Investments Considered:
Min Size of Investment Considered (000s): $3,000
Max Size of Investment Considered (000s): $25,000

Geographical Preferences

United States Preferences:
Midwest
Southeast
Southwest
Texas
All U.S.

Industry Preferences

In Business Serv. prefer:
Services
Distribution

In Manufact. prefer:
Manufacturing

Additional Information
Year Founded: 2003
Capital Under Management: $170,000,000
Current Activity Level: Actively seeking new investments

BLUE SKY PRIVATE EQUITY
130 Commercial Road
Teneriffe
Brisbane City, Australia 4005
Phone: 61-07-3852-2240
E-mail: info@bspe.com.au
Website: www.bspe.com.au

Management and Staff
Mark Sowerby, Managing Director

Type of Firm
Private Equity Firm

Association Membership
Australian Venture Capital Association (AVCAL)

Project Preferences

Type of Financing Preferred:
Leveraged Buyout
Generalist PE
Expansion

Geographical Preferences

International Preferences:
Australia

Industry Preferences

In Financial Services prefer:
Real Estate

In Agr/Forestr/Fish prefer:
Agribusiness
Mining and Minerals

In Other prefer:
Environment Responsible

Additional Information

Year Founded: 2007
Current Activity Level: Actively seeking new investments

BLUE WATER CAPITAL LLC

1420 Beverly Road
Suite 300
McLean, VA USA 22101
Phone: 703-790-8821
Fax: 703-448-1849
Website: www.bluewatercapital.com

Management and Staff

Henry Barratt, Managing Director
Kim Cooke, Managing Director
Michael Acheson, Managing Director
Philip Snare, Managing Director

Type of Firm

Private Equity Firm

Association Membership

Mid-Atlantic Venture Association
Western Association of Venture Capitalists (WAVC)

Project Preferences

Role in Financing:
Prefer role as deal originator but will also invest in deals created by others

Type of Financing Preferred:
Expansion

Size of Investments Considered:
Min Size of Investment Considered (000s): $5,000
Max Size of Investment Considered (000s): $7,000

Geographical Preferences

United States Preferences:
Mid Atlantic
Midwest
East Coast
All U.S.

Canadian Preferences:
All Canada

Industry Focus

(% based on actual investment)

Internet Specific	57.0%
Computer Software and Services	16.9%
Communications and Media	12.3%
Other Products	9.7%
Computer Hardware	3.9%
Semiconductors/Other Elect.	0.2%

Additional Information

Name of Most Recent Fund: Blue Water Venture Fund III, LLC
Most Recent Fund Was Raised: 04/30/2002
Year Founded: 1995
Capital Under Management: $98,700,000
Current Activity Level: Reducing investment activity
Method of Compensation: Return on investment is of primary concern, do not charge fees

BLUE WOLF CAPITAL MANAGEMENT LLC

48 Wall Street
31st Floor
New York, NY USA 10005
Phone: 212-488-1340
Fax: 917-677-8233
E-mail: info@blue-wolf.com
Website: www.blue-wolf.com

Management and Staff

Josh Wolf-Powers, Founding Partner
Michael Ranson, Partner
Mike Musuraca, Managing Director

Type of Firm

Private Equity Firm

Project Preferences

Type of Financing Preferred:
Leveraged Buyout
Turnaround
Special Situation
Distressed Debt

Size of Investments Considered:
Min Size of Investment Considered (000s): $5,000
Max Size of Investment Considered (000s): $30,000

Geographical Preferences

United States Preferences:
All U.S.

Canadian Preferences:
All Canada

Additional Information

Year Founded: 2005
Capital Under Management: $173,500,000
Current Activity Level: Actively seeking new investments

BLUECAR PARTNERS

405 Lexington Avenue
26th Floor
New York, NY USA 10174
Phone: 212-907-6444
Fax: 775-796-3875
E-mail: info@bluecarpartners.com
Website: www.bluecarpartners.com

Other Offices

5307 Duvall Drive
Bethesda, MD USA 20816

1800 Century Park East
Los Angeles, CA USA 90067

721 Noble Oak Drive
Marietta, GA USA 30068

1632 Union Street
San Francisco, CA USA 94123

Via Alzaia Naviglio Grande, 14
Milan, Italy 20144

Management and Staff

Alma Derricks, Vice President
Granger Whitelaw, Managing Director
Lee Olsen, Founding Partner
Thomas Tauzin, Vice President

Type of Firm

Service Provider

Project Preferences

Type of Financing Preferred:
Early Stage
Seed

Industry Preferences

In Communications prefer:
Telecommunications
Wireless Communications

In Internet Specific prefer:
E-Commerce Technology

In Biotechnology prefer:
Biotechnology

In Medical/Health prefer:
Medical/Health
Health Services

In Transportation prefer:
Aerospace

Additional Information

Year Founded: 2001
Capital Under Management: $100,000,000
Current Activity Level: Actively seeking new investments

BLUEFIRE PARTNERS CAPITAL MARKETS

1300 Fifth Street Towers
150 South Fifth Street
Minneapolis, MN USA 55402
Phone: 612-344-1000

Fax: 612-344-1001
Website: www.bluefirepartners.com

Other Offices

1300 Fifth Street Towers
150 South Fifth Street
Minneapolis, MN USA 55402
Phone: 612-344-1000
Fax: 612-344-1001

Management and Staff

Joanne Henry, Managing Director
Lee Schafer, Managing Director
William Bartkowsk, Chief Executive Officer

Type of Firm

Private Equity Firm

Additional Information

Year Founded: 2009
Current Activity Level: Actively seeking new investments

BLUEGEM CAPITAL PARTNERS LLP

16 Berkeley Street
London, United Kingdom W1J 8DZ
Phone: 44-20-7647-9710
Fax: 44-20-7681-1304
E-mail: info@bluegemcp.com
Website: www.bluegemcp.com

Management and Staff

Emilio Di Spiezio Sardo, Partner
Marco Anatriello, Partner

Type of Firm

Private Equity Firm

Project Preferences

Type of Financing Preferred:
Leveraged Buyout
Generalist PE
Expansion
Acquisition

Geographical Preferences

International Preferences:
Italy
United Kingdom
Europe

Additional Information

Year Founded: 2006
Capital Under Management: $269,100,000
Current Activity Level: Actively seeking new investments

BLUELINE PARTNERS, LLC

4115 Blackhawk Plaza Circle
Suite 100
Danville, CA USA 94506
Phone: 925-648-2085
Fax: 925-648-2086
E-mail: contact @ bluelinepartners.com
Website: www.bluelinepartners.com

Management and Staff

Scott Shuda, Co-Founder
Timothy Bacci, Managing Director

Type of Firm

Private Equity Firm

Project Preferences

Type of Financing Preferred:
Public Companies
Private Placement

Industry Preferences

In Medical/Health prefer:
Medical/Health

Additional Information

Year Founded: 2002
Capital Under Management: $600,000
Current Activity Level: Actively seeking new investments

BLUEORCHARD INVESTMENTS SARL

32 rue de Malatrex
Geneva, Switzerland 1201
Phone: 41-22-596-4750
Fax: 41-22-596-4751
E-mail: infoinvest@blueorchard.com
Website: www.blueorchard.com

Management and Staff

Jean-Philippe De Schrevel, Chief Executive Officer

Type of Firm

Bank Affiliated

Project Preferences

Type of Financing Preferred:
Acquisition

Geographical Preferences

International Preferences:
Latin America
Eastern Europe
Africa

Industry Preferences

In Financial Services prefer:
Financial Services

Additional Information

Year Founded: 2008
Capital Under Management: $111,000,000
Current Activity Level: Actively seeking new investments

BLUEPRINT VENTURES LLC

601 Gateway Boulevard
Suite 1140
South San Francisco, CA USA 94080
Phone: 415-901-4000
Fax: 415-901-4035
E-mail: info@blueprintventures.com
Website: www.blueprintventures.com

Management and Staff

Bart Schachter, Managing Director
David Frankel, Venture Partner
George Hoyem, Managing Director
Jim Huston, Managing Director
Richard Yen, Principal

Type of Firm

Private Equity Firm

Association Membership

National Venture Capital Association - USA (NVCA)

Project Preferences

Role in Financing:
Prefer role as deal originator but will also invest in deals created by others

Type of Financing Preferred:
Second Stage Financing
Early Stage
Seed
First Stage Financing

Size of Investments Considered:
Min Size of Investment Considered (000s): $500
Max Size of Investment Considered (000s): $3,000

Geographical Preferences

United States Preferences:
West Coast

Canadian Preferences:
All Canada

Industry Preferences

In Communications prefer:
Wireless Communications

In Computer Software prefer:
Software

In Semiconductor/Electr prefer:
Semiconductor

Additional Information

Name of Most Recent Fund: Blueprint Ventures II, L.P.

Most Recent Fund Was Raised: 08/01/2001
Year Founded: 1999
Capital Under Management: $200,000,000
Current Activity Level: Actively seeking new investments
Method of Compensation: Return on investment is of primary concern, do not charge fees

---

BLUERUN VENTURES

545 Middlefield Road
Suite 210
Menlo Park, CA USA 94025
Phone: 650-462-7250
Fax: 650-462-7252
E-mail: ventures@brv.com
Website: www.brv.com

Other Offices

11 Hamenofim Street
Herzelia Pituach, Ackerstein Towers
Herzelia, Israel 46120
Phone: 972-9-951-4884

Room 2736, K. Wah Center
No. 1010 Huaihai Zhong Road
Shanghai, China 200031
Phone: 86-21-6103-1266
Fax: 86-21-6103-1288

POSCO Center Bldg. West Tower 11th Floor
892 Daechi-4dong, Kangnam-gu
Seoul, South Korea 135-777
Phone: 82-2559-0655
Fax: 82-2559-0656

804, Maker Chamber V
8th floor Nariman Point
Mumbai , India 400 021
Phone: 91-22-2687-6785
Fax: 91-22-2820-2005

Unit 802, Office Tower 1, China Central
No. 81 Jianguo Road, Chaoyang District
Beijing, China 100025
Phone: 86-10-5969-5680
Fax: 86-10-59695681

Haarniskakuja 4a
Espoo, Finland 02610
Phone: 358-50-486-0044

Management and Staff

Andrew Chen, Partner
Antti Kokkinen, Partner
John Malloy, Partner
Jonathan Ebinger, Partner
Jui Tan, Partner
Karen Eliadis, Chief Financial Officer
Kwan Yoon, Partner
W. Peter Buhl, Partner
Yossi Hasson, Partner

Type of Firm

Private Equity Firm

Association Membership

Western Association of Venture Capitalists (WAVC)
National Venture Capital Association - USA (NVCA)

Project Preferences

Role in Financing:

Prefer role as deal originator but will also invest in deals created by others

Type of Financing Preferred:

Second Stage Financing
Early Stage
Balanced
Seed
First Stage Financing
Startup

Size of Investments Considered:

Min Size of Investment Considered (000s): $2,000
Max Size of Investment Considered (000s): $8,000

Geographical Preferences

Canadian Preferences:

All Canada

International Preferences:

India
China
Hong Kong
Western Europe
Israel
Korea, South
Asia
Japan
All International

Industry Focus

(% based on actual investment)	
Semiconductors/Other Elect.	22.1%
Communications and Media	21.9%
Internet Specific	20.4%
Computer Software and Services	15.4%
Computer Hardware	14.4%
Other Products	2.8%
Industrial/Energy	2.4%
Consumer Related	0.7%

Additional Information

Name of Most Recent Fund: BlueRun Ventures IV, L.P.
Most Recent Fund Was Raised: 02/12/2008
Year Founded: 1998
Capital Under Management: $1,000,000,000
Current Activity Level: Actively seeking new investments
Method of Compensation: Return on investment is of primary concern, do not charge fees

---

BLUESTAR VENTURES L.P.

208 South LaSalle Street
Suite 1020
Chicago, IL USA 60604
Phone: 312-384-5000
Fax: 312-384-5005
E-mail: info@bluestarventures.com
Website: www.bluestarventures.com

Management and Staff

Grant Patrick, Vice President
Patrick Pollard, Managing Director
Richard Flynn, Managing Director
William Steinmetz, Managing Director

Type of Firm

Private Equity Firm

Project Preferences

Role in Financing:

Will function either as deal originator or investor in deals created by others

Type of Financing Preferred:

Second Stage Financing
Early Stage
First Stage Financing
Startup

Size of Investments Considered:

Min Size of Investment Considered (000s): $500
Max Size of Investment Considered (000s): $3,000

Geographical Preferences

United States Preferences:

Mid Atlantic
Midwest
Northwest
Southeast
Southwest

Industry Preferences

In Communications prefer:

Telecommunications
Wireless Communications
Data Communications

In Computer Software prefer:

Computer Services
Software
Systems Software
Applications Software
Artificial Intelligence

In Internet Specific prefer:

Internet
Ecommerce
Web Aggregration/Portals

Additional Information

Year Founded: 2000
Capital Under Management: $40,000,000
Current Activity Level: Actively seeking new investments
Method of Compensation: Return on investment is of primary concern, do not charge fees

BLUESTEM CAPITAL PARTNERS

122 South Phillips Avenue
Suite 300
Sioux Falls, SD USA 57104-6706
Phone: 605-331-0091
Fax: 605-334-1218
Website: www.bluestemcapital.com

Management and Staff

Paul Schock, President
Sandy Horst, Chief Financial Officer
Steve Kirby, Vice President

Type of Firm

Private Equity Firm

Association Membership

Natl Assoc of Small Bus. Inv. Co (NASBIC)

Project Preferences

Role in Financing:
Will function either as deal originator or investor in deals created by others

Type of Financing Preferred:
Expansion
Later Stage
Private Placement

Size of Investments Considered:
Min Size of Investment Considered (000s): $250
Max Size of Investment Considered (000s): $3,000

Geographical Preferences

United States Preferences:
Midwest

Industry Focus

(% based on actual investment)	
Industrial/Energy	42.3%
Internet Specific	25.6%
Computer Software and Services	13.9%
Consumer Related	12.5%
Communications and Media	4.5%
Medical/Health	0.5%
Computer Hardware	0.4%
Other Products	0.3%

Additional Information

Name of Most Recent Fund: Bluestem Capital Partners III, L.P.
Most Recent Fund Was Raised: 11/30/2000
Year Founded: 1991
Capital Under Management: $76,000,000
Current Activity Level: Actively seeking new investments
Method of Compensation: Return on invest. most important, but chg. closing fees, service fees, etc.

BLUESTREAM VENTURES

225 South Sixth Street
Suite 4350
Minneapolis, MN USA 55402
Phone: 612-333-8110
Fax: 612-766-4040
E-mail: info@bluestreamventures.com
Website: www.bluestreamventures.com

Other Offices

203 Redwood Shores Parkway
Suite 200
Redwood City, CA USA 94065
Phone: 650-592-3677
Fax: 650-592-3664

Management and Staff

Constance Paiement, Chief Financial Officer
Raj Gollamudi, Founding Partner
Steve Sigmond, Venture Partner
Thomas Erickson, Founding Partner

Type of Firm

Private Equity Firm

Project Preferences

Role in Financing:
Will function either as deal originator or investor in deals created by others

Type of Financing Preferred:
Second Stage Financing
Early Stage
Expansion
First Stage Financing
Startup
Recapitalizations

Size of Investments Considered:
Min Size of Investment Considered (000s): $1,000
Max Size of Investment Considered (000s): $15,000

Geographical Preferences

United States Preferences:
All U.S.

Industry Preferences

In Communications prefer:
Telecommunications
Wireless Communications
Data Communications
Other Communication Prod.

In Computer Software prefer:
Data Processing
Software
Systems Software
Applications Software

In Internet Specific prefer:
E-Commerce Technology
Web Aggregration/Portals

In Semiconductor/Electr prefer:
Semiconductor
Laser Related
Fiber Optics

Additional Information

Name of Most Recent Fund: BlueStream Ventures, L.P.
Most Recent Fund Was Raised: 07/28/2000
Year Founded: 2000
Capital Under Management: $280,000,000
Current Activity Level: Actively seeking new investments
Method of Compensation: Return on investment is of primary concern, do not charge fees

BLUMBERG CAPITAL VENTURES

580 Howard Street
Suite 101
San Francisco, CA USA 94105
Phone: 415-905-5000
Fax: 415-357-5027
E-mail: info@blumbergcapital.com
Website: www.blumbergcapital.com

Management and Staff

Bipul Sinha, Vice President
Bruce Taragin, Managing Director
David Blumberg, Managing Partner
Margot Giusti, Chief Financial Officer
Sharon Azulai, Venture Partner

Type of Firm

Private Equity Firm

Association Membership

Israel Venture Association
European Private Equity and Venture Capital Assoc.

Project Preferences

Role in Financing:
Will function either as deal originator or investor in deals created by others

Type of Financing Preferred:
Early Stage
Seed

Size of Investments Considered:
Min Size of Investment Considered (000s): $500
Max Size of Investment Considered (000s): $3,000

Geographical Preferences

International Preferences:
Israel

Industry Preferences

In Communications prefer:
Wireless Communications

In Computer Software prefer:
Computer Services
Software
Systems Software
Applications Software

In Internet Specific prefer:
E-Commerce Technology
Internet

Additional Information
Name of Most Recent Fund: Blumberg Capital II, L.P.
Most Recent Fund Was Raised: 04/26/2007
Year Founded: 2000
Capital Under Management: $60,000,000
Current Activity Level: Actively seeking new investments
Method of Compensation: Return on investment is of primary concern, do not charge fees

BLUO SICAV-SIF
2, Rue Heinrich Heine
Luxembourg, Luxembourg 1720
Phone: 352-2630-2605
Fax: 352-2630-2607
E-mail: contact@blu-o.lu
Website: www.blu-o.lu

Type of Firm
Private Equity Firm

Project Preferences

Type of Financing Preferred:
Leveraged Buyout
Recapitalizations

Geographical Preferences

International Preferences:
Luxembourg
Switzerland
Austria
Germany

Additional Information
Year Founded: 2008
Capital Under Management: $382,100,000
Current Activity Level: Actively seeking new investments

BM-T BETEILIGUNGSMANAGEMENT THUERINGEN GMBH
Gorkistrasse 9
Erfurt, Germany 99084
Phone: 49-361-7447-601
Fax: 49-361-7447-635
Website: www.bm-t.de

Management and Staff
Guido Bohnenkamp, Managing Director

Type of Firm
Private Equity Firm

Association Membership
German Venture Capital Association (BVK)

Project Preferences

Type of Financing Preferred:
Early Stage
Expansion
Mezzanine
Startup

Geographical Preferences

International Preferences:
Germany

Industry Preferences

In Communications prefer:
Telecommunications

In Semiconductor/Electr prefer:
Electronics
Micro-Processing

In Industrial/Energy prefer:
Process Control

Additional Information
Year Founded: 1994
Capital Under Management: $17,200,000
Current Activity Level: Actively seeking new investments

BMI - SBI
Avenue de Tervurenlaan 168
Brussels, Belgium 1150
Phone: 32-2-776-0100
Fax: 32-2-770-6638
E-mail: info@bmi-sbi.be
Website: www.bmi-sbi.be

Type of Firm
Private Equity Firm

Association Membership
Belgium Venturing Association

Project Preferences

Type of Financing Preferred:
Balanced

Size of Investments Considered:
Min Size of Investment Considered (000s): $668
Max Size of Investment Considered (000s): $3,338

Geographical Preferences

International Preferences:
Europe

Additional Information
Year Founded: 2004
Current Activity Level: Actively seeking new investments

BMO CAPITAL CORPORATION
100 King Street West
First Canadian Place, 11th Flo
Toronto, Canada M5X 1A1
Phone: 416-867-7341
Fax: 416-867-4108
E-mail: darren.yaworsky@bmo.com
Website: www.bmo.com/bmocc

Other Offices
100 King Street West
First Canadian Place, 11th Flo
Toronto, Canada M5X 1A1
Phone: 416-867-7341
Fax: 416-867-4108

Three Times Square
29th Floor
New York, NY USA 10036
Phone: 212-605-1512

111 West Monroe Streeet
Chicago, IL USA 60603
Phone: 312-461-3668

Management and Staff
Claude Miron, Managing Director
Darren Yaworsky, Managing Director
Eric Ehgoetz, Managing Director
John Honney, Vice President
Nadim Hirji, Managing Director
Peter Hurwitz, Managing Director
Robert Nolan, Managing Partner

Type of Firm
Investment Management Firm

Project Preferences

Type of Financing Preferred:
Early Stage
Expansion
Turnaround
Other
Seed
Acquisition
Startup

Geographical Preferences

Canadian Preferences:
All Canada
Eastern Canada
Western Canada

International Preferences:
Western Europe

Additional Information
Year Founded: 1996
Current Activity Level: Actively seeking new investments

BMP AG

Schluterstrasse 38
Berlin, Germany D-10629
Phone: 49-30-2030-5503
Fax: 49-30-2030-5555
E-mail: bmp@bmp.com
Website: www.bmp.com

Other Offices

ul. Koszykowa 54
Warsaw, Poland PL-00675
Phone: 48-22-630-8575
Fax: 48-22-630-8569

Management and Staff

Andreas Van Bon, Chief Financial Officer
Jens Spyrka, Managing Director
Ralph Gunther, Managing Partner

Type of Firm

Private Equity Firm

Association Membership

German Venture Capital Association (BVK)
Polish Venture Capital Association (PSIC/PPEA)
European Private Equity and Venture Capital Assoc.

Project Preferences

Role in Financing:
Prefer role as deal originator but will also invest in deals created by others

Type of Financing Preferred:
Fund of Funds
Early Stage
Expansion
Balanced
Seed
Startup
Acquisition

Size of Investments Considered:
Min Size of Investment Considered (000s): $706
Max Size of Investment Considered (000s): $7,061

Geographical Preferences

International Preferences:
Europe
Switzerland
Western Europe
Poland
Germany

Industry Focus

(% based on actual investment)

Other Products	29.8%
Internet Specific	21.0%
Medical/Health	19.4%
Biotechnology	17.2%
Computer Software and Services	11.2%
Communications and Media	1.1%
Consumer Related	0.2%

Additional Information

Name of Most Recent Fund: bmp Media Investors AG & Co. KGaA
Most Recent Fund Was Raised: 04/30/2007
Year Founded: 1997
Capital Under Management: $29,400,000
Current Activity Level: Actively seeking new investments

BNFL ENTERPRISE (INVESTMENT MANAGEMENT) LIMITED

Beech House, Garstang Road
Harris Knowledge Park, Preston
Lancashire, United Kingdom PR2 9AB
Phone: 44-1772-717-577
Fax: 44-1772-788-692
E-mail: bnfle@4-mat.net
Website: www.bnfl.com

Other Offices

University of Central Lancashire
Adelphi Building
Preston, United Kingdom PR1 2HE
Phone: 44-1772-894-476
Fax: 44-1772-894-497

Type of Firm

Incubator/Development Program

Project Preferences

Type of Financing Preferred:
Early Stage
Expansion
Startup

Geographical Preferences

United States Preferences:
Utah

International Preferences:
United Kingdom

Industry Preferences

In Communications prefer:
Commercial Communications

In Computer Other prefer:
Computer Related

In Semiconductor/Electr prefer:
Electronics

In Biotechnology prefer:
Biotechnology

In Medical/Health prefer:
Medical/Health

In Industrial/Energy prefer:
Energy
Industrial Products
Materials

In Transportation prefer:
Transportation

In Manufact. prefer:
Manufacturing

In Agr/Forestr/Fish prefer:
Agriculture related

Additional Information

Year Founded: 2000
Capital Under Management: $3,700,000
Current Activity Level: Actively seeking new investments

BNP PARIBAS ASSET MANAGEMENT SGR SPA (FKA: BNL GESTIONI SGR)

5 avenue Kleber
Paris, France 75016
Phone: 33-1-5897-2525
Website: www.bnpparibas-am.com

Other Offices

Via Dante 15
Milan, Italy 20123
Phone: 39-2-7247-5100

UGB Tower Building
440 Diplomatic Area Road
Manama, Bahrain
Phone: 973-17-531-152

Type of Firm

Private Equity Firm

Association Membership

Italian Venture Capital Association (AIFI)

Project Preferences

Role in Financing:
Prefer role as deal originator but will also invest in deals created by others

Type of Financing Preferred:
Leveraged Buyout
Expansion

Size of Investments Considered:
Min Size of Investment Considered (000s): $1,428
Max Size of Investment Considered (000s): $12,848

Geographical Preferences

International Preferences:
Italy
Middle East

Industry Focus

(% based on actual investment)

Consumer Related	53.7%
Other Products	46.3%

Additional Information

Year Founded: 1998
Capital Under Management: $50,000,000
Current Activity Level: Actively seeking new investments

BNP PARIBAS DEVELOPPEMENT SAS

20 rue Chauchat
Paris, France 75009
Phone: 33-1-4014-6463
Fax: 33-1-4014-2968
Website: www.bnpparibas.com

Type of Firm

Bank Affiliated

Association Membership

French Venture Capital Association (AFIC)

Project Preferences

Type of Financing Preferred:
Early Stage
Expansion
Balanced

Geographical Preferences

International Preferences:
Europe
France

Additional Information

Year Founded: 1989
Current Activity Level: Actively seeking new investments

BNP PARIBAS PRINCIPAL, INC.

787 Seventh Avenue
32nd Floor
New York, NY USA 10019
Phone: 212-841-2005
Fax: 212-841-3558
Website: www.bnpparibas.com

Management and Staff

Gerry Esposito, Chief Financial Officer
Steven Alexander, Managing Director

Type of Firm

Bank Affiliated

Association Membership

Natl Assoc of Small Bus. Inv. Co (NASBIC)

Project Preferences

Role in Financing:
Prefer role as deal originator but will also invest in deals created by others

Type of Financing Preferred:
Leveraged Buyout
Control-block Purchases
Special Situation

Size of Investments Considered:
Min Size of Investment Considered (000s): $50,000
Max Size of Investment Considered: No Limit

Geographical Preferences

United States Preferences:
All U.S.

Industry Preferences

In Communications prefer:
Commercial Communications
Radio & TV Broadcasting
Satellite Microwave Comm.

In Computer Software prefer:
Computer Services

In Semiconductor/Electr prefer:
Electronic Components
Sensors
Component Testing Equipmt
Analytic/Scientific

In Medical/Health prefer:
Medical Diagnostics
Diagnostic Services
Diagnostic Test Products
Medical Therapeutics
Drug/Equipmt Delivery
Other Therapeutic
Disposable Med. Products
Hospitals/Clinics/Primary
Hospital/Other Instit.

In Consumer Related prefer:
Entertainment and Leisure
Retail
Franchises(NEC)
Food/Beverage
Consumer Products
Consumer Services
Other Restaurants

In Industrial/Energy prefer:
Materials
Machinery
Environmental Related

In Transportation prefer:
Transportation

In Business Serv. prefer:
Distribution

In Manufact. prefer:
Office Automation Equipmt
Publishing

Additional Information

Year Founded: 1989
Capital Under Management: $250,000,000
Current Activity Level: Actively seeking new investments
Method of Compensation: Return on invest. most important, but chg. closing fees, service fees, etc.

BNP PRIVATE EQUITY

32 boulevard Haussmann
Paris, France 75009
Phone: 33-1-5577-9141
Fax: 33-1-4014-9119
E-mail: bnppe.info@bnpgroup.com
Website: www.bnpparibas.com

Other Offices

Limmatquai 4
Zurich, Switzerland 8024
Phone: 41-1-267-93-67
Fax: 41-1-267-93-70

Management and Staff

Jean-Jacques Bertrand, Partner
Michel Bouissou, Partner
Patrick Perez, Partner

Type of Firm

Bank Affiliated

Association Membership

French Venture Capital Association (AFIC)
European Private Equity and Venture Capital Assoc.

Project Preferences

Role in Financing:
Prefer role as deal originator but will also invest in deals created by others

Type of Financing Preferred:
Leveraged Buyout
Early Stage
Expansion
Mezzanine
Generalist PE
Balanced
Later Stage
Management Buyouts
Recapitalizations

Size of Investments Considered:
Min Size of Investment Considered (000s): $189
Max Size of Investment Considered (000s): $28,248

Geographical Preferences

International Preferences:
Europe
Middle East
France

Industry Focus

(% based on actual investment)	
Internet Specific	39.2%
Communications and Media	13.6%
Semiconductors/Other Elect.	12.0%
Biotechnology	11.7%
Computer Software and Services	7.4%
Consumer Related	7.3%
Other Products	3.7%
Computer Hardware	2.8%
Medical/Health	2.1%
Industrial/Energy	0.2%

Additional Information

Year Founded: 1997
Capital Under Management: $649,800,000
Current Activity Level: Actively seeking new investments
Method of Compensation: Return on investment is of primary concern, do not charge fees

BOATHOUSE CAPITAL

435 Devon Park Drive
Building 700
Wayne, PA USA 19087
Phone: 610-977-2787
Website: www.boathousecapital.com

Management and Staff

Chong Moua, Partner
Kenneth Jones, Managing Partner
Steven Gord, Partner
William Dyer, Partner

Type of Firm

Private Equity Firm

Project Preferences

Type of Financing Preferred:
Leveraged Buyout
Mezzanine
Acquisition
Recapitalizations

Additional Information

Year Founded: 2008
Current Activity Level: Actively seeking new investments

BOBCOCK & BROWN

680 George Street
Level 12
Sydney, Australia NSW2000
Phone: 612-8280-7452
E-mail: bobcockbrown@linkmarketservices.com.au
Website: www.bobcockbrown.com.au

Type of Firm

Private Equity Firm

Geographical Preferences

Canadian Preferences:
British Columbia

Additional Information

Year Founded: 2006
Current Activity Level: Actively seeking new investments

BOC INTERNATIONAL HOLDINGS, LTD.

26/F, Bank of China Tower
1 Garden Road
Hong Kong, Hong Kong
Phone: 852-2230-8888
Fax: 825-2147-9065
E-mail: info@bocigroup.com
Website: www.bocigroup.com

Other Offices

28/F, Tower B ICTC
59, MaChang Road, Hexi District
Tianjin, China 300203
Phone: 86-22-8386
Fax: 86-22-8386-7810

Management and Staff

Simon Ting, Managing Director

Type of Firm

Bank Affiliated

Project Preferences

Type of Financing Preferred:
Mezzanine
Expansion

Geographical Preferences

International Preferences:
China
Hong Kong

Industry Focus

(% based on actual investment)

Other Products	98.1%
Industrial/Energy	1.9%

Additional Information

Year Founded: 1998
Capital Under Management: $806,000,000
Current Activity Level: Actively seeking new investments

BOFORSSTIFTELSEN

P.O. Box 8023
Obrero, Sweden 700 08
Phone: 46-19-174-810
Fax: 46-70-576-1435
E-mail: info@boforsstiftelsen.se
Website: www.boforsstiftelsen.se

Type of Firm

Private Equity Firm

Association Membership

European Private Equity and Venture Capital Assoc.

Project Preferences

Type of Financing Preferred:
Balanced

Geographical Preferences

International Preferences:
Sweden

Additional Information

Year Founded: 2006
Capital Under Management: $2,000,000
Current Activity Level: Actively seeking new investments

BOHAI SEA REGION VENTURE CAPITAL MANAGEMENT COMPANY, LTD.

7/F, No. 13 Bldg, Tibei
Weijin South Rd., Hexi Dist.
Tianjin, China 300060
Phone: 86-22-2334-1562
Fax: 86-22-2334-1533
E-mail: cvcm@cvcm.com.cn
Website: www.cvcm.com.cn

Management and Staff

Li Mingyan, Chief Financial Officer
Zhang Renliang, President

Type of Firm

Private Equity Firm

Project Preferences

Type of Financing Preferred:
Balanced

Geographical Preferences

International Preferences:
China

Additional Information

Year Founded: 2000
Current Activity Level: Actively seeking new investments

BOI VENTURE CAPITAL LIMITED

40 Mespil Road
Dublin, Ireland 4
Phone: 353-1-665-3443
Fax: 353-1-665-3484
E-mail: business.banking@boimail.com
Website: www.boi.ie/venturecapital

Type of Firm

Bank Affiliated

Association Membership
Irish Venture Capital Association

Project Preferences
Role in Financing:
Will function either as deal originator or investor in deals created by others

Type of Financing Preferred:
Expansion
Management Buyouts

Geographical Preferences
International Preferences:
Ireland

Additional Information
Year Founded: 2003
Current Activity Level: Actively seeking new investments

BOKWANG INVESTMENT CORPORATION
946-1 Daechi-done
8F Glass Tower
Seoul, South Korea 135-280
Phone: 822-558-2092
Fax: 822-567-1673
Website: www.bokwang.co.kr

Management and Staff
Hong Seok-kyu, Chief Executive Officer
Kwang Lyul Oh, President
Moon Soo Park, Chief Executive Officer

Type of Firm
Private Equity Firm

Association Membership
Korean Venture Capital Association (KVCA)

Project Preferences
Type of Financing Preferred:
Balanced

Geographical Preferences
International Preferences:
Korea, South
Asia

Additional Information
Year Founded: 1989
Capital Under Management: $52,300,000
Current Activity Level: Actively seeking new investments

BOLDCAP VENTURES LLC
969 Third Avenue
4th Floor
New York, NY USA 10036
Phone: 212-730-5498
Fax: 212-208-0925
Website: www.boldcap.com

Management and Staff
Amy Wildstein, Managing Partner
Jed Freifeld, Managing Partner
Kay Koplovitz, Managing Partner
Penny Zuckerwise, Managing Partner

Type of Firm
Private Equity Firm

Association Membership
National Venture Capital Association - USA (NVCA)

Project Preferences
Role in Financing:
Will function either as deal originator or investor in deals created by others

Type of Financing Preferred:
Early Stage
Expansion

Size of Investments Considered:
Min Size of Investment Considered (000s): $250
Max Size of Investment Considered (000s): $500

Geographical Preferences
United States Preferences:
All U.S.

Industry Preferences
In Computer Software prefer:
Software
Systems Software
Applications Software

In Internet Specific prefer:
Internet
Ecommerce
Web Aggregration/Portals

In Computer Other prefer:
Computer Related

In Biotechnology prefer:
Human Biotechnology
Agricultural/Animal Bio.

In Medical/Health prefer:
Medical Diagnostics
Diagnostic Services
Health Services

In Other prefer:
Women/Minority-Owned Bus.

Additional Information
Year Founded: 2001
Capital Under Management: $5,000,000
Current Activity Level: Actively seeking new investments
Method of Compensation: Return on investment is of primary concern, do not charge fees

BOLDER CAPITAL LLC
875 North Michigan Avenue
John Hancock Ctr., Suite 4020
Chicago, IL USA 60611
Phone: 312-573-6420
Fax: 312-573-6420
E-mail: info@boldercapital.com
Website: www.boldercapital.com

Management and Staff
David Tolmie, Managing Director
Gregory Jones, Managing Director
James Gordon, Managing Director
Jeffrey Frient, Managing Director
Robert Growney, Managing Director
Todd Hamilton, Managing Director

Type of Firm
Private Equity Firm

Project Preferences
Type of Financing Preferred:
Leveraged Buyout
Expansion
Acquisition
Recapitalizations

Geographical Preferences
United States Preferences:
All U.S.

Canadian Preferences:
All Canada

Industry Preferences
In Business Serv. prefer:
Services

In Manufact. prefer:
Manufacturing

Additional Information
Year Founded: 2004
Current Activity Level: Actively seeking new investments

BOND CAPITAL PARTNERS, LTD.
1040 West Georgia Street
Suite 940
Vancouver, Canada V6E 4H1
Phone: 604-687-2663
Fax: 604-688-6527
E-mail: info@bondcapital.ca
Website: www.bondcapital.ca

Other Offices
1040 West Georgia Street
Suite 940
Vancouver, Canada

Phone: 604-687-2663
Fax: 604-688-6527

Type of Firm
Private Equity Firm

Additional Information
Year Founded: 2003
Current Activity Level: Actively seeking new investments

BONSAI VENTURE CAPITAL
Avda. Valdelaparra, 27
Alcobendas
Madrid, Spain 28108
Phone: 34-91-661-7987
Fax: 34-91-661-6658
E-mail: atencion.cliente@bonsaitech.com
Website: www.bonsaitech.com

Type of Firm
Private Equity Firm

Project Preferences
Type of Financing Preferred:
Balanced

Geographical Preferences
International Preferences:
Spain

Industry Preferences
In Internet Specific prefer:
Internet

In Biotechnology prefer:
Biotechnology

Additional Information
Year Founded: 2007
Current Activity Level: Actively seeking new investments

BONVENTURE MANAGEMENT GMBH
Pettenkoferstrasse 37
Munich, Germany 80336
Phone: 49-89-544-606-0
Fax: 49-89-544-60135
E-mail: info@bonventure.de
Website: www.bonventure.de

Management and Staff
Erwin Stahl, Chief Executive Officer

Type of Firm
Endowment, Foundation or Pension Fund

Project Preferences
Type of Financing Preferred:
Early Stage
Balanced

Geographical Preferences
International Preferences:
Germany

Industry Preferences
In Other prefer:
Socially Responsible

Additional Information
Year Founded: 2005
Capital Under Management: $13,100,000
Current Activity Level: Actively seeking new investments

BOREA AS
P.O. Box 580
Bergen, Norway 5808
Phone: 47-55-301-980
Fax: 47-55-301-981
E-mail: borea@borea.no
Website: www.borea.no

Management and Staff
Finn Kinserdal, Chief Executive Officer
Gudmund Ronningen, Partner
Harald Mowinckel Troye, Partner
Helge Lundefaret, Partner
Jorgen Lorentz, Partner

Type of Firm
Private Equity Firm

Project Preferences
Type of Financing Preferred:
Leveraged Buyout
Balanced
Management Buyouts

Geographical Preferences
International Preferences:
Norway

Industry Preferences
In Industrial/Energy prefer:
Industrial Products

Additional Information
Year Founded: 2002
Current Activity Level: Actively seeking new investments

BOREALIS INFRASTRUCTURE MANAGEMENT, INC.
Royal Bank Plaza, South Tower
200 Bay Street
Toronto, Canada M5J 2J2
Phone: 416-361-1011
E-mail: info@borealisinfrastructure.com
Website: www.borealisinfrastructure.com

Other Offices
Ernst & Young Tower
440 - 2nd Avenue South West, Suite 700
Calgary, Canada T2P 5E9
Phone: 403-206-6529

Management and Staff
Darren Soanes, Vice President
J. Michael Rolland, President
Rheal Ranger, Chief Executive Officer
Robert Deutschmann, Vice President
Sebastian Sherman, Vice President
Steven Zucchet, Vice President
Tenio Evangelista, Vice President

Type of Firm
Private Equity Firm

Project Preferences
Type of Financing Preferred:
Leveraged Buyout

Geographical Preferences
United States Preferences:
All U.S.

Canadian Preferences:
All Canada

Additional Information
Year Founded: 2005
Current Activity Level: Actively seeking new investments

BOREALIS VENTURES
Ten Allen Street
Upper Level
Hanover, NH USA 03755
Phone: 603-643-1500
Fax: 603-643-7600
E-mail: info@borealisventures.com
Website: www.borealisventures.com

Other Offices
114 North Main Street
Suite 201
Concord, NH USA 03301
Phone: 603-226-4480
Fax: 603-226-4485

Management and Staff
Jesse Devitte, Managing Director

Matt Rightmire, Managing Director
Philip Ferneau, Managing Director

Type of Firm
Private Equity Firm

Association Membership
National Venture Capital Association - USA (NVCA)

Project Preferences

n Financing:
Prefer role as deal originator

Type of Financing Preferred:
Early Stage
Balanced
Seed
First Stage Financing
Startup

Size of Investments Considered:
Min Size of Investment Considered (000s): $250
Max Size of Investment Considered (000s): $5,000

Geographical Preferences

United States Preferences:
Northeast
All U.S.

Industry Preferences

In Computer Software prefer:
Applications Software

In Internet Specific prefer:
Internet

In Medical/Health prefer:
Medical/Health

Additional Information
Year Founded: 2002
Capital Under Management: $50,000,000
Current Activity Level: Actively seeking new investments
Method of Compensation: Return on investment is of primary concern, do not charge fees

---

BOSTON CAPITAL VENTURES
114 State Street
Sixth Floor
Boston, MA USA 02109
Phone: 617-227-6550
Fax: 617-227-3847
E-mail: info.z572@bcv.com
Website: www.bcv.com

Management and Staff
Alex Wilmerding, Partner
Alexander Von der Goltz, Partner
Charles Bridge, Chief Financial Officer
Johan Von der Goltz, Partner
John Shields, General Partner

Type of Firm
Private Equity Firm

Project Preferences

Role in Financing:
Prefer role as deal originator but will also invest in deals created by others

Type of Financing Preferred:
Second Stage Financing
Leveraged Buyout
Expansion
Start-up Financing
First Stage Financing
Recapitalizations

Size of Investments Considered:
Min Size of Investment Considered (000s): $500
Max Size of Investment Considered (000s): $3,000

Geographical Preferences

United States Preferences:
Northeast

Canadian Preferences:
All Canada

Industry Focus

(% based on actual investment)	
Internet Specific	28.7%
Computer Software and Services	24.7%
Communications and Media	18.7%
Other Products	12.3%
Medical/Health	9.5%
Consumer Related	1.7%
Industrial/Energy	1.3%
Semiconductors/Other Elect.	1.2%
Biotechnology	1.2%
Computer Hardware	0.6%

Additional Information
Name of Most Recent Fund: Boston Capital Ventures V, L.P.
Most Recent Fund Was Raised: 09/01/2000
Year Founded: 1982
Capital Under Management: $111,000,000
Current Activity Level: Actively seeking new investments
Method of Compensation: Return on investment is of primary concern, do not charge fees

---

BOSTON INVESTMENT COMPANY, LTD.
13th Floor, Mihae Building
18 Nonhyun-Dong, Kangnam-Gu
Seoul, South Korea 135-813
Phone: 822-3444-5335
Fax: 822-3444-5344
Website: www.bostonvc.co.kr

Management and Staff
Hee Chang Kim, Managing Director
Hyun Woo Kim, Chief Executive Officer
Jong Yoon Noh, Managing Director

Type of Firm
Investment Management Firm

Association Membership
Korean Venture Capital Association (KVCA)

Project Preferences

Type of Financing Preferred:
Balanced

Geographical Preferences

International Preferences:
Korea, South
Asia

Industry Preferences

In Communications prefer:
Media and Entertainment

In Semiconductor/Electr prefer:
Electronics

In Biotechnology prefer:
Biotechnology

In Business Serv. prefer:
Services

Additional Information
Year Founded: 2004
Capital Under Management: $56,700,000
Current Activity Level: Actively seeking new investments

BOSTON MEDICAL INVESTORS
23 Marlborough Street
Boston, MA USA 02116

Management and Staff
Robert Carpenter, President

Type of Firm
Private Equity Firm

Additional Information
Year Founded: 1994
Current Activity Level: Actively seeking new investments

BOSTON MILLENNIA PARTNERS
30 Rowes Wharf
Suite 500
Boston, MA USA 02110
Phone: 617-428-5150
Fax: 617-428-5160
E-mail: info@millenniapartners.com
Website: www.millenniapartners.com

Management and Staff

A. Dana Callow, Managing General Partner
Jean-Yves Lagarde, Partner
Martin Hernon, General Partner
Patrick Fortune, Partner
Robert Jevon, Partner
Robert Sherman, General Partner
Stephen Stickells, Principal

Type of Firm

Private Equity Firm

Association Membership

Mid-Atlantic Venture Association
National Venture Capital Association - USA (NVCA)

Project Preferences

Role in Financing:

Prefer role as deal originator but will also invest in deals created by others

Type of Financing Preferred:

Early Stage
Balanced

Size of Investments Considered:

Min Size of Investment Considered (000s): $2,000
Max Size of Investment Considered (000s): $15,000

Geographical Preferences

United States Preferences:

Northeast

Industry Focus

(% based on actual investment)	
Internet Specific	26.3%
Computer Software and Services	25.2%
Medical/Health	21.4%
Communications and Media	13.7%
Biotechnology	6.5%
Semiconductors/Other Elect.	3.5%
Computer Hardware	1.8%
Other Products	1.3%
Consumer Related	0.4%

Additional Information

Year Founded: 1997
Capital Under Management: $600,000,000
Current Activity Level: Actively seeking new investments
Method of Compensation: Return on investment is of primary concern, do not charge fees

BOSTON UNIVERSITY TECHNOLOGY DEVELOPMENT FUND

53 Bay State Road
Boston, MA USA 02215
Phone: 617-353-4550
Fax: 617-353-6141
E-mail: otd@bu.edu
Website: www.bu.edu/otd

Type of Firm

University Program

Association Membership

National Venture Capital Association - USA (NVCA)

Project Preferences

Role in Financing:

Will function either as deal originator or investor in deals created by others

Type of Financing Preferred:

Second Stage Financing
Early Stage
Expansion
Start-up Financing
Seed
First Stage Financing

Size of Investments Considered:

Min Size of Investment Considered (000s): $250
Max Size of Investment Considered (000s): $2,000

Geographical Preferences

United States Preferences:

Northeast

Industry Focus

(% based on actual investment)	
Medical/Health	28.7%
Biotechnology	21.9%
Semiconductors/Other Elect.	21.4%
Computer Software and Services	10.2%
Internet Specific	7.8%
Communications and Media	4.5%
Computer Hardware	3.7%
Industrial/Energy	0.7%
Consumer Related	0.6%
Other Products	0.4%

Additional Information

Name of Most Recent Fund: OTD Fund/Boston University FKA: Community Tech Foundation BU
Most Recent Fund Was Raised: 06/01/1982
Year Founded: 1975
Capital Under Management: $43,000,000
Current Activity Level: Actively seeking new investments
Method of Compensation: Return on investment is of primary concern, do not charge fees

BOSTON VENTURES MANAGEMENT, INC.

125 High Street
17th Floor
Boston, MA USA 02110
Phone: 617-350-1500
Fax: 617-350-1509
E-mail: info@bvlp.com
Website: www.bostonventures.com

Other Offices

919 Third Avenue
Suite 620
New York, NY USA 10021
Phone: 212-593-0095
Fax: 212-593-0094

Management and Staff

Andrew Davis, Managing Director
Anthony Bolland, Managing Director
Barbara Ginader, Managing Director
Barry Baker, Managing Director
Catherine Bird, Chief Financial Officer
Elizabeth Granville-Smith, Managing Director
James Wilson, Managing Director
Justin Harrison, Partner
Louis Bertocci, Partner
Marco Ferrari, Principal
Matthew Kinsey, Principal
Roy Coppedge, Managing Director
Vikrant Raina, Managing Director

Type of Firm

Private Equity Advisor or Fund of Funds

Project Preferences

Role in Financing:

Prefer role as deal originator

Type of Financing Preferred:

Leveraged Buyout
Later Stage
Management Buyouts
Recapitalizations

Size of Investments Considered:

Min Size of Investment Considered (000s): $10,000
Max Size of Investment Considered (000s): $125,000

Geographical Preferences

International Preferences:

United Kingdom
Europe
All International

Industry Focus

(% based on actual investment)	
Communications and Media	46.9%
Other Products	30.8%
Consumer Related	12.8%
Semiconductors/Other Elect.	4.4%
Internet Specific	2.5%
Biotechnology	1.7%
Computer Software and Services	0.5%
Medical/Health	0.4%

Additional Information

Name of Most Recent Fund: Boston Ventures Ltd. Partnership VI
Most Recent Fund Was Raised: 05/31/2000
Year Founded: 1983
Capital Under Management: $1,454,000,000
Current Activity Level: Actively seeking new investments
Method of Compensation: Return on investment is of primary concern, do not charge fees

BOULDER VENTURES, LTD.

1900 Ninth Street
Suite 200
Boulder, CO USA 80302
Phone: 303-444-6950
Fax: 303-444-0267
E-mail: info@boulderventures.com
Website: www.boulderventures.com

Other Offices

5425 Wisconsin Avenue
Suite 704
Chevy Chase, MD USA 20815
Phone: 301-913-0213
Fax: 301-913-0434

Management and Staff

Andrew Jones, General Partner
Frank Bonsal, Venture Partner
Jonathan Perl, General Partner
Josh Fidler, Founding Partner
Lawrence Macks, Founding Partner
Marvin Caruthers, Venture Partner
Peter Roshko, General Partner
Timothy Hoogheem, Chief Financial Officer

Type of Firm

Private Equity Firm

Association Membership

Mid-Atlantic Venture Association

Project Preferences

Role in Financing:
Will function either as deal originator or investor in deals created by others

Type of Financing Preferred:
Early Stage
Seed
Startup

Size of Investments Considered:
Min Size of Investment Considered (000s): $1,000
Max Size of Investment Considered (000s): $8,000

Geographical Preferences

United States Preferences:
Mid Atlantic
Colorado

Industry Focus

(% based on actual investment)

Computer Software and Services	31.2%
Communications and Media	18.6%
Internet Specific	14.2%
Biotechnology	9.0%
Computer Hardware	8.5%
Semiconductors/Other Elect.	7.0%
Other Products	6.0%
Consumer Related	3.7%
Industrial/Energy	1.1%
Medical/Health	0.8%

Additional Information

Name of Most Recent Fund: Boulder Ventures V
Most Recent Fund Was Raised: 05/03/2007
Year Founded: 1995
Capital Under Management: $282,000,000
Current Activity Level: Actively seeking new investments
Method of Compensation: Return on investment is of primary concern, do not charge fees

BOUNTY EQUITY FUND, LLC

2 West 2nd Street
Suite # 210
Tulsa, OK USA 74103
Phone: 866-885-0264
Fax: 212-898-0397
Website: www.bountyequityfund.com

Management and Staff

Elizabeth Kopple, Managing Partner

Type of Firm

Private Equity Advisor or Fund of Funds

Association Membership

National Venture Capital Association - USA (NVCA)

Project Preferences

Type of Financing Preferred:
Early Stage
Seed

Geographical Preferences

United States Preferences:
All U.S.

Additional Information

Year Founded: 2007
Current Activity Level: Actively seeking new investments

BOW RIVER CAPITAL PARTNERS

1490 Lafayette Street
Suite 400
Denver, CO USA 80218
Phone: 303-861-8466
Fax: 303-861-8557
E-mail: noble@bowrivercapital.com
Website: www.bowrivercapital.com

Management and Staff

Bruno Darre, Co-Founder
Eric Wolf, Co-Founder

Type of Firm

Private Equity Firm

Project Preferences

Role in Financing:
Prefer role as deal originator but will also invest in deals created by others

Type of Financing Preferred:
Leveraged Buyout
Expansion
Mezzanine
Turnaround
Management Buyouts
Acquisition
Recapitalizations

Size of Investments Considered:
Min Size of Investment Considered (000s): $1,000
Max Size of Investment Considered (000s): $5,000

Geographical Preferences

United States Preferences:
Northwest
Rocky Mountain
West Coast
Colorado
All U.S.

Canadian Preferences:
All Canada

Industry Preferences

In Industrial/Energy prefer:
Oil & Gas Drilling,Explor

Additional Information

Year Founded: 2004
Capital Under Management: $75,200,000
Current Activity Level: Actively seeking new investments

BOWMARK CAPITAL (FKA: SAGITTA PRIVATE EQUITY)

3 Saint James's Square
London, United Kingdom SW1Y 4JU
Phone: 44-20-7189-9000
Fax: 44-20-7189-9044
E-mail: info@bowmark.com
Website: www.bowmark.com

Other Offices

34 Molesworth Street
Dublin 2, Ireland
Phone: 353-1-661-5253
Fax: 353-1-676-9484

Management and Staff

Bob Michaelson, Managing Director
Charles Ind, Managing Director
Julian Masters, Partner

Type of Firm

Bank Affiliated

Association Membership
British Venture Capital Association (BVCA)

Project Preferences

Type of Financing Preferred:
Leveraged Buyout
Expansion
Later Stage
Management Buyouts
Acquisition
Industry Rollups

Size of Investments Considered:
Min Size of Investment Considered (000s): $19,725
Max Size of Investment Considered (000s): $147,938

Geographical Preferences

International Preferences:
United Kingdom
Western Europe

Industry Preferences

In Medical/Health prefer:
Medical/Health

In Consumer Related prefer:
Entertainment and Leisure
Retail
Food/Beverage

In Business Serv. prefer:
Services
Media

Additional Information
Year Founded: 1997
Capital Under Management: $1,380,800,000
Current Activity Level: Actively seeking new investments

BOXWOOD CAPITAL PARTNERS, LLC
Nine South 12th Street
Second Floor
Richmond, VA USA 23219
Phone: 804-343-3300
Fax: 804-343-3440
Website: www.boxwoodpartnersllc.com

Management and Staff
Bobby Morris, Partner
Bryan Burden, Vice President
Chris Deel, Partner
Matt Schumacher, Vice President
Patrick Galleher, Partner

Type of Firm
Bank Affiliated

Project Preferences

Role in Financing:
Prefer role as deal originator

Type of Financing Preferred:
Leveraged Buyout
Early Stage
Expansion
Management Buyouts
Acquisition

Size of Investments Considered:
Min Size of Investment Considered (000s): $500
Max Size of Investment Considered (000s): $100,000

Geographical Preferences

United States Preferences:
All U.S.

Industry Preferences

In Computer Software prefer:
Software
Systems Software
Applications Software

In Internet Specific prefer:
E-Commerce Technology
Internet
Ecommerce
Web Aggregration/Portals

In Medical/Health prefer:
Diagnostic Services
Medical Products
Health Services

In Consumer Related prefer:
Consumer
Entertainment and Leisure
Sports
Retail
Franchises(NEC)
Food/Beverage
Education Related

In Financial Services prefer:
Financial Services

In Business Serv. prefer:
Services
Distribution
Media

In Manufact. prefer:
Manufacturing

Additional Information
Year Founded: 2008
Current Activity Level: Actively seeking new investments

BPB INVESTIMENTI
12, Corso Europa
Milan, Italy 20122
Phone: 39-2-7781-4621
Fax: 39-2-7781-4626
E-mail: bpbinv@tin.it

Type of Firm
Bank Affiliated

Association Membership
Italian Venture Capital Association (AIFI)

Project Preferences

Type of Financing Preferred:
Expansion
Turnaround

Geographical Preferences

International Preferences:
Italy

Additional Information
Year Founded: 1996
Current Activity Level: Actively seeking new investments

BPE INVESTIMENTOS
Avenida Ibirapuera 2907
cj. 303
Sao Paulo, Brazil
Phone: 55-11-5561-9544
Fax: 55-11-3285-6582
Website: www.bpei.com.br

Management and Staff
Claudio Pecanha, Partner
Luis Fernando Salem, Partner
Paulo Chueri, Partner
Robert Duncan Littlejohn, Partner

Type of Firm
Private Equity Firm

Association Membership
Brazilian Venture Capital Association (ABCR)

Project Preferences

Type of Financing Preferred:
Balanced

Geographical Preferences

International Preferences:
Brazil

Additional Information
Year Founded: 2006
Current Activity Level: Actively seeking new investments

BPE PRIVATE EQUITY (FKA: BERENBERG PRIVATE EQUITY GMBH)
Schleusenbrucke 1
Ecke Neuer Wall
Hamburg, Germany 20354
Phone: 49-40-361-5700
Fax: 49-40-3615-7070
E-mail: info@bpe.de
Website: www.bpe.de

Management and Staff

Andreas M. Odefey, Managing Partner
Jens Achilles, Partner
Stephan Gummert, Partner

Type of Firm

Bank Affiliated

Association Membership

German Venture Capital Association (BVK)
European Private Equity and Venture Capital Assoc.

Project Preferences

Type of Financing Preferred:

Leveraged Buyout
Expansion

Geographical Preferences

International Preferences:

Switzerland
Austria
Germany

Industry Focus

(% based on actual investment)

Internet Specific	42.3%
Semiconductors/Other Elect.	32.4%
Other Products	25.3%

Additional Information

Name of Most Recent Fund: BPE2 Private Equity GmbH & Co. KG
Most Recent Fund Was Raised: 10/31/2005
Year Founded: 1999
Capital Under Management: $55,200,000
Current Activity Level: Actively seeking new investments

BPEP INTERNATIONAL

39/F One Intl. Finance Centre
1 Harbour View Street
Central, Hong Kong
Phone: 852-2843-9327
Fax: 852-2843-9372
Website: www.bpepasia.com

Other Offices

24/F, Mirae Asset Tower
166 Luijiazui Ring Road
Shanghai, China 200120
Phone: 86-21-3135-9500
Fax: 86-21-3135-9499

9th Floor, Infinity Tower-A
DLF Phase-II
Gurgaon, India 122 002
Phone: 91-124-432-1100
Fax: 91-124-432-1155

53a George Calinescu Street
4th Floor, Sector 1
Bucharest, Romania
Phone: 40-1-230-5072
Fax: 40-1-230-5075

50 Raffles Place
#34-02 Singapore Land Tower
Singapore, Singapore 048623
Phone: 65-6232-6312
Fax: 65-6532-0660

7-501-967-1308
9th Floor
Sao Paulo SP, Brazil 01451-000
Phone: 5511-3847-6490
Fax: 5511-3847-8490

1-12-32 Akasaka, Minato-ku
22/F Ark Mori Building
Tokyo, Japan 107-6022
Phone: 81-3-5545-7200
Fax: 81-3-5545-7201

230 Park Avenue, 13th Floor
New York, NY USA 10169
Phone: 212-901-2615
Fax: 212-901-2614

10 Uspenski Pereulok
5th Floor
Moscow, Russia 103006
Phone: 7-501-967-1307
Fax: 7-501-967-1308

C./ Hermosilla
11-5a Planta
Madrid, Spain 28001
Phone: 34-91-781-8870
Fax: 34-91-781-8877

66 Palmer Avenue
Suite 34
Bronxville, NY USA 10708

13-15 Victoria Street
St. Peter Port
Guernsey, Channel Islands GY13ZD

Unit 2903-05A, Tower 3
China Central Place, No.77 Jian Guo Road
Beijing, China 100025
Phone: 86-10-5904-7300
Fax: 86-10-5904-7333

Zeppelinallee 77
Frankfurt, Germany 60487
Phone: 49-69-714-070
Fax: 49-69-713-980

C./ Luis Vives, 6 - 2
Valencia, Spain 56003
Phone: 34-96-392-4505
Fax: 34-96-392-4561

3 via della Moscova
Milan, Italy 20121
Phone: 39-02-6361-251
Fax: 39-02-2900-5411

ul. Wspolna 47/49
Warsaw, Poland 00-684
Phone: 48-22-627-4000
Fax: 48-22-627-4001

Homero No. 440
9 Piso Desp. 901-901
Col. Polanco, Mexico 11560
Phone: 5255-5254-3280
Fax: 5255-5254-3270

Ducat Place II, Suite 750
Gasheka str. 7, bldg 1
Moscow, Russia 123056
Phone: 7-495-967-1307
Fax: 7-495-967-1308

950 Tower Lane
18th Floor
Foster , CA USA 94404
Phone: 1-650-378-1150
Fax: 1-650-378-4710

Management and Staff

Alexei Kalinin, Managing Partner
Antonio Vertiz, Partner
Caroline Wee, Principal
Colin Lau, Chief Financial Officer
Dar Chen, Principal
David Huckfield, Chief Operating Officer
Dick Kwan, Managing Director
Edward Yang, Partner
Erik Carlberg, Partner
Evan McCordick, Partner
Felix Fong, Partner
Gilbert Chalk, Partner
Giuseppe Turri, Partner
Gordon Shaw, Partner
Hedley Mayor, Partner
Jack Hennessy, Partner
Jean Eric Salata, Managing Partner
Joanna Lei, Partner
Jose Angel Sarasa, Managing Partner
Jun Chen, Partner
Kenneth Cheong, Principal
Leo Gherghina, Partner
Marcio Souza, Partner
Michael Calvey, Managing Partner
N Subramanian, Partner
Peter Chan, Partner
Posner Dirk, Partner
Rahul Bhasin, Managing Partner
Wai San Loke, Principal

Type of Firm

Bank Affiliated

Association Membership

Venture Capital Association of Beijing (VCAB)
Australian Venture Capital Association (AVCAL)
Hong Kong Venture Capital Association (HKVCA)
British Venture Capital Association (BVCA)
Polish Venture Capital Association (PSIC/PPEA)
European Private Equity and Venture Capital Assoc.
Singapore Venture Capital Association (SVCA)
Spanish Venture Capital Association (ASCRI)

Indian Venture Capital Association (IVCA)

Project Preferences

Role in Financing:
Will function either as deal originator or investor in deals created by others

Type of Financing Preferred:
Leveraged Buyout
Early Stage
Expansion
Mezzanine
Generalist PE
Balanced
Start-up Financing
Turnaround
Seed
Management Buyouts
Recapitalizations

Size of Investments Considered:
Min Size of Investment Considered (000s): $100,000
Max Size of Investment Considered: No Limit

Geographical Preferences

International Preferences:
Laos
Vietnam
Hungary
Indonesia
India
Slovak Repub.
United Kingdom
Czech Republic
Portugal
Taiwan
Central Europe
Europe
Brunei
Hong Kong
Poland
China
Thailand
Brazil
Mexico
Philippines
Cambodia
Bulgaria
Spain
Ukraine
Australia
Romania
Singapore
Korea, South
Asia
Burma
Japan
Malaysia
Russia

Industry Focus
(% based on actual investment)

Other Products	29.2%
Computer Software and Services	13.9%
Industrial/Energy	13.3%
Computer Hardware	11.6%
Internet Specific	10.4%
Semiconductors/Other Elect.	7.7%
Consumer Related	5.6%
Communications and Media	5.2%
Biotechnology	3.0%
Medical/Health	0.1%

Additional Information
Name of Most Recent Fund: Baring Private Equity Asia GP III, L.P.
Most Recent Fund Was Raised: 08/17/2006
Year Founded: 1984
Capital Under Management: $2,500,000,000
Current Activity Level: Actively seeking new investments
Method of Compensation: Return on investment is of primary concern, do not charge fees

---

BPI PRIVATE EQUITY (AKA: INTER-RISCO SOC. DE CAP. DE RISCO)

Rua Tenente Valadim, 284
Porto, Portugal 4100-476
Phone: 351-2-2607-2270
Fax: 351-2-2600-6751
E-mail: rlf@bpi.pt
Website: www.bancobpi.pt

Management and Staff
Artur Santos Silva, Founder

Type of Firm
Bank Affiliated

Association Membership
Portuguese Venture Capital Association (APCRI)
European Private Equity and Venture Capital Assoc.

Project Preferences

Role in Financing:
Prefer role as deal originator

Type of Financing Preferred:
Leveraged Buyout
Expansion
Early Stage
Balanced
Acquisition
Startup
Recapitalizations

Size of Investments Considered:
Min Size of Investment Considered (000s): $700
Max Size of Investment Considered: No Limit

Geographical Preferences

International Preferences:
Portugal

Industry Preferences

In Communications prefer:
Communications and Media

In Medical/Health prefer:
Medical/Health

In Industrial/Energy prefer:
Industrial Products

Additional Information
Name of Most Recent Fund: Fundo Caravela
Most Recent Fund Was Raised: 12/01/2002
Year Founded: 1988
Capital Under Management: $70,200,000
Current Activity Level: Actively seeking new investments

BPN GESTAO DE ACTIVOS, SGFIM, S.A.

Av. Antonio Augusto Aguiar 132
5 Piso
Lisbon, Portugal 1050-020
Phone: 351-21-359-8000
Fax: 351-21-094-8679
Website: www.bpn.pt

Type of Firm
Private Equity Firm

Association Membership
European Private Equity and Venture Capital Assoc.

Project Preferences

Type of Financing Preferred:
Balanced

Geographical Preferences

International Preferences:
Portugal
Europe

Additional Information
Year Founded: 1991
Capital Under Management: $57,200,000
Current Activity Level: Actively seeking new investments

BR VENTURES

304 Sage Hall
Cornell University
Ithaca, NY USA 14853
Phone: 607-255-6599
Website: www.johnson.cornell.edu

Type of Firm
University Program

Project Preferences

Type of Financing Preferred:
Balanced
Start-up Financing
Seed

Size of Investments Considered:
Min Size of Investment Considered (000s): $50
Max Size of Investment Considered (000s): $200

Geographical Preferences

United States Preferences:
All U.S.

Additional Information
Year Founded: 2003
Current Activity Level: Actively seeking new investments

BRACKEN PARTNERS LIMITED
50 Liverpool Street
London, United Kingdom EC2M 7PR
Phone: 44-207-456-9880
Fax: 44-207-247-5156
E-mail: info@brackenpartners.com
Website: www.brackenpartners.com

Management and Staff
Barry Gold, Founding Partner
Kevin DeLeon, Founding Partner
Stuart Lucas, Founding Partner

Type of Firm
Private Equity Firm

Association Membership
British Venture Capital Association (BVCA)

Project Preferences

Type of Financing Preferred:
Early Stage

Geographical Preferences

International Preferences:
United Kingdom
Europe

Additional Information
Year Founded: 1999
Current Activity Level: Actively seeking new investments

BRADFORD EQUITIES MANAGEMENT LLC
360 Hamilton Avenue
Suite 425
White Plains, NY USA 10601
Phone: 914-922-7171
Fax: 914-922-7172
Website: www.bradfordequities.com

Management and Staff
Jon Van Tuin, Principal
Neil Taylor, Chief Financial Officer
Richard Rudolph, Managing Director
Robert Simon, Senior Managing Director

Type of Firm
Private Equity Firm

Project Preferences

Role in Financing:
Prefer role as deal originator

Type of Financing Preferred:
Leveraged Buyout

Size of Investments Considered:
Min Size of Investment Considered (000s): $10,000
Max Size of Investment Considered (000s): $70,000

Geographical Preferences

United States Preferences:
Mid Atlantic
Southeast
Northeast

Industry Preferences

In Business Serv. prefer:
Distribution

In Manufact. prefer:
Manufacturing

Additional Information
Name of Most Recent Fund: Bradford Equities Fund III, L.P.
Most Recent Fund Was Raised: 08/15/2000
Year Founded: 1974
Capital Under Management: $120,000,000
Current Activity Level: Actively seeking new investments
Method of Compensation: Return on invest. most important, but chg. closing fees, service fees, etc.

BRADSTONE EQUITY PARTNERS
1103 - 1166 Alberni Street
Vancouver, Canada V6E 3Z3
Phone: 604-688-3410
Fax: 604-683-2235

Type of Firm
Private Equity Firm

Additional Information
Year Founded: 2009
Current Activity Level: Actively seeking new investments

BRAEMAR ENERGY VENTURES
340 Madison Avenue
18th Floor
New York, NY USA 10017
Phone: 212-697-0900
Fax: 212-210-5788
Website: www.braemarenergy.com

Management and Staff
Dennis Costello, Managing Director
Eric Schultz, Chief Financial Officer
George Reichenbach, Managing Director
Jiong Ma, Principal
Neil Suslak, Managing Director
William Lese, Managing Director

Type of Firm
Private Equity Firm

Association Membership
National Venture Capital Association - USA (NVCA)

Project Preferences

Type of Financing Preferred:
Early Stage
Expansion
Public Companies
Later Stage
Other

Size of Investments Considered:
Min Size of Investment Considered (000s): $1,000
Max Size of Investment Considered (000s): $5,000

Industry Preferences

In Communications prefer:
Communications and Media

In Industrial/Energy prefer:
Energy

Additional Information
Year Founded: 2002
Capital Under Management: $60,000,000
Current Activity Level: Actively seeking new investments

BRAHMAN MANAGEMENT, LLC
350 Main Avenue
22nd Floor
New York, NY USA 10017
Phone: 212-681-9797

Management and Staff
Mitchell Kuflik, General Partner
Peter Hochfelder, General Partner
Robert Sobel, General Partner

Type of Firm
Private Equity Firm

Additional Information
Year Founded: 2002
Capital Under Management: $13,000,000
Current Activity Level: Actively seeking new investments

BRAINHEART CAPITAL AB

Skeppsbron 44
PO Box 1238
Stockholm, Sweden SE-111 82
Phone: 46-733-779-900
Fax: 46-733-779-901
E-mail: info@brainheart.com
Website: www.brainheart.com

Management and Staff

Cynthia Suzuma Jonstromer, Venture Partner
Magnus Melander, Partner
Michael Mandahl, Venture Partner

Type of Firm

Private Equity Firm

Association Membership

Swedish Venture Capital Association (SVCA)
European Private Equity and Venture Capital Assoc.

Project Preferences

Type of Financing Preferred:
Leveraged Buyout
Early Stage
Expansion
Seed
Startup

Geographical Preferences

International Preferences:
Europe
Scandanavia/Nordic Region

Industry Preferences

In Communications prefer:
Telecommunications

In Computer Software prefer:
Software

In Internet Specific prefer:
Internet

Additional Information

Year Founded: 2000
Capital Under Management: $210,000,000
Current Activity Level: Actively seeking new investments

BRAIT CAPITAL PARTNERS

9 Fricker Road
Illovo Boulevard, Illovo
Sandton, South Africa
Phone: 27-11-507-1000
Fax: 27-11-507-1001
Website: www.brait.com

Other Offices

19 Baarerstrasse
Zug, Switzerland
Phone: 41-42-710-6066
Fax: 41-42-710-3377

The Terraces, 2nd Floor
25 Protea Road
Cape Town, South Africa 7708
Phone: 27-21-673-7800
Fax: 27-21-673-7801

180 rue des Aubepines
Luxembourg, Luxembourg L-1145
Phone: 352-4590-4794
Fax: 352-4590-3642

Suite 509 - 510
St. James Court, St. Denis Street
Port Louis, Mauritius
Phone: 230-213-6909
Fax: 230-213-6913

Management and Staff

John Gnodde, Chief Executive Officer

Type of Firm

Private Equity Firm

Association Membership

South African Venture Capital Association (SAVCA)

Project Preferences

Type of Financing Preferred:
Early Stage
Balanced
Later Stage
Startup

Geographical Preferences

International Preferences:
Israel
South Africa
Africa

Industry Preferences

In Communications prefer:
Communications and Media

In Semiconductor/Electr prefer:
Electronics

In Medical/Health prefer:
Medical/Health

In Consumer Related prefer:
Retail
Food/Beverage
Consumer Products
Consumer Services

In Transportation prefer:
Transportation

In Business Serv. prefer:
Distribution
Media

In Manufact. prefer:
Manufacturing
Publishing

Additional Information

Year Founded: 1991
Capital Under Management: $650,000,000
Current Activity Level: Actively seeking new investments

BRAMDEAN ASSET MANAGEMENT

100 Brompton Road
London, United Kingdom SW3 1ER
Phone: 44-20-7052-9272
Website: www.bramdean.com

Management and Staff

Nicola Horlick, Chief Executive Officer

Type of Firm

Private Equity Advisor or Fund of Funds

Project Preferences

Type of Financing Preferred:
Balanced

Geographical Preferences

International Preferences:
Europe

Additional Information

Year Founded: 2005
Capital Under Management: $263,500,000
Current Activity Level: Actively seeking new investments

BRAND JOURNEY CAPITAL LP

2609 Production Road
Virginia Beach, VA USA 23451
Website: www.brandjourney.net

Management and Staff

Brian Mankwitz, Vice President
David Wolfe, Managing Director
Peter Murane, Managing Director
Tyler Tysdal, Managing Director

Type of Firm

Private Equity Firm

Project Preferences

Type of Financing Preferred:
Balanced

Geographical Preferences

United States Preferences:
All U.S.

Additional Information

Year Founded: 2008
Current Activity Level: Actively seeking new investments

BRANDON CAPITAL PARTNERS

210 George Street
Level 2
Sydney, Australia 2000
Phone: 612-9247-2577
Fax: 612-9247-7344
E-mail: info@brandoncapital.com.au
Website: www.brandoncapital.com.au

Other Offices

257 Collins Street
Level 1
Melbourne, Australia 3000
Phone: 61-3-9657-0700
Fax: 61-3-9657-0777

Management and Staff

Andrea Tobias, Venture Partner
Christopher Nave, Founding Partner
David Fisher, Founding Partner
Michael Ball, Chief Financial Officer
Stephen Thompson, Founding Partner

Type of Firm

Private Equity Firm

Association Membership

Australian Venture Capital Association (AVCAL)

Project Preferences

Type of Financing Preferred:

Early Stage
Balanced
Seed

Size of Investments Considered:

Min Size of Investment Considered (000s): $403
Max Size of Investment Considered (000s): $4,835

Geographical Preferences

International Preferences:

Pacific
Australia

Industry Preferences

In Biotechnology prefer:

Biotechnology

In Medical/Health prefer:

Medical/Health

Additional Information

Year Founded: 1999
Capital Under Management: $71,700,000
Current Activity Level: Actively seeking new investments

BRANFORD CASTLE, INC.

150 East 58th Street
37th Floor
New York, NY USA 10155
Phone: 212-317-2020
Fax: 212-656-1324
Website: www.branfordcastle.com

Management and Staff

David Castle, President
Howard Morgan, Partner

Type of Firm

Private Equity Firm

Project Preferences

Role in Financing:

Prefer role as deal originator but will also invest in deals created by others

Type of Financing Preferred:

Leveraged Buyout

Geographical Preferences

Canadian Preferences:

All Canada

Additional Information

Year Founded: 1986
Current Activity Level: Actively seeking new investments
Method of Compensation: Return on investment is of primary concern, do not charge fees

---

BRANTLEY PARTNERS

3201 Enterprise Parkway
Suite 350
Beachwood, OH USA 44122
Phone: 216-464-8400
Fax: 216-464-8405
E-mail: info@brantleypartners.com
Website: www.brantleypartners.com

Management and Staff

Curtis Witchey, Chief Financial Officer
James Bergman, General Partner
Kevin Cook, General Partner
Paul Cascio, General Partner
Robert Pinkas, Managing General Partner

Type of Firm

Private Equity Firm

Project Preferences

Role in Financing:

Prefer role as deal originator

Type of Financing Preferred:

Leveraged Buyout
Expansion
Mezzanine
Generalist PE
Later Stage
Management Buyouts
Acquisition
Private Placement
Recapitalizations

Size of Investments Considered:

Min Size of Investment Considered (000s): $2,000
Max Size of Investment Considered (000s): $20,000

Geographical Preferences

United States Preferences:

All U.S.

Canadian Preferences:

All Canada

Industry Focus

(% based on actual investment)

Other Products	60.2%
Industrial/Energy	17.0%
Consumer Related	6.7%
Medical/Health	4.8%
Biotechnology	4.0%
Computer Software and Services	3.1%
Semiconductors/Other Elect.	2.5%
Communications and Media	1.2%
Internet Specific	0.5%

Additional Information

Name of Most Recent Fund: Brantley Equity Partners
Most Recent Fund Was Raised: 06/30/2007
Year Founded: 1987
Capital Under Management: $310,000,000
Current Activity Level: Actively seeking new investments
Method of Compensation: Return on investment is of primary concern, do not charge fees

---

BRASS RING CAPITAL, INC.

301 Carlson Parkway
Suite 265
Minnetonka, MN USA 55305
Phone: 952-473-2710
Fax: 952-473-3607
Website: www.brassringcapital.com

Other Offices

826 North Plankinton
Suite 500
Milwaukee, WI USA 53203
Phone: 414-225-0228
Fax: 414-225-0229

Management and Staff

David Raffel, Managing Director
Steven Peterson, Managing Director

Type of Firm

Private Equity Firm

Project Preferences

Type of Financing Preferred:
Leveraged Buyout
Acquisition
Recapitalizations

Geographical Preferences

United States Preferences:
Midwest

Industry Preferences

In Business Serv. prefer:
Services

In Manufact. prefer:
Manufacturing

Additional Information

Name of Most Recent Fund: Renovare Capital Partners, L.P.
Most Recent Fund Was Raised: 07/01/2004
Year Founded: 2004
Capital Under Management: $13,700,000
Current Activity Level: Actively seeking new investments

BRAVEHEART VENTURES, LTD.

The Cherrybank Centre
Cherrybank Gardens
Perth, United Kingdom PH20PF
Phone: 44-1738-587555
Fax: 44-1738-587666
E-mail: mail@braveheart-ventures.co.uk
Website: www.braveheart-ventures.co.uk

Management and Staff

Geoffrey Thomson, Chief Executive Officer

Type of Firm

Private Equity Firm

Association Membership

British Venture Capital Association (BVCA)

Project Preferences

Type of Financing Preferred:
Early Stage
Expansion

Geographical Preferences

International Preferences:
United Kingdom

Industry Preferences

In Consumer Related prefer:
Retail

In Business Serv. prefer:
Services

In Manufact. prefer:
Manufacturing

Additional Information

Year Founded: 1997
Capital Under Management: $4,000,000
Current Activity Level: Actively seeking new investments

BRAZOS PRIVATE EQUITY PARTNERS LLC

100 Crescent Court
Suite 1777
Dallas, TX USA 75201
Phone: 214-756-6500
Fax: 214-756-6505
Website: www.brazosinv.com

Management and Staff

Benjamin Gaw, Managing Director
David Mann, Partner
F.Russell Beard, Vice President
Glenn Askew, Managing Director
Jason Sutherland, Vice President
Jeff Fronterhouse, Partner
Lucas Cutler, Managing Director
Michael Salim, Partner
Patrick McGee, Partner
Randall Fojtasek, Partner

Type of Firm

Private Equity Firm

Project Preferences

Role in Financing:
Will function either as deal originator or investor in deals created by others

Type of Financing Preferred:
Leveraged Buyout
Control-block Purchases
Expansion
Generalist PE
Management Buyouts
Acquisition
Recapitalizations

Size of Investments Considered:
Min Size of Investment Considered (000s): $10,000
Max Size of Investment Considered (000s): $40,000

Geographical Preferences

United States Preferences:
All U.S.
Southwest
Texas

Industry Focus

(% based on actual investment)

Industrial/Energy	35.9%
Other Products	27.3%
Medical/Health	22.5%
Consumer Related	8.9%
Internet Specific	5.4%

Additional Information

Name of Most Recent Fund: Brazos Equity Fund, L.P.
Most Recent Fund Was Raised: 04/01/2000
Year Founded: 1999
Capital Under Management: $400,000,000
Current Activity Level: Actively seeking new investments
Method of Compensation: Return on invest. most important, but chg. closing fees, service fees, etc.

BREAKAWAY VENTURES

800 Boylston Street
33rd Floor
Boston, MA USA 02199
Phone: 617-399-0635
Fax: 617-671-0557
E-mail: info@breakawayventures.com
Website: www.breakawayventures.com

Management and Staff

Marcus Wilson, Managing Director

Type of Firm

Private Equity Firm

Project Preferences

Role in Financing:
Will function either as deal originator or investor in deals created by others

Type of Financing Preferred:
Early Stage
Expansion

Size of Investments Considered:
Min Size of Investment Considered (000s): $500
Max Size of Investment Considered (000s): $10,000

Geographical Preferences

International Preferences:
United Kingdom

Industry Preferences

In Communications prefer:
Media and Entertainment

In Internet Specific prefer:
Internet
Ecommerce

In Consumer Related prefer:
Consumer
Entertainment and Leisure
Retail
Food/Beverage
Consumer Products

Additional Information

Year Founded: 2006
Capital Under Management: $25,000,000
Current Activity Level: Actively seeking new investments
Method of Compensation: Return on investment is of primary concern, do not charge fees

BREGAL INVESTMENTS

Standbrook House, 4th Floor
2-5 Old Bond Street
London, United Kingdom W1S 4PD
Phone: 44-207-408-1663
Fax: 44-207-491-9228
E-mail: management@bregal.com
Website: www.bregal.com

Other Offices

9 Hope Street
St Helier
Jersey, United Kingdom JE4 9XQ
Phone: 44-1534-754-500
Fax: 44-1534-879-988

360 Madison Avenue, 20th Floor
New York, NY USA 10017
Phone: 1-212-573-6235
Fax: 1-212-573-6234

Management and Staff

Bernard Brenninkmeijer, Partner
Charles Flynn, Partner
David Young, Partner
Edwin Niers, Chief Financial Officer
Jan Faber, Partner
Joost Becker, Partner
Wolter Brenninkmeijer, Partner

Type of Firm

Corporate PE/Venture

Project Preferences

Type of Financing Preferred:
Fund of Funds

Geographical Preferences

United States Preferences:
All U.S.

International Preferences:
Western Europe

Additional Information

Year Founded: 2002
Capital Under Management: $3,048,400,000
Current Activity Level: Actively seeking new investments

BRENTWOOD ASSOCIATES

11150 Santa Monica Boulevard
Suite 1200
Los Angeles, CA USA 90025
Phone: 310-477-6611
Fax: 310-477-1011
E-mail: mailbox@brentwood.com
Website: www.brentwood.com

Management and Staff

Anthony Choe, General Partner
Edward McCall, General Partner
Matthew Whelan, Managing Director
Randolph Brown, Principal
Roger Goddu, General Partner
William Barnum, Co-Founder

Type of Firm

Private Equity Firm

Project Preferences

Role in Financing:
Will function either as deal originator or investor in deals created by others

Type of Financing Preferred:
Second Stage Financing
Leveraged Buyout
Generalist PE
Start-up Financing
Seed
First Stage Financing
Acquisition

Size of Investments Considered:
Min Size of Investment Considered (000s): $1,000
Max Size of Investment Considered: No Limit

Geographical Preferences

United States Preferences:
All U.S.

Industry Focus

(% based on actual investment)

Consumer Related	28.2%
Computer Hardware	21.4%
Other Products	13.7%
Semiconductors/Other Elect.	10.1%
Communications and Media	8.0%
Medical/Health	6.1%
Computer Software and Services	5.2%
Industrial/Energy	3.9%
Biotechnology	3.2%
Internet Specific	0.2%

Additional Information

Name of Most Recent Fund: Brentwood Associates Private Equity III, L.P.
Most Recent Fund Was Raised: 05/19/1999
Year Founded: 1972
Capital Under Management: $600,000,000
Current Activity Level: Actively seeking new investments
Method of Compensation: Return on invest. most important, but chg. closing fees, service fees, etc.

BRENTWOOD VENTURE CAPITAL

11150 Santa Monica Boulevard
Suite 1200
Los Angeles, CA USA 90025
Phone: 310-477-7678
Fax: 310-312-1868
Website: www.brentwoodvc.com

Other Offices

450 Newport Center Drive
Suite 600
Newport Beach, CA USA 92660
Phone: 949-729-4500
Fax: 949-729-4501

3000 Sand Hill Road
Building Four, Suite 210
Menlo Park, CA USA 94025
Phone: 650-233-7877
Fax: 650-854-9513

3000 Sand Hill Road
Building Two, Suite 290
Menlo Park, CA USA 94025
Phone: 650-926-5600
Fax: 650-854-5762

Management and Staff

Brian Atwood, General Partner
G. Bradford Jones, General Partner
Jeffrey Brody, General Partner
John Walecka, General Partner
Ross Jaffe, General Partner
William Link, General Partner

Type of Firm

Private Equity Firm

Association Membership

Western Association of Venture Capitalists (WAVC)

Project Preferences

Type of Financing Preferred:
Second Stage Financing
Seed
Startup

Geographical Preferences

United States Preferences:
West Coast

Industry Preferences

In Communications prefer:
Communications and Media

In Computer Software prefer:
Software

In Internet Specific prefer:
Internet

In Biotechnology prefer:
Biotechnology

In Medical/Health prefer:
Medical/Health
Health Services

Additional Information

Year Founded: 1972
Capital Under Management: $675,000,000
Current Activity Level: Actively seeking new investments

BRETAGNE PARTICIPATIONS

20 quai Duguay Trouin
Rennes, France 35000
Phone: 33-2-9967-9769
Fax: 33-2-9967-4600
E-mail: bretagne.participations@bretpart.com
Website: www.bretagne-participations.com

Management and Staff

Jacques Boulau, Managing Director
Jean-Yves Ruaudel, Managing Director

Type of Firm

Private Equity Firm

Project Preferences

Type of Financing Preferred:
Early Stage
Expansion

Size of Investments Considered:
Min Size of Investment Considered (000s): $41
Max Size of Investment Considered (000s): $412

Geographical Preferences

International Preferences:
France

Additional Information

Year Founded: 1999
Capital Under Management: $13,700,000
Current Activity Level: Actively seeking new investments

BRIDGE INVESTMENT FUND

11000 Cedar Avenue
Suite 100
Cleveland, OH USA 44106
Phone: 216-658-5470
Fax: 216-658-3998
Website: www.bridgefundllc.com

Other Offices

11 Tuval Street
Ramat Gan, Israel 52522
Phone: 972-3-7529590

Management and Staff

Avshalom Horan, Partner

Type of Firm

Private Equity Firm

Project Preferences

Type of Financing Preferred:
Balanced

Geographical Preferences

United States Preferences:
Ohio

International Preferences:
Israel

Industry Preferences

In Biotechnology prefer:
Biotechnology

Additional Information

Year Founded: 2005
Capital Under Management: $5,400,000
Current Activity Level: Actively seeking new investments

BRIDGE STREET CAPITAL PARTNERS, LLC

40 Pearl Street Northwest
Suite 1040
Grand Rapids, MI USA 49503
Phone: 616-732-1050
Fax: 616-732-1055
Website: www.bridgestreetcapital.com

Other Offices

52 Village Place
Hinsdale, IL USA 60521
Phone: 630-323-9222
Fax: 630-323-9224

311 South Wacker Drive
Suite 4400
Chicago, IL USA 60606
Phone: 312-786-3870
Fax: 312-786-3871

Management and Staff

John Meilner, Managing Director
William Kaczynski, Managing Director

Type of Firm

Private Equity Firm

Project Preferences

Role in Financing:
Prefer role as deal originator but will also invest in deals created by others

Type of Financing Preferred:
Leveraged Buyout
Management Buyouts
Acquisition
Recapitalizations

Size of Investments Considered:
Min Size of Investment Considered (000s): $2,500
Max Size of Investment Considered (000s): $7,500

Additional Information

Year Founded: 2004
Capital Under Management: $41,000,000
Current Activity Level: Actively seeking new investments
Method of Compensation: Return on investment is of primary concern, do not charge fees

BRIDGEPOINT CAPITAL, LTD. (FKA: NWEP & NATWEST VENTURES LTD)

30 Warwick Street
London, United Kingdom W1B 5AL
Phone: 44-20-7432-3500
Fax: 44-20-7432-3600
E-mail: info@bridgepoint.eu
Website: www.bridgepoint.eu

Other Offices

ul. Rondo ONZ 1
Warszawa, Poland 00-124
Phone: 48-22-544-8282
Fax: 48-22-544-8299

Via F.lli Gabba 1/a
Milan, Italy 20121
Phone: 39-02-806-951
Fax: 39-02-8645-2424

Calle de Rafael Calvo 39A-4
Madrid, Spain 28010
Phone: 34-91-702-2490
Fax: 34-91-319-6092

Neue Mainzer Strasse 28
Frankfurt, Germany D-60311
Phone: 49-69-210-8770
Fax: 49-69-2108-7777

24 rue Beaumont
Luxembourg, Luxembourg L-1219
Phone: 352-26-4756
Fax: 352-26-2705-74

37-39 rue de la Bienfaisance
Paris, France 75008
Phone: 33-1-4429-2100
Fax: 33-1-4429-2110

Master Samuelsgatan 1
Stockholm, Sweden 111 44
Phone: 46-8-5451-6820
Fax: 46-8-5451-6821

Management and Staff

Alan Lewis, Partner
Alastair Gibbons, Partner
Benoit Bassi, Partner
Christopher Bley, Partner
Graham Oldroyd, Partner
Guy Weldon, Partner
James Murray, Partner
Jose Maria Maldonado, Partner
Juan Lopez-Quesada, Partner
Kevin Reynolds, Partner
Khai Tan, Partner

Michael Davy, Partner
Michael Black, Partner
Raoul Hughes, Chief Financial Officer
Rob Moores, Partner
Stephen Green, Partner
Uwe Kolb, Partner
Valerie Texier, Partner
Vince Gwilliam, Partner
William Jackson, Managing Partner

Type of Firm

Private Equity Firm

Association Membership

Italian Venture Capital Association (AIFI)
British Venture Capital Association (BVCA)
French Venture Capital Association (AFIC)
European Private Equity and Venture Capital Assoc.

Project Preferences

Type of Financing Preferred:

Leveraged Buyout
Expansion
Turnaround
Management Buyouts
Acquisition
Recapitalizations

Size of Investments Considered:

Min Size of Investment Considered (000s): $19,000
Max Size of Investment Considered (000s): $125,000

Geographical Preferences

International Preferences:

United Kingdom
Europe
Western Europe
France

Industry Focus

(% based on actual investment)

Other Products	41.0%
Consumer Related	27.8%
Industrial/Energy	13.4%
Computer Hardware	6.5%
Communications and Media	3.6%
Medical/Health	2.2%
Computer Software and Services	2.2%
Biotechnology	1.6%
Semiconductors/Other Elect.	1.6%
Internet Specific	0.1%

Additional Information

Year Founded: 1983
Capital Under Management: $8,000,000,000
Current Activity Level: Actively seeking new investments

BRIDGEPOINT DEVELOPMENT CAPITAL

c/o Bridgepoint Capital, Ltd.
30 Warwick Street
London, United Kingdom W1B 5AL
Phone: 44-20-7432-3500
Fax: 44-20-7432-3600

Management and Staff

Justin Ward, Partner
Peter Gissel, Partner
Rod Selkirk, Chief Executive Officer
Shane Feeney, Partner
Tim Thomas, Partner

Type of Firm

Private Equity Firm

Project Preferences

Type of Financing Preferred:

Leveraged Buyout

Size of Investments Considered:

Min Size of Investment Considered (000s): $7,131
Max Size of Investment Considered (000s): $71,305

Geographical Preferences

International Preferences:

United Kingdom
Europe

Additional Information

Name of Most Recent Fund: Hermes Private Equity Partners II
Most Recent Fund Was Raised: 09/12/2005
Year Founded: 2009
Capital Under Management: $1,065,200,000
Current Activity Level: Actively seeking new investments

BRIDGES COMMUNITY VENTURES, LTD.

One Craven Hill
London, United Kingdom W2 3EN
Phone: 44-207-262-5566
Fax: 44-207-262-6389
E-mail: Info@bridgesventures.com
Website: www.bridgesventures.com

Management and Staff

Rory Maw, Chief Financial Officer

Type of Firm

Incubator/Development Program

Association Membership

British Venture Capital Association (BVCA)

Project Preferences

Type of Financing Preferred:

Second Stage Financing
Leveraged Buyout
Early Stage
Expansion
Balanced
Turnaround
Startup

Geographical Preferences

International Preferences:

United Kingdom
Europe

Industry Preferences

In Other prefer:

Socially Responsible

Additional Information

Year Founded: 2001
Capital Under Management: $61,900,000
Current Activity Level: Actively seeking new investments

BRIDGESCALE PARTNERS

3000 Sand Hill Road
Bldg 3, Suite 290
Menlo Park, CA USA 94025
Phone: 650-854-7236
Website: www.bridgescale.com

Management and Staff

Matthew Cowan, Co-Founder
Robert Chaplinsky, Co-Founder

Type of Firm

Private Equity Firm

Project Preferences

Type of Financing Preferred:

Expansion

Additional Information

Name of Most Recent Fund: Bridgescale Partners, L.P.
Most Recent Fund Was Raised: 12/01/2005
Year Founded: 2005
Capital Under Management: $160,000,000
Current Activity Level: Actively seeking new investments

BRIGHTON PARTNERS, LLC

3414 Peachtree Road
Suite 730
Atlanta, GA USA 30326
Fax: 404-926-3497
Website: www.bpequity.com

Type of Firm

Private Equity Firm

Project Preferences

Type of Financing Preferred:

Leveraged Buyout
Acquisition
Recapitalizations

Geographical Preferences

United States Preferences:
Midwest
Southeast

Additional Information

Year Founded: 2007
Current Activity Level: Actively seeking new investments

BRIGHTPATH CAPITAL, INC.

11590 North Meridian Street
Suite 100
Carmel, IN USA 46032
Phone: 317-818-2680
Fax: 317-818-2681
E-mail: info@bpathcap.com
Website: www.brightpathcapital.com

Management and Staff

Douglas Conner, Principal
J. Mitchell Rader, Principal
James Budzynski, Principal

Type of Firm

Private Equity Firm

Project Preferences

Type of Financing Preferred:
Leveraged Buyout
Expansion
Industry Rollups
Acquisition

Size of Investments Considered:
Min Size of Investment Considered (000s): $2,000
Max Size of Investment Considered (000s): $20,000

Geographical Preferences

United States Preferences:
All U.S.

Industry Preferences

In Agr/Forestr/Fish prefer:
Agribusiness
Agriculture related

Additional Information

Year Founded: 2008
Current Activity Level: Actively seeking new investments

BRIGHTSPARK VENTURES

4711 Yonge Street
Suite 506
Toronto, Canada M2N 6K8
Phone: 416-488-1999
Fax: 416-488-1988
E-mail: info@brightspark.com
Website: www.brightspark.com

Other Offices

481 Viger Street West
Suite 300
Montreal, Canada H2Z 1G6
Phone: 514-448-2238
Fax: 514-448-5101

Management and Staff

Mark Skapinker, Managing Partner
Salim Teja, Partner
Sophie Forest, Managing Partner
Tony Davis, Managing Partner

Type of Firm

Private Equity Firm

Association Membership

Canadian Venture Capital Association

Project Preferences

Role in Financing:
Prefer role as deal originator but will also invest in deals created by others

Type of Financing Preferred:
Early Stage
Start-up Financing
Seed

Size of Investments Considered:
Min Size of Investment Considered (000s): $500
Max Size of Investment Considered (000s): $5,000

Geographical Preferences

United States Preferences:
Northwest
Northern California
Northeast

Canadian Preferences:
All Canada

Industry Preferences

In Communications prefer:
Commercial Communications
Telecommunications
Wireless Communications

In Computer Software prefer:
Computer Services
Software
Systems Software
Applications Software

In Internet Specific prefer:
E-Commerce Technology
Internet
Ecommerce

Additional Information

Name of Most Recent Fund: Brightspark Ventures II
Most Recent Fund Was Raised: 12/01/2004
Year Founded: 1999
Capital Under Management: $54,300,000
Current Activity Level: Actively seeking new investments
Method of Compensation: Return on investment is of primary concern, do not charge fees

---

BRIGHTSTONE CAPITAL

4700 IDS Center
80 South Eighth Street
Minneapolis, MN USA 55402
Phone: 612-313-0738
Fax: 763-278-0005
E-mail: plan@brightstonevc.com
Website: www.brightstonevc.com

Other Offices

7200 Metro Boulevard
Edina, MN USA 55439
Phone: 952-831-6499
Fax: 952-831-1219

13055 15th Avenue North
Plymouth, MN USA 55441
Phone: 763-278-0017
Fax: 763-278-0005

Management and Staff

David Dalvey, Principal
James Bernards, President

Type of Firm

SBIC

Association Membership

Natl Assoc of Small Bus. Inv. Co (NASBIC)

Project Preferences

Role in Financing:
Will function either as deal originator or investor in deals created by others

Type of Financing Preferred:
Expansion
Balanced

Size of Investments Considered:
Min Size of Investment Considered (000s): $1,000
Max Size of Investment Considered (000s): $5,000

Geographical Preferences

United States Preferences:
Minnesota

Industry Preferences

In Communications prefer:
Communications and Media

In Computer Software prefer:
Software

In Computer Other prefer:
Computer Related

In Semiconductor/Electr prefer:
Electronics
Semiconductor

In Biotechnology prefer:
Biotechnology

In Medical/Health prefer:
Medical/Health

Additional Information
Name of Most Recent Fund: Dougherty Brightstone Fund II
Most Recent Fund Was Raised: 05/01/2000
Year Founded: 1985
Capital Under Management: $105,000,000
Current Activity Level: Actively seeking new investments
Method of Compensation: Return on investment is of primary concern, do not charge fees

---

BRITISH COLUMBIA INVESTMENT MANAGEMENT CORPORATION (BCIMC)
Sawmill Point, 2940 Jutland Rd
Victoria, Canada V8T 5K6
Phone: 250-356-0263
Fax: 250-387-7874
Website: www.bcimc.com

Management and Staff
Doug Pearce, Chief Executive Officer

Type of Firm
Endowment, Foundation or Pension Fund

Additional Information
Year Founded: 1999
Current Activity Level: Actively seeking new investments

BRITISH COLUMBIA MINISTRY OF ECONOMIC DEVELOPMENT
1675 Douglas Street
Suite 250
Victoria, Canada V8W 2G5
Phone: 250-952-0612
Fax: 250 356-6376
Website:
www.cse.gov.bc.ca/TRI/Pages/BCRCF.aspx#

Type of Firm
Government Affiliated Program

Additional Information
Year Founded: 2008
Current Activity Level: Actively seeking new investments

BRITTANY VENTURES
Nestadio
Plouhinec, France 56680
Phone: 33-2-9736-6674
E-mail: contact@investissement-bretagne.com
Website: www.brittany-ventures.com

Type of Firm
Private Equity Firm

Project Preferences

Type of Financing Preferred:
Balanced

Geographical Preferences

International Preferences:
France

Additional Information
Year Founded: 2005
Current Activity Level: Actively seeking new investments

BRM CAPITAL
825 3rd Avenue
32nd Floor
New York, NY USA 10022
Phone: 212-918-0551
Fax: 212-918-0674
E-mail: info@brm.com
Website: www.brm.com

Other Offices
Akerstein Building B
11 Hamenofim Street
Herzliya Pituach , Israel 46725
Phone: 972-9-954-9555
Fax: 972-9-954-9557

Management and Staff
Eli Barkat, Managing Director
Noga Kap, Managing Director
Yuval Rakavy, Venture Partner

Type of Firm
Private Equity Firm

Association Membership
Israel Venture Association

Project Preferences

Role in Financing:
Prefer role as deal originator but will also invest in deals created by others

Type of Financing Preferred:
Early Stage
Expansion
Balanced
Seed

Size of Investments Considered:
Min Size of Investment Considered (000s): $1,000
Max Size of Investment Considered (000s): $5,000

Geographical Preferences

International Preferences:
Israel

Industry Preferences

In Communications prefer:
Commercial Communications
Wireless Communications
Data Communications

In Computer Software prefer:
Software
Applications Software

In Internet Specific prefer:
Internet

In Semiconductor/Electr prefer:
Semiconductor

Additional Information
Year Founded: 2000
Capital Under Management: $150,000,000
Current Activity Level: Actively seeking new investments

BROADMARK CAPITAL CORP.
600 University
Suite 2800
Seattle, WA USA 98101-2333
Phone: 206-623-1200
Fax: 206-623-2213
E-mail: seattle@broadmark.com
Website: www.broadmark.com

Management and Staff
Aidan Stretch, Managing Director
James Walsh, Managing Director
Joseph Schocken, President
Scott Feldman, Managing Director

Type of Firm
Bank Affiliated

Project Preferences

Role in Financing:
Prefer role as deal originator but will also invest in deals created by others

Type of Financing Preferred:
Generalist PE

Size of Investments Considered:
Min Size of Investment Considered (000s): $10,000
Max Size of Investment Considered: No Limit

Geographical Preferences

Canadian Preferences:
All Canada

Industry Focus

(% based on actual investment)

Communications and Media	100.0%

Additional Information

Year Founded: 1986
Capital Under Management: $20,000,000
Current Activity Level: Actively seeking new investments
Method of Compensation: Function primarily in service area, receive contingent fee in cash or equity

BROCKHAUS PRIVATE EQUITY GMBH

Myliusstrasse 30
Frankfurt am Main, Germany 60323
Phone: 49-6971-9161-70
Fax: 49-6971-9161-71
E-mail: info@brockhaus-pe.com
Website: www.brockhaus-pe.de

Management and Staff

Uwe Steinbacher, Managing Director

Type of Firm

Private Equity Firm

Association Membership

German Venture Capital Association (BVK)
European Private Equity and Venture Capital Assoc.

Project Preferences

Type of Financing Preferred:

Leveraged Buyout
Expansion
Balanced

Geographical Preferences

International Preferences:

Switzerland
Europe
Austria
Germany

Industry Preferences

In Communications prefer:

Communications and Media
Telecommunications

In Internet Specific prefer:

Internet

In Computer Other prefer:

Computer Related

In Semiconductor/Electr prefer:

Electronics

In Business Serv. prefer:

Services

Additional Information

Year Founded: 2000
Capital Under Management: $224,600,000
Current Activity Level: Actively seeking new investments

BROCKTON CAPITAL LLP

Level 1
87 Wardour Street
London, France W1F 0UA
Phone: 44-20-7220-2500
Fax: 44-20-7734-3655
Website: www.brocktoncapital.com

Management and Staff

David Marks, Managing Partner

Type of Firm

Private Equity Firm

Project Preferences

Type of Financing Preferred:

Balanced

Geographical Preferences

International Preferences:

United Kingdom

Additional Information

Year Founded: 2005
Current Activity Level: Actively seeking new investments

BROCKWAY MORAN & PARTNERS, INC.

225 Northeast Mizner Boulevard
Suite 700
Boca Raton, FL USA 33432
Phone: 561-750-2000
Fax: 561-750-2001
Website: www.brockwaymoran.com

Management and Staff

Ari Zur, Managing Director
Christopher Blythe, Vice President
James Davis, Managing Director
Lawrence Shagrin, Partner
Mark Eidemueller, Partner
Michael Moran, Managing Partner
Patrick Boroian, Partner
Peter Brockway, Managing Partner
Peter Klein, Partner
Richard Wandoff, Partner
T. Andrew Boswell, Vice President

Type of Firm

Private Equity Firm

Project Preferences

Role in Financing:

Prefer role as deal originator but will also invest in deals created by others

Type of Financing Preferred:

Leveraged Buyout
Later Stage
Management Buyouts
Acquisition
Special Situation
Recapitalizations

Size of Investments Considered:

Min Size of Investment Considered (000s): $50,000
Max Size of Investment Considered (000s): $300,000

Industry Focus

(% based on actual investment)

Consumer Related	52.7%
Other Products	40.8%
Semiconductors/Other Elect.	6.3%
Industrial/Energy	0.3%

Additional Information

Year Founded: 1998
Capital Under Management: $1,310,000,000
Current Activity Level: Actively seeking new investments
Method of Compensation: Return on invest. most important, but chg. closing fees, service fees, etc.

BROOK STREET INVESTMENTS LLC

50 Hood Road
Ardmore, PA USA 19003
Phone: 215-620-6993
Fax: 413-691-0316
Website: www.brookstreetinvestments.com

Management and Staff

Chris Randazzo, Founding Partner
Jonathan Costello, Founding Partner

Type of Firm

Private Equity Firm

Project Preferences

Type of Financing Preferred:

Leveraged Buyout
Management Buyouts
Recapitalizations

Size of Investments Considered:

Min Size of Investment Considered (000s): $250
Max Size of Investment Considered (000s): $5,000

Geographical Preferences

United States Preferences:

Mid Atlantic

Industry Preferences

In Computer Software prefer:

Software

In Industrial/Energy prefer:

Industrial Products
Machinery

In Business Serv. prefer:
Services

In Manufact. prefer:
Manufacturing

Additional Information
Year Founded: 2005
Current Activity Level: Actively seeking new investments

BROOK VENTURE PARTNERS LLC
301 Edgewater Place
Fourth Floor
Wakefield, MA USA 01880
Phone: 781-295-4000
Fax: 781-295-4007
E-mail: info@gatewayfinancial.com
Website: www.brookventure.com

Management and Staff
Andrew Clapp, Partner
Edward Williams, Partner
Frederic Morris, Partner
Jeff Emig, Principal
Rick Waldo, Vice President
Walter Beinecke, Partner

Type of Firm
Private Equity Firm

Association Membership
Natl Assoc of Small Bus. Inv. Co (NASBIC)

Project Preferences
Role in Financing:
Prefer role as deal originator but will also invest in deals created by others

Type of Financing Preferred:
Second Stage Financing
Expansion
First Stage Financing

Size of Investments Considered:
Min Size of Investment Considered (000s): $1,000
Max Size of Investment Considered (000s): $4,000

Geographical Preferences
United States Preferences:
New Hampshire
Rhode Island
Vermont
Northeast
Massachusetts
Connecticut
D. of Columbia
Maine
New York

Industry Preferences
In Computer Software prefer:
Data Processing
Software
Systems Software
Applications Software

In Internet Specific prefer:
E-Commerce Technology
Internet
Ecommerce

In Medical/Health prefer:
Medical/Health
Medical Diagnostics
Medical Products
Disposable Med. Products
Health Services

In Manufact. prefer:
Publishing

Additional Information
Name of Most Recent Fund: Brook Co-Investment II, LP
Most Recent Fund Was Raised: 01/30/2004
Year Founded: 1995
Capital Under Management: $100,000,000
Current Activity Level: Actively seeking new investments
Method of Compensation: Return on investment is of primary concern, do not charge fees

BROOKE PRIVATE EQUITY MANAGEMENT LLC
84 State Street
Suite 320
Boston, MA USA 02109
Phone: 617-227-3160
Fax: 617-227-4128
E-mail: info@brookepea.com
Website: www.brookepea.com

Management and Staff
Johan Von der Goltz, General Partner
Peter Brooke, General Partner

Type of Firm
Private Equity Advisor or Fund of Funds

Project Preferences
Type of Financing Preferred:
Fund of Funds
Early Stage
Expansion

Geographical Preferences
United States Preferences:
All U.S.

Industry Preferences
In Medical/Health prefer:
Medical/Health

Additional Information
Name of Most Recent Fund: Brooke Private Equity Advisors Fund I-D, L.P.
Most Recent Fund Was Raised: 01/06/2004
Year Founded: 2003
Capital Under Management: $133,000,000
Current Activity Level: Actively seeking new investments

BROOKFIELD ASSET MANAGEMENT
181 Bay Street
Suite 300, P.O. Box 771
Toronto, Canada M5J 2T3
Phone: 416-363-0061
Fax: 416-365-9642
Website: www.brascanfinancial.ca

Other Offices
One Liberty Plaza
New York, NY USA 10006
Phone: 212- 417-7195
Fax: 212-417-7000

2050, 1055 West Georgia Street
P.O. Box 11179, Royal Centre
Vancouver, Canada V6E 3R5
Phone: 604-669-3141
Fax: 604-687-3419
150 - 6 Avenue SW
Suite 3370
Calgary, Canada T2P 3Y7
Phone: 403-663-3335
Fax: 403-663-3340

Management and Staff
Peter Gordon, Managing Partner
Sam Pollock, Managing Partner
Steve Riedel, Vice President

Type of Firm
Corporate PE/Venture

Project Preferences
Type of Financing Preferred:
Expansion
Other
Distressed Debt

Geographical Preferences
Canadian Preferences:
All Canada

Industry Preferences
In Financial Services prefer:
Financial Services
Real Estate

In Manufact. prefer:
Manufacturing

Additional Information
Name of Most Recent Fund: Tricap Restructuring Fund
Most Recent Fund Was Raised: 12/01/2001
Year Founded: 2001

Capital Under Management: $3,070,900,000
Current Activity Level: Actively seeking new investments

BROOKLINE VENTURE PARTNERS

20 William Street
Suite G55
Wellesley, MA USA 02481
Phone: 781-235-5755
Website: www.brooklineventures.com

Management and Staff

Ken Levine, Founding Partner
Mark Goodman, Founding Partner

Type of Firm

Private Equity Firm

Project Preferences

Type of Financing Preferred:
Early Stage
Balanced

Size of Investments Considered:
Min Size of Investment Considered (000s): $250
Max Size of Investment Considered (000s): $10,000

Geographical Preferences

United States Preferences:
All U.S.

Additional Information

Year Founded: 2004
Current Activity Level: Actively seeking new investments

BROOKS, HOUGHTON & COMPANY, INC.

444 Madison Avenue
25th Floor
New York, NY USA 10022
Phone: 212-753-1991
Fax: 212-753-7730
E-mail: info@brookshoughton.com
Website: www.bhcinterimfunding.com

Other Offices

263 Tresser Boulevard
Stamford, CT USA 06901
Phone: 203-564-1979
Fax: 203-564-1402

Management and Staff

Andrew Shiftan, Managing Director
David DiPaolo, Managing Director
Deane Driscoll, Managing Director
Gerald Houghton, President
John Cappellari, Vice President
Steven Brooks, Senior Managing Director
Thomas Ivanyi, Managing Director

Type of Firm

Bank Affiliated

Project Preferences

Type of Financing Preferred:
Leveraged Buyout
Mezzanine
Acquisition
Industry Rollups
Recapitalizations

Size of Investments Considered:
Min Size of Investment Considered (000s): $2,000
Max Size of Investment Considered (000s): $15,000

Industry Focus

(% based on actual investment)

Consumer Related	66.7%
Communications and Media	33.3%

Additional Information

Year Founded: 1999
Capital Under Management: $200,000,000
Current Activity Level: Actively seeking new investments

BROOKSTONE CAPITAL, INC.

3800 Howard Hughes Parkway
Suite 550
Las Vegas, NV USA 89109
Phone: 702-307-8090

Management and Staff

Robert Carver, President
Scott Moonly, Vice President

Type of Firm

Private Equity Firm

Industry Preferences

In Biotechnology prefer:
Biotechnology

Additional Information

Year Founded: 2006
Current Activity Level: Actively seeking new investments

BROOKSTONE PARTNERS

317 Madison Avenue
Suite 405
New York, NY USA 10017
Phone: 212-302-0066
Fax: 212-302-5888
Website: www.brookstonepartners.com

Management and Staff

Bardia Mesbah, Principal
Greg Meisenzahl, Vice President
Michael Toporek, Managing General Partner
Perry Jacobson, Managing Director

Type of Firm

Private Equity Firm

Project Preferences

Size of Investments Considered:
Min Size of Investment Considered (000s): $3,000
Max Size of Investment Considered (000s): $15,000

Geographical Preferences

United States Preferences:
Mid Atlantic
Midwest
Northeast
Southwest

Industry Preferences

In Semiconductor/Electr prefer:
Analytic/Scientific

In Business Serv. prefer:
Services
Distribution

In Manufact. prefer:
Manufacturing

Additional Information

Year Founded: 2003
Current Activity Level: Actively seeking new investments

BROWN BROTHERS HARRIMAN & COMPANY (AKA: BBH)

140 Broadway
New York, NY USA 10005
Phone: 212-483-1818
Fax: 212-493-7293
E-mail: invmgmt@bbh.com
Website: www.bbh.com

Other Offices

1-2-8 Toranomon, Minato-ku
Tokyo, Japan 105-0001
Phone: 81-3-6361-6500

125 Finsbury Pavement
Veritas House
London, United Kingdom EC2A 1PN
Phone: 44-207-588-6166

Barengasse 25
Zurich, Switzerland CH-8001
Phone: 41-44-227-1818

50 Milk Street
Boston, MA USA 02109-3661
Phone: 617-742-1818

227 West Trade Street
Suite 2100 Carillion Building
Charlotte, NC USA 28202-1675
Phone: 704-370-0500

240 Royal Palm Way
Palm Beach, FL USA 33480
Phone: 561-832-4262

1531 Walnut Street
Philadelphia, PA USA 19102-3098
Phone: 215-864-1818

Unit 1507, Level 15, Int'l Commerce Ctr.
1 Austin Road West
Kowloon, Hong Kong
Phone: 852-3756-1600
Fax: 852-3756-1799

150 South Wacker Drive
Suite 3250
Chicago, IL USA 60606
Phone: 312-781-7111
Fax: 800-325-1818

Butterfield House, Fort Street
P.O. Box 2330, George Town
Grand Cayman, Cayman Islands
Phone: 345-945-2719

Styne House
Upper Hatch Street
Dublin, Ireland
Phone: 353-1-603-6200
Fax: 353-1-603-6300

2001 Ross Avenue
Suite 2500
Dallas, TX USA 75201
Phone: 214-303-5600

525 Washington Boulevard
Newport Tower
Jersey City, NJ USA 07310
Phone: 201-418-5600

40 Water Street
Boston, MA USA 02109-3661
Phone: 617-742-1818
Fax: 617-742-1148

2-8 Avenue Charles De Gaulle
B.P. 403
Luxembourg, Luxembourg L-2014
Phone: 352-474-0661

Management and Staff

Charles Schreiber, Chief Financial Officer
Edmund Marcarelli, Managing Director
Geoffrey Mills, Managing Director
Gerard McCauley, Managing Director
Jeffrey Meskin, Managing Director
Jeffrey Lockwood, Managing Director
John Nelson, Managing Director
Lawrence Tucker, Partner
Peter Lorraine, Managing Director
T. Michael Long, Partner
Walter Grist, Managing Director

Type of Firm

Bank Affiliated

Project Preferences

Type of Financing Preferred:

Leveraged Buyout
Expansion
Mezzanine
Management Buyouts
Acquisition
Recapitalizations

Size of Investments Considered:

Min Size of Investment Considered (000s): $5,000
Max Size of Investment Considered (000s): $30,000

Geographical Preferences

United States Preferences:

All U.S.

Industry Focus

(% based on actual investment)

Other Products	29.4%
Communications and Media	23.0%
Industrial/Energy	12.1%
Medical/Health	11.9%
Internet Specific	10.4%
Consumer Related	7.0%
Computer Software and Services	5.9%
Semiconductors/Other Elect.	0.2%

Additional Information

Name of Most Recent Fund: BBH Private Equity Partners IV (Offshore), L.P.
Most Recent Fund Was Raised: 05/09/2007
Year Founded: 1989
Capital Under Management: $2,000,000,000
Current Activity Level: Actively seeking new investments

BROWN GIBBONS LANG & COMPANY LLC

1111 Superior Avenue
Suite 900
Cleveland, OH USA 44114
Phone: 216-241-2800
Fax: 216-241-7417
Website: www.bglco.com

Other Offices

Two International Place
16th Floor
Boston, MA USA 02110
Phone: 617-235-7207
Fax: 617-235-7297

Two Prudential Plaza, 180 N. Stetson Ave
Suite 4300
Chicago, IL USA 60601
Phone: 312-658-1600
Fax: 312-368-1988

Management and Staff

Andrew Petryk, Managing Director
Cameron Miele, Vice President
Charles Fultz, Vice President
David C. Sulaski, Managing Director
Effram Kaplan, Vice President
H. Glen Clarke, Managing Director
James MIller, Managing Director
John Tilson, Managing Director
Kevin Sargent, Vice President
Michael Shaffer, Vice President
Michael Gibbons, Senior Managing Director
Paul Mariani, Vice President
Scott Lang, Senior Managing Director
Scott Berlin, Managing Director
Sean Sullivan, Vice President
Thomas West, Chief Financial Officer
Thomas Denison, Senior Managing Director

Type of Firm

Bank Affiliated

Project Preferences

Type of Financing Preferred:

Leveraged Buyout
Acquisition

Geographical Preferences

United States Preferences:

All U.S.

Industry Preferences

In Consumer Related prefer:

Consumer

In Industrial/Energy prefer:

Industrial Products

In Transportation prefer:

Transportation

Additional Information

Year Founded: 1989
Current Activity Level: Actively seeking new investments

BRUCE S BRICKMAN & ASSOCIATES, INC.

712 Fifth Avenue
Sixth Floor
New York, NY USA 10019
Phone: 212-541-5500
Fax: 212-956-5961

Management and Staff

Bruce Brickman, President
Michael Esquenazi, Vice President

Type of Firm

Private Equity Firm

Industry Preferences

In Financial Services prefer:
Real Estate

Additional Information

Name of Most Recent Fund: Brickman Real Estate Fund I, L.P.
Most Recent Fund Was Raised: 04/09/2002
Year Founded: 2002
Capital Under Management: $61,900,000
Current Activity Level: Actively seeking new investments

BRUCKMANN, ROSSER, SHERRILL & CO.

126 East 56th Street
New York, NY USA 10022
Phone: 212-521-3755
Fax: 212-521-3799
E-mail: info@brs.com
Website: www.brs.com

Other Offices

700 Cass Street
Suite 200
Monterey, CA USA 93940

Management and Staff

Brett Pertuz, Vice President
Bruce Bruckmann, Managing Director
Harold Rosser, Managing Director
J. Rice Edmonds, Principal
James Collins, Vice President
Paul Kaminski, Managing Director & CFO
Richard Leonard, Vice President
Stephen Sherrill, Managing Director
Thomas Baldwin, Managing Director

Type of Firm

Private Equity Firm

Project Preferences

Role in Financing:
Will function either as deal originator or investor in deals created by others

Type of Financing Preferred:
Leveraged Buyout
Generalist PE
Management Buyouts
Recapitalizations

Size of Investments Considered:
Min Size of Investment Considered (000s): $10,000
Max Size of Investment Considered (000s): $60,000

Geographical Preferences

United States Preferences:
All U.S.

Canadian Preferences:
All Canada

Industry Focus

(% based on actual investment)

Consumer Related	50.0%
Other Products	38.9%
Industrial/Energy	6.4%
Communications and Media	2.4%
Internet Specific	1.3%
Medical/Health	0.9%

Additional Information

Name of Most Recent Fund: Bruckmann, Rosser, Sherill & Co. II, L.P.
Most Recent Fund Was Raised: 05/21/1999
Year Founded: 1995
Capital Under Management: $1,200,000,000
Current Activity Level: Actively seeking new investments

BRUSSELS I3 FUND NV (AKA:VRIJE UNIVERSITEIT BRUSSEL)

Pleinlaan 2
Elsene, Belgium B-1050
Phone: 32-2-629-2111
Fax: 32-2-710-7853
E-mail: info@vub.ac.be
Website: www.vub.ac.be

Other Offices

Laarbeeklaan 103
Brussel, Belgium 1090
Phone: 32-2-477-4111
Type of Firm
University Program

Association Membership

European Private Equity and Venture Capital Assoc.

Project Preferences

Type of Financing Preferred:
Balanced
Start-up Financing
Seed

Geographical Preferences

International Preferences:
Belgium

Additional Information

Year Founded: 2005
Current Activity Level: Actively seeking new investments

BRYNWOOD PARTNERS L.P.

8 Sound Shore Drive
Suite 265
Greenwich, CT USA 06830
Phone: 203-622-1790
Fax: 203-622-0559
E-mail: info@brynwoodpartners.com
Website: www.brynwoodpartners.com

Management and Staff

Dario Margve, Managing Partner
Hendrik Hartong, Managing Partner
Hendrik Hartong, Senior Managing Director
Ian MacTaggart, Managing Partner
Joan McCabe, Managing Partner
Kevin Hartnett, Managing Partner
Robert Sperry, Managing Partner

Type of Firm

Private Equity Firm

Project Preferences

Type of Financing Preferred:
Leveraged Buyout
Mezzanine
Management Buyouts
Acquisition
Recapitalizations

Geographical Preferences

United States Preferences:
All U.S.

Industry Focus

(% based on actual investment)

Consumer Related	60.3%
Other Products	38.2%
Computer Software and Services	1.5%

Additional Information

Name of Most Recent Fund: Brynwood Partners V, L.P.
Most Recent Fund Was Raised: 08/27/2004
Year Founded: 1984
Capital Under Management: $175,000,000
Current Activity Level: Actively seeking new investments

BS PRIVATE EQUITY SPA (FKA: B&S PRIVATE EQUITY GROUP)

Via dell Orso, 8
Milan, Italy 20121
Phone: 39-2-762-1131
Fax: 39-2-7621-1340
E-mail: info@bspeg.com
Website: www.bspeg.com

Other Offices

Via San Paolo 7
Milan, Italy 20121

Piazzetta S.Carlo 2
Lugano, Switzerland CH-6900
Phone: 41-91-911-1060
Fax: 41-91-911-1069

Management and Staff

Alessandra Gavirati, Partner
Andrea Frecchiami, Partner
Antonio Perricone, Managing Partner
Francesco Sironi, Managing Partner
Lidia Carbonetti, Partner
Matteo Facoetti, Chief Financial Officer
Paolo Pendenza, Partner
Paolo Baretta, Managing Partner
Ugo Pivato, Partner

Type of Firm

Private Equity Firm

Association Membership

Italian Venture Capital Association (AIFI)
European Private Equity and Venture Capital Assoc.

Project Preferences

Type of Financing Preferred:
Leveraged Buyout
Early Stage
Expansion
Balanced
Later Stage
Management Buyouts
Recapitalizations

Size of Investments Considered:
Min Size of Investment Considered (000s): $2,300
Max Size of Investment Considered: No Limit

Geographical Preferences

International Preferences:
Italy
Europe

Industry Focus

(% based on actual investment)

Consumer Related	38.2%
Semiconductors/Other Elect.	15.1%
Other Products	14.0%
Communications and Media	12.2%
Computer Software and Services	10.0%
Medical/Health	5.7%
Industrial/Energy	4.8%

Additional Information

Year Founded: 1990
Capital Under Management: $1,205,600,000
Current Activity Level: Actively seeking new investments

BSD VENTURE CAPITAL LLC

2221 Camino del Rio South
Suite 308
San Diego, CA USA 92108
Phone: 619-682-3834
Website: www.bsdventurecapital.com

Management and Staff

Bruce Dolle, Managing Partner

Type of Firm

Private Equity Firm

Industry Preferences

In Medical/Health prefer:
Medical/Health
Medical Therapeutics
Health Services

Additional Information

Name of Most Recent Fund: BSD Venture Capital Fund I, L.P.
Most Recent Fund Was Raised: 02/09/2009
Year Founded: 2009
Capital Under Management: $250,000,000
Current Activity Level: Actively seeking new investments

BT VENTURE FUND MANAGEMENT, LLC

175 Federal Street
Suite 1350
Boston, MA USA 02210
Phone: 617-439-0770

Management and Staff

Bagus Tjahjono, General Partner

Type of Firm

Private Equity Firm

Project Preferences

Type of Financing Preferred:
Balanced

Additional Information

Year Founded: 2004
Capital Under Management: $1,500,000
Current Activity Level: Actively seeking new investments

BTG BETEILIGUNGSGESELLSCHAFT HAMBURG MBH

Habichtstrasse 41
Hamburg, Germany 22305
Phone: 49 40611 700-0
Fax: 49 40611 700-99
E-mail: info@btg-hamburg.de
Website: www.btg-hamburg.de

Type of Firm

Bank Affiliated

Association Membership

German Venture Capital Association (BVK)

Project Preferences

Type of Financing Preferred:
Expansion
Management Buyouts
Startup
Recapitalizations

Geographical Preferences

International Preferences:
Germany

Industry Preferences

In Industrial/Energy prefer:
Industrial Products

In Business Serv. prefer:
Media

In Manufact. prefer:
Manufacturing

Additional Information

Year Founded: 1970
Current Activity Level: Actively seeking new investments

BTG INTERNATIONAL (AKA: BRITISH TECHNOLOGY GROUP)

10 Fleet Place
Limeburner Lane
London, United Kingdom EC4M 7SB
Phone: 44-20-7575-0000
Fax: 44-20-7575-0010
E-mail: info@btgplc.com
Website: www.btgplc.com

Other Offices

Five Tower Bridge
300 Barr Harbour Drive; 7th Floor
West Conshohocken, PA USA 19428
Phone: 610-278-1660
Fax: 610-278-1605

Management and Staff

Ian Harvey, Chief Executive Officer
Rusi Kathoke, Chief Financial Officer

Type of Firm

Corporate PE/Venture

Additional Information

Year Founded: 1982
Current Activity Level: Actively seeking new investments

BTP CAPITAL INVESTISSEMENT SA

41, rue des Trois Fontanot
BP 211
Nanterre Cedex, France 92002
Phone: 33-1-4724-8108
Fax: 33-1-4724-8437
E-mail: btk@btp-banque.fr
Website: www.btp-banque.fr

Type of Firm
Private Equity Firm

Association Membership
French Venture Capital Association (AFIC)

Project Preferences

Type of Financing Preferred:
Balanced

Geographical Preferences

International Preferences:
Europe

Additional Information
Year Founded: 2003
Current Activity Level: Actively seeking new investments

BTS INVESTMENT ADVISORS, LTD.

704/705, Balarama
Bandra (East)
Mumbai, India 400 021
Phone: 91-22-6697-8292
Fax: 91-22-6697-8299
E-mail: info@btsadvisors.com
Website: www.btsadvisors.com

Other Offices
P.O. Box 1573
Gotthardstrasse 21
Zurich, Switzerland CH-8027
Phone: 41-44-289-9050
Fax: 41-44-289-9059

Management and Staff
Bharat Dighe, Vice President
K Srinivas, Managing Partner
Rajiv Sharma, Chief Financial Officer
Subhash Baliga, Vice President
Suneet Gupta, Vice President
Susanne Grossmann, Managing Partner

Type of Firm
Private Equity Firm

Association Membership
Indian Venture Capital Association (IVCA)

Project Preferences

Type of Financing Preferred:
Expansion
Mezzanine
Balanced
Turnaround
Later Stage
Management Buyouts

Size of Investments Considered:
Min Size of Investment Considered (000s): $3,000
Max Size of Investment Considered (000s): $8,000

Geographical Preferences

International Preferences:
India
Europe
Asia

Industry Preferences

In Communications prefer:
Communications and Media
Telecommunications
Entertainment

In Computer Software prefer:
Software

In Biotechnology prefer:
Biotechnology
Agricultural/Animal Bio.

In Medical/Health prefer:
Medical/Health
Health Services
Pharmaceuticals

In Consumer Related prefer:
Consumer

In Industrial/Energy prefer:
Oil & Gas Drilling,Explor

In Business Serv. prefer:
Distribution

In Manufact. prefer:
Manufacturing

Additional Information
Year Founded: 1996
Capital Under Management: $22,000,000
Current Activity Level: Actively seeking new investments

BTV BETEILIGUNGSVERWALTUNG GMBH & CO. KG

Pettenkoferstrasse 37
Munich, Germany D-80336
Phone: 49-89-544-6060
Fax: 49-89-5446-0620
E-mail: btvbeteiligung@btv-holding.de

Management and Staff
Horst Goss, Managing Director
Thomas Gerstner, Managing Director

Type of Firm
Private Equity Firm

Association Membership
German Venture Capital Association (BVK)

Project Preferences

Type of Financing Preferred:
Expansion
Seed
Startup

Size of Investments Considered:
Min Size of Investment Considered (000s): $200
Max Size of Investment Considered (000s): $200,000

Geographical Preferences

International Preferences:
Western Europe
Germany

Industry Preferences

In Communications prefer:
Communications and Media

In Internet Specific prefer:
Internet

In Biotechnology prefer:
Biotechnology

In Medical/Health prefer:
Medical/Health

In Financial Services prefer:
Financial Services

In Other prefer:
Environment Responsible

Additional Information
Year Founded: 2001
Current Activity Level: Actively seeking new investments

BTV INVEST

Leirvollen 19
Skien, Norway N-3736
Phone: 47-35-505-550
Fax: 47-35-505-555
E-mail: post@btv-invest.no
Website: www.btv-invest.no

Type of Firm
Private Equity Firm

Association Membership
European Private Equity and Venture Capital Assoc.

Project Preferences

Type of Financing Preferred:
Balanced

Geographical Preferences

International Preferences:
Europe
Norway

Industry Preferences

In Industrial/Energy prefer:
Energy
Environmental Related

Additional Information
Year Founded: 2000

Capital Under Management: $33,000,000
Current Activity Level: Actively seeking new investments

BUCKHEAD INVESTMENT PARTNERS LLC

3525 Piedmont Road
Building Eight, Suite 515
Atlanta, GA USA 30305
Phone: 404-495-5230
Fax: 404-495-5239
Website: www.buckheadinvestments.com

Management and Staff

Bill Harris, Managing Partner
Mark Buffington, Managing Partner

Type of Firm

Private Equity Firm

Project Preferences

Type of Financing Preferred:
Early Stage
Expansion

Size of Investments Considered:
Min Size of Investment Considered (000s): $500
Max Size of Investment Considered (000s): $4,000

Geographical Preferences

United States Preferences:
All U.S.
Georgia

Industry Preferences

In Medical/Health prefer:
Health Services

In Industrial/Energy prefer:
Alternative Energy
Energy Conservation Relat

In Financial Services prefer:
Financial Services

In Business Serv. prefer:
Services
Media

Additional Information

Year Founded: 2009
Capital Under Management: $9,500,000
Current Activity Level: Actively seeking new investments

BUCKINGHAM CAPITAL PARTNERS

950 Third Avenue
19th Floor
New York, NY USA 10022
Phone: 212-752-0500
Fax: 212-752-0505
Website: www.buckinghamcapital.com

Management and Staff

Guy Naggar, Founder

Type of Firm

Private Equity Firm

Project Preferences

Type of Financing Preferred:
Leveraged Buyout
Management Buyouts
Recapitalizations

Geographical Preferences

United States Preferences:
All U.S.

Industry Preferences

In Industrial/Energy prefer:
Industrial Products

In Manufact. prefer:
Manufacturing

Additional Information

Year Founded: 2003
Capital Under Management: $26,300,000
Current Activity Level: Actively seeking new investments

BUERK DALE VICTOR LLC (FKA:BUERK CRAIG VICTOR LLC)

1200 Fifth Avenue
Suite 1800
Seattle, WA USA 98101
Phone: 206-956-0898
Fax: 206-956-0863
E-mail: info@bcvllc.com
Website: www.bcvllc.com

Other Offices

One Capital Center
999 Main Street, Suite 102-A
Boise, ID USA 83702
Phone: 208-342-2989
Fax: 206-956-0863

1120 Northwest Couch Street
Portland, OR USA 97209
Phone: 503-542-1101
Fax: 206-956-0863

Management and Staff

Andrew Dale, Managing Director
Arthur Buerk, Managing Director
Dale Vogel, Managing Director
James Wagar, Principal
John O Donnel, Venture Partner
Paul Reed, Venture Partner
Rob Wiltbank, Venture Partner
Todd Marker, Principal
Tom Kealy, Venture Partner

Type of Firm

Investment Management Firm

Association Membership

National Venture Capital Association - USA (NVCA)

Project Preferences

Role in Financing:
Prefer role as deal originator but will also invest in deals created by others

Type of Financing Preferred:
Early Stage
Expansion

Size of Investments Considered:
Min Size of Investment Considered (000s): $1,000
Max Size of Investment Considered (000s): $5,000

Geographical Preferences

United States Preferences:
Northwest

Additional Information

Name of Most Recent Fund: Buerk Dale Victor II, L.P.
Most Recent Fund Was Raised: 08/03/2006
Year Founded: 1999
Capital Under Management: $93,000,000
Current Activity Level: Actively seeking new investments
Method of Compensation: Return on invest. most important, but chg. closing fees, service fees, etc.

BUGIN CAPITAL CO., LTD.

1-10-8 Sakuragi-cho
Omiya shi
Saitama, Japan 331-0852
Phone: 81-48-657-0931
Fax: 81-48-657-0932

Type of Firm

Bank Affiliated

Additional Information

Year Founded: 1997
Current Activity Level: Actively seeking new investments

BULGARIAN-AMERICAN ENTERPRISE FUND, THE

333 West Wacker Drive
Suite 2080
Chicago, IL USA 60606
Phone: 312-629-2500
Fax: 312-629-2929
E-mail: info@baefinvest.com
Website: www.baefinvest.com

Other Offices

3 Shipka Street
Sofia, Bulgaria 1504
Phone: 359-2-946-0119
Fax: 359-2-946-0118

Management and Staff

Thomas Higgins, Managing Director

Type of Firm

Private Equity Firm

Project Preferences

Type of Financing Preferred:

Balanced

Size of Investments Considered:

Min Size of Investment Considered (000s): $100
Max Size of Investment Considered (000s): $5,000

Geographical Preferences

International Preferences:

Bulgaria

Industry Preferences

In Internet Specific prefer:

Internet

In Medical/Health prefer:

Medical/Health

In Business Serv. prefer:

Distribution

In Manufact. prefer:

Manufacturing

In Agr/Forestr/Fish prefer:

Agribusiness

Additional Information

Year Founded: 1991
Current Activity Level: Actively seeking new investments

BULLET TIME VENTURES

1375 Walnut Street
Suite 010
Boulder, CO USA 80302
Phone: 303-957-0226

Type of Firm

Private Equity Firm

Project Preferences

Type of Financing Preferred:

Seed

Industry Preferences

In Computer Software prefer:

Software

In Internet Specific prefer:

Internet
Web Aggregration/Portals

Additional Information

Year Founded: 2009
Capital Under Management: $2,300,000
Current Activity Level: Actively seeking new investments

BULLNET CAPITAL SCR SA

Paseo del Club Deportivo,1
Edif. 3, Pozuelo de Alarcon
Madrid, Spain 28223
Phone: 34-91-799-7206
Fax: 34-91-799-5372
Website: www.grupobullnet.com

Management and Staff

Bruno Entrecanales, Co-Founder
Javier Ulecia, Co-Founder
Miguel del Canizo, Co-Founder

Type of Firm

Private Equity Firm

Project Preferences

Type of Financing Preferred:

Leveraged Buyout
Early Stage
Expansion
Balanced
Management Buyouts

Geographical Preferences

International Preferences:

Portugal
Europe
Spain

Industry Preferences

In Communications prefer:

Telecommunications

In Computer Software prefer:

Software

In Computer Other prefer:

Computer Related

In Business Serv. prefer:

Services

Additional Information

Year Founded: 2001
Capital Under Management: $25,600,000
Current Activity Level: Actively seeking new investments

BUNAOARBANKINN VEROBREF

Hafnarstraeti 5
Reykjavik, Iceland 155
Phone: 354-525-6000
Fax: 354-525-6099

Type of Firm

Private Equity Firm

Project Preferences

Type of Financing Preferred:

Balanced

Geographical Preferences

International Preferences:

Europe
Iceland

Additional Information

Year Founded: 2004
Current Activity Level: Actively seeking new investments

BUNKER HILL CAPITAL

260 Franklin Street
Suite 1860
Boston, MA USA 02110
Phone: 617-720-4030
Fax: 617-720-4037
E-mail: marketing@bunkerhillcapital.com
Website: www.bunkerhillcapital.com

Other Offices

12625 High Bluff Drive
Suite 210
San Diego, CA USA 92130
Phone: 858-793-4560
Fax: 858-793-4562

Management and Staff

Brian Kinsman, Managing Partner
Jason Hurd, Partner
Mark DeBlois, Managing Partner
Rufus Clark, Managing Partner
Theresa Nibi, Managing Partner
Timothy Sheehy, Principal

Type of Firm

Private Equity Firm

Project Preferences

Type of Financing Preferred:

Leveraged Buyout
Acquisition

Geographical Preferences

United States Preferences:

All U.S.

Canadian Preferences:
All Canada

Industry Preferences

In Consumer Related prefer:
Consumer
Retail
Other Restaurants

In Industrial/Energy prefer:
Industrial Products

In Business Serv. prefer:
Services

In Manufact. prefer:
Manufacturing

Additional Information

Year Founded: 2003
Capital Under Management: $79,700,000
Current Activity Level: Actively seeking new investments

BURDA DIGITAL VENTURES GMBH

Arabellastrasse 23
Munich, Germany 81925
Phone: 49-899-250-3861
Fax: 49-899-250-3727
Website: www.ventures.burdadigital.de

Management and Staff

Christoph Braun, Managing Director
Frank Seehaus, Managing Director

Type of Firm

Private Equity Firm

Project Preferences

Type of Financing Preferred:
Balanced

Geographical Preferences

International Preferences:
All International

Additional Information
Year Founded: 2008
Current Activity Level: Actively seeking new investments

BURDARAS HF

Sigtun 42
PO Box 220
Reykjavic, Iceland
Phone: 354-578-7800
Fax: 354-578-7819
E-mail: frj@burdaras.is
Website: www.burdaras.is

Management and Staff

Egill Truyggvason, Partner

Type of Firm

Corporate PE/Venture

Project Preferences

Type of Financing Preferred:
Balanced

Geographical Preferences

International Preferences:
Europe
Scandanavia/Nordic Region

Industry Preferences

In Industrial/Energy prefer:
Industrial Products

Additional Information

Year Founded: 1997
Capital Under Management: $256,200,000
Current Activity Level: Actively seeking new investments

BURE EQUITY

Box 5419
Gothenburg, Sweden SE-402 29
Phone: 46-31-708-6400
Fax: 46-31-708-6480
E-mail: info@bure.se
Website: www.bure.se

Other Offices

Sodra Kungstornet
Kungsgatan 33
Stockholm, Sweden 111 56
Phone: 46-8-791-7700
Fax: 46-8-791-7775

Management and Staff

Anders Morck, Chief Financial Officer
Benny Averpil, Chief Financial Officer
Mikael Nachemson, President

Type of Firm

Private Equity Firm

Association Membership

Swedish Venture Capital Association (SVCA)
European Private Equity and Venture Capital Assoc.

Project Preferences

Type of Financing Preferred:
Balanced

Geographical Preferences

International Preferences:
Europe

Industry Preferences

In Communications prefer:
Telecommunications

In Internet Specific prefer:
Internet

In Medical/Health prefer:
Medical/Health

In Consumer Related prefer:
Entertainment and Leisure

In Business Serv. prefer:
Media

Additional Information

Year Founded: 1992
Current Activity Level: Actively seeking new investments

BURELLE PARTICIPATIONS SA

1, rue Francois 1er
Paris, France 75008
Phone: 33-1-4087-6500
Fax: 33-1-4087-9680
Website: www.burelle.fr

Management and Staff

Jean Burelle, President

Type of Firm

Corporate PE/Venture

Association Membership

French Venture Capital Association (AFIC)
European Private Equity and Venture Capital Assoc.

Project Preferences

Type of Financing Preferred:
Leveraged Buyout
Expansion

Size of Investments Considered:
Min Size of Investment Considered (000s): $934
Max Size of Investment Considered (000s): $9,338

Geographical Preferences

International Preferences:
Europe
France

Industry Preferences

In Consumer Related prefer:
Consumer
Food/Beverage

In Industrial/Energy prefer:
Industrial Products
Environmental Related

In Transportation prefer:
Transportation

In Business Serv. prefer:
Services

Additional Information

Year Founded: 2002
Capital Under Management: $10,100,000
Current Activity Level: Actively seeking new investments

BURRILL & COMPANY

One Embarcadero Center
Suite 2700
San Francisco, CA USA 94111
Phone: 415-591-5400
Fax: 415-591-5401
E-mail: burrill@b-c.com
Website: www.burrillandco.com

Management and Staff

Ann Hanham, Managing Director
Anton Gueth, Managing Director
Benjamin Chen, Managing Director
Bryant Fong, Principal
Caroline Kovac, Managing Director
G. Steven Burrill, Chief Executive Officer
Giovanni Ferrara, Managing Director
Hal Gerber, Managing Director
James Watson, Managing Director
Joao Paulo Poiares Baptista, Managing Director
John Hamer, Managing Director
John Kim, Managing Director
Mohan Iyer, Managing Director
Randy Guggenheimer, Managing Director
Roger Wyse, Managing Director
Stephen Sammut, Managing Director
Victor Hebert, Managing Director

Type of Firm

Bank Affiliated

Association Membership

National Venture Capital Association - USA (NVCA)

Project Preferences

Role in Financing:
Will function either as deal originator or investor in deals created by others

Type of Financing Preferred:
Second Stage Financing
Early Stage
Mezzanine
Balanced
Seed
First Stage Financing
Acquisition

Size of Investments Considered:
Min Size of Investment Considered (000s): $1,000
Max Size of Investment Considered (000s): $11,000

Geographical Preferences

United States Preferences:
All U.S.

Canadian Preferences:
All Canada

International Preferences:
Italy
India
United Kingdom
Latin America
Luxembourg
Netherlands
Portugal
Europe
China
Hong Kong
Western Europe
Mexico
Eastern Europe
Middle East
Spain
Australia
Belgium
New Zealand
Germany
France
Japan
Africa
All International

Industry Focus

(% based on actual investment)

Biotechnology	63.4%
Medical/Health	25.5%
Consumer Related	5.3%
Computer Software and Services	2.5%
Internet Specific	2.5%
Industrial/Energy	0.8%

Additional Information

Year Founded: 1994
Capital Under Management: $625,000,000
Current Activity Level: Actively seeking new investments
Method of Compensation: Return on investment is of primary concern, do not charge fees

---

BUSH O'DONNELL CAPITAL PARTNERS

101 South Hanley
Suite 1250
Saint Louis, MO USA 63105
Phone: 314-727-4555
Fax: 314-727-8829
Website: www.bushodonnell.com

Management and Staff

Benjamin Geis, Principal
James O'Donnell, President
Matthew Koster, Principal
Scott Fesler, Partner
Wayne Smith, Principal
William Bush, Principal

Type of Firm

Investment Management Firm

Project Preferences

Type of Financing Preferred:
Leveraged Buyout
Mezzanine
Management Buyouts
Recapitalizations

Size of Investments Considered:
Min Size of Investment Considered (000s): $2,000
Max Size of Investment Considered (000s): $10,000

Geographical Preferences

United States Preferences:
All U.S.

Industry Preferences

In Consumer Related prefer:
Consumer
Retail

In Business Serv. prefer:
Services
Distribution

In Manufact. prefer:
Manufacturing

Additional Information

Name of Most Recent Fund: Eagle Fund II
Most Recent Fund Was Raised: 10/05/2007
Year Founded: 1986
Capital Under Management: $250,000,000
Current Activity Level: Actively seeking new investments

BUSHIDO CAPITAL PARTNERS, L.P.

145 East 57th Street
Eleventh Floor
New York, NY USA 10022
Phone: 212-750-5200
Fax: 649-219-3695
E-mail: info@bushidocapital.com
Website: www.bushidocapital.com

Type of Firm

Private Equity Firm

Project Preferences

Type of Financing Preferred:
Balanced

Geographical Preferences

United States Preferences:
All U.S.

Additional Information

Year Founded: 2006
Current Activity Level: Actively seeking new investments

BUSINESS ARTS, LTD.

90 Burnhhamthrope Road West
Suite 1504
Mississauga, Canada L5B 3C3
Phone: 905-281-0766
Fax: 905-281-2496

Other Offices

90 Burnhhamthrope Road West
Suite 1504
Mississauga, Canada L5B 3C3
Phone: 905-281-0766
Fax: 905-281-2496

Management and Staff

W. David Breukelman, President

Type of Firm

Private Equity Firm

Additional Information

Year Founded: 2009
Current Activity Level: Actively seeking new investments

BUSINESS CREATION MANAGEMENT AG

Im Bohl 2
Postfach 26
St. Gallen, Switzerland 9004
Phone: 41-71-230-00-66
Fax: 41-71-230-00-76

Type of Firm

Private Equity Firm

Additional Information

Current Activity Level: Actively seeking new investments

BUSINESS DEVELOPMENT BANK OF CANADA(AKA:BDC VENTURE CAPITAL)

5 Place Ville Marie
Suite 400
Montreal, Canada H3B 5E7
Phone: 514-283-8030
Fax: 514-283-7675
Website: www.bdc.ca

Other Offices

150 King Street West, Suite 1101
P.O. Box 23
Toronto, Canada M5H 1J9
Fax: 416-973-5529

Cogswell Tower, 2000
Barrington Street, Suite 1400
Halifax, Canada B3J 2Z7
Fax: 902-426-9033

444 - 7th Avenue SW, Suite 110
Barclay Centre
Calgary, Canada T2P 0X8
Fax: 403-292-6951

55 Metcalfe Street
Suite 1400
Ottawa, Canada K1P 6L5
Fax: 613-996-7331

1 - 505 Burrard Street
BDC Tower - Bentall Centre
Vancouver, Canada V7X 1V3
Fax: 604-666-7650

Management and Staff

Brian Elder, Managing Director
Charles Cazabon, Managing Director
Claude Miron, Vice President
Frank Pho, Managing Director
G. Rick Cornwall, Managing Director
Jim Orgill, Managing Director
Robert Inglese, Managing Director

Type of Firm

Bank Affiliated

Association Membership

Canadian Venture Capital Association

Project Preferences

Type of Financing Preferred:

Early Stage
Expansion
Mezzanine
Balanced
Later Stage
Seed
Startup

Geographical Preferences

Canadian Preferences:

All Canada
Quebec

Industry Preferences

In Communications prefer:

Telecommunications

In Computer Software prefer:

Software

In Internet Specific prefer:

E-Commerce Technology
Internet

In Computer Other prefer:

Computer Related

In Semiconductor/Electr prefer:

Electronics
Semiconductor

Additional Information

Year Founded: 1985
Capital Under Management: $283,000,000
Current Activity Level: Actively seeking new investments

BUSINESS MANAGEMENT, LTD.

123 Eagle Street
Level 37 Riverside Centre
Brisbane, Australia 4000
Phone: 617-3832-4928
Fax: 617-3832-3234
E-mail: bml@businessmanagement.com.au
Website: www.businessmanagement.com.au

Management and Staff

Brian Jones, Founder
Peter Blizzard, Managing Director

Type of Firm

Private Equity Firm

Association Membership

Australian Venture Capital Association (AVCAL)

Project Preferences

Type of Financing Preferred:

Leveraged Buyout
Early Stage
Expansion
Generalist PE
Balanced
Turnaround
Later Stage
Management Buyouts

Size of Investments Considered:

Min Size of Investment Considered (000s): $805
Max Size of Investment Considered (000s): $4,029

Geographical Preferences

International Preferences:

Australia

Industry Preferences

In Medical/Health prefer:

Medical/Health

In Consumer Related prefer:

Entertainment and Leisure
Retail
Food/Beverage
Education Related

In Industrial/Energy prefer:

Industrial Products

In Transportation prefer:

Transportation

In Financial Services prefer:

Financial Services

In Business Serv. prefer:
Distribution

In Manufact. prefer:
Manufacturing

Additional Information

Name of Most Recent Fund: Business Equity Fund
Most Recent Fund Was Raised: 06/28/2000
Year Founded: 2000
Capital Under Management: $35,300,000
Current Activity Level: Actively seeking new investments

BUSINESS PARTNERS

Business Partners Centre
Parktown
Johannesburg, South Africa 2193
Phone: 27-11-480-8700
Fax: 27-11-642-2791
Website: www.businesspartners.co.za

Other Offices

3 Caxton Road
Industria
Johannesburg, South Africa 2000
Phone: 27-11-470-3111
Fax: 27 -11-470-3123

Business Partners Centre
266 Govan Mbeki Avenue
Port Elizabeth, South Africa 6000
Phone: 27-41-582-1601
Fax: 27-41-585-2297

Business Partners Centre
60 Sir Lowry Road
Cape Town, South Africa 8000
Phone: 27-21-464-3600
Fax: 27-21-461-8720

Business Partners Centre
23 Jan Hofmeyr Road
Westville, South Africa 3630
Phone: 27-31-240-7700
Fax: 27-31-266-3600

Management and Staff

Ben Bierman, Chief Financial Officer
J. Schwenke, Managing Director
Paul Malherbe, Chief Operating Officer
Willem Bosch, Chief Operating Officer

Type of Firm

Private Equity Firm

Association Membership

South African Venture Capital Association (SAVCA)

Project Preferences

Type of Financing Preferred:
Leveraged Buyout
Early Stage
Expansion
Turnaround
Seed
Startup

Geographical Preferences

International Preferences:
South Africa

Additional Information

Year Founded: 1981
Current Activity Level: Actively seeking new investments

BUTLER CAPITAL CORPORATION

745 5th Avenue
Suite 1702
New York, NY USA 10151
Phone: 212-980-0606
Fax: 212-759-0876

Type of Firm

Bank Affiliated

Industry Focus

(% based on actual investment)

Other Products	46.8%
Consumer Related	46.7%
Industrial/Energy	5.0%
Communications and Media	1.5%

Additional Information

Name of Most Recent Fund: Senior Lending II
Most Recent Fund Was Raised: 01/01/1990
Year Founded: 1981
Current Activity Level: Making few, if any, new investments

BUTLER CAPITAL PARTNERS SA

30 Cours Albert 1er
Paris, France 75008
Phone: 33-1-4561-5580
Fax: 33-1-4561-9794
E-mail: contact@butlercapitalpartners.com
Website: www.butlercapitalpartners.com

Management and Staff

Arnaud Leleux, Partner
Christophe Ambrosi, Partner
Cyrille Teinturier, Partner
Franck Kelif, Partner
Frederic Favreau, Partner
Imene Maharzi, Partner
Jean-Louis Grevet, Partner
Karine Jacquemart-Pernod, Partner
Laurent Parquet, Partner
Lise Nobre, Partner
Mael De Calan, Partner
Maharzi Imene, Partner
Michel Vedrines, Partner
Rodolphe Frege, Partner

Type of Firm

Private Equity Firm

Association Membership

French Venture Capital Association (AFIC)
European Private Equity and Venture Capital Assoc.

Project Preferences

Role in Financing:
Prefer role as deal originator

Type of Financing Preferred:
Leveraged Buyout
Turnaround
Special Situation
Distressed Debt

Size of Investments Considered:
Min Size of Investment Considered (000s): $2,674
Max Size of Investment Considered (000s): $40,113

Geographical Preferences

International Preferences:
Switzerland
Europe
Belgium
France

Industry Preferences

In Communications prefer:
Other Communication Prod.

In Computer Other prefer:
Computer Related

In Semiconductor/Electr prefer:
Electronics

In Medical/Health prefer:
Medical/Health

In Consumer Related prefer:
Consumer

In Business Serv. prefer:
Services

Additional Information

Name of Most Recent Fund: France Private Equity III
Most Recent Fund Was Raised: 07/01/2005
Year Founded: 1990
Capital Under Management: $222,900,000
Current Activity Level: Actively seeking new investments
Method of Compensation: Return on invest. most important, but chg. closing fees, service fees, etc.

BUY-OUT CENTRAL EUROPE

Mariahilfer Strasse 19-21
Vienna, Austria 1060
Phone: 431581839084

Management and Staff
Kurt Stiassny, Founder
Michael Tojner, Founder

Type of Firm
Private Equity Firm

Project Preferences
Type of Financing Preferred:
Leveraged Buyout

Geographical Preferences
International Preferences:
Europe

Additional Information
Year Founded: 2007
Capital Under Management: $136,400,000
Current Activity Level: Actively seeking new investments

BV CAPITAL (FKA: BERTELSMANN VENTURES, LP)

600 Montgomery Street
43rd Floor
San Francisco, CA USA 94111
Phone: 415-869-5200
Fax: 415-869-5201
E-mail: info@bvcapital.com
Website: www.bvcapital.com

Other Offices
Grosse Elbstrasse 145D
Hamburg, Germany D-22767
Phone: 49-40-82225550
Fax: 49-40-8222-55599

Management and Staff
Andreas Von Blottnitz, Partner
Jan Buettner, Partner
Mathias Schilling, Partner
Thomas Gieselman, General Partner
Wolfgang Rose, General Partner

Type of Firm
Private Equity Firm

Project Preferences
Role in Financing:
Will function either as deal originator or investor in deals created by others
Type of Financing Preferred:
Second Stage Financing
Early Stage
Expansion
First Stage Financing
Size of Investments Considered:
Min Size of Investment Considered (000s): $1,000
Max Size of Investment Considered (000s): $5,000

Geographical Preferences
United States Preferences:
West Coast
International Preferences:
United Kingdom
Luxembourg
Belgium
Germany
France

Industry Focus
(% based on actual investment)

Internet Specific	45.0%
Computer Software and Services	23.6%
Communications and Media	20.4%
Consumer Related	11.0%

Additional Information
Year Founded: 1997
Current Activity Level: Actively seeking new investments
Method of Compensation: Return on investment is of primary concern, do not charge fees

---

BV HOLDING AG

Hotelgasse 1
Bern, Switzerland 3011
Phone: 41-31-310-0130
Fax: 41-31-310-0139
Website: www.bvgroup.ch

Other Offices
Seehof strasse 6
Zurich, Switzerland 8008
Phone: 41-44-251-1880
Fax: 41-44-269-6065

Management and Staff
Roman Strutynski, Partner

Type of Firm
Private Equity Firm

Association Membership
Swiss Venture Capital Association (SECA)
European Private Equity and Venture Capital Assoc.

Project Preferences
Type of Financing Preferred:
Expansion
Turnaround
Acquisition
Startup

Geographical Preferences
International Preferences:
Switzerland

Industry Preferences
In Communications prefer:
Telecommunications
In Computer Software prefer:
Data Processing
In Internet Specific prefer:
Internet
In Biotechnology prefer:
Biotechnology
In Medical/Health prefer:
Medical/Health
Pharmaceuticals
In Industrial/Energy prefer:
Industrial Products
In Business Serv. prefer:
Media

Additional Information
Year Founded: 1997
Capital Under Management: $31,700,000
Current Activity Level: Actively seeking new investments

BV MANAGEMENT MKB FONDSEN

Ondernemingencentrum
Ravelijn 1
Lelystad, Netherlands 8200 AC
Phone: 31-320-286-748
Fax: 31-320-286-747
Website: www.mkbfondsen-flevoland.nl

Type of Firm
Private Equity Firm

Association Membership
European Private Equity and Venture Capital Assoc.

Project Preferences
Type of Financing Preferred:
Early Stage
Expansion
Balanced

Geographical Preferences
International Preferences:
Europe

Additional Information
Year Founded: 2003
Capital Under Management: $11,800,000
Current Activity Level: Actively seeking new investments

BV VENTURE CAPITAL INVESTORS (VCI)

Herengracht 468
Amsterdam, Netherlands 1017 CA
Phone: 31-20-62-61-696
Fax: 31-20-626-80-86
E-mail: VCI@VCI.nl

Type of Firm
Private Equity Firm

Additional Information
Current Activity Level: Actively seeking new investments

BV-CORNERSTONE VENTURES, L.P.
11001 West 120th Avenue
Suite 310
Broomfield, CO USA 80021
Phone: 303-410-2500
Fax: 303-466-9316
E-mail: info@BVCV.com
Website: www.bvcv.com

Other Offices
1650 Tysons Boulevard
Suite 950
McLean, VA USA 22102
Phone: 703-748-4000
Fax: 703-748-7401

Management and Staff
Alex Vahabzadeh, Managing Director
John Ord, Chief Financial Officer
Neville Vere Nicoll, Managing Director
Reid Miles, Managing Director
Thomas McCloskey, Managing Director

Type of Firm
Private Equity Firm

Association Membership
Mid-Atlantic Venture Association
Natl Assoc of Small Bus. Inv. Co (NASBIC)

Project Preferences

Role in Financing:
Will function either as deal originator or investor in deals created by others

Type of Financing Preferred:
Later Stage

Size of Investments Considered:
Min Size of Investment Considered (000s): $2,000
Max Size of Investment Considered (000s): $5,000

Geographical Preferences

United States Preferences:
Industry Preferences

In Communications prefer:
Telecommunications
Data Communications

In Computer Software prefer:
Applications Software

In Internet Specific prefer:
E-Commerce Technology

Additional Information
Name of Most Recent Fund: BV-Cornerstone Ventures, L.P.
Most Recent Fund Was Raised: 03/31/2000
Year Founded: 2000
Capital Under Management: $100,000,000
Current Activity Level: Actively seeking new investments
Method of Compensation: Return on investment is of primary concern, do not charge fees

BWK GMBH UNTERNEHMENSBETEILIGUNGSGESELLSCHAFT
Thouretstrasse 27
Stuttgart, Germany 70173
Phone: 49-711-225576-0
Fax: 49-711-22557610
E-mail: info@bw-kap.de
Website: www.bw-kap.de

Management and Staff
Jochen Wolf, Managing Director
Matthias Heining, Managing Director

Type of Firm
Private Equity Firm

Association Membership
German Venture Capital Association (BVK)

Project Preferences

Type of Financing Preferred:
Balanced

Geographical Preferences

International Preferences:
Germany

Additional Information
Year Founded: 1990
Current Activity Level: Actively seeking new investments

- C -

C&B CAPITAL (AKA: CROFT & BENDER)
4200 Northside Parkway, NW
Building One, Suite 100
Atlanta, GA USA 30327
Phone: 404-841-3131
Fax: 404-841-3135
E-mail: info@croft-bender.com
Website: www.croft-bender.com

Management and Staff
Edward Croft, Managing Director
Frank Briggs, Managing Director
Ronald Goldman, Managing Director
Theodore Bender, Managing Director

Type of Firm
Private Equity Firm

Project Preferences

Role in Financing:
Prefer role as deal originator but will also invest in deals created by others

Type of Financing Preferred:
Second Stage Financing
Leveraged Buyout
Early Stage
Expansion
Balanced
Later Stage
Management Buyouts
First Stage Financing
Acquisition
Industry Rollups
Recapitalizations

Size of Investments Considered:
Min Size of Investment Considered (000s): $250
Max Size of Investment Considered (000s): $1,500

Geographical Preferences

United States Preferences:
Mid Atlantic
Southeast
Northeast

Industry Focus
(% based on actual investment)

Computer Software and Services	29.6%
Other Products	21.5%
Internet Specific	20.3%
Computer Hardware	15.1%
Medical/Health	7.7%
Communications and Media	4.5%
Semiconductors/Other Elect.	1.3%

Additional Information
Year Founded: 2000
Capital Under Management: $19,100,000
Current Activity Level: Actively seeking new investments

Method of Compensation: Return on investment is of primary concern, do not charge fees

C&T ACCESS VENTURES

5805 Bridge Avenue
Cleveland, OH USA 44102
Phone: 216-928-1908
Fax: 216-928-1909
E-mail: info@accessventures.com
Website: www.accessventures.com

Management and Staff

William Trainor, Managing Director

Type of Firm

Corporate PE/Venture

Project Preferences

Role in Financing:
Prefer role in deals created by others

Type of Financing Preferred:
Second Stage Financing
Early Stage
Mezzanine
First Stage Financing

Size of Investments Considered:
Min Size of Investment Considered (000s): $250
Max Size of Investment Considered (000s): $2,000

Geographical Preferences

United States Preferences:
All U.S.

Industry Preferences

In Communications prefer:
Commercial Communications
Telecommunications
Wireless Communications
Data Communications
Satellite Microwave Comm.
Other Communication Prod.

In Computer Hardware prefer:
Mainframes / Scientific
Computer Graphics and Dig

In Computer Software prefer:
Software
Systems Software
Applications Software
Artificial Intelligence

In Internet Specific prefer:
Internet

In Semiconductor/Electr prefer:
Electronic Components
Semiconductor
Micro-Processing
Controllers and Sensors
Sensors
Circuit Boards
Component Testing Equipmt
Laser Related
Fiber Optics
Analytic/Scientific

Additional Information

Name of Most Recent Fund: Access Ventures
Most Recent Fund Was Raised: 12/29/2000
Year Founded: 2000
Capital Under Management: $10,000,000
Current Activity Level: Actively seeking new investments
Method of Compensation: Return on investment is of primary concern, do not charge fees

C.A. BANCORP, INC.

130 King St West, Suite 2810
The Exchange Tower
Toronto, Canada M5X 1A4
Phone: 416-214-5985
Fax: 416-861-8166
E-mail: info@cabancorp.com
Website: www.cabancorp.com

Management and Staff

John Driscoll, Chairman & CEO
Mark MacDonald, Managing Director
Mark Gardhouse, President

Type of Firm

Investment Management Firm

Additional Information

Year Founded: 2009
Current Activity Level: Actively seeking new investments

C.W. DOWNER & COMPANY (FKA: DOWNER & COMPANY)

60 State Street
Boston, MA USA 02109
Phone: 617-482-6200
Fax: 617-482-6201
E-mail: info@cwdowner.com
Website: www.cwdowner.com

Other Offices

3 Fitzwilliam Place
Dublin, Ireland 2
Phone: 353-1-662-0175
Fax: 353-1-662-0176

32 bis, boulevard Haussmann
Paris, France 75009
Phone: 33-1-4800-2700
Fax: 33-1-4800-2710
Level 25, Chifley Tower
2 Chifley Square
Sydney, Australia NSW 2000
Phone: 61-2-9327-4426
Fax: 61-2-9327-3673

Bockenheimer Landstrasse 20
Frankfurt am Main, Germany D-60323
Phone: 49-69-297-2820
Fax: 49-69-297-2829

Management and Staff

Ashley Rountree, Managing Director
Joseph Downing, Managing Director
Karine Curtis Osorovitz, Managing Director
Michael Howell, Managing Director
Paul Colone, Managing Director
R. Wade Aust, Managing Director
Robert Reilly, Managing Director
Thomas Munnell, Managing Director

Type of Firm

Bank Affiliated

Project Preferences

Role in Financing:
Prefer role as deal originator but will also invest in deals created by others

Type of Financing Preferred:
Second Stage Financing
Mezzanine
Start-up Financing
First Stage Financing

Size of Investments Considered:
Min Size of Investment Considered (000s): $300
Max Size of Investment Considered (000s): $500

Geographical Preferences

United States Preferences:
Northeast

Canadian Preferences:
All Canada

Industry Preferences

In Computer Hardware prefer:
Mini and Personal/Desktop
Computer Graphics and Dig
Terminals

In Computer Software prefer:
Computer Services
Applications Software

In Semiconductor/Electr prefer:
Electronics
Electronic Components
Controllers and Sensors
Sensors
Component Testing Equipmt
Analytic/Scientific

In Medical/Health prefer:
Diagnostic Test Products
Other Therapeutic

Hospitals/Clinics/Primary
Pharmaceuticals

In Consumer Related prefer:
Retail
Computer Stores

Food/Beverage
Consumer Products

In Industrial/Energy prefer:
Industrial Products
Materials
Factory Automation
Machinery
Environmental Related

In Manufact. prefer:
Office Automation Equipmt

Additional Information
Year Founded: 1975
Capital Under Management: $100,000,000
Current Activity Level: Actively seeking new investments
Method of Compensation: Professional fee required whether or not deal closes

---

C3 CAPITAL LLC
4520 Main Street
Suite 1600
Kansas City, MO USA 64111
Phone: 816-756-2225
Fax: 816-756-5552
Website: www.c3cap.com

Other Offices
2100 McKinney Avenue
Suite 1550
Dallas, TX USA 75201
Phone: 214-292-2000
Fax: 214-292-2007

Management and Staff
A.Baron Cass, Principal
D. Patrick Curran, Principal
Patrick Healy, Principal
Robert Smith, Principal
Steven Swartzman, Principal

Type of Firm
Private Equity Firm

Association Membership
Natl Assoc of Small Bus. Inv. Co (NASBIC)

Project Preferences

Role in Financing:
Prefer role as deal originator

Type of Financing Preferred:
Expansion
Mezzanine
Management Buyouts
Acquisition
Recapitalizations

Size of Investments Considered:
Min Size of Investment Considered (000s): $2,000
Max Size of Investment Considered (000s): $10,000

Industry Preferences

In Consumer Related prefer:
Franchises(NEC)

In Industrial/Energy prefer:
Energy
Industrial Products

In Business Serv. prefer:
Services
Distribution

In Manufact. prefer:
Manufacturing

Additional Information
Year Founded: 1994
Capital Under Management: $260,000,000
Current Activity Level: Actively seeking new investments
Method of Compensation: Return on invest. most important, but chg. closing fees, service fees, etc.

CA CONSULT (AKA:CAIXA CENTRAL DE CREDITO AGRICOLA MUTUO CRL)
Avenue da Republica, n 23
Lisboa, Portugal 1050-185
Phone: 351-21-111-1810
Fax: 351-21-111-1899
E-mail: geral@caconsult.pt
Website: www.creditoagricola.pt

Type of Firm
Bank Affiliated

Association Membership
Portuguese Venture Capital Association (APCRI)
European Private Equity and Venture Capital Assoc.

Project Preferences

Type of Financing Preferred:
Expansion
Balanced

Geographical Preferences

International Preferences:
Czech Republic
Portugal

Industry Preferences

In Consumer Related prefer:
Consumer

In Industrial/Energy prefer:
Industrial Products

In Agr/Forestr/Fish prefer:
Agriculture related

Additional Information
Name of Most Recent Fund: Agrocapital 1 SCR
Most Recent Fund Was Raised: 06/30/2005
Year Founded: 1999
Capital Under Management: $33,700,000
Current Activity Level: Actively seeking new investments

CABOT PROPERTIES, INC.
One Beacon Street
Suite 1700
Boston, MA USA 02108
Phone: 617-723-7400
Fax: 617-723-4200
E-mail: investorrelations@CabotProp.com
Website: www.cabotprop.com

Management and Staff
Ferdinand Colloredo-Mansfeld, Chief Executive Officer
Franz Colloredo-Mansfeld, Chief Executive Officer
Kelly Stevens, Vice President
Mark Stevens, Vice President
Mark Bechard, Chief Financial Officer
Patrick Mullaney, Vice President

Type of Firm
Private Equity Firm

Project Preferences

Role in Financing:
Prefer role as deal originator

Type of Financing Preferred:
Acquisition

Size of Investments Considered:
Min Size of Investment Considered (000s): $1,000
Max Size of Investment Considered (000s): $100,000

Industry Preferences

In Financial Services prefer:
Real Estate

Additional Information
Name of Most Recent Fund: Cabot Industrial Value Fund II, L.P.
Most Recent Fund Was Raised: 07/26/2005
Year Founded: 2001
Capital Under Management: $450,000,000
Current Activity Level: Actively seeking new investments

CABOT SQUARE CAPITAL, LTD.
Byron House
7 St. James's Street
London, United Kingdom SW1A 1EE
Phone: 44-20-7579-9320
Fax: 44-20-7579-9330
E-mail: contact@cabotsquare.com
Website: www.cabotsquare.com

Management and Staff
Chris Sales, Partner
James Clark, Partner
John Van Deventer, Partner
Keith Maddin, Partner

Type of Firm
Private Equity Firm

Association Membership
British Venture Capital Association (BVCA)
European Private Equity and Venture Capital Assoc.

Project Preferences

Type of Financing Preferred:
Leveraged Buyout
Expansion
Generalist PE
Balanced
Turnaround
Startup

Geographical Preferences

International Preferences:
United Kingdom
Europe
Western Europe

Industry Preferences

In Communications prefer:
Commercial Communications

In Consumer Related prefer:
Entertainment and Leisure

In Transportation prefer:
Transportation

In Financial Services prefer:
Financial Services

In Business Serv. prefer:
Services

In Agr/Forestr/Fish prefer:
Mining and Minerals

In Utilities prefer:
Utilities

Additional Information
Year Founded: 1996
Capital Under Management: $300,000,000
Current Activity Level: Actively seeking new investments

CAHN MEDICAL TECHNOLGIES, LLC (CMT)
16 Lancaster Road
Tenafly, NJ USA 07670
Phone: 201-503-1003
Fax: 201-816-9443
E-mail: cahnmedtech@att.net
Website: www.cahnmedtech.com

Type of Firm
Private Equity Firm

Association Membership
National Venture Capital Association - USA (NVCA)

Project Preferences

Type of Financing Preferred:
Early Stage

Geographical Preferences

United States Preferences:
All U.S.

Industry Preferences

In Medical/Health prefer:
Medical/Health
Medical Diagnostics
Medical Therapeutics
Medical Products

Additional Information
Year Founded: 2002
Current Activity Level: Actively seeking new investments

CAI CAPITAL MANAGEMENT COMPANY
Royal Bank Plaza - South Tower
200 Bay Street, Suite 2320
Toronto, Canada M5J 2J1
Phone: 416-306-9810
Fax: 416-306-9816
E-mail: info@caifunds.com
Website: www.caifunds.com

Other Offices
1508A - 999 West Hastings Street
PO Box 46
Vancouver, Canada V6C 2W2
Phone: 604-694-2525
Fax: 604-694-2524

540 Madison Avenue
22nd Floor
New York, NY USA 10022
Phone: 212-319-2525
Fax: 212-319-0232

3429 Drummond Street
Suite 200
Montreal, Canada H3G 1X6
Phone: 514-849-1642
Fax: 514-849-1788

Management and Staff
Craig Skolnick, Chief Financial Officer
David Culver, Principal
Leslie Daniels, Principal
Manfred Yu, Principal
Peter Restler, Principal
Peter Gottsegen, Principal
Richard Schmeelk, Principal
Tim Patterson, Managing Director
Tracey McVicar, Managing Director

Type of Firm
Private Equity Firm

Association Membership
Canadian Venture Capital Association

Project Preferences

Type of Financing Preferred:
Leveraged Buyout
Management Buyouts
Acquisition

Geographical Preferences

Canadian Preferences:
All Canada

Additional Information
Year Founded: 1990
Capital Under Management: $277,000,000
Current Activity Level: Actively seeking new investments
Method of Compensation: Return on invest. most important, but chg. closing fees, service fees, etc.

CAI DESARROLLO EMPRESARIAL S.C.R. S.A.
Paseo de la Independencia
No 10
Zaragoza, Spain 50004
Phone: 34-976-718-191
E-mail: cai@cai.es
Website: www.cai.es

Type of Firm
Bank Affiliated

Project Preferences

Type of Financing Preferred:
Balanced

Geographical Preferences

International Preferences:
Spain

Additional Information
Year Founded: 2003
Current Activity Level: Actively seeking new investments

CAIXA CAPITAL - SOCIEDADE DE CAPITAL DE RISCO S.A.
Rua Barata Salgueiro, n 33
Lisbon, Portugal 1269-057
Phone: 351-21-313-7300

Fax: 351-21-352-6327
E-mail: caixabi@caixabi.pt
Website: www.caixabi.pt

Other Offices

Calle Maria de Molina, 39
Madrid, Spain 28006
Phone: 34-91-745-0540
Fax: 34-91-563-9559

Type of Firm

Bank Affiliated

Association Membership

Portuguese Venture Capital Association (APCRI)
European Private Equity and Venture Capital Assoc.

Project Preferences

Type of Financing Preferred:
Leveraged Buyout
Early Stage
Expansion

Size of Investments Considered:
Min Size of Investment Considered (000s): $200
Max Size of Investment Considered (000s): $200,000

Geographical Preferences

International Preferences:
Portugal

Industry Preferences

In Medical/Health prefer:
Medical/Health

In Consumer Related prefer:
Consumer

In Industrial/Energy prefer:
Industrial Products

In Manufact. prefer:
Manufacturing

Additional Information

Year Founded: 2002
Capital Under Management: $316,700,000
Current Activity Level: Actively seeking new investments

CAIXA CAPITAL DESARROLLO, SCR (AKA: CCD)

Av. Diagonal, 621-629
Barcelona, Spain 08028
Phone: 34-934-046-000
Fax: 34-933-395-703
Website: www.lacaixa.com

Type of Firm

Bank Affiliated

Project Preferences

Type of Financing Preferred:
Early Stage
Expansion

Geographical Preferences

International Preferences:
Europe
Spain

Additional Information

Year Founded: 2002
Current Activity Level: Actively seeking new investments

CAJA DE AHORROS Y MONTE DE PIEDAD DE NAVARRA

Avda. Carlos III, 8
Pamplona, Spain 31002
Phone: 34-948-208-208
Fax: 34-948-224-179
E-mail: can@can.es
Website: www.cajanavarra.es

Type of Firm

Bank Affiliated

Project Preferences

Type of Financing Preferred:
Balanced

Geographical Preferences

International Preferences:
Spain

Industry Preferences

In Industrial/Energy prefer:
Alternative Energy
Environmental Related

In Other prefer:
Environment Responsible

Additional Information

Year Founded: 2007
Current Activity Level: Actively seeking new investments

CALERA CAPITAL (FKA: FREMONT PARTNERS)

580 California Street
Suite 2200
San Francisco, CA USA 94104
Phone: 415-632-5200
Fax: 415-632-5201
E-mail: inquiry@caleracapital.com
Website: www.caleracapital.com

Other Offices

222 Berkeley Street
Suite 1760
Boston, MA USA 02116
Phone: 617-578-0790
Fax: 617-578-0077

Management and Staff

Carol Foster, Chief Financial Officer
David Lorsch, Principal
James Farrell, Managing Partner
Mark Williamson, Managing Partner
Michael Moon, Principal
Robert Jaunich, Managing Partner
William Lenihan, Managing Director

Type of Firm

Bank Affiliated

Project Preferences

Role in Financing:
Prefer role as deal originator

Type of Financing Preferred:
Leveraged Buyout
Management Buyouts
Acquisition

Size of Investments Considered:
Min Size of Investment Considered (000s): $50,000
Max Size of Investment Considered (000s): $250,000

Geographical Preferences

United States Preferences:
All U.S.

Canadian Preferences:
All Canada

Industry Focus

(% based on actual investment)

Consumer Related	29.8%
Other Products	23.4%
Medical/Health	14.3%
Internet Specific	13.2%
Semiconductors/Other Elect.	11.7%
Communications and Media	4.9%
Computer Software and Services	1.8%
Computer Hardware	0.9%

Additional Information

Name of Most Recent Fund: Fremont SBI Co-Investment
Most Recent Fund Was Raised: 11/21/2002
Year Founded: 1991
Capital Under Management: $1,800,000,000
Current Activity Level: Actively seeking new investments
Method of Compensation: Return on invest. most important, but chg. closing fees, service fees, etc.

CALGARY ENTERPRISES, INC.

Four Park Avenue
Suite 12G
New York, NY USA 10016-5310
Phone: 212-683-0119
Fax: 212-683-3119
Website: www.calgaryenterprises.com

Management and Staff

Steven Insalaco, President

Type of Firm

Investment Management Firm

Project Preferences

Role in Financing:
Prefer role as deal originator

Type of Financing Preferred:
Second Stage Financing
Mezzanine
Generalist PE
Start-up Financing
Private Placement
Recapitalizations

Size of Investments Considered:
Min Size of Investment Considered (000s): $5,000
Max Size of Investment Considered: No Limit

Geographical Preferences

United States Preferences:
All U.S.

Canadian Preferences:
All Canada

Additional Information

Year Founded: 1988
Current Activity Level: Actively seeking new investments
Method of Compensation: Professional fee required whether or not deal closes

CALIFORNIA PUBLIC EMPLOYEES RETIREMENT SYSTEM (AKA:CALPERS)

Lincoln Plaza North
400 Q Street
Sacramento, CA USA 95811
Phone: 916-795-3829
Website: www.calpers.com

Other Offices

650 East Hospitality Lane
Suite 330
San Bernardino, CA USA 92408
Phone: 877-720-7377
Fax: 909-806-4820

7676 Hazard Center Drive
Suite 350
San Diego, CA USA 92108
Phone: 877-720-7377
Fax: 619-220-7201

500 North State College Boulevard
Suite 750
Orange, CA USA 92868
Phone: 877-720-7377
Fax: 714-939-4701

Glendale Plaza
655 North Central Avenue, Suite 1400
Glendale, CA USA 91203
Phone: 877-720-7377
Fax: 818-662-4304

2750 Gateway Oaks Drive
Room 140, P.O. Box 942710
Sacramento, CA USA 95833
Phone: 877-720-7377
Fax: 916-231-7878

10 River Park Place East
Suite 230
Fresno, CA USA 93720
Phone: 877-720-7377
Fax: 559-440-4901

301 Howard Street
Suite 2020
San Francisco, CA USA 94105
Phone: 877-720-7377
Fax: 415-369-8501

650 Castro Street
Suite 240
Mountain View, CA USA 94041
Phone: 877-720-7377
Fax: 650-428-4601

Management and Staff

Anne Stausboll, Chief Executive Officer
Richard Hayes, Principal
Rob Feckner, President
Sean Harrigan, President

Type of Firm

Endowment, Foundation or Pension Fund

Project Preferences

Type of Financing Preferred:
Generalist PE

Industry Focus

(% based on actual investment)	
Communications and Media	52.3%
Internet Specific	31.1%
Industrial/Energy	7.7%
Biotechnology	3.9%
Medical/Health	3.5%
Semiconductors/Other Elect.	1.5%

Additional Information

Year Founded: 1932
Current Activity Level: Actively seeking new investments

CALIFORNIA TECHNOLOGY VENTURES LLC

670 North Rosemead Boulevard
Suite 201
Pasadena, CA USA 91107
Phone: 626-351-3700
Fax: 626-351-3702
E-mail: info@ctventures.com
Website: www.ctventures.com

Management and Staff

Alexander Suh, Managing Director
Dorothy Pavloff, Managing Director
William Hanna, Managing Director

Type of Firm

Private Equity Firm

Project Preferences

Role in Financing:
Will function either as deal originator or investor in deals created by others

Type of Financing Preferred:
Second Stage Financing
Early Stage
First Stage Financing

Size of Investments Considered:
Min Size of Investment Considered (000s): $500
Max Size of Investment Considered (000s): $5,000

Geographical Preferences

United States Preferences:
Southern California
Northern California
California
All U.S.

Industry Preferences

In Communications prefer:
Communications and Media
Telecommunications
Wireless Communications
Data Communications
Other Communication Prod.

In Computer Hardware prefer:

Computers
Computer Graphics and Dig

In Computer Software prefer:
Data Processing
Software
Systems Software
Applications Software
Artificial Intelligence

In Internet Specific prefer:
Internet
Web Aggregration/Portals

In Semiconductor/Electr prefer:
Electronics
Electronic Components
Semiconductor
Micro-Processing
Controllers and Sensors
Sensors
Laser Related
Fiber Optics

In Biotechnology prefer:
Biotechnology
Human Biotechnology
Industrial Biotechnology
Biosensors
Biotech Related Research

In Medical/Health prefer:
Medical Therapeutics
Drug/Equipmt Delivery
Medical Products
Pharmaceuticals

In Consumer Related prefer:
Consumer

In Industrial/Energy prefer:
Factory Automation
Robotics

Additional Information
Name of Most Recent Fund: California Technology Ventures II
Most Recent Fund Was Raised: 06/30/2006
Year Founded: 2000
Capital Under Management: $150,000,000
Current Activity Level: Actively seeking new investments
Method of Compensation: Return on investment is of primary concern, do not charge fees

---

CALIM PRIVATE EQUITY, LLC
320 West Main Street
Aspen, CO USA 81611
Phone: 970-920-6944
E-mail: info@calimpe.com
Website: www.calimpe.com

Other Offices
14 Wall Street
11th Floor
New York, NY USA 10005
Phone: 212-461-4200

Management and Staff
Patrick Imeson, Managing Director

Type of Firm
Private Equity Firm

Project Preferences

Type of Financing Preferred:
Early Stage
Expansion
Mezzanine
Turnaround
Later Stage

Industry Preferences

In Biotechnology prefer:
Biotechnology

In Consumer Related prefer:
Entertainment and Leisure
Food/Beverage

In Industrial/Energy prefer:
Energy

In Transportation prefer:
Transportation

Additional Information
Year Founded: 1998
Capital Under Management: $2,700,000
Current Activity Level: Actively seeking new investments

CALLIODE II
50 Rue Marcel Dassault
Boulogne-Billancourt, France 92100

Management and Staff
Guillaume Lauilhe, Chief Executive Officer

Type of Firm
Private Equity Firm

Additional Information
Year Founded: 2006
Current Activity Level: Actively seeking new investments

CALLISTO CAPITAL
BCE Place, 161 Bay Street
Suite 4620, P.O. Box 709
Toronto, Canada M5J 2S1
Phone: 416-868-4900
Fax: 416-868-4910
E-mail: info@callistocapital.ca
Website: www.callistocapital.ca

Management and Staff
Graham Savage, Co-Founder
Jim Walker, Founder
Joe Shlesinger, Managing Director
Larry Stevenson, Managing Director

Type of Firm
Private Equity Firm

Project Preferences

Type of Financing Preferred:
Leveraged Buyout

Size of Investments Considered:
Min Size of Investment Considered (000s): $8,841
Max Size of Investment Considered (000s): $30,943

Geographical Preferences

Canadian Preferences:
All Canada

Additional Information
Year Founded: 2002
Capital Under Management: $62,200,000
Current Activity Level: Actively seeking new investments

CALTIUS EQUITY PARTNERS
11766 Wilshire Boulevard
Suite 850
Los Angeles, CA USA 90025
Phone: 310-996-9585
Fax: 310-996-9577
Website: www.caltius.com

Management and Staff
Garrick Ahn, Managing Director
Gregory Brackett, Chief Financial Officer
Jeffrey Holdsberg, Managing Director
Jess Ravich, Co-Founder
Michael Morgan, Managing Director

Type of Firm
Private Equity Firm

Project Preferences

Role in Financing:
Prefer role as deal originator but will also invest in deals created by others

Type of Financing Preferred:
Leveraged Buyout
Expansion
Generalist PE
Balanced
Management Buyouts
Acquisition
Recapitalizations

Size of Investments Considered:
Min Size of Investment Considered (000s): $1,000
Max Size of Investment Considered (000s): $20,000

Geographical Preferences

United States Preferences:
Rocky Mountain
All U.S.

Canadian Preferences:
All Canada

Industry Focus
(% based on actual investment)

Medical/Health	32.6%
Computer Hardware	20.1%
Semiconductors/Other Elect.	15.9%
Consumer Related	15.2%
Other Products	14.1%
Industrial/Energy	2.2%

Additional Information

Name of Most Recent Fund: Caltius Private Equity I (FKA: Libra Capital Partners)
Most Recent Fund Was Raised: 09/01/1998
Year Founded: 1998
Capital Under Management: $133,000,000
Current Activity Level: Actively seeking new investments

CALTIUS MEZZANINE

11766 Wilshire Boulevard
Suite 850
Los Angeles, CA USA 90025
Phone: 310-996-9585
Fax: 310-996-9577
E-mail: info@caltius.com
Website: www.caltius.com

Management and Staff

Gavin Bates, Principal
Greg Howorth, Managing Director
Gregory Brackett, Chief Financial Officer
M. Todd Stemler, Principal
Michael Kane, Managing Director

Type of Firm

Private Equity Firm

Project Preferences

Role in Financing:

Will function either as deal originator or investor in deals created by others

Type of Financing Preferred:

Leveraged Buyout
Mezzanine
Turnaround
Management Buyouts
Acquisition
Recapitalizations

Size of Investments Considered:

Min Size of Investment Considered (000s): $10,000
Max Size of Investment Considered (000s): $75,000

Geographical Preferences

United States Preferences:

West Coast
All U.S.

Industry Focus

(% based on actual investment)

Other Products	46.0%
Computer Hardware	18.3%
Consumer Related	17.8%
Industrial/Energy	9.4%
Medical/Health	6.1%
Semiconductors/Other Elect.	1.9%
Biotechnology	0.4%

Additional Information

Year Founded: 1997
Capital Under Management: $1,000,000,000
Current Activity Level: Actively seeking new investments
Method of Compensation: Return on invest. most important, but chg. closing fees, service fees, etc.

CALVERT FUNDS

4550 Montgomery Avenue
Suite 1000N
Bethesda, MD USA 20814
Phone: 301-961-4788
Fax: 301-657-1982
E-mail: ventures@calvert.com
Website: www.calvert.com

Management and Staff

Steve Moody, Principal

Type of Firm

Bank Affiliated

Association Membership

Mid-Atlantic Venture Association

Project Preferences

Role in Financing:

Prefer role in deals created by others

Type of Financing Preferred:

Fund of Funds
Early Stage
Expansion
Other

Size of Investments Considered:

Min Size of Investment Considered (000s): $100
Max Size of Investment Considered (000s): $2,500

Geographical Preferences

United States Preferences:

Mid Atlantic

Industry Preferences

In Biotechnology prefer:

Human Biotechnology

In Medical/Health prefer:

Medical Diagnostics
Diagnostic Services
Diagnostic Test Products
Medical Therapeutics
Drug/Equipmt Delivery
Medical Products
Health Services
Pharmaceuticals

In Consumer Related prefer:

Education Related

In Industrial/Energy prefer:

Energy
Process Control

In Other prefer:

Socially Responsible
Environment Responsible
Women/Minority-Owned Bus.

Additional Information

Year Founded: 1976
Capital Under Management: $25,000,000
Current Activity Level: Actively seeking new investments
Method of Compensation: Return on investment is of primary concern, do not charge fees

CALVERT SOCIAL VENTURE PARTNERS, L.P.

402 Maple Avenue West
Vienna, VA USA 22180
Phone: 703-255-4930
Fax: 703-255-4931
Website: www.calvertventures.com

Management and Staff

John May, Managing Partner
Steve Moody, Principal

Type of Firm

Private Equity Firm

Association Membership

Mid-Atlantic Venture Association

Project Preferences

Role in Financing:

Will function either as deal originator or investor in deals created by others

Type of Financing Preferred:

Second Stage Financing
First Stage Financing
Startup

Size of Investments Considered:

Min Size of Investment Considered (000s): $250
Max Size of Investment Considered (000s): $1,000

Geographical Preferences

United States Preferences:

Industry Preferences

In Other prefer:

Socially Responsible
Environment Responsible

Additional Information

Year Founded: 1989
Capital Under Management: $10,000,000
Current Activity Level: Making few, if any, new investments
Method of Compensation: Return on investment is of primary concern, do not charge fees

CALVERT STREET CAPITAL PARTNERS, INC. (FKA: LEGG MASON)

111 South Calvert Street
Suite 1800
Baltimore, MD USA 21202

Phone: 443-573-3700
Fax: 443-573-3702
E-mail: cscp@cscp.com
Website: www.cscp.com

Management and Staff

Aidan Riordan, Partner
Andrew John, Managing Director
Brian Guerin, Principal
Christopher Hammond, Principal
Colleen Kammar, Chief Financial Officer
Gregory Barger, Managing Director
Joseph Hasse, Partner
Michael Booth, Partner
Steven Axel, Managing Director

Type of Firm

Bank Affiliated

Project Preferences

Role in Financing:

Prefer role as deal originator

Type of Financing Preferred:

Leveraged Buyout
Mezzanine
Management Buyouts
Acquisition
Recapitalizations

Size of Investments Considered:

Min Size of Investment Considered (000s): $5,000
Max Size of Investment Considered (000s): $25,000

Geographical Preferences

United States Preferences:

Mid Atlantic
Southeast
Northeast

Industry Focus

(% based on actual investment)

Industrial/Energy	39.7%
Internet Specific	29.6%
Computer Software and Services	10.0%
Biotechnology	9.3%
Consumer Related	9.1%
Other Products	2.2%

Additional Information

Name of Most Recent Fund: Calvert Street Capital Partners III, L.P.
Most Recent Fund Was Raised: 05/24/2005
Year Founded: 1994
Capital Under Management: $500,000,000
Current Activity Level: Actively seeking new investments
Method of Compensation: Return on invest. most important, but chg. closing fees, service fees, etc.

CALYON (FKA: CREDIT AGRICOLE INDOSUEZ)

9 Quai President Paul Doumer
Paris-la-Defense-Cedex, France 92920
Phone: 33-1-4189-0000
Fax: 33-1-4189-2956
E-mail: infoweb@calyon.com
Website: www.calyon.com

Other Offices

1301 Avenue of the Americas
New York, USA 10019
Phone: 1-212-261-7000
Fax: 1-212-261-3289

39 Allee Scheffer
Luxembourg, Luxembourg 2520
Phone: 352-4767-2659
Fax: 352-4767-3659

Ruben Dario 281
Piso 21
Mexico D. F., Mexico 11580
Phone: 52-55-9138-1380
Fax: 52-55-5280-9720

Savoie, 11, avenue d'Albigny
Annecy Cedex, France 74000
Phone: 33-4-5066-2063
Fax: 33-4-5027-8833

30, rue Thiers
Lille Cedex, France 59005
Phone: 33-3-20-63-6300
Fax: 33-3-20-57-6374

Alameda ITU, 852
16 Andar, Cerqueira Cesar
Sao Paulo, Brazil 01421-001
Phone: 55-11-3896-6300
Fax: 55-11-3896-6363

2200 Ross Avenue
Suite 4400W
Dallas, TX USA 75201
Phone: 1-214-220-2300
Fax: 1-214-220-2323

Circunvalacion Durango 1378
Plaza Zabala
Montevideo, Uruguay 1100
Phone: 11-598-2916-3514
Fax: 11-598-2916-3520

Succursale de Dijon, 3 Place Grangier
Dijon, France 21024
Phone: 33-3-80-54-1770
Fax: 33-3-80-49-9752

227 W Monroe Street
Suite 3800
Chicago, IL USA 60606
Phone: 1-312-641-0500
Fax: 1-312-641-0527

A.M.G. Building, Rue du lac Windermere
Les Berges du lac
Tunis, Tunisia 1053
Phone: 21-67-196-0008
Fax: 21-67-196-0029

Aleksanterinkatu 15 B, P.O. Box 688
Helsinki, Finland FI-00101
Phone: 35-89-69-6991
Fax: 35-89-6969-9200

2000 McGill College Ave
Suite 1900
Montreal, Canada H3A 3H3
Phone: 1-51-4982-6200
Fax: 1-51-4982-6298

Algeria Building, , Business Center Moha
Les Pins Maritimes
Alger, Algeria 16000
Phone: 213-2189-1300
Fax: 213-2189-1199

Torre Mene Grande, Piso 9, Ofic. 9-4
Avenida Francisco de Miranda, Los Paolos
Caracas, Venezuela 1060
Phone: 58-21-2285-1942
Fax: 58-21-2285-3254

Succursale Dauphine, 5, rue Felix Poulat
Grenoble Cedex, France 38010
Phone: 33-4-76-86-6400
Fax: 33-4-76-86-0325

4 quai General Guisan
Geneva, Switzerland 1204
Phone: 41-58-321-9000
Fax: 41-58-321-9100

44/F One Exchange Square
8 Connaught Place
Central, Hong Kong
Phone: 852-2820-7373
Fax: 852-2868-1524

1301 Travis Street
Suite 2100
Houston, TX USA 75201
Phone: 1-713-890-8600
Fax: 1-713-890-8668

23 Melrose Boulevard, Melrose North
Johannesburg, South Africa 2076
Phone: 27-11-448-3300
Fax: 27-11-448-3370

122 Leadenhall Street
London, United Kingdom EC3V 4QH
Phone: 44-20-7971-4454
Fax: 44-20-7971-4362

Torre Alem Plaza
Avda. Leonardo N. Alem 855 - piso 24
Buenos Aires, Argentina 1001
Phone: 54-11-4317-7900
Fax: 54-11-4317-7950

Succursale de Bruxelles
Chaussee de la Hulpe 166
Brussels, Belgium B1170
Phone: 32-2661-3350
Fax: 32-2661-3360

Succursale Aquitaine, 31
Allees de Chartres
Bordeaux Cedex, France 33025
Phone: 33-5-5600-2550
Fax: 33-5-5648-2869

Management and Staff

Edouard Esparbes, CEO & Managing Director
Kenneth Kencel, Managing Director

Type of Firm

Bank Affiliated

Association Membership

British Venture Capital Association (BVCA)
Hong Kong Venture Capital Association (HKVCA)
European Private Equity and Venture Capital Assoc.

Project Preferences

Type of Financing Preferred:

Expansion
Mezzanine
Management Buyouts
Recapitalizations

Geographical Preferences

International Preferences:

Europe

Additional Information

Year Founded: 1997
Capital Under Management: $56,600,000
Current Activity Level: Actively seeking new investments

CAMBRIA GROUP, THE

1600 El Camino Real
Suite 155
Menlo Park, CA USA 94025
Phone: 650-329-8600
Fax: 650-329-8601
Website: www.cambriagroup.com

Management and Staff

Christopher Sekula, Principal
Rene Lajous, Principal

Type of Firm

Private Equity Firm

Project Preferences

Role in Financing:

Prefer role as deal originator but will also invest in deals created by others

Type of Financing Preferred:

Leveraged Buyout
Control-block Purchases
Mezzanine
Expansion
Management Buyouts
Special Situation
Industry Rollups
Recapitalizations

Geographical Preferences

United States Preferences:

All U.S.

Industry Preferences

In Communications prefer:

Commercial Communications
CATV & Pay TV Systems
Radio & TV Broadcasting
Satellite Microwave Comm.

In Semiconductor/Electr prefer:

Electronic Components
Component Testing Equipmt
Analytic/Scientific

In Medical/Health prefer:

Disposable Med. Products

In Consumer Related prefer:

Entertainment and Leisure
Retail
Franchises(NEC)
Food/Beverage
Consumer Products
Consumer Services
Other Restaurants
Hotels and Resorts
Education Related

In Industrial/Energy prefer:

Oil and Gas Exploration
Alternative Energy
Coal Related
Energy Conservation Relat
Industrial Products

In Transportation prefer:

Transportation

In Business Serv. prefer:

Services
Distribution

In Manufact. prefer:

Manufacturing
Office Automation Equipmt
Publishing

In Agr/Forestr/Fish prefer:

Mining and Minerals

Additional Information

Year Founded: 1996
Capital Under Management: $6,000,000
Current Activity Level: Actively seeking new investments
Method of Compensation: Return on invest. most important, but chg. closing fees, service fees, etc.

CAMBRIAN VENTURES

444 Castro Street
Suite 109
Mountain View, CA USA 94041
Phone: 650-938-5900
Fax: 650-938-5959
E-mail: info@cambrianventures.com
Website: www.cambrianventures.com

Management and Staff

Anand Rajaraman, Founding Partner
Henry Huff, Chief Financial Officer
Venkatesh Harinarayan, Founding Partner

Type of Firm

Private Equity Firm

Project Preferences

Role in Financing:

Will function either as deal originator or investor in deals created by others

Type of Financing Preferred:

Early Stage
Seed

Industry Preferences

In Internet Specific prefer:

Internet

Additional Information

Year Founded: 2000
Current Activity Level: Actively seeking new investments

CAMBRIDGELIGHT PARTNERS

955 Massachusetts Avenue
Suite 304
Cambridge, MA USA 02139
Phone: 617-497-6310
E-mail: info@cambridgelight.com
Website: www.cambridgelight.com

Management and Staff

Daniel Alexander, Co-Founder
Eugene Pettinelli, Co-Founder

Type of Firm

Corporate PE/Venture

Association Membership

National Venture Capital Association - USA (NVCA)

Project Preferences

Role in Financing:

Prefer role as deal originator but will also invest in deals created by others

Type of Financing Preferred:

Early Stage
Seed

Size of Investments Considered:

Min Size of Investment Considered (000s): $50
Max Size of Investment Considered (000s): $2,000

Geographical Preferences

United States Preferences:
Massachusetts

Industry Preferences

In Communications prefer:
Telecommunications
Wireless Communications

In Computer Software prefer:
Software
Systems Software
Applications Software
Artificial Intelligence

In Internet Specific prefer:
Internet
Ecommerce
Web Aggregration/Portals

In Semiconductor/Electr prefer:
Electronic Components
Analytic/Scientific

Additional Information

Year Founded: 2000
Current Activity Level: Actively seeking new investments
Method of Compensation: Return on invest. most important, but chg. closing fees, service fees, etc.

CAMDEN PARTNERS HOLDINGS LLC

500 East Pratt Street
Suite 1200
Baltimore, MD USA 21202
Phone: 410-878-6800
Fax: 410-878-6850
E-mail: info@camdenpartners.com
Website: www.camdenpartners.com

Type of Firm

Private Equity Firm

Additional Information

Year Founded: 1995
Current Activity Level: Actively seeking new investments

CAMDEN PARTNERS, INC. (FKA: CAHILL, WARNOCK & CO. LLC)

500 East Pratt Street
Suite 1200
Baltimore, MD USA 21202
Phone: 410-878-6800
Fax: 410-878-6850
E-mail: info@camdenpartners.com
Website: www.camdenpartners.com

Management and Staff

Catharine Burkett, Principal
David Warnock, Partner
Donald Hughes, Partner
F. Mackey Hughes, Partner
Richard Berkeley, Partner
Richard Johnston, Partner
Shane Kim, Principal

Type of Firm

Private Equity Firm

Project Preferences

Role in Financing:
Will function either as deal originator or investor in deals created by others

Type of Financing Preferred:
Fund of Funds
Expansion
Mezzanine
Public Companies
Turnaround
Balanced
Later Stage
Private Placement
Special Situation
Recapitalizations

Size of Investments Considered:
Min Size of Investment Considered (000s): $3,000
Max Size of Investment Considered (000s): $10,000

Geographical Preferences

United States Preferences:
Mid Atlantic
Southeast
Northeast

Industry Focus

(% based on actual investment)

Medical/Health	41.7%
Computer Software and Services	23.6%
Internet Specific	13.8%
Consumer Related	11.1%
Other Products	7.2%
Computer Hardware	2.6%
Communications and Media	0.1%

Additional Information

Year Founded: 1995
Capital Under Management: $359,000,000
Current Activity Level: Actively seeking new investments
Method of Compensation: Return on investment is of primary concern, do not charge fees

---

CAMELOT CAPITAL CORPORATION

84 Winchester Street
Ontario, Canada M4X 1B2
Phone: 416-922-9172
Fax: 416-922-3189

Type of Firm

Private Equity Firm

Additional Information

Year Founded: 2009
Current Activity Level: Actively seeking new investments

CAMELOT VENTURES

20555 Victor Parkway
Suite 100
Livonia, MI USA 48152
Phone: 734-805-5125
E-mail: scicurel@camelotventures.com
Website: www.camelotventures.com

Management and Staff

Daniel Gilbert, Partner
David Katzman, Managing Partner
Nicholas Pyett, Chief Financial Officer

Type of Firm

Investment Management Firm

Association Membership

Natl Assoc of Small Bus. Inv. Co (NASBIC)

Project Preferences

Role in Financing:
Will function either as deal originator or investor in deals created by others

Type of Financing Preferred:
Second Stage Financing
Early Stage
Expansion
Mezzanine
Generalist PE
Balanced
Later Stage
Private Placement

Size of Investments Considered:
Min Size of Investment Considered (000s): $5,000
Max Size of Investment Considered (000s): $150,000

Geographical Preferences

Canadian Preferences:
All Canada

Industry Preferences

In Communications prefer:
Telecommunications
Wireless Communications
Data Communications
Other Communication Prod.

In Computer Hardware prefer:
Mainframes / Scientific
Integrated Turnkey System
Disk Relat. Memory Device

In Computer Software prefer:
Computer Services
Data Processing
Software
Systems Software
Applications Software

In Internet Specific prefer:
E-Commerce Technology
Internet
Web Aggregration/Portals

In Semiconductor/Electr prefer:
Micro-Processing
Fiber Optics

In Consumer Related prefer:
Retail

In Financial Services prefer:
Financial Services

In Business Serv. prefer:
Services
Consulting Services

Additional Information

Year Founded: 1999
Current Activity Level: Actively seeking new investments
Method of Compensation: Return on investment is of primary concern, do not charge fees

---

CAMERON CAPITAL MANAGEMENT

Three Radnor Corporate Center
100 Matsonford Road, Suite 304
Wayne, PA USA 19087
Phone: 610-688-7711
Fax: 610-688-7722
E-mail: info@cameroncap.com
Website: www.cameroncap.com

Management and Staff

Denean Williams, President

Type of Firm

Private Equity Firm
Additional Information
Year Founded: 2004
Current Activity Level: Actively seeking new investments

CAMERON HOLDINGS CORPORATION

1200 Prospect Street
Suite 325
La Jolla, CA USA 92037
Phone: 858-551-1335
Fax: 858-551-1343
Website: www.cameron-holdings.com

Other Offices

13515 Barrett Parkway Drive
Suite 200
Ballwin, MO USA 63021
Phone: 314-984-0700
Fax: 314-984-0751

Management and Staff

Bradley Stack, Vice President
Donald Metzger, Vice President
Kevin Fritzmeyer, Vice President

Type of Firm

Private Equity Firm

Project Preferences

Type of Financing Preferred:
Leveraged Buyout
Acquisition

Size of Investments Considered:
Min Size of Investment Considered (000s): $20,000
Max Size of Investment Considered (000s): $100,000

Geographical Preferences

United States Preferences:
Northwest
Northeast

International Preferences:
Europe
Australia

Additional Information

Year Founded: 1978
Current Activity Level: Actively seeking new investments

CAMPBELL RESOURCES

1155, University
Suite 1405
Montreal, Canada H3B 3A7
Phone: 514-875-9033
Fax: 514-875-9764
E-mail: invest@campbellresources.com
Website: www.resoucescampbell.com

Other Offices

1155, University
Suite 1405
Montreal, Canada
Phone: 514-875-9033
Fax: 514-875-9764

Management and Staff

Alain Blais, Vice President

Type of Firm

Private Equity Firm

Additional Information

Year Founded: 2009
Current Activity Level: Actively seeking new investments

CAMPUS KJELLER AS

Gasevikveien 4
P.O. Box 102
Kjeller, Norway 2027
Phone: 47-64-844-300
Fax: 47-64-844-301
Website: www.campuskjeller.no

Management and Staff

Eva Karal, Managing Director

Type of Firm

Private Equity Firm

Association Membership

Norwegian Venture Capital Association
European Private Equity and Venture Capital Assoc.

Project Preferences

Type of Financing Preferred:
Balanced

Geographical Preferences

International Preferences:
Europe
Norway

Additional Information

Year Founded: 2004
Current Activity Level: Actively seeking new investments

CAMPVENTURES

280 Second Street
Suite 280
Los Altos, CA USA 94022
Phone: 650-949-0804
Fax: 650-618-1719
E-mail: submit@campventures.com
Website: www.campventures.com

Management and Staff

Jerome Camp, Managing General Partner
Justin Camp, Managing General Partner
Kevin Negus, Venture Partner
Steven Brightfield, Venture Partner
Thomas Gutshall, Venture Partner

Type of Firm

Private Equity Firm

Association Membership

National Venture Capital Association - USA (NVCA)

Project Preferences

Type of Financing Preferred:
Early Stage
Start-up Financing
Seed
Startup

Size of Investments Considered:
Min Size of Investment Considered (000s): $300
Max Size of Investment Considered (000s): $500

Geographical Preferences

United States Preferences:
California

Industry Preferences

In Communications prefer:
Communications and Media
Wireless Communications

In Computer Software prefer:
Software

In Semiconductor/Electr prefer:
Semiconductor

Additional Information
Name of Most Recent Fund: CampVentures III (Q), L.P.
Most Recent Fund Was Raised: 12/18/2006
Year Founded: 1997
Capital Under Management: $13,700,000
Current Activity Level: Actively seeking new investments

CANAAN PARTNERS
285 Riverside Avenue
Suite 250
Westport, CT USA 06880
Phone: 203-855-0400
Fax: 203-854-9117
Website: www.canaan.com

Other Offices
2765 Sand Hill Road
Suite 115
Menlo Park, CA USA 94025
Phone: 650-854-8092
Fax: 650-854-8127

11 HaMenofim Street, Ackerstein Towers
Building B, Floor 5
Hertzliya Pituach, Israel 46120
Phone: 972-9-971-5719
Fax: 972-9-972-6859

Ground Floor, Vatika Towers
DLF Golf Course Road, Sector 54
Gurgaon, India 122002
Phone: 91-124-430-1841
Fax: 91-124-430-1850

Management and Staff
Alok Mittal, General Partner
Brent Ahrens, General Partner
Daniel Ciporin, Venture Partner
Deepak Kamra, General Partner
Eric Young, General Partner
Gregory Kopchinsky, Venture Partner
Izhar Shay, General Partner
James Furnivall, General Partner
John Balen, General Partner
Maha Ibrahim, General Partner
Mark Mangiola, Venture Partner
Mickey Kim, Principal
Seth Rudnick, General Partner
Stephen Bloch, General Partner
Stephen Green, Venture Partner
Warren Lee, Venture Partner
Wende Hutton, General Partner

Type of Firm
Private Equity Firm
Association Membership
National Venture Capital Association - USA (NVCA)

Project Preferences

Role in Financing:
Prefer role as deal originator but will also invest in deals created by others

Type of Financing Preferred:
Second Stage Financing
Leveraged Buyout
Early Stage
Balanced
Seed
First Stage Financing
Startup

Size of Investments Considered:
Min Size of Investment Considered (000s): $5,000
Max Size of Investment Considered (000s): $20,000

Geographical Preferences

United States Preferences:
Northeast
West Coast
All U.S.

International Preferences:
India
Israel
Asia

Industry Focus
(% based on actual investment)

Internet Specific	25.2%
Computer Software and Services	19.1%
Medical/Health	16.0%
Communications and Media	11.5%
Biotechnology	8.8%
Semiconductors/Other Elect.	5.7%
Computer Hardware	5.7%
Other Products	5.4%
Industrial/Energy	1.5%
Consumer Related	1.0%

Additional Information
Name of Most Recent Fund: Canaan VIII, L.P.
Most Recent Fund Was Raised: 02/06/2008
Year Founded: 1987
Capital Under Management: $3,000,000,000
Current Activity Level: Actively seeking new investments
Method of Compensation: Return on investment is of primary concern, do not charge fees

CANACCORD CAPITAL
609 Granville Street
Suite 2200
Vancouver, Canada V7Y 1H2
Phone: 604-643-7300
Fax: 604-643-7606
E-mail: info@canaccord.com
Website: www.canaccord.com

Other Offices
609 Granville Street
Suite 2200
Vancouver, Canada V7Y 1H2
Phone: 604-643-7300
Fax: 604-643-7606

Management and Staff
Brad Kotush, Chief Financial Officer
Mark Maybank, Chief Operating Officer
Paul Reynolds, Chief Executive Officer

Type of Firm
Private Equity Firm

Additional Information
Year Founded: 1992
Current Activity Level: Actively seeking new investments

CANADIAN CORPORATE FUNDING , LTD.
70 University Avenue
Suite 1450
Toronto, Canada M5J 2M4
Phone: 416-977-1450
Fax: 416-977-6764

Management and Staff
Paul E. Benson, President

Type of Firm
Private Equity Firm

Additional Information
Year Founded: 2009
Current Activity Level: Actively seeking new investments

CANADIAN IMPERIAL BANK OF COMMERCE (AKA: CIBC)
Commerce Court
Toronto, Canada M5L 1A2
Phone: 416-980-2211
Fax: 416-594-8024
Website: www.cibc.com

Management and Staff

John Penhale, Vice President
John Hunkin, Chairman & CEO

Type of Firm

Bank Affiliated

Additional Information

Year Founded: 1961
Current Activity Level: Actively seeking new investments

CANADIAN MEDICAL DISCOVERIES FUND

26 Wellington Street East
Suite 700
Toronto, Canada M5E 1S2
Phone: 416-601-2440
Fax: 416-601-2434
E-mail: info@cmdf.com
Website: www.cmdf.com

Management and Staff

Jason Mackey, Chief Financial Officer

Type of Firm

Endowment, Foundation or Pension Fund

Association Membership

Canadian Venture Capital Association

Project Preferences

Type of Financing Preferred:

Early Stage
Balanced

Size of Investments Considered:

Min Size of Investment Considered (000s): $250
Max Size of Investment Considered (000s): $15,000

Geographical Preferences

Canadian Preferences:

All Canada
Quebec
Ontario
British Columbia

Industry Preferences

In Biotechnology prefer:

Biotechnology
Biotech Related Research

In Medical/Health prefer:

Medical/Health

Additional Information

Year Founded: 1994
Capital Under Management: $200,000,000
Current Activity Level: Actively seeking new investments

CANAL PARTNERS LLC

7114 East Stetson
Drive 360
Scottsdale, AZ USA 85251
Phone: 480-291-9255
Website: www.canalpartnersllc.com

Management and Staff

Jay Poplawski, Managing Partner
Jim Armstrong, Managing Partner
Todd Belfer, Managing Partner

Type of Firm

Private Equity Firm

Project Preferences

Type of Financing Preferred:

Leveraged Buyout

Industry Preferences

In Internet Specific prefer:

Internet
Web Aggregration/Portals

Additional Information

Year Founded: 2008
Current Activity Level: Actively seeking new investments

CANBANK VENTURE CAPITAL FUND LIMITED

6th Floor Naveen Complex
No. 14, M.G. Road
Bangalore, India 560 001
Phone: 91-80-2558-6506
Fax: 91-80-2558-3909
E-mail: info@canbankventure.com
Website: www.canbankventure.com

Other Offices

P.O. Box 174, Longbow House
14/20 Chiswell St.
London, United Kingdom EC1Y4TW
Phone: 0171-628-2187
Fax: 0171-374-2468

Management and Staff

P.G. Chawla, Managing Director
R Rajee, Vice President
Suresh Gadwal, Managing Director

Type of Firm

Bank Affiliated

Association Membership

Indian Venture Capital Association (IVCA)

Project Preferences

Role in Financing:

Prefer role as deal originator but will also invest in deals created by others

Type of Financing Preferred:

Early Stage
Expansion
Mezzanine
Balanced
Later Stage
Startup

Size of Investments Considered:

Min Size of Investment Considered (000s): $21
Max Size of Investment Considered (000s): $42

Geographical Preferences

International Preferences:

India

Industry Preferences

In Communications prefer:

Communications and Media
Telecommunications
Satellite Microwave Comm.

In Computer Software prefer:

Software

In Computer Other prefer:

Computer Related

In Semiconductor/Electr prefer:

Electronics
Semiconductor

In Biotechnology prefer:

Biotechnology
Industrial Biotechnology

In Medical/Health prefer:

Medical Diagnostics
Medical Therapeutics
Health Services
Pharmaceuticals

In Consumer Related prefer:

Consumer

In Industrial/Energy prefer:

Energy
Alternative Energy
Industrial Products
Materials
Factory Automation
Environmental Related

In Business Serv. prefer:

Distribution

In Manufact. prefer:

Manufacturing

Additional Information

Year Founded: 1995
Capital Under Management: $100,000
Current Activity Level: Actively seeking new investments
Method of Compensation: Return on invest. most important, but chg. closing fees, service fees, etc.

CANDOVER INVESTMENTS PLC

20 Old Bailey
London, United Kingdom EC4M 7LN
Phone: 44-20-7489-9848
Fax: 44-20-7248-5483
E-mail: info@candover.com
Website: www.candover.com

Other Offices

Via Boito 8
Milan, Italy 20121
Phone: 39-02-854-650
Fax: 39-02-7209-5679

Ste 1701, 17F, One Ex. Square
8 Connaught Place
Hong Kong, Hong Kong
Phone: 852-3665-1300
Fax: 852-2537-3990

21-25 rue Balzac
Paris, France 75008
Phone: 33-1-5836-4350
Fax: 33-1-5836-4361

Jorge Juan 15-1 Izq
Madrid, Spain 28001
Phone: 34-91-432-2497
Fax: 34-91-435-7043

Rm 209, Taj Mahal Palace And Towers
Apollo Bunder
Mumbai, India 400 001
Phone: 91-22-6606-5555

Management and Staff

Alexis Dormandy, Managing Director
Allen Gu, Vice President
Charlie Green, Managing Director
Clive Dolman, Managing Director
Harsha Raghavan, Managing Director
Ian Gray, Managing Director
John Arney, Managing Partner
Malcolm Fallen, Chief Executive Officer
Oliver Stratton, Managing Director
Piers Dennison, Managing Director
Simon Leefe, Managing Director

Type of Firm

Private Equity Firm

Association Membership

British Venture Capital Association (BVCA)
European Private Equity and Venture Capital Assoc.

Project Preferences

Role in Financing:

Prefer role as deal originator

Type of Financing Preferred:

Leveraged Buyout
Mezzanine
Management Buyouts
Industry Rollups

Size of Investments Considered:

Min Size of Investment Considered (000s): $150
Max Size of Investment Considered (000s): $500

Geographical Preferences

International Preferences:

Italy
United Kingdom
Luxembourg
Netherlands
Europe
Spain
Scandanavia/Nordic Region
Belgium
Germany
France

Industry Focus

(% based on actual investment)

Other Products	40.6%
Consumer Related	31.6%
Communications and Media	7.1%
Biotechnology	6.1%
Industrial/Energy	5.8%
Computer Software and Services	3.6%
Semiconductors/Other Elect.	2.6%
Internet Specific	2.5%
Medical/Health	0.1%

Additional Information

Name of Most Recent Fund: Candover 2005 Fund
Most Recent Fund Was Raised: 08/19/2005
Year Founded: 1980
Capital Under Management: $13,017,400,000
Current Activity Level: Actively seeking new investments
Method of Compensation: Return on invest. most important, but chg. closing fees, service fees, etc.

CANEC INTERNATIONAL

5 rue Chevalier de St-George
Paris, France 75008
Phone: 33-158-62-5974
Fax: 33-158-62-5976
E-mail: contact@canec.com
Website: www.canec.com

Management and Staff

Jean-Rene Hartpence, Founder

Type of Firm

Private Equity Firm

Project Preferences

Type of Financing Preferred:

Leveraged Buyout
Acquisition

Geographical Preferences

Canadian Preferences:

All Canada

International Preferences:

Europe
France

Additional Information

Year Founded: 1989
Current Activity Level: Actively seeking new investments

CANELCO CAPITAL OY

Savilahdentie 6
Kuopio, Finland 70210
Phone: 354-0531-9307
Fax: 351-7580-0241
Website: www.sentica.fi

Type of Firm

Private Equity Firm

Project Preferences

Type of Financing Preferred:

Management Buyouts

Additional Information

Year Founded: 2008
Current Activity Level: Actively seeking new investments

CANOPY GROUP

333 South 520 West
Suite 300
Lindon, UT USA 84042
Phone: 801-229-2223
Fax: 801-229-2458
E-mail: info@canopy.com
Website: www.canopy.com

Management and Staff

Brandon Tidwell, Managing Director
Ronald Heinz, Managing Director

Type of Firm

Private Equity Firm

Project Preferences

Type of Financing Preferred:

Seed
Startup

Geographical Preferences

United States Preferences:

All U.S.

Additional Information

Name of Most Recent Fund: Canopy Ventures II
Most Recent Fund Was Raised: 05/20/2008
Year Founded: 1995
Capital Under Management: $100,000,000
Current Activity Level: Actively seeking new investments

CANSBRIDGE CAPITAL CORPORATION

725-625 Howe Street
Vancouver, Canada V6C 2T6
Phone: 604-684-8368
Fax: 604-684-9369
Website: www.cansbridge.com

Management and Staff

Diana Liu, Partner
Wiliam Yu, Partner

Type of Firm

Private Equity Firm

Additional Information

Year Founded: 2000
Current Activity Level: Actively seeking new investments

CANTABRIA CAPITAL

C./ Gandara 6
principal dcha
Santander, Spain 39003
Phone: 34-94-231-8656
Fax: 34-94-222-7481
E-mail: informacion@cantabriacapital.com
Website: www.cantabriacapital.com

Management and Staff

Carlos Hazas Guerra, President

Type of Firm

Private Equity Firm

Association Membership

Spanish Venture Capital Association (ASCRI)

Project Preferences

Type of Financing Preferred:
Expansion
Management Buyouts

Geographical Preferences

International Preferences:
Europe
Spain

Additional Information

Year Founded: 2004
Current Activity Level: Actively seeking new investments

CANTERBURY PARK CAPITAL

Commodity Exchange Tower
1500-360 Main Street
Winnipeg, Canada R3C 3Z3
Phone: 204-954-5100
Fax: 204-954-5185
E-mail: info@canparkcap.com
Website: www.canparkcap.com

Other Offices

Royal Trust Tower, Suite 4545
77 King Street West, Box 298
Toronto, Canada M5K 1K2
Phone: 416-861-9155
Fax: 416-861-9268

Management and Staff

Denis Taillieu, Chief Financial Officer
Eugene Siklos, Managing Director
Gregory Milavsky, Senior Managing Director
Jason Stefanson, Managing Director
Martin Weinberg, Senior Managing Director

Type of Firm

Private Equity Firm

Association Membership

Canadian Venture Capital Association

Project Preferences

Role in Financing:
Prefer role as deal originator

Type of Financing Preferred:
Leveraged Buyout
Expansion

Size of Investments Considered:
Min Size of Investment Considered (000s): $10,000
Max Size of Investment Considered (000s): $50,000

Geographical Preferences

Canadian Preferences:
Western Canada

Industry Preferences

In Medical/Health prefer:
Medical Products

Additional Information

Year Founded: 2006
Capital Under Management: $154,200,000
Current Activity Level: Actively seeking new investments
Method of Compensation: Return on invest. most important, but chg. closing fees, service fees, etc.

CANTON VENTURE CAPITAL CO., LTD.

11/F Metro Plaza
183 North Tianhe Road
Guangzhou, China 510075
Phone: 86-20-8755-6020
Fax: 86-20-8755-6023
E-mail: cvcc@c-vcc.com
Website: www.c-vcc.com

Management and Staff

HongHong Zheng, Chief Financial Officer

Type of Firm

Private Equity Firm

Project Preferences

Type of Financing Preferred:
Balanced
Later Stage
Seed
Startup

Geographical Preferences

International Preferences:
China

Industry Preferences

In Communications prefer:
Telecommunications

In Computer Software prefer:
Systems Software

In Internet Specific prefer:
Internet

In Biotechnology prefer:
Biotechnology

In Agr/Forestr/Fish prefer:
Agriculture related

Additional Information

Year Founded: 1999
Capital Under Management: $75,000,000
Current Activity Level: Actively seeking new investments

CANYON CAPITAL

9665 Wilshire Boulevard
Suite 200
Beverly Hills, CA USA 90212
Phone: 310-247-2700
Fax: 310-247-8067
E-mail: rcbe@canyonpartners.com
Website: www.canyonpartners.com

Management and Staff

Joshua Friedman, Managing Partner
K. Robert Turner, Managing Partner
Mitchell Julis, Managing Partner
R. Christian Evensen, Managing Partner

Type of Firm

Private Equity Firm

Additional Information

Year Founded: 1990
Capital Under Management: $3,500,000,000
Current Activity Level: Actively seeking new investments

CAP DECISIF MANAGEMENT SAS

21 bis rue Lord Byron
Paris, France 75008
Phone: 33-1-7500-0100
Fax: 33-1-7500-0115
Website: www.capdecisif.com

Type of Firm

Private Equity Firm

Association Membership

French Venture Capital Association (AFIC)

Project Preferences

Type of Financing Preferred:
Balanced

Size of Investments Considered:
Min Size of Investment Considered (000s): $1,408
Max Size of Investment Considered (000s): $2,815

Geographical Preferences

International Preferences:
France

Industry Preferences

In Communications prefer:
Telecommunications

In Computer Software prefer:
Software

In Industrial/Energy prefer:
Energy

Additional Information

Year Founded: 2003
Capital Under Management: $15,700,000
Current Activity Level: Actively seeking new investments

CAP FINANCE INTERNATIONAL

Manoir de la Bourgeraie
La Vieille Lyre, France 27330

Type of Firm

Private Equity Firm

Project Preferences

Type of Financing Preferred:
Early Stage
Seed
Startup

Geographical Preferences

International Preferences:
Europe
France

Additional Information

Year Founded: 2000
Current Activity Level: Actively seeking new investments

CAP ISF SA

12-14 Rond Point des Champs
Elysees
Paris, France 75008
Phone: 33-1-5353-1510
E-mail: contact@capisf.com
Website: www.capisf.com

Management and Staff

Benjamin Pitcho, General Director
Jeremy Oinino, General Director
Oleg Tscheltzoff, General Director
Olivier Cahane, General Director
Robert Gogel, General Director

Type of Firm

Private Equity Firm

Project Preferences

Type of Financing Preferred:
Early Stage

Additional Information

Year Founded: 2009
Current Activity Level: Actively seeking new investments

CAPE FUND MANAGEMENT, INC.

759 Square-Victoria
Suite 300
Montreal, Canada H2Y 2J7
Phone: 514-982-3905
Fax: 514-982-3803
Website: www.capefund.ca

Other Offices

759 Square-Victoria
Suite 300
Montreal, Canada H2Y 2J7
Phone: 514-982-3905
Fax: 514-982-3803

Management and Staff

Peter Forton, Managing Director

Type of Firm

Private Equity Firm

Additional Information

Year Founded: 2008
Current Activity Level: Actively seeking new investments

CAPEXIT BETEILIGUNGS-MANAGEMENT AG

Rathausstrasse 19/1/Top 53
Vienna, Austria A-1010
Phone: 43-1-4023-7520
Fax: 43-1-4023-75210
E-mail: office@capexit.at
Website: www.capexit.at

Management and Staff

Christian Kaltenegger, Partner
Johannes Krahwinkler, Partner
Siegfried Morz, Partner

Type of Firm

Bank Affiliated

Association Membership

European Private Equity and Venture Capital Assoc.

Project Preferences

Type of Financing Preferred:
Second Stage Financing
Expansion
Seed
First Stage Financing
Startup

Size of Investments Considered:
Min Size of Investment Considered (000s): $1,868
Max Size of Investment Considered (000s): $4,669

Geographical Preferences

International Preferences:
Hungary
Czech Republic
Europe
Austria

Industry Preferences

In Communications prefer:
Communications and Media

In Computer Software prefer:
Software

In Semiconductor/Electr prefer:
Electronics

In Medical/Health prefer:
Medical/Health

In Consumer Related prefer:
Consumer Products

In Industrial/Energy prefer:
Industrial Products
Environmental Related

Additional Information

Year Founded: 2001
Capital Under Management: $20,100,000
Current Activity Level: Actively seeking new investments

CAPI VENTURE INC.

No.7 Hou Yuan En Si Lane
Jiaodaokou
Beijing, China
Phone: 86-10-8401-6277

Type of Firm

Private Equity Firm

Association Membership

Venture Capital Association of Beijing (VCAB)

Project Preferences

Type of Financing Preferred:
Balanced

Geographical Preferences

International Preferences:
China

Additional Information

Year Founded: 1998
Current Activity Level: Actively seeking new investments

CAPIDEA MANAGEMENT APS

Poul Ankers Gade 2
2 Tv
Copenhagen, Denmark 1271
Phone: 45-3338-6800
Fax: 45-3338-6819
Website: www.capidea.dk

Management and Staff

Jens Thoger Hansen, Partner
Nicolai Jungersen, Partner

Type of Firm

Private Equity Firm

Project Preferences

Type of Financing Preferred:
Leveraged Buyout

Geographical Preferences

International Preferences:
Europe

Additional Information

Year Founded: 2008
Current Activity Level: Actively seeking new investments

CAPIMONT INC

393, Saint-Jacques Ouest
Bureau 258
Montreal, Canada H2Y 1N9
Phone: 514-281-0903
Fax: 514-2810906
Website: www.capimont.com

Type of Firm

Private Equity Firm

Project Preferences

Type of Financing Preferred:
Expansion
Balanced
Acquisition

Geographical Preferences

Canadian Preferences:
Quebec

Industry Preferences

In Communications prefer:
Telecommunications

In Semiconductor/Electr prefer:
Electronics

In Industrial/Energy prefer:
Industrial Products

Additional Information

Year Founded: 1996
Current Activity Level: Actively seeking new investments

CAPITAL ALIANZA PRIVATE EQUITY INVESTMENT SA

Plaza del Marques
de Salamanca 9,4
Madrid, Spain 28006
Phone: 34-91-435-3088
Fax: 34-91-575-9468
E-mail: info@capitalalianza.com
Website: www.capitalalianza.com

Management and Staff

Jose Marie Castane, President
Renaud Rivain, Vice President

Type of Firm

Private Equity Firm

Association Membership

Spanish Venture Capital Association (ASCRI)

Project Preferences

Type of Financing Preferred:
Startup
Recapitalizations

Size of Investments Considered:
Min Size of Investment Considered (000s): $7,348
Max Size of Investment Considered (000s): $24,494

Geographical Preferences

International Preferences:
Portugal
Spain

Industry Preferences

In Consumer Related prefer:
Consumer

In Transportation prefer:
Aerospace

In Manufact. prefer:
Manufacturing
Publishing

Additional Information

Year Founded: 1980
Current Activity Level: Actively seeking new investments

CAPITAL BENOIT, INC.

1155 Metcalfe
Suite 1115
Montreal, Canada H3B2V6
Phone: 514-398-0960
Fax: 514-398-0962

Management and Staff

Bernard Deschamps, Vice President

Type of Firm

Private Equity Firm

Project Preferences

Type of Financing Preferred:
Leveraged Buyout
Expansion
Acquisition

Additional Information

Year Founded: 1970
Current Activity Level: Actively seeking new investments

CAPITAL CONNECT VENTURE PARTNERS S.A.

6, Pontou Street
Kifisia, Greece 14563
Phone: 30-210-625-4063
Fax: 30-210-625-4763
E-mail: info@capitalconnect.gr
Website: www.capitalconnect.gr

Management and Staff

Mathios Rigas, Managing Director

Type of Firm

Private Equity Firm

Project Preferences

Type of Financing Preferred:
Early Stage
Mezzanine
Startup

Size of Investments Considered:
Min Size of Investment Considered (000s): $1,322
Max Size of Investment Considered (000s): $3,967

Geographical Preferences

International Preferences:
Greece

Industry Preferences

In Communications prefer:
Communications and Media

In Computer Software prefer:
Software

In Computer Other prefer:
Computer Related

In Semiconductor/Electr prefer:
Electronics

In Biotechnology prefer:
Biotechnology

In Medical/Health prefer:
Medical/Health

In Industrial/Energy prefer:
Industrial Products

Additional Information

Name of Most Recent Fund: Capital Connect Venture Partners
Most Recent Fund Was Raised: 05/29/2003
Year Founded: 2003
Capital Under Management: $30,400,000
Current Activity Level: Actively seeking new investments

CAPITAL DEVELOPMENT & INVESTMENT CO., LTD.

40, NDB Building
Nawam Mawatha
Colombo, Sri Lanka 02
Phone: 941-243-7701
Fax: 941-234-1047
Website: www.boc.lk

Type of Firm

Bank Affiliated

Project Preferences

Role in Financing:
Prefer role as deal originator but will also invest in deals created by others

Type of Financing Preferred:
Second Stage Financing
Start-up Financing
Balanced
First Stage Financing

Size of Investments Considered:
Min Size of Investment Considered (000s): $300
Max Size of Investment Considered (000s): $500

Geographical Preferences

International Preferences:
Pacific Rim

Industry Preferences

In Communications prefer:
Communications and Media
Telecommunications

In Computer Software prefer:
Computer Services
Systems Software

In Internet Specific prefer:
Internet

In Semiconductor/Electr prefer:
Electronic Components

In Biotechnology prefer:
Biotechnology

In Medical/Health prefer:
Health Services

In Consumer Related prefer:
Consumer Services
Education Related

In Industrial/Energy prefer:
Energy
Industrial Products
Materials
Environmental Related

In Business Serv. prefer:
Media

In Manufact. prefer:
Manufacturing

Additional Information

Year Founded: 1983
Capital Under Management: $8,100,000
Current Activity Level: Actively seeking new investments
Method of Compensation: Return on investment is of primary concern, do not charge fees

---

CAPITAL DYNAMICS

Bahnhofstrasse 22
Zug, Switzerland 6301
Phone: 41-417-488-444
Fax: 41-417-488-440
E-mail: info@capdyn.com
Website: www.capdyn.com

Other Offices

21 Sackville Street
First Floor
London, United Kingdom W1S 3DN
Phone: 44-20-7297-0200
Fax: 44-20-7297-0299

16/F Nexxus Building
41 Connaught Road
Central, Hong Kong
Phone: 852-3757-9818
Fax: 852-2166-8999

645 Madison Avenue
19th Floor
New York, NY USA 10022
Phone: 212-798-3400
Fax: 212-798-3499

Spear Tower
One Market Street, 36th Floor
San Francisco, CA USA 94105
Phone: 415-243-4100
Fax: 415-293-8417

9 Colmore Row
Birmingham, United Kingdom B3 2BJ
Phone: 44-121-200-8800
Fax: 44-121-200-8899

Possartstrasse 13
Munich, Germany 81679
Phone: 49-892-00-04180
Fax: 49-892-00041899

Management and Staff

Christian Diller, Vice President
Ivan Herger, Vice President
Katharina Lichtner, Managing Director
Olav Koenig, Managing Director
Stefan Amman, Managing Director & CFO
Thomas Kubr, CEO & Managing Director

Type of Firm

Private Equity Advisor or Fund of Funds

Association Membership

British Venture Capital Association (BVCA)
Swiss Venture Capital Association (SECA)
European Private Equity and Venture Capital Assoc.

Project Preferences

Type of Financing Preferred:
Fund of Funds
Leveraged Buyout
Early Stage
Generalist PE
Seed
Later Stage
Fund of Funds of Second

Geographical Preferences

United States Preferences:
All U.S.

International Preferences:
Europe
Taiwan
Western Europe

Hong Kong
Singapore
New Zealand
Asia
Australia
Japan

Additional Information

Year Founded: 1988
Capital Under Management: $20,000,000,000
Current Activity Level: Actively seeking new investments

CAPITAL E GROUP

598 Madison Avenue
9th Floor
New York, NY USA 10022
Phone: 212-752-3566
Fax: 212-319-6551
Website: www.capitalegroup.com

Type of Firm

Private Equity Advisor or Fund of Funds

Additional Information

Year Founded: 2003
Current Activity Level: Actively seeking new investments

CAPITAL FINANCIERE AGRICOLE,, INC.

1400, boulevard de la Rive-Sud
Saint-Romuald, Canada G6W 8K7
Phone: 418-834-6857
Fax: 418-834-3083
E-mail: cfai@fadq.qc.ca
Website: www.cfai.qc.ca

Type of Firm

Government Affiliated Program

Additional Information

Year Founded: 2002
Current Activity Level: Actively seeking new investments

CAPITAL FOR BUSINESS, INC.

11 South Meramec Street
Suite 1430
Clayton, MO USA 63105
Phone: 314-746-7427
Fax: 314-746-8739
Website: www.capitalforbusiness.com

Other Offices

1000 Walnut Street
18th Floor
Kansas City, MO USA 64106
Phone: 816-234-2375
Fax: 816-234-2952

Management and Staff

James O'Donnell, Chairman & CEO
Wes Hampp, Vice President
William Witzofsky, Vice President

Type of Firm

Bank Affiliated

Association Membership

Natl Assoc of Small Bus. Inv. Co (NASBIC)

Project Preferences

Role in Financing:
Will function either as deal originator or investor in deals created by others

Type of Financing Preferred:
Leveraged Buyout
Expansion
Mezzanine
Later Stage
Management Buyouts
Acquisition

Size of Investments Considered:
Min Size of Investment Considered (000s): $500
Max Size of Investment Considered (000s): $5,000

Geographical Preferences

United States Preferences:
Midwest

Industry Focus

(% based on actual investment)

Industrial/Energy	33.2%
Other Products	25.0%
Medical/Health	13.2%
Internet Specific	7.7%
Communications and Media	5.9%
Consumer Related	4.8%
Semiconductors/Other Elect.	4.5%
Computer Hardware	3.3%
Biotechnology	2.4%

Additional Information

Name of Most Recent Fund: CFB Venture Fund III
Most Recent Fund Was Raised: 08/01/2001
Year Founded: 1959
Capital Under Management: $100,600,000
Current Activity Level: Actively seeking new investments
Method of Compensation: Return on investment is of primary concern, do not charge fees

CAPITAL FOR ENTERPRISE, LTD.

1 Broadfield Close
Broadfield Business Park
Sheffield, United Kingdom S8 0XN
Phone: 44-114-206-2131
Fax: 44-114-206-2146
E-mail: info@capitalforenterprise.gov.uk
Website: www.capitalforenterprise.gov.uk

Management and Staff

David Campbell, Chief Financial Officer
Ken Cooper, Managing Director
Rory Earley, Chief Executive Officer

Type of Firm

Private Equity Advisor or Fund of Funds

Association Membership

British Venture Capital Association (BVCA)

Project Preferences

Type of Financing Preferred:
Fund of Funds
Expansion

Size of Investments Considered:
Min Size of Investment Considered (000s): $131
Max Size of Investment Considered (000s): $2,637

Geographical Preferences

International Preferences:
Europe

Additional Information

Year Founded: 2009
Capital Under Management: $109,700,000
Current Activity Level: Actively seeking new investments

CAPITAL IDEAS PLC (FKA:LEISURE VENTURES PLC)

42 Carter Lane
London, United Kingdom EC4V 5EA
Phone: 44-20-7329-4000
Fax: 44-20-7236-0331
E-mail: info@capitalideasplc.com
Website: www.capitalideasplc.com

Type of Firm

Investment Management Firm

Project Preferences

Type of Financing Preferred:
Balanced

Geographical Preferences

International Preferences:
United Kingdom

Industry Preferences

In Consumer Related prefer:
Entertainment and Leisure

Additional Information

Year Founded: 2001
Current Activity Level: Actively seeking new investments

CAPITAL INTERNATIONAL RESEARCH, INC.

135 South State College Blvd.
Brea, CA USA 92821-5804
Phone: 714-671-7000
E-mail: private_equity@capgroup.com
Website: www.capgroup.com

Other Offices

1 Raffles Place
#24-00 OUB Place
Singapore, Singapore 0104
Phone: 65-6535-1680
Fax: 65-6535-5148

Hibiya Kokusai Building, 19th Floor
2-2-3 Uchisaiwaicho, Chiyoda-ku
Tokyo, Japan 100-0011
Phone: 81-3-3595-1911
Fax: 81-3-3595-1910

3 Place des Bergues
Geneva, Sweden 1201
Phone: 41-22-807-4000
Fax: 41-22-807-4001

One Market, Steuart Tower
Suite 1800
San Francisco, CA USA 94105-1409
Phone: 415-646-7515
Fax: 415-263-7906

2601 One International Finance Centre
No. 1 Harbour View Street
Hong Kong, Hong Kong
Phone: 852-2842-1000
Fax: 852-2810-6788

40 Grosvenor Place
London, United Kingdom SW1X 7GG
Phone: 44-20-7864-5000
Fax: 44-20-7864-5773

Management and Staff

Ashley Dunster, Vice President
Clark Taber, Vice President
James Ho, Vice President
James McGuigan, Vice President
Leonard Kim, Vice President
Naomi Kobayashi, Vice President
Stewart Gibson, Vice President
Vivek Kalra, Vice President
William Bannister-Parker, Vice President

Type of Firm

Private Equity Firm

Association Membership

European Private Equity and Venture Capital Assoc.

Project Preferences

Type of Financing Preferred:
Leveraged Buyout
Expansion
Generalist PE
Balanced
Turnaround
Management Buyouts

Geographical Preferences

International Preferences:
Hungary
Latin America
Indonesia
India
Czech Republic
Taiwan
Central Europe
Europe
Argentina
China
Poland
Brazil
Eastern Europe
Korea, South
Asia
All International
Russia
Africa

Industry Focus

(% based on actual investment)

Other Products	35.1%
Consumer Related	26.9%
Internet Specific	17.5%
Communications and Media	10.4%
Industrial/Energy	7.9%
Computer Software and Services	2.2%

Additional Information

Year Founded: 1992
Capital Under Management: $3,188,200,000
Current Activity Level: Actively seeking new investments

CAPITAL MIDWEST FUND, L.P.

2675 North Mayfair Road
Suite 410
Milwaukee, WI USA 53226
Phone: 414-453-4488
Fax: 414-453-4831
Website: www.capitalmidwest.com

Management and Staff

Alvin Vitangcol, Principal
Daniel Einhorn, Principal
Stephen Einhorn, Principal
Teresa Esser, Principal

Type of Firm

Private Equity Firm

Project Preferences

Type of Financing Preferred:
Early Stage

Geographical Preferences

United States Preferences:
Midwest
Wisconsin

Industry Preferences

In Industrial/Energy prefer:
Environmental Related

In Other prefer:
Socially Responsible
Environment Responsible

Additional Information

Year Founded: 2009
Current Activity Level: Actively seeking new investments

CAPITAL MONTEREGIE, INC.

1550, Rue Ampere
Beureau 300
Boucherville, Canada J4B7L4
Phone: 514-449-2009
Fax: 514-449-6472

Type of Firm

Private Equity Firm

Additional Information

Year Founded: 1993
Current Activity Level: Actively seeking new investments

CAPITAL PARTNERS CORPORATION

70 York Street
Suite 1500
Toronto, Canada
Phone: 416-968-9800

Type of Firm

Private Equity Firm

Additional Information

Year Founded: 2009
Current Activity Level: Actively seeking new investments

CAPITAL PARTNERS, INC.

8 Greenwich Office Park
3rd Floor
Greenwich, CT USA 06831
Phone: 203-625-0770
Fax: 203-625-0423
Website: www.capitalpartners.com

Management and Staff

A. George Gebauer, Managing Director
Brian Fitzgerald, President
Ryan Bell, Vice President

Type of Firm

Private Equity Firm

Project Preferences

Role in Financing:

Prefer role as deal originator

Type of Financing Preferred:

Leveraged Buyout
Acquisition

Size of Investments Considered:

Min Size of Investment Considered (000s): $4,400
Max Size of Investment Considered (000s): $15,000

Geographical Preferences

Canadian Preferences:

All Canada

International Preferences:

Mexico

Industry Focus

(% based on actual investment)

Consumer Related	77.5%
Computer Software and Services	9.2%
Industrial/Energy	6.6%
Communications and Media	4.2%
Internet Specific	2.6%

Additional Information

Name of Most Recent Fund: Capital Partners III
Most Recent Fund Was Raised: 01/01/1995
Year Founded: 1982
Capital Under Management: $264,300,000
Current Activity Level: Actively seeking new investments

CAPITAL POINT PARTNERS

4801 Woodway
Suite 300 East
Houston, TX USA 77056
Phone: 713-964-2765
Fax: 713-964-2769
E-mail: info@cappoint.com
Website: www.cappoint.com

Management and Staff

Darl Petty, Managing Director

Type of Firm

Private Equity Firm

Project Preferences

Type of Financing Preferred:

Leveraged Buyout
Mezzanine
Expansion
Acquisition
Recapitalizations

Size of Investments Considered:

Min Size of Investment Considered (000s): $3,000
Max Size of Investment Considered (000s): $15,000

Geographical Preferences

United States Preferences:

All U.S.

Additional Information

Year Founded: 2008
Current Activity Level: Actively seeking new investments

CAPITAL POINT, LTD. (FKA: ARCHIQUEST TECHNOLOGIES)

Azrieli Center, Round Twr. 13F
132 Menachem Begin Road
Tel Aviv, Israel 67021
Phone: 972-3-6070-320
Fax: 972-3-6070-323
E-mail: info@capitalpoint.co.il
Website: www.capitalpoint.co.il

Type of Firm

Incubator/Development Program

Project Preferences

Type of Financing Preferred:

Early Stage
Seed
Startup

Geographical Preferences

International Preferences:

Israel

Industry Preferences

In Internet Specific prefer:

Internet

In Semiconductor/Electr prefer:

Electronics

In Biotechnology prefer:

Biotechnology

In Medical/Health prefer:

Medical Products

In Industrial/Energy prefer:

Environmental Related

Additional Information

Year Founded: 2000
Current Activity Level: Actively seeking new investments

CAPITAL RESOURCE CO. OF CONNECTICUT

2558 Albany Avenue
West Hartford, CT USA 06117
Phone: 203-236-4336
Fax: 203-232-8161

Management and Staff

Morris Morgenstein, General Partner

Type of Firm

SBIC

Association Membership

Natl Assoc of Small Bus. Inv. Co (NASBIC)

Project Preferences

Type of Financing Preferred:

Expansion
Balanced

Geographical Preferences

United States Preferences:

Northeast

Additional Information

Year Founded: 1977
Capital Under Management: $5,500,000
Current Activity Level: Actively seeking new investments

CAPITAL RESOURCE PARTNERS

200 State Street
Boston, MA USA 02109
Phone: 617-478-9600
Fax: 617-478-9605
Website: www.crp.com

Management and Staff

Nick Scola, Partner
Peter Kagunye, Chief Financial Officer
Robert Ammerman, Managing Partner

Type of Firm

Private Equity Firm

Association Membership

Natl Assoc of Small Bus. Inv. Co (NASBIC)

Project Preferences

Role in Financing:

Prefer role as deal originator

Type of Financing Preferred:

Expansion
Mezzanine
Later Stage
Acquisition
Recapitalizations

Size of Investments Considered:
Min Size of Investment Considered (000s): $5,000
Max Size of Investment Considered (000s): $25,000

Industry Focus
(% based on actual investment)

Computer Software and Services	17.9%
Other Products	17.2%
Medical/Health	16.5%
Communications and Media	16.4%
Consumer Related	12.2%
Industrial/Energy	10.4%
Internet Specific	6.4%
Semiconductors/Other Elect.	1.8%
Biotechnology	1.1%

Additional Information
Name of Most Recent Fund: Capital Resource Partners V, L.P.
Most Recent Fund Was Raised: 07/03/2003
Year Founded: 1987
Capital Under Management: $1,071,000,000
Current Activity Level: Actively seeking new investments
Method of Compensation: Return on invest. most important, but chg. closing fees, service fees, etc.

CAPITAL ROYALTY PARTNERS

1000 Main
Suite 2500
Houston, TX USA 77002
Phone: 713-209-7350
Fax: 713-209-7351
Website: www.capitalroyalty.com

Management and Staff
David Carter, Principal
Harry Loveys, Principal
Jim Webster, Managing Partner
Mary Logan, Chief Financial Officer
Michael Weinmann, Principal
Nathan Hukill, Managing Director

Type of Firm
Private Equity Firm

Project Preferences

Role in Financing:
Will function either as deal originator or investor in deals created by others

Type of Financing Preferred:
Other

Industry Preferences

In Biotechnology prefer:
Human Biotechnology

In Medical/Health prefer:
Medical Therapeutics
Pharmaceuticals

Additional Information
Year Founded: 2003
Capital Under Management: $325,000,000
Current Activity Level: Actively seeking new investments
Method of Compensation: Return on investment is of primary concern, do not charge fees

---

CAPITAL SERVICES & RESOURCES, INC.

5159 Wheelis Drive
Suite 106
Memphis, TN USA 38117
Phone: 901-761-2156
Fax: 901-767-0060

Management and Staff
Charles Bancroft, Principal

Type of Firm
Service Provider

Association Membership
Natl Assoc of Small Bus. Inv. Co (NASBIC)

Project Preferences

Role in Financing:
Prefer role as deal originator

Type of Financing Preferred:
Second Stage Financing
Leveraged Buyout
Expansion
Research and Development
Public Companies
Strategic Alliances
Special Situation
Recapitalizations

Size of Investments Considered:
Min Size of Investment Considered (000s): $10
Max Size of Investment Considered (000s): $15,000

Geographical Preferences

United States Preferences:
All U.S.

Canadian Preferences:
All Canada

Additional Information
Year Founded: 1976
Current Activity Level: Actively seeking new investments
Method of Compensation: Return on investment is of primary concern, do not charge fees

---

CAPITAL SOUTHWEST CORPORATION

12900 Preston Road
Suite 700
Dallas, TX USA 75230
Phone: 972-233-8242
Fax: 972-233-7362
E-mail: cscinfo@capitalsouthwest.com
Website: www.capitalsouthwest.com

Management and Staff
Jeffrey Peterson, Vice President

Type of Firm
Incubator/Development Program

Association Membership
Natl Assoc of Small Bus. Inv. Co (NASBIC)
National Venture Capital Association - USA (NVCA)

Project Preferences

Role in Financing:
Will function either as deal originator or investor in deals created by others

Type of Financing Preferred:
Early Stage
Expansion
Later Stage
Management Buyouts
Recapitalizations

Size of Investments Considered:
Min Size of Investment Considered (000s): $1,000
Max Size of Investment Considered (000s): $6,000

Geographical Preferences

United States Preferences:
All U.S.

Industry Focus
(% based on actual investment)

Consumer Related	28.2%
Other Products	20.5%
Industrial/Energy	14.5%
Communications and Media	9.6%
Internet Specific	9.5%
Medical/Health	8.1%
Computer Hardware	5.9%
Biotechnology	1.6%
Semiconductors/Other Elect.	1.6%
Computer Software and Services	0.5%

Additional Information
Name of Most Recent Fund: CSC Capital Corporation
Most Recent Fund Was Raised: 06/01/1983
Year Founded: 1961
Capital Under Management: $400,000,000
Current Activity Level: Actively seeking new investments
Method of Compensation: Return on investment is of primary concern, do not charge fees

---

CAPITAL STAGE AG

Brodschrangen 4
Hamburg, Germany 20457
Phone: 49-4037-8562-0
Fax: 49-4037-8562129

E-mail: info@capitalstage.com
Website: www.capitalstage.com

Other Offices

Feldeggstrasse 55
Zurich, Switzerland 8008
Phone: 41-1-360-5775
Fax: 41 1 360 57 77

Type of Firm

Private Equity Firm

Association Membership

German Venture Capital Association (BVK)

Project Preferences

Type of Financing Preferred:

Expansion
Other
Seed
Startup

Geographical Preferences

International Preferences:

Europe
Germany
Japan

Industry Preferences

In Communications prefer:

Communications and Media

In Semiconductor/Electr prefer:

Analytic/Scientific

In Biotechnology prefer:

Biotechnology

In Industrial/Energy prefer:

Alternative Energy
Advanced Materials

Additional Information

Year Founded: 2007
Current Activity Level: Actively seeking new investments

CAPITAL STOCK SCR SA

Fortuny 45 Bjo Dcha.
Madrid, Spain 28010
Phone: 34-91-319-3301
Fax: 34-91-319-1839
E-mail: mpl@inversiones-europeas.com

Type of Firm

Private Equity Firm

Association Membership

Swedish Venture Capital Association (SVCA)

Project Preferences

Type of Financing Preferred:

Leveraged Buyout
Expansion
Seed
Startup

Geographical Preferences

International Preferences:

Spain

Additional Information

Year Founded: 2001
Current Activity Level: Actively seeking new investments

CAPITAL STRATEGY MANAGEMENT CO., THE

233 South Wacker Drive
Box 06334
Chicago, IL USA 60606
Phone: 312-444-1170
Website: www.capitalstrategymanagement.com

Management and Staff

Eric von Bauer, President

Type of Firm

Private Equity Firm

Project Preferences

Role in Financing:

Prefer role as deal originator but will also invest in deals created by others

Type of Financing Preferred:

Second Stage Financing
Leveraged Buyout
Control-block Purchases
Early Stage
Expansion
Generalist PE
Public Companies
Turnaround
Management Buyouts
First Stage Financing
Strategic Alliances
Acquisition
Joint Ventures
Industry Rollups
Special Situation
Startup
Recapitalizations

Size of Investments Considered:

Min Size of Investment Considered (000s): $200
Max Size of Investment Considered (000s): $30,000

Geographical Preferences

United States Preferences:

All U.S.

Canadian Preferences:

All Canada

International Preferences:

United Kingdom
Germany

Industry Preferences

In Communications prefer:

Commercial Communications
CATV & Pay TV Systems
Radio & TV Broadcasting
Telecommunications
Wireless Communications
Data Communications
Satellite Microwave Comm.
Other Communication Prod.

In Computer Hardware prefer:

Mainframes / Scientific
Mini and Personal/Desktop
Computer Graphics and Dig
Integrated Turnkey System
Terminals
Disk Relat. Memory Device

In Computer Software prefer:

Computer Services
Data Processing
Software
Systems Software
Applications Software
Artificial Intelligence

In Internet Specific prefer:

E-Commerce Technology
Internet
Ecommerce
Web Aggregration/Portals

In Semiconductor/Electr prefer:

Electronic Components
Semiconductor
Micro-Processing
Controllers and Sensors
Sensors
Circuit Boards
Component Testing Equipmt
Laser Related
Fiber Optics
Analytic/Scientific
Optoelectronics

In Biotechnology prefer:

Biotech Related Research

In Medical/Health prefer:

Medical Diagnostics
Diagnostic Test Products
Drug/Equipmt Delivery
Medical Products
Disposable Med. Products

In Consumer Related prefer:

Consumer
Retail
Franchises(NEC)
Food/Beverage
Education Related

In Industrial/Energy prefer:

Energy
Industrial Products
Factory Automation
Robotics
Machinery

In Transportation prefer:
Transportation
Aerospace

In Business Serv. prefer:
Services
Distribution
Consulting Services
Media

In Manufact. prefer:
Manufacturing

In Agr/Forestr/Fish prefer:
Agriculture related

In Utilities prefer:
Utilities

In Other prefer:
Environment Responsible
Women/Minority-Owned Bus.

Additional Information
Year Founded: 1982
Current Activity Level: Actively seeking new investments
Method of Compensation: Return on invest. most important, but chg. closing fees, service fees, etc.

CAPITAL TODAY
88 Century Street
Suite 3808, 38/F Jinmao Bldg.
Shanghai, China
Phone: 86-21-5098-8886
Fax: 86-21-5098-8050
E-mail: info@capitaltoday.com
Website: www.capitaltoday.com

Other Offices
39/F, Zhonghuan Jiaoyi Square
China
Phone: 852-2868-5526
Fax: 852-2868-5226

Type of Firm
Private Equity Firm

Project Preferences

Type of Financing Preferred:
Expansion

Geographical Preferences

International Preferences:
China

Additional Information
Year Founded: 2006
Capital Under Management: $280,000,000
Current Activity Level: Actively seeking new investments

CAPITAL TRUST, LTD.
49 Mount Street
London, United Kingdom W1K 2SD
Phone: 44-20-7491-4230
Fax: 44-20-7499-0524
Website: www.capitaltrustltd.com

Other Offices
Starco Center
Block C, Eight Floor
Beirut, Lebanon
Phone: 961-1-368-968
Fax: 961-1-368-324

655 Madison Avenue
17th Floor
New York, NY USA 10021
Phone: 212-277-1010
Fax: 212-277-1011

1717 Pennsylvania Avenue Northwest
Washington, DC USA 20006
Phone: 202-887-6171
Fax: 202-887-6786

Management and Staff
Brian Hammond, Chief Financial Officer
Romen Mathieu, Managing Director

Type of Firm
Bank Affiliated

Project Preferences

Type of Financing Preferred:
Mezzanine
Generalist PE
Balanced

Geographical Preferences

United States Preferences:
All U.S.

International Preferences:
Tunisia
Europe
Jordan
Egypt
Lebanon
Middle East
Algeria
Morocco
Syria
South Africa
Africa

Additional Information
Year Founded: 1985
Capital Under Management: $63,000,000
Current Activity Level: Actively seeking new investments

CAPITAL VENTURE PARTNERS AG (AKA: CAPVENT AG)
Dufoustrasse 24
Zurich, Switzerland 8008
Phone: 41-43-500-5070
Fax: 41-43-500-5079
E-mail: info@capvent.com
Website: www.capvent.com

Other Offices
7/2 Edward Road
Bangalore, India 560052
Phone: 91-80-4112-8900
Fax: 91-80-4112-7700

Management and Staff
Joe Sovran, Partner
Tom F. Clausen, Managing Partner
Varun Sood, Managing Partner

Type of Firm
Private Equity Firm

Association Membership
Swiss Venture Capital Association (SECA)
European Private Equity and Venture Capital Assoc.

Project Preferences

Type of Financing Preferred:
Fund of Funds
Leveraged Buyout
Expansion
Mezzanine
Special Situation

Geographical Preferences

United States Preferences:
All U.S.

International Preferences:
Europe
Asia

Additional Information
Year Founded: 2000
Capital Under Management: $400,000,000
Current Activity Level: Actively seeking new investments

CAPITAL Z INVESTMENT PARTNERS (FKA: UNION SQUARE PARTNERS)
230 Park Avenue South
Eleventh Floor
New York, NY USA 10003
Phone: 212-965-2400
Fax: 212-965-2301
E-mail: information@capitalz.com
Website: www.capitalz.com

Other Offices

84 Brook Street
London, United Kingdom W1K 5EH
Phone: 44-207-8666133
Fax: 44-207-8666110

Unit 1208-9 Level 12 Core F Cyberport 3
Lippo Centre, 89 Queensway
Hong Kong, Hong Kong
Phone: 852-2230-9800
Fax: 852-2230-9898

Management and Staff

Andrew Huang, Principal
Bradley Cooper, Partner
Daniel Lieber, Principal
Elizabeth Flisser, President
Elizabeth Danes, Principal
Eric Rahe, Partner
Flisser Elizabeth, Vice President
Frederick Rook, Principal
Harlan Zimmerman, Partner
John Kim, Principal
John Massy, Vice President
John Crocker, Partner
Joseph Tomei, Principal
L. Spencer Greenwald, Partner
Lawrence Cheng, Chairman & CEO
Mani Sadeghi, Partner
Mark Gormley, Partner
Mark Hanley, Partner
Michael Bolner, Principal
Oliver Bergmann, Principal
Robert Spass, Partner
Roland Bernardon, Chief Financial Officer
Scott Delman, President
Sharissa Jones, Partner
Susan Fleming, Principal
Timothy Wright, Vice President
Vincent Fan, Partner

Type of Firm

Private Equity Firm

Project Preferences

Type of Financing Preferred:

Fund of Funds
Leveraged Buyout

Geographical Preferences

International Preferences:

Europe
Asia

Industry Focus

(% based on actual investment)

Other Products	89.1%
Internet Specific	7.5%
Medical/Health	2.2%
Computer Software and Services	1.2%

Additional Information

Year Founded: 1998
Capital Under Management: $4,840,000,000
Current Activity Level: Actively seeking new investments

CAPITAL+ A/S

Agern Alle
Horsholm, Denmark 2970
Phone: 45 3337 8622
Fax: 45 3337 9820
E-mail: info@capitalplus.dk
Website: www.capitalplus.dk

Management and Staff

Jakob Sand, Chief Executive Officer

Type of Firm

Private Equity Firm
Association Membership
Danish Venture Capital Association (DVCA)

Additional Information

Year Founded: 2008
Current Activity Level: Actively seeking new investments

CAPITAL-C VENTURES B.V. (FKA: RESIDEX VENTURES)

Kosterijland 70-78
Bunnik, Netherlands 3981 AJ
Phone: 31-30-659-5500
Fax: 31-30-659-5511
E-mail: info@capital-Cventures.com
Website: www.capital-cventures.com

Management and Staff

De Heer Tom Paffen, Partner
Joris Van Rijn, Partner
Paul Schroder, Managing Partner

Type of Firm

Bank Affiliated

Association Membership

Dutch Venture Capital Associaton (NVP)
European Private Equity and Venture Capital Assoc.

Project Preferences

Type of Financing Preferred:

Fund of Funds
Leveraged Buyout
Early Stage
Expansion
Later Stage
Startup

Size of Investments Considered:

Min Size of Investment Considered (000s): $446
Max Size of Investment Considered (000s): $17,828

Geographical Preferences

International Preferences:

Europe

Industry Preferences

In Communications prefer:

Communications and Media
Telecommunications
Wireless Communications
Data Communications

In Internet Specific prefer:

Internet

In Industrial/Energy prefer:

Industrial Products

In Financial Services prefer:

Financial Services

Additional Information

Year Founded: 2001
Capital Under Management: $79,200,000
Current Activity Level: Actively seeking new investments

CAPITAL-E

Karel Oomsstraat 4
Antwerpen, Belgium B 2018
Phone: 32-3-303-37-30
Fax: 32-3-303-37-39
E-mail: contact@capital-e.be
Website: www.capital-e.be

Management and Staff

Marc Wachsmuth, Co-Founder
Pascal Vanluchene, Co-Founder
Wim De Graeve, Co-Founder

Type of Firm

Private Equity Firm

Project Preferences

Type of Financing Preferred:

Early Stage
Seed
Startup

Geographical Preferences

International Preferences:

Europe
Belgium

Industry Preferences

In Semiconductor/Electr prefer:

Electronics

Additional Information

Year Founded: 2006
Capital Under Management: $40,800,000
Current Activity Level: Actively seeking new investments

CAPITALIA SOFIPA SGR (FKA: MCC SOFIPA)

Via Boncompagni, 14
Rome, Italy 00187
Phone: 39-06-420-3021
Fax: 39-06-4782-3570
E-mail: sofipa.sgr@sofipa.it
Website: www.capitalia.it

Other Offices

Via Hoepli 5
Milan, Italy 21121
Phone: 39-02-725-9271
Fax: 39-02-8901-1027

Via Paisiello 39
Rome, Italy 00198
Phone: 39-06-844-0261
Fax: 39-06-8530-2559

Management and Staff

Enrico De Cecco, Managing Director
Enrico Duranti, Partner
Federico Aloisi, Partner
Giovanni Braccini, Partner

Type of Firm

Bank Affiliated

Association Membership

Italian Venture Capital Association (AIFI)
European Private Equity and Venture Capital Assoc.

Project Preferences

Type of Financing Preferred:
Leveraged Buyout
Early Stage
Expansion
Mezzanine
Balanced
Turnaround
Startup
Recapitalizations

Size of Investments Considered:
Min Size of Investment Considered (000s): $500
Max Size of Investment Considered (000s): $500,000

Geographical Preferences

International Preferences:
Italy
Europe

Industry Focus

(% based on actual investment)

Other Products	68.4%
Consumer Related	24.2%
Communications and Media	6.4%
Semiconductors/Other Elect.	0.9%

Additional Information

Name of Most Recent Fund: Sofipa Equity Fund II
Most Recent Fund Was Raised: 06/01/2004
Year Founded: 1982
Capital Under Management: $110,100,000
Current Activity Level: Actively seeking new investments

CAPITALINE ADVISORS, LLC

111 Main Avenue
Brookings, SD USA 57006
Phone: 605-696-3100
Fax: 605-696-3103
E-mail: info@capitaline.net
Website: www.capitaline.net

Management and Staff

Gordon Ommen, Principal
Steve Myers, President

Type of Firm

Investment Management Firm

Project Preferences

Type of Financing Preferred:
Leveraged Buyout

Geographical Preferences

United States Preferences:
All U.S.

Additional Information

Year Founded: 2005
Current Activity Level: Actively seeking new investments

CAPITALSOURCE HOLDINGS, INC.

4445 Willard Avenue
12th Floor
Chevy Chase, MD USA 20815
Phone: 301-841-2700
Fax: 301-841-2370
E-mail: info@capitalsource.com
Website: www.capitalsource.com

Other Offices

One Maritime Plaza
25th Floor
San Francisco, CA USA 94111
Phone: 415-393-7340
Fax: 415-393-7341

Management and Staff

Cheryl Carner, Managing Director
Dean Graham, President & COO
John Delaney, Chairman & CEO
Michael Szwaikowski, President

Type of Firm

Private Equity Firm

Project Preferences

Type of Financing Preferred:
Mezzanine
Later Stage

Size of Investments Considered:
Min Size of Investment Considered (000s): $1,000
Max Size of Investment Considered (000s): $50,000

Industry Preferences

In Medical/Health prefer:
Medical/Health
Health Services

In Consumer Related prefer:
Consumer Services

In Financial Services prefer:
Financial Services
Real Estate
Investment Groups

In Manufact. prefer:
Manufacturing

Additional Information

Year Founded: 2002
Capital Under Management: $2,500,000,000
Current Activity Level: Actively seeking new investments

CAPITALSOUTH PARTNERS, L.L.C.

1011 East Morehead Street
Suite 150
Charlotte, NC USA 28204
Phone: 704-376-5502
Fax: 704-376-5877
E-mail: info@capitalsouthpartners.com
Website: www.capitalsouthpartners.com

Management and Staff

Elyn Dortch, Managing Director
Hunt Broyhill, Partner

Type of Firm

Private Equity Firm

Association Membership

Mid-Atlantic Venture Association
Natl Assoc of Small Bus. Inv. Co (NASBIC)

Project Preferences

Role in Financing:
Will function either as deal originator or investor in deals created by others

Type of Financing Preferred:
Leveraged Buyout
Expansion
Mezzanine
Acquisition
Recapitalizations

Size of Investments Considered:
Min Size of Investment Considered (000s): $1,000
Max Size of Investment Considered (000s): $5,000

Geographical Preferences

United States Preferences:
Southeast

Industry Preferences

In Business Serv. prefer:
Services
Distribution

In Manufact. prefer:
Manufacturing

Additional Information
Year Founded: 1998
Capital Under Management: $75,000,000
Current Activity Level: Actively seeking new investments
Method of Compensation: Return on investment is of primary concern, do not charge fees

---

CAPITALSPRING LLC

488 Madison Avenue
24th Floor
New York, NY USA 10022
Phone: 212-981-0148
Fax: 212-981-0159

Management and Staff
Jim Ellis, Vice President
Lara Adin, Vice President

Type of Firm
Private Equity Firm

Project Preferences

Type of Financing Preferred:
Generalist PE
Balanced

Industry Preferences

In Consumer Related prefer:
Consumer

Additional Information
Year Founded: 2005
Capital Under Management: $40,400,000
Current Activity Level: Actively seeking new investments

CAPITALWORKS LLC

Eaton Center
1111 Superior Avenue, # 970
Cleveland, OH USA 44114
Phone: 216-781-3233
Fax: 216-781-6670
Website: www.capitalworks.net

Management and Staff
John Mueller, President
W. Todd Martin, Principal
Warren Coleman, Vice President

Type of Firm
Private Equity Firm

Project Preferences

Role in Financing:
Prefer role as deal originator but will also invest in deals created by others

Type of Financing Preferred:
Leveraged Buyout
Management Buyouts
Acquisition
Distressed Debt

Size of Investments Considered:
Min Size of Investment Considered (000s): $2,500
Max Size of Investment Considered (000s): $10,000

Geographical Preferences

United States Preferences:
All U.S.

Industry Preferences

In Semiconductor/Electr prefer:
Electronics
Semiconductor

In Medical/Health prefer:
Medical Products

In Industrial/Energy prefer:
Industrial Products
Factory Automation

Additional Information
Year Founded: 1999
Capital Under Management: $100,000,000
Current Activity Level: Actively seeking new investments

CAPITOL HEALTH PARTNERS, L.P.

152 East
74th Street
New York, NY USA 10021
Phone: 212-249-3666
Fax: 212-249-5130
E-mail: info@capitolhealth.com
Website: www.capitolhealth.com

Management and Staff
Joseph Kelly, Chief Executive Officer

Type of Firm
Private Equity Firm

Association Membership
European Private Equity and Venture Capital Assoc.

Project Preferences

Type of Financing Preferred:
Early Stage
Expansion
Startup

Size of Investments Considered:
Min Size of Investment Considered (000s): $10
Max Size of Investment Considered (000s): $3,852

Geographical Preferences

International Preferences:
Europe

Industry Preferences

In Medical/Health prefer:
Medical/Health

Additional Information
Year Founded: 1995
Capital Under Management: $80,000,000
Current Activity Level: Actively seeking new investments

CAPITON AG

Bleibtreustrasse 33
Berlin, Germany 10707
Phone: 49-30-3159-450
Fax: 49-30-3159-4557
E-mail: info@capiton.de
Website: www.capiton.com

Management and Staff
Christoph Spors, Partner
Christoph Karbenk, Partner
Frank-Marcus Winkler, Partner
Konstantin Von Falkenhausen, Partner

Type of Firm
Private Equity Firm

Association Membership
German Venture Capital Association (BVK)

Project Preferences

Role in Financing:
Prefer role as deal originator

Type of Financing Preferred:
Fund of Funds
Leveraged Buyout
Expansion
Turnaround
Later Stage
Management Buyouts
Special Situation
Startup
Recapitalizations

Size of Investments Considered:
Min Size of Investment Considered (000s): $7,061
Max Size of Investment Considered (000s): $52,253

Geographical Preferences

International Preferences:

Switzerland
Europe
Austria
Germany

Industry Focus

(% based on actual investment)

Industrial/Energy	68.4%
Consumer Related	26.8%
Internet Specific	4.8%

Additional Information

Name of Most Recent Fund: Capiton III
Most Recent Fund Was Raised: 04/08/2006
Year Founded: 2000
Capital Under Management: $436,000,000
Current Activity Level: Actively seeking new investments

CAPMAN PLC

Korkeavuorenkatu 32
Helsinki, Finland 00130
Phone: 358-207-207-500
Fax: 358-207-207-510
Website: www.capman.com

Other Offices

Grev Turegatan 30, Fifth Floor
P.O. Box 5745
Stockholm, Sweden 114 87
Phone: 46-8-5458-5470
Fax: 46-8-5458-5489

Haakon VII's gt 1
PO Box 1235
Oslo, Norway 0110
Phone: 47-23-237-575
Fax: 47-23-237-579

Carre Bonn
20, rue de la Poste
Luxembourg, Luxembourg L-2012
Phone: 352-230-236-812
Fax: 352-230-236-470

Lenbachplatz 4
Munich, Germany D-80333
Phone: 49-89-2555-0610
Fax: 49-89-2555-0620

Esplanaden 7
Second Floor
Copenhagen, Denmark 1263
Phone: 45-3526-0212
Fax: 45-3526-0214

23, Osennij Boulevard
Moscow, Russia 121609
Phone: 7-495-7813-730
Fax: 7-495-7813-729

Hambro Hs, St. Julian's Avenue
P.O. Box 86, St. Peter Port
Guernsey, United Kingdom GY1 3AE
Phone: 44-1481-726-521
Fax: 44-1481-710-742

Management and Staff

Anders Bjorkell, Partner
Goran Barsby, Partner
Hans Tindlund, Partner
Heidi Lepantalo, Chief Financial Officer
Heikki Westerlund, Chief Executive Officer
Jan Mattlin, Partner
Jan Dahlqvist, Partner
Jukka Jarvela, Partner
Kaisa Arovaara, Chief Financial Officer
Lars Hagelstam, Partner
Markus Sjoholm, Partner
Peter Lund, Partner
Sami Lampinen, Partner
Sanna Argillander, Partner
Susanne Sylvest, Partner
Torben Von Lowzow, Partner
Vesa Wallden, Partner

Type of Firm

Private Equity Firm

Association Membership

Finnish Venture Capital Association (FVCA)
Danish Venture Capital Association (DVCA)
Norwegian Venture Capital Association
European Private Equity and Venture Capital Assoc.

Project Preferences

Type of Financing Preferred:

Fund of Funds
Second Stage Financing
Leveraged Buyout
Early Stage
Expansion
Mezzanine
Generalist PE
Balanced
Other
Management Buyouts
Special Situation
Acquisition

Geographical Preferences

International Preferences:

Sweden
Europe
Iceland
Estonia
Scandanavia/Nordic Region
Finland
Norway
Denmark

Industry Focus

(% based on actual investment)

Medical/Health	27.0%
Consumer Related	13.4%
Computer Software and Services	12.3%
Communications and Media	11.4%
Other Products	10.2%
Internet Specific	9.2%
Industrial/Energy	9.1%
Semiconductors/Other Elect.	4.0%
Biotechnology	2.1%
Computer Hardware	1.3%

Additional Information

Name of Most Recent Fund: CapMan Russia Fund (FKA: Norum Russia Fund III)
Most Recent Fund Was Raised: 11/26/2007
Year Founded: 1989
Capital Under Management: $4,747,300,000
Current Activity Level: Actively seeking new investments

CAPRICORN CAPITAL PARTNERS (PTY) LTD

Capricorn House, 32 Impala Rd.
Chislehurston
Johannesburg, South Africa 2196
Phone: 27-11-666-0700
Fax: 27-11-666-0702
E-mail: gavinc@hollard.co.za

Type of Firm

Private Equity Firm

Association Membership

South African Venture Capital Association (SAVCA)

Project Preferences

Type of Financing Preferred:

Balanced

Geographical Preferences

International Preferences:

South Africa

Additional Information

Year Founded: 2004
Current Activity Level: Actively seeking new investments

CAPRICORN INVESTMENT GROUP LLC (AKA: CAPRICORN MANAGEMENT)

250 University Avenue
Suite 300
Palo Alto, CA USA 94301
Phone: 650-331-8800
E-mail: contact@capricornllc.com
Website: www.capricornllc.com

Management and Staff

Andrew Hoffmann, Principal
John Jonson, Chief Operating Officer

Type of Firm

Private Equity Firm

Project Preferences

Type of Financing Preferred:

Generalist PE
Balanced
Public Companies
Recapitalizations

Geographical Preferences

United States Preferences:

All U.S.

Additional Information

Name of Most Recent Fund: Capricorn AIP - Venture Capital I, L.P.
Most Recent Fund Was Raised: 02/08/2008
Year Founded: 2006
Capital Under Management: $16,800,000
Current Activity Level: Actively seeking new investments

CAPRICORN VENTURE PARTNERS N.V.

Lei 19/1, De Jonge St. Jacob
Leuven, Belgium 3000
Phone: 32-16-284-100
Fax: 32-16-284-108
E-mail: capricorn@capricorn.be
Website: www.capricorn.be

Management and Staff

Jacques De Greef, Venture Partner
Jos Peeters, Managing Partner
Liesbet Peeters, Chief Financial Officer

Type of Firm

Private Equity Firm

Association Membership

Belgium Venturing Association
European Private Equity and Venture Capital Assoc.

Project Preferences

Role in Financing:

Prefer role as deal originator but will also invest in deals created by others

Type of Financing Preferred:

Early Stage
Generalist PE
Expansion
Balanced
Seed
Startup

Size of Investments Considered:

Min Size of Investment Considered (000s): $631
Max Size of Investment Considered (000s): $6,312

Geographical Preferences

International Preferences:

Europe
Western Europe
Eastern Europe

Industry Preferences

In Communications prefer:

Telecommunications

In Internet Specific prefer:

Internet

In Computer Other prefer:

Computer Related

In Biotechnology prefer:

Biotechnology
Biotech Related Research

In Medical/Health prefer:

Medical/Health
Medical Diagnostics
Pharmaceuticals

In Industrial/Energy prefer:

Alternative Energy
Energy Conservation Relat
Industrial Products
Materials

In Other prefer:

Environment Responsible

Additional Information

Name of Most Recent Fund: Capricorn Cleantech Fund
Most Recent Fund Was Raised: 11/09/2006
Year Founded: 1993
Capital Under Management: $189,400,000
Current Activity Level: Actively seeking new investments
Method of Compensation: Return on investment is of primary concern, do not charge fees

---

CAPSOURCE FUND, L.P.

795 Woodlands Parkway
Suite 100
Ridgeland, MS USA 39157
Phone: 601-899-8980
Fax: 601-952-1334
E-mail: thefunds@capsources.com
Website: www.capsources.com

Other Offices

14505 Torrey Chase
Suite 325
Houston, TX USA 77014
Phone: 281-893-9494
Fax: 281-893-4508

511 E. John Carpenter Freeway
Suite 220
Irving, TX USA 75062
Fax: 214-638-7612

Management and Staff

Bobby Weatherly, General Partner
Charles Martin, General Partner
James Herndon, Managing Partner
Larry Hicks, Chief Financial Officer

Type of Firm

SBIC

Association Membership

Natl Assoc of Small Bus. Inv. Co (NASBIC)

Project Preferences

Role in Financing:

Will function either as deal originator or investor in deals created by others

Type of Financing Preferred:

Expansion

Size of Investments Considered:

Min Size of Investment Considered (000s): $500
Max Size of Investment Considered (000s): $2,000

Geographical Preferences

United States Preferences:

Southeast
Southwest

Industry Focus

(% based on actual investment)	
Semiconductors/Other Elect.	51.3%
Industrial/Energy	33.3%
Consumer Related	15.4%

Additional Information

Name of Most Recent Fund: CapSource 2000 Fund, L.P.
Most Recent Fund Was Raised: 12/20/2000
Year Founded: 1997
Capital Under Management: $60,000,000
Current Activity Level: Actively seeking new investments
Method of Compensation: Return on invest. most important, but chg. closing fees, service fees, etc.

CAPSTONE CAPITAL PARTNERS LLC

7160 Chagrin Road
Suite 150
Chagrin Falls, OH USA 44023
Phone: 440-247-3646
Fax: 440-247-3604
E-mail: info@capstonecapitalpartnersllc.com
Website: www.capstonecapitalpartnersllc.com

Management and Staff

Rick Collins, Principal
Terry Morgan, Principal

Type of Firm

Private Equity Firm

Project Preferences

Type of Financing Preferred:
Leveraged Buyout
Turnaround
Acquisition
Distressed Debt
Recapitalizations

Geographical Preferences

United States Preferences:
Midwest
All U.S.

Industry Preferences

In Manufact. prefer:
Manufacturing

Additional Information

Year Founded: 2008
Current Activity Level: Actively seeking new investments

CAPSTONE FINANCIAL PARTNERS, LLC

3475 Lenox Road
Suite 400
Atlanta, GA USA 30326
Phone: 404-238-0550

Other Offices

423 Commonwealth Avenue
Newton Center, MA USA 02459

Management and Staff

Gregory Bartko, Managing General Partner
Teo Forcht Dagi, General Partner

Type of Firm

Private Equity Firm

Project Preferences

Type of Financing Preferred:
Mezzanine

Geographical Preferences

United States Preferences:
All U.S.

Additional Information

Year Founded: 2005
Capital Under Management: $800,000
Current Activity Level: Actively seeking new investments

CAPSTREET GROUP LLC, THE (FKA: SUMMIT CAPITAL GROUP)

600 Travis
Suite 6110
Houston, TX USA 77002
Phone: 713-332-2700
Fax: 713-332-2701
E-mail: info@capstreet.com
Website: www.capstreet.com

Management and Staff

George Kelly, Chairman & CEO
M. Neil Kallmeyer, Partner
Park Durrett, Vice President
Paul De Lisi, Vice President
T. Michael Young, Managing Partner

Type of Firm

Private Equity Firm

Project Preferences

Role in Financing:
Prefer role as deal originator

Type of Financing Preferred:
Leveraged Buyout
Generalist PE
Management Buyouts
Recapitalizations

Size of Investments Considered:
Min Size of Investment Considered (000s): $10,000
Max Size of Investment Considered (000s): $50,000

Geographical Preferences

United States Preferences:
Southeast
All U.S.
Southwest
Texas

Industry Focus

(% based on actual investment)	
Computer Software and Services	31.9%
Internet Specific	16.7%
Other Products	13.9%
Industrial/Energy	11.6%
Consumer Related	9.2%
Communications and Media	6.0%
Biotechnology	6.0%
Semiconductors/Other Elect.	4.7%

Additional Information

Name of Most Recent Fund: CapStreet II, L.P. (FKA: Summit Capital II, L.P.)
Most Recent Fund Was Raised: 03/01/2000
Year Founded: 1990
Capital Under Management: $410,000,000
Current Activity Level: Actively seeking new investments
Method of Compensation: Return on invest. most important, but chg. closing fees, service fees, etc.

CAPVEST MANAGEMENT LTD

100 Pall Mall
London, United Kingdom SW1Y 5NQ
Phone: 44-207-389-7940
Fax: 44-207-389-7901
Website: www.capvest.co.uk

Management and Staff

Alberto Cairo, Principal
Doug Evans, Partner
Kate Briant, Principal
Lemy Gresh, Partner
Randl Shure, Managing Partner
Santiago Corral, Principal
Scott Paton, Partner
Seamus FitzPatrick, Partner
Stephen Mostyn-Williams, Partner

Type of Firm

Private Equity Firm

Project Preferences

Type of Financing Preferred:
Expansion
Mezzanine
Later Stage

Size of Investments Considered:
Min Size of Investment Considered (000s): $13,400
Max Size of Investment Considered: No Limit

Geographical Preferences

International Preferences:
United Kingdom
Europe
Western Europe
Scandanavia/Nordic Region

Industry Preferences

In Communications prefer:
Telecommunications

In Business Serv. prefer:
Services

Additional Information

Name of Most Recent Fund: CapVest Equity Partners II, L.P.
Most Recent Fund Was Raised: 08/25/2006
Year Founded: 1999
Capital Under Management: $50,000,000
Current Activity Level: Actively seeking new investments

CAPVEST VENTURE FUND (FKA: VIRGIN VENTURES FUND LP)

14 South High Street
New Albany, OH USA 43054
Phone: 614-855-9980

Fax: 614-855-9979
Website: www.capvestvc.com

Management and Staff

Jakki Haussler, Partner
Mike Bacevich, Partner
Tony Ragio, Partner

Type of Firm

Private Equity Firm

Project Preferences

Type of Financing Preferred:

Early Stage
Seed
Startup

Geographical Preferences

United States Preferences:

Ohio

Additional Information

Year Founded: 2001
Current Activity Level: Actively seeking new investments

CAPVIS EQUITY PARTNERS AG

Talacker 42
Zurich, Switzerland 8022
Phone: 41-43-300-5858
Fax: 41-43-300-5859
E-mail: info@capvis.com
Website: www.capvis.com

Other Offices

Florianstrasse 8
Kirchheim, Germany 85551
Phone: 49-89-903-4390
Fax: 49-89-9048-0750

21J Huadu Mansion
838 Zhangyang Road
Shanghai, China 200122
Phone: 86-21-5830-1200
Fax: 86-21-5830-1201

Management and Staff

Daniel Flaig, Partner
Rolf Friedli, Partner
Tobias Ursprung, Partner
Yves Dudli, Partner

Type of Firm

Private Equity Firm

Association Membership

Swiss Venture Capital Association (SECA)
European Private Equity and Venture Capital Assoc.

Project Preferences

Role in Financing:

Prefer role as deal originator

Type of Financing Preferred:

Leveraged Buyout
Management Buyouts
Recapitalizations

Size of Investments Considered:

Min Size of Investment Considered (000s): $22,540
Max Size of Investment Considered (000s): $225,395

Geographical Preferences

International Preferences:

Switzerland
Austria
Germany

Industry Preferences

In Communications prefer:

Commercial Communications
Telecommunications
Data Communications

In Computer Software prefer:

Computer Services
Systems Software

In Semiconductor/Electr prefer:

Electronic Components

In Medical/Health prefer:

Medical Diagnostics
Diagnostic Services
Diagnostic Test Products
Medical Therapeutics
Drug/Equipmt Delivery
Other Therapeutic
Disposable Med. Products

In Consumer Related prefer:

Entertainment and Leisure
Retail
Computer Stores
Franchises(NEC)
Food/Beverage
Consumer Products
Consumer Services
Education Related

In Industrial/Energy prefer:

Factory Automation
Machinery
Environmental Related

In Business Serv. prefer:

Distribution
Consulting Services

In Manufact. prefer:

Office Automation Equipmt
Publishing

Additional Information

Year Founded: 1995
Capital Under Management: $1,553,300,000
Current Activity Level: Actively seeking new investments
Method of Compensation: Return on invest. most important, but chg. closing fees, service fees, etc.

CAPYBARA VENTURES LLC

319 Southwest Washington St.
Suite 720
Portland, OR USA 97204
Phone: 503-943-0844
Fax: 503-222-2834
E-mail: info@capybaraventures.com
Website: www.capybaraventures.com

Management and Staff

Eric Rosenfeld, Managing Partner
Robert Ward, Managing Partner

Type of Firm

Private Equity Firm

Project Preferences

Role in Financing:

Prefer role as deal originator but will also invest in deals created by others

Type of Financing Preferred:

Early Stage
Seed

Geographical Preferences

United States Preferences:

Northwest
Oregon

Industry Preferences

In Communications prefer:

Communications and Media
Commercial Communications
Telecommunications
Wireless Communications
Data Communications
Satellite Microwave Comm.
Other Communication Prod.

In Computer Hardware prefer:

Computers
Mini and Personal/Desktop
Computer Graphics and Dig
Integrated Turnkey System
Disk Relat. Memory Device

In Computer Software prefer:

Computer Services
Data Processing
Software
Systems Software
Applications Software
Artificial Intelligence

In Internet Specific prefer:

E-Commerce Technology
Internet
Ecommerce
Web Aggregration/Portals

In Computer Other prefer:
Computer Related

In Semiconductor/Electr prefer:
Electronics
Electronic Components
Semiconductor
Micro-Processing
Controllers and Sensors
Sensors
Circuit Boards
Component Testing Equipmt
Analytic/Scientific
Optoelectronics

In Medical/Health prefer:
Diagnostic Services
Diagnostic Test Products

In Industrial/Energy prefer:
Energy
Industrial Products
Advanced Materials
Superconductivity
Robotics

In Business Serv. prefer:
Media

Additional Information

Name of Most Recent Fund: Capybara Ventures LLC
Most Recent Fund Was Raised: 03/31/2004
Year Founded: 2004
Capital Under Management: $2,000,000
Current Activity Level: Actively seeking new investments
Method of Compensation: Return on investment is of primary concern, do not charge fees

---

CAPZANINE

242, rue de Rivoli
Paris, France 75001
Phone: 33-1-4260-3805
Fax: 33-1-4260-1433
E-mail: contact@capzanine.com
Website: www.capzanine.com

Type of Firm

Private Equity Firm

Association Membership

French Venture Capital Association (AFIC)

Project Preferences

Type of Financing Preferred:
Leveraged Buyout
Expansion
Mezzanine

Geographical Preferences

International Preferences:
Europe
France

Additional Information

Year Founded: 2004
Capital Under Management: $719,100,000
Current Activity Level: Actively seeking new investments

CARDIFF UNIVERSITY

Cardiff
Wales, United Kingdom CF10 3XQ
Phone: 44-29-2087-4000
Website: www.cardiff.ac.uk

Type of Firm

University Program

Project Preferences

Type of Financing Preferred:
Balanced

Geographical Preferences

International Preferences:
Europe

Additional Information

Year Founded: 1999
Current Activity Level: Actively seeking new investments

CARDINAL EQUITY PARTNERS (FKA: CARDINAL VENTURES)

280 East 96th Street
Suite 350
Indianapolis, IN USA 46240
Phone: 317-663-0205
Fax: 317-663-0215
E-mail: info@cardinalep.com
Website: www.cardvent.com

Management and Staff

James Smeltzer, Managing Director
John Ackerman, Managing Director
Peter Munson, Managing Director

Type of Firm

Private Equity Firm

Project Preferences

Type of Financing Preferred:
Leveraged Buyout
Balanced
Management Buyouts
Recapitalizations

Geographical Preferences

United States Preferences:
Midwest

Industry Preferences

In Manufact. prefer:
Manufacturing

Additional Information

Year Founded: 1993
Current Activity Level: Actively seeking new investments

CARDINAL PARTNERS

230 Nassau Street
Princeton, NJ USA 08542
Phone: 609-924-6452
Fax: 609-683-0174
E-mail: info@cardinalpartners.com
Website: www.cardinalpartners.com

Other Offices

1200 Liberty Ridge Drive
Suite 300
Wayne, PA USA 19087
Phone: 610-254-4212
Fax: 610-964-8136

Management and Staff

Brandon Hull, Partner
Charles Hadley, Partner
John Clarke, Managing Partner
Lisa Skeete Tatum, Partner
Thomas McKinley, Partner

Type of Firm

Private Equity Firm

Association Membership

Mid-Atlantic Venture Association
National Venture Capital Association - USA (NVCA)

Project Preferences

Role in Financing:
Will function either as deal originator or investor in deals created by others

Type of Financing Preferred:
Second Stage Financing
Early Stage
Seed
First Stage Financing
Startup

Size of Investments Considered:
Min Size of Investment Considered (000s): $4,000
Max Size of Investment Considered (000s): $15,000

Geographical Preferences

United States Preferences:
All U.S.

Industry Focus

(% based on actual investment)

Medical/Health	30.5%
Biotechnology	16.5%
Computer Software and Services	15.7%

Internet Specific	9.8%
Semiconductors/Other Elect.	8.5%
Computer Hardware	6.8%
Communications and Media	5.2%
Industrial/Energy	3.1%
Consumer Related	2.2%
Other Products	1.7%

Additional Information

Name of Most Recent Fund: CHP III, L.P.
Most Recent Fund Was Raised: 12/05/2006
Year Founded: 1968
Capital Under Management: $400,000,000
Current Activity Level: Actively seeking new investments
Method of Compensation: Return on investment is of primary concern, do not charge fees

CARDINAL VENTURE CAPITAL

1010 El Camino Real
Suite 250
Menlo Park, CA USA 94025
Phone: 650-289-4700
Fax: 650-614-4865
Website: www.cardinalvc.com

Management and Staff

Angela Lee, Chief Financial Officer
Christian Borcher, General Partner
Christopher Hadsell, General Partner
Derek Blazensky, General Partner
Eric Dunn, General Partner

Type of Firm

Private Equity Firm

Association Membership

Western Association of Venture Capitalists (WAVC)
Natl Assoc of Small Bus. Inv. Co (NASBIC)

Project Preferences

Role in Financing:

Will function either as deal originator or investor in deals created by others

Type of Financing Preferred:

Second Stage Financing
Start-up Financing
Later Stage
Seed
First Stage Financing

Size of Investments Considered:

Min Size of Investment Considered (000s): $500
Max Size of Investment Considered (000s): $5,000

Geographical Preferences

United States Preferences:

West Coast

Industry Preferences

In Computer Software prefer:

Software

In Internet Specific prefer:

Internet
Ecommerce

Additional Information

Name of Most Recent Fund: Cardinal Venture Capital
Most Recent Fund Was Raised: 04/14/2000
Year Founded: 2000
Capital Under Management: $126,000,000
Current Activity Level: Actively seeking new investments
Method of Compensation: Return on investment is of primary concern, do not charge fees

CARDO PARTNERS

P.O.Box 1979 Vika
Oslo, Norway N-0125
Phone: 47-24-13-43-60
Fax: 47-24-13-43-61
Website: www.cardopartners.com

Type of Firm

Private Equity Firm

Project Preferences

Type of Financing Preferred:

Turnaround

Additional Information

Current Activity Level: Actively seeking new investments

CARE CAPITAL, LLC

47 Hulfish Street
Suite 310
Princeton, NJ USA 08542
Phone: 609-683-8300
Fax: 609-683-5787
E-mail: info@carecapital.com
Website: www.carecapital.com

Management and Staff

Argeris Karabelas, Partner
Daniel Cabo, Chief Financial Officer
David Ramsay, Partner
Lorenzo Pellegrini, Principal
Richard Markham, Partner
Robert Seltzer, Principal
William Clark, Principal

Type of Firm

Private Equity Firm

Project Preferences

Role in Financing:

Prefer role as deal originator but will also invest in deals created by others

Type of Financing Preferred:

Balanced

Size of Investments Considered:

Min Size of Investment Considered (000s): $5,000
Max Size of Investment Considered (000s): $15,000

Geographical Preferences

International Preferences:

United Kingdom
Luxembourg
Netherlands
Europe
Belgium
Germany
France
Japan

Industry Preferences

In Biotechnology prefer:

Biotechnology
Human Biotechnology
Biotech Related Research

In Medical/Health prefer:

Medical/Health
Diagnostic Test Products
Drug/Equipmt Delivery
Pharmaceuticals

In Industrial/Energy prefer:

Energy

Additional Information

Year Founded: 2000
Capital Under Management: $100,000,000
Current Activity Level: Actively seeking new investments
Method of Compensation: Return on investment is of primary concern, do not charge fees

CARGILL VENTURES

12700 Whitewater Drive
MS 143
Minnetonka, MN USA 55343
Phone: 952-984-3735
Fax: 952-984-3923
Website: www.cargillventures.com

Other Offices

15407 McGinty Road West
MS 68
Wayzata, MN USA 55391
Phone: 952-742-2178
Fax: 952-742-2992

Management and Staff

Anne Pedrero, Principal
David Patchen, Managing Director

Deepak Malik, Managing Director
James Sayre, President
Jonathan Tsou, Principal
Mike Muston, Venture Partner
Monica Morse, Managing Director
Sanjiv Arora, Principal

Type of Firm

Corporate PE/Venture

Association Membership

National Venture Capital Association - USA (NVCA)

Project Preferences

Role in Financing:

Prefer role in deals created by others

Type of Financing Preferred:

Second Stage Financing
Early Stage
First Stage Financing

Size of Investments Considered:

Min Size of Investment Considered (000s): $1,000
Max Size of Investment Considered (000s): $10,000

Geographical Preferences

Canadian Preferences:

All Canada

International Preferences:

Italy
India
United Kingdom
Latin America
Luxembourg
Netherlands
Portugal
China
Hong Kong
Spain
Belgium
Germany
France
Japan

Industry Preferences

In Communications prefer:

Wireless Communications

In Computer Software prefer:

Software

In Internet Specific prefer:

Internet
Ecommerce
Web Aggregration/Portals

In Semiconductor/Electr prefer:

Electronics

In Biotechnology prefer:

Biotechnology
Agricultural/Animal Bio.

In Medical/Health prefer:

Medical/Health

In Industrial/Energy prefer:

Advanced Materials

Additional Information

Year Founded: 1999
Current Activity Level: Actively seeking new investments
Method of Compensation: Return on investment is of primary concern, do not charge fees

---

CARIBBEAN DEVELOPMENT CAPITAL, LTD. (AKA: DEVCAP)

Ten Cipriani Boulevard
Port-of-Spain, Trinidad/Tob.
Phone: 868-623-4665
Fax: 868-623-3563
Website: www.devcapital.net

Management and Staff

Gerard Pemberton, CEO & Managing Director

Type of Firm

Private Equity Firm

Project Preferences

Type of Financing Preferred:

Balanced

Geographical Preferences

International Preferences:

Aruba
St Lucia
Grenada
Trinidad/Tob.
Guyana
Surinam

Industry Preferences

In Medical/Health prefer:

Health Services

In Consumer Related prefer:

Education Related

In Manufact. prefer:

Manufacturing

In Agr/Forestr/Fish prefer:

Agribusiness

Additional Information

Year Founded: 1988
Current Activity Level: Actively seeking new investments

CARIBBEAN EQUITY PARTNERS LIMITED

2nd Floor Kingston 5
Eight Dominica Drive
Kingston, Jamaica
Phone: 876-906-3372
Fax: 876-754-5875
E-mail: info@caribequity.com
Website: www.caribequity.com

Management and Staff

David Panton, Managing Director
Jeffrey Hall, Managing Director
Nigel Clarke, Managing Director

Type of Firm

Private Equity Firm

Project Preferences

Type of Financing Preferred:

Generalist PE
Balanced

Geographical Preferences

International Preferences:

Latin America

Additional Information

Year Founded: 2004
Current Activity Level: Actively seeking new investments

CARIS, LTD.

5215 North O'Connor Blvd.
Suite 2650
Irving, TX USA 75039
Phone: 972-590-2100
Fax: 972-590-2103
E-mail: info@carisltd.com
Website: www.carisltd.com

Management and Staff

Laurie Johansen, Partner
Leslie Shaffer, Chief Financial Officer
Steve Houk, Partner

Type of Firm

Private Equity Firm

Project Preferences

Type of Financing Preferred:

Leveraged Buyout
Turnaround
Recapitalizations

Size of Investments Considered:

Min Size of Investment Considered (000s): $10,000
Max Size of Investment Considered (000s): $100,000

Additional Information

Year Founded: 2004
Capital Under Management: $350,000,000
Current Activity Level: Actively seeking new investments

CARLYLE GROUP, THE

1001 Pennsylvania Avenue, NW
Suite 220 South
Washington, DC USA 20004
Phone: 202-729-5626
Fax: 202-347-1818
Website: www.carlyle.com

Other Offices

Piazza Cavour 2
Milan, Italy 20121
Phone: 39-2-620-0461
Fax: 39-2-2901-3559

112, Avenue Kleber
Paris, France 75116
Phone: 331-5370-3520
Fax: 331-5370-3530

Shin-Marunouchi Building
1-5-1 Marunouchi, Chiyoda-ku
Tokyo, Japan 100-6535
Phone: 813-5208-4350
Fax: 813-5208-4351

Senckenberganlage 16
Frankfurt, Germany 60325
Phone: 49-69-5050-6570
Fax: 49-69-5050-65765

128 South Tryon Street
Charlotte, NC USA 28202
Phone: 704-632-0200
Fax: 704-632-0299

Cornish El Nil - Boulaq
Nile City Towers, South Tower
Cairo, Egypt 11221
Phone: 202-2461-8100
Fax: 202-2461-8110

11100 Santa Monica Boulevard
Los Angeles, CA USA 90025
Phone: 310-575-1700
Fax: 310-575-1740

Gagnam Finance Center
Yeoksam I-dong, Gangnam-gu
Seoul, South Korea 135-984
Phone: 822-2112-1900
Fax: 822-2112-1899

Intl. Financial Centre, Precinct Bldg. 3
Level 7 East, P.O. Box 506564
Dubai, Utd. Arab Em.
Phone: 971-4-427-5600
Fax: 971-4-427-5610
Promenadeplatz 8
Munich, Germany D-80333
Phone: 49-89-2444-600
Fax: 49-89-2444-60460

264 George Street
Sydney, Australia 2000
Phone: 61-2-9270-3500
Fax: 61-2-9270-3520

2, Avenue Charles de Gaulle
Luxembourg, Luxembourg L-1653
Phone: 352-2686-2200
Fax: 352-2686-2110

South Office Tower, Beijing Kerry Centre
No.1 Guang Hua Road, Chaoyang District
Beijing, China 100020
Phone: 86-10-8529-8823
Fax: 86-10-8529-9877

Buyukdere Cad.
Yapi Kredi Plaza, B Blok
Istanbul, Turkey 34330
Phone: 90-212-385-9800
Fax: 90-212-385-9898

Pau Casals, 13
Barcelona, Spain 08021
Phone: 34-93-200-0906
Fax: 34-93-209-3510

1 Temasek Avenue
Millenia Tower
Singapore, Singapore 039192
Phone: 65-6212-9600
Fax: 65-6212-9620

Montes Urales, Suite 720
Colonia Lomas de Chapultepec
Mexico, Mexico 11000
Phone: 52-55-524-98020
Fax: 52-55-524-98030

Avenue Brigadeiro Faria Lima, 3900
Sao Paolo, Brazil 04538
Phone: 55-11-3568-7700
Fax: 55-11-3568-7750

Kungsgatan 30
Stockholm, Sweden 11135
Phone: 46-8-510-69600
Fax: 46-8-510-69610
2 Pacific Place
88 Queensway
Hong Kong, Hong Kong
Phone: 852-2878-7000
Fax: 852-2878-7007

520 Madison Avenue
New York, NY USA 10022
Phone: 212-381-4900
Fax: 212-381-4901

12 Yoido-dong Youngdeungpo-gu
CCMM Building
Seoul, South Korea 150-869
Phone: 822-2004-8400
Fax: 822-2004-8440

Plaza 66 1266 Nan Jing Xi Road
Nanjing District
Shanghai, China
Phone: 86-21-6103-3200
Fax: 86-21-6103-3210

Quadrant A The IL&FS Financial Centre
Bandra-Kurla Complex
Mumbai, India 400 051
Phone: 91-22-6647-0800
Fax: 91-22-6647-0803

1050 17th Street
Suite 1875
Denver, CO USA 80265
Phone: 303-405-8300
Fax: 303-405-8310

57 Berkeley Square
Lansdowne House
London, United Kingdom W1J 6ER
Phone: 44-20-7894-1200
Fax: 44-20-7894-1600

Calle Alcala 73
Madrid, Spain 28001
Phone: 34-91-432-9555
Fax: 34-91-432-9570

Al Moutran Street
Building 142 Marfaa
Beirut, Lebanon 20127106
Phone: 961-197-2701
Fax: 961-197-2760

Management and Staff

A. Reed Deupree, Vice President
Aaron Benway, Vice President
Adam Buchwald, Vice President
Adam Palmer, Managing Director
Allan Holt, Managing Director
Andrea Pekala, Vice President
Andrew Marino, Principal
Andrew Burgess, Managing Director
Andrew Chung, Principal
Anita Balaji, Vice President
Barbara Murphy, Principal
Barry Gold, Managing Director
Benoit Colas, Managing Director
Brett Wyard, Managing Director
Brian Bernasek, Principal
Brian Hayhurst, Managing Director
Brian Canann, Vice President
Brooke Coburn, Managing Director
Bruce Rosenblum, Managing Director
Bryan Corbett, Principal
Bryan Lin, Principal
Campbell Dyer, Principal
Can Deldag, Managing Director
Carolyn Weimer, Principal
Catherine Ziobro, Principal
Catherine Simoni, Managing Director
Chip Lippman, Managing Director
Christopher Finn, Managing Director
Claudius Watts, Managing Director
Colin Atkins, Managing Director
Curt Buser, Managing Director
Daisuke Takatsuki, Principal

Dan Pryor, Managing Director
Daniel Akerson, Managing Director
Daniel D Aniello, Founder
David Daniel, Managing Director
David Roth, Managing Director
David Fitzgerald, Managing Director
David Kingery, Principal
David Willich, Principal
David Tung, Managing Director
David Rubenstein, Founder
Debra Pedersen, Managing Director
Devinjit Singh, Managing Director
Eduardo Machado, Managing Director
Edward Samek, Principal
Edward Mathias, Managing Director
Eric Sasson, Managing Director
Erica Herberg, Principal
Feng Xiao, Managing Director
Firas Nasir, Managing Director
Francis Finelli, Managing Director
Franck Falezan, Managing Director
Frazer Burkart, Principal
Gary Bleiberg, Managing Director
Geoff Blades, Vice President
Gerardo Ruiz, Principal
Glenn Youngkin, Managing Director
Glori Holzman-Graziano, Managing Director
Gregor Bohm, Managing Director
Gregory Zeluck, Managing Director
Gregory Ledford, Managing Director
Guido Audagna, Managing Director
Han Chen, Managing Director
Harry Alverson, Managing Director
Hassan El-Khatib, Managing Director
Hayden Jones, Principal
Herman Chang, Managing Director
Ian Fujiyama, Managing Director
James Burr, Managing Director
James McGee, Managing Director
James Williams, Principal
James Attwood, Managing Director
James Kim, Managing Director
James Shevlet, Managing Director
Janine Feng, Managing Director
Jason Lee, Managing Director
Jean-Pierre Millet, Managing Director
Jeff Ferguson, Managing Director
Jeremy Anderson, Principal
Joaquin Avila, Managing Director
John Flaherty, Principal
Jonathan Colby, Managing Director
Jonathan Bylin, Managing Director
Karen Bechtel, Managing Director
Kazuhiro Yamada, Managing Director
Keith Taylor, Principal
Ken Tidwell, Managing Director
Lauren Dillard, Principal
Lee Landrum, Principal
Lee Carson, Managing Director
Leo Helmers, Managing Director
Leslie Eglin, Principal
Linda Pace, Managing Director
Lori Sabet, Managing Director
Maki Mitsui, Managing Director
Marco De Benedetti, Managing Director
Mark Alter, Managing Director
Mark Johnson, Principal
Mark Schoenfeld, Managing Director
Masao Hirano, Managing Director
Masato Marumo, Managing Director
Matthew Stanczuk, Principal
Michael Hadley, Vice President
Michael Wand, Managing Director
Michael Zupon, Managing Director
Michael Gershenson, Principal
Michael Stewart, Managing Director
Mike Ramsay, Managing Director
Nicholas Shao, Managing Director
Norbert Reis, Managing Director
Olivier Sarkozy, Managing Director
Pam Bentley, Principal
Patrick Siewert, Managing Director
Paul Bagatelas, Managing Director
Pauline Brown, Managing Director
Pedro De Esteban, Managing Director
Peter Clare, Managing Director
Peter Nachtwey, Chief Financial Officer
Raymond Whiteman, Managing Director
Raymond Albright, Principal
Richard Chang, Principal
Rio Minami, Managing Director
Robert Stuckey, Managing Director
Robert Dove, Managing Director
Robert Hodges, Managing Director
Robert Brown, Managing Director
Robert Easton, Managing Director
Rodrigo Fonseca, Principal
Russell Farscht, Vice President
Ryan Schwarz, Managing Director
Sam Block, Principal
Sameer Bhargava, Principal
Sandra Horbach, Managing Director
Sang Pil Park, Principal
Satoru Hayashi, Managing Director
Sean He, Managing Director
Shankar Narayanan, Managing Director
Shary Moalemzadeh, Principal
Simon Moore, Managing Director
Stephen Wise, Principal
Stephen Bailey, Managing Director
Takaomi Tomioka, Managing Director
Tamotsu Adachi, Managing Director
Thaddeus Paul, Principal
Thomas Fousse, Managing Director
Thomas Garrigan, Principal
Thomas Lindstrom, Managing Director
Thomas Ray, Managing Director
Todd Newnam, Managing Director
Vipul Amin, Vice President
Wael Bayazid, Managing Director
William Kennard, Managing Director
William Darman, Vice President
William Allen, Vice President
William Conway, Founder
Wolfgang Hanrieder, Managing Director
Wulf Meinel, Managing Director
Xiang-Dong Yang, Managing Director
Yasushi Kamei, Vice President
Yi Luo, Managing Director

Type of Firm

Private Equity Firm

Association Membership

Italian Venture Capital Association (AIFI)
Mid-Atlantic Venture Association
National Venture Capital Association - USA (NVCA)
Singapore Venture Capital Association (SVCA)
European Private Equity and Venture Capital Assoc.
Private Equity Council (PEC)
Spanish Venture Capital Association (ASCRI)
Indian Venture Capital Association (IVCA)

Project Preferences

Role in Financing:

Prefer role as deal originator but will also invest in deals created by others

Type of Financing Preferred:

Leveraged Buyout
Control-block Purchases
Early Stage
Expansion
Mezzanine
Generalist PE
Balanced
Later Stage
Other
Seed
Management Buyouts
Strategic Alliances
Acquisition
Distressed Debt

Size of Investments Considered:

Min Size of Investment Considered (000s): $10,000
Max Size of Investment Considered: No Limit

Geographical Preferences

United States Preferences:

All U.S.

Canadian Preferences:

All Canada

International Preferences:

Italy
Bahrain
India
Tunisia
United Kingdom
Jordan
Qatar
Taiwan
Europe
China
Egypt
Hong Kong
Lebanon
Utd. Arab Em.
Western Europe
Algeria
Mexico
Middle East
Saudi Arabia
Spain
Scandanavia/Nordic Region

South Africa
Morocco
Korea, South
Germany
Asia
Africa
France
Japan
Kuwait
Libya
All International

Industry Focus

(% based on actual investment)

Other Products	33.0%
Medical/Health	18.9%
Industrial/Energy	15.9%
Communications and Media	10.5%
Consumer Related	8.1%
Semiconductors/Other Elect.	5.4%
Computer Software and Services	3.4%
Computer Hardware	2.4%
Internet Specific	2.2%
Biotechnology	0.1%

Additional Information

Name of Most Recent Fund: Carlyle Asia Growth Partners IV, L.P.
Most Recent Fund Was Raised: 06/24/2008
Year Founded: 1987
Capital Under Management: $91,521,000,000
Current Activity Level: Actively seeking new investments
Method of Compensation: Return on invest. most important, but chg. closing fees, service fees, etc.

CARMEL CAPITAL MANAGEMENT

26350 Carmel Rancho Lane
Suite 225
Carmel, CA USA 93923
Phone: 831-625-1375
Fax: 831-325-6493
Website: www.carmelcapital.com

Management and Staff

West Whittaker, President

Type of Firm

Private Equity Firm

Additional Information

Year Founded: 2009
Current Activity Level: Actively seeking new investments

CARMEL VENTURES

16 Abba Eban Avenue
Herzeliya, Israel 46725
Phone: 972-9-9720-400
Fax: 971-9-9720-401
E-mail: contacts@carmelventures.com
Website: www.carmelventures.com

Other Offices

Possartstrasse 9
Munich, Germany D-81679
Phone: 49-89-457-69780
Fax: 49-89-457-6978-98

Management and Staff

Amit Frenkel, General Partner
Asher Kutner, Venture Partner
Avi Zeevi, General Partner
Benny Levin, Venture Partner
Dana Gross, Venture Partner
Doron Inbar, Venture Partner
Gilad De Vries, Principal
Harel Beit-On, General Partner
Isaac Applbaum, Venture Partner
Itzik Avidor, Partner
Ori Bendori, General Partner
Rina Shainski, General Partner
Ron Berman, Principal
Ronen Nir, Partner
Shlomo Dovrat, General Partner
Tomer Michaeli, Principal
Walter Grassl, General Partner

Type of Firm

Private Equity Firm

Association Membership

Israel Venture Association

Project Preferences

Type of Financing Preferred:

Early Stage
Balanced
Seed

Geographical Preferences

United States Preferences:

All U.S.

International Preferences:

Europe
Israel

Industry Preferences

In Communications prefer:

Communications and Media
Wireless Communications

In Computer Software prefer:

Software

In Internet Specific prefer:

Internet

In Semiconductor/Electr prefer:

Semiconductor

Additional Information

Name of Most Recent Fund: Carmel Ventures II
Most Recent Fund Was Raised: 05/03/2005
Year Founded: 2000
Capital Under Management: $170,000,000
Current Activity Level: Actively seeking new investments

CARNEGIE FUND

20 West 55th Street
New York, NY USA 10019
Phone: 212-262-5800
Website: www.carnegieinc.com

Type of Firm

Private Equity Firm

Additional Information

Year Founded: 1803
Current Activity Level: Actively seeking new investments

CAROUSEL CAPITAL PARTNERS

201 North Tryon Street
Suite 2450
Charlotte, NC USA 28202
Phone: 704-372-2040
Fax: 704-372-1040
E-mail: whobbs@carouselcapital.com
Website: www.carouselcap.com

Management and Staff

Brian Bailey, Managing Director
Charles Grigg, Partner
Erskine Bowles, Managing Director
Jason Schmidly, Partner
Joseph Pitt, Vice President
Nelson Schwab, Managing Director
William Hobbs, Partner

Type of Firm

Private Equity Firm

Project Preferences

Role in Financing:

Will function either as deal originator or investor in deals created by others

Type of Financing Preferred:

Leveraged Buyout
Expansion
Later Stage
Recapitalizations

Size of Investments Considered:

Min Size of Investment Considered (000s): $10,000
Max Size of Investment Considered (000s): $20,000

Geographical Preferences

United States Preferences:

Southeast

Industry Focus

(% based on actual investment)

Other Products	40.0%
Communications and Media	33.7%
Medical/Health	11.8%
Industrial/Energy	5.9%
Internet Specific	5.4%
Computer Software and Services	2.8%
Consumer Related	0.3%

Additional Information

Name of Most Recent Fund: Carousel Capital Partners III, L.P.
Most Recent Fund Was Raised: 02/13/2006
Year Founded: 1996
Capital Under Management: $300,000,000
Current Activity Level: Actively seeking new investments
Method of Compensation: Return on invest. most important, but chg. closing fees, service fees, etc.

CARROT CAPITAL LLC

140 West 57th Street
Suite 3B
New York, NY USA 10019
Phone: 212-586-2226
Fax: 212-586-2246
E-mail: info@carrotcapital.com
Website: www.carrotcapital.com

Management and Staff

David Geliebter, Managing Partner

Type of Firm

Private Equity Firm

Project Preferences

Role in Financing:

Prefer role as deal originator but will also invest in deals created by others

Type of Financing Preferred:

Early Stage
Seed
Startup

Size of Investments Considered:

Min Size of Investment Considered (000s): $50
Max Size of Investment Considered (000s): $1,000

Geographical Preferences

Canadian Preferences:

All Canada

Industry Preferences

In Communications prefer:

Telecommunications
Wireless Communications
Data Communications
Satellite Microwave Comm.
Other Communication Prod.

In Computer Hardware prefer:

Mainframes / Scientific
Mini and Personal/Desktop
Computer Graphics and Dig
Disk Relat. Memory Device

In Computer Software prefer:

Data Processing
Systems Software
Artificial Intelligence

In Semiconductor/Electr prefer:

Electronic Components
Semiconductor
Micro-Processing
Controllers and Sensors
Sensors
Circuit Boards
Component Testing Equipmt
Laser Related
Fiber Optics
Analytic/Scientific
Optoelectronics

In Biotechnology prefer:

Human Biotechnology
Genetic Engineering
Agricultural/Animal Bio.
Biosensors
Biotech Related Research

In Medical/Health prefer:

Medical Diagnostics
Diagnostic Test Products
Medical Therapeutics
Drug/Equipmt Delivery
Medical Products
Disposable Med. Products
Pharmaceuticals

In Industrial/Energy prefer:

Industrial Products
Robotics
Machinery

Additional Information

Year Founded: 2001
Capital Under Management: $5,000,000
Current Activity Level: Actively seeking new investments
Method of Compensation: Function primarily in service area, receive contingent fee in cash or equity

---

CARTESIAN CAPITAL GROUP, LLC

505 Fifth Avenue
15th Floor
New York, NY USA 10017
Phone: 212-461-6363
Fax: 212-461-6366
Website: www.cartesiangroup.com

Management and Staff

Geoffrey Hamlin, Partner
Paul Pizzani, Partner
Peter Yu, Managing Partner
Tom Armstrong, Partner
William Jarosz, Partner

Type of Firm

Private Equity Firm

Project Preferences

Type of Financing Preferred:

Leveraged Buyout

Geographical Preferences

United States Preferences:

All U.S.

Additional Information

Year Founded: 2005
Capital Under Management: $1,050,000,000
Current Activity Level: Actively seeking new investments

CARVEST (AKA: CREDIT AGRICOLE REGIONS INVESTISSEMENT)

25 rue Libergier
Reims, France 51100
Phone: 33-3-2683-3050
Fax: 33-3-2683-3554
E-mail: contact@carvest.fr
Website: www.carvest.fr

Management and Staff

Bernard Mary, President

Type of Firm

Bank Affiliated

Association Membership

French Venture Capital Association (AFIC)

Project Preferences

Type of Financing Preferred:

Leveraged Buyout
Expansion
Balanced

Geographical Preferences

International Preferences:

Europe
France

Additional Information

Year Founded: 2004
Current Activity Level: Actively seeking new investments

CAS CAPITAL, INC.

5F Parkside House
2 Ichibancho, Chiyoda-ku
Tokyo, Japan 102-0082
Phone: 81-3-3556-5990
Fax: 81-3-3556-5731
E-mail: cc@cascapital.com
Website: www.cascapital.com

Other Offices

NM Plaza Midosuji
3-6-3 Awajimachi, Chuo-ku
Osaka-shi, Japan 541-0047
Phone: 81-6-4706-5026

Unit 1505, Azia Center,
1233 Lujiazui Ring Road,
Shanghai, China 200120
Phone: 86-21-6160-8200

12F
No.100,Minsheng E. Road
Taipei City, Taiwan 105
Phone: 886-2-8712-3200

15F-4
No.101,Sec.1, Zihyou Rd.,
Taichung, Taiwan 403
Phone: 886-7-241-1800

17F Philam Life Tower,
8767 Paseo de Roxas,
Makati City, Manila, Philippines 1226
Phone: 63-2-856-0888

Management and Staff

Kazuyoshi Komiya, Partner
Nobukazu Sawamura, Managing Partner
Yasuji Kibayashi, Managing Partner

Type of Firm

Private Equity Firm

Project Preferences

Role in Financing:

Unknown

Type of Financing Preferred:

Leveraged Buyout

Geographical Preferences

International Preferences:

Japan

Industry Preferences

In Consumer Related prefer:

Food/Beverage

Additional Information

Year Founded: 2003
Current Activity Level: Actively seeking new investments

CASCADIA CAPITAL LLC

701 Fifth Avenue
Suite 2600
Seattle, WA USA 98104
Phone: 206-436-2500
Fax: 206-436-2501
E-mail: info@cascadiacapital.com
Website: www.cascadiacapital.com

Other Offices

9100 East Panorama Drive
Suite 350
Englewood, CO USA 80112
Phone: 720-212-0554
Fax: 303-645-0501

1230 Avenue of the Americas
7th Floor
New York, NY USA 10020
Phone: 917-639-4160
Fax: 917-639-4159

Management and Staff

Boyd Boyd, Vice President
Christian Schiller, Managing Director
Jonathan Roth, Vice President
Michael Butler, Chairman & CEO
Michael Maruhashi, Vice President
Tom Newell, Managing Director
Warren Gouk, Managing Director

Type of Firm

Bank Affiliated

Project Preferences

Role in Financing:

Prefer role as deal originator

Type of Financing Preferred:

First Stage Financing

Size of Investments Considered:

Min Size of Investment Considered (000s): $100
Max Size of Investment Considered (000s): $1,000

Geographical Preferences

United States Preferences:

Northwest
Colorado

Canadian Preferences:

British Columbia

Industry Preferences

In Communications prefer:

Communications and Media

In Internet Specific prefer:

Internet

In Semiconductor/Electr prefer:

Electronics

In Consumer Related prefer:

Consumer
Retail

In Industrial/Energy prefer:

Industrial Products

In Transportation prefer:

Transportation

In Business Serv. prefer:

Distribution

In Manufact. prefer:

Manufacturing

Additional Information

Year Founded: 1999
Capital Under Management: $10,500,000
Current Activity Level: Actively seeking new investments
Method of Compensation: Return on investment is of primary concern, do not charge fees

---

CASE TECHNOLOGY VENTURES

10900 Euclid Avenue
Adelbert Hall, Suite 203
Cleveland, OH USA 44106
Phone: 216-368-6124
E-mail: techventures@case.edu
Website: www.ora.ra.cwru.edu/ctv/

Management and Staff

Mark Coticchia, Managing Director

Type of Firm

University Program

Project Preferences

Type of Financing Preferred:

Early Stage
Seed
Startup

Size of Investments Considered:

Min Size of Investment Considered (000s): $50
Max Size of Investment Considered (000s): $250

Geographical Preferences

United States Preferences:

Ohio
All U.S.

Additional Information

Year Founded: 2002
Current Activity Level: Actively seeking new investments

CASPIAN ADVISORS PVT. LTD.

3rd Floor, 8-2-596/5/B/1
Road No:10, Banjara Hills
Hyderabad, India 500034
Phone: 91-40-6646-0505
Fax: 91-40-6646-5884
E-mail: info@caspian.in
Website: www.caspianadvisors.com

Other Offices

Level 4, Augusta Point
Sector 53, Golf Course Road
Gurgaon, India 122002
Phone: 91-124-435-4021
Fax: 91-124-435-4021

Management and Staff

R. Venkatram Reddy, Principal
S.Vishwanatha Prasad, Managing Director
Shilpa Sudhakar, Principal

Type of Firm

Private Equity Firm

Project Preferences

Type of Financing Preferred:

Balanced

Geographical Preferences

International Preferences:

India

Industry Preferences

In Financial Services prefer:

Financial Services

Additional Information

Year Founded: 2004
Capital Under Management: $58,000,000
Current Activity Level: Actively seeking new investments

CASSELS BROCK LAWYERS

2100 Scotia Plaza
40 King Street West
Toronto, Canada M5H3C2
Phone: 416-869-5300
Fax: 416-360-8877
E-mail: postmaster@casselsbrock.com
Website: www.casselsbrock.com

Management and Staff

Lori Prokopich, Partner

Type of Firm

Private Equity Firm

Additional Information

Year Founded: 2009
Current Activity Level: Actively seeking new investments

CASTANEA PARTNERS

Three Newton Executive Park
Suite 304
Newton, MA USA 02462
Phone: 617-630-2400
Fax: 617-630-2424
E-mail: info@castaneapartners.com
Website: www.castaneapartners.com

Management and Staff

Adam Garcia Eveloff, Principal
Andrew Collina, Principal
Brian Knez, Managing Partner
Colleen Love, Chief Financial Officer
David Flaschen, Partner
Juan Marcos Hill, Principal
Paul Gibbons, Partner
Robert Smith, Managing Partner
Steven Berg, Partner
Suzanne Obenshain, Principal
Troy Stanfield, Partner

Type of Firm

Private Equity Firm

Project Preferences

Role in Financing:

Prefer role as deal originator but will also invest in deals created by others

Type of Financing Preferred:

Leveraged Buyout
Generalist PE
Turnaround
Management Buyouts
Acquisition
Industry Rollups
Special Situation
Recapitalizations

Size of Investments Considered:

Min Size of Investment Considered (000s): $10,000
Max Size of Investment Considered (000s): $20,000

Geographical Preferences

United States Preferences:

All U.S.

Industry Preferences

In Consumer Related prefer:

Retail
Food/Beverage
Consumer Products
Education Related

In Business Serv. prefer:

Services

In Manufact. prefer:

Publishing

Additional Information

Name of Most Recent Fund: Castanea Partners Fund II
Most Recent Fund Was Raised: 05/26/2004
Year Founded: 2001
Capital Under Management: $207,000,000
Current Activity Level: Actively seeking new investments
Method of Compensation: Return on investment is of primary concern, do not charge fees

---

CASTILE VENTURES

930 Winter Street
Suite 500
North Waltham, MA USA 02451
Phone: 781-890-0060
Fax: 781-890-0065
Website: www.castileventures.com

Management and Staff

Carl Stjernfeldt, General Partner
Jason King, Chief Financial Officer
Nina Saberi, Managing General Partner
Roger Walton, General Partner
Skip Besthoff, General Partner

Type of Firm

Private Equity Firm

Association Membership

National Venture Capital Association - USA (NVCA)

Project Preferences

Role in Financing:

Prefer role as deal originator but will also invest in deals created by others

Type of Financing Preferred:

Early Stage
Seed

Size of Investments Considered:

Min Size of Investment Considered (000s): $1,000
Max Size of Investment Considered (000s): $10,000

Geographical Preferences

United States Preferences:

Mid Atlantic
Northeast

Industry Preferences

In Communications prefer:

Communications and Media
Telecommunications
Data Communications

In Computer Software prefer:

Software

In Internet Specific prefer:

Internet

Additional Information

Name of Most Recent Fund: Castile Ventures III, L.P.
Most Recent Fund Was Raised: 01/10/2006
Year Founded: 1998
Capital Under Management: $200,000,000
Current Activity Level: Actively seeking new investments
Method of Compensation: Return on investment is of primary concern, do not charge fees

---

CASTLE CREEK CAPITAL LLC

6051 El Tordo
Rancho Santa Fe, CA USA 92067
Phone: 858-756-8300
Fax: 858-756-8301
E-mail: accountinfo@castlecreek.com
Website: www.castlecreek.com

Management and Staff

David Volk, Vice President
J. Mikesell Thomas, Principal
John Pietrzak, Vice President
William Black, Vice President
William Moody, Chief Financial Officer

Type of Firm

Private Equity Firm

Project Preferences

Type of Financing Preferred:

Leveraged Buyout
Turnaround
Acquisition
Recapitalizations

Geographical Preferences

United States Preferences:

All U.S.

Industry Preferences

In Financial Services prefer:

Financial Services

Additional Information

Name of Most Recent Fund: Castle Creek Capital Partners Fund III, L.P.
Most Recent Fund Was Raised: 01/03/2006
Year Founded: 1996
Capital Under Management: $225,700,000
Current Activity Level: Actively seeking new investments

CASTLE HARLAN, INC.

150 East 58th Street
37th Floor
New York, NY USA 10155
Phone: 212-644-8600
Fax: 212-207-8042
E-mail: info@castleharlan.com
Website: www.castleharlan.com

Management and Staff

David Pittaway, Senior Managing Director
Howard Morgan, Senior Managing Director
John Morningstar, Vice President
Justin Wender, President
Marcel Fournier, Senior Managing Director
Robert Wages, Managing Director
Thomas Hickey, Managing Director
William Pruellage, Managing Director

Type of Firm

Private Equity Firm

Project Preferences

Type of Financing Preferred:

Leveraged Buyout
Management Buyouts

Geographical Preferences

International Preferences:

Australia
New Zealand

Industry Focus

(% based on actual investment)

Consumer Related	62.5%
Other Products	29.8%
Industrial/Energy	6.5%
Communications and Media	1.2%

Additional Information

Name of Most Recent Fund: Castle Harlan Partners IV, L.P.
Most Recent Fund Was Raised: 05/16/2002
Year Founded: 1987
Capital Under Management: $2,338,000,000
Current Activity Level: Actively seeking new investments

CASTLETOP CAPITAL

5000 Plaza On The Lake
Suite 170
Austin, TX USA 78746
Phone: 512-329-6600
E-mail: info@castletopcapital.com
Website: www.castletopcapital.com

Management and Staff

Alan Topfer, Managing Director
Morton Topfer, Managing Director
Richard Topfer, Managing Director

Type of Firm

Private Equity Firm

Project Preferences

Role in Financing:

Will function either as deal originator or investor in deals created by others

Type of Financing Preferred:

Second Stage Financing
Early Stage
Turnaround

Size of Investments Considered:

Min Size of Investment Considered (000s): $2,000
Max Size of Investment Considered (000s): $5,000

Geographical Preferences

United States Preferences:

Texas

Industry Preferences

In Communications prefer:

Wireless Communications

In Computer Software prefer:

Software
Systems Software
Applications Software

In Semiconductor/Electr prefer:

Sensors

In Medical/Health prefer:

Medical Diagnostics
Diagnostic Services
Diagnostic Test Products

In Financial Services prefer:

Real Estate

Additional Information

Name of Most Recent Fund: Castletop Capital Fund I
Most Recent Fund Was Raised: 12/31/2001
Year Founded: 2000
Capital Under Management: $63,000,000
Current Activity Level: Actively seeking new investments
Method of Compensation: Return on investment is of primary concern, do not charge fees

---

CAT SEED A/S

Frederiksborgvej 399
Roskilde, Denmark 4000
Phone: 45-4677-5919
Fax: 45-730-9100
E-mail: cat@catscience.dk
Website: www.catscience.dk

Type of Firm

Private Equity Firm

Project Preferences

Type of Financing Preferred:

Balanced

Additional Information

Year Founded: 2007
Current Activity Level: Actively seeking new investments

CATALANA D INICIATIVES CR SA

Passeig de Gracia 2, 2n 2B
Barcelona, Spain 08007
Phone: 34-93-317-8161
Fax: 34-93-318-9287
E-mail: catalana@iniciatives.es
Website: www.iniciatives.es

Other Offices

Velazquez 17, 3r esquerra
Madrid, Spain 28001
Phone: 34-91-426-0303
Fax: 34-91-426-0304

Management and Staff

Francesc Raventos, Chief Executive Officer
Joan Carbonell, General Director
Manuel Albanell, General Director

Type of Firm

Private Equity Firm

Association Membership

European Private Equity and Venture Capital Assoc.
Spanish Venture Capital Association (ASCRI)

Project Preferences

Type of Financing Preferred:
Leveraged Buyout
Early Stage
Startup

Size of Investments Considered:
Min Size of Investment Considered (000s): $1,500
Max Size of Investment Considered: No Limit

Geographical Preferences

International Preferences:
Latin America
Spain

Additional Information

Year Founded: 1993
Capital Under Management: $88,300,000
Current Activity Level: Actively seeking new investments

CATALYST CAPITAL MANAGMENT

549 West Randolph
Suite 430
Chicago, IL USA 60661
Phone: 312-441-9590
Website: www.catalyst-cap.com

Management and Staff

Bruce Quade, Partner
Michael Mikolajczyk, Partner

Type of Firm

Private Equity Firm

Project Preferences

Role in Financing:
Prefer role in deals created by others

Type of Financing Preferred:
Early Stage

Geographical Preferences

United States Preferences:
Midwest

Industry Preferences

In Medical/Health prefer:
Medical/Health

In Business Serv. prefer:
Services

Additional Information

Year Founded: 2001
Current Activity Level: Actively seeking new investments

CATALYST EQUITY GROUP LLC

One Compound Drive
Hutchinson, KS USA 67502
Phone: 620-663-1127
Fax: 877-349-6902
Website: www.catalystequitygroup.com

Management and Staff

John Claxton, Chief Financial Officer
Robert Green, Chief Executive Officer
Robert Brown, Partner

Type of Firm

Private Equity Firm

Project Preferences

Type of Financing Preferred:
Acquisition

Additional Information

Year Founded: 2000
Current Activity Level: Actively seeking new investments

CATALYST HEALTH AND TECHNOLOGY PARTNERS LLC

One Gateway Center
Suite 312
Newton, MA USA 02458
Phone: 617-964-3100
Fax: 617-964-8887
E-mail: info@catalystpartners.com
Website: www.catalystpartners.com

Management and Staff

David Hendren, General Partner
Joshua Phillips, General Partner
Kevin McCafferty, Partner
Robert Vigoda, Partner

Type of Firm

Private Equity Firm

Project Preferences

Role in Financing:
Prefer role as deal originator but will also invest in deals created by others

Type of Financing Preferred:
Early Stage
First Stage Financing
Startup

Size of Investments Considered:
Min Size of Investment Considered (000s): $500
Max Size of Investment Considered (000s): $5,000

Geographical Preferences

United States Preferences:
Northeast

Industry Preferences

In Medical/Health prefer:
Medical/Health

Additional Information

Name of Most Recent Fund: Catalyst Health Ventures, L.P.
Most Recent Fund Was Raised: 02/14/2008
Year Founded: 1998
Capital Under Management: $35,000,000
Current Activity Level: Actively seeking new investments
Method of Compensation: Return on investment is of primary concern, do not charge fees

---

CATALYST INVESTMENT MANAGERS PTY, LTD.

151 Macquarie Street
Level 9
Sydney, Australia 2000
Phone: 612-9270-1200
Fax: 612-9270-1222
E-mail: enquiries@catalystinvest.com.au
Website: www.catalystinvest.com.au

Other Offices

91-93 Flinders Lane
Level 4
Melbourne, Australia 3000
Phone: 613-9659-1800
Fax: 613-9659-1899

Management and Staff

John Story, Managing Director
Simon Dighton, Managing Director
Tony Yap, Chief Financial Officer
Trent Peterson, Managing Director

Type of Firm

Private Equity Firm

Association Membership

Australian Venture Capital Association (AVCAL)

Project Preferences

Role in Financing:
Prefer role as deal originator but will also invest in deals created by others

Type of Financing Preferred:
Leveraged Buyout
Management Buyouts

Geographical Preferences

International Preferences:

Pacific Rim
Pacific
Australia
New Zealand
Asia

Industry Focus

(% based on actual investment)	
Consumer Related	60.3%
Other Products	26.9%
Semiconductors/Other Elect.	3.9%
Industrial/Energy	3.6%
Internet Specific	2.8%
Computer Software and Services	2.4%

Additional Information

Year Founded: 1989
Capital Under Management: $722,800,000
Current Activity Level: Actively seeking new investments
Method of Compensation: Return on invest. most important, but chg. closing fees, service fees, etc.

CATALYST INVESTORS

711 Fifth Avenue
Suite 402
New York, NY USA 10022
Phone: 212-863-4848
Fax: 212-319-5771
Website: www.catalystinvestors.com

Management and Staff

Brian Rich, Managing Partner
Christopher Shipman, Partner
D. Ryan McNally, Partner
Gene Wolfson, Partner

Type of Firm

Private Equity Firm

Project Preferences

Role in Financing:

Prefer role as deal originator but will also invest in deals created by others

Type of Financing Preferred:

Second Stage Financing
Leveraged Buyout
Control-block Purchases
Early Stage
Expansion
Turnaround
Later Stage
Management Buyouts
Industry Rollups
Special Situation
Recapitalizations

Size of Investments Considered:

Min Size of Investment Considered (000s): $1,000
Max Size of Investment Considered: No Limit

Geographical Preferences

Canadian Preferences:

All Canada

International Preferences:

All International

Industry Preferences

In Communications prefer:

Communications and Media
Commercial Communications
CATV & Pay TV Systems
Radio & TV Broadcasting
Telecommunications
Wireless Communications
Data Communications
Satellite Microwave Comm.
Media and Entertainment
Other Communication Prod.

In Computer Software prefer:

Software
Applications Software

In Internet Specific prefer:

E-Commerce Technology
Ecommerce
Web Aggregration/Portals

In Consumer Related prefer:

Entertainment and Leisure

In Business Serv. prefer:

Media

In Other prefer:

Women/Minority-Owned Bus.

Additional Information

Name of Most Recent Fund: Catalyst Investors II, L.P.
Most Recent Fund Was Raised: 10/26/2005
Year Founded: 2000
Capital Under Management: $110,000,000
Current Activity Level: Actively seeking new investments
Method of Compensation: Return on investment is of primary concern, do not charge fees

---

CATALYST MICROFINANCE INVESTMENT COMPANY

ASA Tower, 23/3 Khilji Road
Shyamoli Mohammadpur
Dhaka, Bangladesh 1207
Phone: 880-2-911-6375
Fax: 880-2-912-1861
E-mail: dhaka@catalyst-microfinance.com
Website: www.catalyst-microfinance.com

Other Offices

Nieuwegracht 29
Utrecht, Netherlands 3512 LD
Phone: 31-30-234-3430
Fax: 31-30-233-1849

Type of Firm

Private Equity Firm

Project Preferences

Type of Financing Preferred:

Expansion

Geographical Preferences

International Preferences:

India
Pakistan
Ghana
Asia
Africa

Industry Preferences

In Financial Services prefer:

Financial Services

Additional Information

Year Founded: 2005
Capital Under Management: $100,000,000
Current Activity Level: Actively seeking new investments

CATALYST PRIVATE EQUITY

Suite no. 3, Hajabi Complex
Mecca Street
Amman, Jordan 111821
Phone: 962-6-581-3411
Fax: 962-6-581-3412
E-mail: info@catalystpe.com
Website: www.catalystpe.com

Type of Firm

Private Equity Firm

Project Preferences

Type of Financing Preferred:

Balanced

Geographical Preferences

International Preferences:

Jordan
Utd. Arab Em.
Middle East
Saudi Arabia

Industry Preferences

In Industrial/Energy prefer:

Energy

In Utilities prefer:

Utilities

Additional Information

Year Founded: 2007
Current Activity Level: Actively seeking new investments

CATAMOUNT VENTURES, L.P.

400 Pacific Avenue
Third Floor
San Francisco, CA USA 94133
Phone: 415-277-0300
Fax: 415-277-0301
E-mail: info@catamountventures.com
Website: www.catamountventures.com

Management and Staff

Jed Smith, Managing Director
Mark Silverman, Managing Director
Tamin Pechet, Principal

Type of Firm

Private Equity Firm

Association Membership

National Venture Capital Association - USA (NVCA)

Project Preferences

Type of Financing Preferred:
Early Stage
Seed

Size of Investments Considered:
Min Size of Investment Considered (000s): $500
Max Size of Investment Considered (000s): $4,000

Geographical Preferences

United States Preferences:
All U.S.

Additional Information

Name of Most Recent Fund: Catamount Ventures IV, L.P.
Most Recent Fund Was Raised: 12/10/2008
Year Founded: 2000
Capital Under Management: $189,200,000
Current Activity Level: Actively seeking new investments

CATAPULT VENTURE MANAGERS, LTD.

Malt House, 13 Narborough Wood
Business Park, Desford Road
Leicester, United Kingdom LE19 4XT
Phone: 44-116-238-8200
Fax: 44-116-239-6997
E-mail: mail@catapult-vm.co.uk
Website: www.catapult-vm.co.uk

Other Offices

One Victoria Square
Birmingham, United Kingdom B1 1BD
Phone: 44-870-116-3000
Fax: 44-870-116-3010

Management and Staff

Rob Carroll, Managing Director

Type of Firm

Private Equity Firm

Association Membership

British Venture Capital Association (BVCA)

Project Preferences

Type of Financing Preferred:
Leveraged Buyout
Early Stage
Expansion
Startup

Size of Investments Considered:
Min Size of Investment Considered (000s): $308
Max Size of Investment Considered (000s): $3,079

Geographical Preferences

International Preferences:
United Kingdom
Europe

Additional Information

Year Founded: 1999
Capital Under Management: $47,300,000
Current Activity Level: Actively seeking new investments

CATELLA HOLDING AB

Birger Jarlsgatan 6
P.O. Box 5894
Stockholm, Sweden 102 40
Phone: 46-8-463-3300
Fax: 46-8-463-3399
E-mail: catellait@catella.se
Website: www.catella.se

Management and Staff

Annika Espander, Chief Executive Officer
Johan Bjorklund, CEO & Managing Director

Type of Firm

Bank Affiliated

Association Membership

Swedish Venture Capital Association (SVCA)
European Private Equity and Venture Capital Assoc.

Project Preferences

Type of Financing Preferred:
Leveraged Buyout
Early Stage
Turnaround
First Stage Financing
Management Buyouts
Startup

Geographical Preferences

International Preferences:
Sweden
Europe

Industry Preferences

In Communications prefer:
Communications and Media
Publishing

In Internet Specific prefer:
Internet

Additional Information

Year Founded: 1998
Capital Under Management: $30,000,000
Current Activity Level: Actively seeking new investments

CATHAY CAPITAL PRIVATE EQUITY SAS

9-11
avenue Franklin D. Roosevelt
Paris, France 75008
Phone: 33-1-4225-2800
Fax: 33-1-5828-5225
Website: www.cathay.fr

Other Offices

28, rue des Jardins
LILLE, France 59000

12K, Pufa Tower
588 Pudong Nan Road
Shanghai, China 200120
Phone: 86-21-6888-8069

Management and Staff

Edouard Moinet, Partner
Ming-Po Cai, President

Type of Firm

Private Equity Firm

Association Membership

French Venture Capital Association (AFIC)

Project Preferences

Type of Financing Preferred:
Leveraged Buyout
Generalist PE
Mezzanine
Expansion
Acquisition

Geographical Preferences

International Preferences:
China
France

Additional Information

Year Founded: 2007
Capital Under Management: $68,100,000
Current Activity Level: Actively seeking new investments

CATHAY FINANCIAL HOLDINGS CO., LTD.

16th Floor, 296, Sec. 4
Ren Ai Road
Taipei, Taiwan 106
Phone: 886-2-2708-7698
Fax: 886-2-2325-2488
E-mail: service@cathayholdings.com.tw
Website: www.cathayholdings.com.tw

Management and Staff

Cheng-Cheng Tung, President

Type of Firm

Bank Affiliated

Project Preferences

Type of Financing Preferred:
Balanced

Geographical Preferences

International Preferences:
Taiwan

Additional Information

Year Founded: 2003
Capital Under Management: $36,000,000
Current Activity Level: Actively seeking new investments

CATTERTON PARTNERS

599 West Putnam Avenue
Greenwich, CT USA 06830
Phone: 203-629-4901
Fax: 203-629-4903
E-mail: info@cpequity.com
Website: www.cpequity.com

Management and Staff

Andrew Taub, Partner
David Heidecorn, Partner
Farah Khan, Vice President
Frank Vest, Founding Partner
Howard Steyn, Principal
John Scerbo, Chief Financial Officer
Jonathan Owsley, Partner
Marc Magliacano, Principal
Mark Grabowski, Vice President
Michael Farello, Partner
Neda Daneshzadeh, Principal
Nikhil Thukral, Partner
Richard Gersten, Partner
Robert Callahan, Vice President
Scott Dahnke, Managing Partner

Type of Firm

Bank Affiliated

Project Preferences

Role in Financing:
Prefer role as deal originator but will also invest in deals created by others

Type of Financing Preferred:
Leveraged Buyout
Expansion
Turnaround
Acquisition
Recapitalizations

Size of Investments Considered:
Min Size of Investment Considered (000s): $5,000
Max Size of Investment Considered: No Limit

Geographical Preferences

United States Preferences:
All U.S.

Canadian Preferences:
All Canada

Industry Focus

(% based on actual investment)

Consumer Related	54.9%
Other Products	18.3%
Computer Software and Services	12.3%
Internet Specific	9.5%
Medical/Health	2.6%
Biotechnology	2.4%

Additional Information

Name of Most Recent Fund: Catterton Partners VI, L.P.
Most Recent Fund Was Raised: 06/06/2006
Year Founded: 1990
Capital Under Management: $500,000,000
Current Activity Level: Actively seeking new investments
Method of Compensation: Return on invest. most important, but chg. closing fees, service fees, etc.

CAURIS MANAGEMENT

69 av de la Liberation
BP 1172
Lome, Togo
Phone: 228-22-59-57
Fax: 228-22-59-64
E-mail: cauris@boad.org
Website: www.caurismanagement.com

Management and Staff

Noel Eklo, Managing Director

Type of Firm

Private Equity Firm

Association Membership

African Venture Capital Association (AVCA)

Project Preferences

Type of Financing Preferred:
Early Stage
Generalist PE
Later Stage

Size of Investments Considered:
Min Size of Investment Considered (000s): $180
Max Size of Investment Considered (000s): $3,866

Geographical Preferences

International Preferences:
Togo
Morocco
Africa

Industry Preferences

In Communications prefer:
Communications and Media

In Biotechnology prefer:
Agricultural/Animal Bio.

In Financial Services prefer:
Financial Services

Additional Information

Name of Most Recent Fund: Cauris Croissance
Most Recent Fund Was Raised: 07/20/2005
Year Founded: 1997
Capital Under Management: $17,300,000
Current Activity Level: Actively seeking new investments

CAVALRY ASSET MANAGEMENT

600 Townsend Street
Suite 130E
San Francisco, CA USA 94103
Phone: 415-503-4070
Fax: 415-439-7171

Type of Firm

Private Equity Firm

Additional Information

Year Founded: 2003
Capital Under Management: $129,100,000
Current Activity Level: Actively seeking new investments

CAVALRY INVESTMENTS LLC

Seven Skyline Drive
Hawthorne, NY USA 10532
Phone: 914-347-3440
Fax: 914-347-1973
E-mail: newyork@CavalryInvestments.com
Website: www.cavalryinvestments.com

Management and Staff

John Plum, Managing Partner
Michael Godner, Managing Partner

Type of Firm
Bank Affiliated

Project Preferences

Type of Financing Preferred:
Leveraged Buyout
Acquisition
Distressed Debt

Industry Preferences

In Financial Services prefer:
Financial Services

Additional Information
Year Founded: 1991
Current Activity Level: Actively seeking new investments

CAVE CREEK CAPITAL MANAGEMENT (AKA: CCCM)
14646 North Kierland Boulevard
Suite 238
Scottsdale, AZ USA 85254
Phone: 480-659-4699
Fax: 480-664-3952
Website: www.cavecreekcapital.com

Management and Staff
G. Kevin Fechtmeyer, President
Richard Freeman, Managing Director

Type of Firm
Private Equity Firm

Project Preferences

Type of Financing Preferred:
Leveraged Buyout
Management Buyouts

Size of Investments Considered:
Min Size of Investment Considered (000s): $2,000
Max Size of Investment Considered (000s): $40,000

Industry Preferences

In Communications prefer:
Communications and Media

In Medical/Health prefer:
Medical Products
Health Services

In Consumer Related prefer:
Consumer Products
Consumer Services

In Financial Services prefer:
Financial Services

In Manufact. prefer:
Manufacturing

Additional Information
Year Founded: 1990
Current Activity Level: Actively seeking new investments

CAVIPAR SASU
68 rue du Faubourg St. Honore
Paris, France 75008
Phone: 33-1-3949-9703
Fax: 33-1-3429-2297
E-mail: info@cavipar.com
Website: www.cavipar.com

Management and Staff
Charles-Henri Rossignol, Managing Partner
Richard Schreiber, Managing Partner

Type of Firm
Private Equity Firm

Association Membership
French Venture Capital Association (AFIC)

Project Preferences

Type of Financing Preferred:
Early Stage
Balanced

Size of Investments Considered:
Min Size of Investment Considered (000s): $7,038
Max Size of Investment Considered (000s): $42,230

Geographical Preferences

International Preferences:
Europe
France

Additional Information
Year Founded: 1999
Current Activity Level: Actively seeking new investments

CAYUGA VENTURE FUND
15 Thornwood Drive
Cornell Business & Technology
Ithaca, NY USA 14850
Phone: 607-266-9266
Fax: 607-266-9267
Website: www.cvf.biz

Management and Staff
Cliff Lardin, Principal
Jennifer Tegan, Partner
Philip Proujansky, Managing Partner
Zachary Shulman, Managing Partner

Type of Firm
Private Equity Firm

Project Preferences

Role in Financing:
Prefer role as deal originator but will also invest in deals created by others

Type of Financing Preferred:
Early Stage
Seed
First Stage Financing

Size of Investments Considered:
Min Size of Investment Considered (000s): $200
Max Size of Investment Considered (000s): $3,000

Geographical Preferences

United States Preferences:
New York

Industry Preferences

In Communications prefer:
Communications and Media
Telecommunications
Data Communications

In Internet Specific prefer:
E-Commerce Technology

In Semiconductor/Electr prefer:
Semiconductor
Controllers and Sensors
Sensors
Laser Related
Optoelectronics

In Biotechnology prefer:
Biotechnology

In Medical/Health prefer:
Medical Diagnostics
Diagnostic Services

In Consumer Related prefer:
Food/Beverage
Consumer Products

In Industrial/Energy prefer:
Energy
Alternative Energy
Advanced Materials

Additional Information
Name of Most Recent Fund: Cayuga Venture Fund III, L.P.
Most Recent Fund Was Raised: 01/20/2006
Year Founded: 1994
Capital Under Management: $35,000,000
Current Activity Level: Actively seeking new investments
Method of Compensation: Return on investment is of primary concern, do not charge fees

---

CB HEALTH VENTURES LLC
800 Boylston Street
Suite 800
Boston, MA USA 02199

Phone: 617-450-9800
Fax: 617-450-9749
Website: www.health-ventures.com

Other Offices

360 Madison Avenue
Fifth Floor
New York, NY USA 10017
Phone: 212-869-5600
Fax: 212-869-6418

Management and Staff

Daniel Cain, General Partner
Enrico Petrillo, Managing Director
Frederick Blume, Managing Director
Robert Schulz, General Partner

Type of Firm

Private Equity Firm

Association Membership

National Venture Capital Association - USA (NVCA)

Project Preferences

Role in Financing:
Prefer role as deal originator but will also invest in deals created by others

Type of Financing Preferred:
Early Stage
Expansion
Later Stage

Size of Investments Considered:
Min Size of Investment Considered (000s): $500
Max Size of Investment Considered (000s): $7,000

Geographical Preferences

United States Preferences:
All U.S.

Canadian Preferences:
All Canada

Industry Focus

(% based on actual investment)

Medical/Health	50.0%
Biotechnology	27.3%
Internet Specific	12.7%
Computer Software and Services	7.6%
Other Products	2.5%

Additional Information

Year Founded: 1997
Capital Under Management: $150,000,000
Current Activity Level: Making few, if any, new investments
Method of Compensation: Return on investment is of primary concern, do not charge fees

CBC PENSION

1204- 99 Metcalfe Street
Ottawa, Canada K1P 6L7
Website: www3.cbc.ca/aboutcbc/pension/

Type of Firm

Endowment, Foundation or Pension Fund

Additional Information

Year Founded: 2009
Current Activity Level: Actively seeking new investments

CBF TECHNOLOGY INVESTMENT CORPORATION

601 Hanil offictel
815 Moonhyun-4Dong Namgu
Pusan, South Korea
Phone: 82-51-633-7001
Fax: 82-51-633-7006
Website: www.cbffn.com

Management and Staff

Chang-Ho Kim, President

Type of Firm

Private Equity Firm

Association Membership

Korean Venture Capital Association (KVCA)

Project Preferences

Type of Financing Preferred:
Balanced

Geographical Preferences

International Preferences:
Korea, South

Additional Information

Year Founded: 1986
Current Activity Level: Actively seeking new investments

CBPE CAPITAL, LLP (AKA: CLOSE BROTHERS PRIVATE EQUITY, LTD.)

10 Throgmorton Avenue
London, United Kingdom EC2N 2DL
Phone: 44-20-7065-1100
Fax: 44-20-7588-6815
E-mail: enquiries@cbpel.com
Website: www.cbpel.com

Other Offices

10 Crown Place
London, United Kingdom EC2A 4FT
Phone: 44-20-7426-4000

Neue Mainzer Str. 1
Frankfurt, Germany 60311
Phone: 49-69-972-0040
Fax: 49-69-972004-15

Management and Staff

Ben Alexander, Partner
Burkhard Weber, Managing Director
David Benin, Managing Director
Francois Wohrer, Managing Director
Iain Slater, Partner
John Fisher, Partner
John Snook, Managing Partner
Mathew Hutchinson, Partner
Neil Murphy, Partner
Nick MacNay, Partner
Sean Dinnen, Partner
Simon Wildig, Partner

Type of Firm

Private Equity Firm

Association Membership

British Venture Capital Association (BVCA)
European Private Equity and Venture Capital Assoc.

Project Preferences

Type of Financing Preferred:
Leveraged Buyout
Turnaround
Management Buyouts

Geographical Preferences

International Preferences:
United Kingdom
Europe

Industry Preferences

In Consumer Related prefer:
Entertainment and Leisure

In Industrial/Energy prefer:
Industrial Products

In Transportation prefer:
Transportation

In Business Serv. prefer:
Services

In Manufact. prefer:
Manufacturing

Additional Information

Year Founded: 1984
Capital Under Management: $1,262,500,000
Current Activity Level: Actively seeking new investments

CBR MANAGEMENT GMBH (DBA: EQUIVEST GMBH & CO.)

Theatinerstrasse 7
Munich, Germany D-80333
Phone: 49-89-2113-777
Fax: 49-89-2113-7788
E-mail: info@cbr-gmbh.de
Website: www.equivest.de

Management and Staff

Christoph Schubert, Partner
Eberhard Crain, Founding Partner
Gernot Overbeck, Partner
Michael Welzel, Partner
Michael Hessing, Partner
Peter Brock, Founding Partner
Wolfgang Behrens-Ramberg, Founding Partner

Type of Firm

Private Equity Firm

Project Preferences

Type of Financing Preferred:

Expansion
Management Buyouts

Geographical Preferences

International Preferences:

Switzerland
Austria
Germany

Additional Information

Year Founded: 1991
Capital Under Management: $140,000,000
Current Activity Level: Actively seeking new investments

CCB INTERNATIONAL (HOLDINGS), LTD.

Suite 3408, Two Pacific Place
88 Queensway, Admiralty
Central, Hong Kong
Phone: 852-2532-6100
Fax: 852-2530-1496
Website: www.ccbintl.com

Management and Staff

Alvin Li, Managing Director
Hu Zhanghong, Chief Executive Officer

Type of Firm

Bank Affiliated

Project Preferences

Type of Financing Preferred:

Balanced
Later Stage

Geographical Preferences

International Preferences:

China

Industry Preferences

In Medical/Health prefer:

Medical/Health
Other Therapeutic
Medical Products
Health Services
Pharmaceuticals

Additional Information

Year Founded: 2008
Capital Under Management: $234,300,000
Current Activity Level: Actively seeking new investments

CCF SA (AKA: CENTRE DE COMPETENCES FINANCIERES)

Pre-Fleuri 6 CP 286
Sion, Switzerland 1951
Phone: 41-27-327-3550
Fax: 41-27-327-3551
E-mail: info@ccf-valais.ch
Website: www.ccf-valais.ch

Type of Firm

Private Equity Firm

Project Preferences

Type of Financing Preferred:

Leveraged Buyout
Expansion
Balanced
Seed

Geographical Preferences

International Preferences:

Switzerland
Europe

Additional Information

Year Founded: 2003
Capital Under Management: $2,000,000
Current Activity Level: Actively seeking new investments

CCG VENTURE PARTNERS, LLC

14405 Brown Road
Tomball, TX USA 77377
Phone: 281-290-8331
Fax: 281-290-8332
Website: www.ccgvp.com

Management and Staff

Jeff Presnal, Partner
Rick Davis, Chief Executive Officer
Sam Loughlin, Partner

Type of Firm

Private Equity Firm

Additional Information

Year Founded: 1999
Current Activity Level: Actively seeking new investments

CCMP CAPITAL ADVISORS LLC

245 Park Avenue
16th Floor
New York, NY USA 10167
Phone: 212-600-9600
Fax: 212-599-3481
Website: www.ccmpcapital.com

Other Offices

23 King Street
St James's House
London, United Kingdom SW1Y6QY
Phone: 44-207-389-9100
Fax: 44-207-839-2192

24 Waterway Avenue
Suite 750
The Woodlands, TX USA 77380
Phone: 281-363-2013
Fax: 281-363-2097

Management and Staff

Allison Cole, Vice President
Benjamin Edmands, Managing Director
Christopher Behrens, Managing Director
Dana Ardi, Managing Director
Esana Blank, Vice President
Heinz Holsten, Principal
Joe Delgado, Managing Director
John Warner, Principal
Jonathan Lynch, Managing Director
Julie Casella-Esposito, Managing Director
Karl Kurz, Managing Director
Karla Popper, Vice President
Kevin O'Brien, Managing Director
Mark McFadden, Principal
Matthew Reed, Vice President
Michael Hannon, Managing Director
Mit Mehta, Principal
Raf Goovaerts, Principal
Richard Zannino, Managing Director
Rossella Curci, Vice President
Ryan Anderson, Principal
Stephen McKenna, Managing Director
Sunil Mishra, Managing Director
Timothy Walsh, Managing Director
Umur Hursever, Principal

Type of Firm

Private Equity Firm

Project Preferences

Type of Financing Preferred:

Leveraged Buyout
Expansion
Generalist PE

Geographical Preferences

United States Preferences:

All U.S.

International Preferences:
Europe
Asia
All International

Industry Preferences

In Communications prefer:
Telecommunications

In Medical/Health prefer:
Hospitals/Clinics/Primary

In Consumer Related prefer:
Retail
Consumer Services

In Industrial/Energy prefer:
Energy
Industrial Products

In Financial Services prefer:
Financial Services

In Business Serv. prefer:
Media

Additional Information
Year Founded: 2006
Capital Under Management: $3,400,000,000
Current Activity Level: Actively seeking new investments

CCP EQUITY PARTNERS
100 Pearl Street
14th Floor
Hartford, CT USA 06103
Phone: 860-249-7104
Fax: 860-249-7001
E-mail: info@ccpequitypartners.com
Website: www.ccpequitypartners.com

Management and Staff
David Young, Managing Partner
John Clinton, Managing Partner
Michael Aspinwall, Managing Partner
Steven Piaker, Managing Partner

Type of Firm
Private Equity Firm

Project Preferences

Role in Financing:
Prefer role as deal originator but will also invest in deals created by others

Type of Financing Preferred:
Expansion
First Stage Financing

Size of Investments Considered:
Min Size of Investment Considered (000s): $5,000
Max Size of Investment Considered (000s): $20,000

Geographical Preferences

United States Preferences:
All U.S.

Canadian Preferences:
All Canada

International Preferences:
United Kingdom
Bermuda

Industry Focus
(% based on actual investment)

Other Products	50.4%
Internet Specific	15.7%
Medical/Health	15.4%
Computer Software and Services	10.6%
Consumer Related	5.7%
Computer Hardware	2.1%

Additional Information
Name of Most Recent Fund: Conning Capital Partners VI, L.P.
Most Recent Fund Was Raised: 03/31/2000
Year Founded: 1985
Capital Under Management: $532,000,000
Current Activity Level: Actively seeking new investments
Method of Compensation: Return on investment is of primary concern, do not charge fees

CD VENTURES, LLC
1235 Westlakes Drive
Suite 160
Berwyn, PA USA 19312
Phone: 610-640-4900
Fax: 610-640-4981
E-mail: debbas@ix.netcom.com
Website: www.cdventures.net

Management and Staff
Christopher Debbas, Partner
James Griffiths, Partner
Matthew Brach, Vice President

Type of Firm
Private Equity Firm

Project Preferences

Type of Financing Preferred:
Leveraged Buyout

Size of Investments Considered:
Min Size of Investment Considered (000s): $15,000
Max Size of Investment Considered (000s): $50,000

Additional Information
Year Founded: 1996
Capital Under Management: $300,000,000
Current Activity Level: Actively seeking new investments

CDC CAPITAL INVESTISSEMENT (AKA: CDC PARTICIPATIONS)
148, rue de l'Universite
Paris, France 75007
Phone: 33-1-5850-9091
Fax: 33-1-5850-8960
E-mail: info@cdcci.fr
Website: www.cdcci.fr

Management and Staff
Jean Eichenlaub, President

Type of Firm
Bank Affiliated

Association Membership
French Venture Capital Association (AFIC)
European Private Equity and Venture Capital Assoc.

Project Preferences

Type of Financing Preferred:
Fund of Funds
Leveraged Buyout
Early Stage
Expansion
Generalist PE
Recapitalizations

Size of Investments Considered:
Min Size of Investment Considered (000s): $1,000
Max Size of Investment Considered: No Limit

Geographical Preferences

United States Preferences:
All U.S.

International Preferences:
Europe
France

Industry Focus
(% based on actual investment)

Other Products	87.5%
Consumer Related	5.2%
Biotechnology	4.6%
Computer Software and Services	0.9%
Semiconductors/Other Elect.	0.9%
Communications and Media	0.5%
Industrial/Energy	0.2%
Medical/Health	0.2%

Additional Information
Name of Most Recent Fund: FCPR CDC Developpement Transmission II
Most Recent Fund Was Raised: 07/31/2005
Year Founded: 1985
Capital Under Management: $1,455,000,000
Current Activity Level: Actively seeking new investments

CDC CORPORATION (FKA: CHINADOTCOM VENTURES)

11/F, ING Tower
308 Des Voeux Road
Central, Hong Kong
Phone: 852-2893-8200
Fax: 852-2893-5245
E-mail: contact@cdccorporation.net
Website: www.cdccorporation.net

Other Offices

2002 Summit Boulevard
Suite 700
Atlanta, GA USA 30319
Phone: 770-351-9600
Fax: 770-351-0036

Management and Staff

Frank Hung, Managing Director
Matthew Lavelle, Chief Financial Officer
William Geist, Chief Operating Officer

Type of Firm

Corporate PE/Venture

Project Preferences

Type of Financing Preferred:
Balanced

Additional Information

Year Founded: 2000
Current Activity Level: Actively seeking new investments

CDC ENTREPRISES SAS

137, rue de l'Universite
Paris, France 75007
Phone: 33-1-5850-7171
E-mail: contact-cdcentreprises@cdcentreprises.fr
Website: www.cdcentreprises.fr

Management and Staff

Albert Olivier, President
Jerome Gallot, President

Type of Firm

Bank Affiliated

Association Membership

French Venture Capital Association (AFIC)
European Private Equity and Venture Capital Assoc.

Project Preferences

Type of Financing Preferred:
Leveraged Buyout
Expansion
Balanced
Turnaround

Size of Investments Considered:
Min Size of Investment Considered (000s): $880
Max Size of Investment Considered (000s): $7,042

Geographical Preferences

International Preferences:
Europe
France

Industry Preferences

In Industrial/Energy prefer:
Industrial Products

In Transportation prefer:
Transportation

In Business Serv. prefer:
Services

In Manufact. prefer:
Manufacturing

Additional Information

Name of Most Recent Fund: ElectroPar France (EPF)
Most Recent Fund Was Raised: 04/28/2000
Year Founded: 1994
Capital Under Management: $221,000,000
Current Activity Level: Actively seeking new investments

CDC GROUP PLC (FKA: COMMONWEALTH DEVELOPMENT CORPORATION)

Cardinal Place
80 Victoria Street
London, United Kingdom SW1E 5JL
Phone: 44-20-7963-4700
Fax: 44-20-7963-4750
E-mail: enqueries@cdcgroup.com
Website: www.cdcgroup.com

Other Offices

Room 2401, China World Tower 2
No. 1 Jian Guo Men Wai Street
Beijing, China 100004
Phone: 86-10-6505-6655
Fax: 86-10-6505-8111

16 Raffles Quay
#19-02 Hong Leong Building
Singapore, Singapore 048581
Phone: 65-6227-8632
Fax: 65-6227-1004

Management and Staff

Anubha Shrivastava, Managing Director
Godfrey Davies, Chief Financial Officer
Hywel Rees-Jones, Managing Director
Shonaid Jemmet-Page, Chief Operating Officer

Type of Firm

Government Affiliated Program

Association Membership

Emerging Markets Private Equity Association
European Private Equity and Venture Capital Assoc.
African Venture Capital Association (AVCA)

Project Preferences

Type of Financing Preferred:
Fund of Funds
Leveraged Buyout
Expansion
Generalist PE
Management Buyouts
Private Placement

Size of Investments Considered:
Min Size of Investment Considered (000s): $2,500
Max Size of Investment Considered (000s): $310,000

Geographical Preferences

International Preferences:
India
Latin America
Pacific
Asia
Africa
All International

Industry Preferences

In Communications prefer:
Telecommunications

In Medical/Health prefer:
Medical/Health

In Consumer Related prefer:
Consumer
Food/Beverage
Hotels and Resorts

In Industrial/Energy prefer:
Energy
Oil and Gas Exploration

In Transportation prefer:
Transportation

In Financial Services prefer:
Financial Services
Real Estate

In Agr/Forestr/Fish prefer:
Agribusiness
Mining and Minerals

Additional Information

Year Founded: 1948
Capital Under Management: $2,800,000,000
Current Activity Level: Actively seeking new investments

CDC INNOVATION SAS (FKA: CDC IXIS INNOVATION)

63 avenue des Champs Elysees
Paris, France 75008
Phone: 33-1-4076-9900
Fax: 33-1-4561-2478
E-mail: businnesplan@cdcinnovation.com
Website: www.cdcinnovation.com

Management and Staff

Bertrand Limoges, Principal
Daniel Balmisse, General Partner
Franck Noiret, General Partner
Herve De Kergrohen, Venture Partner
Jean-Christophe Renondin, General Partner
Jean-Francois Bru, General Partner
Michel Desbard, Venture Partner
Valery Huot, Managing Partner

Type of Firm

Bank Affiliated

Association Membership

French Venture Capital Association (AFIC)
European Private Equity and Venture Capital Assoc.

Project Preferences

Type of Financing Preferred:
Leveraged Buyout
Early Stage
Expansion
Balanced
Start-up Financing
Later Stage
Seed
Startup

Geographical Preferences

International Preferences:
Central Europe
Europe
France

Industry Focus

(% based on actual investment)	
Biotechnology	22.7%
Internet Specific	20.9%
Medical/Health	13.4%
Computer Software and Services	12.5%
Computer Hardware	11.3%
Semiconductors/Other Elect.	8.0%
Industrial/Energy	4.3%
Communications and Media	3.8%
Other Products	3.1%

Additional Information

Name of Most Recent Fund: FCPR Science et Innovation 2001
Most Recent Fund Was Raised: 10/31/2001
Year Founded: 1996
Capital Under Management: $185,700,000
Current Activity Level: Actively seeking new investments

CDC IXIS ENVIRONNEMENT & INFRASTRUCTURES

47 quai d'Austerlitz
Paris, France 75648
Phone: 33-1-5855-6600
Fax: 33-1-5855-6699

Management and Staff

Sebastien Clerc, President

Type of Firm

Private Equity Firm

Association Membership

French Venture Capital Association (AFIC)

Project Preferences

Type of Financing Preferred:
Leveraged Buyout
Expansion

Geographical Preferences

International Preferences:
Europe
France

Industry Preferences

In Industrial/Energy prefer:
Energy

In Agr/Forestr/Fish prefer:
Agribusiness

Additional Information

Year Founded: 2000
Capital Under Management: $57,000,000
Current Activity Level: Actively seeking new investments

CDH CHINA MANAGEMENT CO., LTD.

2601, 26/F, Lippo Center
Tower 2, 89 Queensway
Admirality, Hong Kong
Phone: 852-2810-7003

Other Offices

Suite 318, Tower B, Grand Pacific Trade
8A Guanghua Road, Chaoyang Dist
Beijing, China 100026
Phone: 86-10-6581-8388
Fax: 86-10-6581-8388

Ugland House, P.O. Box 309 GT
South Church Street
George Town, Grand Cayman, Cayman Islands
Phone: 345-949-8066

Level 30
Six Battery Road
Singapore, Singapore
Phone: 65-6550-9708
Fax: 65-6550-9828

Management and Staff

KH Lew, Chief Financial Officer
Shangzhi Wu, Chief Executive Officer
Stuart Schonberger, Managing Director
Zhen Jiao, Managing Partner

Type of Firm

Private Equity Firm

Project Preferences

Type of Financing Preferred:
Leveraged Buyout
Generalist PE
Early Stage
Expansion
Mezzanine
Balanced
Later Stage

Geographical Preferences

International Preferences:
China
Asia

Industry Preferences

In Medical/Health prefer:
Medical/Health

In Consumer Related prefer:
Consumer Services

In Manufact. prefer:
Manufacturing

Additional Information

Name of Most Recent Fund: CDH Venture Partners, L.P.
Most Recent Fund Was Raised: 06/12/2006
Year Founded: 2002
Capital Under Management: $600,000,000
Current Activity Level: Actively seeking new investments

CDIB BIOSCIENCE VENTURE MANAGEMENT

9191 Towne Centre Drive
Suite 575
San Diego, CA USA 92122
Phone: 858-552-6808
Fax: 858-552-6811
Website: www.cdibbiosciencevc.com

Other Offices

30F, 99, Section 2
Tun-Hwa South Road
Taipei, Taiwan
Phone: 886-2-2325-0556

Fax: 886-2-2754-7708

Management and Staff

Tai-Sen Soong, President

Type of Firm

Private Equity Firm

Association Membership

Taiwan Venture Capital Association(TVCA)

Project Preferences

Role in Financing:

Will function either as deal originator or investor in deals created by others

Type of Financing Preferred:

Second Stage Financing
Expansion
Mezzanine
Strategic Alliances
Joint Ventures
Recapitalizations

Size of Investments Considered:

Min Size of Investment Considered (000s): $2,000
Max Size of Investment Considered (000s): $5,000

Geographical Preferences

United States Preferences:

Mid Atlantic
Midwest
Northwest
West Coast
Southwest

International Preferences:

Taiwan

Industry Preferences

In Biotechnology prefer:

Human Biotechnology
Genetic Engineering
Industrial Biotechnology

In Medical/Health prefer:

Medical Therapeutics
Drug/Equipmt Delivery
Medical Products
Disposable Med. Products
Pharmaceuticals

Additional Information

Year Founded: 2001
Capital Under Management: $75,000,000
Current Activity Level: Actively seeking new investments
Method of Compensation: Return on investment is of primary concern, do not charge fees

---

CDP CAPITAL - TECHNOLOGY VENTURES (FKA: CDP SOFINOV)

1801, avenue McGill College
13th Floor
Montreal, Canada H3A 3C7
Phone: 514-847-2613
Fax: 514-847-2628
E-mail: info@lacaisse.com
Website: www.lacaisse.com

Other Offices

Stabilitas Rt.
Vaci utca 16/b
Budapest, Hungary 1052
Phone: 36-1-235-0224
Fax: 36-1-235-0228

Four Bentall Center, Suite 1800
1055 Dunsmuir Street , PO Box 49001
Vancouver, Canada V7X 1B1
Phone: 1-604-661-5000
Fax: 1-604-661-5055

ul. Nowy Swiat 54/56
Warsaw, Poland 00-363
Phone: 48-22-828-3470
Fax: 48-22-828-3474

9200 Sunset Boulevard
Suite 520
Los Angeles, CA USA 90069
Phone: 1-310-281-0031
Fax: 1-310-281-0020

5/F., Bio House Building 55 Soi Prompong
Sukhumvit 39 Road, Klongton-Nua, Wattana
Bangkok, Thailand 10110
Phone: 662-262-0581
Fax: 662-262-0580

Suite 5408, Central Plaza
18 Harbour Road
Wanchai, Hong Kong
Phone: 852-2586-6222
Fax: 852-2802-3803

Price Building, 65 Sainte-Anne Street
12th Floor
Quebec, Canada G1R 3X5
Phone: 418-684-8165
Fax: 418-684-8166

2680 Skymark Avenue
Suite 100, PO Box 50
Missisauga, Canada L4W 5L6
Phone: 1-905-624-3330
Fax: 1-905-624-2141

Ruben Dario 281, piso 21
Col. Bosque de Chapultepec
Mexico City, Mexico 11580
Phone: 52-55-5281-8080
Fax: 52-55-5281-7975

Avenue Louise 500
Brussels, Belgium 1050
Phone: 32-2644-4165
Fax: 32-2644-4806

Suite 602, Korea City Air Terminal
159-6 Samsung-dong, Kangnam-gu
Seoul, South Korea 135-728
Phone: 822-2016-5925
Fax: 822-2016-5930

Shiroyama MT Building, 8th Floor
4-1-17 Toranomon, Minato-ku
Tokyo, Japan 105-0001
Phone: 81-3-5776-4470
Fax: 81-3-5776-4477

BCE Place, 161 Bay Street
Suite 2800
Toronto, Canada M5J 2S1
Phone: 1-416-214-0603
Fax: 1-416-214-3414

128 rue du Faubourg Sainte-Honore
Paris, France 75008
Phone: 33-15-669-2530
Fax: 33-14-562-0204

199 Angle Bd Zeriktouni & rue D'Avignon
5th etage
Casablanca, Morocco BN 10
Phone: 212-22-95-15-97
Fax: 212-22-95-09-53

118 Mittal Chambers
228 Nariman Point
Mumbai, India 400021
Phone: 91-22-2255-9007
Fax: 91-22-2235-1442

Management and Staff

Denis Dionne, General Partner
Didier Benchimol, Partner
Ernest Bastien, Vice President
Ginette Hains, Vice President
Gordon Fyfe, President
Henri-Paul Rousseau, President, CEO, Chairman
Jean-Francois L Her, Vice President
Karen Laflamme, Vice President
Luc Vallee, Vice President
Michel Nadeau, President
Philippe Gabelier, Vice President
Philippe Halley, Vice President
Pierre Jette, Vice President
Yannis Papageorgiou, Vice President

Type of Firm

Private Equity Advisor or Fund of Funds

Project Preferences

Type of Financing Preferred:

Balanced

Geographical Preferences

United States Preferences:
All U.S.

Canadian Preferences:
All Canada

International Preferences:
Europe
Asia

Industry Preferences

In Biotechnology prefer:
Biotechnology

In Industrial/Energy prefer:
Industrial Products

In Transportation prefer:
Aerospace

Additional Information

Name of Most Recent Fund: CDP Capital - Technology Ventures U.S. Fund 2002
Most Recent Fund Was Raised: 05/17/2002
Year Founded: 1995
Capital Under Management: $65,000,000
Current Activity Level: Actively seeking new investments

CDP CAPITAL PRIVATE EQUITY

1000, place Jean-Paul-Riopelle
Montreal, Canada H2Z 2B3
Phone: 514-842-3261
Fax: 514-842-4833
Website: www.cdpcapital.com

Other Offices

1540 Broadway
Suite 1600
New York, NY USA 10036
Phone: 212-596-6300
Fax: 212-730-2356

Type of Firm

Endowment, Foundation or Pension Fund

Project Preferences

Type of Financing Preferred:
Expansion
Early Stage
Turnaround
Seed
Other
Startup
Acquisition

Geographical Preferences

United States Preferences:
All U.S.

Canadian Preferences:
All Canada
Quebec

International Preferences:
Europe

Additional Information

Year Founded: 1965
Current Activity Level: Actively seeking new investments

CE UNTERBERG TOWBIN (FKA:UNTERBERG HARRIS CAPITAL PARTNERS)

350 Madison Avenue
New York, NY USA 10017
Phone: 212-572-8000
Fax: 212-389-8810
E-mail: info@unterberg.com
Website: www.unterberg.com

Other Offices

456 Montgomery Street
San Francisco, CA USA 94104
Phone: 415-659-2222

The Graf Building
4 Shenkar Street
Hertzlia, Israel 46120
Phone: 972-9961-3000

Management and Staff

Andrew Arno, Chairman & CEO
George Abraham, Managing Director
Mark Hadlock, Vice President

Type of Firm

Bank Affiliated

Project Preferences

Role in Financing:
Prefer role as deal originator but will also invest in deals created by others

Type of Financing Preferred:
Second Stage Financing
Mezzanine

Industry Focus

(% based on actual investment)

Internet Specific	41.9%
Computer Software and Services	19.4%
Communications and Media	11.8%
Consumer Related	7.4%
Medical/Health	5.7%
Computer Hardware	5.1%
Semiconductors/Other Elect.	5.1%
Biotechnology	3.2%
Industrial/Energy	0.3%

Additional Information

Year Founded: 1989
Capital Under Management: $75,000,000
Current Activity Level: Actively seeking new investments
Method of Compensation: Return on investment is of primary concern, do not charge fees

---

CEA VALORISATION SA

17, rue des Martyrs
Cedex 9
Grenoble, France 38054
Phone: 33-4-3878-9400
Fax: 33-4-3878-5674
E-mail: ceavalo@cea.fr
Website: www.cea-valorisation.com

Management and Staff

Guy Labrunie, Chief Executive Officer
Regis Saleur, Chief Executive Officer

Type of Firm

Government Affiliated Program

Association Membership

French Venture Capital Association (AFIC)

Project Preferences

Type of Financing Preferred:
Early Stage
Research and Development
Seed
Startup

Geographical Preferences

International Preferences:
Europe
France

Industry Preferences

In Communications prefer:
Telecommunications

In Biotechnology prefer:
Biotechnology

In Medical/Health prefer:
Medical/Health

In Industrial/Energy prefer:
Energy
Advanced Materials

Additional Information

Year Founded: 1999
Current Activity Level: Actively seeking new investments

CEDAR FUND

9 Keren Hayesod Street
PO Box 505
Herzelia, Israel 46105
Phone: 972-9-957-7227
Fax: 972-9-957-7228
Website: www.cedarfund.com

Management and Staff

Allen Bernardo, Partner
Amnon Shoham, Managing Director

Dorin Miller, Venture Partner
Gal Israely, Co-Founder
Moshe Tur, Venture Partner
Roy Erez, Partner

Type of Firm

Private Equity Firm

Project Preferences

Type of Financing Preferred:

Early Stage
Seed

Geographical Preferences

International Preferences:

Asia
Israel

Industry Preferences

In Communications prefer:

Communications and Media

In Computer Software prefer:

Software

In Internet Specific prefer:

Internet

Additional Information

Year Founded: 1997
Capital Under Management: $50,000,000
Current Activity Level: Actively seeking new investments

CEDARPOINT INVESTMENTS, INC.

30 Saint Clair Avenue West
Suite 900
Toronto, Canada M4V3A1
Phone: 416-927-200
Fax: 416-927-2013

Management and Staff

Sydney Loftus, Managing Director

Type of Firm

Private Equity Firm

Additional Information

Year Founded: 1996
Current Activity Level: Actively seeking new investments

CEI COMMUNITY VENTURES, INC. (AKA: CCVI)

Two Portland Fish Pier
Suite 201
Portland, ME USA 04101
Phone: 207-772-5356
Fax: 207-772-5503
E-mail: info@ceicommunityventures.com
Website: www.ceicommunityventures.com

Management and Staff

Michael Gurau, President

Type of Firm

Private Equity Firm

Association Membership

Natl Assoc of Small Bus. Inv. Co (NASBIC)

Project Preferences

Role in Financing:

Will function either as deal originator or investor in deals created by others

Type of Financing Preferred:

Second Stage Financing
Leveraged Buyout
Early Stage
Expansion
Seed
Management Buyouts
First Stage Financing
Special Situation
Startup
Recapitalizations

Size of Investments Considered:

Min Size of Investment Considered (000s): $100
Max Size of Investment Considered (000s): $500

Geographical Preferences

United States Preferences:

New Hampshire
Vermont
Northeast
Maine

Industry Preferences

In Communications prefer:

Communications and Media
Commercial Communications
CATV & Pay TV Systems
Radio & TV Broadcasting
Telecommunications
Wireless Communications
Data Communications
Satellite Microwave Comm.
Media and Entertainment

In Computer Hardware prefer:

Computers
Mainframes / Scientific
Mini and Personal/Desktop
Computer Graphics and Dig
Integrated Turnkey System
Terminals
Disk Relat. Memory Device

In Computer Software prefer:

Computer Services
Data Processing
Software
Systems Software
Applications Software
Artificial Intelligence

In Internet Specific prefer:

E-Commerce Technology
Internet
Ecommerce
Web Aggregration/Portals

In Computer Other prefer:

Computer Related

In Semiconductor/Electr prefer:

Electronics
Electronic Components
Semiconductor
Micro-Processing
Controllers and Sensors
Sensors
Circuit Boards
Component Testing Equipmt
Fiber Optics
Analytic/Scientific
Optoelectronics

In Biotechnology prefer:

Biotechnology
Human Biotechnology
Genetic Engineering
Agricultural/Animal Bio.
Industrial Biotechnology
Biotech Related Research

In Medical/Health prefer:

Medical/Health
Medical Diagnostics
Diagnostic Services
Diagnostic Test Products
Medical Therapeutics
Drug/Equipmt Delivery
Medical Products
Disposable Med. Products
Health Services
Hospitals/Clinics/Primary
Pharmaceuticals

In Consumer Related prefer:

Retail
Franchises(NEC)
Food/Beverage
Education Related

In Industrial/Energy prefer:

Industrial Products
Factory Automation
Machinery

In Transportation prefer:

Transportation

In Business Serv. prefer:

Services

In Manufact. prefer:

Manufacturing

In Other prefer:

Socially Responsible
Environment Responsible
Women/Minority-Owned Bus.

Additional Information

Year Founded: 2001
Capital Under Management: $10,000,000

Current Activity Level: Actively seeking new investments
Method of Compensation: Return on invest. most important, but chg. closing fees, service fees, etc.

CEI VENTURES, INC. (AKA: CVI)

Two Portland Fish Pier
Suite 201
Portland, ME USA 04101
Phone: 207-772-5356
Fax: 207-772-5503
Website: www.ceiventures.com

Management and Staff

Mark Kaplan, Vice President
Nathaniel Henshaw, President

Type of Firm

Corporate PE/Venture

Association Membership

Community Development Venture Capital Alliance
National Venture Capital Association - USA (NVCA)

Project Preferences

Role in Financing:

Will function either as deal originator or investor in deals created by others

Type of Financing Preferred:

Balanced

Size of Investments Considered:

Min Size of Investment Considered (000s): $250
Max Size of Investment Considered (000s): $2,000

Geographical Preferences

United States Preferences:

Northeast

Additional Information

Name of Most Recent Fund: Coastal Ventures II LLC
Most Recent Fund Was Raised: 03/06/2001
Year Founded: 1994
Capital Under Management: $25,500,000
Current Activity Level: Actively seeking new investments

CELERITY PARTNERS

11111 Santa Monica Boulevard
Suite 1127
Los Angeles, CA USA 90025
Phone: 310-268-1710
Fax: 310-268-1712
E-mail: info@celeritypartners.com
Website: www.celeritypartners.com

Other Offices

3000 Sand Hill Road
Building 3, Suite 105
Menlo Park, CA USA 94025
Phone: 650-233-7800
Fax: 650-233-8230

Management and Staff

Clifford Lyon, Chief Financial Officer
Mark Benham, Partner
Matthew Kraus, Principal
Stephen Adamson, Partner

Type of Firm

Private Equity Firm

Project Preferences

Role in Financing:

Will function either as deal originator or investor in deals created by others

Type of Financing Preferred:

Second Stage Financing
Leveraged Buyout
Mezzanine
Generalist PE
Later Stage
Management Buyouts
Acquisition
Recapitalizations

Geographical Preferences

Canadian Preferences:

All Canada

Industry Focus

(% based on actual investment)

Computer Hardware	38.1%
Semiconductors/Other Elect.	31.7%
Internet Specific	7.9%
Medical/Health	7.3%
Communications and Media	7.2%
Consumer Related	5.0%
Biotechnology	2.7%

Additional Information

Year Founded: 1994
Capital Under Management: $191,000,000
Current Activity Level: Actively seeking new investments

CELGENE CORPORATION

Seven Powder Horn Drive
Warren, NJ USA 07059
Phone: 732-271-1001
Website: www.celgene.com

Management and Staff

John Jackson, Chief Executive Officer
Robert Hugin, Chief Financial Officer
Sol Barer, President & COO

Type of Firm

Private Equity Firm

Additional Information

Year Founded: 2009
Current Activity Level: Actively seeking new investments

CELTIC HOUSE VENTURE PARTNERS

303 Terry Fox Drive
Suite 120
Kanata, Canada K2K 3J1
Phone: 613-271-2020
Fax: 613-271-2025
E-mail: info@celtic-house.com
Website: www.celtic-house.com

Other Offices

MaRS Centre, Heritage Building
101 College Street, Suite 155
Toronto, Canada M5G 1L7
Phone: 416-924-7000
Fax: 416-924-7090

Management and Staff

Brian Antonen, Partner
Julie Fallon, Chief Financial Officer
Pierre-Andre Meunier, Partner
Roger Maggs, Partner
Tom Valis, Partner

Type of Firm

Private Equity Firm

Association Membership

Canadian Venture Capital Association

Project Preferences

Type of Financing Preferred:

Early Stage
Seed
Startup

Geographical Preferences

United States Preferences:

All U.S.

Canadian Preferences:

All Canada

International Preferences:

United Kingdom
Europe

Industry Focus

(% based on actual investment)

Semiconductors/Other Elect.	45.4%
Computer Software and Services	21.0%
Internet Specific	15.3%
Communications and Media	13.7%
Medical/Health	4.7%

Additional Information

Name of Most Recent Fund: Celtic House Venture Partners Fund III, L.P.

Most Recent Fund Was Raised: 12/23/2004
Year Founded: 1994
Capital Under Management: $395,000,000
Current Activity Level: Actively seeking new investments
Method of Compensation: Return on invest. most important, but chg. closing fees, service fees, etc.

CELTIC PHARMA MANAGEMENT, LP

Wessex House
45 Reid Street, 4th Floor
Hamilton, Bermuda HM 12
Phone: 441-299-7440
E-mail: info@celticpharma.com
Website: www.celticpharma.com

Other Offices

663 Fifth Avenue
New York, NY USA 10022
Phone: 212-616-4000

Mercury House, Triton Court
14 Finsbury Square
London, United Kingdom EC2A 1BR
Phone: 44-20-7786-5550

Management and Staff

Averill Powers, Managing Director
John Mayo, Managing General Partner
Radomir Julina, Managing Director
Reinaldo Diaz, Partner
Stephen Parker, Managing Director
Stephen Evans-Freke, Managing General Partner

Type of Firm

Private Equity Firm

Project Preferences

Type of Financing Preferred:
Leveraged Buyout
Acquisition

Geographical Preferences

International Preferences:
All International

Industry Preferences

In Biotechnology prefer:
Biotechnology

In Medical/Health prefer:
Medical/Health
Diagnostic Services
Diagnostic Test Products
Drug/Equipmt Delivery
Pharmaceuticals

Additional Information

Year Founded: 2005
Capital Under Management: $350,000,000
Current Activity Level: Actively seeking new investments

CELTIC THERAPEUTICS MANAGEMENT, L.L.L.P.

34-35 Dronningens Gade
Hibiscus Alley
Saint Thomas, Am. Virgin Is. 00801
Phone: 340-779-6908
Fax: 340-714-5192
E-mail: info@celtictherapeutics.com
Website: www.celtictherapeutics.com

Other Offices

663 Fifth Avenue
New York, NY USA 10022
Phone: 212-616-4061

Management and Staff

Alexandre L Heureux, Chief Financial Officer
Averill Powers, Managing Director
Michael Forer, Partner
Peter Corr, General Partner
Reinaldo Diaz, Partner
Stephen Evans-Freke, Managing General Partner

Type of Firm

Private Equity Firm

Project Preferences

Type of Financing Preferred:
Leveraged Buyout
Acquisition

Industry Preferences

In Medical/Health prefer:
Medical/Health

Additional Information

Year Founded: 2007
Current Activity Level: Actively seeking new investments

CENTARA CORPORATION

One Lombard Place
Suite 2620
Winnipeg, Canada R3B0X5
Phone: 204-982-6977
Fax: 204-982-6970
Website: www.centara.ca

Management and Staff

James Schellenberg, Vice President

Type of Firm

Private Equity Firm

Project Preferences

Type of Financing Preferred:
Early Stage
Other

Geographical Preferences

United States Preferences:
East Coast

Canadian Preferences:
All Canada

Additional Information

Year Founded: 1998
Current Activity Level: Actively seeking new investments

CENTENIUM-PINETREE CHINA PRIVATE EQUITY

56 Boyun Road
Zhangjiang Hi-tech Park
Shanghai, China
Phone: 86-21-5855-9818
Website: www.cpchinacapital.com

Other Offices

300 Park Avenue
17th Floor
New York, NY USA 10022
Phone: 212-572-4896

89 West Third Ring North Road
China Foreign Building B, Suite 1106
Beijing, China
Phone: 86-21-5855-8859

Management and Staff

Andy Yu, Vice President
Angela Luo, Vice President
Hong Ke, Vice President
Junbin Li, Vice President
Lynn Wang, Vice President
Tony Wang, Vice President

Type of Firm

Private Equity Advisor or Fund of Funds

Project Preferences

Type of Financing Preferred:
Leveraged Buyout
Acquisition

Geographical Preferences

International Preferences:
China

Industry Preferences

In Medical/Health prefer:
Health Services

In Industrial/Energy prefer:
Energy
Alternative Energy

In Business Serv. prefer:
Services

In Manufact. prefer:
Manufacturing

Additional Information

Year Founded: 2009
Capital Under Management: $6,000,000
Current Activity Level: Actively seeking new investments

CENTENNIAL VENTURES

1125 Seventeenth Street
Suite 740
Denver, CO USA 80202
Phone: 303-405-7500
Fax: 303-405-7575
Website: www.centennial.com

Other Offices

4605 Post Oak Place
Suite 202
Houston, TX USA 77027
Phone: 713-627-9200
Fax: 713-627-9292

600 Congress Avenue
Suite 200
Austin, TX USA 78701
Phone: 512-505-4500
Fax: 512-505-4550

Management and Staff

Ben Moss, Principal
David Hull, Managing Director
Duncan Butler, Managing Director
Jeffrey Schutz, Managing Director
Neel Sarkar, Managing Director
Rand Lewis, Managing Director
Steven Halstedt, Managing Director

Type of Firm

Private Equity Firm

Association Membership

Natl Assoc of Small Bus. Inv. Co (NASBIC)
National Venture Capital Association - USA (NVCA)

Project Preferences

Role in Financing:
Prefer role as deal originator but will also invest in deals created by others

Type of Financing Preferred:
Early Stage
Balanced
Later Stage
Seed
First Stage Financing
Startup

Size of Investments Considered:
Min Size of Investment Considered (000s): $100
Max Size of Investment Considered: No Limit

Industry Focus

(% based on actual investment)

Communications and Media	39.7%
Internet Specific	27.4%
Computer Hardware	8.4%
Semiconductors/Other Elect.	8.2%
Computer Software and Services	7.0%
Other Products	4.5%
Medical/Health	2.0%
Biotechnology	1.8%
Consumer Related	0.6%
Industrial/Energy	0.3%

Additional Information

Name of Most Recent Fund: Centennial Ventures VII, L.P.
Most Recent Fund Was Raised: 12/28/2000
Year Founded: 1981
Capital Under Management: $100,000,000
Current Activity Level: Actively seeking new investments
Method of Compensation: Return on investment is of primary concern, do not charge fees

---

CENTERBRIDGE PARTNERS

375 Park Avenue
12th Floor
New York, NY USA 10019
Phone: 212-672-5000
Fax: 212-672-5001
E-mail: info@centerbridge.com
Website: www.centerbridge.com

Management and Staff

Jeffrey Gelfand, Managing Director
Jeffrey Aronson, Managing Director
Mark Gallogly, Managing Director
Steven Price, Managing Director

Type of Firm

Private Equity Firm

Project Preferences

Type of Financing Preferred:
Leveraged Buyout
Distressed Debt

Additional Information

Name of Most Recent Fund: Centerbridge Capital Partners, L.P.
Most Recent Fund Was Raised: 05/24/2006
Year Founded: 2006
Capital Under Management: $4,158,100,000
Current Activity Level: Actively seeking new investments

CENTERFIELD CAPITAL PARTNERS (FKA: MWV CAPITAL PARTNERS)

Ten West Market Street
3030 Market Tower
Indianapolis, IN USA 46204
Phone: 317-237-2323
Fax: 317-237-2325
E-mail: info@centerfieldcapital.com
Website: www.centerfieldcapital.com

Management and Staff

Faraz Abbasi, Partner
Matt Hook, Partner
Michael Miller, Chief Financial Officer
Scott Lutzke, Founding Partner
Thomas Hiatt, Founding Partner

Type of Firm

Private Equity Firm

Association Membership

Natl Assoc of Small Bus. Inv. Co (NASBIC)

Project Preferences

Role in Financing:
Will function either as deal originator or investor in deals created by others

Type of Financing Preferred:
Expansion
Mezzanine
Management Buyouts
Acquisition
Industry Rollups
Recapitalizations

Size of Investments Considered:
Min Size of Investment Considered (000s): $2,000
Max Size of Investment Considered (000s): $15,000

Geographical Preferences

United States Preferences:
Midwest

Industry Preferences

In Medical/Health prefer:
Health Services

In Transportation prefer:
Transportation

In Manufact. prefer:
Manufacturing

Additional Information

Name of Most Recent Fund: Centerfield Capital Partners (FKA: MWV Capital Partners III)
Most Recent Fund Was Raised: 07/01/2000
Year Founded: 2000
Capital Under Management: $190,000,000
Current Activity Level: Actively seeking new investments
Method of Compensation: Return on invest. most important, but chg. closing fees, service fees, etc.

CENTERPOINT VENTURE PARTNERS

Two Galleria Tower
13455 Noel Road, 16th Floor
Dallas, TX USA 75240
Phone: 972-702-1101
Fax: 972-702-1103
E-mail: info@cpventures.com
Website: www.cpventures.com

Other Offices

6300 Bridge Point Parkway
Building One, Suite 500
Austin, TX USA 78730
Phone: 512-795-5800
Fax: 512-795-5849

Management and Staff

Cameron McMartin, Managing Director
David Schaller, Managing Director
Eric Jones, Managing Director
Robert Paluck, Managing Director
Terry Rock, Managing Director

Type of Firm

Private Equity Firm

Association Membership

National Venture Capital Association - USA (NVCA)

Project Preferences

Role in Financing:

Prefer role as deal originator but will also invest in deals created by others

Type of Financing Preferred:

Second Stage Financing
Early Stage
First Stage Financing

Size of Investments Considered:

Min Size of Investment Considered (000s): $60
Max Size of Investment Considered (000s): $10,000

Geographical Preferences

United States Preferences:

Southwest
Texas

Industry Focus

(% based on actual investment)

Communications and Media	24.5%
Computer Software and Services	24.0%
Semiconductors/Other Elect.	16.2%
Internet Specific	13.7%
Medical/Health	8.3%
Computer Hardware	6.2%
Other Products	3.1%
Industrial/Energy	2.2%
Consumer Related	1.8%

Additional Information

Name of Most Recent Fund: CenterPoint Venture Fund III
Most Recent Fund Was Raised: 02/01/2001
Year Founded: 1996
Capital Under Management: $450,000,000
Current Activity Level: Actively seeking new investments

CENTERVIEW PARTNERS LLC

640 Fifth Avenue
19th Floor
New York, NY USA 10019
Phone: 212-380-2650
Fax: 212-380-2651
Website: www.centerviewpartners.com

Management and Staff

Adam Chinn, Partner
Alan Hartman, Partner
Anthony Kim, Partner
Blair Effron, Principal
Bryan Spielman, Partner
David Handler, Partner
David St. Jean, Partner
David Hooper, Partner
James Kilts, Founding Partner
Lisbeth Barron, Partner
Mark Robinson, Partner
Robert Pruzan, Partner
Stephen Crawford, Principal

Type of Firm

Private Equity Firm

Project Preferences

Type of Financing Preferred:

Leveraged Buyout
Balanced

Geographical Preferences

United States Preferences:

All U.S.

International Preferences:

All International

Industry Preferences

In Consumer Related prefer:

Consumer

Additional Information

Year Founded: 2006
Capital Under Management: $485,000,000
Current Activity Level: Actively seeking new investments

CENTINELA CAPITAL PARTNERS LLC

152 West 57th Street
34th Floor
New York, NY USA 10019
Phone: 212-823-0280
E-mail: admin@centinelacapital.com
Website: www.centinelacapital.com

Other Offices

777 South Figueroa Street
Suite 390
Los Angeles, CA USA 90017
Phone: 213-542-1800

Management and Staff

Fidel Vargas, Founding Partner
Robert Taylor, Founding Partner

Type of Firm

Private Equity Advisor or Fund of Funds

Project Preferences

Type of Financing Preferred:

Fund of Funds
Leveraged Buyout
Expansion

Additional Information

Year Founded: 2006
Capital Under Management: $400,000,000
Current Activity Level: Actively seeking new investments

CENTIVA CAPITAL

200 Bay Street, P.O. Box 84
Royal Bank Plaza, South Tower,
Toronto, Canada M5J 2Z4
Phone: 416-956-4926
Website: www.centivacapital.com/

Type of Firm

Investment Management Firm

Additional Information

Year Founded: 2007
Current Activity Level: Actively seeking new investments

CENTRAL AFRICAN INVESTMENT CORPORATION (AKA: CENAINVEST SA)

Quartier Fouda
Yaounde, Cameroon 11838
Phone: 237-793-6067
Fax: 237-223-3295
E-mail: info@cinainvest.com
Website: www.cenainvest.com

Type of Firm

Private Equity Advisor or Fund of Funds

Association Membership

African Venture Capital Association (AVCA)

Project Preferences

Type of Financing Preferred:
Early Stage
Expansion
Balanced
Seed
Startup

Size of Investments Considered:
Min Size of Investment Considered (000s): $178
Max Size of Investment Considered (000s): $1,184

Geographical Preferences

International Preferences:
Rwanda
Albania
Gabon
Congo
Cameroon
Chad
Equator Guinea
C. African Rep
Sao Tome

Industry Preferences

In Communications prefer:
Communications and Media

In Semiconductor/Electr prefer:
Electronics

In Biotechnology prefer:
Agricultural/Animal Bio.

In Medical/Health prefer:
Pharmaceuticals

In Industrial/Energy prefer:
Energy

In Transportation prefer:
Transportation

In Financial Services prefer:
Financial Services
Insurance
Real Estate

In Manufact. prefer:
Manufacturing

Additional Information

Year Founded: 1998
Capital Under Management: $19,100,000
Current Activity Level: Actively seeking new investments

CENTRAS CAPITAL PARTNERS

Manas strasse, 32-A
Almaty, Kazakhstan 050008
Phone: 7-727-311-1111
Fax: 7-727-237-8478
E-mail: mail@centrascapital.com
Website: www.centrascapital.com

Management and Staff

Dauren Alipbayev, Managing Director
Eldar Abdrazakov, Managing Director

Type of Firm

Investment Management Firm

Project Preferences

Type of Financing Preferred:
Early Stage
Expansion

Size of Investments Considered:
Min Size of Investment Considered (000s): $4,500
Max Size of Investment Considered (000s): $7,500

Geographical Preferences

International Preferences:
Kazakhstan
Asia
Russia

Industry Preferences

In Communications prefer:
Telecommunications

In Consumer Related prefer:
Consumer

In Industrial/Energy prefer:
Materials
Environmental Related

In Financial Services prefer:
Financial Services

Additional Information

Year Founded: 2004
Capital Under Management: $10,000,000
Current Activity Level: Actively seeking new investments

CENTRE CAPITAL DEVELOPPEMENT SA

38, rue de la Marine de Loire
Le Verlaine
Orleans Cedex 1, France 45100
Phone: 33-2-3822-3060
Fax: 33-2-3856-6225
E-mail: ccd@sofimacpartners.com
Website: www.centrecapitaldeveloppement.com

Management and Staff

Catherine Kraft Le Marec, President

Type of Firm

Private Equity Firm

Association Membership

French Venture Capital Association (AFIC)

Project Preferences

Type of Financing Preferred:
Balanced

Geographical Preferences

International Preferences:
Europe
France

Additional Information

Year Founded: 1987
Current Activity Level: Actively seeking new investments

CENTRE LOIRE EXPANSION SAS

26 rue de la Godde
St Jean de Braye, France
Phone: 33-23860-2000
Fax: 33-23860-2020
E-mail: centreloire.expansion@ca-centreloire.fr
Website: www.ca-centreloire.fr

Type of Firm

Bank Affiliated

Project Preferences

Type of Financing Preferred:
Generalist PE

Geographical Preferences

International Preferences:
France

Additional Information

Year Founded: 2005
Current Activity Level: Actively seeking new investments

CENTRE PARTNERS MANAGEMENT LLC

30 Rockefeller Plaza
Suite 5050
New York, NY USA 10020
Phone: 212-332-5800
Fax: 212-332-5801
E-mail: info@centrepartners.com
Website: www.centrepartners.com

Other Offices

11726 San Vicente Boulevard
Suite 450
Los Angeles, CA USA 90049
Phone: 310-207-9170
Fax: 310-207-9180

Management and Staff

Bruce Pollack, Managing Partner
David Blatte, Managing Director

David Jaffe, Managing Partner
Jeffrey Bartoli, Managing Director
William Tomai, Chief Financial Officer

Type of Firm

Private Equity Firm

Project Preferences

Role in Financing:

Prefer role as deal originator but will also invest in deals created by others

Type of Financing Preferred:

Leveraged Buyout
Generalist PE
Public Companies
Management Buyouts
Industry Rollups
Recapitalizations

Size of Investments Considered:

Min Size of Investment Considered (000s): $15,000
Max Size of Investment Considered (000s): $100,000

Geographical Preferences

United States Preferences:

All U.S.

Canadian Preferences:

All Canada

Industry Focus

(% based on actual investment)	
Other Products	60.2%
Consumer Related	30.0%
Industrial/Energy	2.7%
Computer Hardware	2.5%
Semiconductors/Other Elect.	2.4%
Internet Specific	1.4%
Communications and Media	0.7%

Additional Information

Name of Most Recent Fund: Centre Capital Investors IV, L.P.
Most Recent Fund Was Raised: 11/06/2003
Year Founded: 1986
Capital Under Management: $2,600,000,000
Current Activity Level: Actively seeking new investments
Method of Compensation: Return on invest. most important, but chg. closing fees, service fees, etc.

CENTRE QUEBECOIS DE VALORISATION DES BIOTECHNOLOGIES (CQVB)

2875, Boulevard Laurier
Bureau 620
Quebec, Canada G1V 2M2
Phone: 418-657-3853
Fax: 418-657-7934
E-mail: cqvb@cqvb.qc.ca
Website: www.cqvb.qc.ca

Management and Staff

Jean-Maurice Plourde, President

Type of Firm

Private Equity Firm

Additional Information

Year Founded: 2009
Current Activity Level: Actively seeking new investments

CENTRE SOUTHWEST PARTNERS LLC

2001 Ross Avenue
31st Floor
Dallas, TX USA 75201
Phone: 214-239-8640
Fax: 214-239-8644
E-mail: info@centresw.com
Website: www.centresw.com

Management and Staff

J. Kent Sweezey, Principal
Todd Tomlin, Principal

Type of Firm

Private Equity Firm

Project Preferences

Type of Financing Preferred:

Leveraged Buyout
Mezzanine
Acquisition

Geographical Preferences

United States Preferences:

Southwest

Industry Preferences

In Medical/Health prefer:

Medical/Health

In Consumer Related prefer:

Consumer
Education Related

In Industrial/Energy prefer:

Energy
Industrial Products

In Transportation prefer:

Transportation
Aerospace

In Financial Services prefer:

Financial Services

In Business Serv. prefer:

Services

In Manufact. prefer:

Manufacturing

Additional Information

Year Founded: 2007
Current Activity Level: Actively seeking new investments

CENTRESTONE VENTURES INC.

1250 Waverley Street
Suite 7
Winnipeg, Canada R3T 6C6
Phone: 204-477-7590
Fax: 204-453-1293
E-mail: info@CentreStoneVentures.com
Website: www.CentreStoneVentures.com

Management and Staff

Albert Friesen, Chief Executive Officer
Rick Pauls, Managing Director

Type of Firm

Private Equity Firm

Project Preferences

Type of Financing Preferred:

Early Stage

Geographical Preferences

United States Preferences:

Midwest

Canadian Preferences:

Western Canada

Industry Preferences

In Medical/Health prefer:

Medical Diagnostics
Medical Therapeutics
Medical Products

Additional Information

Year Founded: 2004
Capital Under Management: $21,100,000
Current Activity Level: Actively seeking new investments

CENTRIPETAL CAPITAL PARTNERS, INC.

100 Prospect Street
Suite 201 South
Stamford, CT USA 06901
Phone: 203-326-7600
Fax: 203-316-9329
E-mail: info@centricap.com
Website: www.centricap.com

Other Offices

57 Danbury Road
Suite 103
Wilton, CT USA 06897

Phone: 203-834-6222
Fax: 203-834-2473

Management and Staff

Jeffrey Brodlieb, Principal
Stephen Rossetter, Principal

Type of Firm

Private Equity Firm

Project Preferences

Type of Financing Preferred:
Leveraged Buyout
Early Stage
Mezzanine
Management Buyouts
Acquisition

Size of Investments Considered:
Min Size of Investment Considered (000s): $2,000
Max Size of Investment Considered (000s): $20,000

Geographical Preferences

United States Preferences:
All U.S.

Additional Information

Year Founded: 2004
Current Activity Level: Actively seeking new investments

CENTRO VENTURE - SOCIEDADE CAPITAL RISCO, S.A.

Rua Coronel
Julio Veiga Simao
Coimbra, Portugal 3000
Phone: 351-239-497-167
Fax: 351-239-497-168

Type of Firm

Private Equity Firm

Association Membership

European Private Equity and Venture Capital Assoc.

Project Preferences

Type of Financing Preferred:
Balanced

Geographical Preferences

International Preferences:
Portugal

Additional Information

Year Founded: 2006
Current Activity Level: Actively seeking new investments

CENTROBANCA

Viale Maino, 7
16, Corso Europa
Milan, Italy 20122
Phone: 39-02-7781-4630
Fax: 39-02-7781-4402
E-mail: privateequity@centrobanca.it
Website: www.centrobanca.it

Type of Firm

Bank Affiliated

Association Membership

Italian Venture Capital Association (AIFI)

Project Preferences

Type of Financing Preferred:
Leveraged Buyout
Expansion
Management Buyouts

Geographical Preferences

International Preferences:
Italy
Europe

Industry Preferences

In Medical/Health prefer:
Medical/Health
Health Services

In Financial Services prefer:
Financial Services

In Manufact. prefer:
Manufacturing

Additional Information

Year Founded: 1946
Current Activity Level: Actively seeking new investments

CENTROBANCA SVILUPPO IMPRESA SGR

Corso Europa 16
Milan, Italy 20122
Phone: 39-02-77814621
Fax: 39-02-77814626

Type of Firm

Bank Affiliated

Additional Information

Year Founded: 2003
Current Activity Level: Actively seeking new investments

CENTUM INVESTMENT (FKA: ICDC INVESTMENT CO., LTD.)

International Life House
Mama Ngina Street
Nairobi, Kenya
Phone: 254-20-316-303
Fax: 254-20-223-223
E-mail: info@centum.co.ke
Website: www.icdci.co.ke

Management and Staff

Peter Mwangi, Managing Director

Type of Firm

Private Equity Firm

Project Preferences

Type of Financing Preferred:
Balanced

Geographical Preferences

International Preferences:
Kenya

Additional Information

Year Founded: 1967
Current Activity Level: Actively seeking new investments

CENTURION CAPITAL LTD

C/O Hogan and Hartson
One Angel Court
London, United Kingdom EC2R 7HJ
Phone: 44-207-629-2669
Website: www.centcap.co.uk

Management and Staff

Edwin Richards, Managing Director
Richard Waryn, Chief Executive Officer

Type of Firm

Private Equity Firm

Association Membership

European Private Equity and Venture Capital Assoc.

Project Preferences

Type of Financing Preferred:
Expansion
Turnaround

Size of Investments Considered:
Min Size of Investment Considered (000s): $6,079
Max Size of Investment Considered (000s): $36,474

Geographical Preferences

International Preferences:
Central Europe
Europe

Eastern Europe

Industry Preferences

In Consumer Related prefer:
Consumer
Publishing-Retail
Consumer Products
Consumer Services

Additional Information

Year Founded: 2003
Capital Under Management: $182,400,000
Current Activity Level: Actively seeking new investments

CENTURION CAPITAL LTD (FKA: FINARTIS PRIVATE EQUITY, LTD.)

C/O Hogan & Hartson
One Angel Court
London, United Kingdom EC2R7HJ
Phone: 44-20-7866-6075
E-mail: info@finartis.co.uk

Management and Staff

Richard Waryn, Managing Director

Type of Firm

Bank Affiliated

Association Membership

European Private Equity and Venture Capital Assoc.

Project Preferences

Type of Financing Preferred:
Expansion
Balanced
Turnaround

Size of Investments Considered:
Min Size of Investment Considered (000s): $6,079
Max Size of Investment Considered (000s): $36,474

Geographical Preferences

International Preferences:
Europe
Central Europe
Eastern Europe

Industry Preferences

In Consumer Related prefer:
Consumer
Publishing-Retail
Consumer Products
Consumer Services

Additional Information

Year Founded: 2004
Capital Under Management: $182,400,000
Current Activity Level: Actively seeking new investments

CENTURION INVESTMENT MANAGEMENT

80 Raffles Place
No. 28-02 UOB Plaza 1
Singapore, Singapore 048624
Phone: 65-6100-1288
Fax: 65-6438-0320
Website: www.centurion-investment.com

Other Offices

183 Queen's Road Central
Unit 4007 COSCO Tower
Hong Kong, Hong Kong
Phone: 852-2169-0966
Fax: 852-2907-7669

268 Xi Zang Road
Suite 4906-41 Raffles City Office Tower
Shanghai, China
Phone: 86-21-6340-4081
Fax: 86-21-6340-4187

Management and Staff

Kay Hua Tang, Chief Executive Officer

Type of Firm

Private Equity Firm

Project Preferences

Type of Financing Preferred:
Expansion
Generalist PE
Management Buyouts

Geographical Preferences

International Preferences:
China

Industry Preferences

In Consumer Related prefer:
Consumer
Food/Beverage

In Manufact. prefer:
Manufacturing

In Other prefer:
Environment Responsible

Additional Information

Year Founded: 2004
Current Activity Level: Actively seeking new investments

CENTURY CAPITAL MANAGEMENT, INC.

100 Federal Street
29th Floor
Boston, MA USA 02110
Phone: 617-482-3060
Fax: 617-542-9398
E-mail: info@centurycap.com
Website: www.centurycap.com

Management and Staff

Charles Kline, Managing Director
Chris Lalonde, Principal
Davis Fulkerson, Managing Director
Gerard Vecchio, Managing Director
James Stradtner, Managing Director
Kevin Callahan, Managing Director
Patrick Carolan, Managing Director
Richard Smith, Managing Director
Steven Alfano, Chief Financial Officer

Type of Firm

Private Equity Firm

Project Preferences

Type of Financing Preferred:
Leveraged Buyout
Balanced
Later Stage
Startup

Size of Investments Considered:
Min Size of Investment Considered (000s): $5,000
Max Size of Investment Considered (000s): $15,000

Geographical Preferences

United States Preferences:
All U.S.

Industry Focus

(% based on actual investment)

Other Products	40.7%
Internet Specific	38.0%
Computer Hardware	8.6%
Medical/Health	7.4%
Computer Software and Services	5.2%
Communications and Media	0.1%

Additional Information

Name of Most Recent Fund: Century Capital Partners IV, L.P.
Most Recent Fund Was Raised: 05/07/2006
Year Founded: 1987
Capital Under Management: $224,000,000
Current Activity Level: Actively seeking new investments

CENTURY PARK CAPITAL PARTNERS

10250 Constellation Boulevard
Suite 2850
Los Angeles, CA USA 90067
Phone: 310-867-2210
Fax: 310-867-2212
E-mail: info@cpclp.com
Website: www.cpclp.com

Other Offices

1010 El Camino Real
Suite 300

Menlo Park, CA USA 94025
Phone: 650-324-1956
Fax: 650-322-1550

Management and Staff

Charles Roellig, Partner
Guy Zaczepinski, Vice President
Martin Sarafa, Managing Partner
Martin Jelenko, Managing Partner
Paul Wolf, Partner

Type of Firm

Bank Affiliated

Project Preferences

Type of Financing Preferred:
Leveraged Buyout
Management Buyouts
Recapitalizations

Size of Investments Considered:
Min Size of Investment Considered (000s): $5,000
Max Size of Investment Considered (000s): $20,000

Geographical Preferences

United States Preferences:
All U.S.

Industry Focus

(% based on actual investment)

Other Products	68.1%
Consumer Related	31.9%

Additional Information

Year Founded: 1999
Capital Under Management: $107,000,000
Current Activity Level: Actively seeking new investments

CEPHAS CAPITAL PARTNERS, L.P.

57 Monroe Avenue
Suite D
Pittsford, NY USA 14534
Phone: 585-383-1610
Fax: 585-383-1613
Website: cephascapital.com/

Type of Firm

Private Equity Firm

Additional Information

Year Founded: 1998
Capital Under Management: $10,000,000
Current Activity Level: Actively seeking new investments

CERBERUS CAPITAL MANAGEMENT, L.P.

299 Park Avenue
New York, NY USA 10171
Phone: 212-891-2100
Fax: 212-891-1545
Website: www.cerberuscapital.com

Management and Staff

Jeffrey Lomasky, Chief Financial Officer
Kevin Genda, Senior Managing Director
Lenard Tessler, Managing Director
Mark Neporent, Senior Managing Director
Seth Plattus, Senior Managing Director
Steven Mayer, Managing Director
William Richter, President

Type of Firm

Private Equity Firm

Project Preferences

Type of Financing Preferred:
Leveraged Buyout
Turnaround
Acquisition
Distressed Debt
Recapitalizations

Geographical Preferences

United States Preferences:
All U.S.

Canadian Preferences:
All Canada

International Preferences:
Thailand
Asia
Japan
All International

Industry Focus

(% based on actual investment)

Other Products	85.8%
Consumer Related	10.5%
Computer Software and Services	2.1%
Industrial/Energy	1.0%
Biotechnology	0.4%
Communications and Media	0.2%

Additional Information

Name of Most Recent Fund: Blackacre Institutional Partners, L.P.
Most Recent Fund Was Raised: 03/22/2004
Year Founded: 1993
Capital Under Management: $7,000,000,000
Current Activity Level: Actively seeking new investments

CEREA GESTION SAS

23 Avenue de Neuilly
Paris, France 75116
Phone: 33-1-4431-1033
Fax: 33-1-4431-1650
Website: www.cereagestion.com

Management and Staff

Jean-Francois Laurain, President

Type of Firm

Private Equity Firm

Association Membership

French Venture Capital Association (AFIC)

Project Preferences

Role in Financing:
Prefer role as deal originator

Type of Financing Preferred:
Leveraged Buyout
Mezzanine

Geographical Preferences

International Preferences:
Europe
France

Industry Preferences

In Biotechnology prefer:
Agricultural/Animal Bio.

Additional Information

Year Founded: 2004
Capital Under Management: $174,400,000
Current Activity Level: Actively seeking new investments
Method of Compensation: Return on invest. most important, but chg. closing fees, service fees, etc.

CERES VENTURE FUND

500 Davis Street
Suite 600
Evanston, IL USA 60201
Phone: 847-492-1111
Fax: 847-864-9692
E-mail: contact@ceresventurefund.com
Website: www.ceresventurefund.com

Management and Staff

Donna Williamson, Managing Director
Laura Pearl, Managing Director
Sona Wang, Managing Director

Type of Firm

Private Equity Firm

Association Membership

Illinois Venture Capital Association

Project Preferences

Type of Financing Preferred:
Early Stage

Size of Investments Considered:
Min Size of Investment Considered (000s): $300
Max Size of Investment Considered (000s): $1,500

Geographical Preferences

United States Preferences:
Midwest
Illinois

Industry Preferences

In Computer Software prefer:
Computer Services
Software
Applications Software

In Internet Specific prefer:
E-Commerce Technology

In Biotechnology prefer:
Human Biotechnology

In Medical/Health prefer:
Diagnostic Services
Medical Therapeutics
Health Services

In Financial Services prefer:
Financial Services

In Business Serv. prefer:
Consulting Services

In Other prefer:
Women/Minority-Owned Bus.

Additional Information

Year Founded: 2006
Capital Under Management: $20,000,000
Current Activity Level: Actively seeking new investments

CEVIAN CAPITAL AB (FKA: AMARANTH CAPITAL)

Engelbrektsgatan 5, 2tr
Stockholm, Sweden 114 32
Phone: 46-8-545-67550
Fax: 46-8-545-67560
E-mail: info@ceviancapital.com
Website: www.ceviancapital.com

Type of Firm

Private Equity Firm

Project Preferences

Type of Financing Preferred:
Generalist PE
Public Companies

Geographical Preferences

International Preferences:
Europe
Greenland
Iceland
Scandanavia/Nordic Region
Finland
Norway
Denmark

Additional Information

Year Founded: 2002
Capital Under Management: $2,521,000,000
Current Activity Level: Actively seeking new investments

CEYUAN VENTURES MANAGEMENT, LLC

No. 35, Qinlao Hutong
Dongcheng District
Beijing, China 100009
Phone: 86-10-8402-8800
Fax: 86-10-8402-0999
E-mail: info@ceyuanvc.com
Website: www.ceyuanvc.com

Other Offices

460 Bush Street
2nd Floor
San Francisco, CA USA 94108
Phone: 415-295-8300
Fax: 415-627-9079

Room 2609 Grand Grateway
Tower 1, 1 Hong Qiao Road
Shanghai, China 200030
Phone: 86-21-6448-5757
Fax: 86-21-6447-8211

Management and Staff

Bo Feng, Managing General Partner
Chen Keyi, Vice President
Chris Wadsworth, Managing General Partner
Wang Yi, Vice President
Zhang Fei, Partner
Zhao Weiguo, Partner

Type of Firm

Bank Affiliated

Project Preferences

Role in Financing:
Prefer role as deal originator but will also invest in deals created by others

Type of Financing Preferred:
Early Stage
Seed

Geographical Preferences

International Preferences:
China
Asia

Industry Preferences

In Communications prefer:
Wireless Communications

In Computer Software prefer:
Software

In Internet Specific prefer:
Internet

In Semiconductor/Electr prefer:
Semiconductor

Additional Information

Year Founded: 2005
Capital Under Management: $212,900,000
Current Activity Level: Actively seeking new investments

CF ADVISORS, LLC

666 Fifth Avenue
New York, NY USA 10103
Phone: 212-689-1203
Fax: 212-484-5020

Management and Staff

Paul Orlin, Principal

Type of Firm

Private Equity Firm

Additional Information

Year Founded: 1997
Capital Under Management: $92,000,000
Current Activity Level: Actively seeking new investments

CF INVESTMENT COMPANY (CAROLINA FIRST)

104 South Main Street
Poinsett Plaza
Greenville, SC USA 29601
Phone: 864-255-4919
Fax: 864-239-6423

Type of Firm

Bank Affiliated

Project Preferences

Size of Investments Considered:
Min Size of Investment Considered (000s): $100
Max Size of Investment Considered (000s): $1,000

Additional Information

Year Founded: 1997
Capital Under Management: $3,000,000
Current Activity Level: Actively seeking new investments

CFC INDUSTRIEBETEILIGUNGEN GMBH & CO. KGAA

Ruhrallee 9
Dortmund, Germany 44139
Phone: 49-231-952-5373
Fax: 49-231-952-545
E-mail: info@cfc-eu.com
Website: www.cfc-eu.com

Management and Staff

Marcus Linnepe, Managing Director

Type of Firm

Private Equity Firm

Project Preferences

Type of Financing Preferred:
Leveraged Buyout

Industry Preferences

In Manufact. prefer:
Manufacturing

Additional Information

Year Founded: 2007
Current Activity Level: Actively seeking new investments

CFI CAPITAL

229 Niagara Street
Toronto, Canada M6J 2L5
Phone: 416-364-6191
Fax: 416-364-1012
E-mail: info@corpfinance.ca
Website: www.corpfinance.ca

Management and Staff

Andre Nadon, Vice President
David Bell, Managing Director
Eric Skillins, Vice President
Gerry Hway, Vice President
Jacques Huot, Vice President
Michael Breen, Vice President
Peter Heffernan, Vice President

Type of Firm

Investment Management Firm

Additional Information

Year Founded: 2004
Current Activity Level: Actively seeking new investments

CFSC WAYLAND ADVISERS, INC.

12700 Whitewater Drive
Minnetonka, MN USA 55343
Phone: 952-984-3178
Fax: 952-345-8901

Type of Firm

Private Equity Firm

Project Preferences

Type of Financing Preferred:
Distressed Debt

Additional Information

Year Founded: 1997
Capital Under Management: $16,700,000
Current Activity Level: Actively seeking new investments

CGS MANAGEMENT GIESINGER GLOOR LANZ&CO (AKA:CGS MANAGEMENT)

Huobstrasse 14
Pfaeffikon, Switzerland 8808
Phone: 41-55-416-1640
Fax: 41-55-416-1641
E-mail: info@cgs-management.com
Website: www.cgs-management.com

Management and Staff

Alexandra Keller, General Partner
Antonio Cives, General Partner
Peter F Gloor, General Partner
Rico M Casparis, General Partner

Type of Firm

Private Equity Firm

Association Membership

Swiss Venture Capital Association (SECA)
European Private Equity and Venture Capital Assoc.

Project Preferences

Type of Financing Preferred:
Leveraged Buyout
Balanced
Management Buyouts
Recapitalizations

Geographical Preferences

International Preferences:
Switzerland
Europe

Industry Preferences

In Semiconductor/Electr prefer:
Electronics

In Medical/Health prefer:
Medical/Health

In Industrial/Energy prefer:
Industrial Products
Machinery

In Manufact. prefer:
Manufacturing

Additional Information

Name of Most Recent Fund: CGS Private Equity Partnership I
Most Recent Fund Was Raised: 06/01/1998
Year Founded: 1998
Capital Under Management: $109,600,000
Current Activity Level: Actively seeking new investments

CGW SOUTHEAST PARTNERS (AKA: CRAVEY, GREEN, & WAHLEN)

12 Piedmont Center
Suite 210
Atlanta, GA USA 30305
Phone: 404-816-3255
Fax: 404-816-3258
Website: www.cgwlp.com

Management and Staff

Bart McLean, Partner
Edwin Wahlen, Managing Partner
Garrison Kitchen, Partner
Michael Long, Partner
Richard Cravey, Managing Partner

Type of Firm

Private Equity Firm

Project Preferences

Role in Financing:
Prefer role as deal originator but will also invest in deals created by others

Type of Financing Preferred:
Acquisition
Recapitalizations

Size of Investments Considered:
Min Size of Investment Considered (000s): $25,000
Max Size of Investment Considered (000s): $200,000

Geographical Preferences

United States Preferences:
All U.S.

International Preferences:
United Kingdom
Luxembourg
Netherlands
Portugal
Spain
Belgium
Germany
France

Industry Focus

(% based on actual investment)

Other Products	38.1%
Industrial/Energy	26.6%

Consumer Related	22.6%
Medical/Health	6.6%
Communications and Media	6.1%

Additional Information

Name of Most Recent Fund: CGW Southeast Partners IV, L.P.
Most Recent Fund Was Raised: 05/01/1999
Year Founded: 1984
Capital Under Management: $750,000,000
Current Activity Level: Reducing investment activity
Method of Compensation: Return on invest. most important, but chg. closing fees, service fees, etc.

CHALLENGE FUND - ETGAR LP

20 Lincoln Street
Rubenstein House, 20/F
Tel Aviv, Israel 67134
Phone: 972-3-562-8555
Fax: 972-3-562-1999
E-mail: etgar@challenge.co.il
Website: www.challenge.co.il

Management and Staff

Joseph Ciechanover, President

Type of Firm

Private Equity Firm

Project Preferences

Type of Financing Preferred:

Early Stage
Expansion
Mezzanine
Turnaround
Balanced

Geographical Preferences

International Preferences:

Israel

Industry Preferences

In Communications prefer:

Communications and Media
Telecommunications

In Computer Software prefer:

Software

In Internet Specific prefer:

Internet

In Biotechnology prefer:

Biotechnology

In Medical/Health prefer:

Pharmaceuticals

Additional Information

Year Founded: 1995
Capital Under Management: $250,000,000
Current Activity Level: Actively seeking new investments

CHALLENGE JAPAN INVESTMENT CO., LTD.

2-5-1 Kita-Aoyama
Minato-ku
Tokyo, Japan 107-0061
Phone: 81-3-3497-8633
Fax: 81-3-3408-5781
Website: www.ganbarefund.com

Other Offices

Chuo-ku, 4-1-3
Taro Hisashi-cho
Osaka, Japan 541-0056
Phone: 83-6-6241-3383
Fax: 83-6-6241-3387

Management and Staff

Tadashi Nakamura, President

Type of Firm

Corporate PE/Venture

Additional Information

Year Founded: 2003
Capital Under Management: $36,900,000
Current Activity Level: Actively seeking new investments

CHALLENGER INTERNATIONAL LTD.

Level 41, Aurora Place
88 Philip Street
Sydney, Australia 2000
Phone: 612-9994-7000
Fax: 612-9994-7777
E-mail: info@challenger.com.au
Website: www.challenger.com.au

Other Offices

Level Three
55 St Georges Terrace
Perth, Australia 6000
Phone: 618-9223-7800
Fax: 618-9221-2499

Level Ten
101 Collins Street
Melbourne, Australia 3000
Phone: 613-8616-1000
Fax: 613-8616-1111

Level Nine
175 Eagle Street
Brisbane, Australia 4000
Phone: 617-3218-8000
Fax: 617-3220-3132

Level One
212 Pirie Street
Adelaide, Australia 5000
Phone: 618-8211-7777
Fax: 618-8212-1661

Level One
27 Elizabeth Street
Hobart, Australia 7000

Management and Staff

Dominic Stevens, Managing Director
Mike Tilley, Chief Executive Officer
Paul Rogan, Chief Financial Officer

Type of Firm

Bank Affiliated

Project Preferences

Type of Financing Preferred:

Early Stage
Expansion
Mezzanine
Balanced

Size of Investments Considered:

Min Size of Investment Considered (000s): $1,127
Max Size of Investment Considered (000s): $2,254
Geographical Preferences

International Preferences:

Pacific
Australia

Industry Preferences

In Internet Specific prefer:

Internet

In Biotechnology prefer:

Biotechnology

Additional Information

Name of Most Recent Fund: eFinancial Capital Ltd.
Most Recent Fund Was Raised: 08/09/2000
Year Founded: 1987
Capital Under Management: $2,226,400,000
Current Activity Level: Actively seeking new investments

CHALMERS INNOVATION

Stena Center 1D
Goteborg, Sweden 412 92
Phone: 46-31-772-8100
Fax: 46-31-772-8091
Website: www.chalmersinnovation.com

Management and Staff

Olle Stenberg, President

Type of Firm

Private Equity Firm

Association Membership

Swedish Venture Capital Association (SVCA)
European Private Equity and Venture Capital Assoc.

Project Preferences

Type of Financing Preferred:

Early Stage

Seed
Startup

Geographical Preferences

International Preferences:

Sweden
Europe

Additional Information

Year Founded: 1997
Capital Under Management: $1,700,000
Current Activity Level: Actively seeking new investments

CHAMP PRIVATE EQUITY PTY LTD.

31 Alfred Street
Level 4, Customs House
Sydney, Australia 2000
Phone: 612-8248-8888
Fax: 612-8248-8877
E-mail: champ@champequity.com.au
Website: www.champmbo.com

Other Offices

150 East 58th Street
37th Floor
New York, NY USA 10155
Phone: 212-644-8600
Fax: 212-207-8042

Level 25
North Tower, One Raffles Quay
Singapore, Singapore 048583
Phone: 65-6622-5628
Fax: 65-6622-5629

Level 36 Riparian Plaza
71 Eagle Street
Brisbane, Australia 4000
Phone: 617-3121-3122
Fax: 617-3121-3030

Management and Staff

Benjamin Sebel, Managing Director
Cameron Buchanan, Managing Director
David Jones, Managing Director
Joseph Skrzynski, Founding Partner
Nathaniel Childres, Managing Director
Su-Ming Wong, Managing Director

Type of Firm

Bank Affiliated

Association Membership

Australian Venture Capital Association (AVCAL)

Project Preferences

Role in Financing:

Prefer role as deal originator but will also invest in deals created by others

Type of Financing Preferred:

Leveraged Buyout
Early Stage
Expansion
Mezzanine
Generalist PE
Later Stage
Seed
Management Buyouts

Size of Investments Considered:

Min Size of Investment Considered (000s): $12,117
Max Size of Investment Considered (000s): $36,351

Geographical Preferences

Canadian Preferences:

Alberta

International Preferences:

Europe
China
Hong Kong
Pacific
Australia
Asia
New Zealand

Industry Focus

(% based on actual investment)

Other Products	35.4%
Consumer Related	32.5%
Industrial/Energy	23.1%
Communications and Media	5.7%
Medical/Health	1.1%
Biotechnology	0.6%
Internet Specific	0.5%
Computer Hardware	0.5%
Semiconductors/Other Elect.	0.4%
Computer Software and Services	0.2%

Additional Information

Name of Most Recent Fund: CHAMP Buyout II Trust (AKA: CHAMP II Worldwide, L.P.)
Most Recent Fund Was Raised: 06/17/2005
Year Founded: 1987
Capital Under Management: $401,500,000
Current Activity Level: Actively seeking new investments
Method of Compensation: Return on invest. most important, but chg. closing fees, service fees, etc.

CHAMP VENTURE PTY LTD.

31 Alfred Street
Level 4 Customs House
Sydney, Australia 2000
Phone: 612-8248-8888
Fax: 612-8248-8877
E-mail: champ@champequity.com.au
Website: www.champmbo.com

Other Offices

6 Battery Road
Suite 12-08
Singapore, Singapore 049909
Phone: 65-6576-9179
Fax: 65-6576-9170

Type of Firm

Private Equity Firm

Association Membership

Australian Venture Capital Association (AVCAL)

Project Preferences

Type of Financing Preferred:

Early Stage
Expansion
Later Stage

Size of Investments Considered:

Min Size of Investment Considered (000s): $12,087
Max Size of Investment Considered (000s): $36,261

Additional Information

Name of Most Recent Fund: CHAMP Ventures Investments Trust No. 6 Funds
Most Recent Fund Was Raised: 04/24/2006
Year Founded: 1998
Capital Under Management: $370,700,000
Current Activity Level: Actively seeking new investments

CHAMPAGNE ARDENNE CROISSANCE

2 Rue Carnot
Reims, France 51100
Phone: 33-3-2640-0326
Fax: 33-3-26-88-3750
E-mail: irpac@wandoo.fr
Website: perso.wanadoo.fr/irpac-cac/

Management and Staff

Dominique Minevielle, President

Type of Firm

Government Affiliated Program

Project Preferences

Type of Financing Preferred:

Early Stage
Startup

Geographical Preferences

International Preferences:

France

Additional Information

Year Founded: 2000
Current Activity Level: Actively seeking new investments

CHAMPLAIN CAPITAL MANAGEMENT LLC

44 Montgomery Street
Suite 1920
San Francisco, CA USA 94104
Phone: 415-281-4181
Fax: 415-362-3211
Website: www.champlaincapital.com

Management and Staff

Dennis Leary, Partner
Eric Menke, Partner
Frohman Anderson, Partner
Warren Feldberg, Partner

Type of Firm

Private Equity Firm

Project Preferences

Type of Financing Preferred:
Leveraged Buyout
Recapitalizations

Industry Preferences

In Business Serv. prefer:
Services
Distribution

In Manufact. prefer:
Manufacturing

Additional Information

Year Founded: 2002
Capital Under Management: $146,000,000
Current Activity Level: Actively seeking new investments

CHANG AN CAPITAL

No. 23 Xihaibeiyan
Xicheng
Beijing, China 100035
Phone: 86-10-8400-2728
Fax: 86-10-8400-2716
Website: www.changancap.com

Type of Firm

Private Equity Firm

Project Preferences

Type of Financing Preferred:
Balanced

Geographical Preferences

International Preferences:
China

Industry Preferences

In Consumer Related prefer:
Consumer

In Industrial/Energy prefer:
Environmental Related

In Agr/Forestr/Fish prefer:
Agribusiness

Additional Information

Year Founded: 1998
Current Activity Level: Actively seeking new investments

CHANGE CAPITAL PARTNERS LLP

College House
272 Kings Road
London, United Kingdom SW3 5AW
Phone: 44-207-808-9110
Fax: 44-207-808-9111
E-mail: info@changecapitalpartners.com
Website: www.changecapitalpartners.com

Management and Staff

Patrick Burke, Partner
Steven Petrow, Partner

Type of Firm

Private Equity Firm

Project Preferences

Type of Financing Preferred:
Leveraged Buyout
Management Buyouts

Geographical Preferences

International Preferences:
United Kingdom
Europe

Industry Preferences

In Consumer Related prefer:
Consumer
Entertainment and Leisure
Retail

Additional Information

Year Founded: 2003
Capital Under Management: $324,700,000
Current Activity Level: Actively seeking new investments

CHANGE PARTNERS, S.A.

Avenida da Boavista
1281-3
Porto, Portugal 4100-130
Phone: 351-22-607-5700
Fax: 351-22-607-5709
E-mail: cppe@changepartners.pt
Website: www.changepartners.pt

Management and Staff

Paulo Ribeiro, Founding Partner

Type of Firm

Private Equity Firm

Association Membership

European Private Equity and Venture Capital Assoc.

Project Preferences

Type of Financing Preferred:
Leveraged Buyout
Early Stage
Expansion
Later Stage
Special Situation
Startup

Geographical Preferences

International Preferences:
Portugal
Spain

Industry Preferences

In Communications prefer:
Communications and Media
Telecommunications

In Computer Other prefer:
Computer Related

In Semiconductor/Electr prefer:
Electronics

In Biotechnology prefer:
Biotechnology

In Medical/Health prefer:
Medical/Health

In Consumer Related prefer:
Consumer
Consumer Products

In Industrial/Energy prefer:
Energy
Industrial Products

In Business Serv. prefer:
Media

Additional Information

Year Founded: 2000
Capital Under Management: $30,600,000
Current Activity Level: Actively seeking new investments

CHANGSHA HIGH-TECH VENTURE CAPITAL CO., LTD.

No. 101 Xiangjiang South Road
5/F Huiyuan Building
Changsha, China 410002
Phone: 86-731-8286-868
Fax: 86-731-8286-898
Website: www.cshvc.com

Type of Firm
Private Equity Firm

Project Preferences

Type of Financing Preferred:
Balanced

Geographical Preferences

International Preferences:
China

Additional Information
Year Founded: 2000
Current Activity Level: Actively seeking new investments

CHANGSHA SCIENCE & TECHNOLOGY VENTURE CAPITAL CO., LTD.

No. 101 Xiangjiang Road
5/F Huiyuan Building
Changsha, China 410002
Phone: 86-731-8286-887
Fax: 86-731-8286-892
Website: www.csvvc.cn

Type of Firm
Government Affiliated Program

Project Preferences

Type of Financing Preferred:
Early Stage
Expansion
Balanced
Later Stage
Startup

Size of Investments Considered:
Min Size of Investment Considered (000s): $293
Max Size of Investment Considered (000s): $2,933

Geographical Preferences

International Preferences:
China

Industry Preferences

In Semiconductor/Electr prefer:
Electronics

In Biotechnology prefer:
Biotechnology

In Medical/Health prefer:
Medical/Health

In Industrial/Energy prefer:
Energy
Materials
Environmental Related

In Agr/Forestr/Fish prefer:
Agriculture related

Additional Information
Year Founded: 2000
Current Activity Level: Actively seeking new investments

CHANGZHOU AOYANG VENTURE CAPITAL COMPANY

Wujin Economic Dev'l Zone
Changzhou, China

Type of Firm
Private Equity Firm

Project Preferences

Type of Financing Preferred:
Balanced

Geographical Preferences

International Preferences:
China

Additional Information
Year Founded: 2009
Current Activity Level: Actively seeking new investments

CHANNEL GROUP LLC, THE (TCG)

1133 Broadway
Suite 706
New York, NY USA 10010
Phone: 212-330-8076
Fax: 212-627-8877
E-mail: info@thechannelgroup.com
Website: www.thechannelgroup.com

Management and Staff
Allan Goldberg, Managing Director
Philip Sussman, Managing Partner
Robert Beckman, Managing Director

Type of Firm
Incubator/Development Program

Project Preferences

Type of Financing Preferred:
Seed
Startup
Special Situation

Geographical Preferences

United States Preferences:
All U.S.

International Preferences:
Western Europe
All International

Industry Preferences

In Medical/Health prefer:
Medical/Health
Pharmaceuticals

Additional Information
Year Founded: 2001
Current Activity Level: Actively seeking new investments

CHANNEL MEDICAL PARTNERS

5750 Old Orchard Road
Suite 310
Skokie, IL USA 60077
Phone: 847-779-1500
Fax: 847-779-1535
E-mail: info@chanmed.com
Website: www.chanmed.com

Management and Staff
Carol Winslow, Principal
W. Gregory Shearer, Principal

Type of Firm
Private Equity Firm

Association Membership
Natl Assoc of Small Bus. Inv. Co (NASBIC)

Project Preferences

Role in Financing:
Prefer role as deal originator but will also invest in deals created by others

Type of Financing Preferred:
Expansion
Later Stage

Size of Investments Considered:
Min Size of Investment Considered (000s): $1,500
Max Size of Investment Considered (000s): $2,500

Industry Preferences

In Medical/Health prefer:
Medical Therapeutics
Medical Products

Additional Information
Name of Most Recent Fund: Channel Medical Partners, L.P.
Most Recent Fund Was Raised: 12/28/2000
Year Founded: 2000
Capital Under Management: $40,000,000
Current Activity Level: Actively seeking new investments
Method of Compensation: Return on investment is of primary concern, do not charge fees

CHANNELSTONE PARTNERS LLC

156 West 56th Street
Suite 904
New York, NY USA 10019
Phone: 212-757-8774
Fax: 212-757-8972
E-mail: info@channelstone.com
Website: www.channelstone.com

Management and Staff

R.T. Arnold, Partner
Rush McCloy, Partner

Type of Firm

Private Equity Firm

Project Preferences

Type of Financing Preferred:

Leveraged Buyout
Expansion
Management Buyouts
Acquisition

Size of Investments Considered:

Min Size of Investment Considered (000s): $5,000
Max Size of Investment Considered (000s): $20,000

Geographical Preferences

United States Preferences:

All U.S.

Additional Information

Year Founded: 2008
Current Activity Level: Actively seeking new investments

CHARLEMAGNE CAPITAL (UK) LIMITED

39 St James's Street
London, United Kingdom SW1A 1JD
Phone: 44-207-518-2100
Fax: 44-207-518-2198
E-mail: marketing@charlemagnecapital.com
Website: www.charlemagnecapital.com

Other Offices

Tsum Business Centre
2 Kniagina Maria Louisa
Sofia, Bulgaria 1550
Phone: 359-2-926-0600
Fax: 359-2-926-0692

16-18 Ridgeway Street
Douglas
Isle of Man, United Kingdom IM1 1EN
Phone: 44-1624-640-200
Fax: 44-1624-614-474

Management and Staff

Hans Van Griethuysen, Chief Executive Officer

Type of Firm

Investment Management Firm

Project Preferences

Type of Financing Preferred:

Leveraged Buyout
Expansion
Turnaround
Other
Management Buyouts
Acquisition

Geographical Preferences

International Preferences:

Slovenia
Turkey
Central Europe
Argentina
Croatia
Eastern Europe
Bulgaria
Romania

Additional Information

Year Founded: 1997
Capital Under Management: $38,000,000
Current Activity Level: Actively seeking new investments

CHARLES RIVER VENTURES

1000 Winter Street
Suite 3300
Waltham, MA USA 02451
Phone: 781-768-6000
Fax: 781-768-6100
Website: www.crv.com

Other Offices

2800 Sand Hill Road
Suite 150
Menlo Park, CA USA 94025
Phone: 650-687-5600
Fax: 650-687-5699

Management and Staff

Austin Westerling, Partner
Bruce Sachs, Partner
Chris Baldwin, Partner
Devdutt Yellurkar, Venture Partner
George Zachary, Partner
Izhar Armony, General Partner
Jack Genest, Chief Financial Officer
Jon Auerbach, Partner
Michael Zak, Partner
Richard Burnes, Partner
Saar Gur, Partner
Swapnil Shah, Venture Partner
Ted Dintersmith, Partner
William Tai, Partner

Type of Firm

Private Equity Firm

Association Membership

National Venture Capital Association - USA (NVCA)

Project Preferences

Role in Financing:

Will function either as deal originator or investor in deals created by others

Type of Financing Preferred:

Early Stage
Start-up Financing
Seed
First Stage Financing

Size of Investments Considered:

Min Size of Investment Considered (000s): $3,000
Max Size of Investment Considered (000s): $10,000

Geographical Preferences

United States Preferences:

All U.S.

Industry Focus

(% based on actual investment)

Internet Specific	31.6%
Computer Software and Services	23.2%
Communications and Media	22.8%
Computer Hardware	6.4%
Semiconductors/Other Elect.	5.6%
Other Products	3.9%
Industrial/Energy	3.1%
Medical/Health	1.9%
Consumer Related	0.9%
Biotechnology	0.5%

Additional Information

Name of Most Recent Fund: Charles River Partnership XIV, L.P.
Most Recent Fund Was Raised: 03/30/2009
Year Founded: 1970
Capital Under Management: $1,774,000,000
Current Activity Level: Actively seeking new investments
Method of Compensation: Return on investment is of primary concern, do not charge fees

CHARLESBANK CAPITAL PARTNERS LLC

200 Clarendon Street
54th Floor
Boston, MA USA 02116
Phone: 617-619-5400
Fax: 617-619-5402
E-mail: info@charlesbank.com
Website: www.charlesbank.com

Other Offices

70 East 55th Street
20th Floor
New York, NY USA 10022

Phone: 212-903-1880
Fax: 212-903-1890

Management and Staff

Andrew Janower, Managing Director
Brandon White, Managing Director
Charles Wu, Managing Director
J. Ryan Carroll, Vice President
Jon Biotti, Managing Director
Josh Klevens, Vice President
Kim Davis, Managing Director
Mark Rosen, Managing Director
Michael Choe, Managing Director
Michael Eisenson, CEO & Managing Director
Michael Thonis, Chief Operating Officer
Sam Bartlett, Vice President
Tim Palmer, Managing Director

Type of Firm

Investment Management Firm

Project Preferences

Role in Financing:

Prefer role as deal originator but will also invest in deals created by others

Type of Financing Preferred:

Leveraged Buyout
Expansion
Mezzanine
Generalist PE
Turnaround
Later Stage
Other
Management Buyouts
Acquisition
Special Situation
Recapitalizations

Size of Investments Considered:

Min Size of Investment Considered (000s): $20,000
Max Size of Investment Considered (000s): $75,000

Geographical Preferences

United States Preferences:

All U.S.

Canadian Preferences:

All Canada

Industry Focus

(% based on actual investment)

Other Products	54.1%
Consumer Related	21.1%
Computer Software and Services	5.5%
Medical/Health	5.0%
Communications and Media	4.9%
Semiconductors/Other Elect.	4.1%
Internet Specific	2.2%
Industrial/Energy	2.0%
Biotechnology	1.2%

Additional Information

Name of Most Recent Fund: CB Offshore Equity Fund, VI, L.P.
Most Recent Fund Was Raised: 06/08/2005
Year Founded: 1998
Capital Under Management: $2,300,000,000
Current Activity Level: Actively seeking new investments
Method of Compensation: Return on invest. most important, but chg. closing fees, service fees, etc.

CHARLOTTE ANGEL PARTNERS

5615 Laurium Road
Charlotte, NC USA 28226
Phone: 704-362-4659
Fax: 704-362-4659
E-mail: capllc@hotmail.com
Website: www.capnc.com

Type of Firm

Angel Group

Project Preferences

Role in Financing:

Prefer role in deals created by others

Type of Financing Preferred:

Early Stage
Expansion

Size of Investments Considered:

Min Size of Investment Considered (000s): $1,000
Max Size of Investment Considered (000s): $26,000

Geographical Preferences

United States Preferences:

North Carolina
South Carolina
Virginia

Additional Information

Year Founded: 2000
Capital Under Management: $8,000,000
Current Activity Level: Actively seeking new investments
Method of Compensation: Return on investment is of primary concern, do not charge fees

---

CHARMEX VENTURES LIMITED

The Oast House
5 Mead Lane
Farnham, United Kingdom GU9 7DY
Phone: 44-12-5273-4411
Fax: 44-12-5273-4536

Type of Firm

Private Equity Firm

Association Membership

European Private Equity and Venture Capital Assoc.

Project Preferences

Type of Financing Preferred:

Early Stage
Expansion
Turnaround
Seed
Startup

Geographical Preferences

International Preferences:

Europe

Industry Preferences

In Communications prefer:

Communications and Media

In Internet Specific prefer:

Internet

In Biotechnology prefer:

Biotechnology

In Medical/Health prefer:

Medical/Health

Additional Information

Year Founded: 1998
Capital Under Management: $1,500,000
Current Activity Level: Actively seeking new investments

CHART CAPITAL MANAGEMENT LLC

75 Rockefeller Plaza
14th Floor
New York, NY USA 10019
Phone: 212-350-8200
Fax: 212-350-8299
E-mail: info@chartcapital.com
Website: www.chartcapital.com

Management and Staff

Christopher Brady, Co-Founder
David Collier, Managing Director

Type of Firm

Bank Affiliated

Project Preferences

Role in Financing:

Prefer role as deal originator

Type of Financing Preferred:

Leveraged Buyout
Expansion
Recapitalizations

Size of Investments Considered:

Min Size of Investment Considered (000s): $10,000
Max Size of Investment Considered (000s): $40,000

Geographical Preferences

United States Preferences:

All U.S.

Industry Preferences

In Communications prefer:
Telecommunications

In Consumer Related prefer:
Consumer

In Industrial/Energy prefer:
Energy
Industrial Products

In Business Serv. prefer:
Media

In Manufact. prefer:
Manufacturing

Additional Information

Year Founded: 2000
Capital Under Management: $250,000,000
Current Activity Level: Actively seeking new investments

CHART VENTURE PARTNERS

75 Rockefeller Plaza
14th Floor
New York, NY USA 10019
Phone: 212-350-8224
Fax: 212-350-8299
Website: www.chartventure.com

Other Offices

3305 Main Road
Suite 104
Picatinny Arsenal, NJ USA 07806

Management and Staff

Cole Van Nice, Partner
Michael Wu, Principal
Ted Hobart, Partner

Type of Firm

Private Equity Firm

Project Preferences

Role in Financing:
Will function either as deal originator or investor in deals created by others

Type of Financing Preferred:
Second Stage Financing
Early Stage
Expansion
Balanced
First Stage Financing
Startup
Industry Rollups
Joint Ventures

Size of Investments Considered:
Min Size of Investment Considered (000s): $500
Max Size of Investment Considered (000s): $3,500

Geographical Preferences

United States Preferences:
All U.S.

Additional Information

Year Founded: 2006
Capital Under Management: $93,000,000
Current Activity Level: Actively seeking new investments
Method of Compensation: Return on investment is of primary concern, do not charge fees

CHARTER COMMUNICATIONS

12405 Powerscou Drive
Saint Louis, MO USA 63131
Website: www.charter.com

Management and Staff

Carl Vogel, Chief Executive Officer
Maggie Bellville, Chief Operating Officer

Type of Firm

Private Equity Firm

Additional Information

Year Founded: 2009
Current Activity Level: Actively seeking new investments

CHARTER LIFE SCIENCES

525 University Avenue
Suite 1400
Palo Alto, CA USA 94301
Phone: 650-325-6953
Fax: 650-325-4762
Website: www.clsvc.com

Other Offices

3130 Highland Avenue
Suite 3205
Cincinnati, OH USA 45219
Phone: 513-475-6643
Fax: 513-475-6645

Management and Staff

A. Barr Dolan, Managing Partner
Andrew Klatt, Chief Financial Officer
Donald Harrison, Managing Partner
Fred Schwarzer, Managing Partner
Gino Di Sciullo, Venture Partner
Martin Sanders, Venture Partner
Nelson Teng, Managing Partner

Type of Firm

Private Equity Firm

Project Preferences

Role in Financing:
Prefer role as deal originator but will also invest in deals created by others

Type of Financing Preferred:
Early Stage
Seed
First Stage Financing

Size of Investments Considered:
Min Size of Investment Considered (000s): $500
Max Size of Investment Considered (000s): $8,000

Geographical Preferences

United States Preferences:
Midwest
West Coast
All U.S.

Industry Preferences

In Biotechnology prefer:
Human Biotechnology

In Medical/Health prefer:
Medical Therapeutics
Medical Products

Additional Information

Name of Most Recent Fund: Charter Life Sciences II, L.P.
Most Recent Fund Was Raised: 05/05/2008
Year Founded: 2003
Capital Under Management: $66,200,000
Current Activity Level: Actively seeking new investments
Method of Compensation: Return on investment is of primary concern, do not charge fees

CHARTER VENTURE CAPITAL (AKA: CHARTER VENTURES)

525 University Avenue
Suite 1400
Palo Alto, CA USA 94301
Phone: 650-325-6953
Fax: 650-325-4762
E-mail: info@charterventures.com
Website: www.charterventures.com

Management and Staff

A. Barr Dolan, General Partner
Johnson Cha, General Partner

Type of Firm

Private Equity Firm

Association Membership

Western Association of Venture Capitalists (WAVC)

Project Preferences

Role in Financing:
Prefer role as deal originator but will also invest in deals created by others

Type of Financing Preferred:
Early Stage

Size of Investments Considered:
Min Size of Investment Considered (000s): $500
Max Size of Investment Considered (000s): $10,000

Geographical Preferences

United States Preferences:
All U.S.

Industry Focus

(% based on actual investment)

Internet Specific	21.4%
Medical/Health	21.0%
Biotechnology	17.3%
Computer Software and Services	16.0%
Communications and Media	8.4%
Computer Hardware	6.5%
Semiconductors/Other Elect.	6.1%
Other Products	2.7%
Industrial/Energy	0.6%

Additional Information

Year Founded: 1982
Capital Under Management: $378,000,000
Current Activity Level: Actively seeking new investments
Method of Compensation: Return on investment is of primary concern, do not charge fees

CHARTERHOUSE CAPITAL PARTNERS LLP

Warwick Court
Paternoster Square
London, United Kingdom EC4M 7DX
Phone: 44-20-7334-5300
Fax: 44-20-7334-5333
Website: www.charterhouse.co.uk

Other Offices

1, rue Paul Cezanne
Paris, France 75008
Phone: 33-1-7039-7500
Fax: 33-1-7039-7548

Type of Firm

Private Equity Firm

Association Membership

British Venture Capital Association (BVCA)
French Venture Capital Association (AFIC)
European Private Equity and Venture Capital Assoc.

Project Preferences

Role in Financing:
Prefer role as deal originator but will also invest in deals created by others

Type of Financing Preferred:
Second Stage Financing
Leveraged Buyout
Expansion
Later Stage

Geographical Preferences

International Preferences:
United Kingdom
Europe
Western Europe

Industry Focus

(% based on actual investment)

Other Products	88.2%
Consumer Related	10.3%
Semiconductors/Other Elect.	1.1%
Industrial/Energy	0.2%
Medical/Health	0.1%
Computer Hardware	0.1%

Additional Information

Name of Most Recent Fund: Charterhouse Capital Partners VIII
Most Recent Fund Was Raised: 03/31/2006
Year Founded: 1934
Capital Under Management: $16,432,500,000
Current Activity Level: Actively seeking new investments
Method of Compensation: Return on invest. most important, but chg. closing fees, service fees, etc.

CHARTERHOUSE GROUP INTERNATIONAL, INC.

535 Madison Avenue
28th Floor
New York, NY USA 10022-4299
Phone: 212-584-3200
Fax: 212-750-9704
E-mail: info@charterhousegroup.com
Website: www.charterhousegroup.com

Management and Staff

A. Lawrence Fagan, Partner
C.Taylor Cole, Partner
Cheri Lieberman, Chief Financial Officer
Christian Hensley, Vice President
David Hoffman, Partner
James Silver, Partner
Jay Gates, Partner
Joseph Rhodes, Partner
Lori Livers-Hess, Partner
Mitchell Quain, Principal
Paul Verrochi, Principal
Phyllis Haberman, Partner
Richard Henshaw, Partner
Thomas Dircks, Managing Partner

Type of Firm

Private Equity Firm

Project Preferences

Type of Financing Preferred:
Leveraged Buyout

Industry Focus

(% based on actual investment)

Communications and Media	29.1%
Consumer Related	15.1%
Other Products	14.9%
Medical/Health	12.8%
Industrial/Energy	12.6%
Computer Software and Services	6.5%
Semiconductors/Other Elect.	6.2%
Computer Hardware	2.2%
Internet Specific	0.7%

Additional Information

Year Founded: 1973
Capital Under Management: $320,000,000
Current Activity Level: Actively seeking new investments

CHATHAM CAPITAL

400 Galleria Parkway
Suite 1950
Atlanta, GA USA 30339
Phone: 770-618-2100
Fax: 770-618-2101
Website: www.chathamcapital.com

Management and Staff

Brian Reynolds, Managing Partner
Cheryl Boyd, Partner
Jack Guy, Partner
Nick Anacreonte, Partner

Type of Firm

Private Equity Firm

Project Preferences

Role in Financing:
Will function either as deal originator or investor in deals created by others

Type of Financing Preferred:
Leveraged Buyout
Expansion
Mezzanine
Turnaround
Later Stage
Management Buyouts
Acquisition
Private Placement

Size of Investments Considered:
Min Size of Investment Considered (000s): $700
Max Size of Investment Considered (000s): $60,000

Geographical Preferences

United States Preferences:
Mid Atlantic
Southeast

Industry Preferences

In Medical/Health prefer:
Medical/Health
Medical Diagnostics

Medical Products
Health Services
Hospitals/Clinics/Primary

In Financial Services prefer:
Financial Services

In Business Serv. prefer:
Services
Distribution

In Manufact. prefer:
Manufacturing

Additional Information
Year Founded: 2001
Capital Under Management: $150,000,000
Current Activity Level: Actively seeking new investments
Method of Compensation: Return on invest. most important, but chg. closing fees, service fees, etc.

CHAZEN CAPITAL PARTNERS
767 Fifth Avenue
26th Floor
New York, NY USA 10153
Phone: 212-888-7800
Fax: 212-888-4580
E-mail: info@chazen.com
Website: www.chazen.com

Type of Firm
Private Equity Firm

Additional Information
Year Founded: 1997
Current Activity Level: Actively seeking new investments

CHB CAPITAL PARTNERS
511 Sixteenth Street
Suite 600
Denver, CO USA 80202
Phone: 303-552-5400
Fax: 303-552-5424
Website: www.chbcapital.com

Other Offices
75 Fifth Street, NW
Suite 1025
Atlanta, GA USA 30308
Phone: 404-806-7520

Management and Staff
Blake Morris, Partner
Grant Clayton, Partner
John Flanigan, Managing Partner
Sean McClenaghan, Partner
Tad Kelly, Managing Partner

Type of Firm
Private Equity Firm

Project Preferences

Role in Financing:
Prefer role as deal originator

Type of Financing Preferred:
Expansion
Generalist PE
Management Buyouts
Recapitalizations

Size of Investments Considered:
Min Size of Investment Considered (000s): $2,000
Max Size of Investment Considered (000s): $20,000

Geographical Preferences

United States Preferences:
All U.S.

Additional Information
Name of Most Recent Fund: CHB Capital Partners III, L.P.
Most Recent Fund Was Raised: 06/10/2004
Year Founded: 1995
Capital Under Management: $114,000,000
Current Activity Level: Actively seeking new investments
Method of Compensation: Return on invest. most important, but chg. closing fees, service fees, etc.

CHENG XIN TECHNOLOGY DEVELOPMENT CORP. (FKA: FIDELITY VC)
5/F, No 143 Min-Sheng East Rd.
Section 2
Taipei, Taiwan
Phone: 886-2-2507-2960
Fax: 886-2-2500-6908
E-mail: info@chengxin.com.tw
Website: www.chengxin.com.tw

Management and Staff
Han-Ton Lim, President & Chairman
Jerry Chen, Managing Director

Type of Firm
Private Equity Firm

Association Membership
Taiwan Venture Capital Association(TVCA)

Project Preferences

Type of Financing Preferred:
Early Stage
Expansion
Mezzanine
Balanced

Size of Investments Considered:
Min Size of Investment Considered (000s): $1,000
Max Size of Investment Considered (000s): $2,000

Geographical Preferences

International Preferences:
Taiwan

Industry Preferences

In Communications prefer:
Telecommunications

In Computer Software prefer:
Software

In Internet Specific prefer:
Internet

In Semiconductor/Electr prefer:
Electronics
Semiconductor
Optoelectronics

In Biotechnology prefer:
Biotechnology

In Medical/Health prefer:
Medical/Health
Pharmaceuticals

In Industrial/Energy prefer:
Advanced Materials

In Other prefer:
Environment Responsible

Additional Information
Name of Most Recent Fund: Bio 21 Venture Capital Corporation
Most Recent Fund Was Raised: 09/01/2002
Year Founded: 1990
Capital Under Management: $160,000,000
Current Activity Level: Actively seeking new investments

CHENGDU VENTURE CAPITAL CO., LTD.
No. 308 Shuncheng Street
22/F Guancheng Guangchang
Chengdu, China 610017
Phone: 86-28-8652-8368
Fax: 86-28-8652-8268
E-mail: cdvc@cd-vc.com
Website: www.cd-vc.com

Type of Firm
Private Equity Firm

Project Preferences

Type of Financing Preferred:
Balanced

Geographical Preferences

International Preferences:
China

Industry Preferences

In Computer Software prefer:
Software

In Semiconductor/Electr prefer:
Electronics

In Biotechnology prefer:
Biotechnology

In Medical/Health prefer:
Medical/Health

In Industrial/Energy prefer:
Energy
Materials
Environmental Related

Additional Information

Year Founded: 2001
Current Activity Level: Actively seeking new investments

CHENGDU YINKE VENTURE CAPITAL CO., LTD.

No. 1480 Tianfu Beidao
Room 501 Gaoxin Fuhuayuan
Chengdu, China 610041

Type of Firm

Government Affiliated Program

Project Preferences

Type of Financing Preferred:
Fund of Funds
Balanced

Geographical Preferences

International Preferences:
China

Industry Preferences

In Semiconductor/Electr prefer:
Electronics

In Industrial/Energy prefer:
Machinery

Additional Information

Year Founded: 2009
Capital Under Management: $219,400,000
Current Activity Level: Actively seeking new investments

CHENGWEI VENTURES

Lane 672 Changle Road
Suite 33C
Shanghai, China 200040
Phone: 86-21-5404-8566
Fax: 86-21-5404-8766
E-mail: general@chengwei.com
Website: www.chengwei.com

Other Offices

58 West Portal Avenue #146
San Francisco, CA USA 94127

Management and Staff

Eric Xun Li, Managing Director
Griffith Baker, Venture Partner
Pei Kang, Managing Director
Ping Ping, Managing Director
Yang Dong Shao, Managing Director
Ye Sha, Venture Partner

Type of Firm

Private Equity Firm

Project Preferences

Type of Financing Preferred:
Balanced

Geographical Preferences

International Preferences:
China
All International

Industry Preferences

In Computer Software prefer:
Software

In Semiconductor/Electr prefer:
Electronic Components

In Medical/Health prefer:
Medical/Health

In Financial Services prefer:
Financial Services

In Business Serv. prefer:
Media

In Manufact. prefer:
Manufacturing

Additional Information

Year Founded: 1999
Current Activity Level: Actively seeking new investments

CHEQUERS CAPITAL (FKA: CHARTERHOUSE SA)

48 bis, avenue Montaigne
Paris, France 75008
Phone: 33-1-5357-6100
Fax: 33-1-5357-6111
E-mail: mail@chequerscapital.com

Management and Staff

Anne-Claire Louvet, Partner
Dominique Du Pelloux, Partner
Guillaume Planchon, Partner
Jerome Kinas, Partner

Type of Firm

Private Equity Firm

Association Membership

French Venture Capital Association (AFIC)

Project Preferences

Type of Financing Preferred:
Leveraged Buyout
Management Buyouts

Geographical Preferences

International Preferences:
Europe
France

Additional Information

Year Founded: 2001
Capital Under Management: $761,800,000
Current Activity Level: Actively seeking new investments

CHERINGTON CAPITAL

50 Church Street
Fourth Floor
Cambridge, MA USA 02142
Phone: 617-497-8282
Fax: 617-838-3053
Website: www.cherington.com

Management and Staff

Charles Cherington, Managing Partner

Type of Firm

Private Equity Firm

Additional Information

Year Founded: 2009
Current Activity Level: Actively seeking new investments

CHERRY TREE INVESTMENTS, INC.

301 Carlson Parkway
Suite 103
Minnetonka, MN USA 55305
Phone: 952-893-9012
Fax: 952-893-9036
E-mail: info@cherrytree.com
Website: www.cherrytree.com

Other Offices

20323 Bald Mountain Court
Monument, CO USA 80132
Phone: 303-683-4674
Fax: 720-294-0284

Management and Staff

Chad Johnson, Principal
Charles Gorman, Managing Director
David Latzke, Managing Director
Gordon Stofer, Managing Partner
John Hammett, Managing Director

Kevin McKenna, Managing Director
Larry Pape, Managing Director
Rob Martin, Principal
Tony Christianson, Managing Partner
Ty Schlobohm, Managing Director
Wayne Atkins, Managing Director

Type of Firm

Bank Affiliated

Association Membership

National Venture Capital Association - USA (NVCA)

Project Preferences

Role in Financing:

Prefer role as deal originator but will also invest in deals created by others

Type of Financing Preferred:

Second Stage Financing
Early Stage
Mezzanine
Turnaround
Later Stage
Management Buyouts
First Stage Financing
Private Placement
Special Situation
Recapitalizations

Size of Investments Considered:

Min Size of Investment Considered (000s): $250
Max Size of Investment Considered (000s): $1,000

Geographical Preferences

United States Preferences:

Midwest

Industry Preferences

In Communications prefer:

Commercial Communications
CATV & Pay TV Systems
Radio & TV Broadcasting
Telecommunications
Wireless Communications
Data Communications
Satellite Microwave Comm.
Other Communication Prod.

In Computer Hardware prefer:

Computer Graphics and Dig

In Computer Software prefer:

Computer Services
Software
Systems Software
Applications Software
Artificial Intelligence

In Internet Specific prefer:

Internet
Ecommerce
Web Aggregration/Portals

In Semiconductor/Electr prefer:

Controllers and Sensors
Sensors
Laser Related
Fiber Optics
Analytic/Scientific

In Biotechnology prefer:

Human Biotechnology
Agricultural/Animal Bio.
Industrial Biotechnology
Biosensors
Biotech Related Research

In Medical/Health prefer:

Drug/Equipmt Delivery
Disposable Med. Products
Health Services

In Consumer Related prefer:

Consumer
Retail
Franchises(NEC)
Education Related

In Financial Services prefer:

Financial Services

In Business Serv. prefer:

Services
Distribution

In Agr/Forestr/Fish prefer:

Agriculture related

Additional Information

Name of Most Recent Fund: Cherry Tree Ventures IV
Most Recent Fund Was Raised: 04/01/1991
Year Founded: 1980
Capital Under Management: $37,200,000
Current Activity Level: Actively seeking new investments
Method of Compensation: Return on investment is of primary concern, do not charge fees

---

CHESAPEAKE EMERGING OPPORTUNITIES CLUB LLC

8808 Centre Park Drive
Suite 204
Columbia, MD USA 21045
Phone: 443-367-0101
Fax: 410-964-8302
Website: www.ceopportunities.com

Management and Staff

John May, Partner
Patrick Huddie, Partner
Steve Dubin, Partner

Type of Firm

Angel Group

Association Membership

Mid-Atlantic Venture Association

Project Preferences

Role in Financing:

Will function either as deal originator or investor in deals created by others

Type of Financing Preferred:

Early Stage

Size of Investments Considered:

Min Size of Investment Considered (000s): $150
Max Size of Investment Considered (000s): $200

Geographical Preferences

United States Preferences:

Mid Atlantic

Industry Preferences

In Biotechnology prefer:

Human Biotechnology
Industrial Biotechnology
Biotech Related Research

In Medical/Health prefer:

Medical Diagnostics
Diagnostic Test Products
Disposable Med. Products

Additional Information

Year Founded: 2001
Capital Under Management: $4,000,000
Current Activity Level: Actively seeking new investments
Method of Compensation: Return on investment is of primary concern, do not charge fees

---

CHESS VENTURES

One Embarcadero Centre
Suite 4100
San Francisco, CA USA 94111
Phone: 415-315-1250
Fax: 415-315-1253
Website: www.chessventures.com

Other Offices

40 Saint James's Place
London, United Kingdom SW1A 1NS
Phone: 44-20-7629-9233
Fax: 44-20-7629-9244

Type of Firm

Private Equity Firm

Additional Information

Year Founded: 2004
Current Activity Level: Actively seeking new investments

CHEVRILLON & ASSOCIES SCA

4 Champs Elysees M Dassault
Paris, France 75008

Type of Firm

Investment Management Firm

Project Preferences

Type of Financing Preferred:
Generalist PE

Geographical Preferences

International Preferences:
Europe

Additional Information

Year Founded: 1992
Current Activity Level: Actively seeking new investments

CHEVRON TECHNOLOGY VENTURES (CTTV INVESTMENTS LLC)

6121 Bollinger Canyon Road
San Ramon, CA USA 94583
Phone: 925-358-7777
Fax: 925-807-0385
E-mail: CTVLLC@Chevron.com
Website: www.chevron.com/ctv/ctvi/

Other Offices

3901 Briarpark
Houston, TX USA 77042
Phone: 713-954-6360
Fax: 925-807-0385

Management and Staff

Matt McElhattan, Principal
Richard Pardoe, Principal
Trond Unneland, Vice President

Type of Firm

Corporate PE/Venture

Association Membership

National Venture Capital Association - USA (NVCA)

Project Preferences

Role in Financing:
Prefer role in deals created by others

Type of Financing Preferred:
Second Stage Financing
Early Stage
Expansion
Balanced
Later Stage
First Stage Financing

Size of Investments Considered:
Min Size of Investment Considered (000s): $500
Max Size of Investment Considered (000s): $7,000

Industry Preferences

In Communications prefer:
Wireless Communications

In Computer Hardware prefer:
Computer Graphics and Dig

In Computer Software prefer:
Systems Software

In Semiconductor/Electr prefer:
Controllers and Sensors
Analytic/Scientific

In Industrial/Energy prefer:
Energy
Oil and Gas Exploration
Oil & Gas Drilling,Explor
Alternative Energy
Materials
Process Control

Additional Information

Name of Most Recent Fund: Chevron Technology Ventures Fund IV
Most Recent Fund Was Raised: 08/31/2007
Year Founded: 1999
Capital Under Management: $245,000,000
Current Activity Level: Actively seeking new investments
Method of Compensation: Return on investment is of primary concern, do not charge fees

---

CHEYENNE CAPITAL FUND, L.P.

1900 Wazee Street
Suite 311
Denver, CO USA 80202
Phone: 303-454-5453
Website: www.cheyennefund.com

Management and Staff

John Fitzgerald, Founder

Type of Firm

Private Equity Firm

Project Preferences

Type of Financing Preferred:
Fund of Funds
Leveraged Buyout
Expansion
Acquisition
Recapitalizations

Geographical Preferences

United States Preferences:
All U.S.

Industry Preferences

In Consumer Related prefer:
Consumer Products
Consumer Services

In Industrial/Energy prefer:
Energy

In Financial Services prefer:
Financial Services

In Business Serv. prefer:
Services
Media

In Manufact. prefer:
Manufacturing

Additional Information

Year Founded: 2003
Capital Under Management: $280,000,000
Current Activity Level: Actively seeking new investments

CHIBAGIN CAPITAL COMPANY, LTD.

Nihon Kowa Bldg.
8-4 Chibakou, Chuo-ku
Chiba-shi, Japan 260-0026
Phone: 81-43-248-8822
Fax: 81-43-248-8821
Website: www.chibagincapital.co.jp

Type of Firm

Private Equity Firm

Project Preferences

Type of Financing Preferred:
Balanced

Geographical Preferences

International Preferences:
Japan

Additional Information

Year Founded: 1984
Capital Under Management: $9,800,000
Current Activity Level: Actively seeking new investments

CHICAGO GROWTH PARTNERS (WILLIAM BLAIR CAPITAL PARTNERS)

303 West Madison
Suite 1200
Chicago, IL USA 60606
Phone: 312-201-0720
Fax: 312-201-0703
E-mail: info@cgp.com
Website: www.cgp.com

Management and Staff

Arda Minocherhomjee, Managing Director
Corey Dossett, Chief Financial Officer
David Chandler, Managing Director
Robert Healy, Managing Director
Robert Blank, Managing Director
Timothy Murray, Managing Director

Type of Firm

Bank Affiliated

Project Preferences

Role in Financing:
Prefer role as deal originator but will also invest in deals created by others

Type of Financing Preferred:
Leveraged Buyout
Early Stage
Expansion
Generalist PE
Later Stage
Management Buyouts
Special Situation
Recapitalizations

Size of Investments Considered:
Min Size of Investment Considered (000s): $10,000
Max Size of Investment Considered (000s): $40,000

Geographical Preferences

United States Preferences:
All U.S.

Industry Focus

(% based on actual investment)

Other Products	22.0%
Consumer Related	19.0%
Medical/Health	16.0%
Industrial/Energy	13.4%
Computer Software and Services	12.2%
Biotechnology	5.7%
Internet Specific	4.8%
Computer Hardware	2.8%
Communications and Media	2.5%
Semiconductors/Other Elect.	1.5%

Additional Information

Year Founded: 1982
Capital Under Management: $1,070,000,000
Current Activity Level: Actively seeking new investments
Method of Compensation: Return on investment is of primary concern, do not charge fees

---

CHINA CAPITAL MANAGEMENT COMPANY, LTD.

415, Tower B, Tongtai Mansion
33 Finance St., Xicheng Dist.
Beijing, China 100032
Phone: 86-10-8808-7300
Fax: 86-10-8808-7216
E-mail: invest@ccmcllc.com
Website: www.ccmcllc.com

Other Offices

2206, Bank of America Tower
12 Harcourt Road
Central, Hong Kong
Phone: 852-2810-8155
Fax: 852-2522-9976

5784 Post Road, Suite 5
East Greenwich, RI USA 02818
Phone: 401-398-0260
Fax: 401-885-4686

Management and Staff

Cui Ming, Managing Director
Penny Fang, Chief Financial Officer
Samuel Lou, Managing Director

Type of Firm

Private Equity Firm

Project Preferences

Type of Financing Preferred:
Leveraged Buyout
Balanced
Turnaround
Later Stage
Acquisition

Geographical Preferences

International Preferences:
China

Additional Information

Year Founded: 2004
Capital Under Management: $20,000,000
Current Activity Level: Actively seeking new investments

CHINA CENTURY VENTURE CAPITAL COMPANY, LTD.

No.68 Xinzhong Street
Dongcheng District
Beijing, China
Phone: 86-10-6708-3157
Website: www.ccvc.com.cn

Type of Firm

Private Equity Firm

Association Membership

Venture Capital Association of Beijing (VCAB)

Project Preferences

Type of Financing Preferred:
Expansion
Startup

Geographical Preferences

International Preferences:
China

Industry Preferences

In Communications prefer:
Telecommunications

In Computer Software prefer:
Software

In Semiconductor/Electr prefer:
Electronics

In Biotechnology prefer:
Biotechnology

n Industrial/Energy prefer:
Energy
Materials

In Other prefer:
Environment Responsible

Additional Information

Year Founded: 2000
Current Activity Level: Actively seeking new investments

CHINA DEVELOPMENT FINANCE CO., LTD.

c/o China Development Bank
No. 29 Fucheng Menwai Street
Beijing, China 100037
Phone: 86-10-6830-6688
Fax: 86-10-6830-6699

Type of Firm

Bank Affiliated

Project Preferences

Type of Financing Preferred:
Balanced

Geographical Preferences

International Preferences:
China

Additional Information

Year Founded: 2009
Current Activity Level: Actively seeking new investments

CHINA DEVELOPMENT FINANCIAL HOLDING CORPORATION

125 Nanking East Road
Section 5
Taipei, Taiwan 105
Phone: 886-2-2763-8800
Fax: 886-2-2756-2144
E-mail: ir@cdibh.com
Website: www.cdibh.com

Management and Staff

Simon Dzeng, President

Type of Firm

Bank Affiliated

Project Preferences

Type of Financing Preferred:
Balanced

Geographical Preferences

International Preferences:
Asia

Industry Preferences

In Computer Software prefer:
Software

In Internet Specific prefer:
Internet

In Biotechnology prefer:
Biotechnology

Additional Information

Year Founded: 2001
Current Activity Level: Actively seeking new investments

CHINA DEVELOPMENT INDUSTRIAL BANK (CDIB)

No. 125, Section 5
Nanjing East Road
Taipei, Taiwan 10572
Phone: 886-2-2763-8800
Fax: 886-2-2756-2144
E-mail: ir@cdibh.com
Website: www.cdibank.com

Management and Staff

Angelo Koo, Chairman & CEO
Lawrence Liu, President

Type of Firm

Bank Affiliated

Project Preferences

Role in Financing:
Prefer role as deal originator but will also invest in deals created by others

Type of Financing Preferred:
Early Stage
Expansion
Research and Development
Balanced
Seed

Geographical Preferences

United States Preferences:
All U.S.

International Preferences:
Indonesia
Taiwan
Thailand
Philippines
Australia
Singapore
Korea, South
Japan
Malaysia

Industry Preferences

In Communications prefer:
Telecommunications

In Computer Other prefer:
Computer Related

In Semiconductor/Electr prefer:
Electronics

In Medical/Health prefer:
Medical/Health

In Transportation prefer:
Transportation

In Business Serv. prefer:
Distribution

In Manufact. prefer:
Manufacturing

In Agr/Forestr/Fish prefer:
Agriculture related
Additional Information
Year Founded: 1959
Current Activity Level: Actively seeking new investments

CHINA EQUITY LINKS

9 avenue de l'Opera
Paris, France 75001
E-mail: contact@chinaequitylinks.com
Website: www.chinaequitylinks.com

Type of Firm

Private Equity Firm

Project Preferences

Type of Financing Preferred:
Generalist PE

Size of Investments Considered:
Min Size of Investment Considered (000s): $2,671
Max Size of Investment Considered (000s): $6,678

Geographical Preferences

International Preferences:
China

Industry Preferences

In Business Serv. prefer:
Services

In Manufact. prefer:
Manufacturing

Additional Information

Year Founded: 2006
Capital Under Management: $57,400,000
Current Activity Level: Actively seeking new investments

CHINA EVERBRIGHT BANK CO., LTD.

No. 6 Fuxingmenwai Avenue
Everbright Building
Beijing, China 100045
Phone: 86-10-6809-8000
Fax: 86-10-6856-1260
Website: www.cebbank.com

Management and Staff

You Guo, President

Type of Firm

Bank Affiliated

Project Preferences

Type of Financing Preferred:
Balanced

Geographical Preferences

International Preferences:
China

Additional Information

Year Founded: 2009
Current Activity Level: Actively seeking new investments

CHINA INTERNATIONAL CAPITAL CORPORATION, LTD.

No. 1 Jian Guo Men Wai Avenue
28/F China World Tower 2
Beijing, China 100004
Phone: 86-10-6505-1166
Fax: 86-10-6505-1156
Website: www.cicc.com.cn

Management and Staff

Yunlai Zhu, President

Type of Firm

Bank Affiliated

Project Preferences

Type of Financing Preferred:
Leveraged Buyout
Expansion
Generalist PE
Later Stage

Geographical Preferences

International Preferences:
China

Industry Preferences

In Financial Services prefer:
Insurance
Financial Services

Additional Information

Year Founded: 1995
Current Activity Level: Actively seeking new investments

CHINA ISRAEL VALUE CAPITAL (AKA: CIVC)

No. 88 Fuhua First Road
Rm. 801 Central Tower
Shenzhen, China
Phone: 86755-3335-9986
Fax: 86755-3335-9970
Website: www.civcfund.com

Other Offices

4 Shenkar Street
Beit Graph, 1st Floor
Herzelia, Israel 46725
Phone: 972-9-950-5478
Fax: 972-9-950-5475

Management and Staff

Ami Dotan, General Partner
Haim Shafrir, Venture Partner
Jiang Weiping, General Partner
Jin Haitao, General Partner
Jonathan Chee, Venture Partner
Liora Shpindler, Chief Financial Officer
Ornit Avidar, Partner
Yigal Livne, General Partner

Type of Firm

Private Equity Firm

Project Preferences

Type of Financing Preferred:
Balanced

Geographical Preferences

International Preferences:
China
Israel

Additional Information

Year Founded: 2005
Current Activity Level: Actively seeking new investments

CHINA MERCHANTS & FORTUNE ASSET MANAGEMENT, LTD.

Rm 1903, 19/F, West Tower
Shun Tak Center, Connaught Rd
Central, Hong Kong 168-200
Phone: 852-2857-0388
Fax: 852-2857-0288
Website: www.cmfvc.com

Other Offices

Suite 1115, Lippo Plaza
222 Central Huai Hai Rd
Shanghai, China
Phone: 8621-5396-5589
Fax: 8621-5396-5530

Management and Staff

Luke Lu, Venture Partner

Type of Firm

Private Equity Firm

Project Preferences

Type of Financing Preferred:
Early Stage
Expansion
Later Stage
Seed
Startup

Geographical Preferences

United States Preferences:
All U.S.

International Preferences:
China

Industry Preferences

In Communications prefer:
Communications and Media

In Computer Software prefer:
Software

In Semiconductor/Electr prefer:
Semiconductor

In Biotechnology prefer:
Biotechnology

In Transportation prefer:
Transportation

Additional Information

Name of Most Recent Fund: China Merchant and Fortune Technology Fund 1
Most Recent Fund Was Raised: 01/01/2001
Year Founded: 2001
Current Activity Level: Actively seeking new investments

CHINA MERCHANTS CHINA INVESTMENTS, LTD.

1803 China Merchants Tower
168-200 Connaught Road Central
Central, Hong Kong
Phone: 852-2858-9089
Fax: 852-2858-8455
E-mail: info@cmcdi.com.hk
Website: www.cmcdi.com.hk

Management and Staff

Richard Zhang, Managing Director

Type of Firm

Bank Affiliated

Project Preferences

Type of Financing Preferred:
Balanced

Geographical Preferences

International Preferences:
China

Industry Preferences

In Financial Services prefer:
Financial Services
Real Estate

In Manufact. prefer:
Manufacturing

Additional Information

Year Founded: 1993
Current Activity Level: Actively seeking new investments

CHINA MERCHANTS SECURITIES CO., LTD

38/F, Block A, Jiangsu Bldg
Yitian Road
Shenzhen, China 518026
Website: www.newone.com.cn

Type of Firm

Bank Affiliated

Project Preferences

Type of Financing Preferred:
Later Stage

Geographical Preferences

International Preferences:
China

Industry Preferences

In Communications prefer:
Communications and Media
Media and Entertainment

In Biotechnology prefer:
Agricultural/Animal Bio.

In Medical/Health prefer:
Health Services

In Industrial/Energy prefer:
Alternative Energy
Industrial Products
Environmental Related

Additional Information

Year Founded: 2009

Capital Under Management: $14,600,000
Current Activity Level: Actively seeking new investments

CHINA NEW ENTERPRISE INVESTMENT (AKA: CNEI)

Rm.1003, Twr E3 Oriental Plaza
No.1 East Chang'an Ave.
Beijing, China
Phone: 86-10-8518-5285
Fax: 86-10-8518-4966

Management and Staff

Austin Liu, Vice President
Hirosuke Sakai, Principal
Johannes Schoeter, Principal
Xiaoyang Yu, Principal

Type of Firm

Private Equity Firm

Association Membership

Hong Kong Venture Capital Association (HKVCA)

Project Preferences

Type of Financing Preferred:
Generalist PE
Expansion

Size of Investments Considered:
Min Size of Investment Considered (000s): $10,000
Max Size of Investment Considered (000s): $50,000

Geographical Preferences

International Preferences:
China

Industry Preferences

In Medical/Health prefer:
Medical/Health

In Consumer Related prefer:
Retail
Consumer Products
Consumer Services

In Industrial/Energy prefer:
Environmental Related

In Manufact. prefer:
Manufacturing

In Agr/Forestr/Fish prefer:
Agribusiness

Additional Information

Year Founded: 2006
Capital Under Management: $113,000,000
Current Activity Level: Actively seeking new investments

CHINA RENAISSANCE CAPITAL INVESTMENT

Suite 305, St. George's Bldg.
2 Ice House Street
Central, Hong Kong
Phone: 852-2521-8013
Fax: 852-2521-8023
Website: www.crcicapital.com

Other Offices

Suite 4105A, Bund Center
222 Yan An Road East
Shanghai, China 200002
Phone: 86-21-6335-1018
Fax: 86-21-6335-1919

Tower E1, Beijing Oriental Plaza Office
1 East Chang An Avenue
Beijing, China 100738
Phone: 86-10-8518-5686
Fax: 86-10-8515-1898

Management and Staff

Frances Wang, Vice President

Type of Firm

Private Equity Firm

Project Preferences

Type of Financing Preferred:
Balanced

Geographical Preferences

International Preferences:
China
Asia

Additional Information

Year Founded: 2005
Capital Under Management: $917,200,000
Current Activity Level: Actively seeking new investments

CHINA SCIENCE & MERCHANTS INVESTMENT (FUND) MANAGEMENT CO.

No. 12 Madianqiao Yumin Road
11/F China Int'l Keji Huizhan
Beijing, China 100029
Phone: 86-10-5165-8558
Fax: 86-10-8225-0616
Website: www.leadvc.com

Other Offices

No. 4009 Shennan Dadao
13C Investment Building
Shenzhen, China 518026
Phone: 86-755-82912699
Fax: 86-755-82913291

Management and Staff

Xiangshuang Shan, President & Chairman

Type of Firm

Private Equity Firm

Project Preferences

Type of Financing Preferred:
Balanced

Geographical Preferences

International Preferences:
China

Industry Preferences

In Biotechnology prefer:
Biotechnology

In Medical/Health prefer:
Medical/Health

In Consumer Related prefer:
Consumer
Education Related

In Industrial/Energy prefer:
Energy

In Financial Services prefer:
Financial Services

In Manufact. prefer:
Manufacturing

In Agr/Forestr/Fish prefer:
Agribusiness

Additional Information

Year Founded: 2000
Capital Under Management: $81,000,000
Current Activity Level: Actively seeking new investments

CHINA VENTURE MANAGEMENT, INC.

27/F, No 99 Tun-Hwa South Rd
Section 2
Taipei, Taiwan 106
Phone: 886-2-2705-1006
Fax: 886-2-2705-1008
E-mail: cvm@ms14.hinet.net

Other Offices

15/F, No 376 Jen-Ai Road
Section 4
Taipei, Taiwan
Phone: 886-2-2784-5589
Fax: 886-2-2754-4926

12/F, No 125 Nan-King East Rd
Section 5
Taipei, Taiwan
Phone: 886-2-2705-1006
Fax: 886-2-2705-1008

Management and Staff

Chin Lin, President
James Liang, Vice President
Jeng-Ming Pai, Vice President
Wayne Lo, Vice President

Type of Firm

Private Equity Firm

Association Membership

Taiwan Venture Capital Association(TVCA)

Project Preferences

Role in Financing:

Prefer role as deal originator but will also invest in deals created by others

Type of Financing Preferred:

Second Stage Financing
Leveraged Buyout
Mezzanine
Research and Development
Start-up Financing
Later Stage
Seed
First Stage Financing

Size of Investments Considered:

Min Size of Investment Considered (000s): $1,000
Max Size of Investment Considered (000s): $5,000

Geographical Preferences

United States Preferences:

All U.S.

Canadian Preferences:

All Canada

International Preferences:

Italy
United Kingdom
Taiwan
China
Bermuda
Spain
Australia
Germany
France
Japan

Industry Focus

(% based on actual investment)

Internet Specific	33.5%
Other Products	22.1%
Communications and Media	19.7%
Computer Software and Services	17.9%
Semiconductors/Other Elect.	6.8%

Additional Information

Year Founded: 1985
Capital Under Management: $329,000,000
Current Activity Level: Actively seeking new investments
Method of Compensation: Return on invest. most important, but chg. closing fees, service fees, etc.

CHINA-SINGAPORE SUZHOU INDUSTRIAL PARK (AKA: CS-SIP)

No. 999 Modern Boulevard
Modern Bldg, Suzhou Ind'l Park
Jiangsu, China 215021
Phone: 86-512-66681517
Fax: 86-512-66681599
Website: www.sipac.gov.cn

Management and Staff

Lee Kuan Yew, Co-Founder
Li Lanqing, Co-Founder

Type of Firm

Government Affiliated Program

Project Preferences

Type of Financing Preferred:

Balanced

Geographical Preferences

International Preferences:

China
Singapore

Industry Preferences

In Semiconductor/Electr prefer:

Semiconductor

In Industrial/Energy prefer:

Industrial Products

Additional Information

Year Founded: 1994
Current Activity Level: Actively seeking new investments

CHINAEQUITY GROUP, INC.

Unit 806 North Tower
Beijing Kerry Ctr 1 GuanghuaRd
Beijing, China 100020
Phone: 86-10-8529-7418
Fax: 86-10-8529-7419
E-mail: webmaster@chinaequity.net
Website: www.chinaequity.net

Other Offices

22E Huadu Mansion
838 Zhangyang Road
Shanghai, China 200122
Phone: 86-21-5820-1409

Management and Staff

Chao Wang, Chairman & CEO
Rocky Shao, Managing Director
Wayne Huang, Managing Director

Type of Firm

Bank Affiliated

Association Membership

China Venture Capital Association

Project Preferences

Type of Financing Preferred:

Balanced

Geographical Preferences

International Preferences:

China
New Zealand
Australia
All International

Industry Preferences

In Communications prefer:

Telecommunications
Media and Entertainment

In Agr/Forestr/Fish prefer:

Agriculture related

Additional Information

Year Founded: 1999
Current Activity Level: Actively seeking new investments

CHINAVEST, LTD.

No. 7 Zhong Shan Dong Yi Road
4th Floor
Shanghai, China 200002
Phone: 86-21-6323-2255
Fax: 86-21-6329-3951
E-mail: info@chinavest.com.cn
Website: www.chinavest.com

Other Offices

101 California Strret
Suite 2800
San Francisco, CA USA 94111
Phone: 415-276-8888
Fax: 415-276-8885

19-27 Wyndham Street
Room 1103 Wilson House
Central, Hong Kong
Phone: 852-2810-1638
Fax: 852-2868-3788

7/F Beijing China Resources Building
Suite 706, 8 Jian Guo Men Bei Avenue
Beijing, China 100005
Phone: 8610-8519-1535
Fax: 8610-8519-1530

Management and Staff

Alex Xu, Vice President
Daniel Bao, Vice President
Jenny Hsui, President
Karen Fang, Vice President
Robert Theleen, Chairman & CEO
Robert Daudt, Managing Director
Tao Tao, Managing Director

Type of Firm
Private Equity Firm

Association Membership
Hong Kong Venture Capital Association (HKVCA)

Project Preferences

Type of Financing Preferred:
Leveraged Buyout
Early Stage
Expansion
Research and Development
Later Stage
Management Buyouts

Geographical Preferences

International Preferences:
Taiwan
China
Hong Kong

Industry Preferences

In Communications prefer:
Telecommunications

In Medical/Health prefer:
Medical/Health

In Consumer Related prefer:
Consumer
Consumer Services

In Transportation prefer:
Transportation

In Business Serv. prefer:
Distribution
Media

In Manufact. prefer:
Manufacturing

Additional Information
Year Founded: 1981
Capital Under Management: $300,000,000
Current Activity Level: Actively seeking new investments

CHISHOLM PRIVATE CAPITAL PARTNERS, LC

800 Research Parkway
Suite 385
Oklahoma City, OK USA 73104
Phone: 405-605-1111
Fax: 405-605-1115
E-mail: info@chisholmvc.com
Website: www.chisholmvc.com

Other Offices
2435 North Central Expressway
Suite 600
Richardson, TX USA 75080
Phone: 214-236-9509

805 ONEOK Plaza
100 West Fifth Street
Tulsa, OK USA 74103
Phone: 918-584-0440

Management and Staff
John Frick, Partner
William Paiva, Partner

Type of Firm
Private Equity Firm

Association Membership
Natl Assoc of Small Bus. Inv. Co (NASBIC)

Project Preferences

Role in Financing:
Will function either as deal originator or investor in deals created by others

Type of Financing Preferred:
Early Stage
Expansion
Generalist PE

Size of Investments Considered:
Min Size of Investment Considered (000s): $1,000
Max Size of Investment Considered (000s): $4,000

Geographical Preferences

United States Preferences:
Oklahoma
All U.S.

Industry Focus
(% based on actual investment)

Computer Software and Services	34.1%
Medical/Health	18.1%
Communications and Media	15.0%
Internet Specific	13.2%
Semiconductors/Other Elect.	9.8%
Biotechnology	4.0%
Other Products	4.0%
Industrial/Energy	1.1%
Computer Hardware	0.7%

Additional Information
Name of Most Recent Fund: Oklahoma Life Sciences Fund LLC (AKA: OLSF)
Most Recent Fund Was Raised: 07/01/2000
Year Founded: 1989
Capital Under Management: $60,000,000
Current Activity Level: Actively seeking new investments
Method of Compensation: Return on investment is of primary concern, do not charge fees

---

CHL MEDICAL PARTNERS

1055 Washington Boulevard
Sixth Floor
Stamford, CT USA 06901
Phone: 203-324-7700
Fax: 203-324-3636
E-mail: info@chlmedical.com
Website: www.chlmedical.com

Management and Staff
Gregory Weinhoff, Partner
Jeffrey Collinson, Managing Partner
Myles Greenberg, Partner
Ronald Lennox, Partner
Timothy Howe, Partner

Type of Firm
Private Equity Firm

Association Membership
National Venture Capital Association - USA (NVCA)

Project Preferences

Role in Financing:
Will function either as deal originator or investor in deals created by others

Type of Financing Preferred:
Early Stage
Seed
Startup

Size of Investments Considered:
Min Size of Investment Considered (000s): $250
Max Size of Investment Considered (000s): $12,000

Industry Focus
(% based on actual investment)

Medical/Health	57.0%
Biotechnology	35.1%
Computer Hardware	3.9%
Other Products	2.5%
Internet Specific	1.4%

Additional Information
Year Founded: 1990
Capital Under Management: $340,000,000
Current Activity Level: Actively seeking new investments
Method of Compensation: Return on investment is of primary concern, do not charge fees

---

CHONGQING KEJI VENTURE CAPITAL CO., LTD.

Shiqiao Puyizhou Road
2nd Floor
Chongqing, China 630039
Phone: 86-23-6861-5989
Fax: 86-23-8615-989

Type of Firm
Government Affiliated Program

Project Preferences

Type of Financing Preferred:
Balanced

Geographical Preferences

International Preferences:
China

Industry Preferences

In Semiconductor/Electr prefer:
Electronics

In Biotechnology prefer:
Biotechnology

Additional Information

Year Founded: 1992
Current Activity Level: Actively seeking new investments

CHONGQING YUFU ASSETS MANAGEMENT CO., LTD.

No. 12 Hongshi Road
Jiangbei District
Chongqing, China 400020
Phone: 86-23-6767-8200
Fax: 86-23-6767-8299
E-mail: cqyfgs@cqyfgs.com
Website: www.cqyfgs.com

Type of Firm

Bank Affiliated

Project Preferences

Type of Financing Preferred:
Balanced

Geographical Preferences

International Preferences:
China

Industry Preferences

In Medical/Health prefer:
Medical Products
Pharmaceuticals

In Consumer Related prefer:
Consumer

Additional Information

Year Founded: 2004
Current Activity Level: Actively seeking new investments

CHOONGNAM VENTURE CAPITAL (FKA: CHOONGNAM KI VENTURE CAPITAL)

409 Mutimedia Center
511 Sameun-ri, Jiksan-eup
Chungcheongnam-do, South Korea 330-816
Phone: 8241-589-0820
Fax: 8241-589-0822

Other Offices

2nd Floor, Room 7, Haseong Building
548-1 Kumhodong 4 Ga
Seoul, South Korea 133-809

Type of Firm

Bank Affiliated

Project Preferences

Type of Financing Preferred:
Balanced

Geographical Preferences

International Preferences:
Korea, South

Additional Information

Year Founded: 2007
Current Activity Level: Actively seeking new investments

CHORD CAPITAL, LTD. (FKA: GENERICS GROUP, THE)

Harston Mill
Harston
Cambridge, United Kingdom CB2 5GG
Phone: 44-1223-875-200
Fax: 44-1223-875-201

Other Offices

Generics Group Inc
1601 Trapelo Road
Waltham, MA USA 02451
Phone: 781-290-0500
Fax: 781-290-0501

Catella Generics AB
Veddestavagen
Jarfalla, Sweden SE-175 62
Phone: 46-8-445-7960
Fax: 46-8-445-7999

15/F, Block B, Veristrong Ind. Ctr.
34-36 Au Pui Wan Street
Fotan, Hong Kong

11403 Cronhill Drive
Suite B
Owings Mills, MD USA 21117

Gruneburgweg
Frankfurt, Germany D-60322

Management and Staff

Christopher Coggill, Managing Director
Gordon Edge, Founder
Martin Frost, Managing Director
Peter Hyde, Managing Director

Type of Firm

Corporate PE/Venture

Association Membership

European Private Equity and Venture Capital Assoc.

Project Preferences

Type of Financing Preferred:
Early Stage
Expansion
Seed
Startup

Geographical Preferences

United States Preferences:
All U.S.

International Preferences:
United Kingdom
Europe

Additional Information

Year Founded: 1987
Current Activity Level: Actively seeking new investments

CHRYSALIS VCT

46 Dorset Street
London, United Kingdom W1U 7NB
Phone: 44-20-7486-7454
Fax: 44-20-7486-7463
E-mail: info@chrysalisvct.co.uk
Website: www.chrysalisvct.co.uk

Management and Staff

Chris Kay, Chief Executive Officer

Type of Firm

Private Equity Firm

Project Preferences

Type of Financing Preferred:
Early Stage
Expansion
Balanced
Management Buyouts
Acquisition
Recapitalizations

Size of Investments Considered:
Min Size of Investment Considered (000s): $183
Max Size of Investment Considered (000s): $1,933

Geographical Preferences

International Preferences:
United Kingdom

Additional Information

Year Founded: 2007
Current Activity Level: Actively seeking new investments

CHRYSALIS VENTURES

101 South Fifth Street
Suite 1650
Louisville, KY USA 40202
Phone: 502-583-7644
Fax: 502-583-7648
E-mail: info@chrysalisventures.com
Website: www.chrysalisventures.com

Other Offices

2000 Technology Drive
Suite 250
Pittsburgh, PA USA 15219
Phone: 412-235-0302
Fax: 216-274-0244

122 West Huron Street
Ann Arbor, MI USA 48104
Phone: 734-864-0237

737 Bolivar Road
Suite 1500
Cleveland, OH USA 44115
Phone: 216-453-1299
Fax: 216-274-0244

Management and Staff

David Jones, Chairman & Managing Director
Greg Richey, Chief Operating Officer
John Willmoth, Venture Partner
Koleman Karleski, Managing Director
Wright Steenrod, Principal

Type of Firm

Private Equity Firm

Association Membership

Mid-Atlantic Venture Association
Natl Assoc of Small Bus. Inv. Co (NASBIC)
Illinois Venture Capital Association
National Venture Capital Association - USA (NVCA)

Project Preferences

Role in Financing:

Will function either as deal originator or investor in deals created by others

Type of Financing Preferred:

Second Stage Financing
Early Stage
Expansion
Balanced
Later Stage
First Stage Financing
Industry Rollups

Size of Investments Considered:

Min Size of Investment Considered (000s): $1,000
Max Size of Investment Considered (000s): $20,000

Geographical Preferences

United States Preferences:

Mid Atlantic
Midwest
Southeast
All U.S.

Industry Focus

(% based on actual investment)

Internet Specific	33.8%
Medical/Health	22.2%
Computer Software and Services	17.0%
Industrial/Energy	9.1%
Communications and Media	8.5%
Consumer Related	4.6%
Biotechnology	1.9%
Other Products	1.6%
Semiconductors/Other Elect.	1.3%

Additional Information

Year Founded: 1993
Capital Under Management: $373,000,000
Current Activity Level: Actively seeking new investments
Method of Compensation: Return on invest. most important, but chg. closing fees, service fees, etc.

CHRYSALIX ENERGY

1367 West Broadway
Suite 400
Vancouver, Canada V6J 4A7
Phone: 604-659-5499
Fax: 604-659-5479
E-mail: info@chrysalix.com
Website: www.chrysalix.com

Management and Staff

Christine Bergeron, Vice President
Greg Sullivan, Managing Director
Jim Fletcher, Managing Director
Michael Walkinshaw, Managing Director
Michael Sherman, Vice President

Type of Firm

Private Equity Firm

Project Preferences

Role in Financing:

Will function either as deal originator or investor in deals created by others

Type of Financing Preferred:

Early Stage
Start-up Financing
Seed
First Stage Financing
Startup

Size of Investments Considered:

Min Size of Investment Considered (000s): $100
Max Size of Investment Considered (000s): $2,500

Geographical Preferences

Canadian Preferences:

All Canada

International Preferences:

United Kingdom
Europe
Western Europe
China
Eastern Europe
Israel
Germany
France

Industry Preferences

In Industrial/Energy prefer:

Energy

Additional Information

Name of Most Recent Fund: Chrysalix Energy II U.S. Limited Partnership
Most Recent Fund Was Raised: 02/16/2005
Year Founded: 2001
Capital Under Management: $50,000,000
Current Activity Level: Actively seeking new investments

CHRYSCAPITAL MANAGEMENT COMPANY (FKA:CHRYSALIS MANAGEMENT)

IFS Court, 28, Cybercity
Ebene, Mauritius
Phone: 230-467-3000
Fax: 230-467-4000
E-mail: info@chryscapital.com
Website: www.chryscapital.com

Other Offices

Suite 111, Maker Chambers IV
11th Floor, Nariman Point
Mumbai, India 400021
Phone: 91-22-4066-8000
Fax: 91-22-4066-8080

Suite 101, The Oberoi
Dr. Zakir Hussain Marg
New Delhi, India 110003
Phone: 91-11-4129-1000
Fax: 91-11-4129-1010

285, Hamilton Ave.
Suite 300
Palo Alto, CA USA 94301
Phone: 650-752-0890
Fax: 650-752-0891

Management and Staff

Ashish Dhawan, Senior Managing Director
Ashish Agrawal, Vice President
Ashley Menezes, Chief Financial Officer
Brahmal Vasudevan, Managing Director
Gaurav Ahuja, Vice President
Kunal Shroff, Managing Director
Raghav Ramdev, Vice President
Ravi Bahl, Managing Director
Sanjiv Kaul, Managing Director

Type of Firm

Private Equity Firm

Association Membership

Indian Venture Capital Association (IVCA)

Project Preferences

Type of Financing Preferred:

Leveraged Buyout
Expansion
Mezzanine
Balanced
Later Stage

Size of Investments Considered:

Min Size of Investment Considered (000s): $10,000
Max Size of Investment Considered (000s): $30,000

Geographical Preferences

International Preferences:

India
Asia

Industry Focus

(% based on actual investment)

Other Products	42.5%
Computer Software and Services	36.9%
Communications and Media	7.2%
Medical/Health	5.3%
Internet Specific	4.7%
Industrial/Energy	3.3%

Additional Information

Name of Most Recent Fund: ChrysCapital II, LLC (AKA: Raga Fund)
Most Recent Fund Was Raised: 09/15/2000
Year Founded: 1999
Capital Under Management: $2,250,000,000
Current Activity Level: Actively seeking new investments

CHUGIN LEASE CO., LTD.

1-14-17 Marunouchi
Okayama-shi, Japan 700-0823
Phone: 81-86-232-7060
Website: www.chugin.co.jp

Type of Firm

Private Equity Firm

Additional Information

Year Founded: 1982
Current Activity Level: Actively seeking new investments

CHUO MITSUI CAPITAL CO., LTD.

3 Choume, 2-8 Nihonbashi
Muromachi, Chuo-ku
Tokyo, Japan 103-0022
Phone: 81-3-4520-8906
Fax: 81-3-6385-7623
Website: www.cm-capital.con

Management and Staff

Kiichiro Kurimoto, President
Makoto Ishii, Managing Director

Type of Firm

Bank Affiliated

Project Preferences

Type of Financing Preferred:

Fund of Funds
Leveraged Buyout
Mezzanine
Expansion
Generalist PE
Later Stage
Management Buyouts
Acquisition
Recapitalizations

Geographical Preferences

International Preferences:

Japan

Additional Information

Year Founded: 2000
Current Activity Level: Actively seeking new investments

CHURCHILL EQUITY, INC. (FKA: CHURCHILL CAPITAL, INC.)

333 South Seventh Street
Suite 3100
Minneapolis, MN USA 55402-2435
Phone: 612-673-6680
Fax: 612-673-6732
Website: www.churchillequity.com

Management and Staff

Gary Gottschalk, Partner
Michael Bender, Vice President
Mitchell Kern, Partner
Sameer Vijayakar, Partner

Type of Firm

Private Equity Firm

Project Preferences

Role in Financing:

Prefer role as deal originator but will also invest in deals created by others

Type of Financing Preferred:

Leveraged Buyout
Mezzanine
Later Stage
Management Buyouts
Acquisition
Private Placement
Industry Rollups
Recapitalizations

Size of Investments Considered:

Min Size of Investment Considered (000s): $5,000
Max Size of Investment Considered (000s): $30,000

Geographical Preferences

United States Preferences:

All U.S.

Canadian Preferences:

All Canada

Industry Focus

(% based on actual investment)

Industrial/Energy	46.9%
Other Products	24.0%
Consumer Related	12.9%
Medical/Health	10.9%
Semiconductors/Other Elect.	4.5%
Computer Software and Services	0.8%

Additional Information

Name of Most Recent Fund: Churchill Capital Partners IV, LP
Most Recent Fund Was Raised: 10/16/2000
Year Founded: 1988
Capital Under Management: $558,000,000
Current Activity Level: Actively seeking new investments
Method of Compensation: Return on invest. most important, but chg. closing fees, service fees, etc.

CI CAPITAL PARTNERS LLC (FKA: CAXTON-ISEMAN CAPITAL, INC)

500 Park Avenue
Eighth Floor
New York, NY USA 10022
Phone: 212-752-1850
Fax: 212-832-9450
E-mail: info@cicaplic.com
Website: www.caxton-iseman.com

Management and Staff

Frederick Iseman, Chairman & CEO
Joost Thesseling, Principal
Robert Ferris, General Partner
Steven Lefkowitz, President
Timothy Hall, Principal
Tom Ritchie, Principal

Type of Firm

Bank Affiliated

Project Preferences

Role in Financing:

Prefer role in deals created by others

Type of Financing Preferred:

Leveraged Buyout
Acquisition

Industry Focus

(% based on actual investment)

Consumer Related	75.7%
Other Products	18.1%
Computer Software and Services	5.6%
Biotechnology	0.5%

Additional Information

Year Founded: 1993
Capital Under Management: $2,000,000,000
Current Activity Level: Actively seeking new investments

CIBC CAPITAL PARTNERS

BCE Place
161 Bay Street, Box 500
Toronto, Canada M5J 2S8
Phone: 416-594-7443
Fax: 416-594-8037
Website: www.cibcwm.com

Other Offices

425 Lexington Avenue
New York, NY USA 10017
Phone: 212-856-4000

Cottons Centre
Cottons Lane
United Kingdom SE1 2QL
Phone: 44-20-7234-6000
Fax: 44-20-7407-4127

One Post Street
San Francisco, CA USA 94104
Phone: 415-399-5700

222 Berkeley Street
19th Floor
Boston, MA USA 02116
Phone: 617-375-7875

Management and Staff

David Shotland, Managing Director
Edward P Nash, Managing Director
Mark Hastings, Managing Director
Michele Buchignani, Managing Director
Paul Farrell, Managing Director
Teddy Rosenberg, Managing Director
Thomas Cusick, Managing Director
Todd Worsley, Managing Director
William Phoenix, Managing Director

Type of Firm

Bank Affiliated

Association Membership

Canadian Venture Capital Association
European Private Equity and Venture Capital Assoc.

Project Preferences

Type of Financing Preferred:

Second Stage Financing
Leveraged Buyout
Early Stage
Mezzanine

Size of Investments Considered:

Min Size of Investment Considered (000s): $3,000
Max Size of Investment Considered (000s): $20,000

Geographical Preferences

Canadian Preferences:

All Canada

International Preferences:

Europe
Mexico
Australia

Industry Preferences

In Communications prefer:

Communications and Media

In Medical/Health prefer:

Medical/Health

In Consumer Related prefer:

Consumer Products
Consumer Services

In Industrial/Energy prefer:

Industrial Products

In Transportation prefer:

Transportation

In Financial Services prefer:

Real Estate

In Manufact. prefer:

Publishing

In Agr/Forestr/Fish prefer:

Agriculture related

Additional Information

Year Founded: 1989
Current Activity Level: Actively seeking new investments

CIBC WOOD GUNDY CAPITAL

BCE Place Branch
161 Bay Street, 11th Floor
Toronto, Canada M5J 2S8
Phone: 416-594-7000
Fax: 416-594-7069
Website: www.cibcwoodgundy.com

Other Offices

161 Bay Street
8th Floor
Toronto, Canada M5J 2S8
Phone: 416-594-8021
Fax: 416-594-8037

One Post Street
Suite 3550
San Francisco, CA USA 94104
Phone: 415-399-5723
Fax: 415-399-1224

Management and Staff

P. Kenneth Kilgour, Managing Director
Richard White, Managing Director

Type of Firm

Bank Affiliated

Association Membership

Western Association of Venture Capitalists (WAVC)
Canadian Venture Capital Association
Natl Assoc of Small Bus. Inv. Co (NASBIC)

Project Preferences

Role in Financing:

Prefer role as deal originator but will also invest in deals created by others

Type of Financing Preferred:

Second Stage Financing
Leveraged Buyout
Mezzanine
Other
Special Situation

Size of Investments Considered:

Min Size of Investment Considered (000s): $2,000
Max Size of Investment Considered: No Limit

Geographical Preferences

United States Preferences:

All U.S.

Canadian Preferences:

All Canada

International Preferences:

United Kingdom

Industry Focus

(% based on actual investment)

Internet Specific	41.3%
Communications and Media	20.6%
Semiconductors/Other Elect.	11.9%
Computer Software and Services	9.5%
Medical/Health	6.0%
Other Products	5.7%
Biotechnology	1.8%
Consumer Related	1.3%
Computer Hardware	1.0%
Industrial/Energy	0.8%

Additional Information

Year Founded: 1993
Capital Under Management: $75,000,000
Current Activity Level: Actively seeking new investments
Method of Compensation: Return on invest. most important, but chg. closing fees, service fees, etc.

CIC FINANCE SA

4-6 Rue Gaillon
Paris, France 75002
Phone: 33-1-4266-7663

Fax: 33-1-4266-7871
E-mail: cic-finance@cic.fr
Website: www.cicfinance.com

Other Offices

28 avenue de l'Opera
Paris, France 75002
Phone: 33-1-4266-7959

2 bis rue Duguay Trouin
Rouen, France 76000
Phone: 33-2-3508-6406

33 avenue Le Corbusier
Lille, France 59000
Phone: 33-3-2012-6729

4 Place Andre Maginot
Nancy, France 84000
Phone: 33-3-8334-5192

31 rue Jean Wenger-Valentin
Strasbourg, France 67000
Phone: 33-3-8837-7485

Management and Staff

Sydney Cabessa, Chairman & CEO

Type of Firm

Private Equity Firm

Association Membership

French Venture Capital Association (AFIC)

Project Preferences

Type of Financing Preferred:

Leveraged Buyout
Expansion

Geographical Preferences

International Preferences:

Europe
France

Additional Information

Year Founded: 2003
Current Activity Level: Actively seeking new investments

CIC LBO PARTNERS

28 avenue de l'Opera
Paris, France 75002
Phone: 33-1-4266-7057

Type of Firm

Private Equity Firm

Association Membership

French Venture Capital Association (AFIC)

Project Preferences

Type of Financing Preferred:

Leveraged Buyout
Balanced

Geographical Preferences

International Preferences:

France

Additional Information

Year Founded: 2004
Current Activity Level: Actively seeking new investments

CIC PARTNERS, L.P. (FKA: CARDINAL INVESTMENT COMPANY, INC.)

500 Crescent Court
Suite 250
Dallas, TX USA 75201
Phone: 214-871-6863
Fax: 214-880-4491
E-mail: info@cicpartners.com
Website: www.cicpartners.com

Management and Staff

Aaron Enrico, Principal
Amir Yoffe, Principal
Diane Gross, Vice President
Drew Johnson, Partner
Fouad Bashour, Partner
Marshall Payne, Partner
Michael Rawlings, Managing Partner

Type of Firm

Private Equity Firm

Project Preferences

Type of Financing Preferred:

Leveraged Buyout
Balanced
Management Buyouts
Acquisition
Recapitalizations

Size of Investments Considered:

Min Size of Investment Considered (000s): $3,000
Max Size of Investment Considered (000s): $100,000

Geographical Preferences

United States Preferences:

All U.S.

Industry Preferences

In Medical/Health prefer:

Health Services

In Consumer Related prefer:

Retail
Other Restaurants

In Industrial/Energy prefer:

Energy

In Manufact. prefer:

Manufacturing

Additional Information

Year Founded: 1973
Capital Under Management: $500,000,000
Current Activity Level: Actively seeking new investments

CIC REGIONS EXPANSION

33 avenue Le Corbusier
Lille, France 59800
Phone: 33-3-2012-6464
Fax: 33-3-2012-6742
Website: www.cic.fr

Type of Firm

Bank Affiliated

Project Preferences

Type of Financing Preferred:

Leveraged Buyout
Expansion

Size of Investments Considered:

Min Size of Investment Considered (000s): $609
Max Size of Investment Considered (000s): $3,044

Geographical Preferences

International Preferences:

France

Additional Information

Year Founded: 1990
Current Activity Level: Actively seeking new investments

CICLAD

8 avenue Franklin Roosevelt
Paris, France 75008
Phone: 33-1-5659-7733
Fax: 33-1-5376-2210
E-mail: info@ciclad.com
Website: www.ciclad.com

Management and Staff

Jean-Francois Vaury, Founding Partner
Lionel Lambert, Founding Partner
Thierry Thomann, Founding Partner

Type of Firm

Private Equity Firm

Association Membership

French Venture Capital Association (AFIC)

Project Preferences

Role in Financing:

Prefer role as deal originator but will also invest in deals created by others

Type of Financing Preferred:

Leveraged Buyout
Management Buyouts
Special Situation

Size of Investments Considered:
Min Size of Investment Considered (000s): $718
Max Size of Investment Considered (000s): $7,177

Geographical Preferences

International Preferences:
France

Additional Information
Year Founded: 1988
Capital Under Management: $100,000,000
Current Activity Level: Actively seeking new investments
Method of Compensation: Return on invest. most important, but chg. closing fees, service fees, etc.

CID EQUITY PARTNERS
201 West 103rd Street
Suite 200
Indianapolis, IN USA 46290
Phone: 317-818-5030
Fax: 317-571-1867
E-mail: info@cidcap.com
Website: www.cidcap.com

Other Offices
200 West Madison Street
Suite 3500
Chicago, IL USA 60606
Phone: 312-578-5350
Fax: 312-578-5358

180 East Broad Street
Suite 1701
Columbus, OH USA 43215
Phone: 614-222-8185
Fax: 614-222-8190

Management and Staff
John Aplin, Managing Director
Peter Kleinhenz, Managing Director
Robert O'Brien, Managing Director

Type of Firm
Private Equity Firm

Association Membership
Illinois Venture Capital Association
Natl Assoc of Small Bus. Inv. Co (NASBIC)

Project Preferences

Role in Financing:
Prefer role as deal originator but will also invest in deals created by others

Type of Financing Preferred:
Second Stage Financing
Leveraged Buyout
Early Stage
Mezzanine
Balanced
Start-up Financing
Later Stage
First Stage Financing
Industry Rollups
Special Situation

Size of Investments Considered:
Min Size of Investment Considered (000s): $500
Max Size of Investment Considered (000s): $10,000

Geographical Preferences

United States Preferences:
Midwest
Rocky Mountain
Indiana

Industry Focus
(% based on actual investment)

Computer Software and Services	27.1%
Medical/Health	15.0%
Other Products	14.1%
Communications and Media	9.6%
Internet Specific	9.2%
Biotechnology	6.8%
Consumer Related	5.6%
Semiconductors/Other Elect.	5.4%
Industrial/Energy	4.5%
Computer Hardware	2.7%

Additional Information
Year Founded: 1981
Capital Under Management: $321,000,000
Current Activity Level: Actively seeking new investments
Method of Compensation: Return on investment is of primary concern, do not charge fees

---

CID GROUP (FKA: CHINA INTERNATIONAL DEVELOPMENT CONSULTING)
28/F, No.97 Tun Hwa South Road
Section 2
Taipei, Taiwan 106
Phone: 886-2-2325-7998
Fax: 886-2-2325-7933
E-mail: inquiries@cidgroup.com
Website: www.cidvc.com

Other Offices
35th Floor, The Center
989 ChangLe Road
Shanghai, China 200031
Phone: 86-21-5407-5466
Fax: 86-21-5407-5499

Suite 710, China World Trade Ctr Tower 2
No. 1 Jianguomenwai Avenue
Beijing, China 100004
Phone: 86-10-6505-7734
Fax: 86-10-6505-7934

Management and Staff
Aggie Chen, Principal
Cory Chen, Principal
Eric Tan, Principal
Han-Fei Lin, Partner
Jason Hsieh, Partner
Joseph Chan, Principal
Lisa Lo, Partner
Roy Chaung, Principal
Tony Hwang, Partner
Vincent Hou, Partner

Type of Firm
Private Equity Firm

Association Membership
Taiwan Venture Capital Association(TVCA)

Project Preferences

Type of Financing Preferred:
Balanced

Geographical Preferences

International Preferences:
Taiwan
China
Asia
Korea, South

Additional Information
Year Founded: 1998
Capital Under Management: $300,000,000
Current Activity Level: Actively seeking new investments

CIDC CONSULTANTS, INC. (AKA: CHINA INVESTMENT & DEVELOPMENT)
16/F, 563 Chung-Hsiao East Rd.
Section 4
Taipei, Taiwan
Phone: 886-2-2763-6276
Fax: 886-2-2763-7870
E-mail: info@cidc.com.tw
Website: www.cidc.com.tw

Management and Staff
Alice Chen, Vice President
Edward Chang, President

Type of Firm
Private Equity Firm

Association Membership
Taiwan Venture Capital Association(TVCA)

Project Preferences

Type of Financing Preferred:
Balanced

Geographical Preferences

International Preferences:
Taiwan

Industry Preferences

In Communications prefer:
Telecommunications

In Computer Software prefer:
Software

In Internet Specific prefer:
Internet

In Semiconductor/Electr prefer:
Electronics
Semiconductor

In Biotechnology prefer:
Biotechnology

In Medical/Health prefer:
Pharmaceuticals

In Industrial/Energy prefer:
Factory Automation
Machinery

Additional Information

Year Founded: 1988
Capital Under Management: $114,600,000
Current Activity Level: Actively seeking new investments

CIMB PRIVATE EQUITY SDN BHD

10th Floor Bangunan CIMB
Jalan Semantan, Damansara Hts.
Kuala Lumpur, Malaysia 50490
Phone: 60-3-2084-8888
Fax: 60-3-2084-8899
Website: www.cimb.com

Other Offices

The Jakarta Stock Exchange Bldg. II
20/F Jl Jend, Sudirman Kav 52-53
Jakarta, India 12190
Phone: 62-21-515-1330
Fax: 62-21-515-1335
Unit 3502 35/F, Q. House Lumpini Bldg.
1 South Sathorn Road
Bangkok, Thailand 10120
Phone: 662-687-0888
Fax: 662-677-7538

50 Raffles Place
#19-00 Singapore Land Tower
Singapore, Singapore 048623
Phone: 65-6225-1228
Fax: 65-6225-1522

540 Madison Avenue
Eleventh Floor
New York, NY USA 10022
Phone: 212-616-8600
Fax: 212-828-9633

Almoayyed Tower, Suite 304
Road 283, Al Seef 428
Manama, Bahrain

25th Floor Central Tower
28 Queen's Road Central
Hong Kong, Hong Kong
Phone: 852-2868-0380
Fax: 852-2537-1928

27 Knightbridge
London, United Kingdom SW1X 7YB
Phone: 44-207-201-2199
Fax: 44-207-201-2191

14th Floor PGGMB Building
Jalan Kianggeh
Bandar Seri Begawan, Brunei BS8811
Phone: 673-224-1888
Fax: 673-224-0999

35 (D) Pyay Road
7th Miles Mayangone Tsp
Yangon, Burma
Phone: 951-660-919
Fax: 951-650-838

Management and Staff

Dato Nazir Razak, Chief Executive Officer
Lim Tiang Siew, Chief Financial Officer

Type of Firm

Bank Affiliated

Project Preferences

Type of Financing Preferred:
Leveraged Buyout
Early Stage
Expansion
Mezzanine
Balanced
Management Buyouts
Startup

Geographical Preferences

International Preferences:
Asia
Malaysia

Additional Information

Year Founded: 2004
Capital Under Management: $49,000,000
Current Activity Level: Actively seeking new investments

CINCLUS AS

Rosenkrantzgate 22
Oslo, Norway 0166
Phone: 47-2-282-5152
Fax: 47-2-310-0761
Website: www.cinclus-invest.no

Management and Staff

Sven Petter Omdal, Managing Director

Type of Firm

Private Equity Firm

Project Preferences

Type of Financing Preferred:
Leveraged Buyout

Geographical Preferences

International Preferences:
Sweden
Greenland
Iceland
Finland
Norway
Denmark
Faroe Islands

Additional Information

Year Founded: 2006
Current Activity Level: Actively seeking new investments

CINCYTECH

30 West Third Street
Sixth Floor
Cincinnati, OH USA 45202
Phone: 513-263-2720
Fax: 513-381-5093
E-mail: contactus@cincytechusa.com
Website: www.cincytechventures.com

Management and Staff

Bob Coy, President

Type of Firm

Private Equity Firm

Association Membership

National Venture Capital Association - USA (NVCA)

Project Preferences

Type of Financing Preferred:
Early Stage
Seed

Geographical Preferences

United States Preferences:
Ohio

Industry Preferences

In Biotechnology prefer:
Biotechnology

In Industrial/Energy prefer:
Advanced Materials

In Manufact. prefer:
Manufacturing

Additional Information

Year Founded: 2001
Current Activity Level: Actively seeking new investments

CINVEN, LTD.

Warwick Court
Paternoster Square
London, United Kingdom EC4M 7AG
Phone: 44-20-7661-3333
Fax: 44-20-7661-3888
E-mail: info@cinven.com
Website: www.cinven.com

Other Offices

Via Manzoni, 30
Milan, Italy 20121
Phone: 39-02-3211-1700
Fax: 39-02-3211-1800

Neue Mainzer Str 52
Main Tower
Frankfurt am Main, Germany 60311
Phone: 49-69-900-270
Fax: 49-69-9002-7100

4 square Edouard VII
26 Boulevard des Capucines
Paris, France 75009
Phone: 33-1-4471-4444
Fax: 33-1-4471-4499

Management and Staff

Alex Leslie, Principal
Alexandra Hess, Partner
Alexis Le Marie, Principal
Amelie Brossier, Principal
Andrew Joy, Partner
Anthony Garton, Principal
Benoit Ficheur, Principal
Benoit Valentin, Partner
Brian Linden, Partner
Bruno Schick, Principal
Caspar Berendsen, Partner
Charles Miller-Jones, Principal
Chris Good, Principal
Christian Dosch, Partner
Christoph Hobo, Principal
David Barker, Partner
Dick Munton, Partner
Geoffroy Willaume, Principal
Gordon Moore, Partner
Guy Davison, Partner
Hugh Langmuir, Managing Partner
Jonathan Clarke, Partner
Joseph Wan, Partner
Julian Carreras, Principal
Karin Himmelreich, Principal
Magnus Hildingsson, Principal
Marcus Wood, Partner
Matthew Sabben-Clare, Partner
Nicolas Paulmier, Partner
Olaf Hartmann, Principal
Pascal Heberling, Partner
Peter Catterall, Partner
Rebecca Gibson, Principal
Richard Cheung, Principal
Roberto Italia, Partner
Simon Rowlands, Partner
Soren Christensen, Principal
Stefan Franssen, Principal
Stuart McAlpine, Partner
Supraj Rajagopalan, Principal
Thierry Celestin, Principal
Tobias Knechtle, Principal
Valerio Massimo, Principal
Xavier Geismar, Partner
Yagnish Chotai, Partner
Yalin Karadogan, Principal

Type of Firm

Private Equity Firm

Association Membership

British Venture Capital Association (BVCA)
French Venture Capital Association (AFIC)
European Private Equity and Venture Capital Assoc.

Project Preferences

Role in Financing:

Prefer role as deal originator but will also invest in deals created by others

Type of Financing Preferred:

Leveraged Buyout
Balanced
Management Buyouts
Acquisition

Size of Investments Considered:

Min Size of Investment Considered (000s): $205,571
Max Size of Investment Considered: No Limit

Geographical Preferences

International Preferences:

United Kingdom
Europe
Germany
France

Industry Focus

(% based on actual investment)

Consumer Related	40.8%
Other Products	27.0%
Industrial/Energy	16.5%
Communications and Media	12.2%
Medical/Health	3.4%

Additional Information

Name of Most Recent Fund: Fourth Cinven Fund, The
Most Recent Fund Was Raised: 06/30/2006
Year Founded: 1977
Capital Under Management: $8,771,400,000
Current Activity Level: Actively seeking new investments
Method of Compensation: Return on invest. most important, but chg. closing fees, service fees, etc.

CIPIO PARTNERS

Palais am Lenbachplatz
Ottostrasse 8
Munich, Germany 80333
Phone: 49-89-550-6960
Fax: 49-89-5506-9699
E-mail: info@cipiopartners.com
Website: www.cipiopartners.com

Other Offices

560 South Winchester Boulevard
Suite 500
San Jose, CA USA 95128
Phone: 408-236-7654
Fax: 408-236-7651

Management and Staff

Anubha Shrivastava, Managing Director
David Mes, Principal
Diana Meyel, Partner
Fabian Ruechardt, Venture Partner
Gerhard Miller, Principal
Hans-Dieter Koch, Managing Partner
Hywel Rees-Jones, Managing Director
Maximilian Schroeck, Managing Partner
Rod Evison, Managing Director
Roland Dennert, Partner
Sven Weber, Principal
Thomas Anthofer, Managing Partner
Werner Dreesbach, Managing Partner

Type of Firm

Private Equity Firm

Association Membership

European Private Equity and Venture Capital Assoc.

Project Preferences

Type of Financing Preferred:

Leveraged Buyout
Early Stage
Expansion
Generalist PE
Balanced
Seed
Startup
Acquisition
Recapitalizations

Geographical Preferences

United States Preferences:

All U.S.

Canadian Preferences:

All Canada

International Preferences:

United Kingdom
Europe
Switzerland
Netherlands
Middle East
Germany
Israel
Belgium
Singapore
Asia
All International
France

Industry Preferences

In Communications prefer:
Communications and Media
Telecommunications

In Computer Software prefer:
Software

In Computer Other prefer:
Computer Related

In Semiconductor/Electr prefer:
Electronics
Semiconductor
Optoelectronics

In Medical/Health prefer:
Medical/Health

In Industrial/Energy prefer:
Energy

In Financial Services prefer:
Financial Services

Additional Information

Name of Most Recent Fund: Cipio Partners Fund IV GmbH & Co. KG
Most Recent Fund Was Raised: 07/14/2005
Year Founded: 2003
Capital Under Management: $104,100,000
Current Activity Level: Actively seeking new investments

CIRCLE PEAK CAPITAL LLC (AKA: CPC)

1325 Avenue of the Americas
25th floor
New York, NY USA 10019
Phone: 646-230-8812
Fax: 646-349-2743
E-mail: info@circlepeakcapital.com
Website: www.circlepeakcapital.com

Management and Staff

Holbrook Forusz, Principal
James Clippard, Principal
John Jonge Poerink, Senior Managing Director

Type of Firm

Private Equity Firm

Project Preferences

Role in Financing:
Prefer role as deal originator but will also invest in deals created by others

Size of Investments Considered:
Min Size of Investment Considered (000s): $2,500
Max Size of Investment Considered (000s): $25,000

Industry Preferences

In Consumer Related prefer:
Consumer
Retail
Food/Beverage

In Financial Services prefer:
Financial Services

In Business Serv. prefer:
Services
Distribution

In Manufact. prefer:
Manufacturing

Additional Information

Year Founded: 2002
Current Activity Level: Actively seeking new investments

CIRRUS INVESTMENT PARTNERS LLC

1560 Broadway
Suite 2200
Denver, CO USA 80202
Phone: 303-863-3015
Fax: 303-863-3006

Management and Staff

Elisabeth Ireland, Managing Partner
Fred Hamilton, Managing Partner
Thomas Hamilton, Managing Partner

Type of Firm

Private Equity Firm

Additional Information

Year Founded: 2002
Capital Under Management: $3,200,000
Current Activity Level: Actively seeking new investments

CISCO SYSTEMS, INC.

170 West Tasman Drive
San Jose, CA USA 95134
Phone: 408-526-4000
Fax: 408-526-4100
Website: www.cisco.com

Other Offices

SEZ Unit, Cessna, Business Park
Sarjapur Marathalli, Outer Ring Road
Bangalore, India 560 087
Phone: 91-80-4426-3335
Fax: 91-80-4426-4031

Type of Firm

Corporate PE/Venture

Project Preferences

Type of Financing Preferred:
Early Stage
Expansion
Startup

Size of Investments Considered:
Min Size of Investment Considered (000s): $2,000
Max Size of Investment Considered (000s): $60,000

Industry Preferences

In Communications prefer:
Telecommunications

In Semiconductor/Electr prefer:
Electronics

Additional Information

Year Founded: 1986
Current Activity Level: Actively seeking new investments

CIT GAP FUNDS (AKA: CENTER FOR INNOVATIVE TECHNOLOGY)

2214 Rock Hill Road
Suite 600
Herndon, VA USA 20170
Phone: 703-689-3000
Fax: 703-689-3041
E-mail: gap@cit.org
Website: www.citgapfunds.org

Management and Staff

Tom Weithman, Managing Director

Type of Firm

Incubator/Development Program

Association Membership

Mid-Atlantic Venture Association
National Venture Capital Association - USA (NVCA)

Project Preferences

Role in Financing:
Prefer role as deal originator but will also invest in deals created by others

Type of Financing Preferred:
Early Stage
Seed

Size of Investments Considered:
Min Size of Investment Considered (000s): $50
Max Size of Investment Considered (000s): $300

Geographical Preferences

United States Preferences:
Virginia

Industry Preferences

In Communications prefer:
Wireless Communications
Data Communications

In Computer Hardware prefer:
Mainframes / Scientific

In Computer Software prefer:
Software
Artificial Intelligence

In Internet Specific prefer:
Internet

In Semiconductor/Electr prefer:
Electronics
Electronic Components
Micro-Processing
Controllers and Sensors
Sensors
Circuit Boards

In Biotechnology prefer:
Human Biotechnology
Agricultural/Animal Bio.
Industrial Biotechnology
Biotech Related Research

In Medical/Health prefer:
Medical Diagnostics
Medical Therapeutics
Drug/Equipmt Delivery
Pharmaceuticals

In Consumer Related prefer:
Consumer Products
Consumer Services

In Industrial/Energy prefer:
Energy
Alternative Energy
Coal Related
Energy Conservation Relat
Materials
Advanced Materials
Factory Automation

In Transportation prefer:
Aerospace

In Agr/Forestr/Fish prefer:
Agriculture related

Additional Information
Year Founded: 2004
Capital Under Management: $12,000,000
Current Activity Level: Actively seeking new investments
Method of Compensation: Return on investment is of primary concern, do not charge fees

---

CITA GESTION
11 bis rue Balzac
Paris, France 75008
Phone: 33-1-4225-7676
Fax: 33-14-225-7685
E-mail: info@cita.fr
Website: www.cita.fr

Management and Staff
Dominique De la Martiniere, Vice President
Philippe Queveau, Managing Director

Type of Firm
Bank Affiliated

Association Membership
French Venture Capital Association (AFIC)
European Private Equity and Venture Capital Assoc.

Project Preferences

Type of Financing Preferred:
Leveraged Buyout
Expansion
Startup

Size of Investments Considered:
Min Size of Investment Considered (000s): $1,000
Max Size of Investment Considered (000s): $7,000

Geographical Preferences

International Preferences:
Europe
France

Additional Information
Year Founded: 1985
Capital Under Management: $133,700,000
Current Activity Level: Actively seeking new investments

CITADEL CAPITAL
Nile Plaza
1089 Corniche El-Nil
Cairo, Egypt
Phone: 20-2-2791-4440
Fax: 20-2-2791-4448
E-mail: info@citadelcapital.com
Website: www.citadelcapital.com

Management and Staff
Abdalla El Ebiary, Managing Director
Ahmed El Shamy, Managing Director
Ahmed El Houssieny, Managing Director
Ahmed El Sharkawy, Principal
Alaa El Afifi, Principal
Hisham El Khazindar, Managing Director
Karim Ragab, Principal
Karim Sadek, Managing Director
Karim Badr, Vice President
Marwan El Araby, Managing Director
Mohamed Abdellah, Vice President
Mostafa Sowelem, Vice President
Raouf Tawfik, Vice President
Shereef El Prince, Principal
Tarek Hayaly, Vice President

Type of Firm
Private Equity Firm

Project Preferences

Type of Financing Preferred:
Leveraged Buyout
Turnaround
Distressed Debt

Geographical Preferences

International Preferences:
Egypt
Middle East
Algeria
Africa
Libya

Industry Preferences

In Industrial/Energy prefer:
Oil and Gas Exploration
Alternative Energy
Materials
Advanced Materials
Environmental Related

In Transportation prefer:
Transportation

In Financial Services prefer:
Financial Services

In Business Serv. prefer:
Services

In Manufact. prefer:
Manufacturing

In Agr/Forestr/Fish prefer:
Agribusiness
Agriculture related

Additional Information
Year Founded: 2007
Capital Under Management: $7,000,000,000
Current Activity Level: Actively seeking new investments

CITI VENTURE CAPITAL INTERNATIONAL
731 Lexington Avenue
21st Floor
New York, NY USA 10022
Phone: 212-559-4676
Fax: 212-793-2799
Website: www.citigroupai.com

Other Offices
2nd Floor, Plot C 61 Citigroup Center
Bandra Kurla Complex
Mumbai, India 400051
Phone: 91-22-4001-5757
Fax: 91-22-2653-5816

33 Cavendish Square
London, United Kingdom W1A 2SY
Phone: 44-207-508-1330
Fax: 44-207-508-1493

25/F, Two Exchange Square
Eight Connaught Place
Central, Hong Kong
Phone: 852-2868-6559
Fax: 852-2868-6667

Management and Staff
Ajit Bhushan, Managing Director
Bob Khanna, Managing Director
Boris Bakal, Managing Director
Bruce Catania, Managing Director
Enrique Bascur, Managing Director
Gisele Everett, Partner
Gordon Lam, Managing Director

Ji Min, Managing Director
Marc Desaedeleer, Managing Director
Murtaza Moochhala, Managing Director
PR Srinivasan, Managing Director
Paulo Caldeira, Managing Director
Rahul Yadav, Managing Director
Sunil Nair, Managing Director

Type of Firm

Bank Affiliated

Association Membership

Hong Kong Venture Capital Association (HKVCA)

Project Preferences

Role in Financing:

Prefer role as deal originator but will also invest in deals created by others

Type of Financing Preferred:

Leveraged Buyout
Expansion
Generalist PE
Management Buyouts
Recapitalizations

Geographical Preferences

International Preferences:

India
Latin America
Taiwan
Central Europe
China
Eastern Europe
Russia

Industry Preferences

In Communications prefer:

Telecommunications

In Medical/Health prefer:

Pharmaceuticals

In Consumer Related prefer:

Consumer
Retail

In Industrial/Energy prefer:

Energy
Alternative Energy

In Financial Services prefer:

Financial Services

Additional Information

Year Founded: 2001
Capital Under Management: $5,500,000
Current Activity Level: Actively seeking new investments

CITIBANK VENTURE CAPITAL INDIA

Jeevan Vihar
3 Sansad Marg
New Delhi, India 110001
Phone: 91-11-2371-4211
Fax: 91-11-2336-1045

Management and Staff

Joy Basu, Vice President
P.R. Srinivasan, Managing Director
Vivek Chhachhi, Vice President

Type of Firm

Bank Affiliated

Project Preferences

Role in Financing:

Will function either as deal originator or investor in deals created by others

Type of Financing Preferred:

Balanced

Geographical Preferences

International Preferences:

India
Asia

Additional Information

Year Founded: 2000
Current Activity Level: Actively seeking new investments
Method of Compensation: Return on investment is of primary concern, do not charge fees

---

CITIC CAPITAL PARTNERS (FKA: CITIC PROVIDENT CAPITAL MGT.)

28/F CITIC Tower
1 Tim Mei Avenue
Central, Hong Kong
Phone: 852-2237-6888
Fax: 852-2523-8312
E-mail: info@citiccapital.com
Website: www.citiccapital.com

Other Offices

23F Tokyo Sankei Bldg.
1-7-2 Otemachi, Chiyoda-ku
Tokyo, Japan 1020094
Phone: 81-3-3243-8990
Fax: 81-3-5216-6389

1120 Avenue of the Americas
Suite 1501
New York, NY USA 10036
Phone: 212-395-9767
Fax: 212-395-9787

Room 1607, 17/F Capital Mansion
No. 6 Xin Yuan Nan Lu
Beijing, China 100004
Phone: 86-10-8486-2966
Fax: 86-10-8486-8998

Unit 1211, The Center
989 Changle Road
Shanghai, China 200031
Phone: 86-21-5407-5511
Fax: 86-21-5407-5022

Management and Staff

Annie Fung, Managing Director
Ben Yu, Managing Director
Emil Cheung, Managing Director
Eric Xin, Managing Director
Eric Chan, Chief Financial Officer
Hironobu Nakano, Managing Director
Kei Okuno, Managing Director
Rikizo Matsukawa, Managing Director
Stanley Ching, Managing Director
Xiaoping Liu, Managing Director
Yi-Chen Zhang, Chief Executive Officer
Yichen Zhang, Chief Executive Officer

Type of Firm

Bank Affiliated

Project Preferences

Type of Financing Preferred:

Leveraged Buyout
Expansion
Balanced
Later Stage

Geographical Preferences

United States Preferences:

All U.S.

International Preferences:

China
Japan

Industry Preferences

In Consumer Related prefer:

Consumer Products

In Industrial/Energy prefer:

Industrial Products

In Manufact. prefer:

Manufacturing

Additional Information

Year Founded: 2003
Capital Under Management: $750,000,000
Current Activity Level: Actively seeking new investments

CITIC PRIVATE EQUITY FUNDS MANAGEMENT CO., LTD.

c/o CITIC Securities Co., Ltd.
No. 6 Xinyuan South Road
Beijing, China 100004
Phone: 86-10-8458-8581
Fax: 86-10-8486-5567

Type of Firm

Bank Affiliated

Project Preferences

Type of Financing Preferred:
Generalist PE
Balanced
Acquisition

Geographical Preferences

International Preferences:
China

Additional Information
Year Founded: 2008
Current Activity Level: Actively seeking new investments

CITIC SECURITIES INTERNATIONAL PARTNERS, LTD.

26/F, CITIC Tower
1 Tim Mei Avenue
Central , Hong Kong
Phone: 852-2237-6899
Fax: 852-2104-6862
E-mail: info@citics.com.hk
Website: www.citics.com.hk

Management and Staff
Donald Tang, Chief Executive Officer

Type of Firm
Bank Affiliated

Project Preferences

Type of Financing Preferred:
Generalist PE

Geographical Preferences

International Preferences:
China

Additional Information
Year Founded: 2009
Current Activity Level: Actively seeking new investments

CITICORP VENTURE CAPITAL, LTD.

399 Park Avenue
14th Floor, Zone Four
New York, NY USA 10043
Phone: 212-559-1127
Fax: 212-888-2940

Management and Staff
Thomas McWilliams, Managing Director

Type of Firm
Bank Affiliated

Association Membership
Natl Assoc of Small Bus. Inv. Co (NASBIC)

Project Preferences

Role in Financing:
Prefer role as deal originator

Type of Financing Preferred:
Second Stage Financing
Leveraged Buyout
Special Situation

Size of Investments Considered:
Min Size of Investment Considered (000s): $50,000
Max Size of Investment Considered: No Limit

Geographical Preferences

United States Preferences:
All U.S.

International Preferences:
United Kingdom
Bermuda
Germany
France

Industry Focus
(% based on actual investment)

Semiconductors/Other Elect.	28.0%
Medical/Health	21.0%
Internet Specific	12.7%
Consumer Related	10.1%
Other Products	9.0%
Computer Hardware	5.6%
Communications and Media	5.5%
Industrial/Energy	5.3%
Computer Software and Services	2.3%
Biotechnology	0.4%

Additional Information
Year Founded: 1968
Capital Under Management: $250,000,000
Current Activity Level: Actively seeking new investments
Method of Compensation: Return on investment is of primary concern, do not charge fees

---

CITIGROUP PRINCIPAL INVESTMENT JAPAN CO., LTD.

Tokyo Ginko Kyokai Bldg.
3-1- Marunouchi, Chiyoda-ku
Tokyo, Japan 100-0005
Phone: 81-3-5223-9650
Website: www.citigroup.jp

Type of Firm
Bank Affiliated

Additional Information
Year Founded: 2006
Current Activity Level: Actively seeking new investments

CITIGROUP PRIVATE BANK

153 East 53rd Street
Third Floor
New York, NY USA 10043
Phone: 212-559-6093
Fax: 212-559-0036

Other Offices
41 Berkeley Square
London, United Kingdom W1S 5AN
Phone: 44-207-508-8000

Management and Staff
Annie Fung, Managing Director
Sitaraman Mani, Managing Director

Type of Firm
Bank Affiliated

Project Preferences

Type of Financing Preferred:
Leveraged Buyout

Geographical Preferences

International Preferences:
Western Europe

Additional Information
Year Founded: 2002
Capital Under Management: $19,500,000
Current Activity Level: Actively seeking new investments

CITIGROUP PRIVATE EQUITY

731 Lexington Avenue
27th Floor
New York, NY USA 10022
Phone: 212-783-1088
Website: www.citigroupai.com

Other Offices
33 Cavendish Square
8th Floor
London, United Kingdom W1A 2SY

Parliament Street
New Delhi, India 110001
Phone: 91-11-2371-4211
Fax: 91-11-2374-7450

Management and Staff
Cali Cole, Managing Director
Craig Farnsworth, Partner
Darren Friedman, Partner
Hunter Reisner, Managing Partner
Michael Whitman, Partner
Robert Womsley, Partner

Type of Firm
Bank Affiliated

Project Preferences
Role in Financing:
Will function either as deal originator or investor in deals created by others

Type of Financing Preferred:
Fund of Funds
Leveraged Buyout
Mezzanine
Distressed Debt

Geographical Preferences
United States Preferences:
All U.S.

International Preferences:
All International

Industry Preferences
In Medical/Health prefer:
Pharmaceuticals

In Consumer Related prefer:
Retail

In Industrial/Energy prefer:
Energy

Additional Information
Name of Most Recent Fund: Citigroup Capital Partners II Offshore, L.P.
Most Recent Fund Was Raised: 09/11/2006
Year Founded: 1998
Capital Under Management: $8,300,000,000
Current Activity Level: Actively seeking new investments
Method of Compensation: Return on investment is of primary concern, do not charge fees

---

CITIZEN CAPITAL
16, rue Martel
Paris, France 75010
Phone: 33-1-7674-7720
E-mail: contact@citizencapital.fr
Website: www.citizencapital.fr

Management and Staff
Laurence Mehaignerie, President

Type of Firm
Private Equity Firm

Association Membership
French Venture Capital Association (AFIC)

Project Preferences
Type of Financing Preferred:
Generalist PE
Expansion
Early Stage

Geographical Preferences
International Preferences:
Europe
France

Additional Information
Year Founded: 2008
Current Activity Level: Actively seeking new investments

CITIZENS CAPITAL, INC.
28 State Street
15th Floor
Boston, MA USA 02109
Phone: 617-725-5636
Fax: 617-725-5630
Website: www.citizenscapital.com

Type of Firm
Private Equity Firm

Association Membership
Natl Assoc of Small Bus. Inv. Co (NASBIC)

Project Preferences
Role in Financing:
Prefer role in deals created by others

Type of Financing Preferred:
Generalist PE

Size of Investments Considered:
Min Size of Investment Considered (000s): $1,000
Max Size of Investment Considered (000s): $5,000

Geographical Preferences
United States Preferences:
Northeast

Industry Focus
(% based on actual investment)

Semiconductors/Other Elect.	26.6%
Communications and Media	23.1%
Consumer Related	13.8%
Other Products	10.4%
Computer Software and Services	9.3%
Industrial/Energy	7.8%
Internet Specific	7.7%
Computer Hardware	1.3%

Additional Information
Year Founded: 1996
Capital Under Management: $450,000,000
Current Activity Level: Actively seeking new investments
Method of Compensation: Return on invest. most important, but chg. closing fees, service fees, etc.

CITY LIGHT CAPITAL
295 Madison Avenue
Fifth Floor
New York, NY USA 10017
Phone: 212-403-9586
Fax: 212-403-9552
E-mail: info@citylightcap.com
Website: www.citylightcap.com

Management and Staff
Jamie Daves, Venture Partner
Josh Cohen, Managing Partner
Matt Cohen, Principal
Tom Groos, Partner

Type of Firm
Private Equity Firm

Project Preferences
Type of Financing Preferred:
Early Stage
Expansion

Industry Preferences
In Consumer Related prefer:
Education Related

In Industrial/Energy prefer:
Energy
Energy Conservation Relat

In Business Serv. prefer:
Media

Additional Information
Year Founded: 2009
Current Activity Level: Actively seeking new investments

CIVC PARTNERS LP (FKA: CONTINENTAL ILLINOIS VENTURE CORP.)
191 North Wacker Drive
Suite 1100
Chicago, IL USA 60606
Phone: 312-873-7300
Fax: 312-873-7301
E-mail: civc_partners@CIVC.com
Website: www.civc.com

Management and Staff
Christopher Perry, Partner
Christopher Geneser, Chief Financial Officer
Christopher McLaughlin, Vice President
Daniel Helle, Partner
David Miller, Vice President
John Compall, Principal
Keith Yamada, Partner
Marcus Wedner, Partner
Mark McManus, Vice President
Michael Miller, Principal
Scott Schwartz, Principal

Type of Firm
Bank Affiliated

Association Membership
Illinois Venture Capital Association
Natl Assoc of Small Bus. Inv. Co (NASBIC)

Project Preferences

Role in Financing:
Prefer role as deal originator but will also invest in deals created by others

Type of Financing Preferred:
Leveraged Buyout
Expansion
Generalist PE
Later Stage
Management Buyouts
Acquisition
Recapitalizations

Size of Investments Considered:
Min Size of Investment Considered (000s): $10,000
Max Size of Investment Considered (000s): $75,000

Geographical Preferences

Canadian Preferences:
All Canada

Industry Preferences

In Communications prefer:
Communications and Media
Commercial Communications
Radio & TV Broadcasting
Telecommunications
Data Communications
Other Communication Prod.

In Computer Software prefer:
Computer Services
Data Processing

In Semiconductor/Electr prefer:
Electronic Components
Controllers and Sensors
Sensors
Component Testing Equipmt
Analytic/Scientific

In Consumer Related prefer:
Food/Beverage
Education Related

In Industrial/Energy prefer:
Industrial Products

In Financial Services prefer:
Financial Services
Insurance

In Business Serv. prefer:
Services
Media

In Manufact. prefer:
Manufacturing

Additional Information
Name of Most Recent Fund: CIVC Partners Fund II
Most Recent Fund Was Raised: 01/01/1999
Year Founded: 1970
Capital Under Management: $1,300,000,000
Current Activity Level: Actively seeking new investments
Method of Compensation: Return on invest. most important, but chg. closing fees, service fees, etc.

CLAFLIN CAPITAL MANAGEMENT, INC.
10 Liberty Square
Suite 300
Boston, MA USA 02109
Phone: 617-426-6505
Fax: 617-482-0016
E-mail: Office@clafcap.com
Website: www.claflincapital.com

Management and Staff
George Aggouras, Chief Financial Officer
Joseph Stavenhagen, General Partner
Thomas Claflin, Managing Partner
Walter Bird, Managing Partner
William Wilcoxson, General Partner

Type of Firm
Private Equity Firm

Project Preferences

Role in Financing:
Prefer role as deal originator but will also invest in deals created by others

Type of Financing Preferred:
Early Stage
Startup

Size of Investments Considered:
Min Size of Investment Considered (000s): $250
Max Size of Investment Considered (000s): $1,000

Geographical Preferences

United States Preferences:
Northeast

Industry Focus
(% based on actual investment)

Computer Software and Services	25.1%
Internet Specific	24.5%
Computer Hardware	13.1%
Medical/Health	9.7%
Communications and Media	6.8%
Biotechnology	5.7%
Semiconductors/Other Elect.	5.4%
Consumer Related	5.3%
Industrial/Energy	3.2%
Other Products	1.4%

Additional Information
Year Founded: 1978
Capital Under Management: $70,000,000
Current Activity Level: Actively seeking new investments
Method of Compensation: Return on investment is of primary concern, do not charge fees

---

CLAL VENTURE CAPITAL MANAGEMENT, LTD. (AKA: CVC MANAGEMENT)
3 Azrieli Center
45 floor
Tel Aviv, Israel 67023
Phone: 972-3-607-5777
Fax: 972-3-607-5778
E-mail: cii@cii.co.il

Management and Staff
Avi Fischer, Chief Executive Officer
Zvi Livnat, Chief Executive Officer

Type of Firm
Corporate PE/Venture

Project Preferences

Type of Financing Preferred:
Early Stage
Expansion
Startup

Geographical Preferences

International Preferences:
Middle East
Israel

Industry Preferences

In Computer Software prefer:
Software

In Medical/Health prefer:
Medical/Health

Additional Information
Year Founded: 1995
Capital Under Management: $36,000,000
Current Activity Level: Actively seeking new investments

CLAREMONT CREEK VENTURES
300 Frank H. Ogawa Plaza
Suite 350
Oakland, CA USA 94612
Phone: 510-740-5001
Fax: 510-287-9937
Website: www.claremontvc.com

Management and Staff
Brad Webb, Venture Partner
John Steuart, Managing Director
Nathaniel Goldhaber, Managing Director
Paul Straub, Principal
Randy Hawks, Managing Director
Ted Driscoll, Venture Partner

Type of Firm
Private Equity Firm

Association Membership
Western Association of Venture Capitalists (WAVC)

Project Preferences

Role in Financing:
Prefer role as deal originator

Type of Financing Preferred:
Early Stage

Size of Investments Considered:
Min Size of Investment Considered (000s): $500
Max Size of Investment Considered (000s): $3,000

Geographical Preferences

United States Preferences:
Northern California
California

Industry Preferences

In Communications prefer:
Wireless Communications

In Internet Specific prefer:
E-Commerce Technology
Internet
Ecommerce

In Semiconductor/Electr prefer:
Sensors

In Medical/Health prefer:
Medical/Health
Medical Products
Health Services

In Industrial/Energy prefer:
Alternative Energy

Additional Information
Year Founded: 2005
Capital Under Management: $300,000,000
Current Activity Level: Actively seeking new investments

CLARET CAPITAL, LTD.
The Oval, Building 3
Shelbourne Road
Dublin, Ireland
Phone: 353-1-231-5888
Fax: 353-1-231-5889
Website: www.claretcapital.net

Other Offices
1540 Broadway
Suite 1400
New York, NY USA 10036
Phone: 212-471-1873

Management and Staff
Dermot Hanley, Managing Director
Domhnal Slattery, Managing Partner
Tom McAleese, Chief Operating Officer
Yuki Narula, Managing Director

Type of Firm
Private Equity Firm

Additional Information
Year Founded: 2007
Current Activity Level: Actively seeking new investments

CLAREY CAPITAL LLC
131 Innovation
Suite 150
Irvine, CA USA 92617
Phone: 949-468-5757
Fax: 949-823-3956
E-mail: info@clarey.net
Website: www.clarey.net

Management and Staff
James Righeimer, Principal
John Clarey, Managing Director
Rodney Allen, Chief Financial Officer

Type of Firm
Private Equity Firm

Additional Information
Year Founded: 2007
Current Activity Level: Actively seeking new investments

CLARIAN HEALTH VENTURES, INC.
340 West Tenth Street
Suite 2100
Indianapolis, IN USA 46202
Phone: 317-963-7800
Fax: 317-963-7801
E-mail: chventures@clarian.org
Website: www.clarianhealthventures.com

Management and Staff
Kyle Salyers, Managing Director

Type of Firm
Corporate PE/Venture

Association Membership
National Venture Capital Association - USA (NVCA)

Project Preferences

Type of Financing Preferred:
Early Stage

Size of Investments Considered:
Min Size of Investment Considered (000s): $250
Max Size of Investment Considered (000s): $3,000

Geographical Preferences

United States Preferences:
Indiana

Industry Preferences

In Medical/Health prefer:
Medical/Health
Medical Products

Additional Information
Year Founded: 2008
Current Activity Level: Actively seeking new investments

CLARICA
227 King Street South
Waterloo, Canada N2J4C5
Phone: 888-864-5463
Website: www.clarica.com

Type of Firm
Endowment, Foundation or Pension Fund

Additional Information
Year Founded: 2009
Current Activity Level: Actively seeking new investments

CLARION CAPITAL PARTNERS LLC
110 East 59th Street
New York, NY USA 10022-1304
Phone: 212-821-0176
Fax: 212-371-7597
Website: www.clarion-capital.com

Management and Staff
Marc Utay, Managing Partner

Type of Firm
Private Equity Firm

Project Preferences

Type of Financing Preferred:
Leveraged Buyout
Generalist PE

Size of Investments Considered:
Min Size of Investment Considered (000s): $20,000
Max Size of Investment Considered (000s): $50,000

Additional Information
Year Founded: 1999
Capital Under Management: $300,000,000
Current Activity Level: Actively seeking new investments

CLARITAS CAPITAL LLC (FKA: VERTICAL INVESTMENTS)

One Burton Hills Boulevard
Suite 215
Nashville, TN USA 37215
Phone: 615-665-8550
Fax: 615-665-2550
E-mail: info@claritascapital.com
Website: www.claritascapital.com

Other Offices

1776 One Street Northwest
Ninth Floor
Washington, DC USA 20006
Phone: 202-756-1616
Fax: 202-756-1531

Management and Staff

J. Donald McLemore, Managing Partner
John Chadwick, Managing Partner
Theresa Sexton, Vice President

Type of Firm

Private Equity Firm

Association Membership

National Venture Capital Association - USA (NVCA)

Project Preferences

Role in Financing:
Prefer role as deal originator

Type of Financing Preferred:
Early Stage
Expansion
First Stage Financing

Size of Investments Considered:
Min Size of Investment Considered (000s): $250
Max Size of Investment Considered (000s): $2,000

Geographical Preferences

United States Preferences:
Southeast

Industry Preferences

In Communications prefer:
Wireless Communications

In Computer Software prefer:
Computer Services
Data Processing
Software

In Internet Specific prefer:
Internet
Ecommerce
Web Aggregration/Portals

In Medical/Health prefer:
Medical Diagnostics
Diagnostic Services
Diagnostic Test Products
Medical Products
Disposable Med. Products
Health Services
Hospitals/Clinics/Primary
Hospital/Other Instit.

In Consumer Related prefer:
Consumer
Entertainment and Leisure

In Financial Services prefer:
Financial Services

In Business Serv. prefer:
Distribution
Media

Additional Information

Name of Most Recent Fund: Claritas Opportunity Fund, L.P.
Most Recent Fund Was Raised: 07/15/2008
Year Founded: 2002
Capital Under Management: $40,000,000
Current Activity Level: Actively seeking new investments
Method of Compensation: Return on investment is of primary concern, do not charge fees

CLARITY CAPITAL

5964 Centre Street South East
Calgary, Canada T2H0C1
Phone: 403-543-2587
Fax: 403-543-2599
E-mail: info@claritycapital.com
Website: www.claritycapital.com

Other Offices

The Guinness Tower
suite 300, 1055 West Hastings Street
Vancouver, Canada V6E2E9
Phone: 604-609-6177
Fax: 604-684-6024

Type of Firm

Private Equity Firm

Additional Information

Year Founded: 2009
Current Activity Level: Actively seeking new investments

CLARITY PARTNERS

100 North Crescent Drive
Suite 300
Beverly Hills, CA USA 90210
Phone: 310-432-0100
Fax: 310-432-5000
E-mail: info@claritypartners.net
Website: www.claritypartners.net

Other Offices

Suite 4701, Plaza 66
1366 West Nanjing Road
Shanghai, China 200040
Phone: 86-21-6288-7575
Fax: 86-21-6288-3376

Suite 2003, Capital Mansion
6 Xin Yuan Nan Lu, Chaoyang
Beijing, China 100004
Phone: 86-10-8486-8560
Fax: 86-10-8486-8563

Management and Staff

Barry Porter, Managing General Partner
Clinton Walker, General Partner
Cong Gen Zhou, Managing Director
David Lee, Managing General Partner
Gary Wilson, General Partner
Joshua Gutfreund, General Partner
R. Rudolph Reinfrank, Managing General Partner
Sheldon Liu, General Partner
Stephen Rader, Managing General Partner
T. Leo Griffin, Vice President

Type of Firm

Private Equity Firm

Project Preferences

Role in Financing:
Prefer role as deal originator

Type of Financing Preferred:
Leveraged Buyout
Early Stage
Generalist PE
Balanced
Later Stage

Size of Investments Considered:
Min Size of Investment Considered (000s): $20,000
Max Size of Investment Considered (000s): $60,000

Geographical Preferences

United States Preferences:
California
All U.S.

International Preferences:
China
All International

Industry Focus

(% based on actual investment)

Semiconductors/Other Elect.	55.5%
Communications and Media	16.1%
Other Products	11.5%
Internet Specific	11.0%
Computer Software and Services	4.5%
Computer Hardware	1.5%

Additional Information

Year Founded: 1997
Capital Under Management: $1,260,000,000
Current Activity Level: Actively seeking new investments
Method of Compensation: Return on invest. most important, but chg. closing fees, service fees, etc.

CLARUS VENTURES

101 Main Street
Suite 1210
Cambridge, MA USA 02142
Phone: 617-949-2200
Fax: 617-949-2201
Website: www.clarusventures.com

Other Offices

801 Gateway Boulevard
Suite 410
South San Francisco, CA USA 94080
Phone: 650-238-5000

Fax: 650-238-5001

Management and Staff
Dennis Henner, Managing Director
Edward Scolnick, Venture Partner
Emmett Cunningham, Partner
Finny Kuruvilla, Principal
Jeffrey Leiden, Managing Director
Kurt Wheeler, Managing Director
Michael Steinmetz, Managing Director
Michele Park, Principal
Nicholas Galakatos, Managing Director
Nicholas Simon, Managing Director
Robert Liptak, Managing Director
Scott Requadt, Partner
Type of Firm
Private Equity Firm

Association Membership

National Venture Capital Association - USA (NVCA)

Project Preferences

Type of Financing Preferred:
Balanced
Private Placement

Size of Investments Considered:
Min Size of Investment Considered (000s): $15,000
Max Size of Investment Considered (000s): $50,000

Geographical Preferences

International Preferences:
Europe

Industry Preferences

In Biotechnology prefer:
Biotechnology

In Medical/Health prefer:
Medical Products
Pharmaceuticals

Additional Information

Name of Most Recent Fund: Clarus Lifesciences II, L.P.
Most Recent Fund Was Raised: 02/15/2008
Year Founded: 2005
Capital Under Management: $1,160,000,000
Current Activity Level: Actively seeking new investments

CLAVE MAYOR S.A.

C/Emilio Arrieta
11 bis-2
Pamplona, Spain 31002
Phone: 34-94-820-3960
Fax: 34-94-822-8902
E-mail: info@clavemayor.com
Website: www.clavemayor.com

Type of Firm

Private Equity Firm

Association Membership

Spanish Venture Capital Association (ASCRI)

Project Preferences

Type of Financing Preferred:
Expansion
Early Stage
Balanced
Startup

Geographical Preferences

International Preferences:
Europe
Spain

Industry Preferences

In Communications prefer:
Communications and Media

In Semiconductor/Electr prefer:
Electronics

In Biotechnology prefer:
Biotechnology

In Transportation prefer:
Transportation

Additional Information

Year Founded: 1998
Capital Under Management: $5,800,000
Current Activity Level: Actively seeking new investments

CLAVEL INVESTISSEMENT (FKA: CITY STAR PRIVATE EQUITY)

61 Avenue Victor Hugo
Paris, France 75116
Phone: 33-1-5364-2200
Fax: 33-1-4500-1716
Website: www.citystarcapital.com

Type of Firm

Private Equity Firm

Association Membership

French Venture Capital Association (AFIC)

Project Preferences

Type of Financing Preferred:
Leveraged Buyout
Balanced

Geographical Preferences

International Preferences:
Europe
France

Additional Information

Year Founded: 2004
Current Activity Level: Actively seeking new investments

CLAYTON ASSOCIATES LLC

113 Seaboard Lane
Suite A-250
Franklin, TN USA 37067
Phone: 615-320-3070
Fax: 615-320-0224
E-mail: info@claytonassociates.com
Website: www.claytonassociates.com

Management and Staff

Christopher Kyriopoulos, Partner
Gary Cordell, Chief Operating Officer
Matthew King, Partner
Richard Rodgers, Chief Financial Officer
Stuart McWhorter, Managing Partner

Type of Firm

Private Equity Firm

Association Membership

Natl Assoc of Small Bus. Inv. Co (NASBIC)

Project Preferences

Role in Financing:
Will function either as deal originator or investor in deals created by others

Type of Financing Preferred:
Early Stage
Expansion

Size of Investments Considered:
Min Size of Investment Considered (000s): $500
Max Size of Investment Considered (000s): $4,000

Geographical Preferences

United States Preferences:
Southeast

Industry Preferences

In Medical/Health prefer:
Health Services

Additional Information

Name of Most Recent Fund: FCA Venture Partners IV, L.P.

Most Recent Fund Was Raised: 05/10/2006
Year Founded: 1996
Capital Under Management: $100,000,000
Current Activity Level: Actively seeking new investments
Method of Compensation: Return on invest. most important, but chg. closing fees, service fees, etc.

CLAYTON CAPITAL

8820 Ladue
Suite 201
Saint Louis, MO USA 63124
Phone: 314-725-9939
Fax: 314-725-9938
E-mail: info@claytoncapitalpartners.com
Website: www.claytoncapitalpartners.com

Management and Staff

Brent Baxter, Managing Director
Craig Herron, Principal
Kevin Short, Managing Director

Type of Firm

Private Equity Firm

Additional Information

Year Founded: 2009
Current Activity Level: Actively seeking new investments

CLAYTON, DUBILIER & RICE, INC.

375 Park Avenue
18th Floor
New York, NY USA 10152
Phone: 212-407-5200
Fax: 212-407-5252
E-mail: info@cdr-ltd.com
Website: www.cdr-inc.com

Other Offices

Ugland House
P.O. Box 309
George Town, Grand Cayman, Cayman Islands

33 King Street
Cleveland House
London, United Kingdom SW1Y 6RJ
Phone: 44-207-747-3800
Fax: 44-207-747-3801

Management and Staff

Amyn Pesnani, Principal
Christine Vanden Beukel, Senior Managing Director
Clayton Armstrong, Principal
David Novak, Partner
David Wasserman, Partner
Edward Liddy, Partner
Eric Rahe, Principal
Fred Kindle, Partner
George Jaquette, Partner
J. L. Zrebiec, Principal
James Berges, Partner
Kenneth Giuriceo, Partner
Kevin Conway, Managing Partner
Michael Babiarz, Partner
Nathan Sleeper, Principal
Richard Schnall, Partner
Roberto Quarta, Partner
Stephen Shapiro, Principal
Thomas Franco, Partner

Type of Firm

Private Equity Firm

Association Membership

British Venture Capital Association (BVCA)
French Venture Capital Association (AFIC)

Project Preferences

Type of Financing Preferred:
Leveraged Buyout
Acquisition

Geographical Preferences

rences:

International Preferences:
Europe
All International

Industry Focus

(% based on actual investment)

Other Products	45.1%
Medical/Health	18.1%
Consumer Related	14.6%
Communications and Media	10.1%
Industrial/Energy	8.2%
Computer Hardware	2.3%
Internet Specific	1.5%
Computer Software and Services	0.1%

Additional Information

Name of Most Recent Fund: CDR USF Co-Investor, L.P.
Most Recent Fund Was Raised: 06/26/2007
Year Founded: 1978
Capital Under Management: $5,098,000,000
Current Activity Level: Actively seeking new investments

CLB PARTNERS, LLC

1160 East Jericho Turnpike
Suite 207
Huntington, NY USA 11743
Phone: 631-425-0710
Fax: 631-824-9118
Website: www.clb-partners.com

Management and Staff

Alex Abreu, Managing Director

Type of Firm

Bank Affiliated

Additional Information

Year Founded: 2004
Capital Under Management: $40,000,000
Current Activity Level: Actively seeking new investments

CLEAN PACIFIC VENTURES

425 California Street
Suite 2450
San Francisco, CA USA 94104
Phone: 415-433-0123
Fax: 415-433-0161
Website: www.cleanpacific.com

Management and Staff

Dave Herron, Principal
Denise Davis, Chief Financial Officer
Jay Thomson, Venture Partner
Jeff Barnes, General Partner
Sean Schickedanz, General Partner

Type of Firm

Private Equity Firm

Project Preferences

Type of Financing Preferred:
Early Stage
Seed
Startup

Industry Preferences

In Consumer Related prefer:
Food/Beverage

In Industrial/Energy prefer:
Alternative Energy
Energy Conservation Relat
Materials
Environmental Related

In Other prefer:
Environment Responsible

Additional Information

Year Founded: 2006
Capital Under Management: $10,000,000
Current Activity Level: Actively seeking new investments

CLEANTECH VENTURES PTY, LTD.

Suite 609, Level 6
2 Queen Street
Melbourne, Australia 3000
Phone: 613-9607-7100
Fax: 613-9670-7988
E-mail: info@cleantechventures.com.au
Website: www.cleantechventures.com.au

Management and Staff

Andrew Pickering, Principal
Jan Dekker, Principal

Type of Firm

Private Equity Firm

Project Preferences

Role in Financing:

Will function either as deal originator or investor in deals created by others

Type of Financing Preferred:

Early Stage
Seed

Geographical Preferences

International Preferences:

Switzerland
Asia
New Zealand
Singapore
Australia

Industry Preferences

In Industrial/Energy prefer:

Environmental Related

Additional Information

Year Founded: 2003
Capital Under Management: $76,700,000
Current Activity Level: Actively seeking new investments
Method of Compensation: Return on investment is of primary concern, do not charge fees

---

CLEARLAKE CAPITAL GROUP

650 Madison Avenue
23rd Floor
New York, NY USA 10022
Phone: 212-610-9120
E-mail: info@clearlakecapital.com
Website: www.clearlakecapital.com

Management and Staff

Behdad Eghbali, Principal
Jose Feliciano, Principal
Steven Chang, Principal

Type of Firm

Private Equity Firm

Project Preferences

Type of Financing Preferred:

Leveraged Buyout
Expansion
Special Situation
Acquisition
Distressed Debt
Recapitalizations

Geographical Preferences

United States Preferences:

All U.S.

Additional Information

Year Founded: 2007
Capital Under Management: $103,000,000
Current Activity Level: Actively seeking new investments

CLEARLIGHT PARTNERS LLC

100 Bayview Circle
Suite 5000
Newport Beach, CA USA 92660
Phone: 949-725-6610
Fax: 949-725-6611
E-mail: info@clearlightpartners.com
Website: www.clearlightpartners.com

Management and Staff

Jay Shepherd, Partner
Lawrence Ward, Partner
Michael Kaye, Senior Managing Director
Patrick Haiz, Partner
Peter Nanula, Partner

Type of Firm

Private Equity Firm

Geographical Preferences

United States Preferences:

West Coast

Industry Preferences

In Consumer Related prefer:

Education Related

Additional Information

Year Founded: 2000
Capital Under Management: $300,000,000
Current Activity Level: Actively seeking new investments

CLEARSTONE VENTURE PARTNERS (FKA: IDEALAB! CAPITAL PARTNERS)

1351 Fourth Street
Fourth Floor
Santa Monica, CA USA 90401
Phone: 310-460-7900
Fax: 310-460-7901
E-mail: info@clearstone.com
Website: www.clearstone.com

Other Offices

2180 Sand Hill Road
Suite 200
Menlo Park, CA USA 94025
Phone: 650-234-0400
Fax: 650-234-0401

608, St. James Court
St. Dennis Street
Port Louis, Mauritius
Phone: 230-210-9000
Fax: 230-210-9001

Dhanraj Mahal, Block F, Unit 35
Apollo Bunder
Mumbai, India 400 001
Phone: 91-22-6630-7257
Fax: 91-22-6630-7258

Management and Staff

Anil Patel, Venture Partner
Dana Moraly, Chief Financial Officer
David Stern, Venture Partner
Erik Lasilla, Managing Director
James Armstrong, Managing Director
Rajan Mehra, Venture Partner
Shailesh Mehta, Venture Partner
Sumant Mandal, Managing Director
William Quigley, Managing Director
William Elkus, Managing Director

Type of Firm

Private Equity Firm

Association Membership

National Venture Capital Association - USA (NVCA)

Project Preferences

Role in Financing:

Prefer role as deal originator but will also invest in deals created by others

Type of Financing Preferred:

Early Stage
Expansion
Seed

Size of Investments Considered:

Min Size of Investment Considered (000s): $2,000
Max Size of Investment Considered (000s): $10,000

Geographical Preferences

United States Preferences:

Southern California
Northern California
West Coast
California

International Preferences:

India

Industry Focus

(% based on actual investment)

Internet Specific	46.6%
Computer Software and Services	23.0%
Communications and Media	11.9%
Computer Hardware	5.9%
Semiconductors/Other Elect.	5.1%
Other Products	4.7%
Consumer Related	2.8%

Additional Information

Name of Most Recent Fund: Clearstone Venture Partners III-A, L.P.
Most Recent Fund Was Raised: 10/15/2004
Year Founded: 1998

Capital Under Management: $651,000,000
Current Activity Level: Actively seeking new investments
Method of Compensation: Return on investment is of primary concern, do not charge fees

CLEARVIEW CAPITAL LLC

1445 East Putnam Avenue
Old Greenwich, CT USA 06870
Phone: 203-698-2777
Fax: 203-698-9194
E-mail: info@clearviewcap.com
Website: www.clearviewcap.com

Other Offices

223 West Jackson Boulevard
Suite 1010
Chicago, IL USA 60606
Phone: 312-288-0123
Fax: 312-583-1700

12100 Wilshire Boulevard
Suite 800
West Los Angeles, CA USA 90025
Phone: 310-806-9555
Fax: 310-806-9556

336 Deer Run Drive South
Ponte Vedra Beach
West Los Angeles, CA USA 90025
Phone: 904-280-7810
Fax: 904-285-5870

Management and Staff

Anthony Veith, Principal
Calvin Neider, Managing Partner
H.F. Doolittle, Partner
James Andersen, Managing Partner
Lawrence Simon, Principal
Matt Rumilly, Vice President
Paul Caliento, Partner
William Case, Partner

Type of Firm

Private Equity Firm

Project Preferences

Role in Financing:
Prefer role as deal originator

Type of Financing Preferred:
Leveraged Buyout
Control-block Purchases
Generalist PE
Management Buyouts
Industry Rollups
Acquisition
Recapitalizations

Size of Investments Considered:
Min Size of Investment Considered (000s): $5,000
Max Size of Investment Considered (000s): $15,000

Geographical Preferences

Canadian Preferences:
All Canada

Industry Focus

(% based on actual investment)

Industrial/Energy	52.7%
Consumer Related	23.1%
Other Products	22.9%
Biotechnology	1.2%

Additional Information

Name of Most Recent Fund: Clearview Capital Fund II, L.P.
Most Recent Fund Was Raised: 10/12/2006
Year Founded: 1999
Capital Under Management: $360,000,000
Current Activity Level: Actively seeking new investments
Method of Compensation: Return on invest. most important, but chg. closing fees, service fees, etc.

CLEARWATER CAPITAL MANAGEMENT

614 Academy Avenue
Sewickley, PA USA 15143
Phone: 412-749-0396
Fax: 412-749-1220
E-mail: info@clearwatercapital.com
Website: www.clearwatercapital.com

Type of Firm

Private Equity Firm

Project Preferences

Type of Financing Preferred:
Early Stage
Other

Additional Information

Year Founded: 2003
Current Activity Level: Actively seeking new investments

CLEARWATER CAPITAL PARTNERS, LLC

485 Madison Avenue
18th Floor
New York, NY USA 10022
Phone: 212-201-8544
E-mail: information@clearwatercp.com
Website: www.clearwatercapitalpartners.com

Other Offices

808, Tower C2, Oriental Plaza
No. 1 East Chang An Av
Beijing, China 100738

4 Battery Road #34-01
Bank of China Building
Singapore, Singapore 049908

Suite 2205A
No. 9 Queens Road
Central, Hong Kong, China

201, 2nd Floor, Central Plaza
166 CST Road
Kalina Mumbai, India 400 098

10th Floor KTB Network Building
826-14 Yeoksam-Dong
Gangham-Gu, Seoul, South Korea 135-080

Management and Staff

Amit Gupta, Partner
Bruno Beuque, Partner
Cameron Hillyer, Chief Financial Officer
Robert Petty, Managing Partner
Yao-Chye Chiang, Chief Operating Officer

Type of Firm

Private Equity Firm

Project Preferences

Type of Financing Preferred:
Leveraged Buyout
Distressed Debt

Geographical Preferences

United States Preferences:
All U.S.

International Preferences:
Asia

Additional Information

Name of Most Recent Fund: Clearwater Capital Partners Fund III, LP
Most Recent Fund Was Raised: 02/22/2007
Year Founded: 2001
Capital Under Management: $1,160,800,000
Current Activity Level: Actively seeking new investments

CLESSIDRA CAPITAL

Via del Lauro 7
Milan, Italy 20121
Phone: 39-2-869-5221
Fax: 39-2-869-522522
E-mail: info@clessidrasgr.it
Website: www.clessidrasgr.it

Management and Staff

Alessandro Papetti, Partner
Claudio Sposito, Chairman & CEO
Manuel Catalano, Partner
Matteo Ricatti, Partner
Ugo Belardi, Chief Operating Officer

Type of Firm

Private Equity Firm

Association Membership

European Private Equity and Venture Capital Assoc.

Project Preferences

Type of Financing Preferred:
Leveraged Buyout
Management Buyouts

Geographical Preferences

International Preferences:
Italy
Europe

Additional Information

Name of Most Recent Fund: Clessidra Capital Partners
Most Recent Fund Was Raised: 10/16/2003
Year Founded: 2003
Capital Under Management: $1,340,100,000
Current Activity Level: Actively seeking new investments

CLIMATE CHANGE CAPITAL, LTD.

3 More London Riverside
London, United Kingdom SE1 2AQ
Phone: 44-20-7939-5000
Fax: 44-20-7939-5030
Website: www.climatechangecapital.com

Other Offices

12th Floor, Tower 2
5 Guanghua Road
Beijing, China 100020
Phone: 86-10-6589-0888
Fax: 86-10-8525-3197

Calle Jose Ortega y Gasset
Planta Baja
Madrid, Spain 28006
Phone: 34-91-576-4837

1331 L. Street
North West
Washington, DC USA 20005
Phone: 202-557-7404
Fax: 202-408-4963

Management and Staff

Alex Betts, Partner
Andrew Pearson, Managing Director
Anthony White, Managing Director
Brian Prusnek, Vice President
Bruno Derungs, Partner
Charles Conner, Managing Director
Esme Lowe, Managing Director
Ian Temperton, Managing Director
Jon Sohn, Vice President
Justin Mundy, Managing Director
KK Chan, Managing Director
Laurence Fumagalli, Managing Director
Malcolm Brown, Managing Director
Mark Ellis, Managing Director
Mark Woodall, Chief Executive Officer
Mark Macleod, Chief Financial Officer
Nigel Scott, Managing Director
Paul Udall, Managing Director
Ronnie Lim, Managing Director
Shaun Mays, Chief Executive Officer
Simon Robert-Tissot, Managing Director
Simon Drury, Partner
Steve Read, Managing Director
Tim Mockett, Managing Director
Yuebing Lu, Managing Director

Type of Firm

Private Equity Firm

Project Preferences

Type of Financing Preferred:
Leveraged Buyout
Expansion
Balanced
Later Stage
Management Buyouts

Geographical Preferences

International Preferences:
United Kingdom
Latin America
Europe
Western Europe

Industry Preferences

In Industrial/Energy prefer:
Energy
Alternative Energy
Energy Conservation Relat

Additional Information

Year Founded: 2004
Capital Under Management: $1,600,000,000
Current Activity Level: Actively seeking new investments

CLIMATE SOLUTIONS MANAGEMENT GMBH

Grueneburgweg 18
Frankfurt am Main, Germany
Phone: 49-69719-159660
Fax: 49-69-713758811
E-mail: info@altira-ag.de
Website: www.altira-ag.com

Management and Staff

Philipp Proemm, Chief Operating Officer
Ralf Jungebloed, Chief Executive Officer

Type of Firm

Private Equity Firm

Project Preferences

Type of Financing Preferred:
Generalist PE

Geographical Preferences

International Preferences:
Europe
Germany

Industry Preferences

In Other prefer:
Environment Responsible

Additional Information

Year Founded: 2007
Capital Under Management: $22,000,000
Current Activity Level: Actively seeking new investments

CLOQUET CAPITAL PARTNERS

One Northfield Plaze
Suite 300
Northfield, IL USA 60093
Phone: 847-441-2945
Fax: 877-867-5954
Website: www.cloquetcapital.com

Management and Staff

Burton McGillivray, President

Type of Firm

Private Equity Firm

Project Preferences

Type of Financing Preferred:
Expansion
Turnaround
Management Buyouts
Special Situation
Recapitalizations

Size of Investments Considered:
Min Size of Investment Considered (000s): $5,000
Max Size of Investment Considered (000s): $30,000

Industry Preferences

In Business Serv. prefer:
Distribution

In Manufact. prefer:
Manufacturing

Additional Information

Year Founded: 2002
Capital Under Management: $50,000,000
Current Activity Level: Actively seeking new investments

CLSA CAPITAL PARTNERS (AKA: CREDIT LYONNAIS SECURITIES ASIA)

18/F One Pacific Place
88 Queensway
Admiralty, Hong Kong

Phone: 852-2600-8888
Fax: 852-2868-0189
E-mail: capital@clsa.com
Website: www.clsacapital.com

Other Offices

Room 3111, Shun Hing Square
333 Shennan Road East
Shenzen, China 518008
Phone: 86-755-246-1755
Fax: 86-755-246-1754

WISMA GKBI Suite 1501
Jl. Jendral Sudirman No. 28
Jakarta, Indonesia 10210
Phone: 62-21-574-2626
Fax: 62-21-574-6920

Broadwalk House
5 Appold Street, Broadgate
London, United Kingdom EC2A 2DA
Phone: 44-207-696-9190
Fax: 44-207-214-5401
8/F Dalamal House
Nariman Point
Mumbai, India 400 021
Phone: 91-22-5650-5050
Fax: 91-22-2284-0271

15th Floor Sean Building
116, 1-ka, Shinmun-Ro, Chongro-ku
Seoul, South Korea 110-061
Phone: 82-2397-7300
Fax: 82-2771-8583

18th Floor Tower 1,The Enterprise Center
6766 Ayala Ave., corner Paseo de Roxas
Makati City, Philippines
Phone: 63-2-886-5637
Fax: 63-2-886-5692

1301 Avenue of The Americas
New York, NY USA 10019
Phone: 212-408-5888
Fax: 212-261-2502

4 rue du Parc
Geneva, Switzerland 1207
Phone: 41-22-718-03-03
Fax: 41-22-718-03-13

Eight Floor Dalamal House
Nariman Point
Mumbai, India 40021
Phone: 91-22-5650-5050
Fax: 91-22-2284-0271

9 Raffles Place, #19-20/21
Republic Plaza II
Singapore, Singapore 048619
Phone: 65-6416-7888
Fax: 65-6533-8922

Room 03, 16/F Jin Mao Tower
88 Century Boulevard
Pudong Shanghai, China 200121
Phone: 86-21-5047-1118
Fax: 86-21-5047-3533

25/F Unit 10-12, China Tower 2
One Jian Guo Men Wai Avenue
Beijing, China 100004
Phone: 86-10-6505-0248
Fax: 86-10-6505-2209

14F Shidome Sumitomo Bldg.
1-9-2, Higashi-Shimbashi, Minato-ku
Tokyo, Japan 105-0021
Phone: 81-3-4580-5050
Fax: 81-3-4580-5051
6/F, No. 117, Sec. 3
Min-sheng E. Road
Taipei, Taiwan
Phone: 886-2-2717-0737
Fax: 886-2-2717-0738

Suite 15-2 Level 15, Menara PanGlobal
8 Lorong P. Ramlee, Off Jalan P Ramlee

Kuala Lumpur, Malaysia 50250
Phone: 603-2072-4288

16th Fl, M.Thai Tower, All Seasons Place
87 Wireless Road, Lumpini Pathumwan
Bangkok, Thailand
Phone: 66-2-253-2945
Fax: 66-2-253-0543

4th Floor, C-Wing
Panchsheel Tech Park, Yerwada
Pune, India 411 006
Phone: 91-20-6646-8888

Management and Staff

Alvin Ho, Managing Director
Chris Boyle, Managing Director
Christopher Seaver, Chief Executive Officer
David Cheung, Chief Financial Officer
Gary Coull, Chairman & CEO
Genevieve Heng, Managing Director
J Niranjan, Managing Director
John Pattar, Managing Director
Miranda Tang, Managing Director

Type of Firm

Bank Affiliated

Association Membership

Hong Kong Venture Capital Association (HKVCA)

Project Preferences

Type of Financing Preferred:

Leveraged Buyout
Expansion
Mezzanine
Early Stage
Public Companies
Balanced
Other
Later Stage
Private Placement
Acquisition
Distressed Debt

Size of Investments Considered:

Min Size of Investment Considered (000s): $8,000
Max Size of Investment Considered (000s): $25,000

Geographical Preferences

International Preferences:

Vietnam
India
Indonesia
Taiwan
China
Hong Kong
Thailand
Asia
Korea, South
Singapore
Japan
Malaysia

Industry Preferences

In Consumer Related prefer:

Consumer
Education Related

In Industrial/Energy prefer:

Alternative Energy
Environmental Related

In Transportation prefer:

Transportation

In Financial Services prefer:

Real Estate

In Manufact. prefer:

Manufacturing

In Utilities prefer:

Utilities

Additional Information

Name of Most Recent Fund: Aria Investment Partners III, L.P.
Most Recent Fund Was Raised: 04/01/2006
Year Founded: 1995
Capital Under Management: $1,000,000,000
Current Activity Level: Actively seeking new investments

CLUBINVEST PRIVATE EQUITY

Via G. Carducci 19
Milan, Italy 20123
Phone: 39-023652-5525
Fax: 39-029998-2170
E-mail: info@clubinvest-europe.com
Website: www.clubinvest-europe.com

Management and Staff

Massimo Quattrocchi, Founder

Type of Firm

Private Equity Firm

Association Membership
Italian Venture Capital Association (AIFI)

Project Preferences

Type of Financing Preferred:
Expansion
Acquisition
Recapitalizations

Size of Investments Considered:
Min Size of Investment Considered (000s): $635
Max Size of Investment Considered (000s): $3,837

Geographical Preferences

International Preferences:
Italy
India
Switzerland
Spain

Additional Information
Year Founded: 2004
Capital Under Management: $12,800,000
Current Activity Level: Actively seeking new investments

CLYDESDALE BANK PLC

30 St. Vincent Place
Glasgow, United Kingdom G1 2HL
Phone: 44-141-951-7320
Website: www.cbonline.co.uk

Type of Firm
Bank Affiliated

Project Preferences

Type of Financing Preferred:
Balanced

Geographical Preferences

International Preferences:
Europe

Additional Information
Year Founded: 1989
Current Activity Level: Actively seeking new investments

CLYDESDALE VENTURES LLC

160 Spear Street
Suite 230
San Francisco, CA USA 94105
Phone: 415-391-4085
Fax: 415-243-3000
E-mail: info@clydesdaleventures.com
Website: www.clydesdaleventures.com

Management and Staff
Paul Klapper, Principal

Type of Firm
Private Equity Firm

Project Preferences

Type of Financing Preferred:
Early Stage
Seed

Size of Investments Considered:
Min Size of Investment Considered (000s): $25
Max Size of Investment Considered (000s): $1,500

Geographical Preferences

United States Preferences:
All U.S.

Industry Preferences

In Communications prefer:
Communications and Media
Wireless Communications

In Computer Software prefer:
Systems Software

In Internet Specific prefer:
Internet

In Consumer Related prefer:
Entertainment and Leisure
Food/Beverage
Consumer Services

In Financial Services prefer:
Financial Services

In Business Serv. prefer:
Media

Additional Information
Year Founded: 1990
Current Activity Level: Actively seeking new investments

CM CIC MEZZANINE

4 rue Gaillon
Paris, France 75002
Phone: 33-1-4266-7433

Type of Firm
Bank Affiliated

Association Membership
French Venture Capital Association (AFIC)

Project Preferences

Type of Financing Preferred:
Balanced

Geographical Preferences

International Preferences:
Europe
France

Additional Information
Year Founded: 2006
Current Activity Level: Actively seeking new investments

CM EQUITY PARTNERS (FKA; LYNX INVESTMENT MANAGEMENT, L.P.)

900 Third Avenue
33rd Floor
New York, NY USA 10022
Phone: 212-909-8400
Fax: 212-371-7254
Website: www.cmequity.com

Management and Staff
Daniel Colon, Partner
Joel Jacks, Managing Partner
Peter Schulte, Managing Partner
Robert Hopkins, Partner
Sary Awad, Partner
Wesley Gaus, Partner

Type of Firm
Bank Affiliated

Project Preferences

Type of Financing Preferred:
Leveraged Buyout
Acquisition

Geographical Preferences

Canadian Preferences:
All Canada

International Preferences:
United Kingdom

Industry Focus

(% based on actual investment)	
Other Products	98.5%
Communications and Media	1.0%
Internet Specific	0.6%

Additional Information
Name of Most Recent Fund: CM Equity Partners, L.P.
Most Recent Fund Was Raised: 04/16/1997
Year Founded: 1997
Capital Under Management: $90,000,000
Current Activity Level: Actively seeking new investments

CM-CIC CAPITAL PRIVE

28 avenue de l' Opera
Paris, France 75002
Phone: 33-1-4266-7959
Fax: 33-1-4266-7086
E-mail: info@cic.fr
Website: www.cic.fr

Type of Firm
Bank Affiliated

Association Membership
French Venture Capital Association (AFIC)

Project Preferences

Type of Financing Preferred:
Leveraged Buyout
Early Stage

Geographical Preferences

International Preferences:
Europe
France

Industry Preferences

In Communications prefer:
Telecommunications

In Computer Software prefer:
Software

Additional Information
Year Founded: 1997
Capital Under Management: $22,100,000
Current Activity Level: Actively seeking new investments

CMEA CAPITAL

One Embarcadero Center
Suite 3250
San Francisco, CA USA 94111
Phone: 415-352-1520
Fax: 415-352-1524
Website: www.cmea.com

Management and Staff
Bruce Pasternack, Venture Partner
David Tuckerman, Venture Partner
David Collier, Managing Director
Faysal Sohail, Managing Director
James Hornthal, Venture Partner
James Watson, Managing General Partner
Karl Handelsman, Managing Director
Michael Melnick, Principal
Saad Khan, Partner
Thomas Baruch, Managing Director

Type of Firm
Private Equity Firm

Association Membership
Mid-Atlantic Venture Association
Western Association of Venture Capitalists (WAVC)
National Venture Capital Association - USA (NVCA)

Project Preferences

Role in Financing:
Will function either as deal originator or investor in deals created by others

Type of Financing Preferred:
Second Stage Financing
Expansion
Early Stage
Mezzanine
Balanced
Later Stage
First Stage Financing
Startup

Size of Investments Considered:
Min Size of Investment Considered (000s): $250
Max Size of Investment Considered (000s): $10,000

Geographical Preferences

United States Preferences:
Northwest
West Coast

Industry Focus
(% based on actual investment)

Biotechnology	23.5%
Medical/Health	17.3%
Semiconductors/Other Elect.	14.3%
Computer Software and Services	12.3%
Industrial/Energy	9.8%
Internet Specific	7.8%
Other Products	5.5%
Communications and Media	5.2%
Computer Hardware	4.4%

Additional Information
Name of Most Recent Fund: CMEA Ventures VII, L.P. (CMEA 7)
Most Recent Fund Was Raised: 06/29/2007
Year Founded: 1989
Capital Under Management: $1,091,000,000
Current Activity Level: Actively seeking new investments
Method of Compensation: Return on investment is of primary concern, do not charge fees

---

CMHJ PARTNERS

Suite 803, Lippo Plaza
222 Huai Hai Zhong Road
Shanghai, China 200021
Phone: 86-21-5396-5500
Fax: 86-21-5396-5530
Website: www.cmhjpartners.com

Other Offices
Suite 3002, 30/F, Excellence Times Sq.
4068 Yi Tian Road, Futian District
Shenzhen, China 518048
Phone: 86-755-2399-5380
Fax: 86-755-2399-5382

Management and Staff
Darren Ho, Managing Partner
George Li, Managing Partner
HongBin Liu, Partner
James Jin, Partner
Roger Zha, Partner

Type of Firm
Private Equity Firm

Project Preferences

Type of Financing Preferred:
Early Stage
Expansion

Geographical Preferences

International Preferences:
China

Additional Information
Year Founded: 2007
Current Activity Level: Actively seeking new investments

CMIA CAPITAL PARTNERS (AKA: CM INVESTMENT ADVISERS PTE LTD.)

50 Raffles Place
47-01 Singapore Land Tower
Singapore, Singapore 048623
Phone: 65-6236-1288
Fax: 65-6536-6316
E-mail: info@cmia.com
Website: www.cmia.com

Other Offices
8 Connaught Road Central
Suite 1606, Chater House
Central, Hong Kong
Phone: 852-2251-1968
Fax: 852-2849-4185

No. 233 Taicang Road
Platinum, 20th Flr Unit-04, Luwan Dist.
Shanghai, China
Phone: 86-21-6141-5788
Fax: 86-21-6141-5700

Management and Staff
Chan Hock Eng, Partner
Danny Ho, Partner
Edmund Tan, Partner
Wang Jianming, Partner
Xie Dahong, Partner
Yong Ho Hsiang, Chief Financial Officer

Type of Firm
Private Equity Firm

Project Preferences

Type of Financing Preferred:
Leveraged Buyout
Expansion

Geographical Preferences

International Preferences:
China
Asia

Industry Preferences

In Medical/Health prefer:
Medical/Health

In Consumer Related prefer:
Consumer

In Industrial/Energy prefer:
Industrial Products
Environmental Related

In Transportation prefer:
Transportation

In Manufact. prefer:
Manufacturing

In Agr/Forestr/Fish prefer:
Agribusiness
Mining and Minerals

Additional Information

Year Founded: 2003
Capital Under Management: $61,300,000
Current Activity Level: Actively seeking new investments

CMS COMPANIES

1926 Arch Street
Philadelphia, PA USA 19103
Phone: 215-246-3000
Fax: 215-246-3083
Website: www.cmsco.com

Type of Firm

Bank Affiliated

Additional Information

Year Founded: 2000
Capital Under Management: $1,000,000,000
Current Activity Level: Actively seeking new investments

CNET

235 Second Street
San Francisco, CA USA 94105
Phone: 415-395-7800
Fax: 415-395-9330
Website: www.cnet.com

Management and Staff

Trina Wagner, Principal

Type of Firm

Corporate PE/Venture

Additional Information

Year Founded: 1997
Current Activity Level: Actively seeking new investments

CNF INVESTMENTS, LLC

c/o Clark Enterprises, Inc
7500 Old Georgetown Road, 15/F
Bethesda, MD USA 20814
Phone: 301-657-7100
E-mail: cnfinvestments@clarkus.com
Website: www.clarkenterprisesinc.com

Management and Staff

Joseph Del Guercio, Principal
Robert Flanagan, Managing Director

Type of Firm

Private Equity Firm

Project Preferences

Type of Financing Preferred:
Early Stage
Expansion

Geographical Preferences

United States Preferences:
All U.S.

Industry Preferences

In Communications prefer:
Communications and Media

In Computer Software prefer:
Software

In Biotechnology prefer:
Biotechnology

In Medical/Health prefer:
Medical Products

In Consumer Related prefer:
Consumer Products

In Industrial/Energy prefer:
Energy
Oil and Gas Exploration

In Financial Services prefer:
Financial Services

Additional Information

Year Founded: 1997
Capital Under Management: $125,000,000
Current Activity Level: Actively seeking new investments

CNOOC , LTD.

1 Garden Road
65/F, Bank of China Tower
Hong Kong, Hong Kong
Phone: 852-2213-2500
Fax: 852-2525-9322
Website: www.cnoocltd.com

Type of Firm

Private Equity Firm

Additional Information

Year Founded: 2009
Current Activity Level: Actively seeking new investments

CO-INVESTOR AG

Zugerstrasse 74
Baar, Switzerland 6340
Phone: 41-41-7693533
Fax: 41-41-7693534
E-mail: baaroffice@co-investor.com
Website: www.co-investor.com

Other Offices

Hohlbeinstrasse 31
Zurich, Switzerland 8008
Phone: 41-43-2682018
Fax: 41-43-2682019

Management and Staff

Hans-Dieter Cleven, Founding Partner
Hans-Dieter Rompel, Founding Partner
Juerg Kallay, Founding Partner
Roman Kainz, Founding Partner
Timo Kipp, Partner

Type of Firm

Angel Group

Association Membership

European Private Equity and Venture Capital Assoc.

Project Preferences

Type of Financing Preferred:
Balanced

Geographical Preferences

International Preferences:
Europe

Additional Information

Year Founded: 2004
Current Activity Level: Actively seeking new investments

CO-INVESTOR CAPITAL PARTNERS PTY., LTD.

Level 3 Barrack House
343 George Street
Sydney, Australia 2000
Phone: 612-8235-3880
Fax: 612-8235-3883
E-mail: mail@co-investor.net
Website: www.co-investor.net

Management and Staff

Phillip Pryke, Partner
Roger Croker, Chief Financial Officer
Roger Sharp, Managing Director

Type of Firm

Private Equity Firm

Project Preferences

Type of Financing Preferred:
Public Companies

Geographical Preferences

International Preferences:
Australia
New Zealand

Additional Information
Year Founded: 2007
Current Activity Level: Actively seeking new investments

COACH & CAPITAL NORDIC 1 AB
Sveavagen 17, 12th floor
Box 3209
Stockholm, Sweden SE-103 64
Phone: 46-738-558-118
Website: www.coachandcapital.se

Type of Firm
Private Equity Firm

Project Preferences

Type of Financing Preferred:
Early Stage
Expansion
Seed
Startup

Geographical Preferences

International Preferences:
Sweden

Industry Preferences

In Communications prefer:
Commercial Communications

In Computer Other prefer:
Computer Related

In Semiconductor/Electr prefer:
Electronics

In Medical/Health prefer:
Medical/Health

In Industrial/Energy prefer:
Energy
Industrial Products

Additional Information
Year Founded: 2007
Capital Under Management: $11,000,000
Current Activity Level: Actively seeking new investments

COASTVIEW CAPITAL
11111 Santa Monica Boulevard
Suite 1850
Los Angeles, CA USA 90025
Phone: 310-473-8440
Fax: 310-473-3478
E-mail: info@coastviewcapital.com
Website: www.coastviewcapital.com

Management and Staff
Bill Ouchi, Principal
Edmund Olivier, Partner
Gordon Binder, Principal
Lyndon Lien, Principal
Stella Sung, Managing Director
Todd Binder, Principal

Type of Firm
Private Equity Firm

Project Preferences

Type of Financing Preferred:
Second Stage Financing
Balanced
Later Stage
First Stage Financing

Size of Investments Considered:
Min Size of Investment Considered (000s): $1,000
Max Size of Investment Considered (000s): $10,000

Geographical Preferences

United States Preferences:
Southern California
Massachusetts
Maryland
All U.S.

Industry Preferences

In Biotechnology prefer:
Biotechnology

Additional Information
Name of Most Recent Fund: Coastview Capital II, L.P.
Most Recent Fund Was Raised: 05/28/2004
Year Founded: 2002
Capital Under Management: $72,000,000
Current Activity Level: Actively seeking new investments

COATES MYER & CO. PTY LTD.
167 Eagle Street
Level 4 Emirates House
Brisbane, Australia 4000
Phone: 617-3838-2800
Fax: 617-3831-1256
E-mail: cmcideals@cmcapital.com
Website: www.cmcapital.com

Management and Staff
Andy Jane, Partner
Carrie Hillyard, Partner
Jerry Lim, Chief Financial Officer
John Brennan, Partner
Jonathan Whitehouse, Chief Financial Officer
Mark Gill, Partner
Michael Begun, Managing Partner
Steve Lane, Partner

Type of Firm
Private Equity Firm

Association Membership
Australian Venture Capital Association (AVCAL)

Project Preferences

Role in Financing:
Will function either as deal originator or investor in deals created by others

Type of Financing Preferred:
Early Stage
Expansion
Balanced
Seed
Startup

Size of Investments Considered:
Min Size of Investment Considered (000s): $1,209
Max Size of Investment Considered (000s): $12,087

Geographical Preferences

International Preferences:
Australia
New Zealand

Industry Preferences

In Communications prefer:
Telecommunications

In Computer Software prefer:
Software

In Biotechnology prefer:
Biotechnology

In Medical/Health prefer:
Medical Diagnostics
Medical Products

Additional Information
Name of Most Recent Fund: CM Capital Venture Trust No. 4
Most Recent Fund Was Raised: 07/01/2006
Year Founded: 1998
Capital Under Management: $208,700,000
Current Activity Level: Actively seeking new investments
Method of Compensation: Return on investment is of primary concern, do not charge fees

COBALT CAPITAL (FKA: LGV SA)

63, avenue des Champs-Elysees
Paris, France 75008
Phone: 33-1-4312-9110
Fax: 33-1-4312-9111
E-mail: info@cobalt-cap.com
Website: www.cobalt-cap.com

Management and Staff

Brigitte Neveu, Chief Financial Officer
Christophe Fercocq, Managing Partner

Type of Firm

Private Equity Firm

Association Membership

French Venture Capital Association (AFIC)

Project Preferences

Type of Financing Preferred:
Leveraged Buyout
Management Buyouts
Acquisition

Size of Investments Considered:
Min Size of Investment Considered (000s): $14,122
Max Size of Investment Considered (000s): $70,611

Geographical Preferences

International Preferences:
Europe
France

Industry Preferences

In Communications prefer:
Communications and Media
Data Communications

In Computer Software prefer:
Software

In Semiconductor/Electr prefer:
Semiconductor

In Medical/Health prefer:
Medical/Health

In Consumer Related prefer:
Entertainment and Leisure

In Industrial/Energy prefer:
Alternative Energy
Industrial Products

In Agr/Forestr/Fish prefer:
Agriculture related

Additional Information

Name of Most Recent Fund: Cobalt Sante
Most Recent Fund Was Raised: 11/07/2005
Year Founded: 2004
Capital Under Management: $191,800,000
Current Activity Level: Actively seeking new investments

COBALT CAPITAL, INC.

1540 Cornwall Road
Suite 103
Oakville, Canada L6J 7W5
Phone: 905-815-9755
Fax: 905-815-8385
Website: www.cobaltcapital.ca

Management and Staff

Deb Powis, Partner
Patrick Keane, Partner
Peter Albion, Partner

Type of Firm

Private Equity Firm

Additional Information

Year Founded: 2005
Current Activity Level: Actively seeking new investments

COBE CAPITAL LLC

P.O. Box 4552
New York, NY USA 10163
Phone: 212-338-0235
Fax: 212-338-0238
Website: www.cobecapital.com

Type of Firm

Private Equity Firm

Additional Information

Year Founded: 2009
Current Activity Level: Actively seeking new investments

COBURN VENTURES, LLC

Ten Chestnut Street
Pleasantville, NY USA 10570
E-mail: info@coburnventures.com
Website: www.coburnventures.com

Management and Staff

Brynne Stevens, Partner
Dave Bujnowski, Partner
David Harvey, Chief Operating Officer
Faye Hou, Partner
Helen Rattee, Partner
Pip Coburn, Founder

Type of Firm

Private Equity Firm

Project Preferences

Type of Financing Preferred:
Balanced

Additional Information

Year Founded: 2005
Capital Under Management: $1,700,000
Current Activity Level: Actively seeking new investments

CODE, HENNESSY & SIMMONS LLC

Ten South Wacker Drive
Suite 3175
Chicago, IL USA 60606
Phone: 312-876-1840
Fax: 312-876-3854
E-mail: chs@chsonline.com
Website: www.chsonline.com

Management and Staff

Andrew Code, Partner
Brian Simmons, Partner
Daniel Hennessy, Partner
David Spinola, Vice President
David Hawkins, Partner
Douglas Knoch, Principal
Edward Lhee, Partner
Jon Vesely, Partner
Krista Hatcher, Principal
Marcus George, Partner
Michael Hendrie, Vice President
Mike Keesey, Chief Financial Officer
Peter Gotsch, Partner
Peter Pettit, Vice President
Richard Lobo, Partner
Robert Hogan, Principal
Steven Brown, Partner
Thomas Formolo, Partner

Type of Firm

Private Equity Firm

Association Membership

Illinois Venture Capital Association

Project Preferences

Role in Financing:
Prefer role as deal originator

Type of Financing Preferred:
Leveraged Buyout

Geographical Preferences

United States Preferences:
All U.S.

Industry Focus

(% based on actual investment)

Other Products	53.7%
Consumer Related	13.7%
Medical/Health	12.3%
Computer Hardware	10.2%
Industrial/Energy	8.7%
Semiconductors/Other Elect.	0.7%
Communications and Media	0.7%

Additional Information

Name of Most Recent Fund: CHS Private Equity V LP

Most Recent Fund Was Raised: 02/18/2005
Year Founded: 1988
Capital Under Management: $1,500,000,000
Current Activity Level: Actively seeking new investments
Method of Compensation: Return on invest. most important, but chg. closing fees, service fees, etc.

COFIDES - COMPANIA ESPANOLA DE FINANCIACION DEL DESARROLO SA

Principe de Vergara, 132 - 12
Madrid, Spain 28002
Phone: 34-91-562-6008
Fax: 34-91-561-0015
E-mail: cofides@cofides.es
Website: www.cofides.es

Management and Staff

Jose Gasset Loring, President

Type of Firm

Government Affiliated Program

Association Membership

Spanish Venture Capital Association (ASCRI)

Project Preferences

Type of Financing Preferred:
Second Stage Financing
Expansion
Balanced
Seed

Size of Investments Considered:
Min Size of Investment Considered (000s): $219
Max Size of Investment Considered (000s): $21,880

Geographical Preferences

International Preferences:
Hungary
Latin America
China
Morocco
All International

Industry Preferences

In Industrial/Energy prefer:
Industrial Products

In Business Serv. prefer:
Services

In Other prefer:
Environment Responsible

Additional Information

Year Founded: 1990
Current Activity Level: Actively seeking new investments

COFINA, SGPS SA

Rua General Norton de Matos
No. 68 - R/C
Porto, Portugal 4050-424
Phone: 351-22-834-6500
Fax: 351-22-834-6509
E-mail: sede@cofina.pt
Website: www.cofina.pt

Management and Staff

Paulo Fernandes, President

Type of Firm

Private Equity Firm

Project Preferences

Type of Financing Preferred:
Leveraged Buyout

Additional Information

Year Founded: 2004
Current Activity Level: Actively seeking new investments

COFIRI

26 Via Compagni
Rome, Italy 00187
Phone: 39-06-47-331
Fax: 39-0-6853-31410
E-mail: e.arduini@cofiri.it

Management and Staff

Alfredo De Marzio, President

Type of Firm

Bank Affiliated

Association Membership

Italian Venture Capital Association (AIFI)

Project Preferences

Type of Financing Preferred:
Early Stage
Startup

Geographical Preferences

International Preferences:
Italy

Industry Preferences

In Communications prefer:
Telecommunications

In Biotechnology prefer:
Biotechnology

In Industrial/Energy prefer:
Energy
Materials

In Transportation prefer:
Transportation

Additional Information

Year Founded: 1999
Capital Under Management: $13,500,000
Current Activity Level: Actively seeking new investments

COGENE VENTURES

4400 Post Oak Parkway
Suite 1400
Houston, TX USA 77027
Phone: 713-336-7858
Fax: 713-336-7741
E-mail: info@cogeneventures.com
Website: www.cogeneventures.com

Management and Staff

C. Thomas Caskey, Managing Director
Lloyd Bentsen, Managing Director

Type of Firm

Private Equity Firm

Project Preferences

Type of Financing Preferred:
Early Stage
Expansion
Later Stage

Size of Investments Considered:
Min Size of Investment Considered (000s): $1,000
Max Size of Investment Considered (000s): $10,000

Geographical Preferences

United States Preferences:
Southwest
All U.S.

Industry Preferences

In Biotechnology prefer:
Human Biotechnology
Genetic Engineering
Agricultural/Animal Bio.
Industrial Biotechnology
Biosensors
Biotech Related Research

In Medical/Health prefer:
Medical Diagnostics
Diagnostic Services
Diagnostic Test Products
Medical Therapeutics
Drug/Equipmt Delivery
Medical Products
Disposable Med. Products
Health Services
Hospitals/Clinics/Primary
Hospital/Other Instit.
Pharmaceuticals

Additional Information

Name of Most Recent Fund: Cogene Ventures II, L.P.
Most Recent Fund Was Raised: 10/01/2004

Year Founded: 2000
Capital Under Management: $207,000,000
Current Activity Level: Actively seeking new investments

COGNETAS LLP (FKA: ELECTRA PARTNERS EUROPE LLP)

Paternoster House
65 St. Paul's Churchyard
London, United Kingdom EC4M 8AB
Phone: 44-20-7214-4800
Fax: 44-20-7214-4801
Website: www.cognetas.com

Other Offices

Via Manzoni 3
Milano, Italy 20121
Phone: 39-2-888-9001
Fax: 39-2-8889-0040

49-51, avenue George V
Paris, France 75008
Phone: 33-1-5383-7910
Fax: 33-1-5383-7920

An der Hauptwache 5
Frankfurt am Main, Germany 60313
Phone: 49-69-299-2360
Fax: 49-69-2992-3699

Management and Staff

Andreas Kraemer, Principal
Brian Veitch, Partner
Cedric Rays, Partner
Charles St. John, Partner
Chris Collins, Partner
Damien Lane, Partner
Edward Koopman, Partner
Federico Pastura, Principal
Frank Hermann, Partner
Giovanna Voltolina, Principal
Johannes Meran, Principal
Jonathan Mussellwhite, Partner
Jorge Mataix, Partner
Julian Knott, Partner
Mark Elborn, Partner
Mark Weston, Partner
Maurizio Bianco, Partner
Michael Boltz, Partner
Nigel McConnell, Managing Partner
Patrick Eisenchteter, Partner
Philipp Amereller, Principal
Simon Brown, Partner

Type of Firm

Private Equity Firm

Association Membership

British Venture Capital Association (BVCA)
French Venture Capital Association (AFIC)
German Venture Capital Association (BVK)
European Private Equity and Venture Capital Assoc.

Project Preferences

Type of Financing Preferred:
Leveraged Buyout
Public Companies
Turnaround
Management Buyouts
Special Situation

Size of Investments Considered:
Min Size of Investment Considered (000s): $47,080
Max Size of Investment Considered (000s): $188,320

Geographical Preferences

International Preferences:
Italy
United Kingdom
Europe
Spain
Scandanavia/Nordic Region
Germany
France

Industry Focus

(% based on actual investment)

Other Products	49.2%
Consumer Related	31.2%
Industrial/Energy	13.5%
Semiconductors/Other Elect.	4.1%
Medical/Health	1.9%

Additional Information

Name of Most Recent Fund: Cognetas Fund II (FKA: Electra European Fund II)
Most Recent Fund Was Raised: 07/25/2005
Year Founded: 2000
Capital Under Management: $2,424,200,000
Current Activity Level: Actively seeking new investments

COGNITION VENTURES AB

Sodra Hamngatan 19-21
Goteborg, Sweden 41114
Phone: 46-31-107-030
Fax: 46-31-107-031
E-mail: info@cognitionventures.com
Website: www.cognitionventures.com

Other Offices

221 Eastwood Road
Toronto, Canada MYL 2E2
Phone: 416-895-8098

P.O. Box 1716 Vika
Oslo, Norway 0121
Phone: 47-23-115-950
Fax: 47-23-115-951

2 Brompton Road #439
London, United Kingdom SW7 3DQ
Phone: 44-20-7851-0200
Fax: 44-20-7851-0201

174 Hudson Street
3rd Floor
New York, NY USA 10013
Phone: 212-590-6051
Fax: 212-590-6097

Management and Staff

Bjorn Olegard, Chief Financial Officer

Type of Firm

Private Equity Firm

Association Membership

European Private Equity and Venture Capital Assoc.

Project Preferences

Type of Financing Preferred:
Early Stage
Expansion
Turnaround
Seed
Startup

Size of Investments Considered:
Min Size of Investment Considered (000s): $400
Max Size of Investment Considered (000s): $400,000

Geographical Preferences

United States Preferences:
All U.S.

International Preferences:
Europe
Asia

Industry Preferences

In Communications prefer:
Communications and Media

In Internet Specific prefer:
Internet

Additional Information

Year Founded: 2000
Capital Under Management: $64,600,000
Current Activity Level: Actively seeking new investments

COLLABORATIVE SEED & GROWTH PARTNERS LLC

1340 Centre Street
Suite 207
Newton, MA USA 02459
Phone: 617-969-3066

Management and Staff

Walter Winshall, Managing Director

Type of Firm

Private Equity Firm

Project Preferences

Type of Financing Preferred:
Early Stage
Expansion

Geographical Preferences

United States Preferences:
All U.S.

Additional Information
Name of Most Recent Fund: Alpha Technology Fund, LP
Most Recent Fund Was Raised: 01/10/2005
Year Founded: 2004
Capital Under Management: $1,300,000
Current Activity Level: Actively seeking new investments

COLLER CAPITAL
33 Cavendish Square
London, United Kingdom W1G 0TT
Phone: 44-20-7631-8500
Fax: 44-20-7631-8555
E-mail: mail@collercapital.com
Website: www.collercapital.com

Other Offices
Level 58 Republic Plaza
9 Raffles Place
Singapore, Singapore 048619
Phone: 65-6823-1267
Fax: 65-6823-1377

410 Park Avenue
New York, NY USA 10022
Phone: 212-644-8500
Fax: 212-644-9133

Management and Staff
Alex Sao-Wei Lee, Principal
Andrew Caspersen, Principal
Axel Hansing, Partner
Crispin Payne, Principal
Daniel Dupont, Partner
Erwin Roex, Partner
Frank Morgan, Partner
Hiromichi Mizuno, Partner
Jonathan Gutstein, Partner
Jonathon Freeman, Partner
Joseph Marks, Principal
Luca Salvato, Principal
Patrick Knechtli, Principal
Peter Holden, Partner
Pinal Nicum, Principal
Sebastien Burdel, Principal
Stephen Ziff, Principal
Tim Jones, Partner

Type of Firm
Private Equity Advisor or Fund of Funds

Association Membership
Italian Venture Capital Association (AIFI)
Japan Venture Capital Association
Australian Venture Capital Association (AVCAL)
British Venture Capital Association (BVCA)
Emerging Markets Private Equity Association
French Venture Capital Association (AFIC)
Canadian Venture Capital Association
European Private Equity and Venture Capital Assoc.
Singapore Venture Capital Association (SVCA)

Project Preferences

Type of Financing Preferred:
Fund of Funds
Fund of Funds of Second

Geographical Preferences

International Preferences:
United Kingdom
Europe
Western Europe
All International

Industry Focus
(% based on actual investment)

Other Products	58.4%
Computer Software and Services	8.9%
Medical/Health	8.1%
Biotechnology	7.5%
Communications and Media	7.0%
Semiconductors/Other Elect.	5.0%
Internet Specific	3.6%
Computer Hardware	1.0%
Industrial/Energy	0.4%
Consumer Related	0.1%

Additional Information
Name of Most Recent Fund: Coller International Partners V-B, L.P.
Most Recent Fund Was Raised: 09/13/2006
Year Founded: 1990
Capital Under Management: $8,000,000,000
Current Activity Level: Actively seeking new investments

COLONNADE CAPITAL, LLC
10001 Patterson Avenue
Suite 100
Richmond, VA USA 23233
Phone: 804-741-2189
Fax: 804-754-7092
Website: www.colonnadecapital.com

Type of Firm
Private Equity Firm

Project Preferences

Role in Financing:
Prefer role as deal originator but will also invest in deals created by others

Type of Financing Preferred:
Leveraged Buyout

Geographical Preferences

United States Preferences:
All U.S.

Canadian Preferences:
All Canada

International Preferences:
Italy
United Kingdom
China
Bermuda
Spain
Australia
South Africa
Germany
France

Industry Preferences

In Communications prefer:
Radio & TV Broadcasting
Data Communications

In Semiconductor/Electr prefer:
Sensors

In Medical/Health prefer:
Diagnostic Services
Diagnostic Test Products
Other Therapeutic
Medical Products
Disposable Med. Products

In Consumer Related prefer:
Entertainment and Leisure
Retail
Food/Beverage
Consumer Products
Consumer Services
Other Restaurants

In Industrial/Energy prefer:
Industrial Products
Factory Automation
Machinery
Environmental Related

In Manufact. prefer:
Publishing

Additional Information
Name of Most Recent Fund: Commonwealth Investors II, L.P.
Most Recent Fund Was Raised: 07/03/1996
Year Founded: 1996
Capital Under Management: $60,000,000
Current Activity Level: Actively seeking new investments
Method of Compensation: Return on invest. most important, but chg. closing fees, service fees, etc.

COLONY CAPITAL LLC

2450 Broadway,
6th Floor
Santa Monica, CA USA 90404
Phone: 310-282-8820
Fax: 310-282-8808
Website: www.colonyinc.com

Other Offices

5701 Two International
Finance Center
Hong Kong, Hong Kong
Phone: 852-3119-9800
Fax: 852-3119-9811

66-1685 Kohala Mountain Road
Kamuela, HI USA 96743
Phone: 808-885-8668

Unit 1901, Level 19, Tower E2
No.1, East Chang An Ave., Dong Cheng
Beijing , China 100738
Phone: 86-10-852-00596

Palazzo Pecci Blunt
3, Piazza Ara Coeli
Rome, Italy 00186
Phone: 39-6-6994-1890
10/F Marunouchi Mitsui Bldg.
2-2-2 Marunoushi, Chiyoda-ku
Tokyo, Japan 100-0005
Phone: 813-5220-2255

c/ Miguel Angel #23
Madrid 28010, Spain
Phone: 34-91-308-2653

660 Madison Avenue
Suite 1600
New York, NY USA 10013
Phone: 212-230-3300

Two International Place
Suite 2500
Boston, MA USA 02110
Phone: 617-235-6300

3F, An Nahar Building
Marfaa Street
Beirut, Lebanon 20-145401
Phone: 96-11-973-370

24/F, ING Tower Bldg.
Yeoksam-dong, Kangnam-ku
Seoul, South Korea 135-977
Phone: 822-3468-2700

Leconfield House
Curzon Street
London, United Kingdom W1J 5JA
Phone: 44-20-7016-8030

6, rue Christophe Colomb
Paris, France 75008
Phone: 33-1-5357-4600

16/F No. 460 Hsin Yi Road
Section 4
Taipei, Taiwan 110
Phone: 886-227-2278

Management and Staff

Alain Chetrit, Vice President
Aleksandra Dubrova, Vice President
Alexandra Hill, Vice President
C. Christopher Alberti, Principal
Christophe Fournage, Managing Director
Darren Tangen, Principal
David Monahan, Vice President
Grant Kelley, Chief Executive Officer
Henry Brauer, Senior Managing Director
Jean-Romain Lhomme, Vice President
Jennifer Arrache, Vice President
Jon Halvorsen, Vice President
Joy Mallory, Vice President
Kevin Traenkle, Principal
Marie-Luce Geahchan, Managing Director
Mark Harmeling, Senior Managing Director
Mark Layther, Chief Financial Officer
Michel Sengsuwan, Managing Director
Nadra Moussalem, Vice President
Naji Buotros, Principal
Philippe Lenglet, Managing Director
Richard Nanula, Principal
Richard Saltzman, President
Ronald Sanders, Principal
Scott Freeman, Senior Managing Director
Sebastien Bazin, CEO & Managing Director
Serge Platonow, Managing Director
Sung Je Lee, Chief Executive Officer
Thomas Harrison, Principal
Toshio Masui, Principal
Varun Pathria, Vice President
Wilson Magee, President

Type of Firm

Private Equity Firm

Association Membership

French Venture Capital Association (AFIC)

Project Preferences

Type of Financing Preferred:
Leveraged Buyout
Balanced
Turnaround
Other
Special Situation
Recapitalizations
Distressed Debt

Geographical Preferences

International Preferences:
China
Western Europe
All International

Industry Preferences

In Financial Services prefer:
Financial Services
Real Estate

Additional Information

Year Founded: 1995
Capital Under Management: $4,377,200,000
Current Activity Level: Actively seeking new investments

COLORADO VENTURE MANAGEMENT (AKA: CVM EQUITY FUNDS)

2575 Park Lane
Suite 200
Lafayette, CO USA 80026
Phone: 303-440-4055
Fax: 303-440-4636
Website: www.cvmequity.com

Type of Firm

Private Equity Firm

Project Preferences

Role in Financing:
Will function either as deal originator or investor in deals created by others

Type of Financing Preferred:
Early Stage
Start-up Financing
Seed

Size of Investments Considered:
Min Size of Investment Considered (000s): $50
Max Size of Investment Considered (000s): $1,000

Geographical Preferences

United States Preferences:
Midwest
Rocky Mountain

Industry Focus

(% based on actual investment)

Computer Software and Services	16.7%
Medical/Health	15.1%
Communications and Media	12.9%
Internet Specific	11.9%
Computer Hardware	10.8%
Semiconductors/Other Elect.	8.4%
Biotechnology	8.1%
Consumer Related	6.5%
Industrial/Energy	5.1%
Other Products	4.5%

Additional Information

Name of Most Recent Fund: CVM Equity Fund V, L.P.
Most Recent Fund Was Raised: 10/01/1998
Year Founded: 1979
Capital Under Management: $13,200,000

Current Activity Level: Actively seeking new investments
Method of Compensation: Return on invest. most important, but chg. closing fees, service fees, etc.

COLUMBIA CAPITAL GROUP, INC.

3924 Forest Drive
Suite 9
Columbia, SC USA 29204
Phone: 803-782-5666
Fax: 803-782-0056
E-mail: info@columbiacapitalgroup.com
Website: www.columbiacapitalgroup.com

Management and Staff

Lloyd Arrington, President
Richard Williams, Jr., Vice President

Type of Firm

Government Affiliated Program

Project Preferences

Role in Financing:

Prefer role as deal originator but will also invest in deals created by others

Type of Financing Preferred:

Second Stage Financing
Mezzanine
First Stage Financing

Geographical Preferences

United States Preferences:

D. of Columbia

Industry Focus

(% based on actual investment)

Communications and Media	63.7%
Computer Software and Services	18.9%
Semiconductors/Other Elect.	13.3%
Computer Hardware	4.2%

Additional Information

Year Founded: 1988
Capital Under Management: $10,000,000
Current Activity Level: Actively seeking new investments
Method of Compensation: Return on invest. most important, but chg. closing fees, service fees, etc.

COLUMBIA CAPITAL LLC

201 North Union Street
Suite 300
Alexandria, VA USA 22314
Phone: 703-519-2000
Fax: 703-519-5870
E-mail: info@colcap.com
Website: www.colcap.com

Other Offices

1601 Trapelo Road
Suite 268
Waltham, MA USA 02451
Phone: 781-290-2240
Fax: 781-290-2241

Management and Staff

Arun Gupta, Partner
Brady Rafuse, Venture Partner
David Mixer, Venture Partner
Edward Kennedy, Venture Partner
Harry Hopper, Partner
Hemant Kanakia, Partner
James Fleming, Partner
Jason Booma, Principal
Jay Markley, Partner
Jeffrey Patterson, Partner
John Siegel, Partner
Karl Khoury, Partner
Matthew Newton, Partner
Nigel Morris, Venture Partner
Patrick Hendy, Principal
Phil Herget, Partner
Tom Bain, Principal

Type of Firm

Private Equity Firm

Association Membership

Mid-Atlantic Venture Association
National Venture Capital Association - USA (NVCA)

Project Preferences

Type of Financing Preferred:

Early Stage
Seed
Startup

Size of Investments Considered:

Min Size of Investment Considered (000s): $100
Max Size of Investment Considered (000s): $75,000

Geographical Preferences

United States Preferences:

All U.S.

Industry Preferences

In Communications prefer:

Communications and Media
Wireless Communications
Data Communications

In Internet Specific prefer:

E-Commerce Technology
Internet

In Business Serv. prefer:

Media

Additional Information

Name of Most Recent Fund: Columbia Capital Equity Partners IV (Non-US), L.P.
Most Recent Fund Was Raised: 08/19/2005
Year Founded: 1989
Capital Under Management: $1,400,000,000
Current Activity Level: Actively seeking new investments

COLUMBIA EQUITY PARTNERS

1625 Federal Avenue East
Seattle, WA USA 98102
Phone: 206-325-4453
Fax: 206-260-7473
E-mail: info@columbiaequitypartners.com
Website: www.columbiaequitypartners.com

Other Offices

546 Lombard Street
San Francisco, CA USA 94112
Phone: 415-722-0262

Management and Staff

Brian Flynn, Managing Director
Manuel Rubio, Co-Founder
Marc Dien, Managing Director
William Donovan, Managing Director

Type of Firm

Private Equity Firm

Project Preferences

Type of Financing Preferred:

Early Stage
Expansion
Generalist PE
Balanced

Size of Investments Considered:

Min Size of Investment Considered (000s): $2,000
Max Size of Investment Considered (000s): $25,000

Geographical Preferences

United States Preferences:

All U.S.

International Preferences:

Europe
Asia
Africa

Industry Preferences

In Computer Software prefer:

Computer Services
Software

In Consumer Related prefer:

Entertainment and Leisure
Consumer Services

Additional Information

Year Founded: 1994
Capital Under Management: $26,500,000
Current Activity Level: Actively seeking new investments

COLUMBIA PARTNERS LLC

5425 Wisconsin Avenue
Suite 700
Chevy Chase, MD USA 20815
Phone: 240-482-0400
Fax: 240-482-0401
Website: www.columbiaptrs.com

Management and Staff

Christopher Doherty, Managing Director
Jason Crist, Managing Director
K. Dunlop Scott, President & COO
Thomas Bain, Vice President

Type of Firm

Bank Affiliated

Project Preferences

Type of Financing Preferred:

Balanced
Later Stage

Size of Investments Considered:

Min Size of Investment Considered (000s): $5,000
Max Size of Investment Considered (000s): $40,000

Geographical Preferences

United States Preferences:

All U.S.

Industry Preferences

In Communications prefer:

Communications and Media
Telecommunications

In Medical/Health prefer:

Health Services

In Industrial/Energy prefer:

Energy

Additional Information

Year Founded: 1995
Capital Under Management: $250,000,000
Current Activity Level: Actively seeking new investments

COLUMBUS HILL CAPITAL PARTNERS, LLC

830 Morris Turnpike
2nd Floor
Short Hills, NJ USA 07078
Phone: 973-921-3425

Management and Staff

David Ambrosia, Managing Partner
Howard Kaminsky, Managing Partner
Kevin Eng, Managing Partner

Type of Firm

Private Equity Firm

Project Preferences

Type of Financing Preferred:

Generalist PE

Additional Information

Year Founded: 2006
Capital Under Management: $660,000,000
Current Activity Level: Actively seeking new investments

COLUMN GROUP, THE

425 Market Street
Suite 2200
San Francisco, CA USA 94105
Phone: 415-255-2050
Fax: 415-255-2048
E-mail: info@thecolumngroup.net
Website: www.thecolumngroup.net

Management and Staff

David Goeddel, Managing Partner
Harald Eckman, Managing Partner
Jeff Baxter, Managing Partner
Peter Svennilson, Managing Partner
Richard Klausner, Managing Partner
Willian Rapeport, Managing Partner

Type of Firm

Private Equity Firm

Project Preferences

Type of Financing Preferred:

Early Stage

Geographical Preferences

United States Preferences:

All U.S.

Industry Preferences

In Medical/Health prefer:

Pharmaceuticals

Additional Information

Name of Most Recent Fund: Column Group, L.P., The
Most Recent Fund Was Raised: 02/28/2007
Year Founded: 2007
Capital Under Management: $252,600,000
Current Activity Level: Actively seeking new investments

COMCAST INTERACTIVE CAPITAL

One Comcast Center, 55th Floor
1701 John F. Kennedy Blvd.
Philadelphia, PA USA 19103
Phone: 215-981-8450
Fax: 215-981-8429
E-mail: info@civentures.com
Website: www.civentures.com

Management and Staff

Adam Black, Chief Financial Officer
David Horowitz, Principal
Deepak Sindwani, Principal
Julian Brodsky, Founding Partner
Louis Toth, Managing Director
Samuel Schwartz, Senior Managing Director
Warren Lee, Principal

Type of Firm

Corporate PE/Venture

Project Preferences

Type of Financing Preferred:

Second Stage Financing
Mezzanine
Later Stage
Seed
First Stage Financing
Joint Ventures
Private Placement
Startup

Size of Investments Considered:

Min Size of Investment Considered (000s): $2,000
Max Size of Investment Considered (000s): $10,000

Industry Preferences

In Communications prefer:

Communications and Media
Commercial Communications
CATV & Pay TV Systems
Telecommunications
Wireless Communications
Data Communications
Other Communication Prod.

In Computer Software prefer:

Software
Applications Software

In Internet Specific prefer:

E-Commerce Technology
Internet
Ecommerce

In Semiconductor/Electr prefer:

Fiber Optics

In Consumer Related prefer:

Entertainment and Leisure
Sports

In Business Serv. prefer:

Services
Media

Additional Information

Year Founded: 1999
Capital Under Management: $350,000,000
Current Activity Level: Actively seeking new investments

COMERICA BANK

1717 Main Street
Comerica Bank Tower
Dallas, TX USA 75201
Phone: 800-266-3742
Website: www.comerica.com

Type of Firm

Private Equity Firm

Additional Information

Year Founded: 2009
Current Activity Level: Actively seeking new investments

COMERICA VENTURE CAPITAL GROUP

2500 Sand Hill Road
Suite 110
Menlo Park, CA USA 94025
Phone: 650-233-3082
Fax: 650-230-3075
Website: www.comerica.com

Other Offices

211 North Union Street #100
Alexandria, VA USA 22314
Phone: 703-684-4829
Fax: 703-838-5579

11512 El Camino Real
Suite 350
San Diego, CA USA 92103
Phone: 858-509-2370
Fax: 858-509-2365

1100 Glendon Avenue
Suite 2020
Westwood, CA USA 90024
Phone: 310-481-1001
Fax: 310-481-1099

Management and Staff

Mark Horn, Vice President

Type of Firm

Corporate PE/Venture

Association Membership

Western Association of Venture Capitalists (WAVC)
Natl Assoc of Small Bus. Inv. Co (NASBIC)
National Venture Capital Association - USA (NVCA)

Project Preferences

Role in Financing:

Prefer role as deal originator but will also invest in deals created by others

Type of Financing Preferred:

Second Stage Financing
Leveraged Buyout

Size of Investments Considered:

Min Size of Investment Considered (000s): $500
Max Size of Investment Considered (000s): $2,000

Geographical Preferences

United States Preferences:

California

Industry Preferences

In Semiconductor/Electr prefer:

Electronics

In Medical/Health prefer:

Medical/Health

Additional Information

Year Founded: 1979
Capital Under Management: $18,000,000
Current Activity Level: Actively seeking new investments
Method of Compensation: Other

COMMAND EQUITY GROUP

1213 South High Street
Bloomington, IN USA 47401
Phone: 812-339-3690
Fax: 812-339-3794
Website: www.commandequity.com

Type of Firm

Private Equity Firm

Project Preferences

Type of Financing Preferred:

Early Stage
Start-up Financing

Additional Information

Name of Most Recent Fund: Command Equity Fund III, LLC
Most Recent Fund Was Raised: 05/31/2006
Year Founded: 1998
Capital Under Management: $10,000,000
Current Activity Level: Actively seeking new investments

COMMERCIAL CAPITAL CORPORATION

150 King Street West
Suite 2020, P.O. Box 20
Toronto, Canada M5H 1J9
Phone: 416-599-4206
Fax: 416-599-9250
Website: www.commercialcapital.ca

Management and Staff

Michael Klax, Vice President
Rob Bird, Vice President
William Rogers, President

Type of Firm

Investment Management Firm

Additional Information

Year Founded: 1975
Current Activity Level: Actively seeking new investments

COMMERZBANK AG

60261 Frankfurt am Main
Frankfurt, Germany
Phone: 49-69-136200
Fax: 49-69-285389
E-mail: info@commerzbank.com
Website: www.commerzbank.com

Management and Staff

Eric Strutz, Chief Financial Officer
Klaus-Peter Muller, Chief Executive Officer
Leibniz Gemeinschaft, President

Type of Firm

Private Equity Firm

Additional Information

Year Founded: 1870
Current Activity Level: Actively seeking new investments

COMMONANGELS

One Cranberry Hill
Lexington, MA USA 02421
Phone: 781-274-9124
Fax: 781-862-8367
E-mail: info@commonangels.com
Website: www.commonangels.com

Management and Staff

Chris Sheehan, Managing Director
James Geshwiler, Managing Director

Type of Firm

Private Equity Advisor or Fund of Funds

Association Membership

National Venture Capital Association - USA (NVCA)

Project Preferences

Role in Financing:

Prefer role as deal originator

Type of Financing Preferred:

Early Stage

Size of Investments Considered:

Min Size of Investment Considered (000s): $500
Max Size of Investment Considered (000s): $2,000

Geographical Preferences

United States Preferences:

Northeast

Industry Preferences

In Communications prefer:

Communications and Media
Telecommunications

In Computer Software prefer:

Software
Applications Software

In Internet Specific prefer:

Internet
Ecommerce

In Computer Other prefer:

Computer Related

In Semiconductor/Electr prefer:

Semiconductor
Controllers and Sensors

In Consumer Related prefer:

Consumer Services

In Industrial/Energy prefer:

Industrial Products

In Financial Services prefer:

Financial Services

Additional Information

Year Founded: 1998
Capital Under Management: $20,000,000
Current Activity Level: Actively seeking new investments

COMMONFUND CAPITAL, INC. (FKA: COMMON FUND)

15 Old Danbury Road
Wilton, CT USA 06897
Phone: 203-563-5000
Fax: 203-762-0921
Website: www.commonfund.org

Other Offices

1801 Century Park East
Suite 2220
Los Angeles, CA USA 90067
Phone: 310-788-0500

Berkeley Square House, Second Floor
Berkeley Square
London, United Kingdom W1J 6BD
Phone: 44-20-7887-1540
Fax: 44-20-7887-1541

Management and Staff

A. Nicholas De Monico, Managing Director
E. Lyndon Tefft, Chief Operating Officer
Jeffrey Long, Managing Director
Mary Ellen Beaudreault, Managing Director
Sarah Clark, Managing Director

Type of Firm

Private Equity Advisor or Fund of Funds

Project Preferences

Role in Financing:

Prefer role in deals created by others

Type of Financing Preferred:

Fund of Funds
Early Stage
Expansion
Generalist PE
Seed
Distressed Debt

Geographical Preferences

United States Preferences:

Mid Atlantic
Midwest
Southeast
Northeast
West Coast
Southwest
All U.S.

Canadian Preferences:

All Canada

International Preferences:

Europe
Western Europe
Pacific Rim
Middle East
Asia
Africa
All International

Industry Focus

(% based on actual investment)

Other Products	100.0%

Additional Information

Name of Most Recent Fund: Commonfund Capital Venture Partners VII, L.P.
Most Recent Fund Was Raised: 04/06/2005
Year Founded: 1988
Capital Under Management: $5,765,000,000
Current Activity Level: Actively seeking new investments
Method of Compensation: Return on invest. most important, but chg. closing fees, service fees, etc.

COMMONFUND REALTY

15 Old Danbury Road
Wilton, CT USA 06897
Phone: 203-563-5000
Fax: 203-762-0921
Website: www.commonfund.org

Management and Staff

Hugh Scott, Managing Director
Timothy Shine, Managing Director

Type of Firm

Private Equity Advisor or Fund of Funds

Project Preferences

Type of Financing Preferred:

Other

Industry Preferences

In Financial Services prefer:

Real Estate

Additional Information

Year Founded: 1987
Current Activity Level: Actively seeking new investments

COMMONS CAPITAL, L.P.

320 Washington Street
Fourth Floor
Brookline, MA USA 02445
Phone: 617-739-3500
Fax: 617-739-3550
Website: www.commonscapital.com

Management and Staff

Elizabeth Bailey, Principal

Type of Firm

Private Equity Firm

Association Membership

National Venture Capital Association - USA (NVCA)

Project Preferences

Type of Financing Preferred:

Second Stage Financing
Early Stage
Expansion
Start-up Financing
Seed
First Stage Financing

Size of Investments Considered:

Min Size of Investment Considered (000s): $250
Max Size of Investment Considered (000s): $500

Geographical Preferences

United States Preferences:

Massachusetts

Industry Preferences

In Medical/Health prefer:
Medical/Health

In Consumer Related prefer:
Education Related

In Industrial/Energy prefer:
Energy
Energy Conservation Relat
Industrial Products

In Other prefer:
Environment Responsible
Women/Minority-Owned Bus.

Additional Information

Name of Most Recent Fund: Commons Capital Fund I
Most Recent Fund Was Raised: 03/30/2001
Year Founded: 1993
Current Activity Level: Actively seeking new investments

COMMONWEALTH ASSOCIATES

CityPlace Tower
525 Okeechobee Blvd Suite 1050
West Palm Beach, FL USA 33401
Phone: 561-727-2000
Website: www.comvest.com

Other Offices

830 Third Avenue
Eighth Floor
New York, NY USA 10022
Phone: 212-829-5825
Fax: 212-829-5974

Management and Staff

Daniel Nenadovic, Partner
Geoff Alexander, Partner
Joe Pallota, Vice President
Keith Rosenbloom, Managing Partner
Louis Colosimo, Partner
Michael Falk, Managing Partner
Pete Kight, Managing Partner
Robert Priddy, Managing Partner

Type of Firm

Private Equity Firm

Project Preferences

Role in Financing:
Prefer role as deal originator

Type of Financing Preferred:
Leveraged Buyout
Early Stage
Mezzanine
Balanced
Turnaround
Seed
Special Situation
Recapitalizations
Distressed Debt

Size of Investments Considered:
Min Size of Investment Considered (000s): $5,000
Max Size of Investment Considered (000s): $50,000

Geographical Preferences

United States Preferences:
All U.S.

Industry Preferences

In Computer Software prefer:
Software

In Medical/Health prefer:
Medical Diagnostics
Diagnostic Services
Diagnostic Test Products
Medical Products
Health Services

In Consumer Related prefer:
Education Related

In Transportation prefer:
Transportation

Additional Information

Year Founded: 1988
Capital Under Management: $774,000,000
Current Activity Level: Actively seeking new investments
Method of Compensation: Return on invest. most important, but chg. closing fees, service fees, etc.

COMMONWEALTH CAPITAL PARTNERS LP

509 Madison
New York, NY USA 10022
Phone: 212-317-2500

Management and Staff

Elliot Stein, Managing Director

Type of Firm

Private Equity Firm

Project Preferences

Type of Financing Preferred:
Leveraged Buyout

Additional Information

Name of Most Recent Fund: Commonwealth Capital Partners
Most Recent Fund Was Raised: 04/01/1989
Year Founded: 1989
Current Activity Level: Actively seeking new investments

COMMONWEALTH CAPITAL VENTURES

Bay Colony Corporate Center
950 Winter Street, Suite 4100
Waltham, MA USA 02451
Phone: 781-890-5554
Fax: 781-890-3414
Website: www.commonwealthvc.com

Management and Staff

Elliot Katzman, General Partner
Jeffrey Hurst, General Partner
Justin Perreault, General Partner
Michael Fitzgerald, General Partner
R. Stephen McCormack, General Partner

Type of Firm

Private Equity Firm

Association Membership

National Venture Capital Association - USA (NVCA)

Project Preferences

Role in Financing:
Will function either as deal originator or investor in deals created by others

Type of Financing Preferred:
Second Stage Financing
Early Stage
Expansion
First Stage Financing

Size of Investments Considered:
Min Size of Investment Considered (000s): $1,000
Max Size of Investment Considered (000s): $6,000

Geographical Preferences

United States Preferences:
All U.S.

Canadian Preferences:
All Canada

Industry Focus

(% based on actual investment)

Computer Software and Services	49.7%
Internet Specific	15.8%
Industrial/Energy	8.1%
Semiconductors/Other Elect.	7.9%
Communications and Media	6.9%
Medical/Health	4.1%
Computer Hardware	2.6%
Other Products	2.0%
Biotechnology	1.6%
Consumer Related	1.2%

Additional Information

Name of Most Recent Fund: Commonwealth Capital Ventures IV, LP
Most Recent Fund Was Raised: 02/09/2007
Year Founded: 1995
Capital Under Management: $580,000,000
Current Activity Level: Actively seeking new investments

Method of Compensation: Return on investment is of primary concern, do not charge fees

COMPAGNIA FINANZIARIA INDUSTRIALE (CFI)

5/A Via Vicenza
Rome, Italy 00185
Phone: 39-06-4440-284
Fax: 39-06-4451-766
E-mail: info@cfi.it
Website: www.cfi.it

Type of Firm

Private Equity Firm

Association Membership

Italian Venture Capital Association (AIFI)

Project Preferences

Type of Financing Preferred:
Leveraged Buyout
Startup

Geographical Preferences

International Preferences:
Italy

Additional Information

Year Founded: 1987
Capital Under Management: $64,100,000
Current Activity Level: Actively seeking new investments

COMPAGNIE DU BOIS SAUVAGE

Rue du Bois Sauvage 17
Bruxelles, Belgium 1000
Phone: 32-2-227-5450
Fax: 32-2-219-2520
E-mail: info@bois-sauvage.be
Website: www.bois-sauvage.be

Type of Firm

Private Equity Firm

Project Preferences

Type of Financing Preferred:
Balanced

Geographical Preferences

International Preferences:
Belgium

Additional Information

Year Founded: 1957
Current Activity Level: Actively seeking new investments

COMPANION CAPITAL MANAGEMENT, INC.

4101 Percival Road
AX-200
Columbia, SC USA 29223
Phone: 803-264-5591
Fax: 803-264-8077
E-mail: information@companioncm.com
Website: www.companioncm.com

Management and Staff

Mike Mizeur, President

Type of Firm

Corporate PE/Venture

Association Membership

National Venture Capital Association - USA (NVCA)

Project Preferences

Role in Financing:
Prefer role as deal originator

Type of Financing Preferred:
Second Stage Financing
Expansion
Balanced
Seed
First Stage Financing
Strategic Alliances
Startup

Size of Investments Considered:
Min Size of Investment Considered (000s): $5,000
Max Size of Investment Considered (000s): $100,000

Geographical Preferences

United States Preferences:
Southeast
All U.S.

Industry Preferences

In Computer Software prefer:
Software
Applications Software

In Medical/Health prefer:
Health Services

In Financial Services prefer:
Insurance
Financial Services

Additional Information

Year Founded: 2005
Capital Under Management: $5,600,000
Current Activity Level: Actively seeking new investments
Method of Compensation: Return on investment is of primary concern, do not charge fees

COMPANY GUIDES, LTD. (AKA: COMPANY GUIDES VENTURE PARTNERS)

13 Christopher Street
London, United Kingdom EC2A 2BS
Phone: 44-20-7247-6300
Fax: 44-20-7247-6900
E-mail: enquiries@companyguides.com
Website: www.companyguides.com

Management and Staff

Tony Diment, Managing Director

Type of Firm

Investment Management Firm

Project Preferences

Type of Financing Preferred:
Early Stage
Seed
Startup

Size of Investments Considered:
Min Size of Investment Considered (000s): $88
Max Size of Investment Considered (000s): $442

Geographical Preferences

International Preferences:
United Kingdom
Europe

Industry Preferences

In Communications prefer:
Commercial Communications
Telecommunications

In Computer Hardware prefer:
Computers

In Computer Software prefer:
Computer Services

In Internet Specific prefer:
Internet

In Computer Other prefer:
Computer Related

In Semiconductor/Electr prefer:
Electronics

In Biotechnology prefer:
Biotechnology

In Medical/Health prefer:
Medical/Health

In Consumer Related prefer:
Entertainment and Leisure

In Industrial/Energy prefer:
Energy
Materials

In Business Serv. prefer:
Media

Additional Information

Year Founded: 1996
Capital Under Management: $1,400,000
Current Activity Level: Actively seeking new investments

COMPASS CAPITAL FUND MANAGEMENT LLC

7525 Southeast 24th Street
Suite 450
Mercer Island, WA USA 98040-2334
Phone: 206-236-2100
Fax: 206-926-2300
E-mail: info@compasscapital.com
Website: www.compasscapital.com

Management and Staff

Chris Nicholson, Managing Partner
Malcolm Witter, Partner

Type of Firm

Private Equity Firm

Project Preferences

Role in Financing:

Prefer role as deal originator but will also invest in deals created by others

Type of Financing Preferred:

Early Stage
Expansion

Size of Investments Considered:

Min Size of Investment Considered (000s): $500
Max Size of Investment Considered (000s): $5,000

Geographical Preferences

Canadian Preferences:

All Canada

Industry Preferences

In Communications prefer:

Wireless Communications

In Computer Software prefer:

Software
Systems Software
Applications Software

In Semiconductor/Electr prefer:

Semiconductor
Controllers and Sensors
Sensors
Laser Related
Fiber Optics

In Biotechnology prefer:

Human Biotechnology
Industrial Biotechnology
Biosensors
Biotech Related Research

In Medical/Health prefer:

Medical Diagnostics
Diagnostic Services
Drug/Equipmt Delivery
Medical Products

Additional Information

Year Founded: 1994
Current Activity Level: Actively seeking new investments
Method of Compensation: Return on investment is of primary concern, do not charge fees

COMPASS GROUP INTERNATIONAL LLC, THE

61 Wilton Road
Second Floor
Westport, CT USA 06880
Phone: 203-221-1703
Fax: 203-221-8253
E-mail: info@compassequity.com
Website: www.compassequity.com

Other Offices

24422 Avenida de la Carlota
Suite 370
Laguna Hills, CA USA 92653
Phone: 949-420-0700
Fax: 949-420-0771

Management and Staff

Alan Offenberg, Principal
David Swanson, Vice President
David Browne, Vice President
Elias Sabo, Principal
I. Joseph Massoud, President

Type of Firm

Private Equity Firm

Project Preferences

Role in Financing:

Prefer role as deal originator

Type of Financing Preferred:

Recapitalizations

Geographical Preferences

United States Preferences:

All U.S.

Canadian Preferences:

All Canada

International Preferences:

Latin America
Europe
Middle East
Africa

Industry Focus

(% based on actual investment)

Other Products	100.0%

Additional Information

Year Founded: 1998
Capital Under Management: $140,000,000
Current Activity Level: Actively seeking new investments
Method of Compensation: Return on investment is of primary concern, do not charge fees

COMPASS GROUP, INC

23 Cielo Vista Drive
Monterey, CA USA 93940
Phone: 831-375-5116
Fax: 831-375-0250

Management and Staff

Ryan Kelly, President & Chairman

Type of Firm

Private Equity Firm

Project Preferences

Role in Financing:

Prefer role as deal originator

Type of Financing Preferred:

Expansion
Acquisition
Private Placement
Startup

Size of Investments Considered:

Min Size of Investment Considered (000s): $5,000
Max Size of Investment Considered (000s): $20,000

Industry Focus

(% based on actual investment)

Medical/Health	80.2%
Other Products	10.1%
Consumer Related	9.7%

Additional Information

Year Founded: 1997
Capital Under Management: $500,000,000
Current Activity Level: Actively seeking new investments
Method of Compensation: Return on invest. most important, but chg. closing fees, service fees, etc.

COMPASS TECHNOLOGY PARTNERS

261 Hamilton Avenue
Suite 200
Palo Alto, CA USA 94301
Phone: 650-322-7595
Fax: 650-322-0588
Website: www.compasstechpartners.com

Management and Staff

Alain Harrus, Partner
Benjamin Miller, Partner
David Arscott, Partner
Martha Arscott, Partner
Paul Yau, Partner

Type of Firm

Private Equity Firm

Association Membership
National Venture Capital Association - USA (NVCA)

Project Preferences
Role in Financing:
Will function either as deal originator or investor in deals created by others

Type of Financing Preferred:
Early Stage
Expansion
Public Companies
Seed
First Stage Financing
Private Placement
Startup

Size of Investments Considered:
Min Size of Investment Considered (000s): $250
Max Size of Investment Considered (000s): $1,250

Geographical Preferences
United States Preferences:
California
All U.S.

Industry Focus
(% based on actual investment)

Internet Specific	23.9%
Computer Software and Services	22.3%
Medical/Health	15.2%
Semiconductors/Other Elect.	14.7%
Other Products	11.3%
Industrial/Energy	8.0%
Communications and Media	4.5%

Additional Information
Name of Most Recent Fund: Compass Venture Partners II
Most Recent Fund Was Raised: 10/01/2002
Year Founded: 1988
Capital Under Management: $50,000,000
Current Activity Level: Actively seeking new investments
Method of Compensation: Return on investment is of primary concern, do not charge fees

COMPOUND SEMICONDUCTOR TECHNOLOGIES LTD
Block 6.3, Kelvin Campus,
West of Scotland Science Park,
Glasgow, United Kingdom G20 OSP
Phone: 44-141-579-3000
Fax: 44-141-579-3040
Website: www.compoundsemi.co.uk

Type of Firm
Incubator/Development Program

Project Preferences
Type of Financing Preferred:
Seed
Startup

Geographical Preferences
International Preferences:
United Kingdom

Industry Preferences
In Communications prefer:
Telecommunications

In Semiconductor/Electr prefer:
Electronics
Semiconductor
Fiber Optics

Additional Information
Year Founded: 1998
Capital Under Management: $10,900,000
Current Activity Level: Actively seeking new investments

COMSPACE DEVELOPMENT LLC
12521 Manderlay Way
Oak Hill, VA USA 20171
Phone: 703-716-0675
Website: www.comspacedev.com

Management and Staff
Michael Miller, Managing Director
W. Theodore Pierson, Managing Director

Type of Firm
Private Equity Firm

Association Membership
Mid-Atlantic Venture Association

Project Preferences
Type of Financing Preferred:
Early Stage

Size of Investments Considered:
Min Size of Investment Considered (000s): $100
Max Size of Investment Considered (000s): $1,000

Geographical Preferences
United States Preferences:
Mid Atlantic

Industry Preferences
In Communications prefer:
Telecommunications

In Transportation prefer:
Aerospace

Additional Information
Year Founded: 1997
Capital Under Management: $10,000,000
Current Activity Level: Actively seeking new investments

COMSTAR MEDIA
5057 Keller Springs Road
Suite 110
Addison, TX USA 75001
Phone: 831-521-6690
Website: www.comstarmedia.com

Type of Firm
Private Equity Firm

Industry Preferences
In Communications prefer:
Communications and Media

Additional Information
Name of Most Recent Fund: ComStar Media Fund, L.P.
Most Recent Fund Was Raised: 02/27/2009
Year Founded: 2009
Capital Under Management: $300,000
Current Activity Level: Actively seeking new investments

COMTECH INVEST A/S (FKA: AHEAD ENTERPRISE SA)
Falkoner Alle 7, 2.
Frederiksberg, Denmark 2000
Phone: 45-383-353-45
Fax: 45-383-482-39
Website: www.comtechinvest.com

Management and Staff
Peder Pedersen, Managing Partner

Type of Firm
Private Equity Firm

Association Membership
Danish Venture Capital Association (DVCA)

Project Preferences
Type of Financing Preferred:
Seed
Startup

Geographical Preferences
International Preferences:
Sweden
Denmark

Industry Preferences
In Communications prefer:
Communications and Media
Wireless Communications

In Internet Specific prefer:
Internet

Additional Information

Year Founded: 1999
Current Activity Level: Actively seeking new investments

CONCENTRIC EQUITY PARTNERS, L.P.

50 East Washington Street
Suite 400
Chicago, IL USA 60602
Phone: 312-494-4513
Website: www.fic-cep.com

Management and Staff

Allan Martin, Partner
Dan Kotynski, General Partner
Frank Reppenhagen, Vice President
Harrison Steans, Partner
Ian Ross, Vice President
James Watt, Partner
Jeffrey Prough, Partner
Jennifer Steans, Partner
Joseph Chillura, Partner
Judy Dabertin, Partner
Kenneth Hooten, Partner
Mike Ayars, Partner
Neele Stearns, Partner
Thomas McMurtrey, Partner

Type of Firm

Private Equity Firm

Association Membership

Illinois Venture Capital Association

Project Preferences

Role in Financing:
Will function either as deal originator or investor in deals created by others

Type of Financing Preferred:
Leveraged Buyout
Expansion
Generalist PE
Later Stage
Recapitalizations

Size of Investments Considered:
Min Size of Investment Considered (000s): $1,000
Max Size of Investment Considered (000s): $10,000

Geographical Preferences

United States Preferences:
All U.S.

Industry Preferences

In Computer Software prefer:
Computer Services

In Medical/Health prefer:
Health Services

In Consumer Related prefer:
Consumer
Franchises(NEC)

In Business Serv. prefer:
Services

Additional Information

Name of Most Recent Fund: Concentric Equity Partners, L.P.
Most Recent Fund Was Raised: 08/21/2003
Year Founded: 2003
Capital Under Management: $40,000,000
Current Activity Level: Actively seeking new investments
Method of Compensation: Return on invest. most important, but chg. closing fees, service fees, etc.

CONCEPT DEVELOPMENT ASSOCIATES, INC.

P.O. Box 15245
Evansville, IN USA 47716-0245
Phone: 812-471-3334
Fax: 812-477-6499
E-mail: dealmakeracademy@aol.com

Other Offices

1375 Central Avenue
Santa Rosa, CA USA 95401
Phone: 707-546-4470
Fax: 707-546-4720

Type of Firm

Private Equity Firm

Project Preferences

Role in Financing:
Will function either as deal originator or investor in deals created by others

Type of Financing Preferred:
Early Stage
Research and Development
Start-up Financing
Seed

Size of Investments Considered:
Min Size of Investment Considered (000s): $250
Max Size of Investment Considered (000s): $5,000

Geographical Preferences

United States Preferences:
All U.S.

Canadian Preferences:
All Canada

International Preferences:
Italy
India
Latin America
Luxembourg
Netherlands
Portugal
China
Hong Kong
Mexico
Middle East
Spain
Australia
Belgium
New Zealand
Germany
All International
France
Japan
Africa

Industry Preferences

In Consumer Related prefer:
Consumer
Entertainment and Leisure
Retail
Franchises(NEC)
Food/Beverage
Education Related

In Industrial/Energy prefer:
Industrial Products

In Financial Services prefer:
Financial Services

In Business Serv. prefer:
Services
Distribution
Consulting Services
Media

In Manufact. prefer:
Manufacturing

In Agr/Forestr/Fish prefer:
Agriculture related

In Other prefer:
Socially Responsible
Environment Responsible
Women/Minority-Owned Bus.

Additional Information

Year Founded: 1986
Capital Under Management: $22,800,000
Current Activity Level: Actively seeking new investments
Method of Compensation: Return on invest. most important, but chg. closing fees, service fees, etc.

CONCEPT VENTURES MANAGEMENT LLC

4800 Great America Parkway
Suite 530
Santa Clara, CA USA 95054
Phone: 650-575-5739
Website: www.conceptvc.com

Management and Staff

Anne De Gheest, Managing Director

Type of Firm

Private Equity Firm

Project Preferences

Type of Financing Preferred:
Expansion

Geographical Preferences

United States Preferences:
All U.S.

Additional Information

Name of Most Recent Fund: Concept Ventures I, L.P.
Most Recent Fund Was Raised: 06/15/2005
Year Founded: 2005
Capital Under Management: $10,800,000
Current Activity Level: Actively seeking new investments

CONCORD VENTURES (FKA: NITZANIM)

85 Medinat Hayehudim Street
Seventh Floor, P.O.Box 4011
Herzelia, Israel 46140
Phone: 972-9-960-2020
Fax: 972-9-960-2022
E-mail: office@concordventures.com
Website: www.concord-ventures.co.il

Management and Staff

Avi Domoshevizki, General Partner
Avigdor Willenz, Venture Partner
Batsheva Elran, General Partner
Geva Rechav, Principal
Isaac Shpantzer, Venture Partner
Matty Karp, Managing Partner
Shai Schiller, General Partner
Yair Safrai, General Partner
Yaron Rosenboim, Chief Financial Officer
Yigal Koltin, Venture Partner

Type of Firm

Investment Management Firm

Project Preferences

Role in Financing:
Prefer role as deal originator but will also invest in deals created by others

Type of Financing Preferred:
Second Stage Financing
Leveraged Buyout
Early Stage
Balanced
Later Stage
Seed
First Stage Financing
Private Placement
Startup

Size of Investments Considered:
Min Size of Investment Considered (000s): $100
Max Size of Investment Considered (000s): $15,000

Geographical Preferences

United States Preferences:
All U.S.

International Preferences:
Middle East
Israel

Industry Preferences

In Communications prefer:
Communications and Media
Telecommunications
Wireless Communications
Data Communications

In Computer Hardware prefer:
Integrated Turnkey System

In Computer Software prefer:
Data Processing
Software
Systems Software
Applications Software
Artificial Intelligence

In Internet Specific prefer:
Internet

In Semiconductor/Electr prefer:
Semiconductor
Micro-Processing
Controllers and Sensors
Circuit Boards
Component Testing Equipmt
Fiber Optics

In Biotechnology prefer:
Human Biotechnology
Biosensors
Biotech Related Research

In Medical/Health prefer:
Medical/Health
Medical Diagnostics
Diagnostic Test Products
Drug/Equipmt Delivery
Medical Products

In Industrial/Energy prefer:
Robotics

Additional Information

Year Founded: 1993
Capital Under Management: $260,000,000
Current Activity Level: Actively seeking new investments
Method of Compensation: Return on investment is of primary concern, do not charge fees

---

CONCORDIA FUND

Delftweg 96
Rotterdam, Netherlands 3043 NA
Phone: 31-10-240-0504
Fax: 31-10-240-0506
E-mail: info@concordiafund.nl
Website: www.concordiafund.nl

Management and Staff

Saskia Van Walsum, Chief Executive Officer

Type of Firm

Private Equity Firm

Project Preferences

Type of Financing Preferred:
Expansion
Management Buyouts
Recapitalizations

Geographical Preferences

International Preferences:
Netherlands
All International

Additional Information

Year Founded: 2008
Capital Under Management: $55,700,000
Current Activity Level: Actively seeking new investments

CONDOR CAPITAL MANAGEMENT

1973 Washington Valley road
Martinsville, NJ USA 08836
Phone: 732-356-7323
Fax: 732-356-5875
Website: www.condorcapital.com

Management and Staff

Ken Schapiro, Managing Partner
Stephen Tipping, Vice President

Type of Firm

Private Equity Firm

Additional Information

Year Founded: 1988
Current Activity Level: Actively seeking new investments

CONDUIT CAPITAL PARTNERS, LLC

488 Madison Avenue
New York, NY USA 10022
Phone: 212-485-8900
Fax: 212-485-8939
E-mail: info@conduitcap.com
Website: www.conduitcap.com

Management and Staff
Eyob Easwaran, Partner
George Osorio, Managing Director
Juan Fernando Paez, Partner
Liliana Rauch, Partner
Marc Frishman, Partner
Marcelo Vandelli, Chief Financial Officer
Samuel Gomez, Partner

Type of Firm
Private Equity Firm

Project Preferences
Type of Financing Preferred:
Leveraged Buyout

Size of Investments Considered:
Min Size of Investment Considered (000s): $60,000
Max Size of Investment Considered (000s): $300,000

Geographical Preferences
International Preferences:
Latin America

Industry Preferences
In Utilities prefer:
Utilities

Additional Information
Name of Most Recent Fund: Latin Power III
Most Recent Fund Was Raised: 07/21/2005
Year Founded: 2003
Capital Under Management: $393,000,000
Current Activity Level: Actively seeking new investments

CONDUIT VENTURES LIMITED

Unit B,2nd Floor Colonial Bldg
59-61 Hatton Garden
London, United Kingdom EC1N 8LS
Phone: 44-207-242-9595
Fax: 44-207-405-2863
E-mail: info@conduit-ventures.com
Website: www.conduit-ventures.com

Management and Staff
John Butt, Chief Executive Officer

Type of Firm
Private Equity Firm

Project Preferences
Type of Financing Preferred:
Early Stage
Expansion
Later Stage
Startup

Geographical Preferences
Canadian Preferences:
All Canada

International Preferences:
Europe

Industry Preferences
In Industrial/Energy prefer:
Energy

Additional Information
Year Founded: 2001
Current Activity Level: Actively seeking new investments

CONETWORK ERNEUERBARE ENERGIEN MANAGMENT GMBH

Brandstwiete 1
Hamburg, Germany DE-20457
Phone: 49-40-6887-880
Fax: 49-40-6887-8870
E-mail: hamburg@lampe-cf.de
Website: www.cee-holding.de

Type of Firm
Bank Affiliated

Project Preferences
Type of Financing Preferred:
Mezzanine
Generalist PE
Management Buyouts

Size of Investments Considered:
Min Size of Investment Considered (000s): $1,568
Max Size of Investment Considered (000s): $7,842

Geographical Preferences
International Preferences:
Switzerland
Europe
Germany

Industry Preferences
In Industrial/Energy prefer:
Alternative Energy
Energy Conservation Relat
Environmental Related

In Other prefer:
Environment Responsible

Additional Information
Year Founded: 2007
Capital Under Management: $146,000,000
Current Activity Level: Actively seeking new investments

CONEXUS CAPITAL MANAGEMENT, INC.

Post Office Box 835
Somerville, NJ USA 08876
Phone: 908-231-9101
Fax: 908-231-9103
E-mail: info@conexuscapital.com
Website: www.conexuscapital.com

Management and Staff
Dietmar Hirt, Managing Director
G. Robert Marcus, Managing Director
Graham May, Managing Director

Type of Firm
Private Equity Firm

Project Preferences
Role in Financing:
Prefer role as deal originator but will also invest in deals created by others

Type of Financing Preferred:
Second Stage Financing
Early Stage
Expansion
First Stage Financing

Size of Investments Considered:
Min Size of Investment Considered (000s): $1,000
Max Size of Investment Considered (000s): $4,000

Geographical Preferences
United States Preferences:
Mid Atlantic
Northeast

Additional Information
Name of Most Recent Fund: Conexus Financial Partners, L.P.
Most Recent Fund Was Raised: 05/01/2001
Year Founded: 2000
Capital Under Management: $45,000,000
Current Activity Level: Actively seeking new investments
Method of Compensation: Return on investment is of primary concern, do not charge fees

CONNECTICUT INNOVATIONS, INC.

200 Corporate Place
Third Floor
Rocky Hill, CT USA 06067
Phone: 860-563-5851
Fax: 860-563-4877
E-mail: info@ctinnovations.com
Website: www.ctinnovations.com

Management and Staff
Russell Tweeddale, Managing Director

Type of Firm
Government Affiliated Program

Association Membership

National Venture Capital Association - USA (NVCA)

Project Preferences

Role in Financing:

Will function either as deal originator or investor in deals created by others

Type of Financing Preferred:

Early Stage
Balanced
Later Stage
Seed
First Stage Financing
Startup

Size of Investments Considered:

Min Size of Investment Considered (000s): $100
Max Size of Investment Considered (000s): $4,000

Geographical Preferences

United States Preferences:

Connecticut
All U.S.

Industry Focus

(% based on actual investment)

Industrial/Energy	31.0%
Computer Software and Services	20.3%
Biotechnology	18.0%
Internet Specific	15.8%
Medical/Health	4.8%
Other Products	3.0%
Communications and Media	2.9%
Computer Hardware	1.8%
Consumer Related	1.4%
Semiconductors/Other Elect.	1.0%

Additional Information

Year Founded: 1989
Capital Under Management: $70,700,000
Current Activity Level: Actively seeking new investments
Method of Compensation: Return on investment is of primary concern, do not charge fees

---

CONOR VENTURE PARTNERS OY

Innopoli 2
Tekniikkatie 14
Espoo, Finland FI-02150
Phone: 358-9-2517-7370
Fax: 358-9-812-7305
Website: www.conor.vc

Management and Staff

Jari Mieskonen, Managing Partner
Manu Makela, Partner
Sami Ahvenniemi, Partner

Type of Firm

Private Equity Firm

Project Preferences

Type of Financing Preferred:

Early Stage

Size of Investments Considered:

Min Size of Investment Considered (000s): $286
Max Size of Investment Considered (000s): $4,283

Geographical Preferences

International Preferences:

Sweden
Western Europe
Estonia
Finland
Latvia
Lithuania

Industry Preferences

In Communications prefer:

Communications and Media
Wireless Communications

In Computer Software prefer:

Software

In Semiconductor/Electr prefer:

Fiber Optics

Additional Information

Year Founded: 2005
Capital Under Management: $28,600,000
Current Activity Level: Actively seeking new investments

CONSECO GLOBAL INVESTMENT

18/F, Room 18
China World Tower 1
Beijing, China
Phone: 86-10-6505-0636
Fax: 86-10-6505-5635
E-mail: conseco@public.bta.net.cn

Type of Firm

Insurance Firm Affiliate

Association Membership

Venture Capital Association of Beijing (VCAB)

Project Preferences

Type of Financing Preferred:

Balanced

Geographical Preferences

International Preferences:

China

Additional Information

Year Founded: 1997
Current Activity Level: Actively seeking new investments

CONSILIUM SGR

Via Sacchi 7
Milan, Italy 20121
Phone: 39-02726-0191
Fax: 39-027209-5768
E-mail: info@consiliumsgr.it
Website: www.consiliumsgr.it

Type of Firm

Private Equity Firm

Association Membership

Italian Venture Capital Association (AIFI)

Project Preferences

Type of Financing Preferred:

Leveraged Buyout
Expansion
Recapitalizations

Size of Investments Considered:

Min Size of Investment Considered (000s): $3,811
Max Size of Investment Considered (000s): $7,621

Geographical Preferences

International Preferences:

Italy

Additional Information

Year Founded: 2006
Capital Under Management: $56,900,000
Current Activity Level: Actively seeking new investments

CONSOR CAPITAL LLC

475 Gate Five Road
Suite 320
Sausalito, CA USA 94965
Phone: 415-559-9913
Fax: 415-332-1491
Website: www.consorcapital.com

Other Offices

Three Greenwich Office Park
Second Floor
Greenwich, CT USA 06831
Phone: 203-661-3405
Fax: 720-294-1304

Type of Firm

Private Equity Firm

Project Preferences

Type of Financing Preferred:

Early Stage

Geographical Preferences

United States Preferences:

All U.S.

Industry Preferences

In Consumer Related prefer:
Consumer
Sports

In Business Serv. prefer:
Services

Additional Information
Year Founded: 2002
Current Activity Level: Actively seeking new investments

CONSTELLATION VENTURES (AKA: CONSTELLATION GROWTH CAPITAL)

40 West 57th Street
30th Floor
New York, NY USA 10019
Phone: 212-287-6792
Fax: 212-272-9256
E-mail: constellationventures@bear.com
Website: www.constellationventures.com

Other Offices
Shiroyama JT Trust Tower 16F
4-3-1 Toranomon Minato-ku
Tokyo, Japan
Phone: 81-3-5219-0606

Management and Staff
Bryan Rubin, Vice President
Clifford Friedman, Senior Managing Director
Liza Boyd, Managing Director
Thomas Wasserman, Managing Director

Type of Firm
Bank Affiliated

Project Preferences

Role in Financing:
Will function either as deal originator or investor in deals created by others

Type of Financing Preferred:
Second Stage Financing
Early Stage
Balanced
First Stage Financing

Size of Investments Considered:
Min Size of Investment Considered (000s): $5,000
Max Size of Investment Considered (000s): $25,000

Geographical Preferences

United States Preferences:
Northeast
West Coast
All U.S.

Industry Focus
(% based on actual investment)

Other Products	53.9%
Computer Software and Services	22.0%
Internet Specific	17.2%
Communications and Media	6.3%
Consumer Related	0.3%
Industrial/Energy	0.2%

Additional Information
Name of Most Recent Fund: Constellation Ventures III
Most Recent Fund Was Raised: 02/08/2007
Year Founded: 1998
Capital Under Management: $450,000,000
Current Activity Level: Actively seeking new investments
Method of Compensation: Return on investment is of primary concern, do not charge fees

---

CONSTITUTION CAPITAL PARTNERS, LLC

300 Brickstone Square
Sixth Floor
Andover, MA USA 01810
Phone: 978-749-9600
Fax: 978-749-9669
E-mail: info@concp.com
Website: www.concp.com

Management and Staff
Alexander Tatum, Principal
Dan Cahill, Managing Partner
John Guinee, Managing Partner
Robert Hatch, Partner
Vicente Miguel Ramos, Partner
William Richardson, Partner

Type of Firm
Private Equity Advisor or Fund of Funds

Project Preferences

Type of Financing Preferred:
Fund of Funds
Leveraged Buyout

Geographical Preferences

United States Preferences:
All U.S.

Additional Information
Year Founded: 2008
Capital Under Management: $750,000,000
Current Activity Level: Actively seeking new investments

CONSUMER GROWTH PARTNERS

233 West 47th Street
Country Club Plaza
Kansas City, MO USA 64112
Phone: 816-960-1771
Fax: 816-960-1777
E-mail: info@consumergrowth.com
Website: www.consumergrowth.com

Other Offices
445 Hamilton Avenue
Suite 1102
White Plains, NY USA 10601
Phone: 914-220-8337
Fax: 914-428-4001

Management and Staff
Bill Reisler, Managing Partner
Jeffrey Teeven, Partner
Peter Bennett, Partner
Richard Baum, Managing Partner

Type of Firm
Private Equity Firm

Project Preferences

Type of Financing Preferred:
Management Buyouts

Size of Investments Considered:
Min Size of Investment Considered (000s): $10,000
Max Size of Investment Considered (000s): $100,000

Geographical Preferences

United States Preferences:
All U.S.

Industry Preferences

In Consumer Related prefer:
Retail
Consumer Products

Additional Information
Year Founded: 2006
Current Activity Level: Actively seeking new investments

CONTINENTAL CAPITAL PARTNERS, LTD.

CCP House
8 Wilfred Street
London, United Kingdom SW1E 6PL
Phone: 44-207-630-2010
Fax: 44-207-630-2011
E-mail: info@dealmaker.co.uk
Website: www.ccpltd.net

Management and Staff

Roger C. Luscombe, Founder

Type of Firm

Private Equity Firm

Project Preferences

Type of Financing Preferred:

Fund of Funds
Leveraged Buyout
Generalist PE
Mezzanine
Management Buyouts
Acquisition
Recapitalizations

Geographical Preferences

International Preferences:

United Kingdom
Europe

Additional Information

Year Founded: 1997
Current Activity Level: Actively seeking new investments

CONTINENTAL S.B.I.C.

4141 North Henderson Road
Suite #8
Arlington, VA USA 22203
Phone: 703-527-5200
Fax: 703-527-3700

Management and Staff

Arthur Walters, President
Mark Walters, Vice President
Thomas Goodfellow, Chief Financial Officer

Type of Firm

Bank Affiliated

Association Membership

Mid-Atlantic Venture Association
Natl Assoc of Small Bus. Inv. Co (NASBIC)

Project Preferences

Role in Financing:

Will function either as deal originator or investor in deals created by others

Type of Financing Preferred:

Fund of Funds
Leveraged Buyout
Expansion
Mezzanine
Generalist PE
Early Stage
Later Stage
Management Buyouts
Acquisition
Joint Ventures
Private Placement
Special Situation
Distressed Debt

Size of Investments Considered:

Min Size of Investment Considered (000s): $250
Max Size of Investment Considered (000s): $5,100

Geographical Preferences

United States Preferences:

Mid Atlantic
Midwest
Southeast
Northeast
Southwest

Canadian Preferences:

Quebec
Ontario

International Preferences:

United Kingdom
Latin America
Luxembourg
Netherlands
China
Mexico
Australia
Belgium
Germany
France
Japan

Industry Preferences

In Communications prefer:

Commercial Communications
Radio & TV Broadcasting
Wireless Communications

In Semiconductor/Electr prefer:

Electronic Components
Semiconductor
Micro-Processing
Controllers and Sensors
Laser Related

In Biotechnology prefer:

Biotech Related Research

In Medical/Health prefer:

Diagnostic Test Products
Medical Therapeutics
Hospitals/Clinics/Primary
Pharmaceuticals

In Consumer Related prefer:

Hotels and Resorts

In Industrial/Energy prefer:

Energy
Robotics

In Financial Services prefer:

Financial Services
Insurance
Real Estate

In Utilities prefer:

Utilities

In Other prefer:

Women/Minority-Owned Bus.

Additional Information

Name of Most Recent Fund: Continental S.B.I.C.
Most Recent Fund Was Raised: 03/31/1990
Year Founded: 1990
Capital Under Management: $2,000,000
Current Activity Level: Actively seeking new investments
Method of Compensation: Return on invest. most important, but chg. closing fees, service fees, etc.

CONTOUR VENTURE PARTNERS

317 Madison Avenue
Suite 1124
New York, NY USA 10017
Phone: 212-644-5481
Fax: 203-552-5381
E-mail: businessplan@contourventures.com
Website: www.contourventures.com

Management and Staff

Matthew Gorin, General Partner
Robert Greene, Managing Partner

Type of Firm

Private Equity Firm

Association Membership

National Venture Capital Association - USA (NVCA)

Project Preferences

Role in Financing:

Prefer role as deal originator but will also invest in deals created by others

Type of Financing Preferred:

Early Stage
Seed
First Stage Financing
Startup

Size of Investments Considered:

Min Size of Investment Considered (000s): $250
Max Size of Investment Considered (000s): $1,500

Geographical Preferences

United States Preferences:

Northeast

Industry Preferences

In Computer Software prefer:

Software

In Internet Specific prefer:

Internet
Ecommerce

In Medical/Health prefer:

Health Services

In Financial Services prefer:

Financial Services

In Business Serv. prefer:

Media

Additional Information

Name of Most Recent Fund: Contour Venture Partners, L.P.
Most Recent Fund Was Raised: 06/30/2006
Year Founded: 2006
Capital Under Management: $17,000,000
Current Activity Level: Actively seeking new investments

CONVERGENCE PARTNERS

800 West El Camino Real
Suite 180
Mountain View, CA USA 94040
Phone: 650-854-3010
Fax: 650-462-8415
E-mail: info@convergencepartners.com
Website: www.convergencepartners.com

Management and Staff

Eric DiBenedetto, General Partner
Russel Irwin, General Partner
Type of Firm
Private Equity Firm

Association Membership

Western Association of Venture Capitalists (WAVC)

Project Preferences

Role in Financing:
Prefer role as deal originator but will also invest in deals created by others

Type of Financing Preferred:
Early Stage
Seed
First Stage Financing

Size of Investments Considered:
Min Size of Investment Considered (000s): $2,000
Max Size of Investment Considered (000s): $10,000

Industry Focus

(% based on actual investment)

Internet Specific	53.1%
Computer Software and Services	18.0%
Semiconductors/Other Elect.	10.4%
Computer Hardware	8.1%
Industrial/Energy	3.8%
Other Products	3.4%
Communications and Media	3.2%

Additional Information

Year Founded: 1997
Capital Under Management: $200,000,000
Current Activity Level: Actively seeking new investments
Method of Compensation: Return on invest. most important, but chg. closing fees, service fees, etc.

CONVERGENT CAPITAL

52, avenue de l'Europe
Marly le Roi, France 78160
Phone: 33-1-3008-8101
Fax: 33-1-3008-8111
E-mail: info@convergent-capital.com
Website: www.convergent-capital.com

Management and Staff

Alain Meller, Partner
Armand Sibony, Managing Partner
Philippe De Bellefonds, Partner

Type of Firm

Private Equity Firm

Association Membership

French Venture Capital Association (AFIC)

Project Preferences

Type of Financing Preferred:
Early Stage

Size of Investments Considered:
Min Size of Investment Considered (000s): $1,788
Max Size of Investment Considered (000s): $5,363

Geographical Preferences

United States Preferences:
All U.S.

International Preferences:
Europe
Israel
France

Industry Preferences

In Communications prefer:
Communications and Media

In Computer Software prefer:
Software

Additional Information

Year Founded: 2001
Capital Under Management: $17,000,000
Current Activity Level: Actively seeking new investments

CONVERGENT CAPITAL MANAGEMENT, INC. (AKA: CCM)

190 South LaSalle Street
Suite 2800
Chicago, IL USA 60603
Phone: 312-444-6000
Fax: 312-444-6034
E-mail: ccm@convergentcapital.com
Website: www.convergentcapital.com

Management and Staff

Gregory Francoeur, Chief Financial Officer
H. Tom Griffith, Co-Founder
James Hayes, Co-Founder
Jon Hunt, Managing Director
Richard Adler, Co-Founder

Type of Firm

Bank Affiliated

Additional Information

Year Founded: 1994
Capital Under Management: $6,300,000,000
Current Activity Level: Actively seeking new investments

CONVERGENT CAPITAL PARTNERS

5353 Wayzata Boulevard
Suite 205
Minneapolis, MN USA 55416
Phone: 952-595-8022
Fax: 952-595-8113
Website: www.cvcap.com

Management and Staff

John Mason, Managing Partner
Keith Bares, Partner

Type of Firm

Private Equity Firm

Project Preferences

Type of Financing Preferred:
Expansion
Management Buyouts
Acquisition
Recapitalizations

Additional Information

Year Founded: 1998
Current Activity Level: Actively seeking new investments

CONVERGENT INVESTORS, LLC

111 Congress Avenue
Suite 3000
Austin, TX USA 78701
Phone: 512-472-2077
Fax: 512-472-9018
E-mail: info@convergentinvestors.com
Website: www.convergentinvestors.com

Other Offices

5251 Westheimer
Suite 800
Houston, TX USA 77056
Phone: 713-993-9310
Fax: 713-993-9335

Management and Staff

Brian Smith, Principal
Henry James, Principal
James Mansour, Principal
John Chaney, Principal
Robert Gauntt, Principal
Steve Shaper, Principal
Willard Hanzlik, Principal

Type of Firm

Private Equity Firm

Project Preferences

Type of Financing Preferred:

Early Stage

Geographical Preferences

United States Preferences:

Southwest

Industry Preferences

In Communications prefer:

Telecommunications

In Internet Specific prefer:

E-Commerce Technology

Additional Information

Name of Most Recent Fund: Convergent Investors VI, LP
Most Recent Fund Was Raised: 06/30/2000
Year Founded: 2000
Current Activity Level: Actively seeking new investments

CONVEXA CAPITAL AS

Ruselokkveien 6
Oslo, Norway N-0251
Phone: 47-23-118-550
Fax: 47-23-118-570
E-mail: post@convexa.com
Website: www.convexa.no

Management and Staff

Anne Young Syrrist, Partner
Bjorge Gretland, Managing Partner
J. Frode Vaksvik, Managing Partner
Lars Krogh, Partner
Nicolai Malling, Partner

Type of Firm

Private Equity Firm

Association Membership

Norwegian Venture Capital Association
European Private Equity and Venture Capital Assoc.

Project Preferences

Type of Financing Preferred:

Early Stage
Expansion
Balanced
Seed
First Stage Financing

Geographical Preferences

International Preferences:

Europe
Scandanavia/Nordic Region
Norway

Industry Preferences

In Communications prefer:

Telecommunications
Wireless Communications
Data Communications

In Computer Software prefer:

Software

In Industrial/Energy prefer:

Energy
Oil and Gas Exploration

Additional Information

Year Founded: 2000
Capital Under Management: $92,400,000

Current Activity Level: Actively seeking new investments

COOLEY GODWARD LLP

One Maritime Plaza
20th Floor
San Francisco, CA USA 94111
Phone: 415-693-2000
Fax: 415-951-3699
Website: www.cooley.com

Management and Staff

Eric Jensen, Partner
Gordon Atkinson, Partner
Joe Conroy, Partner
Mark Pitchford, Chief Operating Officer
Richard Climan, Partner
Stephen Neal, Chairman & CEO
Suzanne Hooper, Partner

Type of Firm

Service Provider

Additional Information

Year Founded: 1996
Current Activity Level: Actively seeking new investments

COOPFOND SPA

Via Guattani, 9
Rome, Italy 0061
Phone: 39-06-4424-9435
Fax: 39-06-4424-9659
Website: www.coopfond.it

Other Offices

Via Cairoli, 11
Bologna, Italy 40121
Phone: 39-051-5282-811
Fax: 39-051-5282-888

Type of Firm

Private Equity Firm

Additional Information

Year Founded: 2003
Current Activity Level: Actively seeking new investments

COPAN, INC

2000 University Avenue
Suite 610
Palo Alto, CA USA 94303
Phone: 650-838-1100
Fax: 650-838-9183
E-mail: info@copan.com
Website: www.copan.com

Other Offices

Maximilianstr. 45
Munich, Germany D-80538
Phone: 49-89-2126-780
Fax: 49-89-2126-7878

Kensington Square House
12-14 Ansdell Street
London, United Kingdom W8 5TR
Phone: 44-207-073-2667
Fax: 44-207-073-2690

Management and Staff

Christian Wedell, Partner

Type of Firm

Private Equity Firm

Project Preferences

Type of Financing Preferred:

Expansion
Balanced

Geographical Preferences

International Preferences:

Europe

Additional Information

Year Founded: 1998
Capital Under Management: $30,000,000
Current Activity Level: Actively seeking new investments

COPELEY CAPITAL PARTNERS

101 South Tryon Street
Suite 2410
Charlotte, NC USA 28280
Phone: 704-409-3070
Fax: 704-409-3075
Website: www.copeleycapital.com

Management and Staff

Lane Faison, Principal
William Lunsford, Principal

Type of Firm

Private Equity Firm

Project Preferences

Type of Financing Preferred:
Management Buyouts
Recapitalizations

Geographical Preferences

United States Preferences:
Mid Atlantic
Southeast

Additional Information

Year Founded: 2003
Capital Under Management: $20,000,000
Current Activity Level: Actively seeking new investments

COPERNICUS CAPITAL PARTNERS, LTD.

Saski Crescent
16 Krolewska Street
Warsaw, Poland 00-103
Phone: 48-22-330-6333
Fax: 48-22-330-6300
E-mail: warsaw@copernicus-capital.com
Website: www.copernicus-capital.com

Other Offices

Trg Nikole Subica Zrinskog 6
Zagreb, Croatia 10000
Phone: 385-1-487-7900
Fax: 385-1-487-7901

Smithfield House
92 North Street
Leeds, United Kingdom LS2 7PN
Phone: 44-113-222-3555
Fax: 44-113-222-3550

Francuska 5
Belgrade, Serbia and Montenegro 11000
Phone: 381-11-262-3100
Fax: 381-11-328-8661

26/1 Pictor Barbu Iscovescu Street
Bucharest, Romania 011937
Phone: 40-21-230-7485
Fax: 40-21-230-9331

Management and Staff

Hajdi Mostic, Managing Director
Janusz Skrzypkowsk, Managing Director
Keith Mellors, Managing Partner
Leslie Carver, Managing Director
Neil Milne, Managing Director
Pawel Gierynski, Managing Partner
Radoslaw Solan, Vice President

Type of Firm

Bank Affiliated

Association Membership

Polish Venture Capital Association (PSIC/PPEA)
European Private Equity and Venture Capital Assoc.

Project Preferences

Role in Financing:
Will function either as deal originator or investor in deals created by others

Type of Financing Preferred:
Leveraged Buyout
Early Stage
Expansion
Later Stage
Management Buyouts
Startup

Size of Investments Considered:
Min Size of Investment Considered (000s): $1,000
Max Size of Investment Considered (000s): $2,500

Geographical Preferences

International Preferences:
Central Europe
Poland
Eastern Europe

Industry Focus

(% based on actual investment)	
Internet Specific	42.5%
Computer Software and Services	27.2%
Other Products	18.0%
Consumer Related	12.2%

Additional Information

Year Founded: 1994
Capital Under Management: $3,000,000
Current Activity Level: Actively seeking new investments
Method of Compensation: Return on investment is of primary concern, do not charge fees

COPIA ASSOCIATES LLC

18 Crow Canyon Court
Suite 300
San Ramon, CA USA 94583
Website: www.copiainc.com

Management and Staff

Sudhir Aggarwal, Partner
Tom Liguori, Partner

Type of Firm

Private Equity Firm

Project Preferences

Type of Financing Preferred:
Expansion
Turnaround

Size of Investments Considered:
Min Size of Investment Considered (000s): $2,000
Max Size of Investment Considered (000s): $15,000

Geographical Preferences

United States Preferences:
All U.S.

Additional Information

Year Founded: 2006
Current Activity Level: Actively seeking new investments

COPPERMINE CAPITAL LLC

950 Winter Street
Suite 3200
Waltham, MA USA 02451
Phone: 781-684-0400
Fax: 781-684-0405
E-mail: info@copperminecapital.com
Website: www.copperminecapital.com

Management and Staff

Edward Honos, Managing Director
Grant Gund, Managing Partner
Zachary Gund, Managing Partner

Type of Firm

Private Equity Firm

Project Preferences

Type of Financing Preferred:
Leveraged Buyout
Management Buyouts
Acquisition
Recapitalizations

Size of Investments Considered:
Min Size of Investment Considered (000s): $2,000
Max Size of Investment Considered (000s): $8,000

Geographical Preferences

United States Preferences:
All U.S.

Canadian Preferences:
All Canada

Industry Preferences

In Business Serv. prefer:
Services

In Manufact. prefer:
Manufacturing

Additional Information

Year Founded: 2008
Current Activity Level: Actively seeking new investments

CORADIN, INC.

675, Saint Charles
Marieville, Canada J3M1B3
Phone: 514-658-0661
Fax: 514-658-9158

Management and Staff

Pierre Lizotte, Vice President

Type of Firm

Private Equity Firm

Additional Information

Year Founded: 1976
Current Activity Level: Actively seeking new investments

CORAL CAPITAL MANAGEMENT

60 South Sixth Street
Suite 3510
Minneapolis, MN USA 55402
Phone: 612-335-8698
Fax: 612-335-8668
Website: www.coralcm.com

Management and Staff

Linda Watchmaker, Managing Director & CFO
Mark Headrick, Managing Director
Steve Gordon, Managing Director
Todd Ortberg, Managing Director
Yuval Almog, Senior Managing Director

Type of Firm

Private Equity Firm

Project Preferences

Type of Financing Preferred:
Later Stage

Industry Preferences

In Communications prefer:
Communications and Media

In Computer Software prefer:
Software
Applications Software

Additional Information

Year Founded: 2002
Capital Under Management: $53,300,000
Current Activity Level: Actively seeking new investments

CORAL VENTURES

60 South Sixth Street
Suite 2210
Minneapolis, MN USA 55402
Phone: 612-335-8666
Fax: 612-335-8668
Website: www.coralventures.com

Other Offices

1001 Bayhill Drive
Suite 255
San Bruno, CA USA 94066
Phone: 650-616-4173

Management and Staff

Karen Boezi, General Partner
Linda Watchmaker, Chief Financial Officer
Peter McNerney, Managing Partner
Yuval Almog, Managing Partner

Type of Firm

Private Equity Firm

Project Preferences

Role in Financing:
Will function either as deal originator or investor in deals created by others

Type of Financing Preferred:
Second Stage Financing
Leveraged Buyout
Early Stage
Expansion
Mezzanine
Start-up Financing
Later Stage
Seed
First Stage Financing

Size of Investments Considered:
Min Size of Investment Considered (000s): $1,000
Max Size of Investment Considered (000s): $10,000

Geographical Preferences

Canadian Preferences:
All Canada

Industry Focus

(% based on actual investment)

Medical/Health	24.7%
Communications and Media	23.2%
Computer Software and Services	15.9%
Internet Specific	14.7%
Semiconductors/Other Elect.	8.3%
Biotechnology	5.6%
Computer Hardware	4.6%
Industrial/Energy	2.5%
Other Products	0.6%

Additional Information

Name of Most Recent Fund: Coral Partners V, L.P.
Most Recent Fund Was Raised: 03/18/1998
Year Founded: 1993
Capital Under Management: $253,100,000
Current Activity Level: Actively seeking new investments
Method of Compensation: Return on investment is of primary concern, do not charge fees

---

CORDIANT CAPITAL

1010 Sherbrooke Street West
Suite 2400
Montreal, Canada H3A 2R7
Phone: 514-286-1142
Fax: 514-286-4203
E-mail: info@cordiantcap.com
Website: www.cordiantcap.com

Type of Firm

Investment Management Firm

Association Membership

Emerging Markets Private Equity Association
Canadian Venture Capital Association
African Venture Capital Association (AVCA)

Project Preferences

Type of Financing Preferred:
Generalist PE
Balanced

Geographical Preferences

United States Preferences:
All U.S.

International Preferences:
Asia
Africa

Additional Information

Year Founded: 1999
Capital Under Management: $930,000,000
Current Activity Level: Actively seeking new investments

CORDOVA VENTURES (FKA:CORDOVA CAPITAL)

2500 North Winds Parkway
Suite 475
Alpharetta, GA USA 30004
Phone: 678-942-0300
Fax: 678-942-0301
Website: www.cordovaventures.com

Management and Staff

Chris Valianos, Partner
Frank Dalton, Partner
Gerald Schmidt, Managing Partner
L. Edward Wilson, Venture Partner
Paul DiBella, Partner

Type of Firm

Private Equity Firm

Association Membership

Natl Assoc of Small Bus. Inv. Co (NASBIC)

Project Preferences

Role in Financing:
Will function either as deal originator or investor in deals created by others

Type of Financing Preferred:
Expansion
Later Stage
Acquisition

Size of Investments Considered:
Min Size of Investment Considered (000s): $1,000
Max Size of Investment Considered (000s): $5,000

Industry Focus

(% based on actual investment)

Computer Software and Services	21.8%
Medical/Health	18.2%
Internet Specific	16.5%
Communications and Media	12.4%
Industrial/Energy	9.5%
Other Products	8.3%
Biotechnology	5.9%
Semiconductors/Other Elect.	4.3%
Consumer Related	3.1%

Additional Information

Name of Most Recent Fund: Cordova Intellimedia Ventures, LP (CIV)
Most Recent Fund Was Raised: 02/24/2000
Year Founded: 1989
Capital Under Management: $200,000,000
Current Activity Level: Actively seeking new investments
Method of Compensation: Return on invest. most important, but chg. closing fees, service fees, etc.

CORDOVA, SMART & WILLIAMS, LLC

845 Third Avenue
21st Floor
New York, NY USA 10022
Phone: 212-920-3700
Fax: 212-920-3710
E-mail: info@cswprivateequity.com
Website: www.cswprivateequity.com

Management and Staff

A. Jabbar Abdi, Principal
Carl Cordova, Managing Partner
Joli Cooper, Partner
Michael Smart, Managing Partner
Robert Holland, Partner
Tannis Fussell, Principal

Type of Firm

Private Equity Firm

Project Preferences

Type of Financing Preferred:
Leveraged Buyout
Later Stage
Recapitalizations

Size of Investments Considered:
Min Size of Investment Considered (000s): $10,000
Max Size of Investment Considered (000s): $20,000

Industry Preferences

In Consumer Related prefer:
Consumer Products
Consumer Services

In Business Serv. prefer:
Distribution

In Manufact. prefer:
Manufacturing

Additional Information

Year Founded: 2005
Current Activity Level: Actively seeking new investments

CORE CAPITAL PARTNERS

1401 I Street Northwest
Suite 1000
Washington, DC USA 20005
Phone: 202-589-0090
Fax: 202-589-0091
E-mail: info@core-capital.com
Website: www.core-capital.com

Management and Staff

Mark Levine, Managing Director
Pascal Luck, Managing Director
Randy Klueger, Chief Financial Officer
Thomas Wheeler, Managing Director
William Dunbar, Managing Director

Type of Firm

Private Equity Firm

Association Membership

Mid-Atlantic Venture Association
Natl Assoc of Small Bus. Inv. Co (NASBIC)
National Venture Capital Association - USA (NVCA)

Project Preferences

Role in Financing:
Prefer role as deal originator but will also invest in deals created by others

Type of Financing Preferred:
Second Stage Financing
Early Stage
Expansion
Balanced
Later Stage
First Stage Financing
Startup

Size of Investments Considered:
Min Size of Investment Considered (000s): $1,000
Max Size of Investment Considered (000s): $10,000

Geographical Preferences

United States Preferences:
Mid Atlantic
Southeast
Northeast
All U.S.
East Coast

Industry Preferences

In Communications prefer:
Communications and Media
Commercial Communications
Telecommunications

In Computer Software prefer:
Software

In Computer Other prefer:
Computer Related

In Semiconductor/Electr prefer:
Electronics
Optoelectronics

In Medical/Health prefer:
Medical Products
Health Services

In Consumer Related prefer:
Consumer Products

Additional Information

Name of Most Recent Fund: Core Capital Partners Fund II, L.P.
Most Recent Fund Was Raised: 12/28/2005
Year Founded: 1999
Capital Under Management: $370,000,000
Current Activity Level: Actively seeking new investments
Method of Compensation: Return on investment is of primary concern, do not charge fees

CORE GROWTH CAPITAL LLP

103 Baker Street
2nd Floor
London, United Kingdom W1U 6LN
Phone: 44-20-7317-0155
Fax: 44-20-7900-2316
E-mail: info@core-cap.com
Website: www.@core-cap.com

Management and Staff

Angad Paul, Partner
David Dancaster, Partner
Stephen Edwards, Partner
Walid Fakhry, Partner

Type of Firm

Private Equity Firm

Project Preferences

Type of Financing Preferred:
Leveraged Buyout
Later Stage
Management Buyouts

Size of Investments Considered:
Min Size of Investment Considered (000s): $3,793
Max Size of Investment Considered (000s): $9,482

Geographical Preferences

International Preferences:
United Kingdom
Europe

Additional Information

Year Founded: 2004
Capital Under Management: $27,200,000
Current Activity Level: Actively seeking new investments

CORE PARTNERS, INC.

120-Tenth Street North West
Suite 200
Calgary, Canada T2N1V3
Phone: 403-270-9772
Fax: 403-270-4594
Website: www.corepartners.ca

Management and Staff

Don Short, Partner
Jim Gibson, Partner
Ken Maclean, Partner
Kevin Weatherston, Partner
Martin Bunting, Partner
Neil Bowker, Partner
Rick Shannon, Partner

Type of Firm

Private Equity Firm

Project Preferences

Type of Financing Preferred:
Early Stage

Geographical Preferences

United States Preferences:
East Coast

Additional Information

Year Founded: 2009
Current Activity Level: Actively seeking new investments

CORECAP LIMITED

P.O. Box 66916
Dubai, Utd. Arab Em.
Phone: 971-4-391-0627
Fax: 971-4-390-4361
E-mail: info@cc-corecap.com
Website: www.cc-corecap.com

Other Offices

Liejyklos 8
Vilnius, Lithuania LT-01120
Phone: 370-5212-2176
Fax: 370-5263-9621

Management and Staff

Hatem Saad Hendawi, Chief Financial Officer
Omar Adel El Maghawry, Managing Director
Susan Gay, Vice President

Type of Firm

Private Equity Firm

Project Preferences

Type of Financing Preferred:
Leveraged Buyout
Balanced
Management Buyouts
Recapitalizations

Geographical Preferences

International Preferences:
Europe
Middle East
Africa

Additional Information

Year Founded: 2000
Current Activity Level: Actively seeking new investments

COREST AG

Inselstrasse 24
Dusseldorf, Germany 40479
Phone: 49-211-5136472
Fax: 49-211-5136449
E-mail: info@COREST.de
Website: www.corest.de

Type of Firm

Private Equity Firm

Project Preferences

Type of Financing Preferred:
Leveraged Buyout
Turnaround
Other
Special Situation
Recapitalizations

Geographical Preferences

International Preferences:
Germany

Industry Preferences

In Manufact. prefer:
Manufacturing

Additional Information

Year Founded: 2006
Current Activity Level: Actively seeking new investments

CORINTHIAN CAPITAL GROUP LLC

601 Lexington Avenue
59th Floor
New York, NY USA 10022
Phone: 212-920-2300
Fax: 212-920-2399
E-mail: contact@corinthiancap.com
Website: www.corinthiancap.com

Other Offices

70 West Madison Street
Suite 1400
Chicago, IL USA 60602
Phone: 312-899-9988
Fax: 312-899-9099

Management and Staff

C. Kenneth Clay, Senior Managing Director
James McNair, Senior Managing Director
Nora De la Serna, Chief Financial Officer
Peter Van Raalte, Senior Managing Director
Steven Kumble, Chairman & CEO
Tony Pucillo, Managing Director

Type of Firm

Private Equity Firm

Project Preferences

Role in Financing:
Prefer role as deal originator

Type of Financing Preferred:
Leveraged Buyout
Acquisition
Recapitalizations

Size of Investments Considered:
Min Size of Investment Considered (000s): $5,000
Max Size of Investment Considered (000s): $50,000

Geographical Preferences

United States Preferences:
Mid Atlantic
Northwest
Southeast
Hawaii
Southern California
Northern California
Rocky Mountain
Alaska

Industry Preferences

In Consumer Related prefer:
Consumer

In Business Serv. prefer:
Services
Distribution

In Manufact. prefer:
Manufacturing

Additional Information
Year Founded: 2005
Current Activity Level: Actively seeking new investments
Method of Compensation: Return on invest. most important, but chg. closing fees, service fees, etc.

CORIOLIS VENTURES LLC
218 East 63rd Street
Suite B
New York, NY USA 10055
E-mail: contact@coriolisventures.com
Website: www.coriolisventures.com

Management and Staff
William Jaris, Partner

Type of Firm
Private Equity Firm

Project Preferences

Type of Financing Preferred:
Early Stage
Seed

Industry Preferences

In Internet Specific prefer:
Internet

In Business Serv. prefer:
Media

Additional Information
Year Founded: 2008
Current Activity Level: Actively seeking new investments

CORNERSTONE ADVISORS, INC.
4725 North Scottsdale Road
Suite 250
Scottsdale, AZ USA 85251
Phone: 480-423-2030
Fax: 480-481-6076
Website: www.crnrstone.com

Management and Staff
Joseph Franzi, Managing Director

Type of Firm
Investment Management Firm

Project Preferences

Type of Financing Preferred:
Balanced

Additional Information
Year Founded: 1983
Capital Under Management: $1,700,000,000
Current Activity Level: Actively seeking new investments

CORNERSTONECAPITAL AG
Westendstrasse 41
Frankfurt am Main, Germany 60325
Phone: 49-6978-9047-0
Fax: 49-6978-904710
E-mail: equity@cornerstonecapital.de
Website: www.cornerstone-capital.de

Management and Staff
Pieter Van Halem, Managing Partner
Sascha Rangoonwala, Partner
Stephan Helmstadter, Managing Partner

Type of Firm
Private Equity Firm

Association Membership
European Private Equity and Venture Capital Assoc.

Project Preferences

Type of Financing Preferred:
Generalist PE
Public Companies
Management Buyouts

Size of Investments Considered:
Min Size of Investment Considered (000s): $2,685
Max Size of Investment Considered (000s): $67,132

Geographical Preferences

International Preferences:
Switzerland
Austria
Germany

Industry Preferences

In Computer Software prefer:
Software

In Medical/Health prefer:
Medical/Health

In Industrial/Energy prefer:
Industrial Products

In Business Serv. prefer:
Services

Additional Information
Year Founded: 2001
Capital Under Management: $41,300,000
Current Activity Level: Actively seeking new investments

CORNESTONE CAPITAL PARTNERS
555 Fifth Avenue
14th Floor
New York, NY USA 10017
Phone: 212-986-5470
Fax: 212-986-5316
Website: www.cornerstonecappartners.com

Management and Staff
Jerry Donatelli, Founding Partner
Norman Silberdick, Partner
Stephen Altman, Partner

Type of Firm
Private Equity Firm

Additional Information
Year Founded: 1990
Current Activity Level: Actively seeking new investments

CORNING INNOVATION VENTURES
Eight Denison Parkway
Corning, NY USA 14830
Phone: 607-936-4000
Fax: 607-936-4000
E-mail: civ@corning.com

Management and Staff
Eric Urruti, General Partner
Greg Smith, President
Jeff Jacobs, Principal
Myron Thomas, Chief Financial Officer

Type of Firm
Private Equity Firm

Project Preferences

Role in Financing:
Will function either as deal originator or investor in

deals created by others

Type of Financing Preferred:

Second Stage Financing
Early Stage
First Stage Financing

Size of Investments Considered:

Min Size of Investment Considered (000s): $300
Max Size of Investment Considered (000s): $15,000

Geographical Preferences

Canadian Preferences:

All Canada

Industry Preferences

In Communications prefer:

Commercial Communications
CATV & Pay TV Systems
Telecommunications
Wireless Communications
Data Communications
Other Communication Prod.

In Semiconductor/Electr prefer:

Laser Related
Fiber Optics
Optoelectronics

Additional Information

Name of Most Recent Fund: Corning Innovation Ventures
Most Recent Fund Was Raised: 09/30/2000
Year Founded: 2000
Capital Under Management: $120,000,000
Current Activity Level: Actively seeking new investments
Method of Compensation: Return on investment is of primary concern, do not charge fees

---

CORONIS MEDICAL VENTURES

1368 Bordeaux Drive
Sunnyvale, CA USA 94089
Phone: 925-314-9488
Fax: 925-888-8686
Website: www.coronismedical.com

Management and Staff

Carl Simpson, Venture Partner
Mark Klopp, Managing Director
Roger Stern, Managing Director
Wil Samson, Managing Director

Type of Firm

Private Equity Firm

Association Membership

National Venture Capital Association - USA (NVCA)

Project Preferences

Type of Financing Preferred:

Early Stage
Seed

Geographical Preferences

United States Preferences:

All U.S.

Additional Information

Year Founded: 2006
Capital Under Management: $10,000,000
Current Activity Level: Actively seeking new investments

CORPFIN CAPITAL ASESORES SA

Marques de Villamejor, 3
Madrid, Spain 28006
Phone: 34-91-781-2800
Fax: 34-91-577-8583
E-mail: contacto@corpfincapital.com
Website: www.corpfincapital.com

Management and Staff

Carlos Lavilla, Partner
Juan Cuesta, Partner
Patrick Gandarias, Partner

Type of Firm

Private Equity Firm

Association Membership

European Private Equity and Venture Capital Assoc.
Spanish Venture Capital Association (ASCRI)

Project Preferences

Role in Financing:

Prefer role as deal originator but will also invest in deals created by others

Type of Financing Preferred:

Leveraged Buyout
Expansion
Later Stage
Management Buyouts

Size of Investments Considered:

Min Size of Investment Considered (000s): $14,122
Max Size of Investment Considered (000s): $42,367

Geographical Preferences

International Preferences:

Europe
Spain

Industry Focus

(% based on actual investment)

Consumer Related	34.5%
Industrial/Energy	28.4%
Other Products	28.2%
Semiconductors/Other Elect.	8.8%

Additional Information

Name of Most Recent Fund: Corpfin Capital Fund III
Most Recent Fund Was Raised: 09/30/2006
Year Founded: 1990
Capital Under Management: $474,400,000
Current Activity Level: Actively seeking new investments
Method of Compensation: Return on invest. most important, but chg. closing fees, service fees, etc.

CORPORACION SANT BERNAT SA (AKA:CORSABE)

Balmes, 76
Barcelona, Spain 08007
Phone: 34-93-487-4007
Fax: 34-93-487-9684
E-mail: info@corsabe.es
Website: www.corsabe.com

Type of Firm

Private Equity Firm

Association Membership

Spanish Venture Capital Association (ASCRI)

Project Preferences

Type of Financing Preferred:

Second Stage Financing
Expansion

Geographical Preferences

International Preferences:

Europe
Spain

Industry Preferences

In Internet Specific prefer:

Internet

Additional Information

Year Founded: 1986
Current Activity Level: Actively seeking new investments

CORPORATE EQUITY PARTNERS AG

Obmoos 4
Zug, Switzerland 6301
Phone: 41-43-268-4649
Fax: 41-43-268-4643
Website: www.corporate-equity.com

Type of Firm

Private Equity Firm

Additional Information

Year Founded: 2006
Current Activity Level: Actively seeking new investments

CORPORATE FUEL PARTNERS

119 Fifth Avenue
Seventh Floor
New York, NY USA 10003
Phone: 212-260-2743
Fax: 212-260-2748
E-mail: info@corporatefuelpartners.com
Website: www.corporatefuelpartners.com

Management and Staff

Alan Breitman, Managing Director
Cathleen Cote, Vice President
Charles Lachman, Partner
George Hansen, Partner
John Simons, Partner
Kevin Bodnar, Managing Director
Russ Fein, Managing Director
Samuel Ticknor, Vice President

Type of Firm

Bank Affiliated

Project Preferences

Role in Financing:
Prefer role as deal originator

Type of Financing Preferred:
Leveraged Buyout
Expansion
Balanced
Management Buyouts
Acquisition
Recapitalizations

Size of Investments Considered:
Min Size of Investment Considered (000s): $2,000
Max Size of Investment Considered (000s): $5,000

Geographical Preferences

United States Preferences:
New Hampshire
Rhode Island
Vermont
Massachusetts
Connecticut
New York
Maine

Additional Information

Year Founded: 2005
Capital Under Management: $25,000,000
Current Activity Level: Actively seeking new investments
Method of Compensation: Return on invest. most important, but chg. closing fees, service fees, etc.

CORPORATE GROWTH ASSISTANCE, LTD.

19 York Ridge Road
North York, Canada M2P 1R8
Phone: 416-222-7772
Fax: 416-222-6091

Management and Staff

Millard Roth, President

Type of Firm

Bank Affiliated

Project Preferences

Role in Financing:
Prefer role as deal originator but will also invest in deals created by others

Type of Financing Preferred:
Second Stage Financing
Leveraged Buyout
Mezzanine
Recapitalizations

Size of Investments Considered:
Min Size of Investment Considered (000s): $1,000
Max Size of Investment Considered: No Limit

Geographical Preferences

United States Preferences:
Midwest
Northwest

Canadian Preferences:
Ontario
Western Canada

Industry Preferences

In Communications prefer:
CATV & Pay TV Systems
Data Communications
Other Communication Prod.

In Computer Software prefer:
Computer Services
Applications Software

In Semiconductor/Electr prefer:
Component Testing Equipmt

In Medical/Health prefer:
Disposable Med. Products
Hospital/Other Instit.
Pharmaceuticals

In Consumer Related prefer:
Food/Beverage
Consumer Products
Consumer Services

In Industrial/Energy prefer:
Energy Conservation Relat
Industrial Products
Materials
Machinery

In Manufact. prefer:
Publishing

Additional Information

Year Founded: 1967
Current Activity Level: Actively seeking new investments
Method of Compensation: Return on invest. most important, but chg. closing fees, service fees, etc.

CORRIDOR CAPITAL, LLC

11611 San Vicente Boulevard
Suite 800
Los Angeles, CA USA 90049
Phone: 310-442-7000
Fax: 310-442-7010
E-mail: investments@corridorcap.com
Website: www.corridorcap.com

Management and Staff

Carolyn Enenstein, Partner
Craig Enenstein, Chief Executive Officer
Edward Monnier, Principal

Type of Firm

Private Equity Firm

Project Preferences

Type of Financing Preferred:
Leveraged Buyout
Balanced
Later Stage

Size of Investments Considered:
Min Size of Investment Considered (000s): $3,000
Max Size of Investment Considered (000s): $15,000

Geographical Preferences

United States Preferences:
All U.S.

Industry Preferences

In Consumer Related prefer:
Consumer

In Financial Services prefer:
Financial Services

In Business Serv. prefer:
Services

In Manufact. prefer:
Manufacturing

Additional Information

Year Founded: 2005
Current Activity Level: Actively seeking new investments

CORRIDOR MANAGEMENT COMPANY LLC

222 Third Avenue Southeast
Suite 12
Cedar Rapids, IA USA 52406
Phone: 319-364-4411
Fax: 319-364-4422

Type of Firm

Private Equity Firm

Project Preferences

Type of Financing Preferred:
Leveraged Buyout
Early Stage
Expansion
Later Stage

Size of Investments Considered:
Min Size of Investment Considered (000s): $100
Max Size of Investment Considered (000s): $500

Geographical Preferences

United States Preferences:
Iowa

Industry Preferences

In Computer Software prefer:
Software

In Biotechnology prefer:
Biotechnology

Additional Information

Year Founded: 2006
Capital Under Management: $6,900,000
Current Activity Level: Actively seeking new investments

CORSAIR CAPITAL LLC

717 Fifth Avenue
24th Floor
New York, NY USA 10022
Phone: 212-224-9400
Fax: 212-224-9445
E-mail: corsair@corsairinvestments.com
Website: www.corsairinvestments.com

Management and Staff

Amy Soeda, Chief Financial Officer
Clifford Brokaw, Managing Director
D.T. Ignacio Jayanti, President
Derrick Estes, Vice President
Hari Rajan, Principal
James Kirk, Vice President
Jeremy Schein, Principal
Michael Poe, Principal

Type of Firm

Private Equity Firm

Project Preferences

Type of Financing Preferred:
Leveraged Buyout
Generalist PE
Acquisition

Geographical Preferences

International Preferences:
All International

Industry Preferences

In Financial Services prefer:
Financial Services

Additional Information

Year Founded: 1999
Capital Under Management: $1,003,000,000
Current Activity Level: Actively seeking new investments

CORSTONE CORPORATION

7361 Calhoun Place
Suite 510
Rockville, MD USA 20855
Phone: 866-367-2100
Fax: 240-238-5017
E-mail: info@corstone.com
Website: www.corstone.com

Type of Firm

Bank Affiliated

Project Preferences

Type of Financing Preferred:
Early Stage

Size of Investments Considered:
Min Size of Investment Considered (000s): $3,000
Max Size of Investment Considered (000s): $7,000

Geographical Preferences

International Preferences:
China

Additional Information

Year Founded: 1991
Capital Under Management: $100,000,000
Current Activity Level: Actively seeking new investments

CORTEC GROUP, INC.

200 Park Avenue
20th Floor
New York, NY USA 10166
Phone: 212-370-5600
Fax: 212-682-4195
Website: www.cortecgroup.com

Management and Staff

Bruce Taylor, Senior Managing Director
David Schnadig, Partner
Jared Friedberg, Vice President
Jeffrey Lipsitz, Managing Director
Jonathan Stein, Managing Director
Neal Kayes, Partner
R. Scott Schafler, President
Richard Fishbein, Partner

Type of Firm

Private Equity Firm

Project Preferences

Type of Financing Preferred:
Leveraged Buyout
Acquisition
Recapitalizations

Geographical Preferences

United States Preferences:
All U.S.

Industry Focus

(% based on actual investment)	
Other Products	55.3%
Consumer Related	36.9%
Semiconductors/Other Elect.	3.2%
Biotechnology	3.2%
Industrial/Energy	1.4%

Additional Information

Name of Most Recent Fund: Cortec Group Fund III
Most Recent Fund Was Raised: 03/09/2000
Year Founded: 1984
Capital Under Management: $560,000,000
Current Activity Level: Actively seeking new investments

CORVINUS INTERNATIONAL INVESTMENT RT

Nagymezo utca 46-48
Budapest, Hungary 1065
Phone: 36-1-354-3000
Fax: 36-1-354-3001
E-mail: info@corvinus.hu
Website: www.corvinus.hu

Management and Staff

Akos Benke, Chief Executive Officer

Type of Firm

Incubator/Development Program

Association Membership

European Private Equity and Venture Capital Assoc.

Project Preferences

Type of Financing Preferred:
Expansion

Geographical Preferences

International Preferences:
Central Europe
Eastern Europe

Additional Information
Year Founded: 1997
Capital Under Management: $5,300,000
Current Activity Level: Actively seeking new investments

COSTELLA KIRSCH, INC.

873 Santa Cruz Avenue
Suite 207
Menlo Park, CA USA 94025
Phone: 650-462-1888
Fax: 650-462-1891
E-mail: info@costellakirsch.com
Website: www.costellakirsch.com

Other Offices
14395 Saratoga Avenue
Suite 140
Saratoga, CA USA 95070
Phone: 408-867-9021

Management and Staff
Bill Kirsch, Managing Partner
Dave Campbell, Principal

Type of Firm
Service Provider

Project Preferences

Role in Financing:
Prefer role as deal originator but will also invest in deals created by others

Type of Financing Preferred:
Second Stage Financing
Early Stage
Seed
First Stage Financing
Startup

Size of Investments Considered:
Min Size of Investment Considered (000s): $750
Max Size of Investment Considered (000s): $4,000

Geographical Preferences

United States Preferences:
Northwest

Industry Preferences

In Communications prefer:
Telecommunications
Wireless Communications
Data Communications

In Computer Software prefer:
Software

In Internet Specific prefer:
Ecommerce

In Semiconductor/Electr prefer:
Semiconductor
Circuit Boards
Laser Related
Fiber Optics

In Biotechnology prefer:
Biotech Related Research

In Medical/Health prefer:
Medical Products
Pharmaceuticals

Additional Information
Year Founded: 1986
Capital Under Management: $128,000,000
Current Activity Level: Actively seeking new investments
Method of Compensation: Return on invest. most important, but chg. closing fees, service fees, etc.

COUNCIL VENTURES

150 Second Avenue North
Suite 415
Nashville, TN USA 37201
Phone: 615-255-3707
Fax: 615-255-3709
E-mail: info@councilventures.com
Website: www.councilventures.com

Management and Staff
Dennis Bottorff, General Partner
Gary Peat, General Partner
Grant Jackson, General Partner
Jennifer Bottorff, Partner
Katie Gamball, Chief Executive Officer

Type of Firm
Private Equity Firm

Project Preferences

Role in Financing:
Will function either as deal originator or investor in deals created by others

Type of Financing Preferred:
Early Stage
Expansion

Size of Investments Considered:
Min Size of Investment Considered (000s): $2,000
Max Size of Investment Considered (000s): $5,000

Geographical Preferences

United States Preferences:
Southeast

Canadian Preferences:
All Canada

Industry Preferences

In Communications prefer:
Telecommunications
Wireless Communications
Data Communications

In Computer Hardware prefer:
Mainframes / Scientific
Mini and Personal/Desktop
Computer Graphics and Dig
Integrated Turnkey System
Terminals
Disk Relat. Memory Device

In Computer Software prefer:
Software
Systems Software
Applications Software
Artificial Intelligence

In Internet Specific prefer:
Internet
Ecommerce

In Semiconductor/Electr prefer:
Electronic Components
Semiconductor
Micro-Processing
Controllers and Sensors
Sensors
Circuit Boards
Component Testing Equipmt
Laser Related
Fiber Optics

In Medical/Health prefer:
Diagnostic Test Products
Medical Products
Disposable Med. Products

In Consumer Related prefer:
Retail
Hotels and Resorts

In Industrial/Energy prefer:
Industrial Products

In Transportation prefer:
Aerospace

In Financial Services prefer:
Financial Services
Insurance

In Business Serv. prefer:
Media

Additional Information
Name of Most Recent Fund: Council Ventures II, L.P.
Most Recent Fund Was Raised: 03/14/2008
Year Founded: 2000
Capital Under Management: $52,000,000
Current Activity Level: Actively seeking new investments
Method of Compensation: Return on investment is of primary concern, do not charge fees

COURT SQUARE CAPITAL PARTNERS

Park Avenue Plaza
55 East 52nd Street, 34th Fl.
New York, NY USA 10055
Phone: 212-752-6110
Fax: 212-752-6184
Website: www.courtsquare.com

Management and Staff

Andrew Gesell, Partner
Anthony Mirra, Chief Financial Officer
Christopher Bloise, Principal
Christopher Hojlo, Partner
David Thomas, Managing Partner
David Nguyen, Vice President
Ian Highet, Managing Partner
James Urry, Partner
Jeffrey Vogel, Vice President
John Civantos, Partner
John Kim, Partner
John Overbay, Vice President
John Weber, Managing Partner
Joseph Silvestri, Managing Partner
Kevin Brown, Principal
Kurt Hilzinger, Partner
Michael Delaney, Managing Partner
Michael Finley, Partner
Michael Gollner, Partner
Thomas McWilliams, Managing Partner
William Comfort, Managing Partner

Type of Firm

Private Equity Firm

Project Preferences

Type of Financing Preferred:
Leveraged Buyout

Geographical Preferences

United States Preferences:
All U.S.

Additional Information

Name of Most Recent Fund: Court Square Capital Partners (Executive) II, L.P.
Most Recent Fund Was Raised: 06/29/2007
Year Founded: 2002
Capital Under Management: $6,494,300,000
Current Activity Level: Actively seeking new investments

COURT SQUARE VENTURES, LLC

Zero Court Square
Charlottesville, VA USA 22903
Phone: 434-817-3300
Fax: 434-817-3299
E-mail: info@courtsquareventures.com
Website: www.courtsquareventures.com

Management and Staff

Christopher Holden, Managing Partner
James Murray, Managing General Partner
W.Randy Castleman, Managing Partner

Type of Firm

Private Equity Firm

Association Membership

Mid-Atlantic Venture Association

Project Preferences

Role in Financing:
Prefer role as deal originator but will also invest in deals created by others

Type of Financing Preferred:
Early Stage
Expansion
Seed
First Stage Financing
Startup

Size of Investments Considered:
Min Size of Investment Considered (000s): $500
Max Size of Investment Considered (000s): $20,000

Geographical Preferences

United States Preferences:
All U.S.

Industry Preferences

In Communications prefer:
Commercial Communications
CATV & Pay TV Systems
Radio & TV Broadcasting
Telecommunications
Wireless Communications
Data Communications
Satellite Microwave Comm.

In Computer Hardware prefer:
Disk Relat. Memory Device

In Computer Software prefer:
Computer Services
Software
Systems Software
Applications Software

In Internet Specific prefer:
Internet
Web Aggregration/Portals

In Semiconductor/Electr prefer:
Electronic Components
Semiconductor
Micro-Processing
Controllers and Sensors
Sensors
Circuit Boards
Component Testing Equipmt
Laser Related
Fiber Optics
Analytic/Scientific

Additional Information

Name of Most Recent Fund: Court Square Ventures-E, L.P.
Most Recent Fund Was Raised: 08/15/2006
Year Founded: 2001
Capital Under Management: $118,000,000
Current Activity Level: Actively seeking new investments
Method of Compensation: Return on investment is of primary concern, do not charge fees

COVENT INDUSTRIAL CAPITAL INVESTMENT CO., LTD.

H-1122 Budapest
Maros u. 27
Budapest, Hungary 1122
Phone: 36-1-355-2493
Fax: 36-1-202-2381
E-mail: mail@covent.hu
Website: www.covent.hu

Management and Staff

Janos Bolyky, Chief Executive Officer

Type of Firm

Private Equity Firm

Association Membership

Hungarian Venture Capital Association (HVCA)

Project Preferences

Role in Financing:
Prefer role as deal originator but will also invest in deals created by others

Type of Financing Preferred:
Expansion
Turnaround
Startup

Geographical Preferences

International Preferences:
Hungary
Sweden
Scandanavia/Nordic Region

Industry Preferences

In Financial Services prefer:
Real Estate

In Business Serv. prefer:
Consulting Services

Additional Information

Year Founded: 1993
Capital Under Management: $7,900,000
Current Activity Level: Actively seeking new investments

COVESTIA CAPITAL PARTNERS

60 South Sixth Street
Suite 3720
Minneapolis, MN USA 55402
Phone: 612-333-0130
Fax: 612-333-0122
Website: www.covestia.com

Other Offices

280 Park Avenue
22nd Floor
New York, NY USA 10017
Phone: 212-883-0130

11111 Santa Monica Boulevard
Suite 1620
West Los Angeles, CA USA 90025
Phone: 310-444-0130
Fax: 310-444-6393

Management and Staff

Jim D Aquila, Managing Director
Randy Bort, Managing Director

Type of Firm

Bank Affiliated

Project Preferences

Type of Financing Preferred:
Leveraged Buyout
Expansion
Recapitalizations

Industry Preferences

In Medical/Health prefer:
Medical Products
Health Services

In Consumer Related prefer:
Retail

In Business Serv. prefer:
Services

In Manufact. prefer:
Manufacturing

Additional Information

Year Founded: 2008
Capital Under Management: $30,000,000
Current Activity Level: Actively seeking new investments

COVINGTON CAPITAL CORPORATION (FKA: C.I. COVINGTON FUND)

200 Front St W
Suite 3003, PO Box 10
Toronto, Canada M5V 3K2
Phone: 416-365-0060
Fax: 416-365-9822
Website: www.covingtoncap.com

Management and Staff

Chip Vallis, Managing Partner
Grant Brown, Managing Partner

Type of Firm

Private Equity Firm

Project Preferences

Type of Financing Preferred:
Early Stage
Expansion
Balanced
Later Stage

Size of Investments Considered:
Min Size of Investment Considered (000s): $1,000
Max Size of Investment Considered (000s): $15,000

Geographical Preferences

Canadian Preferences:
All Canada
Ontario

Industry Preferences

In Communications prefer:
Wireless Communications

In Internet Specific prefer:
Internet

In Consumer Related prefer:
Consumer

Additional Information

Year Founded: 1998
Current Activity Level: Actively seeking new investments

COWEN CAPITAL PARTNERS LLC (FKA: SG CAPITAL PARTNERS LLC)

1221 Avenue of the Americas
14th Floor
New York, NY USA 10020
Phone: 646-562-1189
Fax: 646-562-1132
E-mail: CowenCapitalPartners@cowen.com
Website: www.cowencapitalpartners.com

Other Offices

181 West Madison Street
Chicago, IL USA 60602
Phone: 312-578-5000
Fax: 312-578-5099

3200 Cherry Creek South Drive
Suite 280
Denver, CO USA 80209
Phone: 303-282-3100
Fax: 303-778-7340

118, Rue du Rhone
Geneva, Switzerland 1204
Phone: 41-22-707-6900
Fax: 41-22-707-6999

Tour Societe Generale
17 Cours Valmy
Paris la Defense , France
Phone: 331-4213-5500
Fax: 331-4244-1745

100 Yonge Street
Suite 1002
Toronto, Canada M5C 2W1
Phone: 416-362-2229
Fax: 416-362-5373

Talstrasse 20
Zurich , Switzerland 8001
Phone: 411-225-2040
Fax: 411-225-2040
Exchange House
Primrose Street
London, United Kingdom EC2A 2DD
Phone: 44-207-762-4444
Fax: 44-207-762-5578

Four Embarcadero Center
Suite 1200
San Francisco, CA USA 94111
Phone: 415-646-7200
Fax: 415-646-7455

Trammel Crow Center
2001 Ross Avenue, 49th Floor
Dallas, TX USA 75201
Phone: 214-979-2735
Fax: 214-979-2795

Two International Place
Boston, MA USA 02110
Phone: 617-946-3700
Fax: 617-946-3758

20006 Detroit Road
Suite 100
Cleveland, OH USA 44116
Phone: 440-331-3631
Fax: 440-331-7237

Management and Staff

Sengal Selassie, Managing Director

Type of Firm

Bank Affiliated

Project Preferences

Role in Financing:
Prefer role in deals created by others

Type of Financing Preferred:
Leveraged Buyout
Generalist PE
Later Stage
Management Buyouts

Geographical Preferences

United States Preferences:
All U.S.

Industry Focus

(% based on actual investment)	
Medical/Health	25.2%
Internet Specific	20.3%
Computer Software and Services	20.0%
Semiconductors/Other Elect.	18.5%
Communications and Media	9.1%
Computer Hardware	3.0%
Other Products	2.6%
Biotechnology	1.4%

Additional Information

Name of Most Recent Fund: SG Mechant Banking Fund (FKA: SG Capital Partners LLC)
Most Recent Fund Was Raised: 08/01/1998
Year Founded: 1983
Capital Under Management: $500,000,000
Current Activity Level: Actively seeking new investments
Method of Compensation: Return on investment is of primary concern, do not charge fees

CPP INVESTMENT BOARD

One Queen Street East
Suite 2600, P.O. Box 101
Toronto, Canada M5C2W5
Phone: 416-868-4075
Fax: 416-868-8689
E-mail: csr@cppib.ca
Website: www.cppib.ca

Management and Staff

Alaine Carrier, Managing Director
Andre Bourbonnais, Vice President
Erik Levy, Principal
John Breen, Vice President
Robert Grossi, Principal
Ryan Selwood, Principal
Scott Taylor, Principal

Type of Firm

Endowment, Foundation or Pension Fund

Additional Information

Year Founded: 1996

Current Activity Level: Actively seeking new investments

CRATON EQUITY PARTNERS (FKA:PALADIN PRIVATE EQUITY PARTNERS)

10880 Wilshire Boulevard
Suite 1400
Westwood, CA USA 90024
Phone: 310-996-8759
Fax: 310-996-8757
Website: www.cratonep.com

Other Offices

310 South Street
Morristown, NJ USA 07960

Management and Staff

Michael Lenard, Partner
Robert McDonald, Managing Partner
Tom Soto, Managing Partner

Type of Firm

Private Equity Firm

Project Preferences

Type of Financing Preferred:
Balanced

Geographical Preferences

United States Preferences:
All U.S.

Industry Preferences

In Industrial/Energy prefer:
Energy
Alternative Energy

In Manufact. prefer:
Manufacturing

Additional Information

Year Founded: 2005
Capital Under Management: $82,500,000
Current Activity Level: Actively seeking new investments

CREADEV

50 bd du General de Gaulle
Roubaix, France 59100
Website: www.creadev.fr

Management and Staff

Jerome Mulliez, President

Type of Firm

Private Equity Firm

Association Membership

French Venture Capital Association (AFIC)

Additional Information

Year Founded: 2002
Current Activity Level: Actively seeking new investments

CREAFUND MANAGEMENT NV

Kapitein Maenhoutstraat 77B
Sint-Martens-Latem, Belgium 9830
Phone: 32-9-272-6200
Fax: 32-9-272-6209
E-mail: info@creafund.be
Website: www.creafund.be

Type of Firm

Private Equity Firm

Association Membership

Belgium Venturing Association
European Private Equity and Venture Capital Assoc.

Project Preferences

Type of Financing Preferred:
Fund of Funds
Early Stage
Later Stage
Seed
Startup

Size of Investments Considered:
Min Size of Investment Considered (000s): $220
Max Size of Investment Considered (000s): $4,404

Geographical Preferences

International Preferences:
Belgium

Industry Preferences

In Communications prefer:
Telecommunications

In Computer Software prefer:
Software

In Biotechnology prefer:
Biotechnology

In Transportation prefer:
Transportation

In Business Serv. prefer:
Media

In Manufact. prefer:
Manufacturing

Additional Information

Year Founded: 1997
Capital Under Management: $34,400,000
Current Activity Level: Actively seeking new investments

CREANDUM KB

Jakobsbergsgatan 18
11th Floor
Stockholm, Sweden 111 40
Phone: 46-8-5246-3630
Fax: 46-8-221-175
E-mail: info@creandum.com
Website: www.creandum.com

Management and Staff

Asa Lindercrona, Chief Financial Officer
Daniel Blomquist, Principal
Fredrik Cassel, Partner
Martin Hauge, General Partner

Staffan Helgesson, Managing General Partner
Stefan Lindeberg, General Partner

Type of Firm
Bank Affiliated

Project Preferences
Type of Financing Preferred:
Early Stage

Geographical Preferences
International Preferences:
Europe
Scandanavia/Nordic Region

Industry Preferences
In Internet Specific prefer:
Internet

In Computer Other prefer:
Computer Related

In Semiconductor/Electr prefer:
Semiconductor

Additional Information
Name of Most Recent Fund: Creandum KB
Most Recent Fund Was Raised: 03/25/2003
Year Founded: 2002
Capital Under Management: $35,300,000
Current Activity Level: Actively seeking new investments

CREATE PARTNERS LTD
Victory House, Vision Park
Histon
Cambridge, United Kingdom CB24 9ZR
Phone: 44-1223-202-876
Fax: 44-1223-484-511
E-mail: enquiries@createpartners.com
Website: www.createpartners.com

Management and Staff
Boyd Mulvey, Chief Executive Officer

Type of Firm
Private Equity Firm

Association Membership
British Venture Capital Association (BVCA)

Project Preferences
Type of Financing Preferred:
Early Stage

Geographical Preferences
International Preferences:
United Kingdom
Europe

Industry Preferences
In Computer Software prefer:
Software

Additional Information
Name of Most Recent Fund: Create East of England Fund
Most Recent Fund Was Raised: 08/11/2003
Year Founded: 2003
Capital Under Management: $32,100,000
Current Activity Level: Actively seeking new investments

CREATHOR VENTURE GMBH
Marienbader Platz 1
Bad Homburg, Germany 61348
Phone: 49-6172-139-720
Fax: 49-6172-1397229
E-mail: creathor@creathor.de
Website: www.creathor.de

Management and Staff
Gert Koehler, Chief Executive Officer
Ingo Franz, Partner
Karlheinz Schmelig, Partner

Type of Firm
Private Equity Firm

Project Preferences
Type of Financing Preferred:
Early Stage

Geographical Preferences
International Preferences:
Switzerland
Germany
All International
France

Industry Preferences
In Communications prefer:
Communications and Media

In Computer Other prefer:
Computer Related

In Semiconductor/Electr prefer:
Electronics

In Biotechnology prefer:
Biotechnology

In Medical/Health prefer:
Medical/Health

In Industrial/Energy prefer:
Energy
Industrial Products
Materials

Additional Information
Year Founded: 2005
Capital Under Management: $78,200,000
Current Activity Level: Actively seeking new investments

CREATION CAPITAL LLC
630 Fifth Avenue
Suite 2000
New York, NY USA 10111
Phone: 212-332-1618
Fax: 212-332-1626
Website: www.creationcapital.com

Management and Staff
Gregg Honigblum, Chief Executive Officer
Michael Morris, President

Type of Firm
Bank Affiliated

Project Preferences
Type of Financing Preferred:
Early Stage
Expansion
Later Stage

Geographical Preferences
United States Preferences:
All U.S.

Industry Preferences
In Biotechnology prefer:
Biotechnology

Additional Information
Year Founded: 2000
Current Activity Level: Actively seeking new investments

CREATIVE INDUSTRIES MANAGEMENT OY (CIM)
Fabianinkatu Four b
Helsinki, Finland 00130
Phone: 358-9-681-2350
Fax: 358-9-692-2631
E-mail: cim@cimfunds.com
Website: www.cimfunds.com

Management and Staff
Heikki Masalin, Managing Director

Type of Firm
Private Equity Firm

Project Preferences
Type of Financing Preferred:
Early Stage
Expansion

Geographical Preferences

International Preferences:
Europe

Industry Preferences

In Communications prefer:
Radio & TV Broadcasting
Wireless Communications

In Internet Specific prefer:
Internet

In Consumer Related prefer:
Entertainment and Leisure

In Business Serv. prefer:
Media

Additional Information

Year Founded: 2001
Capital Under Management: $27,800,000
Current Activity Level: Actively seeking new investments

CREDELITY CAPITAL

Linnegatan 18
Box 5352
Stockholm, Sweden 102 49
Phone: 46-8-663-2160
Fax: 46-8-663-3631
E-mail: inof@credelity.se
Website: www.credelity.se

Type of Firm

Private Equity Firm

Project Preferences

Type of Financing Preferred:
Leveraged Buyout
Expansion

Geographical Preferences

International Preferences:
Scandanavia/Nordic Region

Additional Information

Year Founded: 2004
Current Activity Level: Actively seeking new investments

CREDEM VENTURE CAPITAL

Via Che Guevara, 4
Reggio Emilia, Italy 42100
Phone: 39-522-323-123
Fax: 39-522-582-087
Website: www.credempriveq.it

Type of Firm

Private Equity Firm

Project Preferences

Type of Financing Preferred:
Balanced

Geographical Preferences

International Preferences:
Italy

Additional Information

Year Founded: 2006
Current Activity Level: Actively seeking new investments

CREDIT AGRICOLE PRIVATE EQUITY SA (FKA: CREDIT LYONNAIS PE)

100 Boulevard du Montparnasse
Paris Cedex 14, France 75682
Phone: 33-1-4323-2121
Fax: 33-1-5844-5109
E-mail: cape.contact@ca-privateequity.fr
Website: www.ca-privateequity.com

Type of Firm

Bank Affiliated

Association Membership

French Venture Capital Association (AFIC)
European Private Equity and Venture Capital Assoc.

Project Preferences

Type of Financing Preferred:
Fund of Funds
Leveraged Buyout
Early Stage
Expansion
Mezzanine
Generalist PE
Balanced
Other
Startup
Special Situation
Fund of Funds of Second

Size of Investments Considered:
Min Size of Investment Considered (000s): $1,372
Max Size of Investment Considered (000s): $68,595

Geographical Preferences

United States Preferences:
Alaska

International Preferences:
Europe
Eastern Europe
France

Industry Focus

(% based on actual investment)

Industrial/Energy	21.1%
Biotechnology	17.6%
Other Products	15.2%
Medical/Health	11.7%
Computer Software and Services	10.7%
Internet Specific	8.7%
Computer Hardware	4.7%
Semiconductors/Other Elect.	4.4%
Consumer Related	3.2%
Communications and Media	2.7%

Additional Information

Year Founded: 2000
Capital Under Management: $586,400,000
Current Activity Level: Actively seeking new investments

CREDIT SUISSE ASSET MANAGEMENT

355 Madison Avenue
New York, NY USA 10017
Phone: 800-401-2230
Fax: 212-355-2099
Website: www.credit-suisse.com

Other Offices

Giesshuebelstrasse 40
PO Box 800
Zurich, Switzerland 8070
Phone: 41-1-333-42-45
Fax: 41-1-333-41-98

Management and Staff

Jack DiMaio, Chief Executive Officer
Keith Schappert, Managing Director

Type of Firm

Bank Affiliated

Additional Information

Year Founded: 1992
Current Activity Level: Actively seeking new investments

CREDIT SUISSE FIRST BOSTON DVTM, BRASIL

Avenida Brig. Faria Lima, 3064
Suite 13
Sao Paulo, SP, Brazil
Phone: 5511-3841-6331
Fax: 5511-3841-6949

Type of Firm

Bank Affiliated

Project Preferences

Type of Financing Preferred:
Leveraged Buyout

Geographical Preferences

International Preferences:
Brazil

Additional Information

Year Founded: 1995
Current Activity Level: Actively seeking new investments

CREDIT SUISSE PRIVATE EQUITY (FKA: CSFB PRIVATE EQUITY)

Eleven Madison Avenue
New York, NY USA 10010
Phone: 212-325-2000
Fax: 212-325-6665
Website: www.credit-suisse.com

Other Offices

Campos Eliseos # 345
Piso 9
Chapultepec Polanco, Mexico 11560
Phone: 52-5-5283-8900
Fax: 52-5-5283-8930

1250 Rene Levesque Boulevard West
Suite 3935
Montreal , Canada H3B 4W8
Phone: 514-933-8774
Fax: 514-933-7699

2400 Hanover Street
Palo Alto, CA USA 94304
Phone: 650-614-5000
Fax: 650-614-5030

34 Chervonoarmiyska Street
Kiev, Ukraine 252004
Phone: 380-44-247-1900
Fax: 380-44-247-5790
One Raffles Link
Number 05-02
Singapore, Singapore 039393
Phone: 65-6212-6000
Fax: 65-6212-6200
Paradeplatz 8
Zurich, Switzerland 8070
Phone: 41-44-212-1616
Fax: 41-44-333-2587

21 Boulevard de la Madeleine
Cedex 01
Paris, France 75001
Phone: 33-1-40-76-8888
Fax: 33-1-42-56-1082

Izumi Garden Tower
6-1, Roppongi 1-Chome, Minato-ku
Tokyo, Japan 106-6024
Phone: 81-3-4550-9000
Fax: 81-3-4550-9800

Karntner Ring 11-13
Wien, Austria A-1010
Phone: 43-1-512-3023
Fax: 43-1-512-3023-23

5/39 Free Press House, 3rd Floor
215 Free Press Journal Marg, Nariman Pt.
Mumbai, India 400 021
Phone: 91-22-230-6333
Fax: 91-22-285-1949

Three Exchange Square, 22nd Floor
8 Connaught Place
Central, Hong Kong
Phone: 852-2101-6000
Fax: 852-2101-7990

5 Nikitsky Pereulok
Moscow, Russia 103 009
Phone: 7-501-967-8200
Fax: 7-501-967-8210

6th Floor, Union Enterprise Plaza
No. 109, Section 3, Min Sheng East Road
Taipei, Taiwan
Phone: 886-2-2715-6388
Fax: 886-2-2718-8934

Via Principe Amedeo 2
Milano, Italy 20121
Phone: 39-02-7702-1
Fax: 39-02-7702-2216

101 Collins Street
27th Floor
Melbourne, Victoria , Australia 3000
Phone: 61-3-9280-1666
Fax: 61-3-9280-1890

Bahamas Financial Centre, 4th Floor
Shirley & Charlotte St., P.O. Box N4928
Nassau, Bahamas
Phone: 242-356-8100
Fax: 242-326-6589

Avenida Brigadeiro Faria
Lima, 3064
Sao Paulo, Brazil 01451 000

Phone: 55-11-3841-6000
Fax: 55-11-3841-6900

One Cabot Square
London, United Kingdom E14 4QJ
Phone: 44-20-7888-8888
Fax: 44-20-7888-1600

Ortega y Gasset
22 24 Floor 6th
Madrid, Spain 28006
Phone: 34-91-423-1600
Fax: 34-91-423-1638

BritCay House
P.O. Box 10344 APO
Grand Cayman, Cayman Islands
Phone: 345-946-9920
Fax: 345-946-9921

Management and Staff

Albert Sohn, Vice President
Barbara Yastine, Chief Financial Officer
Charles Pieper, Managing Director
David DeNunzio, Chief Executive Officer
George Horning, Chief Operating Officer
Harjit Bhatia, Managing Partner
Lucinda Bloom, Vice President
Melissa Anderson, Vice President
Michael Arpey, Managing Director
Paul Aliprandi, Vice President
Peter Thomas, Managing Director
Robert Rivett, Managing Director
Socorro Barraquias, Managing Director
Sokho Jung, Managing Director
Stephen Can, Managing Director
Steven Kwok, Managing Director

Type of Firm

Bank Affiliated

Association Membership

Illinois Venture Capital Association

Project Preferences

Type of Financing Preferred:

Fund of Funds
Leveraged Buyout
Expansion
Mezzanine
Generalist PE
Balanced
Fund of Funds of Second

Geographical Preferences

United States Preferences:

Midwest
Ohio
Indiana
All U.S.

International Preferences:

Europe
Asia
All International

Industry Focus

(% based on actual investment)

Other Products	37.2%
Industrial/Energy	16.7%
Consumer Related	12.1%
Internet Specific	10.3%
Computer Software and Services	8.3%
Medical/Health	5.9%
Biotechnology	4.5%
Communications and Media	2.6%
Semiconductors/Other Elect.	1.3%
Computer Hardware	1.0%

Additional Information

Year Founded: 1985
Capital Under Management: $28,000,000,000
Current Activity Level: Actively seeking new investments

CREO CAPITAL PARTNERS, LLC

17383 Sunset Boulevard
Suite A210
Pacific Palisades, CA USA 90272
Phone: 310-230-8600
Fax: 310-230-6206
E-mail: reception@creocapitalpartners.com
Website: www.creocapitalpartners.com

Management and Staff

Gregory Bortz, Managing Partner
Nick Sternberg, Partner
Rob Holland, Partner

Type of Firm

Private Equity Firm

Project Preferences

Role in Financing:
Prefer role as deal originator

Type of Financing Preferred:
Turnaround
Balanced
Special Situation
Distressed Debt
Recapitalizations

Size of Investments Considered:
Min Size of Investment Considered (000s): $5,000
Max Size of Investment Considered (000s): $100,000

Geographical Preferences

United States Preferences:
All U.S.

Industry Preferences

In Consumer Related prefer:
Consumer
Food/Beverage
Hotels and Resorts

In Industrial/Energy prefer:
Industrial Products
Robotics
Machinery

In Transportation prefer:
Transportation
Aerospace

In Financial Services prefer:
Insurance
Real Estate
Financial Services

In Manufact. prefer:
Manufacturing

In Utilities prefer:
Utilities

Additional Information

Year Founded: 2005
Capital Under Management: $181,800,000
Current Activity Level: Actively seeking new investments
Method of Compensation: Return on invest. most important, but chg. closing fees, service fees, etc.

CREO VENTURES AS

Oscarsgate 57
Oslo, Norway 0258
Phone: 47-22-56-38-00
Fax: 47-24-11-96-50
E-mail: mail@creo.no
Website: www.creo.no

Type of Firm

Private Equity Firm

Additional Information

Current Activity Level: Actively seeking new investments

CRESCENDO VENTURE MANAGEMENT LLC

480 Cowper Street
Suite 300
Palo Alto, CA USA 94301
Phone: 650-470-1200
Fax: 650-470-1201
E-mail: investorservices@crescendoventures.com
Website: www.crescendoventures.com

Management and Staff

Clint Korver, Venture Partner
David Spreng, Managing General Partner
John Borchers, General Partner
Peter Van Cuylenberg, General Partner
Wayne Cantwell, General Partner

Type of Firm

Private Equity Firm

Association Membership

National Venture Capital Association - USA (NVCA)
European Private Equity and Venture Capital Assoc.

Project Preferences

Role in Financing:
Prefer role as deal originator but will also invest in deals created by others

Type of Financing Preferred:
Early Stage
Seed
First Stage Financing
Startup

Size of Investments Considered:
Min Size of Investment Considered (000s): $5,000
Max Size of Investment Considered (000s): $30,000

Geographical Preferences

United States Preferences:
All U.S.

International Preferences:
Western Europe
Israel

Industry Focus

(% based on actual investment)

Internet Specific	28.3%
Computer Software and Services	20.4%
Semiconductors/Other Elect.	20.3%
Communications and Media	16.8%
Medical/Health	4.9%
Other Products	3.4%
Computer Hardware	2.0%
Biotechnology	1.9%
Industrial/Energy	1.2%
Consumer Related	0.8%

Additional Information

Year Founded: 1993
Capital Under Management: $1,128,600,000
Current Activity Level: Actively seeking new investments
Method of Compensation: Return on investment is of primary concern, do not charge fees

CRESCENT CAPITAL (NI) LTD

7 Upper Crescent
Belfast, United Kingdom BT7 1NT
Phone: 44-28-9023-3633
Fax: 44-28-9032-9525
E-mail: mail@crescentcapital.co.uk
Website: www.crescentcapital.co.uk

Management and Staff

Colin Walsh, Managing Director
Ed Finnegan, Chief Financial Officer

Type of Firm

Private Equity Firm

Project Preferences

Type of Financing Preferred:
Early Stage
Expansion
Management Buyouts

Size of Investments Considered:
Min Size of Investment Considered (000s): $400
Max Size of Investment Considered (000s): $400,000

Geographical Preferences

International Preferences:
Ireland
United Kingdom

Industry Preferences

In Communications prefer:
Communications and Media

In Computer Other prefer:
Computer Related

In Semiconductor/Electr prefer:
Electronics

In Medical/Health prefer:
Medical/Health

In Industrial/Energy prefer:
Industrial Products
Materials
Factory Automation

In Manufact. prefer:
Manufacturing

Additional Information

Year Founded: 1995
Capital Under Management: $20,500,000
Current Activity Level: Actively seeking new investments

CRESCENT CAPITAL PARTNERS LIMITED

75 Elizabeth Street
Level 7
Sydney, Australia 2000
Phone: 612-9220-8100
Fax: 612-9221-9650
E-mail: mail@crescentcap.com.au
Website: www.crescentcap.com.au

Management and Staff

Peter Lyon-Mercado, Chief Financial Officer

Type of Firm

Private Equity Firm

Association Membership

Australian Venture Capital Association (AVCAL)

Project Preferences

Type of Financing Preferred:
Leveraged Buyout
Generalist PE
Early Stage
Expansion
Mezzanine
Balanced
Later Stage
Management Buyouts

Size of Investments Considered:
Min Size of Investment Considered (000s): $16,116
Max Size of Investment Considered (000s): $64,464

Geographical Preferences

International Preferences:
Pacific
Australia

Industry Preferences

In Communications prefer:
Telecommunications

In Computer Other prefer:
Computer Related

In Medical/Health prefer:
Medical Diagnostics

In Consumer Related prefer:
Food/Beverage

In Financial Services prefer:
Financial Services

Additional Information

Year Founded: 2000
Capital Under Management: $360,900,000
Current Activity Level: Actively seeking new investments

CRESCENT CAPITAL PARTNERS MANAGEMENT PTY., LTD.

Level 7
75 Elizabeth Street
Sydney, Australia 2000
Phone: 612-9220-8100
Fax: 612-9221-9650
E-mail: mail@crescentcap.com.au
Website: www.crescentcap.com.au

Management and Staff

Peter Lyon-Mercado, Chief Financial Officer

Type of Firm

Private Equity Firm

Project Preferences

Role in Financing:
Prefer role as deal originator

Type of Financing Preferred:
Leveraged Buyout
Generalist PE
Expansion
Management Buyouts

Size of Investments Considered:
Min Size of Investment Considered (000s): $16,116
Max Size of Investment Considered (000s): $64,464

Geographical Preferences

International Preferences:
Pacific
Australia
New Zealand

Additional Information

Year Founded: 2004
Capital Under Management: $424,600,000
Current Activity Level: Actively seeking new investments
Method of Compensation: Return on invest. most important, but chg. closing fees, service fees, etc.

CRESCENT POINT ENERGY TRUST

500 - 4th Avenue South West
Suite 1800
Calgary, Canada T2P 2V6
Phone: 403-693-0020
Fax: 403-693-0070
Website: www.crescentpointenergy.com

Type of Firm

Private Equity Firm

Additional Information

Year Founded: 2001
Current Activity Level: Actively seeking new investments

CRESCENT PRIVATE CAPITAL, L.P.

One Copley Place
Suite 602
Boston, MA USA 02116
Phone: 617-638-0050
Fax: 617-638-0090
Website: www.crescentlp.com

Management and Staff

Hugh O'Donnell, General Partner
Nancy Amer, General Partner

Type of Firm

Private Equity Firm

Project Preferences

Type of Financing Preferred:
Leveraged Buyout
Mezzanine
Management Buyouts
Acquisition
Recapitalizations

Geographical Preferences

United States Preferences:
All U.S.

Additional Information

Year Founded: 1999
Capital Under Management: $75,000,000
Current Activity Level: Actively seeking new investments

CRESSEY & COMPANY, L.P.

233 South Wacker Drive
9200 Sears Tower
Chicago, IL USA 60606

Phone: 312-777-4444
Fax: 312-777-4445
Website: www.cresseyco.com

Other Offices

2525 West End Avenue
Suite 1175
Nashville, TN USA 37203
Phone: 615-369-8400
Fax: 615-369-8444

Management and Staff

Bryan Cressey, Partner
David Rogero, Vice President
David Schuppan, Principal
Merrick Axel, Principal
Peter Ehrich, Partner
Ralph Davis, Partner
William Frist, Partner

Type of Firm

Private Equity Firm

Project Preferences

Type of Financing Preferred:

Balanced

Geographical Preferences

United States Preferences:

All U.S.

Industry Preferences

In Medical/Health prefer:

Medical/Health
Health Services

Additional Information

Year Founded: 2007
Current Activity Level: Actively seeking new investments

CREST CAPITAL PARTNERS

50 Raffles Place #34-03
Singapore Land Tower
Singapore, Singapore 048623
Phone: 65-6533-2002
Fax: 65-6532-2002
Website: www.crest-capital.com

Other Offices

Plaza ABDA 23rd floor
Jalan Jend. Sudirman Kav 59
Jakarta, Indonesia 12190
Phone: 62-21-5140-1133
Fax: 62-21-5140-1599

Suite 8-1, Level 8, Faber Imperial Court
Jaltan Sultan Ismail
Kuala Lumpur, Malaysia 50250
Phone: 603-2693-8008
Fax: 603-2698-2088

16th FL, FKI B/D,
28-1, Yoido-dong
Seoul, South Korea
Phone: 821-6231-7601

Room 1212A No. 689 Guang Dong Road
Haitong Securities Tower
Shanghai, China 200001
Phone: 86-21-6341-0319
Fax: 86-21-6341-0329

Management and Staff

Angela Tan, Principal
David Tan, Principal
Glendon Tan, Principal
Peter Chan, Managing Partner

Type of Firm

Private Equity Firm

Project Preferences

Type of Financing Preferred:

Expansion
Public Companies
Management Buyouts
Acquisition

Geographical Preferences

International Preferences:

Asia

Industry Preferences

In Communications prefer:

Communications and Media
Telecommunications

In Computer Software prefer:

Software

In Internet Specific prefer:

E-Commerce Technology
Internet

In Consumer Related prefer:

Consumer

In Industrial/Energy prefer:

Industrial Products

In Business Serv. prefer:

Services

In Manufact. prefer:

Manufacturing

Additional Information

Year Founded: 1987
Capital Under Management: $55,000,000
Current Activity Level: Actively seeking new investments

CRESTVIEW PARTNERS L.P. (FKA: CRESTVIEW, LLC)

667 Madison Avenue
Tenth Floor
New York, NY USA 10065
Phone: 212-906-0700
Website: www.crestview.com

Management and Staff

Adam Klein, Vice President
Alex Rose, Vice President
Alex Binderow, Vice President
Brian Cassidy, Principal
Quentin Chu, Principal
Wing Keith, Chief Operating Officer

Type of Firm

Private Equity Firm

Project Preferences

Type of Financing Preferred:

Generalist PE

Industry Preferences

In Medical/Health prefer:

Health Services

In Consumer Related prefer:

Food/Beverage

In Financial Services prefer:

Financial Services

In Business Serv. prefer:

Media

Additional Information

Year Founded: 2004
Capital Under Management: $4,000,000,000
Current Activity Level: Actively seeking new investments

CRG PARTNERS

711 Third Avenue
Suite 1803
New York, NY USA 10017
Phone: 370-5550
E-mail: info@crgpartners.com
Website: www.crgpartners.com

Other Offices

13355 Noel Road
Suite 1825
Dallas, TX USA 75240
Phone: 972-702-7333

Two Atlantic Avenue
Boston, MA USA 02110
Phone: 617-482-4242

11835 West Olympic Boulevard
Suite 705E
Los Angeles, CA USA 90064
Phone: 310-954-8755

1870 The Exchange
Suite 100
Atlanta, GA USA 30339
Phone: 770-989-7370

One Park Plaza
Sixth Floor
Irvine, CA USA 92614
Phone: 949-833-7143

203 North LaSalle Street
Suite 2100
Chicago, IL USA 60601
Phone: 312-264-2777

Wipplingerstrasse 25
Vienna, Austria A-1013
Phone: 43-532-0466-422
212 South Tyron Street
Suite 1750
Charlotte, NC USA 28281
Phone: 704-332-2800
7625 Wisconsin Avenue
Bethesda, MD USA 20814
Phone: 240-482-4737

Management and Staff

Ethan Buyon, Managing Partner
John Sumner, Managing Partner
Mark Barbeau, Managing Partner
Michael Epstein, Managing Partner
Parham Pouladdej, Managing Partner
Rod Carringer, Managing Partner
Stephen Gray, Managing Partner
T. Scott Avila, Managing Partner
Tom O'Donoghue, Managing Partner
William Snyder, Managing Partner

Type of Firm

Private Equity Firm

Project Preferences

Type of Financing Preferred:
Turnaround
Distressed Debt
Recapitalizations

Geographical Preferences

United States Preferences:
All U.S.

International Preferences:
Central Europe
Eastern Europe

Industry Preferences

In Communications prefer:
Radio & TV Broadcasting
Telecommunications

In Medical/Health prefer:
Medical/Health

In Consumer Related prefer:
Other Restaurants

In Industrial/Energy prefer:
Energy

In Transportation prefer:
Transportation
Aerospace

In Financial Services prefer:
Real Estate
Financial Services

In Business Serv. prefer:
Media

In Manufact. prefer:
Manufacturing

In Agr/Forestr/Fish prefer:
Agriculture related

Additional Information

Year Founded: 2007
Current Activity Level: Actively seeking new investments

CRIMSON

260 Sheridan Avenue
Suite 300
Palo Alto, CA USA 94306
Phone: 650-233-6900
Fax: 650-233-6919
Website: www.crimsoninvestment.com

Other Offices

13F, 109, Sec. 3, Min Sheng E. Road
Taipei, Taiwan 105
Phone: 886-2-2717-9900
Fax: 886-2-2546-2302

35 SiNan Road
2nd Floor North Wing
Shanghai, China 200020
Phone: 86-21-5306-2299
Fax: 86-21-6386-0166

Management and Staff

Alfredo Ayala, Partner
Cliff Chen, Partner
David Ventura, Principal
Drew Peck, Partner
Ian Morton, Partner
John-Paul Ho, Partner
Steve Dollinger, Managing Director
T.G. Wang, Partner

Type of Firm

Private Equity Firm

Association Membership

Hong Kong Venture Capital Association (HKVCA)
Taiwan Venture Capital Association(TVCA)
Singapore Venture Capital Association (SVCA)

Project Preferences

Role in Financing:
Prefer role as deal originator but will also invest in deals created by others

Type of Financing Preferred:
Leveraged Buyout
Generalist PE
Balanced
Later Stage
Management Buyouts
Acquisition
Special Situation
Recapitalizations

Size of Investments Considered:
Min Size of Investment Considered (000s): $1,000
Max Size of Investment Considered (000s): $30,000

Geographical Preferences

International Preferences:
Pacific Rim
Asia

Industry Focus

(% based on actual investment)	
Consumer Related	62.2%
Internet Specific	16.4%
Semiconductors/Other Elect.	8.1%
Communications and Media	7.7%
Computer Software and Services	5.3%
Computer Hardware	0.2%

Additional Information

Name of Most Recent Fund: Crimson Velocity Fund, L.P.
Most Recent Fund Was Raised: 05/01/2000
Year Founded: 1993
Capital Under Management: $850,000,000
Current Activity Level: Actively seeking new investments
Method of Compensation: Return on invest. most important, but chg. closing fees, service fees, etc.

CRIMSON CAPITAL CHINA

Unit 1025, Tower 1
China World Trade Center
Beijing, China 100004
Phone: 86-10-6505-8668
Fax: 86-10-6505-8667
E-mail: info@crimcap.com
Website: www.crimcap.com

Other Offices

Unit 4808, Tower 2
Plaza 66, #1366, West Nanjing Road
Shanghai, China 200040
Phone: 86-21-6113-0177
Fax: 86-21-6113-0176

Management and Staff

Eileen Yang, Managing Director
Real Lin, Vice President
Zack Ren, Managing Director

Type of Firm
Private Equity Firm

Project Preferences

Type of Financing Preferred:
Generalist PE

Additional Information
Year Founded: 1991
Capital Under Management: $100,000,000
Current Activity Level: Actively seeking new investments

CRISPIAN VENTURE CAPITAL, LLC

5000 Legacy Drive
Suite 140
Plano, TX USA 75024
Phone: 972-608-8753
Fax: 972-608-8816
Website: www.crispianvc.com

Management and Staff
David Machemehl, Managing Partner

Type of Firm
Private Equity Firm

Project Preferences

Type of Financing Preferred:
Early Stage
Balanced
Seed
First Stage Financing
Startup

Size of Investments Considered:
Min Size of Investment Considered (000s): $25
Max Size of Investment Considered (000s): $100

Geographical Preferences

United States Preferences:
Southeast
Southwest

Additional Information
Year Founded: 2005
Capital Under Management: $1,000,000
Current Activity Level: Actively seeking new investments

CRITICAL CAPITAL GROWTH FUND, LP

90 Park Avenue
New York, NY USA 10016
Phone: 212-697-5200
Fax: 212-697-1096

Management and Staff
Charlie Robinson, Managing Director
Jeff Krentz, Vice President

Type of Firm
Private Equity Firm

Association Membership
Natl Assoc of Small Bus. Inv. Co (NASBIC)

Project Preferences

Type of Financing Preferred:
Expansion
Mezzanine
Management Buyouts

Size of Investments Considered:
Min Size of Investment Considered (000s): $1,000
Max Size of Investment Considered (000s): $2,000

Geographical Preferences

United States Preferences:
All U.S.

Industry Preferences

In Communications prefer:
Communications and Media

In Semiconductor/Electr prefer:
Electronics

In Consumer Related prefer:
Consumer

In Industrial/Energy prefer:
Machinery

In Business Serv. prefer:
Services

In Manufact. prefer:
Manufacturing

Additional Information
Year Founded: 1999
Capital Under Management: $10,000,000
Current Activity Level: Actively seeking new investments

CROCKER CAPITAL

One Post Street
Suite 2515
San Francisco, CA USA 94104
Phone: 415-956-5250
Fax: 415-959-5710

Type of Firm
Bank Affiliated

Association Membership
Western Association of Venture Capitalists (WAVC)

Project Preferences

Role in Financing:
Prefer role as deal originator

Type of Financing Preferred:
Second Stage Financing
Leveraged Buyout
Startup

Size of Investments Considered:
Min Size of Investment Considered (000s): $500
Max Size of Investment Considered (000s): $5,000

Geographical Preferences

United States Preferences:
West Coast

Industry Preferences

In Semiconductor/Electr prefer:
Electronic Components
Controllers and Sensors
Sensors
Optoelectronics

In Biotechnology prefer:
Human Biotechnology
Agricultural/Animal Bio.
Industrial Biotechnology
Biosensors

In Medical/Health prefer:
Medical Diagnostics
Diagnostic Services
Diagnostic Test Products
Medical Therapeutics
Drug/Equipmt Delivery
Medical Products
Disposable Med. Products
Pharmaceuticals

Additional Information
Name of Most Recent Fund: Crocker Capital/Crocker Assoc.
Most Recent Fund Was Raised: 01/01/1976
Year Founded: 1969
Capital Under Management: $50,000,000
Current Activity Level: Actively seeking new investments
Method of Compensation: Return on investment is of primary concern, do not charge fees

---

CROCUS INVESTMENT FUND

275 Broadway
Suite 303
Winnipeg, Canada R3C 4M6
Phone: 204-925-2401
Fax: 204-942-2785
Website: www.crocusfund.com

Management and Staff
James Umlah, Vice President

Type of Firm
Private Equity Firm

Project Preferences

Type of Financing Preferred:
Early Stage
Turnaround
Later Stage
Management Buyouts
Special Situation
Startup

Geographical Preferences

Canadian Preferences:
All Canada
Manitoba

Industry Preferences

In Communications prefer:
Telecommunications

In Computer Other prefer:
Computer Related

In Semiconductor/Electr prefer:
Electronics

In Biotechnology prefer:
Biotechnology

In Medical/Health prefer:
Medical/Health

In Consumer Related prefer:
Consumer

Additional Information
Year Founded: 1995
Current Activity Level: Making few, if any, new investments

CROISSANCE NORD - PAS DE CALAIS
2 avenue de Kaarst
BP 52004
Lille cedex, France 59777
Phone: 33-3-5931-2021
Fax: 33-3-2063-6495
Website: www.nordfinancement.com

Other Offices
Euroalliance Port A
2 avenue de Kaarst BP52004
Euralille, France 59777
Phone: 33-35-931-2020
Fax: 33-32-063-6495

Type of Firm
Private Equity Firm

Association Membership
French Venture Capital Association (AFIC)

Project Preferences

Type of Financing Preferred:
Expansion

Geographical Preferences

International Preferences:
Europe
France

Additional Information
Year Founded: 1991
Capital Under Management: $35,200,000
Current Activity Level: Actively seeking new investments

CRONUS VENTURES
6517, 151st PL Southeast
Bellevue, WA USA 98006
Phone: 425-641-4497
Fax: 419-793-1451
E-mail: info@cronusventures.com
Website: www.cronusventures.com

Management and Staff
Rao Remala, Partner

Type of Firm
Private Equity Firm

Additional Information
Year Founded: 2000
Current Activity Level: Actively seeking new investments

CROSBY ASSET MANAGEMENT, INC. (FKA: CROSBY CAPITAL PARTNERS)
Six Battery Road
#14-02
Singapore, Singapore 049909
Phone: 65-6325-1960
Fax: 65-6223-0451
E-mail: singapore.info@techpacific.com
Website: www.crosby.com

Other Offices
2701, Citibank Tower
3 Garden Road
Central, Hong Kong
Phone: 852-2169-2800
Fax: 852-2169-0008

8 Grafton Street
London, United Kingdom W1S 4EL
Phone: 44-203-291-2863
Fax: 44-203-291-2943

8th Floor, PIC Towers
M T Khan Road
Karachi, Pakistan
Phone: 92-21-111-1883
Fax: 92-21-561-1886

Wisma Metropolitan 1, 10th Floor
Kav. 29, Jl. Jend. Sudirman
Jakarta, Indonesia 12920
Phone: 62-21-526-1794
Fax: 62-21-526-4101

Management and Staff
Martin Angus, Chief Financial Officer
Simon Fry, Chief Executive Officer
Steve Fletcher, Chief Operating Officer
Surapol Viryasathien, Managing Director
Will Hoon, Managing Director

Type of Firm
Private Equity Firm

Association Membership
Hong Kong Venture Capital Association (HKVCA)

Project Preferences

Role in Financing:
Will function either as deal originator or investor in deals created by others

Type of Financing Preferred:
Second Stage Financing
Early Stage
Management Buyouts
First Stage Financing
Special Situation

Size of Investments Considered:
Min Size of Investment Considered (000s): $1,000
Max Size of Investment Considered (000s): $20,000

Geographical Preferences

United States Preferences:
New York

International Preferences:
Indonesia
China
Pacific Rim
Thailand
Asia

Industry Preferences

In Communications prefer:
Telecommunications

In Medical/Health prefer:
Pharmaceuticals

In Consumer Related prefer:
Consumer
Food/Beverage

Additional Information
Year Founded: 1984
Capital Under Management: $150,000,000
Current Activity Level: Actively seeking new investments
Method of Compensation: Professional fee required whether or not deal closes

CROSS ATLANTIC CAPITAL PARTNERS

Five Radnor Corporate Center
100 Matsonford Road, Suite 555
Radnor, PA USA 19087
Phone: 610-995-2650
Fax: 610-971-2062
E-mail: info@xacp.com
Website: www.xacp.com

Other Offices

Alexandra House
The Sweepstakes
Dublin, Ireland
Phone: 353-1-664-1721
Fax: 353-1-664-1806

152 Morrison Street
Conference House
Edinburgh, Scotland, United Kingdom EH3 8EB
Phone: 44-131-343-1361

Management and Staff

Frederick Tecce, Managing Director
Gerry McCrory, Managing Director
Hazel Cameron, Managing Director
Richard Fox, Managing Director

Type of Firm

Private Equity Firm

Association Membership

Mid-Atlantic Venture Association
National Venture Capital Association - USA (NVCA)

Project Preferences

Role in Financing:

Will function either as deal originator or investor in deals created by others

Type of Financing Preferred:

Early Stage
Balanced

Size of Investments Considered:

Min Size of Investment Considered (000s): $2,000
Max Size of Investment Considered (000s): $7,000

Geographical Preferences

United States Preferences:

Mid Atlantic

International Preferences:

Ireland
United Kingdom

Industry Focus

(% based on actual investment)

Internet Specific	26.5%
Computer Software and Services	24.2%
Other Products	13.5%
Semiconductors/Other Elect.	12.7%
Communications and Media	8.5%
Biotechnology	6.7%
Computer Hardware	4.7%
Medical/Health	2.1%
Industrial/Energy	1.1%

Additional Information

Name of Most Recent Fund: Co-Investment Fund II, The
Most Recent Fund Was Raised: 11/17/2005
Year Founded: 1999
Capital Under Management: $420,000,000
Current Activity Level: Actively seeking new investments
Method of Compensation: Return on investment is of primary concern, do not charge fees

CROSS ATLANTIC PARTNERS, INC.

551 Madison Avenue
7th Floor
New York, NY USA 10022
Phone: 646-521-7500
Fax: 646-497-0061
E-mail: info@crossatlanticpartners.com
Website: www.crossatlanticpartners.com

Management and Staff

James Dougherty, Venture Partner
John Cassis, Managing Partner
Sandra Panem, Managing Partner
Steven Soignet, Venture Partner

Type of Firm

Private Equity Firm

Association Membership

National Venture Capital Association - USA (NVCA)

Project Preferences

Role in Financing:

Will function either as deal originator or investor in deals created by others

Type of Financing Preferred:

Public Companies
Later Stage

Size of Investments Considered:

Min Size of Investment Considered (000s): $2,000
Max Size of Investment Considered (000s): $6,000

Industry Preferences

In Biotechnology prefer:

Human Biotechnology

In Medical/Health prefer:

Medical Diagnostics
Diagnostic Services
Diagnostic Test Products
Medical Therapeutics
Drug/Equipmt Delivery
Medical Products
Disposable Med. Products
Health Services
Pharmaceuticals

Additional Information

Name of Most Recent Fund: Cross Atlantic Partners V, K/S
Most Recent Fund Was Raised: 03/31/2004
Year Founded: 1994
Capital Under Management: $155,000,000
Current Activity Level: Actively seeking new investments
Method of Compensation: Return on investment is of primary concern, do not charge fees

CROSS CREEK CAPITAL, AN AFFILIATE OF WASATCH ADVISORS

150 Social Hall Avenue
Fourth Floor
Salt Lake City, UT USA 84111
Phone: 801-415-5525
Fax: 801-533-9828
E-mail: info@crosscreekcapital.com
Website: www.crosscreekcapital.com

Management and Staff

Greg Bohlen, Managing Director
John Scowcroft, Managing Director
Karey Barker, Managing Director

Type of Firm

Bank Affiliated

Project Preferences

Type of Financing Preferred:

Later Stage

Geographical Preferences

United States Preferences:

All U.S.

Industry Preferences

In Medical/Health prefer:

Medical/Health

Additional Information

Year Founded: 1999
Capital Under Management: $120,000,000
Current Activity Level: Actively seeking new investments

CROSS EQUITY PARTNERS AG

Kreuzstrasse 60
Zurich, Switzerland CH-8008
Phone: 41-44-269-9393
Website: www.crossequitypartners.ch

Management and Staff

Markus Reich, Managing Partner
Michael Petersen, Managing Partner

Type of Firm
Private Equity Firm

Project Preferences

Type of Financing Preferred:
Generalist PE
Expansion
Balanced
Management Buyouts
Acquisition

Geographical Preferences

International Preferences:
Switzerland
Liechtenstein
Luxembourg
Austria
Germany
Belgium

Industry Preferences

In Industrial/Energy prefer:
Industrial Products
Machinery

In Business Serv. prefer:
Services

Additional Information
Year Founded: 2009
Current Activity Level: Actively seeking new investments

CROSS ROAD BIOTECH S.C.R.
C/ Almagro no 1, bajo derecha
Madrid, Spain 28010
Phone: 34-914-467-897
Fax: 34-915-938-262
E-mail: crb@crossroadbiotech.com
Website: www.crossroadbiotech.com

Type of Firm
Private Equity Firm

Project Preferences

Type of Financing Preferred:
Balanced

Geographical Preferences

International Preferences:
Spain

Additional Information
Year Founded: 2008
Current Activity Level: Actively seeking new investments

CROSSBOW VENTURES
One North Clematis Street
Suite 510
West Palm Beach, FL USA 33401-5523
Phone: 561-838-9005
Fax: 561-838-4105
E-mail: mail@crossbowventures.com
Website: www.crossbowventures.com

Other Offices
Dufourstrasse 60
Zollikon-Zurich, Switzerland 8702
Phone: 41-43-499-4010
Fax: 41-43-499-4019

Management and Staff
Brian Bilnoski, Principal
George Philippidis, Venture Partner
Mark Patten, Principal
Ravi Ugale, Managing Director
Rene Eichenberger, Managing Director
Rita Soto, Chief Financial Officer
Stephen Warner, Managing Director

Type of Firm
Private Equity Firm

Association Membership
Natl Assoc of Small Bus. Inv. Co (NASBIC)
National Venture Capital Association - USA (NVCA)

Project Preferences

Role in Financing:
Prefer role as deal originator

Type of Financing Preferred:
Early Stage
Expansion

Size of Investments Considered:
Min Size of Investment Considered (000s): $1,000
Max Size of Investment Considered (000s): $10,000

Geographical Preferences

United States Preferences:
Southeast

Industry Focus
(% based on actual investment)

Internet Specific	39.6%
Computer Software and Services	14.4%
Medical/Health	13.4%
Semiconductors/Other Elect.	10.9%
Other Products	8.1%
Consumer Related	6.3%
Communications and Media	2.8%
Computer Hardware	2.4%
Industrial/Energy	2.2%

Additional Information
Year Founded: 1999
Capital Under Management: $173,000,000
Current Activity Level: Actively seeking new investments
Method of Compensation: Return on investment is of primary concern, do not charge fees

---

CROSSBRIDGE VENTURE PARTNERS
1001 Bayhill Drive
Suite 289
San Bruno, CA USA 94066
Phone: 650-616-4104
Fax: 650-239-3678
Website: www.crossbridgevp.com

Other Offices
5th Floor Ariasu Minami Aoyama
1-10-2 Minami Aoyama
Minato-Ku, Tokyo, Japan 107-0062
Phone: 81-3-5414-7182
Fax: 81-3-5414-7184

Management and Staff
Herman White, General Partner
Katsuhiko Saito, General Partner
Shinji Miyashita, General Partner
Takaharu Yamagami, General Partner

Type of Firm
Private Equity Firm

Project Preferences

Role in Financing:
Will function either as deal originator or investor in deals created by others

Type of Financing Preferred:
Second Stage Financing
Expansion
Generalist PE
Start-up Financing
First Stage Financing

Size of Investments Considered:
Min Size of Investment Considered (000s): $2,000
Max Size of Investment Considered (000s): $10,000

Geographical Preferences

United States Preferences:
All U.S.

Canadian Preferences:
All Canada

International Preferences:
India
Hong Kong
China
Japan

Industry Preferences

In Communications prefer:
Commercial Communications
Telecommunications
Wireless Communications
Data Communications
Satellite Microwave Comm.
Other Communication Prod.

In Computer Hardware prefer:
Mainframes / Scientific
Mini and Personal/Desktop
Computer Graphics and Dig
Integrated Turnkey System
Terminals
Disk Relat. Memory Device

In Computer Software prefer:
Computer Services
Data Processing
Software
Systems Software
Applications Software
Artificial Intelligence

In Internet Specific prefer:
E-Commerce Technology
Internet
Ecommerce
Web Aggregration/Portals

In Semiconductor/Electr prefer:
Electronic Components
Semiconductor
Micro-Processing
Controllers and Sensors
Component Testing Equipmt
Laser Related
Fiber Optics

In Medical/Health prefer:
Diagnostic Test Products
Medical Products
Disposable Med. Products

In Consumer Related prefer:
Entertainment and Leisure
Retail
Franchises(NEC)

In Industrial/Energy prefer:
Robotics

In Financial Services prefer:
Financial Services

In Business Serv. prefer:
Services
Media

Additional Information

Name of Most Recent Fund: CrossBridge Side Fund I
Most Recent Fund Was Raised: 03/27/2001
Year Founded: 2000
Capital Under Management: $28,000,000
Current Activity Level: Actively seeking new investments
Method of Compensation: Return on investment is of primary concern, do not charge fees

---

CROSSCUT VENTURES

1918 Main Street
Santa Monica, CA USA 90405
Phone: 310-650-4777
Website: www.crosscutventures.com

Management and Staff

Brian Garrett, Principal
Rick Smith, Principal

Type of Firm

Private Equity Firm

Project Preferences

Type of Financing Preferred:
Early Stage
Seed
Startup

Industry Preferences

In Business Serv. prefer:
Media

Additional Information

Name of Most Recent Fund: Crosscut Ventures I, LP.
Most Recent Fund Was Raised: 08/12/2008
Year Founded: 2008
Capital Under Management: $5,100,000
Current Activity Level: Actively seeking new investments

CROSSHARBOR CAPITAL PARTNERS LLC

One Boston Place
Suite 2300
Boston, MA USA 02108
Phone: 617-624-8300
Fax: 617-624-8399
E-mail: info@crossharborcapital.com
Website: www.crossharborcapital.com

Management and Staff

Daniel Jacobson, Vice President
David Jones, Vice President
Gregory Dewitt, Managing Director
Stephen Steinour, Managing Partner
William Kremer, Managing Partner

Type of Firm

Private Equity Firm

Project Preferences

Role in Financing:
Prefer role as deal originator

Type of Financing Preferred:
Leveraged Buyout

Geographical Preferences

United States Preferences:
All U.S.

Industry Preferences

In Financial Services prefer:
Financial Services

In Business Serv. prefer:
Services

Additional Information

Year Founded: 1993
Current Activity Level: Actively seeking new investments

CROSSHILL FINANCIAL GROUP, INC

1000 Wilson Boulevard
Suite 1850
Arlington, VA USA 22209
Phone: 703-526-1340
Fax: 703-526-3088
E-mail: crosshill@crosshill.com
Website: www.crosshill.com

Management and Staff

Mark Alarie, Principal
Stuart Yarbrough, General Partner
Stuart Graham, Principal

Type of Firm

Private Equity Firm

Association Membership

Mid-Atlantic Venture Association

Project Preferences

Type of Financing Preferred:
Leveraged Buyout
Acquisition
Private Placement
Recapitalizations

Size of Investments Considered:
Min Size of Investment Considered (000s): $500
Max Size of Investment Considered (000s): $1,000

Industry Preferences

In Communications prefer:
Telecommunications

In Industrial/Energy prefer:
Energy

In Financial Services prefer:
Financial Services

In Business Serv. prefer:
Media

In Manufact. prefer:
Manufacturing

Additional Information

Year Founded: 1998
Capital Under Management: $10,000,000
Current Activity Level: Actively seeking new investments

CROSSLINK CAPITAL (FKA: OMEGA VENTURE PARTNERS)

Two Embarcadero Center
Suite 2200
San Francisco, CA USA 94111
Phone: 415-617-1800
Fax: 415-617-1801
E-mail: info@crosslinkcapital.com
Website: www.crosslinkcapital.com

Management and Staff

Alain Harrus, Partner
Bruce MacNaughton, Partner
Dan Myers, General Partner
Daniel Dunn, General Partner
David Epstein, Venture Partner
Dennis Puri, Vice President
Gary Hromadko, Venture Partner
Isabelle Fymat, Partner
James Feuille, General Partner
Jerome Contro, Chief Operating Officer
Jon Schwartz, Vice President
Lou DiNardo, Partner
Mihaly Szigeti, Chief Financial Officer
Nick Mignano, Vice President
Peter Rip, General Partner
Seymour Kaufman, Founder
Stacy Nieuwoudt, Vice President
Stephen Perkins, General Partner
Thomas Bliska, General Partner

Type of Firm

Private Equity Firm

Association Membership

Western Association of Venture Capitalists (WAVC)
National Venture Capital Association - USA (NVCA)

Project Preferences

Role in Financing:
Prefer role as deal originator but will also invest in deals created by others

Type of Financing Preferred:
Second Stage Financing
Leveraged Buyout
Early Stage
Expansion
Balanced
Public Companies
Later Stage
Seed
First Stage Financing

Size of Investments Considered:
Min Size of Investment Considered (000s): $3,000
Max Size of Investment Considered (000s): $14,000

Geographical Preferences

United States Preferences:
California
All U.S.

International Preferences:
Western Europe

Industry Focus

(% based on actual investment)

Internet Specific	29.8%
Computer Software and Services	22.6%
Semiconductors/Other Elect.	18.3%
Communications and Media	10.5%
Computer Hardware	8.4%
Industrial/Energy	7.2%
Other Products	1.5%
Medical/Health	0.7%
Consumer Related	0.6%
Biotechnology	0.4%

Additional Information

Year Founded: 1989
Capital Under Management: $1,400,000,000
Current Activity Level: Actively seeking new investments

CROSSOVER ADVISORS PVT., LTD. (FKA: META CROSSOVER ADVISORS)

318, Maker Chambers V
Nariman Point
Mumbai, India 400 021
Phone: 91-22-6610-7030
Fax: 91-22-6610-7033
E-mail: info@crossoveradvisors.com
Website: www.crossoveradvisors.com

Other Offices

A1, Deepak Complex
6, National Games Road, Yerawada
Pune, India 411006

Bharat Mekani, 1 , Amber Road
#17-03 Amber point
Singapore, Singapore 439845

Management and Staff

S Chandrasekaran, Chief Operating Officer
Vinnie Vyas, Chief Executive Officer

Type of Firm

Private Equity Firm

Association Membership

Indian Venture Capital Association (IVCA)

Project Preferences

Type of Financing Preferred:
Balanced

Size of Investments Considered:
Min Size of Investment Considered (000s): $2,000
Max Size of Investment Considered (000s): $20,000

Geographical Preferences

International Preferences:
India
China

Industry Preferences

In Manufact. prefer:
Manufacturing

Additional Information

Year Founded: 2007
Current Activity Level: Actively seeking new investments

CROSSPOINT VENTURE PARTNERS

The Pioneer Hotel Building
2925 Woodside Road
Woodside, CA USA 94062
Phone: 650-851-7600
Fax: 650-851-7661
E-mail: partners@cpvp.com
Website: www.cpvp.com

Other Offices

18552 MacArthur Boulevard
Suite 400
Irvine, CA USA 92612
Phone: 949-852-1611
Fax: 949-852-9804

Management and Staff

Andy Alcon, Chief Financial Officer
Donald Milder, General Partner
James Dorrian, General Partner
John Mumford, Founding Partner
Rich Shapero, Managing Partner
Robert Hoff, General Partner
Seth Neiman, Managing Partner

Type of Firm

Private Equity Firm

Association Membership

Western Association of Venture Capitalists (WAVC)

Project Preferences

Role in Financing:
Prefer role as deal originator

Type of Financing Preferred:
Early Stage
Seed

Size of Investments Considered:
Min Size of Investment Considered (000s): $100
Max Size of Investment Considered: No Limit

Geographical Preferences

United States Preferences:
West Coast
Southwest

Industry Preferences

In Communications prefer:
Communications and Media

In Internet Specific prefer:
E-Commerce Technology
Internet

In Semiconductor/Electr prefer:
Electronics

In Medical/Health prefer:
Medical/Health

In Financial Services prefer:
Financial Services

Additional Information

Name of Most Recent Fund: Crosspoint Ventures 2000 Late Stage Fund, L.P.
Most Recent Fund Was Raised: 06/01/2000
Year Founded: 1972
Capital Under Management: $225,000,000
Current Activity Level: Actively seeking new investments
Method of Compensation: Return on investment is of primary concern, do not charge fees

CROSSROADS CAPITAL PARTNERS, LLC

9 Executive Circle
Suite 190
Irvine, CA USA 92614
Phone: 949-261-1600
Fax: 949-567-1655
Website: www.xroadsllc.com

Other Offices

885 3rd Avenue
Suite 2900
New York, NY USA 10022
Phone: 212-829-5794
Fax: 212-829-5795

Management and Staff

Dennis Simon, Managing Director
James Skelton, Principal
Jim Neidhart, Principal
Mark Barbeau, Principal

Type of Firm

Private Equity Firm

Project Preferences

Role in Financing:
Prefer role as deal originator

Size of Investments Considered:
Min Size of Investment Considered (000s): $3,000
Max Size of Investment Considered (000s): $25,000

Additional Information

Name of Most Recent Fund: Crossroads Capital Partners
Most Recent Fund Was Raised: 01/01/1997
Year Founded: 1997
Current Activity Level: Actively seeking new investments

CROUPIER PRIVE PRIVATE EQUITY PARTNERS LLC

470 Park Avenue
4th Floor
New York, NY USA 10016
Phone: 646-495-7333

Type of Firm

Private Equity Firm

Project Preferences

Type of Financing Preferred:
Leveraged Buyout
Balanced

Geographical Preferences

United States Preferences:
All U.S.

Additional Information

Year Founded: 2007
Capital Under Management: $3,500,000
Current Activity Level: Actively seeking new investments

CROWN CAPITAL CORPORATION

13321 North Forty Drive
Suite 212
Saint Louis, MO USA 63141
Phone: 314-590-5100
Fax: 314-590-5105
Website: www.crown-cap.com

Other Offices

83 Meadow Road West
Trumbull, CT USA 06611
Phone: 203-459-1553

15201 Medici Way
Naples, FL USA 34110
Phone: 239-593-4500
Fax: 314-576-1525

880 Third Avenue
New York, NY USA 10022
Phone: 212-380-2840
Fax: 314-576-1525

Management and Staff

Kyla Krahl, Vice President

Type of Firm

Bank Affiliated

Project Preferences

Role in Financing:
Will function either as deal originator or investor in deals created by others

Type of Financing Preferred:
Leveraged Buyout
Control-block Purchases
Expansion
Mezzanine
Later Stage
Management Buyouts
Private Placement
Acquisition
Recapitalizations
Distressed Debt

Size of Investments Considered:
Min Size of Investment Considered (000s): $1,000
Max Size of Investment Considered (000s): $500,000

Industry Preferences

In Communications prefer:
Commercial Communications
CATV & Pay TV Systems
Radio & TV Broadcasting
Telecommunications
Wireless Communications
Satellite Microwave Comm.
Other Communication Prod.

In Computer Software prefer:
Computer Services
Data Processing
Software
Systems Software
Applications Software

In Internet Specific prefer:
E-Commerce Technology
Internet
Ecommerce

In Semiconductor/Electr prefer:
Electronic Components
Semiconductor
Micro-Processing
Sensors
Circuit Boards
Component Testing Equipmt
Laser Related
Fiber Optics
Analytic/Scientific
Optoelectronics

In Medical/Health prefer:
Medical Diagnostics
Diagnostic Services
Diagnostic Test Products
Medical Therapeutics
Drug/Equipmt Delivery
Medical Products
Disposable Med. Products
Health Services
Pharmaceuticals

In Consumer Related prefer:
Consumer
Entertainment and Leisure
Sports
Retail
Franchises(NEC)
Food/Beverage

Hotels and Resorts
Education Related

In Industrial/Energy prefer:

Industrial Products
Factory Automation
Robotics
Machinery

In Financial Services prefer:

Financial Services
Real Estate

In Business Serv. prefer:

Services
Distribution
Consulting Services
Media

In Agr/Forestr/Fish prefer:

Agriculture related

In Other prefer:

Women/Minority-Owned Bus.

Additional Information

Year Founded: 1985
Capital Under Management: $200,000,000
Current Activity Level: Actively seeking new investments
Method of Compensation: Return on invest. most important, but chg. closing fees, service fees, etc.

CROWN CAPITAL PARTNERS INC.

1874 Scarth Street
Suite 1900
Regina, Canada S4P 4B3
Phone: 306-546-8000
Fax: 306-546-8010
Website: www.crowncapital.ca

Other Offices

175 Bloor Street East
Suite 1316
Toronto, Canada M4W 3R8
Phone: 416-927-1851
Fax: 416-927-0863

Management and Staff

Alan Rowe, Partner
Brent Hughes, Partner
Brian Johnson, Partner
Christopher Johnson, Partner
Christopher Anderson, Partner
Laurie Powers, Chief Financial Officer

Type of Firm

Private Equity Firm

Association Membership

Canadian Venture Capital Association

Project Preferences

Type of Financing Preferred:

Mezzanine

Size of Investments Considered:

Min Size of Investment Considered (000s): $5,000
Max Size of Investment Considered (000s): $25,000

Geographical Preferences

Canadian Preferences:

All Canada

Additional Information

Year Founded: 2005
Capital Under Management: $150,000,000
Current Activity Level: Actively seeking new investments

CRP (AKA: COMPANHIA DE PARTICIPACOES)

Rua General Camara
243 - 8 Andar
Porto Alegre - RS, Brazil 90010-230
Phone: 55-51-3211-0777
Fax: 55-51-3211-0777
E-mail: crp@crp.com.br
Website: www.crp.com.br

Other Offices

AV. Rio Branco 404/sala 901
Florianopolis, SC, Brazil 88015-201
Phone: 5551-3211-0777
Fax: 5551-3211-0777

Management and Staff

Andre Burger, Chief Operating Officer
Clovis Benoni Meurer, Managing Partner
Olga Maria Kolesza, Chief Financial Officer

Type of Firm

Incubator/Development Program

Association Membership

Brazilian Venture Capital Association (ABCR)

Project Preferences

Type of Financing Preferred:

Balanced
Startup

Geographical Preferences

International Preferences:

Brazil

Industry Preferences

In Communications prefer:

Communications and Media

In Computer Hardware prefer:

Mainframes / Scientific

In Computer Software prefer:

Software

In Semiconductor/Electr prefer:

Electronic Components

In Biotechnology prefer:

Biotechnology

In Medical/Health prefer:

Medical/Health

In Business Serv. prefer:

Services
Consulting Services

Additional Information

Year Founded: 1981
Capital Under Management: $12,000,000
Current Activity Level: Actively seeking new investments

CRYSTAL CAPITAL

Two International Place, 17/F
Boston, MA USA 02110
Phone: 617-428-8700
Fax: 617-428-8701
E-mail: crystal@crystalcapital.com
Website: www.crystalcapital.com

Other Offices

5928 Tuxedo Terrace
Los Angeles, CA USA 90068
Phone: 323-839-5526
Fax: 310-774-3943

225 West Washington Street
Suite 2200
Chicago, IL USA 60606
Phone: 312-924-0228
Fax: 312-277-9005

Management and Staff

Colin Cross, Managing Director
Lauren Endicott, Managing Director
Michael Pizette, Managing Director
Paul Feinstein, Chief Financial Officer
Robert DeAngelis, Managing Director
Stephen Krawchuk, Managing Director
Steve Migliero, Managing Director

Type of Firm

Private Equity Firm

Project Preferences

Type of Financing Preferred:

Balanced

Geographical Preferences

United States Preferences:

All U.S.

Additional Information

Year Founded: 2007
Current Activity Level: Actively seeking new investments

CRYSTAL INTERNET VENTURE FUND, L.P.

1120 Chester Avenue
Suite 418
Cleveland, OH USA 44114
Phone: 216-263-5515
Fax: 216-263-5518
E-mail: info@crystalventures.com
Website: www.crystalventures.com

Management and Staff

Cameron Rubino, Chief Financial Officer
Daniel Kellogg, Managing Director
John Hsin, General Partner
Joseph Tzeng, Managing Director
Sybil Yang, General Partner

Type of Firm

Private Equity Firm

Project Preferences

Role in Financing:
Prefer role as deal originator but will also invest in deals created by others

Type of Financing Preferred:
Second Stage Financing
Early Stage
Expansion
Later Stage
Seed
First Stage Financing
Startup

Size of Investments Considered:
Min Size of Investment Considered (000s): $1,000
Max Size of Investment Considered (000s): $6,000

Geographical Preferences

Canadian Preferences:
All Canada

International Preferences:
Taiwan
China
Singapore

Industry Focus

(% based on actual investment)

Internet Specific	64.5%
Computer Software and Services	20.8%
Communications and Media	8.7%
Semiconductors/Other Elect.	4.3%
Computer Hardware	1.8%

Additional Information

Year Founded: 1997
Capital Under Management: $170,000,000
Current Activity Level: Actively seeking new investments
Method of Compensation: Return on investment is of primary concern, do not charge fees

CRYSTAL PARTNERS & CO., LLP

Chancery Lane
1 Quality Court
London, United Kingdom WC2A 1HR
Phone: 44-20-7061-6250
Fax: 44-20-7061-6251
E-mail: info@crystalpartners-llp.com
Website: www.crystalpartners-llp.com

Type of Firm

Private Equity Advisor or Fund of Funds

Project Preferences

Type of Financing Preferred:
Fund of Funds

Geographical Preferences

United States Preferences:
All U.S.

International Preferences:
Western Europe
Asia

Additional Information

Year Founded: 2005
Current Activity Level: Actively seeking new investments

CRYSTAL RIDGE PARTNERS, LLC

17 Hulfish Street
Suite 200
Princeton, NJ USA 08542
Phone: 609-924-2088
E-mail: info@crystalridgepartners.com
Website: www.crystalridgepartners.com

Management and Staff

Brian Toolan, Managing Director
Rodney Eshelman, Managing Director

Type of Firm

Private Equity Firm

Project Preferences

Type of Financing Preferred:
Leveraged Buyout

Geographical Preferences

United States Preferences:
All U.S.

Additional Information

Year Founded: 2004
Capital Under Management: $28,000,000
Current Activity Level: Actively seeking new investments

CS CAPITAL PARTNERS LLC

415 Cedar Bridge Avenue
Lakewood, NJ USA 08701
Phone: 732-901-1111
E-mail: info@cs-capital.com

Other Offices

5616 Park Heights Avenue
Baltimore, MD USA 21215

Management and Staff

Charles Nebenzahl, Managing Partner
Solomon Lax, Managing Partner

Type of Firm

Private Equity Firm

Project Preferences

Role in Financing:
Prefer role as deal originator

Type of Financing Preferred:
Second Stage Financing
Early Stage
Expansion
Turnaround
First Stage Financing
Acquisition
Special Situation
Distressed Debt
Recapitalizations

Size of Investments Considered:
Min Size of Investment Considered (000s): $500
Max Size of Investment Considered (000s): $3,000

Geographical Preferences

United States Preferences:
Mid Atlantic
Southeast
Northeast

Industry Focus

(% based on actual investment)

Internet Specific	57.8%
Computer Software and Services	22.9%
Other Products	9.0%
Communications and Media	7.6%
Medical/Health	2.7%

Additional Information

Name of Most Recent Fund: CS Private Equity Fund, L.P.
Most Recent Fund Was Raised: 12/31/1998
Year Founded: 1999
Capital Under Management: $24,000,000
Current Activity Level: Actively seeking new investments
Method of Compensation: Return on invest. most important, but chg. closing fees, service fees, etc.

CSI (FKA: VIRGINIA COMMUNITY DEVELOPMENT LOAN FUND)

2317 Westwood Avenue
Suite 204
Richmond, VA USA 23230
Phone: 804-340-1988
Fax: 804-340-2836
Website: www.vcdlf.org

Other Offices

The Mason Enterprise Center
4031 University Drive, Suite 200
Fairfax, VA USA 22030
Phone: 703-277-7706

Management and Staff

Kirsten Sachwitz, Managing Director
Timothy Hayes, President

Type of Firm

Incubator/Development Program

Project Preferences

Type of Financing Preferred:

Early Stage

Size of Investments Considered:

Min Size of Investment Considered (000s): $50
Max Size of Investment Considered (000s): $500

Geographical Preferences

United States Preferences:

Maryland
Virginia
D. of Columbia

Industry Preferences

In Business Serv. prefer:

Services

Additional Information

Year Founded: 1995
Capital Under Management: $3,000,000
Current Activity Level: Actively seeking new investments

CSK VENTURE CAPITAL CO., LTD.

CSK Aoyama Building
2-26-1, Minami-Aoyama, Minato-Tokyo, Japan 107-0062
Phone: 81-3-5771-6411
Fax: 81-3-5771-6412
E-mail: info@cskvc.co.jp
Website: www.cskvc.co.jp

Management and Staff

Alessandro Araldi, Partner
Makoto Kaneshiro, Managing Director
Osamu Hori, Managing Director

Type of Firm

Investment Management Firm

Project Preferences

Role in Financing:

Prefer role in deals created by others

Type of Financing Preferred:

Second Stage Financing
Early Stage
Balanced
Start-up Financing
Seed
First Stage Financing

Size of Investments Considered:

Min Size of Investment Considered (000s): $500
Max Size of Investment Considered (000s): $3,000

Geographical Preferences

United States Preferences:

Northeast
West Coast

International Preferences:

Israel
Japan
All International

Industry Focus

(% based on actual investment)

Internet Specific	25.8%
Consumer Related	17.6%
Computer Software and Services	14.1%
Communications and Media	12.4%
Semiconductors/Other Elect.	11.1%
Biotechnology	11.0%
Medical/Health	4.2%
Industrial/Energy	3.0%
Computer Hardware	0.9%

Additional Information

Year Founded: 2003
Capital Under Management: $300,000,000
Current Activity Level: Actively seeking new investments
Method of Compensation: Return on investment is of primary concern, do not charge fees

CSV CAPITAL PARTNERS (FKA: CHINA SEED VENTURES)

Room 104, Building 18
No. 800 Huashan Road
Shanghai, China 200050
Phone: 86-21-6225-8579
Fax: 86-21-6225-8573
Website: www.csvcp.com

Other Offices

920, Marunouchi Nakadori Building
2-2-3 Marunouchi, Chiyoda-ku
Tokyo, Japan 100-0005
Phone: 813-3210-9673
Fax: 813-3210-9668

88 West Shore Road
Belvedere, CA USA 94920
Phone: 415-298-9729

Rm. 806-808, Wayson Commercial Bldg.
28 Connaught Road West
Central, Hong Kong
Phone: 852-2155-4477
Fax: 852-2155-9008

Management and Staff

Earl Yen, Managing Director
Jianzhong Qu, Vice President
Johnson Liu, Vice President
Lucene Tong, Venture Partner
Michael Liao, Principal
Ralph Ungermann, Managing Director
Ricky Huang, Vice President
William Stewart, Venture Partner
Yongfei Zhao, Vice President
Yukihiro Kayama, Managing Director

Type of Firm

Private Equity Firm

Project Preferences

Type of Financing Preferred:

Early Stage
Seed

Size of Investments Considered:

Min Size of Investment Considered (000s): $100
Max Size of Investment Considered (000s): $3,000

Geographical Preferences

International Preferences:

China

Industry Preferences

In Communications prefer:

Wireless Communications

In Internet Specific prefer:

Internet

In Consumer Related prefer:

Consumer

In Industrial/Energy prefer:

Energy

In Business Serv. prefer:

Services
Media

Additional Information

Year Founded: 2004
Capital Under Management: $45,000,000
Current Activity Level: Actively seeking new investments

CT HOLDINGS

5420 LBJ Freeway
Suite 1600
Dallas, TX USA 75240
Phone: 214-520-9292
Fax: 214-520-9293
E-mail: invest@citadel.com
Website: www.ct-holdings.com

Management and Staff

Carl Banzhof, General Partner
Lester Sideropoulos, General Partner
Steven Solomon, Chief Executive Officer
Victor Kiam, General Partner

Type of Firm

Incubator/Development Program

Project Preferences

Type of Financing Preferred:
Early Stage

Industry Preferences

In Internet Specific prefer:
Internet

Additional Information

Year Founded: 1999
Current Activity Level: Actively seeking new investments

CT INVESTMENT MANAGEMENT CO. (AKA: CAPITAL TRUST)

410 Park Avenue
14th Floor
New York, NY USA 10022
Phone: 212-655-0220
Fax: 212-655-0044
E-mail: investorrelations@capitaltrust.com
Website: www.capitaltrust.com

Management and Staff

John Klopp, Chief Executive Officer
Stephen Plavin, Chief Operating Officer

Type of Firm

Bank Affiliated

Project Preferences

Type of Financing Preferred:
Mezzanine

Additional Information

Name of Most Recent Fund: CT Mezzanine Partners II, L.P.
Most Recent Fund Was Raised: 05/29/2001
Year Founded: 2000
Capital Under Management: $1,045,100,000
Current Activity Level: Actively seeking new investments

CT INVESTMENT PARTNERS LLP

8th Floor
3 Clement's Inn
London, United Kingdom WC2A 2AZ
Phone: 44-8000-852-005
Fax: 44-2071-707-020

Other Offices

The Innovation Centre
Queen's Road, Queen's Island
Belfast, United Kingdom BT3 9DT
Phone: 44-2890-737-912

Albion House
Oxford Street, Nantgarw
Cardiff, United Kingdom CF15 7TR
Phone: 44-1443-845-944

The Technology Centre
Scottish Enterprise Technology Park
East Kilbride, United Kingdom G75 0QF
Phone: 44-1355-581-810

Management and Staff

Peter Linthwaite, Managing Partner

Type of Firm

Corporate PE/Venture

Project Preferences

Type of Financing Preferred:
Expansion
Balanced

Geographical Preferences

International Preferences:
United Kingdom
Qatar
Europe
Middle East

Industry Preferences

In Industrial/Energy prefer:
Alternative Energy
Energy Conservation Relat
Environmental Related

Additional Information

Year Founded: 2007
Capital Under Management: $191,300,000
Current Activity Level: Actively seeking new investments

CUBERA PRIVATE EQUITY

Rosenkrantzgate 22
Oslo, Norway 0160
Phone: 47-23-100-760
Fax: 47-23-100-761
E-mail: info@cubera.no
Website: www.cubera.no

Other Offices

Kungsgatan 26
Stockholm, Sweden 111 35
Phone: 46-8-1411-9033

Management and Staff

Jorgen Kjaernes, Managing Partner
Kine Buroy Ianssen, Partner
Niclas Ekestubbe, Partner
Svein Lien, Partner
Tim Gutzen, Partner

Type of Firm

Private Equity Firm

Association Membership

Norwegian Venture Capital Association
Swedish Venture Capital Association (SVCA)

Additional Information

Year Founded: 1998
Capital Under Management: $100,000,000
Current Activity Level: Actively seeking new investments

CUBIC VENTURE CAPITAL CO.,LTD (FKA DAIICHI MUTUAL LIFE CAPI)

10/F Shin Yurakucho Building
1-12-1 Yurakucho,Chiyoda-ku
Tokyo, Japan 100-0006
Phone: 81-3-3216-7800
Fax: 81-3-3216-7803
Website: www.cubic-vc.co.jp

Type of Firm

Insurance Firm Affiliate

Additional Information

Year Founded: 1989
Capital Under Management: $25,000,000
Current Activity Level: Actively seeking new investments

CUE BALL GROUP, LLC, THE

Nine East Street
Boston, MA USA 02111
Phone: 617-542-0100
Fax: 617-542-0033
Website: www.cueball.com

Management and Staff
Anthony Tjan, CEO & Managing Director
John Hamel, Partner

Type of Firm
Private Equity Firm

Association Membership
National Venture Capital Association - USA (NVCA)

Project Preferences

Type of Financing Preferred:
Early Stage
Expansion
Seed

Geographical Preferences

United States Preferences:
All U.S.

Industry Preferences

In Consumer Related prefer:
Consumer

In Business Serv. prefer:
Media

Additional Information
Year Founded: 2007
Capital Under Management: $5,000,000
Current Activity Level: Actively seeking new investments

CULBRO, LLC
880 Third Avenue
18th Floor
New York, NY USA 10022
Phone: 646-461-9270
E-mail: info@culbro.com
Website: www.culbro.com

Type of Firm
Private Equity Firm

Project Preferences

Type of Financing Preferred:
Balanced

Size of Investments Considered:
Min Size of Investment Considered (000s): $10,000
Max Size of Investment Considered (000s): $15,000

Geographical Preferences

United States Preferences:
All U.S.

Industry Preferences

In Internet Specific prefer:
Ecommerce

In Consumer Related prefer:
Consumer
Food/Beverage
Education Related

In Business Serv. prefer:
Services

Additional Information
Year Founded: 2005
Current Activity Level: Actively seeking new investments

CURZON PARK CAPITAL, LTD.
25 Park Lane
London, United Kingdom W1K 1RA
Phone: 44-20-3358-0000
Fax: 44-20-7491-3735
Website: www.curzonparkcapital.com

Type of Firm
Private Equity Firm

Project Preferences

Type of Financing Preferred:
Balanced

Geographical Preferences

International Preferences:
United Kingdom

Industry Preferences

In Industrial/Energy prefer:
Alternative Energy

In Other prefer:
Environment Responsible

Additional Information
Year Founded: 2007
Capital Under Management: $40,000,000
Current Activity Level: Actively seeking new investments

CUSTER CAPITAL, INC.
14 South High Street
P.O. Box 673
New Albany, OH USA 43054
Phone: 614-855-9980
Fax: 614-855-9979
Website: www.custercapital.com

Management and Staff
Donald O Shea, Managing Director

Type of Firm
Private Equity Firm

Project Preferences

Role in Financing:
Will function either as deal originator or investor in deals created by others

Type of Financing Preferred:
Second Stage Financing
Early Stage
Later Stage
First Stage Financing

Size of Investments Considered:
Min Size of Investment Considered (000s): $100
Max Size of Investment Considered (000s): $1,000

Geographical Preferences

United States Preferences:
Midwest
Southeast
All U.S.

Canadian Preferences:
Ontario

Industry Preferences

In Communications prefer:
Telecommunications
Wireless Communications
Data Communications

In Computer Software prefer:
Software

In Internet Specific prefer:
E-Commerce Technology
Internet

In Semiconductor/Electr prefer:
Semiconductor
Analytic/Scientific

In Medical/Health prefer:
Medical Diagnostics
Diagnostic Test Products
Medical Therapeutics
Drug/Equipmt Delivery
Medical Products
Health Services

In Business Serv. prefer:
Media

Additional Information
Year Founded: 1985
Capital Under Management: $65,000,000
Current Activity Level: Actively seeking new investments
Method of Compensation: Return on invest. most important, but chg. closing fees, service fees, etc.

CUTLASS CAPITAL
84 State Street
Suite 1040
Boston, MA USA 02109
Phone: 617-202-9550
Fax: 617-624-9669
Website: www.cutlasscapital.com

Other Offices
1750 Montgomery Street
San Francisco, CA USA 94111
Phone: 415-954-7163

Fax: 415-954-7164

Management and Staff

Nimesh Shah, Principal
Stephen Solomon, Venture Partner
Urs Baertschi, Principal

Type of Firm

Private Equity Firm

Association Membership

National Venture Capital Association - USA (NVCA)

Project Preferences

Type of Financing Preferred:

Early Stage
Expansion
Later Stage

Geographical Preferences

United States Preferences:

All U.S.

Industry Preferences

In Medical/Health prefer:

Medical/Health

Additional Information

Year Founded: 2001
Current Activity Level: Actively seeking new investments

CVC ASIA PACIFIC, LTD.

Suite 901-3, ICBC Tower
Citibank Plaza, 3 Garden Road
Central, Hong Kong
Phone: 852-3518-6360
Fax: 852-3518-6380
Website: www.cvcasia.com

Other Offices

21/F Seoul Finance Center
Taepyeongro 1-ga, Jung-gu
Seoul, South Korea 100-768
Phone: 82-2-2075-8500
Fax: 82-2-2075-8511

Atago Green Hills MORI Tower 38F
2-5-1 Atago
Tokyo, Japan 105-6238
Phone: 813-5402-5300
Fax: 813-5402-5301

Level 45 Citigroup Centre
2 Park Street
Sydney, Australia 2000
Phone: 612-9260-9800
Fax: 612-9260-9820

712 Fifth Avenue
43rd Floor
New York, NY USA 10019
Phone: 212-265-6222
Fax: 212-265-6375

1 Temasek Avenue
#24-01A Millenia Tower
Singapore, Singapore 039192
Phone: 65-6500-7328
Fax: 65-6500-7323

Lvl 16, Units 25-29, China World Tower 1
Jianguomenwai Dajie No.1, Chaoyang
Beijing, China
Phone: 86-10-6535-1800
Fax: 86-10-6535-1811

Management and Staff

Adrian MacKenzie, Managing Partner
Alvin Lam, Managing Director
Ben Keeble, Managing Director
Brian Hong, Managing Director
Graham Brooke, Managing Director
Hans Wang, Managing Director
Hemal Mirani, Managing Director
Kamil Salame, Partner
Kei Mizukami, Senior Managing Director
Maarten Ruijs, Managing Partner
Norimitsu Niwa, Managing Director
Roy Kuan, Managing Partner
Sigit Prasetya, Senior Managing Director
William Ho, Senior Managing Director

Type of Firm

Private Equity Firm

Project Preferences

Type of Financing Preferred:

Leveraged Buyout
Management Buyouts

Geographical Preferences

International Preferences:

Taiwan
Hong Kong
Asia
Australia
Singapore
Korea, South
Japan

Industry Preferences

In Communications prefer:

Telecommunications

In Medical/Health prefer:

Medical/Health
Pharmaceuticals

In Consumer Related prefer:

Entertainment and Leisure
Retail
Food/Beverage
Consumer Products
Hotels and Resorts
Education Related

In Transportation prefer:

Transportation

In Financial Services prefer:

Financial Services

In Business Serv. prefer:

Distribution

In Manufact. prefer:

Manufacturing

In Agr/Forestr/Fish prefer:

Agribusiness

Additional Information

Name of Most Recent Fund: CVC Capital Partners Asia Pacific II, LP
Most Recent Fund Was Raised: 05/04/2005
Year Founded: 1999
Capital Under Management: $6,800,000,000
Current Activity Level: Actively seeking new investments

CVC CAPITAL PARTNERS (EUROPE), LTD.

111 Strand
London, United Kingdom WC2R 0AG
Phone: 44-20-7420-4200
Fax: 44-20-7420-4231
E-mail: info@cvceurope.com
Website: www.cvc.com

Other Offices

40 Rue La Perouse
Paris, France 75116
Phone: 33-1-4502-2300
Fax: 33-1-4502-2301

WestendDuo
Bockenheimer Landstrasse 24
Frankfurt am Main, Germany D-60323
Phone: 49-69-975-8350
Fax: 49-69-9758-3511

Level 16th, Units 25-29
China World Tower 1 Jianguomenwai Dajie
Beijing , China 100004
Phone: 86-10-6535-1800
Fax: 86-10-6535-1811

Bredgade 31
3rd Floor
Copenhagen, Denmark 1260 K
Phone: 45-3312-0010
Fax: 45-3312-0015

Hamngatan 13
Stockholm, Sweden 11147
Phone: 46-8-407-8790
Fax: 46-8-611-0565

20 Avenue Monterey
Luxembourg, Luxembourg L-2163
Phone: 352-2647-8368
Fax: 352-2647-8367

Kabushiki Kaisha Atago, Green Hills MORI Tower 38F 2-5-1 Atago, Minato-ku

Tokyo, Japan 105-6238
Phone: 813-5402-5300
Fax: 813-5402-5301

Jose Ortega y Gasset 25-1
Madrid, Spain 28006
Phone: 34-91-436-4280
Fax: 34-91-436-4282

Bahnhofstrasse 94
Zurich, Switzerland 8001
Phone: 41-44-217-7000
Fax: 41-44-217-70001

18-22 Grenville Street,
St. Helier, United Kingdom JE4 8PX
Phone: 44-15-3460-9000
Fax: 44-15-3460-9333

712 Fifth Avenue
43rd Floor
New York, NY USA 10019
Phone: 212-265-6222
Fax: 212-265-6375

1 Temasek Avenue
#24-01A Millenia Tower
Singapore , Singapore 039192
Phone: 65-6500-7328
Fax: 65-6500-7323
21/F Seoul Finance Center
Taepyeongro 1-ga, Jung-gu
Seoul, South Korea 100-768
Phone: 822-2075-8500
Fax: 822-2075-8511

World Trade Centre, Schiphol Airport
Tower B, 6/F Schiphol Boulevard 285
Amsterdam, Netherlands 1118BH
Phone: 31-20-354-8051
Fax: 31-20-354-8052

Via Senato 12
Milan, Italy 20121
Phone: 39-2-760-7571
Fax: 39-2-7607-5799

Chausse de la Hulpe 166
Brussels, Belgium 1170
Phone: 32-2-663-8090
Fax: 32-2-663-8099

Suite 901-3, ICBC Tower, Citibank Plaza
3 Garden Road
Central Hong Kong, Hong Kong
Phone: 852-3518-6360
Fax: 852-3518-6380

Level 45, Citigroup Centre
2 Park Street
Sydney, Australia NSW 2000
Phone: 612-9260-9800
Fax: 612-9260-9820

Management and Staff

Adrian MacKenzie, Managing Partner
Alfredo Zamarriego, Managing Director
Alvin Lam, Managing Director
Ben Keeble, Managing Director
Brian Hong, Managing Director
Charles Schwarck, Managing Director
Chris Wildmoser, Partner
Christian Wildmoser, Partner
Christopher Stadler, Managing Partner
Daniel Schmitz, Partner
David Milne, Senior Managing Director
Domnin De Kerdaniel, Senior Managing Director
Domnin de Kerdaniel, Senior Managing Director
Donald Mackenzie, Managing Partner
Fred Watt, Chief Operating Officer
Geert Duyck, Managing Partner
Gijsbert Vuursteen, Managing Director
Gregoire Poux-Guillaume, Managing Director
Gregor Hilverkus, Managing Director
Hans Wang, Managing Director
Hardy McLain, Managing Partner
Hemal Mirani, Managing Director
Hugh Briggs, Managing Director
Hugo Van Berckel, Partner
Iain Parham, Managing Partner
Inaki Cobo, Managing Director
Istvan Szoke, Senior Managing Director
Jan Reinier Voute, Managing Partner
Janish Patel, Managing Partner
Javier De Jaime, Managing Partner
Jean-Remy Roussel, Partner
Johan Sjogren, Managing Director
Jonathan Feuer, Managing Partner
Jose Antonio Torre de Silva, Managing Director
Kamil Salame, Partner
Kei Mizukami, Senior Managing Director
Lorne Somerville, Partner
Luigi Lanari, Partner
Maarten Ruijs, Managing Director
Marc St John, Partner
Marc Strobel, Partner
Mark Grizzelle, Partner
Nick Archer, Partner
Nick Clarry, Managing Director
Norimitsu Niwa, Managing Director
Patrick Verschelde, Partner
Peter Tornquist, Partner
Pev Hooper, Managing Director
Rob Lucas, Managing Partner
Robert Berner, Partner
Robert-Jan Van Ogtrop, Partner
Robert-Jan Ogtrop, Partner
Rolly Van Rappard, Managing Partner
Roy Kuan, Managing Director
Sigit Prasetya, Senior Managing Director
Soren Vestergaard-Poulsen, Partner
Stephen Vineburg, Chief Executive Officer
Steve Koltes, Managing Partner
Steven Buyse, Managing Director
Tim Parker, Partner
William Ho, Senior Managing Director

Type of Firm

Private Equity Firm

Association Membership

Italian Venture Capital Association (AIFI)
Hong Kong Venture Capital Association (HKVCA)
British Venture Capital Association (BVCA)
French Venture Capital Association (AFIC)
European Private Equity and Venture Capital Assoc.
Spanish Venture Capital Association (ASCRI)

Project Preferences

Role in Financing:

Prefer role as deal originator but will also invest in deals created by others

Type of Financing Preferred:

Leveraged Buyout
Expansion
Generalist PE
Balanced
Management Buyouts
Acquisition

Geographical Preferences

Canadian Preferences:

Alberta

International Preferences:

Italy
United Kingdom
Luxembourg
Netherlands
Taiwan
Europe
China
Hong Kong
Western Europe
Spain
Scandanavia/Nordic Region
Pacific
Australia
Belgium
Singapore
Korea, South
Germany
Asia
France
Japan
All International

Industry Focus

(% based on actual investment)

Consumer Related	45.0%
Other Products	39.1%
Industrial/Energy	5.0%
Medical/Health	4.8%
Internet Specific	3.0%
Communications and Media	1.7%
Biotechnology	1.3%
Computer Hardware	0.1%

Additional Information

Name of Most Recent Fund: CVC European Equity Partners Tandem Fund
Most Recent Fund Was Raised: 01/31/2007
Year Founded: 1981
Capital Under Management: $40,144,400,000
Current Activity Level: Actively seeking new investments

Method of Compensation: Return on investment is of primary concern, do not charge fees

CVC MANAGERS PTY LTD (CONTINENTAL VENTURE CAPITAL)

Level 42, Suncorp Place
259 George Street
Sydney, Australia 2000
Phone: 612-9087-8000
Fax: 612-9087-8088
E-mail: cvc@cvcltd.com.au
Website: www.cvc.com.au

Other Offices

Level 5, 432 St. Kilda Road
Melbourne, Australia 3004
Phone: 613-9867-2811
Fax: 613-9820-5957

Type of Firm

Private Equity Firm

Project Preferences

Role in Financing:
Will function either as deal originator or investor in deals created by others

Type of Financing Preferred:
Second Stage Financing
Leveraged Buyout
Early Stage
Expansion
Mezzanine
Generalist PE
Balanced
Turnaround
Later Stage
Seed
Management Buyouts
First Stage Financing
Acquisition
Private Placement
Special Situation
Startup
Distressed Debt
Recapitalizations

Size of Investments Considered:
Min Size of Investment Considered (000s): $282
Max Size of Investment Considered (000s): $1,691

Geographical Preferences

International Preferences:
Europe
Pacific
Australia
Asia

Industry Focus

(% based on actual investment)

Other Products	49.3%
Industrial/Energy	17.2%
Medical/Health	12.2%
Consumer Related	7.3%
Semiconductors/Other Elect.	6.9%
Biotechnology	3.5%
Computer Software and Services	1.7%
Communications and Media	1.0%
Internet Specific	0.9%

Additional Information

Name of Most Recent Fund: CVC Sustainable Investments Ltd. (FKA: Eco Fund Ltd, The)
Most Recent Fund Was Raised: 06/30/2002
Year Founded: 1985
Capital Under Management: $73,300,000
Current Activity Level: Actively seeking new investments
Method of Compensation: Return on invest. most important, but chg. closing fees, service fees, etc.

CW GROUP, INC.

1041 Third Avenue
Second Floor
New York, NY USA 10021
Phone: 212-308-5266
Fax: 212-644-0354
E-mail: cweast@cwventures.com
Website: www.cwventures.com

Other Offices

2683 Via De La Valle
#204, Suite G
Del Mar, CA USA 92014
Phone: 858-759-8693
Fax: 858-759-8299

Management and Staff

Barry Weinberg, General Partner
Lawrence Bock, General Partner
Walter Channing, General Partner

Type of Firm

Private Equity Firm

Project Preferences

Role in Financing:
Prefer role as deal originator but will also invest in deals created by others

Type of Financing Preferred:
Second Stage Financing
Leveraged Buyout
Control-block Purchases
Early Stage
Research and Development
Balanced
Start-up Financing
Seed
First Stage Financing
Special Situation

Size of Investments Considered:
Min Size of Investment Considered (000s): $500
Max Size of Investment Considered (000s): $5,000

Geographical Preferences

United States Preferences:
All U.S.

Industry Focus

(% based on actual investment)

Medical/Health	41.7%
Biotechnology	35.9%
Computer Software and Services	9.6%
Semiconductors/Other Elect.	4.8%
Industrial/Energy	2.9%
Other Products	2.4%
Internet Specific	1.5%
Computer Hardware	1.2%

Additional Information

Name of Most Recent Fund: CW Ventures III-A Co-Investment Fund, L.P.
Most Recent Fund Was Raised: 03/31/1998
Year Founded: 1982
Capital Under Management: $200,000,000
Current Activity Level: Actively seeking new investments
Method of Compensation: Return on invest. most important, but chg. closing fees, service fees, etc.

CWC CAPITAL MANAGEMENT LLC

ul. Pulawska 17
Warsaw, Poland 02-515
Phone: 48-22-852-8193
Fax: 48-22-852-8190
Website: www.cwcpartners.com

Other Offices

MOM Park Centrum
Building D Alkotas u. 53
Budapest, Hungary 1123
Phone: 36-1-487-8010

Type of Firm

Private Equity Firm

Project Preferences

Type of Financing Preferred:
Balanced

Geographical Preferences

International Preferences:
Europe
Poland

Additional Information

Year Founded: 2004
Current Activity Level: Actively seeking new investments

CYBERNAUT (CHINA) CAPITAL MANAGEMENT

176 Tianmu Shan Road
3/F Shuyuan Keji Yuan
Hangzhou, China 310012
Phone: 86-571-89939898
Fax: 86-571-89939834
E-mail: contact@cybernaut.com.cn
Website: www.cybernaut.com.cn

Other Offices

20/F China Everbright Bank Building
Zhu Zi Lin, Futian District
Shenzhen, China 518040

No. 11 Chang Chun Bridge Road
Room 1502 Wan Liu Yi Cheng Center
Beijing, China 100089
Phone: 86-1-5881-9698
Fax: 86-1-5881-9566

No. 200 Yincheng Middle Road
Room 2705 Bank of China Tower
Shanghai, China 200120
Phone: 86-21-5037-2257

Management and Staff

Daryl Magana, Partner
David Ren, General Partner
Irwin Lan, Partner
Jason Zhao, General Partner
Lan Shi, Partner
Min Zhu, Founder
Minghai Zhou, Venture Partner
Paul Chen, Partner
Sha Wang, Principal
Tom Chen, General Partner
Wei Lu, Partner
Xuanyu Shang, General Partner
Yan Gu, Partner

Type of Firm

Bank Affiliated

Project Preferences

Type of Financing Preferred:
Early Stage
Expansion
Balanced

Geographical Preferences

International Preferences:
China

Industry Preferences

In Internet Specific prefer:
Internet
Ecommerce

In Medical/Health prefer:
Medical/Health

In Consumer Related prefer:
Consumer
Retail
Consumer Services
Education Related

In Industrial/Energy prefer:
Environmental Related

In Financial Services prefer:
Financial Services

In Business Serv. prefer:
Services
Media

In Manufact. prefer:
Manufacturing

Additional Information

Year Founded: 2006
Capital Under Management: $345,200,000
Current Activity Level: Actively seeking new investments

CYCAD GROUP LLC

6187 Carpinteria Avenue
Suite 300
Carpinteria, CA USA 93014
Phone: 805-684-6515
Fax: 805-684-6511
Website: www.cycadvc.com

Management and Staff

K. Leonard Judson, Managing Director
Robert Balch, Vice President

Type of Firm

Private Equity Firm

Project Preferences

Type of Financing Preferred:
Balanced

Geographical Preferences

United States Preferences:
All U.S.

Industry Preferences

In Semiconductor/Electr prefer:
Electronics

In Biotechnology prefer:
Biotechnology

In Medical/Health prefer:
Medical/Health
Medical Products
Pharmaceuticals

In Industrial/Energy prefer:
Energy
Advanced Materials

Additional Information

Year Founded: 2000
Current Activity Level: Actively seeking new investments

CYCLE CAPITAL MANAGEMENT

4050, rue Molson
Bureau 340
Montreal, Canada H1Y3N1
Phone: 514-495-1022
Fax: 514-495-8034
Website: www.cyclecapital.net

Management and Staff

Alain-Oliver Desbois, Partner
Andree-lise Methot, Founder

Type of Firm

Private Equity Firm

Project Preferences

Type of Financing Preferred:
Expansion
Early Stage

Additional Information

Year Founded: 2003
Current Activity Level: Actively seeking new investments

CYPRESSTREE INVESTMENT MANAGEMENT COMPANY, INC.

One Washington Mall
6th Floor
Boston, MA USA 02108
Phone: 617-371-9300
Fax: 617-371-9362
E-mail: info@cyptree.com
Website: www.cyptree.com

Management and Staff

Paul Foley, Chief Financial Officer

Type of Firm

Bank Affiliated

Additional Information

Year Founded: 1998
Current Activity Level: Actively seeking new investments

CYPRUS DEVELOPMENT BANK, THE

Alpha House
50 Arch. Makarios III Ave.
Nicosia, Cyprus 1508
Phone: 357-22-846-575
Fax: 357-22-846-600
Website: www.cyprusdevelopmentbank.com

Type of Firm
Bank Affiliated

Project Preferences

Type of Financing Preferred:
Balanced

Geographical Preferences

International Preferences:
Europe

Additional Information
Year Founded: 1963
Current Activity Level: Actively seeking new investments

CYRTE INVESTMENTS BV (FKA: TALPA CAPITAL BEHEER)
Flevolaan 41 A
Naarden, Netherlands 1411
Phone: 31-35-695-9090
Fax: 31-35-695-9044
Website: www.cyrte.com

Type of Firm
Private Equity Firm

Additional Information
Year Founded: 2004
Current Activity Level: Actively seeking new investments

- D -

D. CARNEGIE & CO AB
Gustav Adolfs Torg 18
Vastra Tradgardsgatan 15
Stockholm, Sweden SE-103 38
Phone: 46-8-676-8800
Fax: 46-8-676-8895
Website: www.carnegie.se

Management and Staff
Kristina Schauman, Chief Financial Officer
Mikael Ericson, Chief Executive Officer

Type of Firm
Bank Affiliated

Project Preferences

Type of Financing Preferred:
Fund of Funds
Expansion

Geographical Preferences

International Preferences:
Sweden
Scandanavia/Nordic Region

Additional Information
Year Founded: 1999
Current Activity Level: Actively seeking new investments

D. E. SHAW GROUP, THE
120 West Forty-Fifth Street
39th Floor
New York, NY USA 10036
Phone: 212-478-0000
Fax: 212-478-0100
E-mail: inquiries@deshaw.com
Website: www.deshaw.com

Other Offices
Vatika Towers, Tower B, 15th Floor
Sector 54, Golf Course Road
Gurgaon, India 122 002
Phone: 91-124-451-8300
Fax: 91-124-451-8400

3 Bethesda Metro Center
Suite 1450
Bethesda, MD USA 20814
Phone: 301-634-3000
Fax: 301-634-3050

44 Church Street West
Hamilton, Bermuda HM 12
Phone: 441-294-6650
Fax: 441-294-6670

One Embarcadero Center
Suite 3860
San Francisco, CA USA 94111
Phone: 415-268-2800
Fax: 415-268-2850

110 Newport Center Drive
Suite 200
Newport Beach, CA USA 92660
Phone: 949-719-1142
Fax: 949-719-1144

Sanali Infopark
8-2-120/113, Road No.2, Banjara Hills
Hyderabad, India 500 034
Phone: 91-40-6639-0000
Fax: 91-40-4016-4284

305, Ceejay House, Third Floor
Shiv Sagar Estate, Dr. Annie Besant Road
Mumbai, India 400 018
Phone: 91-22-4341-2000
Fax: 91-22-6747-0990

10000 Memorial Drive
Suite 500
Houston, TX USA 77024
Phone: 713-292-5400
Fax: 713-292-5450

20400 Stevens Creek Boulevard
Suite 850
Cupertino, CA USA 95014
Phone: 408-352-9600
Fax: 408-352-9670

19th Floor, York House
The Landmark,15 Queen's Road Central
Hong Kong, Hong Kong
Phone: 852-3521-2500
Fax: 852-3521-2600

Seventh Floor
55 Baker Street
London, United Kingdom W1U 8EW
Phone: 44-20-7409-4300
Fax: 44-20-7409-4350

Management and Staff
Alexander Wong, Managing Director

Type of Firm
Corporate PE/Venture

Association Membership
National Venture Capital Association - USA (NVCA)

Project Preferences

Role in Financing:
Will function either as deal originator or investor in deals created by others

Type of Financing Preferred:
Early Stage
Expansion
Later Stage
Seed

Size of Investments Considered:
Min Size of Investment Considered (000s): $1,000
Max Size of Investment Considered (000s): $50,000

Additional Information
Year Founded: 1988
Capital Under Management: $29,000,000,000
Current Activity Level: Actively seeking new investments

DA VINCI CAPITAL MANAGEMENT
Martello Court
Admiral Park, St Peter Port
Guernsey, United Kingdom GY1 3HB
E-mail: info@dvcap.com
Website: www.dvcap.com

Other Offices
Lotte Plaza 9th Floor
8-10, Novinsky Boulevard
Moscow, Russia 121099
Phone: 7-495-662-6370

7 Old Park Lane, Level 3
mayfair
London, United Kingdom W1K 1QR
Phone: 44-20-7529-6647

Management and Staff
Gleb Yakovlev, Partner
Natalia Ivanova, Partner
Oleg Jelezko, Chief Executive Officer
Steven Philipp, Chief Operating Officer

Type of Firm
Private Equity Firm

Project Preferences

Type of Financing Preferred:
Leveraged Buyout
Mezzanine
Balanced
Management Buyouts

Geographical Preferences

United States Preferences:
All U.S.

International Preferences:
Kazakhstan
Ukraine
Asia
Russia

Industry Preferences

In Consumer Related prefer:
Consumer Products
Consumer Services

In Financial Services prefer:
Real Estate
Investment Groups
Financial Services

Additional Information
Year Founded: 2008
Capital Under Management: $110,000,000
Current Activity Level: Actively seeking new investments

DACE VENTURES
31 St. James Avenue
Suite 850
Boston, MA USA 02116
Phone: 617-399-6931
E-mail: info@daceventures.com
Website: www.daceventures.com

Management and Staff
David Andonian, Managing General Partner
Jonathan Chait, Partner

Type of Firm
Private Equity Firm

Project Preferences

Type of Financing Preferred:
Early Stage
Balanced

Geographical Preferences

United States Preferences:
All U.S.

Industry Preferences

In Internet Specific prefer:
Internet

Additional Information
Year Founded: 2007
Capital Under Management: $78,000,000
Current Activity Level: Actively seeking new investments

DACHA CAPITAL, INC.
1801 McGill College Avenue
Suite 1260
Montreal, Canada H3A 2N4
Phone: 514-286-1660
Fax: 514-286-7811

Type of Firm
Private Equity Firm

Additional Information
Year Founded: 1996
Current Activity Level: Actively seeking new investments

DAEGYEONG VENTURE CAPITAL CORPORATION
4th Flr., Daegu Venture Center
Shincheon-dong, Dong-Gu
Daegu, South Korea 701-020
Phone: 82-53-751-2537
Fax: 82-53-751-2538
Website: www.dvc.co.kr

Other Offices
Maru Building, 6th Floor
942-20, Daechi-dong, Gangnam-gu
Seoul, South Korea 135-845
Phone: 82-2-553-2304
Fax: 82-2-553-2305

Type of Firm
Private Equity Firm

Association Membership
Korean Venture Capital Association (KVCA)

Project Preferences

Type of Financing Preferred:
Balanced

Geographical Preferences

International Preferences:
Korea, South

Industry Preferences

In Business Serv. prefer:
Services

Additional Information
Year Founded: 2006
Capital Under Management: $40,300,000
Current Activity Level: Actively seeking new investments

DAEYANG VENTURE CAPITAL CO., LTD.
2nd Floor, Samsung Fire
1329-3, Seocho-dong, Seocho-ku
Seoul, South Korea
Phone: 82-2-523-0256
Fax: 82-2-523-0618
Website: www.dyvc.com

Type of Firm
Corporate PE/Venture

Project Preferences

Type of Financing Preferred:
Early Stage
Seed

Geographical Preferences

International Preferences:
Asia

Industry Preferences

In Semiconductor/Electr prefer:
Semiconductor

In Biotechnology prefer:
Biotechnology

Additional Information

Year Founded: 1996
Current Activity Level: Actively seeking new investments

DAIWA SECURITIES SMBC PRINCIPAL INVESTMENTS CO. LTD.

Gran Tokyo North Tower
1-9-1 Marunouchi, Chiyoda-Ku
Tokyo, Japan 100-6754
Phone: 81-3-5555-6111
Fax: 81-3-3286-1815
Website: www.daiwasmbcpi.co.jp

Other Offices

1-14-5 Eidai
Koto-ku
Tokyo, Japan 135-0034
Phone: 81-3-5620-7111

3-15-30, Nishiki
Naka-ku
Nagoya, Japan 460-8691
Phone: 81-52-963-7200

1-13-20, Sonezakishinchi
Kita-ku
Osaka, Japan 530-8231
Phone: 81-6-6454-7000

Level 26, One Pacific Place
88 Queensway
Hong Kong, Hong Kong
Phone: 852-2848-4955
Fax: 852-2848-4012

Management and Staff

Akio Takahashi, Managing Director
Akira Inoue, President
Hideo Watanabe, Senior Managing Director
Ikuo Mori, Senior Managing Director
Kazuhiko Akamatsu, Senior Managing Director
Masaki Yamane, Managing Director
Mitsuharu Tanaka, Managing Director
Nobuaki Ohmura, President
Shin Yoshidome, President
Takashi Yamaguchi, Managing Director
Teruaki Ueda, Managing Director
Toshihiko Onishi, Managing Director

Type of Firm

Bank Affiliated

Project Preferences

Type of Financing Preferred:
Balanced

Geographical Preferences

International Preferences:
Japan

Additional Information

Year Founded: 2001
Capital Under Management: $18,300,000
Current Activity Level: Actively seeking new investments

DAIWA SMBC CAPITAL CO., LTD.

12F, Sumitomofudosan Kudan Bdg
1-8-10, Kudan-Kita, Chiyoda-ku
Tokyo, Japan 102-0073
Phone: 81-3-6910-2600
Fax: 81-3-3234-5013
Website: www.daiwasmbc-cap.co.jp

Other Offices

6 Shenton Way, #21-11
DBS Building Tower Two
Singapore, Singapore 068809
Phone: 65-6227-8121
Fax: 65-6224-6153

2300 Geng Road, Suite 220
Palo Alto, CA USA 94303

04-B, 15F, Aurora Plaza
No. 99 Fucheng Road, Pudong
Shanghai, China
Phone: 86-21-5879-4255
Fax: 86-21-5879-4208

Suites 250608,Two Pacific Place
88 Queensway
Hong Kong, Hong Kong
Phone: 852-2918-4111
Fax: 852-2918-4666

Management and Staff

Hisao Katsuta, Managing Director
Junichiro Wakimizu, President
Kazuo Ariake, President
Kohei Katsukawa, President
Yoshihide Shimamura, Senior Managing Director
Yoshio Narukage, Senior Managing Director

Type of Firm

Private Equity Firm

Association Membership

Singapore Venture Capital Association (SVCA)

Project Preferences

Type of Financing Preferred:
Early Stage
Expansion
Balanced
Seed
Later Stage
Management Buyouts
Startup
Recapitalizations

Geographical Preferences

International Preferences:
China
Asia
Japan

Industry Preferences

In Communications prefer:
Communications and Media

In Semiconductor/Electr prefer:
Electronics

In Biotechnology prefer:
Biotechnology

In Consumer Related prefer:
Consumer
Education Related

In Industrial/Energy prefer:
Energy Conservation Relat
Environmental Related

Additional Information

Year Founded: 1983
Capital Under Management: $735,300,000
Current Activity Level: Actively seeking new investments

DAKOTA CAPITAL

400 Oyster Point Boulevard
Suite 525
South San Francisco, CA USA 94080
Phone: 650-233-0808
Fax: 707-221-0542
E-mail: info@dakota.com
Website: www.dakota.com

Management and Staff

Andre Thomas, Venture Partner
Brooke Seawell, Venture Partner
Matt Freivald, Venture Partner
Stephen Meyer, Managing Partner
Tom Fisher, Venture Partner

Type of Firm

Private Equity Firm

Project Preferences

Role in Financing:
Prefer role as deal originator but will also invest in deals created by others

Type of Financing Preferred:
Second Stage Financing
Early Stage
Start-up Financing
Seed
First Stage Financing
Special Situation
Recapitalizations

Size of Investments Considered:
Min Size of Investment Considered (000s): $300
Max Size of Investment Considered (000s): $500

Geographical Preferences

United States Preferences:
Northwest
Southeast
Northeast
Rocky Mountain
Southwest

International Preferences:
United Kingdom
China
Middle East
Spain
Australia
Germany
France
Japan

Industry Preferences

In Communications prefer:
Commercial Communications
CATV & Pay TV Systems
Telecommunications
Data Communications

In Computer Software prefer:
Computer Services
Systems Software
Applications Software

In Consumer Related prefer:
Education Related

In Manufact. prefer:
Publishing

Additional Information
Year Founded: 1990
Capital Under Management: $25,000,000
Current Activity Level: Actively seeking new investments
Method of Compensation: Return on invest. most important, but chg. closing fees, service fees, etc.

DALIAN KAIDA VENTURE CAPITAL CO., LTD.
Room 2504 Tianan Int'l Bldg.
Zhongshan District
Dalian, China 116001
Phone: 86-411-39856899
Fax: 86-411-39805933
Website: www.dlkdvc.com

Management and Staff
Yulong Wang, President & Chairman

Type of Firm
Private Equity Firm

Project Preferences

Type of Financing Preferred:
Expansion
Later Stage

Geographical Preferences

International Preferences:
China

Industry Preferences

In Biotechnology prefer:
Biotechnology

In Medical/Health prefer:
Medical/Health
Health Services

In Industrial/Energy prefer:
Energy

In Financial Services prefer:
Financial Services

Additional Information
Year Founded: 2008
Current Activity Level: Actively seeking new investments

DANCAP PRIVATE EQUITY INC.
5000 Yonge Street
Suite 1705
Toronto, Canada M2N 7E9
Phone: 416-590-9398
Fax: 416-590-9488
Website: www.dancap.ca

Management and Staff
Aubrey Dan, President
Elias Toby, Chief Operating Officer
Shaun Kobrin, Managing Director

Type of Firm
Private Equity Firm

Association Membership
Canadian Venture Capital Association

Project Preferences

Type of Financing Preferred:
Expansion

Geographical Preferences

Canadian Preferences:
All Canada

Additional Information
Year Founded: 2002
Current Activity Level: Actively seeking new investments
Method of Compensation: Return on invest. most important, but chg. closing fees, service fees, etc.

DANFOSS CORPORATE VENTURES (AKA: INNOVATION A/S)
Nordborgvej 81
Nordborg, Denmark 6430
Phone: 45-748-822-22
Fax: 45-748-869-99
E-mail: danfoss@danfoss.com
Website: www.ventures.danfoss.com

Management and Staff
Hans Jorgen Pedersen, President

Type of Firm
Corporate PE/Venture

Association Membership
Danish Venture Capital Association (DVCA)
European Private Equity and Venture Capital Assoc.

Project Preferences

Type of Financing Preferred:
Second Stage Financing
Early Stage
Expansion

Geographical Preferences

Canadian Preferences:
All Canada

International Preferences:
Europe

Industry Preferences

In Industrial/Energy prefer:
Energy
Alternative Energy
Coal Related
Materials

Additional Information
Year Founded: 2000
Current Activity Level: Actively seeking new investments

DANIA CAPITAL K/S
Borgergade 111
Copenhagen, Denmark 1300
Phone: 45-7011-6663
Fax: 45-3347-6663
E-mail: info@daniacapital.dk
Website: www.daniacapital.dk

Management and Staff

Jorgen Jensen, Partner
Lars Fejer, Partner
Soren Jessen Nielsen, Partner
Thomas Dywremose, Managing Partner

Type of Firm

Private Equity Firm

Association Membership

European Private Equity and Venture Capital Assoc.

Project Preferences

Role in Financing:

Prefer role as deal originator

Type of Financing Preferred:

Generalist PE

Geographical Preferences

International Preferences:

Europe
Norway
Denmark

Industry Preferences

In Business Serv. prefer:

Services
Distribution

Additional Information

Year Founded: 2003
Capital Under Management: $106,700,000
Current Activity Level: Actively seeking new investments

DANISCO VENTURE

Langebrogade 1
P.O. Box 17
Copenhagen, Denmark DK-1001
Phone: 45-3266-2300
Fax: 45-3266-2159
E-mail: venture@danisco.com
Website: www.danisco.com

Management and Staff

Lars Dybkjaer, Venture Partner
Leif Kjaergaard, President

Type of Firm

Corporate PE/Venture

Association Membership

Danish Venture Capital Association (DVCA)
European Private Equity and Venture Capital Assoc.

Project Preferences

Type of Financing Preferred:

Early Stage
Seed
Startup

Geographical Preferences

International Preferences:

Scandanavia/Nordic Region

Industry Preferences

In Biotechnology prefer:

Biotechnology

In Consumer Related prefer:

Food/Beverage

In Business Serv. prefer:

Services

Additional Information

Year Founded: 2001
Capital Under Management: $60,000,000
Current Activity Level: Actively seeking new investments

DANISH INTERNATIONAL INVESTMENT FUND, THE (AKA: IFU)

Bremerholm 4
Copenhagen, Denmark 1069
Phone: 45-3363-7500
Fax: 45-3335-2524
Website: www.ifu.dk

Other Offices

Room 804, Diyang Tower
No. 2H Dongsanhuan Beilu
Beijing, China 100027
Phone: 86-10-6460-9797
Fax: 86-10-6460-9799

Rua Riachuelo 460, Edifico Trade Tower
Office 1105
Sao Paulo, Brazil 18035-330
Phone: 55-15-3224-1030
Fax: 55-15-3231-4442

2nd Floor, SPWD Building
14 A, Vishnu Digambhar Marg
New Delhi, India 110002
Phone: 91-11-2321-7160
Fax: 91-11-2321-7167

32 Belmont Avenue
Oranjezicht
Cape Town, South Africa 8001
Phone: 27-21-465-5701
Fax: 27-21-465-5701

1016 Oak Hill Fourways Golf Park
Roos Street Fourways
Johannesburg, South Africa 2055
Phone: 27-11-467-4070
Fax: 27-11-467-4079

13 Runda Drive
Runda
Nairobi, Kenya 00100 GPO
Phone: 254-712-980-553
Fax: 254-204-451-474

ul. Mokotowska 23/8
Warsaw, Poland 00-560
Phone: 48-22-621-1377
Fax: 48-22-621-8363

21, rue du Chemin de Fer, B.P.
Lome, Togo 7373
Phone: 228-221-7807
Fax: 228-221-7513

Management and Staff

Svend Risaer, Managing Director
Torben Huss, Managing Director

Type of Firm

Private Equity Firm

Association Membership

European Private Equity and Venture Capital Assoc.
African Venture Capital Association (AVCA)
Indian Venture Capital Association (IVCA)

Project Preferences

Type of Financing Preferred:

Expansion

Size of Investments Considered:

Min Size of Investment Considered (000s): $136
Max Size of Investment Considered (000s): $9,137

Geographical Preferences

International Preferences:

Latin America
Central Europe
Eastern Europe
Middle East
Pacific
Africa
All International

Additional Information

Year Founded: 1967
Capital Under Management: $224,600,000
Current Activity Level: Actively seeking new investments

DANSK ERHVERVSUDVIKLING A/S

Lemchesvej 6
Hellerup, Denmark 2900
Phone: 45-7020-8013
Fax: 45-7020-8003
E-mail: d-e@d-e.dk
Website: www.d-e.dk

Type of Firm

Private Equity Firm

Project Preferences

Type of Financing Preferred:
Leveraged Buyout

Size of Investments Considered:
Min Size of Investment Considered (000s): $2,451
Max Size of Investment Considered (000s): $18,386

Geographical Preferences

International Preferences:
Denmark

Industry Focus

(% based on actual investment)

Computer Software and Services	90.3%
Consumer Related	9.7%

Additional Information

Year Founded: 1997
Capital Under Management: $4,400,000
Current Activity Level: Actively seeking new investments

DANSK KAPITALANLAEG AKTIESELSKAB

Gothersgade 103
Copenhagen , Denmark DK-1123
Phone: 45-33-157-030
Fax: 45-33-369-444
E-mail: dankap@dankap.dk
Website: www.dankap.dk

Management and Staff

Kjeld Bock, Partner
Lars Dybkjaer, Partner
Niels Kristian Agner, Managing Director
Steen Lonberg Jorgensen, Managing Partner

Type of Firm

Private Equity Firm

Association Membership

European Private Equity and Venture Capital Assoc.

Project Preferences

Type of Financing Preferred:
Fund of Funds
Leveraged Buyout
Expansion
Start-up Financing
Turnaround
Recapitalizations

Size of Investments Considered:
Min Size of Investment Considered (000s): $625
Max Size of Investment Considered (000s): $18,735

Geographical Preferences

International Preferences:
Europe
Denmark

Industry Focus

(% based on actual investment)

Medical/Health	29.4%
Other Products	21.5%
Biotechnology	21.0%
Internet Specific	11.1%
Industrial/Energy	7.9%
Semiconductors/Other Elect.	6.7%
Computer Software and Services	1.9%
Consumer Related	0.7%

Additional Information

Year Founded: 1984
Capital Under Management: $275,000,000
Current Activity Level: Actively seeking new investments

DANSKE PRIVATE EQUITY A/S

Ny Kongensgade 10
Copenhagen, Denmark DK-1472
Phone: 45-3344-6300
Fax: 45-3344-6301
E-mail: info@danskeprivateequity.com
Website: www.danskeprivateequity.com

Management and Staff

Carsten Ronfeldt, Chief Financial Officer
Dan Kjerulf, Partner
John Danielsen, Managing Partner
Klaus Friis, Partner

Type of Firm

Private Equity Advisor or Fund of Funds

Association Membership

Danish Venture Capital Association (DVCA)
European Private Equity and Venture Capital Assoc.

Project Preferences

Role in Financing:
Other

Type of Financing Preferred:
Fund of Funds

Geographical Preferences

United States Preferences:
All U.S.

Canadian Preferences:
All Canada

International Preferences:
Western Europe

Additional Information

Name of Most Recent Fund: Danske Private Equity Partners III (DPEP III)
Most Recent Fund Was Raised: 12/01/2005
Year Founded: 2000
Capital Under Management: $505,500,000
Current Activity Level: Actively seeking new investments
Method of Compensation: Other

DANUBE EQUITY INVEST-MANAGEMENT GMBH

Hafenstrasse 47-51
Linz, Austria 4020
Phone: 43-732-90155360
Fax: 43-732-90155370
E-mail: office@danubequity.com
Website: www.danubequity.com

Type of Firm

Corporate PE/Venture

Association Membership

Austrian PE and Venture Capital Association (AVCO)
European Private Equity and Venture Capital Assoc.

Project Preferences

Type of Financing Preferred:
Early Stage
Expansion

Size of Investments Considered:
Min Size of Investment Considered (000s): $600
Max Size of Investment Considered: No Limit

Geographical Preferences

International Preferences:
Europe
Eastern Europe

Industry Preferences

In Internet Specific prefer:
Internet

In Semiconductor/Electr prefer:
Electronics

In Industrial/Energy prefer:
Industrial Products
Materials
Factory Automation

In Other prefer:
Environment Responsible

Additional Information

Year Founded: 2000
Capital Under Management: $33,000,000
Current Activity Level: Actively seeking new investments

DANVILLE PARTNERS, LLC

815 Superior Avenue
Cleveland, OH USA 44114
Phone: 216-928-4342
E-mail: info@danvillepartners.com
Website: www.danvillepartners.com

Management and Staff

Michael Gaudiani, Managing Partner

Type of Firm
Private Equity Firm

Project Preferences

Type of Financing Preferred:
Balanced

Size of Investments Considered:
Min Size of Investment Considered (000s): $2,000
Max Size of Investment Considered (000s): $15,000

Geographical Preferences

United States Preferences:
All U.S.

Industry Preferences

In Computer Software prefer:
Software

In Semiconductor/Electr prefer:
Component Testing Equipmt

In Medical/Health prefer:
Medical/Health

In Industrial/Energy prefer:
Industrial Products
Environmental Related

In Business Serv. prefer:
Services
Distribution

In Manufact. prefer:
Manufacturing

Additional Information
Year Founded: 2000
Current Activity Level: Actively seeking new investments

DARBY OVERSEAS INVESTMENTS, LTD.
1133 Connecticut Avenue, NW
Suite 400
Washington, DC USA 20036
Phone: 202-872-0500
Fax: 202-872-1816
Website: www.darbyoverseas.com

Other Offices
Templeton Research Poland
Rondo 1, 29th floor
Warsaw, Poland 00-124
Phone: 48-22-337-1380
Fax: 48-22-337-1373

Tesvikiye Bostani Sokak
Orjin Apartment Number 15, Kat 8
Istanbul, Turkey 34367
Phone: 90-212-291-5222
Fax: 90-212-291-5223

Montes Urales 770
Oficina 401
Col. Lomas de Chapultepec, Mexico DF 11000
Phone: 52-55-5002-0660
Fax: 52-55-2623-0661

12 Youido-dong, Youngdungpo-gu
10th Floor, CCMM Building
Seoul, South Korea 150-968
Phone: 822-3774-0605
Fax: 822-3774-06617

Avenida Brigadeiro Faria Lima, 3311
5 andar
Sao Paulo, Brazil 04538-133
Phone: 5511-3206-0080
Fax: 5511-3077-3775

200 South Biscayne Boulevard
Suite 3050
Miami, FL USA 33131
Phone: 305-982-1592
Fax: 305-982-1593

7 Temasek Blvd. #38-03 Suntec Tower One
Templeton Asset Management, Ltd.
Singapore, Singapore 038987
Phone: 65-6-338-6100
Fax: 65-332-1088

Dr. Karl Lueger-Ring 10
Vienna, Austria A-1010
Phone: 43-1-53226-5500
Fax: 43-1-53226-5550

600 Fifth Avenue, Fourth Floor
Fiduciary Trust Company, International
New York, NY USA 10020
Phone: 212-632-3000
Fax: 212-632-3265

Suites 911-919
Jardine House, 1 Connaught Place
Central, Hong Kong
Phone: 852-2910-9200
Fax: 852-2521-9815

Bank Centre, Citibank Tower, First Floor
Szabadsag ter 7
Budapest, Hungary H-1054
Phone: 36-1-474-8192
Fax: 36-1-474-8404

Wockhardt Tower (East Wing), Level 4
C-2, G-Block, Bandra Kurla Complex
Mumbai, India 400051
Phone: 91-22-6751-9100
Fax: 91-22-6649-0622

Management and Staff
Bong Kyun Shin, Principal
Burak Dalgin, Vice President
Cathina Poon, Principal
Clark Nielsen, Senior Managing Director
David Wong, Vice President
David Hudson, Senior Managing Director
Deepa Sankaran, Principal
Diane Smith, Principal
Eduardo Farhat, Principal
Fernando Luque, Vice President
Fernando Gentil, Managing Director
Jang Yeon Kim, Principal
Jonathan Whittle, Principal
Julio Lastres, Senior Managing Director
Jun Suk Hwang, Vice President
Kyu-Hwan Lee, Principal
Nicholas Kabcenell, Managing Director
Patrick Zee, Vice President
Phil Patman, Principal
R. Michael Barth, Senior Managing Director
Richard Frank, Chief Executive Officer
Robert Graffam, Senior Managing Director
Simon Sham, Managing Director
Thomas Niss, Vice President
Woonki Sung, Managing Director

Type of Firm
Private Equity Firm

Association Membership
European Private Equity and Venture Capital Assoc.

Project Preferences

Role in Financing:
Prefer role as deal originator but will also invest in deals created by others

Type of Financing Preferred:
Leveraged Buyout
Expansion
Mezzanine
Generalist PE
Balanced
Management Buyouts

Geographical Preferences

International Preferences:
India
Latin America
Central Europe
China
Brazil
Mexico
Eastern Europe
Korea, South
Asia
Colombia

Industry Focus
(% based on actual investment)

Communications and Media	26.9%
Other Products	25.5%
Consumer Related	18.2%
Internet Specific	9.5%
Medical/Health	9.4%
Industrial/Energy	7.2%
Computer Software and Services	2.2%
Biotechnology	1.2%

Additional Information
Year Founded: 1994
Capital Under Management: $1,800,000,000
Current Activity Level: Actively seeking new investments

Method of Compensation: Return on invest. most important, but chg. closing fees, service fees, etc.

DARBY TECHNOLOGY VENTURES GROUP (AKA: DTV)

1133 Conneticut Avenue, NW
Suite 400
Washington, DC USA 20036
Phone: 202-872-0500
Fax: 202-872-1816
Website: www.darbyoverseas.com

Management and Staff

Jonathan Whittle, Principal
Julio Lastres, Senior Managing Director
Richard Frank, Chief Executive Officer

Type of Firm

Private Equity Firm

Project Preferences

Type of Financing Preferred:
Early Stage
Expansion
Later Stage

Geographical Preferences

International Preferences:
Latin America
Argentina
Mexico

Industry Preferences

In Communications prefer:
Communications and Media

In Computer Software prefer:
Software

In Internet Specific prefer:
Internet

Additional Information

Year Founded: 2000
Current Activity Level: Actively seeking new investments

DARWIN PRIVATE EQUITY LLP

29 St. James's Place
London, United Kingdom SW1A 1NP
Website: www.darwinpe.com

Management and Staff

Derek Elliott, Co-Founder
Jonathan Kaye, Co-Founder
Kevin Street, Co-Founder

Type of Firm

Private Equity Firm

Association Membership

British Venture Capital Association (BVCA)

Project Preferences

Type of Financing Preferred:
Leveraged Buyout

Size of Investments Considered:
Min Size of Investment Considered (000s): $96,000
Max Size of Investment Considered (000s): $193,200

Geographical Preferences

International Preferences:
United Kingdom

Industry Preferences

In Industrial/Energy prefer:
Industrial Products

In Financial Services prefer:
Financial Services

Additional Information

Year Founded: 2007
Capital Under Management: $96,000,000
Current Activity Level: Actively seeking new investments

DARWIN VENTURE CAPITAL CO., LTD.

No. 1407 SK Leader's View
168 Dogok-dong, Gangam-gu
Seoul, South Korea 135-270
Phone: 822-575-5200
Fax: 822-575-3223

Management and Staff

Yongdong Yeo, Chief Executive Officer

Type of Firm

Private Equity Firm

Project Preferences

Type of Financing Preferred:
Balanced

Additional Information

Year Founded: 2008
Current Activity Level: Actively seeking new investments

DARWIN VENTURES LLC

One Embarcadero Center
Suite 2310
San Francisco, CA USA 94111
Phone: 415-362-0794
Fax: 415-362-7006
E-mail: info@darwinvc.com
Website: www.darwinvc.com

Management and Staff

Frank Caufield, Managing Partner
Ken Hausman, Partner
Peter Freudenthal, Managing Partner
Robert Young, Partner
Sunil Kurkure, Principal

Type of Firm

Private Equity Advisor or Fund of Funds

Project Preferences

Type of Financing Preferred:
Fund of Funds

Geographical Preferences

United States Preferences:
All U.S.

Additional Information

Year Founded: 2002
Capital Under Management: $92,100,000
Current Activity Level: Actively seeking new investments

DASSAULT DEVELOPPEMENT

8 avenue Franklin Roosevelt
Paris, France 75008
Phone: 33-1-5688-3200
Fax: 33-1-5688-3209
E-mail: info@dassault-developpement.fr
Website: www.dassault-developpement.fr

Management and Staff

Benoit Habert, Partner
Jean-Claude Leveque, Partner
Jean-Marie Chauvet, Partner
Luc Lechelle, Partner

Type of Firm

Corporate PE/Venture

Association Membership

European Private Equity and Venture Capital Assoc.

Project Preferences

Type of Financing Preferred:
Early Stage
Expansion
Startup

Geographical Preferences

United States Preferences:
All U.S.

International Preferences:
Europe
Israel

Industry Focus

(% based on actual investment)

Internet Specific	54.9%
Computer Software and Services	15.5%
Semiconductors/Other Elect.	14.1%
Consumer Related	10.3%
Biotechnology	4.1%
Other Products	1.2%

Additional Information

Year Founded: 1995
Capital Under Management: $89,100,000
Current Activity Level: Actively seeking new investments

DATABANK FINANCIAL SERVICES LTD

61 Barnes Road Adabraca
Accra, Ghana
Phone: 233-21-610610
Fax: 233-21-681443
E-mail: info@databankgh.com
Website: www.databankgroup.com

Other Offices

Meridian Plaza, Room 206 & 207, 2nd Floo
Community 1
Tema, Ghana
Phone: 233-22-210050
Fax: 233-22-203438

SSNIT Office Complex, Block B 2nd Floor
Harper Road
Kumasi, Ghana
Phone: 233-51-23487
Fax: 233-51-29740

Type of Firm

Private Equity Advisor or Fund of Funds

Association Membership

African Venture Capital Association (AVCA)

Project Preferences

Type of Financing Preferred:
Early Stage
Expansion
Turnaround
Management Buyouts
Recapitalizations

Size of Investments Considered:
Min Size of Investment Considered (000s): $50
Max Size of Investment Considered (000s): $500

Geographical Preferences

International Preferences:
Ghana

Industry Preferences

In Consumer Related prefer:
Food/Beverage

Additional Information

Year Founded: 2004
Capital Under Management: $7,000,000
Current Activity Level: Actively seeking new investments

DAUPHIN CAPITAL PARTNERS

108 Forest Avenue
Locust Valley, NY USA 11560
Phone: 516-759-3339
Fax: 516-759-3322
Website: www.dauphincapital.com

Management and Staff

James Hoover, Managing Partner

Type of Firm

Private Equity Firm

Project Preferences

Role in Financing:
Prefer role as deal originator but will also invest in deals created by others

Type of Financing Preferred:
Second Stage Financing
Expansion
Management Buyouts
First Stage Financing
Acquisition

Size of Investments Considered:
Min Size of Investment Considered (000s): $1,000
Max Size of Investment Considered (000s): $10,000

Geographical Preferences

United States Preferences:
Mid Atlantic
Southeast
Northeast

Industry Preferences

In Medical/Health prefer:
Diagnostic Services
Health Services
Hospitals/Clinics/Primary
Hospital/Other Instit.

Additional Information

Name of Most Recent Fund: Dauphin Capital Partners II, L.P.
Most Recent Fund Was Raised: 10/01/2001
Year Founded: 1998
Capital Under Management: $36,000,000
Current Activity Level: Actively seeking new investments
Method of Compensation: Return on investment is of primary concern, do not charge fees

---

DAVIES WARD PHILLIPS & VINEBERG

44th Floor
First Canadian Place
Toronto, Canada M5X1B1
Phone: 416-367-6972
Fax: 416-863-0871
E-mail: mduncan@dwpv.com
Website: www.dwpv.com

Management and Staff

Carol Pennycook, Partner

Type of Firm

Private Equity Firm

Additional Information

Year Founded: 2009
Current Activity Level: Actively seeking new investments

DAVIS, TUTTLE VENTURE PARTNERS, L.P. (AKA: DTVP)

110 West Seventh Street
Suite 1000
Tulsa, OK USA 74106-3703
Phone: 918-584-7272
Fax: 918-582-3404
Website: www.davistuttle.com

Other Offices

Eight Greenway Plaza
Suite 1320
Houston, TX USA 77046
Phone: 713-993-0440
Fax: 713-621-2297

Management and Staff

Albert Laverty, Partner
Barry Davis, Managing General Partner
H. Lee Frost, Chief Financial Officer
Philip Tuttle, General Partner
W. Michael Partain, Partner

Type of Firm

Private Equity Firm

Association Membership

National Venture Capital Association - USA (NVCA)
Natl Assoc of Small Bus. Inv. Co (NASBIC)

Project Preferences

Role in Financing:
Prefer role as deal originator but will also invest in deals created by others

Type of Financing Preferred:
Second Stage Financing
Leveraged Buyout
Early Stage

Expansion
Mezzanine
Balanced
First Stage Financing
Acquisition

Size of Investments Considered:
Min Size of Investment Considered (000s): $1,000
Max Size of Investment Considered (000s): $4,500

Geographical Preferences

United States Preferences:
Southwest

Industry Focus

(% based on actual investment)

Medical/Health	27.2%
Industrial/Energy	23.5%
Consumer Related	19.6%
Other Products	15.6%
Computer Software and Services	4.5%
Semiconductors/Other Elect.	3.6%
Internet Specific	3.1%
Communications and Media	3.0%

Additional Information
Year Founded: 1998
Capital Under Management: $45,300,000
Current Activity Level: Actively seeking new investments
Method of Compensation: Return on investment is of primary concern, do not charge fees

---

DAWN CAPITAL

14 Buckingham Street
London, United Kingdom WC2N 6DF

Type of Firm
Private Equity Firm

Project Preferences

Type of Financing Preferred:
Balanced

Geographical Preferences

International Preferences:
United Kingdom

Additional Information
Year Founded: 2008
Current Activity Level: Actively seeking new investments

DAWNAY DAY PRINCIPAL INVESTMENTS

15 Grosvenor Gardens
London, United Kingdom SW1W 0BD
Phone: 44-207-834-8060
Fax: 44-207-828-1992
Website: www.dawnayday.com

Type of Firm
Bank Affiliated

Project Preferences

Type of Financing Preferred:
Leveraged Buyout
Management Buyouts
Acquisition

Geographical Preferences

International Preferences:
United Kingdom
Europe

Industry Preferences

In Consumer Related prefer:
Consumer
Entertainment and Leisure

In Financial Services prefer:
Real Estate

Additional Information
Year Founded: 2003
Current Activity Level: Actively seeking new investments

DAWNTREADER VENTURES

520 Madison Avenue
Ninth Floor
New York, NY USA 10022
Phone: 646-452-6100
Fax: 646-452-6101
E-mail: info@dtventures.com
Website: www.dtventures.com

Management and Staff
Daniel DeWolf, Managing Director
Edward Sim, Managing Director
Jennifer Moy, Vice President
Ned Carlson, Managing Director
Sang Ahn, Principal

Type of Firm
Private Equity Firm

Project Preferences

Role in Financing:
Will function either as deal originator or investor in deals created by others

Type of Financing Preferred:
Second Stage Financing
Early Stage
Seed
First Stage Financing

Size of Investments Considered:
Min Size of Investment Considered (000s): $1,000
Max Size of Investment Considered (000s): $15,000

Geographical Preferences

United States Preferences:
Mid Atlantic
Northeast

Industry Focus

(% based on actual investment)

Internet Specific	53.6%
Computer Software and Services	32.4%
Semiconductors/Other Elect.	4.8%
Communications and Media	4.5%
Other Products	3.2%
Consumer Related	1.4%

Additional Information
Year Founded: 1998
Capital Under Management: $300,000,000
Current Activity Level: Actively seeking new investments

DB CAPITAL PARTNERS AUSTRALIA

c/o Propel Investments
Level 12, 201 Kent Street
Sydney, Australia 2000
Phone: 612-8272-5200
Fax: 612-8272-5222

Type of Firm
Private Equity Firm

Project Preferences

Type of Financing Preferred:
Balanced

Additional Information
Year Founded: 1994
Current Activity Level: Actively seeking new investments

DBL INVESTORS (AKA: DOUBLE BOTTOM LINE VENTURE CAPITAL)

One Bush Street
12th floor
San Francisco, CA USA 94104
Phone: 415-354-2867
Fax: 415-986-3230
Website: www.dblinvestors.com

Management and Staff
Cynthia Ringo, Managing Partner
Mark Perutz, Partner
Michael Dorsey, Managing Partner
Nancy Pfund, Managing Partner
Seth Miller, Partner

Type of Firm
Private Equity Firm

Project Preferences

Type of Financing Preferred:
Expansion
Later Stage

Geographical Preferences

United States Preferences:
California
All U.S.

Industry Preferences

In Medical/Health prefer:
Health Services

In Consumer Related prefer:
Consumer Products
Consumer Services

Additional Information
Name of Most Recent Fund: Bay Area Equity Fund II, L.P.
Most Recent Fund Was Raised: 12/23/2008
Year Founded: 2008
Capital Under Management: $109,400,000
Current Activity Level: Actively seeking new investments

DBS PRIVATE EQUITY
6 Shenton Way
30F, DBS Building Tower
Singapore, Singapore 068809
Phone: 65-6878-6446
Fax: 65-6227-6811
E-mail: contactgts@dbs.com
Website: www.DBS.com.sg

Other Offices
22F, The Center
99 Queen's Road
Central, Hong Kong
Phone: 852-2218-2723
Fax: 852-2259-5106

Management and Staff
Joan Tan, Vice President
Melvin Teo Tian Sing, Managing Director
Teo Eu Seng, Vice President

Type of Firm
Bank Affiliated

Association Membership
Korean Venture Capital Association (KVCA)
Singapore Venture Capital Association (SVCA)

Project Preferences

Role in Financing:
Prefer role as deal originator but will also invest in deals created by others

Type of Financing Preferred:
Second Stage Financing
Leveraged Buyout
Mezzanine
Expansion
Generalist PE
Balanced
Turnaround
Management Buyouts
First Stage Financing
Acquisition

Geographical Preferences

International Preferences:
China
Pacific
Asia

Industry Preferences

In Communications prefer:
Telecommunications

In Computer Other prefer:
Computer Related

In Semiconductor/Electr prefer:
Electronics

In Consumer Related prefer:
Food/Beverage
Consumer Products
Consumer Services

In Financial Services prefer:
Financial Services

In Business Serv. prefer:
Media

Additional Information
Year Founded: 1986
Capital Under Management: $171,500,000
Current Activity Level: Actively seeking new investments
Method of Compensation: Return on investment is of primary concern, do not charge fees

---

DC CAPITAL PARTNERS LLC
975 F Street North West
Suite 1050
Washington, DC USA 20004
Phone: 202-737-5220
Fax: 202-737-5225
E-mail: info@dccapitalpartners.com
Website: www.dccapitalpartners.com

Other Offices
11 Canal Center Plaza
Suite 110
Alexandria, VA USA 22314

Management and Staff
Gail Dady, Partner
Thomas Campbell, President, Founder

Type of Firm
Private Equity Firm

Project Preferences

Type of Financing Preferred:
Leveraged Buyout

Geographical Preferences

United States Preferences:
All U.S.

Additional Information
Year Founded: 1988
Current Activity Level: Actively seeking new investments

DC THOMSON & CO
185 Fleet Street
London, United Kingdom EC4A 2HS
Phone: 020-7400-1030
Fax: 020-7831-9440
E-mail: mail@sundaypost.com
Website: www.dcthomson.co.uk

Type of Firm
Private Equity Firm

Additional Information
Year Founded: 2004
Current Activity Level: Actively seeking new investments

DCA PARTNERS, INC.
3721 Douglas Boulevard
Suite 350
Roseville, CA USA 95661
Phone: 916-960-5350
Fax: 916-960-5360
E-mail: contact@dcapartners.com
Website: www.dcapartners.com

Other Offices
2425 East Camelback Road
Suite 850
Phoenix, AZ USA 85016

Management and Staff
Casey Layton, Chief Financial Officer
Curtis Rocca, Managing Director
Steven Mills, General Partner

Type of Firm
Private Equity Firm

Project Preferences

Type of Financing Preferred:
Leveraged Buyout
Generalist PE
Later Stage
Acquisition
Recapitalizations

Size of Investments Considered:
Min Size of Investment Considered (000s): $3,000
Max Size of Investment Considered (000s): $10,000

Geographical Preferences

United States Preferences:
Northern California
California
Southwest

Industry Preferences

In Medical/Health prefer:
Health Services

In Consumer Related prefer:
Retail

In Financial Services prefer:
Financial Services

In Business Serv. prefer:
Services
Distribution
Media

In Manufact. prefer:
Manufacturing
Publishing

Additional Information
Year Founded: 2005
Capital Under Management: $20,000,000
Current Activity Level: Actively seeking new investments

DCM (FKA: DOLL CAPITAL MANAGEMENT)
2420 Sand Hill Road
Suite 200
Menlo Park, CA USA 94025
Phone: 650-233-1400
Fax: 650-854-9159
Website: www.dcm.com

Other Offices
Yamato Seimei Building 5F
1-1-7 Uchisaiwaicho, Chiyoda-ku
Tokyo, Japan
Phone: 11-813-3580-1451
Fax: 11-813-3580-5840

Unit 1, Level 10, Tower W2, The Towers
Oriental Plaza No. 1 East Chang An Ave.
Beijing, China 100738
Phone: 8610-8515-1180
Fax: 8610-8515-1179

Management and Staff
Bob Hawk, Venture Partner
Carl Amdahl, General Partner
David Chao, General Partner
Dixon Doll, General Partner
Gen Isayama, Partner
Hurst Lin, General Partner
Lisa Harris, Chief Financial Officer
Osuke Honda, Principal
Peter Moran, General Partner
Ruby Lu, Partner
Scott Alberts, Venture Partner
Thomas Blaisdell, General Partner

Type of Firm
Private Equity Firm

Association Membership
Western Association of Venture Capitalists (WAVC)
National Venture Capital Association - USA (NVCA)

Project Preferences

Role in Financing:
Will function either as deal originator or investor in deals created by others

Type of Financing Preferred:
Second Stage Financing
Early Stage
Mezzanine
Later Stage
Seed
First Stage Financing

Size of Investments Considered:
Min Size of Investment Considered (000s): $3,000
Max Size of Investment Considered (000s): $7,000

Geographical Preferences

United States Preferences:
Northwest
Northern California
West Coast

International Preferences:
China
Asia
Japan
All International

Industry Focus
(% based on actual investment)

Internet Specific	37.1%
Computer Software and Services	19.3%
Communications and Media	12.9%
Semiconductors/Other Elect.	12.3%
Other Products	7.7%
Computer Hardware	7.3%
Industrial/Energy	2.4%
Consumer Related	1.0%

Additional Information
Year Founded: 1996
Capital Under Management: $1,600,000,000
Current Activity Level: Actively seeking new investments
Method of Compensation: Return on investment is of primary concern, do not charge fees

DDJ CAPITAL MANAGEMENT, LLC
130 Turner Street
Building 3 Suite 600
Waltham, MA USA 02453
Phone: 781-283-8500
Fax: 781-283-8555
E-mail: inforequest@ddjcap.com
Website: www.ddjcap.com

Management and Staff
Jackson Craig, Managing Partner
Jay Russell, Chief Financial Officer

Type of Firm
Bank Affiliated

Project Preferences

Type of Financing Preferred:
Leveraged Buyout
Turnaround
Other
Distressed Debt

Industry Focus
(% based on actual investment)

Internet Specific	32.5%
Medical/Health	29.4%
Consumer Related	23.6%
Computer Software and Services	4.8%
Industrial/Energy	3.9%
Semiconductors/Other Elect.	3.1%
Other Products	1.8%
Communications and Media	1.0%

Additional Information
Year Founded: 1996
Capital Under Management: $444,000,000
Current Activity Level: Actively seeking new investments

DE KRUIJFF VENTURE PARTNERS
Postbus 40280
Utrecht, Netherlands 3504 AB
Phone: 31-34-628-28-93
Fax: 31-34-628-26-13

Type of Firm
Private Equity Firm

Additional Information
Current Activity Level: Actively seeking new investments

DE NOVO VENTURES
400 Hamilton Avenue
Suite 300
Palo Alto, CA USA 94301

Phone: 650-329-1999
Fax: 650-329-1315
Website: www.denovovc.com

Management and Staff

Cathy Minshall, Chief Financial Officer
David Mauney, Managing Director
Frederick Dotzler, Managing Director
Jay Watkins, Managing Director
Joseph Mandato, Managing Director
Richard Ferrari, Managing Director

Type of Firm

Private Equity Firm

Association Membership

Western Association of Venture Capitalists (WAVC)
National Venture Capital Association - USA (NVCA)

Project Preferences

Role in Financing:

Will function either as deal originator or investor in deals created by others

Type of Financing Preferred:

Early Stage
Expansion
Seed
First Stage Financing
Startup

Size of Investments Considered:

Min Size of Investment Considered (000s): $1,000
Max Size of Investment Considered (000s): $10,000

Geographical Preferences

United States Preferences:

Northwest
Rocky Mountain
West Coast
Southwest

Industry Preferences

In Internet Specific prefer:

Internet

In Biotechnology prefer:

Biotechnology
Human Biotechnology
Industrial Biotechnology
Biosensors
Biotech Related Research

In Medical/Health prefer:

Medical Diagnostics
Diagnostic Test Products
Medical Therapeutics
Drug/Equipmt Delivery
Medical Products
Disposable Med. Products
Pharmaceuticals

Additional Information

Name of Most Recent Fund: De Novo Ventures III, L.P.
Most Recent Fund Was Raised: 08/01/2006
Year Founded: 2000
Capital Under Management: $650,000,000
Current Activity Level: Actively seeking new investments
Method of Compensation: Return on investment is of primary concern, do not charge fees

---

DEAL MANAGEMENT LTD.

Longboat
56 Sir John Rogersons Quay
Dublin 2, Ireland
Phone: 353-1-677 0365
Fax: 353-1-677 0483
E-mail: dealman@eircom.net
Website: www.glanbiaenterprisefund.com

Type of Firm

Private Equity Advisor or Fund of Funds

Project Preferences

Type of Financing Preferred:

Second Stage Financing
Early Stage
Expansion
First Stage Financing

Size of Investments Considered:

Min Size of Investment Considered (000s): $355
Max Size of Investment Considered (000s): $710

Geographical Preferences

International Preferences:

Ireland

Industry Preferences

In Consumer Related prefer:

Food/Beverage

Additional Information

Year Founded: 1998
Capital Under Management: $7,300,000
Current Activity Level: Actively seeking new investments

DEBAEQUE VENTURE CAPITAL

Edificio Nexus II
Calle Jordi Girona 29
Barcelona, Spain 08034
Phone: 34-93-252-1193
Fax: 34-93-252-1194
E-mail: info@debaeque.com
Website: www.debaeque.com

Management and Staff

Marc Ferrero, Partner
Patrick Raibaut, Partner

Type of Firm

Private Equity Firm

Project Preferences

Type of Financing Preferred:

Early Stage
Startup

Geographical Preferences

International Preferences:

All International

Industry Preferences

In Communications prefer:

Communications and Media

Additional Information

Year Founded: 2001
Capital Under Management: $113,800,000
Current Activity Level: Actively seeking new investments

DECISAO GESTAO FINANCEIRA (AKA: DGF INVESTIMENTOS)

Av. Paulista 1337
2nd Floor
Sao Paulo, Brazil
Phone: 55- 1-3521-3700
Fax: 55-11-3884-5827
Website: www.dgf.com.br

Management and Staff

Eduardo Pamplona, Managing Partner
Frederico Greve, Managing Partner
Sidney Chameh, Founding Partner

Type of Firm

Private Equity Firm

Association Membership

Brazilian Venture Capital Association (ABCR)

Project Preferences

Type of Financing Preferred:

Expansion
Balanced
Startup

Geographical Preferences

International Preferences:

Brazil

Industry Preferences

In Communications prefer:

Communications and Media

In Computer Software prefer:

Software

In Semiconductor/Electr prefer:

Electronics

In Consumer Related prefer:
Consumer

In Industrial/Energy prefer:
Energy

In Transportation prefer:
Transportation

In Financial Services prefer:
Financial Services
Insurance

In Agr/Forestr/Fish prefer:
Agribusiness
Agriculture related

Additional Information

Year Founded: 2001
Capital Under Management: $224,600,000
Current Activity Level: Actively seeking new investments

DECORUM CAPITAL PARTNERS (PTY) LTD

P O Box 11708
Craighall, South Africa 2027
Phone: 27-11-380-3540
E-mail: arthurm@decorumsa.co.za

Type of Firm

Private Equity Firm

Association Membership

South African Venture Capital Association (SAVCA)

Project Preferences

Type of Financing Preferred:
Early Stage

Geographical Preferences

International Preferences:
South Africa

Industry Preferences

In Agr/Forestr/Fish prefer:
Mining and Minerals

Additional Information

Year Founded: 2000
Capital Under Management: $50,000,000
Current Activity Level: Actively seeking new investments

DEFI GESTION SA

Boulevard de Grancy 1
Lausanne, Switzerland CH-1006
Phone: 41-21-614-3444
Fax: 41-21-614-3445
E-mail: defi@defigestion.ch
Website: www.defigestion.ch

Management and Staff

Claude Suard, Chief Financial Officer
Francois Marcos, Principal
Jacques Berger, Chief Executive Officer
Mohammed Diab, Managing Director

Type of Firm

Private Equity Firm

Association Membership

Swiss Venture Capital Association (SECA)
French Venture Capital Association (AFIC)
European Private Equity and Venture Capital Assoc.

Project Preferences

Type of Financing Preferred:
Leveraged Buyout
Expansion
Balanced
Later Stage
Management Buyouts
Recapitalizations

Geographical Preferences

International Preferences:
Italy
Switzerland
Netherlands
Luxembourg
Germany
Belgium
France

Industry Focus

(% based on actual investment)	
Consumer Related	50.9%
Biotechnology	34.5%
Other Products	14.6%

Additional Information

Year Founded: 1990
Capital Under Management: $141,300,000
Current Activity Level: Actively seeking new investments

DEFTA PARTNERS

111 Pine Street
Suite 1410
San Francisco, CA USA 94111
Phone: 415-433-2262
Fax: 415-433-2264
Website: www.defta-partners.com

Other Offices

6 Alon Street
Rosh Ha'ain, Israel 48560
Phone: 972-3-938-4940
Fax: 972-3-938-8965

Marpol House 6 The Green
Richmond, Surrey, United Kingdom TW9 1PL
Phone: 44-208-940-1001
Fax: 44-208-940-6792

7-22-17 Nishi-Gotanda
Shinagawa-ku, Tokyo, Japan 141-0031
Phone: 81-3-3495-2049
Fax: 81-3-5487-0815

Management and Staff

Arie Kahana, Partner
George Hara, Managing Partner
Masa Isono, Principal
Stan Sakai, Partner

Type of Firm

Service Provider

Association Membership

National Venture Capital Association - USA (NVCA)

Project Preferences

Role in Financing:
Prefer role in deals created by others

Type of Financing Preferred:
Early Stage
Start-up Financing
Seed

Size of Investments Considered:
Min Size of Investment Considered (000s): $500
Max Size of Investment Considered (000s): $3,000

Geographical Preferences

United States Preferences:
All U.S.

International Preferences:
United Kingdom
China
Hong Kong
Israel
Japan

Industry Focus

(% based on actual investment)	
Computer Software and Services	48.7%
Internet Specific	25.1%
Semiconductors/Other Elect.	19.4%
Medical/Health	4.0%
Communications and Media	1.5%
Computer Hardware	1.3%

Additional Information

Year Founded: 1985
Capital Under Management: $100,000,000
Current Activity Level: Actively seeking new investments
Method of Compensation: Professional fee required whether or not deal closes

---

DEHOU FUND MANAGEMENT CO., LTD. (AKA: DOHOLD CAPITAL)

No. 360 Pudong South Road
21B New Shanghai Int'l Bldg.
Shanghai, China

Phone: 86-21-5528-0598
Fax: 86-21-6886-3501
Website: www.doholdcapital.com

Type of Firm

Private Equity Firm

Project Preferences

Type of Financing Preferred:

Public Companies
Later Stage

Industry Preferences

In Industrial/Energy prefer:

Energy
Materials
Environmental Related

Additional Information

Year Founded: 2008
Current Activity Level: Actively seeking new investments

DELANY CAPITAL MANAGEMENT CORPORATION (DCM)

41 North Broadway
Irvington, NY USA 10533
Phone: 914-591-5969
Fax: 914-591-7783
Website: www.dcmcorp.com

Management and Staff

Jim Elsner, Principal
Joel Motley, Principal
Logan Delany, President

Type of Firm

Private Equity Firm

Project Preferences

Type of Financing Preferred:

Leveraged Buyout

Industry Preferences

In Semiconductor/Electr prefer:

Electronic Components

In Business Serv. prefer:

Services

Additional Information

Year Founded: 2005
Current Activity Level: Actively seeking new investments

DELAWARE INNOVATION FUND (AKA: DIF)

Three Mill Road
Suite 201
Wilmington, DE USA 19806
Phone: 302-777-1616
Fax: 302-777-1620
E-mail: info@difonline.com
Website: www.difonline.com

Management and Staff

Patrick Foley, Managing Director
Sherri Schaeffer, Vice President

Type of Firm

Private Equity Firm

Association Membership

Mid-Atlantic Venture Association

Project Preferences

Type of Financing Preferred:

Early Stage
Seed
Startup

Size of Investments Considered:

Min Size of Investment Considered (000s): $100
Max Size of Investment Considered (000s): $250

Geographical Preferences

United States Preferences:

Mid Atlantic
Delaware

Industry Preferences

In Communications prefer:

Telecommunications

In Computer Software prefer:

Software

In Internet Specific prefer:

Internet

In Industrial/Energy prefer:

Industrial Products

In Business Serv. prefer:

Services

Additional Information

Name of Most Recent Fund: Innovation Ventures
Most Recent Fund Was Raised: 08/18/2004
Year Founded: 1995
Capital Under Management: $10,000,000
Current Activity Level: Actively seeking new investments

DELPHI VENTURES

3000 Sand Hill Road
Building One, Suite 135
Menlo Park, CA USA 94025
Phone: 650-854-9650
Website: www.delphiventures.com

Management and Staff

David Douglass, Partner
Deepa Pakianathan, Partner
Donald Lothrop, Partner
Douglas Roeder, Partner
James Bochnowski, Partner
John Maroney, Partner
Kevin Roberg, Partner
Matthew Potter, Chief Financial Officer

Type of Firm

Private Equity Firm

Association Membership

Western Association of Venture Capitalists (WAVC)
National Venture Capital Association - USA (NVCA)

Project Preferences

Role in Financing:

Will function either as deal originator or investor in deals created by others

Type of Financing Preferred:

Second Stage Financing
Early Stage
Expansion
Start-up Financing
Later Stage
Seed
First Stage Financing

Size of Investments Considered:

Min Size of Investment Considered (000s): $500
Max Size of Investment Considered (000s): $12,000

Industry Focus

(% based on actual investment)

Medical/Health	65.5%
Biotechnology	19.5%
Internet Specific	6.6%
Computer Software and Services	4.0%
Industrial/Energy	1.6%
Computer Hardware	1.5%
Other Products	1.2%
Communications and Media	0.2%

Additional Information

Name of Most Recent Fund: Delphi Ventures VIII, L.P.
Most Recent Fund Was Raised: 06/10/2008
Year Founded: 1988
Capital Under Management: $850,000,000
Current Activity Level: Actively seeking new investments
Method of Compensation: Return on investment is of primary concern, do not charge fees

DELTA ADVISORS, LLC

One Financial Center
Suite 1600
Boston, MA USA 02111
Phone: 617-526-8929

Type of Firm
Private Equity Firm

Project Preferences
Type of Financing Preferred:
Other

Additional Information
Year Founded: 2002
Capital Under Management: $800,000
Current Activity Level: Actively seeking new investments

DELTA CAPITAL MANAGEMENT (AKA:DELTA PRIVATE EQUITY PARTNERS)
2/3 Paveletskaya Square
Moscow, Russia 115054
Phone: 7-495-960-3131
Fax: 7-495-960-3132
E-mail: reception@deltacap.ru
Website: www.deltacap.ru

Other Offices
545 Fifth Avenue
Suite 300
New York, NY USA 10017
Phone: 1 212 818 0444
Fax: 1 212 818 0445

Management and Staff
Lori Singer, Chief Financial Officer
Patricia Cloherty, Chairman & CEO
Roman Simonov, Managing Director

Type of Firm
Private Equity Firm

Association Membership
Russian Venture Capital Association (RVCA)

Project Preferences
Type of Financing Preferred:
Early Stage
Expansion
Later Stage

Size of Investments Considered:
Min Size of Investment Considered (000s): $1,000
Max Size of Investment Considered (000s): $500,000

Geographical Preferences
International Preferences:
Russia

Industry Preferences
In Communications prefer:
Communications and Media
Telecommunications

In Medical/Health prefer:
Medical/Health

In Consumer Related prefer:
Consumer
Food/Beverage
Consumer Products

In Financial Services prefer:
Financial Services

In Business Serv. prefer:
Media

Additional Information
Name of Most Recent Fund: Delta Russia Fund
Most Recent Fund Was Raised: 06/16/2004
Year Founded: 1999
Capital Under Management: $440,000,000
Current Activity Level: Actively seeking new investments

DELTA CAPITAL MANAGEMENT LLC
70 Timber Creek Drive
Suite 3
Cordova, TN USA 38018
Phone: 901-755-0949
Fax: 901-755-0436
E-mail: info@deltacapital.com
Website: www.deltacapital.com

Management and Staff
Don Mundie, Managing Partner
Joel Wood, Partner
Pat Yearwood, Vice President

Type of Firm
Private Equity Firm

Association Membership
Natl Assoc of Small Bus. Inv. Co (NASBIC)

Project Preferences
Role in Financing:
Will function either as deal originator or investor in deals created by others

Type of Financing Preferred:
Leveraged Buyout
Early Stage
Expansion
Balanced
Later Stage
Industry Rollups

Size of Investments Considered:
Min Size of Investment Considered (000s): $500
Max Size of Investment Considered (000s): $1,500

Geographical Preferences
United States Preferences:
Tennessee
Mississippi
Southeast
Alabama
Arkansas

Industry Preferences
In Communications prefer:
Telecommunications
Wireless Communications

In Computer Software prefer:
Software
Applications Software

In Internet Specific prefer:
Internet
Ecommerce

In Medical/Health prefer:
Medical/Health
Medical Diagnostics
Diagnostic Services
Diagnostic Test Products
Medical Therapeutics
Drug/Equipmt Delivery
Medical Products
Disposable Med. Products
Health Services

In Transportation prefer:
Transportation

In Business Serv. prefer:
Distribution

Additional Information
Year Founded: 1992
Capital Under Management: $90,000,000
Current Activity Level: Actively seeking new investments
Method of Compensation: Return on investment is of primary concern, do not charge fees

---

DELTA PARTNERS FZ LLC
Shatha Tower, 12th Floor
Dubai Internet City
Dubai, Utd. Arab Em.
Phone: 971-4-369-2999
Fax: 971-4-368-8408
E-mail: privateequity@deltapartnersgroup.com
Website: www.deltapartnersgroup.com

Other Offices
P.O. Box 783719
Santon
Johannesburg, South Africa 2146
Phone: 27-11-881-5957
Fax: 27-11-881-5611

Management and Staff
Antonio Carvalho, Partner
Federico Membrillera, Partner
Javier Alvarez, Partner
Josep Maria Moya, Partner
Juan Ignacio Cifre, Partner
Kristoff Puelinckx, Managing Partner
Mauricio Franca, Partner
Rogier Van Driessche, Partner

Victor Font, Managing Partner

Type of Firm

Investment Management Firm

Project Preferences

Type of Financing Preferred:

Expansion

Geographical Preferences

International Preferences:

Middle East
Africa

Industry Preferences

In Communications prefer:

Telecommunications

In Business Serv. prefer:

Media

Additional Information

Year Founded: 2007
Capital Under Management: $80,000,000
Current Activity Level: Actively seeking new investments

DELTA PARTNERS, LTD.

South County Business Park
Leopardstown, Fujitsu Bldg.
Dublin, Ireland 18
Phone: 353-1-294-0870
Fax: 353-1-294-0877
E-mail: venture@delta.ie
Website: www.delta.ie

Other Offices

18a St. James's Place
London, United Kingdom SW1A 1NH
Phone: 44-20-7290-3040
Fax: 44-20-7495-7881

Management and Staff

Dermot Berkery, General Partner
John O'Sullivan, Chief Financial Officer
Juan Ignacio Cifre, Partner
Maurice Roche, General Partner
Rob Johnson, Partner
Shay Garvey, General Partner

Type of Firm

Private Equity Firm

Association Membership

Irish Venture Capital Association
European Private Equity and Venture Capital Assoc.

Project Preferences

Role in Financing:

Prefer role as deal originator but will also invest in deals created by others

Type of Financing Preferred:

Second Stage Financing
Early Stage
Balanced
Seed
Startup

Size of Investments Considered:

Min Size of Investment Considered (000s): $500
Max Size of Investment Considered (000s): $500,000

Geographical Preferences

International Preferences:

Ireland
United Kingdom
Germany
France

Industry Focus

(% based on actual investment)

Other Products	29.5%
Internet Specific	24.6%
Computer Software and Services	17.7%
Medical/Health	12.7%
Communications and Media	8.4%
Biotechnology	4.1%
Semiconductors/Other Elect.	3.0%

Additional Information

Name of Most Recent Fund: Delta Equity Fund III
Most Recent Fund Was Raised: 10/08/2007
Year Founded: 1994
Capital Under Management: $173,400,000
Current Activity Level: Actively seeking new investments
Method of Compensation: Return on investment is of primary concern, do not charge fees

---

DELTAPOINT CAPITAL MANAGEMENT LLC

45 East Avenue
Sixth Floor
Rochester, NY USA 14604
Phone: 585-454-6990
Fax: 585-454-3204
E-mail: info@deltapointcapital.com
Website: www.deltapointcapital.com

Management and Staff

David Waterman, Managing Director
Kevin Halpin, Vice President
Thomas Cimino, Managing Director

Type of Firm

Private Equity Firm

Association Membership

Natl Assoc of Small Bus. Inv. Co (NASBIC)

Project Preferences

Role in Financing:

Prefer role as deal originator but will also invest in deals created by others

Type of Financing Preferred:

Leveraged Buyout
Expansion
Generalist PE
Later Stage
Management Buyouts
Acquisition
Industry Rollups

Size of Investments Considered:

Min Size of Investment Considered (000s): $2,000
Max Size of Investment Considered (000s): $6,000

Geographical Preferences

United States Preferences:

New York

Industry Preferences

In Business Serv. prefer:

Services
Distribution

In Manufact. prefer:

Manufacturing

Additional Information

Year Founded: 1997
Capital Under Management: $45,000,000
Current Activity Level: Actively seeking new investments
Method of Compensation: Return on investment is of primary concern, do not charge fees

---

DEMETER PARTNERS S.A.

23 rue de l'Arcade
Paris, France 75008
Phone: 33-1-4312-5333
Fax: 33-1-4312-5330
E-mail: contact@demeter-partners.com
Website: www.demeter-partners.com

Other Offices

c/ Jose Abascal 52 2izda
Madrid, Spain 28003
Phone: 34-915-639-704
Fax: 34-915-619-506

Kurfurstendamm 119
Berlin, Germany

Management and Staff

Anselm Adams, Venture Partner
Lionel Cormier, Partner
Marcos Semmler, Venture Partner
Michel Ronc, Partner
Sophie Paturle Guesnerot, Partner
Stephane Villecroze, Partner

Type of Firm

Corporate PE/Venture

Association Membership

French Venture Capital Association (AFIC)

Project Preferences

Type of Financing Preferred:
Leveraged Buyout
Early Stage
Expansion
Acquisition
Startup

Geographical Preferences

International Preferences:
Europe
France

Industry Preferences

In Industrial/Energy prefer:
Energy
Alternative Energy
Energy Conservation Relat

In Other prefer:
Environment Responsible

Additional Information

Year Founded: 2005
Capital Under Management: $321,500,000
Current Activity Level: Actively seeking new investments

DENTSU.COM, INC.

6F, Ichikudo Building
1-9-5, Tsukiji, Chuo-ku
Tokyo, Japan 104-0045
Phone: 81-3-5551-8021
Website: www.dentsu.com

Management and Staff

Tateo Mataki, Chairman & CEO
Tatsuyoshi Takashima, President & COO

Type of Firm

Corporate PE/Venture

Project Preferences

Type of Financing Preferred:
Balanced
Geographical Preferences

International Preferences:
Asia

Additional Information

Year Founded: 2000
Current Activity Level: Actively seeking new investments

DERBYSHIRE FIRST INVESTMENTS LIMITED (DFI)

95 Sheffield Road
Chesterfied
Derbyshire, United Kingdom S4I 7JH
Phone: 44-12-4620-7390
Fax: 44-12-4622-1080
E-mail: info@dfil.co.uk
Website: www.dfil.co.uk

Management and Staff

Andrew Hay, Partner

Type of Firm

Private Equity Firm

Association Membership

British Venture Capital Association (BVCA)

Project Preferences

Type of Financing Preferred:
Leveraged Buyout
Early Stage
Expansion
Turnaround

Geographical Preferences

International Preferences:
United Kingdom

Industry Preferences

In Communications prefer:
Communications and Media

In Computer Other prefer:
Computer Related

In Semiconductor/Electr prefer:
Electronics

In Medical/Health prefer:
Medical/Health

In Consumer Related prefer:
Consumer

In Industrial/Energy prefer:
Energy
Industrial Products

In Financial Services prefer:
Financial Services

Additional Information

Year Founded: 1987
Capital Under Management: $4,500,000
Current Activity Level: Actively seeking new investments

DERWENT LONDON PLC (FKA: LONDON MERCHANT SECURITIES)

25 Savile Row
London, United Kingdom W1S 2ER
Phone: 44-20-7659-3000
Fax: 44-20-7659-3100
E-mail: mail@derwentlondon.com
Website: www.derwentlondon.com

Other Offices

2 The Cross Court
Glasgow, United Kingdom G64 2RD
Phone: 44-141-761-1200
Fax: 44-141-762-5600

Management and Staff

Robert Rayne, Managing Director

Type of Firm

Private Equity Firm

Project Preferences

Role in Financing:
Prefer role in deals created by others

Type of Financing Preferred:
Early Stage
Expansion
Balanced

Geographical Preferences

International Preferences:
United Kingdom
All International

Industry Preferences

In Communications prefer:
Communications and Media

In Computer Software prefer:
Software

In Internet Specific prefer:
Internet

Additional Information

Name of Most Recent Fund: Westpool Investment Trust PLC
Most Recent Fund Was Raised: 08/01/1983
Year Founded: 1983
Capital Under Management: $200,000,000
Current Activity Level: Actively seeking new investments
Method of Compensation: Return on investment is of primary concern, do not charge fees

---

DESERT CEDARS, LLC

5346 Calle Del Norte
Phoenix, AZ USA 85018
Phone: 602-840-8611

Management and Staff

Michael Koslow, Managing Partner
Patricia Koslow, Managing Partner

Type of Firm

Private Equity Firm

Industry Preferences

In Financial Services prefer:
Real Estate

Additional Information

Year Founded: 2002
Capital Under Management: $1,900,000
Current Activity Level: Actively seeking new investments

DESEVEN AB

Birger Jarlsgatan 13
Stockholm, Sweden SE-111 45
Phone: 46-8-5450-1680
Fax: 46-8-648-6356
E-mail: info@deseven.com
Website: www.deseven.com

Management and Staff

Jorgen Larsson, Managing Partner
Marcus Backlund, Partner
Petter Lundgren, Partner
Sten Wranne, Partner

Type of Firm

Private Equity Firm

Association Membership

Singapore Venture Capital Association (SVCA)

Project Preferences

Type of Financing Preferred:

Leveraged Buyout
Expansion
Early Stage
Balanced
Management Buyouts
Recapitalizations

Geographical Preferences

International Preferences:

Scandanavia/Nordic Region

Additional Information

Year Founded: 2000
Current Activity Level: Actively seeking new investments

DESIGN INVESTORS LLC

61 Wilton Road
Westport, CT USA 06880
Phone: 203-227-2500
Fax: 203-341-9409
Website: www.designinvestors.com

Management and Staff

A. Peter Sallick, Managing Partner
Amanda D.H. Smith, Vice President
Margaret Touborg, Managing Partner

Type of Firm

Private Equity Firm

Project Preferences

Type of Financing Preferred:

Leveraged Buyout
Acquisition

Industry Preferences

In Consumer Related prefer:

Consumer
Retail
Consumer Products
Consumer Services

In Business Serv. prefer:

Services
Media

Additional Information

Year Founded: 2007
Current Activity Level: Actively seeking new investments

DESTINATION GROUP, THE

2121 Rosecrans Avenue
Suite 2390
El Segundo, CA USA 90245
Phone: 310-414-8400
Website: www.dgrp.com

Management and Staff

John Brady, Chief Executive Officer
Sean Prendergast, Vice President
Simon Todd, Principal

Type of Firm

Private Equity Firm

Additional Information

Year Founded: 2009
Current Activity Level: Actively seeking new investments

DETROIT RENAISSANCE

600 Renaissance Center
Suite 1760
Detroit, MI USA 48243
Phone: 313-259-5400
Fax: 313-567-8355
E-mail: info@detroitrenaissance.com
Website: www.detroitrenaissance.com

Management and Staff

Doug Rothwell, President
Sabrina Keeley, Vice President

Type of Firm

Private Equity Advisor or Fund of Funds

Project Preferences

Type of Financing Preferred:

Fund of Funds

Geographical Preferences

United States Preferences:

Michigan

Additional Information

Year Founded: 2007
Capital Under Management: $57,000,000
Current Activity Level: Actively seeking new investments

DEUTSCHE BANC ALEX BROWN (FKA: BANKERS TRUST NEW YORK CORP)

345 Park Avenue
16th Floor
New York, NY USA 10154
Phone: 212-454-7241
Fax: 212-454-0530
Website: www.alexbrown.db.com

Management and Staff

Colleen Sellers, Chief Operating Officer

Type of Firm

Bank Affiliated

Project Preferences

Role in Financing:

Prefer role as deal originator but will also invest in deals created by others

Type of Financing Preferred:

Fund of Funds
Second Stage Financing
Leveraged Buyout
Mezzanine
Generalist PE
Special Situation

Geographical Preferences

International Preferences:

Europe

Industry Focus

(% based on actual investment)

Other Products	49.9%
Consumer Related	15.9%
Internet Specific	12.8%
Communications and Media	11.4%
Computer Software and Services	4.8%
Medical/Health	1.8%
Semiconductors/Other Elect.	1.8%
Industrial/Energy	1.6%
Computer Hardware	0.1%

Additional Information

Year Founded: 1972
Capital Under Management: $1,200,000,000
Current Activity Level: Actively seeking new investments
Method of Compensation: Return on invest. most important, but chg. closing fees, service fees, etc.

DEUTSCHE BANK CORPORATE INVESTMENTS (FKA: DB INVESTOR)

Taunusanlage 12
Frankfurt, Germany 60325
Phone: 4969-91000
Fax: 49-69-9103-3983
Website: www.deutsche-bank.de

Type of Firm

Bank Affiliated

Association Membership

European Private Equity and Venture Capital Assoc.

Project Preferences

Type of Financing Preferred:
Expansion
Unknown
Later Stage

Geographical Preferences

International Preferences:
Europe
Germany
All International

Industry Preferences

In Communications prefer:
Communications and Media
Commercial Communications
Telecommunications

In Internet Specific prefer:
Internet
Ecommerce

In Computer Other prefer:
Computer Related

In Business Serv. prefer:
Media

Additional Information

Year Founded: 1998
Current Activity Level: Reducing investment activity

DEUTSCHE BETEILIGUNGS AG

Kleine Wiesenau 1
Frankfurt am Main, Germany D-60323
Phone: 49-69-957-8701
Fax: 49-69-9578-7199
E-mail: welcome@deutsche-beteiligung.de
Website: www.deutsche-beteiligung.com

Management and Staff

Gustav Egger, Chief Financial Officer

Type of Firm

Private Equity Firm

Association Membership

German Venture Capital Association (BVK)
European Private Equity and Venture Capital Assoc.

Project Preferences

Role in Financing:
Prefer role as deal originator but will also invest in deals created by others

Type of Financing Preferred:
Leveraged Buyout
Expansion
Balanced
Management Buyouts
Recapitalizations

Size of Investments Considered:
Min Size of Investment Considered (000s): $8,914
Max Size of Investment Considered (000s): $53,484

Geographical Preferences

United States Preferences:
All U.S.

International Preferences:
Italy
United Kingdom
Liechtenstein
Luxembourg
Switzerland
Austria
Namibia
Belgium
Romania
Germany
Asia
France

Industry Focus

(% based on actual investment)

Other Products	48.8%
Industrial/Energy	29.2%
Internet Specific	21.9%

Additional Information

Name of Most Recent Fund: DBAG Fund V
Most Recent Fund Was Raised: 12/22/2005
Year Founded: 1965
Capital Under Management: $1,271,800,000
Current Activity Level: Actively seeking new investments

DEVA GROUP AB

Stansargrand 4
Vasteras, Sweden 72130
Phone: 46-7-0426-6267
Fax: 46-21-314-459
Website: www.deva.se

Type of Firm

Private Equity Firm

Association Membership

Swedish Venture Capital Association (SVCA)

Project Preferences

Type of Financing Preferred:
Leveraged Buyout

Geographical Preferences

International Preferences:
Sweden

Additional Information

Year Founded: 2009
Current Activity Level: Actively seeking new investments

DEVELOPMENT CAPITAL SA (AKA: ALTO PARTNERS SRL)

Via Monte di Pieta 1/A
Milano, Italy 20121
Phone: 39-02-720-95041
Fax: 39-02-720-95012
E-mail: info@altopartners.it
Website: www.altopartners.it

Other Offices

Via Monte di Pieta 1/A
Milan, Italy 20121
Phone: 39-02-7209-5019
Fax: 39-02-7209-5049

Piazza Galvani, 3
Bologna, Italy 40124
Phone: 39-051-234-931

Corso Palladio, 15
Vicenza, Italy 36100
Phone: 39-044-454-4040

Management and Staff

Alberto Craici, Partner
Mario Visioni, Partner
Massimo Perona, Founding Partner
Raffaele De Courten, Founding Partner

Type of Firm

Private Equity Advisor or Fund of Funds

Association Membership

Italian Venture Capital Association (AIFI)
European Private Equity and Venture Capital Assoc.

Project Preferences

Type of Financing Preferred:
Leveraged Buyout
Early Stage
Expansion
Startup

Size of Investments Considered:
Min Size of Investment Considered (000s): $437
Max Size of Investment Considered (000s): $30,597

Geographical Preferences

International Preferences:
Italy
Europe

Industry Preferences

In Consumer Related prefer:
Consumer
Entertainment and Leisure
Food/Beverage

In Industrial/Energy prefer:
Machinery

Additional Information

Name of Most Recent Fund: Alto Capital II
Most Recent Fund Was Raised: 11/24/2005
Year Founded: 1997
Capital Under Management: $270,600,000
Current Activity Level: Actively seeking new investments

DEVELOPMENT PARTNERS INTERNATIONAL

28 Chelsea Wharf
Lots Road
London, United Kingdom SW10 0QJ
Phone: 44-20-7349-5030
Fax: 44-20-7349-5038
E-mail: info@dpi-llp.com
Website: www.dpi-llp.com

Management and Staff

Runa Alam, Chief Executive Officer

Type of Firm

Private Equity Firm

Project Preferences

Type of Financing Preferred:
Balanced

Geographical Preferences

International Preferences:
South Africa
France

Additional Information

Year Founded: 2007
Capital Under Management: $425,000,000
Current Activity Level: Actively seeking new investments

DEVELOPMENT PRINCIPLES GROUP, LTD.

New World Tower One, 15/F
18 Queen's Road Central
Central, Hong Kong
Phone: 852-2258-7068
Fax: 852-2258-7022
Website: www.developmentprinciplesgroup.com

Other Offices

708, Building 10, Wanda Plaza 93
Jianguo Road, Chao Yang District
Beijing, China 100 022
Phone: 86-10-5820-7048
Fax: 86-10-5820-5012

Management and Staff

Arthur Wang, Vice President
Bingming Peng, Vice President
Lisa Kim, Vice President
Mark Kooijman, Managing Partner
Qi Wang, Managing Partner
Simon He, Vice President

Type of Firm

Private Equity Firm

Project Preferences

Type of Financing Preferred:
Expansion

Geographical Preferences

International Preferences:
Mongolia
China

Industry Preferences

In Medical/Health prefer:
Pharmaceuticals

In Consumer Related prefer:
Food/Beverage

In Industrial/Energy prefer:
Energy
Alternative Energy

In Transportation prefer:
Transportation

In Financial Services prefer:
Financial Services

In Business Serv. prefer:
Distribution

In Manufact. prefer:
Manufacturing

In Agr/Forestr/Fish prefer:
Agriculture related

Additional Information

Year Founded: 2005
Capital Under Management: $80,000,000
Current Activity Level: Actively seeking new investments

DEVELOPPEMENT & PARTENARIAT

152 avenue de Malakoff
Paris, France 75116
Phone: 33-1-5679-7900
Fax: 33-1-5679-7910

Management and Staff

Didier Calmels, President
Thierry Jullien, Vice President

Type of Firm

Private Equity Firm

Association Membership

French Venture Capital Association (AFIC)

Project Preferences

Type of Financing Preferred:
Leveraged Buyout
Early Stage
Expansion
Turnaround
Distressed Debt
Recapitalizations

Geographical Preferences

International Preferences:
Europe
France

Industry Preferences

In Industrial/Energy prefer:
Industrial Products

In Business Serv. prefer:
Services

Additional Information

Year Founded: 1994
Capital Under Management: $83,500,000
Current Activity Level: Actively seeking new investments

DEVON PARK BIOVENTURES

435 Devon Park Drive
700 Building
Wayne, PA USA 19087
Phone: 610-977-7520
Fax: 484-582-1065
Website: www.dpbioventures.com

Management and Staff

Christopher Moller, General Partner
Devang Kantesaria, General Partner
Marc Ostro, General Partner

Type of Firm

Private Equity Firm

Project Preferences

Role in Financing:
Prefer role as deal originator but will also invest in deals created by others

Type of Financing Preferred:
Later Stage

Size of Investments Considered:
Min Size of Investment Considered (000s): $5,000
Max Size of Investment Considered (000s): $10,000

Geographical Preferences

Canadian Preferences:
All Canada

Industry Preferences

In Biotechnology prefer:
Biotechnology

In Medical/Health prefer:
Medical/Health
Medical Therapeutics
Drug/Equipmt Delivery
Medical Products

Additional Information
Name of Most Recent Fund: Devon Park Bioventures, L.P.
Most Recent Fund Was Raised: 02/28/2006
Year Founded: 2006
Capital Under Management: $100,000,000
Current Activity Level: Actively seeking new investments
Method of Compensation: Return on investment is of primary concern, do not charge fees

---

DEWB AG (FKA: DEUTSCHE EFFECTEN UND WECHSELBETEILIGUNGSGES)
Leutagraben 1
Jena, Germany 07743
Phone: 49-3641-5733600
Fax: 49-3641-5733601
E-mail: info@dewb-vc.com
Website: www.dewb-vc.com

Management and Staff
Dietmar Kubis, Chief Executive Officer

Type of Firm
Private Equity Firm

Association Membership
German Venture Capital Association (BVK)

Project Preferences

Type of Financing Preferred:
Expansion
Seed
Startup

Geographical Preferences

International Preferences:
Europe
Germany

Industry Preferences

In Communications prefer:
Telecommunications

In Semiconductor/Electr prefer:
Fiber Optics

In Biotechnology prefer:
Biotechnology

Additional Information
Year Founded: 1872
Capital Under Management: $110,900,000
Current Activity Level: Actively seeking new investments

DFJ ATHENA
100 Hamilton Avenue
Suite 225
Palo Alto, CA USA 94301
Phone: 650-470-0370
Fax: 650-470-0378
E-mail: info@dfjathena.com
Website: www.dfjathena.com

Other Offices
Suite 301 , Poongsung Building
51-12 Banpo-dong, Seocho-ku
Seoul, South Korea
Phone: 82-2-2194-3800
Fax: 82-2-2194-3809

Management and Staff
Henry Chung, Managing Director
Perry Ha, Managing Director
Steven Lee, Venture Partner
Warren Packard, Managing Director

Type of Firm
Private Equity Firm

Project Preferences

Type of Financing Preferred:
Balanced

Geographical Preferences

International Preferences:
Korea, South

Additional Information
Name of Most Recent Fund: DFJ Athena, L.P.
Most Recent Fund Was Raised: 12/28/2007
Year Founded: 2007
Capital Under Management: $28,100,000
Current Activity Level: Actively seeking new investments

DFJ ATHENA (FKA: ATHENA TECHNOLOGY VENTURES)
2882 Sand Hill Road
Suite 150
Menlo Park, CA USA 94025
Phone: 650-233-9000
Fax: 650-234-8533
Website: www.dfjathena.com

Other Offices
10th Floor Samjeong Building
Yoksam-dong 701-2 Kangnam-gu
Seoul , South Korea 135-080
Phone: 82-2-554-3131-
Fax: 82-2-553-2201

Management and Staff
Henry Chung, Managing Director
Margot Giusti, Chief Financial Officer
Perry Ha, Managing Director
Robert Tomkinson, Venture Partner
Steven Lee, Venture Partner
Warren Packard, Managing Director

Type of Firm
Private Equity Firm

Project Preferences

Role in Financing:
Will function either as deal originator or investor in deals created by others

Type of Financing Preferred:
Early Stage
Seed
First Stage Financing
Startup

Geographical Preferences

United States Preferences:
West Coast

Industry Focus
(% based on actual investment)

Internet Specific	44.6%
Computer Software and Services	28.4%
Communications and Media	10.7%
Semiconductors/Other Elect.	8.5%
Computer Hardware	5.7%
Consumer Related	2.0%

Additional Information
Name of Most Recent Fund: Athena Venture Fund II
Most Recent Fund Was Raised: 03/01/2000
Year Founded: 1998
Capital Under Management: $55,000,000
Current Activity Level: Actively seeking new investments

DFJ ESPRIT (FKA: ESPRIT CAPITAL PARTNERS)

14 Buckingham Gate
London, United Kingdom SW1E 6LB
Phone: 44-20-7931-8800
Fax: 44-20-7931-8866
E-mail: enquiries@espritcp.com
Website: www.espritcp.com

Other Offices

Sycamore Studios
New Road, Over
Cambridge, United Kingdom CB24 5PJ
Phone: 44-1223-307-770
Fax: 44-1223-307-771

Management and Staff

Alan Duncan, Partner
Catrina Holme, Partner
Nic Brisbourne, Partner
Paul Murray, Partner
Robert James, Partner
Simon Cook, Chief Executive Officer
Stuart Chapman, Partner
Tom Bradley, Partner
William Reeves, Venture Partner

Type of Firm

Private Equity Firm

Association Membership

British Venture Capital Association (BVCA)

Project Preferences

Type of Financing Preferred:
Early Stage
Expansion
Balanced
Later Stage
Startup

Size of Investments Considered:
Min Size of Investment Considered (000s): $500
Max Size of Investment Considered (000s): $25,000

Geographical Preferences

International Preferences:
Europe
Western Europe

Industry Preferences

In Communications prefer:
Telecommunications

In Medical/Health prefer:
Medical/Health

In Business Serv. prefer:
Media

Additional Information

Year Founded: 2006
Capital Under Management: $500,000,000
Current Activity Level: Actively seeking new investments

DFJ FRONTIER

800 Anacapa Street
Suite A
Santa Barbara, CA USA 93101
Phone: 805-963-2277
Website: www.dfjfrontier.com

Other Offices

2545 Boatman Ave
West Sacramento, CA USA 95691
Phone: 916-372-3700

Management and Staff

Brian Danella, Venture Partner
David Cremin, Managing Director
Frank Foster, Managing Director
Jim Schraith, Venture Partner
Oleg Kaganovich, Principal
Scott Lenet, Managing Director
Tony Perkins, Venture Partner

Type of Firm

Private Equity Firm

Project Preferences

Role in Financing:
Prefer role as deal originator but will also invest in deals created by others

Type of Financing Preferred:
Early Stage
Seed

Size of Investments Considered:
Min Size of Investment Considered (000s): $100
Max Size of Investment Considered (000s): $1,500

Geographical Preferences

United States Preferences:
Oregon
Washington
California

Industry Preferences

In Communications prefer:
Communications and Media
Wireless Communications
Data Communications

In Computer Software prefer:
Software

In Internet Specific prefer:
Internet

In Semiconductor/Electr prefer:
Electronics
Semiconductor

In Biotechnology prefer:
Biotechnology
Human Biotechnology

In Medical/Health prefer:
Health Services

In Consumer Related prefer:
Consumer
Consumer Services

In Industrial/Energy prefer:
Energy
Alternative Energy
Industrial Products

In Financial Services prefer:
Financial Services

In Agr/Forestr/Fish prefer:
Agriculture related

Additional Information

Name of Most Recent Fund: DFJ Frontier Fund II, L.P.
Most Recent Fund Was Raised: 06/25/2007
Year Founded: 2002
Capital Under Management: $80,000,000
Current Activity Level: Actively seeking new investments
Method of Compensation: Return on investment is of primary concern, do not charge fees

DFJ INCUBE VENTURES

1390 Willow Road
Menlo Park, CA USA 94025
Phone: 650-289-5100
Fax: 650-853-8830
Website: www.dfjincubevc.com

Management and Staff

Andrew Farquharson, Managing Director
Mir Imran, Managing Director
Wayne Roe, Managing Director

Type of Firm

Private Equity Firm

Project Preferences

Type of Financing Preferred:
Early Stage

Industry Preferences

In Medical/Health prefer:
Medical/Health

Additional Information

Year Founded: 2008
Capital Under Management: $10,000,000
Current Activity Level: Actively seeking new investments

DFJ MERCURY

One Greenway Plaza
Suite 930
Houston, TX USA 77046
Phone: 713-715-6820
Fax: 713-715-6826
E-mail: info@dfjmercury.com
Website: www.dfjmercury.com

Management and Staff
Blair Garrou, Managing Director
Daniel Watkins, Managing Director
Ned Hill, Managing Director

Type of Firm
Private Equity Firm

Association Membership
National Venture Capital Association - USA (NVCA)

Project Preferences

Role in Financing:
Prefer role as deal originator but will also invest in deals created by others

Type of Financing Preferred:
Early Stage
Seed
Startup

Size of Investments Considered:
Min Size of Investment Considered (000s): $100
Max Size of Investment Considered (000s): $1,000

Geographical Preferences

United States Preferences:
Midwest
Texas
Southwest

Industry Preferences

In Industrial/Energy prefer:
Advanced Materials

Additional Information
Name of Most Recent Fund: DFJ Mercury II, L.P.
Most Recent Fund Was Raised: 02/28/2008
Year Founded: 2005
Capital Under Management: $20,000,000
Current Activity Level: Actively seeking new investments
Method of Compensation: Return on investment is of primary concern, do not charge fees

---

DFW CAPITAL PARTNERS (AKA:DEMUTH, FOLGER & WETHERILL)
Glenpointe Centre East- 5th Fl
300 Frank W. Burr Boulevard
Teaneck, NJ USA 07666
Phone: 201-836-6000
Fax: 201-836-5666
E-mail: info@dfwcapital.com
Website: www.dfwcapital.com

Management and Staff
Donald DeMuth, General Partner
Keith Pennell, General Partner
Thomas Folger, General Partner

Type of Firm
Private Equity Firm

Project Preferences

Role in Financing:
Prefer role as deal originator but will also invest in deals created by others

Type of Financing Preferred:
Leveraged Buyout
Control-block Purchases
Expansion
Later Stage
Management Buyouts
Acquisition
Special Situation
Recapitalizations

Size of Investments Considered:
Min Size of Investment Considered (000s): $5,000
Max Size of Investment Considered (000s): $10,000

Geographical Preferences

United States Preferences:
All U.S.

Industry Focus
(% based on actual investment)

Medical/Health	30.9%
Consumer Related	14.9%
Communications and Media	13.4%
Computer Hardware	9.0%
Internet Specific	8.4%
Semiconductors/Other Elect.	8.3%
Other Products	7.7%
Computer Software and Services	5.2%
Industrial/Energy	2.3%

Additional Information
Name of Most Recent Fund: DFW Capital Partners III, L.P.
Most Recent Fund Was Raised: 02/07/2007
Year Founded: 1983
Capital Under Management: $40,000,000
Current Activity Level: Actively seeking new investments
Method of Compensation: Return on investment is of primary concern, do not charge fees

---

DGPA SGR SPA
via dei Bossi 6
Milan, Italy 20121
Phone: 39-0280-6241
Fax: 39-02890-12321
E-mail: info@dgpa.it
Website: www.dgpa.it

Type of Firm
Private Equity Advisor or Fund of Funds

Additional Information
Year Founded: 2006
Capital Under Management: $83,000,000
Current Activity Level: Actively seeking new investments

DHFL VENTURE CAPITAL INDIA PVT LTD.
6th Floor,Dheeraj Arma
Anand Kanekar Road, Bandra(E)
Mumbai, India 400051
Phone: 91-22-2658-3333
Fax: 91-22-2658-3344
E-mail: info@dhfl.com
Website: www.dhfl.com

Management and Staff
Arun Goel, Chief Executive Officer

Type of Firm
Bank Affiliated

Association Membership
Indian Venture Capital Association (IVCA)

Project Preferences

Type of Financing Preferred:
Balanced

Geographical Preferences

International Preferences:
India

Industry Preferences

In Financial Services prefer:
Real Estate

Additional Information
Year Founded: 2006
Capital Under Management: $57,900,000
Current Activity Level: Actively seeking new investments

DIAMOND CAPITAL MANAGEMENT
5311 N Plaza Drive
Menomonee Falls, WI USA 53051
Phone: 262-790-9175
Fax: 262-790-9175
Website: www.diamond-hill.com

Type of Firm
Private Equity Firm

Additional Information
Year Founded: 2009
Current Activity Level: Actively seeking new investments

DIAMOND CASTLE HOLDINGS LLC
280 Park Avenue
25th Floor, East Tower
New York, NY USA 10017

Phone: 212-300-1900
Fax: 212-983-1234
E-mail: info@dchold.com
Website: www.dchold.com

Management and Staff

Aalok Jain, Vice President
Andrew Rush, Senior Managing Director
Ari Benacerraf, Senior Managing Director
Daniel Clare, Principal
David Wittels, Senior Managing Director
Eric Nadan, Vice President
Lee Wright, Principal
Linda Grogan, Chief Financial Officer
Michael Langer, Vice President
Michael Ranger, Senior Managing Director
Stephen Bassford, Principal

Type of Firm

Private Equity Firm

Project Preferences

Type of Financing Preferred:

Leveraged Buyout
Expansion
Management Buyouts

Industry Preferences

In Medical/Health prefer:

Medical/Health

In Industrial/Energy prefer:

Energy

In Financial Services prefer:

Financial Services

In Business Serv. prefer:

Media

Additional Information

Name of Most Recent Fund: Diamond Castle Partners IV, L.P.
Most Recent Fund Was Raised: 10/27/2005
Year Founded: 2004
Capital Under Management: $1,850,000,000
Current Activity Level: Actively seeking new investments

DIAMOND STATE VENTURES, L.P.

200 South Commerce
Suite 400
Little Rock, AR USA 72201
Phone: 501-374-9247
Fax: 501-374-9425
Website: dsv.arcapital.com

Other Offices

2905 King Street
Jonesboro, AR USA 72403
Phone: 870-932-8002
Fax: 870-932-0135

The Chamber Building
West 3rd
Fordyce, AR USA 71742
Phone: 870-352-2853
Fax: 870-352-5126

700 Research Centre Boulevard
Suite 1608
Fayetteville, AR USA 72701
Phone: 479-444-8881
Fax: 479-444-8882

Management and Staff

Joe Hays, President
Larry Carter, Partner
Todd Brogdon, Chief Financial Officer

Type of Firm

SBIC

Association Membership

Natl Assoc of Small Bus. Inv. Co (NASBIC)

Project Preferences

Role in Financing:

Will function either as deal originator or investor in deals created by others

Type of Financing Preferred:

Early Stage
Expansion
Mezzanine
Later Stage
Management Buyouts
Acquisition

Size of Investments Considered:

Min Size of Investment Considered (000s): $250
Max Size of Investment Considered (000s): $3,000

Geographical Preferences

United States Preferences:

Midwest
Southeast
Southwest
Arkansas

Additional Information

Name of Most Recent Fund: Diamond State Ventures, L.P.
Most Recent Fund Was Raised: 07/01/1999
Year Founded: 1999
Capital Under Management: $56,000,000
Current Activity Level: Actively seeking new investments
Method of Compensation: Return on invest. most important, but chg. closing fees, service fees, etc.

DIAMONDHEAD VENTURES, L.P.

2200 Sand Hill Road
Suite 110
Menlo Park, CA USA 94025
Phone: 650-233-7526
Fax: 650-233-7527
E-mail: info@dhven.com
Website: www.dhven.com

Management and Staff

David Lane, Managing Director
Raman Khanna, Managing Director

Type of Firm

Private Equity Firm

Association Membership

Western Association of Venture Capitalists (WAVC)

Project Preferences

Type of Financing Preferred:

Second Stage Financing
Early Stage
Start-up Financing
Seed
First Stage Financing

Size of Investments Considered:

Min Size of Investment Considered (000s): $500
Max Size of Investment Considered (000s): $5,000

Geographical Preferences

United States Preferences:

Northern California
West Coast

Industry Preferences

In Communications prefer:

Communications and Media
Telecommunications
Wireless Communications
Data Communications

In Computer Software prefer:

Software

In Internet Specific prefer:

Internet
Ecommerce
Web Aggregration/Portals

In Semiconductor/Electr prefer:

Semiconductor
Fiber Optics

Additional Information

Year Founded: 2000
Capital Under Management: $140,000,000
Current Activity Level: Actively seeking new investments

DIANA CAPITAL SGECR S.A.

Paseo Castellana, 95
29/F Torre Europa
Madrid, Spain 28046
Phone: 34-914-262-329
Fax: 34-914-262-330
E-mail: diana@dianacapital.com
Website: www.dianacapital.com

Management and Staff

Francisco Gomez-Zubeldia, Managing Director

Type of Firm

Investment Management Firm

Association Membership

European Private Equity and Venture Capital Assoc.
Spanish Venture Capital Association (ASCRI)

Project Preferences

Role in Financing:

Prefer role as deal originator

Type of Financing Preferred:

Leveraged Buyout
Expansion
Management Buyouts
Acquisition

Size of Investments Considered:

Min Size of Investment Considered (000s): $5,592
Max Size of Investment Considered (000s): $16,777

Geographical Preferences

International Preferences:

Portugal
Spain

Industry Focus

(% based on actual investment)

Other Products	69.3%
Industrial/Energy	18.9%
Consumer Related	11.8%

Additional Information

Year Founded: 2000
Capital Under Management: $93,000,000
Current Activity Level: Actively seeking new investments

DIATEM NETWORKS

350 Terry Fox Drive
Suite 320
Ottawa, Canada K2K2W5
Phone: 613-592-3525
Fax: 613-592-4570
E-mail: info@diatem.com
Website: www.diatem.com

Type of Firm

Private Equity Firm

Additional Information

Year Founded: 2009
Current Activity Level: Actively seeking new investments

DICK ISRAEL & PARTNERS (FKA: SPONSORED CONSULTING SERVICES)

8929 Wilshire Boulevard
Suite 214
Beverly Hills, CA USA 90211
Phone: 310-208-1234
Fax: 310-657-4486

Type of Firm

Private Equity Firm

Project Preferences

Role in Financing:

Prefer role as deal originator

Type of Financing Preferred:

Second Stage Financing
Leveraged Buyout
Mezzanine
First Stage Financing
Special Situation

Size of Investments Considered:

Min Size of Investment Considered (000s): $10,000
Max Size of Investment Considered: No Limit

Geographical Preferences

United States Preferences:

All U.S.

Industry Preferences

In Communications prefer:

Commercial Communications
Radio & TV Broadcasting

In Internet Specific prefer:

Internet

In Medical/Health prefer:

Diagnostic Services
Disposable Med. Products

In Consumer Related prefer:

Entertainment and Leisure
Retail
Computer Stores
Franchises(NEC)
Food/Beverage
Consumer Products
Consumer Services
Education Related

In Industrial/Energy prefer:

Factory Automation
Machinery

In Financial Services prefer:

Financial Services
Real Estate

In Business Serv. prefer:

Distribution
Consulting Services

In Manufact. prefer:

Publishing

In Agr/Forestr/Fish prefer:

Agriculture related

Additional Information

Year Founded: 1974
Current Activity Level: Actively seeking new investments
Method of Compensation: Function primarily in service area, receive contingent fee in cash or equity

---

DIE PROTEKTUS AG (FKA: AAFORTUNA VENTURE CAPITAL & MGMT AG)

Grunewaldstrasse 22
Berlin, Germany 12165
Phone: 49-302190-880
Fax: 49-302190-8890
E-mail: info@protektus.ag
Website: www.protektus.ag

Type of Firm

Service Provider

Project Preferences

Type of Financing Preferred:

Later Stage
Seed
Management Buyouts
First Stage Financing
Startup

Industry Preferences

In Communications prefer:

Communications and Media

In Semiconductor/Electr prefer:

Electronics

In Biotechnology prefer:

Biotechnology

In Medical/Health prefer:

Medical/Health

In Industrial/Energy prefer:

Energy

In Other prefer:

Environment Responsible

Additional Information

Year Founded: 1998
Current Activity Level: Actively seeking new investments

DIF CAPITAL PARTNERS, LTD.

Level 23, The Chifley Tower
2 Chifley Square
Sydney, Australia 2000
Phone: 612-9375-2475
Fax: 612-9375-2121

E-mail: info@dif.com.au
Website: www.dif.com.au

Management and Staff

Fergus Neilson, Chief Executive Officer

Type of Firm

Bank Affiliated

Association Membership

Australian Venture Capital Association (AVCAL)

Project Preferences

Role in Financing:

Will function either as deal originator or investor in deals created by others

Type of Financing Preferred:

Leveraged Buyout
Expansion
Mezzanine
Generalist PE
Balanced
Turnaround

Size of Investments Considered:

Min Size of Investment Considered (000s): $10,000
Max Size of Investment Considered (000s): $37,100

Geographical Preferences

United States Preferences:

All U.S.

Canadian Preferences:

All Canada

International Preferences:

United Kingdom
Europe
Pacific
Singapore
Australia
New Zealand
Japan

Additional Information

Year Founded: 2003
Capital Under Management: $266,600,000
Current Activity Level: Actively seeking new investments
Method of Compensation: Return on invest. most important, but chg. closing fees, service fees, etc.

DIFKO VENTURE A/S

Nyhavn 31G
Kobenhavn K, Denmark 1051
Phone: 45-3369-1414
Fax: 45-3369-1417
E-mail: difko@difko.dk

Type of Firm

Private Equity Firm

Project Preferences

Type of Financing Preferred:

Balanced

Geographical Preferences

International Preferences:

Denmark

Additional Information

Year Founded: 2000
Current Activity Level: Actively seeking new investments

DIGITAL PARTNERS

303 Parkplace Center
Suite G130
Kirkland, WA USA 98033
Phone: 425-468-3950
Fax: 425-468-3901
E-mail: info@digitalpartnersvc.com
Website: www.digitalpartnersvc.com

Management and Staff

Bill Tenneson, Managing Director
Daniel Regis, Managing Director
Pamela Gaspers, Managing Director

Type of Firm

Private Equity Firm

Association Membership

Western Association of Venture Capitalists (WAVC)

Project Preferences

Role in Financing:

Will function either as deal originator or investor in deals created by others

Type of Financing Preferred:

Second Stage Financing
Early Stage
Seed
First Stage Financing
Startup

Size of Investments Considered:

Min Size of Investment Considered (000s): $100
Max Size of Investment Considered (000s): $3,000

Geographical Preferences

United States Preferences:

West Coast

Industry Preferences

In Communications prefer:

Telecommunications
Wireless Communications
Data Communications

In Computer Software prefer:

Software
Applications Software

In Internet Specific prefer:

Internet

In Medical/Health prefer:

Medical Products
Health Services

Additional Information

Year Founded: 1999
Capital Under Management: $36,000,000
Current Activity Level: Actively seeking new investments
Method of Compensation: Return on investment is of primary concern, do not charge fees

---

DIGITAL POWER CAPITAL, LLC

411 West Putnam Avenue
Suite 125, Wexford Plaza
Greenwich, CT USA 06830
Phone: 203-862-7040
Website: www.digitalpower.com

Other Offices

1615 M Street NW
Suite 400
Washington, DC USA 20036
Phone: 202-367-7750

Management and Staff

Mark Mills, Founding Partner
Peter Huber, Partner

Type of Firm

Private Equity Firm

Additional Information

Year Founded: 2002
Current Activity Level: Actively seeking new investments

DIH DEUTSCHE INDUSTRIE-HOLDING GMBH

Friedrichstrasse 34
Frankfurt, Germany 60323
Phone: 49-69-71214-0
Fax: 49-69-71212-44
E-mail: info@dih-ffm.de
Website: www.dih-ffm.de

Management and Staff

Diethard Freiherr von Tettau, Managing Partner
Peter Zuehlsdorff, Managing Partner

Type of Firm

Private Equity Firm

Project Preferences

Type of Financing Preferred:

Recapitalizations

Geographical Preferences

International Preferences:
Germany

Industry Preferences

In Industrial/Energy prefer:
Industrial Products

Additional Information
Year Founded: 2005
Current Activity Level: Actively seeking new investments

DINVEST B.V.
Luchthavenweg 1
Budel, Netherlands 6021 PX
Phone: 31-495-583-390
Fax: 31-495-583-399
E-mail: info@dinvest.nl
Website: www.dinvest.nl

Type of Firm
Private Equity Firm

Project Preferences

Type of Financing Preferred:
Balanced

Geographical Preferences

International Preferences:
Netherlands

Additional Information
Year Founded: 1996
Current Activity Level: Actively seeking new investments

DIOGENES BUSINESS INCUBATOR
91 Aglandjia Avenue, 2/F
P.O. Box 20537
Nicosia, Cyprus 1678
Phone: 357-22-892-220
Fax: 357-22-892-211
E-mail: info@diogenes.com.cy
Website: www.diogenes.com.cy

Type of Firm
Private Equity Firm

Association Membership
European Private Equity and Venture Capital Assoc.

Project Preferences

Type of Financing Preferred:
Balanced
Startup

Geographical Preferences

International Preferences:
Cyprus

Additional Information
Year Founded: 2005
Current Activity Level: Actively seeking new investments

DIRECT CAPITAL PRIVATE EQUITY
Level 6
2 Kitchener Street
Auckland, New Zealand 6466
Phone: 64-9-307-2562
Fax: 64-9-307-2349
Website: www.directcapital.co.nz

Management and Staff
Aki Von Roy, Partner
Erich Sieber, Partner
Paul Van Tol, Chief Executive Officer
Ross George, Managing Director

Type of Firm
Private Equity Firm

Association Membership
Australian Venture Capital Association (AVCAL)

Project Preferences

Role in Financing:
Prefer role as deal originator but will also invest in deals created by others

Type of Financing Preferred:
Leveraged Buyout
Early Stage
Expansion
Generalist PE
Later Stage
Seed
Management Buyouts
Startup
Acquisition

Size of Investments Considered:
Min Size of Investment Considered (000s): $2,500
Max Size of Investment Considered (000s): $12,500

Geographical Preferences

International Preferences:
Pacific
Australia
New Zealand
Asia

Industry Preferences

In Communications prefer:
Telecommunications
Media and Entertainment

In Computer Software prefer:
Computer Services

In Semiconductor/Electr prefer:
Electronic Components

In Biotechnology prefer:
Biotechnology
Agricultural/Animal Bio.

In Medical/Health prefer:
Medical/Health

In Consumer Related prefer:
Entertainment and Leisure
Food/Beverage

In Transportation prefer:
Transportation
Aerospace

In Business Serv. prefer:
Media

In Manufact. prefer:
Manufacturing

Additional Information
Name of Most Recent Fund: Direct Capital Partners III
Most Recent Fund Was Raised: 04/01/2005
Year Founded: 1994
Capital Under Management: $2,200,000
Current Activity Level: Actively seeking new investments
Method of Compensation: Return on invest. most important, but chg. closing fees, service fees, etc.

DISCOVERY CAPITAL
Fifth Floor
1199 West Hastings
Vancouver, Canada V6E 3T5
Phone: 604-683-3000
Fax: 604-662-3457
E-mail: info@discoverycapital.com
Website: www.discoverycapital.com

Type of Firm
Private Equity Firm

Project Preferences

Role in Financing:
Prefer role as deal originator

Type of Financing Preferred:
Early Stage
Balanced
Startup

Geographical Preferences

Canadian Preferences:
All Canada
British Columbia

Industry Preferences

In Communications prefer:
Communications and Media

In Internet Specific prefer:
Internet

Additional Information
Year Founded: 1986
Current Activity Level: Actively seeking new investments

DISNEY (AKA THE WALT DISNEY COMPANY)
500 South Buena Vista Street
Burbank, CA USA 91521
Phone: 818-560-1000
Fax: 818-560-1930
Website: www.disney.go.com

Type of Firm
Corporate PE/Venture

Additional Information
Year Founded: 1995
Current Activity Level: Actively seeking new investments

DIVERGENT CAPITAL PARTNERS (FKA: BLUEFIRE INNOVATION)
Level 1, 505 Balmain Road
Lilyfield, Australia 2040
Phone: 614-0214-4898
Fax: 612-9818-3191
E-mail: info@divergent.com.au
Website: www.divergent.com.au

Management and Staff
David Nelson, Managing Director

Type of Firm
Incubator/Development Program

Project Preferences

Role in Financing:
Prefer role as deal originator but will also invest in deals created by others

Type of Financing Preferred:
Early Stage
Start-up Financing
Seed

Size of Investments Considered:
Min Size of Investment Considered (000s): $390
Max Size of Investment Considered (000s): $781

Geographical Preferences

International Preferences:
Australia
New Zealand

Industry Preferences

In Communications prefer:
Telecommunications
Wireless Communications
Data Communications

In Computer Hardware prefer:
Computer Graphics and Dig

In Computer Software prefer:
Computer Services
Data Processing
Software
Systems Software
Applications Software
Artificial Intelligence

In Internet Specific prefer:
Internet
Ecommerce

In Semiconductor/Electr prefer:
Electronic Components
Controllers and Sensors

In Consumer Related prefer:
Consumer
Entertainment and Leisure
Retail

In Business Serv. prefer:
Services

Additional Information
Year Founded: 1999
Capital Under Management: $7,800,000
Current Activity Level: Actively seeking new investments
Method of Compensation: Return on investment is of primary concern, do not charge fees

---

DIVERGENT VENTURES
2011 East Olive Street
Seattle, WA USA 98122
Phone: 206-709-3090
Fax: 206-709-3008
E-mail: info@divergent.com
Website: www.divergent.com

Management and Staff
Kevin Ober, Managing Director
Kevin Doren, Managing Director
Robert Shurtleff, Managing Director

Type of Firm
Private Equity Firm

Project Preferences

Role in Financing:
Prefer role as deal originator but will also invest in deals created by others

Type of Financing Preferred:
Early Stage

Size of Investments Considered:
Min Size of Investment Considered (000s): $200
Max Size of Investment Considered (000s): $1,000

Geographical Preferences

United States Preferences:
Northwest

Industry Preferences

In Computer Software prefer:
Software

In Business Serv. prefer:
Services

Additional Information
Year Founded: 2003
Capital Under Management: $100,000,000
Current Activity Level: Actively seeking new investments
Method of Compensation: Return on investment is of primary concern, do not charge fees

---

DKB WAGNISKAPITAL UNTERNEHMENSBETEILIGUNGSGESELLSCHAFT MBH
Kronenstrasse 11
Berlin, Germany 10117
Phone: 49-30-201-55676
Fax: 49-30-201-55851

Management and Staff
Axel Bublitz, Managing Partner
Manfred Mende, Managing Partner

Type of Firm
Bank Affiliated

Project Preferences

Type of Financing Preferred:
Balanced

Geographical Preferences

International Preferences:
Germany

Additional Information
Year Founded: 2005
Current Activity Level: Actively seeking new investments

DLJ MERCHANT BANKING PARTNERS
11 Madison Avenue
New York, NY USA 10010
Phone: 212-892-3000
Fax: 646-658-0728
E-mail: askdlj@dlj.com
Website: www.csfb.com

Other Offices

One Cabot Square
London, United Kingdom E14 4QJ
Phone: 44-207-888-8888
Fax: 44-207-888-1600

Uetlibergstrasse 231
P.O. Box 700
Zurich, Switzerland CH 8070
Phone: 411-332-6400
Fax: 411-333-5555

201 West Big Beaver Road
Columbia Center Suite 950
Troy, MI USA 48084

Management and Staff

Allen Yurko, Partner
Dominick Schiano, Partner
John Janitz, Partner
Neal Pomroy, Managing Director
Nicole Arnaboldi, Chairman & Managing Director
Ron Beegle, Managing Director
Steven Rattner, Managing Director

Type of Firm

Bank Affiliated

Project Preferences

Type of Financing Preferred:

Fund of Funds
Leveraged Buyout
Mezzanine
Generalist PE

Geographical Preferences

United States Preferences:

Northwest
All U.S.

Canadian Preferences:

All Canada

International Preferences:

Europe
All International

Industry Focus

(% based on actual investment)

Other Products	26.1%
Consumer Related	22.1%
Industrial/Energy	16.4%
Medical/Health	14.7%
Communications and Media	8.7%
Computer Software and Services	4.7%
Internet Specific	3.9%
Semiconductors/Other Elect.	2.9%
Computer Hardware	0.3%
Biotechnology	0.2%

Additional Information

Year Founded: 1972
Capital Under Management: $3,740,500,000
Current Activity Level: Actively seeking new investments

DMC CAPITAL FUNDING LLC

105 Madison Avenue
New York, NY USA 10016
Phone: 212-779-8400
Fax: 212-779-2333
E-mail: info@dmccapitalfunding.com
Website: www.dmccapitalfunding.com

Management and Staff

Andrew Lowinger, Chief Executive Officer

Type of Firm

Private Equity Firm

Project Preferences

Role in Financing:

Prefer role as deal originator

Type of Financing Preferred:

Leveraged Buyout
Generalist PE
Expansion
Acquisition

Industry Preferences

In Consumer Related prefer:

Consumer

Additional Information

Year Founded: 2008
Current Activity Level: Actively seeking new investments

DN CAPITAL, LTD. (FKA: DIGITAL NETWORKS GLOBAL VENTURES)

2 Queen Anne's Gate Buildings
Darmouth Street
London, United Kingdom SW1H 9BP
Phone: 44-20-7340-1600
Fax: 44-20-7340-1601
E-mail: info@dncapital.com
Website: www.dncapital.com

Other Offices

228 Hamilton Avenue
Third Floor
Palo Alto, CA USA 94301
Phone: 650-798-5424

Management and Staff

Nenad Marovac, Managing Partner
Pierre Suhrcke, Managing Partner
Steven Schlenker, Managing Partner
Tom Bradley, Principal

Type of Firm

Private Equity Firm

Association Membership

European Private Equity and Venture Capital Assoc.

Project Preferences

Role in Financing:

Will function either as deal originator or investor in deals created by others

Type of Financing Preferred:

Early Stage
Expansion
Balanced
Later Stage

Size of Investments Considered:

Min Size of Investment Considered (000s): $100
Max Size of Investment Considered (000s): $100,000

Geographical Preferences

International Preferences:

United Kingdom
Central Europe
Western Europe
Eastern Europe
Scandanavia/Nordic Region
Israel
Germany
France

Industry Preferences

In Communications prefer:

Communications and Media

In Computer Software prefer:

Software

In Internet Specific prefer:

Internet

In Computer Other prefer:

Computer Related

In Semiconductor/Electr prefer:

Electronics

Additional Information

Name of Most Recent Fund: European Digital Infrastructure Fund I
Most Recent Fund Was Raised: 06/21/2001
Year Founded: 2000
Capital Under Management: $62,600,000
Current Activity Level: Actively seeking new investments

DOCOMO CAPITAL

181 Metro Drive
Suite 300
San Jose, CA USA 95110
Phone: 408-573-8840
Fax: 408-451-4770
Website: www.docomo-capital.com

Management and Staff

Ichiro Okajima, Managing Director

Koji Hiratsuka, Principal
Shinichiro Tonooka, Principal

Type of Firm

Corporate PE/Venture

Project Preferences

Type of Financing Preferred:
Expansion
Later Stage

Geographical Preferences

United States Preferences:
Northern California

Industry Preferences

In Communications prefer:
Wireless Communications

Additional Information

Year Founded: 2005
Current Activity Level: Actively seeking new investments

DOCOR INTERNATIONAL B.V.

65 Yigal Alon Street
Toyota Tower, 14th Floor
Tel Aviv, Israel 67443
Phone: 972-3-562-0311
Fax: 972-3-562-0312
E-mail: info@docor.co.il
Website: www.docor.co.il

Management and Staff

Alon Dumanis, Chief Executive Officer
Tsachy Shasha, Managing Director

Type of Firm

Endowment, Foundation or Pension Fund

Project Preferences

Type of Financing Preferred:
Balanced
Startup

Geographical Preferences

International Preferences:
Israel

Industry Preferences

In Computer Software prefer:
Software

In Biotechnology prefer:
Biotechnology

In Medical/Health prefer:
Medical Products

In Industrial/Energy prefer:
Industrial Products
Materials

Additional Information

Year Founded: 2005
Current Activity Level: Actively seeking new investments

DOEN PARTICIPATIES BV

Havenstraat 68
Huizen, Netherlands 1271 AG
Phone: 31-35-526-8808
Fax: 31-35-526-8614
E-mail: info@doenp.nl
Website: www.doenparticipaties.nl

Type of Firm

Private Equity Firm

Association Membership

European Private Equity and Venture Capital Assoc.
Dutch Venture Capital Associaton (NVP)

Project Preferences

Type of Financing Preferred:
Expansion
Turnaround
Seed
Management Buyouts
Startup

Geographical Preferences

International Preferences:
Netherlands
Europe
All International

Industry Preferences

In Other prefer:
Socially Responsible
Environment Responsible

Additional Information

Year Founded: 1991
Capital Under Management: $29,300,000
Current Activity Level: Actively seeking new investments

DOGAN INVESTMENTS, INC.

3F Shin Nihon Bldg.
2-4-22 Daimyo Chuo-ku
Fukuoka-shi, Japan
Phone: 81-92-739-2311
Fax: 81-92-739-2317
E-mail: info@dogan.jp
Website: www.dogan.jp

Management and Staff

Masatoshi Matsuo, Managing Director

Type of Firm

SBIC

Project Preferences

Type of Financing Preferred:
Leveraged Buyout
Generalist PE
Balanced

Geographical Preferences

International Preferences:
Asia

Additional Information

Year Founded: 2004
Capital Under Management: $8,500,000
Current Activity Level: Actively seeking new investments

DOGWOOD EQUITY

316 West Edenton Street
Suite 110
Raleigh, NC USA 27603
Phone: 919-256-5000
Fax: 919-256-5015
E-mail: info@dogwoodequity.com
Website: www.dogwoodequity.com

Other Offices

1901 Roxborough Road
Suite 116
Charlotte, NC USA 28211
Phone: 704-362-1800
Fax: 704-366-1850

Management and Staff

David Cox, Vice President
H. Dabney Smith, General Partner
Rick Carlisle, Managing Partner
Stephen Buchanan, General Partner

Type of Firm

Private Equity Firm

Association Membership

Natl Assoc of Small Bus. Inv. Co (NASBIC)

Project Preferences

Role in Financing:
Prefer role as deal originator but will also invest in deals created by others

Type of Financing Preferred:
Leveraged Buyout
Expansion
Balanced
Later Stage
Management Buyouts

Size of Investments Considered:
Min Size of Investment Considered (000s): $1,000
Max Size of Investment Considered (000s): $7,000

Geographical Preferences

United States Preferences:
Southeast

Industry Preferences

In Computer Software prefer:
Software

In Medical/Health prefer:
Medical Products
Disposable Med. Products

In Consumer Related prefer:
Food/Beverage
Consumer Products

In Business Serv. prefer:
Distribution

In Manufact. prefer:
Manufacturing

Additional Information
Year Founded: 2001
Capital Under Management: $75,000,000
Current Activity Level: Actively seeking new investments
Method of Compensation: Return on investment is of primary concern, do not charge fees

---

DOJANE CAPITAL
1604, Bldg. B, JinYing Mansion
1518 MinSheng Road
Shanghai, China 200135
Phone: 86-21-6104-9522
Fax: 86-21-6104-9527
E-mail: info@dojane.com.cn
Website: www.dojane.com.cn

Management and Staff
TieCheng Yu, Managing Partner
Xiaoyun Cai, Managing Director
YuXin Zhang, Founding Partner

Type of Firm
Bank Affiliated

Project Preferences

Type of Financing Preferred:
Early Stage
Expansion
Later Stage

Size of Investments Considered:
Min Size of Investment Considered (000s): $10,000
Max Size of Investment Considered (000s): $100,000

Geographical Preferences

International Preferences:
China
Asia

Industry Preferences

In Biotechnology prefer:
Agricultural/Animal Bio.

In Industrial/Energy prefer:
Alternative Energy
Environmental Related

Additional Information
Year Founded: 2009
Current Activity Level: Actively seeking new investments

DOLPHIN CAPITAL GROUP, LLC
1679 West Village Round Drive
Park City, UT USA 84068
Phone: 435-649-0406
Fax: 435-649-0522
E-mail: info@dolphincapitalgroup.com
Website: www.dolphincapitalgroup.com

Other Offices
Three Devon Road
Westport, CT USA 06880
Phone: 917-860-7440

Management and Staff
Daniel Schley, Co-Founder
Eric Jacobsen, Co-Founder
Jill Dempsey, Partner
Ken Jacquin, Partner
Mike Dutton, Partner

Type of Firm
Private Equity Firm

Project Preferences

Type of Financing Preferred:
Expansion
Early Stage
Acquisition
Industry Rollups

Geographical Preferences

United States Preferences:
Rocky Mountain

Additional Information
Year Founded: 2007
Capital Under Management: $41,700,000
Current Activity Level: Actively seeking new investments

DOLPHIN CAPITAL PARTNERS
Four Kaplanon Street
Athens, Greece 10680
Phone: 30-210-361-4255
Fax: 30-210-361-4243
Website: www.dolphincp.com

Other Offices
12 Themistocles Dervis Avenue
P.O. Box 21762 - Palais D'Ivoire House
Nicosia, Cyprus 1513
Fax: 357-22-67-2075

Management and Staff
Miltos Kambourides, Managing Partner
Pierre Charalambides, Partner

Type of Firm
Private Equity Firm

Project Preferences

Type of Financing Preferred:
Generalist PE

Geographical Preferences

International Preferences:
Europe

Industry Preferences

In Consumer Related prefer:
Entertainment and Leisure
Sports
Consumer Services
Hotels and Resorts

Additional Information
Year Founded: 2004
Capital Under Management: $119,400,000
Current Activity Level: Actively seeking new investments

DOLPHIN EQUITY PARTNERS
750 Lexington Avenue
16th Floor
New York, NY USA 10022
Phone: 212-446-1600
Fax: 212-446-1638
E-mail: info@dolphinequity.com
Website: www.dolphinequity.com

Management and Staff
Adam Greene, Venture Partner
Dennis O'Connell, Partner
R.Gregory Breetz, Chief Financial Officer
Richard Brekka, Managing Partner

Type of Firm
Private Equity Firm

Association Membership
National Venture Capital Association - USA (NVCA)

Project Preferences

Role in Financing:

Prefer role as deal originator but will also invest in deals created by others

Type of Financing Preferred:

Second Stage Financing
Expansion
Balanced
Later Stage
Recapitalizations

Size of Investments Considered:

Min Size of Investment Considered (000s): $10,000
Max Size of Investment Considered (000s): $75,000

Geographical Preferences

Canadian Preferences:

All Canada

Industry Focus

(% based on actual investment)

Internet Specific	35.0%
Computer Software and Services	21.2%
Communications and Media	21.2%
Semiconductors/Other Elect.	14.7%
Computer Hardware	5.8%
Other Products	1.2%
Medical/Health	1.0%

Additional Information

Name of Most Recent Fund: Dolphin Communications Fund II, L.P.
Most Recent Fund Was Raised: 07/01/2000
Year Founded: 1998
Capital Under Management: $350,000,000
Current Activity Level: Actively seeking new investments
Method of Compensation: Return on investment is of primary concern, do not charge fees

---

DOMAIN ASSOCIATES LLC

One Palmer Square
Suite 515
Princeton, NJ USA 08542
Phone: 609-683-5656
Fax: 609-683-9789
E-mail: domain@domainvc.com
Website: www.domainvc.com

Other Offices

12481 High Bluff Drive
Suite 150
San Diego, CA USA 92130
Phone: 858-480-2400
Fax: 858-480-2401

Management and Staff

Brian Dovey, Partner
Brian Halak, Partner
Debra Liebert, Principal
Dennis Podlesak, Partner
Eckard Weber, Partner
James Blair, Partner
Jesse Treu, Partner
Kim Kamdar, Principal
Nicole Vitullo, Partner
Nimesh Shah, Principal
Todd Brady, Principal

Type of Firm

Private Equity Firm

Association Membership

National Venture Capital Association - USA (NVCA)

Project Preferences

Role in Financing:

Will function either as deal originator or investor in deals created by others

Type of Financing Preferred:

Second Stage Financing
Early Stage
Expansion
Mezzanine
Research and Development
Balanced
Public Companies
Later Stage
Seed
First Stage Financing
Private Placement
Startup

Size of Investments Considered:

Min Size of Investment Considered (000s): $1,000
Max Size of Investment Considered (000s): $20,000

Industry Focus

(% based on actual investment)

Medical/Health	48.5%
Biotechnology	45.3%
Internet Specific	2.4%
Consumer Related	1.2%
Computer Software and Services	1.0%
Industrial/Energy	1.0%
Semiconductors/Other Elect.	0.7%

Additional Information

Name of Most Recent Fund: Domain Partners VII, L.P.
Most Recent Fund Was Raised: 08/15/2006
Year Founded: 1985
Capital Under Management: $2,475,500,000
Current Activity Level: Actively seeking new investments
Method of Compensation: Return on investment is of primary concern, do not charge fees

---

DOMINION VENTURES, INC.

1656 North California Blvd.
Suite 300
Walnut Creek, CA USA 94596
Phone: 925-280-6300
Fax: 925-280-6338
E-mail: info@dominion.com

Other Offices

Dominion Capital Management
75 Park Place, 4th Floor
Boston, MA USA 02116
Phone: 617-848-5980
Fax: 617-249-1806

Dominion Capital Management
885 Oak Grove Avenue; Suite 102
Menlo Park, CA USA 94025
Phone: 650-854-1800
Fax: 650-618-2639

Management and Staff

Brian Smith, General Partner
Michael Lee, General Partner

Type of Firm

Private Equity Firm

Project Preferences

Role in Financing:

Will function either as deal originator or investor in deals created by others

Type of Financing Preferred:

Second Stage Financing
Start-up Financing
First Stage Financing

Size of Investments Considered:

Min Size of Investment Considered (000s): $2,000
Max Size of Investment Considered (000s): $4,000

Geographical Preferences

United States Preferences:

All U.S.

Industry Focus

(% based on actual investment)

Internet Specific	41.1%
Computer Software and Services	22.9%
Medical/Health	9.9%
Communications and Media	7.5%
Computer Hardware	4.8%
Semiconductors/Other Elect.	4.7%
Other Products	4.2%
Consumer Related	2.7%
Biotechnology	2.1%

Additional Information

Name of Most Recent Fund: Dominion Fund V, L.P.
Most Recent Fund Was Raised: 01/01/2000
Year Founded: 1985
Capital Under Management: $500,000,000
Current Activity Level: Actively seeking new investments
Method of Compensation: Return on investment is of primary concern, do not charge fees

---

DOMINUS CAPITAL, L.P.

623 Fifth Avenue
29th Floor
New York, NY USA 10022
Phone: 212-784-5440

Fax: 212-784-5441
E-mail: Dominus@dominuscap.com
Website: www.dominuscap.com

Management and Staff

Ashish Rughwani, Partner
Gary Binning, Managing Partner
Robert Haswell, Partner

Type of Firm

Private Equity Firm

Project Preferences

Type of Financing Preferred:

Leveraged Buyout
Management Buyouts
Acquisition
Recapitalizations

Industry Preferences

In Consumer Related prefer:

Retail
Food/Beverage
Consumer Products
Consumer Services
Other Restaurants

In Industrial/Energy prefer:

Industrial Products
Materials

In Business Serv. prefer:

Distribution

In Manufact. prefer:

Manufacturing

Additional Information

Year Founded: 2008
Capital Under Management: $102,600,000
Current Activity Level: Actively seeking new investments

DOR VENTURES MANAGEMENT SA

161 Dreve Richelle
Waterloo, Belgium 1410
Phone: 32-2-352-8911
Fax: 32-2-352-8889
Website: www.dorventures.com

Management and Staff

Arie Rosenfeld, Managing Partner
Ilan Neugarten, Managing Director

Type of Firm

Private Equity Firm

Project Preferences

Type of Financing Preferred:

Early Stage

Geographical Preferences

International Preferences:

Europe
Israel

Industry Preferences

In Communications prefer:

Publishing

Additional Information

Year Founded: 2000
Current Activity Level: Actively seeking new investments

DORSET CAPITAL

Pier 1
Bay 2
San Francisco, CA USA 94111
Phone: 415-398-7101
Fax: 415-398-7141
E-mail: info@dorsetcapital.com
Website: www.dorsetcapital.com

Management and Staff

Jeffrey Mills, General Partner
John Berg, Managing Partner

Type of Firm

Private Equity Firm

Project Preferences

Role in Financing:

Will function either as deal originator or investor in deals created by others

Type of Financing Preferred:

Second Stage Financing
Leveraged Buyout
Expansion
Generalist PE
Later Stage
Management Buyouts
First Stage Financing
Recapitalizations

Size of Investments Considered:

Min Size of Investment Considered (000s): $5,000
Max Size of Investment Considered (000s): $30,000

Geographical Preferences

United States Preferences:

All U.S.

Industry Preferences

In Consumer Related prefer:

Consumer
Retail
Food/Beverage
Consumer Products
Consumer Services

In Financial Services prefer:

Financial Services

In Business Serv. prefer:

Services
Distribution

In Manufact. prefer:

Manufacturing

In Other prefer:

Socially Responsible
Environment Responsible
Women/Minority-Owned Bus.

Additional Information

Name of Most Recent Fund: Dorset Capital, L.P.
Most Recent Fund Was Raised: 06/30/1999
Year Founded: 1999
Capital Under Management: $70,000,000
Current Activity Level: Actively seeking new investments
Method of Compensation: Return on investment is of primary concern, do not charge fees

---

DOT EDU VENTURES

514 Bryant Street
Suite 108
Palo Alto, CA USA 94301
Phone: 650-321-3804
Fax: 650-321-3808
Website: www.doteduventures.com

Management and Staff

Asha Jadeja, Managing Partner
J. Casey McGlynn, General Partner

Type of Firm

Private Equity Firm

Project Preferences

Role in Financing:

Will function either as deal originator or investor in deals created by others

Type of Financing Preferred:

Early Stage
Seed

Industry Preferences

In Internet Specific prefer:

Internet

Additional Information

Year Founded: 2000
Current Activity Level: Actively seeking new investments

DOUGHTY HANSON & CO., LTD.

Times Place
45 Pall Mall
London, United Kingdom SW1Y 5JG
Phone: 44-207-663-9300
Fax: 44-207-663-9352

E-mail: info@doughtyhanson.com
Website: www.doughtyhanson.com

Other Offices

Platz der Einheit 2
Frankfurt, Germany D-60327
Phone: 49-69-971-2020
Fax: 49-69-9712-0299

Biblioteksgatan 6-8
Stockholm, Sweden S-111 46
Phone: 46-8-5450-6030
Fax: 46-8611-3840

Via Dei Bossi 4
Milan, Italy 20121
Phone: 39-02-806-0681
Fax: 39-02-8060-6820

28 Boulevard Royal
Luxembourg, Luxembourg L-2449
Phone: 352-26-27-561
Fax: 352-26-275-620

Shlafflerhof
Windenmacherstrasse 2
Munich, Germany D-80 333
Phone: 49-89-244-4060
Fax: 49-89-2444-0688

60 Avenue Hoche
Paris, France 75008
Phone: 33-1-5668-5515
Fax: 33-1-5668-5524

Calle Pinar 5
Madrid, Spain 28006
Phone: 34-91-745-6819
Fax: 34-91-745-6626

Management and Staff

Anders Tagt, Principal
Chris Wallis, Partner
Douglas Edwards, Principal
Ken Terry, Partner
Marc Mogull, Partner
Mark Florman, Principal
Nigel Doughty, Partner
Nigel Grierson, Founder
Richard Hanson, Partner
Yann Duchesne, Managing Director

Type of Firm

Private Equity Firm

Association Membership

British Venture Capital Association (BVCA)
Swedish Venture Capital Association (SVCA)
European Private Equity and Venture Capital Assoc.

Project Preferences

Type of Financing Preferred:

Leveraged Buyout
Expansion
Other

Geographical Preferences

International Preferences:

Italy
Sweden
United Kingdom
Switzerland
Europe
Iceland
Finland
Norway
Germany
Denmark
France

Industry Focus

(% based on actual investment)	
Other Products	38.5%
Communications and Media	21.4%
Semiconductors/Other Elect.	14.3%
Consumer Related	10.8%
Computer Software and Services	5.0%
Industrial/Energy	4.2%
Internet Specific	3.6%
Medical/Health	1.4%
Computer Hardware	0.5%
Biotechnology	0.2%

Additional Information

Year Founded: 1986
Capital Under Management: $2,000,000,000
Current Activity Level: Actively seeking new investments

DPE DEUTSCHE PRIVATE EQUITY GMBH (AKA: PARCOM DEUTSCHE PE)

Ludwigstrasse 7
Munich, Germany 80539
Phone: 49-89-200-0380
Fax: 49-89-200038111
E-mail: info@pdpe.de
Website: www.pdpe.com

Management and Staff

Marc Thiery, Managing Partner
Uwe Schweda, Chief Financial Officer
Volker Hichert, Managing Partner

Type of Firm

Private Equity Firm

Project Preferences

Type of Financing Preferred:

Leveraged Buyout
Management Buyouts
Acquisition
Recapitalizations

Size of Investments Considered:

Min Size of Investment Considered (000s): $6,467
Max Size of Investment Considered (000s): $64,666

Geographical Preferences

International Preferences:

Switzerland
Austria
Germany

Industry Preferences

In Medical/Health prefer:

Health Services

In Consumer Related prefer:

Education Related

In Industrial/Energy prefer:

Alternative Energy
Industrial Products
Environmental Related

In Business Serv. prefer:

Services

Additional Information

Year Founded: 2007
Capital Under Management: $330,400,000
Current Activity Level: Actively seeking new investments

DR SCHMIDT BIOTECH GMBH

Max-Planck-Ring 21
Wiesbaden, Germany 65205
Phone: 49-6122-9988400
Fax: 49-6122-9988401
Website: www.drschmidt-biotech.de

Type of Firm

Corporate PE/Venture

Project Preferences

Type of Financing Preferred:

Balanced

Additional Information

Year Founded: 2007
Current Activity Level: Actively seeking new investments

DRAGON CAPITAL

1901 Me Linh Point
2 Ngo Duc Ke St., District 1
Ho Chi Minh , Vietnam
Phone: 84-8-3823-9355
Fax: 84-8-3823-9366
E-mail: info@dragoncapital.com
Website: www.dragoncapital.com

Other Offices

1505 Vietcombank Tower
198 Tran Quang Khai St., Hoan Kiem Dist.
Hanoi, Vietnam
Phone: 84-8-3936-0203
Fax: 84-8-3936-0204

The Tramshed, Beehive Yard
Walcot Street
Bath, United Kingdom BA1 5BB
Phone: 44-122-573-1402
Fax: 44-207-149-9969

15 Douglas Street
Okitu
Gisborne, New Zealand
Phone: 64-6-867-0882

Type of Firm

Bank Affiliated

Project Preferences

Type of Financing Preferred:
Early Stage
Balanced

Geographical Preferences

International Preferences:
Vietnam
Belarus
Moldova
Ukraine

Additional Information

Year Founded: 1994
Capital Under Management: $200,000,000
Current Activity Level: Actively seeking new investments

DRAGON CAPITAL

36D Saksahanskoho
Kyiv, Ukraine 01 033
Phone: 380-44-490-7120
Fax: 380-44-490-7121
E-mail: dragon@dragon-capital.com
Website: www.dragon-capital.com

Other Offices

Dlouha 35
Sebel Development BC
Prague, Czech Republic 110 00
Phone: 420-224-827-830
Fax: 420-224-828-010

Management and Staff

Brian Best, Managing Director
Dmytro Tarabakin, Managing Director
Tomas Fiala, Managing Director

Type of Firm

Bank Affiliated

Project Preferences

Type of Financing Preferred:
Leveraged Buyout

Geographical Preferences

International Preferences:
Eastern Europe

Industry Preferences

In Communications prefer:
Communications and Media
Telecommunications

In Medical/Health prefer:
Pharmaceuticals

In Consumer Related prefer:
Retail
Consumer Products

Additional Information

Year Founded: 2000
Current Activity Level: Actively seeking new investments

DRAGONTECH VENTURES MANAGEMENT, LTD.

Unit 504 Lippo Center, Tower 2
89 Queensway
Admiralty, Hong Kong
Phone: 852-2801-7333
Fax: 852-2899-2711
E-mail: info@dragontechventures.com
Website: www.dragontechventures.com

Other Offices

Room 516, Tower A, COFCO Plaza
No. 8 Jianguomennei Avenue
Beijing, China
Phone: 86-10-6524-4083
Fax: 86-10-6513-7941

Management and Staff

Cathy Zhang, Managing Director
Lynn Ta, Vice President
Roman Shaw, CEO & Managing Director
Sean Wang, Managing Director
Zhizhong Qiu, Chairman & CEO

Type of Firm

Private Equity Firm

Association Membership

Venture Capital Association of Beijing (VCAB)
Hong Kong Venture Capital Association (HKVCA)

Project Preferences

Type of Financing Preferred:
Early Stage
Expansion
Balanced

Geographical Preferences

International Preferences:
Taiwan
China
Hong Kong
Singapore
Asia

Industry Preferences

In Communications prefer:
Telecommunications

In Computer Software prefer:
Software

In Semiconductor/Electr prefer:
Semiconductor

Additional Information

Year Founded: 2000
Capital Under Management: $135,100,000
Current Activity Level: Actively seeking new investments

DRAGONVENTURE, INC.

2882 Sand Hill Road
Suite 150
Menlo Park, CA USA 94025
Phone: 650-233-9000
Fax: 650-234-8533
E-mail: info@dragonventure.com
Website: www.dragonventure.com

Other Offices

801 Haidian Science Plaza
3 Zhong Guan Cun Rd. South, Haidian Dist
Beijing, China

Suite 301, Tower A, 560 Songtao Road
Zhangjiang High-tech Park
Shanghai, China

Management and Staff

Tony Luh, Managing Director

Type of Firm

Private Equity Firm

Project Preferences

Type of Financing Preferred:
Early Stage
Expansion
Balanced
Seed

Geographical Preferences

International Preferences:
Taiwan
China

Industry Preferences

In Communications prefer:
Telecommunications

In Computer Software prefer:
Software

In Internet Specific prefer:
Internet

In Semiconductor/Electr prefer:
Semiconductor

Additional Information

Name of Most Recent Fund: DFJ DragonFund China II, L.P.
Most Recent Fund Was Raised: 11/12/2008
Year Founded: 2000
Capital Under Management: $71,700,000
Current Activity Level: Actively seeking new investments

DRAGONVEST PARTNERS

Unit 303, Building 27
879 Zhongjiang Road
Shanghai, China 200333
Phone: 86-21-6142-3234
Fax: 86-21-6142-3239
Website: www.dragonvestpartners.com.cn

Other Offices

20 Farnham Circle
Needham, MA USA 02492

Management and Staff

Alice Ye, Vice President
Cha Li, Managing General Partner
Jesse Parker, Managing Director
Lena Li, Managing General Partner

Type of Firm

Angel Group

Project Preferences

Role in Financing:

Prefer role as deal originator but will also invest in deals created by others

Type of Financing Preferred:

Early Stage
Seed

Size of Investments Considered:

Min Size of Investment Considered (000s): $100
Max Size of Investment Considered (000s): $500

Geographical Preferences

International Preferences:

Taiwan
China
Hong Kong

Industry Preferences

In Communications prefer:

Telecommunications
Wireless Communications

In Computer Software prefer:

Software

In Semiconductor/Electr prefer:

Semiconductor

In Medical/Health prefer:

Medical Products

Additional Information

Year Founded: 2004
Capital Under Management: $1,100,000
Current Activity Level: Actively seeking new investments

DRAPER FISHER JURVETSON

2882 Sand Hill Road
Suite 150
Menlo Park, CA USA 94025
Phone: 650-233-9000
Fax: 650-233-9233
E-mail: mail@dfj.com
Website: www.dfj.com

Other Offices

1366 West Nanjing Road
Plaza 6611, Suite 4709
Shanghai, China 200040
Phone: 86-21-6288-4000

2/1 First Floor, Stylus Office
Embassy Icon Annexe
Bangalore, India 560001
Phone: 91-80-6644-5100
Fax: 91-80-6644-5200

2 Kensington Square
London, United Kingdom W8 5EP
Phone: 44-207-3610140

Management and Staff

Andreas Stavropoulos, Managing Director
Donald Wood, Managing Director
Jennifer Fonstad, Managing Director
John Fisher, Managing Director
Josh Stein, Managing Director
Mark Greenstein, Chief Financial Officer
Rajesh Atluru, Managing Director
Sachin Maheshwari, Principal
Sateesh Andra, Venture Partner
Songbo Li, Venture Partner
Steven Jurvetson, Managing Director
Timothy Draper, Managing Director
Warren Packard, Managing Director
William Bryant, Venture Partner

Type of Firm

Private Equity Firm

Association Membership

Western Association of Venture Capitalists (WAVC)
National Venture Capital Association - USA (NVCA)

Project Preferences

Role in Financing:

Prefer role as deal originator but will also invest in deals created by others

Type of Financing Preferred:

Leveraged Buyout
Expansion
Early Stage
Start-up Financing
Balanced
Seed
First Stage Financing

Size of Investments Considered:

Min Size of Investment Considered (000s): $500
Max Size of Investment Considered (000s): $1,000

Geographical Preferences

United States Preferences:

Mid Atlantic
Southeast
Northeast

International Preferences:

Russia
All International

Industry Focus

(% based on actual investment)	
Internet Specific	32.5%
Computer Software and Services	22.5%
Semiconductors/Other Elect.	12.3%
Communications and Media	11.9%
Industrial/Energy	7.9%
Other Products	4.0%
Biotechnology	3.0%
Computer Hardware	2.6%
Medical/Health	2.4%
Consumer Related	1.0%

Additional Information

Year Founded: 1986
Capital Under Management: $4,000,000,000
Current Activity Level: Actively seeking new investments
Method of Compensation: Function primarily in service area, receive contingent fee in cash or equity

---

DRAPER FISHER JURVETSON EPLANET VENTURES, L.P.

5300 Stevens Creek Boulevard
Suite 500
San Jose, CA USA 95129
Phone: 408-236-6501
Fax: 408-554-6600
E-mail: mail@drapervc.com
Website: www.dfjeplanet.com

Other Offices

30th Floor ASEM Tower
159-1 Samsung-dong, Kangnam-ku
Seoul, South Korea 135-798
Phone: 822-6001-2920
Fax: 822-6001-2922

Level 11 Park West Building
6-2-1 Nishi-Shinjuku
Shinjuku-ku, Tokyo, Japan
Phone: 81-3-5325-3212
Fax: 81-3-3816-5689

1168 Nanjing Xi Road
Suite 4105, CITIC Square
Shanghai, China 200041

Phone: 86-21-5292-9911
Fax: 86-21-5292-5026

2 Kensington Square
London, United Kingdom W8 5EP
Phone: 44-20-7361-0140
Fax: 44-20-7361-0149

Room 2113-2114, Tower I
No. 1 Jianguomen Wai Da Jie
Beijing, China 100004
Phone: 86-10-6505-9398
Fax: 86-10-6505-9395

30 Cecil Street
Prudential Tower 27th Floor
Singapore, Singapore 049712
Phone: 65-6538-3353
Fax: 65-6538-5755

W-2 First Floor
Greater Kailash Part I
New Delhi, India 110 048
Phone: 91-11-4141-4107

21/F, ICBC Tower, Citibank Plaza
No. 3 Garden Road
Central, Hong Kong
Phone: 852-2273-5749
Fax: 852-2273-5999

202 B Rear, II Floor
Sobha Alexander Plaza, Commissariat Road
Bangalore, India 560 001
Phone: 91-80-4154-0240
Fax: 91-80-4154-0250

Management and Staff

Ayaz ul Haque, Managing Director
Chandrasekar Kandasamy, Managing Director
Cynthia Zhang, Vice President
Francis Egan, Venture Partner
Fredrik Brag, Venture Partner
Gupta Manish, Venture Partner
Henry Wong, Venture Partner
Huateng Ma, Venture Partner
Jerry Ilhyun Cho, Managing Director
Jung-kyoo Yang, Venture Partner
Mir Imran, Venture Partner
Morten Lund, Venture Partner
Neil Adams, Managing Director
Nick Yang, Venture Partner
Pratap Reddy, Venture Partner
Rajesh Atluru, Managing Director
Roderick Thomson, Managing Director
Rupam Shrivastava, Vice President
Saad Raja, Managing Director
Scott Walchek, Venture Partner

Type of Firm

Bank Affiliated

Association Membership

National Venture Capital Association - USA (NVCA)
European Private Equity and Venture Capital Assoc.
Singapore Venture Capital Association (SVCA)

Project Preferences

Type of Financing Preferred:

Mezzanine
Early Stage
Expansion
Balanced
Later Stage
Seed
Acquisition
Startup

Geographical Preferences

United States Preferences:

All U.S.

International Preferences:

Israel
Asia

Industry Preferences

In Communications prefer:

Communications and Media
Wireless Communications
Data Communications

In Computer Software prefer:

Software
Applications Software

In Internet Specific prefer:

Internet

In Semiconductor/Electr prefer:

Electronic Components
Semiconductor
Fiber Optics
Optoelectronics

Additional Information

Year Founded: 1999
Capital Under Management: $4,500,000,000
Current Activity Level: Actively seeking new investments

DRAPER FISHER JURVETSON GOTHAM VENTURE PARTNERS

132 West 31st Street
Suite 1102
New York, NY USA 10001
Phone: 212-279-3980
Fax: 212-279-3825
E-mail: mail@dfjgotham.com
Website: www.dfjgotham.com

Management and Staff

Daniel Schultz, Managing Partner
Jed Katz, Venture Partner
Ross Goldstein, Managing Partner
Thatcher Bell, Principal
Timothy Draper, Managing Director

Type of Firm

Bank Affiliated

Association Membership

National Venture Capital Association - USA (NVCA)

Project Preferences

Type of Financing Preferred:

Early Stage
Seed
First Stage Financing

Size of Investments Considered:

Min Size of Investment Considered (000s): $100
Max Size of Investment Considered (000s): $5,000

Geographical Preferences

United States Preferences:

Northeast
New York

Industry Preferences

In Communications prefer:

Communications and Media

In Computer Software prefer:

Software

In Internet Specific prefer:

Internet

Additional Information

Year Founded: 2000
Capital Under Management: $107,000,000
Current Activity Level: Actively seeking new investments

DRAPER FISHER JURVETSON NEW ENGLAND (AKA: DFJ/NE)

One Broadway
14th Floor
Cambridge, MA USA 02142
Phone: 617-758-4275
Fax: 617-758-4101
E-mail: info@dfjne.com
Website: www.dfjne.com

Management and Staff

Scott Johnson, Managing Director
Todd Hixon, Managing Director

Type of Firm

Private Equity Firm

Association Membership

New England Venture Capital Association
Natl Assoc of Small Bus. Inv. Co (NASBIC)
National Venture Capital Association - USA (NVCA)

Project Preferences

Role in Financing:
Prefer role as deal originator but will also invest in deals created by others

Type of Financing Preferred:
Early Stage
Seed
First Stage Financing

Size of Investments Considered:
Min Size of Investment Considered (000s): $500
Max Size of Investment Considered (000s): $2,000

Geographical Preferences

United States Preferences:
Mid Atlantic
Southeast
Northeast

Industry Preferences

In Communications prefer:
Commercial Communications
Telecommunications
Wireless Communications
Data Communications

In Computer Hardware prefer:
Mainframes / Scientific
Mini and Personal/Desktop
Computer Graphics and Dig
Integrated Turnkey System
Terminals
Disk Relat. Memory Device

In Computer Software prefer:
Computer Services
Data Processing
Software
Systems Software
Applications Software
Artificial Intelligence

In Internet Specific prefer:
E-Commerce Technology
Internet
Ecommerce
Web Aggregration/Portals

In Semiconductor/Electr prefer:
Electronic Components
Semiconductor
Micro-Processing
Controllers and Sensors
Sensors
Circuit Boards
Component Testing Equipmt
Laser Related
Fiber Optics
Optoelectronics

In Consumer Related prefer:
Consumer Services

In Industrial/Energy prefer:
Energy

In Business Serv. prefer:
Distribution

Additional Information
Name of Most Recent Fund: Draper Fisher Jurvetson New England Fund, The
Most Recent Fund Was Raised: 03/05/2001
Year Founded: 2001
Capital Under Management: $45,000,000
Current Activity Level: Actively seeking new investments
Method of Compensation: Return on investment is of primary concern, do not charge fees

---

DRAPER INVESTMENT COMPANY

Dreikonigstrasse 31a
Zurich, Switzerland CH-8002
Phone: 41-44-208-32-37
Fax: 41-44-208-35-00
E-mail: info@draperco.com
Website: www.draperco.com

Management and Staff
Don Plaisted, Managing Director
William H. Draper III, General Partner

Type of Firm
Private Equity Firm

Project Preferences

Type of Financing Preferred:
Early Stage
Startup

Geographical Preferences

International Preferences:
Europe
Asia

Industry Preferences

In Computer Software prefer:
Software

Additional Information
Year Founded: 2001
Current Activity Level: Actively seeking new investments

DRAPER RICHARDS, L.P.

50 California Street
Suite 2925
San Francisco, CA USA 94111
Phone: 415-616-4050
Fax: 415-616-4060
Website: www.draperrichards.com

Management and Staff
Cynthia Lam, Chief Financial Officer
Robin Donohoe, General Partner
William Draper, General Partner

Type of Firm
Private Equity Firm

Association Membership
Western Association of Venture Capitalists (WAVC)
National Venture Capital Association - USA (NVCA)

Project Preferences

Role in Financing:
Will function either as deal originator or investor in deals created by others

Type of Financing Preferred:
Second Stage Financing
Early Stage
First Stage Financing

Geographical Preferences

United States Preferences:
Mid Atlantic
Northern California
Northeast
West Coast

Industry Focus
(% based on actual investment)

Internet Specific	50.5%
Computer Software and Services	26.5%
Communications and Media	8.6%
Semiconductors/Other Elect.	5.1%
Consumer Related	2.4%
Biotechnology	2.2%
Industrial/Energy	2.1%
Computer Hardware	1.3%
Other Products	1.2%

Additional Information
Name of Most Recent Fund: Draper Richards, L.P.
Most Recent Fund Was Raised: 12/31/1996
Year Founded: 1996
Capital Under Management: $30,000,000
Current Activity Level: Actively seeking new investments
Method of Compensation: Return on investment is of primary concern, do not charge fees

---

DRAPER TRIANGLE VENTURES

Two Gateway Center
Suite 2000
Pittsburgh, PA USA 15222
Phone: 412-288-9800
Fax: 412-288-9799
Website: www.drapertriangle.com

Other Offices
737 Bolivar Road
Suite 1500
Cleveland, OH USA 44115
Phone: 216-363-5300
Fax: 216-363-5440

30 West Third Street
Sixth Floor
Cincinnati, OH USA 45206
Phone: 513-297-3420
Fax: 513-381-5093

Management and Staff

D. Thompson Jones, Managing Director
Donald Jones, Managing Director
Jay Katarincic, Managing Director
Mark Richey, Managing Director
Michael Stubler, Managing Director

Type of Firm

Private Equity Firm

Project Preferences

Role in Financing:

Will function either as deal originator or investor in deals created by others

Type of Financing Preferred:

Early Stage
Expansion
First Stage Financing

Size of Investments Considered:

Min Size of Investment Considered (000s): $500
Max Size of Investment Considered (000s): $3,000

Geographical Preferences

United States Preferences:

Midwest
Ohio
Northeast

Industry Preferences

In Communications prefer:

Wireless Communications

In Computer Software prefer:

Software
Systems Software
Applications Software
Artificial Intelligence

In Internet Specific prefer:

E-Commerce Technology
Internet

In Semiconductor/Electr prefer:

Semiconductor
Micro-Processing

In Medical/Health prefer:

Medical Diagnostics
Diagnostic Test Products
Health Services

In Industrial/Energy prefer:

Factory Automation
Robotics

Additional Information

Name of Most Recent Fund: Draper Triangle Ventures II, L.P.
Most Recent Fund Was Raised: 09/30/2004
Year Founded: 1999
Capital Under Management: $125,000,000
Current Activity Level: Actively seeking new investments
Method of Compensation: Return on investment is of primary concern, do not charge fees

---

DRAUPNIR LLC

515 North State Street
Suite 2650
Chicago, IL USA 60610
Phone: 312-527-9636
Fax: 312-527-3964
E-mail: info@draupnirllc.com
Website: www.draupnirllc.com

Management and Staff

Allen Petersen, Chairman & Managing Director
Jeremy Hobbs, Managing Director

Type of Firm

Private Equity Firm

Project Preferences

Role in Financing:

Prefer role as deal originator

Type of Financing Preferred:

Leveraged Buyout
Management Buyouts
Acquisition

Size of Investments Considered:

Min Size of Investment Considered (000s): $1,000
Max Size of Investment Considered (000s): $25,000

Industry Preferences

In Industrial/Energy prefer:

Industrial Products

In Manufact. prefer:

Manufacturing

Additional Information

Year Founded: 2002
Capital Under Management: $300,000,000
Current Activity Level: Actively seeking new investments

DREAM VENTURE INVESTMENT (FKA: BASIC VENTURE INVESTMENT)

316, G-Five Central Plaza
1685-8, Seocho-dong
Seoul, South Korea 137-070
Phone: 82-2-539-7220
Fax: 82-2-539-8995
Website: www.dreamvi.co.kr

Management and Staff

Chung Hae Lim, President

Type of Firm

Corporate PE/Venture

Association Membership

Korean Venture Capital Association (KVCA)

Project Preferences

Type of Financing Preferred:

Mezzanine

Geographical Preferences

International Preferences:

Korea, South

Additional Information

Year Founded: 2000
Current Activity Level: Actively seeking new investments

DRESNER PARTNERS (FKA: DRESNER CAPITAL RESOURCES, INC.)

20 North Clark Street
Suite 3550
Chicago, IL USA 60602
Phone: 312-726-3600
Fax: 312-726-7448
E-mail: info@dresnerco.com
Website: www.dresnerco.com

Management and Staff

Ejaz Elahi, Vice President
Gian Ricco, Vice President
Gregg Pollack, Managing Director
John Riddle, Managing Director
Joseph Kacergis, Vice President
Keith Koeneman, Vice President
M. Roderick Rivera, Senior Managing Director
Michael McCoy, Managing Director
Paul Hoffman, Vice President
Richard Wottrich, Managing Director
Steven Dresner, President
Timothy Coleman, Senior Managing Director
Vincent Pappalardo, Managing Director

Type of Firm

Bank Affiliated

Project Preferences

Role in Financing:

Prefer role as deal originator

Type of Financing Preferred:

Second Stage Financing
Leveraged Buyout
Mezzanine

Size of Investments Considered:

Min Size of Investment Considered (000s): $500
Max Size of Investment Considered (000s): $1,000

Industry Preferences

In Communications prefer:

Commercial Communications
Telecommunications

Data Communications
Satellite Microwave Comm.

In Computer Hardware prefer:
Computers
Mini and Personal/Desktop
Computer Graphics and Dig
Disk Relat. Memory Device

In Computer Software prefer:
Computer Services
Systems Software
Applications Software

In Internet Specific prefer:
Internet

In Semiconductor/Electr prefer:
Semiconductor
Sensors
Circuit Boards
Component Testing Equipmt
Laser Related
Fiber Optics
Analytic/Scientific

In Medical/Health prefer:
Medical/Health
Medical Products

In Consumer Related prefer:
Entertainment and Leisure
Retail
Computer Stores
Franchises(NEC)
Food/Beverage
Consumer Products
Consumer Services
Other Restaurants

In Industrial/Energy prefer:
Industrial Products
Materials
Factory Automation
Robotics
Machinery

In Financial Services prefer:
Financial Services

In Business Serv. prefer:
Consulting Services

In Manufact. prefer:
Office Automation Equipmt
Publishing

Additional Information
Year Founded: 1991
Current Activity Level: Actively seeking new investments
Method of Compensation: Return on investment is of primary concern, do not charge fees

---

DRIVE SOCIEDADE DE CAPITAL DE RISCO, SA
Avenida 5 de Outubro 68
11B
Lisboa, Portugal 1050-059
Phone: 351-217-994-550
Fax: 351-217-994-555
E-mail: drive@drive.pt
Website: www.drive.pt

Management and Staff
Cristina Almeida, Partner
Pedro Braga, Partner
Pedro Murta, Partner
Rui Val Ferreira, Partner

Type of Firm
Private Equity Firm

Association Membership
European Private Equity and Venture Capital Assoc.

Project Preferences

Role in Financing:
Prefer role in deals created by others

Type of Financing Preferred:
Generalist PE
Balanced

Size of Investments Considered:
Min Size of Investment Considered (000s): $94
Max Size of Investment Considered (000s): $615

Geographical Preferences

International Preferences:
Portugal
Spain

Additional Information
Year Founded: 2004
Capital Under Management: $1,300,000
Current Activity Level: Actively seeking new investments

DRUM CAPITAL MANAGEMENT
18 Marshall Street
Suite 330
South Norwalk, CT USA 06854
Phone: 203-604-2621
Fax: 203-604-1263
Website: www.drumcapital.com

Management and Staff
Duran Curis, Managing Director
Peter Notz, Vice President
Timothy Ortez, Managing Director

Type of Firm
Private Equity Advisor or Fund of Funds

Project Preferences

Type of Financing Preferred:
Fund of Funds
Special Situation
Fund of Funds of Second

Additional Information
Year Founded: 2005
Capital Under Management: $545,000,000
Current Activity Level: Actively seeking new investments

DSE INVESTMENT SERVICES, LTD.
38/F Dah Sing Financial Centre
108 Gloucester Road
Wanchai, Hong Kong
Phone: 852-2507-8122
Fax: 852-2845-9926
E-mail: ops@dahsing.com.hk
Website: www.cbd.dahsing.com

Management and Staff
Nicholas Mayhew, Managing Director

Type of Firm
Bank Affiliated

Association Membership
Hong Kong Venture Capital Association (HKVCA)

Project Preferences

Role in Financing:
Prefer role as deal originator but will also invest in deals created by others

Type of Financing Preferred:
Early Stage
Expansion
Mezzanine
Balanced
Turnaround
Later Stage

Size of Investments Considered:
Min Size of Investment Considered (000s): $1,281
Max Size of Investment Considered (000s): $12,814

Geographical Preferences

International Preferences:
China
Hong Kong

Industry Preferences

In Communications prefer:
Telecommunications

In Semiconductor/Electr prefer:
Electronic Components

In Medical/Health prefer:
Pharmaceuticals

In Consumer Related prefer:
Entertainment and Leisure
Food/Beverage
Consumer Products
Consumer Services

In Industrial/Energy prefer:
Machinery

In Financial Services prefer:
Financial Services

In Business Serv. prefer:
Distribution

Additional Information
Year Founded: 1995
Capital Under Management: $60,000,000
Current Activity Level: Actively seeking new investments
Method of Compensation: Return on invest. most important, but chg. closing fees, service fees, etc.

DSM
Het Overloon 1
Heerlen, Netherlands 6411
Phone: 31-45-578-81-11
Fax: 31-45-571-97-53
Website: www.dsm.com

Type of Firm
Private Equity Firm

Project Preferences

Type of Financing Preferred:
Early Stage

Additional Information
Year Founded: 1902
Current Activity Level: Actively seeking new investments

DSM CORPORATE VENTURING
Mauritslaan 49
Urmond, Netherlands 6129 EL
Phone: 31-45-578-8111
Fax: 31-45-571-9753
E-mail: info@dsm.com
Website: www.dsm-venturing.com

Type of Firm
Corporate PE/Venture

Association Membership
European Private Equity and Venture Capital Assoc.

Project Preferences

Type of Financing Preferred:
Early Stage
Expansion
Seed
Startup

Geographical Preferences

International Preferences:
Netherlands
Europe
All International

Industry Preferences

In Biotechnology prefer:
Biotechnology

In Industrial/Energy prefer:
Materials

Additional Information
Year Founded: 1902
Capital Under Management: $1,000,000
Current Activity Level: Actively seeking new investments

DT CAPITAL PARTNERS
No.1 Gao Lan Road
Shanghai, China 200020
Phone: 86-21-5383-5999
Fax: 86-21-5383-5998
E-mail: info@dtcap.com
Website: www.dtcap.com

Other Offices
3000 Sand Hill Road
Building One, Suite 150
Menlo Park, CA USA 94025
Phone: 650-854-8301
Fax: 650-233-9352

No. 189 Guangzhou Road
5th Floor Ming Fang Mansion
Nanjing, China 210008
Phone: 86-25-6660-5601
Fax: 86-25-6660-5602

Rm 1005A, China Resources Building
No. 8 Jianguomenbei Avenue
Beijing, China 100005
Phone: 86-10-8519-2121
Fax: 86-10-8519-2100

No. 58 North Ke Hua Road
14F-18, Building C, Bi-Pacific Plaza
Sichuan, China 610041
Phone: 86-28-8523-1260
Fax: 86-28-8523-8917

19 Des Voeux Road
Suite 1505 World Wide House
Central, Hong Kong
Phone: 852-3107-0682
Fax: 852-3107-0683

No. 151 Cuiyuan Road
5th Floor Suzhou Industrial Park
Suzhou, China 215122
Phone: 86-512-6660-0512
Fax: 86-512-6660-0515

Management and Staff
Daming Zhu, Principal
Greg Penner, General Partner
Jason Li, Principal
Joe Tian, Managing Partner
Jun Zhao, Managing Partner
Roman Shaw, Founding Partner
William Chen, General Partner

Type of Firm
Private Equity Firm

Project Preferences

Type of Financing Preferred:
Early Stage
Expansion
Balanced

Geographical Preferences

International Preferences:
China
Asia

Industry Preferences

In Consumer Related prefer:
Consumer

In Industrial/Energy prefer:
Energy

In Business Serv. prefer:
Media

Additional Information
Year Founded: 2006
Capital Under Management: $135,500,000
Current Activity Level: Actively seeking new investments

DTA CAPITAL
24A, Jalan Datuk Sulaiman
Taman Tun Dr. Ismail
Kuala Lumpur, Malaysia 60000
Phone: 603-7722-2560
Fax: 603-7722-2570
Website: www.dtacapital.com

Management and Staff
Dali Sardar, Chief Executive Officer
Kong Cheng Tan, Chief Operating Officer
Nikhil Kothari, Chief Financial Officer

Type of Firm
Private Equity Advisor or Fund of Funds

Project Preferences

Type of Financing Preferred:
Early Stage
Expansion
Mezzanine
Seed
Startup

Size of Investments Considered:
Min Size of Investment Considered (000s): $100
Max Size of Investment Considered (000s): $500

Geographical Preferences

International Preferences:
Malaysia

Industry Preferences

In Communications prefer:
Telecommunications
Wireless Communications

In Computer Software prefer:
Applications Software

In Internet Specific prefer:
Ecommerce
Web Aggregration/Portals

Additional Information

Year Founded: 1996
Capital Under Management: $6,600,000
Current Activity Level: Actively seeking new investments

DTE ENERGY TECHNOLOGIES

37849 Interchange Drive
Farmington, MI USA 48335
Phone: 248-427-2200
Fax: 248-427-2265
Website: www.dtetech.com

Management and Staff

Michael McNally, President

Type of Firm

Private Equity Firm

Additional Information

Year Founded: 2004
Current Activity Level: Actively seeking new investments

DTU INNOVATION A/S

Danmarks Tekniske Universitet
Bygning 404
Lyngby, Denmark 2800
Phone: 45-4525-6155
Fax: 45-4525-6159
E-mail: info@dtu-innovation.dk
Website: www.dtu-innovation.dk

Management and Staff

Ulla Brockenhuus-Schack, Chief Executive Officer

Type of Firm

University Program

Association Membership

Danish Venture Capital Association (DVCA)

Project Preferences

Type of Financing Preferred:
Early Stage
Seed
Startup

Geographical Preferences

International Preferences:
Denmark

Industry Preferences

In Biotechnology prefer:
Biotechnology

In Consumer Related prefer:
Food/Beverage

Additional Information

Year Founded: 1998
Capital Under Management: $10,400,000
Current Activity Level: Actively seeking new investments

DUBAI INTERNATIONAL CAPITAL LLC

The Gate, East Wing
13th Floor, DIFC
Dubai, Utd. Arab Em.
Phone: 971-4-362-1888
Fax: 971-4-362-0888
E-mail: info@dubaiic.com
Website: www.dubaiic.com

Other Offices

9th Floor
21 Palmer Street
London, United Kingdom SW1H 0AD
Phone: 44-207-808-1700

Management and Staff

Anand Krishnan, Chief Executive Officer
Andrew Wright, Managing Director
Eric Kump, Managing Director
Michel Gaudreau, Managing Director
Sameer Al Ansari, Chairman & CEO
Samer Al Saifi, Chief Executive Officer

Type of Firm

Private Equity Firm

Project Preferences

Type of Financing Preferred:
Leveraged Buyout
Balanced
Other
Acquisition

Geographical Preferences

United States Preferences:
All U.S.

International Preferences:
India
Europe
China
Utd. Arab Em.
Middle East
Japan
Africa

Industry Preferences

In Medical/Health prefer:
Medical/Health
Health Services

In Consumer Related prefer:
Consumer Products
Consumer Services
Education Related

In Industrial/Energy prefer:
Energy
Oil and Gas Exploration

In Transportation prefer:
Transportation

In Business Serv. prefer:
Services

Additional Information

Year Founded: 2004
Capital Under Management: $2,500,000,000
Current Activity Level: Actively seeking new investments

DUBAI INVESTMENT GROUP (AKA: DIG)

Emirates Towers Office
Sheikh Zayed Road
Dubai, Utd. Arab Em.
Phone: 971-4-330-0707
Fax: 971-4-330-3260
E-mail: info@dubaigroup.com
Website: www.dubaigroup.com

Other Offices

4th Floor, DIFC, 5th Precinct
Sheikh Zayed Road
Dubai, Utd. Arab Em.
Phone: 971-4-363-7070
Fax: 971-4-363-7066

1 Rockefeller Plaza
30th Floor, Suite 3001
New York, NY USA 10020
Phone: 212-218-7400
Fax: 212-218-7401

3107 - 3109 AIG Tower
1 Connaught Road
Central, Hong Kong
Phone: 852-2-219-2111
Fax: 852-2-219-2112

58th Floor, Petronas Twin Towers
Kuala Lumpur City Centre
Kuala Lumpur, Malaysia 50088
Phone: 60-3-216-85288
Fax: 60-3-2168-5388

5th Floor, Berkeley Square House
Berkeley Square
London, United Kingdom W1J 6BR
Phone: 44-20-7907-2992
Fax: 44-20-7907-2990

Management and Staff

Jacqueline Asher, Chief Operating Officer

Type of Firm

Private Equity Firm

Project Preferences

Type of Financing Preferred:
Mezzanine
Balanced
Public Companies

Geographical Preferences

International Preferences:
India
Asia

Industry Preferences

In Communications prefer:
Telecommunications

In Industrial/Energy prefer:
Energy
Industrial Products

In Transportation prefer:
Transportation

Additional Information

Year Founded: 2007
Current Activity Level: Actively seeking new investments

DUCHOSSOIS TECHNOLOGY PARTNERS LLC (DTEC)

845 Larch Avenue
Elmhurst, IL USA 60126
Phone: 630-993-8606
Fax: 630-993-6920
E-mail: duchtec@duch.com
Website: www.duchtech.com

Other Offices

6300 Bridge Point Parkway
Building 1, Suite 500
Austin, TX USA 78730
Phone: 512-795-5814
Fax: 512-795-5849

Management and Staff

Robert Fealy, Managing Director
Rohit Seth, General Partner

Type of Firm

Private Equity Firm

Association Membership

National Venture Capital Association - USA (NVCA)

Project Preferences

Role in Financing:
Will function either as deal originator or investor in deals created by others

Type of Financing Preferred:
Second Stage Financing
Expansion
Later Stage

Size of Investments Considered:
Min Size of Investment Considered (000s): $2,000
Max Size of Investment Considered (000s): $7,000

Industry Preferences

In Communications prefer:
Communications and Media

In Computer Software prefer:
Software

In Semiconductor/Electr prefer:
Semiconductor

In Consumer Related prefer:
Retail
Consumer Products

Additional Information

Year Founded: 1998
Capital Under Management: $100,000,000
Current Activity Level: Actively seeking new investments
Method of Compensation: Return on investment is of primary concern, do not charge fees

---

DUET CAPITAL

27 Hill Street
London, United Kingdom W1J 5LP
Phone: 44-20-7290-9800
E-mail: info@duetgroup.net
Website: www.duetgroup.net

Management and Staff

Joe McManus, Chief Operating Officer
Osman Semerci, Chief Executive Officer

Type of Firm

Private Equity Firm

Project Preferences

Type of Financing Preferred:
Early Stage
Turnaround
Later Stage
Startup

Geographical Preferences

International Preferences:
United Kingdom
Europe
Israel

Industry Preferences

In Communications prefer:
Communications and Media

In Computer Software prefer:
Software

In Internet Specific prefer:
Ecommerce

In Medical/Health prefer:
Medical/Health

In Consumer Related prefer:
Sports

Additional Information

Year Founded: 2002
Current Activity Level: Actively seeking new investments

DUFF ACKERMAN & GOODRICH LLC (AKA: DAG VENTURES)

Two Embarcadero Center
Suite 2300
San Francisco, CA USA 94111
Phone: 415-788-2755
Fax: 415-788-7311
E-mail: dag@dagllc.com
Website: www.dagllc.com

Other Offices

251 Lytton Avenue
Suite 200
Palo Alto, CA USA 94301
Phone: 415-788-2755
Fax: 650-328-2921

Management and Staff

Arnold Ackerman, Managing Director
Dick Williams, General Partner
John Duff, Managing Director
John Cadeddu, Managing Director
Thomas Goodrich, Managing Director
Young Chung, Principal

Type of Firm

Private Equity Firm

Association Membership

National Venture Capital Association - USA (NVCA)

Project Preferences

Type of Financing Preferred:
Leveraged Buyout
Balanced

Size of Investments Considered:
Min Size of Investment Considered (000s): $5,000
Max Size of Investment Considered (000s): $15,000

Industry Focus
(% based on actual investment)

Internet Specific	32.6%
Communications and Media	17.0%
Semiconductors/Other Elect.	11.6%
Biotechnology	11.0%
Computer Software and Services	10.0%
Other Products	8.1%
Medical/Health	4.4%
Industrial/Energy	2.8%
Computer Hardware	2.4%

Additional Information
Year Founded: 1991
Capital Under Management: $100,000,000
Current Activity Level: Actively seeking new investments

DUKE EQUITY PARTNERS
10866 Wilshire Boulevard
Suite 740
Westwood, CA USA 90024
Phone: 310-553-5777
Fax: 310-553-9405
E-mail: info@dukeequity.com
Website: www.dukeequity.com

Other Offices
IndiaCo Innovation Center
214 Navi Peth, L.B.S. Marg
Pune, India 411 030
Phone: 91-20-2433-5710
Fax: 91-20-2433-4978

Dubai International Financial Centre
Level 12, The Gate
Dubai, Utd. Arab Em.
Phone: 971-4-361-1949
Fax: 971-4-361-1950

84 Brook Street
Mayfair
London, United Kingdom W1K 5EH
Phone: 44-20-7866-6230
Fax: 44-20-7866-6231

Management and Staff
Patwardhan Gopal, Managing Partner
Rigved Joshi, Principal

Type of Firm
Private Equity Firm

Project Preferences
Type of Financing Preferred:
Public Companies
Private Placement

Size of Investments Considered:
Min Size of Investment Considered (000s): $2,000
Max Size of Investment Considered (000s): $6,000

Geographical Preferences
United States Preferences:
All U.S.

International Preferences:
India

Industry Preferences
In Communications prefer:
Telecommunications
Wireless Communications
Data Communications

In Computer Software prefer:
Applications Software

In Semiconductor/Electr prefer:
Semiconductor
Controllers and Sensors

In Biotechnology prefer:
Biotechnology

In Medical/Health prefer:
Medical Diagnostics
Medical Therapeutics
Medical Products

In Industrial/Energy prefer:
Alternative Energy

In Financial Services prefer:
Financial Services

In Manufact. prefer:
Manufacturing

Additional Information
Year Founded: 2007
Current Activity Level: Actively seeking new investments

DUKE STREET CAPITAL
Nations House
103 Wigmore Street
London, United Kingdom W1U 1QS
Phone: 44-20-7663-8500
Fax: 44-20-7663-8501
E-mail: mail@dukestreetcapital.com
Website: www.dukestreetcapital.com

Other Offices
Centre d'Affaires Paris Victoire
52 rue de la Victoire
Paris, France 75009
Phone: 33-1-5343-5444
Fax: 33-1-5343-5440

Management and Staff
Charlie Troup, Partner
Colin Curvey, Partner
Didier Bismuth, Partner
Frederic Chauffier, Managing Partner
Iain Kennedy, Partner
Jean-Marc Dayan, Partner
Jeffrey Belkin, Partner
John Harper, Partner
Miles Cresswell-Turner, Partner
Peter Taylor, Managing Partner
Sharon Jebb, Partner
Timothy Lebus, Partner

Type of Firm
Private Equity Firm

Association Membership
British Venture Capital Association (BVCA)
French Venture Capital Association (AFIC)
European Private Equity and Venture Capital Assoc.

Project Preferences
Role in Financing:
Prefer role as deal originator but will also invest in deals created by others

Type of Financing Preferred:
Leveraged Buyout
Expansion
Turnaround
Management Buyouts
Recapitalizations

Size of Investments Considered:
Min Size of Investment Considered (000s): $29,800
Max Size of Investment Considered (000s): $383,642

Geographical Preferences
International Preferences:
United Kingdom
Europe
France

Industry Focus
(% based on actual investment)

Consumer Related	58.6%
Medical/Health	19.6%
Industrial/Energy	9.9%
Communications and Media	7.1%
Other Products	4.7%
Internet Specific	0.1%
Computer Software and Services	0.1%

Additional Information
Year Founded: 1988
Capital Under Management: $1,522,700,000
Current Activity Level: Actively seeking new investments
Method of Compensation: Return on invest. most important, but chg. closing fees, service fees, etc.

DUMONT VENTURE HOLDING GMBH & CO. KG
Amsterdamer Strasse 192
Cologne, Germany 50735
Phone: 49-221-224-3320
Fax: 49-211224402092
E-mail: info@dumontventure.de
Website: www.dumontventure.de

Management and Staff

Joerg Binnenbruecker, Managing Director
Olaf Cordt, Principal

Type of Firm

Private Equity Firm

Project Preferences

Type of Financing Preferred:

Expansion

Geographical Preferences

International Preferences:

Europe

Industry Preferences

In Communications prefer:

Media and Entertainment

In Internet Specific prefer:

Ecommerce

Additional Information

Year Founded: 2007
Current Activity Level: Actively seeking new investments

DUNEDIN CAPITAL PARTNERS, LTD. (FKA: DUNEDIN VENTURES, LTD.)

10 George Street
Edinburgh, United Kingdom EH2 2DW
Phone: 44-131-225-6699
Fax: 44-131-718-2300
E-mail: info@dunedin.com
Website: www.dunedin.com

Other Offices

28 Savile Row
London, United Kingdom W1S 2EU
Phone: 44-20-7292-2110
Fax: 44-20-7292-2111

Management and Staff

Brian Scouler, Managing Director
Ross Marshall, Chief Executive Officer
Shaun Middleton, Managing Director

Type of Firm

Bank Affiliated
Association Membership
British Venture Capital Association (BVCA)
European Private Equity and Venture Capital Assoc.

Project Preferences

Role in Financing:

Prefer role as deal originator but will also invest in deals created by others

Type of Financing Preferred:

Leveraged Buyout
Management Buyouts
Acquisition

Size of Investments Considered:

Min Size of Investment Considered (000s): $2,985
Max Size of Investment Considered (000s): $17,912

Geographical Preferences

International Preferences:

United Kingdom
Europe

Industry Preferences

In Medical/Health prefer:

Medical/Health

In Consumer Related prefer:

Consumer
Entertainment and Leisure
Consumer Products

In Industrial/Energy prefer:

Industrial Products

In Financial Services prefer:

Financial Services

In Business Serv. prefer:

Consulting Services

In Manufact. prefer:

Manufacturing

Additional Information

Name of Most Recent Fund: Dunedin Buyout Fund II
Most Recent Fund Was Raised: 05/31/2006
Year Founded: 1983
Capital Under Management: $320,800,000
Current Activity Level: Actively seeking new investments
Method of Compensation: Return on invest. most important, but chg. closing fees, service fees, etc.

DUNRATH CAPITAL, INC.

53 West Jackson Boulevard
Suite 715
Chicago, IL USA 60604
Phone: 312-546-4700
Fax: 312-386-9454
E-mail: info@dunrath.com
Website: www.dunrath.com

Other Offices

1140 Connecticut Avenue
Suite 350
Washington, DC USA 20036
Phone: 202-360-4060

Management and Staff

Brian Gannon, Managing Director
John Abernethy, Managing Director & CFO
Richard Earley, Managing Director
Stephen Beitler, Managing Director

Type of Firm

Private Equity Firm

Association Membership

Illinois Venture Capital Association
Natl Assoc of Small Bus. Inv. Co (NASBIC)

Project Preferences

Role in Financing:

Will function either as deal originator or investor in deals created by others

Type of Financing Preferred:

Early Stage
Balanced

Size of Investments Considered:

Min Size of Investment Considered (000s): $500
Max Size of Investment Considered (000s): $10,000

Geographical Preferences

United States Preferences:

All U.S.

Industry Preferences

In Communications prefer:

Telecommunications

In Semiconductor/Electr prefer:

Sensors

In Medical/Health prefer:

Medical Diagnostics

In Industrial/Energy prefer:

Alternative Energy

Additional Information

Year Founded: 2002
Capital Under Management: $50,000,000
Current Activity Level: Actively seeking new investments
Method of Compensation: Return on investment is of primary concern, do not charge fees

---

DUPONT VENTURES

Chestnut Run Plaza; Bldg 708
P.O. Box 80708
Wilmington, DE USA 19880
Phone: 302-999-2927
Fax: 302-999-4083
Website: www2.dupont.com

Management and Staff

Robert Keller, Venture Partner

Type of Firm

Corporate PE/Venture

Association Membership

National Venture Capital Association - USA (NVCA)

Additional Information

Name of Most Recent Fund: DuPont
Most Recent Fund Was Raised: 01/01/1985

Year Founded: 1985
Current Activity Level: Actively seeking new investments

DUTCHESS ADVISORS LLC

50 Commonwealth Avenue
Suite 2
Boston, MA USA 02116
Phone: 617-301-4700
Fax: 617-249-0947
Website: www.dutchessadvisors.com

Other Offices

1110 Route 55
Suite 206, Town Square
Lagrangeville, NY USA 12540
Phone: 845-575-6770
Fax: 845-575-6772

Management and Staff

Louis Posner, Vice President

Type of Firm

Private Equity Advisor or Fund of Funds

Project Preferences

Type of Financing Preferred:
Public Companies

Geographical Preferences

United States Preferences:
All U.S.

Additional Information

Year Founded: 1996
Capital Under Management: $110,000,000
Current Activity Level: Actively seeking new investments

DVC DEUTSCHE VENTURE CAPITAL

Rindermarkt 7
Munich, Germany 80331
Phone: 49-89-20000990
Fax: 49-89-200009999
E-mail: info@dvcg.de
Website: www.dvcg.de

Management and Staff

Alexander Asam, Chief Executive Officer
Bernhard Schmid, Partner
Cyril Bertrand, Partner
Frank Schuhardt, Partner
Jorg Neermann, Managing Partner
Jurgen Gerlach, Managing Partner

Type of Firm

Private Equity Firm

Association Membership

German Venture Capital Association (BVK)
European Private Equity and Venture Capital Assoc.

Project Preferences

Type of Financing Preferred:
Early Stage
Expansion
Seed
Startup

Size of Investments Considered:
Min Size of Investment Considered (000s): $1,250
Max Size of Investment Considered (000s): $12,494

Geographical Preferences

United States Preferences:
All U.S.

International Preferences:
Europe
Germany

Industry Focus

(% based on actual investment)

Biotechnology	31.2%
Computer Software and Services	16.9%
Medical/Health	14.9%
Internet Specific	14.8%
Communications and Media	12.9%
Semiconductors/Other Elect.	9.3%

Additional Information

Year Founded: 1998
Capital Under Management: $395,600,000
Current Activity Level: Actively seeking new investments

DW HEALTHCARE PARTNERS

6440 South Wasatch Boulevard
Suite 105
Salt Lake City, UT USA 84121-3511
Phone: 801-365-4000
Fax: 801-365-4444
Website: www.dwhp.com

Management and Staff

Andrew Carragher, Managing Director
Douglas Schillinger, Managing Director
John Benear, Managing Director
Justin Pettit, Vice President
William Klintworth, Managing Director

Type of Firm

Private Equity Firm

Project Preferences

Type of Financing Preferred:
Leveraged Buyout
Expansion
Later Stage
Recapitalizations

Size of Investments Considered:
Min Size of Investment Considered (000s): $5,000
Max Size of Investment Considered (000s): $15,000

Geographical Preferences

United States Preferences:
All U.S.

Industry Preferences

In Medical/Health prefer:
Medical Diagnostics
Diagnostic Services
Diagnostic Test Products
Drug/Equipmt Delivery
Medical Products
Disposable Med. Products
Health Services

Additional Information

Name of Most Recent Fund: DW Healthcare Affiliates II, L.P.
Most Recent Fund Was Raised: 11/17/2006
Year Founded: 2002
Capital Under Management: $29,400,000
Current Activity Level: Actively seeking new investments

DYAD PARTNERS

701 Oak Knoll Terrace
Rockville, MD USA 20850
Phone: 703-969-6285
Fax: 608-531-3487
E-mail: info@dyadpartners.com
Website: www.dyadpartners.com

Management and Staff

David Lesser, Principal
Jack Hans, Principal
Ray Lund, Principal
Tim Lex, Principal

Type of Firm

Private Equity Firm

Project Preferences

Type of Financing Preferred:
Leveraged Buyout
Early Stage
Balanced

Geographical Preferences

United States Preferences:
East Coast
All U.S.

Industry Preferences

In Biotechnology prefer:
Biotechnology

In Medical/Health prefer:
Medical/Health

In Business Serv. prefer:
Distribution

In Manufact. prefer:
Manufacturing

Additional Information

Year Founded: 2005
Current Activity Level: Actively seeking new investments

DYNAFUND VENTURES LLC

21250 Hawthorne Boulevard
Suite 700
Torrance, CA USA 90503
Phone: 310-543-5477
Fax: 310-543-8733
E-mail: info@dynafundventures.com
Website: www.dynafundventures.com

Other Offices

1555 Wilson Boulevard
Suite 320
Arlington, VA USA 22209
Phone: 703-841-1925
Fax: 703-841-8395

900 Hamilton Avenue
Suite 100
Campbell, CA USA 95008
Phone: 408-868-9901
Fax: 408-868-9909

Management and Staff

David Lam, Venture Partner
Peter Lee, Partner
Richard Whiting, General Partner
Tony Hung, General Partner

Type of Firm

Private Equity Firm

Association Membership

Mid-Atlantic Venture Association

Project Preferences

Role in Financing:
Will function either as deal originator or investor in deals created by others

Type of Financing Preferred:
Second Stage Financing
Early Stage
First Stage Financing

Size of Investments Considered:
Min Size of Investment Considered (000s): $1,000
Max Size of Investment Considered (000s): $4,000

Geographical Preferences

United States Preferences:
All U.S.

Industry Focus

(% based on actual investment)

Semiconductors/Other Elect.	48.7%
Communications and Media	15.2%
Internet Specific	14.6%
Computer Software and Services	13.8%
Computer Hardware	4.1%
Biotechnology	3.1%
Industrial/Energy	0.5%

Additional Information

Name of Most Recent Fund: DynaFund II
Most Recent Fund Was Raised: 02/01/2000
Year Founded: 1997
Capital Under Management: $220,000,000
Current Activity Level: Actively seeking new investments
Method of Compensation: Return on investment is of primary concern, do not charge fees

DYNAMIC EQUITY, LTD.

92-96 Saint Vincent Street
6th Floor
Port of Spain, Trinidad/Tob.
Phone: 868-627-7450
Fax: 868-623-3697
E-mail: contact@dynamic-equity.com
Website: www.dynamic-equity.com

Management and Staff

Jelle Sjoerdsma, Managing Director

Type of Firm

Private Equity Firm

Project Preferences

Type of Financing Preferred:
Generalist PE
Balanced

Size of Investments Considered:
Min Size of Investment Considered (000s): $162
Max Size of Investment Considered (000s): $813

Geographical Preferences

International Preferences:
Trinidad/Tob.

Additional Information

Year Founded: 2000
Capital Under Management: $35,000,000
Current Activity Level: Actively seeking new investments

DYNAMICS VENTURE MANAGEMENT GMBH (FKA: RWE DYNAMICS VENTURE)

Residenzstrasse 9
Munich, Germany 80333
Phone: 49-89-2050-890
Fax: 49-89-2050-8999
Website: www.dynamicsventure.com

Management and Staff

Dietmar Bauer, Managing Partner
Pieter Van Halem, Managing Partner
Ulrich Gleissner, Managing Partner

Type of Firm

Corporate PE/Venture

Association Membership

German Venture Capital Association (BVK)
European Private Equity and Venture Capital Assoc.

Project Preferences

Type of Financing Preferred:
Early Stage
Expansion
Startup

Geographical Preferences

International Preferences:
Europe
Germany

Industry Preferences

In Communications prefer:
Commercial Communications

In Biotechnology prefer:
Biotechnology

In Industrial/Energy prefer:
Energy
Energy Conservation Relat
Environmental Related

Additional Information

Year Founded: 2001
Capital Under Management: $50,600,000
Current Activity Level: Actively seeking new investments

DYNAMIS ADVISORS LLC

310 Fourth Street
Suite 101
Charlottesville, VA USA 22902
Phone: 434-220-0234
E-mail: info@dynamis.com
Website: www.dynamisfunds.com

Management and Staff

George McVey, Chief Financial Officer

Type of Firm

Private Equity Firm

Project Preferences

Type of Financing Preferred:
Balanced

Geographical Preferences

United States Preferences:
All U.S.

Additional Information

Name of Most Recent Fund: Dynamis Venture Partners, LP
Most Recent Fund Was Raised: 10/02/2007
Year Founded: 2007
Capital Under Management: $9,000,000
Current Activity Level: Actively seeking new investments

DYNEX CAPITAL CORPORATION

475 Dumont Ave
Suite 300
Dorval, Canada H9S5W2
Phone: 514-631-2682
Fax: 514-631-1257
Website: www.dynexcapitalcorp.com

Other Offices

150 William Street
Kingston, Canada K7L2C9
Phone: 613-532-1290
Fax: 613-549-3054

Management and Staff

Peter Blaney, President

Type of Firm

Private Equity Firm

Project Preferences

Type of Financing Preferred:
Early Stage
Startup

Geographical Preferences

Canadian Preferences:
Quebec
Ontario

Additional Information

Year Founded: 2009
Current Activity Level: Actively seeking new investments

DZ EQUITY PARTNER GMBH (FKA: DG PRIVATE EQUITY GMBH)

Platz der Republik
Frankfurt am Main, Germany 60265
Phone: 49-69-7447-7209
Fax: 49-69-7447-1632
E-mail: mail@dzpe.de
Website: www.dzep.de

Management and Staff

Bernd Sexauer, Managing Director

Type of Firm

Bank Affiliated

Association Membership

German Venture Capital Association (BVK)

Project Preferences

Type of Financing Preferred:
Expansion
Mezzanine
Balanced
Later Stage
Recapitalizations

Geographical Preferences

International Preferences:
Europe
Germany

Industry Focus

(% based on actual investment)

Computer Software and Services	66.3%
Other Products	23.2%
Internet Specific	5.9%
Industrial/Energy	4.5%

Additional Information

Year Founded: 1970
Capital Under Management: $698,000,000
Current Activity Level: Actively seeking new investments

- E -

E TRUST VENTURE CAPITAL

#2512 Techno Mart
546-4 Koowui-Dong Kwangjin-Gu
Seoul, South Korea
Phone: 822-3424-1989
Fax: 822-3424-1983

Type of Firm

Private Equity Firm

Association Membership

Korean Venture Capital Association (KVCA)

Project Preferences

Type of Financing Preferred:
Balanced

Geographical Preferences

International Preferences:
Korea, South

Industry Preferences

In Semiconductor/Electr prefer:
Electronics

Additional Information

Year Founded: 1999
Capital Under Management: $13,100,000
Current Activity Level: Actively seeking new investments

E+CO

383 Franklin Street
Bloomfield, NJ USA 07003
Phone: 973-680-9100
Fax: 973-680-8066
Website: www.eandco.net

Other Offices

Av. Santa Cruz No. 1274
Piso 7, Oficina No. 3
Cochabamba, Bolivia
Phone: 5914-429-4006
Fax: 5914-429-4007

P.O. Box 11454
Tangal
Kathmandu, Nepal
Phone: 977-1-410-146
Fax: 977-1-438-442

P.O. Box 13443-1000
San Jose, Costa Rica
Phone: 506-296-3532
Fax: 506-296-4810

Hanoi School of Business
144 Xuan Thuy, Cau Giay district
Hanoi, Vietnam
Phone: 84-4-768-0456
Fax: 84-4-768-0455

P.O. Box 34921
Glenstantia, South Africa 0010
Phone: 27-12-998-8280
Fax: 27-12-998-8401

Management and Staff

Steve Cunningham, Chief Financial Officer

Type of Firm

Private Equity Firm

Project Preferences

Type of Financing Preferred:
Early Stage
Expansion
Seed

Geographical Preferences

International Preferences:
Latin America
Asia
Africa

Industry Preferences

In Industrial/Energy prefer:
Energy

Additional Information

Year Founded: 1994
Capital Under Management: $5,000,000
Current Activity Level: Actively seeking new investments

E-CAPITAL MANAGEMENT

Square Vergote 41
Brussels, Belgium 1050
Phone: 32-2-642-2000
Fax: 32-2-642-2009
E-mail: info@e-capital.be
Website: www.e-capital.be

Type of Firm

Private Equity Firm

Association Membership

Belgium Venturing Association
European Private Equity and Venture Capital Assoc.

Project Preferences

Type of Financing Preferred:
Expansion
Mezzanine
Management Buyouts

Size of Investments Considered:
Min Size of Investment Considered (000s): $1,287
Max Size of Investment Considered (000s): $3,862

Geographical Preferences

International Preferences:
United Kingdom
Luxembourg
Netherlands
Belgium
Germany
France

Industry Preferences

In Computer Other prefer:
Computer Related

In Semiconductor/Electr prefer:
Electronics

In Biotechnology prefer:
Biotechnology

In Medical/Health prefer:
Medical/Health

In Industrial/Energy prefer:
Industrial Products
Materials

In Business Serv. prefer:
Services

Additional Information

Year Founded: 1999
Capital Under Management: $31,300,000
Current Activity Level: Actively seeking new investments

E-CELERATE, INC.

350 Bay Street
Seventh Floor
Toronto, Canada M5H2S6
Phone: 800-621-3130
Website: www.e-celerateinc.com

Management and Staff

Ron Weinberger, President

Type of Firm

Private Equity Firm

Additional Information

Year Founded: 2009
Current Activity Level: Actively seeking new investments

E-KATALYST

ul. Podwale 13
Third Floor
Warsaw, Poland 00-950
Phone: 48-22-635-7754
Fax: 48-22-831-7920
E-mail: info@e-katalyst.pl
Website: www.e-katalyst.pl

Type of Firm

Incubator/Development Program

Association Membership

Polish Venture Capital Association (PSIC/PPEA)

Project Preferences

Type of Financing Preferred:
Early Stage
Seed
Startup

Geographical Preferences

International Preferences:
Poland

Industry Preferences

In Internet Specific prefer:
Internet

Additional Information

Year Founded: 2000
Capital Under Management: $6,900,000
Current Activity Level: Actively seeking new investments

E-LAUNCHER

St John's Innovation Centre
Cowley Road
Cambridge, United Kingdom CB4 4WS
Phone: 44-122-342-2010
Fax: 44-122-342-2011
E-mail: info@e-launcher.com
Website: www.e-launcher.com

Management and Staff

Robert Harris, Chief Executive Officer

Type of Firm

Incubator/Development Program

Project Preferences

Type of Financing Preferred:
Seed
Startup

Geographical Preferences

United States Preferences:
Utah

International Preferences:
United Kingdom

Industry Preferences

In Internet Specific prefer:
Internet

Additional Information

Year Founded: 2000
Current Activity Level: Actively seeking new investments

E-SYNERGY

6-7 New Bridge Street
London, United Kingdom EC4V 6AB
Phone: 44-20-7583-3503
Fax: 44-20-7583-3474
E-mail: enquiries@e-synergy.com
Website: www.e-synergy.com

Management and Staff

Andrew Stevenson, Partner
John White, Partner
Robert Brook, Partner
Ronald Armstrong, Partner

Type of Firm

Private Equity Firm

Project Preferences

Type of Financing Preferred:
Early Stage
Start-up Financing

Geographical Preferences

International Preferences:
United Kingdom
Europe
Eastern Europe

Industry Preferences

In Other prefer:
Environment Responsible

Additional Information

Year Founded: 1999
Capital Under Management: $9,400,000
Current Activity Level: Actively seeking new investments

E-TRUST INVESTMENT GROUP

Regus business center
3, Smolenskaya sq.
Moscow, Russia 119099
Phone: 7-095-933-8944
Fax: 7-095-937-8290
E-mail: info@e-trustgroup.com
Website: www.e-trustgroup.com

Management and Staff

Maxim Karimov, Managing Director

Type of Firm

Private Equity Firm

Project Preferences

Type of Financing Preferred:
Balanced

Geographical Preferences

International Preferences:
Europe

Additional Information

Year Founded: 2003
Current Activity Level: Actively seeking new investments

E-VENTURE.IT

Via Carlo Leoni 7
Padova, Italy 35139
Phone: 39-049-657-884
Fax: 39-049-660-151
E-mail: info@e-venture.it
Website: www.e-venture.it

Management and Staff

Amedeo Levorato, Managing Director

Type of Firm

Bank Affiliated

Association Membership

Italian Venture Capital Association (AIFI)

Project Preferences

Type of Financing Preferred:
Early Stage
Expansion
Startup

Geographical Preferences

United States Preferences:
All U.S.

International Preferences:
Italy
Europe

Industry Preferences

In Computer Software prefer:
Software

In Biotechnology prefer:
Biotechnology

In Consumer Related prefer:
Entertainment and Leisure

In Financial Services prefer:
Financial Services

Additional Information

Year Founded: 1999
Current Activity Level: Actively seeking new investments

EAGLE TRADING SYSTEMS, INC.

47 Hulfish Street
Suite 410
Princeton, NJ USA 08542
Phone: 609-688-2060
Fax: 609-688-2099
E-mail: eagleinfo@eaglets.com
Website: www.eaglets.com

Management and Staff

Menachem Sternberg, Chief Executive Officer

Type of Firm

Private Equity Firm

Additional Information

Year Founded: 2002
Capital Under Management: $16,300,000
Current Activity Level: Actively seeking new investments

EAGLE VENTURE PARTNERS

Chernogryazskaya, 1
Sadovaya
Moscow, Russia 105064
Phone: 7-095-771-7115
Fax: 7-095-771-7116
E-mail: eagle@comail.ru
Website: www.evp.ru

Other Offices

Room 501
Zhibek Zholy 64
Almaty, Kazakhstan 480002
Phone: 7-571-360-3296
Fax: 7-571-360-3295

Vorobiova st. 17
Smolensk, Russia 214013
Phone: 7-0812-66-0693
Fax: 7-095-943-5524

Karel Oomsstraat 37
Antwerpen, Belgium B-2018
Phone: 32-32-90-2100
Fax: 32-32-90-2105

ul. Stepana Razina 38
Voronezh, Russia 394000
Phone: 7-073-271-3180
Fax: 7-073-271-2303

Antona Valeka str. 15A
Office 405
Ekaterinburg, Russia 620026
Phone: 7-343-378-7174
Fax: 7-343-378-7175

Wageningselaan 6
LA Veenendaal, Netherlands 3903
Phone: 32-3-290-2120
Fax: 32-3-290-2105

Management and Staff

Hans Vreeman, Managing Director
Jan Dewijngaert, Managing Director

Type of Firm

Bank Affiliated

Project Preferences

Type of Financing Preferred:
Second Stage Financing
Early Stage
Expansion

Geographical Preferences

International Preferences:
Eastern Europe
Russia

Additional Information

Year Founded: 2000
Current Activity Level: Actively seeking new investments

EARLY STAGE ENTERPRISES, L.P.

103 Carnegie Center
Suite 200
Princeton, NJ USA 08540
Phone: 609-921-8896
Fax: 609-921-8703
E-mail: partners@esevc.com
Website: www.esevc.com

Management and Staff

James Millar, Partner
Kef Kasdin, Partner
Ronald Hahn, Partner

Type of Firm

Private Equity Firm

Association Membership

Mid-Atlantic Venture Association
Natl Assoc of Small Bus. Inv. Co (NASBIC)

Project Preferences

Role in Financing:
Prefer role as deal originator but will also invest in deals created by others

Type of Financing Preferred:
Early Stage
Seed
First Stage Financing
Startup

Size of Investments Considered:
Min Size of Investment Considered (000s): $500
Max Size of Investment Considered (000s): $1,000

Geographical Preferences

United States Preferences:
Mid Atlantic

Industry Focus

(% based on actual investment)

Computer Software and Services	48.0%
Internet Specific	19.6%
Other Products	9.2%
Communications and Media	8.8%
Medical/Health	7.7%
Biotechnology	6.8%

Additional Information

Year Founded: 1996
Capital Under Management: $44,000,000
Current Activity Level: Actively seeking new investments
Method of Compensation: Return on investment is of primary concern, do not charge fees

EARLY STAGE PARTNERS, L.P.

1801 East Ninth Street
Suite 1700
Cleveland, OH USA 44114
Phone: 216-781-4600
Fax: 216-781-0158
E-mail: inbox@esplp.com
Website: www.esplp.com

Management and Staff

Charles MacMillan, Principal
James Petras, Principal
James Ireland, Principal
Jonathan Murray, Principal

Type of Firm

Private Equity Firm

Project Preferences

Role in Financing:
Will function either as deal originator or investor in deals created by others

Type of Financing Preferred:
Early Stage

Size of Investments Considered:
Min Size of Investment Considered (000s): $250
Max Size of Investment Considered (000s): $5,000

Geographical Preferences

United States Preferences:
Midwest
Ohio

Industry Preferences

In Computer Software prefer:
Software

In Industrial/Energy prefer:
Advanced Materials

In Manufact. prefer:
Manufacturing

Additional Information

Name of Most Recent Fund: Early Stage Partners II, L.P.
Most Recent Fund Was Raised: 03/10/2008
Year Founded: 2002
Capital Under Management: $26,700,000
Current Activity Level: Actively seeking new investments
Method of Compensation: Return on investment is of primary concern, do not charge fees

EARLYBIRD VENTURE CAPITAL

Van-der-Smissen-Strasse 3
Hamburg, Germany 22767
Phone: 49-40-432-9410
Fax: 49-40-432-94129
E-mail: hamburg@earlybird.com
Website: www.earlybird.com

Other Offices

Maximilianstrasse 14
Munich, Germany 80539
Phone: 49-89-2907-020
Fax: 49-89-2907-0222

Management and Staff

Christian Nagel, Managing Partner
Hendrik Brandis, Managing Partner
Marion Jung, Principal
Matias Collan, Venture Partner
Roland Manger, Managing Partner
Rolf Mathies, Managing Partner
Sven Schmidt, Venture Partner
Thom Rasche, Partner
Thorsten Schaefer, Venture Partner
Wolfgang Seibold, Partner

Type of Firm

Private Equity Firm

Association Membership

European Private Equity and Venture Capital Assoc.

Project Preferences

Role in Financing:
Will function either as deal originator or investor in deals created by others

Type of Financing Preferred:
Early Stage
Expansion
Startup

Size of Investments Considered:
Min Size of Investment Considered (000s): $1,412
Max Size of Investment Considered (000s): $16,947

Geographical Preferences

International Preferences:
Europe

Industry Focus

(% based on actual investment)

Internet Specific	40.7%
Computer Software and Services	17.4%
Medical/Health	14.1%
Biotechnology	11.4%
Semiconductors/Other Elect.	9.4%
Computer Hardware	3.1%
Communications and Media	2.7%
Other Products	1.1%

Additional Information

Name of Most Recent Fund: Earlybird IV
Most Recent Fund Was Raised: 05/03/2007
Year Founded: 1997
Capital Under Management: $530,100,000
Current Activity Level: Actively seeking new investments
Method of Compensation: Return on investment is of primary concern, do not charge fees

EARLYBIRDCAPITAL, INC.

275 Madison Avenue
27th Floor
New York, NY USA 10016
Phone: 212-661-0200
Website: www.earlybirdcapital.com

Type of Firm

Bank Affiliated

Project Preferences

Type of Financing Preferred:
Early Stage

Industry Preferences

In Communications prefer:
Telecommunications

In Internet Specific prefer:
Internet

In Medical/Health prefer:
Medical/Health

In Business Serv. prefer:
Media

Additional Information

Year Founded: 2000
Current Activity Level: Actively seeking new investments

EARTHRISE CAPITAL PARTNERS LLC

45 Rockefeller Plaza
20th Floor
New York, NY USA 10111
Phone: 212-757-1007
Website: www.earthrisecapital.com

Management and Staff

Ann Partlow, Principal
Jim LoGerfo, Principal

Type of Firm

Private Equity Firm

Project Preferences

Type of Financing Preferred:
Early Stage

Industry Preferences

In Industrial/Energy prefer:
Alternative Energy

Additional Information

Name of Most Recent Fund: Earthrise Capital Fund, L.P.
Most Recent Fund Was Raised: 05/12/2008
Year Founded: 2008
Capital Under Management: $2,700,000
Current Activity Level: Actively seeking new investments

EAST AFRICA CAPITAL PARTNERS

P O Box 15538
Nairobi, Kenya 00503
Phone: 254-733-617-186

Type of Firm

Private Equity Firm

Project Preferences

Type of Financing Preferred:
Leveraged Buyout
Expansion

Size of Investments Considered:
Min Size of Investment Considered (000s): $500
Max Size of Investment Considered (000s): $5,000

Geographical Preferences

International Preferences:
Rwanda
Malawi
Uganda
Tanzania
Kenya
Africa

Industry Preferences

In Communications prefer:
Communications and Media
Telecommunications

In Business Serv. prefer:
Media

Additional Information

Year Founded: 2005
Capital Under Management: $100,000,000
Current Activity Level: Actively seeking new investments

EAST CAPITAL PRIVATE EQUITY AB

Kungsgatan 33
1st Floor
Stockholm, Sweden 111 93
Phone: 46-8-5058-8500
Fax: 46-8-5058-8509
E-mail: private.equity@eastcapital.com
Website: www.eastcapital.com

Other Offices

42 Avenue Montaigne
Paris, France 75008
Phone: 33-1-7274-1189
Fax: 33-1-7274-1188

Management and Staff

Justas Pipinis, Managing Director
Karine Hirn, Founding Partner
Kestutis Sasnauskas, Chief Executive Officer

Type of Firm

Bank Affiliated

Association Membership

Swedish Venture Capital Association (SVCA)

Project Preferences

Type of Financing Preferred:
Leveraged Buyout
Generalist PE
Balanced
Special Situation

Geographical Preferences

International Preferences:
Europe
Kazakhstan
Eastern Europe
Russia
Georgia

Industry Preferences

In Consumer Related prefer:
Consumer

In Industrial/Energy prefer:
Energy

In Financial Services prefer:
Financial Services

In Business Serv. prefer:
Services
Distribution

Additional Information

Year Founded: 1997
Capital Under Management: $15,000,000
Current Activity Level: Actively seeking new investments

EAST FUND MANAGEMENTBERATUNG GMBH

Biberstrasse 11/8
Vienna, Austria 1010
Phone: 43-1-512-4290
Fax: 43-1-5124290400
E-mail: office@hkkpartners.com
Website: www.eastfund.com

Other Offices

George Enescu Street 43/6
Bucharest, Romania
Phone: 40-1-211-5968

Podhaj 15
Bratislava, Slovakia 841 05
Phone: 421-2-254418319

Management and Staff

Dave Williams, Partner
Mark Kaltenbacher, Managing Director
Reba White-Williams, Partner
Roland Haas, Managing Director & CFO

Type of Firm

Private Equity Firm

Association Membership

European Private Equity and Venture Capital Assoc.

Project Preferences

Type of Financing Preferred:
Leveraged Buyout
Early Stage
Expansion
Mezzanine
Later Stage
Management Buyouts
Startup
Recapitalizations

Size of Investments Considered:
Min Size of Investment Considered (000s): $3,634
Max Size of Investment Considered (000s): $36,348

Geographical Preferences

International Preferences:
Central Europe
Austria
Eastern Europe

Industry Preferences

In Communications prefer:
Media and Entertainment

In Consumer Related prefer:
Food/Beverage

In Transportation prefer:
Transportation

In Financial Services prefer:
Financial Services

In Business Serv. prefer:
Services

Additional Information

Name of Most Recent Fund: EFM Partners
Most Recent Fund Was Raised: 04/08/1999
Year Founded: 1994
Capital Under Management: $164,000,000
Current Activity Level: Actively seeking new investments

EAST GATE PRIVATE EQUITY PARTNERS LLC

514 High Street
Suite 5
Palo Alto, CA USA 94301
Phone: 650-325-5077
Fax: 650-325-5072
Website: www.eg-group.com

Management and Staff

Hsiao-wen Kao, President
Kenneth Choi, Managing Director

Type of Firm

Private Equity Firm

Association Membership

National Venture Capital Association - USA (NVCA)

Project Preferences

Role in Financing:
Will function either as deal originator or investor in deals created by others

Type of Financing Preferred:
Startup

Size of Investments Considered:
Min Size of Investment Considered (000s): $500
Max Size of Investment Considered (000s): $2,000

Geographical Preferences

United States Preferences:
Northern California

Additional Information
Name of Most Recent Fund: East Gate Private Equity Fund III, L.P.
Most Recent Fund Was Raised: 04/01/2000
Year Founded: 1997
Capital Under Management: $60,000,000
Current Activity Level: Actively seeking new investments

EAST HILL MANAGEMENT

200 Clarendon Street
Suite 6000
Boston, MA USA 02116
Phone: 617-450-015
Fax: 617-450-0151
Website: www.easthillmgt.com

Other Offices

Oxford University Begbroke Science Park
Sandy Lane, Yarnton
Oxford, United Kingdom OX5 1PF
Phone: 44-1865-283-792

Management and Staff

Larry Grantham, Principal

Type of Firm

Private Equity Advisor or Fund of Funds

Project Preferences

Type of Financing Preferred:
Early Stage
Balanced

Geographical Preferences

United States Preferences:
All U.S.

International Preferences:
United Kingdom

Industry Preferences

In Biotechnology prefer:
Biotechnology

Additional Information

Year Founded: 2000
Capital Under Management: $16,800,000
Current Activity Level: Actively seeking new investments

EAST WEST CAPITAL PARTNERS PTE, LTD.

14 Robinson Road
06-01 Far East Finanace Bldg.
Singapore, Singapore 048545
Phone: 65-9675-6436
Fax: 65-6325-2789
Website: www.eastwestcap.com

Management and Staff

Duncan Moore, Partner
Hans Brenner, Partner
Ram Radhakrishnan, Partner
Sanjay Sehgal, CEO & Managing Director

Type of Firm

Private Equity Firm

Association Membership

Singapore Venture Capital Association (SVCA)

Project Preferences

Role in Financing:
Prefer role as deal originator

Type of Financing Preferred:
Research and Development
Public Companies

Turnaround
Later Stage
Management Buyouts
Private Placement
Recapitalizations

Geographical Preferences

International Preferences:
India
China
Asia

Industry Preferences

In Medical/Health prefer:
Medical Products
Health Services
Hospitals/Clinics/Primary
Pharmaceuticals

Additional Information

Year Founded: 2005
Current Activity Level: Actively seeking new investments

EASTMAN KODAK COMPANY

1999 Lake Avenue
Rochester, NY USA 14650
Phone: 585-722-3122
Fax: 585-477-5010
Website: www.kodak.com

Type of Firm

Corporate PE/Venture

Project Preferences

Role in Financing:
Prefer role in deals created by others

Type of Financing Preferred:
Second Stage Financing
Early Stage
Later Stage
First Stage Financing

Size of Investments Considered:
Min Size of Investment Considered (000s): $250
Max Size of Investment Considered (000s): $1,000

Geographical Preferences

United States Preferences:
All U.S.

International Preferences:
Europe

Industry Preferences

In Computer Software prefer:
Software

In Semiconductor/Electr prefer:
Sensors

In Consumer Related prefer:
Consumer Services

In Industrial/Energy prefer:
Advanced Materials

In Business Serv. prefer:
Media

Additional Information

Year Founded: 1983
Capital Under Management: $30,000,000
Current Activity Level: Actively seeking new investments
Method of Compensation: Other

EASTMAN VENTURES

100 North Eastman Road
P.O. Box 511
Kingsport, TN USA 37662
Phone: 423-229-2000
Fax: 423-224-0314
E-mail: ventures@eastman.com
Website: www.eastmanventures.com

Management and Staff

Fouad Azzam, Venture Partner
Jim Lowery, Venture Partner

Type of Firm

Corporate PE/Venture

Association Membership

Western Association of Venture Capitalists (WAVC)
European Private Equity and Venture Capital Assoc.

Project Preferences

Role in Financing:
Will function either as deal originator or investor in deals created by others

Type of Financing Preferred:
Second Stage Financing
Early Stage
Expansion
Later Stage

Size of Investments Considered:
Min Size of Investment Considered (000s): $500
Max Size of Investment Considered (000s): $2,000

Geographical Preferences

United States Preferences:
All U.S.

International Preferences:
Western Europe
Asia

Industry Preferences

In Computer Software prefer:
Software

In Internet Specific prefer:
E-Commerce Technology
Internet

In Semiconductor/Electr prefer:
Electronics
Electronic Components
Semiconductor
Optoelectronics

In Biotechnology prefer:
Biotechnology
Industrial Biotechnology
Biosensors

In Medical/Health prefer:
Medical/Health
Medical Diagnostics
Diagnostic Test Products
Drug/Equipmt Delivery
Medical Products
Disposable Med. Products

In Industrial/Energy prefer:
Energy
Alternative Energy
Energy Conservation Relat
Industrial Products
Materials
Advanced Materials
Environmental Related

In Manufact. prefer:
Manufacturing

In Other prefer:
Environment Responsible

Additional Information

Year Founded: 1999
Capital Under Management: $50,000,000
Current Activity Level: Reducing investment activity
Method of Compensation: Return on investment is of primary concern, do not charge fees

---

EASTON HUNT CAPITAL PARTNERS, L.P.

767 Third Avenue
Seventh Floor
New York, NY USA 10017
Phone: 212-702-0950
Fax: 212-702-0952
E-mail: info@eastoncapital.com
Website: www.eastoncapital.com

Other Offices

11 Summer Street
Buffalo, NY USA 14209
Phone: 716-885-0119

2151 Le Jeune Road
Suite 303
Miami, FL USA 33134
Phone: 305-361-6479
Fax: 305-444-7964

Management and Staff

Anup Arora, Vice President
Charles Hughes, Managing Director
Daniel Googel, Principal

Edward Meyer, Managing Director
Francisco Garcia, Managing Director
John Friedman, Managing Partner
Mark Chen, Venture Partner
Milena Adamian, Vice President
Richard Schneider, Managing Director
Seth Orlow, Venture Partner

Type of Firm

Private Equity Firm

Association Membership

Natl Assoc of Small Bus. Inv. Co (NASBIC)

Project Preferences

Role in Financing:

Prefer role as deal originator but will also invest in deals created by others

Type of Financing Preferred:

Second Stage Financing
Early Stage
Expansion
Later Stage
Management Buyouts
First Stage Financing
Private Placement

Size of Investments Considered:

Min Size of Investment Considered (000s): $2,000
Max Size of Investment Considered (000s): $7,500

Industry Preferences

In Communications prefer:

Media and Entertainment

In Internet Specific prefer:

Internet

In Semiconductor/Electr prefer:

Electronics
Controllers and Sensors

In Biotechnology prefer:

Biotechnology
Biotech Related Research

In Medical/Health prefer:

Medical Diagnostics
Diagnostic Test Products
Drug/Equipmt Delivery
Medical Products

In Consumer Related prefer:

Entertainment and Leisure

Additional Information

Year Founded: 1999
Capital Under Management: $140,000,000
Current Activity Level: Actively seeking new investments
Method of Compensation: Return on invest. most important, but chg. closing fees, service fees, etc.

EASTSIDE PARTNERS

207 East Side Square
2nd Floor
Huntsville, AL USA 35801
Phone: 256-327-8777
Fax: 256-883-8558
E-mail: info@eastsidepartners.com
Website: www.eastsidepartners.com

Management and Staff

Emerson Fann, Managing Director
Tina Corley, Chief Financial Officer

Type of Firm

Private Equity Firm

Project Preferences

Type of Financing Preferred:

Early Stage
Expansion

Size of Investments Considered:

Min Size of Investment Considered (000s): $2,000
Max Size of Investment Considered (000s): $6,000

Geographical Preferences

United States Preferences:

Southeast

Industry Preferences

In Medical/Health prefer:

Health Services

In Financial Services prefer:

Financial Services

Additional Information

Year Founded: 2005
Capital Under Management: $60,000,000
Current Activity Level: Actively seeking new investments

EASTWARD CAPITAL

432 Cherry Street
West Newton, MA USA 02465
Phone: 617-969-6700
Fax: 617-969-7900
E-mail: contacts@eastwardcp.com
Website: www.eastwardcp.com

Management and Staff

David Alpert, Partner
Dennis Cameron, Managing Director
Douglas Brian, Chief Operating Officer
Edward Dresner, Principal
Michael Dale, Chief Financial Officer
Ted Stecko, Principal

Type of Firm

Service Provider

Additional Information

Year Founded: 1994
Capital Under Management: $235,000,000
Current Activity Level: Actively seeking new investments

EBM SOCIEDAD GESTORA DE ENTIDADES DE CAPITAL RIESGO SA

Almagro 46
Plaza Ruben Dario
Madrid, Spain 28010
Phone: 34-91-700-9800
Fax: 34-91-700-9829
E-mail: capitalriesgo@bnbanco.com

Type of Firm

Bank Affiliated

Association Membership

Spanish Venture Capital Association (ASCRI)

Project Preferences

Type of Financing Preferred:

Balanced

Size of Investments Considered:

Min Size of Investment Considered (000s): $500
Max Size of Investment Considered (000s): $500,000

Geographical Preferences

International Preferences:

Spain

Additional Information

Year Founded: 1999
Capital Under Management: $62,600,000
Current Activity Level: Actively seeking new investments

EBT VENTURE FUND, LTD.

38-42 Hill Street
Belfast, Ireland BT1 2LB
Phone: 44-28-9031-1770
Fax: 44-28-9031-1880
E-mail: info@emergingbusinesstrust.com
Website: www.emergingbusinesstrust.com

Type of Firm

Private Equity Firm

Additional Information

Current Activity Level: Actively seeking new investments

ECAPITAL ENTREPRENEURIAL PARTNERS AG

Hafenweg 24
Munster, Germany 48155
Phone: 49-251-7037-670
Fax: 49-251-70376722
E-mail: info@ecapital.de
Website: www.ecapital.de

Type of Firm
Private Equity Firm

Project Preferences

Type of Financing Preferred:
Early Stage
Expansion
Seed
Startup

Geographical Preferences

International Preferences:
Europe
Germany

Industry Preferences

In Communications prefer:
Communications and Media
Wireless Communications

In Computer Software prefer:
Software

In Internet Specific prefer:
Internet

In Semiconductor/Electr prefer:
Optoelectronics

In Industrial/Energy prefer:
Materials

Additional Information
Year Founded: 1999
Capital Under Management: $53,000,000
Current Activity Level: Actively seeking new investments

ECART INVEST 1 BV
Javastraat 78
Den Haag, Netherlands 2585 AS
Phone: 31-70-355-4788
Fax: 31-70-350-0523
E-mail: info@ecart.nl
Website: www.ecart.nl

Type of Firm
Private Equity Firm

Association Membership
Dutch Venture Capital Associaton (NVP)

Project Preferences

Type of Financing Preferred:
Balanced

Size of Investments Considered:
Min Size of Investment Considered (000s): $88
Max Size of Investment Considered (000s): $1,104

Geographical Preferences

International Preferences:
Netherlands
Europe

Industry Preferences

In Business Serv. prefer:
Services

Additional Information
Year Founded: 1993
Capital Under Management: $4,400,000
Current Activity Level: Actively seeking new investments

ECD INVESTMENTS LLC/ECD INVESTMENTS BIDCO
222 North President Street
Suite 200
Jackson, MS USA 39201
Phone: 601-944-1100
Fax: 601-944-0808
E-mail: info@ecd.org
Website: www.ecd.org

Other Offices
8869 Centre Street
Suite C
Southaven, MS USA 38671
Phone: 662-342-5555
Fax: 662-342-5590

121 West Sixth Street
Suite 2F
Pine Bluff, AR USA 71601
Phone: 870-535-8775
Fax: 870-535-8776

1301 Washington Street
Vicksburg, MS USA 39180
Phone: 601-636-4741
Fax: 601-636-2195

909 North 18th Street
Suite 223
Monroe, LA USA 71201
Phone: 318-340-9898
Fax: 318-340-9613

1720 South Caraway Road
Suite 3040
Jonesboro, AR USA 72401
Phone: 870-972-8417
Fax: 870-972-8427

Stevens Building, Suite 205
110 Yazoo
Clarksdale, MS USA 38614
Phone: 662-621-1995
Fax: 662-621-1951

Management and Staff
Alan Branson, Vice President

Type of Firm
Incubator/Development Program

Association Membership
Community Development Venture Capital Alliance

Project Preferences

Role in Financing:
Prefer role as deal originator but will also invest in deals created by others

Type of Financing Preferred:
Second Stage Financing
Early Stage
Expansion
Mezzanine

Size of Investments Considered:
Min Size of Investment Considered (000s): $250
Max Size of Investment Considered (000s): $1,000

Geographical Preferences

United States Preferences:
Mississippi
Southeast
Louisiana
Arkansas

Industry Preferences

In Communications prefer:
Wireless Communications

In Computer Software prefer:
Software
Systems Software
Applications Software

In Internet Specific prefer:
Internet

In Medical/Health prefer:
Medical Products

In Agr/Forestr/Fish prefer:
Agriculture related

In Other prefer:
Women/Minority-Owned Bus.

Additional Information
Year Founded: 1995
Capital Under Management: $18,000,000
Current Activity Level: Actively seeking new investments
Method of Compensation: Return on investment is of primary concern, do not charge fees

---

ECENTURY CAPITAL PARTNERS, L.P.
8180 Greensboro Drive
Suite 1150
McLean, VA USA 22102
Phone: 703-442-4480
Fax: 703-448-1816
E-mail: info@ecenturycapital.com
Website: www.ecenturycapital.com

Management and Staff

Hank Tuten, Managing Director
J. Christian Fritz, Principal
James Broder, Managing Director
Marsh Marshall, Managing Director
Thomas Dann, Managing Director

Type of Firm

Private Equity Firm

Association Membership

Mid-Atlantic Venture Association
Natl Assoc of Small Bus. Inv. Co (NASBIC)

Project Preferences

Type of Financing Preferred:

Second Stage Financing
Early Stage
Expansion
Seed
First Stage Financing

Size of Investments Considered:

Min Size of Investment Considered (000s): $100
Max Size of Investment Considered (000s): $4,000

Geographical Preferences

United States Preferences:

All U.S.

Industry Preferences

In Communications prefer:

Data Communications

In Computer Software prefer:

Software
Applications Software

In Semiconductor/Electr prefer:

Semiconductor

In Industrial/Energy prefer:

Advanced Materials

Additional Information

Name of Most Recent Fund: ECentury Capital Partners I
Most Recent Fund Was Raised: 09/30/2000
Year Founded: 2000
Capital Under Management: $90,000,000
Current Activity Level: Actively seeking new investments

ECHELON VENTURES LLC

300 Fifth Avenue
Third Floor
North Waltham, MA USA 02451
Phone: 781-419-9850
Fax: 781-419-9851
E-mail: info@echelonventures.com
Website: www.echelonventures.com

Management and Staff

Alfred Woodworth, Managing Director

Type of Firm

Private Equity Firm

Project Preferences

Role in Financing:

Prefer role as deal originator but will also invest in deals created by others

Type of Financing Preferred:

Early Stage

Size of Investments Considered:

Min Size of Investment Considered (000s): $1,000
Max Size of Investment Considered (000s): $5,000

Geographical Preferences

United States Preferences:

Northeast

Industry Preferences

In Computer Software prefer:

Software

In Semiconductor/Electr prefer:

Semiconductor

In Biotechnology prefer:

Human Biotechnology

In Medical/Health prefer:

Medical Diagnostics

In Industrial/Energy prefer:

Alternative Energy

Additional Information

Name of Most Recent Fund: Echelon Ventures II, L.P.
Most Recent Fund Was Raised: 08/04/2004
Year Founded: 2000
Capital Under Management: $15,700,000
Current Activity Level: Actively seeking new investments
Method of Compensation: Return on invest. most important, but chg. closing fees, service fees, etc.

ECHO CAPITAL

1234 Rena-Levesque Ouest
Montreal, Canada H3X2K6
Phone: 514-555-1212
Fax: 514-555-1213
E-mail: enquiries@echocapital.ca
Website: echo.ashtoncole.com

Management and Staff

Jacques Lacroix, Partner
Philippe Huneault, Partner
Terry Enepekides, Partner

Type of Firm

Government Affiliated Program

Additional Information

Year Founded: 2009
Current Activity Level: Actively seeking new investments

ECHO STREET CAPITAL ADVISORS

850 Third Avenue
New York, NY USA 10022

Type of Firm

Private Equity Firm

Additional Information

Year Founded: 2002
Capital Under Management: $3,600,000
Current Activity Level: Actively seeking new investments

ECI PARTNERS LLP

Brettenham House
Lancaster Place
London, United Kingdom WC2E 7EN
Phone: 44-20-7606-1000
Fax: 44-20-7240-5050
E-mail: enquiries@ecipartners.com
Website: www.ecipartners.com

Other Offices

Royal House
Sovereign Street
Leeds, United Kingdom LS1 4BJ
Phone: 44-113- 234-3401
Fax: 44-113-234-3402

40 Peter Street
Manchester, United Kingdom M2 5GP
Phone: 44-161-819-3160
Fax: 44-161-819-3161

Management and Staff

Ken Landsberg, Managing Director
Richard Chapman, Partner
Steven Tudge, Managing Director
Tim Raffle, Managing Director

Type of Firm

Private Equity Firm

Association Membership

British Venture Capital Association (BVCA)
European Private Equity and Venture Capital Assoc.

Project Preferences

Role in Financing:

Prefer role as deal originator but will also invest in deals created by others

Type of Financing Preferred:

Leveraged Buyout
Control-block Purchases
Expansion
Generalist PE
Balanced
Later Stage
Management Buyouts
Acquisition

Industry Rollups
Special Situation
Recapitalizations

Size of Investments Considered:

Min Size of Investment Considered (000s): $8,925
Max Size of Investment Considered (000s): $89,250

Geographical Preferences

International Preferences:

United Kingdom
Europe

Industry Focus

(% based on actual investment)

Computer Software and Services	29.5%
Consumer Related	22.0%
Other Products	19.1%
Industrial/Energy	12.6%
Communications and Media	12.1%
Computer Hardware	2.8%
Medical/Health	1.1%
Biotechnology	0.9%

Additional Information

Name of Most Recent Fund: ECI 8
Most Recent Fund Was Raised: 04/11/2005
Year Founded: 1976
Capital Under Management: $305,600,000
Current Activity Level: Actively seeking new investments
Method of Compensation: Return on invest. most important, but chg. closing fees, service fees, etc.

ECLIPSE RT.

Alkotas ut 50.
Budapest, Hungary 1123
Phone: 36-1-489-2286
Fax: 36-1-489-2290

Type of Firm

Private Equity Firm

Association Membership

Hungarian Venture Capital Association (HVCA)
Additional Information
Current Activity Level: Actively seeking new investments

ECM EQUITY CAPITAL MANAGEMENT GMBH

Oberlindau 80-82
Frankfurt/Main, Germany 60323
Phone: 49-69-971020
Fax: 49-69-9710224
E-mail: info@ecm-ffm.de
Website: www.ecm-pe.de

Type of Firm

Private Equity Firm

Association Membership

German Venture Capital Association (BVK)

Project Preferences

Type of Financing Preferred:

Leveraged Buyout
Expansion
Mezzanine
Turnaround
Management Buyouts

Geographical Preferences

International Preferences:

Switzerland
Austria
Germany

Additional Information

Name of Most Recent Fund: German Equity Partners III LP
Most Recent Fund Was Raised: 09/28/2006
Year Founded: 1996
Capital Under Management: $317,600,000
Current Activity Level: Actively seeking new investments

ECM-BULGARIAN POST-PRIVATISATION FUND

Svoboda Square 1
Fourth Floor
Sofia, Bulgaria 1421
Phone: 359-2-960-0200
Fax: 359-2-981-5812
Website: www.ecm.bg

Management and Staff

Antonio Perez-Montes, Managing Director

Type of Firm

Private Equity Firm

Project Preferences

Type of Financing Preferred:

Balanced

Geographical Preferences

International Preferences:

Europe

Additional Information

Year Founded: 2005
Current Activity Level: Actively seeking new investments

ECO UNTERNEHMENS-BETEILIGUNGS-AG (ECO UB-AG)

Boersegasse 14
Vienna, Austria 1010
Phone: 43-1-0501-000
Fax: 431-05010017608
E-mail: eco@erstebank.at

Management and Staff

Leopold Bednar, Partner
Thomas Poll, Partner

Type of Firm

Bank Affiliated

Association Membership

Austrian PE and Venture Capital Association (AVCO)

Project Preferences

Type of Financing Preferred:

Management Buyouts

Size of Investments Considered:

Min Size of Investment Considered (000s): $300
Max Size of Investment Considered (000s): $300,000

Geographical Preferences

International Preferences:

Austria

Industry Focus

(% based on actual investment)

Consumer Related	57.2%
Industrial/Energy	42.8%

Additional Information

Year Founded: 1995
Capital Under Management: $10,300,000
Current Activity Level: Actively seeking new investments

ECOENTERPRISES FUND

The Nature Conservancy
4245 North Fairfax Drive
Arlington, VA USA 22203
Phone: 703-841-5692
Fax: 703-841-9059
E-mail: ecoenterprises@tnc.org
Website: www.ecoenterprisesfund.com

Other Offices

Apdo. Postal 230-1225
Plaza Mayor
San Jose, Costa Rica
Phone: 506-296-5000
Fax: 506-220-2551

Management and Staff

Tammy Newmark, President

Type of Firm
Private Equity Firm

Project Preferences

Type of Financing Preferred:
Balanced

Size of Investments Considered:
Min Size of Investment Considered (000s): $50
Max Size of Investment Considered (000s): $800

Geographical Preferences

International Preferences:
Latin America

Industry Preferences

In Industrial/Energy prefer:
Environmental Related

In Business Serv. prefer:
Services

In Agr/Forestr/Fish prefer:
Agriculture related

In Other prefer:
Socially Responsible
Environment Responsible

Additional Information
Year Founded: 2001
Capital Under Management: $5,000,000
Current Activity Level: Actively seeking new investments

ECOMPARK INC.

BCE Place, 181 Bay Street
Suite 3100, P.O. Box 830
Toronto, Canada M5J2T3
Phone: 416-216-0822
Fax: 416-216-0823

Type of Firm
Private Equity Firm

Project Preferences

Type of Financing Preferred:
Early Stage
Seed
Startup

Geographical Preferences

Canadian Preferences:
All Canada

Additional Information
Year Founded: 2009
Current Activity Level: Actively seeking new investments

ECONERGY INTERNATIONAL CORPORATION

1881 Ninth Street
Suite 300
Boulder, CO USA 80302
Phone: 303-473-9007
Fax: 303-473-9060
Website: www.econergy.net

Other Offices
Plaza Roble, Escazu
Edificio El Portico, Piso 1
San Jose, Costa Rica
Phone: 506-201-1543

1925 K Street North West
Washington, DC USA 20006
Phone: 202-822-4980
Fax: 202-822-4986

Avenida Angelica 2530
Conjunto 111
Sao Paulo, Brazil 01228-200
Phone: 55-11-3555-5700
Fax: 55-11-3555-5735

22 Billiter Street
London, United Kingdom EC3M 2RY
Phone: 44-203-102-3403
Fax: 44-203-102-3401

Management and Staff
Lee Atkins, Chief Financial Officer
Rick Renner, Chief Operating Officer
Tom Stoner, General Partner

Type of Firm
Corporate PE/Venture

Project Preferences

Type of Financing Preferred:
Early Stage

Geographical Preferences

International Preferences:
Latin America

Industry Preferences

In Industrial/Energy prefer:
Energy
Alternative Energy
Energy Conservation Relat

Additional Information
Year Founded: 1994
Capital Under Management: $16,300,000
Current Activity Level: Actively seeking new investments

ECOS VENTURE CAPITAL BETEILIGUNGS AG

Doeblinger Hauptstrasse 66/11
Vienna, Austria A-1190
Phone: 43-1-368-9125
Fax: 43-1-3689-12522
E-mail: office@ecosventure.com
Website: www.ecosventure.com

Management and Staff
Hans-Jurgen Schmitz, Managing Director
Werner Edlinger, Managing Director

Type of Firm
Private Equity Firm

Association Membership
European Private Equity and Venture Capital Assoc.

Project Preferences

Type of Financing Preferred:
Early Stage
Expansion

Size of Investments Considered:
Min Size of Investment Considered (000s): $714
Max Size of Investment Considered (000s): $2,141

Geographical Preferences

International Preferences:
Switzerland
Europe
Austria
Germany

Industry Preferences

In Communications prefer:
Communications and Media
Wireless Communications

In Computer Software prefer:
Software

In Semiconductor/Electr prefer:
Electronics
Semiconductor

In Medical/Health prefer:
Medical/Health

In Industrial/Energy prefer:
Factory Automation

Additional Information
Year Founded: 1999
Capital Under Management: $28,600,000
Current Activity Level: Actively seeking new investments

ECOSYSTEM VENTURES LLC

P.O. Box 3347
Saratoga, CA USA 95070
Phone: 408-426-8040
Fax: 408-867-1441
E-mail: info@ecosystemventures.com
Website: www.ecosystemventures.com

Other Offices

60 Weingartenstrasse
Mannedorf
Zurich, Switzerland 8708
Phone: 41-44-586-7108
Fax: 41-44-790-2187

Management and Staff

Alexander Fries, President, Founder

Type of Firm

Private Equity Firm

Project Preferences

Type of Financing Preferred:
Early Stage
Seed

Geographical Preferences

International Preferences:
Europe

Additional Information

Year Founded: 2005
Current Activity Level: Actively seeking new investments

ECS CAPITAL, S.A.

Rua Castilho 20, 6
Lisbon, Portugal 1250-069
Phone: 351-21-380-2500
Fax: 351-21-380-2499
E-mail: info@ecscapital.com
Website: www.ecscapital.com

Management and Staff

Antonio de Sousa, Partner
Fernando Esmeraldo, Partner

Type of Firm

Private Equity Firm

Project Preferences

Type of Financing Preferred:
Leveraged Buyout
Expansion
Management Buyouts
Distressed Debt
Recapitalizations

Geographical Preferences

International Preferences:
Portugal
Spain

Additional Information

Year Founded: 2006
Capital Under Management: $148,500,000
Current Activity Level: Actively seeking new investments

ECT MERCHANT INVESTMENTS CORP (ENRON CORP.)

Four Houston Center
1331 Lamar, Suite 1600
Houston, TX USA 77010
Phone: 713-853-6161
Website: www.enron.com

Type of Firm

Private Equity Firm

Additional Information

Year Founded: 2009
Current Activity Level: Actively seeking new investments

EDBV MANAGEMENT PTE LTD.

250 North Bridge Road
20-03 Raffles City Tower
Singapore, Singapore 179101
Phone: 65-6832-6117
E-mail: edbvm@edb.gov.sg
Website: www.edbvm.com.sg

Other Offices

210 Twin Dolphin Drive
Redwood City, CA USA 94065
Phone: 650-591-9102
Fax: 650-591-1328

Type of Firm

Government Affiliated Program

Association Membership

Korean Venture Capital Association (KVCA)
Singapore Venture Capital Association (SVCA)

Project Preferences

Type of Financing Preferred:
Early Stage
Expansion
Balanced
Seed
Startup

Geographical Preferences

United States Preferences:
All U.S.

International Preferences:
Europe
Western Europe
Israel
Singapore
Asia
All International

Industry Preferences

In Communications prefer:
Communications and Media
Telecommunications
Wireless Communications

In Computer Software prefer:
Software

In Internet Specific prefer:
E-Commerce Technology

In Computer Other prefer:
Computer Related

In Semiconductor/Electr prefer:
Electronic Components
Semiconductor
Circuit Boards

In Biotechnology prefer:
Biotechnology

In Consumer Related prefer:
Retail
Consumer Services

In Industrial/Energy prefer:
Industrial Products

In Financial Services prefer:
Financial Services

Additional Information

Year Founded: 1991
Capital Under Management: $400,000,000
Current Activity Level: Actively seeking new investments
Method of Compensation: Return on investment is of primary concern, do not charge fees

EDELSON TECHNOLOGY PARTNERS

300 Tice Boulevard
Woodcliff Lake, NJ USA 07677
Phone: 201-930-9898
Fax: 201-930-8899
Website: www.edelsontech.com

Management and Staff

Harry Edelson, General Partner
Nicholas Puro, Partner

Type of Firm

Private Equity Firm

Project Preferences

Role in Financing:
Will function either as deal originator or investor in deals created by others

Type of Financing Preferred:
Generalist PE

Size of Investments Considered:
Min Size of Investment Considered (000s): $500
Max Size of Investment Considered (000s): $2,000

Geographical Preferences

Canadian Preferences:
All Canada

International Preferences:
Europe
Asia

Industry Focus

(% based on actual investment)

Computer Software and Services	19.1%
Other Products	18.0%
Medical/Health	17.7%
Communications and Media	16.3%
Industrial/Energy	10.1%
Consumer Related	5.5%
Semiconductors/Other Elect.	5.4%
Internet Specific	3.9%
Computer Hardware	3.7%
Biotechnology	0.3%

Additional Information

Name of Most Recent Fund: Edelson V, L.P.
Most Recent Fund Was Raised: 03/01/2001
Year Founded: 1984
Capital Under Management: $125,000,000
Current Activity Level: Actively seeking new investments
Method of Compensation: Return on investment is of primary concern, do not charge fees

EDEN VENTURES (UK), LTD.

1 Widcombe Crescent
Bath, United Kingdom BA2 6AH
Phone: 44-1225-472-950
Fax: 44-1225-481-767
E-mail: info@edenventures.co.uk
Website: www.edenventures.co.uk

Management and Staff

Ben Tompkins, General Partner

Type of Firm

Private Equity Firm

Project Preferences

Type of Financing Preferred:
Early Stage
Seed

Geographical Preferences

International Preferences:
Ireland
United Kingdom
Europe

Industry Preferences

In Communications prefer:
Telecommunications
Media and Entertainment

In Computer Software prefer:
Software

Additional Information

Year Founded: 2005
Capital Under Management: $58,700,000
Current Activity Level: Actively seeking new investments

EDF VENTURES (FKA: ENTERPRISE DEVELOPMENT FUND)

425 North Main Street
Ann Arbor, MI USA 48104
Phone: 734-663-3213
Fax: 734-663-7358
E-mail: contact@edfvc.com
Website: www.edfvc.com

Other Offices

4670 Fulton Street East
Suite 202
Ada, MI USA 49301
Phone: 616-956-8025
Fax: 616-956-8026

12531 High Bluff Drive, Suite 100
Office 444
San Diego, CA USA 92130
Phone: 858-259-9474
Fax: 734-663-7358

Management and Staff

Linda Fingerle, Chief Financial Officer
Mary Campbell, Managing Director
Michael DeVries, Managing Director

Type of Firm

Private Equity Firm

Association Membership

National Venture Capital Association - USA (NVCA)

Project Preferences

Role in Financing:
Will function either as deal originator or investor in deals created by others

Type of Financing Preferred:
Second Stage Financing
Early Stage
Research and Development
Seed
First Stage Financing
Startup

Size of Investments Considered:
Min Size of Investment Considered (000s): $1,500
Max Size of Investment Considered (000s): $6,000

Geographical Preferences

United States Preferences:
Midwest

Industry Focus

(% based on actual investment)

Medical/Health	28.5%
Other Products	20.2%
Computer Software and Services	18.5%
Internet Specific	12.4%
Semiconductors/Other Elect.	9.5%
Biotechnology	5.5%
Communications and Media	2.4%
Computer Hardware	1.7%
Consumer Related	1.2%

Additional Information

Name of Most Recent Fund: EDF Ventures III Sidecar, L.P. (FKA: REI Ventures, L.P.)
Most Recent Fund Was Raised: 08/04/2004
Year Founded: 1987
Capital Under Management: $186,000,000
Current Activity Level: Actively seeking new investments
Method of Compensation: Return on investment is of primary concern, do not charge fees

EDGESTONE CAPITAL PARTNERS INC. (FKA: NB CAPITAL PARTNERS)

130 King Street West
Suite 600
Toronto, Canada M5X 1A6
Phone: 416-860-3740
Fax: 416-860-9838
E-mail: info@edgestone.com
Website: www.edgestone.com

Other Offices

1010, rue Sherbrooke Ouest
Bureau 500
Montreal, Canada H3A 2R7
Phone: 514-282-2100
Fax: 514-282-1944

221 10 Avenue SE
Suite 201
Calgary, Canada T2G 0V9
Phone: 403-775-1075
Fax: 403-303-4489

Management and Staff

Bryan Kerdman, Partner
Derek Smyth, Partner

Gilbert Palter, Managing Partner
Guthrie Stewart, Partner
Samuel Duboc, Managing Partner
Sandra Bosela, Partner
Sandra Cowan, Partner
Stephen Marshall, Partner

Type of Firm
Private Equity Firm

Project Preferences

Role in Financing:
Prefer role as deal originator but will also invest in deals created by others

Type of Financing Preferred:
Fund of Funds
Leveraged Buyout
Early Stage
Expansion
Mezzanine
Generalist PE
Management Buyouts
Acquisition
Startup
Recapitalizations

Geographical Preferences

Canadian Preferences:
All Canada

Industry Focus
(% based on actual investment)

Other Products	52.2%
Consumer Related	22.7%
Computer Software and Services	11.3%
Industrial/Energy	7.4%
Communications and Media	3.0%
Computer Hardware	1.2%
Semiconductors/Other Elect.	1.2%
Internet Specific	1.0%

Additional Information
Year Founded: 1999
Capital Under Management: $1,510,000,000
Current Activity Level: Actively seeking new investments

EDGEWATER CAPITAL GROUP, INC.
100 North Main Street
Suite 235
Chagrin Falls, OH USA 44022
Phone: 440-893-1600
Fax: 440-893-9060
E-mail: info@edgewatercapital.com
Website: www.edgewatercapital.com

Management and Staff
Chris Childres, President
Edward Sawyer, Founder
Ryan Meany, Vice President

Type of Firm
Private Equity Firm

Project Preferences

Type of Financing Preferred:
Leveraged Buyout

Geographical Preferences

United States Preferences:
All U.S.

Industry Focus
(% based on actual investment)

Other Products	100.0%

Additional Information
Year Founded: 1982
Capital Under Management: $30,000,000
Current Activity Level: Actively seeking new investments

EDGEWATER FUNDS, THE
900 North Michigan Avenue
Suite 1800
Chicago, IL USA 60611
Phone: 312-649-5666
Fax: 312-664-8649
E-mail: info@edgewaterfunds.com
Website: www.edgewaterfunds.com

Management and Staff
David Tolmie, Partner
Gregory Jones, Partner
James Gordon, Managing Partner
Jeffrey Frient, Principal
Robert Growney, Partner
Robert Allison, Venture Partner
Ward McNally, Principal

Type of Firm
Private Equity Firm

Association Membership
Illinois Venture Capital Association

Project Preferences

Role in Financing:
Prefer role as deal originator but will also invest in deals created by others

Type of Financing Preferred:
Leveraged Buyout
Early Stage
Expansion
Generalist PE
Balanced
Public Companies
Later Stage
Management Buyouts
Acquisition
Private Placement
Industry Rollups
Recapitalizations

Size of Investments Considered:
Min Size of Investment Considered (000s): $5,000
Max Size of Investment Considered (000s): $20,000

Geographical Preferences

United States Preferences:
All U.S.

Industry Preferences

In Communications prefer:
Communications and Media
Telecommunications
Data Communications

In Computer Software prefer:
Computer Services
Data Processing
Applications Software

In Internet Specific prefer:
E-Commerce Technology
Internet
Ecommerce

In Consumer Related prefer:
Consumer
Entertainment and Leisure
Food/Beverage
Consumer Products
Consumer Services
Education Related

In Transportation prefer:
Aerospace

In Financial Services prefer:
Financial Services

In Business Serv. prefer:
Services
Distribution
Media

In Manufact. prefer:
Manufacturing

Additional Information
Name of Most Recent Fund: Edgewater Growth Capital Partners III, L.P.
Most Recent Fund Was Raised: 06/05/2009
Year Founded: 1991
Capital Under Management: $538,000,000
Current Activity Level: Actively seeking new investments
Method of Compensation: Return on investment is of primary concern, do not charge fees

---

EDISON VENTURE FUND
1009 Lenox Drive
Suite Four
Lawrenceville, NJ USA 08648
Phone: 609-896-1900
Fax: 609-896-0066
E-mail: info@edisonventure.com
Website: www.edisonventure.com

Other Offices

1025 Andrew Drive
Suite 100
West Chester, PA USA 19380
Phone: 609-873-9212
Fax: 609-896-0066

8405 Greensboro Drive
Suite 210
McLean, VA USA 22102
Phone: 703-903-9546
Fax: 703-903-9528

Eleven Penn Plaza
Fifth floor, Suite 5144
New York, NY USA 10001
Phone: 609-896-1900
Fax: 609-896-0066

117 Kendrick Street
Suite 200
Needham, MA USA 02494
Phone: 718-251-4302
Fax: 609-896-0066

Management and Staff

Christopher Sugden, Managing Partner
Darry Oliver, Chief Financial Officer
Gary Golding, General Partner
John Martinson, Managing Partner
Joseph Allegra, General Partner
Michael Kopelman, Principal
Michael Balmuth, General Partner
Orlando Mendoza, Principal
Ross Martinson, Partner
Ryan Ziegler, Principal
Sever Totia, Principal
Tom Vander Schaaff, Vice President

Type of Firm

Private Equity Firm

Association Membership

Mid-Atlantic Venture Association
National Venture Capital Association - USA (NVCA)
Natl Assoc of Small Bus. Inv. Co (NASBIC)

Project Preferences

Role in Financing:

Prefer role as deal originator but will also invest in deals created by others

Type of Financing Preferred:

Second Stage Financing
Leveraged Buyout
Early Stage
Expansion
Later Stage
Management Buyouts
Recapitalizations

Size of Investments Considered:

Min Size of Investment Considered (000s): $4,000
Max Size of Investment Considered (000s): $8,000

Geographical Preferences

United States Preferences:

Mid Atlantic
Pennsylvania
Delaware
Northeast
Maryland
Virginia
New Jersey
New York

Industry Focus

(% based on actual investment)

Computer Software and Services	45.3%
Internet Specific	17.7%
Other Products	12.2%
Computer Hardware	6.8%
Medical/Health	6.4%
Industrial/Energy	5.2%
Communications and Media	4.1%
Semiconductors/Other Elect.	1.5%
Consumer Related	0.9%

Additional Information

Name of Most Recent Fund: Edison Venture Fund VI
Most Recent Fund Was Raised: 04/26/2006
Year Founded: 1986
Capital Under Management: $680,000,000
Current Activity Level: Actively seeking new investments
Method of Compensation: Return on investment is of primary concern, do not charge fees

---

EDMOND DE ROTHSCHILD CAPITAL PARTNERS

47, rue du Faubourg
Saint Honore
Paris, France 75401
Phone: 33-1-4017-2169
Fax: 33-1-4017-2391
Website: www.lcf-rothschild.fr

Other Offices

Hotel de Saige
23, cours du Chapeau, Rouge
Bordeaux, France 33000
Phone: 33-05-56-44-2066

55, avenue Foch
Lyon, France 69006
Phone: 33-04-72-82-3525

10-12, rue du President
Herriot
Nantes, France 44000

165, avenue du Prado
Marseille Cedex , France 13272
Phone: 33-04-91-29-9080

Management and Staff

Christophe Marchand, Managing Director
Herve Fonta, Partner

Type of Firm

Bank Affiliated

Association Membership

French Venture Capital Association (AFIC)
European Private Equity and Venture Capital Assoc.

Project Preferences

Type of Financing Preferred:

Leveraged Buyout
Balanced

Geographical Preferences

International Preferences:

France

Industry Preferences

In Communications prefer:

Media and Entertainment

In Medical/Health prefer:

Medical/Health

In Consumer Related prefer:

Consumer

In Industrial/Energy prefer:

Industrial Products

In Business Serv. prefer:

Distribution

Additional Information

Name of Most Recent Fund: Edmond de Rothschild LBO Fund
Most Recent Fund Was Raised: 07/31/2003
Year Founded: 2003
Capital Under Management: $688,100,000
Current Activity Level: Actively seeking new investments

EDMOND DE ROTHSCHILD INVESTMENT PARTNERS

47 rue du Faubourg
Saint-Honore
Paris, France 75401
Phone: 33-1-4017-2525
Fax: 33-1-4017-2402
E-mail: info@lcfr.fr
Website: www.lcf-rothschild.fr

Management and Staff

Sylvie Verges, Chief Financial Officer

Type of Firm

Bank Affiliated

Association Membership

French Venture Capital Association (AFIC)
European Private Equity and Venture Capital Assoc.

Project Preferences

Type of Financing Preferred:
Leveraged Buyout
Early Stage
Expansion
Balanced
Seed
Startup

Size of Investments Considered:
Min Size of Investment Considered (000s): $446
Max Size of Investment Considered (000s): $13,371

Geographical Preferences

United States Preferences:
All U.S.

International Preferences:
United Kingdom
Switzerland
Europe
Israel
Germany
France

Industry Preferences

In Communications prefer:
Communications and Media
Telecommunications
Wireless Communications

In Internet Specific prefer:
Internet

In Computer Other prefer:
Computer Related

In Semiconductor/Electr prefer:
Electronics

In Biotechnology prefer:
Biotechnology

In Medical/Health prefer:
Medical/Health
Medical Diagnostics
Medical Therapeutics
Pharmaceuticals

In Consumer Related prefer:
Food/Beverage
Consumer Products

In Industrial/Energy prefer:
Industrial Products
Environmental Related

In Financial Services prefer:
Financial Services

In Business Serv. prefer:
Services
Distribution
Media

In Agr/Forestr/Fish prefer:
Agriculture related

In Other prefer:
Environment Responsible

Additional Information
Name of Most Recent Fund: Winch Capital FCPR
Most Recent Fund Was Raised: 02/02/2006
Year Founded: 1986
Capital Under Management: $693,500,000
Current Activity Level: Actively seeking new investments

EDMOND DE ROTHSCHILD VENTURE CAPITAL MANAGEMENT
The Technology Park
Building 8
Manhat, Jerusalem, Israel 96251
Phone: 972-2-649-0670
Fax: 972-2-649-0680
E-mail: mail@rvcm.co.il
Website: www.rvcm.co.il

Management and Staff
Erick Fouque, President
Samuel Katz, Vice President

Type of Firm
Private Equity Firm

Project Preferences

Type of Financing Preferred:
Balanced

Geographical Preferences

International Preferences:
Israel

Additional Information
Year Founded: 2000
Current Activity Level: Actively seeking new investments

EDP
5/F 105 Piccadilly
London, United Kingdom W1J 7NJ
Phone: 44-20-7318-5300
Fax: 44-20-7318-5313
E-mail: info@edcapital.com
Website: www.edcapital.com

Other Offices
Hovslagargatan 5B, 5tr
Stockholm, Sweden 111 48
Phone: 46-8-407-7470
Fax: 46-8-611-8150

Type of Firm
Private Equity Firm

Project Preferences

Type of Financing Preferred:
Expansion
Balanced
Turnaround

Geographical Preferences

International Preferences:
Europe

Industry Preferences

In Financial Services prefer:
Financial Services

Additional Information
Year Founded: 2000
Current Activity Level: Actively seeking new investments

EFG-HERMES PRIVATE EQUITY (FKA: EFG-HERMES)
9 Mohamed Fahmy Street
Garden City
Cairo, Egypt
Phone: 20-2-2792-3875
Fax: 20-2-2792-3869
E-mail: pegroup@efg-hermes.com
Website: www.efg-hermes.com

Other Offices
Mohamed Darwish El-Dib (Ismailiya)
39 Roshdy
Alexandria, Egypt
Phone: 20-3-544-2100
Fax: 20-3-544-2101

5 Gomhoreya we Assaf Street
Dakahleya
Mansoura, Egypt
Phone: 20-050-229-5300
Fax: 20-050-229-5301

Emirates Towers, 11th Floor
Sheikh Zayed Road
Dubai, Utd. Arab Em.
Phone: 971-4-306-9471
Fax: 971-4-330-0046

Management and Staff
Ayman El Gammal, Managing Director
Gehan Fathi, Partner
Hany Al Sonbaty, Partner
Hazem Shawki, Managing Partner
Kashif Siddiqui, Managing Partner
Samer Yassa, Partner
Walid Zein, Managing Partner

Type of Firm
Bank Affiliated

Association Membership
African Venture Capital Association (AVCA)

Project Preferences

Type of Financing Preferred:
Leveraged Buyout
Early Stage
Expansion
Generalist PE
Balanced
Later Stage
Management Buyouts

Size of Investments Considered:
Min Size of Investment Considered (000s): $500
Max Size of Investment Considered (000s): $7,000

Geographical Preferences

International Preferences:
Jordan
Egypt
Middle East
Africa

Industry Preferences

In Communications prefer:
Communications and Media
Telecommunications

In Consumer Related prefer:
Retail
Food/Beverage

In Industrial/Energy prefer:
Energy
Industrial Products

In Financial Services prefer:
Financial Services
Real Estate

In Agr/Forestr/Fish prefer:
Agribusiness

Additional Information
Year Founded: 1997
Capital Under Management: $1,000,000,000
Current Activity Level: Actively seeking new investments

EFIBANCA PALLADIO FINANZIARIA SGR

Strada Statale
Padana verso Verona, 6
Vicenza, Italy 36100
Phone: 39-444-650-500
Fax: 39-444-650-580
E-mail: vicenza@palladiofinanziaria.it
Website: www.palladiofinanziaria.it

Other Offices
Via Fiori Oscuri, 11
Milan, Italy 20121
Phone: 39-2-7273-0700
Fax: 39-2-7273-0730

Type of Firm
Bank Affiliated

Association Membership
Italian Venture Capital Association (AIFI)

Project Preferences

Type of Financing Preferred:
Leveraged Buyout
Generalist PE

Geographical Preferences

International Preferences:
Italy
France

Industry Preferences

In Communications prefer:
Communications and Media

In Medical/Health prefer:
Medical/Health

In Industrial/Energy prefer:
Industrial Products

Additional Information
Name of Most Recent Fund: Star Bridge Social Responsible Fund
Most Recent Fund Was Raised: 04/07/2006
Year Founded: 2003
Capital Under Management: $186,900,000
Current Activity Level: Actively seeking new investments

EFIBANCA SPA

Via Boncompagni, 71
Rome, Italy 00187
Phone: 39-06-4229-8791
Fax: 39-06-4229-8902
E-mail: efibanca@bipielle.it
Website: www.efibanca.it

Other Offices
Via S. Vittore al Teatro, 1
Milan, Italy 20121

Type of Firm
Bank Affiliated

Association Membership
Italian Venture Capital Association (AIFI)
European Private Equity and Venture Capital Assoc.

Project Preferences

Type of Financing Preferred:
Leveraged Buyout
Expansion
Generalist PE
Turnaround
Later Stage
Recapitalizations

Size of Investments Considered:
Min Size of Investment Considered (000s): $6,340
Max Size of Investment Considered (000s): $50,723

Geographical Preferences

International Preferences:
Italy

Industry Focus
(% based on actual investment)

Other Products	56.3%
Consumer Related	23.5%
Industrial/Energy	16.7%
Communications and Media	3.2%
Internet Specific	0.4%

Additional Information
Year Founded: 1999
Capital Under Management: $434,900,000
Current Activity Level: Actively seeking new investments

EFO HOLDINGS, L.P.

2828 Routh
Suite 500
Dallas, TX USA 75201
Phone: 214-849-9800
Fax: 214-849-9807
E-mail: info@efoholdings.com
Website: www.efoholdings.com

Management and Staff
William Esping, General Partner

Type of Firm
Private Equity Firm

Project Preferences

Type of Financing Preferred:
Leveraged Buyout
Expansion
Generalist PE
Balanced
Acquisition

Geographical Preferences

United States Preferences:
All U.S.

Industry Focus
(% based on actual investment)

Industrial/Energy	75.5%
Computer Software and Services	16.4%
Other Products	8.1%

Additional Information
Year Founded: 1994
Current Activity Level: Actively seeking new investments

EFUND, LLC

10500 North East Eighth Street
Suite 1550
Bellevue, WA USA 98004
Phone: 206-389-4901
Fax: 206-389-4901
Website: www.efundllc.com

Management and Staff

Daniel Kranzler, Managing Partner
Jeff Canin, Partner
Joe Tanous, Partner
John Forbes, Partner

Type of Firm

Private Equity Firm

Project Preferences

Type of Financing Preferred:
Early Stage

Industry Preferences

In Communications prefer:
Communications and Media

In Internet Specific prefer:
Internet

Additional Information

Year Founded: 1999
Current Activity Level: Actively seeking new investments

EG CAPITAL GROUP LLC

39 West 54th Street
New York, NY USA 10019
Phone: 212-956-2600
Fax: 212-956-2699
Website: www.egcapitalgroup.com

Management and Staff

Jay Eastman, Managing Director

Type of Firm

Private Equity Firm

Project Preferences

Type of Financing Preferred:
Leveraged Buyout

Geographical Preferences

United States Preferences:
All U.S.

Canadian Preferences:
All Canada

Industry Preferences

In Consumer Related prefer:
Retail
Food/Beverage
Other Restaurants

Additional Information

Year Founded: 2003
Current Activity Level: Actively seeking new investments

EGAN-MANAGED CAPITAL

30 Federal Street
Boston, MA USA 02110
Phone: 617-695-2600
Fax: 617-695-2699
Website: www.egancapital.com

Management and Staff

Frank Andrasco, Partner
John Egan, Managing Partner
Michael Shanahan, Managing Partner
Travis Connors, Partner

Type of Firm

Private Equity Firm

Association Membership

New England Venture Capital Association

Project Preferences

Role in Financing:
Will function either as deal originator or investor in deals created by others

Type of Financing Preferred:
Early Stage
Seed
First Stage Financing
Startup

Size of Investments Considered:
Min Size of Investment Considered (000s): $2,000
Max Size of Investment Considered (000s): $5,000

Geographical Preferences

United States Preferences:
Northeast

Industry Focus

(% based on actual investment)

Internet Specific	46.7%
Computer Software and Services	42.3%
Semiconductors/Other Elect.	7.5%
Communications and Media	2.1%
Computer Hardware	1.4%

Additional Information

Name of Most Recent Fund: Egan-Managed Capital III
Most Recent Fund Was Raised: 10/01/2003
Year Founded: 1997
Capital Under Management: $233,000,000
Current Activity Level: Actively seeking new investments
Method of Compensation: Return on investment is of primary concern, do not charge fees

EGARDEN VENTURES HONG KONG, LTD.

4/F, New East Ocean Center
9 Science Museum Road
Kowloon, Hong Kong
Phone: 852-2311-7996
Fax: 852-2312-1909
Website: www.egardenvc.com

Type of Firm

Private Equity Firm

Project Preferences

Type of Financing Preferred:
Balanced

Geographical Preferences

International Preferences:
China
Asia

Industry Preferences

In Communications prefer:
Telecommunications
Wireless Communications
Media and Entertainment

In Internet Specific prefer:
Internet

In Medical/Health prefer:
Health Services

In Consumer Related prefer:
Consumer Products

Additional Information

Year Founded: 2000
Current Activity Level: Actively seeking new investments

EGERIA B.V.

Nieuwe Herengracht 51
Amsterdam, Netherlands 1011 RN
Phone: 31-20-530-6868
Fax: 31-20-530-6869
E-mail: egeria@egeria.nl
Website: www.egeria.nl

Management and Staff

Jan Niessen, Managing Partner

Type of Firm

Private Equity Firm

Association Membership

European Private Equity and Venture Capital Assoc.

Project Preferences

Type of Financing Preferred:
Leveraged Buyout

Expansion
Mezzanine
Management Buyouts
Recapitalizations

Size of Investments Considered:
Min Size of Investment Considered (000s): $20,970
Max Size of Investment Considered (000s): $69,901

Geographical Preferences

International Preferences:
Netherlands
Europe
Germany

Industry Preferences

In Communications prefer:
Communications and Media

In Medical/Health prefer:
Medical/Health

In Consumer Related prefer:
Consumer

In Industrial/Energy prefer:
Energy
Industrial Products

Additional Information
Year Founded: 1997
Capital Under Management: $1,537,800,000
Current Activity Level: Actively seeking new investments

EGIS CAPITAL PARTNERS LLC
Four Becker Farm Road
Roseland, NJ USA 07068
Phone: 973-994-1172
Fax: 973-992-6336
Website: www.egiscp.com

Management and Staff
Joe Falkenstein, Founding Partner
John Mack, Founding Partner
Robert Chefitz, Founding Partner

Type of Firm
Private Equity Firm

Project Preferences

Type of Financing Preferred:
Leveraged Buyout
Management Buyouts

Size of Investments Considered:
Min Size of Investment Considered (000s): $5,000
Max Size of Investment Considered (000s): $40,000

Geographical Preferences

United States Preferences:
Virginia
New Jersey
California

Canadian Preferences:
All Canada

Additional Information
Year Founded: 1997
Capital Under Management: $3,700,000
Current Activity Level: Actively seeking new investments

EGS BETEILIGUNGEN AG
Dufourstrasse 29
Zurich, Switzerland 8032
Phone: 41-44-250-75-00
Website: www.egs-beteiligungen.ch

Management and Staff
Dominik Sauter, Chief Executive Officer

Type of Firm
Private Equity Firm

Project Preferences

Type of Financing Preferred:
Balanced
Management Buyouts

Geographical Preferences

International Preferences:
Switzerland

Industry Preferences

In Business Serv. prefer:
Services

Additional Information
Year Founded: 2009
Current Activity Level: Actively seeking new investments

EGS HEALTHCARE CAPITAL PARTNERS, LLC
One Lafayette Place
Second Floor
Greenwich, CT USA 06830
Phone: 203-422-0581
Fax: 203-422-0574
E-mail: info@egshealthcare.com
Website: www.egshealthcare.com

Management and Staff
Abhijeet Lele, General Partner
Frederic Greenberg, General Partner
Terry Vance, General Partner

Type of Firm
Private Equity Firm

Project Preferences

Role in Financing:
Prefer role as deal originator

Type of Financing Preferred:
Expansion
Public Companies
Later Stage

Geographical Preferences

United States Preferences:
Massachusetts
California

Industry Preferences

In Biotechnology prefer:
Biotechnology

In Medical/Health prefer:
Medical Products
Health Services
Pharmaceuticals

Additional Information
Year Founded: 1999
Capital Under Management: $135,000,000
Current Activity Level: Actively seeking new investments

EGS PARTNERS
Route De Soleure 12
St-Blaise, Switzerland 2072
Phone: 032-753-0270
Fax: 032-753-0275
Website: www.eg-software.com

Type of Firm
Private Equity Firm

Additional Information
Year Founded: 1989
Current Activity Level: Actively seeking new investments

EGYPT KUWAIT HOLDING COMPANY
Hassan Mohamed El Razzaz St.
Agouza
Giza, Egypt
Phone: 202-336-3300
Fax: 202-335-8989
E-mail: info@ekholding.com
Website: www.ekholding.com

Management and Staff
Moataz Al-Alfi, Managing Director

Type of Firm
Private Equity Firm

Project Preferences

Type of Financing Preferred:
Balanced

Geographical Preferences

International Preferences:
Egypt
Kuwait

Additional Information

Year Founded: 1997
Current Activity Level: Actively seeking new investments

EIG VENTURE CAPITAL, LTD. (AKA: EVC)

Sveavagen 74
Stockholm, Sweden 113 59
Phone: 46-8-440-2600
Fax: 46-8-411-2460
E-mail: evc@eigcapital.com
Website: www.eigcapital.com

Other Offices

P.O. Box 925
Marbella, Spain 29600
Phone: 34-952-766-250
Fax: 34-952-858-068

Type of Firm

Private Equity Firm
Association Membership
European Private Equity and Venture Capital Assoc.

Project Preferences

Type of Financing Preferred:
Early Stage
Balanced
Seed
Startup

Geographical Preferences

International Preferences:
Sweden

Additional Information

Year Founded: 2001
Current Activity Level: Actively seeking new investments

EINDIA VENTURE MANAGEMENT

001,Turf Estate
Shakti Mills Lane, Mahalakshmi
Mumbai, India 400 011
Phone: 91-22-2490-2201
Fax: 91-22-2490-2205
Website: www.eindiaventure.com

Other Offices

515 Madison Avenue 53rd Street
21st Floor
New York, NY USA 10022
Phone: 212-838-6360
Fax: 212-838-7818

Management and Staff

Gaurav Dalmia, Venture Partner
Mehool Parekh, Managing Partner
Nilesh Mehta, Managing Partner
Pravin Gandhi, Venture Partner
Saurabh Srivastava, Venture Partner

Type of Firm

Private Equity Firm

Association Membership

Indian Venture Capital Association (IVCA)

Project Preferences

Type of Financing Preferred:
Early Stage
Mezzanine
Startup

Size of Investments Considered:
Min Size of Investment Considered (000s): $1,000
Max Size of Investment Considered (000s): $5,000

Geographical Preferences

International Preferences:
India
Europe
Singapore

Industry Preferences

In Communications prefer:
Communications and Media
Telecommunications

In Computer Software prefer:
Software

In Computer Other prefer:
Computer Related

In Semiconductor/Electr prefer:
Electronics

Additional Information

Year Founded: 2000
Capital Under Management: $18,000,000
Current Activity Level: Actively seeking new investments

EK MITTELSTANDSFINANZIERUNGS AG

Operngasse 6
Vienna, Austria 1010
Phone: 43-1-532897911
Fax: 43-1-513220115
E-mail: office@ekfin.at
Website: www.ekfin.at

Type of Firm

Private Equity Firm

Association Membership

European Private Equity and Venture Capital Assoc.

Project Preferences

Type of Financing Preferred:
Leveraged Buyout
Expansion

Geographical Preferences

International Preferences:
Austria

Additional Information

Year Founded: 2002
Capital Under Management: $48,800,000
Current Activity Level: Actively seeking new investments

EKK DR. ENGELHARDT, KAUPP, KIEFER BETEILIGUNGSBERATUNG GMBH

Marienstrasse 39
Berlin, Germany 70178
Phone: 49-7115-1876400
E-mail: info@EKK-Beteiligungen.de
Website: www.ekk-beteiligungen.de

Other Offices

Leipziger Platz 7
Berlin, Germany 10117

Management and Staff

Betina Fecker, Partner
Georg Kiefer, Managing Director
Karl Friedrich Kaupp, Managing Director
Thomas Heiden, Partner
Tobias Engelhardt, Managing Director
Volker Horst, Partner

Type of Firm

Private Equity Firm

Project Preferences

Type of Financing Preferred:
Expansion
Start-up Financing

Additional Information

Year Founded: 2004
Current Activity Level: Actively seeking new investments

EKO INVESTORS

Brivibas iela 85
Riga, Latvia
Phone: 371-7843-794
Fax: 371-7843-765
Website: www.ekoinvestors.lv

Type of Firm

Private Equity Firm

Project Preferences

Type of Financing Preferred:
Generalist PE

Geographical Preferences

International Preferences:
Latvia

Additional Information

Year Founded: 2004
Capital Under Management: $19,500,000
Current Activity Level: Actively seeking new investments

EL DORADO VENTURES

2440 Sand Hill Road
Suite 200
Menlo Park, CA USA 94025
Phone: 650-854-1200
Fax: 650-854-1202
E-mail: info@eldorado.com
Website: www.eldorado.com

Other Offices

601 Carlson Parkway
Suite 600
Minnetonka, MN USA 55305
Phone: 952-995-7499
Fax: 952-995-7493

Management and Staff

Charles Beeler, General Partner
Gary Kalbach, Founding Partner
Jeffrey Hinck, General Partner
Jim Kunse, Chief Financial Officer
Michael Scott Irwin, General Partner
Ray Schuder, Principal
Shanda Bahles, Venture Partner
Thomas Peterson, General Partner

Type of Firm

Private Equity Firm

Association Membership

Western Association of Venture Capitalists (WAVC)
Natl Assoc of Small Bus. Inv. Co (NASBIC)

Project Preferences

Role in Financing:
Prefer role as deal originator but will also invest in deals created by others

Type of Financing Preferred:
Early Stage
Seed
First Stage Financing
Startup

Size of Investments Considered:
Min Size of Investment Considered (000s): $500
Max Size of Investment Considered (000s): $4,000

Geographical Preferences

United States Preferences:
West Coast

Industry Focus

(% based on actual investment)

Internet Specific	27.4%
Computer Software and Services	25.1%
Semiconductors/Other Elect.	18.1%
Communications and Media	17.5%
Computer Hardware	5.5%
Consumer Related	3.5%
Medical/Health	1.3%
Other Products	1.0%
Industrial/Energy	0.4%
Biotechnology	0.3%

Additional Information

Year Founded: 1986
Capital Under Management: $750,000,000
Current Activity Level: Actively seeking new investments
Method of Compensation: Return on investment is of primary concern, do not charge fees

ELAB TECHNOLOGY VENTURES INC.

One Richmond Street West
Eight Floor
Toronto, Canada M5H3W4
Phone: 416-313-5206
Fax: 416-313-5200
Website: www.elabventure.com

Type of Firm

Private Equity Firm

Additional Information

Year Founded: 2001
Current Activity Level: Actively seeking new investments

ELADDAN CAPITAL PARTNERS

48 St. Clair Avenue West
Suite 1100
Toronto, Canada M4V2Z2
Phone: 416-961-9956
Fax: 416-961-0696

Type of Firm

Private Equity Firm

Additional Information

Year Founded: 1997
Current Activity Level: Actively seeking new investments

ELAIA PARTNERS

54, rue de Ponthieu
Paris, France 75008
Phone: 33-1-7674-9250
Fax: 33-1-7674-9260
Website: www.elaia.fr

Management and Staff

Marie Ekeland, Partner
Maryline Kulawik, Venture Partner
Philippe Gire, Partner
Xavier Lazarus, Partner

Type of Firm

Private Equity Firm

Association Membership

French Venture Capital Association (AFIC)

Project Preferences

Type of Financing Preferred:
Leveraged Buyout
Early Stage
Expansion
Balanced
Turnaround
Seed
Startup

Size of Investments Considered:
Min Size of Investment Considered (000s): $650
Max Size of Investment Considered (000s): $5,220

Geographical Preferences

International Preferences:
United Kingdom
Europe
France
All International

Industry Preferences

In Computer Software prefer:
Software

In Computer Other prefer:
Computer Related

In Business Serv. prefer:
Services

Additional Information

Year Founded: 2002
Capital Under Management: $59,600,000
Current Activity Level: Actively seeking new investments

ELDERSTREET INVESTMENTS LIMITED

32 Bedford Row
London, United Kingdom WC1R 4HE
Phone: 44-20-7831-5088
Fax: 44-20-7831-5077
Website: www.elderstreet.com

Management and Staff

Barnaby Terry, Partner
Paul Frew, Partner
Vin Murria, Partner

Type of Firm

Private Equity Firm

Association Membership

European Private Equity and Venture Capital Assoc.

Project Preferences

Type of Financing Preferred:

Leveraged Buyout
Generalist PE
Early Stage
Expansion
Turnaround
Seed
Management Buyouts
Recapitalizations

Size of Investments Considered:

Min Size of Investment Considered (000s): $400
Max Size of Investment Considered (000s): $400,000

Geographical Preferences

International Preferences:

United Kingdom
Western Europe

Industry Focus

(% based on actual investment)

Internet Specific	44.5%
Computer Software and Services	43.8%
Communications and Media	5.8%
Consumer Related	3.1%
Semiconductors/Other Elect.	1.9%
Other Products	0.9%

Additional Information

Year Founded: 1990
Capital Under Management: $169,800,000
Current Activity Level: Actively seeking new investments

ELEMENT PARTNERS (FKA: DFJ ELEMENT, L.P.)

Three Radnor Corporate Centre
Suite 410, 100 Matsonford Rd.
Radnor, PA USA 19087
Phone: 610-964-8004
Fax: 610-964-8005
E-mail: info@elementpartners.com
Website: www.elementpartners.com

Other Offices

2882 Sand Hill Road
Suite 150
Menlo Park, CA USA 94025
Phone: 650-234-8500
Fax: 650-234-8533

Management and Staff

David Lincoln, Managing Director
John Rockwell, Managing Director
Michael Todd, Chief Financial Officer
Michael Bevan, Managing Director
Michael DeRosa, Managing Director
Sam Gabbita, Principal

Type of Firm

Private Equity Firm

Association Membership

National Venture Capital Association - USA (NVCA)

Project Preferences

Role in Financing:

Prefer role as deal originator but will also invest in deals created by others

Type of Financing Preferred:

Expansion
Early Stage

Size of Investments Considered:

Min Size of Investment Considered (000s): $1,000
Max Size of Investment Considered (000s): $35,000

Geographical Preferences

United States Preferences:

All U.S.

Industry Preferences

In Semiconductor/Electr prefer:

Controllers and Sensors
Sensors

In Biotechnology prefer:

Industrial Biotechnology
Biosensors

In Industrial/Energy prefer:

Energy
Oil and Gas Exploration
Oil & Gas Drilling,Explor
Alternative Energy
Coal Related
Energy Conservation Relat
Industrial Products
Materials
Advanced Materials
Superconductivity
Factory Automation
Process Control
Robotics
Environmental Related

In Transportation prefer:

Transportation

In Manufact. prefer:

Manufacturing

In Agr/Forestr/Fish prefer:

Agriculture related
Mining and Minerals

In Other prefer:

Socially Responsible
Environment Responsible

Additional Information

Name of Most Recent Fund: Element Partners II, L.P.
Most Recent Fund Was Raised: 04/30/2008
Year Founded: 2006
Capital Under Management: $800,000,000
Current Activity Level: Actively seeking new investments

ELEVATION ASSOCIATES LLC

2800 Sand Hill Road
Suite 160
Menlo Park, CA USA 94025
Phone: 650-687-6700
Fax: 650-687-6710
E-mail: info@elevation.com
Website: www.elevation.com

Other Offices

70 East 55th Street
12th Floor
New York, NY USA 10022
Phone: 212-317-6555
Fax: 212-317-6556

Management and Staff

Adam Hopkins, Principal
Bret Pearlman, Managing Director
Fred Anderson, Managing Director
Kevin Albert, Managing Director
Marc Bodnick, Managing Director
Martin Fichtner, Principal
Patty Halfen, Principal
Paul David Hewson, Managing Director
Roger McNamee, Managing Director
Sherwin Chen, Principal
Tracy Hogan, Chief Financial Officer

Type of Firm

Private Equity Firm

Project Preferences

Type of Financing Preferred:

Generalist PE
Later Stage

Industry Preferences

In Communications prefer:

Data Communications
Media and Entertainment

In Consumer Related prefer:
Consumer Services

In Business Serv. prefer:
Media

Additional Information

Name of Most Recent Fund: Elevation Partners, L.P.
Most Recent Fund Was Raised: 09/03/2004
Year Founded: 2004
Capital Under Management: $211,000,000
Current Activity Level: Actively seeking new investments

ELLERINE BROS. (PTY) LTD

51 West Street
Houghton, South Africa
Phone: 27-11-483-4700
Fax: 27-11-483-1554

Type of Firm

Private Equity Advisor or Fund of Funds

Association Membership

South African Venture Capital Association (SAVCA)

Project Preferences

Type of Financing Preferred:
Balanced

Geographical Preferences

International Preferences:
Africa

Additional Information

Year Founded: 2004
Current Activity Level: Actively seeking new investments

ELM CREEK PARTNERS

300 Crescent Court
Suite 1000
Dallas, TX USA 75201
Phone: 214-871-5650
Fax: 214-975-5650
Website: www.elmcreekpartners.com

Management and Staff

Aaron Handler, Founder
Zach Wooldridge, Founder

Type of Firm

Private Equity Firm

Project Preferences

Type of Financing Preferred:
Leveraged Buyout
Acquisition

Size of Investments Considered:

Min Size of Investment Considered (000s): $3,000
Max Size of Investment Considered (000s): $6,000

Industry Preferences

In Financial Services prefer:
Financial Services

In Business Serv. prefer:
Distribution

In Manufact. prefer:
Manufacturing

Additional Information

Year Founded: 2008
Current Activity Level: Actively seeking new investments

ELM STREET VENTURES

300 George Street
New Haven, CT USA 06511
Phone: 203-401-4201
Fax: 203-401-4235
E-mail: venture@elmvc.com
Website: www.elmvc.com

Management and Staff

Gregory Gardiner, Partner
Michael Sherman, Partner
Rob Bettigole, Managing Partner
Thomas Wood, Partner

Type of Firm

Private Equity Firm

Association Membership

National Venture Capital Association - USA (NVCA)

Project Preferences

Role in Financing:
Will function either as deal originator or investor in deals created by others

Type of Financing Preferred:
Early Stage
Seed

Geographical Preferences

United States Preferences:
New York

Industry Preferences

In Computer Software prefer:
Software

In Internet Specific prefer:
Internet
Ecommerce

In Biotechnology prefer:
Human Biotechnology
Genetic Engineering
Agricultural/Animal Bio.
Industrial Biotechnology
Biosensors
Biotech Related Research

In Medical/Health prefer:
Medical Diagnostics
Diagnostic Services
Diagnostic Test Products
Medical Therapeutics
Drug/Equipmt Delivery
Medical Products
Disposable Med. Products
Health Services
Hospitals/Clinics/Primary
Hospital/Other Instit.
Pharmaceuticals

Additional Information

Name of Most Recent Fund: Elm Street Ventures, L.P.
Most Recent Fund Was Raised: 02/21/2006
Year Founded: 2004
Capital Under Management: $22,000,000
Current Activity Level: Actively seeking new investments

ELNOS

31 Nova Scotia Walk, 3rd Floor
Elliot Lake, Canada P5A1V9
Phone: 705-256-7299
Fax: 705-848-1539

Management and Staff

John Stenger, Chief Operating Officer

Type of Firm

Private Equity Firm

Geographical Preferences

Canadian Preferences:
All Canada

Additional Information

Year Founded: 1993
Current Activity Level: Actively seeking new investments

ELRON ELECTRONIC INDUSTRIES

The Triangle Building, 42nd Fl
3 Azrieli Center
Tel Aviv, Israel 67023
Phone: 972-3-607-5555
Fax: 972-3-6075556
E-mail: elron@elron.net
Website: www.elron.com

Type of Firm

Corporate PE/Venture

Additional Information

Year Founded: 2002

Current Activity Level: Actively seeking new investments

ELYSIAN CAPITAL

Ingram House
15 John Adam Street
London, United Kingdom WC2N 6LU
Phone: 44-20-7925-8050
Fax: 44-207-925-8069
Website: www.elysiancapital.com

Type of Firm

Private Equity Firm

Project Preferences

Type of Financing Preferred:
Leveraged Buyout
Mezzanine
Management Buyouts

Size of Investments Considered:
Min Size of Investment Considered (000s): $19,680
Max Size of Investment Considered (000s): $137,760

Geographical Preferences

International Preferences:
United Kingdom

Additional Information

Year Founded: 2008
Current Activity Level: Actively seeking new investments

EMALTERNATIVES LLC

1010 Wisconsin Avenue NW
Suite 520
Washington, DC USA 20007
Phone: 202-659-5959
Fax: 202-659-5960
E-mail: info@emalternatives.com
Website: www.emalternatives.com

Other Offices

6th Floor, Building Kennemerhaghe
Leidsevaartweg 99
Heemstede, Netherlands 2106 AS
Phone: 31-23-510-0560
Fax: 31-23-510-0569

Level 5, North Block
159 Madang Road
Shanghai, China 200021
Phone: 86-21-6135-7208
Fax: 86-21-6135-7207

Management and Staff

Alexandra Gardiner, Chief Financial Officer
John Stephens, Managing Partner
Nicholas Morriss, Managing Partner

Type of Firm

Private Equity Advisor or Fund of Funds

Project Preferences

Type of Financing Preferred:
Fund of Funds

Geographical Preferences

International Preferences:
India
Soviet Union
Latin America
Central Europe
China
Eastern Europe
Middle East
Australia
Asia
Korea, South
Japan
Africa

Additional Information

Year Founded: 2007
Current Activity Level: Actively seeking new investments

EMANO AB

Vasagatan 1
Umea, Sweden 903 29
Phone: 46-90-702-150
Fax: 46-90-702-155
E-mail: info@emano.se
Website: www.emano.se

Management and Staff

Tomas Lindstrom, Managing Director

Type of Firm

Private Equity Firm

Association Membership

Swedish Venture Capital Association (SVCA)
European Private Equity and Venture Capital Assoc.

Project Preferences

Type of Financing Preferred:
Leveraged Buyout
Expansion
Startup

Size of Investments Considered:
Min Size of Investment Considered (000s): $106
Max Size of Investment Considered (000s): $1,593

Geographical Preferences

International Preferences:
Scandanavia/Nordic Region

Additional Information

Year Founded: 1998
Capital Under Management: $20,900,000
Current Activity Level: Actively seeking new investments

EMBL VENTURE CAPITAL PARTNERS GMBH

Boxbergring 107
Heidelberg, Germany D-69126
Phone: 49-62-2138-9330
Fax: 49-62-2138-9331
E-mail: info@embl-ventures.com
Website: www.embl-ventures.com

Management and Staff

Christof Antz, Managing Partner
Stefan Herr, Managing Partner

Type of Firm

University Program

Association Membership

European Private Equity and Venture Capital Assoc.

Project Preferences

Type of Financing Preferred:
Early Stage
Seed
Startup

Size of Investments Considered:
Min Size of Investment Considered (000s): $60
Max Size of Investment Considered (000s): $12,000

Geographical Preferences

International Preferences:
Europe
Germany

Industry Preferences

In Medical/Health prefer:
Medical Diagnostics
Medical Therapeutics

In Industrial/Energy prefer:
Advanced Materials

Additional Information

Name of Most Recent Fund: EMBL Technology Fund
Most Recent Fund Was Raised: 12/06/2001
Year Founded: 2001
Capital Under Management: $31,600,000
Current Activity Level: Actively seeking new investments

EMEDICI CAPITAL, INC. (ACCOLADE CAPITAL, INC.)

427 Eleventh Avenue North East
Calgary, Canada T2E0Z4
Phone: 403-701-2700
Fax: 403-221-0909
Website: www.emedici.net/accolade_capital.shtml

Management and Staff

Grant Howard, President
Stace Wills, Managing Partner

Type of Firm

Private Equity Firm

Project Preferences

Type of Financing Preferred:
Seed

Geographical Preferences

Canadian Preferences:
All Canada

Additional Information

Year Founded: 2009
Current Activity Level: Actively seeking new investments

EMERALD HILL CAPITAL PARTNERS, LTD.

16 Ice House Street
19th Floor
Central, Hong Kong
Phone: 852-2248-8000
Fax: 852-2248-8001
E-mail: info@ehcp.com
Website: www.ehcp.com

Other Offices

1512 Larimer Street
Suite 200
Denver, CO USA 80202
Phone: 303-825-3550
Fax: 303-825-1874

Management and Staff

David Spencer, Managing Director
Michael Smith, Managing Director & CFO
S. Eugene Choung, Managing Director
Tommy Y. Yip, Principal

Type of Firm

Private Equity Advisor or Fund of Funds

Project Preferences

Type of Financing Preferred:
Fund of Funds

Geographical Preferences

International Preferences:
Asia

Additional Information

Year Founded: 2005
Capital Under Management: $164,200,000
Current Activity Level: Actively seeking new investments

EMERALD STAGE2 VENTURES (AKA: STAGE2 CAPITAL VENTURES)

4801 South Broad Street
Suite 400
Philadelphia, PA USA 19112
Phone: 215-972-1502
Fax: 215-689-4886
E-mail: bizplans@s2vc.com
Website: www.s2vc.com

Other Offices

500 North Gulph Road
Suite 101
King of Prussia, PA USA 19406
Phone: 610-994-4929
Fax: 215-689-4886

Management and Staff

Bruce Luehrs, Partner
Saul Richter, Managing Partner

Type of Firm

Private Equity Firm

Association Membership

National Venture Capital Association - USA (NVCA)

Project Preferences

Role in Financing:
Prefer role as deal originator but will also invest in deals created by others

Type of Financing Preferred:
Early Stage

Size of Investments Considered:
Min Size of Investment Considered (000s): $400
Max Size of Investment Considered (000s): $1,250

Geographical Preferences

United States Preferences:
Mid Atlantic
Pennsylvania
Delaware
Washington
New Jersey
New York
Industry Preferences

In Computer Software prefer:
Computer Services

In Medical/Health prefer:
Medical/Health

In Financial Services prefer:
Financial Services

Additional Information

Name of Most Recent Fund: Emerald Stage2 Ventures, LP (FKA: Stage2 Capital Ventures)
Most Recent Fund Was Raised: 03/05/2008
Year Founded: 2008
Capital Under Management: $13,600,000
Current Activity Level: Actively seeking new investments
Method of Compensation: Return on investment is of primary concern, do not charge fees

EMERALD TECHNOLOGY VENTURES (FKA:SAM SUSTAINABLE ASSET MNGT)

Seefeldstrasse 215
Zurich, Switzerland 8008
Phone: 41-44-269-61-00
Fax: 41-44-269-61-01
E-mail: info@emerald-ventures.com
Website: www.emerald-ventures.com

Other Offices

999, Boul. De Maisonneuve O.
Suite 1700
Montreal, Canada H3A 3L4
Phone: 514-789-6441
Fax: 514-286-9817

Management and Staff

Charles Vaslet, Partner
Gianni Operto, Partner
Gina Domanig, Managing Partner
Hans Dellenbach, Chief Financial Officer
Luc Charron, Partner
Markus Moor, Partner
Peter Crombie, Partner
Scott MacDonald, Partner
Whitney Rockley, General Partner

Type of Firm

Private Equity Firm

Association Membership

Swiss Venture Capital Association (SECA)

Project Preferences

Role in Financing:
Will function either as deal originator or investor in deals created by others

Type of Financing Preferred:
Early Stage
Expansion
Balanced
Startup

Size of Investments Considered:
Min Size of Investment Considered (000s): $2,987
Max Size of Investment Considered (000s): $14,936

Geographical Preferences

United States Preferences:
All U.S.

Canadian Preferences:
All Canada

International Preferences:
Europe

Industry Preferences

In Semiconductor/Electr prefer:
Semiconductor

In Industrial/Energy prefer:
Energy
Alternative Energy
Coal Related
Materials
Environmental Related

Additional Information
Name of Most Recent Fund: Emerald Technology Ventures II, L.P.
Most Recent Fund Was Raised: 03/29/2007
Year Founded: 2000
Capital Under Management: $473,600,000
Current Activity Level: Actively seeking new investments

EMERGE VENTURE CAPITAL (AKA: EMERGE VC)
70 Danbury Road
Second Floor
Wilton, CT USA 06897
Phone: 203-210-7477
E-mail: info@emergevc.com
Website: www.emergevc.com

Management and Staff
Geoff Schneider, Managing Partner
Kevin Lynch, Chief Financial Officer

Type of Firm
Private Equity Firm

Project Preferences

Type of Financing Preferred:
Early Stage
Seed

Additional Information
Year Founded: 2008
Current Activity Level: Actively seeking new investments

EMERGENCE CAPITAL PARTNERS LLC
160 Bovet Road
Suite 300
San Mateo, CA USA 94402
Phone: 650-573-3100
Fax: 650-573-3119
E-mail: info@emcap.com
Website: www.emcap.com

Management and Staff
Brian Jacobs, General Partner
Gordon Ritter, General Partner
Jason Green, General Partner
Jeffrey Stiefler, Venture Partner
John Dillon, Venture Partner
Kevin Spain, Principal
Margot Giusti, Chief Financial Officer
Richard Yanowitch, Venture Partner

Type of Firm
Private Equity Firm

Association Membership
National Venture Capital Association - USA (NVCA)

Project Preferences

Role in Financing:
Prefer role as deal originator but will also invest in deals created by others

Type of Financing Preferred:
Early Stage
Expansion
Start-up Financing
Seed

Size of Investments Considered:
Min Size of Investment Considered (000s): $1,000
Max Size of Investment Considered (000s): $15,000

Geographical Preferences

United States Preferences:
All U.S.

Industry Preferences

In Computer Software prefer:
Computer Services
Software

Internet Specific prefer:
Internet

In Semiconductor/Electr prefer:
Electronics

In Consumer Related prefer:
Consumer Services

In Financial Services prefer:
Financial Services

In Business Serv. prefer:
Services

Additional Information
Name of Most Recent Fund: Emergence Capital Partners II, L.P.
Most Recent Fund Was Raised: 06/21/2007
Year Founded: 2003
Capital Under Management: $347,100,000
Current Activity Level: Actively seeking new investments
Method of Compensation: Return on investment is of primary concern, do not charge fees

---

EMERGENCES
12 cours Xavier Arnozan
Bordeaux, France 33000
Phone: 33-5-5644-0407
Fax: 33-5-5679-3311
Website: www.emergences.com

Type of Firm
Service Provider

Project Preferences

Type of Financing Preferred:
Leveraged Buyout
Early Stage
Expansion
Seed
Startup

Geographical Preferences

International Preferences:
France

Additional Information
Year Founded: 2001
Capital Under Management: $800,000
Current Activity Level: Actively seeking new investments

EMERGENT MEDICAL VENTURES, LLP
3282 Alpine Road
Portola Valley, CA USA 94028
Phone: 650-851-0091
Fax: 650-851-0095
Website: www.emvllp.com

Management and Staff
Allan May, Managing Director
Chris Adams, Chief Financial Officer
Robert Brownell, Managing Director
Thomas Fogarty, Managing Director

Type of Firm
Private Equity Firm

Project Preferences

Role in Financing:
Will function either as deal originator or investor in deals created by others

Type of Financing Preferred:
Early Stage

Size of Investments Considered:
Min Size of Investment Considered (000s): $200
Max Size of Investment Considered (000s): $8,000

Geographical Preferences

United States Preferences:
All U.S.

Industry Preferences

In Medical/Health prefer:
Medical Diagnostics
Diagnostic Services
Diagnostic Test Products
Medical Therapeutics
Drug/Equipmt Delivery
Medical Products
Disposable Med. Products
Health Services
Hospitals/Clinics/Primary
Hospital/Other Instit.
Pharmaceuticals

Additional Information
Year Founded: 2007
Capital Under Management: $70,000,000
Current Activity Level: Actively seeking new investments
Method of Compensation: Return on investment is of primary concern, do not charge fees

---

EMERGING ISV CAPITAL PARTNERS
179 Riverview Circle SouthEast
Calgary, Canada T2C4J9
Phone: 403-560-5469
E-mail: info@emergingisv.com
Website: www.emergingisv.com

Management and Staff
Brent Stankowski, General Partner
Kevin Hein, General Partner
Richard Weston, Venture Partner

Type of Firm
Private Equity Firm

Additional Information
Year Founded: 2009
Current Activity Level: Actively seeking new investments

EMERGING MARKETS PARTNERSHIP
2020 K Street Northwest
Suite 400
Washington, DC USA 20006
Phone: 202-331-9051
Fax: 202-331-9250
E-mail: inquiries@empw.com
Website: www.empwdc.com

Other Offices
Unit 1-4, Ground Floor
RBA Plaza, Bandar Seri Begawan
Negara Darussalam , Brunei BS 8811
Phone: 673-2-222-920
Fax: 673-2-22-923

10th Floor, Al Salam Tower, Bldg. 722
Road No. 1708, Diplomatic Area
Manama, Bahrain 317
Phone: 973-17-537-301
Fax: 973-17-537-660

18 Charter Road
33rd Floor, Alexander House
Central, Hong Kong
Phone: 852-2844-1900
Fax: 852-2877-3748

Management and Staff
Chung Min Pang, Managing Director
Darren Tan, Managing Director
Donald Roth, Managing Partner
Edward Hummer, Managing Director
Edward V Jaycox, Managing Director
Hurley Doddy, Chief Operating Officer
James Seymour, Managing Director
James Martin, Managing Director
Judy Mackay, Chief Financial Officer
Katherine Downs, Managing Director
Michael Lee, Managing Director
Ming Yee Ho, Managing Director
Monica Tsui, Managing Director
Mumtaz Khan, Managing Director
Roberta Brzezinski, Partner
Samir Soota, Managing Director
Teseo Bergoglio, Managing Director
Thomas Gibian, Chief Executive Officer
Vincent Le Guennou, Managing Director
Wilfried Kaffenberger, Managing Director

Type of Firm
Private Equity Firm

Association Membership
British Venture Capital Association (BVCA)
Hong Kong Venture Capital Association (HKVCA)
European Private Equity and Venture Capital Assoc.
Project Preferences

Role in Financing:
Will function either as deal originator or investor in deals created by others

Type of Financing Preferred:
Early Stage
Expansion
Mezzanine
Generalist PE
Start-up Financing
Turnaround
Acquisition
Recapitalizations

Size of Investments Considered:
Min Size of Investment Considered (000s): $10,000
Max Size of Investment Considered (000s): $40,000

Geographical Preferences

International Preferences:
Hungary
Slovak Repub.
Latin America
Albania
Czech Republic
Turkey
Macedonia
Poland
Croatia
Bulgaria
Estonia
Bosnia
Romania
Asia
Cyprus
Latvia
Lithuania
Africa

Industry Preferences

In Communications prefer:
Telecommunications

In Industrial/Energy prefer:
Energy
Industrial Products

In Transportation prefer:
Transportation

In Financial Services prefer:
Financial Services

In Agr/Forestr/Fish prefer:
Agribusiness

In Utilities prefer:
Utilities

In Other prefer:
Environment Responsible

Additional Information
Year Founded: 1992
Capital Under Management: $5,700,000,000
Current Activity Level: Actively seeking new investments

EMERGING MARKETS PARTNERSHIP (BAHRAIN) E.C.
10th Flr, Al Salam Twr
Bldg 722 Diplomatic Area
Manama , Bahrain
Phone: 973-17-537-301
Fax: 973-17-537-660
E-mail: emp@emp.com.bh
Website: www.bahrain.empglobal.com

Type of Firm
Private Equity Firm

Additional Information
Current Activity Level: Actively seeking new investments

EMERGING POWER PARTNERS LTD
Tekniikantie 4 D
Espoo, Finland 02151
Phone: 358-9-469-1201
Fax: 358-9-469-1207
Website: www.pemfund.com
Management and Staff
Herkko Lehdonvirta, Managing Partner

Type of Firm
Private Equity Advisor or Fund of Funds

Association Membership
Finnish Venture Capital Association (FVCA)
European Private Equity and Venture Capital Assoc.

Project Preferences

Type of Financing Preferred:
Expansion
Turnaround
Startup

Geographical Preferences

International Preferences:
Central Europe
Europe
Eastern Europe
Scandanavia/Nordic Region
Asia

Industry Preferences

In Industrial/Energy prefer:
Energy

Additional Information
Year Founded: 1999
Capital Under Management: $50,400,000
Current Activity Level: Actively seeking new investments

EMERGING TECHNOLOGY PARTNERS, LLC
Six Taft Court
Suite 388
Rockville, MD USA 20850
Phone: 301-222-2200
Fax: 301-340-0879
Website: www.etpvc.com

Management and Staff
Bill Snider, General Partner
Wei-Wu He, General Partner

Type of Firm
Private Equity Firm
Association Membership
Mid-Atlantic Venture Association
Project Preferences

Role in Financing:
Will function either as deal originator or investor in deals created by others

Type of Financing Preferred:
Early Stage
Expansion

estments Considered:
Min Size of Investment Considered (000s): $500
Max Size of Investment Considered (000s): $5,000

Industry Preferences

In Biotechnology prefer:
Human Biotechnology
Genetic Engineering
Biotech Related Research

Additional Information
Year Founded: 2000
Capital Under Management: $40,000,000
Current Activity Level: Actively seeking new investments
Method of Compensation: Return on investment is of primary concern, do not charge fees

---

EMERTEC GESTION
17 rue de la Frise
Grenoble, France 38000
Phone: 33-4-3812-3895
Fax: 33-4-3812-3464
E-mail: info@emertec.fr
Website: www.emertec.fr

Type of Firm
Private Equity Firm

Association Membership
French Venture Capital Association (AFIC)

Project Preferences

Type of Financing Preferred:
Early Stage
Seed
Startup

Geographical Preferences

International Preferences:
Europe
Western Europe
France

Industry Preferences

In Computer Other prefer:
Computer Related

In Semiconductor/Electr prefer:
Electronics
Semiconductor

In Industrial/Energy prefer:
Energy
Industrial Products
Advanced Materials
Robotics
Environmental Related

Additional Information
Name of Most Recent Fund: Emertec 4
Most Recent Fund Was Raised: 02/19/2008
Year Founded: 1999
Capital Under Management: $17,100,000
Current Activity Level: Actively seeking new investments

EMIGRANT CAPITAL
Six East 43rd Street
Eight Floor
New York, NY USA 10017
Phone: 212-850-4460
Fax: 212-850-4839
E-mail: info@emigrantcapital.com
Website: www.emigrantcapital.com

Management and Staff
Edward Burns, Vice President
John Appel, Managing Director
Katherine Butkevich, Vice President
Kenneth Walters, Senior Managing Director

Type of Firm
Bank Affiliated

Project Preferences

Role in Financing:
Will function either as deal originator or investor in deals created by others

Type of Financing Preferred:
Generalist PE

Industry Focus
(% based on actual investment)

Computer Software and Services	40.8%
Biotechnology	24.2%
Other Products	22.6%
Industrial/Energy	6.4%
Consumer Related	6.0%

Additional Information
Year Founded: 1999
Capital Under Management: $150,000,000
Current Activity Level: Actively seeking new investments

EMINENT VENTURE CAPITAL CORPORATION

11F, No.19-11 San Choung Road
Nan Kang
Taipei, Taiwan
Phone: 886-2-655-3010
Fax: 886-2-655-3209

Type of Firm

Private Equity Firm

Project Preferences

Type of Financing Preferred:
Balanced

Additional Information

Year Founded: 2005
Current Activity Level: Actively seeking new investments

EMP AFRICA FUND MANAGEMENT (AKA: EMERGING CAPITAL PARTNERS)

1602 L Street North West
6th Floor
Washington, DC USA 20036
Phone: 202-280-200
Fax: 202-331-8255
E-mail: inquiries@ecpinvestments.com
Website: www.ecpinvestments.com

Other Offices

316 Victoria Street
4th Floor, Victoria Building
Douala, Cameroon 753
Phone: 237-33-424-861
Fax: 237-33-424-851

South Atlantic Petroleum Towers
7 Adeola Odeku Street
Victoria Island, Lagos, Nigeria

8th Floor, The Forum Building
Corner 5th and Maude St., Sandton
Johannesburg, South Africa 2196
Phone: 27-11-685-0830
Fax: 27-11-784-9112

Immeuble N'Zarama
Boulevard Lagunaire - Plateau
Abidjan, Ivory Coast
Phone: 225-20-310-731
Fax: 225-203-338-651

Immeuble Miniar Bloc B 2eme Etage
Les Berges du Lac
Tunis, Tunisia 1053
Phone: 216-71-962-590
Fax: 216-71-962-608

Management and Staff

Hurley Doddy, Chief Operating Officer
Thomas Gibian, Chief Executive Officer
Vincent Le Guennou, Managing Director

Type of Firm

Private Equity Firm

Project Preferences

Type of Financing Preferred:
Leveraged Buyout
Expansion
Generalist PE
Acquisition
Recapitalizations

Geographical Preferences

International Preferences:
Africa

Industry Preferences

In Communications prefer:
Telecommunications

In Medical/Health prefer:
Medical/Health

In Consumer Related prefer:
Consumer

In Industrial/Energy prefer:
Energy

In Transportation prefer:
Transportation

In Financial Services prefer:
Financial Services

In Business Serv. prefer:
Distribution
Media

In Agr/Forestr/Fish prefer:
Agribusiness
Mining and Minerals

Additional Information

Year Founded: 1997
Capital Under Management: $1,152,100,000
Current Activity Level: Actively seeking new investments

EMPIRE INVESTMENT HOLDINGS, LLC

703 Waterford Way
Suite 520
Miami, FL USA 33126
Phone: 305-403-1111
Fax: 305-403-1112
E-mail: info@empireih.com
Website: www.empireih.com

Management and Staff

David Alfonso, Chairman & CEO
Gene Bardakjy, Vice President

Type of Firm

Private Equity Firm

Project Preferences

Type of Financing Preferred:
Leveraged Buyout

Size of Investments Considered:
Min Size of Investment Considered (000s): $10,000
Max Size of Investment Considered (000s): $100,000

Geographical Preferences

United States Preferences:
All U.S.

Industry Preferences

In Business Serv. prefer:
Services
Distribution

In Manufact. prefer:
Manufacturing

Additional Information

Year Founded: 2004
Current Activity Level: Actively seeking new investments

EMPIRE VENTURES

1020 SW Taylor Street
Suite 415
Portland, OR USA 97205
Phone: 503-222-1556
Fax: 503-222-1607
E-mail: inquiries@empireventures.com
Website: www.empireventures.com

Management and Staff

Wade Bradley, Managing Partner

Type of Firm

Private Equity Firm

Project Preferences

Type of Financing Preferred:
Early Stage
Balanced

Additional Information

Name of Most Recent Fund: Empire Ventures Information Technology Fund
Most Recent Fund Was Raised: 07/01/1998
Year Founded: 1998
Capital Under Management: $10,000,000
Current Activity Level: Actively seeking new investments

EMPRESERIAL CAJA DE MADRID, S.A.

Paseo de la Castellana 189
Madrid, Spain 28046
Phone: 34-91-423-9516
Fax: 34-91-423-5223
Website: www.cajamadrid.es

Type of Firm

Bank Affiliated

Association Membership

European Private Equity and Venture Capital Assoc.
Spanish Venture Capital Association (ASCRI)

Project Preferences

Role in Financing:
Prefer role in deals created by others

Type of Financing Preferred:
Second Stage Financing
Expansion
Generalist PE
Other
Management Buyouts
Acquisition

Size of Investments Considered:
Min Size of Investment Considered (000s): $1,339
Max Size of Investment Considered (000s): $10,714

Geographical Preferences

International Preferences:
Eastern Europe
Spain
Romania

Industry Preferences

In Medical/Health prefer:
Medical/Health
Pharmaceuticals

In Consumer Related prefer:
Entertainment and Leisure
Consumer Services

In Industrial/Energy prefer:
Industrial Products

In Manufact. prefer:
Manufacturing

Additional Information

Year Founded: 1988
Capital Under Management: $848,300,000
Current Activity Level: Actively seeking new investments

EMX CAPITAL

Montes Urales 720
5/F, Lomas de Chapultepec
Mexico, Mexico 11000
Phone: 52-55-5249-8020
E-mail: contact@emxcapital.com
Website: www.emxcapital.com

Type of Firm

Private Equity Firm

Project Preferences

Type of Financing Preferred:
Leveraged Buyout
Expansion

Geographical Preferences

International Preferences:
Mexico

Additional Information

Name of Most Recent Fund: Carlyle Mexico Partners-TE, L.P.
Most Recent Fund Was Raised: 02/09/2007
Year Founded: 2009
Capital Under Management: $220,400,000
Current Activity Level: Actively seeking new investments

ENCORE CONSUMER CAPITAL LLC

2333 San Ramon Valley Blvd.
Suite 160
San Ramon, CA USA 94583
Phone: 925-837-6933
Fax: 925-837-6948
E-mail: info@encoreconsumercapital.com
Website: www.encoreconsumercapital.com

Other Offices

100 California Street
Suite 670
San Francisco, CA USA 94111
Phone: 415-296-9850
Fax: 415-296-9075

Management and Staff

Bill Shen, Vice President
Gary Smith, Managing Director
Kevin Murphy, Vice President
Megan Pirsch, Vice President
Robert Brown, Managing Director
Ryan Caldbeck, Vice President
Scott Sellers, Managing Director
Vanessa Stanley-Miller, Vice President

Type of Firm

Private Equity Firm

Project Preferences

Role in Financing:
Prefer role as deal originator

Type of Financing Preferred:
Leveraged Buyout
Expansion
Management Buyouts
Recapitalizations

Size of Investments Considered:
Min Size of Investment Considered (000s): $5,000
Max Size of Investment Considered (000s): $25,000

Geographical Preferences

Canadian Preferences:
All Canada

Industry Preferences

In Consumer Related prefer:
Food/Beverage
Consumer Products

In Manufact. prefer:
Manufacturing

Additional Information

Year Founded: 2005
Capital Under Management: $175,000,000
Current Activity Level: Actively seeking new investments

ENDEAVOR CAPITAL MANAGEMENT

49 Richmondville Avenue
Suite 215
Westport, CT USA 06880
Phone: 203-341-7788
Fax: 203-341-7799
E-mail: contactus@endeavorcap.com
Website: www.endeavorcap.com

Other Offices

Via Le Corbusier, 19
Ravenna, Italy 48110
Phone: 39-0-54-427-6084
Fax: 39-0-54-440-8520

437 Huntington Road
Union, NJ USA 07083
Phone: 908-851-2805
Fax: 908-851-2804

Management and Staff

Anthony Buffa, Managing General Partner
Nancy Haar, General Partner

Type of Firm

Private Equity Firm

Association Membership

National Venture Capital Association - USA (NVCA)

Project Preferences

Role in Financing:
Prefer role as deal originator but will also invest in deals created by others

Type of Financing Preferred:
Early Stage
Expansion

Size of Investments Considered:
Min Size of Investment Considered (000s): $50
Max Size of Investment Considered (000s): $10,000

Geographical Preferences

Canadian Preferences:
All Canada

International Preferences:
Europe

Industry Focus

(% based on actual investment)

Other Products	26.8%
Communications and Media	22.8%
Internet Specific	21.1%
Medical/Health	11.6%
Consumer Related	11.5%
Computer Hardware	3.5%
Industrial/Energy	1.5%
Computer Software and Services	1.2%

Additional Information

Year Founded: 1992
Capital Under Management: $80,000,000
Current Activity Level: Actively seeking new investments
Method of Compensation: Return on investment is of primary concern, do not charge fees

ENDEAVOUR CAPITAL

920 SW Sixth Avenue
Suite 1400
Portland, OR USA 97204
Phone: 503-223-2721
Fax: 503-223-1384
E-mail: reception@endeavourcapital.com
Website: www.endeavourcapital.com

Other Offices

1000 Second Avenue
Suite 3700
Seattle, WA USA 98104
Phone: 206-621-7060
Fax: 206-621-1075

Management and Staff

Aaron Richmond, Principal
Chad Heath, Principal
D. Mark Dorman, Principal
John Dixon, Managing Director
John E. von Schlegell, Managing Director
Leland Jones, Principal
Randy Miller, Chief Financial Officer
Stephen Babson, Principal

Type of Firm

Private Equity Firm

Project Preferences

Type of Financing Preferred:
Leveraged Buyout
Mezzanine
Early Stage
Management Buyouts
Acquisition
Industry Rollups
Recapitalizations

Geographical Preferences

United States Preferences:
Northwest
All U.S.

Industry Focus

(% based on actual investment)

Communications and Media	59.0%
Internet Specific	29.0%
Other Products	12.0%
Consumer Related	0.1%

Additional Information

Name of Most Recent Fund: Endeavour Associates Fund IV, L.P.
Most Recent Fund Was Raised: 01/01/2004
Year Founded: 1991
Capital Under Management: $400,000,000
Current Activity Level: Actively seeking new investments

ENDEAVOUR CAPITAL AUSTRALIA PTY, LTD.

Level 14, 309 Kent Street
GPO Box 3966
Sydney, Australia 2001
Phone: 612-9994-8942
Fax: 612-9994-8008
E-mail: pw@endeavourcapital.com.au
Website: www.endeavourcapital.com.au

Management and Staff

Peter Wallace, Managing Director

Type of Firm

Private Equity Firm

Project Preferences

Type of Financing Preferred:
Early Stage
Expansion
Management Buyouts

Size of Investments Considered:
Min Size of Investment Considered (000s): $781
Max Size of Investment Considered (000s): $23,418

Geographical Preferences

International Preferences:
Pacific

Industry Focus

(% based on actual investment)

Computer Hardware	51.7%
Computer Software and Services	48.3%

Additional Information

Year Founded: 1998
Capital Under Management: $15,600,000
Current Activity Level: Making few, if any, new investments

ENDEAVOUR CAPITAL, LTD.

Level 5, Wakefield House
90 The Terrace
Wellington, New Zealand
Phone: 644-499-5140
Fax: 644-499-5141
Website: www.ecap.co.nz

Other Offices

10 Jane Deans Close
Riccarton
Christchurch, New Zealand
Phone: 643-343-5997
Fax: 643-343-5987

24 Earnoch Avenue
Takapuna
Auckland, New Zealand
Phone: 649-489-1895
Fax: 649-489-1896

Management and Staff

Dennis Row, General Partner
Neil Campbell, General Partner
Stuart McKenzie, General Partner

Type of Firm

Private Equity Firm

Project Preferences

Type of Financing Preferred:
Early Stage
Expansion
Balanced
Seed
Startup

Geographical Preferences

International Preferences:
Pacific
New Zealand

Industry Preferences

In Communications prefer:
Communications and Media
Commercial Communications

In Computer Software prefer:
Software

In Semiconductor/Electr prefer:
Electronics

In Biotechnology prefer:
Biotechnology

Additional Information

Year Founded: 1999
Capital Under Management: $40,000,000
Current Activity Level: Actively seeking new investments

ENDEAVOUR VISION SA

6 rue de la Croix d'Or
Geneva, Switzerland 1204
Phone: 41-22-544-6000
Fax: 41-22-544-6006
E-mail: info@endeavourvision.com
Website: www.endeavourvision.com

Management and Staff

Bernard Vogel, Managing Partner
Dominik Ellenrieder, Venture Partner
Olivier Valdenaire, Venture Partner
Sven Lingjaerde, Managing Partner

Type of Firm

Private Equity Firm

Association Membership

Swiss Venture Capital Association (SECA)
European Private Equity and Venture Capital Assoc.

Project Preferences

Type of Financing Preferred:
Second Stage Financing
Other
Special Situation

Size of Investments Considered:
Min Size of Investment Considered (000s): $1,428
Max Size of Investment Considered (000s): $7,138

Geographical Preferences

International Preferences:
Switzerland
Europe

Industry Preferences

In Communications prefer:
Commercial Communications
Wireless Communications
Data Communications

In Computer Hardware prefer:
Computer Graphics and Dig
Integrated Turnkey System

In Internet Specific prefer:
Internet

In Semiconductor/Electr prefer:
Semiconductor

In Biotechnology prefer:
Biotechnology
Human Biotechnology
Industrial Biotechnology
Biosensors
Biotech Related Research

In Medical/Health prefer:
Medical Diagnostics
Medical Products

Additional Information

Name of Most Recent Fund: Endeavour LP
Most Recent Fund Was Raised: 06/08/2000
Year Founded: 1989
Capital Under Management: $142,800,000
Current Activity Level: Actively seeking new investments

ENDLESS LLP

3 Whitehall Quay
Leeds, United Kingdom LS16 0AY
Phone: 44-113-210-4000
Fax: 44-845-280-2411
Website: www.endlessllp.com

Other Offices

Fourth Floor, The Chambers
13 Police Street
Manchester, United Kingdom M2 7LQ
Phone: 44-161-837-6030
Fax: 44-161-837-6031

Solihull
PO Box 13876
Birmingham, United Kingdom B91 9HA
Phone: 44-845-094-6140

PO Box 62757
London, United Kingdom SW12 0UY
Phone: 44-845-370-0101
Fax: 44-845-280-2411

Management and Staff

Darren Forshaw, Partner
Del Huse, Managing Director
Garry Wilson, Partner

Type of Firm

Private Equity Firm

Project Preferences

Type of Financing Preferred:
Leveraged Buyout
Turnaround
Management Buyouts
Recapitalizations

Size of Investments Considered:
Min Size of Investment Considered (000s): $929
Max Size of Investment Considered (000s): $37,154

Geographical Preferences

International Preferences:
United Kingdom

Additional Information

Year Founded: 2005
Capital Under Management: $324,900,000
Current Activity Level: Actively seeking new investments

ENERCAP CAPITAL PARTNERS

Burzovni palac
Rybna 14
Prague, Czech Republic 110 00
Phone: 420-227-316-222
Fax: 420-227-316-444
Website: www.enercap.com

Management and Staff

Alastair Hammond, Chief Operating Officer
Ewan Gibb, Partner
George Formandl, Partner
Michael White, Partner
Type of Firm
Private Equity Firm

Project Preferences

Type of Financing Preferred:
Leveraged Buyout

Geographical Preferences

International Preferences:
Central Europe
Europe
Eastern Europe

Industry Preferences

In Industrial/Energy prefer:
Energy
Alternative Energy
Energy Conservation Relat

Additional Information

Year Founded: 2007
Capital Under Management: $108,800,000
Current Activity Level: Actively seeking new investments

ENERGIE CAPITAL INVESTISSEMENTS, SEC

85, rue Ste-Catherine Ouest
Tene etage
Montreal, Canada H2X3P4
Phone: 514-842-8875
Fax: 514-842-7274

Management and Staff

Jeanne Wojas, President

Type of Firm

Private Equity Firm

Additional Information

Year Founded: 1999
Current Activity Level: Actively seeking new investments

ENERGY VENTURES A.S.

Kongsgaardbakken 1
Stavanger, Norway N-4001
Phone: 47-51-841-295
Fax: 47-51-524-607
E-mail: mail@energyventures.no
Website: www.energyventures.no

Other Offices

Rubislaw Den House
23 Rubislaw Den North
Aberdeen, United Kingdom AB15 4AL
Phone: 44-1224-329-077

10375 Richmond Avenue
Suit 295
Houston, TX USA 77042
Phone: 281-768-6722
Fax: 281-768-6726

Management and Staff

Bob Schwart, Vice President
Einar Gamman, Partner
Greg Herrera, Partner
Kjell Jacobsen, Partner
Leif Andre Skare, Partner
Ole Melberg, Managing Partner
Pelle Bildsten, Chief Financial Officer

Type of Firm

Private Equity Firm

Association Membership

Norwegian Venture Capital Association
European Private Equity and Venture Capital Assoc.

Project Preferences

Type of Financing Preferred:
Second Stage Financing
Expansion
Balanced

Geographical Preferences

International Preferences:
Scandanavia/Nordic Region

Industry Preferences

In Industrial/Energy prefer:
Energy
Oil and Gas Exploration
Oil & Gas Drilling,Explor
Alternative Energy

Additional Information

Year Founded: 2002
Capital Under Management: $25,600,000
Current Activity Level: Actively seeking new investments

ENERGY VENTURES GROUP LLC

3050 K Street, NW.
Suite 205
Washington, DC USA 20007
Phone: 202-944-4141
Fax: 202-944-4145
E-mail: aweissman@energyvg.com
Website: www.energyvg.com

Type of Firm

Private Equity Firm

Additional Information

Year Founded: 2001
Current Activity Level: Actively seeking new investments

ENERTECH CAPITAL (FKA: ENERTECH CAPITAL PARTNERS, L.P.)

625 West Ridge Pike
Building D, Suite 105
Conshohocken, PA USA 19428
Phone: 484-539-1860
Fax: 484-539-1870
Website: www.enertechcapital.com

Other Offices

111 Richmond Street West
Suite 1014
Toronto, Canada M5H 2G4
Phone: 610-254-4141
Fax: 610-254-4188

Management and Staff

Bill Kingsley, Managing Partner
Scott Ungerer, Managing Partner
Tucker Twitmyer, Managing Partner
Wally Hunter, Managing Partner

Type of Firm

Private Equity Firm

Association Membership

Mid-Atlantic Venture Association
National Venture Capital Association - USA (NVCA)

Project Preferences

Role in Financing:
Prefer role as deal originator

Type of Financing Preferred:
Early Stage
Expansion
Balanced
Seed

Size of Investments Considered:
Min Size of Investment Considered (000s): $1,000
Max Size of Investment Considered (000s): $10,000

Geographical Preferences

United States Preferences:
All U.S.

Canadian Preferences:
All Canada

International Preferences:
United Kingdom

Industry Focus

(% based on actual investment)

Internet Specific	34.9%
Industrial/Energy	21.4%
Computer Software and Services	13.6%
Semiconductors/Other Elect.	13.5%
Other Products	13.1%
Communications and Media	3.1%
Consumer Related	0.5%

Additional Information

Name of Most Recent Fund: EnerTech Capital Partners III, L.P.
Most Recent Fund Was Raised: 08/09/2007
Year Founded: 1996
Capital Under Management: $365,000,000
Current Activity Level: Actively seeking new investments
Method of Compensation: Return on investment is of primary concern, do not charge fees

ENGLEFIELD CAPITAL

Michelin House
81 Fulham Road
London, United Kingdom SW3 6RD
Phone: 44-20-7591-4200
Fax: 44-20-7591-4222
E-mail: englefield@engcap.com
Website: www.englefieldcapital.com

Management and Staff

Adam Barron, Partner
Dominic Shorthouse, Founder
Dwight Cupit, Chief Financial Officer
Edmund Lazarus, Partner
Eric Walters, Partner
Etienne De Villiers, Partner
Sam Abboud, Partner

Type of Firm

Private Equity Firm

Project Preferences

Type of Financing Preferred:
Leveraged Buyout
Expansion

Geographical Preferences

International Preferences:
United Kingdom
Europe
Germany
France

Industry Preferences

In Medical/Health prefer:
Health Services

In Consumer Related prefer:
Education Related

In Industrial/Energy prefer:
Energy
Alternative Energy

In Financial Services prefer:
Financial Services

Additional Information

Name of Most Recent Fund: Englefield Fund, The
Most Recent Fund Was Raised: 03/31/2003
Year Founded: 2001
Capital Under Management: $2,179,100,000
Current Activity Level: Actively seeking new investments

ENHANCED CAPITAL PARTNERS, LLC

201 St. Charles Avenue
Suite 3700
New Orleans, LA USA 70170
Phone: 504-569-7900
Fax: 504-569-7910
E-mail: info@enhancedcap.com
Website: www.enhancedcapital.net

Other Offices

350 Park Avenue
24th Floor
New York, NY USA 10022
Phone: 212-207-3385
Fax: 212-207-3386

8310 South Valley Highway
Third Floor
Englewood, CO USA 80112
Phone: 303-524-1313
Fax: 303-524-1278

500 Beacon Parkway West
c/o Redmont Venture Partners
Birmingham, AL USA 35209
Phone: 205-943-5646
Fax: 205-943-4748

Management and Staff

David Orlandella, Managing Director
Gingee Prince, Managing Director
Jim Stanislaus, Chief Operating Officer
Ranjit Bhonsle, Managing Director
Robert Dennen, Managing Director
Thomas Davidson, Managing Director

Type of Firm

Incubator/Development Program

Project Preferences

Type of Financing Preferred:
Early Stage
Expansion
Balanced

Size of Investments Considered:
Min Size of Investment Considered (000s): $500
Max Size of Investment Considered (000s): $3,000

Geographical Preferences

United States Preferences:
Alabama
Colorado
Louisiana
New York
All U.S.

Industry Preferences

In Communications prefer:
Communications and Media

In Biotechnology prefer:
Biotechnology

In Medical/Health prefer:
Health Services

Additional Information

Year Founded: 1999
Capital Under Management: $24,400,000
Current Activity Level: Actively seeking new investments

ENHANCED EQUITY FUND, L.P.

350 Park Avenue
24th Floor
New York, NY USA 10022
Phone: 212-207-3385
Fax: 212-207-3386
Website: www.enhancedequity.com

Management and Staff

Andrew Paul, Managing General Partner
Brett Fliegler, General Partner
David Howe, Managing General Partner
Malcolm Kostuchenko, General Partner

Type of Firm

Private Equity Firm

Project Preferences

Type of Financing Preferred:
Leveraged Buyout
Expansion
Acquisition
Recapitalizations

Size of Investments Considered:
Min Size of Investment Considered (000s): $5,000
Max Size of Investment Considered (000s): $25,000

Geographical Preferences

United States Preferences:
All U.S.

Industry Preferences

In Medical/Health prefer:
Medical/Health

In Business Serv. prefer:
Services

Additional Information

Year Founded: 2007
Capital Under Management: $225,000,000
Current Activity Level: Actively seeking new investments

ENHANCED PERFORMANCE, INC.

179 Waldoncroft Crescent
Burlington, Canada

Type of Firm

Private Equity Firm

Additional Information

Year Founded: 1996
Current Activity Level: Actively seeking new investments

ENTERASYS NETWORKS (FKA: CABLETRON SYSTEMS, INC.)

50 Minuteman Road
Andover, MA USA 01810
Phone: 978-684-1000
Website: www.enterasys.com

Management and Staff

Robert Gagalis, Chief Financial Officer

Type of Firm

Corporate PE/Venture

Additional Information

Year Founded: 1996
Current Activity Level: Actively seeking new investments

ENTERPRISE 2000 FUND

43 Pearse Street
Dublin 2, Ireland
Phone: 353-1-677-5570
Fax: 353-1-677-5588
E-mail: capital@enterprise2000fund.ie
Website: www.enterprise2000fund.ie

Type of Firm
Bank Affiliated

Project Preferences

Type of Financing Preferred:
Early Stage

Geographical Preferences

International Preferences:
Ireland

Industry Preferences

In Computer Software prefer:
Software

In Biotechnology prefer:
Biotechnology

In Consumer Related prefer:
Food/Beverage

In Business Serv. prefer:
Media

In Manufact. prefer:
Manufacturing

Additional Information
Year Founded: 1998
Capital Under Management: $11,400,000
Current Activity Level: Actively seeking new investments

ENTERPRISE EQUITY VENTURE CAPITAL GROUP
Dublin Road
Co. Louth
Dundalk, Ireland
Phone: 353-42-933-3167
Fax: 353-42-933-4857
E-mail: info@enterpriseequity.ie
Website: www.enterpriseequity.ie

Other Offices
Mervue Business and Technology Park
Galway, Ireland
Phone: 353-91-764-614
Fax: 353-91-764-615

NSC Campus
Mahon
Cork, Ireland
Phone: 353-21-230-7127
Fax: 353-21-230-7070

78a Dublin Road
Belfast, Ireland BT2 7HP
Phone: 353-48-90242500
Fax: 353-48-90242487

Management and Staff
Bob McGowan-Smyth, Chief Executive Officer
Conor O Connor, Chief Executive Officer

Type of Firm
Private Equity Firm

Association Membership
British Venture Capital Association (BVCA)
European Private Equity and Venture Capital Assoc.

Project Preferences

Role in Financing:
Prefer role as deal originator but will also invest in deals created by others

Type of Financing Preferred:
Second Stage Financing
Leveraged Buyout
Early Stage
Balanced
Start-up Financing
Seed
First Stage Financing
Startup

Size of Investments Considered:
Min Size of Investment Considered (000s): $100
Max Size of Investment Considered (000s): $100,000

Geographical Preferences

International Preferences:
Ireland
United Kingdom
Europe

Industry Preferences

In Communications prefer:
Data Communications

In Computer Software prefer:
Computer Services
Applications Software

In Internet Specific prefer:
Internet

In Semiconductor/Electr prefer:
Semiconductor
Sensors
Component Testing Equipmt
Analytic/Scientific

In Biotechnology prefer:
Industrial Biotechnology
Biosensors

In Medical/Health prefer:
Medical Diagnostics
Diagnostic Services
Diagnostic Test Products
Drug/Equipmt Delivery
Medical Products

In Consumer Related prefer:
Entertainment and Leisure
Food/Beverage
Consumer Products

In Industrial/Energy prefer:
Alternative Energy
Industrial Products
Factory Automation

In Manufact. prefer:
Publishing

In Agr/Forestr/Fish prefer:
Agriculture related

Additional Information
Year Founded: 1987
Capital Under Management: $20,000,000
Current Activity Level: Actively seeking new investments
Method of Compensation: Return on invest. most important, but chg. closing fees, service fees, etc.

ENTERPRISE INVESTORS
31/F Warsaw Financial Center
53 Emilii Plater Street
Warsaw, Poland 00-113
Phone: 48-22-458-8500
Fax: 48-22-458-8555
E-mail: info@ei.com.pl
Website: www.ei.com.pl

Other Offices
Domus Center, Str. Stirbei Voda
Nr. 36, Etaj 5
Bucharest, Romania
Phone: 40-21-314-6685
Fax: 40-21-314-8191

Management and Staff
Agnieszka Kowalska, Partner
Cristian Nacu, Partner
Dariusz Pronczuk, Managing Partner
Jacek Wozniak, Partner
Michal Rusiecki, Managing Partner
Monika Nachya, Partner
Piotr Augustyniak, Partner
Rafal Bator, Partner
Robert Manz, Managing Partner
Sebastian Krol, Partner
Stanislaw Knaflewski, Partner

Type of Firm
Private Equity Firm

Association Membership
Polish Venture Capital Association (PSIC/PPEA)
European Private Equity and Venture Capital Assoc.

Project Preferences

Role in Financing:
Prefer role as deal originator but will also invest in deals created by others

Type of Financing Preferred:
Second Stage Financing
Leveraged Buyout
Early Stage
Expansion
Mezzanine
Generalist PE
Turnaround

Management Buyouts
First Stage Financing
Joint Ventures
Special Situation
Startup
Acquisition

Size of Investments Considered:

Min Size of Investment Considered (000s): $3,000
Max Size of Investment Considered (000s): $30,000

Geographical Preferences

International Preferences:

Hungary
Slovak Repub.
Czech Republic
Central Europe
Poland
Eastern Europe
Bulgaria
Romania

Industry Preferences

In Communications prefer:

Communications and Media
Telecommunications
Media and Entertainment

In Computer Hardware prefer:

Integrated Turnkey System

In Computer Software prefer:

Computer Services
Systems Software
Applications Software

In Internet Specific prefer:

Internet

In Semiconductor/Electr prefer:

Electronic Components
Sensors
Component Testing Equipmt
Analytic/Scientific

In Biotechnology prefer:

Industrial Biotechnology

In Medical/Health prefer:

Medical/Health
Medical Diagnostics
Medical Therapeutics
Health Services
Pharmaceuticals

In Consumer Related prefer:

Consumer
Entertainment and Leisure
Retail
Computer Stores
Franchises(NEC)
Food/Beverage
Consumer Products
Consumer Services
Education Related

In Industrial/Energy prefer:

Energy Conservation Relat
Materials
Factory Automation
Machinery
Environmental Related

In Transportation prefer:

Transportation

In Financial Services prefer:

Financial Services

In Business Serv. prefer:

Distribution
Media

In Manufact. prefer:

Manufacturing
Office Automation Equipmt
Publishing

In Agr/Forestr/Fish prefer:

Agriculture related
Mining and Minerals

Additional Information

Name of Most Recent Fund: Polish Enterprise Fund V, L.P.
Most Recent Fund Was Raised: 02/18/2004
Year Founded: 1990
Capital Under Management: $1,344,900,000
Current Activity Level: Actively seeking new investments
Method of Compensation: Return on investment is of primary concern, do not charge fees

---

ENTERPRISE IRELAND

The Plaza
East Point Business Park
Dublin 3, Ireland
Phone: 353-1-727-2000
Fax: 353-1-808-2020
E-mail: client.service@enterprise-ireland.com
Website: www.enterprise-ireland.com

Type of Firm

Government Affiliated Program

Project Preferences

Type of Financing Preferred:

Early Stage
Expansion
Startup

Geographical Preferences

International Preferences:

Ireland
Europe

Additional Information

Year Founded: 1998
Capital Under Management: $772,000,000
Current Activity Level: Actively seeking new investments

ENTERPRISE PARTNERS VENTURE CAPITAL (AKA: EPVC)

2223 Avenida de la Playa
Suite 300
La Jolla, CA USA 92037
Phone: 858-731-0300
E-mail: innovations@epvc.com
Website: www.epvc.com

Management and Staff

Andrew Senyei, Managing Director
Carl Eibl, Managing Director

Type of Firm

Private Equity Firm

Association Membership

Western Association of Venture Capitalists (WAVC)
National Venture Capital Association - USA (NVCA)

Project Preferences

Role in Financing:

Will function either as deal originator or investor in deals created by others

Type of Financing Preferred:

Early Stage
Seed
Later Stage
Management Buyouts

Size of Investments Considered:

Min Size of Investment Considered (000s): $2,000
Max Size of Investment Considered (000s): $20,000

Geographical Preferences

United States Preferences:

Southern California
Southwest
All U.S.

Industry Focus

(% based on actual investment)

Computer Software and Services	22.4%
Communications and Media	20.8%
Biotechnology	13.0%
Internet Specific	12.9%
Medical/Health	10.4%
Semiconductors/Other Elect.	10.1%
Consumer Related	4.3%
Computer Hardware	2.3%
Industrial/Energy	2.3%
Other Products	1.5%

Additional Information

Year Founded: 1985
Capital Under Management: $1,016,000,000
Current Activity Level: Actively seeking new investments
Method of Compensation: Return on invest. most important, but chg. closing fees, service fees, etc.

ENTERPRISE PRIVATE CAPITAL GP

35 South County Hall
London, United Kingdom SE1 7GB
Phone: 44-871-871-0788
Fax: 44-1832-720-304
E-mail: contact@enterpriseprivatecapital.com

Type of Firm

Private Equity Firm

Project Preferences

Type of Financing Preferred:
Early Stage
Expansion
Seed
Startup

Geographical Preferences

International Preferences:
United Kingdom
Europe

Additional Information

Year Founded: 2003
Current Activity Level: Actively seeking new investments

ENTERPRISE VENTURES, LTD. (FKA:LANCASHIRE ENTERPRISES PLC)

Preston Technology Mgt. Centre
Marsh Lane
Preston, United Kingdom PR1 8UQ
Phone: 44-870-766-8237
Fax: 44-870-766-828
E-mail: info@enterprise-ventures.co.uk
Website: www.enterprise-ventures.co.uk

Other Offices

Pall Mall Court
67 King Street
Manchester, United Kingdom M2 4PD

1 Whitehall
Whitehall Road
Leeds, United Kingdom LS1 4HR

Management and Staff

Jonathan Diggines, Chief Executive Officer
Roger Hoyle, Managing Director

Type of Firm

Private Equity Firm

Association Membership

British Venture Capital Association (BVCA)

Project Preferences

Role in Financing:
Prefer role as deal originator but will also invest in deals created by others

Type of Financing Preferred:
Early Stage
Expansion
Generalist PE
Start-up Financing
Turnaround
Seed
Management Buyouts
Startup
Recapitalizations

Size of Investments Considered:
Min Size of Investment Considered (000s): $75
Max Size of Investment Considered (000s): $746

Geographical Preferences

International Preferences:
United Kingdom
Europe

Industry Focus

(% based on actual investment)

Industrial/Energy	30.7%
Medical/Health	23.6%
Biotechnology	15.3%
Other Products	9.2%
Computer Hardware	7.8%
Computer Software and Services	7.6%
Internet Specific	5.8%
Consumer Related	0.1%

Additional Information

Name of Most Recent Fund: Coalfields Enterprise Fund
Most Recent Fund Was Raised: 05/28/2004
Year Founded: 1982
Capital Under Management: $44,800,000
Current Activity Level: Actively seeking new investments

ENTERPRISEASIA PLC (FKA: ENTERPIRSEASIA.COM PLC)

Albion Mills Greengates
Bradford
West Yorkshire, United Kingdom BD10 9TQ
Phone: 44-1274-623-478
Fax: 44-1274-622-032
E-mail: contact-us@enterpriseasia.com.hk
Website: www.enterpriseasia.com.hk

Other Offices

Room 501, 5/F Nan Fung Tower
173 Des Voeux Road
Central, Hong Kong
Phone: 852-2116-5900
Fax: 852-2151-0955

Management and Staff

Benjamin Ng, Chief Executive Officer

Type of Firm

Private Equity Firm

Association Membership

Hong Kong Venture Capital Association (HKVCA)

Project Preferences

Type of Financing Preferred:
Early Stage
Balanced

Geographical Preferences

International Preferences:
Asia

Industry Preferences

In Internet Specific prefer:
Internet

Additional Information

Year Founded: 2000
Current Activity Level: Actively seeking new investments

ENTREPIA VENTURES, INC.

5201 Great America Parkway
Suite 456
Santa Clara, CA USA 95054
Phone: 408-492-9040
Fax: 408-492-9540
E-mail: info@entrepia.com
Website: www.entrepia.com

Other Offices

Nagatacho TBR Bldg. 8F
2-10-2 Nagatacho, Chiyoda-ku
Tokyo , Japan 100-6014
Phone: 81-3-5521-2040
Fax: 813-3591-6540

1010 Sherbrooke Street West
Suite 820
Montreal, Canada H3A 2R7
Phone: 514-842-7400
Fax: 514-842-9847

Management and Staff

Amit Srivastava, Chief Executive Officer

Type of Firm

Private Equity Firm

Association Membership

National Venture Capital Association - USA (NVCA)

Project Preferences

Role in Financing:
Will function either as deal originator or investor in

deals created by others

Type of Financing Preferred:
Expansion

Size of Investments Considered:
Min Size of Investment Considered (000s): $2,000
Max Size of Investment Considered (000s): $4,000

Geographical Preferences

Canadian Preferences:
Quebec

International Preferences:
Japan

Industry Preferences

In Communications prefer:
Commercial Communications
Telecommunications
Wireless Communications
Data Communications
Other Communication Prod.

In Computer Hardware prefer:
Integrated Turnkey System

In Computer Software prefer:
Software
Systems Software
Applications Software

In Internet Specific prefer:
E-Commerce Technology
Internet
Ecommerce
Web Aggregration/Portals

In Semiconductor/Electr prefer:
Electronic Components
Semiconductor
Fiber Optics
Analytic/Scientific
Optoelectronics

Additional Information
Name of Most Recent Fund: Le Fonds Entrepia Nord S.E.C.
Most Recent Fund Was Raised: 02/11/2003
Year Founded: 1999
Capital Under Management: $95,000,000
Current Activity Level: Actively seeking new investments
Method of Compensation: Return on invest. most important, but chg. closing fees, service fees, etc.

ENTREPRENEUR PARTNERS, L.P.
1820 Rittenhouse Square
Philadelphia, PA USA 19103
Phone: 215-893-1530
Fax: 215-689-2529

Management and Staff
Bruce Newman, Partner
Salem Shuchman, Partner

Type of Firm
Private Equity Firm

Additional Information
Year Founded: 2005
Capital Under Management: $15,000,000
Current Activity Level: Actively seeking new investments

ENTREPRENEUR VENTURE GESTION
39, avenue Pierre 1er de Serbie
Paris, France 75008
Phone: 33-1-5818-6180
Fax: 33-1-5818-6189
Website: www.entrepreneurventure.com

Other Offices
23 F/Asia Orient Tower
128 Lockhart Road, Wanchai
Hong Kong, Hong Kong
Phone: 852-9131-8099
Fax: 852-2520-1213

Type of Firm
Private Equity Firm

Association Membership
French Venture Capital Association (AFIC)

Project Preferences

Type of Financing Preferred:
Early Stage
Seed
Startup

Size of Investments Considered:
Min Size of Investment Considered (000s): $472
Max Size of Investment Considered (000s): $3,777

Geographical Preferences

International Preferences:
Europe
France

Industry Preferences

In Communications prefer:
Commercial Communications

In Computer Software prefer:
Software

In Internet Specific prefer:
Ecommerce

Additional Information
Year Founded: 2000
Current Activity Level: Actively seeking new investments

ENTREPRENEURS FUND MANAGEMENT LLP
3rd Floor, Standbrook House
2-5 Old Bond Street
London, United Kingdom W1S 4PD
Phone: 44-20-7355-1011
Fax: 44-20-7355-6199
E-mail: info@entrepreneursfund.com
Website: www.efbv.net

Management and Staff
Alexis Figeac, Partner
Klaas De Boer, Managing Partner

Type of Firm
Private Equity Firm

Project Preferences

Type of Financing Preferred:
Expansion

Industry Preferences

In Communications prefer:
Communications and Media

In Medical/Health prefer:
Medical/Health

In Industrial/Energy prefer:
Energy

Additional Information
Year Founded: 2002
Capital Under Management: $413,000,000
Current Activity Level: Actively seeking new investments

ENTROPY VENTURES, LTD.
30/F, Bank of China Tower
One Garden Road
Central, Hong Kong
Phone: 852-2251-8213
Fax: 852-2251-8383
E-mail: info@entropyventures.com
Website: www.entropyventures.com

Other Offices
Cricket Square
Hutchins Drive P.O. Box 2681
Grand Cayman, Cayman Islands KY1-1111

Management and Staff
Carol Lee, Partner
Fergie May, Founding Partner

Type of Firm
Private Equity Firm

Project Preferences

Type of Financing Preferred:
Expansion

Size of Investments Considered:
Min Size of Investment Considered (000s): $3,000
Max Size of Investment Considered (000s): $15,000

Geographical Preferences

International Preferences:
China
Pacific
Asia

Industry Preferences

In Industrial/Energy prefer:
Alternative Energy
Environmental Related

Additional Information
Year Founded: 2008
Capital Under Management: $35,000,000
Current Activity Level: Actively seeking new investments

ENTRUST CAPITAL
717 Fifth Avenue
25th Floor
New York, NY USA 10022
Phone: 212-888-1040
Fax: 212-888-0751
E-mail: info@entrustcapital.com
Website: www.entrustcapital.com

Management and Staff
Mark Fife, Managing Partner

Type of Firm
Private Equity Firm

Additional Information
Year Founded: 2009
Current Activity Level: Actively seeking new investments

ENVEST VENTURES
2101 Parks Avenue
Suite 401
Virginia Beach, VA USA 23451
Phone: 757-437-3000
Fax: 757-437-3884
E-mail: information@envestventures.com
Website: www.envestventures.com

Management and Staff
David Kaufman, Senior Managing Director
John Garel, Senior Managing Director
Kevin Wilson, Managing Director

Type of Firm
Private Equity Firm

Association Membership
Mid-Atlantic Venture Association
National Venture Capital Association - USA (NVCA)

Project Preferences

Role in Financing:
Prefer role as deal originator but will also invest in deals created by others

Type of Financing Preferred:
Leveraged Buyout
Early Stage
Expansion
Later Stage
Management Buyouts

Size of Investments Considered:
Min Size of Investment Considered (000s): $1,000
Max Size of Investment Considered (000s): $5,000

Geographical Preferences

United States Preferences:
Mid Atlantic
Southeast
Virginia

Industry Preferences

In Computer Software prefer:
Computer Services

In Consumer Related prefer:
Retail
Franchises(NEC)

In Business Serv. prefer:
Services
Distribution
Media

In Manufact. prefer:
Manufacturing

Additional Information
Name of Most Recent Fund: Envest II LLC
Most Recent Fund Was Raised: 04/19/2004
Year Founded: 2000
Capital Under Management: $89,100,000
Current Activity Level: Actively seeking new investments
Method of Compensation: Return on investment is of primary concern, do not charge fees

---

ENVIROCAPITAL, INC.
2540, boul. Daniel-Johnson
Bureau 910
Laval, Canada
Phone: 514-687-2040
Fax: 514-687-9283

Management and Staff
Raymond Brouzes, Vice President

Type of Firm
Private Equity Firm

Additional Information
Year Founded: 1992
Current Activity Level: Actively seeking new investments

ENVIRONMENTAL CAPITAL PARTNERS LLC
Six East 43rd Street
20th Floor
New York, NY USA 10017
Phone: 917-262-5240
Fax: 917-262-5259
Website: www.ecpcapital.com

Management and Staff
Christopher Staudt, Principal
Michael Richter, Partner
Robert Egan, Managing Partner
William Staudt, Managing Partner

Type of Firm
Private Equity Firm

Project Preferences

Type of Financing Preferred:
Leveraged Buyout
Expansion
Generalist PE
Acquisition
Recapitalizations

Size of Investments Considered:
Min Size of Investment Considered (000s): $5,000
Max Size of Investment Considered (000s): $25,000

Geographical Preferences

International Preferences:
All International

Industry Preferences

In Industrial/Energy prefer:
Energy
Alternative Energy
Energy Conservation Relat
Industrial Products
Environmental Related

In Utilities prefer:
Utilities

Additional Information
Year Founded: 2009
Current Activity Level: Actively seeking new investments

ENVIRONMENTAL R&D CAPITAL CORPORATION

One Toronto Street, Suite 806
Toronto, Canada M5C2V6
Phone: 416-777-0530
Fax: 416-777-0457

Type of Firm

Private Equity Firm

Additional Information

Year Founded: 1994
Current Activity Level: Actively seeking new investments

EONBUSINESS CORPORATION

7430 East Caley Avenue
Suite 200
Centennial, CO USA 80111
Phone: 303-850-9300
E-mail: inquiry@eonbusiness.com
Website: www.eonbusiness.com

Type of Firm

Private Equity Firm

Project Preferences

Type of Financing Preferred:
Early Stage
Seed

Geographical Preferences

United States Preferences:
Rocky Mountain

Industry Preferences

In Internet Specific prefer:
E-Commerce Technology
Ecommerce

Additional Information

Year Founded: 1997
Current Activity Level: Actively seeking new investments

EONTECH VENTURES (FKA: TRITON VENTURES)

5 rue Guillame Kroll
Luxembourg, Luxembourg L-1025
Phone: 41-78-728-7023
Fax: 44-870-912-8059
E-mail: info@eontechventures.com
Website: www.eontechventures.com

Management and Staff

James Carter, Partner
Neil Shah, Partner
Nicola Bettio, Partner
Sandro Grigolli, Partner

Type of Firm

Private Equity Firm

Association Membership

European Private Equity and Venture Capital Assoc.

Project Preferences

Type of Financing Preferred:
Early Stage
Expansion

Geographical Preferences

International Preferences:
Italy
United Kingdom
Europe
France

Industry Preferences

In Communications prefer:
Media and Entertainment

In Computer Software prefer:
Software

In Internet Specific prefer:
Internet

Additional Information

Year Founded: 2000
Capital Under Management: $26,400,000
Current Activity Level: Actively seeking new investments

EOS ASIA INVESTMENTS, LTD. (FKA: JCAR FUNDS, LTD.)

No. 12 Chaoyangmenwai Avenue
Rm. 2516 Kuntai Int'l Mansion
Chaoyang, Beijing, China 100020
Website: www.eosfunds.com

Other Offices

No. 19 Renmin South Road Section 4
Room 1817 Western Tower
Chengdu, China 610041

1068 East Main Street
Suite 140E
Ventura, CA USA 93001
Phone: 310-878-9021

Management and Staff

Bernard Goh, Vice President
Beth Liu, Vice President
Biqiang Huang, Vice President
Christian Arnell, Vice President
David Zhuang, Vice President
George Zhou, Partner
Jon Carnes, President
Shuyun Zhu, Vice President
Xiping Wang, Vice President

Type of Firm

Private Equity Firm

Project Preferences

Type of Financing Preferred:
Public Companies
Private Placement

Size of Investments Considered:
Min Size of Investment Considered (000s): $25,000
Max Size of Investment Considered (000s): $150,000

Geographical Preferences

International Preferences:
China

Additional Information

Year Founded: 2001
Current Activity Level: Actively seeking new investments

EOS PARTNERS, L.P.

320 Park Avenue
9th Floor
New York, NY USA 10022
Phone: 212-832-5800
Fax: 212-832-5815
E-mail: mfirst@eospartners.com
Website: www.eospartners.com

Management and Staff

Beth Berstein, Chief Financial Officer
Jason Pike, Vice President
Mark First, Managing Director
Samuel Levine, Managing Director
Stenning Schueppert, Principal

Type of Firm

Private Equity Firm

Project Preferences

Role in Financing:
Prefer role as deal originator but will also invest in deals created by others

Type of Financing Preferred:
Second Stage Financing
Leveraged Buyout
Expansion
Mezzanine
Later Stage
First Stage Financing
Acquisition
Industry Rollups
Special Situation
Startup
Recapitalizations

Size of Investments Considered:
Min Size of Investment Considered (000s): $3,000
Max Size of Investment Considered: No Limit

Geographical Preferences

United States Preferences:
All U.S.

Canadian Preferences:
All Canada

International Preferences:
South Africa

Industry Focus

(% based on actual investment)

Industrial/Energy	39.8%
Other Products	26.4%
Communications and Media	10.7%
Medical/Health	7.4%
Consumer Related	5.6%
Semiconductors/Other Elect.	4.6%
Computer Software and Services	4.1%
Internet Specific	1.4%

Additional Information

Name of Most Recent Fund: Eos Capital Parners III, L.P.
Most Recent Fund Was Raised: 07/14/2004
Year Founded: 1994
Capital Under Management: $300,000,000
Current Activity Level: Making few, if any, new investments
Method of Compensation: Return on investment is of primary concern, do not charge fees

---

EPF PARTNERS

152 avenue des Champs-Elysees
Paris, France 75008
Phone: 33-1-5643-6520
Fax: 33-1-5819-2190
E-mail: contact@epf-partners.com
Website: www.epf-partners.com

Management and Staff

Christian D Argoubet, Managing Director

Type of Firm

Bank Affiliated

Association Membership

French Venture Capital Association (AFIC)

Project Preferences

Type of Financing Preferred:
Early Stage
Expansion
Later Stage
Acquisition

Geographical Preferences

International Preferences:
Europe
France

Additional Information

Year Founded: 1996
Capital Under Management: $152,000,000
Current Activity Level: Actively seeking new investments

EPI-V LLP

Winchfield Lodge
Old Potbridge Road
Winchfield, United Kingdom RG27 8BT
Phone: 44-1252-849-072
Fax: 44-1252-848-800
E-mail: info@epi-v.com
Website: www.epi-v.com

Management and Staff

Glynn Williams, Founding Partner
Nigel Leggett, Partner
Robert Preston, Founding Partner

Type of Firm

Private Equity Firm

Association Membership

British Venture Capital Association (BVCA)

Project Preferences

Type of Financing Preferred:
Early Stage
Expansion
Start-up Financing
Management Buyouts
Startup

Size of Investments Considered:
Min Size of Investment Considered (000s): $3,917
Max Size of Investment Considered (000s): $19,587

Geographical Preferences

United States Preferences:
All U.S.

Canadian Preferences:
All Canada

International Preferences:
United Kingdom
Europe
Western Europe

Industry Preferences

In Industrial/Energy prefer:
Energy
Oil and Gas Exploration
Oil & Gas Drilling,Explor

Additional Information

Year Founded: 2007
Capital Under Management: $101,800,000
Current Activity Level: Actively seeking new investments

EPIC INVESTMENT PARTNERS (AKA: EPIC PRIVATE EQUITY)

22 Billiter Street
London, United Kingdom EC3M 2RY
Phone: 44-20-7984-8884
Fax: 44-20-7984-8661
E-mail: info@epicip.com
Website: www.epicip.com

Management and Staff

Andrew Castle, Founder
Giles Brand, Founding Partner

Type of Firm

Private Equity Firm

Association Membership

British Venture Capital Association (BVCA)

Project Preferences

Type of Financing Preferred:
Leveraged Buyout
Early Stage
Expansion
Mezzanine
Turnaround
Management Buyouts

Size of Investments Considered:
Min Size of Investment Considered (000s): $1,729
Max Size of Investment Considered (000s): $17,290

Geographical Preferences

International Preferences:
United Kingdom
Europe
Western Europe

Additional Information

Year Founded: 2001
Capital Under Management: $138,200,000
Current Activity Level: Actively seeking new investments

EPIC VENTURES

One South Main Street
Eighth Floor
Salt Lake City, UT USA 84101
Phone: 801-524-8939
Fax: 801-524-8941
E-mail: slcinfo@wasatchvc.com
Website: www.epicvc.com

Other Offices

301 Griffin Street
Santa Fe, NM USA 87501
Phone: 505-603-1720

Management and Staff

Christopher Stone, Managing Director

Kent Madsen, Managing Director
Nicholaus Efstratis, Managing Director
Ryan Davis, Chief Financial Officer
Stephanie Spong, Principal
Todd Stevens, Venture Partner

Type of Firm

Bank Affiliated

Association Membership

National Venture Capital Association - USA (NVCA)
Natl Assoc of Small Bus. Inv. Co (NASBIC)

Project Preferences

Role in Financing:

Prefer role as deal originator but will also invest in deals created by others

Type of Financing Preferred:

Second Stage Financing
Early Stage
Seed
First Stage Financing

Size of Investments Considered:

Min Size of Investment Considered (000s): $500
Max Size of Investment Considered (000s): $5,000

Geographical Preferences

United States Preferences:

Rocky Mountain
West Coast
California
Southwest

Industry Focus

(% based on actual investment)

Internet Specific	36.1%
Computer Software and Services	17.6%
Computer Hardware	9.8%
Industrial/Energy	7.8%
Semiconductors/Other Elect.	6.9%
Communications and Media	6.6%
Biotechnology	5.8%
Consumer Related	5.3%
Medical/Health	3.3%
Other Products	0.8%

Additional Information

Name of Most Recent Fund: Epic Venture Fund IV (FKA: Wasatch Venture Fund IV)
Most Recent Fund Was Raised: 03/24/2008
Year Founded: 1994
Capital Under Management: $220,000,000
Current Activity Level: Actively seeking new investments
Method of Compensation: Return on invest. most important, but chg. closing fees, service fees, etc.

EPS FINANZ AG

Bodmerstrasse 9
Postfach 432
Zurich, Switzerland 8027
Phone: 41-43-344-3800
Fax: 41-43-344-3801
E-mail: info@epsvalueplus.ch
Website: www.epsvalueplus.ch

Other Offices

26 rue Adrian Lachenal
Geneva, Switzerland 1207
Phone: 41-22-700-2488
Fax: 41-22-786-0449

Management and Staff

Peter Letter, Chief Executive Officer

Type of Firm

Private Equity Firm

Association Membership

Swiss Venture Capital Association (SECA)
European Private Equity and Venture Capital Assoc.

Project Preferences

Type of Financing Preferred:

Early Stage
Expansion
Balanced

Geographical Preferences

International Preferences:

Switzerland
Europe

Industry Preferences

In Other prefer:

Socially Responsible
Environment Responsible

Additional Information

Year Founded: 1998
Capital Under Management: $18,500,000
Current Activity Level: Actively seeking new investments

EQT PARTNERS (AKA: EQT FUNDS MANAGEMENT, LTD.)

PO Box 269, Isabelle Chambers
Route Isabelle, St Peter Port
Guernsey, United Kingdom GY1 3RA
Phone: 44-1481-722-278
Fax: 44-1481-722-442
E-mail: info@eqt.se
Website: www.eqt.se

Other Offices

Taunusanlage 16
Frankfurt, Germany 60325
Phone: 49-69-247-0450
Fax: 49-69-247-045122

78 Brook Street
Ground Floor
London, United Kingdom W1K 5EF

Postboks 1241 Vika
Oslo, Norway 0110
Phone: 47-2323-7550
Fax: 47-2323-7560

Unit 2901, 29th Floor
Tower II, Plaza 66, 1366 Nanjing W Rd
Shanghai, China 200040
Phone: 86-21-6113-5868
Fax: 86-21-6113-5866

Pohjoisesplanadi 25A
Helsinki, Finland 00100
Phone: 358-9-696-2470
Fax: 358-9-6962-4710

One North Lexington Avenue
Eleventh Floor
White Plains, NY USA 10601
Phone: 914-220-0900
Fax: 914-428-0649

Grzybowska Park, 7th Floor
Grzybowska 5a Street
Warsaw, Poland 00-132
Phone: 48-22-324-5820
Fax: 48-22-324-5838

P.O. Box 16409
Stockholm, Sweden 10327
Phone: 46-8-5065-5300
Fax: 46-8-5065-5319

Dampfaergevej 27-29
Third Floor
Copenhagen, Denmark 2100
Phone: 45-3312-1236
Fax: 45-3312-1836

Leopoldstrasse 8
Munich, Germany D-80802
Phone: 49-892-554-990
Fax: 49-892-554-9999

1701 Hutchison House
10 Harcourt Road
Central, Hong Kong
Phone: 85-2-2801-6823
Fax: 85-2-2810-4188

Muhlebachstrasse 20
Zurich, Switzerland 8008
Phone: 41-43-244-8191
Fax: 41-43-244-8190

Management and Staff

Bengt Hellstrom, General Partner
Caspar Callerstrom, Partner
Christian Sinding, Partner
Conni Jonsson, Chief Executive Officer
David Chen, Vice President
Fredrik Atting, Managing Director
Jochen Martin, Partner
Jonas Ragnarsson, Chief Financial Officer
Juha Lindfors, Partner
Juhani Mikola, Partner

Mads Ditlevsen, Vice President
Martin Mok, Partner
Mikael Dahl, Partner
Peter Korsholm, Partner
Piotr Czapski, Partner
Thomas Ramsay, Partner

Type of Firm

Private Equity Firm

Association Membership

Hong Kong Venture Capital Association (HKVCA)
Swedish Venture Capital Association (SVCA)
European Private Equity and Venture Capital Assoc.

Project Preferences

Type of Financing Preferred:

Leveraged Buyout
Expansion
Mezzanine
Balanced
Later Stage
Management Buyouts
Special Situation

Size of Investments Considered:

Min Size of Investment Considered (000s): $13,700

Max Size of Investment Considered (000s): $118,700

Geographical Preferences

United States Preferences:

All U.S.

International Preferences:

Sweden
Switzerland
Taiwan
Europe
China
Hong Kong
Austria
Iceland
Eastern Europe
Scandanavia/Nordic Region
Finland
Germany
Norway
Denmark

Industry Focus

(% based on actual investment)

Medical/Health	39.7%
Consumer Related	32.3%
Other Products	11.0%
Industrial/Energy	6.2%
Computer Hardware	5.4%
Semiconductors/Other Elect.	5.0%
Communications and Media	0.4%

Additional Information

Name of Most Recent Fund: EQT Opportunity Fund
Most Recent Fund Was Raised: 12/19/2005
Year Founded: 1994
Capital Under Management: $12,000,000,000
Current Activity Level: Actively seeking new investments

EQUAL ELEMENTS

530 Wilshire Boulevard
Suite 100-101
Santa Monica, CA USA 90401
Phone: 619-985-7057

Management and Staff

David Mandel, Managing Director
Mark Anten, Chief Financial Officer
Rowland Hanson, Managing Partner
Steve Gormley, Managing Director

Type of Firm

Incubator/Development Program

Project Preferences

Type of Financing Preferred:

Early Stage

Geographical Preferences

United States Preferences:

All U.S.

Additional Information

Year Founded: 2006
Current Activity Level: Actively seeking new investments

EQUATIS AG

Seefeldstrasse 9
Zurich, Switzerland 8008
Phone: 41-1-250-20-80
Fax: 41-43-488-35-00
E-mail: nfo@equatis.com
Website: www.equatis.com

Type of Firm

Private Equity Firm

Additional Information

Current Activity Level: Actively seeking new investments

EQUEST PARTNERS, LTD.

Manfield House
1 Southampton Street
London, United Kingdom WC2R 0LR
Phone: 44-20-7240-7600
Fax: 44-20-7240-9555
E-mail: info@equest-partners.com
Website: www.equest-partners.com

Other Offices

No. 20 Malog Radojice
Belgrade, Serbia and Montenegro 11000
Phone: 381-11-266-0353

49, Patriarh Evtimi Boulevard
Sofia, Bulgaria
Phone: 359-2-851-9120
Fax: 359-2-851-9102

Management and Staff

George Krumov, Managing Partner
Kari Haataja, Managing Partner
Petri Karjalainen, Managing Partner

Type of Firm

Private Equity Firm

Project Preferences

Type of Financing Preferred:

Early Stage
Expansion
Start-up Financing
Seed
Startup

Geographical Preferences

International Preferences:

Bulgaria

Industry Preferences

In Communications prefer:

Telecommunications

In Consumer Related prefer:

Consumer
Retail

In Financial Services prefer:

Financial Services
Real Estate

Additional Information

Year Founded: 2000
Capital Under Management: $38,600,000
Current Activity Level: Actively seeking new investments

EQUIFIN CAPITAL PARTNERS

Seven Times Square
Suite 2106
New York, NY USA 10036
Phone: 212-382-6000
Website: www.equifincapital.com

Management and Staff

Douglas Goodman, Partner
Joseph Tomei, Managing Partner
Mani Sadeghi, Managing Partner

Type of Firm

Private Equity Firm

Project Preferences

Type of Financing Preferred:

Generalist PE

Geographical Preferences

United States Preferences:
All U.S.

Additional Information

Year Founded: 2005
Current Activity Level: Actively seeking new investments

EQUINOX CAPITAL, INC.

41 West Putnam Avenue
Greenwich, CT USA 06830
Phone: 203-622-1605
Fax: 203-622-4684
E-mail: info@equinox-capital.com
Website: www.equinox-capital.com

Management and Staff

John Wechsler, Partner
Kevin Lynch, Chief Financial Officer
Patrick Donnellan, Principal

Type of Firm

Private Equity Firm

Association Membership

Natl Assoc of Small Bus. Inv. Co (NASBIC)

Project Preferences

Role in Financing:
Prefer role as deal originator but will also invest in deals created by others

Type of Financing Preferred:
Leveraged Buyout
Expansion
Mezzanine
Generalist PE
Later Stage
Management Buyouts
Special Situation
Recapitalizations

Size of Investments Considered:
Min Size of Investment Considered (000s): $250
Max Size of Investment Considered (000s): $2,500

Geographical Preferences

United States Preferences:
All U.S.

Industry Preferences

In Semiconductor/Electr prefer:
Electronic Components
Analytic/Scientific
Optoelectronics

In Medical/Health prefer:
Medical Diagnostics
Diagnostic Services
Diagnostic Test Products
Drug/Equipmt Delivery
Medical Products
Disposable Med. Products
Health Services
Hospitals/Clinics/Primary

In Consumer Related prefer:
Education Related

In Industrial/Energy prefer:
Machinery

In Manufact. prefer:
Manufacturing

Additional Information

Year Founded: 1996
Capital Under Management: $75,000,000
Current Activity Level: Actively seeking new investments
Method of Compensation: Return on invest. most important, but chg. closing fees, service fees, etc.

EQUINOX S.A.

Boulevard du Prince Henri, 35
Luxembourg City, Luxembourg L-1724
Phone: 352-262-9861
Fax: 39-02-36516180
E-mail: info@eqx.ch
Website: www.eqx.com.ch

Other Offices

Riva Albertolli 1
Palazzo Gargantini
Lugano, Switzerland CH-6900
Phone: 41-91-911-5490
Fax: 41-91-911-5499

Management and Staff

Salvatore Mancuso, President, Founder

Type of Firm

Private Equity Firm

Project Preferences

Type of Financing Preferred:
Start-up Financing
Recapitalizations

Geographical Preferences

International Preferences:
Europe

Industry Preferences

In Medical/Health prefer:
Health Services

In Consumer Related prefer:
Food/Beverage
Consumer Products

In Transportation prefer:
Transportation

Additional Information

Year Founded: 2003
Current Activity Level: Actively seeking new investments

EQUINOX SECURITIES LIMITED (AKA: FASTVENTURES)

29 Harley Street
61-65 Conduit Street
London, United Kingdom WIG9QR
Phone: 44-20-7509-9500
Fax: 44-20-7509-9602
Website: www.equinoxonline.com

Type of Firm

Private Equity Firm

Additional Information

Current Activity Level: Actively seeking new investments

EQUIP VENTURES LLC

60 East 42nd Street
Suite 501
New York, NY USA 10165
Phone: 646-291-6310
Fax: 646-205-9136
E-mail: info@equipventures.com
Website: www.equipventures.com

Other Offices

2626 Hidden Valley Road
La Jolla, CA USA 92037
Phone: 858-551-1280
Fax: 858-551-1708

Management and Staff

David Waxman, Managing Partner
Mark Goros, Managing Partner

Type of Firm

Private Equity Firm

Project Preferences

Type of Financing Preferred:
Early Stage
Seed
Startup

Geographical Preferences

United States Preferences:
Southern California

International Preferences:
Israel

Industry Preferences

In Communications prefer:
Communications and Media

In Computer Software prefer:
Software

Additional Information

Year Founded: 2002

Current Activity Level: Actively seeking new investments

EQUIS CAPITAL PARTNERS

165 11th Street
Hoboken, NJ USA 07030
Website: www.equiscapitalpartners.com

Management and Staff

John Sheehan, Founder

Type of Firm

Private Equity Firm

Project Preferences

Type of Financing Preferred:
Balanced
Management Buyouts
Recapitalizations

Geographical Preferences

United States Preferences:
All U.S.

Industry Preferences

In Consumer Related prefer:
Consumer

In Business Serv. prefer:
Services

In Manufact. prefer:
Manufacturing

Additional Information

Year Founded: 2002
Current Activity Level: Actively seeking new investments

EQUITA MANAGEMENT GMBH (FKA: HARALD QUANDT PRIVATE EQUITY)

Inge Quandt Haus
Am Pilgerrain 15
Bad Homburg, Germany D-61352
Phone: 49-6172-9441-0
Fax: 49-6172-9441335
E-mail: info@equita.de
Website: www.equita.de

Management and Staff

Hans Moock, Managing Director
Hans Jurgen Wiemker, Chief Financial Officer
Hansjorg Schnabel, Managing Director
Michael Honig, Managing Partner
Werner Quillmann, Managing Partner

Type of Firm

Private Equity Firm

Association Membership

German Venture Capital Association (BVK)

Project Preferences

Type of Financing Preferred:
Leveraged Buyout
Expansion
Later Stage
Management Buyouts
Recapitalizations

Geographical Preferences

International Preferences:
Germany

Additional Information

Year Founded: 1991
Capital Under Management: $428,000,000
Current Activity Level: Actively seeking new investments

EQUITEK CAPITAL

2000 Auburn Drive
Suite 200
Beachwood, OH USA 44122
Phone: 216-378-7568
Fax: 216-378-7578
E-mail: info@equitekcapital.com
Website: www.equitekcapital.com

Other Offices

17 State Street
41st Floor
New York, NY USA 10004
Phone: 212-943-2170
Fax: 212-785-4834

4819 Emperor Boulevard
4th Floor
Durham, NC USA 27703
Phone: 919-313-4532
Fax: 919-313-4505

Management and Staff

Greg Somer, Managing Director
J. Paul Reilly Grim, Managing Director
John Gannon, Managing Director
Ken Ehrhart, Managing Director

Type of Firm

Private Equity Firm

Project Preferences

Type of Financing Preferred:
Expansion
Balanced

Size of Investments Considered:
Min Size of Investment Considered (000s): $500
Max Size of Investment Considered (000s): $1,500

Geographical Preferences

International Preferences:
All International

Industry Preferences

In Semiconductor/Electr prefer:
Semiconductor

In Manufact. prefer:
Manufacturing

Additional Information

Year Founded: 2000
Capital Under Management: $10,000,000
Current Activity Level: Actively seeking new investments

EQUITIS

9, rue de Teheran
Paris, France 75008
Phone: 33-1-5688-1616
Fax: 33-1-5688-1618
Website: www.equitis.fr

Type of Firm

Private Equity Firm

Association Membership

French Venture Capital Association (AFIC)
European Private Equity and Venture Capital Assoc.

Project Preferences

Type of Financing Preferred:
Early Stage
Expansion

Geographical Preferences

International Preferences:
Europe
France

Additional Information

Year Founded: 2000
Current Activity Level: Actively seeking new investments

EQUITRUST AG

ABC-Strasse 19
Hamburg, Germany 20354
Phone: 49-4037-48340
Fax: 49-4037-483410
E-mail: info@equitrust.de
Website: www.equitrust.de

Management and Staff

Guenther Casjens, Chief Executive Officer

Type of Firm

Private Equity Firm

Project Preferences

Type of Financing Preferred:
Fund of Funds
Generalist PE

Geographical Preferences

International Preferences:
Switzerland
Austria
Germany
All International

Additional Information
Year Founded: 2001
Capital Under Management: $305,100,000
Current Activity Level: Actively seeking new investments

EQUITY 11, LTD.

2701 Cambridge Court
Suite 420
Auburn Hills, MI USA 48326
Phone: 248-377-8012
E-mail: contact@equity11.com
Website: www.equity11.com

Management and Staff
JB Smith, Managing Partner
Larry Lee, Partner
Ralph Terry, Partner

Type of Firm
Private Equity Firm

Project Preferences

Type of Financing Preferred:
Expansion
Balanced

Additional Information
Year Founded: 2007
Current Activity Level: Actively seeking new investments

EQUITY AFRICA TRUST

No 3 Sherwood Road
Forest Town
Johannesburg, South Africa 2193
Phone: 27-11-646-1390
Fax: 27-11-646-1325
E-mail: info@equityafrica.com
Website: www.equityafrica.com

Type of Firm
Private Equity Firm

Association Membership
African Venture Capital Association (AVCA)

Project Preferences

Type of Financing Preferred:
Startup

Geographical Preferences

International Preferences:
South Africa

Industry Preferences

In Consumer Related prefer:
Consumer Products

In Agr/Forestr/Fish prefer:
Agriculture related

Additional Information
Year Founded: 2004
Current Activity Level: Actively seeking new investments

EQUITY PARTNERS GMBH

Konigsallee 60c
Dusseldorf, Germany 40212
Phone: 49-211-878-1181
Fax: 49-211-878-1189
E-mail: info@eqpa.com
Website: www.eqpa.com

Management and Staff
Carsten Schmeding, Managing Director

Type of Firm
Private Equity Firm

Project Preferences

Role in Financing:
Will function either as deal originator or investor in deals created by others

Type of Financing Preferred:
Fund of Funds
Generalist PE
Mezzanine
Public Companies

Size of Investments Considered:
Min Size of Investment Considered (000s): $7,742
Max Size of Investment Considered (000s): $23,227

Additional Information
Year Founded: 2006
Current Activity Level: Actively seeking new investments

EQUITY PARTNERS MANAGEMENT PTY LTD.

201 Kent Street
Level 12
Sydney, Australia 2000
Phone: 612-8298-5100
Fax: 612-8298-5150
E-mail: enquiries@equitypartners.com.au
Website: www.equitypartners.com.au

Management and Staff
Quentin Jones, Partner
Rajeev Dhawan, Partner
Richard Gregson, Partner

Type of Firm
Private Equity Firm

Association Membership
Australian Venture Capital Association (AVCAL)

Project Preferences

Role in Financing:
Will function either as deal originator or investor in deals created by others

Type of Financing Preferred:
Leveraged Buyout
Expansion
Later Stage
Management Buyouts
Acquisition
Industry Rollups
Private Placement

Size of Investments Considered:
Min Size of Investment Considered (000s): $5,641
Max Size of Investment Considered (000s): $16,116

Geographical Preferences

International Preferences:
Australia
New Zealand

Industry Focus
(% based on actual investment)

Other Products	41.1%
Computer Software and Services	16.9%
Medical/Health	16.9%
Consumer Related	15.2%
Internet Specific	4.9%
Industrial/Energy	4.9%

Additional Information
Year Founded: 1995
Capital Under Management: $144,600,000
Current Activity Level: Actively seeking new investments
Method of Compensation: Return on invest. most important, but chg. closing fees, service fees, etc.

EQUUS CAPITAL CORP.

2727 Allen Parkway
13th Floor
Houston, TX USA 77019
Phone: 713-529-0900
Fax: 713-529-9545
E-mail: cohen@equuscap.com
Website: www.equuscap.com

Management and Staff

Gary Forbes, Vice President
Hank Nicodemus, Chief Financial Officer

Type of Firm

Private Equity Firm

Project Preferences

Role in Financing:

Prefer role as deal originator but will also invest in deals created by others

Type of Financing Preferred:

Leveraged Buyout
Mezzanine
Special Situation

Size of Investments Considered:

Min Size of Investment Considered (000s): $2,000
Max Size of Investment Considered (000s): $5,000

Geographical Preferences

United States Preferences:

All U.S.

Industry Focus

(% based on actual investment)

Other Products	36.2%
Industrial/Energy	24.2%
Consumer Related	18.7%
Medical/Health	12.9%
Communications and Media	7.1%
Biotechnology	0.7%
Computer Software and Services	0.2%
Internet Specific	0.1%

Additional Information

Name of Most Recent Fund: Equus Equity Appreciation Fund
Most Recent Fund Was Raised: 01/01/1991
Year Founded: 1983
Capital Under Management: $150,000,000
Current Activity Level: Actively seeking new investments
Method of Compensation: Return on invest. most important, but chg. closing fees, service fees, etc.

EQUUS CHANDLER, LLC

800 Silverado Street
Suite 300
La Jolla, CA USA 92037
Phone: 858-551-8800
Management and Staff
David Bourne, General Partner

Type of Firm

Private Equity Advisor or Fund of Funds

Industry Preferences

In Financial Services prefer:

Real Estate

Additional Information

Year Founded: 2002
Capital Under Management: $800,000
Current Activity Level: Actively seeking new investments

EQVITEC PARTNERS OY

Fabianinkatu 8
P.O. Box 148
Helsinki, Finland FIN-00101
Phone: 358-20-780-9800
Fax: 358-20-780-9801
E-mail: info@eqvitec.com
Website: www.eqvitec.com

Other Offices

Brunnsgatan 7
Stockholm, Sweden SE-111 38
Phone: 46-8-676-6560
Fax: 46-8-676-6569

Management and Staff

Jari Mieskonen, Partner
Jukka Hayrynen, Partner
Jukka Makinen, Managing Partner
Kimmo Jyllila, Managing Partner
Pertti Nurmio, Partner

Type of Firm

Private Equity Firm

Association Membership

Finnish Venture Capital Association (FVCA)
Swedish Venture Capital Association (SVCA)
European Private Equity and Venture Capital Assoc.

Project Preferences

Type of Financing Preferred:

Early Stage
Expansion
Mezzanine
Balanced
Startup

Size of Investments Considered:

Min Size of Investment Considered (000s): $200
Max Size of Investment Considered (000s): $200,000

Geographical Preferences

United States Preferences:

All U.S.

International Preferences:

Sweden
Europe
Scandanavia/Nordic Region
Finland
Norway
Denmark
All International

Industry Preferences

In Communications prefer:

Communications and Media
Wireless Communications

In Computer Other prefer:

Computer Related

In Semiconductor/Electr prefer:

Electronics

In Industrial/Energy prefer:

Industrial Products
Materials

Additional Information

Name of Most Recent Fund: Eqvitec Technology Mezzanine Fund II
Most Recent Fund Was Raised: 03/16/2005
Year Founded: 1997
Capital Under Management: $524,800,000
Current Activity Level: Actively seeking new investments

ERASMUS MC

Dr. Molewaterplein 50
Kamer EE 19-14, Postbus 2040
Rotterdam, Netherlands 3000 CA
Website: www.erasmusmcfund.nl

Management and Staff

Harm De Vries, Partner
Tom Schwarz, Partner

Type of Firm

Private Equity Firm

Project Preferences

Type of Financing Preferred:

Early Stage
Seed

Geographical Preferences

International Preferences:

Netherlands

Industry Preferences

In Biotechnology prefer:

Biotechnology

In Medical/Health prefer:

Pharmaceuticals

Additional Information

Year Founded: 2007
Capital Under Management: $15,600,000
Current Activity Level: Actively seeking new investments

ERHVERVSINVEST NORD A/S

Nytorv 6
Postbox 1519
Aalborg, Denmark 9100
Phone: 45-702-032-93
Fax: 45-963-444-54
Website: www.erhvervsinvestnord.dk

Type of Firm

Bank Affiliated

Association Membership

Danish Venture Capital Association (DVCA)

Project Preferences

Type of Financing Preferred:
Expansion
Startup

Geographical Preferences

International Preferences:
Denmark

Additional Information

Year Founded: 2000
Capital Under Management: $28,300,000
Current Activity Level: Actively seeking new investments

ERICSSON VENTURE PARTNERS

712 Fifth Avenue
11th Floor
New York, NY USA 10019
Phone: 212-485-1100
Fax: 212-485-1194
E-mail: info@evp.com
Website: www.evp.com

Management and Staff

Jeff Low, Partner
Mark Maybell, Partner
Mark McAndrews, Partner
Scott Seidelmann, Partner
Sharat Raghavan, Partner

Type of Firm

Corporate PE/Venture

Project Preferences

Role in Financing:
Prefer role as deal originator but will also invest in deals created by others

Type of Financing Preferred:
Second Stage Financing
Early Stage
First Stage Financing

Size of Investments Considered:
Min Size of Investment Considered (000s): $2,240
Max Size of Investment Considered (000s): $30,000

Geographical Preferences

International Preferences:
Europe
Middle East

Industry Preferences

In Communications prefer:
Commercial Communications
CATV & Pay TV Systems
Radio & TV Broadcasting
Telecommunications
Wireless Communications
Data Communications
Satellite Microwave Comm.
Other Communication Prod.

In Internet Specific prefer:
E-Commerce Technology

Additional Information

Year Founded: 2001
Capital Under Management: $304,500,000
Current Activity Level: Actively seeking new investments

ERIMED BETEILIGUNGS-GESELLSCHAFT MBH

Hartmannstrasse 65
Erlangen, Germany D-91052
Phone: 49-9131-8924892
Fax: 49-9131-8924899
Website: www.erimed.de

Management and Staff

Peter Thumann, Managing Director

Type of Firm

Private Equity Firm

Project Preferences

Type of Financing Preferred:
Startup

Geographical Preferences

International Preferences:
Germany

Industry Preferences

In Computer Software prefer:
Software

In Medical/Health prefer:
Medical/Health

Additional Information

Year Founded: 1999
Current Activity Level: Actively seeking new investments

ERNSTROM INVEST AB

Ostra Hamngatan 19
Box 11304
Goteborg, Sweden 404 27
Phone: 46-31-890-300
Fax: 46-31-493-500
E-mail: info@ernstrom.se
Website: www.ernstrom.se

Management and Staff

Anne Gentzel, Managing Director

Type of Firm

Corporate PE/Venture

Association Membership

Swedish Venture Capital Association (SVCA)
European Private Equity and Venture Capital Assoc.

Project Preferences

Type of Financing Preferred:
Fund of Funds
Leveraged Buyout
Expansion
Turnaround

Size of Investments Considered:
Min Size of Investment Considered (000s): $106
Max Size of Investment Considered (000s): $2,655

Geographical Preferences

International Preferences:
Scandanavia/Nordic Region

Additional Information

Year Founded: 1918
Capital Under Management: $8,400,000
Current Activity Level: Actively seeking new investments

ESCALATE CAPITAL

150 Almaden Boulevard
Suite 925
San Jose, CA USA 95113
Phone: 408-200-0095
Fax: 650-854-5062
E-mail: info@escalatecapital.com
Website: www.escalatecapital.com

Other Offices

300 West Sixth Street
Suite 2300
Austin, TX USA 78701
Phone: 512-651-2100
Fax: 408-200-0099

Management and Staff

Chris Julich, Principal
Larry Bradshaw, Principal
Ross Cockrell, Managing Director
Tony Schell, Managing Director

Type of Firm
Private Equity Firm

Project Preferences

Type of Financing Preferred:
Expansion
Later Stage

Geographical Preferences

United States Preferences:
All U.S.

Additional Information
Name of Most Recent Fund: Escalate Capital I, L.P.
Most Recent Fund Was Raised: 05/15/2005
Year Founded: 2005
Capital Under Management: $192,000,000
Current Activity Level: Actively seeking new investments

ESFIN GESTION
2 place des Vosges
Immeuble La Fayette
Courbevoie, France 92022
Phone: 33-1-5523-0710
Fax: 33-1-4900-1982
E-mail: esfin-gestion@esfingestion.fr
Website: www.esfin-ides.com

Type of Firm
Private Equity Firm

Association Membership
French Venture Capital Association (AFIC)

Project Preferences

Type of Financing Preferred:
Balanced

Size of Investments Considered:
Min Size of Investment Considered (000s): $100
Max Size of Investment Considered (000s): $100,000

Geographical Preferences

International Preferences:
France

Industry Preferences

In Business Serv. prefer:
Services

Additional Information
Year Founded: 1983
Current Activity Level: Actively seeking new investments

ESP EQUITY PARTNERS LLC
172 45 Park Place South
Morristown, NJ USA 07960
Phone: 973-886-3422
Website: www.espequity.com

Management and Staff
Howard Weisman, General Partner
Jeffery Li, General Partner
S. Douglas Sheldon, General Partner

Type of Firm
Private Equity Firm

Project Preferences

Type of Financing Preferred:
Generalist PE

Geographical Preferences

United States Preferences:
All U.S.

International Preferences:
Europe
Asia

Industry Preferences

In Biotechnology prefer:
Biotechnology

In Medical/Health prefer:
Pharmaceuticals

Additional Information
Year Founded: 2005
Current Activity Level: Actively seeking new investments

ESPERANTE BV
Siriusdreef 22
Hoofddorp, Netherlands 2132 WT
Phone: 31-23-556-0466
Fax: 31-23-556-0461
Website: www.esperanteventures.com

Other Offices
216 Boulevard Saint Germain
Paris, France 75007
Phone: 33-1-5363-5087
Fax: 33-1-5363-5090

Management and Staff
Dean Slagel, Managing Director

Type of Firm
Private Equity Firm

Project Preferences

Type of Financing Preferred:
Early Stage
Balanced
Seed
Startup

Geographical Preferences

International Preferences:
Europe

Industry Preferences

In Medical/Health prefer:
Medical/Health
Medical Therapeutics
Other Therapeutic

Additional Information
Year Founded: 2004
Current Activity Level: Actively seeking new investments

ESPIGA CAPITAL GESTION SCR SA
C/ Alfonso XII 22, 4 izq.
Madrid, Spain 28014
Phone: 34-91-531-7277
Fax: 34-91-531-2552
E-mail: contact@espiga.com
Website: www.espiga.com

Management and Staff
Carlos Prado Perez-Seoane, Founding Partner
Juan Carvajal, Founding Partner

Type of Firm
Private Equity Firm

Association Membership
Spanish Venture Capital Association (ASCRI)

Project Preferences

Role in Financing:
Will function either as deal originator or investor in deals created by others

Type of Financing Preferred:
Leveraged Buyout
Expansion
Management Buyouts
Acquisition
Special Situation

Size of Investments Considered:
Min Size of Investment Considered (000s): $4,653
Max Size of Investment Considered (000s): $13,960

Geographical Preferences

International Preferences:
Portugal
Spain

Industry Focus
(% based on actual investment)

Consumer Related	35.7%
Other Products	30.3%

Semiconductors/Other Elect.	24.0%
Industrial/Energy	5.6%
Computer Software and Services	3.0%
Communications and Media	1.3%

Additional Information

Year Founded: 1998
Capital Under Management: $198,100,000
Current Activity Level: Actively seeking new investments

ESPIRITO SANTO (ES) VENTURES - SOCIEDADE DE CAPITAL DE RISCO

Praca Marques de Pombal
n 3A, 4 piso
Lisbon, Portugal 1250-161
Phone: 351-21-310-6490
Fax: 351-21-310-6425
E-mail: info@es-ventures.com
Website: www.es-ventures.com

Management and Staff

Jose Guerreiro de Sousa, Venture Partner

Type of Firm

Bank Affiliated

Project Preferences

Type of Financing Preferred:

Early Stage
Expansion
Private Placement
Startup

Size of Investments Considered:

Min Size of Investment Considered (000s): $1,000
Max Size of Investment Considered (000s): $10,000

Geographical Preferences

International Preferences:

Portugal

Industry Preferences

In Medical/Health prefer:

Medical/Health
Health Services

In Industrial/Energy prefer:

Energy Conservation Relat

Additional Information

Name of Most Recent Fund: FCR Espirito Santo Ventures II
Most Recent Fund Was Raised: 09/30/2006
Year Founded: 2000
Capital Under Management: $201,800,000
Current Activity Level: Actively seeking new investments

ESPIRITO SANTO CAPITAL - SOCIEDADE DE CAPITAL DE RISCO SA

Rua Alexandre Herculano, 38, 1
Lisboa, Portugal 1269-161
Phone: 351-21-351-5840
Fax: 351-21-351-5846
E-mail: es-capital@ip.pt
Website: www.escapital.pt

Other Offices

Calle Serrano
88-4 Planta
Madrid, Spain 28006
Phone: 34-91-400-5464
Fax: 34-91-435-3593

Av. Brigadeiro Faria Lima
3729-6 Itaim Bibi
Sao Paulo, Brazil 04538-905
Phone: 55-11-3074-7445
Fax: 55-11-3074-7462

Management and Staff

Antonio Silva Ricciardi, Managing Director
Emilia Franco Frazao, Managing Director
Joao Arantes e Oliveira, Chief Executive Officer

Type of Firm

Bank Affiliated

Association Membership

Portuguese Venture Capital Association (APCRI)
European Private Equity and Venture Capital Assoc.

Project Preferences

Role in Financing:

Will function either as deal originator or investor in deals created by others

Type of Financing Preferred:

Leveraged Buyout
Generalist PE
Expansion
Later Stage
Seed
Management Buyouts
Acquisition

Size of Investments Considered:

Min Size of Investment Considered (000s): $1,300
Max Size of Investment Considered (000s): $25,990

Geographical Preferences

International Preferences:

Liberia
Europe
Portugal
Switzerland
Brazil
Norway
France

Industry Preferences

In Computer Other prefer:

Computer Related

In Semiconductor/Electr prefer:

Electronics

In Biotechnology prefer:

Biotechnology

In Medical/Health prefer:

Medical/Health

In Consumer Related prefer:

Consumer

In Industrial/Energy prefer:

Energy
Industrial Products

Additional Information

Name of Most Recent Fund: Espirito Santo Infrastructure Fund I
Most Recent Fund Was Raised: 07/31/2007
Year Founded: 1988
Capital Under Management: $266,600,000
Current Activity Level: Actively seeking new investments

ESPIRITO SANTO TECH VENTURES

Rua das Amoreiras Tower 3
Suite 509
Lisbon, Portugal P-1070-274
Phone: 351-1-383-1529
Fax: 351-1-385-9237

Management and Staff

Michael E.S. De Mello, Principal

Type of Firm

Bank Affiliated

Project Preferences

Type of Financing Preferred:

Balanced

Additional Information

Year Founded: 2000
Current Activity Level: Actively seeking new investments

ESSEX WOODLANDS HEALTH VENTURES (FKA: WOODLANDS VENTURE)

717 Fifth Avenue
14th Floor, Suite B
New York, NY USA 10022
Phone: 646-429-1251
Fax: 212-355-2313
E-mail: ca@essexwoodlands.com
Website: www.ewhv.com

Other Offices

335 Bryant Street
Third Floor
Palo Alto, CA USA 94301
Phone: 650-543-1555
Fax: 650-327-9755

21 Waterway Avenue
Suite 225
The Woodlands, TX USA 77380
Phone: 281-364-1555
Fax: 281-364-9755

Berkeley Square House
Berkeley Square
London, United Kingdom W1J 6BR
Phone: 44-20-7529-2500
Fax: 44-20-7529-2501

Management and Staff

C. Thomas Caskey, Partner
Christopher Shen, Principal
Cynthia Doerr, Partner
Frank Young, Partner
Gilbert Gonzales, Partner
Guido Neels, Managing Director
Immanuel Thangaraj, Managing Director
James Currie, Managing Director
Jeff Himawan, Managing Director
Lisa Ricciardi, Partner
Mark Pacala, Managing Director
Martin Sutter, Managing Director
Michael Gertner, Partner
Nicolas Chronos, Partner
Petri Vainio, Managing Director
Phyllis Gardner, Partner
R.Scott Barry, Partner
Richard Kolodziejcyk, Chief Financial Officer
Ronald Eastman, Managing Director
Steve Wiggins, Managing Director
Tamara Elias, Principal
Toby Sykes, Principal

Type of Firm

Private Equity Firm

Association Membership

National Venture Capital Association - USA (NVCA)

Project Preferences

Role in Financing:

Prefer role as deal originator but will also invest in deals created by others

Type of Financing Preferred:

Second Stage Financing
Early Stage
Expansion
Balanced
Later Stage
First Stage Financing
Private Placement

Size of Investments Considered:

Min Size of Investment Considered (000s): $2,000
Max Size of Investment Considered (000s): $30,000

Geographical Preferences

International Preferences:

Europe
Asia

Industry Focus

(% based on actual investment)

Medical/Health	53.8%
Biotechnology	36.3%
Internet Specific	3.5%
Computer Software and Services	2.2%
Computer Hardware	2.0%
Communications and Media	1.1%
Other Products	0.6%
Consumer Related	0.3%
Industrial/Energy	0.1%

Additional Information

Name of Most Recent Fund: Essex Woodlands Health Ventures Fund VIII, L.P.
Most Recent Fund Was Raised: 02/11/2008
Year Founded: 1985
Capital Under Management: $2,400,000,000
Current Activity Level: Actively seeking new investments
Method of Compensation: Return on investment is of primary concern, do not charge fees

---

ESTAG CAPITAL AG

Fasanenstrasse 28
Berlin, Germany D-10719
Phone: 49-30-889249520
Fax: 49-30-889249528
E-mail: info@estag.de
Website: www.estag.de

Management and Staff

Karoly Horvath, Chief Executive Officer

Type of Firm

Private Equity Firm

Project Preferences

Type of Financing Preferred:

Fund of Funds
Early Stage
Expansion
Seed

Industry Preferences

In Computer Software prefer:

Software

In Consumer Related prefer:

Consumer

In Industrial/Energy prefer:

Alternative Energy
Environmental Related

Additional Information

Year Founded: 1998
Current Activity Level: Actively seeking new investments

ESTONIAN DEVELOPMENT FUND

Tornimae 5
Talinn, Estonia 10145
Phone: 372-616-1100
Fax: 372-616-1101
E-mail: info@arengufond.ee
Website: www.arengufond.ee

Type of Firm

Government Affiliated Program

Project Preferences

Type of Financing Preferred:

Early Stage

Geographical Preferences

International Preferences:

Europe

Additional Information

Year Founded: 2007
Current Activity Level: Actively seeking new investments

ETECH MANAGEMENT GMBH

Wagistrasse 6
Zurich, Switzerland 8592
Phone: 41-44-2046010
Fax: 41-44-2046011
E-mail: info@etech.ch
Website: www.etech.ch

Type of Firm

Private Equity Firm

Project Preferences

Type of Financing Preferred:

Seed

Geographical Preferences

International Preferences:

Europe

Additional Information

Year Founded: 2002
Capital Under Management: $3,900,000
Current Activity Level: Actively seeking new investments

ETF GROUP - NEXTFUND CAPITAL

Via Praccio 27
Massagno, Switzerland 6900
Phone: 41-91-961-6200
Fax: 41-91-961-6266

Website: www.etfgroup.com

Other Offices

Pilotystrasse 4
Munich, Germany 80538
Phone: 49-89-2303-5175
Fax: 49-89-2303-5298

Largo Quinto Alpini 12
Milan, Italy 20145
Phone: 39 02 4804 8401
Fax: 39 02 4802 4885

11, rue Lincoln
Paris, France 75008
Phone: 33-1-5689-0851
Fax: 33-1-5689-0859

100 Walker Street
Suite 15 Level 9
North Sydney, Australia NSW 2060
Phone: 61-2-9922-4256
Fax: 61-2-9954-3583

230 Park Avenue
Suite 814
New York, NY USA 10169
Phone: 1-212-983-7003
Fax: 1-212-983-7002

Ms Building 6F
2-4 Mita, 3-Chrome
Minato-ku Tokyo, Japan 108-0074
Phone: 81 3 5439 5601
Fax: 81 3 5439 5603

28 Saville Row
London, United Kingdom W1S 2EU
Phone: 44 20 7440 5300
Fax: 44 20 7440 5333

Management and Staff

Aldo Monteforte, Managing Director
Chris Pelly, Chief Financial Officer
Giorgio Ronchi, Chairman & CEO
Jens Bodenkamp, Managing Director
Lorcan Burke, Vice President
Maurice Khawam, Managing Director
Michael Smith, Vice President
Michael Sheldon, President
Olav Ostin, Managing Director
Peter Thompson, President
Robert Logan, Vice President
Stefano Devescovi, Managing Director
Sven Lung, Partner
Tetsushi Yamada, President

Type of Firm

Private Equity Firm

Association Membership

French Venture Capital Association (AFIC)

Project Preferences

Type of Financing Preferred:

Early Stage
Expansion
Startup

Geographical Preferences

Canadian Preferences:

All Canada

International Preferences:

Italy
Sweden
United Kingdom
Europe
Belgium
Germany
France

Industry Focus

(% based on actual investment)

Internet Specific	71.1%
Computer Software and Services	14.9%
Communications and Media	14.0%

Additional Information

Year Founded: 1996
Capital Under Management: $233,700,000
Current Activity Level: Actively seeking new investments

ETF MANAGER LLP (AKA: ENVIRONMENTAL TECHNOLOGIES FUND)

20 Berkeley Square
London, United Kingdom W1J 6EQ
Phone: 44-20-7318-0700
Fax: 44-20-7629-3338
E-mail: Info@etf.eu.com
Website: www.etf.eu.com

Management and Staff

Henrik Olsen, Partner
Patrick Sheehan, Partner
Per Ericsson, Venture Partner
Peter Horsburgh, Partner

Type of Firm

Private Equity Firm

Project Preferences

Role in Financing:

Prefer role as deal originator but will also invest in deals created by others

Type of Financing Preferred:

Expansion
Research and Development
Distressed Debt

Size of Investments Considered:

Min Size of Investment Considered (000s): $2,920
Max Size of Investment Considered (000s): $21,413

Geographical Preferences

International Preferences:

Western Europe

Industry Preferences

In Semiconductor/Electr prefer:

Electronic Components
Semiconductor

In Industrial/Energy prefer:

Alternative Energy
Energy Conservation Relat
Environmental Related

In Transportation prefer:

Transportation

In Manufact. prefer:

Manufacturing

In Agr/Forestr/Fish prefer:

Agriculture related

In Utilities prefer:

Utilities

Additional Information

Name of Most Recent Fund: Environmental Technologies Fund (AKA: ETF)
Most Recent Fund Was Raised: 11/30/2006
Year Founded: 2006
Capital Under Management: $173,800,000
Current Activity Level: Actively seeking new investments

ETF VENTURE FUNDS

100 Four Falls Corp. Center
Suite 101
West Conshohocken, PA USA 19428
Phone: 610-825-0250
Fax: 610-825-0205
E-mail: info@etfventurefunds.com
Website: www.etfventurefunds.com

Management and Staff

Howard Smith, Managing Director
Ian Berg, Managing Partner
Scott Bohrer, Principal
Tony Bifano, Managing Partner
Wayne Kimmel, Managing Partner

Type of Firm

Private Equity Firm

Association Membership

Mid-Atlantic Venture Association
National Venture Capital Association - USA (NVCA)

Project Preferences

Role in Financing:

Prefer role as deal originator but will also invest in deals created by others

Type of Financing Preferred:

Early Stage

Size of Investments Considered:
Min Size of Investment Considered (000s): $500
Max Size of Investment Considered (000s): $2,000

Geographical Preferences

United States Preferences:
Mid Atlantic
Pennsylvania
Delaware
Maryland
Virginia
Connecticut
New Jersey
New York
D. of Columbia

Industry Preferences

In Internet Specific prefer:
Internet

In Medical/Health prefer:
Medical/Health
Health Services

In Consumer Related prefer:
Entertainment and Leisure

In Financial Services prefer:
Financial Services

In Business Serv. prefer:
Services
Media

Additional Information
Name of Most Recent Fund: ETF Venture Fund II, L.P.
Most Recent Fund Was Raised: 07/01/2007
Year Founded: 2000
Capital Under Management: $50,000,000
Current Activity Level: Actively seeking new investments

ETHANOL CAPITAL MANAGEMENT, LLC
1230 Avenue of the Americas
7th Floor
New York, NY USA 10020
Phone: 917-639-4025
Fax: 917-639-4005
Website: www.ecapitalpartners.com

Management and Staff
Jack Porter, Chief Operating Officer

Type of Firm
Private Equity Firm

Project Preferences

Type of Financing Preferred:
Early Stage

Geographical Preferences

United States Preferences:
All U.S.

Industry Preferences

In Industrial/Energy prefer:
Energy
Alternative Energy

Additional Information
Name of Most Recent Fund: Ethanol Capital Partners, L.P.
Most Recent Fund Was Raised: 10/13/2004
Year Founded: 2003
Capital Under Management: $140,000,000
Current Activity Level: Actively seeking new investments

ETHEMBA CAPITAL, LTD.
P.O. Box 1234GT
South Church Street
Grand Cayman, Cayman Islands
Phone: 345-949-9876
Fax: 345-949-9877
E-mail: info@ethembacapital.com
Website: www.ethembacapital.co.uk

Other Offices
43 Portland Place
London, United Kingdom W1B 1QH
Phone: 44-207-299-8960
Fax: 44-207-299-8966

15 Boulevard Heletique
Geneva, Switzerland 1207
Phone: 41-22-718-7200
Fax: 41-22-718-7201

Management and Staff
Mark Jacobson, Managing Partner

Type of Firm
Private Equity Firm

Project Preferences

Type of Financing Preferred:
Leveraged Buyout
Turnaround
Acquisition

Geographical Preferences

International Preferences:
India
Central Europe
Turkey
Eastern Europe
Middle East
Africa

Industry Preferences

In Medical/Health prefer:
Medical/Health
Pharmaceuticals

In Consumer Related prefer:
Consumer
Entertainment and Leisure
Retail
Consumer Products

In Industrial/Energy prefer:
Industrial Products

In Financial Services prefer:
Real Estate

Additional Information
Year Founded: 2006
Current Activity Level: Actively seeking new investments

ETHOS PRIVATE EQUITY
35 Fricker Road
Illovo, South Africa 2196
Phone: 27-11-328-7400
Website: www.ethos.co.za

Management and Staff
Anthonie De Beer, Partner
Bill Ashmore, Partner
Busi Mabuza, Partner
Christo Roos, Partner
Claudia Koch, Partner
Craig Dreyer, Chief Financial Officer
Danie Jordaan, Partner
Garry Boyd, Partner
Ngalaah Chuphi, Partner
Rod Fehrsen, Partner
Shaun Zagnoev, Partner
Stuart Mackenzie, Partner

Type of Firm
Private Equity Firm

Association Membership
South African Venture Capital Association (SAVCA)

Project Preferences

Type of Financing Preferred:
Leveraged Buyout
Expansion
Turnaround
Management Buyouts
Acquisition

Geographical Preferences

International Preferences:
South Africa
Africa

Industry Focus
(% based on actual investment)

Consumer Related	91.0%

Other Products	7.7%
Communications and Media	1.0%
Computer Hardware	0.3%

Additional Information

Name of Most Recent Fund: Ethos Private Equity Fund IV (FKA: FirstCorp Capital IV)
Most Recent Fund Was Raised: 12/22/1998
Year Founded: 1984
Capital Under Management: $750,000,000
Current Activity Level: Actively seeking new investments

ETOILE ID (FKA: SPTF)

59 boulevard Haussman
Paris, France 75008
Phone: 33-1-4022-2046
Fax: 33-1-4022-4379
Website: www.credit-du-nord.fr

Type of Firm

Private Equity Firm

Association Membership

French Venture Capital Association (AFIC)

Project Preferences

Type of Financing Preferred:

Leveraged Buyout
Balanced

Size of Investments Considered:

Min Size of Investment Considered (000s): $619
Max Size of Investment Considered (000s): $2,474

Geographical Preferences

International Preferences:

France

Additional Information

Year Founded: 1987
Current Activity Level: Actively seeking new investments

EUCLIDSR PARTNERS

45 Rockefeller Plaza
Suite 3240
New York, NY USA 10111
Phone: 212-218-6880
Fax: 212-218-6877
Website: www.euclidsr.com

Management and Staff

A Bliss McCrum, General Partner
Barbara Dalton, General Partner
Elaine Jones, General Partner
Frank Lin, Principal
Graham D.S. Anderson, General Partner
Matthew Rothman, Principal
Milton Pappas, General Partner
Raymond Whitaker, General Partner
Stephen Reidy, General Partner

Type of Firm

Private Equity Firm

Project Preferences

Role in Financing:

Prefer role as deal originator but will also invest in deals created by others

Type of Financing Preferred:

Second Stage Financing
Later Stage
First Stage Financing

Geographical Preferences

International Preferences:

Italy
United Kingdom
Germany
France

Industry Focus

(% based on actual investment)

Computer Software and Services	22.5%
Biotechnology	22.3%
Internet Specific	22.1%
Medical/Health	18.5%
Semiconductors/Other Elect.	5.5%
Industrial/Energy	3.3%
Computer Hardware	2.7%
Communications and Media	1.5%
Consumer Related	1.4%
Other Products	0.3%

Additional Information

Year Founded: 2000
Capital Under Management: $282,000,000
Current Activity Level: Actively seeking new investments
Method of Compensation: Return on investment is of primary concern, do not charge fees

EURAZEO (FKA: GAZ-ET-EAUX & AZEO)

3 rue Jacques Bingen
Paris, France 75017
Phone: 33-1-4415-0111
Fax: 33-1-4766-8441
E-mail: webmaster@eurazeo.com
Website: www.eurazeo.com

Management and Staff

Patrick Sayer, President

Type of Firm

Corporate PE/Venture

Association Membership

French Venture Capital Association (AFIC)
European Private Equity and Venture Capital Assoc.

Project Preferences

Type of Financing Preferred:

Leveraged Buyout
Expansion
Other
Recapitalizations

Geographical Preferences

International Preferences:

Europe
Asia
France

Industry Preferences

In Communications prefer:

Communications and Media

In Internet Specific prefer:

Internet

In Semiconductor/Electr prefer:

Electronics

In Consumer Related prefer:

Consumer

In Industrial/Energy prefer:

Industrial Products

In Business Serv. prefer:

Media

Additional Information

Name of Most Recent Fund: Eurazeo Co-Investment Partners
Most Recent Fund Was Raised: 07/06/2006
Year Founded: 2000
Capital Under Management: $3,144,300,000
Current Activity Level: Actively seeking new investments

EUREFI

Maison de la Formation
Centre Jean Monnet
Longwy, France 54414
Phone: 33-352-307-2891
Fax: 33-352-30728944
E-mail: info@eurefi.org
Website: www.eurefi.org

Management and Staff

Bernard Moreau, Vice President
Georges Schmit, President
Rene Delcomminette, Vice President

Type of Firm

Private Equity Firm

Association Membership

French Venture Capital Association (AFIC)

Project Preferences

Type of Financing Preferred:

Leveraged Buyout

Early Stage
Expansion
Startup

Size of Investments Considered:
Min Size of Investment Considered (000s): $123
Max Size of Investment Considered (000s): $1,229

Geographical Preferences

International Preferences:
Luxembourg
Belgium
France

Additional Information
Year Founded: 1995
Current Activity Level: Actively seeking new investments

EUREKA GROWTH CAPITAL
3420 Bell Atlantic Tower
1717 Arch Street
Philadelphia, PA USA 19103
Phone: 267-238-4200
Fax: 267-238-4201
Website: www.eurekagrowth.com

Other Offices
770 Township Line Road
Suite 150
Yardley, PA USA 19067
Phone: 267-238-4205
Fax: 267-288-4201

Management and Staff
Christian Miller, Vice President
Christopher Hanssens, Managing Partner
Jonathan Chou, Vice President
Jonathan Zimbalist, Partner
Michael Foran, Chief Financial Officer
Thomas Calibeo, Partner

Type of Firm
Private Equity Firm

Association Membership
Mid-Atlantic Venture Association

Project Preferences

Role in Financing:
Prefer role as deal originator but will also invest in deals created by others

Type of Financing Preferred:
Leveraged Buyout
Expansion
Generalist PE
Later Stage
Management Buyouts
Acquisition
Recapitalizations

Size of Investments Considered:
Min Size of Investment Considered (000s): $4,000
Max Size of Investment Considered (000s): $10,000

Geographical Preferences

United States Preferences:
Mid Atlantic
Pennsylvania

Industry Focus
(% based on actual investment)

Other Products	54.1%
Medical/Health	15.9%
Consumer Related	14.1%
Computer Software and Services	13.2%
Communications and Media	2.6%

Additional Information
Name of Most Recent Fund: Eureka II, L.P.
Most Recent Fund Was Raised: 12/31/2005
Year Founded: 1999
Capital Under Management: $215,000,000
Current Activity Level: Actively seeking new investments
Method of Compensation: Return on invest. most important, but chg. closing fees, service fees, etc.

EURIDI
18 avenue Matignon
Paris, France 75008
Phone: 33-1-5527-8040
Fax: 33-1-4017-0444
Website: www.euridi.fr

Type of Firm
Private Equity Firm

Project Preferences

Type of Financing Preferred:
Leveraged Buyout
Expansion

Geographical Preferences

International Preferences:
Europe
France

Additional Information
Year Founded: 1991
Current Activity Level: Actively seeking new investments

EURO CAPITAL
3, rue Francois de Curel
Metz, France 57000
Phone: 33-3-8737-7065
Fax: 33-3-8737-7281

Type of Firm
Bank Affiliated

Project Preferences

Type of Financing Preferred:
Expansion

Geographical Preferences

International Preferences:
France

Additional Information
Year Founded: 1999
Current Activity Level: Actively seeking new investments

EURO CAPITAL PARTNERS
Kohlmarkt 3
Vienna, Austria 1010
Phone: 43-1-535-4545
Fax: 43-1-535-3655
E-mail: office@ecp.co.at
Website: www.eurocapitalpartners.com

Management and Staff
Johannes Strohmayer, Partner
Robert Schaechter, Partner

Type of Firm
Corporate PE/Venture

Association Membership
European Private Equity and Venture Capital Assoc.

Project Preferences

Type of Financing Preferred:
Leveraged Buyout
Expansion

Geographical Preferences

United States Preferences:
All U.S.

International Preferences:
Europe

Industry Preferences

In Communications prefer:
Other Communication Prod.

In Semiconductor/Electr prefer:
Electronics

In Biotechnology prefer:
Biotechnology

In Medical/Health prefer:
Medical/Health

In Industrial/Energy prefer:
Industrial Products

In Financial Services prefer:
Financial Services
Insurance
Real Estate

Additional Information

Year Founded: 2002
Current Activity Level: Actively seeking new investments

EUROCOM HOLDINGS

2 Don Friedman Street
Ramat Gan, Israel 52141
Phone: 972-3-7530000
Fax: 972-3-7530001
E-mail: info@eurocomco.il
Website: www.eurocom.co.il

Type of Firm

Private Equity Firm

Additional Information

Year Founded: 2009
Current Activity Level: Actively seeking new investments

EUROFUND LP

87 Hayarkon Street
Tel Aviv, Israel 63432
Phone: 972 3 520 2447
Fax: 972 3 527 0041
E-mail: info@eurofund.co.il
Website: www.eurofund.co.il

Management and Staff

Gidi Federmann, Partner
Ron Hiram, Managing Partner

Type of Firm

Private Equity Firm

Association Membership

Israel Venture Association

Project Preferences

Type of Financing Preferred:

Early Stage

Geographical Preferences

International Preferences:

Europe

Industry Preferences

In Communications prefer:

Communications and Media

In Internet Specific prefer:

Internet

Additional Information

Year Founded: 1994
Capital Under Management: $72,000,000
Current Activity Level: Actively seeking new investments

EUROMEZZANINE CONSEIL (AKA: EUROMEZZANINE GESTION)

11, rue Scribe
Paris, France 75009
Phone: 33-1-5330-2330
Fax: 33-1-5330-2340
Website: www.euromezzanine.com

Management and Staff

Guy Fabritius, President
Thierry Raiff, General Director

Type of Firm

Investment Management Firm

Association Membership

French Venture Capital Association (AFIC)
European Private Equity and Venture Capital Assoc.

Project Preferences

Role in Financing:

Will function either as deal originator or investor in deals created by others

Type of Financing Preferred:

Leveraged Buyout
Mezzanine
Turnaround
Balanced
Acquisition
Recapitalizations

Size of Investments Considered:

Min Size of Investment Considered (000s): $9,050
Max Size of Investment Considered (000s): $103,426

Geographical Preferences

International Preferences:

Europe
France

Industry Focus

(% based on actual investment)

Other Products	67.9%
Computer Software and Services	18.2%
Medical/Health	13.7%
Consumer Related	0.2%

Additional Information

Name of Most Recent Fund: Euromezzanine 5 FCPR
Most Recent Fund Was Raised: 07/29/2005
Year Founded: 1990
Capital Under Management: $1,939,200,000
Current Activity Level: Actively seeking new investments

EUROPEAN BANK FOR RECONSTRUCTION AND DEVELOPMENT (AKA: EBRD)

36 str.1
Bolshaya Molchanovka
Moscow, Russia 121069
Phone: 7-95-787-1111
Fax: 7-95-787-1122
E-mail: generalenquiries@ebrd.com
Website: www.ebrd.com

Other Offices

One Exchange Square
London, United Kingdom EC2A 2JN
Phone: 44-20-7338-6372
Fax: 44-20-7338-6690

Kalku Street
Riga, Latvia 1050
Phone: 371-7-830-300
Fax: 371-7-830-301

Type of Firm

Government Affiliated Program

Association Membership

Russian Venture Capital Association (RVCA)

Project Preferences

Type of Financing Preferred:

Leveraged Buyout
Balanced

Geographical Preferences

International Preferences:

Europe
Russia

Industry Preferences

In Communications prefer:

Communications and Media
Telecommunications

In Industrial/Energy prefer:

Energy
Environmental Related

In Transportation prefer:

Transportation

In Financial Services prefer:

Real Estate

In Agr/Forestr/Fish prefer:

Agribusiness

Additional Information

Year Founded: 1991
Current Activity Level: Actively seeking new investments

EUROPEAN CAPITAL FINANCIAL SERVICES LTD.

112 avenue Kleber
Paris, France 75784
Phone: 33-1-4068-0666
Fax: 33-1-4068-0688
E-mail: info@europeancapital.com
Website: www.europeancapital.com

Other Offices

25 Bedford Street
London, United Kingdom WC2E 9ES
Phone: 44-207-539-7000
Fax: 44-207-539-7001

Taunusanlage 18
Frankfurt, Germany 60325
Phone: 49-69-7171-2970
Fax: 49-69-717-129-730

C/Lopez de Hoyos, 35, 1
Madrid, Spain 28002
Phone: 34-91-745-9963

Management and Staff

Didier Lefevre, Principal
Etienne Haubold, Vice President
Ira Wagner, President
Juan Carlos Morales Cortes, Vice President
Luis Felipe Castellanos, Managing Director
Malon Wilkus, Chairman & CEO
Nathalie Faure Beaulieu, Managing Director
Robert Von Finckenstein, Managing Director
Roland Cline, Partner
Tristan Parisot, Managing Director
Walter Munnich, Managing Director

Type of Firm

Private Equity Firm

Association Membership

French Venture Capital Association (AFIC)

Project Preferences

Type of Financing Preferred:
Leveraged Buyout
Mezzanine
Generalist PE
Acquisition
Recapitalizations

Size of Investments Considered:
Min Size of Investment Considered (000s): $6,980
Max Size of Investment Considered (000s): $698,032

Geographical Preferences

International Preferences:
Europe

Industry Preferences

In Business Serv. prefer:
Services
Distribution

In Manufact. prefer:
Manufacturing

Additional Information

Name of Most Recent Fund: European Capital Ltd.
Most Recent Fund Was Raised: 08/18/2005
Year Founded: 2004
Capital Under Management: $1,306,800,000
Current Activity Level: Actively seeking new investments

EUROPEAN EQUITY PARTNERS

76 Brook Street
London, United Kingdom W1K 5EE
Phone: 44-207-629-9992
Fax: 44-207-629-2072
E-mail: mail@eeplp.com
Website: www.eeplp.com

Other Offices

Grevture Gatan 30
6th Floor
Stockholm, Sweden 114 38
Phone: 46-8-679-5704
Fax: 46-8701-371-789

8 Rue Montesquieu
Paris, France 75001
Phone: 33-1-7543-5530
Fax: 33-1-7543-5533

Management and Staff

David Kauffmann, General Partner
Hans Blomberg, Founder
Neil Boughton, Chief Financial Officer

Type of Firm

Private Equity Firm

Project Preferences

Type of Financing Preferred:
Early Stage
Balanced
Later Stage

Geographical Preferences

International Preferences:
Europe

Industry Preferences

In Communications prefer:
Telecommunications

In Medical/Health prefer:
Health Services

Additional Information

Year Founded: 1999
Capital Under Management: $47,000,000
Current Activity Level: Actively seeking new investments

EUROPEAN FOUNDERS FUND GMBH

Lindenalle 45
Cologne, Germany 50698
E-mail: info@europeanfounders.com
Website: www.europeanfounders.com

Management and Staff

Alexander Samwer, Co-Founder
Marc Samwer, Co-Founder
Oliver Samwer, Co-Founder

Type of Firm

Private Equity Firm

Project Preferences

Type of Financing Preferred:
Early Stage
Seed

Size of Investments Considered:
Min Size of Investment Considered (000s): $500
Max Size of Investment Considered (000s): $2,000

Geographical Preferences

Canadian Preferences:
All Canada

International Preferences:
Europe

Industry Preferences

In Communications prefer:
Wireless Communications

In Computer Software prefer:
Software

In Internet Specific prefer:
Internet

Additional Information

Year Founded: 2007
Current Activity Level: Actively seeking new investments

EUROPEAN HOTEL CAPITAL

Herengracht 469
Amsterdam, Netherlands 1017 BS
Phone: 31-20-522-6330
Fax: 31-20-522-6333
Website: www.europeanhotelcapital.com

Type of Firm

Private Equity Firm

Project Preferences

Type of Financing Preferred:
Leveraged Buyout

Geographical Preferences

International Preferences:
Netherlands
Western Europe
Belgium
France

Industry Preferences

In Consumer Related prefer:
Hotels and Resorts

Additional Information
Year Founded: 2003
Current Activity Level: Actively seeking new investments

EUROPEAN INVESTMENT BANK, THE (AKA: EIB)

100, boulevard Konrad Adenauer
Luxembourg, Luxembourg L - 2950
Phone: 352-4379-1
Fax: 352-4379-6897
E-mail: info@eib.org
Website: www.eib.org

Management and Staff
Carlos Da Silva Costa, Vice President
Dario Scannapieco, Vice President
Eva Srejber, Vice President
Marta Gajecka, Vice President
Matthias Kollatz-Ahnen, Vice President
Philippe Maystadt, President
Philippe De Fontaine Vive Curtaz, Vice President
Simon Brooks, Vice President
Torsten Gersfelt, Vice President

Type of Firm
Bank Affiliated

Association Membership
Emerging Markets Private Equity Association
African Venture Capital Association (AVCA)

Project Preferences

Type of Financing Preferred:
Fund of Funds
Expansion
Generalist PE
Balanced

Size of Investments Considered:
Min Size of Investment Considered (000s): $2,368
Max Size of Investment Considered (000s): $11,841

Geographical Preferences

International Preferences:
Tunisia
Jordan
Europe
Egypt
Lebanon
Algeria
Pacific Rim
Israel
Morocco
Syria
Africa

Industry Preferences

In Communications prefer:
Communications and Media

In Internet Specific prefer:
Internet

In Computer Other prefer:
Computer Related

In Semiconductor/Electr prefer:
Electronics
Semiconductor

In Biotechnology prefer:
Biotechnology

In Medical/Health prefer:
Medical/Health

In Consumer Related prefer:
Consumer
Education Related

In Industrial/Energy prefer:
Energy

In Transportation prefer:
Transportation

In Financial Services prefer:
Real Estate
Financial Services

In Manufact. prefer:
Manufacturing

In Utilities prefer:
Utilities

Additional Information
Year Founded: 1957
Capital Under Management: $462,900,000
Current Activity Level: Actively seeking new investments

EUROPEAN INVESTMENT FUND (AKA: EIF)

43, avenue J.F. Kennedy
Luxembourg, Luxembourg L-2968
Phone: 352-42-66-881
Fax: 352-42-668-8200
E-mail: info@eif.org
Website: www.eif.org

Management and Staff
Richard Pelly, Chief Executive Officer
Thomas Meyer, Managing Director

Type of Firm
Bank Affiliated

Association Membership
European Private Equity and Venture Capital Assoc.

Project Preferences

Type of Financing Preferred:
Fund of Funds
Early Stage
Expansion

Size of Investments Considered:
Min Size of Investment Considered (000s): $1,000
Max Size of Investment Considered: No Limit

Geographical Preferences

International Preferences:
Portugal
Europe
Germany

Industry Preferences

In Industrial/Energy prefer:
Energy

Additional Information
Year Founded: 1994
Capital Under Management: $3,619,800,000
Current Activity Level: Actively seeking new investments

EUROPEAN ISLAMIC INVESTMENT BANK PLC

131 Finsbury Pavement
London, United Kingdom EC2A 1NT
Phone: 44-20-7847-9900
Fax: 44-20-7847-901
E-mail: contactus@eiib.co.uk
Website: www.eiib.co.uk

Management and Staff
Danie Marx, Managing Director
John Weguelin, Chief Executive Officer

Type of Firm
Bank Affiliated

Project Preferences

Type of Financing Preferred:
Generalist PE
Balanced
Public Companies

Geographical Preferences

International Preferences:
Europe
Middle East
Africa

Industry Preferences

In Consumer Related prefer:
Retail
Consumer Products

In Industrial/Energy prefer:
Energy

In Transportation prefer:
Transportation

In Financial Services prefer:
Real Estate

In Business Serv. prefer:
Services

In Agr/Forestr/Fish prefer:
Agriculture related

Additional Information
Year Founded: 2005
Current Activity Level: Actively seeking new investments

EUROPEAN TECHNOLOGY VENTURES SA (AKA: ETV CAPITAL SA)
1 Tenterden Street
1st Floor
London, United Kingdom W1S 1TA
Phone: 44-20-7907-2370
Fax: 44-20-7907-2399
Website: www.etvcapital.com

Type of Firm
Private Equity Firm

Project Preferences

Type of Financing Preferred:
Balanced

Geographical Preferences

International Preferences:
Ireland
United Kingdom
Europe

Additional Information
Year Founded: 2003
Current Activity Level: Actively seeking new investments

EUROUS VENTURES
101 California Street
Suite 2710
San Francisco, CA USA 94111
Phone: 415-409-1116
E-mail: info@eurousventures.com
Website: www.eurousventures.com

Other Offices
2000 Commonwealth Avenue
Auburndale, MA USA 02466

Dolderstr. 14
Zurich, Switzerland
Phone: 41-79-792-9066

Management and Staff
Alain Renaud, Venture Partner
Cindy Steiner, Venture Partner
Jan Nygren, Venture Partner
John Turner, General Partner
Jon Rortveit, Venture Partner
Kay Thompson, Venture Partner
Lucian Wagner, General Partner
Vincent Titolo, General Partner
William Wick, Chief Financial Officer

Type of Firm
Private Equity Firm

Project Preferences

Type of Financing Preferred:
Expansion
Later Stage

Geographical Preferences

International Preferences:
Europe

Industry Preferences

In Communications prefer:
Communications and Media
Wireless Communications

In Computer Software prefer:
Software

In Semiconductor/Electr prefer:
Semiconductor

Additional Information
Year Founded: 2005
Current Activity Level: Actively seeking new investments

EUROVENTURES CAPITAL KFT. (AKA: EV CAPITAL PARTNERS LTD.)
HegMartonhegyi str. 61/A
H Budapest
Budapest, Hungary 1124
Phone: 36-1-309-7900
Fax: 36-1-319-4762
E-mail: office@euroventures.hu
Website: www.euroventures.hu

Management and Staff
Andras Geszti, Managing Partner
Ivan Halasz, Principal
Peter Tanczos, Partner
Thomas Howells, Partner

Type of Firm
Private Equity Firm

Association Membership
Hungarian Venture Capital Association (HVCA)
European Private Equity and Venture Capital Assoc.

Project Preferences

Type of Financing Preferred:
Early Stage
Expansion
Start-up Financing
Seed

Size of Investments Considered:
Min Size of Investment Considered (000s): $650
Max Size of Investment Considered (000s): $6,000

Geographical Preferences

International Preferences:
Hungary
Slovak Repub.
Czech Republic
Central Europe
Poland
Eastern Europe
Estonia
Latvia
Lithuania

Industry Preferences

In Consumer Related prefer:
Consumer

In Industrial/Energy prefer:
Industrial Products

In Transportation prefer:
Transportation
Aerospace

In Business Serv. prefer:
Services

Additional Information
Year Founded: 1989
Capital Under Management: $99,400,000
Current Activity Level: Actively seeking new investments

EUROVESTECH PLC
29 Curzon Street
London, United Kingdom W1J 7TR
Phone: 44-207-491-0770
Fax: 44-207-491-9595
E-mail: enquiries@eurovestech.com
Website: www.eurovestech.co.uk

Management and Staff
Ariella Berger, President
Richard Bernstein, Chief Executive Officer

Type of Firm
Private Equity Firm

Project Preferences

Type of Financing Preferred:
Early Stage

Geographical Preferences

International Preferences:
United Kingdom
Europe
Israel

Additional Information
Year Founded: 2000
Capital Under Management: $14,000,000
Current Activity Level: Actively seeking new investments

EVALUATION ASSOCIATES
200 Connecticut Avenue
Suite 700
Norwalk, CT USA 06854-1958
Phone: 203-855-2200
Fax: 203-855-2373
Website: www.evaluationassociates.com

Type of Firm
Service Provider

Additional Information
Year Founded: 1976
Current Activity Level: Actively seeking new investments

EVERCORE PARTNERS
55 East 52nd Street
43rd Floor
New York, NY USA 10055
Phone: 212-857-3100
Fax: 212-857-3101
E-mail: info@evercore.com
Website: www.evercore.com

Other Offices
Lazaro Cardenas 2400 Pte.
Los Soles, Torre D, D-33
Graza Garcia, Nuevo Leon, Mexico 66267

10 Hill Street
London, United Kingdom W1J 5NQ
Phone: 44-207-268-2700
Fax: 44-207-268-2710

Three Embarcadero Center
Suite 560
San Francisco, CA USA 94111
Phone: 415-989-8900
Fax: 415-989-8929

Blvd. Manuel Avila Camacho 36
piso 22 Torre Esmeralda II
Mexico City, Distrito Federal , Mexico 11000

Management and Staff
Adam Frankel, Senior Managing Director
Ciara Burnham, Senior Managing Director
Daniel Ross, Managing Director
George Ackert, Senior Managing Director
James Matthews, Senior Managing Director
John Dillon, Senior Managing Director
Justin Steil, Vice President
Kathleen Reiland, Senior Managing Director
Mark Burton, Senior Managing Director
Mark Friedman, Senior Managing Director
Mayer Bick, Vice President
Nancy Bryson, Managing Director
Neeraj Mital, Senior Managing Director
Philippe Camus, Senior Managing Director
Ralph Schlosstein, Chief Executive Officer
Ray Newton, Senior Managing Director
Robert Walsh, Chief Financial Officer
Robert Pacha, Senior Managing Director
Robert Gillespie, Senior Managing Director
Roger Altman, Chairman & CEO
Sangam Pant, Senior Managing Director
Sky Dayton, Venture Partner
Stephen Sieh, Managing Director

Type of Firm
Private Equity Firm

Project Preferences

Type of Financing Preferred:
Leveraged Buyout
Early Stage
Generalist PE

Size of Investments Considered:
Min Size of Investment Considered (000s): $1,000
Max Size of Investment Considered (000s): $5,000

Geographical Preferences

United States Preferences:
All U.S.

International Preferences:
Mexico

Industry Focus
(% based on actual investment)

Other Products	77.8%
Medical/Health	17.9%
Communications and Media	1.9%
Internet Specific	1.1%
Computer Software and Services	1.1%
Computer Hardware	0.2%

Additional Information
Name of Most Recent Fund: Evercore Capital Partners II, L.P.
Most Recent Fund Was Raised: 12/03/2002
Year Founded: 1996
Capital Under Management: $120,000,000
Current Activity Level: Actively seeking new investments

EVERGREEN CAPITAL PARTNERS, INC.
150 East 58th Street
New York, NY USA 10155
Phone: 212-813-0758
Fax: 212-813-0754
Website: www.evergreencap.ca

Management and Staff
Richard Smith, President

Type of Firm
Service Provider

Project Preferences

Role in Financing:
Prefer role as deal originator

Type of Financing Preferred:
Leveraged Buyout
Expansion
Generalist PE
Later Stage
Management Buyouts
Acquisition
Private Placement

Size of Investments Considered:
Min Size of Investment Considered (000s): $3,000
Max Size of Investment Considered (000s): $300,000

Geographical Preferences

United States Preferences:
All U.S.

Canadian Preferences:
All Canada

Industry Preferences

In Communications prefer:
Communications and Media

In Computer Other prefer:
Computer Related

In Semiconductor/Electr prefer:
Laser Related
Analytic/Scientific

In Biotechnology prefer:
Biotechnology

In Medical/Health prefer:
Medical/Health

In Consumer Related prefer:
Consumer
Education Related

In Industrial/Energy prefer:
Alternative Energy
Energy Conservation Relat
Industrial Products

In Transportation prefer:
Transportation

In Financial Services prefer:
Financial Services

In Business Serv. prefer:
Distribution

In Manufact. prefer:
Publishing

Additional Information

Year Founded: 1993
Current Activity Level: Actively seeking new investments
Method of Compensation: Function primarily in service area, receive contingent fee in cash or equity

---

EVERGREEN PACIFIC PARTNERS LLC

1700 Seventh Avenue
Suite 2300
Seattle, WA USA 98101
Phone: 206-262-4709
Fax: 206-262-4715
Website: www.eppcapital.com

Management and Staff

Michael Nibarger, Partner
T.J. McGill, Partner
Tim Brillon, Chief Financial Officer
Timothy Bernardez, Partner

Type of Firm

Private Equity Firm

Project Preferences

Type of Financing Preferred:

Leveraged Buyout
Management Buyouts

Geographical Preferences

United States Preferences:

Northwest
All U.S.

Canadian Preferences:

Western Canada

Industry Preferences

In Communications prefer:

Radio & TV Broadcasting

In Consumer Related prefer:

Consumer Products

In Business Serv. prefer:

Distribution

In Manufact. prefer:

Manufacturing

Additional Information

Year Founded: 2003
Capital Under Management: $227,700,000
Current Activity Level: Actively seeking new investments

EVERGREEN VENTURE PARTNERS

96 Rothschild Boulevard
P.O. Box 14111
Tel Aviv, Israel 65224
Phone: 972-3-710-8282
Fax: 972-3-710-8210
E-mail: info@evergreen.co.il
Website: www.evergreen.co.il

Management and Staff

Adi Gan, General Partner
Alan Adler, Venture Partner
Amichai Hammer, Chief Financial Officer
Boaz Dinte, Managing Director
Erez Shachar, Managing Partner
Limor Sandach, Principal
Moty Hoss, Chief Financial Officer

Type of Firm

Private Equity Firm

Project Preferences

Role in Financing:

Prefer role as deal originator but will also invest in deals created by others

Type of Financing Preferred:

Fund of Funds
Second Stage Financing
Leveraged Buyout
Early Stage
Expansion
Mezzanine
Research and Development
Balanced
Start-up Financing
Seed
First Stage Financing
Startup

Size of Investments Considered:

Min Size of Investment Considered (000s): $300
Max Size of Investment Considered: No Limit

Geographical Preferences

International Preferences:

Middle East
Israel

Industry Preferences

In Communications prefer:

Communications and Media
Commercial Communications
CATV & Pay TV Systems
Telecommunications
Data Communications
Satellite Microwave Comm.
Other Communication Prod.

In Computer Hardware prefer:

Computers

In Computer Software prefer:

Computer Services
Software
Systems Software
Applications Software

In Internet Specific prefer:

Internet

In Semiconductor/Electr prefer:

Semiconductor
Laser Related
Fiber Optics

In Biotechnology prefer:

Biotechnology

In Medical/Health prefer:

Medical/Health
Diagnostic Test Products

In Consumer Related prefer:

Computer Stores

Additional Information

Year Founded: 1996
Capital Under Management: $500,000,000
Current Activity Level: Actively seeking new investments
Method of Compensation: Return on investment is of primary concern, do not charge fees

---

EVO HOLDING A/S (AKA: EVO MANAGEMENT A/S)

Vestergade 74
Aarhus, Denmark 8000
Phone: 45-7020-4086
Fax: 45-7020-4087
Website: www.evoholding.dk

Management and Staff

Peter Sonderlyng, Chief Financial Officer

Type of Firm

Private Equity Firm

Association Membership

Danish Venture Capital Association (DVCA)

Project Preferences

Type of Financing Preferred:

Leveraged Buyout
Other

Industry Preferences

In Consumer Related prefer:

Retail

In Industrial/Energy prefer:

Industrial Products

In Business Serv. prefer:

Services

Additional Information

Year Founded: 2007
Capital Under Management: $177,400,000
Current Activity Level: Actively seeking new investments

EVOLEM

11, Rue de la Republique
Cedex 01
Lyon, France 69281

Phone: 33-4-7268-9800
Fax: 33-4-7268-9809
E-mail: contact@evolem.fr
Website: www.evolem.fr

Other Offices

6 rue d'Antin
Paris, France 75002
Phone: 44-1-4020-0363
Fax: 44-1-4015-0017

65, rue Blatin
Clermont-Ferrand, France 63000
Phone: 33-4-7268-9800
Fax: 33-4-7268-9809

Management and Staff

Bruno Rousset, President
Marie-Christine Varnier, Chief Financial Officer
Vanessa Rousset, Managing Director

Type of Firm

Private Equity Firm

Association Membership

French Venture Capital Association (AFIC)

Project Preferences

Type of Financing Preferred:

Leveraged Buyout
Expansion

Geographical Preferences

International Preferences:

Europe
France

Additional Information

Year Founded: 2002
Current Activity Level: Actively seeking new investments

EVOLUTION CAPITAL PARTNERS, LLC

29325 Chagrin Boulevard
Suite 105
Pepper Pike, OH USA 44122
Phone: 216-593-0402
Fax: 216-593-0403
Website: www.evolutioncp.com

Management and Staff

Brendan Anderson, Principal
Jeffrey Kadlic, Principal
Paul Gierosky, Principal

Type of Firm

Private Equity Firm

Project Preferences

Type of Financing Preferred:

Turnaround
Management Buyouts
Acquisition
Recapitalizations

Geographical Preferences

United States Preferences:

Midwest
Ohio

Additional Information

Year Founded: 2007
Current Activity Level: Actively seeking new investments

EVOLUTION GROUP (FKA: EVC CHRISTOWS PLC)

100 Wood Street
London, United Kingdom EC2V 7AN
Phone: 44-20-7071-4300
Fax: 44-20-7071-4450
E-mail: enquiries@evgplc.com
Website: www.evgplc.com

Other Offices

223A Kensington High Street
London, United Kingdom W8 6SG

Management and Staff

Alex Snow, Chief Executive Officer
James Chilcott, Managing Director
James Kenny, Chief Executive Officer
Oliver Vaughan, Founder

Type of Firm

Private Equity Firm

Project Preferences

Role in Financing:

Prefer role as deal originator

Type of Financing Preferred:

Early Stage
Balanced
Startup

Geographical Preferences

United States Preferences:

All U.S.

International Preferences:

United Kingdom
Europe

Industry Preferences

In Communications prefer:

Communications and Media
Telecommunications
Wireless Communications

In Internet Specific prefer:

Internet

Additional Information

Year Founded: 1997
Capital Under Management: $21,900,000
Current Activity Level: Actively seeking new investments
Method of Compensation: Return on invest. most important, but chg. closing fees, service fees, etc.

EVOLUTION VENTURE CAPITAL

32A Habarzel Street
Tel Aviv, Israel 69710
Phone: 972-3-768-6776
Fax: 972-3-648-4104
E-mail: info@evolutionvc.com
Website: www.evolutionvc.com

Type of Firm

Private Equity Firm

Project Preferences

Type of Financing Preferred:

Expansion
Later Stage

Geographical Preferences

International Preferences:

Israel

Industry Preferences

In Biotechnology prefer:

Biotechnology
Human Biotechnology
Industrial Biotechnology

Additional Information

Year Founded: 2006
Capital Under Management: $20,000,000
Current Activity Level: Actively seeking new investments

EVOLVE CAPITAL

2200 Ross Avenue
Suite 4050
Dallas, TX USA 75201
Phone: 214-220-4800
E-mail: evolve@evolvecapital.com
Website: www.evolvecapital.com

Type of Firm

Private Equity Firm

Project Preferences

Type of Financing Preferred:

Leveraged Buyout
Expansion
Balanced
Acquisition
Recapitalizations

Industry Preferences

In Communications prefer:
Wireless Communications

In Semiconductor/Electr prefer:
Electronics

In Biotechnology prefer:
Biotechnology

In Medical/Health prefer:
Medical/Health

In Transportation prefer:
Transportation

In Business Serv. prefer:
Services

Additional Information

Year Founded: 2005
Current Activity Level: Actively seeking new investments

EVOLVENCE CAPITAL

Level 15, Park Place
API Tower, Sheik Zayed Road
Dubai, Utd. Arab Em.
Phone: 971-4-315-8100
Fax: 971-4-329-6500
E-mail: info@evolvence.com
Website: www.evolvence.com

Other Offices

150 East 58th Street
14th Floor
New York, NY USA 10155

8th Floor, Narain Manzil
Barakhamba Road, Connaught Place
New Delhi, India 110 001
Phone: 91-11-4151-9292
Fax: 91-11-4151-9393

Management and Staff

Ezaldeen El-Araj, Chief Financial Officer
Jay Jegannathan, Managing Director
Mustafa Sinno, Vice President
Paresh Thakker, Managing Director
Robert Pardi, President

Type of Firm

Private Equity Firm

Association Membership
Indian Venture Capital Association (IVCA)

Project Preferences

Type of Financing Preferred:
Fund of Funds
Expansion

Geographical Preferences

International Preferences:
India

Industry Preferences

In Biotechnology prefer:
Biotechnology

In Medical/Health prefer:
Pharmaceuticals

In Financial Services prefer:
Real Estate

In Utilities prefer:
Utilities

Additional Information

Year Founded: 2001
Capital Under Management: $163,000,000
Current Activity Level: Actively seeking new investments

EVP CAPITAL MANAGEMENT AG

Wilhelm-Leuschner-Strasse 68
Frankfurt am Main, Germany DE - 60487
Phone: 49-6940-325-970
Fax: 49-6940-3259749
E-mail: info@evp-capital.com
Website: www.evp-capital.com

Management and Staff

Farsin Yadegardjam, Partner
Gerald Worner, Partner
Gerrit Imsieke, Partner
Gert Purkert, Partner
Thomas Hoch, Managing Partner

Type of Firm

Private Equity Firm

Association Membership

German Venture Capital Association (BVK)
European Private Equity and Venture Capital Assoc.

Project Preferences

Type of Financing Preferred:
Early Stage
Expansion
Other
Seed
Startup

Geographical Preferences

International Preferences:
Europe
Germany

Industry Preferences

In Communications prefer:
Communications and Media

In Internet Specific prefer:
Internet

In Computer Other prefer:
Computer Related

In Biotechnology prefer:
Biotechnology

In Medical/Health prefer:
Medical/Health

In Industrial/Energy prefer:
Materials

Additional Information

Year Founded: 2000
Capital Under Management: $19,700,000
Current Activity Level: Actively seeking new investments

EWING MANAGEMENT GROUP LLC

3824 Cedar Springs Road
Suite 101-407
Dallas, TX USA 75219
Phone: 214-756-6260
Fax: 214-756-6299
E-mail: investorrelations@emglp.com
Website: www.emglp.com

Other Offices

1266 Nan Jing West Road
Suite 6306, Plaza 66
Shanghai, China 200040
Phone: 86-21-6288-0111
Fax: 8621-6288-4778

Management and Staff

Thomas Keene, Vice President

Type of Firm

Private Equity Firm

Project Preferences

Type of Financing Preferred:
Leveraged Buyout
Turnaround

Additional Information

Year Founded: 2004
Capital Under Management: $1,000,000,000
Current Activity Level: Actively seeking new investments

EXCALIBUR FUND MANAGERS, LTD. (FKA: MERLIN BIOSCIENCES, LTD.)

33 King Street
St James's
London, United Kingdom SW1Y 6RJ
Phone: 44-20-7811-4000
Fax: 44-20-7811-4001
E-mail: info@excaliburfundmanagers.co.uk
Website: www.excaliburfundmanagers.co.uk

Other Offices

Sophia House
28 Cathedral Road
Cardiff, United Kingdom CF11 9LJ
Phone: 44-29-2066-0150

Management and Staff

Mark Clement, Chief Executive Officer
Martin Brennan, Chief Operating Officer

Type of Firm

Private Equity Firm

Association Membership

British Venture Capital Association (BVCA)
European Private Equity and Venture Capital Assoc.

Project Preferences

Role in Financing:

Prefer role as deal originator

Type of Financing Preferred:

Second Stage Financing
Early Stage
Expansion
Seed
Startup

Size of Investments Considered:

Min Size of Investment Considered (000s): $400
Max Size of Investment Considered (000s): $400,000

Geographical Preferences

International Preferences:

United Kingdom
Europe

Industry Focus

(% based on actual investment)	
Biotechnology	56.7%
Medical/Health	40.8%
Computer Software and Services	2.5%

Additional Information

Name of Most Recent Fund: Merlin Biosciences Fund III, L.P. (Fund III)
Most Recent Fund Was Raised: 09/09/2002
Year Founded: 1996
Capital Under Management: $511,100,000
Current Activity Level: Actively seeking new investments

EXCEL PARTNERS

Claudio Coello 78, 3
Madrid, Spain 28001
Phone: 34-91-781-2941
Fax: 34-91-431-9303
E-mail: excel@excelpartners.com
Website: www.excelpartners.com

Management and Staff

David Bendel, Partner
Jose De Letona, Managing Partner
Ramon Menendez De Luarca, Principal

Type of Firm

Private Equity Firm

Association Membership

European Private Equity and Venture Capital Assoc.

Project Preferences

Type of Financing Preferred:

Leveraged Buyout
Early Stage
Expansion
Later Stage

Size of Investments Considered:

Min Size of Investment Considered (000s): $4,500
Max Size of Investment Considered: No Limit

Geographical Preferences

International Preferences:

Portugal
Spain

Additional Information

Name of Most Recent Fund: Excel Capital Partners I & II, Ltd.
Most Recent Fund Was Raised: 01/01/1992
Year Founded: 1991
Capital Under Management: $188,700,000
Current Activity Level: Actively seeking new investments

EXCEL VENTURE MANAGEMENT

800 Boylston Street
Suite 1585
Boston, MA USA 02199
Phone: 617-450-9800
Fax: 617-450-9749
E-mail: info@emven.com
Website: www.emven.com

Management and Staff

Caleb Winder, Vice President
Enrico Petrillo, Managing Director
Frederick Blume, Managing Director
Juan Enriquez, Managing Director
Steve Gullans, Managing Director

Type of Firm

Private Equity Firm

Project Preferences

Type of Financing Preferred:

Early Stage
Expansion
Later Stage

Industry Preferences

In Medical/Health prefer:

Medical Diagnostics
Diagnostic Services
Disposable Med. Products
Health Services

In Industrial/Energy prefer:

Energy
Materials

In Agr/Forestr/Fish prefer:

Agriculture related

Additional Information

Year Founded: 2007
Capital Under Management: $125,000,000
Current Activity Level: Actively seeking new investments

EXCELLERE CAPITAL MANAGEMENT

100 Fillmore Street
Suite 300
Denver, CO USA 80206
Phone: 303-765-2400
Fax: 303-765-2411
Website: www.excellerepartners.com

Management and Staff

David Kessenich, Managing Partner
Matthew Hicks, Partner
Patrick O'Keefe, Vice President
Robert Martin, Managing Partner

Type of Firm

Private Equity Firm

Project Preferences

Type of Financing Preferred:

Leveraged Buyout
Recapitalizations

Geographical Preferences

United States Preferences:

All U.S.

Industry Preferences

In Medical/Health prefer:

Health Services

In Consumer Related prefer:

Food/Beverage
Consumer Services
Education Related

In Industrial/Energy prefer:

Industrial Products

Additional Information

Name of Most Recent Fund: Excellere Capital Partners I, L.P.
Most Recent Fund Was Raised: 12/22/2006
Year Founded: 2007
Capital Under Management: $265,000,000
Current Activity Level: Actively seeking new investments

EXCLAMATION, INC.

134 Peter Street
Suite 333
Toronto, Canada M5H3R3
Phone: 416-978-6052
Fax: 416-978-6052
Website: www.exclamation.com

Management and Staff

Steve Yuzpe, Chief Financial Officer

Type of Firm

Private Equity Firm

Additional Information

Year Founded: 2009
Current Activity Level: Actively seeking new investments

EXECUTIVE VENTURE PARTNERS (AKA: EVP)

Arena House
Arena Road, Sandyford
Dublin, Ireland
Phone: 353-1-213-0711
Fax: 353-1-213-0515
E-mail: info@evp.ie
Website: www.evp.ie

Type of Firm

Private Equity Firm

Project Preferences

Type of Financing Preferred:

Early Stage
Expansion
Start-up Financing

Additional Information

Year Founded: 2002
Capital Under Management: $13,000,000
Current Activity Level: Actively seeking new investments

EXETER CAPITAL PARTNERS

10 East 53rd Street
32nd Floor
New York, NY USA 10022
Phone: 212-872-1172
Fax: 212-872-1198
E-mail: info@exeterfunds.com
Website: www.exeterfunds.com

Management and Staff

Ghaitrie Ganesh, Chief Financial Officer
Keith Fox, President
Kurt Bergquist, General Partner
Michael Golden, Vice President

Type of Firm

Private Equity Firm

Association Membership

Natl Assoc of Small Bus. Inv. Co (NASBIC)

Project Preferences

Role in Financing:

Prefer role as deal originator but will also invest in deals created by others

Type of Financing Preferred:

Leveraged Buyout
Expansion
Mezzanine
Balanced
Later Stage
Management Buyouts

Size of Investments Considered:

Min Size of Investment Considered (000s): $2,000
Max Size of Investment Considered (000s): $20,000

Geographical Preferences

United States Preferences:

All U.S.

Industry Focus

(% based on actual investment)

Other Products	37.3%
Consumer Related	17.6%
Medical/Health	15.0%
Internet Specific	13.1%
Computer Software and Services	9.6%
Computer Hardware	5.1%
Communications and Media	2.3%

Additional Information

Name of Most Recent Fund: Exeter Capital Partners V, L.P.
Most Recent Fund Was Raised: 04/17/2002
Year Founded: 1986
Capital Under Management: $135,000,000
Current Activity Level: Actively seeking new investments
Method of Compensation: Return on investment is of primary concern, do not charge fees

EXFUND GROUP OF COMPANIES

1177 West Hastings Street
Fifth Floor
Vancouver, Canada V6E 3T5
Phone: 604-683-3000
Fax: 604-662-3457

Type of Firm

Private Equity Firm

Additional Information

Year Founded: 1993
Current Activity Level: Actively seeking new investments

EXPANSION CAPITAL PARTNERS LLC

One Embarcadero Centre
Suite 4100
San Francisco, CA USA 94111
Phone: 415-788-8802
Fax: 415-358-4907
E-mail: info@expansioncapital.com
Website: www.expansioncapital.com

Other Offices

230 Park Avenue
Tenth Floor
New York, NY USA 10016
Phone: 212-786-7408
Fax: 646-514-8492

Two Summer Street
Suite Two
Natick, MA USA 01760
Phone: 508-651-2277

Management and Staff

Bernardo Llovera, Managing Partner
Diana Propper de Callejon, Managing Partner
Kjartan Jansen, Principal

Type of Firm

Private Equity Firm

Association Membership

National Venture Capital Association - USA (NVCA)

Project Preferences

Role in Financing:

Prefer role as deal originator

Type of Financing Preferred:

Expansion
Later Stage

Size of Investments Considered:

Min Size of Investment Considered (000s): $3,000
Max Size of Investment Considered (000s): $10,000

Geographical Preferences

Canadian Preferences:

All Canada

Industry Preferences

In Semiconductor/Electr prefer:

Controllers and Sensors
Sensors
Component Testing Equipmt

In Biotechnology prefer:

Biosensors

In Industrial/Energy prefer:

Energy
Oil and Gas Exploration
Oil & Gas Drilling,Explor
Alternative Energy
Coal Related
Energy Conservation Relat

Industrial Products
Materials
Advanced Materials
Factory Automation
Process Control
Robotics
Machinery
Environmental Related

In Transportation prefer:
Transportation

In Manufact. prefer:
Manufacturing
Office Automation Equipmt

In Agr/Forestr/Fish prefer:
Agriculture related

In Utilities prefer:
Utilities

In Other prefer:
Environment Responsible

Additional Information

Name of Most Recent Fund: Clean Technology Fund II, LP
Most Recent Fund Was Raised: 03/31/2006
Year Founded: 2002
Capital Under Management: $103,100,000
Current Activity Level: Actively seeking new investments
Method of Compensation: Return on investment is of primary concern, do not charge fees

EXPLOIT TECHNOLOGIES PTE, LTD.

30 Biopolis Street
No 09-02 Matrix
Singapore, Singapore 138671
Phone: 65-6478-8420
Fax: 65-6873-7192
Website: www.exploit-tech.com

Management and Staff

Barbara Lim-Nothacker, Vice President
Muhammad Tani, Vice President

Type of Firm

Government Affiliated Program

Project Preferences

Type of Financing Preferred:
Early Stage
Seed
Startup

Geographical Preferences

International Preferences:
Singapore

Industry Preferences

In Computer Other prefer:
Computer Related

In Biotechnology prefer:
Biotechnology

Additional Information

Year Founded: 2002
Current Activity Level: Actively seeking new investments

EXPLORER INVESTMENTS SCR, S.A.

Av. Eng. Duarte Pacheco
N 26 - 8
Lisboa, Portugal 1070-110
Phone: 351-21-324-1820
Fax: 351-21-324-1829
E-mail: explorer@explorerinvestments.com
Website: www.explorerinvestments.com

Management and Staff

Rodrigo Guimaraes, Partner

Type of Firm

Private Equity Firm

Association Membership

European Private Equity and Venture Capital Assoc.
Project Preferences

Type of Financing Preferred:
Leveraged Buyout
Expansion
Acquisition

Size of Investments Considered:
Min Size of Investment Considered (000s): $29,000
Max Size of Investment Considered (000s): $59,000

Geographical Preferences

International Preferences:
Portugal
Europe
Spain

Industry Preferences

In Industrial/Energy prefer:
Industrial Products

In Business Serv. prefer:
Services

Additional Information

Name of Most Recent Fund: Explorer I
Most Recent Fund Was Raised: 06/30/2004
Year Founded: 2003
Capital Under Management: $356,000,000
Current Activity Level: Actively seeking new investments

EXPONENT PRIVATE EQUITY LLP (FKA: SQUARE CAPITAL MANAGEMENT)

12 Henrietta Street
London, United Kingdom WC2E 8LH
Phone: 44-20-7845-8520
Fax: 44-20-7845-8521
Website: www.exponentpe.com

Management and Staff

Chris Graham, Founder
Richard Campin, Founder
Simon Baines, Partner
Tom Sweet-Escott, Founder

Type of Firm

Private Equity Firm

Association Membership

British Venture Capital Association (BVCA)

Project Preferences

Type of Financing Preferred:
Leveraged Buyout
Management Buyouts
Acquisition

Size of Investments Considered:
Min Size of Investment Considered (000s): $29,586
Max Size of Investment Considered (000s): $147,930

Geographical Preferences

International Preferences:
United Kingdom
Europe

Industry Preferences

In Communications prefer:
Media and Entertainment

In Financial Services prefer:
Financial Services

Additional Information

Year Founded: 2004
Capital Under Management: $2,317,700,000
Current Activity Level: Actively seeking new investments

EXPORT DEVELOPMENT CANADA

151 O'Connor
Ottawa, Canada K1A1K3
Phone: 613-597-8523
Fax: 613-598-3811
Website: www.edc.ca

Type of Firm

Government Affiliated Program

Project Preferences

Type of Financing Preferred:
Expansion
Early Stage

Geographical Preferences

United States Preferences:
All U.S.

Canadian Preferences:
All Canada

Additional Information
Year Founded: 1994
Current Activity Level: Actively seeking new investments

EXPORT VENTURE CAPITAL CORPORATION (PTY) LTD.
1st Fl. North Wing, Workshop
70-7th Ave.
Parktown North, South Africa
Phone: 27-11-214-2700
Fax: 27-11-214-2714
E-mail: info@exportcapital.co.za
Website: www.exportcapital.co.za

Management and Staff
Pieter Wesselink, Managing Director

Type of Firm
Private Equity Firm

Association Membership
South African Venture Capital Association (SAVCA)

Project Preferences

Type of Financing Preferred:
Leveraged Buyout
Early Stage
Expansion
Management Buyouts
Startup

Geographical Preferences

International Preferences:
South Africa

Industry Preferences

In Business Serv. prefer:
Services

Additional Information
Year Founded: 2003
Current Activity Level: Actively seeking new investments

EXPORT-IMPORT BANK OF CHINA, THE
30, FuXingMenNei Street
Xicheng District
Beijing, China 100031
Phone: 86-10-8357-9000
Fax: 86-10-6606-0636
Website: www.eximbank.gov.cn

Type of Firm
Government Affiliated Program

Project Preferences

Type of Financing Preferred:
Balanced

Geographical Preferences

International Preferences:
China
Asia

Industry Preferences

In Communications prefer:
Telecommunications

In Industrial/Energy prefer:
Oil & Gas Drilling,Explor

In Transportation prefer:
Transportation

In Agr/Forestr/Fish prefer:
Mining and Minerals

Additional Information
Year Founded: 1994
Current Activity Level: Actively seeking new investments

EXTREME VENTURE PARTNERS, INC.
67 Yonge Street
Suite 1600
Toronto, Canada M5E 1J8
Website: www.extremevp.com

Management and Staff
Imran Bashir, Founding Partner
Ken Teslia, Founding Partner
Ray Sharma, Founding Partner

Type of Firm
Private Equity Firm

Additional Information
Year Founded: 2009
Current Activity Level: Actively seeking new investments

EXXEL GROUP S.A.
Avenida del Libertador 602
22nd floor
Buenos Aires, Argentina 1001
Phone: 5411-4129-8854
Fax: 5411-4814-1201
E-mail: exxel@exxelgroup.com
Website: www.exxelgroup.com

Type of Firm
Private Equity Firm

Project Preferences

Role in Financing:
Other

Type of Financing Preferred:
Leveraged Buyout

Geographical Preferences

International Preferences:
Latin America
Argentina

Industry Focus
(% based on actual investment)

Computer Software and Services	50.4%
Semiconductors/Other Elect.	29.4%
Medical/Health	20.2%

Additional Information
Name of Most Recent Fund: Exxel Capital Partners VI, L.P.
Most Recent Fund Was Raised: 08/01/2000
Year Founded: 1991
Capital Under Management: $550,000,000
Current Activity Level: Actively seeking new investments
Method of Compensation: Return on invest. most important, but chg. closing fees, service fees, etc.

- F -

401 CAPITAL PARTNERS, INC.

150 Randall Street
Suite 103
Oakville, Canada L6J1P4
Phone: 905-481-1677
E-mail: info@401capital.com
Website: www.401capital.com

Management and Staff

George Georgiou, Managing Director
Robert Manherz, President

Type of Firm

Private Equity Firm

Additional Information

Year Founded: 2009
Current Activity Level: Actively seeking new investments

4D GLOBAL ENERGY ADVISORS

15 Rue de la Baume
Paris, France 75008
Phone: 33-1-5643-3860
Fax: 33-1-4225-5459
E-mail: contact@4dgea.com
Website: www.4dgea.com

Management and Staff

Jerome Halbout, Partner
Paola Chiecchio, Chief Operating Officer
Simon Eyers, Partner
Tighe Noonan, Partner

Type of Firm

Private Equity Firm

Association Membership

French Venture Capital Association (AFIC)

Project Preferences

Type of Financing Preferred:

Expansion
Other

Size of Investments Considered:

Min Size of Investment Considered (000s): $5,000
Max Size of Investment Considered (000s): $15,000

Geographical Preferences

International Preferences:

Europe
All International

Industry Preferences

In Industrial/Energy prefer:

Energy

Additional Information

Year Founded: 2002
Capital Under Management: $264,000,000
Current Activity Level: Actively seeking new investments

5280 PARTNERS

360 South Monroe Street
Suite 600
Denver, CO USA 80209
Phone: 303-333-1215
Fax: 303-322-3553
Website: www.5280partners.com

Management and Staff

Jeffrey Bennis, Principal
Kevin Allen, Principal
Peter Smith, Principal

Type of Firm

Private Equity Firm

Project Preferences

Role in Financing:

Will function either as deal originator or investor in deals created by others

Type of Financing Preferred:

Second Stage Financing
Balanced
First Stage Financing

Size of Investments Considered:

Min Size of Investment Considered (000s): $500
Max Size of Investment Considered (000s): $2,500

Geographical Preferences

United States Preferences:

Rocky Mountain
All U.S.

Industry Preferences

In Communications prefer:

Wireless Communications
Data Communications

In Computer Software prefer:

Applications Software

In Internet Specific prefer:

Internet
Ecommerce

Additional Information

Name of Most Recent Fund: 5280 Partners I, LP
Most Recent Fund Was Raised: 12/01/2000
Year Founded: 2000
Capital Under Management: $15,300,000
Current Activity Level: Actively seeking new investments
Method of Compensation: Return on investment is of primary concern, do not charge fees

5AM VENTURES (AKA: 5AM PARTNERS)

2200 Sand Hill Road
Suite 110
Menlo Park, CA USA 94025
Phone: 650-233-8600
Fax: 650-233-8923
E-mail: info@5amventures.com
Website: www.5amventures.com

Other Offices

Suite 140, 890 Winter Street
Waltham Woods Corporate Center
Waltham, MA USA 02451
Phone: 781-890-4480
Fax: 781-890-3565

Management and Staff

James Young, Venture Partner
Kevin Forrest, Principal
Mark Colella, Principal
R.Andrew McMillan, Principal
Richard Ulevitch, Venture Partner
Scott Rocklage, Managing Partner

Type of Firm

Private Equity Firm

Association Membership

National Venture Capital Association - USA (NVCA)

Project Preferences

Type of Financing Preferred:

Early Stage
Seed
Startup

Size of Investments Considered:

Min Size of Investment Considered (000s): $250
Max Size of Investment Considered (000s): $15,000

Geographical Preferences

United States Preferences:

All U.S.

Canadian Preferences:

All Canada

Industry Preferences

In Biotechnology prefer:

Biotechnology

Additional Information

Name of Most Recent Fund: 5AM Ventures III, L.P.
Most Recent Fund Was Raised: 03/18/2009
Year Founded: 2002
Capital Under Management: $215,000,000
Current Activity Level: Actively seeking new investments

F&C ASSET MANAGEMENT PLC

Exchange House
Primorose Street
London, United Kingdom EC2A2NY
Phone: 44-2076288000
Fax: 44-2076288188
E-mail: enquiriesi@fandc.com
Website: www.fandc.com

Type of Firm

Investment Management Firm

Project Preferences

Type of Financing Preferred:
Fund of Funds
Balanced

Geographical Preferences

International Preferences:
United Kingdom
Europe

Additional Information

Year Founded: 1997
Capital Under Management: $271,600,000
Current Activity Level: Actively seeking new investments

F. HOFFMANN - LA ROCHE, LTD.

Grenzacherstrasse 124
Basel, Switzerland 4070
Phone: 41-61-688-1111
Fax: 41-61-691-9391
Website: www.roche.com

Management and Staff

Erich Hunziker, Chief Financial Officer
Franz Humer, Chairman & CEO

Type of Firm

Corporate PE/Venture

Project Preferences

Type of Financing Preferred:
Early Stage

Geographical Preferences

International Preferences:
All International

Industry Preferences

In Biotechnology prefer:
Biotechnology

In Medical/Health prefer:
Medical Diagnostics

Additional Information

Year Founded: 1896
Current Activity Level: Actively seeking new investments

F. TURISMO - CAPITAL DE RISCO SA

Rua Ivone Silva
lote 6-3 Esq.
Lisboa, Portugal 1050-124
Phone: 351-217-815-800
Fax: 351-217-815-809
E-mail: cr_mail@ifturismo.min-economia.pt

Type of Firm

Government Affiliated Program

Association Membership

Portuguese Venture Capital Association (APCRI)
European Private Equity and Venture Capital Assoc.

Project Preferences

Role in Financing:
Prefer role in deals created by others

Type of Financing Preferred:
Early Stage
Expansion
Turnaround
Startup
Recapitalizations

Size of Investments Considered:
Min Size of Investment Considered (000s): $161
Max Size of Investment Considered (000s): $1,879

Geographical Preferences

International Preferences:
Portugal
Cape Verde
Brazil

Industry Preferences

In Consumer Related prefer:
Hotels and Resorts

In Business Serv. prefer:
Services

Additional Information

Year Founded: 1991
Capital Under Management: $27,400,000
Current Activity Level: Actively seeking new investments
Method of Compensation: Return on invest. most important, but chg. closing fees, service fees, etc.

F. VAN LANSCHOT PARTICIPATIES BV

Hooge Steenweg 29
's-Hertogenbosch, Netherlands 5211 JN
Phone: 31-73-548-3548
Fax: 31-73-548-3648
E-mail: corporate.finance@vanlanschot.com
Website: www.vanlanschot.com

Management and Staff

Floris G. Deckers, Chief Executive Officer
Ieko Sevinga, Managing Director
Paul A. Loven, Managing Director

Type of Firm

Bank Affiliated

Association Membership

Dutch Venture Capital Associaton (NVP)

Project Preferences

Type of Financing Preferred:
Leveraged Buyout
Expansion
Management Buyouts

Geographical Preferences

International Preferences:
Netherlands

Industry Preferences

In Communications prefer:
Communications and Media

In Computer Other prefer:
Computer Related

In Consumer Related prefer:
Consumer
Consumer Products

Additional Information

Year Founded: 2005
Current Activity Level: Actively seeking new investments

FA TECHNOLOGY VENTURES

677 Broadway
Albany, NY USA 12207
Phone: 518-447-8525
Fax: 518-447-8524
E-mail: info@fatechventures.com
Website: www.fatechventures.com

Other Offices

150 Federal Street
Suite 1105
Boston, MA USA 02110
Phone: 617-757-3880
Fax: 617-757-3881

Management and Staff

George McNamee, Managing Partner
Giri Sekhar, Managing Partner
Gregory Hulecki, Managing Partner
John Cococcia, Partner
Kenneth Mabbs, Managing Partner

Type of Firm

Bank Affiliated

Project Preferences

Role in Financing:

Will function either as deal originator or investor in deals created by others

Type of Financing Preferred:

Early Stage
Expansion
First Stage Financing

Size of Investments Considered:

Min Size of Investment Considered (000s): $2,500
Max Size of Investment Considered (000s): $8,000

Geographical Preferences

United States Preferences:

New York

Industry Preferences

In Computer Software prefer:

Applications Software

In Internet Specific prefer:

Internet
Ecommerce
Web Aggregration/Portals

In Semiconductor/Electr prefer:

Electronics
Electronic Components
Semiconductor
Laser Related
Fiber Optics
Optoelectronics

In Industrial/Energy prefer:

Alternative Energy
Energy Conservation Relat
Industrial Products
Materials
Factory Automation

Additional Information

Name of Most Recent Fund: FA Technology Ventures
Most Recent Fund Was Raised: 10/20/2000
Year Founded: 2000
Capital Under Management: $175,000,000
Current Activity Level: Actively seeking new investments
Method of Compensation: Return on investment is of primary concern, do not charge fees

---

FABREL LOTOS (AKA: FABREL AG)

Lagerstrasse 33
Zurich, Switzerland 8021
Phone: 41-1-246-7040
Fax: 41-1-246-7059
Website: www.fabrellotos.ch

Management and Staff

Hans Von Weissenfluh, Partner
Juerg Muffler, Partner
Martin Mader, Managing Partner

Type of Firm

Corporate PE/Venture

Association Membership

Swiss Venture Capital Association (SECA)

Project Preferences

Type of Financing Preferred:

Expansion
Turnaround
Management Buyouts
Acquisition
Startup
Recapitalizations

Size of Investments Considered:

Min Size of Investment Considered (000s): $17,270
Max Size of Investment Considered (000s): $34,539

Geographical Preferences

International Preferences:

Switzerland
Austria
Germany

Industry Preferences

In Internet Specific prefer:

Internet

In Financial Services prefer:

Financial Services

Additional Information

Year Founded: 1999
Current Activity Level: Actively seeking new investments

FACILITIES CORPORATE MANAGEMENT

100 Barbirolli Square
Manchester, United Kingdom

Management and Staff

Paul Davidson, Founder

Type of Firm

Incubator/Development Program

Project Preferences

Type of Financing Preferred:

Seed
Startup

Geographical Preferences

International Preferences:

United Kingdom

Additional Information

Year Founded: 2001
Current Activity Level: Actively seeking new investments

FAIR VALUE INVESTMENT (AKA: SHANGHAI ANYI INVESTMENT)

No. 107 Zunyi Road
Room 409 An Tai Building
Shanghai, China 200100
Phone: 86-21-6237-5485
Fax: 86-21-6237-5482
E-mail: aytz888@126.com
Website: www.fairvalueinvestment.cn

Management and Staff

Bin Zhou, Partner
Dong Bing Ma, Partner
Pei Feng Zhu, Partner
Wei Hong Luo, Partner

Type of Firm

Private Equity Firm

Project Preferences

Type of Financing Preferred:

Balanced

Additional Information

Year Founded: 2007
Capital Under Management: $25,600,000
Current Activity Level: Actively seeking new investments

FAIRFORD HOLDINGS SCANDINAVIA AB (AKA: FAIRFORD HOLDINGS)

P.O. Box 40
Ostersund, Sweden 831 21
Phone: 46-6313-4686
Fax: 46-6313-3825
E-mail: juvenis@telia.com
Website: www.fairfordholdings.com

Management and Staff

Salah Osseiran, President

Type of Firm

Private Equity Firm

Association Membership

Swedish Venture Capital Association (SVCA)

Project Preferences

Type of Financing Preferred:

Leveraged Buyout
Expansion
Seed
Startup

Geographical Preferences

International Preferences:
Scandanavia/Nordic Region

Additional Information

Year Founded: 2000
Capital Under Management: $53,100,000
Current Activity Level: Actively seeking new investments

FAIRHAVEN CAPITAL PARTNERS

101 Federal Street
29th Floor
Boston, MA USA 02110
Phone: 617-425-0800
Fax: 617-425-0801
Website: www.fairhavencapital.com

Management and Staff

Daniel Keshian, Managing Director
James Goldinger, Managing Director
Paul Ciriello, Managing Partner
Richard Grinnell, Managing Director

Type of Firm

Private Equity Firm

Association Membership

National Venture Capital Association - USA (NVCA)

Project Preferences

Type of Financing Preferred:
Early Stage

Industry Preferences

In Communications prefer:
Commercial Communications

In Computer Hardware prefer:
Integrated Turnkey System

In Consumer Related prefer:
Consumer

Additional Information

Name of Most Recent Fund: Fairhaven Capital Partners, L.P.
Most Recent Fund Was Raised: 06/24/2008
Year Founded: 2007
Capital Under Management: $200,000,000
Current Activity Level: Actively seeking new investments

FAIRMONT CAPITAL, INC.

18200 Yorba Linda Boulevard
Suite 211
Yorba Linda, CA USA 92886
Phone: 714-524-4770
Fax: 714-524-4775
E-mail: info@fairmontcapital.com
Website: www.fairmontcapital.com

Management and Staff

Mark Gill, Principal
Michael Gibbons, President
Timothy Greenleaf, Managing Director

Type of Firm

Private Equity Firm

Project Preferences

Type of Financing Preferred:
Leveraged Buyout
Acquisition

Geographical Preferences

United States Preferences:
All U.S.

Industry Focus

(% based on actual investment)

Consumer Related	99.1%
Industrial/Energy	0.9%

Additional Information

Year Founded: 2000
Capital Under Management: $25,000,000
Current Activity Level: Actively seeking new investments

FAIRWATER GROWTH RESOURCES, INC.

130 Adelaide Street West
Suite 1010
Toronto, Canada M5H3P5
Phone: 416-369-1499
Fax: 416-369-0280
E-mail: info@fairwater.ca
Website: www.fairwater.ca

Management and Staff

Terry Mactaggart, President

Type of Firm

Private Equity Firm

Additional Information

Year Founded: 2001
Current Activity Level: Actively seeking new investments

FAJR CAPITAL LTD

Gate Village 10, Level 3
Office 34,Dubai Intl Fnl Centr
Dubai, Utd. Arab Em.
Phone: 9714-401-9734
Fax: 9714-401-9730
Website: www.fajrcapital.com
Other Offices
4, Royal Mint Court
EC3N 4HJ
London, United Kingdom EC3N
Phone: 4420-7073-7960
Fax: 4420-7073-7951

Level 40, Tower 2
Petronas Twin Towers
Kuala Lumpur, Malaysia 50088
Phone: 603-2168-4249
Fax: 603-2168-4622

Management and Staff

Aamir Rehman, Managing Director
Chris Masterson, Chief Executive Officer
Dato Noor Aziz, Managing Director
Iqbal Khan, Chief Executive Officer
Javed Ahmed, Managing Director
Kamran Faridi, Managing Director
Rafe Haneef, Managing Director
Rizwan Kherati, Managing Director & CFO
Saud Hashimi, Managing Director

Type of Firm

Private Equity Firm

Project Preferences

Type of Financing Preferred:
Balanced

Geographical Preferences

International Preferences:
Middle East

Industry Preferences

In Financial Services prefer:
Financial Services

Additional Information

Year Founded: 2009
Current Activity Level: Actively seeking new investments

FALCON CAPITAL, LLC

1111 Brickell Avenue
Suite 1100
Miami, FL USA 33131
Phone: 305-913-7130
Fax: 305-675-0925
E-mail: investors@falconcapital.net
Website: www.falconcapital.net

Management and Staff

Eric Schaer, Managing Director

Type of Firm

Private Equity Firm

Project Preferences

Type of Financing Preferred:
Generalist PE
Turnaround

Acquisition
Startup

Size of Investments Considered:
Min Size of Investment Considered (000s): $1,000
Max Size of Investment Considered (000s): $5,000

Geographical Preferences

United States Preferences:
All U.S.

Additional Information
Year Founded: 2004
Current Activity Level: Actively seeking new investments

FALCON INVESTMENT ADVISORS LLC
21 Custom House Street
10th Floor
Boston, MA USA 02110
Phone: 617-412-2700
Website: www.falconinvestments.com

Management and Staff
Eric Rogoff, Partner
John Schnabel, Partner
Rafael Fogel, Partner
Sandeep Alva, Managing Partner
William Kennedy, Managing Partner

Type of Firm
Private Equity Firm

Project Preferences

Role in Financing:
Will function either as deal originator or investor in deals created by others

Type of Financing Preferred:
Leveraged Buyout
Mezzanine
Public Companies
Management Buyouts
Acquisition
Special Situation
Recapitalizations

Size of Investments Considered:
Min Size of Investment Considered (000s): $10,000
Max Size of Investment Considered (000s): $50,000

Geographical Preferences

United States Preferences:
All U.S.

Canadian Preferences:
All Canada

International Preferences:
Mexico

Additional Information
Name of Most Recent Fund: Falcon Mezzanine Partners, L.P.
Most Recent Fund Was Raised: 06/01/2002
Year Founded: 2000
Capital Under Management: $630,000,000
Current Activity Level: Actively seeking new investments

FALCONER BELLOMO AND CO., LTD.
Sargood House, Suite 404
73 Flinders Lane
Melbourne, Australia 3000
Phone: 613-9650-8911
Fax: 613-9650-4911
E-mail: falconerbellomo@bigpond.com

Type of Firm
Private Equity Firm

Project Preferences

Role in Financing:
Prefer role as deal originator

Type of Financing Preferred:
Early Stage
Expansion
Mezzanine
Later Stage
First Stage Financing
Acquisition
Private Placement

Geographical Preferences

International Preferences:
China
Australia

Industry Preferences

In Communications prefer:
Telecommunications
Wireless Communications
Satellite Microwave Comm.

In Biotechnology prefer:
Agricultural/Animal Bio.

In Consumer Related prefer:
Entertainment and Leisure
Sports
Food/Beverage
Hotels and Resorts

In Industrial/Energy prefer:
Energy

In Financial Services prefer:
Financial Services

In Business Serv. prefer:
Media

In Agr/Forestr/Fish prefer:
Agribusiness
Agriculture related
Mining and Minerals

Additional Information
Year Founded: 1997
Current Activity Level: Actively seeking new investments
Method of Compensation: Function primarily in service area, receive contingent fee in cash or equity

---

FALCONHEAD CAPITAL (FKA: SPORTS CAPITAL PARTNERS)
450 Park Avenue
Third Floor
New York, NY USA 10022
Phone: 212-634-3304
Fax: 212-634-3305
E-mail: info@falconheadcapital.com
Website: www.falconheadcapital.com

Management and Staff
Brian Crosby, General Partner
David Gubbay, General Partner
Glen Bushery, Chief Financial Officer
Zuher Ladak, General Partner

Type of Firm
Private Equity Firm

Project Preferences

Role in Financing:
Prefer role as deal originator but will also invest in deals created by others

Type of Financing Preferred:
Leveraged Buyout

Size of Investments Considered:
Min Size of Investment Considered (000s): $5,000
Max Size of Investment Considered (000s): $25,000

Geographical Preferences

International Preferences:
United Kingdom

Industry Preferences

In Internet Specific prefer:
Internet

In Consumer Related prefer:
Entertainment and Leisure
Sports
Hotels and Resorts

In Business Serv. prefer:
Media

Additional Information
Name of Most Recent Fund: Falconhead Capital Partners II, L.P.
Most Recent Fund Was Raised: 01/05/2006
Year Founded: 1998
Capital Under Management: $170,000,000
Current Activity Level: Actively seeking new investments

Method of Compensation: Return on invest. most important, but chg. closing fees, service fees, etc.

FALFURRIAS CAPITAL PARTNERS

100 North Tryon Street
Suite 5120
Charlotte, NC USA 28202
Phone: 704-371-3220
Fax: 704-333-0185
Website: www.falfurriascapital.com

Management and Staff

Ed McMahan, Principal
Marc Oken, Managing Director

Type of Firm

Private Equity Firm

Project Preferences

Type of Financing Preferred:
Leveraged Buyout
Generalist PE
Expansion
Recapitalizations

Geographical Preferences

United States Preferences:
All U.S.

Industry Preferences

In Consumer Related prefer:
Retail
Consumer Products

In Industrial/Energy prefer:
Industrial Products

In Financial Services prefer:
Financial Services

In Business Serv. prefer:
Services

In Manufact. prefer:
Manufacturing

Additional Information

Year Founded: 2006
Capital Under Management: $97,000,000
Current Activity Level: Actively seeking new investments

FAMA PRIVATE EQUITY

R. Samuel Morse
Brooklin
Sao Paulo, Brazil 04576-060
Phone: 55-11-5508-1188
Website: www.famape.com.br

Management and Staff

Fabio Alperwitch, Founder

Type of Firm

Bank Affiliated

Project Preferences

Type of Financing Preferred:
Leveraged Buyout
Acquisition

Geographical Preferences

International Preferences:
Brazil

Additional Information

Year Founded: 2008
Capital Under Management: $110,000,000
Current Activity Level: Actively seeking new investments

FAR PACIFIC CAPITAL LIMITED

6th Floor Change House
150 Featherstone Street
Wellington, New Zealand
Phone: 644-473-3877
Fax: 644-473-3836
E-mail: info@far.co.nz
Website: www.farpacific.co.nz

Type of Firm

Private Equity Firm

Project Preferences

Type of Financing Preferred:
Early Stage
Expansion
Turnaround
Seed
Startup

Geographical Preferences

International Preferences:
New Zealand

Additional Information

Year Founded: 2001
Current Activity Level: Actively seeking new investments

FAVONIUS VENTURES

Mollaan 1a
Bloemendaal, Netherlands 2061 CR
Phone: 31-23-541-1222
Fax: 31-23-541-1200
E-mail: info@favoniusventures.com
Website: www.favoniusventures.com

Other Offices

20 Balderton Street
8th Floor
London, United Kingdom W1K 6TL
Phone: 44-207-629-8035
Fax: 44-207-491-2645

Management and Staff

Jan De Jong, Managing Director
Maarten Boasson, Venture Partner
Marius Abel, Venture Partner
Matthias Allgaier, Managing Director
Roel Pieper, Managing Director
Stephen Duckett, Managing Director

Type of Firm

Private Equity Firm

Project Preferences

Type of Financing Preferred:
Balanced

Size of Investments Considered:
Min Size of Investment Considered (000s): $3,000
Max Size of Investment Considered (000s): $5,000

Geographical Preferences

International Preferences:
Europe

Industry Preferences

In Communications prefer:
Wireless Communications

In Computer Software prefer:
Software

In Internet Specific prefer:
Internet

Additional Information

Name of Most Recent Fund: Favonius Insight Ventures
Most Recent Fund Was Raised: 09/09/2001
Year Founded: 2001
Capital Under Management: $330,000,000
Current Activity Level: Actively seeking new investments

FBR COMOTION VENTURE CAPITAL

200 West Mercer Street
E-207
Seattle, WA USA 98119
Phone: 206-382-9191
Fax: 206-382-9199
E-mail: partners@comotionvc.com
Website: www.comotionvc.com

Other Offices

208 Southwest First Avenue
Suite 300
Portland, OR USA 97204
Phone: 503-221-0200
Fax: 503-478-0559

Management and Staff

David Billstrom, Managing Partner
Will Neuhauser, Managing Partner

Type of Firm

Private Equity Firm

Project Preferences

Role in Financing:

Will function either as deal originator or investor in deals created by others

Type of Financing Preferred:

Early Stage
Start-up Financing
Seed
First Stage Financing

Size of Investments Considered:

Min Size of Investment Considered (000s): $100
Max Size of Investment Considered (000s): $5,000

Geographical Preferences

United States Preferences:

Northwest

Industry Focus

(% based on actual investment)

Internet Specific	80.3%
Computer Software and Services	19.7%

Additional Information

Year Founded: 2000
Capital Under Management: $50,000,000
Current Activity Level: Actively seeking new investments
Method of Compensation: Return on investment is of primary concern, do not charge fees

---

FCC VENTURES

1800 Hamilton Street
2nd Floor
Regina, Canada S4P 4L3
Phone: 306-780-8100
Fax: 306-780-5456

Other Offices

1030 Gordon Street
Guelph, Canada N5A 5T7
Phone: 519-826-2007
Fax: 519-826-2006

Type of Firm

Private Equity Firm

Additional Information

Year Founded: 2002
Capital Under Management: $41,000,000
Current Activity Level: Actively seeking new investments

FCP INVESTORS

101 East Kennedy Boulevard
Suite 3925
Tampa, FL USA 33602
Phone: 813-222-8000
Fax: 813-222-8001
E-mail: postmaster@fcpinvestors.com
Website: www.fcpinvestors.com

Management and Staff

Chenier Christian, Vice President
David Haas, Principal
Felix Wong, Managing Director
Joshua Kuder, Vice President
Peter Franz, Managing Director
Scott Herberlein, Vice President

Type of Firm

Private Equity Firm

Project Preferences

Role in Financing:

Prefer role as deal originator but will also invest in deals created by others

Type of Financing Preferred:

Leveraged Buyout
Recapitalizations

Size of Investments Considered:

Min Size of Investment Considered (000s): $3,000
Max Size of Investment Considered: No Limit

Geographical Preferences

United States Preferences:

All U.S.

Canadian Preferences:

All Canada

Industry Focus

(% based on actual investment)

Consumer Related	49.8%
Other Products	23.1%
Industrial/Energy	20.9%
Medical/Health	6.1%

Additional Information

Name of Most Recent Fund: FCP Investors VI
Most Recent Fund Was Raised: 10/01/2000
Year Founded: 1988
Capital Under Management: $214,000,000
Current Activity Level: Actively seeking new investments
Method of Compensation: Return on invest. most important, but chg. closing fees, service fees, etc.

FELICIS VENTURES

268 Bush Street
Suite 800
San Francisco, CA USA 94104
Phone: 650-714-7292
Fax: 650-649-1976
Website: www.felicisvc.com

Management and Staff

Aydin Senkut, President

Type of Firm

Private Equity Firm

Association Membership

National Venture Capital Association - USA (NVCA)

Project Preferences

Role in Financing:

Will function either as deal originator or investor in deals created by others

Type of Financing Preferred:

Early Stage
Seed

Size of Investments Considered:

Min Size of Investment Considered (000s): $25
Max Size of Investment Considered (000s): $150

Geographical Preferences

United States Preferences:

All U.S.

Industry Preferences

In Internet Specific prefer:

Internet

Additional Information

Year Founded: 2005
Capital Under Management: $5,000,000
Current Activity Level: Actively seeking new investments
Method of Compensation: Other

FENNO MANAGEMENT OY

Toppelundintie 5 B 10
Espoo, Finland 02170
Phone: 358-400-706-072
Fax: 358-9-2517-2202
Website: www.fennomanagement.com

Management and Staff

Aaro Cantell, Managing Partner
Janne Huhtala, Partner

Type of Firm

Private Equity Firm

Association Membership

Finnish Venture Capital Association (FVCA)
European Private Equity and Venture Capital Assoc.

Project Preferences

Type of Financing Preferred:

Leveraged Buyout
Expansion

Size of Investments Considered:

Min Size of Investment Considered (000s): $1,000
Max Size of Investment Considered (000s): $40,000

Geographical Preferences

International Preferences:

Europe
Finland

Industry Focus

(% based on actual investment)

Communications and Media	82.6%
Other Products	17.4%

Additional Information

Name of Most Recent Fund: Fenno Rahasto Ky (AKA: Fenno Program)
Most Recent Fund Was Raised: 06/17/1997
Year Founded: 1997
Capital Under Management: $85,600,000
Current Activity Level: Actively seeking new investments

FENWAY PARTNERS, INC.

152 West 57th Street
59th Floor
New York, NY USA 10019
Phone: 212-698-9400
Fax: 212-581-1205
E-mail: contact_us@fenwaypartners.com
Website: www.fenwaypartners.com

Other Offices

10880 Wilshire Boulevard
Suite 1101
Westwood, CA USA 90024
Phone: 310-689-0129
Fax: 310-689-0126

Management and Staff

Aron Schwartz, Managing Director
Bradley Smiedt, Vice President
David Richman, Vice President
Hans Allegaert, Vice President
James Shillito, Vice President
Marc Kramer, Managing Director
Peter Lamm, Managing Partner
Richard Dresdale, Managing Director
Timothy Mayhew, Managing Director

Type of Firm

Private Equity Firm

Project Preferences

Role in Financing:

Prefer role as deal originator but will also invest in deals created by others

Type of Financing Preferred:

Leveraged Buyout
Management Buyouts
Acquisition
Recapitalizations

Size of Investments Considered:

Min Size of Investment Considered (000s): $50,000
Max Size of Investment Considered (000s): $75,000

Industry Focus

(% based on actual investment)

Consumer Related	62.2%
Other Products	26.9%
Internet Specific	6.4%
Computer Software and Services	2.1%
Communications and Media	1.6%
Industrial/Energy	0.7%
Semiconductors/Other Elect.	0.1%

Additional Information

Name of Most Recent Fund: Fenway Partners Capital Fund III, L.P.
Most Recent Fund Was Raised: 02/24/2006
Year Founded: 1994
Capital Under Management: $1,673,000,000
Current Activity Level: Actively seeking new investments
Method of Compensation: Return on investment is of primary concern, do not charge fees

---

FEO VENTURES PTE., LTD.

14 Scotts Road
#06-00 Far East Plaza
Singapore, Singapore 228213
Phone: 65-6235-2411
Fax: 65-6235-3316
E-mail: feoca@fareast.com.sg
Website: www.fareast.com.sg

Other Offices

1 Tanglin Road
#04-18 Orchard Parade Hotel
Singapore, Singapore 247905
Phone: 65-833-6666
Fax: 75-736-2043

Management and Staff

Philip Ng, Chief Executive Officer

Type of Firm

Corporate PE/Venture

Project Preferences

Role in Financing:

Will function either as deal originator or investor in deals created by others

Type of Financing Preferred:

Expansion
Start-up Financing

Geographical Preferences

International Preferences:

Asia

Industry Preferences

In Internet Specific prefer:

Internet

Additional Information

Year Founded: 2000
Capital Under Management: $1,700,000
Current Activity Level: Actively seeking new investments
Method of Compensation: Return on investment is of primary concern, do not charge fees

---

FERD VENTURE

Strandveien 50
P.O.Box 34
Lysaker, Norway N-1324
Phone: 47-67-108-000
Fax: 47-67-108-001
E-mail: post@ferd.no
Website: www.ferd.no

Management and Staff

Bjorn Erik Reinseth, Partner
Erik Olsen, Managing Partner
Helge Hellebust, Partner
Pal Rodseth, Partner

Type of Firm

Private Equity Firm

Association Membership

Norwegian Venture Capital Association

Project Preferences

Type of Financing Preferred:

Early Stage

Size of Investments Considered:

Min Size of Investment Considered (000s): $2,666
Max Size of Investment Considered (000s): $14,216

Geographical Preferences

International Preferences:

Norway

Additional Information

Year Founded: 2009
Capital Under Management: $177,700,000
Current Activity Level: Actively seeking new investments

FF ASSET MANAGEMENT LLC

830 Morris Turnpike
Second Floor
Short Hills, NJ USA 07078
Phone: 973-488-7110
Fax: 973-488-7117
E-mail: inquiries@ffassetmanagement.com
Website: www.ffassetmanagement.com

Management and Staff

Alex Katz, Chief Financial Officer
John Frankel, Founder

Type of Firm

Private Equity Firm

Project Preferences

Type of Financing Preferred:
Early Stage

Industry Preferences

In Internet Specific prefer:
Internet

Additional Information

Name of Most Recent Fund: ff Blue Private Equity Fund, L.P.
Most Recent Fund Was Raised: 11/26/2008
Year Founded: 2000
Capital Under Management: $2,500,000
Current Activity Level: Actively seeking new investments

FFR CAPITAL PARTNERS

141 Avondale Road
Ridgewood, NJ USA 07450
Website: www.frrcapital.com

Management and Staff

Robert Rosenberg, Partner
Thomas Ferguson, Partner

Type of Firm

Private Equity Advisor or Fund of Funds

Project Preferences

Type of Financing Preferred:
Leveraged Buyout

Geographical Preferences

United States Preferences:
Midwest
Northeast

Additional Information

Year Founded: 2006
Current Activity Level: Actively seeking new investments

FIANCHETTO VENTURE CAPITAL AB (FVC)

Akervagen 26
Rosersberg, Sweden S-195 71
Phone: 46-8-558-01433
Fax: 46-8-558-01434
Website: www.fianchettovc.com

Management and Staff

Gustav Kamperman, Chief Executive Officer

Type of Firm

Private Equity Firm

Project Preferences

Type of Financing Preferred:
Balanced

Geographical Preferences

International Preferences:
Scandanavia/Nordic Region

Industry Preferences

In Medical/Health prefer:
Medical/Health

Additional Information

Year Founded: 2005
Current Activity Level: Actively seeking new investments

FIDELITY ASIA VENTURES

17/F, 1 International Finance
1 Harbour View Street
Central, Hong Kong
Phone: 852-2629-2800
Fax: 852-2509-0371
E-mail: fidelityasiaventures@fidelity.com
Website: www.fidelityasiaventures.com

Other Offices

222 Hubin Road, Luwan District
Suite 1502-03, One Corporate Avenue
Shanghai, China 200021
Phone: 86-21-6340-6555
Fax: 86-21-6340-6618

Management and Staff

Albert Cheng, Partner
Benson Tam, Partner
Daniel Auerbach, Managing Director
Norman Chen, Partner
Qian Yu, Vice President
Rebecca Lin, Vice President
Ted Chua, Principal

Type of Firm

Corporate PE/Venture

Association Membership

Hong Kong Venture Capital Association (HKVCA)

Project Preferences

Type of Financing Preferred:
Expansion
Mezzanine
Seed
Later Stage
Startup

Size of Investments Considered:
Min Size of Investment Considered (000s): $300
Max Size of Investment Considered (000s): $20,000

Geographical Preferences

International Preferences:
China
Asia

Industry Preferences

In Communications prefer:
Telecommunications
Other Communication Prod.

In Computer Hardware prefer:
Computers

In Computer Other prefer:
Computer Related

In Medical/Health prefer:
Medical/Health

In Consumer Related prefer:
Consumer

Additional Information

Year Founded: 1995
Capital Under Management: $250,000,000
Current Activity Level: Actively seeking new investments

FIDELITY BIOSCIENCES (FKA: FIDELITY BIOSCIENCES GROUP)

One Main Street
13th Floor
Cambridge, MA USA 02142
Phone: 617-231-2400
Fax: 617-231-2425
E-mail: fidelitybiosciences@fmr.com
Website: www.fidelitybiosciences.com

Other Offices

82 Devonshire Street
EPC13A
Boston, MA USA 02109

Management and Staff

Ben Auspitz, Principal
Declan Doogan, Venture Partner
Richard Fedorowich, Chief Financial Officer
Robert Weisskoff, Partner
Stephen Knight, Managing Partner
Thomas Beck, Venture Partner

Type of Firm

Bank Affiliated

Association Membership

National Venture Capital Association - USA (NVCA)

Project Preferences

Role in Financing:
Will function either as deal originator or investor in deals created by others

Type of Financing Preferred:
Second Stage Financing
Early Stage
Expansion
Research and Development
Balanced
Start-up Financing
First Stage Financing

Size of Investments Considered:
Min Size of Investment Considered (000s): $500
Max Size of Investment Considered (000s): $15,000

Geographical Preferences

United States Preferences:
All U.S.

International Preferences:
Europe
Asia

Industry Preferences

In Biotechnology prefer:
Biotechnology
Biosensors
Biotech Related Research

In Medical/Health prefer:
Medical Diagnostics
Diagnostic Services
Diagnostic Test Products
Medical Therapeutics
Drug/Equipmt Delivery
Medical Products
Hospitals/Clinics/Primary
Pharmaceuticals

Additional Information
Year Founded: 2002
Capital Under Management: $400,000,000
Current Activity Level: Actively seeking new investments
Method of Compensation: Return on investment is of primary concern, do not charge fees

---

FIDELITY CAPITAL PARTNERS LTD.
18 Aviation Road
Cantonments
Accra, Ghana
Phone: 233-21-782-625
Fax: 233-21-782-627
E-mail: info@fidelitycapitalpartners.com
Website: www.fidelitycapitalpartners.com

Management and Staff
Stephen Antwi-Asimeng, Managing Director

Type of Firm
Private Equity Firm

Association Membership
African Venture Capital Association (AVCA)

Project Preferences

Type of Financing Preferred:
Expansion
Generalist PE
Balanced

Size of Investments Considered:
Min Size of Investment Considered (000s): $200
Max Size of Investment Considered (000s): $800

Geographical Preferences

International Preferences:
Ghana
Africa

Additional Information
Year Founded: 1997
Capital Under Management: $8,500,000
Current Activity Level: Actively seeking new investments

FIDELITY EQUITY PARTNERS
One Federal Street
27th Floor
Boston, MA USA 02110
Phone: 617-563-7000
Fax: 617-476-9023
E-mail: info@fidelityprivateequity.com
Website: www.fidelityequitypartners.com

Other Offices
10 Paternoster Square
London, United Kingdom EC4M 7LS
Phone: 44-20-7184-3630

Management and Staff
Andrew Flaster, Chief Financial Officer
Brooke Ablon, Partner
David Nemeskal, Vice President
Ian Blasco, Partner
Nick Martin, Partner
Paul Lipson, Vice President
Robert Ketterson, Managing Partner
Sebastian McKinlay, Partner
Stephen Findlay, Vice President

Type of Firm
Bank Affiliated

Project Preferences

Type of Financing Preferred:
Leveraged Buyout
Expansion

Geographical Preferences

United States Preferences:
All U.S.

International Preferences:
Europe

Industry Preferences

In Communications prefer:
Communications and Media

In Computer Software prefer:
Software

In Medical/Health prefer:
Health Services

In Consumer Related prefer:
Consumer Services

In Financial Services prefer:
Financial Services

In Business Serv. prefer:
Services

Additional Information
Year Founded: 2007
Capital Under Management: $500,000,000
Current Activity Level: Actively seeking new investments

FIDELITY INVESTMENTS
82 Devonshire Street
R25E
Boston, MA USA 02109
Phone: 617-563-7000
Website: www.fidelity.com

Type of Firm
Bank Affiliated

Project Preferences

Type of Financing Preferred:
Balanced

Geographical Preferences

United States Preferences:
All U.S.

Additional Information
Name of Most Recent Fund: Fidelity Investors VI Limited Partnership
Most Recent Fund Was Raised: 07/13/2004
Year Founded: 1971
Capital Under Management: $2,100,000
Current Activity Level: Actively seeking new investments

FIDELITY VENTURES
One Federal Street
27th Floor
Boston, MA USA 02110
Phone: 617-830-2100
Fax: 617-476-9023
E-mail: ventures@fidelityventures.com
Website: www.fidelityventures.com

Other Offices

One Corporate Avenue
222 Hubin Road, Luwam District
Shanghai, China 200021
Phone: 86-21-6340-6555

Mail Zone XGM #56
5th Floor, Maker Chambers VI
Mumbai, India 400021

25 Cannon Street
London, United Kingdom EC4M 5TA
Phone: 44-20-7074-5610

8 Finance St., Two Int'l Finance Centre
Suites 7013-7015, 70th Floor
Central, Hong Kong
Phone: 852-2629-2800

Unit 2207, 22F, Twr 2, China Central Plc
No. 79 Jianguo Road
Beijing, China 100025
Phone: 86-10-6598-9336

Management and Staff

Anne Mitchell, Partner
David Power, Partner
Davor Hebel, Vice President
Don Haile, Venture Partner
Frank Panaccio, Vice President
Lawrence Cheng, Partner
Robert Ketterson, Managing Partner
Roger Hurwitz, Partner
Simon Clark, Partner

Type of Firm

Bank Affiliated

Association Membership

National Venture Capital Association - USA (NVCA)
European Private Equity and Venture Capital Assoc.

Project Preferences

Role in Financing:

Will function either as deal originator or investor in deals created by others

Type of Financing Preferred:

Second Stage Financing
Early Stage
Expansion
Balanced
Start-up Financing
Seed
First Stage Financing

Size of Investments Considered:

Min Size of Investment Considered (000s): $3,000
Max Size of Investment Considered (000s): $10,000

Geographical Preferences

Canadian Preferences:

All Canada

International Preferences:

Italy
Ireland
United Kingdom
Luxembourg
Netherlands
Belgium
Israel
Germany
France

Industry Focus

(% based on actual investment)

Computer Software and Services	39.1%
Internet Specific	33.1%
Communications and Media	16.7%
Biotechnology	3.9%
Consumer Related	2.1%
Computer Hardware	2.1%
Medical/Health	2.0%
Semiconductors/Other Elect.	1.0%

Additional Information

Name of Most Recent Fund: Fidelity Ventures IV, L.P.
Most Recent Fund Was Raised: 11/23/2004
Year Founded: 1969
Capital Under Management: $800,000,000
Current Activity Level: Actively seeking new investments
Method of Compensation: Return on investment is of primary concern, do not charge fees

---

FIDES CAPITAL SCR SA

Velazquez 3
4th Floor
Madrid, Spain 28001
Phone: 34-91-781-1638
Fax: 34-91-576-9351
E-mail: fmb@fidescapital.es
Website: www.fidescapital.es

Type of Firm

Private Equity Firm

Association Membership

Spanish Venture Capital Association (ASCRI)

Project Preferences

Type of Financing Preferred:

Second Stage Financing
Expansion

Geographical Preferences

International Preferences:

Europe
Spain

Industry Preferences

In Internet Specific prefer:

Internet

Additional Information

Year Founded: 1999
Capital Under Management: $20,900,000
Current Activity Level: Actively seeking new investments

FIDUS CAPITAL

121 West Trade Street
Suite 1800
Charlotte, NC USA 28202
Phone: 704-334-2222
Fax: 704-334-2202
E-mail: info@fiduspartners.com
Website: www.fiduspartners.com

Other Offices

190 South LaSalle Street
Suite 2140
Chicago, IL USA 60603
Phone: 312-284-5200
Fax: 312-284-5212

70 East 55th Street
Tenth Floor
New York, NY USA 10022
Phone: 212-750-6400
Fax: 212-750-6411

Management and Staff

B. Bragg Comer, Managing Partner
Cary Schaefer, Vice President
Christopher Haza, Vice President
Edward Ross, Managing Director
J. Stephen Dockery, Managing Partner
John Cheek, Vice President
Robert Kreidler, Chief Operating Officer
Ted Swimmer, Managing Partner
W. Andrew Worth, Principal

Type of Firm

Bank Affiliated

Project Preferences

Type of Financing Preferred:

Leveraged Buyout
Mezzanine
Expansion
Later Stage
Management Buyouts
Acquisition
Recapitalizations

Geographical Preferences

United States Preferences:

Industry Preferences

In Medical/Health prefer:

Health Services

In Consumer Related prefer:

Consumer Products

In Transportation prefer:

Aerospace

In Business Serv. prefer:

Services
Distribution

Additional Information

Year Founded: 2008
Capital Under Management: $200,000,000
Current Activity Level: Actively seeking new investments

FIER SUCCES

350 Rue Franquet
Porte 20, Sainte-Foy
Quebec, Canada G1P 4N3
Phone: 418-683-0011
Fax: 418-650-2359
Website: www.fiersucces.com

Type of Firm

Government Affiliated Program

Additional Information

Year Founded: 2005
Current Activity Level: Actively seeking new investments

FIFTH STREET CAPITAL LLC

Ten Bank Street
12th Floor
White Plains, NY USA 10606
Phone: 914-286-6800
Fax: 914-328-4214
Website: www.fifthstreetfinance.com

Other Offices

15233 Ventura Boulevard
Penthouse Two
Sherman Oaks, CA USA 91403
Phone: 818-990-3144
Fax: 818-990-3147

Management and Staff

Brian Finkelstein, Vice President
Casey Zmijeski, Managing Director
Ivelin Dimitrov, Partner
Juan Alva, Partner
Robert Kiesel, Principal
William Craig, Chief Financial Officer

Type of Firm

Private Equity Firm

Project Preferences

Type of Financing Preferred:

Leveraged Buyout
Expansion
Mezzanine
Recapitalizations

Size of Investments Considered:

Min Size of Investment Considered (000s): $3,000
Max Size of Investment Considered (000s): $20,000

Additional Information

Year Founded: 1998
Capital Under Management: $100,000,000
Current Activity Level: Actively seeking new investments

FILAS - FINANZIARIA LAZIALE DI SVILUPPO SPA

Via Alessandro Farnese, 3
Roma, Italy 00192
Phone: 39-06-328851
Fax: 39-06-3600-6808
E-mail: filas@filas.it
Website: www.filas.it

Type of Firm

Private Equity Firm

Association Membership

Italian Venture Capital Association (AIFI)
European Private Equity and Venture Capital Assoc.

Project Preferences

Type of Financing Preferred:

Early Stage
Expansion
Generalist PE
Startup

Geographical Preferences

International Preferences:

Italy
Spain

Additional Information

Year Founded: 2000
Capital Under Management: $45,200,000
Current Activity Level: Actively seeking new investments

FILTARN

4 rue Augustin-Malroux
Albi, France 81000
Phone: 33-5-6348-8740
Fax: 33-5-6338-9750

Type of Firm

Private Equity Firm

Project Preferences

Type of Financing Preferred:

Leveraged Buyout
Early Stage
Expansion

Geographical Preferences

International Preferences:

France

Additional Information

Year Founded: 1990
Capital Under Management: $1,500,000
Current Activity Level: Actively seeking new investments

FIN ACTIVE

96 rue de la Victoire
Paris, France 75009
Phone: 33-1-4463-1540
Fax: 33-1-4463-0311
Website: www.finactive.fr

Management and Staff

Eric Etcharry, Partner
Francis Pelligrono, Partner
Gilles Roland, President

Type of Firm

Private Equity Firm

Association Membership

French Venture Capital Association (AFIC)

Project Preferences

Role in Financing:

Prefer role as deal originator

Type of Financing Preferred:

Turnaround
Special Situation

Size of Investments Considered:

Min Size of Investment Considered (000s): $125
Max Size of Investment Considered (000s): $6,000

Geographical Preferences

International Preferences:

Europe
France

Additional Information

Year Founded: 2004
Capital Under Management: $243,400,000
Current Activity Level: Actively seeking new investments
Method of Compensation: Return on invest. most important, but chg. closing fees, service fees, etc.

FIN.CO

Verbindingsdok
Oostkaai 13
Antwerp, Belgium 2000
Phone: 32-3-202-0453
Fax: 32-3-226-4194
E-mail: info@finco.be
Website: www.finco.be

Other Offices

Napoleonkaai 19
Antwerp 1, Belgium B-2000

Management and Staff
Hubert Plouvier, Managing Director

Type of Firm
Private Equity Firm

Association Membership
European Private Equity and Venture Capital Assoc.

Project Preferences
Type of Financing Preferred:
Leveraged Buyout
Turnaround
Later Stage
Management Buyouts

Geographical Preferences
International Preferences:
Netherlands
Belgium

Industry Preferences
In Industrial/Energy prefer:
Energy
Industrial Products

In Business Serv. prefer:
Services

Additional Information
Year Founded: 2000
Current Activity Level: Actively seeking new investments

FINADVANCE SA
Le Derby
570 Avenue du Club Hippique
Aix en Provence, France 13090
Phone: 33-4-4252-9130
Fax: 33-4-4252-9139
E-mail: finadvance@aol.com
Website: www.finadvance.fr

Other Offices
82 rue Saint-Lazare
Paris, France 75009
Phone: 33-1-4874-7770
Fax: 33-14874-2169

Type of Firm
Private Equity Firm

Association Membership
French Venture Capital Association (AFIC)

Project Preferences
Role in Financing:
Prefer role as deal originator but will also invest in deals created by others

Type of Financing Preferred:
Leveraged Buyout
Expansion
Management Buyouts
Acquisition

Geographical Preferences
International Preferences:
France

Industry Preferences
In Industrial/Energy prefer:
Industrial Products

In Business Serv. prefer:
Services

Additional Information
Year Founded: 1988
Capital Under Management: $41,000,000
Current Activity Level: Actively seeking new investments
Method of Compensation: Return on invest. most important, but chg. closing fees, service fees, etc.

FINANCE SOUTH EAST, LTD.
Devonshire Place
New Road
Crowthorne, United Kingdom RG45 6NA
Phone: 44-134-475-8540
Fax: 44-134-476-2002
E-mail: mail@financesoutheast.com
Website: www.financesoutheast.com

Management and Staff
Sally Goodsell, Chief Executive Officer

Type of Firm
Incubator/Development Program

Project Preferences
Type of Financing Preferred:
Early Stage
Seed
Startup

Geographical Preferences
International Preferences:
United Kingdom

Additional Information
Year Founded: 2004
Capital Under Management: $18,400,000
Current Activity Level: Actively seeking new investments

FINANCE WALES PLC
Oakleigh House
Park Place
Cardiff, United Kingdom CF10 3DQ
Phone: 44-29-2033-8100
Fax: 44-29-2033-8101
E-mail: info@financewales.co.uk
Website: www.financewales.co.uk

Management and Staff
Sian Lloyd Jones, Chief Executive Officer

Type of Firm
Incubator/Development Program

Association Membership
British Venture Capital Association (BVCA)
European Private Equity and Venture Capital Assoc.

Project Preferences
Type of Financing Preferred:
Leveraged Buyout
Early Stage
Expansion
Mezzanine
Balanced
Seed
Startup

Geographical Preferences
International Preferences:
United Kingdom

Additional Information
Year Founded: 1999
Capital Under Management: $38,000,000
Current Activity Level: Actively seeking new investments

FINANCIERE DES ENTERPRISES CULTURELLES (AKA: FIDEC)
215, rue Sainte-Jacques,
Bureau 800
Montreal, Canada H2Y 1M6
Phone: 514-940-2200
Fax: 514-940-1528
E-mail: info@fidecinvest.com

Type of Firm
Private Equity Firm

Additional Information
Year Founded: 2009
Current Activity Level: Actively seeking new investments

FINANCIERE GALLIERA
21, rue du Mont-Thabor
Paris, France 75001
Phone: 33-1-4286-0902
Fax: 33-1-4286-0988

Type of Firm
Private Equity Firm

Association Membership
French Venture Capital Association (AFIC)

Project Preferences

Type of Financing Preferred:
Balanced

Geographical Preferences

International Preferences:
France

Additional Information
Current Activity Level: Actively seeking new investments

FINANCIERE SAINT MERRI

75 boulevard Haussmann
Paris, France 75008
Phone: 33-1-4268-5107
Website: www.saintmerri.com

Management and Staff
Jean Luc Rivoire, President

Type of Firm
Private Equity Firm

Project Preferences

Type of Financing Preferred:
Leveraged Buyout
Expansion
Balanced

Geographical Preferences

International Preferences:
France

Industry Preferences

In Industrial/Energy prefer:
Energy

In Financial Services prefer:
Real Estate

Additional Information
Year Founded: 1999
Current Activity Level: Actively seeking new investments

FINANCIERE VECTEUR

9 avenue Newton
Montigny-le-Bretonneux
St-Quentin-en-Yvelines Cedex, France 78183
Phone: 33-1-3014-6730
Fax: 33-1-3014-6736
E-mail: info@vecteur.fr

Type of Firm
Bank Affiliated

Project Preferences

Type of Financing Preferred:
Leveraged Buyout
Expansion

Geographical Preferences

International Preferences:
France

Additional Information
Year Founded: 1995
Capital Under Management: $21,500,000
Current Activity Level: Actively seeking new investments

FINANZIARA SENESE DI SVILUPPO SPA

Piazza Matteotti 30
Palazzo Camerale
Siena, Romania 153100
Phone: 39-57-74-8102
Fax: 39-57-74-3068
E-mail: info@fises.it
Website: www.fises.it

Type of Firm
Private Equity Firm

Association Membership
Italian Venture Capital Association (AIFI)

Project Preferences

Type of Financing Preferred:
Early Stage
Expansion
Seed

Geographical Preferences

International Preferences:
Italy
Europe

Additional Information
Year Founded: 1998
Current Activity Level: Actively seeking new investments

FINATEM GMBH

Freiherr-vom-Stein-Strasse 7
Frankfurt, Germany 60323
Phone: 49-69-509-5640
Fax: 49-69-5095-6430
E-mail: info@finatem.de
Website: www.finatem.de

Management and Staff
Christophe Hemmerle, Managing Director
Robert Hennigs, Managing Director

Type of Firm
Private Equity Firm

Project Preferences

Type of Financing Preferred:
Leveraged Buyout
Early Stage
Expansion
Management Buyouts
Recapitalizations

Geographical Preferences

International Preferences:
Switzerland
Austria
Germany

Additional Information
Year Founded: 2000
Capital Under Management: $119,000,000
Current Activity Level: Actively seeking new investments

FINAVENTURES

3000 Ocean Park Boulevard
Suite 1022
Santa Monica, CA USA 90405
Phone: 310-399-5011
Fax: 310-452-5492
E-mail: info@finaventures.com
Website: www.finaventures.com

Management and Staff
Abdou Bensouda, Managing Director
Rachid Sefrioui, Managing Director
Sam Lee, Managing Director
Suresh Nihalani, Venture Partner

Type of Firm
Private Equity Firm

Association Membership
National Venture Capital Association - USA (NVCA)

Project Preferences

Role in Financing:
Will function either as deal originator or investor in deals created by others

Type of Financing Preferred:
Second Stage Financing
Early Stage
Expansion
Balanced
First Stage Financing

Size of Investments Considered:
Min Size of Investment Considered (000s): $500
Max Size of Investment Considered (000s): $3,000

Geographical Preferences

United States Preferences:
Southern California
Northern California

Industry Preferences

In Communications prefer:
Commercial Communications
Telecommunications
Wireless Communications
Data Communications
Satellite Microwave Comm.
Other Communication Prod.

In Computer Software prefer:
Software
Systems Software
Applications Software

In Semiconductor/Electr prefer:
Electronic Components
Semiconductor
Micro-Processing
Controllers and Sensors
Sensors
Circuit Boards
Component Testing Equipmt
Laser Related
Fiber Optics
Analytic/Scientific
Optoelectronics

Additional Information

Name of Most Recent Fund: Fina Fund I, L.P.
Most Recent Fund Was Raised: 10/24/2000
Year Founded: 2000
Capital Under Management: $22,000,000
Current Activity Level: Actively seeking new investments
Method of Compensation: Return on investment is of primary concern, do not charge fees

---

FINCALABRA SPA

274 Viale De Filippis
Catanzaro, Italy 88100
Phone: 39-09-6177-0775
Fax: 39-09-6177-0226
E-mail: fincalabra@libero.it
Website: www.fincalabra.it

Type of Firm

Incubator/Development Program

Association Membership

Italian Venture Capital Association (AIFI)

Project Preferences

Type of Financing Preferred:
Balanced

Geographical Preferences

International Preferences:
Italy

Industry Preferences

In Industrial/Energy prefer:
Industrial Products
Materials

In Manufact. prefer:
Manufacturing

Additional Information

Year Founded: 1999
Current Activity Level: Actively seeking new investments

FINDOS INVESTOR GMBH

Giselastrasse 12
Munich, Germany D-80802
Phone: 49-89-2000-0950
Fax: 49-89-2000-9595
E-mail: findos@findos.eu
Website: www.findos-cdo.de

Management and Staff

Hans Freudenberg, Partner
Olaf Rogowski, Partner
Wolfgang Ziegler, Partner

Type of Firm

Private Equity Firm

Project Preferences

Type of Financing Preferred:
Leveraged Buyout

Additional Information

Year Founded: 2008
Current Activity Level: Actively seeking new investments

FINIMMO

64 rue Galilee
Paris, France 75008
Phone: 33-1-4070-2045
Fax: 33-1-4952-0667

Management and Staff

Philippe De Verdalle, Chief Executive Officer

Type of Firm

Private Equity Firm

Project Preferences

Type of Financing Preferred:
Expansion
Later Stage

Geographical Preferences

International Preferences:
Europe

Additional Information

Year Founded: 1995
Capital Under Management: $100,000,000
Current Activity Level: Actively seeking new investments

FININT & PARTNERS SPA

1 Via Vittorio Alfieri
Conegliano (TV), Italy 31015
Phone: 39-04-3836-0900
Fax: 39-04-3841-1901
E-mail: finint@finint.it
Website: www.finint.it

Management and Staff

Domenico Tonussi, Managing Director
Matteo Patrone, Managing Director

Type of Firm

Bank Affiliated

Association Membership

Italian Venture Capital Association (AIFI)

Project Preferences

Type of Financing Preferred:
Expansion

Geographical Preferences

International Preferences:
Italy

Additional Information

Year Founded: 2001
Capital Under Management: $32,300,000
Current Activity Level: Actively seeking new investments

FINISTERE PARTNERS LLC

12555 High Bluff Drive
Suite 175
San Diego, CA USA 92130
Phone: 858-552-8454
Fax: 858-793-7120
E-mail: info@finisterepartners.com
Website: www.finisterepartners.com

Management and Staff

Rob Ayling, Managing Director
Robert Gilmour, Managing Director

Type of Firm

Private Equity Firm

Project Preferences

Role in Financing:
Prefer role as deal originator but will also invest in deals created by others

Type of Financing Preferred:
Early Stage
Expansion
Seed
Startup

Size of Investments Considered:
Min Size of Investment Considered (000s): $500
Max Size of Investment Considered (000s): $5,000

Geographical Preferences

United States Preferences:
All U.S.

International Preferences:
Taiwan
China
New Zealand

Industry Preferences

In Biotechnology prefer:
Agricultural/Animal Bio.
Industrial Biotechnology

In Medical/Health prefer:
Medical Diagnostics
Medical Products
Disposable Med. Products

In Consumer Related prefer:
Food/Beverage

In Agr/Forestr/Fish prefer:
Agriculture related

In Other prefer:
Environment Responsible

Additional Information
Name of Most Recent Fund: Finistere-AgResearch Strategic Fund I, L.P.
Most Recent Fund Was Raised: 09/05/2005
Year Founded: 2005
Capital Under Management: $46,000,000
Current Activity Level: Actively seeking new investments
Method of Compensation: Return on invest. most important, but chg. closing fees, service fees, etc.

FINISTERE VENTURES LLC
12555 High Bluff Drive
Suite 175
San Diego, CA USA 92130
Phone: 858-552-8454
Fax: 858-793-7120
E-mail: info@finistereventures.com
Website: www.finistereventures.com

Management and Staff
Arama Kukutai, Managing Director
Bruce Brumfield, Managing Director
Kenneth Selzer, Venture Partner
Paul Zorner, Venture Partner

Type of Firm
Private Equity Firm

Project Preferences

Type of Financing Preferred:
Early Stage
Startup

Geographical Preferences

International Preferences:
Australia
New Zealand

Industry Preferences

In Biotechnology prefer:
Agricultural/Animal Bio.
Industrial Biotechnology

In Medical/Health prefer:
Medical Products
Disposable Med. Products

In Industrial/Energy prefer:
Energy Conservation Relat

In Agr/Forestr/Fish prefer:
Agriculture related

In Other prefer:
Environment Responsible

Additional Information
Name of Most Recent Fund: Finistere - Oceania Partners I
Most Recent Fund Was Raised: 06/30/2005
Year Founded: 2005
Capital Under Management: $34,000,000
Current Activity Level: Actively seeking new investments

FINLOMBARDA GESTIONI SGR SPA
Piazza Belgioioso, 2
Milan, Italy 20121
Phone: 39-02-760-441
Fax: 39-02-780-819
E-mail: flsegreteria@finlombardia.it
Website: www.finlombarda.it

Management and Staff
Marco Nicholai, Managing Director

Type of Firm
Government Affiliated Program

Association Membership
Italian Venture Capital Association (AIFI)

Project Preferences

Type of Financing Preferred:
Early Stage
Expansion

Geographical Preferences

International Preferences:
Italy
Europe
All International

Additional Information
Year Founded: 1971
Capital Under Management: $112,600,000
Current Activity Level: Actively seeking new investments

FINNISH FUND FOR INDUSTRIAL COOPERATION, LTD. (AKA:FINNFUND)
Uudenmaankatu 16 B
4th Floor
Helsinki, Finland FI-00120
Phone: 358-9-348-434
Fax: 358-9-3484-3346
E-mail: finnfund@finnfund.fi
Website: www.finnfund.fi

Management and Staff
Jaakko Kangasniemi, CEO & Managing Director

Type of Firm
Private Equity Firm

Association Membership
Finnish Venture Capital Association (FVCA)

Project Preferences

Role in Financing:
Prefer role as deal originator but will also invest in deals created by others

Type of Financing Preferred:
Second Stage Financing
Expansion
Mezzanine
Start-up Financing
Seed
First Stage Financing
Startup

Geographical Preferences

International Preferences:
Eastern Europe
Middle East
Afghanistan
Asia
Russia

Industry Preferences

In Communications prefer:
Communications and Media

in Computer Other prefer:
Computer Related

In Semiconductor/Electr prefer:
Electronic Components

In Biotechnology prefer:
Biotechnology

In Medical/Health prefer:
Medical/Health

In Consumer Related prefer:
Consumer

In Industrial/Energy prefer:
Energy
Industrial Products

In Business Serv. prefer:
Distribution

In Agr/Forestr/Fish prefer:
Agriculture related

Additional Information

Year Founded: 1980
Capital Under Management: $101,900,000
Current Activity Level: Actively seeking new investments
Method of Compensation: Return on investment is of primary concern, do not charge fees

FINNISH INDUSTRY INVESTMENT (AKA: SUOMEN TEOLLISUUSSIJOITUS)

Kalevankatu 9 A
P.O. Box 685
Helsinki, Finland 00101
Phone: 358-9-680-3680
Fax: 358-9-612-1680
E-mail: tesi@teollisuussijoitus.fi
Website: www.teollisuussijoitus.fi

Management and Staff

Marko Haikio, Chief Financial Officer

Type of Firm

Government Affiliated Program

Association Membership

Finnish Venture Capital Association (FVCA)
European Private Equity and Venture Capital Assoc.

Project Preferences

Role in Financing:
Will function either as deal originator or investor in deals created by others

Type of Financing Preferred:
Fund of Funds
Early Stage
Expansion
Mezzanine
Generalist PE
Start-up Financing
Turnaround
Seed

Size of Investments Considered:
Min Size of Investment Considered (000s): $2,000
Max Size of Investment Considered (000s): $7,000

Geographical Preferences

International Preferences:
Central Europe
Europe
Finland

Industry Focus

(% based on actual investment)

Other Products	65.8%
Semiconductors/Other Elect.	9.9%
Industrial/Energy	8.2%
Computer Software and Services	5.6%
Medical/Health	3.9%
Communications and Media	2.6%
Consumer Related	1.8%
Biotechnology	1.3%
Internet Specific	0.6%
Computer Hardware	0.3%

Additional Information

Name of Most Recent Fund: Start Fund I KY
Most Recent Fund Was Raised: 04/03/2005
Year Founded: 1954
Capital Under Management: $222,900,000
Current Activity Level: Actively seeking new investments
Method of Compensation: Return on invest. most important, but chg. closing fees, service fees, etc.

FINORPA

23 rue du 11 novembre
BP 351
Lens Cedex, France 62334
Phone: 33-3-2113-6060
Fax: 33-3-2113-6069
E-mail: finorpa@finorpa.fr
Website: www.finorpa.fr

Other Offices

50 Boulevard Jacquard
Calais, France 62100
Phone: 33 3 2185 5460
Fax: 33 3 2185 0758

21 avenue Le Corbusier
Lille, France 59800
Phone: 33 3 2031 5954
Fax: 33 3 2031 2265

17 rue Capron
Valenciennes, France 59300
Phone: 33 3 2747 4707
Fax: 33 3 2733 5177

Management and Staff

Antoine Harleaux, General Director
Jean-Marie Duvivier, President

Type of Firm

Incubator/Development Program

Project Preferences

Type of Financing Preferred:
Expansion
Turnaround
Management Buyouts
Startup

Geographical Preferences

International Preferences:
France

Industry Preferences

In Semiconductor/Electr prefer:
Electronics

In Consumer Related prefer:
Food/Beverage

In Industrial/Energy prefer:
Industrial Products
Materials

In Manufact. prefer:
Manufacturing
Publishing

Additional Information

Year Founded: 1984
Current Activity Level: Actively seeking new investments

FINPRO, SGPS SA

Av. Barbosa do Bocage, 85, 5o
Lisboa, Portugal 1050-030
Phone: 351-21-793-4234
Fax: 351-21-799-3774
E-mail: finpro@mail.telepac.pt
Website: www.finpro.pt

Type of Firm

Private Equity Firm

Project Preferences

Type of Financing Preferred:
Balanced

Additional Information

Year Founded: 2007
Current Activity Level: Actively seeking new investments

FINSBURY LIFE SCIENCES INVESTMENT TRUST

10 Crown Place
London, United Kingdom EC2B 2BR
Phone: 800-169-6968
Fax: 20-7247-4722
E-mail: info@closefinsbury.com
Website: www.closefinsbury.com

Management and Staff

Alastair Smith, Managing Director

Type of Firm

Private Equity Firm

Additional Information

Year Founded: 2009
Current Activity Level: Actively seeking new investments

FIR CAPITAL PARTNERS, LTD.

Rua Carlos Chagas, 49/ 9 andar
Santo Lourdes
Belo Horizonte, MG, Brazil
Phone: 55-31-3074-0020
Fax: 55-31-3074-0015
E-mail: info@fircapital.com
Website: www.fircapital.com

Management and Staff

Christiano Moyses, Partner

Type of Firm

Private Equity Firm

Association Membership

Brazilian Venture Capital Association (ABCR)

Project Preferences

Type of Financing Preferred:
Early Stage
Expansion
Balanced
Other
Seed
Startup

Size of Investments Considered:
Min Size of Investment Considered (000s): $100
Max Size of Investment Considered (000s): $2,000

Geographical Preferences

International Preferences:
Brazil

Industry Preferences

In Computer Software prefer:
Software

In Biotechnology prefer:
Biotechnology

In Medical/Health prefer:
Medical/Health

In Business Serv. prefer:
Services

Additional Information

Year Founded: 1999
Capital Under Management: $65,000,000
Current Activity Level: Actively seeking new investments

FIRE CAPITAL

104, Ashoka Estate
24 Barakhamba, Connaught Place
New Delhi, India 110001
Phone: 91-11-2372-3909
Website: www.firecapital.com

Management and Staff

Om Chaudhry, Managing Director

Type of Firm

Private Equity Firm

Project Preferences

Type of Financing Preferred:
Balanced

Geographical Preferences

International Preferences:
India

Industry Preferences

In Financial Services prefer:
Real Estate

Additional Information

Year Founded: 2005
Current Activity Level: Actively seeking new investments

FIREBIRD MANAGEMENT LLC

152 West 57th Street
24th Floor
New York, NY USA 10019
Phone: 212-698-9260
Fax: 212-698-9266
E-mail: firebird@fbird.com
Website: www.fbird.com

Other Offices

52, route d'Esch
Luxembourg, Luxembourg 2965
Phone: 35-240-654-0459
Fax: 35-240-654-0459

Management and Staff

Indrek Kasela, Partner
Joanne Tuckman, Chief Financial Officer
Martynas Cesnavicius, Partner

Type of Firm

Investment Management Firm

Project Preferences

Type of Financing Preferred:
Leveraged Buyout

Geographical Preferences

International Preferences:
Sweden
Luxembourg
Eastern Europe
Estonia
Finland
Latvia
Russia
Lithuania

Additional Information

Year Founded: 2005
Capital Under Management: $203,100,000
Current Activity Level: Actively seeking new investments

FIRELAKE CAPITAL MANAGEMENT

575 High Street
Suite 330
Palo Alto, CA USA 94301-1648
Phone: 650-321-0880
Fax: 650-321-0882
Website: www.firelakecapital.com

Management and Staff

Candice Eggerss, Managing Director
Fred Kittler, Managing Director
Martin Lagod, Managing Director
Peter Shannon, Partner

Type of Firm

Private Equity Firm

Additional Information

Year Founded: 2009
Current Activity Level: Actively seeking new investments

FIRESTARTER PARTNERS LLC

1055 Minnesota Avenue
Suite 3
San Jose, CA USA 95125
Phone: 408-288-5100
Fax: 408-873-0550
Website: www.firestarter-llc.com

Management and Staff

Peter Verbica, Managing Partner

Type of Firm

Private Equity Advisor or Fund of Funds

Project Preferences

Type of Financing Preferred:
Fund of Funds
Early Stage

Expansion
Mezzanine
Seed

Additional Information

Year Founded: 1999
Current Activity Level: Making few, if any, new investments

FIRM FACTORY NETWORK

Karlavagen 50
Stockholm, Sweden 114-49
E-mail: info@firmfactory.com
Website: www.firmfactory.com

Management and Staff

Alexander Murad, Partner
Arwind Malhotra, Founder
Daniel Kaplan, Managing Partner
David Ekenvi, Partner
Lars Procheus, Partner
Maria Groschopp, Founder
Oskar Bjursten, Founder
Peter Settman, Partner
Peter Ahlgren, Founder
Samuel Asarnoj, Partner

Type of Firm

Private Equity Firm

Association Membership

Swedish Venture Capital Association (SVCA)

Additional Information

Year Founded: 2005
Current Activity Level: Actively seeking new investments

FIRMAINVEST A/S

Europaplads 2, 7
Arhus, Denmark 8000
Phone: 45-8610-4814
Fax: 45-8610-4815
Website: www.firmainvest.com

Type of Firm

Private Equity Firm

Project Preferences

Type of Financing Preferred:

Balanced

Geographical Preferences

International Preferences:

Denmark

Additional Information

Year Founded: 2008
Current Activity Level: Actively seeking new investments

FIRST ANALYSIS CORPORATION

One South Wacker Drive
Suite 3900
Chicago, IL USA 60606
Phone: 312-258-1400
Fax: 312-258-0334
E-mail: info@facvc.com
Website: www.firstanalysis.com

Management and Staff

Allan Cohen, Managing Director
Angela Soliz, Vice President
Clement Erbmann, Managing Director
Daniel Smereczynski, Vice President
F. Oliver Nicklin, President
Howard Smith, Managing Director
James Macdonald, Managing Director
John Dexheimer, Partner
Joseph Chopp, Chief Financial Officer
Tracy Marshbanks, Vice President

Type of Firm

Private Equity Firm

Association Membership

Illinois Venture Capital Association

Project Preferences

Role in Financing:

Prefer role as deal originator but will also invest in deals created by others

Type of Financing Preferred:

Early Stage
Expansion
Mezzanine
Balanced
Later Stage

Size of Investments Considered:

Min Size of Investment Considered (000s): $3,000
Max Size of Investment Considered (000s): $10,000

Geographical Preferences

United States Preferences:

All U.S.

Industry Focus

(% based on actual investment)	
Internet Specific	24.9%
Other Products	18.2%
Computer Software and Services	17.4%
Industrial/Energy	15.1%
Communications and Media	8.3%
Medical/Health	5.7%
Semiconductors/Other Elect.	3.7%
Biotechnology	2.9%
Consumer Related	2.1%
Computer Hardware	1.6%

Additional Information

Name of Most Recent Fund: FA Private Equity IV
Most Recent Fund Was Raised: 08/28/2001
Year Founded: 1981
Capital Under Management: $490,000,000
Current Activity Level: Actively seeking new investments
Method of Compensation: Return on investment is of primary concern, do not charge fees

FIRST ASSOCIATES INVESTMENTS, INC.

6 Wellington Street, West
Suite 5200, P.O. Box 357
Toronto, Canada M5K 1K7
Phone: 416-601-9030
Fax: 416-601-0396
Website: www.firstassociates.com

Management and Staff

David Burrows, President
John Playfair, Managing Director
Richard Stuchberry, Chairman & CEO

Type of Firm

Private Equity Firm

Additional Information

Year Founded: 1991
Current Activity Level: Actively seeking new investments

FIRST ATLANTIC CAPITAL, LTD.

135 East 57th Street
New York, NY USA 10022
Phone: 212-207-0300
Fax: 212-207-8842
E-mail: general@first-atlantic.com
Website: www.firstatlanticcapital.com

Management and Staff

Charles Shaw, Managing Director
Mahesh Saladi, Managing Director & CFO
Noel Wilens, Principal

Type of Firm

Bank Affiliated

Project Preferences

Type of Financing Preferred:

Leveraged Buyout
Special Situation

Geographical Preferences

United States Preferences:

All U.S.

Industry Preferences

In Consumer Related prefer:

Food/Beverage
Consumer Products

In Industrial/Energy prefer:
Industrial Products
Materials

In Business Serv. prefer:
Services

Additional Information

Name of Most Recent Fund: Atlantic Equity Partners IV, L.P.
Most Recent Fund Was Raised: 07/17/2006
Year Founded: 1989
Capital Under Management: $490,000,000
Current Activity Level: Actively seeking new investments

FIRST AVENUE PARTNERS, L.P.

30 Burton Hills Boulevard
Suite 550
Nashville, TN USA 37201
Phone: 615-370-0056
Fax: 615-376-6310
Website: www.1stpartners.com

Management and Staff

David Wilds, Managing Partner
Mark Isaacs, Partner

Type of Firm

Private Equity Firm

Project Preferences

Type of Financing Preferred:
Later Stage

Size of Investments Considered:
Min Size of Investment Considered (000s): $3,000
Max Size of Investment Considered (000s): $4,000

Geographical Preferences

United States Preferences:
All U.S.

Industry Preferences

In Medical/Health prefer:
Health Services

Additional Information

Name of Most Recent Fund: First Avenue Partners II
Most Recent Fund Was Raised: 08/01/2005
Year Founded: 1998
Capital Under Management: $71,500,000
Current Activity Level: Actively seeking new investments

FIRST CANADIAN TITLE

1290 Central Parkway West
Suite 900
Mississauga, Canada L5C 4R3
Phone: 905-566-0425
Fax: 905-566-8613
Website: www.firstcanadiantitle.com

Type of Firm

Investment Management Firm

Additional Information

Year Founded: 2009
Current Activity Level: Actively seeking new investments

FIRST CAPITAL GROUP MANAGEMENT CO. LLC (AKA: FCG)

P.O. Box 15616
750 East Mulberry, Suite 305
San Antonio, TX USA 78212
Phone: 210-736-4233
Fax: 210-736-5449
E-mail: info@firstcapitalgroup.com
Website: www.firstcapitalgroup.com

Other Offices

12400 Coit Road
Suite 910
Dallas, TX USA 75251
Phone: 214-382-1916
Fax: 214-382-1915

Management and Staff

James O'Donnell, Managing Director
Jeffrey Blanchard, Managing Director
Paul Williams, Principal

Type of Firm

Private Equity Firm

Association Membership

Natl Assoc of Small Bus. Inv. Co (NASBIC)

Project Preferences

Role in Financing:
Will function either as deal originator or investor in deals created by others

Type of Financing Preferred:
Second Stage Financing
Leveraged Buyout
Early Stage
Expansion
Later Stage
Management Buyouts
First Stage Financing
Special Situation

Size of Investments Considered:
Min Size of Investment Considered (000s): $1,000
Max Size of Investment Considered (000s): $6,000

Geographical Preferences

United States Preferences:
Southeast
Southwest
Texas

Industry Focus

(% based on actual investment)

Communications and Media	25.8%
Semiconductors/Other Elect.	24.9%
Internet Specific	13.3%
Consumer Related	13.3%
Computer Software and Services	6.0%
Industrial/Energy	5.3%
Other Products	4.8%
Medical/Health	4.7%
Computer Hardware	1.7%
Biotechnology	0.1%

Additional Information

Name of Most Recent Fund: First Capital Group of Texas Fund III, L.P.
Most Recent Fund Was Raised: 01/01/2001
Year Founded: 1984
Capital Under Management: $150,000,000
Current Activity Level: Actively seeking new investments
Method of Compensation: Return on investment is of primary concern, do not charge fees

---

FIRST CAPITAL PARTNERS LLC

1620 Dodge Street
Stop 1052
Omaha, NE USA 68197
Phone: 402-633-3396
E-mail: info@firstmezzanine.com
Website: www.firstmezzanine.com

Management and Staff

David McLeese, Managing Partner
Eric Gustavson, Managing Director
Wes Hampp, Managing Director

Type of Firm

Private Equity Firm

Project Preferences

Type of Financing Preferred:
Balanced

Geographical Preferences

United States Preferences:
All U.S.

Additional Information

Year Founded: 2001
Current Activity Level: Actively seeking new investments

FIRST EASTERN (SHANGHAI) INVESTMENT MANAGEMENT, LTD.

No. 68 Yincheng East Road
33/F Shidai Finance Building
Shanghai, China

Type of Firm
Private Equity Firm

Project Preferences
Type of Financing Preferred:
Balanced

Geographical Preferences
International Preferences:
China

Industry Preferences
In Industrial/Energy prefer:
Environmental Related

Additional Information
Year Founded: 2009
Capital Under Management: $5,000,000
Current Activity Level: Actively seeking new investments

FIRST EASTERN INVESTMENT GROUP
77th Floor, Tower II
International Finance Centre
Central, Hong Kong
Phone: 852-2956-3838
Fax: 852-2956-1132

Management and Staff
Elisabeth Kan, Managing Director

Type of Firm
Private Equity Firm

Association Membership
Hong Kong Venture Capital Association (HKVCA)

Project Preferences
Type of Financing Preferred:
Generalist PE
Expansion
Acquisition

Size of Investments Considered:
Min Size of Investment Considered (000s): $1,000
Max Size of Investment Considered (000s): $10,000

Geographical Preferences
International Preferences:
Indonesia
Taiwan
Hong Kong
China
Thailand
Philippines
Asia
Korea, South
Singapore
Malaysia
Japan

Industry Preferences
In Computer Hardware prefer:
Computer Graphics and Dig

In Consumer Related prefer:
Education Related

In Financial Services prefer:
Financial Services
Real Estate

In Business Serv. prefer:
Services

In Manufact. prefer:
Manufacturing

Additional Information
Year Founded: 1988
Capital Under Management: $100,000,000
Current Activity Level: Actively seeking new investments

FIRST ELEMENTS VENTURES, LTD. (FKA: SFS CORPORATE ANALYSIS)
Ellinas House, 6 Theotoki St.
P.O. Box 22379
Nicosia, Cyprus 1521
Phone: 357-22-554-300
Fax: 357-22-343-589
Website: www.firstelements.com.cy

Management and Staff
Christodoulos Ellinas, Partner
John Pitsillos, Partner
Marios Joannides, Partner
Marios Argyris, Managing Director
Neofytos Neofytou, Partner
Philip X. Larkos, Partner

Type of Firm
Private Equity Firm

Association Membership
European Private Equity and Venture Capital Assoc.

Project Preferences
Type of Financing Preferred:
Leveraged Buyout
Early Stage
Expansion
Mezzanine
Turnaround
Seed
Startup
Recapitalizations

Size of Investments Considered:
Min Size of Investment Considered (000s): $280
Max Size of Investment Considered (000s): $3,735

Geographical Preferences
International Preferences:
Greece
Europe
Israel
Romania
Cyprus

Industry Preferences
In Consumer Related prefer:
Food/Beverage

In Financial Services prefer:
Real Estate

Additional Information
Year Founded: 2001
Capital Under Management: $356,600,000
Current Activity Level: Actively seeking new investments

FIRST ENERGY CAPITAL CORPORATION
1600, 333 - 7 Avenue SouthWest
Calgary, Canada T2P 2Z1
Phone: 403-262-0600
Fax: 403-262-0666
Website: www.firstenergy.com

Type of Firm
Investment Management Firm

Additional Information
Year Founded: 2009
Current Activity Level: Actively seeking new investments

FIRST FUNDS LTD
Bull Plaza (9th Floor)
38/39 Marina
Lagos, Nigeria 1001
Phone: 234-1-266-5211
Fax: 234-1-266-0784
Website: www.firstfundsltd.com

Management and Staff
Kayode Ayeni, CEO & Managing Director

Type of Firm
Private Equity Firm

Association Membership
African Venture Capital Association (AVCA)

Project Preferences
Type of Financing Preferred:
Generalist PE
Balanced

Size of Investments Considered:
Min Size of Investment Considered (000s): $77
Max Size of Investment Considered (000s): $1,536

Geographical Preferences

International Preferences:
Nigeria

Industry Preferences

In Communications prefer:
Other Communication Prod.

In Biotechnology prefer:
Agricultural/Animal Bio.

In Medical/Health prefer:
Medical/Health

In Industrial/Energy prefer:
Energy

In Manufact. prefer:
Manufacturing

Additional Information

Year Founded: 2003
Capital Under Management: $42,500,000
Current Activity Level: Actively seeking new investments

FIRST ISRAEL MEZZANINE INVESTORS, LTD. (AKA: FIMI)

FIMI Rubinstein House
37 Menachem Begin Road
Tel Aviv, Israel 67137
Phone: 972-3-565-2244
Fax: 972-3-565-2245
E-mail: fimi@fimi.co.il
Website: www.fimi.co.il

Management and Staff

Ami Boehm, Partner
Ron Ben-Haim, Partner

Type of Firm

Private Equity Firm

Project Preferences

Type of Financing Preferred:
Leveraged Buyout
Mezzanine
Generalist PE
Management Buyouts
Acquisition

Geographical Preferences

International Preferences:
Israel
All International

Additional Information

Year Founded: 1996
Capital Under Management: $125,000,000
Current Activity Level: Actively seeking new investments

FIRST NATIONS EQUITY, INC.

145 King Street West
Tenth Floor
Toronto, Canada M5H 1J8
Phone: 416-947-9191
Fax: 416-483-5117
Website: www.firstnationsequity.com

Management and Staff

Andrew Szonyi, Co-Founder
Brian Davey, Founder

Type of Firm

Private Equity Firm

Project Preferences

Type of Financing Preferred:
Expansion
Start-up Financing

Geographical Preferences

United States Preferences:
Northwest

Canadian Preferences:
Yukon

Additional Information

Year Founded: 2000
Current Activity Level: Actively seeking new investments

FIRST NEW ENGLAND CAPITAL, L.P.

100 Pearl Street
Hartford, CT USA 06103
Phone: 860-293-3333
Fax: 860-293-3338
E-mail: info@fnec.com
Website: www.firstnewenglandcapital.com

Management and Staff

John Ritter, Principal
Lawrence Stillman, Principal
Seth Alvord, Principal

Type of Firm

SBIC

Association Membership

Natl Assoc of Small Bus. Inv. Co (NASBIC)

Project Preferences

Role in Financing:
Will function either as deal originator or investor in deals created by others

Type of Financing Preferred:
Leveraged Buyout
Mezzanine
Later Stage
Management Buyouts
Acquisition
Private Placement
Industry Rollups
Recapitalizations

Size of Investments Considered:
Min Size of Investment Considered (000s): $1,000
Max Size of Investment Considered (000s): $4,500

Industry Focus

(% based on actual investment)

Industrial/Energy	76.4%
Other Products	9.5%
Consumer Related	8.8%
Computer Hardware	3.7%
Medical/Health	1.7%

Additional Information

Name of Most Recent Fund: First New England Capital II, L.P.
Most Recent Fund Was Raised: 09/01/1998
Year Founded: 1987
Capital Under Management: $75,000,000
Current Activity Level: Actively seeking new investments
Method of Compensation: Return on invest. most important, but chg. closing fees, service fees, etc.

FIRST ONTARIO LABOUR SPONSORED INVESTMENT FUND, LTD.

234 Eglinton Avenue East
Suite 310
Toronto, Canada M4P 1K5
Phone: 416-487-5444
Fax: 416-487-1345
Website: www.firstontariofund.com

Management and Staff

Don McDonald, Vice President
Jeff McRae, Chief Financial Officer

Type of Firm

Private Equity Firm

Project Preferences

Type of Financing Preferred:
Expansion

Geographical Preferences

Canadian Preferences:
All Canada

Additional Information

Year Founded: 1994
Current Activity Level: Actively seeking new investments

FIRST RESERVE CORPORATION

One Lafayette Place
Greenwich, CT USA 06830
Phone: 203-661-6601
Fax: 203-661-6729
E-mail: info@firstreserve.com
Website: www.firstreserve.com

Other Offices

68 Pall Mall
2nd Floor
London, United Kingdom SW1Y 5ES
Phone: 44-207-930-2120
Fax: 44-207-930-2130

600 Travis
Suite 6000
Houston, TX USA 77002
Phone: 713 227-7890
Fax: 713 224-0771

Management and Staff

Alan Schwartz, Managing Director
Alex Krueger, Managing Director
Anastasia Deulina, Vice President
Brian Lee, Vice President
Cathleen Ellsworth, Managing Director
Christopher Hearn, Managing Director
Edward Bialas, Vice President
J. Hardy Murchison, Managing Director
Jeffrey MacDonald, Managing Director
Jennifer Zarrilli, Managing Director & CFO
Joe Bob Edwards, Managing Director
Kenneth Moore, Managing Director
Mark Florian, Managing Director
Mark McComiskey, Managing Director
Michael France, Vice President
Neil Wizel, Vice President
Thomas Sikorski, Managing Director
Timothy Day, Managing Director
Timothy O Keeffe, Vice President
Will Honeybourne, Managing Director
William Macaulay, Chairman & CEO

Type of Firm

Private Equity Firm

Project Preferences

Role in Financing:
Prefer role as deal originator but will also invest in deals created by others

Type of Financing Preferred:
Leveraged Buyout
Later Stage
Management Buyouts
Private Placement

Size of Investments Considered:
Min Size of Investment Considered (000s): $50,000
Max Size of Investment Considered (000s): $500,000

Geographical Preferences

International Preferences:
All International

Industry Focus

(% based on actual investment)

Industrial/Energy	61.9%
Other Products	37.9%
Computer Software and Services	0.1%

Additional Information

Name of Most Recent Fund: First Reserve Fund XI, L.P.
Most Recent Fund Was Raised: 08/10/2006
Year Founded: 1980
Capital Under Management: $4,700,000,000
Current Activity Level: Actively seeking new investments
Method of Compensation: Return on investment is of primary concern, do not charge fees

FIRST ROUND CAPITAL

100 Four Falls Corporate Ctr.
Suite 104
West Conshohocken, PA USA 19428
Phone: 610-834-7686
Fax: 610-834-7635
E-mail: info@firstround.com
Website: www.firstround.com

Other Offices

217 Second Street
Fifth Floor
San Francisco, CA USA 94105
Phone: 415-646-0072
Fax: 415-646-0074

Management and Staff

Christine Herron, Principal
Christopher Fralic, Partner
Howard Morgan, Partner
Joshua Kopelman, Managing Partner
Kent Goldman, Principal
Phin Barnes, Principal
Robert Hayes, Partner

Type of Firm

Private Equity Firm

Association Membership

National Venture Capital Association - USA (NVCA)

Project Preferences

Type of Financing Preferred:
Early Stage
Seed

Size of Investments Considered:
Min Size of Investment Considered (000s): $180
Max Size of Investment Considered (000s): $325

Additional Information

Name of Most Recent Fund: First Round Capital II
Most Recent Fund Was Raised: 01/23/2008
Year Founded: 2004
Capital Under Management: $25,000,000
Current Activity Level: Actively seeking new investments

FIRST SOUTH INVESTMENT MANAGERS

Block D, Rosebank Office Park
181 Jan Smuts Ave.
Rosebank, South Africa 2121
Phone: 27-11-448-8200
Fax: 27-11-448-8215
E-mail: info@firstsouth.co.za
Website: www.Firstsouthgroup.co.za

Management and Staff

Duarte Da Silva, Co-Founder
Fawzia Suliman, Chief Financial Officer
Jayendra Naidoo, Chief Executive Officer

Type of Firm

Private Equity Firm

Association Membership

South African Venture Capital Association (SAVCA)

Project Preferences

Type of Financing Preferred:
Balanced

Size of Investments Considered:
Min Size of Investment Considered (000s): $1,517
Max Size of Investment Considered (000s): $7,586

Geographical Preferences

International Preferences:
South Africa

Industry Preferences

In Industrial/Energy prefer:
Industrial Products

In Financial Services prefer:
Financial Services

Additional Information

Year Founded: 2003
Capital Under Management: $34,900,000
Current Activity Level: Actively seeking new investments

FIRST STEP LTD.

Jefferson House, Eglinton Road
Donnybrook
Dublin, Ireland 4
Phone: 353-1-260-0988
Fax: 353-1-260-0989
E-mail: firststep@eircom.net
Website: www.first-step.ie

Type of Firm
Private Equity Firm

Additional Information
Year Founded: 2003
Current Activity Level: Actively seeking new investments

FIRSTHAND CAPITAL MANAGEMENT
125 South Market
Suite 1200
San Jose, CA USA 95113
Phone: 888-884-2675
E-mail: inforequests@firsthandfunds.com
Website: www.firsthandfunds.com

Type of Firm
Private Equity Firm

Additional Information
Year Founded: 1984
Current Activity Level: Actively seeking new investments

FIRSTMARK CAPITAL, LLC (FKA: PEQUOT VENTURES)
1221 Avenue of the Americas
26th Floor
New York, NY USA 10020
Phone: 212-792-2200
Fax: 212-391-5700
E-mail: info@firstmarkcap.com
Website: www.firstmarkcap.com

Other Offices
1901 Assembly Street
Suite 390
Columbia, SC USA 29201
Phone: 803-251-7994

Management and Staff
Amish Jani, General Partner
Brian Kempner, Chief Operating Officer
Gerald Poch, Chairman & Managing Director
Larry Wilson, Venture Partner
Lawrence Lenihan, CEO & Managing Director
Sterling Phillips, Venture Partner

Type of Firm
Private Equity Firm

Project Preferences

Role in Financing:
Prefer role as deal originator but will also invest in deals created by others

Type of Financing Preferred:
Second Stage Financing
Early Stage
Mezzanine
Later Stage
Seed
First Stage Financing
Startup

Size of Investments Considered:
Min Size of Investment Considered (000s): $1,000
Max Size of Investment Considered (000s): $10,000

Geographical Preferences

International Preferences:
Middle East

Industry Preferences

In Communications prefer:
Communications and Media

In Computer Hardware prefer:
Computers

In Computer Software prefer:
Data Processing
Software
Applications Software

In Semiconductor/Electr prefer:
Electronics
Semiconductor

In Biotechnology prefer:
Biotechnology

In Medical/Health prefer:
Health Services

In Consumer Related prefer:
Entertainment and Leisure

In Transportation prefer:
Transportation

In Financial Services prefer:
Financial Services

In Business Serv. prefer:
Services

Additional Information
Name of Most Recent Fund: FirstMark IV (FKA: Pequot Private Equity Fund IV, LP)
Most Recent Fund Was Raised: 11/21/2006
Year Founded: 1999
Capital Under Management: $2,000,000,000
Current Activity Level: Actively seeking new investments
Method of Compensation: Return on investment is of primary concern, do not charge fees

FIRSTVENTURES
Elsinore House
77 Fulham Palace Road
London, United Kingdom IP4 3QE
Phone: 44-20-8563-1563
Fax: 44-20-8563-2767
E-mail: info@firstventures.co.uk
Website: www.firstventures.co.uk

Other Offices
Hill Farm
128 Green End, Comberton
Cambridge, United Kingdom CB3 7DY
Phone: 44-1223-264-125

Management and Staff
Hazel Moore, Managing Partner
Paul Atherton, Venture Partner
Peter Wolfers, Partner

Type of Firm
Private Equity Firm

Project Preferences

Type of Financing Preferred:
Early Stage

Geographical Preferences

International Preferences:
United Kingdom
Europe

Industry Preferences

In Communications prefer:
Communications and Media
Telecommunications

In Semiconductor/Electr prefer:
Electronics

In Medical/Health prefer:
Medical Products
Health Services

In Industrial/Energy prefer:
Alternative Energy
Materials

Additional Information
Year Founded: 2001
Current Activity Level: Actively seeking new investments

FIRSTVENTURY GMBH
Aeris Capital AG
Seedammstrasse 3
Pfaffikon, Switzerland CH-8808
Phone: 41-55-417-4666
E-mail: info@firstventury.com
Website: www.firstventury.com

Management and Staff
David Hartford, Managing Partner
Frank Muehlenbeck, Partner
George Rehm, Managing Partner
Gordon Summer, Partner
Michael W. Kelly, Chief Financial Officer
Niall Davis, Partner
Uwe R. Feuersenger, Managing Partner

Type of Firm
Private Equity Firm

Association Membership
European Private Equity and Venture Capital Assoc.

Project Preferences

Type of Financing Preferred:
Early Stage
Expansion
Mezzanine
Seed
Startup

Geographical Preferences

United States Preferences:
All U.S.

International Preferences:
Switzerland
Europe
Austria
Germany

Industry Preferences

In Computer Software prefer:
Software

In Internet Specific prefer:
Internet

In Computer Other prefer:
Computer Related

In Biotechnology prefer:
Biotechnology

In Medical/Health prefer:
Medical/Health

Additional Information
Year Founded: 2000
Capital Under Management: $9,000,000
Current Activity Level: Actively seeking new investments

FISHER CAPITAL PARTNERS
5619 DTC Parkway
Suite 1150
Englewood, CO USA 80111
Phone: 303-414-9900
Fax: 303-414-9905
E-mail: info@fisher-capital.com
Website: www.fisher-capital.com

Management and Staff
Bill Fisher, Co-Founder
Don Fisher, Co-Founder

Type of Firm
Private Equity Firm

Additional Information
Year Founded: 2002
Current Activity Level: Actively seeking new investments

FISHER LYNCH CAPITAL
The Pilot House
Lewis Wharf
Boston, MA USA 02110
Phone: 617-854-3840
Fax: 617-854-3839
Website: www.fisherlynch.com

Other Offices
2929 Campus Drive
Suite 410
San Mateo, CA USA 94403
Phone: 650-287-2700
Fax: 650-240-0277

Management and Staff
Anthony Limberis, Managing Director
Brett Fisher, Managing Director
Debbie Richard, Chief Financial Officer
Georgeanne Perkins, Managing Director
Leon Kuan, Managing Director
Linda Lynch, Managing Director
Marshall Bartlett, Managing Director

Type of Firm
Private Equity Advisor or Fund of Funds

Association Membership
National Venture Capital Association - USA (NVCA)

Project Preferences

Type of Financing Preferred:
Fund of Funds
Leveraged Buyout

Geographical Preferences

United States Preferences:
All U.S.

Canadian Preferences:
All Canada

International Preferences:
Italy
United Kingdom
Luxembourg
Netherlands
Portugal
Europe
Western Europe
Eastern Europe
Spain
Belgium
Germany
France

Additional Information
Year Founded: 2003
Capital Under Management: $112,000,000
Current Activity Level: Actively seeking new investments
Method of Compensation: Return on investment is of primary concern, do not charge fees

---

FISK VENTURES, INC. (AKA: FVI)
555 North Main Street
Suite 500
Racine, WI USA 53403

Management and Staff
H. Fisk Johnson, Founder

Type of Firm
Private Equity Firm

Additional Information
Year Founded: 2003
Current Activity Level: Actively seeking new investments

FITECH VENTURE PARTNERS COMPANY, LTD.
8/F, KyoungRim Building, 253-4
Seohyeon-dong, Bundang-gu
Gyeonggi-do, South Korea 463824
Phone: 82-31-278-9503
Fax: 82-31-278-9504
Website: www.fitech.co.kr

Other Offices
111-7, Kuyun-dong
Kwonsun-gu, Suwon
Kyeunggi-do, South Korea

Management and Staff
Jongsu Lee, Managing Director
Younggeun Kang, President

Type of Firm
Corporate PE/Venture

Project Preferences

Type of Financing Preferred:
Fund of Funds
Balanced

Geographical Preferences

International Preferences:
Korea, South

Industry Preferences

In Consumer Related prefer:
Entertainment and Leisure

Additional Information
Year Founded: 1999
Capital Under Management: $34,700,000
Current Activity Level: Actively seeking new investments

FIVE ELMS CAPITAL

4520 Main Street
Suite 1650
Kansas City, MO USA 64111
Phone: 212-951-8625
Fax: 816-298-0241
E-mail: ws@fiveelms.com
Website: www.fiveelms.com

Management and Staff

Fred Coulson, Managing Director

Type of Firm

Private Equity Firm

Project Preferences

Type of Financing Preferred:
Leveraged Buyout
Expansion
Public Companies
Later Stage

Industry Preferences

In Consumer Related prefer:
Entertainment and Leisure

In Financial Services prefer:
Financial Services

Additional Information

Name of Most Recent Fund: Five Elms Equity Fund I, L.P.
Most Recent Fund Was Raised: 10/24/2007
Year Founded: 2007
Capital Under Management: $30,000,000
Current Activity Level: Actively seeking new investments

FJARFESTINGAFELAG SUOURLANDS EHF

Borgartuni 35
Reykjavik, Iceland 105
Phone: 354-510-1800
Fax: 354-510-1809

Type of Firm

Private Equity Firm

Project Preferences

Type of Financing Preferred:
Balanced

Geographical Preferences

International Preferences:
Europe

Additional Information

Year Founded: 2004
Current Activity Level: Actively seeking new investments

FJORD INVEST MANAGEMENT AS

Firdavegen 6
Forde, Norway 6800
Phone: 47- 91-335-724
Fax: 47-94-774-175
E-mail: post@fjordinvest.no
Website: www.fjordinvest.no

Management and Staff

Aud Ingrid Espeland, Managing Director

Type of Firm

Private Equity Firm

Association Membership

Norwegian Venture Capital Association

Project Preferences

Type of Financing Preferred:
Generalist PE

Geographical Preferences

International Preferences:
Norway

Industry Preferences

In Industrial/Energy prefer:
Energy

In Business Serv. prefer:
Services

In Agr/Forestr/Fish prefer:
Agribusiness

Additional Information

Year Founded: 2001
Current Activity Level: Actively seeking new investments

FJORD VENTURES, LLC

26051 Merit Circle
Suite 104
Laguna Hills, CA USA 92653
Phone: 949-348-1188
Fax: 949-348-1866
E-mail: info@fjordventures.com
Website: www.fjordventures.com

Type of Firm

Private Equity Firm

Project Preferences

Type of Financing Preferred:
Early Stage

Geographical Preferences

United States Preferences:
All U.S.

Additional Information

Year Founded: 2005
Current Activity Level: Actively seeking new investments

FL PARTNERS

Stradbrook House, Stradbrook Road, Blackrock
Dublin, Ireland
Phone: 353-1-663-7630
Fax: 353-1-663-6831
E-mail: info@flpartners.ie
Website: www.flpartners.ie

Management and Staff

Kevin Crowley, Founder
Neill Hughes, Founder

Type of Firm

Private Equity Firm

Project Preferences

Type of Financing Preferred:
Leveraged Buyout

Geographical Preferences

International Preferences:
Europe

Additional Information

Year Founded: 2008
Current Activity Level: Actively seeking new investments

FLAGSHIP VENTURES

One Memorial Drive
Seventh Floor
Cambridge, MA USA 02142
Phone: 617-868-1888
Fax: 617-868-1115
Website: www.flagshipventures.com

Management and Staff

Brian Baynes, Partner
Chris Varma, Partner
David Berry, Partner
Douglas Levinson, Partner
Douglas Cole, General Partner
James Matheson, General Partner
William Strecker, Partner

Type of Firm

Private Equity Firm

Association Membership

National Venture Capital Association - USA (NVCA)

Project Preferences

Role in Financing:
Prefer role as deal originator but will also invest in deals created by others

Type of Financing Preferred:
Start-up Financing
Startup

Size of Investments Considered:
Min Size of Investment Considered (000s): $500
Max Size of Investment Considered (000s): $15,000

Industry Focus
(% based on actual investment)

Biotechnology	29.6%
Computer Software and Services	21.5%
Communications and Media	16.0%
Medical/Health	10.2%
Internet Specific	8.2%
Semiconductors/Other Elect.	6.2%
Computer Hardware	3.1%
Other Products	2.6%
Industrial/Energy	2.6%

Additional Information
Name of Most Recent Fund: Flagship Ventures Fund 2007, L.P.
Most Recent Fund Was Raised: 07/17/2007
Year Founded: 1999
Capital Under Management: $603,000,000
Current Activity Level: Actively seeking new investments
Method of Compensation: Return on investment is of primary concern, do not charge fees

FLAGSTONE CAPITAL LLC
8608 E. Gail Road
Scottsdale, AZ USA 85260
Phone: 480-634-7440
Fax: 480-634-7444
Website: www.flagstonecapital.net

Management and Staff
Larry Heath, Founder

Type of Firm
Corporate PE/Venture

Additional Information
Year Founded: 2009
Current Activity Level: Actively seeking new investments

FLATWORLD CAPITAL LLC
The Empire State Building
350 Fifth Avenue, Suite 7519
New York, NY USA 10118
Phone: 212-796-4001
Fax: 212-796-4002
E-mail: info@flatworldcapital.com
Website: www.flatworldcapital.com

Other Offices
Usha Kiran 1-8-165
S.D. Road
Secunderabad, India 500-033
Phone: 91-40-2781-0633

Management and Staff
Jeffrey Valenty, Partner
Raj Gupta, Partner

Type of Firm
Private Equity Firm

Project Preferences

Type of Financing Preferred:
Leveraged Buyout
Expansion
Acquisition
Recapitalizations

Industry Preferences

In Business Serv. prefer:
Services

Additional Information
Year Founded: 2008
Current Activity Level: Actively seeking new investments

FLAVIN VENTURES LLC
1440 Davey Road
Woodridge, IL USA 60517
Phone: 630-739-2018
Fax: 630-739-6754
Website: www.flavinventures.com

Management and Staff
John Flavin, Managing Director
Michael Flavin, Managing Director

Type of Firm
Private Equity Firm

Project Preferences

Type of Financing Preferred:
Early Stage
Startup

Size of Investments Considered:
Min Size of Investment Considered (000s): $250
Max Size of Investment Considered (000s): $1,000

Geographical Preferences

United States Preferences:
Midwest

Additional Information
Year Founded: 2003
Current Activity Level: Actively seeking new investments

FLEMING FAMILY & PARTNERS, LTD. (AKA: FF&P)
15 Suffolk Street
London, United Kingdom SW1Y 4HG
Phone: 44-20-7036-5722
Fax: 44-20-7036-5651
Website: www.ffandppe.com

Management and Staff
David Donnelly, Chief Executive Officer

Type of Firm
Private Equity Firm

Project Preferences

Type of Financing Preferred:
Leveraged Buyout
Expansion
Generalist PE

Size of Investments Considered:
Min Size of Investment Considered (000s): $8,855
Max Size of Investment Considered (000s): $177,100

Geographical Preferences

International Preferences:
United Kingdom
Europe

Additional Information
Year Founded: 2005
Current Activity Level: Actively seeking new investments

FLETCHER SPAGHT ASSOCIATES
222 Berkeley Street
20th Floor
Boston, MA USA 02116
Phone: 617-247-6700
Fax: 617-247-7757
Website: www.fletcherspaght.com

Management and Staff
Bob Schmidt, Vice President
Guy Fish, Vice President
Linda Tufts, Vice President
Lisa Granick, Vice President
Peary Spaght, President

Type of Firm
Private Equity Firm

Association Membership
National Venture Capital Association - USA (NVCA)

Project Preferences

Role in Financing:
Prefer role in deals created by others

Type of Financing Preferred:
Generalist PE
Early Stage

Geographical Preferences

United States Preferences:
All U.S.

Industry Preferences

In Communications prefer:
Telecommunications
Wireless Communications
Data Communications
Satellite Microwave Comm.

In Computer Hardware prefer:
Mainframes / Scientific
Computer Graphics and Dig
Integrated Turnkey System

In Computer Software prefer:
Computer Services
Data Processing
Software
Systems Software
Applications Software
Artificial Intelligence

In Internet Specific prefer:
E-Commerce Technology
Web Aggregration/Portals

In Semiconductor/Electr prefer:
Electronic Components
Semiconductor
Micro-Processing
Controllers and Sensors
Sensors
Circuit Boards
Component Testing Equipmt
Laser Related
Fiber Optics
Analytic/Scientific
Optoelectronics

In Biotechnology prefer:
Human Biotechnology
Genetic Engineering
Agricultural/Animal Bio.
Industrial Biotechnology
Biotech Related Research

In Medical/Health prefer:
Medical Diagnostics
Drug/Equipmt Delivery
Pharmaceuticals

In Industrial/Energy prefer:
Factory Automation
Robotics

In Transportation prefer:
Aerospace

In Financial Services prefer:
Financial Services

Additional Information
Year Founded: 2001
Capital Under Management: $30,300,000
Current Activity Level: Actively seeking new investments

FLEXPOINT FORD (FKA: FLEXPOINT PARTNERS LLC)
676 North Michigan Avenue
Suite 3300
Chicago, IL USA 60611
Phone: 312-327-4520
Fax: 312-327-4525
Website: www.flexpointpartners.com

Management and Staff
Charles Glew, Principal
Ethan Budin, Principal

Type of Firm
Private Equity Firm

Project Preferences

Type of Financing Preferred:
Leveraged Buyout

Geographical Preferences

United States Preferences:
All U.S.

Industry Preferences

In Medical/Health prefer:
Medical/Health

In Financial Services prefer:
Financial Services

Additional Information
Year Founded: 2004
Capital Under Management: $1,495,000,000
Current Activity Level: Actively seeking new investments

FLEXTRONICS INTERNATIONAL, LTD.
2 Changi South Lane
Singapore, Singapore 486123
Phone: 65-6299-8888
Fax: 65-6543-1888
E-mail: info@sg.flextronics.com
Website: www.flextronics.com

Other Offices
12 Kallang Way
Singapore 349216

31 Joo Koon Circle
Singapore 349216

Management and Staff
Marks Michael, Chairman & CEO
Robert Dykes, Chief Financial Officer

Type of Firm
Corporate PE/Venture

Project Preferences

Type of Financing Preferred:
Balanced

Geographical Preferences

International Preferences:
All International

Additional Information
Year Founded: 1999
Current Activity Level: Actively seeking new investments

FLOW VENTURES
1470 Peel Street
Suite 910
Montreal, Canada
E-mail: info@flowventures.com
Website: www.flowventures.com

Management and Staff
Raymond Luk, Founder

Type of Firm
Private Equity Firm
Project Preferences

Type of Financing Preferred:
Early Stage
Seed
Startup

Additional Information
Year Founded: 2009
Current Activity Level: Actively seeking new investments

FLUKE VENTURE PARTNERS
11400 Southeast Sixth Street
Suite 230
Bellevue, WA USA 98004
Phone: 425-453-4590
Fax: 425-453-4675
Website: www.flukeventures.com

Management and Staff
Dennis Weston, Senior Managing Director
Kevin Gabelein, Managing Director

Type of Firm
Private Equity Firm

Project Preferences

Role in Financing:
Will function either as deal originator or investor in deals created by others

Type of Financing Preferred:
Second Stage Financing
Early Stage
Balanced
Seed

Size of Investments Considered:
Min Size of Investment Considered (000s): $500
Max Size of Investment Considered (000s): $4,000

Geographical Preferences

United States Preferences:
Northwest

Industry Focus

(% based on actual investment)

Computer Software and Services	21.9%
Medical/Health	18.6%
Internet Specific	16.3%
Communications and Media	16.0%
Other Products	7.4%
Computer Hardware	7.0%
Semiconductors/Other Elect.	6.0%
Consumer Related	2.7%
Industrial/Energy	2.5%
Biotechnology	1.7%

Additional Information

Name of Most Recent Fund: Fluke Venture Partners II
Most Recent Fund Was Raised: 04/13/2004
Year Founded: 1974
Capital Under Management: $100,000,000
Current Activity Level: Actively seeking new investments
Method of Compensation: Return on investment is of primary concern, do not charge fees

FLYBRIDGE CAPITAL PARTNERS (FKA: IDG VENTURES BOSTON)

500 Boylston Street
18th Floor
Boston, MA USA 02116
Phone: 617-307-9292
Fax: 617-307-9293
Website: www.flybridge.com

Management and Staff

Bruce Revzin, Chief Financial Officer
Chip Hazard, General Partner
David Aronoff, General Partner
Jeffrey Bussgang, General Partner
John Karlen, General Partner
Michael Greeley, General Partner

Type of Firm

Private Equity Firm

Association Membership

National Venture Capital Association - USA (NVCA)

Project Preferences

Role in Financing:
Prefer role as deal originator but will also invest in deals created by others

Type of Financing Preferred:
Early Stage
Balanced
Seed
First Stage Financing

Geographical Preferences

United States Preferences:
All U.S.

Industry Focus

(% based on actual investment)

Internet Specific	28.0%
Communications and Media	16.0%
Computer Software and Services	15.0%
Other Products	13.3%
Medical/Health	7.5%
Biotechnology	7.4%
Semiconductors/Other Elect.	6.3%
Consumer Related	3.0%
Computer Hardware	2.0%
Industrial/Energy	1.5%

Additional Information

Name of Most Recent Fund: Flybridge Capital Partners III, L.P.
Most Recent Fund Was Raised: 03/21/2008
Year Founded: 2001
Capital Under Management: $560,000,000
Current Activity Level: Actively seeking new investments
Method of Compensation: Other

FLYWHEEL VENTURES

341 East Alameda Street
Santa Fe, NM USA 87501
Phone: 800-750-7870
Fax: 800-750-7870
E-mail: info@flywheelventures.com
Website: www.flywheelventures.com

Other Offices

9204 San Mateo Boulevard
Northeast
Albuquerque, NM USA 87113
Phone: 800-750-7870
Fax: 800-750-7870

400 Montgomery Street
Suite 1040
San Francisco, CA USA 94104
Phone: 800-750-7870
Fax: 800-750-7870

Management and Staff

Kim Sanchez Rael, General Partner
Scott Caruso, General Partner
Trevor Loy, Managing Partner

Type of Firm

Private Equity Firm

Association Membership

National Venture Capital Association - USA (NVCA)

Project Preferences

Role in Financing:
Prefer role as deal originator but will also invest in deals created by others

Type of Financing Preferred:
Early Stage
Seed
Special Situation
Startup

Size of Investments Considered:
Min Size of Investment Considered (000s): $100
Max Size of Investment Considered (000s): $1,000

Geographical Preferences

United States Preferences:
New Mexico
Arizona
Rocky Mountain
West Coast
Colorado
Utah
Southwest

Industry Preferences

In Computer Software prefer:
Software

In Internet Specific prefer:
Internet
Ecommerce

In Semiconductor/Electr prefer:
Electronics
Semiconductor
Optoelectronics

In Industrial/Energy prefer:
Advanced Materials
Environmental Related

Additional Information

Name of Most Recent Fund: New Mexico Gap Fund I, L.P.
Most Recent Fund Was Raised: 02/28/2007
Year Founded: 1999
Capital Under Management: $32,500,000
Current Activity Level: Actively seeking new investments
Method of Compensation: Return on investment is of primary concern, do not charge fees

FOCUS EQUITY PARTNERS, LLC

700 Commerce Drive
Suite 140
Hinsdale, IL USA 60523

Phone: 630-571-1141
Fax: 630-571-1143
E-mail: info@focusequity.com
Website: www.focusequity.com

Management and Staff

David Duerr, Founding Partner
Michael Cahr, Partner

Type of Firm

Private Equity Advisor or Fund of Funds

Project Preferences

Type of Financing Preferred:
Expansion
Mezzanine
Management Buyouts
Recapitalizations

Size of Investments Considered:
Min Size of Investment Considered (000s): $3,000
Max Size of Investment Considered (000s): $10,000

Industry Preferences

In Medical/Health prefer:
Health Services

In Business Serv. prefer:
Distribution

Additional Information

Year Founded: 2007
Current Activity Level: Actively seeking new investments

FOCUS GESTIONI SGR

Via Ghislieri 6
Jesi (AN), Italy 60035
Phone: 39-0731-539619

Type of Firm

Private Equity Firm

Association Membership

Italian Venture Capital Association (AIFI)

Project Preferences

Type of Financing Preferred:
Balanced

Geographical Preferences

International Preferences:
Italy
Europe

Additional Information

Year Founded: 2004
Current Activity Level: Actively seeking new investments

FOCUS VENTURES

525 University Avenue
Suite 1400
Palo Alto, CA USA 94301
Phone: 650-325-7400
Fax: 650-325-8400
E-mail: info@focusventures.com
Website: www.focusventures.com

Management and Staff

James Boettcher, General Partner
Kevin McQuillan, General Partner
Steven Bird, General Partner
Tara Farnsworth, Chief Financial Officer

Type of Firm

Private Equity Firm

Association Membership

Western Association of Venture Capitalists (WAVC)
National Venture Capital Association - USA (NVCA)

Project Preferences

Role in Financing:
Will function either as deal originator or investor in deals created by others

Type of Financing Preferred:
Expansion

Size of Investments Considered:
Min Size of Investment Considered (000s): $2,000
Max Size of Investment Considered (000s): $10,000

Geographical Preferences

United States Preferences:
All U.S.

Industry Focus

(% based on actual investment)

Internet Specific	40.0%
Computer Software and Services	27.4%
Communications and Media	18.5%
Semiconductors/Other Elect.	8.7%
Consumer Related	2.3%
Computer Hardware	1.4%
Medical/Health	1.0%
Biotechnology	0.3%
Other Products	0.3%

Additional Information

Name of Most Recent Fund: FV Investors III, L.P.
Most Recent Fund Was Raised: 11/17/2006
Year Founded: 1997
Capital Under Management: $830,000,000
Current Activity Level: Actively seeking new investments
Method of Compensation: Return on investment is of primary concern, do not charge fees

---

FONDACTION

2175, bd De Maisonneuve Est
Bureau 103
Montreal, Canada
Phone: 514-525-5505
E-mail: investissement@fondaction.com
Website: www.fondaction.com

Type of Firm

Private Equity Firm

Project Preferences

Type of Financing Preferred:
Generalist PE

Geographical Preferences

Canadian Preferences:
Quebec

Additional Information

Year Founded: 1996
Current Activity Level: Actively seeking new investments

FONDAMENTA SGR SPA

Via Mazzini 2
Milan, Italy
E-mail: info@fondamentasgr.com
Website: www.fondamentasgr.com

Type of Firm

Private Equity Firm

Project Preferences

Type of Financing Preferred:
Early Stage

Geographical Preferences

International Preferences:
Europe

Additional Information

Year Founded: 2009
Current Activity Level: Actively seeking new investments

FONDATIONS CAPITAL SAS

3 rue Paul Cezanne
Paris, France 75008
Phone: 33-1-5535-5500
Fax: 33-1-5535-5529
E-mail: contact@fondcap.com
Website: www.fondationscapital.com

Other Offices

121 avenue de la Faiencerie
Luxembourg, Luxembourg L-1511

Management and Staff

Philippe Renaud, Partner

Type of Firm

Private Equity Advisor or Fund of Funds

Association Membership

French Venture Capital Association (AFIC)

Project Preferences

Role in Financing:
Prefer role as deal originator but will also invest in deals created by others

Type of Financing Preferred:
Early Stage

Geographical Preferences

International Preferences:
Europe
France

Additional Information

Year Founded: 2007
Current Activity Level: Actively seeking new investments
Method of Compensation: Return on invest. most important, but chg. closing fees, service fees, etc.

FONDINVEST CAPITAL (GRP. CAISSE DE DEPOTS)

33 rue de la Baume
Paris, France 75008
Phone: 33-1-5836-4800
Fax: 33-1-5836-4829
E-mail: mailbox@fondinvest.com
Website: www.fondinvest.com

Management and Staff

Charles Soulignac, Chairman & CEO
Emmanuel Roubinowitz, Managing Director
Francois Gamblin, Managing Director
Marc-Eric Flory, Chief Operating Officer

Type of Firm

Bank Affiliated

Association Membership

French Venture Capital Association (AFIC)
European Private Equity and Venture Capital Assoc.

Project Preferences

Role in Financing:
Prefer role as deal originator but will also invest in deals created by others

Type of Financing Preferred:
Fund of Funds
Fund of Funds of Second

Geographical Preferences

United States Preferences:
All U.S.

International Preferences:
Europe
Western Europe
Eastern Europe
Asia
France

Additional Information

Year Founded: 1994
Capital Under Management: $561,100,000
Current Activity Level: Actively seeking new investments
Method of Compensation: Return on invest. most important, but chg. closing fees, service fees, etc.

FONDS BIOALIMENTAIRE

5050, boul. des Gradins
Bureau 130
Quebec, Canada G2J 1P8
Phone: 418-628-5737
Fax: 418-624-8975
E-mail: fondsbio@fondsftq.com
Website: www.fondsbio.com

Management and Staff

Serge Yelle, Chief Executive Officer

Type of Firm

Government Affiliated Program

Project Preferences

Type of Financing Preferred:
Expansion

Additional Information

Year Founded: 1991
Current Activity Level: Actively seeking new investments

FONDS D INVESTISSEMENT DE LA CULTURE ET DES COMMUNICATIONS

1155, rue University
Bureau 1308
Montreal, Canada H3B 3A7
Phone: 514-394-0700
Fax: 514-394-0708
Website: www.ficc.qc.ca

Management and Staff

Marcel Choquette, President

Type of Firm

Government Affiliated Program

Project Preferences

Type of Financing Preferred:
Expansion

Geographical Preferences

Canadian Preferences:
Quebec

Additional Information

Year Founded: 1997
Current Activity Level: Actively seeking new investments

FONDS DE DEVELOPPMENT ECONOM. LAPRADE CHAMPLIN INC.

290, rue St-Jeseph C.P. 607
La Tuque, Canada G9X 3P5
Phone: 819-523-2375
Fax: 819-523-7843

Type of Firm

Government Affiliated Program

Additional Information

Year Founded: 1987
Current Activity Level: Actively seeking new investments

FONDS DE RESERVE POUR LES RETRAITES (AKA: FRR)

84, rue de Lille
Paris, France 75007
Phone: 33-1-5850-9986
Website: www.fondsdereserve.fr

Management and Staff

Augustin De Romanet, President

Type of Firm

Government Affiliated Program

Project Preferences

Type of Financing Preferred:
Fund of Funds

Geographical Preferences

International Preferences:
Europe

Additional Information

Year Founded: 2006
Current Activity Level: Actively seeking new investments

FONDS PARTENAIRES GESTION

10, avenue Percier
Paris, France 75008
Phone: 33-1-5383-8000
Fax: 33-1-5383-8020
E-mail: contact@fondspartenairesgestion.com
Website: www.fondspartenairesgestion.com

Management and Staff

Gilles Etrillard, President, CEO, Director
Jean Eichenlaub, Partner

Type of Firm

Private Equity Firm

Association Membership

French Venture Capital Association (AFIC)
European Private Equity and Venture Capital Assoc.

Project Preferences

Type of Financing Preferred:
Leveraged Buyout
Management Buyouts

Geographical Preferences

International Preferences:
Europe
France

Industry Focus

(% based on actual investment)
Other Products 100.0%

Additional Information

Name of Most Recent Fund: Groupe LFPI
Most Recent Fund Was Raised: 06/30/2004
Year Founded: 1985
Capital Under Management: $329,600,000
Current Activity Level: Actively seeking new investments

FONTAINEBLEAU VENTURES

16, rue de Turbigo
Paris, France 75002
Phone: 33-1-4482-7777
Fax: 33-1-4482-7776
E-mail: contact@fontainebleau-ventures.com

Type of Firm

Private Equity Firm

Project Preferences

Type of Financing Preferred:
Seed
Startup

Geographical Preferences

International Preferences:
Europe
France

Industry Preferences

In Communications prefer:
Telecommunications
Media and Entertainment

Additional Information

Year Founded: 2000
Current Activity Level: Actively seeking new investments

FONTERELLI GMBH & CO KGAA

Postfach 33 07 05
Munchen, Germany 80067
Phone: 49-89-230-010
Fax: 49-89-2300-1111
E-mail: info@fonterelli.de
Website: www.fonterelli.de

Type of Firm

Bank Affiliated

Project Preferences

Type of Financing Preferred:
Leveraged Buyout
Management Buyouts

Geographical Preferences

International Preferences:
Europe
Germany

Additional Information

Year Founded: 2007
Current Activity Level: Actively seeking new investments

FOO BRAINS&CAPITAL, THE

Agnes-Pockels-Bogen 1
Muenchner Technologie Zentrum
Munich, Germany 80922
Phone: 49-89-7874-9680
E-mail: mail@the-foo.de
Website: www.the-foo.de

Management and Staff

Ulrich Frey, President
Werner Roth, Managing Director

Type of Firm

Private Equity Firm

Project Preferences

Type of Financing Preferred:
Early Stage

Geographical Preferences

International Preferences:
Europe

Industry Preferences

In Other prefer:
Environment Responsible

Additional Information

Year Founded: 2009
Current Activity Level: Actively seeking new investments

FOOTPRINT VENTURES

Plot No.16, 2/F, 7th Main
1st Block, Koramangala
Bangalore, India 560 034
Phone: 91-80-4110-1910
Fax: 91-80-4110-1913
E-mail: info@footprintventures.com
Website: www.footprintventures.com

Management and Staff

Anjana Kaul, Co-Founder
Larry Glaeser, Co-Founder
Linda Brownstein, Co-Founder
Neill Brownstein, General Partner
Shalini Elassery, Co-Founder

Type of Firm

Private Equity Firm

Project Preferences

Type of Financing Preferred:
Early Stage

Geographical Preferences

International Preferences:
India
Israel

Industry Preferences

In Communications prefer:
Telecommunications
Wireless Communications

In Computer Software prefer:
Software

In Biotechnology prefer:
Biotechnology

In Medical/Health prefer:
Health Services

In Consumer Related prefer:
Consumer Services

In Industrial/Energy prefer:
Alternative Energy

Additional Information

Year Founded: 2007
Current Activity Level: Actively seeking new investments

FORAGEN TECHNOLOGIES MANAGEMENT

74 Wyndham Street North
2nd Floor
Guelph, Canada N1E 6W8
Phone: 519-824-7923
Fax: 519-824-9146
Website: www.foragen.com

Other Offices

7333 rue Berri
Montreal, Canada H2R 2G6
Phone: 514 217-6775
Fax: 514 217-1754

105-111 Research Drive
Canada S7N 3R2
Phone: 306-651-1066
Fax: 306-651-1067

Management and Staff

Armand Lavoie, Vice President
David Gauthier, Vice President
Roger Bernier, Vice President

Type of Firm

Private Equity Firm

Project Preferences

Type of Financing Preferred:
Early Stage
Seed

Geographical Preferences

Canadian Preferences:
All Canada

Industry Preferences

In Agr/Forestr/Fish prefer:
Agriculture related

Additional Information

Year Founded: 2000
Current Activity Level: Actively seeking new investments

FORBES ALLIANCE PARTNERS INC.

4880, Sherbrooke St. West
Suite 170
Montreal, Canada H3Z 1H1
Phone: 514-282-1500
Fax: 514-369-9223
E-mail: info@forbesalliance.com
Website: www.forbesalexander.com

Management and Staff

Eric Melka, President

Type of Firm

Incubator/Development Program

Project Preferences

Role in Financing:
Prefer role as deal originator

Type of Financing Preferred:
Early Stage
Expansion

Size of Investments Considered:
Min Size of Investment Considered (000s): $1,000
Max Size of Investment Considered (000s): $5,000

Geographical Preferences

Canadian Preferences:
All Canada

Industry Preferences

In Internet Specific prefer:
Internet

Additional Information

Year Founded: 2000
Current Activity Level: Actively seeking new investments

FORBION CAPITAL PARTNERS

Gooimeer 2-35
Naarden, Netherlands 1411 DC
Phone: 31-35-699-3000
Fax: 31-35-699-3001
E-mail: info@forbion.com
Website: www.forbion.com

Management and Staff

Avi Molcho, Venture Partner
Bart Bergstein, Managing Partner
Christina Takke, Principal
Geert-Jan Mulder, General Partner
Martien Van Osch, General Partner
Sander Van Deventer, General Partner
Sander Slootweg, General Partner

Type of Firm

Private Equity Firm

Project Preferences

Role in Financing:
Prefer role as deal originator but will also invest in deals created by others

Type of Financing Preferred:
Balanced

Size of Investments Considered:
Min Size of Investment Considered (000s): $4,080
Max Size of Investment Considered (000s): $9,520

Geographical Preferences

International Preferences:
Europe

Industry Preferences

In Biotechnology prefer:
Biotechnology

Additional Information

Year Founded: 2007
Capital Under Management: $272,000,000
Current Activity Level: Actively seeking new investments

FORE C INVESTMENT AB

Nasets Backavag 60
Vastra Frolunda, Sweden 421 66
Phone: 46-704-331-320
Fax: 46-31-68-13-20
E-mail: info@4c.se
Website: www.4c.se

Type of Firm

Private Equity Firm

Association Membership

Swedish Venture Capital Association (SVCA)

Project Preferences

Type of Financing Preferred:
Balanced

Geographical Preferences

International Preferences:
Sweden
Europe

Additional Information

Year Founded: 2003
Current Activity Level: Actively seeking new investments

FORESIGHT GROUP (FKA: FORESIGHT VCF PARTNERS)

ECA Court
South Park
Sevenoaks Kent, United Kingdom TN13 1DU
Phone: 44-1732-471-800
Fax: 44-1732-471-810
E-mail: info@foresightgroup.eu
Website: www.foresightgroup.eu

Other Offices

Via Marche 23
Rome, Italy 00187

Management and Staff

Andrew Page, Partner
Bernard Fairman, Managing Partner
David Hughes, Partner
Donald MacLennan, Partner
Jamie Richards, Partner
Matt Taylor, Partner
Peter English, Partner
Russell Healey, Partner

Type of Firm

Private Equity Firm

Project Preferences

Type of Financing Preferred:

Second Stage Financing
Leveraged Buyout
Early Stage
Expansion
Balanced
Management Buyouts

Size of Investments Considered:

Min Size of Investment Considered (000s): $1,120
Max Size of Investment Considered (000s): $2,985

Geographical Preferences

International Preferences:

United Kingdom
Europe

Industry Preferences

In Communications prefer:

Communications and Media
Commercial Communications
Telecommunications

In Computer Software prefer:

Software

In Internet Specific prefer:

Internet

In Computer Other prefer:

Computer Related

In Semiconductor/Electr prefer:

Electronics

In Biotechnology prefer:

Biotechnology

In Industrial/Energy prefer:

Alternative Energy
Energy Conservation Relat
Industrial Products

In Manufact. prefer:

Manufacturing

In Other prefer:

Environment Responsible

Additional Information

Year Founded: 1984
Capital Under Management: $83,400,000
Current Activity Level: Actively seeking new investments

FOREST HILL PARTNERS LLC

300 East Long Lake Road
Suite 200
Bloomfield Hills, MI USA 48304
Phone: 248-798-6915
Fax: 734-264-6127
E-mail: info@foresthillpartners.com
Website: www.foresthillpartners.com

Other Offices

1115 Aldine Avenue
Park Ridge, IL USA 60068
Phone: 773-909-1239
Fax: 847-939-1700

Management and Staff

John Carretta, Founding Partner
Michael Sullivan, Founding Partner

Type of Firm

Private Equity Firm

Project Preferences

Type of Financing Preferred:

Leveraged Buyout
Expansion
Management Buyouts
Acquisition
Recapitalizations

Geographical Preferences

United States Preferences:

Midwest
All U.S.

Industry Preferences

In Industrial/Energy prefer:

Industrial Products

In Transportation prefer:

Transportation
Aerospace

In Business Serv. prefer:

Services
Distribution

In Manufact. prefer:

Manufacturing

Additional Information

Year Founded: 2002
Current Activity Level: Actively seeking new investments

FORETAGSBYGGARNA AB (AKA: BUSINESS BUILDERS)

Norrmalmstorg 14
Stockholm, Sweden 111 46
Phone: 46-8-678-1450
Fax: 46-8-678-1460
E-mail: partners@businessbuilders.se
Website: www.businessbuilders.se

Management and Staff

Birgitta Johansson, Chief Financial Officer
Johan Edfeldt, Partner
Martin Gemvik, Partner
Per-Henrik Norhagen, Partner

Type of Firm

Private Equity Firm

Association Membership

Swedish Venture Capital Association (SVCA)

Project Preferences

Role in Financing:

Prefer role as deal originator

Type of Financing Preferred:

Early Stage
Expansion
Seed
Startup

Geographical Preferences

International Preferences:

Sweden

Industry Preferences

In Communications prefer:

Communications and Media
Commercial Communications
Telecommunications
Data Communications

In Computer Software prefer:

Computer Services

In Internet Specific prefer:

Internet

In Medical/Health prefer:

Diagnostic Test Products
Drug/Equipmt Delivery
Pharmaceuticals

Additional Information

Name of Most Recent Fund: ForetagsByggarna AB (AKA: Business Builders)
Most Recent Fund Was Raised: 01/01/1993
Year Founded: 1984
Capital Under Management: $7,000,000
Current Activity Level: Actively seeking new investments
Method of Compensation: Return on invest. most important, but chg. closing fees, service fees, etc.

FORMATIVE VENTURES

2061 Avy Avenue
Menlo Park, CA USA 94025
Phone: 650-461-8000
Fax: 650-461-8010
E-mail: info@formative.com
Website: www.formative.com

Management and Staff

Bernard Xavier, Venture Partner
Bill Burger, Venture Partner
Brian Connors, General Partner
Brooke Seawell, Venture Partner
Clint Chao, General Partner
Dino Vendetti, General Partner
Doug Laird, Venture Partner
Ian Crayford, Venture Partner
James Burke, Venture Partner
John Hagedorn, Venture Partner
Joseph Hutt, Venture Partner
Mark Allen, Venture Partner
Michael Boich, Venture Partner
Michael Ricks, Venture Partner
Mike Ingster, Venture Partner
Peter Zaballos, Venture Partner
Ziya Boyacigiller, Venture Partner

Type of Firm

Private Equity Firm

Association Membership

National Venture Capital Association - USA (NVCA)

Project Preferences

Role in Financing:

Will function either as deal originator or investor in deals created by others

Type of Financing Preferred:

Second Stage Financing
Early Stage
Seed

Size of Investments Considered:

Min Size of Investment Considered (000s): $1,000
Max Size of Investment Considered (000s): $4,000

Geographical Preferences

United States Preferences:

Northwest
West Coast
Southwest

Industry Preferences

In Communications prefer:

Telecommunications
Wireless Communications
Media and Entertainment
Other Communication Prod.

In Computer Software prefer:

Systems Software

In Internet Specific prefer:

Internet

In Semiconductor/Electr prefer:

Semiconductor

Additional Information

Year Founded: 2000
Capital Under Management: $95,000,000
Current Activity Level: Actively seeking new investments
Method of Compensation: Return on investment is of primary concern, do not charge fees

FORREST BINKLEY & BROWN

19800 MacArthur Boulevard
Suite 690
Irvine, CA USA 92612
Phone: 949-222-1987
Fax: 949-222-1988
E-mail: fbb@fbbvc.com
Website: www.fbbvc.com

Other Offices

265 Santa Helena
Suite 110
Solana Beach, CA USA 92075
Phone: 858-259-4105
Fax: 858-259-4108

Management and Staff

Ashish Kaul, Principal
Gregory Forrest, Partner
Jeff Brown, Partner
Joseph Galligan, Chief Financial Officer
Nicholas Binkley, Partner

Type of Firm

Private Equity Advisor or Fund of Funds

Association Membership

Natl Assoc of Small Bus. Inv. Co (NASBIC)

Project Preferences

Role in Financing:

Prefer role as deal originator but will also invest in deals created by others

Type of Financing Preferred:

Leveraged Buyout
Expansion
Generalist PE
Later Stage
Management Buyouts
Acquisition

Size of Investments Considered:

Min Size of Investment Considered (000s): $250
Max Size of Investment Considered (000s): $6,000

Geographical Preferences

United States Preferences:

All U.S.

Industry Focus

(% based on actual investment)

Computer Software and Services	27.8%
Internet Specific	15.5%
Semiconductors/Other Elect.	13.8%
Communications and Media	10.6%
Consumer Related	10.0%
Other Products	9.0%
Biotechnology	7.2%
Medical/Health	4.7%
Computer Hardware	1.1%
Industrial/Energy	0.3%

Additional Information

Name of Most Recent Fund: Forrest Binkley & Brown Capital Partners LLC
Most Recent Fund Was Raised: 09/01/2001
Year Founded: 1993
Capital Under Management: $260,000,000
Current Activity Level: Actively seeking new investments
Method of Compensation: Return on invest. most important, but chg. closing fees, service fees, etc.

FORSTA ENTREPRENORS-FONDEN I NORDEN AB

Grev Turegatan 14
Stockholm, Sweden 114 46
Phone: 41-8-611-4140
E-mail: info@forstaentreprenorsfonden.se
Website: www.forstaentreprenorsfonden.se

Other Offices

Arvid Hedvalls Backe 4
Goteborg, Sweden 411 33
Phone: 41-733-130-095

Management and Staff

Pelle Snarelid, Partner
Peter Wendel, Partner
Peter Werme, Partner
Rune Nordlander, Partner

Type of Firm

Private Equity Firm

Project Preferences

Type of Financing Preferred:

Early Stage
Seed
Startup

Size of Investments Considered:

Min Size of Investment Considered (000s): $14
Max Size of Investment Considered (000s): $725

Geographical Preferences

International Preferences:

Sweden

Additional Information

Year Founded: 2004
Current Activity Level: Actively seeking new investments

FORSTMANN LITTLE & COMPANY

767 Fifth Avenue
44th Floor
New York, NY USA 10153
Phone: 212-355-5656
Fax: 212-759-9059

Other Offices

2 N. Riverside Plaza
Suite 600
Chicago, IL USA 60606
Phone: 312-454-1800
Fax: 312-454-0610

Management and Staff

Daniel Akerson, Managing Director
Greg Stegimen, Chief Financial Officer
Jamie Nicholls, General Partner
Sheli Rosenberg, Chief Executive Officer
Steven Klinsky, General Partner
Winston Hutchins, General Partner

Type of Firm

Private Equity Firm

Project Preferences

Type of Financing Preferred:
Leveraged Buyout

Industry Focus

(% based on actual investment)

Internet Specific	62.2%
Communications and Media	18.1%
Consumer Related	15.1%
Industrial/Energy	2.9%
Other Products	1.8%

Additional Information

Name of Most Recent Fund: Forstmann Little Sub. Debt & Equity MBO Fund VIII
Most Recent Fund Was Raised: 06/30/2000
Year Founded: 1978
Current Activity Level: Making few, if any, new investments

FORSYTH CAPITAL INVESTORS LLC

8040 Forsyth Boulevard
Saint Louis, MO USA 63105
Phone: 314-726-2152
Fax: 314-726-2132
Website: www.forsythcapital.com

Management and Staff

Chet Walker, Senior Managing Director
Kyle Chapman, Managing Director

Type of Firm

Private Equity Firm

Project Preferences

Type of Financing Preferred:
Leveraged Buyout
Expansion
Management Buyouts
Special Situation
Recapitalizations

Size of Investments Considered:
Min Size of Investment Considered (000s): $10,000
Max Size of Investment Considered (000s): $30,000

Industry Preferences

In Communications prefer:
Telecommunications

In Medical/Health prefer:
Health Services

In Consumer Related prefer:
Consumer Products

In Industrial/Energy prefer:
Factory Automation

In Financial Services prefer:
Financial Services
Insurance

In Business Serv. prefer:
Services
Distribution
Media

In Manufact. prefer:
Manufacturing

Additional Information

Year Founded: 2009
Current Activity Level: Actively seeking new investments

FORT HILL PARTNERS, INC.

159 Stanwich Road
Greenwich, CT USA 06830
Phone: 203-661-9827
Fax: 203-661-9821

Management and Staff

John Hall, President

Type of Firm

Private Equity Firm

Project Preferences

Role in Financing:
Prefer role as deal originator

Type of Financing Preferred:
Leveraged Buyout
Management Buyouts
Acquisition
Industry Rollups
Recapitalizations

Size of Investments Considered:
Min Size of Investment Considered (000s): $1,000
Max Size of Investment Considered (000s): $5,000

Geographical Preferences

United States Preferences:
Mid Atlantic
Midwest
Southeast
Northeast
Rocky Mountain

Additional Information

Year Founded: 1997
Capital Under Management: $30,000,000
Current Activity Level: Actively seeking new investments
Method of Compensation: Return on invest. most important, but chg. closing fees, service fees, etc.

FORT WASHINGTON CAPITAL PARTNERS GROUP

303 Broadway
Suite 1200
Cincinnati, OH USA 45202
Phone: 513-361-7600
Fax: 513-361-7605
E-mail: infofw@fortwashington.com
Website: www.fortwashington.com

Other Offices

The Huntington Center, Suite 2495
41 South High Street
Columbus, OH USA 43215
Phone: 614-222-6500
Fax: 614-222-6535

299 South Main Street
Suite 1301
Salt Lake City, UT USA 84111
Phone: 801-535-4350
Fax: 801-535-4351

263 Staab Street
Santa Fe, NM USA 87501
Phone: 505-986-1552
Fax: 505-986-1592

Management and Staff

Christopher Baucom, Managing Director
John O'Connor, Managing Director
John Bessone, Vice President
Joseph Michael, Managing Director
Paul Cohn, Vice President
Stephen Baker, Managing Director

Type of Firm

Private Equity Advisor or Fund of Funds

Association Membership

National Venture Capital Association - USA (NVCA)

Project Preferences

Role in Financing:
Prefer role in deals created by others

Type of Financing Preferred:
Fund of Funds
Second Stage Financing
Leveraged Buyout
Early Stage
Expansion
Mezzanine
Other
Later Stage
Seed
Management Buyouts
Startup
Fund of Funds of Second

Size of Investments Considered:
Min Size of Investment Considered (000s): $250
Max Size of Investment Considered (000s): $5,000

Geographical Preferences

United States Preferences:
New Mexico
Mid Atlantic
Northwest
Southeast
Hawaii
Southern California
Northern California
Rocky Mountain
Alaska
New York
Southwest

International Preferences:
Europe
Asia

Industry Preferences

In Communications prefer:
Communications and Media
Commercial Communications
CATV & Pay TV Systems
Radio & TV Broadcasting
Telecommunications
Wireless Communications
Data Communications
Satellite Microwave Comm.
Media and Entertainment

In Computer Software prefer:
Data Processing
Software
Applications Software

In Internet Specific prefer:
Internet
Web Aggregration/Portals

In Computer Other prefer:
Computer Related

In Semiconductor/Electr prefer:
Electronics
Semiconductor
Sensors
Circuit Boards
Component Testing Equipmt
Laser Related
Fiber Optics

In Biotechnology prefer:
Biotechnology
Human Biotechnology
Agricultural/Animal Bio.
Industrial Biotechnology
Biotech Related Research

In Medical/Health prefer:
Medical/Health
Medical Therapeutics
Drug/Equipmt Delivery
Medical Products
Health Services
Pharmaceuticals

In Consumer Related prefer:
Consumer
Retail
Consumer Products
Consumer Services
Education Related

In Industrial/Energy prefer:
Energy
Alternative Energy
Industrial Products
Superconductivity
Process Control

In Transportation prefer:
Aerospace

In Business Serv. prefer:
Media

In Manufact. prefer:
Manufacturing

In Utilities prefer:
Utilities

Additional Information
Year Founded: 1999
Capital Under Management: $1,819,100,000
Current Activity Level: Actively seeking new investments
Method of Compensation: Return on investment is of primary concern, do not charge fees

---

FORTIS HAITONG INVESTMENT MANAGEMENT CO., LTD.
Unit 3701, Jin Mao Tower
88 Century Blvd., Pudong
Shanghai, China 200121
Phone: 86-21-3865-0999
Fax: 86-21-5047-9997
E-mail: info@hftfund.com
Website: www.hftfund.com

Type of Firm
Bank Affiliated

Project Preferences

Type of Financing Preferred:
Expansion
Balanced

Geographical Preferences

International Preferences:
China
Belgium

Additional Information
Year Founded: 2003
Capital Under Management: $24,000,000
Current Activity Level: Actively seeking new investments

FORTIS PRIVATE EQUITY FRANCE (FKA: ROBERTSAU GESTION)
25 allee de la Robertsau
Strasbourg, France 67000
Phone: 33-3-9022-1100
Fax: 33-3-9022-1101
E-mail: info@robertsau-gestion.com
Website: www.robertsau-gestion.com

Other Offices
23 boulevard Jules Favre
Lyon, France 69459
Phone: 33-4-3724-7796
Fax: 33-4-3724-7800

6 rue de Ponthieu
Paris, France 75008
Phone: 33-1-5836-4460
Fax: 33-1-5836-4461

Management and Staff
Lionel Robin, President
Philippe Aubert, Chief Executive Officer

Type of Firm
Bank Affiliated

Association Membership
French Venture Capital Association (AFIC)

Project Preferences

Type of Financing Preferred:
Leveraged Buyout
Expansion

Size of Investments Considered:
Min Size of Investment Considered (000s): $270
Max Size of Investment Considered (000s): $2,026

Geographical Preferences

International Preferences:
France

Industry Preferences

In Manufact. prefer:
Manufacturing

Additional Information
Year Founded: 1999
Capital Under Management: $40,000,000
Current Activity Level: Actively seeking new investments

FORTIS PRIVATE EQUITY NV/SA (FKA: VIV NV)
Rue Royale 20
Brussels, Belgium 1000
Phone: 32-2-565-1111
Fax: 32-2-565-4222
E-mail: info@fortisprivateequity.com
Website: www.fortis.com

Other Offices
Archimedeslaan 6
Utrecht, Netherlands 3584 BA
Phone: 31-30-226-6222
Fax: 31-30-226-9835

6 rue de Ponthieu
Paris, France 75008
Phone: 33-1-5836-4460
Fax: 33-1-5836-4461

25 Allee de la Robertsau
Strasbourg, France 67000
Phone: 33-3-9022-1100
Fax: 33-3-9022-1101

Fortuny 37
3 Dcha.
Madrid, Spain 28010
Phone: 34-91-700-0501
Fax: 34-91-700-0514

Management and Staff
Brigitte Boone, Managing Director
Eric Spliet, Partner
Filip Dierckx, Chief Executive Officer
Frank Claeys, Managing Director
Georges Noel, Partner
Jean-Paul Votron, Chief Executive Officer
Julien Smets, Managing Director
Pieter Demuynck, Partner
Raf Moons, Partner

Type of Firm
Bank Affiliated

Association Membership
Belgium Venturing Association
European Private Equity and Venture Capital Assoc.

Project Preferences

Role in Financing:
Prefer role as deal originator but will also invest in deals created by others

Type of Financing Preferred:
Fund of Funds
Leveraged Buyout
Early Stage
Expansion
Later Stage
Seed
Startup
Recapitalizations

Size of Investments Considered:
Min Size of Investment Considered (000s): $471
Max Size of Investment Considered (000s): $7,533

Geographical Preferences

International Preferences:
Luxembourg
Netherlands
Belgium
Germany
France

Industry Focus
(% based on actual investment)

Consumer Related	25.4%
Biotechnology	24.3%
Other Products	22.9%
Semiconductors/Other Elect.	7.5%
Computer Software and Services	7.4%
Medical/Health	7.3%
Internet Specific	3.3%
Industrial/Energy	1.9%

Additional Information
Year Founded: 1987
Capital Under Management: $372,300,000
Current Activity Level: Actively seeking new investments
Method of Compensation: Return on invest. most important, but chg. closing fees, service fees, etc.

FORTRESS INVESTMENT GROUP LLC
1345 Avenue of the Americas
New York, NY USA 10105
Phone: 212-798-6100
Fax: 212-798-6092
Website: www.fortressinv.com

Other Offices
Level 43, AMP Centre
50 Bridge Street
Sydney, Australia 2000
Phone: 612-8239-1960

One Market Street
Spear Tower, 35th Floor
San Francisco, CA USA 94105
Phone: 415-293-7965

Drawbridge (Suisse) SARL
Place Longemalle 6-8
Geneva, Switzerland 1204
Phone: 41-22-310-5790

750 B Street
Suite 2700
San Diego, CA USA 92101
Phone: 619-881-6910

10250 Constellation Boulevard
23rd Floor
Los Angeles, CA USA 90067
Phone: 310-228-3030

200 South Wacker Drive
31st Floor
Chicago, IL USA 60606
Phone: 312-674-4954

5 Savile Row
London, United Kingdom W1S 3PD
Phone: 44-207-290-5600

5221 North O'Connor Boulevard
Suite 700
Irving, TX USA 75039
Phone: 972-532-4300

Junghofstrasse 22
Frankfurt, Germany 60311
Phone: 49-69-2549-670

Cheung Kong Centre, Suite 4701
2 Queen's Road
Central, Hong Kong
Phone: 852-2251-1881

220 Elm Street
Suite 201
New Canaan, CT USA 06840
Phone: 203-442-2450

Via del Tritone 181
Rome, Italy 00187
Phone: 39-06-47971

Bay Wellington Tower, Suite 3210
181 Bay Street, BCE Place
Toronto, Canada M5J 2T3
Phone: 416-862-8720

Midtown Towers, 23rd Floor
9-7-1 Akasaka, Minato-ku
Tokyo, Japan 107-6223
Phone: 81-3-6438-4400

Feringastr. 6
Munich, Germany 85774
Phone: 49-89-9921-6265

Management and Staff
Daniel Mudd, Chief Executive Officer
Daniel Bass, Chief Financial Officer
Lilly Donohue, Managing Director

Type of Firm
Investment Management Firm

Project Preferences

Type of Financing Preferred:
Leveraged Buyout
Early Stage
Generalist PE
Distressed Debt

Geographical Preferences

United States Preferences:
All U.S.

International Preferences:
Western Europe
All International

Industry Preferences

In Communications prefer:
Communications and Media
Telecommunications

In Transportation prefer:
Transportation

In Financial Services prefer:
Financial Services
Real Estate

Additional Information
Name of Most Recent Fund: Fortress Investment Fund V (Coinvesment A-F), L.P.
Most Recent Fund Was Raised: 06/15/2007
Year Founded: 1998
Capital Under Management: $3,000,000,000
Current Activity Level: Actively seeking new investments

FORTUNE VENTURE CAPITAL, INC.

2F, No. 76, Tun-Hwa South Road
Section 2
Taipei, Taiwan
Phone: 886-2-2700-6999
Fax: 886-2-2702-6208

Management and Staff
Robert Tsao, President & Chairman

Type of Firm
Private Equity Firm

Association Membership
Taiwan Venture Capital Association(TVCA)

Project Preferences

Type of Financing Preferred:
Early Stage
Expansion
Start-up Financing
Turnaround
Later Stage
Seed

Geographical Preferences

International Preferences:
Taiwan
China

Industry Preferences

In Communications prefer:
Telecommunications

In Computer Software prefer:
Software

In Semiconductor/Electr prefer:
Semiconductor
Circuit Boards

Additional Information
Year Founded: 1993
Capital Under Management: $62,100,000
Current Activity Level: Actively seeking new investments

FORTUNE VENTURE INVESTMENT GROUP (AKA:FORTUNE CONSULTING)

13/F-1, 128 Min-Sheng East Rd.
Section 3
Taipei, Taiwan
Phone: 886-2-2718-2330
Fax: 886-2-2546-7182
Website: www.vcfortune.com

Other Offices
80 Robinson Road
#25-01B
Singapore, Singapore 068898
Phone: 65-6238-1911
Fax: 65-6738-1511

No. 93 Huai Hai M. Road
Suite 1103-04 Shanghai Times Square
Shanghai, China
Phone: 86-21-5386-8989
Fax: 86-21-5386-8099

535 Middlefield Road
Suite 280
Menlo Park, CA USA 94025
Phone: 408-489-9215
Fax: 408-725-8654

Management and Staff
Jack Tao, Partner
James Chew, Managing Partner
Jason Chen, Partner
Jesffer Liu, Partner
KC Tay, President
Luke Lu, Partner
Philip Wang, Partner

Type of Firm
Bank Affiliated

Association Membership
Hong Kong Venture Capital Association (HKVCA)
Taiwan Venture Capital Association(TVCA)
Singapore Venture Capital Association (SVCA)

Project Preferences

Type of Financing Preferred:
Early Stage
Expansion
Mezzanine
Balanced
Later Stage
Seed
Startup

Size of Investments Considered:
Min Size of Investment Considered (000s): $500
Max Size of Investment Considered (000s): $5,000

Geographical Preferences

United States Preferences:
All U.S.

International Preferences:
Taiwan
China
Hong Kong
Singapore

Industry Preferences

In Communications prefer:
Communications and Media
Commercial Communications
Telecommunications
Data Communications

In Computer Hardware prefer:
Computer Graphics and Dig

In Computer Software prefer:
Software

In Internet Specific prefer:
Internet
Ecommerce

In Semiconductor/Electr prefer:
Electronics
Semiconductor
Fiber Optics
Optoelectronics

In Biotechnology prefer:
Biotechnology

In Transportation prefer:
Transportation

Additional Information
Name of Most Recent Fund: Fortune Asia Pacific Technology Fund
Most Recent Fund Was Raised: 03/31/2002
Year Founded: 1984
Capital Under Management: $400,000,000
Current Activity Level: Actively seeking new investments

FORUM CAPITAL PARTNERS

330 Madison Avenue
Ninth Floor
New York, NY USA 10017
Phone: 212-290-1787
Fax: 212-290-1763
E-mail: info@forumcp.com
Website: www.forumcp.com

Management and Staff

Jeffrey Stern, Managing Director
Robert Schwabe, Managing Director

Type of Firm

Private Equity Firm

Additional Information

Year Founded: 2009
Current Activity Level: Actively seeking new investments

FORWARD VENTURES

9393 Towne Centre Drive
Suite 200
San Diego, CA USA 92121
Phone: 858-677-6077
Fax: 858-452-8799
E-mail: info@forwardventures.com
Website: www.forwardventures.com

Management and Staff

Stuart Collinson, Partner

Type of Firm

Private Equity Firm

Association Membership

Western Association of Venture Capitalists (WAVC)
National Venture Capital Association - USA (NVCA)

Project Preferences

Role in Financing:

Prefer role as deal originator but will also invest in deals created by others

Type of Financing Preferred:

Second Stage Financing
Early Stage
Balanced
Later Stage
Seed
First Stage Financing

Size of Investments Considered:

Min Size of Investment Considered (000s): $500
Max Size of Investment Considered (000s): $10,000

Geographical Preferences

United States Preferences:

Southern California
Northern California
West Coast
All U.S.

Canadian Preferences:

Eastern Canada

Industry Focus

(% based on actual investment)

Biotechnology	68.6%
Medical/Health	29.2%
Industrial/Energy	1.6%
Internet Specific	0.5%

Additional Information

Name of Most Recent Fund: Forward Ventures V, L.P.
Most Recent Fund Was Raised: 04/28/2003
Year Founded: 1990
Capital Under Management: $444,000,000
Current Activity Level: Actively seeking new investments
Method of Compensation: Return on investment is of primary concern, do not charge fees

FOUNDATION CAPITAL

250 Middlefield Road
Menlo Park, CA USA 94025
Phone: 650-614-0500
Fax: 650-614-0505
E-mail: info@foundationcapital.com
Website: www.foundationcapital.com

Management and Staff

Adam Grosser, General Partner
Ashmeet Sidana, General Partner
Ashu Garg, Venture Partner
Charles Moldow, General Partner
Gail Haney, Chief Financial Officer
Michael Schuh, General Partner
Mike Brown, Principal
Paul Holland, General Partner
Paul Koontz, General Partner
Richard Redelfs, General Partner
Steve Vassallo, Principal
Warren Weiss, General Partner
William Elmore, General Partner

Type of Firm

Private Equity Firm

Association Membership

Western Association of Venture Capitalists (WAVC)
National Venture Capital Association - USA (NVCA)

Project Preferences

Role in Financing:

Prefer role as deal originator but will also invest in deals created by others

Type of Financing Preferred:

Second Stage Financing
Early Stage
Research and Development
Balanced
Start-up Financing
Seed
First Stage Financing

Size of Investments Considered:

Min Size of Investment Considered (000s): $1,000
Max Size of Investment Considered (000s): $10,000

Geographical Preferences

United States Preferences:

West Coast
All U.S.

Industry Focus

(% based on actual investment)

Computer Software and Services	34.8%
Communications and Media	21.7%
Internet Specific	15.9%
Semiconductors/Other Elect.	9.8%
Computer Hardware	8.2%
Industrial/Energy	4.4%
Other Products	3.3%
Consumer Related	1.1%
Biotechnology	0.4%
Medical/Health	0.3%

Additional Information

Name of Most Recent Fund: Foundation Capital VI, L.P.
Most Recent Fund Was Raised: 04/07/2008
Year Founded: 1995
Capital Under Management: $200,000,000
Current Activity Level: Actively seeking new investments
Method of Compensation: Return on investment is of primary concern, do not charge fees

FOUNDATION CAPITAL, LTD.

P.O Box Z5350
St. George's Terrace
Perth, Australia 6831
Phone: 618-9267-4766
Fax: 618-9325-8837
E-mail: first@foundationcap.com.au
Website: www.foundationcap.com.au

Other Offices

Suite G 113, Paspalis Centerpoint
48-50 Smith Street Mall
Darwin, Australia 0801
Phone: 618-8941-5538
Fax: 618-9841-0848

Management and Staff

Jose Martins, Chief Financial Officer

Type of Firm

Private Equity Firm

Project Preferences

Role in Financing:

Prefer role in deals created by others

Type of Financing Preferred:
Second Stage Financing
Leveraged Buyout
Early Stage
Expansion
Mezzanine
Generalist PE
Seed
Management Buyouts
First Stage Financing
Acquisition
Startup

Size of Investments Considered:
Min Size of Investment Considered (000s): $762
Max Size of Investment Considered (000s): $7,627

Geographical Preferences

International Preferences:
Australia

Industry Preferences

In Communications prefer:
Communications and Media
Telecommunications

In Computer Software prefer:
Software

In Computer Other prefer:
Computer Related

In Semiconductor/Electr prefer:
Electronic Components
Laser Related

In Biotechnology prefer:
Biotechnology

In Industrial/Energy prefer:
Energy
Industrial Products
Materials

In Transportation prefer:
Transportation

In Financial Services prefer:
Financial Services

In Business Serv. prefer:
Services
Distribution

In Manufact. prefer:
Manufacturing

Additional Information
Year Founded: 1994
Capital Under Management: $59,000,000
Current Activity Level: Actively seeking new investments

FOUNDATION EQUITY CORPORATION
22 Sir Winston Churchill
Avenue 603
Edmonton, Canada T8N1B4
Phone: 780-460-1242

Type of Firm
Private Equity Firm

Additional Information
Year Founded: 2009
Current Activity Level: Actively seeking new investments

FOUNDATION FOR ASSISTANCE TO SMALL INNOVATIVE ENTERPRISES
49 Leninsky prospekt
Moscow, Romania 119991
Phone: 7-95-135-7734
Fax: 7-95-132-8993
E-mail: fond@com2com.ru
Website: www.fasie.ru

Type of Firm
Government Affiliated Program

Association Membership
Russian Venture Capital Association (RVCA)

Project Preferences

Type of Financing Preferred:
Balanced

Geographical Preferences

International Preferences:
Europe

Industry Preferences

In Biotechnology prefer:
Biotechnology

In Medical/Health prefer:
Medical/Health

Additional Information
Year Founded: 1994
Current Activity Level: Actively seeking new investments

FOUNDATION MEDICAL PARTNERS
105 Rowayton Avenue
Rowayton, CT USA 06853
Phone: 203-851-3900
Fax: 203-831-8289
Website: www.foundmed.com

Management and Staff
Andrew Firlik, General Partner
Harry Rein, General Partner
John Sullivan, Principal
Lee Wrubel, General Partner

Type of Firm
Private Equity Firm

Association Membership
National Venture Capital Association - USA (NVCA)

Project Preferences

Role in Financing:
Will function either as deal originator or investor in deals created by others

Type of Financing Preferred:
Second Stage Financing
Early Stage
First Stage Financing

Size of Investments Considered:
Min Size of Investment Considered (000s): $1,000
Max Size of Investment Considered (000s): $8,000

Geographical Preferences

United States Preferences:
All U.S.

Industry Preferences

In Biotechnology prefer:
Human Biotechnology
Biosensors

In Medical/Health prefer:
Medical Diagnostics
Medical Therapeutics
Medical Products

Additional Information
Year Founded: 2001
Capital Under Management: $215,000,000
Current Activity Level: Actively seeking new investments
Method of Compensation: Return on investment is of primary concern, do not charge fees

---

FOUNDATION VENTURE CAPITAL GROUP LLC
120 Albany Street
Tower II
New Brunswick, NJ USA 08901
Phone: 732-235-5400
Website: www.foundationventure.com

Management and Staff
James Golubieski, President

Type of Firm
Private Equity Firm

Project Preferences

Type of Financing Preferred:
Startup

Geographical Preferences

United States Preferences:
New Jersey

Industry Preferences

In Biotechnology prefer:
Biotech Related Research

In Medical/Health prefer:
Diagnostic Test Products

Additional Information

Year Founded: 2006
Current Activity Level: Actively seeking new investments

FOUNDER COLLECTIVE

130 Liberty Road
Somerville, MA USA 02144
Phone: 617-270-4569
Website: www.foundercollective.com

Type of Firm

Private Equity Firm

Project Preferences

Type of Financing Preferred:
Seed

Additional Information

Year Founded: 2009
Capital Under Management: $24,400,000
Current Activity Level: Actively seeking new investments

FOUNDERS CAPITAL PARTNERS

1615 Lasuen Road
Santa Barbara, CA USA 93103
Phone: 805-963-4600
Fax: 805-963-4704
Website: www.founderscapitalpartners.com

Management and Staff

Robert Johnson, Managing Partner

Type of Firm

Angel Group

Project Preferences

Type of Financing Preferred:
Early Stage

Geographical Preferences

United States Preferences:
California

Industry Preferences

In Computer Software prefer:
Software

In Internet Specific prefer:
Internet

In Semiconductor/Electr prefer:
Electronics
Sensors

In Biotechnology prefer:
Industrial Biotechnology

In Industrial/Energy prefer:
Industrial Products

Additional Information

Year Founded: 1995
Current Activity Level: Actively seeking new investments

FOUNDERS EQUITY, INC.

711 Fifth Avenue
Fifth Floor
New York, NY USA 10022
Phone: 212-829-0900
Fax: 212-829-0901
Website: www.fequity.com

Type of Firm

Private Equity Firm

Association Membership

Natl Assoc of Small Bus. Inv. Co (NASBIC)

Project Preferences

Role in Financing:
Prefer role as deal originator but will also invest in deals created by others

Type of Financing Preferred:
Leveraged Buyout
Expansion
Public Companies
Turnaround
Later Stage
Management Buyouts
Industry Rollups
Special Situation
Recapitalizations

Size of Investments Considered:
Min Size of Investment Considered (000s): $3,000
Max Size of Investment Considered (000s): $15,000

Geographical Preferences

United States Preferences:
Mid Atlantic
Midwest
Southeast
Northeast

Industry Preferences

In Medical/Health prefer:
Health Services

In Consumer Related prefer:
Consumer
Franchises(NEC)
Food/Beverage

In Industrial/Energy prefer:
Industrial Products

In Business Serv. prefer:
Services
Distribution
Consulting Services
Media

In Manufact. prefer:
Manufacturing

In Other prefer:
Environment Responsible

Additional Information

Year Founded: 1969
Capital Under Management: $150,000,000
Current Activity Level: Actively seeking new investments
Method of Compensation: Return on invest. most important, but chg. closing fees, service fees, etc.

FOUNDERS FUND, THE

One Letterman Drive
Bldg. C, Suite 400
San Francisco, CA USA 94129
E-mail: info@thefoundersfund.com
Website: www.thefoundersfund.com

Management and Staff

Ken Howery, Managing Partner
Luke Nosek, Venture Partner
Peter Thiel, Managing Partner
Sean Parker, Managing Partner

Type of Firm

Private Equity Firm

Project Preferences

Type of Financing Preferred:
Early Stage
Seed
Strategic Alliances
Startup

Size of Investments Considered:
Min Size of Investment Considered (000s): $500
Max Size of Investment Considered (000s): $1,000

Geographical Preferences

United States Preferences:
All U.S.

Industry Preferences

In Internet Specific prefer:
Internet

In Consumer Related prefer:
Consumer

Additional Information

Name of Most Recent Fund: Founders Fund II
Most Recent Fund Was Raised: 12/18/2007
Year Founded: 2005
Capital Under Management: $50,000,000
Current Activity Level: Actively seeking new investments

FOUNDRY GROUP

1050 Walnut Street
Suite 210
Boulder, CO USA 80302
Phone: 303-642-4050
Fax: 303-642-4001
Website: www.foundrygroup.com

Management and Staff

Bradley Feld, Managing Director
Jason Mendelson, Managing Director
Ryan McIntyre, Managing Director
Seth Levine, Managing Director

Type of Firm

Private Equity Firm

Association Membership

National Venture Capital Association - USA (NVCA)

Project Preferences

Type of Financing Preferred:
Balanced
Seed

Geographical Preferences

United States Preferences:
Colorado
All U.S.

Additional Information

Name of Most Recent Fund: Foundry Venture Capital 2007, L.P.
Most Recent Fund Was Raised: 09/13/2007
Year Founded: 2007
Capital Under Management: $225,000,000
Current Activity Level: Actively seeking new investments

FOUNDRY LLC, THE

199 Jefferson Drive
Menlo Park, CA USA 94025
Phone: 650-326-2656
Fax: 650-326-3108
E-mail: info@the-foundry.com
Website: www.the-foundry.com

Management and Staff

Erik Engelson, Managing Partner
Hanson Gifford, Partner
Jeffrey Grainger, Managing Partner
Kara Liebig, Managing Partner
Mark Deem, Managing Partner

Type of Firm

Incubator/Development Program

Project Preferences

Type of Financing Preferred:
Early Stage
Seed

Industry Preferences

In Medical/Health prefer:
Medical Products

Additional Information

Year Founded: 1998
Capital Under Management: $89,500,000
Current Activity Level: Actively seeking new investments

FOUNDRY VENTURES, INC.

513 Eighth Avenue South West
Suite 204
Calgary, Canada T2P 1G3
Phone: 403-571-2195
Fax: 403-571-2197
Website: www.foundryventures.com

Management and Staff

Hal Peters, Partner
Kim Wong, Partner
Vince Krynski, Partner

Type of Firm

Private Equity Firm

Project Preferences

Type of Financing Preferred:
Early Stage

Geographical Preferences

Canadian Preferences:
Western Canada

Additional Information

Year Founded: 2002
Current Activity Level: Actively seeking new investments

FOUNTAINHEAD CAPITAL LTD

1 Beach Queen, J.P. Road
Versova Andheri (W)
Mumbai, India 400061
Phone: 91-22-633-0688
Fax: 91-22-629-0914

Management and Staff

Chiranjit Banerjee, Managing Director

Type of Firm

Private Equity Advisor or Fund of Funds

Project Preferences

Role in Financing:
Prefer role in deals created by others

Type of Financing Preferred:
Mezzanine
Balanced

Geographical Preferences

International Preferences:
India

Industry Preferences

In Communications prefer:
Communications and Media

In Consumer Related prefer:
Consumer

Additional Information

Year Founded: 1995
Current Activity Level: Actively seeking new investments

FOUNTAINVEST PARTNERS (ASIA), LTD.

3 Garden Road
Suite 906, ICBC Tower
Central, Hong Kong
Phone: 852-3972-3900
Fax: 852-3107-2490
E-mail: enquiry@fountainvest.com
Website: www.fountainvest.com

Other Offices

1010 Huahai Middle Road
Suite 1602 K. Wah Center
Shanghai, China 200031
Phone: 86-21-2419-0868
Fax: 86-21-2419-0888

Management and Staff

Chenning Zhao, Managing Director
Frank Tang, CEO & Managing Director
George Chuang, Managing Director
Terry Yongmin Hu, Managing Director

Type of Firm
Private Equity Firm

Project Preferences

Type of Financing Preferred:
Expansion

Size of Investments Considered:
Min Size of Investment Considered (000s): $50,000
Max Size of Investment Considered (000s): $150,000

Geographical Preferences

International Preferences:
China

Additional Information
Year Founded: 2007
Capital Under Management: $950,000,000
Current Activity Level: Actively seeking new investments

FOUR HATS CAPITAL PTY, LTD.

P.O. Box H89
Australia Square
Sydney, Australia 1215
Phone: 61-403-181-418
Fax: 612-9909-3927
Website: www.fourhats.com.au

Type of Firm
Private Equity Firm

Association Membership
Australian Venture Capital Association (AVCAL)

Project Preferences

Type of Financing Preferred:
Early Stage
Expansion

Geographical Preferences

International Preferences:
Pacific
Australia

Industry Preferences

In Medical/Health prefer:
Medical/Health

Additional Information
Name of Most Recent Fund: Nanyang Innovation Fund (FKA: St. George Innovation Fund)
Most Recent Fund Was Raised: 04/05/2001
Year Founded: 2008
Current Activity Level: Actively seeking new investments

FOUR RIVERS PARTNERS

2441 Fillmore Street
Suite Two
San Francisco, CA USA 94115
Phone: 415-250-4643

Management and Staff
Farouk Ladha, Founder

Type of Firm
Private Equity Advisor or Fund of Funds

Additional Information
Name of Most Recent Fund: Four Rivers Partners, L.P.
Most Recent Fund Was Raised: 03/20/2007
Year Founded: 2007
Capital Under Management: $21,300,000
Current Activity Level: Actively seeking new investments

FOURTH LEVEL VENTURES (AKA: 4TH LEVEL VENTURES)

The Tower, Pearse Street
Trinity College Enterprise Ctr
Dublin 2, Ireland
Phone: 353-1-671-1288
Fax: 353-1-671-1339
E-mail: info@4thLevelVentures.ie
Website: www.4thlevelventures.ie

Management and Staff
Dennis Jennings, Founder
Ray Naughton, Founder
Ronan Reid, Managing Director

Type of Firm
Private Equity Firm

Association Membership
European Private Equity and Venture Capital Assoc.

Project Preferences

Type of Financing Preferred:
Early Stage
Expansion
Seed
Startup

Geographical Preferences

International Preferences:
Ireland
Europe

Industry Preferences

In Communications prefer:
Communications and Media

Additional Information
Name of Most Recent Fund: 4th Level Ventures University Seed Fund
Most Recent Fund Was Raised: 12/31/2002
Year Founded: 2002
Capital Under Management: $25,500,000
Current Activity Level: Actively seeking new investments

FOX PAINE & COMPANY, LLC

950 Tower Lane
Suite 1150
Foster City, CA USA 94404-2131
Phone: 650-235-2075
Fax: 650-525-1396
E-mail: info@foxpaine.com
Website: www.foxpaine.com

Management and Staff
Erik Glover, Principal
Saul Fox, Chief Executive Officer

Type of Firm
Private Equity Firm

Project Preferences

Role in Financing:
Prefer role as deal originator

Type of Financing Preferred:
Leveraged Buyout
Expansion
Later Stage
Management Buyouts
Acquisition
Special Situation
Recapitalizations

Size of Investments Considered:
Min Size of Investment Considered (000s): $30,000
Max Size of Investment Considered (000s): $200,000

Geographical Preferences

United States Preferences:
All U.S.

Canadian Preferences:
All Canada

International Preferences:
Europe

Industry Focus
(% based on actual investment)

Other Products	56.9%
Medical/Health	18.9%
Communications and Media	17.2%
Semiconductors/Other Elect.	6.8%
Biotechnology	0.2%

Additional Information

Name of Most Recent Fund: Fox Paine Capital Fund III Co-Investors, L.P.
Most Recent Fund Was Raised: 02/14/2007
Year Founded: 1997
Capital Under Management: $1,500,000,000
Current Activity Level: Actively seeking new investments

FR2 CAPITAL B.V.

Smidswater 13
The Hague, Netherlands 2514 BW
Phone: 31-70-364-2420
Fax: 31-70-364-2602
E-mail: management@fr2capital.com
Website: www.fr2.nl

Management and Staff

Adu Advaney, Managing Director
Hans Ouwendijk, Managing Director

Type of Firm

Private Equity Firm

Project Preferences

Type of Financing Preferred:
Leveraged Buyout
Management Buyouts
Startup

Size of Investments Considered:
Min Size of Investment Considered (000s): $7,323
Max Size of Investment Considered (000s): $36,614

Geographical Preferences

International Preferences:
Europe

Industry Preferences

In Consumer Related prefer:
Consumer Products

Additional Information

Year Founded: 2006
Capital Under Management: $131,800,000
Current Activity Level: Actively seeking new investments

FRAMTAK INVESTMENT BANK (AKA: ALBJOOAF-JARFESTINGARFELAG EFA)

Sioumuli 28
Reykjavik, Iceland 108
Phone: 354-588-3370
Fax: 354-588-3340

Type of Firm

Private Equity Firm

Project Preferences

Type of Financing Preferred:
Balanced

Geographical Preferences

International Preferences:
Europe
Iceland

Additional Information

Year Founded: 2004
Current Activity Level: Actively seeking new investments

FRANCHE-COMTE PME GESTION

28, rue de la Republique
Besancon, France 25013
Phone: 33-38125-0614
Fax: 33-38125-0613

Management and Staff

Patrick Blasselle, General Director
Philippe Lafaurie, President

Type of Firm

Bank Affiliated

Project Preferences

Type of Financing Preferred:
Leveraged Buyout
Expansion

Geographical Preferences

International Preferences:
Europe
France

Additional Information

Year Founded: 2004
Capital Under Management: $13,000,000
Current Activity Level: Actively seeking new investments

FRANCISCO PARTNERS

One Letterman Drive
Building C, Suite 410
San Francisco, CA USA 94129
Phone: 415-418-2900
Fax: 415-418-2999
E-mail: info@franciscopartners.com
Website: www.franciscopartners.com

Other Offices

100 Pall Mall
Fourth Floor
London, United Kingdom SW1Y 5NQ
Phone: 44-207-907-8600
Fax: 44-207-907-8650

Management and Staff

Andrew Kowal, Principal
Ann Savellano, Chief Financial Officer
Ashutosh Agrawal, Principal
Benjamin Ball, Founding Partner
Chris Adams, Vice President
David Golob, Partner
David Stanton, Founding Partner
Deep Shah, Principal
Dipanjan Deb, Partner
Ezra Perlman, Partner
Keith Toh, Principal
Keith Geeslin, Partner
Matthew Spetzler, Vice President
Neil Garfinkel, Partner
Noaman Ahmad, Vice President
Petri Oksanen, Vice President
Phokion Potamianos, Partner
Sanford Robertson, Partner
Thomas Ludwig, Principal

Type of Firm

Private Equity Firm

Project Preferences

Role in Financing:
Prefer role as deal originator

Type of Financing Preferred:
Leveraged Buyout
Management Buyouts
Acquisition
Recapitalizations

Industry Focus

(% based on actual investment)

Computer Software and Services	41.5%
Internet Specific	35.1%
Other Products	23.4%

Additional Information

Name of Most Recent Fund: Francisco Partners II, L.P.
Most Recent Fund Was Raised: 07/14/2005
Year Founded: 1999
Capital Under Management: $4,831,900,000
Current Activity Level: Actively seeking new investments

FRANK RUSSELL CAPITAL

909 A Street
Tacoma, WA USA 98402
Phone: 253-572-9500
Fax: 253-502-2500
Website: www.russell.com

Other Offices

1 First Canadian Place
100 King St. W, Ste 5900, PO Box 476
Toronto, Canada M5X 1E4
Phone: 416-362-8411

590 Madison Avenue
New York, NY USA 10022

Phone: 212-702-7900
Fax: 212-702-7944

6 Shenton Way #25-11 A
DBS Building Tower Two
Singapore, Singapore 068809
Phone: 65-325-4336

PO Box 105-191
Auckland, New Zealand
Phone: 649-357-6633

6 Rue Christophe Colomb
Paris, France 75008
Phone: 331-5357-4020
Fax: 331-5357-4021

Level 24, Maritime Centre
207 Kent Street
Sydney, Australia NSW 2000
Phone: 612-9770-8000

Place Canada
7-3-37, Akasaka
Minato-ku, Tokyo , Japan 107-0052
Phone: 81-3-5411-3500

Rex House
10 Regent Street
London, United Kingdom SW1Y 4PE
Phone: 44-20-7024-6000

Management and Staff

Hal Strong, Managing Director
Helen Steers, Managing Director
Jeff Watts, Managing Director
Karl Smith, Managing Director
Len Brennan, Managing Director
Michael Phillips, Chairman & CEO

Type of Firm

Bank Affiliated

Project Preferences

Type of Financing Preferred:

Fund of Funds

Additional Information

Year Founded: 1995
Capital Under Management: $3,127,000,000
Current Activity Level: Actively seeking new investments

FRANKFURT CAPITAL-PARTNERS AG (AKA: FCP)

Zeppelinallee 77
Frankfurt, Germany 60487
Phone: 49-69-298028890
Fax: 49-69-298028899
Website: www.frankfurtcapitalpartners.com

Management and Staff

Andreas Steinmann, Partner
Dirk Sachse, Partner
Michael Vogt, Partner

Type of Firm

Private Equity Firm

Project Preferences

Type of Financing Preferred:

Generalist PE
Management Buyouts
Special Situation
Recapitalizations
<@Subhead2:>Size of Investments Considered:
Min Size of Investment Considered (000s): $11,883
Max Size of Investment Considered (000s): $118,830

Geographical Preferences

International Preferences:

Europe
Germany

Additional Information

Year Founded: 2008
Current Activity Level: Actively seeking new investments

FRANKLIN STREET PARTNERS

1450 Raleigh Road
Suite 300
Chapel Hill, NC USA 27517
Phone: 919-489-2600
Fax: 919-489-1666
Website: www.franklin-street.com

Management and Staff

Stuart Frantz, President

Type of Firm

Private Equity Firm

Project Preferences

Role in Financing:

Prefer role in deals created by others

Type of Financing Preferred:

Leveraged Buyout

Industry Focus

(% based on actual investment)

Medical/Health	68.1%
Other Products	16.1%
Biotechnology	15.7%

Additional Information

Year Founded: 1990
Current Activity Level: Actively seeking new investments

FRANTZ MEDICAL VENTURES

7740 Metric Drive
Mentor, OH USA 44060
Phone: 440-266-5800
Fax: 440-266-5801
Website: www.frantzgroup.com

Type of Firm

Corporate PE/Venture

Project Preferences

Type of Financing Preferred:

Balanced

Additional Information

Year Founded: 2004
Current Activity Level: Actively seeking new investments

FRAZIER HEALTHCARE AND TECHNOLOGY VENTURES

601 Union Street
Suite 3200
Seattle, WA USA 98101
Phone: 206-621-7200
Fax: 206-621-1848
E-mail: businessplan@fraziertechnology.com
Website: www.frazierco.com

Other Offices

550 Hamilton Avenue
Suite 100
Palo Alto, CA USA 94301
Phone: 650-325-5156
Fax: 650-325-5157

Management and Staff

Alan Levy, Venture Partner
Ben Magnano, Vice President
Bob More, General Partner
Brian Morfitt, Principal
David Kosloff, Principal
Gary Gigot, General Partner
James Topper, General Partner
Julian Nikolchev, Venture Partner
Len Jordan, General Partner
Nader Naini, General Partner
Nathan Every, General Partner
Patrick Heron, General Partner
Paul Bialek, General Partner
Peter Zaballos, Vice President
Sam Brasch, Vice President
Scott Darling, Partner
Shelley Chu, Principal
Steve Bailey, Chief Financial Officer
Trevor Moody, General Partner
W.Michael Gallatin, Venture Partner

Type of Firm
Private Equity Firm

Association Membership
National Venture Capital Association - USA (NVCA)

Project Preferences

Role in Financing:
Prefer role as deal originator but will also invest in deals created by others

Type of Financing Preferred:
Early Stage
Balanced
Later Stage

Size of Investments Considered:
Min Size of Investment Considered (000s): $500
Max Size of Investment Considered (000s): $15,000

Geographical Preferences

United States Preferences:
Midwest
Northwest
All U.S.

Industry Focus

(% based on actual investment)

Medical/Health	51.5%
Biotechnology	29.0%
Internet Specific	5.8%
Computer Software and Services	4.6%
Other Products	3.9%
Communications and Media	2.1%
Consumer Related	1.2%
Computer Hardware	1.1%
Semiconductors/Other Elect.	0.4%
Industrial/Energy	0.4%

Additional Information
Name of Most Recent Fund: Frazier Healthcare VI, L.P.
Most Recent Fund Was Raised: 11/28/2007
Year Founded: 1991
Capital Under Management: $1,993,000,000
Current Activity Level: Actively seeking new investments
Method of Compensation: Return on investment is of primary concern, do not charge fees

---

FRDCM
8, Rue du Nil
Gafsa, Tunisia 2100
Phone: 216-7620-0000
Fax: 216-7622-4036
Website: www.frdcmgafsa.com.tn

Type of Firm
Private Equity Firm

Project Preferences

Type of Financing Preferred:
Balanced

Geographical Preferences

International Preferences:
Tunisia

Additional Information
Year Founded: 2004
Current Activity Level: Actively seeking new investments

FREEBIRD PARTNERS, LP
2800 Post Oak Boulevard
Houston, TX USA 77056
Phone: 713-961-0118

Type of Firm
Private Equity Firm

Project Preferences

Type of Financing Preferred:
Balanced

Geographical Preferences

United States Preferences:
All U.S.

Additional Information
Year Founded: 2002
Capital Under Management: $25,000,000
Current Activity Level: Actively seeking new investments

FREEMAN SPOGLI & CO.
11100 Santa Monica Boulevard
Suite 1900
Los Angeles, CA USA 90025
Phone: 310-444-1822
Fax: 310-444-1870
E-mail: info@freemanspogli.com
Website: www.freemanspogli.com

Other Offices
299 Park Avenue
20th Floor
New York, NY USA 10171
Phone: 212-758-2555
Fax: 212-758-7499

Management and Staff
Brad Brutocao, General Partner
Brad Freeman, Co-Founder
Charles Rullman, General Partner
J. Frederick Simmons, General Partner
John Roth, General Partner
Jon Ralph, General Partner
Lou Losorelli, Chief Financial Officer
Mark Doran, General Partner
Ron Spogli, Co-Founder
Todd Halloran, General Partner
William Wardlaw, General Partner

Type of Firm
Bank Affiliated

Project Preferences

Type of Financing Preferred:
Leveraged Buyout

Size of Investments Considered:
Min Size of Investment Considered (000s): $50,000
Max Size of Investment Considered (000s): $100,000

Industry Focus

(% based on actual investment)

Consumer Related	43.9%
Other Products	26.1%
Internet Specific	13.0%
Industrial/Energy	7.0%
Communications and Media	4.0%
Medical/Health	3.3%
Semiconductors/Other Elect.	2.7%

Additional Information
Year Founded: 1983
Capital Under Management: $1,813,200,000
Current Activity Level: Actively seeking new investments
Method of Compensation: Return on investment is of primary concern, do not charge fees

---

FREMONT GROUP
199 Fremont Street
Suite 2400
San Francisco, CA USA 94105
Phone: 415-284-8500
Fax: 415-284-8187
E-mail: info@fremontgroup.com
Website: www.fremontgroup.com

Type of Firm
Private Equity Firm

Additional Information
Year Founded: 2000
Current Activity Level: Actively seeking new investments

FREMONT VENTURES
199 Fremont Street
19th Floor
San Francisco, CA USA 94105
Phone: 415-284-8800
Fax: 415-284-8102
E-mail: ventures@fremontgroup.com
Website: www.fremontventures.com

Management and Staff
W. Blake Winchell, Managing General Partner

Type of Firm
Private Equity Firm

Association Membership

Western Association of Venture Capitalists (WAVC)

Project Preferences

Role in Financing:

Prefer role as deal originator but will also invest in deals created by others

Type of Financing Preferred:

Second Stage Financing
Early Stage
Expansion
Start-up Financing
Public Companies
Seed
First Stage Financing
Special Situation

Size of Investments Considered:

Min Size of Investment Considered (000s): $500
Max Size of Investment Considered (000s): $10,000

Industry Preferences

In Communications prefer:

Wireless Communications

In Internet Specific prefer:

E-Commerce Technology

In Biotechnology prefer:

Human Biotechnology
Industrial Biotechnology
Biosensors
Biotech Related Research

In Medical/Health prefer:

Medical Diagnostics
Diagnostic Services
Medical Therapeutics
Drug/Equipmt Delivery
Medical Products
Disposable Med. Products
Health Services
Pharmaceuticals

Additional Information

Name of Most Recent Fund: Fremont Ventures II
Most Recent Fund Was Raised: 02/01/2000
Year Founded: 1999
Capital Under Management: $200,000,000
Current Activity Level: Actively seeking new investments
Method of Compensation: Return on investment is of primary concern, do not charge fees

---

FRESHTRACKS CAPITAL

29 Harbor Road, Suite 200
P.O. Box 849
Shelburne, VT USA 05482
Phone: 802-923-1500
Fax: 802-923-1506
E-mail: info1@freshtrackscap.com
Website: www.freshtrackscap.com

Management and Staff

Cairn Cross, Managing Director
Charles Kireker, Managing Director
Lee Bouyea, Managing Director
Timothy Davis, Managing Director

Type of Firm

Private Equity Firm

Project Preferences

Role in Financing:

Prefer role as deal originator but will also invest in deals created by others

Type of Financing Preferred:

Early Stage
Seed
First Stage Financing

Size of Investments Considered:

Min Size of Investment Considered (000s): $500
Max Size of Investment Considered (000s): $1,500

Geographical Preferences

United States Preferences:

Vermont
Northeast

Industry Preferences

In Communications prefer:

Communications and Media

In Computer Software prefer:

Software
Applications Software

In Semiconductor/Electr prefer:

Electronics
Semiconductor

In Medical/Health prefer:

Medical Products
Health Services

In Consumer Related prefer:

Consumer

In Industrial/Energy prefer:

Energy
Factory Automation

In Business Serv. prefer:

Media

Additional Information

Name of Most Recent Fund: FreshTracks Capital II, L.P.
Most Recent Fund Was Raised: 06/05/2007
Year Founded: 2001
Capital Under Management: $22,000,000
Current Activity Level: Actively seeking new investments
Method of Compensation: Return on investment is of primary concern, do not charge fees

---

FRESHWATER VENTURE PARTNERS

Laan Van Niftarlake 54
Tienhoven, Netherlands 3612 BT
Phone: 31-346-28-2893
Fax: 31-346-28-2613
E-mail: proposals@freshwater.biz
Website: www.Freshwater.biz

Management and Staff

Cathrien De Liagre Bohl, General Partner
Feico Elhorst, General Partner
Gepco De Kruijff, Managing Partner

Type of Firm

Private Equity Firm

Association Membership

European Private Equity and Venture Capital Assoc.

Project Preferences

Type of Financing Preferred:

Early Stage
Start-up Financing

Size of Investments Considered:

Min Size of Investment Considered (000s): $188
Max Size of Investment Considered (000s): $2,825

Geographical Preferences

International Preferences:

Luxembourg
Netherlands
Belgium
Germany

Industry Preferences

In Computer Software prefer:

Software

In Internet Specific prefer:

Internet

In Computer Other prefer:

Computer Related

Additional Information

Year Founded: 1999
Capital Under Management: $9,400,000
Current Activity Level: Actively seeking new investments

FREUDENBERG VENTURE CAPITAL GMBH

Hohnerweg 2-4
Weinheim, Germany D-69465
Phone: 49-6201-804-455
Fax: 49-6201-883-063
E-mail: info@freudenberg-venture.de
Website: www.freudenberg-venture.de

Management and Staff

Rudiger Braun, Managing Director
Thomas Barth, Managing Director
Wolfgang Scheffler, Managing Director

Type of Firm

Corporate PE/Venture

Association Membership

German Venture Capital Association (BVK)

Project Preferences

Type of Financing Preferred:

Expansion
Seed
Startup

Geographical Preferences

International Preferences:

Europe
Germany

Industry Preferences

In Computer Software prefer:

Software

In Industrial/Energy prefer:

Advanced Materials

In Manufact. prefer:

Manufacturing

Additional Information

Year Founded: 2001
Current Activity Level: Actively seeking new investments

FRIEDBERGMILSTEIN, LLC

Six East 43rd Street
21st Floor
New York, NY USA 10017
Phone: 212-407-6700
Fax: 212-407-6789
Website: www.friedbergmilstein.com

Management and Staff

David Moszer, Principal
David Yoon, Vice President
James Feeley, Partner
Michael Weinberg, Chief Financial Officer

Type of Firm

Bank Affiliated

Project Preferences

Role in Financing:

Will function either as deal originator or investor in deals created by others

Type of Financing Preferred:

Leveraged Buyout
Expansion
Mezzanine
Generalist PE
Balanced
Public Companies
Turnaround
Later Stage
Management Buyouts
Acquisition
Industry Rollups
Special Situation
Distressed Debt
Recapitalizations

Size of Investments Considered:

Min Size of Investment Considered (000s): $10,000
Max Size of Investment Considered (000s): $25,000

Geographical Preferences

United States Preferences:

All U.S.

Canadian Preferences:

All Canada

Industry Preferences

In Communications prefer:

Commercial Communications
CATV & Pay TV Systems
Radio & TV Broadcasting
Telecommunications
Wireless Communications
Data Communications
Satellite Microwave Comm.
Entertainment
Other Communication Prod.

In Computer Hardware prefer:

Mainframes / Scientific
Mini and Personal/Desktop
Computer Graphics and Dig
Integrated Turnkey System
Terminals
Disk Relat. Memory Device

In Computer Software prefer:

Computer Services
Data Processing
Software
Systems Software
Applications Software

In Internet Specific prefer:

E-Commerce Technology
Internet
Ecommerce
Web Aggregration/Portals

In Semiconductor/Electr prefer:

Electronic Components
Semiconductor
Micro-Processing
Controllers and Sensors
Sensors
Circuit Boards
Component Testing Equipmt
Laser Related
Fiber Optics
Analytic/Scientific
Optoelectronics

In Medical/Health prefer:

Medical Diagnostics
Diagnostic Services
Diagnostic Test Products
Medical Therapeutics
Drug/Equipmt Delivery
Medical Products
Disposable Med. Products
Health Services
Hospitals/Clinics/Primary
Hospital/Other Instit.
Pharmaceuticals

In Consumer Related prefer:

Consumer
Retail
Franchises(NEC)
Food/Beverage
Hotels and Resorts
Education Related

In Industrial/Energy prefer:

Energy
Industrial Products
Factory Automation
Robotics
Machinery

In Transportation prefer:

Transportation
Aerospace

In Financial Services prefer:

Insurance
Real Estate
Financial Services

In Business Serv. prefer:

Services
Distribution
Consulting Services
Media

In Manufact. prefer:

Manufacturing

In Other prefer:

Socially Responsible
Environment Responsible
Women/Minority-Owned Bus.

Additional Information

Name of Most Recent Fund: FriedbergMilstein Leveraged Capital Fund I
Most Recent Fund Was Raised: 12/22/2005
Year Founded: 2003
Capital Under Management: $1,100,000,000
Current Activity Level: Actively seeking new investments
Method of Compensation: Return on invest. most important, but chg. closing fees, service fees, etc.

FRIEDLI CORPORATE FINANCE AG

Freigutstrasse 5
Zurich, Switzerland 8002
Phone: 41-1283-2900

Fax: 41-1283-2901
E-mail: peter.friedli@friedlicorp.ch
Website: www.friedlicorp.com

Management and Staff

Peter Friedli, President

Type of Firm

Private Equity Firm

Project Preferences

Type of Financing Preferred:
Early Stage
Startup

Additional Information

Name of Most Recent Fund: InVenture, Inc.
Most Recent Fund Was Raised: 01/01/1999
Year Founded: 1986
Capital Under Management: $900,000,000
Current Activity Level: Actively seeking new investments

FRIEDMAN, FLEISCHER & LOWE, LLC

One Maritime Plaza
22nd Floor
San Francisco, CA USA 94111
Phone: 415-402-2100
Fax: 415-402-2111
E-mail: contact@fflpartners.com
Website: www.fflpartners.com

Management and Staff

Christopher Masto, Managing Director
Jeremy Thatcher, Chief Financial Officer
Tully Friedman, Chairman & CEO

Type of Firm

Private Equity Firm

Project Preferences

Type of Financing Preferred:
Leveraged Buyout

Industry Focus

(% based on actual investment)

Other Products	90.6%
Consumer Related	8.1%
Computer Software and Services	1.3%

Additional Information

Name of Most Recent Fund: Friedman, Fleischer & Lowe Capital Partners II, LP
Most Recent Fund Was Raised: 04/01/2004
Year Founded: 1999
Capital Under Management: $2,250,000,000
Current Activity Level: Actively seeking new investments

FRIEND SKOLER & CO., L.L.C.

Park 80 West
Plaza One
Saddle Brook, NJ USA 07663
Phone: 201-712-0075
Fax: 201-712-1525
E-mail: mail@friendskoler.com
Website: www.friendskoler.com

Management and Staff

Alexander Friend, Managing Director
Chris Temple, Managing Director
Gregory Sullivan, Chief Financial Officer
Hunter Mccrossin, Vice President
Steven Skoler, Managing Director

Type of Firm

Private Equity Firm

Project Preferences

Type of Financing Preferred:
Leveraged Buyout
Later Stage
Acquisition

Size of Investments Considered:
Min Size of Investment Considered (000s): $10,000
Max Size of Investment Considered (000s): $50,000

Geographical Preferences

Canadian Preferences:
All Canada

Industry Preferences

In Consumer Related prefer:
Consumer
Retail
Consumer Products

In Industrial/Energy prefer:
Industrial Products

In Business Serv. prefer:
Services
Distribution

In Manufact. prefer:
Manufacturing

Additional Information

Name of Most Recent Fund: Friend Skoler Equity Investors
Most Recent Fund Was Raised: 11/17/2003
Year Founded: 1998
Capital Under Management: $212,000,000
Current Activity Level: Actively seeking new investments

FRIESLAND BANK INVESTMENTS BV

Beursplein 1
P.O. Box 1
Leeuwarden, Netherlands 8900 AA
Phone: 31-58-299-4451
Fax: 31-58-299-4515
E-mail: investments@frieslandbank.nl
Website: www.frieslandbankinvestments.nl

Other Offices

Postbus 241
M.H. Tromplaan 52
Enschede, Netherlands 7500 AE
Phone: 31-53-480-5858
Fax: 31-53-432-3437

Museumplein 17
Amsterdam, Netherlands

Management and Staff

Ids Van der Weij, Managing Director

Type of Firm

Bank Affiliated

Association Membership

European Private Equity and Venture Capital Assoc.

Project Preferences

Type of Financing Preferred:
Balanced

Geographical Preferences

International Preferences:
Netherlands

Additional Information

Year Founded: 1913
Capital Under Management: $275,900,000
Current Activity Level: Actively seeking new investments

FRIULIA SPA FIN.REG.FRIULI-VENEZIA

19 Via Vittorio Locchi n. 19
Trieste, Italy 34123
Phone: 39-040-31-971
Fax: 39-040-319-7400
E-mail: mail@friulia.it
Website: www.friulia.it

Other Offices

Via Liruti, 18
Udine, Italy 33100
Phone: 39-0432-275-911
Fax: 39-0432-501-290

Piazzetta del Portello n. 2
Pordenone, Italy 33170

Phone: 39-0434-247-666
Fax: 39-0434-246-304

Management and Staff

Federico Marescotti, Vice President
Luigi Glarey, Chief Financial Officer
Michele Degrassi, Managing Director

Type of Firm

Government Affiliated Program

Association Membership

Italian Venture Capital Association (AIFI)
European Private Equity and Venture Capital Assoc.

Project Preferences

Role in Financing:

Prefer role as deal originator but will also invest in deals created by others

Type of Financing Preferred:

Second Stage Financing
Leveraged Buyout
Early Stage
Expansion
Mezzanine
Turnaround
First Stage Financing

Size of Investments Considered:

Min Size of Investment Considered (000s): $47
Max Size of Investment Considered (000s): $14,124

Geographical Preferences

International Preferences:

Italy

Industry Focus

(% based on actual investment)

Consumer Related	57.7%
Industrial/Energy	32.6%
Other Products	7.9%
Medical/Health	1.1%
Computer Software and Services	0.8%

Additional Information

Year Founded: 1967
Capital Under Management: $234,500,000
Current Activity Level: Actively seeking new investments
Method of Compensation: Professional fee required whether or not deal closes

---

FROG CAPITAL (FKA: FOURSOME INVESTMENTS, LTD.)

The Mews
1A Birkenhead Street
London, United Kingdom WC1H 8BA
Phone: 44-207-833-0555
Fax: 44-207-833-8322
E-mail: info@foursome.net
Website: www.frogcapital.com

Management and Staff

Mike Reid, Managing Partner
Piers Clark, Venture Partner
Sue Hunter, Partner

Type of Firm

Private Equity Firm

Association Membership

British Venture Capital Association (BVCA)

Project Preferences

Type of Financing Preferred:

Second Stage Financing
Early Stage
Expansion
Seed
Startup

Size of Investments Considered:

Min Size of Investment Considered (000s): $200
Max Size of Investment Considered (000s): $1,000

Geographical Preferences

International Preferences:

United Kingdom
Europe
Western Europe

Industry Preferences

In Communications prefer:

Communications and Media

In Computer Software prefer:

Software

In Internet Specific prefer:

Internet

In Industrial/Energy prefer:

Energy Conservation Relat
Environmental Related

In Financial Services prefer:

Financial Services

Additional Information

Year Founded: 1998
Capital Under Management: $122,300,000
Current Activity Level: Actively seeking new investments

FRONT STREET CAPITAL

33 Yonge Street
Suite 600
Toronto, Canada M5E 1G4
Phone: 416-597-9595
Fax: 416-364-8893
Website: www.frontstreetcapital.com

Type of Firm

Private Equity Firm

Additional Information

Year Founded: 2009
Current Activity Level: Actively seeking new investments

FRONTENAC COMPANY

135 South LaSalle Street
Suite 3800
Chicago, IL USA 60603
Phone: 312-368-0044
Fax: 312-368-9520
E-mail: info@frontenac.com
Website: www.frontenac.com

Management and Staff

James Cowie, Managing Director
Jeremy Silverman, Managing Director
Marcus Badger, Vice President
Martin Koldyke, Founder
Paul Carbery, Managing Director
Rodney Goldstein, Chairman & Managing Director
Troy Noard, Managing Director
Walter Florence, Managing Director

Type of Firm

Private Equity Firm

Association Membership

Illinois Venture Capital Association
National Venture Capital Association - USA (NVCA)

Project Preferences

Role in Financing:

Prefer role as deal originator

Type of Financing Preferred:

Leveraged Buyout
Expansion
Balanced
Later Stage
Management Buyouts
Acquisition
Recapitalizations

Size of Investments Considered:

Min Size of Investment Considered (000s): $10,000
Max Size of Investment Considered (000s): $50,000

Geographical Preferences

United States Preferences:

All U.S.

Industry Focus

(% based on actual investment)

Consumer Related	23.0%
Other Products	20.4%
Computer Software and Services	15.7%
Medical/Health	12.7%
Internet Specific	11.4%
Industrial/Energy	9.5%
Communications and Media	5.3%
Computer Hardware	1.2%
Semiconductors/Other Elect.	0.5%
Biotechnology	0.3%

Additional Information

Name of Most Recent Fund: Frontenac Masters VIII, L.P.
Most Recent Fund Was Raised: 01/19/2001
Year Founded: 1971
Capital Under Management: $1,500,000,000
Current Activity Level: Actively seeking new investments
Method of Compensation: Return on investment is of primary concern, do not charge fees

---

FRONTERA GROUP LLC

15303 Ventura Boulevard
Suite 1510
Sherman Oaks, CA USA 91403
Phone: 818-450-3601
Fax: 818-450-3636
E-mail: info@fronteracapital.com
Website: www.fronteracapital.com

Management and Staff

Eric Manlunas, Managing Director

Type of Firm

Private Equity Firm

Association Membership

National Venture Capital Association - USA (NVCA)

Project Preferences

Type of Financing Preferred:

Early Stage

Geographical Preferences

United States Preferences:

West Coast
All U.S.

Additional Information

Year Founded: 2002
Current Activity Level: Actively seeking new investments

FRONTERIS BUSINESS DEVELOPMENT GMBH

Furtmayrstr. 3
Regensburg, Germany
Phone: 49-941-9920-886
Fax: 49-941-9920-883
E-mail: info@fronteris.com
Website: www.fronteris.com

Type of Firm

Private Equity Firm

Project Preferences

Type of Financing Preferred:

Expansion
Start-up Financing

Geographical Preferences

International Preferences:

Germany

Industry Preferences

In Industrial/Energy prefer:

Alternative Energy

In Financial Services prefer:

Financial Services

Additional Information

Year Founded: 2000
Current Activity Level: Actively seeking new investments

FRONTERIS ENERGY FUND GMBH

Furtmayrstrasse 3
Regensburg, Germany
Phone: 49-941-9920-886
Fax: 49-941-9920-883
E-mail: info@fronteris.de
Website: www.fronteris.de

Type of Firm

Private Equity Firm

Project Preferences

Type of Financing Preferred:

Start-up Financing
Startup

Geographical Preferences

International Preferences:

Germany

Industry Preferences

In Industrial/Energy prefer:

Oil and Gas Exploration
Environmental Related

Additional Information

Year Founded: 2006
Current Activity Level: Actively seeking new investments

FRONTERIS PRIVATE EQUITY AG

Furtmayrstrasse 3
Regensburg, Germany 93053
Phone: 49-941-9920-886
Fax: 49-941-9920-883
E-mail: info@fronteris.de
Website: www.fronteris.com

Type of Firm

Private Equity Firm

Project Preferences

Type of Financing Preferred:

Later Stage

Geographical Preferences

International Preferences:

Germany

Industry Preferences

In Industrial/Energy prefer:

Alternative Energy

In Financial Services prefer:

Financial Services

Additional Information

Year Founded: 2003
Current Activity Level: Actively seeking new investments

FRONTIER CAPITAL LLC

1111 Metropolitan Avenue
Suite 1050
Charlotte, NC USA 28203
Phone: 704-414-2880
Fax: 704-414-2881
E-mail: info@frontiercapital-llc.com
Website: www.frontierfunds.com

Management and Staff

Andrew Lindner, Managing Partner
J. Michael Ramich, Partner
Joel Lanik, Principal
Lori Shell, Chief Financial Officer
Richard Maclean, Managing Partner

Type of Firm

Private Equity Firm

Association Membership

Mid-Atlantic Venture Association
Natl Assoc of Small Bus. Inv. Co (NASBIC)

Project Preferences

Role in Financing:

Will function either as deal originator or investor in deals created by others

Type of Financing Preferred:

Second Stage Financing
Expansion
Balanced
First Stage Financing

Size of Investments Considered:

Min Size of Investment Considered (000s): $5,000
Max Size of Investment Considered (000s): $10,000

Geographical Preferences

United States Preferences:

Mid Atlantic
Southeast

Industry Preferences

In Communications prefer:
Telecommunications

In Computer Software prefer:
Computer Services
Software

In Medical/Health prefer:
Health Services

In Financial Services prefer:
Financial Services

In Business Serv. prefer:
Services
Consulting Services

Additional Information

Name of Most Recent Fund: Frontier Fund II, L.P.
Most Recent Fund Was Raised: 09/30/2006
Year Founded: 1999
Capital Under Management: $160,000,000
Current Activity Level: Actively seeking new investments
Method of Compensation: Return on investment is of primary concern, do not charge fees

---

FRONTIER CAPITAL PARTNERS (FCP)

444 St. Mary Avenue
Suite 1445
Winnipeg, Canada R3C 3T1
Phone: 204-925-8402
Fax: 204-949-0602
E-mail: frontier.capital@shawlink.ca

Type of Firm

Private Equity Firm

Additional Information

Year Founded: 2002
Current Activity Level: Actively seeking new investments

FRONTIER INVESTMENT & DEVELOPMENT PARTNERS

5 Shenton Way
#26-01 UIC Building
Singapore, Singapore 068808
Phone: 65-8121-0031
Fax: 65-6333-6487
Website: www.fidp-funds.com

Other Offices

7/F Phnom Penh Center, Complex F
Sothearos & Sihanouk Boulevard
Phnom Penh, Cambodia
Phone: 855-23-997-492
Fax: 855-23-997-493

Management and Staff

Kim Song Tan, Partner
Marvin Yeo, Partner

Type of Firm

Private Equity Firm

Project Preferences

Type of Financing Preferred:
Balanced

Geographical Preferences

International Preferences:
Mongolia
Cambodia

Industry Preferences

In Communications prefer:
Telecommunications

In Consumer Related prefer:
Education Related

In Industrial/Energy prefer:
Oil and Gas Exploration

In Transportation prefer:
Transportation

In Financial Services prefer:
Financial Services
Real Estate

In Business Serv. prefer:
Services

In Manufact. prefer:
Manufacturing

In Agr/Forestr/Fish prefer:
Agribusiness
Mining and Minerals

Additional Information

Year Founded: 2008
Current Activity Level: Actively seeking new investments

FRONTIERS CAPITAL, LTD.

75 Wells Street
Second Floor, Castle House
London, United Kingdom W1T 3QH
Phone: 44-20-7182-7700
Fax: 44-20-7182-7701
E-mail: info@frontierscapital.com
Website: www.frontierscapital.com

Management and Staff

Benn Mikula, Partner
Nigel Spray, Managing Partner
Pierre Nadeau, Partner
Tim Horlick, Managing Partner

Type of Firm

Private Equity Firm

Association Membership

British Venture Capital Association (BVCA)

Project Preferences

Type of Financing Preferred:
Second Stage Financing
Early Stage
Expansion
Startup

Geographical Preferences

International Preferences:
United Kingdom
Europe
Western Europe

Industry Preferences

In Communications prefer:
Commercial Communications
Telecommunications
Wireless Communications

In Computer Software prefer:
Software

In Internet Specific prefer:
Internet

Additional Information

Year Founded: 2003
Capital Under Management: $151,000,000
Current Activity Level: Actively seeking new investments

FRONTLINE STRATEGY PTE. LTD.

212 Turf Estate
Shakti Mills Lane, Mahalaxmi
Mumbai, India 400 011
Phone: 91-22-2826-4534
Fax: 91-22-2826-3926
E-mail: info@frontlinestrategy.com
Website: www.frontlinestrategy.com

Other Offices

#03-19 Orchard Parade Hotel
1 Tanglin Road
Singapore, Singapore 247905

Management and Staff

Atim Kabra, Founding Partner
J Venkatadas, Principal
Sanjay Bhattacharya, Chief Operating Officer

Type of Firm

Private Equity Advisor or Fund of Funds

Association Membership

Indian Venture Capital Association (IVCA)

Project Preferences

Role in Financing:
Prefer role as deal originator

Type of Financing Preferred:
Expansion
Generalist PE
Management Buyouts
Strategic Alliances
Joint Ventures

Size of Investments Considered:
Min Size of Investment Considered (000s): $2,000
Max Size of Investment Considered (000s): $5,000

Geographical Preferences

International Preferences:
India
Middle East
Asia

Industry Preferences

In Communications prefer:
Communications and Media
Telecommunications

In Computer Hardware prefer:
Computers

In Computer Software prefer:
Software

In Internet Specific prefer:
Internet

In Semiconductor/Electr prefer:
Electronics

In Biotechnology prefer:
Biotechnology

In Medical/Health prefer:
Medical/Health
Medical Therapeutics
Pharmaceuticals

In Consumer Related prefer:
Consumer
Retail

In Industrial/Energy prefer:
Energy
Alternative Energy
Industrial Products

In Transportation prefer:
Transportation

In Financial Services prefer:
Financial Services
Insurance

In Business Serv. prefer:
Services
Distribution

In Manufact. prefer:
Manufacturing

In Agr/Forestr/Fish prefer:
Agriculture related

Additional Information
Year Founded: 2000
Capital Under Management: $150,000,000
Current Activity Level: Actively seeking new investments

FRYE-LOUIS CAPITAL ADVISORS LLC
225 West Wacker Drive
Suite 1000
Chicago, IL USA 60606
Phone: 312-541-4650
Fax: 312-541-9140
Website: www.fryelouis.com

Management and Staff
Tim Maloney, Principal

Type of Firm
Private Equity Advisor or Fund of Funds

Project Preferences

Type of Financing Preferred:
Fund of Funds
Early Stage
Expansion
Balanced
Acquisition
Distressed Debt

Size of Investments Considered:
Min Size of Investment Considered (000s): $2,000
Max Size of Investment Considered: No Limit

Additional Information
Year Founded: 1992
Capital Under Management: $70,000,000
Current Activity Level: Actively seeking new investments

FSN CAPITAL PARTNERS AS
Karl Johansgate 27
Oslo, Norway NO-0159
Phone: 47-24-147-300
Fax: 47-24-147-301
E-mail: admin@fsncapital.no
Website: www.fsncapital.no

Other Offices
Esplanaden 7
Copenhagen, Denmark 1263
Phone: 45-3313-4800
Fax: 45-3391-1608

Master Samuelsgatan 4
Stockholm, Sweden 111 44
Phone: 46-85-450-3930
Fax: 46-86-113-305

Management and Staff
Dan Johnson, Partner
Frode Strand Nielsen, Managing Partner
Henrik Lisaeth, Partner
Marianne Michelsen, Chief Operating Officer
Peter Moller, Partner
Thomas Broe-Andersen, Partner

Type of Firm
Private Equity Firm

Association Membership
Norwegian Venture Capital Association
European Private Equity and Venture Capital Assoc.

Project Preferences

Type of Financing Preferred:
Leveraged Buyout
Early Stage
Expansion

Size of Investments Considered:
Min Size of Investment Considered (000s): $4,513
Max Size of Investment Considered (000s): $25,270

Geographical Preferences

International Preferences:
Iceland
Scandanavia/Nordic Region
Finland
Norway

Industry Preferences

In Industrial/Energy prefer:
Industrial Products

Additional Information
Year Founded: 1999
Capital Under Management: $292,800,000
Current Activity Level: Actively seeking new investments

FTV CAPITAL (FKA: FTVENTURES)
555 California Street
Suite 2900
San Francisco, CA USA 94104
Phone: 415-229-3000
Fax: 415-229-3005
E-mail: info@ftventures.com
Website: www.ftventures.com

Other Offices
540 Madison Avenue
Suite 2600
New York, NY USA 10022
Phone: 212-682-4800
Fax: 212-682-4480

Management and Staff
Alexander Harrison, Vice President
Benjamin Cukier, Partner

Borris Rapoport, Principal
Brad Bernstein, Partner
Chris Winship, Partner
Christopher Tan, Vice President
Craig Hanson, Vice President
David Haynes, Chief Operating Officer
Derek Lemke-von Ammon, Partner
Eric Byunn, Partner
James Hale, Founding Partner
Karen Derr Gilbert, Managing Director
Liron Gitig, Principal
Mohit Daswani, Principal
Peter Casella, Vice President
Richard Garman, Managing Partner
Robert Barrett, Venture Partner
Robert Huret, Founding Partner

Type of Firm

Private Equity Firm

Association Membership

National Venture Capital Association - USA (NVCA)

Project Preferences

Role in Financing:
Prefer role as deal originator but will also invest in deals created by others

Type of Financing Preferred:
Second Stage Financing
Expansion
Later Stage

Size of Investments Considered:
Min Size of Investment Considered (000s): $5,000
Max Size of Investment Considered (000s): $50,000

Geographical Preferences

Canadian Preferences:
All Canada

International Preferences:
United Kingdom
All International

Industry Focus

(% based on actual investment)

Computer Software and Services	48.6%
Other Products	31.3%
Internet Specific	16.8%
Computer Hardware	1.7%
Communications and Media	1.5%

Additional Information

Name of Most Recent Fund: FTVentures III, L.P. (AKA: FTV III)
Most Recent Fund Was Raised: 04/04/2007
Year Founded: 1998
Capital Under Management: $623,500,000
Current Activity Level: Actively seeking new investments
Method of Compensation: Other

FUJIAN INVESTMENT & DEVELOPMENT CO., LTD.

No. 169 Hudong Road
14/F Zhongmin Tianao Building
Fuzhou, Fujian, China 350001
Website: www.fidc.com.cn

Type of Firm

Government Affiliated Program

Project Preferences

Type of Financing Preferred:
Early Stage
Expansion
Balanced
Seed
Later Stage

Geographical Preferences

International Preferences:
China

Additional Information

Year Founded: 1988
Capital Under Management: $87,900,000
Current Activity Level: Actively seeking new investments

FUJIAN VENTURE CAPITAL CO., LTD.

Software Park B11
Room 510-511
Fuzhou, Fujian, China 350001
Phone: 86-591-87303311
Fax: 86-591-87303322
Website: www.fjvc.com.cn

Other Offices

No. 820 Xiahe Road
Room 1308 Dihao Building
Xiamen, Fujian, China 361004
Phone: 86-592-2966-650
Fax: 86-592-2966-656

No. 1000 Maanshan South Road
Room 3101 Xinduhui Huanqiu
Hafei, Anhui, China 230001
Phone: 86-551-4682-777
Fax: 86-551-4681-877

No. 13 Wenhua West Road
Room 808 Haichen Building B
Jinan, Shandong, China 250014
Phone: 86-531-82660679
Fax: 86-531-82660679

Management and Staff

Shaobing Huang, President

Type of Firm

Private Equity Firm

Project Preferences

Type of Financing Preferred:
Balanced

Geographical Preferences

International Preferences:
China

Industry Preferences

In Consumer Related prefer:
Sports

In Business Serv. prefer:
Media

Additional Information

Year Founded: 2000
Current Activity Level: Actively seeking new investments

FUJISAWA RESEARCH INSTITUTE OF AMERICA (FRIA)

Evanston Research Park
1801 Maple Avenue
Evanston, IL USA 60201-3135
Phone: 847-467-4472
Fax: 847-467-4471
Website: www.fujisawa.com/fitefund

Type of Firm

Corporate PE/Venture

Project Preferences

Role in Financing:
Will function either as deal originator or investor in deals created by others

Type of Financing Preferred:
Early Stage
Start-up Financing
Seed
First Stage Financing

Size of Investments Considered:
Min Size of Investment Considered (000s): $200
Max Size of Investment Considered (000s): $500

Geographical Preferences

International Preferences:
All International

Industry Preferences

In Biotechnology prefer:
Human Biotechnology

In Medical/Health prefer:
Medical Therapeutics
Pharmaceuticals

Additional Information

Year Founded: 1999
Capital Under Management: $7,500,000
Current Activity Level: Actively seeking new investments

FUKUI JAFCO COMPANY, LTD.

1-10-5 Junka
Fukui, Japan 910-0023
Phone: 81-77-623-8444
Fax: 81-77-623-8410
E-mail: jafcof@po.incl.ne.jp

Management and Staff

Masaru Hayashida, Managing Director

Type of Firm

Private Equity Firm

Project Preferences

Type of Financing Preferred:

Balanced

Geographical Preferences

International Preferences:

Japan

Additional Information

Year Founded: 2000
Capital Under Management: $11,100,000
Current Activity Level: Actively seeking new investments

FUKUOKA CAPITAL PARTNERS

2-14-8 Tenjin, Chuo-Ku
Fukuoka-Shi
Fukuoka, Japan 810-0001
Phone: 81-92-736-8787

Type of Firm

Private Equity Firm

Project Preferences

Type of Financing Preferred:

Leveraged Buyout

Geographical Preferences

International Preferences:

Japan

Additional Information

Year Founded: 2008
Current Activity Level: Actively seeking new investments

FULCRUM CAPITAL PARTNERS LIMITED

25 Bligh Street
Level 28
Sydney, Australia 2000
Phone: 612-9237-2700
Fax: 612-9235-0773
E-mail: info@fulcrumcap.com.au
Website: www.fulcrumcap.com.au

Management and Staff

Andrew Boss, Chief Financial Officer
Paul Riley, Founding Partner
Tim Downing, Founding Partner

Type of Firm

Private Equity Firm

Association Membership

Australian Venture Capital Association (AVCAL)

Project Preferences

Type of Financing Preferred:

Leveraged Buyout
Generalist PE
Expansion

Size of Investments Considered:

Min Size of Investment Considered (000s): $4,029
Max Size of Investment Considered (000s): $16,116

Geographical Preferences

International Preferences:

Pacific

Additional Information

Year Founded: 2006
Capital Under Management: $63,100,000
Current Activity Level: Actively seeking new investments

FULCRUM MANAGEMENT, INC.

245 Park Avenue
24th Floor
New York, NY USA 10167
Phone: 212-439-1512
Fax: 212-208-6810
Website: www.fulcrummgt.com

Management and Staff

Robert Crary, Managing Director

Type of Firm

Private Equity Firm

Project Preferences

Role in Financing:

Prefer role as deal originator but will also invest in deals created by others

Type of Financing Preferred:

Leveraged Buyout
Expansion
Management Buyouts
Acquisition
Recapitalizations

Size of Investments Considered:

Min Size of Investment Considered (000s): $10,000
Max Size of Investment Considered (000s): $75,000

Additional Information

Year Founded: 1994
Current Activity Level: Actively seeking new investments
Method of Compensation: Return on invest. most important, but chg. closing fees, service fees, etc.

FULCRUM VENTURE CAPITAL CORPORATION

300 Corporate Pointe
Suite 380
Culver City, CA USA 90230
Phone: 310-645-1271
Fax: 310-645-1272
E-mail: info@fulcrumventures.com
Website: www.fulcrumventures.com

Management and Staff

Roy Doumani, Venture Partner

Type of Firm

SBIC

Project Preferences

Type of Financing Preferred:

Leveraged Buyout
Expansion
Acquisition
Recapitalizations

Geographical Preferences

United States Preferences:

Southern California

Industry Preferences

In Other prefer:

Women/Minority-Owned Bus.

Additional Information

Year Founded: 1977
Current Activity Level: Actively seeking new investments

FULCRUM VENTURES

1040 Crown Point Parkway
Suite 330
Atlanta, GA USA 30338
Phone: 770-551-6300
Fax: 770-551-6330

Website: www.fulcrumvp.com

Management and Staff

Alston Gardner, Founding Partner
Frank Dalton, Founding Partner
Jeffrey Muir, Founding Partner
Thomas Greer, Founding Partner

Type of Firm

Private Equity Firm

Association Membership

National Venture Capital Association - USA (NVCA)

Project Preferences

Type of Financing Preferred:
Leveraged Buyout
Generalist PE
Expansion
Management Buyouts

Size of Investments Considered:
Min Size of Investment Considered (000s): $1,000
Max Size of Investment Considered (000s): $4,000

Geographical Preferences

United States Preferences:
Southeast
All U.S.

Industry Preferences

In Computer Software prefer:
Software

In Internet Specific prefer:
E-Commerce Technology
Internet
Ecommerce

In Medical/Health prefer:
Health Services

In Business Serv. prefer:
Services

Additional Information

Name of Most Recent Fund: Fulcrum Fund, LLC
Most Recent Fund Was Raised: 10/06/2006
Year Founded: 2006
Capital Under Management: $40,000,000
Current Activity Level: Actively seeking new investments

FULHAM & COMPANY, INC.

593 Washington Street
Wellesley, MA USA 02482
Phone: 781-235-2266
Fax: 781-235-2009
Website: www.fulhamco.com

Management and Staff

John Fulham, Principal, Founder
Timothy Fulham, Principal

Type of Firm

Investment Management Firm

Project Preferences

Type of Financing Preferred:
Leveraged Buyout

Industry Preferences

In Manufact. prefer:
Manufacturing

Additional Information

Name of Most Recent Fund: Fulham Investors II, L.P.
Most Recent Fund Was Raised: 08/05/2005
Year Founded: 1985
Capital Under Management: $115,000,000
Current Activity Level: Actively seeking new investments

FUNAI CAPITAL CO., LTD

5F Urban Square Yaesu
2-4-13 Yaesu, Chuo-ku
Tokyo, Japan 104-0028
Phone: 81-3-6225-5911
Fax: 81-3-6225-5912
E-mail: info@funaicapital.co.jp
Website: www.funaicapital.co.jp

Type of Firm

Private Equity Firm

Project Preferences

Type of Financing Preferred:
Expansion

Geographical Preferences

International Preferences:
Japan

Additional Information

Year Founded: 1990
Current Activity Level: Actively seeking new investments

FUND CREATION CO., LTD.

37/F Roppongi Hills Mori Tower
6-10-1 Roppongi, Minato-ku
Tokyo, Japan 106-6137
Phone: 81-3-5413-5355
Website: www.fundcreation.co.jp

Management and Staff

Katsuhiro Tashima, Chief Executive Officer
Kenichi Nagao, Senior Managing Director
Koji Sakamoto, Managing Director
Mikio Hashimoto, Managing Director
Takashi Yoshida, Managing Director
Tatsuya Oyama, Senior Managing Director
Yuji Miyamoto, Senior Managing Director

Type of Firm

Private Equity Firm

Additional Information

Year Founded: 2002
Capital Under Management: $13,500,000
Current Activity Level: Actively seeking new investments

FUNDAMENTAL CAPITAL, LLC

455 Market Street
Suite 1460
San Francisco, CA USA 94105
Phone: 415-782-0000
E-mail: info@fundamentalcapital.com
Website: www.fundamentalcapital.com

Type of Firm

Private Equity Firm

Project Preferences

Type of Financing Preferred:
Leveraged Buyout
Generalist PE
Expansion
Other
Management Buyouts
Recapitalizations

Size of Investments Considered:
Min Size of Investment Considered (000s): $2,000
Max Size of Investment Considered (000s): $10,000

Geographical Preferences

United States Preferences:
All U.S.

Industry Preferences

In Consumer Related prefer:
Retail
Consumer Products

In Business Serv. prefer:
Services
Distribution

In Manufact. prefer:
Manufacturing

Additional Information

Year Founded: 2004
Current Activity Level: Actively seeking new investments

FUNDAMENTAL MANAGEMENT CORPORATION

8567 Coral Way
Suite 138
Miami, FL USA 33165
Phone: 305-288-3020

Management and Staff
Carl Singer, Founder

Type of Firm
Private Equity Firm

Additional Information
Year Founded: 1994
Current Activity Level: Actively seeking new investments

FUNDO PARA A INTERNACIONALIZACAO DAS EMPRESAS PORTUGUESAS
Edificio Heron Castilho
Rua Braamcamp, 40-11
Lisbon, Portugal 1250
Phone: 351-21-382-5635
Fax: 351-21-386-7273
E-mail: fiep@fiep.pt
Website: www.fiep.pt

Type of Firm
Private Equity Firm

Project Preferences
Type of Financing Preferred:
Second Stage Financing
Early Stage
Expansion

Geographical Preferences
International Preferences:
Portugal

Additional Information
Year Founded: 1997
Capital Under Management: $104,600,000
Current Activity Level: Making few, if any, new investments

FUNDUS
Serkampsteenweg 52
Wetteren, Belgium B 9030
Phone: 32-9-365-60-80
Fax: 32-9-365-60-75
E-mail: info@fundus.be
Website: www.fundus.be

Type of Firm
Private Equity Firm

Project Preferences
Type of Financing Preferred:
Early Stage

Geographical Preferences
International Preferences:
Europe
Belgium

Industry Preferences
In Biotechnology prefer:
Biotechnology

In Medical/Health prefer:
Pharmaceuticals

Additional Information
Year Founded: 2006
Capital Under Management: $6,900,000
Current Activity Level: Actively seeking new investments

FUNK VENTURES, INC.
1453 Third Street Promenade
Suite 370
Santa Monica, CA USA 90401
Phone: 310-395-5703
Fax: 310-395-5813
Website: www.funkventures.com

Management and Staff
Andy Funk, Managing Director
David Krasnow, Principal
Fran Seegull, Managing Director
Jan Smith, Venture Partner
Ron Garret, Venture Partner

Type of Firm
Bank Affiliated

Association Membership
National Venture Capital Association - USA (NVCA)

Project Preferences
Role in Financing:
Prefer role as deal originator but will also invest in deals created by others

Type of Financing Preferred:
Second Stage Financing
Early Stage
Start-up Financing
Seed
First Stage Financing
Startup

Size of Investments Considered:
Min Size of Investment Considered (000s): $100
Max Size of Investment Considered (000s): $5,000

Geographical Preferences
United States Preferences:
All U.S.

Industry Preferences
In Biotechnology prefer:
Human Biotechnology
Genetic Engineering

In Medical/Health prefer:
Medical/Health
Medical Diagnostics
Medical Therapeutics
Medical Products
Disposable Med. Products
Health Services
Hospitals/Clinics/Primary
Hospital/Other Instit.

In Consumer Related prefer:
Food/Beverage

In Industrial/Energy prefer:
Alternative Energy
Energy Conservation Relat
Environmental Related

In Other prefer:
Socially Responsible
Environment Responsible

Additional Information
Year Founded: 2000
Capital Under Management: $20,000,000
Current Activity Level: Actively seeking new investments
Method of Compensation: Return on invest. most important, but chg. closing fees, service fees, etc.

FUQUA VENTURES LLC
1201 West Peachtree Street NW
Suite 5000
Atlanta, GA USA 30309
Phone: 404-815-4500
Fax: 404-815-4528
E-mail: info@fuquaventures.com
Website: www.fuquaventures.com

Type of Firm
Private Equity Firm

Association Membership
Natl Assoc of Small Bus. Inv. Co (NASBIC)

Project Preferences
Role in Financing:
Will function either as deal originator or investor in deals created by others

Type of Financing Preferred:
Balanced

Size of Investments Considered:
Min Size of Investment Considered (000s): $500
Max Size of Investment Considered (000s): $2,500

Geographical Preferences
United States Preferences:
Mid Atlantic
Southeast

Industry Focus

(% based on actual investment)

Internet Specific	46.7%
Biotechnology	26.4%
Computer Software and Services	21.2%
Computer Hardware	4.5%
Communications and Media	1.1%

Additional Information

Year Founded: 1997
Capital Under Management: $25,000,000
Current Activity Level: Actively seeking new investments
Method of Compensation: Return on investment is of primary concern, do not charge fees

---

FUSE CAPITAL

305 Lytton Avenue
Palo Alto, CA USA 94301
Phone: 650-325-9600
Fax: 650-325-9608
E-mail: info@fusecapital.com
Website: www.fusecapital.com

Other Offices

204 Santa Monica Boulevard
Suite A
Santa Monica, CA USA 90401
Phone: 310-857-5780

02 Shil, Mayur Colony
Near Textile Traders Co-operative Bank
Ahmedabad, India 380 009

Management and Staff

Charles Noreen, Chief Financial Officer
David Britts, Partner
Keyur Patel, Partner
Roland Van der Meer, Partner
Ross Levinsohn, Partner

Type of Firm

Private Equity Firm

Association Membership

Western Association of Venture Capitalists (WAVC)
National Venture Capital Association - USA (NVCA)

Project Preferences

Role in Financing:

Prefer role as deal originator but will also invest in deals created by others

Type of Financing Preferred:

Second Stage Financing
Early Stage
Expansion
Start-up Financing
Seed
Later Stage
First Stage Financing

Size of Investments Considered:

Min Size of Investment Considered (000s): $3,000
Max Size of Investment Considered (000s): $25,000

Geographical Preferences

United States Preferences:

All U.S.

Canadian Preferences:

All Canada

International Preferences:

India
China
Israel

Industry Focus

(% based on actual investment)

Communications and Media	35.3%
Internet Specific	29.2%
Semiconductors/Other Elect.	16.1%
Computer Software and Services	14.8%
Industrial/Energy	1.8%
Computer Hardware	1.8%
Other Products	0.7%
Consumer Related	0.3%

Additional Information

Name of Most Recent Fund: ComVentures VI, L.P.
Most Recent Fund Was Raised: 09/29/2003
Year Founded: 1987
Capital Under Management: $1,500,000,000
Current Activity Level: Actively seeking new investments
Method of Compensation: Return on investment is of primary concern, do not charge fees

---

FUTURE CAPITAL AG

Westendstr. 16-22
Frankfurt am Main, Germany 60325
Phone: 49-69-24-2421-0
Fax: 49-69-24242150
E-mail: info@future-capital.com
Website: www.future-capital.com

Management and Staff

Wrede Michael, Chief Executive Officer

Type of Firm

Corporate PE/Venture

Project Preferences

Type of Financing Preferred:

Early Stage
Expansion
Later Stage
Seed
Startup

Size of Investments Considered:

Min Size of Investment Considered (000s): $3,000
Max Size of Investment Considered: No Limit

Geographical Preferences

International Preferences:

Germany

Additional Information

Name of Most Recent Fund: Future Capital AG
Most Recent Fund Was Raised: 01/01/1999
Year Founded: 1999
Current Activity Level: Actively seeking new investments

FUTURE CAPITAL HOLDINGS

FCH House, Peninsula
Corp. Park, Lower Parel
Mumbai, India 400 013
Phone: 91-22-4043-6000
Fax: 91-22-4043-6068
E-mail: fch.contactus@fch.in
Website: www.fch.in

Management and Staff

N Shridhar, Chief Financial Officer
Sameer Sain, CEO & Managing Director
Shishir Baijal, Chief Executive Officer
Venkatesh Srinivasan, Chief Operating Officer

Type of Firm

Corporate PE/Venture

Project Preferences

Type of Financing Preferred:

Balanced

Geographical Preferences

International Preferences:

India

Additional Information

Year Founded: 2005
Capital Under Management: $425,000,000
Current Activity Level: Actively seeking new investments

FUTURE FUND, THE

215 South Main Street
Suite One
Zelienople, PA USA 16063
Phone: 724-453-6150
Fax: 724-453-6151
Website: www.future-fund.com

Management and Staff

Esther Dormer, Founder
Richard Madden, Founder

Type of Firm

Private Equity Firm

Project Preferences

Role in Financing:

Will function either as deal originator or investor in deals created by others

Type of Financing Preferred:
Seed
Startup

Size of Investments Considered:
Min Size of Investment Considered (000s): $100
Max Size of Investment Considered (000s): $1,500

Industry Preferences

In Communications prefer:
Data Communications

In Computer Software prefer:
Software
Systems Software

In Internet Specific prefer:
Internet

In Semiconductor/Electr prefer:
Electronic Components

In Biotechnology prefer:
Human Biotechnology
Biotech Related Research

In Medical/Health prefer:
Diagnostic Services
Diagnostic Test Products

In Business Serv. prefer:
Services

Additional Information
Name of Most Recent Fund: Future Fund, The
Most Recent Fund Was Raised: 07/01/1999
Year Founded: 1999
Capital Under Management: $10,000,000
Current Activity Level: Making few, if any, new investments
Method of Compensation: Return on investment is of primary concern, do not charge fees

---

FUTURE INTERNATIONAL CO., LTD.
4-6-21-301
Takanawa, Minato-ku
Tokyo, Japan
Phone: 81-3-5447-6581
Fax: 81-3-5447-6583
Website: www.future-intl.com

Type of Firm
Private Equity Firm

Additional Information
Year Founded: 1997
Current Activity Level: Actively seeking new investments

FUTURE VALUE VENTURES, INC.
330 East Kibourn Avenue
Suite 711
Milwaukee, WI USA 53203
Phone: 414-278-0377
Fax: 414-278-7321
E-mail: fvvventures@aol.com

Management and Staff
William Beckett, President

Type of Firm
SBIC

Association Membership
Natl Assoc of Investment Cos. (NAIC)
Natl Assoc of Small Bus. Inv. Co (NASBIC)

Project Preferences

Role in Financing:
Prefer role as deal originator but will also invest in deals created by others

Type of Financing Preferred:
Second Stage Financing
Mezzanine
Start-up Financing
First Stage Financing

Size of Investments Considered:
Min Size of Investment Considered (000s): $100
Max Size of Investment Considered (000s): $300

Geographical Preferences

United States Preferences:
All U.S.

Additional Information
Year Founded: 1984
Capital Under Management: $3,500,000
Current Activity Level: Actively seeking new investments
Method of Compensation: Return on invest. most important, but chg. closing fees, service fees, etc.

- G -

G-51 CAPITAL LLC
901 South Mo Pac Expressway
Building III, Suite 410
Austin, TX USA 78746
Phone: 512-929-5151
Fax: 512-732-0886
E-mail: info@g51.com
Website: www.g51.com

Management and Staff
Lauranne Jarrett, Partner
N. Rudy Garza, General Partner
Rick Timmins, Venture Partner
Theresa Garza, Venture Partner

Type of Firm
Private Equity Firm

Association Membership
National Venture Capital Association - USA (NVCA)

Project Preferences

Role in Financing:
Prefer role as deal originator but will also invest in deals created by others

Type of Financing Preferred:
Early Stage
Start-up Financing
Seed

Size of Investments Considered:
Min Size of Investment Considered (000s): $250
Max Size of Investment Considered (000s): $1,000

Geographical Preferences

United States Preferences:
Southwest

Industry Focus
(% based on actual investment)

Internet Specific	44.8%
Computer Software and Services	27.2%
Computer Hardware	16.4%
Consumer Related	11.6%

Additional Information
Year Founded: 1996
Capital Under Management: $22,000,000
Current Activity Level: Actively seeking new investments
Method of Compensation: Return on investment is of primary concern, do not charge fees

---

G.A. HERRERA & CO., LLC
600 Jefferson
Suite 1080
Houston, TX USA 77002
Phone: 713-978-6590

Fax: 713-978-6599
E-mail: info@herrera-co.com
Website: www.herrera-co.com

Type of Firm
Private Equity Firm

Project Preferences

Role in Financing:
Will function either as deal originator or investor in deals created by others

Type of Financing Preferred:
Balanced

Size of Investments Considered:
Min Size of Investment Considered (000s): $500
Max Size of Investment Considered (000s): $25,000

Geographical Preferences

United States Preferences:
Midwest
Rocky Mountain
Southwest

Additional Information
Year Founded: 1992
Current Activity Level: Actively seeking new investments
Method of Compensation: Professional fee required whether or not deal closes

---

G.L. OHRSTROM & CO., INC. (AKA: GLO & CO.)
370 Lexington Avenue
21st Floor
New York, NY USA 10017
Phone: 212-759-5380
Fax: 212-486-0935
E-mail: info@glohrstrom.com
Website: www.glohrstrom.com

Management and Staff
Donald Calder, President
George Pfeil, Managing Director
Michael Horgan, Managing Director
Wright Ohrstrom, Managing Partner

Type of Firm
Private Equity Firm

Project Preferences

Type of Financing Preferred:
Leveraged Buyout

Geographical Preferences

United States Preferences:
All U.S.

Canadian Preferences:
All Canada

Industry Preferences

In Semiconductor/Electr prefer:
Analytic/Scientific

In Medical/Health prefer:
Medical/Health
Medical Products
Disposable Med. Products

In Consumer Related prefer:
Consumer

In Industrial/Energy prefer:
Energy
Alternative Energy
Industrial Products

Additional Information
Year Founded: 1948
Current Activity Level: Actively seeking new investments

GABES INVEST SICAR
Centre Dorra,Esc A Appt n 8
El Manar III
Tunis, Tunisia 2092
Phone: 216-7188-6922
Fax: 216-7188-7477
Website: www.gabesinvest-sicar.com

Type of Firm
Private Equity Firm

Project Preferences

Type of Financing Preferred:
Balanced

Geographical Preferences

International Preferences:
Tunisia

Additional Information
Year Founded: 2004
Current Activity Level: Actively seeking new investments

GABRIEL VENTURE PARTNERS
350 Marine Parkway
Suite 200
Redwood Shores, CA USA 94065
Phone: 650-551-5000
Fax: 650-551-5001
E-mail: info@gabrielvp.com
Website: www.gabrielvp.com

Other Offices
14900 Conference Center Drive
Suite 300
Chantilly, VA USA 20151
Phone: 703-636-4440

Management and Staff
Frederick Bolander, Managing Director
Helen MacKenzie, Chief Financial Officer
J.Phillip Samper, Founding Partner
Jim Long, Venture Partner
Scott Chou, Managing Director

Type of Firm
Private Equity Firm

Association Membership
Mid-Atlantic Venture Association
Western Association of Venture Capitalists (WAVC)
National Venture Capital Association - USA (NVCA)

Project Preferences

Role in Financing:
Prefer role as deal originator but will also invest in deals created by others

Type of Financing Preferred:
Early Stage
Seed
First Stage Financing

Size of Investments Considered:
Min Size of Investment Considered (000s): $250
Max Size of Investment Considered (000s): $7,000

Geographical Preferences

United States Preferences:
Mid Atlantic
Northern California
Northeast
West Coast
California

Industry Focus
(% based on actual investment)

Communications and Media	43.8%
Internet Specific	30.9%
Computer Software and Services	10.6%
Semiconductors/Other Elect.	10.6%
Computer Hardware	2.5%
Industrial/Energy	1.6%

Additional Information
Name of Most Recent Fund: Gabriel Venture Partners II
Most Recent Fund Was Raised: 01/12/2001
Year Founded: 1999
Capital Under Management: $260,000,000
Current Activity Level: Actively seeking new investments
Method of Compensation: Return on investment is of primary concern, do not charge fees

---

GAEL PARTNERS, LLC
1590 Drew Avenue
Suite 110
Davis, CA USA 95618
Phone: 530-757-7004
Fax: 530-757-1316
Website: www.centralvalleyfund.com

Other Offices

5010 Woodrow Avenue, Lyles Center
Suite WC 142
Fresno, CA USA 93740
Phone: 559-294-6668
Fax: 559-294-6655

Management and Staff

Brad Triebsch, Principal
Daniel Jessee, Principal
Edward McNulty, Principal
Jose Blanco, Principal

Type of Firm

Private Equity Firm

Project Preferences

Role in Financing:

Will function either as deal originator or investor in deals created by others

Type of Financing Preferred:

Mezzanine
Generalist PE
Management Buyouts

Size of Investments Considered:

Min Size of Investment Considered (000s): $1,000
Max Size of Investment Considered (000s): $6,000

Geographical Preferences

United States Preferences:

Southern California
Northern California
California

Industry Preferences

In Business Serv. prefer:

Services
Distribution

In Manufact. prefer:

Manufacturing

Additional Information

Year Founded: 2005
Capital Under Management: $55,000,000
Current Activity Level: Actively seeking new investments
Method of Compensation: Return on invest. most important, but chg. closing fees, service fees, etc.

GAJA CAPITAL PARTNERS

Publicis Zen House
Kamala Mill Compound
Mumbai, India 400 013
Phone: 91-22-2490-3047
Fax: 91-22-2490-3057
E-mail: info@gajacapital.com
Website: www.gajacapital.com

Management and Staff

Avinash Luthria, Principal
Gopal Jain, Partner
Imran Jafar, Principal
Praveen Chennareddy, Principal
Ranjit Shah, Partner
Sanjay Patel, Co-Founder
Vikas Arya, Principal

Type of Firm

Private Equity Firm

Association Membership

Indian Venture Capital Association (IVCA)

Project Preferences

Type of Financing Preferred:

Leveraged Buyout
Expansion
Turnaround
Balanced
Acquisition

Geographical Preferences

International Preferences:

India

Industry Preferences

In Business Serv. prefer:

Services

In Manufact. prefer:

Manufacturing

Additional Information

Year Founded: 2005
Capital Under Management: $144,000,000
Current Activity Level: Actively seeking new investments

GALA CAPITAL PARTNERS (AKA: GCP)

P de la Castellana 32
Madrid, Spain 28046
Website: www.galacapital.com

Management and Staff

Carlos Tejera, Co-Founder
Jaime Bergel, Co-Founder

Type of Firm

Private Equity Firm

Project Preferences

Type of Financing Preferred:

Leveraged Buyout
Balanced

Geographical Preferences

International Preferences:

Europe
Spain

Additional Information

Year Founded: 2004
Current Activity Level: Actively seeking new investments

GALEN ASSOCIATES (FKA:GALEN PARTNERS)

680 Washington Boulevard
Eleventh Floor
Stamford, CT USA 06901
Phone: 203-653-6400
Fax: 203-653-6499
Website: www.galen-partners.com

Management and Staff

Andrew Isaacson, Vice President
Bill Williams, Venture Partner
Bruce Wesson, Managing Director
David Azad, Principal
David Jahns, Managing Director
Howard Zauberman, Venture Partner
Jeffrey Soinski, Venture Partner
Judith Starkey, Venture Partner
L.John Wilkerson, Managing Director
Michael Koby, Principal
Neil MacAllister, Venture Partner
Stacey Bauer, Chief Financial Officer
Steve Shapiro, Venture Partner
Terrance Gregg, Venture Partner
Zubeen Shroff, Managing Director

Type of Firm

Private Equity Firm

Project Preferences

Role in Financing:

Prefer role as deal originator but will also invest in deals created by others

Type of Financing Preferred:

Second Stage Financing
Later Stage

Size of Investments Considered:

Min Size of Investment Considered (000s): $10,000
Max Size of Investment Considered: No Limit

Geographical Preferences

United States Preferences:

All U.S.

Industry Focus

(% based on actual investment)

Medical/Health	63.2%
Computer Software and Services	15.7%
Internet Specific	7.9%
Communications and Media	4.4%
Industrial/Energy	3.7%
Other Products	2.0%
Biotechnology	1.6%
Consumer Related	1.5%

Additional Information

Name of Most Recent Fund: Galen Partners V, L.P.
Most Recent Fund Was Raised: 07/11/2007

Year Founded: 1990
Capital Under Management: $397,000,000
Current Activity Level: Actively seeking new investments
Method of Compensation: Return on investment is of primary concern, do not charge fees

GALIA GESTION

2 rue des Piliers de Tutelle
BP 149
Bordeaux Cedex, France 33025
Phone: 33-557-818-810
Fax: 33-556-521-734
E-mail: contact@galia-gestion.com
Website: www.galia-gestion.com

Management and Staff

Christian Joubert, General Director
Yves Bardinet, President

Type of Firm

Private Equity Firm

Association Membership

French Venture Capital Association (AFIC)

Project Preferences

Type of Financing Preferred:
Generalist PE
Early Stage
Expansion
Balanced
Later Stage

Size of Investments Considered:
Min Size of Investment Considered (000s): $67
Max Size of Investment Considered (000s): $1,338

Geographical Preferences

International Preferences:
Europe
France

Additional Information

Name of Most Recent Fund: EXPANSO Investissements
Most Recent Fund Was Raised: 12/22/2002
Year Founded: 2000
Capital Under Management: $72,500,000
Current Activity Level: Actively seeking new investments

GALILEO EQUITY MANAGEMENT

161 Bay Street
Suite 4730
Toronto, Canada M5J 2S1
Phone: 416-594-0606

Type of Firm

Private Equity Firm

Additional Information

Year Founded: 2009
Current Activity Level: Actively seeking new investments

GALILEO PARTNERS

106, rue de l'Universite
Paris Cedex, France 75340
Phone: 33-1-5359-4500
Fax: 33-1-5359-9200
E-mail: contact@galileo.fr
Website: www.galileo.fr

Management and Staff

Corrine D Agrain, Chief Financial Officer
Joel Flichy, Co-Founder
Louis-Michel Angue, Co-Founder

Type of Firm

Private Equity Firm

Association Membership

French Venture Capital Association (AFIC)
European Private Equity and Venture Capital Assoc.

Project Preferences

Type of Financing Preferred:
Early Stage
Expansion
Seed
Startup
Fund of Funds of Second

Size of Investments Considered:
Min Size of Investment Considered (000s): $1,883
Max Size of Investment Considered (000s): $18,832

Geographical Preferences

International Preferences:
United Kingdom
Europe
France

Industry Preferences

In Communications prefer:
Communications and Media
Telecommunications

In Computer Software prefer:
Software

In Internet Specific prefer:
Internet

In Computer Other prefer:
Computer Related

In Semiconductor/Electr prefer:
Electronics

In Business Serv. prefer:
Media

Additional Information

Year Founded: 1989
Capital Under Management: $400,000
Current Activity Level: Actively seeking new investments

GALLEON GROUP

135 East 57th Street
16th Floor
New York, NY USA 10022
Phone: 212-371-2939
Fax: 212-371-0092
E-mail: info@galleongrp.com
Website: www.galleongrp.com

Type of Firm

Private Equity Firm

Association Membership

National Venture Capital Association - USA (NVCA)

Project Preferences

Type of Financing Preferred:
Balanced

Additional Information

Year Founded: 1997
Current Activity Level: Actively seeking new investments

GAMBRO AB

Jakobsgatan Six
Stockholm, Sweden SE-103 91
Phone: 46-8-613-6500
Fax: 46-8-611-2830
Website: www.gambro.com

Type of Firm

Corporate PE/Venture

Association Membership

Swedish Venture Capital Association (SVCA)

Project Preferences

Type of Financing Preferred:
Leveraged Buyout
Expansion
Seed
Startup

Geographical Preferences

International Preferences:
Sweden

Industry Preferences

In Biotechnology prefer:
Biotechnology

In Medical/Health prefer:
Medical/Health
Medical Products
Pharmaceuticals

Additional Information

Year Founded: 2000
Current Activity Level: Actively seeking new investments

GAMMA INVESTORS LLC

758 Harrison Road
Suite 111
Villanova, PA USA 19085
Phone: 610-203-9337
Fax: 215-827-5198
E-mail: ExecutiveCommittee@GammaInvestors.com
Website: www.gammainvestors.com

Type of Firm

Private Equity Firm

Project Preferences

Type of Financing Preferred:
Second Stage Financing
Early Stage
First Stage Financing

Size of Investments Considered:
Min Size of Investment Considered (000s): $250
Max Size of Investment Considered (000s): $3,000

Geographical Preferences

United States Preferences:
All U.S.

Industry Preferences

In Internet Specific prefer:
Internet

Additional Information

Year Founded: 1998
Capital Under Management: $15,000,000
Current Activity Level: Actively seeking new investments

GANNETT

1100 Wilson Blvd
Arlington, VA USA 22234
Phone: 703-284-6000
Fax: 703-558-3819
Website: www.gannett.com

Type of Firm

Corporate PE/Venture

Project Preferences

Type of Financing Preferred:
Balanced

Additional Information

Year Founded: 1996
Current Activity Level: Actively seeking new investments

GAO SHENG ASSET MANAGEMENT COMPANY, LTD.

Room 2101 Jingcheng Mansion
Six Xinyuan South Street
Beijing, China

Type of Firm

Private Equity Firm

Association Membership

Venture Capital Association of Beijing (VCAB)

Project Preferences

Type of Financing Preferred:
Seed
Startup

Geographical Preferences

International Preferences:
China

Industry Preferences

In Semiconductor/Electr prefer:
Electronics

In Biotechnology prefer:
Biotechnology

In Business Serv. prefer:
Services

In Manufact. prefer:
Manufacturing

Additional Information

Year Founded: 1999
Current Activity Level: Actively seeking new investments

GARAGE TECHNOLOGY VENTURES CANADA

1501 McGill College Avenue
Suite 2240
Montreal, Canada H3A 3M8
Phone: 514-878-1400
Fax: 514-878-2446
E-mail: info@garagecanada.com
Website: www.garagecanada.com

Management and Staff

Louis Desmarais, Co-Founder
Tom Sweeney, Co-Founder

Type of Firm

Private Equity Firm

Additional Information

Year Founded: 2004
Current Activity Level: Actively seeking new investments

GARAGE TECHNOLOGY VENTURES LLC (FKA: GARAGE.COM)

360 Bryant Street
Suite 100
Palo Alto, CA USA 94304
Phone: 650-838-0811
Fax: 650-853-2416
Website: www.garage.com

Management and Staff

Bill Reichert, Managing Director
Guy Kawasaki, Managing Director
Henry Wong, Venture Partner
Joyce Chung, Managing Director
Mohanjit Jolly, Managing Director

Type of Firm

Corporate PE/Venture

Association Membership

National Venture Capital Association - USA (NVCA)

Project Preferences

Role in Financing:
Will function either as deal originator or investor in deals created by others

Type of Financing Preferred:
Second Stage Financing
Early Stage
Seed
First Stage Financing

Size of Investments Considered:
Min Size of Investment Considered (000s): $500
Max Size of Investment Considered (000s): $3,000

Geographical Preferences

United States Preferences:
West Coast
California
All U.S.

Industry Preferences

In Computer Software prefer:
Software

In Consumer Related prefer:
Consumer Services

In Industrial/Energy prefer:
Materials

In Other prefer:
Environment Responsible

Additional Information

Year Founded: 1997
Capital Under Management: $20,000,000
Current Activity Level: Actively seeking new investments

GARBER VENTURE CAPITAL CENTER, THE

FCFE Smeal College of Business
The Pennsylvania State Univ.
University Park, PA USA 16802
Phone: 814-865-4593
Fax: 814-865-7425
E-mail: mediarelations@smeal.psu.edu
Website: www.smeal.psu.edu

Type of Firm

University Program

Project Preferences

Type of Financing Preferred:
Balanced

Geographical Preferences

United States Preferences:
All U.S.

Industry Preferences

In Business Serv. prefer:
Services

Additional Information

Year Founded: 1999
Current Activity Level: Actively seeking new investments

GARIBALDI PARTICIPATIONS SCR

141, rue Garibaldi
Lyon, France 69003
Website: www.garibaldi-participations.com

Other Offices

1, place de l'Hotel de Ville
Saint-Etienne, France 42000

Type of Firm

Bank Affiliated

Association Membership

French Venture Capital Association (AFIC)

Project Preferences

Type of Financing Preferred:
Leveraged Buyout
Expansion
Research and Development
Early Stage
Acquisition

Size of Investments Considered:
Min Size of Investment Considered (000s): $388
Max Size of Investment Considered (000s): $2,588

Geographical Preferences

International Preferences:
France

Additional Information

Year Founded: 2004
Capital Under Management: $19,500,000
Current Activity Level: Actively seeking new investments

GARMARK ADVISORS, L.L.C.

One Landmark Square
6th Floor
Stamford, CT USA 06901
Phone: 203-325-8500
Fax: 203-325-8522
Website: www.garmark.com

Management and Staff

Christopher Smith, Principal
David Scopelliti, Principal
Richard Davies, Vice President
Robert Shaykin, Chief Financial Officer
Steven Pickhardt, Principal

Type of Firm

Private Equity Firm

Project Preferences

Type of Financing Preferred:
Leveraged Buyout
Mezzanine
Acquisition

Size of Investments Considered:
Min Size of Investment Considered (000s): $5,000
Max Size of Investment Considered (000s): $50,000

Industry Focus

(% based on actual investment)

Other Products	25.1%
Consumer Related	22.9%
Industrial/Energy	20.8%
Semiconductors/Other Elect.	16.5%
Medical/Health	10.9%
Computer Hardware	3.3%
Internet Specific	0.6%

Additional Information

Name of Most Recent Fund: GarMark Partners II, L.P.
Most Recent Fund Was Raised: 06/27/2005
Year Founded: 1996
Capital Under Management: $330,400,000
Current Activity Level: Actively seeking new investments

GARNETT & HELFRICH CAPITAL

1200 Park Place
Suite 200
San Mateo, CA USA 94403
Phone: 650-234-4200
Fax: 650-234-4299
E-mail: info@garnetthefrich.com
Website: www.garnetthelfrich.com

Management and Staff

David Helfrich, Managing Director
Terence Garnett, Managing Director

Type of Firm

Private Equity Firm

Association Membership

National Venture Capital Association - USA (NVCA)

Project Preferences

Type of Financing Preferred:
Leveraged Buyout

Industry Preferences

In Communications prefer:
Communications and Media

In Computer Software prefer:
Software

In Internet Specific prefer:
Internet

In Semiconductor/Electr prefer:
Semiconductor

Additional Information

Year Founded: 2004
Capital Under Management: $350,300,000
Current Activity Level: Actively seeking new investments

GARON FINANCIAL GROUP, THE

1220 Howard Avenue
Second Floor
Burlingame, CA USA 94011
Phone: 650-548-9511

Type of Firm

Service Provider

Project Preferences

Role in Financing:
Will function either as deal originator or investor in deals created by others

Type of Financing Preferred:
Second Stage Financing
Research and Development
Start-up Financing
Seed

First Stage Financing
Special Situation

Size of Investments Considered:
Min Size of Investment Considered (000s): $100
Max Size of Investment Considered (000s): $1,000

Additional Information
Year Founded: 1994
Current Activity Level: Actively seeking new investments
Method of Compensation: Function primarily in service area, receive contingent fee in cash or equity

---

GARTMORE INVESTMENT LIMITED
Gartmore House
8 Fenchurch Place
London, United Kingdom EC3M 4PB
Phone: 44-20-7782-2836
Fax: 44-20-7782-2034
Website: www.gartmore.co.uk

Type of Firm
Investment Management Firm

Project Preferences

Type of Financing Preferred:
Early Stage
Expansion
Public Companies

Geographical Preferences

International Preferences:
United Kingdom
Western Europe

Additional Information
Year Founded: 2001
Current Activity Level: Actively seeking new investments

GARTNER GROUP, INC.
56 Top Gallant Road
P.O. Box 10212
Stamford, CT USA 06904
Website: www3.gartner.com

Type of Firm
Service Provider

Additional Information
Year Founded: 1985
Current Activity Level: Actively seeking new investments

GARUDA CAPITAL PARTNERS
Plaza Bapindo- Citibank Tower
12/F, Jl Jendral Sudirman
Jakarta, Indonesia
Phone: 62-21-524-030
Fax: 62-21-526-7516
E-mail: info@garudacapitalfunds.com
Website: www.garudacapitalfunds.com

Management and Staff
Patrick Alexander, Managing Partner

Type of Firm
Private Equity Firm

Project Preferences

Type of Financing Preferred:
Leveraged Buyout
Management Buyouts

Geographical Preferences

International Preferences:
Indonesia

Industry Preferences

In Consumer Related prefer:
Consumer

In Industrial/Energy prefer:
Energy

In Agr/Forestr/Fish prefer:
Agriculture related

Additional Information
Year Founded: 2004
Current Activity Level: Actively seeking new investments

GASSER+PARTNER
Viktringer Ring 21
Klagenfurt, Austria 9020
Phone: 43-463-504404
Fax: 43-463-50440415
E-mail: office@gasser-partner.at
Website: www.gasser-partner.at

Type of Firm
Private Equity Firm

Association Membership
Austrian PE and Venture Capital Association (AVCO)

Project Preferences

Type of Financing Preferred:
Early Stage

Geographical Preferences

International Preferences:
Austria

Additional Information
Year Founded: 1999
Capital Under Management: $6,600,000
Current Activity Level: Actively seeking new investments

GATEHOUSE VENTURES, L.P.
920 Cassatt Road
Suite 100
Berwyn, PA USA 19312
Phone: 610-560-4700
Fax: 610-560-4707
Website: www.gatehouseventures.com

Management and Staff
Christopher Jansen, Managing Director
David Jorgensen, Chief Financial Officer
Geoffrey Warrell, Founding Partner
Karl Buettner, Founding Partner

Type of Firm
Private Equity Firm

Project Preferences

Type of Financing Preferred:
Leveraged Buyout

Geographical Preferences

United States Preferences:
Mid Atlantic
Pennsylvania
Northeast
Maryland
New Jersey
Connecticut
New York

Industry Preferences

In Communications prefer:
Commercial Communications

In Consumer Related prefer:
Food/Beverage

In Transportation prefer:
Aerospace

In Financial Services prefer:
Real Estate
Financial Services

In Business Serv. prefer:
Services

In Manufact. prefer:
Manufacturing

Additional Information
Year Founded: 2001
Current Activity Level: Actively seeking new investments

GATEWAY GLOBAL (FKA:NW BROWN CAPITAL PARTNERS)

Saint Andrew's House
Saint Andrew's Road
Cambridge, United Kingdom CB4 1DL
Phone: 44-1223-535-185
Fax: 44-1223-535-187
E-mail: info@cambridgegateway.com
Website: www.cambridgegateway.com

Type of Firm

Private Equity Firm

Association Membership

European Private Equity and Venture Capital Assoc.

Project Preferences

Type of Financing Preferred:
Early Stage
Expansion
Balanced
Later Stage
Seed
Startup

Geographical Preferences

International Preferences:
United Kingdom
Europe

Industry Preferences

In Biotechnology prefer:
Biotechnology

In Industrial/Energy prefer:
Environmental Related

Additional Information

Name of Most Recent Fund: GEIF Ventures (AKA: GEIFV)
Most Recent Fund Was Raised: 04/01/2003
Year Founded: 1974
Capital Under Management: $46,500,000
Current Activity Level: Actively seeking new investments

GATX EUROPEAN TECHNOLOGY VENTURES

First Floor
Tendernden Street
London, United Kingdom W1S1TA
Phone: 44-20-7499-0163
Fax: 44-20-7491-1935
Website: www.gatxetv.com

Management and Staff

Humphrey Nokes, Managing Director

Type of Firm

Private Equity Firm

Additional Information

Current Activity Level: Actively seeking new investments

GAVEA INVESTIMENTOS

Rua Dias Ferreira 190, 7 andar
Leblon
Rio de Janeiro, Brazil 22431-050
Phone: 55-21-3206-9000
Fax: 55-21-3206-9001
E-mail: gavea@gaveainvest.com.br
Website: www.gaveainvest.com.br

Other Offices

Rua Amauri, 255, 7 andar
Itaim Bibi
Sao Paulo, Brazil 01448-000
Phone: 55-11-3526-9100
Fax: 55-11-3526-9101

Type of Firm

Private Equity Firm

Association Membership

Brazilian Venture Capital Association (ABCR)

Project Preferences

Type of Financing Preferred:
Balanced

Geographical Preferences

International Preferences:
Brazil

Additional Information

Year Founded: 2006
Current Activity Level: Actively seeking new investments

GAZELLE TECHVENTURES

11611 North Meridian Street
Suite 310
Carmel, IN USA 46032
Phone: 317-275-6800
Fax: 317-275-1100
E-mail: inquiries@gazellevc.com
Website: www.gazellevc.com

Management and Staff

Bryan Smith, Venture Partner
Don Aquilano, Managing Director
Matthew Ridenour, Venture Partner
Thomas Palmer, Venture Partner

Type of Firm

Private Equity Firm

Project Preferences

Role in Financing:
Will function either as deal originator or investor in deals created by others

Type of Financing Preferred:
Early Stage
Expansion
Later Stage

Size of Investments Considered:
Min Size of Investment Considered (000s): $1,000
Max Size of Investment Considered (000s): $3,000

Geographical Preferences

United States Preferences:
Midwest
Illinois
Michigan
Ohio
Indiana
Kentucky

Industry Preferences

In Communications prefer:
Communications and Media
CATV & Pay TV Systems
Radio & TV Broadcasting
Telecommunications
Data Communications
Satellite Microwave Comm.
Entertainment
Publishing

In Computer Hardware prefer:
Computers

In Computer Software prefer:
Software
Systems Software
Applications Software

In Biotechnology prefer:
Biotechnology
Human Biotechnology
Genetic Engineering

In Medical/Health prefer:
Medical/Health
Medical Diagnostics
Diagnostic Services
Diagnostic Test Products
Medical Therapeutics
Drug/Equipmt Delivery
Other Therapeutic
Medical Products
Disposable Med. Products
Health Services
Hospitals/Clinics/Primary
Hospital/Other Instit.
Pharmaceuticals

In Consumer Related prefer:
Consumer Services

In Industrial/Energy prefer:
Energy
Superconductivity

In Agr/Forestr/Fish prefer:
Agriculture related

Additional Information

Year Founded: 2000
Capital Under Management: $63,000,000
Current Activity Level: Actively seeking new investments
Method of Compensation: Return on investment is of primary concern, do not charge fees

GB MERCHANT PARTNERS, LLC (FKA: GB PALLADIN CAPITAL LLC)

One Rockefellar Plaza
Suite 110
New York, NY USA 10020
Phone: 212-218-6800
Fax: 212-218-6802
E-mail: equityinfo@gbmerchantpartners.com
Website: www.gbmerchantpartners.com

Other Offices

101 Huntington Avenue
Tenth Floor
Boston, MA USA 02199
Phone: 617-422-6240
Fax: 617-422-6240

Management and Staff

Alan Taylor, Managing Director
Brian Cooper, Vice President
James Dworkin, Managing Director
Larry Klaff, Managing Director
Matthew Kahn, Managing Director
Michael Rand, Managing Director
Scott Strasser, Managing Director

Type of Firm

Bank Affiliated

Project Preferences

Type of Financing Preferred:
Leveraged Buyout
Mezzanine
Turnaround
Management Buyouts
Acquisition

Geographical Preferences

United States Preferences:
All U.S.

Industry Preferences

In Consumer Related prefer:
Consumer Products
Consumer Services

Additional Information

Year Founded: 2003
Capital Under Management: $320,000,000
Current Activity Level: Actively seeking new investments

GBP CAPITAL (AKA: GREENWICH BIOTECH PARTNERS)

537 Steamboat Road
Suite 200
Greenwich, CT USA 06830
Phone: 203-769-2345
Fax: 203-769-2322
Website: www.gbpcap.com

Management and Staff

David Wetherell, Managing Partner
Douglas Lind, Managing Partner

Type of Firm

Private Equity Firm

Project Preferences

Role in Financing:
Prefer role as deal originator but will also invest in deals created by others

Type of Financing Preferred:
Early Stage
Research and Development
Start-up Financing
First Stage Financing

Size of Investments Considered:
Min Size of Investment Considered (000s): $500
Max Size of Investment Considered (000s): $10,000

Geographical Preferences

United States Preferences:
All U.S.

Industry Preferences

In Biotechnology prefer:
Biotechnology
Human Biotechnology
Genetic Engineering

In Medical/Health prefer:
Medical/Health
Medical Diagnostics
Diagnostic Test Products
Medical Therapeutics
Medical Products

Additional Information

Year Founded: 2006
Capital Under Management: $20,000,000
Current Activity Level: Actively seeking new investments

GBS VENTURE PARTNERS, LTD.

71 Collins Street
Harley House, Level 5
Melbourne, Australia 3000
Phone: 613-8650-9900
Fax: 613-8650-9901
E-mail: investment@gbsventures.com.au
Website: www.gbsventures.com.au

Other Offices

25 Henry Street
Queens Park
Sydney, Australia 2022
Phone: 612-9389-0765
Fax: 613-8650-9901

Management and Staff

Brigitte Smith, Managing Director
Carolyn Ireland, Chief Financial Officer
Geoffrey Brooke, Managing Director
Susan Wolff, Chief Financial Officer

Type of Firm

Private Equity Firm

Association Membership

Australian Venture Capital Association (AVCAL)

Project Preferences

Role in Financing:
Prefer role as deal originator but will also invest in deals created by others

Type of Financing Preferred:
Early Stage
Expansion
Seed
Startup

Size of Investments Considered:
Min Size of Investment Considered (000s): $40
Max Size of Investment Considered (000s): $9,670

Geographical Preferences

United States Preferences:
All U.S.

International Preferences:
Pacific
Australia

Industry Preferences

In Biotechnology prefer:
Biotechnology
Human Biotechnology
Agricultural/Animal Bio.

In Medical/Health prefer:
Medical/Health
Medical Diagnostics
Diagnostic Services
Medical Therapeutics
Other Therapeutic
Medical Products
Pharmaceuticals

Additional Information

Year Founded: 1996
Capital Under Management: $329,900,000
Current Activity Level: Actively seeking new investments
Method of Compensation: Return on investment is of primary concern, do not charge fees

GC&H PARTNERS

One Maritime Plaza
20th Floor
San Francisco, CA USA 94110
Phone: 415-693-2000

Other Offices

1200 17th Street
Denver, CO USA 80202
Phone: 303-606-4800

Type of Firm

Service Provider

Project Preferences

Type of Financing Preferred:
Early Stage
Balanced

Additional Information

Year Founded: 1981
Capital Under Management: $2,200,000
Current Activity Level: Actively seeking new investments

GCC ENERGY FUND, THE

Sheik Zayed Road
22nd Floor, Emirates Tower
Dubai, Utd. Arab Em. 504946
Phone: 971-4-330-0202
Fax: 971-4-330-0510
E-mail: invest@gccenergyfund.ae
Website: www.gccenergyfund.com

Management and Staff

Adil Toubia, Chief Executive Officer

Type of Firm

Bank Affiliated

Project Preferences

Type of Financing Preferred:
Balanced

Geographical Preferences

International Preferences:
Bahrain
Oman
Qatar
Utd. Arab Em.
Saudi Arabia
Kuwait

Industry Preferences

In Industrial/Energy prefer:
Energy
Oil & Gas Drilling,Explor
Alternative Energy

Additional Information

Year Founded: 2005
Current Activity Level: Actively seeking new investments

GCI MANAGEMENT

Brienner Strasse 10
Munich, Germany D - 80333
Phone: 49-89-20500-500
Fax: 49-89-20500-555
E-mail: gci@gci-management.com
Website: www.gci-management.com

Type of Firm

Private Equity Firm

Project Preferences

Type of Financing Preferred:
Early Stage
Startup

Geographical Preferences

International Preferences:
Switzerland
Germany

Industry Preferences

In Computer Software prefer:
Software

In Internet Specific prefer:
Internet

In Medical/Health prefer:
Medical/Health

In Business Serv. prefer:
Services

Additional Information

Year Founded: 1991
Current Activity Level: Actively seeking new investments

GCP GAMMA CAPITAL PARTNERS (FKA: ILAB24 AG)

Reisnerstrasse 40/3
Vienna, Austria A-1030
Phone: 43-1-513-1072
Fax: 43-1-5131072200
E-mail: office@gamma-capital.com
Website: www.gamma-capital.com

Other Offices

Businesspark Lindenberg
Lauenbuhlstrasse 59
Lindenberg, Germany D-88161
Phone: 49-8381-807-771
Fax: 49-8381-807-773

Zamocka 22
Bratislava, Slovakia SK-811 01
Phone: 421-2-5413-1378
Fax: 43-1-513-107-2200

Management and Staff

Christian Lutz, Venture Partner
Jurgen Wahl, Venture Partner
Karl Krista, Venture Partner
Klaus Matzka, Founding Partner
Markus Wagner, Venture Partner
Nikolaus Spieckermann-Hutter, Partner
Oliver Grabherr, Founding Partner
Rupert Nagler, Venture Partner

Type of Firm

Private Equity Firm

Association Membership

Austrian PE and Venture Capital Association (AVCO)
European Private Equity and Venture Capital Assoc.

Project Preferences

Role in Financing:
Prefer role as deal originator but will also invest in deals created by others

Type of Financing Preferred:
Early Stage
Expansion
Seed
Startup

Size of Investments Considered:
Min Size of Investment Considered (000s): $62
Max Size of Investment Considered (000s): $4,993

Geographical Preferences

International Preferences:
Switzerland
Europe
Austria
Eastern Europe
Germany

Industry Preferences

In Communications prefer:
Communications and Media

In Computer Software prefer:
Software

In Computer Other prefer:
Computer Related

In Semiconductor/Electr prefer:
Electronics

In Biotechnology prefer:
Biotechnology

In Medical/Health prefer:
Pharmaceuticals

In Industrial/Energy prefer:
Alternative Energy
Advanced Materials

Additional Information

Name of Most Recent Fund: GAMMA III
Most Recent Fund Was Raised: 07/18/2007
Year Founded: 2002
Capital Under Management: $119,400,000
Current Activity Level: Actively seeking new investments

GE ANTARES CAPITAL CORPORATION

500 West Monroe Street
Chicago, IL USA 60661
Phone: 312-697-3999
Fax: 312-697-3998
Website: www.antareslev.com

Other Offices

100 California Street
San Francisco, CA USA 94111
Phone: 415-277-7400

125 Summer Street
Suite 1230
Boston, MA USA 02110
Phone: 617-378-4778

2611 Internet Boulevard
Suite 105
Frisco, TX USA 75034
Phone: 972-334-1216

201 Merritt 7 PO Box 5201
Norwalk, CT USA 06851
Phone: 866-243-5537

299 Park Avenue
New York, NY USA 10001
Phone: 212-370-8000

350 South Beverly Drive
Beverly Hills, CA USA 90212
Phone: 310-203-0335

Management and Staff

Barry Shear, Senior Managing Director
Chester Zara, Senior Managing Director
Daniel Glickman, Managing Director
Daniel Barry, Senior Managing Director
David Brackett, Senior Managing Director
David Mahon, Managing Director
David Swanson, Managing Director
David Schmuck, Chief Financial Officer
Eric Hansen, Managing Director
Gerard Hanabergh, Managing Director
Hugh Wilder, Senior Managing Director
John Martin, Senior Managing Director
Kathleen Hockman, Vice President
Kristin Clark, Vice President
Mary Gaede, Vice President
Michael Chirillo, Senior Managing Director
Michael King, Managing Director
Michael Hynes, Vice President
Robert Tuchscherer, Vice President
Stefano Robertson, Managing Director
Steven Robinson, Managing Director
Timothy Lyne, Senior Managing Director

Type of Firm

Private Equity Firm

Project Preferences

Role in Financing:

Prefer role as deal originator but will also invest in deals created by others

Type of Financing Preferred:

Second Stage Financing
Leveraged Buyout
Mezzanine
First Stage Financing
Special Situation
Distressed Debt

Size of Investments Considered:

Min Size of Investment Considered (000s): $10,000
Max Size of Investment Considered (000s): $130,000

Geographical Preferences

United States Preferences:

Southeast
All U.S.

Canadian Preferences:

All Canada

Industry Preferences

In Communications prefer:

Commercial Communications
Telecommunications
Data Communications
Satellite Microwave Comm.

In Computer Hardware prefer:

Mini and Personal/Desktop
Computer Graphics and Dig
Disk Relat. Memory Device

In Computer Software prefer:

Computer Services
Systems Software
Applications Software
Artificial Intelligence

In Internet Specific prefer:

Internet

In Semiconductor/Electr prefer:

Electronic Components
Controllers and Sensors
Sensors
Laser Related
Fiber Optics
Analytic/Scientific

In Medical/Health prefer:

Medical/Health
Diagnostic Services
Diagnostic Test Products
Drug/Equipmt Delivery
Other Therapeutic
Disposable Med. Products
Hospitals/Clinics/Primary
Hospital/Other Instit.

In Consumer Related prefer:

Retail
Computer Stores
Food/Beverage
Consumer Products
Consumer Services
Other Restaurants
Education Related

In Industrial/Energy prefer:

Materials
Factory Automation
Robotics
Machinery

In Financial Services prefer:

Financial Services

In Business Serv. prefer:

Services

In Manufact. prefer:

Manufacturing
Office Automation Equipmt
Publishing

Additional Information

Year Founded: 1996
Capital Under Management: $1,500,000,000
Current Activity Level: Actively seeking new investments
Method of Compensation: Return on investment is of primary concern, do not charge fees

---

GE COMMERCIAL FINANCE - EQUITY

120 Long Ridge Road
Stamford, CT USA 06927
Phone: 203-357-3100
Fax: 203-357-3657
Website: www.geequity.com

Other Offices

Block 4A, DLF Corporate Park
Qutub Enclave, Phase III,Mehrauli
Gurgaon , India 122002
Phone: 91-12-4235-8030
Fax: 91-12-4235-8044

Level 14
255 George Street
Sydney , Australia NSW 2000
Phone: 61-2-9324-7565
Fax: 61-2-9324-7570

Martin Behaim-Strasse 10
Neu-Isenburg, Germany D-63263
Phone: 49-6102-361600
Fax: 49-6102-361611

16/F Three Exchange Square
Central, Hong Kong
Phone: 852-2100-6871
Fax: 852-2100-6733

5th Floor, Via Gabrio Casati
(angolo via Cordusio 2)
Milan, Italy 20123
Phone: 39-02-7259-591
Fax: 39-02-7259-5959

622 Third Avenue
New York, NY USA 10017
Phone: 212-880-7000

Prolongacion Reforma 490
3rd Floor
Col. Santa Fe, Mexico 01217D.F.
Phone: 525-257-6200
Fax: 525-257-6239

GE International Inc.
Eliahu House
Tel Aviv , Israel 64077
Phone: 972-3-695-8466
Fax: 972-3-696-9436

Clarges House
6-12 Clarges Street
London, United Kingdom W1J 8DH
Phone: 44-207-302-6000
Fax: 44-207-302-6936

Warsaw Financial Center
ul. Emilii Plater 53
Warsaw, Poland 00-113
Phone: 48-22-520-5303
Fax: 48-22-520-5301

Kowa 35 Building 2F
14-14, Akasaka 1-chome
Minato-ku, Japan 107-8453
Phone: 81-3-3588-6126
Fax: 81-3-3588-6159

Av. L.N. Alem 619
4th Floor
Buenos Aires, Argentina 1001
Phone: 54-11-4317-8755
Fax: 54-11-4317-8789

Av. Nove De Julho, 5229
11th Andar, Itaim Bibi
Sao Paulo, SP, Brazil 01407-907
Phone: 55-11-3067-8487
Fax: 55-11-3067-8398

Management and Staff

Ab Igram, Vice President
Alan Sadayasu, Vice President
Andrew Bonanno, Vice President
Brian Keil, Vice President
Eduardo Guemez, Vice President
Harjit Bhatia, Senior Managing Director
Henrik Olsen, Managing Director
Jerome Marcus, Managing Director
Jonathan Glass, Vice President
Joseph Freeman, Vice President
Kathleen Konopka, Vice President
Luca Giacometti, Managing Director
Mark Muth, Managing Director
Mark Chen, Senior Managing Director
Michael Fisher, Managing Director
Nicola Baker, Vice President
Patricio Sabaini, Managing Director
Patrick Dowling, Managing Director
Patrick Kocsi, Vice President
Pierre Casanova, Vice President
Robert Cioffi, Vice President
Roger Keane, Vice President
Samuel Cubac, Vice President
Sherwood Dodge, Managing Director
Stefan Abbruzzese, Vice President
Steve Warner, Vice President
Steven Smith, Managing Director
Sunil Sabharwal, Managing Director
Todd Wong, Vice President
Trevor Kienzle, Vice President
Vicki Harris, Vice President

Type of Firm

Corporate PE/Venture

Association Membership

Italian Venture Capital Association (AIFI)
Hong Kong Venture Capital Association (HKVCA)

Project Preferences

Role in Financing:

Will function either as deal originator or investor in deals created by others

Type of Financing Preferred:

Leveraged Buyout
Early Stage
Expansion
Research and Development
Turnaround
Later Stage
Management Buyouts
Startup
Recapitalizations

Size of Investments Considered:

Min Size of Investment Considered (000s): $5,000
Max Size of Investment Considered (000s): $20,000

Geographical Preferences

Canadian Preferences:

All Canada

International Preferences:

Latin America
Europe
Asia

Industry Focus

(% based on actual investment)	
Internet Specific	28.7%
Other Products	24.2%
Computer Software and Services	16.9%
Communications and Media	14.4%
Semiconductors/Other Elect.	5.9%
Medical/Health	4.1%
Industrial/Energy	3.6%
Biotechnology	1.0%
Consumer Related	0.7%
Computer Hardware	0.5%

Additional Information

Year Founded: 1991
Capital Under Management: $28,200,000
Current Activity Level: Reducing investment activity

GED GROUP

Strada Frumoasa 42 A
Sector 1
Bucharest, Romania 010987
Phone: 40-21-317-5884
Fax: 40-21-318-1483
E-mail: ged@com.pcnet.ro
Website: www.gedprivateequity.com

Other Offices

R. Viana de Lima 155
Oporto, Portugal 4150-746
Phone: 351-225-322-810

Marques de Riscal 12
4o izq
Madrid, Spain 28010
Phone: 34-91-702-2255
Fax: 34-91-702-1764

14, Saborna Str.,
Second Floor
Sofia, Bulgaria 1000
Phone: 35-929-817-469
Fax: 35-928-117-607

Edificio Arttysur, 2 planta, modulo A
Avda. de la Palmera, 27-29
Sevilla, Spain 41013
Phone: 34-954-490-180
Fax: 34-954-560-857

Management and Staff

Alberto Ales, Managing Director
Enrique Centelles, President
Felix Guerrero Igea, Managing Director
Joaquim Hierro Lopes, Managing Director
Juan Puertas, Managing Director
Marcelo Ca?ellas, Managing Director
Robert Luke, Managing Director

Type of Firm

Private Equity Firm

Association Membership

European Private Equity and Venture Capital Assoc.
Spanish Venture Capital Association (ASCRI)

Project Preferences

Type of Financing Preferred:

Second Stage Financing
Leveraged Buyout
Expansion
Balanced
Startup

Size of Investments Considered:

Min Size of Investment Considered (000s): $1,883
Max Size of Investment Considered (000s): $14,124

Geographical Preferences

International Preferences:

Portugal
Eastern Europe
Bulgaria
Spain
Romania

Additional Information

Year Founded: 1996
Capital Under Management: $198,000,000
Current Activity Level: Actively seeking new investments

GEDEFI TECHNOLOGY VENTURE SERVICES SA

Rue De XXXI Decembre 42
Geneva, Switzerland 1211
Phone: 41-22-707-43-77
Fax: 41-22-707-43-78
Website: www.gedefi.com

Type of Firm

Corporate PE/Venture
Additional Information
Current Activity Level: Actively seeking new investments

GEFINOR VENTURES (FKA: INMAN VENTURES)

301 Congress
Suite 1350
Austin, TX USA 78701
Phone: 512-346-7111
Fax: 512-346-2111
E-mail: info@gefinorventures.com
Website: www.gefinorventures.com

Other Offices

375 Park Avenue
Suite 2401
New York, NY USA 10152
Phone: 212-308-1111
Fax: 212-308-1182

Management and Staff

Bobby Inman, Managing Director
Greg Carlisle, Managing Director
Mohamed Ousseimi, Managing Director
Robert Porell, Vice President
Thomas Inman, Principal
William Beckett, Chief Financial Officer

Type of Firm

Private Equity Firm

Association Membership

National Venture Capital Association - USA (NVCA)

Project Preferences

Role in Financing:

Will function either as deal originator or investor in deals created by others

Type of Financing Preferred:

Early Stage

Size of Investments Considered:

Min Size of Investment Considered (000s): $500
Max Size of Investment Considered (000s): $2,000

Geographical Preferences

United States Preferences:

California
Colorado
D. of Columbia
New York
Texas

Industry Preferences

In Communications prefer:

Wireless Communications

In Computer Software prefer:

Software

In Internet Specific prefer:

Internet

In Semiconductor/Electr prefer:

Semiconductor

In Medical/Health prefer:

Medical Products

Additional Information

Name of Most Recent Fund: GEFUS SBIC, L.P.
Most Recent Fund Was Raised: 03/01/2000
Year Founded: 2002
Capital Under Management: $48,000,000
Current Activity Level: Actively seeking new investments
Method of Compensation: Return on investment is of primary concern, do not charge fees

---

GEMINI CAPITAL FUND MANAGEMENT, LTD.

9 Hamenofim Street
Herzliya Pituach, Israel 46725
Phone: 972-9-971-9111
Fax: 972-9-958-4842
E-mail: info@gemini.co.il
Website: www.gemini.co.il

Other Offices

525 University Avenue
Suite 700
Palo Alto, CA USA 94301
Phone: 650-289-5506
Fax: 650-233-7515

Management and Staff

Adi Pundak-Mintz, General Partner
Avi Hassan, General Partner
Carmel Sofer, General Partner
Daniel Cohen, General Partner
Jonathan Saacks, Principal
Lior Berger, General Partner
Orna Berry, Venture Partner
Tali Aben, General Partner
Yossi Sela, Managing Partner

Type of Firm

Private Equity Advisor or Fund of Funds

Association Membership

National Venture Capital Association - USA (NVCA)

Project Preferences

Role in Financing:

Prefer role as deal originator but will also invest in deals created by others

Type of Financing Preferred:

Early Stage
Expansion
Balanced
Seed
Startup

Size of Investments Considered:

Min Size of Investment Considered (000s): $500
Max Size of Investment Considered (000s): $5,000

Geographical Preferences

International Preferences:

Europe
Israel

Industry Focus

(% based on actual investment)	
Computer Hardware	29.4%
Computer Software and Services	23.1%
Communications and Media	16.2%
Semiconductors/Other Elect.	12.4%
Medical/Health	8.3%
Internet Specific	7.3%
Other Products	2.2%
Industrial/Energy	0.6%
Biotechnology	0.4%

Additional Information

Name of Most Recent Fund: Gemini Israel IV
Most Recent Fund Was Raised: 08/31/2004
Year Founded: 1993
Capital Under Management: $350,000,000
Current Activity Level: Actively seeking new investments
Method of Compensation: Return on investment is of primary concern, do not charge fees

---

GEMINI INVESTORS (AKA: GMN INVESTORS)

20 William Street
Suite 250
Wellesley, MA USA 02481
Phone: 781-237-7001
Fax: 781-237-7233

Website: www.gemini-investors.com

Other Offices

225 South Sixth Street
Suite 4350
Minneapolis, MN USA 55406
Phone: 612-766-4073
Fax: 612-766-4040

Management and Staff

David Millet, Managing Director
James Goodman, President
James Rich, Managing Director
Jeffrey Newton, Managing Director
Matthew Keis, Managing Director
Molly Simmons, Managing Director

Type of Firm

SBIC

Association Membership

Natl Assoc of Small Bus. Inv. Co (NASBIC)

Project Preferences

Role in Financing:
Will function either as deal originator or investor in deals created by others

Type of Financing Preferred:
Expansion
Generalist PE
Balanced
Later Stage
Private Placement
Recapitalizations

Size of Investments Considered:
Min Size of Investment Considered (000s): $3,000
Max Size of Investment Considered (000s): $8,000

Industry Focus

(% based on actual investment)

Other Products	19.1%
Consumer Related	17.2%
Internet Specific	13.5%
Computer Software and Services	12.2%
Communications and Media	11.7%
Medical/Health	11.4%
Semiconductors/Other Elect.	6.9%
Industrial/Energy	4.5%
Computer Hardware	3.5%

Additional Information
Name of Most Recent Fund: Gemini Investors IV, L.P.
Most Recent Fund Was Raised: 07/22/2005
Year Founded: 1993
Capital Under Management: $300,000,000
Current Activity Level: Actively seeking new investments
Method of Compensation: Return on invest. most important, but chg. closing fees, service fees, etc.

GEMINI ISRAEL FUNDS

525 University Avenue
Suite 700
Palo Alto, CA USA 94301
Phone: 650-289-5506
Fax: 650-233-7515
E-mail: tali@gemini.co.il
Website: www.gemini.co.il

Management and Staff

Tali Aben, General Partner

Type of Firm

Private Equity Firm

Additional Information

Year Founded: 2004
Current Activity Level: Actively seeking new investments

GEMINI PARTNERS, INC.

10900 Wilshire Boulevard
Suite 500
Westwood, CA USA 90024
Phone: 310-696-4001
Fax: 310-507-0263
Website: www.geminipartners.net

Management and Staff

Adam Eckhart, Vice President
Faiz Bhora, Principal
John Garofolo, Principal
Matthew Johnson, Principal
Nathan Johnson, Principal
Tad Neeley, Principal

Type of Firm

Bank Affiliated

Project Preferences

Type of Financing Preferred:
Leveraged Buyout
Expansion
Mezzanine
Generalist PE
Public Companies
Private Placement
Distressed Debt

Size of Investments Considered:
Min Size of Investment Considered (000s): $1,000
Max Size of Investment Considered (000s): $5,000

Geographical Preferences

International Preferences:
Europe

Additional Information

Year Founded: 2003
Current Activity Level: Actively seeking new investments

GEMISA

Calea Rahovei Nr. 266 - 268
Sector 5
Bucharest, Romania 050912
Phone: 40-21-404-1400
Fax: 40-21-404-1401
E-mail: office@gemisa-inv.ro
Website: www.gemisa.ro

Type of Firm

Private Equity Firm

Project Preferences

Type of Financing Preferred:
Early Stage
Generalist PE
Startup

Size of Investments Considered:
Min Size of Investment Considered (000s): $350
Max Size of Investment Considered (000s): $4,194

Geographical Preferences

International Preferences:
Romania

Additional Information

Year Founded: 2004
Capital Under Management: $15,400,000
Current Activity Level: Actively seeking new investments

GEMPLUS SCA

Avenue Du Pic De Bertagne
Parc D'Actvites
Gemenos, France 13881
Phone: 33-442-36-46-07
E-mail: info.gemventures@gemplus.com
Website: www.gemplus.com

Other Offices

2-4 Place des Alpes
Geneva, Switzerland 1201
Phone: 41-22-544-50-45
Fax: 41-22-544-50-40

12 Ayer Rajah Crescent
Singapore, Singapore 068912
Phone: 65-6889-3303
Fax: 65-6889-6891

Management and Staff

Michael Ng, Principal

Type of Firm

Corporate PE/Venture

Association Membership

Singapore Venture Capital Association (SVCA)

Project Preferences

Type of Financing Preferred:
Early Stage
Balanced
Seed

Geographical Preferences

International Preferences:
Europe
Australia
Asia

Industry Preferences

In Internet Specific prefer:
Internet

Additional Information

Year Founded: 1999
Current Activity Level: Actively seeking new investments

GEN 3 PARTNERS

Ten Post Office Square
Ninth Floor
Boston, MA USA 02109
Phone: 617-728-7000
Fax: 617-728-7500
Website: www.gen3partners.com

Management and Staff

Sam Kogan, President & COO

Type of Firm

Service Provider

Project Preferences

Type of Financing Preferred:
Early Stage
Balanced

Geographical Preferences

United States Preferences:
All U.S.

International Preferences:
Russia

Industry Preferences

In Communications prefer:
Wireless Communications

In Medical/Health prefer:
Medical Products

In Industrial/Energy prefer:
Energy

Additional Information

Name of Most Recent Fund: GEN3 Capital I, L.P.
Most Recent Fund Was Raised: 07/31/2005
Year Founded: 1999
Capital Under Management: $17,900,000
Current Activity Level: Actively seeking new investments

GEN CAP AMERICA, INC.

40 Burton Hills Boulevard
Suite 420
Nashville, TN USA 37215
Phone: 615-256-0231
Fax: 615-256-2487
E-mail: info@gencapamerica.com
Website: www.gencapamerica.com

Management and Staff

Christopher Hammond, Vice President
Mark Isaacs, Vice President
Matthew Lane, Vice President

Type of Firm

Private Equity Firm

Project Preferences

Role in Financing:
Prefer role as deal originator

Type of Financing Preferred:
Leveraged Buyout
Mezzanine
Generalist PE
Management Buyouts
Acquisition
Recapitalizations

Geographical Preferences

United States Preferences:
All U.S.

Canadian Preferences:
All Canada

Additional Information

Name of Most Recent Fund: Southvest Fund V, L.P.
Most Recent Fund Was Raised: 12/30/2004
Year Founded: 1985
Capital Under Management: $134,000,000
Current Activity Level: Actively seeking new investments

GENECHEM FINANCIAL CORPORATION

1001 De Maisonneuve Blvd, West
Suite 920
Montreal, Canada H3A 3C8
Phone: 514-849-7696
Fax: 514-849-5191
Website: www.genechem.com

Type of Firm

Corporate PE/Venture

Project Preferences

Type of Financing Preferred:
Early Stage

Geographical Preferences

Canadian Preferences:
Quebec

Additional Information

Name of Most Recent Fund: GeneChem Technologies Venture Fund L.P.
Most Recent Fund Was Raised: 01/01/1997
Year Founded: 1997
Capital Under Management: $57,900,000
Current Activity Level: Actively seeking new investments

GENENTECH CORPORATION

One DNA Way
South San Francisco, CA USA 94080
Phone: 650-225-1000
Fax: 650-225-6000
E-mail: medinfo@gene.com
Website: www.gene.com

Type of Firm

Corporate PE/Venture

Additional Information

Name of Most Recent Fund: Genentech Corporation
Most Recent Fund Was Raised: 04/01/1986
Year Founded: 1986
Current Activity Level: Actively seeking new investments

GENERA NAVARRA INICIATIVAS EMPRESARIALES SA

Carlos III, 11 1 1 zda
Pamplona, Spain 31001
Phone: 34-948-207-350
Fax: 34-948-204-139
E-mail: genera@genera21.com
Website: www.genera21.com

Type of Firm

Private Equity Firm

Association Membership

Spanish Venture Capital Association (ASCRI)

Project Preferences

Type of Financing Preferred:
Second Stage Financing
Expansion
Management Buyouts

Geographical Preferences

International Preferences:
Spain

Industry Preferences

In Computer Software prefer:
Computer Services
Software

In Biotechnology prefer:
Biotechnology
Biotech Related Research

In Industrial/Energy prefer:
Industrial Products

Additional Information
Year Founded: 2001
Current Activity Level: Actively seeking new investments

GENERAL ATLANTIC LLC
Three Pickwick Plaza
Suite 200
Greenwich, CT USA 06830-5538
Phone: 203-629-8600
Fax: 203-622-8818
E-mail: gainfo@gapartners.com
Website: www.generalatlantic.com

Other Offices
No. 2 Jianguomenwai Avenue
15F Yintai Office Tower Suite 1545
Beijing, China 100022
Phone: 86-10-6563-7948
Fax: 86-10-6563-7999

83 Pall Mall
Fourth Floor
London, United Kingdom SW1Y 5ES
Phone: 44-20-7484-3200
Fax: 44-20-7484-3290

Room 151-152, 15th Floor
Maker Chambers VI, Nariman Point
Mumbai, India 400 021
Phone: 91-22-6656-1400
Fax: 91-22-6631-7893

Park Avenue Plaza
55 East 52nd Street, 32nd Floor
New York, NY USA 10055
Phone: 212-715-4000
Fax: 212-759-5708

Koenigsallee 62
Dusseldorf, Germany 40212
Phone: 4921-1602-88880
Fax: 4921-1602-88857

Suite 2007-10, 20th Floor
One IFC, 1 Harbour View Street
Central, Hong Kong
Phone: 852-3602-2600
Fax: 852-3602-2611

Av. Brigadeiro Faria Lima
3729 - 50 Andar
Sao Paulo SP, Brazil 04538-133
Phone: 55-11- 3443-6257
Fax: 55-11- 3443-6201

228 Hamilton Avenue
Palo Alto, CA USA 94301
Phone: 650-251-7800
Fax: 650-251-9672

Management and Staff
Aaron Goldman, Vice President
Abhay Havaldar, Managing Director
Abhishek Agrawal, Vice President
Adrianna Ma, Managing Director
Alexander Chulack, Principal
Amit Soni, Vice President
Anthony McNulty, Vice President
Anton Levy, Managing Director
Arne Hartmann, Vice President
Brett Rochkind, Principal
Christopher Lanning, Managing Director
David Hodgson, Managing Director
David Rosenstein, Managing Director
David Lisewski, Vice President
Doug Scherrer, Vice President
Drew Pearson, Managing Director
Fernando Olveira, Managing Director
Florian Wendelstadt, Managing Director
Franchon Smithson, Managing Director
Gabriel Caillaux, Principal
H. Raymond Bingham, Managing Director
James Franzone, Vice President
Jan Hammer, Principal
Jeff Leng, Managing Director
Jing Hong, Principal
Joern Nikolay, Vice President
John Bernstein, Managing Director
Jonathan Korngold, Managing Director
Klaus Esser, Managing Director
Marc McMorris, Managing Director
Mark Dzialga, Managing Director
Matthew Nimetz, Managing Director
Mauro Bonugli, Vice President
Minesh Mistry, Vice President
Nick Nash, Vice President
Nishant Mittal, Vice President
Nishant Sharma, Vice President
Parker Hume, Vice President
Peter Bloom, Managing Director
Phil Trahanas, Managing Director
Ranjit Pandit, Managing Director
Raul Rai, Managing Director
Rene Kern, Managing Director
Robbert Vorhoff, Vice President
Shirley Chen, Vice President
Sunish Sharma, Managing Director
T.R. Newcomb, Vice President
Thomas Murphy, Managing Director & CFO
Tom Collier Tinsley, Managing Director
William Grabe, Managing Director
William Ford, Chief Executive Officer

Type of Firm
Private Equity Firm

Association Membership
Venture Capital Association of Beijing (VCAB)
Hong Kong Venture Capital Association (HKVCA)
German Venture Capital Association (BVK)
European Private Equity and Venture Capital Assoc.
Indian Venture Capital Association (IVCA)

Project Preferences

Role in Financing:
Prefer role as deal originator but will also invest in deals created by others

Type of Financing Preferred:
Leveraged Buyout
Early Stage
Expansion
Mezzanine
Generalist PE
Later Stage

Size of Investments Considered:
Min Size of Investment Considered (000s): $50,000
Max Size of Investment Considered (000s): $500,000

Geographical Preferences

United States Preferences:
All U.S.

International Preferences:
India
Latin America
Europe
China

Industry Focus
(% based on actual investment)

Computer Software and Services	42.3%
Other Products	24.6%
Internet Specific	17.0%
Computer Hardware	8.0%
Communications and Media	3.6%
Medical/Health	2.1%
Consumer Related	1.5%
Industrial/Energy	0.6%
Semiconductors/Other Elect.	0.2%

Additional Information
Year Founded: 1980
Capital Under Management: $14,000,000,000
Current Activity Level: Actively seeking new investments

GENERAL CATALYST PARTNERS (FKA: GENERAL CATALYST GROUP LLC)
20 University Road
Suite 450
Cambridge, MA USA 02138
Phone: 617-234-7000
Fax: 617-234-7040
E-mail: info@generalcatalyst.com
Website: www.generalcatalyst.com

Management and Staff

Adrienne Sweetser, Vice President
Bilal Zuberi, Principal
Bill Kung, Principal
Brian Shortsleeve, Principal
David Fialkow, Managing Director
David Orfao, Managing Director
George Bell, Managing Director
Hemant Taneja, Managing Director
Isaac Kato, Principal
Joel Cutler, Managing Director
John Simon, Managing Director
Laurence Bohn, Managing Director
Neil Sequeira, Managing Director
Terry Jones, Venture Partner
William Fitzgerald, Managing Director & CFO

Type of Firm

Private Equity Firm

Project Preferences

Role in Financing:

Prefer role as deal originator but will also invest in deals created by others

Type of Financing Preferred:

Early Stage
First Stage Financing
Startup

Size of Investments Considered:

Min Size of Investment Considered (000s): $1,000
Max Size of Investment Considered (000s): $25,000

Geographical Preferences

United States Preferences:

Northeast

Industry Focus

(% based on actual investment)

Internet Specific	51.5%
Computer Software and Services	22.4%
Communications and Media	8.2%
Industrial/Energy	6.7%
Other Products	5.0%
Semiconductors/Other Elect.	3.0%
Computer Hardware	2.2%
Medical/Health	0.7%
Consumer Related	0.4%

Additional Information

Name of Most Recent Fund: General Catalyst Group V, L.P.
Most Recent Fund Was Raised: 10/02/2007
Year Founded: 2000
Capital Under Management: $1,000,000,000
Current Activity Level: Actively seeking new investments

GENERAL ENTERPRISE MANAGEMENT SERVICES LTD (AKA: GEMS)

3601, Cheung Kong Center
2 Queen's Road Central
Central, Hong Kong
Phone: 852-2838-0093
Fax: 852-2838-0292
E-mail: contact@gems.com.hk
Website: www.gems.com.hk

Management and Staff

Geoff Spender, Managing Partner
John Cheuck, Partner

Type of Firm

Private Equity Firm

Association Membership

Hong Kong Venture Capital Association (HKVCA)

Project Preferences

Type of Financing Preferred:

Expansion
Mezzanine
Balanced
Later Stage
Management Buyouts

Size of Investments Considered:

Min Size of Investment Considered (000s): $10,000
Max Size of Investment Considered (000s): $50,000

Geographical Preferences

International Preferences:

Indonesia
India
China
Hong Kong
Thailand
Philippines
Singapore
Korea, South
Asia
Japan
Malaysia

Industry Preferences

In Communications prefer:

Telecommunications

In Semiconductor/Electr prefer:

Electronics

In Consumer Related prefer:

Retail
Consumer Products
Consumer Services

In Industrial/Energy prefer:

Energy

In Transportation prefer:

Transportation

In Financial Services prefer:

Financial Services

In Business Serv. prefer:

Media

In Manufact. prefer:

Manufacturing

Additional Information

Name of Most Recent Fund: GEMS Oriental & General Fund Limited II
Most Recent Fund Was Raised: 06/01/2001
Year Founded: 1998
Capital Under Management: $700,000,000
Current Activity Level: Actively seeking new investments

GENERATION CAPITAL PARTNERS

One Greenwich Office Park
Greenwich, CT USA 06831
Phone: 203-422-8200
Fax: 203-422-8250
Website: www.generation.com

Other Offices

One Maritime Plaza
Suite 1555
San Francisco, CA USA 94111
Phone: 415-646-8620
Fax: 415-646-8625

Management and Staff

Andrew Hertzmark, Partner
Erich Vaden, Vice President
John Hawkins, Managing Partner
Lloyd Mandell, Partner
Mark Jennings, Managing Partner
Peter Campbell, Partner
Robert Pflieger, Partner
Russ Hawkins, Managing Partner

Type of Firm

Private Equity Firm

Association Membership

Western Association of Venture Capitalists (WAVC)

Project Preferences

Role in Financing:

Prefer role as deal originator but will also invest in deals created by others

Type of Financing Preferred:

Second Stage Financing
Leveraged Buyout
Early Stage
Generalist PE
Start-up Financing
First Stage Financing

Size of Investments Considered:

Min Size of Investment Considered (000s): $5,000
Max Size of Investment Considered: No Limit

Geographical Preferences

United States Preferences:
All U.S.

Canadian Preferences:
All Canada

Industry Focus

(% based on actual investment)

Internet Specific	82.8%
Communications and Media	6.3%
Medical/Health	5.6%
Consumer Related	3.1%
Computer Software and Services	1.9%
Industrial/Energy	0.3%

Additional Information

Name of Most Recent Fund: Generation Capital Partners VRC LP
Most Recent Fund Was Raised: 04/30/2007
Year Founded: 1995
Capital Under Management: $325,000,000
Current Activity Level: Actively seeking new investments
Method of Compensation: Return on invest. most important, but chg. closing fees, service fees, etc.

GENERATION EQUITY INVESTORS

345 East 12th Street
Suite 28
New York, NY USA 10003
Phone: 617-935-9149
Fax: 617-663-6186
Website: www.generation-equity.com

Other Offices

164 Chestnut Street
West Newton, MA USA 02465
Phone: 508-962-5723
Fax: 617-965-6776

Management and Staff

Brian Colton, Co-Founder
Gary Furst, Co-Founder

Type of Firm

Private Equity Firm

Project Preferences

Type of Financing Preferred:
Leveraged Buyout

Additional Information

Year Founded: 2005
Capital Under Management: $2,300,000
Current Activity Level: Actively seeking new investments

GENERATION GROWTH CAPITAL, INC.

411 East Wisconsin Avenue
Suite 1710
Milwaukee, WI USA 53202
Phone: 414-291-8908
Fax: 414-291-8918
E-mail: info@generationgrowth.com
Website: www.generationgrowth.com

Management and Staff

Cory Nettles, Managing Director

Type of Firm

Private Equity Firm

Project Preferences

Type of Financing Preferred:
Leveraged Buyout
Turnaround

Size of Investments Considered:
Min Size of Investment Considered (000s): $1,000
Max Size of Investment Considered (000s): $5,000

Industry Preferences

In Business Serv. prefer:
Services
Distribution

In Manufact. prefer:
Manufacturing

Additional Information

Year Founded: 2007
Current Activity Level: Actively seeking new investments

GENERATION INVESTMENT MANAGEMENT LLP

One Vine Street
London, United Kingdom W1J 0AH
Phone: 44-207-534-4700
Fax: 44-207-534-4701
Website: www.generationim.com

Other Offices

One Bryant Park
48th Floor
New York, NY USA 10036
Phone: 212-584-3650
Fax: 212-584-3652

29 Chifley Tower
2 Chifley Square
Sydney, Australia 2000
Phone: 61-2-9375-2243
Fax: 61-2-9375-2121

Management and Staff

Peter Harris, Chief Operating Officer

Type of Firm

Private Equity Firm

Industry Preferences

In Industrial/Energy prefer:
Energy
Alternative Energy
Energy Conservation Relat

In Other prefer:
Environment Responsible

Additional Information

Year Founded: 2008
Capital Under Management: $683,000,000
Current Activity Level: Actively seeking new investments

GENERIS CAPITAL PARTNERS

8 rue Montesquieu
Paris, France 75001
Phone: 33-1-7894-8710
Fax: 33-1-7894-8729
E-mail: generis@generiscapital.com
Website: www.generiscapital.com

Management and Staff

David Kauffmann, Venture Partner
John Fromson, Venture Partner
Paul Toon, Managing Partner
Thibaut De Roux, Managing Partner

Type of Firm

Private Equity Firm

Association Membership

French Venture Capital Association (AFIC)

Project Preferences

Type of Financing Preferred:
Early Stage
Expansion
Public Companies
Later Stage
Seed

Geographical Preferences

International Preferences:
United Kingdom
Luxembourg
Netherlands
Europe
Scandanavia/Nordic Region
Belgium
Germany
France

Additional Information

Year Founded: 2009
Current Activity Level: Actively seeking new investments

GENESIS CAMPUS

16475 Dallas Parkway
Suite 620
Addison, TX USA 75001
Phone: 972-991-9942
Fax: 972-669-7873
E-mail: info@genesiscampus.com
Website: www.genesiscampus.com

Management and Staff

Laszlo Szerenyi, Venture Partner
Michael Buckland, Venture Partner
Ray Jamp, Partner
Roman Kikta, General Partner
Wu-Fu Chen, General Partner

Type of Firm

Incubator/Development Program

Project Preferences

Role in Financing:

Will function either as deal originator or investor in deals created by others

Type of Financing Preferred:

Second Stage Financing
Early Stage
Start-up Financing
Balanced
Seed
First Stage Financing

Size of Investments Considered:

Min Size of Investment Considered (000s): $100
Max Size of Investment Considered (000s): $4,000

Geographical Preferences

United States Preferences:

Southern California
Northern California
Texas
Southwest

Industry Preferences

In Communications prefer:

Commercial Communications
Telecommunications
Wireless Communications
Data Communications
Other Communication Prod.

In Computer Software prefer:

Applications Software

In Internet Specific prefer:

Internet
Ecommerce
Web Aggregration/Portals

In Semiconductor/Electr prefer:

Semiconductor
Circuit Boards

Additional Information

Year Founded: 2001
Capital Under Management: $48,000,000
Current Activity Level: Actively seeking new investments
Method of Compensation: Return on investment is of primary concern, do not charge fees

GENESIS CAPITAL CONSULTING & MANAGEMENT, LTD.

20/F, Rouy Chai Int'l Bldg.
No.8 Yong An Dongli
Beijing, China 100022
Phone: 86-10-8528-8998
Fax: 86-10-8528-8890
Website: www. genesis-cap.com

Other Offices

Suite 3008, 30/F One Int'l Finance Ctr.
1 Harbour View Street Central
Hong Kong, Hong Kong
Phone: 852-2295-1120
Fax: 852-2295-1121

Management and Staff

Pu Zhang, Managing Director
Stan Yue, Managing Director

Type of Firm

Private Equity Firm

Association Membership

Venture Capital Association of Beijing (VCAB)

Project Preferences

Type of Financing Preferred:

Startup

Geographical Preferences

International Preferences:

China

Industry Preferences

In Communications prefer:

Telecommunications

In Computer Software prefer:

Software

Additional Information

Year Founded: 2000
Current Activity Level: Actively seeking new investments

GENESIS CAPITAL CORP.

8 King Street East
Suite 1400
Toronto, Canada M5C 1B5
Phone: 416-214-2225
Fax: 416-214-0593
E-mail: info@genesiscapitalcorp.com
Website: www.genesiscapitalcorp.com

Management and Staff

Martin Philp, Managing Partner
Mike Wilson, Managing Partner
Paul Massara, President

Type of Firm

Private Equity Firm

Association Membership

Canadian Venture Capital Association

Project Preferences

Type of Financing Preferred:

Acquisition

Geographical Preferences

United States Preferences:

All U.S.

Canadian Preferences:

All Canada

Industry Preferences

In Industrial/Energy prefer:

Energy

In Business Serv. prefer:

Services
Distribution

In Manufact. prefer:

Manufacturing

In Other prefer:

Environment Responsible

Additional Information

Year Founded: 2006
Current Activity Level: Actively seeking new investments

GENESIS CAPITAL, INC.

250 West 57th Street
Suite 2214
New York, NY USA 10169
Phone: 212-682-3603
Fax: 212-682-4025

Management and Staff

Jeffrey Parker, President

Type of Firm

Bank Affiliated

Project Preferences

Role in Financing:

Prefer role as deal originator but will also invest in deals created by others

Type of Financing Preferred:

Second Stage Financing
Leveraged Buyout
Special Situation

Size of Investments Considered:
Min Size of Investment Considered (000s): $10,000
Max Size of Investment Considered: No Limit

Industry Preferences

In Communications prefer:
Commercial Communications
CATV & Pay TV Systems
Radio & TV Broadcasting
Telecommunications
Data Communications

In Computer Hardware prefer:
Computer Graphics and Dig
Integrated Turnkey System

In Computer Software prefer:
Computer Services
Systems Software
Applications Software
Artificial Intelligence

In Semiconductor/Electr prefer:
Electronic Components
Semiconductor
Component Testing Equipmt
Laser Related
Fiber Optics
Analytic/Scientific

In Biotechnology prefer:
Biotech Related Research

In Medical/Health prefer:
Medical/Health
Medical Diagnostics
Medical Therapeutics

In Consumer Related prefer:
Retail
Food/Beverage
Consumer Products
Education Related

In Industrial/Energy prefer:
Alternative Energy
Environmental Related

In Financial Services prefer:
Real Estate

In Business Serv. prefer:
Consulting Services

In Manufact. prefer:
Office Automation Equipmt
Publishing

In Agr/Forestr/Fish prefer:
Agriculture related

Additional Information
Year Founded: 1981
Capital Under Management: $50,000,000
Current Activity Level: Actively seeking new investments
Method of Compensation: Return on invest. most important, but chg. closing fees, service fees, etc.

GENESIS CAPITAL, S.R.O.
Na Safrance 22
Praha 10
Prague, Czech Republic 101 00
Phone: 420-271-740-207
Fax: 420-271-740-208
E-mail: genesis@genesis.cz
Website: www.genesis.cz

Other Offices
Jelenia 4
Bratislava, Slovakia 814 99
Phone: 421-2-5262-6614
Fax: 421-2-5262-6615

Management and Staff
Jan Tauber, Managing Director

Type of Firm
Private Equity Firm

Association Membership
Czech Venture Capital Association (CVCA)
European Private Equity and Venture Capital Assoc.

Project Preferences

Role in Financing:
Prefer role as deal originator but will also invest in deals created by others

Type of Financing Preferred:
Leveraged Buyout
Early Stage
Expansion
Generalist PE
Balanced
Later Stage
Management Buyouts
Acquisition

Size of Investments Considered:
Min Size of Investment Considered (000s): $2,097
Max Size of Investment Considered (000s): $12,582

Geographical Preferences

International Preferences:
Slovak Repub.
Czech Republic
Eastern Europe

Industry Preferences

In Communications prefer:
Communications and Media

In Consumer Related prefer:
Consumer Products

In Industrial/Energy prefer:
Energy

In Manufact. prefer:
Manufacturing

Additional Information
Name of Most Recent Fund: Genesis Private Equity Fund
Most Recent Fund Was Raised: 02/07/2003
Year Founded: 1999
Capital Under Management: $42,900,000
Current Activity Level: Actively seeking new investments

GENESIS PARK VENTURES
2131 San Felipe
Houston, TX USA 77019
Phone: 713-533-5898
E-mail: info@genesis-park.com
Website: www.genesis-park.com

Management and Staff
Bonnie Lewis, Chief Financial Officer
Neil Kelley, Founding Partner
Paul Hobby, Founding Partner
Peter Shaper, Founding Partner

Type of Firm
Private Equity Firm

Project Preferences

Role in Financing:
Prefer role as deal originator but will also invest in deals created by others

Type of Financing Preferred:
Early Stage
First Stage Financing
Startup

Size of Investments Considered:
Min Size of Investment Considered (000s): $500
Max Size of Investment Considered (000s): $2,000

Geographical Preferences

United States Preferences:
Texas

Industry Preferences

In Communications prefer:
Telecommunications

In Computer Software prefer:
Software

In Industrial/Energy prefer:
Energy

Additional Information
Name of Most Recent Fund: Genesis Park Ventures
Most Recent Fund Was Raised: 03/01/2000
Year Founded: 2000
Capital Under Management: $27,000,000
Current Activity Level: Actively seeking new investments
Method of Compensation: Return on investment is of primary concern, do not charge fees

GENESIS PARTNERS

P.O. Box 12866
Herzliya Pituach, Israel 46733
Phone: 972-9-972-9000
Fax: 972-9-972-9001
E-mail: office@genesisvp.com
Website: www.genesispartners.co.il

Other Offices

Ackerstein Towers, Building B
11 Hamenofim Street, 4th Floor
Herzliya Pituach, Israel

Management and Staff

Debbie Haim, Principal
Eddy Shalev, Managing General Partner
Eyal Kishon, Managing Partner
Gary Gannot, General Partner
Mark Ziering, Principal
Ron Yachini, General Partner
Vered Assulin, Partner
Yair Shoham, General Partner
Yaron Polak, Venture Partner

Type of Firm

Private Equity Firm

Project Preferences

Type of Financing Preferred:
Early Stage
Expansion
Balanced
Later Stage
Seed
Startup

Geographical Preferences

International Preferences:
Middle East
Israel

Industry Focus

(% based on actual investment)

Communications and Media	31.7%
Computer Software and Services	29.9%
Semiconductors/Other Elect.	14.3%
Industrial/Energy	9.5%
Internet Specific	7.2%
Computer Hardware	5.2%
Other Products	1.7%
Medical/Health	0.6%

Additional Information

Name of Most Recent Fund: Genesis Partners III, L.P.
Most Recent Fund Was Raised: 03/29/2005
Year Founded: 1997
Capital Under Management: $618,000,000
Current Activity Level: Actively seeking new investments

GENESYS CAPITAL PARTNERS, INC.

200 Front Street West
Suite 3004, P.O. Box 31
Toronto, Canada M5V 3K2
Phone: 416-598-4900
Fax: 416-598-3328
E-mail: info@genesyscapital.com
Website: www.genesyscapital.com

Management and Staff

Damian Lamb, Managing Director
Jack Cashman, Venture Partner
Judy Blumstock, Principal
Kelly Holman, Managing Director

Type of Firm

Private Equity Firm

Project Preferences

Type of Financing Preferred:
Early Stage
Balanced
Seed
Startup

Geographical Preferences

Canadian Preferences:
All Canada
Ontario

Industry Preferences

In Biotechnology prefer:
Biotechnology
Biotech Related Research

In Medical/Health prefer:
Medical/Health
Additional Information
Year Founded: 2001
Current Activity Level: Actively seeking new investments

GENEVEST CONSULTING GROUP, S.A.

6, rue Croix d'Or
Geneve, Switzerland 1204
Phone: 41-22-312-3333
Fax: 41-22-544-6030
Website: www.genevest.ch

Type of Firm

Service Provider

Association Membership

European Private Equity and Venture Capital Assoc.

Project Preferences

Role in Financing:
Prefer role as deal originator but will also invest in deals created by others

Type of Financing Preferred:
Early Stage
Expansion
Unknown
Startup

Geographical Preferences

International Preferences:
Switzerland
Europe

Industry Preferences

In Computer Software prefer:
Software

In Computer Other prefer:
Computer Related

In Semiconductor/Electr prefer:
Electronics

In Business Serv. prefer:
Media

Additional Information

Year Founded: 1983
Capital Under Management: $60,400,000
Current Activity Level: Actively seeking new investments
Method of Compensation: Return on invest. most important, but chg. closing fees, service fees, etc.

GENIUS VENTURE CAPITAL GMBH

Hagenower Strasse 73
Schwerin, Germany 19601
Phone: 49-3-8539-93500
Fax: 49-3-8539-93510
E-mail: info@genius-vc.de
Website: www.genius-vc.de

Type of Firm

Private Equity Firm

Project Preferences

Type of Financing Preferred:
Early Stage
Startup

Geographical Preferences

International Preferences:
Europe
Germany

Industry Preferences

In Communications prefer:
Communications and Media

In Biotechnology prefer:
Biotechnology

In Medical/Health prefer:
Medical/Health

In Industrial/Energy prefer:
Advanced Materials

Additional Information
Year Founded: 1998
Current Activity Level: Actively seeking new investments

GENNX360 CAPITAL PARTNERS
300 Park Avenue
17th Floor
New York, NY USA 10022
Phone: 888-215-6992
Fax: 212-572-6472
E-mail: info@gennx360.biz
Website: www.gennx360.biz

Other Offices
701 Fifth Avenue
42nd Floor
Seattle, WA USA 98104

245 First Street
Suite 1800
Cambridge, MA USA 02142

DLF City, PhaseV (Churchhill, 2nd floor)
Sector 53, Gurgaon
Haryana, India 122002
Phone: 91-124-402-3047

Management and Staff
Matthew Guenther, Principal
Monty York, Managing Partner
Rena Clark, Principal

Type of Firm
Private Equity Firm

Project Preferences

Type of Financing Preferred:
Leveraged Buyout

Size of Investments Considered:
Min Size of Investment Considered (000s): $250,000
Max Size of Investment Considered: No Limit

Geographical Preferences

International Preferences:
All International

Industry Preferences

In Industrial/Energy prefer:
Industrial Products

In Business Serv. prefer:
Services

Additional Information
Year Founded: 2006
Capital Under Management: $560,000,000
Current Activity Level: Actively seeking new investments

GENOPOLE 1ER JOUR (AKA: G1J)
5, rue Henri Desbrueres
Evry Cedex, France 91030
Phone: 33-1-6087-8300
Fax: 33-1-6087-8301
E-mail: presse@genopole.fr
Website: www.genopole.com

Management and Staff
Pierre Tambourin, Chief Executive Officer
Thierry Mandon, President

Type of Firm
Private Equity Firm

Association Membership
French Venture Capital Association (AFIC)

Project Preferences

Type of Financing Preferred:
Early Stage
Seed
Startup

Geographical Preferences

International Preferences:
Europe
France

Industry Preferences

In Biotechnology prefer:
Biotechnology
Human Biotechnology

Additional Information
Year Founded: 1999
Current Activity Level: Actively seeking new investments

GENSEC IRELAND LTD
Beech House
Beech Hill Road, Clonskeagh
Dublin 4, Ireland
Phone: 353-1-261-4000
Fax: 353-1-260-3175
Website: www.gensec.com

Type of Firm
Bank Affiliated

Project Preferences

Type of Financing Preferred:
Expansion
Later Stage

Geographical Preferences

International Preferences:
Ireland
Europe

Industry Preferences

In Communications prefer:
Commercial Communications

In Computer Software prefer:
Software

In Internet Specific prefer:
Internet

Additional Information
Year Founded: 2001
Capital Under Management: $4,700,000
Current Activity Level: Actively seeking new investments

GENSTAR CAPITAL LLC
Four Embarcadero Center
Suite 1900
San Francisco, CA USA 94111
Phone: 415-834-2350
Fax: 415-834-2383
E-mail: info@gencap.com
Website: www.gencap.com

Management and Staff
Darren Gold, Managing Director
J. Ryan Clark, Principal
James Nadauld, Principal
Jean-Pierre Conte, Chairman & Managing Director
Mark Hanson, Managing Director
Melissa Dickerson, Chief Financial Officer
Richard Paterson, Managing Director
Richard Hoskins, Managing Director
Robert Weltman, Managing Director

Type of Firm
Private Equity Firm

Project Preferences

Role in Financing:
Prefer role as deal originator but will also invest in deals created by others

Type of Financing Preferred:
Leveraged Buyout
Management Buyouts
Recapitalizations

Size of Investments Considered:
Min Size of Investment Considered (000s): $10,000
Max Size of Investment Considered (000s): $50,000

Geographical Preferences

Canadian Preferences:
All Canada

Industry Focus
(% based on actual investment)

Other Products	38.4%
Industrial/Energy	35.5%
Medical/Health	20.2%
Biotechnology	3.3%
Communications and Media	2.5%
Consumer Related	0.1%

Additional Information

Name of Most Recent Fund: Genstar Capital Partners IV, L.P.
Most Recent Fund Was Raised: 10/29/2004
Year Founded: 1988
Capital Under Management: $810,800,000
Current Activity Level: Actively seeking new investments
Method of Compensation: Return on invest. most important, but chg. closing fees, service fees, etc.

GENUITY CAPITAL PARTNERS

40 King Street West
Suite 4900, Scotia Plaza
Toronto, Canada M5H 3Y2
Phone: 416-603-6000
Fax: 416-603-3099
E-mail: investor.relations@genuitycm.com
Website: www.genuitycm.com

Other Offices

Bentall Tower Five
1068-550 Burrard Street
Vancouver, Canada V6C 2B5
Phone: 604-331-1444
Fax: 604-331-1446

1800 McGill College Avenue
Suite 3000
Montreal, Canada H3A 3J6
Phone: 514-281-3250
Fax: 514-281-3022

One Federal Street
25th Floor
Boston, MA USA 02110
Phone: 617-338-1008
Fax: 617-338-1016

717 Fifth Avenue
Suite 1403
New York, NY USA 10022
Phone: 212-644-0001
Fax: 212-644-1341

1700 Stock Exchange Tower
300 Fifth Avenue SouthWest
Calgary, Canada T2P 3C4
Phone: 403-266-3400
Fax: 403-266-1755

Management and Staff

Conrad Beyleveldt, Chief Financial Officer
David Kassie, Chief Executive Officer

Type of Firm

Bank Affiliated

Project Preferences

Type of Financing Preferred:

Leveraged Buyout
Strategic Alliances
Acquisition
Joint Ventures
Recapitalizations

Geographical Preferences

Canadian Preferences:

All Canada

Additional Information

Year Founded: 2005
Current Activity Level: Actively seeking new investments

GEOCAPITAL PARTNERS, LLC

One Executive Drive
Suite 160
Fort Lee, NJ USA 07024
Phone: 201-461-9292
Fax: 201-461-7793
E-mail: investments@geocapital.com
Website: www.geocapital.com

Other Offices

8311 Brier Creek Parkway
Suite 105-128
Raleigh, NC USA 27617
Phone: 919-479-9525
Fax: 919-477-7804

Management and Staff

James Basili, Principal
Judith Benardete, Principal
Lawrence Lepard, Managing General Partner
Richard Vines, General Partner
Shakir Merali, Principal
Stephen Clearman, Managing General Partner
Tushar Shah, Principal

Type of Firm

Bank Affiliated

Association Membership

British Venture Capital Association (BVCA)
European Private Equity and Venture Capital Assoc.

Project Preferences

Role in Financing:

Prefer role as deal originator but will also invest in deals created by others

Type of Financing Preferred:

Early Stage
Expansion
Start-up Financing
Later Stage
Seed
First Stage Financing
Private Placement

Size of Investments Considered:

Min Size of Investment Considered (000s): $2,000
Max Size of Investment Considered (000s): $20,000

Geographical Preferences

Canadian Preferences:

All Canada

International Preferences:

Luxembourg
Netherlands
Portugal
Albania
Western Europe
Spain
Belgium
Germany
France

Industry Focus

(% based on actual investment)

Computer Software and Services	40.2%
Internet Specific	34.5%
Communications and Media	12.7%
Other Products	5.8%
Computer Hardware	4.2%
Consumer Related	2.1%
Industrial/Energy	0.2%
Medical/Health	0.2%
Semiconductors/Other Elect.	0.2%

Additional Information

Year Founded: 1984
Capital Under Management: $490,300,000
Current Activity Level: Making few, if any, new investments
Method of Compensation: Return on investment is of primary concern, do not charge fees

---

GEORGETOWN VENTURE PARTNERS (AKA: GVP)

318 Old Brompton Road
Second Floor
London, United Kingdom SW5 9JH
Phone: 44-20-7373-4823
Fax: 801-681-3604
E-mail: inquiries@georgetownventures.com
Website: www.georgetownventures.com

Management and Staff

Andrew Romans, Managing Partner

Type of Firm

Private Equity Firm

Project Preferences

Type of Financing Preferred:

Expansion

Size of Investments Considered:
Min Size of Investment Considered (000s): $5,000
Max Size of Investment Considered (000s): $50,000

Geographical Preferences

Canadian Preferences:
All Canada

International Preferences:
United Kingdom
Europe

Industry Preferences

In Communications prefer:
Communications and Media

Additional Information

Year Founded: 2004
Current Activity Level: Actively seeking new investments

GEORGIA VENTURE PARTNERS LLC

75 Fifth Street Northwest
Suite 860
Atlanta, GA USA 30308
Phone: 404-920-2041
Fax: 404-920-2054
Website: www.georgiavc.com

Management and Staff

Jim Heitner, Principal
John Richard, Managing Director
Thomas Callaway, Managing Director

Type of Firm

Private Equity Firm

Project Preferences

Type of Financing Preferred:
Early Stage
Seed

Size of Investments Considered:
Min Size of Investment Considered (000s): $100
Max Size of Investment Considered (000s): $500

Geographical Preferences

United States Preferences:
Georgia

Additional Information

Name of Most Recent Fund: GVP Seed Fund
Most Recent Fund Was Raised: 04/29/2005
Year Founded: 2004
Capital Under Management: $3,500,000
Current Activity Level: Actively seeking new investments

GEORGIAN PARTNERS

Eight Price Street
Third Floor
Toronto, Canada M4W 1Z4
Phone: 416-868-9696
Fax: 416-868-1514
E-mail: info@georgianpartners.com
Website: www.georgianpartners.com

Other Offices

Eight Price Street
Third Floor
Toronto, Canada M4W 1Z4
Phone: 416-868-9696
Fax: 416-868-1514

Management and Staff

John Berton, Partner
Justin LaFayette, Partner
Simon Chong, Partner

Type of Firm

Private Equity Firm

Geographical Preferences

Canadian Preferences:
Ontario

Additional Information

Year Founded: 2009
Current Activity Level: Actively seeking new investments

GERKEN CAPITAL ASSOCIATES

110 Tiburon Boulevard
Suite 5
Mill Valley, CA USA 94941
Phone: 415-383-1464
Fax: 415-383-1253
E-mail: info@gerkencapital.com
Website: www.gerkencapital.com

Type of Firm

Bank Affiliated

Additional Information

Year Founded: 2002
Current Activity Level: Actively seeking new investments

GERMANINCUBATOR (AKA: GI VENTURES AG)

Gundelindenstrasse 2
Munich, Germany 80805
Phone: 49-89-3838-9220
Fax: 49-89-3838-9299
E-mail: info@gi-ag.com
Website: www.gi-ag.com

Management and Staff

Jurgen Diegruber, Chief Executive Officer
Peter G Nietzer, Chief Financial Officer

Type of Firm

Incubator/Development Program

Association Membership

European Private Equity and Venture Capital Assoc.

Project Preferences

Type of Financing Preferred:
Early Stage
Expansion
Seed
Management Buyouts
Startup

Geographical Preferences

International Preferences:
Switzerland
Austria
Germany
Asia

Industry Preferences

In Communications prefer:
Telecommunications

In Internet Specific prefer:
Internet

In Business Serv. prefer:
Media

Additional Information

Year Founded: 2000
Capital Under Management: $8,700,000
Current Activity Level: Actively seeking new investments

GERRITY CAPITAL PARTNERS, LLC (FKA: MULTI-CHANNEL VENTURES)

1000 Universal Studios Plaza
Building 22-A
Orlando, FL USA 32819
Phone: 407-224-6847
Fax: 407-224-8490
Website: www.gerritycapital.com

Type of Firm

Private Equity Firm

Project Preferences

Role in Financing:
Prefer role as deal originator but will also invest in deals created by others

Type of Financing Preferred:
Early Stage

Expansion
Public Companies
Acquisition
Joint Ventures
Private Placement
Industry Rollups
Startup

Size of Investments Considered:

Min Size of Investment Considered (000s): $1,000
Max Size of Investment Considered (000s): $25,000

Geographical Preferences

United States Preferences:

Mid Atlantic
Northern California
California
Florida
New York
All U.S.

Industry Preferences

In Communications prefer:

Communications and Media
CATV & Pay TV Systems
Radio & TV Broadcasting
Telecommunications
Media and Entertainment

In Internet Specific prefer:

E-Commerce Technology
Internet
Web Aggregration/Portals

In Consumer Related prefer:

Entertainment and Leisure
Consumer Services
Hotels and Resorts

In Financial Services prefer:

Real Estate

Additional Information

Year Founded: 2002
Capital Under Management: $100,000,000
Current Activity Level: Actively seeking new investments
Method of Compensation: Return on invest. most important, but chg. closing fees, service fees, etc.

GESCAIXA GALICIA SGECR SA

Linares Rivas 30
Coruna, Spain 15005
Phone: 34-981-121-530
Fax: 34-981-123-052
E-mail: gescaixa@caixagalicia.es
Website: www.caixagalicia.es

Type of Firm

Bank Affiliated

Association Membership

Spanish Venture Capital Association (ASCRI)

Project Preferences

Type of Financing Preferred:

Expansion

Geographical Preferences

International Preferences:

Spain

Industry Preferences

In Computer Hardware prefer:

Computers

In Internet Specific prefer:

Internet

Additional Information

Year Founded: 2000
Current Activity Level: Actively seeking new investments

GESD CAPITAL PARTNERS, LLC

221 Main Street
Suite 1450
San Francisco, CA USA 94105
Phone: 415-477-8200
Fax: 415-495-8211
Website: www.gesd.com

Management and Staff

Daniel Stromberg, Partner
Louis Giraudo, Partner
Mark Briggs, Partner
Sharon Duvall, Partner
Shonn Tom, Vice President
William Dozier, Chief Financial Officer

Type of Firm

Private Equity Firm

Project Preferences

Type of Financing Preferred:

Leveraged Buyout
Later Stage

Industry Preferences

In Consumer Related prefer:

Retail
Food/Beverage

In Financial Services prefer:

Financial Services

Additional Information

Year Founded: 2001
Capital Under Management: $150,000,000
Current Activity Level: Actively seeking new investments

GESTION CAPIDEM, INC.

1595, boulevard Wilfrid-Hamel
Edifice B
Quebec City, Canada G1N 3Y7
Phone: 418-681-1910
Fax: 418-527-1967

Type of Firm

Other

Project Preferences

Role in Financing:

Will function either as deal originator or investor in deals created by others

Type of Financing Preferred:

Second Stage Financing
Leveraged Buyout
Start-up Financing
First Stage Financing

Size of Investments Considered:

Min Size of Investment Considered (000s): $300
Max Size of Investment Considered (000s): $500

Additional Information

Year Founded: 1988
Capital Under Management: $10,500,000
Current Activity Level: Actively seeking new investments
Method of Compensation: Return on invest. most important, but chg. closing fees, service fees, etc.

GESTION DE CAPITAL RIESGO DEL PAIS VASCO

Gran Via 35 - 3 planta
Bilbao, Spain 48009
Phone: 34-94-479-0192
Fax: 34-94-479-0050
E-mail: info@spri.es
Website: www.gestioncapitalriesgo.com

Type of Firm

Private Equity Firm

Association Membership

Spanish Venture Capital Association (ASCRI)

Project Preferences

Type of Financing Preferred:

Second Stage Financing
Early Stage
Expansion
Turnaround
Balanced
Later Stage
Seed
Startup

Size of Investments Considered:

Min Size of Investment Considered (000s): $100
Max Size of Investment Considered (000s): $100,000

Geographical Preferences

International Preferences:
Europe
Spain

Additional Information

Year Founded: 1985
Capital Under Management: $47,500,000
Current Activity Level: Actively seeking new investments

GET CAPITAL

620 Service Building
80 Lanyue Road
Guangzhou, China 510660
Phone: 86-20-3221-1153
Fax: 86-20-3221-1146
Website: www.getcapitalgz.com

Management and Staff

Peigu Liu, Managing Director

Type of Firm

Private Equity Firm

Project Preferences

Type of Financing Preferred:
Early Stage
Expansion
Later Stage
Seed
Startup

Geographical Preferences

International Preferences:
China
Asia

Additional Information

Year Founded: 2008
Capital Under Management: $117,200,000
Current Activity Level: Actively seeking new investments

GEVAERT N.V.

Septestraat 27
Mortsel, Belgium 2640
Phone: 32-3-443-0216
Fax: 32-3-443-0210
E-mail: directie@gevaert.be
Website: www.gevaert.be

Type of Firm

Private Equity Firm

Project Preferences

Type of Financing Preferred:
Balanced

Geographical Preferences

International Preferences:
Belgium

Additional Information

Year Founded: 2004
Current Activity Level: Actively seeking new investments

GEZINA AS

Kronprinsesse Marthas
Plass 1
Oslo, Norway N-0160
Phone: 47-22-40-3080
Fax: 47-22-40-3081
E-mail: ee@brovig.no
Website: www.brovig.no

Other Offices

Havnegaten 29
Farsund, Norway N-4550
Phone: 47-38-39-5670
Fax: 47-38-39-5690

Management and Staff

Erik Engebretsen, Managing Director

Type of Firm

Private Equity Firm

Project Preferences

Type of Financing Preferred:
Balanced

Geographical Preferences

International Preferences:
Europe

Industry Preferences

In Biotechnology prefer:
Biotechnology

In Medical/Health prefer:
Pharmaceuticals

Additional Information

Year Founded: 1889
Current Activity Level: Actively seeking new investments

GF CAPITAL MANAGEMENT & ADVISORS LLC

767 Fifth Avenue
46th Floor
New York, NY USA 10153
Phone: 212-433-1234
Fax: 212-433-1239
E-mail: info@gfcap.com
Website: www.gfcap.com

Management and Staff

Christina Hull, Vice President
David Basner, Co-Founder
Erik Baker, Co-Founder
Neil Shapiro, Co-Founder

Type of Firm

Private Equity Firm

Project Preferences

Type of Financing Preferred:
Leveraged Buyout
Acquisition
Industry Rollups
Recapitalizations

Geographical Preferences

United States Preferences:
All U.S.

Industry Preferences

In Communications prefer:
Telecommunications
Media and Entertainment

In Computer Software prefer:
Software

In Consumer Related prefer:
Consumer Products

Additional Information

Year Founded: 2006
Current Activity Level: Actively seeking new investments

GF PRIVATE EQUITY GROUP, LLC

175 Mercado Street
Suite 201
Durango, CO USA 81301
Phone: 970-764-6300
Fax: 970-764-6301
E-mail: info@gfprivateequity.com
Website: www.gfprivateequity.com

Management and Staff

Chris Metcalf, Vice President
David Fallace, Vice President
Elliott Wimberly, Vice President
James Thompson, Vice President
Ken Lucas, Vice President
Mahesh Vaidya, Vice President
Thomas Arland, President

Type of Firm

Private Equity Advisor or Fund of Funds

Project Preferences

Type of Financing Preferred:
Fund of Funds
Leveraged Buyout
Early Stage

Industry Preferences

In Communications prefer:
Telecommunications

In Computer Software prefer:
Software

In Medical/Health prefer:
Medical Products

In Industrial/Energy prefer:
Alternative Energy

In Financial Services prefer:
Financial Services

Additional Information

Year Founded: 2003
Current Activity Level: Actively seeking new investments

GFE (GESELLSCHAFT FR ELEKTROMETALLURGIE MBH)

Hoefener Strasse 45
Nuremberg, Germany D-90431
E-mail: contact@gfe-online.de

Type of Firm

Private Equity Firm

Additional Information

Year Founded: 2009
Current Activity Level: Actively seeking new investments

GFI ENERGY VENTURES

11611 San Vicente Boulevard
Suite 710
Los Angeles, CA USA 90049
Phone: 310-442-0542
Fax: 310-442-0540
E-mail: info@gfienergy.com
Website: www.gfienergy.com

Management and Staff

Andrew Osler, Partner
Ian Schapiro, Partner
J. Bradford Forth, Partner
R. Chad Van Sweden, Vice President
Richard Landers, Partner

Type of Firm

Private Equity Firm

Project Preferences

Type of Financing Preferred:
Leveraged Buyout
Acquisition

Industry Preferences

In Industrial/Energy prefer:
Energy

Additional Information

Year Founded: 1995
Current Activity Level: Actively seeking new investments

GGV CAPITAL

2494 Sand Hill Road
Suite 100
Menlo Park, CA USA 94025
Phone: 650-475-2150
Fax: 650-475-2151
E-mail: info@ggvc.com
Website: www.ggvc.com

Other Offices

Venture TDF Pte. Ltd.
19A Ann Siang Road
Singapore, Singapore 069699
Phone: 65-6236-6920
Fax: 65-6887-0535

Suite 38, 11th FL, North Building
Kerry Centre, One Guang Hua Road
Beijing, China 100020
Phone: 86-10-6599-7907
Fax: 86-10-6599-7959

Unit 3701, K. Wah Center
1010 Huaihai Zhong Road
Shanghai, China 200031
Phone: 86-21-6161-1717
Fax: 86-21-5404-7667

Management and Staff

Alvin Wenhai Sun, Partner
Fumin Zhuo, Managing Partner
Glenn Solomon, Managing Partner
Hany Nada, Managing Partner
Helen Wong, Partner
Jeff Richards, Partner
Jenny Lee, Managing Partner
Jessie Jin, Managing Partner
Jia Fen Wang, Venture Partner
Jixun Foo, Managing Partner
Joel Kellman, Managing Partner
Kheng Nam Lee, Venture Partner
Michael Kuan, Venture Partner
Scott Bonham, Managing Partner
Stephen Hyndman, Chief Financial Officer
Steve Chu, Venture Partner
Thomas Ng, Managing Partner
Yi Pin Ng, Principal
Zhuo Fumin, Managing Partner

Type of Firm

Private Equity Firm

Association Membership

National Venture Capital Association - USA (NVCA)

Project Preferences

Role in Financing:
Will function either as deal originator or investor in deals created by others

Type of Financing Preferred:
Expansion
Later Stage

Size of Investments Considered:
Min Size of Investment Considered (000s): $5,000
Max Size of Investment Considered (000s): $25,000

Geographical Preferences

International Preferences:
Hong Kong
China
Asia

Industry Preferences

In Communications prefer:
Communications and Media
Wireless Communications

In Computer Software prefer:
Software
Systems Software
Applications Software

In Internet Specific prefer:
E-Commerce Technology
Internet

In Semiconductor/Electr prefer:
Semiconductor

In Medical/Health prefer:
Medical/Health
Drug/Equipmt Delivery
Pharmaceuticals

In Business Serv. prefer:
Media

Additional Information

Year Founded: 2000
Capital Under Management: $1,000,000,000
Current Activity Level: Actively seeking new investments
Method of Compensation: Return on investment is of primary concern, do not charge fees

---

GIBRALT CAPITAL CORPORATION

1075 West Georgia Street
Suite 2600
Vancouver, Canada V6E 3C9
Phone: 604-687-3707
Fax: 604-661-4873
Website: www.gibralt.com

Other Offices

1075 West Georgia Street
Suite 2600
Vancouver, Canada V6E 3C9

Phone: 604-687-3707
Fax: 604-661-4873

Type of Firm

Private Equity Firm

Additional Information

Year Founded: 2009
Current Activity Level: Actively seeking new investments

GIC SPECIAL INVESTMENTS PTE, LTD.

168 Robinson Road
#37-01 Capital Tower
Singapore, Singapore 068912
Phone: 65-6889-8888
Fax: 65-6889-6891
E-mail: contactsi@gic.com.sg
Website: www.gic.com.sg

Other Offices

225 Shoreline Drive
Suite 600
Redwood City, CA USA 94065
Phone: 650-593-3100
Fax: 650-802-1212

Cityspire, 156 West 56th Street
19th Floor
New York, NY USA 10019
Phone: 212-468-1900
Fax: 212-468-1901

Unit 15/17, Level 12
#1 Jian Guo Men Wai Avenue
Beijing, China 100004
Phone: 86-10-6505-5920
Fax: 86-10-6505-5914

First Floor, York House
45 Seymour Street
London, United Kingdom W1H 7LX
Phone: 44-20-7725-3888
Fax: 44-20-7725-3511

10/F Shiodome City Center
Minato-ku Higabashi-Shinbashi
Tokyo, Japan 105-7110
Phone: 81-3-3289-8868
Fax: 81-3-3289-8869

Management and Staff

Ng Kok Song, Managing Director
Teh Kok Peng, President

Type of Firm

Government Affiliated Program

Association Membership

Singapore Venture Capital Association (SVCA)

Project Preferences

Type of Financing Preferred:

Fund of Funds
Leveraged Buyout
Expansion
Mezzanine
Balanced
Recapitalizations

Geographical Preferences

United States Preferences:

All U.S.

International Preferences:

India
Europe
China
Asia
Korea, South
Australia
Japan

Additional Information

Year Founded: 1982
Current Activity Level: Actively seeking new investments

GIDEON HIXON FUND

800 Ancapa Street
Suite A
Santa Barbara, CA USA 93101
Phone: 805-963-2277
Fax: 805-565-0929
Website: www.gideonhixonfund.com

Other Offices

315 East Commerce Street
Suite 300
San Antonio, TX USA 78205
Phone: 210-225-3053
Fax: 210-225-5910

Management and Staff

Benson Whitney, Managing Partner

Type of Firm

Private Equity Firm

Project Preferences

Role in Financing:

Prefer role as deal originator but will also invest in deals created by others

Type of Financing Preferred:

Second Stage Financing
Start-up Financing
Seed
First Stage Financing

Size of Investments Considered:

Min Size of Investment Considered (000s): $300
Max Size of Investment Considered (000s): $500

Geographical Preferences

United States Preferences:

West Coast

Industry Focus

(% based on actual investment)

Internet Specific	40.2%
Medical/Health	29.5%
Computer Software and Services	11.6%
Biotechnology	10.3%
Other Products	5.5%
Semiconductors/Other Elect.	3.0%

Additional Information

Year Founded: 1989
Capital Under Management: $30,000,000
Current Activity Level: Actively seeking new investments
Method of Compensation: Return on investment is of primary concern, do not charge fees

---

GIFUSHIN FINANCE CO., LTD.

7-66 Shikishima-cho
Gifu-shi, Japan 500-8369
Phone: 81-58-252-3130

Type of Firm

Bank Affiliated

Additional Information

Year Founded: 2007
Current Activity Level: Actively seeking new investments

GILBERT GLOBAL EQUITY CAPITAL, L.L.C.

320 Park Avenue
17th Floor
New York, NY USA 10022
Phone: 212-584-6200
Fax: 212-584-6211
Website: www.gilbertglobal.com

Other Offices

P.O. Box 984
New Canaan, CT USA 06840
Phone: 203-966-6022
Fax: 203-972-0250

1302 Bank of America Tower
12 Harcourt Road
Admiralty, Hong Kong
Phone: 852-2524-6100
Fax: 852-2970-0078

100 North Crescent Drive
Suite 305
Beverly Hills, CA USA 90210
Phone: 310-385-3688
Fax: 310-248-3639

Bucklersbury House
3 Queen Victoria Street
London, United Kingdom EC4N 8EL
Phone: 20-7246-6201
Fax: 20-7329-3730

Management and Staff

Arakin Gaw, Partner
David Filippone, Partner
Eric Wei, Managing Director
Eric Bunting, Partner
Paul Deuticke, Partner
Richard Gaenzle, Partner

Type of Firm

Private Equity Firm

Project Preferences

Type of Financing Preferred:

Second Stage Financing
Leveraged Buyout
Expansion
Mezzanine
Later Stage
Management Buyouts
Acquisition
Special Situation
Distressed Debt
Recapitalizations

Size of Investments Considered:

Min Size of Investment Considered (000s): $10,000
Max Size of Investment Considered (000s): $150,000

Geographical Preferences

International Preferences:

All International

Industry Focus

(% based on actual investment)

Communications and Media	39.2%
Semiconductors/Other Elect.	31.7%
Internet Specific	11.2%
Other Products	10.5%
Computer Software and Services	5.1%
Computer Hardware	2.3%

Additional Information

Name of Most Recent Fund: Gilbert Global Equity Partners, L.P.
Most Recent Fund Was Raised: 12/01/1997
Year Founded: 1997
Capital Under Management: $1,158,600,000
Current Activity Level: Actively seeking new investments

GILD BANKERS (FKA: LHV VENTURES)

City Plaza, Tartu mnt 2
Tallinn, Estonia 10145
Phone: 372-6-800-401
Fax: 372-6-800-410
E-mail: gild@gildbankers.com
Website: www.gildbankers.com

Other Offices

Brivibas Street 40-31
Riga, Latvia LV-1050
Phone: 371-6-750-2000
Fax: 371-6-750-2001

1 Ropemaker Street
City Point
London, United Kingdom EC2Y HT
Phone: 44-20-7153-1017

27 Pushkinskaya Street
Kiev, Ukraine 01601
Phone: 380-44-235-7991

Saborna 2a
Sofia, Bulgaria 1000
Phone: 359-29-264-260
Fax: 359-29-264-262

A. Tumeno g. 4
Vilnius, Lithuania LT- 01109
Phone: 370-5-268-5179
Fax: 370-5-279-1598

Management and Staff

Heikki Kallu, Partner
Joel Aasmae, Partner
Karolis Pocius, Partner
Kimmo Irpola, Partner
Lauri Isotamm, Partner
Pirje Raidma, Chief Financial Officer
Rain Tamm, Managing Partner
Rain Lohmus, Founder
Sarunas Skyrius, Partner
Taavi Lepmets, Partner
Tarmo Juristo, Partner
Tomas Marcinkus, Partner
Tonis Haavel, Partner
Tonno Vahk, Partner

Type of Firm

Bank Affiliated

Association Membership

European Private Equity and Venture Capital Assoc.

Project Preferences

Type of Financing Preferred:

Leveraged Buyout
Expansion
Mezzanine
Seed
Management Buyouts
Startup
Acquisition

Geographical Preferences

International Preferences:

Central Europe
Eastern Europe
Estonia
Latvia
Lithuania

Industry Preferences

In Computer Software prefer:

Software

In Internet Specific prefer:

Internet

In Business Serv. prefer:

Services

Additional Information

Year Founded: 1999
Current Activity Level: Actively seeking new investments

GILDE BUY OUT PARTNERS

Newtonlaan 91
P.O. Box 85067
Utrecht, Netherlands 3508 AB
Phone: 31-30-219-2535
Fax: 31-30-219-2530
Website: www.gilde.com

Other Offices

69, Boulevard
Haussmann
Paris, France 75008
Phone: 33-1-4098-0515
Fax: 33-1-4098-0518
Holbeinstrasse 31
Zurich, Switzerland 8008
Phone: 41-43-268-2030
Fax: 41-43-268-2035

Management and Staff

Boudewijn Molenaar, Partner
Eric-Jan B. Vink, Partner
Hubert Lange, Partner
Martijn Schreurs, Partner
Nikolai R.D. Pronk, Partner
Paul A. Bekx, Partner
Ralph Wyss, Partner
Robert M. Thole, Partner

Type of Firm

Private Equity Firm

Project Preferences

Role in Financing:

Prefer role as deal originator

Type of Financing Preferred:

Leveraged Buyout
Management Buyouts

Geographical Preferences

International Preferences:

Netherlands
Luxembourg
Europe

Austria
Belgium
Germany
France

Industry Preferences

In Industrial/Energy prefer:

Energy
Industrial Products
Materials
Machinery

In Business Serv. prefer:

Consulting Services

Additional Information

Name of Most Recent Fund: Gilde Buyout Fund III
Most Recent Fund Was Raised: 05/12/2005
Year Founded: 1996
Capital Under Management: $1,817,400,000
Current Activity Level: Actively seeking new investments

GILDE EQUITY MANAGEMENT BENELUX B.V.

Newtonlaan 91
P.O. Box 85067
Utrecht, Netherlands 3508 AB
Phone: 31-30-219-2555
Fax: 31-30-219-2575
E-mail: info@gilde.nl
Website: www.gembenelux.com

Management and Staff

Gerhard H. Nordemann, Managing Partner
Paul Lamers, Managing Partner
Remko Jager, Managing Partner

Type of Firm

Private Equity Firm

Project Preferences

Type of Financing Preferred:

Second Stage Financing
Leveraged Buyout
Management Buyouts

Size of Investments Considered:

Min Size of Investment Considered (000s): $23,339
Max Size of Investment Considered (000s): $116,695

Geographical Preferences

International Preferences:

Netherlands
Luxembourg
Belgium

Additional Information

Year Founded: 2006
Capital Under Management: $191,000,000
Current Activity Level: Actively seeking new investments

GILDE HEALTHCARE PARTNERS B.V.

Newtonlaan 91
Utrecht, Netherlands 3584 BP
Phone: 31-30-219-2536
Fax: 31-30-219-2596
E-mail: healthcare@gilde.nl
Website: www.gildehealthcare.nl

Management and Staff

Arthur Franken, Partner
Dirk Kersten, Partner
Jasper Van Gorp, Partner

Type of Firm

Private Equity Firm

Project Preferences

Type of Financing Preferred:

Early Stage
Expansion

Geographical Preferences

International Preferences:

Europe

Industry Preferences

In Medical/Health prefer:

Medical/Health

Additional Information

Year Founded: 2000
Capital Under Management: $427,900,000
Current Activity Level: Actively seeking new investments

GILDE INVESTMENT MANAGEMENT B.V.

Newtonlaan 91
P.O. Box 85067
Utrecht, Netherlands 3508 AB
Phone: 31-30-219-2555
Fax: 31-30-219-2575
E-mail: info@gilde.nl
Website: www.gilde.nl

Other Offices

Holbeinstrasse 31
Zurich, Switzerland 8008
Phone: 41-43-268-2030
Fax: 41-43-268-2035

69 Boulevard Haussmann
Haussmann
Paris, France 75008
Phone: 33-1-4098-0515
Fax: 33-1-4098-0518

Management and Staff

Boudewijn Molenaar, Managing Director
Dirk Kersten, Partner
Paul A. Bekx, Managing Director
Ralph Wyss, Managing Director
Robert M. Thole, Managing Director

Type of Firm

Private Equity Firm

Association Membership

Swiss Venture Capital Association (SECA)
Dutch Venture Capital Associaton (NVP)
European Private Equity and Venture Capital Assoc.

Project Preferences

Role in Financing:

Prefer role as deal originator but will also invest in deals created by others

Type of Financing Preferred:

Second Stage Financing
Leveraged Buyout
Early Stage
Expansion
Mezzanine
Generalist PE
Balanced
Later Stage
Management Buyouts
First Stage Financing
Startup

Size of Investments Considered:

Min Size of Investment Considered (000s): $4,708
Max Size of Investment Considered (000s): $9,416

Geographical Preferences

United States Preferences:

All U.S.

Canadian Preferences:

All Canada

International Preferences:

Italy
United Kingdom
Luxembourg
Netherlands
Europe
Bermuda
Middle East
Spain
Scandanavia/Nordic Region
Australia
Belgium
Germany
France

Industry Focus

(% based on actual investment)

Biotechnology	21.6%
Computer Software and Services	16.9%
Internet Specific	16.7%
Communications and Media	14.9%
Industrial/Energy	8.7%
Medical/Health	7.1%
Consumer Related	6.6%
Semiconductors/Other Elect.	3.0%

Other Products	2.5%
Computer Hardware	2.0%

Additional Information

Year Founded: 1982
Capital Under Management: $1,979,900,000
Current Activity Level: Actively seeking new investments
Method of Compensation: Return on invest. most important, but chg. closing fees, service fees, etc.

GILO VENTURES

P.O. Box 620925
Redwood City, CA USA 94062-0925
Phone: 650-851-5060
Fax: 650-851-2887
E-mail: contactus@giloventures.com
Website: www.giloventures.com

Other Offices

Three Daniel Frisch Street
Tel-Aviv, Israel 64731
Phone: 972-3-6957740
Fax: 972-3-6957762

Management and Staff

Gil Perez, CEO & Managing Director
Rick Bottomley, Chief Financial Officer

Type of Firm

Private Equity Firm

Project Preferences

Type of Financing Preferred:

Early Stage
Expansion
Balanced
Startup

Size of Investments Considered:

Min Size of Investment Considered (000s): $250
Max Size of Investment Considered (000s): $20,000

Geographical Preferences

International Preferences:

United Kingdom

Industry Preferences

In Communications prefer:

Communications and Media
Wireless Communications

In Semiconductor/Electr prefer:

Fiber Optics

Additional Information

Year Founded: 2000
Current Activity Level: Actively seeking new investments

GIMAR CAPITAL INVESTISSEMENT

9, Avenue de l'Opera
Paris, France 75001
Phone: 33-1-5504-7100
Fax: 33-1-5504-7104
E-mail: contact@gimar-finance.com
Website: www.gimar-finance.com

Management and Staff

Lionel Giacomotto, Managing Partner
Pierre Dauvillaire, Managing Partner

Type of Firm

Private Equity Advisor or Fund of Funds

Association Membership

French Venture Capital Association (AFIC)

Project Preferences

Type of Financing Preferred:

Fund of Funds

Additional Information

Year Founded: 2005
Current Activity Level: Actively seeking new investments

GIMV ASIA MANAGEMENT PTE., LTD.

298 Tiong Bahru Rd.
#08-04 Central Plaza
Singapore, Singapore 168730
Phone: 65-6278-3881
Fax: 65-6278-3991
E-mail: info@gimv.com
Website: www.gimv.com

Type of Firm

Bank Affiliated

Project Preferences

Type of Financing Preferred:

Fund of Funds
Leveraged Buyout
Expansion
Balanced
Startup
Recapitalizations

Geographical Preferences

International Preferences:

Indonesia
Taiwan
China
Hong Kong
Thailand
Philippines
Singapore
Asia
Malaysia

Industry Preferences

In Communications prefer:

Communications and Media
Telecommunications

In Computer Software prefer:

Software
Applications Software

In Internet Specific prefer:

Internet

In Semiconductor/Electr prefer:

Semiconductor

In Consumer Related prefer:

Entertainment and Leisure
Food/Beverage
Consumer Products

In Business Serv. prefer:

Distribution
Media

Additional Information

Year Founded: 1999
Capital Under Management: $60,000,000
Current Activity Level: Actively seeking new investments

GIMV N.V.

Karel Oomsstraat 37
Antwerp, Belgium 2018
Phone: 32-3-290-2100
Fax: 32-3-290-2105
E-mail: info@gimv.be
Website: www.gimv.com

Other Offices

38, Avenue Hoche
Paris, France 75008
Phone: 33-1-5836-4560

Lange Voorhout 9
The Hague, Netherlands 2514 EA
Phone: 31-70-361-8618
Fax: 31-70-361-8616

Barckhausstrasse 12-16
Frankfurt am Main, Germany 60325
Phone: 49-69-242-5330
Fax: 49-69-236-866

60 Cannon Street
London, United Kingdom EC4N 6NP
Phone: 44-20-7618-6428
Fax: 44-20-7618-8498

Management and Staff

Elderd Land, Partner
Hansjoerg Sage, Partner
Herman Daems, President, CEO, Chairman
Marc Vercruysse, Chief Financial Officer
Peter Maenhout, Vice President

Type of Firm
Private Equity Firm

Association Membership
Belgium Venturing Association
French Venture Capital Association (AFIC)
Dutch Venture Capital Associaton (NVP)
European Private Equity and Venture Capital Assoc.

Project Preferences

Role in Financing:
Prefer role as deal originator but will also invest in deals created by others

Type of Financing Preferred:
Leveraged Buyout
Early Stage
Expansion
Balanced
Start-up Financing
Turnaround
Seed
Management Buyouts
Startup
Recapitalizations

Size of Investments Considered:
Min Size of Investment Considered (000s): $1,883
Max Size of Investment Considered (000s): $28,248

Geographical Preferences

United States Preferences:
All U.S.

International Preferences:
Central Europe
Europe
Western Europe
Eastern Europe
Belgium
Germany
Russia

Industry Focus
(% based on actual investment)

Biotechnology	28.1%
Consumer Related	13.2%
Communications and Media	12.1%
Other Products	10.5%
Medical/Health	9.8%
Internet Specific	8.5%
Computer Software and Services	7.7%
Semiconductors/Other Elect.	5.6%
Computer Hardware	3.5%
Industrial/Energy	0.9%

Additional Information
Name of Most Recent Fund: Halder GIMV Germany Fund
Most Recent Fund Was Raised: 11/18/2003
Year Founded: 1980
Capital Under Management: $847,400,000
Current Activity Level: Actively seeking new investments

GIRAFFE CAPITAL LP
780 Third Avenue
45th Floor
New York, NY USA 10128
Phone: 212- 833-9983
Fax: 314-754-8363
E-mail: info@giraffecapital.net
Website: www.giraffecapital.net

Type of Firm
Private Equity Firm

Additional Information
Year Founded: 2009
Current Activity Level: Actively seeking new investments

GIV VENTURE PARTNERS (AKA: GLOBAL INTERNET VENTURES)
1350 Edgmont Avenue
Suite 2550
Chester, PA USA 19013
Phone: 484-823-8008
Fax: 302-239-9322
E-mail: info@givventurepartners.com
Website: www.givventurepartners.com

Other Offices
Suite 11, 3/F Beijing Kerry Center
1 Guanghua Road, Chaoyand District
Beijing, China
Phone: 8610-8529-8905
Fax: 8610-8529-8866

No. 714 Carlton Towers
No. 1 Airport Road
Bangalore, India
Phone: 9180-521-6066
Fax: 9180-521-6077

601 Edgewater Drive
Suite 345
Wakefield, MA USA 01880
Phone: 781-213-9344
Fax: 781-213-9345

Management and Staff
Bill McHale, Venture Partner
Michael Long, Chief Financial Officer
Vijay Khanna, General Partner

Type of Firm
Private Equity Firm

Association Membership
Mid-Atlantic Venture Association
National Venture Capital Association - USA (NVCA)

Project Preferences

Role in Financing:
Will function either as deal originator or investor in deals created by others

Type of Financing Preferred:
Early Stage

Size of Investments Considered:
Min Size of Investment Considered (000s): $2,000
Max Size of Investment Considered (000s): $4,000

Geographical Preferences

United States Preferences:
Mid Atlantic

International Preferences:
India
China

Industry Preferences

In Communications prefer:
Telecommunications
Data Communications

In Computer Software prefer:
Computer Services
Data Processing
Software
Systems Software
Applications Software

In Internet Specific prefer:
Internet

In Medical/Health prefer:
Health Services

Additional Information
Year Founded: 1999
Capital Under Management: $75,000,000
Current Activity Level: Actively seeking new investments

GIZA VENTURE CAPITAL (FKA: GIZA INVESTMENT MANAGEMENT)
Ramat Aviv Tower
40 Einstein St., 12th Floor
Tel Aviv, Israel 61172
Phone: 972-3-640-2318
Fax: 972-3-640-2319
E-mail: info@gizavc.com
Website: www.gizavc.com

Other Offices
250 North Bridge Road, #30-05
Raffles City Tower
Singapore, Singapore 179101
Phone: 65-6334-8533
Fax: 65-6334-3083

Management and Staff
Allon Reiter, Vice President
Eitan Ben-Eliahu, Venture Partner
Elka Nir, Managing Director
Eyal Niv, Managing Director
Ezer Soref, Managing Director

Meir Weinstein, Venture Partner
Moshe Nazarathy, Venture Partner
Ori Israely, Managing Director
Ori Kirshner, Managing Partner
Shuki Ehrlich, Managing Director
Udi Ziv, Venture Partner
Yaron Valler, Vice President
Zvi Shechter, Managing Director

Type of Firm

Bank Affiliated

Association Membership

Israel Venture Association

Project Preferences

Role in Financing:

Prefer role as deal originator

Type of Financing Preferred:

Second Stage Financing
Early Stage
Balanced
Start-up Financing
First Stage Financing

Size of Investments Considered:

Min Size of Investment Considered (000s): $3,000
Max Size of Investment Considered (000s): $5,000

Geographical Preferences

International Preferences:

Taiwan
Israel
All International

Industry Focus

(% based on actual investment)

Medical/Health	23.1%
Internet Specific	18.7%
Communications and Media	16.9%
Computer Software and Services	13.3%
Semiconductors/Other Elect.	13.3%
Computer Hardware	8.8%
Biotechnology	3.1%
Other Products	2.8%

Additional Information

Name of Most Recent Fund: Giza Venture Fund IV, L.P.
Most Recent Fund Was Raised: 04/28/2004
Year Founded: 1992
Capital Under Management: $316,000,000
Current Activity Level: Actively seeking new investments
Method of Compensation: Return on investment is of primary concern, do not charge fees

---

GKM NEWPORT GENERATION FUNDS

11150 Santa Monica Boulevard
Suite 825
Los Angeles, CA USA 90025
Phone: 310-268-2650
Fax: 310-268-0870
Website: www.gkmnewport.com

Management and Staff

Anthony Rust, Managing Director
Diane Peek, Managing Director
Erica Bushner, Managing Director
Jeff Scheinrock, Managing Director
Jonathan Bloch, Managing Director

Type of Firm

Private Equity Advisor or Fund of Funds

Project Preferences

Type of Financing Preferred:

Fund of Funds

Additional Information

Year Founded: 2002
Capital Under Management: $154,000,000
Current Activity Level: Actively seeking new investments

GKM VENTURES

11150 Santa Monica Boulevard
Suite 825
Los Angeles, CA USA 90025
Phone: 310-268-2637
Fax: 310-268-0870
E-mail: info@gkmventures.com
Website: www.gkmventures.com

Other Offices

203 Redwood Shores Parkway
Suite 630
Redwood City, CA USA 94065
Phone: 650-620-9455
Fax: 650-620-9458

Management and Staff

David Stastny, Managing Director
Emanuel Gerard, Managing Director
Eric Risley, Venture Partner
John Morris, Managing Director
Jonathan Bloch, Managing Director
Paul Sherer, Venture Partner
Ralph Eschenbach, Venture Partner
Ravi Chiruvolu, Venture Partner

Type of Firm

Private Equity Firm

Association Membership

Natl Assoc of Investment Cos. (NAIC)
Natl Assoc of Small Bus. Inv. Co (NASBIC)
Project Preferences

Role in Financing:

Will function either as deal originator or investor in deals created by others

Type of Financing Preferred:

Fund of Funds
Second Stage Financing
Early Stage
Expansion
Balanced
Later Stage
Private Placement

Size of Investments Considered:

Min Size of Investment Considered (000s): $1,500
Max Size of Investment Considered (000s): $4,000

Geographical Preferences

United States Preferences:

Arizona
Southern California
Northern California
Colorado
Southwest
Texas
All U.S.

International Preferences:

All International

Industry Preferences

In Communications prefer:

Commercial Communications
CATV & Pay TV Systems
Telecommunications
Wireless Communications
Data Communications
Satellite Microwave Comm.
Other Communication Prod.

In Computer Software prefer:

Software
Systems Software
Applications Software

In Internet Specific prefer:

Internet

In Computer Other prefer:

Computer Related

In Semiconductor/Electr prefer:

Electronics
Electronic Components
Semiconductor
Micro-Processing
Circuit Boards

In Consumer Related prefer:

Consumer

In Industrial/Energy prefer:

Advanced Materials

Additional Information

Name of Most Recent Fund: GKM SBIC, L.P.
Most Recent Fund Was Raised: 09/09/2002
Year Founded: 2000
Capital Under Management: $90,000,000
Current Activity Level: Actively seeking new investments
Method of Compensation: Return on investment is of primary concern, do not charge fees

GLASTAD INVEST AS

Grev Wedels Plass 5
P.O. Box 772
Oslo, Norway 0151
Phone: 47-22-478-070
Fax: 47-22-478-071
Website: www.glastadinvest.com

Other Offices

Gaseholmen Brygge Three
PO Box 113
Farsund, Norway 4551
Phone: 47-38-39-9600
Fax: 47-38-39-9701

Management and Staff

Patrick Stephansen, Chief Executive Officer

Type of Firm

Private Equity Firm

Association Membership

Norwegian Venture Capital Association

Project Preferences

Type of Financing Preferred:
Second Stage Financing
Early Stage
Expansion

Geographical Preferences

International Preferences:
United Kingdom
Scandanavia/Nordic Region

Industry Preferences

In Communications prefer:
Telecommunications

In Medical/Health prefer:
Medical Products

In Industrial/Energy prefer:
Energy

In Business Serv. prefer:
Media

In Other prefer:
Environment Responsible

Additional Information

Year Founded: 2000
Current Activity Level: Actively seeking new investments

GLEACHER & CO.

660 Madison Avenue
19th Floor
New York, NY USA 10065
Phone: 212-418-4200
Fax: 212-752-2711
Website: www.gleacher.com

Other Offices

Cleveland House
33 King Street
London, United Kingdom SW1Y 6RJ
Phone: 020-7484-1150
Fax: 020-7484-1160

Management and Staff

Ben Nickoll, Managing Director
Bruce Ruehl, Managing Director
Eliott Jones, Managing Director
Emil Henry, Managing Director
Eric Gleacher, President, CEO, Chairman
Frederick Wahl, Managing Director
H. Conrad Meyer, Managing Director
James Raith, Managing Director
Jeffrey Tepper, Managing Director
John Huwiler, Managing Director
Mary Price Gay, Managing Director
Michiel McCarty, Managing Director
Phillip Krall, Managing Director
Robert A. Engel, Partner
Simon Murray, Partner
William Payne, Managing Director
William Forrest, Managing Director

Type of Firm

Bank Affiliated

Project Preferences

Type of Financing Preferred:
Early Stage
Expansion
Mezzanine
Later Stage

Geographical Preferences

United States Preferences:

Industry Focus

(% based on actual investment)

Other Products	39.4%
Consumer Related	29.8%
Internet Specific	20.6%
Communications and Media	6.5%
Semiconductors/Other Elect.	2.2%
Computer Software and Services	1.5%

Additional Information

Name of Most Recent Fund: Gleacher Mezzanine Partners II, L.P.
Most Recent Fund Was Raised: 11/17/2006
Year Founded: 1990
Capital Under Management: $720,000,000
Current Activity Level: Actively seeking new investments

GLENALTA CAPITAL LLP

Hudson House
8, Tavistock Street
London, United Kingdom WC2E 7PP
Phone: 44-20-7559-6672
Fax: 44-20-7559-6501
E-mail: enquiries@glenalta.com
Website: www.glenalta.com

Other Offices

Frankfurter Strasse 5
Wiesbaden, Germany 65189
Phone: 49-175-414-0408

Via Avezzana, 1
Milan, Italy 20139
Phone: 39-335-634-9843

Management and Staff

Andrew Beaton, Managing Partner
David Smith, Managing Partner
Luca Giacometti, Partner
Oliver Schumann, Partner

Type of Firm

Private Equity Firm

Project Preferences

Type of Financing Preferred:
Balanced

Geographical Preferences

International Preferences:
Europe

Additional Information

Year Founded: 2005
Current Activity Level: Actively seeking new investments

GLENCOE CAPITAL LLC (FKA: GLENCOE INVESTMENT CORPORATION)

222 West Adams Street
Suite 1000
Chicago, IL USA 60606
Phone: 312-795-6300
Fax: 312-795-0455
E-mail: info@glencap.com
Website: www.glencap.com

Management and Staff

Christopher Collins, Vice President
David Evans, Chairman & Managing Director
G. Douglas Patterson, Managing Director
Jason Duzan, Managing Director

Type of Firm

Private Equity Advisor or Fund of Funds

Project Preferences

Role in Financing:
Prefer role as deal originator but will also invest in deals created by others

Type of Financing Preferred:
Leveraged Buyout
Expansion
Recapitalizations

Size of Investments Considered:
Min Size of Investment Considered (000s): $10,000
Max Size of Investment Considered (000s): $75,000
Geographical Preferences

United States Preferences:
Michigan
All U.S.

Canadian Preferences:
All Canada

Industry Focus

(% based on actual investment)

Consumer Related	81.6%
Other Products	16.8%
Industrial/Energy	0.8%
Semiconductors/Other Elect.	0.6%
Biotechnology	0.2%

Additional Information

Name of Most Recent Fund: Glencoe Capital Partners III, L.P.
Most Recent Fund Was Raised: 12/28/2001
Year Founded: 1993
Capital Under Management: $457,000,000
Current Activity Level: Actively seeking new investments
Method of Compensation: Return on invest. most important, but chg. closing fees, service fees, etc.

GLENGARY LLC

P.O. Box 202526
Cleveland, OH USA 44120
Phone: 216-491-4700
Website: www.glengaryventures.com

Management and Staff

Stephen Haynes, Managing Director
Thomas Tyrrell, Managing Director

Type of Firm

Private Equity Firm

Project Preferences

Type of Financing Preferred:
Early Stage

Industry Preferences

In Computer Software prefer:
Software

In Medical/Health prefer:
Health Services

In Consumer Related prefer:
Consumer Products

In Business Serv. prefer:
Services

Additional Information

Year Founded: 2008
Current Activity Level: Actively seeking new investments

GLENHOVE FUND MANAGERS (PTY) LTD

PO Box 72425
Parkview, South Africa 2122
Phone: 27-11-507-2000
Fax: 27-11-507-2004

Type of Firm

Private Equity Firm

Association Membership

South African Venture Capital Association (SAVCA)

Project Preferences

Type of Financing Preferred:
Balanced

Geographical Preferences

International Preferences:
South Africa

Industry Preferences

In Other prefer:
Women/Minority-Owned Bus.

Additional Information

Year Founded: 2003
Capital Under Management: $12,700,000
Current Activity Level: Actively seeking new investments

GLENMONT PARTNERS, LLC

54 State Street
Suite 110
Albany, NY USA 12207
Phone: 518-431-1300
Fax: 518-431-1302
E-mail: info@glenmontpartners.com
Website: www.glenmontpartners.com

Management and Staff

Dara Shareef, Partner
Jeffrey Wetherbee, Partner
Laura Mann, Partner

Type of Firm

Private Equity Firm

Project Preferences

Type of Financing Preferred:
Early Stage

Geographical Preferences

United States Preferences:
Pennsylvania
Massachusetts
New Jersey
Connecticut
New York

Additional Information

Year Founded: 2007
Current Activity Level: Actively seeking new investments

GLENMOUNT, LLC

1048 Irvine Avenue
Suite 763
Newport Beach, CA USA 92660
Phone: 949-475-0055
Fax: 949-475-1990

Management and Staff

Michael Johnson, Managing Director
Robert Forbes, Managing Director

Type of Firm

Private Equity Firm

Project Preferences

Role in Financing:
Prefer role as deal originator but will also invest in deals created by others

Type of Financing Preferred:
Leveraged Buyout
Expansion
Later Stage
Management Buyouts
Acquisition

Size of Investments Considered:
Min Size of Investment Considered (000s): $2,000
Max Size of Investment Considered (000s): $20,000

Geographical Preferences

Canadian Preferences:
All Canada

Industry Focus

(% based on actual investment)

Computer Software and Services	100.0%

Additional Information

Name of Most Recent Fund: Glenmount International, L.P.
Most Recent Fund Was Raised: 10/21/1998
Year Founded: 1998
Current Activity Level: Actively seeking new investments
Method of Compensation: Return on invest. most important, but chg. closing fees, service fees, etc.

GLENROCK ISRAEL, LTD.

85 Merdinat Hayehudim St.
Tower G, 8th Floor
Herzliya, Israel
Phone: 972-9-970-1800
Fax: 972-9-970-1866
E-mail: info@grg.co.il

Website: www.grg.co.il

Management and Staff

Leon Recanati, Founder

Type of Firm

Private Equity Firm

Project Preferences

Role in Financing:
Will function either as deal originator or investor in deals created by others

Type of Financing Preferred:
Leveraged Buyout
Mezzanine
Balanced
Later Stage

Geographical Preferences

International Preferences:
Israel

Additional Information

Year Founded: 2003
Capital Under Management: $20,000,000
Current Activity Level: Actively seeking new investments

GLOBAL ASIA PARTNERS

1 Crystal Creek Drive
Larkspur, CA USA 94939
Phone: 415-235-6061
Fax: 415-924-7773
Website: www.gapvc.com

Management and Staff

Ajoy Khanderia, General Partner
John Cornell, Chief Financial Officer

Type of Firm

Private Equity Firm

Project Preferences

Type of Financing Preferred:
Early Stage
Later Stage

Geographical Preferences

International Preferences:
Asia

Industry Preferences

In Communications prefer:
Telecommunications
Wireless Communications

In Computer Software prefer:
Software

Additional Information

Year Founded: 2002
Capital Under Management: $10,000,000
Current Activity Level: Actively seeking new investments

GLOBAL ASSET CAPITAL LLC

2460 Sand Hill Road
Suite 100
Menlo Park, CA USA 94025
Phone: 650-233-1999
Fax: 650-233-1901
E-mail: padmini@gacapital.com
Website: www.gacapital.com

Type of Firm

Private Equity Firm

Additional Information

Year Founded: 2000
Current Activity Level: Actively seeking new investments

GLOBAL CAPITAL FINANCE

4 Manhattanville Road
Suite 104
Purchase, NY USA 10577
Phone: 212-660-7600
Fax: 212-660-7660
E-mail: info@globalcapitalfinance.com
Website: www.globalcapitalfinance.com

Other Offices

45 Lime Street
Suite 403
Sydney, Australia NSW 2000
Phone: 61-2-9279-0443
Fax: 61-2-9279-0283

Bertalanffy u. 49
Szombathely, Hungary 9700
Phone: 36-94-344-745
Fax: 36-94-344-745

1 Ropemaker Street
London, United Kingdom EC2Y 9HD

10th Fl, 120, 2-ka Taepyungro
Chung-ku
Seoul, South Korea 110-724
Phone: 82-2-772-2872
Fax: 82-2-772-2835

Westendstrasse 74
Frankfurt am Main, United Kingdom 60325
Phone: 49-69-4786-6370
Fax: 49-69-7430-8607

Burgemeester Haspelslaan 67
Amstelveen, United Kingdom 1181 NB
Phone: 31-20-347-5015
Fax: 31-20-347-5011

Narodni 41/973
Prague, United Kingdom 110 00
Phone: 420-225-574-460
Fax: 420-574-999

Stadiongasse 5/2a
Vienna, Austria 1010
Phone: 43-1-990-7174
Fax: 43-1-990-2393

Mohrlistrasse 97
Zurich, United Kingdom CH-8006
Phone: 41-44-363-9436
Fax: 41-44-363-9436

Management and Staff

Christine Brockwell, Vice President
Juergen Moessner, President

Type of Firm

Bank Affiliated

Project Preferences

Type of Financing Preferred:
Expansion
Acquisition

Geographical Preferences

United States Preferences:
All U.S.

Canadian Preferences:
All Canada

International Preferences:
United Kingdom
Australia

Industry Preferences

In Industrial/Energy prefer:
Energy

In Transportation prefer:
Transportation
Aerospace

In Financial Services prefer:
Real Estate

In Utilities prefer:
Utilities

Additional Information

Current Activity Level: Actively seeking new investments

GLOBAL CAPITAL PRIVATE EQUITY LTD

21 West Street
Houghton
Johannesburg, South Africa 2198
Phone: 27-11-728-0255
Fax: 27-11-728-8921
E-mail: info@glocapital.com
Website: www.glocapital.com

Management and Staff
Frank Boner, Chief Executive Officer

Type of Firm
Private Equity Firm

Association Membership
South African Venture Capital Association (SAVCA)

Project Preferences

Type of Financing Preferred:
Expansion
Management Buyouts
Acquisition

Geographical Preferences

International Preferences:
United Kingdom
Australia
Africa

Additional Information
Year Founded: 2002
Current Activity Level: Actively seeking new investments

GLOBAL CATALYST PARTNERS
255 Shoreline Drive
Suite 520
Redwood Shores, CA USA 94065
Phone: 650-486-2420
Fax: 650-593-0419
Website: www.gc-partners.com

Other Offices
2-15-1-107, Hamadayama Suginami-ku
Tokyo, Japan 168-0065
Phone: 81-3-6750-9321
Fax: 81-3-6750-9321

3/F Beijing Kerry Centre
North Tower, 1 Guanghua Road
Chaoyang District, Beijing, China 100020
Phone: 86-10-8529-8955
Fax: 86-10-8529-8866

Management and Staff
Arthur Schneiderman, Principal
Jenny Lee, Chief Financial Officer

Type of Firm
Private Equity Firm

Association Membership
Singapore Venture Capital Association (SVCA)
Indian Venture Capital Association (IVCA)

Project Preferences

Role in Financing:
Will function either as deal originator or investor in deals created by others

Type of Financing Preferred:
Second Stage Financing
Early Stage
Start-up Financing
Seed
First Stage Financing
Strategic Alliances
Joint Ventures
Startup

Size of Investments Considered:
Min Size of Investment Considered (000s): $3,000
Max Size of Investment Considered (000s): $15,000

Geographical Preferences

United States Preferences:
All U.S.

International Preferences:
Europe
Asia
All International

Industry Preferences

In Communications prefer:
Communications and Media

In Computer Software prefer:
Software
Systems Software
Applications Software

In Semiconductor/Electr prefer:
Electronics
Semiconductor

Additional Information
Name of Most Recent Fund: Global Catalyst Partners III, L.P.
Most Recent Fund Was Raised: 04/07/2005
Year Founded: 1999
Capital Under Management: $245,000,000
Current Activity Level: Actively seeking new investments
Method of Compensation: Return on investment is of primary concern, do not charge fees

---

GLOBAL ENVIRONMENT FUND MANAGEMENT CORP. (GEF)
5471 Wisconsin Avenue
Suite 300
Chevy Chase, MD USA 20815
Phone: 240-482-8900
Fax: 240-482-8908
E-mail: info@globalenvironmentfund.com
Website: www.globalenvironmentfund.com

Other Offices
352 3rd Street
Suite 306
Laguna Beach, CA USA 92651
Phone: 949-497-6049
Fax: 949-497-7800

Management and Staff
Barry Ulrich, Managing Director
Benjamin Session, Managing Director
Jay Powell, Managing Partner
Joan Larrea, Managing Director
Julia Pulzone, Senior Managing Director
Lisa Schule, Managing Director
Rajesh Pai, Managing Director
Samrat Ganguly, Principal
Scott Vicary, Managing Director
Scott MacLeod, Managing Director
Todd Cater, Principal
Wendell Robinson, Managing Partner

Type of Firm
Private Equity Firm

Association Membership
Mid-Atlantic Venture Association

Project Preferences

Type of Financing Preferred:
Balanced

Geographical Preferences

United States Preferences:
All U.S.

International Preferences:
Asia

Industry Preferences

In Medical/Health prefer:
Health Services

In Industrial/Energy prefer:
Energy
Alternative Energy
Environmental Related

Additional Information
Year Founded: 1989
Capital Under Management: $425,000,000
Current Activity Level: Actively seeking new investments

GLOBAL EQUITY CAPITAL LLC
6260 Lookout Road
Boulder, CO USA 80301
Phone: 303-531-1000
Fax: 303-531-1001
Website: www.globalequitycap.com

Other Offices
10940 Wilshire Boulevard
Suite 600
Westwood, CA USA 90024
Phone: 310-443-4246
Fax: 310-443-4247

Management and Staff
Angela Blatteis, Managing Director

Catherine Scanlon, Chief Financial Officer

Type of Firm
Private Equity Firm

Project Preferences
Type of Financing Preferred:
Management Buyouts
Recapitalizations

Geographical Preferences
United States Preferences:
All U.S.

Industry Preferences
In Communications prefer:
Telecommunications

In Industrial/Energy prefer:
Industrial Products

In Business Serv. prefer:
Services

Additional Information
Year Founded: 2002
Current Activity Level: Actively seeking new investments

GLOBAL EQUITY PARTNERS BETEILIGUNGS-MANAGEMENT AG
Mariahilfer Strasse 1
Getreidemarkt 17
Vienna, Austria A-1060
Phone: 43-1-581-8390
Fax: 43-1-581-7611
E-mail: office@gep.at
Website: www.gep.at

Management and Staff
Reinhard Fischer, Partner

Type of Firm
Private Equity Firm

Association Membership
Austrian PE and Venture Capital Association (AVCO)
European Private Equity and Venture Capital Assoc.

Project Preferences
Type of Financing Preferred:
Leveraged Buyout
Early Stage
Expansion
Generalist PE
Balanced
Turnaround
Later Stage
Other
Seed
Management Buyouts
Private Placement
Startup
Recapitalizations

Size of Investments Considered:
Min Size of Investment Considered (000s): $364
Max Size of Investment Considered (000s): $4,669

Geographical Preferences
International Preferences:
Switzerland
Austria
Eastern Europe
Germany

Industry Preferences
In Communications prefer:
Communications and Media

In Computer Other prefer:
Computer Related

In Industrial/Energy prefer:
Industrial Products

In Business Serv. prefer:
Distribution

In Manufact. prefer:
Manufacturing

Additional Information
Year Founded: 1998
Capital Under Management: $188,700,000
Current Activity Level: Actively seeking new investments
Method of Compensation: Return on invest. most important, but chg. closing fees, service fees, etc.

GLOBAL FINANCE SA
14 Filikis Eterias Square
Athens, Greece 10673
Phone: 30-210-720-8900
Fax: 30-210-729-2643
E-mail: office@globalfinance.gr
Website: www.globalfinance.gr

Other Offices
39 Vitosha Blvd.
1st Floor
Sofia, Bulgaria 1000
Phone: 359-2-980-8246
Fax: 359-2-980-8245

115E, Mihaila Pupina Boulevard
Belgrade, Serbia and Montenegro 11000
Phone: 381112123342
Fax: 381112123350

Bd Aviatorilor nr. 60-62, ap.1
sector 1
Bucharast, Romania 70401
Phone: 40-1-2315-5713
Fax: 40-1-2315-5713

Management and Staff
Angelos Plakopitas, Managing Partner
George Kourtis, Partner
Ivana Bozjak, Partner
Kostis Glavas, Partner
Mihalis Madianos, Partner
Theodore Kiakidis, Partner

Type of Firm
Private Equity Firm

Association Membership
European Private Equity and Venture Capital Assoc.

Project Preferences
Role in Financing:
Prefer role as deal originator but will also invest in deals created by others

Type of Financing Preferred:
Leveraged Buyout
Early Stage
Expansion
Mezzanine
Later Stage

Size of Investments Considered:
Min Size of Investment Considered (000s): $1,000
Max Size of Investment Considered: No Limit

Geographical Preferences
International Preferences:
Greece
Central Europe
Eastern Europe
Bulgaria
Romania

Additional Information
Year Founded: 1991
Capital Under Management: $154,000,000
Current Activity Level: Actively seeking new investments
Method of Compensation: Return on invest. most important, but chg. closing fees, service fees, etc.

GLOBAL FUND 1 GO TOSHI JIGYO KUMIAI
3-8-25 Toranomon
Minato-Ku
Tokyo, Japan 105-0001

Type of Firm
Private Equity Firm

Project Preferences
Type of Financing Preferred:
Leveraged Buyout

Geographical Preferences
International Preferences:
Japan
Additional Information

Year Founded: 2008
Current Activity Level: Actively seeking new investments

GLOBAL INFRASTRUCTURE PARTNERS

225 High Ridge Road
Suite 260 West Building
Stamford, CT USA 06905
Phone: 203-355-3270
Website: www.global-infra.com

Other Offices

315 Park Avenue South
8th Floor
New York, NY USA 10010
Phone: 212-325-8888

80 Victoria Street
Cardinal Place
London, United Kingdom SW1E 5JL
Phone: 44-20-7883-3100

16-20 Chater Road
20th Floor, Alexandra House
Central, Hong Kong
Phone: 852-3556-0184

Management and Staff

Adebayo Ogunlesi, Managing Partner
Jonathan Bram, Partner
Matthew Harris, Partner
Mehrdad Noorani, Partner
Michael McGhee, Partner
Mike Nikkel, Partner
William Woodburn, Partner

Type of Firm

Private Equity Firm

Project Preferences

Type of Financing Preferred:
Leveraged Buyout

Geographical Preferences

International Preferences:
Europe
Asia

Industry Preferences

In Industrial/Energy prefer:
Energy

In Transportation prefer:
Transportation

In Business Serv. prefer:
Services

In Other prefer:
Environment Responsible

Additional Information

Year Founded: 2007
Current Activity Level: Actively seeking new investments

GLOBAL INNOVATION PARTNERS LLC (AKA: GI PARTNERS)

2180 Sand Hill Road
Suite 210
Menlo Park, CA USA 94025
Phone: 650-233-3600
Fax: 650-233-3601
E-mail: info@gipartners.com
Website: www.gipartners.com

Other Offices

35 Portman Square
Fifth Floor
London, United Kingdom W1H 6LR
Phone: 44-20-7034-1120
Fax: 44-20-7034-1156

Management and Staff

Al Foglio, Managing Director
Andrew Tainiter, Managing Director
Brad Altberger, Managing Director
Eric Harrison, Managing Director
Howard Park, Managing Director
Mark Tagliaferri, Managing Director
Phil Kaziewicz, Managing Director

Type of Firm

Private Equity Firm

Association Membership

European Private Equity and Venture Capital Assoc.

Project Preferences

Role in Financing:
Prefer role as deal originator

Type of Financing Preferred:
Leveraged Buyout
Expansion
Generalist PE
Later Stage
Management Buyouts
Acquisition
Joint Ventures

Size of Investments Considered:
Min Size of Investment Considered (000s): $10,000
Max Size of Investment Considered (000s): $100,000

Geographical Preferences

United States Preferences:
All U.S.

International Preferences:
Europe
Western Europe

Industry Focus

(% based on actual investment)

Consumer Related	46.7%
Other Products	21.6%
Industrial/Energy	14.9%
Internet Specific	8.4%
Semiconductors/Other Elect.	8.4%

Additional Information

Name of Most Recent Fund: Global Innovation Partners I
Most Recent Fund Was Raised: 03/15/2001
Year Founded: 2000
Capital Under Management: $2,000,000,000
Current Activity Level: Actively seeking new investments

GLOBAL INVESTMENT HOUSE

Sharq, Shuhada Street
P.O. Box 28807
Safat, Kuwait 13149
Phone: 965-2295-1000
Fax: 965-2295-1005
Website: www.globalinv.net

Other Offices

7 Abdel Hadi Salah Street
El-Nasr Tower
Giza, Egypt 12411
Phone: 20-2-3760-9398
Fax: 20-2-3760-9506

AL-Mather Street
PO. Box 66930
Riyadh, Saudi Arabia 11586
Phone: 966-1-219-9966
Fax: 966-1-217-8481

Abu Dhabi Commercial Bank Building
Intersection of Al Salam and Electra St.
Abu Dhabi, Utd. Arab Em.
Phone: 971-2-678-9808
Fax: 971-2-6790-0601

First Floor, Flat No. 2
Sagar Apartments, CBD Belapur
Navi Mumbai, India 400 614
Phone: 91-982-078-2884
Fax: 91-981-940-0280

Bldg. No. 131, Office No. 191
P.O.Box 855
Manama, Bahrain
Phone: 973-17-210-011
Fax: 973-17-210-222

Burj Dubai Square
Bldg 1- Office 402, Sheikh Zayed Road
Dubai, Utd. Arab Em.
Phone: 971-4-425-7977
Fax: 971-4-425-7960

Khartoum - Al Barakah Tower
1st Floor - Flat 407
Sudan, Sudan
Phone: 249-1-8376-7324
Fax: 249-1-8374-7260

Al-Jazaer St., Sana'a Trade Center
Northern Tower, 3rd Floor
Sana'a, Yemen
Phone: 967-1-448-3502
Fax: 967-1-448-353

Shmeisani - Al Sharef Abdelhameed
Sharaf Street
Jordan 11180
Phone: 962-6-500-5060
Fax: 962-6-500-5066

QFC Tower, Office 1902
P.O.Box: 18126
Doha, Qatar
Phone: 974-496-7305
Fax: 974-496-7307

Management and Staff

Arunesh Madan, Vice President
Elena Ayub, Vice President
Ismail Odeh, Vice President
Maha Al-Ghunaim, Managing Director
Mohamed Abdelsalam, Partner
Sunny Bhatia, Chief Financial Officer

Type of Firm

Investment Management Firm

Project Preferences

Type of Financing Preferred:

Fund of Funds
Leveraged Buyout
Mezzanine
Generalist PE
Balanced
Public Companies

Geographical Preferences

International Preferences:

India
Pakistan
Turkey
Qatar
China
Utd. Arab Em.
Middle East
Saudi Arabia
Asia
All International
Africa

Additional Information

Year Founded: 2006
Capital Under Management: $2,553,500,000
Current Activity Level: Actively seeking new investments

GLOBAL INVESTMENT SERVICES

Happy World House
Port Louis, Mauritius
Phone: 650-429-2130
Fax: 650-429-2130
E-mail: gis@globalinvest.org
Website: www.globalnvest.org

Type of Firm

Private Equity Firm

Association Membership

African Venture Capital Association (AVCA)

Project Preferences

Type of Financing Preferred:

Leveraged Buyout
Expansion
Management Buyouts
Acquisition
Joint Ventures
Recapitalizations

Size of Investments Considered:

Min Size of Investment Considered (000s): $50
Max Size of Investment Considered (000s): $50,000

Geographical Preferences

International Preferences:

Mauritius
Africa

Additional Information

Year Founded: 2004
Current Activity Level: Actively seeking new investments

GLOBAL LEISURE PARTNERS LLP

17/18 Old Bond Street
London, United Kingdom W1S4PT
Phone: 44- 2070168050
Fax: 44-2070168060
Website: www.globalleisurepartners.com

Management and Staff

Robert L. Decker, Managing Director
Tina Palastanga, Vice President
W.B. Harms, CEO & Managing Director

Type of Firm

Bank Affiliated

Project Preferences

Type of Financing Preferred:

Balanced

Geographical Preferences

International Preferences:

United Kingdom

Industry Preferences

In Consumer Related prefer:

Entertainment and Leisure

Additional Information

Year Founded: 2004
Current Activity Level: Actively seeking new investments

GLOBAL LIFE SCIENCE VENTURES GMBH

Von-der-Tann-Strasse 3
Munich, Germany D-80539
Phone: 49-89-2881-510
Fax: 49-89-2881-5130
E-mail: mailbox@glsv-vc.com
Website: www.glsv-vc.com

Other Offices

Postplatz 1
Zug, Switzerland CH - 6301
Phone: 41-41-727-1940
Fax: 41-41-727-1945

Management and Staff

Hanns-Peter Wiese, Partner
Hans Kupper, Partner
Holger Reithinger, Partner
Kuno Jung, Principal
Peter Reinisch, Partner

Type of Firm

Private Equity Firm

Association Membership

British Venture Capital Association (BVCA)
German Venture Capital Association (BVK)
European Private Equity and Venture Capital Assoc.

Project Preferences

Role in Financing:

Prefer role as deal originator but will also invest in deals created by others

Type of Financing Preferred:

Second Stage Financing
Leveraged Buyout
Early Stage
Expansion
Balanced
Later Stage
Seed
Management Buyouts
Startup
Acquisition

Size of Investments Considered:

Min Size of Investment Considered (000s): $2,796
Max Size of Investment Considered (000s): $19,572

Geographical Preferences

International Preferences:

Europe
Germany

Industry Focus

(% based on actual investment)

Biotechnology	55.7%
Medical/Health	44.0%
Computer Software and Services	0.4%

Additional Information

Year Founded: 1996
Capital Under Management: $289,400,000
Current Activity Level: Actively seeking new investments

GLOBAL MARITIME VENTURES BHD

15/F, Bangunan Bank Pembangnan
Bandar Wawasan
Kuala Lumpur, Malaysia 50790
Phone: 603-2733-9962
Fax: 603-2694-0860
E-mail: global@gmv.com.my
Website: www.gmv.com.my

Management and Staff

Norulhadi Bin Md Shariff, Chief Executive Officer

Type of Firm

Private Equity Firm

Project Preferences

Type of Financing Preferred:
Balanced

Geographical Preferences

International Preferences:
Asia

Industry Preferences

In Transportation prefer:
Transportation

Additional Information

Year Founded: 2000
Current Activity Level: Actively seeking new investments

GLOBAL PRIVATE EQUITY PLC

4 Royal Mint Court
London, United Kingdom EC3N 4HJ
Phone: 44-20-7073-7888
Fax: 44-20-7073-7889
E-mail: mailto:info@global.cn
Website: www.globalprivateequity.plc.uk

Management and Staff

Adam Palin, Chief Executive Officer
Johnny Hon, Chairman & CEO
Rebecca Wong, Chief Financial Officer
Simmy Ho, Chief Operating Officer

Type of Firm

Private Equity Firm

Project Preferences

Type of Financing Preferred:
Leveraged Buyout
Early Stage
Seed
Acquisition

Geographical Preferences

International Preferences:
Vietnam
Indonesia
United Kingdom
China
Thailand
Philippines
Singapore
Korea, South
Malaysia

Industry Preferences

In Communications prefer:
Communications and Media

In Semiconductor/Electr prefer:
Electronic Components

In Consumer Related prefer:
Entertainment and Leisure

In Industrial/Energy prefer:
Alternative Energy

In Financial Services prefer:
Financial Services

Additional Information

Year Founded: 2008
Current Activity Level: Actively seeking new investments

GLOBAL TECH MANAGEMENT CONSULTING CORPORATION

9F-6, No. 2, Lane 150
Shin-Yi Rd., Sec. 5
Taipei, Taiwan
Phone: 886-2-2758-5565
Fax: 886-2-2758-5805

Type of Firm

Private Equity Firm

Association Membership

Taiwan Venture Capital Association(TVCA)

Project Preferences

Type of Financing Preferred:
Early Stage
Expansion
Balanced
Seed

Geographical Preferences

International Preferences:
Taiwan

Industry Preferences

In Communications prefer:
Telecommunications

In Computer Software prefer:
Software

In Internet Specific prefer:
Internet

In Semiconductor/Electr prefer:
Electronics
Semiconductor
Optoelectronics

In Biotechnology prefer:
Biotechnology

In Industrial/Energy prefer:
Advanced Materials

Additional Information

Name of Most Recent Fund: Technology Partners II Venture Capital Corporation
Most Recent Fund Was Raised: 12/01/1999
Year Founded: 1998
Capital Under Management: $42,500,000
Current Activity Level: Actively seeking new investments

GLOBAL TECHNOLOGY INVESTMENT (GTI)

375 Park Avenue
Suite 1505
New York, NY USA 10152
Phone: 212-755-9100
Fax: 212-755-2018
E-mail: info@gti-llc.com
Website: www.gti-llc.com

Other Offices

1049 Camino Dos Rios
Thousand Oaks, CA USA 91360
Phone: 805-373-4390

Management and Staff

Hendrik Susanto, Partner
Jonathan Schulhof, Partner
Michael Schulhof, General Partner
Robert Kay, Partner
Suresh Soni, Partner

Type of Firm

Private Equity Firm

Association Membership

National Venture Capital Association - USA (NVCA)

Project Preferences

Type of Financing Preferred:
Leveraged Buyout
Early Stage

Geographical Preferences

International Preferences:
All International

Industry Preferences

In Industrial/Energy prefer:
Industrial Products

In Transportation prefer:
Aerospace

Additional Information

Year Founded: 2006
Current Activity Level: Actively seeking new investments

GLOBAL VENTURE CAPITAL, INC.

6F Toranomon Suzuki Bldg.
20-4 Toranomon Minato-ku
Tokyo, Japan 105-0001
Phone: 81-3-5403-8451
Fax: 81-3-3437-1802
Website: www.gvc.jp

Management and Staff

Hirokazu Hasegawa, Managing Partner
Michael Korver, Managing Partner
Tomohiko Hasegawa, Partner
Yoshitaka Matsubara, Partner

Type of Firm

Private Equity Firm

Project Preferences

Type of Financing Preferred:
Early Stage
Expansion
Balanced
Later Stage
Startup

Geographical Preferences

International Preferences:
All International
Japan

Industry Preferences

In Communications prefer:
Telecommunications

In Medical/Health prefer:
Health Services

In Industrial/Energy prefer:
Environmental Related

Additional Information

Year Founded: 1996
Capital Under Management: $32,000,000
Current Activity Level: Actively seeking new investments

GLOBAL VISION AG

Westendstrasse 16-22
Frankfurt, Germany 60325
Phone: 49-69-978-40005
Fax: 49-69-978-80006
E-mail: info@globalvision-ag.de
Website: www.globalvision-ag.de

Other Offices

Palmaille 67
Hamburg, Germany 22767
Phone: 49-40-3802-2126
Fax: 49-40-3802-2194

Type of Firm

Bank Affiliated

Project Preferences

Type of Financing Preferred:
Fund of Funds

Geographical Preferences

Canadian Preferences:
All Canada

International Preferences:
United Kingdom
Europe
Australia
Israel
Germany
Asia
All International

Industry Focus

(% based on actual investment)

Industrial/Energy	25.8%
Computer Software and Services	24.2%
Medical/Health	19.0%
Biotechnology	8.5%
Semiconductors/Other Elect.	8.3%
Other Products	6.2%
Internet Specific	4.4%
Computer Hardware	3.6%

Additional Information

Year Founded: 1999
Capital Under Management: $343,200,000
Current Activity Level: Actively seeking new investments

GLOBESPAN CAPITAL PARTNERS

One Boston Place
Suite 2810
Boston, MA USA 02108
Phone: 617-305-2300
Fax: 617-305-2301
E-mail: east@globespancapital.com
Website: www.globespancapital.com

Other Offices

300 Hamilton Avenue
Palo Alto, CA USA 94301
Phone: 650-328-2828
Fax: 650-328-2818

1-1-1 Uchisaiwai-cho
Chiyoda-ku
Tokyo, Japan 100-0011
Phone: 81-3-3507-5660
Fax: 81-3-3507-5601

Management and Staff

Daniel Leff, Venture Partner
David Fachetti, Managing Director
Eugene Yoo, Vice President
Jonathan Seelig, Managing Director
Mary Bevelock, Chief Financial Officer
Ullas Naik, Managing Director
Venky Ganesan, Managing Director

Type of Firm

Private Equity Firm

Association Membership

Western Association of Venture Capitalists (WAVC)
National Venture Capital Association - USA (NVCA)

Project Preferences

Role in Financing:
Will function either as deal originator or investor in deals created by others

Type of Financing Preferred:
Second Stage Financing
Early Stage
Mezzanine
Balanced
Later Stage
Seed
First Stage Financing

Size of Investments Considered:
Min Size of Investment Considered (000s): $500
Max Size of Investment Considered (000s): $15,000

Geographical Preferences

Canadian Preferences:
All Canada

International Preferences:
Asia

Industry Focus

(% based on actual investment)

Computer Software and Services	34.8%
Communications and Media	20.7%
Internet Specific	18.5%
Semiconductors/Other Elect.	7.8%
Industrial/Energy	5.8%
Consumer Related	5.3%
Computer Hardware	2.4%
Medical/Health	2.2%
Biotechnology	1.8%
Other Products	0.7%

Additional Information

Name of Most Recent Fund: Globespan Capital Partners V, L.P.
Most Recent Fund Was Raised: 06/28/2006
Year Founded: 1984
Capital Under Management: $1,100,000,000
Current Activity Level: Actively seeking new investments
Method of Compensation: Return on investment is of primary concern, do not charge fees

---

GLOBIS CAPITAL PARTNERS & CO. (FKS: APAX GLOBIS PARTNERS)

5F Sumitomo Fudosan Kojimachi
5-1 Nibancho, Chiyoda-ku
Tokyo, Japan 102-0084
Phone: 81-3-5275-3939
Fax: 81-3-5275-3825
E-mail: info-gcp@globis.co.jp
Website: www.globis.co.jp

Management and Staff

Akihiro Ideguchi, Principal
Soichi Kariyazono, Partner
Takaaki Hata, Partner
Takuo Inoue, Principal
Tetsushi Kawaguchi, Principal

Type of Firm

Private Equity Advisor or Fund of Funds

Association Membership

Japan Venture Capital Association

Project Preferences

Type of Financing Preferred:

Early Stage
Expansion
Start-up Financing
Later Stage
Seed

Geographical Preferences

International Preferences:

Japan

Industry Preferences

In Communications prefer:

Telecommunications

In Computer Software prefer:

Software

In Semiconductor/Electr prefer:

Semiconductor

In Medical/Health prefer:

Medical/Health
Health Services

In Consumer Related prefer:

Retail

In Business Serv. prefer:

Services

Additional Information

Name of Most Recent Fund: Globis Fund III, L.P.
Most Recent Fund Was Raised: 06/15/2006
Year Founded: 1992
Capital Under Management: $180,000,000
Current Activity Level: Actively seeking new investments

GLYNN CAPITAL MANAGEMENT

3000 Sand Hill Road
Building 4, Suite 235
Menlo Park, CA USA 94025
Phone: 650-854-2215
Fax: 650-854-8083
E-mail: info@glynncapital.com
Website: www.glynncapital.com

Management and Staff

Jacqueline Glynn Brandin, Vice President
John Glynn, President
Sarah Rogers, Managing Director
Scott Jordon, Partner
Steven Rosston, Vice President
Vivian Loh Nahmias, Chief Financial Officer

Type of Firm

Private Equity Firm

Association Membership

Western Association of Venture Capitalists (WAVC)
National Venture Capital Association - USA (NVCA)

Project Preferences

Role in Financing:

Prefer role in deals created by others

Type of Financing Preferred:

Expansion
Open Market
Private Placement

Size of Investments Considered:

Min Size of Investment Considered (000s): $200
Max Size of Investment Considered (000s): $500

Industry Preferences

In Communications prefer:

Communications and Media

In Computer Other prefer:

Computer Related

In Semiconductor/Electr prefer:

Electronics

In Biotechnology prefer:

Biotechnology

In Medical/Health prefer:

Medical/Health

In Financial Services prefer:

Financial Services

Additional Information

Name of Most Recent Fund: Glynn Ventures V
Most Recent Fund Was Raised: 01/10/2001
Year Founded: 1970
Capital Under Management: $250,000,000
Current Activity Level: Actively seeking new investments
Method of Compensation: Return on investment is of primary concern, do not charge fees

---

GMAC - RESIDENTIAL FUNDING CORPORATION

8400 Normandale Lake Boulevard
Suite 250
Minneapolis, MN USA 55437
Phone: 952-832-7000
Fax: 952-857-7252
Website: www.gmacrfc.com

Other Offices

Periferico Sur #4829, 2nd Floor
Parques Del Pedregal, Mexico 14010
Phone: 52-55-5447-8300
Fax: 52-55-5447-8313

Kreuzberger Ring 24
Wiesbaden, Germany 65205
Phone: 49-611-9884-0
Fax: 49-611-9884-110

2625 South Plaza Drive
Suite 400
Tempe, AZ USA 85282
Phone: 480-902-3133
Fax: 480-902-3132

7501 Wisconsin Avenue
Suite 900
Bethesda, MD USA 20814
Phone: 301-215-6200
Fax: 301-664-6999

Alexanderveld 84
Den Haag, Netherlands 2585 DB
Phone: 31-703-117-920
Fax: 31-704-278-888

41-44 Great Queen Street
London, United Kingdom WC2B5AA
Phone: 44-20-7841-1155
Fax: 44-20-7841-1166

2255 N. Ontario Street
Suite 400
Burbank, CA USA 91504-3120
Phone: 818-260-1400
Fax: 818-260-1835

4650 SW Macadam Avenue
Suite 240
Portland, OR USA 97201
Phone: 503-419-2100
Fax: 503-419-2121

18-26 Rue Goubet
Paris, France 75019
Phone: 33-1-4040-5600
Fax: 33-1-4202-3974

Type of Firm

Incubator/Development Program

Project Preferences

Role in Financing:

Prefer role in deals created by others

Type of Financing Preferred:

Expansion
Mezzanine
Acquisition
Joint Ventures
Distressed Debt

Size of Investments Considered:

Min Size of Investment Considered (000s): $5,000
Max Size of Investment Considered (000s): $50,000

Geographical Preferences

International Preferences:

Italy
United Kingdom
Netherlands
Europe
China
Poland
Spain
Australia
Germany
Japan

Industry Preferences

In Financial Services prefer:

Financial Services

Additional Information

Year Founded: 1982
Capital Under Management: $50,000,000
Current Activity Level: Actively seeking new investments
Method of Compensation: Return on investment is of primary concern, do not charge fees

---

GMB MEZZANINE CAPITAL, L.P.

50 South Sixth Street
Suite 1460
Minneapolis, MN USA 55402
Phone: 612-243-4400
Fax: 612-243-4446
Website: www.gmbmezz.com

Management and Staff

Daniel Hemiadan, Principal
Susan Edmonds, Principal

Type of Firm

Private Equity Firm

Project Preferences

Type of Financing Preferred:

Leveraged Buyout
Mezzanine
Expansion
Management Buyouts
Acquisition

Size of Investments Considered:

Min Size of Investment Considered (000s): $3,000
Max Size of Investment Considered (000s): $13,000

Geographical Preferences

United States Preferences:

All U.S.

Industry Preferences

In Business Serv. prefer:

Services
Distribution

In Manufact. prefer:

Manufacturing

Additional Information

Year Founded: 2004
Capital Under Management: $198,000,000
Current Activity Level: Actively seeking new investments

GMG CAPITAL PARTNERS (FKA: GMS CAPITAL PARTNERS)

399 Park Avenue
36th Floor
New York, NY USA 10022
Phone: 212-832-4013
Fax: 212-980-1695
E-mail: info@gmgpartners.net
Website: www.gmgpartners.net

Other Offices

9350 South 150 East
9th Floor
Salt Lake City, UT USA 84107
Phone: 801-208-8100
Fax: 801-937-8101

Management and Staff

Bill Kesselring, General Partner
Byrren Yates, Chief Financial Officer
Jeffrey Gilfix, Managing Director
Joachim Gfoeller, Managing General Partner

Type of Firm

Private Equity Firm

Project Preferences

Type of Financing Preferred:

Early Stage

Industry Preferences

In Communications prefer:

Telecommunications
Data Communications

In Internet Specific prefer:

Internet

Additional Information

Year Founded: 1997
Current Activity Level: Actively seeking new investments

GMT COMMUNICATIONS PARTNERS LLP

Sackville House
40 Piccadilly
London, United Kingdom W1J 0DR
Phone: 44-20-7292-9333
Fax: 44-20-7292-9390
Website: www.gmtpartners.com

Management and Staff

Ashley Long, Partner
Jeffrey Montgomery, Managing Partner
Jonathan Gillbanks, Managing Director
Massimo Prelz, Partner
Nora Kerppola, Partner
Sebastian Sipp, Principal
Sebastien Canderle, Principal
Timothy Green, Managing Partner

Type of Firm

Private Equity Firm

Association Membership

British Venture Capital Association (BVCA)
European Private Equity and Venture Capital Assoc.

Project Preferences

Role in Financing:

Prefer role as deal originator but will also invest in deals created by others

Type of Financing Preferred:

Leveraged Buyout

Early Stage
Expansion
Management Buyouts
Acquisition

Size of Investments Considered:
Min Size of Investment Considered (000s): $28,245
Max Size of Investment Considered (000s): $70,612

Geographical Preferences

International Preferences:
Europe
Western Europe

Industry Focus
(% based on actual investment)

Communications and Media	71.2%
Internet Specific	12.7%
Computer Software and Services	12.3%
Consumer Related	2.3%
Other Products	1.4%

Additional Information
Name of Most Recent Fund: GMT Communications Partners III, L.P.
Most Recent Fund Was Raised: 05/11/2006
Year Founded: 1993
Capital Under Management: $819,000,000
Current Activity Level: Actively seeking new investments

GMUL INVESTMENT COMPANY, LTD.
Levinstein Tower
23 Menahem Begin Road
Tel Aviv, Israel 66184
Phone: 972-3-710-4400
Fax: 972-3-710-4455
E-mail: office@gmul.co.il
Website: www.gmul.co.il

Management and Staff
Doron Shechter, Chief Operating Officer
Tal Mish-Vered, Chief Financial Officer
Uri Omid, Chief Executive Officer

Type of Firm
Corporate PE/Venture

Project Preferences

Type of Financing Preferred:
Balanced

Geographical Preferences

International Preferences:
Israel
Asia

Industry Preferences

In Communications prefer:
Communications and Media

In Financial Services prefer:
Real Estate

Additional Information
Year Founded: 1950
Current Activity Level: Actively seeking new investments

GOBI PARTNERS, INC.
Zhangjiang Innovation Park
399 Keyuan Road
Shanghai, China 201203
Phone: 86-21-5292-9729
Fax: 86-21-5292-9730
E-mail: email@gobivc.com
Website: www.gobivc.com

Other Offices
4th Floor, Sohu.com, Internet Plaza
1 East Zhongguan Road, Haidian District
Beijing, China 100084
Phone: 86-10-8215-1502
Fax: 86-10-8215-1503

Management and Staff
Ken Xu, General Partner
Lawrence Tse, General Partner
Thomas Tsao, General Partner
Wai Kit Lau, General Partner

Type of Firm
Private Equity Firm

Project Preferences

Type of Financing Preferred:
Early Stage
Expansion
Balanced
Seed
Startup

Size of Investments Considered:
Min Size of Investment Considered (000s): $1,000
Max Size of Investment Considered (000s): $3,000

Geographical Preferences

International Preferences:
China

Industry Preferences

In Communications prefer:
Telecommunications

In Industrial/Energy prefer:
Energy

In Business Serv. prefer:
Media

Additional Information
Year Founded: 2002
Capital Under Management: $51,800,000
Current Activity Level: Actively seeking new investments

GOEAST VENTURES, LTD.
Universal House
88-94 Wentworth Street
London, United Kingdom E1 7SA
Phone: 44-20-7456-0448
Fax: 44-20-7247-8729

Management and Staff
Eddie Yongo, Chief Executive Officer

Type of Firm
Private Equity Firm

Project Preferences

Type of Financing Preferred:
Balanced

Additional Information
Year Founded: 2002
Current Activity Level: Actively seeking new investments

GOENSE BOUNDS & PARTNERS, LP
272 East Deerpath Road
Suite 300
Lake Forest, IL USA 60045
Phone: 847-735-2000
Fax: 847-735-2003
E-mail: slc@goensebounds.com
Website: www.goensebounds.com

Management and Staff
John Goense, Managing Director
Mark Bounds, Managing Director

Type of Firm
Private Equity Advisor or Fund of Funds

Project Preferences

Role in Financing:
Prefer role as deal originator

Type of Financing Preferred:
Leveraged Buyout
Expansion
Management Buyouts
Acquisition
Recapitalizations

Size of Investments Considered:
Min Size of Investment Considered (000s): $10,000
Max Size of Investment Considered (000s): $40,000

Industry Focus
(% based on actual investment)

Other Products	60.4%
Consumer Related	39.6%

Additional Information
Name of Most Recent Fund: Goense Bounds & Partners, L.P.

Most Recent Fund Was Raised: 06/28/2000
Year Founded: 2000
Capital Under Management: $300,000,000
Current Activity Level: Actively seeking new investments
Method of Compensation: Return on invest. most important, but chg. closing fees, service fees, etc.

GOFF MOORE STRATEGIC PARTNERS

777 Main Street
Suite 2100
Fort Worth, TX USA 76102
Phone: 817-321-1209
Fax: 817-321-2939
Website: www.goff-moore.com

Other Offices

500 West Putnam Avenue
4th Floor
Greenwich, CT USA 06830
Phone: 203-983-6666
Fax: 203-983-6653

Management and Staff

Darla Moore, Principal
Hugh Balloch, Principal
John Goff, Managing Director

Type of Firm

Private Equity Firm

Project Preferences

Type of Financing Preferred:
Balanced

Industry Focus

(% based on actual investment)

Communications and Media	45.4%
Computer Software and Services	29.0%
Internet Specific	23.6%
Semiconductors/Other Elect.	2.0%

Additional Information

Year Founded: 1998
Capital Under Management: $2,000,000,000
Current Activity Level: Actively seeking new investments

GOGIN CAPITAL COMPANY, LTD., THE

71 Shirakata Hon-machi
Matsue-shi, Japan 690-0061
Phone: 81-852-28-7170
Fax: 81-852-28-7177
E-mail: gogin-cp@mx.miracle.ne.jp
Website: fish.miracle.ne.jp/gogin-cp

Management and Staff

Hiroshi Watanabe, President
Shohei Ikebuchi, Managing Director

Type of Firm

Private Equity Firm

Project Preferences

Type of Financing Preferred:
Balanced

Geographical Preferences

International Preferences:
Japan

Additional Information

Year Founded: 1996
Current Activity Level: Actively seeking new investments

GOLD HILL CAPITAL MANAGEMENT LLC

One Almaden Boulevard
Suite 630
San Jose, CA USA 95113
Phone: 408-200-7840
Fax: 408-200-7841
E-mail: info@goldhillcapital.com
Website: www.goldhillcapital.com

Other Offices

Two Newton Executive Park
Suite 203
Newton, MA USA 02462
Phone: 617-243-2616

Management and Staff

Dave Fischer, Partner
Frank Tower, Partner
Rob Helm, Managing Director
Sean Lynden, Partner
Tim Waterson, Partner
Tim McDonough, Principal

Type of Firm

Private Equity Firm

Project Preferences

Type of Financing Preferred:
Balanced
Other

Geographical Preferences

United States Preferences:
Additional Information
Name of Most Recent Fund: Gold Hill Venture Lending 03-C, L.P.
Most Recent Fund Was Raised: 01/12/2005
Year Founded: 2003
Capital Under Management: $19,800,000
Current Activity Level: Actively seeking new investments

GOLD STONE INVESTMENT, LTD.

25A, New Poly Plaza
1 Chaoyangmenbei Avenue
Beijing, China 100010
Phone: 86-10-6408-2278
Fax: 86-10-6408-2728
Website: www.goldstone-investment.com

Management and Staff

Bruce Fan, Vice President
Charles Qian, Vice President
Hong-Ru Yang, Managing Director
Jianguo Cui, Chief Executive Officer
Megan Gao, Vice President
Randy Zhang, Vice President
Stephany Shuang Liang, Vice President
Tianjiao Mao, Vice President

Type of Firm

Bank Affiliated

Project Preferences

Type of Financing Preferred:
Expansion
Later Stage

Geographical Preferences

International Preferences:
China
Asia

Additional Information

Year Founded: 2007
Current Activity Level: Actively seeking new investments

GOLDEN GATE CAPITAL

One Embarcadero Center
39th Floor
San Francisco, CA USA 94111
Phone: 415-983-2700
Fax: 415-983-2701
Website: www.goldengatecap.com

Management and Staff

David Dominik, Managing Director
Jesse Rogers, Managing Director
Kenneth Diekroeger, Managing Director
Prescott Ashe, Managing Director

Type of Firm

Private Equity Firm

Project Preferences

Type of Financing Preferred:
Leveraged Buyout
Expansion
Generalist PE
Balanced

Other
Management Buyouts
Recapitalizations

Geographical Preferences

United States Preferences:
All U.S.

International Preferences:
Asia
All International

Industry Focus

(% based on actual investment)

Computer Software and Services	60.1%
Consumer Related	15.1%
Communications and Media	12.2%
Other Products	10.5%
Computer Hardware	1.0%
Semiconductors/Other Elect.	0.8%
Medical/Health	0.2%
Internet Specific	0.2%

Additional Information

Name of Most Recent Fund: Golden Gate Capital Investment Annex Fund II, L.P.
Most Recent Fund Was Raised: 04/11/2007
Year Founded: 2000
Capital Under Management: $700,000,000
Current Activity Level: Actively seeking new investments

GOLDFISH HOLDINGS, INC.

8037 South Datura Street
Littleton, CO USA 80120
Phone: 303-795-7167
Fax: 303-265-9490
E-mail: info@goldfish-holdings.com
Website: www.goldfish-holdings.com

Other Offices

Benrather Schlossallee 121
Dusseldorf, Germany 40597
Phone: 49-211-770 58 6-0
Fax: 49-211-770 58 6-11

Management and Staff

Tobias Janssen, Chairman & CEO

Type of Firm

Private Equity Firm

Project Preferences

Type of Financing Preferred:
Early Stage
Generalist PE
Acquisition

Geographical Preferences

International Preferences:
Western Europe

Industry Preferences

In Biotechnology prefer:
Biotechnology

In Medical/Health prefer:
Medical/Health

In Industrial/Energy prefer:
Alternative Energy

Additional Information

Year Founded: 2002
Current Activity Level: Actively seeking new investments

GOLDING CAPITAL PARTNERS GMBH

Moehlstrasse 10
Munich, Germany 81675
Phone: 49-89-419-9970
Fax: 49-89-419-99750
E-mail: info@goldingcapital.com
Website: www.goldingcapital.com

Management and Staff

Jeremy P. Golding, Managing Director

Type of Firm

Private Equity Advisor or Fund of Funds

Association Membership

German Venture Capital Association (BVK)
European Private Equity and Venture Capital Assoc.

Project Preferences

Type of Financing Preferred:
Fund of Funds

Geographical Preferences

United States Preferences:
All U.S.

International Preferences:
United Kingdom
Europe
Scandanavia/Nordic Region
Germany
France

Additional Information

Year Founded: 1999
Capital Under Management: $49,000,000
Current Activity Level: Actively seeking new investments

GOLDIS BERHAD (FKA: GOLD IS BHD)

Penthouse, Menara Tan & Tan
207 Jalan Tun Razak
Kuala Lumpur, Malaysia 50400
Phone: 603-2163-1111
Fax: 603-2163-7020
E-mail: tslim@goldis.com.my
Website: www.goldis.com.my

Management and Staff

Tan Lei Cheng, Chief Executive Officer

Type of Firm

Private Equity Firm

Project Preferences

Type of Financing Preferred:
Balanced

Geographical Preferences

International Preferences:
China
Malaysia

Additional Information

Year Founded: 2000
Current Activity Level: Actively seeking new investments

GOLDMAN SACHS JBWERE (NZ) LTD. (FKA: JBWERE (NZ) LTD.)

Level 38, Vero Centre
48 Shortland Street
Auckland, New Zealand 1001
Phone: 649-357-3200
Fax: 649-353-2396
E-mail: jbwere@gsjbw.co.nz
Website: www.jbwere.co.nz

Other Offices

65-67 Thomas Drive
Chevron Island
Gold Coast, Australia 4217
Phone: 617-5582-2444
Fax: 617-5582-2400

Level 16
101 Collins Street
Melbourne, Australia 3000
Phone: 613-9679-1111
Fax: 613-9679-1493

Level 42, Governor Phillip Tower
1 Farrer Place
Sydney, Australia 2000
Phone: 612-9321-8777
Fax: 612-9321-8640

60 Marcus Clarke Street
Canberra, Australia 2601
Phone: 612-6218-2000
Fax: 612-6218-2001

Level 13
45 Perie Street
Adelaide, Australia 5000

Phone: 618-8407-1111
Fax: 618-8407-1112

37/F Riverside Centre
123 Eagle Street
Brisbane, Australia 4000
Phone: 617-3258-1111
Fax: 617-3258-1112

Level 49
Republic Plaza
Singapore, Singapore 048619
Phone: 65-415-6111
Fax: 65-415-6112

Level 1
36 King Street
London, United Kingdom EC2V 8BB
Phone: 44-20-7367-8400
Fax: 44-20-7367-8452

Level 5
Taunusanlage 21
Frankfurt, Germany 60325
Phone: 49-69-7953-8800
Fax: 49-69-7953-8888

Level 28 New Otani Garden Court
4-1 Kioi-Cho, Chiyoda-ku
Tokyo, Japan 102-0094
Phone: 81-03-5214-0938
Fax: 81-03-5214-0935

Level 19
140 St. George's Terrace
Perth, Australia 6000
Phone: 618-9422-3333
Fax: 618-9422-3399

34th Floor
101 East 52nd Street
New York, NY USA 10022
Phone: 1-212-824-4500
Fax: 1-212-824-4501

Level 1
141 Cambridge Terrace
Christchurch, New Zealand 8001
Phone: 643-364-5601
Fax: 643-364-5611

Level 8, BNZ Centre
1 Willis Street
Wellington, New Zealand 6001
Phone: 644-471-6260
Fax: 644-471-6261

Type of Firm

Investment Management Firm

Project Preferences

Type of Financing Preferred:

Leveraged Buyout
Expansion
Mezzanine
Balanced
Later Stage

Geographical Preferences

International Preferences:

Pacific
New Zealand

Additional Information

Name of Most Recent Fund: Hauraki Private Equity No.2 Fund
Most Recent Fund Was Raised: 05/03/2004
Year Founded: 1930
Capital Under Management: $56,900,000
Current Activity Level: Actively seeking new investments

GOLDMAN SACHS JBWERE PRIVATE EQUITY (FKA:JBWERE PRV EQUITY)

1 Farrer Place
Level 42, Gov. Phillip Tower
Sydney, Australia 2000
Phone: 612-9321-8533
Fax: 612-9521-2318
E-mail: privateequity@gsjbw.com
Website: www.gsjbw.com

Other Offices

141 Cambridge Terrace
Level 1
Christchurch, New Zealand 8001
Phone: 64-3-364-5610
Fax: 64-3-364-5611

60 Marcus Clarke Street
Level 3
Canberra, Australia 2600
Phone: 61-2-6218-2000
Fax: 61-2-6218-2001

48 Shortland Street
Level 38, Vero Center
Auckland, New Zealand 1001
Phone: 64-9-357-3200
Fax: 64-9-357-3248

45 Pirie Street
Level 13
Adelaide, Australia 5000
Phone: 61-8-8407-1111
Fax: 61-8-8407-1112

123 Eagle Street
37th Floor, Riverside Center
Brisbane, Australia
Phone: 61-7-3258-1111
Fax: 61-7-3258-1112

1 Willis Street
Level 8, BNZ Center
Wellington, New Zealand
Phone: 64-4-471-6260
Fax: 64-4-471-6261

One New York Plaza
Level 42
New York, NY USA 10004
Phone: 212-357-6550
Fax: 212-357-1100
108 St. George's Terrace
BankWest Tower, Level 44
Perth, Australia 6000
Phone: 61-8-9422-3333
Fax: 61-8-9422-3399

133 Fleet Street
Level 6, Daniel House
London, United Kingdom EC4A 2BB
Phone: 44-207-774-2002
Fax: 44-207-552-2278

Management and Staff

Mark Wilson, Managing Director

Type of Firm

Bank Affiliated

Association Membership

Australian Venture Capital Association (AVCAL)

Project Preferences

Role in Financing:

Will function either as deal originator or investor in deals created by others

Type of Financing Preferred:

Control-block Purchases
Leveraged Buyout
Generalist PE
Expansion
Public Companies
Turnaround
Later Stage
Management Buyouts
Acquisition
Industry Rollups
Special Situation
Distressed Debt
Recapitalizations

Size of Investments Considered:

Min Size of Investment Considered (000s): $16,984
Max Size of Investment Considered (000s): $84,920

Geographical Preferences

International Preferences:

Pacific
New Zealand
Australia

Industry Preferences

In Computer Software prefer:

Software

In Semiconductor/Electr prefer:

Controllers and Sensors

In Medical/Health prefer:
Medical/Health
Health Services
Hospital/Other Instit.
Pharmaceuticals

In Consumer Related prefer:
Consumer
Entertainment and Leisure
Casino/Gambling
Retail
Food/Beverage
Consumer Products
Consumer Services
Education Related

In Industrial/Energy prefer:
Industrial Products

In Transportation prefer:
Transportation

In Financial Services prefer:
Financial Services

In Business Serv. prefer:
Distribution
Media

In Manufact. prefer:
Manufacturing

Additional Information
Name of Most Recent Fund: JBWere Private Equity Fund
Most Recent Fund Was Raised: 08/15/2000
Year Founded: 2000
Capital Under Management: $424,600,000
Current Activity Level: Actively seeking new investments
Method of Compensation: Return on invest. most important, but chg. closing fees, service fees, etc.

GOLDMAN SACHS URBAN INVESTMENT GROUP
85 Broad Street
Ninth Floor
New York, NY USA 10004
Phone: 888-902-5197
Fax: 212-357-5505
E-mail: urbaninvestment@gs.com
Website: www.gs.com/client_services/urban_investment_group

Management and Staff
Martin Chavez, Managing Director

Type of Firm
Bank Affiliated

Project Preferences

Type of Financing Preferred:
Expansion
Mezzanine
Balanced
Recapitalizations

Geographical Preferences

United States Preferences:
All U.S.

Industry Preferences

In Communications prefer:
Communications and Media

In Medical/Health prefer:
Medical/Health

In Consumer Related prefer:
Retail
Food/Beverage
Consumer Products
Consumer Services

In Industrial/Energy prefer:
Industrial Products

In Financial Services prefer:
Financial Services

In Other prefer:
Socially Responsible
Women/Minority-Owned Bus.

Additional Information
Year Founded: 2003
Current Activity Level: Actively seeking new investments

GOLDMAN, SACHS & CO.
85 Broad Street
New York, NY USA 10004
Phone: 212-902-0300
E-mail: gs-investor-relations@gs.com
Website: www2.goldmansachs.com

Other Offices
Second Floor
Hardwicke House, Upper Hatch Street
Dublin, Ireland 2
Phone: 35-31-439-6000

Passaggio Centrale 2
Milan, Italy 20123
Phone: 39-02-8022-1000

Akasaka Tameike Towers
17-7, Akasaka 2-chome
Minato-ku, Tokyo, Japan 107-0052
Phone: 81-3-5573-7800

1 Raffles Link
#07-01 South Lobby
Singapore, Singapore 039393
Phone: 65-889-1000

Peterborough Court
133 Fleet Street
London, United Kingdom EC4A 2BB
Phone: 44-207-774-1000
Fax: 44-207-774-4123

150 King Street West
Suite 1201
Toronto, Canada M5H 1J9
Phone: 416-343-8900

MesseTurm
Friedrich-Ebert-Anlage 49
Frankfurt am Main, Germany 60308
Phone: 49-69-7532-1000
Shibuya Cross Tower
15-1, Shibuya 2-chome
Shibuya-ku, Tokyo, Japan 150-0002
Phone: 81-3-5469-4400

21/F, HungKuk Life Insurance Building
226 Shin Mun Ro 1Ga
Chong Ro-Gu, Seoul, South Korea
Phone: 822-3788-1000

Avda. del Libertador, 498
19th Floor
Buenos Aires, Argentina 1001
Phone: 54-11-4323-0500

Suite 505, Shanghai Centre
1376 Nanjing Xi Lu
Shanghai, China 200040
Phone: 86-21-6279-7261

1 Rue des Moulins
P.O. Box 3666
Geneva, Sweden 1211
Phone: 41-228-166-000

3835,855 - 2nd Street SW
Bankers Hall - East Tower
Calgary, Canada T2P 4J8
Phone: 403-233-9293

600 boul. de Maisonneuve Ouest
Bureau 2350
Montreal, Canada H3A 3J2
Phone: 514-499-1510

8th Floor, Usadba Center
22/13 Voznesensky Per.
Moscow, Russia 103009
Phone: 7-095-785-1818

Paseo de la Castellana, 21
2nd and 3rd Floors
Madrid, Spain 28046
Phone: 34-91-700-6000

24/F Sindhorn Building, Tower 3
130-132 Wireless Road
Bangkok, Thailand 10330
Phone: 66-2650-8381
Fax: 66-2650-8382

Av. Pres. Juscelino
Kubitscheck, 510-6th Floor
Sao Paulo, Brazil 04543-000
Phone: 55-11-3371-0700

Torre Optima Building

Paseo de las Palmas 405, 18th Floor
Col. Lomas de Chapultepec, Mexico 11000
Phone: 52-55-5540-8100

13th Floor, The Forum
2 Maude Street, Sandton 2196
Sandton, South Africa 2196
Phone: 27-11-303-2700

Cheung Kong Center, 68th Floor
2 Queens Road
Central, Hong Kong, China
Phone: 852-2978-1000

555 California Street
San Francisco, CA USA 94104
Phone: 415-393-7628
Fax: 415-249-7400

37/F, 01-02, 12-18 China World Tower 2
No. 1 Jian Guo Men Wai Avenue
Beijing, China
Phone: 86-10-6505-6888

ARK Mori Building
12-32, Akasaka 1-chome
Minato-ku, Tokyo, Japan 107-6005
Phone: 81-3-3589-7000

2, rue de Thann
Paris, France
Phone: 33-1-42-12-1000

Birger Jarlsgatan, 12
Second Floor
Stockholm, Sweden S114 34
Phone: 46-8-407-0500

Munsterhof 4, Postfach
Zurich, Sweden CH-8022
Phone: 41-1-224-1000

Taipei Metro Tower, 11th Floor
207 Tun Hua South Road, Sec. 2
Taipei, Taiwan
Phone: 886-2-2730-4000

Management and Staff

Abraham Bleiberg, Managing Director
Adrian Jones, Managing Director
Antoine Schwartz, Managing Director
Atul Kapur, Managing Director
David Heller, Managing Director
Douglas Londall, Managing Director
Elizabeth Fascitelli, Managing Director
Elizabeth Marcellino, Managing Director
Henry Cornell, Managing Director
Huges Lepic, Managing Director
Jerome Truzzolino, Vice President
John Thain, President & COO
Jon Winkelried, President
Joseph DiSabato, Managing Director
Joseph Gleberman, Managing Director
Katherine Enquist, Managing Director
Larry Kellerman, Managing Director
Lloyd Blankfein, Chairman & CEO
Marc Spilker, Managing Director
Melina Higgins, Managing Director
Ming Maa, Principal
Muneer Satter, Managing Director
Peter Perrone, Vice President
Ram Venkateswaran, Vice President
Richard Sharp, Managing Director
Richard Friedman, Managing Director
Richard Sherlund, Managing Director
Robert Mancini, Managing Director
Robert Doumar, Managing Director
Robert Gheewalla, Managing Director
Robin Neustein, Managing Director
Sanjeev Mehra, Managing Director
Stephen Trevor, Managing Director
Terence O'Toole, Managing Director

Type of Firm

Bank Affiliated

Association Membership

National Venture Capital Association - USA (NVCA)
European Private Equity and Venture Capital Assoc.

Project Preferences

Type of Financing Preferred:

Fund of Funds
Leveraged Buyout
Generalist PE
Expansion
Mezzanine
Balanced
Turnaround
Later Stage
Other
Management Buyouts
Distressed Debt
Fund of Funds of Second
Recapitalizations

Geographical Preferences

United States Preferences:

All U.S.

Canadian Preferences:

All Canada

International Preferences:

Italy
Latin America
Netherlands
Switzerland
Europe
Austria
Mexico
Eastern Europe
Belgium
Germany
Asia
France
All International

Industry Focus

(% based on actual investment)

Other Products	35.0%
Communications and Media	16.6%
Internet Specific	12.8%
Consumer Related	9.7%
Medical/Health	6.9%
Industrial/Energy	6.7%
Computer Hardware	4.4%
Computer Software and Services	4.2%
Semiconductors/Other Elect.	3.0%
Biotechnology	0.6%

Additional Information

Name of Most Recent Fund: GS Capital Partners VI PIA PMD QP Fund, L.P.
Most Recent Fund Was Raised: 03/22/2007
Year Founded: 1869
Capital Under Management: $23,620,800,000
Current Activity Level: Actively seeking new investments

GOLDNER HAWN JOHNSON & MORRISON, INC.

3700 Wells Fargo Center
90 South Seventh Street
Minneapolis, MN USA 55402
Phone: 612-338-5912
Fax: 612-338-2860
Website: www.ghjm.com

Management and Staff

Darren Acheson, Managing Director
Gary Obermiller, Managing Director
Jason Brass, Principal
John Morrison, Managing Director
Joseph Heinen, Principal
Lisa Kro, Managing Director & CFO
Michael Healy, Vice President
Michael Israel, Managing Director
Michael Sweeney, Managing Partner
Paul Grangaard, Managing Director
Timothy Johnson, Managing Director
Van Zandt Hawn, Managing Director

Type of Firm

Private Equity Firm

Project Preferences

Role in Financing:

Prefer role as deal originator

Type of Financing Preferred:

Leveraged Buyout

Geographical Preferences

United States Preferences:

Midwest
Northwest
Rocky Mountain

Industry Preferences

In Semiconductor/Electr prefer:

Sensors

In Medical/Health prefer:

Health Services

In Consumer Related prefer:
Entertainment and Leisure
Retail
Food/Beverage
Consumer Products
Consumer Services
Other Restaurants

In Industrial/Energy prefer:
Industrial Products
Materials
Machinery

In Manufact. prefer:
Publishing

Additional Information
Year Founded: 1989
Capital Under Management: $325,000,000
Current Activity Level: Actively seeking new investments
Method of Compensation: Return on invest. most important, but chg. closing fees, service fees, etc.

GOLUB CAPITAL
551 Madison Avenue
New York, NY USA 10022
Phone: 212-750-6060
Fax: 212-750-5505
E-mail: info@golubcapital.com
Website: www.golubcapital.com

Other Offices
150 South Wacker Drive
Suite 800
Chicago, IL USA 60606
Phone: 312-205-5050
Fax: 312-201-9167

3343 Peachtree Road, North East
East Tower, Suite 331
Atlanta, GA USA 30326
Phone: 404-495-4520
Fax: 404-495-4526

Management and Staff
Allan Marzen, Vice President
Andrew Steuerman, Senior Managing Director
Charles Riceman, Managing Director
Gregory Robbins, Principal
Gregory Cashman, Senior Managing Director
James Higgins, Principal
John Geisler, Chief Financial Officer
Jonathan Pearl, Vice President
Joseph Longosz, Managing Director
Lawrence Golub, President, Founder
Matthew Fulk, Vice President
Michael Griffin, Vice President
Paul Stern, Vice President
Scott Reilly, Vice President
Sean Coleman, Principal
Stefano Robertson, Principal
Thomas Turmell, Principal
Troy Oder, Principal

Type of Firm
Private Equity Firm

Association Membership
Natl Assoc of Small Bus. Inv. Co (NASBIC)

Project Preferences

Role in Financing:
Will function either as deal originator or investor in deals created by others

Type of Financing Preferred:
Mezzanine
Generalist PE
Balanced
Later Stage
Private Placement
Recapitalizations

Size of Investments Considered:
Min Size of Investment Considered (000s): $4,000
Max Size of Investment Considered (000s): $25,000

Geographical Preferences

United States Preferences:
All U.S.

Canadian Preferences:
All Canada

Industry Preferences

In Semiconductor/Electr prefer:
Semiconductor

In Medical/Health prefer:
Medical/Health
Diagnostic Services
Health Services

In Consumer Related prefer:
Consumer
Sports
Retail
Consumer Products
Other Restaurants
Hotels and Resorts
Education Related

In Industrial/Energy prefer:
Industrial Products
Factory Automation
Process Control

In Transportation prefer:
Transportation
Aerospace

In Business Serv. prefer:
Services
Distribution
Media

In Manufact. prefer:
Manufacturing

Additional Information
Year Founded: 1994
Capital Under Management: $313,000,000
Current Activity Level: Actively seeking new investments
Method of Compensation: Return on invest. most important, but chg. closing fees, service fees, etc.

GOOD CAPITAL
2601 Mission Street
Suite 400B
San Francisco, CA USA 94110
Phone: 415-285-5601
Fax: 415-285-5565
E-mail: info@goodcap.net
Website: www.goodcap.net

Management and Staff
Joy Anderson, Principal
Kevin Jones, Principal
Tim Freundlich, Principal

Type of Firm
Private Equity Firm

Project Preferences

Type of Financing Preferred:
Expansion
Later Stage

Size of Investments Considered:
Min Size of Investment Considered (000s): $1,000
Max Size of Investment Considered (000s): $3,000

Industry Preferences

In Medical/Health prefer:
Health Services

In Consumer Related prefer:
Food/Beverage
Education Related

In Business Serv. prefer:
Services

Additional Information
Name of Most Recent Fund: Social Enterprise Expansion Fund, L.P. (AKA: SEEF)
Most Recent Fund Was Raised: 03/20/2008
Year Founded: 2008
Capital Under Management: $3,700,000
Current Activity Level: Actively seeking new investments

GOOD ENERGIES, INC.
Grafenauweg 4
Zug, Switzerland CH-6301
Phone: 41-41-560-6660
Fax: 41-41-560-6666
E-mail: mail@goodenergies.com
Website: www.goodenergies.com

Management and Staff
Andrew Lee, Managing Director
Richard Kauffman, Chief Executive Officer
William Nesbitt, Managing Director

Type of Firm
Private Equity Firm

Project Preferences
Type of Financing Preferred:
Generalist PE

Geographical Preferences
International Preferences:
Italy
Ireland
Western Europe
Spain
France

Industry Preferences
In Industrial/Energy prefer:
Energy
Alternative Energy

Additional Information
Year Founded: 2004
Current Activity Level: Actively seeking new investments

GOODE PARTNERS LLC
667 Madison Avenue
21st Floor
New York, NY USA 10021
Phone: 646-722-9454
Fax: 212-317-2827
E-mail: info@goodepartners.com
Website: www.thevine.com

Other Offices
150 North Santa Anita Avenue
Suite 300
Arcadia, CA USA 91006
Phone: 626-821-1877
Fax: 626-821-1876

Management and Staff
David Oddi, Partner
Jose Ferreira, Principal
Keith Miller, Partner
Mark Dolfato, Principal
Neal Goldman, Partner
Paula Semelmacher, Chief Financial Officer
Ron Beegle, Principal
Thomas Saunders, Partner

Type of Firm
Private Equity Firm

Project Preferences
Type of Financing Preferred:
Leveraged Buyout
Management Buyouts

Geographical Preferences
United States Preferences:
All U.S.

Industry Preferences
In Consumer Related prefer:
Consumer
Consumer Services
Other Restaurants

In Business Serv. prefer:
Services

Additional Information
Year Founded: 2005
Capital Under Management: $225,000,000
Current Activity Level: Actively seeking new investments

GORDON RIVER CAPITAL
350 5th Avenue South
Suite 203
Naples, FL USA 34102
Phone: 239-659-0288
Fax: 239-262-2212
E-mail: inquiries@gulfshorecap.com
Website: www.gordonriver.com

Management and Staff
Patrick George, Principal
Richard Molloy, Principal

Type of Firm
Private Equity Firm

Project Preferences
Type of Financing Preferred:
Second Stage Financing
Leveraged Buyout
Expansion
Generalist PE
Later Stage
Management Buyouts

Geographical Preferences
United States Preferences:
Florida

Industry Preferences
In Medical/Health prefer:
Medical Products

In Consumer Related prefer:
Consumer Products

In Business Serv. prefer:
Services

Additional Information
Year Founded: 2005
Current Activity Level: Actively seeking new investments

GORES GROUP LLC, THE (AKA: GORES TECHNOLOGY GROUP)
10877 Wilshire Boulevard
18th Floor
Los Angeles, CA USA 90024
Phone: 310-209-3010
Fax: 310-209-3310
Website: www.gores.com

Other Offices
52 Conduit Street
4th Floor
London, United Kingdom W1S 2YX
Phone: 44-870-060-1190
Fax: 44-870-060-1191

6260 Lookout Road
Boulder, CO USA 80301
Phone: 303-531-3100
Fax: 303-531-3200

Management and Staff
Anne Philips, Vice President
Anthony Chirikos, Vice President
Ashley Abdo, Managing Director
Eric Tis, Vice President
Fernando Goni, Principal
Ian Weingarten, Managing Director
Jonathan Gimbel, Vice President
Jordan Katz, Managing Director
Joseph Page, Chief Operating Officer
Kurt Hans, Vice President
Mark Stone, Senior Managing Director
Ryan Wald, Managing Director
Scott Honour, Senior Managing Director
Steven Yager, Managing Director
Steven Eisner, Vice President

Type of Firm
Private Equity Advisor or Fund of Funds

Project Preferences
Role in Financing:
Prefer role as deal originator

Type of Financing Preferred:
Leveraged Buyout
Turnaround
Acquisition

Size of Investments Considered:
Min Size of Investment Considered (000s): $5,000
Max Size of Investment Considered (000s): $100,000

Geographical Preferences
International Preferences:
Europe

Industry Preferences
In Communications prefer:
Telecommunications

Additional Information

Year Founded: 1987
Capital Under Management: $400,000,000
Current Activity Level: Actively seeking new investments

GORNOSLASKI FUNDUSZ RESTRUKTURYZACYJNY SA

40-203 Katowice
Al. Rozdzienskiego 91
Katowice, Poland 40-203
Phone: 48-32-209-0330
Fax: 48-32-209-0585
E-mail: biuro@gfr.com.pl
Website: www.gfr.com.pl

Management and Staff

Marek Palus, President

Type of Firm

Government Affiliated Program

Association Membership

European Private Equity and Venture Capital Assoc.

Project Preferences

Type of Financing Preferred:

Early Stage
Balanced
Later Stage
Startup

Geographical Preferences

International Preferences:

Poland

Industry Preferences

In Communications prefer:

Communications and Media

In Consumer Related prefer:

Consumer

In Industrial/Energy prefer:

Industrial Products

Additional Information

Year Founded: 1995
Current Activity Level: Actively seeking new investments

GOTHAM PARTNERS

888 Seventh Avenue
42nd Floor
New York, NY USA 10019

Type of Firm

Private Equity Firm

Additional Information

Year Founded: 1995
Current Activity Level: Actively seeking new investments

GOVERNANCA & GESTAO INVESTIMENTOS

Rua Alexandre Dumas, 1630
2 andar, Chacara Santo Antonio
Rio de Janeiro, Brazil 04717-004
Phone: 55-11-5181-5655
Fax: 55-11-5181-6236
E-mail: gg@gginvestimentos.com.br
Website: www.gginvestimentos.com.br

Type of Firm

Private Equity Firm

Association Membership

Brazilian Venture Capital Association (ABCR)

Project Preferences

Type of Financing Preferred:

Balanced

Geographical Preferences

International Preferences:

Brazil

Additional Information

Year Founded: 2006
Current Activity Level: Actively seeking new investments

GP INVESTIMENTOS

Av. Brig. Faria Lima, 3900
7th Andar, Jardim Paulistano
Sao Paulo, SP, Brazil 01451-000
Phone: 55-11-3131-5505
Fax: 55-11-3131-5566
Website: www.gp.com.br

Management and Staff

Marcus Marques Martino, Managing Partner
Nelson Rozental, Managing Partner

Type of Firm

Private Equity Firm

Association Membership

Brazilian Venture Capital Association (ABCR)

Project Preferences

Role in Financing:

Prefer role as deal originator

Type of Financing Preferred:

Leveraged Buyout
Generalist PE
Balanced
Management Buyouts
Acquisition

Size of Investments Considered:

Min Size of Investment Considered (000s): $50,000
Max Size of Investment Considered (000s): $200,000

Geographical Preferences

International Preferences:

Latin America
Brazil

Additional Information

Name of Most Recent Fund: GP Capital Partners III, L.P.
Most Recent Fund Was Raised: 06/17/2005
Year Founded: 1993
Capital Under Management: $1,300,000,000
Current Activity Level: Actively seeking new investments
Method of Compensation: Function primarily in service area, receive contingent fee in cash or equity

GRACE VENTURE PARTNERS

201 South Orange Avenue
Suite 880, Seaside Plaza
Orlando, FL USA 32801
Phone: 407-835-7900
Fax: 407-835-7901
E-mail: info@graceventure.com
Website: www.graceventure.com

Management and Staff

Edward Grace, Managing Director

Type of Firm

Private Equity Firm

Project Preferences

Role in Financing:

Will function either as deal originator or investor in deals created by others

Type of Financing Preferred:

Second Stage Financing
Early Stage
Seed
First Stage Financing
Startup

Size of Investments Considered:

Min Size of Investment Considered (000s): $500
Max Size of Investment Considered (000s): $2,000

Geographical Preferences

United States Preferences:

Southeast
Northeast
East Coast

Industry Preferences

In Communications prefer:
Telecommunications
Wireless Communications
Data Communications

In Computer Software prefer:
Software
Systems Software
Applications Software

In Semiconductor/Electr prefer:
Semiconductor
Laser Related
Fiber Optics

In Consumer Related prefer:
Retail
Food/Beverage
Consumer Products
Consumer Services

Additional Information
Year Founded: 1999
Capital Under Management: $20,000,000
Current Activity Level: Actively seeking new investments
Method of Compensation: Return on investment is of primary concern, do not charge fees

---

GRAHAM PARTNERS, INC.
3811 Westchester Pike
Building 2, Suite 200
Newtown Square, PA USA 19073
Phone: 610-408-0500
Fax: 610-408-0600
E-mail: gpinc@grahampartners.net
Website: www.grahampartners.net

Management and Staff
Anthony Folino, Chief Financial Officer
Christopher Lawler, Principal
Robert Newbold, Principal
Steven Graham, Senior Managing Director
William McKee, Managing Partner

Type of Firm
Corporate PE/Venture

Project Preferences

Type of Financing Preferred:
Leveraged Buyout

Size of Investments Considered:
Min Size of Investment Considered (000s): $15,000
Max Size of Investment Considered (000s): $40,000

Geographical Preferences

United States Preferences:
All U.S.

Canadian Preferences:
All Canada

International Preferences:
Western Europe

Industry Focus
(% based on actual investment)

Industrial/Energy	55.7%
Other Products	38.4%
Internet Specific	4.4%
Communications and Media	0.9%
Computer Software and Services	0.6%

Additional Information
Name of Most Recent Fund: Graham Partners II (A), L.P.
Most Recent Fund Was Raised: 10/15/2004
Year Founded: 1988
Capital Under Management: $227,000,000
Current Activity Level: Actively seeking new investments

GRAND SUD OUEST CAPITAL
304 Bd du President Wilson
Bordeaux Cedex, France 33076
Phone: 33-5-5690-4287
Fax: 33-5-5690-4296
E-mail: gsocapital@gsocapital.com
Website: www.gsocapital.com

Other Offices
9 rue Ozenne
Toulouse, France 31000
Phone: 33-5-6114-5004
Fax: 33-5-6114-5032

Management and Staff
Didier Mathieu, Partner
Francois De Vaugelas, General Director
Laurent Mazard, Partner

Type of Firm
Private Equity Firm

Association Membership
French Venture Capital Association (AFIC)

Project Preferences

Role in Financing:
Unknown

Type of Financing Preferred:
Early Stage
Expansion
Management Buyouts

Geographical Preferences

International Preferences:
Europe
Western Europe
France

Additional Information
Year Founded: 1988
Capital Under Management: $39,800,000
Current Activity Level: Actively seeking new investments
Method of Compensation: Unknown

GRANDBANKS CAPITAL
65 William Street
Suite 330
Wellesley, MA USA 02481
Phone: 781-997-4300
Fax: 781-997-4301
E-mail: info@grandbankscapital.com
Website: www.grandbankscapital.com

Management and Staff
Charles Lax, Managing General Partner
J J Healy, Venture Partner
Jeffrey Parker, Venture Partner
Ryan Moore, General Partner
Tim Wright, General Partner

Type of Firm
Private Equity Firm

Association Membership
New England Venture Capital Association
National Venture Capital Association - USA (NVCA)

Project Preferences

Role in Financing:
Prefer role as deal originator but will also invest in deals created by others

Type of Financing Preferred:
Early Stage
Seed

Size of Investments Considered:
Min Size of Investment Considered (000s): $1,000
Max Size of Investment Considered (000s): $12,000

Geographical Preferences

United States Preferences:
Mid Atlantic
Southeast
Northeast
East Coast

Canadian Preferences:
All Canada
Quebec
Ontario
Eastern Canada

Industry Preferences

In Communications prefer:
Communications and Media
Telecommunications
Wireless Communications
Data Communications

In Computer Software prefer:
Computer Services
Software
Systems Software
Applications Software

In Internet Specific prefer:
E-Commerce Technology
Internet
Ecommerce
Web Aggregration/Portals

In Semiconductor/Electr prefer:
Semiconductor

In Consumer Related prefer:
Consumer

In Financial Services prefer:
Financial Services
Insurance

In Business Serv. prefer:
Consulting Services
Media

Additional Information
Year Founded: 2000
Capital Under Management: $125,000,000
Current Activity Level: Actively seeking new investments
Method of Compensation: Return on investment is of primary concern, do not charge fees

GRANDE VENTURES
7160 Riverwood Drive
Suite 150
Columbia, MD USA 21045
Phone: 443-516-1312
Fax: 443-285-0050
Website: www.grandeventures.com

Management and Staff
David Huber, General Partner
Greg Denicola, Partner
Michael Antone, Partner

Type of Firm
Private Equity Firm

Association Membership
Mid-Atlantic Venture Association

Project Preferences

Type of Financing Preferred:
Early Stage
Expansion
Seed
Later Stage
Startup

Geographical Preferences

United States Preferences:
All U.S.

International Preferences:
All International

Industry Preferences

In Communications prefer:
Communications and Media
Wireless Communications

In Computer Other prefer:
Computer Related

In Semiconductor/Electr prefer:
Electronics

In Biotechnology prefer:
Biotechnology

In Consumer Related prefer:
Consumer Products

In Industrial/Energy prefer:
Energy
Industrial Products

Additional Information
Year Founded: 2006
Current Activity Level: Actively seeking new investments

GRANITE CAPITAL PARTNERS
251 River Park Drive
Suite 325
Provo, UT USA 84604
Phone: 801-426-9292
Fax: 801-426-9299
E-mail: info@granitecp.com
Website: www.granitecp.com

Management and Staff
Adam Rasmussen, Partner
Richard Ehlert, Managing Director
Robb Taylor, Managing Director

Type of Firm
Private Equity Firm

Project Preferences

Role in Financing:
Prefer role as deal originator but will also invest in deals created by others

Type of Financing Preferred:
Leveraged Buyout
Expansion
Later Stage
Management Buyouts
Recapitalizations

Size of Investments Considered:
Min Size of Investment Considered (000s): $1,000
Max Size of Investment Considered (000s): $20,000

Geographical Preferences

United States Preferences:
Northern California
Rocky Mountain
West Coast

Industry Focus
(% based on actual investment)

Internet Specific	69.4%
Computer Software and Services	22.6%
Industrial/Energy	3.5%
Other Products	2.8%
Computer Hardware	1.7%

Additional Information
Name of Most Recent Fund: Granite Capital Partners LLC
Most Recent Fund Was Raised: 09/01/1999
Year Founded: 1999
Capital Under Management: $30,000,000
Current Activity Level: Actively seeking new investments
Method of Compensation: Return on investment is of primary concern, do not charge fees

GRANITE CREEK PARTNERS
222 West Adams Street
Suite 1980
Chicago, IL USA 60606
Phone: 312-895-4500
Fax: 312-895-4509
E-mail: info@granitecreek.com
Website: www.granitecreek.com

Management and Staff
Brian Boorstein, Principal
Mark Radzik, Principal
Peter Lehman, Principal

Type of Firm
Private Equity Firm

Project Preferences

Type of Financing Preferred:
Expansion
Mezzanine
Acquisition
Recapitalizations

Geographical Preferences

United States Preferences:
All U.S.

Additional Information
Year Founded: 2007
Current Activity Level: Actively seeking new investments

GRANITE EQUITY PARTNERS
3051 2nd Street South
Suite 105
Saint Cloud, MN USA 56301
Phone: 320-251-1800

Fax: 320-251-1804
Website: www.graniteequity.com

Other Offices

7701 France Avenue South
Suite 200
Minneapolis, MN USA 55435
Phone: 612-605-8017
Fax: 612-395-9295

Management and Staff

Art Monaghan, Principal
Patrick Edeburn, Principal
Rick Bauerly, Principal

Type of Firm

Private Equity Firm

Project Preferences

Type of Financing Preferred:

Leveraged Buyout
Expansion
Recapitalizations

Geographical Preferences

United States Preferences:

South Dakota
North Dakota
Wisconsin
Minnesota

Industry Preferences

In Communications prefer:

Media and Entertainment

In Business Serv. prefer:

Services
Distribution

In Manufact. prefer:

Manufacturing

In Agr/Forestr/Fish prefer:

Agriculture related

Additional Information

Year Founded: 2002
Current Activity Level: Actively seeking new investments

GRANITE HALL PARTNERS (FKA: SPORTS VENTURE PARTNERS, LLC)

190 South LaSalle Street
Suite 540
Chicago, IL USA 60603
Phone: 312-444-6360
Fax: 312-444-6369
E-mail: info@granitehall.com
Website: www.granitehall.com

Management and Staff

Darrell Green, Managing Director
Gregory Anthony, Managing Director
James Flanigan, Managing Director
John Wagner, Managing Director

Type of Firm

Private Equity Advisor or Fund of Funds

Project Preferences

Type of Financing Preferred:

Fund of Funds
Leveraged Buyout

Additional Information

Year Founded: 2000
Capital Under Management: $2,400,000
Current Activity Level: Actively seeking new investments

GRANITE HILL CAPITAL PARTNERS

2180 Sand Hill Road
Suite 200
Menlo Park, CA USA 94025
Phone: 650-787-2716
E-mail: info@granitehill.net
Website: www.granitehill.net

Management and Staff

Kamil Hasan, General Partner
Sameet Mehta, General Partner
Shailesh Mehta, Managing General Partner
Talat Hasan, Venture Partner

Type of Firm

Private Equity Firm

Project Preferences

Type of Financing Preferred:

Expansion

Geographical Preferences

International Preferences:

India

Industry Preferences

In Communications prefer:

Communications and Media

In Consumer Related prefer:

Consumer Products

In Financial Services prefer:

Financial Services

Additional Information

Name of Most Recent Fund: Granite Hill India Opportunities Fund, L.P.
Most Recent Fund Was Raised: 07/02/2008
Year Founded: 2008
Capital Under Management: $16,400,000
Current Activity Level: Actively seeking new investments

GRANITE VENTURES LLC

One Bush Street
Suite 1350
San Francisco, CA USA 94104
Phone: 415-591-7700
Fax: 415-591-7720
Website: www.granitevc.com

Management and Staff

Brian Panoff, Vice President
Chris Hollenbeck, Managing Director
Chris McKay, Managing Director
Eric Zimits, Managing Director
Jackie Berterretche, Chief Financial Officer
Len Rand, Managing Director
Samuel Kingsland, Managing Director
Savinay Berry, Vice President
Standish O Grady, Managing Director
Tom Furlong, Managing Director

Type of Firm

Bank Affiliated

Association Membership

National Venture Capital Association - USA (NVCA)

Project Preferences

Role in Financing:

Prefer role as deal originator but will also invest in deals created by others

Type of Financing Preferred:

Early Stage
Expansion
Research and Development
First Stage Financing
Special Situation
Startup

Size of Investments Considered:

Min Size of Investment Considered (000s): $100
Max Size of Investment Considered (000s): $3,500

Geographical Preferences

United States Preferences:

All U.S.

Industry Focus

(% based on actual investment)

Computer Software and Services	38.8%
Internet Specific	27.4%
Semiconductors/Other Elect.	14.0%
Communications and Media	11.5%
Computer Hardware	3.6%
Consumer Related	2.0%
Medical/Health	1.4%
Other Products	0.8%
Biotechnology	0.2%
Industrial/Energy	0.2%

Additional Information

Name of Most Recent Fund: Granite Ventures II, L.P.
Most Recent Fund Was Raised: 06/27/2005
Year Founded: 1998
Capital Under Management: $465,000,000

Current Activity Level: Actively seeking new investments
Method of Compensation: Return on investment is of primary concern, do not charge fees

GRAPHITE CAPITAL (FKA: F&C VENTURES, LTD.)

Berkeley Square House
Berkeley Square
London, United Kingdom W1J 6BQ
Phone: 44-207-825-5300
Fax: 44-207-825-5399
E-mail: info@graphitecapital.com
Website: www.graphitecapital.com

Management and Staff

Anne Hoffmann, Partner
Jenny Michelman, Partner
Jeremy Gough, Partner
John O'Neill, Partner
Mark Hudson, Partner
Mike Tilbury, Partner
Mike Innes, Partner
Rod Richards, Managing Partner

Type of Firm

Private Equity Firm

Association Membership

British Venture Capital Association (BVCA)

Project Preferences

Role in Financing:

Prefer role as deal originator but will also invest in deals created by others

Type of Financing Preferred:

Leveraged Buyout
Expansion
Balanced
Turnaround
Management Buyouts

Size of Investments Considered:

Min Size of Investment Considered (000s): $2,985
Max Size of Investment Considered (000s): $44,781

Geographical Preferences

International Preferences:

Italy
United Kingdom
Europe
Western Europe
Bermuda
Spain
Germany
France

Industry Focus

(% based on actual investment)

Consumer Related	38.5%
Other Products	25.1%
Medical/Health	14.1%
Industrial/Energy	11.3%
Communications and Media	5.6%
Computer Hardware	2.1%
Computer Software and Services	1.7%
Semiconductors/Other Elect.	1.4%
Biotechnology	0.1%

Additional Information

Name of Most Recent Fund: Graphite Capital Partners VII
Most Recent Fund Was Raised: 05/16/2007
Year Founded: 1981
Capital Under Management: $750,000,000
Current Activity Level: Actively seeking new investments
Method of Compensation: Return on invest. most important, but chg. closing fees, service fees, etc.

GRAYHAWK CAPITAL (FKA: IRONWOOD CAPITAL, GREYHAWK VP)

5050 North 40th Street
Suite 310
Phoenix, AZ USA 85018
Phone: 602-956-8700
Fax: 602-956-8080
E-mail: info@grayhawkcapital.uc
Website: www.grayhawkcapital.us

Management and Staff

Brian Burns, Partner
John Bentley, Partner
Sherman Chu, Partner

Type of Firm

SBIC

Association Membership

Natl Assoc of Small Bus. Inv. Co (NASBIC)

Project Preferences

Role in Financing:

Will function either as deal originator or investor in deals created by others

Type of Financing Preferred:

Second Stage Financing
Leveraged Buyout
Early Stage
Expansion
Generalist PE
Later Stage
First Stage Financing
Special Situation
Recapitalizations

Size of Investments Considered:

Min Size of Investment Considered (000s): $1,000
Max Size of Investment Considered (000s): $3,500

Geographical Preferences

United States Preferences:

Arizona
Rocky Mountain
West Coast
Texas
Southwest

Industry Focus

(% based on actual investment)

Computer Software and Services	39.6%
Other Products	28.3%
Internet Specific	12.3%
Medical/Health	4.6%
Semiconductors/Other Elect.	4.6%
Computer Hardware	4.2%
Communications and Media	3.4%
Biotechnology	2.9%

Additional Information

Name of Most Recent Fund: Grayhawk Venture Fund I, L.P.
Most Recent Fund Was Raised: 05/31/2000
Year Founded: 1995
Capital Under Management: $150,000,000
Current Activity Level: Actively seeking new investments
Method of Compensation: Return on investment is of primary concern, do not charge fees

GRAYSON & ASSOCIATES, INC.

10147 Bluffmont Lane
Lone Tree, CO USA 80124
Phone: 303-768-8664
Fax: 303-484-7679
E-mail: enquiries@grayson-and-associates.com
Website: www.grayson-and-associates.com

Other Offices

5209 Ocean Front Walk
Suite 302
Marina del Rey, CA USA 90292
Phone: 310-306-0850
Fax: 303-484-7679

2638 Juniper Hills Road
Aspen, CO USA 81611
Phone: 970-925-4049
Fax: 303-484-7679

155 Riverside Drive
Suite 7B
New York, NY USA 10024
Phone: 212-580-8817
Fax: 212-580-8827

Management and Staff

F. Joseph Daugherty, Managing Director
Gerald Grayson, President

Type of Firm

Service Provider

Project Preferences

Role in Financing:

Prefer role as deal originator but will also invest in

deals created by others

Type of Financing Preferred:
Later Stage

Size of Investments Considered:
Min Size of Investment Considered (000s): $1,000
Max Size of Investment Considered: No Limit

Industry Preferences

In Biotechnology prefer:
Human Biotechnology

In Medical/Health prefer:
Medical Diagnostics
Diagnostic Services
Diagnostic Test Products
Medical Therapeutics
Drug/Equipmt Delivery
Medical Products
Disposable Med. Products

Additional Information
Year Founded: 1986
Current Activity Level: Actively seeking new investments
Method of Compensation: Function primarily in service area, receive contingent fee in cash or equity

---

GRAZIA EQUITY GMBH
Breitscheidstrasse 10
Stuttgart, Germany 70174
Phone: 49-71-1907-1090
Fax: 49-711-90710918
E-mail: info@grazia-equity.de
Website: www.grazia-equity.de

Management and Staff
Alec Rauschenbusch, Managing Director

Type of Firm
Private Equity Firm

Project Preferences

Type of Financing Preferred:
Leveraged Buyout
Early Stage
Expansion
Management Buyouts

Geographical Preferences

International Preferences:
Europe
Germany

Industry Preferences

In Industrial/Energy prefer:
Alternative Energy

In Manufact. prefer:
Manufacturing

Additional Information
Year Founded: 2000
Current Activity Level: Actively seeking new investments

GREAT HILL EQUITY PARTNERS LLC
One Liberty Square
Boston, MA USA 02109
Phone: 617-790-9400
Fax: 617-790-9401
E-mail: info@greathillpartners.com
Website: www.greathillpartners.com

Management and Staff
Aaron Miller, Vice President
Charlie Papazian, Vice President
Christopher Gaffney, Managing Partner
Christopher Busby, Principal
John Hayes, Managing Partner
Laurie Gerber, Chief Financial Officer
Mark Taber, Partner
Matthew Vettel, Managing Partner
Michael Kumin, Partner
Nicholas Cayer, Vice President
Peter Garran, Vice President
Peter Freeland, Vice President
Philip Yates, Principal
Stephen Gormley, Managing Partner

Type of Firm
Private Equity Firm

Association Membership
National Venture Capital Association - USA (NVCA)

Project Preferences

Role in Financing:
Prefer role as deal originator but will also invest in deals created by others

Type of Financing Preferred:
Leveraged Buyout
Expansion
Balanced
Later Stage
Acquisition
Recapitalizations

Size of Investments Considered:
Min Size of Investment Considered (000s): $50,000
Max Size of Investment Considered (000s): $150,000

Geographical Preferences

United States Preferences:
All U.S.

International Preferences:
Latin America
Europe

Industry Focus
(% based on actual investment)

Computer Software and Services	34.4%
Internet Specific	29.3%
Other Products	14.8%
Communications and Media	10.4%
Semiconductors/Other Elect.	6.5%
Consumer Related	4.7%

Additional Information
Name of Most Recent Fund: Great Hill Equity Partners IV, L.P.
Most Recent Fund Was Raised: 06/11/2008
Year Founded: 1993
Capital Under Management: $790,000,000
Current Activity Level: Actively seeking new investments

GREAT PACIFIC CAPITAL, LLC
610 Anacapa Street
Santa Barbara, CA USA 93101
Phone: 805-966-1000
Fax: 805-413-2019
E-mail: info@greatpacificcapital.com
Website: www.greatpacificcapital.com

Management and Staff
David Gross, Managing Partner
Jason Spievak, Venture Partner
Rusty Reed, Managing Partner

Type of Firm
Private Equity Firm

Project Preferences

Role in Financing:
Prefer role as deal originator but will also invest in deals created by others

Type of Financing Preferred:
Early Stage
Expansion
Seed

Size of Investments Considered:
Min Size of Investment Considered (000s): $500
Max Size of Investment Considered (000s): $3,000

Geographical Preferences

United States Preferences:
California

Industry Preferences

In Internet Specific prefer:
Internet
Ecommerce

In Medical/Health prefer:
Medical Diagnostics

Additional Information
Year Founded: 2005
Capital Under Management: $15,000,000
Current Activity Level: Actively seeking new investments
Method of Compensation: Return on investment is of primary concern, do not charge fees

GREAT POINT PARTNERS LLC

165 Mason Street
Third Floor
Greenwich, CT USA 06830
Phone: 203-971-3300
Fax: 203-971-3320
Website: www.gppfunds.com

Management and Staff

Adam Dolder, Managing Director
Christopher Laitala, Managing Director
David Gerber, Chief Financial Officer
David Kroin, Managing Director
Jeffrey Jay, Managing Director

Type of Firm

Private Equity Firm

Project Preferences

Type of Financing Preferred:
Balanced

Additional Information

Year Founded: 2005
Capital Under Management: $124,500,000
Current Activity Level: Actively seeking new investments

GREAT RIVER CAPITAL LLC

131 West Second Street
Suite 305
Davenport, IA USA 52801
Website: www.greatrivercapital.com

Management and Staff

Andrew Axel, Chief Operating Officer

Type of Firm

Private Equity Advisor or Fund of Funds

Project Preferences

Type of Financing Preferred:
Fund of Funds

Geographical Preferences

United States Preferences:
Iowa

Industry Preferences

In Biotechnology prefer:
Biotechnology

Additional Information

Year Founded: 2002
Current Activity Level: Actively seeking new investments

GREATER PACIFIC CAPITAL LLP

77 Wimpole Street
London, United Kingdom W1G 9RU
Phone: 44-20-7935-6752
Fax: 44-20-7935-6648
E-mail: contact@greaterpacificcapital.com
Website: www.greaterpacificcapital.com

Other Offices

Cayman Financial Centre
Tower C, 36 Dr. Roy's Drive
Cayman Islands

#B-2, First Floor, Amarchand Mansion
Madam Carna Road
Mumbai, India 400 020

Management and Staff

Francis Crispino, Founding Partner
Joe Sealy, Founding Partner
Ketan Patel, Founding Partner
Pradeep Udhas, Managing Director

Type of Firm

Private Equity Firm

Project Preferences

Type of Financing Preferred:
Leveraged Buyout
Acquisition

Geographical Preferences

International Preferences:
India
China

Industry Preferences

In Medical/Health prefer:
Pharmaceuticals

In Consumer Related prefer:
Retail

In Industrial/Energy prefer:
Alternative Energy
Robotics
Machinery

In Financial Services prefer:
Financial Services

Additional Information

Year Founded: 2005
Capital Under Management: $345,000,000
Current Activity Level: Actively seeking new investments

GREATWALL SECURITIES COMPANY, LTD.

Shenzhen Special Area
6008 Shennan Rd., Futian Dist.
Shenzhen, China
Phone: 86-755-82288968

Type of Firm

Bank Affiliated

Project Preferences

Type of Financing Preferred:
Balanced

Additional Information

Year Founded: 1995
Capital Under Management: $287,800,000
Current Activity Level: Actively seeking new investments

GREEN BUSAN INVESTMENT CO., LTD.

87-7 Jungang-Dong 4Ga, Jung-Ku
11/F Busan Trade Center
Busan, South Korea 600-014
Phone: 82-51-465-1214
Fax: 82-51-465-1216
Website: www.greeninvestments.co.kr

Other Offices

705-19 Yeoksam-Dong, Gangam-Gu
7/F Green Non-Insurance Building
Seoul, South Korea 135-922

Type of Firm

Private Equity Firm

Project Preferences

Type of Financing Preferred:
Balanced

Additional Information

Year Founded: 2008
Capital Under Management: $7,200,000
Current Activity Level: Actively seeking new investments

GREEN RECOVERY

21 Avenue Edouard Belin
Rueil Malmaison, France 92500
Phone: 33-1-7061-1264
Fax: 33-1-7272-9309
E-mail: info@green-recovery.com
Website: www.green-recovery.com

Management and Staff

Christophe Talon, President
Type of Firm
Corporate PE/Venture

Association Membership
French Venture Capital Association (AFIC)

Project Preferences

Type of Financing Preferred:
Turnaround

Geographical Preferences

International Preferences:
Europe
France

Additional Information
Year Founded: 2006
Current Activity Level: Actively seeking new investments

GREEN SPARK VENTURES LLC
1580 Lincoln Street
Suite 1120
Denver, CO USA 80203
Phone: 303-884-5733
Website: www.greensparkventures.net

Management and Staff
Dave Ryan, Managing Director

Type of Firm
Private Equity Firm

Project Preferences

Type of Financing Preferred:
Early Stage
Startup

Size of Investments Considered:
Min Size of Investment Considered (000s): $500
Max Size of Investment Considered (000s): $2,000

Geographical Preferences

United States Preferences:
Rocky Mountain
Colorado

Industry Preferences

In Industrial/Energy prefer:
Alternative Energy

Additional Information
Year Founded: 2008
Current Activity Level: Actively seeking new investments

GREEN TREE CAPITAL
135 Camino Dorado
Suite Number Seven
Napa, CA USA 94558
Phone: 707-251-0994
Fax: 707-251-0940
E-mail: info@greentreecapital.com
Website: www.greentreecapital.com

Type of Firm
Bank Affiliated

Project Preferences

Role in Financing:
Prefer role as deal originator

Type of Financing Preferred:
Leveraged Buyout
Management Buyouts
Recapitalizations

Geographical Preferences

United States Preferences:
West Coast

Additional Information
Year Founded: 1985
Current Activity Level: Actively seeking new investments
Method of Compensation: Unknown

GREENBRIAR EQUITY GROUP LLC
555 Theodore Fremd Avenue
Suite A-201
Rye, NY USA 10580
Phone: 914-925-9600
Fax: 914-925-9699
E-mail: info@greenbriarequity.com
Website: www.greenbriarequity.com

Management and Staff
Alan Howard, Managing Director
Gerald Greenwald, Managing Partner
Jill Raker, Managing Director
Joel Beckman, Managing Partner
John Daileader, Managing Director
Kathleen Moran, Managing Director
Noah Roy, Managing Director
Raynard Benvenuti, Managing Director
Reginald Jones, Managing Partner

Type of Firm
Private Equity Firm

Project Preferences

Role in Financing:
Prefer role as deal originator but will also invest in deals created by others

Type of Financing Preferred:
Leveraged Buyout
Management Buyouts
Joint Ventures
Recapitalizations

Geographical Preferences

International Preferences:
All International

Industry Focus
(% based on actual investment)

Other Products	57.7%
Industrial/Energy	42.3%

Additional Information
Name of Most Recent Fund: Greenbriar Equity Fund II-A, L.P.
Most Recent Fund Was Raised: 03/13/2007
Year Founded: 2000
Capital Under Management: $700,000,000
Current Activity Level: Actively seeking new investments
Method of Compensation: Return on invest. most important, but chg. closing fees, service fees, etc.

GREENFIELD CAPITAL PARTNERS
Huizerstraatweg 111
Naarden, Netherlands 1411 GM
Phone: 31-35-699-3900
Fax: 31-35-695-0444
E-mail: info@greenfield.nl
Website: www.greenfield.nl

Other Offices
747 Third Avenue
Suite 34A
New York, NY USA 10017
Phone: 212-317-2662
Fax: 212-679-2940

Scharlooweg 81
Willemstad
Curacao, Neth. Antilles
Phone: 5999-461-8866
Fax: 5999-461-8130

Management and Staff
Bart Zanderbergen, Managing Partner
Enneus Lodewijk, Managing Partner
Leo Deuzeman, Managing Partner
Marc Renne, Managing Partner
Martin Bleijendaal, Chief Financial Officer
Paul Janssens, Managing Partner
Stef Van Doesburg, Managing Partner

Type of Firm
Private Equity Firm

Association Membership
European Private Equity and Venture Capital Assoc.
Dutch Venture Capital Associaton (NVP)

Project Preferences

Type of Financing Preferred:
Fund of Funds
Leveraged Buyout

Early Stage
Expansion
Mezzanine
Generalist PE
Balanced
Turnaround
Management Buyouts
Acquisition

Size of Investments Considered:

Min Size of Investment Considered (000s): $942
Max Size of Investment Considered (000s): $4,708

Geographical Preferences

United States Preferences:

All U.S.

International Preferences:

Netherlands
Europe
Western Europe

Industry Focus

(% based on actual investment)

Other Products	68.9%
Communications and Media	18.3%
Internet Specific	5.0%
Computer Software and Services	4.6%
Consumer Related	3.2%
Industrial/Energy	0.1%

Additional Information

Year Founded: 1981
Capital Under Management: $264,000,000
Current Activity Level: Actively seeking new investments

GREENFIELD HILL CAPITAL LLC

133 Farmstead Hill Road
Fairfield, CT USA 06824

Type of Firm

Private Equity Firm

Industry Preferences

In Communications prefer:

Communications and Media

Additional Information

Year Founded: 2001
Capital Under Management: $1,600,000
Current Activity Level: Actively seeking new investments

GREENHILL CAPITAL PARTNERS

300 Park Avenue
23rd Floor
New York, NY USA 10022
Phone: 212-389-1800
Fax: 212-389-1700
E-mail: investorrelations@greenhill-co.com
Website: www.greenhill-co.com

Other Offices

Neue Mainzer Strasse 52
D-60311 Frankfurt am Main
Frankfurt, Germany 60311
Phone: 49-69-2722-7200
Fax: 49-69-2722-7233

300 Crescent Court
Suite 200
Dallas, TX USA 75201
Phone: 214-443-5400
Fax: 214-443-5401

Lansdowne House
57 Berkeley Square
London, United Kingdom W1J 6ER
Phone: 44-20-7198-7400
Fax: 44-20-7198-7500

One California Street
26th Floor
San Francisco, CA USA 94111
Phone: 212-389-1594

79 Wellington Street West
Suite 3403, P.O. Box 333
Toronto, Canada M5K 1K7
Phone: 416-601-2560
Fax: 416-214-4886

Management and Staff

Aaron Hoover, Managing Director
Adam Maidment, Principal
Anand Jagannathan, Managing Director
Andrew Woeber, Managing Director
Anthony Samengo-Turner, Vice President
Ashish Contractor, Vice President
Ben Lamb, Vice President
Ben Loomes, Vice President
Birger Berendes, Vice President
Boris Gutin, Vice President
Brad Crompton, Managing Director
Bradley Robins, Managing Director
Brian Hirsch, Managing Director
Bryan Cassin, Managing Director
Cameron Crockett, Principal
Charles Barlow, Managing Director
Christopher Mize, Managing Director
Christopher Kirsten, Managing Director
Christopher Riley, Principal
Christopher Cooke, Managing Director
Colin Roy, Managing Director
Dave Brown, Principal
David Skatoff, Principal
David Burns, Vice President
David Wyles, Managing Director
Dhiren Shah, Managing Director
Edward Wakefield, Principal
George Estey, Managing Director
Gregory Miller, Managing Director
Gregory Randolph, Managing Director
Harold Rodriguez, Chief Financial Officer
Hugh Tidbury, Managing Director
Jacob Spens, Vice President
James Flicker, Managing Director
James Lupton, Managing Director
Jan Werner, Managing Director
Jean-Philippe Verdier, Vice President
Jeff Sands, Principal
Jeffrey Buckalew, Managing Director
Jennifer Cobleigh, Principal
Jonathan Rezneck, Vice President
Julie Betts, Vice President
Kenneth Crews, Managing Director
Kevin Bousquette, Managing Director
Kevin Constantino, Vice President
Markus Schneider, Principal
Martin Lewis, Managing Director
Mathias Kiep, Vice President
Meghan Kelly, Vice President
Michael Cramer, Vice President
Michael Giaquinto, Managing Director
Neil Banta, Managing Director
Patrick Dunleavy, Managing Director
Peter Krause, Managing Director
Peter Stott, Managing Director
Phillip Meyer-Horn, Managing Director
Pieter-Jan Bouten, Vice President
Rachel Clark, Principal
Rahul Mody, Principal
Rakesh Chawla, Principal
Richard Jacobsen, Managing Director
Richard Steinman, Managing Director
Richard Morse, Managing Director
Richard Hoyle, Principal
Robert Smith, Managing Director
Robert Hyer, Managing Director
Robert Greenhill, Chairman & Managing Director
Simon Borrows, Managing Director
Steve Brotman, Managing Director
Timothy George, Managing Director
Ulrika Ekman, Managing Director

Type of Firm

Bank Affiliated

Association Membership

British Venture Capital Association (BVCA)

Project Preferences

Type of Financing Preferred:

Leveraged Buyout

Geographical Preferences

United States Preferences:

All U.S.

International Preferences:

United Kingdom
Europe
Australia
Asia

Industry Focus

(% based on actual investment)

Communications and Media	61.1%
Industrial/Energy	18.3%
Other Products	16.1%
Computer Software and Services	4.5%

Additional Information

Name of Most Recent Fund: Greenhill Capital Partners Europe (Employees) L.P.
Most Recent Fund Was Raised: 05/24/2007
Year Founded: 1996
Capital Under Management: $1,340,200,000
Current Activity Level: Actively seeking new investments

GREENHILL SAVP (FKA: SILICON ALLEY VENTURE PARTNERS LLC)

300 Park Avenue
New York, NY USA 10022
Phone: 212-389-1500
Fax: 212-389-1700
E-mail: partners@savp.com
Website: www.greenhill.com

Other Offices

79 Wellington Street West
Suite 3403
Toronto, Canada M5K 1K7
Phone: 416-601-2560
Fax: 416-214-4886

Neue Mainzer Strasse 52
Frankfurt, Georgia D-60311
Phone: 49-69-2722-7200
Fax: 49-69-2722-7233

300 Crescent Court
Suite 200
Dallas, TX USA 75201
Phone: 214-443-5400
Fax: 214-443-5401

One South Dearborn
Suite 2100
Chicago, IL USA 60603
Phone: 312-846-5000
Fax: 312-846-5001

Lansdowne House
57 Berkeley Square
London, United Kingdom W1J 6ER
Phone: 44-20-7198-7400
Fax: 44-20-7198-7500

One California Street
26th Floor
San Francisco, CA USA 94111
Phone: 415-216-4100
Fax: 415-216-4101

Marunouchi Building
2-4-1, Marunouchi, Chiyoda-ku
Tokyo, Japan 100-6309
Phone: 81-3-4520-5100
Fax: 81-3-4520-5101

Management and Staff

Brian Hirsch, Managing Director
James Lockhart, Vice President
Somak Chattopadhyay, Vice President
Steve Brotman, Managing Director

Type of Firm

Private Equity Firm

Association Membership

National Venture Capital Association - USA (NVCA)

Project Preferences

Role in Financing:

Will function either as deal originator or investor in deals created by others

Type of Financing Preferred:

Second Stage Financing
Early Stage
Start-up Financing
Seed
First Stage Financing
Startup

Size of Investments Considered:

Min Size of Investment Considered (000s): $100
Max Size of Investment Considered (000s): $5,000

Geographical Preferences

United States Preferences:

Northeast
Connecticut
New Jersey
New York
All U.S.

Industry Preferences

In Communications prefer:

Wireless Communications
Media and Entertainment

In Computer Software prefer:

Computer Services
Software
Systems Software
Applications Software

In Internet Specific prefer:

E-Commerce Technology
Internet
Ecommerce
Web Aggregration/Portals

In Computer Other prefer:

Computer Related

In Consumer Related prefer:

Publishing-Retail
Consumer Services
Education Related

In Business Serv. prefer:

Media

Additional Information

Name of Most Recent Fund: Greenhill SAVP
Most Recent Fund Was Raised: 06/30/2006
Year Founded: 1998
Capital Under Management: $115,000,000
Current Activity Level: Actively seeking new investments
Method of Compensation: Return on investment is of primary concern, do not charge fees

---

GREENHOUSE CAPITAL PARTNERS

480 Gate Five Road
Suite 210
Sausalito, CA USA 94965
Phone: 415-279-5083
Website: www.greenhousecapital.net

Management and Staff

David Ferrara, Venture Partner
Michael Schwab, General Partner
Peter Henig, Managing Partner

Type of Firm

Private Equity Firm

Project Preferences

Type of Financing Preferred:

Early Stage
Seed

Size of Investments Considered:

Min Size of Investment Considered (000s): $250
Max Size of Investment Considered (000s): $1,000
Geographical Preferences

United States Preferences:

All U.S.

Industry Preferences

In Industrial/Energy prefer:

Alternative Energy

Additional Information

Year Founded: 2006
Capital Under Management: $11,000,000
Current Activity Level: Actively seeking new investments

GREENLIGHT CAPITAL

Two Grand Central Tower
140 East 45 Street, 24/F
New York, NY USA 10017
Phone: 212-973-1900
Fax: 212-973-9219
E-mail: info@greenlightcapital.com
Website: www.greenlightcapital.com

Type of Firm

Private Equity Firm

Additional Information

Year Founded: 2002
Current Activity Level: Actively seeking new investments

GREENMONT CAPITAL PARTNERS

1628 Walnut Street
Boulder, CO USA 80302
Phone: 303-444-0599
Fax: 303-444-0603
E-mail: inquiry@greenmontcapital.com
Website: www.greenmontcapital.com

Management and Staff

Barnet Feinblum, Managing Director
David Haynes, Managing Director
Kim Bixel, Partner
Pam Shepherd, Principal
S.M. Hassan, Managing Director
Todd Woloson, Managing Director

Type of Firm

Private Equity Firm

Project Preferences

Role in Financing:
Will function either as deal originator or investor in deals created by others

Type of Financing Preferred:
Second Stage Financing
Early Stage
Expansion
Balanced
First Stage Financing

Size of Investments Considered:
Min Size of Investment Considered (000s): $500
Max Size of Investment Considered (000s): $2,000

Geographical Preferences

International Preferences:
United Kingdom

Industry Preferences

In Consumer Related prefer:
Consumer
Retail
Food/Beverage
Consumer Products
Consumer Services

In Industrial/Energy prefer:
Alternative Energy
Energy Conservation Relat

In Agr/Forestr/Fish prefer:
Agriculture related

In Other prefer:
Socially Responsible
Environment Responsible

Additional Information

Name of Most Recent Fund: Greenmont Capital Partners II, L.P.
Most Recent Fund Was Raised: 06/20/2008
Year Founded: 2004
Capital Under Management: $20,000,000
Current Activity Level: Actively seeking new investments
Method of Compensation: Return on investment is of primary concern, do not charge fees

GREENPARK CAPITAL, LTD.

57-59 St James's Street
London, United Kingdom SW1A 1LD
Phone: 44-20-7647-1400
Fax: 44-20-7647-1440
E-mail: mail@greenparkcapital.com
Website: www.greenparkcapital.com

Type of Firm

Private Equity Advisor or Fund of Funds

Association Membership

French Venture Capital Association (AFIC)

Project Preferences

Type of Financing Preferred:
Fund of Funds
Leveraged Buyout
Mezzanine
Fund of Funds of Second

Geographical Preferences

International Preferences:
Europe

Additional Information

Year Founded: 2000
Capital Under Management: $1,174,000,000
Current Activity Level: Actively seeking new investments

GREENSTONE PARTNERS PRIVATE CAPITAL PTY, LTD.

56 Pitt Street
Level 25
Sydney, Australia 2000
Phone: 612-9252-4224
Fax: 612-9252-4227
Website: www.greenstonepartners.com.au

Management and Staff

Heath Kerr, Partner
Jesse Sully, Chief Financial Officer
Scott Malcolm, Founding Partner

Type of Firm

Bank Affiliated

Association Membership

Australian Venture Capital Association (AVCAL)

Project Preferences

Type of Financing Preferred:
Leveraged Buyout
Expansion
Management Buyouts

Size of Investments Considered:
Min Size of Investment Considered (000s): $3,223
Max Size of Investment Considered (000s): $6,446

Geographical Preferences

International Preferences:
Australia

Additional Information

Year Founded: 2006
Capital Under Management: $28,600,000
Current Activity Level: Actively seeking new investments

GREENWICH BETEILIGUNGEN AG (FKA: PEGASUS BETEILIGUNGEN AG)

Rossmarkt 14
Frankfurt am Main, Germany 60311
Phone: 49-69-9709-890
Fax: 49-69-9709-8920
Website: www.greenwich-ag.de

Type of Firm

Private Equity Firm

Project Preferences

Type of Financing Preferred:
Early Stage
Expansion

Geographical Preferences

International Preferences:
Germany

Industry Preferences

In Computer Software prefer:
Software

In Internet Specific prefer:
Internet
Ecommerce

Additional Information

Year Founded: 1985
Capital Under Management: $8,900,000
Current Activity Level: Actively seeking new investments

GREENWOODS CAPITAL PARTNERS

24 Greenwoods Road West
P.O. Box 572
Norfolk, CT USA 06058

Phone: 860-542-3935
Fax: 860-542-3936
Website: www.greenwoodscapital.com

Other Offices

245 Fifth Avenue
25th Floor
New York, NY USA 10016
Phone: 212-683-5328
Fax: 212-213-9607

Management and Staff

Frank Gallagi, Principal

Type of Firm

Private Equity Firm

Project Preferences

Type of Financing Preferred:

Expansion
Management Buyouts
Acquisition

Size of Investments Considered:

Min Size of Investment Considered (000s): $1,000
Max Size of Investment Considered (000s): $3,000

Industry Preferences

In Consumer Related prefer:

Retail

In Business Serv. prefer:

Services

Additional Information

Year Founded: 2005
Current Activity Level: Actively seeking new investments

GREER CAPITAL ADVISORS LLC

2200 Woodcrest Place
Suite 309
Birmingham, AL USA 35209
Phone: 205-445-0800
Fax: 205-445-1013
E-mail: info@greercap.com
Website: www.greercap.com

Management and Staff

Hewes Hull, Managing Partner
Jennifer King, Managing Partner
Lawrence Greer, Managing Partner

Type of Firm

Private Equity Firm

Project Preferences

Role in Financing:

Will function either as deal originator or investor in deals created by others

Type of Financing Preferred:

Early Stage
Mezzanine
Later Stage

Size of Investments Considered:

Min Size of Investment Considered (000s): $250
Max Size of Investment Considered (000s): $2,500

Geographical Preferences

United States Preferences:

Southeast
Alabama

Industry Preferences

In Biotechnology prefer:

Biotechnology

In Medical/Health prefer:

Medical/Health
Medical Diagnostics
Medical Therapeutics
Pharmaceuticals

Additional Information

Year Founded: 2002
Capital Under Management: $18,000,000
Current Activity Level: Actively seeking new investments
Method of Compensation: Return on investment is of primary concern, do not charge fees

---

GRESHAM LLP

One South Place
London, United Kingdom EC2M 2GT
Phone: 44-20-7309-5000
Fax: 44-20-7374-0707
E-mail: info@greshampe.com
Website: www.greshampe.com

Other Offices

12-22 Newhall Street
Edmund House
Birmingham, United Kingdom B3 3GT
Phone: 44-121-200-0050
Fax: 44-121-200-0055

82 King Street
Manchester, United Kingdom M2 4WQ
Phone: 44-161-833-7500
Fax: 44-161-833-7575

Management and Staff

Alastair Mills, Partner
Andrew Marsh, Partner
Andy Tupholme, Partner
Christian Bruning, Partner
Gary Ward, Partner
Iain Wolstenholme, Partner
James Barbour-Smith, Partner
James Slipper, Partner
Ken Lawrence, Partner
Mike O'Brien, Partner
Mike Henebery, Partner
Mitch Titley, Partner
Neil Scragg, Partner
Paul Franks, Partner
Paul Thomas, Partner
Paul Marson-Smith, Managing Partner
Pauline Abbie, Partner
Simon Inchley, Partner
Simon Hemley, Partner

Type of Firm

Private Equity Firm

Association Membership

British Venture Capital Association (BVCA)
European Private Equity and Venture Capital Assoc.

Project Preferences

Type of Financing Preferred:

Leveraged Buyout
Expansion
Management Buyouts
Acquisition
Recapitalizations

Size of Investments Considered:

Min Size of Investment Considered (000s): $8,661
Max Size of Investment Considered (000s): $129,908

Geographical Preferences

International Preferences:

United Kingdom
Europe
Western Europe

Industry Focus

(% based on actual investment)

Other Products	32.2%
Consumer Related	30.9%
Medical/Health	22.5%
Communications and Media	5.2%
Industrial/Energy	4.8%
Computer Software and Services	2.8%
Semiconductors/Other Elect.	1.6%

Additional Information

Name of Most Recent Fund: Gresham IV
Most Recent Fund Was Raised: 06/30/2006
Year Founded: 1982
Capital Under Management: $262,800,000
Current Activity Level: Actively seeking new investments

GRESHAM PRIVATE EQUITY, LTD.

Level 17
167 Macquarie Street
Sydney, Australia 2000
Phone: 612-9221-5133
Fax: 612-9223-9072
E-mail: gpe@gresham.com.au
Website: www.gresham.com.au

Other Offices

Level Three

The Esplanade
Perth, Australia
Phone: 618-9486-7077
Fax: 618-9486-7024

Level 10
One Collins Street
Melbourne, Australia 3000
Phone: 613-9664-0300
Fax: 613-9650-7722

Management and Staff

Roger Casey, Managing Director
Roy McKelvie, Managing Director

Type of Firm

Bank Affiliated

Association Membership

Australian Venture Capital Association (AVCAL)

Project Preferences

Role in Financing:
Prefer role as deal originator but will also invest in deals created by others

Type of Financing Preferred:
Leveraged Buyout
Expansion
Later Stage
Management Buyouts

Size of Investments Considered:
Min Size of Investment Considered (000s): $11,130
Max Size of Investment Considered (000s): $44,520

Geographical Preferences

International Preferences:
Australia
New Zealand

Industry Focus

(% based on actual investment)

Other Products	76.1%
Consumer Related	20.8%
Communications and Media	3.1%

Additional Information

Name of Most Recent Fund: Gresham Private Equity Fund 2
Most Recent Fund Was Raised: 02/29/2004
Year Founded: 1998
Capital Under Management: $249,200,000
Current Activity Level: Actively seeking new investments
Method of Compensation: Return on invest. most important, but chg. closing fees, service fees, etc.

GRESHAM RABO MANAGEMENT, LTD.

Level 17
167 Macquarie Street
Sydney, Australia 2000
Phone: 612-9221-4133
Fax: 612-9232-3352
E-mail: inquiries@faif.com.au
Website: www.faif.com.au

Type of Firm

Bank Affiliated

Project Preferences

Type of Financing Preferred:
Second Stage Financing
Leveraged Buyout
Expansion
Balanced
Turnaround
Later Stage
Management Buyouts
First Stage Financing
Acquisition
Special Situation
Startup
Recapitalizations

Size of Investments Considered:
Min Size of Investment Considered (000s): $2,288
Max Size of Investment Considered (000s): $11,440

Geographical Preferences

International Preferences:
Australia
New Zealand

Industry Preferences

In Biotechnology prefer:
Biotechnology

In Consumer Related prefer:
Food/Beverage

In Agr/Forestr/Fish prefer:
Agribusiness

Additional Information

Name of Most Recent Fund: Food and Agribusiness Investment Fund 2
Most Recent Fund Was Raised: 04/03/2002
Year Founded: 1997
Capital Under Management: $70,000,000
Current Activity Level: Actively seeking new investments

GREY CORPORATE INVESTMENTS AG

Pfingstweidstrasse 60
Zurich, Switzerland 8005

Type of Firm

Private Equity Firm

Additional Information

Year Founded: 2008
Current Activity Level: Actively seeking new investments

GREY MOUNTAIN PARTNERS

1426 Pearl Street
Suite 400
Boulder, CO USA 80302
Phone: 303-449-5692
Fax: 303-449-3194
E-mail: info@greymountain.com
Website: www.greymountain.com

Other Offices

590 Madison Avenue
21st Floor
New York, NY USA 10022
Phone: 212-588-8845
Fax: 212-588-8853

Management and Staff

Ben Ault, Vice President
Dan Crouse, Vice President
Jeffrey Vincent, Managing Director
Mark Jennings, Managing Director

Type of Firm

Private Equity Firm

Project Preferences

Role in Financing:
Prefer role as deal originator

Type of Financing Preferred:
Leveraged Buyout
Recapitalizations

Geographical Preferences

Canadian Preferences:
All Canada

Industry Preferences

In Business Serv. prefer:
Services
Distribution

In Manufact. prefer:
Manufacturing

Additional Information

Year Founded: 2003
Current Activity Level: Actively seeking new investments
Method of Compensation: Return on investment is of primary concern, do not charge fees

GREY VENTURES

777 Third Avenue
New York, NY USA 10017
Phone: 212-546-1280
Website: www.grey.com

Type of Firm

Corporate PE/Venture

Project Preferences

Type of Financing Preferred:
Balanced

Additional Information

Year Founded: 2000
Current Activity Level: Actively seeking new investments

GREYCROFT PARTNERS

153 East 53rd Street
53rd Floor
New York, NY USA 10022
Phone: 212-756-3508
Fax: 212-832-0117
Website: www.greycroftpartners.com

Other Offices

100 Wilshire Boulevard
Suite 1830
Santa Monica, CA USA 90401
Phone: 310-566-5961

Management and Staff

Alan Patricof, Managing Director
Andrew Lipsher, Partner
Dana Settle, Partner
Ian Sigalow, Principal

Type of Firm

Private Equity Firm

Project Preferences

Type of Financing Preferred:
Early Stage
Expansion
Balanced

Size of Investments Considered:
Min Size of Investment Considered (000s): $500
Max Size of Investment Considered (000s): $3,000

Industry Preferences

In Communications prefer:
Wireless Communications
Media and Entertainment

In Internet Specific prefer:
Internet

In Consumer Related prefer:
Consumer

Additional Information

Year Founded: 2006
Capital Under Management: $75,000,000
Current Activity Level: Actively seeking new investments

GREYLOCK PARTNERS

880 Winter Street
Suite 300
Waltham, MA USA 02451
Phone: 781-622-2200
Fax: 781-622-2300
E-mail: greylock-info@greylock.com
Website: www.greylock.com

Other Offices

2929 Campus Drive
Suite 400
San Mateo, CA USA 94403
Phone: 650-493-5525
Fax: 650-493-5575

10 Abba Eban Blvd.
Building C, 9th floor, POB 12298
Herzliya Pituach , Israel 46733
Phone: 972-9-958-0007
Fax: 972-9-958-0009

Management and Staff

Aneel Bhusri, Partner
Arnon Dinur, Partner
Arvin Babu, Partner
Asheem Chandna, Partner
Ashutosh Ashutosh, Partner
Charles Chi, Partner
David Sze, Partner
David Thacker, Principal
David Strohm, Partner
Donald Fischer, Principal
Howard Cox, Partner
Isaac Fehrenbach, Principal
Ivy Li, Managing Director
James Slavet, Partner
Michael Stankey, Partner
Roger Evans, Partner
Thomas Bogan, Partner
William Kaiser, Partner
William Helman, Partner

Type of Firm

Private Equity Firm

Association Membership

Western Association of Venture Capitalists (WAVC)
National Venture Capital Association - USA (NVCA)

Project Preferences

Role in Financing:
Prefer role as deal originator but will also invest in deals created by others

Type of Financing Preferred:
Early Stage
Expansion
Start-up Financing
Later Stage
Seed
First Stage Financing

Size of Investments Considered:
Min Size of Investment Considered (000s): $250
Max Size of Investment Considered: No Limit

Geographical Preferences

International Preferences:
China
Israel

Industry Focus

(% based on actual investment)	
Computer Software and Services	37.3%
Internet Specific	25.7%
Communications and Media	11.5%
Semiconductors/Other Elect.	9.1%
Computer Hardware	4.3%
Other Products	4.0%
Industrial/Energy	2.6%
Medical/Health	2.2%
Consumer Related	1.6%
Biotechnology	1.6%

Additional Information

Name of Most Recent Fund: Greylock Israel
Most Recent Fund Was Raised: 07/17/2006
Year Founded: 1965
Capital Under Management: $2,200,000,000
Current Activity Level: Actively seeking new investments
Method of Compensation: Return on investment is of primary concern, do not charge fees

GREYROCK CAPITAL GROUP

Ten Wright Street
Suite 110
Westport, CT USA 06880
Phone: 203-429-2010
Website: www.greyrockcapital.com

Other Offices

582 Market Street
Suite 1117
San Francisco, CA USA 94104
Phone: 415-288-0284

230 West Monroe Street
Suite 2000
Chicago, IL USA 60606
Phone: 312-849-0000

Management and Staff

Mark French, Principal
Mark Shufro, Managing Partner
Stephen Etter, Partner
Steve Dempsey, Principal
Todd Osburn, Partner
Tracy Perkins, Partner

Type of Firm

Private Equity Firm

Association Membership

Illinois Venture Capital Association
Project Preferences

Type of Financing Preferred:
Leveraged Buyout
Mezzanine
Recapitalizations

Size of Investments Considered:
Min Size of Investment Considered (000s): $3,000
Max Size of Investment Considered (000s): $15,000

Geographical Preferences

United States Preferences:
All U.S.

Additional Information
Year Founded: 2002
Capital Under Management: $263,100,000
Current Activity Level: Actively seeking new investments

GRIDIRON CAPITAL LLC
220 Elm Street
New Canaan, CT USA 06840
Phone: 203-972-1100
Fax: 203-801-0602
Website: www.gridironcapital.com

Management and Staff
Donald Cihak, Managing Director
Eugene Conese, Managing Director
Geoffrey Spillane, Principal
Joseph Saldutti, Managing Director
Michael Walsh, Chief Financial Officer
Owen Tharrington, Principal
Peter Kotz, Vice President
Thomas Burger, Managing Director
Timothy Clark, Managing Director

Type of Firm
Private Equity Firm

Project Preferences

Type of Financing Preferred:
Leveraged Buyout
First Stage Financing

Size of Investments Considered:
Min Size of Investment Considered (000s): $5,000
Max Size of Investment Considered (000s): $25,000

Geographical Preferences

United States Preferences:
All U.S.

Canadian Preferences:
Central Canada

Industry Preferences

In Consumer Related prefer:
Consumer Products
Consumer Services

In Industrial/Energy prefer:
Industrial Products

In Transportation prefer:
Aerospace

In Business Serv. prefer:
Services

In Manufact. prefer:
Manufacturing

Additional Information
Name of Most Recent Fund: Gridiron Capital Fund, L.P.
Most Recent Fund Was Raised: 02/14/2006
Year Founded: 2006
Capital Under Management: $300,000,000
Current Activity Level: Actively seeking new investments

GRIFFON VENTURE PARTNERS
6711 Forest Glen Road
Pittsburgh, PA USA 15217
Phone: 412-904-4743

Management and Staff
Gary Schwager, Managing Partner

Type of Firm
Private Equity Advisor or Fund of Funds

Project Preferences

Type of Financing Preferred:
Fund of Funds

Additional Information
Year Founded: 2008
Current Activity Level: Actively seeking new investments

GRIPEN INTERNATIONAL
Vaci ut 22-24
Budapest, Hungary 1132
Phone: 36-1-270-0582
Fax: 36-1-270-0584
Website: www.gripen.hu

Type of Firm
Corporate PE/Venture

Additional Information
Current Activity Level: Actively seeking new investments

GROFIN CAPITAL
224 Loristo Street
Pretorius Park
Pretoria, South Africa 0010
Phone: 27-12-998-8280
Fax: 27-12-998-8401
E-mail: info@grofin.com
Website: www.grofin.com

Other Offices
9 Abimbola Awoniyi Close
Lagos, Nigeria
Phone: 234-1-279-8046
Fax: 234-1-279-8049

No 7 NME Lane
Airport Residential Area
Accra, Ghana
Phone: 233-21-774-777
Fax: 233-21-760-457

4th Floor Tele10 Building
Airport Boulevard, Nyarutarama, Remera
Kigali, Rwanda
Phone: 250-587-150
Fax: 250-587-152

Unit 107, il Palazzo
Cnr Zenith & Solstice Roads
Durban, South Africa
Phone: 27-31-584-6079
Fax: 27-31-566-3075

Ground Floor, CIC Plaza
Mara Road, Upper Hill
Nairobi, Kenya
Phone: 254-20-273-0280
Fax: 254-20-273-0279

Office 229A, 2nd Floor
Harbour View Towers Centre, Samora Ave.
Dar es Salaam, Tanzania
Phone: 255-22-212-0815
Fax: 255-22-212-0871

1st Floor, Global house
Plot 38B Winsor Crescent
Kampala, Uganda
Phone: 256-41-423-7482
Fax: 256-41-423-7481

House No 1305, Way No 3017
Shatti Al Qurum
Muscat, Oman
Phone: 968-24-697-949
Fax: 968-24-697-323

Management and Staff
Jurie Willemse, Managing Director
William Morkel, Chief Financial Officer

Type of Firm
Incubator/Development Program

Association Membership
South African Venture Capital Association (SAVCA)
African Venture Capital Association (AVCA)

Project Preferences

Type of Financing Preferred:
Early Stage
Expansion
Generalist PE

Balanced
Startup

Size of Investments Considered:
Min Size of Investment Considered (000s): $50
Max Size of Investment Considered (000s): $1,000

Geographical Preferences

International Preferences:
Rwanda
Mauritius
Uganda
Nigeria
Tanzania
Kenya
Ghana
South Africa
Africa

Industry Preferences

In Consumer Related prefer:
Retail
Consumer Products
Education Related

In Industrial/Energy prefer:
Energy

In Transportation prefer:
Transportation

In Business Serv. prefer:
Services

In Manufact. prefer:
Manufacturing

In Agr/Forestr/Fish prefer:
Agribusiness

Additional Information
Year Founded: 2003
Capital Under Management: $45,700,000
Current Activity Level: Actively seeking new investments

GROSVENOR FUNDS, THE
1808 Eye Street Northwest
Suite 900
Washington, DC USA 20006
Phone: 202-861-5650
Fax: 202-861-5653
Website: www.grosvenorfund.com

Other Offices
57 Old Post Road #2
2nd Floor
Greenwich, CT USA 06830
Phone: 203-629-8337
Fax: 203-629-8506

Management and Staff
Bruce Dunnan, Managing Partner
C. Bowdoin Train, Managing Partner
Douglas Dunnan, Managing Partner

Type of Firm
Private Equity Firm

Association Membership
Mid-Atlantic Venture Association
National Venture Capital Association - USA (NVCA)

Project Preferences

Type of Financing Preferred:
Early Stage
Balanced
Later Stage
Seed

Size of Investments Considered:
Min Size of Investment Considered (000s): $1,000
Max Size of Investment Considered (000s): $3,000

Industry Preferences

In Communications prefer:
Telecommunications

In Internet Specific prefer:
Internet

In Semiconductor/Electr prefer:
Fiber Optics

In Biotechnology prefer:
Biotechnology

Additional Information
Year Founded: 1994
Current Activity Level: Actively seeking new investments

GROTECH VENTURES (FKA: GROTECH CAPITAL GROUP)
230 Schilling Circle
Suite 362
Hunt Valley, MD USA 21031
Phone: 410-560-2000
Fax: 410-527-1307
E-mail: info@grotech.com
Website: www.grotech.com

Other Offices
2255 Glades Road, Building 1110
Suite 324A
Boca Raton, FL USA 33431
Phone: 561-988-8731
Fax: 561-997-9392

8000 Towers Crescent Drive
Suite 850
Vienna, VA USA 22182
Phone: 703-637-9555
Fax: 703-827-9088

Management and Staff
Donald Rainey, General Partner
Frank Adams, Managing General Partner
Joseph Zell, General Partner
Lawson DeVries, Vice President
Patrick Cairns, Principal
Stephen Fredrick, General Partner
Stuart Frankel, General Partner

Type of Firm
Private Equity Firm

Association Membership
Mid-Atlantic Venture Association
National Venture Capital Association - USA (NVCA)

Project Preferences

Role in Financing:
Prefer role as deal originator

Type of Financing Preferred:
Second Stage Financing
Leveraged Buyout
Early Stage
Expansion
Balanced
Later Stage
First Stage Financing
Private Placement

Size of Investments Considered:
Min Size of Investment Considered (000s): $3,000
Max Size of Investment Considered (000s): $40,000

Geographical Preferences

United States Preferences:
Mid Atlantic
Southeast

Industry Focus
(% based on actual investment)

Internet Specific	25.0%
Consumer Related	17.5%
Computer Software and Services	16.0%
Medical/Health	14.4%
Communications and Media	11.1%
Other Products	5.2%
Industrial/Energy	4.0%
Semiconductors/Other Elect.	3.2%
Computer Hardware	2.3%
Biotechnology	1.2%

Additional Information
Name of Most Recent Fund: Grotech Partners VII, L.P.
Most Recent Fund Was Raised: 03/10/2009
Year Founded: 1984
Capital Under Management: $1,000,000,000
Current Activity Level: Actively seeking new investments
Method of Compensation: Return on invest. most important, but chg. closing fees, service fees, etc.

GROUND SWELL EQUITY PARTNERS
P.O. Box 2370
Del Mar, CA USA 92014
Phone: 858-345-2637

E-mail: info@groundswellequity.com
Website: www.groundswellequity.com

Management and Staff

Robert Bennett, Founder

Type of Firm

Private Equity Firm

Project Preferences

Type of Financing Preferred:
Leveraged Buyout

Size of Investments Considered:
Min Size of Investment Considered (000s): $50,000
Max Size of Investment Considered (000s): $200,000

Geographical Preferences

United States Preferences:
All U.S.

Industry Preferences

In Communications prefer:
Data Communications

In Medical/Health prefer:
Health Services
Pharmaceuticals

In Consumer Related prefer:
Sports
Consumer Services
Education Related

In Financial Services prefer:
Financial Services

In Business Serv. prefer:
Services

In Manufact. prefer:
Manufacturing
Publishing

In Other prefer:
Environment Responsible

Additional Information

Year Founded: 2003
Current Activity Level: Actively seeking new investments

GROUPAMA PRIVATE EQUITY (FKA: FINAMA PRIVATE EQUITY SA)

148 boulevard Hausmann
Paris, France 75008
Phone: 33-1-53-935-151
Fax: 33-1-53-935-152
E-mail: info@finama-pe.fr
Website: www.finama-pe.fr

Management and Staff

Didier Levy-Rueff, General Partner
Stephane D'agostino, Chief Financial Officer

Type of Firm

Insurance Firm Affiliate

Association Membership

French Venture Capital Association (AFIC)

Project Preferences

Type of Financing Preferred:
Fund of Funds
Leveraged Buyout
Early Stage
Expansion
Mezzanine
Generalist PE
Fund of Funds of Second
Recapitalizations

Size of Investments Considered:
Min Size of Investment Considered (000s): $1,372
Max Size of Investment Considered (000s): $5,488

Geographical Preferences

United States Preferences:
All U.S.

International Preferences:
Europe
France

Industry Preferences

In Financial Services prefer:
Real Estate

Additional Information

Year Founded: 2000
Capital Under Management: $2,410,200,000
Current Activity Level: Actively seeking new investments

GROUPE ARNAULT SAS

41, Avenue Montaigne
Paris, France 75008
Phone: 33-14070-0127
Fax: 33-14070-0128
Website: www.groupe-arnault.com

Type of Firm

Private Equity Firm

Project Preferences

Type of Financing Preferred:
Generalist PE

Geographical Preferences

International Preferences:
Europe

Additional Information

Year Founded: 2006
Current Activity Level: Actively seeking new investments

GROUPE BRUXELLES LAMBERT S.A. (GBL)

Avenue Marnix 24
Brussels, Belgium 1000
Phone: 322-547-2352
Fax: 322-547-3633
Website: www.gbl.be

Management and Staff

Gerald Frere, Managing Director
Thierry De Rudder, Managing Director

Type of Firm

Private Equity Firm

Project Preferences

Type of Financing Preferred:
Fund of Funds
Generalist PE
Public Companies

Geographical Preferences

International Preferences:
Italy
Europe
Belgium
France

Additional Information

Year Founded: 1999
Capital Under Management: $190,000,000
Current Activity Level: Actively seeking new investments

GROUPE CAISSE D EPARGNE (AKA: GCE CAPITAL)

47, avenue George V
Paris, France 75008
Phone: 33-1-5364-8770
Fax: 33-1-5364-8773
Website: www.groupe.caisse-epargne.com

Management and Staff

Jean-Claude Crequit, Vice President
Nicolas Merindol, President

Type of Firm

Bank Affiliated

Association Membership

French Venture Capital Association (AFIC)

Project Preferences

Type of Financing Preferred:
Leveraged Buyout
Early Stage
Expansion
Seed

Later Stage
Startup

Additional Information

Year Founded: 2009
Current Activity Level: Actively seeking new investments

GROUPE SADE

4, allee de la Robertsau
Strasbourg, France 67000
Phone: 33-3-8845-5151
Fax: 33-3-8860-4420
E-mail: info@groupesade.com
Website: www.groupesade.com

Type of Firm

Private Equity Firm

Project Preferences

Type of Financing Preferred:

Generalist PE
Balanced

Geographical Preferences

International Preferences:

Europe
France

Additional Information

Year Founded: 1960
Capital Under Management: $29,000,000
Current Activity Level: Actively seeking new investments

GROUPE SOFIMAC (AKA: SOFIMAC PARTNERS)

24 avenue de l'Agriculture
Clermont-Ferrand, France 63028
Phone: 33-4-7374-5757
Fax: 33-4-7374-5758
E-mail: sofimac@sofimac.fr
Website: www.sofimac.fr

Management and Staff

Pascal Voulton, President

Type of Firm

Private Equity Firm

Association Membership

French Venture Capital Association (AFIC)

Project Preferences

Type of Financing Preferred:

Leveraged Buyout
Early Stage
Expansion
Startup

Geographical Preferences

International Preferences:

Europe
France

Industry Preferences

In Biotechnology prefer:

Biotechnology

In Medical/Health prefer:

Medical/Health

In Consumer Related prefer:

Retail

In Industrial/Energy prefer:

Industrial Products
Materials

In Business Serv. prefer:

Services

Additional Information

Year Founded: 1977
Capital Under Management: $34,100,000
Current Activity Level: Actively seeking new investments

GROVE STREET ADVISORS LLC

20 William Street
Suite 230
Wellesley, MA USA 02481
Phone: 781-263-6100
Fax: 781-263-6101
E-mail: info@grovestreetadvisors.com
Website: www.grovestreetadvisors.com

Other Offices

425 Market St.
Suite 2200
San Francisco, CA USA 94105
Phone: 415-955-2741
Fax: 415-955-2745

Management and Staff

Ann St. Germain, Chief Financial Officer
Barry Gonder, General Partner
Catherine Crockett, General Partner
Chris Yang, General Partner
Clinton Harris, Managing General Partner
Frank Angella, General Partner
Kiran Rao, Principal

Type of Firm

Private Equity Advisor or Fund of Funds

Association Membership

National Venture Capital Association - USA (NVCA)

Project Preferences

Role in Financing:

Will function either as deal originator or investor in deals created by others

Type of Financing Preferred:

Fund of Funds

Size of Investments Considered:

Min Size of Investment Considered (000s): $1,000
Max Size of Investment Considered (000s): $7,500

Industry Preferences

In Communications prefer:

Commercial Communications
Wireless Communications
Data Communications

In Computer Hardware prefer:

Integrated Turnkey System

In Computer Software prefer:

Software
Systems Software
Applications Software
Artificial Intelligence

In Internet Specific prefer:

Internet

In Semiconductor/Electr prefer:

Fiber Optics

In Consumer Related prefer:

Consumer

In Industrial/Energy prefer:

Industrial Products

In Business Serv. prefer:

Distribution

Additional Information

Year Founded: 1999
Capital Under Management: $4,165,000,000
Current Activity Level: Actively seeking new investments
Method of Compensation: Return on investment is of primary concern, do not charge fees

GROW UTAH VENTURES

P.O. Box 764
Kaysville, UT USA 84037
Phone: 801-479-5525
E-mail: info@growutahventures.com
Website: www.growutahventures.com

Management and Staff

Kent Thomas, Chief Financial Officer

Type of Firm

Private Equity Firm

Project Preferences

Type of Financing Preferred:

Early Stage
Seed

Geographical Preferences

United States Preferences:

Utah

Additional Information

Year Founded: 2004
Current Activity Level: Actively seeking new investments

GROWCORP GROUP, LTD.

3015 Lake Drive
National Digital Park
Dublin, Ireland
Phone: 353-1-466-1000
Fax: 353-1-466-1002
E-mail: grow@growcorp.net
Website: www.growcorp.net

Management and Staff

Fintan Maher, Managing Director

Type of Firm

Incubator/Development Program

Association Membership

European Private Equity and Venture Capital Assoc.

Project Preferences

Type of Financing Preferred:

Seed
Startup

Geographical Preferences

International Preferences:

Ireland
United Kingdom
Europe

Industry Preferences

In Communications prefer:

Communications and Media

In Biotechnology prefer:

Biotechnology

In Medical/Health prefer:

Medical Diagnostics
Medical Products

Additional Information

Name of Most Recent Fund: European Bioscience Fund 1, The
Most Recent Fund Was Raised: 12/17/2002
Year Founded: 1999
Capital Under Management: $8,700,000
Current Activity Level: Actively seeking new investments

GROWTH CAPITAL PARTNERS (FKA: CLOSE BROTHERS GROWTH CAPITAL)

Second Floor
96-98 Baker Street
London, United Kingdom W1U 6TJ
Phone: 44-20-7563-1760
Fax: 44-20-7563-1761
E-mail: cgc@growthcapital.co.uk
Website: www.growthcapital.co.uk

Management and Staff

Bill Crossan, Managing Director
Garrett Curran, Partner
James Blake, Partner
John Paul McGarth, Managing Director

Type of Firm

Bank Affiliated

Project Preferences

Type of Financing Preferred:

Leveraged Buyout
Expansion
Mezzanine
Management Buyouts

Size of Investments Considered:

Min Size of Investment Considered (000s): $8,729
Max Size of Investment Considered (000s): $43,645

Geographical Preferences

International Preferences:

United Kingdom
Western Europe

Industry Focus

(% based on actual investment)

Other Products	83.0%
Internet Specific	17.0%

Additional Information

Year Founded: 1999
Capital Under Management: $71,200,000
Current Activity Level: Actively seeking new investments

GROWTH CAPITAL PARTNERS, L.P.

363 N. Sam Houston Pkwy. E.
Suite 550
Houston, TX USA 77060
Phone: 281-445-6611
Fax: 281-445-4298
Website: www.growth-capital.com

Other Offices

Two Sound View Drive
Suite 100
Greenwich, CT USA 06830
Phone: 203-622-3916
Fax: 203-622-3917

9600 Crumley Ranch Road
Austin, TX USA 78738
Phone: 512-263-2938
Fax: 512-263-2864

2626 Cole Avenue
Suite 240
Dallas, TX USA 75204
Phone: 214-303-1177
Fax: 214-303-1172

Management and Staff

Drew Sudduth, Managing Director
Edward DiPaolo, Partner
George Khouri, Managing Director
James Rebello, Managing Director
John Grimes, Managing Director
Stephanie Malone, Chief Financial Officer

Type of Firm

Bank Affiliated

Project Preferences

Type of Financing Preferred:

Expansion
Mezzanine
Acquisition
Recapitalizations

Size of Investments Considered:

Min Size of Investment Considered (000s): $1,000
Max Size of Investment Considered (000s): $5,000

Geographical Preferences

United States Preferences:

Southwest

Additional Information

Name of Most Recent Fund: Southwest Mezzanine Investments II, L.P.
Most Recent Fund Was Raised: 07/29/2005
Year Founded: 1992
Capital Under Management: $78,000,000
Current Activity Level: Actively seeking new investments

GROWTHGATE CAPITAL CORPORATION

Level 22, World Trade Center
Sheikh Zayed Road
Dubai, Utd. Arab Em.
Phone: 971-4-329-5537
Fax: 971-4-329-5538
Website: www.growthgatecapitalcorp.com

Management and Staff

Ahmed Doumani, Partner
Haythem Macki, Partner
Joelle Achkar-Juvelekian, Managing Director
Karim Souaid, Managing Partner

Type of Firm

Private Equity Firm

Project Preferences

Type of Financing Preferred:

Generalist PE
Management Buyouts
Recapitalizations

Size of Investments Considered:
Min Size of Investment Considered (000s): $25,000
Max Size of Investment Considered (000s): $100,000

Geographical Preferences

International Preferences:
Europe
Utd. Arab Em.
Asia

Additional Information
Year Founded: 2007
Current Activity Level: Actively seeking new investments

GROWTHPATH CAPITAL, LLC (FKA: TANGRAM PARTNERS, INC.)
200 South Wacker Drive
Suite 3100
Chicago, IL USA 60606
Phone: 312-674-4531
Fax: 312-674-4532
Website: www.growthpathcapital.com

Management and Staff
Andrew Bahnfleth, Managing Partner
Bruce Stevens, Managing Partner
David Dolan, Managing Partner

Type of Firm
Private Equity Firm

Project Preferences

Type of Financing Preferred:
Leveraged Buyout

Size of Investments Considered:
Min Size of Investment Considered (000s): $20,000
Max Size of Investment Considered (000s): $40,000

Industry Focus
(% based on actual investment)

Industrial/Energy	100.0%

Additional Information
Year Founded: 1990
Capital Under Management: $49,000,000
Current Activity Level: Actively seeking new investments

GROWTHWORKS
2600-1055 West Georgia Street
Box 11169, Royal Centre
Vancouver, Canada V6E 3R5
Phone: 604-633-1418
Fax: 604-688-9039
E-mail: info@growthworks.ca
Website: www.growthworks.ca

Other Offices
20 Queen Street West
Suite 3504, PO Box 35
Toronto, Canada M5H 3R3
Phone: 416-934-7777
Fax: 416-929-0901

77 Westmorland Street
Fredericton, Canada E3B 6Z3
Phone: 506-444-0091
Fax: 506-444-0816

410-22nd Street East
Suite 830
Saskatoon, Canada S7K 5T6
Phone: 306-242-1023
Fax: 306-242-9959

Purdy's Wharf Tower 1
1959 Upper Water Street, Suite 1401
Halifax, Canada B3J 3N2
Phone: 902-492-5164
Fax: 902-421-1808

275 Slater Street
Suite 900
Ottawa, Canada K1P 5H9
Phone: 613-567-3225
Fax: 613-567-3979

Highland Business Centre
239 Major's Path
St. John's, Canada A1A 5A1
Phone: 709-757-6221
Fax: 709-722-1136

Management and Staff
Brad Munro, Vice President
David Wilson, Vice President
Harold Heide, Vice President
Joe Timlin, Vice President
John Proven, Vice President
Joseph Regan, Vice President
Les Lyall, Chief Operating Officer
Pat Brady, Vice President
Richard Charlebois, Vice President
Rolf Dekleer, Vice President
Scott Pelton, Vice President
Steven Stang, Vice President
Todd Farrell, Vice President
Tom Hayes, Vice President

Type of Firm
Private Equity Firm

Association Membership
Canadian Venture Capital Association

Project Preferences

Role in Financing:
Will function either as deal originator or investor in deals created by others

Type of Financing Preferred:
Early Stage
Expansion
Balanced
Turnaround
Later Stage
Seed
Private Placement

Size of Investments Considered:
Min Size of Investment Considered (000s): $500
Max Size of Investment Considered (000s): $10,000

Geographical Preferences

Canadian Preferences:
Nova Scotia
Prince Edward Island
All Canada
New Brunswick
Manitoba
Ontario
British Columbia
Saskatchewan
Western Canada
Newfoundland

Industry Preferences

In Computer Software prefer:
Software

In Internet Specific prefer:
E-Commerce Technology

In Computer Other prefer:
Computer Related

In Semiconductor/Electr prefer:
Electronics

In Biotechnology prefer:
Biotechnology

In Medical/Health prefer:
Pharmaceuticals

In Consumer Related prefer:
Consumer Products

In Industrial/Energy prefer:
Alternative Energy
Advanced Materials

In Transportation prefer:
Aerospace

Additional Information
Year Founded: 1999
Capital Under Management: $750,000,000
Current Activity Level: Actively seeking new investments
Method of Compensation: Return on invest. most important, but chg. closing fees, service fees, etc.

GRP PARTNERS (AKA: GLOBAL RETAIL PARTNERS)
2121 Avenue of the Stars
Suite 1630
Los Angeles, CA USA 90067
Phone: 310-785-5100

Fax: 310-785-5111
Website: www.grpvc.com

Management and Staff

Brian McLoughlin, Partner
Mark Suster, Partner
Steven Dietz, General Partner
Steven Lebow, Managing Partner
Yves Sisteron, Managing Partner

Type of Firm

Private Equity Firm

Project Preferences

Role in Financing:

Prefer role as deal originator but will also invest in deals created by others

Type of Financing Preferred:

Second Stage Financing
Early Stage
Expansion
Balanced
Later Stage
First Stage Financing

Size of Investments Considered:

Min Size of Investment Considered (000s): $3,000
Max Size of Investment Considered (000s): $25,000

Geographical Preferences

United States Preferences:

All U.S.

International Preferences:

United Kingdom
Europe
Germany
Asia
All International
France

Industry Focus

(% based on actual investment)

Internet Specific	53.2%
Computer Software and Services	17.6%
Consumer Related	12.3%
Other Products	11.3%
Computer Hardware	3.0%
Communications and Media	2.0%
Industrial/Energy	0.6%

Additional Information

Name of Most Recent Fund: GRP III, L.P.
Most Recent Fund Was Raised: 01/28/2008
Year Founded: 1996
Capital Under Management: $650,000,000
Current Activity Level: Actively seeking new investments
Method of Compensation: Return on investment is of primary concern, do not charge fees

GRUENDERFONDS GMBH & COKEG

Operngasse 6
2. Stock
Vienna, Austria 1010
Phone: 43-1-512-4811
Fax: 43-1-512-481160
E-mail: office@gruenderfonds.at
Website: www.gruenderfonds.at

Management and Staff

Gero Parfuss, Chief Executive Officer
Jonathan Toth, Managing Director
Martin Breuner, Managing Director

Type of Firm

Bank Affiliated

Association Membership

European Private Equity and Venture Capital Assoc.

Project Preferences

Type of Financing Preferred:

Early Stage
Expansion
Seed
Management Buyouts

Size of Investments Considered:

Min Size of Investment Considered (000s): $100
Max Size of Investment Considered (000s): $100,000

Geographical Preferences

International Preferences:

Austria

Industry Focus

(% based on actual investment)

Semiconductors/Other Elect.	44.7%
Biotechnology	31.3%
Industrial/Energy	12.5%
Computer Software and Services	10.7%
Other Products	0.8%

Additional Information

Year Founded: 2001
Current Activity Level: Actively seeking new investments

GRUENWALD EQUITY MANAGEMENT GMBH

Suedliche Muenchner Strasse 15
Gruenwald, Germany 82031
Phone: 49-89500-80860
Fax: 49-895008086160
Website: www.gruenwaldequity.com

Type of Firm

Private Equity Firm

Project Preferences

Type of Financing Preferred:

Generalist PE

Geographical Preferences

International Preferences:

Switzerland
Austria
Germany

Additional Information

Year Founded: 2007
Current Activity Level: Actively seeking new investments

GRUSS & CO.

667 Madison Avenue
Third Floor
New York, NY USA 10021
Phone: 212-688-1500
Fax: 212-688-2138
Website: www.gruss.com

Type of Firm

Private Equity Firm

Project Preferences

Type of Financing Preferred:

Distressed Debt

Additional Information

Year Founded: 2001
Capital Under Management: $26,600,000
Current Activity Level: Actively seeking new investments

GRYFFINDOR CAPITAL PARTNERS LLC

150 North Wacker Drive
Suite 800
Chicago, IL USA 60606
Phone: 312-827-2280
Fax: 312-827-2281
E-mail: info@gryffindorcapital.com
Website: www.gcpfunds.com

Management and Staff

Shelby Pruett, Managing Partner
Stuart Fuchs, Managing Partner

Type of Firm

Private Equity Firm

Project Preferences

Role in Financing:

Will function either as deal originator or investor in deals created by others

Type of Financing Preferred:

Expansion

Public Companies
Later Stage
Other
Joint Ventures
Special Situation

Size of Investments Considered:
Min Size of Investment Considered (000s): $500
Max Size of Investment Considered (000s): $2,000

Geographical Preferences

United States Preferences:
All U.S.

Industry Preferences

In Computer Software prefer:
Software

In Semiconductor/Electr prefer:
Electronic Components
Controllers and Sensors
Sensors
Analytic/Scientific

In Medical/Health prefer:
Medical Therapeutics
Drug/Equipmt Delivery
Medical Products
Health Services
Pharmaceuticals

In Consumer Related prefer:
Consumer
Entertainment and Leisure

In Industrial/Energy prefer:
Energy

In Business Serv. prefer:
Services
Distribution
Media

Additional Information
Year Founded: 2000
Capital Under Management: $2,000,000,000
Current Activity Level: Actively seeking new investments
Method of Compensation: Return on investment is of primary concern, do not charge fees

---

GRYPHON INVESTORS, INC.
One Market Plaza
Steuart Tower, 24/F
San Francisco, CA USA 94105
Phone: 415-217-7400
Fax: 415-217-7447
E-mail: info@gryphoninvestors.com
Website: www.gryphoninvestors.com

Management and Staff
Alexander Earls, Principal
Dennis O Brien, Partner
Dorian Faust, Principal
Felix Park, Vice President
James Gillette, Principal
Janet Kluzik, Vice President
Jef Rogers, Principal
John Rogers, Principal
Keith Stimson, Principal
Kurtis Kaull, Partner
Luke Schroeder, Vice President
Matthew Farron, Vice President
Nicholas Orum, Partner
Patrick Fallon, Partner
R. David Andrews, Managing General Partner
Timothy Bradley, Vice President
Williard Lynn, Partner

Type of Firm
Private Equity Firm

Project Preferences

Type of Financing Preferred:
Leveraged Buyout

Geographical Preferences

United States Preferences:
All U.S.

Industry Focus
(% based on actual investment)

Consumer Related	44.4%
Other Products	20.0%
Industrial/Energy	11.5%
Semiconductors/Other Elect.	10.4%
Medical/Health	7.9%
Computer Software and Services	3.2%
Internet Specific	1.6%
Communications and Media	1.0%

Additional Information
Year Founded: 1995
Capital Under Management: $554,900,000
Current Activity Level: Actively seeking new investments

GS CAPITAL PARTNERS, L.P.
85 Broad Street
New York, NY USA 10004
Phone: 212-902-1000
Fax: 212-902-3000
Website:
www.gs.com/client_services/merchant_banking

Other Offices
50 Raffles Place
#29-01 Singapore Land Tower
Singapore, Singapore 048623
Phone: 65-228-8100
Fax: 65-228-8128

Peterborough Court
133 Fleet Street
London, United Kingdom EC4A 2DBB
Phone: 020-7774-1000
Fax: 020-7529-2351

Management and Staff
Henry Cornell, Managing Director
Milton Berlinski, Principal
Richard Sharp, Managing Director

Type of Firm
Bank Affiliated

Project Preferences

Role in Financing:
Prefer role as deal originator

Type of Financing Preferred:
Leveraged Buyout
Management Buyouts
Acquisition
Special Situation
Recapitalizations

Geographical Preferences

International Preferences:
All International

Additional Information
Year Founded: 1986
Capital Under Management: $4,000,000
Current Activity Level: Actively seeking new investments
Method of Compensation: Return on investment is of primary concern, do not charge fees

---

GSC PARTNERS (FKA: GREENWICH STREET CAPITAL PARTNERS)
500 Campus Drive
Suite 220
Florham Park, NJ USA 07932
Phone: 973-437-1000
Fax: 973-437-1037
E-mail: info@gscpartners.com
Website: www.gscpartners.com

Other Offices
888 Seventh Avenue
New York, NY USA 10019
Phone: 212-884-6200
Fax: 212-884-6184

68 Pall Mall
First Floor
London, United Kingdom SW1Y 5ES
Phone: 44-20-7968-3600
Fax: 44-20-7968-3636

Management and Staff
Alexander Wright, Managing Director
Alexander Zabik, Senior Managing Director
Alfred Eckert, Chairman & CEO
Andrew Wagner, Chief Financial Officer
Brian Oswald, Chief Financial Officer
Carl Crosetto, Managing Director
Christine Vanden Beukel, Senior Managing Director

Daniel Lukas, Managing Director
Daniel Castro, Managing Director
David Robbins, Managing Director
David Goret, Senior Managing Director
Edward Steffelin, Managing Director
Frederick Horton, Senior Managing Director
Georges Courtadon, Managing Director
Harvey Siegel, Managing Director
Jay Merves, Managing Director
Jeremy Soames, Managing Director
John Mills, Managing Director
Joshua Kane, Managing Director
Marc Ciancimino, Managing Director
Matthew Kaufman, Senior Managing Director
Mayur Patel, Managing Director
Michael Lynch, Senior Managing Director
Nick Petrusic, Managing Director
Peter Firth, Managing Director
Peter Frank, Senior Managing Director
Philip Raygorodetsky, Managing Director
Robert Cummings, Senior Managing Director
Robert Hamwee, Senior Managing Director
Robert Paine, Senior Managing Director
Seth Katzenstein, Managing Director
Stanislaw Maliszewski, Managing Director
Thomas Libassi, Senior Managing Director
Thomas Inglesby, Senior Managing Director
Wenbo Zhu, Managing Director

Type of Firm

Private Equity Firm

Project Preferences

Role in Financing:

Will function either as deal originator or investor in deals created by others

Type of Financing Preferred:

Leveraged Buyout
Mezzanine
Acquisition
Distressed Debt
Recapitalizations

Size of Investments Considered:

Min Size of Investment Considered (000s): $10,000
Max Size of Investment Considered (000s): $25,000

Geographical Preferences

International Preferences:

Latin America
Europe
Western Europe
Mexico
Asia

Industry Focus

(% based on actual investment)

Consumer Related	46.6%
Industrial/Energy	20.4%
Medical/Health	16.5%
Other Products	13.8%
Computer Software and Services	1.7%
Internet Specific	1.0%

Additional Information

Name of Most Recent Fund: GSC European Mezzanine Offshore Capital II, L.P.
Most Recent Fund Was Raised: 05/02/2005
Year Founded: 1999
Capital Under Management: $9,200,000,000
Current Activity Level: Actively seeking new investments
Method of Compensation: Return on investment is of primary concern, do not charge fees

GSIM CORPORATION (AKA: GLOBAL STRATEGIC INVESTMENT MGMT.)

4th Floor, No. 65, Sec. 2
Tun Hwa S. Road
Taipei, Taiwan
Phone: 88-62-2325-0777
Fax: 88-62-2754-4778
E-mail: cs@globalsif.com
Website: www.globalsif.com

Other Offices

15997 Grandview Ave.
Monte Sereno
Los Gatos, CA USA 95030
Phone: 408-395-7838
Fax: 408-395-7838

100 Memorial Dr. 11-21C
Cambridge, MA USA 02142
Phone: 617-576-0950
Fax: 617-576-0950

1624 Via Margarita
Palos Verdes
Los Angeles, CA USA 90274
Phone: 310-373-9925

1111 Jupiter Road
Suite 100B
Plano, TX USA 75074
Phone: 972-509-8588
Fax: 972-509-8587

Management and Staff

Erh-Cheng Hwa, Chief Operating Officer
Shih-Chien Yang, Chairman & CEO

Type of Firm

Private Equity Firm

Project Preferences

Type of Financing Preferred:

Expansion
Later Stage

Geographical Preferences

United States Preferences:

All U.S.

International Preferences:

Taiwan
China

Industry Preferences

In Communications prefer:

Communications and Media

In Internet Specific prefer:

Internet

In Semiconductor/Electr prefer:

Electronics

In Biotechnology prefer:

Biotechnology

Additional Information

Year Founded: 2001
Capital Under Management: $11,900,000
Current Activity Level: Actively seeking new investments

GSO INVESTISSEMENTS

Rue Ampere
Labege, France 31670
Phone: 33-5-6224-1010

Type of Firm

Private Equity Firm

Project Preferences

Type of Financing Preferred:

Seed
Startup

Geographical Preferences

International Preferences:

France

Additional Information

Year Founded: 2006
Capital Under Management: $1,000,000
Current Activity Level: Actively seeking new investments

GSR VENTURES

Tsinghua Science Park Bldg. 8
SP Tower A, Suite 907
Beijing, China 100084
Phone: 86-10-8215-1166
Fax: 86-10-8215-1018
E-mail: finance@gsrventures.com
Website: www.gsrventures.com

Other Offices

101 University Avenue
Fourth Floor
Palo Alto, CA USA 94301
Phone: 650-331-7300
Fax: 650-331-7301

Management and Staff

Alex Pan, Managing Director
Allen Zhu, Partner
James Ding, Managing Director
Kevin Yin, Partner
Richard Lim, Managing Director
Sonny Wu, Managing Director

Type of Firm

Private Equity Firm

Project Preferences

Type of Financing Preferred:
Early Stage
Balanced
Startup

Geographical Preferences

International Preferences:
China

Industry Preferences

In Semiconductor/Electr prefer:
Semiconductor

Additional Information

Name of Most Recent Fund: GSR Associates II, L.P.
Most Recent Fund Was Raised: 03/12/2007
Year Founded: 2004
Capital Under Management: $735,000,000
Current Activity Level: Actively seeking new investments

GTCR GOLDER RAUNER LLC

6100 Sears Tower
Chicago, IL USA 60606
Phone: 312-382-2200
Fax: 312-382-2201
E-mail: info@gtcr.com
Website: www.gtcr.com

Management and Staff

Aaron Cohen, Vice President
Anna May Trala, Chief Financial Officer
Barry Dunn, Principal
Ben Daverman, Vice President
Benjamin Remmert, Vice President
Collin Roche, Principal
Constantine (Dean) Mihas, Principal
Craig Bondy, Principal
David Katz, Principal
David Donnini, Principal
Edgar Jannotta, Principal
Eric Sondag, Vice President
George Sperzel, Principal
James Cantu, Vice President
Jay Pauley, Vice President
John Dills, Vice President
John Hofmann, Vice President
Joseph Nolan, Principal
Joshua Earl, Vice President
Mark Springer, Vice President
Mark Anderson, Vice President
Michael Karamouzis, Vice President
Philip Canfield, Principal
Sean Cunningham, Vice President
Shakeel Abdul, Vice President
Vincent Hemmer, Principal

Type of Firm

Private Equity Firm

Association Membership

National Venture Capital Association - USA (NVCA)
Illinois Venture Capital Association

Project Preferences

Role in Financing:
Prefer role as deal originator

Type of Financing Preferred:
Leveraged Buyout
Expansion
Generalist PE
Management Buyouts
Acquisition
Industry Rollups
Recapitalizations

Size of Investments Considered:
Min Size of Investment Considered (000s): $10,000
Max Size of Investment Considered (000s): $300,000

Industry Focus

(% based on actual investment)

Other Products	34.5%
Communications and Media	21.6%
Computer Software and Services	14.2%
Medical/Health	8.4%
Consumer Related	8.4%
Semiconductors/Other Elect.	5.9%
Internet Specific	4.0%
Industrial/Energy	2.2%
Computer Hardware	0.8%

Additional Information

Year Founded: 1980
Capital Under Management: $8,000,000,000
Current Activity Level: Actively seeking new investments
Method of Compensation: Return on invest. most important, but chg. closing fees, service fees, etc.

GTD CAPITAL

1155 Dairy Ashford Street
Suite 806
Houston, TX USA 77079
Phone: 713-621-2693

Management and Staff

Brenda Heartfield, President

Type of Firm

Private Equity Firm

Additional Information

Year Founded: 2009
Current Activity Level: Actively seeking new investments

GTI CAPITAL INC.

255, Rue Saint-Jacques
2nd Floor
Montreal, Canada H2Y 1M6
Phone: 514-845-3800
Fax: 514-845-3810
E-mail: info@gticapital.com
Website: www.gticapital.com

Management and Staff

Francois Veilleux, Chief Financial Officer
Jean Desjardins, Partner
Jean-Francois Couturier, General Partner

Type of Firm

Private Equity Firm

Project Preferences

Type of Financing Preferred:
Early Stage
Expansion
Seed
Later Stage
Startup

Geographical Preferences

Canadian Preferences:
All Canada
Quebec

Industry Preferences

In Communications prefer:
Telecommunications

In Computer Other prefer:
Computer Related

In Semiconductor/Electr prefer:
Electronics

In Industrial/Energy prefer:
Energy

Additional Information

Year Founded: 1993
Capital Under Management: $100,000,000
Current Activity Level: Actively seeking new investments

GUANGDONG INVESTMENT (FKA: GUANGDONG INVESTMENT MANAGEMENT)

28F & 29F Guandong Inv. Tower
148 Connaught Rd.
Central, Hong Kong
Phone: 852-2860-4368

Fax: 852-2528-4386
Website: www.gdi.com.hk

Management and Staff

Hui Zhang, Managing Director

Type of Firm

Private Equity Firm

Project Preferences

Type of Financing Preferred:
Expansion

Geographical Preferences

International Preferences:
China

Industry Preferences

In Semiconductor/Electr prefer:
Electronics

In Consumer Related prefer:
Food/Beverage
Consumer Products

In Industrial/Energy prefer:
Industrial Products
Materials
Additional Information
Year Founded: 1993
Current Activity Level: Actively seeking new investments

GUANGDONG TECHNOLOGY VENTURE CAPITAL GROUP., LTD

14F, Hi-Tech R&D Center
100 Mid Xianlie Road
Guangzhou, China 510070
Phone: 86-20-8768-0388
Fax: 86-20-8761-2766
E-mail: gvcgc@gvcgc.com
Website: www.gdtvic.com

Management and Staff

He Rong, President
Liang Xiang, Chief Executive Officer

Type of Firm

Private Equity Firm

Project Preferences

Type of Financing Preferred:
Early Stage
Expansion
Balanced
Later Stage

Size of Investments Considered:
Min Size of Investment Considered (000s): $1,464
Max Size of Investment Considered (000s): $4,391

Geographical Preferences

International Preferences:
China

Industry Preferences

In Semiconductor/Electr prefer:
Electronics

In Biotechnology prefer:
Biotechnology

In Industrial/Energy prefer:
Energy

In Other prefer:
Environment Responsible

Additional Information

Year Founded: 2000
Current Activity Level: Actively seeking new investments

GUARD, INC.

Research Park Centre
150 Research Lane
Guelph, Canada N1G 4T2
Phone: 519-767-2020
Fax: 519-767-2614

Other Offices

Research Park Centre
150 Research Lane
Guelph, Canada N1G 4T2
Phone: 519-767-2020
Fax: 519-767-2614

Management and Staff

Brian Cox, Partner

Type of Firm

Private Equity Firm

Additional Information

Year Founded: 2009
Current Activity Level: Actively seeking new investments

GUARDIAN CAPITAL PARTNERS

353 West Lancaster Avenue
Suite 130
Wayne, PA USA 19087
Phone: 610-964-1500
Fax: 610-465-8900
E-mail: gcp@guardiancp.com
Website: www.guardiancp.com

Management and Staff

Hugh Kenworthy, Managing Partner
Peter Haabestad, Managing Partner
Scott Evans, Managing Partner

Type of Firm

Private Equity Firm

Project Preferences

Type of Financing Preferred:
Leveraged Buyout
Management Buyouts

Size of Investments Considered:
Min Size of Investment Considered (000s): $5,000
Max Size of Investment Considered (000s): $15,000

Geographical Preferences

United States Preferences:
All U.S.

Industry Preferences

In Medical/Health prefer:
Medical Products

In Consumer Related prefer:
Consumer Products

In Industrial/Energy prefer:
Industrial Products

In Business Serv. prefer:
Services

In Manufact. prefer:
Manufacturing

Additional Information

Year Founded: 2008
Capital Under Management: $37,000,000
Current Activity Level: Actively seeking new investments

GUGGENHEIM VENTURE PARTNERS LLC

227 West Monroe
Chicago, IL USA 60606
Phone: 312-827-0100
Website: www.guggenheimpartners.com

Other Offices

8, rue Saint-Leger
Geneva, Switzerland 1205
Phone: 41-22-704-0666

1111 Brickell Avenue
Miami, FL USA 33131
Phone: 305-373-8033

25 Old Broad Street
London, United Kingdom EC2N 1HN
Phone: 44-207-877-0723

Four Copley Place
Boston, MA USA 02116
Phone: 617-536-5515

231 South Bemiston
Saint Louis, MO USA 63105
Phone: 314-862-4848

Six South Bryn Mawr Avenue
Bryn Mawr, PA USA 19010
Phone: 610-313-0910

135 East 57th Street
New York, NY USA 10022
Phone: 212-739-0700

1301 McKinney
Houston, TX USA 77010
Phone: 713-300-1330

64 Knightsbridge
London, United Kingdom SW1X 7JF
Phone: 44-207-590-3145

200 East 10th Street
Sioux Falls, SD USA 57104
Phone: 605-782-1930

One Exchange Square
8 Connaught Place
Central, Hong Kong
Phone: 852-3119-0135

100 Wilshire Boulevard
Santa Monica, CA USA 90401
Phone: 310-576-1270

Management and Staff

Eric Rothfus, Managing Director
Michael Burns, Managing Director

Type of Firm

Private Equity Firm

Project Preferences

Type of Financing Preferred:

Early Stage
Mezzanine
Distressed Debt

Geographical Preferences

United States Preferences:

Mid Atlantic
Northwest
Southwest

Industry Preferences

In Communications prefer:

Communications and Media
Commercial Communications

In Internet Specific prefer:

Internet

Additional Information

Year Founded: 2006
Capital Under Management: $10,000,000
Current Activity Level: Actively seeking new investments

GUIDANT CORPORATION

3200 Lakeside Drive
Santa Clara, CA USA 95054
Phone: 408-845-3000
Fax: 408-845-3333
Website: www.guidant.com

Other Offices

111 Monument Circle
29th Floor
Indianapolis, IN USA 46204

Management and Staff

Mark Bartell, President

Type of Firm

Corporate PE/Venture

Project Preferences

Role in Financing:

Will function either as deal originator or investor in deals created by others

Type of Financing Preferred:

Second Stage Financing
Early Stage
Expansion
Mezzanine
Start-up Financing
Later Stage
Seed
First Stage Financing

Industry Preferences

In Medical/Health prefer:

Medical Therapeutics

Additional Information

Year Founded: 1994
Capital Under Management: $30,000,000
Current Activity Level: Actively seeking new investments

GUIDE VENTURES LLC

12509 Bel-Red Road
Suite 201
Bellevue, WA USA 98005
Phone: 425-450-0062
Fax: 425-688-7980
E-mail: info@guideventures.com
Website: www.guideventures.com

Management and Staff

James Thornton, Managing Director
Michael Templeman, Managing Director
Russ Aldrich, Managing Director

Type of Firm

Private Equity Firm

Project Preferences

Role in Financing:

Prefer role as deal originator but will also invest in deals created by others

Type of Financing Preferred:

Early Stage
Expansion
Seed

Size of Investments Considered:

Min Size of Investment Considered (000s): $200
Max Size of Investment Considered (000s): $2,000

Geographical Preferences

United States Preferences:

Northwest
West Coast
Southwest

Industry Preferences

In Communications prefer:

Telecommunications
Wireless Communications
Data Communications

In Computer Software prefer:

Computer Services
Data Processing
Software
Systems Software
Applications Software
Artificial Intelligence

In Internet Specific prefer:

Internet
Ecommerce
Web Aggregration/Portals

In Biotechnology prefer:

Biotech Related Research

Additional Information

Year Founded: 1999
Capital Under Management: $21,000,000
Current Activity Level: Actively seeking new investments
Method of Compensation: Return on investment is of primary concern, do not charge fees

---

GUIGU TIANTANG VENTURE CAPITAL CO., LTD.

No. 12 Zhongguancun Street A
Huantai Building
Beijing, China 100081
Phone: 86-10-6212-5588
Fax: 86-10-6210-9119
Website: www.ggttvc.com

Other Offices

Qintai Wenhua Yishu Center
No. 8 Gujianzhu A District
Wuhan, China 430050
Phone: 86-27-8484-2218

Fax: 86-27-8484-2228
No. 76 Yuhuang Shan Road
Haiqin Liaoyang Yuan
Hangzhou, China 310002
Phone: 86-571-87083018
Fax: 86-571-87089718

Jintian Road, Futian District
Rongchao Jingmao Center
Shenzhen, China 518035
Phone: 86-755-33226099
Fax: 86-755-33226069

No. 439 Chunxiao Road
Zhangjiang Gaokeji Yuan District
Shanghai, China 201203
Phone: 86-21-5027-4986
Fax: 86-21-5027-5016

Management and Staff

Yue Bao, Chief Executive Officer

Type of Firm

Private Equity Firm

Project Preferences

Type of Financing Preferred:

Expansion
Early Stage
Balanced
Public Companies
Seed
Later Stage
Private Placement

Geographical Preferences

International Preferences:

China

Industry Preferences

In Computer Other prefer:

Computer Related

In Industrial/Energy prefer:

Energy
Materials
Environmental Related

In Transportation prefer:

Transportation

Additional Information

Year Founded: 2001
Capital Under Management: $90,600,000
Current Activity Level: Actively seeking new investments

GULF CAPITAL PRIVATE JOINT STOCK COMPANY

Al Ferdous Tower
Salam St., 15th Floor
Abu Dhabi, Utd. Arab Em.
Phone: 971-2-671-6060
Fax: 971-2-694-2703
E-mail: info@gulfcapital.com
Website: www.gulfcapital.com

Management and Staff

Imad Ghandour, Principal
Magellan Makhlouf, Managing Director
Mayas Ghosheh, Vice President
Mohamed Sharara, Principal
Muhannad Qubbai, Managing Director
Wassim Assaad, Principal

Type of Firm

Private Equity Firm

Project Preferences

Type of Financing Preferred:

Early Stage
Balanced
Later Stage

Geographical Preferences

International Preferences:

Middle East

Industry Preferences

In Medical/Health prefer:

Health Services

In Industrial/Energy prefer:

Oil and Gas Exploration
Oil & Gas Drilling,Explor

In Transportation prefer:

Transportation

Additional Information

Year Founded: 2005
Capital Under Management: $476,800,000
Current Activity Level: Actively seeking new investments

GULFSTAR GROUP

700 Louisiana Street
Suite 3800
Houston, TX USA 77002
Phone: 713-300-2020
Fax: 713-300-2021
E-mail: info@gulfstargroup.com
Website: www.gulfstargroup.com

Other Offices

100 Crescent Court
Suite 700
Dallas, TX USA 75201
Phone: 214-459-2755
Fax: 214-459-2756

Management and Staff

Alan Blackburn, Managing Director
Bradley Alexander, Vice President
Christopher Williams, Managing Director
F.W. Luedde, Managing Director
G. Kent Kahle, Managing Director
Richard Wilson, Managing Director
Stephen Lasher, Managing Director
Stewart Cureton, Managing Director
Thomas Hargrove, Managing Director
Thomas Bartlett, Managing Director
Todd Mehall, Vice President
W. Clifford Atherton, Managing Director

Type of Firm

Bank Affiliated

Geographical Preferences

United States Preferences:

Southwest

Additional Information

Year Founded: 1990
Current Activity Level: Actively seeking new investments

GUNNALLEN VENTURE PARTNERS

5002 West Waters Avenue
Tampa, FL USA 33634
Phone: 813-282-0808
Fax: 813-282-1275
Website: www.gunnallen.com

Management and Staff

Christopher Frankel, Chief Operating Officer
Jon Goldberg, Managing Director

Type of Firm

Private Equity Firm

Additional Information

Year Founded: 1996
Capital Under Management: $15,000,000
Current Activity Level: Actively seeking new investments

GUOTAI JUNAN INNOVATION INVESTMENT CO., LTD.

c/o Guotai Junan Securities Co
29/F, Shanghai Bank Building
Shanghai, China 200120
Fax: 86-21-3867-0666

Type of Firm

Bank Affiliated

Project Preferences

Type of Financing Preferred:

Expansion

Geographical Preferences

International Preferences:

China
Asia

Industry Preferences

In Medical/Health prefer:
Medical/Health

In Consumer Related prefer:
Consumer Products

In Industrial/Energy prefer:
Environmental Related

In Business Serv. prefer:
Services

In Manufact. prefer:
Manufacturing

Additional Information
Year Founded: 2009
Capital Under Management: $73,200,000
Current Activity Level: Actively seeking new investments

GUSTAFSON & CO., INC.
1866 Commerce Street
Yorktown Heights, NY USA 10598
Phone: 914-962-2200
Fax: 914-962-2204
E-mail: mark.r.gustafson@gustafsoninc.com

Management and Staff
Mark Gustafson, President

Type of Firm
Private Equity Firm

Project Preferences

Role in Financing:
Unknown

Type of Financing Preferred:
Leveraged Buyout
Turnaround
Management Buyouts
Recapitalizations

Geographical Preferences

International Preferences:
United Kingdom
France

Additional Information
Current Activity Level: Actively seeking new investments
Method of Compensation: Return on invest. most important, but chg. closing fees, service fees, etc.

GVFL LIMITED (FKA: GUJARAT VENTURE FINANCE LIMITED)
1st Flr, Premchand House Annex
B/h Popular House, Ashram Road
Ahmedabad, India 380 009
Phone: 91-79-2658-8741
Fax: 91-79-2658-5226
Website: www.gvfl.com

Other Offices
#45 Trade Centre
Bangalore, India 560 042

Management and Staff
Bharat Kanani, Chief Operating Officer
Sanjeev Sharma, Vice President
Vinodkumar Chopra, Vice President

Type of Firm
Private Equity Firm

Association Membership
Indian Venture Capital Association (IVCA)

Project Preferences

Role in Financing:
Prefer role as deal originator but will also invest in deals created by others

Type of Financing Preferred:
Leveraged Buyout
Early Stage
Expansion
Balanced
Seed
Management Buyouts
Startup

Size of Investments Considered:
Min Size of Investment Considered (000s): $55
Max Size of Investment Considered (000s): $2,200

Geographical Preferences

International Preferences:
India

Industry Focus

(% based on actual investment)	
Industrial/Energy	22.7%
Communications and Media	18.3%
Other Products	13.8%
Computer Software and Services	10.8%
Semiconductors/Other Elect.	10.1%
Computer Hardware	9.6%
Internet Specific	5.8%
Consumer Related	4.3%
Medical/Health	3.1%
Biotechnology	1.5%

Additional Information
Year Founded: 1990
Capital Under Management: $34,600,000
Current Activity Level: Actively seeking new investments
Method of Compensation: Return on investment is of primary concern, do not charge fees

---

GYLLING INVEST AB
Vendevagen 90
Danderyd, Sweden 182 32
Phone: 46-854-49-8980
Fax: 46-854-49-8990
Website: www.gylling.se

Management and Staff
Bengt Hagander, CEO & Managing Director
Bertil Gylling, Partner

Type of Firm
Private Equity Firm

Association Membership
Swedish Venture Capital Association (SVCA)

Project Preferences

Type of Financing Preferred:
Early Stage
Expansion
Seed
Startup

Geographical Preferences

International Preferences:
Sweden
Europe

Additional Information
Year Founded: 2004
Capital Under Management: $27,300,000
Current Activity Level: Actively seeking new investments

GZ GROUP (AKA: GATENBECK ZAKRISSON GROUP)
Master Samuelsgatan 42
Stockholm, Sweden SE-111 57
Phone: 46-8-5456-8060
Fax: 46-8-5456-8070
E-mail: info@gzgroup.se
Website: www.gzgroup.se

Management and Staff
Lars Gatenbeck, Chief Executive Officer
Peter Zakrisson, General Partner

Type of Firm
Private Equity Firm

Association Membership
Swedish Venture Capital Association (SVCA)
European Private Equity and Venture Capital Assoc.

Project Preferences

Type of Financing Preferred:
Expansion
Balanced

Size of Investments Considered:
Min Size of Investment Considered (000s): $1,062
Max Size of Investment Considered (000s): $10,620

Geographical Preferences

International Preferences:
Sweden
Scandanavia/Nordic Region

Industry Preferences

In Biotechnology prefer:
Biotechnology

In Medical/Health prefer:
Medical/Health

In Consumer Related prefer:
Consumer
Consumer Products

Additional Information
Year Founded: 1999
Capital Under Management: $208,500,000
Current Activity Level: Actively seeking new investments

- H -

H & S CAPITAL (AKA: HEIDRICK & STRUGGLES CAPITAL)
Sears Tower
233 Wacker Dr, Suite 7000
Chicago, IL USA 60606-6402
Phone: 312-496-1000
Fax: 312-496-1048
E-mail: Chicago@h-s.com
Website: www.heidrick.com

Other Offices
950 Tower Lane
Sixth Floor
Foster City, CA USA 94404
Phone: 650-234-1500
Fax: 650-350-1000

Management and Staff
Bradley Holden, Managing Partner
Jean-Louis Alpeyrie, Partner
Kevin Smith, Chief Financial Officer
Michael Hunter, Principal

Type of Firm
Corporate PE/Venture

Project Preferences

Type of Financing Preferred:
Early Stage

Geographical Preferences

International Preferences:
All International

Additional Information
Year Founded: 1999
Current Activity Level: Actively seeking new investments

H&Q ASIA PACIFIC
400 Hamilton Avenue
Suite 250
Palo Alto, CA USA 94301
Phone: 650-838-8088
Fax: 650-838-0801
E-mail: hqap@hqap.com
Website: www.hqap.com

Other Offices
MID Nihonbashi-Horidome-cho Bldg. 7F
1-7-7 Nihonbashi-Horidome-cho, Chuo-ku
Tokyo, Japan 103-0012
Phone: 81-3-6206-2399
Fax: 81-3-3249-5950

3F Wonseo Bldg., 171 Wonseo-Dong
Jongno-Gu
Seoul, South Korea 110-280
Phone: 822-782-2288
Fax: 822-3775-4589

Suite 2405, Union Bank Plaza
Meralco Avenue, Ortigas Center
Pasig City, Philippines 1605
Phone: 63-2-706-0835
Fax: 63-2-638-5128

Suite 2011, 20/FL CitiGroup Tower
33 HuaYuanShiQiao Road
Shanghai, China 200120
Phone: 86-21-6887-8080
Fax: 86-21-6887-8011

32F-1, International Trade Bldg.
333 Kee-Lung Road, Sec.1
Taipei, Taiwan 110
Phone: 886-2-2720-9855
Fax: 886-2-2722-2106

Suite 2018, Hutchison House
10 Harcourt Road, Central
Hong Kong, Hong Kong
Phone: 852-2868-4800
Fax: 852-2810-4883

Management and Staff
Jarlon Tsang, Chief Operating Officer
Jong Won (John) Lee, Managing Director
Jung-Jin Lee, Managing Director
Mark Hsu, Managing Director
Peter Pil Jae Ko, Managing Director
Rick Chiang, Managing Director
Robert Shen, Managing Director
Shigeaki Koga, Managing Director
Solomon Tsai, Managing Director
Teck Shang Ang, Managing Director
Virapan Pulges, Managing Director
Yuchul (YC) Rhim, Managing Director

Type of Firm
Private Equity Firm

Association Membership
Hong Kong Venture Capital Association (HKVCA)
Taiwan Venture Capital Association(TVCA)

Project Preferences

Role in Financing:
Prefer role as deal originator but will also invest in deals created by others

Type of Financing Preferred:
Leveraged Buyout
Early Stage
Expansion
Balanced
Later Stage
Management Buyouts
Acquisition
Special Situation

Size of Investments Considered:

Min Size of Investment Considered (000s): $150
Max Size of Investment Considered (000s): $50,000

Geographical Preferences

United States Preferences:

California

International Preferences:

India
Taiwan
China
Thailand
Singapore
Asia
Korea, South
Japan

Industry Focus

(% based on actual investment)

Other Products	36.1%
Semiconductors/Other Elect.	14.7%
Internet Specific	13.9%
Industrial/Energy	10.1%
Computer Hardware	9.9%
Computer Software and Services	9.1%
Consumer Related	2.6%
Medical/Health	1.7%
Communications and Media	1.3%
Biotechnology	0.7%

Additional Information

Year Founded: 1985
Capital Under Management: $2,691,000,000
Current Activity Level: Actively seeking new investments

H.I.G. CAPITAL LLC

1001 Brickell Bay Drive
27th Floor
Miami, FL USA 33131
Phone: 305-379-2322
Fax: 305-379-2013
E-mail: info@higcapital.com
Website: www.higcapital.com

Other Offices

One Market - Spear Tower
18th Floor
San Francisco, CA USA 94105
Phone: 415-439-5500
Fax: 415-439-5525

855 Boylston Street
Eleventh Floor
Boston, MA USA 02116
Phone: 617-262-8455
Fax: 617-262-1505

Warburgstrasse 50
Hamburg, Germany 20354
Phone: 49-40-4133-06100
Fax: 49-40-4133-06200

600 Fifth Avenue
24th Floor
New York, NY USA 10020
Phone: 212-506-0500
Fax: 212-506-0559

25 St. George Street
First Floor
London, United Kingdom W1S 1FS
Phone: 44-207-318-5700
Fax: 44-207-318-5749

3050 Peachtree Road NorthWest
Suite 360, Two Buckhead Plaza
Atlanta, GA USA 30305
Phone: 404-504-9333
Fax: 404-504-9370

44, avenue George V
Paris, France 75008
Phone: 33-1-5357-5060
Fax: 33-1-5357-5089

Management and Staff

Aaron Davidson, Managing Director
Andrew Steel, Principal
Austin Scee, Vice President
Bret Wiener, Managing Director
Brian Schwartz, Managing Director
Bruce Robertson, Managing Director
Charles Hanemann, Managing Director
Craig Burson, Managing Director
Douglas Berman, Managing Director
Elliot Maluth, Managing Director
Fred Sturgis, Managing Director
Hank Boughner, Managing Director
Jens Alsleben, Managing Director
John Bolduc, Managing Director
John Black, Managing Director
John Kim, Managing Director
Jorn-Marc Vogler, Principal
Lars Hirche, Managing Director
Lewis Schoenwetter, Managing Director
Mark Kelly, Principal
Matt Sanford, Managing Director
Matthias Allgaier, Managing Director
Olivier Boyadjian, Managing Director
Patrick Caron, Managing Director
Rick Rosen, Managing Director
Sami Mnaymneh, Managing Partner
Thibaud Caulier, Principal
Tony Tamer, Managing Partner
Wolfgang Biedermann, Managing Director
Zoltan Bognar, Principal

Type of Firm

Private Equity Firm

Association Membership

French Venture Capital Association (AFIC)
National Venture Capital Association - USA (NVCA)

Project Preferences

Role in Financing:

Will function either as deal originator or investor in deals created by others

Type of Financing Preferred:

Second Stage Financing
Leveraged Buyout
Early Stage
Expansion
Later Stage
Seed
Management Buyouts
First Stage Financing
Startup
Distressed Debt
Recapitalizations

ize of Investments Considered:

Min Size of Investment Considered (000s): $500
Max Size of Investment Considered (000s): $40,000

Geographical Preferences

United States Preferences:

All U.S.

International Preferences:

Europe

Industry Focus

(% based on actual investment)

Consumer Related	27.4%
Industrial/Energy	23.5%
Other Products	20.9%
Computer Software and Services	6.1%
Biotechnology	5.3%
Internet Specific	5.0%
Semiconductors/Other Elect.	4.4%
Medical/Health	3.6%
Communications and Media	3.2%
Computer Hardware	0.5%

Additional Information

Name of Most Recent Fund: H.I.G. Bayside Debt & LBO Fund II, L.P.
Most Recent Fund Was Raised: 06/11/2008
Year Founded: 1993
Capital Under Management: $4,500,000,000
Current Activity Level: Actively seeking new investments
Method of Compensation: Return on invest. most important, but chg. closing fees, service fees, etc.

H2 EQUITY PARTNERS BV

Oosteinde 19
Amsterdam, Netherlands NL-1017
Phone: 31-20-679-0822
Fax: 31-20-675-8359
E-mail: info@h2.nl
Website: www.h2.nl

Management and Staff

Age Hollander, Managing Partner
Gert Jan Van der Hoeven, Managing Partner

Type of Firm

Private Equity Firm

Project Preferences

Type of Financing Preferred:
Leveraged Buyout
Expansion
Turnaround
Recapitalizations

Geographical Preferences

International Preferences:
United Kingdom
Netherlands
Belgium
Germany

Industry Preferences

In Medical/Health prefer:
Medical/Health
Pharmaceuticals

In Consumer Related prefer:
Hotels and Resorts
Education Related

In Industrial/Energy prefer:
Industrial Products

Additional Information
Year Founded: 1991
Capital Under Management: $234,400,000
Current Activity Level: Actively seeking new investments

HACHIJUNI CAPITAL COMPANY, LTD.
6F Choei Dai-ichi Bldg. 282-11
MinamiSekidomachi,Oaza-Minami-Nagano, Nagano-shi, Japan 380-0824
Phone: 026-227-6887
Fax: 026-227-6989
Website: www.hcc82.co.jp

Type of Firm
Private Equity Firm

Project Preferences

Type of Financing Preferred:
Balanced

Geographical Preferences

International Preferences:
Japan

Industry Preferences

In Computer Other prefer:
Computer Related

In Consumer Related prefer:
Consumer Services

Additional Information
Year Founded: 1984
Capital Under Management: $50,500,000
Current Activity Level: Actively seeking new investments

HADDINGTON VENTURES, LLC
2603 Augusta
Suite 1130
Houston, TX USA 77057
Phone: 713-532-7992
Fax: 713-532-9922
E-mail: sec@hvllc.com
Website: www.hvllc.com

Management and Staff
J. Chris Jones, Managing Director
John Strom, Managing Director
M. Scott Jones, Managing Director

Type of Firm
Private Equity Firm

Project Preferences

Role in Financing:
Prefer role as deal originator but will also invest in deals created by others

Type of Financing Preferred:
Balanced

Size of Investments Considered:
Min Size of Investment Considered (000s): $5,000
Max Size of Investment Considered (000s): $50,000

Geographical Preferences

United States Preferences:
All U.S.

Canadian Preferences:
All Canada

Industry Preferences

In Industrial/Energy prefer:
Energy

In Utilities prefer:
Utilities

Additional Information
Name of Most Recent Fund: Haddington Energy Partners III, L.P.
Most Recent Fund Was Raised: 08/22/2005
Year Founded: 1997
Capital Under Management: $150,000,000
Current Activity Level: Actively seeking new investments
Method of Compensation: Return on invest. most important, but chg. closing fees, service fees, etc.

HADLEY CAPITAL
111 West Washington Street
Suite 1340
Chicago, IL USA 60602
Phone: 312-201-9900
Fax: 312-201-9923
E-mail: info@hadleycapital.com
Website: www.hadleycapital.com

Management and Staff
Clay Brock, Managing Partner
Paul Wormley, Partner
Scott Dickes, Managing Partner

Type of Firm
Private Equity Firm

Project Preferences

Type of Financing Preferred:
Leveraged Buyout
Expansion
Generalist PE
Management Buyouts
Acquisition
Recapitalizations

Industry Preferences

In Business Serv. prefer:
Distribution

In Manufact. prefer:
Manufacturing

Additional Information
Year Founded: 1998
Capital Under Management: $40,000,000
Current Activity Level: Actively seeking new investments

HAFSLUND VENTURE AS
P.O. Box 2468
Solli, Norway N-0202
Phone: 47-22-435-000
Website: www.hafslund.com

Management and Staff
Christian Berg, Chief Financial Officer

Type of Firm
Private Equity Firm

Association Membership
Norwegian Venture Capital Association

Industry Preferences

In Communications prefer:
Communications and Media

Additional Information
Year Founded: 1898
Current Activity Level: Actively seeking new investments

HAKON INVEST AB (FKA: ICA FORBUNDET INVEST)

Svetsarvagen 16
Box 1508
Solna, Sweden 171 29
Phone: 46-8-5533-9900
Fax: 46-8-5533-9933
Website: www.hakoninvest.se

Management and Staff

Claes-Goran Sylven, President
Goran Hesseborn, Chief Financial Officer

Type of Firm

Private Equity Firm

Association Membership

Swedish Venture Capital Association (SVCA)

Project Preferences

Type of Financing Preferred:
Expansion
Balanced

Geographical Preferences

International Preferences:
Sweden
Estonia
Norway
Finland
Latvia
Lithuania
Denmark

Industry Preferences

In Consumer Related prefer:
Retail

Additional Information

Year Founded: 2005
Current Activity Level: Actively seeking new investments

HAL INVESTMENTS BV

Millennium Tower
Weena 696
Rotterdam, Netherlands 3012 CN
Phone: 31-10-281-6500
Fax: 31-10-281-6528
E-mail: info@halinvestments.nl
Website: www.halinvestments.nl

Other Offices

Tower D, 4th Floor
Schiphol Boulevard 123
Schiphol Airport, Netherlands 1118 BG
Phone: 31-20-446-9555
Fax: 31-20-446-9550

Type of Firm

Bank Affiliated

Project Preferences

Type of Financing Preferred:
Leveraged Buyout
Expansion
Balanced
Acquisition
Recapitalizations

Geographical Preferences

International Preferences:
Western Europe

Industry Focus

(% based on actual investment)

Internet Specific	100.0%

Additional Information

Year Founded: 1989
Current Activity Level: Actively seeking new investments

HALDER HOLDINGS BV

Lange Voorhout 9
The Hague, Netherlands 2514 EA
Phone: 31-70-361-8618
Fax: 31-70-361-8616
E-mail: info@halder.eu
Website: www.halder.nl

Other Offices

Barckhausstrasse 12-16
Frankfurt, Germany 60325
Phone: 49-69-242-5330
Fax: 49-69-236-866

Karel Oomsstraat 37
Antwerp, Belgium 2018
Phone: 32-3-290-2100
Fax: 32-3-290-2105

Management and Staff

Geert-Jan Van Logtestijn, Managing Director
Marcel Van Wijk, Partner
Michael Wahl, Partner
Paul De Ridder, Partner
Susanne Quint, Partner
Thomas Fotteler, Partner
Ward Bouwers, Managing Director

Type of Firm

Private Equity Firm

Association Membership

German Venture Capital Association (BVK)
European Private Equity and Venture Capital Assoc.
Indian Venture Capital Association (IVCA)

Project Preferences

Role in Financing:
Prefer role as deal originator but will also invest in deals created by others

Type of Financing Preferred:
Leveraged Buyout
Expansion
Generalist PE
Management Buyouts
Recapitalizations

Size of Investments Considered:
Min Size of Investment Considered (000s): $7,172
Max Size of Investment Considered (000s): $14,345

Geographical Preferences

International Preferences:
Netherlands
Belgium
Germany

Industry Focus

(% based on actual investment)

Industrial/Energy	33.7%
Consumer Related	32.2%
Other Products	26.9%
Computer Software and Services	6.2%
Internet Specific	1.0%
Medical/Health	0.1%

Additional Information

Year Founded: 1983
Capital Under Management: $384,200,000
Current Activity Level: Actively seeking new investments
Method of Compensation: Return on investment is of primary concern, do not charge fees

HALE FUND MANAGEMENT, L.P.

570 Lexington Avenue
49th Floor
New York, NY USA 10022
Phone: 212-751-8802
E-mail: contact@halefunds.com
Website: www.halefunds.com

Management and Staff

Martin Hale, Chief Executive Officer

Type of Firm

Private Equity Firm

Project Preferences

Type of Financing Preferred:
Leveraged Buyout
Acquisition

Additional Information

Year Founded: 2009
Current Activity Level: Actively seeking new investments

HALIFAX GROUP, THE

1133 Connecticut Avenue, NW
Suite 725
Washington, DC USA 20036
Phone: 202-530-8300
Fax: 202-296-7133
Website: www.thehalifaxgroup.com

Other Offices

2840 Plaza Place
Suite 103
Raleigh, NC USA 27612
Phone: 919-786-4420
Fax: 919-786-4428

201 Main Street
Suite 2420
Fort Worth, TX USA 76102
Phone: 817-332-9811
Fax: 817-332-7474

1999 Avenue of the Stars
Suite 1200
Los Angeles, CA USA 90067
Phone: 310-282-8820
Fax: 310-282-8813

Management and Staff

Bill Rogers, Managing Director
Billie Ellis, Managing Director
Brent Williams, Principal
David Dupree, Managing Director
Kenneth Doyle, Principal
Michael Marshall, Chief Financial Officer
Scott Plumridge, Vice President

Type of Firm

Private Equity Firm

Association Membership

Mid-Atlantic Venture Association

Project Preferences

Type of Financing Preferred:
Leveraged Buyout

Size of Investments Considered:
Min Size of Investment Considered (000s): $5,000
Max Size of Investment Considered (000s): $30,000

Geographical Preferences

United States Preferences:
All U.S.

Industry Focus

(% based on actual investment)

Other Products	51.8%
Medical/Health	25.5%
Internet Specific	20.5%
Communications and Media	2.2%

Additional Information

Name of Most Recent Fund: Halifax Capital Partners II, L.P.
Most Recent Fund Was Raised: 02/25/2005
Year Founded: 1999
Capital Under Management: $200,000,000
Current Activity Level: Actively seeking new investments

HALL CAPITAL PARTNERS LLC (FKA: OFFIT HALL CAPITAL MGMT)

One Maritime Plaza
Fifth Floor
San Francisco, CA USA 94111
Phone: 415-288-0544
Fax: 415-288-4694
E-mail: general.inquiries@hallcapital.com
Website: www.hallcapital.com

Other Offices

597 Fifth Avenue
Eight Floor
New York, NY USA 10017
Phone: 212-407-0700

Management and Staff

Brian Taylor, Principal
John Boneparth, President
John Buoymaster, President
Kathryn Hall, Chairman & CEO
R. Rachel Hsu, Principal

Type of Firm

Investment Management Firm

Project Preferences

Type of Financing Preferred:
Fund of Funds

Additional Information

Year Founded: 1994
Capital Under Management: $2,000,000,000
Current Activity Level: Actively seeking new investments

HALPERN, DENNY & COMPANY

399 Boylston Street
Third Floor
Boston, MA USA 02116
Phone: 617-536-6602
Fax: 617-536-8535
E-mail: Info@HalpernDenny.com
Website: www.halperndenny.com

Management and Staff

Barbara Eastman, Vice President
David Malm, Partner
George Denny, Partner
John Halpern, Partner
Mark Greene, Chief Financial Officer
William LaPoint, Partner
William Nimmo, Partner

Type of Firm

Private Equity Firm

Project Preferences

Role in Financing:
Will function either as deal originator or investor in deals created by others

Type of Financing Preferred:
Second Stage Financing
Leveraged Buyout
Control-block Purchases
Early Stage
Expansion
Mezzanine
Generalist PE
Balanced
Turnaround
Later Stage
Seed
Management Buyouts
First Stage Financing
Acquisition
Joint Ventures
Recapitalizations

Size of Investments Considered:
Min Size of Investment Considered (000s): $5,000
Max Size of Investment Considered (000s): $40,000

Industry Focus

(% based on actual investment)

Medical/Health	25.9%
Consumer Related	24.4%
Internet Specific	19.4%
Other Products	16.6%
Communications and Media	5.7%
Industrial/Energy	4.5%
Computer Software and Services	3.6%

Additional Information

Year Founded: 1990
Capital Under Management: $615,000,000
Current Activity Level: Actively seeking new investments
Method of Compensation: Return on invest. most important, but chg. closing fees, service fees, etc.

HALYARD PARTNERS

600 Fifth Avenue
17th Floor
New York, NY USA 10020
Phone: 212-554-2121
Fax: 212-554-2120
E-mail: info@halyard.com
Website: www.halyard.com

Management and Staff

Bruce Eatroff, Founding Partner
Jonathan Barnes, Principal
Michael Furey, Principal
Robert Nolan, Managing Partner

Sarah Kim, Principal
Timothy Brown, Principal

Type of Firm

Private Equity Firm

Project Preferences

Type of Financing Preferred:
Leveraged Buyout
Expansion
Management Buyouts

Industry Preferences

In Communications prefer:
Communications and Media
Media and Entertainment

In Business Serv. prefer:
Services

Additional Information

Name of Most Recent Fund: Halyard Capital Fund II (Parallel), L.P.
Most Recent Fund Was Raised: 05/09/2007
Year Founded: 2000
Capital Under Management: $450,000,000
Current Activity Level: Actively seeking new investments

HAMBRECHT & QUIST CAPITAL MANAGEMENT (H&Q) LLC

30 Rowes Wharf
4th Floor
Boston, MA USA 02110
Phone: 617-772-8500
Website: www.hqcm.com

Management and Staff

Dan Omstead, Managing Director

Type of Firm

Private Equity Firm

Additional Information

Year Founded: 2009
Current Activity Level: Actively seeking new investments

HAMILTON BIOVENTURES (FKA HAMILTON APEX TECHNOLOGY VENTURES)

12555 High Bluff Drive
Suite 310
San Diego, CA USA 92130
Phone: 858-314-2350
Fax: 858-314-2355
E-mail: info@hamiltonapex.com
Website: www.hamiltonbioventures.com

Management and Staff

Kerry Dance, Managing Director
Richard Crosby, Managing Director

Type of Firm

Private Equity Firm

Association Membership

Natl Assoc of Small Bus. Inv. Co (NASBIC)

Project Preferences

Role in Financing:
Will function either as deal originator or investor in deals created by others

Type of Financing Preferred:
Second Stage Financing
Early Stage
First Stage Financing

Size of Investments Considered:
Min Size of Investment Considered (000s): $1,000
Max Size of Investment Considered (000s): $5,600

Geographical Preferences

United States Preferences:
Southern California
Northern California
West Coast

Industry Preferences

In Biotechnology prefer:
Human Biotechnology
Genetic Engineering

In Medical/Health prefer:
Medical Therapeutics
Drug/Equipmt Delivery
Medical Products
Pharmaceuticals

Additional Information

Name of Most Recent Fund: Hamilton BioVentures (FKA:Hamilton Apex Tech. Ventures)
Most Recent Fund Was Raised: 01/01/2000
Year Founded: 2000
Capital Under Management: $100,000,000
Current Activity Level: Actively seeking new investments
Method of Compensation: Return on investment is of primary concern, do not charge fees

---

HAMILTON BRADSHAW

10 Stratton Street
London, United Kingdom W1J 8DA
Phone: 44-207-101-7100
Fax: 44-207-491-3759
E-mail: enquiry@hamiltonbradshaw.com
Website: www.hamiltonbradshaw.com

Management and Staff

Tony Sarin, Chief Executive Officer

Type of Firm

Private Equity Firm

Project Preferences

Type of Financing Preferred:
Leveraged Buyout
Expansion
Turnaround
Later Stage
Management Buyouts
Recapitalizations

Size of Investments Considered:
Min Size of Investment Considered (000s): $892
Max Size of Investment Considered (000s): $8,921

Geographical Preferences

International Preferences:
Europe

Industry Preferences

In Communications prefer:
Communications and Media

In Computer Software prefer:
Software

In Medical/Health prefer:
Health Services

In Financial Services prefer:
Financial Services

Additional Information

Year Founded: 2004
Current Activity Level: Actively seeking new investments

HAMILTON INVESTMENTS

375 Park Avenue
Suite 3407
New York, NY USA 10152
Phone: 646-285-0341
Fax: 646-285-0347
Website: www.hamltoninvestment.com

Management and Staff

Douglas Hamilton, Managing Partner
Marc Cole, Founding Partner
Veronica La Voun, Chief Operating Officer

Type of Firm

Private Equity Firm

Additional Information

Year Founded: 2005
Current Activity Level: Actively seeking new investments

HAMILTON LANE ADVISORS, INC.

One Presidential Boulevard
Fourth Floor
Bala Cynwyd, PA USA 19004
Phone: 610-934-2222
Fax: 610-617-9853
E-mail: information@hamiltonlane.com
Website: www.hamiltonlane.com

Other Offices

825 Third Avenue
35th Floor
New York, NY USA 10022
Phone: 212-752-7667
Fax: 212-752-7865

Buchanan House
3 St. James's Square
London, United Kingdom SW1Y 4JU
Phone: 44-207-484-0650
Fax: 44-207-484-0655

80 Raffles Place
UOB Plaza 1, 35th Floor
Singapore, Singapore 048624
Phone: 65-6248-4741
Fax: 65-6248-4501

17F, Imperial Hotel Tower
1-1-1, Uchisaiwai-cho
Tokyo, Japan 100-0011
Phone: 81-3-3580-4000
Fax: 81-3-3580-4600

14 Shenkar Street
Nolton House
Herzalia Pituach, Israel 46733
Phone: 972-9-958-6620
Fax: 972-9-956-8205

200 California Street
Suite 400
San Francisco, CA USA 94111
Phone: 415-365-1056
Fax: 415-365-1057

Level 8, Two Exchange Square
8 Connaught Place, Central
Hong Kong, Hong Kong
Phone: 852-2297-2370
Fax: 852-2297-0066

7777 Fay Avenue
Suite 206
La Jolla, CA USA 92037
Phone: 858-410-9967
Fax: 858-410-9968

Management and Staff

Allen Williams, Vice President
Ana Lei Ortiz, Vice President
Andrea Kramer, Principal
Anthony Donofrio, Vice President
Christopher Priebe, Vice President
David Helgerson, Vice President
Elizabeth Foo, Vice President
Jacqueline Rantanen, Principal
Janet Bauman, Vice President
Jeffrey Meeker, Vice President
Jisoo Noh, Vice President
John Mensack, Vice President
Joshua Kahn, Vice President
Juan Delgado-Moreira, Managing Director
Keith Spears, Vice President
Kevin Lucey, Managing Director
Mario Giannini, Chief Executive Officer
Michael Ryan, Vice President
Michael Kelly, Managing Director
Michael McCabe, Vice President
Michael Palone, Vice President
Michael Koenig, Vice President
Paul Yett, Managing Director
Peter Larsen, Vice President
Randy Stilman, Chief Financial Officer
Stephen Brennan, Principal
Tara Blackburn, Managing Director
Thomas Kerr, Principal
W. Duke DeGrassi, Managing Director

Type of Firm

Private Equity Advisor or Fund of Funds

Project Preferences

Type of Financing Preferred:

Fund of Funds
Later Stage
Fund of Funds of Second

Size of Investments Considered:

Min Size of Investment Considered (000s): $5,000
Max Size of Investment Considered (000s): $5,000

Geographical Preferences

United States Preferences:

California
New York
All U.S.

International Preferences:

United Kingdom
Latin America
Europe
Asia
Australia

Industry Focus

(% based on actual investment)

Other Products	99.4%
Computer Software and Services	0.6%

Additional Information

Name of Most Recent Fund: Hamilton Lane Private Equity Offshore Fund VI, L.P.
Most Recent Fund Was Raised: 05/25/2007
Year Founded: 1991
Capital Under Management: $62,900,000
Current Activity Level: Actively seeking new investments

HAMILTONTECH CAPITAL PARTNERS, LP

8880 Rio San Diego Drive
Suite 500
San Diego, CA USA 92109
Phone: 619-291-2777
Fax: 619-295-0189
E-mail: info@hamiltontechcapital.com
Website: www.hamiltontechcapital.com

Other Offices

18101 Von Karman Avenue
Suite 1050
Irvine, CA USA 92612
Phone: 949-851-4856
Fax: 949-851-4860

Management and Staff

F. Duwaine Townsen, Senior Managing Director
Jay Kear, Senior Managing Director
Paul Bouchard, Senior Managing Director
Randy Berholtz, Venture Partner
Richard Sandfer, Managing Director & CFO
Terry Moore, Managing Director

Type of Firm

Private Equity Firm

Project Preferences

Type of Financing Preferred:

Second Stage Financing
Expansion
First Stage Financing

Geographical Preferences

United States Preferences:

All U.S.

Industry Preferences

In Computer Hardware prefer:

Computers

In Computer Software prefer:

Software

Additional Information

Year Founded: 1999
Current Activity Level: Actively seeking new investments

HAMMERMAN CAPITAL, LLC

One Federal Street
18th Floor
Boston, MA USA 02110
Phone: 617-574-6150

Type of Firm

Other

Additional Information

Year Founded: 2002
Capital Under Management: $79,000,000
Current Activity Level: Actively seeking new investments

HAMMOND KENNEDY WHITNEY & CO

8888 Keystone Crossing
Suite 600
Indianapolis, IN USA 46240
Phone: 317-574-6900
Fax: 317-574-7515
E-mail: hk@hkwinc.com
Website: www.hkwinc.com

Other Offices

Suite 1807 An Tai Building
No. 107 Zunyi Road
Shanghai, China 200051
Phone: 86-21-6237-5801
Fax: 86-21-6237-5836

333 N. Michigan Avenue
Suite 501
Chicago, IL USA 60601
Phone: 312-458-0060
Fax: 312-458-0072

230 Park Avenue
Suite 1616
New York, NY USA 10169
Phone: 212-867-1010
Fax: 212-867-1312

Management and Staff

Andrew McNally, Partner
Forrest Crisman, Partner
James Snyder, Partner
James Futterknecht, Partner
Ted Kramer, Principal

Type of Firm

Bank Affiliated

Project Preferences

Role in Financing:

Prefer role as deal originator

Type of Financing Preferred:

Leveraged Buyout
Generalist PE
Management Buyouts
Acquisition
Recapitalizations

Size of Investments Considered:

Min Size of Investment Considered (000s): $5,000
Max Size of Investment Considered (000s): $15,000

Geographical Preferences

United States Preferences:

All U.S.

Canadian Preferences:

All Canada

Industry Focus

(% based on actual investment)

Industrial/Energy	53.8%
Other Products	46.2%

Additional Information

Year Founded: 1903
Capital Under Management: $66,900,000
Current Activity Level: Actively seeking new investments
Method of Compensation: Return on invest. most important, but chg. closing fees, service fees, etc.

HAMPSHIRE EQUITY PARTNERS (FKA: ING EQUITY PARTNERS)

520 Madison Avenue
33rd Floor
New York, NY USA 10022
Phone: 212-453-1600
Fax: 212-750-2970
E-mail: info@hampep.com
Website: www.hampep.com

Management and Staff

Gregory Flynn, Managing Partner
Jason Meyer, Partner
John Lenahan, Vice President
Laurens Goff, Principal
Michael McGovern, Partner
Paul Cabral, Chief Financial Officer
Tracey Rudd, Managing Partner

Type of Firm

Investment Management Firm

Project Preferences

Role in Financing:

Will function either as deal originator or investor in deals created by others

Type of Financing Preferred:

Leveraged Buyout
Expansion
Generalist PE
Later Stage
Management Buyouts
Acquisition
Joint Ventures
Recapitalizations

Size of Investments Considered:

Min Size of Investment Considered (000s): $7,000
Max Size of Investment Considered (000s): $70,000

Geographical Preferences

United States Preferences:

All U.S.

Industry Focus

(% based on actual investment)

Industrial/Energy	54.9%
Computer Software and Services	19.3%
Other Products	16.7%
Consumer Related	4.2%
Medical/Health	3.0%
Internet Specific	1.8%

Additional Information

Name of Most Recent Fund: Hampshire Equity Partners III, L.P.
Most Recent Fund Was Raised: 12/01/2000
Year Founded: 1993
Capital Under Management: $873,000,000
Current Activity Level: Actively seeking new investments
Method of Compensation: Return on invest. most important, but chg. closing fees, service fees, etc.

HANA INVESTMENT, INC. (AKA: HANA VENTURE CAPITAL)

508# Kins Tower, 25-1
Jeongja-dong, Bundang-gu
Gyeonggi-do, South Korea 463-844
Phone: 82-31-782-3290
Fax: 82-31-782-3292

Management and Staff

Kwangsoo Kim, Chief Executive Officer

Type of Firm

Corporate PE/Venture

Project Preferences

Type of Financing Preferred:

Balanced

Additional Information

Year Founded: 2007
Current Activity Level: Actively seeking new investments

HANCOCK CAPITAL MANAGEMENT LLC

197 Clarendon Street
Second Floor
Boston, MA USA 02117
Phone: 617-572-9624
Website: www.hancockcapitalllc.com

Management and Staff

John Pluta, Senior Managing Director

Type of Firm

Insurance Firm Affiliate

Project Preferences

Type of Financing Preferred:
Mezzanine
Acquisition
Recapitalizations

Industry Focus

(% based on actual investment)

Consumer Related	42.1%
Other Products	40.5%
Semiconductors/Other Elect.	13.7%
Computer Software and Services	3.6%

Additional Information

Name of Most Recent Fund: Hancock Mezzanine Partners, L.P.
Most Recent Fund Was Raised: 01/01/1999
Year Founded: 1999
Capital Under Management: $430,900,000
Current Activity Level: Actively seeking new investments

HANCOCK PARK ASSOCIATES

1880 Century Park East
Suite 900
Los Angeles, CA USA 90067
Phone: 310-228-6900
Fax: 310-228-6939
E-mail: info@hpcap.com
Website: www.hpcap.com

Other Offices

1330 Post Oak
Suite 2300
Houston, TX USA 77056
Phone: 713-333-2580
Fax: 713-209-7451

Management and Staff

Brian McDermott, Partner
Kenton Van Harten, Partner
Kevin Listen, Partner
Michael Fourticq, Managing Partner
Michael Fourticq, Partner

Type of Firm

Private Equity Firm

Project Preferences

Type of Financing Preferred:
Leveraged Buyout
Expansion
Later Stage
Acquisition

Size of Investments Considered:
Min Size of Investment Considered (000s): $5,000
Max Size of Investment Considered (000s): $10,000

Geographical Preferences

United States Preferences:
Northwest
West Coast
Southwest

Industry Focus

(% based on actual investment)

Other Products	52.8%
Consumer Related	47.2%

Additional Information

Name of Most Recent Fund: Hancock Park Capital II, L.P. (AKA: HPC-II, L.P.)
Most Recent Fund Was Raised: 11/22/2002
Year Founded: 1986
Capital Under Management: $158,000,000
Current Activity Level: Actively seeking new investments

HANJU INVESTMENT CORP.

14-15 Yoido-dong
Yongdungpo-gu
Seoul, South Korea
Phone: 822-783-7101
Fax: 822-783-7104

Management and Staff

Oh Jin Kim, President

Type of Firm

Private Equity Firm

Project Preferences

Type of Financing Preferred:
Balanced

Geographical Preferences

International Preferences:
Korea, South

Additional Information

Year Founded: 2000
Current Activity Level: Actively seeking new investments

HANMI VENTURE CAPITAL (FKA: CHEIL VENTURE CAPITAL)

2/F Jeil Building, 168-26
Samsung-dong, Kangnam-ku
Seoul, South Korea 135-882
Phone: 822-555-0781
Fax: 822-557-2570
Website: www.hanmivc.co.kr

Other Offices

1133-10 Ingue-dong
Suwon
Kyonggi-do, South Korea
Phone: 82-331-38-1761
Fax: 82-331-36-1637

Management and Staff

Kicheon Shin, President

Type of Firm

Corporate PE/Venture

Association Membership

Korean Venture Capital Association (KVCA)

Project Preferences

Type of Financing Preferred:
Balanced

Geographical Preferences

International Preferences:
Korea, South

Additional Information

Year Founded: 1988
Capital Under Management: $87,300,000
Current Activity Level: Actively seeking new investments

HANNOVER FINANZ AUSTRIA GMBH

Guenthergasse 3
Vienna, Austria A-1090
Phone: 43-1-505-8000
Fax: 43-1-505-800030
E-mail: mail@hannoverfinanz.at
Website: www.hannoverfinanz.at

Management and Staff

Harald Parapatits, Managing Director
Martin Walka, Managing Director

Type of Firm

Private Equity Firm

Project Preferences

Type of Financing Preferred:
Early Stage
Expansion
Management Buyouts

Size of Investments Considered:
Min Size of Investment Considered (000s): $300
Max Size of Investment Considered (000s): $300,000

Geographical Preferences

International Preferences:
Austria

Industry Focus

(% based on actual investment)

Consumer Related	42.3%
Semiconductors/Other Elect.	24.5%
Other Products	17.5%
Industrial/Energy	15.8%

Additional Information

Year Founded: 1995
Capital Under Management: $2,400,000
Current Activity Level: Actively seeking new investments

HANNOVER FINANZ GMBH

Gunther-Wagner-Allee 13
Hannover, Germany 30177
Phone: 49-511-28007-0
Fax: 49-511-28007-37
E-mail: mail@hannoverfinanz.de
Website: www.hannoverfinanz.de

Type of Firm

Private Equity Firm

Association Membership

German Venture Capital Association (BVK)
European Private Equity and Venture Capital Assoc.

Project Preferences

Type of Financing Preferred:
Expansion
Mezzanine
Generalist PE
Turnaround
Management Buyouts
Startup
Recapitalizations

Geographical Preferences

International Preferences:
Europe
Germany

Additional Information

Year Founded: 1979
Capital Under Management: $366,400,000
Current Activity Level: Actively seeking new investments

HANOVER PARTNERS, INC

425 California Street
Suite 1700
San Francisco, CA USA 94104
Phone: 415-788-8222
Fax: 415-788-8444
Website: www.hanoverpartners.com

Other Offices

340 Oswego Pointe Drive
Suite 207
Lake Oswego, OR USA 97034
Phone: 503-699-6410
Fax: 503-699-6490

Management and Staff

Andrew Ford, Principal
John Palmer, Principal

Type of Firm

Private Equity Firm

Project Preferences

Role in Financing:
Prefer role as deal originator

Type of Financing Preferred:
Leveraged Buyout
Management Buyouts
Acquisition

Size of Investments Considered:
Min Size of Investment Considered (000s): $5,000
Max Size of Investment Considered (000s): $75,000

Geographical Preferences

Canadian Preferences:
All Canada

Industry Focus

(% based on actual investment)

Industrial/Energy	61.4%
Other Products	38.6%

Additional Information

Year Founded: 1994
Current Activity Level: Actively seeking new investments
Method of Compensation: Return on invest. most important, but chg. closing fees, service fees, etc.

HANWHA VENTURE CAPITAL CORPORATION

2/F, Junghyun Building, 944-3
Daechi 3 Dong, Kangnam-ku
Seoul, South Korea 135-846
Phone: 822-568-4982
Fax: 822-568-0661
Website: www.hwvc.co.kr

Management and Staff

Juntae Park, Chief Executive Officer

Type of Firm

Investment Management Firm

Project Preferences

Type of Financing Preferred:
Fund of Funds
Early Stage
Balanced
Later Stage
Seed
Recapitalizations

Geographical Preferences

International Preferences:
Korea, South

Industry Preferences

In Communications prefer:
Commercial Communications
Media and Entertainment

In Semiconductor/Electr prefer:
Electronics
Semiconductor

In Biotechnology prefer:
Biotechnology

In Consumer Related prefer:
Entertainment and Leisure

In Industrial/Energy prefer:
Industrial Products

Additional Information

Year Founded: 2000
Capital Under Management: $118,700,000
Current Activity Level: Actively seeking new investments

HARBERT MANAGEMENT CORPORATION

2100 Third Avenue North
Suite 600
Birmingham, AL USA 35203
Phone: 205-987-5500
Fax: 205-987-5568
E-mail: irelations@harbert.net
Website: www.harbert.net

Other Offices

One Riverchase Parkway South
Birmingham, AL USA 35244
Phone: 205-987-5500
Fax: 205-987-5568

618 Church Street
Suite 500
Nashville, TN USA 37219

36 rue Beaujon
Office 4.08
Paris, France 75008

Suite 204, Second Floor
Pinar 5
Madrid, Spain 28006

1210 East Cary Street
Suite 400
Richmond, VA USA 23219

425 Market Street
22nd Floor
San Francisco, CA USA 94105

555 Madison Avenue
16th Floor
New York, NY USA 10022

3715 Northside Parkway
Northcreek Building 300, Suite 150
Atlanta, GA USA 30327

44 Davies Street, Brookfield House
Fifth Floor
London, United Kingdom W1K 5JA

Management and Staff

Alan Fuller, Vice President
James Flood, Vice President
Jeff Harris, Principal
Jeffrey Seidman, Vice President
John Uhrin, Venture Partner
Jon-Paul Momsen, Managing Director
Jonathan Campbell, Vice President
Michael Luce, President & COO
Michael White, Vice President
Peter Land, Principal
Raymond Harbert, Chairman & CEO
Roque Rotaeche, Principal
Scott O'Donnell, Senior Managing Director
Thomas Roberts, Partner
Wayne Hunter, Managing Partner
William Brooke, Managing Partner

Type of Firm

Private Equity Firm

Association Membership

Australian Venture Capital Association (AVCAL)
National Venture Capital Association - USA (NVCA)
Project Preferences

Type of Financing Preferred:

Mezzanine
Generalist PE
Balanced
Turnaround
Distressed Debt

Geographical Preferences

International Preferences:

Europe
Australia

Additional Information

Year Founded: 1999
Capital Under Management: $3,706,800,000
Current Activity Level: Actively seeking new investments

HARBERT VENTURE PARTNERS

1210 East Cary Street
Suite 400
Richmond, VA USA 23219
Phone: 804-782-3800
Fax: 804-782-3810
Website: www.harbert.net

Other Offices

618 Church Street
Suite 500
Nashville, TN USA 37219
Phone: 615-301-6400
Fax: 615-301-6401

One Riverchase Parkway
Birmingham, AL USA 35244
Phone: 205-987-5500
Fax: 205-987-5568

555 Madison Avenue
16th Floor
New York, NY USA 10022
Phone: 212-521-6970
Fax: 212-521-6972

34 Brook Street
Mayfair
London, United Kingdom W1K 5DN
Phone: 4420-7408-4120
Fax: 4420-7408-4121

Management and Staff

Jeff Harris, Principal
John Uhrin, Venture Partner
Michael Luce, President & COO
Patrick Molony, Vice President
Robert Crutchfield, Venture Partner
Thomas Roberts, Partner
Wayne Hunter, Managing Partner
William Brooke, Managing Partner

Type of Firm

Investment Management Firm
Association Membership
Mid-Atlantic Venture Association
National Venture Capital Association - USA (NVCA)

Project Preferences

Role in Financing:

Prefer role as deal originator but will also invest in deals created by others

Type of Financing Preferred:

Early Stage
Startup

Size of Investments Considered:

Min Size of Investment Considered (000s): $500
Max Size of Investment Considered (000s): $3,000

Geographical Preferences

United States Preferences:

Mid Atlantic
Southeast

Industry Preferences

In Communications prefer:

Telecommunications

In Computer Other prefer:

Computer Related

In Biotechnology prefer:

Biotechnology

In Medical/Health prefer:

Medical/Health

In Industrial/Energy prefer:

Advanced Materials

Additional Information

Name of Most Recent Fund: Harbert Venture Partners II, L.P.
Most Recent Fund Was Raised: 06/23/2008
Year Founded: 1997
Capital Under Management: $110,000,000
Current Activity Level: Actively seeking new investments
Method of Compensation: Return on investment is of primary concern, do not charge fees

---

HARBINGER VENTURE MANAGEMENT

Three Results Way
Cupertino, CA USA 95014
Phone: 408-861-3683
E-mail: USContact@harbingervc.com
Website: www.harbingervc.com

Other Offices

No. 187 Tiding Boulevard
7th Floor, Sec 2, Neihu
Taipei, Taiwan 114
Phone: 886-22657-9368

10th Floor, Tower D
No. 1068 Tian Shan West Road
Shanghai, China
Phone: 86-21-6120-9980

Management and Staff

Chih-Kai Cheng, General Partner
David Chin, Vice President
John Tzeng, Vice President
Moun-Rong Lin, Venture Partner
Ronald Han, Vice President
Ru Guang Bai, Vice President

Type of Firm

Private Equity Firm

Project Preferences

Role in Financing:

Will function either as deal originator or investor in deals created by others

Type of Financing Preferred:

Early Stage
Expansion
Balanced
Later Stage

Size of Investments Considered:

Min Size of Investment Considered (000s): $1,000
Max Size of Investment Considered (000s): $5,000

Geographical Preferences

International Preferences:
China

Industry Preferences

In Communications prefer:
Wireless Communications

In Computer Software prefer:
Software

In Internet Specific prefer:
Internet

In Computer Other prefer:
Computer Related

In Semiconductor/Electr prefer:
Semiconductor

In Consumer Related prefer:
Consumer

Additional Information
Year Founded: 2000
Capital Under Management: $150,000,000
Current Activity Level: Actively seeking new investments
Method of Compensation: Return on investment is of primary concern, do not charge fees

---

HARBOUR GROUP, LTD.
7701 Forsyth Boulevard
Suite 600
St. Louis, MO USA 63105
Phone: 314-727-5550
Fax: 314-727-9912
Website: www.harbourgroup.com

Management and Staff
Jeff Fox, Chief Executive Officer

Type of Firm
Private Equity Firm

Project Preferences

Role in Financing:
Prefer role as deal originator but will also invest in deals created by others

Type of Financing Preferred:
Leveraged Buyout

Geographical Preferences

International Preferences:
Mexico

Industry Focus
(% based on actual investment)

Other Products	100.0%

Additional Information
Name of Most Recent Fund: Harbour Group Investments IV
Most Recent Fund Was Raised: 02/01/1999
Year Founded: 1976
Capital Under Management: $706,500,000
Current Activity Level: Actively seeking new investments
Method of Compensation: Return on investment is of primary concern, do not charge fees

---

HARBOURVEST PARTNERS LLC
One Financial Center
44th Floor
Boston, MA USA 02111
Phone: 617-348-3707
Fax: 617-350-0305
E-mail: usinfo@harbourvest.com
Website: www.harbourvest.com

Other Offices
Suite 1207, Citibank Tower
3 Garden Road
Central, Hong Kong
Phone: 852-2525-2214
Fax: 852-2525-2241

Berkeley Square House
8th Floor, Berkeley Square
London, United Kingdom W1J 6DB
Phone: 44-20-7399-9820
Fax: 44-20-7399-9840

Management and Staff
Alex Rogers, Managing Director
Amanda McCrystal, Vice President
Amanda Outerbridge, Vice President
Aris Hatch, Vice President
Brett Gordon, Managing Director
Carolina De Carulla, Vice President
Christopher Walker, Principal
Claudio Siniscalco, Vice President
Corentin Du Roy, Vice President
D. Brooks Zug, Senior Managing Director
David Atterbury, Principal
David Zug, Vice President
Edward Kane, Senior Managing Director
Frederick Maynard, Managing Director
George Anson, Managing Director
Gregory Stento, Managing Director
Hannah Tobin, Vice President
Ian Lane, Vice President
Jack Wagner, Vice President
Jeffrey Keay, Principal
John Morris, Managing Director
John Begg, Managing Director
John Toomey, Managing Director
John Fiato, Vice President
John Nelson, Vice President
Julia Ocko, Principal
Kathleen Bacon, Managing Director
Kevin Delbridge, Senior Managing Director
Leila Blodgett, Vice President
Martha Vorlicek, Managing Director
Mary Traer, Principal
Michael Taylor, Managing Director
Michael Pugatch, Vice President
Nathan Bishop, Vice President
Ofer Nemirovsky, Managing Director
Peter Wilson, Managing Director
Peter Lipson, Principal
Philip Bilden, Managing Director
Robert Wadsworth, Managing Director
Sandra Pasquale, Vice President
Scott Voss, Principal
Sebastiaan Van den Berg, Vice President
Stephen Belgrad, Principal
Tim Flower, Vice President
Valerie Handal, Vice President
William Johnston, Managing Director

Type of Firm
Private Equity Advisor or Fund of Funds

Association Membership
Australian Venture Capital Association (AVCAL)
Hong Kong Venture Capital Association (HKVCA)
British Venture Capital Association (BVCA)
National Venture Capital Association - USA (NVCA)
European Private Equity and Venture Capital Assoc.

Project Preferences

Role in Financing:
Prefer role as deal originator but will also invest in deals created by others

Type of Financing Preferred:
Fund of Funds
Leveraged Buyout
Mezzanine
Generalist PE
Balanced
Later Stage
Acquisition
Distressed Debt
Fund of Funds of Second
Recapitalizations

Size of Investments Considered:
Min Size of Investment Considered (000s): $5,000
Max Size of Investment Considered (000s): $100,000

Geographical Preferences

United States Preferences:
Mid Atlantic
Northeast
Rocky Mountain
West Coast
All U.S.

International Preferences:
Italy
Ireland
Sweden
United Kingdom
Latin America
Europe
Netherlands
Portugal
Switzerland
Poland
Middle East

Pacific
Spain
Australia
Finland
Germany
Asia
All International
Denmark
France
Africa

Industry Focus

(% based on actual investment)

Other Products	22.2%
Computer Software and Services	16.8%
Internet Specific	13.9%
Communications and Media	12.9%
Consumer Related	9.3%
Computer Hardware	6.7%
Medical/Health	6.3%
Industrial/Energy	5.8%
Semiconductors/Other Elect.	4.1%
Biotechnology	1.9%

Additional Information

Year Founded: 1997
Capital Under Management: $33,670,000,000
Current Activity Level: Actively seeking new investments
Method of Compensation: Return on invest. most important, but chg. closing fees, service fees, etc.

HARDT GROUP CAPITAL PARTNERS LIMITED

Stubenring 18/ 6
Vienna, Austria 1010
Phone: 43-1-5138365407
Fax: 43-1-5138365468
Website: www.hardtgroup.com

Other Offices

99 Park Avenue, Suite 1550
New York, NY USA 10016
Phone: 212-523-0211
Fax: 212-523-0214

Grabenstrasse 42
Zug, Switzerland 6301

42 Berkeley Square
London, United Kingdom WIJ 5AW
Phone: 44-20-7409-5070
Fax: 44-20-7409-5071

Management and Staff

Alexander Schweikhardt, Chief Executive Officer
Alexander Gotzinger, Managing Director
Evi Schachenhofer, Chief Operating Officer
Petra Schiendl, Managing Director

Type of Firm

Private Equity Firm

Project Preferences

Type of Financing Preferred:

Balanced

Geographical Preferences

International Preferences:

Europe
Western Europe
Eastern Europe

Industry Preferences

In Communications prefer:

Media and Entertainment

In Consumer Related prefer:

Consumer

Additional Information

Year Founded: 2004
Current Activity Level: Actively seeking new investments

HARGAN VENTURES, INC.

4850 Keele Street, First Floor
Computer Methods Building
Toronto, Canada M3J 3K1
Phone: 416-923-0660
Fax: 416-495-9750
E-mail: info@harganvc.com
Website: www.harganvc.com

Other Offices

4850 Keele Street, First Floor
Computer Methods Building
Toronto, Canada M3J 3K1
Phone: 416-923-0660
Fax: 416-495-9750

Management and Staff

Lance Soskin, Vice President
Les Nochomovitz, Chief Financial Officer

Type of Firm

Private Equity Firm

Additional Information

Year Founded: 1999
Current Activity Level: Actively seeking new investments

HARREN EQUITY PARTNERS

123 East Main Street
Fifth Floor
Charlottesville, VA USA 22902
Phone: 434-245-5800
Fax: 434-245-5802
E-mail: info@harrenequity.com
Website: www.harrenequity.com

Other Offices

350 East Las Olas Boulevard
Suite 980
Fort Lauderdale, FL USA 33301
Phone: 954-745-9000
Fax: 954-764-9137

Management and Staff

George Urban, Vice President
Jonathan Earnhardt, Vice President
Lee Monahan, Partner
Thomas Carver, Managing Partner

Type of Firm

Private Equity Firm

Project Preferences

Type of Financing Preferred:

Expansion
Balanced
Acquisition
Recapitalizations

Geographical Preferences

United States Preferences:

All U.S.

Industry Preferences

In Business Serv. prefer:

Services
Distribution

In Manufact. prefer:

Manufacturing

Additional Information

Year Founded: 2004
Current Activity Level: Actively seeking new investments

HARRIS & HARRIS GROUP, INC.

111 West 57th Street
Suite 1100
New York, NY USA 10019
Phone: 212-582-0900
Fax: 212-582-9563
E-mail: admin@tinytechvc.com
Website: www.hhvc.com

Other Offices

420 Florence Street
Suite 200
Palo Alto, CA USA 94301
Phone: 650-321-2668
Fax: 650-321-1561

Management and Staff

Alexei Andreev, Managing Director
Douglas Jamison, Chairman & CEO
Michael Janse, Managing Director
Misti Ushio, Vice President

Type of Firm
Private Equity Firm

Project Preferences

Role in Financing:
Will function either as deal originator or investor in deals created by others

Type of Financing Preferred:
Early Stage
Start-up Financing
First Stage Financing
Startup

Industry Preferences

In Semiconductor/Electr prefer:
Electronics
Electronic Components
Laser Related
Analytic/Scientific
Optoelectronics

In Biotechnology prefer:
Biotechnology
Human Biotechnology
Agricultural/Animal Bio.
Industrial Biotechnology
Biosensors
Biotech Related Research

In Medical/Health prefer:
Medical Diagnostics
Medical Therapeutics
Medical Products
Pharmaceuticals

In Industrial/Energy prefer:
Energy
Alternative Energy
Coal Related
Energy Conservation Relat
Materials

Additional Information
Year Founded: 1983
Capital Under Management: $150,000,000
Current Activity Level: Actively seeking new investments
Method of Compensation: Return on investment is of primary concern, do not charge fees

---

HARRIS CORPORATION
1025 West NASA Blvd.
Melbourne, FL USA 32919
Phone: 321-727-9207
Website: www.harris.com

Type of Firm
Corporate PE/Venture

Additional Information
Year Founded: 1999
Current Activity Level: Actively seeking new investments

HARRIS PRESTON & PARTNERS, LLC
One American Center
600 Congress Ave. Ste 200
Austin, TX USA 78701
Phone: 512-505-4111
Fax: 512-505-4110
Website: www.harrispreston.com

Management and Staff
Charles Preston, Managing Director
Ron Harris, Managing Director

Type of Firm
Private Equity Firm

Project Preferences

Type of Financing Preferred:
Balanced

Geographical Preferences

United States Preferences:
All U.S.

Additional Information
Year Founded: 2007
Current Activity Level: Actively seeking new investments

HARVARD MANAGEMENT COMPANY, INC.
600 Atlantic Avenue
Boston, MA USA 02210
Phone: 617-523-4400
E-mail: general@hmc.harvard.edu
Website: www.hmc.harvard.edu

Type of Firm
Endowment, Foundation or Pension Fund

Additional Information
Year Founded: 1990
Current Activity Level: Actively seeking new investments

HARVEST PARTNERS, LLC
280 Park Avenue
25th Floor
New York, NY USA 10017
Phone: 212-599-6300
Fax: 212-812-0100
E-mail: harvestpartners@harvpart.com
Website: www.harvpart.com

Management and Staff
Andrew Schoenthal, Principal
Christopher Whalen, Principal
Harvey Mallement, Principal
Harvey Wertheim, Principal
Ira Kleinman, Senior Managing Director
Michael DeFlorio, Senior Managing Director
Michael Cardito, Principal
Richard Moreau, Principal
Stephen Eisenstein, Senior Managing Director
Thomas Arenz, Senior Managing Director

Type of Firm
Private Equity Advisor or Fund of Funds

Association Membership
Natl Assoc of Small Bus. Inv. Co (NASBIC)

Project Preferences

Role in Financing:
Will function either as deal originator or investor in deals created by others

Type of Financing Preferred:
Leveraged Buyout
Later Stage
Management Buyouts
Acquisition

Size of Investments Considered:
Min Size of Investment Considered (000s): $100,000
Max Size of Investment Considered (000s): $600,000

Geographical Preferences

International Preferences:
Italy
United Kingdom
Luxembourg
Netherlands
Portugal
Spain
Belgium
Germany
France

Industry Focus
(% based on actual investment)

Other Products	59.2%
Industrial/Energy	18.4%
Consumer Related	8.0%
Communications and Media	5.4%
Medical/Health	4.5%
Internet Specific	4.5%

Additional Information
Name of Most Recent Fund: Harvest Strategic Associates V, L.P.
Most Recent Fund Was Raised: 03/08/2007
Year Founded: 1981
Capital Under Management: $1,400,000,000
Current Activity Level: Actively seeking new investments
Method of Compensation: Return on invest. most important, but chg. closing fees, service fees, etc.

HASPA BGM

Moenkedamm 11
Hamburg, Germany 20457
Phone: 49-40-8222-0950
Fax: 49-40-822209595
E-mail: info@haspa-bgm.de
Website: www.haspa-bgm.de

Management and Staff

Carsten Roehrs, Managing Director
York Heitmann, Managing Director

Type of Firm

Bank Affiliated

Project Preferences

Type of Financing Preferred:
Leveraged Buyout
Generalist PE
Expansion
Startup

Geographical Preferences

International Preferences:
Europe
Germany

Industry Preferences

In Biotechnology prefer:
Biotechnology

In Business Serv. prefer:
Media

Additional Information

Year Founded: 1998
Capital Under Management: $13,500,000
Current Activity Level: Actively seeking new investments

HASSO PLATTNER VENTURES MANAGEMENT GMBH

August-Bebel-Strasse 88
Potsdam, Germany 14482
Phone: 49-331-97992120
E-mail: info@hp-ventures.com
Website: www.hp-ventures.com

Type of Firm

Private Equity Firm

Project Preferences

Type of Financing Preferred:
Early Stage

Geographical Preferences

International Preferences:
Europe
South Africa
Israel

Industry Preferences

In Communications prefer:
Telecommunications
Wireless Communications

In Computer Software prefer:
Software

In Industrial/Energy prefer:
Alternative Energy
Energy Conservation Relat

In Business Serv. prefer:
Media

Additional Information

Year Founded: 2005
Capital Under Management: $233,300,000
Current Activity Level: Actively seeking new investments

HASTINGS EQUITY PARTNERS LLC

179 Bear Hill Road
Waltham, MA USA 02451
Phone: 781-209-8801
Fax: 781-209-8802
Website: www.hastingsequity.com

Management and Staff

Bruce MacRae, Managing Director
Ted Patton, Managing Director

Type of Firm

Private Equity Firm

Project Preferences

Type of Financing Preferred:
Leveraged Buyout
Management Buyouts
Recapitalizations

Size of Investments Considered:
Min Size of Investment Considered (000s): $4,000
Max Size of Investment Considered (000s): $15,000

Geographical Preferences

United States Preferences:
All U.S.

Industry Preferences

In Business Serv. prefer:
Services
Distribution

In Manufact. prefer:
Manufacturing

Additional Information

Year Founded: 2002
Capital Under Management: $55,900,000
Current Activity Level: Actively seeking new investments

HASTINGS FUNDS MANAGEMENT, LTD. (AKA: MAINRIDGE CAPITAL)

Level 16, 90 Collins Street
Melbourne, Australia 3000
Phone: 613-9654-4477
Fax: 613-9650-6555
Website: www.mainridgecapital.com.au

Other Offices

Level 39
575 Fifth Avenue
New York, NY USA 10017
Phone: 212-551-1976
Fax: 212-551-1997

Level 23, Gold Fields House
1 Alfred Street
Sydney, Australia 2000
Phone: 612-9251-4220
Fax: 612-9251-7709

63, St. Mary Axe
Level 2
London, United Kingdom EC3A 8LE
Phone: 44-20-7337-6720
Fax: 44-20-7929-2502

Management and Staff

Dominic Leary, Managing Director
Rose Schiavello, Chief Financial Officer

Type of Firm

Investment Management Firm

Association Membership

Australian Venture Capital Association (AVCAL)

Project Preferences

Role in Financing:
Will function either as deal originator or investor in deals created by others

Type of Financing Preferred:
Leveraged Buyout
Expansion
Generalist PE
Later Stage
Management Buyouts
Acquisition
Industry Rollups

Size of Investments Considered:
Min Size of Investment Considered (000s): $627
Max Size of Investment Considered (000s): $6,694

Geographical Preferences

International Preferences:
Australia

Additional Information

Name of Most Recent Fund: Hastings Private Equity Fund 2
Most Recent Fund Was Raised: 11/26/2005
Year Founded: 2001
Capital Under Management: $200,600,000
Current Activity Level: Actively seeking new investments
Method of Compensation: Return on investment is of primary concern, do not charge fees

HATTERAS VENTURE PARTNERS (FKA: CATALYSTA PARTNERS)

280 South Magnum Street
Suite 350
Durham, NC USA 27701
Phone: 919-484-0730
Fax: 919-484-0364
Website: www.hatterasvp.com

Management and Staff

Dana Fowlkes, Venture Partner
Douglas Reed, General Partner
John Crumpler, General Partner
Kenneth Lee, General Partner
Robert Ingram, General Partner
Robert Morff, Venture Partner

Type of Firm

Private Equity Firm

Project Preferences

Role in Financing:

Will function either as deal originator or investor in deals created by others

Type of Financing Preferred:

Early Stage
Seed
Special Situation

Size of Investments Considered:

Min Size of Investment Considered (000s): $2,000
Max Size of Investment Considered (000s): $5,000

Geographical Preferences

United States Preferences:

Mid Atlantic
Southeast

Industry Preferences

In Biotechnology prefer:

Biotechnology
Human Biotechnology

Additional Information

Year Founded: 2000
Capital Under Management: $120,000,000
Current Activity Level: Actively seeking new investments

HAWKESBRIDGE PRIVATE EQUITY

23 Hunter Street
Level 14, Currency House
Sydney, Australia 2000
Phone: 612-9233-7200
Fax: 612-9233-7544
E-mail: contact@hawkesbridge.com.au
Website: www.hawkesbridge.com.au

Other Offices

10 Airlie Street
Claremont
Perth, Australia 6010
Phone: 618-9384-3963
Fax: 618-9284-4915

Management and Staff

David Plumridge, Partner
Joshua Rowe, Partner
Rosemary Nolan, Chief Financial Officer

Type of Firm

Private Equity Firm

Association Membership

Australian Venture Capital Association (AVCAL)

Project Preferences

Role in Financing:

Will function either as deal originator or investor in deals created by others

Type of Financing Preferred:

Leveraged Buyout
Expansion
Generalist PE
Balanced
Management Buyouts

Size of Investments Considered:

Min Size of Investment Considered (000s): $8,058
Max Size of Investment Considered (000s): $40,290

Geographical Preferences

International Preferences:

Australia

Additional Information

Year Founded: 2001
Capital Under Management: $174,700,000
Current Activity Level: Actively seeking new investments
Method of Compensation: Return on investment is of primary concern, do not charge fees

HAWKEYE CAPITAL

800 Third Avenue
10th Floor
New York, NY USA 10022

Type of Firm

Private Equity Firm

Project Preferences

Type of Financing Preferred:

Balanced

Geographical Preferences

United States Preferences:

All U.S.

Additional Information

Year Founded: 2007
Current Activity Level: Actively seeking new investments

HAWTHORNE GROUP

381 Mansfield Avenue
Pittsburgh, PA USA 15220
Phone: 412-928-7700

Management and Staff

Henry Posner, Co-Founder
Thomas Wright, Co-Founder

Type of Firm

Private Equity Firm

Project Preferences

Type of Financing Preferred:

Leveraged Buyout

Additional Information

Year Founded: 1987
Current Activity Level: Actively seeking new investments

HAYNES AND BOONE LLC

2505 North Plano Road
Suite 4000
Richardson, TX USA 75082
Phone: 972-680-7550
Fax: 972-680-7551
Website: www.haynesboone.com

Other Offices

7501 North Capital of Texas Highway
Building A, Suite 130
Austin, TX USA 78731
Phone: 512-692-8300
Fax: 512-692-8370

1000 Louisiana Street
Suite 4300
Houston, TX USA 77002-5012
Phone: 713-547-2000
Fax: 713-547-2600

Management and Staff

Charles Powell, Partner

David Burton, Partner
David Oden, Partner
Jim Miller, Chief Financial Officer
Richard Rafferty, Partner

Type of Firm

Service Provider

Project Preferences

Type of Financing Preferred:

Second Stage Financing

Industry Preferences

In Semiconductor/Electr prefer:

Electronics

In Consumer Related prefer:

Entertainment and Leisure
Food/Beverage

In Business Serv. prefer:

Distribution

In Manufact. prefer:

Manufacturing

Additional Information

Year Founded: 1970
Current Activity Level: Actively seeking new investments

HB EQUITY PARTNERS, L.P.

405 Park Avenue
Suite 701
New York, NY USA 10022
Phone: 212-980-5510
Fax: 212-980-5517
Website: www.hbequity.com

Management and Staff

Andrew Hubregsen, General Partner
Jonathan Gormin, General Partner
Michael Bonnet, General Partner

Type of Firm

Private Equity Firm

Project Preferences

Role in Financing:

Prefer role as deal originator

Type of Financing Preferred:

Leveraged Buyout
Expansion
Generalist PE
Later Stage
Management Buyouts
Acquisition
Industry Rollups
Recapitalizations

Size of Investments Considered:

Min Size of Investment Considered (000s): $5,000
Max Size of Investment Considered (000s): $25,000

Geographical Preferences

United States Preferences:

All U.S.

Canadian Preferences:

All Canada

Industry Preferences

In Communications prefer:

Radio & TV Broadcasting
Telecommunications
Wireless Communications

In Semiconductor/Electr prefer:

Electronic Components
Controllers and Sensors
Sensors

In Consumer Related prefer:

Consumer
Entertainment and Leisure
Hotels and Resorts

In Industrial/Energy prefer:

Industrial Products
Machinery

In Financial Services prefer:

Financial Services
Insurance

In Business Serv. prefer:

Services
Distribution

In Manufact. prefer:

Manufacturing

Additional Information

Year Founded: 2002
Capital Under Management: $30,000,000
Current Activity Level: Actively seeking new investments
Method of Compensation: Return on invest. most important, but chg. closing fees, service fees, etc.

HBG HOLDINGS, LTD.

Level 27, Al Moosa Tower II
Sheikh Zayed Road
Dubai, Utd. Arab Em.
Phone: 971-4-331-4133
Fax: 971-4-331-4134
E-mail: info@hbgholdings.com
Website: www.hbgholdings.com

Management and Staff

Zulfi Hydari, Managing Director

Type of Firm

Investment Management Firm

Project Preferences

Type of Financing Preferred:

Leveraged Buyout
Early Stage
Acquisition
Recapitalizations

Geographical Preferences

International Preferences:

United Kingdom
Uruguay
Middle East
Asia

Industry Preferences

In Consumer Related prefer:

Retail
Consumer Products

In Transportation prefer:

Transportation

In Financial Services prefer:

Real Estate

In Manufact. prefer:

Manufacturing

Additional Information

Year Founded: 2004
Capital Under Management: $350,000,000
Current Activity Level: Actively seeking new investments

HBM BIOVENTURES AG (FKA: HBM PARTNERS AG)

Bundesplatz 1
Zug, Switzerland 6300
Phone: 41-43-888-7171
Fax: 41-43-888-7172
Website: www.hbmpartners.com

Other Offices

Centennial Towers, Suite 305
2454 West Bay Road
Grand Cayman, Cayman Islands
Phone: 345-946-8002
Fax: 345-946-8003

Management and Staff

Andreas Wicki, Chief Executive Officer
Jean-Marc LeSieur, Managing Director
Joachim Rudolf, Chief Financial Officer
John Arnold, Chief Executive Officer

Type of Firm

Private Equity Firm

Association Membership

European Private Equity and Venture Capital Assoc.

Project Preferences

Type of Financing Preferred:

Fund of Funds
Early Stage
Public Companies
Later Stage
Seed

Geographical Preferences

International Preferences:
Europe
Western Europe

Industry Preferences

In Biotechnology prefer:
Biotechnology

In Medical/Health prefer:
Medical/Health
Medical Diagnostics
Medical Products
Pharmaceuticals

Additional Information
Year Founded: 2001
Capital Under Management: $1,100,000,000
Current Activity Level: Actively seeking new investments

HDFC VENTURE CAPITAL, LTD.
Ramon House, 169, Backbay
HT Parekh Marg, Churchgate
Mumbai, India 400 020
Phone: 91-22-6631-6000
Fax: 91-22-22048834
E-mail: info@hdfc.com
Website: www.hdfc.com

Management and Staff
K. G. Krishnamurthy, CEO & Managing Director

Type of Firm
Bank Affiliated

Association Membership
Indian Venture Capital Association (IVCA)

Project Preferences

Type of Financing Preferred:
Balanced
Other

Geographical Preferences

International Preferences:
India

Industry Preferences

In Financial Services prefer:
Real Estate

Additional Information
Year Founded: 2005
Capital Under Management: $230,300,000
Current Activity Level: Actively seeking new investments

HEAD INDUSTRIAL PARTNER OY
Pohjoisesplanadi 25 A 8
Helsinki, Finland 00100
Phone: 358-9-251-1520
Fax: 358-9-2511-5351
Website: www.headteam.com

Other Offices
P.O.Box 557
Uusikatu 53
Oulu, Finland 90101
Phone: 358-201-432-300
Fax: 358-201-432-301

Management and Staff
Arto Ylimartino, Managing Director
Veikko Lesonen, Founder

Type of Firm
Bank Affiliated

Association Membership
Finnish Venture Capital Association (FVCA)

Project Preferences

Type of Financing Preferred:
Leveraged Buyout
Early Stage
Expansion
Generalist PE
Balanced

Geographical Preferences

International Preferences:
Finland

Industry Preferences

In Computer Other prefer:
Computer Related

In Semiconductor/Electr prefer:
Electronics

In Industrial/Energy prefer:
Energy
Energy Conservation Relat
Industrial Products

Additional Information
Year Founded: 2000
Capital Under Management: $5,700,000
Current Activity Level: Actively seeking new investments

HEADLINE MEDIA GROUP (WEB CAPITAL PARTNERS)
1605 Main Street West
Hamilton, Canada L8S 1E6
Phone: 905-522-4269
Fax: 905-522-9744
Website: www.webcapitalpartners.com

Other Offices
1605 Main Street West
Hamilton, Canada L8S 1E6
Phone: 905-522-4269
Fax: 905-522-9744

Type of Firm
Private Equity Firm

Project Preferences

Type of Financing Preferred:
Early Stage
Startup

Geographical Preferences

Canadian Preferences:
All Canada

Additional Information
Year Founded: 1999
Current Activity Level: Actively seeking new investments

HEADWATERS MERCHANT BANK
One Tabor Center
1200 17th Street, Suite 900
Denver, CO USA 80202
Phone: 303-572-6000
Fax: 303-572-6001
Website: www.headwatersmb.com

Other Offices
111 Hunington Avenue
Suite 2850
Boston, MA USA 02199
Phone: 781-710-5691
Fax: 509-461-0746

3184-H Airway Avenue
Costa Mesa, CA USA 92626
Phone: 714-800-1770
Fax: 714-850-1511

Tower Place 100, Suite 450
3340 Peachtree Road
Atlanta, GA USA 30326
Phone: 404-495-5000
Fax: 404-495-5001

2211 Michelson Drive
Suite 530
Irvine, CA USA 92612
Phone: 714-800-1770
Fax: 949-679-9550

Management and Staff
Aaron Osmundson, Principal
Andrew Paff, Managing Director
Brian Mulvaney, Managing Director

C.J. Hummel, Principal
Chris Battel, Managing Director
Chris Wilson, Managing Director
Dave Prieto, Principal
David Duke, Principal
David Dodson, Managing Director
David Heilman, Principal
Douglas Reynolds, Managing Director
Edward Shaoul, Principal
Grant Garbers, Managing Director
Gretchen Lium, Managing Director
James Von Kreuter, Managing Director
Jason Ficken, Managing Director
Joseph Radecki, Managing Director
Mark Guilford, Principal
Michael Thomsic, Principal
Patrick Seese, Managing Director
Paul Janson, President
Rob Heilbronner, Managing Director
Scott Teagle, Principal
Sivaprakash Siva Shanmugam, Principal
Ted Kinsman, Principal
Toby Nuber, Principal
Todd Hellman, Managing Director
Travis Rue, Principal
Tucker Morrison, Managing Director

Type of Firm

Bank Affiliated

Project Preferences

Type of Financing Preferred:
Balanced

Geographical Preferences

United States Preferences:
All U.S.

Additional Information

Year Founded: 2002
Capital Under Management: $600,000
Current Activity Level: Actively seeking new investments

HEADWAY CAPITAL PARTNERS LLP

16 Old Bond Street
4th Floor
London, United Kingdom W1S 4PS
Phone: 44-20-7518-8888
Fax: 44-20-7900-3160
E-mail: info@headwaycap.com
Website: www.headwaycap.com

Management and Staff

Christiaan De Lint, Partner
David Toon, Chief Financial Officer
Laura Shen, Partner
Sebastian Junoy, Partner

Type of Firm

Private Equity Firm

Association Membership

French Venture Capital Association (AFIC)

Project Preferences

Type of Financing Preferred:
Leveraged Buyout
Other
Acquisition

Geographical Preferences

International Preferences:
United Kingdom
Europe

Additional Information

Year Founded: 2004
Capital Under Management: $297,200,000
Current Activity Level: Actively seeking new investments

HEALTH ENTERPRISE PARTNERS (AKA: HEP FUND)

360 Madison Avenue
Fifth Floor
New York, NY USA 10017
Phone: 212-869-5833
Fax: 212-869-6418
E-mail: info@hepfund.com
Website: www.hepfund.com

Management and Staff

Daniel Cain, General Partner
Richard Stowe, General Partner
Robert Schulz, General Partner

Type of Firm

Private Equity Firm

Project Preferences

Type of Financing Preferred:
Balanced

Geographical Preferences

United States Preferences:
All U.S.

Industry Preferences

In Medical/Health prefer:
Medical/Health

Additional Information

Name of Most Recent Fund: Health Enterprise Partners, L.P.
Most Recent Fund Was Raised: 11/13/2006
Year Founded: 2005
Capital Under Management: $82,800,000
Current Activity Level: Actively seeking new investments

HEALTH EVOLUTION PARTNERS LLC

One Maritime Plaza
Suite 2250
San Francisco, CA USA 94111
Phone: 415-362-5800
Fax: 415-520-5656
E-mail: info@healthevolutionpartners.com
Website: www.healthevolutionpartners.com

Other Offices

888 Seventh Avenue
43rd Floor
New York, NY USA 10019
Phone: 212-660-8099
Fax: 212-660-8098

Management and Staff

Adam Grossman, Principal
Brian Kirkbride, Principal
Christopher McFadden, Managing Director
Nina Labatt, Chief Financial Officer

Type of Firm

Private Equity Firm

Project Preferences

Type of Financing Preferred:
Leveraged Buyout
Expansion
Later Stage
Recapitalizations

Size of Investments Considered:
Min Size of Investment Considered (000s): $10,000
Max Size of Investment Considered (000s): $80,000

Industry Preferences

In Medical/Health prefer:
Medical/Health

Additional Information

Year Founded: 2007
Capital Under Management: $500,000,000
Current Activity Level: Actively seeking new investments

HEALTH SHARES INC (FKA:WELLSPRING BIO-CAPITAL PARTNERS, LLC)

420 Lexington Avenue
Suite 2550
New York, NY USA 10170
Phone: 212-867-7400
Fax: 212-867-3857
Website: www.healthsharesinc.com

Type of Firm

Private Equity Firm

Project Preferences

Type of Financing Preferred:
Early Stage
Balanced

Geographical Preferences

United States Preferences:
All U.S.

Industry Preferences

In Biotechnology prefer:
Biotechnology

In Medical/Health prefer:
Medical/Health

Additional Information

Year Founded: 2004
Capital Under Management: $1,100,000
Current Activity Level: Actively seeking new investments

HEALTHCARE CAPITAL PARTNERS

6065 Roswell Road
Suite 800
Atlanta, GA USA 30328
Phone: 678-244-5874
Fax: 404-250-9431
Website: www.healthcarecp.com

Type of Firm

Private Equity Firm

Project Preferences

Role in Financing:
Prefer role as deal originator

Type of Financing Preferred:
Early Stage

Size of Investments Considered:
Min Size of Investment Considered (000s): $250
Max Size of Investment Considered (000s): $3,000

Geographical Preferences

United States Preferences:
Southeast

Industry Preferences

In Medical/Health prefer:
Medical Diagnostics
Diagnostic Test Products
Medical Therapeutics
Drug/Equipmt Delivery
Medical Products

Additional Information

Year Founded: 2003
Capital Under Management: $50,000,000
Current Activity Level: Actively seeking new investments
Method of Compensation: Return on investment is of primary concern, do not charge fees

---

HEALTHCARE VENTURES LLC

55 Cambridge Parkway
Suite 301
Cambridge, MA USA 02142
Phone: 617-252-4343
Fax: 617-252-4342
Website: www.hcven.com

Other Offices

44 Nassau Street
Princeton, NJ USA 08542
Phone: 609-430-3900
Fax: 609-430-9525

Management and Staff

Augustine Lawlor, Managing Partner
Christopher Mirabelli, Managing Director
Douglas Onsi, Venture Partner
Harold Werner, Managing Director
James Cavanaugh, Managing Director
John Littlechild, Managing Director

Type of Firm

Private Equity Firm

Association Membership

Mid-Atlantic Venture Association
National Venture Capital Association - USA (NVCA)

Project Preferences

Role in Financing:
Will function either as deal originator or investor in deals created by others

Type of Financing Preferred:
Second Stage Financing
Early Stage
Expansion
Mezzanine
Research and Development
Start-up Financing
Later Stage
Seed
First Stage Financing

Size of Investments Considered:
Min Size of Investment Considered (000s): $500
Max Size of Investment Considered (000s): $25,000

Geographical Preferences

United States Preferences:
All U.S.
Industry Focus
(% based on actual investment)

Biotechnology	53.0%
Medical/Health	45.2%
Consumer Related	1.3%
Internet Specific	0.5%

Additional Information

Name of Most Recent Fund: Healthcare Ventures VIII, L.P.
Most Recent Fund Was Raised: 07/28/2005
Year Founded: 1985
Capital Under Management: $1,409,100,000
Current Activity Level: Actively seeking new investments
Method of Compensation: Return on investment is of primary concern, do not charge fees

---

HEALTHEDGE INVESTMENT PARTNERS

100 South Ashley Drive
Suite 650
Tampa, FL USA 33602
Phone: 813-490-7100
Fax: 813-490-7111
E-mail: info@healthedgepartners.com
Website: www.healthedgepartners.com

Management and Staff

Brian Anderson, Managing Partner
Harold Blue, Managing Partner
Phillip Dingle, Managing Partner

Type of Firm

Private Equity Firm

Project Preferences

Type of Financing Preferred:
Leveraged Buyout
Recapitalizations

Size of Investments Considered:
Min Size of Investment Considered (000s): $5,000
Max Size of Investment Considered (000s): $15,000

Geographical Preferences

United States Preferences:
All U.S.

Industry Preferences

In Medical/Health prefer:
Medical/Health
Drug/Equipmt Delivery
Medical Products
Health Services
Pharmaceuticals

In Business Serv. prefer:
Distribution

Additional Information

Year Founded: 2005
Capital Under Management: $60,800,000
Current Activity Level: Actively seeking new investments

HEALTHPOINTCAPITAL LLC

505 Park Avenue
12th Floor
New York, NY USA 10022
Phone: 212-935-7780
Fax: 212-935-6878
E-mail: info@healthpointcapital.com
Website: www.healthpointcapital.com

Management and Staff

Elizabeth Varley Camp, Managing Director
John McCormick, Managing Director
John Foster, Chairman & Managing Director
Joseph Fitzpatrick, Chief Financial Officer
Laing Rikkers, Managing Director
Mortimer Berkowitz, Managing Director

Type of Firm

Private Equity Firm

Project Preferences

Type of Financing Preferred:
Leveraged Buyout

Geographical Preferences

International Preferences:
All International

Industry Preferences

In Medical/Health prefer:
Medical Therapeutics
Medical Products

Additional Information

Year Founded: 2002
Capital Under Management: $125,000,000
Current Activity Level: Actively seeking new investments

HEALTHRIGHT PARTNERS

10939 N. Alpine Highway
Suite 505
American Fork, UT USA 84003
Phone: 801-772-0403
Website: www.healthright.org

Management and Staff

Shawn Smart, General Partner

Type of Firm

Private Equity Firm

Project Preferences

Type of Financing Preferred:
Balanced

Additional Information

Year Founded: 2005
Capital Under Management: $2,000,000
Current Activity Level: Actively seeking new investments

HEALY CIRCLE CAPITAL, LLC

153 East 53rd Street
48th Floor
New York, NY USA 10022
Phone: 212-446-2440

Type of Firm

Private Equity Firm

Additional Information

Year Founded: 2002
Capital Under Management: $10,400,000
Current Activity Level: Actively seeking new investments

HEARST CORPORATION

300 West 57th Street
New York, NY USA 10019
Phone: 212-649-2211
Fax: 212-649-2166
Website: www.hearst.com

Management and Staff

Kenneth Bronfin, President
Scott English, Vice President

Type of Firm

Corporate PE/Venture

Project Preferences

Role in Financing:
Prefer role in deals created by others

Type of Financing Preferred:
Second Stage Financing
Early Stage
Balanced
First Stage Financing
Joint Ventures

Size of Investments Considered:
Min Size of Investment Considered (000s): $1,000
Max Size of Investment Considered (000s): $10,000

Geographical Preferences

International Preferences:
All International

Industry Preferences

In Communications prefer:
Radio & TV Broadcasting
Media and Entertainment

In Internet Specific prefer:
Internet
Web Aggregration/Portals

In Consumer Related prefer:
Entertainment and Leisure

In Business Serv. prefer:
Media

In Manufact. prefer:
Publishing

Additional Information

Year Founded: 1995
Current Activity Level: Actively seeking new investments

HEARTLAND CAPITAL NETWORK

124 SW Adams Street
Suite 300
Peoria, IL USA 61602
Phone: 309-495-5900

Type of Firm

Angel Group

Project Preferences

Type of Financing Preferred:
Early Stage

Geographical Preferences

United States Preferences:
Midwest
Illinois

Additional Information

Name of Most Recent Fund: Tri-County Venture Capital Fund I, LLC
Most Recent Fund Was Raised: 11/04/2004
Year Founded: 2003
Capital Under Management: $1,800,000
Current Activity Level: Actively seeking new investments

HEARTLAND INDUSTRIAL PARTNERS

55 Railroad Avenue
Greenwich, CT USA 06830
Phone: 203-861-2622
Fax: 203-861-2722
E-mail: info@heartlandpartners.com
Website: www.heartlandpartners.com

Other Offices

320 Park Avenue
33rd Floor
New York, NY USA 10022
Phone: 212-981-5613
Fax: 212-981-3535

39400 Woodward Avenue
Suite 130
Bloomfield Hills, MI USA 48304

Phone: 248-593-8814
Fax: 248-631-5444

Management and Staff

Cindy Hess, General Partner
Daniel Tredwell, General Partner
David A. Stockman, General Partner
Gary Banks, Partner
J. Michael Stepp, Partner
Perry Lewis, Partner
Sam Valenti, Partner
Timothy D. Leuliette, General Partner
W. Gerald McConnell, Partner

Type of Firm

Private Equity Firm

Project Preferences

Type of Financing Preferred:

Leveraged Buyout
Acquisition

Industry Focus

(% based on actual investment)

Other Products	72.3%
Consumer Related	24.5%
Computer Hardware	3.1%

Additional Information

Name of Most Recent Fund: Heartland Industrial Partners, L.P.
Most Recent Fund Was Raised: 05/10/2000
Year Founded: 1999
Current Activity Level: Actively seeking new investments

HEBEI TECHNOLOGY VENTURE CAPITAL CO., LTD.

No. 55 Kunlun Street
Gaoxin Technology Dev'l
Shijiazhuang, China 050035
Phone: 86-311-85961617
Fax: 86-311-85961613
E-mail: hebvc@hebvc.com
Website: www.hebvc.com

Type of Firm

Private Equity Firm

Project Preferences

Type of Financing Preferred:

Early Stage
Balanced
Seed

Geographical Preferences

International Preferences:

China

Industry Preferences

In Biotechnology prefer:

Biotechnology

In Medical/Health prefer:

Medical/Health

In Industrial/Energy prefer:

Industrial Products
Materials

In Manufact. prefer:

Manufacturing

Additional Information

Year Founded: 2001
Current Activity Level: Actively seeking new investments

HEIDELBERG CAPITAL ASSET MANAGEMENT GMBH

Alte Glockengiesserei 9
Heidelberg, Germany 69115
Phone: 49-6221-867630
Fax: 49-6221-8676310
Website: www.heidelbergcapital.de

Type of Firm

Private Equity Firm

Project Preferences

Type of Financing Preferred:

Leveraged Buyout

Geographical Preferences

International Preferences:

Germany

Additional Information

Year Founded: 2007
Current Activity Level: Actively seeking new investments

HEIDELBERG INNOVATION FONDS MANAGEMENT GMBH

Waldhofer Strasse 11/5
Heidelberg, Germany 69123
Phone: 49-6221-64680
Fax: 49-6221-646864
E-mail: lifescience@hd-innovation.de
Website: www.hd-innovation.de

Type of Firm

Private Equity Firm

Additional Information

Year Founded: 2009
Current Activity Level: Actively seeking new investments

HEIDELBERG INNOVATION GMBH

Im Neuenheimer Feld 581
Heidelberg, Germany 69120
Phone: 49-6221-64680
Fax: 49-6221-646868
E-mail: info@hd-innovation.de
Website: www.hd-innovation.de

Management and Staff

Berthold Hackl, Managing Partner
Cristoph Kronabel, Managing Partner
Ulrich Abshagen, Managing Partner

Type of Firm

Private Equity Firm

Association Membership

German Venture Capital Association (BVK)
European Private Equity and Venture Capital Assoc.

Project Preferences

Type of Financing Preferred:

Early Stage
Expansion
Mezzanine
Seed
Startup

Size of Investments Considered:

Min Size of Investment Considered (000s): $471
Max Size of Investment Considered (000s): $4,708

Geographical Preferences

International Preferences:

Germany

Industry Preferences

In Biotechnology prefer:

Biotechnology

In Medical/Health prefer:

Medical/Health

Additional Information

Year Founded: 1997
Capital Under Management: $170,100,000
Current Activity Level: Actively seeking new investments

HEIRS CAPITAL LTD

H.E.I.R. Place, 33A Bishop
Aboyade Cole,V/I
Lagos, Nigeria
Phone: 234-1-461-6466
Fax: 234-1-461-6785
Website: www.heirsalliance.com

Type of Firm

Private Equity Firm
Project Preferences

Type of Financing Preferred:
Balanced

Geographical Preferences

International Preferences:
Nigeria

Additional Information

Year Founded: 2004
Current Activity Level: Actively seeking new investments

HELION VENTURE PARTNERS

Les Cascades Building
Edith Cavell Street
Port Louis, Mauritius
Phone: 230-212-9800
Fax: 230-212-9833
E-mail: contact@helionvc.com
Website: www.helionvc.com

Other Offices

Block B, 9th Floor
Vatika Towers, Sector 54
Gurgaon, India 122 002
Phone: 91-124-461-5333
Fax: 91-124-461-5345

First Floor, Pine Valley, Embassy
Golflinks Business Park, Koramangala
Bangalore , India 560 071
Phone: 91-80-4018-3333
Fax: 91-80-4018-3456

Management and Staff

Natarajan Ranganathan, Chief Financial Officer
Rahul Chowdhri, Vice President

Type of Firm

Private Equity Firm

Project Preferences

Type of Financing Preferred:
Early Stage
Expansion
Balanced
Seed

Size of Investments Considered:
Min Size of Investment Considered (000s): $2,000
Max Size of Investment Considered (000s): $10,000

Geographical Preferences

International Preferences:
India

Industry Preferences

In Communications prefer:
Wireless Communications

In Internet Specific prefer:
Internet

In Consumer Related prefer:
Consumer Services

In Business Serv. prefer:
Services

Additional Information

Year Founded: 2006
Capital Under Management: $140,000,000
Current Activity Level: Actively seeking new investments

HELIOS INVESTMENT PARTNERS

19 Bruton Place
London, United Kingdom W1J 6LZ
Phone: 44-207-491-4841
Fax: 44-207-491-4905
Website: www.heliosinvestment.com/

Management and Staff

Babatunde Soyoye, Managing Director
Tope Lawani, Managing Director

Type of Firm

Private Equity Firm

Project Preferences

Type of Financing Preferred:
Fund of Funds
Generalist PE

Geographical Preferences

International Preferences:
Nigeria
South Africa
Africa

Industry Preferences

In Communications prefer:
Communications and Media
Telecommunications

In Transportation prefer:
Transportation

In Utilities prefer:
Utilities

Additional Information

Year Founded: 2006
Capital Under Management: $400,000
Current Activity Level: Actively seeking new investments

HELIX INVESTMENTS

Corner St. Georges
de Chazal Street
Port Louis, Mauritius
Phone: 230-203-6600
Website: www.helix-investments.com

Other Offices

1421 Maker Chamber V
Nariman Point
Mumbai, India 400 021
Phone: 91-22-6615-7324
Fax: 91-22-6615-7328

Management and Staff

Raj Shastri, Vice President

Type of Firm

Private Equity Firm

Project Preferences

Type of Financing Preferred:
Leveraged Buyout
Management Buyouts
Acquisition

Size of Investments Considered:
Min Size of Investment Considered (000s): $5,000
Max Size of Investment Considered (000s): $15,000

Geographical Preferences

International Preferences:
India

Industry Preferences

In Medical/Health prefer:
Health Services

In Consumer Related prefer:
Consumer Services
Education Related

Additional Information

Year Founded: 2007
Current Activity Level: Actively seeking new investments

HELIX VENTURES

1717 Embarcadero Road
Palo Alto, CA USA 94303
Phone: 650-565-2223
E-mail: info@helixventure.com
Website: www.helixventure.com

Management and Staff

Evgeny Zaytsev, General Partner
Graham Crooke, General Partner
Philip Sawyer, General Partner

Type of Firm

Private Equity Firm

Project Preferences

Type of Financing Preferred:
Early Stage
Later Stage

Industry Preferences

In Medical/Health prefer:

Medical/Health
Health Services
Pharmaceuticals

Additional Information

Year Founded: 2008
Current Activity Level: Actively seeking new investments

HELLMAN & FRIEDMAN LLC

One Maritime Plaza
12th Floor
San Francisco, CA USA 94111
Phone: 415-788-5111
Fax: 415-788-0176
E-mail: info@hf.com
Website: www.hf.com

Other Offices

30th Floor Millbank tower
21-24 Millbank Tower
London, United Kingdom SW1P 4QP
Phone: 44-20-7839-5111
Fax: 44-20-7839-5711

390 Park Avenue
21st Floor
New York, NY USA 10022
Phone: 212-871-6680
Fax: 212-871-6688

Management and Staff

Adam Durrett, Principal
Allen Thorpe, Managing Director
Benjamin Farkas, Principal
Brian Powers, Chief Executive Officer
C. Andrew Ballard, Managing Director
David Tunnell, Managing Director
Edward Woiteshek, Principal
Erik Ragatz, Managing Director
Frank Zarb, Managing Director
Georgia Lee, Managing Director & CFO
Jeffrey Goldstein, Managing Director
P. Hunter Philbrick, Principal
Patrick Healy, Managing Director
Philip Sternheimer, Principal
Philip Hammarskjold, Managing Director
Robert Henske, Managing Director
Saloni Saraiya, Principal
Stephen Duckett, Managing Director
Thomas Steyer, Managing Director
Zita Saurel, Principal

Type of Firm

Private Equity Firm

Association Membership

Private Equity Council (PEC)

Project Preferences

Role in Financing:

Prefer role as deal originator

Type of Financing Preferred:

Second Stage Financing
Leveraged Buyout
Mezzanine
Special Situation

Size of Investments Considered:

Min Size of Investment Considered (000s): $50,000
Max Size of Investment Considered (000s): $300,000

Geographical Preferences

United States Preferences:

All U.S.

International Preferences:

Europe
China
Australia
South Africa
Asia
Japan

Industry Focus

(% based on actual investment)

Other Products	54.5%
Computer Software and Services	23.1%
Consumer Related	14.0%
Communications and Media	5.7%
Medical/Health	2.1%
Internet Specific	0.7%

Additional Information

Name of Most Recent Fund: Hellman & Friedman Capital Partners VI, L.P.
Most Recent Fund Was Raised: 11/09/2006
Year Founded: 1984
Capital Under Management: $8,000,000,000
Current Activity Level: Actively seeking new investments

HELMET BUSINESS MENTORS

Runeberginkatu 5 B
Helsinki, Finland 00100
Phone: 358-9-6869-2210
Fax: 358-9-6869-2241
E-mail: info@helmetcapital.fi
Website: www.helmetcapital.fi

Management and Staff

Berndt Blomqvist, Partner
Heikki Koivisto, Founding Partner
Jorma Petajisto, Managing Director
Pentti Kulmala, Partner
Reijo Kaukonen, Founding Partner
Seppo Ahonen, Founding Partner

Type of Firm

Private Equity Firm

Association Membership

Finnish Venture Capital Association (FVCA)
European Private Equity and Venture Capital Assoc.

Project Preferences

Type of Financing Preferred:

Second Stage Financing
Leveraged Buyout
Expansion
Balanced
Turnaround
Management Buyouts
Startup

Size of Investments Considered:

Min Size of Investment Considered (000s): $1,225
Max Size of Investment Considered (000s): $5,021

Geographical Preferences

International Preferences:

Estonia
Scandanavia/Nordic Region
Finland
Latvia
Lithuania

Industry Preferences

In Industrial/Energy prefer:

Industrial Products

Additional Information

Year Founded: 1995
Capital Under Management: $62,800,000
Current Activity Level: Actively seeking new investments

HELMSMAN FUNDS MANAGEMENT PTY LTD.

23 Hunter Street
Suite 503, Level 5
Sydney, Australia 2000
Phone: 612-9239-8100
Fax: 612-9239-8199
Website: www.helmsman.com.au

Type of Firm

Bank Affiliated

Association Membership

Australian Venture Capital Association (AVCAL)

Project Preferences

Role in Financing:

Prefer role as deal originator but will also invest in deals created by others

Type of Financing Preferred:

Turnaround
Special Situation
Distressed Debt

Geographical Preferences

International Preferences:
Pacific
Australia
New Zealand

Additional Information
Name of Most Recent Fund: Helmsman Capital Fund
Most Recent Fund Was Raised: 12/23/2002
Year Founded: 2002
Capital Under Management: $85,900,000
Current Activity Level: Actively seeking new investments
Method of Compensation: Return on invest. most important, but chg. closing fees, service fees, etc.

HELVETIC CAPITAL VENTURES AG
Sihlamtsstrasse 5
Zurich, Switzerland 8002

Type of Firm
Private Equity Firm

Project Preferences

Type of Financing Preferred:
Leveraged Buyout
Balanced

Additional Information
Year Founded: 2008
Current Activity Level: Actively seeking new investments

HEMISPHERE CAPITAL LLC
84 Brook Street
London, United Kingdom W1K 5EY
Phone: 44-20-7886-6028
E-mail: info@hemispherecapital.com
Website: www.hemispherecapital.com

Management and Staff
Daniel Sasaki, Managing Partner
Heather Killen, Managing Partner
Jesse Parker, Managing Director
Matt Rothman, Managing Partner

Type of Firm
Private Equity Firm

Project Preferences

Type of Financing Preferred:
Expansion

Size of Investments Considered:
Min Size of Investment Considered (000s): $3,000
Max Size of Investment Considered (000s): $5,000

Geographical Preferences

International Preferences:
Sweden
United Kingdom
Iceland
Norway
Finland
Denmark

Industry Preferences

In Communications prefer:
Telecommunications

Additional Information
Year Founded: 2004
Current Activity Level: Actively seeking new investments

HENDERSON EQUITY PARTNERS (AKA: HENDERSON PRIVATE CAPITAL)
201 Bishopgate
London, United Kingdom EC2M 2AE
Phone: 44-20-7818-2965
Fax: 44-20-7818-7310
Website: www.hendersonequitypartners.com

Other Offices
Frauenplatz 11
Munchen, Germany 80331
Phone: 49-89-2102-9714
Fax: 49-89-2102-9729

Via Agnello, 8
Milan, Italy 20121
Phone: 39-02-7214-7330
Fax: 39-02-7214-7350

6 Battery Road, #12-01
Singapore, Singapore 049909
Phone: 65-6836-6175
Fax: 65-6223-3536

Suites 3905-3908 Jardine House
1 Connaught Place
Central, Hong Kong
Phone: 852-2905-5188
Fax: 852-2905-5199

C/-The Oberoi Hotel
Suite 110, Dr. Zakir Hussain Marg
New Delhi, India 110003
Phone: 91-11-2430-4029
Fax: 91-11-2430-4030

Management and Staff
Chris Tanner, Principal
Guy Pigache, Partner
Hannah Gilbey, Principal
Jasvinder Bal, Principal
Melissa Deniz, Principal
Michael Jaffe, Principal
Ming Shu, Principal
Paul Woodbury, Partner
Roger Yates, Managing Director
Roger Greville, Managing Partner
Scott Greck, Partner
Steven Proctor, Principal
Vicky McDonagh, Principal
Vishal Marwaha, Partner

Type of Firm
Investment Management Firm

Association Membership
Hong Kong Venture Capital Association (HKVCA)
European Private Equity and Venture Capital Assoc.

Project Preferences

Type of Financing Preferred:
Fund of Funds
Leveraged Buyout
Expansion
Balanced
Management Buyouts
Acquisition

Size of Investments Considered:
Min Size of Investment Considered (000s): $10,000
Max Size of Investment Considered (000s): $50,000

Geographical Preferences

International Preferences:
India
Europe
China
Asia
Korea, South

Industry Preferences

In Communications prefer:
Telecommunications

In Medical/Health prefer:
Health Services

In Consumer Related prefer:
Entertainment and Leisure
Retail
Consumer Products

In Industrial/Energy prefer:
Alternative Energy

In Transportation prefer:
Transportation

In Business Serv. prefer:
Media

Additional Information
Name of Most Recent Fund: Henderson Asia Pacific Equity Partners I, L.P.
Most Recent Fund Was Raised: 01/01/2001
Year Founded: 1998
Capital Under Management: $2,400,000,000
Current Activity Level: Actively seeking new investments

HENKEL VENTURE CAPITAL

Henkelstrasse 67
Dusseldorf, Germany 40191
Phone: 49-211-797-1331
Fax: 49-211-798-2342
E-mail: venture.capital@henkel.de
Website: www.henkel.com

Type of Firm

Bank Affiliated

Association Membership

German Venture Capital Association (BVK)

Project Preferences

Type of Financing Preferred:
Early Stage
Expansion
Seed
Startup

Geographical Preferences

United States Preferences:
All U.S.

International Preferences:
Europe

Industry Preferences

In Biotechnology prefer:
Biotechnology

In Consumer Related prefer:
Consumer Products

In Industrial/Energy prefer:
Materials
Factory Automation

Additional Information

Year Founded: 2001
Current Activity Level: Actively seeking new investments

HENQ INVEST

Lloydstraat 136
Rotterdam, Netherlands 3024 EA
Phone: 31-10-452-1346
Fax: 31-10-452-8846
E-mail: info@henq.nl
Website: www.henq.nl

Type of Firm

Private Equity Firm

Project Preferences

Type of Financing Preferred:
Early Stage
Seed
Startup

Additional Information

Year Founded: 2006
Current Activity Level: Actively seeking new investments

HENRY INVESTMENT TRUST, L.P.

255 South 17th Street
Suite 2501
Philadelphia, PA USA 19103
Phone: 215-985-4484

Type of Firm

Private Equity Firm

Additional Information

Year Founded: 2001
Capital Under Management: $5,800,000
Current Activity Level: Actively seeking new investments

HERALD INVESTMENT MANAGEMENT LTD (HIML)

10-11 Charterhouse Square
London, United Kingdom EC1M 6EE
Phone: 44-20-7553-6300
Fax: 44-20-7490-8026
E-mail: info@heralduk.com
Website: www.heralduk.com

Management and Staff

Katie Potts, Managing Director
Robert Gorton, Partner
Simon Roberts, Partner

Type of Firm

Private Equity Firm

Association Membership

British Venture Capital Association (BVCA)

Project Preferences

Role in Financing:
Will function either as deal originator or investor in deals created by others

Type of Financing Preferred:
Early Stage
Startup

Size of Investments Considered:
Min Size of Investment Considered (000s): $400
Max Size of Investment Considered (000s): $400,000

Geographical Preferences

International Preferences:
United Kingdom

Industry Preferences

In Communications prefer:
Communications and Media

In Internet Specific prefer:
Internet

In Business Serv. prefer:
Media

Additional Information

Year Founded: 1999
Capital Under Management: $29,600,000
Current Activity Level: Actively seeking new investments

HERCULES TECHNOLOGY GROWTH CAPITAL, INC.

400 Hamilton Avenue
Suite 310
Palo Alto, CA USA 94301
Phone: 650-289-3060
Fax: 650-473-9194
E-mail: info@htgc.com
Website: www.htgc.com

Other Offices

11001 West 120th Avenue
Suite 400
Broomfield, CO USA 80021
Phone: 303-410-4417
Fax: 866-212-1031

934 Church
Elmhurst, IL USA 60126
Phone: 630-279-6017
Fax: 866-369-2815

31 St. James Avenue
Suite 790
Boston, MA USA 02116
Phone: 617-314-9973
Fax: 617-314-9997

Management and Staff

Arip Tirta, Principal
Bryan Jadot, Managing Director
David Lund, Chief Financial Officer
Greg Roth, Managing Director
Kathy Conte, Managing Director
Kevin Grossman, Managing Director
Mark Denomme, Managing Director
Mat Glauninger, Managing Director
Parag Shah, Senior Managing Director
Roy Liu, Managing Director
Sean Holland, Managing Director
Steve Kuo, Managing Director

Type of Firm

Private Equity Firm

Association Membership

National Venture Capital Association - USA (NVCA)

Project Preferences

Type of Financing Preferred:
Generalist PE

Size of Investments Considered:
Min Size of Investment Considered (000s): $1,000
Max Size of Investment Considered (000s): $30,000

Geographical Preferences

United States Preferences:
All U.S.

Additional Information
Year Founded: 2003
Capital Under Management: $452,000,000
Current Activity Level: Actively seeking new investments

HERE BE DRAGONS (HBD) MGT SERVICES (AKA:HBD VENTURE CAPITAL)

PO Box 1159
Durbanville, South Africa 7551
Phone: 27-21-970-1000
Fax: 27-21-970-1001
E-mail: webmaster@hbd.co.za
Website: www.hbdvc.com

Management and Staff
Julia Long, Chief Executive Officer
Stuart Kirkman, Chief Financial Officer
Vicki Shaw, Chief Executive Officer

Type of Firm
Private Equity Firm

Association Membership
South African Venture Capital Association (SAVCA)

Project Preferences

Type of Financing Preferred:
Balanced

Geographical Preferences

International Preferences:
South Africa

Additional Information
Year Founded: 2000
Capital Under Management: $10,000,000
Current Activity Level: Actively seeking new investments

HERITAGE PARTNERS

800 Boylston Street
Suite 401
Boston, MA USA 02199
Phone: 617-439-0688
Fax: 617-439-0689
E-mail: info@heritagepartnersinc.com
Website: www.heritagepartnersinc.com

Management and Staff
Charles Gifford, Partner
Mark Jrolf, General Partner
Matthew Mitchell, Vice President
Melissa Meyers, Vice President
Michael Gilligan, General Partner
Nickie Norris, Partner
Peter Hermann, General Partner

Type of Firm
Private Equity Firm

Project Preferences

Role in Financing:
Prefer role as deal originator

Type of Financing Preferred:
Leveraged Buyout
Industry Rollups

Size of Investments Considered:
Min Size of Investment Considered (000s): $60,000
Max Size of Investment Considered: No Limit

Geographical Preferences

United States Preferences:
All U.S.

Industry Focus

(% based on actual investment)	
Medical/Health	61.7%
Other Products	23.7%
Consumer Related	9.2%
Industrial/Energy	4.8%
Internet Specific	0.3%
Semiconductors/Other Elect.	0.2%

Additional Information
Name of Most Recent Fund: Heritage Fund III, L.P.
Most Recent Fund Was Raised: 06/30/1999
Year Founded: 1987
Capital Under Management: $1,433,000,000
Current Activity Level: Reducing investment activity
Method of Compensation: Return on investment is of primary concern, do not charge fees

---

HERKULES CAPITAL AS (FKA: FERD VENTURE)

Haakon VII's gt. 5B
P.O. Box 1793, Vika
Oslo, Norway 0161
Phone: 47-22-090-600
Fax: 47-22-090-601
E-mail: post@herkulescapital.no
Website: www.herkulescapital.no

Management and Staff
Adele Bugge Norman Pran, Chief Financial Officer
Erik Olsen, Managing Partner
Gert Munthe, Managing Partner
Tore Rynning-Nielsen, Partner

Type of Firm
Private Equity Firm

Association Membership
Norwegian Venture Capital Association

Project Preferences

Type of Financing Preferred:
Leveraged Buyout
Early Stage
Expansion
Mezzanine
Later Stage
Seed
Management Buyouts
Acquisition
Startup
Recapitalizations

Size of Investments Considered:
Min Size of Investment Considered (000s): $564
Max Size of Investment Considered (000s): $2,256

Geographical Preferences

International Preferences:
Sweden
Greenland
Iceland
Scandanavia/Nordic Region
Finland
Norway
Denmark
Faroe Islands

Industry Preferences

In Communications prefer:
Telecommunications

In Biotechnology prefer:
Biotechnology

In Medical/Health prefer:
Health Services

In Consumer Related prefer:
Consumer
Retail

In Industrial/Energy prefer:
Energy
Oil and Gas Exploration

In Business Serv. prefer:
Services

In Other prefer:
Environment Responsible

Additional Information
Year Founded: 2000
Capital Under Management: $1,865,000,000
Current Activity Level: Actively seeking new investments

HERMES PRIVATE EQUITY MANAGEMENT, LTD.

Lloyds Chambers
One Portsoken Street
London, United Kingdom E1 8HZ
Phone: 44-20-7702-0888
Fax: 44-20-7702-9452
Website: www.hermesprivateequity.co.uk

Management and Staff

Adrian White, Chief Operating Officer
Colin Melvin, Chief Executive Officer
David Pitt-Watson, Managing Director
John Mould, Chief Operating Officer
Simon Jennings, Partner
Tony Watson, Chief Executive Officer

Type of Firm

Private Equity Firm

Association Membership

British Venture Capital Association (BVCA)
European Private Equity and Venture Capital Assoc.

Project Preferences

Type of Financing Preferred:
Fund of Funds
Leveraged Buyout
Balanced

Size of Investments Considered:
Min Size of Investment Considered (000s): $7,533
Max Size of Investment Considered (000s): $47,080

Geographical Preferences

International Preferences:
United Kingdom
Europe
Asia

Industry Preferences

In Communications prefer:
Communications and Media

In Semiconductor/Electr prefer:
Electronics
Semiconductor

Additional Information

Year Founded: 1983
Capital Under Management: $33,943,500,000
Current Activity Level: Actively seeking new investments

HERMIS CAPITAL, JSC

K. Kalinausko str. 2B
4 floor
Vilnius, Lithuania 03107
Phone: 370-5-264-4740
Fax: 370-5-264-4747
E-mail: info@hermis.lt
Website: www.hermis.lt

Type of Firm

Private Equity Firm

Project Preferences

Type of Financing Preferred:
Leveraged Buyout
Balanced

Geographical Preferences

International Preferences:
Central Europe
Eastern Europe
Lithuania

Industry Preferences

In Consumer Related prefer:
Consumer
Food/Beverage

In Transportation prefer:
Transportation

Additional Information

Year Founded: 2000
Current Activity Level: Actively seeking new investments

HERO VENTURES

30 St. Clair Avenue West
Suite 103
Toronto, Canada M4V 3A1
Phone: 416-922-0941
Fax: 416-922-7963
Website: www.herovc.com

Type of Firm

Private Equity Firm

Additional Information

Year Founded: 2008
Current Activity Level: Actively seeking new investments

HERON CAPITAL LLC

One Indiana Square
Suite 2250
Indianapolis, IN USA 46204
Phone: 317-686-1950
Fax: 317-686-1954
Website: www.heroncap.com

Other Offices

3006 Lime Kiln Lane
Louisville, KY USA 40222
Phone: 317-686-1950
Fax: 502-339-1789

Management and Staff

Greg Maurer, Managing Director
Kevin Etzkorn, Managing Director
Michael Shepard, Principal
Shannon Rothschild, Vice President

Type of Firm

Private Equity Firm

Project Preferences

Role in Financing:
Will function either as deal originator or investor in deals created by others

Type of Financing Preferred:
Early Stage
Balanced
First Stage Financing

Size of Investments Considered:
Min Size of Investment Considered (000s): $250
Max Size of Investment Considered (000s): $2,000

Geographical Preferences

United States Preferences:
Midwest
Indiana
All U.S.

Industry Preferences

In Medical/Health prefer:
Medical/Health
Medical Diagnostics
Medical Products

Additional Information

Name of Most Recent Fund: Heron Capital Venture Fund I, L.P.
Most Recent Fund Was Raised: 12/14/2006
Year Founded: 2005
Capital Under Management: $24,000,000
Current Activity Level: Actively seeking new investments

HEUNGKOOK VENTURE CAPITAL COMPANY, LTD.

667-1 Buan-dong
Jin-gu
Pusan, South Korea
Phone: 82-51-816-3753
Fax: 82-51-817-5746

Management and Staff

Young Chul Hong, President

Type of Firm

Private Equity Firm

Project Preferences

Type of Financing Preferred:
Balanced

Geographical Preferences

International Preferences:
Korea, South

Additional Information

Year Founded: 2000
Current Activity Level: Actively seeking new investments

HEXAGRAM INVESTMENT ADVISORS PVT, LTD.

15-B Chandramukhi
Nariman Point
Mumbai, India 400 021

Management and Staff

S.N. Subramanya, Managing Partner

Type of Firm

Private Equity Firm

Project Preferences

Type of Financing Preferred:
Balanced

Geographical Preferences

International Preferences:
India

Industry Preferences

In Consumer Related prefer:
Entertainment and Leisure

In Business Serv. prefer:
Media

Additional Information

Year Founded: 2001
Current Activity Level: Actively seeking new investments

HFIC PARTNERS, LLC

925 Westchester Avenue
Suite 105
White Plains, NY USA 10604
Phone: 914-798-7600

Management and Staff

Mark Jurish, Founder

Type of Firm

Private Equity Firm

Additional Information

Year Founded: 2001
Capital Under Management: $100,000,000
Current Activity Level: Actively seeking new investments

HGCAPITAL (FKA: MERCURY PRIVATE EQUITY)

2 More London Riverside
London, United Kingdom SE1 2AP
Phone: 44-20-7089-7888
Fax: 44-20-7089-7999
E-mail: info@hgcapital.com
Website: www.hgcapital.net

Other Offices

3rd Floor
Jan Luijkenstraat 92k
Amsterdam, Netherlands 1071 CT
Phone: 31-20-572-7140
Fax: 31-20-572-7141

Salvatorstrasse 3
Munich, Germany 80333
Phone: 49-89-2554-9550
Fax: 49-89-2554-95550

Management and Staff

Justin Von Simson, Partner
Karsten Hartman, Partner
Martin Block, Partner
Nic Humphries, Chief Executive Officer
Richard Donner, Partner

Type of Firm

Private Equity Firm

Association Membership

British Venture Capital Association (BVCA)
European Private Equity and Venture Capital Assoc.

Project Preferences

Type of Financing Preferred:
Leveraged Buyout
Expansion
Generalist PE
Balanced
Turnaround
Later Stage
Other
Management Buyouts

Geographical Preferences

International Preferences:
Ireland
United Kingdom
Europe
Western Europe
Germany

Industry Preferences

In Communications prefer:
Communications and Media
Media and Entertainment

In Medical/Health prefer:
Medical/Health

In Consumer Related prefer:
Consumer
Entertainment and Leisure

In Industrial/Energy prefer:
Alternative Energy
Industrial Products

In Business Serv. prefer:
Services

Additional Information

Name of Most Recent Fund: HgCapital5
Most Recent Fund Was Raised: 02/28/2006
Year Founded: 1985
Capital Under Management: $3,276,000,000
Current Activity Level: Actively seeking new investments

HICKORY VENTURE CAPITAL CORPORATION

301 Washington St. NW
Suite 301
Huntsville, AL USA 35801
Phone: 256-539-1931
Fax: 256-539-5130
E-mail: info@hvcc.com
Website: www.hvcc.com

Management and Staff

J. Thomas Noojin, President
Monro Lanier, Vice President
Paul Brashier, Vice President

Type of Firm

SBIC

Project Preferences

Role in Financing:
Will function either as deal originator or investor in deals created by others

Type of Financing Preferred:
Leveraged Buyout
Mezzanine
Later Stage
Management Buyouts

Size of Investments Considered:
Min Size of Investment Considered (000s): $2,000
Max Size of Investment Considered (000s): $13,000

Geographical Preferences

United States Preferences:
Mid Atlantic
Midwest
Southeast
Southwest

Industry Focus

(% based on actual investment)

Internet Specific	25.7%
Medical/Health	18.7%
Other Products	15.3%
Computer Software and Services	15.2%
Communications and Media	8.6%
Consumer Related	7.8%

Semiconductors/Other Elect.	4.5%
Biotechnology	2.3%
Industrial/Energy	1.7%
Computer Hardware	0.2%

Additional Information

Year Founded: 1985
Capital Under Management: $175,000,000
Current Activity Level: Actively seeking new investments
Method of Compensation: Return on invest. most important, but chg. closing fees, service fees, etc.

HICKS EQUITY PARTNERS

c/o Hicks Holdings LLC
100 Crescent Court, Ste 1200
Dallas, TX USA 75201

Type of Firm

Private Equity Firm

Project Preferences

Type of Financing Preferred:

Leveraged Buyout

Geographical Preferences

United States Preferences:

All U.S.

Canadian Preferences:

Alberta

Additional Information

Year Founded: 2004
Current Activity Level: Actively seeking new investments

HIGH COUNTRY VENTURE LLC

831 Pearl Street
Boulder, CO USA 80302
Phone: 303-381-2638
E-mail: Coloradofund1@tangogroup.com
Website: www.coloradofund1.com

Management and Staff

Chris Marks, Principal
Mark Lupa, Principal

Type of Firm

Private Equity Firm

Project Preferences

Role in Financing:

Will function either as deal originator or investor in deals created by others

Type of Financing Preferred:

Early Stage
Seed

Size of Investments Considered:

Min Size of Investment Considered (000s): $250
Max Size of Investment Considered (000s): $3,000

Geographical Preferences

United States Preferences:

Rocky Mountain
Colorado

Industry Preferences

In Computer Software prefer:

Software
Systems Software
Applications Software

In Internet Specific prefer:

Internet
Ecommerce
Web Aggregration/Portals

In Semiconductor/Electr prefer:

Analytic/Scientific

In Biotechnology prefer:

Human Biotechnology
Genetic Engineering
Agricultural/Animal Bio.
Industrial Biotechnology
Biosensors
Biotech Related Research

In Medical/Health prefer:

Medical Diagnostics
Medical Therapeutics
Drug/Equipmt Delivery
Medical Products
Disposable Med. Products
Pharmaceuticals

In Consumer Related prefer:

Consumer
Retail
Food/Beverage
Education Related

In Financial Services prefer:

Financial Services

Additional Information

Year Founded: 2005
Capital Under Management: $25,000,000
Current Activity Level: Actively seeking new investments
Method of Compensation: Return on investment is of primary concern, do not charge fees

---

HIGH PEAKS VENTURE PARTNERS, LLC

10 Second Street
Troy, NY USA 12180
Phone: 518-720-3087
Fax: 518-720-3091
Website: www.hpvp.com

Management and Staff

Bela Musits, Managing Director
Bradley Svrluga, Managing Director
Russell Howard, Managing Director

Type of Firm

Private Equity Firm

Project Preferences

Type of Financing Preferred:

Early Stage

Geographical Preferences

United States Preferences:

Northeast
New York

Additional Information

Name of Most Recent Fund: High Peaks Ventures, L.P.
Most Recent Fund Was Raised: 04/22/2003
Year Founded: 2001
Capital Under Management: $46,000,000
Current Activity Level: Actively seeking new investments

HIGH ROAD CAPITAL PARTNERS

1251 Avenue of the Americas
Suite 525
New York, NY USA 10016
Phone: 212-554-3265
Fax: 212-554-3284
Website: www.highroadcap.com

Management and Staff

Adi Blum, Vice President
Ben Schnakenberg, Vice President
Jeffrey Goodrich, Partner
Robert Fitzsimmons, Managing Partner
William Hobbs, Partner
William Connel, Partner

Type of Firm

Private Equity Firm

Project Preferences

Role in Financing:

Prefer role as deal originator

Type of Financing Preferred:

Leveraged Buyout
Management Buyouts
Acquisition
Recapitalizations

Size of Investments Considered:

Min Size of Investment Considered (000s): $5,000
Max Size of Investment Considered (000s): $20,000

Geographical Preferences

United States Preferences:

All U.S.

Industry Preferences

In Communications prefer:
Commercial Communications
CATV & Pay TV Systems
Radio & TV Broadcasting
Telecommunications
Wireless Communications
Data Communications
Satellite Microwave Comm.
Other Communication Prod.

In Computer Hardware prefer:
Mainframes / Scientific
Mini and Personal/Desktop
Computer Graphics and Dig
Integrated Turnkey System
Terminals
Disk Relat. Memory Device

In Computer Software prefer:
Computer Services
Data Processing
Software
Systems Software
Applications Software
Artificial Intelligence

In Internet Specific prefer:
E-Commerce Technology
Internet
Ecommerce
Web Aggregration/Portals

In Semiconductor/Electr prefer:
Electronic Components
Semiconductor
Micro-Processing
Controllers and Sensors
Sensors
Circuit Boards
Component Testing Equipmt
Laser Related
Fiber Optics
Analytic/Scientific
Optoelectronics

In Biotechnology prefer:
Agricultural/Animal Bio.
Industrial Biotechnology
Biosensors
Biotech Related Research

In Medical/Health prefer:
Medical Diagnostics
Diagnostic Services
Diagnostic Test Products
Medical Therapeutics
Medical Products
Disposable Med. Products
Health Services
Pharmaceuticals

In Consumer Related prefer:
Consumer
Franchises(NEC)
Food/Beverage
Education Related

In Industrial/Energy prefer:
Energy
Industrial Products
Factory Automation
Robotics
Machinery
Environmental Related

In Transportation prefer:
Transportation
Aerospace

In Financial Services prefer:
Financial Services

In Business Serv. prefer:
Services
Distribution
Consulting Services
Media

In Manufact. prefer:
Manufacturing

In Utilities prefer:
Utilities

In Other prefer:
Socially Responsible

Additional Information
Year Founded: 2007
Capital Under Management: $150,000,000
Current Activity Level: Actively seeking new investments
Method of Compensation: Return on invest. most important, but chg. closing fees, service fees, etc.

HIGH STREET CAPITAL
Eleven South LaSalle Street
Fifth Floor
Chicago, IL USA 60603
Phone: 312-423-2650
Fax: 312-423-2655
Website: www.highstreetcapital.com

Management and Staff
Joseph Katcha, Principal
Kent Haeger, Principal
Richard McClain, Principal
Robert France, Vice President
William Oberholtzer, Principal

Type of Firm
Private Equity Firm

Association Membership
Natl Assoc of Investment Cos. (NAIC)
Natl Assoc of Small Bus. Inv. Co (NASBIC)

Project Preferences

Role in Financing:
Prefer role as deal originator but will also invest in deals created by others

Type of Financing Preferred:
Leveraged Buyout
Expansion
Generalist PE
Later Stage
Management Buyouts
Acquisition
Special Situation
Recapitalizations

Size of Investments Considered:
Min Size of Investment Considered (000s): $2,000
Max Size of Investment Considered (000s): $15,000

Industry Preferences

In Medical/Health prefer:
Medical Diagnostics
Diagnostic Services
Disposable Med. Products
Health Services

In Consumer Related prefer:
Food/Beverage

In Industrial/Energy prefer:
Industrial Products
Machinery

In Financial Services prefer:
Insurance

In Business Serv. prefer:
Services
Distribution
Consulting Services

In Manufact. prefer:
Manufacturing

Additional Information
Year Founded: 1997
Capital Under Management: $120,000,000
Current Activity Level: Actively seeking new investments
Method of Compensation: Return on investment is of primary concern, do not charge fees

---

HIGH TECH PRIVATE EQUITY (FKA: HIGH TECH MANAGEMENT GMBH)
Steinstrasse 20
Dusseldorf, Germany 40212
Phone: 49-211-13608460
Fax: 49-211-13608465
E-mail: info@hightech-pe.com
Website: www.hightech-pe.de

Management and Staff
Christian Schutte, Managing Director
Erich Hacker, Managing Director
Georg Ludwig, Managing Director
Jochen Kalbe, Managing Director

Type of Firm
Private Equity Firm

Association Membership
German Venture Capital Association (BVK)

Project Preferences

Type of Financing Preferred:
Expansion
Other
Management Buyouts
Recapitalizations

Size of Investments Considered:
Min Size of Investment Considered (000s): $4,194
Max Size of Investment Considered (000s): $13,980

Geographical Preferences

International Preferences:
Europe
Germany

Industry Focus
(% based on actual investment)

Semiconductors/Other Elect.	100.0%

Additional Information
Year Founded: 2000
Capital Under Management: $211,100,000
Current Activity Level: Actively seeking new investments

HIGH-TECH GRUNDERFONDS MANAGEMENT GMBH
Ludwig-Erhard-Allee 2
Bonn, Germany 53175
Phone: 49-228-96568500
Fax: 49-228-96568550
E-mail: info@high-tech-gruenderfonds.de
Website: www.high-tech-gruenderfonds.de

Management and Staff
Alexander Von Frankenberg, Managing Director
Guido Schlitzer, Chief Financial Officer
Michael Brandkamp, Managing Director

Type of Firm
Government Affiliated Program

Project Preferences

Type of Financing Preferred:
Early Stage
Seed
Startup

Geographical Preferences

International Preferences:
Europe
Germany

Additional Information
Year Founded: 2004
Capital Under Management: $369,700,000
Current Activity Level: Actively seeking new investments

HIGHBAR VENTURES
660 Windsor Drive
Menlo Park, CA USA 94025
E-mail: info@highbarventures.com
Website: www.highbarventures.com

Management and Staff
Roy Thiele-Sardina, General Partner

Type of Firm
Private Equity Firm

Project Preferences

Type of Financing Preferred:
Early Stage

Additional Information
Year Founded: 2000
Current Activity Level: Actively seeking new investments

HIGHGATE VENTURE CAPITAL FUND
Eight King Street East
Suite 202
Toronto, Canada M5C 1B5
Phone: 416-362-7668
Fax: 416-863-5161

Type of Firm
Private Equity Firm

Additional Information
Year Founded: 1988
Current Activity Level: Actively seeking new investments

HIGHGROWTH PARTNERS SGECR SA (AKA: BCNHIGHGROWTH)
Tuset 20-24
Barcelona, Spain 08006
Phone: 34-93-363-0386
Fax: 34-93-218-3333
E-mail: info@hg.com.es
Website: www.highgrowth.net

Other Offices
Calle Velazquez 41 4o
Madrid, Spain 28001
Phone: 34-91-5782600
Fax: 34-91-5778995

Management and Staff
Ferran Lemus, Managing Director

Type of Firm
Private Equity Firm

Association Membership
Spanish Venture Capital Association (ASCRI)

Project Preferences

Type of Financing Preferred:
Early Stage
Expansion
Balanced
Start-up Financing
Seed
Startup

Size of Investments Considered:
Min Size of Investment Considered (000s): $582
Max Size of Investment Considered (000s): $2,908

Geographical Preferences

International Preferences:
Portugal
Argentina
Spain
France

Additional Information
Name of Most Recent Fund: Highgrowth - Innovation FCR
Most Recent Fund Was Raised: 07/13/2007
Year Founded: 1999
Capital Under Management: $70,200,000
Current Activity Level: Actively seeking new investments

HIGHLAND CAPITAL MANAGEMENT, L.P. (FKA: PAMCO)
Nexbank Tower
13455 Noel Road, Eighth Floor
Dallas, TX USA 75240
Phone: 972-628-4100
Fax: 972-308-6747
E-mail: hfinfo@hcmlp.com
Website: www.hcmlp.com

Other Offices
Nine West 57th Street
38th Floor
New York, NY USA 10019
Phone: 212-792-6900
Fax: 212-792-6920

130 Jermyn Street
4th Floor
London, United Kingdom SW1Y 4UR
Phone: 11-44-20-7747-8000
Fax: 11-44-20-7747-8001

Management and Staff
Amit Walia, Partner
Appu Mundassery, Partner
Bernard Vonderhaar III, Managing Director
Brad Borud, Partner
Brad Means, Partner

Christopher Harrison, Managing Director
David Walls, Partner
Davis Deadman, Partner
Elizabeth Goldstein, Managing Director
Eugene Miao, Managing Director
Gregory Stuecheli, Partner
Harold Siegel, Managing Director
Jack Yang, Partner
James Dondero, President
Joe Dougherty, Partner
John Honis, Partner
John Morgan, Partner
John Mackin, Managing Director
Kevin Latimer, Partner
Maureen Mitchell, Managing Director
Patrick Conner, Partner
Patrick Boyce, Chief Financial Officer
Patrick Daugherty, Partner
Paul Adkins, Managing Director
Paul Kauffman, Partner
Roger Li, Managing Director
Saukok Chu Tiampo, Managing Director
Todd Travers, Partner

Type of Firm

Private Equity Firm

Project Preferences

Type of Financing Preferred:

Expansion
Turnaround
Special Situation
Distressed Debt

Geographical Preferences

United States Preferences:

All U.S.

International Preferences:

Europe

Additional Information

Year Founded: 1993
Capital Under Management: $200,000,000
Current Activity Level: Actively seeking new investments

HIGHLAND CAPITAL PARTNERS LLC

92 Hayden Avenue
Lexington, MA USA 02421
Phone: 781-861-5500
Fax: 781-861-5499
E-mail: info@hcp.com
Website: www.hcp.com

Other Offices

2420 Sand Hill Road
Suite 300
Menlo Park, CA USA 94025
Phone: 650-687-3800
Fax: 650-687-3899

6 rue de la Croix d'Or
Geneva, Switzerland 1204
Phone: 41-22-817-7200
Fax: 41-22-817-7219

288 Nan Jin Road
Financial Centre, Suite 2606
Shanghai , China 200003
Phone: 86-21-2890-9888
Fax: 86-21-2890-9999

Management and Staff

Bijan Salehizadeh, General Partner
Chuan Thor, Managing Director
Corey Mulloy, General Partner
Daniel Rosen, Principal
Daniel Nova, General Partner
Fergal Mullen, General Partner
Gaurav Tewari, Principal
Irena Goldenberg, Principal
John St. Amand, Venture Partner
John Hsin, Managing Director
John Burns, General Partner
Kuantai Yeh, Managing Director
Matthew Nichols, Principal
Neill Occhiogrosso, Principal
Paul Maeder, General Partner
Peter Bell, General Partner
Richard DeSilva, General Partner
Robert Higgins, General Partner
Robert Davis, General Partner
Sean Dalton, General Partner
Ted Philip, Managing General Partner
Thomas Stemberg, Managing General Partner
Thomas Guilfoile, General Partner

Type of Firm

Private Equity Firm

Association Membership

Mid-Atlantic Venture Association
National Venture Capital Association - USA (NVCA)
European Private Equity and Venture Capital Assoc.

Project Preferences

Role in Financing:

Prefer role as deal originator but will also invest in deals created by others

Type of Financing Preferred:

Early Stage
Balanced
Later Stage
Seed

Size of Investments Considered:

Min Size of Investment Considered (000s): $100
Max Size of Investment Considered (000s): $20,000

Geographical Preferences

United States Preferences:

All U.S.

Canadian Preferences:

All Canada

International Preferences:

Europe

Industry Focus

(% based on actual investment)

Internet Specific	34.6%
Communications and Media	15.8%
Computer Software and Services	13.9%
Biotechnology	7.4%
Other Products	6.7%
Medical/Health	6.5%
Consumer Related	6.3%
Semiconductors/Other Elect.	4.7%
Industrial/Energy	2.1%
Computer Hardware	2.0%

Additional Information

Name of Most Recent Fund: Highland Consumer Fund I Family
Most Recent Fund Was Raised: 02/15/2007
Year Founded: 1988
Capital Under Management: $2,966,000,000
Current Activity Level: Actively seeking new investments
Method of Compensation: Return on invest. most important, but chg. closing fees, service fees, etc.

HIGHTECH VENTURE PARTNERS GMBH

Wendelsweg 64
Frankfurt am Main, Germany 60599
Phone: 49-699637687714
Fax: 49-699637687710
E-mail: info@htvp.de
Website: www.htvp.de

Management and Staff

Bernd Kemmler, Founder
Daniel Hopp, Founder
Kai Kremer, Founder
Rainer Marquardt, Founder

Type of Firm

Private Equity Firm

Project Preferences

Type of Financing Preferred:

Early Stage
Seed

Geographical Preferences

International Preferences:

Switzerland
Austria
Germany

Additional Information

Year Founded: 2007
Capital Under Management: $136,900,000
Current Activity Level: Actively seeking new investments

HIGHWAY 12 VENTURES

802 West Bannock
Seventh Floor, Hoff Building
Boise, ID USA 83702
Phone: 208-345-8383
Fax: 208-345-8484
E-mail: inform@highway12ventures.com
Website: www.highway12ventures.com

Management and Staff

Archie Clemins, Venture Partner
George Mulheen, Venture Partner
Glenn Michael, General Partner
Mark Solon, Managing Partner
Phillip Reed, General Partner

Type of Firm

Private Equity Firm

Association Membership

National Venture Capital Association - USA (NVCA)

Project Preferences

Role in Financing:
Will function either as deal originator or investor in deals created by others

Type of Financing Preferred:
Early Stage
Expansion
Seed

Size of Investments Considered:
Min Size of Investment Considered (000s): $500
Max Size of Investment Considered (000s): $5,000

Geographical Preferences

United States Preferences:
Midwest
Rocky Mountain
Idaho

Industry Preferences

In Communications prefer:
Wireless Communications

In Computer Hardware prefer:
Computer Graphics and Dig

In Computer Software prefer:
Computer Services
Data Processing
Software
Systems Software
Applications Software

In Internet Specific prefer:
Internet
Ecommerce
Web Aggregration/Portals

In Consumer Related prefer:
Retail
Education Related

In Industrial/Energy prefer:
Energy

Additional Information

Year Founded: 2001
Capital Under Management: $100,000,000
Current Activity Level: Actively seeking new investments
Method of Compensation: Return on investment is of primary concern, do not charge fees

HIH DEVELOPMENT A/S

Birk Centerpark 40
Herning, Denmark 7400
Phone: 45-9627-0100
Fax: 45-9627-0109
Website: www.hih-development.dk

Type of Firm

Incubator/Development Program

Project Preferences

Type of Financing Preferred:
Seed
Startup

Geographical Preferences

International Preferences:
Denmark

Additional Information

Year Founded: 2004
Current Activity Level: Actively seeking new investments

HIKARI PRIVATE EQUITY, INC.

1-16-15 Minami Ikebukuro,
Toshima-Ku
Tokyo, Japan 150-0002
Phone: 813-5951-8497
Fax: 813-5951-8597
Website: www.hpe.co.jp

Management and Staff

Hirokazu Mashita, Chairman & CEO
Shinya Nakayama, President & COO

Type of Firm

Private Equity Firm

Project Preferences

Type of Financing Preferred:
Balanced

Geographical Preferences

International Preferences:
Taiwan
China
Hong Kong
Singapore
Asia
Japan

Industry Preferences

In Internet Specific prefer:
Internet

Additional Information

Year Founded: 1999
Current Activity Level: Actively seeking new investments

HILCO CONSUMER CAPITAL CORPORATION

40 King Street West
Scotia Plaza, Suite 3201
Toronto, Canada M5H 3Y2
Phone: 416-361-6336
E-mail: mail@hilcocc.com
Website: www.hilcocc.com

Type of Firm

Private Equity Firm

Additional Information

Year Founded: 2009
Current Activity Level: Actively seeking new investments

HILCO EQUITY MANAGEMENT, LLC

5 Revere Drive
Suite 300
Northbrook, IL USA 60062
Phone: 847-509-1100
Fax: 847-714-1580
E-mail: mail@hilcoequity.com
Website: www.hilcoequity.com

Other Offices

38/F One Exchange Square
8 Connaught Place
Central, Hong Kong
Phone: 852-3101-7385
Fax: 852-3101-7384

Management and Staff

John Tomes, Managing Director
Keith Freeman, Principal
Ryan Bohr, Principal
Taffy Gutu, Vice President

Type of Firm

Private Equity Firm

Association Membership

Illinois Venture Capital Association

Project Preferences

Type of Financing Preferred:
Leveraged Buyout

Size of Investments Considered:
Min Size of Investment Considered (000s): $3,000
Max Size of Investment Considered (000s): $10,000

Industry Preferences

In Consumer Related prefer:
Consumer
Retail

In Business Serv. prefer:
Services

In Manufact. prefer:
Manufacturing

Additional Information
Year Founded: 2005
Capital Under Management: $73,000,000
Current Activity Level: Actively seeking new investments

HILL-ROM HOLDINGS, INC. (FKA: HILLENBRAND INDUSTRIES)
1069 State Route
46 East
Batesville, IN USA 47006
Phone: 812-934-7777
Fax: 812-934-8189
Website: www.hillenbrand.com

Management and Staff
Don Berger, Chief Financial Officer
Michael Buettner, Vice President
W. August Hillenbrand, Chief Executive Officer

Type of Firm
Private Equity Firm

Project Preferences

Role in Financing:
Prefer role as deal originator but will also invest in deals created by others

Type of Financing Preferred:
Leveraged Buyout
Acquisition

Geographical Preferences

International Preferences:
United Kingdom
Latin America
Spain
Germany
Japan

Additional Information
Year Founded: 1999
Current Activity Level: Actively seeking new investments
Method of Compensation: Return on investment is of primary concern, do not charge fees

---

HIMALAYA CAPITAL
489 5th Avenue
Suite 1200
New York, NY USA 10017
Phone: 212-687-9271
Fax: 212-856-9759
E-mail: businessplans@himalayacapital.com
Website: www.himcapventures.com

Management and Staff
Li Lu, Founding Partner
Paul Kahn, General Partner
Saul Richter, Principal

Type of Firm
Private Equity Firm

Project Preferences

Role in Financing:
Prefer role as deal originator

Type of Financing Preferred:
Early Stage

Size of Investments Considered:
Min Size of Investment Considered (000s): $500
Max Size of Investment Considered (000s): $3,000

Geographical Preferences

United States Preferences:
Northeast
Connecticut
New Jersey
New York

Industry Preferences

In Computer Software prefer:
Software

In Biotechnology prefer:
Biotechnology

In Medical/Health prefer:
Medical/Health

In Business Serv. prefer:
Media

Additional Information
Name of Most Recent Fund: Himalaya Capital Ventures II, L.P.
Most Recent Fund Was Raised: 01/14/2003
Year Founded: 1998
Capital Under Management: $40,000,000
Current Activity Level: Actively seeking new investments

HINA GROUP, THE
2445 Faber Place
Suite 101
Palo Alto, CA USA 94303
Phone: 650-331-8780
Fax: 650-331-8790
Website: www.hinagroup.com

Other Offices
Pacific Century Place 2A, Unit 810
Gongti Bei Lu, Chaoyang District
Beijing, China 100027
Phone: 8610-6539-1368
Fax: 8610-6539-1369

Management and Staff
Eric Clow, Vice President
Hong Chen, Chairman & CEO
Ken Tsang, Vice President

Type of Firm
Investment Management Firm

Geographical Preferences

International Preferences:
China
Asia

Industry Preferences

In Communications prefer:
Telecommunications

Additional Information
Year Founded: 2003
Current Activity Level: Actively seeking new investments

HIROGIN CAPITAL COMPANY, LTD.
1-3-8 Kamiya machi
Naka-ku
Hiroshima City, Japan
Phone: 81-82-504-3979
Fax: 81-82-246-7002

Type of Firm
Private Equity Firm

Project Preferences

Type of Financing Preferred:
Balanced

Geographical Preferences

International Preferences:
Japan

Additional Information
Year Founded: 1995
Capital Under Management: $16,400,000
Current Activity Level: Actively seeking new investments

HIROSHIMA VENTURE CAPITAL CO., LTD.

5F Koden Bldg.
1-2-22 Kamiyacho,Naka-ku
Hiroshima-shi, Japan 730-0031
Phone: 81-82-504-3979
Fax: 81-82-246-7002
Website: www.h-vc.co.jp

Management and Staff

Kenji Harada, President

Type of Firm

Private Equity Firm

Additional Information

Year Founded: 1995
Current Activity Level: Actively seeking new investments

HISPANIA CAPITAL PARTNERS (HCP)

311 South Wacker Drive
Suite 4200
Chicago, IL USA 60606
Phone: 312-697-4611
Fax: 312-697-4598
E-mail: hispania@hispaniapartners.com
Website: www.hispaniapartners.com

Other Offices

2029 Century Park East
Suite 820
Los Angeles, CA USA 90067
Phone: 310-284-8008
Fax: 310-284-8130

2725 Southwest Third Avenue
Miami, FL USA 33129
Phone: 305-285-4160
Fax: 305-285-4115

Management and Staff

Carlos Signoret, Principal
Victor Maruri, Principal

Type of Firm

Private Equity Firm

Project Preferences

Type of Financing Preferred:
Leveraged Buyout
Expansion
Later Stage

Geographical Preferences

International Preferences:
Latin America

Industry Preferences

In Communications prefer:
Media and Entertainment

In Medical/Health prefer:
Medical/Health

In Consumer Related prefer:
Consumer
Entertainment and Leisure
Food/Beverage
Education Related

In Financial Services prefer:
Financial Services

In Business Serv. prefer:
Services
Media

Additional Information

Year Founded: 2003
Capital Under Management: $103,000,000
Current Activity Level: Actively seeking new investments

HITACHI AMERICA, LTD.

750 Central Expressway
MS 3201
Santa Clara, CA USA 95050-2627
Phone: 408-970-7138
Fax: 408-327-3474
E-mail: info@cvc.hitachi.com
Website: www.hitachi.com/cvc

Management and Staff

Vinie Zhang, Vice President

Type of Firm

Incubator/Development Program

Project Preferences

Role in Financing:
Prefer role in deals created by others

Type of Financing Preferred:
Fund of Funds
Second Stage Financing
Early Stage
Expansion
Mezzanine
Research and Development
Generalist PE
Balanced
Later Stage
Seed
First Stage Financing
Joint Ventures
Private Placement

Size of Investments Considered:
Min Size of Investment Considered (000s): $100
Max Size of Investment Considered (000s): $10,000

Geographical Preferences

International Preferences:
Italy
India
United Kingdom
Latin America
China
Mexico
Eastern Europe
Spain
Australia
Germany
France
Japan

Industry Preferences

In Communications prefer:
Commercial Communications
CATV & Pay TV Systems
Radio & TV Broadcasting
Telecommunications
Wireless Communications
Data Communications
Satellite Microwave Comm.

In Computer Hardware prefer:
Computers
Mainframes / Scientific
Mini and Personal/Desktop
Computer Graphics and Dig
Integrated Turnkey System
Terminals
Disk Relat. Memory Device

In Computer Software prefer:
Computer Services
Data Processing
Software
Systems Software
Applications Software
Artificial Intelligence

In Internet Specific prefer:
Internet
Ecommerce
Web Aggregration/Portals

In Semiconductor/Electr prefer:
Electronic Components
Semiconductor
Micro-Processing
Controllers and Sensors
Sensors
Circuit Boards
Component Testing Equipmt
Laser Related
Fiber Optics
Analytic/Scientific

In Biotechnology prefer:
Human Biotechnology
Biosensors
Biotech Related Research

In Medical/Health prefer:
Diagnostic Services
Diagnostic Test Products
Medical Products

Disposable Med. Products
Health Services

In Consumer Related prefer:

Consumer
Entertainment and Leisure
Retail

In Industrial/Energy prefer:

Energy
Industrial Products
Factory Automation
Process Control
Robotics
Machinery

In Transportation prefer:

Transportation

In Financial Services prefer:

Financial Services

In Business Serv. prefer:

Services
Distribution
Consulting Services
Media

In Manufact. prefer:

Manufacturing

Additional Information

Year Founded: 2000
Capital Under Management: $95,000,000
Current Activity Level: Actively seeking new investments
Method of Compensation: Function primarily in service area, receive contingent fee in cash or equity

HITACHI, LTD.

6, Kanda-Surugadai 4-chome
Chiyoda-ku
Tokyo, Japan 1018010
Phone: 813-3258-1111
Website: www.hitachi.co.jp

Type of Firm

Corporate PE/Venture

Project Preferences

Type of Financing Preferred:

Balanced

Geographical Preferences

International Preferences:

Asia

Industry Preferences

In Semiconductor/Electr prefer:

Electronics

Additional Information

Year Founded: 1910
Current Activity Level: Actively seeking new investments

HITECVISION AS

Jattavagveien 7 (Building A)
P.O. Box 8120
Stavanger, Norway 4068
Phone: 47-51-202-020
Fax: 47-51-202-051
E-mail: contact@hitecvision.com
Website: www.hitecvision.com

Other Offices

Union Plaza 2nd floor
1 Union Wynd
Aberdeen, United Kingdom AB10 ISL
Phone: 44-2242218-558

Ruselokkveien 6
Oslo, Norway 0251
Phone: 47-22-014-030

15995 N. Bakers Landing
Suite 310
Houston, TX USA 77079
Phone: 281-598-2500

Management and Staff

Egil Stokka, Chief Financial Officer
Finn Marum, Partner
Ola Saetre, Founding Partner
Pal Reed, Partner
Per Hatlem, Partner

Type of Firm

Private Equity Firm

Association Membership

Norwegian Venture Capital Association

Project Preferences

Type of Financing Preferred:

Second Stage Financing
Leveraged Buyout
Early Stage
Expansion
Public Companies
Management Buyouts
Industry Rollups

Size of Investments Considered:

Min Size of Investment Considered (000s): $30,000
Max Size of Investment Considered (000s): $150,000

Geographical Preferences

International Preferences:

Europe

Industry Preferences

In Industrial/Energy prefer:

Energy
Oil and Gas Exploration
Oil & Gas Drilling,Explor

Additional Information

Name of Most Recent Fund: HitecVision Private Equity IV
Most Recent Fund Was Raised: 01/24/2006
Year Founded: 1985
Capital Under Management: $1,140,000,000
Current Activity Level: Actively seeking new investments

HLM VENTURE PARTNERS

222 Berkeley Street
21st Floor
Boston, MA USA 02116
Phone: 617-266-0030
Fax: 617-266-3619
E-mail: info@hlm.net
Website: www.hlmventurepartners.com

Other Offices

201 Mission Street
Suite 2240
San Francisco, CA USA 94105
Phone: 415-814-6110
Fax: 415-986-3050

Management and Staff

Albert Weigman, General Partner
Daniel Galles, General Partner
Edward Cahill, Managing Partner
Enrico Picozza, Venture Partner
Martin Felsenthal, General Partner
Peter Grua, Managing Partner
Russell Ray, Managing Partner
Teo Forcht Dagi, General Partner

Type of Firm

Private Equity Firm

Association Membership

National Venture Capital Association - USA (NVCA)

Project Preferences

Role in Financing:

Will function either as deal originator or investor in deals created by others

Type of Financing Preferred:

Second Stage Financing
Early Stage
Expansion
Balanced
Later Stage

Size of Investments Considered:

Min Size of Investment Considered (000s): $3,000
Max Size of Investment Considered (000s): $15,000

Industry Preferences

In Medical/Health prefer:

Medical/Health
Medical Diagnostics
Medical Therapeutics
Drug/Equipmt Delivery
Medical Products
Health Services
Hospitals/Clinics/Primary

Hospital/Other Instit.

Additional Information

Name of Most Recent Fund: HLM Venture Partners II, LP
Most Recent Fund Was Raised: 09/30/2005
Year Founded: 1983
Capital Under Management: $500,000,000
Current Activity Level: Actively seeking new investments
Method of Compensation: Other

HM CAPITAL PARTNERS LLC

200 Cresent Court
Suite 1600
Dallas, TX USA 75201
Phone: 214-740-7300
Fax: 214-720-7888
Website: www.hmcapital.com

Management and Staff

Andrew Rosen, Partner
Daniel Hokin, Vice President
Daniel Hopkins, Vice President
Dave Knickel, Chief Financial Officer
Edward Herring, Partner
Jason Downie, Partner
Joe Colonnetta, Partner
Nirav Shah, Vice President
Peter Brodsky, Partner
Williams Jaudes, Vice President

Type of Firm

Private Equity Firm

Project Preferences

Role in Financing:

Prefer role as deal originator

Type of Financing Preferred:

Leveraged Buyout
Acquisition

Size of Investments Considered:

Min Size of Investment Considered (000s): $19
Max Size of Investment Considered (000s): $665

Geographical Preferences

United States Preferences:

All U.S.

Canadian Preferences:

All Canada

Industry Focus

(% based on actual investment)

Communications and Media	42.0%
Other Products	21.4%
Consumer Related	13.8%
Industrial/Energy	12.9%
Internet Specific	4.8%
Computer Software and Services	2.4%
Medical/Health	1.2%
Semiconductors/Other Elect.	1.2%
Biotechnology	0.4%

Additional Information

Year Founded: 1989
Capital Under Management: $11,000,000,000
Current Activity Level: Actively seeking new investments
Method of Compensation: Return on invest. most important, but chg. closing fees, service fees, etc.

HMS HAWAII MANAGEMENT PARTNERS

Pacific Guardian Center
733 Bishop Street, Suite 2500
Honolulu, HI USA 96813
Phone: 808-545-3755
Fax: 808-546-2211
E-mail: info@hmshawaii.com
Website: www.hmshawaii.com

Other Offices

280 Second Street
Suite 240
Los Altos, CA USA 94022
Phone: 650-941-5105
Fax: 650-941-5106

Management and Staff

Richard Grey, General Partner
William Richardson, General Partner

Type of Firm

Private Equity Firm

Project Preferences

Role in Financing:

Prefer role as deal originator but will also invest in deals created by others

Type of Financing Preferred:

Early Stage
Start-up Financing
Seed
Joint Ventures

Size of Investments Considered:

Min Size of Investment Considered (000s): $500
Max Size of Investment Considered (000s): $1,500

Geographical Preferences

United States Preferences:

Hawaii
West Coast

Industry Focus

(% based on actual investment)

Communications and Media	39.7%
Other Products	38.8%
Internet Specific	18.0%
Industrial/Energy	2.6%
Medical/Health	0.9%

Additional Information

Name of Most Recent Fund: HMS Hawaii III, LP
Most Recent Fund Was Raised: 03/01/2004
Year Founded: 1995
Capital Under Management: $15,000,000
Current Activity Level: Making few, if any, new investments
Method of Compensation: Return on investment is of primary concern, do not charge fees

HO2 PARTNERS

Two Galleria Tower
13455 Noel Rd. Suite 1670
Dallas, TX USA 75240
Phone: 972-702-1144
Fax: 972-702-8234
Website: www.ho2.com

Management and Staff

Charles Humphreyson, General Partner
Daniel Owen, General Partner
Diane Gross, Chief Financial Officer

Type of Firm

Private Equity Firm

Project Preferences

Role in Financing:

Will function either as deal originator or investor in deals created by others

Type of Financing Preferred:

Early Stage
Seed
Startup

Size of Investments Considered:

Min Size of Investment Considered (000s): $750
Max Size of Investment Considered (000s): $3,000

Geographical Preferences

United States Preferences:

Texas

Industry Preferences

In Communications prefer:

Wireless Communications
Media and Entertainment

In Computer Software prefer:

Software

Additional Information

Year Founded: 1999
Capital Under Management: $35,000,000
Current Activity Level: Making few, if any, new investments
Method of Compensation: Return on investment is of primary concern, do not charge fees

HOAK & CO.

500 Crescent Court
Suite 220
Dallas, TX USA 75201
Phone: 214-855-2288
Fax: 972-960-4899
E-mail: confidential@hoak.net
Website: www.hoakco.com

Management and Staff

Eric Stroud, Principal
J.Hale Hoak, Principal

Type of Firm

Private Equity Firm

Project Preferences

Role in Financing:
Prefer role as deal originator but will also invest in deals created by others

Type of Financing Preferred:
Leveraged Buyout
Control-block Purchases
Industry Rollups
Special Situation

Size of Investments Considered:
Min Size of Investment Considered (000s): $35,000
Max Size of Investment Considered: No Limit

Geographical Preferences

United States Preferences:
All U.S.

Industry Focus

(% based on actual investment)

Communications and Media	38.3%
Consumer Related	28.2%
Other Products	18.6%
Semiconductors/Other Elect.	8.7%
Industrial/Energy	2.7%
Internet Specific	2.4%
Computer Software and Services	1.2%

Additional Information

Name of Most Recent Fund: Hoak Communications Partners, L.P.
Most Recent Fund Was Raised: 04/19/1996
Year Founded: 1991
Capital Under Management: $174,000,000
Current Activity Level: Actively seeking new investments
Method of Compensation: Return on investment is of primary concern, do not charge fees

HOKKAIDO VENTURE CAPITAL, INC.

Tokyo Tatemono Sapporo Bldg.
2F, 20 North 7, West 2, Kitaku
Sapporo, Japan 060-0807
Phone: 81-11-738-7380
Fax: 81-11-738-7387
Website: www.hokkaido-vc.com

Other Offices

Yaesu Kato Bldg. 3F,
15-12 Nihonbashi Kabutocho, Chuo-ku
Tokyo, Japan 103-0026

Management and Staff

Ikkei Matsuda, President

Type of Firm

Private Equity Firm

Project Preferences

Type of Financing Preferred:
Early Stage
Expansion
Balanced
Later Stage
Seed

Geographical Preferences

United States Preferences:
All U.S.

International Preferences:
Japan

Industry Preferences

In Computer Software prefer:
Software

In Biotechnology prefer:
Biotechnology

In Medical/Health prefer:
Medical/Health

Additional Information

Year Founded: 1999
Capital Under Management: $9,300,000
Current Activity Level: Actively seeking new investments

HOKURIKU CAPITAL CO., LTD

1-8-10 Marunouchi
Toyama-shi, Japan 930-0085
Phone: 81-76-431-2440
Fax: 81-76-431-2401
Website: www.hokuhoku-fg.co.jp

Type of Firm

Private Equity Firm

Additional Information

Year Founded: 2007
Current Activity Level: Actively seeking new investments

HOLDING CAPITAL GROUP, INC.

630 Third Avenue
7th Floor
New York, NY USA 10017
Phone: 212-486-6670
Fax: 212-486-0843
Website: www.holdingcapital.com

Other Offices

1111 Third Avenue
Suite 2400
Seattle, WA USA 98101
Phone: 206-219-1535

Type of Firm

Private Equity Firm

Project Preferences

Role in Financing:
Prefer role as deal originator but will also invest in deals created by others

Type of Financing Preferred:
Leveraged Buyout

Size of Investments Considered:
Min Size of Investment Considered (000s): $5,000
Max Size of Investment Considered: No Limit

Geographical Preferences

United States Preferences:
All U.S.

International Preferences:
China
Australia

Additional Information

Year Founded: 1975
Capital Under Management: $100,000,000
Current Activity Level: Actively seeking new investments
Method of Compensation: Return on invest. most important, but chg. closing fees, service fees, etc.

HOLDING VC

Ten Hangzhou Staff Road
23/F Bainao Hui Tech. Bldg.
Hangzhou, China 310012
Phone: 86-571-28938600
Fax: 86-571-28938511
E-mail: holdingvc@163.com
Website: www.holdingvc.com

Other Offices

No. 10 Huixin Lijia
303-B Taideshang Huayuan
Beijing, China 100029

Management and Staff

Jian Biao Xiang, Chief Executive Officer

Ming Ye, Founder
Xiao Ren Liu, Founder

Type of Firm

Private Equity Firm

Project Preferences

Type of Financing Preferred:
Seed

Geographical Preferences

International Preferences:
China

Industry Preferences

In Communications prefer:
Communications and Media
Wireless Communications

In Computer Other prefer:
Computer Related

In Medical/Health prefer:
Medical/Health

Additional Information

Year Founded: 2006
Current Activity Level: Actively seeking new investments

HOLDING VENTURE CAPITAL, LTD.

10/F, Bainaohui Keji Building
23 Jiaogong Road
Zhejiang, China 310012
Phone: 86-571-28938600
Fax: 86-571-28938511
E-mail: holdingvc@163.com
Website: www.holdingvc.com

Other Offices

Suite 303, Block B, Qinde Shangwu Garden
10 Huixinli, Zhaoyang District
Beijing, China 100029

Management and Staff

Ming Ye, Co-Founder
Xiaoren Liu, President, Founder

Type of Firm

Private Equity Firm

Project Preferences

Type of Financing Preferred:
Seed

Geographical Preferences

International Preferences:
China

Industry Preferences

In Communications prefer:
Communications and Media
Wireless Communications

In Internet Specific prefer:
Internet

In Semiconductor/Electr prefer:
Semiconductor
Additional Information

Year Founded: 2006

Current Activity Level: Actively seeking new investments

HOLLAND PRIVATE EQUITY B.V.

Strawinskylaan 711
World Trade Center A7
Amsterdam, Netherlands 1077 XX
Phone: 31-20-714-3400
Fax: 31-20-714-3419
Website: www.hollandpe.com

Management and Staff

Hans Van Ierland, Managing Partner
Tim Van Delden, Managing Partner

Type of Firm

Private Equity Firm

Project Preferences

Type of Financing Preferred:
Expansion
Public Companies
Later Stage
Acquisition

Geographical Preferences

International Preferences:
Europe

Industry Preferences

In Communications prefer:
Wireless Communications

In Computer Software prefer:
Software

In Semiconductor/Electr prefer:
Electronics

In Medical/Health prefer:
Medical/Health

In Industrial/Energy prefer:
Energy
Factory Automation
Environmental Related

In Financial Services prefer:
Financial Services

Additional Information

Year Founded: 2008
Capital Under Management: $51,000,000
Current Activity Level: Actively seeking new investments

HOLLAND VENTURE III B.V. (FKA: HOLLAND VENTURE B.V.)

Dreeftoren 14e etage
Haaksbergweg 55
Amsterdam Zuidoost, Netherlands 1101 BR
Phone: 31-20-311-9411
Fax: 31-20-697-3326
E-mail: info@hollandventure.com
Website: www.hventure.nl

Management and Staff

E Deves, Chief Executive Officer

Type of Firm

Private Equity Firm

Association Membership

European Private Equity and Venture Capital Assoc.

Project Preferences

Type of Financing Preferred:
Expansion
Management Buyouts

Size of Investments Considered:
Min Size of Investment Considered (000s): $1,300
Max Size of Investment Considered (000s): $5,000

Geographical Preferences

International Preferences:
Netherlands
Europe
Scandanavia/Nordic Region
Israel

Industry Focus

(% based on actual investment)

Computer Software and Services	36.4%
Internet Specific	26.9%
Communications and Media	26.5%
Computer Hardware	10.2%

Additional Information

Year Founded: 1981
Capital Under Management: $135,900,000
Current Activity Level: Actively seeking new investments

HOLLAND VENTURE PARTNERS BV

Stadhouderskade 14d
Byzantium
Amsterdam, Netherlands 1054 ES

Phone: 31-20-3119-411
Fax: 31-20-3119-412
E-mail: info@hollandventure.com
Website: www.hventure.nl

Type of Firm

Private Equity Firm

Association Membership

European Private Equity and Venture Capital Assoc.

Additional Information

Year Founded: 2009
Capital Under Management: $97,700,000
Current Activity Level: Actively seeking new investments

HOLTZBRINCK VENTURES GMBH

Bayerstrasse 21
Munich, Germany 80335
Phone: 49-89-2060-77-0
Fax: 49-89-2060-7742
E-mail: info@holtzbrinck.net
Website: www.holtzbrinck-ventures.com

Other Offices

Georg von Holtzbrinck GmbH & Co. KG
Gansheidestrasse 26
Stuttgart, Germany D-70184
Phone: 49-711-2150-0
Fax: 49-711-2150-269

Management and Staff

Helmar Hipp, Chief Executive Officer
Konstantin Urban, Chief Executive Officer
Martin Weber, Chief Financial Officer

Type of Firm

Corporate PE/Venture

Association Membership

European Private Equity and Venture Capital Assoc.

Project Preferences

Type of Financing Preferred:

Early Stage
Startup

Geographical Preferences

International Preferences:

Germany

Industry Preferences

In Internet Specific prefer:

Internet

Additional Information

Year Founded: 1998
Capital Under Management: $52,300,000
Current Activity Level: Actively seeking new investments

HOMELAND DEFENSE VENTURES

153 East 53rd Street
35th Floor
New York, NY USA 10022
Phone: 212-651-3545
Fax: 212-655-0174
Website: www.homelanddefenseventures.com

Management and Staff

Ken Jennings, Partner
Richard Barker, Partner
Valerie Ceva, Partner

Type of Firm

Private Equity Firm

Project Preferences

Type of Financing Preferred:

Balanced

Industry Preferences

In Computer Software prefer:

Artificial Intelligence

In Semiconductor/Electr prefer:

Sensors

In Biotechnology prefer:

Industrial Biotechnology

In Medical/Health prefer:

Pharmaceuticals

In Other prefer:

Socially Responsible

Additional Information

Year Founded: 2001
Current Activity Level: Actively seeking new investments

HONDA STRATEGIC VENTURING (HSV)

800 California Street
Suite 300
Mountain View, CA USA 94041
Phone: 650-314-0400
Fax: 650-314-0405
Website: www.hsv.honda.com

Other Offices

8-1, Honcho
Wako-shi
Saitama, Japan 351-0114
Phone: 048-462-5219
Fax: 048-462-5221

Management and Staff

Nick Sugimoto, Principal
Paul Cummings, Principal

Type of Firm

Corporate PE/Venture

Project Preferences

Role in Financing:

Prefer role in deals created by others

Type of Financing Preferred:

Early Stage
Seed
First Stage Financing
Strategic Alliances

Size of Investments Considered:

Min Size of Investment Considered (000s): $10
Max Size of Investment Considered (000s): $1,000

Geographical Preferences

United States Preferences:

All U.S.

International Preferences:

Europe
Japan

Industry Preferences

In Communications prefer:

Communications and Media

In Semiconductor/Electr prefer:

Electronic Components
Semiconductor
Sensors

In Biotechnology prefer:

Agricultural/Animal Bio.

In Industrial/Energy prefer:

Alternative Energy
Advanced Materials
Robotics

Additional Information

Year Founded: 2003
Capital Under Management: $100,000,000
Current Activity Level: Actively seeking new investments

HONY CAPITAL LTD.

6F S. Twr C, Raycom InfoTech
2, Ke Xue Yuan Nanlu, Haidian
Beijing, China 100090
Phone: 86-10-6250-9998
Fax: 86-10-6250-9181
E-mail: honymaster@honycapital.com
Website: www.honycapital.com

Management and Staff

David Qiu, Managing Director
Jianguo Li, Managing Director
John Zhao, CEO & Managing Director
Michael Luo, Managing Director
Owen Guo, Managing Director
Xihong Deng, Managing Director

Type of Firm

Private Equity Firm

Project Preferences

Type of Financing Preferred:

Leveraged Buyout
Expansion

Geographical Preferences

International Preferences:

China

Industry Preferences

In Communications prefer:

Media and Entertainment

In Medical/Health prefer:

Pharmaceuticals

In Consumer Related prefer:

Consumer Products
Education Related

In Industrial/Energy prefer:

Materials

Additional Information

Year Founded: 2003
Capital Under Management: $125,000,000
Current Activity Level: Actively seeking new investments

HOOK PARTNERS

One Lincoln Centre, Suite 1550
5400 LBJ Freeway
Dallas, TX USA 75240
Phone: 972-991-5457
Fax: 972-991-5458
Website: www.hookpartners.com

Management and Staff

David Hook, General Partner
John Hook, General Partner

Type of Firm

Private Equity Firm

Project Preferences

Role in Financing:

Prefer role as deal originator but will also invest in deals created by others

Type of Financing Preferred:

Second Stage Financing
Balanced
First Stage Financing

Size of Investments Considered:

Min Size of Investment Considered (000s): $100
Max Size of Investment Considered (000s): $1,000

Geographical Preferences

United States Preferences:

West Coast
Southwest

Industry Focus

(% based on actual investment)	
Communications and Media	27.7%
Computer Software and Services	26.1%
Computer Hardware	22.1%
Semiconductors/Other Elect.	12.6%
Internet Specific	9.0%
Consumer Related	1.3%
Biotechnology	0.7%
Industrial/Energy	0.3%
Medical/Health	0.2%

Additional Information

Name of Most Recent Fund: Hook Partners V
Most Recent Fund Was Raised: 05/15/2000
Year Founded: 1978
Capital Under Management: $77,000,000
Current Activity Level: Actively seeking new investments
Method of Compensation: Return on investment is of primary concern, do not charge fees

---

HOPEWELL VENTURES

20 North Wacker Drive
Suite 2200
Chicago, IL USA 60606
Phone: 312-357-9600
Fax: 312-357-9620
E-mail: info@hopewellventures.com
Website: www.hopewellventures.com

Other Offices

801 Main Street
Peoria, IL USA 61606
Phone: 309-495-7251
Fax: 309-495-7255

Management and Staff

Brian Williams, Venture Partner
Craig Overmyer, Principal
David Wilhelm, Principal
Jeffrey Lampe, Principal
Jude Conway, Principal
Matthew McCue, Vice President
Thomas Parkinson, Principal
William Sutter, Principal

Type of Firm

SBIC

Association Membership

Natl Assoc of Small Bus. Inv. Co (NASBIC)
Illinois Venture Capital Association

Project Preferences

Role in Financing:

Prefer role as deal originator but will also invest in deals created by others

Type of Financing Preferred:

Leveraged Buyout
Early Stage
Expansion
Balanced
Later Stage
Management Buyouts

Size of Investments Considered:

Min Size of Investment Considered (000s): $2,000
Max Size of Investment Considered (000s): $7,000

Geographical Preferences

United States Preferences:

Midwest

Industry Preferences

In Communications prefer:

Communications and Media

In Computer Hardware prefer:

Computer Graphics and Dig
Integrated Turnkey System

In Computer Software prefer:

Software

In Medical/Health prefer:

Medical/Health
Medical Products

In Consumer Related prefer:

Consumer Products
Education Related

In Industrial/Energy prefer:

Energy
Environmental Related

In Business Serv. prefer:

Distribution
Media

In Agr/Forestr/Fish prefer:

Agriculture related

Additional Information

Name of Most Recent Fund: Hopewell Ventures, L.P.
Most Recent Fund Was Raised: 05/05/2004
Year Founded: 2004
Capital Under Management: $110,000,000
Current Activity Level: Actively seeking new investments
Method of Compensation: Return on investment is of primary concern, do not charge fees

---

HORATIO ENTERPRISE FUND

16 Donwoods Drive
Toronto, Canada M4N2G1
Phone: 416-544-9863
Fax: 416-544-9862

Management and Staff

Greig Clark, Managing Partner

Type of Firm

Private Equity Firm

Geographical Preferences

Canadian Preferences:
All Canada

Additional Information

Year Founded: 1991
Current Activity Level: Actively seeking new investments

HORIZON 21 PRIVATE EQUITY

Poststrasse 4
Pfaeffikon, Switzerland 8808
Phone: 41-55-415-2200
Fax: 41-55-415-2201
Website: www.horizon21.com

Management and Staff

Beat Buehlmann, Managing Director
Rene Eichenberger, Chief Executive Officer

Type of Firm

Private Equity Firm

Association Membership

Swiss Venture Capital Association (SECA)

Additional Information

Year Founded: 2004
Current Activity Level: Actively seeking new investments

HORIZON CAPITAL MANAGEMENT (FKA:WESTERN NIS ENTERPRISE FUND)

4 Mykoly Rayevskoho Street
Kyiv, Ukraine 01042
Phone: 380-44-490-5580
Fax: 380-44-490-5589
E-mail: info@horizoncapital.com.ua
Website: www.horizoncapital.com.ua

Other Offices

Str. Petru Movila 12
ap. 4
Chisinau, Moldova 2004
Phone: 373-2288-7200
Fax: 373-2288-7201

175 West Jackson Boulevard
Suite 2225
Chicago, IL USA 60604
Phone: 312-939-7003
Fax: 312-939-7004

Management and Staff

Alexander Kuprasov, Principal
Iryna Starodubova, Partner
Jeffrey Neal, Founding Partner
Mark Iwashko, Managing Partner
Natalie A. Jaresko, Managing Partner
Oksana Strashna, Partner
Peter Charchalis, Partner

Type of Firm

Investment Management Firm

Association Membership

European Private Equity and Venture Capital Assoc.

Project Preferences

Type of Financing Preferred:
Leveraged Buyout
Expansion
Balanced

Size of Investments Considered:
Min Size of Investment Considered (000s): $15,000
Max Size of Investment Considered (000s): $40,000

Geographical Preferences

International Preferences:
Belarus
Moldova
Ukraine

Industry Preferences

In Consumer Related prefer:
Retail
Consumer Products

In Industrial/Energy prefer:
Industrial Products

In Financial Services prefer:
Financial Services

In Manufact. prefer:
Manufacturing

Additional Information

Year Founded: 1995
Capital Under Management: $647,000,000
Current Activity Level: Actively seeking new investments

HORIZON HOLDINGS, LLC

Three Embarcadero Center
Suite 2360
San Francisco, CA USA 94111
Phone: 415-788-2000
Fax: 415-788-2030
E-mail: hh@horizonholdings.com
Website: www.horizonholdings.com

Management and Staff

James Shorin, Managing Partner
Phillip Estes, Managing Partner

Type of Firm

Private Equity Firm

Project Preferences

Type of Financing Preferred:
Leveraged Buyout

Additional Information

Year Founded: 1989
Current Activity Level: Actively seeking new investments

HORIZON VENTURES

Four Main Street
Suite 50
Los Altos, CA USA 94022
Phone: 650-917-4100
Fax: 650-917-4109
E-mail: info@horizonvc.com
Website: www.horizonvc.com

Management and Staff

Ash Dhar, Venture Partner
Bob Dahlberg, Venture Partner
Doug Tsui, Managing Director
George Schneer, Venture Partner
Geri Brown, Chief Financial Officer
Jack Carsten, Managing Director
John Hall, Managing Director

Type of Firm

Private Equity Firm

Association Membership

Western Association of Venture Capitalists (WAVC)
Natl Assoc of Small Bus. Inv. Co (NASBIC)

Project Preferences

Role in Financing:
Will function either as deal originator or investor in deals created by others

Type of Financing Preferred:
Second Stage Financing
Seed
First Stage Financing

Size of Investments Considered:
Min Size of Investment Considered (000s): $500
Max Size of Investment Considered (000s): $8,000

Geographical Preferences

United States Preferences:
Northwest
Southern California
Northern California
Southwest

Industry Focus

(% based on actual investment)

Semiconductors/Other Elect.	39.5%
Communications and Media	23.3%
Internet Specific	15.5%
Computer Hardware	11.7%
Computer Software and Services	8.8%
Industrial/Energy	1.2%

Additional Information

Name of Most Recent Fund: Horizon Ventures Fund II, L.P.
Most Recent Fund Was Raised: 11/19/2003
Year Founded: 1999
Capital Under Management: $176,800,000
Current Activity Level: Actively seeking new investments
Method of Compensation: Return on investment is of primary concern, do not charge fees

---

HORIZONTE VENTURE MANAGEMENT GMBH

Bauernmarkt 6
Vienna, Austria A-1010
Phone: 43-1-533-5601
Fax: 43-1-5335-6014
E-mail: office@horizonte.at
Website: www.horizonte.at

Other Offices

Vlaska 99
Zagreb, Croatia HR-10000
Phone: 385-1-466-5322
Fax: 385-1-466-4850

Teslova 30
Ljubljana, Slovenia SLO-1000
Phone: 386-1-241-4780
Fax: 386-1-241-4788

ul. Ferhadija 11 br
Sarajevo, Bosnia/Herz. BiH-71000
Phone: 387-33-207-087
Fax: 387-33-207-463

Management and Staff

Alfred Matzka, Managing Partner
Franz Krejs, Managing Partner
Martin Wodak, Partner
Matej Penca, Managing Partner

Type of Firm

Private Equity Firm

Association Membership

Austrian PE and Venture Capital Association (AVCO)
European Private Equity and Venture Capital Assoc.

Project Preferences

Role in Financing:

Prefer role as deal originator but will also invest in deals created by others

Type of Financing Preferred:

Early Stage
Seed

Size of Investments Considered:

Min Size of Investment Considered (000s): $141
Max Size of Investment Considered (000s): $2,825

Geographical Preferences

International Preferences:

Slovenia
Austria
Croatia
Bosnia
Germany
Industry Preferences

In Communications prefer:

Communications and Media

In Computer Software prefer:

Software

In Semiconductor/Electr prefer:

Electronics

In Medical/Health prefer:

Medical/Health
Drug/Equipmt Delivery
Pharmaceuticals

In Industrial/Energy prefer:

Energy
Environmental Related

Additional Information

Name of Most Recent Fund: Horizonte Alpe Adria Fund (HAAF)
Most Recent Fund Was Raised: 11/01/2001
Year Founded: 1985
Capital Under Management: $49,600,000
Current Activity Level: Actively seeking new investments
Method of Compensation: Function primarily in service area, receive contingent fee in cash or equity

---

HORSLEY BRIDGE PARTNERS

505 Montgomery Street
21st Floor
San Francisco, CA USA 94111
Phone: 415-986-7733
Fax: 415-986-7744

Other Offices

Four Cork Street
London, United Kingdom W1S 3LG
Phone: 44-207-534-9700
Fax: 44-207-534-9711

8 Jianguomenbei Avenue
Beijing, China
Phone: 86-1-6517-5988
Fax: 86-1-6517-5788

Management and Staff

Alexa Zhang, Principal
Alfred Giuffrida, Managing Director
Duane Phillips, Managing Director
Elizabeth Obershaw, Managing Director
Fred Berkowitz, Managing Director
Gary Bridge, Managing Director
Josh Freeman, Managing Director
Kate Murphy, Managing Director
Kathryn Abbott, Managing Director
Lance Cottrill, Managing Director
N. Dan Reeve, Managing Director
Phillip Horsley, Managing Director
Yi Sun, Principal

Type of Firm

Private Equity Advisor or Fund of Funds

Project Preferences

Type of Financing Preferred:

Fund of Funds
Leveraged Buyout
Early Stage
Balanced
Later Stage
Seed

Size of Investments Considered:

Min Size of Investment Considered (000s): $25,000
Max Size of Investment Considered (000s): $500,000

Geographical Preferences

International Preferences:

India
Europe
Australia
Israel
Asia
All International

Industry Focus

(% based on actual investment)

Other Products	48.4%
Computer Hardware	22.6%
Communications and Media	8.5%
Computer Software and Services	6.1%
Semiconductors/Other Elect.	3.7%
Industrial/Energy	2.7%
Consumer Related	2.6%
Biotechnology	2.2%
Medical/Health	2.0%
Internet Specific	1.3%

Additional Information

Name of Most Recent Fund: Horsley Bridge International IV, L.P.
Most Recent Fund Was Raised: 09/14/2006
Year Founded: 1979
Capital Under Management: $11,452,000,000
Current Activity Level: Actively seeking new investments
Method of Compensation: Return on invest. most important, but chg. closing fees, service fees, etc.

HOTBED, LTD.

10 Albemarle Street
London, United Kingdom W1S 4HH
Phone: 44-20-7569-1440
Fax: 44-20-7629-2826
E-mail: enquiries@hotbed.uk.com
Website: www.hotbed.uk.com

Management and Staff

Gary Robins, Chief Executive Officer

Type of Firm

Angel Group

Project Preferences

Type of Financing Preferred:

Early Stage
Expansion
Management Buyouts
Startup

Size of Investments Considered:

Min Size of Investment Considered (000s): $423
Max Size of Investment Considered (000s): $8,460

Geographical Preferences

International Preferences:

United Kingdom
Europe

Additional Information

Year Founded: 2002
Current Activity Level: Actively seeking new investments

HOTUNG INTERNATIONAL COMPANY, LTD.

10/F, No. 261 Sung-Chiang Rd
Taipei, Taiwan
Phone: 886-2-2500-6700
Fax: 886-2-2502-9716
E-mail: hotung@equity.com.tw
Website: www.hotung.com.tw

Other Offices

5201 Great America Parkway, No. 356
Techmart
Santa Clara, CA USA 95054
Phone: 408-577-1380
Fax: 408-907-0147

Management and Staff

Ben Chang, President
Cheng-Nan Chou, Vice President
George Huang, Vice President
Steven Huang, Vice President
Tsui Hui Huang, President
Vincent Chang, Vice President

Type of Firm

Private Equity Firm

Association Membership

Taiwan Venture Capital Association(TVCA)

Project Preferences

Role in Financing:

Prefer role as deal originator

Type of Financing Preferred:

Second Stage Financing
Expansion
Mezzanine
Balanced
Later Stage
Seed
Startup

Geographical Preferences

United States Preferences:

West Coast
All U.S.

Canadian Preferences:

Quebec
Western Canada

International Preferences:

United Kingdom
Taiwan
China
Middle East
Israel
Germany
France
Japan
All International

Industry Preferences

In Communications prefer:

Communications and Media
Telecommunications
Data Communications
Satellite Microwave Comm.

In Computer Hardware prefer:

Disk Relat. Memory Device

In Computer Software prefer:

Software

In Internet Specific prefer:

Internet

In Semiconductor/Electr prefer:

Electronics
Electronic Components
Semiconductor
Circuit Boards
Fiber Optics

In Biotechnology prefer:

Biotechnology
Biosensors
Biotech Related Research

In Medical/Health prefer:

Diagnostic Services
Other Therapeutic
Pharmaceuticals

In Consumer Related prefer:

Retail

In Industrial/Energy prefer:

Advanced Materials
Machinery
Environmental Related

Additional Information

Name of Most Recent Fund: Hotung Investment Holdings, Ltd.
Most Recent Fund Was Raised: 07/01/2000
Year Founded: 1997
Capital Under Management: $511,300,000
Current Activity Level: Actively seeking new investments
Method of Compensation: Return on investment is of primary concern, do not charge fees

---

HOULIHAN, LOKEY, HOWARD & ZUKIN

1930 Century Park West
Los Angeles, CA USA 90067
Phone: 310-553-8871
Fax: 310-553-2173
Website: www.hlhz.com

Other Offices

Citicorp Center - One Sansome Street
Suite 1700
San Francisco, CA USA 94104
Phone: 415-974-5888
Fax: 415-974-5969

11/F Hong Kong Club Building
3A Chater Road
Hong Kong, China
Phone: 852-3551-2300
Fax: 852-3551-2551

200 Crescent Court
Suite 1900
Dallas, TX USA 75201
Phone: 214-220-8470
Fax: 214-220-3808

225 South Sixth Street
Suite 4950
Minneapolis, MN USA 55402
Phone: 612-338-2910
Fax: 612-338-2938

123 North Wacker Drive
Fourth Floor
Chicago, IL USA 60606
Phone: 312-456-4700
Fax: 312-346-0951

83 Pall Mall
3rd Floor
London, United Kingdom SW1Y 5ES
Phone: 44-20-7839-3355
Fax: 44-20-7839-5566

3475 Piedmont Road
Suite 950
Atlanta, GA USA 30305
Phone: 404-495-7000
Fax: 404-495-9545

Taunusanlage 1 (Skyper)
60329 Frankfurt am Main
Frankfurt, Germany
Phone: 49-692-562-460
Fax: 49-692-5624-6136

1800 Tysons Boulevard
Suite 300
McLean, VA USA 22102
Phone: 703-847-5225
Fax: 703-848-9667

15/17 rue Auber
Paris, France 75009
Phone: 33-1-7500-1400
Fax: 33-1-7500-1499

245 Park Avenue
New York, NY USA 10167-0001
Phone: 212-497-4100
Fax: 212-661-3070

Management and Staff

Andrew Stull, Managing Director
Andrew Silver, Managing Director
Ben Buettell, Managing Director
Bill Peluchiwski, Managing Director
Bradley Pickard, Managing Director
Geoffrey Ligibel, Vice President
Irwin Gold, Senior Managing Director
James Zukin, Senior Managing Director
Jason Apple, Vice President
Jay Novak, Managing Director
Jim Massey, Managing Director
John Mavredakais, Senior Managing Director
John Carsello, Vice President
Jon Melzer, Managing Director
Jonathan Guise, Managing Director
Joseph Wallace, Vice President
Julie Levenson, Managing Director
Justin Abelow, Managing Director
Marc Gondek, Vice President
Matthew Niemann, Managing Director
Michael McMahon, Managing Director
O. Kit Lokey, President
Patrick Hurst, Managing Director
Paul Much, Senior Managing Director
Ralph Montgomery, Vice President
Reid Snellenbarger, Vice President
Rick Lackler, Managing Director
Robert Hotz, Senior Managing Director
Robert Howard, Senior Managing Director
Romain Cattet, Vice President
Sandy Purcell, Managing Director
Scott Adelson, Senior Managing Director
Terence Flynn, Managing Director
Timothy Smith, Vice President
Todd Watkins, Managing Director
Tom Hartfield, Managing Director
Willaim Smith, Managing Director
William Allen, Managing Director

Type of Firm

Bank Affiliated

Project Preferences

Role in Financing:

Prefer role as deal originator but will also invest in deals created by others

Type of Financing Preferred:

Leveraged Buyout
Early Stage
Management Buyouts
Recapitalizations

Industry Focus

(% based on actual investment)

Industrial/Energy	100.0%

Additional Information

Year Founded: 1970
Current Activity Level: Actively seeking new investments
Method of Compensation: Unknown

HOUSATONIC PARTNERS

44 Montgomery Street
Suite 4010
San Francisco, CA USA 94104
Phone: 415-955-9020
Fax: 415-955-9053
Website: www.housatonicpartners.com

Other Offices

800 Boylston Street
Suite 2220, Prudential Tower
Boston, MA USA 02199
Phone: 617-399-9200
Fax: 617-267-5565

Management and Staff

Barry Reynolds, General Partner
Eliot Wadsworth, Founding Partner
Glenn Healey, Principal
Jill Raimondi, Chief Financial Officer
John Chendo, Principal
Joseph Niehaus, General Partner
Karen Liesching, Principal
Mark Hilderbrand, General Partner
Michael Jackson, Founding Partner
William Thorndike, General Partner

Type of Firm

Private Equity Firm

Project Preferences

Type of Financing Preferred:

Leveraged Buyout
Balanced
Later Stage
Management Buyouts
Acquisition
Recapitalizations

Size of Investments Considered:

Min Size of Investment Considered (000s): $3,000
Max Size of Investment Considered (000s): $10,000

Geographical Preferences

United States Preferences:

All U.S.

Canadian Preferences:

All Canada

Industry Preferences

In Communications prefer:

Communications and Media
Radio & TV Broadcasting
Telecommunications

In Financial Services prefer:

Financial Services

In Business Serv. prefer:

Services
Media

Additional Information

Name of Most Recent Fund: Housatonic Equity Affiliates IV, L.P.
Most Recent Fund Was Raised: 10/10/2007
Year Founded: 1994
Capital Under Management: $600,000,000
Current Activity Level: Actively seeking new investments

HOYA CORPORATION

7-5, Naka-Ochiai
2-chome, Shinjuku-ku
Tokyo, Japan 161-8
Phone: 813-3952-1151
Fax: 813-3952-1314
Website: www.hoya.co.jp

Type of Firm

Corporate PE/Venture

Project Preferences

Type of Financing Preferred:

Balanced

Geographical Preferences

International Preferences:

Japan

Additional Information

Year Founded: 1941
Current Activity Level: Actively seeking new investments

HPJ MEDIA VENTURES FUND LLC

127 El Paseo
Santa Barbara, CA USA 93101
Phone: 805-884-1111
Fax: 804-884-1114
Website: www.hpjmedia.com

Management and Staff

Jack Theimer, Chief Executive Officer
Mark Justh, Managing Partner
Michael Alcamo, Managing Partner

Type of Firm

Private Equity Firm

Project Preferences

Type of Financing Preferred:
Leveraged Buyout

Industry Preferences

In Communications prefer:
Communications and Media

In Business Serv. prefer:
Media

Additional Information

Year Founded: 2000
Capital Under Management: $21,700,000
Current Activity Level: Actively seeking new investments

HRJ CAPITAL (FKA: CHAMPION VENTURES)

2965 Woodside Road
Suite A
Woodside, CA USA 94062
Phone: 650-327-5023
Fax: 650-327-5235
E-mail: info@hrjcapital.com
Website: www.hrjcapital.com

Other Offices

Suite 2761, 27/F K. Wah Center
No.1010 Huaihai Middle Road
Shanghai, China 200031
Phone: 86-21-6103-1219
Fax: 86-21-6103-1220

Othmarstrasse 8
Zurich, Switzerland 8008
Phone: 41-44-250-5131
Fax: 41-44-250-5130

1170 Peachtree Street
Suite 1200
Atlanta, GA USA 30309
Phone: 404-885-5732
Fax: 404-538-9197

82 Washington Street
Marblehead, MA USA 01945

800 Westchester Avenue
Suite S322
Port Chester, NY USA 10573
Phone: 914-417-3184
Fax: 914-417-3180

430 Park Avenue
Suite 2B
Highland Park, IL USA 60035
Phone: 847-748-9300
Fax: 847-681-1440

Management and Staff

Carlton Forrester, Vice President
Chris Hecht, Vice President
Cory Pavlik, Chief Financial Officer
Darren Wong, Managing Director
Duran Curis, Managing Director
Geoff LeMieux, Vice President
Harris Barton, Managing Partner
Howard Fields, Managing Director
Jeffrey Bloom, Managing Director
Jennifer Coffey, Managing Director
Linda Waissar, Vice President
Megan Fielding, Vice President
Michael Merrigan, Vice President
Ronnie Lott, Founding Partner
Theodore Deutz, Managing Director

Type of Firm

Private Equity Advisor or Fund of Funds

Project Preferences

Type of Financing Preferred:
Fund of Funds
Other

Geographical Preferences

United States Preferences:
All U.S.

International Preferences:
All International

Industry Preferences

In Financial Services prefer:
Real Estate

Additional Information

Name of Most Recent Fund: HRJ Special Opportunities I-D, L.P.
Most Recent Fund Was Raised: 05/23/2007
Year Founded: 1999
Capital Under Management: $225,000,000
Current Activity Level: Actively seeking new investments

HSBC CAPITAL (CANADA)

70 York Street
7th Floor
Toronto, Canada M5J 1S9
Phone: 416-864-2897
Fax: 416-868-0067
Website: www.hsbccanada/ca.com

Other Offices

452 Fifth Avenue
14th Floor
New York, NY USA 10018
Phone: 212-525-5969
Fax: 212-525-8047

885 West Georgia Street
Suite 1100
Vancouver, Canada V6C 3E8
Phone: 604-631-8088
Fax: 604-631-8073

Management and Staff

David Mullen, Chief Executive Officer
John Philp, Managing Director
Neil Johansen, Managing Director

Type of Firm

Bank Affiliated

Association Membership

Canadian Venture Capital Association

Project Preferences

Type of Financing Preferred:
Fund of Funds
Leveraged Buyout
Mezzanine
Later Stage
Management Buyouts
Acquisition

Geographical Preferences

Canadian Preferences:
All Canada
Alberta
Ontario
British Columbia

Industry Focus

(% based on actual investment)

Communications and Media	40.7%
Industrial/Energy	33.8%
Biotechnology	15.1%
Consumer Related	10.4%

Additional Information

Name of Most Recent Fund: HSBC Capital Canada Private Equity Fund
Most Recent Fund Was Raised: 11/18/1998
Year Founded: 1998
Capital Under Management: $483,000,000
Current Activity Level: Actively seeking new investments

HSBC PRIVATE EQUITY LATIN AMERICA

Avenida de Mayo 701
8th Floor
Buenos Aires, Argentina
Phone: 54-11-4345-1930
Fax: 54-11-4345-1984

Management and Staff

Carlos Wagener, Managing Director

Type of Firm

Bank Affiliated

Project Preferences

Type of Financing Preferred:
Fund of Funds
Expansion
Management Buyouts

Acquisition
Recapitalizations

Geographical Preferences

International Preferences:
Uruguay
Argentina
Bolivia
Peru
Paraguay
Brazil
Mexico
Chile
Venezuela

Additional Information

Name of Most Recent Fund: HSBC Tower II Equity Partners (Cayman), L.P.
Most Recent Fund Was Raised: 05/14/2001
Year Founded: 1995
Capital Under Management: $79,800,000
Current Activity Level: Actively seeking new investments

HSBC PRIVATE EQUITY MIDDLE EAST

HSBC House Esplanade
St. Helier
Jersey, United Kingdom JE4 8UB
Website: www.middleeast.hsbc.com

Other Offices

8 Canada Square
London, United Kingdom E14 5HQ

Management and Staff

Niall Booker, Chief Executive Officer

Type of Firm

Bank Affiliated

Project Preferences

Type of Financing Preferred:
Expansion
Generalist PE
Later Stage
Management Buyouts

Geographical Preferences

International Preferences:
Middle East

Industry Preferences

In Consumer Related prefer:
Retail

In Industrial/Energy prefer:
Energy

In Manufact. prefer:
Manufacturing

Additional Information

Year Founded: 1959
Capital Under Management: $118,000,000
Current Activity Level: Actively seeking new investments

HSBC PTE EQUITY (ASIA), LTD. (FKA: HSBC PRIVATE EQUITY MGT.)

Level 17, HSBC Main Building
One Queen's Road
Central, Hong Kong
Phone: 852-2845-7688
Fax: 852-2845-9992
E-mail: hpea@hsbc.com.hk
Website: www.hsbcnet.com/pi/asia

Other Offices

India Liason Office, 3/F Ashoka Estate
24, Barakhamba Road
New Delhi, India 110001
Phone: 911-1372-1234
Fax: 911-1332-8501

Management and Staff

George Raffini, Managing Director
Shane Yau, Chief Financial Officer

Type of Firm

Bank Affiliated

Association Membership

Hong Kong Venture Capital Association (HKVCA)

Project Preferences

Role in Financing:
Prefer role as deal originator but will also invest in deals created by others

Type of Financing Preferred:
Second Stage Financing
Leveraged Buyout
Control-block Purchases
Early Stage
Expansion
Mezzanine
Balanced
Public Companies
Management Buyouts
Special Situation

Size of Investments Considered:
Min Size of Investment Considered (000s): $1,000
Max Size of Investment Considered (000s): $80,000

Geographical Preferences

International Preferences:
Indonesia
India
Taiwan
China
Hong Kong
Thailand
Philippines
Pacific
Singapore
Korea, South
Asia
Japan

Industry Focus

(% based on actual investment)

Other Products	35.9%
Consumer Related	23.5%
Semiconductors/Other Elect.	9.6%
Industrial/Energy	8.3%
Computer Software and Services	6.9%
Communications and Media	6.7%
Computer Hardware	3.4%
Medical/Health	2.8%
Internet Specific	2.8%

Additional Information

Name of Most Recent Fund: HSBC Asian Ventures Fund 2 Limited (HAV2)
Most Recent Fund Was Raised: 03/01/2005
Year Founded: 1988
Capital Under Management: $900,000,000
Current Activity Level: Actively seeking new investments
Method of Compensation: Return on investment is of primary concern, do not charge fees

---

HSD PARTNERS, INC.

181 Bay Street
Suite 3620
Toronto, Canada M5J2S1
Phone: 416-367-4200
Fax: 416-863-1030

Management and Staff

Gerard Hurlow, Partner
Jon Gill, Partner
Michael Henthorn, Chief Financial Officer
Michael Liik, Partner
Philip Deck, Partner
Terrence Smith, Partner

Type of Firm

Private Equity Firm

Additional Information

Year Founded: 1987
Current Activity Level: Actively seeking new investments

HSH NORDBANK KAPITAL (FKA: SCHLESWIG-HOLSTEINISCHE)

Domstrasse 17-19
Hamburg, Germany 20095
Phone: 49-40-30700700
Fax: 49-40-30700777
Website: www.hsh-pe.de

Management and Staff
Joerg Richard, Managing Director

Type of Firm
Bank Affiliated

Association Membership
German Venture Capital Association (BVK)

Project Preferences
Type of Financing Preferred:
Expansion
Balanced
Management Buyouts
Recapitalizations

Geographical Preferences
International Preferences:
Germany

Additional Information
Year Founded: 2000
Capital Under Management: $22,500,000
Current Activity Level: Actively seeking new investments

HST VENTURE CAPITAL
44-22 Yuido-Dong, 150-890
Rm. 610 Hosung Building
Seoul, South Korea 150-010
Phone: 822-780-2317
Fax: 822-780-2317

Management and Staff
Jongkyu Shin, President

Type of Firm
Private Equity Firm

Project Preferences
Type of Financing Preferred:
Balanced

Geographical Preferences
International Preferences:
Korea, South

Additional Information
Year Founded: 2006
Current Activity Level: Actively seeking new investments

HT CAPITAL ADVISORS LLC
437 Madison Avenue
New York, NY USA 10022
Phone: 212-759-9080
Fax: 212-759-0299
E-mail: finance@htcapital.com
Website: www.htcapital.com

Management and Staff
C.A. Burkhardt, Senior Managing Director
Eric Lomas, President
Peter Offermann, Managing Director
Sharif Tanamli, Managing Director
Stephen Tardio, Managing Director

Type of Firm
Bank Affiliated

Association Membership
Natl Assoc of Investment Cos. (NAIC)

Project Preferences
Role in Financing:
Will function either as deal originator or investor in deals created by others

Type of Financing Preferred:
Second Stage Financing
Leveraged Buyout
Expansion
Balanced
Turnaround
Later Stage
Strategic Alliances
Acquisition
Joint Ventures
Distressed Debt

Size of Investments Considered:
Min Size of Investment Considered (000s): $2,000
Max Size of Investment Considered (000s): $10,000

Geographical Preferences
United States Preferences:
All U.S.

International Preferences:
United Kingdom
Germany
France

Additional Information
Year Founded: 1932
Current Activity Level: Actively seeking new investments
Method of Compensation: Return on invest. most important, but chg. closing fees, service fees, etc.

HUA NAN VENTURE CAPITAL CO., LTD.
38, Sec. 1
Chungching South Road
Taipei, Taiwan
Phone: 886-2-2371-3111
Fax: 886-2-2331-6741
E-mail: public@hnfhc.com.tw
Website: www.hnfhc.com.tw

Type of Firm
Bank Affiliated

Project Preferences
Type of Financing Preferred:
Balanced

Geographical Preferences
International Preferences:
Taiwan

Additional Information
Year Founded: 2001
Capital Under Management: $1,832,400,000
Current Activity Level: Actively seeking new investments

HUA YU INVESTMENT MANAGEMENT LIMITED
Suite 51, 5F New Henry House
10 Ice House Street
Central, Hong Kong
Phone: 852-2804-6188
Fax: 852-2804-6197

Type of Firm
Investment Management Firm

Project Preferences
Type of Financing Preferred:
Balanced

Geographical Preferences
International Preferences:
Hong Kong

Additional Information
Year Founded: 2002
Capital Under Management: $6,000,000
Current Activity Level: Actively seeking new investments

HUBEI HI-TECH INDUSTRIAL INVESTMENT CO., LTD.
12/F, Huale Business Center
716 Luoyu Road, Hongshan Dist.
Wuhan, China 430074
Phone: 86-27-8744-0890
Fax: 86-27-8744-0849
Website: www.cnhbgt.com

Type of Firm
Private Equity Firm

Project Preferences
Type of Financing Preferred:
Fund of Funds
Expansion
Later Stage
Seed

Geographical Preferences

International Preferences:
China
Asia

Additional Information

Year Founded: 2005
Capital Under Management: $58,600,000
Current Activity Level: Actively seeking new investments

HUDSON CAPITAL MANAGEMENT, L.P.

400 Frank W. Burr Boulevard
Suite 37
Teaneck, NJ USA 07666
Phone: 201-287-4100
E-mail: inquiries@hudsoncep.com
Website: www.hudsoncep.com

Management and Staff

Craig Cornelius, Principal
John Cavalier, Managing Partner
Larry Henry, Managing Director
Nick Sangermano, Chief Operating Officer
Paul Ho, Principal
Shaun Kingsbury, Partner

Type of Firm

Bank Affiliated

Project Preferences

Type of Financing Preferred:
Leveraged Buyout

Geographical Preferences

United States Preferences:
All U.S.

Industry Preferences

In Industrial/Energy prefer:
Energy
Alternative Energy

Additional Information

Year Founded: 2008
Capital Under Management: $800,000,000
Current Activity Level: Actively seeking new investments

HUDSON FERRY CAPITAL LLC

153 East 53rd Street
29th Floor
New York, NY USA 10022
Phone: 212-308-3079
Fax: 212-308-3893
E-mail: info@hudsonferry.com
Website: www.hudsonferry.com

Type of Firm

Private Equity Firm

Project Preferences

Type of Financing Preferred:
Leveraged Buyout

Size of Investments Considered:
Min Size of Investment Considered (000s): $100,000
Max Size of Investment Considered (000s): $300,000

Geographical Preferences

United States Preferences:
All U.S.

Industry Preferences

In Business Serv. prefer:
Services

In Manufact. prefer:
Manufacturing

Additional Information

Year Founded: 2006
Capital Under Management: $40,000,000
Current Activity Level: Actively seeking new investments

HUDSON VENTURE PARTNERS

535 Fifth Avenue
14th Floor
New York, NY USA 10017
Phone: 212-644-9797
Fax: 212-644-7430
E-mail: info@hudsonptr.com
Website: www.hudsonptr.com

Management and Staff

Bill Carson, Managing Director
Glen Lewy, Senior Managing Director
Jay Goldberg, Senior Managing Director
John Truehart, Chief Financial Officer
Kim Goh, Senior Managing Director
Lawrence Howard, Senior Managing Director

Type of Firm

SBIC

Association Membership

Natl Assoc of Small Bus. Inv. Co (NASBIC)

Project Preferences

Role in Financing:
Will function either as deal originator or investor in deals created by others

Type of Financing Preferred:
Second Stage Financing
Early Stage
Later Stage
First Stage Financing

Size of Investments Considered:
Min Size of Investment Considered (000s): $2,000
Max Size of Investment Considered (000s): $8,000

Geographical Preferences

United States Preferences:
Mid Atlantic
Northeast

Industry Focus

(% based on actual investment)

Computer Software and Services	42.5%
Internet Specific	31.2%
Computer Hardware	12.2%
Biotechnology	4.6%
Medical/Health	3.6%
Communications and Media	3.0%
Other Products	2.0%
Semiconductors/Other Elect.	0.9%

Additional Information

Name of Most Recent Fund: Hudson Venture Partners II, LP
Most Recent Fund Was Raised: 11/29/2000
Year Founded: 1996
Capital Under Management: $175,000,000
Current Activity Level: Actively seeking new investments
Method of Compensation: Return on investment is of primary concern, do not charge fees

---

HULL CAPITAL MANAGEMENT, LLC

78 Forest Avenue
Locust Valley, NY USA 11560
Phone: 516-609-2500
Fax: 516-977-3058
E-mail: mhull@hullcap.com
Website: www.hullcap.com

Management and Staff

George Holland, Managing Director
James Mitchell Hull, Managing Director

Type of Firm

Other

Project Preferences

Role in Financing:
Unknown

Additional Information

Year Founded: 2003
Capital Under Management: $18,000,000
Current Activity Level: Actively seeking new investments
Method of Compensation: Unknown

HUMMER WINBLAD VENTURE PARTNERS

One Lombard Street
Suite 300
San Francisco, CA USA 94111
Phone: 415-979-9600
Fax: 415-979-9601
Website: www.humwin.com

Management and Staff

Ann Winblad, Founding Partner
Douglas Hickey, Managing Partner
John Hummer, Founding Partner
Lars Leckie, Principal
Mark Gorenberg, Managing Partner
Mitchell Kertzman, Managing Partner
Prashant Shah, Managing Director

Type of Firm

Private Equity Firm

Association Membership

National Venture Capital Association - USA (NVCA)

Project Preferences

Role in Financing:
Prefer role as deal originator but will also invest in deals created by others

Type of Financing Preferred:
Early Stage
First Stage Financing

Size of Investments Considered:
Min Size of Investment Considered (000s): $1,000
Max Size of Investment Considered (000s): $10,000

Geographical Preferences

United States Preferences:
Northwest
Northern California
Northeast
West Coast

Industry Focus

(% based on actual investment)

Computer Software and Services	53.1%
Internet Specific	35.2%
Computer Hardware	3.5%
Communications and Media	2.9%
Consumer Related	2.8%
Other Products	2.6%

Additional Information

Name of Most Recent Fund: Hummer Winblad Venture Partners VI, L.P.
Most Recent Fund Was Raised: 08/03/2007
Year Founded: 1989
Capital Under Management: $1,000,000,000
Current Activity Level: Actively seeking new investments
Method of Compensation: Return on investment is of primary concern, do not charge fees

HUMPHREY ENTERPRISES, LLC

One Beacon Street
Suite 2320
Boston, MA USA 02108
Phone: 617-720-5222
Fax: 617-720-5507
E-mail: info@humphreyenterprises.com
Website: www.humphreyenterprises.com

Management and Staff

Daniel Brennan, Principal
James Green, Principal
James Humphrey, Principal

Type of Firm

Private Equity Firm

Project Preferences

Type of Financing Preferred:
Leveraged Buyout

Size of Investments Considered:
Min Size of Investment Considered (000s): $250
Max Size of Investment Considered (000s): $4,000

Geographical Preferences

United States Preferences:
All U.S.

Industry Preferences

In Medical/Health prefer:
Health Services

In Consumer Related prefer:
Education Related

In Transportation prefer:
Transportation

Additional Information

Year Founded: 2002
Current Activity Level: Actively seeking new investments

HUNAN HIGH-TECH VENTURE CAPITAL

No. 1 Chengnan West Road
Changsha, China
Phone: 86-731-5165-403
Fax: 86-731-5165-400
Website: www.hhtvc.com

Type of Firm

Private Equity Firm

Project Preferences

Type of Financing Preferred:
Balanced

Geographical Preferences

International Preferences:
China

Industry Preferences

In Biotechnology prefer:
Biotechnology

In Medical/Health prefer:
Medical/Health

In Industrial/Energy prefer:
Energy
Advanced Materials
Machinery

In Manufact. prefer:
Manufacturing

Additional Information

Year Founded: 2007
Current Activity Level: Actively seeking new investments

HUNAN XIANGTOU HIGH-TECH VENTURE CAPITAL CO., LTD.

No. 279, Furong Zhong Road
10/F South Jinyuan Hotel
Changsha, Hunan, China 410007
Phone: 86-731-85167219
Fax: 86-731-85167227
Website: www.hnhvc.com

Type of Firm

Private Equity Firm

Project Preferences

Type of Financing Preferred:
Balanced

Geographical Preferences

International Preferences:
China

Industry Preferences

In Semiconductor/Electr prefer:
Electronics

In Biotechnology prefer:
Biotechnology

In Medical/Health prefer:
Medical/Health

In Industrial/Energy prefer:
Materials

Additional Information

Year Founded: 2000
Current Activity Level: Actively seeking new investments

HUNT BIOVENTURES

1900 North Akard Street
Dallas, TX USA 75201
Phone: 214-978-8690
E-mail: huntbioventures@huntbioventures.com
Website: www.huntbioventures.com

Management and Staff

Fulton Murray, Managing Director
Mike Bierman, Managing Director

Type of Firm

Corporate PE/Venture

Project Preferences

Type of Financing Preferred:
Early Stage
Public Companies
Private Placement

Size of Investments Considered:
Min Size of Investment Considered (000s): $2,000
Max Size of Investment Considered (000s): $7,000

Geographical Preferences

United States Preferences:
All U.S.

Industry Preferences

In Biotechnology prefer:
Agricultural/Animal Bio.

In Medical/Health prefer:
Medical Products
Pharmaceuticals

Additional Information

Year Founded: 2001
Current Activity Level: Actively seeking new investments

HUNT CAPITAL GROUP

1601 Elm Street
Suite 4000
Dallas, TX USA 75201
Phone: 214-720-1600
Fax: 214-720-1662
E-mail: info@huntcapital.com
Website: www.huntcapital.com

Management and Staff

Peter Stein, Partner
Scott Colvert, Partner

Type of Firm

Private Equity Firm

Project Preferences

Role in Financing:
Will function either as deal originator or investor in deals created by others

Type of Financing Preferred:
Second Stage Financing
Expansion
Generalist PE
Later Stage
Management Buyouts
Acquisition
Recapitalizations

Size of Investments Considered:
Min Size of Investment Considered (000s): $3,000
Max Size of Investment Considered (000s): $10,000

Geographical Preferences

United States Preferences:
Midwest
Southeast
Southwest
All U.S.

Canadian Preferences:
All Canada

Industry Focus

(% based on actual investment)

Other Products	37.1%
Communications and Media	17.0%
Computer Software and Services	14.3%
Internet Specific	9.6%
Industrial/Energy	9.2%
Medical/Health	6.4%
Semiconductors/Other Elect.	5.5%
Consumer Related	1.0%

Additional Information

Name of Most Recent Fund: Hunt Capital Growth Fund II, L.P.
Most Recent Fund Was Raised: 10/01/1998
Year Founded: 1993
Capital Under Management: $120,000,000
Current Activity Level: Actively seeking new investments
Method of Compensation: Return on invest. most important, but chg. closing fees, service fees, etc.

HUNT PRIVATE EQUITY GROUP, INC. (FKA: HUNT FINANCIAL CORP.)

1900 North Akard Street
Dallas, TX USA 75201
Phone: 214-978-8550
Fax: 214-855-6999
E-mail: huntpeginfo@huntpeg.com
Website: www.huntpeg.com

Management and Staff

Andy Foskey, Vice President
Matt Malone, Vice President
Stephen Smiley, President

Type of Firm

Corporate PE/Venture

Association Membership

National Venture Capital Association - USA (NVCA)

Project Preferences

Role in Financing:
Prefer role as deal originator but will also invest in deals created by others

Type of Financing Preferred:
Leveraged Buyout
Expansion
Generalist PE
Later Stage
Management Buyouts
Acquisition
Private Placement
Industry Rollups
Recapitalizations

Size of Investments Considered:
Min Size of Investment Considered (000s): $5,000
Max Size of Investment Considered (000s): $20,000

Geographical Preferences

United States Preferences:
Mid Atlantic
Midwest
Southeast
Rocky Mountain
Southwest
All U.S.

Industry Focus

(% based on actual investment)

Other Products	57.4%
Internet Specific	28.9%
Consumer Related	9.9%
Computer Software and Services	3.8%

Additional Information

Year Founded: 1990
Capital Under Management: $107,500,000
Current Activity Level: Actively seeking new investments
Method of Compensation: Return on invest. most important, but chg. closing fees, service fees, etc.

HUNT SPECIAL SITUATIONS GROUP

Fountain Place
1445 Ross At Field, Suite 1400
Dallas, TX USA 75202
Phone: 214-978-8107
Fax: 214-978-8000
E-mail: huntssg@huntssg.com
Website: www.huntssg.com

Management and Staff

James Lee, Vice President
Phillip Arra, President

Type of Firm

Corporate PE/Venture

Project Preferences

Role in Financing:
Prefer role as deal originator but will also invest in deals created by others

Type of Financing Preferred:
Turnaround
Acquisition
Special Situation
Recapitalizations

Size of Investments Considered:
Min Size of Investment Considered (000s): $2,000
Max Size of Investment Considered (000s): $20,000

Geographical Preferences

United States Preferences:
All U.S.

Additional Information
Year Founded: 2004
Current Activity Level: Actively seeking new investments

HUNT VENTURES
6300 Bridgepoint Parkway
Bldg 1, Suite 500
Austin, TX USA 78730
Phone: 512-795-5870
Fax: 512-795-5879
E-mail: huntventuresinfo@huntventures.com
Website: www.huntventures.com

Other Offices
1900 North Akard Street
Dallas, TX USA 75201
Phone: 214-978-8690
Fax: 214-978-8588

Two Galleria Tower
13455 Noel Road, Suite 1670
Dallas, TX USA 75240
Phone: 972-776-1575
Fax: 972-767-4250

Management and Staff
Christopher Kleinert, Managing Director
Jeff Williams, Managing Director
Steven Coffey, Managing Director

Type of Firm
Corporate PE/Venture

Association Membership
National Venture Capital Association - USA (NVCA)

Project Preferences

Role in Financing:
Will function either as deal originator or investor in deals created by others

Type of Financing Preferred:
Second Stage Financing
Early Stage
Seed
First Stage Financing

Size of Investments Considered:
Min Size of Investment Considered (000s): $500
Max Size of Investment Considered (000s): $5,000

Geographical Preferences

United States Preferences:
All U.S.

Industry Preferences

In Communications prefer:
Communications and Media
Telecommunications
Wireless Communications

In Computer Software prefer:
Software
Applications Software

In Internet Specific prefer:
Internet

In Semiconductor/Electr prefer:
Semiconductor

Additional Information
Name of Most Recent Fund: Hunt Ventures Fund I, L.P.
Most Recent Fund Was Raised: 05/28/2008
Year Founded: 1998
Capital Under Management: $140,000,000
Current Activity Level: Actively seeking new investments
Method of Compensation: Return on investment is of primary concern, do not charge fees

---

HUNTINGTON CAPITAL
11988 El Camino Real
Suite 160
San Diego, CA USA 92130
Phone: 858-259-7654
Fax: 858-259-0074
E-mail: info@huntingtoncapital.com
Website: www.huntingtoncapital.com

Other Offices
5251 California Avenue
Suite 120
Irvine, CA USA 92612
Phone: 949-679-9826
Fax: 949-679-9801

Management and Staff
Barry Wilson, Managing Partner
Tim Bubnack, Partner

Type of Firm
Private Equity Firm

Project Preferences

Type of Financing Preferred:
Mezzanine
Acquisition

Geographical Preferences

United States Preferences:
Southwest

Additional Information
Year Founded: 2000
Capital Under Management: $78,000,000
Current Activity Level: Actively seeking new investments

HUNTINGTON VENTURES
19700 Fairchild Road
Suite 290
Irvine, CA USA 92612
Phone: 949-442-9990
Fax: 949-442-9992
E-mail: info@huntingtonventures.com
Website: www.huntingtonventures.com

Management and Staff
Douglas Broyles, General Partner
Scott Burri, Managing General Partner

Type of Firm
Private Equity Firm

Project Preferences

Role in Financing:
Prefer role as deal originator but will also invest in deals created by others

Type of Financing Preferred:
Second Stage Financing
Early Stage
Expansion

Size of Investments Considered:
Min Size of Investment Considered (000s): $500
Max Size of Investment Considered (000s): $1,500

Geographical Preferences

United States Preferences:
Oregon
California
Washington
Texas

Industry Preferences

In Communications prefer:
Communications and Media
Telecommunications
Wireless Communications
Data Communications

In Computer Hardware prefer:
Computer Graphics and Dig

In Computer Software prefer:
Software

In Internet Specific prefer:
E-Commerce Technology

In Computer Other prefer:
Computer Related

In Semiconductor/Electr prefer:
Electronic Components
Semiconductor
Micro-Processing
Sensors
Component Testing Equipmt
Fiber Optics

In Industrial/Energy prefer:
Advanced Materials

Additional Information
Year Founded: 2000
Capital Under Management: $35,000,000
Current Activity Level: Actively seeking new investments
Method of Compensation: Return on investment is of primary concern, do not charge fees

---

HUNTSMAN GAY GLOBAL CAPITAL LLC
1900 University Avenue
Palo Alto, CA USA 94303
Phone: 650-321-4910
Fax: 650-321-4911
E-mail: info@hgequity.com
Website: www.hgequity.com

Other Offices
26 Patriot Place
Foxboro, MA USA 02035
Phone: 508-549-8800
Fax: 508-546-7867

9815 South Monroe Street
Sandy, UT USA 840703
Phone: 801-984-2700
Fax: 801-984-2701

222 Lakeview Avenue
West Palm Beach, FL USA 33401
Phone: 561-491-6300
Fax: 561-491-6301

Management and Staff
David Topham, Vice President
Gary Crittenden, Managing Director
Gregory Benson, Managing Director
J. Steven Young, Managing Director
Jacob Hodgman, Vice President
James Colyer, Vice President
Jared Archibald, Vice President
Jon Huntsman, Managing Director
Judy Frodigh, Managing Director
Leslie Brown, Chief Financial Officer
Rhett Neuenschwander, Managing Director
Richard Lawson, Managing Director
Robert Gay, Managing Director
Ronald Mika, Managing Director
Ryan Stratton, Principal
Suken Shah, Principal

Type of Firm
Private Equity Firm

Project Preferences

Type of Financing Preferred:
Leveraged Buyout
Expansion

Additional Information
Year Founded: 2007
Capital Under Management: $1,188,800,000
Current Activity Level: Actively seeking new investments

HUPOMONE CAPITAL PARTNERS
79 Robinson Road
15-01 CPF Building
Singapore, Singapore 068897
Website: www.hupomonepartners.com

Management and Staff
Chan Kok-Pun, Chief Operating Officer
Siew Wing Keong, President

Type of Firm
Private Equity Firm

Project Preferences

Type of Financing Preferred:
Early Stage
Balanced

Geographical Preferences

International Preferences:
Indonesia
Philippines
Asia
Malaysia

Additional Information
Year Founded: 2004
Capital Under Management: $5,000,000
Current Activity Level: Actively seeking new investments

HURON CAPITAL PARTNERS LLC
500 Griswold
Suite 2700
Detroit, MI USA 48226
Phone: 313-962-5800
Fax: 313-962-5820
Website: www.huroncapital.com

Other Offices
100 King Street West
37th Floor
Toronto, Canada M5X 1C9
Phone: 416-234-0313
Fax: 416-234-1980

225 Ross Street
Fourth Floor
Pittsburgh, PA USA 15219
Phone: 412-201-7040
Fax: 412-201-7041

Management and Staff
Christian Moye, Principal
Christopher Sheeren, Partner
Frederick Quinn, Partner
Greg Steve, Principal
James Mahomey, Vice President
James Clegg, Partner
Jeffrey Wasson, Partner
Jeremy Busch, Principal
John Williams, Partner
John Higgins, Partner
Merle Smith, Partner
Michael Beauregard, Partner
Nicholas Barker, Vice President
Peter Mogk, Partner
Robert Cronin, Partner

Type of Firm
Private Equity Firm

Project Preferences

Role in Financing:
Prefer role as deal originator but will also invest in deals created by others

Type of Financing Preferred:
Leveraged Buyout
Later Stage
Management Buyouts
Acquisition
Special Situation
Recapitalizations

Size of Investments Considered:
Min Size of Investment Considered (000s): $10,000
Max Size of Investment Considered (000s): $70,000

Geographical Preferences

United States Preferences:
All U.S.

Canadian Preferences:
All Canada

Industry Focus
(% based on actual investment)

Other Products	92.4%
Medical/Health	7.6%

Additional Information
Name of Most Recent Fund: Huron Fund III, L.P.
Most Recent Fund Was Raised: 01/09/2008
Year Founded: 1999
Capital Under Management: $72,000,000
Current Activity Level: Actively seeking new investments
Method of Compensation: Return on invest. most important, but chg. closing fees, service fees, etc.

HURRAY INC.

30F ARK Mori Bldg.
1-12-32 Akasaka, Minato-ku
Tokyo, Japan 107-6030
Phone: 81-3-3560-2010
Fax: 81-3-3560-2015
Website: www.hurray.co.jp

Type of Firm

Private Equity Firm

Additional Information

Year Founded: 2004
Current Activity Level: Actively seeking new investments

HUTTON COLLINS & COMPANY LIMITED

50 Pall Mall
Kingsbury House
London, United Kingdom SW1Y 5JH
Phone: 44-207-004-7000
Fax: 44-207-004-7001
E-mail: enquiries@huttoncollins.com
Website: www.huttoncollins.com

Management and Staff

Graham Hutton, Founding Partner
Matthew Collins, Founding Partner

Type of Firm

Private Equity Firm

Project Preferences

Type of Financing Preferred:

Leveraged Buyout
Expansion
Mezzanine
Management Buyouts
Recapitalizations

Geographical Preferences

International Preferences:

United Kingdom
Europe

Additional Information

Year Founded: 2001
Capital Under Management: $934,900,000
Current Activity Level: Actively seeking new investments

HUVUDKONTORET (AKA: HK MANAGEMENT I KRISTINEHAMN AB)

Strandvagen 30
Kristinehamn, Sweden 681 38
Phone: 46-550-39100
Fax: 46-550-39199
E-mail: info@hkkristinehamn.se
Website: www.hkkristinehamn.se

Management and Staff

Hans Andreasson, Chief Financial Officer

Type of Firm

Private Equity Firm

Project Preferences

Type of Financing Preferred:

Balanced

Geographical Preferences

International Preferences:

Sweden
Europe

Additional Information

Year Founded: 2007
Capital Under Management: $3,900,000
Current Activity Level: Actively seeking new investments

HVB RUSSELL MANAGEMENT GMBH

Arabellastrasse 12
Munich, Germany 81925
Phone: 49-89-3781-4367
Fax: 49-89-3781-5162

Management and Staff

Aris Aristidou, Managing Director
Axel Gruber, Managing Director
Hal Strong, Managing Director
Harald Lusser, Managing Director
Helen Steers, Managing Director

Type of Firm

Bank Affiliated

Project Preferences

Type of Financing Preferred:

Fund of Funds

Geographical Preferences

International Preferences:

Latin America
Western Europe
Israel
Asia

Additional Information

Year Founded: 2001
Current Activity Level: Actively seeking new investments

HYDERABAD INFORMATION TECHNOLOGY VENTURE ENTERPRISES, LTD.

Parishram Bhavan, 1st Floor
Fateh Maidan Road
Hyderabad, India 500 044
Phone: 91-40-2323-7995
Fax: 91-40-2323-5516
E-mail: info@hitvel.co.in
Website: www.hitvel.co.in

Management and Staff

C. Balagopal, Chief Executive Officer

Type of Firm

Government Affiliated Program

Association Membership

Indian Venture Capital Association (IVCA)

Project Preferences

Role in Financing:

Prefer role as deal originator but will also invest in deals created by others

Type of Financing Preferred:

Early Stage
Expansion
Seed
Startup

Size of Investments Considered:

Min Size of Investment Considered (000s): $250
Max Size of Investment Considered (000s): $750

Geographical Preferences

International Preferences:

India

Industry Preferences

In Computer Hardware prefer:

Computers

In Computer Software prefer:

Software

In Computer Other prefer:

Computer Related

Additional Information

Year Founded: 1998
Capital Under Management: $3,300,000
Current Activity Level: Actively seeking new investments

HYDRO-QUEBEC CAPITECH INC.

75 Boul. Rene Levesque Ouest
22e etage
Montreal, Canada H2Z 1A4
Phone: 514-289-4783

Fax: 514-289-5420
Website: www.hqcapitech.com

Management and Staff

Jean-Claude Sinard, Vice President
Michel DeBroux, Vice President

Type of Firm

Corporate PE/Venture

Association Membership

Canadian Venture Capital Association

Project Preferences

Type of Financing Preferred:
Second Stage Financing
Early Stage
Expansion
Mezzanine
Balanced
Seed
First Stage Financing
Startup

Geographical Preferences

Canadian Preferences:
All Canada

Industry Preferences

In Communications prefer:
Wireless Communications
Data Communications
Other Communication Prod.

In Internet Specific prefer:
Internet

In Semiconductor/Electr prefer:
Electronic Components
Semiconductor

In Industrial/Energy prefer:
Energy
Superconductivity

In Utilities prefer:
Utilities

Additional Information

Year Founded: 1998
Capital Under Management: $320,000,000
Current Activity Level: Actively seeking new investments

HYIELD CONSULTING GROUP

5F-3, 380 Fu Hsing South Road
Section 1
Taipei, Taiwan
Phone: 886-2-2708-1915
Fax: 886-2-2708-1932
E-mail: hyield@ms34.com.tw

Management and Staff

Hong-Jen Chung, President

Type of Firm

Private Equity Firm

Association Membership

Taiwan Venture Capital Association(TVCA)

Project Preferences

Type of Financing Preferred:
Expansion
Mezzanine
Balanced
Seed

Geographical Preferences

International Preferences:
Taiwan

Industry Preferences

In Communications prefer:
Telecommunications

In Computer Software prefer:
Software

In Semiconductor/Electr prefer:
Electronic Components
Semiconductor

Additional Information

Name of Most Recent Fund: Hyield Venture Capital Company, Ltd.
Most Recent Fund Was Raised: 10/01/1996
Year Founded: 1995
Capital Under Management: $58,800,000
Current Activity Level: Actively seeking new investments

HYPO EQUITY MANAGEMENT AG

Bahnhofstrasse 14
Bregenz, Austria 6900
Phone: 43-5574-471920
Fax: 43-557447192599
E-mail: office@hypoequity.at
Website: www.hypoequity.at

Management and Staff

Harald Poettinger, Managing Director
Omer Rehman, Managing Director

Type of Firm

Bank Affiliated

Association Membership

Austrian PE and Venture Capital Association (AVCO)
European Private Equity and Venture Capital Assoc.

Project Preferences

Type of Financing Preferred:
Fund of Funds
Leveraged Buyout
Early Stage
Expansion
Turnaround
Startup
Recapitalizations

Size of Investments Considered:
Min Size of Investment Considered (000s): $471
Max Size of Investment Considered (000s): $4,708

Geographical Preferences

International Preferences:
Liechtenstein
Switzerland
Austria
Germany

Industry Focus

(% based on actual investment)

Industrial/Energy	30.6%
Computer Software and Services	29.1%
Other Products	17.6%
Medical/Health	13.2%
Biotechnology	5.2%
Semiconductors/Other Elect.	2.4%
Consumer Related	1.7%

Additional Information

Year Founded: 1999
Capital Under Management: $92,400,000
Current Activity Level: Actively seeking new investments

HYUNDAI VENTURE INVESTMENT CORPORATION

4F, Nat'l Info Soc Agency Bldg
Mookyo-dong, Chung-ku
Seoul, South Korea 100-170
Phone: 822-728-8990
Fax: 822-728-8999
Website: www.hvic.co.kr

Management and Staff

Mong-il Chung, Chairman & CEO

Type of Firm

Corporate PE/Venture

Association Membership

Korean Venture Capital Association (KVCA)

Project Preferences

Type of Financing Preferred:
Early Stage
Expansion
Balanced

Geographical Preferences

International Preferences:
Korea, South

Industry Preferences

In Computer Hardware prefer:
Computers

In Computer Software prefer:
Software

In Internet Specific prefer:
Internet

In Semiconductor/Electr prefer:
Electronics
Electronic Components

In Biotechnology prefer:
Biotechnology

In Industrial/Energy prefer:
Materials

Additional Information

Year Founded: 1997
Capital Under Management: $24,200,000
Current Activity Level: Actively seeking new investments

- I -

I VENTURE INVESTMENT CO., LTD.

4/F Samik Electron Building
Nonhyeon-dong, Gangam-gu
Seoul, South Korea 135-010
Phone: 822-557-7005
Fax: 822-557-7006

Other Offices

12/F Yeondan Building
Samsung-dong, Kangam-ku
Seoul, South Korea

Management and Staff

Kwang Myung Jung, Chief Executive Officer

Type of Firm

Private Equity Firm

Project Preferences

Type of Financing Preferred:
Balanced

Geographical Preferences

International Preferences:
Korea, South

Industry Preferences

In Communications prefer:
Media and Entertainment
Entertainment

Additional Information

Year Founded: 2000
Capital Under Management: $16,100,000
Current Activity Level: Actively seeking new investments

I&P MANAGEMENT LTD. (AKA: INDIAN OCEAN)

6th Floor, Harbour Front Bldg.
President John Kennedy St.
Port Louis, Mauritius
Phone: 230-213-8190
Fax: 230-213-8191
Website: www.ip-mngt.com

Other Offices

Lot IVG 204, Lot IV - 3rd Floor
Santa Building - Antanimena
Antananarivo, Madagascar
Phone: 261-320-784-878
Fax: 260-202-265-494

Management and Staff

Antoine Delaporte, Managing Director

Type of Firm

Private Equity Firm

Association Membership

African Venture Capital Association (AVCA)

Project Preferences

Type of Financing Preferred:
Leveraged Buyout
Expansion
Balanced
Start-up Financing

Size of Investments Considered:
Min Size of Investment Considered (000s): $1,460
Max Size of Investment Considered (000s): $7,299

Geographical Preferences

International Preferences:
Mauritius

Additional Information

Year Founded: 2003
Capital Under Management: $58,400,000
Current Activity Level: Actively seeking new investments

I-CAP PARTNERS,LTD. (AKA:INTELLECTUAL CAPITAL PARTNERS,LTD.)

12 Viaduct Harbour Ave.
Level 3, Maritime Square
Auckland, New Zealand 1001
Phone: 649-913-3370
Fax: 649-913-3377
E-mail: auckland@i-cappartners.com
Website: www.i-cappartners.com

Other Offices

2nd Floor
76 Brook Street
London, United Kingdom W1K 5EF
Phone: 44-207-408-0814
Fax: 44-207-681-1326

2000 Powell Street
Suite 510
Emeryville, CA USA 94608
Phone: 510-450-6720
Fax: 510-985-1741

Management and Staff

Nick Lodge, Managing Director
Tony Hannon, Managing Director

Type of Firm

Private Equity Firm

Project Preferences

Type of Financing Preferred:
Early Stage
Expansion

Mezzanine
Balanced
Later Stage
Management Buyouts

Geographical Preferences

International Preferences:
Pacific Rim
Pacific
Australia
New Zealand
Asia

Industry Preferences

In Communications prefer:
Telecommunications

In Computer Hardware prefer:
Computers

In Computer Software prefer:
Software
Applications Software

In Internet Specific prefer:
Internet
Ecommerce

In Semiconductor/Electr prefer:
Semiconductor

In Medical/Health prefer:
Medical/Health

In Industrial/Energy prefer:
Industrial Products

In Manufact. prefer:
Manufacturing

Additional Information

Year Founded: 1999
Capital Under Management: $286,700,000
Current Activity Level: Actively seeking new investments

I-CUBE S.A.

377 Syngrou Avenue
Palaio Faliro
Athens, Greece 175 64
Phone: 30-210-948-4280
Fax: 30-210-942-0287
E-mail: info@i-cube.gr
Website: www.i-cube.gr

Type of Firm

Private Equity Firm

Project Preferences

Type of Financing Preferred:
Expansion
Seed
Startup

Additional Information

Year Founded: 2000
Capital Under Management: $6,800,000
Current Activity Level: Actively seeking new investments

I-HATCH VENTURES LLC

584 Broadway
Suite 1103
New York, NY USA 10012
Phone: 212-651-1750
Fax: 212-208-4590
E-mail: info@i-hatch.com
Website: www.i-hatch.com

Management and Staff

Bradford Farkas, General Partner
Randolph Austin, General Partner

Type of Firm

Private Equity Firm

Project Preferences

Role in Financing:
Will function either as deal originator or investor in deals created by others

Type of Financing Preferred:
Early Stage
Seed
First Stage Financing

Size of Investments Considered:
Min Size of Investment Considered (000s): $1,000
Max Size of Investment Considered (000s): $15,000

Geographical Preferences

United States Preferences:
Northeast
All U.S.

Industry Focus

(% based on actual investment)

Communications and Media	38.7%
Internet Specific	30.7%
Other Products	11.0%
Consumer Related	9.9%
Computer Software and Services	9.7%

Additional Information

Name of Most Recent Fund: i-Hatch Ventures, L.P.
Most Recent Fund Was Raised: 01/19/2000
Year Founded: 1999
Capital Under Management: $100,000,000
Current Activity Level: Actively seeking new investments
Method of Compensation: Return on investment is of primary concern, do not charge fees

---

I-SOURCE GESTION

1-3, Avenue Jean Jaures
Versailles, France 78000
Phone: 33-1-3923-0200
Fax: 33-1-3923-0209
E-mail: info@isourcegestion.fr
Website: www.isourcegestion.fr

Management and Staff

Francois-Rene Letourneur, Partner
Nicolas Landrin, Partner
Nicolas Boulay, Principal
Pierre Fiorini, Venture Partner
Yvan-Michel Ehkirch, Principal

Type of Firm

Private Equity Firm

Association Membership

French Venture Capital Association (AFIC)
European Private Equity and Venture Capital Assoc.

Project Preferences

Type of Financing Preferred:
Early Stage
Seed
Startup

Size of Investments Considered:
Min Size of Investment Considered (000s): $645
Max Size of Investment Considered (000s): $1,934

Geographical Preferences

International Preferences:
Europe
Western Europe
France

Industry Preferences

In Communications prefer:
Communications and Media
Other Communication Prod.

In Computer Software prefer:
Software

In Internet Specific prefer:
Internet

In Computer Other prefer:
Computer Related

In Medical/Health prefer:
Medical/Health

In Business Serv. prefer:
Media

Additional Information

Year Founded: 1998
Capital Under Management: $200,000,000
Current Activity Level: Actively seeking new investments

IAME CAPITAL RIESGO SGECR SA

Plaza Marques de Salamanca, 10
5 Planta Derecha
Madrid, Spain 28006
Phone: 34-91-432-3628

Fax: 34-91-576-1285
E-mail: info@iame.es
Website: www.iame.es

Management and Staff
Amalio Marichalar, Managing Director
Cesar Vacchiano, Managing Director
Guillermo Romanos, Managing Director
Jose Luis Echarri, Managing Director
Juan Iranzo, Managing Director
Luis Sans Huecas, Chairman & CEO
Victorio Valle, Managing Director

Type of Firm
Private Equity Firm

Project Preferences
Type of Financing Preferred:
Balanced

Geographical Preferences
International Preferences:
Spain

Industry Preferences
In Consumer Related prefer:
Retail
Consumer Products

Additional Information
Year Founded: 2008
Capital Under Management: $93,300,000
Current Activity Level: Actively seeking new investments

IB H BETEILIGUNGS-MANAGEMENTGESELLSCHAFT HESSEN MBH (BM H)
Schumannstrasse 4-6
Frankfurt, Germany 60325
Phone: 49-1338-507841
Fax: 49-1338-507860
E-mail: info@bmh-hessen.de
Website: www.bmh-hessen.de

Type of Firm
Bank Affiliated

Association Membership
German Venture Capital Association (BVK)

Project Preferences
Type of Financing Preferred:
Leveraged Buyout
Expansion
Generalist PE
Early Stage

Geographical Preferences
International Preferences:
Germany

Additional Information
Year Founded: 1998
Capital Under Management: $2,900,000
Current Activity Level: Actively seeking new investments

IB INDUSTRIE-BETEILIGUNGEN GMBH
Marktstrasse 3
TZE 1
Eisenstadt, Austria 7000
Phone: 43-590-1026910
Fax: 43-590-1026911
Website: www.ib-industrie.at

Type of Firm
Private Equity Firm

Association Membership
Austrian PE and Venture Capital Association (AVCO)

Project Preferences
Type of Financing Preferred:
Balanced

Geographical Preferences
International Preferences:
Austria

Additional Information
Year Founded: 2005
Current Activity Level: Actively seeking new investments

IBB BETEILIGUNGSGESELLSCHAFT MBH
Bundesallee 171
Berlin, Germany 10715
Phone: 49-30-2125-3201
Fax: 49-30-2125-3202
E-mail: venture@ibb-bet.de
Website: www.ibb-bet.de

Management and Staff
Marco Zeller, Managing Director

Type of Firm
Bank Affiliated

Association Membership
German Venture Capital Association (BVK)
European Private Equity and Venture Capital Assoc.

Project Preferences
Type of Financing Preferred:
Early Stage
Expansion
Start-up Financing
Startup

Geographical Preferences
International Preferences:
Germany

Industry Preferences
In Communications prefer:
Communications and Media

In Computer Hardware prefer:
Computers

In Semiconductor/Electr prefer:
Electronics

In Biotechnology prefer:
Biotechnology

In Industrial/Energy prefer:
Energy

Additional Information
Name of Most Recent Fund: IBB Beteilgungsgesellschaft
Most Recent Fund Was Raised: 10/01/1997
Year Founded: 1997
Capital Under Management: $25,500,000
Current Activity Level: Actively seeking new investments

IBERCAJA GESTION SGICC SA
Paseo De La Constitucion 4
Zaragoza, Spain
Phone: 34-9762-39484
Fax: 34-9767-67772
Website: www.ibercaja.es

Type of Firm
Bank Affiliated

Additional Information
Year Founded: 2006
Current Activity Level: Actively seeking new investments

IBG BETEILIGUNGSGESELLSCHAFT SACHSEN-ANHALT MBH
Kantstrasse 5
Magdeburg, Germany 39104
Phone: 49-391-53281-40
Fax: 49-391-53281-59
E-mail: klemm@ibg-vc.de
Website: www.ibg-vc.de

Type of Firm
Incubator/Development Program

Additional Information
Year Founded: 2000
Current Activity Level: Actively seeking new investments

IBG MANAGEMENT

24B Kifisias
Marousi
Athens, Greece 15125
Phone: 30-21081-71953
Fax: 30-21081-71969
Website: www.marfingroup.gr

Type of Firm

Bank Affiliated

Project Preferences

Type of Financing Preferred:
Generalist PE

Geographical Preferences

International Preferences:
Greece

Industry Preferences

In Industrial/Energy prefer:
Alternative Energy

Additional Information

Year Founded: 2006
Capital Under Management: $24,300,000
Current Activity Level: Actively seeking new investments

IBH INNOVACIOS ES BEFEKTETESI HOLDING RT.

Regiposta u. 12
Budapest, Hungary 1052
Phone: 36-1-266-2181
Fax: 36-1-266-1489
E-mail: ibh@ibh.hu

Type of Firm

Private Equity Firm

Project Preferences

Type of Financing Preferred:
Balanced

Geographical Preferences

International Preferences:
Hungary
Europe

Additional Information

Year Founded: 2000
Current Activity Level: Actively seeking new investments

IBIS CAPITAL, LTD.

22 Soho Square
London, United Kingdom W1D 4NS
Phone: 44-20-7070-7080
Fax: 44-20-7070-7081
E-mail: info@ibiscapital.co.uk
Website: www.ibiscapital.co.uk

Management and Staff

Charles McIntyre, Partner
David Forster, Partner

Type of Firm

Investment Management Firm

Project Preferences

Type of Financing Preferred:
Expansion
Mezzanine
Management Buyouts
Acquisition

Size of Investments Considered:
Min Size of Investment Considered (000s): $1,013
Max Size of Investment Considered (000s): $2,026

Geographical Preferences

International Preferences:
United Kingdom

Industry Preferences

In Business Serv. prefer:
Media

Additional Information

Year Founded: 2003
Capital Under Management: $10,600,000
Current Activity Level: Actively seeking new investments

IBM CORPORATION

One New Orchard Road
Armonk, NY USA 10504
Phone: 914-499-1900
Fax: 914-499-6020
Website: www.ibm.com

Management and Staff

Donna Ewart, Partner
Drew Clark, Partner
Ellen Warms, Partner
Hisashi Katsuya, Partner
Richard Birney, Vice President
Wendy Lung, Partner

Type of Firm

Corporate PE/Venture

Association Membership

National Venture Capital Association - USA (NVCA)

Project Preferences

Role in Financing:
Prefer role in deals created by others

Type of Financing Preferred:
Fund of Funds
Early Stage
Private Placement

Size of Investments Considered:
Min Size of Investment Considered (000s): $1,000
Max Size of Investment Considered (000s): $5,000

Geographical Preferences

International Preferences:
India
Europe
China
Asia

Industry Preferences

In Communications prefer:
Communications and Media

In Computer Software prefer:
Software

In Internet Specific prefer:
Internet

In Biotechnology prefer:
Biotechnology

In Industrial/Energy prefer:
Energy

In Transportation prefer:
Transportation

In Financial Services prefer:
Financial Services

Additional Information

Year Founded: 1999
Capital Under Management: $500,000,000
Current Activity Level: Actively seeking new investments

IBTC VENTURES LIMITED

C/o IBTC Place P.O. Box 71707
Walter Carrington Crescent
Victoria Island, Lagos, Nigeria
Phone: 234-1-262-6520
Fax: 234-1-262-6541
E-mail: ibtcnet@ibtc.com
Website: www.ibtclagos.com

Management and Staff

Atedo N.A. Peterside, Chief Executive Officer
Yinka Sanni, Chief Executive Officer

Type of Firm

Bank Affiliated

Association Membership

Nigerian Venture Capital Association
African Venture Capital Association (AVCA)

Project Preferences

Type of Financing Preferred:
Expansion
Generalist PE

Geographical Preferences

International Preferences:
Nigeria
Africa

Industry Preferences

In Communications prefer:
Communications and Media

In Industrial/Energy prefer:
Energy
Industrial Products

In Manufact. prefer:
Manufacturing

Additional Information
Year Founded: 1992
Capital Under Management: $2,700,000
Current Activity Level: Actively seeking new investments

IC2 CAPITAL LLP
Three Bunhill Row
London, United Kingdom EC1Y 8YZ
Phone: 44-20-7847-4020
Fax: 44-20-7847-4005
E-mail: info@ic2capital.co.uk
Website: www.ic2capital.com

Other Offices
A-67 Mount Kailash
New Delhi, India 110065
Phone: 91-99-103-35485

Management and Staff
Anmol Nayyar, Managing Director
Kuldip Clair, Chief Operating Officer

Type of Firm
Private Equity Firm

Project Preferences

Type of Financing Preferred:
Leveraged Buyout
Expansion
Acquisition

Size of Investments Considered:
Min Size of Investment Considered (000s): $5,000
Max Size of Investment Considered (000s): $30,000

Geographical Preferences

International Preferences:
India
Europe
Middle East

Industry Preferences

In Medical/Health prefer:
Medical/Health
Health Services
Hospitals/Clinics/Primary

In Transportation prefer:
Transportation
Aerospace

In Business Serv. prefer:
Services
Media

In Manufact. prefer:
Manufacturing

In Agr/Forestr/Fish prefer:
Agriculture related

In Other prefer:
Socially Responsible

Additional Information
Year Founded: 2008
Current Activity Level: Actively seeking new investments

ICAPITAL (M) SDN BHD
11th Floor, Block C
Kelana Centrepoint Petaling Ja
Selangor, Malaysia
Phone: 603-7491-9100
Fax: 603-7491-9101

Management and Staff
Christine Lim, Partner
Nethan Pillai, Partner

Type of Firm
Private Equity Firm

Project Preferences

Type of Financing Preferred:
Seed

Geographical Preferences

International Preferences:
Hong Kong
Philippines
Singapore
Malaysia

Industry Preferences

In Internet Specific prefer:
Internet

Additional Information
Year Founded: 2000
Current Activity Level: Actively seeking new investments

ICCP MANAGEMENT CORPORATION
15/F, PSBank Center
777 Paseo de Roxas
Makati City, Philippines 1226
Phone: 63-2-811-4656
Fax: 63-2-819-0941
E-mail: info@iccpventureparnters.com
Website: www.iccpventurepartners.com

Management and Staff
Edwin Lau, Managing Director
William Valtos, Senior Managing Director

Type of Firm
Bank Affiliated

Project Preferences

Role in Financing:
Will function either as deal originator or investor in deals created by others

Type of Financing Preferred:
Leveraged Buyout
Early Stage
Expansion
Mezzanine
Turnaround
Startup

Size of Investments Considered:
Min Size of Investment Considered (000s): $500
Max Size of Investment Considered (000s): $500,000

Geographical Preferences

International Preferences:
Europe
Hong Kong
Philippines
Singapore

Industry Preferences

In Communications prefer:
Telecommunications

In Computer Other prefer:
Computer Related

In Semiconductor/Electr prefer:
Electronics

In Consumer Related prefer:
Consumer Products
Consumer Services

In Business Serv. prefer:
Services

Additional Information
Year Founded: 1989
Current Activity Level: Actively seeking new investments

ICEANGELS LLP

100 Adelaide Street West
Toronto, Canada M5H 1S3
Phone: 416-815-8889
Website: www.iceangels.com

Type of Firm

Private Equity Firm

Project Preferences

Type of Financing Preferred:
Early Stage

Geographical Preferences

Canadian Preferences:
All Canada

Additional Information

Year Founded: 2000
Current Activity Level: Actively seeking new investments

ICICI VENTURE FUNDS MANAGEMENT CO., PVT. LTD. (FKA: TDICI)

Ground Floor, Stanrose House
Appasaheb Marathe Marg
Mumbai, India 400025
Phone: 91-22-6655-5050
Fax: 91-22-6655-5055
E-mail: info@iciciventure.com
Website: www.iciciventure.com

Other Offices

Ground Floor, Scindia House
N.M.Marg, Ballard Estate
Mumbai, India 400 038
Phone: 9122-266-4767
Fax: 9122-266-4769

ICICI Towers
Bandra Kurla Complex
Mumbai, India 400051
Phone: 9122-653-8818

10th Floor, Prestige Obelisk
Kasturba Road
Bangalore, India 560 001
Phone: 91-80-4149-7021
Fax: 91-80-4149-7027

501, 5th Floor, World Trade Tower,
Barakhamba Road, Connaught Place
New Delhi, India 110001
Phone: 91-11-6618-4440
Fax: 91-11-6618-4450

Management and Staff

Akash Jain, Vice President
Aseem Rangnekar, Principal
Beena Chotai, Chief Financial Officer
Hoshedur Patel, Principal
Parth Gandhi, President
Prashant Purkar, President
Rajeev Bakshi, Managing Director
Ruchir Lahoty, Vice President
Suketu Kumar, Vice President
Sumant Kasliwal, Principal
Vishakha Mulye, CEO & Managing Director

Type of Firm

Bank Affiliated

Association Membership

Indian Venture Capital Association (IVCA)

Project Preferences

Role in Financing:
Prefer role as deal originator but will also invest in deals created by others

Type of Financing Preferred:
Leveraged Buyout
Early Stage
Expansion
Mezzanine
Balanced
Turnaround
Later Stage
Seed
Management Buyouts
Startup

Size of Investments Considered:
Min Size of Investment Considered (000s): $416
Max Size of Investment Considered (000s): $20,810

Geographical Preferences

United States Preferences:
All U.S.

International Preferences:
India
Asia
All International

Industry Focus

(% based on actual investment)

Other Products	34.6%
Medical/Health	23.2%
Consumer Related	15.9%
Internet Specific	10.9%
Communications and Media	4.5%
Computer Software and Services	4.4%
Industrial/Energy	3.0%
Biotechnology	1.8%
Semiconductors/Other Elect.	0.9%
Computer Hardware	0.8%

Additional Information

Name of Most Recent Fund: India Advantage Fund I
Most Recent Fund Was Raised: 02/01/2003
Year Founded: 1988
Capital Under Management: $2,000,000,000
Current Activity Level: Actively seeking new investments

ICON CAPITAL GROUP AS

PO Box 1767, Vika
Olso, Norway 0122
Phone: 47-23-30-8800
Fax: 47-23-30-8801
E-mail: post@icon-cg.com
Website: www.icon-cg.com

Management and Staff

Espen Magnussen, Partner

Type of Firm

Private Equity Firm

Additional Information

Current Activity Level: Actively seeking new investments

ICOS CAPITAL

Haaksbergweg 55
Amsterdam Z.O.
Amsterdam, Netherlands 1101 BR
Phone: 31-20-453-0777
Fax: 31-20-452-9286
E-mail: info@icoscapital.com
Website: www.icoscapital.com

Management and Staff

Fred van Efferink, Partner
Nityen Lal, General Partner
Peter van Gelderen, General Partner

Type of Firm

Private Equity Firm

Association Membership

Indian Venture Capital Association (IVCA)

Project Preferences

Type of Financing Preferred:
Early Stage
Startup

Geographical Preferences

International Preferences:
India
Netherlands

Industry Preferences

In Consumer Related prefer:
Food/Beverage

In Industrial/Energy prefer:
Energy Conservation Relat
Environmental Related

Additional Information

Year Founded: 2007
Current Activity Level: Actively seeking new investments

ICSO PRIVATE EQUITY (FKA: ICSO GESTION)

18 Place Dupuy
BP 808
Toulouse Cedex 6, France 31080
Phone: 33-5-3441-7418
Fax: 33-5-3441-7419
E-mail: contact.icso@wanadoo.fr
Website: www.icso.fr

Type of Firm

Private Equity Firm

Association Membership

French Venture Capital Association (AFIC)

Project Preferences

Type of Financing Preferred:
Fund of Funds
Leveraged Buyout
Generalist PE
Expansion
Early Stage
Balanced

Geographical Preferences

International Preferences:
France

Additional Information

Year Founded: 2003
Capital Under Management: $116,400,000
Current Activity Level: Actively seeking new investments

ICV CAPITAL PARTNERS LLC

The Chrysler Center
666 Third Avenue, 29th Floor
New York, NY USA 10017
Phone: 212-455-9600
Fax: 212-455-9603
Website: www.icvcapital.com

Management and Staff

Cory Mims, Managing Director
Lloyd Metz, Managing Director
Tarrus Richardson, Managing Director
Willie Woods, Managing Director
Zeena Rao, Vice President

Type of Firm

Private Equity Firm

Project Preferences

Type of Financing Preferred:
Leveraged Buyout
Expansion
Recapitalizations

Industry Focus

(% based on actual investment)

Consumer Related	76.5%
Medical/Health	23.5%

Additional Information

Year Founded: 2000
Capital Under Management: $313,000,000
Current Activity Level: Actively seeking new investments

ID CAPITAL

1250 Rene-Levesque Blvd. West
38th Floor
Montreal, Canada H3B 4W8
Phone: 514-397-8477
Fax: 514-673-8477
E-mail: info@idcapital.ca
Website: www.idcapital.ca

Management and Staff

Daniel Cyr, Managing Partner
David Bernardi, Managing Partner
Jean Paul Tardif, Managing Partner
Louis Saint-Jacques, Principal

Type of Firm

Private Equity Firm

Project Preferences

Type of Financing Preferred:
Early Stage
Seed
Startup

Geographical Preferences

Canadian Preferences:
Quebec

Additional Information

Year Founded: 2006
Capital Under Management: $50,800,000
Current Activity Level: Actively seeking new investments

ID TECHVENTURES, INC. (FKA: ACER TECHNOLOGY VENTURES)

7F, 122, DunHua North Road
Taipei, Taiwan 10595
Phone: 886-2-3518-3999
Fax: 886-2-6606-0021
E-mail: contact@idtvc.com
Website: www.idtvc.com

Other Offices

Room 1802
168 Xizang Zhong Road
Shanghai, China 200001
Phone: 86-21-6386-8708
Fax: 86-21-6386-8709

Room 1506, West Tower, Twin Towers, B-12
Jianguomenwai Dajie
Beijing, China 100022
Phone: 86-10-6568-4161
Fax: 86-10-6568-4162

Management and Staff

Edward Leung, Partner
Frank Lu, Partner
Ralph Cho, Partner
York Chen, Managing Partner

Type of Firm

Private Equity Firm

Project Preferences

Type of Financing Preferred:
Early Stage
Expansion
Balanced

Geographical Preferences

United States Preferences:
All U.S.

International Preferences:
Taiwan
China
Pacific
Asia

Industry Preferences

In Communications prefer:
Telecommunications

In Computer Software prefer:
Software

In Internet Specific prefer:
Internet

In Semiconductor/Electr prefer:
Semiconductor

In Business Serv. prefer:
Media

Additional Information

Year Founded: 2000
Capital Under Management: $171,000,000
Current Activity Level: Actively seeking new investments

ID VENTURES AMERICA, LLC (AKA: ACER TECHNOLOGY VENTURES)

5201 Great America Parkway
Suite 270
Santa Clara, CA USA 95054
Phone: 408-894-7900
Fax: 408-894-7939

E-mail: info@idsoftcapital.com
Website: www.idsoftcapital.com

Other Offices

7/F, No. 122
Dun Hwa N. Road
Taipei, Taiwan 105
Phone: 886-2-8712-9090
Fax: 886-2-8712-9091

Room 9C, Zhong Hai Building
398 Huai Hai Zhong Road
Shanghai, China 200020
Phone: 86-21-6386-8708
Fax: 86-21-6386-8709

Management and Staff

James Lu, General Partner
Pyramyth Liu, Venture Partner
Roger Liao, Venture Partner
Ronald Chwang, President & Chairman
Ted Lai, Chief Financial Officer

Type of Firm

Corporate PE/Venture

Association Membership

Singapore Venture Capital Association (SVCA)
Indian Venture Capital Association (IVCA)

Project Preferences

Role in Financing:

Prefer role as deal originator but will also invest in deals created by others

Type of Financing Preferred:

Second Stage Financing
Early Stage
Mezzanine
Balanced
Start-up Financing
Later Stage
Seed
First Stage Financing
Startup

Size of Investments Considered:

Min Size of Investment Considered (000s): $500
Max Size of Investment Considered (000s): $3,000

Geographical Preferences

United States Preferences:

All U.S.

Canadian Preferences:

All Canada

International Preferences:

India
Taiwan
China
Australia
Singapore
All International

Industry Preferences

In Communications prefer:

Communications and Media
Telecommunications
Wireless Communications
Data Communications

In Computer Hardware prefer:

Mini and Personal/Desktop
Computer Graphics and Dig
Disk Relat. Memory Device

In Computer Software prefer:

Software
Systems Software
Applications Software
Artificial Intelligence

In Internet Specific prefer:

Internet

In Semiconductor/Electr prefer:

Electronics
Electronic Components
Semiconductor
Controllers and Sensors
Component Testing Equipmt
Fiber Optics

In Consumer Related prefer:

Consumer Products

In Financial Services prefer:

Insurance

Additional Information

Year Founded: 1998
Capital Under Management: $340,000,000
Current Activity Level: Actively seeking new investments
Method of Compensation: Return on investment is of primary concern, do not charge fees

---

IDA CAPITAL COMPANY LIMITED

8F New Kudan Building
3-7-1 Kandajimbo-cho,Chiyodaku
Tokyo, Japan 101-0051
Phone: 813-3288-2786
Fax: 813-3288-2787
E-mail: info@idacapital.co.jp
Website: www.idacapital.co.jp

Type of Firm

Private Equity Firm

Project Preferences

Type of Financing Preferred:

Mezzanine
Balanced
Management Buyouts

Geographical Preferences

International Preferences:

Asia

Additional Information

Year Founded: 2002
Capital Under Management: $24,000,000
Current Activity Level: Actively seeking new investments

IDANTA PARTNERS, LTD.

12526 High Bluff Drive
Suite 925
San Diego, CA USA 92130
Phone: 858-356-0150
Website: www.idanta.com

Other Offices

4660 La Jolla Village Drive
Suite 775
San Diego, CA USA 92122
Phone: 619-452-9690

Management and Staff

Anita Colmie, Chief Financial Officer
David Dunn, Managing Partner
Jonathan Huberman, General Partner

Type of Firm

Private Equity Firm

Project Preferences

Role in Financing:

Prefer role as deal originator but will also invest in deals created by others

Type of Financing Preferred:

Second Stage Financing
Early Stage
Balanced
Seed
Management Buyouts
First Stage Financing
Acquisition

Size of Investments Considered:

Min Size of Investment Considered (000s): $500
Max Size of Investment Considered (000s): $10,000

Geographical Preferences

United States Preferences:

All U.S.

Industry Focus

(% based on actual investment)

Semiconductors/Other Elect.	42.5%
Computer Hardware	15.6%
Communications and Media	14.3%
Computer Software and Services	13.3%
Internet Specific	5.0%
Other Products	4.5%
Consumer Related	3.5%
Medical/Health	1.4%

Additional Information

Year Founded: 1971
Capital Under Management: $400,000,000
Current Activity Level: Actively seeking new investments

Method of Compensation: Return on investment is of primary concern, do not charge fees

IDEA CAPITAL FUNDS SGR SPA

Via dell'Annunciata 23/4
Milan, Italy 20121
Phone: 39-2-2906-631
Fax: 39-2-2906-6320
E-mail: info@ideasgr.com
Website: www.ideasgr.com

Management and Staff

Danilo Beltramino, Chief Financial Officer
Franco Mosca, Managing Director
Mario Barozzi, Chief Executive Officer

Type of Firm

Investment Management Firm

Project Preferences

Type of Financing Preferred:

Fund of Funds
Leveraged Buyout
Acquisition

Geographical Preferences

United States Preferences:

All U.S.

International Preferences:

Italy
Europe
Asia

Additional Information

Year Founded: 2006
Capital Under Management: $1,570,800,000
Current Activity Level: Actively seeking new investments

IDEA FUND PARTNERS

4505 Emperor Boulevard
Suite 130
Durham, NC USA 27703
Phone: 919-941-5600
Fax: 919-941-5630
E-mail: info@ideafundpartners.com
Website: www.ideafundpartners.com

Management and Staff

David Rizzo, Managing Partner
Lister Delgado, Partner
W. Merrette Moore, Partner

Type of Firm

Private Equity Firm

Association Membership

National Venture Capital Association - USA (NVCA)

Project Preferences

Role in Financing:

Will function either as deal originator or investor in deals created by others

Type of Financing Preferred:

Second Stage Financing
Early Stage
Seed
First Stage Financing

Size of Investments Considered:

Min Size of Investment Considered (000s): $250
Max Size of Investment Considered (000s): $1,000

Geographical Preferences

United States Preferences:

Southwest

Industry Preferences

In Communications prefer:

Wireless Communications

In Computer Software prefer:

Software

In Semiconductor/Electr prefer:

Semiconductor

In Medical/Health prefer:

Medical Diagnostics
Medical Products

In Industrial/Energy prefer:

Energy
Advanced Materials

Additional Information

Name of Most Recent Fund: IDEA Fund I, L.P.
Most Recent Fund Was Raised: 02/14/2007
Year Founded: 2003
Capital Under Management: $25,000,000
Current Activity Level: Actively seeking new investments
Method of Compensation: Return on investment is of primary concern, do not charge fees

IDEALAB!

130 West Union Street
Pasadena, CA USA 91103
Phone: 626-585-6900
Fax: 626-535-2701
Website: www.idealab.com

Other Offices

58-59 Haymarket
Fifth Floor
London, United Kingdom SW1Y 4QX
Phone: 20-7968-4700
Fax: 20-7930-4310

675 Avenue of the Americas
New York, NY USA 10010
Phone: 212-420-7700
Fax: 212-929-4423

380 Portage Avenue
Palo Alto, CA USA 94306
Phone: 650-251-5500
Fax: 650-251-5501

Management and Staff

Bradley Ramberg, Chief Financial Officer
Howard Morgan, President
Marcia Goodstein, President & COO
William Gross, Managing Director

Type of Firm

Incubator/Development Program

Project Preferences

Type of Financing Preferred:

Early Stage

Industry Preferences

In Internet Specific prefer:

Internet

Additional Information

Year Founded: 1996
Current Activity Level: Actively seeking new investments

IDEB (INSTITUT DE DEVELOPPEMENT ECONOMIQUE DE LA BOURGOGNE)

7, Bd de la Tremouille
BP 1449
Dijon Cedex, France 21052
Phone: 33-3-8060-0800
Fax: 33-3-8060-0804
Website: www.ideb.fr

Type of Firm

Private Equity Firm

Project Preferences

Type of Financing Preferred:

Leveraged Buyout
Early Stage
Expansion

Size of Investments Considered:

Min Size of Investment Considered (000s): $38
Max Size of Investment Considered (000s): $377

Geographical Preferences

International Preferences:

France

Additional Information

Year Founded: 1984
Current Activity Level: Actively seeking new investments

IDFC CAPITAL (SINGAPORE) PTE., LTD.

One Finlayson Green #16-02
Singapore, Singapore 049246
Phone: 65-6499-0700
Fax: 65-6536-3359

Management and Staff

Melissa Brown, Managing Director
Veronica John, Chief Executive Officer

Type of Firm

Private Equity Advisor or Fund of Funds

Project Preferences

Type of Financing Preferred:
Fund of Funds

Geographical Preferences

International Preferences:
India
China
Asia
Africa

Additional Information

Year Founded: 2008
Current Activity Level: Actively seeking new investments

IDFC PRIVATE EQUITY CO., LTD.

17, Vaswani Mansion, 3rd Floor
Dinshaw Vachha Rd, Churchgate
Mumbai, India 400 020
Phone: 91-22-2202-0748
Fax: 91-22-2202-0798
E-mail: fund@idfcpe.com
Website: www.idfcpe.com

Management and Staff

Nimesh Grover, Principal
Prasad Gadkari, Principal
Raja Parthasarathy, Managing Director
Rajiv Lall, CEO & Managing Director
Rupa Vora, Chief Financial Officer
S.G. Shyam Sundar, Managing Director
Satish Mandhana, Managing Director
Shivani Bhasin, Principal
Vineet Sachdeva, Principal
Vinod Giri, Principal

Type of Firm

Bank Affiliated

Association Membership

Indian Venture Capital Association (IVCA)

Project Preferences

Type of Financing Preferred:
Early Stage
Expansion
Mezzanine
Balanced
Turnaround
Later Stage
Seed
Startup

Size of Investments Considered:
Min Size of Investment Considered (000s): $7,000
Max Size of Investment Considered (000s): $33,000

Geographical Preferences

International Preferences:
India

Industry Preferences

In Communications prefer:
Telecommunications

In Medical/Health prefer:
Medical/Health

In Consumer Related prefer:
Hotels and Resorts
Education Related

In Industrial/Energy prefer:
Energy
Oil and Gas Exploration

In Transportation prefer:
Transportation

In Business Serv. prefer:
Services
Distribution

Additional Information

Year Founded: 2002
Capital Under Management: $185,000,000
Current Activity Level: Actively seeking new investments

IDG INTERNATIONAL DATA GROUP AB

Sturegatan 11
Stockholm, Sweden 106 78
Phone: 46-8-453-60-00
Fax: 46-8-453-60-05
Website: www.idg.se

Type of Firm

Corporate PE/Venture
Additional Information
Current Activity Level: Actively seeking new investments

IDG TECHNOLOGY VENTURE INVESTMENT, INC.

Room 616 Tower A, COFCO Plaza
Eight Jianguomen Nei Dajie
Beijing, China 100005
Phone: 86-10-6526-2400
Fax: 86-10-6526-0700
E-mail: idgvc@idgvc.com.cn
Website: www.idgvc.com

Other Offices

Unit 1509, 15th Floor., The Center
99 Queen's Road
Central, Hong Kong
Phone: 852-2529-1016
Fax: 852-2529-1619

Room 1105, Aetna Tower
Number 107 Zunyi Road
Shanghai, China 200051
Phone: 86-21-6237-5408
Fax: 86-21-6237-5899

One Exeter Plaza
15th Floor Penthouse Suite
Boston, MA USA 02116
Phone: 617-534-1243
Fax: 617-277-0626

Room 2609B Jinzhonghuan Business Building, No.3037 Jintian Road, Futian
Shenzhen, China 518048
Phone: 86-755-8280-5462
Fax: 86-755-8280-5475

2635 North First Street
Suite 150
San Jose, CA USA 95134
Phone: 408-907-0040
Fax: 408-456-0688

Management and Staff

Dongliang Lin, General Partner
Fei Yang, General Partner
Gongquan Wang, General Partner
Hugo Shong, Managing Partner
Jianguang Li, General Partner
Michael Mao, Partner
Quan Zhou, Managing Director
Simon Ho, Vice President
Suyang Zhang, Managing Partner
Xi Stella Jin, Venture Partner
Young Guo, Vice President

Type of Firm

Private Equity Firm

Project Preferences

Role in Financing:
Prefer role in deals created by others

Type of Financing Preferred:
Expansion
Early Stage

Balanced

Size of Investments Considered:
Min Size of Investment Considered (000s): $500
Max Size of Investment Considered (000s): $5,000

Geographical Preferences

International Preferences:
China

Industry Preferences

In Communications prefer:
Communications and Media
Telecommunications

In Computer Software prefer:
Computer Services
Software

In Internet Specific prefer:
Internet

In Computer Other prefer:
Computer Related

In Biotechnology prefer:
Biotechnology

In Medical/Health prefer:
Medical/Health
Pharmaceuticals

In Consumer Related prefer:
Consumer

In Manufact. prefer:
Publishing

Additional Information
Year Founded: 1992
Capital Under Management: $247,900,000
Current Activity Level: Actively seeking new investments
Method of Compensation: Return on investment is of primary concern, do not charge fees

---

IDG VENTURES INDIA
7B, 7F, Sobha Pearl
1, Commissariat Road
Bangalore, India 560 025
Phone: 91-80-4132-9225
Fax: 91-80-4132-9226
E-mail: contact@idgvcindia.com
Website: www.idgvcindia.com

Other Offices
C/o. Int. Financial Services Limited
IFS Court, TwentyEight, Cybercity
Ebene,, Mauritius
Phone: 230-467-3000
Fax: 230-467-4000

Trident Hotel
Number 1212 Nariman Point
Mumbai, India 400 021
Phone: 91-22-6630-6010
Fax: 91-80-4132-9226

Management and Staff
Manik Arora, Managing Director
Sudhir Sethi, Chairman & Managing Director
T.C. Meenakshisundaram, Managing Director

Type of Firm
Private Equity Firm

Project Preferences

Type of Financing Preferred:
Early Stage
Expansion
Balanced

Size of Investments Considered:
Min Size of Investment Considered (000s): $500
Max Size of Investment Considered (000s): $10,000

Geographical Preferences

International Preferences:
India

Industry Preferences

In Communications prefer:
Wireless Communications

In Computer Software prefer:
Software

In Financial Services prefer:
Financial Services

Additional Information
Year Founded: 2006
Capital Under Management: $150,000,000
Current Activity Level: Actively seeking new investments

IDG VENTURES KOREA
9th Fl. Landmark B/D 77-11
Samsung-Dong, Gangnam-Gu
Seoul, South Korea 135-090
Phone: 822-3447-0510
Fax: 822-3447-0520
Website: www.idgvk.com

Management and Staff
Dong-Jo Choi, Principal
Duk-Hwan Oh, Chief Executive Officer
Matthew Lee, Chief Financial Officer
Suk Geun Chung, Principal
Sungtae Jin, Vice President

Type of Firm
Private Equity Firm

Project Preferences

Type of Financing Preferred:
Early Stage

Geographical Preferences

International Preferences:
Korea, South

Industry Preferences

In Medical/Health prefer:
Health Services

In Consumer Related prefer:
Education Related

In Business Serv. prefer:
Services
Media

In Other prefer:
Environment Responsible

Additional Information
Year Founded: 2007
Capital Under Management: $100,000,000
Current Activity Level: Actively seeking new investments

IDG VENTURES SF (FKA: IDG VENTURES PACIFIC)
One Letterman Drive
Building D, Suite 100
San Francisco, CA USA 94129
Phone: 415-439-4420
Fax: 415-439-4428
E-mail: sf@idgventures.com
Website: www.idgventures.com

Management and Staff
Alexander Rosen, Managing Director
Patrick Kenealy, Managing Director
Philip Sanderson, Managing Director
Susan Cheng, Chief Financial Officer

Type of Firm
Private Equity Firm

Association Membership
Western Association of Venture Capitalists (WAVC)
National Venture Capital Association - USA (NVCA)

Project Preferences

Type of Financing Preferred:
Early Stage
Other
Seed
First Stage Financing

Size of Investments Considered:
Min Size of Investment Considered (000s): $1,000
Max Size of Investment Considered (000s): $8,000

Geographical Preferences

United States Preferences:
Midwest
Northwest
Southern California
Northern California
West Coast
California

Industry Preferences

In Computer Software prefer:
Software

In Internet Specific prefer:
E-Commerce Technology
Ecommerce

In Business Serv. prefer:
Services
Media

In Other prefer:
Environment Responsible

Additional Information

Name of Most Recent Fund: IDG Ventures SF
Most Recent Fund Was Raised: 12/03/2007
Year Founded: 1996
Capital Under Management: $100,000,000
Current Activity Level: Actively seeking new investments

IDG VENTURES VIETNAM

Vincom City Tower B, 15th Fl.
Unit 2-3, 191 Ba Trieu Street
Hai Ba Trung District, Hanoi, Vietnam
Phone: 84-4-220-0348
Fax: 84-4-220-0349
E-mail: info@idgvv.com.vn
Website: www.idgvv.com.vn

Other Offices

Sunwah Tower, 11th Floor, Suite 1108
115 Nguyen Hue Street, District 1
Ho Chi Minh City, Vietnam
Phone: 84-8-827-8888
Fax: 84-8-827-8899

Management and Staff

Duc Tran, General Partner
Frederic De Bure, Venture Partner
Hiep Do, Vice President
Hoang Bao Nguyen, Managing General Partner
Rachan Reddy, General Partner
Reza Behnam, Venture Partner
Vu Thanh Trung, Chief Financial Officer

Type of Firm

Private Equity Firm

Project Preferences

Role in Financing:
Prefer role as deal originator but will also invest in deals created by others

Type of Financing Preferred:
Early Stage
Seed
Startup

Geographical Preferences

International Preferences:
Vietnam

Industry Preferences

In Communications prefer:
Telecommunications
Wireless Communications

In Internet Specific prefer:
E-Commerce Technology
Internet
Ecommerce
Web Aggregration/Portals

In Consumer Related prefer:
Consumer
Entertainment and Leisure

In Business Serv. prefer:
Media

Additional Information

Year Founded: 2003
Capital Under Management: $100,000,000
Current Activity Level: Actively seeking new investments
Method of Compensation: Return on investment is of primary concern, do not charge fees

---

IDI ASSET MANAGEMENT

18 avenue Matignon
Paris, France 75008
Phone: 33-1-5527-8040
Fax: 33-1-4017-0444
E-mail: idi@idi.fr
Website: www.idi.fr

Management and Staff

Christian Langlois-Meurinne, President
Jacques Halperin, Chief Executive Officer

Type of Firm

Private Equity Firm

Association Membership

French Venture Capital Association (AFIC)

Project Preferences

Type of Financing Preferred:
Leveraged Buyout
Early Stage
Expansion

Geographical Preferences

International Preferences:
United Kingdom
Europe
France

Industry Preferences

In Communications prefer:
Telecommunications

In Computer Software prefer:
Software

Additional Information

Year Founded: 1970
Capital Under Management: $284,400,000
Current Activity Level: Actively seeking new investments

IDIA AGRICAPITAL

100 Montparnasse Boulevard
Paris, France 75682
Phone: 33-1-4323-2434
Fax: 33-1-4323-6582
Website: www.ca-idia.com

Management and Staff

Herve Delachaume, Managing Director
Hubert Achard, Partner

Type of Firm

Bank Affiliated

Association Membership

French Venture Capital Association (AFIC)

Project Preferences

Type of Financing Preferred:
Leveraged Buyout
Expansion

Geographical Preferences

International Preferences:
France

Industry Preferences

In Consumer Related prefer:
Food/Beverage

In Agr/Forestr/Fish prefer:
Agriculture related

Additional Information

Year Founded: 2004
Current Activity Level: Actively seeking new investments

IDP INDUSTRIAL DEVELOPMENT PARTNERS GMBH & CO KG

Postfach 1226
Limburger Strasse 9
Konigstein, Germany 61452
Phone: 49-6174-4017
Fax: 49-6174-4010
E-mail: Germany@idp-investments.com
Website: www.idp-investments.com

Other Offices

Baarerstrasse 12
Zug, Switzerland 6300
Phone: 41-41-7123412
Fax: 41-41-7291559

211 Congress Street
2nd Floor
Boston, MA USA 02110
Phone: 617-350-3100
Fax: 617-350-7222

Type of Firm

Private Equity Firm

Association Membership

German Venture Capital Association (BVK)

Project Preferences

Type of Financing Preferred:

Mezzanine
Expansion
Early Stage
Management Buyouts
Recapitalizations

Geographical Preferences

International Preferences:

Germany

Industry Preferences

In Medical/Health prefer:

Medical/Health

In Consumer Related prefer:

Retail

In Manufact. prefer:

Manufacturing

Additional Information

Year Founded: 1980
Capital Under Management: $19,900,000
Current Activity Level: Actively seeking new investments

IDPC (INSTITUT DE DEVELOPPEMENT ET PARTICIPATION AU CAPITAL)

6 avenue Pierre Mendes France
Parthenay, France 79200
Phone: 33-5-4964-0186
Fax: 33-5-4994-6889
E-mail: infos@idpc.fr
Website: www.idpc.fr

Type of Firm

Private Equity Firm

Project Preferences

Type of Financing Preferred:

Leveraged Buyout
Expansion

Geographical Preferences

International Preferences:

France

Additional Information

Year Founded: 2000
Current Activity Level: Actively seeking new investments

IEUROPE CAPITAL LLC

1199 Park Avenue
Suite 19A
New York, NY USA 10128
Phone: 212-828-0037
Fax: 212-410-6196
E-mail: info@ieurope.com
Website: www.ieurope.com

Other Offices

Zugligeti ut 41.
Budapest, Hungary 1121
Phone: 36-1-200-4015
Fax: 36-1-200-5707

Management and Staff

Charles Huebner, Partner
Kristina Davison, Founding Partner
Laszlo Czirjak, Founding Partner

Type of Firm

Private Equity Firm

Association Membership

European Private Equity and Venture Capital Assoc.

Project Preferences

Role in Financing:

Prefer role as deal originator but will also invest in deals created by others

Type of Financing Preferred:

Leveraged Buyout
Generalist PE
Expansion
Acquisition

Size of Investments Considered:

Min Size of Investment Considered (000s): $300
Max Size of Investment Considered (000s): $3,000

Geographical Preferences

International Preferences:

Hungary
Slovenia
Slovak Repub.
Central Europe
Czech Republic
Western Europe
Croatia
Romania

Industry Preferences

In Communications prefer:

Communications and Media
Telecommunications

In Consumer Related prefer:

Food/Beverage
Consumer Products
Consumer Services

In Industrial/Energy prefer:

Environmental Related

Additional Information

Year Founded: 2000
Current Activity Level: Actively seeking new investments

IFCI VENTURE CAPITAL FUNDS, LTD. (FKA: RISK CAPITAL & TECH.)

IFCI Tower, 13th Floor
61 Nehru Place
New Delhi, India 110 019
Phone: 91-11-2645-3343
Fax: 91-11-2645-3348
E-mail: business@ifciventure.com
Website: www.ifciventure.com

Management and Staff

A.C. Ahuja, Chairman & Managing Director
Atual Kumar Rai, CEO & Managing Director
S.P. Lavakara, Chief Executive Officer
Shri B.N. Nayak, Managing Director

Type of Firm

Bank Affiliated

Association Membership

Indian Venture Capital Association (IVCA)

Project Preferences

Role in Financing:

Prefer role as deal originator but will also invest in deals created by others

Type of Financing Preferred:

Early Stage
Expansion
Balanced
Later Stage
Startup

Size of Investments Considered:

Min Size of Investment Considered (000s): $220
Max Size of Investment Considered (000s): $660

Geographical Preferences

International Preferences:

India
Europe
Mauritius
Cyprus

Industry Preferences

In Communications prefer:

Communications and Media

In Computer Software prefer:

Software

In Biotechnology prefer:
Biotechnology
In Medical/Health prefer:
Pharmaceuticals
In Industrial/Energy prefer:
Machinery
Environmental Related
In Transportation prefer:
Transportation
In Manufact. prefer:
Manufacturing
In Other prefer:
Environment Responsible

Additional Information
Year Founded: 1975
Capital Under Management: $17,600,000
Current Activity Level: Actively seeking new investments
Method of Compensation: Return on invest. most important, but chg. closing fees, service fees, etc.

IFE MEZZANINE (FKA: IFE CONSEIL)
41 avenue George V
Paris, France 75008
Phone: 33-1-5652-0240
Fax: 33-1-4720-0694
E-mail: info@ifeconseil.com
Website: www.ifemezzanine.com

Management and Staff
Dominique Fouquoire, Partner
Jean-Pascal Ley, Partner
Jean-Pierre Molin, Partner
Regis Mitjavile, Managing Director

Type of Firm
Bank Affiliated

Association Membership
French Venture Capital Association (AFIC)
European Private Equity and Venture Capital Assoc.

Project Preferences
Role in Financing:
Will function either as deal originator or investor in deals created by others
Type of Financing Preferred:
Leveraged Buyout
Expansion
Mezzanine
Size of Investments Considered:
Min Size of Investment Considered (000s): $9,886
Max Size of Investment Considered (000s): $41,940

Geographical Preferences
International Preferences:
Italy
Luxembourg
Netherlands
Switzerland
Europe
Spain
Belgium
Germany
France

Industry Focus
(% based on actual investment)

Industrial/Energy	57.3%
Communications and Media	39.0%
Other Products	3.8%

Additional Information
Name of Most Recent Fund: IFE Fund II
Most Recent Fund Was Raised: 07/22/2005
Year Founded: 1999
Capital Under Management: $397,600,000
Current Activity Level: Actively seeking new investments

IGLOBE PARTNERS, LTD.
5201 Great America Parkway
Suite 320
Santa Clara, CA USA 95054
Phone: 408-982-2126
Fax: 408-982-2129
Website: www.iglobepartners.com

Other Offices
Neustadt Gasse 12
Zurich, Switzerland 8001

435 Orchard Road
#19-03 Wisma Atria
Singapore, Singapore 238877
Phone: 65-6836-9119
Fax: 65-6732-9787

Goetheplatz 9
Frankfurt am Main, Germany 60313
Phone: 49-17269-21534

Management and Staff
Bill Barmeier, General Partner
Doris Yee, General Partner
Frankie Siew Teck Tan, Venture Partner
Jean-Philippe Sarraut, Venture Partner
Joseph Zaelit, Venture Partner
Peng Ang, Managing Partner
Soo Boon Koh, Managing Partner
Trudi Schifter, General Partner
XiaoBao Hu, Venture Partner

Type of Firm
Private Equity Firm

Association Membership
Singapore Venture Capital Association (SVCA)

Project Preferences
Type of Financing Preferred:
Early Stage
Mezzanine
Balanced
Size of Investments Considered:
Min Size of Investment Considered (000s): $1
Max Size of Investment Considered (000s): $10

Geographical Preferences
United States Preferences:
All U.S.
International Preferences:
Europe
Singapore
Asia

Industry Preferences
In Communications prefer:
Communications and Media
Wireless Communications
Media and Entertainment
In Internet Specific prefer:
Internet
In Semiconductor/Electr prefer:
Semiconductor
In Medical/Health prefer:
Health Services

Additional Information
Year Founded: 1999
Capital Under Management: $92,000,000
Current Activity Level: Actively seeking new investments

IGLOBE TREASURY MANAGEMENT, LTD.
Unit 16, 43D Apollo Drive
Mairangi Bay
Auckland, New Zealand
Phone: 649-915-3401
Fax: 649-968-8431
Website: www.iglobetreasury.com

Other Offices
11 Biopolis Way
Helios #09-03
Singapore, Singapore 138667
Phone: 65-6478-9716
Fax: 65-6478-9717

Management and Staff
Anthony Paul Bishop, Managing Partner
Christopher Due, Venture Partner
Colin Harvey, Venture Partner
Doris Yee, General Partner
Joseph Platnick, Venture Partner
Koh Soo Boon, Managing Partner
Martin Greenberg, Venture Partner

Michael Standbridge, Venture Partner
N. Ganesan, Venture Partner
Philip Lum, General Partner

Type of Firm
Private Equity Firm

Project Preferences

Type of Financing Preferred:
Early Stage

Geographical Preferences

International Preferences:
New Zealand

Industry Preferences

In Communications prefer:
Communications and Media

In Semiconductor/Electr prefer:
Electronics

In Biotechnology prefer:
Biotechnology

In Medical/Health prefer:
Health Services
Pharmaceuticals

In Industrial/Energy prefer:
Environmental Related

In Agr/Forestr/Fish prefer:
Agriculture related

Additional Information
Name of Most Recent Fund: iGlobe Treasury Fund
Most Recent Fund Was Raised: 06/24/2003
Year Founded: 2002
Capital Under Management: $19,000,000
Current Activity Level: Actively seeking new investments

IGNIA PARTNERS LLC
Av. Ricardo Margain 575
Parque Corp Sta. Engracia
San Pedro Garza Garcia, Mexico 66267
Phone: 52-81-8000-7165
Fax: 52-81-8000-7095
E-mail: info@ignia.com.mx
Website: www.ignia.com.mx

Management and Staff
Alvaro Rodriguez Arrequi, Managing Director
Michael Chu, Managing Director

Type of Firm
Private Equity Firm

Project Preferences

Type of Financing Preferred:
Leveraged Buyout
Early Stage
Expansion
Balanced
Startup

Geographical Preferences

International Preferences:
Latin America
Mexico

Industry Preferences

In Medical/Health prefer:
Medical/Health

In Consumer Related prefer:
Education Related

In Utilities prefer:
Utilities

Additional Information
Year Founded: 2008
Capital Under Management: $40,700,000
Current Activity Level: Actively seeking new investments

IGNITE GROUP, THE (AKA: IGNITE ASSOCIATES, LLC)
255 Shoreline Drive
Suite 510
Redwood City, CA USA 94065
Phone: 650-622-2000
Fax: 650-622-2015
E-mail: info@ignitegroup.com
Website: www.ignitegroup.com

Other Offices
Burex Kyobashi Bldg., 6th Floor
7-14, Kyobashi 2-Chome
Chuo-ku, Tokyo, Japan 104-0031
Phone: 81-3-5159-0535
Fax: 81-3-5159-0534

Management and Staff
Akihiro Takagi, General Partner
Deanne Kenneally, General Partner
Hiroaki Yano, President
Hiroshi Sakai, General Partner
Masato Kikuchi, Venture Partner
Nobuo Mii, Managing Partner
Ryu Hoshino, Principal
Steve Payne, General Partner
Tony Cannestra, Principal

Type of Firm
Private Equity Firm

Project Preferences

Role in Financing:
Will function either as deal originator or investor in deals created by others

Type of Financing Preferred:
Second Stage Financing
Early Stage
Start-up Financing
Seed
First Stage Financing

Size of Investments Considered:
Min Size of Investment Considered (000s): $2,000
Max Size of Investment Considered (000s): $10,000

Geographical Preferences

United States Preferences:
Southern California
Northern California

International Preferences:
India
China
Japan

Industry Focus
(% based on actual investment)

Internet Specific	41.2%
Computer Software and Services	21.0%
Semiconductors/Other Elect.	19.4%
Communications and Media	14.2%
Computer Hardware	3.2%
Medical/Health	0.9%

Additional Information
Year Founded: 1998
Capital Under Management: $200,000,000
Current Activity Level: Actively seeking new investments
Method of Compensation: Return on invest. most important, but chg. closing fees, service fees, etc.

IGNITION CAPITAL
1500 Fourth Avenue
Suite 200
Seattle, WA USA 98101
Phone: 206-438-0777
Fax: 206-971-5055
Website: www.igncap.com

Management and Staff
Darrell Walker, Principal
John Zagula, Founding Partner
Jon Anderson, Founding Partner
Richard Tong, Founding Partner
Robert Headley, Founding Partner

Type of Firm
Private Equity Firm

Project Preferences

Type of Financing Preferred:
Expansion
Generalist PE
Later Stage

Industry Preferences

In Communications prefer:
Communications and Media

In Medical/Health prefer:
Health Services

In Industrial/Energy prefer:
Energy

In Business Serv. prefer:
Services

Additional Information
Name of Most Recent Fund: Ignition Growth Capital I, L.P.
Most Recent Fund Was Raised: 09/30/2007
Year Founded: 2007
Capital Under Management: $672,000,000
Current Activity Level: Actively seeking new investments

IGNITION PARTNERS (FKA: IGNITION CORPORATION)

11400 Southeast Sixth Street
Suite 100
Bellevue, WA USA 98004
Phone: 425-709-0772
Fax: 425-709-0798
E-mail: info@ignitionpartners.com
Website: www.ignitionpartners.com

Other Offices
1500 Fourth Avenue
Suite 200
Seattle, WA USA 98101
Phone: 206-438-0777
Fax: 206-971-5055

Management and Staff
Adrian Smith, Partner
Brad Silverberg, Partner
Cameron Myhrvold, Partner
Carolyn Duffy, Principal
Jack Ferry, Chief Financial Officer
John Zagula, Partner
John Ludwig, Partner
John Connors, Partner
Jon Anderson, Partner
Jonathan Roberts, Partner
Martin Tobias, Venture Partner
Michelle Goldberg, Partner
Richard Fade, Partner
Richard Tong, Partner
Robert Headley, Partner
Steven Hooper, Partner

Type of Firm
Private Equity Firm

Project Preferences

Role in Financing:
Prefer role as deal originator but will also invest in deals created by others

Type of Financing Preferred:
Second Stage Financing
Expansion
Early Stage
Generalist PE
Seed
Later Stage
First Stage Financing
Startup

Size of Investments Considered:
Min Size of Investment Considered (000s): $1,000
Max Size of Investment Considered (000s): $30,000

Geographical Preferences

United States Preferences:
Northwest
Northern California
Rocky Mountain
West Coast

Canadian Preferences:
Western Canada

Industry Preferences

In Communications prefer:
Telecommunications
Wireless Communications
Data Communications
Other Communication Prod.

In Computer Software prefer:
Software
Systems Software
Applications Software

In Internet Specific prefer:
Internet
Web Aggregration/Portals

In Medical/Health prefer:
Medical/Health

In Consumer Related prefer:
Consumer Services
Education Related

Additional Information
Name of Most Recent Fund: Ignition Venture Partners III, L.P.
Most Recent Fund Was Raised: 11/10/2004
Year Founded: 2000
Capital Under Management: $2,011,000,000
Current Activity Level: Actively seeking new investments
Method of Compensation: Return on investment is of primary concern, do not charge fees

---

IK INVESTMENT PARTNERS, LTD. (FKA: INDUSTRI KAPITAL, LTD.)

Brettenham House
5 Lancaster Place
London, United Kingdom WC2E 7EN
Phone: 44-20-7304-4300
Fax: 44-20-7304-0124
Website: www.ikinvest.com

Other Offices
30-32 New Street
Charles Bisson House, 3rd Floor
St. Helier, Japan JE2 3RA
Phone: 44-1534-639-380
Fax: 44-1534-639-382

ABC-Bogen
ABC-Strasse 19
Hamburg, Germany D-20354
Phone: 49-40-369-8850
Fax: 49-40-3698-8530

Olav V's gate 5
9th Floor, Postboks 1273
Oslo, Norway 0111
Phone: 47-23-114-650
Fax: 47-22-839-058

Birger Jarlsgatan 4
Stockholm, Sweden 11434
Phone: 46-8678-9500
Fax: 46-8678-0336

6 rue Christophe Colomb
Paris, France 75008
Phone: 33-144-430-660
Fax: 33-144-430-670

Management and Staff
Christopher Masek, Managing Partner
Dan Soudry, Partner
Detlef Dinsel, Managing Partner
Gerard De Geer, Partner
Gustav Ohman, Managing Partner
Helena Stjernholm, Partner
James Yates, Partner
Kristiaan Nieuwenburg, Partner
Mads Larsen, Partner
Michael Rosenlew, Managing Partner
Trygve Grindheim, Partner

Type of Firm
Private Equity Firm

Association Membership
British Venture Capital Association (BVCA)
French Venture Capital Association (AFIC)
Swedish Venture Capital Association (SVCA)
European Private Equity and Venture Capital Assoc.

Project Preferences

Type of Financing Preferred:
Leveraged Buyout
Management Buyouts

Size of Investments Considered:
Min Size of Investment Considered (000s): $18,000
Max Size of Investment Considered (000s): $359,800

Geographical Preferences

International Preferences:
Sweden
United Kingdom
Europe
Scandanavia/Nordic Region

Industry Focus

(% based on actual investment)

Industrial/Energy	35.9%
Consumer Related	24.7%
Other Products	24.6%
Medical/Health	6.6%
Biotechnology	5.5%
Internet Specific	2.4%
Communications and Media	0.3%

Additional Information

Year Founded: 1989
Capital Under Management: $5,592,200,000
Current Activity Level: Actively seeking new investments

IK INVESTMENTBANK AG

Renngasse 10
Vienna, Austria 1010
Phone: 43-1-53-135-668
Fax: 43-1-53-135-923
Website: www.ikib.at

Management and Staff

Robert Hufnugel, Vice President

Type of Firm

Bank Affiliated

Association Membership

European Private Equity and Venture Capital Assoc.

Project Preferences

Type of Financing Preferred:

Balanced

Geographical Preferences

International Preferences:

Europe

Additional Information

Year Founded: 1998
Capital Under Management: $58,100,000
Current Activity Level: Actively seeking new investments

IKB PRIVATE EQUITY GMBH (AKA: IKB BETEILIGUNGSGESELLSCHAFT)

Wilhelm-Botzkes-Strasse 1
Dusseldorf, Germany 40474
Phone: 49-211-822114
Fax: 49-211-82213949
E-mail: info@ikp-pe.de
Website: www.ikb-private-equity.de

Management and Staff

Anne Osthaus, Managing Director

Type of Firm

Bank Affiliated

Association Membership

German Venture Capital Association (BVK)
European Private Equity and Venture Capital Assoc.

Project Preferences

Type of Financing Preferred:

Early Stage
Expansion
Mezzanine
Seed
Management Buyouts
Startup
Recapitalizations

Geographical Preferences

International Preferences:

Germany

Industry Preferences

In Communications prefer:

Communications and Media
Telecommunications

In Semiconductor/Electr prefer:

Electronics

In Biotechnology prefer:

Biotechnology

In Medical/Health prefer:

Medical/Health

Additional Information

Year Founded: 2000
Capital Under Management: $403,600,000
Current Activity Level: Actively seeking new investments

IKEGIN CAPITAL CO., LTD.

4F OsakaUmeda Ikegin Bldg.
18-14 Chaya-machi,Kita-ku
Osaka, Japan 530-0013
Phone: 81-6-6375-7204
Fax: 81-3-6375-7214
Website: www.ikegin-c.jp

Type of Firm

Bank Affiliated

Additional Information

Year Founded: 1989
Current Activity Level: Actively seeking new investments

IL&FS INVESTMENT MANAGERS LTD (FKA: IL&FS VENTURE CORP)

1st Flr, Plot No.C-22, G Block
Bandra Kurla Complex, Bandra E
Mumbai, India 400 051
Phone: 91-22-2653-3333
Fax: 91-22-2653-3056
E-mail: fund_info@ivcindia.com
Website: www.ilfsinvestmentmanagers.com

Other Offices

Aum Plaza First Floor, No 76,
3rd Cross, Residency Road
Bangalore, India 560025
Phone: 9180-4034-3333
Fax: 9180-4034-3310

Management and Staff

Arun Prakash Korati, Vice President
Guhan Subramaniam, Managing Partner
Hetal Gandhi, Managing Director
Kuldeep Chawla, Vice President
Manoj Borkar, Chief Financial Officer
Mark Silgardo, Managing Partner
Muneesh Chawla, Managing Director
Rahul Shah, Managing Partner
Shahzaad Dalal, Managing Director
Sunil V. Diwakar, Managing Partner

Type of Firm

Bank Affiliated

Association Membership

Indian Venture Capital Association (IVCA)

Project Preferences

Role in Financing:

Prefer role as deal originator but will also invest in deals created by others

Type of Financing Preferred:

Leveraged Buyout
Early Stage
Expansion
Mezzanine
Balanced
Turnaround
Other
Seed
Management Buyouts
Acquisition
Recapitalizations

Size of Investments Considered:

Min Size of Investment Considered (000s): $1,000
Max Size of Investment Considered (000s): $12,000

Geographical Preferences

International Preferences:

Vietnam
India
Thailand
Philippines

Asia
Malaysia

Industry Focus

(% based on actual investment)

Other Products	59.4%
Consumer Related	9.6%
Medical/Health	7.5%
Biotechnology	7.3%
Computer Software and Services	4.2%
Communications and Media	3.9%
Semiconductors/Other Elect.	3.0%
Industrial/Energy	2.4%
Internet Specific	2.2%
Computer Hardware	0.5%

Additional Information

Year Founded: 1986
Capital Under Management: $900,000,000
Current Activity Level: Actively seeking new investments
Method of Compensation: Professional fee required whether or not deal closes

ILAB VENTURES

Ataturk Cad. No. 72
Kozyatagi
Istanbul, Turkey 34736
Phone: 90-216-468-1010
Fax: 90-216-302-8683
E-mail: info@ilab.com.tr
Website: www.ilab.com.tr/tr

Management and Staff

Cem Sertoglu, General Partner

Type of Firm

Private Equity Firm

Project Preferences

Type of Financing Preferred:

Early Stage
Expansion
Balanced
Later Stage

Geographical Preferences

International Preferences:

Turkey

Additional Information

Year Founded: 2000
Current Activity Level: Actively seeking new investments

ILE DE FRANCE DEVELOPPEMENT (AKA: IDFD)

3 parc des Erables
66 route de Sartrouville
Le Parc cedex, France 78232
Phone: 33-1-3015-6400
Fax: 33-1-3015-6409
E-mail: contact@idfd.fr
Website: www.idfd.fr

Type of Firm

Bank Affiliated

Project Preferences

Type of Financing Preferred:

Early Stage
Expansion

Size of Investments Considered:

Min Size of Investment Considered (000s): $15
Max Size of Investment Considered (000s): $151

Geographical Preferences

International Preferences:

France

Industry Preferences

In Industrial/Energy prefer:

Industrial Products

n Business Serv. prefer:

Services

Additional Information

Year Founded: 1995
Current Activity Level: Actively seeking new investments

ILLINOIS DEVELOPMENT FINANCE AUTHORITY

233 South Wacker Drive
Suite 4000
Chicago, IL USA 60606
Phone: 312-627-1434
Fax: 312-496-0578
E-mail: info@idfa.com
Website: www.idfa.com

Type of Firm

Investment Management Firm

Project Preferences

Type of Financing Preferred:

Balanced

Additional Information

Year Founded: 2001
Current Activity Level: Actively seeking new investments

ILLINOIS INNOVATION ACCELERATOR FUND (I2A)

200 E. Randolph St., Ste 2200
Aon Center
Chicago, IL USA 60601
Phone: 312-494-6773
E-mail: info@I2Afund.com
Website: www.i2afund.com

Management and Staff

Kapil Chaudhary, Principal

Type of Firm

Private Equity Firm

Project Preferences

Type of Financing Preferred:

Seed
Strategic Alliances

Geographical Preferences

United States Preferences:

Midwest
Illinois

Industry Preferences

In Communications prefer:

Communications and Media

In Consumer Related prefer:

Consumer
Retail
Consumer Products
Consumer Services
Education Related

Additional Information

Name of Most Recent Fund: Illinois Innovation Accelerator Fund
Most Recent Fund Was Raised: 02/26/2007
Year Founded: 2007
Capital Under Management: $6,400,000
Current Activity Level: Actively seeking new investments

ILLINOIS PARTNERS, LLC

60 Hazelwood Drive
Suite 226
Champaign, IL USA 61820
Phone: 312-404-3507
E-mail: info@illinoispartners.com
Website: www.illinoispartners.com

Management and Staff

Neil Kane, Managing Director

Type of Firm

Private Equity Firm

Project Preferences

Type of Financing Preferred:

Seed

Geographical Preferences

United States Preferences:

Illinois

Industry Preferences

In Semiconductor/Electr prefer:
Laser Related
Fiber Optics

Additional Information

Year Founded: 2001
Current Activity Level: Actively seeking new investments

ILLINOIS VENTURES LLC

20 North Wacker Drive
Suite 1201
Chicago, IL USA 60606
Phone: 312-251-0700
Fax: 312-251-0701
Website: www.illinoisventures.com

Management and Staff

John Banta, Managing Director

Type of Firm

Private Equity Firm

Association Membership

Illinois Venture Capital Association

Project Preferences

Type of Financing Preferred:
Early Stage
Seed
Startup

Size of Investments Considered:
Min Size of Investment Considered (000s): $250
Max Size of Investment Considered (000s): $3,000

Geographical Preferences

United States Preferences:
Midwest
Illinois

Industry Preferences

In Semiconductor/Electr prefer:
Semiconductor
Sensors

In Industrial/Energy prefer:
Energy
Alternative Energy
Advanced Materials

Additional Information

Name of Most Recent Fund: Illinois Emerging Technologies Fund, LP
Most Recent Fund Was Raised: 05/26/2005
Year Founded: 2002
Capital Under Management: $40,000,000
Current Activity Level: Actively seeking new investments

ILSHIN INVESTMENT CO., LTD. (AKA:ILSHIN VENTURE CAPITAL)

100, Im-dong, Buk-gu
Gwangju
Seoul, South Korea 150-872
Phone: 822-767-6400
Fax: 822-786-6051
Website: www.ilshin.co.kr

Other Offices

15-15, Yeouido-dong
Yeongdeungpo-gu
Seoul, South Korea 150-872

Management and Staff

Kwanghee Oh, Vice President

Type of Firm

Bank Affiliated

Association Membership

Korean Venture Capital Association (KVCA)

Project Preferences

Type of Financing Preferred:
Leveraged Buyout
Early Stage
Expansion
Balanced
Later Stage

Size of Investments Considered:
Min Size of Investment Considered (000s): $385
Max Size of Investment Considered (000s): $16,000

Geographical Preferences

International Preferences:
Korea, South

Industry Preferences

In Communications prefer:
Telecommunications
Media and Entertainment

In Computer Hardware prefer:
Computers

In Consumer Related prefer:
Consumer
Entertainment and Leisure
Retail

In Business Serv. prefer:
Distribution
Media

In Manufact. prefer:
Manufacturing

Additional Information

Year Founded: 1990
Capital Under Management: $60,800,000
Current Activity Level: Actively seeking new investments

IMBEWU CAPITAL PARTNERS

Suite 5, Rydall Vale Ofc. Park
10 Rydall Vale Crescent
La Lucia Ridge, South Africa 4051
Phone: 27-31-566-1484
Fax: 27-31-566-3925
E-mail: office@imbewucapital.co.za
Website: www.imbewucapital.co.za

Management and Staff

Gcina Zondi, Chief Executive Officer

Type of Firm

Private Equity Firm

Project Preferences

Type of Financing Preferred:
Leveraged Buyout
Management Buyouts

Additional Information

Year Founded: 2005
Current Activity Level: Actively seeking new investments

IMLAY INVESTMENTS

945 East Paces Ferry Road
Suite 2450
Atlanta, GA USA 30326
Phone: 404-239-1799
Fax: 404-239-1779

Management and Staff

I. Sigmund Mosley, President

Type of Firm

Private Equity Firm

Project Preferences

Role in Financing:
Will function either as deal originator or investor in deals created by others

Type of Financing Preferred:
Seed
First Stage Financing

Size of Investments Considered:
Min Size of Investment Considered (000s): $100
Max Size of Investment Considered (000s): $1,000

Geographical Preferences

United States Preferences:
Mid Atlantic
Southeast

Industry Focus

(% based on actual investment)

Computer Software and Services	40.2%
Internet Specific	35.5%

Computer Hardware	9.6%
Semiconductors/Other Elect.	6.6%
Communications and Media	4.1%
Other Products	2.1%
Biotechnology	1.0%
Consumer Related	0.9%

Additional Information

Year Founded: 1990
Current Activity Level: Actively seeking new investments
Method of Compensation: Return on investment is of primary concern, do not charge fees

---

IMPACT VENTURE PARTNERS

One Penn Plaza
Suite 2207
New York, NY USA 10019
Phone: 212-219-3931
Fax: 212-214-0909
Website: www.impactvp.com

Management and Staff

Adam Dell, Managing General Partner
Michael Rosenfelt, Venture Partner
Satin Mirchandani, General Partner
Steven Dell, Venture Partner

Type of Firm

Private Equity Firm

Project Preferences

Type of Financing Preferred:
Early Stage

Size of Investments Considered:
Min Size of Investment Considered (000s): $3,000
Max Size of Investment Considered (000s): $5,000

Geographical Preferences

United States Preferences:
Northeast
Texas

Industry Focus

(% based on actual investment)

Internet Specific	52.9%
Computer Software and Services	19.0%
Computer Hardware	15.5%
Communications and Media	12.6%

Additional Information

Name of Most Recent Fund: Impact Venture Partners II
Most Recent Fund Was Raised: 11/01/2001
Year Founded: 1999
Capital Under Management: $100,000,000
Current Activity Level: Actively seeking new investments

IMPALA CAPITAL PARTNERS (FKA; SUALA CAPITAL ADVISORS)

Pedro de Valdivia 10
4/F Planta
Madrid, Spain 28006
Phone: 34-91-411-9290
Fax: 34-91-411-9331
E-mail: info@impalacapital.com
Website: www.impalacapital.com

Management and Staff

Gonzalo Diaz-Rato, Partner
Gonzalo De Rivera, Partner
Pierre Saenz, Partner

Type of Firm

Private Equity Firm

Association Membership

European Private Equity and Venture Capital Assoc.
Spanish Venture Capital Association (ASCRI)

Project Preferences

Type of Financing Preferred:
Leveraged Buyout
Expansion
Management Buyouts
Recapitalizations

Size of Investments Considered:
Min Size of Investment Considered (000s): $8,754
Max Size of Investment Considered (000s): $37,642

Geographical Preferences

International Preferences:
Spain

Additional Information

Year Founded: 2000
Capital Under Management: $176,400,000
Current Activity Level: Actively seeking new investments

IMPAX ASSET MANAGEMENT

Mezzanine Floor, Pegasus House
37-43 Sackville Street
London, United Kingdom W1S 3EH
Phone: 44-20-7434-1122
Fax: 44-20-7434-1123
E-mail: info@impax.co.uk
Website: www.impax.co.uk

Management and Staff

Bruce Jenkyn-Jones, Managing Director
Daniel Von Preyss, Managing Director
Ian Simm, Chief Executive Officer
Nigel Taunt, Managing Director
Peter Rossbach, Managing Director

Type of Firm

Bank Affiliated

Association Membership

British Venture Capital Association (BVCA)

Project Preferences

Type of Financing Preferred:
Early Stage
Expansion
Balanced

Geographical Preferences

International Preferences:
United Kingdom
Europe
Western Europe

Industry Preferences

In Industrial/Energy prefer:
Alternative Energy
Energy Conservation Relat
Environmental Related

In Other prefer:
Environment Responsible

Additional Information

Year Founded: 1994
Capital Under Management: $134,600,000
Current Activity Level: Actively seeking new investments

IMPERIAL CAPITAL CORPORATION

200 King Street West
Suite 1701, P.O. Box 57
Toronto, Canada M5H 3T4
Phone: 416-362-3658
Fax: 416-362-8660
E-mail: icl@imperialcap.com
Website: www.imperialcap.com

Management and Staff

Edward Truant, Principal
Jeffrey Rosenthal, Managing Partner
Jonathan Sherman, Vice President
Robert Molyneux, Principal
Stephen Lister, Managing Partner

Type of Firm

Bank Affiliated

Project Preferences

Type of Financing Preferred:
Leveraged Buyout
Acquisition

Geographical Preferences

Canadian Preferences:
All Canada

Industry Preferences

In Medical/Health prefer:
Medical/Health

In Consumer Related prefer:
Consumer

In Business Serv. prefer:
Services

Additional Information

Year Founded: 1989
Capital Under Management: $204,200,000
Current Activity Level: Actively seeking new investments
Method of Compensation: Return on invest. most important, but chg. closing fees, service fees, etc.

IMPERIAL CAPITAL, LLC

150 South Rodeo Drive
Suite 100
Beverly Hills, CA USA 90212
Phone: 310-246-3700
Fax: 310-777-3000
E-mail: info@imperialcapital.com
Website: www.imperialcapital.com

Other Offices

P.O. Box 664
Ketchum, ID USA 83340
Phone: 208-727-1000
Fax: 208-727-1019

280 Park Avenue
39th Floor West
New York, NY USA 10017
Phone: 212-490-0004
Fax: 212-490-5956

Management and Staff

James Stone, Managing Director
Jeff Kessler, Managing Director
Mark Martis, Chief Operating Officer
Robert Wagner, Managing Director

Type of Firm

Bank Affiliated

Industry Focus

(% based on actual investment)

Internet Specific	100.0%

Additional Information

Year Founded: 1997
Current Activity Level: Actively seeking new investments

IMPERIAL INNOVATIONS (AKA: IMPERIAL COLLEGE INNOVATIONS)

Imperial College London
Exhibition Road
London, United Kingdom SW7 2AZ
Phone: 44-20-7581-4949
Fax: 44-20-7589-3553
E-mail: info@imperialinnovations.co.uk
Website: www.imperialinnovations.co.uk

Management and Staff

Julian Smith, Chief Financial Officer
Susan Searle, Chief Executive Officer

Type of Firm

University Program

Project Preferences

Type of Financing Preferred:
Early Stage
Seed
Startup

Geographical Preferences

International Preferences:
United Kingdom

Industry Preferences

In Biotechnology prefer:
Biotechnology

In Medical/Health prefer:
Medical/Health

In Industrial/Energy prefer:
Alternative Energy

Additional Information

Year Founded: 1986
Capital Under Management: $4,000,000
Current Activity Level: Actively seeking new investments

IMPRESA E FINANZA SGR

via F. Lippi 11
Brescia, Italy 25134
Phone: 39-030-230-6904
Fax: 39-030-230-6930
E-mail: info@impresa-finanza.it
Website: www.impresa-finanza.it

Management and Staff

Marco Tabladini, Managing Director

Type of Firm

Private Equity Firm

Association Membership

Italian Venture Capital Association (AIFI)

Project Preferences

Type of Financing Preferred:
Leveraged Buyout
Expansion
Balanced

Geographical Preferences

International Preferences:
Italy
Europe

Additional Information

Year Founded: 2005
Current Activity Level: Actively seeking new investments

IMPRIMATUR CAPITAL, LTD.

2nd Floor, Staple Hall
Stone House Court, 87-90
Houndsditch, London, United Kingdom EC3A 7NP
Phone: 44-20-7929-4467
Fax: 44-20-7929-4500
E-mail: iw@impcap.com
Website: www.imprimaturcapital.com

Other Offices

Elizabetes Street 85a
Berga Bazar, II, 19a, 2nd Floor
Riga, Latvia LV-1050
Phone: 371-7-365-275
Fax: 371-7-365-281

Unit 31, 39th Floor
One Exchange Square
Central, Hong Kong
Phone: 852-3101-70-90
Fax: 852-3101-75-30

Av.Jose de Souza
Campos, k550, Sala 81
Campinas, Brazil 13.092-123
Phone: 55-19-3251-8713

Level 26, 44 Market Street
Sydney, Australia NSW 2000
Phone: 612-9089-8688
Fax: 612-9089-8989

PO Box 211
Carterton, New Zealand
Phone: 64-6379-9271
Fax: 64-6379-9272

20 Cecil Street #15 - 07
Equity Plaza
Singapore, Singapore 049705
Phone: 65-6535-3454
Fax: 65-6535-3494

4 Khreschatyk
StreetSuite 20, 6th Floor

Kyiv, Ukraine 01001
Phone: 380-44-494-1898
Fax: 380-44-278-0920

Management and Staff

Ben Ferrari, Managing Director
Charles Scott, Managing Director

Type of Firm

Private Equity Firm

Project Preferences

Type of Financing Preferred:
Early Stage

Geographical Preferences

International Preferences:
Hungary
United Kingdom
Hong Kong
China
Brazil
Ukraine
Spain
Singapore
Australia
New Zealand
Russia

Industry Preferences

In Communications prefer:
Communications and Media

In Internet Specific prefer:
Internet

In Semiconductor/Electr prefer:
Optoelectronics

In Medical/Health prefer:
Medical/Health

Additional Information

Year Founded: 2008
Current Activity Level: Actively seeking new investments

IN PARTNERS LLC (AKA: MIDPOINT)

11550 North Meridian Street
Suite 310
Carmel, IN USA 46032
Phone: 317-750-4076
Website: www.midpointvc.com

Management and Staff

Andrew Ziolkowski, Partner
Clint Dederick, Partner
Ronald Meeusen, Partner

Type of Firm

Private Equity Firm

Association Membership

National Venture Capital Association - USA (NVCA)

Project Preferences

Type of Financing Preferred:
Early Stage
Expansion
Balanced

Geographical Preferences

United States Preferences:
Midwest

Industry Preferences

In Medical/Health prefer:
Other Therapeutic

In Consumer Related prefer:
Food/Beverage
Consumer Products

In Industrial/Energy prefer:
Energy
Environmental Related

In Agr/Forestr/Fish prefer:
Agriculture related

In Other prefer:
Environment Responsible

Additional Information

Name of Most Recent Fund: MidPoint Food & Ag Fund, L.P.
Most Recent Fund Was Raised: 12/16/2008
Year Founded: 2008
Capital Under Management: $27,800,000
Current Activity Level: Actively seeking new investments

IN-Q-TEL, INC.

1000 Wilson Blvd
29th Floor
Arlington, VA USA 22209
Phone: 703-248-3000
Fax: 703-248-3001
E-mail: info@in-q-tel.org
Website: www.in-q-tel.org

Management and Staff

Christopher Darby, Chief Executive Officer
Eric Kaufmann, General Partner
Ronald Richard, Chief Operating Officer
William Johnson, Partner

Type of Firm

Government Affiliated Program

Association Membership

Mid-Atlantic Venture Association
National Venture Capital Association - USA (NVCA)

Project Preferences

Type of Financing Preferred:
Early Stage

Size of Investments Considered:
Min Size of Investment Considered (000s): $100
Max Size of Investment Considered (000s): $2,500

Industry Preferences

In Communications prefer:
Data Communications

In Computer Hardware prefer:
Computers

In Computer Software prefer:
Data Processing

In Internet Specific prefer:
Internet

Additional Information

Name of Most Recent Fund: Information Technology Fund 2000
Most Recent Fund Was Raised: 02/01/1999
Year Founded: 1999
Capital Under Management: $40,000,000
Current Activity Level: Actively seeking new investments

INC3 VENTURES, LLC

5201 Great America Parkway
Suite 457
Santa Clara, CA USA 95054
Phone: 408-330-0917
Fax: 408-317-2300
Website: www.inc3vc.com

Management and Staff

Bipin Shah, Managing Partner
Dhimant Bhayani, Managing Partner

Type of Firm

Private Equity Firm

Project Preferences

Role in Financing:
Prefer role in deals created by others

Type of Financing Preferred:
Second Stage Financing
Early Stage
Expansion
Seed
First Stage Financing
Private Placement
Startup

Size of Investments Considered:
Min Size of Investment Considered (000s): $250
Max Size of Investment Considered (000s): $1,250

Geographical Preferences

United States Preferences:
Northern California
West Coast

International Preferences:
India

Industry Preferences

In Communications prefer:
Commercial Communications
Telecommunications
Wireless Communications
Data Communications

In Computer Hardware prefer:
Disk Relat. Memory Device

In Internet Specific prefer:
Internet

In Semiconductor/Electr prefer:
Electronic Components
Semiconductor
Micro-Processing
Controllers and Sensors

Additional Information

Year Founded: 2000
Capital Under Management: $15,000,000
Current Activity Level: Actively seeking new investments
Method of Compensation: Return on investment is of primary concern, do not charge fees

---

INCITE.CAPITAL MANAGEMENT PTY, LTD.

Level 9, 132 Arthur Street
North Sydney, Australia 2060
Phone: 612-8920-2300
Fax: 612-8920-2400
E-mail: info@incitecapital.com.au
Website: www.incitecapital.com.au

Management and Staff

Lindsay Rowlands, Managing Director

Type of Firm

Private Equity Firm

Project Preferences

Type of Financing Preferred:
Early Stage
Expansion
Mezzanine
Management Buyouts
Acquisition

Size of Investments Considered:
Min Size of Investment Considered (000s): $255
Max Size of Investment Considered (000s): $1,274

Geographical Preferences

International Preferences:
Pacific

Additional Information

Year Founded: 1999
Capital Under Management: $5,200,000
Current Activity Level: Actively seeking new investments

INCLUSIVE VENTURES, LLC

P.O. Box 1492
Millbrook, NY USA 12545
Phone: 917-733-6733
Fax: 212-202-4391
Website: www.inclusive-ventures.com

Management and Staff

Charles Weeden, Managing Partner

Type of Firm

Private Equity Firm

Project Preferences

Role in Financing:
Prefer role as deal originator

Type of Financing Preferred:
Seed
Startup

Size of Investments Considered:
Min Size of Investment Considered (000s): $100
Max Size of Investment Considered (000s): $1,000

Industry Preferences

In Financial Services prefer:
Financial Services

Additional Information

Year Founded: 1992
Capital Under Management: $7,000,000
Current Activity Level: Actively seeking new investments

INCTANK INC.

411 Massachusetts Avenue
Cambridge, MA USA 02139
Phone: 617-576-9555
Fax: 617-576-9551
E-mail: Info@inctank.com
Website: www.inctank.com

Other Offices

University of Tokyo RCAST #14-212
4-6-1 Meguro-ku
Tokyo, Japan 153-8904
Phone: 81-3-5453-5317
Fax: 81-3-5453-5318

Management and Staff

Chad Jackson, General Partner
Christian Bailey, General Partner
Masanobu Tsukagoshi, General Partner

Type of Firm

Private Equity Firm

Project Preferences

Role in Financing:
Prefer role as deal originator

Type of Financing Preferred:
Early Stage
Seed
Startup

Size of Investments Considered:
Min Size of Investment Considered (000s): $100
Max Size of Investment Considered (000s): $1,000

Geographical Preferences

United States Preferences:
Northeast
All U.S.

Industry Preferences

In Industrial/Energy prefer:
Materials

Additional Information

Year Founded: 1999
Current Activity Level: Actively seeking new investments

INCUBATION FOR GROWTH

21 A.Tritsi st,
Thessaloniki, Greece 57001
Website: www.i4g.gr

Management and Staff

Paris Kokorotsikos, Managing Director
Stathis Tavridis, Managing Director

Type of Firm

Incubator/Development Program

Project Preferences

Type of Financing Preferred:
Early Stage

Geographical Preferences

International Preferences:
Greece

Additional Information

Year Founded: 2003
Current Activity Level: Actively seeking new investments

INCUBIC VENTURE CAPITAL

545 Middlefield Road
Suite 130
Menlo Park, CA USA 94025
Phone: 650-617-2380

Fax: 650-617-2381
E-mail: info@incubic.com
Website: www.incubic.com

Management and Staff

Milton Chang, Managing Director
Nicholas Colella, Partner
William Nighan Jr., Managing Director

Type of Firm

Private Equity Firm

Project Preferences

Type of Financing Preferred:

Balanced

Additional Information

Year Founded: 2001
Capital Under Management: $100,000,000
Current Activity Level: Actively seeking new investments

INDECATUR VENTURES LLC

130 North Water Street
Decatur, IL USA 62523
Fax: 217-425-8366
E-mail: inquire@indecaturventures.com
Website: www.indecaturventures.com

Management and Staff

Christopher Shroyer, Vice President
Larry Haab, President

Type of Firm

Private Equity Firm

Project Preferences

Role in Financing:

Will function either as deal originator or investor in deals created by others

Type of Financing Preferred:

Second Stage Financing
Early Stage
Mezzanine
Balanced
Later Stage
First Stage Financing

Size of Investments Considered:

Min Size of Investment Considered (000s): $100
Max Size of Investment Considered (000s): $1,000

Geographical Preferences

United States Preferences:

Midwest

Industry Preferences

In Communications prefer:

Telecommunications
Wireless Communications
Data Communications

In Computer Hardware prefer:

Mainframes / Scientific
Mini and Personal/Desktop

In Computer Software prefer:

Computer Services
Data Processing
Software
Systems Software
Applications Software
Artificial Intelligence

In Internet Specific prefer:

Internet
Ecommerce

In Semiconductor/Electr prefer:

Electronics

In Biotechnology prefer:

Agricultural/Animal Bio.
Industrial Biotechnology
Biotech Related Research

In Medical/Health prefer:

Medical Diagnostics
Diagnostic Services
Diagnostic Test Products
Medical Therapeutics
Drug/Equipmt Delivery
Medical Products
Disposable Med. Products
Health Services
Pharmaceuticals

In Business Serv. prefer:

Services
Distribution

In Manufact. prefer:

Manufacturing

Additional Information

Name of Most Recent Fund: InDecatur Ventures
Most Recent Fund Was Raised: 10/01/2003
Year Founded: 2003
Capital Under Management: $3,000,000
Current Activity Level: Actively seeking new investments
Method of Compensation: Return on invest. most important, but chg. closing fees, service fees, etc.

INDEPENDENCE HOLDINGS PARTNERS (FKA: NEWBROOK CAPITAL MGMT)

245 Fifth Avenue
25th Floor
New York, NY USA 10016
Phone: 212-213-9614
Fax: 212-213-9607
E-mail: info@independencefund.com
Website: www.independencefund.com

Type of Firm

Private Equity Advisor or Fund of Funds

Project Preferences

Type of Financing Preferred:

Fund of Funds

Geographical Preferences

International Preferences:

Europe

Additional Information

Name of Most Recent Fund: Independence Venture and Technology Fund, LP
Most Recent Fund Was Raised: 05/01/2001
Year Founded: 1999
Capital Under Management: $50,000,000
Current Activity Level: Actively seeking new investments

INDEPENDENT BANKERS CAPITAL FUND

1700 Pacific Avenue
Suite 2740
Dallas, TX USA 75201
Phone: 214-765-1350
Fax: 214-765-1360
E-mail: info@ibcfund.com
Website: www.ibcfund.com

Management and Staff

Meg Taylor, Chief Financial Officer

Type of Firm

Private Equity Firm

Association Membership

Natl Assoc of Small Bus. Inv. Co (NASBIC)

Project Preferences

Role in Financing:

Will function either as deal originator or investor in deals created by others

Type of Financing Preferred:

Leveraged Buyout
Later Stage
Management Buyouts
Acquisition
Recapitalizations

Size of Investments Considered:

Min Size of Investment Considered (000s): $1,000
Max Size of Investment Considered (000s): $4,600

Geographical Preferences

United States Preferences:

Southwest

Industry Preferences

In Medical/Health prefer:

Medical Products
Disposable Med. Products
Health Services

In Business Serv. prefer:
Distribution

In Manufact. prefer:
Manufacturing

Additional Information

Name of Most Recent Fund: Independent Bankers Capital Fund, L.P.
Most Recent Fund Was Raised: 02/09/2000
Year Founded: 2000
Capital Under Management: $70,000,000
Current Activity Level: Actively seeking new investments
Method of Compensation: Return on invest. most important, but chg. closing fees, service fees, etc.

INDEPENDENT CAPITAL UNTERNEHMENSBETEILIGUNGEN AG

Friedrichstrasse 95
Remscheid, Germany 42897
Phone: 49-21-9166-6606
Fax: 49-21-9161-0755
E-mail: mail@independentcapital.de
Website: www.independent-capital.de

Type of Firm

Private Equity Firm

Project Preferences

Type of Financing Preferred:
Early Stage
Expansion
Later Stage
Seed
Startup

Geographical Preferences

International Preferences:
Europe
Germany

Additional Information

Year Founded: 2002
Current Activity Level: Actively seeking new investments

INDEX VENTURES

2 rue de Jargonnant
Geneva, Switzerland 1207
Phone: 41-22-737-0000
Fax: 41-22-737-0099
E-mail: info@indexventures.com
Website: www.indexventures.com

Other Offices

1 Seaton Place
St. Helier
Jersey, United Kingdom JEY 8Y
Phone: 44-1534-753-858
Fax: 44-1534-605-605

52-53 Conduit Street
London, United Kingdom W1S 2YX
Phone: 44-20-7154-2020
Fax: 44-20-7154-2021

Management and Staff

Ben Holmes, Partner
Bernard Dalle, General Partner
Daniel Rimer, General Partner
Dominique Vidal, Partner
Francesco De Rubertis, General Partner
Giuseppe Zocco, Partner
Herve Lebret, Principal
Mark De Boer, Venture Partner
Michelangelo Volpi, Partner
Michele Ollier, Principal
Mike Volpi, Partner
Neil Rimer, General Partner
Richard Rimer, Partner
Roman Fleck, Principal
Saul Klein, Partner
Tony Zappala, Principal

Type of Firm

Private Equity Firm

Association Membership

Swiss Venture Capital Association (SECA)
European Private Equity and Venture Capital Assoc.

Project Preferences

Type of Financing Preferred:
Early Stage
Expansion
Balanced
Later Stage
Seed

Size of Investments Considered:
Min Size of Investment Considered (000s): $500
Max Size of Investment Considered (000s): $20,000

Geographical Preferences

United States Preferences:
All U.S.

International Preferences:
Switzerland
Europe
Israel
All International

Industry Focus

(% based on actual investment)	
Computer Software and Services	46.7%
Internet Specific	26.0%
Biotechnology	12.4%
Medical/Health	3.9%
Semiconductors/Other Elect.	3.5%
Communications and Media	2.0%
Computer Hardware	2.0%
Other Products	1.8%
Industrial/Energy	0.9%
Consumer Related	0.9%

Additional Information

Name of Most Recent Fund: Index Ventures IV
Most Recent Fund Was Raised: 12/22/2006
Year Founded: 1992
Capital Under Management: $646,100,000
Current Activity Level: Actively seeking new investments

INDEXATLAS GROUP

140 Broadway
Suite 4430
New York, NY USA 10005
Phone: 212-514-6010
Fax: 212-514-6037
Website: www.indexatlas.com

Other Offices

Catherine House
76 Gloucester Place
London, United Kingdom W1U 6HJ
Phone: 44-20-7725-0572
Fax: 44-20-7487-4211

5 Nizhniy Kislovskiy pereulok
Moscow, Russia 125993

10 Schottengasse
Vienna, Austria A-1010
Phone: 43-664-528-4623
Fax: 43-664-528-4623

Management and Staff

Elizabeth Dimmitt, Chief Operating Officer
Marina Nacheva, Managing Director
Markus Huber, Managing Director
Michael Moriarty, President
Sergey Skaterschikov, Chief Executive Officer
Simon Vidrevich, Managing Director

Type of Firm

Bank Affiliated

Project Preferences

Type of Financing Preferred:
Generalist PE

Size of Investments Considered:
Min Size of Investment Considered (000s): $3,000
Max Size of Investment Considered (000s): $8,000

Geographical Preferences

International Preferences:
Central Europe
Eastern Europe
Ukraine
Russia
All International

Industry Preferences

In Computer Software prefer:
Software

In Internet Specific prefer:
Internet

In Financial Services prefer:
Financial Services

In Business Serv. prefer:
Services
Media

Additional Information

Year Founded: 2001
Capital Under Management: $400,000,000
Current Activity Level: Actively seeking new investments

INDIA INFOLINE VENTURES CAPITAL (AKA: IIFL CAPITAL)

Bldg. No. 75, Nirlon Complex
Goregoan East
Mumbai, India 400 063
Phone: 91-22-6648-9000
Fax: 91-22-2685-0451
Website: www.indiainfoline.com

Type of Firm

Bank Affiliated

Project Preferences

Type of Financing Preferred:
Seed

Geographical Preferences

International Preferences:
India

Additional Information

Year Founded: 2008
Current Activity Level: Actively seeking new investments

INDIA VALUE FUND ADVISORS PRIVATE LTD. (FKA: GW CAPITAL)

Grand Hyatt Plaza
Santacruz (East)
Mumbai, India 400 055
Phone: 91-22-6695-4888
Fax: 91-22-6695-4777
Website: www.ivfa.com

Other Offices

18, Marshall Street
Suite 112
Norwalk, CT USA 06854
Phone: 203-956-6565
Fax: 203-956-6546

Rocklines House (Ground Floor)
9/2 Museum Road
Bangalore, India 560001
Phone: 91-80-4132-1845
Fax: 91-80-2559-0800

Management and Staff

Jai Rupani, Vice President
Prateek Roongta, Vice President
Satish Chander, Vice President
Siddharth Dhondiyal, Vice President
Srikrishna Dwaram, Vice President
Vishal Nevatia, Chief Executive Officer

Type of Firm

Private Equity Firm

Association Membership

Indian Venture Capital Association (IVCA)

Project Preferences

Type of Financing Preferred:
Leveraged Buyout
Expansion
Generalist PE
Balanced
Later Stage

Size of Investments Considered:
Min Size of Investment Considered (000s): $4,000
Max Size of Investment Considered (000s): $10,000

Geographical Preferences

International Preferences:
India

Industry Preferences

In Communications prefer:
Telecommunications
Media and Entertainment

In Biotechnology prefer:
Biotechnology

In Medical/Health prefer:
Health Services
Pharmaceuticals

In Consumer Related prefer:
Retail

In Financial Services prefer:
Financial Services

In Business Serv. prefer:
Services
Distribution

Additional Information

Year Founded: 2000
Capital Under Management: $600,000,000
Current Activity Level: Actively seeking new investments

INDIACO

4th Floor, Symphony, S.No. 210
A/1, Range Hils Rd, Sivaji Ngr
Pune, India 411 020
Phone: 91-20-2551-3254
Fax: 91-20-2551-3243
E-mail: info@indiaco.com
Website: www.indiaco.com

Management and Staff

Dhananjay Bendre, Managing Director
Rahul Patwardhan, Managing Director

Type of Firm

Private Equity Firm

Project Preferences

Type of Financing Preferred:
Balanced

Geographical Preferences

International Preferences:
India
Ukraine
All International

Industry Preferences

In Biotechnology prefer:
Biotechnology

Additional Information

Year Founded: 2001
Current Activity Level: Actively seeking new investments

INDIACO VENTURES, LTD.

IndiaCo Center, 4th Floor
Symphony, S.No. 210 A/1
Pune, India 411 020
Phone: 91-20-2551-3254
Fax: 91-20-2551-3243
E-mail: info@indiaco.com
Website: www.indiaco.com

Management and Staff

Dhananjay Bendre, Chief Operating Officer
Praveena Chandra, Vice President

Type of Firm

Investment Management Firm

Project Preferences

Type of Financing Preferred:
Expansion

Geographical Preferences

International Preferences:
India

Industry Preferences

In Communications prefer:
Telecommunications

In Medical/Health prefer:
Health Services

In Consumer Related prefer:
Education Related

In Industrial/Energy prefer:
Alternative Energy

In Transportation prefer:
Aerospace

In Manufact. prefer:
Manufacturing

Additional Information
Year Founded: 2000
Current Activity Level: Actively seeking new investments

INDIGO CAPITAL, LTD.
25 Watling Street
London, United Kingdom EC4M 9BR
Phone: 44-20-7710-7800
Fax: 44-20-7710-7777
E-mail: info@indigo-capital.com
Website: www.indigo-capital.com

Other Offices
69 rue de la Boetie
Paris, France 75008
Phone: 33-1-5688-1750
Fax: 33-1-5688-2488

Management and Staff
Martin Hook, Partner
Monique Deloire, Partner

Type of Firm
Private Equity Firm

Association Membership
French Venture Capital Association (AFIC)

Project Preferences

Type of Financing Preferred:
Leveraged Buyout
Expansion
Mezzanine
Recapitalizations

Geographical Preferences

International Preferences:
Italy
Ireland
Sweden
Netherlands
Portugal
Switzerland
Europe
Austria
Iceland
Spain
Belgium
Finland
Norway
Germany
Denmark
France

Industry Focus
(% based on actual investment)

Consumer Related	44.4%
Other Products	34.6%
Computer Hardware	12.5%
Biotechnology	6.1%
Computer Software and Services	2.4%

Additional Information
Year Founded: 1990
Capital Under Management: $589,800,000
Current Activity Level: Actively seeking new investments

INDIGO PARTNERS LLC
2525 East Camelback Road
Phoenix, AZ USA 85016
Phone: 602-224-1500
Fax: 602-956-6306

Management and Staff
William Franke, Managing Partner

Type of Firm
Private Equity Firm

Geographical Preferences

United States Preferences:
All U.S.

International Preferences:
Asia

Industry Preferences

In Transportation prefer:
Transportation

Additional Information
Year Founded: 2002
Current Activity Level: Actively seeking new investments

INDO-NORDIC PRIVATE EQUITY AS
P.O Box 9
Majorstuen
Oslo, Norway 0330
Phone: 47-9801-6573
Website: www.indo-nordic.com

Management and Staff
Suneel Regulla, Managing Director

Type of Firm
Private Equity Firm

Project Preferences

Type of Financing Preferred:
Expansion
Balanced

Geographical Preferences

International Preferences:
India

Industry Preferences

In Industrial/Energy prefer:
Energy
Oil and Gas Exploration
Oil & Gas Drilling,Explor

In Utilities prefer:
Utilities

Additional Information
Year Founded: 2008
Current Activity Level: Actively seeking new investments

INDOCHINA CAPITAL MANAGEMENT
Capital Place, Floors 9-10
06 Thai Van Lung St., Dist. 1
Ho Chi Minh , Vietnam
Phone: 84-8-910-4855
Fax: 84-8-910-4860
E-mail: info@indochinacapital.com
Website: www.indochinacapital.com

Other Offices
77 Tran Phu
Danang, Vietnam
Phone: 84-511-3840-850
Fax: 84-511-3840-851

Saigon Finance Center, Floor 9
9 Dinh Tien Hoang, District 1
Ho Chi Minh , Vietnam
Phone: 84-8-3520-2030
Fax: 84-8-3520-2036

3705 Bank of America Tower, Suite 505
12 Harcourt Road
Central, Hong Kong
Phone: 852-2588-3450
Fax: 852-3010-6880

60 Ly Thai To Street
Floor 9-9A
Hanoi, Vietnam
Phone: 84-4-3930-6399
Fax: 84-4-3935-0251

Management and Staff
Tung Kim Nguyen, Managing Director

Type of Firm
Investment Management Firm

Project Preferences

Type of Financing Preferred:
Mezzanine
Expansion
Public Companies

Geographical Preferences

International Preferences:
Vietnam
Thailand

Additional Information
Year Founded: 1999
Capital Under Management: $500,000,000
Current Activity Level: Actively seeking new investments

INDOFIN
PO Box 23341
Rotterdam, Netherlands 3001 KH
Phone: 31-10-414-4544
Fax: 31-10-433-2879
Website: www.indofin.nl

Other Offices
Suite 260
10375 Richmond Avenue
Houston, TX USA 77042
Phone: 1-713-781-9500

9 place du Bourg de Four
Avobone SA
Geneva, Switzerland 1204
Phone: 41-223-10-2044
Fax: 41-223-10-2045

Management and Staff
Belle De Bruin, Partner
C.J. De Bruin, Partner
Henk Van Den Hoek, Partner
J.D. De Kruif, Partner

Type of Firm
Private Equity Firm

Association Membership
European Private Equity and Venture Capital Assoc.

Project Preferences

Type of Financing Preferred:
Balanced

Size of Investments Considered:
Min Size of Investment Considered (000s): $6,406
Max Size of Investment Considered (000s): $64,062

Geographical Preferences

United States Preferences:
All U.S.

International Preferences:
Europe
All International

Additional Information
Year Founded: 1968
Current Activity Level: Actively seeking new investments

INDUFIN
Dreve Richelle 161
Bat. O, Boite 43
Waterloo, Belgium 1410
Phone: 32-2-351-0805
Fax: 32-2 -351-2544
E-mail: indufin@indufin.be
Website: www.indufin.be

Management and Staff
Jo Santino, Managing Director

Type of Firm
Private Equity Firm

Association Membership
Belgium Venturing Association
European Private Equity and Venture Capital Assoc.

Project Preferences

Type of Financing Preferred:
Balanced

Geographical Preferences

International Preferences:
Belgium

Additional Information
Year Founded: 2003
Current Activity Level: Actively seeking new investments

INDUSTRI UDVIKLING A/S
Vendersgade 28
Kobenhavn, Denmark 1363
Phone: 45-33-36-8999
Fax: 45-33-36-8990
E-mail: iu@industriudvikling.dk
Website: www.industriudvikling.dk

Type of Firm
Private Equity Firm

Association Membership
European Private Equity and Venture Capital Assoc.

Project Preferences

Type of Financing Preferred:
Leveraged Buyout
Early Stage
Expansion
Mezzanine
Turnaround
Startup

Geographical Preferences

International Preferences:
Denmark

Additional Information
Year Founded: 1994
Capital Under Management: $36,300,000
Current Activity Level: Actively seeking new investments

INDUSTRIA & FINANZA SGR S.P.A.
Corso Giovanni Lanza, 101
Torino, Italy 10133
Phone: 39-11-630-2155
Fax: 39-11-630-2199
E-mail: welcome@ifequity.it
Website: www.ifequity.it

Other Offices
Via Donizetti 36
Milan, Italy 20122
Phone: 39-2-3968-0196
Fax: 39-11-6302-199

Management and Staff
Alberto Franchino, Managing Director

Type of Firm
Private Equity Firm

Association Membership
Italian Venture Capital Association (AIFI)

Project Preferences

Role in Financing:
Prefer role as deal originator but will also invest in deals created by others

Type of Financing Preferred:
Generalist PE

Size of Investments Considered:
Min Size of Investment Considered (000s): $6,990
Max Size of Investment Considered (000s): $20,970

Geographical Preferences

International Preferences:
Italy

Industry Preferences

In Medical/Health prefer:
Pharmaceuticals

In Consumer Related prefer:
Consumer Products

In Industrial/Energy prefer:
Machinery

In Financial Services prefer:
Financial Services

In Utilities prefer:
Utilities

Additional Information

Year Founded: 2002
Capital Under Management: $168,100,000
Current Activity Level: Actively seeking new investments

INDUSTRIAL BANK OF KOREA CAPITAL

702-22 Yeoksam-Dong
Kangnam-Ku
Seoul, South Korea
Phone: 822-531-9343
Fax: 822-568-3400
E-mail: kts@ibkc.co.kr
Website: www.ibkc.co.kr

Other Offices

15th Fl., Daeoh Bldg.
26-5 Yeoido-Dong Yeongdeongpo-Gu
Seoul, South Korea
Phone: 822-786-4391
Fax: 822-786-4393

6th Fl., Shinjoo Bldg.
297 Mannyeon-Dong Seo-Gu
Daejeon, South Korea
Phone: 82-42-482-2151
Fax: 82-42-482-2009

5th Fl., Boorim Bldg
42 Uljiro-1-Ga, Joong-Gu
Seoul, South Korea
Phone: 822-319-2141
Fax: 822-319-2143

14th Fl., IPIC Bldg
91-5 Boojeon-Dong Jin-Ku
Pusan, South Korea
Phone: 82-51-818-7260
Fax: 82-051-818-7259

Type of Firm

Bank Affiliated

Association Membership

Korean Venture Capital Association (KVCA)

Project Preferences

Type of Financing Preferred:
Fund of Funds
Leveraged Buyout
Early Stage
Expansion
Balanced

Geographical Preferences

International Preferences:
Korea, South

Industry Preferences

In Computer Software prefer:
Software

In Semiconductor/Electr prefer:
Electronics

In Industrial/Energy prefer:
Industrial Products

Additional Information

Year Founded: 1986
Capital Under Management: $1,700,000
Current Activity Level: Actively seeking new investments

INDUSTRIAL BANK OF TAIWAN

99, Sec. 2, Tiding Boulevard
Neihu District
Taipei, Taiwan
Phone: 886-2-8752-7000
Fax: 886-2-2798-5337
Website: www.ibt.com.tw

Other Offices

12/F No.55 Jungjeng
3rd Road
Kaohsiung, Taiwan
Phone: 886-7-225-0212
Fax: 886-7-225-0221

3/F No.2 Jinshan Street
Hsinchu, Taiwan
Phone: 886-3-563-5666
Fax: 886-3-563-5000

Management and Staff

Henry Peng, President

Type of Firm

Bank Affiliated

Project Preferences

Type of Financing Preferred:
Early Stage
Expansion
Balanced

Geographical Preferences

United States Preferences:
All U.S.

International Preferences:
Taiwan
China

Industry Preferences

In Biotechnology prefer:
Biotechnology

In Medical/Health prefer:
Medical/Health
Pharmaceuticals

Additional Information

Year Founded: 1999
Capital Under Management: $58,800,000
Current Activity Level: Actively seeking new investments

INDUSTRIAL DEVELOPMENT & INVESTMENT AB (AKA: IDI)

Hovslagargatan 5 B
Stockholm, Sweden SE-111 48
Phone: 46-8-407-35-00
Fax: 46-8-611-47-30
E-mail: info@idiab.se
Website: www.idiab.se

Management and Staff

Christer Zetterberg, Founder

Type of Firm

Private Equity Firm

Association Membership

Swedish Venture Capital Association (SVCA)

Project Preferences

Type of Financing Preferred:
Leveraged Buyout
Expansion
Turnaround

Geographical Preferences

International Preferences:
Scandanavia/Nordic Region

Additional Information

Year Founded: 1997
Capital Under Management: $106,200,000
Current Activity Level: Actively seeking new investments

INDUSTRIAL DEVELOPMENT CORPORATION OF SOUTH AFRICA LTD (IDC)

19 Fredman Drive
Sandown, South Africa 2196
Phone: 27-11-269-3000
Fax: 27-11-269-3116
E-mail: callcentre@idc.co.za
Website: www.idc.co.za

Management and Staff

K Ngqula, Chief Executive Officer

Type of Firm

Private Equity Advisor or Fund of Funds

Association Membership

South African Venture Capital Association (SAVCA)

Project Preferences

Type of Financing Preferred:

Fund of Funds
Second Stage Financing
Early Stage
Expansion
Seed
Startup

Geographical Preferences

International Preferences:

South Africa
Africa

Industry Preferences

In Communications prefer:

Telecommunications

In Computer Software prefer:

Applications Software

In Internet Specific prefer:

E-Commerce Technology

In Semiconductor/Electr prefer:

Electronics

In Biotechnology prefer:

Biotechnology

In Medical/Health prefer:

Medical/Health
Medical Products

In Industrial/Energy prefer:

Industrial Products

In Financial Services prefer:

Financial Services

In Agr/Forestr/Fish prefer:

Agriculture related
Mining and Minerals

Additional Information

Year Founded: 2000
Capital Under Management: $75,400,000
Current Activity Level: Actively seeking new investments

INDUSTRIAL GROWTH PARTNERS

100 Spear Street
Suite 1500
San Francisco, CA USA 94105
Phone: 415-882-4550
Fax: 415-882-4551
Website: www.igpequity.com

Management and Staff

Daniel Delaney, Partner
Gottfried Tittiger, Managing Director
Jeffrey Webb, Partner
Karen Greaves, Chief Financial Officer
Matthew Antaya, Partner
Michael Beaumont, Managing Director
Peter Reidencach, Partner
R. Patrick Forster, Managing Director
Robert Groenke, Partner

Type of Firm

Private Equity Firm

Project Preferences

Type of Financing Preferred:

Leveraged Buyout
Expansion
Management Buyouts
Recapitalizations

Geographical Preferences

United States Preferences:

All U.S.

Canadian Preferences:

All Canada

International Preferences:

Mexico

Industry Focus

(% based on actual investment)

Industrial/Energy	62.3%
Other Products	29.7%
Computer Hardware	8.0%

Additional Information

Name of Most Recent Fund: Industrial Growth Partners III, L.P.
Most Recent Fund Was Raised: 09/08/2006
Year Founded: 1997
Capital Under Management: $625,500,000
Current Activity Level: Actively seeking new investments

INDUSTRIAL OPPORTUNITY PARTNERS, LLC

1603 Orrington Avenue
Suite 700
Evanston, IL USA 60201
Phone: 847-556-3460
Fax: 847-556-3461
Website: www.iopfund.com

Management and Staff

Adam Gottlieb, Managing Director
Andrew Weller, Principal
James Todd, Principal
John Colaianne, Principal
Kenneth Tallering, Senior Managing Director
Nicholas Galambos, Principal
Robert Vedra, Managing Director
Thomas Paisley, Principal

Type of Firm

Private Equity Firm

Project Preferences

Type of Financing Preferred:

Leveraged Buyout
Turnaround
Recapitalizations

Size of Investments Considered:

Min Size of Investment Considered (000s): $5,000
Max Size of Investment Considered (000s): $20,000

Industry Preferences

In Semiconductor/Electr prefer:

Electronics

In Industrial/Energy prefer:

Industrial Products
Advanced Materials

In Manufact. prefer:

Manufacturing

Additional Information

Name of Most Recent Fund: IOP Affiliates Fund, L.P.
Most Recent Fund Was Raised: 06/22/2007
Year Founded: 2005
Capital Under Management: $188,000,000
Current Activity Level: Actively seeking new investments

INDUSTRIAL RENAISSANCE INC.

P.O. Box 320595
Fairfield, CT USA 06825
Phone: 203-254-7420
Fax: 203-254-8669
E-mail: info@indren.com
Website: www.indren.com

Management and Staff

Eric Hamburg, President, Founder
Rick Shuart, Managing Director

Type of Firm

Private Equity Firm

Project Preferences

Type of Financing Preferred:

Leveraged Buyout
Management Buyouts
Acquisition

Size of Investments Considered:

Min Size of Investment Considered (000s): $10,000
Max Size of Investment Considered (000s): $100,000

Geographical Preferences

United States Preferences:
All U.S.

Industry Preferences

In Business Serv. prefer:
Services

In Manufact. prefer:
Manufacturing

Additional Information

Year Founded: 1996
Current Activity Level: Actively seeking new investments

INDUSTRIEBERATUNG DR. H.C. HARALD EGGERS

Malerstr. 14
Dresden, Germany 01326
Phone: 49-351-266-6515
Fax: 49-351-266-6516
E-mail: info@ibe-dresden.de
Website: www.ibe-dresden.de

Management and Staff

Harald Eggers, CEO & Managing Director

Type of Firm

Service Provider

Project Preferences

Role in Financing:
Will function either as deal originator or investor in deals created by others

Type of Financing Preferred:
Start-up Financing
Seed

Geographical Preferences

International Preferences:
Germany

Industry Preferences

In Semiconductor/Electr prefer:
Semiconductor

In Industrial/Energy prefer:
Alternative Energy

Additional Information

Year Founded: 2004
Current Activity Level: Actively seeking new investments
Method of Compensation: Unknown

INDUSTRIES ET FINANCES PARTENAIRES SA

134 rue du Faubourg
Saint-Honore
Paris, France 75008
Phone: 33-1-5856-3300
Fax: 33-1-5375-3300
E-mail: ifpart@ifpart.com

Management and Staff

Emmanuel Harle, Chairman & Managing Director

Type of Firm

Private Equity Firm

Association Membership

French Venture Capital Association (AFIC)

Project Preferences

Type of Financing Preferred:
Leveraged Buyout
Management Buyouts

Geographical Preferences

International Preferences:
Europe
France

Additional Information

Year Founded: 1998
Capital Under Management: $91,200,000
Current Activity Level: Actively seeking new investments

INDUSTRY FUNDS MANAGEMENT

Casselden Place, Level 31
2 Lonsdale Street
Melbourne, Australia 3000
Phone: 613-9657-4321
Fax: 613-9657-4322
E-mail: ifsnet@ifs.net.au
Website: www.industryfundservices.com.au

Other Offices

25 Old Broad Street
Level 10, Tower 42
London, United Kingdom EC2N 1HQ
Phone: 4420-7448-9600
Fax: 4420-7448-9640

Times Square Tower
25th Floor, Seven Times Square
New York, NY USA 10036
Phone: 212-575-1055
Fax: 212-575-8738

Management and Staff

Damian Moloney, Chief Executive Officer

Type of Firm

Bank Affiliated

Project Preferences

Type of Financing Preferred:
Fund of Funds

Geographical Preferences

International Preferences:
Australia

Additional Information

Name of Most Recent Fund: IFM International Private Equity Fund II
Most Recent Fund Was Raised: 08/31/2005
Year Founded: 1991
Capital Under Management: $841,000,000
Current Activity Level: Actively seeking new investments

INDUSTRY VENTURES

750 Battery Street
Seventh Floor
San Francisco, CA USA 94111
Phone: 415- 273-4201
Fax: 415-391-7262
E-mail: info@industryventures.com
Website: www.industryventures.com

Management and Staff

Hans Swildens, Principal
Justin Burden, Principal
Michael Gridley, Principal
Robert Raynard, Chief Financial Officer

Type of Firm

Private Equity Firm

Project Preferences

Role in Financing:
Prefer role as deal originator

Type of Financing Preferred:
Later Stage

Size of Investments Considered:
Min Size of Investment Considered (000s): $250
Max Size of Investment Considered (000s): $100,000

Geographical Preferences

United States Preferences:
All U.S.

Industry Preferences

In Communications prefer:
Wireless Communications

In Computer Software prefer:
Data Processing
Software

In Internet Specific prefer:
E-Commerce Technology
Internet

In Consumer Related prefer:
Retail

In Business Serv. prefer:
Media

Additional Information

Name of Most Recent Fund: Industry Ventures Fund V, L.P.
Most Recent Fund Was Raised: 03/26/2008
Year Founded: 2000
Capital Under Management: $450,000,000
Current Activity Level: Actively seeking new investments
Method of Compensation: Return on invest. most important, but chg. closing fees, service fees, etc.

INEKO CAPITAL PARTNERS LLP

62-a Chervonoarmiynska Street
3rd Floor
Kiev, Ukraine 03150
Phone: 380-44-201-6454
Fax: 380-44-201-6417
E-mail: info@inekocapital.com
Website: www.ineko.com

Management and Staff

Chris Kamtsios, Managing Partner
Denis Kopylov, Chief Executive Officer
Eugene Baranov, Chief Financial Officer

Type of Firm

Bank Affiliated

Association Membership

European Private Equity and Venture Capital Assoc.

Project Preferences

Type of Financing Preferred:
Leveraged Buyout
Expansion
Turnaround
Management Buyouts

Size of Investments Considered:
Min Size of Investment Considered (000s): $1,000
Max Size of Investment Considered (000s): $10,000

Geographical Preferences

International Preferences:
Europe
Eastern Europe
Ukraine
Russia

Industry Preferences

In Consumer Related prefer:
Food/Beverage

In Industrial/Energy prefer:
Energy
Materials

In Transportation prefer:
Transportation

In Financial Services prefer:
Real Estate
Financial Services

In Business Serv. prefer:
Distribution

In Manufact. prefer:
Manufacturing

Additional Information

Year Founded: 2002
Current Activity Level: Actively seeking new investments

INETWORKS, LLC

411 Seventh Avenue
14th Floor
Pittsburgh, PA USA 15219
Phone: 412-393-7650
Fax: 412-393-7651
Website: www.inetworksllc.com

Other Offices

National Technology Transfer Center
316 Washington Avenue
Wheeling, WV USA 26003

4548 Market Street
Philadelphia, PA USA 19139
Phone: 215-243-4111
Fax: 215-895-4001

Management and Staff

Anthony Lacenere, Managing Director
Charles Schliebs, Managing Director
Steven Russell, Managing Director

Type of Firm

Private Equity Firm

Project Preferences

Type of Financing Preferred:
Early Stage
Seed

Size of Investments Considered:
Min Size of Investment Considered (000s): $250
Max Size of Investment Considered (000s): $5,000

Geographical Preferences

United States Preferences:
Mid Atlantic
Pennsylvania
West Virginia

International Preferences:
All International

Industry Preferences

In Medical/Health prefer:
Medical/Health
Medical Products

In Other prefer:
Socially Responsible
Women/Minority-Owned Bus.

Additional Information

Name of Most Recent Fund: iNetworks Private Fund, L.P.
Most Recent Fund Was Raised: 02/07/2007
Year Founded: 2003
Capital Under Management: $50,000,000
Current Activity Level: Actively seeking new investments

INFIELD CAPITAL

2033 Eleventh Street
Boulder, CO USA 80302
Phone: 303-449-2921
Fax: 303-449-2936
E-mail: info@infieldcapital.com
Website: www.infieldcapital.com

Management and Staff

David Moll, Managing Director

Type of Firm

Private Equity Firm

Project Preferences

Type of Financing Preferred:
Early Stage

Geographical Preferences

United States Preferences:
All U.S.

Industry Preferences

In Industrial/Energy prefer:
Energy
Environmental Related

In Transportation prefer:
Transportation

Additional Information

Year Founded: 2008
Capital Under Management: $50,000,000
Current Activity Level: Actively seeking new investments

INFINITY ASSET MANAGEMENT LLP

26th Floor, City Tower
Piccadilly Plaza
Manchester, United Kingdom M1 4BD
Phone: 44-161-242-2910

Fax: 44-161-242-2929
E-mail: enquiries@infinityllp.com
Website: www.infinityllp.com

Other Offices

Mayfair
London, United Kingdom

Management and Staff

Daniel Finestein, Partner
Les Lang, Partner
Phil Vickers, Partner
Sarah Butler, Partner
Yitz Jaffe, Partner

Type of Firm

Private Equity Firm

Association Membership

British Venture Capital Association (BVCA)

Project Preferences

Type of Financing Preferred:

Leveraged Buyout
Expansion
Turnaround
Management Buyouts
Acquisition

Size of Investments Considered:

Min Size of Investment Considered (000s): $1,959
Max Size of Investment Considered (000s): $19,591

Geographical Preferences

International Preferences:

United Kingdom

Industry Preferences

In Communications prefer:

Telecommunications

In Consumer Related prefer:

Entertainment and Leisure

In Financial Services prefer:

Financial Services
Real Estate

In Business Serv. prefer:

Consulting Services

Additional Information

Year Founded: 2007
Current Activity Level: Actively seeking new investments

INFINITY CAPITAL LLC

480 Cowper Street
Suite 200
Palo Alto, CA USA 94301
Phone: 650-462-8400
Fax: 650-462-8415
E-mail: info@infinityllc.com
Website: www.infinityllc.com

Management and Staff

Bruce Graham, Managing Director
Sam Lee, Managing Director

Type of Firm

Private Equity Firm

Association Membership

Western Association of Venture Capitalists (WAVC)

Project Preferences

Role in Financing:

Will function either as deal originator or investor in deals created by others

Type of Financing Preferred:

Early Stage

Size of Investments Considered:

Min Size of Investment Considered (000s): $275
Max Size of Investment Considered (000s): $10,000

Industry Focus

(% based on actual investment)

Internet Specific	36.7%
Computer Software and Services	26.2%
Semiconductors/Other Elect.	16.6%
Communications and Media	10.2%
Computer Hardware	8.7%
Medical/Health	0.9%
Other Products	0.6%

Additional Information

Name of Most Recent Fund: Infinity Capital VF 1999
Most Recent Fund Was Raised: 09/30/1999
Year Founded: 1999
Capital Under Management: $207,500,000
Current Activity Level: Actively seeking new investments
Method of Compensation: Return on investment is of primary concern, do not charge fees

---

INFINITY VENTURE CAPITAL

001 Turf Estate, Shakti Mills
Mahalakshmi
Mumbai, India 400011
Phone: 91-22-2490-2201
Fax: 91-22-2490-2205
E-mail: contact.bombay@infinityventure.com
Website: www.infinityventure.com

Other Offices

515 Madison Avenue 53rd Street
21st floor
New York, NY USA 10022
Phone: 212-838-6360
Fax: 212-838-7818

A-32, Shefali Apartments
Aga Abbas Ali Road, Ulsoor
Bangalore, India 560042
Phone: 91-80-2559 7252
Fax: 91-80-559 4752

Management and Staff

Pravin Gandhi, Managing Partner
Rishi Sahai, Managing Partner
Sanjay Bhattacharya, Managing Partner

Type of Firm

Private Equity Firm

Association Membership

Indian Venture Capital Association (IVCA)

Project Preferences

Type of Financing Preferred:

Early Stage
Mezzanine
Expansion
Seed
Startup
Recapitalizations

Size of Investments Considered:

Min Size of Investment Considered (000s): $21
Max Size of Investment Considered (000s): $2,000

Geographical Preferences

International Preferences:

India

Industry Preferences

In Communications prefer:

Telecommunications

In Computer Software prefer:

Software

In Computer Other prefer:

Computer Related

Additional Information

Year Founded: 1999
Capital Under Management: $21,000,000
Current Activity Level: Actively seeking new investments

INFINITY VENTURE CAPITAL FUND (AKA: ISRAEL INFINITY FUND)

3 Azrieli Ctr, Triangle Tower
42nd Floor
Tel Aviv, Israel 67023
Phone: 972-3607-5456
Fax: 972-3607-5455
E-mail: inf@infinity-vc.com
Website: www.infinity-vc.com

Other Offices

1C2F, Sanlake Square, 345 Fengli Road
Suzhou Industrial Park
Jiangsu Province, China 215026
Phone: 86-512-6696-9511
Fax: 86-512-6696-9533

Unit 3501 Lippo Centre, Tower 1
89 Queensway Road, Admiralty
Central, Hong Kong
Phone: 852-21-869-016
Fax: 852-21-693-117

33rd Floor
900 Third Avenue
New York, NY USA 10022
Phone: 212-317-3376
Fax: 212-317-3365

Room 2404
Number 885 Renmin Road
Shanghai, China 200010
Phone: 86-21-3307-0045

Management and Staff

Adiv Baruch, Venture Partner
Amir Gal-Or, Managing Partner
Ariel Poppel, Managing Director
Avishai Silvershatz, Managing Partner
Bella Ohana, Managing Director
Fei Jianjiang, Managing Director
Henry Gong, Venture Partner
Kenneth Rind, Managing Partner
Kersten Hui, Managing Director
Peter Lu, Managing Director
Robert Barasch, Managing Director
Wang Wei, Venture Partner

Type of Firm

Private Equity Firm

Project Preferences

Role in Financing:

Will function either as deal originator or investor in deals created by others

Type of Financing Preferred:

Early Stage
Balanced
Later Stage
Startup

Size of Investments Considered:

Min Size of Investment Considered (000s): $500
Max Size of Investment Considered (000s): $5,000

Geographical Preferences

International Preferences:

China
Israel
Singapore
Asia

Industry Preferences

In Communications prefer:

Telecommunications

In Internet Specific prefer:

Internet

Additional Information

Year Founded: 1998
Capital Under Management: $85,000,000
Current Activity Level: Actively seeking new investments

INFLECTION PARTNERS, LLC

One Sansome Street
Suite 2900
San Francisco, CA USA 94104
Phone: 415-835-3880

Type of Firm

Private Equity Firm

Project Preferences

Type of Financing Preferred:

Balanced

Additional Information

Year Founded: 2004
Current Activity Level: Actively seeking new investments

INFLECTION POINT VENTURES

One Innovation Way
Suite 500
Newark, DE USA 19711
Phone: 302-452-1120
Fax: 302-452-1122
E-mail: info@inflectpoint.com
Website: www.inflectpoint.com

Other Offices

7903 Sleaford Place
Bethesda, MD USA 20814
Phone: 301-656-6837
Fax: 301-656-8056

30 Washington Street
Wellesley, MA USA 02481
Phone: 781-416-5107
Fax: 781-237-6699

Management and Staff

Diane Messick, Chief Financial Officer
Jeffrey Davison, General Partner
Michael O'Malley, General Partner
Timothy Webb, General Partner

Type of Firm

Private Equity Firm

Association Membership

Mid-Atlantic Venture Association
National Venture Capital Association - USA (NVCA)

Project Preferences

Role in Financing:

Prefer role as deal originator

Type of Financing Preferred:

Early Stage
Seed

Size of Investments Considered:

Min Size of Investment Considered (000s): $500
Max Size of Investment Considered (000s): $2,000

Geographical Preferences

United States Preferences:

Mid Atlantic
Northeast

Industry Preferences

In Communications prefer:

Telecommunications

In Internet Specific prefer:

Ecommerce

Additional Information

Year Founded: 1998
Capital Under Management: $50,000,000
Current Activity Level: Actively seeking new investments

INFLEXION PLC (AKA: INFLEXION PRIVATE EQUITY)

43 Welbeck Street
London, United Kingdom W1G 8DX
Phone: 44-20-7487-9888
Fax: 44-20-7487-2774
E-mail: info@inflexion.com
Website: www.inflexion.com

Other Offices

82 King Street
Manchester, United Kingdom M2 4WQ
Phone: 44-161-935-8018
Fax: 44-161-935-8154

Management and Staff

Charles Thompson, Partner
John Hartz, Managing Partner
Simon Turner, Managing Partner
Tim Smallbone, Partner

Type of Firm

Private Equity Firm

Association Membership

British Venture Capital Association (BVCA)
European Private Equity and Venture Capital Assoc.

Project Preferences

Type of Financing Preferred:

Second Stage Financing
Leveraged Buyout
Expansion
Management Buyouts

Size of Investments Considered:
Min Size of Investment Considered (000s): $2,839
Max Size of Investment Considered (000s): $14,195

Geographical Preferences

International Preferences:
United Kingdom
Europe
Western Europe

Industry Preferences

In Communications prefer:
Communications and Media

In Internet Specific prefer:
Internet

In Computer Other prefer:
Computer Related

In Medical/Health prefer:
Medical/Health

In Consumer Related prefer:
Consumer Products
Consumer Services

In Business Serv. prefer:
Services

Additional Information

Year Founded: 1998
Capital Under Management: $51,100,000
Current Activity Level: Actively seeking new investments

INFOCOMM INVESTMENTS PTE., LTD. (FKA: NCB HOLDINGS PTE LTD)

Eight Temasek Boulevard
#14-00 Suntec Tower Three
Singapore, Singapore 038988
Phone: 65-6211-0888
Fax: 65-6211-2222
E-mail: info@ida.gov.sg
Website: www.ida.gov.sg

Other Offices

1038 Nanjing West Road
Westgate Tower 18-01
Shanghai, China 200041
Phone: 86-21-6217-8822
Fax: 86-21-6218-9720

Unit One, Level Three, Explorer Block
International Tech Park, Whitefield Road
Bangalore, India 560 066
Phone: 91-80-5115-6400
Fax: 91-80-5115-6104

Three Twin Dolphin Drive
Suite 150
Redwood City, CA USA 94065
Phone: 650-593-1716
Fax: 650-593-3276

Management and Staff

Ronnie Tay, Chief Executive Officer

Type of Firm

Government Affiliated Program

Project Preferences

Type of Financing Preferred:
Expansion

Size of Investments Considered:
Min Size of Investment Considered (000s): $1,000
Max Size of Investment Considered (000s): $5,000

Geographical Preferences

United States Preferences:
All U.S.

International Preferences:
India
China
Singapore
Asia

Industry Preferences

In Communications prefer:
Communications and Media

Additional Information

Year Founded: 1996
Capital Under Management: $170,000,000
Current Activity Level: Actively seeking new investments

INFORMAL CAPITAL NETWORK (AKA: ICN)

Birkstratt 95/97
Soest, Netherlands 3768 HD
Phone: 31-35-603-3293
Fax: 31-35-603-3295
E-mail: triad@tiin.net
Website: www.tiin.net

Type of Firm

Private Equity Firm

Additional Information

Year Founded: 2004
Current Activity Level: Actively seeking new investments

INFORMATION TECHNOLOGY FARM CORPORATION (AKA: IT FARM)

Shinjuku i-Land Tower 5F
6-5-1 Nishii Shinjuku
Tokyo, Japan 463-1305
Phone: 81-3-5324-3531
Fax: 81-3-5324-3546
E-mail: in-for-ma-tion@it-farm.com
Website: www.it-farm.com

Management and Staff

Akio Kojima, Partner
Morio Kurosaki, President
Satoshi Yamaguchi, Partner
Takehiro Shirai, General Partner

Type of Firm

Incubator/Development Program

Project Preferences

Type of Financing Preferred:
Expansion
Seed
Startup

Geographical Preferences

International Preferences:
Japan

Industry Preferences

In Semiconductor/Electr prefer:
Semiconductor

Additional Information

Year Founded: 1999
Capital Under Management: $412,800,000
Current Activity Level: Actively seeking new investments

INFOTECH PACIFIC VENTURES L.P. (FKA: INFOTECH VENTURES CO.)

Rm. 2003, Cyber Tower B
No. 2 ZhongGuanCun NanDaJie
Beijing, China 100086
Phone: 86-10-8251-2080
Fax: 86-10-8251-5186
Website: www.infotechcapital.com

Other Offices

522 Cambridge Avenue
Palo Alto, CA USA 94302
Phone: 650-278-0276

Management and Staff

Fang Roger Li, General Partner
Ning Zhou, Vice President
Terence Tan, General Partner
Tingru Liu, General Partner
Weijin Liu, Vice President

Type of Firm

Private Equity Firm

Project Preferences

Type of Financing Preferred:
Early Stage
Balanced

Geographical Preferences

International Preferences:
China
All International

Additional Information
Name of Most Recent Fund: Infotech Pacific Ventures Affiliates, L.P.
Most Recent Fund Was Raised: 03/13/2007
Year Founded: 2005
Capital Under Management: $77,400,000
Current Activity Level: Actively seeking new investments

INFRASTRUCTURE FUND, THE
1000 Red River
Rm. E208
Austin, TX USA 78701-2698
Phone: 512-344-4300
Fax: 512-344-4320
Website: www.tifb.state.tx.us

Type of Firm
Private Equity Firm

Additional Information
Year Founded: 2009
Current Activity Level: Actively seeking new investments

ING BARINGS PRIVATE EQUITY
60 London Wall
London, United Kingdom EC2M 5TQ
Phone: 44-207-767-1000
Fax: 44-207-767-7777
Website: www.ingbarings.com

Other Offices
89-91 rue du Faubourg Saint-Honore
Paris, France 75008
Phone: 33 1 44947500
Fax: 33 1 44947555

Management and Staff
Anna Ohlsson, Vice President
Dominique Grey, Managing Director

Type of Firm
Bank Affiliated

Project Preferences

Type of Financing Preferred:
Leveraged Buyout
Expansion
Balanced

Geographical Preferences

International Preferences:
Czech Republic
Portugal
Western Europe
Spain
Scandanavia/Nordic Region
Belgium
France

Industry Preferences

In Communications prefer:
Communications and Media

In Computer Other prefer:
Computer Related

In Semiconductor/Electr prefer:
Electronics

In Biotechnology prefer:
Biotechnology

In Medical/Health prefer:
Medical/Health

In Industrial/Energy prefer:
Industrial Products

Additional Information
Year Founded: 2000
Capital Under Management: $259,800,000
Current Activity Level: Actively seeking new investments

ING BELGIUM (AKA: BANQUE BRUXELLES LAMBERT)
24 Avenue Marnix
Brussels, Belgium 1000
Phone: 32-2-547-3589
Fax: 32-2-547-8482
E-mail: info@bbl.be
Website: www.ing.be

Type of Firm
Bank Affiliated

Project Preferences

Type of Financing Preferred:
Early Stage
Expansion

Geographical Preferences

International Preferences:
Europe
Belgium

Additional Information
Year Founded: 1997
Capital Under Management: $98,900,000
Current Activity Level: Actively seeking new investments

ING INVESTMENT MANAGEMENT
Level 21
83 Clarence Street
Sydney, Australia 2000
Phone: 612-9276-6200
Fax: 612-9276-6400
E-mail: ingpeal@ing.com.au
Website: www.ingim.com

Other Offices
39/F One International Finance Ctr
1 Harbour View Street
Central, Hong Kong
Phone: 852-2846-3938
Fax: 852-2179-5703

17 Lincoln Lodge
Altamount Road
Mumbai, India 400 036
Phone: 91-22-383-7999
Fax: 91-22-383-4668

1 Raffles Place
23-08 Republic
Singapore, Singapore 048619
Phone: 65-6539-7833
Fax: 65-6535-3393

84 Jalan Raja Chulan
Kuala Lumpur, Malaysia 50927
Phone: 603-2161-7255
Fax: 603-2161-2402

Management and Staff
David Hampton, Chief Operating Officer
David McClatchy, Chief Executive Officer

Type of Firm
Insurance Firm Affiliate

Project Preferences

Type of Financing Preferred:
Fund of Funds
Leveraged Buyout

Geographical Preferences

International Preferences:
Australia

Industry Focus
(% based on actual investment)

Other Products	93.2%
Biotechnology	2.7%
Communications and Media	2.3%
Internet Specific	1.7%

Additional Information
Name of Most Recent Fund: ING Private Capital Fund II
Most Recent Fund Was Raised: 08/31/2001
Year Founded: 1998
Capital Under Management: $43,400,000

Current Activity Level: Actively seeking new investments

INGENIOUS HAUS GROUP

111 North Bridge Road
Suite 27-01 Peninsula Plaza
Singapore, Singapore 179098
Phone: 65-9175-8978
Website: www.ingenioushaus.com

Other Offices

No. 1 Medan Syed Putra Utara
Suite 168, A-G-3A North Point
Midvalley, Kuala Lumpur, Malaysia 59200

Type of Firm

Private Equity Firm

Project Preferences

Type of Financing Preferred:
Expansion
Generalist PE
Early Stage
Balanced
Seed
Startup

Geographical Preferences

International Preferences:
Asia
Malaysia

Industry Preferences

In Communications prefer:
Telecommunications
Wireless Communications

Additional Information

Year Founded: 2004
Capital Under Management: $1,400,000
Current Activity Level: Actively seeking new investments

INGENIOUS VENTURES

15 Golden Square
London, United Kingdom W1F 9JG
Phone: 44-20-7319-4000
Fax: 44-20-7319-4001
E-mail: enquiries@ingeniousmedia.co.uk
Website: www.ingeniousmedia.co.uk

Other Offices

P. O. Box 29305
Glasgow
Scotland, United Kingdom G20 8YQ

Management and Staff

Guy Bowles, Managing Director
Kevin Mead, Chief Executive Officer
Nick Harvey, Managing Director

Type of Firm

Private Equity Firm

Project Preferences

Type of Financing Preferred:
Early Stage
Expansion
Balanced

Geographical Preferences

United States Preferences:
Alaska

International Preferences:
United Kingdom
Europe
Western Europe

Industry Preferences

In Communications prefer:
Communications and Media
Media and Entertainment
Entertainment

Additional Information

Year Founded: 1998
Capital Under Management: $311,400,000
Current Activity Level: Actively seeking new investments

INGENIUM CAPITAL GMBH & CO KG

Theatinerstrasse 14
Munich, Germany 80333
Phone: 49-89-208204-80
Fax: 49-89-208024-86
E-mail: info.muenchen@ingenium-capital.com
Website: www.ingcap.com

Management and Staff

Ekkehard Franzke, Managing Partner
Norbert Stelzer, Managing Partner

Type of Firm

Private Equity Firm

Project Preferences

Type of Financing Preferred:
Leveraged Buyout
Management Buyouts

Geographical Preferences

International Preferences:
Germany

Additional Information

Year Founded: 2004
Current Activity Level: Actively seeking new investments

INGLEWOOD VENTURES

12526 Highbluff Drive
Suite 300
San Diego, CA USA 92130
Phone: 858-792-3579
Fax: 858-792-3417
E-mail: info@inglewoodventures.com
Website: www.inglewoodventures.com

Management and Staff

Daniel Wood, General Partner
Killu Tougu Sanborn, Principal
M. Blake Ingle, General Partner

Type of Firm

Private Equity Firm

Association Membership

Natl Assoc of Small Bus. Inv. Co (NASBIC)

Project Preferences

Type of Financing Preferred:
Early Stage
Seed

Size of Investments Considered:
Min Size of Investment Considered (000s): $500
Max Size of Investment Considered (000s): $2,600

Geographical Preferences

United States Preferences:
Southern California
Northern California
West Coast

Industry Preferences

In Biotechnology prefer:
Human Biotechnology
Agricultural/Animal Bio.
Industrial Biotechnology
Biosensors
Biotech Related Research

In Medical/Health prefer:
Medical Diagnostics
Diagnostic Services
Diagnostic Test Products
Medical Therapeutics
Drug/Equipmt Delivery
Medical Products
Disposable Med. Products
Health Services
Pharmaceuticals

Additional Information

Year Founded: 1999
Capital Under Management: $40,000,000
Current Activity Level: Actively seeking new investments
Method of Compensation: Return on investment is of primary concern, do not charge fees

INITIATIVE & FINANCE GESTION

96 Avenue d'Iena
Paris Cedex 16, France 75783
Phone: 33-1-5689-9700
Fax: 33-1-4720-8690
E-mail: infos@initiative-finance.com
Website: www.initiative-finance.com

Other Offices

77, rue du president Edouard Herriot
Lyon, France 69002
Phone: 33-4-7887-8685
Fax: 33-4-7887-8500

Management and Staff

Jean-Bernard Meurisse, Managing Director
Matthieu Douchet, Partner
Thierry Boghossian, Partner
Thierry Giron, Partner
Valerie Bouillier, Partner

Type of Firm

Bank Affiliated

Association Membership

French Venture Capital Association (AFIC)

Project Preferences

Type of Financing Preferred:
Leveraged Buyout
Management Buyouts

Geographical Preferences

International Preferences:
Netherlands
Belgium
Germany
France

Industry Focus

(% based on actual investment)

Medical/Health	45.9%
Consumer Related	32.3%
Internet Specific	14.9%
Industrial/Energy	4.7%
Computer Software and Services	1.6%
Other Products	0.6%

Additional Information

Year Founded: 1984
Current Activity Level: Actively seeking new investments

INITIATIVE CAPITAL SA

C/o Banque CAN-TONAL Vaudoise
Case postale 300
Lausanne, Switzerland CH - 1001
Phone: 41-21-212-3017
Fax: 41-21-212-2166
Website: www.bcv.ch

Type of Firm

Bank Affiliated

Project Preferences

Type of Financing Preferred:
Startup

Geographical Preferences

International Preferences:
Switzerland

Industry Preferences

In Semiconductor/Electr prefer:
Electronic Components

In Biotechnology prefer:
Biotechnology

In Medical/Health prefer:
Medical/Health

Additional Information

Year Founded: 1998
Current Activity Level: Actively seeking new investments

INITIUM CAPITAL LLC

P.O. Box 1585
Dewey, AZ USA 86327
Fax: 928-632-8753
Website: www.initiumcapital.com

Management and Staff

Mark Montgomery, Managing Partner

Type of Firm

Private Equity Firm

Project Preferences

Type of Financing Preferred:
Early Stage
Seed

Industry Preferences

In Communications prefer:
Wireless Communications

In Computer Software prefer:
Software

In Semiconductor/Electr prefer:
Semiconductor

In Medical/Health prefer:
Medical Products
Pharmaceuticals

In Industrial/Energy prefer:
Alternative Energy

Additional Information

Year Founded: 2003
Current Activity Level: Actively seeking new investments

INIZIATIVA GESTIONE INVESTIMENTI SGR

Via Arco 1
Milan, Italy 20121
Phone: 39-2-3657-0550
Fax: 39-2-804-124
E-mail: segretaria@igisgr.it
Website: www.igisgr.it

Other Offices

Piazza Municipio, 4
Napoli, Italy 80133
Phone: 39-081-251-8111
Fax: 39-081-551-7504

Caduti del Lavoro, 40
Ancona, Italy 60131
Phone: 39-071-290-0764
Fax: 39-071-286-1891

Via Michele Scammacca, 5
Catania, Italy 95127
Phone: 39-095-722-5173
Fax: 39-095-722-1296

Mazzini 23
Vicenza, Italy 36100
Phone: 39-0444-540-403
Fax: 39-0444-324-585

Via Emilia Ponente, 317
Bologna, Italy 40125
Phone: 39-051-619-9485
Fax: 39-051-569-481

Via Abruzzi, 6
Rome, Italy
Phone: 39-06-4201-2306
Fax: 39-06-4201-0653

Viale dei Cacciatori 2
Trevisco, Italy 31100
Phone: 39-0422-580-395
Fax: 39-0422-55-199

Amendola, 172/c
Bari, Italy 70126
Phone: 39-080-546-1570
Fax: 39-080-548-1594

Corso Zanardelli 32
Brescia, Italy 25121
Phone: 39-030-280-7402
Fax: 39-030-41-050

Corso Galileo Ferraris 60
Torino, Italy
Phone: 39-011-580-6122
Fax: 39-011-500-567

Management and Staff

Giorgio Cirla, President

Type of Firm
Private Equity Firm

Association Membership
Italian Venture Capital Association (AIFI)
European Private Equity and Venture Capital Assoc.

Project Preferences

Role in Financing:
Will function either as deal originator or investor in deals created by others

Type of Financing Preferred:
Leveraged Buyout
Expansion
Generalist PE
Balanced
Turnaround
Later Stage
Management Buyouts
First Stage Financing

Size of Investments Considered:
Min Size of Investment Considered (000s): $1,500
Max Size of Investment Considered: No Limit

Geographical Preferences

International Preferences:
Italy
Europe

Industry Preferences

In Business Serv. prefer:
Services

In Manufact. prefer:
Manufacturing

Additional Information
Year Founded: 1997
Capital Under Management: $272,700,000
Current Activity Level: Actively seeking new investments

INIZIATIVA PIEMONTE SPA
Corso G. Lanza, 101
Torino, Italy 10133
Phone: 39-011-630-2111
Fax: 39-011-630-2199
E-mail: welcome@ipspa.it
Website: www.iniziativapiemonte.it

Management and Staff
Enrico Amo, Chief Executive Officer
Michele Denegri, Managing Director

Type of Firm
Private Equity Firm

Project Preferences

Type of Financing Preferred:
Early Stage
Balanced
Startup

Geographical Preferences

International Preferences:
Italy

Industry Preferences

In Communications prefer:
Telecommunications

In Financial Services prefer:
Financial Services

In Manufact. prefer:
Manufacturing

Additional Information
Year Founded: 1994
Current Activity Level: Actively seeking new investments

INJAZAT CAPITAL
402, Level 4
Precinct Building 3, The Gate
Dubai, Utd. Arab Em.
Phone: 971-4-365-1500
Fax: 971-4-363-7324
E-mail: info@injazatcapital.com
Website: www.injazatcapital.com

Management and Staff
Declan Duff, Vice President
Edward Nassim, Vice President
Fawzi Zeine, Principal
Hussein Rifai, Chief Executive Officer
Morten Kvammen, Chief Operating Officer
Rami Bazzi, Vice President

Type of Firm
Private Equity Firm

Project Preferences

Type of Financing Preferred:
Balanced

Geographical Preferences

International Preferences:
Utd. Arab Em.
Middle East

Industry Preferences

In Medical/Health prefer:
Health Services

Additional Information
Year Founded: 2001
Current Activity Level: Actively seeking new investments

INNISFREE GROUP
21 Whitefriars Street
London, United Kingdom EC4Y 8JJ
Phone: 44-207583-4040
Fax: 44-207583-4141
E-mail: kashem@innisfree.co.uk
Website: www.innisfree.co.uk

Management and Staff
David Metter, Chief Executive Officer

Type of Firm
Private Equity Firm

Project Preferences

Type of Financing Preferred:
Fund of Funds
Special Situation

Size of Investments Considered:
Min Size of Investment Considered (000s): $6,167
Max Size of Investment Considered (000s): $98,668

Geographical Preferences

International Preferences:
United Kingdom
Europe

Industry Preferences

In Medical/Health prefer:
Medical/Health

In Consumer Related prefer:
Education Related

In Transportation prefer:
Transportation

Additional Information
Year Founded: 2002
Capital Under Management: $561,400,000
Current Activity Level: Actively seeking new investments

INNOCAL VENTURE CAPITAL
600 Anton Boulevard
Suite 1207
Costa Mesa, CA USA 92626
Phone: 714-850-6784
Fax: 714-850-6798
Website: www.innocal.com

Other Offices
180 Lytton Avenue
Palo Alto, CA USA 94301

Management and Staff
Harry Lambert, Managing Director
James Houlihan, Managing Director
Rick Gold, Managing Director

Type of Firm
Private Equity Firm

Project Preferences

Role in Financing:
Prefer role as deal originator but will also invest in deals created by others

Type of Financing Preferred:
Second Stage Financing
Early Stage
Expansion
Turnaround
First Stage Financing
Startup
Recapitalizations

Size of Investments Considered:
Min Size of Investment Considered (000s): $1,000
Max Size of Investment Considered (000s): $5,000

Geographical Preferences

United States Preferences:
Southern California
Northern California
West Coast

International Preferences:
All International

Industry Focus
(% based on actual investment)

Computer Software and Services	34.1%
Medical/Health	19.3%
Internet Specific	14.3%
Communications and Media	14.3%
Semiconductors/Other Elect.	7.6%
Computer Hardware	4.0%
Industrial/Energy	3.9%
Biotechnology	2.5%

Additional Information
Name of Most Recent Fund: InnoCal II, L.P.
Most Recent Fund Was Raised: 12/01/1999
Year Founded: 1993
Capital Under Management: $175,000,000
Current Activity Level: Actively seeking new investments
Method of Compensation: Return on investment is of primary concern, do not charge fees

INNOFINANCE OY (FKA: CULMINATUM OY)
Tekniikantie 12
Innopoli
Espoo, Finland 02150
Phone: 358-20-743-2500
Fax: 358-20-743-2501
E-mail: info@innofinance.fi
Website: www.innofinance.fi

Other Offices
Hatanpaan valtatie 24
Dynamo Business Park
Tampere, Finland 33210
Fax: 358-20-743-2503

Snellmaninkatu 10
Lappeenranta, Finland 53100
Fax: 358-20-743-2502

Management and Staff
Martti Hintikka, Chief Executive Officer

Type of Firm
Incubator/Development Program

Association Membership
Finnish Venture Capital Association (FVCA)
European Private Equity and Venture Capital Assoc.

Project Preferences

Type of Financing Preferred:
Early Stage
Expansion
Balanced
Seed
Startup

Geographical Preferences

International Preferences:
Finland

Industry Preferences

In Semiconductor/Electr prefer:
Electronics

In Biotechnology prefer:
Biotechnology

In Medical/Health prefer:
Medical Products

In Consumer Related prefer:
Consumer Products

In Industrial/Energy prefer:
Energy

Additional Information
Name of Most Recent Fund: Seedcap II Ky
Most Recent Fund Was Raised: 08/01/2005
Year Founded: 1993
Capital Under Management: $21,000,000
Current Activity Level: Actively seeking new investments

INNOGEST
11 , Piazza Solferino
Torino, Italy 10121
Phone: 39-0111950-1401
Fax: 39-011509-7323
E-mail: info@innogest.it
Website: www.innogest.it

Management and Staff
Claudio Giuliano, Managing Director

Type of Firm
Private Equity Firm

Association Membership
Italian Venture Capital Association (AIFI)

Project Preferences

Type of Financing Preferred:
Early Stage

Geographical Preferences

International Preferences:
Italy
Europe

Additional Information
Year Founded: 2005
Current Activity Level: Actively seeking new investments

INNOVA CAPITAL
Rondo ONZ 1, 35th Floor
Warsaw, Poland 00-124
Phone: 48-22-544-9400
Fax: 48-22-544-9403
E-mail: mail@innovacap.com
Website: www.innovacap.com

Management and Staff
Andrzej Bartos, Partner
Arkaduisz Podziewski, Partner
Gregory Krasnov, Managing Director
Krzysztof Krawczyk, Partner
Krzysztof Kulig, Partner
Leszek Muzyczyszyn, Managing Director
Robert Conn, Managing Partner
Steven Buckley, Managing Partner

Type of Firm
Private Equity Firm

Association Membership
Hungarian Venture Capital Association (HVCA)
Polish Venture Capital Association (PSIC/PPEA)
European Private Equity and Venture Capital Assoc.

Project Preferences

Role in Financing:
Prefer role as deal originator but will also invest in deals created by others

Type of Financing Preferred:
Second Stage Financing
Leveraged Buyout
Control-block Purchases
Early Stage
Mezzanine
Expansion
Balanced
Later Stage
Management Buyouts
First Stage Financing
Industry Rollups
Special Situation

Size of Investments Considered:
Min Size of Investment Considered (000s): $6,053
Max Size of Investment Considered (000s): $18,160

Geographical Preferences

International Preferences:
Hungary
Slovak Repub.
Czech Republic
Central Europe
Poland
Austria
Scandanavia/Nordic Region
Germany

Industry Preferences

In Communications prefer:
Telecommunications

In Consumer Related prefer:
Retail

In Financial Services prefer:
Financial Services

In Business Serv. prefer:
Services
Media

In Manufact. prefer:
Manufacturing

Additional Information
Name of Most Recent Fund: Innova/3 LP
Most Recent Fund Was Raised: 02/21/2002
Year Founded: 1994
Capital Under Management: $674,500,000
Current Activity Level: Actively seeking new investments

INNOVA MEMPHIS, INC.
20 South Dudley
Suite 620
Memphis, TN USA 38103
Phone: 901-866-1433
Fax: 901-866-1431
E-mail: contact@innovamemphis.com
Website: www.innovamemphis.com

Management and Staff
Ken Woody, President

Type of Firm
Private Equity Firm

Project Preferences

Role in Financing:
Prefer role as deal originator but will also invest in deals created by others

Type of Financing Preferred:
Early Stage
Startup

Geographical Preferences

United States Preferences:
Tennessee

Industry Preferences

In Biotechnology prefer:
Biotechnology
Agricultural/Animal Bio.

In Medical/Health prefer:
Medical/Health
Medical Therapeutics
Medical Products
Health Services
Pharmaceuticals

In Industrial/Energy prefer:
Energy

In Other prefer:
Women/Minority-Owned Bus.

Additional Information
Year Founded: 2007
Capital Under Management: $12,000,000
Current Activity Level: Actively seeking new investments

INNOVACOM
23, Rue Royale
Paris, France 75008
Phone: 33-1-4494-1500
Fax: 33-1-4494-1515
E-mail: info@innovacom.com
Website: www.innovacomvc.com

Other Offices
One Embarcadero Centre
Skydeck- 41st Floor
San Francisco, CA USA 94111
Phone: 415-288-0680
Fax: 415-288-0685

Birger Jarlsgatan 2
Stockholm, Sweden 11434
Phone: 46-708-112-933

Management and Staff
Aymerik Renard, General Partner
Bruno Dizengremel, General Partner
Denis Champenois, President
Denis Barrier, General Partner
Francois Scolan, General Partner
Frederic Veyssiere, General Partner
Geoffroy Dubus, General Partner
Jacques Meheut, General Partner
Jerome Lecoeur, General Partner

Type of Firm
Private Equity Firm

Association Membership
French Venture Capital Association (AFIC)
European Private Equity and Venture Capital Assoc.

Project Preferences

Type of Financing Preferred:
Second Stage Financing
Early Stage
Balanced
Start-up Financing
Seed
First Stage Financing
Startup

Size of Investments Considered:
Min Size of Investment Considered (000s): $1,180
Max Size of Investment Considered (000s): $7,075

Geographical Preferences

United States Preferences:
West Coast

Canadian Preferences:
All Canada
Quebec

International Preferences:
United Kingdom
Europe
Scandanavia/Nordic Region
France

Industry Focus
(% based on actual investment)

Computer Software and Services	29.7%
Internet Specific	25.4%
Communications and Media	24.4%
Semiconductors/Other Elect.	13.5%
Computer Hardware	6.2%
Consumer Related	0.8%

Additional Information
Name of Most Recent Fund: Innovacom 6
Most Recent Fund Was Raised: 11/12/2007
Year Founded: 1988
Capital Under Management: $341,400,000
Current Activity Level: Actively seeking new investments
Method of Compensation: Return on investment is of primary concern, do not charge fees

---

INNOVAFONDS
157, avenue de l'Eygala
Corenc, France 38700
Phone: 33-4-7608-7946
E-mail: contact@innovafonds.com
Website: www.innovafonds.com

Management and Staff
Emmanuel Arnould, Partner
Frederic Martel, Partner
Jean-Michel Gline, Partner
Vincent Weber, Partner

Type of Firm
Private Equity Firm

Association Membership

French Venture Capital Association (AFIC)

Project Preferences

Type of Financing Preferred:

Expansion
Early Stage
Later Stage

Geographical Preferences

International Preferences:

France

Industry Preferences

In Communications prefer:

Wireless Communications

In Medical/Health prefer:

Medical/Health

In Industrial/Energy prefer:

Energy

Additional Information

Year Founded: 2008
Current Activity Level: Actively seeking new investments

INNOVATECH SUD DU QUEBEC

455 Rue King Ouest
Bureau 305
Sherbrooke, Canada J1H 6E9
Phone: 819-820-3305
Fax: 819-820-3320
E-mail: isq@isq.qc.ca
Website: www.isq.qc.ca

Management and Staff

Jean-Jacques Caron, Vice President

Type of Firm

Government Affiliated Program

Project Preferences

Role in Financing:

Will function either as deal originator or investor in deals created by others

Type of Financing Preferred:

Early Stage
Research and Development
Start-up Financing
Seed
First Stage Financing

Size of Investments Considered:

Min Size of Investment Considered (000s): $83
Max Size of Investment Considered (000s): $4,153

Geographical Preferences

Canadian Preferences:

Quebec

Industry Preferences

In Communications prefer:

Telecommunications
Data Communications

In Biotechnology prefer:

Industrial Biotechnology

Additional Information

Year Founded: 1995
Capital Under Management: $58,300,000
Current Activity Level: Actively seeking new investments
Method of Compensation: Return on invest. most important, but chg. closing fees, service fees, etc.

INNOVATION CAPITAL ASSOCIATES PTY, LTD.

35 Lime Street
Suite 401
Sydney, Australia 2000
Phone: 612-8296-6000
Fax: 612-8296-6066
E-mail: info@innovationcapital.net
Website: www.innovationcapital.net

Other Offices

Level 1, 168 Stirling Highway
Nedlands
Perth, Australia 6009
Phone: 618-9389-7911
Fax: 618-9389-6788

900 Victors Way
Suite 280
Ann Arbor, MI USA 48108
Phone: 734-747-9401
Fax: 734-747-9704

Management and Staff

Fiona Pak-Poy, General Partner
Geoff Dolphin, Chief Financial Officer
Ian Bund, General Partner
Michael Quinn, Chief Executive Officer
Roger Price, General Partner

Type of Firm

Private Equity Firm

Association Membership

Australian Venture Capital Association (AVCAL)

Project Preferences

Type of Financing Preferred:

Early Stage
Seed
Startup

Size of Investments Considered:

Min Size of Investment Considered (000s): $403
Max Size of Investment Considered (000s): $4,835

Geographical Preferences

International Preferences:

Pacific
Australia

Industry Preferences

In Communications prefer:

Telecommunications

In Internet Specific prefer:

Internet

In Biotechnology prefer:

Biotechnology

In Medical/Health prefer:

Medical Products

In Industrial/Energy prefer:

Environmental Related

Additional Information

Year Founded: 1999
Capital Under Management: $69,200,000
Current Activity Level: Actively seeking new investments

INNOVATION ONTARIO CORP.

56 Wellesley Street West
Toronto, Canada M7A 2E7
Phone: 416-326-1025
Fax: 416-326-1109

Type of Firm

Other

Project Preferences

Role in Financing:

Prefer role in deals created by others

Type of Financing Preferred:

Second Stage Financing
Start-up Financing
First Stage Financing

Size of Investments Considered:

Min Size of Investment Considered (000s): $500
Max Size of Investment Considered (000s): $1,000

Additional Information

Year Founded: 1986
Capital Under Management: $80,000,000
Current Activity Level: Actively seeking new investments
Method of Compensation: Return on investment is of primary concern, do not charge fees

INNOVATION PHILADELPHIA

2600 Centre Square West
1500 Market Street
Philadelphia, PA USA 19102

Phone: 215-496-8110
Fax: 215-320-1991
E-mail: ipweb@ipphila.com
Website: www.ipphila.com

Type of Firm

Incubator/Development Program

Project Preferences

Type of Financing Preferred:
Early Stage
Balanced
Seed

Geographical Preferences

United States Preferences:
Pennsylvania
Delaware
New Jersey

Additional Information

Year Founded: 2002
Capital Under Management: $1,100,000
Current Activity Level: Actively seeking new investments

INNOVATION TRANSFER CENTER - CARNEGIE MELLON UNIVERSITY

4615 Forbes Avenue
Suite 302
Pittsburgh, PA USA 15213
Phone: 412-268-7390
Fax: 412-268-7395
E-mail: innovation@cmu.edu
Website: www.cmu.edu/innovationtransfer/

Type of Firm

University Program

Project Preferences

Type of Financing Preferred:
Early Stage
Seed
Startup

Industry Preferences

In Computer Software prefer:
Software

In Consumer Related prefer:
Education Related

Additional Information

Name of Most Recent Fund: Carnegie Mellon University
Most Recent Fund Was Raised: 09/01/1984
Year Founded: 1984
Current Activity Level: Actively seeking new investments

INNOVATION WORKS

Tower C Tsinghua Science Park
Haidian District
Beijing, China 100084
E-mail: contact@innovation-works.com
Website: www.innovation-works.com

Management and Staff

Kai-Fu Lee, Founder

Type of Firm

Incubator/Development Program

Project Preferences

Type of Financing Preferred:
Seed

Geographical Preferences

International Preferences:
China

Industry Preferences

In Internet Specific prefer:
Internet

Additional Information

Year Founded: 2009
Current Activity Level: Actively seeking new investments

INNOVATION WORKS, INC.

2000 Technology Drive
Suite 250
Pittsburgh, PA USA 15219
Phone: 412-681-1520
Fax: 412-681-2625
E-mail: info@innovationworks.org
Website: www.innovationworks.org

Type of Firm

Private Equity Firm

Association Membership

National Venture Capital Association - USA (NVCA)

Project Preferences

Role in Financing:
Prefer role as deal originator

Type of Financing Preferred:
Seed
First Stage Financing
Startup

Size of Investments Considered:
Min Size of Investment Considered (000s): $100
Max Size of Investment Considered (000s): $600

Geographical Preferences

United States Preferences:
Pennsylvania

Industry Preferences

In Communications prefer:
Telecommunications
Wireless Communications

In Computer Hardware prefer:
Mainframes / Scientific
Mini and Personal/Desktop
Computer Graphics and Dig
Integrated Turnkey System
Terminals
Disk Relat. Memory Device

In Computer Software prefer:
Computer Services
Data Processing
Software
Systems Software
Applications Software
Artificial Intelligence

In Internet Specific prefer:
E-Commerce Technology
Internet
Web Aggregration/Portals

In Semiconductor/Electr prefer:
Electronic Components
Semiconductor
Micro-Processing
Controllers and Sensors
Sensors
Circuit Boards
Component Testing Equipmt
Laser Related
Fiber Optics

In Biotechnology prefer:
Human Biotechnology
Industrial Biotechnology

In Medical/Health prefer:
Medical Diagnostics
Diagnostic Services
Diagnostic Test Products
Medical Therapeutics
Drug/Equipmt Delivery
Medical Products
Disposable Med. Products
Health Services
Pharmaceuticals

In Industrial/Energy prefer:
Alternative Energy
Superconductivity
Robotics

Additional Information

Year Founded: 1999
Capital Under Management: $42,000,000
Current Activity Level: Actively seeking new investments
Method of Compensation: Return on investment is of primary concern, do not charge fees

INNOVATIONS-CAPITAL GOTTINGEN GMBH

Wilhelmsplatz 1
Goettingen, Germany 37073
Phone: 49-551-405-2369
Fax: 49-551-405-2310
Website: www.innovations-capital-goettingen.de

Management and Staff

Stefan Keveloh, Chief Executive Officer

Type of Firm

Private Equity Firm

Project Preferences

Type of Financing Preferred:
Expansion
Seed
Startup

Geographical Preferences

International Preferences:
Germany

Industry Preferences

In Biotechnology prefer:
Biotechnology

In Other prefer:
Environment Responsible

Additional Information

Year Founded: 2005
Current Activity Level: Actively seeking new investments

INNOVATIONSKAPITAL

Kungsportsplatsen 1
Goteborg, Sweden SE-411 10
Phone: 46-31-609-190
Fax: 46-31-609-199
E-mail: info@innkap.se
Website: www.innkap.se

Other Offices

1115 Broadway
12th Floor
New York, NY USA 10010
Phone: 917-582-0396
Fax: 212-659-0097

Birger Jarlsgatan 13
Stockholm, Sweden SE-111 45
Phone: 46-8-5450-1490
Fax: 46-8-5450-1499

Management and Staff

Gabriella Ohldin, Chief Financial Officer
Staffan Ingeborn, Chief Executive Officer

Type of Firm

Private Equity Firm

Association Membership

Swedish Venture Capital Association (SVCA)
European Private Equity and Venture Capital Assoc.

Project Preferences

Role in Financing:
Prefer role as deal originator but will also invest in deals created by others

Type of Financing Preferred:
Second Stage Financing
Early Stage
Research and Development
Balanced
Start-up Financing
Seed
First Stage Financing
Startup

Size of Investments Considered:
Min Size of Investment Considered (000s): $200
Max Size of Investment Considered (000s): $3,766

Geographical Preferences

International Preferences:
Europe
Western Europe
Scandanavia/Nordic Region

Industry Focus

(% based on actual investment)

Semiconductors/Other Elect.	29.3%
Biotechnology	20.1%
Medical/Health	12.5%
Internet Specific	11.7%
Communications and Media	7.9%
Computer Software and Services	7.6%
Industrial/Energy	5.5%
Other Products	5.2%
Computer Hardware	0.1%

Additional Information

Name of Most Recent Fund: InnKap 4 Partners
Most Recent Fund Was Raised: 10/01/2005
Year Founded: 1994
Capital Under Management: $400,000
Current Activity Level: Actively seeking new investments
Method of Compensation: Return on investment is of primary concern, do not charge fees

INNOVATIVE VENTURES S.A. (IVEN)

135-137 El. Venizelou Ave
Kallithea
Athens, Greece 17671
Phone: 30-210-331-9950
Fax: 30-210-955-0610
E-mail: info@nbgvc.gr
Website: www.iven.gr

Type of Firm

Incubator/Development Program

Project Preferences

Type of Financing Preferred:
Balanced
Seed

Geographical Preferences

International Preferences:
Greece
Sweden
Europe

Additional Information

Year Founded: 2000
Current Activity Level: Actively seeking new investments

INNOVEN PARTENAIRES S.A.

10 rue de la Paix
Paris, France 75002
Phone: 33-1-4703-1818
Fax: 33-1-4703-1819
E-mail: contact@innoven-partners.com
Website: www.innoven-partners.com

Management and Staff

Bertrand Leblanc, President
Paul Toon, Managing Partner
Thomas Dicker, Managing Partner

Type of Firm

Private Equity Firm

Association Membership

French Venture Capital Association (AFIC)

Project Preferences

Type of Financing Preferred:
Early Stage
Expansion
Generalist PE
Seed

Size of Investments Considered:
Min Size of Investment Considered (000s): $1,098
Max Size of Investment Considered (000s): $2,058

Geographical Preferences

International Preferences:
Europe
France

Industry Preferences

In Communications prefer:
Telecommunications

In Computer Software prefer:
Artificial Intelligence

In Semiconductor/Electr prefer:
Electronics

In Biotechnology prefer:
Biotechnology

Additional Information

Year Founded: 1997
Capital Under Management: $212,700,000
Current Activity Level: Actively seeking new investments

INNOVENTURE A/S

Sortemosemosevej 15
Allerod, Denmark 3450
Phone: 45-48-100-000
Fax: 45-48-100-048

Management and Staff

Torben Ronje, Chief Executive Officer

Type of Firm

Bank Affiliated

Project Preferences

Type of Financing Preferred:
Second Stage Financing
Early Stage
Seed
First Stage Financing
Startup

Geographical Preferences

International Preferences:
Sweden
Denmark

Additional Information

Year Founded: 1999
Capital Under Management: $5,800,000
Current Activity Level: Actively seeking new investments

INNOVENTURES CAPITAL PARTNERS

699 East South Temple
Suite 220
Salt Lake City, UT USA 84102
Phone: 801-741-4200
Fax: 801-741-4249
Website: www.innoventurescapitalpartners.com

Type of Firm

Private Equity Firm

Association Membership

Natl Assoc of Small Bus. Inv. Co (NASBIC)

Project Preferences

Role in Financing:
Prefer role as deal originator but will also invest in deals created by others

Type of Financing Preferred:
Early Stage
Expansion
Mezzanine

Size of Investments Considered:
Min Size of Investment Considered (000s): $100
Max Size of Investment Considered (000s): $500

Geographical Preferences

United States Preferences:
Rocky Mountain
Utah

Industry Preferences

In Communications prefer:
Wireless Communications
Other Communication Prod.

In Computer Software prefer:
Software

In Internet Specific prefer:
E-Commerce Technology

In Business Serv. prefer:
Services

In Manufact. prefer:
Manufacturing

Additional Information

Name of Most Recent Fund: UTFC Fund II LLC
Most Recent Fund Was Raised: 04/30/2007
Year Founded: 2001
Capital Under Management: $19,000,000
Current Activity Level: Actively seeking new investments
Method of Compensation: Return on invest. most important, but chg. closing fees, service fees, etc.

INNVOTEC, LTD.

1 Castle Lane
London, United Kingdom SW1E 6DN
Phone: 44-20-7630-6990
Fax: 44-20-7828-8232
E-mail: cvk@innvotec.co.uk
Website: www.innvotec.co.uk

Other Offices

Business Link House
Salford UBP, 35 Winders Way
Salford, United Kingdom M6 6AR
Phone: 44 161 278 2600
Fax: 44 161 278 2610

MSIF, 5th Floor
Cunard Building, Pier Head
Liverpool, United Kingdom L3 1DS
Phone: 44 151 236 4040
Fax: 44 151 236 3060

Management and Staff

David Hall, Partner
Jeremy Mobbs, Partner

Type of Firm

Private Equity Firm

Association Membership

British Venture Capital Association (BVCA)

Project Preferences

Role in Financing:
Prefer role as deal originator but will also invest in deals created by others

Type of Financing Preferred:
Second Stage Financing
Leveraged Buyout
Early Stage
Expansion
Balanced
Start-up Financing
Seed
First Stage Financing

Size of Investments Considered:
Min Size of Investment Considered (000s): $800
Max Size of Investment Considered: No Limit

Geographical Preferences

International Preferences:
United Kingdom
Europe

Industry Focus

(% based on actual investment)

Internet Specific	33.4%
Computer Software and Services	25.0%
Consumer Related	11.2%
Medical/Health	7.9%
Communications and Media	6.6%
Semiconductors/Other Elect.	5.8%
Computer Hardware	5.5%
Biotechnology	4.6%

Additional Information

Name of Most Recent Fund: Advantage Technology Fund
Most Recent Fund Was Raised: 01/05/2001
Year Founded: 1987
Capital Under Management: $50,100,000
Current Activity Level: Actively seeking new investments
Method of Compensation: Return on investment is of primary concern, do not charge fees

---

INOCAP S.A.

40 rue de la Boetie
Paris, France 75008
Phone: 33-1-4564-0580
Fax: 33-1-4561-6494
Website: www.inocap.fr

Management and Staff
Emmanuel Laussinotte, President
Olivier Bourdelas, Chief Executive Officer
Pierrick Bauchet, Managing Partner

Type of Firm
Private Equity Firm

Association Membership
French Venture Capital Association (AFIC)

Project Preferences
Type of Financing Preferred:
Generalist PE
Early Stage

Geographical Preferences
International Preferences:
Europe
Eastern Europe

Additional Information
Year Founded: 2007
Capital Under Management: $25,400,000
Current Activity Level: Actively seeking new investments

INOVA CAPITAL SCR SA
Paseo de la Castellana 12
Madrid, Spain 28046
Phone: 34-91-426-2590
Fax: 34-91-431-3267
E-mail: info@inovacapital.com
Website: www.inovacapital.com

Management and Staff
Jaime De Gabriel, Chief Financial Officer
Jorge Calvet, President
Jorge Calderon, Managing Director
Jose Tomas Moliner, Managing Director

Type of Firm
Private Equity Firm

Association Membership
Spanish Venture Capital Association (ASCRI)

Project Preferences
Type of Financing Preferred:
Early Stage

Geographical Preferences
International Preferences:
Europe

Industry Preferences
In Communications prefer:
Telecommunications

In Internet Specific prefer:
E-Commerce Technology
Internet

Additional Information
Year Founded: 2000
Capital Under Management: $88,500,000
Current Activity Level: Actively seeking new investments

INOVATE COMMUNICATIONS GROUP
2010 Crow Canyon Place
Suite 270
San Ramon, CA USA 94583
Phone: 925-358-4900
Fax: 925-358-4901
E-mail: info@inovate.com
Website: www.inovate.com

Management and Staff
Bruce Lawler, Managing Director
Issie Rabinovitch, Managing Director
Keith Kaczmarek, Managing Director
Patrizia Owen, Chief Financial Officer

Type of Firm
Incubator/Development Program

Project Preferences
Role in Financing:
Prefer role as deal originator

Type of Financing Preferred:
Early Stage
Seed
Startup

Industry Preferences
In Communications prefer:
Telecommunications

Additional Information
Year Founded: 1999
Current Activity Level: Actively seeking new investments

INOVCAPITAL (AKA: PME CAPITAL)
Av. Dr Antunes Guimaraes 103
Porto, Portugal 4100-079
Phone: 351-22-616-5390
Fax: 351-22-610-2089
E-mail: geral@inovcapital.pt
Website: www.inovcapital.pt

Type of Firm
Private Equity Firm

Association Membership
Portuguese Venture Capital Association (APCRI)
European Private Equity and Venture Capital Assoc.

Project Preferences
Type of Financing Preferred:
Early Stage
Seed
Startup

Geographical Preferences
International Preferences:
Portugal
Africa

Industry Preferences
In Communications prefer:
Communications and Media

In Internet Specific prefer:
Internet

In Computer Other prefer:
Computer Related

In Semiconductor/Electr prefer:
Electronics

In Biotechnology prefer:
Biotechnology

In Industrial/Energy prefer:
Energy
Materials

In Business Serv. prefer:
Media

Additional Information
Year Founded: 1989
Capital Under Management: $89,900,000
Current Activity Level: Actively seeking new investments

INOVIA CAPITAL (FKA: MSBI CAPITAL)
1155 Rene-Levesque Boulevard W
Suite 2701
Montreal, Canada H3B 2K8
Phone: 514-982-2261
Fax: 514-982-2264
Website: www.inoviacapital.com

Management and Staff
Cedric Bisson, Partner
Chris Arsenault, Partner
Christian Zabbal, Venture Partner
Joe Rouse, Venture Partner
John Elton, Partner
Mark De Groot, Managing Partner
Yves Sicard, Venture Partner

Type of Firm
Private Equity Firm

Project Preferences
Type of Financing Preferred:
Early Stage
Seed

Geographical Preferences

Canadian Preferences:
All Canada

Additional Information
Year Founded: 2002
Capital Under Management: $26,000,000
Current Activity Level: Actively seeking new investments

INQLAB
Aithrio Centre Suite A35 40 Ag
Maroussi, Greece GR 151-24
Phone: 30-210-610-0294
Fax: 30-210-617-8140
E-mail: info@inqlab.gr
Website: www.inqlab.gr

Type of Firm
Private Equity Firm

Additional Information
Year Founded: 2001
Capital Under Management: $3,400,000
Current Activity Level: Actively seeking new investments

INSERM-TRANSFERT INITIATIVE
Paris BioPark
7 Rue Watt
Paris, France 75013
Phone: 33-1-55-03-0100
Fax: 33-1-55-03-0160
Website: www.it-initiative.fr

Type of Firm
Private Equity Firm

Project Preferences

Type of Financing Preferred:
Seed
Startup

Geographical Preferences

International Preferences:
Europe
France

Industry Preferences

In Biotechnology prefer:
Human Biotechnology

Additional Information
Year Founded: 2006
Capital Under Management: $5,000,000
Current Activity Level: Actively seeking new investments

INSIGHT EQUITY HOLDINGS LLC
1400 Civic Place
Suite 250
Southlake, TX USA 76092
Phone: 817-488-7775
Fax: 817-488-7739
Website: www.insightequity.com

Management and Staff
Brandon Bethea, Principal
Connor Searcy, Partner
Eliot Kerlin, Principal
Robert Strauss, Principal
Ross Gatlin, Managing Director
Ted Beneski, Chief Executive Officer
Victor Vescovo, Chief Operating Officer

Type of Firm
Private Equity Firm

Project Preferences

Type of Financing Preferred:
Leveraged Buyout
Mezzanine

Size of Investments Considered:
Min Size of Investment Considered (000s): $10,000
Max Size of Investment Considered (000s): $30,000

Geographical Preferences

United States Preferences:
All U.S.

Canadian Preferences:
All Canada

International Preferences:
Mexico

Industry Preferences

In Transportation prefer:
Transportation
Aerospace

In Business Serv. prefer:
Services
Distribution

In Manufact. prefer:
Manufacturing

Additional Information
Year Founded: 2002
Capital Under Management: $250,000,000
Current Activity Level: Actively seeking new investments

INSIGHT VENTURE PARTNERS
680 Fifth Avenue
Eighth Floor
New York, NY USA 10019
Phone: 212-230-9200
Fax: 212-230-9272
E-mail: info_usa@insightpartners.com
Website: www.insightpartners.com

Management and Staff
Alex Crisses, Vice President
Blair Flicker, Managing Director
Bonnie Lewis, Principal
Cian Cotter, Vice President
Deven Parekh, Managing Director
Hilary Gosher, Managing Director
Jeff Lieberman, Managing Director
Jeffrey Horing, Managing Director
Jerry Murdock, Managing Director
Lawrence Handen, Managing Director
Mark Lessing, Chief Financial Officer
Michael Triplett, Managing Director
Nikitas Koutoupes, Managing Director
Peter Sobiloff, Managing Director
Richard Wells, Principal
Ryan Hinkle, Vice President
Ted Bockius, Principal

Type of Firm
Private Equity Firm

Project Preferences

Role in Financing:
Prefer role as deal originator but will also invest in deals created by others

Type of Financing Preferred:
Second Stage Financing
Leveraged Buyout
Expansion
Mezzanine
Generalist PE
Public Companies
Later Stage
Management Buyouts
Acquisition
Private Placement
Industry Rollups
Recapitalizations

Size of Investments Considered:
Min Size of Investment Considered (000s): $5,000
Max Size of Investment Considered (000s): $150,000

Geographical Preferences

Canadian Preferences:
All Canada

International Preferences:
India
United Kingdom
Europe
Australia

Industry Focus
(% based on actual investment)

Computer Software and Services	43.7%
Internet Specific	42.1%
Other Products	8.0%
Communications and Media	2.9%

Computer Hardware 2.6%
Medical/Health 0.7%

Additional Information

Name of Most Recent Fund: Insight Venture Partners VI, L.P.
Most Recent Fund Was Raised: 05/04/2007
Year Founded: 1995
Capital Under Management: $3,000,000,000
Current Activity Level: Actively seeking new investments
Method of Compensation: Return on investment is of primary concern, do not charge fees

INSPIRE TECHNOLOGY RESOURCE MANAGEMENT CORPORATION

Akasaka 1-chome Mori Bldg., 6F
1-11-28, Akasaka, Minato-ku
Tokyo, Japan
Phone: 81-03-5549-4321
Fax: 81-03-5549-4306
E-mail: info@inspire-trm.co.jp
Website: www.inspire-trm.co.jp
Management and Staff
Toshio Ishii, President

Type of Firm

Private Equity Firm

Project Preferences

Type of Financing Preferred:
Seed
Startup

Geographical Preferences

International Preferences:
Japan

Industry Preferences

In Computer Software prefer:
Software

In Semiconductor/Electr prefer:
Electronics

In Biotechnology prefer:
Biotechnology

In Medical/Health prefer:
Medical/Health

In Manufact. prefer:
Manufacturing

Additional Information

Year Founded: 2001
Capital Under Management: $27,400,000
Current Activity Level: Actively seeking new investments

INSPIRED EVOLUTION INVESTMENT MANAGEMENT

1st Floor, Amdec House
Steenberg Office Park, Tokai
Cape Town, South Africa 7945
Phone: 27-21-702-1290
Fax: 27-21-702-1483
E-mail: info@inspiredevolution.co.za
Website: www.inspiredevolution.co.za

Other Offices

2nd Floor, Summit Square
15 School Rd., Cnr Rivonia & Summit Rd.
Johannesburg, South Africa

Management and Staff

Paul Vorster, Principal

Type of Firm

Investment Management Firm

Project Preferences

Type of Financing Preferred:
Expansion
Early Stage
Later Stage
Startup

Geographical Preferences

International Preferences:
South Africa
Africa

Industry Preferences

In Industrial/Energy prefer:
Energy
Energy Conservation Relat
Environmental Related

In Agr/Forestr/Fish prefer:
Agribusiness

In Other prefer:
Environment Responsible

Additional Information

Year Founded: 2008
Capital Under Management: $67,100,000
Current Activity Level: Actively seeking new investments

INSTITUT LORRAIN DE PARTICIPATION - ILP

24 rue du Palais
Metz , France 57000
Phone: 33-3-8775-9350
Fax: 33-3-8775-9358
E-mail: ilp@i-l-p.com.fr
Website: www.i-l-p.com.fr

Management and Staff

Christian Namy, Chairman & Managing Director

Type of Firm

Private Equity Firm

Association Membership

French Venture Capital Association (AFIC)

Project Preferences

Type of Financing Preferred:
Leveraged Buyout
Early Stage
Expansion
Startup

Size of Investments Considered:
Min Size of Investment Considered (000s): $199
Max Size of Investment Considered (000s): $1,727

Geographical Preferences

International Preferences:
France

Additional Information

Year Founded: 1983
Capital Under Management: $24,700,000
Current Activity Level: Actively seeking new investments

INSTITUTIONAL VENTURE PARTNERS

3000 Sand Hill Road
Building Two, Suite 250
Menlo Park, CA USA 94025
Phone: 650-854-0132
Fax: 650-854-2009
Website: www.ivp.com

Other Offices

Two Embarcadero Center
Suite 1680
San Francisco, CA USA 94111
Phone: 415-765-9393
Fax: 415-434-1903

Management and Staff

Dennis Phelps, General Partner
J. Sanford Miller, General Partner
Jules Maltz, Vice President
Melanie Chladek, Chief Financial Officer
Norman Fogelsong, General Partner
Reid Dennis, Founder
Stephen Harrick, General Partner
Todd Chaffee, General Partner

Type of Firm

Private Equity Firm

Association Membership

Western Association of Venture Capitalists (WAVC)
National Venture Capital Association - USA (NVCA)

Project Preferences

Role in Financing:
Will function either as deal originator or investor in deals created by others

Type of Financing Preferred:
Mezzanine
Expansion
Public Companies
Later Stage
Industry Rollups
Recapitalizations

Size of Investments Considered:
Min Size of Investment Considered (000s): $10,000
Max Size of Investment Considered (000s): $50,000

Geographical Preferences

United States Preferences:
West Coast
California
All U.S.

Industry Focus

(% based on actual investment)

Internet Specific	34.2%
Communications and Media	14.1%
Computer Software and Services	13.4%
Medical/Health	11.0%
Semiconductors/Other Elect.	9.1%
Computer Hardware	8.2%
Biotechnology	5.9%
Industrial/Energy	1.9%
Consumer Related	1.3%
Other Products	1.0%

Additional Information

Name of Most Recent Fund: Institutional Venture Partners XII
Most Recent Fund Was Raised: 05/30/2007
Year Founded: 1980
Capital Under Management: $2,200,000,000
Current Activity Level: Actively seeking new investments
Method of Compensation: Return on investment is of primary concern, do not charge fees

---

INSTITUTO ARAGONES DE FOMENTO

Teniente Coronel Valenzuela, 9
Zaragoza, Spain 50004
Phone: 34-97-670-2100
Fax: 34-97-670-2103
E-mail: info@iaf.es
Website: www.iaf.es

Type of Firm
Private Equity Firm

Association Membership
Spanish Venture Capital Association (ASCRI)

Project Preferences

Type of Financing Preferred:
Expansion
Seed

Geographical Preferences

International Preferences:
Europe
Spain

Additional Information

Year Founded: 2004
Current Activity Level: Actively seeking new investments

INTEC IT CAPITAL, INC.

1-3-3 Shinsuna
Koto-ku
Tokyo, Japan 136-0075
Phone: 81-3-5665-5070
Fax: 81-3-5665-5080
E-mail: info@inteccap.co.jp
Website: www.inteccap.co.jp

Type of Firm
Private Equity Firm

Project Preferences

Type of Financing Preferred:
Balanced

Geographical Preferences

International Preferences:
Japan

Industry Preferences

In Computer Software prefer:
Software

Additional Information

Year Founded: 2000
Current Activity Level: Actively seeking new investments

INTEGRA VENTURES

300 East Pine Street
Second Floor
Seattle, WA USA 98122
Phone: 206-832-1990
Fax: 206-832-1991
Website: www.integraventures.net

Management and Staff

Hans Lundin, Managing Director
James Nelson, Partner
Joseph Piper, Managing Director
Tim Black, Partner

Type of Firm
Private Equity Firm

Association Membership
Natl Assoc of Small Bus. Inv. Co (NASBIC)

Project Preferences

Role in Financing:
Will function either as deal originator or investor in deals created by others

Type of Financing Preferred:
Later Stage
Seed
First Stage Financing

Size of Investments Considered:
Min Size of Investment Considered (000s): $500
Max Size of Investment Considered (000s): $2,000

Geographical Preferences

United States Preferences:
Northwest

Industry Preferences

In Biotechnology prefer:
Human Biotechnology
Industrial Biotechnology
Biosensors
Biotech Related Research

In Medical/Health prefer:
Medical/Health
Medical Diagnostics
Diagnostic Services
Diagnostic Test Products
Medical Therapeutics
Drug/Equipmt Delivery
Medical Products
Disposable Med. Products
Health Services
Hospitals/Clinics/Primary
Hospital/Other Instit.
Pharmaceuticals

Additional Information

Name of Most Recent Fund: Integra Ventures III, L.P.
Most Recent Fund Was Raised: 04/01/2002
Year Founded: 1998
Capital Under Management: $40,000,000
Current Activity Level: Actively seeking new investments
Method of Compensation: Return on investment is of primary concern, do not charge fees

---

INTEGRAL CAPITAL PARTNERS

3000 Sand Hill Road
Building 3, Suite 240
Menlo Park, CA USA 94025
Phone: 650-233-0360
Fax: 650-233-0366

Website: www.icp.com

Other Offices

Four Embarcadero Center
Suite 3620
San Francisco, CA USA 94111

100 Light Street
22nd Floor
Baltimore, MD USA 21202
Phone: 410-454-4240

Management and Staff

Brian Stansky, Partner
Charles (Chip) Morris, Partner
Glen Kacher, Partner
John Powell, General Partner
Neil Struminger, Partner
Pamela Hagenah, Managing Partner
Roger McNamee, General Partner

Type of Firm

Private Equity Firm

Project Preferences

Type of Financing Preferred:

Leveraged Buyout
Expansion
Generalist PE

Industry Preferences

In Communications prefer:

Communications and Media

In Computer Software prefer:

Software

In Internet Specific prefer:

Internet

Additional Information

Name of Most Recent Fund: Integral Capital Partners VII, L.P.
Most Recent Fund Was Raised: 05/18/2005
Year Founded: 1991
Capital Under Management: $473,600,000
Current Activity Level: Actively seeking new investments

INTEGRATED PARTNERS

130 Adelaide Street West
Suite 2200
Toronto, Canada M5H 3P5
Phone: 416-360-7667
Fax: 416-360-7446
E-mail: info@iamgroup.ca
Website: www.iamgroup.ca

Management and Staff

Douglas Harris, Vice President
James Ridout, Vice President
Stephen Johnson, Vice President

Type of Firm

Bank Affiliated

Project Preferences

Type of Financing Preferred:

Leveraged Buyout
Expansion
Public Companies
Turnaround
Other
Acquisition
Distressed Debt
Recapitalizations

Size of Investments Considered:

Min Size of Investment Considered (000s): $3,256
Max Size of Investment Considered (000s): $32,560

Geographical Preferences

Canadian Preferences:

All Canada

Additional Information

Year Founded: 1998
Current Activity Level: Actively seeking new investments

INTEL CAPITAL

2200 Mission College Boulevard
RN6-37
Santa Clara, CA USA 95052
Phone: 408-765-8080
Fax: 408-765-1399
E-mail: intelcapital@intel.com
Website: www.intel.com/capital

Other Offices

Dornacher Strasse 1
Feldkirchen
Munich, Germany D-85622
Phone: 49-89-99143-0
Fax: 49-89-9043948

75 Reed Road
Hudson, MA USA 01749
Phone: 978-553-4000

2800 Center Drive
Dupont, WA USA 98327
Phone: 253-371-8080

136 Airport Road
Bangalore, India 560017
Phone: 91-80-2507-5000
Fax: 91-80-2520-2460

5000 West Chandler Boulevard
Chandler, AZ USA 85226
Phone: 480-554-8080

Exchange Plaza, National Stock Exchange
Commercial Wing, 3rd Floor
Mumbai, India 400 051
Phone: 91-22-659-8811
Fax: 91-22-659-8809

Anillo Periferico Sur 7980, Edificio 4-E
col. Santa Maria Tequepexpan
Tlaquepaque, Jalisco, Mexico 45600
Phone: 52-333540-6000
Fax: 52-333540-6099

1900 Prairie City Road
Folsom, CA USA 95630
Phone: 916-356-8080

Kokusai Bldg. 5F
3-1-1 Marunouchi, Chiyoda-ku
Tokyo, Japan 100-0005
Phone: 81-3-5223-9100
Fax: 81-3-5223-9172

Av. Batallon San Patricio 109
Torre Dataflux, 11th Floor, Regus Center
San Pedro Garza Garcia, Mexico 66260
Phone: 53-8625-6570
Fax: 52-8625-6573

22F, Shanghai Mart
2299 Yan'an Road (West)
Shanghai, China 200336
Phone: 8621-5257-4545
Fax: 8621-6236-4545

2, rue de Paris
Meudon cedex, France 92196
Phone: 33-1-5887-7147
Fax: 33-1-5887-7000

15373 Innovation Drive
Suite 250
San Diego, CA USA 92128
Phone: 858-676-2000

Level 17, 111 Pacific Highway
North Sydney, Australia NSW 2060
Phone: 612-9937-5800
Fax: 612-9937-5899

51 Cuppage Road
#06-01/02 StarHub Centre
Singapore, Singapore 229469
Phone: 65-213-1000
Fax: 65-213-1003

Av. Vitacura 2939 - 10th Floor
6760176 - Las Condes
Santiago, Chile
Phone: 562-431-5063
Fax: 562-431-5050

Veldkant 31
Kontich, Belgium 2550
Phone: 32-03-450-0811
Fax: 32-03-450-0990

4100 Sara Road
Rio Rancho, NM USA 87124
Phone: 505-893-7000

Sokol-10 Business Center
14, Chapaevski Pereulok
Moscow, Russia 125252
Phone: 7-095-721-4900
Fax: 7-095-721-4905

Collinstown Industrial Park
Leixlip, County Kildare, Ireland
Phone: 353-1-606-7000

Jerozolimskie Bussiness Park
Al. Jherozolimskie 146C
Warszawa, Poland 02-305
Phone: 48-22-570-8100
Fax: 48-22-570-8140

2111 N.E. 25th Avenue
Hillsboro, OR USA 97124
Phone: 503-696-8080

Avenida Dr. Chucri Zaidan
940 - 10th floor
Sao Paulo, Brazil 04583-110
Phone: 55-11-3365-5500

2000 CentreGreen Way
Suite 100
Cary, NC USA 27513
Phone: 919-678-2890
Fax: 919-678-2819

Calle 129 La Ribera
Belen, Heredia, Costa Rica
Phone: 506-298-6000
Fax: 506-298-7206

94 Em Hamoshavot Road
Park Azorim
Petach Tikva, Israel 49527
Phone: 972-3-920-7111
Fax: 972-3-920-7648

Knarrarnasgatan 15, 5tr
Kista, Sweden 164 40
Phone: 46-8-5946-1700
Fax: 46-8-5946-1701

1501 S. Mopac Expressway
Suite 400
Austin, TX USA 78746
Phone: 512-314-0000

30 Turgeneva Street
Nizhni Novgorod , Russia 603950
Phone: 7-8312-319010
Fax: 7-8312-317839

1515 Route Ten
Parsippany, NJ USA 07054
Phone: 973-993-3030
Fax: 973-967-8780

32 Floor Two Pacific Place
88 Queensway
Central, Hong Kong
Phone: 852-2844-4555
Fax: 852-2868-1989

5/F Daehan Investment & Trust Co Bldg
27-3 Yoido-Doing
Seoul, South Korea 150-010
Phone: 82-2-767-2500
Fax: 82-2-7-67-2509

758 East Utah Valley Drive
American Fork, UT USA 84003
Phone: 801-763-2400

Beijing Kerry Centre 6/F, N Tower
No.1 Guanghua Road
Chao Yang District, Beijing, China 100020
Phone: 8610-85298800
Fax: 8610-85298801

Room 5803 CITIC Plaza
233 Tianhe Road
Guangzhou, China 510613
Phone: 86-20-8332-3333
Fax: 86-20-3877-1399

5-6 Tokodai Tsukuba-shi
Mito, Japan 300-2635
Phone: 81-298-47-8511

Blvd. Manuel Avila Camacho No. 36 Piso 7
Lomas de Chapultepec
D.F., Mexico 11000
Phone: 52-555284-7000
Fax: 52-555540-3161

8/F Bank Tower Bldg.
No. 205 Tun Hwa N. Road
Taipei, Taiwan
Phone: 886-2-716-9660
Fax: 886-2-719-6387

Carrington House
126-130 Regent House
London, United Kingdom W1B 5SE
Phone: 44-20-7292-8782

Management and Staff

Abdul Guefor, Managing Director
Arvind Sodhani, President
Ashish Patel, Managing Director
Bryan Wolf, Managing Director
Cadol Cheung, Managing Director
Curt Nichols, Managing Director
David Earl Thomas, Managing Director
Keith Larson, Managing Director
Lisa Lambert, Managing Director
Mike Buckley, Managing Director
Ranjeet Alexis, Managing Director
Ravi Jacob, Vice President
Sriram Viswanathan, Managing Director
Steve Eichenlaub, Managing Director
Sudheer Kuppam, Managing Director

Type of Firm

Corporate PE/Venture

Association Membership

Brazilian Venture Capital Association (ABCR)
Mid-Atlantic Venture Association
British Venture Capital Association (BVCA)
National Venture Capital Association - USA (NVCA)
European Private Equity and Venture Capital Assoc.
Indian Venture Capital Association (IVCA)

Project Preferences

Type of Financing Preferred:

Second Stage Financing
Balanced
First Stage Financing

Size of Investments Considered:

Min Size of Investment Considered (000s): $5,000
Max Size of Investment Considered (000s): $10,000

Geographical Preferences

United States Preferences:

All U.S.

International Preferences:

India
Latin America
Turkey
Europe
China
Middle East
Israel
Asia
Japan
All International

Industry Preferences

In Communications prefer:

Communications and Media
Telecommunications
Wireless Communications

In Computer Hardware prefer:

Computers
Mini and Personal/Desktop

In Computer Software prefer:

Software

In Internet Specific prefer:

Internet

In Semiconductor/Electr prefer:

Semiconductor

In Industrial/Energy prefer:

Energy Conservation Relat

In Business Serv. prefer:

Media

In Other prefer:

Environment Responsible

Additional Information

Year Founded: 1990
Capital Under Management: $950,000,000
Current Activity Level: Actively seeking new investments

INTELLIGENT VENTURE CAPITAL MANAGEMENT GMBH

Forckenbeckstrasse 6
Aachen, Germany 52074
Phone: 49-241-89499891
Fax: 49-241-89499899
E-mail: office@intelligent-venture-capital.de
Website: www.intelligent-venture-capital.de

Management and Staff

Andreas Tietmann, Managing Director
Florian Geyr, Managing Director
Georg Kox, Managing Director
Wilfried Frohnhofen, Managing Director

Type of Firm

Private Equity Firm

Project Preferences

Type of Financing Preferred:
Seed
Startup

Geographical Preferences

International Preferences:
Germany

Industry Preferences

In Biotechnology prefer:
Biotechnology

In Medical/Health prefer:
Medical/Health

Additional Information

Year Founded: 2001
Current Activity Level: Actively seeking new investments

INTER-ASIA VENTURE MANAGEMENT

Suite 2509, Harcourt House
39 Gloucester Road
Wanchai, Hong Kong
Phone: 852-2528-5717
Fax: 852-2527-9704
E-mail: iavm@iavmhk.com
Website: www.iavmhk.com

Other Offices

63 Robinson Road
#3-16 Afro Asia Building
Singapore, Singapore 068894
Phone: 65-6327-1250
Fax: 65-6327-1251

Suite 4908-06 Raffles City
268 Xi Zang Middle Road
Shanghai, China 200001
Phone: 86-21-6340-5002
Fax: 86-21-6340-4754

Management and Staff

Edward Ee, Partner
James Hawes, Managing Director
Lewis Rutherfurd, Managing Director
Louis S.K. Wong, Chief Financial Officer
May Fung, Chief Operating Officer
Robert Y.C. Lee, Partner

Type of Firm

Private Equity Firm

Association Membership

Hong Kong Venture Capital Association (HKVCA)

Project Preferences

Role in Financing:
Prefer role in deals created by others

Type of Financing Preferred:
Leveraged Buyout
Early Stage
Expansion
Balanced
Seed
First Stage Financing
Startup

Size of Investments Considered:
Min Size of Investment Considered (000s): $500
Max Size of Investment Considered (000s): $5,000

Geographical Preferences

International Preferences:
India
China
Pacific Rim
Asia

Industry Focus

(% based on actual investment)

Industrial/Energy	44.6%
Computer Software and Services	31.5%
Consumer Related	19.3%
Other Products	2.2%
Communications and Media	1.8%
Medical/Health	0.7%

Additional Information

Name of Most Recent Fund: Inter-Asia Capital (IV)
Most Recent Fund Was Raised: 07/01/2003
Year Founded: 1972
Capital Under Management: $25,000,000
Current Activity Level: Actively seeking new investments
Method of Compensation: Return on investment is of primary concern, do not charge fees

INTER-ATLANTIC GROUP

400 Madison Avenue
16th Floor
New York, NY USA 10017
Phone: 212-581-2000
Fax: 212-581-2433
Website: www.interatlanticgroup.com

Management and Staff

Andrew Lerner, Managing Partner
Brett Baris, Partner
D. James Daras, Partner

Type of Firm

Private Equity Firm

Project Preferences

Type of Financing Preferred:
Expansion
Early Stage
Later Stage

Size of Investments Considered:
Min Size of Investment Considered (000s): $3,000
Max Size of Investment Considered (000s): $10,000

Geographical Preferences

United States Preferences:
All U.S.

Industry Preferences

In Financial Services prefer:
Financial Services

Additional Information

Name of Most Recent Fund: Inter-Atlantic Fund II, L.P.
Most Recent Fund Was Raised: 12/30/2005
Year Founded: 2000
Capital Under Management: $76,000,000
Current Activity Level: Actively seeking new investments

INTERA EQUITY PARTNERS OY

Aleksanterinkatu 15 B
3rd floor
Helsinki, Finland 00100
Phone: 358-9-2525-2200
Fax: 358-9-2525-2210
Website: www.interapartners.fi

Management and Staff

Harri Hollmen, Partner
Jokke Paananen, Partner
Martin Grotenfelt, Partner
Tuomas Lang, Partner

Type of Firm

Private Equity Firm

Project Preferences

Type of Financing Preferred:
Leveraged Buyout
Expansion
Management Buyouts
Acquisition

Size of Investments Considered:
Min Size of Investment Considered (000s): $6,242
Max Size of Investment Considered (000s): $31,211

Geographical Preferences

International Preferences:
Finland

Additional Information
Year Founded: 2007
Capital Under Management: $181,500,000
Current Activity Level: Actively seeking new investments

INTERACTIVE PARTNERS
10401 Bubb Road
Cupertino, CA USA 95014
Phone: 408-364-6710
Fax: 408-777-8086
E-mail: hello.ipartners.com
Website: www.ipartners.com

Type of Firm
Private Equity Firm

Additional Information
Year Founded: 1994
Current Activity Level: Actively seeking new investments

INTERBANCA SPA
56, Corso Venezia
Milan, Italy 20121
Phone: 39-02-773-11
Fax: 39-02-7601-4913
Website: www.interbanca.it

Other Offices
via Caduti del Lavoro, 40
Ancona, Italy 60131
Phone: 39-071-290-0764
Fax: 39-071-286-1891

via Mazzini, 23
Vicenza, Italy 36100
Phone: 39-0444-540-403
Fax: 39-0444-324-585

Via Emilia Ponente, 317
Bologna, Italy 40125
Phone: 39-051-619-9485
Fax: 39-051-569-481

Piazza Municipio, 4
Naples, Italy 80133
Phone: 39-081-251-8111
Fax: 39-081-551-7504

Corso Zanardelli, 32
Brescia, Italy 25121
Phone: 39-030-280-7402
Fax: 39-030-415-050

Via Michele Scammacca, 5
Catania, Italy 95127
Phone: 39-095-722-5173
Fax: 39-095-722-1296

Viale dei Cacciatori, 2
Treviso, Zambia 31100
Phone: 39-0422-580-395
Fax: 39-0422-551-99

via Amendola, 172/c
Bari, Italy 70126
Phone: 39-080-546-1570
Fax: 39-080-548-1594

Corso Galileo Ferraris, 60
Torino, Italy 10128
Phone: 39-011-580-6122
Fax: 39-011-500-567

via Abruzzi, 6
Rome, Italy
Phone: 39-06-4201-2306
Fax: 39-06-4201-0653

Management and Staff
Achille Mucci, Managing Director

Type of Firm
Bank Affiliated

Association Membership
Italian Venture Capital Association (AIFI)

Project Preferences

Type of Financing Preferred:
Leveraged Buyout
Expansion

Geographical Preferences

International Preferences:
Italy
Europe

Additional Information
Year Founded: 1961
Current Activity Level: Actively seeking new investments

INTERLEADER CAPITAL, LTD.
29-30/F, 8 Wyndham Street
Central, Hong Kong
Phone: 852-2156-8876
Fax: 852-2156-8870
E-mail: info@interleadercapital.com
Website: www.interleadercapital.com

Management and Staff
Cliff Cheung, Chairman & CEO

Type of Firm
Private Equity Firm

Association Membership
Hong Kong Venture Capital Association (HKVCA)

Geographical Preferences

International Preferences:
China

Industry Preferences

In Financial Services prefer:
Real Estate

Additional Information
Year Founded: 2009
Current Activity Level: Actively seeking new investments

INTERMEDIA PARTNERS
405 Lexington Avenue
48th Floor
New York, NY USA 10174

Management and Staff
Leo Hindery, Managing Director
Peter Kern, Managing Director

Type of Firm
Private Equity Firm

Additional Information
Year Founded: 2005
Capital Under Management: $700,000,000
Current Activity Level: Actively seeking new investments

INTERMEDIATE CAPITAL GROUP PLC
20 Old Broad Street
London, United Kingdom EC2N 1DP
Phone: 44-20-7628-9898
Fax: 44-20-7628-2268
Website: www.icgplc.com

Other Offices
Level 18, 88 Phillip Street
Sydney, Australia 2000
Phone: 612-9241-5525
Fax: 612-9241-5526

12. Stockwerk
An der Welle 5
Frankfurt, Germany 60322
Phone: 49-69-2549-7650
Fax: 49-69-2549-7699

Biger Jarlsgatan 13, 1tr
Stockholm, Sweden 111 45
Phone: 46-8-5450-4150
Fax: 46-8-5450-4151

250 Park Avenue
Suite 810
New York, NY USA 10177
Phone: 212-710-9650
Fax: 212-710-9651

36/F, Edinburgh Tower
15 Queen's Road
Central, Hong Kong
Phone: 852-2297-3080
Fax: 852-2297-3081

Serrano, 30-3 degrees
Madrid, Spain 28001
Phone: 34-91-310-7200
Fax: 34-91-310-7201

Paulus Potterstraat 20 II/III
Amsterdam, Netherlands 1071 DA
Phone: 31-20-305-9600
Fax: 31-20-302-9620

38 Avenue Hoche
Paris, France 75008
Phone: 33-1-4495-8686
Fax: 33-1-4495-8687

Management and Staff

Christophe Evain, Managing Director
Francois De Mitry, Managing Director
Philip Keller, Managing Director
Tom Attwood, Managing Director

Type of Firm

Private Equity Firm

Association Membership

Hong Kong Venture Capital Association (HKVCA)
French Venture Capital Association (AFIC)
European Private Equity and Venture Capital Assoc.

Project Preferences

Role in Financing:

Will function either as deal originator or investor in deals created by others

Type of Financing Preferred:

Leveraged Buyout
Expansion
Mezzanine
Balanced
Public Companies
Management Buyouts
Acquisition
Recapitalizations

Size of Investments Considered:

Min Size of Investment Considered (000s): $4,478
Max Size of Investment Considered (000s): $298,540

Geographical Preferences

International Preferences:

United Kingdom
Europe
Taiwan
Western Europe
China
Hong Kong
Australia
New Zealand
Asia
South Africa
Singapore
Korea, South
Japan

Industry Focus

(% based on actual investment)

Other Products	46.2%
Consumer Related	40.8%
Medical/Health	11.3%
Internet Specific	1.0%
Communications and Media	0.2%
Industrial/Energy	0.2%
Biotechnology	0.2%

Additional Information

Name of Most Recent Fund: Mezzanine Fund 2003
Most Recent Fund Was Raised: 10/02/2003
Year Founded: 1989
Capital Under Management: $7,000,000,000
Current Activity Level: Actively seeking new investments
Method of Compensation: Return on invest. most important, but chg. closing fees, service fees, etc.

INTERNATIONAL FINANCE CORPORATION

2121 Pennsylvania Avenue, NW
Washington, DC USA 20433
Phone: 202-473-1000
Fax: 202-974-4384
Website: www.ifc.org

Other Offices

14th Floor, One Pacific Place
88 Queensway, Admiralty
Hong Kong, Hong Kong
Phone: 852-2509-8100
Fax: 852-2509-9363

50-M, Shanti Path, Gate No. 3
Niti Marg, Chanakyapuri
New Delhi, India 110 021
Phone: 91-11-4111-1000
Fax: 91-11-4111-1001

Kanyon Ofis Blogu Kat 10
Levent
Istanbul, Turkey 34394
Phone: 90-212-385-3000
Fax: 90-212-385-3001

14 Fricker Road
Illovo
Johannesburg, South Africa 2196
Phone: 27-11-731-300
Fax: 27-11-268-0074

P.O. Box 41283
Craighall, South Africa 2024
Phone: 27-11-731-9000

36, Bldg. 1 Bolshaya Molchanovka St.
Third Floor
Moscow, Russia 121069
Phone: 7495-411-7555
Fax: 7495-411-7556

Management and Staff

Declan Duff, Vice President
Edward Nassim, Vice President
Farida Khambata, Vice President
Lars Thunell, Chief Executive Officer
Michel Maila, Vice President

Type of Firm

Bank Affiliated

Association Membership

South African Venture Capital Association (SAVCA)

Project Preferences

Type of Financing Preferred:

Balanced
Recapitalizations

Geographical Preferences

International Preferences:

Latin America
Asia
All International
Africa

Industry Preferences

In Financial Services prefer:

Financial Services

Additional Information

Year Founded: 1956
Capital Under Management: $2,450,000,000
Current Activity Level: Actively seeking new investments

INTERNATIONAL MAGHREB MERCHANT BANK (AKA: IMBANK)

Dar El Maghrebia
Al Bouhaira
Tunis, Tunisia 2045
Phone: 216-71-860-816
Fax: 216-71-860-057
E-mail: imbank@imbank.com.tn
Website: www.imbank.com.tn

Type of Firm

Bank Affiliated

Project Preferences

Type of Financing Preferred:
Balanced

Geographical Preferences

International Preferences:
Tunisia

Additional Information

Year Founded: 1995
Current Activity Level: Actively seeking new investments

INTERNATIONAL SICAR

11 Rue Hedi Nouira Immeuble
BTKD, 9eme etage
Tunis, Tunisia 1000
Phone: 216-71-241-169
Fax: 216-71-240-700

Management and Staff

Khaled Youssef, General Director

Type of Firm

Private Equity Firm

Project Preferences

Type of Financing Preferred:
Balanced

Geographical Preferences

International Preferences:
Tunisia

Additional Information

Year Founded: 2004
Current Activity Level: Actively seeking new investments

INTERNET CAPITAL GROUP

690 Lee Road
Suite 310
Wayne, PA USA 19087
Phone: 610-727-6900
Fax: 610-727-6901
Website: www.internetcapital.com

Other Offices

1201 Third Avenue
Suite 5450
Seattle, WA USA 98101
Phone: 206-494-1100
Fax: 206-494-1101

One Market Street, Spear Tower
Third Floor, Suite 307
San Francisco, CA USA 94105
Phone: 415-343-3700
Fax: 415-343-3740

One Boston Place
23rd Floor
Boston, MA USA 02108
Phone: 617-531-4882
Fax: 617-531-4886

Centre d'Affaires ATEAC
75 Boulevard Haussmann
Paris, France 75008
Phone: 33-1-42- 685186
Fax: 33-1-42- 685185

Cassini House
57 St. James's Street
London, United Kingdom SW1A 1LD
Phone: 44-20-7959-1100
Fax: 44-20-7959-1199

Maximilianstrasse 35
Munich, Germany
Phone: 89-20508-6000
Fax: 89-20508-6900

The Center, 67/f
99 Queen's Road Central
Hong Kong, Hong Kong
Phone: 852-2186-3000
Fax: 852-2186-7388

Management and Staff

Anthony Dolanski, Managing Director
Douglas Alexander, Managing Director
Kamal Advani, Managing Director
Michael Forster, Managing Director
Philip Rooney, Vice President

Type of Firm

Corporate PE/Venture

Association Membership

National Venture Capital Association - USA (NVCA)

Project Preferences

Type of Financing Preferred:
Leveraged Buyout

Geographical Preferences

International Preferences:
Europe
Asia

Industry Preferences

In Internet Specific prefer:
Internet

Additional Information

Year Founded: 1996
Current Activity Level: Actively seeking new investments

INTERROS HOLDING

40 Bolshaya Yakimanka
Moscow, Russia 119049
Phone: 7-495-785-6363
Fax: 7-495-72-65754
E-mail: kirp@pr.interros.ru
Website: www.interros.ru

Type of Firm

Investment Management Firm

Additional Information

Year Founded: 2009
Current Activity Level: Actively seeking new investments

INTERSOUTH PARTNERS

406 Blackwell Street
Suite 200
Durham, NC USA 27701
Phone: 919-493-6640
Fax: 919-493-6649
E-mail: info@intersouth.com
Website: www.intersouth.com

Management and Staff

Bonnie Layman, Chief Financial Officer
David Pierson, Partner
Dennis Dougherty, Founding Partner
Garheng Kong, General Partner
John Glushik, Partner
Kip Frey, Partner
Mitchell Mumma, Founding Partner
Philip Tracy, Venture Partner
Richard Kent, Venture Partner
Robert Bell, Venture Partner
W. Chris Hegele, Venture Partner

Type of Firm

Private Equity Firm

Association Membership

Mid-Atlantic Venture Association
National Venture Capital Association - USA (NVCA)

Project Preferences

Role in Financing:
Prefer role as deal originator but will also invest in deals created by others

Type of Financing Preferred:
Second Stage Financing
Early Stage
Start-up Financing
Seed
First Stage Financing

Size of Investments Considered:
Min Size of Investment Considered (000s): $2,000
Max Size of Investment Considered (000s): $12,000

Geographical Preferences

United States Preferences:
Mid Atlantic
Southeast

Industry Focus

(% based on actual investment)

Biotechnology	38.0%
Medical/Health	16.9%
Computer Software and Services	14.1%
Internet Specific	10.6%
Semiconductors/Other Elect.	7.9%
Communications and Media	6.6%
Industrial/Energy	2.5%
Computer Hardware	1.6%
Consumer Related	1.4%
Other Products	0.4%

Additional Information

Name of Most Recent Fund: Intersouth Partners VII, L.P.
Most Recent Fund Was Raised: 05/26/2006
Year Founded: 1985
Capital Under Management: $780,000,000
Current Activity Level: Actively seeking new investments
Method of Compensation: Return on investment is of primary concern, do not charge fees

INTERVALE CAPITAL

50 Church Street
4th Floor
Cambridge, MA USA 02138
Phone: 617-497-8282
Fax: 617-497-8453
E-mail: inquiries@intervalecapital.com
Website: www.intervalecapital.com

Other Offices

2800 Post Oak Boulevard
Suite 5220
Houston, TX USA 77056
Phone: 713-961-0118
Fax: 713-961-0361

Management and Staff

Charles Cherington, Managing Partner
Curtis Huff, Managing Partner
Erich Horsley, Principal
Frederick Malloy, Principal

Type of Firm

Private Equity Firm

Project Preferences

Type of Financing Preferred:
Leveraged Buyout
Recapitalizations

Size of Investments Considered:
Min Size of Investment Considered (000s): $10,000
Max Size of Investment Considered (000s): $100,000

Geographical Preferences

United States Preferences:
All U.S.

Canadian Preferences:
All Canada

Industry Preferences

In Industrial/Energy prefer:
Energy

Additional Information

Year Founded: 2002
Capital Under Management: $25,000,000
Current Activity Level: Actively seeking new investments

INTERVEST CO., LTD.

1404 Trade Tower Samsung-dong
Kangnam-Ku
Seoul, South Korea 135-729
Phone: 822-551-7340
Fax: 822-551-7350
E-mail: admin@intervest.co.kr
Website: www.intervest.co.kr

Other Offices

No.1 Science Centre Road
#08-01 The Enterprise
Singapore, Singapore 609077
Phone: 65-6822-3491
Fax: 65-3822-3490

Management and Staff

Myengki Kim, Managing Director

Type of Firm

Private Equity Firm
Association Membership
Korean Venture Capital Association (KVCA)

Project Preferences

Type of Financing Preferred:
Early Stage
Expansion
Mezzanine
Balanced
Later Stage
Startup

Size of Investments Considered:
Min Size of Investment Considered (000s): $500
Max Size of Investment Considered (000s): $2,500

Geographical Preferences

International Preferences:
Singapore
Korea, South
Asia

Industry Preferences

In Communications prefer:
Telecommunications
Wireless Communications

In Computer Software prefer:
Software

In Internet Specific prefer:
Internet

In Semiconductor/Electr prefer:
Semiconductor

In Biotechnology prefer:
Biotechnology

In Industrial/Energy prefer:
Energy

Additional Information

Year Founded: 1999
Capital Under Management: $108,700,000
Current Activity Level: Actively seeking new investments

INTERWEST PARTNERS

2710 Sand Hill Road
Second Floor
Menlo Park, CA USA 94025
Phone: 650-854-8585
Fax: 650-854-4706
E-mail: info@interwest.com
Website: www.interwest.com

Other Offices

Two Galleria Tower
13455 Noel Road
Dallas, TX USA 75240
Phone: 972-392-7279
Fax: 972-490-6348

Management and Staff

Arnold Oronsky, General Partner
Bruce Cleveland, Partner
Christopher Ehrlich, General Partner
Doug Fisher, Principal
Douglas Pepper, General Partner
Ellen Koskinas, Partner
Gilbert Kliman, General Partner
H. Berry Cash, General Partner
Khaled Nasr, Partner
Leroy Hood, Partner
Linda Grais, Partner
Michael Sweeney, General Partner
Nina Kjellson, General Partner
Philip Gianos, General Partner
Thomas Rosch, General Partner

Type of Firm

Private Equity Firm

Association Membership

Western Association of Venture Capitalists (WAVC)
National Venture Capital Association - USA (NVCA)

Project Preferences

Role in Financing:

Prefer role as deal originator but will also invest in deals created by others

Type of Financing Preferred:

Second Stage Financing
Early Stage
Expansion
Balanced
Later Stage
Seed
First Stage Financing
Startup

Size of Investments Considered:

Min Size of Investment Considered (000s): $2,000
Max Size of Investment Considered (000s): $25,000

Geographical Preferences

United States Preferences:

All U.S.

Industry Focus

(% based on actual investment)	
Medical/Health	32.0%
Biotechnology	12.9%
Communications and Media	12.3%
Computer Software and Services	9.3%
Semiconductors/Other Elect.	9.0%
Consumer Related	7.4%
Internet Specific	6.2%
Computer Hardware	5.9%
Other Products	2.7%
Industrial/Energy	2.4%

Additional Information

Name of Most Recent Fund: InterWest Partners X, L.P.
Most Recent Fund Was Raised: 08/07/2008
Year Founded: 1979
Capital Under Management: $2,112,000,000
Current Activity Level: Actively seeking new investments
Method of Compensation: Return on investment is of primary concern, do not charge fees

---

INTREPID EQUITY FINANCE, LTD.

266 King Street West
Suite 405
Toronto, Canada M5V 1H8
Phone: 647-288-3006
Fax: 416-360-3819
E-mail: info@intrepidequity.com
Website: www.intrepidequity.com
Management and Staff
Alkarim Jivraj, Founder
Type of Firm
Private Equity Firm

Project Preferences

Type of Financing Preferred:

Early Stage

Geographical Preferences

Canadian Preferences:

All Canada

Industry Preferences

In Computer Software prefer:

Software

Additional Information

Year Founded: 2004
Current Activity Level: Actively seeking new investments

INTREPID VENTURE CAPITAL (PTY) LTD

2 Arnold Road
Rosebank, South Africa 2196
Phone: 27-11-283-0000
E-mail: shane.kidd@oba.co.uk

Type of Firm

Private Equity Firm

Association Membership

South African Venture Capital Association (SAVCA)

Project Preferences

Type of Financing Preferred:

Balanced

Geographical Preferences

International Preferences:

South Africa

Additional Information

Year Founded: 2004
Current Activity Level: Actively seeking new investments

INTRO-VERWALTUNGS GMBH

Schlossweg 14
Reichenschwand, Germany 91244
Phone: 49-9151-8693640
Fax: 49-9151-8693650
E-mail: info@introverwaltung.de
Website: www.introverwaltung.de

Management and Staff

Hans Rudolf Woehrl, Managing Director
Helga Moeschel, Managing Director
Peter Oncken, Managing Director

Type of Firm

Private Equity Firm

Project Preferences

Type of Financing Preferred:

Expansion
Balanced
Startup

Geographical Preferences

International Preferences:

Sweden
Europe
Germany

Additional Information

Year Founded: 2007
Current Activity Level: Actively seeking new investments

INVENCOR, INC.

P.O. Box 7355
Menlo Park, CA USA 94026
Phone: 650-330-1210
Fax: 650-330-1222
Website: www.invencor.com

Other Offices

369 Montezuma Avenue
Suite 588
Santa Fe, NM USA 87506
Phone: 505-995-9910
Fax: 505-995-9929

Management and Staff

D.Kirk Westbrook, Managing Director
Daniel Macuga, Managing Partner
Debra Guerin Beresini, Managing Director
Richard Harding, Managing Partner

Type of Firm

Private Equity Firm

Association Membership

Western Association of Venture Capitalists (WAVC)
National Venture Capital Association - USA (NVCA)
Project Preferences

Type of Financing Preferred:

Early Stage
Start-up Financing
Seed
First Stage Financing

Size of Investments Considered:

Min Size of Investment Considered (000s): $300
Max Size of Investment Considered (000s): $2,000

Geographical Preferences

United States Preferences:

New Mexico
Arizona
Northwest

Hawaii
Northern California
California
Utah

Additional Information

Name of Most Recent Fund: International Venture Fund I, L.P.
Most Recent Fund Was Raised: 04/01/2000
Year Founded: 1997
Capital Under Management: $17,200,000
Current Activity Level: Actively seeking new investments
Method of Compensation: Return on investment is of primary concern, do not charge fees

INVENI CAPITAL

Cultivator I
Viikinkaari 6
Helsinki, Finland FIN-00790
Phone: 358-400-874-546
Fax: 358-9-3193-6570
Website: www.invenicapital.com

Other Offices

Zweibrueckenstr. 8
Munich, Germany D-80331
Phone: 49-892351-5702

Management and Staff

Aki Prihti, Partner
Markku Fagerlund, Partner
Wolfgang Pieken, Partner

Type of Firm

Private Equity Firm

Project Preferences

Type of Financing Preferred:
Early Stage
Expansion

Geographical Preferences

International Preferences:
Europe
Germany
Finland

Industry Preferences

In Medical/Health prefer:
Medical/Health
Pharmaceuticals

Additional Information

Year Founded: 2007
Capital Under Management: $46,900,000
Current Activity Level: Actively seeking new investments

INVENTAGES VENTURE CAPITAL S.A.

36, Route de Morges
Saint Prex, Switzerland 1162
Phone: 41-21-823-0000
Fax: 41-21-823-0001
E-mail: contact@inventages.com
Website: www.inventages.com

Other Offices

Winterbotham Place, P.O.Box N-3026
Marlborough - Queen Streets
Nassau, Bahamas
Phone: 1-242-356-7247
Fax: 1-242-356-9432

Bio Pacific Ventures, Wellesley Street
L6, 2, Kitchener Street, PO Box 6466
Auckland, New Zealand
Phone: 64-9307-2562
Fax: 64-9307-2349

Management and Staff

Aki von Roy, Partner
Erich Sieber, Partner
Robert Schier, Partner
Wolfgang Reichenberger, General Partner

Type of Firm

Corporate PE/Venture

Project Preferences

Type of Financing Preferred:
Early Stage
Expansion
Balanced
Later Stage
Seed
Startup

Geographical Preferences

International Preferences:
India
Switzerland
Europe
Australia
New Zealand
All International

Industry Preferences

In Biotechnology prefer:
Biotechnology
Agricultural/Animal Bio.

In Medical/Health prefer:
Medical/Health
Health Services

In Consumer Related prefer:
Retail
Food/Beverage

Additional Information

Year Founded: 2002
Capital Under Management: $1,342,200,000
Current Activity Level: Actively seeking new investments

INVENTURE CAPITAL A/S

Norregade 26, 2
Arhus C, Denmark DK - 8000
Phone: 45-8734-2400
Fax: 45-8734-2410
E-mail: info@inventurecapital.dk
Website: www.inventurecapital.dk

Management and Staff

Soren Ravn, Chief Executive Officer

Type of Firm

Private Equity Firm

Project Preferences

Type of Financing Preferred:
Early Stage

Geographical Preferences

International Preferences:
Denmark

Industry Preferences

In Communications prefer:
Telecommunications

In Computer Software prefer:
Software

In Biotechnology prefer:
Biotechnology

In Medical/Health prefer:
Medical/Health
Medical Diagnostics
Pharmaceuticals

Additional Information

Year Founded: 2006
Capital Under Management: $95,500,000
Current Activity Level: Actively seeking new investments

INVENTURE OY

Korkeavuorenkatu 22
Helsinki, Finland 00130
Phone: 358-400-399-912
Fax: 358-420-399-912
E-mail: info@inventure.fi
Website: www.inventure.fi

Management and Staff

Sami Lampinen, Managing Director
Timo Tirkkonen, Partner

Type of Firm

Bank Affiliated

Association Membership
Finnish Venture Capital Association (FVCA)
European Private Equity and Venture Capital Assoc.

Project Preferences

Role in Financing:
Prefer role as deal originator

Type of Financing Preferred:
Early Stage
Seed
Startup

Size of Investments Considered:
Min Size of Investment Considered (000s): $374
Max Size of Investment Considered (000s): $1,494

Geographical Preferences

International Preferences:
Scandanavia/Nordic Region
Finland

Industry Preferences

In Communications prefer:
Communications and Media

In Computer Software prefer:
Software

In Internet Specific prefer:
Internet

In Computer Other prefer:
Computer Related

In Semiconductor/Electr prefer:
Semiconductor

Additional Information
Name of Most Recent Fund: Inventure Fund Ky
Most Recent Fund Was Raised: 02/06/2008
Year Founded: 2005
Capital Under Management: $77,700,000
Current Activity Level: Actively seeking new investments

INVENTUS CAPITAL PARTNERS
2735 Sand Hill Road
Menlo Park, CA USA 94025
Phone: 650-292-2530
Fax: 650-292-2570
Website: www.inventuscap.com

Other Offices
507, Fourth Floor
Oxford Towers, 139, Airport Road
Bangalore , India 560 008
Phone: 91-80-4213-1235
Fax: 91-80-4213-1237

Management and Staff
John Dougery, Managing Director
Kanwal Rekhi, Managing Director
Samir Kumar, Managing Director

Type of Firm
Private Equity Firm

Association Membership
Indian Venture Capital Association (IVCA)

Project Preferences

Role in Financing:
Prefer role as deal originator but will also invest in deals created by others

Type of Financing Preferred:
Second Stage Financing
Early Stage
Expansion
First Stage Financing
Startup

Size of Investments Considered:
Min Size of Investment Considered (000s): $250
Max Size of Investment Considered (000s): $1,250

Geographical Preferences

United States Preferences:
California

International Preferences:
India

Industry Preferences

In Communications prefer:
Communications and Media
Wireless Communications
Media and Entertainment

In Computer Software prefer:
Computer Services
Software
Applications Software

In Internet Specific prefer:
E-Commerce Technology
Internet
Ecommerce

In Computer Other prefer:
Computer Related

In Medical/Health prefer:
Health Services

In Consumer Related prefer:
Consumer
Consumer Products
Consumer Services
Education Related

In Business Serv. prefer:
Services

Additional Information
Name of Most Recent Fund: Inventus Capital Partners Fund I, L.P.
Most Recent Fund Was Raised: 11/30/2007
Year Founded: 2007
Capital Under Management: $51,000,000
Current Activity Level: Actively seeking new investments
Method of Compensation: Return on investment is of primary concern, do not charge fees

---

INVERALIA GROUP
Avda. Comunidad Autonoma
de Murcia, 30, CP: 30189
La Copa de Bullas (Murcia), Spain
Phone: 34-968-65-1155
Fax: 34-968-65-1161

Type of Firm
Private Equity Firm

Project Preferences

Type of Financing Preferred:
Expansion
Later Stage

Geographical Preferences

International Preferences:
Spain

Industry Preferences

In Consumer Related prefer:
Food/Beverage
Consumer Products

Additional Information
Year Founded: 2000
Capital Under Management: $76,600,000
Current Activity Level: Actively seeking new investments

INVEREADY SEED CAPITAL
C/ Baldiri Reixac, 4-6
2na Planta
Barcelona, Spain 08028
Phone: 34-93-447-30-63
Fax: 34-93-447-30-63
E-mail: info@inveready.com
Website: www.inveready.com

Management and Staff
Josep Maria Echarri, Partner
Roger Pique, Partner

Type of Firm
Private Equity Firm

Project Preferences

Type of Financing Preferred:
Seed

Geographical Preferences

International Preferences:
Spain

Industry Preferences

In Computer Software prefer:
Software

In Medical/Health prefer:
Medical Products

In Industrial/Energy prefer:
Alternative Energy

Additional Information
Year Founded: 2008
Current Activity Level: Actively seeking new investments

INVERJAEN S.C.R. SA
Plaza de la Constitucion 10, 6
Jaen, Spain 23001
Phone: 34-953-243-228
Fax: 34-953-245-246
E-mail: comunicacion@inverjaen.com
Website: www.inverjaen.com

Management and Staff
Esperanza Notario Romero, Vice President
Francisco Correal Marin, Vice President
Jeronimo Jimenez Martinez, Vice President
Jose Boyano Martinez, Vice President
Jose Antonio Arcos Moya, Vice President
Miguel Angel Perez Jimenez, Vice President
Perez Tomas, President

Type of Firm
Private Equity Firm

Association Membership
European Private Equity and Venture Capital Assoc.
Spanish Venture Capital Association (ASCRI)

Project Preferences

Type of Financing Preferred:
Early Stage
Expansion
Startup

Geographical Preferences

International Preferences:
Spain

Additional Information
Year Founded: 1992
Capital Under Management: $8,600,000
Current Activity Level: Actively seeking new investments

INVERNESS GRAHAM INVESTMENTS (FKA: INVERNESS CAPITAL)
3811 West Chester Pike
Building 2, Suite 100
Newtown Square, PA USA 19073
Phone: 610-722-0300
Fax: 610-251-2880
E-mail: contact@invernesscap.com
Website: www.invernesscap.com

Other Offices
2600 Michelson Drive
Suite 1700
Irvine, CA USA 92612
Phone: 949-221-8200

Management and Staff
Kenneth Graham, Senior Managing Director
Michael Morrissey, Principal
Trey Sykes, Principal

Type of Firm
Bank Affiliated

Association Membership
National Venture Capital Association - USA (NVCA)

Project Preferences

Role in Financing:
Prefer role as deal originator

Type of Financing Preferred:
Expansion
Management Buyouts
Private Placement
Recapitalizations

Size of Investments Considered:
Min Size of Investment Considered (000s): $4,000
Max Size of Investment Considered (000s): $10,000

Geographical Preferences

United States Preferences:
All U.S.

Industry Preferences

In Communications prefer:
Wireless Communications

In Computer Software prefer:
Software

In Semiconductor/Electr prefer:
Electronic Components
Sensors

In Medical/Health prefer:
Drug/Equipmt Delivery
Medical Products

In Consumer Related prefer:
Food/Beverage

In Industrial/Energy prefer:
Energy
Industrial Products
Advanced Materials
Factory Automation
Robotics

In Manufact. prefer:
Manufacturing

Additional Information
Name of Most Recent Fund: Inverness Graham Investments, L.P.
Most Recent Fund Was Raised: 01/07/2008
Year Founded: 2003
Capital Under Management: $125,000,000
Current Activity Level: Actively seeking new investments

INVERPYME SA
Travessera de Gracia, 11
5a planta
Barcelona, Spain 08021
Phone: 34-93-316-3283
Fax: 34-93-316-3264
E-mail: inverpyme@inverpyme.es
Website: www.inverpyme.es

Type of Firm
Private Equity Firm

Association Membership
Spanish Venture Capital Association (ASCRI)

Project Preferences

Type of Financing Preferred:
Expansion
Later Stage
Management Buyouts
Recapitalizations

Size of Investments Considered:
Min Size of Investment Considered (000s): $654
Max Size of Investment Considered (000s): $5,234

Geographical Preferences

International Preferences:
Europe
Spain

Additional Information
Year Founded: 2004
Current Activity Level: Actively seeking new investments

INVERSIONES IBERSUIZAS S.A.
Marques de Villamagna 3
11th Floor
Madrid, Spain 28001
Phone: 34-91-426-4380
Fax: 34-91-431-2011
Website: www.ibersuizas.es

Type of Firm
Bank Affiliated

Association Membership
Spanish Venture Capital Association (ASCRI)

Project Preferences

Type of Financing Preferred:
Expansion
Balanced

Geographical Preferences

International Preferences:
Latin America
Europe
Spain

Additional Information
Year Founded: 1999
Capital Under Management: $551,200,000
Current Activity Level: Actively seeking new investments

INVERSIONES PROGRANADA SA

Reyes Catolicos, 51
Granada, Spain 18001
Phone: 34-958-22-8383
Fax: 34-958-22-9527
E-mail: progran@arrakis.es

Type of Firm
Private Equity Firm

Association Membership
Spanish Venture Capital Association (ASCRI)

Project Preferences

Type of Financing Preferred:
Expansion

Geographical Preferences

International Preferences:
Spain

Industry Preferences

In Biotechnology prefer:
Biotechnology

In Agr/Forestr/Fish prefer:
Agribusiness
Agriculture related

Additional Information
Year Founded: 1989
Current Activity Level: Actively seeking new investments

INVERTEC

Passeig de Gracia, 129
Barcelona, Spain 08008
Phone: 34-93567-4939
Fax: 34-93476-7233

Type of Firm
Incubator/Development Program

Project Preferences

Type of Financing Preferred:
Seed

Geographical Preferences

International Preferences:
Spain

Additional Information
Year Founded: 2006
Capital Under Management: $5,100,000
Current Activity Level: Actively seeking new investments

INVESCO PRIVATE CAPITAL (FKA: CHANCELLOR)

1166 Avenue of the Americas
New York, NY USA 10036
Phone: 212-278-9000
Fax: 404-439-4911
Website: www.invescoprivatecapital.com

Other Offices
30 Finsbury Square
London, United Kingdom EC2A 1AG
Phone: 415-445-3344

101 California Street
Suite 1900
San Francisco, CA USA 94111
Phone: 415-445-3344
Fax: 415-445-7549

Management and Staff
Amit Tiwari, Principal
Esfandiar Lohrasbpour, General Partner
Greg Stoeckle, Managing Director
John Evans, General Partner
Kelvin Liu, Principal
Mary Frances Kelley, General Partner
Michael Gibbons, Chief Financial Officer
Philip Shaw, General Partner
Ray Maxwell, Venture Partner

Type of Firm
Private Equity Advisor or Fund of Funds

Association Membership
National Venture Capital Association - USA (NVCA)

Project Preferences

Role in Financing:
Will function either as deal originator or investor in deals created by others

Type of Financing Preferred:
Leveraged Buyout
Early Stage
Expansion
Balanced
Turnaround
Later Stage
Special Situation
Distressed Debt

Size of Investments Considered:
Min Size of Investment Considered (000s): $5,000
Max Size of Investment Considered (000s): $20,000

Geographical Preferences

United States Preferences:
All U.S.

Canadian Preferences:
All Canada

International Preferences:
United Kingdom
Western Europe
Hong Kong
Israel

Industry Focus
(% based on actual investment)

Other Products	21.4%
Communications and Media	13.7%
Medical/Health	13.2%
Internet Specific	12.8%
Computer Software and Services	12.3%
Biotechnology	12.2%
Semiconductors/Other Elect.	6.4%
Consumer Related	6.4%
Computer Hardware	1.3%
Industrial/Energy	0.4%

Additional Information
Name of Most Recent Fund: INVESCO Partnership Fund IV
Most Recent Fund Was Raised: 02/11/2004
Year Founded: 1982
Capital Under Management: $1,693,600,000
Current Activity Level: Actively seeking new investments
Method of Compensation: Function primarily in service area, receive contingent fee in cash or equity

---

INVEST AD (FKA: ABU DHABI INVESTMENT COMPANY)

Nat'l Bank of Abu Dhabi Bldg.
Khalidiya, Tariq Bin Ziad St.
Abu Dhabi, Utd. Arab Em.
Phone: 971-2-665-8100
Fax: 971-2-665-0575
E-mail: info@adic.ae
Website: www.adic.ae

Management and Staff
Chris Coombe, Chief Operating Officer
Nazem Fawwaz Al Kudsi, Chief Executive Officer

Type of Firm
Government Affiliated Program

Project Preferences

Type of Financing Preferred:
Leveraged Buyout
Unknown
Acquisition

Geographical Preferences

International Preferences:

Bahrain
Oman
Tunisia
Pakistan
Jordan
Qatar
Turkey
Iran
Lebanon
Utd. Arab Em.
Egypt
Algeria
Middle East
Saudi Arabia
Yemen
Israel
Syria
Morocco
All International
Cyprus
Iraq
Kuwait
Libya

Additional Information

Year Founded: 1994
Capital Under Management: $200,000,000
Current Activity Level: Actively seeking new investments

INVEST DEVELOPMENT SICAR (AKA: I.D. SICAR)

Immeuble STB
Avenue Mohamed V
Montplaisir, Tunisia 1002
Phone: 216-71-891-081
Fax: 216-71-890-855
E-mail: stbinvest@planet.tn

Type of Firm

Private Equity Advisor or Fund of Funds

Association Membership

African Venture Capital Association (AVCA)

Project Preferences

Type of Financing Preferred:

Expansion

Size of Investments Considered:

Min Size of Investment Considered (000s): $46
Max Size of Investment Considered (000s): $796

Geographical Preferences

International Preferences:

Africa

Industry Preferences

In Communications prefer:

Telecommunications

In Internet Specific prefer:

Internet

In Biotechnology prefer:

Biotechnology

In Industrial/Energy prefer:

Industrial Products

In Manufact. prefer:

Manufacturing

Additional Information

Year Founded: 2004
Capital Under Management: $14,700,000
Current Activity Level: Actively seeking new investments

INVEST EQUITY MANAGEMENT CONSULTING GMBH

Waechtergasse 1
Top 504
Vienna, Austria A - 1010
Phone: 43-1-532-0551
Fax: 43-1-5320-55120
E-mail: office@investequity.at
Website: www.investequity.at

Other Offices

Klimentska 1216/46
Praha City Center
Czech Republic 110 02
Phone: 420-222-191-105
Fax: 43-1-5320-551-830

Management and Staff

Gunter Lessig, Managing Partner
Helmut Bousek, Managing Partner
Jorgen Hausberger, Managing Partner
Karl Vieider, Partner
Thomas Jud, Partner

Type of Firm

Private Equity Firm

Association Membership

European Private Equity and Venture Capital Assoc.

Project Preferences

Role in Financing:

Prefer role as deal originator

Type of Financing Preferred:

Leveraged Buyout
Early Stage
Expansion
Balanced
Management Buyouts
Acquisition
Private Placement

Size of Investments Considered:

Min Size of Investment Considered (000s): $283
Max Size of Investment Considered (000s): $4,708

Geographical Preferences

International Preferences:

Hungary
Slovenia
Slovak Repub.
Czech Republic
Europe
Austria
Germany

Industry Preferences

In Communications prefer:

Communications and Media

In Semiconductor/Electr prefer:

Electronics

In Medical/Health prefer:

Medical/Health

In Consumer Related prefer:

Consumer
Retail
Food/Beverage

In Industrial/Energy prefer:

Industrial Products

In Business Serv. prefer:

Services

In Manufact. prefer:

Manufacturing

Additional Information

Year Founded: 1998
Capital Under Management: $79,800,000
Current Activity Level: Actively seeking new investments

INVEST MEZZANINE CAPITAL MANAGEMENT GMBH

Renngasse 10
Vienna, Austria A-1013
Phone: 43-1-532-9839
Fax: 43-1-5329839923
E-mail: office@investmezzanin.at
Website: www.investmezzanin.at

Type of Firm

Bank Affiliated

Association Membership

Austrian PE and Venture Capital Association (AVCO)
European Private Equity and Venture Capital Assoc.

Project Preferences

Type of Financing Preferred:

Leveraged Buyout
Expansion
Mezzanine
Balanced
Acquisition
Recapitalizations

Size of Investments Considered:
Min Size of Investment Considered (000s): $891
Max Size of Investment Considered (000s): $4,457

Geographical Preferences

International Preferences:
Switzerland
Central Europe
Europe
Austria
Eastern Europe
Germany

Industry Focus
(% based on actual investment)

Industrial/Energy	53.8%
Other Products	37.0%
Computer Software and Services	9.3%

Additional Information
Year Founded: 2000
Capital Under Management: $35,700,000
Current Activity Level: Actively seeking new investments

INVEST NORTHERN IRELAND
Bedford Square
Bedford Street
Belfast, United Kingdom BT2 7ES
Phone: 44-28-9023-9090
Fax: 44-28-9043-6536
E-mail: nitechgrowthfund@ANGLETechnology.com
Website: www.investni.com

Other Offices
Angle Technology Ltd
12 Cromac Place
Belfast, United Kingdom BT7 2JB
Phone: 44-28-902-44424
Fax: 44-28-903-26473

Management and Staff
Leslie Morrison, Chief Executive Officer

Type of Firm
Government Affiliated Program

Project Preferences

Type of Financing Preferred:
Second Stage Financing
Leveraged Buyout
Early Stage
Expansion
Turnaround
Seed
Startup

Geographical Preferences

International Preferences:
Ireland
United Kingdom

Industry Preferences

In Communications prefer:
Commercial Communications

In Semiconductor/Electr prefer:
Electronics

In Biotechnology prefer:
Biotechnology

In Medical/Health prefer:
Medical/Health

In Industrial/Energy prefer:
Industrial Products
Materials

In Financial Services prefer:
Financial Services

In Business Serv. prefer:
Services
Media

In Manufact. prefer:
Manufacturing

Additional Information
Year Founded: 2004
Capital Under Management: $24,300,000
Current Activity Level: Actively seeking new investments

INVEST UNTERNEHMENS-BETEILIGUNGS AG
Europaplatz 1a
Linz, Austria 4020
Phone: 43-732-65962451
Fax: 43-732-65962403
E-mail: investag@rlbooe.at
Website: www.investag.at

Type of Firm
Bank Affiliated
Association Membership
European Private Equity and Venture Capital Assoc.

Project Preferences

Type of Financing Preferred:
Early Stage
Expansion
Mezzanine
Management Buyouts
Acquisition

Size of Investments Considered:
Min Size of Investment Considered (000s): $60
Max Size of Investment Considered (000s): $605

Geographical Preferences

International Preferences:
Austria
Germany

Additional Information
Year Founded: 1994
Capital Under Management: $198,000,000
Current Activity Level: Actively seeking new investments

INVESTA FORETAGSKAPITAL
Torggatan 8
Sundsvall, Sweden 852 38
Phone: 46-60-600-7111
E-mail: info@investa.se
Website: www.investa.se

Management and Staff
Johan Lindqvist, Chief Executive Officer

Type of Firm
Private Equity Firm

Association Membership
Swedish Venture Capital Association (SVCA)

Project Preferences

Type of Financing Preferred:
Generalist PE

Geographical Preferences

International Preferences:
Sweden

Additional Information
Year Founded: 2005
Current Activity Level: Actively seeking new investments

INVESTAMERICA VENTURE GROUP, INC.
101 Second Street, Southeast
Suite 800
Cedar Rapids, IA USA 52401
Phone: 319-363-8249
Fax: 319-363-9683
Website: www.investamericaventuregroup.com

Other Offices
Commerce Tower
911 Main Street
Kansas City, MO USA 64105
Phone: 816-842-0114
Fax: 816-471-7339

600 East Mason Street
Suite 304
Milwaukee, WI USA 53202
Phone: 414-276-3839
Fax: 414-276-1885

Management and Staff
David Schroder, President

Type of Firm
Private Equity Firm

Association Membership
Natl Assoc of Small Bus. Inv. Co (NASBIC)

Project Preferences

Role in Financing:
Prefer role as deal originator but will also invest in deals created by others

Type of Financing Preferred:
Second Stage Financing
Leveraged Buyout
Early Stage
Expansion
Later Stage
First Stage Financing
Management Buyouts
Special Situation

Size of Investments Considered:
Min Size of Investment Considered (000s): $1,000
Max Size of Investment Considered (000s): $2,000

Geographical Preferences

United States Preferences:
Midwest
South Dakota
Iowa
North Dakota
Oregon
Idaho
Washington
Minnesota
Montana
All U.S.

Industry Focus
(% based on actual investment)

Other Products	19.7%
Communications and Media	19.4%
Industrial/Energy	15.7%
Internet Specific	12.7%
Consumer Related	9.6%
Semiconductors/Other Elect.	8.6%
Computer Hardware	5.8%
Biotechnology	3.4%
Medical/Health	3.3%
Computer Software and Services	1.8%

Additional Information
Year Founded: 1959
Capital Under Management: $48,500,000
Current Activity Level: Actively seeking new investments
Method of Compensation: Return on investment is of primary concern, do not charge fees

INVESTAR CAPITAL, INC.
No. 76, Sec. 2, Dunhua S. Rd.
24/F, Da-an District
Taipei, Taiwan
Phone: 886-2-2706-5500
Fax: 886-2-2706-5511
E-mail: contact@investar-cap.com
Website: www.investar-cap.com

Other Offices
333 West San Carlos Street
14th Floor
San Jose, CA USA 95110
Phone: 408-280-7888
Fax: 408-280-5508

Management and Staff
Fred Wong, Managing Partner
Herbert Chang, General Partner
Kenneth Tai, General Partner
Max Wu, Managing Partner
Michael Lin, Partner

Type of Firm
Private Equity Firm

Association Membership
Taiwan Venture Capital Association(TVCA)

Project Preferences

Role in Financing:
Will function either as deal originator or investor in deals created by others

Type of Financing Preferred:
Early Stage
Expansion

Size of Investments Considered:
Min Size of Investment Considered (000s): $500
Max Size of Investment Considered (000s): $5,000

Geographical Preferences

United States Preferences:
All U.S.

International Preferences:
Taiwan
China
Hong Kong
Japan

Industry Focus
(% based on actual investment)

Semiconductors/Other Elect.	47.3%
Computer Software and Services	16.9%
Communications and Media	16.0%
Computer Hardware	9.5%
Internet Specific	8.4%
Other Products	1.7%
Consumer Related	0.2%

Additional Information
Name of Most Recent Fund: Fuhwa I Venture Capital Co., Ltd.
Most Recent Fund Was Raised: 12/11/2002
Year Founded: 1996
Capital Under Management: $210,000,000
Current Activity Level: Actively seeking new investments
Method of Compensation: Professional fee required whether or not deal closes

INVESTBIO, INC.
135 Fifth Avenue
Tenth Floor
New York, NY USA 10010
Phone: 212-739-7676
Fax: 212-655-3681
E-mail: info@investbio.com
Website: www.investbio.com

Management and Staff
Ronald Robbins, Chief Operating Officer
Scott Mathis, Chairman & CEO

Type of Firm
Private Equity Advisor or Fund of Funds

Project Preferences

Type of Financing Preferred:
Balanced

Industry Preferences

In Biotechnology prefer:
Biotechnology

Additional Information
Name of Most Recent Fund: InvestBio Ventures - Amplimed II, L.P.
Most Recent Fund Was Raised: 07/22/2005
Year Founded: 2003
Capital Under Management: $2,500,000
Current Activity Level: Actively seeking new investments

INVESTCORP BANK B.S.C.
P.O. Box 5340
Manama, Bahrain
Phone: 973-1753-2000
Fax: 973-1753-0816
E-mail: info@investcorp.com
Website: www.investcorp.com

Other Offices
48 Grosvenor Street
London, United Kingdom W1K 3HW
Phone: 44-20-7629-6600
Fax: 44-20-7499-0371

280 Park Avenue
New York, NY USA 10017
Phone: 212-599-4700
Fax: 212-983-7073

Management and Staff
Christopher O'Brien, President
Craig Sinfield-Hain, Principal
Darryl D Souza, Principal
Deborah Smith, Managing Director
Ebrahim Hussain Ebrahim, Principal
Elizabeth Pires, Principal
Firas El Amine, Principal
Gerard DelBene, Principal

Grahame Ivey, Managing Director
Harin Wijeyeratne, Principal
Hasan Chehime, Managing Director
Jonathan Minor, Managing Director
Kamran Zulfiqar, Principal
Karen Van Nouhuys, Principal
Lawrence Kessler, Managing Director
Michael Simatos, Principal
Mohammed Al-Shroogi, President
Mufeed Rajab, Principal
Nemir Kirdar, Chairman & CEO
Ramzi AbdelJaber, Managing Director
Rangarajan Raghavan, Principal
Rishi Kapoor, Chief Financial Officer
Sarah Bradley, Managing Director
Sean Elliot, Principal
Shahbaz Khan, Principal
Shaun Hill, Principal
Sreevatsan Rajagopalan, Principal
Stephanie Bess, Managing Director
Stuart Marshall, Managing Director
Sudip Dey, Principal

Type of Firm

Investment Management Firm

Project Preferences

Type of Financing Preferred:

Leveraged Buyout
Early Stage
Generalist PE
Balanced
Distressed Debt
Fund of Funds of Second

Size of Investments Considered:

Min Size of Investment Considered (000s): $5,000
Max Size of Investment Considered: No Limit

Geographical Preferences

International Preferences:

Bahrain
Western Europe
Middle East
Africa

Industry Focus

(% based on actual investment)

Industrial/Energy	48.7%
Other Products	21.6%
Computer Software and Services	12.5%
Consumer Related	6.7%
Internet Specific	5.5%
Communications and Media	4.9%
Semiconductors/Other Elect.	0.1%
Medical/Health	0.1%

Additional Information
Year Founded: 1982
Capital Under Management: $1,000,000,000
Current Activity Level: Making few, if any, new investments

INVESTCORP TECHNOLOGY INVESTMENTS GROUP (AKA: TI)

280 Park Avenue
New York, NY USA 10017
Phone: 212-599-4700
Fax: 212-983-7073
E-mail: tig@investcorp.com
Website: www.investcorp.com

Other Offices

Investcorp House
48 Grosvenor Street
London, United Kingdom W1K 3HW
Phone: 44-20-7629-6600
Fax: 44-20-7887-3335

Type of Firm

Bank Affiliated

Association Membership

National Venture Capital Association - USA (NVCA)

Project Preferences

Role in Financing:

Prefer role as deal originator but will also invest in deals created by others

Type of Financing Preferred:

Leveraged Buyout
Early Stage
Expansion
Later Stage
Startup

Size of Investments Considered:

Min Size of Investment Considered (000s): $2,000
Max Size of Investment Considered (000s): $15,000

Geographical Preferences

United States Preferences:

All U.S.

Canadian Preferences:

All Canada

International Preferences:

Western Europe
All International

Industry Preferences

In Communications prefer:

Communications and Media
Telecommunications
Data Communications

In Computer Software prefer:

Software

In Internet Specific prefer:

Internet

Additional Information

Name of Most Recent Fund: Investcorp Technology Partners III, L.P. (AKA: ITP Fund III)
Most Recent Fund Was Raised: 10/11/2007
Year Founded: 2000
Capital Under Management: $800,000,000
Current Activity Level: Actively seeking new investments

INVESTEC PRIVATE EQUITY

2 Gresham Street
London, United Kingdom EC2V 7QP
Phone: 44-207-597-4000
Fax: 44-207-597-4070
E-mail: info@investec.com
Website: www.investec.com

Other Offices

300 Middel Street
Brooklyn
Pretoria, South Africa 0075
Phone: 27-12-427-8300
Fax: 27-12-427-8310

36 Hans Strijdom Ave.
Foreshore
Cape Town, South Africa 8001
Phone: 27-21-416-1000
Fax: 27-21-416-1001

100 Grayston Drive
Sandown
Sandton, South Africa 2196
Phone: 27-11-286-7000
Fax: 27-11-286-7777

325 Smith Street
Durban, South Africa 4001
Phone: 27-31-365-4700
Fax: 27-31-365-4800

Pilot Mill House
The Quarry, Selborne
East London, South Africa 5247
Phone: 27-43-721-0660
Fax: 27-43-721-0664

Ascot Office Park, Conyngham Rd.
Green Acres
Port Elizabeth, South Africa 6045
Phone: 27-41-391-9400
Fax: 27-41-374-8346

Type of Firm

Bank Affiliated

Association Membership

South African Venture Capital Association (SAVCA)

Project Preferences

Type of Financing Preferred:

Leveraged Buyout
Early Stage
Expansion
Mezzanine

Management Buyouts
Acquisition
Recapitalizations

Geographical Preferences

International Preferences:

United Kingdom
Europe
Israel
South Africa
Asia
All International

Additional Information

Name of Most Recent Fund: Guinness Mahon Venture Founders Fund
Most Recent Fund Was Raised: 03/01/1985
Year Founded: 1974
Current Activity Level: Actively seeking new investments

INVESTEC WENTWORTH PRIVATE EQUITY PTY., LTD.

2 Chifley Square
Level 31, The Chifley Tower
Sydney, Australia 2000
Phone: 612-9293-2000
Fax: 612-9293-2002
Website: www.investec.com.au

Other Offices

71 Eagle Street
Level 31, Riparian Plaza
Brisbane, Australia 4000
Phone: 617-3018-8100
Fax: 617-3018-8108

140 St.Georges Terrace
Level 21
Perth, Australia
Phone: 618-9289-8000
Fax: 618-9289-8010

120 Collins Street
Level 49
Melbourne, Australia 3000
Phone: 613-8660-1000
Fax: 613-8660-1010

Management and Staff

John Murphy, Managing Director

Type of Firm

Bank Affiliated

Association Membership

Australian Venture Capital Association (AVCAL)

Project Preferences

Role in Financing:

Will function either as deal originator or investor in deals created by others

Type of Financing Preferred:

Leveraged Buyout
Generalist PE

Size of Investments Considered:

Min Size of Investment Considered (000s): $16,116
Max Size of Investment Considered (000s): $161,160

Geographical Preferences

International Preferences:

Australia
New Zealand

Additional Information

Name of Most Recent Fund: MGB Equity Growth Unit Trust 2
Most Recent Fund Was Raised: 02/01/2000
Year Founded: 1998
Capital Under Management: $398,100,000
Current Activity Level: Actively seeking new investments
Method of Compensation: Return on invest. most important, but chg. closing fees, service fees, etc.

INVESTECO CAPITAL CORPORATION

70 Esplanade
Suite 400
Toronto, Canada M5E1R2
Phone: 416-304-1750
Fax: 416-362-2378
E-mail: info@investco.com
Website: www.investco.com

Management and Staff

Alex Chamberlain, Managing Partner
Andrew Heintzman, President
John Cook, Managing Partner
Michael Curry, Managing Partner

Type of Firm

Private Equity Firm

Project Preferences

Type of Financing Preferred:

Expansion
Early Stage
Seed
Startup

Geographical Preferences

Canadian Preferences:

Ontario

Additional Information

Year Founded: 2004
Current Activity Level: Actively seeking new investments

INVESTINDUSTRIAL PARTNERS, LTD.

1 Duchess Street
London, United Kingdom W1W 6AN
Phone: 44-207-631-2777
Fax: 44-207-631-2778
E-mail: info@investindustrial.com
Website: www.investindustrial.com

Other Offices

Via Augusta 200 1-2
Barcelona, Spain 08021
Phone: 34-93-240-5750
Fax: 34-93-240-5755

51 Avenue JF Kennedy
Luxembourg, Luxembourg 1855
Phone: 352-2609-531
Fax: 352-2609-5340

Paseo de la Castellana 31
Madrid, Spain 28046
Phone: 34-91-789-6300
Fax: 34-91-789-6321

Via Nassa 5
Lugano, Switzerland 6900
Phone: 41-91-260-8300
Fax: 41-91-260-8329

Via dei Bossi 4
Milan, Italy 20121
Phone: 39-02-802-7761
Fax: 39-02-8901-1223

Whiteley Chambers
Don Street, St. Helier
Jersey, United Kingdom JE4 9WG
Phone: 44-1534-504-000
Fax: 44-1534-504-444

Management and Staff

Carlo Bonomi, Principal
Dante Razzano, Principal
Filippo Aleotti, Principal
Ignacio Arietta, Principal
John Mowinckel, Principal
Martin Del Valle, Principal
Michele Garulli, Principal
Roberto Maestroni, Principal
Salvatore Catapano, Principal

Type of Firm

Private Equity Firm

Association Membership

European Private Equity and Venture Capital Assoc.

Project Preferences

Type of Financing Preferred:

Second Stage Financing
Leveraged Buyout
Expansion

Mezzanine
Turnaround

Size of Investments Considered:
Min Size of Investment Considered (000s): $18,661
Max Size of Investment Considered (000s): $93,307

Geographical Preferences

International Preferences:
Italy
Greece
United Kingdom
Portugal
Switzerland
Europe
Spain
France

Industry Preferences

In Consumer Related prefer:
Consumer
Food/Beverage

In Industrial/Energy prefer:
Industrial Products
Materials

In Transportation prefer:
Transportation

Additional Information
Name of Most Recent Fund: Investindustrial III, L.P.
Most Recent Fund Was Raised: 10/31/2005
Year Founded: 1990
Capital Under Management: $600,000,000
Current Activity Level: Actively seeking new investments

INVESTINOR AS
Brattorkaia 17B
Trondheim, Norway 7010
Phone: 47-9-574-2000
E-mail: post@investinor.no
Website: www.investinor.no

Management and Staff
Tor Helmersen, Chief Financial Officer

Type of Firm
Government Affiliated Program

Project Preferences

Type of Financing Preferred:
Balanced

Geographical Preferences

International Preferences:
Norway

Additional Information
Year Founded: 2009
Current Activity Level: Actively seeking new investments

INVESTISSEMENT DESJARDINS
2, complexe Desjardins
C.P. 760
Montreal, Canada H5B 1B8
Phone: 514-281-7131
Fax: 514-281-7808
E-mail: invdesj@invdesjardins.qc.ca
Website: www.desjardins.com/id

Type of Firm
Bank Affiliated

Association Membership
Canadian Venture Capital Association

Project Preferences

Role in Financing:
Prefer role as deal originator but will also invest in deals created by others

Type of Financing Preferred:
Second Stage Financing
Leveraged Buyout
Control-block Purchases
Mezzanine
Expansion
Early Stage
Start-up Financing
Later Stage
First Stage Financing
Acquisition
Startup

Size of Investments Considered:
Min Size of Investment Considered (000s): $5,000
Max Size of Investment Considered: No Limit

Geographical Preferences

Canadian Preferences:
Quebec

Industry Focus
(% based on actual investment)

Medical/Health	18.6%
Computer Software and Services	18.3%
Other Products	11.5%
Consumer Related	11.2%
Biotechnology	10.7%
Communications and Media	9.1%
Semiconductors/Other Elect.	8.1%
Internet Specific	7.1%
Industrial/Energy	3.7%
Computer Hardware	1.8%

Additional Information
Year Founded: 1974
Capital Under Management: $150,000,000
Current Activity Level: Actively seeking new investments
Method of Compensation: Return on invest. most important, but chg. closing fees, service fees, etc.

INVESTISSEMENT QUEBEC
393 St-Jacques Street
Suite 500
Montreal, Canada H2Y1N9
Phone: 514-873-4375
Fax: 514-873-5786
Website: www.investquebec.com/en/index.aspx

Management and Staff
Andre Cote, Vice President
Dominique Bonifacio, Vice President
Pierre Lafreniere, Vice President

Type of Firm
Government Affiliated Program

Project Preferences

Type of Financing Preferred:
Expansion
Early Stage
Startup

Geographical Preferences

Canadian Preferences:
Quebec

Additional Information
Year Founded: 1998
Current Activity Level: Actively seeking new investments

INVESTISSEMENTS 3L
3100, boul. le Carrefour
Bureau 660
Laval, Canada

Type of Firm
Private Equity Firm

Additional Information
Year Founded: 1994
Current Activity Level: Actively seeking new investments

INVESTISSEUR ET PARTENAIRE POUR LE DEVELOPPEMENT (AKA: I&P)
c/o I&P Etudes et Conseils
3 rue Casteja
Boulogne-Billancourt, France 92100
Phone: 33-146-090-617
Fax: 33-146-091-897
E-mail: catherine.Leblanc@ip-conseil.com
Website: www.ip-dev.com

Type of Firm
Private Equity Firm

Association Membership

African Venture Capital Association (AVCA)

Project Preferences

Type of Financing Preferred:

Generalist PE

Size of Investments Considered:

Min Size of Investment Considered (000s): $126
Max Size of Investment Considered (000s): $632

Geographical Preferences

International Preferences:

Latin America
Pacific
Africa

Industry Preferences

In Medical/Health prefer:

Medical/Health

In Consumer Related prefer:

Consumer

In Financial Services prefer:

Financial Services

In Manufact. prefer:

Manufacturing

Additional Information

Year Founded: 2002
Capital Under Management: $7,600,000
Current Activity Level: Actively seeking new investments

INVESTITIONS- UND STRUKTURBANK RHEINLAND-PFALZ (ISB) GMBH

Holzhofstrasse 4
Mainz, Germany 55116
Phone: 49-6131-985-0
Fax: 49-6131-985-199
E-mail: isb@isb.rlp.de
Website: www.isb.rlp.de

Management and Staff

Bernhard Wasmayr, Managing Director
Hans-Joachim Metternich, Managing Director
Jutta Lehmann, Partner
Manfred Kramer, Managing Director
Roland C Wagner, Managing Director
Rudiger Bucher, Managing Director

Type of Firm

Bank Affiliated

Project Preferences

Type of Financing Preferred:

Early Stage
Expansion
Balanced
Management Buyouts
Startup

Geographical Preferences

International Preferences:

Germany

Industry Focus

(% based on actual investment)

Biotechnology	44.9%
Semiconductors/Other Elect.	27.9%
Medical/Health	27.2%

Additional Information

Year Founded: 2001
Current Activity Level: Actively seeking new investments

INVESTITORI ASSOCIATI SPA

Via Agnello, 8
Milan, Italy 20121
Phone: 39-02-854-5731
Fax: 39-02-8545-7346
E-mail: info@investitoriassociati.com
Website: www.investitoriassociati.com

Management and Staff

Andrea Gianola, Partner
Carlo Moser, Partner
Filippo Gaggini, Partner
Luca Liberali, Partner
Michele Marini, Partner
Paolo Visioni, Partner
Paolo Melloni, Partner
Renato Peroni, Partner
Valeria Lattuada, Partner

Type of Firm

Private Equity Firm

Association Membership

Italian Venture Capital Association (AIFI)
European Private Equity and Venture Capital Assoc.

Project Preferences

Type of Financing Preferred:

Leveraged Buyout
Expansion
Turnaround
Management Buyouts
Acquisition

Geographical Preferences

International Preferences:

Italy
Europe

Industry Focus

(% based on actual investment)

Consumer Related	52.7%
Industrial/Energy	19.0%
Other Products	16.6%
Medical/Health	10.5%
Internet Specific	1.2%

Additional Information

Year Founded: 1993
Capital Under Management: $1,827,600,000
Current Activity Level: Actively seeking new investments

INVESTMENT AB LATOUR

J A Wettergrens gata 7
P.O. Box 336
Gothenburg, Sweden SE-401 25
Phone: 46-31-891-790
Fax: 46-31-456-063
E-mail: info@latour.se
Website: www.latour.se

Management and Staff

G. Wirenstam, President
Jan Svensson, Chief Executive Officer

Type of Firm

Corporate PE/Venture

Project Preferences

Type of Financing Preferred:

Balanced

Geographical Preferences

International Preferences:

Europe
Scandanavia/Nordic Region

Industry Preferences

In Industrial/Energy prefer:

Industrial Products
Materials

Additional Information

Year Founded: 1999
Current Activity Level: Actively seeking new investments

INVESTMENT AB SPILTAN

Grevgatan 39
Stockholm, Sweden 114 53
Phone: 46-8-5458-1340
Fax: 46-8-5458-1348
Website: www.spiltan.se

Management and Staff

Per Borjesson, Managing Director

Type of Firm

Private Equity Firm

Association Membership

Swedish Venture Capital Association (SVCA)

Project Preferences

Type of Financing Preferred:

Early Stage

Expansion
Seed
Startup

Geographical Preferences

International Preferences:
Scandanavia/Nordic Region

Additional Information
Year Founded: 1985
Current Activity Level: Actively seeking new investments

INVESTMENT CAPITAL PARTNERS PTY., LTD.

Level 3, Lantos Place
80 Stamford Road
Brisbane, Australia 4068
Phone: 617-3378-6033
Fax: 617-3378-6044
E-mail: info@icpartners.com.au
Website: www.icpartners.com.au

Type of Firm
Private Equity Firm

Project Preferences

Type of Financing Preferred:
Balanced

Geographical Preferences

International Preferences:
Pacific

Additional Information
Year Founded: 2007
Current Activity Level: Actively seeking new investments

INVESTMENT FUND FOR FOUNDATIONS

200 Barr Harbor Drive
Suite 100
Conshohocken, PA USA 19428
Phone: 610-684-8000
Fax: 610-684-8080
E-mail: info@tiff.org
Website: www.tiff.org

Management and Staff
Esther Cash, Managing Director
Meredith Shuwall, Managing Director
Nina Scherago, Managing Director
Robert Swain, Managing Director
Tom Felker, Managing Director

Type of Firm
Endowment, Foundation or Pension Fund

Project Preferences

Type of Financing Preferred:
Fund of Funds
Fund of Funds of Second

Geographical Preferences

International Preferences:
All International

Industry Preferences

In Financial Services prefer:
Real Estate

Additional Information
Name of Most Recent Fund: TIFF Partners III (AKA: TP III)
Most Recent Fund Was Raised: 01/20/1999
Year Founded: 1995
Capital Under Management: $474,400,000
Current Activity Level: Actively seeking new investments

INVESTOR GROWTH CAPITAL AB

Arsenalsgatan 8C
Stockholm, Sweden SE-103 32
Phone: 46-8-614-2000
Fax: 46-8-614-2150
Website: www.investorab.com

Other Offices
1701 Hutchison House
10 Harcourt Road
Central, Hong Kong
Phone: 852-2123-8000
Fax: 852-2123-8001

630 Fifth Avenue
Suite 1965
New York, NY USA 10111
Phone: 212-515-9000
Fax: 212-515-9009

Schiphol Boulevard 353
Amsterdam, Netherlands NL-1118
Phone: 31-20-577-6600
Fax: 31-20-577-6609

Unit 1603, 16F, Tower 2
No. 79 Jiangou Road
Beijing, China 100025
Phone: 86-10-6598-9118
Fax: 86-10-5866-9128

333 Middlefield Road
Suite 110
Menlo Park, CA USA 94025
Phone: 650-543-8100
Fax: 650-543-8110

Togin Building, 13F
1-4-2 Marunouchi Chiyoda-ku
Tokyo, Japan 100-0011
Phone: 81-3-5512-4532
Fax: 81-3-5512-4534

Management and Staff
Fredrik Hillelson, Managing Director
Henry Gooss, Managing Director
Jakob Lindberg, Vice President
Lisa Chan, Chief Financial Officer
Pia Rudengren, Managing Director
Ulla Litzen, Managing Director
Winnie Fok, Chief Executive Officer

Type of Firm
Corporate PE/Venture

Association Membership
Hong Kong Venture Capital Association (HKVCA)
European Private Equity and Venture Capital Assoc.

Project Preferences

Type of Financing Preferred:
Generalist PE
Balanced

Geographical Preferences

United States Preferences:
All U.S.

International Preferences:
Sweden
Europe
China
Korea, South
Asia
All International

Industry Focus
(% based on actual investment)

Biotechnology	28.7%
Internet Specific	24.4%
Medical/Health	15.6%
Communications and Media	13.1%
Semiconductors/Other Elect.	7.2%
Other Products	5.3%
Computer Software and Services	4.6%
Industrial/Energy	0.7%
Computer Hardware	0.4%

Additional Information
Year Founded: 1995
Capital Under Management: $321,000,000
Current Activity Level: Actively seeking new investments

INVESTOR GROWTH CAPITAL, INC.

630 Fifth Avenue
Suite 1965
New York, NY USA 10111
Phone: 212-515-9000
Fax: 212-515-9009
E-mail: igc-us@investorab.com

Website: www.investorab.com

Other Offices

Schiphol Boulevard
Schiphol, Netherlands NL-1118 BJ
Phone: 31-20-577-6600
Fax: 31-20-577-6609

Arsenalsgatan 8c
Stockholm, Sweden S-103 32
Phone: 46-8614-1800
Fax: 46-8614-1809

1701 Hutchison House
10 Harcourt Road
Central, Hong Kong
Phone: 852-2123-8000
Fax: 852-2123-8001

Unit 1603, 16Fl, Tower 2, No.79 Jianguo
China Central Place Office Building
Beijing, China 1000025
Phone: 86-10-6598-9118
Fax: 86-10-6598-9128

333 Middlefield Road
Suite 110
Menlo Park, CA USA 94025
Phone: 650-543-8100
Fax: 650-543-8110

10F Imperial Hotel Tower
1-1-1 Uchisaiwaicho, Chiyoda-ku
Tokyo, Japan 100-0011
Phone: 81-3-5512-4532
Fax: 81-3-5512-4534

Management and Staff

Albert Kim, Vice President
Anders Osund, Vice President
Henry Gooss, Chief Executive Officer
Jakob Lindberg, Vice President
Jose Suarez, Managing Director
Karl Swartling, Managing Director
Liza Page Nelson, Managing Director
Michael Oporto, Managing Director & CFO
Mikael Johnsson, Vice President
Noah Walley, Managing Director
Paul Choo, Vice President
Philip Dur, Managing Director
Shinji Yasui, Vice President
Stephen Campe, President
Thomas Eklund, Managing Director
William Fong, Managing Director
Xin Wang, Venture Partner

Type of Firm

Bank Affiliated

Association Membership

Swedish Venture Capital Association (SVCA)
National Venture Capital Association - USA (NVCA)
European Private Equity and Venture Capital Assoc.

Project Preferences

Role in Financing:

Prefer role as deal originator but will also invest in deals created by others

Type of Financing Preferred:

Expansion
Balanced
Later Stage
Open Market
Other

Size of Investments Considered:

Min Size of Investment Considered (000s): $5,000
Max Size of Investment Considered (000s): $50,000

Geographical Preferences

Canadian Preferences:

All Canada

International Preferences:

Europe
Asia

Industry Focus

(% based on actual investment)

Medical/Health	19.4%
Computer Software and Services	18.3%
Biotechnology	17.2%
Communications and Media	16.7%
Internet Specific	11.9%
Semiconductors/Other Elect.	8.1%
Computer Hardware	5.2%
Industrial/Energy	1.9%
Other Products	1.2%
Consumer Related	0.3%

Additional Information

Year Founded: 1995
Capital Under Management: $1,800,000,000
Current Activity Level: Actively seeking new investments
Method of Compensation: Return on investment is of primary concern, do not charge fees

---

INVESTORS IN PRIVATE EQUITY (AKA: IPE)

1 rue Francois 1er
Paris, France 75008
Phone: 33-1-5836-1550
Fax: 33-1-5836-1569
E-mail: ipe@investors-in-private-equity.fr
Website: www.investors-in-private-equity.fr

Management and Staff

Philippe Nguyen, President

Type of Firm

Private Equity Firm

Association Membership

French Venture Capital Association (AFIC)
European Private Equity and Venture Capital Assoc.

Project Preferences

Type of Financing Preferred:

Leveraged Buyout
Management Buyouts

Geographical Preferences

International Preferences:

Europe
France

Industry Preferences

In Communications prefer:

Telecommunications

In Semiconductor/Electr prefer:

Electronics

In Biotechnology prefer:

Biotechnology

In Medical/Health prefer:

Medical/Health

In Consumer Related prefer:

Consumer Products

In Industrial/Energy prefer:

Energy
Industrial Products
Advanced Materials
Factory Automation

In Transportation prefer:

Transportation

In Financial Services prefer:

Financial Services

In Manufact. prefer:

Manufacturing

In Agr/Forestr/Fish prefer:

Agriculture related

Additional Information

Year Founded: 2002
Current Activity Level: Actively seeking new investments

INVESTRA ASA

Cort Adelers gate 17, 6 eta
P.O. Box 2493 Solli
Oslo, Norway 0202
Phone: 47-23-08-40-50
Fax: 47-23-08-40-55
E-mail: investra@investra.no
Website: www.investra.no

Type of Firm

Private Equity Firm

Additional Information

Current Activity Level: Actively seeking new investments

INVESTSUD

Avenue de France 6
Marche-en-Famenne, Belgium 6900
Phone: 32-84-32-0520
Fax: 32-84-31-5723
E-mail: pierre.bernes@investsud.be
Website: www.investsud.be

Type of Firm

Private Equity Firm

Project Preferences

Type of Financing Preferred:
Generalist PE

Geographical Preferences

International Preferences:
Belgium
France

Additional Information

Year Founded: 1983
Current Activity Level: Actively seeking new investments

INVEX CAPITAL PARTNERS

10 Market Mews
London, United Kingdom W1J 7BZ
Phone: 44-20-7408-5000
Fax: 44-20-7408-5001
E-mail: info@invex.co.uk
Website: www.invex.co.uk

Type of Firm

Private Equity Firm

Project Preferences

Type of Financing Preferred:
Generalist PE

Size of Investments Considered:
Min Size of Investment Considered (000s): $9,963
Max Size of Investment Considered (000s): $199,250

Geographical Preferences

International Preferences:
United Kingdom
Europe
Asia

Additional Information

Year Founded: 2007
Current Activity Level: Actively seeking new investments

INVICO CAPITAL CORPORATION

Bankers Hall Hollinsworth BLDG
Suite 600, 301 - Eight Ave SW
Calgary, Canada T2P1C5
Phone: 403-538-4771
Website: www.invicocapital.com

Management and Staff

Allison Taylor, Vice President
Jason Brooks, President

Type of Firm

Private Equity Firm

Project Preferences

Type of Financing Preferred:
Early Stage
Startup

Additional Information

Year Founded: 2006
Current Activity Level: Actively seeking new investments

INVISION PRIVATE EQUITY AG (FKA: INVISION AG)

Grafenaustrasse 7
P.O. Box 4433
Zug, Switzerland 6304
Phone: 41-41-729-0101
Fax: 41-41-729-0100
E-mail: info@invision.ch
Website: www.invision.ch

Management and Staff

Bernd Pfister, Chief Executive Officer
Christian Stoller, Partner
Frank Becker, Chief Financial Officer
Gerhard Weisschaedel, Partner
Marco Martelli, Partner
Martin Staub, Partner

Type of Firm

Private Equity Firm

Association Membership

Swiss Venture Capital Association (SECA)
European Private Equity and Venture Capital Assoc.

Project Preferences

Type of Financing Preferred:
Early Stage
Expansion
Generalist PE
Balanced
Seed
Startup

Size of Investments Considered:
Min Size of Investment Considered (000s): $682
Max Size of Investment Considered (000s): $27,274

Geographical Preferences

International Preferences:
Ireland
Switzerland
Europe
China
Israel
Germany
France

Industry Focus

(% based on actual investment)

Internet Specific	29.1%
Computer Software and Services	23.7%
Medical/Health	18.8%
Computer Hardware	9.7%
Consumer Related	6.6%
Semiconductors/Other Elect.	5.6%
Other Products	5.2%
Communications and Media	1.4%

Additional Information

Name of Most Recent Fund: Invision III (AKA: Mach II)
Most Recent Fund Was Raised: 06/02/2000
Year Founded: 1998
Capital Under Management: $41,900,000
Current Activity Level: Actively seeking new investments

INVIVO VENTURES

404 Dublin
Beaconsfield, Canada H9W 1V4
Phone: 514-697-3175
Fax: 514-697-0908

Management and Staff

Claude Miron, Managing Partner
Trudie Resch, Managing Partner

Type of Firm

Private Equity Firm

Project Preferences

Role in Financing:
Prefer role as deal originator but will also invest in deals created by others

Type of Financing Preferred:
Second Stage Financing
Expansion
Later Stage
Private Placement

Size of Investments Considered:
Min Size of Investment Considered (000s): $5,000
Max Size of Investment Considered (000s): $10,000

Industry Preferences

In Biotechnology prefer:
Biotechnology
Human Biotechnology

In Medical/Health prefer:
Medical/Health
Medical Diagnostics
Medical Therapeutics
Drug/Equipmt Delivery
Medical Products
Health Services
Pharmaceuticals

Additional Information

Year Founded: 2004
Current Activity Level: Actively seeking new investments
Method of Compensation: Return on investment is of primary concern, do not charge fees

---

INVUS GROUP LTD., THE

750 Lexington Avenue
30th Floor
New York, NY USA 10022
Phone: 212-371-1717
Fax: 212-371-1829
E-mail: NYOffice@invus.com
Website: www.invus.com

Other Offices

20th Floor Central Tower
28 Queen's Road
Central, Hong Kong
Phone: 852-2159-9610

170 Piccadillly
London, United Kingdom W1J 9EJ
Phone: 44-20-7493-9133
Fax: 44-20-7518-9629

46, rue Pierre Charron
Paris, France 75008
Phone: 33-1-5690-5000
Fax: 33-1-5690-5010

Management and Staff

Alfalo Guimaraes, Managing Director
Christopher Sobecki, Managing Director
Evren Bilimer, Managing Director
Francis Cukierman, Managing Director
H.Eric Chiang, Principal
Jonas Fajgenbaum, Managing Director
Juan Uribe, Principal
Khalil Barrage, Managing Director
Luc Ta-Ngoc, Managing Director
Philippe Amouyal, Managing Director

Type of Firm

Private Equity Firm

Association Membership

French Venture Capital Association (AFIC)

Project Preferences

Role in Financing:
Will function either as deal originator or investor in deals created by others

Type of Financing Preferred:
Leveraged Buyout
Early Stage
Expansion

Geographical Preferences

United States Preferences:
All U.S.

International Preferences:
Latin America
Europe

Industry Focus

(% based on actual investment)	
Consumer Related	83.6%
Biotechnology	5.6%
Industrial/Energy	5.3%
Computer Software and Services	3.4%
Other Products	1.1%
Internet Specific	0.7%
Medical/Health	0.3%

Additional Information

Year Founded: 1985
Capital Under Management: $1,000,000,000
Current Activity Level: Actively seeking new investments
Method of Compensation: Unknown

ION EQUITY, LTD.

Huguenot House
35/38 St. Stephen's Green
Dublin 2, Ireland
Phone: 353-1-611-0500
Fax: 353-1-611-0510
E-mail: info@ionequity.com
Website: www.ionequity.com

Other Offices

2 Cavendish Square
London, United Kingdom W1G 0PU
Phone: 44-207-043-5188
Fax: 44-207-152-6331

Management and Staff

Joe Devine, Partner
Neil O'Leary, Chairman & CEO
Ulric Kenny, Partner

Type of Firm

Private Equity Firm

Project Preferences

Type of Financing Preferred:
Early Stage

Geographical Preferences

International Preferences:
Ireland

Industry Preferences

In Communications prefer:
Commercial Communications
Telecommunications
Wireless Communications

In Computer Software prefer:
Software

Additional Information

Year Founded: 2001
Capital Under Management: $12,000,000
Current Activity Level: Actively seeking new investments

IP2IPO, LTD. (AKA: IP GROUP PLC)

24 Cornhill
London, United Kingdom EC3V 3ND
Phone: 44-207-444-0050
Fax: 44-845-074-2928
E-mail: enquiries@ip2ipo.com
Website: www.ip2ipo.com

Other Offices

Leeds Innovation Centre
103 Clarendon Road
Leeds, United Kingdom LS2 9DF
Phone: 44-870-126-3200
Fax: 44-870-126-3201

Management and Staff

Alan Aubrey, Chief Executive Officer
Magnus Goodlad, Chief Operating Officer

Type of Firm

Bank Affiliated

Association Membership

European Private Equity and Venture Capital Assoc.

Project Preferences

Type of Financing Preferred:
Balanced

Geographical Preferences

International Preferences:
United Kingdom

Industry Preferences

In Computer Software prefer:
Software

In Internet Specific prefer:
Internet

In Semiconductor/Electr prefer:
Semiconductor

In Biotechnology prefer:
Biotechnology

Additional Information

Year Founded: 1989
Capital Under Management: $63,100,000
Current Activity Level: Actively seeking new investments

IPACIFIC PARTNERS, INC. (FKA: KOLON VENTURE CAPITAL INC)

8th Floor, Samsung Building
170-8 Samsung-dong, Kangnam-gu
Seoul, South Korea 135-090
Phone: 82-2-2052-2310
Fax: 82-2-2052-2319
Website: www.ipacificpartners.com

Type of Firm

Corporate PE/Venture

Association Membership

Korean Venture Capital Association (KVCA)

Project Preferences

Type of Financing Preferred:

Early Stage
Startup

Size of Investments Considered:

Min Size of Investment Considered (000s): $250
Max Size of Investment Considered (000s): $250

Geographical Preferences

International Preferences:

Korea, South

Industry Preferences

In Communications prefer:

Telecommunications
Wireless Communications

In Internet Specific prefer:

E-Commerce Technology
Internet
Ecommerce

In Consumer Related prefer:

Entertainment and Leisure

Additional Information

Year Founded: 2000
Capital Under Management: $33,000,000
Current Activity Level: Actively seeking new investments

IPO (INSTITUT DE PARTICIPATIONS DE L OUEST)

32 avenue Camus
BP 50416
Nantes Cedex 1, France 44004
Phone: 33-2-4035-7531
Fax: 33-2-4035-2737
E-mail: ipo@ipo.fr
Website: www.ipo.fr

Management and Staff

Pierre Tiers, General Director

Type of Firm

Private Equity Firm

Association Membership

French Venture Capital Association (AFIC)

Project Preferences

Type of Financing Preferred:

Leveraged Buyout
Early Stage
Expansion
Mezzanine
Startup
Recapitalizations

Geographical Preferences

International Preferences:

France

Additional Information

Year Founded: 1997
Current Activity Level: Actively seeking new investments

IPO BETEILIGUNGS-MANAGEMENT AG

Argentinierstrasse 42
Vienna, Austria 1040
Phone: 43-1-505-6320
Fax: 43-1-505-632050
E-mail: office@ipo-austria.at
Website: www.ipo-austria.at

Type of Firm

Private Equity Firm

Association Membership

European Private Equity and Venture Capital Assoc.

Project Preferences

Type of Financing Preferred:

Leveraged Buyout
Expansion
Balanced
Start-up Financing
Seed
Other
Management Buyouts
Acquisition
Startup

Size of Investments Considered:

Min Size of Investment Considered (000s): $699
Max Size of Investment Considered (000s): $6,990

Geographical Preferences

International Preferences:

Switzerland
Europe
Austria
Germany

Industry Preferences

In Communications prefer:

Communications and Media

In Semiconductor/Electr prefer:

Electronics

Additional Information

Name of Most Recent Fund: Athena Zweite Beteiligungen AG (AKA: Athena II)
Most Recent Fund Was Raised: 11/29/2000
Year Founded: 2000
Capital Under Management: $161,500,000
Current Activity Level: Actively seeking new investments

IPS INDUSTRIAL PROMOTION SERVICES, LTD.

60 Columbia Way
Suite 720
Markham, Canada L3R 0C9
Phone: 905-475-9400
Fax: 905-475-5003
Website: www.ipscanada.com

Type of Firm

Private Equity Firm

Association Membership

Canadian Venture Capital Association

Project Preferences

Role in Financing:

Prefer role as deal originator but will also invest in deals created by others

Type of Financing Preferred:

Second Stage Financing
Leveraged Buyout
Control-block Purchases
Expansion
Startup
Special Situation

Size of Investments Considered:

Min Size of Investment Considered (000s): $500
Max Size of Investment Considered: No Limit

Geographical Preferences

United States Preferences:

All U.S.

Canadian Preferences:

All Canada

Industry Preferences

In Communications prefer:
Telecommunications

In Computer Hardware prefer:
Mini and Personal/Desktop

In Semiconductor/Electr prefer:
Electronics
Laser Related
Fiber Optics

In Biotechnology prefer:
Industrial Biotechnology

In Medical/Health prefer:
Drug/Equipmt Delivery
Medical Products
Pharmaceuticals

In Consumer Related prefer:
Food/Beverage
Consumer Products

In Industrial/Energy prefer:
Energy Conservation Relat
Industrial Products
Environmental Related

In Transportation prefer:
Transportation

Additional Information

Year Founded: 1979
Capital Under Management: $25,000,000
Current Activity Level: Actively seeking new investments
Method of Compensation: Return on invest. most important, but chg. closing fees, service fees, etc.

IRDI

18 place Dupuy
BP 808
Toulouse, France 31080
Phone: 33-5-3441-7417
Fax: 33-5-3441-7419
E-mail: contact@irdi.fr
Website: www.irdi.fr

Other Offices

9, rue de Conde
Bordeaux, France 33000
Phone: 33-5-5600-1269
Fax: 33-5-5644-2351

Management and Staff

Christian Reynaud, President

Type of Firm

Private Equity Firm

Association Membership

French Venture Capital Association (AFIC)

Project Preferences

Type of Financing Preferred:
Leveraged Buyout
Generalist PE
Early Stage
Expansion
Balanced
Startup

Size of Investments Considered:
Min Size of Investment Considered (000s): $132
Max Size of Investment Considered (000s): $2,648

Geographical Preferences

International Preferences:
France

Additional Information

Year Founded: 1981
Capital Under Management: $129,600,000
Current Activity Level: Actively seeking new investments

IRIS CAPITAL MANAGEMENT (FKA: PART'COM MANAGEMENT S.A.)

62 rue Pierre Charon
Paris, France 75008
Phone: 33-1-4562-7373
Fax: 33-1-4562-7370
E-mail: general@iriscapital.com
Website: www.iriscapital.com

Type of Firm

Bank Affiliated

Association Membership

French Venture Capital Association (AFIC)
European Private Equity and Venture Capital Assoc.

Project Preferences

Type of Financing Preferred:
Early Stage
Expansion
Balanced
Startup

Size of Investments Considered:
Min Size of Investment Considered (000s): $1,167
Max Size of Investment Considered (000s): $23,348

Geographical Preferences

United States Preferences:
All U.S.

International Preferences:
Europe
France

Industry Focus

(% based on actual investment)

Communications and Media	36.2%
Internet Specific	24.8%
Computer Software and Services	14.7%
Consumer Related	11.2%
Semiconductors/Other Elect.	5.1%
Computer Hardware	3.8%
Other Products	3.7%
Medical/Health	0.4%

Additional Information

Year Founded: 1986
Capital Under Management: $508,100,000
Current Activity Level: Actively seeking new investments

IRITECH SPA

Piazza Monte Grappa 4
Rome, Italy 00195
Phone: 39-632-473331
Fax: 39-632-657174

Type of Firm

Corporate PE/Venture

Association Membership

Italian Venture Capital Association (AIFI)
European Private Equity and Venture Capital Assoc.

Project Preferences

Type of Financing Preferred:
Early Stage
Seed
Startup

Geographical Preferences

United States Preferences:
All U.S.

International Preferences:
Europe

Industry Preferences

In Communications prefer:
Communications and Media

In Semiconductor/Electr prefer:
Electronics

In Industrial/Energy prefer:
Energy
Alternative Energy

Additional Information

Year Founded: 1987
Capital Under Management: $14,000,000
Current Activity Level: Actively seeking new investments

IRON CAPITAL PARTNERS

455 Market Street
Suite 550
San Francisco, CA USA 94105
Phone: 415-986-0422
Fax: 415-986-4875
E-mail: info@ironcapitalpartners.com
Website: www.ironcapitalpartners.com

Management and Staff

Brian Dennen, Chief Operating Officer
Donald Basile, Managing Director
Jason Blum, Managing Director

Type of Firm

Private Equity Firm

Project Preferences

Type of Financing Preferred:
Early Stage
Balanced

Industry Preferences

In Communications prefer:
Communications and Media
Wireless Communications

In Computer Software prefer:
Software

In Industrial/Energy prefer:
Environmental Related

Additional Information

Year Founded: 2008
Current Activity Level: Actively seeking new investments

IRON GATE CAPITAL

1400 16th Street
Suite 220
Denver, CO USA 80202
Phone: 303-506-4562
Fax: 866-599-0961
E-mail: info@irongatecapital.com
Website: www.irongatecapital.com

Type of Firm

Private Equity Firm

Project Preferences

Type of Financing Preferred:
Leveraged Buyout
Early Stage
Mezzanine
Balanced
Management Buyouts

Size of Investments Considered:
Min Size of Investment Considered (000s): $750
Max Size of Investment Considered (000s): $10,000

Additional Information

Year Founded: 2005
Capital Under Management: $1,000,000
Current Activity Level: Actively seeking new investments

IRONBRIDGE CAPITAL PTY., LTD.

88 Philip Street
Level 39 Aurora Place
Sydney, Australia 2000
Phone: 612-9250-8700
Fax: 612-9250-8777
E-mail: contact@ironbridge.com.au
Website: www.ironbridge.com.au

Other Offices

188 Quay Street
Level 27 PwC Tower
Auckland, New Zealand
Phone: 649-363-2997
Fax: 649-363-2727

Management and Staff

Greg Ruddock, Managing Partner
Julian Knights, Managing Partner
Neil Broekhuizen, Managing Partner
Paul Evans, Managing Partner
Stuart Mitchell, Chief Financial Officer

Type of Firm

Private Equity Firm

Association Membership

Australian Venture Capital Association (AVCAL)

Project Preferences

Role in Financing:
Will function either as deal originator or investor in deals created by others

Type of Financing Preferred:
Leveraged Buyout
Expansion
Generalist PE
Management Buyouts

Size of Investments Considered:
Min Size of Investment Considered (000s): $46,785
Max Size of Investment Considered (000s): $187,140

Geographical Preferences

International Preferences:
Australia
New Zealand

Industry Preferences

In Communications prefer:
Communications and Media
Radio & TV Broadcasting
Media and Entertainment

In Medical/Health prefer:
Health Services
Pharmaceuticals

In Consumer Related prefer:
Entertainment and Leisure
Retail
Consumer Products

In Financial Services prefer:
Insurance
Financial Services

In Business Serv. prefer:
Services
Distribution

Additional Information

Name of Most Recent Fund: Ironbridge Fund II
Most Recent Fund Was Raised: 11/01/2006
Year Founded: 2003
Capital Under Management: $1,273,800,000
Current Activity Level: Actively seeking new investments
Method of Compensation: Return on invest. most important, but chg. closing fees, service fees, etc.

IRONBRIDGE EQUITY PARTNERS

390 Bay Street
Suite 1200
Toronto, Canada M5H 2Y2
Phone: 416-863-0101
Fax: 416-863-9418
Website: www.ironbridgeequity.com

Management and Staff

Alan Sellery, Partner
James Johnson, Managing Partner
Peter Dowse, Partner

Type of Firm

Private Equity Firm

Project Preferences

Type of Financing Preferred:
Leveraged Buyout
Expansion
Management Buyouts
Recapitalizations

Geographical Preferences

Canadian Preferences:
All Canada

Additional Information

Year Founded: 2006
Capital Under Management: $51,600,000
Current Activity Level: Actively seeking new investments

IRONSIDE CAPITAL GROUP (FKA:IRONSIDE VENTURES LLC)

161 Worcester Road
Suite 602
Framingham, MA USA 01701
Phone: 781-622-5800
Fax: 781-622-5801
Website: www.ironsidecapital.com

Management and Staff

Myles Gilbert, General Partner
Steve Kurylo, Chief Financial Officer
Steven Brackett, General Partner
William Sheehan, General Partner

Type of Firm

Insurance Firm Affiliate

Association Membership

National Venture Capital Association - USA (NVCA)

Project Preferences

Role in Financing:
Prefer role as deal originator but will also invest in deals created by others

Type of Financing Preferred:
Balanced

Size of Investments Considered:
Min Size of Investment Considered (000s): $500
Max Size of Investment Considered (000s): $10,000

Geographical Preferences

Canadian Preferences:
Quebec
Ontario

Industry Preferences

In Communications prefer:
Telecommunications
Data Communications

In Computer Software prefer:
Computer Services
Software
Systems Software
Applications Software

In Internet Specific prefer:
Internet

In Semiconductor/Electr prefer:
Semiconductor
Controllers and Sensors

Additional Information

Year Founded: 1998
Capital Under Management: $175,000,000
Current Activity Level: Actively seeking new investments
Method of Compensation: Return on investment is of primary concern, do not charge fees

IRONWOOD CAPITAL (AKA: IRONWOOD CAPITAL ADVISORS LLC)

55 Nod Road
Avon, CT USA 06001
Phone: 860-409-2100
Fax: 860-409-2120
E-mail: info@ironwoodcap.com
Website: www.ironwoodcap.com

Other Offices

One Beacon Street
34th Floor
Boston, MA USA 02108
Phone: 617-742-7600
Fax: 617-742-7610

Management and Staff

Carolyn Galiette, Senior Managing Director
Christopher Gabrieli, Managing Director
Dickson Suit, Managing Director
James Barra, Managing Director
M. Joshua Tolkoff, Managing Director
Marc Reich, President
Roger Roche, Senior Managing Director
Sanford Cloud, Principal
Susan Sweeney, Senior Managing Director
Victor Budnick, Managing Director

Type of Firm

Investment Management Firm

Project Preferences

Type of Financing Preferred:
Expansion
Mezzanine
Balanced
Management Buyouts
Acquisition
Recapitalizations

Size of Investments Considered:
Min Size of Investment Considered (000s): $2,000
Max Size of Investment Considered (000s): $11,000

Geographical Preferences

United States Preferences:
Northeast
All U.S.

Industry Preferences

In Medical/Health prefer:
Health Services

In Consumer Related prefer:
Consumer Products
Education Related

In Business Serv. prefer:
Services
Distribution

In Manufact. prefer:
Manufacturing

In Other prefer:
Women/Minority-Owned Bus.

Additional Information

Year Founded: 2001
Capital Under Management: $300,000,000
Current Activity Level: Actively seeking new investments

IRONWOOD PARTNERS LLC

420 Lexington Avenue
Suite 2650
New York, NY USA 10170
Phone: 212-682-7100
Website: www.ironwood-partners.com

Management and Staff

John Cosentino, Founding Partner
Michael Jackson, Founding Partner
Paul Balser, Founding Partner

Type of Firm

Private Equity Firm

Project Preferences

Type of Financing Preferred:
Leveraged Buyout
Recapitalizations

Industry Preferences

In Manufact. prefer:
Manufacturing

Additional Information

Year Founded: 2003
Capital Under Management: $20,000,000
Current Activity Level: Actively seeking new investments

IRPAC (INSTITUT REGIONAL DE PARTICIPATION ARDENNE-CHAMPAGNE)

2 Rue Carnot
Reims, France 51100
Phone: 33-3-2640-0326
Fax: 33-3-2688-3750
E-mail: irpac@wanadoo.fr

Type of Firm

Private Equity Firm

Project Preferences

Type of Financing Preferred:
Leveraged Buyout
Expansion

Geographical Preferences

International Preferences:
France

Additional Information

Year Founded: 1984
Current Activity Level: Actively seeking new investments

IRVING PLACE CAPITAL (FKA: BEAR STEARNS MERCHANT BANKING)

277 Park Avenue
39th Floor
New York, NY USA 10172
Phone: 212-272-3287
Fax: 212-272-7425
E-mail: mdoppelt@bear.com
Website: www.bsmb.com

Other Offices

Citicorp Center
One Sansome Street
San Francisco, CA USA 94104
Fax: 212-881-9653

Management and Staff

David King, Senior Managing Director
Doug Korn, Senior Managing Director
Elizabeth Kelly, Managing Director
Gwyneth Ketterer, Senior Managing Director
John Howard, Senior Managing Director
Joshua Neuman, Vice President
Michael Doppelt, Managing Director
Peter Cureton, Vice President
Philip Carpenter, Managing Director
Richard Perkal, Senior Managing Director
Robert Juneja, Managing Director
Theodore Young, Managing Director

Type of Firm

Bank Affiliated

Project Preferences

Type of Financing Preferred:
Fund of Funds
Leveraged Buyout
Management Buyouts
Acquisition
Special Situation
Recapitalizations

Size of Investments Considered:
Min Size of Investment Considered (000s): $100,000
Max Size of Investment Considered (000s): $250,000

Geographical Preferences

International Preferences:
United Kingdom
Western Europe

Industry Focus

(% based on actual investment)	
Consumer Related	48.2%
Industrial/Energy	16.4%
Other Products	15.3%
Internet Specific	12.4%
Semiconductors/Other Elect.	3.6%
Computer Software and Services	2.9%
Medical/Health	0.7%
Communications and Media	0.3%
Biotechnology	0.1%

Additional Information

Name of Most Recent Fund: Bear Stearns Merchant Banking Partners III, LP
Most Recent Fund Was Raised: 02/28/2006
Year Founded: 1997
Capital Under Management: $1,700,000,000
Current Activity Level: Actively seeking new investments

IRWIN VENTURES LLC (FKA: IRWIN VENTURES INCORPORATED)

500 Washington Street-Box 929
Columbus, IN USA 47202
Phone: 812-376-1909
Fax: 812-376-1709
E-mail: info@irwinfinancial.com
Website: www.irwinventures.com

Management and Staff

Thomas Washburn, President
William Miller, Chairman & CEO

Type of Firm

Bank Affiliated

Association Membership

Natl Assoc of Small Bus. Inv. Co (NASBIC)

Project Preferences

Role in Financing:
Will function either as deal originator or investor in deals created by others

Type of Financing Preferred:
Early Stage
Start-up Financing
Seed
First Stage Financing
Joint Ventures

Geographical Preferences

United States Preferences:
Mid Atlantic
Northwest
Northern California
Northeast
West Coast

Industry Preferences

In Communications prefer:
Data Communications

In Computer Other prefer:
Computer Related

In Consumer Related prefer:
Consumer

In Financial Services prefer:
Financial Services
Insurance
Real Estate

In Business Serv. prefer:
Services

Additional Information

Year Founded: 1999
Capital Under Management: $20,000,000
Current Activity Level: Actively seeking new investments
Method of Compensation: Return on investment is of primary concern, do not charge fees

---

IS PRIVATE EQUITY (FKA: IS VENTURE CAPITAL INVESTMENT TRUST)

Is Kuleleri, Kule 2, Kat: 8
Levent
Istanbul, Turkey 34330
Phone: 90-212-325-1744
Fax: 90-212-270-5808
E-mail: info@isgirisim.com.tr
Website: www.isgirisim.com.tr

Management and Staff

A. Murat Ozgen, Chief Executive Officer
Burak Bayhan, Principal
Burcu Kalender, Principal
Cenk Coskunturk, Principal
Yesim Uysal, Principal

Type of Firm

Bank Affiliated

Association Membership

European Private Equity and Venture Capital Assoc.

Project Preferences

Type of Financing Preferred:
Early Stage
Expansion
Later Stage

Geographical Preferences

International Preferences:
Turkey
Europe

Industry Preferences

In Communications prefer:
Telecommunications

In Medical/Health prefer:
Medical/Health

In Consumer Related prefer:
Consumer
Retail
Food/Beverage
Education Related

In Industrial/Energy prefer:
Energy
Materials

In Business Serv. prefer:
Services
Media

Additional Information
Year Founded: 2001
Capital Under Management: $76,000,000
Current Activity Level: Actively seeking new investments

ISABELLA CAPITAL LLC
1995 Madison Road
Cincinnati, OH USA 45208
Phone: 513-721-7110
Fax: 513-871-7150
E-mail: info@fundisabella.com
Website: www.fundisabella.com

Management and Staff
Margaret H. Wyant, Managing Director
Susan Schieman, Chief Financial Officer

Type of Firm
Private Equity Firm

Project Preferences

Role in Financing:
Will function either as deal originator or investor in deals created by others

Type of Financing Preferred:
Early Stage
Expansion

Size of Investments Considered:
Min Size of Investment Considered (000s): $100
Max Size of Investment Considered (000s): $1,000

Geographical Preferences

United States Preferences:
Midwest

Industry Preferences

In Computer Software prefer:
Software

In Biotechnology prefer:
Human Biotechnology
Biotech Related Research

In Other prefer:
Women/Minority-Owned Bus.

Additional Information
Name of Most Recent Fund: Fund Isabella, L.P.
Most Recent Fund Was Raised: 10/01/1999
Year Founded: 1999
Capital Under Management: $10,000,000
Current Activity Level: Actively seeking new investments
Method of Compensation: Return on investment is of primary concern, do not charge fees

---

ISHERPA CAPITAL
6400 S. Fiddler's Green Circle
Suite 650
Greenwood Village, CO USA 80111
Phone: 303-645-0500
Fax: 303-645-0501
E-mail: info@isherpa.net
Website: www.isherpa.com

Management and Staff
Deepu John, Principal
Nim Patel, Principal
Peter Mannetti, Managing Partner

Type of Firm
Private Equity Firm

Project Preferences

Type of Financing Preferred:
Seed

Geographical Preferences

United States Preferences:
All U.S.

International Preferences:
All International

Industry Preferences

In Communications prefer:
Communications and Media
Telecommunications
Wireless Communications

Additional Information
Year Founded: 2000
Capital Under Management: $31,000,000
Current Activity Level: Actively seeking new investments

ISIS EQUITY PARTNERS PLC (FKA: ISIS CAPITAL PLC)
100 Wood Street
2nd Floor
London, United Kingdom EC2V 7AN
Phone: 44-20-7506-5600
Fax: 44-20-7726-8857
Website: www.isisep.com

Other Offices
Bank House
8 Cherry Street
Birmingham, United Kingdom B2 5AN
Phone: 44-121-253-1600
Fax: 44-121-253-1616

First Floor, Colwyn Chambers
19 York Street
Manchester, United Kingdom M2 3BA
Phone: 44-161-912-6500
Fax: 44-161-912-6501

Infirmary Street
3rd Floor, 9 Bond Court
Leeds, United Kingdom LS1 2JZ
Phone: 44-113-291-3200
Fax: 44-113-291-3290

Management and Staff
Sheenagh Egan, Chief Operating Officer
Wol Kolade, Managing Director

Type of Firm
Private Equity Firm

Association Membership
European Private Equity and Venture Capital Assoc.

Project Preferences

Role in Financing:
Prefer role as deal originator but will also invest in deals created by others

Type of Financing Preferred:
Leveraged Buyout
Early Stage
Expansion
Balanced
Public Companies
Acquisition

Size of Investments Considered:
Min Size of Investment Considered (000s): $2,985
Max Size of Investment Considered (000s): $22,391

Geographical Preferences

International Preferences:
United Kingdom
Netherlands
Europe
Germany

Industry Focus
(% based on actual investment)

Other Products	32.7%
Medical/Health	21.3%
Consumer Related	18.7%
Computer Software and Services	8.7%
Computer Hardware	7.0%
Biotechnology	4.7%
Internet Specific	4.3%
Communications and Media	2.8%

Additional Information

Name of Most Recent Fund: Isis Equity Partners III
Most Recent Fund Was Raised: 12/31/2002
Year Founded: 1983
Capital Under Management: $1,046,700,000
Current Activity Level: Actively seeking new investments

ISIS INNOVATION LTD

Ewert House, Ewert Place
Summertown
Oxford, United Kingdom OX2 7SG
Phone: 44-1865-280-830
Fax: 44-1865-280-831
E-mail: innovation@isis.ox.ac.uk
Website: www.isis-innovation.com

Type of Firm

University Program

Association Membership

British Venture Capital Association (BVCA)

Project Preferences

Type of Financing Preferred:

Seed

Geographical Preferences

International Preferences:

United Kingdom

Additional Information

Year Founded: 1988
Capital Under Management: $2,900,000
Current Activity Level: Actively seeking new investments

ISLAMIC DEVELOPMENT BANK, THE

P.O. Box 5925
Jeddah, Saudi Arabia 21432
Phone: 966-2-636-1400
Fax: 966-2-636-6871
E-mail: idbarchives@isdb.org.sa
Website: www.isdb.org

Other Offices

P.O. Box 11545
Muharraq, Bahrain
Phone: 973-536-100
Fax: 973-536-206

Management and Staff

Ahmad Mohamed Ali, President

Type of Firm

Bank Affiliated

Project Preferences

Type of Financing Preferred:

Balanced

Geographical Preferences

International Preferences:

Indonesia
Brunei
Middle East
Malaysia
All International

Industry Preferences

In Communications prefer:

Telecommunications

In Industrial/Energy prefer:

Energy
Oil and Gas Exploration
Coal Related
Energy Conservation Relat
Environmental Related

In Transportation prefer:

Transportation

In Financial Services prefer:

Financial Services

Additional Information

Year Founded: 1975
Current Activity Level: Actively seeking new investments

ISLENSK VEROBREFASTOFAN HF

Suourlandsbraut 20
Reykjavik, Iceland 108
Phone: 354-570-1200
Fax: 35-4570-1209
E-mail: vbs@vbs.is
Website: www.vbs.is

Type of Firm

Private Equity Firm

Project Preferences

Type of Financing Preferred:

Expansion

Geographical Preferences

International Preferences:

Europe

Additional Information

Year Founded: 2004
Current Activity Level: Actively seeking new investments

ISLINGTON CAPITAL PARTNERS

2345 Washington Street
Suite 101
Newton Lower Falls, MA USA 02462
Phone: 617-558-3200
Fax: 617-558-3244
Website: www.islingtoncapital.com

Management and Staff

John Cullinane, Co-Founder
Paul Spinale, Co-Founder

Type of Firm

Private Equity Firm

Project Preferences

Role in Financing:

Prefer role as deal originator

Type of Financing Preferred:

Management Buyouts
Acquisition
Recapitalizations

Size of Investments Considered:

Min Size of Investment Considered (000s): $1,000
Max Size of Investment Considered (000s): $7,000

Geographical Preferences

United States Preferences:

Midwest
Mid Atlantic
Southeast
Northeast
East Coast

Industry Preferences

In Business Serv. prefer:

Services

In Manufact. prefer:

Manufacturing

Additional Information

Year Founded: 2005
Capital Under Management: $20,000,000
Current Activity Level: Actively seeking new investments

ISPRINGCAPITAL SDN BHD (FKA: PRODUCTIVE IDEAS SDN BHD)

P-2-6 Plaza Damas
No. 60 Jalan Sri Hartamas 1
Kuala Lumpur, Malaysia 50480
Phone: 603-6203-3906
Fax: 603-6203-2915
Website: www.ispringcapital.com

Management and Staff

David Fong, Chief Executive Officer

Type of Firm

Private Equity Firm

Project Preferences

Type of Financing Preferred:
Balanced

Geographical Preferences

International Preferences:
Asia

Additional Information

Year Founded: 2000
Current Activity Level: Actively seeking new investments

ISQ, SOCIEDADE CAPITAL DE RISCO, SA

Av. Prof. Dr. Cavaco Silva n33
Taguspark
Porto Salvo, Portugal 2780-994
Phone: 351-21-422-8100
Fax: 351-21-422-8120
E-mail: info@isq.pt
Website: www.isq.pt

Type of Firm

Private Equity Firm

Project Preferences

Type of Financing Preferred:
Early Stage

Geographical Preferences

International Preferences:
Portugal

Industry Preferences

In Communications prefer:
Communications and Media

In Industrial/Energy prefer:
Energy

Additional Information

Name of Most Recent Fund: ISQ, Sociedade Capital de Risco, SA
Most Recent Fund Was Raised: 05/31/2005
Year Founded: 1965
Capital Under Management: $8,400,000
Current Activity Level: Actively seeking new investments

ISRAEL CLEANTECH VENTURES

Hakfar Hayarok
Ramat Hasharon, Israel 47800
Phone: 972-54-622-4663
E-mail: info@israelcleantech.com
Website: www.israelcleantech.com

Management and Staff

Arnon Goldfarb, Venture Partner
Eytan Levy, Venture Partner
Glen Schwaber, General Partner
Israel Kroizer, Venture Partner
Jack Levy, General Partner
Meir Ukeles, General Partner
Yigal Stav, Venture Partner

Type of Firm

Private Equity Firm

Project Preferences

Type of Financing Preferred:
Startup

Geographical Preferences

International Preferences:
Israel

Industry Preferences

In Industrial/Energy prefer:
Energy
Energy Conservation Relat
Environmental Related

In Agr/Forestr/Fish prefer:
Agriculture related

Additional Information

Year Founded: 2006
Capital Under Management: $75,000,000
Current Activity Level: Actively seeking new investments

ISRAEL HEALTHCARE VENTURES

32 Habarzel St.
Ramat Hachayal
Tel Aviv, Israel 69710
Phone: 972-3-648-8566
Fax: 972-3-648-8474
E-mail: ihcv@ihcv.co.il
Website: www.ihcv.co.il

Management and Staff

Hadar Ron, Managing Director

Type of Firm

Private Equity Firm

Project Preferences

Type of Financing Preferred:
Balanced

Geographical Preferences

International Preferences:
Europe
Israel

Industry Preferences

In Biotechnology prefer:
Biotechnology

In Medical/Health prefer:
Medical/Health

Additional Information

Year Founded: 2001
Current Activity Level: Actively seeking new investments

ISRAEL SEED PARTNERS

Jerusalem Technology Park
P O Box 48183
Jerusalem, Israel 91481
Phone: 972-2-565-5111
Fax: 972-2-565-5122
E-mail: info@israelseed.com
Website: www.israelseed.com

Management and Staff

Daphna Pearl, Chief Financial Officer
Jonathan Medved, General Partner
Michael Chinn, General Partner
Michael Berman, Venture Partner
Michael Eisenberg, General Partner

Type of Firm

Private Equity Firm

Project Preferences

Type of Financing Preferred:
Early Stage
Seed

Size of Investments Considered:
Min Size of Investment Considered (000s): $2,500
Max Size of Investment Considered: No Limit

Geographical Preferences

International Preferences:
All International

Industry Focus

(% based on actual investment)

Computer Software and Services	35.2%
Internet Specific	14.5%
Semiconductors/Other Elect.	13.2%
Medical/Health	12.8%
Communications and Media	12.1%
Computer Hardware	10.8%
Biotechnology	1.4%

Additional Information

Year Founded: 1995
Capital Under Management: $300,000,000
Current Activity Level: Actively seeking new investments

ISTITHMAR WORLD CAPITAL

Emirates Towers, Floor 4
Sheikh Zayed Road
Dubai, Utd. Arab Em.
Phone: 971-4-390-2100
Fax: 971-4-390-3818
E-mail: info@istithmarworld.com
Website: www.istithmarworld.com

Other Offices

230 Park Avenue
New York, NY USA 10169
Phone: 212-661-8137

Room 425
12 Zhong Shan Dong Yi Road
Shanghai, China 200002
Phone: 86-21-6323-2599
Fax: 86-21-6323-2112

Management and Staff

David Jackson, Chief Executive Officer
Peter Jodlowski, Chief Financial Officer
Sandesh Pandhare, Vice President

Type of Firm

Investment Management Firm

Project Preferences

Type of Financing Preferred:
Balanced

Geographical Preferences

International Preferences:
All International

Industry Preferences

In Consumer Related prefer:
Consumer

In Industrial/Energy prefer:
Industrial Products

In Financial Services prefer:
Financial Services
Real Estate

Additional Information

Year Founded: 2003
Current Activity Level: Actively seeking new investments

ISTITUTO ATESINO SPA

Via Grazioli, 25
Trento, Italy 38100
Phone: 39-461-98-4798
Fax: 39-461-98-4006
E-mail: isa@isa.tn.it
Website: www.isa.tn.it

Type of Firm

Private Equity Firm

Association Membership

Italian Venture Capital Association (AIFI)

Project Preferences

Type of Financing Preferred:
Balanced

Geographical Preferences

International Preferences:
Italy
Europe

Additional Information

Year Founded: 2004
Current Activity Level: Actively seeking new investments

ISU VENTURE CAPITAL CO., LTD. (FKA: PETA CAPITAL)

6F, ISU Building, Banpo-Dong
112-4 Seocho-Gu
Seoul, South Korea 137-040
Phone: 822-3482-2010
Fax: 822-3482-2015
Website: www.isuvc.com

Management and Staff

Yoon Chae, President

Type of Firm

Private Equity Firm

Project Preferences

Type of Financing Preferred:
Balanced

Industry Preferences

In Communications prefer:
Communications and Media
Media and Entertainment
Entertainment

Additional Information

Year Founded: 2000
Capital Under Management: $64,800,000
Current Activity Level: Actively seeking new investments

IT FORNEBU INKUBATOR AS

Martin Linges vei 15-25
Snaroya, Norway 1367
Phone: 47-67-82-7090
Fax: 47-67-827-051
E-mail: firmapost@itfi.no
Website: www.itfornebu.no

Management and Staff

Jon-Atle Sagabraaten, Vice President

Type of Firm

Incubator/Development Program

Association Membership

Norwegian Venture Capital Association

Project Preferences

Type of Financing Preferred:
Seed

Geographical Preferences

International Preferences:
Norway

Industry Preferences

In Communications prefer:
Commercial Communications

In Business Serv. prefer:
Media

Additional Information

Year Founded: 2001
Current Activity Level: Actively seeking new investments

IT MATRIX VENTURES

1071 Post Road East
Westport, CT USA 06880
Phone: 203-226-7052
Fax: 203-226-5741

Management and Staff

Ronald Klammer, Managing Director

Type of Firm

Bank Affiliated

Project Preferences

Role in Financing:
Prefer role as deal originator

Type of Financing Preferred:
Leveraged Buyout
Control-block Purchases
Expansion
Mezzanine
Turnaround
Public Companies

Later Stage
Management Buyouts
Acquisition
Private Placement
Special Situation
Recapitalizations

Size of Investments Considered:
Min Size of Investment Considered (000s): $1,000
Max Size of Investment Considered (000s): $10,000

Geographical Preferences

United States Preferences:
All U.S.

Industry Preferences

In Communications prefer:
Commercial Communications
Telecommunications
Wireless Communications
Data Communications
Satellite Microwave Comm.
Other Communication Prod.

In Internet Specific prefer:
E-Commerce Technology

In Semiconductor/Electr prefer:
Electronic Components
Semiconductor
Micro-Processing
Controllers and Sensors
Sensors
Circuit Boards
Component Testing Equipmt
Laser Related
Fiber Optics
Analytic/Scientific
Optoelectronics

In Biotechnology prefer:
Biosensors

In Medical/Health prefer:
Diagnostic Test Products

In Industrial/Energy prefer:
Factory Automation
Robotics

Additional Information
Year Founded: 2004
Capital Under Management: $50,000,000
Current Activity Level: Actively seeking new investments
Method of Compensation: Professional fee required whether or not deal closes

---

ITEKSA VENTURE AB
Badhusgatan 5
Linkoping, Sweden 581 89
Phone: 46-13-280-490
Fax: 46-13-280-486
E-mail: info@iteksa.se
Website: www.iteksa.se

Management and Staff
Carl-Henrik Koit, Managing Director
Katarina Segerborg, Managing Director

Type of Firm
Bank Affiliated

Association Membership
Swedish Venture Capital Association (SVCA)

Project Preferences

Type of Financing Preferred:
Early Stage
Seed
Startup

Geographical Preferences

International Preferences:
Sweden
Europe
Scandanavia/Nordic Region

Industry Preferences

In Computer Software prefer:
Software

In Semiconductor/Electr prefer:
Electronics
Electronic Components

In Medical/Health prefer:
Medical Products

Additional Information
Year Founded: 2002
Capital Under Management: $13,200,000
Current Activity Level: Actively seeking new investments

ITHMAR CAPITAL
Belhoul Group Building
Entrance 3 - 3rd floor
Dubai, Utd. Arab Em.
Phone: 971-4-282-5555
Fax: 971-4-283-1155
E-mail: info@ithmar.com
Website: www.ithmar.com

Management and Staff
Khaled Jaouni, Partner
Ranjit Bhonsle, Partner
Samiya Ali, Managing Partner
Shahram Hashemi, Vice President

Type of Firm
Private Equity Firm

Project Preferences

Type of Financing Preferred:
Leveraged Buyout
Generalist PE
Expansion

Geographical Preferences

International Preferences:
Bahrain
Oman
Qatar
Utd. Arab Em.
Middle East
Saudi Arabia
Kuwait

Industry Preferences

In Communications prefer:
Communications and Media
Media and Entertainment

In Medical/Health prefer:
Health Services

In Consumer Related prefer:
Consumer
Franchises(NEC)

In Industrial/Energy prefer:
Oil and Gas Exploration

In Financial Services prefer:
Financial Services

In Business Serv. prefer:
Distribution
Media

Additional Information
Year Founded: 2004
Capital Under Management: $320,000,000
Current Activity Level: Actively seeking new investments

ITI SCOTLAND LTD (AKA: SCOTTISH DEVELOPMENT INTERNATIONAL)
180 St Vincent Street
Glasgow, United Kingdom G2 5SG
Phone: 44-141-204-8000
Fax: 44-141-229-1448
E-mail: email@itiscotland.com
Website: www.itiscotland.com

Other Offices
17 Luna Place
Innovation House, Dundee Technology Park
Dundee, United Kingdom
Phone: 44-1382-56-8060
Fax: 44-1382-56-8061

Balgownie Road
Daividson House, Aberdeen Science Park
Aberdeen, United Kingdom AB228GT
Phone: 44-1224- 70-1200
Fax: 44-1224-70-1211

Type of Firm
Government Affiliated Program

Project Preferences

Type of Financing Preferred:
Research and Development

Geographical Preferences

International Preferences:
United Kingdom

Industry Preferences

In Communications prefer:
Communications and Media

In Industrial/Energy prefer:
Energy

Additional Information

Name of Most Recent Fund: ITI Techmedia
Most Recent Fund Was Raised: 09/30/2003
Year Founded: 2003
Capital Under Management: $717,800,000
Current Activity Level: Actively seeking new investments

ITM VENTURES, INC.

39/F One Exchange Square
Central, Hong Kong
Phone: 852-2187-3200
Fax: 852-2187-2489
Website: www.trans-tele.com

Type of Firm
Corporate PE/Venture

Association Membership
Hong Kong Venture Capital Association (HKVCA)

Project Preferences

Type of Financing Preferred:
Expansion
Early Stage
Balanced
Seed

Geographical Preferences

United States Preferences:
All U.S.

International Preferences:
Taiwan
Hong Kong
China
Asia
Singapore
Australia

Industry Preferences

In Communications prefer:
Telecommunications
Wireless Communications

In Internet Specific prefer:
Internet

In Semiconductor/Electr prefer:
Electronics

In Consumer Related prefer:
Retail

Additional Information

Year Founded: 2003
Current Activity Level: Actively seeking new investments

ITOCHU CORPORATION

5-1, Kita-Aoyama 2-chome
Minato-ku
Tokyo, Japan 107-8077
Phone: 813-3497-2121
Fax: 813-3497-7296
Website: www.itochu.co.jp

Other Offices

1-3, Kyutaromachi 4-chome
Chuo-ku
Osaka, Japan 541-8577
Phone: 816-6241-2121

Management and Staff

Akira Yokota, Chief Operating Officer
Eizo Kobayashi, President, CEO, Chairman
Hiroo Inoue, President
Kouhei Watanabe, Chief Financial Officer
Takeyoshi Ide, Chief Executive Officer
Toshihito Tamba, Chief Operating Officer
Yoshihisa Aoki, Chief Operating Officer

Type of Firm
Corporate PE/Venture

Project Preferences

Type of Financing Preferred:
Balanced

Geographical Preferences

International Preferences:
Asia

Additional Information

Year Founded: 1858
Current Activity Level: Actively seeking new investments

ITOCHU TECHNOLOGY, INC.

3945 Freedom Circle
Suite 350
Santa Clara, CA USA 95054
Phone: 408-727-8810
Fax: 408-727-4619
E-mail: info@itochu.net
Website: www.itochu.net

Other Offices

257 Park Avenue South
Eighth Floor
New York, NY USA 10010
Phone: 212-308-7800
Fax: 212-308-7886

Management and Staff

Takashi Kameda, Vice President
Yo Hoshino, Vice President

Type of Firm
Corporate PE/Venture

Project Preferences

Role in Financing:
Prefer role as deal originator

Type of Financing Preferred:
Second Stage Financing
Early Stage
Expansion
Later Stage

Size of Investments Considered:
Min Size of Investment Considered (000s): $500
Max Size of Investment Considered (000s): $1,000

Industry Focus

(% based on actual investment)	
Computer Software and Services	42.8%
Internet Specific	31.4%
Communications and Media	11.7%
Computer Hardware	6.7%
Semiconductors/Other Elect.	5.5%
Biotechnology	1.9%

Additional Information

Year Founded: 1984
Capital Under Management: $100,000,000
Current Activity Level: Actively seeking new investments
Method of Compensation: Return on investment is of primary concern, do not charge fees

---

ITP INVEST AB (AKA: I TEKNISK PARTNER INVEST AB)

Jakobsbergsgatan 9
Stockholm, Sweden 111 47
Phone: 46-8-611-5320
Fax: 46-8-611-7715
Website: www.itp-invest.se

Management and Staff

Maria Horelli-Rosenlew, Partner
Peter Lindell, Partner
Staffan Persson, Partner

Type of Firm
Private Equity Firm

Association Membership
Swedish Venture Capital Association (SVCA)

Project Preferences
Type of Financing Preferred:
Leveraged Buyout
Expansion
Seed
Startup

Size of Investments Considered:
Min Size of Investment Considered (000s): $9
Max Size of Investment Considered (000s): $1,274

Geographical Preferences
International Preferences:
Sweden
Scandanavia/Nordic Region

Additional Information
Year Founded: 1995
Capital Under Management: $125,100,000
Current Activity Level: Actively seeking new investments

ITP MANAGEMENT NV (AKA: IT-PARTNERS NV)
H. Henneaulaan 105
Zaventem, Belgium 1930
Phone: 32-2-725-1838
Fax: 32-2-721-4435
E-mail: info@it-partners.be
Website: www.it-partners.be

Type of Firm
Private Equity Firm

Project Preferences
Type of Financing Preferred:
Early Stage

Geographical Preferences
United States Preferences:
All U.S.

International Preferences:
Luxembourg
Netherlands
Europe
Belgium
Israel

Industry Preferences
In Communications prefer:
Communications and Media

Additional Information
Name of Most Recent Fund: IT Partners NV
Most Recent Fund Was Raised: 01/01/1999
Year Founded: 1997
Current Activity Level: Actively seeking new investments

ITP-MANAGEMENT N.V.
Excelsiorlaan 13
H. Henneaulaan 366
Zaventum, Belgium 1930
Phone: 32-2-725-1838
Fax: 32-2-721-4435
E-mail: info@it-partners.be
Website: www.it-partners.be

Management and Staff
Paul Verdurme, General Partner
Stefaan Nicolay, General Partner

Type of Firm
Private Equity Firm

Association Membership
European Private Equity and Venture Capital Assoc.
Indian Venture Capital Association (IVCA)

Project Preferences
Type of Financing Preferred:
Early Stage

Geographical Preferences
United States Preferences:
All U.S.

International Preferences:
Luxembourg
Netherlands
Europe
Belgium
Israel

Industry Preferences
In Communications prefer:
Communications and Media

Additional Information
Year Founded: 1997
Capital Under Management: $70,000,000
Current Activity Level: Actively seeking new investments

ITU VENTURES
1900 Avenue of the Stars
Suite 2701
Los Angeles, CA USA 90067
Phone: 310-777-5900
Fax: 310-777-5901
E-mail: info@itu.com
Website: www.itu.com

Other Offices
1660 17th Street
Suite 450
Denver, CO USA 80202
Phone: 303-777-7023

201 Third Street Northwest
Suite 1500
Albuquerque, NM USA 87102
Phone: 505-724-9576

Management and Staff
Adam Winnick, Venture Partner
Andrew Murray, Principal
Chad Brownstein, Managing Partner
Jonah Schnel, Managing Partner
Neel Master, Principal
Steve Schneider, Chief Financial Officer

Type of Firm
Private Equity Firm

Project Preferences
Role in Financing:
Will function either as deal originator or investor in deals created by others

Type of Financing Preferred:
Second Stage Financing
Early Stage
Research and Development
Start-up Financing
Seed
First Stage Financing
Startup

Size of Investments Considered:
Min Size of Investment Considered (000s): $100
Max Size of Investment Considered (000s): $6,500

Geographical Preferences
United States Preferences:
New Mexico
Rocky Mountain
West Coast
California
Colorado
All U.S.

Industry Preferences
In Communications prefer:
Communications and Media

In Internet Specific prefer:
Internet

In Computer Other prefer:
Computer Related

In Semiconductor/Electr prefer:
Electronics

In Industrial/Energy prefer:
Advanced Materials

Additional Information
Year Founded: 2000
Capital Under Management: $80,000,000
Current Activity Level: Actively seeking new investments

ITX INTERNATIONAL HOLDINGS, INC.

700 E.El Camino Real
Suite 200
Mountain View, CA USA 94040
Phone: 650-210-8691
Fax: 650-210-8698
E-mail: info@itxintl.com
Website: www.itxintl.com

Management and Staff

Naoki Yamamoto, Vice President

Type of Firm

Bank Affiliated

Project Preferences

Type of Financing Preferred:
Early Stage

Geographical Preferences

International Preferences:
All International

Additional Information

Year Founded: 2001
Capital Under Management: $30,000,000
Current Activity Level: Actively seeking new investments

IV HOLDINGS

Building 123, 2nd Floor Street
Zahran Street, 4th Circle
Amman, Jordan 11183
Phone: 962-6-593-9094
Fax: 962-6-593-9097
E-mail: info@iv-holdings.com
Website: www.iv-holdings.com

Management and Staff

Emile Cubeisy, Managing Director

Type of Firm

Private Equity Firm

Project Preferences

Role in Financing:
Prefer role as deal originator but will also invest in deals created by others

Type of Financing Preferred:
Early Stage

Size of Investments Considered:
Min Size of Investment Considered (000s): $250
Max Size of Investment Considered (000s): $2,000

Geographical Preferences

International Preferences:
Middle East
Asia

Industry Preferences

In Communications prefer:
Communications and Media
Telecommunications

In Computer Software prefer:
Computer Services

In Business Serv. prefer:
Services

Additional Information

Year Founded: 2008
Current Activity Level: Actively seeking new investments

IVS A/S (AKA: INTERNET VENTURES SCANDINAVIA A/S)

Boge Alle 5, 2
Horsholm, Denmark 2970
Phone: 45-7022-0228
Fax: 45-70220-227
E-mail: info@ivs.dk
Website: www.ivs.dk

Other Offices

6 Arosa Road
Richmond Bridge, East Twickenham
Middlesex, United Kingdom TW1 2TL
Phone: 44 181 408 2041

10420 Little Patuxent Parkway
Suite 301
Columbia, MD USA 21044-3636
Phone: 410 884 1700
Fax: 410 884 6171

Surenweg 6
Walchwil, Switzerland 6318
Phone: 41 417 581 422
Fax: 41 417 581 588

c/o InnovationLab
Finlandsgade 20
Arhus, Denmark 8200

Management and Staff

Benny Guld, Founder
Frank Ewald, Partner
Peter Aagaard, Founding Partner
Preben Mejer, Partner
Soren Fogtdal, Partner
Steen Louis Reinholdt, Founder
Sten Larsen, Chief Financial Officer
Thomas Weilby Knudsen, Chief Executive Officer

Type of Firm

Private Equity Firm

Association Membership

Danish Venture Capital Association (DVCA)
European Private Equity and Venture Capital Assoc.

Project Preferences

Type of Financing Preferred:
Early Stage
Startup

Size of Investments Considered:
Min Size of Investment Considered (000s): $267
Max Size of Investment Considered (000s): $4,457

Geographical Preferences

International Preferences:
Europe

Industry Preferences

In Internet Specific prefer:
Internet

Additional Information

Year Founded: 1999
Capital Under Management: $44,600,000
Current Activity Level: Actively seeking new investments

IVY CAPITAL PARTNERS

One Paragon Drive
Montvale, NJ USA 07645
Phone: 201-573-8400
Fax: 201-573-8403
Website: www.ivycapitalpartners.com

Management and Staff

Robert Pangia, Partner

Type of Firm

Private Equity Firm

Project Preferences

Type of Financing Preferred:
Later Stage

Industry Preferences

In Medical/Health prefer:
Medical/Health

Additional Information

Name of Most Recent Fund: Ivy Healthcare Capital II, L.P.
Most Recent Fund Was Raised: 02/12/2007
Year Founded: 2003
Capital Under Management: $30,000,000
Current Activity Level: Actively seeking new investments

IXCORE

52, avenue de l'Europe
Marly-le-Roi, France 78160
Phone: 33-130-08-8888
Fax: 33-130-08-8880
E-mail: contact@ixcore.com
Website: www.ixcore.com

Management and Staff
Christophe Bottega, Chief Financial Officer

Type of Firm
Private Equity Firm

Project Preferences

Type of Financing Preferred:
Balanced

Geographical Preferences

International Preferences:
Europe
France

Additional Information
Year Founded: 2001
Current Activity Level: Actively seeking new investments

IXEN PARTNERS (FKA: NATEXIS INDUSTRIE MANAGEMENT)

5-7, rue de Monttessuy
Paris, France 75340
Phone: 33-1-5819-2060
Fax: 33-1-5819-2070
E-mail: contact@ixen-partners.com
Website: www.ixen-partners.com

Management and Staff
Pierre Rispoli, Managing Director
Veronique Bernard, Chief Financial Officer
Yves Roucaud, Managing Director

Type of Firm
Private Equity Firm

Association Membership
French Venture Capital Association (AFIC)

Project Preferences

Type of Financing Preferred:
Leveraged Buyout
Mezzanine
Management Buyouts
Recapitalizations

Size of Investments Considered:
Min Size of Investment Considered (000s): $10,000
Max Size of Investment Considered (000s): $80,000

Geographical Preferences

International Preferences:
Europe
France

Industry Preferences

In Consumer Related prefer:
Consumer
Retail
Consumer Products
Other Restaurants

In Manufact. prefer:
Manufacturing

Additional Information
Year Founded: 1988
Capital Under Management: $631,500,000
Current Activity Level: Actively seeking new investments

IYOGIN CAPITAL CO., LTD.

5-12-3 Sanbancho
Matsuyama, Japan
Phone: 81-89-933-8804
Fax: 81-89-943-3443
Website:
www.iyobank.co.jp/profil/group/iyprgu07.htm

Management and Staff
Yuichi Shinoura, Chief Executive Officer

Type of Firm
Bank Affiliated

Association Membership
Japan Venture Capital Association

Project Preferences

Type of Financing Preferred:
Early Stage

Geographical Preferences

International Preferences:
Japan

Additional Information
Year Founded: 2007
Capital Under Management: $4,700,000
Current Activity Level: Actively seeking new investments

- J -

J BRIDGE CORPORATION

Sumitomo Fudosan Ryogoku Bldg.
2-10-6 Ryogoku,
Sumida-Ku, Tokyo, Japan 130-0026
Phone: 81-35-638-8560
Website: www.j-bridge.jp

Type of Firm
Bank Affiliated

Project Preferences

Type of Financing Preferred:
Leveraged Buyout
Acquisition

Geographical Preferences

International Preferences:
Japan

Additional Information
Year Founded: 1922
Current Activity Level: Actively seeking new investments

J&W SELIGMAN & COMPANY

100 Park Avenue
7th Floor
New York, NY USA 10017
Phone: 650-833-4550
Fax: 650-330-1018
Website: www.jwseligman.com

Management and Staff
Ajay Diwan, Managing Director
Sang Peruri, Managing Director
Vishal Saluja, Managing Director

Type of Firm
Private Equity Firm

Project Preferences

Role in Financing:
Prefer role in deals created by others

Type of Financing Preferred:
Later Stage

Size of Investments Considered:
Min Size of Investment Considered (000s): $500
Max Size of Investment Considered (000s): $24,900

Geographical Preferences

United States Preferences:
All U.S.

Industry Focus

(% based on actual investment)

Internet Specific	44.4%
Computer Software and Services	18.9%
Communications and Media	15.9%
Semiconductors/Other Elect.	6.0%
Computer Hardware	4.4%
Other Products	3.4%
Biotechnology	2.9%
Consumer Related	1.9%
Medical/Health	1.5%
Industrial/Energy	0.7%

Additional Information

Year Founded: 1989
Capital Under Management: $1,750,000,000
Current Activity Level: Actively seeking new investments
Method of Compensation: Return on investment is of primary concern, do not charge fees

---

J-STAR CO., LTD.

20F Toranomon Towers Office
4-1-28 Toranomon,Minato-ku
Tokyo, Japan 105-0001
Phone: 81-3-5776-1700
Fax: 81-3-5776-1705
Website: www.j-star.co.jp

Management and Staff

Emiko Iwata, Principal
Hideaki Sakurai, Partner
Kenichi Harada, Partner
Satoru Arakawa, Principal
Satoshi Tsuji, Principal
Tatsuya Yumoto, Partner

Type of Firm

Private Equity Firm

Project Preferences

Type of Financing Preferred:

Balanced

Additional Information

Year Founded: 2006
Capital Under Management: $42,300,000
Current Activity Level: Actively seeking new investments

J-WILL PARTNERS

15F Yurakucho Denki North Bldg
1-7-1 Yurakucho, Chiyoda-ku
Tokyo, Japan 103-0027
Phone: 81-3-6266-5810

Type of Firm

Private Equity Firm
Additional Information
Year Founded: 2003
Current Activity Level: Actively seeking new investments

J. HIRSCH & CO. S.A.R.L.

30, rue Marie Adelaide
Luxembourg, Luxembourg L-2128
Phone: 352-2638-4181
Fax: 352-2638-4183
E-mail: contact@j-hirsch.lu
Website: www.j-hirsch.com

Other Offices

Steinweg 3
Frankfurt, Germany D-60313
Phone: 49-69-2992-53612
Fax: 49-69-2929-53620

Via Brera, 3
Milan, Italy I-20121
Phone: 39-2-721-1741
Fax: 39-2-7211-74219

Management and Staff

Jean-Francois Aron, Managing Director
Mario De Benedetti, Managing Director
Stefano Cassina, Managing Director

Type of Firm

Private Equity Firm

Project Preferences

Type of Financing Preferred:

Leveraged Buyout
Management Buyouts
Acquisition
Recapitalizations

Geographical Preferences

International Preferences:

Italy
Europe

Additional Information

Year Founded: 1997
Capital Under Management: $588,600,000
Current Activity Level: Actively seeking new investments

J.C. FLOWERS & CO. LLC

717 Fifth Avenue
26th Floor
New York, NY USA 10022
Phone: 212-404-6800
Fax: 212-404-6899
Website: www.jcfco.com

Other Offices

10 Gresham Street
Fourth Floor
London, United Kingdom EC2V 7JD
Phone: 44-20-7562-2300
Fax: 44-20-7562-2319
Spitalerstrasse 32
Hamburg, Germany D-20095
Phone: 49-40-244-281-350
Fax: 49-40-244-281-399

Management and Staff

Sally Rocker, Principal

Type of Firm

Private Equity Firm

Project Preferences

Type of Financing Preferred:

Leveraged Buyout

Geographical Preferences

United States Preferences:

All U.S.

Canadian Preferences:

All Canada

International Preferences:

Europe
Mexico

Industry Preferences

In Financial Services prefer:

Financial Services

Additional Information

Name of Most Recent Fund: J.C. Flowers II, L.P.
Most Recent Fund Was Raised: 06/30/2006
Year Founded: 2001
Capital Under Management: $668,000,000
Current Activity Level: Actively seeking new investments

J.F. LEHMAN & COMPANY

450 Park Avenue
6th Floor
New York, NY USA 10022
Phone: 212-634-0100
Fax: 212-634-1155
E-mail: jflc@jflpartners.com
Website: www.jflpartners.com

Other Offices

2001 Jefferson Davis Highway
Suite 607
Arlington, VA USA 22202
Phone: 703-418-6095
Fax: 703-418-6099

4 Grosvenor Place
Third Floor
London, United Kingdom SW1X 7HJ
Phone: 44-207-201-5490
Fax: 44-207-201-5499

Management and Staff

Donald Glickman, Founding Partner
Eric Young, Vice President
Louis Mintz, Partner
Stephen Brooks, Partner
Victor Caruso, Principal

Type of Firm
Private Equity Firm

Project Preferences

Role in Financing:
Prefer role as deal originator but will also invest in deals created by others

Type of Financing Preferred:
Leveraged Buyout
Control-block Purchases
Expansion
Generalist PE
Management Buyouts
Acquisition

Geographical Preferences

United States Preferences:
All U.S.

Canadian Preferences:
All Canada

International Preferences:
United Kingdom
Germany
France

Industry Focus
(% based on actual investment)

Industrial/Energy	51.3%
Semiconductors/Other Elect.	45.9%
Other Products	2.8%

Additional Information
Name of Most Recent Fund: JFL Parallel Fund II, L.P.
Most Recent Fund Was Raised: 12/12/2006
Year Founded: 1992
Capital Under Management: $130,000,000
Current Activity Level: Actively seeking new investments
Method of Compensation: Return on invest. most important, but chg. closing fees, service fees, etc.

J.F. SHEA & COMPANY
655 Brea Canyon Road
P.O. Box 489
Walnut, CA USA 91788-0489
Phone: 909-594-9500
Fax: 909-594-0934
E-mail: investments@jfshea.com
Website: www.jfshea.com

Type of Firm
Private Equity Firm

Project Preferences

Type of Financing Preferred:
Balanced

Industry Focus
(% based on actual investment)

Communications and Media	22.9%
Computer Hardware	19.6%
Internet Specific	14.5%
Computer Software and Services	14.4%
Semiconductors/Other Elect.	11.0%
Biotechnology	4.6%
Other Products	4.5%
Medical/Health	3.5%
Industrial/Energy	3.3%
Consumer Related	1.7%

Additional Information
Name of Most Recent Fund: J.F. Shea & Company
Most Recent Fund Was Raised: 09/01/1981
Year Founded: 1980
Capital Under Management: $50,000,000
Current Activity Level: Actively seeking new investments

J.H. WHITNEY & CO. LLC
130 Main Street
New Canaan, CT USA 06840
Phone: 203-716-6100
Fax: 203-716-6101
E-mail: inquiry@whitney.com
Website: www.whitney.com

Other Offices
580 California Street
20th Floor
San Francisco, CA USA 94104
Phone: 415-229-4000
Fax: 415-229-4001

750 Lexington Avenue
New York, NY USA 10022
Phone: 212-835-1900
Fax: 212-835-1901

Management and Staff
Brian Cherry, Principal
James Fordyce, Managing Director
Paul Vigano, Managing Director
Robert Williams, Managing Director

Type of Firm
Private Equity Firm

Project Preferences

Role in Financing:
Prefer role as deal originator but will also invest in deals created by others

Type of Financing Preferred:
Leveraged Buyout
Mezzanine
Balanced
Turnaround
Later Stage
Acquisition
Recapitalizations

Size of Investments Considered:
Min Size of Investment Considered (000s): $1,000
Max Size of Investment Considered: No Limit

Geographical Preferences

International Preferences:
Europe

Industry Focus
(% based on actual investment)

Medical/Health	18.6%
Internet Specific	15.6%
Other Products	15.3%
Communications and Media	11.0%
Computer Software and Services	10.8%
Consumer Related	7.0%
Computer Hardware	6.5%
Industrial/Energy	6.1%
Semiconductors/Other Elect.	4.7%
Biotechnology	4.4%

Additional Information
Name of Most Recent Fund: J.H. Whitney VI, L.P.
Most Recent Fund Was Raised: 04/14/2005
Year Founded: 1946
Capital Under Management: $6,000,000,000
Current Activity Level: Actively seeking new investments
Method of Compensation: Return on invest. most important, but chg. closing fees, service fees, etc.

J.P. MORGAN ASSET MANAGEMENT
245 Park Avenue
Third Floor
New York, NY USA 10167
Phone: 212-648-2298
Fax: 212-648-2322
E-mail: pe.website@jpmorgan.com
Website: www.jpmorganchase.com

Management and Staff
Ijeoma Agboti, Vice President
Julian Shles, Chief Financial Officer
Katherine Rosa, Managing Director
Lawrence Unrein, Managing Director
Meena Gandhi, Vice President
Naoko Akasaka, Vice President

Type of Firm
Private Equity Advisor or Fund of Funds

Association Membership
National Venture Capital Association - USA (NVCA)

Project Preferences

Type of Financing Preferred:
Fund of Funds
Leveraged Buyout
Early Stage
Expansion
Mezzanine
Turnaround

Industry Rollups
Special Situation
Recapitalizations

Geographical Preferences

United States Preferences:

All U.S.

International Preferences:

Europe
Israel
Asia
All International

Industry Focus

(% based on actual investment)

Communications and Media	51.5%
Medical/Health	26.9%
Biotechnology	11.1%
Computer Software and Services	10.5%

Additional Information

Name of Most Recent Fund: J.P. Morgan European Corporate Finance II
Most Recent Fund Was Raised: 08/01/2002
Year Founded: 1997
Capital Under Management: $18,000,000,000
Current Activity Level: Actively seeking new investments

J.P. MORGAN CAPITAL CORPORATION

1221 Avenue of the Americas
New York, NY USA 10020
Phone: 212-899-3400
Fax: 212-899-3401
E-mail: contactus@jpmorganpartners.com
Website: www.jpmorgan.com

Other Offices

Edinburgh Tower, 15 Queen's Road
Central, Hong Kong
Phone: 852-2841-1168
Fax: 852-2973-5471

Kardinal - Faulhaber-Strasse 10
Munich, Germany 80333
Phone: 49-892-426-890
Fax: 49-8924-268-990

Av. Brigadeiro Faria Lima, 3729
andar 15
Boothbay Harbor, Brazil 04538-905
Phone: 5511-3048-3700
Fax: 5511-3048-3888

Yamato Seimei Bldg. 12F
Uchisaiwaicho, Chiyoda-ku
Tokyo , Japan 100-0011
Phone: 813-3504-2888
Fax: 813-3504-2823

333 South Hope Street
35th Floor
Los Angeles, CA USA 90071
Phone: 213-437-9278
Fax: 213-437-9365

One International Finance Centre
Suite 3003, 1 Harbour View St.
Central, Hong Kong
Phone: 852-2533-1818
Fax: 852-2868-5551

522 5th Avenue
New York, NY USA 10036
Phone: 212-837-2151
Fax: 212-837-2695

125 London Wall
London, United Kingdom EC2Y 5AJ
Phone: 44-207-777-3365
Fax: 44-207-777-4731

Avda. Corrientes, 411
Buenos Aires, Argentina 1043
Phone: 54-11-4325-7292
Fax: 54-11-4348-7238

90 Collins Street
Eighth Floor
Melbourne, Australia 3000
Phone: 613-9631-8300
Fax: 613-9631-8333

50 California Street
29th Floor
San Francisco, CA USA 94111
Phone: 415-591-1200
Fax: 415-591-1205

Walkway Level, Jardine House
One Connaught Place
Central, Hong Kong
Phone: 852-2265-1133
Fax: 852-2868-5013

Management and Staff

Cheryl Eustace, Vice President
John Mayer, Chief Executive Officer
Kevin Alger, Managing Director
Monty Cerf, Managing Director
Sanjay Jain, Vice President
T. Lynne Seden, Vice President
Tim Purcell, Managing Director

Type of Firm

Bank Affiliated

Association Membership

Hungarian Venture Capital Association (HVCA)
Natl Assoc of Small Bus. Inv. Co (NASBIC)

Project Preferences

Role in Financing:

Prefer role as deal originator but will also invest in deals created by others

Type of Financing Preferred:

Early Stage
Balanced

Size of Investments Considered:

Min Size of Investment Considered (000s): $10,000
Max Size of Investment Considered (000s): $20,000

Geographical Preferences

United States Preferences:

All U.S.

Canadian Preferences:

All Canada

International Preferences:

Italy
United Kingdom
China
Bermuda
Spain
Australia
South Africa
Germany
France
Japan
All International

Industry Focus

(% based on actual investment)

Other Products	36.8%
Internet Specific	13.4%
Consumer Related	13.0%
Communications and Media	12.2%
Computer Software and Services	10.8%
Semiconductors/Other Elect.	5.1%
Medical/Health	4.6%
Biotechnology	2.3%
Computer Hardware	1.3%
Industrial/Energy	0.5%

Additional Information

Name of Most Recent Fund: J.P. Morgan Direct Venture Capital Fund II
Most Recent Fund Was Raised: 08/15/2000
Year Founded: 1985
Capital Under Management: $800,000,000
Current Activity Level: Actively seeking new investments
Method of Compensation: Return on investment is of primary concern, do not charge fees

J.P. MORGAN H&Q (FKA: CHASE H&Q)

560 Mission Street
San Francisco, CA USA 94105
Phone: 415-315-5000

Management and Staff

Alan Carr, President
Bruce Crocker, Managing Director
Charles Walker, Managing Partner
Kerri Bisner, Vice President
Nancy Pfund, Partner

Type of Firm

Bank Affiliated

Association Membership
Western Association of Venture Capitalists (WAVC)

Project Preferences

Role in Financing:
Prefer role as deal originator but will also invest in deals created by others

Type of Financing Preferred:
Second Stage Financing
Leveraged Buyout
Control-block Purchases
Generalist PE
Mezzanine
Research and Development
Balanced
Start-up Financing
First Stage Financing
Special Situation

Size of Investments Considered:
Min Size of Investment Considered (000s): $500
Max Size of Investment Considered: No Limit

Geographical Preferences

United States Preferences:
All U.S.

Industry Focus
(% based on actual investment)

Industrial/Energy	100.0%

Additional Information
Year Founded: 1997
Capital Under Management: $55,000,000
Current Activity Level: Actively seeking new investments
Method of Compensation: Return on investment is of primary concern, do not charge fees

---

J.P. MORGAN PARTNERS (FKA: CHASE CAPITAL PARTNERS)
1221 Avenue of the Americas
40th Floor
New York, NY USA 10020
Phone: 212-899-3400
Fax: 212-899-3401
E-mail: contactus@jpmorganpartners.com
Website: www.jpmorganpartners.com

Other Offices
125 London Wall
London, United Kingdom EC2Y 5AJ
Phone: 44-20-7777-3614
Fax: 44-207-777-4731

Str. Vasile Lascar 42-44
Bucharest, Romania
Phone: 40-21-210-7646
Fax: 40-21-210-3137

Yamato Seimei Bldg. 12F
Uchisaiwaicho, Chiyoda-ku
Tokyo , Japan 100-0011
Phone: 813-3504-2888
Fax: 813-3504-2823

Almack House
28 King St.
London, United Kingdom SW1Y 6XA

Suite 3003, 30/Floor, 1 Harbour View St.
One International Finance Centre
Central, Hong Kong
Phone: 852-2533-1818
Fax: 852-2868-5551

Av. Brigadeiro Faria Lima
3729 andar 15
San Paulo , Brazil 04538-905
Phone: 5511-3048-3910
Fax: 5511-3048-3888

90 Collins Street
8th Floor
Melbourne, Australia 3000
Phone: 613-9631-8300
Fax: 613-9631-8333

Avda. Corrientes, 411
Buenos Aires, Argentina 1043
Phone: 54-11-4325-8046
Fax: 54-11-4348-7238

Kardinal - Faulhaber-Strasse 10
Munich, Germany 80333
Phone: 49-89-24-26-89-0
Fax: 49-89-24-26-89-90

50 California Street
29th Floor
San Francisco, CA USA 94111
Phone: 415-591-1200
Fax: 415-591-1205

Management and Staff
Alfred Irigoin, Partner
Andrew Liu, Managing Partner
Brooke Cuddy, Principal
Cathy Zhang, Managing Director
Christopher Albinson, General Partner
Christopher Behrens, Partner
Damion Wicker, General Partner
Elizabeth Patrick, Managing Director
Eugene Suh, Partner
Jeffrey Logan, Principal
Jeffrey Walker, Managing General Partner
John Lewis, Partner
John Reardon, Partner
John Ryan, Principal
Jonathan Lynch, Partner
Michael Jung, Principal
Ming Lu, Partner
Plinio Villares Musetti, Partner
Rodney Ferguson, General Partner
Shahan Soghikian, General Partner
Srinivas Akkaraju, General Partner
Stephen Murray, Partner
Stephen Welton, Partner
Thomas Walker, Partner
Timothy Walsh, Partner
Varun Bery, Managing Director
Vibhav Panandiker, Managing Director
Vikram Gupta, Principal

Type of Firm
Bank Affiliated

Association Membership
Brazilian Venture Capital Association (ABCR)
Hong Kong Venture Capital Association (HKVCA)
Natl Assoc of Small Bus. Inv. Co (NASBIC)
European Private Equity and Venture Capital Assoc.

Project Preferences

Role in Financing:
Will function either as deal originator or investor in deals created by others

Type of Financing Preferred:
Second Stage Financing
Leveraged Buyout
Early Stage
Expansion
Mezzanine
Generalist PE
Balanced
Later Stage
Management Buyouts
First Stage Financing
Acquisition

Size of Investments Considered:
Min Size of Investment Considered (000s): $5,000
Max Size of Investment Considered (000s): $200,000

Geographical Preferences

United States Preferences:
All U.S.

Canadian Preferences:
All Canada

International Preferences:
Italy
India
United Kingdom
Latin America
Portugal
China
Hong Kong
Mexico
Eastern Europe
Spain
Asia
Australia
New Zealand
Germany
France
Japan
All International

Industry Focus

(% based on actual investment)

Other Products	21.3%
Internet Specific	17.1%
Industrial/Energy	14.2%
Computer Software and Services	9.9%
Communications and Media	8.6%
Medical/Health	8.2%
Consumer Related	6.1%
Biotechnology	5.9%
Semiconductors/Other Elect.	4.7%
Computer Hardware	4.1%

Additional Information

Year Founded: 1984
Capital Under Management: $25,000,000,000
Current Activity Level: Actively seeking new investments
Method of Compensation: Return on investment is of primary concern, do not charge fees

J.W. CHILDS ASSOCIATES

111 Huntington Avenue
Suite 2900
Boston, MA USA 02199
Phone: 617-753-1100
Fax: 617-753-1101
E-mail: jwcinfo@jwchilds.com
Website: www.jwchilds.com

Other Offices

33/F., Alexandra House
18 Chater Road
Central, Hong Kong
Phone: 852-2844-1950
Fax: 852-2844-1036

23/F., Unit G, Pufa Tower
588 South Pudong Road
Shanghai, China PC200120
Phone: 8621-5877-8100
Fax: 8621-5877-7007

Management and Staff

Adam Suttin, Partner
David Fiorentino, Partner
Jodie Urquhart, Chief Financial Officer
John Childs, Chairman & CEO
Steven Segal, Partner

Type of Firm

Private Equity Firm

Project Preferences

Type of Financing Preferred:

Leveraged Buyout
Recapitalizations

Geographical Preferences

United States Preferences:

All U.S.

Industry Focus

(% based on actual investment)

Consumer Related	65.5%
Other Products	20.4%
Medical/Health	8.1%
Communications and Media	6.0%

Additional Information

Year Founded: 1995
Capital Under Management: $1,750,000,000
Current Activity Level: Actively seeking new investments

JACOB BALLAS CAPITAL INDIA PVT, LTD. (AKA:JBC)

The Ashok Hotel, Lower Arcade
50-B Chanakapuri
New Delhi, India 110 021
Phone: 91-11-2410-4440
Fax: 91-11-2410-4439
E-mail: jbindia@jbindia.co.in
Website: www.jbindia.co.in

Other Offices

IFS Court,
TwentyEight Cybercity
Ebene, Mauritius
Phone: 230-467-3000
Fax: 230-467-4000

Management and Staff

Anurag Kumar, Chief Financial Officer
Bharat Bakhshi, Partner
Shantanu Pandey, Principal
Srinivas Chidambaram, Managing Director
Sunil Chawla, Partner
Tirumala Rao, Principal

Type of Firm

Private Equity Advisor or Fund of Funds

Project Preferences

Type of Financing Preferred:

Expansion
Balanced

Size of Investments Considered:

Min Size of Investment Considered (000s): $5,000
Max Size of Investment Considered (000s): $30,000

Geographical Preferences

International Preferences:

India

Industry Preferences

In Medical/Health prefer:

Medical/Health
Pharmaceuticals

In Consumer Related prefer:

Consumer
Retail
Consumer Products
Hotels and Resorts

In Industrial/Energy prefer:

Industrial Products

In Financial Services prefer:

Insurance
Financial Services

In Utilities prefer:

Utilities

Additional Information

Year Founded: 1995
Capital Under Management: $440,000,000
Current Activity Level: Actively seeking new investments

JACOBS CAPITAL GROUP, LLC

670 North Rosemead Boulevard
Suite 201
Pasadena, CA USA 91107
Phone: 626-351-3701
Fax: 626-351-3702
E-mail: info@jacobscapitalgroup.com
Website: www.jacobscapitalgroup.com

Management and Staff

Alexander Suh, Managing Director
Joseph Jacobs, Co-Founder
William Hanna, Managing Director

Type of Firm

Private Equity Firm

Project Preferences

Type of Financing Preferred:

Fund of Funds

Geographical Preferences

United States Preferences:

All U.S.

International Preferences:

All International

Additional Information

Year Founded: 2005
Capital Under Management: $125,000,000
Current Activity Level: Actively seeking new investments

JACOBSON PARTNERS

595 Madison Avenue
Suite 3100
New York, NY USA 10022
Phone: 212-758-4500

Management and Staff

Ben Jacobson, Managing General Partner
Harrison Horan, General Partner
Murry Gunty, General Partner

Type of Firm
Bank Affiliated

Industry Preferences
In Medical/Health prefer:
Medical/Health

In Consumer Related prefer:
Other Restaurants

In Manufact. prefer:
Manufacturing

Additional Information
Year Founded: 2003
Current Activity Level: Actively seeking new investments

JADE ALTERNATIVE INVESTMENT ADVISORS
1266 Nanjing West Road
Plaza 66, Suite 4110
Shanghai, China 200040
Phone: 86-21-6101-0060
Fax: 86-21-6101-0061
E-mail: info@jadeadvisors.com
Website: www.jadeadvisors.com

Other Offices
1 East Chang An Avenue
Oriental Plaza, W2 Tower 1010
Beijing, China 100738
Phone: 86-10-8518-1827
Fax: 86-10-8518-7722

Management and Staff
Dayi Sun, General Partner
Jenny Zeng, Venture Partner
Jonas Lindblad, Managing Director
Larry Ma, Venture Partner
Ludvig Nilsson, Managing Partner
Wei Zhou, Venture Partner
Zhou Wei, Venture Partner

Type of Firm
Private Equity Advisor or Fund of Funds

Association Membership
China Venture Capital Association

Project Preferences
Type of Financing Preferred:
Fund of Funds
Expansion

Geographical Preferences
International Preferences:
China

Additional Information
Year Founded: 2005
Capital Under Management: $62,000,000
Current Activity Level: Actively seeking new investments

JADE INVEST SA
Jaquet-Droz 1
Neuchatel, Switzerland CH-2002
Phone: 41-32-720-5134
Fax: 41-32-720-5762
E-mail: info@jade-invest.ch
Website: www.jade-invest.ch

Management and Staff
Anne - Marie Ridout, Managing Director

Type of Firm
Private Equity Firm

Project Preferences
Type of Financing Preferred:
Early Stage
Expansion
Balanced

Industry Preferences
In Communications prefer:
Communications and Media

Additional Information
Year Founded: 2008
Current Activity Level: Actively seeking new investments

JAFCO CO., LTD. (FKA: JAPAN ASSOCIATED FINANCE CO. LTD.)
Tekko Bldg.
1-8-2 Marunouchi, Chiyoda-ku
Tokyo, Japan 100-0005
Phone: 81-3-5223-7536
Fax: 81-3-5223-7561
E-mail: info@jafco.co.jp
Website: www.jafco.co.jp

Other Offices
One Saint Martin's-le-Grand
Nomura House
London, United Kingdom EC1A 4NP
Phone: 44-20-7489-8066
Fax: 44-20-7248-5070

159-9 Samseong-dong, Gangman-gu
18th Floor, Korea City Air Tower
Seol, South Korea
Phone: 822-2016-6100
Fax: 822-2016-6101

505 Hamilton Avenue
Suite 310
Palo Alto, CA USA 94301
Phone: 650-463-8800
Fax: 650-463-8801

Five Dong San Huan North Road
Room 801, Beijing Fortune Building
Beijing, China 100004
Phone: 861-6590-9730
Fax: 861-6590-9729

109 Min-Sheng East Road
14th Floor, Sec. 3
Taipei, Taiwan
Phone: 886-2-2719-0182
Fax: 886-2-2712-4930

Six Battery Road, 42-01
Standard Chartered Bank Building
Singapore, Singapore 04990966
Phone: 656-224-6383
Fax: 656-221-3690

Eight Finance Street, Central
30/F, Two International Finance Centre
Hong Kong, China
Phone: 852-2536-1960
Fax: 852-2536-1979

Management and Staff
Hiroshi Yamada, Managing Director
Tomikazu Kaneko, Managing Director
Yusuke Yamada, Managing Director

Type of Firm
Private Equity Firm

Association Membership
Natl Assoc of Small Bus. Inv. Co (NASBIC)

Project Preferences
Role in Financing:
Will function either as deal originator or investor in deals created by others

Type of Financing Preferred:
Leveraged Buyout
Early Stage
Expansion
Mezzanine
Balanced
Seed
Management Buyouts
Startup

Geographical Preferences
United States Preferences:
All U.S.

International Preferences:
United Kingdom
China
Middle East
Australia
Germany
Asia
Japan

Industry Focus

(% based on actual investment)

Computer Software and Services	23.5%
Consumer Related	15.5%
Industrial/Energy	12.6%
Biotechnology	12.4%
Medical/Health	11.0%
Semiconductors/Other Elect.	10.4%
Internet Specific	8.2%
Other Products	5.0%
Communications and Media	0.8%
Computer Hardware	0.5%

Additional Information

Year Founded: 1973
Capital Under Management: $1,720,100,000
Current Activity Level: Actively seeking new investments
Method of Compensation: Return on investment is of primary concern, do not charge fees

---

JAFCO INVESTMENT (HONG KONG), LTD.

30F, Two International Finance
8 Finance Street
Central, Hong Kong
Phone: 852-2536-1960
Fax: 852-2536-1979
E-mail: enquiry_hongkong@jafcoasia.com
Website: www.jafcoasia.com

Other Offices

5/F, Bank Perdania Bldg. Jl. Jend.
Sudirman Kav. 40-41
Jakarta, Indonesia 10210
Phone: 6221-570-73-21
Fax: 6221-570-73-18

Unit 1404, Tower One, Ayala Triangle
Ayala Avenue
Makati, Philippines
Phone: 632-848-5251
Fax: 632-848-5254

Unit 3, 6th Floor, Tower A
Raycom Infotech Park
Beijing, China 100080
Phone: 86-10-6250-8506

23rd Floor, Tower Block, PNB Building
201-A Jalan Tun Razak
Kuala Lumpur, Taiwan 50400
Phone: 603-213-5100
Fax: 603-213-5232

1770 New Petchburi Road
Bangkok, Thailand 10320
Phone: 66-2-254-8066
Fax: 66-2-254-8075

6 Battery Road #42-01
Singapore, Singapore 049909
Phone: 65-224-6383
Fax: 65-221-3690

Nomura House
1 St. Martin's-le-Grand
London, United Kingdom EC1A 4NP
Phone: 44-207-489-8066
Fax: 44-207-248-5070

Management and Staff

Forrest Zhong, Vice President
Grace Lee, Vice President
Jian Huan Zhu, Managing Director

Type of Firm

Private Equity Firm

Association Membership

Hong Kong Venture Capital Association (HKVCA)

Project Preferences

Role in Financing:

Prefer role as deal originator but will also invest in deals created by others

Type of Financing Preferred:

Second Stage Financing
Early Stage
Expansion
Mezzanine
Balanced
Start-up Financing
Seed
First Stage Financing
Startup

Geographical Preferences

United States Preferences:

All U.S.

International Preferences:

Italy
Vietnam
United Kingdom
China
Hong Kong
Bermuda
Philippines
Spain
Australia
Korea, South
Germany
France
Japan

Industry Preferences

In Communications prefer:

Commercial Communications
CATV & Pay TV Systems
Telecommunications
Data Communications
Satellite Microwave Comm.

In Computer Hardware prefer:

Computer Graphics and Dig
Disk Relat. Memory Device

In Computer Software prefer:

Computer Services
Systems Software
Applications Software
Artificial Intelligence

In Internet Specific prefer:

Internet

In Semiconductor/Electr prefer:

Electronics
Semiconductor
Circuit Boards
Laser Related
Fiber Optics

In Biotechnology prefer:

Biosensors
Biotech Related Research

In Medical/Health prefer:

Medical Diagnostics
Diagnostic Services
Diagnostic Test Products
Medical Therapeutics
Drug/Equipmt Delivery
Other Therapeutic
Disposable Med. Products
Pharmaceuticals

In Consumer Related prefer:

Consumer
Retail
Education Related

In Industrial/Energy prefer:

Energy
Industrial Products

In Transportation prefer:

Transportation

In Business Serv. prefer:

Distribution

In Manufact. prefer:

Publishing

In Agr/Forestr/Fish prefer:

Agriculture related

Additional Information

Year Founded: 1999
Capital Under Management: $748,500,000
Current Activity Level: Actively seeking new investments
Method of Compensation: Return on investment is of primary concern, do not charge fees

---

JAFCO INVESTMENT [FKA: NOMURA/JAFCO INVESTMENT (ASIA), LTD.]

6 Battery Road
#42-01
Singapore, Singapore 049909
Phone: 65-6224-6383
Fax: 65-6221-3690
E-mail: enquiry_singapore@jafcoasia.com
Website: www.jafcoasia.com

Other Offices

Room 801, Beijing Fortune Building
No.5 Dong San Huan Bei Lu
Beijing, China 100004
Phone: 86-10-6590-9730
Fax: 86-10-6590-9729

14/F, 109 Min-Sheng E. Road
Section 3
Taipei, Taiwan
Phone: 886-2-2719-0182
Fax: 886-2-2712-4930

Suite 42-021, 42/F HSBC Tower
1000 Lujiazui Ring Road
Shanghai, China 200120
Phone: 86-21-6841-3818
Fax: 86-21-6841-3800

30/F, Two International Finance Centre
8 Finance Street
Central, Hong Kong
Phone: 852-2536-1960
Fax: 852-2536-1979

18/F Korea City Air Tower
159-9 Samseong-dong Gangnam-gu
Seoul, South Korea 135-973
Phone: 82-2-2016-6100
Fax: 82-2-2016-6101

Management and Staff

Fumito Takashima, Chief Financial Officer
Jian Huan Zhu, Managing Director
Junitsu Uchikata, Managing Director
Michael Chow Ching Ning, Managing Director
Richard Uichel Joung, Managing Director

Type of Firm

Private Equity Firm

Association Membership

Hong Kong Venture Capital Association (HKVCA)
Singapore Venture Capital Association (SVCA)

Project Preferences

Type of Financing Preferred:

Mezzanine
Early Stage
Expansion

Size of Investments Considered:

Min Size of Investment Considered (000s): $1,000
Max Size of Investment Considered (000s): $5,000

Geographical Preferences

International Preferences:

Vietnam
Indonesia
India
Taiwan
China
Hong Kong
Thailand
Philippines
Australia
Israel
Singapore
Korea, South
Asia
Malaysia

Industry Focus

(% based on actual investment)

Communications and Media	26.5%
Internet Specific	17.4%
Industrial/Energy	12.4%
Computer Hardware	11.1%
Semiconductors/Other Elect.	10.2%
Computer Software and Services	9.7%
Medical/Health	6.0%
Other Products	4.3%
Consumer Related	2.5%

Additional Information

Name of Most Recent Fund: JAFCO Asia Technology Fund III L.P.
Most Recent Fund Was Raised: 12/01/2005
Year Founded: 1990
Capital Under Management: $1,000,000,000
Current Activity Level: Actively seeking new investments

JAFCO VENTURES

505 Hamilton Avenue
Suite 310
Palo Alto, CA USA 94301
Phone: 650-463-8800
Fax: 650-463-8801
Website: www.jafco.com

Management and Staff

Ben Shih, Principal
Debby Meredith, Venture Partner
Jeb Miller, General Partner
Joe Horowitz, General Partner
Nick Sturiale, General Partner
Tom Mawhinney, General Partner
Tsunesaburo Sugaya, General Partner

Type of Firm

Private Equity Firm

Association Membership

Western Association of Venture Capitalists (WAVC)
National Venture Capital Association - USA (NVCA)

Project Preferences

Role in Financing:

Prefer role as deal originator but will also invest in deals created by others

Type of Financing Preferred:

Second Stage Financing
Early Stage
Expansion

Size of Investments Considered:

Min Size of Investment Considered (000s): $4,000
Max Size of Investment Considered (000s): $8,000

Industry Preferences

In Communications prefer:

Communications and Media
Commercial Communications
Telecommunications

In Computer Hardware prefer:

Integrated Turnkey System

In Computer Software prefer:

Computer Services
Software

In Internet Specific prefer:

Internet

In Semiconductor/Electr prefer:

Semiconductor

In Consumer Related prefer:

Consumer Products
Consumer Services

Additional Information

Year Founded: 2003
Capital Under Management: $360,000,000
Current Activity Level: Actively seeking new investments
Method of Compensation: Return on investment is of primary concern, do not charge fees

---

JAHANGIR SIDDIQUI GROUP (AKA: JS GROUP)

7/F The Forum
Block 9, Clifton
Karachi, Pakistan 75600
Phone: 92-21-583-9977
Fax: 92-21-536-1721
Website: www.js.com

Other Offices

The Fairmont Hotel, Suite 712
Shaikh Zayed Road
Dubai, Utd. Arab Em.
Phone: 971-4-312-4350
Fax: 971-4-312-4351

Four Old Park Lane
London, United Kingdom W1K 1QW
Phone: 44-20-7399-4350
Fax: 44-20-7399-4351

Management and Staff

Kamran Qadir, Chief Financial Officer
Munaf Ibrahim, Chief Executive Officer

Type of Firm

Bank Affiliated

Project Preferences

Type of Financing Preferred:

Balanced

Geographical Preferences

International Preferences:
Pakistan
Asia

Additional Information
Year Founded: 2006
Capital Under Management: $70,000,000
Current Activity Level: Actively seeking new investments

JAIC-CROSBY INVESTMENT MANAGEMENT CO., LTD.
Suite 1112 Two Pacific Place
88 Queensway, Admiralty
Central, Hong Kong
Phone: 852-2509-3011
Website:
www.crosby.com/web/en/cam/ourBusinesses/cro

Type of Firm
Private Equity Firm

Project Preferences

Type of Financing Preferred:
Balanced

Geographical Preferences

International Preferences:
Taiwan
China
Hong Kong

Additional Information
Year Founded: 2005
Capital Under Management: $10,000,000
Current Activity Level: Actively seeking new investments

JALA CAPITAL (PTY) LTD.
11 Alice Lane
Standard Bank Building
Johannesburg, South Africa 2146
Phone: 27-11-884-2042
Fax: 27-11-884-5309
E-mail: info@jalacapital.co.za
Website: www.jalacapital.co.za

Management and Staff
Salala Lesela, Chief Executive Officer

Type of Firm
Private Equity Firm

Project Preferences

Type of Financing Preferred:
Leveraged Buyout
Acquisition

Size of Investments Considered:
Min Size of Investment Considered (000s): $12,452
Max Size of Investment Considered (000s): $24,905

Industry Preferences

In Medical/Health prefer:
Medical/Health
Health Services

In Industrial/Energy prefer:
Industrial Products
Machinery

In Financial Services prefer:
Real Estate

In Manufact. prefer:
Manufacturing

In Agr/Forestr/Fish prefer:
Mining and Minerals

Additional Information
Year Founded: 2005
Current Activity Level: Actively seeking new investments

JANIVO INVESTMENTS BV
Postbus 544
Zeist, Netherlands 3700 AM
Phone: 31-30-693-7500
Fax: 31-30-693-7550
E-mail: secretariaat@janivo.nl

Type of Firm
Private Equity Firm

Association Membership
Dutch Venture Capital Associaton (NVP)

Project Preferences

Type of Financing Preferred:
Leveraged Buyout
Expansion

Geographical Preferences

International Preferences:
Netherlands
Europe

Additional Information
Year Founded: 2000
Current Activity Level: Actively seeking new investments

JAPAN ASIA INVESTMENT COMPANY, LTD. (AKA: JAIC)
3-11 Kandanishiki-cho
Seiko Takebashi-Kyodo Building
Chiyoda-ku, Tokyo, Japan 101-8570
Phone: 81-3-3259-8518
Fax: 81-3-3259-8511
E-mail: ir@jaic-vc.co.jp
Website: www.jaic-vc.co.jp

Other Offices
10th Floor, MANHYO Daiichi Building
12-14 Nishiki 2-chome, Naka-ku
Nagoya, Japan 460-0003
Phone: 81-52-211-2921
Fax: 81-52-211-2920

7th Floor, Tenjin NK Building
8-36 Tenjin 2-Chome, Chuo-ku
Fukuoka, Japan 810-0001
Phone: 81-92-725-5733
Fax: 81-92-725-5717

3rd Floor, Yodoyabashi Yamamoto Building
3-22 Imabashi 4-chome, Chuo-ku
Osaka, Japan 541-0042
Phone: 81-6-232-2881
Fax: 81-6-6232-2880

2479 East Bayshore Road
Suite 709
Palo Alto, CA USA 94303
Phone: 650-213-9011
Fax: 650-213-9012

2nd Floor, Sakura Hiroden Building
2-26 Kamiyacho 1-Chome, Naka-ku
Hiroshima, Japan 730-0031
Phone: 81-82-504-6920
Fax: 81-82-504-6921

14/F, Sumitomo Life Sendai Bldg,
10-3 Chuo 4-Chome, Aoba-ku
Sendai, Japan 980-0021
Phone: 81-22-216-8551
Fax: 81-22-216-8550

Mayban Ventures Sdn.Bhd.-20/F W. Wing,
Menera Maybank 100 Jalan Tun Perak
Kuala Lumpur, Malaysia 50050
Phone: 603-202-2188
Fax: 603-201-2188

50 Raffles Place #24-03
Singapore Land Tower
Singapore, Singapore 048623
Phone: 65-6557-0511
Fax: 65-6557-0332

Unit 707, Antel 2000 Corp. Center
121 Valero St., Salcedo Vill.
Makati, Philippines
Phone: 632-751-0000
Fax: 632-751-1560

14/F C Room Grand Amarin
Tower 1550 New Petchburi Rd., Makasan
Bangkok, Thailand 10310
Phone: 662-207-0216
Fax: 662-207-0215

Suite 1112, Two Pacific Place
88 Queensway Admiralty
Hong Kong, Hong Kong
Phone: 852-2509-3011
Fax: 852-2509-3025

3/F, Mitsuikaijo Okayama Bldg.
12-1 Yanagimachi 1-Chome
Okayama, Japan 700-0904
Phone: 818-6224-0048
Fax: 818-6224-0040

5th Floor, Puresuto 1-7 Building
1 Kitachijyo Nishi 7-Chome, Chuo-ku
Sapporo, Japan 060-0001
Phone: 81-11-232-3550
Fax: 81-11-232-3556

6/F Kanazawa Fukokuseimei-ekimae
11-7 Honmachi 2-Chome
Kanazawa, Japan 920-0853
Phone: 817-6232-5040
Fax: 817-6232-5043

Management and Staff

Hidetaka Fukuzawa, Managing Director
Makoto Isshi, Senior Managing Director
Tsuneo Kumada, Senior Managing Director
Yoshiki Sasaki, Senior Managing Director

Type of Firm

Bank Affiliated

Association Membership

Singapore Venture Capital Association (SVCA)

Project Preferences

Role in Financing:

Prefer role as deal originator but will also invest in deals created by others

Type of Financing Preferred:

Leveraged Buyout
Early Stage
Expansion
Mezzanine
Balanced
Later Stage
Seed
Distressed Debt

Geographical Preferences

United States Preferences:

All U.S.

International Preferences:

Indonesia
India
China
Hong Kong
Thailand
Singapore
Korea, South
Asia
Japan
Malaysia
All International

Industry Focus

(% based on actual investment)

Medical/Health	30.3%
Computer Hardware	20.2%
Biotechnology	16.3%
Internet Specific	15.5%
Consumer Related	6.4%
Other Products	4.3%
Semiconductors/Other Elect.	3.4%
Computer Software and Services	2.4%
Communications and Media	1.3%

Additional Information

Year Founded: 1981
Capital Under Management: $204,300,000
Current Activity Level: Actively seeking new investments
Method of Compensation: Return on invest. most important, but chg. closing fees, service fees, etc.

JAPAN INDUSTRIAL PARTNERS, INC.

2-1-1 Marunouchi
Chiyoda-ku
Tokyo, Japan
Phone: 813-6266-5781
Fax: 813-6266-5797
Website: www.jipinc.com

Management and Staff

Hidemi Moue, Managing Director
Ryota Suzuki, Vice President

Type of Firm

Private Equity Firm

Project Preferences

Type of Financing Preferred:

Leveraged Buyout
Balanced
Turnaround
Management Buyouts

Geographical Preferences

International Preferences:

Asia
Japan

Additional Information

Year Founded: 2002
Current Activity Level: Actively seeking new investments

JAPAN PRIVATE EQUITY CO., LTD

6F Kudan Ailex Bldg.
1-14-21 Kudankita, Chiyoda-ku
Tokyo, Japan 102-0073
Phone: 81-3-3238-1726
Fax: 81-3-3238-1639
E-mail: info@private-equity.co.jp
Website: www.private-equity.co.jp

Other Offices

10F MANHYO Daiichi Bldg.
2-12-14 Nishiki, Naka-ku,
Nagoya, Japan 460-0003
Phone: 81-52-211-2913
Fax: 81-52-211-2920

Management and Staff

Shinichi Hotta, President & COO
Suguru Miyake, Vice President

Type of Firm

Private Equity Firm

Project Preferences

Type of Financing Preferred:

Leveraged Buyout
Turnaround
Management Buyouts

Geographical Preferences

International Preferences:

Japan

Industry Preferences

In Semiconductor/Electr prefer:

Electronics

Additional Information

Year Founded: 2000
Current Activity Level: Actively seeking new investments

JARDIM BOTANICO PARTNERS (FKA: ARAUJO FONTES CONSULTORIA)

Rua General Garzon, 22 / 408
Jardim Botanico
Rio de Janeiro - RJ, Brazil 22470-010
Phone: 55-21-2512-5574
Fax: 55-21-2512-5575
E-mail: info@jbpartners.com.br
Website: www.jbpartners.com.br

Other Offices

Rua Saguacu 302
40th Floor
Joinville, Brazil
Phone: 55-47-433-8885
Fax: 55-47-433-5558

Rua Paraiba, 1323
7th Floor
Belo Horizonte - MG, Brazil

Rua Said Aiach, 135-Paraiso
Sao Paulo - SP, Brazil

Phone: 55-11-3884-1013
Fax: 55-11-3884-1013

Management and Staff

Ana Siqueira Dantas, Partner
Eduardo Faria, Partner
Eduardo Rezende, Partner
Evaldo Fontes, Partner
Jose Luiz Osorio, Partner

Type of Firm

Private Equity Firm

Association Membership

Brazilian Venture Capital Association (ABCR)

Project Preferences

Type of Financing Preferred:

Mezzanine
Balanced
Public Companies
Seed

Geographical Preferences

International Preferences:

Brazil

Industry Preferences

In Communications prefer:

Communications and Media

In Computer Hardware prefer:

Computers

In Computer Software prefer:

Software

In Computer Other prefer:

Computer Related

In Semiconductor/Electr prefer:

Electronic Components

In Biotechnology prefer:

Biotechnology
Agricultural/Animal Bio.

In Medical/Health prefer:

Medical/Health

In Industrial/Energy prefer:

Energy

In Financial Services prefer:

Financial Services

In Agr/Forestr/Fish prefer:

Agriculture related

Additional Information

Year Founded: 1990
Current Activity Level: Actively seeking new investments

JARVINIAN LLC

101 Federal Street
Suite 1900
Boston, MA USA 02110
Phone: 617-342-7023
Fax: 617-395-2719
E-mail: info@jarvinian.com
Website: www.jarvinian.com

Management and Staff

Christopher Carter, Managing Director
John Dooley, Managing Director
Thomas Eddy, Managing Director

Type of Firm

Private Equity Firm

Project Preferences

Type of Financing Preferred:

Early Stage
Expansion
Mezzanine
Seed
Later Stage
Startup

Size of Investments Considered:

Min Size of Investment Considered (000s): $1,000
Max Size of Investment Considered (000s): $5,000

Industry Preferences

In Communications prefer:

Wireless Communications

In Semiconductor/Electr prefer:

Electronic Components
Semiconductor

In Business Serv. prefer:

Media

Additional Information

Year Founded: 2009
Current Activity Level: Actively seeking new investments

JATOTECH MANAGEMENT LLC

6300 Bridgepoint Parkway
Building 1, Suite 500
Austin, TX USA 78730
Phone: 512-795-5860
Fax: 512-692-2868
E-mail: info@jatotech.com
Website: www.jatotech.com

Other Offices

300 Crescent Court
Suite 850
Dallas, TX USA 75201
Phone: 214-855-3732

Management and Staff

Daniel Ray, Venture Partner
Molly Pieroni, Managing Director
Walter Thirion, Managing Director

Type of Firm

Private Equity Firm

Association Membership

National Venture Capital Association - USA (NVCA)

Project Preferences

Role in Financing:

Prefer role as deal originator but will also invest in deals created by others

Type of Financing Preferred:

Early Stage
Seed

Size of Investments Considered:

Min Size of Investment Considered (000s): $500
Max Size of Investment Considered (000s): $5,000

Geographical Preferences

United States Preferences:

Northern California
Southwest

Industry Preferences

In Communications prefer:

Wireless Communications
Data Communications

In Semiconductor/Electr prefer:

Semiconductor

Additional Information

Year Founded: 1999
Capital Under Management: $56,700,000
Current Activity Level: Actively seeking new investments
Method of Compensation: Return on invest. most important, but chg. closing fees, service fees, etc.

JAVELIN VENTURE PARTNERS

One Rincon Center
101 Spear Street, Suite 255
San Francisco, CA USA 94105
Phone: 415-202-5820
Fax: 415-520-0305
E-mail: info@javelinvp.com
Website: www.javelinvp.com

Management and Staff

Jed Katz, Managing Director
Noah Doyle, Managing Director

Type of Firm

Private Equity Firm

Project Preferences

Type of Financing Preferred:

Early Stage
Seed

Size of Investments Considered:
Min Size of Investment Considered (000s): $1,000
Max Size of Investment Considered (000s): $2,000

Industry Preferences

In Communications prefer:
Communications and Media
Wireless Communications

In Internet Specific prefer:
Internet
Ecommerce

In Medical/Health prefer:
Medical/Health

Additional Information
Year Founded: 2009
Capital Under Management: $70,000,000
Current Activity Level: Actively seeking new investments

JAVELIN VENTURES LIMITED
London Bioscience Innovation
2 Royal College Street
London, United Kingdom NW1 0TU
Phone: 44-207-691-2080
Fax: 44-207-681-9129
E-mail: info@javelin-ventures.com
Website: www.javelin-ventures.com

Type of Firm
University Program

Project Preferences

Type of Financing Preferred:
Early Stage
Seed

Geographical Preferences

International Preferences:
United Kingdom
Europe

Industry Preferences

In Biotechnology prefer:
Biotechnology

In Medical/Health prefer:
Medical/Health

Additional Information
Year Founded: 2004
Capital Under Management: $6,000,000
Current Activity Level: Actively seeking new investments

JBF PARTNERS
8F Marunouchmitsui Bldg.
2-2-2 Marunouchi, Chiyoda-ku
Tokyo, Japan

Management and Staff
Naohiro Takemoto, Partner

Type of Firm
Private Equity Firm

Project Preferences

Type of Financing Preferred:
Leveraged Buyout

Geographical Preferences

International Preferences:
Asia

Additional Information
Year Founded: 2003
Current Activity Level: Actively seeking new investments

JC SIMMONS & ASSOCIATES
206-2187 Oak Bay Avenue
Victoria, Canada V8R1G1
Phone: 250-595-8860
Fax: 250-595-8861

Management and Staff
John Simmons, President

Type of Firm
Private Equity Firm

Additional Information
Year Founded: 1999
Current Activity Level: Actively seeking new investments

JEFFERIES GROUP, INC.
520 Madison Avenue
12th Floor
New York, NY USA 10022
Phone: 212-284-2300
Website: www.jefferies.com

Other Offices
111 Park Place Boulevard
Suite 140
Covington, LA USA 70433
Phone: 985-845-6020

51 JFK Parkway
Third Floor
Short Hills, NJ USA 07078
Phone: 973-912-2900

One Station Place
Three North
Stamford, CT USA 06902
Phone: 203-708-5980

The Taj Mahal Palace & Tower Hotel
Suite 305, Apollo Bunder
Mumbai, India 400 001
Phone: 91-22-2287-7100

1909-1910A, CITIC Square
1168 Nanjing Road (W)
Shanghai, China 200041
Phone: 86-21-5111-8700

One Post Office Square
Suite 3400
Boston, MA USA 02109
Phone: 617-342-7800

55 West Monroe
Suite 3500
Chicago, IL USA 60603
Phone: 312-750-4700

650 California Street
29th Floor
San Francisco, CA USA 94108
Phone: 415-229-1400

8 rue Halevy
Paris, France 5009
Phone: 33-1-5343-6700

Hibiya Marine Building 3F
1-5-1, Yuraku-cho, Chiyoda-ku
Tokyo, Japan 100-0006
Phone: 81-3-5251-6100

13355 Noel Road
Suite 1400
Dallas, TX USA 75240
Phone: 972-701-3000

1050 Winter Street
Suite 2400
Waltham, MA USA 02451
Phone: 781-522-8400

3414 Peachtree Road Northeast
Suite 810
Atlanta, GA USA 30326
Phone: 404-264-5000

11100 Santa Monica
Tenth Floor
West Los Angeles, CA USA 90025
Phone: 310-445-1199

80 Raffles Place
Suite 15-20 UOB Plaza 2
Singapore, Singapore 048624
Phone: 65-6551-3950

Niederlassung Frankfurt
Bockenheimer Landstrasse 24
Frankfurt am Main, Germany 60323
Phone: 49-69-719-1870

4064 Colony Road
Suite 400

Charlotte, NC USA 28211
Phone: 704-943-7400

Vintners Place
68 Upper Thames Street
London, United Kingdom EC4V 3BJ
Phone: 44-20-7029-8000

2nd Floor, Eros Corporate Tower
Nehru Place
New Delhi, India 110019
Phone: 91-11-4059-9500

2525 West End Avenue
Suite 1150
Nashville, TN USA 37203
Phone: 615-963-8300

Uraniastrasse 12
Zurich, Switzerland 8021
Phone: 41-44-227-1600

Harborside Financial Center
34 Exchange Place, Plaza III
Jersey City, NJ USA 07311
Phone: 212-336-7000

Emirates Office Tower, Level 41
Sheikh Zayed Road
Dubai, Utd. Arab Em.
Phone: 971-4-319-7648

909 Fannin Street
Suite 3100
Houston, TX USA 77010
Phone: 800-533-0072

Management and Staff

Christopher Bury, Managing Director
Daniel Markaity, Managing Director
Hal Kennedy, Managing Director
John Shaw, President & COO
Leon Szlezinger, Managing Director
Richard Burke, Managing Director
Richard Handler, Chief Executive Officer

Type of Firm

Bank Affiliated

Project Preferences

Role in Financing:

Prefer role as deal originator but will also invest in deals created by others

Type of Financing Preferred:

Fund of Funds
Second Stage Financing
Leveraged Buyout
Expansion
Later Stage
Management Buyouts
First Stage Financing
Private Placement
Acquisition
Recapitalizations

Size of Investments Considered:

Min Size of Investment Considered (000s): $10,000
Max Size of Investment Considered (000s): $80,000

Geographical Preferences

United States Preferences:

Northern California
All U.S.

Industry Preferences

In Communications prefer:

Commercial Communications
Telecommunications
Wireless Communications

In Computer Software prefer:

Computer Services
Data Processing
Software
Applications Software
Artificial Intelligence

In Internet Specific prefer:

Internet
Web Aggregration/Portals

In Semiconductor/Electr prefer:

Electronic Components
Semiconductor
Laser Related
Fiber Optics

In Industrial/Energy prefer:

Superconductivity
Robotics

In Transportation prefer:

Transportation

Additional Information

Name of Most Recent Fund: Jefferies Capital Partners IV, L.P.
Most Recent Fund Was Raised: 06/06/2005
Year Founded: 1999
Capital Under Management: $600,000,000
Current Activity Level: Actively seeking new investments
Method of Compensation: Return on invest. most important, but chg. closing fees, service fees, etc.

JEFFERSON CAPITAL FUND, LTD.

4149 Old Leeds Road
Birmingham, AL USA 35213

Type of Firm

Private Equity Firm

Project Preferences

Role in Financing:

Prefer role as deal originator but will also invest in deals created by others

Type of Financing Preferred:

Leveraged Buyout
Control-block Purchases
Special Situation

Size of Investments Considered:

Min Size of Investment Considered (000s): $1,000
Max Size of Investment Considered: No Limit

Geographical Preferences

United States Preferences:

Mid Atlantic
Southeast
Northeast

Industry Preferences

In Communications prefer:

Telecommunications
In Semiconductor/Electr prefer:
Sensors

In Medical/Health prefer:

Medical Products
Pharmaceuticals

In Consumer Related prefer:

Entertainment and Leisure
Consumer Products
Education Related

In Industrial/Energy prefer:

Industrial Products
Materials
Factory Automation
Environmental Related

In Manufact. prefer:

Publishing

Additional Information

Year Founded: 1991
Capital Under Management: $10,000,000
Current Activity Level: Actively seeking new investments
Method of Compensation: Return on invest. most important, but chg. closing fees, service fees, etc.

JEFFERSON CAPITAL PARTNERS, LTD.

901 East Cary Street
Suite 1600
Richmond, VA USA 23219
Phone: 804-643-0100
Fax: 804-643-9140
Website: www.jeffersoncapital.com

Management and Staff

Palmer Garson, Partner
R. Timothy O'Donnell, Partner

Type of Firm

Private Equity Firm

Association Membership

Mid-Atlantic Venture Association

Project Preferences

Type of Financing Preferred:
Leveraged Buyout
Expansion
Generalist PE
Later Stage
Management Buyouts
Acquisition
Recapitalizations

Size of Investments Considered:
Min Size of Investment Considered (000s): $2,000
Max Size of Investment Considered (000s): $7,000

Geographical Preferences

United States Preferences:
Mid Atlantic
Midwest
Southeast
Northeast
Southwest

Industry Focus

(% based on actual investment)

Computer Software and Services	39.0%
Consumer Related	27.5%
Other Products	21.2%
Internet Specific	8.6%
Medical/Health	3.7%

Additional Information
Name of Most Recent Fund: Jefferson Capital Partners II, L.P.
Most Recent Fund Was Raised: 09/01/2000
Year Founded: 1997
Capital Under Management: $108,500,000
Current Activity Level: Actively seeking new investments

JEFFERSON PARTNERS
260 Queen Street West
4th Floor
Toronto, Canada M5V 1Z8
Phone: 416-367-1533
Fax: 416-367-5827
Website: www.jefferson.com

Management and Staff
David Folk, Managing General Partner
David Harris Kolada, Venture Partner
Ian Locke, General Partner
Jack Kiervin, Managing General Partner
Jonathan Black, Venture Partner

Type of Firm
Private Equity Firm

Project Preferences

Role in Financing:
Prefer role as deal originator but will also invest in deals created by others

Type of Financing Preferred:
Early Stage
Expansion
Later Stage
Seed

Size of Investments Considered:
Min Size of Investment Considered (000s): $3,000
Max Size of Investment Considered (000s): $10,000

Geographical Preferences

United States Preferences:
Northeast
All U.S.

Canadian Preferences:
All Canada

Industry Preferences

In Communications prefer:
Communications and Media

In Computer Software prefer:
Software

In Internet Specific prefer:
Internet

Additional Information
Name of Most Recent Fund: Jefferson Fund IV
Most Recent Fund Was Raised: 12/24/2002
Year Founded: 1994
Capital Under Management: $110,000,000
Current Activity Level: Actively seeking new investments
Method of Compensation: Return on invest. most important, but chg. closing fees, service fees, etc.

JEGI CAPITAL, LLC
150 East 52nd Street
18th Floor
New York, NY USA 10022
Phone: 212-754-0710
Fax: 212-754-0337
Website: www.jegi.com

Management and Staff
Bill Hitzig, Chief Operating Officer
Kent Hawryluk, General Partner
Roger Krakoff, Managing Director
Wilma Jordan, Chief Executive Officer

Type of Firm
Corporate PE/Venture

Project Preferences

Role in Financing:
Prefer role as deal originator but will also invest in deals created by others

Type of Financing Preferred:
Second Stage Financing
Early Stage
First Stage Financing

Size of Investments Considered:
Min Size of Investment Considered (000s): $2,000
Max Size of Investment Considered (000s): $5,000

Geographical Preferences

United States Preferences:
All U.S.

Industry Preferences

In Computer Hardware prefer:
Disk Relat. Memory Device

In Computer Software prefer:
Computer Services
Data Processing
Software
Systems Software
Applications Software
Artificial Intelligence

In Internet Specific prefer:
E-Commerce Technology
Internet
Web Aggregration/Portals

In Semiconductor/Electr prefer:
Fiber Optics

Additional Information
Name of Most Recent Fund: JEGI Internet Economy Partners
Most Recent Fund Was Raised: 02/17/2000
Year Founded: 1988
Capital Under Management: $100,000,000
Current Activity Level: Actively seeking new investments
Method of Compensation: Return on investment is of primary concern, do not charge fees

JEMISON INVESTMENTS
320 Park Place Tower
Birmingham, AL USA 35203
Phone: 205-324-7681
Management and Staff
J. David Brown, President

Type of Firm
Private Equity Firm

Additional Information
Year Founded: 2009
Current Activity Level: Actively seeking new investments

JEROME CAPITAL LLC
1260 Vallecita Drive
Santa Fe, NM USA 87501
Phone: 505-988-1360
Fax: 505-988-1360

Management and Staff
Halley Faust, Managing Director

Type of Firm
Private Equity Firm

Project Preferences

Role in Financing:
Prefer role as deal originator but will also invest in deals created by others

Type of Financing Preferred:
Second Stage Financing
Early Stage
Seed
First Stage Financing
Startup

Size of Investments Considered:
Min Size of Investment Considered (000s): $50,000
Max Size of Investment Considered (000s): $250,000

Geographical Preferences

United States Preferences:
New Mexico

Industry Preferences

In Semiconductor/Electr prefer:
Laser Related

In Biotechnology prefer:
Human Biotechnology
Genetic Engineering

In Medical/Health prefer:
Medical/Health
Medical Diagnostics
Diagnostic Services
Diagnostic Test Products
Medical Therapeutics
Medical Products
Health Services
Hospitals/Clinics/Primary
Pharmaceuticals

In Consumer Related prefer:
Education Related

In Industrial/Energy prefer:
Alternative Energy

In Financial Services prefer:
Insurance

Additional Information
Year Founded: 1997
Capital Under Management: $10,000,000
Current Activity Level: Actively seeking new investments

JERUSALEM CAPITAL (AKA: JCP)
Jerusalem Technology Park
Building 8, Floor 3, Malcha
Jerusalem, Israel 96251
Phone: 972-542-261-789
Fax: 972-508-970-670
Website: www.jerusalemcapital.net

Management and Staff
Brent James, Venture Partner
Hanan Yona, Chief Financial Officer
Lior Lifshitz, Partner

Type of Firm
Private Equity Firm

Project Preferences

Type of Financing Preferred:
Balanced

Geographical Preferences

International Preferences:
Israel

Industry Preferences

In Business Serv. prefer:
Services

Additional Information
Year Founded: 2006
Current Activity Level: Actively seeking new investments

JERUSALEM GLOBAL VENTURES
8 Hartom Street
Beck Science Building, Floor 3
Jerusalem, Israel 91481
Phone: 972-2-582-8888
Fax: 972-2-648-2451
E-mail: info@jgv.com
Website: www.jgv.com

Other Offices
Beit Hatayalet
Beitar Street 2; Floor 4
Jerusalem, Israel
Phone: 972-2-565-2220

Globus Communication Centre
Suite 220; 2nd Floor
Neve Ilan, Israel
Phone: 972-2-533-2808
Fax: 972-2-570-2352

Management and Staff
Avraham Menachem, Managing Partner
Avrom Gilbert, Principal
Dalia Megiddo, Managing Partner
Erik Grossberg, Principal
Joel Weiss, Chief Operating Officer
Jonathan Adereth, Venture Partner
Micah Avni, Partner
Michael Pliner, Venture Partner
Michael Brous, Co-Founder
Ranan Grobman, Partner
Shlomo Kalish, Founding Partner
Shlomo Caine, Venture Partner
Yoni Hashkes, Managing Partner
Yoseph Linde, Managing Partner
Yossi Tsuria, Venture Partner

Type of Firm
Private Equity Firm

Project Preferences

Role in Financing:
Prefer role as deal originator but will also invest in deals created by others

Type of Financing Preferred:
Early Stage
Later Stage
Seed
First Stage Financing

Size of Investments Considered:
Min Size of Investment Considered (000s): $1,000
Max Size of Investment Considered (000s): $8,000

Geographical Preferences

International Preferences:
Israel

Industry Preferences

In Communications prefer:
Communications and Media
Telecommunications
Wireless Communications
Data Communications
Other Communication Prod.

In Computer Software prefer:
Software

In Semiconductor/Electr prefer:
Semiconductor
Component Testing Equipmt
Fiber Optics

In Medical/Health prefer:
Medical Products

Additional Information
Year Founded: 1994
Capital Under Management: $117,000,000
Current Activity Level: Actively seeking new investments
Method of Compensation: Return on investment is of primary concern, do not charge fees

---

JH PARTNERS, LLC (FKA: JESSE.HANSEN & CO.)
451 Jackson Street
Floor 3
San Francisco, CA USA 94111
Phone: 415-364-0300
Fax: 415-364-0333
E-mail: info@jhpartners.com
Website: www.jhpartners.com

Management and Staff

James Williamson, Chief Financial Officer
John Hansen, President

Type of Firm

Private Equity Firm

Project Preferences

Type of Financing Preferred:
Leveraged Buyout
Expansion
Balanced

Geographical Preferences

United States Preferences:
All U.S.

Additional Information

Name of Most Recent Fund: JH Investment Partners II, L.P.
Most Recent Fund Was Raised: 06/19/2006
Year Founded: 1986
Capital Under Management: $533,500,000
Current Activity Level: Actively seeking new investments

JHP ENTERPRISES LLC

534 West Road
New Canaan, CT USA 06840
Phone: 203-652-0548
Fax: 917-591-7580
E-mail: jhpujol@jhpenter.com
Website: www.jhpenter.com

Management and Staff

Juan Pujol, President

Type of Firm

Bank Affiliated

Project Preferences

Role in Financing:
Unknown

Type of Financing Preferred:
Leveraged Buyout
Management Buyouts
Recapitalizations

Geographical Preferences

International Preferences:
Latin America
Spain

Additional Information

Year Founded: 1988
Current Activity Level: Actively seeking new investments
Method of Compensation: Return on invest. most important, but chg. closing fees, service fees, etc.

JIANGSU HIGH-TECH INVESTMENT GROUP (AKA: GOVTOR CAPITAL)

No. 268 Zhongshan Road
22/F Huijie Guangchang
Nanjing, China 210008
Phone: 86-25-8311-6299
Fax: 86-25-8311-6200
Website: www.js-vc.com

Management and Staff

Shungen Guo, Vice President
Wei Zhang, President
Wenlu Ying, Vice President

Type of Firm

Government Affiliated Program

Project Preferences

Type of Financing Preferred:
Early Stage
Expansion
Seed
Later Stage

Geographical Preferences

International Preferences:
China

Industry Preferences

In Semiconductor/Electr prefer:
Electronics

In Biotechnology prefer:
Biotechnology
Industrial Biotechnology

In Medical/Health prefer:
Medical/Health

In Industrial/Energy prefer:
Energy
Materials
Environmental Related

In Financial Services prefer:
Financial Services

In Business Serv. prefer:
Services

In Manufact. prefer:
Manufacturing

Additional Information

Year Founded: 2005
Capital Under Management: $32,400,000
Current Activity Level: Actively seeking new investments

JIANGSU JIUZHOU CAPITAL CO., LTD.

No. 38 Guanhe East Road
23/F Jiuzhou Huanyu B
Changzhou, China
Phone: 86-519-85228901
Fax: 86-519-85228850
E-mail: jzct@jiuzhouinvest.com
Website: www.jiuzhouinvest.com

Type of Firm

Private Equity Firm

Project Preferences

Type of Financing Preferred:
Expansion
Public Companies
Later Stage
Private Placement

Geographical Preferences

International Preferences:
China

Industry Preferences

In Biotechnology prefer:
Biotechnology

In Industrial/Energy prefer:
Energy
Materials
Environmental Related

Additional Information

Year Founded: 2008
Current Activity Level: Actively seeking new investments

JIANGSU TOP-BRIDGE CAPITAL CO., LTD. (AKA: DINGQIAO)

No. 15 Shenjia Gang
5th Floor Zhong Fang Building
Nantong, China
Phone: 86-513-85512833
Fax: 86-513-85512033
E-mail: tbc@china-tbc.com
Website: www.china-tbc.com

Other Offices

No. 169 Hanzhong Road
Rm. 912 Kinsley Sheraton Hotel
Nanjing, China

Type of Firm

Private Equity Firm

Project Preferences

Type of Financing Preferred:
Balanced

Geographical Preferences

International Preferences:
China

Industry Preferences

In Biotechnology prefer:
Biotechnology

In Industrial/Energy prefer:
Materials
Machinery

In Business Serv. prefer:
Services

Additional Information

Year Founded: 2008
Capital Under Management: $14,600,000
Current Activity Level: Actively seeking new investments

JILIN HUIZHENG INVESTMENT CO.

Jilin Province
Changchun, China

Management and Staff

Wang Xitian, President

Type of Firm

Private Equity Firm

Project Preferences

Type of Financing Preferred:
Balanced

Geographical Preferences

International Preferences:
China

Industry Preferences

In Industrial/Energy prefer:
Oil and Gas Exploration

Additional Information

Year Founded: 2003
Current Activity Level: Actively seeking new investments

JILIN VENTURE CAPITAL FUND OF FUNDS MANAGEMENT CO., LTD.

6788 Yatai Street
5/F Taihu Hotel
Changchun, China 130022
Phone: 86-431-85225526
Fax: 86-431-85225522
E-mail: jlvc@jl-vc.com
Website: www.jl-vc.com

Type of Firm

Private Equity Advisor or Fund of Funds

Project Preferences

Type of Financing Preferred:
Balanced

Size of Investments Considered:
Min Size of Investment Considered (000s): $731
Max Size of Investment Considered (000s): $4,387

Geographical Preferences

International Preferences:
China

Industry Preferences

In Biotechnology prefer:
Biotechnology

In Medical/Health prefer:
Pharmaceuticals

In Industrial/Energy prefer:
Energy
Materials
Environmental Related

In Agr/Forestr/Fish prefer:
Agribusiness

Additional Information

Year Founded: 2007
Current Activity Level: Actively seeking new investments

JINA VENTURES, INC.

425 Park Avenue
31st Floor
New York, NY USA 10022
Phone: 212-888-6008
Fax: 646-514-8026
E-mail: info@jinaventures.com
Website: www.jinaventures.com

Other Offices

1-11-12, Nishikata
Bunkyo-Ku
Tokyo, Japan 113-0024

47 Hill Street, #06-02
Singapore Chamber of Commerce & Industry
Singapore, Singapore 179365

59/112 Soi Sukhumvit
26 Sukhumvit Road, Klongton, Klongtoey
Bangkok, Thailand 10110
Phone: 66-2-259-3078
Fax: 66-2-259-3079

T-1 Cama Industrial Estate
Andheri West
Mumbai, India 400 036

297 Central Avenue
Jersey City, NJ USA 07307

Management and Staff

Chris Kosuke Hosokawa, Managing Partner
Karthik Balakrishnan, Vice President
Samir Mistry, Principal
Umesh Gowda, Principal
Vishal Savani, Partner

Type of Firm

Private Equity Firm

Project Preferences

Type of Financing Preferred:
Leveraged Buyout
Later Stage
Private Placement

Geographical Preferences

United States Preferences:
All U.S.

International Preferences:
India
Europe
Asia

Industry Preferences

In Communications prefer:
Communications and Media

In Consumer Related prefer:
Consumer
Retail

In Manufact. prefer:
Manufacturing

Additional Information

Year Founded: 2002
Current Activity Level: Actively seeking new investments

JINPU INDUSTRIAL INVESTMENT FUND MANAGEMENT COMPANY

c/o Shanghai Int'l Group
No. 111 Jiujiang Road
Shanghai, China 200002
Phone: 86-21-6323-1111
Fax: 86-21-6329-0944

Management and Staff

Duoguang Bei, Chief Executive Officer

Type of Firm

Government Affiliated Program
Project Preferences

Type of Financing Preferred:
Startup

Geographical Preferences

International Preferences:
China

Industry Preferences

In Financial Services prefer:
Financial Services

Additional Information
Year Founded: 2009
Capital Under Management: $29,300,000
Current Activity Level: Actively seeking new investments

JK&B CAPITAL
Two Prudential Plaza
180 N. Stetson Ave, Suite 4500
Chicago, IL USA 60601
Phone: 312-946-1200
Fax: 312-946-1103
E-mail: info@jkbcapital.com
Website: www.jkbcapital.com

Management and Staff
Albert DaValle, Partner
Ali Shadman, Partner
Marc Sokol, Partner
Nancy O'Leary, Chief Financial Officer
Robert Humes, Partner
Tasha Seitz, Partner
Thomas Neustaetter, Partner

Type of Firm
Private Equity Firm

Association Membership
Illinois Venture Capital Association
National Venture Capital Association - USA (NVCA)

Project Preferences

Role in Financing:
Prefer role as deal originator but will also invest in deals created by others

Type of Financing Preferred:
Second Stage Financing
Early Stage
Expansion
Balanced
Later Stage
First Stage Financing

Size of Investments Considered:
Min Size of Investment Considered (000s): $5,000
Max Size of Investment Considered (000s): $30,000

Geographical Preferences

United States Preferences:
All U.S.

Industry Focus
(% based on actual investment)

Internet Specific	33.7%
Computer Software and Services	28.5%
Communications and Media	20.1%
Semiconductors/Other Elect.	11.4%
Computer Hardware	6.1%
Consumer Related	0.2%

Additional Information
Name of Most Recent Fund: JK&B Capital V, L.P.
Most Recent Fund Was Raised: 10/12/2006
Year Founded: 1996
Capital Under Management: $1,112,800,000
Current Activity Level: Actively seeking new investments
Method of Compensation: Return on invest. most important, but chg. closing fees, service fees, etc.

JLA VENTURES (FKA: J.L. ALBRIGHT VENTURE PARTNERS)
Canada Trust Tower, 161 Bay St
Suite 4440; P.O. Box 215
Toronto, Canada M5J 2S1
Phone: 416-367-2440
Fax: 416-367-4604
E-mail: info@jlaventures.com
Website: www.jlaventures.com

Other Offices
481 Viger Ouest
Suite 300
Montreal, Canada H2Z 1G6

Management and Staff
John Albright, Partner
Pierre Donaldson, Partner
Rick Segal, Partner
Stuart Lombard, Partner

Type of Firm
Private Equity Firm

Association Membership
Canadian Venture Capital Association

Project Preferences

Role in Financing:
Prefer role as deal originator but will also invest in deals created by others

Type of Financing Preferred:
Expansion
Early Stage
Seed
Later Stage
First Stage Financing
Startup
Private Placement

Size of Investments Considered:
Min Size of Investment Considered (000s): $3,000
Max Size of Investment Considered (000s): $20,000

Geographical Preferences

Canadian Preferences:
All Canada
Alberta
Quebec
Ontario
British Columbia

Industry Focus
(% based on actual investment)

Internet Specific	49.2%
Computer Software and Services	22.8%
Communications and Media	9.9%
Computer Hardware	6.7%
Other Products	5.3%
Industrial/Energy	5.2%
Consumer Related	1.0%

Additional Information
Name of Most Recent Fund: J.L. Albright IV Venture Fund
Most Recent Fund Was Raised: 05/24/2006
Year Founded: 1996
Capital Under Management: $168,900,000
Current Activity Level: Actively seeking new investments
Method of Compensation: Return on investment is of primary concern, do not charge fees

---

JLL PARTNERS (FKA: JOSEPH, LITTLEJOHN & LEVY, INC.)
450 Lexington Avenue
Suite 3350
New York, NY USA 10017
Phone: 212-286-8600
Fax: 212-286-8626
E-mail: info@jllpartners.com
Website: www.jllpartners.com

Management and Staff
Alexander Castaldi, Senior Managing Director
Dan Agroskin, Principal
Eugene Hann, Principal
James Rauh, Vice President
Jay Rose, Principal
Kevin Hammond, Principal
Michael Legarde, Principal
Michael Schwartz, Chief Financial Officer
Paul Levy, Senior Managing Director
Ramsey Frank, Managing Director

Type of Firm
Bank Affiliated

Project Preferences

Type of Financing Preferred:
Leveraged Buyout
Turnaround
Recapitalizations

Geographical Preferences

United States Preferences:

All U.S.

Industry Focus

(% based on actual investment)

Other Products	65.7%
Consumer Related	22.8%
Medical/Health	10.0%
Industrial/Energy	0.9%
Communications and Media	0.7%

Additional Information

Year Founded: 1988
Capital Under Management: $2,400,000,000
Current Activity Level: Actively seeking new investments

JM FINANCIAL INVESTMENT MANAGERS, LTD.

141, Maker Chambers III
Nariman Point
Mumbai, India 400021
Phone: 91-22-6630-3030
Fax: 91-22-2204-2137
E-mail: corporate@jmfinancial.in
Website: www.jmfinancial.in

Management and Staff

Dilip Kothari, Managing Director

Type of Firm

Bank Affiliated

Project Preferences

Type of Financing Preferred:

Balanced

Geographical Preferences

International Preferences:

India

Additional Information

Year Founded: 2006
Capital Under Management: $90,000,000
Current Activity Level: Actively seeking new investments

JM GALEF & CO., INC.

P.O. Box 7693
Greenwich, CT USA 06830
Phone: 203-625-8600
Fax: 203-625-8682
E-mail: admin@galef.net
Website: www.galef.net

Management and Staff

James Galef, President

Type of Firm

Private Equity Firm

Project Preferences

Role in Financing:

Prefer role as deal originator

Type of Financing Preferred:

Leveraged Buyout
Turnaround
Management Buyouts
Recapitalizations

Geographical Preferences

International Preferences:

United Kingdom
France

Additional Information

Year Founded: 1986
Current Activity Level: Actively seeking new investments
Method of Compensation: Unknown

JMH CAPITAL

890 Winter Street
Suite 110
Waltham, MA USA 02451
Phone: 781-522-1600
Fax: 781-522-1699
E-mail: info@jmhcapital.com
Website: www.jmhcapital.com

Management and Staff

Douglas Rohall, Managing Director
Mike Mullen, Chief Financial Officer
Scott Steele, Managing Director
W. Anthony Brooke, Managing Director

Type of Firm

Private Equity Firm

Project Preferences

Type of Financing Preferred:

Control-block Purchases
Industry Rollups
Recapitalizations

Geographical Preferences

United States Preferences:

All U.S.

Canadian Preferences:

All Canada

International Preferences:

United Kingdom

Industry Preferences

In Medical/Health prefer:

Medical Products

In Consumer Related prefer:

Food/Beverage
Consumer Products

In Financial Services prefer:

Financial Services

In Business Serv. prefer:

Distribution

In Manufact. prefer:

Manufacturing

Additional Information

Year Founded: 2003
Capital Under Management: $100,000,000
Current Activity Level: Actively seeking new investments

JMI EQUITY

Two Hamill Road
Suite 272
Baltimore, MD USA 21210
Phone: 410-951-0200
Fax: 410-951-0201
Website: www.jmiequity.com

Other Offices

7590 Fay Avenue
Suite 301
La Jolla, CA USA 92037
Phone: 858-362-9880
Fax: 858-362-9879

Management and Staff

Bob Nye, Vice President
Bradford Woloson, General Partner
Brian Hersman, Vice President
Charles Noell, Venture Partner
Charles Ramsey, Venture Partner
Harry Gruner, General Partner
Jit Sinha, Principal
Mohit Daswani, Principal
Paul Barber, General Partner
Peter Arrowsmith, General Partner
Robert Smith, General Partner
Robert Sywolski, Venture Partner
Travis Hughes, Vice President

Type of Firm

Private Equity Firm

Association Membership

Mid-Atlantic Venture Association
National Venture Capital Association - USA (NVCA)
Canadian Venture Capital Association

Project Preferences

Role in Financing:

Prefer role as deal originator but will also invest in deals created by others

Type of Financing Preferred:

Second Stage Financing
Leveraged Buyout
Early Stage

Expansion
Later Stage
Management Buyouts
Recapitalizations

Size of Investments Considered:
Min Size of Investment Considered (000s): $10,000
Max Size of Investment Considered (000s): $60,000

Industry Preferences

In Computer Software prefer:
Software
Systems Software

In Internet Specific prefer:
Internet

Additional Information
Name of Most Recent Fund: JMI Equity Fund VI, L.P.
Most Recent Fund Was Raised: 06/26/2007
Year Founded: 1992
Capital Under Management: $1,300,000,000
Current Activity Level: Actively seeking new investments
Method of Compensation: Return on invest. most important, but chg. closing fees, service fees, etc.

JMI INVEST A/S
Lejrvej 19
Vaerlose, Denmark 3500
Phone: 45-7011-4800
Fax: 45-7023-4822
Website: www.jmiinvest.dk

Management and Staff
Lars Hylling Axelsson, Partner

Type of Firm
Private Equity Firm

Project Preferences

Type of Financing Preferred:
Leveraged Buyout
Acquisition

Industry Preferences

In Communications prefer:
Telecommunications

Additional Information
Year Founded: 2003
Current Activity Level: Actively seeking new investments

JO HAMBRO CAPITAL MANAGEMENT
Ryder Court
14 Ryder Street
London, United Kingdom SW1Y 6QB
Phone: 44-20-7747-5678
Fax: 44-20-7747-5647
E-mail: info@johcm.co.uk
Website: www.johcm.co.uk

Management and Staff
Andreas Lehman, Managing Director
David Rhydderch, Chief Operating Officer
Nichola Pease, Chief Executive Officer

Type of Firm
Private Equity Firm

Project Preferences

Type of Financing Preferred:
Balanced

Geographical Preferences

International Preferences:
United Kingdom
Europe

Industry Preferences

In Consumer Related prefer:
Consumer Services
Other Restaurants

In Business Serv. prefer:
Media

Additional Information
Year Founded: 2001
Capital Under Management: $173,400,000
Current Activity Level: Actively seeking new investments

JOG CAPITAL
440 - Second Avenue South West
Suite 2370
Calgary, Canada T2P5E9
Phone: 403-232-3340
Fax: 403-705-3341
Website: www.jogcapital.com

Management and Staff
Chad Weiss, Managing Partner
Daryl Gilbert, Managing Director
Donald Cowie, President
Ryan Crawford, Managing Director

Type of Firm
Private Equity Firm

Additional Information
Year Founded: 2009
Current Activity Level: Actively seeking new investments

JOHNSON & JOHNSON DEVELOPMENT CORPORATION
410 George Street
New Brunswick, NJ USA 08901
Phone: 732-524-3218
Fax: 732-247-5309
Website: www.jjdevcorp.com

Other Offices
c/o Johnson & Johnson Medical Limited
Coronation Road, Ascot
Berks, United Kingdom SL5 9EY
Phone: 44-1344-87-1130
Fax: 44-1344-87-1135

c/o Advanced Sterilization Products
33 Technology Drive
Irvine, CA USA 92618
Phone: 949-789-3819
Fax: 949-789-3869

c/o Alza Corporation
1900 Charleston Road, Suite M12-2110
Mountain View, CA USA 94039
Phone: 650-564-7124
Fax: 650-564-3514

Kibbutz Shefayim
Jerusalem, Israel 60990
Phone: 972-9-959-1176
Fax: 972-9-951-9797

c/o Janssen Pharmaceutica N.V.
Turnhoutseweg 30
Beerse, Belgium 2340
Phone: 32-14-60-7119
Fax: 32-14-60-3999

c/o RWJ PRI
3210 Merryfield Row
San Diego, CA USA 92121
Phone: 858-784-3220
Fax: 858-784-3221

Management and Staff
Asish Xavier, Vice President
Brad Vale, Vice President
Carol Marino, Vice President
Roger Guidi, Vice President
Roy Davis, President
Sarita Jain, Principal
Scott Moonly, Principal
Stacey Davis, Principal
V. Kadir Kadhiresan, Principal
Zeev Zehavi, Vice President

Type of Firm
Corporate PE/Venture

Association Membership
National Venture Capital Association - USA (NVCA)
European Private Equity and Venture Capital Assoc.

Project Preferences

Role in Financing:
Prefer role as deal originator but will also invest in deals created by others

Type of Financing Preferred:
Second Stage Financing
Start-up Financing
Seed
First Stage Financing

Geographical Preferences

International Preferences:
All International

Industry Focus
(% based on actual investment)

Medical/Health	74.4%
Biotechnology	17.3%
Computer Software and Services	4.0%
Internet Specific	2.3%
Semiconductors/Other Elect.	1.1%
Computer Hardware	0.6%
Industrial/Energy	0.2%
Other Products	0.1%

Additional Information
Name of Most Recent Fund: Johnson & Johnson Development Corp.
Most Recent Fund Was Raised: 01/01/1978
Year Founded: 1973
Capital Under Management: $16,200,000
Current Activity Level: Actively seeking new investments
Method of Compensation: Return on investment is of primary concern, do not charge fees

---

JOLIMONT CAPITAL PTY., LTD. (FKA: JOLIMONT VENTURES)
133 Flinders Lane
Melbourne, Australia 3000
Phone: 613-9038-8808
Fax: 613-9639-5228
Website: www.jolimontcapital.com.au

Management and Staff
Charles Gillies, Managing Partner
Lex McArthur, Managing Partner
Teresa Engelhard, Venture Partner

Type of Firm
Private Equity Advisor or Fund of Funds

Association Membership
Australian Venture Capital Association (AVCAL)

Project Preferences

Type of Financing Preferred:
Early Stage
Fund of Funds of Second

Size of Investments Considered:
Min Size of Investment Considered (000s): $806
Max Size of Investment Considered (000s): $24,174

Geographical Preferences

International Preferences:
Pacific
Australia

Industry Preferences

In Communications prefer:
Wireless Communications

In Computer Software prefer:
Software

In Semiconductor/Electr prefer:
Laser Related

In Consumer Related prefer:
Consumer Products

Additional Information
Name of Most Recent Fund: Jolimont Secondaries Fund I
Most Recent Fund Was Raised: 10/24/2004
Year Founded: 2003
Capital Under Management: $95,100,000
Current Activity Level: Actively seeking new investments

JORDAN COMPANY, THE
767 Fifth Avenue
48th Floor
New York, NY USA 10153
Phone: 212-572-0829
Fax: 212-355-0622
Website: www.thejordancompany.com

Other Offices
875 North Michigan Avenue
John Hancock Building Suite 4040
Chicago, IL USA 60611
Phone: 312-573-6418
Fax: 312-274-1247

CITIC Square, 1168 Nanjing Xi Lu
Floor 23, Suite 2308
Shanghai, China 200041
Phone: 86-21-5292-5566
Fax: 86-21-5292-8600

Management and Staff
Brian Higgins, Vice President
David Butler, Principal
Douglas Zych, Principal
Eion Hu, Vice President
Joseph Linnen, Principal
Michael Denvir, Vice President
Paul Rodzevik, Chief Financial Officer
Peter Carbonara, Vice President
Young Ye, Managing Director

Type of Firm
Bank Affiliated

Project Preferences

Type of Financing Preferred:
Leveraged Buyout
Mezzanine
Industry Rollups

Geographical Preferences

United States Preferences:
All U.S.

Canadian Preferences:
All Canada

International Preferences:
Italy
United Kingdom
Eastern Europe
Spain
Germany
France

Industry Focus
(% based on actual investment)

Other Products	100.0%

Additional Information
Name of Most Recent Fund: Resolute Fund, L.P., The
Most Recent Fund Was Raised: 09/30/2002
Year Founded: 1982
Capital Under Management: $5,000,000,000
Current Activity Level: Actively seeking new investments
Method of Compensation: Return on invest. most important, but chg. closing fees, service fees, etc.

JORMIAN CAPITAL, INC.
3448, rue Stanley
Montreal, Canada H3A1R8
Phone: 514-284-0110

Management and Staff
Ian Kott, President

Type of Firm
Private Equity Firm

Additional Information
Year Founded: 2009
Current Activity Level: Actively seeking new investments

JOTO INVESTERING
Petroleumsveien 8
P.O.Box 361
Stavanger, Norway 4067
Phone: 51-95-85-00
Fax: 51-95-85-01
E-mail: mail@joto.no
Website: www.joto.no

Type of Firm
Private Equity Firm

Association Membership
Norwegian Venture Capital Association

Project Preferences

Type of Financing Preferred:
Balanced

Geographical Preferences

International Preferences:
Norway

Additional Information
Year Founded: 2004
Current Activity Level: Actively seeking new investments

JOTUNFJELL PARTNERS AS (AKA: JFP)

co/ Convexa AS
Ruselokkveien 6
Oslo, Norway N-0251
Phone: 47-2301-2351
Fax: 47-2283-8183
E-mail: info@jfp.no
Website: www.jfp.no

Other Offices
Strandvagen 7A
Stockholm, Sweden SE-11456
Phone: 46-8-501-648-92
Fax: 46-707-167-113
Management and Staff
Hans Kristian Melbye, Founding Partner
Marco Bolandrina, Partner

Type of Firm
Private Equity Firm

Project Preferences

Type of Financing Preferred:
Turnaround
Balanced
Special Situation

Geographical Preferences

International Preferences:
Scandanavia/Nordic Region

Industry Preferences

In Consumer Related prefer:
Retail
Consumer Products

Additional Information
Year Founded: 2000
Current Activity Level: Actively seeking new investments

JOVFUNDS

26 Wellington Street East
Suite 700
Toronto, Canada M5E1S2
Phone: 416-601-2500
Fax: 416-601-2501
E-mail: info@jovfunds.com
Website: www.jovfunds.com

Management and Staff
Ian Lennox, Partner
Steve Hawkins, Chief Executive Officer

Type of Firm
Private Equity Firm

Project Preferences

Type of Financing Preferred:
Expansion
Early Stage
Startup

Additional Information
Year Founded: 2005
Current Activity Level: Actively seeking new investments

JP CAPITAL PARTNERS, LLC

9701 Wilshire Boulevard
Eleventh Floor
Beverly Hills, CA USA 90212
Phone: 310-691-1700
Website: www.jp-cap.com

Management and Staff
Ethan Goodson, Vice President
Joseph Pretlow, Managing Director
Simon Newman, Managing Director

Type of Firm
Private Equity Firm

Project Preferences

Type of Financing Preferred:
Leveraged Buyout
Turnaround
Management Buyouts
Acquisition
Recapitalizations

Industry Preferences

In Communications prefer:
Telecommunications

In Medical/Health prefer:
Medical/Health
Diagnostic Services
Diagnostic Test Products

In Consumer Related prefer:
Consumer Products
Consumer Services

In Financial Services prefer:
Financial Services

In Business Serv. prefer:
Services
Media

In Manufact. prefer:
Manufacturing

Additional Information
Year Founded: 2006
Current Activity Level: Actively seeking new investments

JS GROUP

7/F The Forum
Block 9, Clifton
Karachi , Pakistan 75600
Phone: 92-21-583-9977
Fax: 92-21-536-1721
Website: www.js.com

Other Offices
4 Old Park Lane
London, United Kingdom W1K 1QW
Phone: 44-20-7399-4350
Fax: 44-20-7399-4351

The Fairmont Hotel, Suite 712
Shaikh Zayed Road
Dubai, Utd. Arab Em.
Phone: 971-4312-4350
Fax: 971-4312-4351

Management and Staff
Stephen Smith, Partner

Type of Firm
Bank Affiliated

Project Preferences

Type of Financing Preferred:
Leveraged Buyout
Expansion

Geographical Preferences

International Preferences:
Pakistan

Additional Information
Year Founded: 2006
Capital Under Management: $158,000,000
Current Activity Level: Actively seeking new investments

JUMPSTART, INC.

737 Bolivar Road
Suite 3000
Cleveland, OH USA 44115
Phone: 216-363-3400
Fax: 216-363-3401
E-mail: ask@jumpstartinc.org
Website: www.jumpstartinc.org

Management and Staff

Jerry Frantz, Venture Partner
Kevin Mendelsohn, Venture Partner
Lee Poseidon, Venture Partner
Mark Smith, Venture Partner
Ray Leach, Chief Executive Officer
Rebecca Braun, President
Richard Jankura, Chief Financial Officer
Theodore Frank, Venture Partner

Type of Firm

Incubator/Development Program

Association Membership

National Venture Capital Association - USA (NVCA)

Project Preferences

Role in Financing:
Prefer role as deal originator but will also invest in deals created by others

Type of Financing Preferred:
Startup

Size of Investments Considered:
Min Size of Investment Considered (000s): $125
Max Size of Investment Considered (000s): $600

Geographical Preferences

United States Preferences:
Ohio

Additional Information

Year Founded: 2003
Current Activity Level: Actively seeking new investments
Method of Compensation: Return on investment is of primary concern, do not charge fees

JUMPSTARTUP FUND ADVISORS PVT. LTD.

206, Raheja Plaza 17
Commissariat Road
Bangalore, India 560 025
Phone: 91-80-536-2780
Fax: 91-80-536-2401
E-mail: info@jumpstartup.net
Website: www.jumpstartup.net

Other Offices

5201 Great America Parkway
Suite 320
Santa Clara, CA USA 95054
Phone: 408-562-6354
Fax: 408-562-5745

Management and Staff

K. Ganapathy Subramanian, Founding Partner
Kiran Nadkarni, Founding Partner
Sanjay Anandaram, Founding Partner

Type of Firm

Private Equity Firm

Association Membership

Indian Venture Capital Association (IVCA)

Project Preferences

Type of Financing Preferred:
Early Stage
Expansion
Seed
Startup

Size of Investments Considered:
Min Size of Investment Considered (000s): $500
Max Size of Investment Considered (000s): $3,000

Geographical Preferences

International Preferences:
India

Industry Preferences

In Communications prefer:
Communications and Media
Telecommunications

In Computer Software prefer:
Software

In Internet Specific prefer:
Internet

In Computer Other prefer:
Computer Related

In Semiconductor/Electr prefer:
Electronics
Semiconductor

Additional Information

Year Founded: 2000
Capital Under Management: $40,000,000
Current Activity Level: Actively seeking new investments

JUNIPER CAPITAL VENTURES PTE, LTD.

29 International Business Park
#08-05/06 Acer Bldg. Tower B
Singapore, Singapore 609923
Phone: 65-6561-7978
Fax: 65-6561-9770
Website: www.engro-global.com

Management and Staff

Cheng Gay Tan, Chief Executive Officer
Chi Tsung Wong, Vice President

Type of Firm

Corporate PE/Venture

Association Membership

Singapore Venture Capital Association (SVCA)

Project Preferences

Role in Financing:
Prefer role as deal originator but will also invest in deals created by others

Type of Financing Preferred:
Fund of Funds
Early Stage
Expansion
Balanced
Seed
Startup

Size of Investments Considered:
Min Size of Investment Considered (000s): $100
Max Size of Investment Considered (000s): $2,000

Geographical Preferences

United States Preferences:
All U.S.

International Preferences:
China
Singapore
Asia

Industry Preferences

In Communications prefer:
Wireless Communications

In Computer Software prefer:
Software

In Semiconductor/Electr prefer:
Semiconductor

In Medical/Health prefer:
Medical Products
Pharmaceuticals

In Industrial/Energy prefer:
Industrial Products
Environmental Related

Additional Information

Year Founded: 2000
Capital Under Management: $50,000,000
Current Activity Level: Actively seeking new investments
Method of Compensation: Return on investment is of primary concern, do not charge fees

JUNIPER NETWORKS

1194 North Mathilda Avenue
Sunnyvale, CA USA 94089
Phone: 408-745-2000
Fax: 408-745-2100
Website: www.juniper.net

Management and Staff

Bjorn Liencres, Founder
Dean Hickman-Smith, Vice President
Dennis Ferguson, Founder
Marcel Gani, Chief Financial Officer
Scott Kriens, Chairman & CEO

Type of Firm

Corporate PE/Venture

Industry Focus

(% based on actual investment)

Communications and Media	48.6%
Computer Software and Services	28.2%
Internet Specific	11.6%
Semiconductors/Other Elect.	11.6%

Additional Information

Year Founded: 1999
Current Activity Level: Actively seeking new investments

JUNSAN CAPITAL (AKA: JUNSHENG INVESTMENT)

No. 7006 Shennan Dadao
Rm. 2101 Fuchun Dongfang Bldg.
Shenzhen, China 518040
Phone: 86-755-82571118
Fax: 86-755-82571198
E-mail: js@junsancapital.com
Website: www.junsancapital.com

Management and Staff

Zijun Liao, President

Type of Firm

Private Equity Firm

Project Preferences

Type of Financing Preferred:

Later Stage
Acquisition

Geographical Preferences

International Preferences:

China

Industry Preferences

In Medical/Health prefer:

Medical/Health

In Consumer Related prefer:

Consumer

In Industrial/Energy prefer:

Energy

In Financial Services prefer:

Financial Services

In Manufact. prefer:

Manufacturing

Additional Information

Year Founded: 2003
Current Activity Level: Actively seeking new investments

JUROKU CAPITAL COMPANY, LTD., THE

7-12 Kanda-cho
Gifu City, Japan
Phone: 81-58-264-7716
Fax: 81-58-264-7718
Website: www.jic-gifu.or.jp

Type of Firm

Private Equity Firm

Project Preferences

Type of Financing Preferred:

Balanced

Geographical Preferences

International Preferences:

Asia
Japan

Additional Information

Year Founded: 2000
Capital Under Management: $11,700,000
Current Activity Level: Actively seeking new investments

JV CAPITAL MANAGEMENT S.R.O. (FKA: CZECH VENTURE PARTNERS)

Filmarska 1153/19
Prague, Czech Republic 152 00
Phone: 420-2-4248-8822
Fax: 420-2-4248-8824
E-mail: vladislav.jez@jvcm.cz
Website: www.cvp.cz

Other Offices

Wenceslas square 48
Prague, Czech Republic 110 00
Phone: 420-5-5670-1900
Fax: 420-5-5670-9123

Management and Staff

Gijsbert Boot, Chief Executive Officer

Type of Firm

Private Equity Firm

Association Membership

European Private Equity and Venture Capital Assoc.

Project Preferences

Role in Financing:

Will function either as deal originator or investor in deals created by others

Type of Financing Preferred:

Leveraged Buyout
Expansion
Acquisition

Size of Investments Considered:

Min Size of Investment Considered (000s): $1,049
Max Size of Investment Considered (000s): $4,194

Geographical Preferences

International Preferences:

Czech Republic

Industry Focus

(% based on actual investment)

Computer Software and Services	92.2%
Consumer Related	4.0%
Internet Specific	3.8%

Additional Information

Name of Most Recent Fund: Czech Top Venture Fund B.V.
Most Recent Fund Was Raised: 03/01/2003
Year Founded: 1997
Capital Under Management: $33,700,000
Current Activity Level: Actively seeking new investments
Method of Compensation: Return on invest. most important, but chg. closing fees, service fees, etc.

JVIC VENTURE CAPITAL CO., LTD.

5F Capital Akasaka Bldg.
1-7-19 Akasaka, MInato-ku
Tokyo, Japan 107-0052
Website: www.jvic-vc.co.jp

Type of Firm

Private Equity Firm

Project Preferences

Type of Financing Preferred:

Balanced

Geographical Preferences

International Preferences:

Japan

Additional Information

Year Founded: 2000
Current Activity Level: Actively seeking new investments

JVP (FKA: JERUSALEM VENTURE PARTNERS)

24 Hebron Road
Jerusalem, Israel 93542
Phone: 972-2-640-9000
Fax: 972-2-640-9001
E-mail: info@jvpvc.com

Website: www.jvpvc.com

Other Offices

2C Drax Avenue
London, United Kingdom SW20 OEH
Phone: 44-20-7758-8200
Fax: 44-20-7758-8208

Jin Mao Tower, 31st Floor
88 Shi Ji Avenue, Pudong
Shanghai, China 200120
Phone: 86-21-2890-9020
Fax: 86-21-6856-6978

156 Fifth Avenue
Suite 410
New York, NY USA 10010
Phone: 212-479-5100
Fax: 212-213-1776

Kyodo Building, 6th Floor
2-13-13, Nihonbashi-Kayabacho
Toyko, Japan 103-0025
Phone: 81-3-3614-7035
Fax: 81-3-3614-7035

Management and Staff

Alex Ott, Venture Partner
Ariel Maislos, Venture Partner
Gadi Tirosh, General Partner
Haim Kopans, Venture Partner
Kobi Rozengarten, General Partner
Raffi Kesten, Venture Partner
Robert Gehorsam, Venture Partner
Ronit Dulberg, Chief Financial Officer
Uri Adoni, Venture Partner

Type of Firm

Private Equity Firm

Association Membership

Israel Venture Association

Project Preferences

Role in Financing:

Prefer role as deal originator but will also invest in deals created by others

Type of Financing Preferred:

Early Stage
Balanced

Size of Investments Considered:

Min Size of Investment Considered (000s): $2,000
Max Size of Investment Considered (000s): $35,000

Geographical Preferences

International Preferences:

Europe
Israel
Asia
All International

Industry Focus

(% based on actual investment)

Communications and Media	32.1%
Internet Specific	22.0%
Computer Software and Services	18.2%
Semiconductors/Other Elect.	17.2%
Computer Hardware	7.2%
Biotechnology	2.5%
Consumer Related	0.6%
Other Products	0.2%

Additional Information

Name of Most Recent Fund: JVP III Annex Fund, L.P.
Most Recent Fund Was Raised: 08/31/2002
Year Founded: 1993
Capital Under Management: $770,000,000
Current Activity Level: Actively seeking new investments

JYSK FYNSK KAPITALANAEG AS

Hojbro Plads 6
Kobenhavn, Denmark 1200
Phone: 45-4015-1477
E-mail: info@jf-kapital.dk
Website: www.jf-kapital.dk

Type of Firm

Private Equity Firm

Project Preferences

Type of Financing Preferred:

Leveraged Buyout

Geographical Preferences

International Preferences:

Denmark

Additional Information

Year Founded: 2005
Current Activity Level: Actively seeking new investments

K+ VENTURE PARTNERS

Postbus 39
Groesbeek, Netherlands 6550
Phone: 31-24-3995-522
Fax: 31-24-3977-619
E-mail: info@kplus.nl
Website: www.kplus.nl

Other Offices

Bd. Natiunil Unite nr 8 bl 104 Sc 5
et 6 ap 100 Sector 5
Bucharest, Romania 705052
Phone: 40-21-266-0632
Fax: 40-21-337-2936

Management and Staff

Gijsbert Maarten Boot, Chief Executive Officer
Michel Hendriks, Chief Operating Officer
Pavel Zabransky, Partner
Viktor Bernat, Partner

Type of Firm

Private Equity Firm

Association Membership

European Private Equity and Venture Capital Assoc.

Project Preferences

Type of Financing Preferred:

Leveraged Buyout
Early Stage
Expansion
Recapitalizations

Geographical Preferences

International Preferences:

Central Europe
Eastern Europe

Industry Preferences

In Communications prefer:

Commercial Communications

In Biotechnology prefer:

Biotechnology

In Medical/Health prefer:

Medical/Health

In Consumer Related prefer:

Food/Beverage
Consumer Products

Additional Information

Year Founded: 1999
Current Activity Level: Actively seeking new investments

K-NET INVESTMENT

1575-3 Seocho 3 dong Seocho-ku
11/F Younghan Building
Seoul, South Korea 137-875

Type of Firm

Private Equity Firm

Project Preferences

Type of Financing Preferred:
Balanced

Additional Information

Year Founded: 2008
Capital Under Management: $33,300,000
Current Activity Level: Actively seeking new investments

K.C. VENTURE GROUP

800 West 47th Street
Suite 300
Kansas City, MO USA 64112
Phone: 816-753-8380
Fax: 816-753-8399
Website: www.kcventuregroup.com

Type of Firm

Private Equity Firm

Additional Information

Current Activity Level: Actively seeking new investments

K9 VENTURES

837 Garland Drive
P.O. Box 901
Palo Alto, CA USA 94302
Phone: 650-838-0600
E-mail: admin@k9ventures.com
Website: www.k9ventures.com

Management and Staff

Manu Kumar, Founder

Type of Firm

Private Equity Firm

Project Preferences

Type of Financing Preferred:
Early Stage
Seed
Startup

Geographical Preferences

United States Preferences:
West Coast

Industry Preferences

In Communications prefer:
Telecommunications

In Computer Software prefer:
Software

In Internet Specific prefer:
Internet

Additional Information

Year Founded: 2009
Capital Under Management: $2,000,000
Current Activity Level: Actively seeking new investments

KACHI PARTNERS

2595 Canyon Boulevard
Suite 420
Boulder, CO USA 80302
Phone: 303-962-4900
Fax: 303-442-1673
Website: www.kachipartners.com

Management and Staff

Eric Weissmann, Managing Director
John Helson, Managing Director
Nathan Drake, Vice President

Type of Firm

Private Equity Firm

Project Preferences

Type of Financing Preferred:
Leveraged Buyout
Management Buyouts
Acquisition
Industry Rollups

Geographical Preferences

United States Preferences:
All U.S.

Industry Preferences

In Business Serv. prefer:
Distribution

In Manufact. prefer:
Manufacturing

Additional Information

Year Founded: 2007
Current Activity Level: Actively seeking new investments

KAGAWAGIN CAPITAL CO., LTD

6F KagawaginKameicho Bldg.
7-1 Kameicho
Takamatsu-shi, Japan 760-0050
Phone: 81-87-836-1310
Fax: 81-87-836-1320
Website: www.kagawabank.co.jp

Type of Firm

Bank Affiliated

Additional Information

Year Founded: 1996
Current Activity Level: Actively seeking new investments

KAGISO VENTURES

Kagiso House, 16 Fricker Road
Illovo Boulevard
Illovo, South Africa 2128
Phone: 27-11-537-0520
Fax: 27-11- 537-0530
E-mail: info@kagisoventures.co.za
Website: www.kagiso.com

Type of Firm

Bank Affiliated

Association Membership

South African Venture Capital Association (SAVCA)

Project Preferences

Type of Financing Preferred:
Early Stage
Expansion

Geographical Preferences

International Preferences:
Africa

Additional Information

Year Founded: 1998
Capital Under Management: $51,000,000
Current Activity Level: Actively seeking new investments

KAHALA INVESTMENTS, INC.

8214 Westchester Drive
Suite 715
Dallas, TX USA 75225
Phone: 214-987-0077
Fax: 214-987-2332

Type of Firm

Service Provider

Project Preferences

Role in Financing:
Prefer role as deal originator but will also invest in deals created by others

Type of Financing Preferred:
Leveraged Buyout
Control-block Purchases
Mezzanine

Industry Rollups
Special Situation

Size of Investments Considered:

Min Size of Investment Considered (000s): $10,000
Max Size of Investment Considered: No Limit

Geographical Preferences

United States Preferences:

Southeast
Southwest

Industry Preferences

In Consumer Related prefer:

Entertainment and Leisure
Retail
Franchises(NEC)
Food/Beverage
Consumer Products
Consumer Services

In Industrial/Energy prefer:

Industrial Products
Machinery

Additional Information

Year Founded: 1978
Capital Under Management: $5,000,000
Current Activity Level: Actively seeking new investments
Method of Compensation: Return on invest. most important, but chg. closing fees, service fees, etc.

KAIROS CAPITAL PARTNERS

Westwood Business Center
690 Canton Street, Suite 250
Westwood, MA USA 02090
Phone: 603-595-5637
E-mail: info@kairoscapitalpartners.com
Website: www.kairoscapitalpartners.com

Other Offices

1375 Broadway
Sixth Floor
New York, NY USA 10018

Management and Staff

Andrew Moser, Founding Partner
Don Jones, General Partner
Lynda Davey, Founding Partner
Robert Corliss, Founding Partner

Type of Firm

Private Equity Firm

Project Preferences

Type of Financing Preferred:

Leveraged Buyout
Expansion
Turnaround
Acquisition
Distressed Debt

Industry Preferences

In Consumer Related prefer:

Consumer
Retail
Consumer Products

Additional Information

Year Founded: 2007
Current Activity Level: Actively seeking new investments

KAISER PERMANENTE VENTURES

One Kaiser Plaza
22nd Floor
Oakland, CA USA 94612
Phone: 510-267-7300
Fax: 510-891-7943
Website: www.kpventures.com

Management and Staff

Bob Ward, Principal
David Schulte, Principal
Sarah Kelly, Principal

Type of Firm

Corporate PE/Venture

Association Membership

National Venture Capital Association - USA (NVCA)

Project Preferences

Role in Financing:

Prefer role in deals created by others

Type of Financing Preferred:

Second Stage Financing
Early Stage
Balanced
First Stage Financing

Size of Investments Considered:

Min Size of Investment Considered (000s): $1,500
Max Size of Investment Considered (000s): $5,000

Geographical Preferences

United States Preferences:

All U.S.

Industry Preferences

In Computer Software prefer:

Applications Software

In Biotechnology prefer:

Human Biotechnology

In Medical/Health prefer:

Medical Diagnostics
Diagnostic Services
Diagnostic Test Products
Medical Therapeutics
Drug/Equipmt Delivery
Medical Products
Disposable Med. Products
Health Services
Hospitals/Clinics/Primary
Hospital/Other Instit.

Additional Information

Name of Most Recent Fund: Kaiser Permanente Healthcare Fund IV
Most Recent Fund Was Raised: 01/01/2006
Year Founded: 1998
Capital Under Management: $200,000,000
Current Activity Level: Actively seeking new investments
Method of Compensation: Return on investment is of primary concern, do not charge fees

---

KAIXIN INVESTMENT CO., LTD.

No. 6 Xinyuan Nan Road
Room 1606 Capital Mansion
Beijing, China 100004
Phone: 86-10-8486-8222
Fax: 86-10-8486-8224
Website: www.kaixininvestment.com

Type of Firm

Bank Affiliated

Project Preferences

Type of Financing Preferred:

Early Stage
Expansion
Seed
Startup

Size of Investments Considered:

Min Size of Investment Considered (000s): $2,932
Max Size of Investment Considered (000s): $29,325

Geographical Preferences

International Preferences:

China

Industry Preferences

In Communications prefer:

Wireless Communications

In Internet Specific prefer:

Internet

In Semiconductor/Electr prefer:

Semiconductor

In Medical/Health prefer:

Medical/Health

In Industrial/Energy prefer:

Energy
Energy Conservation Relat
Materials
Machinery
Environmental Related

In Transportation prefer:

Transportation

In Business Serv. prefer:
Services
Media

In Agr/Forestr/Fish prefer:
Agribusiness

Additional Information
Year Founded: 2008
Capital Under Management: $132,000,000
Current Activity Level: Actively seeking new investments

KAIZEN GLOBAL INDIA PRIVATE, LTD. (AKA: KAIZEN GLOBAL)

805 Mayuresh Chambers Plot 60
Sector 11
Mumbai, India 40061
Phone: 91-222-756-4558

Management and Staff
Akhil Shahani, Managing Partner
Reema Shetty, Managing Partner

Type of Firm
Private Equity Firm

Project Preferences

Type of Financing Preferred:
Balanced

Geographical Preferences

International Preferences:
India

Industry Preferences

In Consumer Related prefer:
Consumer Services

Additional Information
Year Founded: 2009
Capital Under Management: $7,000,000
Current Activity Level: Actively seeking new investments

KAMYLON CAPITAL LLC

70 Walnut Street
Wellesley, MA USA 02481
Phone: 781-263-7373
Fax: 781-263-7379
E-mail: info@kamylon.com
Website: www.kamylon.com

Management and Staff
David Sopp, Principal
Richard Spencer, General Partner

Type of Firm
Private Equity Firm

Project Preferences

Type of Financing Preferred:
Leveraged Buyout
Expansion

Industry Preferences

In Medical/Health prefer:
Health Services

In Consumer Related prefer:
Sports
Retail
Consumer Products
Consumer Services

In Transportation prefer:
Transportation

In Financial Services prefer:
Financial Services

In Business Serv. prefer:
Services
Distribution
Media

In Manufact. prefer:
Manufacturing
Publishing

Additional Information
Year Founded: 2008
Capital Under Management: $100,000,000
Current Activity Level: Actively seeking new investments

KANKAKU INVESTMENT CO., LTD.

3-3-3 Nihonbashi honmachi
Chuo ku
Tokyo, Japan 103-0023
Phone: 813-3246-5821
Fax: 813-3246-5881

Type of Firm
Bank Affiliated

Project Preferences

Role in Financing:
Prefer role in deals created by others

Type of Financing Preferred:
Second Stage Financing
Mezzanine
First Stage Financing

Size of Investments Considered:
Min Size of Investment Considered (000s): $500
Max Size of Investment Considered (000s): $1,000

Geographical Preferences

United States Preferences:
All U.S.

International Preferences:
Western Europe
Pacific Rim
Asia

Industry Preferences

In Communications prefer:
Telecommunications
Data Communications

In Computer Software prefer:
Computer Services
Applications Software

In Internet Specific prefer:
Internet

In Computer Other prefer:
Computer Related

In Semiconductor/Electr prefer:
Electronic Components
Semiconductor

In Consumer Related prefer:
Consumer Services

In Industrial/Energy prefer:
Industrial Products

In Transportation prefer:
Transportation

In Financial Services prefer:
Real Estate

In Manufact. prefer:
Manufacturing
Publishing

Additional Information
Year Founded: 1984
Capital Under Management: $180,000,000
Current Activity Level: Actively seeking new investments
Method of Compensation: Return on invest. most important, but chg. closing fees, service fees, etc.

KANSAS TECHNOLOGY ENTERPRISE CORPORATION

214 SW Sixth Street
First Floor
Topeka, KS USA 66603-3719
Phone: 785-296-5272
Fax: 785-296-1160
E-mail: ktec@ktec.com
Website: www.ktec.com

Management and Staff
Kevin Carr, Chief Operating Officer

Type of Firm
Government Affiliated Program

Association Membership
National Venture Capital Association - USA (NVCA)

Project Preferences

Role in Financing:
Will function either as deal originator or investor in deals created by others

Type of Financing Preferred:
Early Stage
Seed

Size of Investments Considered:
Min Size of Investment Considered (000s): $100
Max Size of Investment Considered (000s): $500

Geographical Preferences

United States Preferences:
Midwest

Industry Preferences

In Communications prefer:
Telecommunications
Wireless Communications

In Computer Software prefer:
Data Processing
Systems Software
Applications Software

In Internet Specific prefer:
E-Commerce Technology
Internet
Ecommerce
Web Aggregration/Portals

In Semiconductor/Electr prefer:
Micro-Processing

In Biotechnology prefer:
Biotechnology
Human Biotechnology
Genetic Engineering
Agricultural/Animal Bio.
Industrial Biotechnology
Biotech Related Research

In Medical/Health prefer:
Medical Diagnostics
Medical Therapeutics
Drug/Equipmt Delivery
Medical Products
Pharmaceuticals

In Consumer Related prefer:
Consumer Products

In Industrial/Energy prefer:
Energy
Alternative Energy
Advanced Materials
Machinery

In Transportation prefer:
Aerospace

In Agr/Forestr/Fish prefer:
Agriculture related

Additional Information
Name of Most Recent Fund: KTEC Investments (FKA: Sunflower Technology Ventures)
Most Recent Fund Was Raised: 12/31/1995
Year Founded: 1987
Capital Under Management: $10,000,000
Current Activity Level: Actively seeking new investments
Method of Compensation: Return on investment is of primary concern, do not charge fees

---

KANSAS VENTURE CAPITAL, INC.
11300 Tomahawk Creek Parkway
Suite 250
Leawood, KS USA 66211
Phone: 913-262-7117
Fax: 913-262-3509
E-mail: jdalton@kvci.com
Website: www.kvci.com

Management and Staff
Thomas Blackburn, President

Type of Firm
SBIC

Association Membership
Natl Assoc of Small Bus. Inv. Co (NASBIC)

Project Preferences

Role in Financing:
Prefer role as deal originator but will also invest in deals created by others

Type of Financing Preferred:
Leveraged Buyout
Expansion
Mezzanine
Turnaround
Later Stage
Management Buyouts
Acquisition
Recapitalizations

Size of Investments Considered:
Min Size of Investment Considered (000s): $500
Max Size of Investment Considered (000s): $250,000

Geographical Preferences

United States Preferences:
Midwest

Industry Preferences

In Communications prefer:
Communications and Media

In Computer Other prefer:
Computer Related

In Semiconductor/Electr prefer:
Electronic Components

In Medical/Health prefer:
Medical/Health

In Consumer Related prefer:
Consumer
Retail

In Industrial/Energy prefer:
Industrial Products

In Business Serv. prefer:
Services
Distribution

In Manufact. prefer:
Manufacturing

Additional Information
Name of Most Recent Fund: Kansas Venture Capital, Inc.
Most Recent Fund Was Raised: 01/01/1988
Year Founded: 1977
Capital Under Management: $50,000,000
Current Activity Level: Actively seeking new investments
Method of Compensation: Return on invest. most important, but chg. closing fees, service fees, etc.

KAOFU VENTURE & INVESTMENT CORP.
15008 Sermiamhoo Place
Surrey, Canada
Phone: 604-535-9238
Fax: 604-535-9238

Type of Firm
Private Equity Firm

Additional Information
Year Founded: 1999
Current Activity Level: Actively seeking new investments

KAPITAL-BETEILIGUNGS AG (KABAG)
Am Modenapark 2
Vienna, Austria A-1030
Phone: 43-1712-52590
Fax: 43-1712-525928
E-mail: info@kabag.at
Website: www.kabag.at

Type of Firm
Incubator/Development Program

Project Preferences

Type of Financing Preferred:
Expansion
Unknown
Turnaround

Geographical Preferences

International Preferences:
Austria

Industry Preferences

In Communications prefer:
Telecommunications

In Consumer Related prefer:
Consumer Services

In Industrial/Energy prefer:
Energy
Industrial Products

Additional Information

Year Founded: 1997
Capital Under Management: $7,600,000
Current Activity Level: Actively seeking new investments

KARNATAKA INFORMATION TECHNOLOGY VENTURE CAPITAL FUND

403, 4th Floor, HVS Court
21 Cunningham Road
Bangalore, India 560052
Phone: 91-80-2228-5627
Fax: 91-80-2238-6836
Website: www.kitven.com

Management and Staff

A.R. Jayakumar, Chief Executive Officer
R.B. Shetty, Managing Director

Type of Firm

Government Affiliated Program

Association Membership

Indian Venture Capital Association (IVCA)

Project Preferences

Type of Financing Preferred:
Early Stage
Expansion
Mezzanine
Startup

Size of Investments Considered:
Min Size of Investment Considered (000s): $5,000
Max Size of Investment Considered (000s): $15,000

Geographical Preferences

International Preferences:
India

Industry Preferences

In Communications prefer:
Communications and Media

In Computer Software prefer:
Software

In Internet Specific prefer:
Internet

In Computer Other prefer:
Computer Related

In Semiconductor/Electr prefer:
Electronics
Semiconductor

Additional Information

Year Founded: 1998
Capital Under Management: $2,200,000
Current Activity Level: Actively seeking new investments

KAROLINSKA DEVELOPMENT AB

Fogdevreten 2
Solna
Stockholm, Sweden S-171 77
Phone: 46-8-524-86591
Fax: 46-8-303-423
E-mail: info@karolinskadevelopment.com
Website: www.karolinskadevelopment.com

Management and Staff

Conny Bogentoft, Chief Executive Officer
Gunnar Casserstedt, Chief Financial Officer

Type of Firm

Private Equity Firm

Project Preferences

Role in Financing:
Prefer role as deal originator

Type of Financing Preferred:
Early Stage
Expansion
Balanced

Geographical Preferences

International Preferences:
Sweden

Additional Information

Year Founded: 2008
Current Activity Level: Actively seeking new investments

KAROLINSKA INVESTMENT MANAGEMENT AB

Nobels Vag 15A
Karolinska Institutet
Stockholm, Sweden 171 77
Phone: 46-8-5088-4450
Fax: 46-8-5088-4459
E-mail: info@karolinskafund.com
Website: www.karolinskafund.com

Management and Staff

Kjell Simonsson, Managing Director

Type of Firm

Private Equity Firm

Association Membership

Swedish Venture Capital Association (SVCA)

Project Preferences

Type of Financing Preferred:
Leveraged Buyout
Expansion
Seed
Startup

Geographical Preferences

International Preferences:
Scandanavia/Nordic Region

Industry Preferences

In Biotechnology prefer:
Biotechnology

In Medical/Health prefer:
Medical Products
Pharmaceuticals

Additional Information

Year Founded: 1999
Capital Under Management: $53,100,000
Current Activity Level: Actively seeking new investments

KARPREILLY LLC

1700 East Putnam
Suite 100
Old Greenwich, CT USA 06870
Phone: 203-504-9900
Fax: 203-504-9901
Website: www.karpreilly.com

Type of Firm

Private Equity Firm

Project Preferences

Type of Financing Preferred:
Leveraged Buyout
Expansion
Management Buyouts
Acquisition
Recapitalizations

Size of Investments Considered:
Min Size of Investment Considered (000s): $10,000
Max Size of Investment Considered (000s): $75,000

Geographical Preferences

United States Preferences:
All U.S.

Industry Preferences

In Medical/Health prefer:
Health Services

In Consumer Related prefer:
Consumer
Retail

Consumer Products
Other Restaurants

Additional Information

Year Founded: 2007
Capital Under Management: $200,000,000
Current Activity Level: Actively seeking new investments

KATALYST VENTURES LIMITED

10 Fenchurch Avenue
London, United Kingdom EC3M 5BN
Phone: 44-870-420-2565
Fax: 44-871-990-6338
E-mail: info@katalystventures.com
Website: www.katalystventures.com

Management and Staff

Alexander Macpherson, Chief Executive Officer

Type of Firm

Private Equity Advisor or Fund of Funds

Association Membership

British Venture Capital Association (BVCA)

Project Preferences

Type of Financing Preferred:
Leveraged Buyout
Early Stage
Expansion
Turnaround
Seed
Management Buyouts
Startup

Size of Investments Considered:
Min Size of Investment Considered (000s): $146
Max Size of Investment Considered (000s): $1,458

Geographical Preferences

International Preferences:
United Kingdom

Additional Information

Year Founded: 2001
Capital Under Management: $6,600,000
Current Activity Level: Actively seeking new investments

KAUPTHING BANK HF.

Borgartun 19
Reykjavik, Sweden IS-105
Phone: 354-444-6000
Fax: 354-444-6009
E-mail: info@kaupthing.net
Website: www.kaupthing.net

Other Offices

Pohjoisesplanadi 37A
6th floor
Helsinki, Finland 00100
Phone: 358-9-4784-000
Fax: 358-9-4784-0111

230 Park Avenue
Suite 1528
New York, NY USA 10169
Phone: 212-457-8700
Fax: 212-457-8725

Armuli 13A
Reykjavik, Iceland 108
Phone: 354-515-1500
Fax: 354-515-1505

Olav V's gt 5
Postboks 1914 Vika
Oslo, Norway 0161
Phone: 47-2414-7400
Fax: 47-2414-7401

Stureplan 19
Stockholm, Sweden 107 81
Phone: 46-8-791-4800
Fax: 46-8-611-2690

One Hanover Street
London, United Kingdom W1S 1AX
Phone: 44-020-3205-5000
Fax: 44-020-3205-5001

Bokbindaragta 8
Postboks 3090
Torshavn, Faroe Islands 110
Phone: 298-351-500
Fax: 298-351-501

35a avenue J.F. Kennedy
Luxembourg, Luxembourg 1855
Phone: 352-46-3131
Fax: 352-46-3132

1 Rue de Rive
Geneva, Switzerland 1204
Phone: 41-22-591-2941
Fax: 41-22-591-2942

Langelinie Alle 43
Copenhagen, Denmark 2100
Phone: 45-7222-5000
Fax: 45-7222-5018

Management and Staff

Ingolfur Helgason, Chief Executive Officer
John Skajem, Managing Director

Type of Firm

Bank Affiliated

Association Membership

Swedish Venture Capital Association (SVCA)
European Private Equity and Venture Capital Assoc.

Project Preferences

Type of Financing Preferred:
Second Stage Financing
Leveraged Buyout
Early Stage
Expansion
Mezzanine
Balanced
Startup

Geographical Preferences

International Preferences:
United Kingdom
Europe
Iceland
Scandanavia/Nordic Region

Industry Preferences

In Communications prefer:
Wireless Communications

In Biotechnology prefer:
Biotechnology

In Medical/Health prefer:
Medical/Health

In Industrial/Energy prefer:
Industrial Products
Materials

In Business Serv. prefer:
Services

Additional Information

Year Founded: 2000
Capital Under Management: $35,700,000
Current Activity Level: Actively seeking new investments

KB INVESTMENT CO., LTD. (FKA: KOOKMIN INVESTMENT COMPANY)

9th Floor, Sinyeong Building
68-5 Cheongdam-dong Gangnam-gu
Seoul, South Korea 135-953
Phone: 822-545-5091
Fax: 822-545-5092
Website: www.kbic.co.kr

Management and Staff

Nam Sik Yang, Chief Executive Officer

Type of Firm

Bank Affiliated

Association Membership

Korean Venture Capital Association (KVCA)

Project Preferences

Type of Financing Preferred:
Leveraged Buyout
Early Stage

Expansion
Balanced
Turnaround
Management Buyouts
Recapitalizations

Geographical Preferences

International Preferences:
Korea, South
Asia
Australia

Industry Preferences

In Semiconductor/Electr prefer:
Electronics

In Consumer Related prefer:
Consumer Products

In Industrial/Energy prefer:
Industrial Products

In Financial Services prefer:
Financial Services

Additional Information
Year Founded: 1990
Capital Under Management: $107,100,000
Current Activity Level: Actively seeking new investments

KB PARTNERS LLC
1780 Green Bay Road
Suite 202
Highland Park, IL USA 60035
Phone: 847-681-1270
Fax: 847681-1370
Website: www.kbpartners.com

Management and Staff
Byron Denenberg, Managing Director
Keith Bank, Managing Director
Robert Zieserl, Managing Director
Robert Garber, Managing Director

Type of Firm
Private Equity Firm

Association Membership
Illinois Venture Capital Association

Project Preferences

Role in Financing:
Will function either as deal originator or investor in deals created by others

Type of Financing Preferred:
Early Stage
Expansion
Startup
Special Situation

Size of Investments Considered:
Min Size of Investment Considered (000s): $1,000
Max Size of Investment Considered (000s): $5,000

Geographical Preferences

United States Preferences:
Midwest
All U.S.

Industry Focus
(% based on actual investment)

Semiconductors/Other Elect.	23.5%
Internet Specific	19.6%
Computer Software and Services	18.2%
Communications and Media	14.9%
Medical/Health	10.6%
Industrial/Energy	6.1%
Biotechnology	4.9%
Computer Hardware	2.2%

Additional Information
Name of Most Recent Fund: KB Partners Venture Fund II, L.P.
Most Recent Fund Was Raised: 06/09/2000
Year Founded: 1996
Capital Under Management: $98,000,000
Current Activity Level: Actively seeking new investments
Method of Compensation: Return on investment is of primary concern, do not charge fees

KBC PRIVATE EQUITY NV
Havenlaan 12
Brussels, Belgium 1080
Phone: 32-2-429-3645
Fax: 32-2-429-0525
E-mail: info@kbcpe.be
Website: www.kbcpe.be

Other Offices
Skretova 12
Prague, Czech Republic 120 00
Phone: 420-2-2142-4111
Fax: 420-2-2142-4204

ul. Chmielna 85/87
Warsaw, Poland 00-805
Phone: 48-22-581-0826
Fax: 48-22-581-0358

68, rue du faubourg Saint-Honore
Paris, France 75008
Phone: 33-1-53-05-2930
Fax: 33-1-53-05-2969

Management and Staff
Floris Vansina, Managing Director
Philippe De Vick, Managing Director

Type of Firm
Bank Affiliated

Association Membership
Belgium Venturing Association
European Private Equity and Venture Capital Assoc.

Project Preferences

Type of Financing Preferred:
Leveraged Buyout
Mezzanine
Early Stage
Expansion
Generalist PE
Balanced
Acquisition

Size of Investments Considered:
Min Size of Investment Considered (000s): $2,790
Max Size of Investment Considered (000s): $69,774

Geographical Preferences

International Preferences:
Netherlands
Central Europe
Eastern Europe
Belgium

Industry Preferences

In Communications prefer:
Communications and Media

In Computer Other prefer:
Computer Related

In Semiconductor/Electr prefer:
Electronics

In Biotechnology prefer:
Biotechnology

In Medical/Health prefer:
Medical/Health

In Consumer Related prefer:
Consumer

In Industrial/Energy prefer:
Energy
Industrial Products
Materials

Additional Information
Year Founded: 1993
Capital Under Management: $596,300,000
Current Activity Level: Actively seeking new investments

KBL HEALTHCARE VENTURES
380 Lexington Avenue
31st Floor
New York, NY USA 10168
Phone: 212-319-5555
Fax: 212-319-5591
E-mail: inquiries@kblvc.com
Website: www.kblvc.com

Management and Staff
Eli Berk, Vice President
Marlene Krauss, Managing Director
Mike Kaswan, Managing Director
Zachary Berk, Managing Director

Type of Firm

Private Equity Firm

Association Membership

National Venture Capital Association - USA (NVCA)
Natl Assoc of Small Bus. Inv. Co (NASBIC)

Project Preferences

Role in Financing:

Will function either as deal originator or investor in deals created by others

Type of Financing Preferred:

Second Stage Financing
Mezzanine
Research and Development
Early Stage
Expansion
Start-up Financing
Public Companies
Turnaround
Later Stage
Seed
First Stage Financing
Private Placement
Recapitalizations

Size of Investments Considered:

Min Size of Investment Considered (000s): $500
Max Size of Investment Considered (000s): $6,000

Industry Focus

(% based on actual investment)

Medical/Health	47.6%
Biotechnology	24.0%
Internet Specific	16.8%
Communications and Media	8.2%
Computer Software and Services	3.4%

Additional Information

Name of Most Recent Fund: KBL Healthcare Ventures
Most Recent Fund Was Raised: 08/06/1999
Year Founded: 1991
Capital Under Management: $100,000,000
Current Activity Level: Actively seeking new investments
Method of Compensation: Return on investment is of primary concern, do not charge fees

---

KCA PARTNERS, LTD.

580 California Street
Suite 1600
San Francisco, CA USA 94104
Phone: 415-433-4494
Fax: 415-433-4493
E-mail: info@kcapartners.com
Website: www.kcapartners.com

Management and Staff

JP Lachance, Vice President
PJ Nora, Partner
Sedge Dienst, Partner

Type of Firm

Private Equity Firm

Project Preferences

Type of Financing Preferred:

Leveraged Buyout
Turnaround
Management Buyouts
Recapitalizations

Geographical Preferences

United States Preferences:

All U.S.

Industry Preferences

In Consumer Related prefer:

Consumer
Food/Beverage
Consumer Products
Consumer Services

In Industrial/Energy prefer:

Alternative Energy

In Transportation prefer:

Aerospace

In Business Serv. prefer:

Distribution

In Manufact. prefer:

Manufacturing

In Other prefer:

Environment Responsible

Additional Information

Year Founded: 1993
Current Activity Level: Actively seeking new investments

KCPS ISRAEL PRIVATE EQUITY PARTNERS

132 Menachem Begin Boulevard
30F, One Azrieli Center
Tel Aviv, Israel 67021
Website: www.kcs-pe.com

Other Offices

540 Madison Avenue
19th Floor
New York, NY USA 10022

Management and Staff

Gilad Shavit, General Partner
Yitzhak Raab, Chief Financial Officer

Type of Firm

Bank Affiliated

Project Preferences

Type of Financing Preferred:

Leveraged Buyout

Geographical Preferences

International Preferences:

Israel

Additional Information

Year Founded: 2005
Current Activity Level: Actively seeking new investments

KD GROUP

Celovska 206
Ljubljana, Slovenia SL 1000
Phone: 386-1-582-6700
Fax: 386-1-519-2847
E-mail: info@kd-group.si
Website: www.kd-group.si

Management and Staff

Gavin Ryan, Partner
Matjaz Peterman, Managing Partner
Matjaz Gantar, President

Type of Firm

Private Equity Firm

Project Preferences

Type of Financing Preferred:

Balanced

Geographical Preferences

International Preferences:

Slovenia
Czech Republic
Europe
Eastern Europe
Bulgaria
Romania

Additional Information

Year Founded: 2005
Current Activity Level: Actively seeking new investments

KD VENTURES, LLC

26 Turtle Rock Court
Tiburon, CA USA 94920
Management and Staff
Kathy Dell, Managing Director

Type of Firm

Private Equity Firm

Project Preferences

Type of Financing Preferred:

Early Stage
Additional Information
Year Founded: 2004
Current Activity Level: Actively seeking new investments

KEARNY VENTURE PARTNERS

88 Kearny Street
4th Floor
San Francisco, CA USA 94108
Phone: 415-364-5991
Fax: 415-364-6944
Website: www.kearnyvp.com

Management and Staff

Andrew Jensen, Chief Financial Officer
Anupam Dalal, General Partner
Caley Castelein, General Partner
James Shapiro, General Partner
Richard Glickman, Partner
Richard Spalding, General Partner

Type of Firm

Private Equity Firm

Association Membership

National Venture Capital Association - USA (NVCA)

Project Preferences

Role in Financing:
Prefer role in deals created by others

Type of Financing Preferred:
Early Stage
Balanced

Size of Investments Considered:
Min Size of Investment Considered (000s): $500
Max Size of Investment Considered (000s): $10,000

Geographical Preferences

United States Preferences:
All U.S.

International Preferences:
All International

Industry Preferences

In Biotechnology prefer:
Biotechnology

In Medical/Health prefer:
Medical/Health
Medical Diagnostics
Medical Therapeutics
Medical Products

Additional Information

Name of Most Recent Fund: Kearny Venture Partners, L.P.
Most Recent Fund Was Raised: 09/13/2006
Year Founded: 2001
Capital Under Management: $300,000,000
Current Activity Level: Actively seeking new investments
Method of Compensation: Return on investment is of primary concern, do not charge fees

KEGONSA CAPITAL PARTNERS, LLC

5520 Nobel Drive
Suite 150
Madison, WI USA 53711
Phone: 608-310-4454
Fax: 608-310-4456
E-mail: info@kegonsapartners.com
Website: www.kegonsapartners.com

Management and Staff

Kenneth Johnson, Managing Director

Type of Firm

Private Equity Firm

Association Membership

National Venture Capital Association - USA (NVCA)

Project Preferences

Role in Financing:
Prefer role as deal originator

Type of Financing Preferred:
Early Stage
Seed

Size of Investments Considered:
Min Size of Investment Considered (000s): $100
Max Size of Investment Considered (000s): $750

Geographical Preferences

United States Preferences:
Midwest

Industry Preferences

In Computer Software prefer:
Software

Additional Information

Name of Most Recent Fund: Kegonsa Seed Fund I, L.P.
Most Recent Fund Was Raised: 04/27/2004
Year Founded: 2004
Capital Under Management: $11,000,000
Current Activity Level: Actively seeking new investments
Method of Compensation: Return on investment is of primary concern, do not charge fees

KEIRETSU FORUM

3466 Mt. Diablo Boulevard
Suite C-205
Lafayette, CA USA 94549
Phone: 925-283-8829
Fax: 925-283-8159
E-mail: sonja@keiretsuforum.com
Website: www.keiretsuforum.com

Management and Staff

Randy Williams, Chief Executive Officer

Type of Firm

Angel Group

Project Preferences

Type of Financing Preferred:
Early Stage
Expansion

Geographical Preferences

Canadian Preferences:
All Canada

Additional Information

Year Founded: 2000
Current Activity Level: Actively seeking new investments
Method of Compensation: Professional fee required whether or not deal closes

KELSO & COMPANY

320 Park Avenue
24th Floor
New York, NY USA 10022
Phone: 212-751-3939
Fax: 212-223-2379
Website: www.kelso.com

Management and Staff

Frank Bynum, Managing Director
Howard Matlin, Chief Financial Officer
Thomas Wall, Managing Director

Type of Firm

Bank Affiliated

Project Preferences

Type of Financing Preferred:
Leveraged Buyout
Mezzanine
Acquisition
Recapitalizations

Geographical Preferences

United States Preferences:
All U.S.

Canadian Preferences:
All Canada

International Preferences:
Mexico
All International

Industry Focus

(% based on actual investment)

Other Products	43.3%
Consumer Related	13.7%
Industrial/Energy	13.6%
Medical/Health	10.2%
Communications and Media	9.9%
Semiconductors/Other Elect.	6.9%
Computer Software and Services	1.5%
Internet Specific	0.5%
Biotechnology	0.4%

Additional Information

Year Founded: 1971
Capital Under Management: $3,378,400,000
Current Activity Level: Actively seeking new investments

KELSO PLACE ASSET MANAGEMENT LIMITED

110 St Martin's Lane
London, United Kingdom WC2N 4BA
Phone: 44-20-7836-0000
Fax: 44-20-7836-1001
E-mail: info@kelsoplace.com
Website: www.kelsoplace.com

Management and Staff

John Drinkwater, Managing Director

Type of Firm

Private Equity Firm

Association Membership

British Venture Capital Association (BVCA)

Project Preferences

Type of Financing Preferred:

Early Stage
Expansion
Turnaround
Special Situation

Geographical Preferences

International Preferences:

United Kingdom
Europe

Additional Information

Year Founded: 2000
Capital Under Management: $204,500,000
Current Activity Level: Actively seeking new investments

KENDALL CAPITAL ASSOCIATES LLC

6817 Fairview Road
Charlotte, NC USA 28210
Phone: 704-366-3880
Fax: 704-366-6177
E-mail: info@kendallcap.com
Website: www.kendallcap.com

Management and Staff

James Phelps, Managing Director

Type of Firm

Bank Affiliated

Project Preferences

Type of Financing Preferred:

Leveraged Buyout
Early Stage
Mezzanine
Generalist PE
Acquisition

Geographical Preferences

United States Preferences:

Southeast

Industry Preferences

In Computer Software prefer:

Software

In Internet Specific prefer:

Ecommerce

In Semiconductor/Electr prefer:

Semiconductor

In Biotechnology prefer:

Biotechnology

In Medical/Health prefer:

Medical/Health

In Business Serv. prefer:

Distribution

In Manufact. prefer:

Manufacturing

Additional Information

Current Activity Level: Actively seeking new investments

KENDALL COURT CAPITAL PARTNERS, LTD.

250 North Bridge Road
#13-02 Raffles City Tower
Singapore, Singapore 179101
Phone: 65-6491-1121
Fax: 65-6491-1147
Website: www.kendallcourt.com

Other Offices

Suite 21-03 Centerpoint South
Lingkaran Syed Putra
Kuala Lumpur, Malaysia 59200
Phone: 603-2282-0780
Fax: 603-2283-1780

22nd Citibank Tower
Jl. Jend. Sudirman Kav. 54-55
Jakarta, Indonesia 12190
Phone: 6221-527-6180
Fax: 6221-527-6181

Management and Staff

Chris Chia, Managing Partner
Dennis Wuisan, Partner

Type of Firm

Private Equity Firm

Project Preferences

Type of Financing Preferred:

Leveraged Buyout
Mezzanine
Expansion
Acquisition
Recapitalizations

Size of Investments Considered:

Min Size of Investment Considered (000s): $5,000
Max Size of Investment Considered (000s): $15,000

Geographical Preferences

International Preferences:

Asia

Additional Information

Year Founded: 2004
Capital Under Management: $152,000,000
Current Activity Level: Actively seeking new investments

KENDALL INVESTMENTS

122 Mount Auburn Street
Cambridge, MA USA 02138
Phone: 617-374-3707
Fax: 617-3743733
Website: www.kendallinvestments.com

Type of Firm

Private Equity Advisor or Fund of Funds

Additional Information

Year Founded: 2006
Current Activity Level: Actively seeking new investments

KENMORE PRIVATE EQUITY, LTD. (AKA: KPE)

58 Davies Street
First Floor
London, United Kingdom W1K 5JF
Phone: 44-207-6294480
Fax: 44-207-3181830
Website: www.kpequity.com

Other Offices

65 Church Street
Birmingham, United Kingdom B3 2DP
Phone: 44-121-2623700
Fax: 44-121-2623711

33 Castle Street
Edinburgh, United Kingdom EH2 3DN
Phone: 44-131-2269000
Fax: 44-131-2269001

Pearl Assurance House
23 Princess Street
Manchester, United Kingdom M2 4EB
Phone: 44-161-2360105
Fax: 44-161-2360106

Norrlandsgatan 18
Stockholm, Sweden SE-11143
Phone: 46-8545-335-60
Fax: 46-8611-4710

Venturers House
Prince Street
Bristol, United Kingdom BS1 4PB
Phone: 44-117-9154022
Fax: 44-117-9154352

Brusselstraat 51
Antwerpen, Belgium B-2018
Phone: 32-3-242-8816

Level Forty One, Emirates Towers
Sheikh Zayed Road, PO Box 282110
Dubai, Utd. Arab Em.
Phone: 971-4-319-9033
Fax: 971-4-319-3365

Potsdamer Platz 11
Berlin, Germany 10785
Phone: 49-30-2589-5020
Fax: 49-30-2589-4100

4 rue de Penthievre
Paris, France 75008
Phone: 33-1-5664-0404
Fax: 33-1-4070-0958

1 City Square
Leeds, United Kingdom LS1 2ES
Phone: 44-113-3663303
Fax: 44-113-3663033

Management and Staff

Simon Dempsey, Managing Director

Type of Firm

Bank Affiliated

Project Preferences

Type of Financing Preferred:

Management Buyouts
Acquisition

Geographical Preferences

International Preferences:

United Kingdom
Europe

Industry Preferences

In Consumer Related prefer:

Entertainment and Leisure
Sports
Consumer Services

In Financial Services prefer:

Investment Groups

In Other prefer:

Environment Responsible

Additional Information

Year Founded: 2006
Current Activity Level: Actively seeking new investments

KENNET VENTURE PARTNERS, LTD. (FKA: KENNET CAPITAL, LTD.)

Nuffield House
41-46 Piccadilly
London, United Kingdom W1J 0DS
Phone: 44-20-7839-8020
Fax: 44-20-7434-2973
E-mail: info@kennet.com
Website: www.kennet.com

Other Offices

950 Tower Lane
Suite 1710
Foster City, CA USA 94404
Phone: 650-573-8700
Fax: 650-573-8712

Management and Staff

David Carratt, Managing Director
Javier Rojas, Managing Director
Maximilian Bleyleben, Partner
Michael Elias, Managing Director

Type of Firm

Private Equity Firm

Association Membership

British Venture Capital Association (BVCA)
European Private Equity and Venture Capital Assoc.

Project Preferences

Role in Financing:

Prefer role as deal originator but will also invest in deals created by others

Type of Financing Preferred:

Early Stage
Expansion
Balanced
Startup

Size of Investments Considered:

Min Size of Investment Considered (000s): $4,000
Max Size of Investment Considered (000s): $20,000

Geographical Preferences

International Preferences:

United Kingdom
Europe
Bermuda
Germany
France

Industry Focus

(% based on actual investment)

Internet Specific	48.3%
Computer Software and Services	34.5%
Communications and Media	7.9%
Semiconductors/Other Elect.	5.5%
Medical/Health	3.8%

Additional Information

Name of Most Recent Fund: Kennet II
Most Recent Fund Was Raised: 12/31/2000
Year Founded: 1997
Capital Under Management: $280,000,000
Current Activity Level: Actively seeking new investments
Method of Compensation: Return on investment is of primary concern, do not charge fees

---

KENSINGTON CAPITAL PARTNERS

95 St. Clair Avenue West
Suite 1401
Toronto, Canada M4V 1N6
Phone: 416-632-9000
Fax: 416-362-0939
Website: www.kcpl.ca

Management and Staff

Mary Ann Leon, Vice President
Rick Nathan, Partner
Thomas Kennedy, President, Founder

Type of Firm

Private Equity Firm

Project Preferences

Type of Financing Preferred:

Fund of Funds

Geographical Preferences

United States Preferences:

All U.S.

Canadian Preferences:

All Canada

Additional Information

Year Founded: 1996
Current Activity Level: Actively seeking new investments

KENSON VENTURES LLC

695 Oak Grove Avenue
Suite 330
Menlo Park, CA USA 94025
Phone: 650-330-0322
Fax: 650-330-0577
Website: www.kensonventures.com

Management and Staff

Joseph Huang, Vice President
Yishan Li, Vice President

Type of Firm

Private Equity Firm

Additional Information

Year Founded: 1999
Current Activity Level: Actively seeking new investments

KENTRA AS

Akersgaten 11
Oslo, Norway 0158
Phone: 47-22-47-4290
Fax: 47-22-47-4291
Website: www.kentra.no

Type of Firm

Private Equity Firm

Additional Information

Current Activity Level: Actively seeking new investments

KENTUCKY SEED CAPITAL FUND

201 East Jefferson Street
Suite 315
Louisville, KY USA 40202
Phone: 502-569-1590
E-mail: info@kyseed.com
Website: www.kyseed.com

Other Offices

1500 Bull Lea Road
Suite 206
Lexington, KY USA 40511
Phone: 502-569-1590

Management and Staff

George Emont, Managing Partner
Steve Gailar, Managing Partner

Type of Firm

Private Equity Firm

Project Preferences

Type of Financing Preferred:

Seed

Geographical Preferences

United States Preferences:

Kansas
Louisiana
Kentucky

Industry Preferences

In Medical/Health prefer:

Medical/Health
Medical Products
Health Services

Additional Information

Year Founded: 2005
Capital Under Management: $5,000,000
Current Activity Level: Actively seeking new investments

KEPHA PARTNERS

1050 Winter Street
Suite 1000
North Waltham, MA USA 02451
Phone: 751-577-0355
E-mail: info@kephapartners.com
Website: www.kephapartners

Management and Staff

Eric Hjerpe, Partner
Jo Tango, Founder

Type of Firm

Private Equity Firm

Project Preferences

Type of Financing Preferred:

Seed
Startup

Additional Information

Name of Most Recent Fund: Kepha Partners I, L.P.
Most Recent Fund Was Raised: 10/14/2008
Year Founded: 2006
Capital Under Management: $94,700,000
Current Activity Level: Actively seeking new investments

KERALA VENTURE CAPITAL FUND PVT, LTD. (AKA: KVCF PVT LTD)

604, Pioneer Towers
Marine Drive
Kochi, India 682 031
Phone: 91-484-236-1279
Fax: 91-484-237-3077
E-mail: kvcf@vsnl.in
Website: www.keralaventure.org

Management and Staff

K.A. Joseph, CEO & Managing Director

Type of Firm

Government Affiliated Program

Association Membership

Indian Venture Capital Association (IVCA)

Project Preferences

Type of Financing Preferred:

Early Stage
Expansion
Mezzanine
Startup

Size of Investments Considered:

Min Size of Investment Considered (000s): $52
Max Size of Investment Considered (000s): $890

Geographical Preferences

International Preferences:

India

Industry Preferences

In Communications prefer:

Communications and Media

In Computer Software prefer:

Software

In Computer Other prefer:

Computer Related

In Semiconductor/Electr prefer:

Electronics

In Biotechnology prefer:

Biotechnology

Additional Information

Year Founded: 1999
Capital Under Management: $4,400,000
Current Activity Level: Actively seeking new investments

KERN PARTNERS

200 Doll Block 116
8th Avenue Southeast
Calgary, Canada T2G 0K4
Phone: 403-517-1500
Website: www.kernpartners.com

Management and Staff

Jeff Van Steenbergen, Founding Partner
Pentti Karkkainen, Founding Partner

Type of Firm

Private Equity Firm

Project Preferences

Type of Financing Preferred:

Leveraged Buyout
Acquisition

Geographical Preferences

Canadian Preferences:

All Canada

Industry Preferences

In Industrial/Energy prefer:

Energy

Oil and Gas Exploration
Oil & Gas Drilling,Explor
Coal Related

Additional Information

Year Founded: 2000
Capital Under Management: $553,200,000
Current Activity Level: Actively seeking new investments

KERN WHELAN CAPITAL, LLC

402 Jackson Street
San Francisco, CA USA 94111
Phone: 415-694-7064
Fax: 415-694-7065
E-mail: info@kernwhelan.com
Website: www.kernwhelan.com

Management and Staff

J.P. Whelan, Founder
Jay Kern, Founder

Type of Firm

Private Equity Firm

Project Preferences

Type of Financing Preferred:

Balanced

Geographical Preferences

United States Preferences:

All U.S.

Additional Information

Year Founded: 2007
Current Activity Level: Actively seeking new investments

KERNEL CAPITAL PARTNERS

Rubicon Centre, Rossa Avenue
Bishopstown
Cork, Ireland
Phone: 353-21-492-8974
Fax: 353-21-492-8977
Website: www.kernelcapital.ie

Other Offices

Eagle House, 16 Wentworth
Lower Grand Canal
Dublin 2, Ireland
Phone: 353-1-424-0040
Fax: 353-21-492-8977

Management and Staff

Niall Olden, Managing Director
Ralph Parkes, Venture Partner

Type of Firm

Private Equity Firm

Association Membership

Irish Venture Capital Association

Project Preferences

Type of Financing Preferred:

Expansion
Early Stage
Balanced
Seed
Later Stage
Management Buyouts

Size of Investments Considered:

Min Size of Investment Considered (000s): $2,974
Max Size of Investment Considered (000s): $14,872

Geographical Preferences

International Preferences:

Ireland
Europe

Additional Information

Year Founded: 2002
Capital Under Management: $141,700,000
Current Activity Level: Actively seeking new investments

KERTEN CAPITAL

Park View
Beech Hill Office Campus
Dublin, Ireland 4
Phone: 353-818-300-181
E-mail: info@kerten.com
Website: www.kerten.com

Other Offices

Warsaw Financial Centre, 17th Flr.
ul. Emili Plater 53
Warszawa, Poland 00-113
Phone: 48-22-540-6150

Str. Sold. Octavian Moraru nr. 1ro
Sector 1
Bucharest, Romania 011893
Phone: 40-21-231-3016

Type of Firm

Private Equity Firm

Geographical Preferences

International Preferences:

Central Europe
Eastern Europe

Industry Preferences

In Medical/Health prefer:

Medical/Health

In Consumer Related prefer:

Food/Beverage

In Industrial/Energy prefer:

Energy
Environmental Related

In Financial Services prefer:

Financial Services

Additional Information

Year Founded: 2008
Current Activity Level: Actively seeking new investments

KESTREL CAPITAL (FKA: NANYANG VENTURES PTY., LTD.)

5 Lime Street
Suite 425
Sydney, Australia 2000
Phone: 612-8243-1600
Fax: 612-9262-5668
E-mail: enquiries@kestrelcapital.com.au
Website: www.kestrelcapital.com.au

Management and Staff

Niall Cairns, Managing Director
Phillip Carter, Managing Director
Wayne Longbottom, Chief Financial Officer

Type of Firm

Private Equity Firm

Association Membership

Australian Venture Capital Association (AVCAL)

Project Preferences

Role in Financing:

Prefer role as deal originator

Type of Financing Preferred:

Control-block Purchases
Leveraged Buyout
Expansion
Later Stage

Size of Investments Considered:

Min Size of Investment Considered (000s): $5,000
Max Size of Investment Considered (000s): $20,000

Geographical Preferences

International Preferences:

Australia
New Zealand

Industry Focus

(% based on actual investment)	
Computer Software and Services	39.4%
Other Products	26.7%
Consumer Related	12.3%
Industrial/Energy	5.8%
Semiconductors/Other Elect.	5.1%
Computer Hardware	5.1%
Medical/Health	2.9%
Communications and Media	2.8%

Additional Information

Name of Most Recent Fund: Nanyang Australia II Ltd (FKA: St.George Dev't Capital II)
Most Recent Fund Was Raised: 11/16/1999
Year Founded: 1993
Capital Under Management: $78,900,000
Current Activity Level: Actively seeking new investments
Method of Compensation: Professional fee required whether or not deal closes

---

KESTREL ENERGY PARTNERS LLC

520 Broad Hollow Road
Melville, NY USA 11747
Phone: 631-421-2711
Fax: 631-214-4238
Website: www.kestrelenergypartners.com

Type of Firm

Private Equity Firm

Project Preferences

Type of Financing Preferred:

Balanced

Geographical Preferences

United States Preferences:

All U.S.

Additional Information

Year Founded: 2005
Current Activity Level: Actively seeking new investments

KESTREL MANAGEMENT LLC

One Liberty Street
Suite 1200
Boston, MA USA 02109
Phone: 617-451-6722
Fax: 617-451-3322
Website: www.kestrelvm.com

Type of Firm

Service Provider

Association Membership

New England Venture Capital Association

Project Preferences

Role in Financing:

Will function either as deal originator or investor in deals created by others

Type of Financing Preferred:

Second Stage Financing
Start-up Financing
Seed
First Stage Financing

Size of Investments Considered:

Min Size of Investment Considered (000s): $250
Max Size of Investment Considered (000s): $1,000

Geographical Preferences

United States Preferences:

Northeast

Industry Focus

(% based on actual investment)

Internet Specific	29.5%
Biotechnology	27.1%
Communications and Media	9.3%
Computer Software and Services	9.1%
Semiconductors/Other Elect.	7.0%
Other Products	5.3%
Consumer Related	4.6%
Computer Hardware	3.3%
Industrial/Energy	2.4%
Medical/Health	2.4%

Additional Information

Name of Most Recent Fund: Mass Ventures Equity Fund, LP
Most Recent Fund Was Raised: 03/10/1997
Year Founded: 1996
Capital Under Management: $25,000,000
Current Activity Level: Actively seeking new investments
Method of Compensation: Return on investment is of primary concern, do not charge fees

---

KETTLE PARTNERS

350 West Hubbard Street
Suite 350
Chicago, IL USA 60610
Phone: 312-329-9300
Fax: 312-329-9310

Management and Staff

David Semmel, Managing Partner

Type of Firm

Private Equity Firm

Project Preferences

Role in Financing:

Prefer role as deal originator but will also invest in deals created by others

Type of Financing Preferred:

Second Stage Financing
Early Stage
Seed
First Stage Financing

Size of Investments Considered:

Min Size of Investment Considered (000s): $1,000
Max Size of Investment Considered (000s): $5,000

Industry Focus

(% based on actual investment)

Internet Specific	68.0%
Communications and Media	15.8%
Other Products	9.8%
Computer Software and Services	6.3%

Additional Information

Name of Most Recent Fund: Kettle Partners II L.P.
Most Recent Fund Was Raised: 05/15/2000
Year Founded: 1997
Capital Under Management: $85,000,000
Current Activity Level: Reducing investment activity
Method of Compensation: Return on investment is of primary concern, do not charge fees

---

KEY BRIDGE PARTNERS LLC

675 East Street Nothwest
Suite 250
Washington, DC USA 20004
Phone: 202-558-3825
Fax: 202-903-0177
Website: www.keybridgepartners.com

Management and Staff

Robert Maruszewski, Founding Partner

Type of Firm

Private Equity Firm

Project Preferences

Type of Financing Preferred:

Leveraged Buyout
Turnaround
Management Buyouts
Recapitalizations

Geographical Preferences

United States Preferences:

All U.S.

Industry Preferences

In Computer Other prefer:

Computer Related

In Industrial/Energy prefer:

Industrial Products

In Transportation prefer:

Transportation
Aerospace

In Business Serv. prefer:

Services

In Manufact. prefer:

Manufacturing

Additional Information

Year Founded: 2007
Capital Under Management: $25,000,000
Current Activity Level: Actively seeking new investments

KEY CAPITAL CORP.

800 Superior Avenue
10th Floor
Cleveland, OH USA 44114
Phone: 216-828-8127
Website: www.key.com

Management and Staff

Chris Hanrahan, Principal

Type of Firm

Bank Affiliated

Project Preferences

Type of Financing Preferred:
Fund of Funds
Strategic Alliances

Size of Investments Considered:
Min Size of Investment Considered (000s): $5,000
Max Size of Investment Considered (000s): $15,000

Geographical Preferences

United States Preferences:
All U.S.

Additional Information

Year Founded: 1990
Capital Under Management: $100,000,000
Current Activity Level: Actively seeking new investments

KEY CAPITAL PARTNERS

Suite 111, Wellington House
East Road
Cambridge, United Kingdom CB1 1BH
Phone: 44-1223-451-060
Fax: 44-1223-451-100
E-mail: cambridge@keycapitalpartners.co.uk
Website: www.keycapitalpartners.co.uk

Other Offices

Princes Exchange
Princes Square
Leeds, United Kingdom LS1 4HY
Phone: 44-113-280-5824
Fax: 44-113-280-5801

Type of Firm

Private Equity Firm

Association Membership

British Venture Capital Association (BVCA)

Project Preferences

Type of Financing Preferred:
Generalist PE
Recapitalizations

Size of Investments Considered:
Min Size of Investment Considered (000s): $1,983
Max Size of Investment Considered (000s): $9,914

Geographical Preferences

International Preferences:
Europe

Additional Information

Year Founded: 2007
Current Activity Level: Actively seeking new investments

KEY PRINCIPAL PARTNERS LLC (AKA: KPP)

800 Superior Avenue
Tenth Floor
Cleveland, OH USA 44114
Phone: 216-828-8125
Fax: 216-828-8135
E-mail: info@kppinvest.com
Website: www.key.com/keyprincipalpartners

Other Offices

Suite 2603, Westgate Mall
No. 1038, West Nanjing Road
Shanghai, China
Phone: 86-21-6271-7199
Fax: 86-21-6271-1850

Nine Greenwich Office Park
Third Floor
Greenwich, CT USA 06831
Phone: 203-862-0555
Fax: 203-422-2517

50 California Street
Suite 2525
San Francisco, CA USA 94111
Phone: 415-692-4660
Fax: 415-402-0472

Management and Staff

Andrew Bacas, Principal
Beth Laschinger, Principal
Cindy Babitt, Partner
Daniel Kessler, Principal
Gregory Davis, Principal
John Sinnenberg, Managing Partner
Jonathon Leffers, Principal
Leland Lewis, Managing Partner
Matthew Brennan, Principal
Michael Conaton, Partner
Philip Curatilo, Principal
Timothy Fay, Managing Partner

Type of Firm

Investment Management Firm

Project Preferences

Role in Financing:
Prefer role as deal originator

Type of Financing Preferred:
Leveraged Buyout
Expansion
Mezzanine
Generalist PE
Balanced
Later Stage
Management Buyouts
Acquisition
Industry Rollups
Recapitalizations
Distressed Debt

Size of Investments Considered:
Min Size of Investment Considered (000s): $7,000
Max Size of Investment Considered (000s): $40,000

Geographical Preferences

Canadian Preferences:
All Canada

International Preferences:
Mexico

Industry Preferences

In Business Serv. prefer:
Services
Distribution

In Manufact. prefer:
Manufacturing

Additional Information

Name of Most Recent Fund: KPP Investors III, L.P.
Most Recent Fund Was Raised: 05/16/2006
Year Founded: 1998
Capital Under Management: $77,500,000
Current Activity Level: Actively seeking new investments

KEY VENTURE PARTNERS

1000 Winter Street
Suite 1400
Waltham, MA USA 02451
Phone: 781-663-2100
Fax: 781-663-2108
Website: www.keyvp.com

Management and Staff

John Ward, Managing Director
Thadeus Mocarski, Managing Director
Vaibhav Nalwaya, Principal

Type of Firm

Bank Affiliated

Association Membership

National Venture Capital Association - USA (NVCA)

Project Preferences

Role in Financing:
Prefer role as deal originator but will also invest in deals created by others

Type of Financing Preferred:
Expansion
Later Stage

Size of Investments Considered:
Min Size of Investment Considered (000s): $5,000
Max Size of Investment Considered (000s): $15,000

Geographical Preferences

United States Preferences:
All U.S.

Industry Preferences

In Communications prefer:
Telecommunications
Wireless Communications
Data Communications

In Computer Software prefer:
Software
Systems Software
Applications Software

In Internet Specific prefer:
E-Commerce Technology
Ecommerce

Additional Information

Year Founded: 2003
Capital Under Management: $200,000,000
Current Activity Level: Actively seeking new investments
Method of Compensation: Return on investment is of primary concern, do not charge fees

KEYHAVEN CAPITAL PARTNERS, LTD.

1 Richmond Mews
London, United Kingdom W1D 3DA
Phone: 44 20 7432 6200
Fax: 4420 7432 6201
E-mail: info@keyhavencapital.com
Website: www.keyhavencapital.com

Management and Staff

Claus Stenbaek, Managing Director
James Donohue, Principal
Sasha Van de Water, Managing Director

Type of Firm

Private Equity Advisor or Fund of Funds

Project Preferences

Type of Financing Preferred:
Fund of Funds

Geographical Preferences

International Preferences:
Europe

Additional Information

Year Founded: 2003
Current Activity Level: Actively seeking new investments

KEYNOTE VENTURES (FKA: DALI, HOOK PARTNERS)

3000 Sand Hill Road
Building One, Suite 185
Menlo Park, CA USA 94025
Phone: 650-926-9820
Fax: 650-926-9825
Website: www.keynoteventures.com

Other Offices

Two Galleria Tower
13455 Noel Road Suite 1670
Dallas, TX USA 75240
Phone: 972-991-5457
Fax: 972-991-5458

Management and Staff

Alessandro Biral, General Partner
Clara Yee, Chief Financial Officer
David Hook, General Partner
Haru Kato, Venture Partner
Paul Dali, Managing Partner

Type of Firm

Private Equity Firm

Project Preferences

Type of Financing Preferred:
Early Stage

Industry Preferences

In Communications prefer:
Other Communication Prod.

In Computer Software prefer:
Software

In Semiconductor/Electr prefer:
Semiconductor

Additional Information

Name of Most Recent Fund: Dali Hook Annex Fund, L.P.
Most Recent Fund Was Raised: 06/05/2006
Year Founded: 1995
Capital Under Management: $40,200,000
Current Activity Level: Actively seeking new investments

KEYSTONE NATIONAL GROUP LLC

2410 Camino Ramon
Suite 120
San Ramon, CA USA 94583
Phone: 925-407-3120
Fax: 925-407-3125
Website: www.keystonenational.net

Management and Staff

Lynette Walbom, Chief Financial Officer

Type of Firm

Private Equity Firm

Project Preferences

Type of Financing Preferred:
Fund of Funds

Additional Information

Name of Most Recent Fund: Keystone Private Equity, L.P.
Most Recent Fund Was Raised: 07/27/2006
Year Founded: 2006
Capital Under Management: $115,300,000
Current Activity Level: Actively seeking new investments

KHALEEJ FINANCE & INVESTMENT

Al Zamil Tower, 6th floor
P.O. Box 5571
Manama, Bahrain
Phone: 973-17-502-222
Fax: 973-17-502-211
Website: www.khaleejfinance.com

Management and Staff

Nabil Mohammed Hadi, Chief Executive Officer

Type of Firm

Private Equity Firm

Project Preferences

Type of Financing Preferred:
Balanced

Geographical Preferences

International Preferences:
Middle East

Industry Preferences

In Communications prefer:
Telecommunications

In Biotechnology prefer:
Biotechnology

In Medical/Health prefer:
Pharmaceuticals

In Consumer Related prefer:
Food/Beverage

In Agr/Forestr/Fish prefer:
Mining and Minerals

Additional Information

Year Founded: 2007
Capital Under Management: $200,000,000
Current Activity Level: Actively seeking new investments

KHAO KLA VENTURE CAPITAL MANAGEMENT CO., LTD.

252/38 Muang Thai Phatra Twr 1
Ratchadapisek Road, Huaykwang
Bangkok, Thailand 10310
Phone: 66-2-693-2333
Fax: 66-2-693-2333
E-mail: info@khaokla.com
Website: www.khaokla.com

Management and Staff

Patamaporn Chaiyakool, Managing Director

Type of Firm

Bank Affiliated

Project Preferences

Type of Financing Preferred:
Balanced

Geographical Preferences

International Preferences:
Asia

Additional Information

Year Founded: 2007
Capital Under Management: $6,400,000
Current Activity Level: Actively seeking new investments

KHAZAEN VENTURE CAPITAL

5F Makki Al-Juma Office Tower
Mubarak al Kabeer Street
Kuwait City, Kuwait
Phone: 965-240-7035
Fax: 965-240-7034
E-mail: info@khazaen.com
Website: www.khazaen.com

Management and Staff

Mansour Al-Khuzam, Managing Director

Type of Firm

Private Equity Firm

Project Preferences

Type of Financing Preferred:
Balanced

Geographical Preferences

International Preferences:
Kuwait

Additional Information

Year Founded: 2002
Current Activity Level: Actively seeking new investments

KHOSLA VENTURES

3000 Sand Hill Road
Building Three, Suite 170
Menlo Park, CA USA 94025
Phone: 650-376-8500
Fax: 650-926-9590
E-mail: kv@khoslaventures.com
Website: www.khoslaventures.com

Management and Staff

Gideon Yu, General Partner
Samir Kaul, Partner
Vinod Khosla, Founder

Type of Firm

Private Equity Firm

Project Preferences

Type of Financing Preferred:
Early Stage
Expansion
Balanced
Seed

Size of Investments Considered:
Min Size of Investment Considered (000s): $100
Max Size of Investment Considered (000s): $20,001

Geographical Preferences

United States Preferences:
All U.S.

Industry Preferences

In Internet Specific prefer:
Internet

In Semiconductor/Electr prefer:
Semiconductor

In Industrial/Energy prefer:
Alternative Energy
Environmental Related

In Other prefer:
Environment Responsible

Additional Information

Year Founded: 2004
Capital Under Management: $1,213,200,000
Current Activity Level: Actively seeking new investments

KHULA ENTERPRISE FINANCE LTD

3rd Floor - Block E(Uuzaji)
77 Meintje Street
Sunnyside, South Africa 0132
Phone: 27-12-394-5560
Fax: 27-12-394-6560
E-mail: helpline@khula.org.za
Website: www.khula.org.za

Type of Firm

Investment Management Firm

Association Membership

South African Venture Capital Association (SAVCA)

Project Preferences

Type of Financing Preferred:
Early Stage
Expansion

Geographical Preferences

International Preferences:
Africa

Additional Information

Year Founded: 2000
Current Activity Level: Actively seeking new investments

KILCULLEN KAPITAL PARTNERS

Burzovni palac
Rybna 682/14
Prague, Czech Republic 110 05
Phone: 420-2-2731-6222
Fax: 420-2-2731-6444
E-mail: info@kilcullen.cz
Website: www.kilcullen.cz

Other Offices

Kilcullen House
One Haigh Tce, Dun Laoghaire
Co. Dublin, Ireland
Phone: 353-1-284-5199
Fax: 353-1-284-5195

Management and Staff

Charles Bergen, Partner
Robert Sheshol, Managing Director
Sean McVeigh, Managing Director

Type of Firm

Private Equity Firm

Association Membership

European Private Equity and Venture Capital Assoc.

Project Preferences

Type of Financing Preferred:
Early Stage
Other
Seed
Startup

Size of Investments Considered:
Min Size of Investment Considered (000s): $268
Max Size of Investment Considered (000s): $893

Geographical Preferences

International Preferences:
Ireland
Czech Republic

Industry Preferences

In Internet Specific prefer:
Internet

In Financial Services prefer:
Financial Services
Insurance
Real Estate

In Business Serv. prefer:
Media

Additional Information
Year Founded: 1999
Capital Under Management: $5,400,000
Current Activity Level: Actively seeking new investments

KILLICK CAPITAL
34 Harvey Road, Fifth Floor
P O Box 5883
St. John's, Canada A1C5W2
Phone: 709-738-6288
Fax: 709-738-5578
Website: www.killickcapital.com

Management and Staff
Tom Williams, Vice President

Type of Firm
Private Equity Firm

Additional Information
Year Founded: 2009
Current Activity Level: Actively seeking new investments

KILMER CAPITAL PARTNERS
40 King Street West
Suite 2700, Scotia Plaza
Toronto, Canada M5H3Y2
Phone: 416-635-6100
Fax: 416-635-7697
E-mail: info@kilmercapital.com
Website: www.kilmercapital.com

Management and Staff
Anthony Sigel, President
Arnie Gross, Partner
Doug Peel, Partner

Type of Firm
Private Equity Firm

Association Membership
Canadian Venture Capital Association

Project Preferences

Role in Financing:
Prefer role as deal originator but will also invest in deals created by others

Type of Financing Preferred:
Leveraged Buyout
Control-block Purchases
Expansion
Turnaround
Later Stage
Management Buyouts
Acquisition
Recapitalizations

Size of Investments Considered:
Min Size of Investment Considered (000s): $4,000
Max Size of Investment Considered (000s): $50,000

Geographical Preferences

Canadian Preferences:
All Canada

Industry Preferences

In Communications prefer:
Wireless Communications

In Computer Hardware prefer:
Integrated Turnkey System

In Computer Software prefer:
Software
Systems Software
Applications Software

In Semiconductor/Electr prefer:
Electronics
Electronic Components
Controllers and Sensors
Sensors
Circuit Boards
Component Testing Equipmt

In Biotechnology prefer:
Human Biotechnology
Agricultural/Animal Bio.
Industrial Biotechnology
Biotech Related Research

In Medical/Health prefer:
Medical Diagnostics
Diagnostic Services
Diagnostic Test Products
Medical Therapeutics
Drug/Equipmt Delivery
Medical Products
Disposable Med. Products
Pharmaceuticals

In Consumer Related prefer:
Consumer
Entertainment and Leisure
Sports
Food/Beverage
Consumer Products
Education Related

In Industrial/Energy prefer:
Industrial Products
Factory Automation

In Financial Services prefer:
Financial Services

In Business Serv. prefer:
Services
Distribution
Consulting Services
Media

In Manufact. prefer:
Manufacturing

Additional Information
Year Founded: 2001
Capital Under Management: $95,800,000
Current Activity Level: Actively seeking new investments
Method of Compensation: Return on invest. most important, but chg. closing fees, service fees, etc.

KIMBERLY-CLARK VENTURES, LLC
2100 Winchester Road
Neenah, WI USA 54956
Phone: 920-721-3034
Fax: 920-380-6719
Website: www.kimberly-clark.com

Type of Firm
Corporate PE/Venture

Project Preferences

Type of Financing Preferred:
Balanced

Industry Preferences

In Medical/Health prefer:
Medical Products

Additional Information
Year Founded: 1999
Capital Under Management: $20,000,000
Current Activity Level: Actively seeking new investments

KINDERHOOK INDUSTRIES
888 Seventh Avenue
16th Floor
New York, NY USA 10106
Phone: 212-201-6780
Fax: 212-201-6790
Website: www.kinderhookindustries.com

Management and Staff
Christian Michalik, Managing Director
Corwynne Carruthers, Principal
Lisa Clarke, Chief Financial Officer
Louis Aurelio, Vice President
Paul Cifelli, Principal
Robert Michalik, Managing Director
Thomas Tuttle, Managing Director

Type of Firm
Private Equity Firm

Project Preferences

Type of Financing Preferred:
Leveraged Buyout
Turnaround
Management Buyouts
Acquisition
Special Situation

Size of Investments Considered:
Min Size of Investment Considered (000s): $10
Max Size of Investment Considered (000s): $100

Additional Information
Year Founded: 2003
Capital Under Management: $470,000,000
Current Activity Level: Actively seeking new investments

KINETIC CAPITAL PARTNERS
777 Hornby Street
Suite 1460
Vancouver, Canada V6Z 1S4
Phone: 604-692-2530
Fax: 604-692-2531
Website: www.kineticcapitalpartners.com

Type of Firm
Private Equity Firm

Project Preferences

Type of Financing Preferred:
Early Stage
Later Stage
Startup

Geographical Preferences

United States Preferences:
All U.S.

Canadian Preferences:
All Canada

Additional Information
Year Founded: 2001
Current Activity Level: Actively seeking new investments

KINETIC VENTURES LLC
Two Wisconsin Circle
Suite 620
Chevy Chase, MD USA 20815
Phone: 301-652-8066
Fax: 301-652-8310
E-mail: kinetic@kineticventures.com
Website: www.kineticventures.com

Other Offices
75 Fifth Street, Northwest
Suite 316
Atlanta, GA USA 30308
Phone: 404-995-8811
Fax: 404-995-4455

Management and Staff
Bernard Tarr, Managing Director
Nelson Chu, Managing Director
William Heflin, Managing Director

Type of Firm
Private Equity Firm

Association Membership
Mid-Atlantic Venture Association
National Venture Capital Association - USA (NVCA)

Project Preferences

Role in Financing:
Will function either as deal originator or investor in deals created by others

Type of Financing Preferred:
Second Stage Financing
Expansion
Early Stage
Balanced
Later Stage
First Stage Financing

Size of Investments Considered:
Min Size of Investment Considered (000s): $2,000
Max Size of Investment Considered (000s): $7,000

Geographical Preferences

United States Preferences:
All U.S.

Industry Focus
(% based on actual investment)

Communications and Media	33.7%
Internet Specific	26.7%
Semiconductors/Other Elect.	18.3%
Computer Software and Services	7.4%
Computer Hardware	7.2%
Other Products	4.7%
Industrial/Energy	1.6%
Medical/Health	0.3%

Additional Information
Year Founded: 1984
Capital Under Management: $195,000,000
Current Activity Level: Actively seeking new investments
Method of Compensation: Return on investment is of primary concern, do not charge fees

---

KINGDOM ZEPHYR AFRICA MANAGEMENT (AKA: KZAM)
Unihold House, 1st floor
22 Hurlingham Road,Illovo Blvd
Johannesburg, South Africa 2196
Phone: 27-11-268-6911
Fax: 27-11-268-6917
E-mail: info@kingdomzephyr.com
Website: www.kingdomzephyr.com

Management and Staff
J.Kofi Bucknor, Managing Director
Lekan Odugbesan, Vice President
NanaAma Dowuona, Chief Operating Officer
Nathan Mintah, Partner
Sofiane Lahmar, Partner

Type of Firm
Private Equity Firm

Project Preferences

Type of Financing Preferred:
Leveraged Buyout
Balanced
Acquisition

Geographical Preferences

International Preferences:
South Africa
Africa

Industry Preferences

In Consumer Related prefer:
Consumer
Education Related

In Financial Services prefer:
Financial Services

In Manufact. prefer:
Manufacturing

Additional Information
Year Founded: 2004
Capital Under Management: $325,000,000
Current Activity Level: Actively seeking new investments

KINGDON CAPITAL
152 West 57th Street
50th Floor
New York, NY USA 10019
Phone: 212-333-0100

Type of Firm
Private Equity Firm

Additional Information
Year Founded: 1996
Current Activity Level: Actively seeking new investments

KINGHAVEN SECURITIES LIMITED / INTELECTUAL INVESTMENTS

20 Queen Street West
Suite316
Toronto, Canada M5H 3R3
Phone: 416-581-8850
Fax: 416-581-0020

Type of Firm

Private Equity Advisor or Fund of Funds

Additional Information

Year Founded: 1995
Current Activity Level: Actively seeking new investments

KINGSMAN CAPITAL LLC

1144 West Randolph Street
Chicago, IL USA 60607
Phone: 312-320-9575
Website: www.kingsmancapital.com

Management and Staff

Keith Koeneman, Managing Partner

Type of Firm

Private Equity Firm

Project Preferences

Type of Financing Preferred:
Leveraged Buyout
Expansion
Industry Rollups
Recapitalizations

Geographical Preferences

United States Preferences:
All U.S.

Canadian Preferences:
All Canada

Industry Preferences

In Medical/Health prefer:
Health Services

In Consumer Related prefer:
Consumer Products
Consumer Services

In Industrial/Energy prefer:
Industrial Products

In Business Serv. prefer:
Services
Distribution

In Manufact. prefer:
Manufacturing

Additional Information

Year Founded: 2008
Current Activity Level: Actively seeking new investments

KINGSWAY CAPITAL OF CANADA, INC.

Eight King Street East
Suite 1400
Toronto, Canada M5C1B5
Phone: 416-861-3099
Fax: 416-861-9027
E-mail: info@kingswaygroup.ca
Website: www.kingswaygroup.ca

Management and Staff

David Charnock, Vice President

Type of Firm

Private Equity Firm

Additional Information

Year Founded: 2001
Current Activity Level: Actively seeking new investments

KIPCO ASSET MANAGEMENT COMPANY (KAMCO)

Al-Shaheed Tower, 12-15 Flrs.
Khalid Bin Waleed St., Sharq
Sharq, Kuwait
Phone: 965-805-885
Fax: 965-805-885
E-mail: info@kamconline.com
Website: www.kamconline.com

Type of Firm

Investment Management Firm

Project Preferences

Type of Financing Preferred:
Balanced

Geographical Preferences

International Preferences:
Kuwait

Additional Information

Year Founded: 1998
Capital Under Management: $45,000,000
Current Activity Level: Actively seeking new investments

KIRCHNER PRIVATE CAPITAL GROUP

36 Toronto Street
Suite 850
Toronto, Canada M5C 2C5
Phone: 416-861-9807
Fax: 954-252-2522
E-mail: info@kcpg.net
Website: www.kcpg.net

Other Offices

2618 Hopewell Place North East
Suite 340
Calgary, Canada T1Y 7J7
Phone: 403-215-5491

1155, boulevard Rene-Levesque Ouest
suite 2500
Montreal, Canada H3B 2K4
Phone: 514-868-1079

Type of Firm

Private Equity Advisor or Fund of Funds

Additional Information

Year Founded: 2009
Current Activity Level: Actively seeking new investments

KIRLAN VENTURE CAPITAL, INC.

221 First Avenue West
Suite 108
Seattle, WA USA 98119-4223
Phone: 206-281-8610
Fax: 206-285-3451
Website: www.kirlanvc.com

Management and Staff

Kenneth Keller, Vice President
Kirk Lanterman, Chairman & CEO

Type of Firm

Private Equity Advisor or Fund of Funds

Project Preferences

Role in Financing:
Prefer role in deals created by others

Type of Financing Preferred:
Early Stage
Expansion
Mezzanine
Balanced
Later Stage
First Stage Financing

Size of Investments Considered:
Min Size of Investment Considered (000s): $200
Max Size of Investment Considered (000s): $2,000

Geographical Preferences

United States Preferences:
Northwest
West Coast
Washington

Canadian Preferences:
Western Canada

Industry Focus

(% based on actual investment)

Computer Software and Services	33.8%
Communications and Media	32.0%
Medical/Health	14.2%
Industrial/Energy	9.6%
Internet Specific	8.3%
Semiconductors/Other Elect.	2.2%

Additional Information

Name of Most Recent Fund: Kirlan Venture Partners II, L.P.
Most Recent Fund Was Raised: 01/01/1997
Year Founded: 1991
Capital Under Management: $20,000,000
Current Activity Level: Actively seeking new investments
Method of Compensation: Return on investment is of primary concern, do not charge fees

KIRTLAND CAPITAL CORPORATION

3201 Enterprise Parkway
Suite 200
Beachwood, OH USA 44122
Phone: 216-593-0100
Fax: 216-593-0240
Website: www.kirtlandcapital.com

Management and Staff

Corrine Menary, Vice President
David Wood, Partner
David Halstead, Managing Partner
James Foley, Partner
John Lalley, Principal
Robert Fines, Managing Partner
Thomas Littman, Managing Partner

Type of Firm

Private Equity Firm

Project Preferences

Role in Financing:
Prefer role as deal originator

Type of Financing Preferred:
Leveraged Buyout
Control-block Purchases
Generalist PE
Management Buyouts
Acquisition

Size of Investments Considered:
Min Size of Investment Considered (000s): $15,000
Max Size of Investment Considered (000s): $75,000

Geographical Preferences

United States Preferences:
Mid Atlantic
Midwest
Southeast
Northeast

Industry Focus

(% based on actual investment)

Industrial/Energy	90.0%
Semiconductors/Other Elect.	10.0%

Additional Information

Name of Most Recent Fund: Kirtland Capital Partners IV L.P.
Most Recent Fund Was Raised: 12/21/2002
Year Founded: 1977
Capital Under Management: $338,900,000
Current Activity Level: Making few, if any, new investments
Method of Compensation: Return on invest. most important, but chg. closing fees, service fees, etc.

KISTEFOS VENTURE CAPITAL AS

Stranden 1A
Oslo, Norway 0250
Phone: 47-23-117-000
Fax: 47-23-117-002
E-mail: info@kistefos.no
Website: www.kistefos.com

Management and Staff

Age Korsvold, Managing Director
Alex Munch-Thore, Partner
Ditlef de Vibe, Managing Director
Kjell E. Sommerseth, Managing Director
Niels Kr. Hodt, Chief Financial Officer

Type of Firm

Bank Affiliated

Association Membership

Norwegian Venture Capital Association
European Private Equity and Venture Capital Assoc.

Project Preferences

Role in Financing:
Prefer role as deal originator

Type of Financing Preferred:
Expansion
Early Stage

Size of Investments Considered:
Min Size of Investment Considered (000s): $773
Max Size of Investment Considered (000s): $4,637

Geographical Preferences

International Preferences:
Scandanavia/Nordic Region
Norway

Industry Preferences

In Communications prefer:
Telecommunications

In Computer Software prefer:
Software

In Industrial/Energy prefer:
Energy Conservation Relat

In Financial Services prefer:
Financial Services

Additional Information

Year Founded: 1997
Capital Under Management: $80,300,000
Current Activity Level: Actively seeking new investments

KISVALLALKOZAS-FEJLESZTO PENZUGYI RT. (AKA: KVFP)

Szep utca 2
Budapest, Hungary 1053
Phone: 36-1-486-3240
Fax: 36-1-486-3232
E-mail: info@kvfp.hu
Website: www.kvfp.hu

Management and Staff

Krisztina Arato, Chief Executive Officer

Type of Firm

Private Equity Firm

Association Membership

European Private Equity and Venture Capital Assoc.

Project Preferences

Type of Financing Preferred:
Expansion
Startup

Size of Investments Considered:
Min Size of Investment Considered (000s): $50
Max Size of Investment Considered (000s): $500

Geographical Preferences

International Preferences:
Hungary

Industry Preferences

In Communications prefer:
Communications and Media

In Computer Other prefer:
Computer Related

In Medical/Health prefer:
Medical/Health

In Industrial/Energy prefer:
Energy
Industrial Products

Additional Information

Year Founded: 2002
Capital Under Management: $17,300,000
Current Activity Level: Actively seeking new investments

KITTY HAWK CAPITAL

2901 Coltsgate Road
Suite 100
Charlotte, NC USA 28211
Phone: 704-362-3909
Fax: 704-362-2774
E-mail: info@kittyhawkcapital.com

Management and Staff

W. Chris Hegele, General Partner
Walter Wilkinson, General Partner

Type of Firm

Private Equity Firm

Project Preferences

Role in Financing:
Other

Type of Financing Preferred:
Other

Geographical Preferences

United States Preferences:
Southeast

Industry Focus

(% based on actual investment)

Medical/Health	27.6%
Biotechnology	15.3%
Industrial/Energy	10.8%
Internet Specific	10.8%
Computer Software and Services	10.7%
Other Products	9.2%
Communications and Media	6.9%
Consumer Related	4.7%
Semiconductors/Other Elect.	3.0%
Computer Hardware	1.0%

Additional Information

Name of Most Recent Fund: Kitty Hawk Capital, L.P. IV
Most Recent Fund Was Raised: 02/01/1998
Year Founded: 1980
Capital Under Management: $69,300,000
Current Activity Level: Making few, if any, new investments
Method of Compensation: Return on investment is of primary concern, do not charge fees

KIWI GROWTH PARTNERS LTD.

57 Killarney Road
Hamilton, New Zealand
Phone: 647-848-2574
Fax: 647-848-2576
Website: www.kiwigrowthpartners.com

Management and Staff

Alvin Donovan, Founder

Type of Firm

Investment Management Firm

Project Preferences

Type of Financing Preferred:
Balanced

Geographical Preferences

International Preferences:
New Zealand

Additional Information

Year Founded: 2006
Current Activity Level: Actively seeking new investments

KIWOOM INVESTMENT COMPANY, LTD.

3/F, Sindo Ricoh Building
943-27 Daechi-dong, Gangnam-gu
Seoul, South Korea 135-845
Phone: 822-3430-4881
Fax: 822-3452-9493
Website: www.kiwoominvest.com

Management and Staff

Yongwon Kwon, Chief Executive Officer

Type of Firm

Corporate PE/Venture

Association Membership

Korean Venture Capital Association (KVCA)

Project Preferences

Type of Financing Preferred:
Early Stage
Expansion
Balanced
Later Stage
Startup

Geographical Preferences

International Preferences:
Korea, South

Industry Preferences

In Industrial/Energy prefer:
Environmental Related

Additional Information

Year Founded: 1999
Capital Under Management: $93,600,000
Current Activity Level: Actively seeking new investments

KKR & CO. (GUERNSEY) L.P.

Trafalgar Court, Les Banques
St. Peter Port
Guernsey, Channel Islands GY1 3QL
Phone: 44-481-745-001
Fax: 44-481-745-074
Website: www.kkrpei.com

Other Offices

9 West 57th Street
Suite 1640
New York, NY USA 10019
Phone: 212-659-2026
Fax: 212-659-2049

Type of Firm

Private Equity Firm

Project Preferences

Type of Financing Preferred:
Balanced

Geographical Preferences

International Preferences:
Europe

Additional Information

Year Founded: 2006
Current Activity Level: Actively seeking new investments

KLARIUS GROUP, LTD.

101 Barbirolli Square
Manchester, United Kingdom M2 3DL

Type of Firm

Private Equity Firm

Project Preferences

Type of Financing Preferred:
Balanced

Geographical Preferences

International Preferences:
United Kingdom

Industry Preferences

In Transportation prefer:
Transportation

Additional Information

Year Founded: 2007
Current Activity Level: Actively seeking new investments

KLEINER PERKINS CAUFIELD & BYERS

2750 Sand Hill Road
Menlo Park, CA USA 94025
Phone: 650-233-2750
Fax: 650-233-0300
Website: www.kpcb.com

Other Offices

Unit 2505, K. Wah Center
1010 Huaihai Zhong Road, Xuhui District
Shanghai, China 200031
Phone: 86-21-5467-0500
Fax: 86-21-5405-7557

Suite 503-504, Tower C1, Oriental Plaza
No. 1 East Chang An Avenue
Beijing, China 100738
Phone: 86-10-8518-
Fax: 86-10-8518-9647

Management and Staff

Aileen Lee, Partner
Ajit Nazre, Partner
Al Gore, Partner
Beth Seidenberg, Partner
Bill Joy, Partner
Brook Byers, General Partner
Chi-Hua Chien, Partner
Dana Mead, Partner
Douglas Mackenzie, Partner
Ellen Pao, Partner
Eric Keller, Chief Operating Officer
James Li, Partner
Jessica Owens, Partner
John Gage, Partner
John Doerr, Partner
John Denniston, Partner
Joseph Lacob, Partner
Juliet Flint, Partner
Kevin Compton, Partner
Matthew Murphy, Partner
Randy Komisar, Partner
Raymond Lane, General Partner
Risa Stack, Partner
Russell Siegelman, Partner
Susan Biglieri, Chief Financial Officer
Ted Schlein, Partner
Thomas Monath, Partner
Trae Vassallo, Partner
Vinod Khosla, Partner
Wen Hsieh, Partner
William Hearst, Partner

Type of Firm

Private Equity Firm

Association Membership

Western Association of Venture Capitalists (WAVC)
National Venture Capital Association - USA (NVCA)

Project Preferences

Role in Financing:

Prefer role as deal originator but will also invest in deals created by others

Type of Financing Preferred:

Early Stage
Expansion
Balanced
Start-up Financing
Seed
First Stage Financing

Size of Investments Considered:

Min Size of Investment Considered (000s): $500
Max Size of Investment Considered: No Limit

Geographical Preferences

United States Preferences:

West Coast

International Preferences:

China

Industry Focus

(% based on actual investment)	
Internet Specific	23.4%
Computer Software and Services	15.7%
Semiconductors/Other Elect.	11.5%
Biotechnology	10.7%
Communications and Media	10.2%
Medical/Health	8.7%
Industrial/Energy	6.7%
Computer Hardware	6.6%
Other Products	4.8%
Consumer Related	1.6%

Additional Information

Name of Most Recent Fund: Kleiner Perkins Caufield & Byers XIII
Most Recent Fund Was Raised: 05/01/2008
Year Founded: 1972
Capital Under Management: $2,700,000,000
Current Activity Level: Actively seeking new investments
Method of Compensation: Return on investment is of primary concern, do not charge fees

KLESCH CAPITAL PARTNERS

105 Wigmore Street
London, United Kingdom W1U 1QY
Phone: 44-20-7493-4300
Fax: 44-20-7493-2525
E-mail: info@klesch.com
Website: www.klesch.co.uk

Management and Staff

Gary Klesch, Founder

Type of Firm

Private Equity Firm

Project Preferences

Role in Financing:

Prefer role in deals created by others

Type of Financing Preferred:

Leveraged Buyout
Turnaround

Geographical Preferences

International Preferences:

United Kingdom
Europe

Additional Information

Year Founded: 1990
Capital Under Management: $76,100,000
Current Activity Level: Actively seeking new investments

KLINE HAWKES & CO.

11726 San Vicente Boulevard
Suite 300
Los Angeles, CA USA 90049
Phone: 310-442-4700
Fax: 310-442-4707
E-mail: info@klinehawkes.com
Website: www.klinehawkes.com

Management and Staff

Frank Kline, General Partner
Greg Arsenault, Chief Financial Officer
Jay Ferguson, General Partner
Nicholas Memmo, General Partner

Type of Firm

Private Equity Firm

Association Membership

National Venture Capital Association - USA (NVCA)
Natl Assoc of Small Bus. Inv. Co (NASBIC)

Project Preferences

Role in Financing:

Prefer role as deal originator but will also invest in deals created by others

Type of Financing Preferred:

Second Stage Financing
Leveraged Buyout
Expansion
Generalist PE
Turnaround
Later Stage
Management Buyouts
Acquisition
Private Placement
Industry Rollups
Recapitalizations

Size of Investments Considered:

Min Size of Investment Considered (000s): $5,000
Max Size of Investment Considered (000s): $10,000

Geographical Preferences

United States Preferences:

Northwest
West Coast
Southwest

Industry Focus

(% based on actual investment)

Medical/Health	31.4%
Internet Specific	17.3%
Other Products	11.9%
Computer Software and Services	10.0%
Communications and Media	8.6%
Computer Hardware	8.2%
Semiconductors/Other Elect.	6.9%
Consumer Related	3.8%
Biotechnology	1.5%
Industrial/Energy	0.3%

Additional Information

Name of Most Recent Fund: Kline Hawkes Pacific, L.P.
Most Recent Fund Was Raised: 04/27/2000
Year Founded: 1995
Capital Under Management: $267,000,000
Current Activity Level: Actively seeking new investments
Method of Compensation: Return on investment is of primary concern, do not charge fees

---

KLM CAPITAL MANAGEMENT, INC.

19925 Stevens Creek Boulevard
Suite 100
Cupertino, CA USA 95014
Phone: 408-970-8888
Fax: 408-725-8885
E-mail: info@klmcapital.com
Website: www.klmtech.com

Other Offices

19 Des Vouex Road Central
2211-2212, World Wide House
Central, Hong Kong
Phone: 852-2537-3318
Fax: 852-2537-3138

Management and Staff

Alfred Li, Co-Founder
Mary Page, Chief Financial Officer
Peter Mok, Managing General Partner

Type of Firm

Private Equity Firm

Association Membership

Hong Kong Venture Capital Association (HKVCA)

Project Preferences

Role in Financing:

Prefer role as deal originator but will also invest in deals created by others

Type of Financing Preferred:

Early Stage
Expansion
Balanced
Later Stage
Seed
Acquisition

Size of Investments Considered:

Min Size of Investment Considered (000s): $500
Max Size of Investment Considered (000s): $5,000

Geographical Preferences

United States Preferences:

All U.S.

Canadian Preferences:

All Canada

International Preferences:

Taiwan
China
Hong Kong
Singapore
All International

Industry Focus

(% based on actual investment)

Semiconductors/Other Elect.	32.3%
Industrial/Energy	25.3%
Internet Specific	19.9%
Computer Software and Services	13.4%
Communications and Media	7.4%
Consumer Related	1.8%

Additional Information

Year Founded: 1996
Capital Under Management: $102,000,000
Current Activity Level: Actively seeking new investments
Method of Compensation: Return on invest. most important, but chg. closing fees, service fees, etc.

KNIGHT S BRIDGE CAPITAL CORPORATION

Scotia Plaza, Suite 3200
40 King Street West
Toronto, Canada M5H3Y2
Phone: 416-866-3132
Website: www.kbcpartners.com

Type of Firm

Private Equity Firm

Geographical Preferences

United States Preferences:

All U.S.

Canadian Preferences:

All Canada

Additional Information

Year Founded: 2007
Current Activity Level: Actively seeking new investments

KNIGHTSBRIDGE MANAGEMENT, L.L.C.

235 West 48th Street
New York, NY USA 10022
Phone: 212-582-4000
Fax: 212-896-2755
Website: www.knightsbridgeny.com

Management and Staff

Steve Vissichelli, Chief Financial Officer

Type of Firm

Private Equity Firm

Additional Information

Name of Most Recent Fund: Knightsbridge Capital Fund I, L.P.
Most Recent Fund Was Raised: 06/05/1995
Year Founded: 1995
Current Activity Level: Actively seeking new investments

KNOWLEDGE UNIVERSE

3351 El Camino Real
Suite 200
Menlo Park, CA USA 94027
Phone: 650-549-3200
Website: www.knowledgeu.com

Type of Firm

Corporate PE/Venture

Additional Information

Year Founded: 2002
Current Activity Level: Actively seeking new investments

KNOX INVESTMENT PARTNERS, LTD.

112 Parnell Road
Suite 1, Level 2, Parnell
Auckland, New Zealand
Phone: 649-307-0552
Fax: 649-307-0558
Website: www.knoxpartners.co.nz

Management and Staff

Bret Jackson, Chairman & Managing Director

Type of Firm

Private Equity Firm

Project Preferences

Type of Financing Preferred:

Leveraged Buyout
Generalist PE
Expansion
Balanced
Acquisition

Geographical Preferences

International Preferences:
Pacific

Additional Information
Year Founded: 2007
Capital Under Management: $46,900,000
Current Activity Level: Actively seeking new investments

KOCH GENESIS LLC
4111 East 37th Street North
Wichita, KS USA 67220
Phone: 316-828-8532
Fax: 316-828-3030
E-mail: info@kochgenesis.com
Website: www.kochgenesis.com

Management and Staff
Brett Chugg, Vice President
Tim Cesarek, President

Type of Firm
Bank Affiliated

Project Preferences

Type of Financing Preferred:
Early Stage

Size of Investments Considered:
Min Size of Investment Considered (000s): $5,000
Max Size of Investment Considered (000s): $10,000

Industry Preferences

In Communications prefer:
Communications and Media

In Semiconductor/Electr prefer:
Semiconductor

In Medical/Health prefer:
Medical Products
Health Services

In Industrial/Energy prefer:
Energy

Additional Information
Current Activity Level: Actively seeking new investments

KODAK EXTERNAL ALLIANCES (FKA: KODAK VENTURES GROUP)
1999 Lake Avenue
Rochester, NY USA 14650-2218
E-mail: ventures@Kodak.com
Website: www.kodak.com/go/kea

Other Offices
Hatnufa 7
Petach-Tikva, Israel 49510
Phone: 972-3-916-7286

Type of Firm
Corporate PE/Venture

Association Membership
European Private Equity and Venture Capital Assoc.

Project Preferences

Role in Financing:
Prefer role in deals created by others

Type of Financing Preferred:
Second Stage Financing
Early Stage
First Stage Financing
Startup

Size of Investments Considered:
Min Size of Investment Considered (000s): $250
Max Size of Investment Considered (000s): $5,000

Geographical Preferences

United States Preferences:
All U.S.

Canadian Preferences:
All Canada

International Preferences:
United Kingdom
Middle East
Israel

Industry Preferences

In Communications prefer:
Communications and Media
Wireless Communications
Data Communications
Other Communication Prod.

In Computer Software prefer:
Software
Systems Software
Applications Software
Artificial Intelligence

In Internet Specific prefer:
Internet
Ecommerce

In Semiconductor/Electr prefer:
Electronic Components
Semiconductor

In Consumer Related prefer:
Consumer
Consumer Products

In Business Serv. prefer:
Services
Media

Additional Information
Year Founded: 1997
Capital Under Management: $30,000,000
Current Activity Level: Actively seeking new investments
Method of Compensation: Return on investment is of primary concern, do not charge fees

KODIAK VENTURE PARTNERS
Bay Colony Corporate Center
1000 Winter Street, Suite 3800
Waltham, MA USA 02451
Phone: 781-672-2500
Fax: 781-672-2501
E-mail: contact@kodiakvp.com
Website: www.kodiakvp.com

Management and Staff
Chip Meakem, Managing Partner
David Furneaux, Managing General Partner
Louis Volpe, Managing Partner

Type of Firm
Private Equity Firm

Association Membership
National Venture Capital Association - USA (NVCA)

Project Preferences

Role in Financing:
Prefer role as deal originator but will also invest in deals created by others

Type of Financing Preferred:
Early Stage
Seed
Startup

Size of Investments Considered:
Min Size of Investment Considered (000s): $250
Max Size of Investment Considered (000s): $15,000

Geographical Preferences

United States Preferences:
Mid Atlantic
Northeast
East Coast

Canadian Preferences:
All Canada
Ontario
Eastern Canada

Industry Preferences

In Communications prefer:
Communications and Media
Telecommunications
Wireless Communications
Data Communications

In Computer Software prefer:
Software

In Internet Specific prefer:
Internet

In Semiconductor/Electr prefer:
Semiconductor

In Consumer Related prefer:
Consumer

In Business Serv. prefer:
Services
Media

Additional Information

Name of Most Recent Fund: Kodiak Venture Partners III, L.P.
Most Recent Fund Was Raised: 01/13/2004
Year Founded: 1999
Capital Under Management: $677,000,000
Current Activity Level: Actively seeking new investments
Method of Compensation: Return on investment is of primary concern, do not charge fees

---

KOHLBERG & COMPANY LLC

111 Radio Circle
Mount Kisco, NY USA 10549
Phone: 914-241-7430
Fax: 914-241-7476
E-mail: info@kohlberg.com
Website: www.kohlberg.com

Other Offices

3000 Alpine Road
Suite 100
Portola Valley, CA USA 94028
Phone: 650-463-1480
Fax: 650-463-1481

Management and Staff

Jerome Kohlberg, Co-Founder
Shant Mardirossian, Chief Financial Officer

Type of Firm

Private Equity Firm

Project Preferences

Type of Financing Preferred:
Leveraged Buyout

Geographical Preferences

United States Preferences:
All U.S.

Canadian Preferences:
All Canada

Industry Focus

(% based on actual investment)

Semiconductors/Other Elect.	42.3%
Other Products	32.1%
Consumer Related	14.7%
Computer Hardware	7.3%
Medical/Health	3.4%
Internet Specific	0.2%

Additional Information

Name of Most Recent Fund: Kohlberg Investors VI, L.P.
Most Recent Fund Was Raised: 06/20/2007
Year Founded: 1987
Capital Under Management: $3,009,000,000
Current Activity Level: Actively seeking new investments

KOHLBERG VENTURES LLC

3000 Alpine Road
Portola Valley, CA USA 94028
Phone: 650-463-1480
Fax: 650-463-1481
E-mail: information@kohlbergventures.com
Website: www.kohlbergventures.com

Management and Staff

Bill Youstra, Partner
Greg Shove, Partner

Type of Firm

Private Equity Firm

Project Preferences

Type of Financing Preferred:
Early Stage

Industry Preferences

In Internet Specific prefer:
Web Aggregration/Portals

In Consumer Related prefer:
Entertainment and Leisure
Food/Beverage
Consumer Products

In Industrial/Energy prefer:
Alternative Energy
Energy Conservation Relat

In Business Serv. prefer:
Media

Additional Information

Year Founded: 2009
Current Activity Level: Actively seeking new investments

KOHLBERG, KRAVIS, ROBERTS & COMPANY, L.P. (AKA: KKR)

Nine West 57th Street
Suite 4200
New York, NY USA 10019
Phone: 212-750-8300
Fax: 212-750-0003
Website: www.kkr.com

Other Offices

Stirling Square
7 Carlton Gardens
London, United Kingdom SW1Y 5AD
Phone: 44-207-839-9800
Fax: 44-207-839-9801

15F Beijing Yintai Office Tower C
No. 2 Jianguomenwai Street
Chaoyang District, China 1000022
Phone: 86-10-6563-7001

Level 42, Gateway Building
One Macquarie Place
Sydney, Australia
Phone: 61-2-8298-5500

24 rue Jean Goujon
Paris, France 75008
Phone: 33-1-5353-9600
Fax: 33-1-5353-9601

555 California Street
50th Floor
San Francisco, CA USA 94104
Phone: 415-315-3620

2800 Sand Hill Road
Suite 200
Menlo Park, CA USA 94025
Phone: 650-233-6560
Fax: 650-233-6561

1 Connaught Road
25/F AIG Tower
Central, Hong Kong
Phone: 852-3602-7300
Fax: 852-2219-3000

600 Travis Street
Suite 6270
Houston, TX USA 77002
Phone: 713-241-1924

6/F, Tokyo Ginko Kyokai Bldg.
3-1, Marunouchi, 1-Chome, Chiyoda-ku
Tokyo, Japan 100-0005
Phone: 813-6268-6000
Fax: 813-5223-2381

Management and Staff

Clive Hollick, Managing Director
David Netjes, Chief Operating Officer
David Liu, Managing Director
Deryck Maughan, Managing Director
Edward Gilhuly, General Partner
George Roberts, Founding Partner
Henry Kravis, Founding Partner
Jacques Garaialde, Managing Director
James Greene, General Partner
Jeffrey Van Horn, Chief Financial Officer
Jesus Olmos Clavijo, Managing Director
Joseph Bae, Partner
Justin Reizes, Managing Director
Ken Mehlman, Managing Director
Makram Azar, Managing Director
Ming Lu, Managing Director
Robert MacDonnell, General Partner
Sanjay Nayar, Chief Executive Officer
Shusaku Minoda, Managing Director
Suzanne Donohoe, Managing Director
Taketo Yamakawa, Managing Director

Type of Firm
Private Equity Firm

Association Membership
Australian Venture Capital Association (AVCAL)
British Venture Capital Association (BVCA)
Private Equity Council (PEC)

Project Preferences
Type of Financing Preferred:
Leveraged Buyout
Mezzanine
Balanced

Geographical Preferences
International Preferences:
India
Taiwan
Europe
China
Hong Kong
Australia
New Zealand
Japan
All International

Industry Focus
(% based on actual investment)

Consumer Related	40.9%
Other Products	29.7%
Communications and Media	10.8%
Semiconductors/Other Elect.	5.4%
Computer Software and Services	5.0%
Industrial/Energy	3.9%
Computer Hardware	2.7%
Internet Specific	1.1%
Medical/Health	0.4%

Additional Information
Name of Most Recent Fund: KKR Asian Fund Private Investors Offshore L.P.
Most Recent Fund Was Raised: 07/11/2007
Year Founded: 1976
Capital Under Management: $27,000,000,000
Current Activity Level: Actively seeking new investments

KOMPANIYA PO UPRAVLENIYU AKTIVAMI TEKT
Velyka Vasylkivska Street
Building 64, 6th floor
Kiev, Ukraine 03150
Phone: 38-44-201-6391
E-mail: office@tekt.com.ua
Website: www.tekt.com

Type of Firm
Private Equity Firm

Project Preferences
Type of Financing Preferred:
Distressed Debt

Additional Information
Year Founded: 2004
Current Activity Level: Actively seeking new investments

KONCEPTKAPITAL AB
Djurgardsvagen 220
Stockholm, Sweden 115 21
Phone: 46-8-5661-5000
Fax: 46-8-5456-5778
Website: www.konceptkapital.com

Management and Staff
Jorgen Wigh, Partner
Par-Jorgen Parson, Managing Partner

Type of Firm
Private Equity Firm

Project Preferences
Type of Financing Preferred:
Expansion
Seed
Startup

Geographical Preferences
International Preferences:
Scandanavia/Nordic Region

Industry Preferences
In Communications prefer:
Communications and Media

In Computer Software prefer:
Computer Services
Software

In Internet Specific prefer:
Internet

In Financial Services prefer:
Financial Services

In Business Serv. prefer:
Services

Additional Information
Year Founded: 2001
Capital Under Management: $1,300,000
Current Activity Level: Actively seeking new investments

KONGSBERG INNOVASJON AS
Postboks 1027
Kongsberg, Norway 3601
Phone: 47-32-28-9859
Website: www.k-i.no

Type of Firm
Corporate PE/Venture

Additional Information
Current Activity Level: Actively seeking new investments

KOREA BIOTECH INVESTMENT COMPANY, LTD.
45th Floor, KWTC Building
159 Samsung-Dong Kangnam-Ku
Seoul, South Korea 135-729
Phone: 82-2-6000-8259
Fax: 82-2-6000-8275
Website: www.kbicventure.com

Management and Staff
Juyeon Kim, President

Type of Firm
Corporate PE/Venture

Project Preferences
Type of Financing Preferred:
Expansion
Balanced

Geographical Preferences
International Preferences:
Korea, South

Industry Preferences
In Biotechnology prefer:
Biotechnology

In Medical/Health prefer:
Medical/Health

Additional Information
Year Founded: 2000
Capital Under Management: $5,400,000
Current Activity Level: Actively seeking new investments

KOREA DEVELOPMENT BANK
16-3 Yeoido-dong
Yeongdeungpo-gu
Seoul, South Korea 150-973
Phone: 822-787-6450
Fax: 822-787-6496
Website: www.kdb.co.kr

Type of Firm
Bank Affiliated

Project Preferences
Type of Financing Preferred:
Leveraged Buyout

Early Stage
Recapitalizations

Geographical Preferences

International Preferences:
Korea, South

Industry Preferences

In Biotechnology prefer:
Biotechnology

In Industrial/Energy prefer:
Environmental Related

In Transportation prefer:
Aerospace

Additional Information

Year Founded: 1954
Capital Under Management: $374,200,000
Current Activity Level: Actively seeking new investments

KOREA INVESTMENT & PARTNERS (AKA: DONGWON VENTURE CAPITAL)

26/F, Gangnam Finance Center
737, YeokSam-dong, Gangnam-gu
Seoul, South Korea 135-925
Phone: 822-2112-5200
Fax: 822-2112-5202
E-mail: dwvc@truefriend.com
Website: www.kipvc.com

Other Offices

16/F, HuaMin Empire Plaza
726 Yanan West Road
Shanghai, China 200050
Phone: 86-21-6212-1522
Fax: 86-21-6212-3012

Management and Staff

Jongpil Kim, Managing Director

Type of Firm

Bank Affiliated

Association Membership

Korean Venture Capital Association (KVCA)

Project Preferences

Type of Financing Preferred:
Early Stage
Balanced

Geographical Preferences

International Preferences:
Korea, South

Industry Preferences

In Communications prefer:
Telecommunications

Additional Information

Year Founded: 1986
Capital Under Management: $200,000,000
Current Activity Level: Actively seeking new investments

KOREA TECHNOLOGY INVESTMENT CORPORATION (AKA: KTIC)

17th Floor, Shinhan Building
943-19, Daechi-dong Gangnam-gu
Seoul, South Korea 135-845
Phone: 822-3467-0600
Fax: 822-3467-0610
Website: www.ktic.co.kr

Other Offices

2180 Sand Hill Road
Suite 450
Menlo Park, CA USA 94025
Phone: 650-321-3899

Management and Staff

Ji Hoon Kim, Managing Director
Se-Hyeon Kim, Managing Director

Type of Firm

Private Equity Firm

Association Membership

Korean Venture Capital Association (KVCA)

Project Preferences

Type of Financing Preferred:
Leveraged Buyout
Early Stage
Expansion
Balanced
Other
Management Buyouts
Startup
Distressed Debt

Geographical Preferences

International Preferences:
Europe
Middle East
Asia
Korea, South

Industry Preferences

In Communications prefer:
Communications and Media
Telecommunications
Media and Entertainment

In Computer Hardware prefer:
Computers

In Semiconductor/Electr prefer:
Electronics

In Biotechnology prefer:
Biotechnology

In Medical/Health prefer:
Medical/Health

In Consumer Related prefer:
Entertainment and Leisure

In Industrial/Energy prefer:
Industrial Products

In Business Serv. prefer:
Services

In Manufact. prefer:
Manufacturing

Additional Information

Year Founded: 1986
Capital Under Management: $122,100,000
Current Activity Level: Actively seeking new investments

KOREA VENTURE CREATIVE INVESTMENT CO., LTD. (AKA: KVCI)

502 choongang royal B/D
1355-8 Seocho-2dong, Seocho-Gu
Seoul, South Korea 137-072
Phone: 822-571-4300
Fax: 822-575-5625
Website: www.kvci.co.kr

Management and Staff

Duksoo Kim, President

Type of Firm

Private Equity Firm

Association Membership

Korean Venture Capital Association (KVCA)

Project Preferences

Type of Financing Preferred:
Early Stage
Startup

Size of Investments Considered:
Min Size of Investment Considered (000s): $3,000
Max Size of Investment Considered (000s): $40,000

Geographical Preferences

International Preferences:
Korea, South

Industry Preferences

In Communications prefer:
Entertainment

Additional Information

Year Founded: 2000
Capital Under Management: $3,200,000
Current Activity Level: Actively seeking new investments

KOREA VENTURE FUND MANAGEMENT

Bigway Tower 19F, 677-25
Yeoksam-Dong, KangNam-Ku
Seoul, South Korea 135-080
Phone: 822-3452-1960
Fax: 822-3452-1690

Type of Firm

Private Equity Firm

Project Preferences

Type of Financing Preferred:
Fund of Funds
Early Stage
Expansion
Mezzanine
Balanced

Geographical Preferences

International Preferences:
Korea, South
Asia

Industry Preferences

In Communications prefer:
Communications and Media

In Computer Software prefer:
Software

In Internet Specific prefer:
Internet

In Semiconductor/Electr prefer:
Electronics
Semiconductor

In Consumer Related prefer:
Entertainment and Leisure

Additional Information

Year Founded: 1999
Current Activity Level: Actively seeking new investments

KOREA VENTURE INVESTMENT CORPORATION

5th Floor, VR Building
1706-5 Seocho-dong, Seocho-gu
Seoul, South Korea 137-070
Phone: 822-2156-2000
Fax: 822-2156-2002
E-mail: kvic@k-vic.co.kr
Website: www.k-vic.co.kr

Management and Staff

Byung hak Moon, Vice President
Cheol-Ho Han, Vice President
Hyo hwan Yoon, Principal
Jeong Seo Park, Chief Operating Officer
Ki Hong Sung, Managing Director
Seungheum Lee, Managing Director
Sungcheol Kwon, President
Yoon Jung Yong, Principal
Young Soo Bae, Vice President

Type of Firm

Government Affiliated Program

Association Membership

Korean Venture Capital Association (KVCA)

Project Preferences

Type of Financing Preferred:
Fund of Funds
Balanced

Geographical Preferences

International Preferences:
Korea, South

Industry Preferences

In Biotechnology prefer:
Biotechnology

Additional Information

Year Founded: 2000
Capital Under Management: $1,000,000,000
Current Activity Level: Actively seeking new investments

KORONA INVEST OY

Tekniikantie 12
Espoo, Finland 02150
Phone: 358-9-2517-2070
Website: www.koronainvest.fi

Type of Firm

Private Equity Firm

Association Membership

Finnish Venture Capital Association (FVCA)
European Private Equity and Venture Capital Assoc.

Project Preferences

Type of Financing Preferred:
Balanced

Geographical Preferences

International Preferences:
Europe
Finland

Additional Information

Year Founded: 2006
Current Activity Level: Actively seeking new investments

KOTAK INVESTMENT ADVISORS, LTD. (AKA: KPEG)

13th Floor, Bakhtawar
229, Nariman Point
Mumbai, India 400 021
Phone: 91-22-6626-0500
Fax: 91-22-2285-5511
E-mail: private.equity@kotak.com
Website: www.kotak.com

Management and Staff

K.V. Ramakrishna, Vice President
Nitin Deshmukh, Founding Partner
Uday Kotak, Managing Director
Vamesh Chovatia, Vice President

Type of Firm

Bank Affiliated

Association Membership

Indian Venture Capital Association (IVCA)

Project Preferences

Role in Financing:
Will function either as deal originator or investor in deals created by others

Type of Financing Preferred:
Control-block Purchases
Early Stage
Expansion
Generalist PE
Balanced
Later Stage
Other
First Stage Financing
Acquisition
Industry Rollups
Private Placement

Size of Investments Considered:
Min Size of Investment Considered (000s): $5,000
Max Size of Investment Considered (000s): $15,000

Geographical Preferences

International Preferences:
India

Industry Preferences

In Communications prefer:
Communications and Media
Commercial Communications
Wireless Communications
Media and Entertainment

In Computer Software prefer:
Software

In Internet Specific prefer:
Internet

In Semiconductor/Electr prefer:
Semiconductor
Optoelectronics

In Biotechnology prefer:
Human Biotechnology
Industrial Biotechnology
Biotech Related Research

In Medical/Health prefer:
Medical/Health
Pharmaceuticals

In Consumer Related prefer:
Consumer
Retail
Consumer Products
Consumer Services

In Industrial/Energy prefer:
Environmental Related

In Transportation prefer:
Transportation

In Financial Services prefer:
Real Estate

In Utilities prefer:
Utilities

Additional Information

Year Founded: 1985
Capital Under Management: $1,200,000,000
Current Activity Level: Actively seeking new investments

KPG VENTURES

Pier 33 South- Embarcadero
Suite 201
San Francisco, CA USA 94111
Phone: 415-781-6800
Fax: 415-781-6805
Website: www.kpgventures.com

Management and Staff

Dave Hills, General Partner
Julia Chang, Principal

Type of Firm

Private Equity Firm

Association Membership

National Venture Capital Association - USA (NVCA)

Project Preferences

Type of Financing Preferred:
Balanced
Seed

Geographical Preferences

United States Preferences:
All U.S.

Industry Preferences

In Internet Specific prefer:
Internet

Additional Information

Year Founded: 2006
Current Activity Level: Actively seeking new investments

KPMG CORPORATE FINANCE

Suite 3300
199 Bay Street
Toronto, Canada M5L1B2
Phone: 416-777-8500
Fax: 416-777-8818
Website: www.kpmg.ca

Type of Firm

Private Equity Firm

Additional Information

Year Founded: 2009
Current Activity Level: Actively seeking new investments

KPS CAPITAL PARTNERS, L.P. (FKA: KEILIN & COMPANY)

485 Lexington Avenue
31st Floor
New York, NY USA 10017
Phone: 212-338-5100
Fax: 646-307-7100
Website: www.kpsfund.com

Management and Staff

Bruce Curley, Managing Director
Eugene Keilin, Co-Founder
Jay Bernstein, Partner
Randy Hicks, Managing Director
Raquel Palmer, Partner

Type of Firm

Bank Affiliated

Project Preferences

Type of Financing Preferred:
Leveraged Buyout
Turnaround
Special Situation
Distressed Debt

Geographical Preferences

United States Preferences:
All U.S.

Canadian Preferences:
All Canada

Industry Focus

(% based on actual investment)

Industrial/Energy	76.3%
Other Products	8.9%
Internet Specific	7.2%
Medical/Health	3.0%
Semiconductors/Other Elect.	2.9%
Consumer Related	1.7%

Additional Information

Name of Most Recent Fund: KPS Special Situations Fund II, L.P.
Most Recent Fund Was Raised: 11/25/2002
Year Founded: 1998
Capital Under Management: $494,000,000
Current Activity Level: Actively seeking new investments

KRAFT GROUP, THE

One Patriot Place
Foxboro, MA USA 02035
Phone: 508-543-8200
E-mail: info@thekraftgroup.com
Website: www.thekraftgroup.com

Management and Staff

Jonathan Kraft, President & COO
Robert Kraft, Chairman & CEO

Type of Firm

Private Equity Firm

Project Preferences

Type of Financing Preferred:
Balanced

Industry Preferences

In Communications prefer:
Entertainment

In Financial Services prefer:
Real Estate

In Manufact. prefer:
Manufacturing

Additional Information

Year Founded: 1963
Current Activity Level: Actively seeking new investments

KRAKOWSKIE CENTRUM INWESTYCYJNE

ul. G.Zapolskiej 38
Krakow, Poland 30-126
Phone: 48-12-257-1101
Fax: 48-12-227-1069
E-mail: kci@kci.com
Website: www.kci.pl

Type of Firm

Private Equity Firm

Association Membership

European Private Equity and Venture Capital Assoc.

Project Preferences

Type of Financing Preferred:
Leveraged Buyout
Balanced

Geographical Preferences

International Preferences:
Europe

Additional Information
Year Founded: 2005
Current Activity Level: Actively seeking new investments

KREDITANSTALT FUER WIEDERAUFBAU (KFW)
Palmengartenstrasse 5-9
Frankfurt, Germany 60325
Phone: 49-69-74-310
Fax: 49-69-7431-2944
E-mail: infocenter@kfw.de
Website: www.kfw.de

Type of Firm
Incubator/Development Program

Association Membership
German Venture Capital Association (BVK)
European Private Equity and Venture Capital Assoc.

Project Preferences

Type of Financing Preferred:
Fund of Funds
Balanced

Geographical Preferences

International Preferences:
Europe
Germany

Additional Information
Year Founded: 1998
Capital Under Management: $971,300,000
Current Activity Level: Actively seeking new investments

KREOS CAPITAL (FKA: EUROPEAN VENTURE PARTNERS)
4th Floor, Cardinal House
39-40 Albemarle Street
London, United Kingdom W1S 4TE
Phone: 44-20-7518-8890
Fax: 44-20-7409-1034
E-mail: info@kreoscapital.com
Website: www.kreoscapital.com

Other Offices
27 Maskit Street
P.O. Box 12226
Herzlya Pituach, Israel 46733
Phone: 972-9-951-44-34
Fax: 972-9-951-44-35

Birger Jarlsgatan 2
Stockholm, Sweden 114 34
Phone: 46-8-678-7200
Fax: 46-8-678-0470

Management and Staff
Maurizio Petitbon, Partner
Ross Ahlgren, Partner
Simon Hirtzel, Chief Operating Officer

Type of Firm
Private Equity Firm

Project Preferences

Type of Financing Preferred:
Early Stage
Startup

Size of Investments Considered:
Min Size of Investment Considered (000s): $1,016
Max Size of Investment Considered (000s): $20,314

Geographical Preferences

International Preferences:
Sweden
United Kingdom
Europe
Netherlands
Israel
Germany
France

Industry Preferences

In Communications prefer:
Communications and Media

In Internet Specific prefer:
Internet

In Semiconductor/Electr prefer:
Semiconductor

In Medical/Health prefer:
Medical/Health

Additional Information
Year Founded: 1998
Capital Under Management: $393,200,000
Current Activity Level: Actively seeking new investments

KRG CAPITAL PARTNERS, LLC
1515 Ararpahoe Street
Tower One, Suite 1500
Denver, CO USA 80202
Phone: 303-390-5001
Fax: 303-390-5015
E-mail: info@krgcapital.com
Website: www.krgcapital.com

Other Offices
11827 Oakland Hills Drive
Las Vegas, NV USA 89141
Phone: 702-897-7753
Fax: 702-897-7544

60 Seminary Cove
Mill Valley, CA USA 94941
Phone: 415-388-6752
Fax: 603-994-6294

Management and Staff
Blair Tikker, Managing Director
Bruce Rogers, Managing Director
Charles Gwirtsman, Managing Director
Christopher Bock, Managing Director
Damon Judd, Principal
Mark King, Managing Director
Steven Neumann, Managing Director
Stewart Fisher, Managing Director
Ted Nark, Managing Director
Theresa Shelton, Chief Operating Officer

Type of Firm
Private Equity Firm

Project Preferences

Role in Financing:
Prefer role as deal originator

Type of Financing Preferred:
Leveraged Buyout
Acquisition

Size of Investments Considered:
Min Size of Investment Considered (000s): $3,000
Max Size of Investment Considered (000s): $40,000

Geographical Preferences

United States Preferences:
All U.S.

Canadian Preferences:
All Canada

International Preferences:
Western Europe

Industry Focus
(% based on actual investment)

Other Products	46.4%
Medical/Health	34.8%
Consumer Related	11.5%
Biotechnology	3.4%
Semiconductors/Other Elect.	2.7%
Internet Specific	0.9%
Industrial/Energy	0.2%

Additional Information
Name of Most Recent Fund: KRG Capital Fund IV, L.P.
Most Recent Fund Was Raised: 06/29/2007
Year Founded: 1999
Capital Under Management: $3,533,600,000

Current Activity Level: Actively seeking new investments

KROKUS PRIVATE EQUITY SP. Z O.O.

Al. Jana Pawla II 25
Warsaw, Poland 00-854
Phone: 48-22-6534700
Fax: 48-22-6534707
E-mail: biuro@krokuspe.pl
Website: www.krokuspe.pl

Management and Staff

Anna Ozimska, Chief Executive Officer

Type of Firm

Private Equity Firm

Project Preferences

Role in Financing:
Will function either as deal originator or investor in deals created by others

Type of Financing Preferred:
Leveraged Buyout
Expansion
Management Buyouts
Acquisition

Size of Investments Considered:
Min Size of Investment Considered (000s): $4,194
Max Size of Investment Considered (000s): $20,970

Geographical Preferences

International Preferences:
Poland

Industry Preferences

In Industrial/Energy prefer:
Materials

In Transportation prefer:
Transportation

In Financial Services prefer:
Financial Services

In Business Serv. prefer:
Services
Distribution

In Manufact. prefer:
Manufacturing

Additional Information

Year Founded: 2007
Capital Under Management: $132,500,000
Current Activity Level: Actively seeking new investments

KSH CAPITAL PARTNERS AG (FKA: UEG BETEILIGUNGS AG)

Eschenburgstrasse 7
Luebeck, Germany 23568
Phone: 49-40-3020267
Fax: 49-40-3020517
E-mail: info@ksh-ag.de
Website: www.ksh-ag.de

Management and Staff

Christoph Heyke, Managing Partner
Frank Schneider, Chief Executive Officer

Type of Firm

Private Equity Firm

Association Membership

German Venture Capital Association (BVK)

Project Preferences

Type of Financing Preferred:
Balanced

Geographical Preferences

International Preferences:
Germany

Additional Information

Year Founded: 2000
Current Activity Level: Actively seeking new investments

KSL CAPITAL PARTNERS

100 Fillmore Street
Suite 600
Denver, CO USA 80206
Phone: 720-284-6400
Fax: 720-284-6401
E-mail: contact@kslcapital.com
Website: www.kslcapital.com

Management and Staff

Bernie Siegel, Principal
Coley Brenan, Vice President
Eric Resnick, Managing Director
Martin Newburger, Principal
Michael Shannon, Managing Director
Peter McDermott, Principal
Steven Siegel, Chief Operating Officer

Type of Firm

Private Equity Firm

Project Preferences

Type of Financing Preferred:
Leveraged Buyout
Acquisition

Geographical Preferences

United States Preferences:
All U.S.

Industry Preferences

In Consumer Related prefer:
Consumer
Entertainment and Leisure

In Financial Services prefer:
Real Estate

In Business Serv. prefer:
Services

Additional Information

Year Founded: 2005
Capital Under Management: $1,337,100,000
Current Activity Level: Actively seeking new investments

KSP (KANAGAWA SCIENCE PARK)

West 304, 3-2-1 Sakado
Takatsu-ku
Kawasaki-shi, Japan 213-0012
Phone: 81-44-819-2001
Fax: 81-44-819-2009
Website: www.ksp.or.jp

Management and Staff

Tomoyoshi Ookita, President

Type of Firm

Incubator/Development Program

Additional Information

Year Founded: 1986
Current Activity Level: Actively seeking new investments

KT CAPITAL MANAGEMENT LLC

One Glenlake Parkway
Suite 1075
Atlanta, GA USA 30328
Phone: 770-753-4323

Management and Staff

Peter Kacer, Founding Partner
Robert Konrad, Founding Partner

Type of Firm

Private Equity Firm

Additional Information

Year Founded: 2008
Capital Under Management: $5,700,000
Current Activity Level: Actively seeking new investments

KT VENTURE GROUP LLC

160 Rio Robles
Building D
San Jose, CA USA 95134-1809
Phone: 408-875-3206
Fax: 408-875-2223
Website: www.ktventuregroup.com

Management and Staff

Robert Lee, Founding Partner
Stefano Concina, General Partner

Type of Firm

Corporate PE/Venture

Association Membership

Western Association of Venture Capitalists (WAVC)

Project Preferences

Role in Financing:
Prefer role in deals created by others

Type of Financing Preferred:
Second Stage Financing
Early Stage
First Stage Financing
Strategic Alliances
Joint Ventures

Size of Investments Considered:
Min Size of Investment Considered (000s): $1,000
Max Size of Investment Considered (000s): $4,000

Geographical Preferences

United States Preferences:
All U.S.

International Preferences:
Italy
United Kingdom
China
Hong Kong
Spain
Germany
France
Japan

Industry Preferences

In Semiconductor/Electr prefer:
Semiconductor
Micro-Processing
Sensors
Laser Related
Optoelectronics

In Biotechnology prefer:
Genetic Engineering
Industrial Biotechnology
Biosensors
Biotech Related Research

In Medical/Health prefer:
Medical Diagnostics

In Industrial/Energy prefer:
Advanced Materials
Process Control

In Manufact. prefer:
Manufacturing

Additional Information

Year Founded: 2000
Capital Under Management: $50,000,000
Current Activity Level: Actively seeking new investments
Method of Compensation: Other

KTB SECURITIES CO., LTD. (FKA: KTB NETWORK CO., LTD.)

826-14 Yeoksam-dong
Gangnam-gu
Seoul, South Korea 135-080
Phone: 822-3466-2000
Fax: 822-3466-2120
Website: www.ktb.co.kr

Other Offices

11/F, 88-7 Kyobo Life Building
Jungang-dong, Jung-gu
Busan, South Korea 600-014
Phone: 82-51-442-5742
Fax: 82-51-465-1136

Unit 14-16, 5Fl., China World Tower 1
No. 1 Jian Guo Men Wai Avenue
Beijing, China 100004
Phone: 86-10-6505-2583
Fax: 86-10-6505-1334

9F, Samsung Life Bldg.,
863-1 Bucheon 1 dong
Pusanjin-Ku Pusan, South Korea
Phone: 82-51-647-0051
Fax: 82-51-647-0054

Unit 03, 25F, West Tower Of Twin Towers
No.B12,Jianguomenwai, Dajie, Chaoyang Di
Beijing, China
Phone: 86-10-6568-1391
Fax: 86-10-6568-1392

720 University Avenue
Suite 100
Palo Alto, CA USA 94301
Phone: 650-324-4681
Fax: 650-324-4682

911 Iino Bldg.
2-1-1 Uchisaiwai-cho, Chiyoda-ku
Tokyo, Japan 100-0011
Phone: 81-3-3509-7588
Fax: 81-3-3509-7586

728 Yanan West Road
HuaMin Empire Plaza, Changning District
Shanghai, China
Phone: 86-10-6568-1391
Fax: 86-10-6568-1392

Management and Staff

Bon-Yong Koo, Senior Managing Director
Hoon Park, Managing Director
Jin-Ho Shin, Senior Managing Director
Kyu-Tae Kim, Senior Managing Director
Moo-Gyung Kang, Managing Director
Young-Soo Choi, Senior Managing Director

Type of Firm

Private Equity Firm

Association Membership

Korean Venture Capital Association (KVCA)

Project Preferences

Type of Financing Preferred:
Leveraged Buyout
Balanced
Turnaround
Acquisition
Recapitalizations

Geographical Preferences

International Preferences:
China
Korea, South
Asia

Industry Preferences

In Communications prefer:
Communications and Media
Telecommunications
Wireless Communications

In Business Serv. prefer:
Services

Additional Information

Year Founded: 1981
Capital Under Management: $1,636,500,000
Current Activity Level: Actively seeking new investments

KTB VENTURES

720 University Avenue
Suite 100
Palo Alto, CA USA 94301
Phone: 650-324-4681
Fax: 650-324-4682
E-mail: info@ktbvc.com
Website: www.ktbvc.com

Other Offices

11th floor, Kyobo Life Building
88-7 Jungang-dong, Jung-gu
Busan, South Korea
Phone: 82- 51-442-5742
Fax: 82-51-465-1136

9F, NH Toranomon Bldg.
2-6-10, Toranomon, Minato-ku
Tokyo, Japan 105-0001
Phone: 81-3-3509-7588
Fax: 81-3-3509-7592

KTB Network Building
826-14 Yeoksam-dong- Kangnam-gu
Seoul, South Korea 135-080
Phone: 82- 2-3466-2000
Fax: 82 2-3466-2120

25F, West Tower of Twin Towers
No. B12 Jianguomenwai, Dajie
Beijing, China 100022
Phone: 86-10-6568-1391
Fax: 86-10-6568-1392

KTB network, #24-03 Singapore Land Tower
50 Raffles Place
Singapore, Singapore 048623
Phone: 65-6557-0559
Fax: 65-6557-0332

Suite 1707, Plaza 66 Tower 1
No. 1266 Nanjing West Road
Shanghai, China 200040
Phone: 86-21-6113-5758
Fax: 86-21-6113-5759

Management and Staff

Ho Chan Lee, Partner
Sung Yoon, Managing Partner

Type of Firm

Private Equity Firm

Project Preferences

Role in Financing:
Will function either as deal originator or investor in deals created by others

Type of Financing Preferred:
Early Stage
Balanced
Start-up Financing
First Stage Financing

Size of Investments Considered:
Min Size of Investment Considered (000s): $500
Max Size of Investment Considered (000s): $5,000

Geographical Preferences

United States Preferences:
All U.S.

Industry Focus

(% based on actual investment)

Internet Specific	29.9%
Communications and Media	28.0%
Semiconductors/Other Elect.	17.3%
Consumer Related	13.6%
Computer Software and Services	5.3%
Other Products	2.9%
Computer Hardware	1.9%
Industrial/Energy	1.1%

Additional Information

Year Founded: 1988
Capital Under Management: $130,000,000
Current Activity Level: Actively seeking new investments
Method of Compensation: Return on investment is of primary concern, do not charge fees

KTH CHALMERS CAPITAL (FKA: KTH SEED CAPITAL)

Lindstedtsvagen 5
Stockholm, Sweden 100 44
Phone: 46-8-752-1965
Fax: 46-8-751-6062
E-mail: info@kthchalmerscapital.se
Website: www.kthchalmerscapital.se

Other Offices

Stena Center
Holtermansgatan 1D
Goteborg, Sweden

Management and Staff

Jakob Svardstrom, Managing Partner
Joachim Karlsson, Partner
Jonas Rahmn, Partner

Type of Firm

University Program

Association Membership

Swedish Venture Capital Association (SVCA)
European Private Equity and Venture Capital Assoc.

Project Preferences

Type of Financing Preferred:
Early Stage
Expansion
Seed
Startup

Size of Investments Considered:
Min Size of Investment Considered (000s): $495
Max Size of Investment Considered (000s): $989

Geographical Preferences

International Preferences:
Sweden

Additional Information

Year Founded: 2002
Capital Under Management: $17,700,000
Current Activity Level: Actively seeking new investments

KTIC GLOBAL INVESTMENT ADVISORY CO., LTD.

5th Fl., ES Tower
144-4 Samsung-dong Kangnam-ku
Seoul, South Korea 144-4
Phone: 822-2040-9800
Fax: 822-2040-9899
Website: www.kicvc.com

Management and Staff

Yongku Yang, President

Type of Firm

Investment Management Firm

Association Membership

Venture Capital Association of Beijing (VCAB)
Korean Venture Capital Association (KVCA)

Project Preferences

Type of Financing Preferred:
Early Stage
Expansion
Balanced
Later Stage

Geographical Preferences

International Preferences:
Korea, South

Industry Preferences

In Industrial/Energy prefer:
Industrial Products

In Business Serv. prefer:
Services

Additional Information

Year Founded: 1986
Capital Under Management: $10,100,000
Current Activity Level: Actively seeking new investments

KUA SVAROG ESSET MENEDZHMENT, TOV

Hospital'na
Building 12
Kiev, Ukraine 01901
Phone: 044-496-1460
Fax: 044-492-7855
E-mail: alfa3@svarog.kiev.ua

Type of Firm

Private Equity Firm

Additional Information

Year Founded: 2009

KUBERA PARTNERS, LLC

60 East 42nd Street, Suite 450
The Lincoln Building
New York, NY USA 10165
Phone: 212-295-2400
Fax: 212-295-2424
E-mail: info@kuberapartners.com
Website: www.kuberapartners.com

Other Offices

Nirlon House, 5th Floor
Dr. Annie Besant Road, Worli
Mumbai, India 400025
Phone: 91-22-4034-8600

Fax: 91-22-4034-8686

Management and Staff

Abhishek Maheshwari, Vice President
Alex Dulac, Vice President
Kumar Mahadeva, Managing Partner
Ramanan Raghavendran, Managing Partner
Tarun Pande, Principal

Type of Firm

Private Equity Advisor or Fund of Funds

Project Preferences

Type of Financing Preferred:
Expansion
Later Stage

Size of Investments Considered:
Min Size of Investment Considered (000s): $20,000
Max Size of Investment Considered (000s): $40,000

Geographical Preferences

United States Preferences:
All U.S.

International Preferences:
India
Western Europe
Asia

Additional Information

Name of Most Recent Fund: Kubera Cross Border Fund
Most Recent Fund Was Raised: 01/25/2007
Year Founded: 2007
Capital Under Management: $225,000,000
Current Activity Level: Actively seeking new investments

KUNWU JIUDING CAPITAL CO., LTD.

No. 2 Wudinghou Street
Taikang International Bldg.
Beijing, China 100140
Phone: 86-10-6629-0123
Fax: 86-10-6629-0128
E-mail: pe@jiudingcapital.com
Website: www.jiudingcapital.com

Management and Staff

Leo Cai, Managing Partner
Xiaojie Huang, President

Type of Firm

Private Equity Firm

Project Preferences

Type of Financing Preferred:
Early Stage
Expansion
Later Stage

Geographical Preferences

International Preferences:
China
Asia

Additional Information

Year Founded: 2007
Current Activity Level: Actively seeking new investments

KUNYOUNG INVESTMENT CO., LTD.

13-4 Yoido-dong
Yongdungpo-gu
Seoul, South Korea
Phone: 822-369-8484
Fax: 822-369-8489

Management and Staff

Tae In Park, President

Type of Firm

Private Equity Firm

Project Preferences

Type of Financing Preferred:
Balanced

Geographical Preferences

International Preferences:
Korea, South

Additional Information

Year Founded: 2000
Current Activity Level: Actively seeking new investments

KUO-CHUN FINANCIAL MANAGEMENT, INC.

3F, No. 233-1, Pao-Chiao Road
Hsin Tien
Taipei, Taiwan
Phone: 886-2-2917-7555
Fax: 886-2-2917-3789

Type of Firm

Private Equity Firm

Association Membership

Taiwan Venture Capital Association(TVCA)

Project Preferences

Type of Financing Preferred:
Expansion
Mezzanine
Balanced
Seed
Startup

Geographical Preferences

International Preferences:
Taiwan

Industry Preferences

In Communications prefer:
Telecommunications

In Computer Software prefer:
Software

In Semiconductor/Electr prefer:
Semiconductor

In Biotechnology prefer:
Biotechnology

Additional Information

Name of Most Recent Fund: Kuo-Ding Venture Investment Company, Ltd.
Most Recent Fund Was Raised: 10/01/1997
Year Founded: 1997
Capital Under Management: $14,700,000
Current Activity Level: Actively seeking new investments

KURT SALMON ASSOCIATES CAPITAL ADVISORS

1355 Peachtree Street
Atlanta, GA USA 30309
Phone: 404-897-7248
Fax: 404-253-0373
E-mail: services@kurtsalmon.com
Website: www.kurtsalmon.com

Management and Staff

Gary Catherman, Managing Director
O. Bradley Payme, Managing Director

Type of Firm

Private Equity Firm

Project Preferences

Role in Financing:
Prefer role as deal originator

Type of Financing Preferred:
Turnaround
Management Buyouts
Acquisition
Recapitalizations

Geographical Preferences

United States Preferences:
All U.S.

International Preferences:
Europe

Additional Information

Year Founded: 1936
Current Activity Level: Actively seeking new investments

KYOTO PLANET CAPITAL PARTNERS

1111 West Georgia Street
24th Floor
Vancouver, Canada V6E4M3
Phone: 604-697-0967
Fax: 604-697-0968
Website: www.kyotocapital.com

Management and Staff

Damien Reynolds, Chief Executive Officer
David Kelly B Eng, Vice President
J. Paul Guedes, Vice President

Type of Firm

Private Equity Firm

Additional Information

Year Founded: 2006
Current Activity Level: Actively seeking new investments

KYUSHU VENTURE CAPITAL CO., LTD.

3/F New Tenjin Building Six
4-3-30 Tenjin, Chuo-ku
Fukuoka-shi, Japan 810-0001
Phone: 81-92-725-1515
Fax: 81-92-725-1545
Website: www.kvp.jp

Type of Firm

Private Equity Firm

Project Preferences

Type of Financing Preferred:
Early Stage

Geographical Preferences

International Preferences:
Japan

Industry Preferences

In Semiconductor/Electr prefer:
Semiconductor

In Biotechnology prefer:
Biotechnology

In Consumer Related prefer:
Consumer

Additional Information

Year Founded: 2003
Capital Under Management: $27,000,000
Current Activity Level: Actively seeking new investments

- L -

L CAPITAL MANAGEMENT SAS

22, avenue Montaigne
Paris, France 75008
Phone: 33-1-4413-2222
Fax: 33-1-4413-2485
E-mail: lcapital@lvmh.fr

Other Offices

Via Tonale, 26
Milan, Italy 20125
Phone: 39-02-6714-111
Fax: 39-02-6714-1192

Management and Staff

Daniel Piette, President

Type of Firm

Corporate PE/Venture

Association Membership

French Venture Capital Association (AFIC)
European Private Equity and Venture Capital Assoc.

Project Preferences

Type of Financing Preferred:
Leveraged Buyout
Expansion

Size of Investments Considered:
Min Size of Investment Considered (000s): $4,457
Max Size of Investment Considered (000s): $26,742

Geographical Preferences

International Preferences:
Europe
France

Industry Focus

(% based on actual investment)

Internet Specific	44.9%
Other Products	29.0%
Communications and Media	14.1%
Consumer Related	11.9%

Additional Information

Name of Most Recent Fund: L Capital 2 FCPR
Most Recent Fund Was Raised: 02/15/2006
Year Founded: 1998
Capital Under Management: $222,900,000
Current Activity Level: Actively seeking new investments

L CAPITAL PARTNERS

Ten East 53rd Street
37th Floor
New York, NY USA 10022
Phone: 212-675-7755
Fax: 212-206-9156
E-mail: info@lcapitalpartners.com
Website: www.lcapitalpartners.com

Other Offices

9 Ahad Ha'am Street
Shalom Tower
Tel-Aviv, Israel 65251
Phone: 972-3-510-8581
Fax: 972-3-516-3413

Management and Staff

John Levy, Partner
Jonathan Leitersdorf, Managing Partner
Ting Pau Oei, Partner
Yair Talmor, Partner

Type of Firm

Private Equity Firm

Association Membership

National Venture Capital Association - USA (NVCA)

Project Preferences

Type of Financing Preferred:
Expansion

Size of Investments Considered:
Min Size of Investment Considered (000s): $4,000
Max Size of Investment Considered (000s): $6,500

Geographical Preferences

United States Preferences:
East Coast

Industry Preferences

In Medical/Health prefer:
Medical/Health

In Industrial/Energy prefer:
Energy
Environmental Related

Additional Information

Year Founded: 2004
Capital Under Management: $170,000,000
Current Activity Level: Actively seeking new investments

L&L CAPITAL PARTNERS, LLC

57 Danbury Road
Suite 103
Wilton, CT USA 06897
Phone: 203-834-6222
Fax: 203-834-2473
E-mail: info@llcapitalpartners.com
Website: www.llcapitalpartners.com

Management and Staff

E. Bulkeley Griswold, Managing Director

Type of Firm
Bank Affiliated

Additional Information
Year Founded: 2002
Current Activity Level: Actively seeking new investments

L&S VENTURE CAPITAL CORPORATION
944-24, Daechi-Dong, Gangam-Gu
5/F Sean Building
Seoul, South Korea 135-846
Phone: 822-501-1031
Fax: 822-501-1029

Management and Staff
Dongshik Chang, Chief Executive Officer
Shincheon Kim, President
Sunglin Ju, Partner

Type of Firm
Private Equity Firm

Project Preferences
Type of Financing Preferred:
Balanced

Geographical Preferences
International Preferences:
Korea, South

Industry Preferences
In Industrial/Energy prefer:
Environmental Related

Additional Information
Year Founded: 2006
Capital Under Management: $15,600,000
Current Activity Level: Actively seeking new investments

L-A FINANCES
16 Place Vendome
Paris, France 75001
Phone: 33-1-4286-6030
Fax: 44-1-4286-6031
E-mail: info@la-finances.fr
Website: www.la-finances.fr

Management and Staff
Antoine Labbe, Chairman & Managing Director
Marc Guyot, Partner

Type of Firm
Private Equity Firm

Association Membership
French Venture Capital Association (AFIC)

Project Preferences
Type of Financing Preferred:
Balanced

Geographical Preferences
International Preferences:
Europe
France

Industry Preferences
In Consumer Related prefer:
Retail

In Business Serv. prefer:
Services

Additional Information
Year Founded: 1997
Current Activity Level: Actively seeking new investments

L-EIGENKAPITALAGENTUR (AKA: L-EA)
Schlossplatz 10
Karlsruhe, Germany 76113
Phone: 49-72-1150-1991
Fax: 49-72-1150-1869
E-mail: info@l-ea.de
Website: www.l-ea.de

Type of Firm
Bank Affiliated

Project Preferences
Type of Financing Preferred:
Seed
Startup

Geographical Preferences
International Preferences:
Europe
Germany

Industry Preferences
In Communications prefer:
Commercial Communications

In Biotechnology prefer:
Biotechnology

Additional Information
Year Founded: 2002
Current Activity Level: Actively seeking new investments

LA FINANCIERE DE BRIENNE
2 place Rio de Janeiro
Paris, France 75008
Phone: 33-1-4495-2991
Fax: 33-1-4495-2969
E-mail: contact@financieredebrienne.fr
Website: www.financieredebrienne.fr

Management and Staff
Edwige Avice, President

Type of Firm
Bank Affiliated

Association Membership
French Venture Capital Association (AFIC)

Project Preferences
Type of Financing Preferred:
Balanced

Geographical Preferences
International Preferences:
France

Additional Information
Year Founded: 1993
Current Activity Level: Actively seeking new investments

LA FINANCIERE PATRIMONIALE D INVESTISSMENT (AKA: LFPI)
128, boulevard Haussmann
Paris, France 75008
Phone: 33-1-5836-4490
Fax: 33-1-5836-4499
Website: www.lapatrimoniale.com

Management and Staff
Gilles Etrillard, President
Jerome Balladur, General Director

Type of Firm
Private Equity Firm

Association Membership
French Venture Capital Association (AFIC)

Project Preferences
Type of Financing Preferred:
Leveraged Buyout
Expansion
Balanced

Geographical Preferences
International Preferences:
France

Industry Preferences
In Financial Services prefer:
Real Estate

Additional Information
Name of Most Recent Fund: LFPI Croissance

Most Recent Fund Was Raised: 04/30/2006
Year Founded: 2002
Capital Under Management: $126,000,000
Current Activity Level: Actively seeking new investments

LAB-ONE INNOVATIONS

6 Ha-nechoshet Street
Ramat-Hachayal
Tel-Aviv, Israel 69710
Phone: 972-3-647-5788
Fax: 972-3-647-3819
E-mail: labone@lab-one.co.il
Website: www.lab-one.co.il

Type of Firm

Private Equity Firm

Project Preferences

Type of Financing Preferred:
Early Stage

Geographical Preferences

International Preferences:
Israel

Additional Information

Year Founded: 2007
Current Activity Level: Actively seeking new investments

LABRADOR VENTURES

101 University Avenue
Fourth Floor
Palo Alto, CA USA 94301
Phone: 650-366-6000
Fax: 650-366-6430
E-mail: BusinessPlans@labrador.com
Website: www.labrador.com

Management and Staff

Larry Kubal, Partner
Sean Foote, Partner
Stuart Davidson, Partner

Type of Firm

Private Equity Firm

Association Membership

Western Association of Venture Capitalists (WAVC)

Project Preferences

Role in Financing:
Will function either as deal originator or investor in deals created by others

Type of Financing Preferred:
Early Stage
Seed
Startup

Size of Investments Considered:
Min Size of Investment Considered (000s): $300
Max Size of Investment Considered (000s): $3,000

Geographical Preferences

United States Preferences:
Northern California
West Coast

Industry Preferences

In Communications prefer:
Wireless Communications
Data Communications
Satellite Microwave Comm.
Other Communication Prod.

In Computer Software prefer:
Computer Services
Data Processing
Software

In Semiconductor/Electr prefer:
Semiconductor
Fiber Optics

Additional Information

Name of Most Recent Fund: Labrador Ventures V, L.P.
Most Recent Fund Was Raised: 08/02/2002
Year Founded: 1989
Capital Under Management: $216,000,000
Current Activity Level: Actively seeking new investments
Method of Compensation: Return on investment is of primary concern, do not charge fees

LACUNA, LLC

1100 Spruce Street
Suite 202
Boulder, CO USA 80302
Phone: 303-447-1700
Fax: 303-447-1710
E-mail: info@lacuna.com
Website: www.lacuna.com

Management and Staff

Rawleigh Ralls, Partner
Rich O'Leary, Partner
Sanford Keziah, Partner
Wink Jones, Partner

Type of Firm

Private Equity Firm

Association Membership

National Venture Capital Association - USA (NVCA)

Project Preferences

Type of Financing Preferred:
Early Stage

Size of Investments Considered:
Min Size of Investment Considered (000s): $500
Max Size of Investment Considered (000s): $3,000

Additional Information

Name of Most Recent Fund: Lacuna Venture Fund LLLP
Most Recent Fund Was Raised: 12/16/2008
Year Founded: 2008
Capital Under Management: $22,300,000
Current Activity Level: Actively seeking new investments

LAGO PARTNERS LTD

207 The Chambers
Chelsea Harbour
London, United Kingdom SW1D OXF
Phone: 44-207-349-8210
Fax: 44-207-351-9966
E-mail: info@lagovc.com
Website: www.lagovc.com

Management and Staff

Nadim Nsouli, Managing Partner

Type of Firm

Private Equity Firm

Association Membership

European Private Equity and Venture Capital Assoc.

Project Preferences

Type of Financing Preferred:
Balanced

Geographical Preferences

International Preferences:
Europe

Industry Preferences

In Communications prefer:
Telecommunications
Wireless Communications

In Internet Specific prefer:
Internet

Additional Information

Year Founded: 2000
Capital Under Management: $77,900,000
Current Activity Level: Actively seeking new investments

LAKE CAPITAL PARTNERS, INC.

676 North Michigan Avenue
Suite 3900
Chicago, IL USA 60611
Phone: 312-640-7050
Fax: 312-640-7051
E-mail: info@lakecapital.com
Website: www.lakecapital.com

Management and Staff

Anthony Broglio, Principal
Bradford Cornell, Vice President
Dan Shockley, Vice President
David Hansen, Vice President
David Martin, Vice President
Edward Kovas, Principal
Eric Hart, Vice President
Kevin Rowe, Principal
Marc Landsberg, Principal
Michael Hayes, Chief Financial Officer
Michael Orend, Vice President
Rob Monahan, Vice President
Robert Austin, Vice President
Scott Rowe, Vice President
Tiffany Obenchain, Vice President
Wade Glisson, Vice President

Type of Firm

Private Equity Firm

Project Preferences

Role in Financing:

Prefer role as deal originator

Type of Financing Preferred:

Leveraged Buyout
Expansion
Acquisition
Startup

Size of Investments Considered:

Min Size of Investment Considered (000s): $50,000
Max Size of Investment Considered (000s): $75,000

Geographical Preferences

International Preferences:

Europe

Industry Preferences

In Medical/Health prefer:

Health Services

In Consumer Related prefer:

Consumer Services

In Financial Services prefer:

Financial Services

In Business Serv. prefer:

Services
Distribution

Additional Information

Name of Most Recent Fund: Lake Capital Partners II, L.P.
Most Recent Fund Was Raised: 10/08/2005
Year Founded: 1997
Capital Under Management: $1,300,000,000
Current Activity Level: Actively seeking new investments
Method of Compensation: Function primarily in service area, receive contingent fee in cash or equity

---

LAKE PACIFIC PARTNERS, LLC

120 South Lasalle Street
Suite 1510
Chicago, IL USA 60603
Phone: 312-578-1110
Fax: 312-578-1414
Website: www.lakepacific.com

Management and Staff

Terry Sebastian, Managing Director
William Voss, Managing Director

Type of Firm

Private Equity Firm

Project Preferences

Role in Financing:

Prefer role as deal originator but will also invest in deals created by others

Type of Financing Preferred:

Leveraged Buyout
Control-block Purchases
Expansion
Public Companies
Turnaround
Later Stage
Management Buyouts
Acquisition
Industry Rollups
Recapitalizations

Size of Investments Considered:

Min Size of Investment Considered (000s): $5,000
Max Size of Investment Considered (000s): $35,000

Geographical Preferences

Canadian Preferences:

All Canada

Industry Focus

(% based on actual investment)

Consumer Related	44.1%
Other Products	34.3%
Communications and Media	21.7%

Additional Information

Year Founded: 2000
Capital Under Management: $101,000,000
Current Activity Level: Actively seeking new investments
Method of Compensation: Return on invest. most important, but chg. closing fees, service fees, etc.

LAKE STREET CAPITAL LLC

655 Montgomery Street
Suite 540
San Francisco, CA USA 94111
Phone: 415-291-0500
Fax: 415-276-9353
E-mail: info@lakestreetcapital.com
Website: www.lakestreetcapital.com

Management and Staff

Craig Such, Partner

Type of Firm

Private Equity Firm

Project Preferences

Type of Financing Preferred:

Later Stage
Fund of Funds of Second

Size of Investments Considered:

Min Size of Investment Considered (000s): $550
Max Size of Investment Considered (000s): $550

Industry Preferences

In Communications prefer:

Telecommunications
Wireless Communications
Data Communications

In Computer Software prefer:

Software

In Internet Specific prefer:

Internet

In Semiconductor/Electr prefer:

Electronics
Semiconductor

Additional Information

Year Founded: 2003
Capital Under Management: $400,000,000
Current Activity Level: Actively seeking new investments

LAKEVIEW EQUITY PARTNERS, LLC

700 North Water Street
Suite 630
Milwaukee, WI USA 53202
Phone: 414-732-2040
Fax: 414-732-2041
E-mail: info@lakeviewequity.com
Website: www.lakeviewequity.com

Management and Staff

Gordon Gunnlaugsson, Principal
Joseph Cesarz, Vice President
Ted Kellner, Principal
W. Kent Velde, President
William Abraham, Principal
William Read, Principal

Type of Firm

Private Equity Firm

Project Preferences

Type of Financing Preferred:
Leveraged Buyout
Later Stage
Management Buyouts
Acquisition
Recapitalizations

Geographical Preferences

United States Preferences:
Midwest
All U.S.

Industry Preferences

In Financial Services prefer:
Financial Services

In Business Serv. prefer:
Services
Distribution

In Manufact. prefer:
Manufacturing

Additional Information
Year Founded: 2005
Capital Under Management: $42,700,000
Current Activity Level: Actively seeking new investments

LAMBDA FUNDS, THE
432 East 84th Street
New York, NY USA 10028
Phone: 212-774-1812
Fax: 212-288-7603
Website: www.lambdafund.com

Management and Staff
Anthony Lamport, General Partner

Type of Firm
Private Equity Firm

Association Membership
National Venture Capital Association - USA (NVCA)

Project Preferences

Role in Financing:
Will function either as deal originator or investor in deals created by others

Type of Financing Preferred:
Leveraged Buyout
Early Stage
First Stage Financing

Size of Investments Considered:
Min Size of Investment Considered (000s): $100
Max Size of Investment Considered (000s): $1,000

Geographical Preferences

United States Preferences:
Mid Atlantic
West Coast

Industry Focus
(% based on actual investment)

Biotechnology	25.1%
Computer Hardware	13.3%
Computer Software and Services	12.9%
Industrial/Energy	11.0%
Other Products	8.9%
Consumer Related	8.8%
Semiconductors/Other Elect.	8.0%
Medical/Health	5.4%
Communications and Media	4.0%
Internet Specific	2.5%

Additional Information
Name of Most Recent Fund: Lambda IV
Most Recent Fund Was Raised: 01/01/1996
Year Founded: 1979
Capital Under Management: $10,000,000
Current Activity Level: Actively seeking new investments
Method of Compensation: Return on investment is of primary concern, do not charge fees

---

LAMINAR DIRECT CAPITAL, L.P.
10000 Memorial Drive
Suite 500
Houston, TX USA 77024
Phone: 713-292-5400
Fax: 713-292-5451
Website: www.laminardirect.com

Other Offices
Three Bethesda Metro Center
Suite 1450
Bethesda, MD USA 20814
Phone: 301-634-3000

One Embarcadero Center
Suite 3860
San Francisco, CA USA 94111
Phone: 415-268-2800

Management and Staff
Robert Ladd, President

Type of Firm
Bank Affiliated

Project Preferences

Type of Financing Preferred:
Leveraged Buyout
Expansion
Mezzanine
Acquisition
Distressed Debt
Recapitalizations

Size of Investments Considered:
Min Size of Investment Considered (000s): $5,000
Max Size of Investment Considered (000s): $150,000

Geographical Preferences

United States Preferences:
Northwest
Northeast

Additional Information
Year Founded: 1988
Current Activity Level: Actively seeking new investments

LANCET CAPITAL (FKA: CADUCEUS CAPITAL PARTNERS)
100 Technology Drive
Suite 400
Pittsburgh, PA USA 15219
Phone: 412-770-1622
Fax: 412-770-1347
Website: www.lancetcapital.com

Other Offices
100 Technology Drive
Suite 200
Pittsburgh, PA USA 15219
Phone: 412-770-1308
Fax: 412-770-1342

Management and Staff
George Sing, Managing Director
William Golden, Managing Director

Type of Firm
SBIC

Association Membership
National Venture Capital Association - USA (NVCA)
Natl Assoc of Small Bus. Inv. Co (NASBIC)

Project Preferences

Role in Financing:
Prefer role as deal originator

Type of Financing Preferred:
Seed
Startup

Size of Investments Considered:
Min Size of Investment Considered (000s): $100
Max Size of Investment Considered (000s): $4,000

Industry Preferences

In Biotechnology prefer:
Human Biotechnology
Biosensors
Biotech Related Research

In Medical/Health prefer:
Medical Diagnostics
Diagnostic Services
Diagnostic Test Products
Medical Therapeutics
Drug/Equipmt Delivery
Medical Products

Disposable Med. Products
Hospitals/Clinics/Primary
Hospital/Other Instit.
Pharmaceuticals

Additional Information

Name of Most Recent Fund: Lancet Capital Health Ventures (FKA: Caduceus Capital Healt)
Most Recent Fund Was Raised: 07/15/1998
Year Founded: 1998
Current Activity Level: Actively seeking new investments
Method of Compensation: Return on investment is of primary concern, do not charge fees

LANDMARK GLOBAL FINANCIAL CORPORATION

56 Temperance Street
Fourth Floor
Toronto, Canada M5H 3V5
Phone: 403-531-2660
Fax: 416 362-6777

Type of Firm

Private Equity Firm

Additional Information

Year Founded: 2009
Current Activity Level: Actively seeking new investments

LANDMARK PARTNERS, INC.

Ten Mill Pond Lane
Simsbury, CT USA 06070
Phone: 860-651-9760
Fax: 860-408-8890
E-mail: info@landmarkpartners.com
Website: www.landmarkpartners.com

Other Offices

One Federal Street
21st Floor
Boston, MA USA 02110
Phone: 617-556-3910
Fax: 617-556-4266

Two Greenwich Office Park
Suite 300
Greenwich, CT USA 06831
Phone: 203-485-7510

29-30 St. James's Street
London, United Kingdom SW1A 1HB
Phone: 44-207-343-4450
Fax: 44-207-343-4488

Management and Staff

Barry Griffiths, Vice President
Chad Alfeld, Partner
Gregory Lombardi, Vice President
Ian Charles, Principal
James McConnell, Partner
Julie Gionfriddo, Vice President
Kathryn Feeney, Vice President
Michael Carrano, Vice President
Paul Giovacchini, Principal
Robert Shanfield, Partner
Scott Conners, Partner
Scott Humber, Principal
Tina St. Pierre, Partner

Type of Firm

Private Equity Advisor or Fund of Funds

Association Membership

European Private Equity and Venture Capital Assoc.

Project Preferences

Role in Financing:
Prefer role as deal originator

Type of Financing Preferred:
Fund of Funds
Other
Fund of Funds of Second

Size of Investments Considered:
Min Size of Investment Considered (000s): $500
Max Size of Investment Considered (000s): $500,000

Geographical Preferences

United States Preferences:
All U.S.

Canadian Preferences:
All Canada

International Preferences:
Europe

Industry Focus

(% based on actual investment)

Other Products	72.6%
Industrial/Energy	6.1%
Computer Software and Services	5.2%
Computer Hardware	4.6%
Medical/Health	4.2%
Semiconductors/Other Elect.	3.5%
Consumer Related	2.0%
Internet Specific	1.1%
Biotechnology	0.7%

Additional Information

Name of Most Recent Fund: Landmark Equity Partners XIII-A, L.P.
Most Recent Fund Was Raised: 03/05/2007
Year Founded: 1989
Capital Under Management: $7,500,000,000
Current Activity Level: Actively seeking new investments
Method of Compensation: Other

LANDON INVESTMENTS, SCR, SA

Via Augusta, 200-6
Barcelona, Spain 08021
Phone: 34-93-240-5200
Fax: 34-93-241-6202

Type of Firm

Private Equity Firm

Association Membership

Spanish Venture Capital Association (ASCRI)

Project Preferences

Type of Financing Preferred:
Leveraged Buyout
Expansion
Balanced
Recapitalizations

Size of Investments Considered:
Min Size of Investment Considered (000s): $3,553
Max Size of Investment Considered (000s): $10,655

Geographical Preferences

International Preferences:
Spain

Additional Information

Year Founded: 2006
Current Activity Level: Actively seeking new investments

LANE FIVE VENTURES LLC (FKA: SWAN HOLDINGS LLC)

726 17th Avenue Northeast
Saint Petersburg, FL USA 33704
Phone: 727-385-7360
Fax: 813-463-1706
Website: www.lanefive.com

Management and Staff

Mark Swanson, Managing Director

Type of Firm

Private Equity Firm

Project Preferences

Type of Financing Preferred:
Startup

Geographical Preferences

United States Preferences:
All U.S.

Additional Information

Year Founded: 2008
Current Activity Level: Actively seeking new investments

LANGHOLM CAPITAL LLP

1st Floor, Charles House
5-11 Regent Street
London, United Kingdom SW1Y 4LR
Phone: 44-20-7484-8850
Fax: 44-20-7484-8851
E-mail: info@langholm.com
Website: www.langholm.com

Management and Staff

Amanda Tonsgaard, Principal
Bert Wiegman, Founding Partner
Christian Lorenzen, Partner
Cyril Albrecht, Principal
Eric Pathe, Principal
Oliver Wyncoll, Partner
Paul Richings, Partner
Tom Sirett, Principal

Type of Firm

Private Equity Firm

Association Membership

British Venture Capital Association (BVCA)
European Private Equity and Venture Capital Assoc.

Project Preferences

Role in Financing:
Prefer role as deal originator but will also invest in deals created by others

Type of Financing Preferred:
Second Stage Financing
Leveraged Buyout
Expansion
Management Buyouts

Size of Investments Considered:
Min Size of Investment Considered (000s): $14,276
Max Size of Investment Considered (000s): $71,378

Geographical Preferences

International Preferences:
United Kingdom
Europe

Industry Preferences

In Consumer Related prefer:
Entertainment and Leisure
Retail
Food/Beverage
Consumer Products
Consumer Services

Additional Information

Name of Most Recent Fund: Langholm Capital LP
Most Recent Fund Was Raised: 09/30/2002
Year Founded: 2002
Capital Under Management: $519,000,000
Current Activity Level: Actively seeking new investments

LANKA VENTURES, LTD.

Ocean Lines Building
46/12, Navam Mawatha
Colombo, Sri Lanka
Phone: 94-11-243-9201
Fax: 94-11-243-9203
Website: www.lankaventures.lk

Management and Staff

Sumith Arangala, Chief Executive Officer

Type of Firm

Bank Affiliated

Project Preferences

Role in Financing:
Prefer role in deals created by others

Type of Financing Preferred:
Leveraged Buyout
Generalist PE
Expansion
Early Stage
Turnaround
Seed
Startup

Size of Investments Considered:
Min Size of Investment Considered (000s): $139
Max Size of Investment Considered (000s): $464

Geographical Preferences

International Preferences:
Sri Lanka

Industry Preferences

In Communications prefer:
Other Communication Prod.

In Medical/Health prefer:
Health Services

In Consumer Related prefer:
Education Related

In Industrial/Energy prefer:
Industrial Products

In Manufact. prefer:
Manufacturing

Additional Information

Year Founded: 1992
Capital Under Management: $10,600,000
Current Activity Level: Actively seeking new investments
Method of Compensation: Return on invest. most important, but chg. closing fees, service fees, etc.

LARSEN MACCOLL PARTNERS

One Liberty Place
1650 Market Street, 36th Floor
Philadelphia, PA USA 19103
Phone: 267-319-7930
Fax: 215-689-0847
E-mail: info@larsenmaccoll.com
Website: www.larsenmaccoll.com

Management and Staff

Jeff Larsen, Managing Partner
Tim MacColl, Managing Partner

Type of Firm

Private Equity Firm

Project Preferences

Type of Financing Preferred:
Leveraged Buyout
Early Stage
Seed
Startup

Geographical Preferences

United States Preferences:
All U.S.

Additional Information

Year Founded: 2007
Capital Under Management: $18,000,000
Current Activity Level: Actively seeking new investments

LASALLE CAPITAL GROUP, INC.

5710 Three First Nat'l Plaza
70 West Madison Street
Chicago, IL USA 60602
Phone: 312-236-7041
Fax: 312-236-0720
E-mail: info@lasallecapitalgroup.com
Website: www.lasallecapitalgroup.com

Other Offices

8730 Sunset Boulevard
Suite 420
Los Angeles, CA USA 90069
Phone: 310-360-0707
Fax: 310-360-7391

Management and Staff

Jeff Walters, Partner
Kelly Cornelis, Managing Director
Nicholas Christopher, Vice President
Rocco Martino, Partner

Type of Firm

Private Equity Firm

Association Membership

Natl Assoc of Small Bus. Inv. Co (NASBIC)

Project Preferences

Role in Financing:
Prefer role as deal originator but will also invest in deals created by others

Type of Financing Preferred:
Leveraged Buyout
Management Buyouts
Acquisition
Industry Rollups
Recapitalizations

Size of Investments Considered:
Min Size of Investment Considered (000s): $2,000
Max Size of Investment Considered (000s): $100,000

Industry Preferences

In Communications prefer:
Radio & TV Broadcasting

In Computer Software prefer:
Artificial Intelligence

In Semiconductor/Electr prefer:
Electronic Components

In Medical/Health prefer:
Medical Diagnostics
Diagnostic Services
Medical Therapeutics
Medical Products
Disposable Med. Products
Health Services

In Consumer Related prefer:
Food/Beverage
Consumer Products
Education Related

In Industrial/Energy prefer:
Industrial Products
Materials
Machinery

In Transportation prefer:
Aerospace

In Business Serv. prefer:
Services
Distribution

In Manufact. prefer:
Manufacturing

In Agr/Forestr/Fish prefer:
Agriculture related

In Utilities prefer:
Utilities

In Other prefer:
Socially Responsible

Additional Information
Year Founded: 1984
Capital Under Management: $115,000,000
Current Activity Level: Actively seeking new investments
Method of Compensation: Return on invest. most important, but chg. closing fees, service fees, etc.

LATHAM & WATKINS
355 South Grand Avenue
Los Angeles, CA USA 90071
Phone: 213-485-1234
Fax: 213-891-8763
Website: www.lw.com

Other Offices
885 Third Avenue
Suite 1000
New York, NY USA 10022
Phone: 212-906-2960
Fax: 212-751-4864

650 Town Center Drive
20th Floor
Costa Mesa, CA USA 92626
Phone: 714-540-1235
Fax: 755-8290

88 Century Boulevard
49/F, Jin Mao Tower
Pudong, Shanghai, China 200121
Phone: 8621-6101-6000
Fax: 8621-6101-6001

233 South Wacker Drive
Sears Tower, Suite 5800
Chicago, IL USA 60606
Phone: 312-876-7700
Fax: 312-993-9767

Maximilianhoefe
Maximilianstrasse 11
Munchen, Germany 80539
Phone: 49-89-20-803-8000
Fax: 49-89-20-803-8080

505 Montgomery Street
Suite 2000
San Francisco, CA USA 94111
Phone: 415-391-0600
Fax: 415-395-8095

Boulevard du Regent, 43-44
Brussels, Belgium 1000
Phone: 32-2-788-6000
Fax: 32-2-788-6060

Reuterweg 20
Frankfurt, Germany 60323
Phone: 49-69-6062-6000
Fax: 49-69-6062-6060

12636 High Bluff Drive
Suite 400
San Diego, CA USA 92130
Phone: 858-523-5400
Fax: 858-523-5450

80 Raffles Place
Suite 14-20, UOB Plaza 2
Singapore, Singapore 048624
Phone: 65-6536-1161
Fax: 65-6536-1171

One Newark Center
16th Floor
Newark, NJ USA 07101
Phone: 973-639-1234
Fax: 973-639-7298

140 Scott Drive
Menlo Park, CA USA 94025
Phone: 650-328-4600
Fax: 650-463-2600

555 Eleventh Street, Northwest
Suite 1000
Washington, DC USA 20004
Phone: 202-637-2200
Fax: 202-637-2201

99 Bishopsgate
London, United Kingdom EC2M 3XF
Phone: 44-20-7710-1000
Fax: 44-20-7374-4460

Corso Giacomo Matteotti, 8
Milan, Italy 20121
Phone: 39-02-3046-2000
Fax: 39-02-3046-2001

41st Floor, One Exchange Square
8 Connaught Place
Central, Hong Kong
Phone: 852-2912-2503
Fax: 852-2522-7006

11955 Freedom Drive
Two Freedom Square, Suite 500
Reston, VA USA 20190
Phone: 703-456-1000
Fax: 703-456-1001

600 West Broadway
Suite 1800
San Diego, CA USA 92101
Phone: 619-236-1234
Fax: 619-696-7419

2-4-1 Marunouchi, Chiyoda-ku
Marunouchi Building, 32nd Floor
Tokyo, Japan 100-6332
Phone: 81-3-6212-7800
Fax: 81-3-6212-7801

Warburgstrasse 50
Hamburg, Germany 20354
Phone: 49-40-41-4030
Fax: 49-40-4140-3130

Ulitsa Gasheka, 7
Ducat II, Suite 900
Moscow, Russia 123056
Phone: 7-501-785-1234
Fax: 7-501-785-1235

53, quai d'Orsay
Paris, France 75007
Phone: 33-1-4062-2000
Fax: 33-1-4062-2062

Management and Staff
Beth Wilkinson, Partner

David Zhang, Partner
Dennis Lamont, Partner
Graeme Sloan, Partner
I. Scott Gottdiener, Partner
Riccardo Agostinelli, Partner

Type of Firm

Corporate PE/Venture

Additional Information

Year Founded: 1934
Current Activity Level: Actively seeking new investments

LATIN AMERICA EQUITY PARTNERS (FKA: LAEP)

Avenida Cidade Jardim 400
Conjunto 81
Sao Paulo, Brazil
Phone: 55-11-3079-4219
Fax: 55-11-3071-3937
Website: www.laepbrasil.com.br

Management and Staff

Carlos Christensen, Partner
Eduardo Aguinaga De Moraes, Partner
Flavio Silva Souto, Partner
Luis Manoel Do Amaral, Partner
Marcus Alberto Elias, Partner

Type of Firm

Private Equity Firm

Association Membership

Brazilian Venture Capital Association (ABCR)

Project Preferences

Type of Financing Preferred:

Balanced

Geographical Preferences

International Preferences:

Brazil

Industry Preferences

In Consumer Related prefer:

Retail
Food/Beverage

In Agr/Forestr/Fish prefer:

Agribusiness

Additional Information

Year Founded: 2006
Current Activity Level: Actively seeking new investments

LATIN IDEA VENTURES, LLC

Paseo de las Palmas 405-601
Col. Lomas de Chapultepec
Mexico City, Mexico 11000
Phone: 52-55-2973-3030
E-mail: info@latinidea.com
Website: www.latinidea.com

Management and Staff

Alexander Rossi, Managing Director

Type of Firm

Private Equity Firm

Project Preferences

Type of Financing Preferred:

Expansion
Later Stage

Size of Investments Considered:

Min Size of Investment Considered (000s): $1,000
Max Size of Investment Considered (000s): $6,000

Geographical Preferences

International Preferences:

Mexico

Industry Preferences

In Communications prefer:

Communications and Media

In Business Serv. prefer:

Services
Media

Additional Information

Year Founded: 2003
Capital Under Management: $30,000,000
Current Activity Level: Actively seeking new investments

LATINVALLEY

Rua Araujo Porto Alegre, 36
Sala 1303, Centro
Rio de Janeiro, RJ, Brazil 20030-010
Phone: 5521-2544-4834
Fax: 5521-2524-5655
E-mail: contact@latinvalley.com
Website: www.latinvalley.com

Type of Firm

Private Equity Firm

Project Preferences

Type of Financing Preferred:

Balanced

Geographical Preferences

International Preferences:

Brazil

Additional Information

Year Founded: 2001
Current Activity Level: Actively seeking new investments

LATITUDE PARTNERS

223 Avenue Road
Toronto, Canada M5R 2J3
Phone: 416-513-9090
Fax: 416-513-9339
Website: www.latitudepartners.com

Management and Staff

Don Bent, Chief Financial Officer
John Sheedy, Partner
Kevin Clay, Partner
Thomas Eisenhauer, Managing Partner

Type of Firm

Private Equity Firm

Project Preferences

Type of Financing Preferred:

Leveraged Buyout

Size of Investments Considered:

Min Size of Investment Considered (000s): $5,000
Max Size of Investment Considered (000s): $10,000

Geographical Preferences

Canadian Preferences:

All Canada

Industry Preferences

In Communications prefer:

Communications and Media

In Internet Specific prefer:

Internet

Additional Information

Year Founded: 1999
Current Activity Level: Actively seeking new investments

LATTERELL VENTURE PARTNERS

One Embarcadero Centre
Suite 4050
San Francisco, CA USA 94111-4106
Phone: 415-399-9880
Fax: 415-399-9879
Website: www.lvpcapital.com

Management and Staff

James Woody, Partner

Kenneth Widder, Partner
Patrick Latterell, Managing Partner
Paul Edwards, Principal
Peter Fitzgerald, Partner
Stephen Salmon, Partner

Type of Firm

Private Equity Firm

Association Membership

National Venture Capital Association - USA (NVCA)

Project Preferences

Role in Financing:

Will function either as deal originator or investor in deals created by others

Type of Financing Preferred:

Early Stage
Balanced
Later Stage

Geographical Preferences

United States Preferences:

All U.S.

International Preferences:

India
United Kingdom
China

Industry Preferences

In Biotechnology prefer:

Biotechnology

In Medical/Health prefer:

Medical/Health

Additional Information

Name of Most Recent Fund: Latterell Venture Partners III, L.P.
Most Recent Fund Was Raised: 06/23/2005
Year Founded: 2001
Capital Under Management: $301,000,000
Current Activity Level: Actively seeking new investments

LAUD COLLIER & COMPANY LLC (AKA: LC & CO.)

466 Southern Boulevard
Jefferson Building
Chatham, NJ USA 07928
Phone: 973-822-1234
Fax: 973-822-1224
E-mail: info@lccap.com
Website: www.lccap.com

Management and Staff

Colby Collier, Co-Founder
Paul Laud, Co-Founder

Type of Firm

Private Equity Firm

Project Preferences

Type of Financing Preferred:

Leveraged Buyout
Acquisition
Recapitalizations

Size of Investments Considered:

Min Size of Investment Considered (000s): $10,000
Max Size of Investment Considered (000s): $20,000

Geographical Preferences

United States Preferences:

All U.S.

Industry Preferences

In Consumer Related prefer:

Entertainment and Leisure
Consumer Products

In Industrial/Energy prefer:

Industrial Products

In Transportation prefer:

Transportation

In Business Serv. prefer:

Services
Distribution

In Manufact. prefer:

Manufacturing

Additional Information

Year Founded: 2002
Current Activity Level: Actively seeking new investments

LAUDER PARTNERS

88 Mercedes Lane
Atherton, CA USA 94027
Phone: 650-323-5700
Fax: 650-323-2171
Website: www.lauderpartners.com

Management and Staff

Gary Lauder, Managing Partner

Type of Firm

Private Equity Firm

Additional Information

Year Founded: 1996
Current Activity Level: Actively seeking new investments

LAUNCHCAPITAL LLC

One Mifflin Place
Suite 300
Cambridge, MA USA 02138
Website: www.launch-capital.com

Management and Staff

Elon Boms, Managing Director

Type of Firm

Private Equity Firm

Association Membership

National Venture Capital Association - USA (NVCA)

Project Preferences

Type of Financing Preferred:

Early Stage

Additional Information

Year Founded: 2009
Current Activity Level: Actively seeking new investments

LAUNCHCYTE LLC

100 Technology Drive
Suite 440
Pittsburgh, PA USA 15219
Phone: 412-770-1630
Fax: 412-770-1638
E-mail: info@launchcyte.com
Website: www.launchcyte.com

Management and Staff

Babs Carryer, President
Thomas Petzinger, Chief Executive Officer

Type of Firm

Incubator/Development Program

Project Preferences

Role in Financing:

Prefer role as deal originator

Type of Financing Preferred:

Startup

Industry Preferences

In Biotechnology prefer:

Biotechnology

Additional Information

Year Founded: 2000
Capital Under Management: $800,000
Current Activity Level: Actively seeking new investments

LAURENCE CAPITAL CORPORATION

75 King Street South
P.O. BOX 40042
Waterloo, Canada
Phone: 519-749-8893
Fax: 519-749-1554
Website: www.laurencecapital.com

Type of Firm

Private Equity Firm

Additional Information

Year Founded: 2009
Current Activity Level: Actively seeking new investments

LAURENTIAN BANK

1981 McGill College
Suite 1660
Montreal, Canada H3A 3K3
Phone: 514-284-3987
Fax: 514-284-3988
Website: www.laurentianbank.ca

Type of Firm

Endowment, Foundation or Pension Fund

Additional Information

Year Founded: 2009
Current Activity Level: Actively seeking new investments

LAUX CAPITAL PARTNERS

672 West Liberty Street
Medina, OH USA 44256
Phone: 330-721-0100

Management and Staff

William Laux, General Partner

Type of Firm

Private Equity Firm

Project Preferences

Type of Financing Preferred:

Mezzanine

Geographical Preferences

United States Preferences:

All U.S.

Additional Information

Year Founded: 2004
Capital Under Management: $200,000
Current Activity Level: Actively seeking new investments

LAVA MANAGEMENT, LLC

1001 Bishop Street
Pauahi Tower, Suite 1570
Honolulu, HI USA 96813
Phone: 808-524-1508

Management and Staff

Gwendolyn Watanabe, General Partner

Type of Firm

Private Equity Firm

Project Preferences

Type of Financing Preferred:

Balanced

Geographical Preferences

United States Preferences:

All U.S.

Additional Information

Name of Most Recent Fund: Lava Ventures VII, L.P.
Most Recent Fund Was Raised: 09/21/2004
Year Founded: 2004
Capital Under Management: $4,900,000
Current Activity Level: Actively seeking new investments

LAWRENCE FINANCIAL GROUP

13320 Westcove Drive
Los Angeles, CA USA 90049
Phone: 310-230-1188
Fax: 310-943-2232
E-mail: info@lawrencefinancial.com
Website: www.lawrencefinancial.com

Type of Firm

Bank Affiliated

Project Preferences

Role in Financing:

Prefer role as deal originator but will also invest in deals created by others

Type of Financing Preferred:

Second Stage Financing

Size of Investments Considered:

Min Size of Investment Considered (000s): $500
Max Size of Investment Considered (000s): $1,000

Geographical Preferences

United States Preferences:

West Coast

Industry Preferences

In Communications prefer:

Telecommunications
Satellite Microwave Comm.

In Computer Other prefer:

Computer Related

In Semiconductor/Electr prefer:

Electronic Components
Circuit Boards
Component Testing Equipmt

In Biotechnology prefer:

Industrial Biotechnology
Biosensors
Biotech Related Research

In Medical/Health prefer:

Medical/Health
Medical Diagnostics
Medical Therapeutics

In Consumer Related prefer:

Consumer
Education Related

In Industrial/Energy prefer:

Oil and Gas Exploration
Oil & Gas Drilling,Explor
Energy Conservation Relat
Industrial Products

In Financial Services prefer:

Financial Services

In Business Serv. prefer:

Distribution

In Agr/Forestr/Fish prefer:

Agriculture related
Mining and Minerals

Additional Information

Year Founded: 1989
Current Activity Level: Actively seeking new investments
Method of Compensation: Function primarily in service area, receive contingent fee in cash or equity

---

LAWRENCE VENTURES

621 Fifth Street
Suite B
Clovis, CA USA 93612
Phone: 559-298-9700
Website: www.lawrenceventures.com

Management and Staff

Case Lawrence, Managing Director
David Mason, Venture Partner
Krishna Krishnamaneni, Venture Partner
Peter Ehat, Venture Partner
Tom McLelland, Venture Partner

Type of Firm

Private Equity Firm

Additional Information

Year Founded: 2005
Current Activity Level: Actively seeking new investments

LAZARD ALTERNATIVE INVESTMENT

30 Rockefeller Plaza
48th Floor
New York, NY USA 10020
Phone: 212-332-5601
Website: www.lazardai.com

Management and Staff

Joseph Josephson, Managing Director
Steve Golub, Chief Financial Officer

Type of Firm

Bank Affiliated

Industry Focus

(% based on actual investment)

Other Products	50.3%
Consumer Related	18.5%
Internet Specific	10.9%
Communications and Media	10.2%
Computer Software and Services	7.0%
Computer Hardware	1.3%
Medical/Health	1.1%
Semiconductors/Other Elect.	0.7%

Additional Information

Year Founded: 1979
Current Activity Level: Actively seeking new investments

LAZARD CAPITAL PARTNERS

30 Rockefeller Plaza
62 Floor
New York, NY USA 10020
Phone: 212-632-6000
Fax: 212-632-6060
Website: www.lazard.com

Other Offices

3414 Peachtree Road North East
Suite 705
Atlanta, GA USA 30326
Phone: 404-442-2144
Fax: 404-442-2155

1999 Avenue of the Stars
Suite 1140
Los Angeles, CA USA 90067
Phone: 310-601-3400
Fax: 310-601-3401

Pariser Platz 4A
First Floor
Berlin, Germany 10117
Phone: 49-30-7261-0190
Fax: 4930-7261-0191

Romm 2601, Henley Building
5 Queen's Road Central
Central, Hong Kong
Phone: 852-2522-8187
Fax: 852-2522-8581

Sanno Park Tower 6th Floor
11-1 Nagatocho 2-Chome
Tokyo, Japan 100-6106
Phone: 81-3-5511-6011
Fax: 81-3-5511-0751

JPMorgan Chase Tower
600 Travis Street, Suite 2300
Houston, TX USA 77002
Phone: 713-236-4600
Fax: 713-236-4620

225 South Sixth Street
Suite 3390
Minneapolis, MN USA 55402
Phone: 612-341-8171

Four Embarcadero Center
Suite 650
San Francisco, CA USA 94111
Phone: 415-623-5000
Fax: 415-421-5050

via Po 25
Rome, Italy 00198
Phone: 33-06-8537-691
Fax: 33-06-8537-6930

Room 1804, Tower E1
No.1 East Chang An AVenue
Beijing, China
Phone: 86-10-8515-0880
Fax: 86-10-8515-0879

200 West Madison Street
Suite 2200
Chicago, IL USA 60606
Phone: 312-407-6600
Fax: 312-407-6620

via Dell'Orso 2
Milan, Italy 20121
Phone: 39-02-723-121
Fax: 39-02-723-121

1501 McGill College
Suite 1610
Montreal, Canada H3A3M8
Phone: 514-397-1016
Fax: 514-397-1317

Neue Mainzer Strasse 69-75
Frankfurt, Germany 60311
Phone: 49-69-170-0730
Fax: 49-69-1700-7310

UOB Plaza II #22-21
80 Raffles Place
Singapore, Singapore 048624
Phone: 65-6534-2011
Fax: 65-6534-2911

Level 39, Gateway
Macquarie Place
Sydney, Australia 2000
Phone: 61-2-9251-8300
Fax: 61-2-9251-8309

Sturegatan 24
Stockholm, Sweden 11436
Phone: 46-8442-5400
Fax: 46-8442-5415

Hanwha Building 801
110 Sogong Dong, Cheung Gu
Seoul, South Korea 100070
Phone: 82-2771-0991
Fax: 82-2771-0996

16, avenue Foch
Lyon, France 69006
Phone: 33-4-7269-6580
Fax: 33-4-7269-6585

121 Boulevard Haussmann
Paris, France 75382
Phone: 33-1-4413-0111
Fax: 33-1-4413-0100

Suite 4610
1 First Canadian Place
Toronto, Canada M5X1E2
Phone: 416-216-5086
Fax: 416-216-5085

20th Floor, Express Towers
Nariman Point
Mumbai, India 400021
Phone: 91-22-6752-6000
Fax: 91-22-6752-6060

Neuer Wall 9
Hamburg, Germany 20354
Phone: 49-40-3572-9020
Fax: 49-40-3572-9029

50 Stratton Street
London, United Kingdom W1J 8LL
Phone: 44-207-187-2000
Fax: 44-207-072-7000

Financieros S.A.
Serrano 28-1 Planta
Madrid, Spain 28001
Phone: 34-91-781-8480
Fax: 34-91-781-8492

Rembrandt Tower
28th Floor, Amstelplein 1
Amsterdam, Netherlands 1096HA
Phone: 31-20-561-1160
Fax: 31-20-561-1150

8 rue du Chatteu-Trompette
Aquitaine, France 33000
Phone: 33-5-5644-3000
Fax: 33-5-5644-3949

Management and Staff

Ali Wambold, Managing Director
B. Timothy O'Gara, Managing Director
Ben Sullivan, Managing Director
Bill Riddle, Managing Director
Eytan Tigay, Principal
Gilles Etrillard, Partner
Gregory Myers, Vice President
J. Michael Sutka, Managing Director
Robert White, Vice President
Scott Church, Managing Director
William Buchanan, Managing Director

Type of Firm

Bank Affiliated

Project Preferences

Type of Financing Preferred:
Expansion

Size of Investments Considered:
Min Size of Investment Considered (000s): $10,000
Max Size of Investment Considered (000s): $50,000

Industry Focus

(% based on actual investment)

Computer Hardware	78.1%
Industrial/Energy	8.2%
Internet Specific	7.2%
Computer Software and Services	6.5%

Additional Information

Year Founded: 1998
Current Activity Level: Actively seeking new investments

LAZARD TECHNOLOGY PARTNERS

30 Rockefeller Plaza
48th Floor
New York, NY USA 10020
Phone: 212-632-6000
Fax: 212-332-8677
Website: www.lazardtp.com

Other Offices

5335 Wisconsin Avenue, Northwest
Suite 410
Washington, DC USA 20015
Phone: 202-895-1515
Fax: 202-895-1501

Type of Firm

Bank Affiliated

Association Membership

Mid-Atlantic Venture Association

Project Preferences

Type of Financing Preferred:
Second Stage Financing
Early Stage
Expansion
Later Stage
First Stage Financing

Size of Investments Considered:
Min Size of Investment Considered (000s): $1,000
Max Size of Investment Considered (000s): $10,000

Geographical Preferences

United States Preferences:
East Coast
D. of Columbia
New York

Industry Focus

(% based on actual investment)

Computer Software and Services	41.6%
Internet Specific	41.1%
Communications and Media	6.2%
Computer Hardware	5.0%
Semiconductors/Other Elect.	4.5%
Consumer Related	1.5%

Additional Information

Name of Most Recent Fund: Lazard Technology Partners II
Most Recent Fund Was Raised: 05/09/2000
Year Founded: 1998
Capital Under Management: $400,000,000
Current Activity Level: Actively seeking new investments

LB INVESTMENT, INC. (FKA: LG VENTURE INVESTMENT, INC.)

13/F, Shinan Building, 943-19
Daechi-Dong, Gangnam-Gu
Seoul, South Korea 135-280
Phone: 822-3467-0500
Fax: 822-3467-0530
Website: www.lginvest.co.kr

Management and Staff

Boncheon Gu, President
Bonwan Koo, General Partner
Brian Koo, CEO & Managing Director
DooSeok Chae, Principal
GunSoo Yoon, General Partner
Haitong Zhung, Principal
Hakkyoon Kim, Principal
Hee-gyoo Lee, Partner
Hong-Chae Kim, Partner
Hyung-Kew Choi, Principal
Hyunkeun Lee, General Partner
Jason Koo, Partner
Jason Jeongseok Lee, Principal
Keunyoung Ahn, Principal
Kiho Park, General Partner
Mahn-Joon Jang, Partner
Qin Wang, Principal
Wonyun Choi, General Partner
Young Kim, President

Type of Firm

Private Equity Firm

Association Membership

Korean Venture Capital Association (KVCA)

Project Preferences

Type of Financing Preferred:
Early Stage
Expansion
Mezzanine
Balanced

Size of Investments Considered:
Min Size of Investment Considered (000s): $500
Max Size of Investment Considered (000s): $3,000

Geographical Preferences

International Preferences:
China
Korea, South

Industry Preferences

In Communications prefer:
Communications and Media
Telecommunications

In Internet Specific prefer:
Internet

In Semiconductor/Electr prefer:
Semiconductor

In Biotechnology prefer:
Biotechnology

Additional Information

Year Founded: 1996
Capital Under Management: $103,400,000
Current Activity Level: Actively seeking new investments

LBBW VENTURE CAPITAL GMBH

Koenigstrasse 10 C
Stuttgart, Germany 70173
Phone: 49-711-30589200
Fax: 49-711305892099
E-mail: Zukunft@LBBW-Venture.de
Website: www.bw-venture.de

Management and Staff

Harald Fuchs, Managing Director

Type of Firm

Bank Affiliated

Association Membership

German Venture Capital Association (BVK)

Project Preferences

Type of Financing Preferred:
Expansion

Geographical Preferences

International Preferences:
Germany

Industry Preferences

In Communications prefer:
Communications and Media

In Internet Specific prefer:
Internet
Ecommerce

In Computer Other prefer:
Computer Related

In Biotechnology prefer:
Biotechnology

In Medical/Health prefer:
Medical/Health

In Industrial/Energy prefer:
Energy
Materials
Environmental Related

In Financial Services prefer:
Financial Services

Additional Information
Year Founded: 1998
Current Activity Level: Actively seeking new investments

LBC CAPITAL, INC.
1981, avenue McGill College
Bureau 1485
Montreal, Canada H3A 3K3
Phone: 514-284-4732
Fax: 514-284-4551

Type of Firm
Investment Management Firm

Additional Information
Year Founded: 1997
Current Activity Level: Actively seeking new investments

LBO FRANCE SAS
148 rue de l'Universite
Paris, France 75007
Phone: 33-1-4062-7767
Fax: 33-1-4062-7555
Website: www.lbofrance.com

Type of Firm
Private Equity Firm

Association Membership
French Venture Capital Association (AFIC)

Project Preferences

Type of Financing Preferred:
Leveraged Buyout
Balanced
Management Buyouts
Acquisition

Size of Investments Considered:
Min Size of Investment Considered (000s): $1,372
Max Size of Investment Considered (000s): $41,157

Geographical Preferences

International Preferences:
Fr Polynesia
Europe
Western Europe
France

Industry Focus
(% based on actual investment)

Other Products	66.5%
Industrial/Energy	32.9%
Semiconductors/Other Elect.	0.3%
Consumer Related	0.2%
Medical/Health	0.1%

Additional Information
Name of Most Recent Fund: White Knight II
Most Recent Fund Was Raised: 12/21/1998
Year Founded: 1984
Capital Under Management: $4,413,500,000
Current Activity Level: Actively seeking new investments

LC CAPITAL
12, rue Marbeuf
Paris, France 75008
Phone: 33-1-5688-3200
Fax: 33-1-5688-3209
E-mail: info@lc-capital.com
Website: www.lc-capital.com

Type of Firm
Private Equity Advisor or Fund of Funds

Association Membership
French Venture Capital Association (AFIC)
European Private Equity and Venture Capital Assoc.

Project Preferences

Role in Financing:
Will function either as deal originator or investor in deals created by others

Type of Financing Preferred:
Early Stage
Expansion

Size of Investments Considered:
Min Size of Investment Considered (000s): $129
Max Size of Investment Considered (000s): $3,889

Geographical Preferences

International Preferences:
United Kingdom
Europe
Spain
France

Industry Preferences

In Communications prefer:
Telecommunications

In Computer Software prefer:
Software

In Medical/Health prefer:
Medical/Health

Additional Information
Name of Most Recent Fund: FCPR LC Capital Fund II
Most Recent Fund Was Raised: 02/28/2005
Year Founded: 2003
Capital Under Management: $35,300,000
Current Activity Level: Actively seeking new investments
Method of Compensation: Return on investment is of primary concern, do not charge fees

---

LD INVEST A/S
Vendersgade 28
Copenhagen, Denmark 1363
Phone: 45-3336-8989
Fax: 45-3336-8904
E-mail: equity@ld-invest.dk
Website: www.ld-invest.dk

Management and Staff
Henrik Parkhoi, Managing Director
Lars Tonnesen, Managing Partner

Type of Firm
Private Equity Firm

Project Preferences

Type of Financing Preferred:
Leveraged Buyout
Acquisition

Size of Investments Considered:
Min Size of Investment Considered (000s): $9,966
Max Size of Investment Considered (000s): $29,898

Geographical Preferences

International Preferences:
Denmark

Industry Preferences

In Business Serv. prefer:
Services

In Manufact. prefer:
Manufacturing

Additional Information
Year Founded: 1983
Capital Under Management: $487,400,000
Current Activity Level: Actively seeking new investments

LD PENSIONS
Vendersgade, 28
Copenhagen, Denmark K - 1363
Phone: 45-33-368-900
Fax: 45-33-368-901
E-mail: info@ld.dk
Website: www.ldpensions.dk

Type of Firm
Endowment, Foundation or Pension Fund

Association Membership

Danish Venture Capital Association (DVCA)

Project Preferences

Type of Financing Preferred:

Fund of Funds
Early Stage
Expansion
Later Stage
Seed
Management Buyouts
Startup

Geographical Preferences

International Preferences:

Europe
Denmark

Industry Preferences

In Business Serv. prefer:

Services

Additional Information

Year Founded: 1980
Current Activity Level: Actively seeking new investments

LDC (FKA: LLOYDS TSB DEVELOPMENT CAPITAL, LTD.)

One Vine Street
London, United Kingdom W1J 0AH
Phone: 44-20-7758-3680
Fax: 44-20-7758-3681
Website: www.ldc.co.uk

Other Offices

First Floor, Abbey corner
Four Kings Road, Reading
Berkshire, United Kingdom RG1 3BB
Phone: 44-118-958-0274
Fax: 44-118-956-8991

Pall Mall House
Mercury Court, Tithebarn Street
Liverpool, United Kingdom L2 2QU
Phone: 44-151-227-5024
Fax: 44-151-236-6773

8 Queen's Road
26/F
Central, Hong Kong
Phone: 852-3416-4400

Butt Dyke House
33 Park Row
Nottingham, United Kingdom NG1 6GZ
Phone: 44-115-947-1280
Fax: 44-115-947-1290

Interchange Place
6th Floor, Edmund Street
Birmingham, United Kingdom B3 2TA
Phone: 44-121-237-6500
Fax: 44-121-236-5269

45 Old Bond Street
London, United Kingdom W1S 4QT
Phone: 44-20-7499-1500
Fax: 44-20-7647-2000

1 City Square
Leeds, United Kingdom LS1 2ES
Phone: 44-113-300-2013
Fax: 44-113-300-2601

One Forbury Square
1st Floor
Reading, United Kingdom RG1 3BB
Phone: 44-118-958-0274
Fax: 44-118-956-8991

Amsterdam Atrium
Strawinskylaan 3051
Amsterdam, Netherlands 1077 ZX
Phone: 31-20-3012-225
Fax: 31-20-3012-232

Enterprise House, Ocean Village
Suite 4
Southampton , United Kingdom S014 3XB
Phone: 44-23-80-488-727
Fax: 44-2380-488-725

P.O. Box 686, Black Horse House
91 Sandyford Road
Newcastle upon Tyne, United Kingdom NE99 1JW
Phone: 44-191-261-1541
Fax: 44-191-261-5934

Quay 2
139 Fountainbridge
Edinburgh, United Kingdom EH3 9QG
Phone: 44-131-257-4500
Fax: 44-131-257-4510

1 Marsden Street
8th Floor
Manchester, United Kingdom M2 1HW
Phone: 44-161-831-1720
Fax: 44-161-831-1730

Kings House
14 Orchard Street
Bristol, United Kingdom BS1 5EH
Phone: 44-117-905-5322
Fax: 44-117-905-9055

Management and Staff

Adrian Willetts, Managing Director
Andrew Ball, Managing Director
Candida Morley, Chief Operating Officer
Darryl Eales, Managing Director
Jonathan Andrew, Chief Operating Officer
Kevan Leggett, Managing Director
Martin Draper, Managing Director
Patrick Sellers, Managing Director
Peter Brooks, Managing Director
Tim Farazmand, Managing Director

Type of Firm

Bank Affiliated

Association Membership

British Venture Capital Association (BVCA)
European Private Equity and Venture Capital Assoc.

Project Preferences

Type of Financing Preferred:

Leveraged Buyout
Expansion
Acquisition

Size of Investments Considered:

Min Size of Investment Considered (000s): $3,600
Max Size of Investment Considered (000s): $54,350

Geographical Preferences

International Preferences:

United Kingdom

Industry Focus

(% based on actual investment)

Other Products	53.8%
Consumer Related	12.0%
Internet Specific	9.6%
Industrial/Energy	8.1%
Computer Software and Services	7.0%
Communications and Media	5.5%
Computer Hardware	1.7%
Biotechnology	1.2%
Medical/Health	0.7%
Semiconductors/Other Elect.	0.5%

Additional Information

Name of Most Recent Fund: Henderson Unquoted Growth Equity II
Most Recent Fund Was Raised: 12/21/1998
Year Founded: 1981
Capital Under Management: $1,551,500,000
Current Activity Level: Actively seeking new investments

LE GROUPE FORCES

444, 5e Rue 2e Etase
Shawinigan, Canada G9N 1E6
Phone: 819-537-5107
Fax: 819-537-5109
Website: www.groupeforces.qc.ca

Type of Firm

Private Equity Firm

Project Preferences

Type of Financing Preferred:

Expansion

Geographical Preferences

Canadian Preferences:
Quebec

Additional Information

Year Founded: 1984
Current Activity Level: Actively seeking new investments

LE PROMOTEUR

53, rue 8600
Z.I. Charguia I
Tunis, Tunisia 2035
Phone: 216-71-771-823
Fax: 216-71-809-408
E-mail: info@lepromoteur.com.tn
Website: www.lepromoteur.com.tn

Type of Firm

Private Equity Firm
Association Membership
Tunisian Venture Capital Association

Project Preferences

Type of Financing Preferred:
Balanced

Geographical Preferences

International Preferences:
Tunisia

Additional Information

Year Founded: 1994
Current Activity Level: Actively seeking new investments

LEAD EQUITIES

Brucknerstrasse 4
Wien, Austria A-1040
Phone: 43-1-503-6086
Fax: 43-1-5036-08610
E-mail: office@leadequities.at
Website: www.leadequities.at

Management and Staff

Dirk Brandis, Managing Partner
Norbert Doll, Managing Partner
Stephan Zochling, Co-Founder

Type of Firm

Private Equity Firm

Association Membership

European Private Equity and Venture Capital Assoc.

Project Preferences

Type of Financing Preferred:
Later Stage

Geographical Preferences

International Preferences:
Central Europe
Austria
Eastern Europe

Industry Preferences

In Semiconductor/Electr prefer:
Electronics

In Medical/Health prefer:
Medical/Health

In Consumer Related prefer:
Consumer

In Transportation prefer:
Transportation

Additional Information

Name of Most Recent Fund: Lead Equities I
Most Recent Fund Was Raised: 01/17/2003
Year Founded: 2003
Capital Under Management: $123,100,000
Current Activity Level: Actively seeking new investments

LEAGUE OF MANAGEMENT COMPANIES

29 str., Bolshaia Ordynka
Moscow, Russia 119017
Phone: 7-95-953-7450
Fax: 7-95-953-7450
E-mail: president@cic.ru
Website: www.nlu.ru

Type of Firm

Private Equity Firm

Association Membership

Russian Venture Capital Association (RVCA)

Project Preferences

Type of Financing Preferred:
Balanced

Geographical Preferences

International Preferences:
Europe

Additional Information

Year Founded: 2005
Current Activity Level: Actively seeking new investments

LEAPFROG VENTURES

3000 Sand Hill Road
Building 1, Suite 280
Menlo Park, CA USA 94025
Phone: 650-926-9900
Fax: 650-233-9063
E-mail: plans@leapfrogventures.com
Website: www.leapfrogventures.com

Management and Staff

Mark Dubovoy, Managing Director
Michael Kranz, Chief Financial Officer
Peter Rip, Venture Partner
Peter Sinclair, Managing Director

Type of Firm

Private Equity Firm

Association Membership

Western Association of Venture Capitalists (WAVC)

Project Preferences

Role in Financing:
Prefer role as deal originator but will also invest in deals created by others

Type of Financing Preferred:
Early Stage
Seed
First Stage Financing
Startup

Size of Investments Considered:
Min Size of Investment Considered (000s): $700
Max Size of Investment Considered (000s): $5,000

Geographical Preferences

United States Preferences:
Northern California
West Coast

Industry Preferences

In Communications prefer:
Communications and Media
Wireless Communications

In Computer Software prefer:
Software
Applications Software

In Internet Specific prefer:
Internet

Additional Information

Name of Most Recent Fund: Leapfrog Venture II, LP
Most Recent Fund Was Raised: 09/16/2004
Year Founded: 2000
Capital Under Management: $100,000,000
Current Activity Level: Actively seeking new investments
Method of Compensation: Return on investment is of primary concern, do not charge fees

---

LEASING & EQUITY INVESTMENTS LTD.

St. Christopher's Place
The Cross
Baltonsborough, United Kingdom BA6 8QW
Phone: 44-1458-851-509
Fax: 44-871-242-6820

E-mail: privateequity@leasingequity.com
Website: www.leasingequity.com

Type of Firm

Private Equity Firm

Project Preferences

Type of Financing Preferred:

Leveraged Buyout
Mezzanine
Management Buyouts
Startup

Size of Investments Considered:

Min Size of Investment Considered (000s): $470,725
Max Size of Investment Considered (000s): $941,450

Geographical Preferences

International Preferences:

United Kingdom

Industry Preferences

In Communications prefer:

Commercial Communications

In Medical/Health prefer:

Medical/Health

In Financial Services prefer:

Financial Services

Additional Information

Year Founded: 2004
Current Activity Level: Actively seeking new investments

LEASING TECHNOLOGIES INTERNATIONAL, INC.

221 Danbury Road
Wilton, CT USA 06897
Phone: 203-563-1100
Fax: 203-563-1111
Website: www.ltileasing.com

Other Offices

Two Clearfield Road
P.O. Box 447
Ardmore, PA USA 19003-0447
Phone: 610-446-4479
Fax: 610-446-3771

655 Montgomery St
Suite 800
San Francisco, CA USA 94121
Phone: 415-834-0773

23 West Park Ave
Suite 1060
Merchantville, NJ USA 08109
Phone: 856-910-9970

10 Liberty Square
Boston, MA USA 02109
Phone: 617-426-4116
Fax: 617-482-6475

Management and Staff

Richard Livingston, Vice President

Type of Firm

Private Equity Firm

Project Preferences

Role in Financing:

Prefer role as deal originator but will also invest in deals created by others

Type of Financing Preferred:

Second Stage Financing
Early Stage
Mezzanine
Balanced
Later Stage
First Stage Financing
Special Situation

Size of Investments Considered:

Min Size of Investment Considered (000s): $500
Max Size of Investment Considered (000s): $2,000

Geographical Preferences

United States Preferences:

All U.S.

Industry Preferences

In Communications prefer:

Commercial Communications
Telecommunications
Data Communications
Satellite Microwave Comm.
Other Communication Prod.

In Computer Hardware prefer:

Computers
Mini and Personal/Desktop
Computer Graphics and Dig

In Computer Software prefer:

Systems Software
Applications Software

In Internet Specific prefer:

Internet

In Computer Other prefer:

Computer Related

In Semiconductor/Electr prefer:

Electronics
Electronic Components

In Biotechnology prefer:

Industrial Biotechnology
Biosensors
Biotech Related Research

In Medical/Health prefer:

Medical Diagnostics
Diagnostic Services
Diagnostic Test Products
Drug/Equipmt Delivery
Other Therapeutic
Medical Products
Pharmaceuticals

In Consumer Related prefer:

Retail
Computer Stores
Food/Beverage

In Industrial/Energy prefer:

Robotics
Machinery

Additional Information

Year Founded: 1983
Capital Under Management: $50,000,000
Current Activity Level: Actively seeking new investments
Method of Compensation: Return on investment is of primary concern, do not charge fees

---

LEDSTIERNAN AB

Grev Turegatan 18
Stockholm, Sweden 11434
Phone: 46-8-5450-3500
Fax: 46-8-5450-3535
E-mail: info@ledstiernan.se
Website: www.ledstiernan.se

Other Offices

10 Hill Street
London, United Kingdom W1J 5NQ
Phone: 44 207 529 5650
Fax: 44 207 529 5659

Management and Staff

Dag Bjurstrom, Founding Partner
Dan Walker, Founding Partner
Fredrik Lindgren, Chief Executive Officer
Hans Risberg, Founding Partner
Mikael Solberg, Founding Partner
Olof Stenhammar, Founding Partner
Per Lundberg, Founding Partner
Thomas Rosen, Founding Partner

Type of Firm

Private Equity Firm

Association Membership

Swedish Venture Capital Association (SVCA)

Project Preferences

Type of Financing Preferred:

Early Stage
Expansion

Size of Investments Considered:

Min Size of Investment Considered (000s): $600
Max Size of Investment Considered: No Limit

Geographical Preferences

International Preferences:

Sweden
Spain
Scandanavia/Nordic Region
Finland
Norway
Denmark

Industry Preferences

In Communications prefer:
Commercial Communications

In Internet Specific prefer:
Internet

In Medical/Health prefer:
Pharmaceuticals

Additional Information
Year Founded: 1994
Capital Under Management: $95,400,000
Current Activity Level: Actively seeking new investments

LEE & COMPANY INVESTMENTS
Cheongbu 118-4 Cheongdam-Dong
Kangnam-Gu
Seoul, South Korea
Phone: 82-2-2088-2600
Fax: 82-2-2088-1699
E-mail: nyhwang@leenco.co.kr
Website: www.leenco.co.kr

Management and Staff
Bo-Hoi Koo, Chief Executive Officer
Hyung-Kie Kim, Managing Director
Seung-Woo Lee, Managing Director
Sung-Il Bae, Managing Director

Type of Firm
Private Equity Firm

Association Membership
Korean Venture Capital Association (KVCA)

Project Preferences

Type of Financing Preferred:
Early Stage
Balanced
Management Buyouts

Geographical Preferences

International Preferences:
Korea, South

Additional Information
Year Founded: 2000
Capital Under Management: $8,300,000
Current Activity Level: Actively seeking new investments

LEE EQUITY PARTNERS
767 Fifth Avenue
17th Floor
New York, NY USA 10022
Phone: 212-888-1500
Fax: 212-888-6388

Management and Staff
Joseph Rotberg, Chief Financial Officer

Type of Firm
Private Equity Firm

Project Preferences

Type of Financing Preferred:
Leveraged Buyout

Geographical Preferences

United States Preferences:
All U.S.

Additional Information
Year Founded: 2006
Capital Under Management: $1,098,300,000
Current Activity Level: Actively seeking new investments

LEEDS EQUITY PARTNERS (FKA: LEEDS EQUITY ADVISORS)
350 Park Avenue
23rd Floor
New York, NY USA 10022
Phone: 212-835-2000
Fax: 212-835-2020
E-mail: info@leedsequity.com
Website: www.leedsequity.com

Management and Staff
Atif Gilani, Managing Director
Bradley Whitman, Managing Director
Carter Harned, Managing Director
Jeffrey Leeds, President, Founder
Joshua Sorensen, Principal
Peter Lyons, Managing Director & CFO
Robert Bernstein, Senior Managing Director

Type of Firm
Private Equity Firm

Project Preferences

Type of Financing Preferred:
Leveraged Buyout

Geographical Preferences

United States Preferences:
All U.S.

Industry Focus
(% based on actual investment)

Consumer Related	43.5%
Computer Software and Services	29.7%
Internet Specific	23.9%
Computer Hardware	2.9%

Additional Information
Name of Most Recent Fund: Leeds Weld Equity Partners IV, L.P.
Most Recent Fund Was Raised: 12/01/2002
Year Founded: 1993
Capital Under Management: $1,000,000
Current Activity Level: Actively seeking new investments

LEEWARD FUND MANAGEMENT
3-5 Place Winston Churchill
Luxembourg, Luxembourg 2019
Phone: 352-2697-971
Fax: 352-2697-73460
E-mail: mail@leeward.lu
Website: www.leewardfund.com

Other Offices
Lyford Financial Centre
P.O. Box N-7776
Nassau, Bahamas

Hunkins Plaza, Main Street
P.O. Box 556
Charlestown, St Kitts/Nevis

67 Wall Street
Suite 2211
New York, NY USA 10005

Management and Staff
Peter Vanderbruggen, Chief Executive Officer

Type of Firm
Investment Management Firm

Project Preferences

Type of Financing Preferred:
Expansion
Balanced
Management Buyouts
Startup
Recapitalizations

Geographical Preferences

International Preferences:
Europe
Asia

Additional Information
Year Founded: 2006
Current Activity Level: Actively seeking new investments

LEGACY VENTURE
180 Lytton Avenue
Palo Alto, CA USA 94301
Phone: 650-324-5980
Fax: 650-324-5982
E-mail: info@legacyventure.com
Website: www.legacyventure.com

Management and Staff

Alan Marty, Managing Partner
Chris Eyre, Managing Partner
Lance Taylor, Chief Financial Officer
Russell Hall, Managing Partner

Type of Firm

Private Equity Advisor or Fund of Funds

Association Membership

Western Association of Venture Capitalists (WAVC)
National Venture Capital Association - USA (NVCA)

Project Preferences

Type of Financing Preferred:
Fund of Funds
Early Stage

Size of Investments Considered:
Min Size of Investment Considered (000s): $5,000
Max Size of Investment Considered (000s): $15,000

Geographical Preferences

International Preferences:
Asia

Additional Information

Year Founded: 1999
Capital Under Management: $725,000,000
Current Activity Level: Actively seeking new investments

LEGATUM CAPITAL

Level 9, Convention Tower
P.O. Box 71082
Dubai, Utd. Arab Em.
Phone: 971-4317-5800
E-mail: hamish.banks@legatum.com
Website: www.legatumcapital.com

Management and Staff

Alan McCormick, Managing Director
Mark Stoleson, President

Type of Firm

Private Equity Firm

Project Preferences

Type of Financing Preferred:
Balanced

Geographical Preferences

International Preferences:
India
Hong Kong
Brazil
New Zealand
Korea, South
Japan
Russia

Industry Preferences

In Communications prefer:
Telecommunications

In Industrial/Energy prefer:
Energy

In Financial Services prefer:
Financial Services

In Utilities prefer:
Utilities

Additional Information

Year Founded: 2006
Current Activity Level: Actively seeking new investments

LEGEND CAPITAL

10/F Tower A, Raycom InfoTech
Zhongguancun, Haidian District
Beijing, China 100080
Phone: 86-10-6250-8000
Fax: 86-10-6250-9100
E-mail: master@legendcapital.com.cn
Website: www.legendcapital.com.cn

Other Offices

2410, Shanghai Times Square
Huai Hai Zhong Road
Shanghai, China 200021
Phone: 86-21-5382-7723
Fax: 86-21-5382-7713

Management and Staff

Erhai Liu, Managing Director
Hao Chen, Managing Director
Jian-guo Li, Managing Director
Li-nan Zhu, Chief Executive Officer
Neng-guang Wang, Managing Director & CFO
Ouyang Xiangyu, Managing Director
Richard Li, Managing Director
Xia Yang, Managing Director

Type of Firm

Corporate PE/Venture

Association Membership

Venture Capital Association of Beijing (VCAB)

Project Preferences

Type of Financing Preferred:
Early Stage
Expansion
Balanced
Later Stage
Startup

Size of Investments Considered:
Min Size of Investment Considered (000s): $2,000
Max Size of Investment Considered (000s): $10,000

Geographical Preferences

International Preferences:
Taiwan
China

Industry Preferences

In Communications prefer:
Telecommunications

In Computer Software prefer:
Applications Software

In Semiconductor/Electr prefer:
Semiconductor

In Business Serv. prefer:
Services
Media

Additional Information

Name of Most Recent Fund: LC Fund III
Most Recent Fund Was Raised: 04/30/2006
Year Founded: 1984
Capital Under Management: $300,000,000
Current Activity Level: Actively seeking new investments

LEGEND PARTNERS, THE

312 Walnut Street
Suite 1151
Cincinnati, OH USA 45202
Phone: 513-651-2300
Fax: 513-651-1084
Website: www.thelegendpartners.com

Management and Staff

James Gould, Managing General Partner
John Bernloehr, Partner
Mark Hauser, Managing General Partner
Patrick McBride, Partner
Paul Swanson, Partner
R. Scott Barnes, Partner
Ronald Tysoe, Managing General Partner

Type of Firm

Private Equity Firm

Project Preferences

Type of Financing Preferred:
Balanced

Industry Preferences

In Consumer Related prefer:
Consumer
Retail

In Business Serv. prefer:
Services

Additional Information

Year Founded: 2008
Current Activity Level: Actively seeking new investments

LEGEND VENTURES LLC

7100 Arrowood Road
Bethesda, MD USA 20817
Phone: 202-258-7462
Fax: 301-365-9359
E-mail: info@legendventures.com
Website: www.legendventures.com

Management and Staff

Todd Klein, Managing Partner

Type of Firm

Private Equity Firm

Project Preferences

Type of Financing Preferred:
Early Stage
Later Stage
Acquisition

Size of Investments Considered:
Min Size of Investment Considered (000s): $500
Max Size of Investment Considered (000s): $2,500

Geographical Preferences

United States Preferences:
All U.S.

Industry Preferences

In Communications prefer:
Telecommunications

In Business Serv. prefer:
Media

Additional Information

Name of Most Recent Fund: Legend Ventures
Most Recent Fund Was Raised: 02/15/2005
Year Founded: 2005
Capital Under Management: $11,000,000
Current Activity Level: Actively seeking new investments

LEGG MASON CAPITAL MANAGEMENT

100 International Drive
Baltimore, MD USA 21202
Phone: 866-410-5500
Website: www.lmcm.com

Management and Staff

Kyle Legg, Chief Executive Officer

Type of Firm

Private Equity Firm

Project Preferences

Type of Financing Preferred:
Balanced

Geographical Preferences

United States Preferences:
All U.S.

Additional Information

Year Founded: 2007
Current Activity Level: Actively seeking new investments

LEHMAN BROTHERS, INC.

1271 Avenue of the Americas
45th Floor
New York, NY USA 10020
Phone: 212-526-7000
Website: www.lehman.com

Other Offices

Roppongi Hills Mori Tower
31st Floor, 6-10-1 Roppongi
Minato-ku, Tokyo , Japan 106-6131
Phone: 81-3-6440-3000

3414 Peachtree Road
Suite 200
Atlanta, GA USA 30326
Phone: 404-262-4800

600 Travis Street
Suite 7200
Houston, TX USA 77002
Phone: 713-236-3950

1111 Brickell Avenue
Miami, FL USA 33131
Phone: 305-789-8700

125 High Street
Boston, MA USA 02110
Phone: 617-330-5800

450 Royal Palm Way
3rd Floor
Palm Beach, FL USA 33480
Phone: 561-671-1250

Bank of America Tower
701 Fifth Avenue, Suite 7101
Seattle, WA USA 98104
Phone: 206-344-5870

Brandywine Building
1000 West Street, Suite 200
Wilmington, DE USA 19801
Phone: 800-372-8464

101 Hudson Street
Jersey City, NJ USA 07302
Phone: 201-524-2000

190 South LaSalle Street
26th Floor
Chicago, IL USA 60603
Phone: 312-609-7200

2600 Corporate Exchange Drive
Suite 110
Columbus, OH USA 43231
Phone: 614-840-9080

10250 Constellation Boulevard
25th Floor
Los Angeles, CA USA 90067
Phone: 800-582-4904

Rincon 477
Montevideo, Uruguay
Phone: 598-2-402-5716

25 Bank Street
30th Floor
London, United Kingdom E14 5LE
Phone: 44-20-7102-1000
Fax: 44-20-7260-2722

200 Crescent Court
Suite 400
Dallas, TX USA 75201
Phone: 214-720-9470

155 Linfield Drive
Menlo Park, CA USA 94025
Phone: 650-289-6000

Torre Alem Plaza
Av. Leandro N. Alem 855
Buenos Aires, Argentina
Phone: 54-11-4319-2700

270 Munoz Rivera
Suite 501
San Juan, PR USA 00918
Phone: 787-296-6831

2001 K Street Northwest
Suite 1125
Washington, DC USA 20006
Phone: 202-452-4700

555 California Street
30th Floor
San Francisco, CA USA 94104
Phone: 415-263-3300

Management and Staff

Eric Johnson, Managing Director
Herbert McDade, President & COO
Ian Lowitt, Chief Financial Officer
Joseph Amato, Managing Director
Mark Bourgeois, Managing Director
Michael Odrich, Managing Director
Richard Fuld, Chairman & CEO
Theodore Janulis, Managing Director

Type of Firm

Bank Affiliated

Project Preferences

Type of Financing Preferred:
Fund of Funds
Leveraged Buyout

Expansion
Mezzanine
Generalist PE
Balanced
Later Stage
Other
Distressed Debt

Geographical Preferences

United States Preferences:

Massachusetts
California
New Jersey

Canadian Preferences:

All Canada

International Preferences:

Europe
Mexico
All International

Industry Preferences

In Communications prefer:

Telecommunications

In Consumer Related prefer:

Food/Beverage

In Financial Services prefer:

Real Estate

In Business Serv. prefer:

Distribution

Additional Information

Name of Most Recent Fund: Lehman Brothers Merchant Banking Partners IV, L.P.
Most Recent Fund Was Raised: 03/21/2007
Year Founded: 1850
Capital Under Management: $5,417,700,000
Current Activity Level: Actively seeking new investments

LEIV EIRIKSSON NYFOTEK AS (FKA: SAKORN MIDT NORGE)

Postboks 1262 Pirsenteret
Trondheim, Norway 7462
Phone: 47-7354-5100
Fax: 47-7354-5110
E-mail: firmapost@len.no
Website: www.len.no

Management and Staff

Malvin Villabo, Managing Director

Type of Firm

Incubator/Development Program

Association Membership

Norwegian Venture Capital Association

Project Preferences

Type of Financing Preferred:

Seed
Startup

Geographical Preferences

International Preferences:

Norway

Industry Preferences

In Computer Software prefer:

Software

In Internet Specific prefer:

Internet

In Business Serv. prefer:

Services
Media

Additional Information

Year Founded: 1998
Current Activity Level: Actively seeking new investments

LEMAN CAPITAL

65, rue du Rhone
Geneva, Switzerland CH-1204
Phone: 41-22-707-4990
Fax: 41-22-707-4999
E-mail: office@leman-capital.com
Website: www.leman-capital.com

Management and Staff

Alyson Greenwood, Chief Financial Officer
Auguste Betschart, Managing Partner
Christian Vassiliu, Founding Partner
Nikolaus Zens, Managing Partner

Type of Firm

Private Equity Firm

Association Membership

Swiss Venture Capital Association (SECA)
European Private Equity and Venture Capital Assoc.

Project Preferences

Type of Financing Preferred:

Leveraged Buyout
Expansion
Management Buyouts

Size of Investments Considered:

Min Size of Investment Considered (000s): $9,416
Max Size of Investment Considered (000s): $47,080

Geographical Preferences

International Preferences:

Italy
Luxembourg
Netherlands
Switzerland
Europe
Austria
Spain
Belgium
Germany
France

Industry Focus

(% based on actual investment)

Industrial/Energy	55.1%
Consumer Related	31.7%
Semiconductors/Other Elect.	13.2%

Additional Information

Name of Most Recent Fund: BVP Europe II
Most Recent Fund Was Raised: 08/28/2002
Year Founded: 1999
Capital Under Management: $319,700,000
Current Activity Level: Actively seeking new investments

LEMHI VENTURES

202 Water Street
Suite 200
Excelsior, MN USA 55331
Phone: 952-908-9680
Fax: 952-908-9780
E-mail: info@lemhiventures.com
Website: www.lemhiventures.com

Management and Staff

Jodi Hubler, Managing Director
Randall Schmidt, Venture Partner
Tony Miller, Managing Partner

Type of Firm

Private Equity Firm

Project Preferences

Type of Financing Preferred:

Balanced

Geographical Preferences

United States Preferences:

All U.S.

Industry Preferences

In Medical/Health prefer:

Medical/Health

Additional Information

Year Founded: 2007
Capital Under Management: $175,000,000
Current Activity Level: Actively seeking new investments

LEO CAPITAL HOLDINGS LLC

1101 Skokie Boulevard
Suite 255
Northbrook, IL USA 60062

Phone: 847-418-3420
Fax: 847-418-3424
E-mail: info@leocapholdings.com
Website: www.leocapholdings.com

Management and Staff

Randy Rissman, Managing Director

Type of Firm

Private Equity Firm

Association Membership

Illinois Venture Capital Association

Project Preferences

Role in Financing:

Will function either as deal originator or investor in deals created by others

Type of Financing Preferred:

Second Stage Financing
Early Stage
Expansion
Turnaround
Later Stage
Seed
First Stage Financing
Special Situation
Startup

Size of Investments Considered:

Min Size of Investment Considered (000s): $1,000
Max Size of Investment Considered (000s): $8,000

Geographical Preferences

Canadian Preferences:

All Canada

Industry Preferences

In Communications prefer:

Wireless Communications
Media and Entertainment

In Consumer Related prefer:

Consumer
Consumer Products

Additional Information

Year Founded: 2000
Capital Under Management: $25,000,000
Current Activity Level: Actively seeking new investments
Method of Compensation: Return on investment is of primary concern, do not charge fees

---

LEONARD GREEN & PARTNERS

11111 Santa Monica Boulevard
Suite 2000
Los Angeles, CA USA 90025
Phone: 310-954-0444
Fax: 310-954-0404
E-mail: info@leonardgreen.com
Website: www.leonardgreen.com

Management and Staff

Alyse Wagner, Vice President
Cody Franklin, Chief Financial Officer
Gregory Annick, Partner
J. Kristopher Galashan, Vice President
James Halper, Partner
John Baumer, Partner
John Danhakl, Managing Partner
Jonathan Seiffer, Partner
Jonathan Sokoloff, Managing Partner
Lily Chang, Chief Operating Officer
Michael Solomon, Principal
Michael Connolly, Partner
Michael Wong, Vice President
Peter Nolan, Managing Partner
Timothy Flynn, Partner
Todd Purdy, Principal
Usama Cortas, Vice President

Type of Firm

Private Equity Advisor or Fund of Funds

Project Preferences

Role in Financing:

Prefer role as deal originator but will also invest in deals created by others

Type of Financing Preferred:

Leveraged Buyout
Management Buyouts
Recapitalizations

Size of Investments Considered:

Min Size of Investment Considered (000s): $25,000
Max Size of Investment Considered (000s): $300,000

Geographical Preferences

United States Preferences:

West Coast
California
All U.S.

Industry Focus

(% based on actual investment)

Consumer Related	55.0%
Other Products	33.2%
Communications and Media	7.2%
Internet Specific	2.8%
Medical/Health	1.0%
Semiconductors/Other Elect.	0.6%
Computer Software and Services	0.2%

Additional Information

Name of Most Recent Fund: Green Equity Investors V, L.P.
Most Recent Fund Was Raised: 12/14/2006
Year Founded: 1989
Capital Under Management: $1,770,400,000
Current Activity Level: Actively seeking new investments
Method of Compensation: Return on invest. most important, but chg. closing fees, service fees, etc.

LEONARDO VENTURE GMBH & CO. KGAA

Augusta Carree
Augustaanlage 32
Mannheim, Germany 68165
Phone: 49-621-438-4300
Fax: 49-621-43843010
E-mail: kontakt@leonardoventure.de
Website: www.leonardoventure.de

Management and Staff

Carsten Felgenhauer, Managing Director
Hans Jochen Koop, CEO & Managing Director

Type of Firm

Private Equity Firm

Project Preferences

Type of Financing Preferred:

Early Stage
Seed
Startup

Geographical Preferences

International Preferences:

Europe

Industry Preferences

In Communications prefer:

Wireless Communications

In Computer Software prefer:

Software

In Internet Specific prefer:

Internet

In Biotechnology prefer:

Biotechnology

In Industrial/Energy prefer:

Advanced Materials

Additional Information

Year Founded: 2000
Current Activity Level: Actively seeking new investments

LEOPARD CAPITAL, LTD.

7B, Hong Kong Jewellery Bldg.
178-180 Queen's Road
Central, Hong Kong
Phone: 852-3904-1015
Fax: 852-3904-1017
E-mail: info@leopardasia.com
Website: www.leopardasia.com

Other Offices

81B Street 57
P.O. Box 1141
Phnom Penh, Cambodia
Phone: 855-2322-1634

Fax: 855-2372-6849

Management and Staff

Douglas Clayton, Managing Partner
Kenneth Stevens, Managing Partner
Scott Lewis, Managing Partner
Stephen Simmons, Managing Partner
Thomas Hugger, Managing Partner

Type of Firm

Private Equity Firm

Project Preferences

Type of Financing Preferred:

Leveraged Buyout
Early Stage
Generalist PE
Expansion
Acquisition

Geographical Preferences

International Preferences:

Cambodia
Asia
Sri Lanka

Industry Preferences

In Biotechnology prefer:

Agricultural/Animal Bio.

In Consumer Related prefer:

Retail
Food/Beverage
Consumer Services

In Industrial/Energy prefer:

Materials

In Financial Services prefer:

Financial Services
Real Estate

In Agr/Forestr/Fish prefer:

Agribusiness

Additional Information

Year Founded: 2007
Capital Under Management: $43,100,000
Current Activity Level: Actively seeking new investments

LEREKO INVESMENTS PROPERTY, LTD.

1st Floor, 3 Commerce Square
39 Rivonia Road
Sandhurst, South Africa 2196
Phone: 27-11-268-0755
Fax: 27-11-268-0756
E-mail: info@lereko.co.za
Website: www.lereko.co.za

Management and Staff

Cedrick Mampuru, Chief Financial Officer
Lulu Gwagwa, Chief Operating Officer
Popo Molefe, Chief Executive Officer

Type of Firm

Private Equity Firm

Project Preferences

Type of Financing Preferred:

Acquisition

Size of Investments Considered:

Min Size of Investment Considered (000s): $6,175
Max Size of Investment Considered (000s): $31,710

Geographical Preferences

International Preferences:

South Africa

Industry Preferences

In Consumer Related prefer:

Food/Beverage
Consumer Products

In Manufact. prefer:

Manufacturing

In Agr/Forestr/Fish prefer:

Mining and Minerals

Additional Information

Year Founded: 2004
Capital Under Management: $200,000
Current Activity Level: Actively seeking new investments

LEVCO GROUP, LTD.

24480 Harbour View Drive
Ponte Vedra Beach, FL USA 32082
Phone: 904-285-4800
Website: www.levcogroup.com

Type of Firm

Private Equity Firm

Project Preferences

Type of Financing Preferred:

Leveraged Buyout
Management Buyouts
Acquisition

Additional Information

Year Founded: 1990
Current Activity Level: Actively seeking new investments

LEVENSOHN VENTURE PARTNERS LLC (FKA: LEVENSOHN CAPITAL MGMT)

260 Townsend Street
Suite 600
San Francisco, CA USA 94107
Phone: 415-217-4710
Fax: 415-217-4727
E-mail: businessplans@levp.com
Website: www.levp.com

Management and Staff

Jeff Karras, General Partner
Keith Benjamin, Managing Partner
Kip Sheeline, Managing Partner
Scott Sillers, General Partner
Steve Reale, General Partner

Type of Firm

Private Equity Firm

Association Membership

Western Association of Venture Capitalists (WAVC)
National Venture Capital Association - USA (NVCA)

Project Preferences

Role in Financing:

Will function either as deal originator or investor in deals created by others

Type of Financing Preferred:

Early Stage
Expansion
Special Situation
Industry Rollups
Recapitalizations

Size of Investments Considered:

Min Size of Investment Considered (000s): $2,000
Max Size of Investment Considered (000s): $10,000

Geographical Preferences

United States Preferences:

California

Industry Preferences

In Communications prefer:

Telecommunications
Wireless Communications

In Computer Software prefer:

Software
Systems Software
Applications Software

In Internet Specific prefer:

E-Commerce Technology
Internet
Ecommerce

In Semiconductor/Electr prefer:

Electronic Components
Semiconductor
Fiber Optics
Optoelectronics

In Industrial/Energy prefer:

Energy
Robotics

In Other prefer:

Women/Minority-Owned Bus.

Additional Information

Year Founded: 1996

Capital Under Management: $202,000,000
Current Activity Level: Actively seeking new investments
Method of Compensation: Return on investment is of primary concern, do not charge fees

LEVESQUE BEAUBIEN GEOFFRION (LBG)

1155 rue Metcalfe
Fifth Floor
Montreal, Canada H3B 4S9
Phone: 514-879-2222
Fax: 514-879-5321
Website: www.lbg.ca

Type of Firm

Endowment, Foundation or Pension Fund

Additional Information

Year Founded: 2009
Current Activity Level: Actively seeking new investments

LEVINE LEICHTMAN CAPITAL PARTNERS, INC.

335 North Maple Drive
Suite 240
Beverly Hills, CA USA 90210
Phone: 310-275-5335
Fax: 310-275-1441
E-mail: Main@llcp.com
Website: www.llcp.com

Other Offices

200 South Wacker Drive
Suite 3100
Chicago, IL USA 60606
Phone: 312-674-4900
Fax: 312-674-4905

100 Crescent Court
Seventh Floor
Dallas, TX USA 75201
Phone: 214-303-0118
Fax: 214-303-0119

415 Madison Avenue
15th Floor, Suite 1513
New York, NY USA 10017
Phone: 646-673-8513
Fax: 646-673-8613

Management and Staff

Aaron Perlmutter, Managing Director
Arthur Levine, President
Gordon Cook, Managing Director
John Klinge, Managing Director
Kimberly Pollack, Managing Director
Lauren Leichtman, Chief Executive Officer
Robert Poletti, Principal
Scott Imbach, Managing Director
Stephen Hogan, Principal
Steven Hartman, Principal

Type of Firm

Private Equity Firm

Project Preferences

Role in Financing:
Prefer role as deal originator

Type of Financing Preferred:
Leveraged Buyout
Management Buyouts
Acquisition
Distressed Debt
Recapitalizations

Size of Investments Considered:
Min Size of Investment Considered (000s): $2,000
Max Size of Investment Considered (000s): $100,000

Geographical Preferences

United States Preferences:
Rocky Mountain
West Coast

Industry Preferences

In Computer Software prefer:
Software

In Medical/Health prefer:
Medical Products

In Consumer Related prefer:
Food/Beverage

In Industrial/Energy prefer:
Industrial Products

In Transportation prefer:
Aerospace

In Financial Services prefer:
Financial Services

Additional Information

Name of Most Recent Fund: Levine Leichtman Capital Partners Deep Value Fund, L.P.
Most Recent Fund Was Raised: 03/23/2005
Year Founded: 1984
Capital Under Management: $1,553,000,000
Current Activity Level: Actively seeking new investments
Method of Compensation: Return on invest. most important, but chg. closing fees, service fees, etc.

LEXINGTON COMMERCIAL HOLDINGS

9350 Wilshire Boulevard
Suite 400
Beverly Hills, CA USA 90212
Phone: 310-271-1990

Management and Staff

Harvey Gettleson, Chief Operating Officer
Louis Gonda, President

Type of Firm

Investment Management Firm

Project Preferences

Type of Financing Preferred:
Balanced

Additional Information

Year Founded: 1995
Current Activity Level: Actively seeking new investments

LFE CAPITAL (FKA: L FRECON ENTERPRISES)

60 South Sixth Street
Suite 2320
Minneapolis, MN USA 55402
Phone: 612-752-1809
Fax: 612-752-1800
E-mail: info@lfecapital.com
Website: www.lfecapital.com

Type of Firm

Private Equity Firm

Association Membership

Natl Assoc of Small Bus. Inv. Co (NASBIC)

Project Preferences

Role in Financing:
Will function either as deal originator or investor in deals created by others

Type of Financing Preferred:
Leveraged Buyout
Generalist PE
Expansion

Size of Investments Considered:
Min Size of Investment Considered (000s): $2,000
Max Size of Investment Considered (000s): $5,000

Geographical Preferences

United States Preferences:
Midwest

Industry Preferences

In Medical/Health prefer:
Medical Products
Health Services

In Consumer Related prefer:
Food/Beverage
Consumer Products
Consumer Services

In Business Serv. prefer:
Services

Additional Information

Year Founded: 1999
Capital Under Management: $25,000,000
Current Activity Level: Actively seeking new investments

Method of Compensation: Return on investment is of primary concern, do not charge fees

LGT CAPITAL PARTNERS AG

Schuetzenstrasse 6
Pfaeffikon, Switzerland CH-8808
Phone: 41-55-415-9600
Fax: 41-55-415-9699
E-mail: lgt.cp@lgt.com
Website: www.lgt-capital-partners.com

Other Offices

20 Grosvenor Place
London, United Kingdom SW1X 7HN
Phone: 44-20-7823-2900
Fax: 44-20-7823-2003

245 Park Avenue
39th Floor
New York, NY USA 10167
Phone: 212-3728716
Fax: 212-3728727

Segrave House
19/20 Earlsfort Terrace
Dublin, Ireland 2
Phone: 353-1-4337440
Fax: 353-1-4337467

Suite 4203 Two Exchange Tower
8 Connaught Place
Central Hong Kong, Hong Kong
Phone: 852-2522-9260
Fax: 852-2868-0059

8th Floor, Pacific Century Place
1-11-1, Marunouchi, Chiyoda-ku
Tokyo, Japan 100-6208
Phone: 813-6860-8353
Fax: 813-6860-8552

Management and Staff

Alexandre Covello, Vice President
Andre Aubert, Vice President
Andrew Kwee, Principal
Cem Meric, Vice President
Hans Markvoort, Principal
Ivan Vercoutere, Partner
Jonas Agesand, Vice President
Maximilian Bronner, Partner
Robert Schlachter, Principal
Roberto Paganoni, Chief Executive Officer
Sascha Gruber, Vice President
Thomas Weber, Partner
Tycho Sneyers, Partner
Wolfgang Muller, Vice President

Type of Firm

Bank Affiliated

Association Membership

Swiss Venture Capital Association (SECA)
European Private Equity and Venture Capital Assoc.

Project Preferences

Type of Financing Preferred:

Fund of Funds
Leveraged Buyout
Early Stage
Expansion
Balanced

Size of Investments Considered:

Min Size of Investment Considered (000s): $471
Max Size of Investment Considered (000s): $94,160

Geographical Preferences

United States Preferences:

All U.S.

International Preferences:

United Kingdom
Europe
Pacific
Asia
All International

Additional Information

Year Founded: 1997
Capital Under Management: $4,000,000,000
Current Activity Level: Actively seeking new investments

LGV CAPITAL, LTD. (FKA: LEGAL & GENERAL VENTURES, LTD.)

One Coleman Street
London, United Kingdom EC2R 5AA
Phone: 44-20-3124-2900
Fax: 44-20-3124-2546
Website: www.lgvcapital.com

Management and Staff

Bill Priestley, Managing Director
Ivan Heywood, Chief Executive Officer
Michael Mowlem, Managing Director
Michael O'Donnell, Managing Director

Type of Firm

Insurance Firm Affiliate

Association Membership

British Venture Capital Association (BVCA)
European Private Equity and Venture Capital Assoc.

Project Preferences

Role in Financing:

Prefer role as deal originator

Type of Financing Preferred:

Leveraged Buyout
Management Buyouts

Size of Investments Considered:

Min Size of Investment Considered (000s): $35,666
Max Size of Investment Considered (000s): $133,748

Geographical Preferences

International Preferences:

United Kingdom

Industry Preferences

In Medical/Health prefer:

Medical/Health

In Consumer Related prefer:

Consumer
Entertainment and Leisure
Food/Beverage
Consumer Products
Consumer Services

In Industrial/Energy prefer:

Factory Automation

In Business Serv. prefer:

Services

Additional Information

Name of Most Recent Fund: LGV 5 Private Equity Fund
Most Recent Fund Was Raised: 12/09/2005
Year Founded: 1988
Capital Under Management: $366,300,000
Current Activity Level: Actively seeking new investments
Method of Compensation: Return on invest. most important, but chg. closing fees, service fees, etc.

LI & FUNG INVESTMENTS (AKA: LF INVESTMENTS)

33rd Floor, Alexandria House
18 Chater Road
Central, Hong Kong
Phone: 852-2844-1937
Fax: 852-2844-1939
E-mail: enquiry@lifunginvestments.com
Website: www.lifunginvestments.com

Other Offices

Four Embarcadero Center
Suite 3400
San Francisco, CA USA 941111
Phone: 415-315-7440

2nd Floor, 93 Newman Street
London, United Kingdom W1T 3EZ
Phone: 44-20-7462-2000

Management and Staff

John Seung, Partner
Jose Cheng, Managing Director
Robert Adams, Managing Director
Tugba Unkan, Managing Director

Type of Firm

Corporate PE/Venture

Association Membership

British Venture Capital Association (BVCA)
Hungarian Venture Capital Association (HVCA)

Project Preferences

Role in Financing:
Prefer role as deal originator but will also invest in deals created by others

Type of Financing Preferred:
Second Stage Financing
Expansion
Generalist PE
Later Stage
Management Buyouts
Private Placement
Joint Ventures

Size of Investments Considered:
Min Size of Investment Considered (000s): $1,000
Max Size of Investment Considered (000s): $10,000

Geographical Preferences

United States Preferences:
All U.S.

International Preferences:
Europe
Taiwan
China
Hong Kong
Thailand
Singapore
Malaysia

Industry Preferences

In Computer Software prefer:
Software

In Internet Specific prefer:
Ecommerce

In Medical/Health prefer:
Medical/Health
Health Services
Pharmaceuticals

In Consumer Related prefer:
Consumer
Entertainment and Leisure
Sports
Retail
Consumer Products

In Business Serv. prefer:
Services
Distribution

Additional Information
Name of Most Recent Fund: Golden Horn (III), L.P.
Most Recent Fund Was Raised: 10/01/1997
Year Founded: 1982
Capital Under Management: $100,000,000
Current Activity Level: Actively seeking new investments
Method of Compensation: Return on investment is of primary concern, do not charge fees

---

LIAONING NEUSOFT VENTURE CAPITAL COMPANY, LTD.

Hun Nan Industrial Area
New & Hi-tech Dev't Zone
Shenyang, China 110179
Phone: 86-24-237-8300
Fax: 86-24-2378-2700

Type of Firm
Private Equity Firm

Project Preferences

Type of Financing Preferred:
Balanced

Geographical Preferences

International Preferences:
China

Additional Information
Year Founded: 2003
Current Activity Level: Actively seeking new investments

LIAONING TECHNOLOGY VENTURE CAPITAL LIMITED LIABILITY CO.

4/F Jiahuan Building
#39 Heping South St., Heping
Shenyang, China 110003
Phone: 86-24-2322-2100
Fax: 86-24-2324-4922
E-mail: lnvc@lnvc.com.cn
Website: www.lnvc.com.cn

Type of Firm
Government Affiliated Program

Project Preferences

Type of Financing Preferred:
Early Stage
Expansion
Start-up Financing
Seed

Size of Investments Considered:
Min Size of Investment Considered (000s): $60
Max Size of Investment Considered (000s): $2,500

Geographical Preferences

International Preferences:
China

Industry Preferences

In Biotechnology prefer:
Biotechnology

In Industrial/Energy prefer:
Advanced Materials
Environmental Related

In Manufact. prefer:
Manufacturing

Additional Information
Year Founded: 2000
Capital Under Management: $24,200,000
Current Activity Level: Actively seeking new investments

LIBERTY CAPITAL MANAGEMENT CORPORATION

1811 East Garry Avenue
Santa Ana, CA USA 92705
Phone: 949-724-8848
Fax: 949-724-8805
E-mail: info@libertycapitalmgt.com
Website: www.libertycapitalmgt.com

Management and Staff
A. Donald McCulloch, Partner
Earl Linehan, Partner
J. Eustace Wolfington, Partner
Jeffrey Levitt, Partner
Joe Zoll, Partner
Kevin Donohoe, Partner
Martin Lautman, Partner
Paul Gardi, Partner

Type of Firm
Bank Affiliated

Project Preferences

Role in Financing:
Prefer role as deal originator but will also invest in deals created by others

Type of Financing Preferred:
Leveraged Buyout
Management Buyouts
Acquisition
Recapitalizations

Geographical Preferences

United States Preferences:
All U.S.

International Preferences:
Europe
Asia

Additional Information
Year Founded: 1994
Current Activity Level: Actively seeking new investments
Method of Compensation: Return on investment is of primary concern, do not charge fees

LIBERTY MUTUAL

175 Berkeley Street
Boston, MA USA 02116
Phone: 617-357-9500
Website: www.libertymutual.com

Type of Firm

Private Equity Firm

Additional Information

Year Founded: 2009
Current Activity Level: Actively seeking new investments

LIBERTY PARTNERS

1370 Avenue Of The Americas
34th & 35th Floor
New York, NY USA 10019
Phone: 212-541-7676
Fax: 212-649-6076
E-mail: info@libertypartners.com
Website: www.libertypartners.com

Management and Staff

Carl Ring, Managing Director
G. Michael Stakias, Managing Director
Michael Levine, Managing Director
Peter Bennett, Managing Director
Stephen Fisher, Managing Director
Thomas Greig, Managing Director
Timothy Ross, Vice President
Yvonne Marsh, Managing Director

Type of Firm

Private Equity Firm

Project Preferences

Type of Financing Preferred:
Leveraged Buyout
Mezzanine
Recapitalizations

Geographical Preferences

United States Preferences:
All U.S.

Industry Focus

(% based on actual investment)

Internet Specific	47.1%
Computer Software and Services	16.2%
Medical/Health	15.5%
Communications and Media	10.5%
Other Products	8.5%
Semiconductors/Other Elect.	1.9%
Industrial/Energy	0.3%

Additional Information

Name of Most Recent Fund: Liberty Partners
Most Recent Fund Was Raised: 09/01/1992
Year Founded: 1992
Capital Under Management: $1,800,000,000
Current Activity Level: Actively seeking new investments

LIBERTY VENTURE PARTNERS, INC.

Two Commerce Square
2001 Market St., Suite 3820
Philadelphia, PA USA 19103
Phone: 267-861-5692
Fax: 267-861-5696
Website: www.libertyvp.com

Management and Staff

David Robkin, Principal
Maria Hahn, Chief Financial Officer
Thomas Morse, Principal

Type of Firm

Private Equity Firm

Association Membership

Natl Assoc of Small Bus. Inv. Co (NASBIC)

Project Preferences

Role in Financing:
Will function either as deal originator or investor in deals created by others

Type of Financing Preferred:
Expansion

Size of Investments Considered:
Min Size of Investment Considered (000s): $1,000
Max Size of Investment Considered (000s): $3,000

Geographical Preferences

United States Preferences:
Mid Atlantic

Industry Focus

(% based on actual investment)

Medical/Health	39.5%
Internet Specific	28.9%
Computer Software and Services	24.2%
Communications and Media	4.3%
Industrial/Energy	3.1%

Additional Information

Name of Most Recent Fund: Liberty Ventures II, L.P.
Most Recent Fund Was Raised: 12/31/1999
Year Founded: 1996
Capital Under Management: $150,000,000
Current Activity Level: Actively seeking new investments
Method of Compensation: Return on investment is of primary concern, do not charge fees

LIFE SCIENCE FONDS ESSLINGEN VERWALTUNGS-GMBH

Rathausplatz 2
Esslingen am Neckar, Germany
Phone: 711-3152-3414
Fax: 711-3152-553414
E-mail: Gottwald.Schaefter@esslingen.de
Website: www.lsc-esslingen.de

Type of Firm

Incubator/Development Program

Additional Information

Year Founded: 2006
Current Activity Level: Actively seeking new investments

LIFE SCIENCES GREENHOUSE OF CENTRAL PENSYLVANIA (LSGPA)

225 Market Street
Suite 500, Fifth Floor
Harrisburg, PA USA 17101
Phone: 717-635-2100
Fax: 717-635-2010
E-mail: info@lsgpa.com
Website: www.lsgpa.com

Management and Staff

Stephen Carpenter, Vice President

Type of Firm

Private Equity Firm

Association Membership

National Venture Capital Association - USA (NVCA)

Project Preferences

Role in Financing:
Prefer role as deal originator

Type of Financing Preferred:
Seed

Size of Investments Considered:
Min Size of Investment Considered (000s): $250
Max Size of Investment Considered (000s): $1,000

Geographical Preferences

United States Preferences:
Pennsylvania

Industry Preferences

In Medical/Health prefer:
Medical/Health
Medical Diagnostics
Medical Therapeutics
Medical Products
Health Services
Pharmaceuticals

Additional Information

Name of Most Recent Fund: Tech and GAP Fund
Most Recent Fund Was Raised: 01/01/2003
Year Founded: 2003
Capital Under Management: $18,000,000
Current Activity Level: Actively seeking new investments
Method of Compensation: Return on investment is of primary concern, do not charge fees

---

LIFE SCIENCES PARTNERS BV

Johannes Vermeerplein 9
Amsterdam, Netherlands 1071 DV
Phone: 31-20-664-5500
Fax: 31-20-676-8810
E-mail: lspamsterdam@lspvc.com
Website: www.lsp.nl

Other Offices

Luisenstrasse 14
Munich, Germany 80333
Phone: 49-89-330-6660
Fax: 49-89-3306-6629

25 First Street
Suite 300
Cambridge, MA USA 02141
Phone: 617-452-1000
Fax: 617-452-1001

Management and Staff

Daan Ellens, Partner
Fouad Azzam, General Partner
Frits Van Der Have, General Partner
Hans Clevers, Venture Partner
Jan Vesseur, Chief Financial Officer
Joachim Rothe, Partner
Joep Muijrers, Partner
Jorg Neermann, Partner
Jorg Riesmeier, General Partner
Mark Wegter, General Partner
Martijn Kleijwegt, Managing Partner
Merijin Klaassen, Chief Financial Officer
Rene Kuijten, General Partner
Tom Schwarz, Venture Partner

Type of Firm

Private Equity Firm

Association Membership

European Private Equity and Venture Capital Assoc.
Dutch Venture Capital Associaton (NVP)

Project Preferences

Type of Financing Preferred:

Early Stage
Expansion
Balanced
Later Stage
Seed
Management Buyouts
Startup

Size of Investments Considered:

Min Size of Investment Considered (000s): $471
Max Size of Investment Considered (000s): $9,416

Geographical Preferences

International Preferences:

Luxembourg
Netherlands
Europe
Belgium
Israel
Germany
Finland

Industry Preferences

In Biotechnology prefer:

Biotechnology
Human Biotechnology

In Medical/Health prefer:

Medical/Health
Medical Diagnostics
Medical Therapeutics
Medical Products

In Consumer Related prefer:

Food/Beverage

Additional Information

Year Founded: 1998
Capital Under Management: $541,800,000
Current Activity Level: Actively seeking new investments

LIGHTHOUSE CAPITAL PARTNERS

500 Drake's Landing Road
Greenbrae, CA USA 94904
Phone: 415-464-5900
Fax: 415-925-3387
E-mail: info@lcpartners.com
Website: www.lcpartners.com

Other Offices

20 University Road
Suite 460
Cambridge, MA USA 02138
Phone: 617-441-9192
Fax: 617-354-4374

3555 Alameda de las Pulgas
Suite 200
Menlo Park, CA USA 94025
Phone: 650-233-1000
Fax: 650-233-7688

Management and Staff

Anurag Chandra, Managing Director
Brian Crews, Principal
Cristy Barnes, Principal
Dennis Ryan, Chief Operating Officer
Gwill York, Managing Director
Jeff Griffor, Principal
Ned Hazen, Managing Director
Richard Stubblefield, Managing Director
Ryan Turner, Principal

Type of Firm

Private Equity Firm

Association Membership

Western Association of Venture Capitalists (WAVC)
National Venture Capital Association - USA (NVCA)

Project Preferences

Role in Financing:

Prefer role in deals created by others

Type of Financing Preferred:

Second Stage Financing
Early Stage
Expansion
Seed
First Stage Financing
Startup

Size of Investments Considered:

Min Size of Investment Considered (000s): $1,000
Max Size of Investment Considered (000s): $10,000

Geographical Preferences

United States Preferences:

Massachusetts
California
All U.S.

Industry Focus

(% based on actual investment)

Internet Specific	36.0%
Communications and Media	21.3%
Computer Software and Services	19.2%
Semiconductors/Other Elect.	17.8%
Biotechnology	3.0%
Other Products	2.7%

Additional Information

Name of Most Recent Fund: Lighthouse Capital Partners VI, L.P.
Most Recent Fund Was Raised: 02/27/2007
Year Founded: 1994
Capital Under Management: $1,000,000,000
Current Activity Level: Actively seeking new investments
Method of Compensation: Return on invest. most important, but chg. closing fees, service fees, etc.

LIGHTHOUSE FUNDS LLC

45 Rockefeller Plaza
20th Floor
New York, NY USA 10111
E-mail: info@lhfunds.com
Website: www.lhfunds.com

Other Offices

18, Jolly Maker Chambers II
Nariman Point
Mumbai, India 400 021

1001 Chestnut Street
Suite 101
Philadelphia, PA USA 19107

Type of Firm

Private Equity Firm

Project Preferences

Type of Financing Preferred:
Balanced
Public Companies
Later Stage

Size of Investments Considered:
Min Size of Investment Considered (000s): $1,000
Max Size of Investment Considered (000s): $10,000

Geographical Preferences

United States Preferences:
All U.S.

International Preferences:
India

Additional Information

Year Founded: 2008
Capital Under Management: $95,400,000
Current Activity Level: Actively seeking new investments

LIGHTSPEED GEMINI INTERNET LAB

11/F, Tower A
9 Hamenofim St. Akerstein Twr
Herzliya, Israel 46725
Phone: 972-9-971-9111
Fax: 972-9-958-4842
E-mail: info@lgilab.com
Website: www.lgilab.com

Type of Firm

Private Equity Firm

Project Preferences

Type of Financing Preferred:
Early Stage
Balanced

Geographical Preferences

International Preferences:
Israel

Industry Preferences

In Internet Specific prefer:
Internet

Additional Information

Year Founded: 2006
Current Activity Level: Actively seeking new investments

LIGHTSPEED VENTURE PARTNERS (FKA: WEISS, PECK & GREER)

2200 Sand Hill Road
Menlo Park, CA USA 94025
Phone: 650-234-8300
Fax: 650-234-8333
E-mail: info@lightspeedvp.com
Website: www.lightspeedvp.com

Other Offices

302 Pride Elite
10 Museum Road
Bangalore, India 560 001
Phone: 91-80-4039-5566
Fax: 91-80-4039-5511

Tian An Center
338 Nanjing West Road
Shanghai, China 200003
Phone: 86-21-6358-6598
Fax: 86-21-6358-6590

Okeanus Building
50 Ramat Yam Street
Herzilya Pituach, Israel 46851
Phone: 972-9-956-1634
Fax: 972-9-954-3423

Management and Staff

Andrew Moley, Chief Financial Officer
Andrew Chung, Principal
Barry Eggers, Managing Director
Bejul Somaia, Managing Director
Christopher Schaepe, Managing Director
David Gussarsky, Managing Director
Eric O'Brien, Managing Director
Jacob Seid, Managing Director
James Mi, Managing Director
Jeremy Liew, Managing Director
John Vrionis, Principal
Peter Nieh, Managing Director
Ravi Mhatre, Managing Director
Ron Cao, Managing Director
Yoni Cheifetz, Managing Director

Type of Firm

Private Equity Firm

Association Membership

Western Association of Venture Capitalists (WAVC)
National Venture Capital Association - USA (NVCA)

Project Preferences

Role in Financing:
Will function either as deal originator or investor in deals created by others

Type of Financing Preferred:
Second Stage Financing
Early Stage
Expansion
Balanced
Seed
First Stage Financing

Size of Investments Considered:
Min Size of Investment Considered (000s): $2,000
Max Size of Investment Considered (000s): $30,000

Geographical Preferences

United States Preferences:
All U.S.

International Preferences:
India
China
Israel

Industry Focus

(% based on actual investment)

Internet Specific	28.2%
Computer Software and Services	24.0%
Semiconductors/Other Elect.	17.1%
Communications and Media	14.0%
Computer Hardware	4.4%
Other Products	3.7%
Medical/Health	3.5%
Industrial/Energy	3.1%
Biotechnology	1.1%
Consumer Related	0.9%

Additional Information

Name of Most Recent Fund: Lightspeed Venture Partners VIII, L.P.
Most Recent Fund Was Raised: 05/12/2008
Year Founded: 1971
Capital Under Management: $2,100,000,000
Current Activity Level: Actively seeking new investments
Method of Compensation: Return on investment is of primary concern, do not charge fees

---

LIGHTYEAR CAPITAL LLC

375 Park Avenue
Eleventh Floor
New York, NY USA 10152
Phone: 212-328-0555
Fax: 212-328-0516
E-mail: lycapinfo@lycap.com
Website: www.lycap.com

Management and Staff

Chris Casciato, Managing Director
Daniel Freyman, Vice President
David Cynn, Managing Director
David Howe, Managing Director
David Glenn, Managing Director
Donald Marron, Chairman & CEO
Mark Vassallo, Managing Director
Michal Petrzela, Vice President
Richard Sterne, Managing Director
Stewart Gross, Managing Director
Thierry Ho, Managing Director
Timothy Kacani, Chief Financial Officer

Type of Firm

Private Equity Firm

Project Preferences

Type of Financing Preferred:
Leveraged Buyout
Turnaround
Later Stage
Acquisition
Recapitalizations

Geographical Preferences

United States Preferences:
All U.S.

International Preferences:
Europe

Industry Preferences

In Communications prefer:
Telecommunications

In Financial Services prefer:
Financial Services

In Business Serv. prefer:
Media

Additional Information

Name of Most Recent Fund: Lightyear Fund II, L.P.
Most Recent Fund Was Raised: 05/10/2007
Year Founded: 2000
Capital Under Management: $2,000,000,000
Current Activity Level: Actively seeking new investments

LILLY BIOVENTURES

Lilly Corporate Center
D.C. 1088
Indianapolis, IN USA 46285
Phone: 317-651-3050
Fax: 317-651-3051
E-mail: lilly_bioventures@lilly.com
Website: www.lillybioventures.com

Other Offices

Saalburgstrasse 153
Bad Homburg, Germany 61350

3650 Danforth Avenue
Toronto, Canada M1N 2E8

Erl Wood Manor
Sunninghill Road
Windlesham, United Kingdom GU20 6PH

POB 2160
Herzeliya Pituach , Israel 46120

112 Wharf Road
West Ryde , Australia NSW 2114

Management and Staff

Charles Schalliol, Managing Director
Ed Seguine, Principal
Nick Colangelo, Managing Director
Pawel Fludzinski, Managing Director
Ron Laufer, Principal
S. Edward Torres, Principal
Thomas Krake, Managing Director
Vanessah Ng, Principal

Type of Firm

Corporate PE/Venture

Association Membership

National Venture Capital Association - USA (NVCA)

Project Preferences

Role in Financing:
Will function either as deal originator or investor in deals created by others

Type of Financing Preferred:
Early Stage

Size of Investments Considered:
Min Size of Investment Considered (000s): $4,500
Max Size of Investment Considered (000s): $4,500

Industry Preferences

In Biotechnology prefer:
Human Biotechnology
Biotech Related Research

Additional Information

Year Founded: 2001
Capital Under Management: $75,000,000
Current Activity Level: Actively seeking new investments
Method of Compensation: Return on investment is of primary concern, do not charge fees

---

LILLY VENTURES (FKA: E.LILLY VENTURES)

Lilly Corporate Center
D.C.1089
Indianapolis, IN USA 46285
Phone: 317-651-3050
Fax: 317-651-3051
E-mail: lilly_ventures@lilly.com
Website: www.lillyventures.com

Management and Staff

Bryan Dunnivant, Principal
Darren Carroll, Senior Managing Director
S. Edward Torres, Managing Director

Type of Firm

Corporate PE/Venture

Association Membership

National Venture Capital Association - USA (NVCA)

Project Preferences

Role in Financing:
Will function either as deal originator or investor in deals created by others

Type of Financing Preferred:
Early Stage
Expansion
Balanced
First Stage Financing

Size of Investments Considered:
Min Size of Investment Considered (000s): $1,000
Max Size of Investment Considered (000s): $10,000

Industry Preferences

In Biotechnology prefer:
Biotechnology
Biotech Related Research

In Medical/Health prefer:
Medical Diagnostics
Medical Therapeutics
Medical Products
Pharmaceuticals

Additional Information

Year Founded: 2000
Capital Under Management: $175,000,000
Current Activity Level: Actively seeking new investments
Method of Compensation: Return on investment is of primary concern, do not charge fees

---

LILY ASIAN VENTURES

D.C. 1089
Lilly Corporate Center
Indianapolis, IN USA 46285
Phone: 317-651-3050
Fax: 317-651-3051
E-mail: lilly_ventures@lilly.com
Website: www.lillybioventures.com

Management and Staff

Bryan Dunnivant, Principal
Darren Carroll, Senior Managing Director
Ron Laufer, Managing Director
S. Edward Torres, Managing Director

Type of Firm

Private Equity Advisor or Fund of Funds

Project Preferences

Type of Financing Preferred:
Fund of Funds

Geographical Preferences

International Preferences:
Asia

Additional Information

Year Founded: 2007
Current Activity Level: Actively seeking new investments

LIME ROCK PARTNERS LLC

274 Riverside Avenue
Westport, CT USA 06880
Phone: 203-293-2750
Fax: 203-293-2760
Website: www.lrpartners.com

Other Offices

38 Carden Place
Aberdeen, United Kingdom AB10 1UP
Phone: 44-1224-267010
Fax: 44-1224-267011

Heritage Plaza
1111 Bagby Street, Suite 4600
Houston, TX USA 77002
Phone: 713-292-9500
Fax: 713-292-9550

Management and Staff

J. McLane, Managing Director
Jason Smith, Vice President
John Reynolds, Managing Director
Jonathan Farber, Managing Director
Lawrence Ross, Managing Director
Mark McCall, Managing Director & CFO
Rajat Barua, Vice President
Saad Bargach, Managing Director
Simon Munro, Managing Director
Thomas Bates, Managing Director
Townes Pressler, Managing Director
Will Franklin, Managing Director

Type of Firm

Private Equity Firm

Project Preferences

Type of Financing Preferred:
Generalist PE
Balanced
Other

Size of Investments Considered:
Min Size of Investment Considered (000s): $25,000
Max Size of Investment Considered (000s): $150,000

Geographical Preferences

United States Preferences:
All U.S.

Canadian Preferences:
All Canada

International Preferences:
United Kingdom

Industry Focus

(% based on actual investment)

Industrial/Energy	95.9%
Other Products	3.1%
Communications and Media	1.0%

Additional Information

Name of Most Recent Fund: Lime Rock Partners V, L.P.
Most Recent Fund Was Raised: 03/12/2008
Year Founded: 1998
Capital Under Management: $425,000,000
Current Activity Level: Actively seeking new investments

LIMOUSIN PARTICIPATIONS

Ester B.P 6922
Limoges Cedex, France 87069
Phone: 33-5-5542-6110
Fax: 33-5-5542-6112
E-mail: courrier@limousin-participations.fr
Website: www.limousin-participations.fr

Type of Firm

Private Equity Firm

Project Preferences

Type of Financing Preferred:
Early Stage
Expansion
Startup

Geographical Preferences

International Preferences:
France

Additional Information

Year Founded: 2002
Capital Under Management: $3,700,000
Current Activity Level: Actively seeking new investments

LINCOLN FUNDS

695 Town Centre Drive
First and Eight Floors
Costa Mesa, CA USA 92626
Phone: 800-918-4352
E-mail: la@lincolnfunds.com
Website: www.lincolnfunds.com

Type of Firm

Private Equity Firm

Additional Information

Year Founded: 2009
Current Activity Level: Actively seeking new investments

LINCOLNSHIRE MANAGEMENT, INC.

780 Third Avenue
39th Floor
New York, NY USA 10017
Phone: 212-319-3633
Fax: 212-755-5457
Website: www.lincolnshiremgmt.com

Other Offices

10990 Wilshire Boulevard
16th Floor
Los Angeles, CA USA 90024
Phone: 310-704-7230
Fax: 310-475-7701

Five Concourse Parkway
Suite 3000
Atlanta, GA USA 30328
Phone: 404-222-9585
Fax: 404-222-9566

60 State Street
Suite 1100
Boston, MA USA 02109
Phone: 617-695-9400
Fax: 617-532-3361

22 West Washington Street
15th Floor
Chicago, IL USA 60602
Phone: 312-899-9000
Fax: 312-899-9009

Management and Staff

Allan Weinstein, Managing Director
Charles Mills, Managing Director
Douglas Bagin, Senior Managing Director
Edwin Moss, Managing Director
George Henry, Managing Director
James Binch, Managing Director
James McLaughlin, Managing Director
John Perrachon, Managing Director
John Camp III, Managing Director
Michael Lyons, Senior Managing Director
Michael Forlenza, Managing Director
Nicholas Nedeau, Managing Director
Nicolo Vergani, Principal
Ottavio Serena di Lapigio, Managing Director
Patrick Coyne, Managing Director
Philip Kim, Principal
Pieter Kodde, Managing Director
Richard Huo, Managing Director
T.J. Maloney, President
Thomas Callahan, Managing Director
Thomas Janes, Managing Director
Vineet Pruthi, Senior Managing Director
William Hall, Managing Director

Type of Firm

Bank Affiliated

Project Preferences

Role in Financing:
Prefer role as deal originator

Type of Financing Preferred:
Leveraged Buyout
Management Buyouts
Acquisition
Recapitalizations

Size of Investments Considered:
Min Size of Investment Considered (000s): $25,000
Max Size of Investment Considered (000s): $150,000

Geographical Preferences

United States Preferences:
All U.S.

Canadian Preferences:
All Canada

Industry Preferences

In Semiconductor/Electr prefer:
Electronic Components
Component Testing Equipmt

In Medical/Health prefer:
Diagnostic Test Products

In Industrial/Energy prefer:
Industrial Products
Factory Automation
Machinery

In Business Serv. prefer:
Distribution

In Manufact. prefer:
Manufacturing

Additional Information

Name of Most Recent Fund: Lincolnshire Equity Fund III, L.P.
Most Recent Fund Was Raised: 09/14/2004
Year Founded: 1985
Capital Under Management: $400,000,000
Current Activity Level: Actively seeking new investments
Method of Compensation: Return on invest. most important, but chg. closing fees, service fees, etc.

LINDEMAN ASIA INVESTMENT

2nd Floor Samik Building
720-2 Yeoksam-dong Gangnam-gu
Seoul, South Korea 135-080
Phone: 82-70-7019-4001
Fax: 822-593-3272
Website: www.lindemanasia.com

Management and Staff

Jinha Kim, Chief Executive Officer

Type of Firm

Private Equity Firm

Project Preferences

Type of Financing Preferred:
Balanced

Geographical Preferences

International Preferences:
China

Industry Preferences

In Other prefer:
Environment Responsible

Additional Information

Year Founded: 2006
Capital Under Management: $7,400,000
Current Activity Level: Actively seeking new investments

LINDEN LLC

111 South Wacker Drive
Suite 3350
Chicago, IL USA 60606
Phone: 312-506-5600
Fax: 312-506-5601
Website: www.lindenllc.com

Management and Staff

Anthony Davis, Partner
Brian Miller, Partner
Eric Larson, Partner
Mary Beth Berkes, Managing Partner
Todd Van Horn, Vice President
William Drehkoff, Principal

Type of Firm

Private Equity Firm

Association Membership

Illinois Venture Capital Association

Project Preferences

Type of Financing Preferred:
Leveraged Buyout
Later Stage
Recapitalizations

Size of Investments Considered:
Min Size of Investment Considered (000s): $10,000
Max Size of Investment Considered: No Limit

Geographical Preferences

United States Preferences:
All U.S.

Industry Preferences

In Medical/Health prefer:
Medical/Health
Medical Diagnostics
Medical Therapeutics
Medical Products
Health Services

Additional Information

Name of Most Recent Fund: Linden Capital Partners-A, L.P.
Most Recent Fund Was Raised: 10/11/2006
Year Founded: 2002
Capital Under Management: $226,500,000
Current Activity Level: Actively seeking new investments

LINDSAY GOLDBERG LLC (FKA: LINDSAY GOLDBERG & BESSEMER GP)

630 Fifth Avenue
30th Floor
New York, NY USA 10011
Phone: 212-651-1100
Fax: 212-651-1101
E-mail: contact@lindsaygoldbergllc.com
Website: www.lindsaygoldbergllc.com

Management and Staff

Adam Godfrey, Partner
Alan Goldberg, Managing Partner
Andrew Weinberg, Principal
J. Russell Triedman, Partner
John A.W. Werwaiss, Principal
Lance Hirt, Partner
Michael Dee, Principal
Robert Lindsay, Managing Partner
Robert Roriston, Partner

Type of Firm

Private Equity Firm

Project Preferences

Type of Financing Preferred:
Leveraged Buyout

Industry Preferences

In Medical/Health prefer:
Health Services

In Financial Services prefer:
Financial Services

In Manufact. prefer:
Manufacturing

Additional Information

Year Founded: 2002
Capital Under Management: $11,189,000,000
Current Activity Level: Actively seeking new investments

LINEAGE CAPITAL LLC

222 Berkeley Street
21st Floor
Boston, MA USA 02116
Phone: 617-778-0660
Fax: 617-778-0659
E-mail: info@lineagecap.com
Website: www.lineagecap.com

Type of Firm

Private Equity Firm

Project Preferences

Type of Financing Preferred:
Leveraged Buyout
Acquisition
Recapitalizations

Geographical Preferences

Canadian Preferences:
All Canada

International Preferences:
Mexico

Additional Information

Year Founded: 2003
Capital Under Management: $157,100,000
Current Activity Level: Actively seeking new investments

LINK VENTURES LLLP

100 Quannapowitt Parkway
Wakefield, MA USA 01880
Website: www.linkventures.com

Management and Staff

Cynthia Birnbaum, Chief Financial Officer

Type of Firm

Private Equity Firm

Project Preferences

Type of Financing Preferred:
Early Stage

Geographical Preferences

United States Preferences:
All U.S.

Industry Preferences

In Internet Specific prefer:
Internet

Additional Information

Year Founded: 2007
Current Activity Level: Actively seeking new investments

LINKAGENE

P.O.Box: 5271
Gan Yavne, Israel 70800
Phone: 08-8574225
Fax: 08-9926581
E-mail: yoelmaya@bezeqint.net
Website: www.ohv.co.il/linkagene.htm

Management and Staff

Sylvia Kachalsky, Chief Executive Officer

Type of Firm

Private Equity Firm

Additional Information

Year Founded: 2000
Current Activity Level: Actively seeking new investments

LINKMED AB

Drottninggatan 33
Box 7710
Stockholm, Sweden 103 95
Phone: 46-8-5089-3992
Fax: 46-8-5089-3950
E-mail: info@linkmed.se
Website: www.linkmed.se

Management and Staff

Ingemar Lagerlof, Vice President
Olle Johansson, President

Type of Firm

Private Equity Firm

Association Membership

Swedish Venture Capital Association (SVCA)

Project Preferences

Type of Financing Preferred:
Early Stage

Size of Investments Considered:
Min Size of Investment Considered (000s): $218
Max Size of Investment Considered (000s): $545

Geographical Preferences

International Preferences:
Sweden

Additional Information

Year Founded: 1998
Current Activity Level: Actively seeking new investments

LINKTECH AB

Agatan 39
Linkoping, Sweden 582 22
Phone: 46-13-136-440
Fax: 46-13-125-095
E-mail: office@linktech.se
Website: www.linktech.se

Management and Staff

Johan Amneus, Managing Director

Type of Firm

Private Equity Firm

Association Membership

Swedish Venture Capital Association (SVCA)

Project Preferences

Type of Financing Preferred:
Early Stage
Expansion
Startup

Size of Investments Considered:
Min Size of Investment Considered (000s): $212
Max Size of Investment Considered (000s): $531

Geographical Preferences

International Preferences:
Scandanavia/Nordic Region

Industry Preferences

In Internet Specific prefer:
Internet

Additional Information

Year Founded: 1998
Capital Under Management: $10,600,000
Current Activity Level: Actively seeking new investments

LINSALATA CAPITAL PARTNERS

5900 Landerbrook Drive
Suite 280
Mayfield Heights, OH USA 44124
Phone: 440-684-1400
Fax: 440-684-0984
E-mail: info@linsalatacapital.com
Website: www.linsalatacapital.com

Management and Staff

Daniel DeSantis, Managing Director
Eric Bacon, Senior Managing Director
Gregory Taber, Managing Director
John Studdard, Vice President
Mark Kirk, Managing Director
Michael Faremouth, Vice President
Michael Moran, Vice President
Murad Beg, Vice President
Stephen Perry, Senior Managing Director
Timothy Healy, Vice President

Type of Firm

Private Equity Firm

Project Preferences

Role in Financing:
Prefer role as deal originator

Type of Financing Preferred:
Leveraged Buyout
Generalist PE
Acquisition
Recapitalizations

Size of Investments Considered:
Min Size of Investment Considered (000s): $10,000
Max Size of Investment Considered (000s): $60,000

Geographical Preferences

United States Preferences:
All U.S.

Industry Focus

(% based on actual investment)

Other Products	92.0%
Industrial/Energy	8.0%

Additional Information

Name of Most Recent Fund: Linsalata Capital Partners V, L.P.
Most Recent Fund Was Raised: 04/05/2005
Year Founded: 1984
Capital Under Management: $975,000,000
Current Activity Level: Actively seeking new investments
Method of Compensation: Return on invest. most important, but chg. closing fees, service fees, etc.

LINX PARTNERS

100 Galleria Parkway
Suite 1300
Atlanta, GA USA 30339
Phone: 770-818-0335
Fax: 770-818-9537
Website: www.linxpartners.com

Other Offices

670 White Plains Road
Suite 201
Scarsdale, NY USA 10583
Phone: 914-472-1835
Fax: 914-472-6721

Management and Staff

Barbara Henagan, Managing Director
Edward Leinss, Managing Director
Mark Niznik, Vice President
Melissa Nims, Chief Financial Officer
Peter Hicks, Managing Director

Type of Firm

Private Equity Firm

Project Preferences

Role in Financing:

Prefer role as deal originator

Type of Financing Preferred:

Leveraged Buyout
Public Companies
Recapitalizations

Size of Investments Considered:

Min Size of Investment Considered (000s): $7,000
Max Size of Investment Considered (000s): $20,000

Geographical Preferences

United States Preferences:

All U.S.

Industry Preferences

In Industrial/Energy prefer:

Industrial Products

In Business Serv. prefer:

Services
Distribution

In Manufact. prefer:

Manufacturing

Additional Information

Year Founded: 1999
Capital Under Management: $188,000,000
Current Activity Level: Actively seeking new investments
Method of Compensation: Function primarily in service area, receive contingent fee in cash or equity

LION CAPITAL (FKA: HICKS MUSE (EUROPE))

21 Grosvenor Place
London, United Kingdom SW1X 7HF
Phone: 44-20-7201-2200
Fax: 44-20-7201-2222
E-mail: info@lioncapital.com
Website: www.lioncapital.com

Management and Staff

Dominik Halstenberg, Principal
George Sewell, Partner
Janet Dunlop, Chief Operating Officer
Javier Ferran, Partner
Kelly Mayer, Partner
Lyndon Lea, Partner
Mary Minnick, Partner
Neil Richardson, Founding Partner
Robert Darwent, Founding Partner

Type of Firm

Private Equity Firm

Association Membership

British Venture Capital Association (BVCA)
European Private Equity and Venture Capital Assoc.

Project Preferences

Type of Financing Preferred:

Leveraged Buyout
Generalist PE

Geographical Preferences

International Preferences:

Europe

Industry Preferences

In Communications prefer:

Media and Entertainment

In Consumer Related prefer:

Consumer Products
Consumer Services

Additional Information

Name of Most Recent Fund: Lion Capital Fund II, L.P.
Most Recent Fund Was Raised: 04/03/2007
Year Founded: 2004
Capital Under Management: $4,029,100,000
Current Activity Level: Actively seeking new investments

LION CAPITAL ADVISERS LTD (FKA: LION CAPITAL PARTNERS PLC)

1 Love Lane
London, United Kingdom EC2V 7JJ
Phone: 44-20-7710-4524
Fax: 44-20-7710-4501
Website: www.lioncapitaladvisers.com

Management and Staff

Simon Stock, Chief Financial Officer
Tony Canning, Chief Executive Officer

Type of Firm

Private Equity Firm

Project Preferences

Type of Financing Preferred:

Leveraged Buyout
Early Stage
Expansion
Management Buyouts

Geographical Preferences

International Preferences:

United Kingdom
Europe

Industry Preferences

In Medical/Health prefer:

Medical Products

Additional Information

Year Founded: 1998
Capital Under Management: $55,000,000
Current Activity Level: Actively seeking new investments

LION CHEMICAL CAPITAL

535 Madison Avenue
Fourth Floor
New York, NY USA 10022
Phone: 212-355-5500
Fax: 212-355-6283
Website: www.lionchemicalcapital.com

Other Offices

9720 Cypresswood Drive
Suite 212
Houston, TX USA 77070
Phone: 281-807-2610
Fax: 281-807-2646

Management and Staff

David De Leeuw, Managing Director
Peter De Leeuw, Managing Director
Stephen Lyttleton, Vice President

Type of Firm

Private Equity Firm

Project Preferences

Type of Financing Preferred:
Leveraged Buyout
Balanced

Industry Preferences

In Industrial/Energy prefer:
Industrial Products
Materials

Additional Information

Year Founded: 2008
Current Activity Level: Actively seeking new investments

LION SELECTION, LTD. (AKA: LION SELECTION GROUP)

Level 4
15 Queen Street
Melbourne, Australia 3000
Phone: 613-9614-8008
Fax: 613-9614-8009
E-mail: info@lionselection.com.au
Website: www.lionselection.com.au

Management and Staff

Luke Smith, Vice President
Peter Maloney, Chief Financial Officer
Robin Widdup, Managing Director

Type of Firm

Private Equity Firm

Project Preferences

Role in Financing:
Will function either as deal originator or investor in deals created by others

Type of Financing Preferred:
Balanced

Size of Investments Considered:
Min Size of Investment Considered (000s): $3,983
Max Size of Investment Considered (000s): $7,966

Geographical Preferences

International Preferences:
Pacific
Asia
Africa

Industry Preferences

In Agr/Forestr/Fish prefer:
Mining and Minerals

Additional Information

Year Founded: 1997
Capital Under Management: $54,100,000
Current Activity Level: Actively seeking new investments

LIONHART INVESTMENTS LTD.

19 Camp Road
Heston Business Court
Wimbledon, United Kingdom SW19 4UW
Phone: 44-20-8947-6934
Fax: 44-20-8947-6936
E-mail: info@lionhart.net
Website: www.lionhart.net

Type of Firm

Bank Affiliated

Project Preferences

Type of Financing Preferred:
Mezzanine
Balanced
Distressed Debt

Geographical Preferences

International Preferences:
Latin America
Europe
Cayman Islands

Industry Preferences

In Industrial/Energy prefer:
Energy
Alternative Energy
Environmental Related

In Financial Services prefer:
Real Estate

In Agr/Forestr/Fish prefer:
Mining and Minerals
Additional Information
Year Founded: 2008
Current Activity Level: Actively seeking new investments

LIONHEART VENTURES

130 Keystone Drive
Montgomeryville, PA USA 18936
Phone: 215-283-8400
Fax: 215-646-5149
Website: www.lionheartventures.com

Other Offices

124 Mount Auburn Street
Suite 200N
Cambridge, MA USA 02138
Phone: 617-576-5888

Management and Staff

Matthew Sutton, Managing Partner
Tim Long, Vice President
Vanessa Mai, Founding Partner

Type of Firm

Private Equity Firm

Project Preferences

Type of Financing Preferred:
Leveraged Buyout
Acquisition

Industry Preferences

In Semiconductor/Electr prefer:
Electronics
Controllers and Sensors

In Industrial/Energy prefer:
Industrial Products

In Transportation prefer:
Transportation

In Manufact. prefer:
Manufacturing

Additional Information

Year Founded: 2008
Current Activity Level: Actively seeking new investments

LIQUID CAPITAL MANAGEMENT GROUP, LLC

8300 Greensboro Drive
Suite 800
McLean, VA USA 22102
Phone: 703-626-3757
Fax: 703-991-2595
E-mail: info@liquidcapitalgroup.com
Website: www.liquidcapitalgroup.com

Management and Staff

Randolph Domolky, Managing Director

Type of Firm

Private Equity Firm

Project Preferences

Type of Financing Preferred:
Early Stage

Industry Preferences

In Communications prefer:
Wireless Communications

In Internet Specific prefer:
Ecommerce

Additional Information

Year Founded: 2000
Capital Under Management: $2,100,000
Current Activity Level: Actively seeking new investments

LIREAS HOLDINGS (PTY) LTD

PO Box 10842
Johannesburg, South Africa 2000
Phone: 27-11-481-6607

Fax: 27-11-643-4245
E-mail: info@hannover-re.com
Website: www.hannover-re.co.za

Type of Firm

Corporate PE/Venture

Association Membership

South African Venture Capital Association (SAVCA)

Project Preferences

Type of Financing Preferred:

Expansion

Geographical Preferences

International Preferences:

Africa

Industry Preferences

In Financial Services prefer:

Financial Services

Additional Information

Year Founded: 2000
Capital Under Management: $3,100,000
Current Activity Level: Actively seeking new investments

LITEXCO MEDITERRANEA

Pau Claris 148
Barcelona, Spain 08009
Phone: 34-93-467-1070
Fax: 34-93-467-9113
E-mail: barcelona@litexco.com
Website: www.litexco.com

Other Offices

Via Cefalonia 55
Brescia, Italy 25124
Phone: 39-30-242-2016
Fax: 39-30-242-2018

Apaca Utca 9
Gyor, Hungary 9022
Phone: 36-96-526-944
Fax: 36-96-312-302

9, Asnyka Street
Krakow, Poland 31144
Phone: 48-12-431-0576
Fax: 48-12-431-0576

104-106, Stirbei Voda Street
Sector 1
Bucharest, Romania
Phone: 40-21-313-6039
Fax: 40-21-313-6039

Saxweg 11
Triesen, Switzerland 9495
Phone: 423-265-5710
Fax: 423-265-5711

Colonia Elena - C.C. 15
San Rafael - Mendoza, Argentina 5600
Phone: 54-9-2627-430-477

Grosslingova 56
Bratislava, Sri Lanka 811 09
Phone: 421-907-984-996
Fax: 421-2-5443-5680

Type of Firm

Private Equity Firm

Project Preferences

Type of Financing Preferred:

Expansion
Balanced
Startup

Size of Investments Considered:

Min Size of Investment Considered (000s): $123
Max Size of Investment Considered (000s): $492

Geographical Preferences

International Preferences:

Gibraltar
Portugal
Europe
Andorra
Eastern Europe
Spain

Additional Information

Year Founded: 1989
Current Activity Level: Actively seeking new investments

LITORINA CAPITAL MANAGEMENT

Kungstradgardsgatan 18, 5 tr
Stockholm, Sweden 111 47
Phone: 46-8-5451-8180
Fax: 46-8-5451-8189
E-mail: litorina@litorina.se
Website: www.litorinakapital.se

Type of Firm

Private Equity Firm

Association Membership

Swedish Venture Capital Association (SVCA)
European Private Equity and Venture Capital Assoc.

Project Preferences

Type of Financing Preferred:

Leveraged Buyout
Expansion

Size of Investments Considered:

Min Size of Investment Considered (000s): $1,100
Max Size of Investment Considered (000s): $11,400

Geographical Preferences

International Preferences:

Sweden
Europe
Scandanavia/Nordic Region
Finland
Norway
Denmark

Industry Focus

(% based on actual investment)

Industrial/Energy	34.9%
Computer Software and Services	25.9%
Communications and Media	15.3%
Internet Specific	13.0%
Medical/Health	11.0%

Additional Information

Name of Most Recent Fund: Litorina Kapital II
Most Recent Fund Was Raised: 12/11/2001
Year Founded: 1998
Capital Under Management: $57,200,000
Current Activity Level: Actively seeking new investments

LITTLEJOHN & COMPANY LLC

Eight Sound Shore Drive
Suite 303
Greenwich, CT USA 06830
Phone: 203-552-3500
Fax: 203-552-3550
E-mail: info@littlejohnllc.com
Website: www.littlejohnllc.com

Management and Staff

Angus Littlejohn, Chairman & CEO
Antonio Miranda, Principal
Brian Ramsay, Managing Director
David Simon, Managing Director
Edmund Feeley, Managing Director
Kenneth Warren, Chief Financial Officer
Michael Kaplan, Principal
Michael Klein, President
Richard Maybaum, Managing Director
Robert Davis, Managing Director
Steven Raich, Managing Director

Type of Firm

Bank Affiliated

Project Preferences

Type of Financing Preferred:

Leveraged Buyout

Geographical Preferences

Canadian Preferences:

All Canada

International Preferences:

Europe

Industry Focus

(% based on actual investment)

Industrial/Energy	44.4%
Consumer Related	44.0%
Other Products	7.5%
Semiconductors/Other Elect.	4.1%

Additional Information

Name of Most Recent Fund: Littlejohn Fund III, L.P.
Most Recent Fund Was Raised: 12/30/2004
Year Founded: 1996
Capital Under Management: $1,287,800,000
Current Activity Level: Actively seeking new investments

LIVEOAK EQUITY PARTNERS

1268 Park Vista Drive
Atlanta, GA USA 30319
Phone: 404-790-2666
Fax: 404-842-1502
E-mail: liveoakequity@bellsouth.net
Website: www.liveoakequity.com

Management and Staff

James Gilbert, Managing Partner

Type of Firm

Private Equity Firm

Project Preferences

Type of Financing Preferred:

Second Stage Financing
Early Stage
Later Stage
Seed
First Stage Financing

Size of Investments Considered:

Min Size of Investment Considered (000s): $500
Max Size of Investment Considered (000s): $6,000

Geographical Preferences

United States Preferences:

Southeast

Industry Focus

(% based on actual investment)

Computer Software and Services	50.3%
Internet Specific	34.3%
Medical/Health	8.6%
Communications and Media	5.8%
Semiconductors/Other Elect.	1.0%

Additional Information

Name of Most Recent Fund: LiveOak Seed Capital
Most Recent Fund Was Raised: 01/30/2001
Year Founded: 1998
Capital Under Management: $70,000,000
Current Activity Level: Actively seeking new investments

LIVINGSTON CAPITAL, LTD.

106 South University Boulevard
Suite 14
Denver, CO USA 80209
Phone: 303-722-4008
Fax: 303-722-4011

Management and Staff

Greg Pusey, President
Jeff McGonegal, Partner

Type of Firm

Private Equity Firm

Association Membership

Natl Assoc of Small Bus. Inv. Co (NASBIC)

Project Preferences

Role in Financing:

Prefer role as deal originator

Type of Financing Preferred:

Early Stage
Expansion
Later Stage

Size of Investments Considered:

Min Size of Investment Considered (000s): $160
Max Size of Investment Considered (000s): $200

Geographical Preferences

United States Preferences:

Rocky Mountain
Southwest
All U.S.

Industry Focus

(% based on actual investment)

Industrial/Energy	80.8%
Biotechnology	7.3%
Computer Software and Services	5.5%
Other Products	3.3%
Computer Hardware	2.9%
Consumer Related	0.1%

Additional Information

Name of Most Recent Fund: Livingston Financial Group
Most Recent Fund Was Raised: 01/01/1990
Year Founded: 1979
Capital Under Management: $232,000,000
Current Activity Level: Actively seeking new investments
Method of Compensation: Return on investment is of primary concern, do not charge fees

---

LJH GLOBAL INVESTMENTS

2640 Golden Gate Parkway
Suite 205
Naples, FL USA 34105
Phone: 239-403-3030
Fax: 239-403-3031
Website: www.ljh.com

Management and Staff

George Gowdey, Vice President
Robert Blabey, Chief Operating Officer
Willis Williams, Chief Financial Officer

Type of Firm

Investment Management Firm

Project Preferences

Role in Financing:

Prefer role in deals created by others

Type of Financing Preferred:

Second Stage Financing
First Stage Financing
Special Situation

Geographical Preferences

United States Preferences:

All U.S.

Industry Preferences

In Communications prefer:

Communications and Media

In Computer Other prefer:

Computer Related

In Semiconductor/Electr prefer:

Electronic Components

In Financial Services prefer:

Financial Services

In Business Serv. prefer:

Distribution

Additional Information

Year Founded: 1992
Capital Under Management: $200,000,000
Current Activity Level: Actively seeking new investments
Method of Compensation: Return on investment is of primary concern, do not charge fees

---

LJH LINLEY CAPITAL LLC

270 Lafayette Street
Suite 610
New York, NY USA 10012
Phone: 212-925-8703
Fax: 212-925-8704
E-mail: info@linleycapital.com
Website: www.linleycapital.com

Management and Staff

John Jonge Poerink, Managing Partner
Robert Blabey, Chief Operating Officer

Type of Firm

Private Equity Firm

Project Preferences

Type of Financing Preferred:
Leveraged Buyout
Expansion
Management Buyouts
Recapitalizations

Geographical Preferences

Canadian Preferences:
All Canada

International Preferences:
Latin America
Europe

Industry Preferences

In Communications prefer:
Media and Entertainment

In Medical/Health prefer:
Health Services

In Consumer Related prefer:
Consumer
Retail
Food/Beverage
Consumer Products
Other Restaurants

In Industrial/Energy prefer:
Energy
Industrial Products

In Transportation prefer:
Transportation
Aerospace

In Financial Services prefer:
Financial Services

In Business Serv. prefer:
Services

In Manufact. prefer:
Manufacturing

Additional Information
Year Founded: 2008
Current Activity Level: Actively seeking new investments

LLM CAPITAL PARTNERS LLC
265 Franklin Street
20th Floor
Boston, MA USA 02110
Phone: 617-330-7755
Fax: 617-330-7759
E-mail: llm@llmcapital.com
Website: www.llmcapital.com

Other Offices
225 Bush Street
16th Floor
San Francisco, CA USA 94104
Phone: 415-439-8315
Fax: 415-439-8316

Management and Staff
Frederick Moseley, Managing Director
Jeffrey Lane, Managing Director
Matthew Hills, Managing Director
Patrick Landers, Managing Director
Samuel Kenna, Vice President

Type of Firm
Private Equity Firm

Project Preferences

Type of Financing Preferred:
Management Buyouts
Acquisition

Geographical Preferences

United States Preferences:
All U.S.

Additional Information
Year Founded: 2006
Capital Under Management: $71,000,000
Current Activity Level: Actively seeking new investments

LLR PARTNERS, INC.
2929 Arch Street
Cira Center, Suite 2700
Philadelphia, PA USA 19104
Phone: 215-717-2900
Fax: 215-717-2270
E-mail: info@llrpartners.com
Website: www.llrpartners.com

Management and Staff
Christian Bullitt, Vice President
David Reuter, Partner
David Stienes, Principal
Gregory Case, Partner
Howard Ross, Partner
Ira Lubert, Partner
Mitchell Hollin, Partner
Paul Winn, Partner
Scott Perricelli, Partner
Seth Lehr, Partner
Todd Morrissey, Principal

Type of Firm
Private Equity Firm

Project Preferences

Role in Financing:
Will function either as deal originator or investor in deals created by others

Type of Financing Preferred:
Leveraged Buyout
Expansion
Generalist PE
Balanced
Public Companies
Turnaround
Later Stage
Management Buyouts
Private Placement
Recapitalizations

Size of Investments Considered:
Min Size of Investment Considered (000s): $10,000
Max Size of Investment Considered (000s): $100,000

Geographical Preferences

United States Preferences:
Mid Atlantic
East Coast
All U.S.

Industry Preferences

In Computer Software prefer:
Software

In Medical/Health prefer:
Health Services

In Consumer Related prefer:
Consumer
Retail
Education Related

In Financial Services prefer:
Financial Services

In Business Serv. prefer:
Services

Additional Information
Year Founded: 1999
Capital Under Management: $140,000,000
Current Activity Level: Actively seeking new investments
Method of Compensation: Return on investment is of primary concern, do not charge fees

---

LMO SAS
14, Avenue Hoche
Paris, France 75008
Phone: 33-14469-3493
Fax: 33-14469-3492
E-mail: info@lmo.fr
Website: www.lmo.fr

Type of Firm
Private Equity Firm

Project Preferences

Type of Financing Preferred:
Generalist PE

Geographical Preferences

International Preferences:
Europe
France

Additional Information
Year Founded: 1989

Current Activity Level: Actively seeking new investments

LMX BUSINESS DEVELOPMENT A/S

Koldingvej 2
Billund, Denmark 7190
Phone: 45-753-386-99
Fax: 45-753-530-02
Website: www.lmx.dk

Management and Staff

Finn Dahlgaard, Chief Executive Officer
Gunnar Brodersen, Chief Financial Officer

Type of Firm

Private Equity Firm

Project Preferences

Type of Financing Preferred:
Expansion
Seed
Startup

Geographical Preferences

International Preferences:
Denmark

Additional Information

Year Founded: 2000
Capital Under Management: $14,100,000
Current Activity Level: Actively seeking new investments

LNK PARTNERS

81 Main Street
White Plains, NY USA 10601
Phone: 914-824-5900
Fax: 914-824-5901
E-mail: info@LNKpartners.com
Website: www.lnkpartners.com

Management and Staff

Bruce Klatsky, Partner
David Landau, Partner
Henry Nasella, Partner
Jeffrey Perlman, Partner
Kayvan Heravi, Principal
Paige Daly, Managing Director
Philip Marineau, Partner

Type of Firm

Private Equity Advisor or Fund of Funds

Project Preferences

Type of Financing Preferred:
Leveraged Buyout
Acquisition
Recapitalizations

Industry Preferences

In Consumer Related prefer:
Consumer
Retail

Additional Information

Year Founded: 2005
Capital Under Management: $400,000,000
Current Activity Level: Actively seeking new investments

LOGISPRING MANAGEMENT COMPANY S.A.R.L.

15, Rue des Alpes
Geneva, Switzerland 1201
Phone: 41-22-716-4230
Fax: 41-22-738-2969
E-mail: info@logispring.com
Website: www.logispring.com

Management and Staff

Brad Corrodi, Partner
Frans Van Schaik, Managing Partner
Marcel Timmer, Partner

Type of Firm

Private Equity Firm

Association Membership

European Private Equity and Venture Capital Assoc.

Project Preferences

Type of Financing Preferred:
Early Stage
Expansion

Size of Investments Considered:
Min Size of Investment Considered (000s): $880
Max Size of Investment Considered (000s): $8,803

Geographical Preferences

United States Preferences:
All U.S.

International Preferences:
Latin America
Europe
Asia

Industry Preferences

In Communications prefer:
Other Communication Prod.

In Internet Specific prefer:
Internet

In Computer Other prefer:
Computer Related

In Semiconductor/Electr prefer:
Electronics

In Industrial/Energy prefer:
Factory Automation

In Transportation prefer:
Transportation

Additional Information

Name of Most Recent Fund: LogiSpring Investment Fund NV/SA
Most Recent Fund Was Raised: 07/27/2001
Year Founded: 2001
Capital Under Management: $221,700,000
Current Activity Level: Actively seeking new investments

LOK CAPITAL GROUP

NBCC Place 1st Flr, East Tower
Bhisham Pitamah Marg
New Delhi , India 110 003
Phone: 91-11-4366-7000
Fax: 91-11-4366-7070
Website: www.lokcapital.com

Management and Staff

Vishal Mehta, Managing Director

Type of Firm

Private Equity Firm

Project Preferences

Type of Financing Preferred:
Balanced

Geographical Preferences

International Preferences:
India

Industry Preferences

In Financial Services prefer:
Financial Services

Additional Information

Year Founded: 2001
Capital Under Management: $22,000,000
Current Activity Level: Actively seeking new investments

LOMBARD INVESTMENTS, INC.

Three Embarcadero Center
Suite 2340
San Francisco, CA USA 94111
Phone: 415-397-5900
Fax: 415-397-5820
E-mail: info@lombardinvestments.com
Website: www.lombardinvestments.com

Other Offices

10/F, CRC Tower
87/2 Wireless Road, Lumpini, Phathumwan
Bangkok, Thailand 10330
Phone: 662-685-3599
Fax: 662-685-3588
Room 2202, 22/F, Tower 1, Lippo Centre

89 Queensway
Central, Hong Kong
Phone: 852-2878-7388
Fax: 852-2878-7288

Management and Staff

Artapong Porndhithi, Vice President
Matthew Taylor, Managing Director
Peter Sullivan, Managing Director
Pote Videt, Managing Director
Scott Sweet, Chief Financial Officer
Thomas Smith, Managing Director

Type of Firm

Investment Management Firm

Association Membership

Hong Kong Venture Capital Association (HKVCA)

Project Preferences

Role in Financing:

Prefer role as deal originator but will also invest in deals created by others

Type of Financing Preferred:

Fund of Funds
Leveraged Buyout
Expansion
Generalist PE
Turnaround
Management Buyouts
Acquisition
Industry Rollups
Recapitalizations

Size of Investments Considered:

Min Size of Investment Considered (000s): $5,000
Max Size of Investment Considered (000s): $35,000

Geographical Preferences

International Preferences:

Asia

Industry Preferences

In Communications prefer:

Communications and Media

In Semiconductor/Electr prefer:

Electronics

In Consumer Related prefer:

Food/Beverage
Consumer Products
Education Related

In Industrial/Energy prefer:

Industrial Products
Materials
Machinery

In Transportation prefer:

Transportation

In Financial Services prefer:

Financial Services

In Business Serv. prefer:

Services
Media

In Manufact. prefer:

Manufacturing

Additional Information

Name of Most Recent Fund: Lombard Asia III L.P.
Most Recent Fund Was Raised: 03/31/2006
Year Founded: 1985
Capital Under Management: $1,000,000,000
Current Activity Level: Actively seeking new investments
Method of Compensation: Return on investment is of primary concern, do not charge fees

---

LOMBARD ODIER DARIER HENTSCH (FKA: LOMBARD ODIER & CIE)

Rue de la Corraterie 11
P.O. Box 5215
Geneva, Switzerland 1211
Phone: 41-22709-2111
Fax: 41-22709-2911
E-mail: contact@lodh.com
Website: www.lombardodier.ch

Type of Firm

Private Equity Advisor or Fund of Funds

Association Membership

European Private Equity and Venture Capital Assoc.

Project Preferences

Type of Financing Preferred:

Fund of Funds
Leveraged Buyout
Early Stage
Expansion
Turnaround
Balanced
Seed
Startup
Fund of Funds of Second

Geographical Preferences

International Preferences:

Europe
Western Europe

Additional Information

Year Founded: 2001
Capital Under Management: $401,100,000
Current Activity Level: Actively seeking new investments

LONDON ASIA CAPITAL PLC (FKA: NETVEST.COM PLC)

197 Providence Square
Jacob Street
London, United Kingdom SE1 2DG
Phone: 44-20-7231-0282
Fax: 44-20-7495-1691
Website: www.londonasiacapital.com

Other Offices

Sukhbaatar Square
Ulaanbaatar, Mongolia

18 Queen's Road Central
21/F, New World Tower 1
Central, Hong Kong

No. 2 Zhong Guan Cun South Avenue
Haidian District
Beijing, China 100085
Phone: 86-10-5172-7918
Fax: 86-10-5172-7915

No. 242,Tianhe East Street
Tianhe District
Guangzhou, China 510620
Phone: 86-20-8759-0487
Fax: 86-20-8757-0377

LAC Canada
Victoria
B.C, Canada
Phone: 778-288-3588

Room 2204 B Building No.18
Hongkong Mid Road
Qingdao, China
Phone: 86-532-6019-280
Fax: 86-)532-6019-111

Central South Forestry University
498 South Shaoshan Road
Changsha, China

Goethestrasse 4
Freiburg, Germany 79100
Phone: 49-761-704-9606
Fax: 49-761-704-9604

141 Market Street
Suite 12-00 Int'l Factors Building
Singapore, Singapore 048944

933 Jianshe Avenue, Suite 17-08
Wuhan Urban Commercial Bank Plaza
Wuhan City, China
Phone: 86-27-8265-6157
Fax: 86-27-8265-6159

B-3A-5, Plaza Mont Kiara
No.2 Jalan Kiara
Kuala Lumpur, Malaysia 50480
1 Garden Road
Level 30, Bank of China Tower
Central, Hong Kong
Phone: 852-2251-8373
Fax: 852-2251-8383

93 He Ping Road
Century Plaza, Zone B Room 1306
Xi'an, China

Management and Staff

Benson Day, Managing Director
Hongtao Liang, Managing Director
John Mi, Chief Executive Officer
Peng Mun Foo, Chief Financial Officer
Shengde Yang, Managing Director

Type of Firm

Bank Affiliated

Project Preferences

Type of Financing Preferred:
Early Stage
Expansion
Later Stage

Geographical Preferences

International Preferences:
Taiwan
China
Hong Kong
Singapore
Asia

Industry Preferences

In Communications prefer:
Communications and Media

In Internet Specific prefer:
Internet

In Medical/Health prefer:
Pharmaceuticals

In Consumer Related prefer:
Consumer Products
Education Related

In Industrial/Energy prefer:
Energy
Environmental Related

In Financial Services prefer:
Financial Services

Additional Information

Year Founded: 1999
Capital Under Management: $300,000,000
Current Activity Level: Actively seeking new investments

LONDON SEED CAPITAL, LTD.

52/54 Southwark Street
London, United Kingdom SE1 1UN
Phone: 44-20-7089-2309
Fax: 44-20-7089-2301
E-mail: info@londonseedcapital.com
Website: www.londonseedcapital.com

Management and Staff

Anthony Clarke, Managing Director

Type of Firm

Bank Affiliated

Project Preferences

Type of Financing Preferred:
Early Stage
Expansion
Seed
Startup

Geographical Preferences

International Preferences:
United Kingdom
Europe

Additional Information

Year Founded: 2002
Capital Under Management: $4,500,000
Current Activity Level: Actively seeking new investments

LONE STAR FUNDS

717 North Harwood Street
Suite 2200
Dallas, TX USA 75204
Phone: 214-754-8300
Website: www.lonestarfunds.com

Other Offices

50 Welbeck Street
London, United Kingdom W1G 9XW
Phone: 44-20-7616-6800

Star Tower 30th Floor
737 Yeoksam-dong, Kangnam-ku
Seoul, South Korea 135-984
Phone: 822-2112-2000

16th Floor, 8 Hsin Yi Road
Section 5
Taipei, Taiwan 110
Phone: 886-2-3725-1500

Holland Hills Mori Tower
17th Floor 5-11-2, Toranomon
Tokyo, Japan 105-0001
Phone: 81-3-5776-8700

Type of Firm

Bank Affiliated

Project Preferences

Type of Financing Preferred:
Leveraged Buyout
Mezzanine
Other

Geographical Preferences

United States Preferences:
All U.S.

International Preferences:
Korea, South
Germany
Japan
All International

Additional Information

Year Founded: 1979
Capital Under Management: $12,500,000,000
Current Activity Level: Actively seeking new investments

LONE STAR INVESTMENT ADVISORS (AKA: LEWIS HOLLINGSWORTH LP)

One Galleria Tower
13355 Noel Road, Suite 1750
Dallas, TX USA 75240
Phone: 972-702-7390
Fax: 972-702-7391
E-mail: info@texasprivateequity.com
Website: www.lonestarcra.com

Management and Staff

Arthur Hollingsworth, Managing Partner
Gregory Campbell, General Partner
Jack Riggs, Principal
Keith Camp, Partner

Type of Firm

Private Equity Firm

Project Preferences

Role in Financing:
Prefer role as deal originator but will also invest in deals created by others

Type of Financing Preferred:
Leveraged Buyout
Control-block Purchases
Generalist PE
Expansion
Turnaround
Later Stage
Management Buyouts
Acquisition

Size of Investments Considered:
Min Size of Investment Considered (000s): $1,000
Max Size of Investment Considered (000s): $10,000

Geographical Preferences

United States Preferences:
Texas

Industry Preferences

In Communications prefer:
Communications and Media

In Consumer Related prefer:
Food/Beverage

In Industrial/Energy prefer:
Industrial Products

In Transportation prefer:
Transportation

In Financial Services prefer:
Insurance

In Business Serv. prefer:
Services
Distribution

In Manufact. prefer:
Manufacturing

Additional Information
Name of Most Recent Fund: North Texas Opportunity Fund
Most Recent Fund Was Raised: 07/24/2000
Year Founded: 1987
Capital Under Management: $112,500,000
Current Activity Level: Actively seeking new investments
Method of Compensation: Return on invest. most important, but chg. closing fees, service fees, etc.

LONESTAR CAPCO FUND LLC
1505 Wallace Drive
Suite 102
Carrollton, TX USA 75006
Phone: 972-849-3550

Type of Firm
Government Affiliated Program

Geographical Preferences

United States Preferences:
Texas
All U.S.

Additional Information
Year Founded: 2005
Current Activity Level: Actively seeking new investments

LONG POINT CAPITAL INC.
767 Fifth Avenue
8th Floor
New York, NY USA 10153
Phone: 212-593-1800
Fax: 212-593-1888
Website: www.longpointcapital.com

Other Offices
26700 Woodward Avenue
Royal Oak, MI USA 48607
Phone: 248-591-6000
Fax: 248-591-6001

Management and Staff
Eric Von Stroh, Vice President
Gerry Bolyan, Partner
Gretchen Perkins, Vice President
Ira Starr, Managing Director
Jonathan Morgan, Partner
William Ughetta, Partner

Type of Firm
Private Equity Firm

Project Preferences

Role in Financing:
Prefer role as deal originator but will also invest in deals created by others

Type of Financing Preferred:
Leveraged Buyout
Expansion
Management Buyouts
Acquisition
Special Situation
Recapitalizations

Size of Investments Considered:
Min Size of Investment Considered (000s): $5,000
Max Size of Investment Considered (000s): $20,000

Geographical Preferences

United States Preferences:
All U.S.

Canadian Preferences:
All Canada

Industry Focus
(% based on actual investment)

Other Products	57.6%
Consumer Related	42.4%

Additional Information
Name of Most Recent Fund: Long Point Capital Fund II, L.P.
Most Recent Fund Was Raised: 11/17/2004
Year Founded: 1998
Capital Under Management: $145,000,000
Current Activity Level: Actively seeking new investments
Method of Compensation: Return on invest. most important, but chg. closing fees, service fees, etc.

LONG RIVER CAPITAL PARTNERS, LLC
100 Venture Way
Suite #4
Hadley, MA USA 01035
Phone: 413-587-2159
Website: www.longriverventures.com

Management and Staff
Tripp Peake, Managing Partner
William Cowen, Partner

Type of Firm
Private Equity Firm

Project Preferences

Type of Financing Preferred:
Early Stage

Size of Investments Considered:
Min Size of Investment Considered (000s): $500
Max Size of Investment Considered (000s): $5,000

Geographical Preferences

United States Preferences:
Northeast
Massachusetts

Industry Preferences

In Communications prefer:
Telecommunications

In Medical/Health prefer:
Health Services

Additional Information
Name of Most Recent Fund: Long River Ventures II, L.P.
Most Recent Fund Was Raised: 07/24/2007
Year Founded: 2000
Capital Under Management: $15,000,000
Current Activity Level: Actively seeking new investments

LONGBOAT CAPITAL MANAGEMENT LLC
139 Freeport Road
Pittsburgh, PA USA 15215
Phone: 412-782-0200
Fax: 412-782-0201
Website: www.thelongboatgroup.com

Management and Staff
Michele DeCarlo, Chief Financial Officer

Type of Firm
Private Equity Firm

Additional Information
Year Founded: 2002
Capital Under Management: $75,700,000
Current Activity Level: Actively seeking new investments

LONGBOW CAPITAL
25 Watling Street
London, United Kingdom EC4M 9BR
Phone: 44-207-332-0320
E-mail: info@longbow.co.uk
Website: www.longbow.co.uk

Other Offices
6a Hope Street
Edinburgh, United Kingdom EH2 4DB
Phone: 44-131-226-3100
Management and Staff
Bill Husselby, Partner
Charles Crick, Partner
Colin Bothway, Co-Founder
Edward Beckett, Managing Partner
Edward Rudd, Co-Founder
Gilmour Thom, Partner

Keith Powell, Partner
Kevin Doyle, Co-Founder
Nicholas Lyons, Partner
Nigel Rudd, Partner
Robin Finlayson, Managing Partner
Ron Petersen, Co-Founder

Type of Firm

Private Equity Firm

Project Preferences

Type of Financing Preferred:

Early Stage
Balanced

Geographical Preferences

International Preferences:

Europe

Industry Preferences

In Medical/Health prefer:

Medical/Health
Health Services

Additional Information

Year Founded: 2004
Capital Under Management: $19,900,000
Current Activity Level: Actively seeking new investments

LONGITUDE CAPITAL MANAGEMENT COMPANY LLC

800 El Camino Real
Suite 220
Menlo Park, CA USA 94025
Phone: 650-854-5700
Fax: 650-854-5705
E-mail: info@longitudecapital.com
Website: www.longitudecapital.com

Management and Staff

David Hirsch, Principal
Douglas Foster, Principal
Jeffrey Gold, Venture Partner
Juliet Bakker, Managing Director
Marc-Henri Galletti, Managing Director
Patrick Enright, Managing Director

Type of Firm

Private Equity Firm

Project Preferences

Type of Financing Preferred:

Balanced

Size of Investments Considered:

Min Size of Investment Considered (000s): $10,000
Max Size of Investment Considered (000s): $30,000

Geographical Preferences

United States Preferences:

All U.S.

Industry Preferences

In Biotechnology prefer:

Biotechnology

In Medical/Health prefer:

Medical Products
Health Services
Pharmaceuticals

Additional Information

Name of Most Recent Fund: Longitude Venture Partners, L.P.
Most Recent Fund Was Raised: 11/19/2007
Year Founded: 2007
Capital Under Management: $325,000,000
Current Activity Level: Actively seeking new investments

LONGREACH GROUP, LTD., THE

1-7 Kojimachi, Chiyoda-ku
Sogo Hanzomon Building 10/F
Tokyo, Japan 102-0083
Phone: 81-3-3556-6740
Fax: 81-3-3556-6739
E-mail: investor-relations@longreachgroup.com
Website: www.longreachgroup.com

Other Offices

18/F, Bund Center
222 Yan An East Road
Shanghai, China 200002
Phone: 86-21-6122-1015
Fax: 86-21-6122-2418

Suite 1004 ICBC Tower
3 Garden Road
Central, Hong Kong
Phone: 852-3175-1700
Fax: 852-3175-1727

Management and Staff

Masamichi Yoshizawa, Partner
Simon Yim, Partner
Tomoya Sugimoto, Partner
Wendy Kok, Chief Financial Officer
Yasuyuki Miyoshi, Partner

Type of Firm

Private Equity Firm

Project Preferences

Type of Financing Preferred:

Leveraged Buyout
Management Buyouts
Acquisition

Size of Investments Considered:

Min Size of Investment Considered (000s): $30,000
Max Size of Investment Considered (000s): $200,000

Geographical Preferences

International Preferences:

Taiwan
China
Korea, South
Asia
Japan

Industry Preferences

In Consumer Related prefer:

Consumer

In Industrial/Energy prefer:

Industrial Products

In Financial Services prefer:

Financial Services

In Business Serv. prefer:

Services

Additional Information

Year Founded: 2003
Capital Under Management: $750,000,000
Current Activity Level: Actively seeking new investments

LONGSTREET PARTNERS, LLC

8270 Greensboro Drive
Suite 1050
McLean, VA USA 22102
Phone: 703-584-8907
Fax: 703-584-8378
Website: www.longstreetpartners.com

Management and Staff

Dan Moore, Managing Partner
Jack Larmer, Partner

Type of Firm

Bank Affiliated

Project Preferences

Role in Financing:

Prefer role as deal originator but will also invest in deals created by others

Type of Financing Preferred:

Early Stage
Expansion
Acquisition

Size of Investments Considered:

Min Size of Investment Considered (000s): $500
Max Size of Investment Considered (000s): $2,000

Geographical Preferences

United States Preferences:

Virginia
D. of Columbia

Industry Preferences

In Communications prefer:
Telecommunications
Wireless Communications
Data Communications

Additional Information
Year Founded: 2001
Capital Under Management: $8,000,000
Current Activity Level: Actively seeking new investments

LONGWORTH VENTURE PARTNERS, L.P.
1050 Winter Street
Suite 2600
Waltham, MA USA 02451
Phone: 781-663-3600
Fax: 781-663-3619
E-mail: businessplans@longworth.com
Website: www.longworth.com

Management and Staff
James Savage, Partner
Nilanjana Bhowmik, Partner
Paul Margolis, Partner
Peter Roberts, Partner

Type of Firm
Private Equity Firm

Association Membership
Mid-Atlantic Venture Association
Natl Assoc of Small Bus. Inv. Co (NASBIC)

Project Preferences

Role in Financing:
Will function either as deal originator or investor in deals created by others

Type of Financing Preferred:
Second Stage Financing
Early Stage
Start-up Financing
Seed
First Stage Financing
Private Placement
Recapitalizations

Size of Investments Considered:
Min Size of Investment Considered (000s): $500
Max Size of Investment Considered (000s): $5,000

Geographical Preferences

United States Preferences:
Mid Atlantic
Midwest
Southeast
Northeast
East Coast

Industry Preferences

In Communications prefer:
Telecommunications
Media and Entertainment

In Computer Hardware prefer:
Computer Graphics and Dig

In Computer Software prefer:
Computer Services
Data Processing
Software
Systems Software
Applications Software
Artificial Intelligence

In Internet Specific prefer:
E-Commerce Technology
Internet
Ecommerce
Web Aggregration/Portals

In Financial Services prefer:
Financial Services

In Business Serv. prefer:
Media

Additional Information
Name of Most Recent Fund: Longworth Venture Partners III, L.P.
Most Recent Fund Was Raised: 08/03/2009
Year Founded: 1999
Capital Under Management: $139,000,000
Current Activity Level: Actively seeking new investments
Method of Compensation: Return on investment is of primary concern, do not charge fees

---

LOUDWATER INVESTMENT PARTNERS, LTD.
Little Tufton House
Three Dean Trench Street
London, United Kingdom SW1P 3HB
Phone: 44-20-3372-6400
Fax: 44-20-7222-2991
Website: www.loudwaterpartners.com

Other Offices
600 Montgomery Street
San Francisco, CA USA 94111
Phone: 415-249-6337

Management and Staff
Edward Forwood, Managing Director

Type of Firm
Private Equity Firm

Association Membership
British Venture Capital Association (BVCA)

Project Preferences

Type of Financing Preferred:
Balanced

Geographical Preferences

International Preferences:
United Kingdom

Additional Information
Year Founded: 2007
Current Activity Level: Actively seeking new investments

LOVELL MINNICK PARTNERS LLC
2141 Rosecrans Avenue
Suite 5150
El Segundo, CA USA 90245
Phone: 310-414-6160
Fax: 310-607-9942
E-mail: info@lovellminnick.com
Website: www.lovellminnick.com

Other Offices
150 North Radnor Chester Road
F110
Radnor, PA USA 19087
Phone: 610-995-9660
Fax: 610-995-9680

Management and Staff
Daniel Kang, Principal
James Minnick, Managing Director
Jennings Newcom, Managing Director
John Cochran, Principal
Robert Belke, Managing Director
Spencer Hoffman, Principal

Type of Firm
Private Equity Firm

Project Preferences

Role in Financing:
Prefer role as deal originator but will also invest in deals created by others

Type of Financing Preferred:
Control-block Purchases
Leveraged Buyout
Expansion
Generalist PE
Later Stage
Management Buyouts
Acquisition
Industry Rollups
Recapitalizations

Size of Investments Considered:
Min Size of Investment Considered (000s): $10,000
Max Size of Investment Considered (000s): $100,000

Geographical Preferences

United States Preferences:
All U.S.

Canadian Preferences:
All Canada

International Preferences:
United Kingdom
Bermuda

Industry Preferences

In Financial Services prefer:
Financial Services
Insurance
Investment Groups

In Business Serv. prefer:
Consulting Services

Additional Information

Year Founded: 1999
Capital Under Management: $700,000,000
Current Activity Level: Actively seeking new investments
Method of Compensation: Return on invest. most important, but chg. closing fees, service fees, etc.

LOVETT MILLER & CO. INCORPORATED

One Independent Square
Suite 1600
Jacksonville, FL USA 32202
Phone: 904-634-0077
Fax: 904-634-0633
E-mail: info@lovettmiller.com
Website: www.lovettmiller.com

Other Offices

100 North Tampa Street
Suite 2675
Tampa, FL USA 33602
Phone: 813-222-1477
Fax: 813-222-1478

Management and Staff

David Smoley, Vice President

Type of Firm

Private Equity Firm

Association Membership

Mid-Atlantic Venture Association

Project Preferences

Type of Financing Preferred:
Leveraged Buyout
Early Stage
Mezzanine
Later Stage
Seed
Startup

Size of Investments Considered:
Min Size of Investment Considered (000s): $2,000
Max Size of Investment Considered (000s): $10,000

Geographical Preferences

United States Preferences:
All U.S.

Industry Focus

(% based on actual investment)	
Computer Software and Services	42.7%
Internet Specific	22.8%
Medical/Health	19.2%
Communications and Media	7.7%
Consumer Related	6.5%
Other Products	1.1%

Additional Information

Name of Most Recent Fund: Lovett Miller Venture Fund III, LP
Most Recent Fund Was Raised: 03/10/2000
Year Founded: 1997
Capital Under Management: $175,000,000
Current Activity Level: Actively seeking new investments

LOW CARBON ACCELERATOR

Ogier House, St. Julian's Ave.
Saint Peter Port
Guernsey, United Kingdom GY1 1WA
E-mail: info@lowcarbonaccelerator.com
Website: www.lowcarbonaccelerator.com

Management and Staff

Andrew Newman, Chief Financial Officer
Mark Shorrock, Chief Executive Officer

Type of Firm

Private Equity Firm

Project Preferences

Type of Financing Preferred:
Balanced

Size of Investments Considered:
Min Size of Investment Considered (000s): $3,924
Max Size of Investment Considered (000s): $9,811

Geographical Preferences

International Preferences:
United Kingdom

Industry Preferences

In Industrial/Energy prefer:
Energy
Alternative Energy
Environmental Related

Additional Information

Year Founded: 2006
Current Activity Level: Actively seeking new investments

LOWER VOLGA RIVER MANAGEMENT INC.

Bolshoy Afanasievsky Perlevlok
Building 8/3, 3rd Floor
Moscow, Russia 121019
Phone: 7-95-234-3095
Fax: 7-95-234-3099

Other Offices

Rockefeller Center
630 5th Avenue, 16th Floor
New York, NY USA
Phone: 1-212-332-5100
Fax: 1-212-332-5120

Management and Staff

Evgeney Gorkov, Managing Director

Type of Firm

Government Affiliated Program

Association Membership

Russian Venture Capital Association (RVCA)

Project Preferences

Type of Financing Preferred:
Balanced

Size of Investments Considered:
Min Size of Investment Considered (000s): $300
Max Size of Investment Considered (000s): $3,000

Geographical Preferences

International Preferences:
Russia

Additional Information

Year Founded: 2000
Capital Under Management: $40,000,000
Current Activity Level: Actively seeking new investments

LOWLAND CAPITAL PARTNERS BV (AKA: LCP)

Koningslaan 24
Bussum, Netherlands 1405 GM
Phone: 31-65-580-2070
E-mail: info@lowlandcapital.com
Website: www.lowlandcapital.com

Type of Firm

Private Equity Firm

Project Preferences

Type of Financing Preferred:
Early Stage
Expansion
Balanced

Size of Investments Considered:
Min Size of Investment Considered (000s): $1,273

Max Size of Investment Considered (000s): $6,366

Geographical Preferences

International Preferences:
Netherlands
Europe

Industry Preferences

In Communications prefer:
Telecommunications
Media and Entertainment

Additional Information

Year Founded: 2003
Current Activity Level: Actively seeking new investments

LOXKO VENTURE MANAGERS, LTD.

22 Henrietta Street
London, United Kingdom WC2E 8ND
Phone: 44-207-240-5024
Fax: 44-20-7420 3993
E-mail: enquiries@loxco.com

Management and Staff

Reg Clark, Chief Executive Officer

Type of Firm

Private Equity Firm

Association Membership

British Venture Capital Association (BVCA)

Project Preferences

Type of Financing Preferred:
Leveraged Buyout
Expansion
Turnaround

Geographical Preferences

International Preferences:
United Kingdom

Additional Information

Year Founded: 1998
Capital Under Management: $4,000,000
Current Activity Level: Actively seeking new investments

LRG CAPITAL GROUP (FKA: BAYSTAR CAPITAL, LLC)

80 East Sir Francis Drake Blvd
Suite 2B
Larkspur, CA USA 94939
Phone: 415-834-4600
Fax: 415-834-4601
E-mail: info@lrgcapital.com
Website: www.lrgcapital.com

Other Offices

717 Fifth Avenue
18th Floor
New York, NY USA 10021
Phone: 212-705-5000
Fax: 212-705-5001

18851 Northeast 29th Avenue
Suite 500
Aventura, FL USA 33180
Phone: 786-528-1418
Fax: 786-787-0346

Management and Staff

Heather Ross, Managing Director
Lawrence Goldfarb, Managing Partner
Mike Randall, Managing Director
Paul Enderle, Managing Director

Type of Firm

Private Equity Firm

Project Preferences

Type of Financing Preferred:
Expansion
Mezzanine
Generalist PE
Early Stage
Public Companies

Geographical Preferences

United States Preferences:
All U.S.

Industry Preferences

In Communications prefer:
Telecommunications
Wireless Communications

In Internet Specific prefer:
Internet

In Consumer Related prefer:
Consumer Services
Other Restaurants

In Business Serv. prefer:
Media

Additional Information

Year Founded: 1998
Capital Under Management: $24,700,000
Current Activity Level: Actively seeking new investments

LRM INVESTERINGS-MAATSCHAPPIJ VOOR LIMBURG

Kempische Steenweg 555
Hasselt, Belgium 3500
Phone: 32-11-246-831
Fax: 32-11-246-850
E-mail: lrm@lrm.be
Website: www.lrm.be

Type of Firm

Government Affiliated Program

Association Membership

European Private Equity and Venture Capital Assoc.
Indian Venture Capital Association (IVCA)

Project Preferences

Type of Financing Preferred:
Leveraged Buyout
Early Stage
Expansion
Mezzanine
Start-up Financing
Management Buyouts
Recapitalizations

Size of Investments Considered:
Min Size of Investment Considered (000s): $188
Max Size of Investment Considered (000s): $9,416

Geographical Preferences

International Preferences:
Europe
Belgium

Industry Preferences

In Industrial/Energy prefer:
Industrial Products

In Business Serv. prefer:
Services

Additional Information

Year Founded: 1993
Capital Under Management: $105,700,000
Current Activity Level: Actively seeking new investments

LRP CAPITAL GMBH

Fort Malakoff Park
Rheinstrasse 4i
Mainz, Germany 55116
Phone: 49-6131-9070030
Fax: 49-6131-9070060
E-mail: info@lrp-capital.de
Website: www.lrp-capital.de

Management and Staff

Peter A. Hallerberg, Chief Executive Officer

Type of Firm

Bank Affiliated

Project Preferences

Type of Financing Preferred:
Expansion
Other
Management Buyouts
Recapitalizations

Geographical Preferences

International Preferences:
Germany

Additional Information

Year Founded: 2005
Current Activity Level: Actively seeking new investments

LS VENTURE CAPITAL, INC. (FKA: IWITH VENTURE CAPITAL, INC.)

63 Korea Life Building
Youngdeungpo-gu
Seoul, South Korea 150-763
Phone: 822-3452-0606
Fax: 822-3452-3050

Other Offices

302 Yookeui Bldg., 376-14
Seokyo-dong, Mapo-ku
Seoul, South Korea

Type of Firm

Private Equity Firm

Project Preferences

Type of Financing Preferred:
Balanced

Geographical Preferences

International Preferences:
Korea, South

Industry Preferences

In Biotechnology prefer:
Biotechnology

Additional Information

Year Founded: 1998
Capital Under Management: $16,500,000
Current Activity Level: Actively seeking new investments

LTG DEVELOPMENT CAPITAL LTD

Chelsea House
West Gate
London, United Kingdom W5 1DR
Phone: 44-20-8991-4577
Fax: 44-20-8991-4572
E-mail: info@ltgdevcap.com
Website: www.ltgdevelopmentgroup.co.uk

Type of Firm

Bank Affiliated

Association Membership

British Venture Capital Association (BVCA)

Project Preferences

Type of Financing Preferred:
Second Stage Financing
Leveraged Buyout
Early Stage
Expansion
Balanced

Size of Investments Considered:
Min Size of Investment Considered (000s): $391
Max Size of Investment Considered (000s): $1,565

Geographical Preferences

International Preferences:
Ireland
United Kingdom
Israel

Industry Preferences

In Communications prefer:
Communications and Media

In Computer Software prefer:
Software

In Computer Other prefer:
Computer Related

In Semiconductor/Electr prefer:
Electronics

In Biotechnology prefer:
Biotechnology

In Medical/Health prefer:
Medical/Health

In Consumer Related prefer:
Consumer

In Industrial/Energy prefer:
Industrial Products

In Financial Services prefer:
Financial Services

In Business Serv. prefer:
Media

Additional Information

Year Founded: 1998
Capital Under Management: $23,500,000
Current Activity Level: Actively seeking new investments

LTI INVESTMENTS

1002 Daechi-dong, Gangam-gu
806 Kosmo Tower
Seoul, South Korea 135-280
Phone: 822-562-9560
Fax: 822-562-9561

Management and Staff

HS Richard Chough, Chief Executive Officer

Type of Firm

Private Equity Firm

Project Preferences

Type of Financing Preferred:
Balanced

Additional Information

Year Founded: 2008
Current Activity Level: Actively seeking new investments

LUCOR HOLDINGS

5111 Ocean Boulevard
Suite J
Sarasota, FL USA 34242
Phone: 941-349-9200
Fax: 941-349-9210

Type of Firm

Private Equity Firm

Additional Information

Year Founded: 2002
Current Activity Level: Actively seeking new investments

LUDGATE INVESTMENTS, LTD.

46 Cannon Street
London, United Kingdom EC4N 6JJ
Phone: 44-20-7236-0973
Fax: 44-20-7329-2100
E-mail: info@ludgate.com
Website: www.ludgate.com

Type of Firm

Private Equity Firm

Association Membership

British Venture Capital Association (BVCA)

Project Preferences

Type of Financing Preferred:
Expansion
Balanced

Geographical Preferences

International Preferences:
United Kingdom

Industry Preferences

In Industrial/Energy prefer:
Energy
Alternative Energy
Energy Conservation Relat
Environmental Related

Additional Information

Name of Most Recent Fund: Ludgate 181 (Jersey) Limited
Most Recent Fund Was Raised: 06/30/2000

Year Founded: 2000
Capital Under Management: $53,300,000
Current Activity Level: Actively seeking new investments

LUMIRA CAPITAL CORPORATION.

20 Bay Street, 11th Floor
Suite 303
Toronto, Canada M5J 2N8
Phone: 416-213-4223
Fax: 416-213-4232
Website: www.lumiracapital.com

Other Offices

245 First Street
Suite 1800
Cambridge, MA USA 02142
Phone: 617-444-8550
Fax: 253-484-4262

435 Tasso Street
Suite 315
Palo Alto, CA USA 94301
Phone: 650-617-0530
Fax: 650-327-7358

1550 Metcalfe Street
Suite 502
Montreal, Canada H3A 1X6
Phone: 514-844-3637
Fax: 514-844-5607

Management and Staff

Benjamin Rovinski, Managing Director
Brian Underdown, Managing Director
Daniel Hetu, Venture Partner
Gerry Brunk, Managing Director
Nandini Tandon, Managing Director
Stephen Cummings, Chief Financial Officer

Type of Firm

Private Equity Firm

Association Membership

National Venture Capital Association - USA (NVCA)

Project Preferences

Role in Financing:
Will function either as deal originator or investor in deals created by others

Type of Financing Preferred:
Early Stage
Expansion
Mezzanine
Balanced
Later Stage
Seed
Startup

Size of Investments Considered:
Min Size of Investment Considered (000s): $500
Max Size of Investment Considered (000s): $5,000

Geographical Preferences

United States Preferences:
All U.S.

Canadian Preferences:
All Canada

Industry Focus

(% based on actual investment)

Biotechnology	52.1%
Medical/Health	29.9%
Internet Specific	12.8%
Computer Software and Services	3.4%
Communications and Media	1.3%
Semiconductors/Other Elect.	0.6%

Additional Information

Name of Most Recent Fund: Lumira Life Science Technology Fund II
Most Recent Fund Was Raised: 06/14/2002
Year Founded: 1988
Capital Under Management: $1,000,000,000
Current Activity Level: Actively seeking new investments
Method of Compensation: Return on investment is of primary concern, do not charge fees

LUMIS PARTNERS

9B, Marble Arch
Prithviraj Road, B3, 2nd Floor
New Delhi, India 110011
Phone: 91-11-4240-3311
Fax: 91-11-4240-3300
E-mail: contact@lumispartners.com
Website: www.lumispartners.com

Other Offices

122, Maker Chamber III
12th Floor, Nariman Point
Mumbai, India 400021
Phone: 91-22-6610-0880
Fax: 91-22-2285-2912

Management and Staff

Lalit Aggarwal, Chief Financial Officer

Type of Firm

Private Equity Firm

Project Preferences

Type of Financing Preferred:
Generalist PE
Public Companies
Management Buyouts
Acquisition

Geographical Preferences

International Preferences:
India

Industry Preferences

In Medical/Health prefer:
Health Services

In Consumer Related prefer:
Education Related

In Business Serv. prefer:
Services

Additional Information

Year Founded: 2009
Current Activity Level: Actively seeking new investments

LUMITEC

Ideon Research Park
Alfahuset
Lund, Sweden 223 70
Phone: 46-46-286-2900
Fax: 46-46-286-8507
E-mail: info@lumitec.se
Website: www.lumitec.se

Type of Firm

Private Equity Firm

Project Preferences

Type of Financing Preferred:
Balanced

Geographical Preferences

International Preferences:
Sweden
Europe

Additional Information

Year Founded: 2003
Current Activity Level: Actively seeking new investments

LUNAR GROUP (AKA: LUNAR CAPITAL MANAGEMENT)

10 Pottinger Street
18th Floor
Central, Hong Kong
Phone: 852-2167-7280
Fax: 852-2167-7281
E-mail: admin@lunarcap.com
Website: www.lunarcap.com

Other Offices

185 South Wulumqi Road
2nd Floor
Shanghai, China
Phone: 86-21-3100-3630
Fax: 86-21-3100-3650

Management and Staff

Hajie Wu, Partner
Patrick Benzie, Co-Founder
Sulger Benzie, Co-Founder

Type of Firm

Private Equity Firm

Project Preferences

Type of Financing Preferred:
Balanced
Seed
Startup

Geographical Preferences

International Preferences:
China

Industry Preferences

In Consumer Related prefer:
Consumer

In Manufact. prefer:
Manufacturing

Additional Information

Year Founded: 1999
Current Activity Level: Actively seeking new investments

LUND UNIVERSITY BIOSCIENCE AB

Ideon
Alfa 5
Lund, Sweden SE-22370
Phone: 46-46-286-4820
E-mail: info@lubio.se
Website: www.lubio.se

Management and Staff

Per-Ola Forsberg, Chief Financial Officer
Thomas Andersson, Chief Executive Officer

Type of Firm

University Program

Project Preferences

Type of Financing Preferred:
Balanced

Geographical Preferences

International Preferences:
Sweden

Additional Information

Year Founded: 2009
Current Activity Level: Actively seeking new investments

LUNOVA AB

Aurorum 2
Lulea, Sweden 977 75
Phone: 46-920-75-915
Fax: 46-920-75-916
E-mail: info@lunova.se
Website: www.lunova.se

Management and Staff

Stefan Lundblom, Chief Executive Officer

Type of Firm

Private Equity Firm

Association Membership

Swedish Venture Capital Association (SVCA)

Project Preferences

Type of Financing Preferred:
Balanced

Geographical Preferences

International Preferences:
Sweden
Europe

Additional Information

Year Founded: 2003
Capital Under Management: $4,200,000
Current Activity Level: Actively seeking new investments

LUX CAPITAL

295 Madison Avenue
24th Floor
New York, NY USA 10167
Phone: 646-475-4385
Fax: 646-349-2960
E-mail: info@luxcapital.com
Website: www.luxcapital.com

Management and Staff

David Sinclair, Partner
Jim Sharpe, Managing Partner
Josh Wolfe, Managing Partner
Peter Hebert, Managing Partner
Rob Paull, Managing Partner

Type of Firm

Private Equity Firm

Project Preferences

Type of Financing Preferred:
Early Stage
Balanced
Startup

Industry Preferences

In Communications prefer:
Communications and Media

In Computer Software prefer:
Software

Additional Information

Year Founded: 2000
Capital Under Management: $37,400,000
Current Activity Level: Actively seeking new investments

LYCEUM CAPITAL (FKA: WEST PRIVATE EQUITY, LTD.)

Burleigh House
357 Strand
London, United Kingdom WC2R 0HS
Phone: 44-20-7632-2480
Fax: 44-20-7836-3138
E-mail: info@lyceumcapital.co.uk
Website: www.lyceumcapital.co.uk

Management and Staff

Andrew Aylwin, Partner
Andy Wilson, Partner
Bill McCall, Partner
Daniel Adler, Partner
Jeremy Hand, Managing Partner
Keith Jelley, Partner
Mark Glatman, Partner
Peter Augherson, Partner
Philip Buscombe, Chief Executive Officer
Ron Elder, Partner
Simon Hitchcock, Partner

Type of Firm

Private Equity Firm

Association Membership

British Venture Capital Association (BVCA)
European Private Equity and Venture Capital Assoc.

Project Preferences

Type of Financing Preferred:
Leveraged Buyout
Expansion
Turnaround
Management Buyouts
Recapitalizations

Size of Investments Considered:
Min Size of Investment Considered (000s): $20,000
Max Size of Investment Considered (000s): $100,000

Geographical Preferences

International Preferences:
United Kingdom
Western Europe

Industry Focus

(% based on actual investment)

Medical/Health	37.4%
Computer Software and Services	33.0%
Consumer Related	29.6%

Additional Information

Name of Most Recent Fund: West Private Equity Fund 2000
Most Recent Fund Was Raised: 07/28/1999
Year Founded: 1999
Capital Under Management: $353,900,000
Current Activity Level: Actively seeking new investments

LYDIAN CAPITAL ADVISORS S.A.

Rue du Rhone 63
Geneva, Switzerland 1204
Phone: 41-22-7187000
Fax: 41-22-7187001
E-mail: info@lydiancapitaladv.com
Website: www.lydiancapitaladv.com

Management and Staff

Denis Brosnan, Founder
Jacques Frehner, Vice President
Mark Benn, Chief Executive Officer

Type of Firm

Private Equity Firm

Project Preferences

Type of Financing Preferred:
Balanced

Size of Investments Considered:
Min Size of Investment Considered (000s): $11,835
Max Size of Investment Considered (000s): $59,175

Geographical Preferences

International Preferences:
Europe
Eastern Europe

Industry Preferences

In Medical/Health prefer:
Medical/Health

Additional Information

Year Founded: 2005
Current Activity Level: Actively seeking new investments

LYRIQUE SARL

Route de Morges 36
St-Prex, Switzerland 1162
Phone: 41-21-806-2614
Fax: 41-21-806-2972
E-mail: info@lyrique.com
Website: www.lyrique.com

Management and Staff

Hans Van Swaay, Partner

Type of Firm

Private Equity Firm

Project Preferences

Type of Financing Preferred:
Fund of Funds
Generalist PE
Recapitalizations

Geographical Preferences

United States Preferences:
All U.S.

International Preferences:
Switzerland
Europe
Germany
Asia
France

Industry Preferences

In Medical/Health prefer:
Medical/Health

Additional Information

Year Founded: 1987
Current Activity Level: Actively seeking new investments

- M -

M SHARIE LLC

Enoc Bldg No.1, 3/F, Bur Dubai
P.O. Box 28171
Dubai, Utd. Arab Em.
Phone: 971-4-337-9333
Fax: 971-4-334-7003
E-mail: info@msharie.com
Website: www.msharie.com

Management and Staff

Abdul Aziz Serkal, Managing Director

Type of Firm

Bank Affiliated

Project Preferences

Type of Financing Preferred:
Leveraged Buyout
Acquisition

Geographical Preferences

International Preferences:
Utd. Arab Em.
Middle East

Industry Preferences

In Business Serv. prefer:
Services

In Manufact. prefer:
Manufacturing

Additional Information

Year Founded: 1998
Current Activity Level: Actively seeking new investments

M&A CAPITAL, LTD.

Kelenhegyi ut 43
Budapest, Hungary 1118
Phone: 36-1-361-5187
Fax: 36-1-361-5190
Website: www.mandaltd.com

Type of Firm

Bank Affiliated

Additional Information

Current Activity Level: Actively seeking new investments

M-CAPITAL S.A.

c/Puerta del Mar, 20
Malaga, Spain 29005
Phone: 34-95-222-2704
Fax: 34-95-222-6304

E-mail: capitalinversion@mcapital.es
Website: www.mcapital.es

Type of Firm

Private Equity Firm

Association Membership

Spanish Venture Capital Association (ASCRI)

Project Preferences

Type of Financing Preferred:
Expansion

Geographical Preferences

International Preferences:
Europe
Western Europe
Spain

Industry Preferences

In Communications prefer:
Communications and Media

In Financial Services prefer:
Financial Services

In Business Serv. prefer:
Consulting Services

In Agr/Forestr/Fish prefer:
Agriculture related

Additional Information

Year Founded: 2004
Current Activity Level: Actively seeking new investments

M-VENTURE INVESTMENT, INC. (FKA: SHINYOUNG VENTURE CAPITAL)

25th Floor, City Air Tower
159-9 Samsung-Dong Kangnam-Gu
Seoul, South Korea 135-973
Phone: 822-6000-5533
Fax: 822-6000-5659
Website: www.m-vc.co.kr

Other Offices

No. 369 Zhaofeng World Trade Building
Jiangsu Road
Shanghai, China 200050
Phone: 86-21-6841-9495
Fax: 86-21-6841-9496

Management and Staff

Daeyup Jeon, Managing Director
Hak-Hyun Lee, Senior Managing Director
Jeong Seo Park, Chief Operating Officer
Kim Doo-Hoon, Principal
Manjun Jang, President
Sejun Jang, Vice President
Steve Zhuang, Vice President
Sunghyuk Hong, Chief Executive Officer

Type of Firm

Private Equity Firm

Association Membership

Korean Venture Capital Association (KVCA)

Project Preferences

Type of Financing Preferred:
Early Stage
Expansion
Mezzanine
Balanced

Geographical Preferences

International Preferences:
China
Korea, South

Industry Preferences

In Communications prefer:
Media and Entertainment

In Computer Software prefer:
Software

In Semiconductor/Electr prefer:
Electronics

In Consumer Related prefer:
Entertainment and Leisure

In Industrial/Energy prefer:
Materials

In Manufact. prefer:
Manufacturing

Additional Information

Year Founded: 1986
Capital Under Management: $60,900,000
Current Activity Level: Actively seeking new investments

M.P.S. MERCHANT SPA- DUCATO GESTIONI SGR P.A.

Viale Mazzini 46
Firenze, Italy
Phone: 39-55-249-8548
E-mail: info@ducatogestioni.it
Website: www.ducatogestioni.it

Type of Firm

Private Equity Firm

Project Preferences

Type of Financing Preferred:
Balanced

Additional Information

Year Founded: 2007
Current Activity Level: Actively seeking new investments

M/C VENTURE PARTNERS

75 State Street
Suite 2500
Boston, MA USA 02109
Phone: 617-345-7200
Fax: 617-345-7201
E-mail: research@mcventurepartners.com
Website: www.mcventurepartners.com

Other Offices

Charles House
18b Charles Street
London, United Kingdom W1J 5DU
Phone: 44-20-7667-6838
Fax: 44-20-7667-6665

235 Pine Street
Suite 165
San Francisco, CA USA 94104
Phone: 415-438-4875
Fax: 415-296-8901

Management and Staff

Andrin Bachmann, Venture Partner
Brian Clark, General Partner
David Croll, Managing General Partner
David Ingraham, Vice President
Edmund Kim, Vice President
Edward Keefe, Chief Financial Officer
Gillis Cashman, General Partner
James Wade, Managing General Partner
John Watkins, Managing General Partner
John Van Hooser, General Partner
Matthew Rubins, General Partner
Robert Savignol, Partner
Salvatore Tirabassi, Partner

Type of Firm

Private Equity Firm

Association Membership

Natl Assoc of Small Bus. Inv. Co (NASBIC)
National Venture Capital Association - USA (NVCA)

Project Preferences

Role in Financing:
Prefer role as deal originator but will also invest in deals created by others

Type of Financing Preferred:
Leveraged Buyout
Early Stage
Expansion
Acquisition

Size of Investments Considered:
Min Size of Investment Considered (000s): $5,000
Max Size of Investment Considered (000s): $50,000

Geographical Preferences

Canadian Preferences:
All Canada

International Preferences:
United Kingdom

Industry Focus

(% based on actual investment)

Communications and Media	49.2%
Internet Specific	27.6%
Other Products	7.1%
Computer Software and Services	5.2%
Semiconductors/Other Elect.	3.9%
Consumer Related	3.9%
Computer Hardware	3.1%

Additional Information

Name of Most Recent Fund: M/C Venture Partners VI, L.P.
Most Recent Fund Was Raised: 07/31/2006
Year Founded: 1976
Capital Under Management: $1,231,000,000
Current Activity Level: Actively seeking new investments
Method of Compensation: Return on investment is of primary concern, do not charge fees

M2 CAPITAL MANAGEMENT AG

Bahnhofplatz
Zug, Switzerland 6300
Phone: 41-41-7268600
E-mail: info@m2capital.ch
Website: www.m2capital.ch

Management and Staff

Hans-Peter Koller, Managing General Partner
Patrick Sidler, Managing Partner
Peter Schiefer, Managing Partner

Type of Firm

Private Equity Firm

Project Preferences

Type of Financing Preferred:

Expansion
Later Stage
Management Buyouts

Size of Investments Considered:

Min Size of Investment Considered (000s): $2,278
Max Size of Investment Considered (000s): $15,186

Geographical Preferences

International Preferences:

Switzerland
Austria
Germany

Industry Focus

(% based on actual investment)

Other Products	100.0%

Additional Information

Year Founded: 1997
Current Activity Level: Actively seeking new investments

M2GROUP

Waanderweg 64
Emmen, Netherlands 7812 HZ
Phone: 31-591-676-009
Fax: 31-591-635-121
Website: www.m2group.nl

Management and Staff

Dick Edelstein, Founder

Type of Firm

Private Equity Firm

Project Preferences

Type of Financing Preferred:

Leveraged Buyout

Geographical Preferences

International Preferences:

Netherlands

Additional Information

Year Founded: 2008
Current Activity Level: Actively seeking new investments

M3 INVESTISSEMENTS

17 Villa Scheffer
Paris, France 75016

Type of Firm

Private Equity Firm

Additional Information

Year Founded: 2005
Current Activity Level: Actively seeking new investments

MAAYAN VENTURES

4 HaNachtom St.
Beltech Building, 5th Floor
Beer-Sheva, Israel 84249
Phone: 972-8-623-1212
Fax: 972-8-623-1246
E-mail: info@maayanventures.com
Website: www.maayanventures.com

Other Offices

3 Azrieli Center
Triangle Tower 42nd Floor
Tel Aviv, Israel 67023
Phone: 972-54-455-5219

Management and Staff

Lior Peleg, Chief Financial Officer
Tsvika Ben-Porat, Managing Director

Type of Firm

Private Equity Firm

Project Preferences

Type of Financing Preferred:

Early Stage
Balanced
Startup

Geographical Preferences

International Preferences:

Israel

Additional Information

Year Founded: 1990
Current Activity Level: Actively seeking new investments

MACANDREWS & FORBES

35 E. 62nd street
New York, NY USA 10021
Phone: 212-688-9000
Fax: 212-572-8400

Management and Staff

Ronald Perelman, Chief Executive Officer

Type of Firm

Private Equity Firm

Additional Information

Year Founded: 2009
Current Activity Level: Actively seeking new investments

MACASSA CAPITAL CORPORATION

20 Queen Street East
Suite 316
Toronto, Canada M6R 3R3

Management and Staff

James Pottow, President

Type of Firm

Private Equity Firm

Additional Information

Year Founded: 1998
Current Activity Level: Actively seeking new investments

MACH VENTURES, LP.

203 Redwood Shores Parkway
Suite 600
Redwood City, CA USA 94065
Phone: 415-987-2273
Fax: 415-358-8564
E-mail: info@machventures.com
Website: www.machventures.com

Management and Staff

Michael Laufer, General Partner

Type of Firm

Private Equity Firm

Project Preferences

Role in Financing:

Prefer role as deal originator but will also invest in deals created by others

Type of Financing Preferred:

Early Stage
Seed
First Stage Financing
Startup

Size of Investments Considered:

Min Size of Investment Considered (000s): $50
Max Size of Investment Considered (000s): $5,000

Geographical Preferences

United States Preferences:

Northern California

Industry Preferences

In Medical/Health prefer:

Medical Products

Additional Information

Year Founded: 2006
Capital Under Management: $100,000,000
Current Activity Level: Actively seeking new investments
Method of Compensation: Return on investment is of primary concern, do not charge fees

---

MACQUARIE CAPITAL ALLIANCE MANAGEMENT LTD.

GPO Box 7045
Sydney, Australia 1115
Phone: 612-8234-5050
Website: www.macquarie.com.au/mcag

Management and Staff

Michael Cook, Chief Executive Officer

Type of Firm

Bank Affiliated

Project Preferences

Type of Financing Preferred:

Balanced

Geographical Preferences

International Preferences:

Australia
All International

Additional Information

Year Founded: 2005
Capital Under Management: $764,000,000
Current Activity Level: Actively seeking new investments

MACQUARIE DIRECT INVESTMENT LTD.

No. 1 Martin Place
Sydney, Australia 2000
Phone: 612-8232-3333
Fax: 612-8232-7780
Website: www.macquarie.com.au

Management and Staff

Alan You Lee, Chief Financial Officer

Type of Firm

Bank Affiliated

Project Preferences

Role in Financing:

Prefer role as deal originator but will also invest in deals created by others

Type of Financing Preferred:

Leveraged Buyout
Mezzanine
Generalist PE
Expansion
Later Stage
Management Buyouts
Recapitalizations

Size of Investments Considered:

Min Size of Investment Considered (000s): $3,491
Max Size of Investment Considered (000s): $20,946

Geographical Preferences

International Preferences:

Australia
New Zealand

Industry Focus

(% based on actual investment)	
Consumer Related	26.2%
Other Products	22.4%
Computer Software and Services	16.3%
Industrial/Energy	13.9%
Semiconductors/Other Elect.	7.1%
Communications and Media	6.0%
Internet Specific	4.7%
Computer Hardware	3.3%

Additional Information

Name of Most Recent Fund: Macquarie Investment Trust IV
Most Recent Fund Was Raised: 01/03/2003
Year Founded: 1988
Capital Under Management: $18,700,000
Current Activity Level: Actively seeking new investments
Method of Compensation: Return on invest. most important, but chg. closing fees, service fees, etc.

MACQUARIE GROUP LIMITED

Computershare Investor Service
GPO Box 7045
Sydney, Australia NSW 1115
Phone: 617-3233-8136
Website: www.macquarie.com.au

Other Offices

100 Wellington Street West
PO Box 234, Suite 2200
Canada M5K 1J3
Phone: 416-607-5000
Fax: 416-607-5051

Type of Firm

Private Equity Firm

Additional Information

Year Founded: 2003
Current Activity Level: Actively seeking new investments

MACQUARIE INVESTMENT MANAGEMENT, LTD. (AKA: MIML)

Level 27
20 Bond Street
Sydney, Australia 2000
Phone: 612-8232-8195
Website: www.macquarie.com.au

Other Offices

Moor House
L1 120 London Wall
London, United Kingdom EC2Y 5ET
Phone: 44-20-3037-4221

Ocean Ridge, 5796 Armada Drive
Suite 150
Carlsbad, CA USA 92008
Phone: 760-688-3811

Level 18, One International Finance Ctr.
1 Harbour View Street
Central, Hong Kong
Phone: 852-3922-1888
Fax: 852-3922-1889

Type of Firm

Bank Affiliated

Project Preferences

Role in Financing:

Prefer role as deal originator but will also invest in deals created by others

Type of Financing Preferred:

Fund of Funds
Leveraged Buyout
Early Stage

Expansion
Mezzanine
Research and Development
Balanced
Management Buyouts

Geographical Preferences

International Preferences:
Western Europe
Pacific
Australia
New Zealand
Asia

Industry Focus

(% based on actual investment)

Other Products	99.0%
Communications and Media	1.0%

Additional Information

Year Founded: 1980
Capital Under Management: $99,000,000
Current Activity Level: Actively seeking new investments
Method of Compensation: Return on investment is of primary concern, do not charge fees

---

MACQUARIE S INFRASTRUCTURE AND SPECIALISED FUNDS DIVISION

CityPoint
One Ropemaker Street
London, United Kingdom EC2Y 9HD
Phone: 44-207-065-2016
Fax: 44-207-065-2041
E-mail: ISFeurope@macquarie.com
Website: www.macquarie.com/eu/infra/index.htm

Type of Firm

Bank Affiliated

Project Preferences

Type of Financing Preferred:
Leveraged Buyout
Balanced
Management Buyouts

Geographical Preferences

International Preferences:
United Kingdom
Portugal
Europe
Chile
Spain
Australia
Korea, South
Germany

Industry Preferences

In Communications prefer:
Communications and Media

In Industrial/Energy prefer:
Energy

In Transportation prefer:
Transportation

In Business Serv. prefer:
Services

In Utilities prefer:
Utilities

Additional Information

Year Founded: 1969
Current Activity Level: Actively seeking new investments

MACQUARIE SHINHAN INFRASTRUCTURE MANAGEMENT CO., LTD.

11F, Hamwha Building
110 Sokong-Dong, Chung-ku
Seoul, South Korea 100-755
Phone: 822-3705-4921
Fax: 822-3705-8585
Website: www.macquarie.com/kr/en/mkif/about.htm

Management and Staff

Alison Tliss-Davie, Chief Financial Officer

Type of Firm

Bank Affiliated

Project Preferences

Type of Financing Preferred:
Balanced
Other

Geographical Preferences

International Preferences:
Korea, South

Industry Preferences

In Business Serv. prefer:
Services

Additional Information

Year Founded: 2003
Capital Under Management: $527,300,000
Current Activity Level: Actively seeking new investments

MADAGASCAR DEVELOPMENT PARTNERS LTD

BP 503
Antananarivo 101, Madagascar
Phone: 261-3202-264-64
E-mail: mail@madapartners.com
Website: www.madapartners.com

Other Offices

8 Palace Gardens
London, United Kingdom 101
Phone: 44-20-7229-6867

Management and Staff

Geoffrey Tassinari, Chief Executive Officer
Richard Rambinintsoa, Chief Operating Officer

Type of Firm

Private Equity Advisor or Fund of Funds

Association Membership

African Venture Capital Association (AVCA)

Project Preferences

Type of Financing Preferred:
Early Stage
Expansion
Turnaround
Recapitalizations

Size of Investments Considered:
Min Size of Investment Considered (000s): $500
Max Size of Investment Considered (000s): $5,000

Geographical Preferences

International Preferences:
Seychelles
Mauritius
Comoros
Madagascar

Industry Preferences

In Communications prefer:
Telecommunications

In Consumer Related prefer:
Food/Beverage

In Financial Services prefer:
Financial Services
Insurance
Real Estate

In Agr/Forestr/Fish prefer:
Agriculture related

Additional Information

Year Founded: 2003
Capital Under Management: $10,000,000
Current Activity Level: Actively seeking new investments

MADISON CAPITAL FUNDING LLC (AKA: MADISON CAPITAL)

30 South Wacker Drive
Suite 3700
Chicago, IL USA 60606
Phone: 312-596-6900
Fax: 312-596-6950
Website: www.nylim.com/madisoncapital

Management and Staff

Christopher Williams, Managing Director
Craig Lacy, Managing Director
David Kulakofsky, Vice President
Devon Russell, Managing Director
Hugh Wade, Senior Managing Director
K. Thomas Klimmeck, Managing Director
Peter Notter, Vice President
Terry Capsay, Managing Director
Trevor Clark, Managing Director
William Kindorf, Vice President

Type of Firm

Bank Affiliated

Project Preferences

Role in Financing:

Prefer role as deal originator but will also invest in deals created by others

Type of Financing Preferred:

Leveraged Buyout
Management Buyouts
Acquisition
Recapitalizations

Size of Investments Considered:

Min Size of Investment Considered (000s): $15,000
Max Size of Investment Considered (000s): $30,000

Industry Preferences

In Business Serv. prefer:

Services
Distribution

In Manufact. prefer:

Manufacturing

Additional Information

Year Founded: 2001
Current Activity Level: Actively seeking new investments

MADISON CAPITAL PARTNERS

500 West Madison
Suite 3890
Chicago, IL USA 60661
Phone: 312-277-0156
Fax: 312-277-0163
Website: www.madisoncapitalpartners.net

Management and Staff

Alice Buechele, Vice President
Brent Campbell, Chief Financial Officer
Larry Geis, President
Scott Murray, Managing Director

Type of Firm

Private Equity Firm

Project Preferences

Role in Financing:

Prefer role as deal originator

Type of Financing Preferred:

Turnaround
Management Buyouts
Acquisition
Industry Rollups

Geographical Preferences

United States Preferences:

All U.S.

International Preferences:

Europe

Industry Focus

(% based on actual investment)

Industrial/Energy	94.7%
Consumer Related	5.3%

Additional Information

Year Founded: 1994
Current Activity Level: Actively seeking new investments
Method of Compensation: Return on invest. most important, but chg. closing fees, service fees, etc.

MADISON DEARBORN PARTNERS LLC

Three First National Plaza
Suite 4600
Chicago, IL USA 60602
Phone: 312-895-1000
Fax: 312-895-1001
E-mail: info@mdcp.com
Website: www.mdcp.com

Management and Staff

Benjamin Chereskin, Managing Director
Christopher McGowan, Managing Director
Douglas Grissom, Managing Director
Edward Magnus, Vice President
Elizabeth Betten, Vice President
George Peinado, Managing Director
James Perry, Managing Director
Mark Tresnowski, Managing Director
Michael Cole, Managing Director
Michael Wilson, Chief Financial Officer
Nicholas Alexos, Managing Director
Patrick Eilers, Managing Director
Richard Copans, Vice President
Rick Desai, Principal
Robin Selati, Managing Director
Thomas Souleles, Managing Director
Thomas Macejko, Vice President
Timothy Sullivan, Managing Director
Timothy Hurd, Managing Director
Zaid Alsikafi, Vice President

Type of Firm

Private Equity Firm

Association Membership

Illinois Venture Capital Association

Project Preferences

Role in Financing:

Prefer role as deal originator

Type of Financing Preferred:

Leveraged Buyout
Public Companies
Management Buyouts
Recapitalizations

Size of Investments Considered:

Min Size of Investment Considered (000s): $100,000
Max Size of Investment Considered (000s): $600,000

Geographical Preferences

United States Preferences:

All U.S.

Canadian Preferences:

All Canada

International Preferences:

Asia

Industry Focus

(% based on actual investment)

Consumer Related	35.1%
Other Products	25.4%
Communications and Media	19.6%
Internet Specific	6.6%
Industrial/Energy	5.6%
Medical/Health	3.7%
Semiconductors/Other Elect.	3.4%
Computer Software and Services	0.4%
Computer Hardware	0.3%

Additional Information

Year Founded: 1992
Capital Under Management: $14,000,000,000
Current Activity Level: Actively seeking new investments
Method of Compensation: Return on invest. most important, but chg. closing fees, service fees, etc.

MADISON PARKER CAPITAL LLC

Seven Harcourt Street
Boston, MA USA 02116
Phone: 617-970-3804
Fax: 617-824-1186
E-mail: info@madisonparkercapital.com
Website: www.madisonparkercapital.com

Type of Firm

Private Equity Firm

Project Preferences

Type of Financing Preferred:

Leveraged Buyout
Expansion

Generalist PE
Management Buyouts
Acquisition
Recapitalizations

Size of Investments Considered:
Min Size of Investment Considered (000s): $5,000
Max Size of Investment Considered (000s): $75,000

Geographical Preferences

United States Preferences:
All U.S.

Industry Preferences

In Consumer Related prefer:
Consumer
Retail
Other Restaurants

In Business Serv. prefer:
Services

In Manufact. prefer:
Manufacturing

Additional Information
Year Founded: 2007
Current Activity Level: Actively seeking new investments

MADISON PRIVATE EQUITY HOLDING AG

Eisengasse 15
P.O. Box 272
Zurich, Switzerland 8034
Phone: 41-44-267-5000
Fax: 41-44-267-5001
E-mail: info@mpeh.ch
Website: www.mpeh.ch

Management and Staff
Bjoern Boeckenforde, Chief Financial Officer
Werner Rudolf Schnorf, Chief Executive Officer

Type of Firm
Private Equity Firm

Association Membership
Swiss Venture Capital Association (SECA)

Project Preferences

Type of Financing Preferred:
Leveraged Buyout
Turnaround
Recapitalizations

Size of Investments Considered:
Min Size of Investment Considered (000s): $6,019
Max Size of Investment Considered (000s): $24,076

Geographical Preferences

International Preferences:
Switzerland
Europe

Industry Preferences

In Consumer Related prefer:
Consumer
Consumer Products
Consumer Services

In Industrial/Energy prefer:
Industrial Products
Factory Automation

In Manufact. prefer:
Manufacturing

Additional Information
Year Founded: 2001
Current Activity Level: Actively seeking new investments

MADRIGAL PARTICIPACIONES, S.A.

Acera de Recoletos 5, 1
Valladolid, Spain 47004
Phone: 34-983-210-734
Fax: 34-983-210-493
E-mail: madrigal@madrigalparticipaciones.com
Website: www.madrigalparticipaciones.com

Type of Firm
Private Equity Firm

Project Preferences

Type of Financing Preferred:
Balanced

Geographical Preferences

International Preferences:
Europe

Additional Information
Year Founded: 2004
Current Activity Level: Actively seeking new investments

MADRONA VENTURE GROUP

1000 Second Avenue
Suite 3700
Seattle, WA USA 98104
Phone: 206-674-3000
Fax: 206-674-8703
E-mail: information@madrona.com
Website: www.madrona.com

Management and Staff
Brian McAndrews, Managing Director
Daniel Weld, Venture Partner
Greg Gottesman, Managing Director
Matt Compton, Venture Partner
Matthew McIlwain, Managing Director
Oren Etzioni, Venture Partner
Paul Goodrich, Managing Director
Scott Jacobson, Partner
Tim Porter, Partner
Tom Alberg, Managing Director

Type of Firm
Private Equity Firm

Association Membership
National Venture Capital Association - USA (NVCA)

Project Preferences

Role in Financing:
Will function either as deal originator or investor in deals created by others

Type of Financing Preferred:
Early Stage
Balanced

Size of Investments Considered:
Min Size of Investment Considered (000s): $1,000
Max Size of Investment Considered (000s): $10,000

Geographical Preferences

United States Preferences:
Northwest
West Coast
All U.S.

Industry Focus

(% based on actual investment)

Internet Specific	52.1%
Computer Software and Services	24.4%
Semiconductors/Other Elect.	11.2%
Communications and Media	6.3%
Other Products	4.1%
Computer Hardware	2.0%

Additional Information
Name of Most Recent Fund: Madrona Venture Fund IV, L.P.
Most Recent Fund Was Raised: 05/23/2008
Year Founded: 1995
Capital Under Management: $667,000,000
Current Activity Level: Actively seeking new investments
Method of Compensation: Return on investment is of primary concern, do not charge fees

MAF OF MISSISSIPPI, INC.

4109 Dogwood Drive
Jackson, MS USA 39211
Phone: 601-366-9791

Management and Staff
O.B. Walton, President

Type of Firm
Private Equity Firm

Project Preferences

Type of Financing Preferred:
Startup

Geographical Preferences

United States Preferences:
Mississippi

Additional Information

Year Founded: 2006
Capital Under Management: $1,400,000
Current Activity Level: Actively seeking new investments

MAGELLAN CAPITAL PARTNERS, LTD.

363 N. Sam Houston Parkway E.
Suite 1100
Houston, TX USA 77060
Phone: 281-405-2620
Fax: 281-405-2619
E-mail: info@magallencap.net
Website: www.magellancap.net

Management and Staff

Greg Miller, Principal
Roy Case, General Partner
Willem Timmermans, General Partner

Type of Firm

Private Equity Firm

Project Preferences

Role in Financing:
Prefer role as deal originator but will also invest in deals created by others

Type of Financing Preferred:
Leveraged Buyout
Turnaround
Acquisition

Geographical Preferences

United States Preferences:
All U.S.

Industry Preferences

In Medical/Health prefer:
Medical/Health

In Industrial/Energy prefer:
Energy

In Transportation prefer:
Aerospace

In Financial Services prefer:
Financial Services

In Manufact. prefer:
Manufacturing

Additional Information

Year Founded: 2004
Capital Under Management: $1,800,000
Current Activity Level: Actively seeking new investments

MAGHREBIA FINANCIERE

Bd. du 7 Novembre
Imm. Maghrebia Tour A
Tunis, Tunisia 1080
Phone: 216-1-704-032
Fax: 216-1-718-243
E-mail: ufi@planet.tn

Type of Firm

Private Equity Firm

Association Membership

Tunisian Venture Capital Association

Project Preferences

Type of Financing Preferred:
Balanced

Geographical Preferences

International Preferences:
Tunisia

Additional Information

Year Founded: 2004
Current Activity Level: Actively seeking new investments

MAGMA VENTURE PARTNERS (FKA: MAGNUM COMMUNICATIONS FUND)

Azrieli Center 1
35th Floor
Tel Aviv, Israel 67021
Phone: 972-3-696-7285
Fax: 972-3-695-5960
E-mail: info@magmavc.com
Website: www.magmavc.com

Management and Staff

Eitan Dekel, General Partner
Modi Rosen, Managing Partner
Yahal Zilka, Managing Partner

Type of Firm

Private Equity Firm

Project Preferences

Type of Financing Preferred:
Early Stage
Later Stage

Geographical Preferences

International Preferences:
Israel
All International

Industry Preferences

In Communications prefer:
Communications and Media

In Internet Specific prefer:
Internet

Additional Information

Year Founded: 1999
Capital Under Management: $70,000,000
Current Activity Level: Actively seeking new investments

MAGNUM CAPITAL INDUSTRIAL PARTNERS

Fortuny 14, 2
Madrid, Spain 28010
Phone: 34-91-310-6342
Fax: 34-91-319-9955
E-mail: info@magnumpartners.es
Website: www.magnumpartners.es

Other Offices

Avenida Liberdade N 249, 4
Lisbon, Portugal 1250-143
Phone: 351-213-163-730
Fax: 351-213-163-731

Management and Staff

Angel Corcostegui, General Partner
Enrique de Leyva, General Partner
Inaki Echave, Partner
Joao Talone, Partner
Joao Coelho Borges, Partner
Jose Manrique, Chief Financial Officer

Type of Firm

Private Equity Firm

Project Preferences

Type of Financing Preferred:
Leveraged Buyout

Size of Investments Considered:
Min Size of Investment Considered (000s): $66,287
Max Size of Investment Considered (000s): $198,860

Geographical Preferences

International Preferences:
Portugal
Spain

Additional Information

Year Founded: 2006
Current Activity Level: Actively seeking new investments

MAGYAR FEJLESZTESI BANK (AKA: HUNGARIAN DEVELOPMENT BANK)

Nador u. 31
Budapest, Hungary 1051
Phone: 36-1-428-1400

Fax: 36-1-428-1605
Website: www.mfb.hu

Type of Firm

Bank Affiliated

Association Membership

Hungarian Venture Capital Association (HVCA)

Project Preferences

Type of Financing Preferred:

Balanced

Geographical Preferences

International Preferences:

Hungary

Additional Information

Year Founded: 2003
Capital Under Management: $75,500,000
Current Activity Level: Actively seeking new investments

MAHON CHINA INVESTMENT MANAGEMENT, LTD.

14/F, Office Tower
Hong Kong-Macau Center
Beijing, China 100027
Phone: 86-10-65068908
Fax: 86-10-65012526
E-mail: info@mahonchina.com
Website: www.mahonchina.com

Type of Firm

Private Equity Firm

Project Preferences

Type of Financing Preferred:

Balanced

Geographical Preferences

International Preferences:

Asia

Industry Preferences

In Transportation prefer:

Transportation

In Manufact. prefer:

Manufacturing

Additional Information

Year Founded: 2007
Current Activity Level: Actively seeking new investments

MAIN CORPORATE FINANCE

Singaporestraat 76B
Linjden, Netherlands 1175 RA
Phone: 31-20-427-4242
Fax: 31-20-427-4141
Website: www.main.nl

Other Offices

Paleisstraat 6
Den Haag, Netherlands 2514 JA
Phone: 31-70-324-3433
Fax: 31-70-328-3354

Management and Staff

Charly Zwemstra, Partner
Lars Van t Hoenderdaal, Partner
Paul Zekveld, Partner

Type of Firm

Private Equity Firm

Association Membership

European Private Equity and Venture Capital Assoc.

Project Preferences

Type of Financing Preferred:

Expansion
Later Stage

Geographical Preferences

International Preferences:

Netherlands

Industry Preferences

In Communications prefer:

Media and Entertainment
Entertainment

In Consumer Related prefer:

Entertainment and Leisure

Additional Information

Name of Most Recent Fund: Main Capital
Most Recent Fund Was Raised: 12/02/2003
Year Founded: 2003
Capital Under Management: $16,500,000
Current Activity Level: Actively seeking new investments

MAIN STREET CAPITAL CORPORATION

1300 Post Oak Boulevard
Suite 800
Houston, TX USA 77056
Phone: 713-350-6000
Fax: 713-350-6042
Website: www.mainstcapital.com

Management and Staff

Curtis Hartman, Managing Director
David Magdol, Managing Director
Dwayne Hyzak, Managing Director
Todd Reppert, Senior Managing Director
Vincent Foster, Senior Managing Director

Type of Firm

Private Equity Firm

Project Preferences

Role in Financing:

Prefer role as deal originator but will also invest in deals created by others

Type of Financing Preferred:

Leveraged Buyout
Expansion
Mezzanine
Later Stage
Management Buyouts
Acquisition
Special Situation
Recapitalizations

Size of Investments Considered:

Min Size of Investment Considered (000s): $2,000
Max Size of Investment Considered (000s): $15,000

Geographical Preferences

United States Preferences:

Southeast
Southwest

Industry Preferences

In Medical/Health prefer:

Medical Products
Health Services

In Industrial/Energy prefer:

Energy
Industrial Products

In Business Serv. prefer:

Services
Distribution

In Manufact. prefer:

Manufacturing

In Utilities prefer:

Utilities

Additional Information

Year Founded: 1997
Capital Under Management: $213,000,000
Current Activity Level: Actively seeking new investments

MAIN STREET CAPITAL HOLDINGS LLC

1001 Corporate Drive
Suite 200
Canonsburg, PA USA 15317
Phone: 724-743-5650

Fax: 724-743-5654
Website: www.mainstreetcapitalholdingsllc.com

Management and Staff

Andrew Bianco, Principal
Andrew Hays, Principal
Dennis Prado, Principal
Donald Jenkins, Principal
Gerald Prado, Principal

Type of Firm

Private Equity Firm

Project Preferences

Role in Financing:

Prefer role as deal originator

Type of Financing Preferred:

Leveraged Buyout
Generalist PE
Management Buyouts
Acquisition

Size of Investments Considered:

Min Size of Investment Considered (000s): $2,000
Max Size of Investment Considered (000s): $10,000

Geographical Preferences

United States Preferences:

Mid Atlantic
Midwest
Southeast
Northeast

Industry Focus

(% based on actual investment)

Computer Software and Services	78.1%
Industrial/Energy	21.9%

Additional Information

Name of Most Recent Fund: Main Street, L.P.
Most Recent Fund Was Raised: 12/31/1995
Year Founded: 1994
Capital Under Management: $100,000,000
Current Activity Level: Actively seeking new investments
Method of Compensation: Return on invest. most important, but chg. closing fees, service fees, etc.

MAIN STREET RESOURCES (FKA: COLT CAPITAL GROUP)

Eight Wright Street
Floor 1
Westport, CT USA 06880
Phone: 203-227-5320
Fax: 203-227-5312
Website: www.mainstreet-resources.com

Management and Staff

Daniel Levinson, Founder
David Schneider, Vice President
Marshall Kiev, Partner

Type of Firm

Private Equity Firm

Project Preferences

Type of Financing Preferred:

Leveraged Buyout
Expansion
Turnaround
Management Buyouts
Startup
Acquisition

Size of Investments Considered:

Min Size of Investment Considered (000s): $2,000
Max Size of Investment Considered (000s): $10,000

Geographical Preferences

United States Preferences:

Northeast

Industry Focus

(% based on actual investment)

Other Products	100.0%

Additional Information

Name of Most Recent Fund: MSR I SBIC, L.P. (FKA: Colt Capital SBIC)
Most Recent Fund Was Raised: 09/30/2000
Year Founded: 1998
Capital Under Management: $66,000,000
Current Activity Level: Actively seeking new investments

MAINSAIL PARTNERS

200 California Street
3rd Floor
San Francisco, CA USA 94111
Phone: 415-391-3150
Fax: 415-727-4111
Website: www.mainsailpartners.com

Management and Staff

C. Jason Payne, Managing Partner
Gavin Turner, Managing Partner
Lars Ahlstrom, Chief Financial Officer
Mark Hamachek, Vice President

Type of Firm

Bank Affiliated

Project Preferences

Type of Financing Preferred:

Expansion
Management Buyouts
Acquisition

Geographical Preferences

United States Preferences:

All U.S.

Canadian Preferences:

All Canada

Industry Preferences

In Internet Specific prefer:

Internet

In Medical/Health prefer:

Health Services
Pharmaceuticals

In Consumer Related prefer:

Education Related

In Financial Services prefer:

Financial Services

In Business Serv. prefer:

Services
Distribution

In Manufact. prefer:

Manufacturing
Publishing

Additional Information

Year Founded: 2003
Capital Under Management: $160,000,000
Current Activity Level: Actively seeking new investments

MAKAIRA VENTURE PARTNERS

75 Mill Street
Stoughton, MA USA 02072
Phone: 508-539-9494
E-mail: info@makairavp.com
Website: www.makairavp.com

Management and Staff

Michael Benoit, Managing Partner
Ronald Murphy, Principal
Steven Tallarida, General Partner

Type of Firm

Private Equity Firm

Project Preferences

Type of Financing Preferred:

Early Stage
Startup

Geographical Preferences

United States Preferences:

Northeast
All U.S.

Industry Preferences

In Medical/Health prefer:

Medical/Health
Medical Products

Additional Information

Year Founded: 2009
Current Activity Level: Actively seeking new investments

MALAYSIAN TECHNOLOGY DEVELOPMENT CORP SDN BHD

Level 8-9, Menara Yayasan
Tun Razak, Jalan Bukit Bintag
Kuala Lumpur, Malaysia 55100
Phone: 603-2161-2000
Fax: 603-2163-7542
E-mail: comms@mtdc.com.my
Website: www.mtdc.com.my

Management and Staff

Affeiz Abdul Razak, Vice President
Norhalim Yunus, Chief Executive Officer
Zaidi Che Man, Vice President

Type of Firm

Government Affiliated Program

Project Preferences

Role in Financing:
Prefer role as deal originator but will also invest in deals created by others

Type of Financing Preferred:
Second Stage Financing
Expansion
Balanced
Start-up Financing
First Stage Financing

Geographical Preferences

United States Preferences:
All U.S.

International Preferences:
United Kingdom
Australia
Asia
France
Malaysia

Industry Preferences

In Communications prefer:
Commercial Communications
Satellite Microwave Comm.

In Computer Hardware prefer:
Disk Relat. Memory Device

In Semiconductor/Electr prefer:
Electronics
Electronic Components
Laser Related
Analytic/Scientific

In Biotechnology prefer:
Human Biotechnology
Agricultural/Animal Bio.
Industrial Biotechnology
Biotech Related Research

In Medical/Health prefer:
Medical Diagnostics
Diagnostic Test Products
Medical Products
Disposable Med. Products
Pharmaceuticals

In Consumer Related prefer:
Retail

In Industrial/Energy prefer:
Alternative Energy
Materials
Robotics

In Manufact. prefer:
Office Automation Equipmt
Publishing

Additional Information

Year Founded: 1992
Capital Under Management: $263,700,000
Current Activity Level: Actively seeking new investments
Method of Compensation: Return on investment is of primary concern, do not charge fees

MALAYSIAN VENTURE CAPITAL MANAGEMENT (MAVCAP)

Level 11, Menara Bank
1016 Jalan Sultan Ismail
Kuala Lumpur, Malaysia 50250
Phone: 603-2050-3000
Fax: 603-2698-3800
E-mail: enquiries@mavcap.com
Website: www.mavcap.com

Management and Staff

Husni Salleh, Chief Executive Officer
Nur Baidzurah Ali, Vice President
Rahmat Ismail, Vice President

Type of Firm

Government Affiliated Program

Project Preferences

Type of Financing Preferred:
Fund of Funds
Leveraged Buyout
Early Stage
Balanced
Turnaround
Seed
Management Buyouts
Startup

Geographical Preferences

International Preferences:
Malaysia

Industry Preferences

In Communications prefer:
Commercial Communications

In Computer Software prefer:
Software

In Computer Other prefer:
Computer Related

In Semiconductor/Electr prefer:
Electronics

In Biotechnology prefer:
Biotechnology

In Medical/Health prefer:
Health Services

In Transportation prefer:
Aerospace

Additional Information

Year Founded: 2001
Capital Under Management: $158,300,000
Current Activity Level: Actively seeking new investments

MALAYSIAN VENTURES MANAGEMENT INCORPORATED SDN BHD

15/F Bangunan Arab-Malaysian
55 Jalan Raja Chulan
Kuala Lumpur, Malaysia 50200
Phone: 603-2078-2392
Fax: 603-2072-8253
Website: www.ambg.com.my

Management and Staff

Cheah Tek Kuang, Managing Director

Type of Firm

Bank Affiliated

Project Preferences

Type of Financing Preferred:
Later Stage

Geographical Preferences

International Preferences:
Malaysia

Additional Information

Year Founded: 2006
Current Activity Level: Actively seeking new investments

MALLIN AS

PO Box 6716
St. Olavs plass
Oslo, Norway N-0130
Phone: 47-23-100-770
Fax: 47-23-100-771
E-mail: mallin@mallin.no
Website: www.mallin.no

Type of Firm

Investment Management Firm

Association Membership
Norwegian Venture Capital Association

Project Preferences

Role in Financing:
Prefer role as deal originator but will also invest in deals created by others

Type of Financing Preferred:
Second Stage Financing

Geographical Preferences

International Preferences:
Norway

Industry Preferences

In Industrial/Energy prefer:
Alternative Energy
Energy Conservation Relat
Environmental Related

Additional Information
Year Founded: 1982
Capital Under Management: $10,000,000
Current Activity Level: Actively seeking new investments
Method of Compensation: Return on investment is of primary concern, do not charge fees

---

MALMOHUS INVEST AB
Storgatan 22 A
Malmo, Sweden SE-211 42
Phone: 46-40-330-280
Fax: 46-40-611-1843
E-mail: info@mhusinvest.se
Website: www.mhusinvest.se

Management and Staff
Christian Ehrenborg, Chief Financial Officer
Hakan Nelson, Chief Executive Officer

Type of Firm
Private Equity Firm

Association Membership
Swedish Venture Capital Association (SVCA)
European Private Equity and Venture Capital Assoc.

Project Preferences

Role in Financing:
Prefer role as deal originator but will also invest in deals created by others

Type of Financing Preferred:
Second Stage Financing
Expansion
Mezzanine
Seed
First Stage Financing
Special Situation
Startup

Size of Investments Considered:
Min Size of Investment Considered (000s): $300
Max Size of Investment Considered (000s): $300,000

Geographical Preferences

International Preferences:
Sweden
Scandanavia/Nordic Region

Industry Preferences

In Communications prefer:
Telecommunications
Data Communications
Satellite Microwave Comm.

In Computer Hardware prefer:
Mini and Personal/Desktop
Computer Graphics and Dig
Disk Relat. Memory Device

In Computer Software prefer:
Systems Software
Applications Software
Artificial Intelligence

In Internet Specific prefer:
Internet

In Semiconductor/Electr prefer:
Electronic Components
Controllers and Sensors
Component Testing Equipmt
Laser Related
Fiber Optics
Analytic/Scientific

In Biotechnology prefer:
Biotechnology

In Medical/Health prefer:
Disposable Med. Products
Hospitals/Clinics/Primary
Hospital/Other Instit.

In Industrial/Energy prefer:
Energy
Industrial Products

Additional Information
Year Founded: 1979
Capital Under Management: $20,600,000
Current Activity Level: Actively seeking new investments
Method of Compensation: Return on invest. most important, but chg. closing fees, service fees, etc.

MAN AGRA CAPITAL, INC.
240 Graham Avenue
Suite 500
Winnipeg, Canada R3C 0J7
Phone: 204-925-5460
Fax: 204-925-5469
Website: www.managracapital.com

Type of Firm
Endowment, Foundation or Pension Fund

Additional Information
Year Founded: 2009
Current Activity Level: Actively seeking new investments

MANAGEMENT & CAPITALI SPA
Via dell'Orso, 6
Milan, Italy 20121
Phone: 39-2-727-371
Fax: 39-2-727-371-77
E-mail: info@management-capitali.com
Website: www.management-capitali.com

Management and Staff
Marco Viberti, Chief Financial Officer

Type of Firm
Private Equity Firm

Association Membership
Italian Venture Capital Association (AIFI)

Project Preferences

Type of Financing Preferred:
Turnaround

Geographical Preferences

International Preferences:
Italy
Europe

Additional Information
Year Founded: 2006
Capital Under Management: $699,300,000
Current Activity Level: Actively seeking new investments

MANAUS HOLDING BV
Postbus 75906
Amsterdam, Netherlands 1070 AX
Phone: 31-20-664-3111
Fax: 31-20-662-9646
E-mail: office@manaus.nl
Website: www.manaus.nl

Type of Firm
Private Equity Firm

Association Membership
Dutch Venture Capital Associaton (NVP)

Project Preferences

Type of Financing Preferred:
Leveraged Buyout
Expansion
Turnaround

Geographical Preferences

International Preferences:
Netherlands

Additional Information
Year Founded: 1993
Current Activity Level: Actively seeking new investments

MANCHESTER TECHNOLOGY FUND LTD, THE
Manchester Science Park
Lloyd Street North
Manchester, United Kingdom M15 6SE
Phone: 44-161-232-6064
Fax: 44-161-226-1001
E-mail: mail@mantechfund.com
Website: www.mantechfund.com

Management and Staff
Richard Young, Managing Director

Type of Firm
University Program

Association Membership
British Venture Capital Association (BVCA)

Project Preferences

Type of Financing Preferred:
Seed
Startup

Geographical Preferences

International Preferences:
United Kingdom

Industry Preferences

In Communications prefer:
Commercial Communications

In Computer Other prefer:
Computer Related

In Biotechnology prefer:
Biotechnology

Additional Information
Year Founded: 1999
Capital Under Management: $9,700,000
Current Activity Level: Actively seeking new investments

MANDARIN CAPITAL PARTNERS
73, Cote d'Eich
Luxembourg, Luxembourg L-1450
Phone: 352-404-546
E-mail: info.europe@mandarincp.com
Website: www.mandarincp.com

Other Offices
Kerry Center
1515 Nanjing Xi Lu
Shanghai, China 200040
Phone: 86-21-5298-6600

Via Brera 3
Milano, Italy 20121
Phone: 39-02-809-401

Management and Staff
Alberto Forchielli, Partner
Enrico Ricotta, Partner
Francesco Della Valentina, Partner
Fusheng Li, Principal
Lorenzo Stanca, Partner

Type of Firm
Private Equity Firm

Project Preferences

Type of Financing Preferred:
Leveraged Buyout
Generalist PE
Expansion
Management Buyouts
Acquisition

Size of Investments Considered:
Min Size of Investment Considered (000s): $12,719
Max Size of Investment Considered (000s): $38,158

Geographical Preferences

International Preferences:
Italy
Europe
China
Hong Kong

Industry Preferences

In Manufact. prefer:
Manufacturing

Additional Information
Year Founded: 2007
Capital Under Management: $482,600,000
Current Activity Level: Actively seeking new investments

MANDELBROT VENTURES, INC.
26610 Harmony Hills
San Antonio, TX USA 78258
Phone: 210-340-0116
Fax: 866-276-0698
Website: www.mandelbrot-ventures.com

Management and Staff
David Spencer, Chief Executive Officer

Type of Firm
Private Equity Firm

Project Preferences

Type of Financing Preferred:
Early Stage
Seed
Startup

Geographical Preferences

United States Preferences:
Texas

Additional Information
Year Founded: 2005
Current Activity Level: Actively seeking new investments

MANGROVE CAPITAL PARTNERS SA
23 Boulevard Grande Duchesse
Charlotte
Luxembourg, Luxembourg L-1331
Phone: 352-26-25-341
Fax: 352-26-253-420
Website: www.mangrove-vc.com

Other Offices
39 allee Scheffer
Luxembourg, Luxembourg 2520
Phone: 352 40 116 2331
Fax: 352 40 116 2331

Management and Staff
Hans-Jurgen Schmitz, Chief Financial Officer

Type of Firm
Private Equity Firm

Project Preferences

Type of Financing Preferred:
Early Stage
Balanced
Seed
Startup

Size of Investments Considered:
Min Size of Investment Considered (000s): $500
Max Size of Investment Considered (000s): $500,000

Geographical Preferences

International Preferences:
Italy
Luxembourg
Netherlands
Europe
Spain
Belgium
Germany
France

Industry Preferences

In Communications prefer:
Communications and Media
Wireless Communications

In Computer Software prefer:
Software

In Internet Specific prefer:
Internet

In Industrial/Energy prefer:
Industrial Products

In Business Serv. prefer:
Services

Additional Information
Year Founded: 2000
Capital Under Management: $226,200,000
Current Activity Level: Actively seeking new investments

MANGROVE EQUITY PARTNERS LLC
101 South Franklin Street
Suite 205
Tampa, FL USA 33602
Phone: 813-868-4500
Fax: 813-224-0922
E-mail: info@mangroveequity.com
Website: www.mangroveequity.com

Management and Staff
Glenn Oken, Managing Director
Hunter Reichert, Managing Director
Matt Young, Managing Director

Type of Firm
Private Equity Firm

Project Preferences

Type of Financing Preferred:
Management Buyouts
Acquisition
Recapitalizations

Size of Investments Considered:
Min Size of Investment Considered (000s): $10,000
Max Size of Investment Considered (000s): $50,000

Geographical Preferences

Canadian Preferences:
All Canada

Additional Information
Year Founded: 2006
Capital Under Management: $50,000,000
Current Activity Level: Actively seeking new investments

MANITOBA CAPITAL FUND
2195-360 Main Street
Winnipeg, Canada R3C 3Z3
Phone: 204-925-8401
Fax: 204-949-0602
Website: www.gov.mb.ca

Management and Staff
Ken Praznuik, President

Type of Firm
Government Affiliated Program

Additional Information
Year Founded: 1996
Current Activity Level: Actively seeking new investments

MAPLE PARTNERS FINANCIAL GROUP, INC.
79 Wellington Street West
Maritime Life Tower Suite3500
Toronto, Canada M5K 1K7
Phone: 416-350-8200
Fax: 416-350-8222
Website: www.maplefinancialgroup.com

Management and Staff
Wolfgang Schuck, Chief Executive Officer

Type of Firm
Private Equity Firm

Additional Information
Year Founded: 1986
Current Activity Level: Actively seeking new investments

MAPLES MANAGEMENT, LLC
2440 Sand Hill Road
Suite 100
Menlo Park, CA USA 94025
Phone: 650-587-5003
Fax: 650-284-2201
Website: www.maples.net

Management and Staff
Ann Miura-Ko, Partner
Michael Maples, Managing Director

Type of Firm
Private Equity Firm

Project Preferences

Type of Financing Preferred:
Balanced

Additional Information
Name of Most Recent Fund: Maples Investments II, L.P.
Most Recent Fund Was Raised: 03/26/2008
Year Founded: 2006
Capital Under Management: $40,200,000
Current Activity Level: Actively seeking new investments

MARANON CAPITAL, L.P.
One North Franklin Street
Suite 2700
Chicago, IL USA 60606
Phone: 312-646-1200
Fax: 312-578-0047
E-mail: info@maranoncapital.com
Website: www.maranoncapital.com

Other Offices
280 North Old Woodward Avenue
Suite 104
Birmingham, MI USA 48009
Phone: 248-220-1804

Management and Staff
Demian Kircher, Managing Director
Greg Long, Managing Director
Ian Larkin, Managing Director
Mike Parilla, Managing Director & CFO
Richard Jander, Principal
Tom Gregory, Managing Director

Type of Firm
Private Equity Firm

Project Preferences

Type of Financing Preferred:
Mezzanine

Geographical Preferences

United States Preferences:
All U.S.

Additional Information
Year Founded: 2009
Capital Under Management: $145,000,000
Current Activity Level: Actively seeking new investments

MARATHON INVESTMENTS (FKA: MARATHON VENTURE CAPITAL FUND)
One Azrieli Center
Tel Aviv, Israel 67021
Phone: 972-3-608-1788
Fax: 972-3-608-1789
E-mail: main@marathon.co.il
Website: www.marathon.co.il

Type of Firm
Private Equity Advisor or Fund of Funds

Project Preferences
Type of Financing Preferred:
Early Stage
Seed

Geographical Preferences
International Preferences:
Israel

Industry Preferences
In Communications prefer:
Commercial Communications

In Computer Software prefer:
Software
Artificial Intelligence

In Semiconductor/Electr prefer:
Electronics

In Biotechnology prefer:
Biotechnology

In Medical/Health prefer:
Medical Products

Additional Information
Year Founded: 1993
Capital Under Management: $22,000,000
Current Activity Level: Actively seeking new investments

MARINER CAPITAL PARTNERS LLC
4200 West 115th Street
Suite 100
Leawood, KS USA 66211
Phone: 913-647-9720
Fax: 913-647-9728
E-mail: info@marinerequity.com
Website: www.marinerequity.com

Management and Staff
Martin Bicknell, Chief Executive Officer
Patrick Doherty, President
S. Kirk Lambright, Chief Operating Officer

Type of Firm
Private Equity Firm

Project Preferences
Type of Financing Preferred:
Leveraged Buyout
Management Buyouts
Acquisition
Recapitalizations

Geographical Preferences
United States Preferences:
Midwest
Southeast
Rocky Mountain
Southwest

Industry Preferences
In Semiconductor/Electr prefer:
Electronics

In Medical/Health prefer:
Medical Products
Disposable Med. Products

In Consumer Related prefer:
Entertainment and Leisure
Food/Beverage
Consumer Products
Consumer Services

In Industrial/Energy prefer:
Alternative Energy
Industrial Products

In Business Serv. prefer:
Distribution

In Other prefer:
Environment Responsible

Additional Information
Year Founded: 2007
Capital Under Management: $65,000,000
Current Activity Level: Actively seeking new investments

MARINER FINANCIAL, LTD. (AKA: MARINER BRAND CAPITAL, LTD.)
Level 40, Chifley Tower
2 Chifley Square
Sydney, Australia 2000
Phone: 612-9238-0750
Fax: 612-9238-0790
E-mail: info@marinerfunds.com.au
Website: www.marinerfunds.com.au

Other Offices
Level 20
101 Collins Street
Melbourne, Australia 3000
Phone: 61-3-8317-1111
Fax: 61-3-8317-1199

Management and Staff
Bill Ireland, Managing Director
Joseph Prsa, Chief Financial Officer

Type of Firm
Investment Management Firm

Project Preferences
Type of Financing Preferred:
Balanced

Geographical Preferences
International Preferences:
Australia

Industry Preferences
In Consumer Related prefer:
Consumer Products

Additional Information
Year Founded: 2003
Capital Under Management: $100,000,000
Current Activity Level: Actively seeking new investments

MARKET CAPITAL ITALIA SRL
Via Dell'Orso 4
Milano, Italy 20121
Phone: 390-289-01-3200
Fax: 390-286-450-765
E-mail: info@marketcapital.it
Website: www.marketcapital.it

Other Offices
10 Stratton Street
Mayfair
London, United Kingdom W1X 5FD
Phone: 44-207-589-6800
Fax: 44-207-589-6900

Type of Firm
Private Equity Firm

Association Membership
European Private Equity and Venture Capital Assoc.

Project Preferences
Type of Financing Preferred:
Leveraged Buyout
Early Stage
Expansion
Mezzanine
Startup

Geographical Preferences
International Preferences:
Europe

Industry Preferences
In Communications prefer:
Commercial Communications
Telecommunications

In Internet Specific prefer:
Internet

In Computer Other prefer:
Computer Related

Additional Information
Year Founded: 2000
Capital Under Management: $9,400,000
Current Activity Level: Actively seeking new investments

MARKPOINT VENTURE PARTNERS

15770 Dallas Parkway
Suite 800
Dallas, TX USA 75248
Phone: 972-490-1976
Fax: 972-490-1980
E-mail: info@markpt.com
Website: www.markpt.com

Management and Staff

Chris Slauer, General Partner
Jeff Williams, Managing General Partner
Tex Sekhon, General Partner

Type of Firm

Private Equity Firm

Project Preferences

Role in Financing:
Will function either as deal originator or investor in deals created by others

Type of Financing Preferred:
Second Stage Financing
Early Stage
Mezzanine
Start-up Financing
Seed
First Stage Financing

Size of Investments Considered:
Min Size of Investment Considered (000s): $250
Max Size of Investment Considered (000s): $2,000

Industry Preferences

In Communications prefer:
Wireless Communications
Data Communications

In Computer Software prefer:
Software

In Semiconductor/Electr prefer:
Semiconductor
Sensors

Additional Information

Year Founded: 1996
Capital Under Management: $10,000,000
Current Activity Level: Actively seeking new investments
Method of Compensation: Return on investment is of primary concern, do not charge fees

MARKSTONE CAPITAL

1801 Century Park East
Suite 2150
Los Angeles, CA USA 90067
Phone: 310-553-5090
Fax: 310-553-3311
E-mail: info@markstonecapital.com
Website: www.markstonecapital.com

Other Offices

46 Rothschild Boulevard
22nd Floor
Tel-Aviv, Israel 66883
Phone: 972-3-710-4242
Fax: 972-3-710-4243

Management and Staff

Amir Kess, Managing Director
Lars Hens, Vice President
Omer Harari, Vice President
Robert Thren, Chief Financial Officer
Ron Lubash, Managing Director
Scott Gluck, Vice President
Shimon Levy, Vice President
Tomer Cohen, Vice President

Type of Firm

Private Equity Firm

Project Preferences

Type of Financing Preferred:
Generalist PE

Additional Information

Name of Most Recent Fund: Markstone Capital Partners, L.P.
Most Recent Fund Was Raised: 01/11/2004
Year Founded: 2003
Capital Under Management: $1,210,000,000
Current Activity Level: Actively seeking new investments

MARLIN EQUITY PARTNERS, LLC

2121 Rosecrans Avenue
Suite 4325
El Segundo, CA USA 90245
Phone: 310-364-0100
Fax: 310-364-0110
E-mail: info@marlinequity.com
Website: www.marlinequity.com

Management and Staff

Andres Martinez, Principal
David McGovern, Managing Partner
George Kase, Partner
Nicholas Kaiser, Partner
Peter Spasov, Principal
Steve Johnson, Principal

Type of Firm

Private Equity Firm

Project Preferences

Role in Financing:
Prefer role as deal originator but will also invest in deals created by others

Type of Financing Preferred:
Leveraged Buyout
Control-block Purchases
Generalist PE
Public Companies
Turnaround
Other
Management Buyouts
Acquisition
Private Placement
Industry Rollups
Special Situation
Distressed Debt
Recapitalizations

Size of Investments Considered:
Min Size of Investment Considered (000s): $5,000
Max Size of Investment Considered (000s): $250,000

Geographical Preferences

United States Preferences:
All U.S.

Canadian Preferences:
All Canada

International Preferences:
United Kingdom
Latin America
Europe
Mexico
Australia
Germany
France

Industry Preferences

In Communications prefer:
Telecommunications
Data Communications

In Computer Hardware prefer:
Computers

In Computer Software prefer:
Software

In Internet Specific prefer:
Internet

In Medical/Health prefer:
Medical/Health
Medical Diagnostics
Medical Therapeutics
Medical Products

In Consumer Related prefer:
Consumer
Entertainment and Leisure
Retail
Consumer Products

In Industrial/Energy prefer:
Industrial Products

In Financial Services prefer:
Financial Services

In Business Serv. prefer:
Services
Distribution
Media

In Manufact. prefer:
Manufacturing

Additional Information

Name of Most Recent Fund: Marlin Equity, L.P.
Most Recent Fund Was Raised: 06/21/2005
Year Founded: 2005
Capital Under Management: $400,000,000
Current Activity Level: Actively seeking new investments

MARLOW CAPITAL

Capricorn House
32 Impala Road, Chislehurston
Johannesburg, South Africa 2196
Phone: 27-11-666-0700
Fax: 27-86-508-8266

Management and Staff

Andrew Hunt, Managing Director

Type of Firm

Private Equity Firm

Association Membership

South African Venture Capital Association (SAVCA)

Project Preferences

Type of Financing Preferred:

Leveraged Buyout

Geographical Preferences

International Preferences:

South Africa
Africa

Additional Information

Year Founded: 2009
Current Activity Level: Actively seeking new investments

MAROCINVEST FINANCE GROUP

82, Angle Bd
18, rue Soumaya
Casablanca, Morocco 20100
Phone: 212-22-259-515
Fax: 212-22-259-960
E-mail: mig@marocinvest.com
Website: www.marocinvest.com

Type of Firm

Private Equity Advisor or Fund of Funds

Association Membership

French Venture Capital Association (AFIC)
African Venture Capital Association (AVCA)

Project Preferences

Type of Financing Preferred:

Expansion

Size of Investments Considered:

Min Size of Investment Considered (000s): $800
Max Size of Investment Considered (000s): $3,300

Geographical Preferences

International Preferences:

Tunisia
Algeria
Morocco

Industry Preferences

In Communications prefer:

Communications and Media

In Computer Software prefer:

Software

In Computer Other prefer:

Computer Related

In Biotechnology prefer:

Biotechnology

In Medical/Health prefer:

Medical/Health

In Consumer Related prefer:

Consumer

In Industrial/Energy prefer:

Industrial Products

In Financial Services prefer:

Financial Services

In Manufact. prefer:

Manufacturing

In Agr/Forestr/Fish prefer:

Agriculture related

Additional Information

Year Founded: 2000
Capital Under Management: $23,000,000
Current Activity Level: Actively seeking new investments

MARQUETTE CAPITAL PARTNERS

60 South Sixth Street
Suite 3900
Minneapolis, MN USA 55402
Phone: 612-661-3990
Fax: 612-661-3999
Website: www.marquettecapitalpartners.com

Other Offices

227 West Monroe Street
Suite 2000
Chicago, IL USA 60606
Phone: 312-624-6920
Fax: 312-624-6921

Management and Staff

David Shapiro, Vice President
Greg Dames, Managing Director
Maggie Yanez, Vice President
Steven Heinen, Managing Director

Type of Firm

Bank Affiliated

Project Preferences

Type of Financing Preferred:

Leveraged Buyout
Expansion
Mezzanine
Management Buyouts
Acquisition
Recapitalizations

Size of Investments Considered:

Min Size of Investment Considered (000s): $2,000
Max Size of Investment Considered (000s): $10,000

Geographical Preferences

United States Preferences:

All U.S.

Industry Preferences

In Consumer Related prefer:

Retail

In Industrial/Energy prefer:

Industrial Products

In Business Serv. prefer:

Services
Distribution

In Manufact. prefer:

Manufacturing

Additional Information

Year Founded: 1997
Capital Under Management: $77,500,000
Current Activity Level: Actively seeking new investments

MARQUETTE VENTURE PARTNERS

676 North Michigan Avenue
Suite 3120
Chicago, IL USA 60611
Phone: 312-932-9230
Fax: 312-787-5907
Website: www.marquetteventures.com

Management and Staff

Chip Ruth, General Partner

Type of Firm

Private Equity Firm

Project Preferences

Type of Financing Preferred:

Second Stage Financing
Start-up Financing
First Stage Financing

Size of Investments Considered:
Min Size of Investment Considered (000s): $1,000
Max Size of Investment Considered (000s): $5,000

Geographical Preferences

United States Preferences:
Mid Atlantic
Midwest
Rocky Mountain
West Coast

Industry Focus
(% based on actual investment)

Consumer Related	28.4%
Medical/Health	26.2%
Computer Software and Services	10.9%
Internet Specific	8.5%
Communications and Media	8.2%
Other Products	7.4%
Biotechnology	6.1%
Semiconductors/Other Elect.	2.5%
Industrial/Energy	1.3%
Computer Hardware	0.4%

Additional Information
Name of Most Recent Fund: Marquette Venture Partners III, L.P.
Most Recent Fund Was Raised: 12/31/1997
Year Founded: 1987
Capital Under Management: $227,700,000
Current Activity Level: Making few, if any, new investments
Method of Compensation: Return on investment is of primary concern, do not charge fees

MARSHALL CAPITAL PARTNERS
Usovo, Building 100
Moscow, Russia 143084
Phone: 7-495-739-7887
Fax: 7-495-739-7898
E-mail: info@marcap.ru
Website: www.marcap.ru

Management and Staff
Alexander Provotorov, Managing Director
Konstantin Malofeev, Managing Partner
Mikhail Leschenko, Managing Director

Type of Firm
Private Equity Firm

Project Preferences

Type of Financing Preferred:
Leveraged Buyout

Geographical Preferences

International Preferences:
Russia

Industry Preferences

In Communications prefer:
Communications and Media
Telecommunications

In Consumer Related prefer:
Retail
Consumer Products
Consumer Services
Hotels and Resorts

In Financial Services prefer:
Real Estate

In Business Serv. prefer:
Media

Additional Information
Year Founded: 2005
Current Activity Level: Actively seeking new investments

MARSMAN-DRYSDALE CORPORATION
45th Flr. Philamlife Tower
8767 Paseo de Roxas Ave.
Makati City, Philippines 1231
Phone: 632-893-0000
Fax: 632-885-0574
E-mail: mdc@marsmandrysdale.com
Website: www.marsmandrysdale.com

Other Offices
177 Bovet Rd., Suite 600
San Mateo, CA USA 94402
Phone: 1650-341-6336
Fax: 1650-341-1329

Management and Staff
Eduardo Castillo, Vice President
George Drysdale, Chief Executive Officer
Roberto Sebastian, President

Type of Firm
Private Equity Firm

Project Preferences

Type of Financing Preferred:
Leveraged Buyout
Early Stage
Startup

Geographical Preferences

International Preferences:
Asia

Industry Preferences

In Communications prefer:
Telecommunications

In Medical/Health prefer:
Medical/Health

In Consumer Related prefer:
Entertainment and Leisure
Consumer Products
Consumer Services
Hotels and Resorts

In Business Serv. prefer:
Media

In Agr/Forestr/Fish prefer:
Agriculture related

Additional Information
Year Founded: 1920
Current Activity Level: Actively seeking new investments

MARTLET VENTURE MANAGEMENT
2135, rue de la Montagne
Montreal, Canada
Phone: 514-499-3443
Fax: 514-499-3448
Website: www.martlet.com

Type of Firm
Private Equity Firm

Additional Information
Year Founded: 2009
Current Activity Level: Actively seeking new investments

MARUBENI CORPORATION
4-2, Ohtemachi 1-chome
Chiyoda-ku
Tokyo, Japan 100-8088
Phone: 81-3-3282-2111
Fax: 81-3-3282-7456
Website: www.marubeni.com

Management and Staff
Michio Kuwahara, Chief Operating Officer

Type of Firm
Corporate PE/Venture

Project Preferences

Type of Financing Preferred:
Expansion

Geographical Preferences

International Preferences:
China
Japan

Industry Preferences

In Semiconductor/Electr prefer:
Electronics

In Medical/Health prefer:
Pharmaceuticals

In Industrial/Energy prefer:
Machinery

Additional Information

Year Founded: 1999
Current Activity Level: Actively seeking new investments

MARWIT CAPITAL, LLC

100 Bayview Circle
Suite 550
Newport Beach, CA USA 92660
Phone: 949-861-3636
Fax: 949-861-3637
E-mail: info@marwit.com
Website: www.marwit.com

Management and Staff

Chris Britt, Managing Partner
David Browne, Principal
Matthew Witte, Chairman & CEO
Thomas Dollhopf, Principal

Type of Firm

Private Equity Firm

Association Membership

Natl Assoc of Small Bus. Inv. Co (NASBIC)

Project Preferences

Role in Financing:
Prefer role as deal originator but will also invest in deals created by others

Type of Financing Preferred:
Leveraged Buyout
Management Buyouts
Acquisition

Size of Investments Considered:
Min Size of Investment Considered (000s): $250
Max Size of Investment Considered: No Limit

Geographical Preferences

United States Preferences:
Southern California
West Coast
California

Industry Preferences

In Medical/Health prefer:
Health Services

In Transportation prefer:
Transportation

In Business Serv. prefer:
Distribution

In Manufact. prefer:
Manufacturing

Additional Information

Year Founded: 1962
Capital Under Management: $42,000,000
Current Activity Level: Actively seeking new investments
Method of Compensation: Return on invest. most important, but chg. closing fees, service fees, etc.

MARWYN INVESTMENT MANAGEMENT, LLP

11 Buckingham Street
London, United Kingdom WC2N 6DF
Phone: 44-20-7004-2700
Fax: 44-20-7004-2701
E-mail: enquiries@marwyn.com
Website: www.marwyn.com

Management and Staff

Benjamin Shaw, Partner
James Corsellis, Managing Partner
Mark Watts, Managing Partner

Type of Firm

Investment Management Firm

Project Preferences

Type of Financing Preferred:
Leveraged Buyout
Expansion
Acquisition
Distressed Debt

Geographical Preferences

International Preferences:
Europe

Industry Preferences

In Computer Software prefer:
Applications Software

In Consumer Related prefer:
Entertainment and Leisure
Food/Beverage

In Financial Services prefer:
Financial Services

In Business Serv. prefer:
Media

Additional Information

Year Founded: 2002
Current Activity Level: Actively seeking new investments

MARYLAND DBED (AKA:DEPT. OF BUSINESS & ECONOMIC DEVELOPMENT)

2401 East Pratt Street
Suite 1760
Baltimore, MD USA 21202
Phone: 410-767-6383
Fax: 410-333-6931
Website: www.choosemaryland.org

Management and Staff

Frank Dickson, Principal

Type of Firm

Government Affiliated Program

Association Membership

Mid-Atlantic Venture Association

Project Preferences

Type of Financing Preferred:
Early Stage
Seed

Size of Investments Considered:
Min Size of Investment Considered (000s): $50
Max Size of Investment Considered (000s): $500

Geographical Preferences

United States Preferences:
Maryland

Industry Preferences

In Biotechnology prefer:
Human Biotechnology
Agricultural/Animal Bio.
Biosensors
Biotech Related Research

Additional Information

Year Founded: 1994
Capital Under Management: $60,000,000
Current Activity Level: Actively seeking new investments
Method of Compensation: Return on investment is of primary concern, do not charge fees

MARYLAND TECHNOLOGY DEVELOPMENT CORPORATION (AKA: TEDCO)

5565 Sterrett Place
Suite 214
Columbia, MD USA 21044
Phone: 410-740-9442
Fax: 410-740-9422
E-mail: info@marylandtedco.org
Website: www.marylandtedco.org

Management and Staff

James Poulos, Vice President

Type of Firm

Government Affiliated Program

Project Preferences

Role in Financing:

Prefer role as deal originator

Type of Financing Preferred:

Early Stage
Seed

Size of Investments Considered:

Min Size of Investment Considered (000s): $50
Max Size of Investment Considered (000s): $150

Geographical Preferences

United States Preferences:

Maryland
All U.S.

Additional Information

Year Founded: 1998
Capital Under Management: $2,900,000
Current Activity Level: Actively seeking new investments
Method of Compensation: Return on investment is of primary concern, do not charge fees

---

MASA LIFE SCIENCE VENTURES, L.P. (AKA: MLSV)

1701 16th Street, Northwest
Suite 716
Washington, DC USA 20009
Phone: 202-309-2071
Fax: 202-478-1619
E-mail: info@mlsvfund.com
Website: www.mlsvfund.com

Management and Staff

Brion Sasaki, President

Type of Firm

Private Equity Firm

Project Preferences

Type of Financing Preferred:

Early Stage

Size of Investments Considered:

Min Size of Investment Considered (000s): $250
Max Size of Investment Considered (000s): $1,500

Geographical Preferences

United States Preferences:

Mid Atlantic
All U.S.

Canadian Preferences:

All Canada

International Preferences:

Europe
Israel

Industry Preferences

In Biotechnology prefer:

Biotechnology

In Medical/Health prefer:

Medical Diagnostics
Medical Products
Health Services

Additional Information

Year Founded: 2005
Capital Under Management: $15,000,000
Current Activity Level: Actively seeking new investments

MASI, LTD.

1419 Lake Cook Road
Suite 220
Deerfield, IL USA 60015
Phone: 847-948-7300
Fax: 847-948-7379
E-mail: masi@masiltd.com
Website: www.masiltd.com

Management and Staff

Art Lyman, Managing Director
Jim Huber, Managing Director
R. Charles McLravy, Managing Director
Raj Bodepudi, Managing Director

Type of Firm

Bank Affiliated

Project Preferences

Role in Financing:

Prefer role as deal originator

Type of Financing Preferred:

Second Stage Financing
Leveraged Buyout
Mezzanine
Generalist PE
Expansion
Later Stage
Management Buyouts
Private Placement
Acquisition
Joint Ventures
Recapitalizations

Geographical Preferences

Canadian Preferences:

All Canada

Additional Information

Year Founded: 1984
Current Activity Level: Actively seeking new investments

MASON WELLS PRIVATE EQUITY (FKA: M&I VENTURES)

411 East Wisconsin Avenue
Suite 1280
Milwaukee, WI USA 53202
Phone: 414-727-6400
Fax: 414-727-6410
E-mail: info@masonwells.com
Website: www.masonwells.com

Management and Staff

Bill Krugler, Managing Director
Jim Domach, Chief Financial Officer
John Byrnes, Chairman & CEO
Thomas Smith, Managing Director
Trevor D Souza, Managing Director

Type of Firm

Private Equity Firm

Project Preferences

Role in Financing:

Prefer role as deal originator

Type of Financing Preferred:

Leveraged Buyout
Early Stage
Start-up Financing
Seed
Management Buyouts

Size of Investments Considered:

Min Size of Investment Considered (000s): $500
Max Size of Investment Considered (000s): $8,000

Geographical Preferences

United States Preferences:

Midwest

Industry Focus

(% based on actual investment)

Other Products	40.1%
Communications and Media	19.7%
Computer Hardware	16.2%
Biotechnology	7.7%
Medical/Health	7.3%
Industrial/Energy	4.7%
Computer Software and Services	3.9%
Consumer Related	0.4%

Additional Information

Name of Most Recent Fund: Mason Wells Buyout Fund II, L.P.
Most Recent Fund Was Raised: 10/07/2004
Year Founded: 1982
Capital Under Management: $500,000,000
Current Activity Level: Actively seeking new investments
Method of Compensation: Return on invest. most important, but chg. closing fees, service fees, etc.

MASSACHUSETTS GREEN ENERGY FUND

320 Washington Street
Fourth Floor
Brookline, MA USA 02445
Phone: 617-739-1155
Fax: 617-739-3550
E-mail: info@massgreenenergy.com
Website: www.massgreenenergy.com

Management and Staff

Eric Emmons, Principal
Jay Fiske, Principal
William Osborn, Managing Director

Type of Firm

Private Equity Firm

Project Preferences

Role in Financing:

Prefer role as deal originator but will also invest in deals created by others

Type of Financing Preferred:

Early Stage
Expansion
Seed

Size of Investments Considered:

Min Size of Investment Considered (000s): $300
Max Size of Investment Considered (000s): $1,600

Geographical Preferences

United States Preferences:

Massachusetts

Industry Preferences

In Industrial/Energy prefer:

Energy
Alternative Energy
Environmental Related

In Other prefer:

Environment Responsible

Additional Information

Name of Most Recent Fund: Massachusetts Green Energy Fund I, LP.
Most Recent Fund Was Raised: 06/01/2004
Year Founded: 2004
Capital Under Management: $16,000,000
Current Activity Level: Actively seeking new investments
Method of Compensation: Return on investment is of primary concern, do not charge fees

MASSACHUSETTS INSTITUTE OF TECHNOLOGY

238 Main Street
Suite 200
Cambridge, MA USA 02142
Phone: 617-253-4900
Fax: 617-258-6676
E-mail: info@mitimco.org
Website: www.mitimco.mit.edu

Management and Staff

Daniel Steele, Managing Director
Philip Rotner, Managing Director
Seth Alexander, President

Type of Firm

University Program

Project Preferences

Type of Financing Preferred:

Fund of Funds
Leveraged Buyout
Early Stage
Expansion
Balanced
Turnaround
Seed
Management Buyouts
First Stage Financing
Acquisition
Startup
Distressed Debt
Recapitalizations

Size of Investments Considered:

Min Size of Investment Considered (000s): $1,000
Max Size of Investment Considered (000s): $150,000

Geographical Preferences

International Preferences:

All International

Industry Focus

(% based on actual investment)

Semiconductors/Other Elect.	33.5%
Computer Software and Services	13.6%
Internet Specific	12.4%
Communications and Media	11.3%
Consumer Related	8.8%
Medical/Health	8.0%
Other Products	6.1%
Industrial/Energy	4.2%
Biotechnology	2.2%

Additional Information

Name of Most Recent Fund: MIT Private Equity Fund III, L.P.
Most Recent Fund Was Raised: 04/16/2006
Year Founded: 1973
Capital Under Management: $320,000,000
Current Activity Level: Actively seeking new investments

MASSACHUSETTS MUTUAL LIFE

1295 State Street
Springfield, MA USA 01111
Phone: 413-744-6062
Fax: 413-846-5002
E-mail: inquiries@dlbabson.com
Website: www.dlbabson.com

Type of Firm

Insurance Firm Affiliate

Project Preferences

Size of Investments Considered:

Min Size of Investment Considered (000s): $10,000
Max Size of Investment Considered (000s): $30,000

Industry Focus

(% based on actual investment)

Medical/Health	34.7%
Other Products	24.6%
Industrial/Energy	17.4%
Semiconductors/Other Elect.	10.7%
Consumer Related	8.2%
Internet Specific	4.0%
Communications and Media	0.4%

Additional Information

Year Founded: 1940
Current Activity Level: Actively seeking new investments

MASSACHUSETTS TECHNOLOGY COLLABORATIVE

75 North Drive
Westborough, MA USA 01581
Phone: 508-870-0312
Fax: 508-898-2275
E-mail: mtc@masstech.org
Website: www.mtpc.org

Type of Firm

Private Equity Firm

Additional Information

Year Founded: 2009
Current Activity Level: Actively seeking new investments

MASSENA CAPITAL PARTNERS

78 Avenue Raymond Poincare
Paris, France 75116
Phone: 33-153-700-700
Fax: 33-153-700-701
E-mail: e-contact@massenacp.com
Website: www.massenacapitalpartners.com

Management and Staff

Claude Lutz, Chief Operating Officer
Didier Choix, Chief Executive Officer
Olivia Bernard, Chief Financial Officer
Romain Lobstein, Managing Director

Type of Firm
Private Equity Firm

Association Membership
French Venture Capital Association (AFIC)

Project Preferences

Role in Financing:
Prefer role as deal originator but will also invest in deals created by others

Type of Financing Preferred:
Generalist PE
Acquisition

Geographical Preferences

International Preferences:
Europe

Industry Preferences

In Financial Services prefer:
Real Estate

Additional Information
Year Founded: 1985
Current Activity Level: Actively seeking new investments
Method of Compensation: Return on invest. most important, but chg. closing fees, service fees, etc.

MASSEY BURCH CAPITAL CORP.

One Burton Hills Boulevard
Suite 350
Nashville, TN USA 37215
Phone: 615-665-3221
Fax: 615-665-3240
Website: www.masseyburch.com

Other Offices
310 25th Avenue North
Suite 103
Nashville, TN USA 37203
Phone: 615-329-9448

1000 Park Forty Plaza
Suite 300
Durham, NC USA 27713
Phone: 919-544-6162
Fax: 919-544-6667

Management and Staff
Donald Johnston, Partner
Lucius Burch, Partner
Vic Gatto, Partner
William Earthman, Partner

Type of Firm
Service Provider

Project Preferences

Role in Financing:
Prefer role as deal originator

Type of Financing Preferred:
Early Stage
Start-up Financing
Seed
First Stage Financing

Size of Investments Considered:
Min Size of Investment Considered (000s): $1,000
Max Size of Investment Considered (000s): $5,000

Geographical Preferences

United States Preferences:
Southeast

Industry Focus
(% based on actual investment)

Other Products	23.5%
Medical/Health	18.4%
Communications and Media	15.3%
Internet Specific	13.4%
Computer Software and Services	8.4%
Consumer Related	5.9%
Biotechnology	4.9%
Industrial/Energy	4.7%
Semiconductors/Other Elect.	2.8%
Computer Hardware	2.7%

Additional Information
Name of Most Recent Fund: Massey Burch Venture Fund II
Most Recent Fund Was Raised: 08/04/1999
Year Founded: 1994
Capital Under Management: $126,000,000
Current Activity Level: Actively seeking new investments
Method of Compensation: Return on investment is of primary concern, do not charge fees

---

MASTHEAD VENTURE PARTNERS

55 Cambridge Parkway
Suite 103
Cambridge, MA USA 02142
Phone: 617-621-3000
Fax: 617-621-3055
E-mail: info@mvpartners.com
Website: www.mvpartners.com

Other Offices
11 Penn Plaza, 5th Floor
New York, NY USA 10001
Phone: 201-602-1100
Fax: 646-619-4466

Management and Staff
Braden Bohrmann, General Partner
Brian Owen, General Partner
Daniel Flatley, General Partner
Mary Shannon, Principal
Stephen Smith, General Partner
Timothy Agnew, Principal

Type of Firm
Private Equity Firm

Project Preferences

Role in Financing:
Prefer role as deal originator but will also invest in deals created by others

Type of Financing Preferred:
Early Stage

Size of Investments Considered:
Min Size of Investment Considered (000s): $500
Max Size of Investment Considered (000s): $5,000

Geographical Preferences

United States Preferences:
Northeast

Industry Preferences

In Communications prefer:
Telecommunications
Wireless Communications
Data Communications

In Computer Software prefer:
Software
Systems Software
Applications Software

In Semiconductor/Electr prefer:
Fiber Optics

In Biotechnology prefer:
Human Biotechnology

In Medical/Health prefer:
Medical/Health

Additional Information
Year Founded: 1997
Capital Under Management: $200,000,000
Current Activity Level: Actively seeking new investments

MATADOR PRIVATE EQUITY AG

Gueterstrasse 3
Sarnen, Switzerland 6060
Phone: 41-41-662-1062
Fax: 41-41-661-0862
E-mail: office@matador-private-equity.com
Website: www.matador-private-equity.com

Type of Firm
Private Equity Firm

Project Preferences

Type of Financing Preferred:
Generalist PE

Geographical Preferences

International Preferences:
Europe
Eastern Europe
All International

Additional Information
Year Founded: 2006
Current Activity Level: Actively seeking new investments

MATHEMATICA CAPITAL MANAGEMENT, LLC
75 Gate Five Road
Sausalito, CA USA 94965
Phone: 415-332-4051
Fax: 415-332-4052
E-mail: info@mathcapm.com
Website: www.mathcapm.com

Type of Firm
Private Equity Firm

Additional Information
Year Founded: 2002
Capital Under Management: $1,500,000
Current Activity Level: Actively seeking new investments

MATIGNON INVESTISSEMENT ET GESTION
5, avenue Matignon
Paris, France 75008
Phone: 33-1-5353-0123
Fax: 33-1-4561-1633
E-mail: mig@matignon-gestion.fr
Website: www.matignon-gestion.fr

Management and Staff
Philippe Dhamelincourt, Managing Director

Type of Firm
Private Equity Firm

Association Membership
French Venture Capital Association (AFIC)

Project Preferences

Type of Financing Preferred:
Early Stage
Balanced

Geographical Preferences

International Preferences:
Europe
France

Industry Preferences

In Medical/Health prefer:
Medical/Health

Additional Information
Year Founded: 1997
Capital Under Management: $109,100,000
Current Activity Level: Actively seeking new investments

MATLINPATTERSON ASSET MANAGEMENT LLC
520 Madison Avenue
New York, NY USA 10022
Phone: 212-651-9500
Fax: 212-651-4011
Website: www.matlinpatterson.com

Other Offices
3 Saint James's Square
London, United Kingdom SW1Y 4JU
Phone: 44-207-747-5400
Fax: 44-207-747-5401

Suite 3803, One Exchange Square
8 Connaught Place
Central, Hong Kong
Phone: 852-2844-7700
Fax: 852-2524-4666

Management and Staff
David Matlin, Chief Executive Officer

Type of Firm
Private Equity Firm

Project Preferences

Type of Financing Preferred:
Distressed Debt

Geographical Preferences

International Preferences:
All International

Industry Preferences

In Communications prefer:
Telecommunications

In Semiconductor/Electr prefer:
Electronic Components

In Industrial/Energy prefer:
Energy
Industrial Products

Additional Information
Name of Most Recent Fund: MatlinPatterson Global Opportunities Fund III, L.P.
Most Recent Fund Was Raised: 06/08/2007
Year Founded: 2001
Capital Under Management: $4,200,000,000
Current Activity Level: Actively seeking new investments

MATON VENTURE
1601 South De Anza Boulevard
Suite 115
Cupertino, CA USA 95014
Phone: 408-786-5168
Fax: 408-996-0728
E-mail: info@maton.com
Website: www.maton.com

Management and Staff
Jaff Lin, Partner
Jesse Chen, Managing Partner

Type of Firm
Private Equity Firm

Association Membership
National Venture Capital Association - USA (NVCA)

Project Preferences

Role in Financing:
Will function either as deal originator or investor in deals created by others

Type of Financing Preferred:
Second Stage Financing
Early Stage
Expansion
Research and Development
Start-up Financing
Turnaround
Seed
First Stage Financing
Private Placement

Size of Investments Considered:
Min Size of Investment Considered (000s): $250
Max Size of Investment Considered (000s): $2,500

Geographical Preferences

United States Preferences:
Northern California

Industry Preferences

In Communications prefer:
Wireless Communications
Data Communications

In Computer Hardware prefer:
Computer Graphics and Dig
Integrated Turnkey System

In Computer Software prefer:
Software
Systems Software
Applications Software
Artificial Intelligence

In Internet Specific prefer:
Internet

In Semiconductor/Electr prefer:
Electronic Components
Semiconductor
Micro-Processing
Controllers and Sensors

Sensors
Circuit Boards
Component Testing Equipmt
Laser Related
Fiber Optics
Analytic/Scientific
Optoelectronics

Additional Information

Year Founded: 1997
Capital Under Management: $42,000,000
Current Activity Level: Actively seeking new investments
Method of Compensation: Return on investment is of primary concern, do not charge fees

MATRIX PARTNERS

Bay Colony Corporate Center
1000 Winter Street, Suite 4500
Waltham, MA USA 02451
Phone: 781-890-2244
Fax: 781-890-2288
E-mail: info@matrixpartners.com
Website: www.matrixpartners.com

Other Offices

2500 Sand Hill Road
Suite 200
Menlo Park, CA USA 94025
Phone: 650-854-3131
Fax: 650-854-3296

Suite 2901, Nexus Center
No. 19A, East 3rd Ring Road North
Beijing, China 100020
Phone: 86-10-6500-0088
Fax: 86-10-6500-0066

Ceejay House #306
Annie Besant Road, Worli
Mumbai, India 400 18
Phone: 91-22-6768-0000
Fax: 91-22-6768-0001

Multiconsult Limited
10, Frere Felix de Valois Street
Port Louis, Mauritius
Phone: 230-202-3000
Fax: 230-212-5265

Management and Staff

Andrew Verhalen, General Partner
Avnish Bajaj, Managing Director
Bo Shao, General Partner
Dana Stalder, General Partner
David Zhang, Managing Partner
David Su, Managing Partner
David Skok, General Partner
Edgar Masri, General Partner
Fang Yuan, Partner
Harry Man, Partner
Ian Goh, Partner
Josh Hannah, General Partner
Michael Humphreys, General Partner
Neeraj Gunsagar, Vice President
Nicholas Beim, General Partner
Paul Ferri, General Partner
Rishi Navani, Managing Director
Robert Soni, General Partner
Robert Lisbonne, General Partner
Rustom Batlivala, Chief Financial Officer
Shirish Sathaye, General Partner
Stanley Reiss, General Partner
Timothy Barrows, General Partner

Type of Firm

Private Equity Firm

Association Membership

Western Association of Venture Capitalists (WAVC)
National Venture Capital Association - USA (NVCA)
Indian Venture Capital Association (IVCA)

Project Preferences

Role in Financing:

Prefer role as deal originator but will also invest in deals created by others

Type of Financing Preferred:

Second Stage Financing
Leveraged Buyout
Early Stage
Balanced
Start-up Financing
First Stage Financing

Size of Investments Considered:

Min Size of Investment Considered (000s): $100
Max Size of Investment Considered (000s): $10,000

Geographical Preferences

United States Preferences:

Massachusetts
California

International Preferences:

India
China

Industry Focus

(% based on actual investment)	
Communications and Media	27.9%
Computer Software and Services	26.8%
Internet Specific	23.9%
Semiconductors/Other Elect.	7.2%
Computer Hardware	4.0%
Consumer Related	4.0%
Other Products	4.0%
Medical/Health	1.3%
Industrial/Energy	0.9%
Biotechnology	0.1%

Additional Information

Year Founded: 1977
Capital Under Management: $2,670,700,000
Current Activity Level: Actively seeking new investments
Method of Compensation: Return on investment is of primary concern, do not charge fees

MATRIX PRIVATE EQUITY PARTNERS LTD.

One Jermyn Street
London, United Kingdom SW1Y 4UH
Phone: 44-20-7925 3300
Fax: 44-20-7925 3285
E-mail: info@matrixpep.co.uk
Website: www.matrixpep.co.uk

Management and Staff

Helen Sinclair, Managing Director
Mark MacLean, Managing Director
Mark Wignall, Chief Executive Officer

Type of Firm

Bank Affiliated

Association Membership

British Venture Capital Association (BVCA)

Project Preferences

Role in Financing:

Prefer role as deal originator

Type of Financing Preferred:

Leveraged Buyout
Balanced
Management Buyouts

Size of Investments Considered:

Min Size of Investment Considered (000s): $3,069
Max Size of Investment Considered (000s): $14,323

Geographical Preferences

International Preferences:

United Kingdom
Europe

Additional Information

Year Founded: 2000
Capital Under Management: $266,000,000
Current Activity Level: Actively seeking new investments

MAVEN CAPITAL MANAGEMENT LLC

6340 International Parkway
Suite 300
Plano, TX USA 75093
Website: www.mavencapital.com

Management and Staff

John Todd, Managing Partner
Mark Bromberg, Managing Partner
Mark Scoular, Managing Partner

Type of Firm

Private Equity Firm

Project Preferences

Type of Financing Preferred:
Balanced
Acquisition

Size of Investments Considered:
Min Size of Investment Considered (000s): $5,000
Max Size of Investment Considered (000s): $25,000

Geographical Preferences

United States Preferences:
All U.S.

Canadian Preferences:
All Canada

Industry Preferences

In Consumer Related prefer:
Other Restaurants

Additional Information
Year Founded: 2007
Current Activity Level: Actively seeking new investments

MAVEN VENTURE PARTNERS
155 Constitution Drive
Menlo Park, CA USA 94025
Phone: 650-324-5175
Website: www.mavenventurepartners.com

Management and Staff
George Richard, Managing Director
Jennifer Gill-Roberts, Managing Director
Laura Gwosden, Chief Financial Officer

Type of Firm
Private Equity Firm

Additional Information
Year Founded: 2005
Current Activity Level: Actively seeking new investments

MAVERICK CAPITAL LTD.
300 Crescent Court
Suite 1850
Dallas, TX USA 75201
Phone: 214-880-4068
Fax: 214-880-4159
Website: www.maverickcap.com

Other Offices
767 Fifth Avenue
11th Floor
New York, NY USA 10153
Phone: 212-418-6900
Fax: 212-752-5713

Management and Staff
Bill Goodell, Chief Operating Officer
David Singer, Partner
Evan Wyly, Managing Partner
Lee Ainslie, Managing Partner
Michael Moore, Managing Director
Thomas Lee, President

Type of Firm
Private Equity Firm

Industry Focus
(% based on actual investment)

Medical/Health	40.8%
Biotechnology	30.8%
Internet Specific	12.6%
Computer Software and Services	11.5%
Other Products	3.8%
Consumer Related	0.5%

Additional Information
Name of Most Recent Fund: Maverick Partners Fund I
Most Recent Fund Was Raised: 07/01/1994
Year Founded: 1990
Current Activity Level: Actively seeking new investments

MAVERON LLC
505 Fifth Avenue South
Suite 600
Seattle, WA USA 98104
Phone: 206-288-1700
Fax: 206-288-1777
E-mail: info@maveron.com
Website: www.maveron.com

Management and Staff
Amy Errett, Partner
Ben Choi, Principal
Dan Levitan, Managing Partner
Debra Somberg, General Partner
Eric Tilenius, Partner
Howard Schultz, Managing Partner
Jonathan Fram, Managing Director
Ron Graves, Principal

Type of Firm
Private Equity Firm

Association Membership
National Venture Capital Association - USA (NVCA)

Project Preferences

Role in Financing:
Prefer role as deal originator but will also invest in deals created by others

Type of Financing Preferred:
Early Stage
Expansion
Balanced

Size of Investments Considered:
Min Size of Investment Considered (000s): $3,000
Max Size of Investment Considered (000s): $15,000

Geographical Preferences

United States Preferences:
All U.S.

Industry Focus
(% based on actual investment)

Internet Specific	48.7%
Consumer Related	19.1%
Other Products	15.7%
Computer Software and Services	7.8%
Computer Hardware	6.0%
Communications and Media	1.5%
Industrial/Energy	1.2%

Additional Information
Name of Most Recent Fund: Maveron Equity Partners IV, L.P.
Most Recent Fund Was Raised: 03/03/2008
Year Founded: 1998
Capital Under Management: $850,000,000
Current Activity Level: Actively seeking new investments
Method of Compensation: Return on investment is of primary concern, do not charge fees

---

MAXUS CAPITAL AB
Birger Jarlsgatan 2
Stockholm, Sweden SE-114 34
Phone: 46-8-611-9460
Fax: 46-8-611-9461

Management and Staff
Magnus Wahlback, Managing Director

Type of Firm
Private Equity Firm

Association Membership
Swedish Venture Capital Association (SVCA)

Project Preferences

Type of Financing Preferred:
Leveraged Buyout
Early Stage
Expansion
Startup

Size of Investments Considered:
Min Size of Investment Considered (000s): $106
Max Size of Investment Considered (000s): $1,062

Geographical Preferences

International Preferences:
Europe

Industry Preferences

In Communications prefer:
Telecommunications

In Computer Software prefer:
Computer Services
Software

In Internet Specific prefer:
Internet

In Consumer Related prefer:
Consumer Products
Consumer Services

In Transportation prefer:
Transportation

In Financial Services prefer:
Financial Services

In Business Serv. prefer:
Services

Additional Information
Year Founded: 1993
Capital Under Management: $15,900,000
Current Activity Level: Actively seeking new investments

MAYBAN-JAIC CAPITAL MANAGEMENT SDN. BHD.
20/F West Wing Menara Maybank
100 Jalan Tun Perak
Kuala Lumpur, Malaysia 50050
Phone: 603-202-2188
Fax: 603-201-2188

Type of Firm
Private Equity Firm

Project Preferences

Type of Financing Preferred:
Balanced
Later Stage

Geographical Preferences

International Preferences:
Vietnam
Indonesia
Thailand
Singapore
Asia
Malaysia

Industry Preferences

In Biotechnology prefer:
Biotechnology

In Consumer Related prefer:
Retail

In Transportation prefer:
Transportation

In Manufact. prefer:
Manufacturing

In Agr/Forestr/Fish prefer:
Agriculture related

Additional Information
Year Founded: 2006
Capital Under Management: $37,000,000
Current Activity Level: Actively seeking new investments

MAYFIELD FUND
2800 Sand Hill Road
Suite 250
Menlo Park, CA USA 94025
Phone: 650-854-5560
Fax: 650-854-5712
E-mail: info@mayfield.com
Website: www.mayfield.com

Management and Staff
Allen Morgan, Venture Partner
David Ladd, Venture Partner
Emily Melton, Partner
James Beck, Managing Director & CFO
Janice Roberts, Managing Director
John Stockton, Venture Partner
Kendall Cooper, Chief Financial Officer
Navin Chaddha, Managing Director
Raj Kapoor, Managing Director
Rajeev Batra, Partner
Robin Vasan, Managing Director
Todd Kimmel, Partner
Tom Fountain, Principal
Yogen Dalal, Managing Director

Type of Firm
Private Equity Firm

Association Membership
Western Association of Venture Capitalists (WAVC)
National Venture Capital Association - USA (NVCA)

Project Preferences

Role in Financing:
Prefer role as deal originator but will also invest in deals created by others

Type of Financing Preferred:
Second Stage Financing
Early Stage
Research and Development
Balanced
Later Stage
Management Buyouts
Strategic Alliances
Acquisition
Joint Ventures
Private Placement

Size of Investments Considered:
Min Size of Investment Considered (000s): $250
Max Size of Investment Considered: No Limit

Geographical Preferences

United States Preferences:
Northwest
Rocky Mountain
West Coast

International Preferences:
India

Industry Focus
(% based on actual investment)

Computer Software and Services	27.9%
Internet Specific	24.8%
Communications and Media	19.4%
Semiconductors/Other Elect.	7.9%
Computer Hardware	5.4%
Medical/Health	5.2%
Biotechnology	5.1%
Other Products	1.6%
Industrial/Energy	1.6%
Consumer Related	1.0%

Additional Information
Name of Most Recent Fund: Mayfield XIII
Most Recent Fund Was Raised: 09/23/2008
Year Founded: 1969
Capital Under Management: $2,300,000,000
Current Activity Level: Actively seeking new investments
Method of Compensation: Return on investment is of primary concern, do not charge fees

---

MAYO MEDICAL VENTURES
200 First Street Southwest
Rochester, MN USA 55905
Phone: 507-284-2511
Fax: 507-284-5410
Website: www.mayo.edu

Type of Firm
Corporate PE/Venture

Association Membership
National Venture Capital Association - USA (NVCA)

Project Preferences

Role in Financing:
Will function either as deal originator or investor in deals created by others

Type of Financing Preferred:
Early Stage
Seed

Size of Investments Considered:
Min Size of Investment Considered (000s): $250
Max Size of Investment Considered (000s): $1,000

Industry Focus
(% based on actual investment)

Medical/Health	68.5%
Computer Software and Services	25.7%
Biotechnology	5.7%

Additional Information
Year Founded: 1998
Capital Under Management: $25,000,000
Current Activity Level: Actively seeking new investments

Method of Compensation: Return on investment is of primary concern, do not charge fees

---

MAZ LEVEL ONE GMBH

Harburger Schlossstrasse 6-12
Hamburg, Germany 21079
Phone: 49-40-766291131
Fax: 49-40-766-29534
E-mail: info@mazlevelone.com
Website: www.mazlevelone.com

Management and Staff

Michael Lubbehusen, Managing Director
Soren Denker, Managing Director

Type of Firm

Incubator/Development Program

Association Membership

German Venture Capital Association (BVK)

Project Preferences

Type of Financing Preferred:
Seed
Startup

Geographical Preferences

International Preferences:
Germany

Industry Preferences

In Communications prefer:
Communications and Media

In Internet Specific prefer:
E-Commerce Technology
internet

In Computer Other prefer:
Computer Related

In Industrial/Energy prefer:
Energy

Additional Information

Year Founded: 2001
Current Activity Level: Actively seeking new investments

MB FUNDS (AKA: MB RAHASTOT OY)

Bulevardi 1A
Helsinki, Finland 00100
Phone: 358-9-131-011
Fax: 358-9-1310-1310
Website: www.mbfunds.com

Management and Staff

Eero Niiva, Partner
Hannu Puhakka, Partner
Juhani Suomela, Managing Partner
Kari Rytkonen, Partner
Matti Mertsola, Partner
Mirja Sundstrom, Partner

Type of Firm

Private Equity Firm

Association Membership

Finnish Venture Capital Association (FVCA)
European Private Equity and Venture Capital Assoc.

Project Preferences

Role in Financing:
Will function either as deal originator or investor in deals created by others

Type of Financing Preferred:
Expansion
Generalist PE
Mezzanine
Management Buyouts

Size of Investments Considered:
Min Size of Investment Considered (000s): $2,858
Max Size of Investment Considered (000s): $71,439

Geographical Preferences

International Preferences:
Scandanavia/Nordic Region
Finland

Industry Focus

(% based on actual investment)

Industrial/Energy	69.3%
Other Products	20.1%
Consumer Related	5.7%
Medical/Health	4.3%
Semiconductors/Other Elect.	0.7%

Additional Information

Name of Most Recent Fund: MB Equity Fund IV
Most Recent Fund Was Raised: 09/21/2007
Year Founded: 1988
Capital Under Management: $571,500,000
Current Activity Level: Actively seeking new investments
Method of Compensation: Return on invest. most important, but chg. closing fees, service fees, etc.

MB VENTURE PARTNERS, LLC

17 West Pontotoc
Suite 200
Memphis, TN USA 38103
Phone: 901-322-0330
Fax: 901-322-0339
Website: www.mbventures.com

Management and Staff

Gary Stevenson, President
J.R. Hyde, General Partner
Stephen Snowdy, Principal

Type of Firm

Private Equity Firm

Project Preferences

Role in Financing:
Prefer role as deal originator

Type of Financing Preferred:
Early Stage
Later Stage
Seed

Geographical Preferences

United States Preferences:
Tennessee
Southeast

Industry Preferences

In Biotechnology prefer:
Biotechnology

In Medical/Health prefer:
Medical Products
Health Services

Additional Information

Name of Most Recent Fund: Memphis Biomed Ventures II, L.P.
Most Recent Fund Was Raised: 05/22/2006
Year Founded: 2001
Capital Under Management: $22,400,000
Current Activity Level: Actively seeking new investments

MBF HEALTHCARE PARTNERS L.P.

121 Alhambra Plaza
Suite 1100
Coral Gables, FL USA 33134
Phone: 305-461-1162
Website: www.mbfhealthcarepartners.com

Management and Staff

Isabel Pena, Chief Financial Officer
Jorge Rico, Managing Director
Marcio Cabrera, Managing Director

Type of Firm

Private Equity Firm

Project Preferences

Type of Financing Preferred:
Leveraged Buyout
Balanced

Geographical Preferences

United States Preferences:
All U.S.

Industry Preferences

In Medical/Health prefer:
Health Services

Additional Information

Year Founded: 2005
Capital Under Management: $200,000,000
Current Activity Level: Actively seeking new investments

MBG BADEN-WUERTEMBERG GMBH

Werastrasse 15-17
Stuttgart, Germany 70182
Phone: 49-7111-6456
Fax: 49-7111-645-777
E-mail: info@mbg.de
Website: www.mbg.de

Type of Firm

Government Affiliated Program

Association Membership

German Venture Capital Association (BVK)

Project Preferences

Type of Financing Preferred:

Expansion
Seed
Management Buyouts
Startup
Recapitalizations

Geographical Preferences

International Preferences:

Germany

Industry Focus

(% based on actual investment)

Medical/Health	100.0%

Additional Information

Year Founded: 1971
Capital Under Management: $446,000,000
Current Activity Level: Actively seeking new investments

MBG SCHLESWIG-HOLSTEIN GMBH

Lorentzendamm 21
Kiel, Germany 24103
Phone: 49-431667013586
Fax: 49-431667013590
E-mail: info@mbg-sh.de
Website: www.mbg-sh.de

Management and Staff

Georg Banner, Partner
Gerd Ruediger, Chief Executive Officer
Hans-Peter Petersen, General Director

Type of Firm

Private Equity Firm

Association Membership

German Venture Capital Association (BVK)

Project Preferences

Type of Financing Preferred:

Leveraged Buyout
Mezzanine
Generalist PE
Seed
Startup

Geographical Preferences

International Preferences:

Germany

Industry Focus

(% based on actual investment)

Internet Specific	100.0%

Additional Information

Year Founded: 1994
Current Activity Level: Actively seeking new investments

MBK PARTNERS

20/F, Seoul Finace Center
84, Taepyung-ro-1-ka, Chung-ku
Seoul, South Korea 100768
Phone: 822-3706-8600
Fax: 822-3706-8615
Website: www.mbkpartnerslp.com

Other Offices

4/F, Akasaka Intercity
1-11-44 Akasaka, Minato-ku
Tokyo, Japan 107-0052
Phone: 813-6229-7960
Fax: 813-6229-7969

Suite 1507, Cheung Kong Center
2 Queen's Road Central
Hong Kong, Hong Kong
Phone: 852-2296-0000
Fax: 852-2297-0038

Unit 3904, K. Wah Center
1010 Huai Hai Middle Road
Shanghai, China 200031
Phone: 86-21-5404-8787
Fax: 86-21-5404-8996

Management and Staff

Kuo-Chuan Kung, Partner

Type of Firm

Private Equity Firm

Project Preferences

Type of Financing Preferred:

Leveraged Buyout

Geographical Preferences

International Preferences:

China
Korea, South
Japan

Industry Preferences

In Communications prefer:

Telecommunications

In Consumer Related prefer:

Consumer Products

In Industrial/Energy prefer:

Industrial Products

In Financial Services prefer:

Financial Services

In Business Serv. prefer:

Services

Additional Information

Year Founded: 2005
Capital Under Management: $3,160,000,000
Current Activity Level: Actively seeking new investments

MBL VENTURE CAPITAL CO., LTD.

Sumitomoshoji Marunouchi Bldg.
5F, 5-10 Marunouchi 3-chome
Nagoya, Japan 460-0002
Website: www.mblvc.co.jp

Other Offices

Shinsei Bldg. 4F, 4-15 Uchikanada
1-chome, Chiyoda-ku
Tokyo, Japan 101-0047

Type of Firm

Private Equity Firm

Project Preferences

Type of Financing Preferred:

Balanced

Geographical Preferences

International Preferences:

Japan

Additional Information

Year Founded: 2000
Current Activity Level: Actively seeking new investments

MBMV MECKLENBURG-VORPOMMERN MBH

Am Grunen Tal 19
Schwerin, Germany 19031
Phone: 49-385-395-550

Fax: 49-385-395-5546
E-mail: info@mbm-v.de
Website: www.mbm-v.de

Management and Staff

Hans-Jurgen Hoerle, Managing Director
Wolfgang Strutz, Managing Director

Type of Firm

Bank Affiliated

Association Membership

German Venture Capital Association (BVK)

Project Preferences

Type of Financing Preferred:

Expansion
Seed
Management Buyouts
Startup
Recapitalizations

Size of Investments Considered:

Min Size of Investment Considered (000s): $500
Max Size of Investment Considered (000s): $1,000

Geographical Preferences

International Preferences:

Germany

Additional Information

Year Founded: 1997
Current Activity Level: Actively seeking new investments

MBO PARTENAIRES

75 bis, avenue Marceau
Paris, France 75116
Phone: 33-1-5664-1700
Fax: 33-1-5664-1719
E-mail: contact@mbopartenaires.com
Website: www.mbopartenaires.com

Other Offices

Espace Europeen, batiment C
4, allee Claude Debussy
Ecully, France 69130
Phone: 33-4-7833-9710
Fax: 33-4-7833-0871

Management and Staff

Eric Dejoie, Partner
Hubert Meraud, Partner
Jean-Michel Rallet, Partner
Jerome De Metz, Partner
Richard Broche, Partner

Type of Firm

Private Equity Firm

Association Membership

French Venture Capital Association (AFIC)
European Private Equity and Venture Capital Assoc.

Project Preferences

Type of Financing Preferred:

Leveraged Buyout
Management Buyouts

Geographical Preferences

International Preferences:

Europe
France

Additional Information

Name of Most Recent Fund: MBO Capital 2, FCPR
Most Recent Fund Was Raised: 06/06/2006
Year Founded: 2002
Capital Under Management: $125,800,000
Current Activity Level: Actively seeking new investments

MC CAPITAL, INC.

655 Third Avenue
2nd Floor
New York, NY USA 10017
Phone: 212-644-1843
Fax: 212-644-2926

Type of Firm

Corporate PE/Venture

Project Preferences

Role in Financing:

Prefer role in deals created by others

Type of Financing Preferred:

Fund of Funds
Second Stage Financing
Leveraged Buyout
Expansion
Generalist PE
Turnaround
Later Stage
First Stage Financing
Acquisition
Joint Ventures
Private Placement
Special Situation

Size of Investments Considered:

Min Size of Investment Considered (000s): $1,000
Max Size of Investment Considered (000s): $30,000

Geographical Preferences

United States Preferences:

All U.S.

Canadian Preferences:

All Canada

International Preferences:

All International

Industry Preferences

In Communications prefer:

Communications and Media

In Computer Hardware prefer:

Computers

In Semiconductor/Electr prefer:

Electronics

In Biotechnology prefer:

Biotechnology

In Medical/Health prefer:

Medical/Health

Additional Information

Year Founded: 1991
Capital Under Management: $200,000,000
Current Activity Level: Actively seeking new investments
Method of Compensation: Return on investment is of primary concern, do not charge fees

---

MC3 VENTURES (FKA: MCKENNA VENTURE ACCELERATOR (MVA))

2130 Pierce Street
San Francisco, CA USA 94115
Phone: 415-290-5532
Other Offices
2350 W. El Camino Real
Suite 210
Mountain View, CA USA 94040

Management and Staff

David McDonnell, Managing Partner
Eric Hall, Venture Partner
Pawan Mehra, Principal
Piers Cooper, Managing Partner
Steve McGrath, Managing Partner

Type of Firm

Private Equity Firm

Project Preferences

Type of Financing Preferred:

Early Stage

Industry Preferences

In Communications prefer:

Telecommunications
Wireless Communications

In Computer Software prefer:

Software

In Medical/Health prefer:

Medical/Health

Additional Information

Year Founded: 2000
Capital Under Management: $25,000,000
Current Activity Level: Reducing investment activity

MCCALL SPRINGER

15332 Antioch Street
Suite 801
Pacific Palisades, CA USA 90272
Phone: 310-573-1172
Website: www.mccallspringer.com

Other Offices

Calle Freixa 37
4th Floor
Barcelona, Spain 08021
Phone: 34-678-49-0150

Type of Firm

Private Equity Firm

Project Preferences

Role in Financing:
Prefer role as deal originator

Type of Financing Preferred:
Leveraged Buyout
Turnaround
Later Stage

Industry Preferences

In Communications prefer:
Telecommunications

In Consumer Related prefer:
Food/Beverage
Consumer Products

In Financial Services prefer:
Real Estate
Financial Services

Additional Information

Year Founded: 1997
Current Activity Level: Actively seeking new investments
Method of Compensation: Return on invest. most important, but chg. closing fees, service fees, etc.

MCCARTHY GROUP, INC.

1125 South 103rd Plaza
Suite 450
Omaha, NE USA 68124
Phone: 402-393-1300
Fax: 402-393-2369
E-mail: info@mccarthyco.com
Website: www.mccarthygroupinc.com

Management and Staff

Robert Emmert, Partner

Type of Firm

Private Equity Firm

Additional Information

Year Founded: 1986
Current Activity Level: Actively seeking new investments

MCG MASTER CONSULTING AG

Zugerstrasse 70
Baar, Switzerland 6340
Phone: 41-41-760-65-45
Fax: 41-41-760-14-40
E-mail: master.consulting@mcg-ch.com
Website: www.mcg-ch.com

Type of Firm

Private Equity Firm

Additional Information

Current Activity Level: Actively seeking new investments

MCGOVERN CAPITAL LLC

16 Roundhill Road
Greenwich, CT USA 06831
Phone: 203-622-1101
Fax: 203-622-9192
Website: www.mcgoverncapital.com

Other Offices

721 Fifth Avenue
Suite 52D
New York, NY USA 10022
Phone: 212-755-8661
Fax: 212-755-8663

Management and Staff

Kevin McGovern, Chairman & CEO

Type of Firm

Private Equity Firm

Project Preferences

Type of Financing Preferred:
Early Stage
Seed

Additional Information

Current Activity Level: Actively seeking new investments

MCGRAW-HILL VENTURES (FKA: MCGRAW-HILL CAPITAL CORP.)

1221 Avenue of the Americas
47th Floor
New York, NY USA 10020-1095
Phone: 212-512-2000
Fax: 212-512-6797
E-mail: ventures@mcgraw-hill.com
Website: www.mcgraw-hill.com

Management and Staff

Brian Casey, Vice President

Type of Firm

Corporate PE/Venture

Project Preferences

Role in Financing:
Prefer role in deals created by others

Type of Financing Preferred:
Second Stage Financing
Early Stage
Expansion
Later Stage

Size of Investments Considered:
Min Size of Investment Considered (000s): $500
Max Size of Investment Considered (000s): $5,000

Geographical Preferences

United States Preferences:
All U.S.

International Preferences:
All International

Industry Preferences

In Communications prefer:
Communications and Media
Commercial Communications
Radio & TV Broadcasting
Wireless Communications
Data Communications
Media and Entertainment

In Computer Software prefer:
Software
Applications Software
Artificial Intelligence

In Internet Specific prefer:
E-Commerce Technology
Internet
Web Aggregration/Portals

In Medical/Health prefer:
Medical/Health

In Consumer Related prefer:
Education Related

In Industrial/Energy prefer:
Energy

In Financial Services prefer:
Financial Services
Real Estate

In Business Serv. prefer:
Consulting Services
Media

In Manufact. prefer:
Publishing

Additional Information

Year Founded: 1995
Capital Under Management: $125,000,000
Current Activity Level: Actively seeking new investments
Method of Compensation: Return on investment is of primary concern, do not charge fees

MCH PRIVATE EQUITY S.A.

Plaza de Colon 2
Torre 1, Planta 15
Madrid, Spain 28046
Phone: 34-91-426-4444
Fax: 34-91-426-4440
E-mail: mch@mch.es
Website: www.mch.es

Management and Staff

Andres Pelaez, Partner
Jaime Hernandez Soto, Partner
Javier Herrero Sorriqueta, Partner
Jose Munoz, Partner

Type of Firm

Private Equity Advisor or Fund of Funds

Association Membership

European Private Equity and Venture Capital Assoc.
Spanish Venture Capital Association (ASCRI)

Project Preferences

Type of Financing Preferred:
Second Stage Financing
Leveraged Buyout
Expansion
Seed

Geographical Preferences

International Preferences:
Portugal
Spain

Industry Preferences

In Communications prefer:
Telecommunications

In Internet Specific prefer:
Internet

In Industrial/Energy prefer:
Industrial Products

In Business Serv. prefer:
Services

Additional Information

Year Founded: 1998
Capital Under Management: $662,600,000
Current Activity Level: Actively seeking new investments

MCI MANAGEMENT

Budynek Business Renaissance
Sw. Mikolaja, Street7
Wroclaw, Poland 50-125
Phone: 48-71-781-7380
Fax: 48-71-781-7383
E-mail: office@mci.com.pl
Website: www.mci.com.pl

Other Offices

V Tunich 10
Prague, Czech Republic 120 00
Phone: 420-296-202-055
Fax: 420-296-202-210

Metav Business Centre, Bldg. F, 2nd fl.
Biharia-Street 67-77
Bucharest, Romania

Suite 3
69 Harrington Gardens
London, United Kingdom SW7 4JZ
Phone: 44-79-8942-5755
Fax: 44-20-8354-3371

IPC Business Center, Bldg. A, 2nd floor
ul. Koszykowa-Street 54
Warsaw, Poland 00-675

Management and Staff

Roman Matkiwsky, Partner
Tomasz Czechowisz, President

Type of Firm

Private Equity Firm

Association Membership

Polish Venture Capital Association (PSIC/PPEA)
European Private Equity and Venture Capital Assoc.

Project Preferences

Type of Financing Preferred:
Expansion

Geographical Preferences

International Preferences:
Central Europe
Poland
Eastern Europe

Industry Preferences

In Communications prefer:
Telecommunications

In Computer Software prefer:
Software

In Internet Specific prefer:
Internet

Additional Information

Year Founded: 1998
Capital Under Management: $14,600,000
Current Activity Level: Actively seeking new investments

MCLEAN WATSON CAPITAL INC.

One First Canadian Place
Suite 1410 P.O. Box 129
Toronto, Canada M5X 1A4
Phone: 416-363-2000
Fax: 416-363-2010
E-mail: info@mcleanwatson.com
Website: www.mcleanwatson.com

Other Offices

Sixty Two John Street
Ottawa, Canada K1M 1M3

04-01, 3 Killiney Road
Winsland House 1
Singapore, Singapore 239519
Phone: 65-6424-0889
Fax: 65-67467117

Management and Staff

Emil Savov, Partner
John Eckert, Partner
John Stewart, Partner
Mclean Owen Loudon, Partner
Stanley Pui-Ling Chan, General Partner
Zachhaeus Boon, Partner

Type of Firm

Private Equity Firm

Association Membership

Singapore Venture Capital Association (SVCA)

Project Preferences

Role in Financing:
Prefer role as deal originator but will also invest in deals created by others

Type of Financing Preferred:
Second Stage Financing
Early Stage
Expansion
Balanced
Later Stage
First Stage Financing

Geographical Preferences

United States Preferences:
All U.S.

Canadian Preferences:
All Canada

International Preferences:
Asia

Industry Preferences

In Communications prefer:
Commercial Communications
Telecommunications
Data Communications
Satellite Microwave Comm.

In Computer Software prefer:
Software

In Computer Other prefer:
Computer Related

In Semiconductor/Electr prefer:
Semiconductor
Laser Related
Fiber Optics

Additional Information

Name of Most Recent Fund: McLean Watson Ventures II, L.P..
Most Recent Fund Was Raised: 01/01/1999
Year Founded: 1993
Capital Under Management: $76,400,000
Current Activity Level: Actively seeking new investments
Method of Compensation: Return on investment is of primary concern, do not charge fees

MCM CAPITAL PARTNERS, LP

25101 Chagrin Boulevard
Suite 310
Cleveland, OH USA 44122
Phone: 216-514-1840
Fax: 216-514-1850
Website: www.mcmcapital.com

Management and Staff

James Poffenberger, Managing Director
Mark Mansour, Managing Director

Type of Firm

Private Equity Firm

Project Preferences

Role in Financing:

Prefer role as deal originator but will also invest in deals created by others

Type of Financing Preferred:

Leveraged Buyout
Management Buyouts
Distressed Debt
Recapitalizations

Size of Investments Considered:

Min Size of Investment Considered (000s): $2,000
Max Size of Investment Considered (000s): $7,500

Industry Preferences

In Business Serv. prefer:

Distribution

In Manufact. prefer:

Manufacturing

Additional Information

Year Founded: 1992
Capital Under Management: $50,000,000
Current Activity Level: Actively seeking new investments

MEAKEM BECKER VENTURE CAPITAL

603 Beaver Street
Sewickley, PA USA 15143
Phone: 412-749-5720
Fax: 412-745-5721
E-mail: info@mbvc.com
Website: www.mbvc.com

Management and Staff

Alan Veeck, Principal
David Becker, Managing Director
Glen Meakem, Managing General Partner

Type of Firm

Private Equity Firm

Project Preferences

Role in Financing:

Prefer role as deal originator but will also invest in deals created by others

Type of Financing Preferred:

Early Stage

Size of Investments Considered:

Min Size of Investment Considered (000s): $1,000
Max Size of Investment Considered (000s): $10,000

Geographical Preferences

United States Preferences:

Mid Atlantic
Southeast
Northern California

Industry Preferences

In Communications prefer:

Wireless Communications

In Computer Software prefer:

Computer Services
Data Processing
Software
Systems Software
Applications Software
Artificial Intelligence

In Internet Specific prefer:

E-Commerce Technology
Internet
Ecommerce
Web Aggregration/Portals

In Semiconductor/Electr prefer:

Semiconductor
Sensors

In Business Serv. prefer:

Services

Additional Information

Name of Most Recent Fund: Meakem Becker Venture Capital I, L.P.
Most Recent Fund Was Raised: 08/31/2006
Year Founded: 2005
Capital Under Management: $75,000,000
Current Activity Level: Actively seeking new investments
Method of Compensation: Return on investment is of primary concern, do not charge fees

MED OPPORTUNITY PARTNERS LLC

Two Sound View Drive
Suite 100
Greenwich, CT USA 06830
Phone: 203-622-1333
Fax: 203-622-1332
Website: www.medopportunity.com

Management and Staff

James Breckenridge, Partner
Robert Vaters, Partner
Vicente Trelles, Partner

Type of Firm

Private Equity Firm

Project Preferences

Type of Financing Preferred:

Leveraged Buyout
Expansion
Recapitalizations

Size of Investments Considered:

Min Size of Investment Considered (000s): $5,000
Max Size of Investment Considered (000s): $30,000

Geographical Preferences

United States Preferences:

All U.S.

Industry Preferences

In Medical/Health prefer:

Medical/Health
Health Services
Pharmaceuticals

Additional Information

Year Founded: 2006
Current Activity Level: Actively seeking new investments

MEDCAP AB (FKA: NEW SCIENCE SVENSKA AB)

Bragevagen 6
Stockholm, Sweden SE-114 26
Phone: 46-8-347-110
Fax: 46-8-347-120
E-mail: info@medcap.se
Website: www.medcap.se

Management and Staff

Sten Soderberg, Chief Financial Officer
Sverker Littorin, Chief Executive Officer

Type of Firm

Private Equity Firm

Association Membership

European Private Equity and Venture Capital Assoc.

Project Preferences

Type of Financing Preferred:
Balanced

Geographical Preferences

International Preferences:
Sweden

Additional Information
Year Founded: 2006
Current Activity Level: Actively seeking new investments

MEDCAPITAL

4287 Beltline Road
Suite 307
Addison, TX USA 75001
Phone: 972-385-8500
Fax: 972-385-8757
E-mail: info@medcapitalgroup.com
Website: www.medcapitalgroup.com

Type of Firm

Private Equity Firm

Additional Information

Year Founded: 2009
Current Activity Level: Actively seeking new investments

MEDEQUITY INVESTORS LLC

16 Laurel Avenue
Suite 150
Wellesley Hills, MA USA 02481
Phone: 781-237-6910
Fax: 781-237-6911
E-mail: info@medequity.com
Website: www.medequity.com

Management and Staff

Jeffrey Ward, Partner
Peter Gates, Partner
W. Brandon Ingersoll, Partner

Type of Firm

Private Equity Firm

Project Preferences

Role in Financing:
Prefer role as deal originator

Type of Financing Preferred:
Expansion
Balanced
Later Stage
Acquisition

Size of Investments Considered:
Min Size of Investment Considered (000s): $5,000
Max Size of Investment Considered (000s): $40,000

Geographical Preferences

United States Preferences:
All U.S.

Industry Preferences

In Medical/Health prefer:
Medical/Health
Health Services

Additional Information

Name of Most Recent Fund: MedEquity Capital, LLC
Most Recent Fund Was Raised: 11/14/2002
Year Founded: 1998
Capital Under Management: $100,000,000
Current Activity Level: Actively seeking new investments

MEDFOCUS FUND LLC

13900 Alton Parkway
Suite 125
Irvine, CA USA 92618
Phone: 949-581-7250
Fax: 949-581-4761
Website: www.fund-mgmt.com

Management and Staff

Michael Henson, Founder

Type of Firm

Private Equity Firm

Project Preferences

Type of Financing Preferred:
Early Stage

Geographical Preferences

United States Preferences:
All U.S.

Industry Preferences

In Medical/Health prefer:
Medical Products

Additional Information

Year Founded: 2001
Current Activity Level: Actively seeking new investments

MEDFORD INVESTMENTS, L.P.

700 Louisiana
Suite 1100
Houston, TX USA 77030
Phone: 713-650-3330
Fax: 713-654-8710

Management and Staff

Gary Winston, Managing Director

Type of Firm

Private Equity Firm

Project Preferences

Role in Financing:
Will function either as deal originator or investor in deals created by others

Type of Financing Preferred:
Leveraged Buyout
Mezzanine
Generalist PE
Later Stage
Management Buyouts
Acquisition
Private Placement
Recapitalizations

Size of Investments Considered:
Min Size of Investment Considered (000s): $2,000
Max Size of Investment Considered (000s): $10,000

Geographical Preferences

United States Preferences:
All U.S.

Industry Preferences

In Semiconductor/Electr prefer:
Electronic Components
Semiconductor
Component Testing Equipmt

In Medical/Health prefer:
Diagnostic Services
Medical Products
Disposable Med. Products
Health Services
Hospitals/Clinics/Primary
Hospital/Other Instit.

In Consumer Related prefer:
Consumer
Retail
Franchises(NEC)
Food/Beverage

In Industrial/Energy prefer:
Energy
Industrial Products
Machinery

In Transportation prefer:
Transportation
Aerospace

In Financial Services prefer:
Financial Services
Insurance
Real Estate

In Business Serv. prefer:
Services
Distribution
Media

In Manufact. prefer:
Manufacturing

In Agr/Forestr/Fish prefer:
Agriculture related

In Utilities prefer:
Utilities

In Other prefer:
Socially Responsible
Environment Responsible
Women/Minority-Owned Bus.

Additional Information

Year Founded: 2003
Capital Under Management: $50,000,000
Current Activity Level: Actively seeking new investments
Method of Compensation: Return on invest. most important, but chg. closing fees, service fees, etc.

MEDIA & PRINT INVESTMENTS PLC

35 Bedford Gardens
London, United Kingdom W8 7EF
Phone: 44-20-7565-9100
Fax: 44-20-7565-9101
E-mail: info@media-print.co.uk
Website: www.media-print.co.uk

Management and Staff

Mike Dolan, Chief Executive Officer

Type of Firm

Private Equity Firm

Project Preferences

Type of Financing Preferred:
Leveraged Buyout

Industry Preferences

In Business Serv. prefer:
Media

In Manufact. prefer:
Publishing

Additional Information

Year Founded: 2007
Current Activity Level: Actively seeking new investments

MEDIA VENTURE PARTNERS

Two Jackson Street
Suite 100
San Francisco, CA USA 94111
Phone: 415-391-4877
Fax: 415-391-4912
Website: www.mediaventurepartners.com

Other Offices

6314 Brookside Plaza
Suite 203
Kansas City, MO USA 64113
Phone: 816-817-0570
Fax: 816-820-0169

75 State Street
Suite 2500
Boston, MA USA 02109
Phone: 617-345-7316
Fax: 617-507-5667

Management and Staff

Adam Altsuler, Vice President
Brian Pryor, Vice President
Elliot Evers, Managing Director
Greg Widroe, Managing Director
Jason Hill, Managing Director
R. Clayton Funk, Managing Director

Type of Firm

Private Equity Advisor or Fund of Funds

Project Preferences

Role in Financing:
Prefer role as deal originator but will also invest in deals created by others

Type of Financing Preferred:
Balanced

Geographical Preferences

United States Preferences:
All U.S.

Additional Information

Year Founded: 1987
Current Activity Level: Actively seeking new investments
Method of Compensation: Return on investment is of primary concern, do not charge fees

---

MEDIA VENTURES GMBH

Wesselinger Strasse 22-30
Cologne, Germany 50999
Phone: 49-2236-480100
Fax: 49-2236-4801001
E-mail: info@mediaventures.de
Website: www.mediaventures.de

Management and Staff

Dirk Stroeer, Chief Executive Officer
Peter Richarz, Chief Executive Officer

Type of Firm

Private Equity Firm

Project Preferences

Type of Financing Preferred:
Early Stage
Expansion
Startup

Geographical Preferences

International Preferences:
Germany

Industry Preferences

In Communications prefer:
Communications and Media

Additional Information

Year Founded: 2006
Current Activity Level: Actively seeking new investments

MEDICA VENTURE PARTNERS

10F, Bldg. B, Ackerstein Tower
11 HaManofim Street
Herzlia, Israel 46725
Phone: 972-9-960-1900
Fax: 972-9-954-2266
E-mail: medica@medicavp.com
Website: www.medicavp.com

Management and Staff

Batsheva Elran, Managing Partner
Jonathan Fleming, Founder
Pennina Safer, Vice President
Yoav Walzer, Chief Financial Officer

Type of Firm

Private Equity Firm

Association Membership

Israel Venture Association

Project Preferences

Type of Financing Preferred:
Early Stage
Expansion
Balanced
Seed
Later Stage
Startup
Special Situation

Size of Investments Considered:
Min Size of Investment Considered (000s): $500
Max Size of Investment Considered (000s): $3,000

Geographical Preferences

International Preferences:
Europe
Israel
Asia

Industry Preferences

In Biotechnology prefer:
Biotechnology

In Medical/Health prefer:
Medical/Health
Medical Therapeutics
Pharmaceuticals

Additional Information

Year Founded: 1995

Capital Under Management: $80,000,000
Current Activity Level: Actively seeking new investments

MEDICAL INNOVATIONS MANAGEMENT, INC.

1095 West Pender Street
Suite 1120
Vancouver, Canada V6E 2M6
Phone: 604-689-0305
Fax: 604-872-2977
E-mail: info@bcmif.com
Website: www.bcmif.com

Management and Staff

Darrell Elliott, Chairman & CEO
Tony Flynn, President

Type of Firm

Private Equity Firm

Project Preferences

Type of Financing Preferred:
Balanced

Geographical Preferences

Canadian Preferences:
All Canada

Additional Information

Year Founded: 2003
Capital Under Management: $1,500,000
Current Activity Level: Actively seeking new investments

MEDICIS AG

Stollbergstrasse 22
Munich, Germany D-80539
Phone: 49-89-5447-920
Fax: 49-89-5447-9222
Website: www.medicis.de

Management and Staff

Matthias Ackermann, Partner
Michael Muth, Partner
Michael Steiner, Partner

Type of Firm

Private Equity Firm

Association Membership

European Private Equity and Venture Capital Assoc.

Project Preferences

Type of Financing Preferred:
Early Stage
Expansion
Seed
Startup

Geographical Preferences

International Preferences:
Europe
Israel

Industry Preferences

In Internet Specific prefer:
Internet

In Biotechnology prefer:
Biotechnology

In Medical/Health prefer:
Medical/Health

In Other prefer:
Environment Responsible

Additional Information

Year Founded: 1999
Capital Under Management: $15,200,000
Current Activity Level: Actively seeking new investments

MEDIMMUNE VENTURES

One MedImmune Way
Gaithersburg, MD USA 20878
Phone: 301-398-0000
E-mail: info@medimmune.com
Website: www.medimmune.com

Management and Staff

Eva Jack, Managing Director
Joseph Amprey, Managing Director
Maggie Flanagan LeFlore, Managing Director

Type of Firm

Corporate PE/Venture

Project Preferences

Type of Financing Preferred:
Balanced

Industry Preferences

In Medical/Health prefer:
Medical Therapeutics

Additional Information

Year Founded: 2002
Capital Under Management: $200,000,000
Current Activity Level: Actively seeking new investments

MEDINNOVA PARTNERS, INC.

117 Centrepointe Drive
Suite 340
Nepean, Canada K2G 5X3
Phone: 613-224-4294
Fax: 613-224-8218
Website: www.medinnova.ca

Other Offices

100 International Blvd.
Toronto, Canada M9W 6J6
Phone: 416-213-4674
Fax: 416-213-4232

1480 Carlton Street
Halifax, Canada B3H 3B7
Phone: 902-422-7439
Fax: 902-422-5384

Management and Staff

Brian Underdown, Chief Executive Officer

Type of Firm

Private Equity Firm

Project Preferences

Type of Financing Preferred:
Seed

Additional Information

Year Founded: 2002
Current Activity Level: Actively seeking new investments

MEDIOLANUM STATE STREET SGRPA

Palazzo Meucci Milano 3
via Francesco Sforza
Basiglio, Milan, Italy 20080
Phone: 39-02-90492403
Fax: 39-02-90492040
E-mail: info@mediolanum.it
Website: www.mediolanum.it

Type of Firm

Endowment, Foundation or Pension Fund

Project Preferences

Type of Financing Preferred:
Fund of Funds
Generalist PE
Joint Ventures

Geographical Preferences

International Preferences:
Italy

Additional Information

Year Founded: 2001
Current Activity Level: Actively seeking new investments

MEDIPHASE VENTURE PARTNERS (FKA: EHEALTH TECHNOLOGY FUND)

Three Newton Executive Park
Suite 104
Newton, MA USA 02462
Phone: 617-332-3408
Fax: 617-332-8463
E-mail: info@mediphaseventure.com
Website: www.mediphaseventure.com

Management and Staff

Eileen Driscoll, Chief Financial Officer
Gerry Gallivan, Venture Partner
Lawrence Miller, Partner
Paul Howard, Partner
Robert Dishman, Venture Partner

Type of Firm

Private Equity Firm

Association Membership

National Venture Capital Association - USA (NVCA)

Project Preferences

Type of Financing Preferred:
Early Stage

Geographical Preferences

United States Preferences:
All U.S.

Industry Preferences

In Internet Specific prefer:
Internet

In Medical/Health prefer:
Medical/Health
Drug/Equipmt Delivery

Additional Information

Year Founded: 2000
Capital Under Management: $20,000,000
Current Activity Level: Actively seeking new investments

MEDTECH PARTNERS, INC.

117 Centrepoint Drive
Suite 340
Nepean, Canada K2G 5X3
Phone: 613-224-4294
Fax: 613-224-8218
Website: www.medtechpartners.com

Management and Staff

Brian Underdown, Chief Executive Officer

Type of Firm

Private Equity Firm

Additional Information

Year Founded: 1997
Current Activity Level: Actively seeking new investments

MEDVENTURE ASSOCIATES (AKA: MVA)

5980 Horton Street
Suite 390
Emeryville, CA USA 94608
Phone: 510-597-7979
Fax: 510-597-9920
E-mail: medven@medven.com
Website: www.medven.com

Management and Staff

Charles Liamos, Partner
Christopher Kaster, Partner
David Holbrooke, Venture Partner
Michael Laufer, Venture Partner
Philip Oyer, Venture Partner
Robert Momsen, Venture Partner
Wally Buch, Venture Partner

Type of Firm

Private Equity Firm

Association Membership

Western Association of Venture Capitalists (WAVC)

Project Preferences

Role in Financing:
Prefer role as deal originator but will also invest in deals created by others

Type of Financing Preferred:
Early Stage
Seed
First Stage Financing
Startup

Size of Investments Considered:
Min Size of Investment Considered (000s): $2,000
Max Size of Investment Considered (000s): $5,000

Geographical Preferences

United States Preferences:
Northwest
Southern California
Northern California
Rocky Mountain
West Coast
California
Southwest

Industry Focus

(% based on actual investment)	
Medical/Health	77.4%
Biotechnology	10.6%
Computer Software and Services	7.3%
Internet Specific	4.4%
Communications and Media	0.3%

Additional Information

Name of Most Recent Fund: MedVenture Affiliates V, L.P.
Most Recent Fund Was Raised: 10/06/2004
Year Founded: 1986
Capital Under Management: $325,000,000
Current Activity Level: Reducing investment activity
Method of Compensation: Return on investment is of primary concern, do not charge fees

MEDVEST

601 13th Street Northwest
Suite 710 North
Washington, DC USA 20005
Phone: 202-638-3356

Type of Firm

Incubator/Development Program
Industry Preferences

In Medical/Health prefer:
Medical/Health

Additional Information

Year Founded: 2002
Current Activity Level: Actively seeking new investments

MEGUNTICOOK MANAGEMENT

143 Newbury Street
Sixth Floor
Boston, MA USA 02116
Phone: 617-986-3000
Fax: 617-986-3100
Website: www.megunticook.com

Management and Staff

Lynne Anderson, Chief Financial Officer
Michelle Fortier, Principal
Thomas Matlack, Managing General Partner

Type of Firm

Private Equity Firm

Project Preferences

Role in Financing:
Prefer role as deal originator but will also invest in deals created by others

Type of Financing Preferred:
Second Stage Financing
Early Stage

Size of Investments Considered:
Min Size of Investment Considered (000s): $1,000
Max Size of Investment Considered (000s): $8,000

Geographical Preferences

United States Preferences:
Northeast

Industry Focus

(% based on actual investment)

Computer Software and Services	22.4%
Internet Specific	19.6%
Semiconductors/Other Elect.	17.9%
Other Products	15.6%
Communications and Media	12.8%
Consumer Related	9.3%
Computer Hardware	2.5%

Additional Information

Year Founded: 1998
Capital Under Management: $159,000,000
Current Activity Level: Actively seeking new investments

MEIJI CAPITAL CO., LTD.

3F Meiji Seimei-kan
2-1-1 Marunouchi, Chiyoda-ku
Tokyo, Japan 100-0005
Phone: 81-3-3283-8705
Fax: 81-3-3212-8048
E-mail: customer@meijicc.co.jp
Website: www.meijicc.co.jp

Other Offices

7F Meiji Yasuda Seimei SakaisujiHoncho
1-7-15 MInamihoncho,Chuo-ku
Osaka, Japan 541-0054
Phone: 81-6-6266-9007
Fax: 81-6-6266-9008

Management and Staff

Kunio Momoi, President

Type of Firm

Insurance Firm Affiliate

Additional Information

Year Founded: 1992
Current Activity Level: Actively seeking new investments

MEKONG CAPITAL, LTD.

Capital Place, 8th Floor
6 Thai Van Lung St., Dist. 1
Ho Chi Minh, Vietnam
Phone: 84-8-3827-3161
Fax: 84-8-3827-3162
E-mail: info@mekongcapital.com
Website: www.mekongcapital.com

Other Offices

12th Floor, HAREC Building
4A Lang Ha Street, Ba Dinh District
Hanoi, Vietnam
Phone: 844-772-4888
Fax: 844-772-4868

Management and Staff

Chris Freund, Managing Partner
Dzung Le Manh, Principal
Hong Tran Thi Thu, Principal

Type of Firm

Private Equity Firm

Project Preferences

Type of Financing Preferred:

Leveraged Buyout
Expansion
Balanced

Geographical Preferences

International Preferences:

Laos
Vietnam
Cambodia

Industry Preferences

In Computer Software prefer:

Software

In Consumer Related prefer:

Consumer
Retail
Consumer Products

In Financial Services prefer:

Financial Services

In Business Serv. prefer:

Distribution
Consulting Services

In Manufact. prefer:

Manufacturing

In Agr/Forestr/Fish prefer:

Agriculture related

Additional Information

Year Founded: 2001
Capital Under Management: $18,500,000
Current Activity Level: Actively seeking new investments

MELLON BANK, N.A.

One Mellon Bank Center
39th Floor
Pittsburgh, PA USA 15258
Phone: 412-236-0299
Fax: 412-234-6179
Website: www.mellon.com

Type of Firm

Private Equity Advisor or Fund of Funds

Project Preferences

Type of Financing Preferred:

Fund of Funds

Geographical Preferences

United States Preferences:

All U.S.

Additional Information

Year Founded: 1983
Capital Under Management: $350,000,000
Current Activity Level: Actively seeking new investments

MENLO VENTURES

3000 Sand Hill Road
Building Four, Suite 100
Menlo Park, CA USA 94025
Phone: 650-854-8540
Fax: 650-854-7059
E-mail: info@menloventures.com
Website: www.menloventures.com

Management and Staff

Arvind Purushotham, Managing Director
Douglas Carlisle, Managing Director
H. DuBose Montgomery, Managing Director
Hal Calhoun, Managing Director
John Jarve, Managing Director
Kirsten Mello, Chief Financial Officer
Mark Siegel, Managing Director
Pravin Vazirani, Managing Director
Shawn Carolan, Managing Director
Sonja Perkins, Managing Director
Thomas Bredt, Venture Partner

Type of Firm

Private Equity Firm

Association Membership

Western Association of Venture Capitalists (WAVC)
National Venture Capital Association - USA (NVCA)

Project Preferences

Role in Financing:

Prefer role as deal originator but will also invest in deals created by others

Type of Financing Preferred:

Second Stage Financing
Early Stage
Expansion
Balanced
Start-up Financing
Later Stage
First Stage Financing

Size of Investments Considered:

Min Size of Investment Considered (000s): $5,000
Max Size of Investment Considered (000s): $20,000

Geographical Preferences

United States Preferences:

All U.S.

Industry Focus

(% based on actual investment)

Computer Software and Services	27.7%
Communications and Media	21.3%
Internet Specific	19.6%
Semiconductors/Other Elect.	13.3%
Medical/Health	6.5%

Computer Hardware	6.1%
Other Products	3.4%
Consumer Related	1.1%
Biotechnology	0.8%
Industrial/Energy	0.1%

Additional Information

Name of Most Recent Fund: Menlo Ventures X, L.P.
Most Recent Fund Was Raised: 04/06/2005
Year Founded: 1976
Capital Under Management: $3,900,000,000
Current Activity Level: Actively seeking new investments
Method of Compensation: Return on investment is of primary concern, do not charge fees

MENTHA CAPITAL BV

Nieuwendammerdijk 538
Amsterdam, Netherlands 1023 BX
Phone: 31-20-6363-140
E-mail: info@menthacapital.com
Website: www.menthacapital.com

Management and Staff

Edo Pfennings, Partner
Gijs Botman, Managing Partner
Raymond Van Nass, Partner

Type of Firm

Private Equity Firm

Project Preferences

Role in Financing:
Prefer role as deal originator but will also invest in deals created by others

Additional Information

Year Founded: 2006
Current Activity Level: Actively seeking new investments

MENTOR CAPITAL GROUP

16371 Belmont Avenue
Monte Sereno, CA USA 95030
Phone: 408-354-6592
Fax: 408-354-6592
Website: www.mentorcapitalpartners.com

Management and Staff

Chris Roon, Partner
David Dury, Partner
Joseph Prang, Partner

Type of Firm

Private Equity Firm

Additional Information

Year Founded: 2000
Current Activity Level: Actively seeking new investments

MENTOR CAPITAL PARTNERS

P.O. Box 560
Yardley, PA USA 19067
Phone: 215-736-8882
Fax: 215-736-8882
Website: www.mentorcapitalpartners.com

Management and Staff

Edward Sager, General Partner

Type of Firm

Bank Affiliated

Project Preferences

Role in Financing:
Prefer role as deal originator but will also invest in deals created by others

Type of Financing Preferred:
Leveraged Buyout
Expansion
Mezzanine
Generalist PE
Balanced
Later Stage
Management Buyouts
Acquisition
Special Situation
Recapitalizations

Geographical Preferences

United States Preferences:
Mid Atlantic
Pennsylvania
New Jersey

Industry Focus

(% based on actual investment)

Biotechnology	45.7%
Computer Software and Services	30.9%
Other Products	10.4%
Internet Specific	5.2%
Medical/Health	5.2%
Industrial/Energy	2.6%

Additional Information

Name of Most Recent Fund: Mentor Special Situation Fund, L.P.
Most Recent Fund Was Raised: 01/01/1996
Year Founded: 1996
Capital Under Management: $5,000,000
Current Activity Level: Actively seeking new investments
Method of Compensation: Return on invest. most important, but chg. closing fees, service fees, etc.

MENTOR CONSULTING CORPORATION

30/F, No 6 Min-Chuan
2nd Road
Kaohsiung, Taiwan 806
Phone: 886-7-338-2288
Fax: 886-7-338-7110

Type of Firm

Private Equity Firm

Association Membership

Taiwan Venture Capital Association(TVCA)

Project Preferences

Type of Financing Preferred:
Balanced

Geographical Preferences

International Preferences:
Taiwan
Tanzania

Industry Preferences

In Communications prefer:
Telecommunications

In Semiconductor/Electr prefer:
Semiconductor
Optoelectronics

In Medical/Health prefer:
Medical/Health

In Industrial/Energy prefer:
Advanced Materials

Additional Information

Year Founded: 1999
Capital Under Management: $194,900,000
Current Activity Level: Actively seeking new investments

MERCANTILE BANCORP LIMITED

999 W. Hastings St.
Suite 1508
Vancouver, Canada V6C 2W2
Phone: 604-685-5765
Fax: 604-685-2755
E-mail: corporate@mercantilebancorp.com
Website: www.mercantilebancorp.com

Management and Staff

Bruce Wendel, Managing Partner
Donald Steele, Managing Partner
Ron Chicoyne, Managing Partner

Type of Firm

Private Equity Firm

Project Preferences

Type of Financing Preferred:
Leveraged Buyout
Turnaround
Acquisition

Geographical Preferences

Canadian Preferences:
Western Canada

Additional Information
Year Founded: 1989
Current Activity Level: Actively seeking new investments

MERCANTILE CAPITAL GROUP (MCG)
1372 Shermer Road
Northbrook, IL USA 60062
Phone: 847-509-3711
Fax: 847-509-3715
E-mail: staff@mcgfunds.com
Website: www.mcgfunds.com

Other Offices
400 Park Avenue
Suite 1440
New York, NY USA 10022
Phone: 212-750-5911
Fax: 212-750-5321

Management and Staff
Amit Bhatnagar, Vice President
Andrew Lask, Vice President
Michael Reinsdorf, Managing Director
Mike Solan, Chief Financial Officer
Nathaniel Kramer, Managing Director
Steven Edelson, Managing Director

Type of Firm
Private Equity Firm

Project Preferences

Type of Financing Preferred:
Early Stage
Expansion
Management Buyouts
Industry Rollups

Geographical Preferences

United States Preferences:
All U.S.

Additional Information
Year Founded: 2000
Current Activity Level: Actively seeking new investments

MERCAPITAL SERVICIOS FINANCIEROS
Paseo del Club Deportivo 1
Bldg. 14, Pozuelo de Alarcon
Madrid, Spain 28223
Phone: 34-91-557-8000
Fax: 34-91-344-9191
Website: www.mercapital.com

Management and Staff
Bruno Delgado, Principal
Carlos Barallobre, Partner
Carlos Puente Costales, Partner
Claudio Aguirre, Vice President
David Estefanell, Partner
Manuel Soto, Vice President
Miguel Zurita, Partner
Nicolas Jimenez-Ugarte, Partner
Ramon Carne, Partner

Type of Firm
Private Equity Firm

Association Membership
European Private Equity and Venture Capital Assoc.
Spanish Venture Capital Association (ASCRI)

Project Preferences

Role in Financing:
Will function either as deal originator or investor in deals created by others

Type of Financing Preferred:
Leveraged Buyout
Expansion
Balanced

Size of Investments Considered:
Min Size of Investment Considered (000s): $13,215
Max Size of Investment Considered (000s): $105,722

Geographical Preferences

International Preferences:
Portugal
Spain

Industry Focus
(% based on actual investment)

Consumer Related	35.5%
Other Products	26.7%
Medical/Health	18.3%
Computer Software and Services	8.0%
Communications and Media	7.6%
Industrial/Energy	3.8%
Internet Specific	0.1%

Additional Information
Year Founded: 1985
Capital Under Management: $1,977,100,000
Current Activity Level: Actively seeking new investments

MERCATO PARTNERS
6405 South 3000 East
Salt Lake City, UT USA 84121
Phone: 801-220-0055
Fax: 801-220-0056
E-mail: info@mercatopartners.com
Website: www.mercatopartners.com

Management and Staff
Alan Hall, Managing Director
Greg Warnock, Managing Director
Ken Krull, Principal

Type of Firm
Private Equity Advisor or Fund of Funds

Association Membership
National Venture Capital Association - USA (NVCA)

Project Preferences

Role in Financing:
Will function either as deal originator or investor in deals created by others

Type of Financing Preferred:
Early Stage
Expansion
Balanced
Later Stage

Additional Information
Year Founded: 2009
Current Activity Level: Actively seeking new investments

MERCATOR INVESTMENTS LIMITED
181 Bay Street
Suite 24520
Toronto, Canada M5J 2T3
Phone: 416-865-0003
Fax: 416-865-9699

Management and Staff
Peter Allen, President
Type of Firm
Private Equity Firm

Additional Information
Year Founded: 1996
Current Activity Level: Actively seeking new investments

MERCATTO VENTURE PARTNERS (AKA: MERCATTO GESTAO DE RECURSOS)
Av. Rio Branco 231
17 andar - Centro
Rio de Janeiro, RJ, Brazil 20030-021
Phone: 5521-2142-6779
Fax: 5521-2142-6701
E-mail: contato@mvpweb.com.br
Website: www.mvpweb.com.br

Type of Firm
Corporate PE/Venture

Association Membership
Brazilian Venture Capital Association (ABCR)

Project Preferences

Type of Financing Preferred:
Balanced

Geographical Preferences

International Preferences:
Brazil

Industry Preferences

In Computer Software prefer:
Software

Additional Information

Year Founded: 2000
Current Activity Level: Actively seeking new investments

MERCHANT EQUITY PARTNERS

10 Bruton Street
London, United Kingdom W1J 6PX
Phone: 44-20-7647-7300
Fax: 44-20-7647-7301
E-mail: info@merchantequity.eu
Website: www.merchantequity.eu

Management and Staff

Joshua Spoerri, Principal

Type of Firm

Private Equity Firm

Project Preferences

Type of Financing Preferred:
Turnaround
Acquisition

Geographical Preferences

International Preferences:
Italy
United Kingdom
Sweden
Europe
Netherlands
Luxembourg
Greenland
Iceland
Spain
Germany
Belgium
Finland
Norway
France
Denmark
Faroe Islands

Industry Preferences

In Consumer Related prefer:
Consumer
Retail

Additional Information

Year Founded: 2006
Current Activity Level: Actively seeking new investments

MERCHANTBANC

66 Hanover Street
Suite 303
Manchester, NH USA 03101
Phone: 603-623-5500
Fax: 603-623-3972
E-mail: info@merchantbanc.com
Website: www.merchantbanc.com

Type of Firm

Bank Affiliated

Project Preferences

Type of Financing Preferred:
Balanced

Geographical Preferences

United States Preferences:
All U.S.

Industry Preferences

In Computer Software prefer:
Software

In Computer Other prefer:
Computer Related

In Semiconductor/Electr prefer:
Laser Related

Additional Information

Name of Most Recent Fund: MB Growth Partners II, L.P.
Most Recent Fund Was Raised: 02/14/2006
Year Founded: 1992
Capital Under Management: $11,700,000
Current Activity Level: Actively seeking new investments

MERCHANTBANSA S.A.

1133 Colon Avenue
Third Floor, Arista Building
Quito, Ecuador
Phone: 5932-255-4016
Fax: 5932-250-4113
Website: www.merchantbansa.com

Management and Staff

Edison Ortiz-Duran, President

Type of Firm

Private Equity Firm

Project Preferences

Type of Financing Preferred:
Balanced

Geographical Preferences

International Preferences:
Ecuador

Additional Information

Year Founded: 2004
Capital Under Management: $8,000,000
Current Activity Level: Actively seeking new investments

MERCK CAPITAL VENTURES LLC

50 Tice Boulevard
Woodcliff Lake, NJ USA 07677
Phone: 201-722-5040
Fax: 201-722-5041
Website: www.merckcapitalventures.com

Management and Staff

James Cooper, Partner

Type of Firm

Corporate PE/Venture

Project Preferences

Type of Financing Preferred:
Balanced

Size of Investments Considered:
Min Size of Investment Considered (000s): $3,000
Max Size of Investment Considered (000s): $8,000

Geographical Preferences

United States Preferences:
All U.S.

Industry Preferences

In Internet Specific prefer:
Internet

In Biotechnology prefer:
Biotechnology

In Medical/Health prefer:
Medical/Health
Pharmaceuticals

Additional Information

Year Founded: 2001
Capital Under Management: $100,000,000
Current Activity Level: Actively seeking new investments

MERCURIUS BELEGGINGSMAATSCHAPPIJ B.V.

Alerstraat 126
Heerlen, Netherlands 6417 BR
Phone: 31-45-560-6222
Fax: 31-45-574-0070
E-mail: merc@wxs.nl

Management and Staff
Frits Vromen, Partner
H.N.F. Stienstra, Partner

Type of Firm

Private Equity Firm

Association Membership

European Private Equity and Venture Capital Assoc.
Dutch Venture Capital Associaton (NVP)

Project Preferences

Type of Financing Preferred:

Leveraged Buyout
Early Stage
Balanced
Start-up Financing
Turnaround

Size of Investments Considered:

Min Size of Investment Considered (000s): $300
Max Size of Investment Considered (000s): $300,000

Geographical Preferences

United States Preferences:

All U.S.

International Preferences:

Europe

Industry Preferences

In Communications prefer:

Communications and Media

In Computer Other prefer:

Computer Related

In Semiconductor/Electr prefer:

Electronics

In Biotechnology prefer:

Biotechnology

In Medical/Health prefer:

Medical/Health

In Industrial/Energy prefer:

Energy

Additional Information

Year Founded: 2007
Capital Under Management: $352,500,000
Current Activity Level: Actively seeking new investments

MERCURY CAPITAL PARTNERS

726 Exchange Street
Suite 410
Buffalo, NY USA 14210
Phone: 716-332-9575
Fax: 716-352-9566
E-mail: info@mercurycapitalpartners.com
Website: www.mercurycapitalpartners.com

Other Offices

One Quincy Lane
White Plains, NY USA 10605
Phone: 917-806-6373

5080 Spectrum Drive
Suite 609
Addison, TX USA 75001
Phone: 972-458-9300

Management and Staff

Allan Grafman, Principal
C. Teo Balbach, Principal
Charles Banta, President
Peter Handy, Principal

Type of Firm

Private Equity Firm

Association Membership

Natl Assoc of Small Bus. Inv. Co (NASBIC)

Project Preferences

Type of Financing Preferred:

Leveraged Buyout
Expansion
Balanced
Management Buyouts

Geographical Preferences

United States Preferences:

All U.S.

Industry Focus

(% based on actual investment)

Consumer Related	100.0%

Additional Information

Name of Most Recent Fund: Mercury Capital Partners III, L.P.
Most Recent Fund Was Raised: 03/26/2004
Year Founded: 1994
Capital Under Management: $19,000,000
Current Activity Level: Actively seeking new investments

MERIDIAN CAPITAL (FKA: OLYMPIC CAPITAL PARTNERS, LLC)

2025 First Avenue
Suite 1170
Seattle, WA USA 98121
Phone: 206-623-4000
Fax: 206-623-8221
Website: www.meridianllc.com

Management and Staff

Brandon Pemberton, Managing Director
Chuck Wilke, Managing Director
Randall Miles, Managing Director
Richard Pratt, Principal

Type of Firm

Bank Affiliated

Project Preferences

Type of Financing Preferred:

Acquisition

Industry Focus

(% based on actual investment)

Computer Software and Services	55.3%
Semiconductors/Other Elect.	44.7%

Additional Information

Name of Most Recent Fund: Northwest Opportunity Fund, L.P.
Most Recent Fund Was Raised: 08/29/2002
Year Founded: 1995
Capital Under Management: $10,100,000
Current Activity Level: Actively seeking new investments

MERIDIAN MANAGEMENT GROUP, INC. (AKA: MMG)

826 East Baltimore Street
Baltimore, MD USA 21202-4702
Phone: 410-333-2548
Fax: 410-333-2552
E-mail: contact@mmggroup.com
Website: www.mmggroup.com

Management and Staff

Anthony Williams, Vice President
David Rice, Vice President
Timothy Smoot, Chief Financial Officer

Type of Firm

Incubator/Development Program

Association Membership

Community Development Venture Capital Alliance
National Venture Capital Association - USA (NVCA)

Project Preferences

Type of Financing Preferred:

Balanced

Geographical Preferences

United States Preferences:

Mid Atlantic
Maryland

Industry Focus

(% based on actual investment)

Communications and Media	68.1%
Computer Software and Services	27.4%
Semiconductors/Other Elect.	4.5%

Additional Information

Year Founded: 1998
Capital Under Management: $16,800,000
Current Activity Level: Actively seeking new investments

MERIDIAN VENTURE PARTNERS (MVP)

201 King of Prussia Road
Suite 240
Radnor, PA USA 19087
Phone: 610-254-2999
Fax: 610-254-2996
E-mail: info@meridian-venture.com
Website: www.meridian-venture.com

Management and Staff

Charlotte Arnold, Vice President
Joseph Hawke, General Partner
Robert Auritt, General Partner
Robert Brown, Managing General Partner
Ryan Northington, Vice President
Thomas Penn, General Partner

Type of Firm

SBIC

Association Membership

Mid-Atlantic Venture Association
Natl Assoc of Small Bus. Inv. Co (NASBIC)

Project Preferences

Role in Financing:

Prefer role as deal originator but will also invest in deals created by others

Type of Financing Preferred:

Leveraged Buyout
Expansion
Later Stage
Management Buyouts
Acquisition
Recapitalizations

Size of Investments Considered:

Min Size of Investment Considered (000s): $2,000
Max Size of Investment Considered (000s): $8,000

Geographical Preferences

United States Preferences:

Mid Atlantic
Midwest
Northwest
Northeast

Industry Focus

(% based on actual investment)

Consumer Related	23.3%
Industrial/Energy	19.4%
Other Products	19.3%
Internet Specific	17.1%
Medical/Health	8.4%
Computer Software and Services	8.2%
Biotechnology	3.1%
Communications and Media	0.7%
Computer Hardware	0.5%

Additional Information

Name of Most Recent Fund: Meridian Venture Partners II
Most Recent Fund Was Raised: 11/01/1999
Year Founded: 1987
Capital Under Management: $110,000,000
Current Activity Level: Actively seeking new investments
Method of Compensation: Return on invest. most important, but chg. closing fees, service fees, etc.

MERIDIUS CAPITAL

349 St. Clair Avenue
Suite 111
Toronto, Canada M5P 1N3
Phone: 416-873-4219

Management and Staff

John DeHart, Partner
Richard Strafehl, Principal

Type of Firm

Private Equity Firm

Additional Information

Year Founded: 2009
Current Activity Level: Actively seeking new investments

MERIFIN CAPITAL GROUP

Place Flagey 18
Brussels, Belgium B-1050
Phone: 32-2-646-2580
Fax: 32-2-646-3036
E-mail: enquiries@merifin.com
Website: www.merifin.com

Other Offices

254, Route de Lausanne
Geneva-Chambesy, Switzerland 1292
Phone: 41-22-770-0088
Fax: 41-22-758-0055

Type of Firm

Private Equity Firm

Association Membership

European Private Equity and Venture Capital Assoc.

Project Preferences

Role in Financing:

Will function either as deal originator or investor in deals created by others

Type of Financing Preferred:

Second Stage Financing
Leveraged Buyout
Control-block Purchases
Early Stage
Expansion
Mezzanine
Generalist PE
Turnaround
Management Buyouts
Private Placement
Special Situation

Size of Investments Considered:

Min Size of Investment Considered (000s): $250
Max Size of Investment Considered (000s): $3,000

Geographical Preferences

United States Preferences:

All U.S.

Canadian Preferences:

All Canada

International Preferences:

Italy
United Kingdom
Latin America
Europe
China
Bermuda
Eastern Europe
Spain
Australia
South Africa
Germany
Asia
France

Additional Information

Year Founded: 1980
Current Activity Level: Actively seeking new investments
Method of Compensation: Return on invest. most important, but chg. closing fees, service fees, etc.

MERION INVESTMENT PARTNERS, L.P.

The Merion Building
700 S. Henderson Rd, Ste 210
King of Prussia, PA USA 19406
Phone: 610-992-5880
Fax: 610-945-1654
E-mail: info@merionpartners.com
Website: www.merionpartners.com

Management and Staff

Anthony Caringi, Partner
Edward Rodgers, Partner
Gayle Hughes, Partner
J. Brian O'Neill, Partner
Sam Brewer, Vice President
William Means, Managing Partner

Type of Firm

Private Equity Firm

Association Membership

Natl Assoc of Small Bus. Inv. Co (NASBIC)

Project Preferences

Role in Financing:

Will function either as deal originator or investor in deals created by others

Type of Financing Preferred:
Leveraged Buyout
Expansion
Mezzanine
Later Stage
Management Buyouts
Acquisition
Industry Rollups

Size of Investments Considered:
Min Size of Investment Considered (000s): $3,000
Max Size of Investment Considered (000s): $15,000

Geographical Preferences

United States Preferences:
Mid Atlantic
Midwest
Southeast
Northeast
East Coast

Industry Preferences

In Computer Software prefer:
Software
Applications Software

In Semiconductor/Electr prefer:
Electronic Components

In Medical/Health prefer:
Medical Diagnostics
Diagnostic Services
Diagnostic Test Products
Medical Products
Disposable Med. Products
Health Services
Hospitals/Clinics/Primary
Hospital/Other Instit.

In Consumer Related prefer:
Consumer
Franchises(NEC)

In Industrial/Energy prefer:
Industrial Products

In Transportation prefer:
Aerospace

In Business Serv. prefer:
Services
Distribution
Consulting Services
Media

In Manufact. prefer:
Manufacturing

In Other prefer:
Women/Minority-Owned Bus.

Additional Information
Year Founded: 2003
Capital Under Management: $115,000,000
Current Activity Level: Actively seeking new investments
Method of Compensation: Return on invest. most important, but chg. closing fees, service fees, etc.

MERIT CAPITAL PARTNERS (FKA:WILLIAM BLAIR MEZZANINE)

303 West Madison Street
Suite 2100
Chicago, IL USA 60606
Phone: 312-592-6111
Fax: 312-592-6112
E-mail: mcp@meritcapital.com
Website: www.meritcapital.com

Other Offices
2415 East Camelback Road
Suite 700
Phoenix, AZ USA 85016
Phone: 602-553-1180
Fax: 602-553-1181

Management and Staff
Benjamin Yarbrough, Vice President
Daniel Pansing, Managing Director
David Jones, Managing Director
Evan Gallinson, Principal
Jason Moskowitz, Vice President
Leonard Lillard, Principal
Marc Walfish, Managing Director
Terrance Shipp, Managing Director
Thomas Campion, Managing Director
Timothy MacKenzie, Managing Director
Van Lam, Chief Financial Officer

Type of Firm
Private Equity Firm

Project Preferences

Role in Financing:
Will function either as deal originator or investor in deals created by others

Type of Financing Preferred:
Leveraged Buyout
Expansion
Mezzanine
Generalist PE
Later Stage
Management Buyouts
Industry Rollups
Acquisition
Recapitalizations

Size of Investments Considered:
Min Size of Investment Considered (000s): $15,000
Max Size of Investment Considered (000s): $60,000

Geographical Preferences

United States Preferences:
All U.S.

Canadian Preferences:
All Canada

Industry Focus
(% based on actual investment)

Other Products	61.0%
Industrial/Energy	17.5%
Consumer Related	12.9%
Computer Hardware	5.5%
Medical/Health	1.4%
Computer Software and Services	1.2%
Semiconductors/Other Elect.	0.5%

Additional Information
Year Founded: 1993
Capital Under Management: $1,070,000,000
Current Activity Level: Actively seeking new investments
Method of Compensation: Return on invest. most important, but chg. closing fees, service fees, etc.

MERITAGE FUNDS (AKA: MERITAGE PRIVATE EQUITY FUNDS)

1600 Wynkoop Street
Suite 300
Denver, CO USA 80202
Phone: 303-352-2040
Fax: 303-352-2050
E-mail: bizplans@meritagefunds.com
Website: www.meritagefunds.com

Management and Staff
G. Jackson Tankersley, Managing Director
John Garrett, Managing Director
Laura Beller, Managing Director
Tom Simonson, Vice President

Type of Firm
Private Equity Firm

Project Preferences

Role in Financing:
Prefer role as deal originator but will also invest in deals created by others

Type of Financing Preferred:
Early Stage
Expansion
Balanced
Public Companies
Turnaround
Later Stage
Seed
Industry Rollups
Special Situation
Recapitalizations

Size of Investments Considered:
Min Size of Investment Considered (000s): $1,000
Max Size of Investment Considered (000s): $50,000

Geographical Preferences

United States Preferences:
All U.S.

Industry Focus

(% based on actual investment)

Internet Specific	49.5%
Communications and Media	39.5%
Computer Hardware	5.9%
Computer Software and Services	5.1%

Additional Information

Name of Most Recent Fund: Meritage Private Equity Fund III
Most Recent Fund Was Raised: 12/10/2008
Year Founded: 1998
Capital Under Management: $476,300,000
Current Activity Level: Actively seeking new investments
Method of Compensation: Return on investment is of primary concern, do not charge fees

MERITECH CAPITAL PARTNERS

245 Lytton Avenue
Suite 350
Palo Alto, CA USA 94301
Phone: 650-475-2200
Fax: 650-475-2222
E-mail: info@meritechcapital.com
Website: www.meritechcapital.com

Management and Staff

George Bischof, Managing Director
Joel Backman, Chief Financial Officer
Michael Gordon, Managing Director
Paul Madera, Managing Director
Robert Ward, Managing Director

Type of Firm

Private Equity Firm

Project Preferences

Role in Financing:
Prefer role as deal originator but will also invest in deals created by others

Type of Financing Preferred:
Leveraged Buyout
Early Stage
Expansion
Mezzanine
Public Companies
Later Stage
Management Buyouts
Industry Rollups

Size of Investments Considered:
Min Size of Investment Considered (000s): $5,000
Max Size of Investment Considered (000s): $25,000

Geographical Preferences

United States Preferences:
All U.S.

International Preferences:
India
Western Europe
Asia

Industry Focus

(% based on actual investment)

Communications and Media	43.4%
Internet Specific	28.8%
Computer Software and Services	14.0%
Semiconductors/Other Elect.	5.5%
Computer Hardware	4.8%
Medical/Health	2.5%
Other Products	0.9%

Additional Information

Name of Most Recent Fund: Meritech Capital Partners III, L.P.
Most Recent Fund Was Raised: 08/25/2005
Year Founded: 1999
Capital Under Management: $2,239,000,000
Current Activity Level: Actively seeking new investments
Method of Compensation: Return on investment is of primary concern, do not charge fees

MERITURN PARTNERS LLC

3030 Bridge Way
Suite 111
Sausalito, CA USA 94965
Phone: 415-616-9800
Fax: 415-362-5623
Website: www.meriturn.com

Other Offices

234 Fayetteville Street
Sixth Floor
Raleigh, NC USA 27601
Phone: 919-821-1550
Fax: 919-573-8200

Management and Staff

Lee Hansen, Partner
Mark Kehaya, Partner
Michael Gillfillan, Partner
T. Ronan Kennedy, Vice President
Vito Russo, Principal

Type of Firm

Private Equity Firm

Project Preferences

Role in Financing:
Prefer role as deal originator

Type of Financing Preferred:
Leveraged Buyout
Turnaround
Acquisition
Special Situation
Distressed Debt
Recapitalizations

Geographical Preferences

United States Preferences:
All U.S.

Canadian Preferences:
All Canada

Industry Preferences

In Consumer Related prefer:
Consumer Products
Consumer Services

In Business Serv. prefer:
Services
Distribution

In Manufact. prefer:
Manufacturing

Additional Information

Year Founded: 2001
Capital Under Management: $40,000,000
Current Activity Level: Actively seeking new investments
Method of Compensation: Return on invest. most important, but chg. closing fees, service fees, etc.

MERITUS VENTURES

P.O. Box 1738
362 Old Whitley Road
London, KY USA 40743
Phone: 606-864-5175
Fax: 606-864-5194
Website: www.meritusventures.com

Other Offices

1020 Commerce Park Drive
Oak Ridge, TN USA 37830
Phone: 865-220-2020
Fax: 865-220-2030

Management and Staff

Brenda McDaniel, Chief Financial Officer

Type of Firm

SBIC

Project Preferences

Role in Financing:
Will function either as deal originator or investor in deals created by others

Type of Financing Preferred:
Expansion

Size of Investments Considered:
Min Size of Investment Considered (000s): $250
Max Size of Investment Considered (000s): $2,500

Geographical Preferences

United States Preferences:
Tennessee
North Carolina
South Carolina
Ohio
Virginia
West Virginia
Arkansas
Kentucky

Industry Preferences

In Computer Software prefer:
Software

In Manufact. prefer:
Manufacturing

Additional Information
Year Founded: 2006
Capital Under Management: $36,600,000
Current Activity Level: Actively seeking new investments

MERIWETHER CAPITAL
30 Rockefeller Plaza
Room 5600
New York, NY USA 10112
Phone: 212-649-5890
Fax: 212-246-7419
E-mail: meriwether@rockco.com
Website: www.meriwethercapital.net

Management and Staff
Grover O Neill, Vice President
Robert Petit, President

Type of Firm
Bank Affiliated

Project Preferences

Role in Financing:
Prefer role as deal originator

Type of Financing Preferred:
Management Buyouts
Acquisition
Industry Rollups
Recapitalizations

Geographical Preferences

United States Preferences:
All U.S.

Industry Focus
(% based on actual investment)

Consumer Related	100.0%

Additional Information
Year Founded: 1976
Current Activity Level: Actively seeking new investments
Method of Compensation: Return on investment is of primary concern, do not charge fees

---

MERLIN NEXUS (FKA: MERLIN BIOMED PRIVATE EQUITY)
230 Park Avenue
Suite 928
New York, NY USA 10169
Phone: 646-227-5270
Fax: 646-227-5201
E-mail: invest@merlinnexus.com
Website: www.merlinnexus.com

Management and Staff
Alberto Bianchinotti, Chief Financial Officer
Bob Ai, Principal
David Gould, Principal

Type of Firm
Private Equity Firm

Project Preferences

Role in Financing:
Will function either as deal originator or investor in deals created by others

Type of Financing Preferred:
Public Companies
Later Stage
Private Placement

Size of Investments Considered:
Min Size of Investment Considered (000s): $2,000
Max Size of Investment Considered (000s): $6,000

Geographical Preferences

International Preferences:
Europe

Industry Preferences

In Biotechnology prefer:
Biotechnology
Human Biotechnology

In Medical/Health prefer:
Medical/Health
Medical Therapeutics
Medical Products
Health Services

Additional Information
Name of Most Recent Fund: Merlin Nexus III
Most Recent Fund Was Raised: 05/19/2008
Year Founded: 2001
Capital Under Management: $175,000,000
Current Activity Level: Actively seeking new investments
Method of Compensation: Return on invest. most important, but chg. closing fees, service fees, etc.

MERRILL LYNCH
Branch B.P. 1058
Luxembourg, Luxembourg L-1010
Phone: 352-342-0101
Fax: 352-342-0102
E-mail: invest_services@ml.com
Website: www.mliminternational.com

Type of Firm
Private Equity Firm

Project Preferences

Type of Financing Preferred:
Expansion
Early Stage

Additional Information
Year Founded: 2009
Current Activity Level: Actively seeking new investments

MERRILL LYNCH CAPITAL PARTNERS
Four World Financial Center
250 Vesey Street
New York, NY USA 10080
Phone: 212-449-1000
Fax: 212-449-7118
Website: www.ml.com

Other Offices
1065 North Pacific Center Drive
Suite 100
Anaheim, CA USA 92806
Phone: 714-237-7838
Fax: 714-237-7843

3000 Sand Hill Road
Building Three
Menlo Park, CA USA 94025
Phone: 415-854-2300

181 Bay Street
Fourth and Fifth Floors
Toronto, Canada M5J 2V8
Phone: 416-369-7400
Fax: 416-369-7966

Mafatlal Centre, 10th Floor
Nariman Point
Mumbai, India 400 021
Phone: 91-22-5632-8000
Fax: 91-22-5632-8000

15th Floor, Citibank Tower
3 Garden Road
Central, Hong Kong
Phone: 852-2536-3888
Fax: 852-2161-7022

One Temasek Avenue
Suite 28-01 Millenia Tower
Singapore, Singapore 039192
Phone: 65-6330-7888
Fax: 65-6330-7800

Management and Staff
Andrew Nevin, Principal
Daniel Pace, Managing Director
Gregory Fleming, President & COO
Jean-Eudes Renier, Managing Director
Nelson Chai, Chief Financial Officer
Stan O Neal, President, CEO, Chairman

Type of Firm
Bank Affiliated

Project Preferences

Role in Financing:
Will function either as deal originator or investor in deals created by others

Type of Financing Preferred:
Fund of Funds
Leveraged Buyout
Mezzanine
Balanced
Start-up Financing
Seed
First Stage Financing

Size of Investments Considered:
Min Size of Investment Considered (000s): $1,000
Max Size of Investment Considered: No Limit

Geographical Preferences

International Preferences:
All International

Industry Preferences

In Communications prefer:
Wireless Communications

In Internet Specific prefer:
E-Commerce Technology

In Medical/Health prefer:
Medical/Health

Additional Information
Year Founded: 1982
Capital Under Management: $180,000,000
Current Activity Level: Actively seeking new investments
Method of Compensation: Return on investment is of primary concern, do not charge fees

MERRILL LYNCH GLOBAL EMERGING MARKETS GROUP
Four World Financial Center
North Tower, 24th Floor
New York, NY USA 10080
Phone: 212-449-4371

Type of Firm
Bank Affiliated

Project Preferences

Type of Financing Preferred:
Generalist PE

Additional Information
Year Founded: 1998
Current Activity Level: Actively seeking new investments

MERRILL LYNCH VENTURE CAPITAL
2 World Financial Center
3rd Floor
New York, NY USA 10281
Phone: 212-236-3328
E-mail: massias_b_bowman@ml.com

Type of Firm
Private Equity Firm

Additional Information
Year Founded: 1995
Current Activity Level: Actively seeking new investments

MERUS CAPITAL INVESTMENT
300 Hamilton Avenue
Suite 400
Palo Alto, CA USA 94301
Phone: 650-838-8888
Fax: 650-838-8887
E-mail: info@meruscap.com
Website: www.meruscap.com

Management and Staff
Peter Hsing, Co-Founder
Salman Ullah, Co-Founder
Sean Dempsey, Co-Founder

Type of Firm
Private Equity Firm

Project Preferences

Role in Financing:
Prefer role as deal originator but will also invest in deals created by others

Type of Financing Preferred:
Early Stage
Seed
Startup

Geographical Preferences

United States Preferences:
All U.S.

Industry Preferences

In Computer Software prefer:
Software

In Internet Specific prefer:
Internet

Additional Information
Year Founded: 2007
Capital Under Management: $37,000,000
Current Activity Level: Actively seeking new investments
Method of Compensation: Return on investment is of primary concern, do not charge fees

MESA CAPITAL PARTNERS
1700 Paseo de Peralta
Suite A
Santa Fe, NM USA 87501
Phone: 505-428-2990
Fax: 505-984-9108
Website: www.mesacapitalpartners.us

Other Offices
12005 North Virginia Avenue
Oklahoma City, OK USA 73120
Phone: 405-755-8448
Fax: 405-755-8449

Management and Staff
Anthony Rippo, Principal
Claudia Casey, Principal
Gregory Edwards, Principal
Jon Bloodworth, Principal
Les Matthews, Principal
Moritz Schlenzig, Principal
W. Douglas Frans, Principal

Type of Firm
Private Equity Firm

Project Preferences

Type of Financing Preferred:
Early Stage

Geographical Preferences

United States Preferences:
Midwest
Oklahoma
Rocky Mountain
Southwest

Industry Preferences

In Industrial/Energy prefer:
Oil and Gas Exploration
Oil & Gas Drilling,Explor

In Utilities prefer:
Utilities

Additional Information
Name of Most Recent Fund: Mesa Oklahoma Growth Fund I, L.P.
Most Recent Fund Was Raised: 11/09/2005
Year Founded: 2004
Capital Under Management: $13,600,000
Current Activity Level: Actively seeking new investments
Method of Compensation: Return on investment is of primary concern, do not charge fees

MESA VERDE VENTURE PARTNERS
12526 High Bluff Drive
San Diego, CA USA 92130
Phone: 858-245-5045

Website: www.mesaverdevp.com

Management and Staff

Daniel Wood, Managing Director

Type of Firm

Private Equity Firm

Additional Information

Name of Most Recent Fund: Mesa Verde Venture Partners, L.P.
Most Recent Fund Was Raised: 12/12/2006
Year Founded: 2006
Capital Under Management: $12,300,000
Current Activity Level: Actively seeking new investments

MESIROW PRIVATE EQUITY INVESTMENTS, INC.

350 North Clark Street
Chicago, IL USA 60610
Phone: 312-595-6099
Fax: 312-595-6211
Website: www.mesirowfinancial.com

Other Offices

321 North Clark Street
Chicago, IL USA 60610
Phone: 312-973-2323

Management and Staff

Brad Busscher, Managing Director
Daniel Howell, Senior Managing Director
Gary Klopfenstein, Senior Managing Director
James Tyree, Chairman & CEO
Joshua Daitch, Vice President
Lester Morris, Senior Managing Director
Marc Sacks, Senior Managing Director
Michael Crowe, Senior Managing Director
Michael Barrett, Managing Director
Paul Rice, Senior Managing Director
Robert DeBolt, Vice President
Thomas Allison, Senior Managing Director
Thomas Galuhn, Senior Managing Director

Type of Firm

Bank Affiliated

Association Membership

Illinois Venture Capital Association
Natl Assoc of Small Bus. Inv. Co (NASBIC)

Project Preferences

Role in Financing:

Will function either as deal originator or investor in deals created by others

Type of Financing Preferred:

Fund of Funds
Leveraged Buyout
Expansion
Generalist PE
Balanced
Later Stage
Management Buyouts
Acquisition
Recapitalizations

Size of Investments Considered:

Min Size of Investment Considered (000s): $2,000
Max Size of Investment Considered (000s): $10,000

Geographical Preferences

United States Preferences:

All U.S.

Canadian Preferences:

All Canada

Industry Focus

(% based on actual investment)

Other Products	53.4%
Computer Software and Services	15.6%
Consumer Related	12.7%
Communications and Media	7.1%
Internet Specific	3.8%
Industrial/Energy	3.2%
Medical/Health	1.8%
Semiconductors/Other Elect.	1.1%
Biotechnology	0.7%
Computer Hardware	0.5%

Additional Information

Name of Most Recent Fund: Mesirow Financial Capital Partners IX, L.P.
Most Recent Fund Was Raised: 05/11/2005
Year Founded: 1981
Capital Under Management: $800,000,000
Current Activity Level: Actively seeking new investments
Method of Compensation: Return on investment is of primary concern, do not charge fees

---

METALMARK CAPITAL LLC

1177 Avenue of the Americas
40th Floor
New York, NY USA 10036
Phone: 212-823-1930
Fax: 212-823-1931
Website: www.metalmarkcapital.com

Management and Staff

Alan Jones, Managing Director
Andrew Feller, Managing Director
David Boudo, Vice President
Eric Fry, Managing Director
Fazle Husain, Managing Director
Gregory Myers, Managing Director
Howard Hoffen, Managing Director
Hwan-Yoon Chung, Principal
Jeffrey Siegal, Managing Director
Kenneth Clifford, Managing Director & CFO
Michael Hoffman, Managing Director
Stephen Trevor, Managing Director
Vanessa Adler, Vice President

Type of Firm

Private Equity Firm

Project Preferences

Type of Financing Preferred:

Leveraged Buyout

Industry Preferences

In Medical/Health prefer:

Medical/Health

In Consumer Related prefer:

Consumer

In Industrial/Energy prefer:

Energy
Industrial Products

Additional Information

Name of Most Recent Fund: Metalmark Capital Partners MS Fund, L.P.
Most Recent Fund Was Raised: 09/12/2006
Year Founded: 2004
Capital Under Management: $3,500,000,000
Current Activity Level: Actively seeking new investments

METAMORPHIC VENTURES, LLC (FKA: GERSH VENTURE PARTNERS)

450 Park Avenue South
Sixth Floor
New York, NY USA 10016
Phone: 212-209-3366
Fax: 646-225-5213
E-mail: info@metamorphic.vc
Website: www.metamorphic.vc

Management and Staff

Alexander Von Summer, Founding Partner
David Hirsch, Managing Partner
Douglas Haynes, Founding Partner
Lewis Gersh, Managing Partner
Marc Michel, Managing Director

Type of Firm

Private Equity Firm

Project Preferences

Role in Financing:

Will function either as deal originator or investor in deals created by others

Type of Financing Preferred:

Early Stage
Seed
Private Placement
Startup

Size of Investments Considered:

Min Size of Investment Considered (000s): $250
Max Size of Investment Considered (000s): $750

Geographical Preferences

United States Preferences:

All U.S.

Industry Preferences

In Financial Services prefer:
Financial Services

In Business Serv. prefer:
Media

Additional Information

Year Founded: 2006
Capital Under Management: $7,000,000
Current Activity Level: Actively seeking new investments
Method of Compensation: Return on investment is of primary concern, do not charge fees

METAPOINT PARTNERS

Three Centennial Drive
Peabody, MA USA 01960
Phone: 978-531-4444
Fax: 978-531-6662
E-mail: info@metapoint.com
Website: www.metapoint.com

Management and Staff

Erik Dykema, Principal
Keith Shaughnessy, Chairman & CEO
Stuart Mathews, President

Type of Firm

Private Equity Firm

Project Preferences

Role in Financing:
Prefer role as deal originator

Type of Financing Preferred:
Leveraged Buyout
Management Buyouts
Acquisition
Recapitalizations

Size of Investments Considered:
Min Size of Investment Considered (000s): $500
Max Size of Investment Considered (000s): $2,500

Geographical Preferences

United States Preferences:
Mid Atlantic
Midwest
Southeast
Northeast
Rocky Mountain

Canadian Preferences:
All Canada

Industry Preferences

In Industrial/Energy prefer:
Industrial Products
Machinery

In Transportation prefer:
Transportation

In Manufact. prefer:
Manufacturing

Additional Information

Year Founded: 1988
Capital Under Management: $91,000,000
Current Activity Level: Actively seeking new investments
Method of Compensation: Return on investment is of primary concern, do not charge fees

METLIFE INVESTMENTS ASIA, LTD.

Level 20, Cityplaza 3
14 Taikoo Wan Road
Taikoo Shing, Hong Kong
Phone: 852-2199-1000
Fax: 852-2956-1485
Website: www.metlife.com.hk

Management and Staff

Boning Tong, Chief Financial Officer
Rory Carson, Chief Executive Officer

Type of Firm

Insurance Firm Affiliate

Association Membership

Hong Kong Venture Capital Association (HKVCA)

Project Preferences

Type of Financing Preferred:
Expansion
Mezzanine
Research and Development
Turnaround
Management Buyouts

Geographical Preferences

International Preferences:
Indonesia
India
China
Hong Kong
Thailand
Philippines
Pacific
Australia
Korea, South
Malaysia

Additional Information

Year Founded: 1996
Capital Under Management: $250,000,000
Current Activity Level: Actively seeking new investments

METROBANK VENTURE CAPITAL CORP.

2/F, Metrobank Plaza Annex
Gil Puyat Avenue
Makati City, Philippines
Phone: 632-818-4462
Fax: 632-816-1012

Type of Firm

Private Equity Firm

Project Preferences

Type of Financing Preferred:
Balanced

Geographical Preferences

International Preferences:
Philippines

Additional Information

Year Founded: 1962
Current Activity Level: Actively seeking new investments

METROPOLITAN VENTURE PARTNERS (METVP)

432 Park Avenue South
12th Floor
New York, NY USA 10016
Phone: 212-561-1219
Fax: 212-561-1201
E-mail: contact@metvp.com
Website: www.metvp.com

Other Offices

Sugar Quay
Lower Thames Street
London, United Kingdom EC3R 6DU
Phone: 44-207-285-590
Fax: 44-207-285-371

Management and Staff

Michael Levin, Managing Director
Paul Lisiak, Managing Director

Type of Firm

Private Equity Firm

Association Membership

European Private Equity and Venture Capital Assoc.

Project Preferences

Role in Financing:
Will function either as deal originator or investor in deals created by others

Type of Financing Preferred:
Second Stage Financing
Early Stage
Expansion

Management Buyouts
First Stage Financing
Special Situation
Recapitalizations

Size of Investments Considered:
Min Size of Investment Considered (000s): $500
Max Size of Investment Considered (000s): $5,000

Geographical Preferences

United States Preferences:
Northeast

International Preferences:
United Kingdom

Industry Preferences

In Communications prefer:
Telecommunications
Wireless Communications
Data Communications

In Computer Software prefer:
Software
Applications Software

In Internet Specific prefer:
E-Commerce Technology
Internet

In Semiconductor/Electr prefer:
Semiconductor
Controllers and Sensors
Sensors

Additional Information
Name of Most Recent Fund: Metropolitan Venture Partners II, L.P.
Most Recent Fund Was Raised: 08/01/2001
Year Founded: 2000
Capital Under Management: $20,000,000
Current Activity Level: Actively seeking new investments
Method of Compensation: Return on investment is of primary concern, do not charge fees

---

MEUSINVEST
Le Vertbois
Rue du Vertbois, 13b
Liege, Belgium 4000
Phone: 32-4-221-6211
Fax: 32-4-223-5765
Website: www.meusinvest.be

Type of Firm
Private Equity Firm

Project Preferences

Type of Financing Preferred:
Early Stage
Expansion

Geographical Preferences

International Preferences:
Belgium

Additional Information
Year Founded: 1986
Capital Under Management: $135,300,000
Current Activity Level: Actively seeking new investments

MEYER VENTURES
107 Portage Avenue
P.O. Box 350
Three Rivers, MI USA 49093
Phone: 269-273-1825
Fax: 269-273-9157
Website: www.meyerventures.com

Management and Staff
Anthony Meyer, Managing Partner

Type of Firm
Private Equity Firm

Additional Information
Year Founded: 2009
Current Activity Level: Actively seeking new investments

MEZZANIN FINANZIERUNGS AG
Operngasse 6
Vienna, Austria 1010
Phone: 43-1-513-4197
Fax: 43-1-513-4175
E-mail: office@mezz.at
Website: www.mezz.at

Type of Firm
Bank Affiliated

Project Preferences

Type of Financing Preferred:
Leveraged Buyout
Expansion
Mezzanine

Geographical Preferences

International Preferences:
Austria

Industry Preferences

In Communications prefer:
Telecommunications

In Consumer Related prefer:
Consumer Products

In Industrial/Energy prefer:
Industrial Products

Additional Information
Year Founded: 2002
Capital Under Management: $132,000,000
Current Activity Level: Actively seeking new investments

MFC CAPITAL FUNDING, INC.
111 South Wacker Drive
Suite 5050
Chicago, IL USA 60606
Phone: 312-376-8500
Fax: 312-376-8475
Website: www.mfccapitalfunding.com

Management and Staff
Andrew Pappas, Managing Director
Chris Randall, Senior Managing Director
Daniel Weiss, Managing Director
Edward Ryczek, Managing Director
Jason Prather, Vice President
Jim Kuncl, Vice President
Kevin Nowak, Vice President
Laura Kraus, Vice President
Monica Briseno, Vice President
Thomas Karle, Managing Director

Type of Firm
Bank Affiliated

Project Preferences

Role in Financing:
Prefer role as deal originator

Type of Financing Preferred:
Leveraged Buyout
Mezzanine

Size of Investments Considered:
Min Size of Investment Considered (000s): $3,000
Max Size of Investment Considered (000s): $25,000

Geographical Preferences

United States Preferences:
All U.S.

Additional Information
Year Founded: 2005
Capital Under Management: $500,000,000
Current Activity Level: Actively seeking new investments

MHI ENERGY PARTNERS
101 South Fifth Street
Suite 3650
Louisville, KY USA 40202
Phone: 502-587-5903
E-mail: mailto:info@mhienergy.com
Website: www.mhienergy.com

Other Offices
300 Fifth Avenue, Southwest
Suite 350
Calgary, Canada T2P 3C4

Type of Firm
Private Equity Firm

Project Preferences

Type of Financing Preferred:
Early Stage
Seed
Startup

Geographical Preferences

United States Preferences:
All U.S.

Canadian Preferences:
All Canada

Industry Preferences

In Industrial/Energy prefer:
Energy

Additional Information

Year Founded: 2003
Capital Under Management: $2,100,000
Current Activity Level: Actively seeking new investments

MHR CAPITAL PARTNERS

40 West 57th Street
20th Floor
New York, NY USA 10019
Phone: 212-262-0005
Fax: 212-262-9356

Management and Staff

Hal Goldstein, Partner
Mark Rachesky, Partner

Type of Firm

Private Equity Firm

Project Preferences

Type of Financing Preferred:
Leveraged Buyout
Distressed Debt

Additional Information

Year Founded: 1996
Capital Under Management: $1,067,000,000
Current Activity Level: Actively seeking new investments

MHS CAPITAL MANAGEMENT, LLC

2201 Pacific Avenue
Suite 503
San Francisco, CA USA 94115
Phone: 415-929-2547

Management and Staff

Mark Sugarman, Managing Director

Type of Firm

Private Equity Firm

Project Preferences

Type of Financing Preferred:
Balanced

Geographical Preferences

United States Preferences:
All U.S.

Additional Information

Name of Most Recent Fund: MHS Capital Partners, L.P.
Most Recent Fund Was Raised: 10/26/2006
Year Founded: 2006
Capital Under Management: $31,800,000
Current Activity Level: Actively seeking new investments

MI3 VENTURE PARTNERS

One Hollis Street
Suite 232
Wellesley, MA USA 02482
Phone: 781-707-5050
Fax: 781-239-1541
E-mail: eileen@mi3.com
Website: www.mi3.com

Management and Staff

Eileen Driscoll, Chief Financial Officer
Mark Carvlin, Venture Partner
Roger Kitterman, General Partner
Ronald Schilling, General Partner
William McPhee, Managing General Partner

Type of Firm

Private Equity Firm

Project Preferences

Role in Financing:
Prefer role as deal originator but will also invest in deals created by others

Type of Financing Preferred:
Early Stage

Size of Investments Considered:
Min Size of Investment Considered (000s): $250
Max Size of Investment Considered (000s): $3,000

Geographical Preferences

Canadian Preferences:
All Canada

Industry Preferences

In Medical/Health prefer:
Medical Products

Additional Information

Name of Most Recent Fund: Mi3, L.P. (AKA:Medical Imaging Innovation & Investments, LP)
Most Recent Fund Was Raised: 01/02/2000
Year Founded: 1998
Capital Under Management: $10,200,000
Current Activity Level: Actively seeking new investments
Method of Compensation: Return on investment is of primary concern, do not charge fees

---

MIAMI VALLEY ECONOMIC DEVELOPMENT

900 Kettering Tower
Dayton, OH USA 45423
Phone: 937-222-4422
Fax: 937-222-1323
Website: www.mvedc.org

Type of Firm

Incubator/Development Program

Project Preferences

Type of Financing Preferred:
Balanced

Additional Information

Name of Most Recent Fund: Miami Valley Venture Fund I, L.P.
Most Recent Fund Was Raised: 10/01/1996
Year Founded: 1997
Current Activity Level: Actively seeking new investments

MIANACH VENTURE CAPITAL

45 Blackbourne Square
Rathfarnham Gate
Dublin 14, Ireland
Phone: 353-1-492-7400
Fax: 353-1-492-7475
E-mail: info@mianach.com
Website: www.mianach.com

Type of Firm

Private Equity Firm

Project Preferences

Role in Financing:
Will function either as deal originator or investor in deals created by others

Type of Financing Preferred:
Early Stage
Seed
Startup

Geographical Preferences

International Preferences:
Ireland

Industry Preferences

In Communications prefer:
Communications and Media

Additional Information

Year Founded: 2009
Current Activity Level: Actively seeking new investments

MIC AG

Tuerkenstrasse 71
Muenchen, Germany 80799
Phone: 49-89-286-7380
Fax: 49-89-286738110
E-mail: info@mic-ag.eu
Website: www.mic-ag.eu

Management and Staff

Claus-Georg Mueller, Chief Executive Officer
Manuel Reitmeier, Chief Financial Officer

Type of Firm

Private Equity Firm

Project Preferences

Type of Financing Preferred:
Early Stage
Expansion
Seed

Geographical Preferences

International Preferences:
Germany

Additional Information

Year Founded: 2006
Current Activity Level: Actively seeking new investments

MICHIGAN ECONOMIC DEVELOPMENT CORPORATION

300 North Washington Square
Lansing, MI USA 48913
Phone: 517-241-8030
Fax: 517-241-0559
E-mail: medcservices@michigan.org
Website: www.michiganadvantage.org

Management and Staff

Cindy Douglas, Vice President

Type of Firm

Government Affiliated Program

Project Preferences

Role in Financing:
Will function either as deal originator or investor in deals created by others

Type of Financing Preferred:
Fund of Funds
Early Stage
Research and Development
Start-up Financing
Seed
Special Situation

Size of Investments Considered:
Min Size of Investment Considered (000s): $50
Max Size of Investment Considered (000s): $7,000

Geographical Preferences

United States Preferences:
Michigan

Industry Preferences

In Biotechnology prefer:
Biotechnology

In Industrial/Energy prefer:
Alternative Energy
Advanced Materials

In Transportation prefer:
Transportation

Additional Information

Year Founded: 1997
Capital Under Management: $160,000,000
Current Activity Level: Actively seeking new investments
Method of Compensation: Other

MICHIGAN VENTURE CAPITAL CO., LTD.

9th Floor, Daedong Building
93 Nonhyun-dong, Kangnam-Ku
Seoul, South Korea 135-010
Phone: 822-3445-1310
Fax: 822-3445-1311
E-mail: info@michiganvc.net
Website: www.michiganvc.net

Management and Staff

Don Kwon, Managing Director
Il Hyung Cho, Chief Financial Officer

Type of Firm

Corporate PE/Venture

Project Preferences

Type of Financing Preferred:
Balanced

Geographical Preferences

International Preferences:
Korea, South

Industry Preferences

In Semiconductor/Electr prefer:
Electronics

In Other prefer:
Environment Responsible

Additional Information

Year Founded: 2002
Capital Under Management: $24,000,000
Current Activity Level: Actively seeking new investments

MICROVEST CAPITAL MANAGEMENT LLC

7514 Wisconsin Avenue
Suite 400
Bethesda, MD USA 20814
Phone: 301-664-6680
Fax: 301-664-6686
E-mail: info@microvestfund.com
Website: www.microvestfund.com

Management and Staff

Candace Smith, Chief Financial Officer
Gil Crawford, Chief Executive Officer

Type of Firm

Private Equity Advisor or Fund of Funds

Project Preferences

Role in Financing:
Will function either as deal originator or investor in deals created by others

Type of Financing Preferred:
Expansion
Later Stage

Size of Investments Considered:
Min Size of Investment Considered (000s): $500
Max Size of Investment Considered (000s): $3,000

Geographical Preferences

International Preferences:
India
Latin America
China
Hong Kong
Eastern Europe
Middle East
All International

Industry Preferences

In Financial Services prefer:
Financial Services

Additional Information

Year Founded: 2003
Capital Under Management: $70,000,000
Current Activity Level: Actively seeking new investments
Method of Compensation: Return on investment is of primary concern, do not charge fees

MID ATLANTIC FINANCIAL MANAGEMENT, INC.

The Times Building
336 Fourth Avenue
Pittsburgh, PA USA 15222
Phone: 412-391-7077

Type of Firm

Private Equity Firm

Additional Information

Year Founded: 2002
Capital Under Management: $16,300,000
Current Activity Level: Actively seeking new investments

MID EUROPA PARTNERS (FKA: EMP EUROPE)

161 Brompton Road
London, United Kingdom SW3 1EX
Phone: 44-20-7886-3600
Fax: 44-20-7886-3639
Website: www.mideuropa.com

Other Offices

Bank Center, Platina Tower, 5th floor
Szabadas Ter 7
Budapest, Hungary 1054
Phone: 36-1-411-1270
Fax: 36-1-411-1271

Warsaw Financial Center, 29th Floor
Ul. Ernilii Plater 53
Warsaw, Poland 00-113
Phone: 48-22-540-7120

Management and Staff

Jacques Du Preez, Chief Operating Officer
Matthew Strassberg, Partner
Robert Knorr, Partner
Thierry Baudon, Managing Partner
Zbigniew Rekusz, Partner

Type of Firm

Private Equity Firm

Association Membership

Hungarian Venture Capital Association (HVCA)
European Private Equity and Venture Capital Assoc.

Project Preferences

Type of Financing Preferred:
Leveraged Buyout
Expansion
Balanced
Turnaround

Geographical Preferences

International Preferences:
Central Europe
Eastern Europe

Industry Preferences

In Communications prefer:
Telecommunications
Wireless Communications

In Industrial/Energy prefer:
Oil and Gas Exploration
Industrial Products

In Transportation prefer:
Transportation

In Manufact. prefer:
Manufacturing

Additional Information

Name of Most Recent Fund: AIG Emerging Europe Infrastructure Fund, L.P.
Most Recent Fund Was Raised: 10/01/1999
Year Founded: 2005
Capital Under Management: $1,442,700,000
Current Activity Level: Actively seeking new investments

MID-ATLANTIC VENTURE FUNDS (FKA: NEPA MANAGEMENT CORP.)

Ben Franklin Technology Center
125 Goodman Drive
Bethlehem, PA USA 18015
Phone: 610-865-6550
Fax: 610-865-6427
Website: www.mavf.com

Other Offices

10461 Sir Walker Drive
Montpelier, VA USA 23192
Phone: 804-883-0152
Fax: 804-883-6164

1850 K Street
Suite 1075
Washington, DC USA 20006
Phone: 202-223-7575
Fax: 202-293-8850

Management and Staff

Donald Yount, Principal
Frederick Beste, Partner
Glen Bressner, Partner
Marc Benson, Partner
Thomas Smith, Partner

Type of Firm

Private Equity Firm

Association Membership

Mid-Atlantic Venture Association
Natl Assoc of Small Bus. Inv. Co (NASBIC)

Project Preferences

Role in Financing:
Prefer role as deal originator but will also invest in deals created by others

Type of Financing Preferred:
Early Stage
Seed
Startup

Size of Investments Considered:
Min Size of Investment Considered (000s): $1,000
Max Size of Investment Considered (000s): $8,000

Geographical Preferences

United States Preferences:
Mid Atlantic

Industry Focus

(% based on actual investment)

Computer Software and Services	32.7%
Internet Specific	21.9%
Communications and Media	18.8%
Medical/Health	14.5%
Semiconductors/Other Elect.	5.2%
Industrial/Energy	4.1%
Other Products	2.1%
Computer Hardware	0.5%
Consumer Related	0.2%
Biotechnology	0.1%

Additional Information

Year Founded: 1984
Capital Under Management: $190,000,000
Current Activity Level: Actively seeking new investments
Method of Compensation: Return on investment is of primary concern, do not charge fees

MIDCOAST CAPITAL, LLC

259 Radnor-Chester Road
Radnor Court, Suite 210
Wayne, PA USA 19087
Phone: 610-687-8580
Fax: 610-971-2154
Website: www.midcoastcapital.com

Type of Firm

Bank Affiliated

Project Preferences

Type of Financing Preferred:
Fund of Funds of Second

Geographical Preferences

United States Preferences:
All U.S.

Additional Information

Year Founded: 2001
Capital Under Management: $4,200,000
Current Activity Level: Actively seeking new investments

MIDF AMANAH VENTURES SDN BHD

Level 4, Menara MIDF
82 Jalan Raja Chulan
Kuala Lumpur, Malaysia 50200
Phone: 603-2173-8888
Fax: 603-2173-8877
E-mail: inquiry@midf.com.my
Website: www.midf.com.my

Type of Firm

Bank Affiliated

Project Preferences

Type of Financing Preferred:
Leveraged Buyout
Expansion
Mezzanine

Size of Investments Considered:
Min Size of Investment Considered (000s): $800
Max Size of Investment Considered (000s): $1,300

Geographical Preferences

International Preferences:
Malaysia

Industry Preferences

In Semiconductor/Electr prefer:
Electronics

In Biotechnology prefer:
Biotechnology

In Industrial/Energy prefer:
Energy
Oil and Gas Exploration
Advanced Materials

In Manufact. prefer:
Manufacturing

Additional Information

Year Founded: 1990
Capital Under Management: $3,900,000
Current Activity Level: Actively seeking new investments

MIDI CAPITAL

42 rue du Languedoc
BP 90112
Toulouse, France 31001
Phone: 33-5-6225-9246
Fax: 33-5-6225-9140
E-mail: contact@midicapital.fr
Website: www.midicapital.fr

Type of Firm

Private Equity Firm

Association Membership

French Venture Capital Association (AFIC)

Project Preferences

Type of Financing Preferred:
Generalist PE
Balanced

Geographical Preferences

International Preferences:
France

Additional Information

Year Founded: 2000
Capital Under Management: $44,800,000
Current Activity Level: Actively seeking new investments

MIDI-PYRENEES CREATION

1 place Alfonse-Jourdain
Toulouse, France 31000
Phone: 33-5-6230-1510
Fax: 33-5-6121-9600
E-mail: irdi@wanadoo.fr

Type of Firm

Private Equity Firm

Project Preferences

Type of Financing Preferred:
Early Stage
Expansion

Geographical Preferences

International Preferences:
France

Industry Preferences

In Business Serv. prefer:
Services

Additional Information

Year Founded: 1996
Capital Under Management: $5,800,000
Current Activity Level: Actively seeking new investments

MIDINVEST MANAGEMENT OY

Kauppakatu 31 C
Survontie 9
Jyvaskyla, Finland 40100
Phone: 358-14-339-3100
Fax: 358-14-339-3111
Website: www.midinvest.fi

Other Offices

Polttimonkatu 4, 4th floor
Tampere, Finland 33210

Puistopolku 15 A
Seinajoki, Finland 60100

Askonkatu 9 A
Lahti, Finland 15100

Management and Staff
Visa Virtanen, Managing Director

Type of Firm

Private Equity Firm

Association Membership

Finnish Venture Capital Association (FVCA)
European Private Equity and Venture Capital Assoc.

Project Preferences

Type of Financing Preferred:
Leveraged Buyout
Early Stage
Expansion
Balanced
Management Buyouts
Startup

Size of Investments Considered:
Min Size of Investment Considered (000s): $100
Max Size of Investment Considered (000s): $100,000

Geographical Preferences

International Preferences:
Europe
Finland

Industry Focus

(% based on actual investment)

Other Products	49.1%
Industrial/Energy	22.8%
Consumer Related	7.5%
Computer Software and Services	6.6%
Semiconductors/Other Elect.	5.4%
Internet Specific	3.1%
Communications and Media	3.0%
Medical/Health	1.5%
Computer Hardware	0.9%

Additional Information

Name of Most Recent Fund: Midinvest Fund II Ky
Most Recent Fund Was Raised: 06/21/2006
Year Founded: 1994
Capital Under Management: $37,600,000
Current Activity Level: Actively seeking new investments

MIDOCEAN PARTNERS (FKA: DEUTSCHE BANK CAPITAL PARTNERS)

320 Park Avenue
Suite 1700
New York, NY USA 10022
Phone: 212-497-1400
Fax: 212-497-1373
Website: www.midoceanpartners.com

Other Offices

No.1 Grosvenor Crescent
Belgravia
London, United Kingdom SW1X 7EF
Phone: 44-20-3178-8492

Management and Staff

Barrett Gilmer, Vice President
Charles Boschetto, Vice President
Christian Purslow, Managing Director
David Basto, Managing Director
Deborah Hodges, Chief Operating Officer
Diarmuid Cummins, Partner
Elias Dokas, Principal
Frank Nash, Managing Director
Frank Schiff, Managing Director
Giampiero Mazza, Principal
Graham Clempson, Managing Partner
Graham Thomas, Partner
Hugh Briggs, Principal
Nicholas McGrane, Managing Director
Nikhil Thukral, Vice President
Richard Braddock, Partner
Robert Sharp, Managing Director
Timothy Billings, Vice President
Tracey Wells, Vice President
Tyler Zachem, Managing Director
Wolfgang Schwerdtle, Principal

Type of Firm

Private Equity Firm

Project Preferences

Type of Financing Preferred:
Fund of Funds
Leveraged Buyout
Management Buyouts

Size of Investments Considered:
Min Size of Investment Considered (000s): $25,000
Max Size of Investment Considered (000s): $150,000

Geographical Preferences

United States Preferences:
All U.S.

International Preferences:
Europe

Industry Preferences

In Communications prefer:
Communications and Media

In Medical/Health prefer:
Health Services

In Consumer Related prefer:
Consumer Products
Consumer Services

In Industrial/Energy prefer:
Industrial Products

In Business Serv. prefer:
Media

Additional Information

Year Founded: 2003
Capital Under Management: $3,000,000,000
Current Activity Level: Actively seeking new investments

MIDVEN, LTD. (AKA: MIDLANDS VENTURE FUND MANAGERS, LTD.)

37 Bennetts Hill
Birmingham, United Kingdom B2 5SN
Phone: 44-121-710-1990
Fax: 44-121-710-1999
E-mail: enquiries@midven.com
Website: www.midven.com

Management and Staff

John O Neill, Managing Director
Tony Stott, Chief Executive Officer

Type of Firm

Private Equity Firm

Association Membership

British Venture Capital Association (BVCA)

Project Preferences

Role in Financing:
Prefer role as deal originator but will also invest in deals created by others

Type of Financing Preferred:
Second Stage Financing
Leveraged Buyout
Early Stage
Expansion
Generalist PE
Turnaround
Seed
Startup
Recapitalizations

Geographical Preferences

International Preferences:
United Kingdom
Europe

Industry Preferences

In Communications prefer:
Communications and Media

In Computer Other prefer:
Computer Related

In Semiconductor/Electr prefer:
Electronics

In Biotechnology prefer:
Biotechnology

In Medical/Health prefer:
Medical/Health

In Consumer Related prefer:
Consumer

In Industrial/Energy prefer:
Energy
Industrial Products
Materials

In Transportation prefer:
Transportation

In Manufact. prefer:
Manufacturing

Additional Information

Name of Most Recent Fund: Advantage Growth Fund
Most Recent Fund Was Raised: 02/07/2003
Year Founded: 1992
Capital Under Management: $11,600,000
Current Activity Level: Actively seeking new investments
Method of Compensation: Return on invest. most important, but chg. closing fees, service fees, etc.

MIDWAY HOLDING AB

Box 42 41
Malmo, Sweden
Phone: 46-40-301-210
Fax: 46-40-301-311
E-mail: midway@midwayholding.se
Website: www.midwayholding.se

Type of Firm

Private Equity Firm

Project Preferences

Type of Financing Preferred:
Balanced

Geographical Preferences

International Preferences:
Sweden
Europe

Additional Information

Year Founded: 2005
Current Activity Level: Actively seeking new investments

MIDWEST MEZZANINE FUNDS

55 West Monroe Street
Suite 3650
Chicago, IL USA 60603
Phone: 312-291-7300
Fax: 312-345-0665
E-mail: info@mmfcapital.com
Website: www.mmfcapital.com

Management and Staff

Ana Winters, Principal

C. Michael Foster, Senior Managing Director
David Gezon, Senior Managing Director
J. Allan Kayler, Senior Managing Director
Jeffrey DeJesus, Managing Director
Paul Kreie, Managing Director

Type of Firm

Bank Affiliated

Project Preferences

Type of Financing Preferred:

Leveraged Buyout
Mezzanine
Expansion
Acquisition
Recapitalizations

Geographical Preferences

United States Preferences:

All U.S.

Canadian Preferences:

All Canada

Industry Focus

(% based on actual investment)

Industrial/Energy	56.1%
Other Products	40.0%
Communications and Media	3.8%

Additional Information

Name of Most Recent Fund: Midwest Mezzanine Fund III, L.P.
Most Recent Fund Was Raised: 10/01/2001
Year Founded: 1992
Capital Under Management: $200,000,000
Current Activity Level: Actively seeking new investments

MIDWEST VENTURE ALLIANCE

7829 East Rockhill Road
Suite 307
Wichita, KS USA 67206
Phone: 316-651-5900
Fax: 866-810-6671
Website: www.midwestventure.com

Management and Staff

Dick West, Co-Founder
Gene Bicknell, Co-Founder
Patricia Brasted, Co-Founder
Stan Brannan, Co-Founder

Type of Firm

Angel Group

Project Preferences

Type of Financing Preferred:

Early Stage
Seed

Geographical Preferences

United States Preferences:

Midwest
All U.S.

Additional Information

Name of Most Recent Fund: 2006 Ventria - I
Most Recent Fund Was Raised: 11/01/2006
Year Founded: 2006
Capital Under Management: $300,000
Current Activity Level: Actively seeking new investments

MIFACTORY

El Bosque Norte 0177 - Of.2101
Las Condes
Santiago, Chile
Phone: 56-2-371-6401
Fax: 56-2-751-9598
E-mail: info@mifactory.com
Website: www.mifactory.com

Other Offices

Rua do Rocio, 423
cj 206
Sao Paulo, Brazil

Management and Staff

Daniel Contreras, Chief Executive Officer
Jaime Said, President

Type of Firm

Corporate PE/Venture

Project Preferences

Type of Financing Preferred:

Early Stage

Geographical Preferences

International Preferences:

Latin America

Industry Preferences

In Communications prefer:

Telecommunications

In Internet Specific prefer:

Internet

Additional Information

Year Founded: 2000
Capital Under Management: $30,000,000
Current Activity Level: Actively seeking new investments

MIG VERWALTUNGS AG

Ismaninger Strasse 102
Munich, Germany 81675
Phone: 49-1805-644-999
Fax: 49-1803-644-999
E-mail: info@mig.ag
Website: www.mig.ag

Type of Firm

Private Equity Firm

Association Membership

German Venture Capital Association (BVK)

Project Preferences

Type of Financing Preferred:

Early Stage
Balanced

Geographical Preferences

International Preferences:

Austria
Germany

Industry Preferences

In Biotechnology prefer:

Biotechnology

Additional Information

Year Founded: 2004
Capital Under Management: $59,000,000
Current Activity Level: Actively seeking new investments

MILESTONE CAPITAL

104 Victoria Street
Fourth Floor
Christchurch, New Zealand 8011
Phone: 643-977-8877
Fax: 649-353-1858
E-mail: info@milestone-cap.com
Website: www.milestone-cap.com

Type of Firm

Private Equity Firm

Project Preferences

Type of Financing Preferred:

Expansion
Early Stage
Later Stage

Geographical Preferences

International Preferences:

China
New Zealand

Industry Preferences

In Industrial/Energy prefer:

Environmental Related

In Other prefer:

Environment Responsible

Additional Information

Year Founded: 2009
Current Activity Level: Actively seeking new investments

MILESTONE CAPITAL MANAGEMENT, LTD.

318 Hua Nan Road
Shanghai, China 200031
Phone: 86-21-6437-9190
Fax: 86-21-6437-9590
E-mail: info@mcmchina.com
Website: www.mcmchina.com

Other Offices

Unit A904-905, Huixin Plaza
No.8 Beichen Road
Beijing, China 100101
Phone: 86-10-8497-1443
Fax: 86-10-8497-1449

Management and Staff

Jonathan Dong, Vice President
Lin Shen, Vice President
Liping Qiu, Managing Director
William Plummer, Vice President
Yangxin Liu, Vice President
Yunli Lou, Managing Director

Type of Firm

Private Equity Firm

Project Preferences

Type of Financing Preferred:
Expansion
Generalist PE
Acquisition

Size of Investments Considered:
Min Size of Investment Considered (000s): $10,000
Max Size of Investment Considered (000s): $40,000

Geographical Preferences

International Preferences:
China

Additional Information

Year Founded: 2003
Capital Under Management: $25,000,000
Current Activity Level: Actively seeking new investments

MILESTONE CAPITAL PARTNERS LTD. (AKA: EAC MANAGER LTD.)

14 Floral Street
London, United Kingdom WC2E 9DH
Phone: 44-20-7420-8800
Fax: 44-20-7420-8827
E-mail: info@milestone-capital.com
Website: www.milestone-capital.com

Other Offices

21 place de la Madeleine
Paris, France 75008
Phone: 33-1-4268-2300
Fax: 33-1-4268-0137

Management and Staff

Erick Rinner, Managing Partner

Type of Firm

Private Equity Firm

Association Membership

British Venture Capital Association (BVCA)
French Venture Capital Association (AFIC)
European Private Equity and Venture Capital Assoc.

Project Preferences

Role in Financing:
Prefer role as deal originator

Type of Financing Preferred:
Second Stage Financing
Leveraged Buyout
Early Stage
Expansion
Turnaround
Management Buyouts
Startup

Size of Investments Considered:
Min Size of Investment Considered (000s): $7,500
Max Size of Investment Considered: No Limit

Geographical Preferences

International Preferences:
United Kingdom
Europe
Western Europe
Germany
France

Industry Focus

(% based on actual investment)

Other Products	33.5%
Medical/Health	25.8%
Consumer Related	19.9%
Computer Software and Services	19.1%
Industrial/Energy	1.8%

Additional Information

Year Founded: 1991
Capital Under Management: $255,700,000
Current Activity Level: Actively seeking new investments

MILESTONE GROWTH FUND, INC.

527 Marquette Avenue
Suite 1915
Minneapolis, MN USA 55402
Phone: 612-338-0090
Fax: 612-338-1172
E-mail: inquirymgf@milestonegrowth.com
Website: www.milestonegrowth.com

Type of Firm

SBIC

Association Membership

Community Development Venture Capital Alliance
Natl Assoc of Small Bus. Inv. Co (NASBIC)

Project Preferences

Role in Financing:
Prefer role as deal originator but will also invest in deals created by others

Type of Financing Preferred:
Early Stage
Mezzanine

Size of Investments Considered:
Min Size of Investment Considered (000s): $200
Max Size of Investment Considered (000s): $600

Geographical Preferences

United States Preferences:
Minnesota

Industry Preferences

In Other prefer:
Women/Minority-Owned Bus.

Additional Information

Year Founded: 1990
Capital Under Management: $26,000,000
Current Activity Level: Actively seeking new investments
Method of Compensation: Return on invest. most important, but chg. closing fees, service fees, etc.

MILESTONE MEDICA CORPORATION

One Richmond Street West
8th Floor
Toronto, Canada M5H 3W4
Phone: 416-974-0340
Fax: 416-974-1288

Type of Firm

Private Equity Firm

Additional Information

Year Founded: 2000
Current Activity Level: Actively seeking new investments

MILESTONE PARTNERS

595 East Lancaster Avenue
Suite 303
Saint Davids, PA USA 19087
Phone: 610-526-2700
Fax: 610-526-2701
E-mail: m2900@milestonepartners.com
Website: www.milestonepartners.com

Management and Staff

Adam Curtin, Vice President
Brooke Hayes, Partner
Geoffrey Veale, Vice President
John Shoemaker, Partner
John Nowaczyk, Vice President
Kenneth Kummerer, Chief Financial Officer
Mark Martinelli, Chief Financial Officer
Robert Levine, Partner
W. Scott Warren, Partner

Type of Firm

Private Equity Firm

Project Preferences

Role in Financing:

Prefer role as deal originator

Type of Financing Preferred:

Leveraged Buyout
Generalist PE
Later Stage
Management Buyouts
Acquisition
Recapitalizations

Size of Investments Considered:

Min Size of Investment Considered (000s): $5,000
Max Size of Investment Considered (000s): $40,000

Geographical Preferences

United States Preferences:

All U.S.

Industry Focus

(% based on actual investment)

Other Products	43.2%
Consumer Related	39.4%
Computer Software and Services	9.6%
Semiconductors/Other Elect.	7.9%

Additional Information

Name of Most Recent Fund: Milestone Partners II, L.P.
Most Recent Fund Was Raised: 07/21/2004
Year Founded: 1995
Capital Under Management: $170,000,000
Current Activity Level: Actively seeking new investments
Method of Compensation: Return on invest. most important, but chg. closing fees, service fees, etc.

MILESTONE RELIGARE INVESTMENT ADVISORS PVT., LTD.

602, Hallmark Business Plaza
Sant Dnyaneshwar Marg, Bandra
Mumbai, India 400051
Phone: 91-22-4235-7000
Fax: 91-22-4235-7077
E-mail: info@milestonereligare.com
Website: www.milestonereligare.com

Management and Staff

Amit Varma, President
Amit Sarup, President
Amitvikram Sharma, Partner
Rajesh Singhal, Managing Partner
Ved Prakash Arya, CEO & Managing Director

Type of Firm

Private Equity Firm

Project Preferences

Type of Financing Preferred:

Expansion

Size of Investments Considered:

Min Size of Investment Considered (000s): $3,993
Max Size of Investment Considered (000s): $11,980

Geographical Preferences

International Preferences:

India

Industry Preferences

In Communications prefer:

Communications and Media

In Medical/Health prefer:

Medical/Health
Medical Diagnostics
Medical Products
Health Services
Pharmaceuticals

In Consumer Related prefer:

Consumer
Food/Beverage
Education Related

Additional Information

Year Founded: 2009
Capital Under Management: $33,900,000
Current Activity Level: Actively seeking new investments

MILESTONE TURNAROUND MANAGEMENT CO., LTD.

1-19-5 Toranomon
4F Toranomon 1 Chome Mori Bldg
Minato-Ku, Tokyo, Japan 105-0001
Phone: 81-3-5501-1441
E-mail: info@milestone-tm.co.jp
Website: www.milestone-tm.co.jp

Type of Firm

Investment Management Firm

Project Preferences

Type of Financing Preferred:

Leveraged Buyout
Turnaround

Geographical Preferences

International Preferences:

Japan

Additional Information

Year Founded: 2005
Current Activity Level: Actively seeking new investments

MILESTONE VENTURE GROUP, INC. (FKA; MILESTONE CAPITAL)

Three Riverway
Suite 1285
Houston, TX USA 77056
Phone: 713-993-0303
Fax: 713-993-0711
Website: www.milestonevg.com

Type of Firm

Private Equity Firm

Project Preferences

Type of Financing Preferred:

Expansion

Size of Investments Considered:

Min Size of Investment Considered (000s): $2,000
Max Size of Investment Considered (000s): $10,000

Geographical Preferences

United States Preferences:

Southwest
Texas

Industry Preferences

In Industrial/Energy prefer:

Oil & Gas Drilling,Explor

In Business Serv. prefer:

Services
Distribution

In Manufact. prefer:

Manufacturing

Additional Information

Year Founded: 2000
Current Activity Level: Actively seeking new investments

MILESTONE VENTURE PARTNERS

551 Madison Avenue
Seventh Floor
New York, NY USA 10022
Phone: 212-223-7400
Fax: 212-223-0315
Website: www.milestonevp.com
Management and Staff

Edwin Goodman, General Partner
F.Morgan Rodd, General Partner
Richard Dumler, General Partner
Todd Pietri, General Partner

Type of Firm

Private Equity Firm

Association Membership

National Venture Capital Association - USA (NVCA)

Project Preferences

Role in Financing:

Will function either as deal originator or investor in deals created by others

Type of Financing Preferred:

Early Stage

Size of Investments Considered:

Min Size of Investment Considered (000s): $250
Max Size of Investment Considered (000s): $1,000

Geographical Preferences

United States Preferences:

Mid Atlantic
Northeast
Connecticut
New Jersey
New York

Industry Preferences

In Communications prefer:

Communications and Media
Data Communications

In Computer Software prefer:

Computer Services
Software
Systems Software
Applications Software

In Internet Specific prefer:

Internet
Web Aggregration/Portals

Additional Information

Name of Most Recent Fund: Milestone Venture Partners III, L.P.
Most Recent Fund Was Raised: 05/10/2006
Year Founded: 1999
Capital Under Management: $45,500,000
Current Activity Level: Actively seeking new investments
Method of Compensation: Return on investment is of primary concern, do not charge fees

---

MILJOUDVIKLING A/S

Tuborg Boulevard 3
Hellerup, Denmark 2900
Phone: 45-3945-4580
Fax: 45-3945-4581
Website: www.investmiljoe.dk

Type of Firm

Private Equity Firm

Project Preferences

Type of Financing Preferred:

Expansion

Geographical Preferences

International Preferences:

Denmark

Additional Information

Year Founded: 2004
Current Activity Level: Actively seeking new investments

MILK CAPITAL

64, Rue Taitbout
Paris, France 75009
Phone: 33-153-328-060
Fax: 33-148-781-446
E-mail: info@milkcapital.com
Website: www.milkcapital.com

Management and Staff

Bruno Bloch, Chief Financial Officer
Marc Eisenberg, Chief Executive Officer
Nathanael Eisenberg, Managing Director

Type of Firm

Private Equity Firm

Project Preferences

Type of Financing Preferred:

Turnaround

Industry Preferences

In Communications prefer:

Telecommunications

In Internet Specific prefer:

Internet

In Industrial/Energy prefer:

Alternative Energy

Additional Information

Year Founded: 2007
Current Activity Level: Actively seeking new investments

MILL ROAD CAPITAL LLC

Two Soundview Drive
Suite 300
Greenwich, CT USA 06830
Phone: 203-987-3500
Website: www.millroadcapital.com

Management and Staff

Charles Goldman, Managing Director

Type of Firm

Private Equity Firm

Project Preferences

Type of Financing Preferred:

Generalist PE
Public Companies

Additional Information

Year Founded: 2006
Capital Under Management: $250,000,000
Current Activity Level: Actively seeking new investments

MILLENNIUM ARK INVESTMENT CO., LTD.

13/F, Fang Yuan Mansion
B56 Zhong Guan Cun, South St.
Beijing, China 100044
Phone: 86-10-8802-6547
Fax: 86-10-8802-6546
E-mail: ark@millenniumark.com.cn
Website: www.millenniumark.com.cn

Management and Staff

Paul Song, President

Type of Firm

Private Equity Firm

Association Membership

Venture Capital Association of Beijing (VCAB)

Project Preferences

Type of Financing Preferred:

Balanced

Geographical Preferences

International Preferences:

China

Additional Information

Year Founded: 1999
Current Activity Level: Actively seeking new investments

MILLENNIUM EQUITY

c/o Empire Capital
One Gorham Island, Suite 201
Westport, CT USA 06880

Management and Staff

Gerald Ramdeen, Founder

Type of Firm

Private Equity Firm

Project Preferences

Type of Financing Preferred:
Leveraged Buyout

Industry Preferences

In Communications prefer:
Telecommunications

In Semiconductor/Electr prefer:
Semiconductor

Additional Information
Year Founded: 2009
Current Activity Level: Actively seeking new investments

MILLENNIUM PRIVATE EQUITY (AKA: MPE)
The Gate, East Wing, Level 2
Dubai Intl Financial Centre
Dubai, Utd. Arab Em.
Phone: 971-4363-4200
Fax: 971-4362-0540
Website: www.mpefunds.com

Management and Staff
Izzet Guney, Managing Director
Walter Brandhuber, Managing Director

Type of Firm
Bank Affiliated

Project Preferences

Type of Financing Preferred:
Leveraged Buyout
Mezzanine
Later Stage
Acquisition
Distressed Debt

Size of Investments Considered:
Min Size of Investment Considered (000s): $20,000
Max Size of Investment Considered (000s): $200,000

Geographical Preferences

International Preferences:
India
Middle East
Africa

Industry Preferences

In Communications prefer:
Telecommunications

In Medical/Health prefer:
Medical/Health

In Consumer Related prefer:
Education Related

In Industrial/Energy prefer:
Energy
Alternative Energy
Energy Conservation Relat

In Financial Services prefer:
Financial Services
Real Estate

In Business Serv. prefer:
Media

Additional Information
Year Founded: 2008
Capital Under Management: $450,000,000
Current Activity Level: Actively seeking new investments

MILLENNIUM TECHNOLOGY VENTURES
747 Third Avenue
38th Floor
New York, NY USA 10017
Phone: 646-521-7800
Fax: 646-521-7878
E-mail: info@mtvlp.com
Website: www.mtvlp.com

Management and Staff
Daniel Burstein, Managing Partner
Daniel Borok, Principal
Jonathan Glass, Chief Financial Officer
Max Chee, Principal
Samuel Schwerin, Managing Partner

Type of Firm
Private Equity Firm

Project Preferences

Type of Financing Preferred:
Leveraged Buyout
Public Companies
Later Stage
Management Buyouts
Acquisition
Special Situation
Recapitalizations

Industry Preferences

In Communications prefer:
Communications and Media

In Internet Specific prefer:
Internet

In Biotechnology prefer:
Biotechnology

In Medical/Health prefer:
Medical/Health
Health Services

In Industrial/Energy prefer:
Alternative Energy
Environmental Related

Additional Information
Year Founded: 1999
Capital Under Management: $130,000,000
Current Activity Level: Actively seeking new investments

MILLENNIUM VENTURES LLC
10777 Westheimer #1100
Houston, TX USA 77042
Phone: 713-260-9666
Fax: 713-260-9667
E-mail: investor@mevco.com
Website: www.mevco.com

Management and Staff
E. Daniel Leightman, Partner
Imran Maniar, Partner
Lamar Loyd, Partner
Phillip Gennarelli, Managing Partner
Ralph Freeman, Partner
Robert Troy, Partner
Steve Hill, Managing Partner

Type of Firm
Private Equity Firm

Project Preferences

Type of Financing Preferred:
Second Stage Financing

Size of Investments Considered:
Min Size of Investment Considered (000s): $1,000
Max Size of Investment Considered (000s): $5,000

Geographical Preferences

International Preferences:
Europe

Industry Preferences

In Communications prefer:
Telecommunications

In Medical/Health prefer:
Medical/Health

In Industrial/Energy prefer:
Energy

In Utilities prefer:
Utilities

Additional Information
Year Founded: 2001
Capital Under Management: $100,000,000
Current Activity Level: Actively seeking new investments

MILLER CAPITAL CORPORATION
4900 North Scottsdale Road
Suite 3800
Scottsdale, AZ USA 85251
Phone: 602-225-0505

Fax: 602-225-9024
E-mail: info@themillergroup.net
Website: www.themillergroup.net

Management and Staff

Rudy Miller, President, CEO, Chairman

Type of Firm

Service Provider

Project Preferences

Role in Financing:

Prefer role as deal originator

Type of Financing Preferred:

Second Stage Financing
Expansion

Size of Investments Considered:

Min Size of Investment Considered (000s): $1,000
Max Size of Investment Considered (000s): $5,000

Geographical Preferences

United States Preferences:

All U.S.

Industry Focus

(% based on actual investment)

Consumer Related	85.0%
Internet Specific	15.0%

Additional Information

Year Founded: 1995
Capital Under Management: $5,000,000
Current Activity Level: Actively seeking new investments
Method of Compensation: Professional fee required whether or not deal closes

---

MILLHOUSEIAG

MillhouseIAG Square
28 Market Street
Brisbane, Australia 4000
Phone: 617-3230-8000
Fax: 617-3230-8001
E-mail: investorservices@millhouseiag.com
Website: www.millhouseiag.com.au

Other Offices

37 Blight Street
Suite 301, Level 3
Sydney, Australia 2000

Millhouse AG Berlin
Alt-Moabit 91 d
Berlin, Germany D-10559
Phone: 49-30-3309-9470
Fax: 49-30-3309-9471

Marsh & McLennan Centre
18 Cross Street, #07-06 / 07
Singapore, Singapore 048423
Phone: 800-616-1511
Fax: 65-6534-5359

Management and Staff

Armand Aguillon, Managing Director
David Millhouse, Founder
Harry Charlton, Chief Financial Officer
Jasper Hagenberg, Managing Partner
Juergen Allesch, Managing Director

Type of Firm

Bank Affiliated

Project Preferences

Type of Financing Preferred:

Balanced

Geographical Preferences

International Preferences:

All International

Industry Preferences

In Biotechnology prefer:

Biotechnology

In Medical/Health prefer:

Medical/Health

Additional Information

Year Founded: 1991
Current Activity Level: Actively seeking new investments

MINAS GMBH

Passauer Platz 2
Vienna, Austria 1010
Phone: 43-1-533-8431
Fax: 43-1-533-843113
Website: www.woltron.com

Type of Firm

Private Equity Firm

Project Preferences

Type of Financing Preferred:

Balanced

Additional Information

Year Founded: 2007
Current Activity Level: Actively seeking new investments

MINATO CAPITAL CO., LTD.

107-1 Ito-cho
Chuo-ku
Kobe-shi, Japan 650-0032
Phone: 81-78-332-0451
Fax: 81-78-327-3205
Website: www.minatocp.co.jp

Type of Firm

Bank Affiliated

Additional Information

Year Founded: 2000
Current Activity Level: Actively seeking new investments

MINATO MIRAI CAPITAL CO., LTD.

No. 7 Naka-ku
Odori Progressive Office, 8/F
Yokohama, Japan
Phone: 81-45-641-3710
Fax: 81-45-641-3714
E-mail: fundmanager@mm-capital.co.jp
Website: www.mm-capital.co.jp

Management and Staff

Yoshiharu Ohta, President
Yoshimi Oota, Managing Director

Type of Firm

Private Equity Firm

Project Preferences

Type of Financing Preferred:

Early Stage
Balanced
Startup

Geographical Preferences

International Preferences:

Japan

Additional Information

Year Founded: 2002
Current Activity Level: Actively seeking new investments

MINERVA CAPITAL

Serrano, 7
Madrid, Spain 28001
Phone: 34-91-426-1790
Fax: 34-91-431-0886
E-mail: administracion@minervacapital.es
Website: www.minervacapital.es

Management and Staff

Alfonso Lopez-Quesada, Partner
David Bendel, Managing Partner
Emilio Ayanz Guillen, Partner

Type of Firm

Private Equity Firm

Project Preferences

Type of Financing Preferred:

Leveraged Buyout
Balanced

Size of Investments Considered:

Min Size of Investment Considered (000s): $4,786

Max Size of Investment Considered (000s): $17,946

Geographical Preferences

International Preferences:

Europe
Spain

Additional Information

Year Founded: 2004
Current Activity Level: Actively seeking new investments

MINORITY BROADCAST INVESTMENT CORPORATION

1001 Connecticut NorthWest
Suite 622
Washington, DC USA 20036
Phone: 202-293-1166
Fax: 202-872-1669

Type of Firm

Private Equity Firm

Association Membership

Natl Assoc of Investment Cos. (NAIC)

Project Preferences

Role in Financing:

Will function either as deal originator or investor in deals created by others

Type of Financing Preferred:

Leveraged Buyout
Special Situation

Size of Investments Considered:

Min Size of Investment Considered (000s): $500
Max Size of Investment Considered (000s): $1,000

Geographical Preferences

United States Preferences:

All U.S.

Industry Preferences

In Communications prefer:

Communications and Media

Additional Information

Year Founded: 1979
Capital Under Management: $4,000,000
Current Activity Level: Actively seeking new investments
Method of Compensation: Return on invest. most important, but chg. closing fees, service fees, etc.

MINT CAPITAL LTD

5/F, 18b Lva Tolstogo Street
11 Timura Frunze Street
Moscow, Russia 119021
Phone: 7-495-780-0424
Fax: 7-495-780-0425
E-mail: info@mintcap.ru
Website: www.mintcap.ru

Management and Staff

Benjamin Wilkening, Partner
Gleb Davidyuk, Partner

Type of Firm

Private Equity Firm

Project Preferences

Type of Financing Preferred:

Expansion

Size of Investments Considered:

Min Size of Investment Considered (000s): $5,000
Max Size of Investment Considered (000s): $15,000

Geographical Preferences

International Preferences:

Russia

Industry Preferences

In Consumer Related prefer:

Consumer
Retail

In Financial Services prefer:

Financial Services

In Business Serv. prefer:

Media

In Manufact. prefer:

Manufacturing

Additional Information

Year Founded: 2000
Capital Under Management: $150,000,000
Current Activity Level: Actively seeking new investments

MIRADERO CAPITAL PARTNERS, INC.

416 Ponce de Leon Avenue
Union Plaza, Suite 1500
San Juan, PR USA 00918
Phone: 787-620-0062
Fax: 787-620-0131
E-mail: info@miraderocapital.com
Website: www.miraderocapital.com

Management and Staff

Abdon Ruiz, Managing Director
Jorge Marti Pena, Chief Financial Officer
Zoilo Mendez, Managing Director

Type of Firm

Private Equity Firm

Association Membership

Natl Assoc of Small Bus. Inv. Co (NASBIC)

Project Preferences

Role in Financing:

Will function either as deal originator or investor in deals created by others

Type of Financing Preferred:

Second Stage Financing
Leveraged Buyout
Expansion
Mezzanine
Balanced
Turnaround
Later Stage
Management Buyouts
Acquisition
Special Situation
Recapitalizations

Size of Investments Considered:

Min Size of Investment Considered (000s): $500
Max Size of Investment Considered (000s): $2,000

Geographical Preferences

United States Preferences:

Southeast
Northeast

International Preferences:

Puerto Rico

Industry Preferences

In Communications prefer:

Telecommunications
Wireless Communications

In Computer Software prefer:

Computer Services
Data Processing
Software

In Internet Specific prefer:

Internet
Web Aggregration/Portals

In Medical/Health prefer:

Health Services
Hospitals/Clinics/Primary
Hospital/Other Instit.
Pharmaceuticals

In Consumer Related prefer:

Consumer
Entertainment and Leisure
Sports
Retail
Franchises(NEC)
Food/Beverage
Hotels and Resorts
Education Related

In Industrial/Energy prefer:

Industrial Products

In Transportation prefer:

Transportation

In Financial Services prefer:

Financial Services

In Business Serv. prefer:
Services
Distribution
Consulting Services
Media

In Manufact. prefer:
Manufacturing

In Agr/Forestr/Fish prefer:
Agriculture related

Additional Information

Year Founded: 2000
Capital Under Management: $31,200,000
Current Activity Level: Actively seeking new investments
Method of Compensation: Return on invest. most important, but chg. closing fees, service fees, etc.

MIRADOR CAPITAL

52 Indian Rock Road
New Canaan, CT USA 06840
Phone: 203-966-8847
Website: www.miradorcap.com

Other Offices

95 Lilac Drive
Atherton, CA USA 94027

Management and Staff

Ken Hausman, Managing Director
Robert Young, Managing Director

Type of Firm

Private Equity Firm

Project Preferences

Type of Financing Preferred:
Fund of Funds

Geographical Preferences

United States Preferences:
All U.S.

Additional Information

Name of Most Recent Fund: Mirador Entreprenuers Fund II, L.P.
Most Recent Fund Was Raised: 08/02/2006
Year Founded: 2003
Capital Under Management: $15,700,000
Current Activity Level: Actively seeking new investments

MIRAE ASSET VENTURE INVESTMENT CO., LTD. (FKA:KOREAN DREAM)

21st Floor, KINS Tower
Bundang-fu, Seongnam
Gyeonggi, South Korea 463-811
Phone: 82-31-784-8500
Fax: 82-31-784-8510
Website: www.venture.miraeasset.co.kr

Management and Staff

Eung-Suk Kim, President
Kyungseok Seol, Chief Executive Officer
Mansoon Park, President
Yong-Moon Kim, Managing Director

Type of Firm

Bank Affiliated

Association Membership

Korean Venture Capital Association (KVCA)

Project Preferences

Type of Financing Preferred:
Early Stage
Balanced

Geographical Preferences

International Preferences:
Korea, South
Asia

Industry Preferences

In Communications prefer:
Telecommunications

In Computer Software prefer:
Software

In Semiconductor/Electr prefer:
Electronics
Electronic Components

In Biotechnology prefer:
Biotechnology

In Industrial/Energy prefer:
Materials

In Manufact. prefer:
Manufacturing

Additional Information

Year Founded: 1999
Capital Under Management: $42,600,000
Current Activity Level: Actively seeking new investments

MIRAIMON OY

Palokulmantie 22
PO Box 61
Ulvila, Finland 28401
Phone: 358-2538-9799
Fax: 358-2538-3049
E-mail: miraimon@miraimon.com

Management and Staff

Kalle Valimaa, Founder

Type of Firm

Private Equity Firm

Association Membership

Finnish Venture Capital Association (FVCA)

Project Preferences

Type of Financing Preferred:
Expansion
Startup

Geographical Preferences

International Preferences:
Europe
Scandanavia/Nordic Region
Finland

Industry Preferences

In Computer Other prefer:
Computer Related

In Semiconductor/Electr prefer:
Electronics

Additional Information

Year Founded: 2000
Capital Under Management: $9,100,000
Current Activity Level: Actively seeking new investments

MIRALTA CAPITAL, INC.

475 Dumont Avenue
Suite 300
Dorval, Canada H9S 5W2
Phone: 514-631-2682
Fax: 514-631-1257

Type of Firm

Private Equity Firm

Project Preferences

Role in Financing:
Prefer role as deal originator

Type of Financing Preferred:
Second Stage Financing
Leveraged Buyout
First Stage Financing

Size of Investments Considered:
Min Size of Investment Considered (000s): $1,000
Max Size of Investment Considered: No Limit

Geographical Preferences

Canadian Preferences:
All Canada

Industry Preferences

In Communications prefer:
Data Communications

In Computer Hardware prefer:
Computer Graphics and Dig
Integrated Turnkey System

In Computer Software prefer:
Computer Services
Systems Software
Applications Software

In Semiconductor/Electr prefer:
Electronics
Electronic Components
Sensors
Analytic/Scientific

In Consumer Related prefer:
Consumer Products

In Industrial/Energy prefer:
Industrial Products
Materials
Factory Automation
Robotics
Machinery

In Manufact. prefer:
Office Automation Equipmt

Additional Information
Year Founded: 1992
Capital Under Management: $28,000,000
Current Activity Level: Actively seeking new investments
Method of Compensation: Return on investment is of primary concern, do not charge fees

---

MIRAMAR VENTURE PARTNERS
2101 East Coast Highway
Suite 300, Third Floor
Corona del Mar, CA USA 92625
Phone: 949-760-4450
Fax: 949-760-4451
Website: www.miramarvp.com

Management and Staff
Bob Holmen, Managing Director
Bruce Hallett, Managing Director
Heiner Sussner, Managing Director
Rick Fink, Managing Director

Type of Firm
Private Equity Firm

Project Preferences
Role in Financing:
Will function either as deal originator or investor in deals created by others

Type of Financing Preferred:
Second Stage Financing
Early Stage
Expansion
Seed
First Stage Financing
Startup

Size of Investments Considered:
Min Size of Investment Considered (000s): $500
Max Size of Investment Considered (000s): $6,000

Geographical Preferences
United States Preferences:
Southern California
West Coast

Industry Preferences
In Communications prefer:
Telecommunications
Wireless Communications
Data Communications
Satellite Microwave Comm.

In Computer Hardware prefer:
Disk Relat. Memory Device

In Computer Software prefer:
Software
Systems Software
Applications Software
Artificial Intelligence

In Internet Specific prefer:
Internet

In Semiconductor/Electr prefer:
Electronic Components
Semiconductor
Micro-Processing
Controllers and Sensors
Sensors
Circuit Boards
Component Testing Equipmt
Laser Related
Fiber Optics
Analytic/Scientific

In Medical/Health prefer:
Medical/Health
Medical Diagnostics

In Industrial/Energy prefer:
Energy

Additional Information
Name of Most Recent Fund: Miramar Venture Partners II, L.P.
Most Recent Fund Was Raised: 05/28/2008
Year Founded: 2001
Capital Under Management: $122,000,000
Current Activity Level: Actively seeking new investments
Method of Compensation: Return on investment is of primary concern, do not charge fees

---

MISSION BAY CAPITAL LLC
1459 18th Street
Suite 263
San Francisco, CA USA 94107
Phone: 415-240-4970

Type of Firm
Private Equity Firm

Project Preferences
Type of Financing Preferred:
Early Stage
Seed

Industry Preferences
In Biotechnology prefer:
Biotechnology

Additional Information
Year Founded: 2009
Capital Under Management: $7,500,000
Current Activity Level: Actively seeking new investments

MISSION VENTURES
11455 El Camino Real
Suite 450
San Diego, CA USA 92130
Phone: 858-350-2100
Fax: 858-350-2101
E-mail: contact@missionventures.com
Website: www.missionventures.com

Other Offices
2951 28th Street
Suite 2060
Santa Monica, CA USA 90405
Phone: 310-396-1420
Fax: 310-396-1353

Management and Staff
Caroline Barberio, Chief Financial Officer
Leo Spiegel, Managing Partner
Ted Alexander, Managing Partner

Type of Firm
Private Equity Firm

Association Membership
Western Association of Venture Capitalists (WAVC)
National Venture Capital Association - USA (NVCA)

Project Preferences
Role in Financing:
Prefer role as deal originator but will also invest in deals created by others

Type of Financing Preferred:
Second Stage Financing
Early Stage
Research and Development
First Stage Financing
Acquisition

Size of Investments Considered:
Min Size of Investment Considered (000s): $2,000
Max Size of Investment Considered (000s): $10,000

Geographical Preferences
United States Preferences:
Southern California

Industry Focus

(% based on actual investment)

Computer Software and Services	30.4%
Internet Specific	27.4%
Semiconductors/Other Elect.	17.0%
Communications and Media	11.0%
Other Products	5.0%
Consumer Related	2.5%
Industrial/Energy	2.4%
Computer Hardware	2.3%
Medical/Health	2.0%

Additional Information

Name of Most Recent Fund: Mission Ventures III, L.P.
Most Recent Fund Was Raised: 09/10/2004
Year Founded: 1997
Capital Under Management: $501,000,000
Current Activity Level: Actively seeking new investments
Method of Compensation: Return on investment is of primary concern, do not charge fees

MISSIONPOINT CAPITAL PARTNERS

20 Marshall Street
Suite 300
Norwalk, CT USA 06854
Phone: 203-286-0400
E-mail: info@missionpointcapital.com
Website: www.missionpointcapital.com

Management and Staff

Jesse Fink, Managing Director
Mark Cirilli, Managing Director

Type of Firm

Private Equity Firm

Project Preferences

Type of Financing Preferred:

Expansion
Management Buyouts
Acquisition
Joint Ventures
Fund of Funds of Second
Recapitalizations

Geographical Preferences

United States Preferences:

All U.S.

Industry Preferences

In Industrial/Energy prefer:

Energy
Alternative Energy
Energy Conservation Relat

In Financial Services prefer:

Financial Services

Additional Information

Year Founded: 2007
Capital Under Management: $335,500,000
Current Activity Level: Actively seeking new investments

MISTRAL EQUITY PARTNERS

650 Fifth Avenue
31st Floor
New York, NY USA 10019
Phone: 212-616-9600
Fax: 212-616-9601
Website: www.mistralequity.com

Management and Staff

Andrew Heyer, Co-Founder
Beth Bronner, Managing Director
William Phoenix, Managing Director

Type of Firm

Private Equity Firm

Project Preferences

Type of Financing Preferred:

Leveraged Buyout

Geographical Preferences

United States Preferences:

All U.S.

Industry Preferences

In Consumer Related prefer:

Consumer
Retail

Additional Information

Name of Most Recent Fund: Mistral Equity GP, L.P.
Most Recent Fund Was Raised: 10/03/2007
Year Founded: 2007
Capital Under Management: $422,000,000
Current Activity Level: Actively seeking new investments

MITHRA GROUP, LLC

205 Newbury Street
Boston, MA USA 02116
Phone: 617-247-4600
Fax: 617-247-4601
E-mail: info@mithragroup.com
Website: www.mithragroup.com

Management and Staff

Nina Ross, Managing Director
Sasha Ebrahimi, Managing Director

Type of Firm

Private Equity Firm

Project Preferences

Type of Financing Preferred:

Early Stage
Expansion
Later Stage

Geographical Preferences

United States Preferences:

All U.S.

International Preferences:

India

Industry Preferences

In Biotechnology prefer:

Biotechnology

In Medical/Health prefer:

Medical/Health

Additional Information

Year Founded: 2004
Capital Under Management: $100,000,000
Current Activity Level: Actively seeking new investments

MITISKA

Greta Baetens
Pontbeekstraat 2
Groot-Bijgaarden, Belgium 1702
Phone: 32-2-583-1950
Fax: 32-2-583-1964
Website: www.mitiska.be

Management and Staff

Leon Seynave, Co-Founder
Michiel Deturck, Managing Partner

Type of Firm

Investment Management Firm

Association Membership

Belgium Venturing Association

Project Preferences

Type of Financing Preferred:

Early Stage
Expansion
Balanced
Seed
Startup

Size of Investments Considered:

Min Size of Investment Considered (000s): $300
Max Size of Investment Considered (000s): $3,000

Geographical Preferences

International Preferences:

Europe

Industry Focus

(% based on actual investment)

Internet Specific	74.1%
Other Products	21.5%
Computer Software and Services	4.4%

Additional Information

Year Founded: 1990
Capital Under Management: $63,400,000
Current Activity Level: Actively seeking new investments

MITSUBISHI CORPORATION

6-1 Marunouchi 2-Chome
Chiyoda-ku
Tokyo, Japan 100-8086
Phone: 81-3-3210-2121
Fax: 81-3-3210-8935
Website: www.mitsubishi.co.jp

Type of Firm

Corporate PE/Venture

Project Preferences

Type of Financing Preferred:
Leveraged Buyout
Expansion

Geographical Preferences

United States Preferences:
All U.S.

International Preferences:
Asia

Industry Preferences

In Communications prefer:
Telecommunications

In Consumer Related prefer:
Food/Beverage

In Industrial/Energy prefer:
Energy
Materials
Machinery

In Manufact. prefer:
Manufacturing

Additional Information

Year Founded: 1950
Capital Under Management: $150,000,000
Current Activity Level: Actively seeking new investments

MITSUBISHI INTERNATIONAL CORP.

6-3 Marunouchi 2 Chome
Chiyoda-ku
Tokyo, Japan 100-8086
Phone: 81-3-3210-2121
Fax: 81-3-3210-8935
E-mail: prdept@org.mitsubishicorp.com
Website: www.mitsubishi.co.jp

Management and Staff

Ichiro Ando, Chief Financial Officer
Kazumi Yoshimura, Chief Operating Officer

Type of Firm

Bank Affiliated

Project Preferences

Role in Financing:
Prefer role as deal originator but will also invest in deals created by others

Type of Financing Preferred:
Second Stage Financing
Mezzanine
First Stage Financing

Geographical Preferences

United States Preferences:
All U.S.

Canadian Preferences:
All Canada

International Preferences:
Asia

Industry Focus

(% based on actual investment)

Other Products	56.1%
Internet Specific	14.1%
Medical/Health	5.8%
Semiconductors/Other Elect.	5.7%
Biotechnology	5.1%
Computer Software and Services	4.6%
Communications and Media	3.6%
Computer Hardware	2.9%
Industrial/Energy	2.1%

Additional Information

Name of Most Recent Fund: Mitsubishi
Most Recent Fund Was Raised: 11/01/1988
Year Founded: 1983
Capital Under Management: $35,000,000
Current Activity Level: Actively seeking new investments

MITSUBISHI UFJ CAPITAL CO., LTD.

Kanematsu Building
2-14-1 Kyobashi, Chuo-ku
Tokyo, Japan 104-0031
Phone: 81-3-3538-8211
Fax: 81-3-3538-7737
Website: www.mucap.co.jp

Management and Staff

Michitaka Mukouhara, President

Type of Firm

Private Equity Firm

Project Preferences

Type of Financing Preferred:
Balanced

Geographical Preferences

International Preferences:
Japan

Additional Information

Year Founded: 1974
Current Activity Level: Actively seeking new investments

MITSUI & CO. VENTURE PARTNERS (MCVP)

200 Park Avenue
36th Floor
New York, NY USA 10166-0130
Phone: 212-878-4066
Fax: 212-878-4070
E-mail: info@mitsuivp.com
Website: www.mitsuivp.com

Other Offices

KKDI Otemachi Bldg.
16F, 1-8-1 Otemachi, Chiyoda-ku
Tokyo, Japan 100-0004
Phone: 81-3-5299-2251
Fax: 81-3-3272-5315

2180 Sand Hill Road
Suite 345
Menlo Park, CA USA 94025
Phone: 650-234-5000
Fax: 650-233-9205

Management and Staff

Yoichiro Endo, CEO & Managing Director
Yoshito Kuroda, Venture Partner
Yoshiyuki Ishii, Venture Partner

Type of Firm

Corporate PE/Venture

Association Membership

National Venture Capital Association - USA (NVCA)

Project Preferences

Role in Financing:
Prefer role as deal originator but will also invest in deals created by others

Type of Financing Preferred:
Second Stage Financing
Early Stage
Research and Development
Start-up Financing
Balanced
Seed
First Stage Financing

Size of Investments Considered:
Min Size of Investment Considered (000s): $5,000
Max Size of Investment Considered (000s): $15,000

Geographical Preferences

United States Preferences:
All U.S.

Canadian Preferences:
All Canada

Industry Focus

(% based on actual investment)

Communications and Media	19.7%
Internet Specific	19.3%
Computer Software and Services	17.4%
Medical/Health	15.2%
Biotechnology	11.2%
Semiconductors/Other Elect.	7.5%
Computer Hardware	4.0%
Industrial/Energy	3.9%
Other Products	1.6%
Consumer Related	0.3%

Additional Information
Name of Most Recent Fund: Mitsui & Co, Ltd.
Most Recent Fund Was Raised: 01/01/1988
Year Founded: 1997
Capital Under Management: $240,000,000
Current Activity Level: Actively seeking new investments
Method of Compensation: Return on investment is of primary concern, do not charge fees

---

MITSUI COMTEK
20300 Stevens Creek Boulevard
Suite 300
Cupertino, CA USA 95014
Phone: 408-725-8525
Fax: 408-725-8527
E-mail: info@mitsuicomtek.com
Website: www.mitsuicomtek.com

Type of Firm
Corporate PE/Venture

Additional Information
Year Founded: 1876
Current Activity Level: Actively seeking new investments

MITSUI INCUBASE CORP.
20400 Steven Creek Boulevard
Suite 300
Cupertino, CA USA 95014
Phone: 408-864-2860
Fax: 408-864-2861

Other Offices
Mitsui & Co. Ltd. IT Business Unit
1-2-1 Ohtemachi
Chiyoda-ku, Tokyo, Japan 100-0004

Phone: 81-3-3285-4338
Fax: 81-3-3285-9389

200 Park Avenue
New York, NY USA 10166
Phone: 212-878-4324
Fax: 212-878-4323

Type of Firm
Corporate PE/Venture

Additional Information
Year Founded: 2005
Current Activity Level: Actively seeking new investments

MITSUI SUMITOMO INSURANCE VENTURE CAPITAL CO., LTD.
2-2-10 Yaesu
Chuo-Ku
Tokyo, Japan 104-0028
Phone: 81-3-3279-3672
Fax: 81-3-3242-3068
Website: www.msivc.co.jp

Type of Firm
Insurance Firm Affiliate

Project Preferences

Type of Financing Preferred:
Balanced

Geographical Preferences

International Preferences:
Japan

Additional Information
Year Founded: 1990
Current Activity Level: Actively seeking new investments

MITTEL SPA
Piazza Armando Diaz 7
Milan, Italy 20123
Phone: 39-02-721-411
E-mail: segreteria@mittel.it
Website: www.mittel.it

Type of Firm
Private Equity Firm

Project Preferences

Type of Financing Preferred:
Balanced

Geographical Preferences

International Preferences:
All International

Additional Information
Year Founded: 1970
Current Activity Level: Actively seeking new investments

MITTELSTANDISCHE BETEILIGUNGSGESELLSCHAFT NIEDERSACHSEN MBG
Schiffgraben 33
Hannover, Germany 30175
Phone: 49 511 33 705-0
Fax: 49 511 33705-55
Website: www.nbb-hannover.de

Type of Firm
Bank Affiliated

Association Membership
German Venture Capital Association (BVK)

Project Preferences

Type of Financing Preferred:
Expansion
Startup
Recapitalizations

Geographical Preferences

International Preferences:
Germany

Additional Information
Year Founded: 2001
Current Activity Level: Actively seeking new investments

MITTELSTANDISCHE BETEILIGUNGSGESELLSCHAFT THURINGEN MBH
Gorkistrasse 9
Erfurt, Germany 99084
Phone: 49 361 7447-132
Fax: 49 361 7447-131
E-mail: info@mbg-thueringen.de
Website: www.mbg-thueringen.de

Management and Staff
Franz Gerstner, Managing Director
Ursula Gabler, Managing Director

Type of Firm
Bank Affiliated

Association Membership
German Venture Capital Association (BVK)

Project Preferences

Type of Financing Preferred:
Expansion
Management Buyouts
Startup
Recapitalizations

Geographical Preferences

International Preferences:
Germany

Additional Information
Year Founded: 1993
Capital Under Management: $9,300,000
Current Activity Level: Actively seeking new investments

MIURA PRIVATE EQUITY
Paseo de Gracia, 79
Principal 1A
Barcelona, Spain 08008
Phone: 34-932-723-440
Fax: 34-932-723-445
E-mail: info@miuraequity.com
Website: www.miuraequity.com

Management and Staff
Juan Leach, Managing Partner
Luis Segui Casas, Managing Partner

Type of Firm
Private Equity Firm

Association Membership
Spanish Venture Capital Association (ASCRI)

Project Preferences

Type of Financing Preferred:
Leveraged Buyout
Expansion

Geographical Preferences

International Preferences:
Portugal
Spain

Industry Preferences

In Medical/Health prefer:
Medical/Health

In Consumer Related prefer:
Entertainment and Leisure
Consumer Products
Consumer Services

In Business Serv. prefer:
Services

Additional Information
Year Founded: 2008
Capital Under Management: $155,300,000
Current Activity Level: Actively seeking new investments

MIYAGIN VENTURE CAPITAL CO., LTD.
1-7-4 Tachibana dori higashi
Miyazaki-shi, Japan
Phone: 81-985-20-0822
Fax: 81-985-31-1757
Website: www.miyagin.co.jp

Type of Firm
Bank Affiliated

Additional Information
Year Founded: 2007
Current Activity Level: Actively seeking new investments

MIZUHO CAPITAL COMPANY, LTD.
1-2-1 Uchisaiwaicho
Chiyoda-ku
Tokyo, Japan 100-0011
Phone: 81-3-3596-1300
Fax: 81-3-3596-1310
Website: www.mizuho-vc.co.jp

Other Offices
4-2-1 Imabashi
Chuo-ku
Osaka, Japan 541-0042
Phone: 81-6-6229-2781
Fax: 81-6-6229-2757

Management and Staff
Akira Kiyohara, President
Hidemasa Ogura, Managing Director
Kengo Numata, Managing Director
Naoto Takano, Senior Managing Director
Seiichi Yagi, Managing Director

Type of Firm
Private Equity Firm

Project Preferences

Type of Financing Preferred:
Balanced

Geographical Preferences

International Preferences:
Asia
Japan

Industry Preferences

In Communications prefer:
Communications and Media

In Computer Software prefer:
Software

In Internet Specific prefer:
Internet

In Semiconductor/Electr prefer:
Electronics
Semiconductor

In Medical/Health prefer:
Medical/Health

In Consumer Related prefer:
Consumer

In Business Serv. prefer:
Services

Additional Information
Year Founded: 1983
Capital Under Management: $567,000,000
Current Activity Level: Actively seeking new investments

MIZUHO CAPITAL PARTNERS CO., LTD.
3rd Floor YUSEN Building
2-3-2 Marunouchi, Chiyoda-ku
Tokyo, Japan 100-0005
Phone: 81-3-3284-1632
Fax: 81-3-3201-1632
E-mail: info@mizuho-ca.co.jp
Website: www.mizuho-cp.co.jp

Management and Staff
Mitsuru Otawa, Managing Director
Tadashi Miyazaki, Managing Director

Type of Firm
Private Equity Firm

Project Preferences

Type of Financing Preferred:
Leveraged Buyout
Balanced
Management Buyouts

Geographical Preferences

International Preferences:
Japan

Additional Information
Year Founded: 2003
Capital Under Management: $341,700,000
Current Activity Level: Actively seeking new investments

MIZUHO SECURITIES ASIA, LTD. (FKA: IBJ ASIA SECURITIES LTD.)
11/F, CITIC Tower
1 Tim Mei Avenue
Central, Hong Kong
Phone: 852-2685-2000
Website: www.mizuho-sc.com/hk

Type of Firm
Private Equity Firm

Project Preferences
Type of Financing Preferred:
Balanced

Geographical Preferences
International Preferences:
Asia

Additional Information
Name of Most Recent Fund: Asian Private Equity Trust
Most Recent Fund Was Raised: 10/01/1997
Year Founded: 1999
Capital Under Management: $50,000,000
Current Activity Level: Actively seeking new investments

MK CAPITAL
1033 Skokie Boulevard
Suite 430
Northbrook, IL USA 60062
Phone: 312-324-7700
Fax: 312-324-7713
Website: www.mkcapital.com

Management and Staff
Bret Maxwell, Managing General Partner
Karen Buckner, Partner
Mark Koulogeorge, Managing General Partner
Mark Terbeek, Partner

Type of Firm
Private Equity Firm

Association Membership
Illinois Venture Capital Association

Project Preferences
Role in Financing:
Prefer role as deal originator but will also invest in deals created by others

Type of Financing Preferred:
Expansion
Turnaround
Balanced
First Stage Financing
Special Situation

Geographical Preferences
United States Preferences:
All U.S.

Industry Preferences
In Communications prefer:
Wireless Communications

In Computer Software prefer:
Software
Applications Software

In Internet Specific prefer:
Web Aggregration/Portals

In Business Serv. prefer:
Services

Additional Information
Year Founded: 2001
Capital Under Management: $150,000,000
Current Activity Level: Actively seeking new investments

MKS PARTNERS, LTD. (FKA: SCHRODER VENTURES K.K.)
Akasaka 81 Building
2-13-5, Nagata-cho, Chiyoda-ku
Tokyo, Japan 100-0014
Phone: 81-3-5251-3911
Fax: 81-3-5251-3950
E-mail: info@mks-c.jp
Website: www.mks-p.jp

Management and Staff
Aida Ryutaro, Principal
Ayumi Sakurai, Partner
Dai Nakamura, Principal
Hidetosi Shibata, Principal
Ken Kato, Partner
Koichiro Yoshizaki, Partner
Masagazu Nakajima, Principal
Masayuki Noguchi, Partner
Ryutaro Aida, Principal
Tetsuro Toyoda, Partner

Type of Firm
Private Equity Firm

Project Preferences
Type of Financing Preferred:
Leveraged Buyout
Expansion
Balanced
Management Buyouts

Geographical Preferences
International Preferences:
Japan

Industry Preferences
In Business Serv. prefer:
Distribution

Additional Information
Year Founded: 1982
Capital Under Management: $492,000,000
Current Activity Level: Actively seeking new investments

MKW CAPITAL, LTD.
Alm Dr. Carlos D' Assumpcao,
181-187 Edf. Jardim Brilhantis
9 andar, Macau
Phone: 853-2872-2376
E-mail: info@mkwcapital.com
Website: www.mkwcapital.com

Other Offices
4009 Gloucester Tower
The Landmark, 11 Pedder Street
Central, Hong Kong

c/o K&E LLP, Citigroup Center
153 East 53rd Street
New York, NY USA 10022-4611

Type of Firm
Private Equity Firm

Project Preferences
Type of Financing Preferred:
Balanced

Geographical Preferences
International Preferences:
Asia

Additional Information
Year Founded: 2006
Capital Under Management: $71,500,000
Current Activity Level: Actively seeking new investments

MMC VENTURES, LTD.
Braywick House
Gregory Place
London, United Kingdom W8 4NG
Phone: 44-20-7938-2220
Fax: 44-20-7938-2259
E-mail: enquiries@mmcventures.com
Website: www.mmcventures.com

Management and Staff
Alan Morgan, Founder

Type of Firm
Private Equity Firm

Association Membership
British Venture Capital Association (BVCA)

Project Preferences
Role in Financing:
Prefer role as deal originator but will also invest in deals created by others

Type of Financing Preferred:
Early Stage
Seed
Startup

Size of Investments Considered:
Min Size of Investment Considered (000s): $800
Max Size of Investment Considered (000s): $3,200

Geographical Preferences

International Preferences:
United Kingdom
Western Europe

Industry Preferences

In Computer Other prefer:
Computer Related

In Consumer Related prefer:
Entertainment and Leisure

In Financial Services prefer:
Financial Services

Additional Information
Year Founded: 2000
Capital Under Management: $19,400,000
Current Activity Level: Actively seeking new investments

MMI GROUP INC.
135 Kingstreet East
Ontario, Canada M5C 1G6
Phone: 416-363-3050
Fax: 416-368-4330
E-mail: info@mmigroup.com

Type of Firm
Private Equity Firm

Additional Information
Year Founded: 2009
Current Activity Level: Actively seeking new investments

MML CAPITAL PARTNERS (FKA: MEZZANINE MANAGEMENT UK, LTD.)
Grand Buildings
1-3 Strand
London, United Kingdom WC2N 5HR
Phone: 44-20-7024-2200
Fax: 44-20-7024-2201
Website: www.mmlcapital.com

Other Offices
12-14 Rond-Point des Champs-Elysees
Paris, France 75008
Phone: 33-1-5353-1508
Fax: 33-1-5353-1575

333 Ludlow Street
Second Floor North Tower
Stamford, CT USA 06902
Phone: 203-323-9118
Fax: 203-323-9119

Bockenheimer Landstrasse 17/19
Franfurt am Main, Germany 60323
Phone: 49-69-710-455-240
Fax: 49-69-710-455-450

Management and Staff
Bal Johal, Partner
Bradley Jay, Partner
Christian Heidl, Partner
George Davidson, Partner
Henry-Louis Merieux, Partner
Ian Wallis, Partner
Jim Read, Founding Partner
Luke Jones, Partner
Mark Evers, Partner
Parag Gandesha, Chief Financial Officer
Robert Davies, Partner
Robin Thywissen, Partner
Rory Brooks, Founding Partner
Shawn St. Jean, Partner
Valerie Lebreton, Partner

Type of Firm
Bank Affiliated

Association Membership
European Private Equity and Venture Capital Assoc.

Project Preferences

Role in Financing:
Prefer role as deal originator but will also invest in deals created by others

Type of Financing Preferred:
Leveraged Buyout
Expansion
Mezzanine
Management Buyouts
Industry Rollups
Special Situation
Recapitalizations

Size of Investments Considered:
Min Size of Investment Considered (000s): $9,416
Max Size of Investment Considered (000s): $94,160

Geographical Preferences

United States Preferences:
All U.S.

Canadian Preferences:
All Canada

International Preferences:
Hungary
Italy
Slovak Repub.
United Kingdom
Turkey
Czech Republic
Central Europe
Europe
Poland
Croatia
Bermuda
Eastern Europe
Bulgaria
Ukraine
Spain
Romania
Germany
Russia
France

Industry Focus
(% based on actual investment)

Other Products	31.9%
Medical/Health	19.7%
Computer Software and Services	13.2%
Industrial/Energy	13.1%
Consumer Related	7.8%
Semiconductors/Other Elect.	5.9%
Communications and Media	4.5%
Internet Specific	4.0%

Additional Information
Year Founded: 1988
Capital Under Management: $1,250,000,000
Current Activity Level: Actively seeking new investments
Method of Compensation: Return on invest. most important, but chg. closing fees, service fees, etc.

MMV FINANCIAL INC. (FKA: MM VENTURE PARTNERS)
370 King Street West
Suite 604
Toronto, Canada M5V 1J9
Phone: 416-977-9718
Fax: 416-591-1393
E-mail: info@mmvf.com
Website: www.mmvf.com

Other Offices
300 Park Avenue
17th Floor
New York, NY USA 10022
Phone: 212-572-4871
Fax: 212-572-6499

366 Cambridge Avenue
Suite 205
Palo Alto, CA USA 94306
Phone: 650-241-0320
Fax: 650-618-1626

11921 Freedom Drive
Suite 550
Reston, VA USA 20190
Phone: 703-397-5157
Fax: 703-904-4399

481 Viger Avenue West
Suite 300
Montreal, Canada H2Z 1G6
Phone: 514-908-9645
Fax: 514-396-4354

Type of Firm
Private Equity Firm

Association Membership
Canadian Venture Capital Association

Project Preferences

Role in Financing:
Will function either as deal originator or investor in deals created by others

Type of Financing Preferred:
Second Stage Financing
Early Stage
Expansion
First Stage Financing
Startup

Size of Investments Considered:
Min Size of Investment Considered (000s): $1,000
Max Size of Investment Considered (000s): $5,000

Geographical Preferences

Canadian Preferences:
All Canada

Industry Focus

(% based on actual investment)

Computer Software and Services	35.3%
Internet Specific	18.8%
Computer Hardware	14.9%
Medical/Health	11.8%
Semiconductors/Other Elect.	6.3%
Communications and Media	6.1%
Biotechnology	2.8%
Consumer Related	1.9%
Industrial/Energy	1.9%

Additional Information
Year Founded: 1998
Capital Under Management: $372,200,000
Current Activity Level: Actively seeking new investments

MOBILE INTERNET CAPITAL CORPORATION

10F, Akasaka 1-chome Mori Bldg
1-11-28, Akasaka Minato-ku
Tokyo, Japan 107-0052
Phone: 813-3568-2979
Fax: 813-3568-2458
E-mail: micinfo@mickk.com
Website: www.mickk.com

Type of Firm
Private Equity Firm

Project Preferences

Type of Financing Preferred:
Early Stage
Startup

Geographical Preferences

International Preferences:
Japan

Industry Preferences

In Communications prefer:
Wireless Communications

In Internet Specific prefer:
Internet

Additional Information
Year Founded: 1999
Current Activity Level: Actively seeking new investments

MOBILITY VENTURES

16475 Dallas Parkway
Suite 620
Addison, TX USA 75001
Phone: 972-991-9942
Fax: 972-669-7873
E-mail: partner@mobilityventures.com
Website: www.mobilityventures.com

Management and Staff
Edward Fernandez, Venture Partner
Krish Prabhu, Venture Partner
Mark Fruehan, Partner
Michael Buckland, Partner
Osmo Hautanen, Partner
Ray Jamp, Venture Partner
Roman Kikta, Managing Partner

Type of Firm
Investment Management Firm

Project Preferences

Type of Financing Preferred:
Early Stage
Seed

Size of Investments Considered:
Min Size of Investment Considered (000s): $100
Max Size of Investment Considered (000s): $2,000

Geographical Preferences

United States Preferences:
All U.S.

Industry Preferences

In Communications prefer:
Wireless Communications

In Computer Software prefer:
Software

In Semiconductor/Electr prefer:
Electronic Components
Semiconductor

Additional Information
Year Founded: 2005
Capital Under Management: $22,000,000
Current Activity Level: Actively seeking new investments

MOBIUS CORPORATE VENTURE CAPITAL SGECR SA

Plaza Manuel Gomez Moreno s/n
Edificio Bronce - Planta 6a
Madrid, Spain 28020
Phone: 34-91-555-0069
Fax: 34-91-555-0036
E-mail: informacion@mobiuscvc.com
Website: www.mobius.es

Type of Firm
Private Equity Firm

Project Preferences

Type of Financing Preferred:
Balanced

Geographical Preferences

International Preferences:
Spain

Additional Information
Year Founded: 2004
Capital Under Management: $36,400,000
Current Activity Level: Actively seeking new investments

MOBIUS VENTURE CAPITAL (FKA: SOFTBANK VENTURE CAPITAL)

1050 Walnut Street
Suite 210
Boulder, CO USA 80302
Phone: 303-642-4000
Fax: 303-642-4001
E-mail: info@mobiusvc.com
Website: www.mobiusvc.com

Management and Staff
Bradley Feld, Managing Director
Jason Mendelson, Managing Director
Ryan McIntyre, Principal
Seth Levine, Principal

Type of Firm
Private Equity Firm

Association Membership
National Venture Capital Association - USA (NVCA)

Project Preferences

Role in Financing:
Prefer role as deal originator

Type of Financing Preferred:
Early Stage
Start-up Financing
Seed
First Stage Financing

Size of Investments Considered:
Min Size of Investment Considered (000s): $2,000
Max Size of Investment Considered (000s): $100,000

Industry Focus

(% based on actual investment)

Internet Specific	49.1%
Computer Software and Services	17.2%
Other Products	10.2%
Semiconductors/Other Elect.	8.1%
Communications and Media	7.4%
Consumer Related	3.4%
Computer Hardware	2.3%
Medical/Health	1.4%
Industrial/Energy	0.4%
Biotechnology	0.4%

Additional Information

Year Founded: 1996
Capital Under Management: $2,210,900,000
Current Activity Level: Making few, if any, new investments
Method of Compensation: Return on investment is of primary concern, do not charge fees

MOBYSON AB (FKA: EXTENDED CAPITAL GROUP ECG AB)

Danvikcenter 28, 11tr
Nacka, Sweden 131-30
Phone: 468-5569-6500
Fax: 468-5569-6501
Website: www.mobyson.se

Type of Firm

Bank Affiliated

Association Membership

Swedish Venture Capital Association (SVCA)

Project Preferences

Type of Financing Preferred:
Later Stage

Geographical Preferences

International Preferences:
Scandanavia/Nordic Region

Industry Preferences

In Communications prefer:
Communications and Media

Additional Information

Year Founded: 2000
Current Activity Level: Actively seeking new investments

MODENA TECHNOLOGIES CAPITAL PARTNERS

Reconquista 865
Pisa 6
Buenos Aires, Argentina C1003ABQ
Phone: 54-11-4317-6812
Fax: 54-11-4317-6814
E-mail: info@modenatcp.com
Website: www.modenatcp.com

Type of Firm

Private Equity Firm

Project Preferences

Type of Financing Preferred:
Early Stage

Geographical Preferences

International Preferences:
All International

Industry Preferences

In Computer Software prefer:
Software

In Internet Specific prefer:
Ecommerce

In Financial Services prefer:
Financial Services

In Business Serv. prefer:
Services

Additional Information

Year Founded: 2004
Current Activity Level: Actively seeking new investments

MODERN AFRICA FUND MANAGERS

7 Arnold Road
Rosebank
Johannesburg, South Africa
Phone: 27-11-447-4834
Fax: 27-11-447-4427
E-mail: ctwood@mafm.com
Website: www.modernafrica.com

Management and Staff

Tim Wood, Managing Director

Type of Firm

Private Equity Firm

Association Membership

African Venture Capital Association (AVCA)

Project Preferences

Type of Financing Preferred:
Expansion
Turnaround
Recapitalizations

Size of Investments Considered:
Min Size of Investment Considered (000s): $2,500
Max Size of Investment Considered (000s): $12,000

Geographical Preferences

International Preferences:
Nigeria
Uganda
Zambia
Tanzania
Ghana
Kenya
South Africa

Industry Preferences

In Communications prefer:
Telecommunications
Other Communication Prod.

In Internet Specific prefer:
Internet

In Financial Services prefer:
Financial Services
Real Estate

In Business Serv. prefer:
Services

In Manufact. prefer:
Manufacturing

Additional Information

Current Activity Level: Actively seeking new investments

MODUS PRIVATE EQUITY

The Edge, Clowes Street
Manchester, United Kingdom M3 5NA
Phone: 44-161-833-0955
Fax: 44-161-833-0956
Website: www.moduspe.co.uk

Other Offices

Lancaster House
67 Newhall Street
Birmingham, United Kingdom B3 1NQ

1st Floor, 32 Dover Street
London, United Kingdom W1S 4NE

Type of Firm

Private Equity Firm

Association Membership

British Venture Capital Association (BVCA)

Project Preferences

Type of Financing Preferred:
Generalist PE

Size of Investments Considered:
Min Size of Investment Considered (000s): $4,023

Max Size of Investment Considered (000s): $20,114

Geographical Preferences

International Preferences:
United Kingdom

Additional Information
Year Founded: 2006
Current Activity Level: Actively seeking new investments

MOFET B-YEHUDA TECHNOLOGICAL AND BUSINESS INCUBATOR
P.O. Box 80
Kiryat Arba, Israel 90100
Phone: 972-2-996-3880
Fax: 972-2-996-1571
E-mail: info@mofet.org.il
Website: www.mofet.org.il

Management and Staff
Yossi Ron, Chief Executive Officer

Type of Firm
Incubator/Development Program

Association Membership
Israel Venture Association

Project Preferences

Type of Financing Preferred:
Seed

Geographical Preferences

International Preferences:
Israel

Additional Information
Year Founded: 1991
Current Activity Level: Actively seeking new investments

MOHR DAVIDOW VENTURES
3000 Sand Hill Road
Building Three, Suite 290
Menlo Park, CA USA 94025
Phone: 650-854-7236
Fax: 650-854-7365
Website: www.mdv.com

Management and Staff
Bryan Stolle, Partner
David Feinleib, Partner
Erik Straser, Partner
Geoffrey Moore, Partner
Jim Smith, Partner
Jonathan Feiber, Partner
Joshua Green, Partner
Katherine Moortgat, Partner
Katherine Barr, Partner
Marianne Wu, Partner
Michael Goldberg, Partner
Michael Lanham, Chief Financial Officer
Moez Virani, Partner
Nancy Schoendorf, Partner
Pamela Mahoney, Partner
Randy Strahan, Partner
Rowan Chapman, Partner
Sue Siegel, Partner
Sven Strohband, Partner
Will Coleman, Partner
William Ericson, Partner
William Davidow, Partner

Type of Firm
Private Equity Firm

Association Membership
Western Association of Venture Capitalists (WAVC)
National Venture Capital Association - USA (NVCA)

Project Preferences

Role in Financing:
Prefer role as deal originator but will also invest in deals created by others

Type of Financing Preferred:
Second Stage Financing
Early Stage
Balanced
Seed
First Stage Financing

Size of Investments Considered:
Min Size of Investment Considered (000s): $500
Max Size of Investment Considered (000s): $10,000

Geographical Preferences

United States Preferences:
Mid Atlantic
Northwest
West Coast
All U.S.

Industry Focus
(% based on actual investment)

Computer Software and Services	28.1%
Internet Specific	20.9%
Semiconductors/Other Elect.	14.5%
Communications and Media	9.0%
Medical/Health	6.8%
Biotechnology	6.2%
Industrial/Energy	5.1%
Computer Hardware	4.2%
Other Products	4.0%
Consumer Related	1.2%

Additional Information
Name of Most Recent Fund: MDV IX, L.P.
Most Recent Fund Was Raised: 08/23/2007
Year Founded: 1983
Capital Under Management: $2,000,000,000
Current Activity Level: Actively seeking new investments
Method of Compensation: Return on invest. most important, but chg. closing fees, service fees, etc.

MOMENTUM CAPITAL LIMITED
42 Brook Street
London, United Kingdom W1K 5DB
Phone: 44-20-7060-5500
Fax: 44-20-7060-5501
Website: www.momentum-capital.com

Management and Staff
Tobias Poensgen, Managing Director

Type of Firm
Private Equity Firm

Association Membership
European Private Equity and Venture Capital Assoc.

Project Preferences

Role in Financing:
Prefer role as deal originator

Type of Financing Preferred:
Second Stage Financing
Early Stage
Expansion
Generalist PE
Turnaround
First Stage Financing
Acquisition

Size of Investments Considered:
Min Size of Investment Considered (000s): $730
Max Size of Investment Considered (000s): $36,502

Geographical Preferences

United States Preferences:
All U.S.

International Preferences:
United Kingdom
Europe

Industry Preferences

In Communications prefer:
Communications and Media

In Computer Software prefer:
Software

In Internet Specific prefer:
E-Commerce Technology
Internet

In Industrial/Energy prefer:
Energy
Alternative Energy
Energy Conservation Relat

In Agr/Forestr/Fish prefer:
Agriculture related

Additional Information
Year Founded: 2002

Capital Under Management: $365,000,000
Current Activity Level: Actively seeking new investments

MOMENTUM TECHNOLOGY PARTNERS LLC

5C North Main Street
Suite 201
Manasquan, NJ USA 08736
Phone: 732-528-4300
E-mail: info@momentumtp.com
Website: www.momentumtp.com

Management and Staff

Bob Beran, Managing Partner
Ed Callahan, Managing Partner
Michael Centrella, Managing Partner

Type of Firm

Private Equity Firm

Project Preferences

Role in Financing:
Prefer role in deals created by others

Type of Financing Preferred:
Mezzanine
Early Stage
Start-up Financing
Later Stage
Seed
First Stage Financing

Size of Investments Considered:
Min Size of Investment Considered (000s): $25
Max Size of Investment Considered (000s): $500

Geographical Preferences

United States Preferences:
Mid Atlantic
Northeast
East Coast

Industry Preferences

In Communications prefer:
Telecommunications
Wireless Communications
Data Communications

In Computer Software prefer:
Computer Services

In Internet Specific prefer:
Internet
Ecommerce

In Semiconductor/Electr prefer:
Semiconductor

In Business Serv. prefer:
Consulting Services

Additional Information

Year Founded: 2001
Capital Under Management: $5,000,000
Current Activity Level: Actively seeking new investments
Method of Compensation: Professional fee required whether or not deal closes

MOMENTUM VENTURE MANAGEMENT LLC

803 South Oakland Avenue
Pasadena, CA USA 91106
Phone: 626-737-9739
E-mail: information@mvmpartners.com
Website: www.mvmpartners.com

Management and Staff

Andrew Wilson, Managing Director
Jonathan Niednagel, Venture Partner
Matthew Ridenour, Managing Director
Stuart MacFarlane, Managing Director

Type of Firm

Private Equity Firm

Project Preferences

Type of Financing Preferred:
Early Stage
Expansion

Geographical Preferences

United States Preferences:
California

Industry Preferences

In Computer Software prefer:
Software
Systems Software
Applications Software

In Internet Specific prefer:
Internet

Additional Information

Name of Most Recent Fund: Momentum Bridge & Opportunity Fund 2, L.P.
Most Recent Fund Was Raised: 01/28/2008
Year Founded: 2004
Capital Under Management: $8,300,000
Current Activity Level: Actively seeking new investments

MONET CAPITAL

3466 Edward Avenue
Santa Clara, CA USA 95054
Phone: 408-748-8840
Fax: 408-748-8842
E-mail: monetcapital@monetcapital.com
Website: www.monetcapital.com

Other Offices

7F-2 51, Sun-Chiang Road
Taipei, Taiwan
Phone: 886-2-2516-7546-9
Fax: 886-2-2504-2980

Management and Staff

HW Chen, Managing Partner
Robert Cheng, Managing Partner

Type of Firm

Private Equity Firm

Additional Information

Year Founded: 1997
Current Activity Level: Actively seeking new investments

MONETA CAPITAL PARTNERS, LTD.

736- 6th Avenue South West
Suite 2050
Calgary, Canada T2P 3T7
Phone: 403-770-4150
Fax: 403-770-4151
E-mail: info@monetacapital.ca
Website: www.monetacapital.ca

Management and Staff

David Blain, Partner
Karen Hanson, Partner
Ken Hergert, Partner
Rex Kary, Managing Partner
Roy Smitshoek, Managing Partner

Type of Firm

Private Equity Firm

Project Preferences

Type of Financing Preferred:
Early Stage
Expansion
Seed
Startup

Additional Information

Year Founded: 2003
Current Activity Level: Actively seeking new investments

MONITOR CLIPPER PARTNERS

Two Canal Park
Fourth Floor
Cambridge, MA USA 02141
Phone: 617-252-2200
Fax: 617-252-2211
E-mail: mcp@monitor.com
Website: www.monitorclipper.com

Other Offices

Muhlebachstrasse 173
Zurich, Switzerland 8034

Phone: 41-44-389-7150
Fax: 41-44-389-7151

Michelin House
81 Fulham Road
London, United Kingdom SW3 6RD
Phone: 44-20-7838-6800
Fax: 44-20-7838-6875

Management and Staff

Adam Doctoroff, Partner
Charles Yoon, Principal
Mark Thomas, Managing Partner
Meg Donigan, Principal
Michael Bell, Managing Partner
Oliver Markl, Principal
Oliver Zugel, Principal
Paul Maxwell, Principal
Peter Laino, Managing Director
Stephen Lehman, Principal
Thomas Perkins, Principal
Travis Metz, Managing Partner
William Young, Managing Partner

Type of Firm

Private Equity Firm

Association Membership

European Private Equity and Venture Capital Assoc.

Project Preferences

Type of Financing Preferred:

Leveraged Buyout
Management Buyouts
Recapitalizations

Size of Investments Considered:

Min Size of Investment Considered (000s): $20,000
Max Size of Investment Considered (000s): $100,000

Geographical Preferences

United States Preferences:

All U.S.

International Preferences:

Europe
Western Europe
All International

Industry Focus

(% based on actual investment)

Other Products	38.7%
Consumer Related	30.2%
Industrial/Energy	9.8%
Computer Software and Services	6.3%
Internet Specific	4.8%
Computer Hardware	4.1%
Communications and Media	3.4%
Biotechnology	1.9%
Medical/Health	0.8%

Additional Information

Name of Most Recent Fund: Monitor Clipper Equity Partners III, L.P.
Most Recent Fund Was Raised: 10/24/2007
Year Founded: 1998
Capital Under Management: $1,500,000,000
Current Activity Level: Actively seeking new investments

MONITOR VENTURE MANAGEMENT, L.L.C.

350 Cambridge Avenue
Suite 325
Palo Alto, CA USA 94306
Phone: 650-475-7300
Fax: 650-475-7301
E-mail: info@monitorvc.com
Website: www.monitorventures.com

Other Offices

100 Wilshire Boulevard
Suite 100
Santa Monica, CA USA 90401
Phone: 310-566-4400
Fax: 310-566-4477

Management and Staff

Bansi Nagji, Venture Partner
Fern Mandelbaum, Partner
George Norsig, Venture Partner
Matthew Le Merle, Venture Partner
Neal Bhadkamkar, Managing Partner
Nicholas Mitsakos, Venture Partner
Teymour Boutros-Ghali, Managing Partner

Type of Firm

Private Equity Firm

Project Preferences

Type of Financing Preferred:

Early Stage
Balanced

Geographical Preferences

United States Preferences:

All U.S.

Additional Information

Name of Most Recent Fund: Monitor Venture Partners, L.P.
Most Recent Fund Was Raised: 07/27/2004
Year Founded: 2002
Capital Under Management: $29,300,000
Current Activity Level: Actively seeking new investments

MONOLITH CAPITAL PARTNERS

817 West Peachtree Street NW
Suite 915
Atlanta, GA USA 30308
Phone: 404-957-2340
E-mail: questions@monolithcapitalpartners.com
Website: www.monolithcapitalpartners.com

Management and Staff

Mark Hoffman, General Partner
Patrick Emmet, Venture Partner
Stacey Anderson, General Partner
Steve Fanning, General Partner

Type of Firm

Service Provider

Project Preferences

Type of Financing Preferred:

Early Stage

Geographical Preferences

United States Preferences:

Southeast
Georgia

Additional Information

Year Founded: 2007
Current Activity Level: Actively seeking new investments

MONOMOY CAPITAL PARTNERS, LLC

152 West 57th Street
Ninth Floor
New York, NY USA 10019
Phone: 212-699-4000
Fax: 212-699-4010
E-mail: info@mcpfunds.com
Website: www.mcpfunds.com

Management and Staff

Andrea Cipriani, Chief Financial Officer
C. Justin Hillenbrand, Partner
David Collin, Partner
Loren Roseman, Vice President
Philip Von Burg, Partner
Stephen Presser, Partner

Type of Firm

Private Equity Firm

Project Preferences

Type of Financing Preferred:

Turnaround

Geographical Preferences

United States Preferences:

All U.S.

Industry Preferences

In Consumer Related prefer:

Retail

In Transportation prefer:

Aerospace

In Manufact. prefer:

Manufacturing

Additional Information

Name of Most Recent Fund: MCP Supplemental Fund, L.P.
Most Recent Fund Was Raised: 05/08/2006
Year Founded: 2005
Capital Under Management: $285,600,000
Current Activity Level: Actively seeking new investments

MONSTER VENTURE PARTNERS

155 108th Avenue Northeast
Suite 810
Bellevue, WA USA 98004
Phone: 425-502-6000
Fax: 425-289-0131
Website: www.monsterventurepartners.com

Management and Staff

Jeff Schrock, Venture Partner
Patrick Pun, Venture Partner
Robert Monster, Managing Director
Todd Humphrey, Venture Partner

Type of Firm

Private Equity Firm

Project Preferences

Type of Financing Preferred:

Early Stage

Size of Investments Considered:

Min Size of Investment Considered (000s): $250
Max Size of Investment Considered (000s): $1,500

Geographical Preferences

United States Preferences:

Washington

International Preferences:

All International

Industry Preferences

In Medical/Health prefer:

Health Services

In Consumer Related prefer:

Consumer Products

Additional Information

Year Founded: 2008
Current Activity Level: Actively seeking new investments

MONTAGU NEWHALL ASSOCIATES

100 Painters Mill Road
Suite 700
Owings Mills, MD USA 21117
Phone: 410-363-2725
Fax: 410-356-9075
E-mail: info@montagunewhall.com
Website: www.montagunewhall.com

Other Offices

303 Twin Dolphin Drive
Suite 600
Redwood City, CA USA 94065
Phone: 650-632-4620
Fax: 650-632-4621

52 Upper Brook Street
London, United Kingdom W1K 2BU
Phone: 44-20-7468-7405
Fax: 44-20-7468-7411

Management and Staff

C. Ashton Newhall, General Partner
James Lim, Partner
Kevin Campbell, Partner
Rupert Montagu, General Partner

Type of Firm

Private Equity Advisor or Fund of Funds

Association Membership

Mid-Atlantic Venture Association
National Venture Capital Association - USA (NVCA)
European Private Equity and Venture Capital Assoc.

Project Preferences

Role in Financing:

Prefer role in deals created by others

Type of Financing Preferred:

Fund of Funds
Early Stage

Size of Investments Considered:

Min Size of Investment Considered (000s): $500
Max Size of Investment Considered (000s): $1,000

Geographical Preferences

International Preferences:

Europe
All International

Industry Preferences

In Biotechnology prefer:

Biotechnology

In Medical/Health prefer:

Medical/Health
Pharmaceuticals

Additional Information

Year Founded: 2001
Capital Under Management: $45,000,000
Current Activity Level: Actively seeking new investments
Method of Compensation: Return on invest. most important, but chg. closing fees, service fees, etc.

MONTAGU PRIVATE EQUITY, LTD. (FKA: HSBC PRIVATE EQUITY LTD.)

Two More London Riverside
London, United Kingdom SE1 2AP
Phone: 44-20-7336-9955
Fax: 44-20-7336-9961
E-mail: enquiries@montagu.com
Website: www.montagu.com

Other Offices

Linnegatan 2
Box 5827
Stockholm, Sweden S-102 48
Phone: 46-8-662-5050
Fax: 46-8-662-5065

Benrather Karree
Benrather Strasse 18-20
Dusseldorf, Germany 40213
Phone: 49-211-867-6930
Fax: 49-211-867-6939

15/F St. James House
Charlotte Street
Manchester, United Kingdom M1 4DZ
Phone: 44-161-233-6660
Fax: 44-161-233-6666

41, avenue George V
Paris, France 75008
Phone: 33-1-4495-1180
Fax: 33-1-4495-1199

Management and Staff

Andy Leach, Managing Director
Chris Masterson, Chief Executive Officer
David Farley, Chief Financial Officer
Ian Forrest, Managing Director
John Brandon, Managing Director
Mamine Soeda, Managing Director
Max Von Drechsel, Managing Director

Type of Firm

Bank Affiliated
Association Membership
British Venture Capital Association (BVCA)
French Venture Capital Association (AFIC)
European Private Equity and Venture Capital Assoc.

Project Preferences

Role in Financing:

Prefer role as deal originator but will also invest in deals created by others

Type of Financing Preferred:

Leveraged Buyout
Expansion
Mezzanine
Balanced
Later Stage
Management Buyouts
Acquisition

Special Situation
Recapitalizations

Size of Investments Considered:

Min Size of Investment Considered (000s): $70,166
Max Size of Investment Considered (000s): $477,126

Geographical Preferences

International Preferences:

Italy
United Kingdom
Europe
Spain
Germany
France
All International

Industry Preferences

In Communications prefer:

Telecommunications

In Semiconductor/Electr prefer:

Electronics

In Medical/Health prefer:

Medical/Health
Pharmaceuticals

In Consumer Related prefer:

Consumer

In Industrial/Energy prefer:

Materials

In Transportation prefer:

Transportation

In Business Serv. prefer:

Media

In Manufact. prefer:

Manufacturing

Additional Information

Year Founded: 1968
Capital Under Management: $3,508,300,000
Current Activity Level: Actively seeking new investments
Method of Compensation: Return on invest. most important, but chg. closing fees, service fees, etc.

MONTAUK TRIGUARD MANAGEMENT, INC.

Two San Joaquin Plaza
Suite 260
Newport Beach, CA USA 92660
Phone: 949-219-3767
Fax: 949-219-5076
Website: www.montauktriguard.com

Other Offices

10529 Dacer Place
Lone Tree, CO USA 80124
Phone: 303-799-1006
Fax: 303-799-1005

4514 Cole Avenue
Suite 600
Dallas, TX USA 75205-4193
Phone: 214-559-7129
Fax: 214-453-3425

Management and Staff

Brian Smith, Principal
Edgar Pfohl, Principal
Ronn Cornelius, Principal
Samuel Tang, Principal

Type of Firm

Private Equity Advisor or Fund of Funds

Project Preferences

Type of Financing Preferred:

Fund of Funds
Fund of Funds of Second

Additional Information

Year Founded: 2008
Capital Under Management: $400,000,000
Current Activity Level: Actively seeking new investments

MONTEFIORE INVESTMENT

17 rue de Miromesnil
Paris, France 75008
Phone: 33-1-5818-6870
Fax: 33-1-588-3027
E-mail: contact@montefiore.fr
Website: www.montefiore.fr

Management and Staff

Alexandre Bonnecuelle, Principal
Daniel Elalouf, Partner
Eric Bismuth, President
Isabelle Fioux, Partner
Thierry Sonalier, Partner

Type of Firm

Private Equity Firm

Association Membership

French Venture Capital Association (AFIC)

Project Preferences

Type of Financing Preferred:

Leveraged Buyout
Expansion

Size of Investments Considered:

Min Size of Investment Considered (000s): $11,419
Max Size of Investment Considered (000s): $28,547

Industry Preferences

In Medical/Health prefer:

Health Services

In Consumer Related prefer:

Consumer Services

In Business Serv. prefer:

Services
Consulting Services

Additional Information

Year Founded: 2005
Capital Under Management: $168,700,000
Current Activity Level: Actively seeking new investments

MONTEFIORE, LLC

14 Wall Street
15th Floor
New York, NY USA 10005

Management and Staff

Daryl Otte, Founding Partner

Type of Firm

Private Equity Firm

Project Preferences

Type of Financing Preferred:

Early Stage

Additional Information

Year Founded: 2003
Capital Under Management: $6,400,000
Current Activity Level: Actively seeking new investments

MONTEREY VENTURE PARTNERS, LLC

2818 Congress Road
Pebble Beach, CA USA 93953
Phone: 831-658-0800
E-mail: info@montereyvp.com
Website: www.montereyvp.com

Management and Staff

Barbara Bellissimo, Partner
David Worrell, Partner
Marshall Frank, Partner
Peter Townshend, Partner
William Manby, Partner

Type of Firm

Private Equity Advisor or Fund of Funds

Project Preferences

Type of Financing Preferred:

Early Stage
Startup

Geographical Preferences

United States Preferences:

California

Industry Preferences

In Consumer Related prefer:
Food/Beverage

In Industrial/Energy prefer:
Energy

In Other prefer:
Environment Responsible

Additional Information

Year Founded: 2001
Current Activity Level: Actively seeking new investments

MONTERREY CAPITAL PARTNERS

Av. Gomez Morin 285 Sur 3 Piso
Valle del Campestre
Monterrey, Mexico 66265
Phone: 52-818-1737303
Fax: 52-818-1737315

Management and Staff

Luis Porras, Principal

Type of Firm

Bank Affiliated

Project Preferences

Type of Financing Preferred:
Expansion

Geographical Preferences

International Preferences:
Mexico

Industry Preferences

In Communications prefer:
Telecommunications

In Medical/Health prefer:
Medical/Health

In Business Serv. prefer:
Media
Additional Information
Year Founded: 2000
Current Activity Level: Actively seeking new investments

MONTGOMERY & CO. (FKA: DIGITAL COAST PARTNERS)

100 Wilshire Boulevard
Suite 400
Santa Monica, CA USA 90401
Phone: 310-260-6006
Fax: 310-260-6095
E-mail: info@monty.com
Website: www.monty.com

Other Offices

Two Embarcadero Center
Suite 2900
San Francisco, CA USA 94111
Phone: 415-962-4560
Fax: 415-962-4567

853 Camino del Mar
Suite 200
Del Mar, CA USA 92014
Phone: 858-947-2800
Fax: 858-947-2801

3720 Carillon Point
Kirkland, WA USA 98033
Phone: 425-576-9850
Fax: 425-576-9868

Management and Staff

Brian Bean, Managing Director
Dan Williams, Principal
Daniel Gossels, Principal
David Michaels, Managing Director
David Horn, Principal
Gee Leung, Vice President
George Montgomery, Managing Director
James Min, Principal
James Schroder, Principal
James Montgomery, Chief Executive Officer
John Cooper, Managing Director
Keith Marshall, Principal
Kevin Covert, Managing Director
Kevin Higgins, Chief Financial Officer
Michael Montgomery, President
Patrick Kratus, Principal
Robert Louv, Managing Director
Thomas Kelly, Managing Director
Tom Newby, Managing Director

Type of Firm

Bank Affiliated

Project Preferences

Type of Financing Preferred:
Seed
Startup

Industry Preferences

In Communications prefer:
Communications and Media
Telecommunications
Wireless Communications
Data Communications
Media and Entertainment

In Computer Software prefer:
Software
Applications Software

In Internet Specific prefer:
Internet
Ecommerce

In Semiconductor/Electr prefer:
Semiconductor

In Biotechnology prefer:
Biotechnology

In Medical/Health prefer:
Medical/Health

In Financial Services prefer:
Financial Services

Additional Information

Year Founded: 2000
Capital Under Management: $35,000,000
Current Activity Level: Actively seeking new investments

MONTIS CAPITAL, LLC

1919 Fourteenth Street
Suite 319
Boulder, CO USA 80302
Phone: 303-440-3352
Fax: 303-449-5626
E-mail: info@montiscapital.com
Website: www.montiscapital.com

Management and Staff

Adam Kimberly, Managing Partner
Andrew Morley, Managing Partner

Type of Firm

Private Equity Advisor or Fund of Funds

Project Preferences

Role in Financing:
Prefer role as deal originator but will also invest in deals created by others

Type of Financing Preferred:
Leveraged Buyout
Expansion
Management Buyouts
Acquisition
Recapitalizations

Size of Investments Considered:
Min Size of Investment Considered (000s): $500,000
Max Size of Investment Considered: No Limit

Geographical Preferences

United States Preferences:
All U.S.

Industry Preferences

In Computer Software prefer:
Computer Services
Software

In Consumer Related prefer:
Consumer Products

In Industrial/Energy prefer:
Industrial Products
Environmental Related

Additional Information

Year Founded: 2007
Capital Under Management: $8,000,000

Current Activity Level: Actively seeking new investments

MONTREUX EQUITY PARTNERS

3000 Sand Hill Road
Building 1, Suite 260
Menlo Park, CA USA 94025
Phone: 650-234-1200
Fax: 650-234-1250
E-mail: information@montreuxequity.com
Website: www.montreuxequity.com

Management and Staff

Daniel Turner, Managing Director
Howard Palefsky, Managing Director
John Savarese, Managing Director
Manish Chapekar, Managing Director
Thomas Fremd, Chief Financial Officer

Type of Firm

Private Equity Firm

Association Membership

Western Association of Venture Capitalists (WAVC)
National Venture Capital Association - USA (NVCA)
Natl Assoc of Small Bus. Inv. Co (NASBIC)

Project Preferences

Role in Financing:
Will function either as deal originator or investor in deals created by others

Type of Financing Preferred:
Second Stage Financing
Early Stage
Balanced
Seed
First Stage Financing
Startup

Size of Investments Considered:
Min Size of Investment Considered (000s): $1,000
Max Size of Investment Considered (000s): $10,000

Geographical Preferences

United States Preferences:
West Coast
All U.S.

Industry Focus

(% based on actual investment)

Medical/Health	73.0%
Biotechnology	18.9%
Consumer Related	2.7%
Internet Specific	2.3%
Computer Software and Services	2.0%
Communications and Media	1.1%

Additional Information

Name of Most Recent Fund: Montreux Equity Partners IV, L.P.
Most Recent Fund Was Raised: 09/01/2006
Year Founded: 1993
Capital Under Management: $440,000,000
Current Activity Level: Actively seeking new investments
Method of Compensation: Return on invest. most important, but chg. closing fees, service fees, etc.

MONUMENT ADVISORS, INC.

Chase Tower
111 Monument Circle,Suite 4500
Indianapolis, IN USA 46204-5172
Phone: 317-656-5065
Fax: 317-656-5060
E-mail: request@monumentadv.com
Website: www.monumentadv.com

Management and Staff

Anthony Walker, Chief Financial Officer
Joseph Schaffer, Managing Director
Larry Wechter, CEO & Managing Director

Type of Firm

Bank Affiliated

Project Preferences

Role in Financing:
Prefer role as deal originator but will also invest in deals created by others

Type of Financing Preferred:
Leveraged Buyout
Expansion
Generalist PE
Later Stage
Management Buyouts
Acquisition
Recapitalizations

Size of Investments Considered:
Min Size of Investment Considered (000s): $1,000
Max Size of Investment Considered (000s): $3,000

Geographical Preferences

United States Preferences:
Midwest

Industry Focus

(% based on actual investment)

Other Products	36.5%
Computer Software and Services	27.0%
Industrial/Energy	16.3%
Communications and Media	12.2%
Consumer Related	4.1%
Medical/Health	4.1%

Additional Information

Year Founded: 1996
Capital Under Management: $35,600,000
Current Activity Level: Actively seeking new investments
Method of Compensation: Return on invest. most important, but chg. closing fees, service fees, etc.

MONUMENTAL VENTURE PARTNERS LLC (AKA: MVP)

8201 Greensboro Drive
Suite 216
McLean, VA USA 22102
Phone: 703-821-0400
Fax: 703-821-0281
E-mail: info@mvpfunds.com
Website: www.mvpfunds.com

Management and Staff

Christopher Dettmar, Managing Director & CFO
Jeff Friedman, Managing Director
Roland Oliver, President & Chairman

Type of Firm

Private Equity Firm

Association Membership

Mid-Atlantic Venture Association

Project Preferences

Role in Financing:
Prefer role as deal originator but will also invest in deals created by others

Type of Financing Preferred:
Early Stage
Expansion
Seed
First Stage Financing
Startup

Size of Investments Considered:
Min Size of Investment Considered (000s): $500
Max Size of Investment Considered (000s): $3,000

Geographical Preferences

United States Preferences:
Mid Atlantic

Industry Preferences

In Communications prefer:
Telecommunications
Wireless Communications
Data Communications

In Computer Hardware prefer:
Disk Relat. Memory Device

In Computer Software prefer:
Software
Applications Software

In Internet Specific prefer:
Internet

In Industrial/Energy prefer:
Energy

Additional Information

Name of Most Recent Fund: MVP America, L.P.
Most Recent Fund Was Raised: 11/01/2000
Year Founded: 1999

Capital Under Management: $15,000,000
Current Activity Level: Actively seeking new investments
Method of Compensation: Return on investment is of primary concern, do not charge fees

MONUMENTS FUNDS GROUP

7920 Norfolk Avenue
Suite 500
Bethesda, MD USA 20817
Phone: 301-215-7550
Fax: 301-215-7558
Website: ralphscherer.com/mfg3

Other Offices

7201 Wisconsin Avenue
Suite 600
Bethesda, MD USA 20814
Phone: 301-657-1700

Type of Firm

Private Equity Firm

Project Preferences

Type of Financing Preferred:
Balanced

Geographical Preferences

International Preferences:
Europe

Industry Preferences

In Communications prefer:
Commercial Communications
CATV & Pay TV Systems
Radio & TV Broadcasting
Telecommunications
Wireless Communications
Data Communications
Satellite Microwave Comm.
Other Communication Prod.

In Computer Hardware prefer:
Mainframes / Scientific
Mini and Personal/Desktop
Computer Graphics and Dig
Integrated Turnkey System
Terminals
Disk Relat. Memory Device

In Computer Software prefer:
Computer Services
Data Processing
Software
Systems Software
Applications Software
Artificial Intelligence

In Internet Specific prefer:
Internet
Web Aggregration/Portals

In Semiconductor/Electr prefer:
Electronic Components
Semiconductor
Micro-Processing
Controllers and Sensors
Sensors
Circuit Boards
Component Testing Equipmt
Laser Related
Fiber Optics
Analytic/Scientific

In Biotechnology prefer:
Biotechnology
Human Biotechnology
Agricultural/Animal Bio.
Industrial Biotechnology
Biosensors
Biotech Related Research

In Medical/Health prefer:
Medical/Health
Medical Diagnostics
Diagnostic Services
Diagnostic Test Products
Medical Therapeutics
Drug/Equipmt Delivery
Disposable Med. Products
Health Services
Hospitals/Clinics/Primary
Hospital/Other Instit.
Pharmaceuticals

Additional Information

Year Founded: 1997
Capital Under Management: $250,000,000
Current Activity Level: Actively seeking new investments

MOORFIELD INVESTMENT MANAGEMENT LTD

Premier House
44-48 Dover Street
London, United Kingdom W1S 4NX
Phone: 44-207-399-1900
Fax: 44-207-499-2114
E-mail: enquiry@moorfield.com
Website: www.moorfield.com

Management and Staff

Marc Gilbard, Managing Director

Type of Firm

Bank Affiliated

Association Membership

British Venture Capital Association (BVCA)
European Private Equity and Venture Capital Assoc.

Project Preferences

Type of Financing Preferred:
Second Stage Financing
Leveraged Buyout
Expansion
Turnaround

Geographical Preferences

International Preferences:
United Kingdom

Industry Preferences

In Consumer Related prefer:
Entertainment and Leisure
Retail

In Financial Services prefer:
Real Estate

In Business Serv. prefer:
Services

Additional Information

Year Founded: 1999
Capital Under Management: $290,000,000
Current Activity Level: Actively seeking new investments

MORGAN CREEK CAPITAL MANAGEMENT LLC

301 West Barbee Chapel Road
Suite 200
Chapel Hill, NC USA 27517
Phone: 919-933-4004
Fax: 919-933-4048
E-mail: investorrelations@morgancreekcap.com
Website: www.morgancreekcap.com

Other Offices

99 Queen's Road
Suite 6803-6805, The Center
Central, Hong Kong
Phone: 852-3550-6000
Fax: 852-3550-6050

100 Park Avenue
28th Floor
New York, NY USA 10017
Phone: 212-692-8660
Fax: 212-692-8661

No. 79 Jian Guo Road
Unit 2305 China Central Place Building
Beijing, China 100025
Phone: 86-10-6598-9518
Fax: 86-10-6598-9528

Management and Staff

Andrea Szigethy, Principal
Brad Briner, Managing Director
Carolyn Anderson, Principal
David Kim, Managing Director
David Welp, Vice President
Dennis Miner, Managing Director
James Spencer, Principal
Jason Zhang, Managing Director
Jim Patrick, Vice President
Josh Tilley, Principal
Mark Morris, Principal
Nirav Kachalia, Managing Director
Robert Durden, Vice President

Type of Firm

Private Equity Advisor or Fund of Funds

Project Preferences

Type of Financing Preferred:

Fund of Funds
Balanced

Geographical Preferences

United States Preferences:

All U.S.

International Preferences:

Asia

Additional Information

Year Founded: 2004
Capital Under Management: $420,400,000
Current Activity Level: Actively seeking new investments

MORGAN KEEGAN MERCHANT BANKING

50 Front Street
17th Floor
Memphis, TN USA 38103
Phone: 901-524-4100
Fax: 901-579-4406
E-mail: info@morgankeegan.com
Website: www.morgankeegan.com

Other Offices

30 Burton Hills Boulevard
Suite 235
Nashville, TN USA 37215
Phone: 615-665-3675

Management and Staff

Alper Cetingok, Vice President
C. Patrick Scholes, Vice President
Charles Shook, Managing Director
Doyle Rippee, Managing Director
Kimble Jenkins, Managing Director

Type of Firm

Bank Affiliated

Project Preferences

Role in Financing:

Will function either as deal originator or investor in deals created by others

Type of Financing Preferred:

Fund of Funds
Early Stage
Expansion
Mezzanine
Balanced
Private Placement
Recapitalizations

Size of Investments Considered:

Min Size of Investment Considered (000s): $500
Max Size of Investment Considered (000s): $3,000

Industry Preferences

In Communications prefer:

Telecommunications

In Semiconductor/Electr prefer:

Semiconductor

In Biotechnology prefer:

Biotechnology

In Medical/Health prefer:

Health Services

Additional Information

Name of Most Recent Fund: Morgan Keegan Private Equity Employee Fund of Funds II, L.P.
Most Recent Fund Was Raised: 09/22/2006
Year Founded: 1999
Capital Under Management: $30,000,000
Current Activity Level: Actively seeking new investments

MORGAN STANLEY ALTERNATIVE INVESTMENT PARTNERS

One Tower Bridge
100 Front Street, Suite 1100
Conshohocken, PA USA 19428
Phone: 610-940-5000
Website: www.morganstanley.com

Other Offices

3 Exchange Square
30th Floor
Central, Hong Kong
Phone: 852-2848-5200

Management and Staff

Joseph Stecher, Managing Director

Type of Firm

Private Equity Advisor or Fund of Funds

Project Preferences

Type of Financing Preferred:

Fund of Funds
Leveraged Buyout
Special Situation
Fund of Funds of Second
Distressed Debt

Geographical Preferences

United States Preferences:

All U.S.

International Preferences:

Europe
All International

Additional Information

Name of Most Recent Fund: Morgan Stanley Private Markets Fund III, L.P.
Most Recent Fund Was Raised: 04/25/2006
Year Founded: 2000
Capital Under Management: $813,400,000
Current Activity Level: Actively seeking new investments

MORGAN STANLEY PRIVATE EQUITY

1585 Broadway
38th Floor
New York, NY USA 10036
Phone: 212-761-4000
E-mail: private.equity@morganstanley.com
Website: www.morganstanley.com/privateequity

Other Offices

30/F Three Exchange Square
Central
Hong Kong, Hong Kong
Phone: 852-2848-5200
Fax: 852-2848-5282

20 Bank Street
Canary Wharf
London, United Kingdom E14 4AD
Phone: 44-207-425-8000
Fax: 44-207-425-4691

3000 Sand Hill Road
Building 4, Suite 250
Menlo Park, CA USA 94025
Phone: 650-233-2600
Fax: 650-233-2626

Management and Staff

Alan Jones, Managing Director
Brian Magnus, Managing Director
David Sidwell, Chief Financial Officer
Debra Abramovitz, Chief Operating Officer
Eric Kanter, Vice President
Eric Fry, Managing Director
Fazle Husain, Principal
Gary Matthews, Managing Director
Ghassan Bejjani, Managing Partner
Graham Keniston-Cooper, Managing Director
H. Chin Chou, Managing Director
Harj Shoan, Vice President
James Howland, Managing Director
Jean-Marc Jabre, Vice President
Jeffrey Booth, Principal
John Moon, Managing Director
John Mack, Chairman & CEO
Kenneth Clifford, Managing Director
Lisa Picardo, Vice President
Mark Bye, Managing Director
Martin Nilsson, Vice President
Michael Hehn, Managing Director
Richard Schultz, Vice President
Scott Cullerton, Vice President
Scott Halsted, Principal
Scott Sang-Won Hahn, Managing Director
Stephen Trevor, Managing Director

Type of Firm
Bank Affiliated

Association Membership
Hungarian Venture Capital Association (HVCA)
Western Association of Venture Capitalists (WAVC)
Natl Assoc of Small Bus. Inv. Co (NASBIC)

Project Preferences

Type of Financing Preferred:
Second Stage Financing
Leveraged Buyout
Expansion
Mezzanine
Generalist PE
Balanced
Later Stage
Other
Management Buyouts
Startup

Size of Investments Considered:
Min Size of Investment Considered (000s): $2,000
Max Size of Investment Considered: No Limit

Geographical Preferences

Canadian Preferences:
All Canada

International Preferences:
Western Europe
Asia
All International

Industry Focus
(% based on actual investment)

Other Products	61.3%
Consumer Related	8.9%
Internet Specific	7.9%
Communications and Media	5.5%
Semiconductors/Other Elect.	4.9%
Industrial/Energy	4.3%
Computer Software and Services	3.9%
Medical/Health	1.4%
Biotechnology	1.2%
Computer Hardware	0.7%

Additional Information
Name of Most Recent Fund: Morgan Stanley Capital Partners V, L.P.
Most Recent Fund Was Raised: 11/20/2008
Year Founded: 1985
Capital Under Management: $6,371,400,000
Current Activity Level: Actively seeking new investments

MORGAN STANLEY VENTURE PARTNERS (AKA: MSDW)
1221 Avenue of the Americas
39th Floor
New York, NY USA 10020
Phone: 212-762-8890
Fax: 212-762-8188
E-mail: msventures@ms.com
Website: www.msvp.com

Other Offices
2725 Sand Hill Road
Suite 130
Menlo Park, CA USA 94025
Phone: 650-233-2600
Fax: 650-233-2626

Management and Staff
Debra Abramovitz, Chief Operating Officer
Fazle Husain, General Partner
Ghassan Bejjani, General Partner
Guy de Chazal, General Partner
Melissa Daniels, Vice President
Patrick Gallagher, Vice President
Richard Schultz, Vice President
Robert Loarie, General Partner
Scott Halsted, General Partner
Shelly Wall, Vice President
William Harding, General Partner

Type of Firm
Bank Affiliated

Association Membership
Western Association of Venture Capitalists (WAVC)
National Venture Capital Association - USA (NVCA)
Natl Assoc of Small Bus. Inv. Co (NASBIC)

Project Preferences

Role in Financing:
Prefer role as deal originator but will also invest in deals created by others

Type of Financing Preferred:
Second Stage Financing
Leveraged Buyout
Mezzanine
Later Stage
Industry Rollups

Size of Investments Considered:
Min Size of Investment Considered (000s): $5,000
Max Size of Investment Considered (000s): $25,000

Geographical Preferences

United States Preferences:
All U.S.

Canadian Preferences:
All Canada

International Preferences:
Western Europe

Industry Focus
(% based on actual investment)

Computer Software and Services	37.3%
Internet Specific	22.7%
Communications and Media	13.6%
Medical/Health	9.8%
Semiconductors/Other Elect.	6.1%
Biotechnology	5.0%
Industrial/Energy	3.1%
Computer Hardware	1.1%
Other Products	0.7%
Consumer Related	0.4%

Additional Information
Name of Most Recent Fund: Morgan Stanley Venture Partners 2002 Fund, L.P.
Most Recent Fund Was Raised: 08/05/2002
Year Founded: 1986
Capital Under Management: $1,100,500,000
Current Activity Level: Actively seeking new investments
Method of Compensation: Return on investment is of primary concern, do not charge fees

---

MORGENTHALER VENTURES
2710 Sand Hill Road
Suite 100
Menlo Park, CA USA 94025
Phone: 650-388-7600
Fax: 650-388-7601
E-mail: companyreports@morgenthaler.com
Website: www.morgenthaler.com

Other Offices
4430 Arapahoe Avenue
Suite 220
Boulder, CO USA 80303
Phone: 303-417-1601
Fax: 303-417-1602

Terminal Tower, 50 Public Square
Suite 2700
Cleveland, OH USA 44113
Phone: 216-416-7500
Fax: 216-416-7501

222 Berkeley Street
20th Floor
Boston, MA USA 02116
Phone: 617-587-7800
Fax: 617-587-7801

120 Woodland Avenue
Summit, NJ USA 07901
Phone: 908-316-5570
Fax: 908-273-3105

Management and Staff
Al Stanley, Managing Director
Alfred Stanley, Partner
Bridget Rauvola, Partner
Ching Wu, Partner
David Morgenthaler, Founding Partner
Drew Lanza, Partner
Gary Morgenthaler, Venture Partner
Gary Little, Partner
Hank Plain, Partner
James Broderick, Partner
Jason Lettmann, Vice President
John Lutsi, Partner
Joseph Machado, Principal
Karen Tuleta, Partner
Ken Gullicksen, Partner

Kevin Macdonald, Managing Partner
Paul Levine, Partner
Peter Taft, Partner
Ralph Christoffersen, Partner
Rebecca Lynn, Principal
Robert Bellas, Partner
Robert Pavey, Partner
Theodore Laufik, Chief Financial Officer

Type of Firm

Private Equity Firm

Association Membership

Western Association of Venture Capitalists (WAVC)
National Venture Capital Association - USA (NVCA)

Project Preferences

Role in Financing:

Prefer role as deal originator

Type of Financing Preferred:

Leveraged Buyout
Mezzanine
Early Stage
Balanced
Later Stage
Management Buyouts
First Stage Financing
Acquisition
Recapitalizations

Size of Investments Considered:

Min Size of Investment Considered (000s): $1,000
Max Size of Investment Considered (000s): $25,000

Industry Focus

(% based on actual investment)

Semiconductors/Other Elect.	22.1%
Medical/Health	16.1%
Communications and Media	15.2%
Biotechnology	10.9%
Internet Specific	10.8%
Industrial/Energy	8.7%
Computer Software and Services	7.6%
Other Products	5.3%
Computer Hardware	1.8%
Consumer Related	1.6%

Additional Information

Name of Most Recent Fund: Morgenthaler Venture Partners IX, L.P.
Most Recent Fund Was Raised: 06/24/2008
Year Founded: 1968
Capital Under Management: $2,600,000,000
Current Activity Level: Actively seeking new investments
Method of Compensation: Return on investment is of primary concern, do not charge fees

---

MORGENTHAU VENTURE PARTNERS, LLC

6750 N. Andrews Avenue
Fort Lauderdale, FL USA 33309
Phone: 954-776-9517
Fax: 954-463-0704
Website: www.morgenthau.com

Management and Staff

Allen Furst, Venture Partner
Anthony Morgenthau, Managing Partner
Doug Betlach, Managing Partner
Larry Dukes, Venture Partner
Michael Andzel, Managing Partner

Type of Firm

Private Equity Firm

Project Preferences

Type of Financing Preferred:

Early Stage
Expansion
Balanced
Later Stage

Geographical Preferences

United States Preferences:

Southeast

Industry Preferences

In Communications prefer:

Communications and Media

In Computer Software prefer:

Software

In Business Serv. prefer:

Services

Additional Information

Year Founded: 2006
Capital Under Management: $14,100,000
Current Activity Level: Actively seeking new investments

MORRISON & FOERSTER

755 Page Mill Road
Palo Alto, CA USA 94304
Phone: 650-813-5600
Fax: 650-494-0792
E-mail: info@mofo.com
Website: www.mofo.com

Other Offices

5200 Republic Plaza
370 Seventeenth Street
Denver, CO USA 80202
Phone: 303-592-1500
Fax: 303-592-1510

555 West Fifth Street
Suite 3500
Los Angeles, CA USA 90013
Phone: 213-892-5200
Fax: 213-892-5454

101 Ygnacio Valley Road
Suite 450
Walnut Creek, CA USA 94596
Phone: 925-295-3300
Fax: 925-946-9912

15 Queen's Road
41/F Edinburgh Tower
Central, Hong Kong
Phone: 852-2585-0888
Fax: 852-2585-0800

One Ropemaker Street
CityPoint
London, United Kingdom EC2Y 9AW
Phone: 4420-7920-4000
Fax: 4420-7496-8500

400 Capitol Mall
Suite 2600
Sacramento, CA USA 95814
Phone: 916-448-3200
Fax: 916-448-3222

12531 High Bluff Drive
Suite 100
San Diego, CA USA 92130
Phone: 858-720-5100
Fax: 858-720-5125

1650 Tysons Boulevard
Suite 400
McLean, VA USA 22102
Phone: 703-760-7700
Fax: 703-760-7777

Yan An East Road No.222
Suite 3501, Bund Center
Shanghai, China 200002
Phone: 86-21-6335-2290
Fax: 86-21-6335-2290

Avenue Moliere 262
Brussels, Belgium 1180
Phone: 322-347-0400
Fax: 322-347-1824

80 Raffles Place
31-04/06 UOB Plaza
Singapore, Singapore 048624
Phone: 65-6532-0151
Fax: 65-6532-3101

No. 1 Jianguomenwai Avenue
Suite 3408, China World Tower 2
Beijing, China
Phone: 86-10-6505-9090
Fax: 86-10-6505-9090

5-1 Marunouchi 1-chrome, Chiyodaku
29th Floor Shin-Marunouchi Building
Tokyo, Japan 100-6529
Phone: 813-3214-6522
Fax: 813-3214-6512

1290 Avenue of the Americas
New York, NY USA 10101
Phone: 212-468-8000
Fax: 212-468-7900

425 Market Street
San Francisco, CA USA 94105
Phone: 415-268-7000
Fax: 415-268-7522

2000 Pennsylvania Avenue Northwest
Suite 5500
Washington, DC USA 20006
Phone: 202-887-1500
Fax: 202-887-0763

Management and Staff

Jack Lewis, Partner
Thomas Chou, Partner
Yukihiro Terazawa, Partner

Type of Firm

Corporate PE/Venture

Additional Information

Year Founded: 2002
Current Activity Level: Actively seeking new investments

MOSAIC VENTURE PARTNERS

49 Wellington Street East
3rd Floor
Toronto, Canada M5E 1C9
Phone: 416-367-2888
Fax: 416-597-2345
Website: www.mosaicvp.com

Management and Staff

David Samuel, Managing Director
Vernon Lobo, Managing Director

Type of Firm

Incubator/Development Program

Project Preferences

Type of Financing Preferred:
Early Stage

Geographical Preferences

Canadian Preferences:
All Canada

Industry Preferences

In Internet Specific prefer:
Internet

Additional Information

Year Founded: 2000
Current Activity Level: Actively seeking new investments

MOSAIX VENTURES

1822 North Mohawk
Chicago, IL USA 60614
Phone: 312-274-0988
Fax: 773-913-2792
E-mail: rlal@mosaixventures.com
Website: www.mosaixventures.com

Management and Staff

Ranjan Lal, Managing Partner

Type of Firm

Private Equity Firm

Project Preferences

Role in Financing:
Will function either as deal originator or investor in deals created by others

Type of Financing Preferred:
Balanced

Size of Investments Considered:
Min Size of Investment Considered (000s): $1,000
Max Size of Investment Considered (000s): $4,000

Geographical Preferences

United States Preferences:
West Coast

Industry Preferences

In Medical/Health prefer:
Medical Products
Health Services

Additional Information

Year Founded: 2000
Capital Under Management: $60,000,000
Current Activity Level: Actively seeking new investments
Method of Compensation: Return on investment is of primary concern, do not charge fees

---

MOSHIR VENTURE PARTNERS

20701 North Scottsdale Road
Suite 107-455
Scottsdale, AZ USA 85255
Phone: 480-515-5200
Fax: 480-699-9491
E-mail: info@moshir.com
Website: www.moshirventure.com

Management and Staff

Kevin Moshir, Partner
Sean Moshir, Partner

Type of Firm

Private Equity Firm

Project Preferences

Type of Financing Preferred:
Early Stage

Size of Investments Considered:
Min Size of Investment Considered (000s): $250
Max Size of Investment Considered (000s): $1,000

Geographical Preferences

United States Preferences:
All U.S.

Industry Preferences

In Communications prefer:
Wireless Communications

Additional Information

Year Founded: 2005
Current Activity Level: Actively seeking new investments

MOTILAL OSWAL PRIVATE EQUITY ADVISORS PVT., LTD.

3rd Floor, Hoechst House
Nariman Point
Mumbai, India 400 021
Phone: 91-22-3982-5500
Fax: 91-22-2282-3499
Website: www.motilaloswal.com

Other Offices

88- Bajaj Bhawan
Nariman Point
Mumbai, India 400 021
Phone: 91-22-3980-4200
Fax: 91-22-2281-6161

Management and Staff

Motilal Oswal, Chairman & Managing Director
Prakash Bagla, Vice President
Vishal Gupta, Vice President
Vishal Tulsyan, Chief Executive Officer

Type of Firm

Bank Affiliated

Association Membership

Indian Venture Capital Association (IVCA)

Project Preferences

Type of Financing Preferred:
Expansion
Balanced

Size of Investments Considered:
Min Size of Investment Considered (000s): $3,000
Max Size of Investment Considered (000s): $7,000

Geographical Preferences

International Preferences:
India

Industry Preferences

In Semiconductor/Electr prefer:
Electronics

In Consumer Related prefer:
Entertainment and Leisure

Consumer Products
Other Restaurants
Education Related

In Transportation prefer:
Transportation

In Financial Services prefer:
Financial Services

Additional Information
Year Founded: 2006
Capital Under Management: $300,000,000
Current Activity Level: Actively seeking new investments

MOTOROLA VENTURES
1303 East Algonquin Road
Sixth Floor
Schaumburg, IL USA 60196
Phone: 847-576-0278
Fax: 847-576-2569
E-mail: motorolaventures@motorola.com
Website: www.motorola.com/ventures

Other Offices
Crockford Lane
Chineham Business Park
Basingstoke, United Kingdom RG24 8WQ

809 11th Avenue
Sunnyvale, CA USA 94089

Shoam Building
16 Kremenetski Street
Tel Aviv, Israel 67899

Management and Staff
Harshul Sanghi, Managing Director
Mony Hassid, Managing Director
Reese Schroeder, Managing Director
Stephen Moore, Managing Director
Tony Palcheck, Managing Director

Type of Firm
Corporate PE/Venture

Association Membership
Illinois Venture Capital Association
Indian Venture Capital Association (IVCA)

Project Preferences

Role in Financing:
Will function either as deal originator or investor in deals created by others

Type of Financing Preferred:
Second Stage Financing
Expansion
Early Stage
Later Stage
First Stage Financing
Startup

Size of Investments Considered:
Min Size of Investment Considered (000s): $1,000
Max Size of Investment Considered (000s): $15,000

Geographical Preferences

United States Preferences:
All U.S.

International Preferences:
United Kingdom
Western Europe
Middle East
Israel

Industry Focus
(% based on actual investment)

Communications and Media	26.5%
Computer Software and Services	20.5%
Internet Specific	18.2%
Semiconductors/Other Elect.	18.1%
Computer Hardware	7.2%
Biotechnology	4.2%
Other Products	3.4%
Medical/Health	1.8%
Consumer Related	0.1%

Additional Information
Year Founded: 1999
Capital Under Management: $400,000,000
Current Activity Level: Actively seeking new investments
Method of Compensation: Return on investment is of primary concern, do not charge fees

MOUNT HOOD EQUITY PARTNERS, L.P.
One Southwest Centerpointe Dr.
Suite 565
Lake Oswego, OR USA 97035
Phone: 503-639-0915
Website: www.mthep.com

Type of Firm
Private Equity Firm

Project Preferences

Type of Financing Preferred:
Early Stage
Startup

Geographical Preferences

United States Preferences:
Northwest

International Preferences:
Pacific

Additional Information
Year Founded: 2008
Current Activity Level: Actively seeking new investments

MOUNT YALE ASSET MANAGEMENT
8000 Norman Center Drive
Suite 630
Minneapolis, MN USA 55437
Phone: 952-897-5390
Website: www.mtyale.com

Management and Staff
Brian McLean, Senior Managing Director
John Sabre, Chairman & CEO
Roger Bowden, President

Type of Firm
Private Equity Advisor or Fund of Funds

Project Preferences

Type of Financing Preferred:
Fund of Funds
Fund of Funds of Second

Geographical Preferences

United States Preferences:
All U.S.

Additional Information
Year Founded: 1998
Capital Under Management: $199,500,000
Current Activity Level: Actively seeking new investments

MOUNTAIN PARTNERS AG
Bondlerstr. 6
Kirchberg/ Zurich, Switzerland 8802
Phone: 41-43-3775313
Fax: 41-43-3775348
E-mail: contact@mountain-partners.ch
Website: www.mountain-partners.ch

Type of Firm
Private Equity Firm

Project Preferences

Type of Financing Preferred:
Early Stage
Seed
Startup

Geographical Preferences

International Preferences:
Switzerland
Austria
Germany

Industry Preferences

In Industrial/Energy prefer:
Alternative Energy
Environmental Related

In Other prefer:
Environment Responsible

Additional Information
Year Founded: 2006
Current Activity Level: Actively seeking new investments

MOUNTAIN SUPER ANGEL AG
Fuhrstrasse 12
Waedenswil, Switzerland 8820
Phone: 41-44-783-8037
Fax: 41-44-783-8040
E-mail: contact@super-angel.ch
Website: www.super-angel.ch

Management and Staff
Daniel Wenzel, Founding Partner
Jorg Arntz, Partner
Sebastian Kofler, Chief Financial Officer

Type of Firm
Private Equity Firm

Project Preferences
Type of Financing Preferred:
Balanced

Geographical Preferences
International Preferences:
Switzerland
Austria
Germany

Industry Preferences
In Communications prefer:
Communications and Media
Telecommunications
Media and Entertainment
Entertainment

In Internet Specific prefer:
Internet

In Medical/Health prefer:
Medical/Health

Additional Information
Year Founded: 2007
Current Activity Level: Actively seeking new investments

MOUNTAIN VENTURES INC.
362 Old Whitley Road
P.O. Box 1738
London, KY USA 40743-1738
Phone: 606-864-5175
Fax: 606-864-5194

Management and Staff
Brenda McDaniel, Chief Financial Officer
Elmer Parlier, Vice President

Type of Firm
Private Equity Firm

Association Membership
Natl Assoc of Small Bus. Inv. Co (NASBIC)

Project Preferences
Role in Financing:
Will function either as deal originator or investor in deals created by others

Type of Financing Preferred:
Start-up Financing
Seed
First Stage Financing

Size of Investments Considered:
Min Size of Investment Considered (000s): $100
Max Size of Investment Considered (000s): $300

Additional Information
Year Founded: 1979
Capital Under Management: $5,000,000
Current Activity Level: Actively seeking new investments
Method of Compensation: Return on investment is of primary concern, do not charge fees

---

MOUNTAINEER CAPITAL, L.P.
107 Capitol Street
Suite 300
Charleston, WV USA 25301
Phone: 304-347-7519
Fax: 304-347-0072
E-mail: info@mountaineercapital.com
Website: www.mountaineercapital.com

Management and Staff
J. Rudy Henley, Partner
Patrick Bond, Partner
William Taylor, Managing General Partner

Type of Firm
SBIC

Association Membership
Natl Assoc of Small Bus. Inv. Co (NASBIC)
National Venture Capital Association - USA (NVCA)

Project Preferences
Role in Financing:
Will function either as deal originator or investor in deals created by others

Type of Financing Preferred:
Expansion
Balanced

Size of Investments Considered:
Min Size of Investment Considered (000s): $250
Max Size of Investment Considered (000s): $3,000

Geographical Preferences
United States Preferences:
Mid Atlantic
West Virginia

Additional Information
Name of Most Recent Fund: Mountaineer Capital, L.P. - SBIC
Most Recent Fund Was Raised: 04/01/2000
Year Founded: 2000
Capital Under Management: $22,300,000
Current Activity Level: Actively seeking new investments
Method of Compensation: Return on invest. most important, but chg. closing fees, service fees, etc.

MOUSAM VENTURES LLC
141 Sea Road
Kennebunk, ME USA 04043
Phone: 978-257-1508
Website: www.mousamventures.com

Type of Firm
Private Equity Firm

Project Preferences
Type of Financing Preferred:
Balanced

Geographical Preferences
United States Preferences:
All U.S.

Additional Information
Year Founded: 2007
Current Activity Level: Actively seeking new investments

MOVENTIS CAPITAL, INC. (FKA:ONLINE INNOVATION, INC.)
1959 152nd Street
Suite 304
White Rock, Canada V4A 9P3
Phone: 604-288-2430
Fax: 604-357-1266
E-mail: info@moventiscapital.com
Website: www.moventiscapital.com

Management and Staff
Blake Ponuick, Chairman & CEO

Type of Firm
Private Equity Advisor or Fund of Funds

Project Preferences

Type of Financing Preferred:
Generalist PE

Additional Information

Year Founded: 1997
Current Activity Level: Actively seeking new investments

MOVIPART BV

De Gorzen 5
Groot-Ammers, Netherlands 2964 AA
Phone: 31-182-614-279
Fax: 31-184-661-785

Type of Firm

Private Equity Firm

Additional Information

Current Activity Level: Reducing investment activity

MP HEALTHCARE VENTURE MANAGEMENT, INC.

33 Arch Street
Suite 2202
Boston, MA USA 02110
Phone: 617-737-4690
Fax: 617-737-4695
E-mail: MPH-WEB@mp-healthcare.com
Website: www.mp-healthcare.com

Management and Staff

Jeffrey Moore, Vice President
Junichi Watanabe, President
Tak Mukohira, Vice President

Type of Firm

Private Equity Firm

Association Membership

National Venture Capital Association - USA (NVCA)

Project Preferences

Type of Financing Preferred:
Early Stage
Seed

Geographical Preferences

United States Preferences:
All U.S.

Canadian Preferences:
All Canada

International Preferences:
Italy
United Kingdom
Luxembourg
Portugal
Europe
Spain
Belgium
Germany
France

Industry Preferences

In Medical/Health prefer:
Medical/Health
Medical Diagnostics
Medical Therapeutics

Additional Information

Year Founded: 2006
Capital Under Management: $100,000,000
Current Activity Level: Actively seeking new investments

MP INVESTMENT BANK

Skipholt 50D - 2.h.
Reykjavik, Iceland 105
Phone: 354-540-3200
Fax: 354-540-3201
Website: www.mp.is

Type of Firm

Bank Affiliated

Additional Information

Year Founded: 2004
Current Activity Level: Actively seeking new investments

MPC CAPITAL AUSTRIA AG

Linke Wienzeile 4
Vienna, Austria 1060
Phone: 43-1-58556700
Fax: 43-1-585567099
E-mail: info@mpc-capital.at
Website: www.mpc-capital.at

Type of Firm

Bank Affiliated

Project Preferences

Type of Financing Preferred:
Fund of Funds

Geographical Preferences

International Preferences:
All International

Additional Information

Year Founded: 2000
Current Activity Level: Actively seeking new investments

MPM CAPITAL (FKA: MPM ASSET MANAGEMENT LLC)

200 Clarendon Street
54th Floor John Hancock Tower
Boston, MA USA 02116
Phone: 617-425-9200
Fax: 617-425-9201
E-mail: info@mpmcapital.com
Website: www.mpmcapital.com

Other Offices

601 Gateway Boulevard
Suite 350
South San Francisco, CA USA 94080
Phone: 650-553-3300
Fax: 650-553-3301

260 Madison Avenue
Eighth Floor (at 38th and Madison)
New York, NY USA 10016

Management and Staff

Ansbert Gadicke, Managing Director
David Stack, Managing Director
Elizabeth Stoner, Managing Director
Frank Baldino, Venture Partner
George Daley, Venture Partner
H.Robert Horvitz, Venture Partner
James Scopa, Managing Director
John McDonald, Managing Director
Kenneth Greenberg, Principal
Robert Millman, Managing Director
Steven St. Peter, Managing Director
Todd Link, Chief Financial Officer
Todd Foley, Managing Director
Vaughn Kailian, Managing Director

Type of Firm

Private Equity Firm

Association Membership

National Venture Capital Association - USA (NVCA)

Project Preferences

Type of Financing Preferred:
Early Stage
Expansion
Mezzanine
Balanced
Later Stage
Other
First Stage Financing
Startup

Size of Investments Considered:
Min Size of Investment Considered (000s): $5,000
Max Size of Investment Considered (000s): $50,000

Geographical Preferences

United States Preferences:
All U.S.

International Preferences:
Europe
Western Europe
Australia
Asia

Industry Focus

(% based on actual investment)

Biotechnology	50.3%
Medical/Health	48.6%
Computer Software and Services	0.6%
Internet Specific	0.5%

Additional Information

Year Founded: 1997
Capital Under Management: $2,100,000,000
Current Activity Level: Actively seeking new investments
Method of Compensation: Return on investment is of primary concern, do not charge fees

MPS VENTURE SGR

Piazza Massimo d'Azeglio 22
Firenze , Italy 50121
Phone: 39-055-249-8553
Fax: 39-055-249-8447
E-mail: mpsventure@mpsventure.it
Website: www.mpsventure.it

Management and Staff

Francesco Saverio Carpinelli, President
Roberto Magnoni, Vice President

Type of Firm

Bank Affiliated

Association Membership

Italian Venture Capital Association (AIFI)
European Private Equity and Venture Capital Assoc.

Project Preferences

Type of Financing Preferred:
Leveraged Buyout
Expansion
Balanced
Management Buyouts
Acquisition
Startup

Geographical Preferences

International Preferences:
Italy
Europe

Industry Preferences

In Consumer Related prefer:
Consumer

In Business Serv. prefer:
Services

In Manufact. prefer:
Manufacturing

Additional Information

Name of Most Recent Fund: Emilia Venture
Most Recent Fund Was Raised: 02/28/2006
Year Founded: 2002
Capital Under Management: $417,500,000
Current Activity Level: Actively seeking new investments

MSD CAPITAL L.P.

645 Fifth Avenue
21st Floor
New York, NY USA 10022
Phone: 212-303-1650
Fax: 212-303-1620
E-mail: investments@msdcapital.com
Website: www.msdcapital.com

Management and Staff

Eric Rosen, Partner
Glenn Fuhrman, Managing Director
Howard Berk, Principal
James Stevens, Chief Financial Officer
John Kim, Principal
Marc Lisker, Chief Operating Officer
Massy Ghausi, Principal
Michael Dell, General Partner

Type of Firm

Private Equity Firm

Project Preferences

Type of Financing Preferred:
Expansion

Additional Information

Year Founded: 1998
Current Activity Level: Actively seeking new investments

MSOUTH EQUITY PARTNERS

12 Piedmont Center
Suite 210
Atlanta, GA USA 30305
Phone: 404-816-3255
Fax: 404-816-3258
Website: www.msouthequity.com

Type of Firm

Private Equity Firm

Project Preferences

Type of Financing Preferred:
Leveraged Buyout
Acquisition
Recapitalizations

Size of Investments Considered:
Min Size of Investment Considered (000s): $25,000
Max Size of Investment Considered (000s): $125,000

Geographical Preferences

United States Preferences:
Southeast
All U.S.

Additional Information

Year Founded: 2007
Capital Under Management: $266,000,000
Current Activity Level: Actively seeking new investments

MST CAPITAL, LTD.

P.O. Box 48855
London, United Kingdom WC1E 7WY
Phone: 44-20-7193-9753
Fax: 44-870-130-7098
Website: www.mstcapital.com

Management and Staff

Fred Mendelsohn, Founding Partner
Ken Terry, Founder
Patrick Smulders, Founder

Type of Firm

Private Equity Firm

Project Preferences

Type of Financing Preferred:
Leveraged Buyout
Balanced

Industry Preferences

In Medical/Health prefer:
Health Services

In Consumer Related prefer:
Food/Beverage

Additional Information

Year Founded: 2005
Current Activity Level: Actively seeking new investments

MTDC (MASSACHUSETTS TECHNOLOGY DEVELOPMENT CORP.)

40 Broad Street
Suite 230
Boston, MA USA 02109
Phone: 617-723-4920
Fax: 617-723-5983
Website: www.mtdc.com

Other Offices

148 State Street
Boston, MA USA 02109
Phone: 617-723-4920

Management and Staff

Dina Routhier, Principal

George Aggouras, Chief Financial Officer
Jerry Bird, Vice President
Paul Tu, Principal
Robert Crowley, President

Type of Firm

Incubator/Development Program

Association Membership

National Venture Capital Association - USA (NVCA)

Project Preferences

Role in Financing:

Prefer role as deal originator but will also invest in deals created by others

Type of Financing Preferred:

Second Stage Financing
Early Stage
Expansion
Seed
First Stage Financing
Joint Ventures
Startup

Size of Investments Considered:

Min Size of Investment Considered (000s): $250
Max Size of Investment Considered (000s): $750

Geographical Preferences

United States Preferences:

Massachusetts

Industry Focus

(% based on actual investment)

Computer Software and Services	32.2%
Internet Specific	23.1%
Semiconductors/Other Elect.	12.5%
Medical/Health	7.4%
Computer Hardware	7.3%
Industrial/Energy	6.6%
Communications and Media	4.9%
Biotechnology	4.6%
Other Products	1.2%
Consumer Related	0.2%

Additional Information

Name of Most Recent Fund: Commonwealth Fund Investment Program II
Most Recent Fund Was Raised: 08/01/2000
Year Founded: 1978
Capital Under Management: $45,000,000
Current Activity Level: Actively seeking new investments
Method of Compensation: Return on invest. most important, but chg. closing fees, service fees, etc.

MTI PARTNERS, LTD.

Langley Place
99 Langley Road
Watford, United Kingdom WD17 4BE
Phone: 44-1923-250-244
Fax: 44-1923-247-783
E-mail: headoffice@mtifirms.com
Website: www.mtifirms.com

Other Offices

Manchester Incubator Building
48 Grafton Street
Manchester, United Kingdom M13 9XX
Phone: 44-161-603-7769
Fax: 44-161-241-5411

Room 404, MWB Business Exchange
1 Berkley Street
London, United Kingdom W1J 8DJ
Phone: 44-20-7016-9516
Fax: 44-20-7016-9100

Waltham - Bay Colony Center
1050 Winter Street, Suite 1000
North Waltham, MA USA 02451
Phone: 781-530-3777
Fax: 781-530-3600

Management and Staff

David Holbrook, General Partner
David Ward, Managing Partner
Ernie Richardson, Managing Partner
Jayne Chace, Venture Partner
Paul Castle, Founder
Ray Sangster, Venture Partner

Type of Firm

Private Equity Firm

Association Membership

British Venture Capital Association (BVCA)
European Private Equity and Venture Capital Assoc.

Project Preferences

Role in Financing:

Prefer role as deal originator but will also invest in deals created by others

Type of Financing Preferred:

Second Stage Financing
Early Stage
Expansion
Start-up Financing
Seed
First Stage Financing
Startup

Size of Investments Considered:

Min Size of Investment Considered (000s): $400
Max Size of Investment Considered (000s): $7,500

Geographical Preferences

International Preferences:

United Kingdom

Industry Focus

(% based on actual investment)

Computer Software and Services	32.6%
Industrial/Energy	25.7%
Semiconductors/Other Elect.	11.9%
Medical/Health	10.6%
Communications and Media	10.1%
Internet Specific	7.8%
Biotechnology	1.0%
Other Products	0.3%

Additional Information

Year Founded: 1983
Capital Under Management: $296,500,000
Current Activity Level: Actively seeking new investments
Method of Compensation: Return on invest. most important, but chg. closing fees, service fees, etc.

MTM CAPITAL PARTNERS

17-23 Willow Place
London, United Kingdom SW1P 1JH
Phone: 44-20-7144-1155
Fax: 44-20-7629-6966
E-mail: mail@mtmcapital.com
Website: www.mtmcapital.com

Management and Staff

James Adams, Vice President
Maria Stratonova, Vice President
Shufang Qiu, Vice President

Type of Firm

Private Equity Firm

Project Preferences

Type of Financing Preferred:

Balanced

Geographical Preferences

International Preferences:

China

Additional Information

Year Founded: 2006
Current Activity Level: Actively seeking new investments

MTN CAPITAL PARTNERS

1114 Avenue of the Americas
38th Floor
New York, NY USA 10036
Phone: 212-400-2670
Fax: 212-986-1781
Website: www.mtncapital.com

Management and Staff

Oliver Trouveroy, Managing Partner

Type of Firm

Private Equity Firm

Additional Information

Year Founded: 2009
Current Activity Level: Actively seeking new investments

MTS HEALTH PARTNERS, L.P.

623 Fifth Avenue
15th Floor
New York, NY USA 10022
Phone: 212-887-2100
Fax: 212-887-2111
E-mail: Stanson@MTSpartners.com
Website: www.mtspartners.com

Other Offices

3200 Park Center Drive
Suite 1160
Costa Mesa, CA USA 92626
Phone: 714-427-0499
Fax: 714-427-0409

Management and Staff

Alexander Buzik, Vice President
Andrew Weisenfeld, Senior Managing Director
Curtis Lane, Senior Managing Director
Jay Shiland, Senior Managing Director
Kenton Rosenberry, Senior Managing Director
Margarita Cervone, Chief Financial Officer
Mark Epstein, Senior Managing Director
Michael Zarriello, Senior Managing Director
Michael Jablon, Vice President
Oliver Moses, Senior Managing Director
Teri Myers, Chief Financial Officer
William Kane, Senior Managing Director

Type of Firm

Bank Affiliated

Project Preferences

Role in Financing:

Will function either as deal originator or investor in deals created by others

Type of Financing Preferred:

Leveraged Buyout
Management Buyouts
Acquisition
Recapitalizations

Size of Investments Considered:

Min Size of Investment Considered (000s): $1,500
Max Size of Investment Considered (000s): $1,500

Industry Focus

(% based on actual investment)

Medical/Health	100.0%

Additional Information

Year Founded: 2000
Capital Under Management: $80,000,000
Current Activity Level: Actively seeking new investments
Method of Compensation: Return on invest. most important, but chg. closing fees, service fees, etc.

MU HANDS-ON CAPITAL LTD. (FKA:TSUBASA HANDS-ON CAPITAL, LTD)

Ishikawa Building 7F, 8-16
Nihombashi-Honcho, Chuo-ku
Tokyo, Japan 103-0023
Phone: 81-3-3245-8300
Fax: 81-3-3245-8311
E-mail: info@hands-on.sc.mufg.jp
Website: www.hands-on.sc.mufg.jp

Management and Staff

Yoshikazu Yabe, President

Type of Firm

Private Equity Firm

Project Preferences

Type of Financing Preferred:

Early Stage
Startup

Geographical Preferences

International Preferences:

Japan

Additional Information

Year Founded: 2000
Capital Under Management: $5,000,000
Current Activity Level: Actively seeking new investments

MUHAN INVESTMENT CO. (FKA: TERASOURCE VENTURE CAPITAL CO.)

4th & 5th Fl., Ku Am Bldg.
249-11 Nonhyun-Dong Kangnam-Ku
Seoul, South Korea
Phone: 822-559-4500
Fax: 822-559-4598
E-mail: area0120@muhanic.com
Website: www.muhanic.com

Other Offices

Daeduck Valley Campus Hannam Univ.
461-7 Jeonmin-Dong Yoosung-Ku
Daegeon , South Korea
Phone: 82-42-863-4600

Management and Staff

Alex Yeon, Chief Executive Officer
Min-Hwa Lee, Founder

Type of Firm

Private Equity Firm

Association Membership

Korean Venture Capital Association (KVCA)

Project Preferences

Type of Financing Preferred:

Balanced

Geographical Preferences

International Preferences:

Korea, South

Industry Preferences

In Internet Specific prefer:

Internet

In Semiconductor/Electr prefer:

Electronics

In Biotechnology prefer:

Biotechnology
Biotech Related Research

In Medical/Health prefer:

Medical/Health

Additional Information

Year Founded: 1996
Capital Under Management: $14,200,000
Current Activity Level: Actively seeking new investments

MULLER & MONROE ASSET MANAGEMENT, LLC (AKA: M2)

180 North Stetson Avenue
Suite 1320
Chicago, IL USA 60601
Phone: 312-782-7771
Fax: 312-782-9290
E-mail: info@m2am.com
Website: www.m2am.com

Management and Staff

Andre Rice, President

Type of Firm

Private Equity Advisor or Fund of Funds

Project Preferences

Type of Financing Preferred:

Fund of Funds

Geographical Preferences

United States Preferences:

Illinois
All U.S.

Industry Preferences

In Financial Services prefer:

Investment Groups

Additional Information

Year Founded: 1999
Capital Under Management: $185,600,000

Current Activity Level: Actively seeking new investments

MULLER-MOHL GROUP

Weinplatz 10
Zurich, Switzerland CH-8022
Phone: 41-43-344-6666
Fax: 41-43-344-6660
E-mail: e-mail@mm-grp.com
Website: www.mm-grp.com

Management and Staff

Beat Naef, Chief Executive Officer

Type of Firm

Private Equity Firm

Association Membership

Swiss Venture Capital Association (SECA)

Additional Information

Year Founded: 2000
Current Activity Level: Actively seeking new investments

MULLIGAN BIOCAPITAL AG

Stubbenhuk 7
8th Floor
Hamburg, Germany D-20459
Phone: 49-40-3703-5422
Fax: 49-40-3703-5410
Website: www.mulliganbiocapital.de

Management and Staff

Hans Hermann Munchmeyer, Managing Director
Jan zur Hausen, Managing Director

Type of Firm

Private Equity Firm

Project Preferences

Type of Financing Preferred:
Early Stage
Expansion
Mezzanine
Later Stage
Startup

Geographical Preferences

United States Preferences:
All U.S.

International Preferences:
Europe

Industry Preferences

In Biotechnology prefer:
Biotechnology

In Medical/Health prefer:
Medical/Health
Medical Therapeutics

Additional Information

Year Founded: 2001
Current Activity Level: Actively seeking new investments

MULTICAPITAL DO BRASIL CONSULTORIA E PARTICIPACOES

Rua Visconde de Piraja
414, Sala 401
Rio de Janeiro, Brazil 22410-002
Phone: 55-21-2287-7819
Fax: 55-21-2287-6921
Website: www.multi-k.com

Other Offices

Avenida Reboucas
1511, sl 83
Sao Paulo - SP, Brazil 05401-200
Phone: 55-11-3062-7915

Management and Staff

Roberto Hesketh, President

Type of Firm

Private Equity Firm

Association Membership

Brazilian Venture Capital Association (ABCR)

Project Preferences

Type of Financing Preferred:
Expansion
Acquisition
Startup

Geographical Preferences

International Preferences:
Brazil

Industry Preferences

In Computer Other prefer:
Computer Related

In Biotechnology prefer:
Biotechnology

In Medical/Health prefer:
Medical/Health

In Industrial/Energy prefer:
Energy

Additional Information

Year Founded: 1987
Current Activity Level: Actively seeking new investments

MULTICROISSANCE SAS

33-43 avenue Georges Pompidou
Balma, France 31130
Website: www.multicroissance.fr

Type of Firm

Bank Affiliated

Project Preferences

Type of Financing Preferred:
Leveraged Buyout
Expansion
Acquisition

Geographical Preferences

International Preferences:
France

Additional Information

Year Founded: 1987
Current Activity Level: Actively seeking new investments

MULTINATIONAL INDUSTRIAL FUND

Boulevard Manuel Avila
Camacho No.1, Eight Floor
Lomos de Chapultepec, Mexico 11009
Phone: 52-55-5395-5222
Fax: 52-55-5395-1008
E-mail: wamex@fondomif.com
Website: www.fondomif.com

Management and Staff

Ernesto Warholtz, President
Jose Antonio Contreras, Partner
Kurt Lipp, Partner

Type of Firm

Private Equity Firm

Project Preferences

Type of Financing Preferred:
Balanced

Size of Investments Considered:
Min Size of Investment Considered (000s): $3,000
Max Size of Investment Considered (000s): $10,000

Geographical Preferences

International Preferences:
Mexico

Industry Preferences

In Communications prefer:
Telecommunications

In Computer Hardware prefer:
Computers

In Semiconductor/Electr prefer:
Electronics

In Transportation prefer:
Transportation

In Manufact. prefer:
Manufacturing

Additional Information

Year Founded: 2004
Current Activity Level: Actively seeking new investments

MULTIPLE CAPITAL INC.

1010 Sherbrooke West
Suite 1200
Montreal, Canada H3A 2R7
Phone: 514-461-9900
Fax: 514-461-9969
E-mail: info@multiplecapital.com
Website: www.multiplecapital.com

Management and Staff

Claude Vachet, Managing Partner
Hubert Manseau, General Partner
Johanne Lemire, Partner
Serge Langford, Managing Partner
Sylvain Bertrand, Principal

Type of Firm

Private Equity Advisor or Fund of Funds

Project Preferences

Type of Financing Preferred:
Fund of Funds of Second

Geographical Preferences

Canadian Preferences:
All Canada

Additional Information

Year Founded: 2005
Current Activity Level: Actively seeking new investments

MUNHWA INVESTMENT CORPORATION (AKA: COMET INVESTMENT)

1607-4, Usang-Dong
Gwangsan-Gu
Gwangju, South Korea 506-050
Phone: 82-2-773-6810
Fax: 82-2-773-6818
Website: www.munhwainvest.com

Other Offices

93-52, Bukchang-Dong, Jung-Gu
Seoul, South Korea

Management and Staff

Un Tae Kim, President

Type of Firm

Bank Affiliated

Association Membership

Korean Venture Capital Association (KVCA)

Project Preferences

Type of Financing Preferred:
Early Stage
Mezzanine
Turnaround
Acquisition

Geographical Preferences

International Preferences:
Korea, South

Industry Preferences

In Communications prefer:
Telecommunications

In Internet Specific prefer:
Internet

In Semiconductor/Electr prefer:
Electronics
Semiconductor

In Biotechnology prefer:
Biotechnology

In Medical/Health prefer:
Medical/Health

Additional Information

Year Founded: 1987
Current Activity Level: Actively seeking new investments

MURCIA EMPRENDE SOCIEDAD DE CAPITAL RIESGO

C/ Jacobo de las Leyes n 12
planta baja
Murcia, Spain 30001
Phone: 34-968-205-051
Fax: 34-968-205-052
Website: www.murciaemprende.com

Type of Firm

Private Equity Firm

Project Preferences

Type of Financing Preferred:
Expansion

Size of Investments Considered:
Min Size of Investment Considered (000s): $60
Max Size of Investment Considered (000s): $150

Geographical Preferences

International Preferences:
Europe
Spain

Additional Information

Year Founded: 2006
Current Activity Level: Actively seeking new investments

MUREX INVESTMENTS, INC.

4700 Wissahickon Avenue
Suite 126
Philadelphia, PA USA 19144
Phone: 215-951-7200
Fax: 215-951-9228
E-mail: murex@rhd.org
Website: www.murexinvests.com

Management and Staff

James Jaffe, Managing Director

Type of Firm

Government Affiliated Program

Association Membership

Community Development Venture Capital Alliance

Project Preferences

Role in Financing:
Will function either as deal originator or investor in deals created by others

Type of Financing Preferred:
Early Stage
Expansion

Size of Investments Considered:
Min Size of Investment Considered (000s): $200
Max Size of Investment Considered (000s): $600

Geographical Preferences

United States Preferences:
Pennsylvania
Delaware
New Jersey

Industry Preferences

In Computer Software prefer:
Computer Services
Software
Applications Software

In Financial Services prefer:
Financial Services

In Business Serv. prefer:
Services

In Manufact. prefer:
Manufacturing

In Other prefer:
Socially Responsible
Women/Minority-Owned Bus.

Additional Information

Year Founded: 2001
Capital Under Management: $13,800,000
Current Activity Level: Actively seeking new investments
Method of Compensation: Return on investment is of primary concern, do not charge fees

MURPHREE COLORADO CAPCO, L.P.

24 South Weber Street
Suite 325
Colorado Springs, CO USA 80903
Phone: 719-634-7070
Fax: 719-634-8544
Website: www.murphreecocapco.com

Other Offices

2005 Tenth Street
Suite D
Boulder, CO USA 80302
Phone: 303-413-1264
Fax: 303-413-1266

Management and Staff

Dennis Murphree, Managing Partner
Pat Long, Venture Partner

Type of Firm

Private Equity Firm

Project Preferences

Role in Financing:

Will function either as deal originator or investor in deals created by others

Type of Financing Preferred:

Mezzanine
Balanced

Size of Investments Considered:

Min Size of Investment Considered (000s): $100
Max Size of Investment Considered (000s): $500

Geographical Preferences

United States Preferences:

Colorado

Additional Information

Year Founded: 2001
Capital Under Management: $6,300,000
Current Activity Level: Actively seeking new investments
Method of Compensation: Return on investment is of primary concern, do not charge fees

MURPHREE VENTURE PARTNERS

1100 Louisiana
Suite 5005
Houston, TX USA 77002
Phone: 713-655-8500
Fax: 713-655-8503
E-mail: webmaster@murphreeventures.com
Website: www.murphreeventures.com

Other Offices

2005 10th Street
Suite D
Boulder, CO USA 80302
Phone: 303-413-1264
Fax: 303-413-1266

9600 Great Hills Trail
Suite 300E
Austin, TX USA 78759
Phone: 512-241-8100
Fax: 512-241-8001

820 Shades Creek Parkway
Suite 3100
Birmingham, AL USA 35209
Phone: 205-870-8050
Fax: 205-870-8052

1155 University Blvd. SE
Albuquerque, NM USA 87106
Phone: 505-843-4277
Fax: 505-843-4278

Management and Staff

Dennis Murphree, Managing General Partner
Ed Perry, Partner
Elliott Boullion, Partner
Geoffrey Tudor, Venture Partner
Steve Dauphin, Partner
Thomas Stephenson, Partner
William Reiser, Partner

Type of Firm

Private Equity Firm

Project Preferences

Role in Financing:

Prefer role as deal originator but will also invest in deals created by others

Type of Financing Preferred:

Early Stage
Balanced
Start-up Financing
Seed
First Stage Financing

Size of Investments Considered:

Min Size of Investment Considered (000s): $250
Max Size of Investment Considered (000s): $10,000

Geographical Preferences

United States Preferences:

Southeast
Southwest

Industry Focus

(% based on actual investment)	
Industrial/Energy	28.9%
Computer Software and Services	25.5%
Computer Hardware	17.8%
Internet Specific	17.1%
Semiconductors/Other Elect.	5.9%
Medical/Health	2.9%
Consumer Related	1.8%
Communications and Media	0.2%

Additional Information

Name of Most Recent Fund: MVP Growth Equity Fund II, L.P.
Most Recent Fund Was Raised: 06/13/2008
Year Founded: 1989
Capital Under Management: $46,400,000
Current Activity Level: Actively seeking new investments
Method of Compensation: Return on investment is of primary concern, do not charge fees

MURPHY & PARTNERS, L.P.

45 Rockefeller Plaza
Suite 1960
New York, NY USA 10111
Phone: 212-332-1000
Fax: 212-332-2920
Website: www.murphy-partners.com

Other Offices

193 Beacon Street
Boston, MA USA 02116
Phone: 617-247-6170
Fax: 617-247-3584

Management and Staff

John Murphy, Managing General Partner
Thomas Keane, General Partner

Type of Firm

Private Equity Firm

Association Membership

Natl Assoc of Small Bus. Inv. Co (NASBIC)

Project Preferences

Role in Financing:

Prefer role as deal originator

Type of Financing Preferred:

Second Stage Financing
Leveraged Buyout
Control-block Purchases
Early Stage
Expansion
Seed

First Stage Financing
Acquisition

Size of Investments Considered:

Min Size of Investment Considered (000s): $1,000
Max Size of Investment Considered (000s): $10,000

Industry Focus

(% based on actual investment)

Other Products	39.5%
Consumer Related	27.0%
Medical/Health	25.3%
Internet Specific	4.3%
Communications and Media	3.9%

Additional Information

Name of Most Recent Fund: Murphy & Partners Fund III LP
Most Recent Fund Was Raised: 11/10/2004
Year Founded: 1988
Capital Under Management: $24,000,000
Current Activity Level: Actively seeking new investments
Method of Compensation: Return on invest. most important, but chg. closing fees, service fees, etc.

MUSHARAKA VENTURE MANAGEMENT SDN BHD

9-2, Platinum Walk
2 Jalan Langkawi, Setapak
Kuala Lumpur, Malaysia 53300
Phone: 603-4142-7285
Fax: 603-4143-6346

Management and Staff

Encick Nor Idzam Yaakub, Managing Director

Type of Firm

Government Affiliated Program

Project Preferences

Type of Financing Preferred:

Mezzanine
Expansion
Generalist PE
Early Stage
Management Buyouts
Startup
Acquisition

Geographical Preferences

International Preferences:

Malaysia

Industry Preferences

In Communications prefer:

Communications and Media

Additional Information

Year Founded: 2008
Capital Under Management: $10,800,000
Current Activity Level: Actively seeking new investments

MUSHUP PARTNERS GODO GAISHA

1-31-3 Bunka
Sumida-Ku, Tokyo, Japan 131-0044

Type of Firm

Private Equity Firm

Project Preferences

Type of Financing Preferred:

Leveraged Buyout

Geographical Preferences

International Preferences:

Asia

Additional Information

Year Founded: 2008
Current Activity Level: Actively seeking new investments

MUSTANG GROUP LLC, THE

339 Auburn Street
Newton, MA USA 02466
Phone: 617-467-6800
Website: www.mustanggroup.com

Management and Staff

Ben Coes, Managing Partner
Bob Crowley, Managing Partner
Carson Biederman, Managing Partner
Eric Tencer, Principal

Type of Firm

Private Equity Firm

Project Preferences

Type of Financing Preferred:

Expansion
Later Stage
Management Buyouts
Recapitalizations

Industry Preferences

In Communications prefer:

Communications and Media

In Consumer Related prefer:

Entertainment and Leisure
Retail
Consumer Products
Consumer Services

In Transportation prefer:

Transportation

In Financial Services prefer:

Financial Services

In Manufact. prefer:

Manufacturing

Additional Information

Year Founded: 2003
Current Activity Level: Actively seeking new investments

MUSTANG VENTURES

505 Hamilton Avenue
Palo Alto, CA USA 94301
Phone: 650-289-4400
Fax: 650-289-4444
Website: www.mustangvc.com

Management and Staff

Robert McCormack, General Partner

Type of Firm

Private Equity Firm

Project Preferences

Type of Financing Preferred:

Balanced

Geographical Preferences

International Preferences:

China

Industry Preferences

In Communications prefer:

Wireless Communications

In Internet Specific prefer:

Internet

In Semiconductor/Electr prefer:

Semiconductor

In Consumer Related prefer:

Education Related

In Business Serv. prefer:

Services

Additional Information

Name of Most Recent Fund: Mustang Venture I, L.P.
Most Recent Fund Was Raised: 09/27/2004
Year Founded: 2004
Capital Under Management: $40,000,000
Current Activity Level: Actively seeking new investments

MUTUAL CAPITAL PARTNERS

5805 Bridge Avenue
Cleveland, OH USA 44102
Phone: 216-928-1908
Fax: 216-928-1909
Website: www.mutualcapitalpartners.com

Management and Staff

Wayne Wallace, Managing Director
William Trainor, Managing Director

Type of Firm

Private Equity Firm

Project Preferences

Role in Financing:

Prefer role as deal originator

Type of Financing Preferred:

Expansion
Balanced
Later Stage

Geographical Preferences

United States Preferences:

Midwest
Pennsylvania
Michigan
Ohio
Indiana
New York

Additional Information

Year Founded: 2004
Capital Under Management: $14,200,000
Current Activity Level: Actively seeking new investments

MVC CAPITAL (FKA: MEVC)

287 Bowman Avenue
2nd Floor
Purchase, NY USA 10577
Phone: 914-701-0310
Fax: 914-701-0315
E-mail: info@mvccapital.com
Website: www.mvccapital.com

Management and Staff

Bruce Shewmaker, Senior Managing Director
Christopher Sullivan, Managing Director
Frances Spark, Chief Financial Officer
Jackie Shapiro, Vice President
James O'Connor, Managing Director
Peter Seidenberg, Chief Financial Officer
Puneet Sanan, Managing Director
Shivani Khurana, Managing Director
William Del Biaggio, President

Type of Firm

Incubator/Development Program

Project Preferences

Role in Financing:

Prefer role as deal originator but will also invest in deals created by others

Type of Financing Preferred:

Generalist PE
Expansion
Management Buyouts
Acquisition

Size of Investments Considered:

Min Size of Investment Considered (000s): $3,000
Max Size of Investment Considered (000s): $25,000

Geographical Preferences

United States Preferences:

All U.S.

International Preferences:

All International

Industry Focus

(% based on actual investment)	
Internet Specific	43.0%
Other Products	19.1%
Computer Software and Services	17.5%
Communications and Media	9.9%
Medical/Health	7.5%
Computer Hardware	1.7%
Consumer Related	1.1%
Industrial/Energy	0.2%

Additional Information

Year Founded: 1999
Capital Under Management: $117,000,000
Current Activity Level: Actively seeking new investments

MVC CORPORATION

16F KDDI Otemachi Bldg.
1-8-1 Otemachi, Chiyoda-ku
Tokyo, Japan 100-0004
Phone: 81-3-5299-2251
Fax: 81-3-3272-5315
Website: www.mvc.co.jp

Other Offices

Room 3101, Kerry Centre
1515 Nanjing Rd. West
Shanghai, China 200040
Phone: 86-21-5298-5959
Fax: 86-21-5298-5177

Room 3303, China World Tower 1
Jian Guo Men wai Avenue
Beijing, China 100004
Phone: 86-10-6505-5308
Fax: 86-21-6506-3128

Management and Staff

Kinji Fuchikami, Venture Partner
Masanobu Hirano, Venture Partner
Shunsuke Masaki, Venture Partner

Type of Firm

Corporate PE/Venture

Project Preferences

Type of Financing Preferred:

Early Stage
Expansion
Balanced

Geographical Preferences

International Preferences:

Japan

Industry Preferences

In Communications prefer:

Communications and Media

In Computer Software prefer:

Software

In Medical/Health prefer:

Medical Products

Additional Information

Year Founded: 1995
Capital Under Management: $19,000,000
Current Activity Level: Actively seeking new investments

MVC UNTERNEHMENS-BETEILIGUNGSGE-SELLSCHAFT MBH (AKA: MVC GMBH)

Kronenstrasse 11
Berlin, Germany 10117
Phone: 49-30-2015-5886
Fax: 49-30-2015-5851
E-mail: info@mvcag.de
Website: www.mvcag.de

Management and Staff

Axel Bublitz, Chief Executive Officer
Manfred Mende, Managing Partner

Type of Firm

Corporate PE/Venture

Association Membership

German Venture Capital Association (BVK)

Project Preferences

Type of Financing Preferred:

Expansion
Mezzanine
Seed
Management Buyouts
Startup
Recapitalizations

Geographical Preferences

International Preferences:

Germany

Industry Preferences

In Communications prefer:

Communications and Media

In Semiconductor/Electr prefer:

Electronics

In Biotechnology prefer:
Biotechnology

In Financial Services prefer:
Financial Services

Additional Information

Year Founded: 1999
Capital Under Management: $21,200,000
Current Activity Level: Actively seeking new investments

MVI ITALIA S.R.L.

Via Santa Marta 19
Milan, Italy 20123
Phone: 39-02720-93833
Fax: 39-02720-15230
E-mail: info@mvi.it

Type of Firm

Private Equity Firm

Association Membership

Italian Venture Capital Association (AIFI)

Project Preferences

Size of Investments Considered:
Min Size of Investment Considered (000s): $191
Max Size of Investment Considered (000s): $6,351

Additional Information

Year Founded: 2006
Capital Under Management: $1,600,000
Current Activity Level: Actively seeking new investments

MVI SVERIGE AB (AKA: MERCHAN VENTURE INVETMENT)

Norrlandsgatan 15
Stockholm, Sweden 111 43
Phone: 46-8-5451-8860
Fax: 46-8-5451-8870
E-mail: info@mvigroup.com
Website: www.mvigroup.com

Other Offices

Plaza Marques de Salamanca
11-4 Izda
Madrid, Spain 28006
Phone: 34-91-426-4974
Fax: 34-91-576-2516

Mezzanine Floor, Menars ING
84 Jalan Raja Chulan
Kuala Lumpur, Malaysia 50200
Phone: 603-2161-1888
Fax: 603-2161-1188

19-20 Woodstock Street
London, United Kingdom W1C 2AN
Phone: 44-207-016-5242
Fax: 44-207-491-1935

Runeberginkatu 5B
7th Floor
Helsinki, Finland 00100
Phone: 358-9-6869-2250
Fax: 358-9-6869-2251

Dronninggaards Alle 136
Holte
Copenhagen, Denmark 2840
Phone: 45-2094-2768

Konigsallee 60 F
Dusseldorf, Germany 40212
Phone: 46-708-365-944

Via Santa Marta 19
Milan, Italy 20123
Phone: 39-02-7209-3833
Fax: 39-02-7209-3745

Inkognitogaten 33
P.O.Box 1890, Vika
Oslo, Norway 0124
Phone: 47-909-16-250
Fax: 47-908-07-250

Rue de Lausanne 31
Morges, Switzerland 1110
Phone: 41-21-804-1090
Fax: 41-21-804-1099

Type of Firm

Private Equity Firm

Association Membership

Swedish Venture Capital Association (SVCA)

Project Preferences

Type of Financing Preferred:
Leveraged Buyout
Balanced
Seed
Startup

Size of Investments Considered:
Min Size of Investment Considered (000s): $1,000
Max Size of Investment Considered: No Limit

Geographical Preferences

International Preferences:
Europe

Additional Information

Year Founded: 1999
Current Activity Level: Actively seeking new investments

MVM LIFE SCIENCE PARTNERS LLP (AKA: MVM, LTD.)

6 Henrietta Street
London, United Kingdom WC2E 8PU
Phone: 44-20-7557-7500
Fax: 44-20-7557-7501
Website: www.mvfund.com

Other Offices

Old City Hall
45 School Street
Boston, MA USA 02108
Phone: 617-383-2101
Fax: 617-383-2106

Management and Staff

Eric Bednarski, Partner

Type of Firm

Private Equity Firm

Project Preferences

Type of Financing Preferred:
Early Stage
Start-up Financing
Seed

Geographical Preferences

International Preferences:
United Kingdom
Europe
Scandanavia/Nordic Region

Industry Preferences

In Biotechnology prefer:
Biotechnology

In Medical/Health prefer:
Medical Diagnostics
Pharmaceuticals

Additional Information

Year Founded: 1997
Capital Under Management: $500,000,000
Current Activity Level: Actively seeking new investments

MVP CAPITAL COMPANY, LTD.

3/F, Ice Castle Building
2 Nonhyun-dong Kangnam-Gu
Seoul, South Korea 135-010
Phone: 822-540-3696
Fax: 822-540-3698
Website: www.mvpc.co.kr

Management and Staff

Dogun Yun, President
Eunkang Song, Chief Executive Officer

Jonghyuk Park, Vice President
Kimoon Nam, President

Type of Firm
Private Equity Firm

Association Membership
Korean Venture Capital Association (KVCA)

Project Preferences

Type of Financing Preferred:
Fund of Funds
Early Stage
Expansion
Balanced
Seed
Startup

Geographical Preferences

International Preferences:
Korea, South

Industry Preferences

In Communications prefer:
Radio & TV Broadcasting
Telecommunications
Media and Entertainment
Entertainment
Other Communication Prod.

In Computer Hardware prefer:
Computers

In Consumer Related prefer:
Consumer
Entertainment and Leisure

Additional Information
Year Founded: 1999
Capital Under Management: $95,500,000
Current Activity Level: Actively seeking new investments

MVP MUNICH VENTURE PARTNERS MANAGEMENTGESELLSCHAFT MBH
Karl-Valentin-Strasse 16
Grunwald, Germany 82031
Phone: 49-89-6130-0105
Fax: 49-89-6130-0106
E-mail: info@munichvp.com
Website: www.munichvp.com

Management and Staff
Rolf Nagel, Managing Partner
Sonke Mehrgardt, Managing Partner
Walter Grassl, Managing Partner

Type of Firm
Private Equity Firm

Project Preferences

Type of Financing Preferred:
Balanced
Startup

Geographical Preferences

International Preferences:
Europe
Germany

Industry Preferences

In Communications prefer:
Communications and Media

In Semiconductor/Electr prefer:
Semiconductor

In Industrial/Energy prefer:
Energy

Additional Information
Year Founded: 2005
Current Activity Level: Actively seeking new investments

MWI & PARTNERS
PO Box 200
161 Bay Street
Toronto, Canada M5J 2S1
Phone: 416-369-3981
Fax: 416-369-3986

Management and Staff
Alan Wearing, Managing Partner
Geoff Browne, Managing Partner

Type of Firm
Private Equity Firm

Project Preferences

Role in Financing:
Prefer role as deal originator but will also invest in deals created by others

Type of Financing Preferred:
Leveraged Buyout
Expansion
Generalist PE
Later Stage
Management Buyouts
Acquisition
Recapitalizations

Size of Investments Considered:
Min Size of Investment Considered (000s): $5,000
Max Size of Investment Considered (000s): $20,000

Geographical Preferences

United States Preferences:
All U.S.

Canadian Preferences:
All Canada

Industry Focus
(% based on actual investment)

Computer Software and Services	100.0%

Additional Information
Year Founded: 1996
Current Activity Level: Actively seeking new investments
Method of Compensation: Return on invest. most important, but chg. closing fees, service fees, etc.

MYQUBE
Rue de Namur 73/D
Bruxelles, Belgium 1000
Phone: 32-2-513-4523
Fax: 32-2-513-6397
E-mail: info@myqube.com
Website: www.myqube.com

Other Offices
10001 North De Anza Boulevard
Suite 301
Cupertino, CA USA 95014
Phone: 1-408-446-1132
Fax: 1-408-446-1155

Bulevardi 5 A
Helsinki, Finland 00120
Phone: 584 242 6001

Corso di Porta Ticinese, 89
Milan, Italy 20123
Phone: 39-2-8311-5211
Fax: 39-2-8311-5227

Rue Maunoir 26
Geneva, Switzerland 1207
Phone: 41-22-8491-000
Fax: 41-22-8491-099

Maximilianstrasse 30
Munchen, Germany 80539
Phone: 49-89-901-09510
Fax: 49-89-901-09575

72, New Bond Street
London, United Kingdom W1Y 9DD
Phone: 44-20-75-145864
Fax: 44-20-74-993417

Management and Staff
Antonio Gambardella, Partner
Ari Aalto, Partner
Domenico Ciccopiedi, Partner
Enzo Torresi, Partner
Gian Luca Braggiotti, Partner
Jan Haglund, Partner
Piero Abbate, Partner
Vittorio Palmieri, Partner

Type of Firm
Incubator/Development Program

Association Membership
Italian Venture Capital Association (AIFI)

Project Preferences

Type of Financing Preferred:
Early Stage
Seed
Startup

Geographical Preferences

International Preferences:
Europe
Israel

Industry Preferences

In Internet Specific prefer:
Internet

In Biotechnology prefer:
Biotechnology

Additional Information
Year Founded: 2000
Capital Under Management: $85,900,000
Current Activity Level: Actively seeking new investments

MYVENTURE PARTNERS, INC.

41/F KWTC Building
Samsung-Dong
Seoul, South Korea 135-757
Phone: 822-6000-5858
Fax: 822-6000-5828
E-mail: contact@myventure.com
Website: www.myventure.com

Management and Staff
Chul-Joo Kim, Vice President
Han Seung Kim, Vice President
Jay Kim, Vice President
Woo-Han Kim, President

Type of Firm
Private Equity Firm

Association Membership
Korean Venture Capital Association (KVCA)

Project Preferences

Type of Financing Preferred:
Balanced

Geographical Preferences

International Preferences:
Korea, South
Asia

Industry Preferences

In Communications prefer:
Telecommunications

In Internet Specific prefer:
Internet

Additional Information
Year Founded: 2000
Capital Under Management: $17,800,000
Current Activity Level: Actively seeking new investment

- N -

N+1

Padilla, 17
Madrid, Spain 28006
Phone: 34-91-745-8484
Fax: 34-91-431-3812
Website: www.nplus1.es

Type of Firm
Private Equity Firm

Project Preferences

Type of Financing Preferred:
Generalist PE
Management Buyouts

Size of Investments Considered:
Min Size of Investment Considered (000s): $21,150
Max Size of Investment Considered (000s): $49,360

Geographical Preferences

International Preferences:
Portugal
Spain

Additional Information
Year Founded: 2008
Capital Under Management: $955,000,000
Current Activity Level : Actively seeking new investments

NAC VENTURES, LLC

8609 Second Avenue
Suite 506B
Silver Spring, MD USA 20910
Phone: 301-587-9003
Fax: 301-587-0264
E-mail: whillabrant@nativeamericancapital.com
Website: www.nativeamericancapital.com

Management and Staff
Christopher Dettmar, General Partner
Jeff Friedman, General Partner
Joseph Falkson, General Partner
Marco Rubin, General Partner
Roland Oliver, General Partner
Walter Hillabrant, General Partner

Type of Firm
Private Equity Firm

Association Membership
Community Development Venture Capital Alliance

Project Preferences

Type of Financing Preferred:
Early Stage
Startup

Geographical Preferences

United States Preferences:
All U.S.

Additional Information

Year Founded: 2003
Current Activity Level : Actively seeking new investments

NAFTA FUND OF MEXICO, LP

Plaza Reforma
Prol. Reforma 600-103
Mexico City, Mexico 01210
Phone: 52-55-5259-6618
Fax: 52-55-5259-3928
Website: www.naftafund.com

Management and Staff

Hernan Sabau, Principal
Jaime Serra, Principal
Luis Perezcano, Partner
Luis Alberto Aziz, Principal
Pedro Noyola, Principal

Type of Firm

Private Equity Firm

Project Preferences

Type of Financing Preferred:
Balanced

Geographical Preferences

International Preferences:
Mexico

Additional Information

Year Founded: 2003
Capital Under Management: $40,000,000
Current Activity Level : Actively seeking new investments

NAGOYA SMALL & MEDIUM BUSINESS INVESTMENT & CONSULTATION CO.

7F Tokai Building, 1-16-30
Meieki Minami, Nakamura-ku
Nagoya, Japan 450-0003
Phone: 815-2581-9541
Fax: 815-2583-8501
Website: www.sbic-cj.co.jp

Management and Staff

Hogen Ikeda, President

Type of Firm

SBIC

Project Preferences

Type of Financing Preferred:
Balanced

Geographical Preferences

International Preferences:
Japan

Additional Information

Year Founded: 1963
Capital Under Management: $166,600,000
Current Activity Level : Actively seeking new investments

NAJAFI COMPANIES (FKA: PIVOTAL PRIVATE EQUITY)

2525 East Camelback Road
Suite 850, The Esplanade
Phoenix, AZ USA 85016
Phone: 602-476-0600
Fax: 602-476-0625
E-mail: info@najafi.com
Website: www.najafi.com

Management and Staff

Jahm Najafi, Chief Executive Officer
Jerry Pence, Vice President
Peter Woog, Partner

Type of Firm

Private Equity Firm

Project Preferences

Role in Financing:
Prefer role as deal originator

Type of Financing Preferred:
Leveraged Buyout
Generalist PE
Later Stage
Management Buyouts
Special Situation

Industry Preferences

In Communications prefer:
Telecommunications
Data Communications

In Internet Specific prefer:
Internet
Ecommerce
Web Aggregration/Portals

In Consumer Related prefer:
Franchises(NEC)
Food/Beverage
Consumer Products

In Industrial/Energy prefer:
Energy
Industrial Products

In Business Serv. prefer:
Distribution

In Manufact. prefer:
Manufacturing

In Utilities prefer:
Utilities

Additional Information

Year Founded: 2003
Current Activity Level : Actively seeking new investments
Method of Compensation: Return on investment is of primary concern, do not charge fees

---

NAJETI FRANCE

Chemin des Bois
Acquin-Westbecourt
Lumbres, France 62380
Phone: 330-321-39789
Fax: 330-321-39745
E-mail: contact.france@najeti.com
Website: www.najeti.com

Type of Firm

Private Equity Firm

Additional Information

Year Founded: 2008
Current Activity Level : Actively seeking new investments

NAJETI VENTURES

Chemin des Bois
Acquin-Westbecourt
Lumbres, France 62380
Phone: 33-3-2139-7891
Fax: 33-3-2139-7458
E-mail: contact.france@najeti.com
Website: www.najeti.com

Other Offices

Najeti US
325 Main Street South
Southbury, CT USA 06488
Phone: 203-262-6336
Fax: 203-262-6666

Najeti Capital SCR, S.A
Calle Serrano 57
Madrid, Spain 28006
Phone: 34-91-781-4960
Fax: 34-91-435-4076

Type of Firm

Incubator/Development Program

Association Membership

European Private Equity and Venture Capital Assoc.

Project Preferences

Type of Financing Preferred:
Early Stage
Seed
Startup

Geographical Preferences

International Preferences:
Spain
France

Industry Preferences

In Communications prefer:
Telecommunications

In Biotechnology prefer:
Biotechnology

In Medical/Health prefer:
Medical/Health

In Industrial/Energy prefer:
Machinery
Environmental Related

Additional Information

Year Founded: 1994
Current Activity Level : Actively seeking new investments

NALANDA CAPITAL PTE, LTD.

#37-03/04 OCBC Center
65 Chulia Street
Singapore, Singapore 049513
Phone: 65-6826-9100
Fax: 65-6826-9101
Website: www.nalandacapital.com

Management and Staff

A.N. Seshadri, Principal
Anand Sridharan, Principal
Ashish Patil, Chief Operating Officer
Pulak Prasad, Managing Partner

Type of Firm

Private Equity Firm

Project Preferences

Type of Financing Preferred:
Public Companies
Acquisition

Geographical Preferences

International Preferences:
India
Asia

Additional Information

Year Founded: 2007
Capital Under Management: $400,000,000
Current Activity Level : Actively seeking new investments

NAMUR INVEST

Av. des Champs Elysees 160
Namur, Belgium 5000
Phone: 32-81-225-903
Fax: 32-81-231-146
E-mail: info@namurinvest.be
Website: www.namurinvest.be

Type of Firm

Private Equity Firm

Project Preferences

Type of Financing Preferred:
Balanced

Additional Information

Year Founded: 2007
Current Activity Level : Actively seeking new investments

NANCHANG VENTURE CAPITAL CO., LTD.

4/F Taihao Xinxi Building A
Nanchang
Jiangxi, China
Phone: 86-791-8105-383
E-mail: lqf@ncct.com.cn
Website: www.ncct.com.cn

Type of Firm

Private Equity Firm

Project Preferences

Type of Financing Preferred:
Balanced

Industry Preferences

In Manufact. prefer:
Manufacturing

Additional Information

Year Founded: 2008
Current Activity Level : Actively seeking new investments

NANCY CREEK CAPITAL

3825 Paces Walk
Suite 350
Atlanta, GA USA 30327
Phone: 678-384-4520
Fax: 678-384-4521
E-mail: info@nancycreek.com
Website: www.nancycreekcapital.com

Management and Staff

Barrington Branch, Principal
Charles Shelton, Principal
Edgar Sims, Principal
Robert Watts, Chief Financial Officer

Type of Firm

Private Equity Firm

Project Preferences

Type of Financing Preferred:
Expansion
Mezzanine
Acquisition
Recapitalizations

Size of Investments Considered:
Min Size of Investment Considered (000s): $1,000
Max Size of Investment Considered (000s): $5,000

Geographical Preferences

United States Preferences:
All U.S.

Industry Preferences

In Medical/Health prefer:
Medical/Health

In Business Serv. prefer:
Distribution

In Manufact. prefer:
Manufacturing

Additional Information

Name of Most Recent Fund: Nancy Creek Capital QP, L.P.
Most Recent Fund Was Raised: 10/26/2005
Year Founded: 2005
Capital Under Management: $40,000,000
Current Activity Level : Actively seeking new investments

NANJING HEDING VENTURE CAPITAL MANAGEMENT CO., LTD.

No. 268 Zhongshan Road
23/F Hui Jie Square
Nanjing, China 210008
Phone: 86-25-8657-9659
Fax: 86-25-8657-9660

Type of Firm

Private Equity Firm

Project Preferences

Type of Financing Preferred:
Expansion
Later Stage

Geographical Preferences

International Preferences:
China

Industry Preferences

In Semiconductor/Electr prefer:
Electronics

In Biotechnology prefer:
Biotechnology

In Medical/Health prefer:
Medical/Health

In Consumer Related prefer:
Education Related

In Industrial/Energy prefer:
Energy
Materials
Environmental Related

In Financial Services prefer:
Financial Services

In Business Serv. prefer:
Media

In Agr/Forestr/Fish prefer:
Agribusiness

Additional Information

Year Founded: 2009
Capital Under Management: $80,000,000
Current Activity Level : Actively seeking new investments

NANJING HI-TECH VENTURE CAPITAL CO., LTD.

268 Hanzhong Road
7th Floor
Nanjing, China 210029
Phone: 86-25-8657-9659
Fax: 86-25-8657-9660
E-mail: info@nj-vc.com
Website: www.nj-vc.com

Management and Staff

Huafei Li, President

Type of Firm

Private Equity Firm

Project Preferences

Type of Financing Preferred:
Expansion
Balanced
Later Stage
Acquisition

Geographical Preferences

International Preferences:
China
Asia

Industry Preferences

In Biotechnology prefer:
Biotechnology

In Medical/Health prefer:
Pharmaceuticals

In Industrial/Energy prefer:
Energy
Materials
Environmental Related

In Financial Services prefer:
Insurance
Real Estate

In Business Serv. prefer:
Services

In Utilities prefer:
Utilities

Additional Information

Year Founded: 2006
Capital Under Management: $55,600,000
Current Activity Level : Actively seeking new investments

NANODIMENSION MANAGEMENT LIMITED

Centennial Towers, Suite 306B
2454 West Bay Road
Grand Cayman, Cayman Islands
Phone: 345-946-5556
E-mail: info@nanodimension.com
Website: www.nanodimension.com

Type of Firm

Private Equity Firm

Project Preferences

Type of Financing Preferred:
Early Stage

Geographical Preferences

International Preferences:
Switzerland

Industry Preferences

In Semiconductor/Electr prefer:
Electronics

In Industrial/Energy prefer:
Energy

Additional Information

Year Founded: 2003
Capital Under Management: $50,000,000
Current Activity Level : Actively seeking new investments

NANOSTART AG

Goethestrasse 26-28
Frankfurt, Germany 60313
Phone: 49-69-2193-9600
Fax: 49-69-219396150
E-mail: info@nanostart.de
Website: www.nanostart.de

Management and Staff

Marco Beckmann, Chief Executive Officer

Type of Firm

Private Equity Firm

Project Preferences

Type of Financing Preferred:
Early Stage
Expansion

Geographical Preferences

International Preferences:
Europe
Germany

Industry Preferences

In Biotechnology prefer:
Biotechnology

Additional Information

Year Founded: 2003
Current Activity Level : Actively seeking new investments

NARRA VENTURE CAPITAL

Northgate Cyberzone
Suite 105, Plaza
Muntinlupa, Philippines 1781
Phone: 632-757-3521
Fax: 632-757-3520
E-mail: info@narravc.com
Website: www.narravc.com

Management and Staff

Arthur Tan, Partner
Delfin Lazaro, Partner
Diosdado Banatao, Partner
Jaime Augusto Zobel de Ayala, Partner
Jose Sandejas, Partner
Paco Sandejas, Managing Partner

Type of Firm

Private Equity Firm

Project Preferences

Type of Financing Preferred:
Balanced

Geographical Preferences

International Preferences:
Philippines
Asia

Industry Preferences

In Communications prefer:
Communications and Media

In Computer Software prefer:
Software

In Semiconductor/Electr prefer:
Electronics
Semiconductor

Additional Information
Year Founded: 2002
Current Activity Level : Actively seeking new investments

NASSAU CAPITAL LLC
22 Chambers Street
Princeton, NJ USA 08542
Phone: 609-924-3555
Fax: 609-924-8887
Website: www.nassau.com

Management and Staff
Curtis Glovier, Managing Director
Jonathan Sweemer, Managing Director
Lisa McGovern, Chief Financial Officer
William Stewart, Managing Director

Type of Firm
Private Equity Firm

Project Preferences

Role in Financing:
Prefer role as deal originator but will also invest in deals created by others

Type of Financing Preferred:
Fund of Funds
Second Stage Financing
Leveraged Buyout
Special Situation

Size of Investments Considered:
Min Size of Investment Considered (000s): $25,000
Max Size of Investment Considered: No Limit

Geographical Preferences

United States Preferences:
All U.S.

Industry Focus
(% based on actual investment)

Medical/Health	55.3%
Communications and Media	17.2%
Computer Software and Services	8.5%
Internet Specific	8.4%
Other Products	6.2%
Semiconductors/Other Elect.	1.9%
Computer Hardware	1.7%
Industrial/Energy	0.9%

Additional Information
Name of Most Recent Fund: Nassau Capital L.P.
Most Recent Fund Was Raised: 01/01/1996
Year Founded: 1995
Capital Under Management: $1,500,000,000
Current Activity Level : Actively seeking new investments

Method of Compensation: Return on investment is of primary concern, do not charge fees

NATCITY INVESTMENTS, INC.
1900 East 9th Street
20th Floor
Cleveland, OH USA 44114
Phone: 216-222-2000
E-mail: resourcecenter@nationalcity.com
Website: www.pia.national-city.com

Management and Staff
Herbert Martens, President
Sean Dorsey, Senior Managing Director
William Haggerty, Senior Managing Director

Type of Firm
Bank Affiliated

Project Preferences

Role in Financing:
Unknown

Type of Financing Preferred:
Management Buyouts
Acquisition
Recapitalizations

Geographical Preferences

United States Preferences:
Midwest

International Preferences:
All International

Additional Information
Year Founded: 1937
Current Activity Level : Actively seeking new investments

NATIONAL BANK FINANCIAL, INC.
130 King Street West
Suite 3200
Toronto, Canada M5H 3T9
Phone: 416-869-3707
Fax: 416-869-3700
Website: www.info.nbfinancial.com

Type of Firm
Investment Management Firm

Additional Information
Year Founded: 2009
Current Activity Level : Actively seeking new investments

NATIONAL CITY EQUITY PARTNERS, INC.
1965 East Sixth Street
Suite 1010
Cleveland, OH USA 44114
Phone: 216-222-2491
Fax: 216-222-9965
Website: www.ncepi.com

Management and Staff
Carl Baldassarre, General Partner
David Sands, Partner
David McCoy, Principal
Edward Pentecost, Managing General Partner
Eric Morgan, Principal
Jay Freund, General Partner
Steve Pattison, Partner

Type of Firm
Bank Affiliated

Association Membership
Natl Assoc of Small Bus. Inv. Co (NASBIC)

Project Preferences

Role in Financing:
Will function either as deal originator or investor in deals created by others

Type of Financing Preferred:
Leveraged Buyout
Expansion
Mezzanine
Generalist PE
Turnaround
Later Stage
Management Buyouts
Acquisition
Special Situation
Recapitalizations

Size of Investments Considered:
Min Size of Investment Considered (000s): $5,000
Max Size of Investment Considered (000s): $20,000

Geographical Preferences

United States Preferences:
All U.S.

Industry Focus
(% based on actual investment)

Industrial/Energy	24.0%
Medical/Health	20.2%
Other Products	17.7%
Semiconductors/Other Elect.	13.0%
Consumer Related	10.1%
Internet Specific	7.9%
Biotechnology	3.5%
Communications and Media	3.4%
Computer Hardware	0.1%

Additional Information
Name of Most Recent Fund: National City Equity Partners

Most Recent Fund Was Raised: 12/01/1981
Year Founded: 1979
Capital Under Management: $950,000,000
Current Activity Level : Actively seeking new investments
Method of Compensation: Return on invest. most important, but chg. closing fees, service fees, etc.

NATIONAL ENDOWMENT FOR SCIENCE, TECHNOLOGY & THE ARTS NESTA

110 Upper Thames Street
Fishmongers' Chambers
London, United Kingdom EC4R 3TW
Phone: 44-20-7645-9500
Fax: 44-20-7645-9501
E-mail: nesta@nesta.org.uk
Website: www.nesta.org.uk

Management and Staff

Jeremy Newton, Chief Executive Officer

Type of Firm

Government Affiliated Program

Project Preferences

Role in Financing:

Prefer role as deal originator

Type of Financing Preferred:

Seed
Startup

Geographical Preferences

International Preferences:

United Kingdom
Europe

Industry Preferences

In Communications prefer:

Entertainment

In Biotechnology prefer:

Human Biotechnology

In Medical/Health prefer:

Medical/Health
Diagnostic Test Products
Drug/Equipmt Delivery
Medical Products

In Industrial/Energy prefer:

Environmental Related

Additional Information

Year Founded: 1998
Capital Under Management: $99,000,000
Current Activity Level : Actively seeking new investments

NATIONAL HEALTHCARE SERVICES

320 Goldenshore Avenue
Suite 120
Long Beach, CA USA 90802
Phone: 562-432-0047
Fax: 562-432-0091
Website: www.nationalhealthcareservices.com

Management and Staff

Brant Heise, Vice President
Gary Vatcher, President

Type of Firm

Private Equity Firm

Association Membership

National Venture Capital Association - USA (NVCA)

Project Preferences

Type of Financing Preferred:

Expansion
Later Stage

Industry Preferences

In Biotechnology prefer:

Biotechnology

In Medical/Health prefer:

Medical/Health

Additional Information

Year Founded: 2005
Capital Under Management: $25,000,000
Current Activity Level : Actively seeking new investments

NATIONAL INVESTMENT BANK LTD.

37, Kwame Nkrumah Avenue
PO Box 3726
Accra, Ghana
Phone: 233-21661-70116
Fax: 233-21-661-730
E-mail: infor@nib-ghana.com
Website: www.nib-ghana.com

Management and Staff

Daniel Charles Gyimah, Managing Director

Type of Firm

Private Equity Firm

Association Membership

African Venture Capital Association (AVCA)

Project Preferences

Type of Financing Preferred:

Balanced

Geographical Preferences

International Preferences:

Ghana

Additional Information

Year Founded: 2004
Current Activity Level : Actively seeking new investments

NATIONAL INVESTOR, THE

Zayed the 1st Street
Khalidiya
Abu Dhabi, Utd. Arab Em.
Phone: 971-2-619-2300
Fax: 971-2-619-2400
E-mail: info@tni.ae
Website: www.tni.ae

Other Offices

DIFC Offices, Gate Precinct Building 4,
P.O. Box 506568
Dubai, Utd. Arab Em.
Phone: 971-4-370-0233
Fax: 971-4-370-0098

ADNIC Building, 6th floor, Khalifa Str.
P.O.Box 47435
Abu Dhabi, Utd. Arab Em.
Phone: 971-2-627-7878
Fax: 971-2-626-5858

Type of Firm

Private Equity Firm

Project Preferences

Type of Financing Preferred:

Early Stage
Mezzanine
Balanced
Later Stage

Geographical Preferences

International Preferences:

Utd. Arab Em.
Middle East
All International

Additional Information

Year Founded: 1994
Current Activity Level : Actively seeking new investments

NATIONAL LIFE

One National Life Drive
Montpelier, VT USA 05604
Phone: 802-229-3333
Website: www.nationallife.com

Type of Firm

Endowment, Foundation or Pension Fund

Additional Information

Year Founded: 2009
Current Activity Level : Actively seeking new investments

NATIONAL TECHNOLOGY ENTERPRISES COMPANY (AKA: NTEC)

Kuwait Chamber of Commerce Bdg
Floor 8
Safat, Kuwait 13023
Phone: 965-223-0300
Fax: 965-240-5926
Website: www.ntec.com.kw

Management and Staff

Adnan Al-Sultan, Managing Director

Type of Firm

Government Affiliated Program

Project Preferences

Role in Financing:
Will function either as deal originator or investor in deals created by others

Type of Financing Preferred:
Fund of Funds
Early Stage
Expansion
Joint Ventures

Industry Preferences

In Communications prefer:
Telecommunications

In Biotechnology prefer:
Biotechnology

In Industrial/Energy prefer:
Energy
Alternative Energy
Environmental Related

Additional Information

Year Founded: 2002
Capital Under Management: $330,900,000
Current Activity Level : Actively seeking new investments

NATIONWIDE MUTUAL CAPITAL LLC

One Nationwide Plaza
Mail Code 1-24-15
Columbus, OH USA 43215-2220
Phone: 614-249-6220
Fax: 614-249-5915
Website: www.nationwide.com

Management and Staff

Ryan Helon, Managing Director

Type of Firm

Insurance Firm Affiliate

Project Preferences

Role in Financing:
Will function either as deal originator or investor in deals created by others

Type of Financing Preferred:
Second Stage Financing
Early Stage
Expansion
Balanced
Later Stage
Acquisition
Recapitalizations

Size of Investments Considered:

Min Size of Investment Considered (000s): $1,000
Max Size of Investment Considered (000s): $4,000

Geographical Preferences

United States Preferences:
All U.S.

International Preferences:
United Kingdom
Europe

Industry Preferences

In Computer Software prefer:
Data Processing
Software
Systems Software
Applications Software

In Internet Specific prefer:
Ecommerce
Web Aggregration/Portals

In Medical/Health prefer:
Health Services

In Financial Services prefer:
Financial Services
Insurance

Additional Information

Year Founded: 2002
Capital Under Management: $40,000,000
Current Activity Level : Actively seeking new investments
Method of Compensation: Return on investment is of primary concern, do not charge fees

NATIVE VENTURE CAPITAL CO., LTD.

21 Artist View Pointe, Box 7
Site 25, RR12
Calgary, Canada T3E 6W3
Phone: 903-208-5380

Management and Staff

MiltPahl

Type of Firm

Other

Project Preferences

Role in Financing:
Prefer role as deal originator but will also invest in deals created by others

Type of Financing Preferred:
Second Stage Financing
Leveraged Buyout
Start-up Financing
Seed
First Stage Financing

Size of Investments Considered:

Min Size of Investment Considered (000s): $300
Max Size of Investment Considered: No Limit

Geographical Preferences

Canadian Preferences:
Western Canada

Additional Information

Year Founded: 1981
Capital Under Management: $10,000,000
Current Activity Level : Actively seeking new investments
Method of Compensation: Return on invest. most important, but chg. closing fees, service fees, etc.

NATIXIS PRIVATE EQUITY

5-7 rue de Monttessuy
Paris, France 75340
Phone: 33-1-5819-2000
Fax: 33-1-5819-2010
E-mail: contact@natexis-pe.com
Website: www.natexis-pe.com

Management and Staff

Caroline Joubin, Chief Operating Officer
Francois Baubeau, Chief Operating Officer
Jean Duhau de Berenx, Chief Executive Officer
Jean-Louis Delvaux, Principal

Type of Firm

Bank Affiliated

Association Membership

French Venture Capital Association (AFIC)
European Private Equity and Venture Capital Assoc.

Project Preferences

Type of Financing Preferred:
Fund of Funds
Leveraged Buyout
Early Stage
Expansion
Mezzanine
Generalist PE
Public Companies
Management Buyouts
Recapitalizations

Size of Investments Considered:
Min Size of Investment Considered (000s): $1,500
Max Size of Investment Considered (000s): $21,200

Geographical Preferences

United States Preferences:
Southern California

International Preferences:
Europe
Germany
Asia
France

Industry Focus
(% based on actual investment)

Internet Specific	44.8%
Communications and Media	35.3%
Other Products	5.4%
Semiconductors/Other Elect.	4.1%
Medical/Health	3.9%
Computer Software and Services	3.5%
Biotechnology	2.6%
Consumer Related	0.4%

Additional Information
Year Founded: 1997
Capital Under Management: $930,000,000
Current Activity Level : Actively seeking new investments

NATIXIS-CAPE SGR SPA (AKA:CIMINO & ASSOCIATI PRIVATE EQUITY)
9, Corso Matteotti
Milan, Italy 20121
Phone: 39-02-7639-0931
Fax: 39-02-7733-1617
E-mail: info@cape.it
Website: www.cape.it

Management and Staff
Guido De Vecchi, Managing Partner

Type of Firm
Private Equity Firm

Association Membership
Italian Venture Capital Association (AIFI)

Project Preferences

Type of Financing Preferred:
Leveraged Buyout
Expansion
Other
Management Buyouts
Acquisition

Geographical Preferences

International Preferences:
Italy
Europe
Western Europe

Industry Preferences

In Medical/Health prefer:
Medical/Health

In Consumer Related prefer:
Food/Beverage

In Industrial/Energy prefer:
Energy
Alternative Energy
Energy Conservation Relat

In Transportation prefer:
Transportation

In Agr/Forestr/Fish prefer:
Agriculture related

Additional Information
Year Founded: 2004
Capital Under Management: $464,100,000
Current Activity Level : Actively seeking new investments

NATURAL GAS PARTNERS (NGP)
125 E. John Carpenter Freeway
Suite 600
Irving, TX USA 75062
Phone: 972-432-1440
Fax: 972-432-1441
E-mail: inquiries@ngptrs.com
Website: www.naturalgaspartners.com

Other Offices
100 North Guadalupe Street
Suite 205
Santa Fe, NM USA 87501
Phone: 505-983-8400
Fax: 505-983-8120

5 Houston Center
1401 McKinney Suite 1025
Houston, TX USA 77010
Phone: 713-579-5700
Fax: 713579-5740

1266 East Main Street
Sixth Floor
Stamford, CT USA 06902
Phone: 203-504-5072
Fax: 203-504-5073

Management and Staff
Brad Barton, Principal
Christopher Sorrells, Managing Director
Christopher Ray, Managing Director
Colin Raymond, Principal
David Hayes, Principal
David Albin, Managing Partner
Eric Pitcher, Venture Partner
John Weinzierl, Managing Director
John Foster, Managing Director
John (Jack) Holmes, Venture Partner
Kenneth Hersh, Managing Partner
Mark Doering, Venture Partner
Ray Davis, Venture Partner
Raymond Edgar, Principal
Richard Covington, Managing Director
Scott Gieselman, Managing Director
Thomas Verhagen, Principal
Tony Weber, Managing Director
William Quinn, Managing Partner

Type of Firm
Private Equity Firm

Project Preferences

Role in Financing:
Prefer role as deal originator

Type of Financing Preferred:
Second Stage Financing
Leveraged Buyout
Start-up Financing
Other
First Stage Financing
Special Situation

Size of Investments Considered:
Min Size of Investment Considered (000s): $5,000
Max Size of Investment Considered (000s): $60,000

Geographical Preferences

United States Preferences:
All U.S.

Canadian Preferences:
All Canada
Central Canada
Western Canada

International Preferences:
Mexico
Middle East
Australia
South Africa

Industry Focus
(% based on actual investment)

Industrial/Energy	91.3%
Other Products	7.2%
Computer Software and Services	0.9%
Internet Specific	0.6%

Additional Information
Year Founded: 1988
Capital Under Management: $3,000,000,000
Current Activity Level : Actively seeking new investments
Method of Compensation: Return on invest. most important, but chg. closing fees, service fees, etc.

NAUTA CAPITAL
Avenida Diagonal, 593
Planta 8
Barcelona, Spain 08014
Phone: 34-93-503-5900
Fax: 34-93-503-5901
E-mail: info@nautacapital.com

Website: www.nautacapital.com

Other Offices

1050 Winter Street
Suite 1000
North Waltham, MA USA 02451
Phone: 781-768-6137
Fax: 781-530-3605

Type of Firm

Private Equity Firm

Project Preferences

Type of Financing Preferred:

Expansion
Generalist PE
Early Stage

Size of Investments Considered:

Min Size of Investment Considered (000s): $682
Max Size of Investment Considered (000s): $6,820

Geographical Preferences

United States Preferences:

All U.S.

International Preferences:

Western Europe
All International

Industry Preferences

In Communications prefer:

Communications and Media
Telecommunications
Media and Entertainment

In Computer Software prefer:

Software

In Internet Specific prefer:

Internet

Additional Information

Year Founded: 2004
Capital Under Management: $156,500,000
Current Activity Level : Actively seeking new investments

NAUTIC PARTNERS LLC

50 Kennedy Plaza
12th Floor
Providence, RI USA 02903
Phone: 401-278-6770
Fax: 401-278-6387
E-mail: nautic@nautic.com
Website: www.nautic.com

Management and Staff

Bernie Buonanno, Managing Director
Bradley Wightman, Managing Director
Chris Crosby, Managing Director
Cynthia Balasco, Chief Financial Officer
Douglas Hill, Managing Director
Elizabeth De Saint-Aignan, Vice President
Fraser Preston, Principal
Habib Gorgi, Managing Director
James LaRowe, Principal
Jim Beakey, Vice President
Michael Joe, Managing Director
Rick Crosier, Managing Director
Robert Van Degna, Managing Director
Scott Hilinski, Managing Director

Type of Firm

Private Equity Firm

Project Preferences

Role in Financing:

Prefer role as deal originator but will also invest in deals created by others

Type of Financing Preferred:

Leveraged Buyout
Expansion
Management Buyouts
Acquisition
Industry Rollups
Recapitalizations

Size of Investments Considered:

Min Size of Investment Considered (000s): $25,000
Max Size of Investment Considered (000s): $100,000

Geographical Preferences

Canadian Preferences:

All Canada

Industry Focus

(% based on actual investment)

Communications and Media	31.5%
Other Products	20.9%
Internet Specific	13.5%
Consumer Related	10.8%
Medical/Health	8.1%
Computer Software and Services	6.5%
Industrial/Energy	3.9%
Semiconductors/Other Elect.	3.8%
Computer Hardware	1.0%

Additional Information

Year Founded: 1986
Capital Under Management: $2,300,000,000
Current Activity Level : Actively seeking new investments
Method of Compensation: Return on invest. most important, but chg. closing fees, service fees, etc.

NAVIGATION CAPITAL PARTNERS

3060 Peachtree Road
Suite 780
Atlanta, GA USA 30305
Phone: 404-264-9180
Fax: 404-264-9305
E-mail: info@navigationcapital.com
Website: www.navigationcapital.com

Management and Staff

David Panton, Founding Partner
Eerik Giles, Founding Partner
Lawrence Mock, Managing Partner
Mark Downs, Founding Partner
Zuri Briscoe, Vice President

Type of Firm

Private Equity Firm

Project Preferences

Type of Financing Preferred:

Leveraged Buyout
Management Buyouts
Acquisition

Size of Investments Considered:

Min Size of Investment Considered (000s): $10,000
Max Size of Investment Considered (000s): $30,000

Geographical Preferences

United States Preferences:

Mid Atlantic
Midwest
Southeast
Southwest

Industry Preferences

In Medical/Health prefer:

Health Services

In Transportation prefer:

Transportation

In Financial Services prefer:

Financial Services

In Business Serv. prefer:

Services
Distribution

Additional Information

Year Founded: 2006
Capital Under Management: $126,300,000
Current Activity Level : Actively seeking new investments

NAVIGATION CAPITAL PARTNERS (AKA: NCP)

One Buckhead Plaza
3060 Peachtree Road, Suite 780
Atlanta, GA USA 30305
Phone: 404-264-9180
Fax: 404-264-9305
E-mail: info@navigationcapital.com
Website: www.navigationcapital.com

Other Offices

1114 Avenue of the Americas
31st Floor
New York, NY USA 10036-7701
Phone: 212-389-2700
Fax: 212-389-2755

400 South Hope Street
Fifth Floor
Los Angeles, CA USA 90071-2806
Phone: 213-553-9685
Fax: 213-553-9690

Management and Staff

Allen Pu, Vice President
Chuck Billerbeck, Senior Managing Director
David Panton, Vice President
Eerik Giles, Vice President
Jeffrey Anderson, Managing Director
John Richardson, Senior Managing Director
John Adams, Partner
Joseph Woods, Vice President
Mark Patton, Vice President
Max Chee, Vice President
Nisha Atre, Vice President
Ron Coombs, Chief Financial Officer
Warren Haber, Partner

Type of Firm

SBIC

Association Membership

Mid-Atlantic Venture Association
Natl Assoc of Small Bus. Inv. Co (NASBIC)

Project Preferences

Role in Financing:

Will function either as deal originator or investor in deals created by others

Type of Financing Preferred:

Second Stage Financing
Leveraged Buyout
Expansion
Mezzanine
Balanced
Start-up Financing
Turnaround
Later Stage
Management Buyouts
First Stage Financing
Strategic Alliances
Acquisition
Joint Ventures
Industry Rollups
Recapitalizations

Size of Investments Considered:

Min Size of Investment Considered (000s): $2,000
Max Size of Investment Considered (000s): $15,000

Geographical Preferences

United States Preferences:

All U.S.

Industry Focus

(% based on actual investment)

Other Products	36.4%
Internet Specific	27.6%
Computer Software and Services	13.5%
Communications and Media	6.8%
Computer Hardware	5.2%
Consumer Related	5.1%
Semiconductors/Other Elect.	2.9%
Industrial/Energy	2.0%
Medical/Health	0.6%

Additional Information

Year Founded: 1995
Capital Under Management: $1,400,000,000
Current Activity Level : Making few, if any, new investments
Method of Compensation: Return on invest. most important, but chg. closing fees, service fees, etc.

NAVIGATOR TECHNOLOGY VENTURES (A.K.A. NTV)

Four Cambridge Center
Second Floor
Cambridge, MA USA 02142
Phone: 617-494-0111
Fax: 617-225-2080
E-mail: info@ntven.com
Website: www.ntven.com

Management and Staff

Alain Hanover, CEO & Managing Director

Type of Firm

Incubator/Development Program

Project Preferences

Role in Financing:

Prefer role as deal originator

Type of Financing Preferred:

Early Stage

Size of Investments Considered:

Min Size of Investment Considered (000s): $200
Max Size of Investment Considered (000s): $2,000

Geographical Preferences

United States Preferences:

Northeast

Industry Preferences

In Communications prefer:

Wireless Communications

In Semiconductor/Electr prefer:

Electronics

In Biotechnology prefer:

Biotechnology

Additional Information

Name of Most Recent Fund: Navigator Technology Ventures
Most Recent Fund Was Raised: 08/01/2000
Year Founded: 2000
Capital Under Management: $15,000,000
Current Activity Level : Actively seeking new investments

NAVIS INVESTMENT PARTNERS (ASIA), LTD.

9 Jalan Stesen Sentral 5
Level 17, Quill 7 Tower
Kuala Lumpur, Malaysia 50470
Phone: 603-2302-3888
Fax: 603-2302-3883
Website: www.naviscapital.com

Other Offices

20, Collyer Quay
#10-06, Tung Center
Singapore
Phone: 65-6438-0711
Fax: 65-6438-0721

Level 2, Elegance
Mathura Road, Jasola
New Delhi, India 110025
Phone: 91-11-406-01528
Fax: 91-11-406-01235

12th Floor, Two Pacific Place
142 Sukhumvit Road, Klongtoey
Bangkok, Thailand 10110
Phone: 66-2-653-2155
Fax: 66-2-653-2158

Suite 2120, Two Pacific Place
88 Queensway
Central, Hong Kong
Phone: 852-2526-0238
Fax: 852-2526-0308

Level 8, 56 Pitt Street
Sydney, Australia 2000
Phone: 612-8024-7800
Fax: 612-8024-7878

Management and Staff

Nicholas Bloy, Managing Partner
Rodney Muse, Managing Partner

Type of Firm

Private Equity Firm

Association Membership

Australian Venture Capital Association (AVCAL)

Project Preferences

Type of Financing Preferred:

Leveraged Buyout
Expansion
Balanced
Public Companies
Turnaround
Management Buyouts
Recapitalizations

Size of Investments Considered:

Min Size of Investment Considered (000s): $10,000
Max Size of Investment Considered (000s): $50,000

Geographical Preferences

International Preferences:
Indonesia
India
Hong Kong
Thailand
Philippines
Pacific
Australia
Singapore
Asia
Malaysia

Industry Focus

(% based on actual investment)	
Computer Software and Services	42.9%
Other Products	29.3%
Consumer Related	27.8%

Additional Information

Name of Most Recent Fund: Navis Asia Fund V-E, L.P.
Most Recent Fund Was Raised: 03/30/2007
Year Founded: 1998
Capital Under Management: $500,000,000
Current Activity Level : Actively seeking new investments

NAVITAS CAPITAL

2920 Domingo Avenue
Suite 207
Berkeley, CA USA 94705
Phone: 510-388-5770
Website: www.navitascap.com

Management and Staff

Jim Pettit, Managing Partner
Travis Putnam, Managing Partner

Type of Firm

Private Equity Firm

Project Preferences

Type of Financing Preferred:
Early Stage

Industry Preferences

In Industrial/Energy prefer:
Environmental Related

In Other prefer:
Environment Responsible

Additional Information

Name of Most Recent Fund: Navitas Capital I, L.P.
Most Recent Fund Was Raised: 04/17/2009
Year Founded: 2008
Capital Under Management: $1,500,000
Current Activity Level : Actively seeking new investments

NAXICAP PARTNERS (FKA: SPEF DEVELOPPEMENT)

5-7 rue de Monttessuy
Paris, France 75340
Phone: 33-1-5819-2220
Fax: 33-1-5819-2230
E-mail: contact@spef-venture.fr
Website: www.naxicap.fr

Other Offices

1, rue de la Republique
Lyon, France 69001
Phone: 33-4-7210-8799
Fax: 33-7210-8770

2, Boulevard de Strasbourg
Toulouse, France 31000
Phone: 33-5-3441-3141
Fax: 33-5-6162-6863

3 rue Francois de Curel
BP 40124
Metz, France 57021
Phone: 33-3-8737-7065
Fax: 33-3-8763-1430

14 boulevard Winston Churchill
Nantes, France 44040
Phone: 33-2-4046-0808
Fax: 33-2-5180-9960

Management and Staff

Amedee Nicolas, President
Daniel Foin, Managing Director
David Giallorenzo, Partner
Marc Wouthoz, Managing Director

Type of Firm

Private Equity Firm

Association Membership

French Venture Capital Association (AFIC)
European Private Equity and Venture Capital Assoc.

Project Preferences

Type of Financing Preferred:
Leveraged Buyout
Early Stage
Expansion
Research and Development
Balanced
Later Stage
Startup

Size of Investments Considered:
Min Size of Investment Considered (000s): $200
Max Size of Investment Considered (000s): $3,800

Geographical Preferences

International Preferences:
Europe
France

Industry Preferences

In Communications prefer:
Communications and Media

In Consumer Related prefer:
Consumer

In Industrial/Energy prefer:
Industrial Products
Materials
Factory Automation

In Other prefer:
Environment Responsible

Additional Information

Year Founded: 1982
Capital Under Management: $261,600,000
Current Activity Level : Actively seeking new investments

NAXOS CAPITAL PARTNERS

No. 44
Chelsea Park Gardens
London, United Kingdom SW3 6AB
E-mail: info@naxoscapital.com
Website: www.naxoscapital.com

Management and Staff

Robert Lezec, Founder

Type of Firm

Private Equity Firm

Project Preferences

Type of Financing Preferred:
Leveraged Buyout
Acquisition

Industry Preferences

In Communications prefer:
Communications and Media

In Business Serv. prefer:
Services
Media

In Manufact. prefer:
Manufacturing

Additional Information

Year Founded: 2009
Current Activity Level : Actively seeking new investments

NAZCA CAPITAL SGECR SA

Fortuny, 37
esc.izda, 3 D
Madrid, Spain 28010
Phone: 39-91-700-0501

Fax: 39-91-700-0514
E-mail: info@nazca.es
Website: www.nazca.es

Management and Staff

Alvaro Mariategui, Managing Partner
Luis Segui Casas, Principal

Type of Firm

Bank Affiliated

Project Preferences

Type of Financing Preferred:
Leveraged Buyout
Expansion
Acquisition

Geographical Preferences

International Preferences:
Europe
Spain

Additional Information

Year Founded: 2001
Capital Under Management: $112,200,000
Current Activity Level : Actively seeking new investments

NB ALTERNATIVES - FUND OF FUNDS

325 North St. Paul Street
Suite 4900
Dallas, TX USA 75219
Phone: 214-647-9500
Fax: 214-647-9501
Website: www.nbprivateequitypartners.com

Other Offices

Two International Finance Centre
26th Floor, 8 Finance Street
Central, Hong Kong

25 Bank Street
London, United Kingdom E14 5LE

605 Third Avenue
New York, NY USA 10158

Management and Staff

Anthony Tutrone, Managing Director
Brien Smith, Managing Director
David Stoneberg, Managing Director
John Buser, Managing Director
Jonathan Shofet, Managing Director
Joseph Malick, Managing Director
Peter Von Lehe, Managing Director

Type of Firm

Investment Management Firm

Association Membership

National Venture Capital Association - USA (NVCA)

Project Preferences

Type of Financing Preferred:
Fund of Funds
Distressed Debt
Fund of Funds of Second

Geographical Preferences

United States Preferences:
All U.S.

International Preferences:
Europe
Pacific
Asia
All International

Additional Information

Name of Most Recent Fund: Lehman Brothers Crossroads XVII, L.P.
Most Recent Fund Was Raised: 07/28/2005
Year Founded: 2002
Capital Under Management: $5,800,000,000
Current Activity Level : Actively seeking new investments

NBC CAPITAL PTY., LTD.

106 Edward Street
Level 2, Sony Centre
Brisbane, Australia 4000
Phone: 617-3233-9200
Fax: 617-3233-9223
E-mail: info@nbccapital.com.au
Website: www.nbccapital.com.au

Management and Staff

Bernard Stapleton, General Partner
Bruce Scott, Managing Director
Peter Lawson, General Partner
Shane Lawrence, General Partner

Type of Firm

Private Equity Firm

Association Membership

Australian Venture Capital Association (AVCAL)

Project Preferences

Type of Financing Preferred:
Leveraged Buyout
Generalist PE
Early Stage
Expansion
Later Stage
Management Buyouts

Geographical Preferences

International Preferences:
Australia

Industry Preferences

In Consumer Related prefer:
Retail
Franchises(NEC)
Food/Beverage
Consumer Services

In Transportation prefer:
Transportation

In Financial Services prefer:
Financial Services

In Business Serv. prefer:
Services

In Manufact. prefer:
Manufacturing

Additional Information

Year Founded: 1999
Capital Under Management: $11,800,000
Current Activity Level : Actively seeking new investments

NBD SANA CAPITAL

P.O. Box 777
Dubai, Utd. Arab Em.
Phone: 971-4-229-8155
Fax: 971-4-224-8157
Website: www.nbdsana.com

Management and Staff

Abrar Mir, Managing Partner
Chris Macklin, Managing Director
Kren Nielson, Managing Director
Masood Razaq, Managing Director
Yalman Khan, Managing Director

Type of Firm

Bank Affiliated

Project Preferences

Type of Financing Preferred:
Leveraged Buyout
Expansion
Generalist PE
Turnaround

Geographical Preferences

International Preferences:
Turkey
Middle East
Asia
Africa

Industry Preferences

In Communications prefer:
Communications and Media
Telecommunications
Media and Entertainment

In Medical/Health prefer:
Medical/Health
Health Services
Pharmaceuticals

In Consumer Related prefer:
Consumer

Retail
Consumer Services

In Industrial/Energy prefer:

Energy

Additional Information

Year Founded: 2007
Capital Under Management: $670,000,000
Current Activity Level : Actively seeking new investments

NBGI PRIVATE EQUITY

Old Change House
128 Queen Victoria Street
London, United Kingdom EC4V 4BJ
Phone: 44-207-661-5678
Fax: 44-207-661-5667
E-mail: info@nbgipe.co.uk
Website: www.nbgiprivateequity.co.uk

Other Offices

44 Avenue Des Champs-Elysees
Paris, France 75008
Phone: 33-1-5856-1908
Fax: 33-1-4562-4166

10th Floor Lowry House
17 Marble Street
Manchester, United Kingdom M2 3AW
Phone: 44-161-214-5290
Fax: 44-161-214-5299

Management and Staff

Alex Borg, Chief Financial Officer
Pavlos Stellakis, Chairman & CEO

Type of Firm

Bank Affiliated

Association Membership

French Venture Capital Association (AFIC)

Project Preferences

Type of Financing Preferred:

Leveraged Buyout
Expansion
Generalist PE
Turnaround
Public Companies
Management Buyouts
Strategic Alliances
Recapitalizations

Size of Investments Considered:

Min Size of Investment Considered (000s): $9,659
Max Size of Investment Considered (000s): $96,585

Geographical Preferences

International Preferences:

Greece
United Kingdom
Europe
Turkey
Western Europe
Eastern Europe
Romania
All International

Industry Preferences

In Medical/Health prefer:

Medical/Health

In Industrial/Energy prefer:

Energy
Environmental Related

In Transportation prefer:

Transportation

In Manufact. prefer:

Manufacturing

Additional Information

Name of Most Recent Fund: NBGI SEE Energy Fund, L.P.
Most Recent Fund Was Raised: 11/20/2008
Year Founded: 2000
Capital Under Management: $128,000,000
Current Activity Level : Actively seeking new investments

NBK CAPITAL, LTD.

17th Floor, Dar Al-Awadi Bldg.
Ahmad Al-Jaber Street
Sharq, Kuwait 13050
Phone: 965-22-246-900
Fax: 965-22-246-904
E-mail: info.request@nbkcapital.com
Website: www.nbkcapital.com

Other Offices

Precinct Building 3, Office 404
Dubai International Financial Centre
Sheikh Zayed Road, Utd. Arab Em.
Phone: 971-4-365-2800
Fax: 971-4-365-2805

SUN Plaza, 30th Floor
Dereboyu Sk. No: 24
Maslak, Turkey 34398
Phone: 90-212-276-5400
Fax: 90-212-276-541

Management and Staff

Ahmet Tataroglu, Managing Director
Amjad Ahmad, Senior Managing Director
Nabil Maroof, Managing Director
Omar Bassal, Vice President
Suhair Khalil, Vice President

Type of Firm

Bank Affiliated

Project Preferences

Type of Financing Preferred:

Expansion
Mezzanine
Generalist PE
Balanced
Turnaround
Acquisition
Recapitalizations

Geographical Preferences

International Preferences:

Bahrain
Oman
Turkey
Egypt
Utd. Arab Em.
Middle East
Kuwait
Africa

Industry Preferences

In Medical/Health prefer:

Health Services

In Consumer Related prefer:

Education Related

In Financial Services prefer:

Investment Groups

In Manufact. prefer:

Manufacturing

Additional Information

Year Founded: 2006
Capital Under Management: $475,000,000
Current Activity Level : Actively seeking new investments

NBT CAPITAL CORPORATION

52 South Broad Street
Norwich, NY USA 13815
Phone: 607-337-6810
Fax: 607-336-6545

Management and Staff

Duke Crandall, Managing Director

Type of Firm

Private Equity Firm

Association Membership

Natl Assoc of Small Bus. Inv. Co (NASBIC)

Project Preferences

Type of Financing Preferred:

Second Stage Financing
Mezzanine
Management Buyouts

Geographical Preferences

United States Preferences:

Pennsylvania
New York

Industry Preferences

In Computer Hardware prefer:
Computers

In Computer Software prefer:
Computer Services

In Biotechnology prefer:
Biotechnology

In Manufact. prefer:
Manufacturing

Additional Information

Year Founded: 1998
Capital Under Management: $5,000,000
Current Activity Level : Actively seeking new investments

NCB PARTICIPATIES

Spoorlaan 350
Tilburg, Netherlands 5038 CC
Phone: 31-13-583-6583
Fax: 31-13-543-5579
Website: www.zlto.nl

Type of Firm

Private Equity Firm

Association Membership

European Private Equity and Venture Capital Assoc.
Dutch Venture Capital Associaton (NVP)

Project Preferences

Type of Financing Preferred:
Generalist PE
Balanced

Geographical Preferences

United States Preferences:
All U.S.

International Preferences:
Netherlands
Scandanavia/Nordic Region
Asia

Additional Information

Year Founded: 2006
Capital Under Management: $12,100,000
Current Activity Level : Actively seeking new investments

NCB VENTURES, LTD.

3 George's Dock
IFSC
Dublin, Ireland 1
Phone: 353-1-611-5611
Fax: 353-1-611-5986
E-mail: info@ncb.ie
Website: www.ncb-ventures.com

Management and Staff

Conor O'Kelly, Chief Executive Officer

Type of Firm

Bank Affiliated

Association Membership

Irish Venture Capital Association

Project Preferences

Type of Financing Preferred:
Early Stage
Expansion
Startup

Size of Investments Considered:
Min Size of Investment Considered (000s): $151
Max Size of Investment Considered (000s): $1,515

Geographical Preferences

International Preferences:
Ireland
Europe

Industry Preferences

In Communications prefer:
Telecommunications
Media and Entertainment

In Computer Software prefer:
Computer Services
Software

In Semiconductor/Electr prefer:
Electronics
Semiconductor

In Biotechnology prefer:
Biotechnology

In Medical/Health prefer:
Medical Products
Health Services

In Industrial/Energy prefer:
Factory Automation
Environmental Related

Additional Information

Year Founded: 1981
Capital Under Management: $42,500,000
Current Activity Level : Actively seeking new investments

NCH CAPITAL, INC.

712 Fifth Avenue
46th Floor
New York, NY USA 10019
Phone: 212-641-3200
Fax: 212-641-3201
Website: www.nchcapital.com

Other Offices

Wilmington-Sucursala Bucuresti
Bd. Pierre de Coubertin, nr. 3-5
Bucharest, Romania 021902

27-T Degtyarevskaya Street
2nd Floor
Kyiv, Ukraine 04119

67-B Hose de San Martin Street
Sofia, Bulgaria 1111

Krzhizhanovskogo Street, 14
Building 3, 5th Floor
Moscow, Russia 117218

SkyTower, Number 72
Rr. Deshmoret e 4 Shkurtit
Tirana, Albania

Armiansky Per. 1/8
BUilding 3
Moscow, Russia 101000

Baznicas 20/22
Riga, Latvia LV 1143

Skytower Office Center, 4F, Office E
63, Vlaicu Pircalab Street
Chisinau, Moldova MD-2012

138 Obvodny Canal Embankment, Bldg. 101
Treugolink Business Center, 3rd Floor
St. Petersburg, Russia 190020

Management and Staff

Andi Ballta, Managing Director
Andrew Radchenko, Vice President
Christopher Abbott, Managing Director
Edna Beaudette, Managing Director
George Rohr, Managing General Partner
Joseph Bond, Managing Director
Mikhail Vasiliev, Vice President
Moris Tabacinic, Managing General Partner
Nikola Zikatanov, Vice President
Patrick Ghidirim, Managing Director
Victor Popusoi, Vice President

Type of Firm

Private Equity Firm

Project Preferences

Type of Financing Preferred:
Balanced

Geographical Preferences

International Preferences:
Russia

Industry Preferences

In Biotechnology prefer:
Agricultural/Animal Bio.

In Financial Services prefer:
Real Estate

Additional Information

Year Founded: 1993
Current Activity Level : Actively seeking new investments

NCI GESTION

57, avenue de Bretagne
Rouen, France 76100
Phone: 33-232-18-6302
Fax: 33-232-18-6393
Website: www.ncigestion.com

Management and Staff

Anne-Cecile Guitton, Partner
Jean-Marc Buchet, President

Type of Firm

Private Equity Firm

Project Preferences

Type of Financing Preferred:
Leveraged Buyout
Early Stage
Expansion
Balanced
Startup

Geographical Preferences

International Preferences:
France

Additional Information

Year Founded: 2000
Capital Under Management: $7,800,000
Current Activity Level : Actively seeking new investments

NCIC CAPITAL FUND

900 Kettering Tower
Dayton, OH USA 45423
Phone: 937-222-4422
Fax: 937-222-1323
Website: www.ncicfund.org

Management and Staff

Frank Winslow, President

Type of Firm

Private Equity Firm

Additional Information

Year Founded: 1995
Current Activity Level : Actively seeking new investments

NCT VENTURES LLC

274 Marconi Boulevard
One Marconi Place, Suite 400
Columbus, OH USA 43215
Phone: 614-794-2732
Fax: 614-794-2738
E-mail: info@nctventures.com
Website: www.nctventures.com

Management and Staff

JT Kreager, Managing Director
Richard Langdale, Managing Director

Type of Firm

Private Equity Firm

Association Membership

National Venture Capital Association - USA (NVCA)

Project Preferences

Type of Financing Preferred:
Early Stage
Balanced
Seed

Geographical Preferences

United States Preferences:
Ohio

Additional Information

Name of Most Recent Fund: NCT Ventures Fund I, L.P.
Most Recent Fund Was Raised: 06/03/2008
Year Founded: 1986
Capital Under Management: $3,100,000
Current Activity Level : Actively seeking new investments

NDI CAPITAL (FKA: NEURO DISCOVERY, INC.)

315-1681 Chestnut Street
Vancouver, Canada V6J 4M6
Phone: 604-736-0634
Fax: 604-736-1616
E-mail: info@neurodiscovery.com
Website: www.ndicapital.com

Other Offices

3150-200 Bay Street
Royal Bank Plaza, South Tower
Toronto, Canada M5J 2J3
Phone: 416-815-1511
Fax: 416-362-7688

Management and Staff

Anthony Phillips, Partner
Gordon McCauley, Partner
James Miller, Managing Director
Matthew Carlyle, Partner

Type of Firm

Corporate PE/Venture

Project Preferences

Role in Financing:
Will function either as deal originator or investor in deals created by others

Type of Financing Preferred:
Early Stage

Size of Investments Considered:
Min Size of Investment Considered (000s): $500
Max Size of Investment Considered (000s): $5,000

Geographical Preferences

Canadian Preferences:
All Canada

Industry Preferences

In Biotechnology prefer:
Human Biotechnology

Additional Information

Year Founded: 2003
Capital Under Management: $23,900,000
Current Activity Level : Actively seeking new investments
Method of Compensation: Return on invest. most important, but chg. closing fees, service fees, etc.

NEA-INDOUS CAPITAL ADVISORS PVT. LTD.

Ground Fl, Unit-2, Navigator
Intl Tech Park Whitefield Road
Bangalore, India 560 066
Phone: 91-80-6616-9500
Fax: 91-80-6616-9506
E-mail: neaiuvinfo@neaiuv.com
Website: www.neaiuv.com

Other Offices

3945 Freedom Circle
Suite 1050
Santa Clara, CA USA 95054
Phone: 408-919-9900
Fax: 408-919-9912

Management and Staff

Kumar Shiralagi, Managing Director
Vani Kola, Managing Director

Type of Firm

Private Equity Firm

Project Preferences

Type of Financing Preferred:
Second Stage Financing
Early Stage
Expansion
First Stage Financing

Geographical Preferences

International Preferences:
India

Industry Preferences

In Internet Specific prefer:
Internet

In Medical/Health prefer:
Medical/Health

In Industrial/Energy prefer:
Energy

In Business Serv. prefer:
Media

Additional Information
Year Founded: 2006
Capital Under Management: $191,000,000
Current Activity Level : Actively seeking new investments

NEC CORPORATION OF AMERICA (FKA: NEC USA, INC.)
2890 Scott Boulevard
Santa Clara, CA USA 95050
Phone: 408-844-1442
Website: www.nec.com

Other Offices
7-1 Shiba 5-Chome
Minato-Ku
Tokyo, Japan 108-8001
Phone: 81-3-3798-9472

Type of Firm
Corporate PE/Venture

Additional Information
Year Founded: 1995
Current Activity Level : Actively seeking new investments

NEDBANK CORPORATE PRIVATE EQUITY
Block F, 6th Floor
135 Rivonia Road
Sandton, South Africa 2196
Phone: 27-11-294-0376
Fax: 27-11-295-0376
Website: www.nedcor.co.za

Type of Firm
Bank Affiliated

Association Membership
South African Venture Capital Association (SAVCA)

Project Preferences

Type of Financing Preferred:
Balanced

Geographical Preferences

International Preferences:
South Africa

Additional Information
Year Founded: 2004
Current Activity Level : Actively seeking new investments

NEEDHAM ASSET MANAGEMENT
445 Park Avenue
Third Floor
New York, NY USA 10022
Phone: 212-705-0311
Fax: 212-705-0455
Website: www.needhamfunds.com

Other Offices
One Post Office Square
Suite 3710
Boston, MA USA 02109
Phone: 617-457-0910
Fax: 617-457-5777

One Ferry Building
Suite 240
San Francisco, CA USA 94111
Phone: 415-262-4860

3000 Sand Hill Road
Building 2, Suite 190
Menlo Park, CA USA 94025
Phone: 650-854-9111
Fax: 650-854-9853

Management and Staff
Ellen McKay, Principal
George Needham, Chief Executive Officer
Glen Albanese, Chief Financial Officer
Jack Iacovone, Principal
John Prior, General Partner
Oliver Gratry, Vice President
Thomas Shanahan, General Partner

Type of Firm
Private Equity Firm

Association Membership
National Venture Capital Association - USA (NVCA)

Project Preferences

Role in Financing:
Will function either as deal originator or investor in deals created by others

Type of Financing Preferred:
Mezzanine
Later Stage
Special Situation

Size of Investments Considered:
Min Size of Investment Considered (000s): $5,000
Max Size of Investment Considered (000s): $10,000

Geographical Preferences

United States Preferences:
All U.S.

Industry Focus
(% based on actual investment)

Computer Software and Services	28.0%
Communications and Media	17.8%
Semiconductors/Other Elect.	16.6%
Computer Hardware	12.5%
Internet Specific	12.3%
Medical/Health	4.1%
Industrial/Energy	3.5%
Consumer Related	3.5%
Biotechnology	1.1%
Other Products	0.7%

Additional Information
Name of Most Recent Fund: Needham Capital International III, Ltd
Most Recent Fund Was Raised: 11/10/2000
Year Founded: 1992
Capital Under Management: $850,000,000
Current Activity Level : Actively seeking new investments
Method of Compensation: Return on invest. most important, but chg. closing fees, service fees, etc.

NEL FUND MANAGERS (FKA: NORTHERN ENTERPRISE, LTD.)
3 Earls Court, 5th Ave Bus Pk
Team Valley Trading Estate
Gateshead, United Kingdom NE11 0HF
Phone: 44-845-111-1850
Fax: 44-845-111-1853
E-mail: enquiries@nel.co.uk
Website: www.nel.co.uk

Other Offices
2 Queens Square
Middlesborough
Cleveland, United Kingdom TS1 2RQ
Phone: 44-1642-341-523
Fax: 44-1642-341-525

Management and Staff
Barrie Hensby, Chief Executive Officer

Type of Firm
Incubator/Development Program

Association Membership
British Venture Capital Association (BVCA)

Project Preferences

Type of Financing Preferred:
Leveraged Buyout
Early Stage
Expansion
Mezzanine
Generalist PE
Balanced
Seed
Management Buyouts
Startup

Geographical Preferences

International Preferences:
United Kingdom
Europe

Industry Preferences

In Computer Other prefer:
Computer Related

In Biotechnology prefer:
Biotechnology

In Business Serv. prefer:
Services

In Manufact. prefer:
Manufacturing

Additional Information

Name of Most Recent Fund: NEL Growth Fund
Most Recent Fund Was Raised: 09/06/2006
Year Founded: 1989
Capital Under Management: $23,700,000
Current Activity Level : Actively seeking new investments

NEM PARTNERS (AKA: NATEXIS EQUITY MANAGEMENT)

5-7, rue de Montessuy
Paris, France 75007
Phone: 33-1-5819-2130
Fax: 33-1-5819-2140
E-mail: contact@nem-sa.com
Website: www.nem-sa.com

Management and Staff

Benoit Bazzocchi, Partner
Hanen Feki-Ben Ayed, Partner
Jean-Yves Noir, Managing Director

Type of Firm

Bank Affiliated

Association Membership
French Venture Capital Association (AFIC)

Project Preferences

Type of Financing Preferred:
Expansion
Public Companies
Turnaround

Geographical Preferences

International Preferences:
Europe
France

Additional Information

Year Founded: 2003
Current Activity Level : Actively seeking new investments

NEM SGR SPA

Viale Mazzini, 77/D
Vicenza, Italy 36100
Phone: 39-444-526-133
Fax: 39-444-545-936
Website: www.nemsgr.it

Type of Firm

Bank Affiliated

Association Membership

Italian Venture Capital Association (AIFI)

Project Preferences

Type of Financing Preferred:
Leveraged Buyout
Generalist PE
Expansion
Management Buyouts
Recapitalizations

Size of Investments Considered:
Min Size of Investment Considered (000s): $1,402
Max Size of Investment Considered (000s): $7,010

Geographical Preferences

International Preferences:
Italy
Europe

Industry Preferences

In Business Serv. prefer:
Services

Additional Information

Year Founded: 2004
Capital Under Management: $35,500,000
Current Activity Level : Actively seeking new investments

NEO TECHNOLOGY VENTURES PTY, LTD.

75 Miller Street
Level 9
North Sydney, Australia 2060
Phone: 612-9409-6700
Fax: 612-9409-6701
E-mail: enquiries@ntfund.com
Website: www.ntfund.com

Type of Firm

Private Equity Firm

Association Membership

Australian Venture Capital Association (AVCAL)

Project Preferences

Role in Financing:
Prefer role as deal originator

Type of Financing Preferred:
Early Stage
Expansion
Seed
Startup

Size of Investments Considered:
Min Size of Investment Considered (000s): $956
Max Size of Investment Considered (000s): $4,778

Geographical Preferences

International Preferences:
Australia

Industry Preferences

In Communications prefer:
Telecommunications

In Internet Specific prefer:
Internet

In Business Serv. prefer:
Media

Additional Information

Name of Most Recent Fund: Neo IIF Fund (FKA: Newport IIF)
Most Recent Fund Was Raised: 05/19/2000
Year Founded: 2000
Capital Under Management: $23,700,000
Current Activity Level : Actively seeking new investments
Method of Compensation: Return on investment is of primary concern, do not charge fees

---

NEOCARTA VENTURES, INC.

45 Fairfield Street
Fourth Floor
Boston, MA USA 02116
Phone: 617-239-9000
Fax: 617-266-4107
E-mail: info@neocarta.com
Website: www.neocarta.com

Other Offices

343 Sansome Street
Suite 525
San Francisco, CA USA 94104
Phone: 415-277-0230
Fax: 415-277-0240

Management and Staff

Anthony Pantuso, Managing Director
Barry Newman, Venture Partner
Jarrett Collins, Managing Director
Lee Pantuso, Chief Financial Officer
Margaret Jackson, Managing Director
Mark Somol, Principal
Paul Hsu, Principal
Tom Naughton, Managing Director

Type of Firm

Private Equity Firm

Project Preferences

Type of Financing Preferred:
Second Stage Financing
Early Stage
Later Stage
Startup

Size of Investments Considered:
Min Size of Investment Considered (000s): $1,000
Max Size of Investment Considered (000s): $5,000

Industry Focus
(% based on actual investment)

Internet Specific	34.8%
Communications and Media	27.8%
Computer Software and Services	16.7%
Semiconductors/Other Elect.	10.8%
Computer Hardware	6.6%
Other Products	3.3%

Additional Information
Name of Most Recent Fund: NeoCarta Ventures, L.P.
Most Recent Fund Was Raised: 11/08/1999
Year Founded: 1999
Capital Under Management: $300,000,000
Current Activity Level : Actively seeking new investments

NEOMARKKA OYJ
Pohjoisesplanadi 27 C
Helsinki, Finland 00100
Phone: 358-9-684-4650
Fax: 358-9-684-6531
E-mail: neonmarkka@neonmarkka.fi
Website: www.neomarkka.fi

Management and Staff
Samuel Martens, Managing Director

Type of Firm
Investment Management Firm

Association Membership
Finnish Venture Capital Association (FVCA)

Project Preferences

Type of Financing Preferred:
Fund of Funds
Expansion

Geographical Preferences

International Preferences:
Scandanavia/Nordic Region
Finland

Industry Preferences

In Communications prefer:
Telecommunications

In Utilities prefer:
Utilities

Additional Information
Year Founded: 1997
Capital Under Management: $65,900,000
Current Activity Level : Actively seeking new investments

NEOMED MANAGEMENT AS
Parkveien 55
Oslo, Norway NO-0256
Phone: 47-22-545-940
Fax: 47-22-545-941
Website: www.neomed.no

Other Offices
111 Devonshire Street
Suite 730
Boston, MA USA 02109
Phone: 617-210-7974

7, Place du Molard
Geneva, Switzerland 1204
Phone: 41-22-566-7802

Management and Staff
Carl Christian Gilhuus-Moe, Partner
Claudio Nessi, Partner
Erik Amble, Partner
Gert Caspritz, Partner
Jeffrey Morris, Vice President
Thomas Goebel, Principal
Tom Pike, Venture Partner

Type of Firm
Private Equity Firm

Association Membership
Norwegian Venture Capital Association
European Private Equity and Venture Capital Assoc.

Project Preferences

Role in Financing:
Will function either as deal originator or investor in deals created by others

Type of Financing Preferred:
Second Stage Financing
Early Stage
Expansion
Mezzanine
Balanced
Public Companies
Later Stage
Open Market
Seed
Private Placement

Size of Investments Considered:
Min Size of Investment Considered (000s): $500
Max Size of Investment Considered (000s): $2,000

Geographical Preferences

United States Preferences:
All U.S.

International Preferences:
Europe
Scandanavia/Nordic Region
All International

Industry Preferences

In Biotechnology prefer:
Biotechnology

In Medical/Health prefer:
Medical/Health
Medical Diagnostics
Diagnostic Services
Diagnostic Test Products
Medical Therapeutics
Drug/Equipmt Delivery
Medical Products
Disposable Med. Products
Health Services
Pharmaceuticals

Additional Information
Name of Most Recent Fund: NeoMed Innovation IV, L.P.
Most Recent Fund Was Raised: 01/04/2005
Year Founded: 1997
Capital Under Management: $202,400,000
Current Activity Level : Actively seeking new investments
Method of Compensation: Return on investment is of primary concern, do not charge fees

NEOPLUX COMPANY, LTD.
Doosan Tower, 15th Floor
Euljiro 6-ga, Jung-gu
Seoul, South Korea 100-730
Phone: 822-3398-1070
Fax: 822-3398-1071
Website: www.neoplux.com

Management and Staff
Jong Gap Lee, President
mTae-won Kim, Senior Managing Director

Type of Firm
Corporate PE/Venture

Association Membership
Korean Venture Capital Association (KVCA)

Project Preferences

Type of Financing Preferred:
Leveraged Buyout
Early Stage
Expansion
Mezzanine
Balanced
Turnaround
Management Buyouts
Startup
Recapitalizations

Size of Investments Considered:
Min Size of Investment Considered (000s): $500
Max Size of Investment Considered (000s): $3,000

Geographical Preferences

International Preferences:
Korea, South
Asia

Industry Preferences

In Communications prefer:
Telecommunications

In Computer Software prefer:
Software

In Semiconductor/Electr prefer:
Electronics
Semiconductor

In Biotechnology prefer:
Biotechnology

In Business Serv. prefer:
Media

Additional Information

Year Founded: 2000
Capital Under Management: $78,900,000
Current Activity Level : Actively seeking new investments

NEST VENTURES

3104 East Camelback Road
Suite 144
Phoenix, AZ USA 85016
Phone: 480-675-7703
Fax: 480-675-8751
E-mail: info@nestventures.com
Website: www.nestventures.com

Type of Firm

Private Equity Firm

Industry Preferences

In Communications prefer:
Communications and Media
Wireless Communications

In Computer Software prefer:
Software

In Biotechnology prefer:
Biotechnology

In Industrial/Energy prefer:
Energy

In Business Serv. prefer:
Media

Additional Information

Year Founded: 2000
Current Activity Level : Actively seeking new investments

NET PARTNERS

375 Avenue Brugmann
2nd floor
Brussels, Belgium 1180
Phone: 32-2-340-9366
Fax: 32-2-340-9363
E-mail: admin@net-partners.com
Website: www.net-partners.com

Other Offices

15 Clifford Street
London, United Kingdom W1S 4JY
Phone: 44-20-7287-4088
Via Sant'Orsola 3
Milan, Italy 20123
Phone: 39-2-880-7731
Fax: 39-2-880-77305

Management and Staff

Alain Dubois, Chief Financial Officer
Danielle Bodor, Managing Director
Fausto Boni, Managing Director
Francois Tison, Partner
Marco Annaratone, Partner
Michele Appendino, Managing Director

Type of Firm

Private Equity Firm

Association Membership

European Private Equity and Venture Capital Assoc.

Project Preferences

Type of Financing Preferred:
Early Stage
Expansion
Later Stage
Seed
Startup

Geographical Preferences

International Preferences:
Italy
United Kingdom
Spain
France

Industry Preferences

In Communications prefer:
Telecommunications
Wireless Communications

In Computer Software prefer:
Software

In Internet Specific prefer:
Internet

Additional Information

Year Founded: 1997
Capital Under Management: $163,000,000
Current Activity Level : Actively seeking new investments

NETHERLANDS DEVELOPMENT FINANCE COMPANY

Anna van Saksenlaan 71
The Hague, Netherlands
Phone: 31-70-314-9696
Fax: 31-70-314-9758
E-mail: info@fmo.nl
Website: www.fmo.nl

Management and Staff

R. Michael Barth, Managing Director

Type of Firm

Incubator/Development Program

Association Membership

African Venture Capital Association (AVCA)

Project Preferences

Type of Financing Preferred:
Early Stage
Expansion

Size of Investments Considered:
Min Size of Investment Considered (000s): $671
Max Size of Investment Considered (000s): $13,419

Geographical Preferences

International Preferences:
Africa

Industry Preferences

In Financial Services prefer:
Financial Services

Additional Information

Year Founded: 2002
Current Activity Level : Actively seeking new investments

NETHERLANDS DEVELOPMENT FINANCE COMPANY (AKA: FMO)

Anna van Saksenlaan 71
P.O. Box 93060
The Hague, Netherlands 2509 AB
Phone: 31-70-314-9696
Fax: 31-70-314-9758
E-mail: info@fmo.nl
Website: www.fmo.nl

Management and Staff

Nanno Kleiterp, Chief Executive Officer
Nico K.G. Pijl, Chief Financial Officer

Type of Firm

Private Equity Firm

Association Membership

Emerging Markets Private Equity Association

European Private Equity and Venture Capital Assoc.
Dutch Venture Capital Associaton (NVP)
African Venture Capital Association (AVCA)

Project Preferences

Size of Investments Considered:
Min Size of Investment Considered (000s): $1,283
Max Size of Investment Considered (000s): $19,247

Industry Preferences

In Communications prefer:
Telecommunications

In Financial Services prefer:
Financial Services

Additional Information

Year Founded: 1970
Capital Under Management: $2,951,100,000
Current Activity Level : Actively seeking new investments

NETSERVICE VENTURES

2108 Sand Hill Road
Menlo Park, CA USA 94025
Phone: 650-234-9955
Fax: 650-234-8322
E-mail: info@nsv.com
Website: www.netserviceventures.com

Other Offices

Shin Marunouchi Building 10F
1-5-1 Marunouchi Chiyoda-Ku
Tokyo, Japan 100-6510
Phone: 81-03-5259-8028

Type of Firm

Private Equity Firm

Additional Information

Year Founded: 2000
Current Activity Level : Actively seeking new investments

NETWORK CAPITAL, INC.

601 - 10 Avenue South West
Kipling Square 175
Calgary, Canada T2R 0B2
Phone: 403-303-4488
Fax: 403-303-4489
Website: www.networkcapital.com

Management and Staff

David Richards, Managing Director
William Bonne, Managing Director

Type of Firm

Private Equity Firm

Project Preferences

Type of Financing Preferred:
Startup

Geographical Preferences

Canadian Preferences:
Western Canada

Additional Information

Year Founded: 1998
Current Activity Level : Actively seeking new investments

NEUBERGER & BERMAN

605 Third Avenue
New York, NY USA 10158
Phone: 212-476-9000
Fax: 212-476-5757
Website: www.nb.com

Management and Staff

Harold Newman, Partner

Type of Firm

Bank Affiliated

Project Preferences

Type of Financing Preferred:
Balanced

Geographical Preferences

United States Preferences:
All U.S.

Additional Information

Name of Most Recent Fund: Amadeus Partners, L.P.
Most Recent Fund Was Raised: 10/18/2007
Year Founded: 1992
Capital Under Management: $45,500,000
Current Activity Level : Actively seeking new investments

NEUHAUS PARTNERS (FKA: DR. NEUHAUS TECHNO NORD GMBH)

Jungfernstieg 30
Hamburg, Germany 20354
Phone: 49-40-355-2820
Fax: 49-40-355-28239
E-mail: gombert@neuhaspartners.com
Website: www.NeuhausPartners.com

Management and Staff

Gottfried Neuhaus, Managing Director
Matthias Grychta, Managing Partner
Pablo Fetter, Managing Partner
Paul Jozefak, Managing Partner
Peter Gombert, Chief Financial Officer

Type of Firm

Private Equity Firm

Association Membership

German Venture Capital Association (BVK)
European Private Equity and Venture Capital Assoc.

Project Preferences

Role in Financing:
Prefer role as deal originator but will also invest in deals created by others

Type of Financing Preferred:
Early Stage
Expansion
Seed
Startup

Size of Investments Considered:
Min Size of Investment Considered (000s): $700
Max Size of Investment Considered (000s): $4,194

Geographical Preferences

International Preferences:
Europe
Scandanavia/Nordic Region
Germany

Industry Preferences

In Communications prefer:
Communications and Media
Commercial Communications
Wireless Communications

In Computer Software prefer:
Software

In Internet Specific prefer:
Internet

In Semiconductor/Electr prefer:
Electronics

In Industrial/Energy prefer:
Industrial Products
Factory Automation

Additional Information

Year Founded: 1998
Capital Under Management: $80,600,000
Current Activity Level : Actively seeking new investments

NEUROSCIENCE DEVELOPMENT, INC.

100 International Blvd.
Toronto, Canada M9W 6J6
Phone: 416-675-7661
Fax: 416-2134232

Management and Staff

Brian Underdown, Managing Director

Type of Firm

Private Equity Firm

Project Preferences

Type of Financing Preferred:
Early Stage
Seed
Startup

Geographical Preferences

Canadian Preferences:
Ontario

Additional Information
Year Founded: 2009
Current Activity Level : Actively seeking new investments

NEUROVENTURES CAPITAL
Zero Court Square
Charlottesville, VA USA 22902
Phone: 434-297-1000
Fax: 434-297-1001
E-mail: info@neuroventures.com
Website: www.neuroventures.com

Management and Staff
Daniel O'Connell, Partner

Type of Firm
Private Equity Firm

Project Preferences

Role in Financing:
Prefer role as deal originator but will also invest in deals created by others

Type of Financing Preferred:
Early Stage
Expansion
First Stage Financing
Startup

Size of Investments Considered:
Min Size of Investment Considered (000s): $250
Max Size of Investment Considered (000s): $2,000

Industry Preferences

In Biotechnology prefer:
Human Biotechnology

In Medical/Health prefer:
Medical Therapeutics
Drug/Equipmt Delivery
Pharmaceuticals

Additional Information
Name of Most Recent Fund: NeuroVentures Fund, L.P.
Most Recent Fund Was Raised: 03/05/2001
Year Founded: 2000
Capital Under Management: $16,000,000
Current Activity Level : Actively seeking new investments
Method of Compensation: Return on investment is of primary concern, do not charge fees

---

NEVADA VENTURES
4781 Caughlin Parkway
Reno, NV USA 89509
Phone: 775-825-5054
Fax: 775-201-7879
Website: www.nevadaventures.com

Management and Staff
Christopher Howard, General Partner
Robb Smith, General Partner

Type of Firm
Private Equity Firm

Project Preferences

Role in Financing:
Will function either as deal originator or investor in deals created by others

Type of Financing Preferred:
Balanced

Size of Investments Considered:
Min Size of Investment Considered (000s): $500
Max Size of Investment Considered (000s): $2,000

Geographical Preferences

United States Preferences:
West Coast
Southwest

Industry Preferences

In Communications prefer:
Communications and Media
Telecommunications
Wireless Communications
Data Communications

In Computer Software prefer:
Software

In Semiconductor/Electr prefer:
Semiconductor
Controllers and Sensors

In Medical/Health prefer:
Medical Diagnostics
Diagnostic Test Products
Medical Products
Health Services

In Financial Services prefer:
Financial Services

Additional Information
Year Founded: 1999
Capital Under Management: $15,000,000
Current Activity Level : Actively seeking new investments
Method of Compensation: Return on investment is of primary concern, do not charge fees

---

NEVIS CAPITAL LLP
177 West George Street
Glasgow, United Kingdom G2 2LB
Phone: 44-141-248-1200
Fax: 44-141-221-7635
E-mail: enquiries@neviscapital.co.uk
Website: www.neviscapital.co.uk

Management and Staff
Brian Aitken, Partner
David Bell, Partner
James Pirrie, Partner
John Pirrie, Partner

Type of Firm
Private Equity Firm

Project Preferences

Type of Financing Preferred:
Leveraged Buyout
Expansion
Management Buyouts

Size of Investments Considered:
Min Size of Investment Considered (000s): $29,364
Max Size of Investment Considered (000s): $58,728

Geographical Preferences

International Preferences:
United Kingdom

Industry Preferences

In Business Serv. prefer:
Services

Additional Information
Year Founded: 2007
Current Activity Level : Actively seeking new investments

NEW AFRICA ADVISERS
Fulham House, 1st Floor
20 Georgian Crescent,Bryanston
Johannesburg, South Africa 2000

Type of Firm
Private Equity Firm

Project Preferences

Type of Financing Preferred:
Balanced

Additional Information
Year Founded: 2005
Current Activity Level : Actively seeking new investments

NEW ASIA PARTNERS, LTD.

18/F, One Lu Jia Zui Building
No. 68 Yin Cheng Middle Road
Shanghai, China
Phone: 86-21-5010-6066
Fax: 86-21-5010-6067
Website: www.newasiapartners.com

Other Offices

705 Kinwick Centre
32 Hollywood Road
Central, Hong Kong 1801-03
Phone: 852-2851-9836
Fax: 852-2544-9816

Management and Staff

Dwight Clark, Managing Director

Type of Firm

Private Equity Firm

Project Preferences

Type of Financing Preferred:
Early Stage
Balanced
Seed

Geographical Preferences

International Preferences:
China
Hong Kong

Industry Preferences

In Biotechnology prefer:
Biotechnology

In Medical/Health prefer:
Medical/Health
Pharmaceuticals

In Consumer Related prefer:
Consumer
Retail

In Industrial/Energy prefer:
Energy
Environmental Related

Additional Information

Year Founded: 2002
Current Activity Level : Actively seeking new investments

NEW ATLANTIC VENTURES (FKA: DRAPER ATLANTIC VENTURE FUND)

11911 Freedom Drive
Suite 1080
Reston, VA USA 20190
Phone: 703-563-4100
Fax: 703-563-4111
Website: www.navfund.com

Other Offices

One Broadway
14th Floor
Cambridge, MA USA 02142
Phone: 617-758-4275
Fax: 617-758-4101

Management and Staff

Geoff Mamlet, Principal
John Backus, Managing Partner
Mel Davidson, Chief Financial Officer
Scott Johnson, Managing Partner
Stephen Marcus, Venture Partner
Thanasis Delistathis, Managing Partner
Timothy Rowe, Venture Partner
Todd Hixon, Managing Partner

Type of Firm

Private Equity Firm

Association Membership

Mid-Atlantic Venture Association
National Venture Capital Association - USA (NVCA)

Project Preferences

Role in Financing:
Will function either as deal originator or investor in deals created by others

Type of Financing Preferred:
Early Stage
Balanced

Size of Investments Considered:
Min Size of Investment Considered (000s): $100
Max Size of Investment Considered (000s): $3,000

Geographical Preferences

United States Preferences:
Mid Atlantic
Southeast
All U.S.

Industry Focus

(% based on actual investment)

Internet Specific	46.4%
Computer Software and Services	31.3%
Communications and Media	14.9%
Semiconductors/Other Elect.	3.6%
Computer Hardware	2.1%
Medical/Health	0.9%
Other Products	0.8%

Additional Information

Name of Most Recent Fund: New Atlantic Entrepreneur Fund III, L.P.
Most Recent Fund Was Raised: 12/21/2007
Year Founded: 1999
Capital Under Management: $300,000,000
Current Activity Level : Actively seeking new investments
Method of Compensation: Return on investment is of primary concern, do not charge fees

NEW BRUNSWICK INNOVATION FOUNDATION

440 King Street
Suite 602, 6Th Floor KingTower
Fredicton, Canada E3B 5h8
Phone: 506-452-2884
Fax: 506-452-2886
E-mail: info@nbif.ca
Website: www.nbif.ca

Type of Firm

Government Affiliated Program

Project Preferences

Type of Financing Preferred:
Startup

Geographical Preferences

Canadian Preferences
New Brunswick

Additional Information

Year Founded: 2003
Current Activity Level : Actively seeking new investments

NEW BRUNSWICK INVESTMENT MANAGEMENT CORPORATION (AKA: NBIMC)

440 Kings Street
York Tower, Suite 581
Fredericton, Canada E3B 5H8
Phone: 506-444-5800
Fax: 506-444-5025
Website: www.nbimc.com

Type of Firm

Endowment, Foundation or Pension Fund

Project Preferences

Type of Financing Preferred:
Expansion
Startup

Geographical Preferences

Canadian Preferences:
Nova Scotia
Prince Edward Island
New Brunswick
Newfoundland

Additional Information

Year Founded: 1996
Current Activity Level : Actively seeking new investments

NEW BUSINESS INVESTMENT CO., LTD.

12F Nihon Bldg.
2-6-2 Otemachi, Chiyoda-ku
Tokyo, Japan 100-0004
Phone: 81-3-3231-2381
Fax: 81-3-3231-2380
Website: www.nbivc.jp

Management and Staff

Shigeki Sugita, Managing Director

Type of Firm

Government Affiliated Program

Additional Information

Year Founded: 1990
Current Activity Level : Actively seeking new investments

NEW CAPITAL - SOCIEDADE DE CAPITAL DE RISCO, S.A.

Rua Tierno Galvan
Torre 3, 14
Lisboa, Portugal 1070-274
Phone: 351-21-381-6200
Fax: 351-21-381-6201
E-mail: banif.investimento@banifinvestimento.pt
Website: www.banifinvestimento.pt

Other Offices

Edifico BCA - Loja do Investidor
Ponta Delgada, Portugal 9500-119
Phone: 351-296-303-144
Fax: 351-296-629-558

Rua Joao Tavira, 30
Funchal, Portugal 9004-509
Phone: 351-291-297-727
Fax: 351-291-207-889

Av. dos Aliados, 107
Porto, Portugal 4000-067
Phone: 351-22-207-8674
Fax: 351-22-207-8679

Type of Firm

Private Equity Firm

Association Membership

Portuguese Venture Capital Association (APCRI)

Project Preferences

Type of Financing Preferred:
Early Stage
Balanced

Geographical Preferences

International Preferences:
Portugal
Europe

Additional Information

Name of Most Recent Fund: New Family Companies Fund, FCRIQ
Most Recent Fund Was Raised: 07/01/2005
Year Founded: 2003
Capital Under Management: $14,800,000
Current Activity Level : Actively seeking new investments

NEW CAPITAL MANAGEMENT, INC.

200 East Washington Street
Appleton, WI USA 54912
Phone: 920-731-5777
Fax: 920-731-5830
Website: www.newcapitalfund.com

Management and Staff

Charles Goff, General Partner

Type of Firm

Private Equity Firm

Association Membership

National Venture Capital Association - USA (NVCA)

Project Preferences

Type of Financing Preferred:
Early Stage
Seed

Size of Investments Considered:
Min Size of Investment Considered (000s): $250
Max Size of Investment Considered (000s): $1,000

Geographical Preferences

United States Preferences:
Wisconsin

Industry Preferences

In Manufact. prefer:
Manufacturing

In Agr/Forestr/Fish prefer:
Agriculture related

Additional Information

Name of Most Recent Fund: NEW Capital Fund, LP
Most Recent Fund Was Raised: 01/10/2006
Year Founded: 2006
Capital Under Management: $9,400,000
Current Activity Level : Actively seeking new investments

NEW CAPITAL PARTNERS

2900 First Avenue South
Suite 200
Birmingham, AL USA 35233
Phone: 205-939-8400
Fax: 205-939-8402
Website: www.newcapitalpartners.com

Other Offices

2101 Cedar Springs Road
Suite 1201
Dallas, TX USA 75201
Phone: 214-871-5408
Fax: 214-871-5401

Management and Staff

Alan Ritchie, General Partner
Gary Culliss, Venture Partner
James Outland, General Partner
Jim Little, General Partner

Type of Firm

Private Equity Firm

Association Membership

National Venture Capital Association - USA (NVCA)

Project Preferences

Role in Financing:
Prefer role as deal originator but will also invest in deals created by others

Type of Financing Preferred:
Early Stage
Expansion
Balanced
Later Stage

Size of Investments Considered:
Min Size of Investment Considered (000s): $500
Max Size of Investment Considered (000s): $3,000

Geographical Preferences

United States Preferences:
Southeast
Southwest
All U.S.

Industry Preferences

In Communications prefer:
Commercial Communications
Telecommunications
Wireless Communications
Data Communications

In Computer Software prefer:
Software
Systems Software
Applications Software

In Internet Specific prefer:
Internet

In Medical/Health prefer:
Medical Diagnostics
Diagnostic Services

Diagnostic Test Products
Drug/Equipmt Delivery
Medical Products
Disposable Med. Products

In Industrial/Energy prefer:
Energy

In Financial Services prefer:
Financial Services
Insurance

In Business Serv. prefer:
Services
Distribution

In Utilities prefer:
Utilities

In Other prefer:
Environment Responsible

Additional Information

Name of Most Recent Fund: New Capital Partners Private Equity Fund II, L.P.
Most Recent Fund Was Raised: 07/02/2008
Year Founded: 2000
Capital Under Management: $152,600,000
Current Activity Level : Actively seeking new investments
Method of Compensation: Return on invest. most important, but chg. closing fees, service fees, etc.

NEW COMMERCIAL ROOM GMBH

Rothenbaumchaussee 116
Hamburg, Germany 20149
Phone: 49-40-23856750
Fax: 49-40-23856759
E-mail: info@necoro.de
Website: www.necoro.de

Type of Firm

Angel Group

Project Preferences

Role in Financing:
Will function either as deal originator or investor in deals created by others

Type of Financing Preferred:
Early Stage
Start-up Financing

Geographical Preferences

International Preferences:
Germany

Additional Information

Year Founded: 2001
Current Activity Level : Actively seeking new investments
Method of Compensation: Unknown

NEW CYCLE CAPITAL LLC

410 Jessie Street
Suite 501
San Francisco, CA USA 94103
Phone: 415-615-0130
Fax: 415-373-3828
E-mail: info@newcyclecapital.com
Website: www.newcyclecapital.com

Management and Staff

Benjamin Black, General Partner
Josh Becker, General Partner

Type of Firm

Private Equity Firm

Project Preferences

Type of Financing Preferred:
Early Stage

Geographical Preferences

United States Preferences:
All U.S.

Industry Preferences

In Other prefer:
Socially Responsible
Environment Responsible

Additional Information

Year Founded: 2007
Capital Under Management: $50,000,000
Current Activity Level : Actively seeking new investments

NEW ECONOMY DEVELOPMENT FUND, THE (AKA: TANEO)

12 Amerikis strasse
6th & 7th Floor
Athens, Greece GR-10671
Phone: 30-210-338-7110
Fax: 30-210-338-7116
E-mail: info@taneo.gr
Website: www.taneo.gr

Type of Firm

Government Affiliated Program

Project Preferences

Type of Financing Preferred:
Fund of Funds

Geographical Preferences

International Preferences:
Greece

Additional Information

Year Founded: 2001
Capital Under Management: $260,900,000
Current Activity Level : Actively seeking new investments

NEW ENERGY CAPITAL CORP.

53 South Main Street
Third Floor
Hanover, NH USA 03755
Phone: 603-643-8885
Fax: 603-653-7524
E-mail: info@newenergycapital.com
Website: www.newenergycapital.com

Other Offices

242 Main Street
PO Box 617
Warren, VT USA 05674
Phone: 802-496-3529
Fax: 253-399-5321

10 Allen Street
Hanover, NH USA 03755
Phone: 603-643-8885
Fax: 206-350-1899

Management and Staff

Dan Reicher, Managing Partner
Everett Smith, Chief Financial Officer
Scott Brown, Chief Executive Officer

Type of Firm

Private Equity Firm

Project Preferences

Type of Financing Preferred:
Later Stage
Acquisition

Geographical Preferences

United States Preferences:
All U.S.

Industry Preferences

In Industrial/Energy prefer:
Energy
Alternative Energy

Additional Information

Name of Most Recent Fund: New Energy Capital Fund I, L.P.
Most Recent Fund Was Raised: 05/09/2005
Year Founded: 2003
Capital Under Management: $400,000
Current Activity Level : Actively seeking new investments

NEW ENGLAND CAPITAL PARTNERS

One Gateway Center
Suite 303
Newton, MA USA 02458
Phone: 617-964-7300
Fax: 617-964-7301
E-mail: info@necapitalpartners.com
Website: www.necapitalpartners.com

Management and Staff

Robert Winneg, General Partner
Vincent Martelli, General Partner

Type of Firm

Private Equity Firm

Project Preferences

Type of Financing Preferred:
Acquisition

Geographical Preferences

United States Preferences:
All U.S.

Industry Preferences

In Business Serv. prefer:
Services
Distribution

In Manufact. prefer:
Manufacturing

Additional Information

Year Founded: 2007
Current Activity Level : Actively seeking new investments

NEW ENGLAND PARTNERS

400 Crown Colony Drive
Suite 104
Quincy, MA USA 02169
Phone: 617-472-2805
Fax: 617-472-3531
E-mail: info@nepartners.com
Website: www.nepartners.com

Management and Staff

Christopher Young, General Partner
David Dullum, General Partner
John Rousseau, Managing General Partner
Robert Hanks, Managing General Partner
Thomas Hancock, Principal
Todd Fitzpatrick, Principal

Type of Firm

Private Equity Firm

Association Membership

Natl Assoc of Small Bus. Inv. Co (NASBIC)

Project Preferences

Role in Financing:
Will function either as deal originator or investor in deals created by others

Type of Financing Preferred:
Second Stage Financing
First Stage Financing

Size of Investments Considered:
Min Size of Investment Considered (000s): $500
Max Size of Investment Considered (000s): $6,000

Geographical Preferences

United States Preferences:
Mid Atlantic
Southeast
Northeast

Industry Focus

(% based on actual investment)

Biotechnology	40.9%
Medical/Health	20.0%
Communications and Media	11.9%
Consumer Related	10.0%
Computer Software and Services	9.1%
Internet Specific	3.1%
Semiconductors/Other Elect.	3.0%
Other Products	1.1%
Industrial/Energy	0.6%
Computer Hardware	0.4%

Additional Information

Name of Most Recent Fund: New England Partners Capital, LP
Most Recent Fund Was Raised: 10/01/1999
Year Founded: 1990
Capital Under Management: $200,000,000
Current Activity Level : Actively seeking new investments
Method of Compensation: Return on investment is of primary concern, do not charge fees

NEW ENTERPRISE ASSOCIATES

1119 Saint Paul Street
Baltimore, MD USA 21202
Phone: 410-244-0115
Fax: 410-752-7721
Website: www.nea.com

Other Offices

2855 Sand Hill Road
Menlo Park, CA USA 94025
Phone: 650-854-9499
Fax: 650-854-9397

5425 Wisconsin Avenue
Suite 800
Chevy Chase, MD USA 20815
Phone: 301-272-2300
Fax: 301-272-1700

Room B1706, Focus Place
No. 19 Financial Street
Beijing, China 100140
Phone: 86-10-6657-5566
Fax: 86-10-6657-3553

Suite 212, 2nd Floor
Prestige Omega, No. 104
Bangalore, India 560 066
Phone: 91-80-4060 0801

Management and Staff

A. Brooke Seawell, Venture Partner
A. Jay Graf, Venture Partner
Ali Behbahani, Principal
Amita Shukla, Principal
Arno Penzias, Venture Partner
Bala Deshpande, Managing Director
Ben Mathias, Vice President
C. Richard Kramlich, General Partner
Charles Linehan, General Partner
Charles Newhall, General Partner
Ching- Ho Fung, Venture Partner
David Mott, General Partner
Ed Mathers, Partner
Eugene Trainor, Chief Operating Officer
Forest Baskett, General Partner
Frank Bonsal, Founding Partner
Frank Torti, Principal
George Stamas, Venture Partner
Harold Weller, General Partner
Hugh Panero, Venture Partner
Jake Nunn, Partner
Jimmy Treybig, Venture Partner
Jon Sakoda, Partner
Joshua Makower, Venture Partner
Justin Klein, Principal
Krishna Kolluri, General Partner
M. James Barrett, General Partner
Mark Perry, General Partner
Michael O Dell, Venture Partner
Michael Ramsay, Venture Partner
Mohamad Makhzoumi, Principal
PM Pai, Venture Partner
Patrick Kerins, General Partner
Patrick Chung, Partner
Paul Hsiao, Partner
Paul Walker, Partner
Peter Behrendt, Venture Partner
Peter Morris, Venture Partner
Peter Barris, General Partner
Peter Sonsini, Partner
Qiang Fu, Vice President
Ralph Snyderman, Venture Partner
Ravi Viswanathan, General Partner
Richard Whitney, Venture Partner
Robert Shawver, Chief Financial Officer
Robert Croce, Venture Partner
Robert Garland, Partner
Rohini Chakravarthy, Partner
Ronald Kase, Venture Partner
Ruchir Lahoty, Vice President
Ryan Drant, General Partner

Scott Sandell, General Partner
Scott Gottlieb, Venture Partner
Sigrid Van Bladel, Partner
Suzanne King, Partner
Tarun Sharma, Vice President
Tim Schaller, Chief Financial Officer
Tom Grossi, Principal
Tony Florence, Partner
Xiaodong Jiang, Managing Director

Type of Firm

Private Equity Firm

Association Membership

Mid-Atlantic Venture Association
Western Association of Venture Capitalists (WAVC)
National Venture Capital Association - USA (NVCA)

Project Preferences

Role in Financing:

Prefer role as deal originator but will also invest in deals created by others

Type of Financing Preferred:

Second Stage Financing
Early Stage
Expansion
Mezzanine
Start-up Financing
Seed
First Stage Financing

Size of Investments Considered:

Min Size of Investment Considered (000s): $1,000
Max Size of Investment Considered (000s): $100,000

Geographical Preferences

United States Preferences:

All U.S.

International Preferences:

India
United Kingdom
China
Belgium
France
All International

Industry Focus

(% based on actual investment)

Medical/Health	18.9%
Communications and Media	18.1%
Internet Specific	18.0%
Computer Software and Services	11.9%
Semiconductors/Other Elect.	9.7%
Biotechnology	9.2%
Other Products	5.0%
Computer Hardware	4.7%
Industrial/Energy	3.5%
Consumer Related	1.0%

Additional Information

Name of Most Recent Fund: New Enterprise Associates 13, L.P.
Most Recent Fund Was Raised: 10/16/2009
Year Founded: 1978
Capital Under Management: $8,500,000,000
Current Activity Level : Actively seeking new investments
Method of Compensation: Return on investment is of primary concern, do not charge fees

NEW ENTERPRISE EAST INVESTMENTS (AKA: NEEI)

Cassells Ghantoot Resort
P.O. Box 126969
Abu Dhabi, Utd. Arab Em.
Phone: 971-2-562-9114
Fax: 971-2-562-9115
Website: www.ip-venturepartners.com

Other Offices

1001 Pennsylvania Avenue
Suite 600 South
Washington, DC USA 20004
Phone: 202-742-6777
Fax: 202-742-6501

Management and Staff

Fouad Al Rumaihi, Managing Director
Harvey Klyce, Managing Director
Jack Roepers, Managing Director

Type of Firm

Private Equity Firm

Project Preferences

Type of Financing Preferred:

Early Stage
Expansion

Size of Investments Considered:

Min Size of Investment Considered (000s): $2,000
Max Size of Investment Considered (000s): $100,000

Geographical Preferences

International Preferences:

Bahrain
Oman
Qatar
Utd. Arab Em.
Iran
Saudi Arabia
Iraq
Kuwait

Industry Preferences

In Communications prefer:

Wireless Communications

In Industrial/Energy prefer:

Alternative Energy
Energy Conservation Relat
Environmental Related

Additional Information

Year Founded: 2008
Capital Under Management: $40,000,000
Current Activity Level : Actively seeking new investments

NEW EQUITY CAPITAL

1310 Greene Avenue
Suite 800
Montreal, Canada H3Z 2B2
Phone: 514-931-0580
Fax: 514-931-3917
E-mail: info@newequity.ca
Website: www.newequity.ca

Type of Firm

Private Equity Firm

Additional Information

Year Founded: 2009
Current Activity Level : Actively seeking new investments

NEW EUROPE VENTURE EQUITY (AKA: NEVEQ)

No. 23, Kustendil str.
Sofia, Bulgaria 1680
Phone: 359-2-850-4000
Fax: 359-2-858-1999
E-mail: office@neveq.com
Website: www.neveq.com

Management and Staff

Pavel Ezekiev, Managing Partner

Type of Firm

Private Equity Firm

Project Preferences

Type of Financing Preferred:

Balanced

Size of Investments Considered:

Min Size of Investment Considered (000s): $691
Max Size of Investment Considered (000s): $6,907

Geographical Preferences

International Preferences:

Turkey
Macedonia
Bulgaria
Romania

Industry Preferences

In Communications prefer:

Communications and Media

In Internet Specific prefer:

E-Commerce Technology
Ecommerce

Additional Information

Year Founded: 2007
Capital Under Management: $310,800,000

Current Activity Level : Actively seeking new investments

NEW HORIZON CAPITAL

Unit 1204, 12/F, Jin Bao Tower
89 Jin Bao Street
Beijing, China 100005
Phone: 86-10-8522-1230
Fax: 86-10-8522-1231
E-mail: webmaster@nhfund.com
Website: www.nhfund.com

Management and Staff

Cher Teck Quek, Managing Director
Jianming Yu, Chief Executive Officer

Type of Firm

Private Equity Firm

Project Preferences

Type of Financing Preferred:
Expansion
Early Stage

Geographical Preferences

International Preferences:
China

Industry Preferences

In Communications prefer:
Other Communication Prod.

In Medical/Health prefer:
Medical Products
Pharmaceuticals

In Consumer Related prefer:
Consumer
Consumer Products

In Industrial/Energy prefer:
Energy
Alternative Energy

In Transportation prefer:
Transportation

In Business Serv. prefer:
Services
Media

In Manufact. prefer:
Manufacturing

Additional Information

Year Founded: 2007
Capital Under Management: $946,000,000
Current Activity Level : Actively seeking new investments

NEW HORIZONS VENTURE CAPITAL

1808 Eye Street, NW
Suite 200
Washington, DC USA 20006
Phone: 202-955-7965
Fax: 202-955-7966
E-mail: info@newhorizonsvc.com
Website: www.newhorizonsvc.com

Management and Staff

T.J. Jubeir, Managing Partner

Type of Firm

Private Equity Firm

Association Membership

Mid-Atlantic Venture Association

Project Preferences

Role in Financing:
Prefer role as deal originator but will also invest in deals created by others

Type of Financing Preferred:
Second Stage Financing
Early Stage
First Stage Financing

Size of Investments Considered:
Min Size of Investment Considered (000s): $500
Max Size of Investment Considered (000s): $5,000

Geographical Preferences

United States Preferences:
Mid Atlantic

Industry Focus

(% based on actual investment)	
Internet Specific	50.4%
Computer Hardware	40.3%
Computer Software and Services	9.2%

Additional Information

Year Founded: 1999
Capital Under Management: $200,000,000
Current Activity Level : Actively seeking new investments

NEW JERSEY ECONOMIC DEVELOPMENT AUTHORITY

36 West State Steet
Trenton, NJ USA 08625
Phone: 609-292-1800
E-mail: njeda@njeda.com
Website: www.njeda.com

Other Offices

Gateway One
Suite 900
Newark, NJ USA 07102
Phone: 973-648-4130

Management and Staff

Caren Franzini, Chief Executive Officer

Type of Firm

Government Affiliated Program

Project Preferences

Type of Financing Preferred:
Early Stage
Startup

Size of Investments Considered:
Min Size of Investment Considered (000s): $100
Max Size of Investment Considered (000s): $1,000

Geographical Preferences

United States Preferences:
New Jersey
All U.S.

Additional Information

Name of Most Recent Fund: Edison Innovation Fund
Most Recent Fund Was Raised: 10/01/2006
Year Founded: 2006
Capital Under Management: $150,000,000
Current Activity Level : Actively seeking new investments

NEW JERSEY TECHNOLOGY COUNCIL (AKA: NJTC)

1001 Briggs Road
Suite 280
Mount Laurel, NJ USA 08054
Phone: 856-273-6800
Fax: 856-273-0990
E-mail: info@njtcvc.com
Website: www.njtcvc.com

Other Offices

Four Becker Farm Road
Roseland, NJ USA 07068
Phone: 973-994-0606
Fax: 973-992-6336

Management and Staff

James Gunton, General Partner
Joe Falkenstein, General Partner
Maxine Ballen, Principal
Phillip Chan, Partner
Robert Chefitz, General Partner

Type of Firm

SBIC

Association Membership

Natl Assoc of Small Bus. Inv. Co (NASBIC)
National Venture Capital Association - USA (NVCA)

Project Preferences

Role in Financing:
Will function either as deal originator or investor in deals created by others

Type of Financing Preferred:
Second Stage Financing
Early Stage
Expansion
Seed
First Stage Financing
Startup

Size of Investments Considered:
Min Size of Investment Considered (000s): $250
Max Size of Investment Considered (000s): $2,000

Geographical Preferences

United States Preferences:
Pennsylvania
Maryland
New Jersey
New York

Industry Preferences

In Communications prefer:
Telecommunications

In Computer Software prefer:
Software

In Internet Specific prefer:
Internet

In Semiconductor/Electr prefer:
Electronics

In Biotechnology prefer:
Biotechnology
Industrial Biotechnology

In Medical/Health prefer:
Health Services

In Industrial/Energy prefer:
Energy
Advanced Materials

In Financial Services prefer:
Financial Services

Additional Information
Name of Most Recent Fund: NJTC Venture Fund
Most Recent Fund Was Raised: 07/02/2001
Year Founded: 2000
Capital Under Management: $80,000,000
Current Activity Level : Actively seeking new investments
Method of Compensation: Return on investment is of primary concern, do not charge fees

NEW LEAF VENTURE PARTNERS LLC
Times Square Tower
Seven Times Square, Suite 1603
New York, NY USA 10036
Phone: 646-871-6400
Fax: 646-871-6450
E-mail: info@nlvpartners.com
Website: www.nlvpartners.com

Other Offices
2500 Sand Hill Road
Suite 203
Menlo Park, CA USA 94025
Phone: 650-234-2700
Fax: 650-234-2704

Management and Staff
Craig Slutzkin, Chief Financial Officer
James Niedel, Managing Director
Jeani Delagardelle, Managing Director
Kathleen LaPorte, Managing Director
Milton McColl, Venture Partner
Philippe Chambon, Managing Director
Ramesh Subramani, Vice President
Ronald Hunt, Managing Director
Srinivas Akkaraju, Managing Director
Vijay Lathi, Managing Director

Type of Firm
Bank Affiliated

Association Membership
National Venture Capital Association - USA (NVCA)

Project Preferences

Role in Financing:
Prefer role as deal originator but will also invest in deals created by others

Type of Financing Preferred:
Leveraged Buyout
Early Stage
Expansion
Balanced
Later Stage
Management Buyouts
Startup

Size of Investments Considered:
Min Size of Investment Considered (000s): $300
Max Size of Investment Considered (000s): $40,000

Geographical Preferences

United States Preferences:
All U.S.

Industry Preferences

In Medical/Health prefer:
Medical/Health
Medical Diagnostics
Health Services
Pharmaceuticals

Additional Information
Year Founded: 2005
Capital Under Management: $1,300,000,000
Current Activity Level : Actively seeking new investments

NEW MARKETS VENTURE PARTNERS (AKA: NEW MARKETS GROWTH FUND)
2518 Van Munching Hall
College Park, MD USA 20742
Phone: 301-405-9499
Fax: 301-314-7971
E-mail: info@newmarketsfund.com
Website: www.newmarketsvp.com

Management and Staff
Donald Spero, General Partner
Frank Bonsal, Partner
Mark Grovic, General Partner
Rajesh Rai, Partner
Robb Doub, General Partner
Sidney Williams, Vice President

Type of Firm
Private Equity Firm

Project Preferences

Role in Financing:
Prefer role as deal originator but will also invest in deals created by others

Type of Financing Preferred:
Second Stage Financing
Early Stage
Turnaround
Later Stage
First Stage Financing
Startup

Size of Investments Considered:
Min Size of Investment Considered (000s): $200
Max Size of Investment Considered (000s): $2,000

Geographical Preferences

United States Preferences:
All U.S.

Industry Preferences

In Communications prefer:
Communications and Media
Telecommunications
Data Communications

In Computer Hardware prefer:
Computer Graphics and Dig

In Computer Software prefer:
Data Processing
Software
Systems Software
Applications Software

In Internet Specific prefer:
E-Commerce Technology
Internet
Ecommerce
Web Aggregration/Portals

In Computer Other prefer:
Computer Related

In Medical/Health prefer:
Medical/Health
Medical Diagnostics
Diagnostic Services
Diagnostic Test Products
Drug/Equipmt Delivery
Medical Products
Disposable Med. Products

In Consumer Related prefer:
Education Related

Additional Information
Year Founded: 2003
Capital Under Management: $20,000,000
Current Activity Level : Actively seeking new investments
Method of Compensation: Return on investment is of primary concern, do not charge fees

---

NEW MEDIA INNOVATION CENTRE
590 - 515 W Hastings Street
Vancouver, Canada V6B 5K3
Phone: 604-268-7968
Fax: 604-268-7967
Website: www.newmic.com

Management and Staff
Fred Lake, Chief Financial Officer

Type of Firm
Private Equity Firm

Project Preferences

Type of Financing Preferred:
Startup

Geographical Preferences

Canadian Preferences:
Western Canada

Additional Information
Year Founded: 2009
Current Activity Level : Actively seeking new investments

NEW MEXICO COMMUNITY CAPITAL
1115 South Camino Pueblo
Bernalillo, NM USA 87004
Phone: 505-924-2820
Fax: 505-213-0333
E-mail: info@nmccap.org
Website: www.nmccap.org

Management and Staff
Christopher Madrid, Vice President
Jarrett Applewhite, Chief Executive Officer
John Rice, President
John Driscoll, Managing Director
Leslie Elgood, Chief Operating Officer
Tammy McCarty, Chief Financial Officer
Thomas Keleher, Co-Founder

Type of Firm
Incubator/Development Program

Project Preferences

Type of Financing Preferred:
Early Stage
Seed
Startup

Geographical Preferences

United States Preferences:
New Mexico

Industry Preferences

In Consumer Related prefer:
Consumer
Food/Beverage

In Manufact. prefer:
Manufacturing

In Other prefer:
Socially Responsible
Environment Responsible

Additional Information
Name of Most Recent Fund: NMCC LP Fund I
Most Recent Fund Was Raised: 05/01/2005
Year Founded: 2004
Capital Under Management: $14,600,000
Current Activity Level : Actively seeking new investments

NEW MILLENNIUM PARTNERS, L.P.
222 Columbus
Suite 412
San Francisco, CA USA 94133
Phone: 415-646-8663
Fax: 415-646-8666
Website: www.nmpartners.com

Type of Firm
Investment Management Firm

Project Preferences

Role in Financing:
Will function either as deal originator or investor in deals created by others

Type of Financing Preferred:
Early Stage

Industry Focus
(% based on actual investment)

Internet Specific	83.1%
Computer Hardware	12.3%
Semiconductors/Other Elect.	2.8%
Communications and Media	1.5%
Consumer Related	0.2%

Additional Information
Year Founded: 1998
Current Activity Level : Actively seeking new investments

NEW MOUNTAIN CAPITAL LLC
787 7th Avenue
49th Floor
New York, NY USA 10019
Phone: 212-720-0300
Fax: 212-582-2277
E-mail: info@newmountaincapital.com
Website: www.newmountaincapital.com

Management and Staff
Adam Collins, Managing Director
Alok Singh, Managing Director
Andre Moura, Vice President
Brad Weckstein, Vice President
David DiDomenico, Managing Director
David Wargo, Managing Director
Douglas Londal, Managing Director
Jeremy Morgan, Vice President
Mathew Lori, Managing Director
Matthew Holt, Vice President
Matthew Ebbel, Vice President
Michael Flaherman, Managing Director
Michael Ajouz, Managing Director
Robert Hamwee, President & Chairman
Sunil Mishra, Managing Director
Thomas Morgan, Managing Director

Type of Firm
Private Equity Firm

Project Preferences

Type of Financing Preferred:
Leveraged Buyout

Size of Investments Considered:
Min Size of Investment Considered (000s): $50,000
Max Size of Investment Considered (000s): $150,000

Geographical Preferences

United States Preferences:
All U.S.

Industry Focus
(% based on actual investment)

Other Products	63.0%
Industrial/Energy	21.9%
Consumer Related	7.6%
Computer Software and Services	7.6%

Additional Information
Name of Most Recent Fund: New Mountain Partners III, L.P.

Most Recent Fund Was Raised: 06/07/2007
Year Founded: 2000
Capital Under Management: $6,864,600,000
Current Activity Level : Actively seeking new investments

NEW RIVER CAPITAL PARTNERS

401 East Las Olas Boulevard
Suite 1140
Fort Lauderdale, FL USA 33316
Phone: 954-713-1160
Fax: 954-713-1175
E-mail: info@newrivercapital.com
Website: www.newrivercapital.com

Management and Staff

John Hall, Partner
Michael Bush, Partner
Mike Van der Kieft, Partner
Steven Berrard, Co-Founder
Thomas Byrne, Co-Founder
Thomas Hawkins, Partner
Thomas Aucamp, Partner

Type of Firm

Private Equity Firm

Project Preferences

Type of Financing Preferred:
Generalist PE

Industry Focus

(% based on actual investment)

Biotechnology	58.9%
Computer Software and Services	22.8%
Internet Specific	11.7%
Consumer Related	6.6%

Additional Information

Year Founded: 1999
Current Activity Level : Actively seeking new investments

NEW SCIENCE VENTURES, LLC

645 Madison Avenue
20th Floor
New York, NY USA 10022
Phone: 212-920-2562
Fax: 212-308-9196
E-mail: info@newscienceventures.com
Website: www.newscienceventures.com

Management and Staff

Somu Subramaniam, Managing Partner
Thomas Lavin, Chief Financial Officer

Type of Firm

Private Equity Firm

Project Preferences

Type of Financing Preferred:
Balanced

Geographical Preferences

United States Preferences:
All U.S.

Industry Preferences

In Medical/Health prefer:
Medical Products

Additional Information

Year Founded: 2004
Capital Under Management: $2,500,000
Current Activity Level : Actively seeking new investments

NEW SILK ROUTE PARTNERS, LTD.

59 Beachside Avenue
Westport, CT USA 06880
Phone: 212-710-5231

Management and Staff

Mark Schwartz, Co-Founder
Raj Rajaratnam, Co-Founder

Type of Firm

Private Equity Firm

Project Preferences

Type of Financing Preferred:
Leveraged Buyout
Expansion

Geographical Preferences

International Preferences:
India
Pakistan
Utd. Arab Em.
Asia

Industry Preferences

In Communications prefer:
Telecommunications

In Consumer Related prefer:
Consumer Products
Consumer Services

In Financial Services prefer:
Financial Services
Real Estate

In Utilities prefer:
Utilities

Additional Information

Year Founded: 2007
Capital Under Management: $1,383,100,000
Current Activity Level : Actively seeking new investments

NEW STAR ASSET MANAGEMENT

1 Knightsbridge Green
London, United Kingdom SW1X 7NE
Phone: 44-20-7225-9200
E-mail: webgroup@newstaram.com
Website: www.newstaram.com

Management and Staff

Howard Covington, Chief Executive Officer
John Mould, Chief Operating Officer
Mark Hilliam, Managing Director
Philip Wagstaff, Managing Director

Type of Firm

Private Equity Advisor or Fund of Funds

Project Preferences

Type of Financing Preferred:
Fund of Funds
Leveraged Buyout

Geographical Preferences

International Preferences:
Europe

Additional Information

Year Founded: 2000
Current Activity Level : Actively seeking new investments

NEW VANTAGE GROUP (FKA: DINNER CLUB LLC, THE)

402 Maple Avenue West
Suite C
Vienna, VA USA 22180
Phone: 703-255-4930
Fax: 703-255-4931
E-mail: info@newvantagegroup.com
Website: www.newvantagegroup.com

Management and Staff

John May, Managing Partner

Type of Firm

Private Equity Firm

Association Membership

Mid-Atlantic Venture Association

Project Preferences

Role in Financing:
Will function either as deal originator or investor in deals created by others

Type of Financing Preferred:
Second Stage Financing
Early Stage
First Stage Financing

Size of Investments Considered:
Min Size of Investment Considered (000s): $250
Max Size of Investment Considered (000s): $1,000

Geographical Preferences

United States Preferences:
Mid Atlantic

Industry Preferences

In Communications prefer:
Telecommunications
Wireless Communications
Data Communications

In Computer Software prefer:
Computer Services
Software
Systems Software
Applications Software

In Internet Specific prefer:
Internet
Ecommerce
Web Aggregration/Portals

In Semiconductor/Electr prefer:
Micro-Processing
Controllers and Sensors
Laser Related
Fiber Optics

In Biotechnology prefer:
Human Biotechnology

In Medical/Health prefer:
Diagnostic Test Products
Medical Products

In Consumer Related prefer:
Education Related

In Financial Services prefer:
Financial Services

Additional Information
Name of Most Recent Fund: Active Angel Investors
Most Recent Fund Was Raised: 01/01/2003
Year Founded: 1999
Capital Under Management: $30,000,000
Current Activity Level : Actively seeking new investments
Method of Compensation: Return on investment is of primary concern, do not charge fees

---

NEW VENTURE DEVELOPMENT SRL

Corso Re Umberto 11
Ivrea, Italy 10015
Phone: 39 0125 64 1183
Fax: 39 0125 48 772
E-mail: info@nvd.it
Website: www.nvd.it

Management and Staff
Mario Ciofalo, Partner

Type of Firm
Private Equity Firm

Association Membership
Italian Venture Capital Association (AIFI)

Project Preferences

Type of Financing Preferred:
Early Stage
Seed

Geographical Preferences

International Preferences:
Italy

Additional Information
Year Founded: 1999
Current Activity Level : Actively seeking new investments

NEW VENTURE PARTNERS

1119 St. Paul Street
Baltimore, MD USA 21202
Phone: 410-244-0115
Fax: 410-752-7721

Management and Staff
Howard Wolfe, General Partner

Type of Firm
Private Equity Firm

Association Membership
Mid-Atlantic Venture Association

Project Preferences

Size of Investments Considered:
Min Size of Investment Considered (000s): $75
Max Size of Investment Considered (000s): $2,400

Additional Information
Year Founded: 1981
Current Activity Level : Actively seeking new investments

NEW VENTURE PARTNERS LLC

430 Mountain Avenue
Murray Hill, NJ USA 07974
Phone: 908-464-0900
Fax: 908-464-8131
E-mail: info@nvpllc.com
Website: www.nvpllc.com

Other Offices
2929 Campus Drive
Suite 410
San Mateo, CA USA 94403
Phone: 650-353-2962

Columba House, NG10
Adastral Park
Ipswich, United Kingdom IP5 3RE
Phone: 44-1473-63670
Fax: 44-1473-636718

Olmenlaan 16
Bussum, Netherlands 1404 DG
Phone: 31-35-697-0015

Management and Staff
Andrew Garman, Managing Partner
Chris Winter, Partner
Daniel Deeney, Partner
David Tennenhouse, Partner
Frank Rimalovski, Partner
Harry Berry, Partner
Jalak Jobanputra, Principal
Robert Rosenberg, Partner
Stephen Socolof, Managing Partner
Thomas Uhlman, Managing Partner

Type of Firm
Private Equity Firm

Association Membership
National Venture Capital Association - USA (NVCA)

Project Preferences

Type of Financing Preferred:
Early Stage
Seed

Industry Preferences

In Communications prefer:
Communications and Media

In Computer Software prefer:
Software

In Semiconductor/Electr prefer:
Semiconductor

Additional Information
Name of Most Recent Fund: NV Partners IV, L.P.
Most Recent Fund Was Raised: 12/29/2005
Year Founded: 1997
Capital Under Management: $167,700,000
Current Activity Level : Actively seeking new investments

NEW VERNON PRIVATE EQUITY (FKA: NEW VERNON BHARAT LTD.)

2330 Plaza Five
Harborside Financial Center
Jersey City, NJ USA 07311
Phone: 201-793-0570

Other Offices
21/22 Free Press House
215 Free Press Journal
Mumbai, India 400 021
Phone: 91-22-6651-1910

Type of Firm
Private Equity Firm

Project Preferences
Type of Financing Preferred:
Balanced

Geographical Preferences
International Preferences:
Asia

Additional Information
Year Founded: 2005
Current Activity Level : Actively seeking new investments

NEW VISTA CAPITAL LLC
161 East Evelyn Avenue
Mountain View, CA USA 94041
Phone: 650-864-2553
Fax: 650-864-2599
Website: www.nvcap.com

Management and Staff
Frank Greene, Managing Partner
Roger Barry, Managing Partner

Type of Firm
SBIC

Association Membership
Western Association of Venture Capitalists (WAVC)

Project Preferences
Role in Financing:
Prefer role as deal originator but will also invest in deals created by others

Type of Financing Preferred:
Second Stage Financing
Early Stage
Start-up Financing
Seed
First Stage Financing

Geographical Preferences
United States Preferences:
Northwest
Rocky Mountain
West Coast
California
Southwest

Industry Focus
(% based on actual investment)

Internet Specific	46.0%
Computer Software and Services	34.0%
Semiconductors/Other Elect.	11.9%
Other Products	2.6%
Communications and Media	2.6%
Computer Hardware	2.6%
Consumer Related	0.3%

Additional Information
Year Founded: 1997
Capital Under Management: $21,000,000
Current Activity Level : Actively seeking new investments
Method of Compensation: Return on investment is of primary concern, do not charge fees

---

NEW WORLD ANGELS, INC.
FAU Boulevard
Suite 210
Boca Raton, FL USA 33431
Phone: 561-620-8494
Fax: 561-620-8493
E-mail: info@newworldangels.com
Website: www.newworldangels.com

Management and Staff
Peter Hairston, President

Type of Firm
Angel Group

Project Preferences
Type of Financing Preferred:
Early Stage

Geographical Preferences
United States Preferences:
Florida

Additional Information
Year Founded: 2006
Current Activity Level : Actively seeking new investments

NEW WORLD VENTURES
1603 Orrington Avenue
Suite 1600
Evanston, IL USA 60201
Phone: 847-328-0300
Fax: 847-328-8297
E-mail: info@newworldvc.com
Website: www.newworldvc.com

Management and Staff
Adam Koopersmith, Vice President
Christopher Girgenti, Managing Partner
J.B. Pritzker, Partner
Kathleen Smith, Chief Financial Officer
Lisa Flashner, Partner

Type of Firm
Private Equity Firm

Association Membership
Illinois Venture Capital Association

Project Preferences
Role in Financing:
Prefer role as deal originator but will also invest in deals created by others

Type of Financing Preferred:
Early Stage

Size of Investments Considered:
Min Size of Investment Considered (000s): $2,000
Max Size of Investment Considered (000s): $4,000

Industry Focus
(% based on actual investment)

Internet Specific	78.4%
Computer Software and Services	17.9%
Communications and Media	3.7%

Additional Information
Year Founded: 1996
Capital Under Management: $90,400,000
Current Activity Level : Actively seeking new investments
Method of Compensation: Return on investment is of primary concern, do not charge fees

---

NEW YORK CITY INVESTMENT FUND
One Battery Park Plaza
5th Floor
New York, NY USA 10004
Phone: 212-493-7400
Fax: 212-809-9815
Website: www.nycif.com

Management and Staff
Anthony Giugliano, Chief Financial Officer

Type of Firm
Private Equity Firm

Association Membership
Community Development Venture Capital Alliance

Project Preferences
Role in Financing:
Will function either as deal originator or investor in deals created by others

Type of Financing Preferred:
Second Stage Financing
Early Stage
Expansion
Research and Development
Generalist PE
Balanced
Start-up Financing
Later Stage
Seed
First Stage Financing
Startup

Size of Investments Considered:
Min Size of Investment Considered (000s): $1,000

Max Size of Investment Considered (000s): $5,000

Geographical Preferences

United States Preferences:

New York

Industry Preferences

In Communications prefer:

Communications and Media
Telecommunications
Wireless Communications
Media and Entertainment

In Computer Software prefer:

Software

In Internet Specific prefer:

Internet

In Biotechnology prefer:

Biotechnology

In Consumer Related prefer:

Retail
Food/Beverage
Education Related

In Industrial/Energy prefer:

Energy
Alternative Energy

In Transportation prefer:

Transportation

In Other prefer:

Socially Responsible
Women/Minority-Owned Bus.

Additional Information

Year Founded: 1996
Capital Under Management: $114,000,000
Current Activity Level : Actively seeking new investments
Method of Compensation: Return on investment is of primary concern, do not charge fees

---

NEW YORK LIFE CAPITAL PARTNERS (AKA: NYLCAP)

51 Madison Avenue
16th Floor
New York, NY USA 10010
Phone: 212-576-7000
Fax: 212-576-5591
Website: www.nylcap.com

Other Offices

1180 Avenue of the Americas
New York, NY USA 10036
Phone: 212-938-6500

Management and Staff

Amanda Parness, Vice President
Quint Barker, Principal
S. Thomas Knoff, Principal
Stephen Williams, Principal
Steven Benevento, Principal

Type of Firm

Insurance Firm Affiliate

Project Preferences

Role in Financing:

Prefer role in deals created by others

Type of Financing Preferred:

Second Stage Financing
Leveraged Buyout
Expansion
Mezzanine
Start-up Financing
Later Stage
First Stage Financing
Acquisition
Distressed Debt
Recapitalizations

Size of Investments Considered:

Min Size of Investment Considered (000s): $15,000
Max Size of Investment Considered (000s): $25,000

Geographical Preferences

United States Preferences:

All U.S.

International Preferences:

India
Europe
All International

Industry Focus

(% based on actual investment)

Other Products	48.7%
Consumer Related	12.1%
Biotechnology	8.0%
Industrial/Energy	7.6%
Internet Specific	5.9%
Computer Hardware	5.3%
Communications and Media	4.9%
Medical/Health	4.7%
Computer Software and Services	2.0%
Semiconductors/Other Elect.	0.8%

Additional Information

Name of Most Recent Fund: NYLIM Mezzanine Partners II Parallel Fund, L.P.
Most Recent Fund Was Raised: 01/11/2007
Year Founded: 1995
Capital Under Management: $3,000,000,000
Current Activity Level : Actively seeking new investments
Method of Compensation: Return on invest. most important, but chg. closing fees, service fees, etc.

NEW YORK TIMES COMPANY,THE

229 West 43rd Street
New York, NY USA 10036
Phone: 212-556-1234
Website: www.nytco.com

Type of Firm

Corporate PE/Venture

Additional Information

Year Founded: 2000
Current Activity Level : Actively seeking new investments

NEWBRIDGE CAPITAL, LTD.

57/F Suite 5704-13 Two IFC
8 Finance Street
Central, Hong Kong
Phone: 852-3515-8888
Fax: 852-3515-8999
Website: www.newbridgecapital.com

Other Offices

Level 31
101 Collins Street
Melbourne, Australia 3000
Phone: 613-9664-4444
Fax: 613-9663-7005

Atago Green Hills MORI Tower 36F
2-5-1 Atago Minato-ku
Tokyo, Japan 1056236
Phone: 81-3-5408-6900
Fax: 81-3-5408-0691

12 Zhongshan Road (E1),
Suite 332
Shanghai, China 200002
Phone: 86-21-3313-0203
Fax: 86-21-6329-9100

301 Commerce Street
Suite 3300
Fort Worth, TX USA 76102
Phone: 817-871-4000
Fax: 817-871-4001

2882 Sand Hill Road
Suite 106
Menlo Park, CA USA 94025
Phone: 650-289-5800
Fax: 650-289-5801

153 Maker Chamber VI
Nariman Point
Mumbai, India 400 02
Phone: 91-22-4039-1000
Fax: 91-22-4039-1002

The Goldbell Centre
5 rue Eugene Ruppert
Luxembourg L-2453
Phone: 352-2700-41251
Fax: 352-2700-412599

Znamenka 7
Building 3
Moscow, Russia 119019

Phone: 7-495-660-8600
Fax: 495-660-8601

One George Street
#14-01
Singapore, Singapore 049145
Phone: 65-6390-5000
Fax: 65-6390-5001

1133 Connecticut Avenue, North West
Suite 700
Washington, DC USA 20036
Phone: 202-530-1400
Fax: 202-496-0051

345 California Street
Suite 3300
San Francisco, CA USA 94104
Phone: 415-743-1500
Fax: 415-743-1507

2nd Floor, Stirling Square
5-7 Carlton Gardens
London, United Kingdom SW1Y 5AD
Phone: 440-20-7544-650
Fax: 440-20-7544-656

Management and Staff

Bien Kiat Tan, Managing Director
Daniel Ashton Carroll, Managing Partner
James Chang, Vice President
Jeff Ekberg, Chief Financial Officer
Jun Tsusaka, Managing Director
Masayuki Yasuoka, Managing Director
Steven Schneider, Partner
Weijian Shan, Managing Partner

Type of Firm

Private Equity Firm

Association Membership

Singapore Venture Capital Association (SVCA)

Project Preferences

Role in Financing:

Prefer role as deal originator but will also invest in deals created by others

Type of Financing Preferred:

Leveraged Buyout
Control-block Purchases
Expansion
Balanced
Public Companies
Turnaround
Later Stage
Management Buyouts
Acquisition
Joint Ventures
Private Placement
Special Situation
Recapitalizations

Size of Investments Considered:

Min Size of Investment Considered (000s): $10,000
Max Size of Investment Considered: No Limit

Geographical Preferences

International Preferences:

Indonesia
India
Taiwan
China
Hong Kong
Thailand
Philippines
Singapore
Korea, South
Asia
Japan
Malaysia

Industry Preferences

In Communications prefer:

Communications and Media

In Computer Software prefer:

Computer Services
Data Processing
Software
Systems Software
Applications Software

In Internet Specific prefer:

Internet
Web Aggregration/Portals

In Semiconductor/Electr prefer:

Electronic Components
Semiconductor
Circuit Boards
Component Testing Equipmt
Laser Related
Fiber Optics

In Biotechnology prefer:

Human Biotechnology
Agricultural/Animal Bio.

In Consumer Related prefer:

Consumer
Entertainment and Leisure
Retail
Food/Beverage
Hotels and Resorts

In Transportation prefer:

Transportation
Aerospace

In Financial Services prefer:

Financial Services
Insurance

In Business Serv. prefer:

Services
Distribution
Consulting Services
Media

In Manufact. prefer:

Manufacturing

Additional Information

Year Founded: 1992
Capital Under Management: $3,200,000,000
Current Activity Level : Actively seeking new investments

NEWBRIDGE NETWORKS

600 March Road
Kanata, Canada K2K 2E6
Phone: 613-599-3600
Fax: 613-599-3673
Website: www.newbridge.com

Type of Firm

Corporate PE/Venture

Additional Information

Year Founded: 1986
Current Activity Level : Actively seeking new investments

NEWBURY PARTNERS LLC

944 Glenwood Station Lane
Suite 301
Charlottesville, VA USA 22901
Phone: 434-220-7495
Fax: 434-220-7496
Website: www.newburypartnersllc.com

Other Offices

977 Seminole Trail
PMB 340
Charlottesville, VA USA 22901

Management and Staff

Michelle Dalton-Hunt, President

Type of Firm

Private Equity Firm

Project Preferences

Type of Financing Preferred:

Early Stage
Seed
Startup

Industry Preferences

In Communications prefer:

Communications and Media

Additional Information

Year Founded: 2007
Current Activity Level : Actively seeking new investments

NEWBURY PARTNERS LLC

100 First Stamford Place
Stamford, CT USA 06902
Phone: 203-428-3600
Fax: 203-428-3601
Website: www.newbury-partners.com

Management and Staff

Gerry Esposito, Chief Financial Officer
Richard Lichter, Managing Director
Warren Symon, Vice President

Type of Firm

Private Equity Advisor or Fund of Funds

Project Preferences

Type of Financing Preferred:
Fund of Funds of Second

Geographical Preferences

Canadian Preferences:
All Canada

International Preferences:
Europe
Asia

Additional Information

Year Founded: 2006
Capital Under Management: $702,000,000
Current Activity Level : Actively seeking new investments

NEWCAP PARTNERS, INC.

5777 West Century Boulevard
Suite 1135
Los Angeles, CA USA 90045
Phone: 310-645-7900
Fax: 310-215-1025
Website: www.newcap.com

Other Offices

Vasagatan 11
Stockholm, Sweden 10139
Phone: 46-8545-13250
Fax: 46-8545-13369

Type of Firm

Bank Affiliated

Additional Information

Year Founded: 2002
Current Activity Level : Actively seeking new investments

NEWFARMERS DEVELOPEMENT COMPANY

Durbanville
Durbanville, South Africa 7551
Phone: 27-21-975-1262
Fax: 27-21-975-1254
E-mail: corporate@newfarmers.co.za

Management and Staff

JP Le Roux, Chief Executive Officer

Type of Firm

Private Equity Firm

Association Membership

South African Venture Capital Association (SAVCA)

Project Preferences

Type of Financing Preferred:
Balanced

Size of Investments Considered:
Min Size of Investment Considered (000s): $274
Max Size of Investment Considered (000s): $1,371

Geographical Preferences

International Preferences:
South Africa

Industry Preferences

In Agr/Forestr/Fish prefer:
Agribusiness

Additional Information

Year Founded: 1995
Current Activity Level : Actively seeking new investments

NEWFUND MANAGEMENT SA

124, Boulevard Haussmann
Paris, France 75008
E-mail: contact@newfund.fr
Website: www.newfund.fr

Management and Staff

Francois Veron, Founder

Type of Firm

Private Equity Firm

Association Membership

French Venture Capital Association (AFIC)

Project Preferences

Type of Financing Preferred:
Expansion
Recapitalizations

Geographical Preferences

International Preferences:
Europe

Industry Preferences

In Communications prefer:
Entertainment

In Consumer Related prefer:
Retail

In Industrial/Energy prefer:
Energy

Additional Information

Year Founded: 2007
Capital Under Management: $99,300,000
Current Activity Level : Actively seeking new investments

NEWION INVESTMENTS B.V.

Postbus 232
Heerenveen, Netherlands 8440 AE
Phone: 31-513-640-633
Fax: 31-513-640-871
E-mail: info@newion-investments .com
Website: www.newion-investments.com

Other Offices

Businesspark Friesland West 27B
Nijehaske, Netherlands 8466

Management and Staff

Jaap Van Barneveld, Founder
Patrick Polak, Founder

Type of Firm

Bank Affiliated

Project Preferences

Type of Financing Preferred:
Early Stage
Generalist PE
Management Buyouts

Size of Investments Considered:
Min Size of Investment Considered (000s): $181
Max Size of Investment Considered (000s): $1,813

Geographical Preferences

International Preferences:
Europe

Industry Preferences

In Communications prefer:
Communications and Media

In Computer Software prefer:
Software

In Internet Specific prefer:
Internet

In Semiconductor/Electr prefer:
Electronic Components

Additional Information

Year Founded: 2000
Capital Under Management: $63,400,000
Current Activity Level : Actively seeking new investments

NEWLIGHT ASSOCIATES

245 Fifth Avenue
25th Floor
Manhattan, NY USA 10016
Phone: 212-675-7354
Fax: 212-675-7381
Website: www.nlventures.com

Other Offices

500 North Broadway
Suite 144
Jericho, NY USA 11753
Phone: 516-433-0090
Fax: 516-433-0412

Management and Staff

Douglas Miscoll, Principal
Michael McMorrow, Chief Financial Officer
Robert Brill, Managing Partner
Robert Raucci, Managing Partner

Type of Firm

Private Equity Firm

Project Preferences

Role in Financing:
Will function either as deal originator or investor in deals created by others

Type of Financing Preferred:
Early Stage
Expansion
Public Companies
Later Stage

Size of Investments Considered:
Min Size of Investment Considered (000s): $1,000
Max Size of Investment Considered (000s): $4,000

Geographical Preferences

United States Preferences:
East Coast

Industry Preferences

In Communications prefer:
Telecommunications

In Computer Software prefer:
Software
Systems Software
Applications Software

In Internet Specific prefer:
Internet

In Semiconductor/Electr prefer:
Semiconductor
Optoelectronics

Additional Information

Year Founded: 1997
Capital Under Management: $120,000,000
Current Activity Level : Actively seeking new investments
Method of Compensation: Return on investment is of primary concern, do not charge fees

NEWMARGIN VENTURES

Villa 3, Radisson Plaza
78 Xing Guo Road
Shanghai, China 200052
Phone: 86-21-6213-8000
Fax: 86-21-6213-7000
E-mail: info@newmargin.com
Website: www.newmargin.com

Other Offices

No. 35 Qin Lao Hutong
Dong Cheng District
Beijing, China 100080
Phone: 86-10-840-22999
Fax: 86-10-840-20555

Management and Staff

Feng Tao, Managing Partner
Xu Hanjie, Partner
Ye Weigang, Partner
Yuan Wei, Partner
Zhou Shuiwen, Partner
Zhou Yongkai, Partner

Type of Firm

Private Equity Firm

Project Preferences

Type of Financing Preferred:
Early Stage
Expansion
Balanced
Seed
Startup

Geographical Preferences

International Preferences:
China
Asia

Industry Preferences

In Communications prefer:
Telecommunications
Wireless Communications

In Semiconductor/Electr prefer:
Fiber Optics

In Biotechnology prefer:
Biotechnology

In Medical/Health prefer:
Medical/Health

In Other prefer:
Environment Responsible

Additional Information

Year Founded: 1999
Capital Under Management: $120,000,000
Current Activity Level : Actively seeking new investments

NEWPATH VENTURES, LLC

3945 Freedom Circle
Suite 1050
Santa Clara, CA USA 95054
Phone: 408-919-9900
Fax: 408-919-9912
Website: www.newpathventures.com

Other Offices

26 Cunningham Road
Bangalore, India 560 052
Phone: 91-80-2226-7272
Fax: 91-80-2225-1133

Type of Firm

Private Equity Firm

Association Membership

Indian Venture Capital Association (IVCA)

Project Preferences

Type of Financing Preferred:
Early Stage
Startup

Geographical Preferences

International Preferences:
India

Industry Preferences

In Computer Software prefer:
Software

In Semiconductor/Electr prefer:
Semiconductor

In Business Serv. prefer:
Services

Additional Information

Year Founded: 2002
Current Activity Level : Actively seeking new investments

NEWPORT PRIVATE EQUITY ASIA

26/F One Int'l Finance Centre
Suite 2616
Central, Hong Kong
Phone: 852-2865-0933
Fax: 852-2164-9000

Type of Firm

Bank Affiliated

Project Preferences

Role in Financing:
Will function either as deal originator or investor in deals created by others

Type of Financing Preferred:
Early Stage
Expansion

Geographical Preferences

International Preferences:
China

Industry Preferences

In Business Serv. prefer:
Services

In Manufact. prefer:
Manufacturing

Additional Information
Year Founded: 2000
Capital Under Management: $75,000,000
Current Activity Level : Actively seeking new investments
Method of Compensation: Return on investment is of primary concern, do not charge fees

---

NEWSCHOOLS VENTURE FUND
49 Stevenson Street
Suite 1275
San Francisco, CA USA 94105
Phone: 415-615-6860
Fax: 415-615-6861
E-mail: info@newschools.org
Website: www.newschools.org

Other Offices
1725 I Street, NW
Suite 300
Washington, DC USA 20006
Phone: 202-349-3912
Fax: 202-349-3915

Management and Staff
Joanne Weiss, Managing Partner
Lauren Dutton, Partner

Type of Firm
Private Equity Firm

Project Preferences

Type of Financing Preferred:
Early Stage
Seed

Geographical Preferences

United States Preferences:
All U.S.

Industry Preferences

In Consumer Related prefer:
Education Related

Additional Information
Year Founded: 1998
Capital Under Management: $20,000,000
Current Activity Level : Actively seeking new investments

NEWSMITH ASSET MANAGEMENT LLP
Lansdowne House
57 Berkeley Square
London, United Kingdom W1J 6ER
Phone: 44-20-7518-3700
Fax: 44-20-7518-3701
E-mail: enquiries@newsmithcapital.com
Website: www.newsmithcapital.com

Other Offices
Suite 701, Ruttonjee House
11 Duddell Street
Central, Hong Kong
Phone: 852-2537-7784
Fax: 852-2537-7794

25-08 One Marina Boulevard
Singapore, Singapore 018989
Phone: 65-6363-7878
Fax: 65-6438-3886

Clover Shibakoen 3F
1-3-12 Shibakoen Minato-ku
Tokyo, Japan 105-0011
Phone: 813-5425-7878
Fax: 813-5425-7900

717 Fifth Avenue, Floor 12-A
New York, NY USA 10022
Phone: 646-520-2900
Fax: 646-520-2999

Management and Staff
Adrian Vanderspuy, Partner
Bob Wong, Chief Operating Officer
Gordon Dunn, Partner
Rob Harley, Partner
Ron Carlson, Partner

Type of Firm
Private Equity Firm

Project Preferences

Type of Financing Preferred:
Generalist PE

Size of Investments Considered:
Min Size of Investment Considered (000s): $8,922
Max Size of Investment Considered (000s): $26,765

Geographical Preferences

International Preferences:
Europe
Asia

Additional Information
Year Founded: 2003
Capital Under Management: $178,400,000
Current Activity Level : Actively seeking new investments
Method of Compensation: Unknown

NEWSPRING CAPITAL
555 East Lancaster Avenue
Radnor Financial Ctr, Ste 520
Radnor, PA USA 19087
Phone: 610-567-2380
Fax: 610-567-2388
E-mail: Info@newspringcapital.com
Website: www.newspringcapital.com

Other Offices
101 JFK Parkway
Fourth Floor
Short Hills, NJ USA 07078
Phone: 973-467-1133
Fax: 973-467-3007

655 15th Street Northwest
Second Floor
Washington, DC USA 20005
Phone: 610-567-2380
Fax: 610-567-2388

Management and Staff
Andrew Panzo, General Partner
Brian Murphy, General Partner
Bruce Downey, Partner
Glenn Rieger, General Partner
Gregory Barger, Principal
Marc Lederman, General Partner
Michael DiPiano, Managing Partner
Steven Hobman, General Partner
Zev Scherl, General Partner

Type of Firm
Private Equity Firm

Association Membership
Mid-Atlantic Venture Association
Natl Assoc of Small Bus. Inv. Co (NASBIC)
National Venture Capital Association - USA (NVCA)

Project Preferences

Role in Financing:
Will function either as deal originator or investor in deals created by others

Type of Financing Preferred:
Leveraged Buyout
Expansion
Mezzanine
Public Companies
Later Stage
Management Buyouts
Recapitalizations

Size of Investments Considered:
Min Size of Investment Considered (000s): $2,000
Max Size of Investment Considered (000s): $10,000

Geographical Preferences

United States Preferences:
Mid Atlantic
Northeast

Industry Preferences

In Communications prefer:
Communications and Media
Wireless Communications
Data Communications

In Computer Software prefer:
Software

In Computer Other prefer:
Computer Related

In Semiconductor/Electr prefer:
Electronics

In Biotechnology prefer:
Biotechnology
Human Biotechnology

In Medical/Health prefer:
Medical/Health
Medical Therapeutics
Medical Products
Health Services
Pharmaceuticals

In Business Serv. prefer:
Media

Additional Information
Name of Most Recent Fund: NewSpring Health Capital II, L.P.
Most Recent Fund Was Raised: 12/31/2007
Year Founded: 1999
Capital Under Management: $500,000,000
Current Activity Level : Actively seeking new investments
Method of Compensation: Return on investment is of primary concern, do not charge fees

---

NEWSTONE CAPITAL PARTNERS
11111 Santa Monica Boulevard
Suite 1100
Los Angeles, CA USA 90025
Phone: 310-689-1710
Fax: 310-689-1717
Website: www.newstonecapital.com

Other Offices
200 Crescent Court
Suite 1600
Dallas, TX USA 75201
Phone: 214-740-7348
Fax: 214-740-7382

Management and Staff
John Rocchio, Managing Director
Robert Brougham, Managing Director
Timothy Costello, Managing Director

Type of Firm
Private Equity Firm

Project Preferences

Type of Financing Preferred:
Leveraged Buyout
Mezzanine
Later Stage
Recapitalizations

Size of Investments Considered:
Min Size of Investment Considered (000s): $20,000
Max Size of Investment Considered (000s): $100,000

Geographical Preferences

United States Preferences:
All U.S.

Industry Preferences

In Consumer Related prefer:
Consumer Products

In Business Serv. prefer:
Services

In Manufact. prefer:
Manufacturing

Additional Information
Year Founded: 2006
Capital Under Management: $374,000,000
Current Activity Level : Actively seeking new investments

NEWTON TECHNOLOGY PARTNERS (NTP)
555 Bryant Street
Suite 584
Palo Alto, CA USA 94301
Phone: 650-331-3990
Fax: 650-745-1222
E-mail: info@newtontp.com
Website: www.newtontp.com

Other Offices
1st Floor, Samhwa Building
144-17 Samseong-dong
Gangnam-gu, Seoul, South Korea 135-090
Phone: 82-2-6410-6100
Fax: 82-2-6410-6101

Management and Staff
John Milburn, General Partner
Mark Shin, Partner

Type of Firm
Private Equity Firm

Project Preferences

Type of Financing Preferred:
Startup

Size of Investments Considered:
Min Size of Investment Considered (000s): $52
Max Size of Investment Considered (000s): $3,000

Geographical Preferences

United States Preferences:
All U.S.

International Preferences:
North Korea
Korea, South
Asia

Industry Preferences

In Communications prefer:
Wireless Communications

In Computer Software prefer:
Software

In Internet Specific prefer:
E-Commerce Technology
Internet

Additional Information
Year Founded: 2000
Capital Under Management: $50,000,000
Current Activity Level : Actively seeking new investments

NEWWEST MEZZANINE FUND, L.P. (FKA:TOUCHSTONE CAPITAL GROUP)
1700 Lincoln Street
Suite 2000
Denver, CO USA 80203
Phone: 303-764-9677
Fax: 303-832-6154
Website: www.mezzcap.com

Management and Staff
Chet Winter, General Partner
Daniel Arenberg, Principal
David Henry, Managing General Partner

Type of Firm
Private Equity Firm

Association Membership
Natl Assoc of Small Bus. Inv. Co (NASBIC)

Project Preferences

Role in Financing:
Will function either as deal originator or investor in deals created by others

Type of Financing Preferred:
Leveraged Buyout
Control-block Purchases
Expansion
Mezzanine
Later Stage
Management Buyouts
Acquisition

Joint Ventures
Recapitalizations

Size of Investments Considered:
Min Size of Investment Considered (000s): $500
Max Size of Investment Considered (000s): $3,000

Geographical Preferences

United States Preferences:
Rocky Mountain
Southwest

Industry Focus
(% based on actual investment)
Internet Specific 100.0%

Additional Information
Year Founded: 1999
Capital Under Management: $60,000,000
Current Activity Level : Actively seeking new investments
Method of Compensation: Return on investment is of primary concern, do not charge fees

NEXIT VENTURES OY

Kaisaniemenkatu 2B
Helsinki, Finland 00100
Phone: 358-9-681-8910
Fax: 358-9-6818-9117
E-mail: info@nexitventures.com
Website: www.nexitventures.com

Other Offices
Norrmalmstorg 14
Stockholm, Sweden SE-111 46
Phone: 46-8-5250-9020
Fax: 46-8-5250-9021

12930 Saratoga Avenue
Suite B-9
Saratoga, CA USA 95070
Phone: 408-725-8400
Fax: 408-725-8405

Management and Staff
Arturi Tarjanne, General Partner
David Aslin, Venture Partner
Michael Mandahl, General Partner
Michel Wendell, General Partner
Patrice Peyret, Venture Partner
Pekka Salonoja, General Partner
Risto Yli-Tainio, Chief Financial Officer

Type of Firm
Private Equity Firm

Association Membership
Finnish Venture Capital Association (FVCA)
Swedish Venture Capital Association (SVCA)
European Private Equity and Venture Capital Assoc.

Project Preferences

Type of Financing Preferred:
Early Stage
Expansion
Seed
Startup

Size of Investments Considered:
Min Size of Investment Considered (000s): $9,416
Max Size of Investment Considered (000s): $23,540

Geographical Preferences

International Preferences:
Scandanavia/Nordic Region
Finland
Norway

Industry Preferences

In Communications prefer:
Communications and Media
Commercial Communications
Wireless Communications

In Internet Specific prefer:
Internet

In Business Serv. prefer:
Services

Additional Information
Name of Most Recent Fund: Nexit Infocom II
Most Recent Fund Was Raised: 03/03/2008
Year Founded: 2000
Capital Under Management: $200,100,000
Current Activity Level : Actively seeking new investments

NEXOS CAPITAL PARTNERS

99 Park Avenue
Suite 1560
New York, NY USA 10016
Phone: 212-907-1450
Fax: 212-907-1450
E-mail: info@nexoscapital.com
Website: www.nexoscapital.com

Other Offices
30211 Avenida de las Banderas
Suite 200
Rancho Santa Margarita, CA USA 92688
Phone: 949-766-6733
Fax: 949-766-6734

Management and Staff
Eduardo Bohorquez, Principal
John McIntire, Principal
Joseph Vadapalas, Principal
Justo Frias, Principal

Type of Firm
Private Equity Firm

Project Preferences

Type of Financing Preferred:
Expansion

Geographical Preferences

United States Preferences:
All U.S.

Industry Preferences

In Communications prefer:
Communications and Media

In Medical/Health prefer:
Health Services

In Consumer Related prefer:
Consumer Products

In Financial Services prefer:
Financial Services

Additional Information
Year Founded: 2008
Current Activity Level : Actively seeking new investments

NEXT CAPITAL PTY., LTD.

25 Bligh Street Level 30/31
GPO Box 4076
Sydney, Australia 2000
Phone: 612-8222-5555
Fax: 612-8222-5556
E-mail: info@nextcapital.com.au
Website: www.nextcapital.com.au

Management and Staff
John White, Founder
Patrick Elliot, Founder
Peter Gibson, Chief Financial Officer
Sandy Lockhart, Founder

Type of Firm
Private Equity Firm

Association Membership
Australian Venture Capital Association (AVCAL)

Project Preferences

Role in Financing:
Will function either as deal originator or investor in deals created by others

Type of Financing Preferred:
Leveraged Buyout
Generalist PE
Expansion

Size of Investments Considered:
Min Size of Investment Considered (000s): $40,290
Max Size of Investment Considered (000s): $161,160

Geographical Preferences

International Preferences:
New Zealand
Australia

Additional Information
Name of Most Recent Fund: Next Capital Fund 1
Most Recent Fund Was Raised: 12/31/2005
Year Founded: 2005
Capital Under Management: $443,200,000
Current Activity Level : Actively seeking new investments

NEXT FRONTIER CAPITAL
700 North Sacramento Boulevard
Suite 130
Chicago, IL USA 60612
Phone: 773-822-0320
Fax: 773-822-0308
E-mail: info@chiventures.org
Website: www.chiventures.org

Management and Staff
Kathleen Wilkerson, Managing Director
Lauren Robinson, Managing Director

Type of Firm
Corporate PE/Venture

Project Preferences
Type of Financing Preferred:
Balanced

Size of Investments Considered:
Min Size of Investment Considered (000s): $250
Max Size of Investment Considered (000s): $2,500

Geographical Preferences
United States Preferences:
Illinois

Industry Preferences
In Other prefer:
Women/Minority-Owned Bus.

Additional Information
Year Founded: 2004
Current Activity Level : Actively seeking new investments

NEXT GENERATION VENTURES, LLC
200 Corporate Place
3rd Floor
Rocky Hill, CT USA 06067
Phone: 860-257-4262
Fax: 860-257-4525
E-mail: info@nextgenven.com
Website: www.nextgenven.com

Management and Staff
Andrew Zaback, Managing Director
Thomas Conroy, President
Todd Becker, Managing Director

Type of Firm
Private Equity Firm

Project Preferences
Type of Financing Preferred:
Seed
Startup

Geographical Preferences
United States Preferences:
Connecticut

Additional Information
Year Founded: 2000
Current Activity Level : Actively seeking new investments

NEXT VENTURE INVESTMENT
18th Floor, ASEM Tower, 159-1
Samsung-dong, Kangnam-Gu
Seoul, South Korea 135-798
Phone: 822-6001-7700
Fax: 822-6001-7709
Website: www.nextvic.com

Management and Staff
Injun Nam, Chief Executive Officer
Jaehwan Song, Vice President

Type of Firm
Private Equity Firm

Project Preferences
Type of Financing Preferred:
Balanced

Geographical Preferences
International Preferences:
Korea, South

Industry Preferences
In Biotechnology prefer:
Biotechnology

Additional Information
Year Founded: 2000
Capital Under Management: $37,200,000
Current Activity Level : Actively seeking new investments

NEXT WAVE FUNDS
P.O. Box 1403
Washington, CT USA 06793
Phone: 860-868-2021
Fax: 860-868-7967
Website: www.nextwavefunds.com

Other Offices
Klostertern 10
Hamburg, Germany 20149
Phone: 49-40-4809-2910
Fax: 49-40-4609-5705

Management and Staff
Elliott Davis, Managing General Partner
Gerlach Wecken, General Partner

Type of Firm
Private Equity Firm

Project Preferences
Type of Financing Preferred:
Fund of Funds
Early Stage
Expansion

Geographical Preferences
International Preferences:
Europe

Additional Information
Year Founded: 1999
Current Activity Level : Actively seeking new investments

NEXT WAVE PARTNERS LLP
71 Wimpole Street
London, United Kingdom W1G 8AY
Website: www.nextwave-ventures.com

Management and Staff
Jonathan Brod, Partner
Stephen Walls, Partner

Type of Firm
Private Equity Firm

Association Membership
British Venture Capital Association (BVCA)

Project Preferences
Type of Financing Preferred:
Leveraged Buyout
Acquisition

Size of Investments Considered:
Min Size of Investment Considered (000s): $3,968
Max Size of Investment Considered (000s): $39,680

Geographical Preferences
International Preferences:
Europe

Industry Preferences
In Consumer Related prefer:
Entertainment and Leisure
Retail

Food/Beverage
Other Restaurants
Education Related

In Industrial/Energy prefer:
Energy Conservation Relat

In Business Serv. prefer:
Services
Media

Additional Information
Year Founded: 2007
Capital Under Management: $39,700,000
Current Activity Level : Actively seeking new investments

NEXTCOM VENTURES
1666 K Street NW
Suite 1200
Washington, DC USA 20006
Website: www.nextcomventures.com

Management and Staff
Ahmed Saeed, Managing Director
Mark Fahlberg, Managing Director

Type of Firm
Private Equity Firm

Association Membership
Mid-Atlantic Venture Association

Project Preferences

Type of Financing Preferred:
Early Stage
Expansion
Later Stage

Size of Investments Considered:
Min Size of Investment Considered (000s): $500
Max Size of Investment Considered (000s): $1,500

Industry Preferences

In Communications prefer:
Communications and Media

In Computer Software prefer:
Software

In Internet Specific prefer:
Internet

Additional Information
Year Founded: 2000
Current Activity Level : Actively seeking new investments

NEXTECH VENTURE, LTD.
Scheuchzerstrasse 35
Zurich, Switzerland CH-8006
Phone: 41-1-366-6611
Fax: 41-1-366-6610
E-mail: info@nextechventure.com
Website: www.nextechventure.com

Management and Staff
Alfred Scheidegger, Managing Partner
Felix Hofstetter, Managing Partner
Myoung-Ok Kwon, Partner
Sven M. Rohmann, Managing Partner

Type of Firm
Investment Management Firm

Project Preferences

Role in Financing:
Prefer role as deal originator but will also invest in deals created by others

Type of Financing Preferred:
Second Stage Financing
Early Stage
Balanced
Later Stage
Private Placement

Size of Investments Considered:
Min Size of Investment Considered (000s): $430
Max Size of Investment Considered (000s): $8,601

Geographical Preferences

United States Preferences:
All U.S.

International Preferences:
Europe
Western Europe
Eastern Europe
Asia

Industry Preferences

In Biotechnology prefer:
Human Biotechnology
Biotech Related Research

In Medical/Health prefer:
Medical Diagnostics
Medical Therapeutics
Pharmaceuticals

Additional Information
Year Founded: 1999
Capital Under Management: $25,800,000
Current Activity Level : Actively seeking new investments

NEXTLEVEL GROUP
6800 Jericho Turnpike
Suite 120W
Syosset, NY USA 11791
Phone: 516-393-5887
Fax: 516-750-9922
E-mail: info@nextlevelvp.com
Website: www.nextlevelvp.com

Management and Staff
Anita Kaufman, Founding Partner
Joe Heller, Managing Director

Type of Firm
Private Equity Firm

Association Membership
Mid-Atlantic Venture Association

Project Preferences

Type of Financing Preferred:
Early Stage

Size of Investments Considered:
Min Size of Investment Considered (000s): $500
Max Size of Investment Considered (000s): $5,000

Geographical Preferences

United States Preferences:
East Coast

Industry Preferences

In Communications prefer:
Telecommunications

In Internet Specific prefer:
E-Commerce Technology
Internet

Additional Information
Year Founded: 2000
Current Activity Level : Making few, if any, new investments

NEXTPOINT PARTNERS, L.P.
701 Pennsylvania Avenue NW
Suite 900
Washington, DC USA 20004
Phone: 202-434-7319
Fax: 202-434-7400
Website: www.nextpointvc.com

Other Offices
One Financial Center
Suite 4100
Boston, MA USA 02111
Phone: 617-348-3023
Fax: 617-542-2241

666 Third Avenue
25th Floor
New York, NY USA 10017
Phone: 212-935-3000
Fax: 212-983-3115

Management and Staff
Bernee D. Strom, Venture Partner
James MacIntyre, General Partner
Jane Dietze, General Partner
Johnathan Peskoff, General Partner
Michael Faber, Managing General Partner

Type of Firm
Private Equity Firm

Project Preferences

Role in Financing:
Will function either as deal originator or investor in deals created by others

Type of Financing Preferred:
Early Stage
Research and Development
Seed
Startup

Size of Investments Considered:
Min Size of Investment Considered (000s): $250
Max Size of Investment Considered (000s): $6,000

Geographical Preferences

United States Preferences:
Mid Atlantic
Midwest
Southeast
Northeast

Industry Preferences

In Communications prefer:
Communications and Media
Telecommunications

In Computer Software prefer:
Software

In Internet Specific prefer:
Internet

In Computer Other prefer:
Computer Related

In Semiconductor/Electr prefer:
Electronic Components

In Industrial/Energy prefer:
Factory Automation
Process Control

In Other prefer:
Socially Responsible

Additional Information
Year Founded: 2000
Capital Under Management: $50,000,000
Current Activity Level : Actively seeking new investments
Method of Compensation: Return on investment is of primary concern, do not charge fees

---

NEXTSTAGE CAPITAL
2570 Boulevard of the Generals
Suite 110
Audubon, PA USA 19403
Phone: 866-892-1500
Fax: 610-635-0304
E-mail: info@nextstagecapital.com
Website: www.nextstagecapital.com

Type of Firm
Private Equity Firm

Project Preferences

Role in Financing:
Prefer role as deal originator but will also invest in deals created by others

Type of Financing Preferred:
Early Stage
Seed

Size of Investments Considered:
Min Size of Investment Considered (000s): $250
Max Size of Investment Considered (000s): $2,000

Geographical Preferences

United States Preferences:
Mid Atlantic

Industry Preferences

In Computer Other prefer:
Computer Related

In Business Serv. prefer:
Services

Additional Information
Name of Most Recent Fund: NextStage Capital, L.P.
Most Recent Fund Was Raised: 03/01/2006
Year Founded: 2004
Capital Under Management: $17,000,000
Current Activity Level : Actively seeking new investments
Method of Compensation: Return on investment is of primary concern, do not charge fees

---

NEXTSTAGE SAS
25, rue Murillo
Paris, France 75008
Phone: 33-1-5393-4940
Fax: 33-1-5393-4941
E-mail: info@nextstage.com
Website: www.nextstage.com

Management and Staff
Gregoire Sentilhes, President
Herve De Bublain, Managing Director
Jean-David Haas, Managing Partner
Keyvan Nilforoushan, Managing Partner

Type of Firm
Private Equity Firm

Association Membership
French Venture Capital Association (AFIC)

Project Preferences

Type of Financing Preferred:
Leveraged Buyout
Early Stage
Expansion
Startup

Geographical Preferences

International Preferences:
Europe
France

Industry Preferences

In Communications prefer:
Communications and Media
Commercial Communications

In Consumer Related prefer:
Retail

In Business Serv. prefer:
Services
Distribution

Additional Information
Year Founded: 2002
Capital Under Management: $118,600,000
Current Activity Level : Actively seeking new investments

NEXTSTART CAPITAL
3650 Mansell Road
Suite 310
Alpharetta, GA USA 30022
Phone: 770-643-5505
Website: www.nextstartcapital.com

Management and Staff
Richard Jackson, Chairman & CEO
Shane Jackson, President & COO

Type of Firm
Private Equity Firm

Project Preferences

Type of Financing Preferred:
Second Stage Financing
Early Stage
First Stage Financing

Geographical Preferences

United States Preferences:
West Coast

Industry Preferences

In Internet Specific prefer:
Internet

Additional Information
Year Founded: 2000
Current Activity Level : Actively seeking new investments

NEXUS GROUP LLC
One Lombard Street
Suite 300
San Francisco, CA USA 94111

Phone: 415-544-6180
Fax: 415-544-6181
E-mail: info@nexusgrp.com
Website: www.nexusgrp.com

Management and Staff

David Leyrer, Founder
Robert Horning, Founder
William Weathersby, Founder

Type of Firm

Private Equity Firm

Industry Focus

(% based on actual investment)

Internet Specific	74.1%
Communications and Media	12.4%
Computer Software and Services	11.2%
Semiconductors/Other Elect.	2.3%

Additional Information

Year Founded: 1996
Capital Under Management: $30,000,000
Current Activity Level : Actively seeking new investments

NEXUS INVESTMENT CORP. (FKA: PUSAN VENTURE TECH. CAPITAL)

6th Floor, Hanil Offcetel, 815
Munhyun-dong, Nam-gu
Busan, South Korea 608-792
Phone: 82-51-633-7001
Fax: 82-51-633-7006
E-mail: info@nesinvest.co.kr
Website: www.nesinvest.co.kr

Other Offices

Level 4, C&H Building
154-8 Samsung-Dong Kangnam-Ku
Seoul, South Korea
Phone: 822-3452-9550
Fax: 822-3452-9577

Management and Staff

Hyo Moon Ahn, President
Yangjin Leem, Chief Executive Officer

Type of Firm

Corporate PE/Venture

Association Membership

Korean Venture Capital Association (KVCA)

Project Preferences

Type of Financing Preferred:

Early Stage
Balanced

Geographical Preferences

International Preferences:

Korea, South

Industry Preferences

In Biotechnology prefer:

Biotechnology

In Medical/Health prefer:

Medical/Health

In Consumer Related prefer:

Entertainment and Leisure

In Industrial/Energy prefer:

Industrial Products

Additional Information

Year Founded: 1986
Capital Under Management: $36,300,000
Current Activity Level : Actively seeking new investments

NEXUS MEDICAL PARTNERS

400 Crown Colony Drive
Suite 104
Quincy, MA USA 02169
Phone: 617-472-2805
Fax: 617-472-3531
E-mail: contact@nexusmp.com
Website: www.nexusmp.com

Other Offices

12, rue Eugene Ruppert
Luxembourg, Luxembourg L-2453

Management and Staff

Edwin Snape, Co-Founder
Gregory Zaic, Principal
John Rousseau, Co-Founder
Thomas Hancock, Principal

Type of Firm

Private Equity Firm

Project Preferences

Type of Financing Preferred:

Balanced

Geographical Preferences

United States Preferences:

All U.S.

International Preferences:

Europe

Industry Preferences

In Biotechnology prefer:

Biotechnology

In Medical/Health prefer:

Medical Products
Pharmaceuticals

Additional Information

Year Founded: 2004
Current Activity Level : Actively seeking new investments

NEXUS PRIVATE EQUITY PARTNERI

I. Lucica 2a
9th Floor, Eurotower
Zagreb, Croatia HR-10000
Phone: 385-1-5499-850
Fax: 385-1-5499-859
E-mail: info@nexus-pe.hr
Website: www.nexus-pe.hr

Management and Staff

Kresimir Ruzdak, Co-Founder
Marko Lesic, Co-Founder

Type of Firm

Private Equity Firm

Project Preferences

Type of Financing Preferred:

Expansion
Early Stage
Generalist PE
Management Buyouts
Startup

Geographical Preferences

International Preferences:

Croatia
Eastern Europe

Industry Preferences

In Financial Services prefer:

Real Estate

Additional Information

Year Founded: 2008
Capital Under Management: $45,300,000
Current Activity Level : Actively seeking new investments

NEXUS VENTURE PARTNERS

2200 Sand Hill Road
Suite 100
Menlo Park, CA USA 94025
Phone: 650-561-0753
Fax: 650-851-1154
Website: www.nexusindiacap.com

Other Offices

201 B Phoenix House, Phoenix Mills
462, S. B. Marg, Lower Parel
Mumbai, India 400013
Phone: 91-22-6626-0000
Fax: 91-22-6626-0001

Management and Staff

Atish Babu, Vice President
Jishnu Bhatacharjee, Vice President
Manoj Gupta, Vice President

Naren Gupta, Managing Director
Sandeep Singhal, Managing Director
Suvir Sujan, Managing Director

Type of Firm
Private Equity Firm

Project Preferences

Type of Financing Preferred:
Early Stage
Later Stage

Size of Investments Considered:
Min Size of Investment Considered (000s): $3,000
Max Size of Investment Considered (000s): $15,000

Geographical Preferences

International Preferences:
India

Industry Preferences

In Consumer Related prefer:
Consumer

In Industrial/Energy prefer:
Environmental Related

In Business Serv. prefer:
Services
Media

Additional Information
Name of Most Recent Fund: Nexus India Capital II, L.P.
Most Recent Fund Was Raised: 08/19/2008
Year Founded: 2006
Capital Under Management: $320,000,000
Current Activity Level : Actively seeking new investments

NEXXUS CAPITAL, S.C.
Guillermo Gonzalez Camarena 16
Fifth Floor
Santa-Fe, Mexico City, Mexico 01210
Phone: 52-55-5292-3400
Fax: 52-55-5292-3410
E-mail: infonexxus@nexxuscapital.com
Website: www.nexxuscapital.com

Management and Staff
Arturo Saval, Managing Director
Luis Harvey, Managing Director

Type of Firm
Private Equity Firm

Project Preferences

Type of Financing Preferred:
Expansion

Geographical Preferences

International Preferences:
Mexico

Industry Preferences

In Consumer Related prefer:
Consumer Products
Consumer Services

In Financial Services prefer:
Financial Services

Additional Information
Year Founded: 1995
Capital Under Management: $144,000,000
Current Activity Level : Actively seeking new investments

NFI MANAGEMENT SP. Z O.O. (AKA: GRUPA CA-IB)
ul. Emilii Plater 53
Warsaw, Poland 00-113
Phone: 48-22-520-9350
Fax: 48-22-520-9351
E-mail: nfimanagement@ca-ib.com.pl
Website: www.ca-ib.com.pl

Management and Staff
Artur Cakala, Partner
Katarzyna Jazdrzyk, Partner
Wojciech Grzybowski, Partner

Type of Firm
Bank Affiliated

Association Membership
Polish Venture Capital Association (PSIC/PPEA)

Project Preferences

Type of Financing Preferred:
Leveraged Buyout
Early Stage
Expansion
Balanced
Management Buyouts

Size of Investments Considered:
Min Size of Investment Considered (000s): $3,103
Max Size of Investment Considered (000s): $12,414

Geographical Preferences

International Preferences:
Europe
Poland

Industry Preferences

In Consumer Related prefer:
Retail
Consumer Products

In Industrial/Energy prefer:
Industrial Products

In Manufact. prefer:
Manufacturing

Additional Information
Year Founded: 2005
Current Activity Level : Actively seeking new investments

NFR ENERGY LLC
c/o First Reserve Corporation
One Lafayette Place
Greenwich, CT USA 06830
Phone: 203 661-6601
Fax: 203 661-6729

Type of Firm
Private Equity Firm

Geographical Preferences

International Preferences:
All International

Industry Preferences

In Industrial/Energy prefer:
Oil and Gas Exploration

Additional Information
Year Founded: 2006
Current Activity Level : Actively seeking new investments

NGEN PARTNERS LLC (FKA: NEXTGEN PARTNERS LLC)
1114 State Street
Suite 247
Santa Barbara, CA USA 93101
Phone: 805-564-3156
Fax: 805-564-1699
Website: www.ngenpartners.com

Management and Staff
Alan Heeger, Venture Partner
Derek Statham, Venture Partner
Edward Kramer, Venture Partner
Jean Frechet, Venture Partner
John Newsam, Venture Partner
Mary Cusenza, Chief Financial Officer
Matthew Tirrell, Venture Partner
Peter Grubstein, Managing Director
Ripley Rosemary, Managing Director
Robert Koch, Managing Director
Robert Lorenzini, Venture Partner
Steven Parry, Managing Director
Steven Worzman, Chief Financial Officer

Type of Firm
Private Equity Firm

Association Membership
National Venture Capital Association - USA (NVCA)

Project Preferences

Role in Financing:
Will function either as deal originator or investor in deals created by others

Type of Financing Preferred:
Second Stage Financing
Early Stage
Expansion
Research and Development
Later Stage
Seed
First Stage Financing
Startup

Size of Investments Considered:
Min Size of Investment Considered (000s): $100
Max Size of Investment Considered (000s): $10,000

Geographical Preferences

United States Preferences:
All U.S.

International Preferences:
Australia
Belgium
All International

Industry Preferences

In Semiconductor/Electr prefer:
Controllers and Sensors

In Biotechnology prefer:
Industrial Biotechnology

In Industrial/Energy prefer:
Energy
Alternative Energy
Energy Conservation Relat
Materials
Advanced Materials
Superconductivity
Process Control
Environmental Related
Environment Responsible

Additional Information
Name of Most Recent Fund: NGEN Partners Fund III
Most Recent Fund Was Raised: 08/14/2008
Year Founded: 1987
Capital Under Management: $250,000,000
Current Activity Level : Actively seeking new investments
Method of Compensation: Return on investment is of primary concern, do not charge fees

---

NGI GROUP (AKA: NETAGE CAPITAL PARTNERS, INC.)
20F, Nakameguro GT Tower
2-1-1 Kamimeguro,Meguro-ku
Tokyo, Japan 153-0051
Phone: 81-3-5725-4760
Fax: 81-3-5725-4761
Website: www.ngigroup.com

Management and Staff
Satoshi Koike, Chief Executive Officer
Yozo Kaneko, Chief Operating Officer

Type of Firm
Corporate PE/Venture

Project Preferences

Type of Financing Preferred:
Balanced

Geographical Preferences

International Preferences:
Asia

Industry Preferences

In Internet Specific prefer:
Internet

Additional Information
Year Founded: 2000
Current Activity Level : Actively seeking new investments

NGN CAPITAL LLC
369 Lexington Avenue
17th Floor
New York, NY USA 10017
Phone: 212-972-0077
Fax: 212-972-0080
E-mail: investorrelations@ngncapital.com
Website: www.ngncapital.com

Other Offices
Bergheimer Strasse 89a
Heidelberg, Germany 69115
Phone: 49-62-2189-3760
Fax: 49-622-1650-5851

c/o Oracle Partners
200 Greenwich Avenue
Greenwich, CT USA 06830
Phone: 203-862-7939
Fax: 203-862-7998

Management and Staff
Austin Broadhurst, Venture Partner
Bernard Peperstraete, Principal
George Nebgen, Managing General Partner
John Costantino, Managing General Partner
Kenneth Abramowitz, Managing General Partner
Kenneth Gorelick, Venture Partner
Leon Recanati, Venture Partner
Leonard Hirsch, Chief Financial Officer
Peter Johann, Managing General Partner

Type of Firm
Private Equity Firm

Association Membership
National Venture Capital Association - USA (NVCA)

Project Preferences

Type of Financing Preferred:
Later Stage

Geographical Preferences

United States Preferences:
All U.S.

International Preferences:
Europe

Industry Preferences

In Medical/Health prefer:
Pharmaceuticals

Additional Information
Year Founded: 2004
Capital Under Management: $97,000,000
Current Activity Level : Actively seeking new investments

NIAGARA GROWTH FUND
509 Glendale Avenue
Suite 302
Niagra-on-the-Lake, Canada L0S1J0
Phone: 905-687-8327
Fax: 905-687-8022
E-mail: gstans@neai.com
Website: www.niagra-growth-fund.com

Type of Firm
Private Equity Firm

Additional Information
Year Founded: 1999
Current Activity Level : Actively seeking new investments

NIB-MDM FUND MANAGERS (PTY) LTD
33 Scott Street
Waverley
Johannesburg, South Africa 2090
Phone: 27-11-885-3690
Fax: 27-11-885-3640

Management and Staff
Malcolm Segal, Chief Executive Officer

Type of Firm
Private Equity Firm

Association Membership
South African Venture Capital Association (SAVCA)

Project Preferences

Type of Financing Preferred:
Expansion
Later Stage
Management Buyouts
Acquisition

Size of Investments Considered:
Min Size of Investment Considered (000s): $411
Max Size of Investment Considered (000s): $1,646

Geographical Preferences

International Preferences:
South Africa

Industry Preferences

In Communications prefer:
Other Communication Prod.

Additional Information

Year Founded: 2001
Current Activity Level : Actively seeking new investments

NIBC PRINCIPAL INVESTMENTS (FKA: PARNIB HOLDING NV)

Carnegieplein 4
Den Haag, Netherlands 2517 KJ
Phone: 31-70-342-5425
Fax: 31-70-342-5698
E-mail: info@nibc.com
Website: www.nibcapital.com

Other Offices

Uitbreidingstraat 10-16
Antwerpen, Belgium B - 2600
Phone: 32-3-286-9140
Fax: 32-3-286-9150

600 Fifth Avenue
17th Floor
New York, NY USA 10020
Phone: 1-212-271-8410
Fax: 1-212-271-8480

Fentener van Vlissingenkade 1
Utrecht, Netherlands 3521 AA
Phone: 31-30-290-8100
Fax: 31-30-290-6199

7 Bishopsgate
London, United Kingdom EC2N 3BX
Phone: 44-20-7375-8080
Fax: 44-20-7588-6483

Management and Staff

Alfred Tulp, Managing Director
C.M. Vermeulen, Managing Director
Charly Zwemstra, Partner
E.J. Van Der Burg, Managing Director
Ernest Lambers, Partner
Gerard Burgers, Managing Director
Hilde Famaey, Partner
J.H. Vermeulen, Managing Director
Joris De Meester, Partner
Niels Ruigrok, Partner
Patrick Paardenkooper, Partner
Paul Zekveld, Partner
Paul De Klerk, Managing Partner
Piet Serrure, Partner

Type of Firm

Bank Affiliated

Association Membership

Natl Assoc of Investment Cos. (NAIC)
European Private Equity and Venture Capital Assoc.

Project Preferences

Role in Financing:
Prefer role as deal originator but will also invest in deals created by others

Type of Financing Preferred:
Second Stage Financing
Leveraged Buyout
Mezzanine
Management Buyouts
Special Situation

Geographical Preferences

United States Preferences:
All U.S.

International Preferences:
Europe
Germany

Industry Focus

(% based on actual investment)

Other Products	100.0%

Additional Information

Year Founded: 1994
Capital Under Management: $1,392,000,000
Current Activity Level : Actively seeking new investments
Method of Compensation: Return on investment is of primary concern, do not charge fees

---

NICHIMEN EUROPE PLC

16 Minories
Latham House
London, United Kingdom EC3N 1EY
Phone: 44-20-7886-7000
Fax: 44-20-7886-7090
Website: www.nichimen.co.uk

Type of Firm

Bank Affiliated

Additional Information

Current Activity Level : Actively seeking new investments

NICOLET CAPITAL PARTNERS LLC

980 North Michigan Avenue
Suite 1400
Chicago, IL USA 60611
Phone: 312-214-3921
Fax: 253-540-2700
Website: www.nicoletcap.com

Management and Staff

Brett Snyder, President

Type of Firm

Private Equity Firm

Project Preferences

Type of Financing Preferred:
Leveraged Buyout
Acquisition

Size of Investments Considered:
Min Size of Investment Considered (000s): $15,000
Max Size of Investment Considered (000s): $50,000

Geographical Preferences

United States Preferences:
All U.S.

Industry Preferences

In Consumer Related prefer:
Consumer

In Business Serv. prefer:
Services
Distribution

In Manufact. prefer:
Manufacturing

Additional Information

Year Founded: 2007
Current Activity Level : Actively seeking new investments

NIKKO PRINCIPAL INVESTMENTS JAPAN, LTD.

Tokyo Bldg. 23F
2-7-3, Marunouchi, Chiyoda-ku
Tokyo, Japan 100-6423
Phone: 81-3-3500-0178
Fax: 81-3-3500-0109
E-mail: contact@pi.nikko.co.jp
Website: www.npi.co.jp

Type of Firm

Bank Affiliated

Project Preferences

Type of Financing Preferred:
Leveraged Buyout
Expansion

Balanced
Management Buyouts

Geographical Preferences

International Preferences:
Japan

Additional Information

Year Founded: 2000
Capital Under Management: $203,000,000
Current Activity Level : Actively seeking new investments

NIKKO PRINCIPAL INVESTMENTS LTD

100 Pall Mall
London, United Kingdom SW1Y 5NN
Phone: 44-20-7799-7700
Fax: 44-20-7930-8726
E-mail: firstcontact@nikko.co.uk
Website: www.npil.co.uk

Type of Firm

Bank Affiliated

Project Preferences

Type of Financing Preferred:
Leveraged Buyout
Early Stage
Acquisition
Startup

Size of Investments Considered:
Min Size of Investment Considered (000s): $44,016
Max Size of Investment Considered (000s): $220,080

Geographical Preferences

International Preferences:
United Kingdom
Western Europe
Austria
Scandanavia/Nordic Region
New Zealand
Japan
All International

Industry Focus

(% based on actual investment)

Other Products	52.7%
Consumer Related	44.0%
Biotechnology	1.3%
Industrial/Energy	0.9%
Medical/Health	0.7%
Computer Software and Services	0.4%

Additional Information

Year Founded: 1998
Capital Under Management: $28,700,000
Current Activity Level : Actively seeking new investments

NIMBUS

Driebergseweg 17
Zeist, Netherlands 3708 JA
Phone: 31-30-697-1410
Fax: 31-30-697-1411
E-mail: info@nimbus.com
Website: www.nimbus.com

Management and Staff

Ed Van Dijk, Managing Partner
Gert Jan Hubers, Managing Partner
Marc Renne, Managing Partner

Type of Firm

Private Equity Firm

Project Preferences

Type of Financing Preferred:
Balanced

Geographical Preferences

International Preferences:
Europe

Additional Information

Year Founded: 2005
Current Activity Level : Actively seeking new investments

NINE RIVERS CAPITAL MANAGEMENT, LTD. (AKA: NRCM)

511-512, Meadows, Sahar Plaza
Andheri Kurla Road, Andheri E.
Mumbai, India 400 059
Phone: 91-22-4063-2800
Fax: 91-22-4063-2801
E-mail: info@nineriverscapital.com
Website: www.nineriverscapital.com

Other Offices

C/o Muticonsult, Ltd.
10, Frere Felix de Valois Street
Port Louis, Mauritius
Phone: 230-202-3000
Fax: 230-212-5265

Management and Staff

Kunal Kumthekar, Co-Founder

Type of Firm

Investment Management Firm

Project Preferences

Type of Financing Preferred:
Early Stage
Expansion

Size of Investments Considered:
Min Size of Investment Considered (000s): $10,000
Max Size of Investment Considered (000s): $15,000

Geographical Preferences

International Preferences:
India
Mauritius

Industry Preferences

In Medical/Health prefer:
Health Services

In Consumer Related prefer:
Consumer
Food/Beverage

In Industrial/Energy prefer:
Energy
Alternative Energy

In Transportation prefer:
Transportation

In Manufact. prefer:
Manufacturing

In Other prefer:
Environment Responsible

Additional Information

Year Founded: 2008
Capital Under Management: $46,000,000
Current Activity Level : Actively seeking new investments

NIPPON ANGELS INVESTMENT CO., LTD

2F Akasaka Hananoki Bldg.
1-5-25 Moto-Akasaka, Minato-ku
Tokyo, Japan 107-0051
Phone: 81-3-5770-6301
Fax: 81-3-5770-6302
E-mail: info@naic.co.jp
Website: www.naic.co.jp

Type of Firm

Angel Group

Additional Information

Year Founded: 2000
Current Activity Level : Actively seeking new investments

NIPPON MIRAI CAPITAL CO., LTD

6F Toranomon 40MT Bldg.
5-13-1 Toranomon, Minato-ku
Tokyo, Japan 105-0001
Phone: 81-3-5425-1900
Fax: 81-3-5425-1901
E-mail: info@miraicapital.co.jp
Website: www.miraicapital.co.jp

Management and Staff

Minoru Honzawa, Chief Financial Officer

Type of Firm
Private Equity Firm

Project Preferences
Type of Financing Preferred:
Leveraged Buyout
Turnaround
Management Buyouts
Recapitalizations

Geographical Preferences
International Preferences:
Japan

Additional Information
Year Founded: 2002
Capital Under Management: $109,000,000
Current Activity Level : Actively seeking new investments

NIPPON MONOZUKURI CAPITAL CO., LTD.
52F Tokyo Opera City
Shinjuku-ku
Tokyo, Japan 163-1452
Phone: 81-3-5351-1919
Fax: 81-3-5351-1920

Management and Staff
Shinjiro Yamada, President

Type of Firm
Private Equity Firm

Project Preferences
Type of Financing Preferred:
Balanced

Geographical Preferences
International Preferences:
Japan

Industry Preferences
In Manufact. prefer:
Manufacturing

Additional Information
Year Founded: 2003
Capital Under Management: $85,000,000
Current Activity Level : Actively seeking new investments

NIPPON TECHNOLOGY VENTURE PARTNERS, LTD.
Akihabara Dai Bldg. 8F 804
1-18-13, Sotokanda
Tokyo, Japan 101-0021
Phone: 813-3526-3131
Fax: 813-3526-3555
Website: www.ntvp.com

Management and Staff
Kazutaka Muraguchi, Chief Executive Officer

Type of Firm
Private Equity Firm

Project Preferences
Type of Financing Preferred:
Early Stage

Geographical Preferences
International Preferences:
Japan

Industry Preferences
In Computer Hardware prefer:
Computers

In Internet Specific prefer:
Internet

In Semiconductor/Electr prefer:
Semiconductor

In Financial Services prefer:
Financial Services

Additional Information
Year Founded: 1998
Capital Under Management: $26,400,000
Current Activity Level : Actively seeking new investments

NIPPON VENTURE CAPITAL CO., LTD.
7/F, Nissei Akasaka Bldg 2
7-1-16 Akasaka, Minato-ku
Tokyo, Japan 107-0052
Phone: 81-3-5413-2680
Fax: 81-3-5413-2688
E-mail: info@nvcc.co.jp
Website: www.nvcc.co.jp

Type of Firm
Private Equity Firm

Project Preferences
Type of Financing Preferred:
Research and Development
Balanced
Seed

Geographical Preferences
International Preferences:
Asia
Japan
All International

Industry Preferences
In Communications prefer:
Commercial Communications

In Biotechnology prefer:
Biotechnology

In Industrial/Energy prefer:
Robotics
Environmental Related

Additional Information
Year Founded: 2000
Capital Under Management: $242,300,000
Current Activity Level : Actively seeking new investments

NISSAY CAPITAL CO., LTD.
10F, No. 1 Yurakucho Bldg.
Yurakuchom Chiyoda-ku
Tokyo, Japan 100-0006
Phone: 813-3287-3150
Fax: 813-3287-3151
Website: www.nissay-cap.co.jp

Type of Firm
Private Equity Firm

Project Preferences
Type of Financing Preferred:
Balanced

Geographical Preferences
International Preferences:
Asia

Additional Information
Year Founded: 1991
Current Activity Level : Actively seeking new investments

NITTANY LION VENTURE CAPITAL
220 Business Building
University Park, PA USA 16802
Phone: 703-405-9602

Management and Staff
Steven Christensen, Managing Director

Type of Firm
Private Equity Firm

Project Preferences
Type of Financing Preferred:
Balanced

Geographical Preferences
United States Preferences:
All U.S.

Additional Information

Year Founded: 2005
Capital Under Management: $5,000,000
Current Activity Level : Actively seeking new investments

NLM CAPITAL PARTNERS, L.P.

125 E. John Carpenter Freeway
Suite 600
Irving, TX USA 75062
Phone: 972-432-1300
Fax: 972-432-1320
E-mail: info@nlmcapital.com
Website: www.nlmcapital.com

Management and Staff

J. Randall Chappel, President
James Collet, Managing Director

Type of Firm

Private Equity Firm

Project Preferences

Type of Financing Preferred:

Leveraged Buyout
Expansion
Generalist PE

Size of Investments Considered:

Min Size of Investment Considered (000s): $20,000
Max Size of Investment Considered (000s): $150,000

Geographical Preferences

United States Preferences:

All U.S.

Industry Preferences

In Medical/Health prefer:

Health Services

In Consumer Related prefer:

Education Related

In Financial Services prefer:

Real Estate

Additional Information

Year Founded: 2004
Capital Under Management: $90,000,000
Current Activity Level : Actively seeking new investments

NMAS1 PRIVATE EQUITY (FKA: NMAS1 ELECTRA CAPITAL PRIVADO)

Padilla, 17
4th floor
Madrid, Spain 28006
Phone: 34-91-745-8484
Fax: 34-91-431-3812
E-mail: info@nmas1.com
Website: www.nmas1.com

Management and Staff

Adolfo Anton, Chief Executive Officer
Joaquin Suarez, Partner
Jorge Mataix, Managing Director
Manuel Gil, Founding Partner
Santiago Eguidazu, President

Type of Firm

Bank Affiliated

Association Membership

European Private Equity and Venture Capital Assoc.
Spanish Venture Capital Association (ASCRI)

Project Preferences

Type of Financing Preferred:

Leveraged Buyout
Early Stage
Expansion
Generalist PE
Balanced
Management Buyouts

Geographical Preferences

International Preferences:

Portugal
Europe
Western Europe
Spain

Industry Focus

(% based on actual investment)

Consumer Related	50.9%
Other Products	28.7%
Industrial/Energy	13.0%
Semiconductors/Other Elect.	6.8%
Computer Software and Services	0.5%

Additional Information

Name of Most Recent Fund: EQMC Europe
Most Recent Fund Was Raised: 07/10/2006
Year Founded: 1990
Capital Under Management: $963,600,000
Current Activity Level : Actively seeking new investments

NO. 8 VENTURES MANAGEMENT LTD (FKA: MOREL VENTURES LTD)

Level 2, The Bond Store
Queens Wharf
Wellington, New Zealand
Phone: 644-499-2029
Fax: 644-471-1612
E-mail: anyone@no8ventures.co.nz
Website: www.no8ventures.co.nz

Management and Staff

Brian Leighs, Chief Financial Officer
Grant McPherson, Chief Executive Officer

Type of Firm

Bank Affiliated

Project Preferences

Role in Financing:

Will function either as deal originator or investor in deals created by others

Type of Financing Preferred:

Early Stage
Expansion
Balanced
Start-up Financing
Seed
Startup

Size of Investments Considered:

Min Size of Investment Considered (000s): $1,000
Max Size of Investment Considered (000s): $5,000

Geographical Preferences

International Preferences:

New Zealand

Industry Preferences

In Communications prefer:

Communications and Media

In Computer Hardware prefer:

Computers

In Computer Software prefer:

Software

In Semiconductor/Electr prefer:

Electronics
Semiconductor

In Biotechnology prefer:

Biotechnology

In Medical/Health prefer:

Medical/Health

Additional Information

Year Founded: 1999
Capital Under Management: $40,000,000
Current Activity Level : Actively seeking new investments
Method of Compensation: Return on investment is of primary concern, do not charge fees

NOBLE FINANCIAL GROUP

6501 Congress Avenue
Suite 100
Boca Raton, FL USA 33487
Phone: 561-994-1191
Fax: 212-664-9345
E-mail: questions@noblefinancialgroup.com
Website: www.noblefinancialgroup.com

Management and Staff
Ben Lichtenberg, Managing Director
Nico Prink, President
Wayne Horne, Managing Partner

Type of Firm
Bank Affiliated

Additional Information
Year Founded: 1984
Current Activity Level : Actively seeking new investments

NOBLE FUND MANAGERS, LTD.

76 George Street
Edinburgh, United Kingdom EH2 3BU
Phone: 44-131-225-9677
Fax: 44-131-225-5479
E-mail: noble@noblegp.com
Website: www.noblegp.com

Other Offices
120 Old Broad Street
5th Floor
London, United Kingdom EC2N 1AR
Phone: 44-20-7763-2200
Fax: 44-20-7763-2399

Management and Staff
Angus Macpherson, Chief Executive Officer
Ben Thomson, Chief Executive Officer
Bruce McLaren, Managing Director
John Llewellyn-Lloyd, Chief Executive Officer

Type of Firm
Bank Affiliated

Association Membership
French Venture Capital Association (AFIC)

Project Preferences

Type of Financing Preferred:
Second Stage Financing
Early Stage
Expansion
Balanced
Later Stage
Distressed Debt

Size of Investments Considered:
Min Size of Investment Considered (000s): $450
Max Size of Investment Considered (000s): $1,350

Geographical Preferences

International Preferences:
United Kingdom
Europe
Western Europe

Industry Preferences

In Computer Software prefer:
Software

In Computer Other prefer:
Computer Related

Additional Information
Name of Most Recent Fund: Noble Venture Finance I L.P. (AKA: NVF)
Most Recent Fund Was Raised: 06/30/2004
Year Founded: 1980
Capital Under Management: $283,000,000
Current Activity Level : Actively seeking new investments

NOBSKA VENTURES

2011 Wiltonwood Road
Stevenson, MD USA 21153
Phone: 410-486-1848
Fax: 410-486-1849
E-mail: info@nobskaventures.com
Website: www.nobskaventures.com

Management and Staff
Charles Moore, Chairman & Managing Director
Franklin Baitman, Venture Partner
J. Ari Tuchman, Managing Director
Laura Moore, Managing Director
Michael Beasley, Venture Partner
Michael Ward, Venture Partner
Robert Rosenbaum, Managing Director

Type of Firm
Bank Affiliated

Project Preferences

Type of Financing Preferred:
Early Stage
Seed

Geographical Preferences

United States Preferences:
Mid Atlantic

Industry Preferences

In Medical/Health prefer:
Medical/Health

Additional Information
Name of Most Recent Fund: Nobska Venture Partners I, LP
Most Recent Fund Was Raised: 04/15/2005
Year Founded: 2005
Capital Under Management: $500,000
Current Activity Level : Actively seeking new investments

NOE BETEILIGUNGSFINANZIERUNGEN GMBH

Gottfried Keller-Gasse 2/3
Vienna, Austria 1030
Phone: 43-17-1052-1025
Fax: 43-17-1052-1040
E-mail: office@noebeg.at
Website: www.noebeg.at

Type of Firm
Bank Affiliated

Association Membership
European Private Equity and Venture Capital Assoc.

Project Preferences

Type of Financing Preferred:
Early Stage
Expansion
Start-up Financing
Management Buyouts

Geographical Preferences

International Preferences:
Austria

Industry Preferences

In Consumer Related prefer:
Consumer

In Industrial/Energy prefer:
Industrial Products

Additional Information
Year Founded: 2003
Capital Under Management: $60,200,000
Current Activity Level : Actively seeking new investments

NOGALES INVESTORS MANAGEMENT, LLC

9229 West Sunset Boulevard
Suite 900
West Hollywood, CA USA 90069
Phone: 310-276-7439
Fax: 310-276-7405
E-mail: info@nogalesinvestors.com
Website: www.nogalesinvestors.com

Management and Staff
Mark Mickelson, Partner
Steven Tolbert, Partner

Type of Firm
Private Equity Firm

Project Preferences

Role in Financing:
Prefer role as deal originator but will also invest in deals created by others

Type of Financing Preferred:
Leveraged Buyout
Expansion
Generalist PE
Turnaround
Management Buyouts
Acquisition
Industry Rollups
Recapitalizations

Size of Investments Considered:
Min Size of Investment Considered (000s): $5,000
Max Size of Investment Considered (000s): $20,000

Geographical Preferences

United States Preferences:
All U.S.

Additional Information

Year Founded: 2004
Capital Under Management: $345,000,000
Current Activity Level : Actively seeking new investments

NOKIA (AKA: NEST MANAGMENT)

Keilalahdentie 4
Espoo, Finland 02150
Phone: 358-7-180-08000
Fax: 358-7-180-62590
Website: www.nokia.com/venturing

Other Offices

Itamerenkatu 11-13
Helsinki, Finland 00045
Phone: 358-718-036-749
Fax: 358-718-037-145

Management and Staff

Petteri Terho, Managing Partner

Type of Firm

Corporate PE/Venture

Project Preferences

Type of Financing Preferred:
Fund of Funds
Early Stage
Seed
Startup

Geographical Preferences

International Preferences:
Europe
Asia

Industry Preferences

In Communications prefer:
Communications and Media
Commercial Communications
Telecommunications
Wireless Communications

Additional Information

Year Founded: 1998
Current Activity Level : Actively seeking new investments

NOKIA GROWTH PARTNERS

545 Middlefield Road
Suite 210
Menlo Park, CA USA 94025
Phone: 650-328-5508
Fax: 650-462-7252
E-mail: ventures@nokia.com
Website: www.nokiagrowthpartners.com

Other Offices

Visiokatu 3
Tampere, Finland 33720
Phone: 358-4-0091-5959
Fax: 358-7-1804-8372

2A Workers Stadium Road
Beijing, China 1000027
Phone: 86-10-8711-2526
Fax: 86-10-8711-4554

Management and Staff

Bo Ilsoe, Partner
John Gardner, Managing Partner
Paul Asel, Managing Partner
Tapio Siik, Partner
Upal Basu, Partner
Weihan Liu, Partner

Type of Firm

Private Equity Firm

Project Preferences

Role in Financing:
Will function either as deal originator or investor in deals created by others

Type of Financing Preferred:
Fund of Funds
Expansion
Balanced

Size of Investments Considered:
Min Size of Investment Considered (000s): $3,000
Max Size of Investment Considered (000s): $7,000

Industry Preferences

In Communications prefer:
Communications and Media
Wireless Communications

Additional Information

Name of Most Recent Fund: Nokia Growth Partners, L.P.
Most Recent Fund Was Raised: 04/20/2005
Year Founded: 2004
Capital Under Management: $350,000,000
Current Activity Level : Actively seeking new investments

Method of Compensation: Return on investment is of primary concern, do not charge fees

---

NOMURA INTERNATIONAL PLC

Nomura House
1 St Martin's-Le-Grand
London, United Kingdom EC1A 4NP
Phone: 44-20-7521-2000
Fax: 44-20-7521-2121
Website: www.nomura.com

Type of Firm

Bank Affiliated

Project Preferences

Type of Financing Preferred:
Fund of Funds
Mezzanine
Later Stage

Geographical Preferences

United States Preferences:
All U.S.

International Preferences:
Europe
Israel
Asia
All International

Industry Focus

(% based on actual investment)

Biotechnology	32.0%
Medical/Health	22.1%
Communications and Media	12.3%
Internet Specific	11.8%
Consumer Related	8.9%
Computer Software and Services	7.1%
Other Products	3.3%
Industrial/Energy	1.5%
Semiconductors/Other Elect.	1.0%

Additional Information

Year Founded: 1998
Capital Under Management: $235,000,000
Current Activity Level : Actively seeking new investments

NOMURA NEW ENERGY & CLEAN TECHNOLOGY VENTURES

Nomura House
1 St. Martin's-le-Grand
London, United Kingdom EC1A 4NP
Phone: 44-20-7521-3539
Fax: 44-20-7521-2235
Website: www.nomura.com

Management and Staff
Whitney Rockley, Principal

Type of Firm
Bank Affiliated

Project Preferences

Type of Financing Preferred:
Expansion

Size of Investments Considered:
Min Size of Investment Considered (000s): $10,000
Max Size of Investment Considered (000s): $25,000

Geographical Preferences

International Preferences:
All International

Industry Preferences

In Computer Software prefer:
Software

In Industrial/Energy prefer:
Alternative Energy
Materials
Environmental Related

Additional Information
Year Founded: 2008
Current Activity Level : Actively seeking new investments

NOMURA PHASE4 VENTURES, LTD.

1 St. Martin's-le-Grand
Nomura House
London, United Kingdom EC1A 4NP
Phone: 44-20-7521-2386
Fax: 44-20-7521-2386
Website: www.nomura.com

Management and Staff
Charles Sermon, Partner
Jennifer Hamilton, Venture Partner
John Westwater, Principal
Jonathan Jones, Principal
Judith Hemberger, Venture Partner
Justin Duckworth, Partner
Naveed Siddiqi, Partner

Type of Firm
Bank Affiliated

Project Preferences

Type of Financing Preferred:
Second Stage Financing
Expansion
Early Stage

Industry Preferences

In Medical/Health prefer:
Medical/Health

Additional Information
Year Founded: 2004
Current Activity Level : Actively seeking new investments

NOMURA RESEARCH & ADVISORY CO., LTD.

Urban Net Otemachi Building
222 Otemachi, Chiyoda-ku
Tokyo, Japan 100-8130
Phone: 81-3-5255-9416
Website: www.nomuraholdings.com/company/group

Management and Staff
Akihito Watanabe, President

Type of Firm
Bank Affiliated

Project Preferences

Type of Financing Preferred:
Balanced

Geographical Preferences

International Preferences:
Japan

Industry Preferences

In Semiconductor/Electr prefer:
Electronics

In Biotechnology prefer:
Biotechnology

Additional Information
Year Founded: 2001
Capital Under Management: $81,000,000
Current Activity Level : Actively seeking new investments

NOORDERHUYS PARTICIPATIES BV

Mercatorweg 2b
Joure, Netherlands 8501 XK
Phone: 31-513-67-2740
Fax: 31-513-41-0400
E-mail: info@noorderhuys.nl
Website: www.noorderhuys.nl

Management and Staff
Alfred Stel, Founder
Jan Ten Cate, Founder
Johannes Osinga, Founder
John Ritchi, Founder

Type of Firm
Private Equity Firm

Project Preferences

Type of Financing Preferred:
Leveraged Buyout
Management Buyouts

Size of Investments Considered:
Min Size of Investment Considered (000s): $14,531
Max Size of Investment Considered (000s): $87,184

Geographical Preferences

International Preferences:
Europe
Germany

Additional Information
Year Founded: 2007
Current Activity Level : Actively seeking new investments

NORD CREATION SAS

2, Avenue de Kaarst
Euralille, France 59777
Phone: 33-3-5931-2099
Fax: 33-3-5930-2059
E-mail: contact@irdnpdc.fr
Website: www.irdnpdc.fr

Management and Staff
Eric Grimonprez, Chief Executive Officer
Gilbert Hennique, President

Type of Firm
Private Equity Firm

Association Membership
European Private Equity and Venture Capital Assoc.

Project Preferences

Role in Financing:
Will function either as deal originator or investor in deals created by others

Type of Financing Preferred:
Early Stage
Seed
Startup

Size of Investments Considered:
Min Size of Investment Considered (000s): $22
Max Size of Investment Considered (000s): $67

Geographical Preferences

International Preferences:
Europe
France

Industry Preferences

In Communications prefer:
Commercial Communications

In Computer Software prefer:
Systems Software
Applications Software

In Consumer Related prefer:
Food/Beverage

In Industrial/Energy prefer:
Industrial Products

In Agr/Forestr/Fish prefer:
Agriculture related

Additional Information
Year Founded: 1991
Capital Under Management: $4,100,000
Current Activity Level : Actively seeking new investments
Method of Compensation: Return on investment is of primary concern, do not charge fees

NORD HOLDING UNTERNEHMENSBETEILIGUNGSGESELLSCHAFT MBH

Villa Venture
Walderseestrasse 23
Hannover, Germany 30177
Phone: 49 511 270415-0
Fax: 49 511 270415-5
E-mail: info@nordholding.de
Website: www.nordholding.de

Management and Staff
Matthias Kues, Chief Executive Officer

Type of Firm
Bank Affiliated

Association Membership
German Venture Capital Association (BVK)

Project Preferences

Type of Financing Preferred:
Expansion
Later Stage
Management Buyouts
Recapitalizations

Geographical Preferences

International Preferences:
Germany

Industry Focus
(% based on actual investment)

Computer Software and Services	51.2%
Industrial/Energy	48.8%

Additional Information
Year Founded: 2001
Capital Under Management: $240,000,000
Current Activity Level : Actively seeking new investments

NORDEA PRIVATE EQUITY

Christiansbro, Strandgade 3
PO Box 850
Copenhagen, Denmark DK-0900
Phone: 45-33-33-3333
Fax: 45-33-33-4873
E-mail: private.equity@nordea.com
Website: www.nordea.com

Other Offices
Hamngatan 10
Stockholm, Sweden SE-105 71
Phone: 46-8-614-7800
Fax: 46-8-20-0846

Middelthunsgt. 17
Oslo, Norway N-0368
Phone: 47-22-48-5000
Fax: 47-22-48-4749

Keskuskatu 3
Helsinki, Finland FIN-00020
Phone: 358-9-1651
Fax: 358-9-165-48368

Management and Staff
Jan Radberg, Partner
Jeppe Starup, Partner
Kim Pedersen, Partner
Lauge Sletting, Partner

Type of Firm
Bank Affiliated

Association Membership
Danish Venture Capital Association (DVCA)

Project Preferences

Type of Financing Preferred:
Fund of Funds
Expansion

Geographical Preferences

International Preferences:
Czech Republic
Turkey
Taiwan
Europe
China
Brazil
Mexico
Thailand
South Africa
Korea, South
Russia

Additional Information
Year Founded: 2000
Capital Under Management: $210,000,000
Current Activity Level : Actively seeking new investments

NORDEST MERCHANT SPA

Viale Appiani, 20/B
Treviso, Italy 31100
Phone: 39-444-235-479
Fax: 39-444-544-754
E-mail: vicenza@nordest-merchant.it
Website: www.nordest-merchant.it

Type of Firm
Bank Affiliated

Association Membership
Italian Venture Capital Association (AIFI)

Project Preferences

Type of Financing Preferred:
Leveraged Buyout
Expansion
Management Buyouts

Geographical Preferences

International Preferences:
Italy
Europe

Additional Information
Year Founded: 1987
Current Activity Level : Actively seeking new investments

NORDIA MANAGEMENT OY (FKA: MATKAILUNKEHITYS NORDIA OY)

Kaisaniemenkatu 3 B
P.O. Box 255
Helsinki, Finland 00101
Phone: 358-9-696-2920
Fax: 358-9-6962-9250
E-mail: info@nordiamanagement.fi
Website: www.nordiamanagement.fi

Other Offices
Sepankatu 4
Jyvaskyla, Finland 40100
Phone: 358-204-602-260
Fax: 358-204-602-297

Management and Staff
Koppinen Pasi, Partner

Type of Firm
Private Equity Firm

Association Membership
Finnish Venture Capital Association (FVCA)

Project Preferences

Type of Financing Preferred:
Leveraged Buyout
Expansion

Turnaround
Seed
Startup

Geographical Preferences

International Preferences:

Europe
Finland

Additional Information

Name of Most Recent Fund: Matkailunkehitys Nordia Oy
Most Recent Fund Was Raised: 12/31/1993
Year Founded: 1989
Capital Under Management: $12,200,000
Current Activity Level : Actively seeking new investments

NORDIC BIOTECH ADVISORS APS

Ostergade Five
Third Floor
Copenhagen K, Denmark DK-1100
Phone: 45-7020-1263
Fax: 45-7020-1264
Website: www.nordicbiotech.com

Management and Staff

Christian Hansen, Partner
Cora Madsen, Chief Financial Officer
Florian Schonharting, Partner
Henrik Nilsson, Principal
Jennifer Glennon, Chief Financial Officer

Type of Firm

Private Equity Firm

Association Membership

European Private Equity and Venture Capital Assoc.

Project Preferences

Type of Financing Preferred:

Early Stage
Balanced
Seed

Geographical Preferences

International Preferences:

Europe
Scandanavia/Nordic Region
Denmark

Industry Preferences

In Biotechnology prefer:

Biotechnology
Human Biotechnology
Agricultural/Animal Bio.
Industrial Biotechnology

In Medical/Health prefer:

Pharmaceuticals

Additional Information

Name of Most Recent Fund: Nordic Biotech Venture Fund II
Most Recent Fund Was Raised: 10/25/2005
Year Founded: 2000
Capital Under Management: $43,000,000
Current Activity Level : Actively seeking new investments

NORDIC CAPITAL (AKA: NC ADVISORY)

Stureplan 4A
Stockholm, Sweden SE-114 35
Phone: 46-8-440-5050
Fax: 46-8-611-7998
E-mail: info@nordiccapital.com
Website: www.nordiccapital.com

Other Offices

Bulevardi 1A
Helsinki, Finland FI-00100
Phone: 358-20-7433-250
Fax: 358-20-7433-259

Westhafen Tower
Westhafenplatz 1
Frankfurt, Germany
Phone: 49-69-710456120
Fax: 49-69-710456123

Berkeley Square House
Berkeley Square
London, United Kingdom W1J 6BY
Phone: 44-20-7355-5700
Fax: 44-20-7355-5749

Sankt Annae Plads 11
Copenhagen, Denmark DK-1250
Phone: 45-3344-7750
Fax: 45-3344-7755

Bygdoey Alle 9
Oslo, Norway NO-0257
Phone: 47-2255-0290
Fax: 47-2255-0291

26 Esplanade
St. Helier
Jersey, Channel Islands JE2 3QA
Phone: 44-1534-605-100
Fax: 44-1534-605-199

Management and Staff

Anders Hultin, Partner
Bo Soderberg, Partner
Christian Peter Dyvig, Partner
Mans Folkesson, Chief Financial Officer
Morgan Olsson, Co-Founder
Toni Weitzberg, Partner
Ulf Rosberg, Partner

Type of Firm

Private Equity Firm

Association Membership

Swedish Venture Capital Association (SVCA)
European Private Equity and Venture Capital Assoc.

Project Preferences

Role in Financing:

Prefer role as deal originator

Type of Financing Preferred:

Leveraged Buyout
Turnaround
Management Buyouts

Size of Investments Considered:

Min Size of Investment Considered (000s): $26,550
Max Size of Investment Considered (000s): $148,680

Geographical Preferences

International Preferences:

Sweden
Europe
Western Europe
Greenland
Iceland
Scandanavia/Nordic Region
Germany
Finland
Norway
Denmark
Faroe Islands

Industry Focus

(% based on actual investment)

Medical/Health	43.3%
Industrial/Energy	24.9%
Other Products	10.2%
Biotechnology	9.4%
Communications and Media	6.8%
Consumer Related	4.7%
Computer Software and Services	0.8%

Additional Information

Name of Most Recent Fund: Nordic Capital VI
Most Recent Fund Was Raised: 03/21/2006
Year Founded: 1989
Capital Under Management: $4,751,700,000
Current Activity Level : Actively seeking new investments

NORDIC GROWTH OY

Etelaesplanadi 14
Helsinki, Finland FI-00130
Phone: 358-9-4241-4450
Fax: 358-9-6122-8357
Website: www.nordicgrowth.com

Other Offices

Stureplan 4C, 4
Stockholm, Sweden SE-114 35
Phone: 46-8-5090-1255
Fax: 46-8-463-1010

Store Strandstraede 19, 2.
Copenhagen K, Denmark DK-1255
Phone: 45-7020-6652
Fax: 45-7020-6653

Type of Firm
Private Equity Firm

Project Preferences
Type of Financing Preferred:
Balanced

Geographical Preferences
International Preferences:
Scandanavia/Nordic Region

Industry Preferences
In Medical/Health prefer:
Medical/Health

In Business Serv. prefer:
Services

Additional Information
Year Founded: 2005
Current Activity Level : Actively seeking new investments

NORDIC MEZZANINE, LTD.
Aleksanterinkatu 15 A
Helsinki, Finland 00100
Phone: 358-9-684-0640
Fax: 358-9-6840-6410
Website: www.nordicmezzanine.com

Other Offices
100 Pall Mall
St James's
London, United Kingdom SW1Y 5HP
Phone: 44-20-7663-9890
Fax: 44-20-7663-9891

Management and Staff
Vesa Suurmunne, Chief Executive Officer

Type of Firm
Private Equity Firm

Association Membership
Finnish Venture Capital Association (FVCA)
European Private Equity and Venture Capital Assoc.

Project Preferences
Role in Financing:
Prefer role in deals created by others

Type of Financing Preferred:
Leveraged Buyout
Expansion
Mezzanine
Turnaround

Size of Investments Considered:
Min Size of Investment Considered (000s): $29,000
Max Size of Investment Considered (000s): $250,000

Geographical Preferences
International Preferences:
United Kingdom
Europe
Poland
Estonia
Scandanavia/Nordic Region
Germany
Latvia
Lithuania

Industry Focus
(% based on actual investment)

Other Products	59.7%
Industrial/Energy	40.3%

Additional Information
Year Founded: 1999
Capital Under Management: $95,000,000
Current Activity Level : Actively seeking new investments

NORDIC RUSSIAN MANAGEMENT COMPANY, LTD. (AKA: NORUM, LTD.)
Kaluzhskij Pereulok 3
St. Petersburg, Russia 191015
Phone: 7-812-320-0404
Fax: 7-812-320-0405
E-mail: main@norum.ru
Website: www.norum.ru

Other Offices
P.O. Box 160
Helsinki, Finland 00181
Phone: 358-9-6189-9400
Fax: 358-9-6189-9550

Forskningsparken
Tromso, Norway 9291
Phone: 47-77-679-250
Fax: 47-77-679-255

Ul. Voskresenskaja 8
Arkhangelsk, Russia 163061
Phone: 7-8182-269-971

Hotel Poliarnie Zori, Office 233
Murmansk, Russia 183038
Phone: 7-8152-289-581

Management and Staff
Ilkka Linnakko, Managing Director
Knut Borch, Managing Director

Type of Firm
Bank Affiliated

Association Membership
European Private Equity and Venture Capital Assoc.
Russian Venture Capital Association (RVCA)

Project Preferences
Type of Financing Preferred:
Early Stage
Expansion

Size of Investments Considered:
Min Size of Investment Considered (000s): $3,000
Max Size of Investment Considered (000s): $8,000

Geographical Preferences
International Preferences:
Russia

Industry Preferences
In Communications prefer:
Telecommunications
Media and Entertainment

In Consumer Related prefer:
Consumer
Retail
Food/Beverage
Consumer Products

In Industrial/Energy prefer:
Industrial Products

In Transportation prefer:
Transportation

In Financial Services prefer:
Financial Services

In Business Serv. prefer:
Services
Media

In Manufact. prefer:
Manufacturing

Additional Information
Year Founded: 1995
Capital Under Management: $64,500,000
Current Activity Level : Actively seeking new investments

NORDIC VENTURE PARTNERS (FKA: DANSKE VENTURE PARTNERS)
Bredgade 75, 3rd floor
Copenhagen, Denmark DK-1260
Phone: 45-3330-7880
Fax: 45-3330-7889
E-mail: sf@dvpvc.com
Website: www.nordicvc.com

Other Offices
Bulevardi 1A
Helsinki, Finland 00100
Phone: 358-9-4282-6100
Fax: 358-9-4282-6110

Birger Jarlsgatan 14, 1st floor
Stockholm, Sweden S-114 34
Phone: 46-8-611-0703
Fax: 46-8-611-0704

Management and Staff
Claus Hojbjerg Andersen, General Partner
Henrik Albertsen, Managing Partner
Jukka Rauhala, General Partner
Per Von Zelowitz, Partner
Thomas Tofte Hansen, General Partner

Type of Firm
Bank Affiliated

Association Membership
Danish Venture Capital Association (DVCA)
European Private Equity and Venture Capital Assoc.

Project Preferences
Type of Financing Preferred:
Early Stage
Expansion
Later Stage
Startup

Geographical Preferences
International Preferences:
Sweden
Europe
Scandanavia/Nordic Region
Finland
Denmark

Industry Preferences
In Communications prefer:
Telecommunications
Wireless Communications
Data Communications

In Computer Software prefer:
Software

Additional Information
Name of Most Recent Fund: NVP II
Most Recent Fund Was Raised: 01/13/2005
Year Founded: 2004
Capital Under Management: $152,000,000
Current Activity Level : Actively seeking new investments

NORDIC WIRELESS AB
Kungsgatan 5, 2tr
Mailbox 398
Stockholm, Sweden 111 73
Phone: 46-8-5552-9800
Fax: 46-8-5552-9899
E-mail: info@nordicwireless.se
Website: www.nordicwireless.se

Management and Staff
Magnus Nilsson, Partner
Peter Blom, Partner

Type of Firm
Private Equity Firm

Association Membership
Swedish Venture Capital Association (SVCA)

Project Preferences
Type of Financing Preferred:
Leveraged Buyout
Expansion
Seed
Startup

Size of Investments Considered:
Min Size of Investment Considered (000s): $531
Max Size of Investment Considered (000s): $2,124

Geographical Preferences
International Preferences:
Scandanavia/Nordic Region

Industry Preferences
In Communications prefer:
Wireless Communications

In Internet Specific prefer:
Internet

Additional Information
Year Founded: 2000
Capital Under Management: $6,400,000
Current Activity Level : Actively seeking new investments

NORDIKA ASSET MANAGEMENT
Radhusgaten 25
Postboks 1464 Vika
Oslo, Norway N-0158
Phone: 47-2233-6481
Fax: 47-229-36821
Website: www.nordika.no

Type of Firm
Private Equity Firm

Additional Information
Year Founded: 2004
Current Activity Level : Actively seeking new investments

NORDSTJERNAN
Stureplan 3
Stockholm, Sweden 103 75
Phone: 46-8-788-5000
Fax: 46-8-788-5010
E-mail: info@nordstjernan.se
Website: www.nordstjernan.se

Type of Firm
Private Equity Firm

Association Membership
Swedish Venture Capital Association (SVCA)

Project Preferences
Type of Financing Preferred:
Expansion
Later Stage
Acquisition

Size of Investments Considered:
Min Size of Investment Considered (000s): $100
Max Size of Investment Considered (000s): $100,000

Geographical Preferences
International Preferences:
Scandanavia/Nordic Region

Industry Focus
(% based on actual investment)

Medical/Health	68.0%
Other Products	21.0%
Industrial/Energy	11.0%

Additional Information
Year Founded: 2001
Capital Under Management: $382,300,000
Current Activity Level : Actively seeking new investments

NORDWIND CAPITAL GMBH
Residenzstrasse 18
Munich, Germany 80333
Phone: 49-8929-19580
Fax: 49-8929-195858
E-mail: info@nordwindcapital.com
Website: www.nordwindcapital.com

Management and Staff
Anton Schneider, Managing Director
Hans Albrecht, Managing Director
Tom Harder, Managing Director

Type of Firm
Private Equity Firm

Association Membership
German Venture Capital Association (BVK)

Project Preferences
Type of Financing Preferred:
Turnaround
Special Situation

Geographical Preferences
International Preferences:
Switzerland
Austria
Germany

Additional Information
Year Founded: 2002
Capital Under Management: $372,000,000
Current Activity Level : Actively seeking new investments

NORFUND

Munkedansveien 45
Oslo, Norway NO 0111
Phone: 47-22-019-393
Fax: 47-22-019-394
E-mail: post@norfund.org
Website: www.norfund.no

Other Offices

Lancaster Gate, Hyde Park Lane
Hyde Park
Johannesburg, South Africa 2196
Phone: 27-11-325-1940
Fax: 27-11-325-1944

Paseo Colon
Torre Mercedes, piso 8
San Jose, Costa Rica 721-1000
Phone: 506-211-1511
Fax: 506-211-1530

Management and Staff

Per Emil Lindoe, Managing Director

Type of Firm

Government Affiliated Program

Association Membership

Norwegian Venture Capital Association
European Private Equity and Venture Capital Assoc.
African Venture Capital Association (AVCA)

Project Preferences

Type of Financing Preferred:
Expansion
Generalist PE
Management Buyouts

Size of Investments Considered:
Min Size of Investment Considered (000s): $400
Max Size of Investment Considered (000s): $20,000

Geographical Preferences

International Preferences:
Latin America
Europe
Pacific
Asia
Africa

Industry Preferences

In Biotechnology prefer:
Agricultural/Animal Bio.

In Industrial/Energy prefer:
Energy

In Financial Services prefer:
Financial Services

In Manufact. prefer:
Manufacturing

Additional Information

Year Founded: 1997
Capital Under Management: $460,000,000
Current Activity Level : Actively seeking new investments

NORGESINVESTOR AS (AKA: NESTOR KAPITAL-FORVALTNING)

Haakon VIIs Gate 6
PO Box 1863
Oslo, Norway 0124
Phone: 47-2201-9330
Fax: 47-2201-9040
E-mail: post@norgesinvestor.no
Website: www.norgesinvestor.no

Management and Staff

Jan Hartvig, Founder
Stein Annexstad, Founder

Type of Firm

Private Equity Firm

Association Membership

European Private Equity and Venture Capital Assoc.

Project Preferences

Type of Financing Preferred:
Leveraged Buyout
Expansion
Later Stage
Management Buyouts

Geographical Preferences

International Preferences:
Europe
Norway

Industry Focus

(% based on actual investment)

Consumer Related	51.8%
Medical/Health	36.7%
Other Products	11.5%

Additional Information

Year Founded: 1996
Capital Under Management: $124,200,000
Current Activity Level : Actively seeking new investments

NORINVEST MANAGEMENT AS (AKA: NORINVEST FORVALTNING AS)

Forskningsparken
Tromso, Norway 9011
Phone: 47-77-679-732
Fax: 47-77-670-750

Type of Firm

Private Equity Firm

Association Membership

Norwegian Venture Capital Association
European Private Equity and Venture Capital Assoc.

Project Preferences

Type of Financing Preferred:
Balanced

Geographical Preferences

International Preferences:
Europe
Norway

Additional Information

Year Founded: 2000
Current Activity Level : Actively seeking new investments

NORO-MOSELEY PARTNERS

Nine North Parkway Square
4200 Northside Parkway, N.W.
Atlanta, GA USA 30327
Phone: 404-233-1966
Fax: 404-239-9280
E-mail: info@noro-moseley.com
Website: www.noro-moseley.com

Management and Staff

Alan Taetle, General Partner
Allen Moseley, General Partner
Charles Moseley, General Partner
Chuck Johnson, General Partner
George Mackie, Venture Partner
Michael Elliott, General Partner

Type of Firm

Private Equity Firm

Association Membership

National Venture Capital Association - USA (NVCA)

Project Preferences

Role in Financing:
Prefer role as deal originator but will also invest in deals created by others

Type of Financing Preferred:
Early Stage
Expansion
Generalist PE
Seed
Acquisition
Startup
Recapitalizations

Size of Investments Considered:
Min Size of Investment Considered (000s): $2,000
Max Size of Investment Considered (000s): $15,000

Geographical Preferences

United States Preferences:

Southeast
All U.S.

Industry Focus

(% based on actual investment)

Computer Software and Services	19.1%
Internet Specific	18.4%
Medical/Health	16.8%
Other Products	13.6%
Communications and Media	10.5%
Consumer Related	10.2%
Semiconductors/Other Elect.	4.4%
Computer Hardware	3.7%
Industrial/Energy	1.7%
Biotechnology	1.6%

Additional Information

Name of Most Recent Fund: Noro-Moseley Partners VI, LP
Most Recent Fund Was Raised: 06/22/2007
Year Founded: 1983
Capital Under Management: $660,000,000
Current Activity Level : Actively seeking new investments
Method of Compensation: Return on investment is of primary concern, do not charge fees

---

NORRSKENET AB (AKA: BOTHNIA)

Foretagarcentrum
Kiruna, Sweden 981 41
Phone: 46-980-12-090
Fax: 46-980-16-694
E-mail: bothnia.invest@kiruna.se
Website: www.norrskenet.se

Other Offices

Hjalmar Lundbomsv. 29
Kiruna, Sweden 981 36
Phone: 46-980-10-210

Type of Firm

Private Equity Firm

Project Preferences

Type of Financing Preferred:

Balanced

Geographical Preferences

International Preferences:

Sweden
Europe

Additional Information

Year Founded: 2003
Current Activity Level : Actively seeking new investments

NORSHIELD CAPITAL MANAGEMENT CORP.

One Place Ville Marie
Montreal, Canada H3B3M5
Phone: 514-875-6755
Fax: 514-875-2940

Type of Firm

Private Equity Firm

Geographical Preferences

United States Preferences:

All U.S.

Canadian Preferences:

Quebec
Ontario

Additional Information

Year Founded: 1982
Current Activity Level : Actively seeking new investments

NORSK HYDRO ASA (AKA: NORSK HYDRO TECHNOLOGY VENTURES)

Drammensveien 260
Oslo, Norway 0283
Phone: 47-22-538-100
Fax: 47-22-532-725
E-mail: corporate@hydro.com
Website: www.hydro.com

Management and Staff

Jorgen Rostrup, Chief Executive Officer
Richard Erskine, Managing Director
Svein Richard Brandtz?g, Chief Executive Officer

Type of Firm

Corporate PE/Venture

Association Membership

Norwegian Venture Capital Association
European Private Equity and Venture Capital Assoc.

Project Preferences

Type of Financing Preferred:

Expansion

Geographical Preferences

International Preferences:

Scandanavia/Nordic Region
Norway

Industry Preferences

In Industrial/Energy prefer:

Energy
Oil & Gas Drilling,Explor

Additional Information

Year Founded: 1986
Capital Under Management: $59,200,000
Current Activity Level : Actively seeking new investments

NORTH ATLANTIC CAPITAL CORPORATION

Two City Center
Fifth Floor
Portland, ME USA 04101
Phone: 207-772-4470
Fax: 207-772-3257
E-mail: nacc@northatlanticcapital.com
Website: www.northatlanticcapital.com

Management and Staff

David Coit, Managing Director
Kimberley Niles, Chief Financial Officer
Mark Morrissette, Managing Director

Type of Firm

Private Equity Advisor or Fund of Funds

Association Membership

National Venture Capital Association - USA (NVCA)
Natl Assoc of Small Bus. Inv. Co (NASBIC)

Project Preferences

Role in Financing:

Will function either as deal originator or investor in deals created by others

Type of Financing Preferred:

Leveraged Buyout
Expansion
Mezzanine
Later Stage
Management Buyouts
Acquisition
Recapitalizations

Size of Investments Considered:

Min Size of Investment Considered (000s): $2,000
Max Size of Investment Considered (000s): $10,000

Geographical Preferences

United States Preferences:

Mid Atlantic
Northeast

Industry Focus

(% based on actual investment)

Communications and Media	17.7%
Computer Software and Services	15.7%
Other Products	12.4%
Internet Specific	11.6%
Computer Hardware	11.0%
Semiconductors/Other Elect.	10.0%
Consumer Related	9.4%
Industrial/Energy	7.4%
Medical/Health	4.0%
Biotechnology	0.7%

Additional Information

Name of Most Recent Fund: North Atlantic SBIC IV
Most Recent Fund Was Raised: 12/31/2007
Year Founded: 1980
Capital Under Management: $198,000,000
Current Activity Level : Actively seeking new investments
Method of Compensation: Return on investment is of primary concern, do not charge fees

---

NORTH BAY EQUITY PARTNERS

1395 Brickell Avenue
Suite 800
Miami, FL USA 33131
Phone: 305-777-2212
Fax: 305-777-2209
E-mail: info@northbayequity.com
Website: www.northbayequity.com

Management and Staff

Alfredo Gutierrez, Partner
Matthew Cole, Partner

Type of Firm

Bank Affiliated

Project Preferences

Role in Financing:

Prefer role as deal originator

Type of Financing Preferred:

Expansion
Later Stage
Management Buyouts

Size of Investments Considered:

Min Size of Investment Considered (000s): $10,000
Max Size of Investment Considered (000s): $25,000

Geographical Preferences

United States Preferences:

Southwest

International Preferences:

Latin America
Brazil
Mexico

Industry Preferences

In Communications prefer:

Commercial Communications
CATV & Pay TV Systems
Radio & TV Broadcasting
Telecommunications
Wireless Communications
Data Communications
Satellite Microwave Comm.
Other Communication Prod.

In Internet Specific prefer:

E-Commerce Technology

In Biotechnology prefer:

Agricultural/Animal Bio.

In Transportation prefer:

Transportation

In Business Serv. prefer:

Media

Additional Information

Year Founded: 2001
Current Activity Level : Actively seeking new investments
Method of Compensation: Function primarily in service area, receive contingent fee in cash or equity

---

NORTH BRIDGE VENTURE PARTNERS

2755 Campus Drive
Suite 165
San Mateo, CA USA 94403
Phone: 650-357-0004
Fax: 650-357-0017
Website: www.northbridge.com

Other Offices

950 Winter Street
Suite 4600
Waltham, MA USA 02451
Phone: 781-290-0004
Fax: 781-290-0999

Management and Staff

Basil Horangic, Partner
Cali Tran, Principal
Carmichael Roberts, Partner
Dayna Grayson, Principal
Edward Anderson, Managing General Partner
James Goldstein, Partner
James Moran, General Partner
Jeffrey McCarthy, Partner
Jeffrey Beir, Partner
Kenneth DiPoto, Chief Financial Officer
Michael Skok, Partner
Paul Santinelli, Partner
Richard D Amore, General Partner
William Geary, Partner

Type of Firm

Private Equity Firm

Association Membership

National Venture Capital Association - USA (NVCA)

Project Preferences

Role in Financing:

Prefer role as deal originator

Type of Financing Preferred:

Leveraged Buyout
Early Stage
Expansion
Public Companies
Later Stage
Acquisition

Size of Investments Considered:

Min Size of Investment Considered (000s): $100
Max Size of Investment Considered (000s): $7,500

Geographical Preferences

United States Preferences:

Southeast
Northeast
All U.S.

Industry Focus

(% based on actual investment)	
Computer Software and Services	29.5%
Internet Specific	24.0%
Communications and Media	22.8%
Semiconductors/Other Elect.	9.4%
Industrial/Energy	4.2%
Computer Hardware	3.5%
Other Products	2.8%
Medical/Health	1.8%
Biotechnology	1.8%
Consumer Related	0.1%

Additional Information

Year Founded: 1994
Capital Under Management: $2,381,000,000
Current Activity Level : Actively seeking new investments
Method of Compensation: Return on investment is of primary concern, do not charge fees

---

NORTH CASTLE PARTNERS

183 East Putnam Avenue
Greenwich, CT USA 06830
Phone: 203-862-3200
Fax: 203-862-3270
Website: www.northcastlepartners.com

Other Offices

One Embarcadero Center
Suite 3810
San Francisco, CA USA 94111
Phone: 415-705-8000
Fax: 415-705-5279

Management and Staff

Alison Minter, Principal
Alyse Skidmore, Chief Financial Officer
Charles Baird, Founder
Douglas Lehrman, Managing Director
Jonathan Canarick, Principal
Louis Marinaccio, Managing Director

Type of Firm

Private Equity Firm

Project Preferences

Type of Financing Preferred:

Leveraged Buyout
Generalist PE

Industry Focus

(% based on actual investment)

Consumer Related	89.0%
Internet Specific	7.4%
Medical/Health	2.2%
Biotechnology	1.0%
Computer Hardware	0.5%

Additional Information

Name of Most Recent Fund: North Castle Partners III - A
Most Recent Fund Was Raised: 05/27/2004
Year Founded: 1997
Capital Under Management: $261,000,000
Current Activity Level : Actively seeking new investments

NORTH COAST ANGEL FUND

737 Bolivar Road
Suite 3000
Cleveland, OH USA 44115
Phone: 800-975-5846
Fax: 800-975-5846
E-mail: Info@northcoastangelfund.com
Website: www.northcoastangels.com

Type of Firm

Angel Group

Project Preferences

Type of Financing Preferred:

Early Stage

Geographical Preferences

United States Preferences:

Ohio

Additional Information

Name of Most Recent Fund: North Coast Angel Fund
Most Recent Fund Was Raised: 09/11/2006
Year Founded: 2006
Capital Under Management: $1,000,000
Current Activity Level : Actively seeking new investments

NORTH COAST TECHNOLOGY INVESTORS, L.P.

206 South Fifth Avenue
Suite 550
Ann Arbor, MI USA 48104
Phone: 734-662-7667
Fax: 734-662-6261
E-mail: partners@northcoastvc.com
Website: www.northcoastvc.com

Other Offices

300 Rodd Street
Suite 201
Midland, MI USA 48640
Phone: 989-832-2300
Fax: 989-832-2301

Management and Staff

Hugo Braun, Managing Partner
Lindsay Aspergren, Managing Partner

Type of Firm

Private Equity Firm

Association Membership

National Venture Capital Association - USA (NVCA)

Project Preferences

Role in Financing:

Will function either as deal originator or investor in deals created by others

Type of Financing Preferred:

Early Stage
Seed
Startup

Size of Investments Considered:

Min Size of Investment Considered (000s): $250
Max Size of Investment Considered (000s): $6,000

Geographical Preferences

United States Preferences:

Midwest
All U.S.

Industry Preferences

In Communications prefer:

Telecommunications

In Computer Software prefer:

Software

In Computer Other prefer:

Computer Related

In Semiconductor/Electr prefer:

Controllers and Sensors

In Biotechnology prefer:

Biotech Related Research

In Medical/Health prefer:

Medical Therapeutics

In Industrial/Energy prefer:

Industrial Products
Materials
Advanced Materials

In Manufact. prefer:

Manufacturing

Additional Information

Name of Most Recent Fund: NCTI III, L.P.
Most Recent Fund Was Raised: 07/03/2008
Year Founded: 1999
Capital Under Management: $100,000,000
Current Activity Level : Actively seeking new investments
Method of Compensation: Return on investment is of primary concern, do not charge fees

NORTH HILL VENTURES

Ten Post Office Square
11th Floor
Boston, MA USA 02109
Phone: 617-788-2150
Fax: 617-788-2152
Website: www.northhillventures.com

Management and Staff

Benjamin Malka, General Partner
Brett Rome, General Partner
Shamez Kanji, General Partner

Type of Firm

Private Equity Firm

Association Membership

Mid-Atlantic Venture Association
Natl Assoc of Small Bus. Inv. Co (NASBIC)
National Venture Capital Association - USA (NVCA)

Project Preferences

Role in Financing:

Will function either as deal originator or investor in deals created by others

Type of Financing Preferred:

Second Stage Financing
Expansion
Later Stage

Size of Investments Considered:

Min Size of Investment Considered (000s): $2,000
Max Size of Investment Considered (000s): $5,000

Geographical Preferences

United States Preferences:

Virginia

Industry Preferences

In Consumer Related prefer:

Consumer

In Financial Services prefer:

Financial Services

In Business Serv. prefer:

Services

Additional Information

Year Founded: 1999
Capital Under Management: $80,000,000
Current Activity Level : Actively seeking new investments
Method of Compensation: Return on investment is of primary concern, do not charge fees

NORTH PEAK CAPITAL, LLC

300 Park Avenue
Suite 1700
New York, NY USA 10022

Phone: 212-687-6800
Fax: 212-572-6499
E-mail: info@northpeakcapital.com
Website: www.northpeakcapital.com

Management and Staff

Michael Kahan, Founding Partner

Type of Firm

Private Equity Firm

Project Preferences

Type of Financing Preferred:

Leveraged Buyout
Expansion

Industry Preferences

In Medical/Health prefer:

Medical/Health

Additional Information

Year Founded: 2005
Current Activity Level : Actively seeking new investments

NORTH WEST DEVELOPMENT AGENCY

P.O. Box 37, Renaissance House
Centre Park
Warrington, Cheshire, United Kingdom WA1 1XB
Phone: 44-1925-400-100
Fax: 44-1925-400-400
E-mail: info@nwda.co.uk
Website: www.nwda.co.uk

Other Offices

Giants Basin
Potato Wharf
Castlefield, United Kingdom M3 4NB
Phone: 44-161-817-7400
Fax: 44-161-831-7051

Ground Floor
12 Princes Parade
Liverpool, United Kingdom L3 1BG
Phone: 44-1925-400-100
Fax: 44-1925-400-400

Gillan Way
Penrith 40 Business Park
Cumbria, United Kingdom CA11 9BP
Phone: 44-1768-867-294
Fax: 44-1768-895-477

18-24 Faraday Road
Wavertree Technology Park
Liverpool, United Kingdom L13 1EH
Phone: 44-1925-400-100
Fax: 44-1925-400-400

Brew House, Wilderspool Park
Greenalls Avenue
Warrington, United Kingdom WA4 6HL
Phone: 44-1925-644-220
Fax: 44-1925-644-222

13 Winkley Street
Preston
Lancashire, United Kingdom PR1 2AA
Phone: 44-1772-206-000
Fax: 44-1772-200-049

Unit 1
Lillyhall Business Centre
Workington, United Kingdom CA14 4HA
Phone: 44-1900-734-000
Fax: 44-1900-606-572

Management and Staff

Steven Broomhead, Chief Executive Officer
Type of Firm
Private Equity Firm

Project Preferences

Type of Financing Preferred:

Early Stage
Seed
Management Buyouts
Startup

Geographical Preferences

International Preferences:

United Kingdom

Additional Information

Current Activity Level : Actively seeking new investments

NORTHCAP PARTNERS

Sundkrogsgade 7
P.O. Box 2672
Copenhagen, Denmark DK-2100
Phone: 45-7730-9000
E-mail: info@northcappartners.com
Website: www.northcappartners.com

Management and Staff

Kim Weincken, Partner
Thomas Weilby Knudsen, Managing Partner

Type of Firm

Private Equity Firm

Project Preferences

Type of Financing Preferred:

Leveraged Buyout
Generalist PE
Early Stage
Expansion

Geographical Preferences

International Preferences:

Switzerland
Austria
Scandanavia/Nordic Region
Germany
Denmark

Additional Information

Year Founded: 2007
Current Activity Level : Actively seeking new investments

NORTHERN LIGHT VENTURE CAPITAL

2855 Sand Hill Road
Suite 201
Menlo Park, CA USA 94025
Phone: 650-585-5450
Fax: 650-585-5451
E-mail: info@northernlightvc.com
Website: www.nlightvc.com

Other Offices

Tsinghua Science Park
23/F, SP Tower A
Beijing, China 100084
Phone: 86-10-8215-1000
Fax: 86-10-5872-2680

1266 Nanjing West Road
Unit 2207 A, Henglong Plaza
Shanghai, China 200040
Phone: 86-21-6113-5855
Fax: 86-21-6138-1010

Management and Staff

Datong Chen, Venture Partner
Elton Jiang, Managing Director
Feng Deng, Managing Director
Figo Zhang, Vice President
Jeffrey Lee, Chief Financial Officer
John Wu, Venture Partner
Lixin Li, Venture Partner
Robert Shuhua Zhou, Managing Director
Summer Xiaopeng Qu, Vice President
Yan Ke, Managing Director
Ying Wang, Vice President
Zhi Tan, Venture Partner

Type of Firm

Private Equity Firm

Association Membership

Western Association of Venture Capitalists (WAVC)
National Venture Capital Association - USA (NVCA)

Project Preferences

Type of Financing Preferred:

Early Stage
Expansion
Balanced

Geographical Preferences

United States Preferences:

California

International Preferences:
China
Asia

Industry Preferences

In Communications prefer:
Telecommunications

In Computer Software prefer:
Software
Systems Software

In Semiconductor/Electr prefer:
Semiconductor

In Consumer Related prefer:
Retail

In Business Serv. prefer:
Services

Additional Information
Name of Most Recent Fund: Northern Light Venture Fund, L.P.
Most Recent Fund Was Raised: 12/12/2005
Year Founded: 2005
Capital Under Management: $471,000,000
Current Activity Level : Actively seeking new investments

NORTHERN LIGHTS VENTURES, LLC

1498 Pacific Avenue
Suite 515
Tacoma, WA USA 98402
Phone: 253-238-0417
E-mail: info@northernlightsventures.com
Website: www.northernlightsventures.com

Management and Staff
Andy Turner, Managing Director
James Wagar, Principal
Paul Greenwood, Managing Director
Timothy Carver, Managing Director

Type of Firm
Private Equity Firm

Project Preferences

Role in Financing:
Prefer role as deal originator but will also invest in deals created by others

Type of Financing Preferred:
Expansion
Later Stage
Management Buyouts

Geographical Preferences

United States Preferences:
All U.S.

Industry Preferences

In Financial Services prefer:
Investment Groups
Financial Services

Additional Information
Name of Most Recent Fund: Northern Lights Capital Partners, LLC
Most Recent Fund Was Raised: 01/24/2007
Year Founded: 2006
Capital Under Management: $60,000,000
Current Activity Level : Actively seeking new investments
Method of Compensation: Return on investment is of primary concern, do not charge fees

---

NORTHERN VENTURE MANAGERS LIMITED (AKA: NVM)

Northumberland House
Princess Square
Newcastle upon Tyne, United Kingdom NE1 8ER
Phone: 44-191-244-6000
Fax: 44-191-244-6001
E-mail: new@nvm.co.uk
Website: www.nvm.co.uk

Other Offices
12 Forbury Road
Reading, United Kingdom RG1 1SB
Phone: 44-118-951-7000
Fax: 44-118-951-7001

50 Moray Place
Edinburgh, United Kingdom EH3 6BQ
Phone: 44-131-260-1000
Fax: 44-131-260-1001

Management and Staff
Alastair Conn, Managing Director

Type of Firm
Bank Affiliated

Association Membership
British Venture Capital Association (BVCA)
European Private Equity and Venture Capital Assoc.

Project Preferences

Role in Financing:
Prefer role as deal originator but will also invest in deals created by others

Type of Financing Preferred:
Second Stage Financing
Leveraged Buyout
Early Stage
Balanced
Turnaround
First Stage Financing
Startup

Size of Investments Considered:
Min Size of Investment Considered (000s): $1,000
Max Size of Investment Considered: No Limit

Geographical Preferences

International Preferences:
United Kingdom

Industry Focus
(% based on actual investment)

Other Products	46.3%
Industrial/Energy	15.2%
Computer Software and Services	8.8%
Biotechnology	8.4%
Medical/Health	8.1%
Consumer Related	6.3%
Computer Hardware	3.3%
Communications and Media	2.5%
Internet Specific	0.9%
Semiconductors/Other Elect.	0.2%

Additional Information
Year Founded: 1984
Capital Under Management: $221,800,000
Current Activity Level : Actively seeking new investments
Method of Compensation: Return on invest. most important, but chg. closing fees, service fees, etc.

NORTHGATE CAPITAL GROUP

649 San Ramon Valley Boulevard
Suite 200
Danville, CA USA 94526
Phone: 925-820-9970
Fax: 925-820-9994
E-mail: info@northgatecapital.com
Website: www.northgatecapital.com

Other Offices
173 Spring Street
Suite 200
Pleasanton, CA USA 94566
Phone: 925-600-9700
Fax: 925-600-9704

1 Jermyn Street
London, United Kingdom SW1Y 4UH
Phone: 44-20-7961-6480
Fax: 44-20-7961-6490

50 Pall Mall
London, United Kingdom SW1Y 5JH
Phone: 44-20-7968-8100
Fax: 44-20-7968-8111

Management and Staff
Brent Jones, Managing Director
Carol Christensen, Chief Financial Officer
Hosein Khajey-Hosseiny, Managing Director
Jared Stone, Managing Director
Kathleen Taradash, Principal
Mark Harris, Managing Director

Thomas Vardell, Managing Director

Type of Firm

Private Equity Advisor or Fund of Funds

Project Preferences

Type of Financing Preferred:

Fund of Funds

Geographical Preferences

United States Preferences:

California
All U.S.

International Preferences:

Europe
All International
Japan

Industry Preferences

In Communications prefer:

Telecommunications
Wireless Communications

In Internet Specific prefer:

Internet

In Medical/Health prefer:

Medical/Health

Additional Information

Name of Most Recent Fund: Northgate Private Equity Partners III-B2, L.P.
Most Recent Fund Was Raised: 04/30/2007
Year Founded: 2000
Capital Under Management: $184,400,000
Current Activity Level : Actively seeking new investments

NORTHROCK CAPITAL PARTNERS

448 Glenlake Avenue
Toronto, Canada M6P 1G8
Phone: 416-760-8819
Fax: 416-760-8427
Website: www.northrockcapital.com

Type of Firm

Private Equity Firm

Project Preferences

Type of Financing Preferred:

Leveraged Buyout
Management Buyouts
Acquisition

Size of Investments Considered:

Min Size of Investment Considered (000s): $5,000
Max Size of Investment Considered (000s): $15,000

Geographical Preferences

Canadian Preferences:

Ontario

Additional Information

Year Founded: 2006
Capital Under Management: $50,000,000
Current Activity Level : Actively seeking new investments
Method of Compensation: Return on invest. most important, but chg. closing fees, service fees, etc.

NORTHSTAR CAPITAL, LLC (FKA: SEIDLER CAPITAL, LTD.)

2310 Plaza VII
45 South 7th Street
Minneapolis, MN USA 55402
Phone: 612-371-5700
Fax: 612-371-5710
Website: www.northstarcapital.com

Management and Staff

Duane Harris, Managing Director
Scott Becker, Managing Director

Type of Firm

Bank Affiliated

Project Preferences

Type of Financing Preferred:

Mezzanine

Geographical Preferences

Canadian Preferences:

All Canada

Industry Focus

(% based on actual investment)

Internet Specific	39.6%
Medical/Health	37.7%
Industrial/Energy	18.4%
Computer Hardware	4.3%

Additional Information

Name of Most Recent Fund: Northstar Mezzanine Partners IV, L.P.
Most Recent Fund Was Raised: 09/09/2005
Year Founded: 1995
Capital Under Management: $898,800,000
Current Activity Level : Actively seeking new investments

NORTHWATER CAPITAL MANAGEMENT

Suite 4700, BCE Place
181 Bay Street P.O. Box 794
Toronto, Canada M5J2T3
Phone: 416-360-5435
Fax: 416-360-0671
E-mail: mpt@northwatercapital.com
Website: www.northwatercapital.com

Management and Staff

Benita Warmbold, Managing Director
Daniel Mills, Managing Director
David Finch, Managing Director
David Patterson, Chairman & CEO
Paul Robson, President

Type of Firm

Private Equity Firm

Additional Information

Year Founded: 1989
Current Activity Level : Actively seeking new investments

NORTHWEST TECHNOLOGY VENTURES (FKA: ORTDF)

663 North West Compton Loop
Murdock Building, Room 516
Beaverton, OR USA 97006
Phone: 503-352-0673
Fax: 503-748-1744
Website: www.nwtechventures.com

Management and Staff

Gordon Hoffman, Managing Director
William Newman, Managing Director

Type of Firm

Endowment, Foundation or Pension Fund

Project Preferences

Role in Financing:

Will function either as deal originator or investor in deals created by others

Type of Financing Preferred:

Early Stage

Size of Investments Considered:

Min Size of Investment Considered (000s): $250
Max Size of Investment Considered (000s): $500

Geographical Preferences

United States Preferences:

Oregon

Industry Focus

(% based on actual investment)

Biotechnology	29.6%
Semiconductors/Other Elect.	28.6%
Computer Software and Services	16.4%
Computer Hardware	7.1%
Medical/Health	6.7%
Other Products	4.9%
Consumer Related	3.7%
Industrial/Energy	2.9%

Additional Information

Name of Most Recent Fund: Northwest Technology Ventures
Most Recent Fund Was Raised: 06/01/2002

Year Founded: 1987
Capital Under Management: $14,000,000
Current Activity Level : Actively seeking new investments
Method of Compensation: Return on investment is of primary concern, do not charge fees

NORTHWEST VENTURE ASSOCIATES, INC. (FKA: SPOKANE CAPITAL MGMT)

221 North Wall Street
Suite 628
Spokane, WA USA 99201
Phone: 509-747-0728
Fax: 509-747-0758
Website: www.nwva.com

Management and Staff

Joe Herzog, Chief Financial Officer
Mark Mecham, Venture Partner
Robert Wolfe, General Partner
Thomas Simpson, Managing Partner

Type of Firm

Private Equity Firm

Association Membership

Natl Assoc of Small Bus. Inv. Co (NASBIC)

Project Preferences

Role in Financing:

Will function either as deal originator or investor in deals created by others

Type of Financing Preferred:

Second Stage Financing
Leveraged Buyout
Early Stage
Expansion
Later Stage
First Stage Financing
Startup

Size of Investments Considered:

Min Size of Investment Considered (000s): $500
Max Size of Investment Considered (000s): $5,000

Geographical Preferences

United States Preferences:

Oregon
Colorado
Idaho
Utah
Washington
Montana

Canadian Preferences:

British Columbia

Industry Focus

(% based on actual investment)

Computer Software and Services	43.4%
Internet Specific	28.1%
Communications and Media	9.8%
Medical/Health	6.8%
Consumer Related	5.8%
Semiconductors/Other Elect.	5.1%
Industrial/Energy	0.8%
Other Products	0.1%

Additional Information

Year Founded: 1986
Capital Under Management: $125,000,000
Current Activity Level : Actively seeking new investments
Method of Compensation: Return on investment is of primary concern, do not charge fees

NORTHWESTERN MUTUAL CAPITAL

720 East Wisconsin Avenue
Milwaukee, WI USA 53202
Phone: 414-665-5499
Fax: 414-665-7124
Website: www.northwesternmutualcapital.com

Other Offices

First Floor
17-19 Maddox Street
London, United Kingdom W1S 2QH
Phone: 44-20-7318-6670

Management and Staff

Jerome Baier, Managing Director
Randal Ralph, Managing Director
Richard Strait, Managing Director

Type of Firm

Insurance Firm Affiliate

Project Preferences

Type of Financing Preferred:

Leveraged Buyout
Expansion
Mezzanine
Distressed Debt

Additional Information

Year Founded: 1978
Capital Under Management: $325,000,000
Current Activity Level : Actively seeking new investments

NORTHWOOD VENTURES

485 Underhill Boulevard
Suite 205
Syosset, NY USA 11791
Phone: 516-364-5544
Fax: 516-364-0879
Website: www.northwoodventures.com

Management and Staff

Henry Wilson, Managing Director
Paul Homer, Vice President
Peter Schiff, President

Type of Firm

Private Equity Firm

Association Membership

National Venture Capital Association - USA (NVCA)

Project Preferences

Role in Financing:

Will function either as deal originator or investor in deals created by others

Type of Financing Preferred:

Second Stage Financing
Leveraged Buyout
Early Stage
Expansion
Generalist PE
Later Stage
Management Buyouts
First Stage Financing
Acquisition
Private Placement
Industry Rollups
Recapitalizations

Size of Investments Considered:

Min Size of Investment Considered (000s): $2,000
Max Size of Investment Considered (000s): $10,000

Geographical Preferences

United States Preferences:

All U.S.

Industry Focus

(% based on actual investment)

Communications and Media	39.7%
Internet Specific	18.0%
Consumer Related	16.4%
Other Products	10.7%
Biotechnology	7.5%
Industrial/Energy	4.7%
Semiconductors/Other Elect.	1.6%
Computer Software and Services	1.0%
Computer Hardware	0.6%

Additional Information

Name of Most Recent Fund: Northwood Ventures
Most Recent Fund Was Raised: 12/01/1982
Year Founded: 1983
Capital Under Management: $150,000,000
Current Activity Level : Actively seeking new investments
Method of Compensation: Return on investment is of primary concern, do not charge fees

NORTHZONE VENTURES AS (FKA: VENTURE PARTNERS AS)

Bygdoy Alle 2
P.O. Box 573 Sentrum
Oslo, Norway 0105

Phone: 47-22-125-010
Fax: 47-22-125-011
E-mail: office@northzone.com
Website: www.northzone.com

Other Offices

HighTech Building
Sveav 9-11
Stockholm, Sweden 101 52
Phone: 46-8-5661-5060
Fax: 46-8-5661-5001

Strandvejen 100, 4th floor
Hellerup
Copenhagen, Denmark 2900
Phone: 45-70-222-475
Fax: 45-7022-2476

Management and Staff

Arve Johan Andresen, General Partner
Bjorn Stray, General Partner
Gregers Kronborg, General Partner
Hans Otterling, General Partner
Jorgen Bladh, General Partner
Karl-Christian Agerup, General Partner
Par-Jorgen Parsson, General Partner
Stine Foss, Chief Financial Officer
Tellef Thorleifsson, General Partner
Torleif Ahlsand, General Partner

Type of Firm

Private Equity Firm

Association Membership

Norwegian Venture Capital Association
European Private Equity and Venture Capital Assoc.

Project Preferences

Type of Financing Preferred:

Early Stage
Expansion
Balanced
Seed
Startup

Size of Investments Considered:

Min Size of Investment Considered (000s): $900
Max Size of Investment Considered (000s): $900,000

Geographical Preferences

International Preferences:

Europe
Scandanavia/Nordic Region

Industry Preferences

In Communications prefer:

Telecommunications

In Computer Software prefer:

Software

In Computer Other prefer:

Computer Related

In Semiconductor/Electr prefer:

Semiconductor

In Consumer Related prefer:

Consumer

Additional Information

Year Founded: 1995
Capital Under Management: $460,800,000
Current Activity Level : Actively seeking new investments

NORTIA CAPITAL PARTNERS, INC. (FKA: BF ACQUISITION GROUP I)

400 Hampton View Court
Alpharetta, GA USA 30004
Phone: 770-777-6795
Fax: 770-777-6799
E-mail: info@nortiacapital.com
Website: www.nortiacapital.com

Other Offices

555 West 5th Street
Suite 3000
Los Angeles, CA USA 90013
Phone: 213-533-4110

Management and Staff

Matthew Henninger, President
William Bosso, Chairman & CEO

Type of Firm

Bank Affiliated

Project Preferences

Type of Financing Preferred:

Leveraged Buyout
Expansion
Mezzanine
Generalist PE
Recapitalizations

Additional Information

Year Founded: 1999
Current Activity Level : Actively seeking new investments

NORVENTUM CAPITAL A/S

Tuborg Boulevard 12
Hellerup, Denmark DK-2900
Phone: 45-7027-5010
E-mail: contact@norventum.com
Website: www.norventum.com

Management and Staff

Jorgen Gransoe, Partner

Type of Firm

Private Equity Firm

Project Preferences

Type of Financing Preferred:

Balanced

Geographical Preferences

International Preferences:

Denmark

Additional Information

Year Founded: 2000
Current Activity Level : Actively seeking new investments

NORVESTOR EQUITY AS (FKA: NORSK VEKST FORVALTNING AS)

Roald Amundsensgt. 6
P.O Box 1223, Vika
Oslo, Norway 0161
Phone: 47-23-000-700
Fax: 47-23-000-701
E-mail: contact@norvestor.com
Website: www.norvestor.com

Other Offices

Vasagatan 36, 1 tr
Stockholm, Sweden 111 20
Phone: 46-827-4792

Management and Staff

Henning Vold, Partner
Jarle Gundersen, Managing Partner
Lars Grinde, Partner
Oyvind Aasbo, Partner
Rolf Straume, Partner
Trond Bjornoy, Partner

Type of Firm

Private Equity Firm

Association Membership

Norwegian Venture Capital Association
Swedish Venture Capital Association (SVCA)
European Private Equity and Venture Capital Assoc.

Project Preferences

Type of Financing Preferred:

Leveraged Buyout
Acquisition

Size of Investments Considered:

Min Size of Investment Considered (000s): $13,017
Max Size of Investment Considered (000s): $58,578

Geographical Preferences

International Preferences:

Scandanavia/Nordic Region
Norway

Industry Preferences

In Communications prefer:
Telecommunications

In Consumer Related prefer:
Retail
Food/Beverage
Consumer Services

In Industrial/Energy prefer:
Energy
Oil & Gas Drilling,Explor

Additional Information

Year Founded: 1997
Capital Under Management: $498,200,000
Current Activity Level : Actively seeking new investments

NORWAY - LATVIA BUSINESS SUPPORT FUND, THE

Perses iela 2-419
Riga, Latvia LV-1011
Phone: 371-722-3321
Fax: 371-728-2445
E-mail: sekretare@nluaf.lv
Website: www.nluaf.lv

Type of Firm

Private Equity Firm

Project Preferences

Type of Financing Preferred:
Expansion

Size of Investments Considered:
Min Size of Investment Considered (000s): $35
Max Size of Investment Considered (000s): $300

Geographical Preferences

International Preferences:
Latvia

Industry Preferences

In Consumer Related prefer:
Consumer

In Industrial/Energy prefer:
Energy
Industrial Products

Additional Information

Year Founded: 1995
Current Activity Level : Actively seeking new investments

NORWEST EQUITY PARTNERS

80 South Eighth Street
Suite 3600
Minneapolis, MN USA 55402
Phone: 612-215-1600
Fax: 612-215-1601
Website: www.nep.com

Management and Staff

Andrew Cantwell, Principal
Erik Torgerson, Partner
John Thomson, Partner
John Lindahl, Managing General Partner
Thomas Schauerman, Principal
Timothy DeVries, Managing General Partner
Timothy Kuehl, Partner
Todd Solow, Partner

Type of Firm

Private Equity Firm

Association Membership

National Venture Capital Association - USA (NVCA)

Project Preferences

Role in Financing:
Prefer role as deal originator but will also invest in deals created by others

Type of Financing Preferred:
Leveraged Buyout
Expansion
Mezzanine
Later Stage
Management Buyouts
Acquisition
Recapitalizations

Size of Investments Considered:
Min Size of Investment Considered (000s): $10,000
Max Size of Investment Considered (000s): $60,000

Geographical Preferences

United States Preferences:
All U.S.

Industry Preferences

In Communications prefer:
Radio & TV Broadcasting

In Computer Software prefer:
Computer Services

In Medical/Health prefer:
Medical/Health
Disposable Med. Products
Health Services

In Consumer Related prefer:
Consumer
Consumer Products
Education Related

In Industrial/Energy prefer:
Industrial Products

In Business Serv. prefer:
Services
Distribution

In Manufact. prefer:
Manufacturing

Additional Information

Name of Most Recent Fund: Norwest Equity Partners VII, L.P.
Most Recent Fund Was Raised: 10/27/1999
Year Founded: 1961
Capital Under Management: $3,000,000,000
Current Activity Level : Actively seeking new investments
Method of Compensation: Return on investment is of primary concern, do not charge fees

---

NORWEST MEZZANINE PARTNERS

80 South Eighth Street
Suite 3600
Minneapolis, MN USA 55402
Phone: 612-215-1600
Fax: 612-215-1602
Website: www.nmp.com

Management and Staff

Carter Balfour, Partner
John Hogan, Partner
John Whaley, Managing Partner
Shani Graber, Principal
Timothy DeVries, General Partner

Type of Firm

Bank Affiliated

Project Preferences

Type of Financing Preferred:
Mezzanine

Geographical Preferences

United States Preferences:
All U.S.

Additional Information

Name of Most Recent Fund: Norwest Mezzanine Partners II, LP
Most Recent Fund Was Raised: 06/15/2004
Year Founded: 2000
Capital Under Management: $900,000,000
Current Activity Level : Actively seeking new investments

NORWEST VENTURE PARTNERS

525 University Avenue
Suite 800
Palo Alto, CA USA 94301
Phone: 650-321-8000
Fax: 650-321-8010
Website: www.nvp.com

Other Offices

Hilton Towers, Suite # 1234
Nariman Point
Mumbai , India 400 021

Management and Staff

Dror Nahumi, Partner
George Still, Managing Partner
James Lussier, General Partner
Jeffrey Crowe, General Partner
Joshua Goldman, Venture Partner
Kurt Betcher, Chief Financial Officer
Matthew Howard, General Partner
Niren Shah, Managing Director
Promod Haque, Managing Partner
Robert Abbott, General Partner
Sergio Monsalve, Principal
Sohil Chand, Managing Director
Timothy Chang, Principal
Vab Goel, General Partner
Venkat Mohan, General Partner

Type of Firm

Bank Affiliated

Association Membership

National Venture Capital Association - USA (NVCA)

Project Preferences

Role in Financing:
Prefer role as deal originator but will also invest in deals created by others

Type of Financing Preferred:
Early Stage
Expansion
Balanced
Seed

Size of Investments Considered:
Min Size of Investment Considered (000s): $1,000
Max Size of Investment Considered (000s): $25,000

Industry Focus

(% based on actual investment)

Internet Specific	38.8%
Computer Software and Services	27.3%
Communications and Media	16.0%
Semiconductors/Other Elect.	8.6%
Computer Hardware	3.1%
Other Products	2.6%
Industrial/Energy	1.5%
Medical/Health	1.3%
Biotechnology	0.5%
Consumer Related	0.4%

Additional Information

Name of Most Recent Fund: Norwest Venture Partners X, L.P.
Most Recent Fund Was Raised: 04/17/2006
Year Founded: 1961
Capital Under Management: $2,500,000,000
Current Activity Level : Actively seeking new investments
Method of Compensation: Return on investment is of primary concern, do not charge fees

NORWICH VENTURES

1210 Broadcasting Road
Suite 201
Wyomissing, PA USA 19610
Phone: 610-373-5320
Fax: 610-373-5520
Website: www.norwichventures.com

Other Offices

101 Main Street
18th Floor
Cambridge, MA USA 02142
Phone: 617-494-1034
Fax: 617-494-1036

Management and Staff

Aaron Sandoski, Managing Director

Type of Firm

Private Equity Firm

Association Membership

National Venture Capital Association - USA (NVCA)

Project Preferences

Type of Financing Preferred:
Early Stage
Seed

Geographical Preferences

United States Preferences:
Mid Atlantic
Northeast

Industry Preferences

In Medical/Health prefer:
Medical/Health

Additional Information

Year Founded: 2005
Capital Under Management: $30,000,000
Current Activity Level : Actively seeking new investments

NOSON LAWEN PARTNERS LLC

19 West 44th Street
Suite 812
New York, NY USA 10036
Phone: 212-302-2435
Website: www.nosonlawenpartners.com

Other Offices

Seven Great Valley Parkway
Suite 211
Malvern, PA USA 19355
Phone: 610-995-9030

Management and Staff

Earl Macomber, Partner
Ted Carroll, Partner

Type of Firm

Private Equity Firm

Project Preferences

Type of Financing Preferred:
Leveraged Buyout
Expansion

Size of Investments Considered:
Min Size of Investment Considered (000s): $3,000
Max Size of Investment Considered (000s): $10,000

Industry Preferences

In Communications prefer:
CATV & Pay TV Systems
Radio & TV Broadcasting
Media and Entertainment
Publishing

In Consumer Related prefer:
Education Related

In Business Serv. prefer:
Media

Additional Information

Name of Most Recent Fund: Noson Lawen Partners, L.P.
Most Recent Fund Was Raised: 02/15/2007
Year Founded: 2007
Capital Under Management: $27,200,000
Current Activity Level : Actively seeking new investments

NOSTRUM VENTURES

Midskogsgrand 11
Stockholm, Sweden 115 43
Phone: 46-8-610-0010
Fax: 46-8-664-1985
E-mail: info@nostrumventures.com
Website: www.nostrumventures.com

Management and Staff

Jonas Bengtsson, Chief Executive Officer

Type of Firm

Private Equity Firm

Association Membership

Swedish Venture Capital Association (SVCA)

Project Preferences

Type of Financing Preferred:
Leveraged Buyout
Early Stage
Expansion
Seed
Startup

Geographical Preferences

International Preferences:
Sweden

Industry Preferences

In Communications prefer:
Wireless Communications

Additional Information

Year Founded: 2002
Capital Under Management: $1,900,000
Current Activity Level : Actively seeking new investments

NOTOS ASSOCIATES S.A.

21 Voukourestiou Str.
Athens, Greece 10671
Phone: 30-210-339-0305
Fax: 30-210-3624337

Management and Staff

Aristos Doxiadis, Partner

Type of Firm

Private Equity Firm

Association Membership

European Private Equity and Venture Capital Assoc.

Project Preferences

Type of Financing Preferred:
Leveraged Buyout
Early Stage
Expansion
Balanced

Geographical Preferences

International Preferences:
Greece
Europe

Additional Information

Year Founded: 2000
Capital Under Management: $46,200,000
Current Activity Level : Actively seeking new investments

NOVA CAPITAL MANAGEMENT LTD. (FKA: LICA DEVELOPMENT CAPITAL)

11 Strand
London, United Kingdom WC2N 5HR
Phone: 44-20-7389-1540
Fax: 44-20-7489-1541
E-mail: info@nova-cap.com
Website: www.nova-cap.com

Other Offices

67 South Main Street
Essex, CT USA 06426
Phone: 860-767-3960

Management and Staff

David Williamson, Managing Director
Kathryn Jones, Partner
Llewellyn John, Partner
Michael Kelly, Managing Director
Simon Bliss, Chief Financial Officer

Type of Firm

Private Equity Firm

Association Membership

European Private Equity and Venture Capital Assoc.

Project Preferences

Type of Financing Preferred:
Leveraged Buyout
Expansion
Balanced
Acquisition

Geographical Preferences

United States Preferences:
All U.S.

International Preferences:
United Kingdom

Industry Focus

(% based on actual investment)	
Medical/Health	57.7%
Internet Specific	17.2%
Other Products	10.0%
Computer Software and Services	9.1%
Communications and Media	6.0%

Additional Information

Year Founded: 2002
Capital Under Management: $768,000,000
Current Activity Level : Actively seeking new investments

NOVA TECHNOLOGY MANAGEMENT LIMITED (NTML)

10 Queens Terrace
Aberdeen, United Kingdom AB10 1YG
Phone: 44-1224-705-471
Fax: 44-1224-705-481
Website: www.novafund.co.uk

Type of Firm

Private Equity Firm

Project Preferences

Type of Financing Preferred:
Second Stage Financing
Early Stage
Expansion

Geographical Preferences

International Preferences:
United Kingdom

Industry Preferences

In Industrial/Energy prefer:
Oil and Gas Exploration
Oil & Gas Drilling,Explor

Additional Information

Year Founded: 2000
Capital Under Management: $7,100,000
Current Activity Level : Actively seeking new investments

NOVABASE CAPITAL

Av. Eng. Duarte Pacheco
15 - F
Lisboa, Portugal 1099-078
Phone: 351-21-383-6300
Fax: 351-21-383-6301
E-mail: info@novabase.pt
Website: www.novabase.pt

Other Offices

Edificio Olympus II
Av. D. Afonso Henriques, 1462
Matosinhos, Portugal 4450-013
Phone: 351-22-608-5100
Fax: 351-22-608-5101

7 andar - Vila Olimpia
Av. Dr. Cardoso de Melo, 1450
Sao Paulo, Brazil
Phone: 55-11-3848-5120
Fax: 55-11-3848-5122

Carrera de San Jeronimo, 15 - 2 piso
Palacio de Miraflores
Madrid, Spain 28014
Phone: 34-91-454-7248
Fax: 34-91-454-7247

Type of Firm

Incubator/Development Program

Project Preferences

Type of Financing Preferred:
Seed
Startup

Geographical Preferences

International Preferences:
Portugal

Industry Preferences

In Internet Specific prefer:
Internet

Additional Information

Year Founded: 1989
Capital Under Management: $8,600,000
Current Activity Level : Actively seeking new investments

NOVAK BIDDLE VENTURE PARTNERS, L.P.

7501 Wisconsin Avenue
East Tower, Suite 1380
Bethesda, MD USA 20814
Phone: 240-497-1910
Fax: 240-223-0255
E-mail: info@novakbiddle.com
Website: www.novakbiddle.com

Management and Staff

A.G.W (Jack) Biddle, General Partner
Andrea Kaufman, General Partner
E. Rogers Novak, General Partner
Janet Yang, Principal
Philip Bronner, General Partner
Thomas Scholl, General Partner

Type of Firm

Private Equity Firm

Association Membership

Mid-Atlantic Venture Association
National Venture Capital Association - USA (NVCA)

Project Preferences

Role in Financing:

Will function either as deal originator or investor in deals created by others

Type of Financing Preferred:

Early Stage
Seed
Startup

Size of Investments Considered:

Min Size of Investment Considered (000s): $100
Max Size of Investment Considered (000s): $10,000

Geographical Preferences

United States Preferences:

Mid Atlantic
Southeast
Northeast

Industry Focus

(% based on actual investment)

Computer Software and Services	36.6%
Internet Specific	31.3%
Communications and Media	13.9%
Semiconductors/Other Elect.	11.4%
Computer Hardware	3.4%
Industrial/Energy	1.9%
Other Products	1.6%

Additional Information

Year Founded: 1997
Capital Under Management: $580,000,000
Current Activity Level : Actively seeking new investments
Method of Compensation: Return on investment is of primary concern, do not charge fees

NOVAQUEST

4709 Creekstone Drive
P.O. Box 13979, RTP
Durham, NC USA 27709
Phone: 919-998-2000
Fax: 919-998-2094
Website: www.novaquest.com

Type of Firm

Private Equity Firm

Additional Information

Year Founded: 2009
Current Activity Level : Actively seeking new investments

NOVARTIS VENTURE FUND (FKA: NOVARTIS CORP.)

608 Fifth Avenue
New York, NY USA 10020
Phone: 212-307-1122
Fax: 212-246-0185
Website: www.venturefund.novartis.com

Other Offices

WSJ-200.220
PO Box
Basel, Switzerland CH-4002
Phone: 41-61-324-6809
Fax: 41-61-324-8679

One Cambridge Center
Cambridge, MA USA 02139
Phone: 617-871-7780
Fax: 617-225-0934

Management and Staff

Campbell Murray, Managing Director
Florent Gros, Managing Director
Lauren Silverman, Managing Director
Markus Goebel, Managing Director
Steve Weinstein, Managing Director
Steven Tregay, Managing Director

Type of Firm

Corporate PE/Venture

Association Membership

National Venture Capital Association - USA (NVCA)

Project Preferences

Type of Financing Preferred:

Early Stage
Startup

Geographical Preferences

International Preferences:

Europe

Industry Focus

(% based on actual investment)

Biotechnology	50.9%
Medical/Health	42.9%
Computer Software and Services	4.9%
Internet Specific	1.2%

Additional Information

Year Founded: 1997
Capital Under Management: $72,500,000
Current Activity Level : Actively seeking new investments

NOVAX AB

Villagatan 6
P.O. Box 26008
Stockholm, Sweden 100 41
Phone: 46-8-700-6660
Fax: 46-8-213-026
E-mail: contact@novax.se
Website: www.novax.se

Type of Firm

Corporate PE/Venture

Association Membership

Swedish Venture Capital Association (SVCA)
European Private Equity and Venture Capital Assoc.

Project Preferences

Type of Financing Preferred:

Expansion

Size of Investments Considered:

Min Size of Investment Considered (000s): $319
Max Size of Investment Considered (000s): $1,487

Geographical Preferences

International Preferences:

Sweden

Industry Preferences

In Consumer Related prefer:

Consumer Products
Consumer Services

In Business Serv. prefer:

Services

Additional Information

Year Founded: 1998
Capital Under Management: $32,100,000
Current Activity Level : Actively seeking new investments

NOVELL TECHNOLOGY CAPITAL

8 Cambridge Center
Cambridge, MA USA 02142
Phone: 617-914-8262

Fax: 617-551-5197
E-mail: ctc-prospects@ctp.com
Website: www.novell.com

Other Offices

1209 Pearl Street
Suite 4
Boulder, CO USA
Phone: 303-390-2310
Fax: 240-269-4090

1800 South Novell Place
Provo, UT USA 84606
Phone: 801-861-1644
Fax: 801-861-1677

Management and Staff

Jack Messman, Managing Director
Ralph Linsalata, Managing Director

Type of Firm

Corporate PE/Venture

Project Preferences

Role in Financing:

Will function either as deal originator or investor in deals created by others

Type of Financing Preferred:

Early Stage
Expansion
Mezzanine
Later Stage

Size of Investments Considered:

Min Size of Investment Considered (000s): $1,000
Max Size of Investment Considered (000s): $5,000

Geographical Preferences

Canadian Preferences:

All Canada

International Preferences:

United Kingdom

Industry Focus

(% based on actual investment)

Computer Software and Services	53.3%
Internet Specific	43.0%
Communications and Media	2.2%
Computer Hardware	1.5%

Additional Information

Name of Most Recent Fund: Novell Technology Capital Fund I, L.P.
Most Recent Fund Was Raised: 12/21/2001
Year Founded: 1991
Capital Under Management: $125,300,000
Current Activity Level : Actively seeking new investments
Method of Compensation: Return on investment is of primary concern, do not charge fees

NOVENTI (FKA: CYPRESS VENTURES) (FKA: CIR VENTURES)

535 Middlefield Road
Suite 100
Menlo Park, CA USA 94025
Phone: 650-325-6699
Fax: 650-325-7799
E-mail: info@noventivc.com
Website: www.noventivc.com

Management and Staff

Giacomo Marini, Managing Director
James Horn, Managing Director
Manfred Ernst, Venture Partner
Masazumi Ishii, Managing Director
Pierluigi Zappacosta, Venture Partner
Pierluigi Ferrero, Venture Partner

Type of Firm

Private Equity Firm

Association Membership

National Venture Capital Association - USA (NVCA)

Project Preferences

Role in Financing:

Will function either as deal originator or investor in deals created by others

Type of Financing Preferred:

Early Stage
Expansion

Size of Investments Considered:

Min Size of Investment Considered (000s): $500
Max Size of Investment Considered (000s): $10,000

Geographical Preferences

United States Preferences:

West Coast
California

Canadian Preferences:

Western Canada

International Preferences:

Italy
Europe

Industry Preferences

In Communications prefer:

Telecommunications
Wireless Communications
Data Communications

In Computer Software prefer:

Systems Software

In Internet Specific prefer:

Internet

In Semiconductor/Electr prefer:

Electronic Components
Semiconductor
Controllers and Sensors
Sensors
Fiber Optics
Optoelectronics

In Biotechnology prefer:

Genetic Engineering
Biosensors

In Consumer Related prefer:

Consumer

In Industrial/Energy prefer:

Energy
Industrial Products
Robotics

In Utilities prefer:

Utilities

Additional Information

Name of Most Recent Fund: Noventi Ventures II, L.P. (FKA: Noventi Sorgenia Ventures)
Most Recent Fund Was Raised: 09/14/2006
Year Founded: 2002
Capital Under Management: $73,000,000
Current Activity Level : Actively seeking new investments
Method of Compensation: Return on invest. most important, but chg. closing fees, service fees, etc.

NOVESTRA AB

Norrlandsgatan 16
Stockholm, Sweden 11143
Phone: 46-8-545-01750
Fax: 46-8-545-01760
E-mail: info@novestra.com
Website: www.novestra.com

Management and Staff

Goran Strandberg, Chief Executive Officer
Johan Heijbel, Chief Financial Officer
Lennart Tengroth, Partner
Nils Bengtsson, Chief Executive Officer
Peter Ekelund, Partner
Theodor Dalenson, Chairman & CEO

Type of Firm

Private Equity Firm

Association Membership

Swedish Venture Capital Association (SVCA)

Project Preferences

Type of Financing Preferred:

Early Stage

Geographical Preferences

International Preferences:

Western Europe

Additional Information

Year Founded: 1997
Current Activity Level : Actively seeking new investments

NOVITAS CAPITAL (FKA: PA EARLY STAGE PARTNERS)

1200 Liberty Ridge Drive
Suite 310
Wayne, PA USA 19087
Phone: 610-293-4075
Fax: 610-254-4240
E-mail: info@novitascapital.com
Website: www.novitascapital.com

Other Offices

1085 Van Voorhis Road
The United Center, Suite 390
Morgantown, WV USA 26507
Phone: 304-599-1032
Fax: 304-599-4272

15 Bonnie Way
Allendale, NJ USA 07401
Phone: 610-254-4286
Fax: 610-254-4246

100 Technology Drive
Suite 400
Pittsburgh, PA USA 15219
Phone: 412-770-1636
Fax: 412-770-1638

Management and Staff

Ching Zhu, Partner
Dean Miller, Managing Director
Michael Bolton, Managing Director
Paul Schmidt, Managing Director
Scott Nissenbaum, Managing Director
Stephen Barnes, Managing Director

Type of Firm

Private Equity Firm

Association Membership

National Venture Capital Association - USA (NVCA)

Project Preferences

Role in Financing:
Will function either as deal originator or investor in deals created by others

Type of Financing Preferred:
Second Stage Financing
Seed
First Stage Financing

Size of Investments Considered:
Min Size of Investment Considered (000s): $100
Max Size of Investment Considered (000s): $5,000

Geographical Preferences

United States Preferences:
Mid Atlantic

Industry Focus

(% based on actual investment)	
Internet Specific	40.5%
Computer Software and Services	16.6%
Biotechnology	13.5%
Semiconductors/Other Elect.	11.8%
Other Products	7.5%
Medical/Health	6.7%
Communications and Media	2.3%
Industrial/Energy	0.7%
Consumer Related	0.5%

Additional Information

Year Founded: 1998
Capital Under Management: $237,500,000
Current Activity Level : Actively seeking new investments
Method of Compensation: Return on investment is of primary concern, do not charge fees

NOVO AS

Krogshoejvej 41
Bagsvaerd, Denmark 2880
Phone: 45-4442-0625
Fax: 45-4444-4627
E-mail: ventures@novo.dk
Website: www.novo.dk

Management and Staff

Heath Lukatch, Partner
Henrik Gurtler, Chief Executive Officer
Jack Nielsen, Partner
Kim Dueholm, Partner
Peter Tuxen Bisgaard, Partner
Soren Carlsen, Managing Partner
Soren Schifter, Partner
Thorkil Kastberg Christensen, Chief Financial Officer

Type of Firm

Corporate PE/Venture

Association Membership

Danish Venture Capital Association (DVCA)
European Private Equity and Venture Capital Assoc.

Project Preferences

Role in Financing:
Will function either as deal originator or investor in deals created by others

Type of Financing Preferred:
Second Stage Financing
Early Stage
Seed
First Stage Financing
Startup

Geographical Preferences

Canadian Preferences:
All Canada

International Preferences:
United Kingdom
Scandanavia/Nordic Region
Denmark
France

Industry Preferences

In Biotechnology prefer:
Biotechnology
Human Biotechnology

In Medical/Health prefer:
Medical/Health
Drug/Equipmt Delivery

Additional Information

Year Founded: 2000
Capital Under Management: $380,000,000
Current Activity Level : Actively seeking new investments
Method of Compensation: Return on investment is of primary concern, do not charge fees

NOVOTECH INVESTMENT

Holland Drive
Block B, Holland Park
Newcastle, United Kingdom NE2 4LD

Type of Firm

Private Equity Firm

Additional Information

Year Founded: 2006
Current Activity Level : Actively seeking new investments

NOVUS VENTURES

20111 Stevens Creek Boulevard
Suite 130
Cupertino, CA USA 95014
Phone: 408-252-3900
Fax: 408-252-1713
E-mail: info@novusventures.com
Website: www.novusventures.com

Management and Staff

Christine Comaford Lynch, Venture Partner
Daniel Tompkins, Managing General Partner
Greg Lahann, General Partner
Henry Wong, Venture Partner
Shirley Cerrudo, General Partner
Stewart Schuster, General Partner

Type of Firm

Private Equity Firm

Association Membership

Western Association of Venture Capitalists (WAVC)
Natl Assoc of Small Bus. Inv. Co (NASBIC)

Project Preferences

Role in Financing:
Will function either as deal originator or investor in deals created by others

Type of Financing Preferred:
Second Stage Financing
Early Stage
Expansion
First Stage Financing

Size of Investments Considered:
Min Size of Investment Considered (000s): $25
Max Size of Investment Considered (000s): $10,000

Geographical Preferences

United States Preferences:
West Coast
California

Industry Focus

(% based on actual investment)

Computer Software and Services	52.8%
Internet Specific	18.5%
Semiconductors/Other Elect.	16.1%
Communications and Media	9.2%
Computer Hardware	1.6%
Medical/Health	1.5%
Biotechnology	0.3%

Additional Information

Name of Most Recent Fund: Artemis Ventures Fund II, L.P.
Most Recent Fund Was Raised: 03/28/2001
Year Founded: 1994
Capital Under Management: $150,000,000
Current Activity Level : Actively seeking new investments
Method of Compensation: Return on investment is of primary concern, do not charge fees

---

NPM CAPITAL (AKA: NEDERLANDSE PARTICIPATIE MIJ NV)

Breitnerstraat 1
Amsterdam, Netherlands 1077 BL
Phone: 31-20-570-5555
Fax: 31-20-470-6454
E-mail: mails@npm-capital.com
Website: www.npm-capital.com

Other Offices

Prinzenallee 7
Dusseldorf, Germany 40549
Phone: 49-21152391122
Fax: 49-21152391200

Rue de Ligne 13
Brussels, Belgium 1000
Phone: 32-2-210-6090
Fax: 32-2-219-6719

Type of Firm

Private Equity Firm

Association Membership

German Venture Capital Association (BVK)
European Private Equity and Venture Capital Assoc.
Dutch Venture Capital Associaton (NVP)

Project Preferences

Role in Financing:
Prefer role as deal originator but will also invest in deals created by others

Type of Financing Preferred:
Leveraged Buyout
Generalist PE
Expansion
Mezzanine
Management Buyouts
Special Situation
Recapitalizations

Geographical Preferences

International Preferences:
Ireland
Netherlands
Belgium
Germany
France

Industry Focus

(% based on actual investment)

Consumer Related	32.6%
Other Products	27.0%
Industrial/Energy	17.9%
Computer Software and Services	8.4%
Semiconductors/Other Elect.	6.8%
Internet Specific	3.2%
Computer Hardware	1.9%
Medical/Health	1.3%
Biotechnology	0.9%

Additional Information

Year Founded: 1948
Capital Under Management: $921,300,000
Current Activity Level : Actively seeking new investments
Method of Compensation: Return on invest. most important, but chg. closing fees, service fees, etc.

NPM-CNP (AKA: COMPAGNIE NATIONALE A PORTEFEUILLE)

Rue de la Blanche Borne 12
Loverval, Belgium 6280
Phone: 32-71-606-060
Fax: 32-71-606-070
E-mail: cnp@cnp.be
Website: www.cnp.be

Type of Firm

Private Equity Firm

Project Preferences

Type of Financing Preferred:
Expansion
Balanced

Geographical Preferences

International Preferences:
Europe

Industry Preferences

In Consumer Related prefer:
Retail
Food/Beverage
Consumer Products

In Industrial/Energy prefer:
Energy

Additional Information

Year Founded: 2005
Current Activity Level : Actively seeking new investments

NRDC EQUITY PARTNERS

Three Manhattanville Road
Purchase, NY USA 10577
Phone: 914-272-8067
Fax: 914-696-1229
Website: www.nrdcequity.com

Management and Staff

Francis Casale, Managing Director
Robert Baker, Chairman & CEO

Type of Firm

Private Equity Firm

Project Preferences

Type of Financing Preferred:
Leveraged Buyout
Acquisition

Size of Investments Considered:
Min Size of Investment Considered (000s): $50,000
Max Size of Investment Considered (000s): $750,000

Geographical Preferences

United States Preferences:
All U.S.

Industry Preferences

In Consumer Related prefer:
Entertainment and Leisure
Retail
Consumer Services

In Financial Services prefer:
Real Estate

Additional Information

Year Founded: 2005
Current Activity Level : Actively seeking new investments

NRG GROUP, THE

Scotia Plaza, 40 King St. West
Suite 5012
Toronto, Canada M5H 3Y2
Phone: 416-867-8592
Fax: 416-867-7595
Website: www.thenrggroup.com

Management and Staff

Anthony Messina, Chief Financial Officer
Robert McLeish, Managing Director

Type of Firm

Private Equity Firm

Project Preferences

Type of Financing Preferred:
Early Stage
Startup

Geographical Preferences

Canadian Preferences:
All Canada

Additional Information

Year Founded: 1995
Current Activity Level : Actively seeking new investments

NRW BANK

Heerdter Lohweg 35
Dussedorf, Germany 40549
Phone: 49-211-82609
Fax: 49-211-82611800
E-mail: info@nrwbank.de
Website: www.nrwbank.de

Other Offices

Friedrichstrasse 1
Munster, Germany 48145
Phone: 49-251-412-09
Fax: 49-251-412-2288

Type of Firm

Bank Affiliated

Project Preferences

Type of Financing Preferred:
Early Stage
Expansion

Geographical Preferences

International Preferences:
Europe

Industry Preferences

In Semiconductor/Electr prefer:
Fiber Optics

Additional Information

Year Founded: 2005
Capital Under Management: $51,900,000
Current Activity Level : Actively seeking new investments

NSBI VENTURE CAPITAL

1800 Argyle Street
Suite 701, P.O. Box 2374
halifax, Canada B3J3E4
Phone: 902-424-6650
Fax: 902-424-5739
E-mail: info@nsbi.ca
Website: www.novascotiabusiness

Management and Staff

Craig Stanfield, Managing Director
Lisa Budgen, Vice President

Type of Firm

Government Affiliated Program

Geographical Preferences

Canadian Preferences:
Nova Scotia

Additional Information

Year Founded: 2001
Current Activity Level : Actively seeking new investments

NSTAR (AKA: NORTHSTAR EQUITY INVESTORS, LTD.)

Ground Floor
1 St James' Gate
Newcastle-upon-Tyne, United Kingdom NE1 4AD
Phone: 44-191-211-2300
Fax: 44-191-211-2323
E-mail: enquiries@nstarfinance.com
Website: www.nstarfinance.com

Management and Staff

Andrew Mitchell, Chief Executive Officer
Jonathan Gold, Chief Operating Officer

Type of Firm

Private Equity Firm

Project Preferences

Type of Financing Preferred:
Early Stage
Seed

Size of Investments Considered:
Min Size of Investment Considered (000s): $2,000
Max Size of Investment Considered (000s): $2,000

Geographical Preferences

International Preferences:
United Kingdom
Europe
Western Europe

Additional Information

Year Founded: 2003
Capital Under Management: $64,600,000
Current Activity Level : Actively seeking new investments

NTH POWER

One Embarcadero Center
Suite 1550
San Francisco, CA USA 94111
Phone: 415-983-9983
Fax: 415-983-9984
E-mail: info@nthpower.com
Website: www.nthpower.com

Management and Staff

Bryant Tong, Managing Director
Elaine Erickson, Chief Financial Officer
Matt Jones, Partner
Nancy Floyd, Managing Director
Rodrigo Prudencio, Partner
Tim Woodward, Managing Director

Type of Firm

Private Equity Firm

Association Membership

Western Association of Venture Capitalists (WAVC)
National Venture Capital Association - USA (NVCA)

Project Preferences

Role in Financing:
Will function either as deal originator or investor in deals created by others

Type of Financing Preferred:
Early Stage

Size of Investments Considered:
Min Size of Investment Considered (000s): $500
Max Size of Investment Considered (000s): $7,000

Geographical Preferences

United States Preferences:
All U.S.

Canadian Preferences:
All Canada

International Preferences:
Italy
India
United Kingdom
China
Hong Kong
Spain
Australia
New Zealand
Germany
France
Japan

Industry Focus

(% based on actual investment)

Industrial/Energy	54.4%
Semiconductors/Other Elect.	11.5%
Computer Software and Services	11.3%
Internet Specific	8.9%
Other Products	6.2%
Communications and Media	5.6%
Computer Hardware	1.3%
Biotechnology	0.7%

Additional Information

Name of Most Recent Fund: Nth Power Technologies Fund IV, L.P.
Most Recent Fund Was Raised: 06/13/2006
Year Founded: 1993
Capital Under Management: $410,000,000
Current Activity Level : Actively seeking new investments
Method of Compensation: Return on investment is of primary concern, do not charge fees

---

NTT LEASING CO., LTD.

Seavance N, 1-2-1
Shibaura, Minato-ku
Tokyo, Japan 105-6791
Phone: 81-3-5445-5400
Website: www.nttl.co.jp

Type of Firm

Corporate PE/Venture

Project Preferences

Type of Financing Preferred:
Balanced

Geographical Preferences

International Preferences:
Japan

Additional Information

Year Founded: 1985
Current Activity Level : Actively seeking new investments

NUEVA VENTURES

770 27th Avenue
San Mateo, CA USA 94403
Phone: 650-350-1191
Fax: 650-240-0170
E-mail: info@nuevaventures.com
Website: www.nuevaventures.com

Management and Staff

Come Lague, Managing Partner
Douglas Fox, Managing Partner

Type of Firm

Private Equity Firm

Project Preferences

Type of Financing Preferred:
Early Stage
Seed
Startup

Size of Investments Considered:
Min Size of Investment Considered (000s): $100
Max Size of Investment Considered (000s): $2,000

Geographical Preferences

United States Preferences:
Northern California

Industry Preferences

In Communications prefer:
Wireless Communications

In Computer Software prefer:
Software

In Internet Specific prefer:
Internet

Additional Information

Year Founded: 2005
Current Activity Level : Actively seeking new investments

NUMENOR VENTURES LLC

1015 East Mountain Drive
Santa Barbara, CA USA 93108
Phone: 805-969-9395
Fax: 805-969-2995
E-mail: inquires@numenorventures.com
Website: www.numenorventures.com

Management and Staff

Michelle Greer, Managing Director
R. Scott Greer, Managing Director

Type of Firm

Private Equity Firm

Project Preferences

Type of Financing Preferred:
Early Stage
Seed
Startup

Geographical Preferences

United States Preferences:
Nevada
Northwest
California
Colorado

Industry Preferences

In Consumer Related prefer:
Consumer

In Financial Services prefer:
Real Estate

Additional Information

Year Founded: 2007
Current Activity Level : Actively seeking new investments

NV BRABANTSE ONTWIKKELINGS MAATSCHAPPIJ (AKA: NV BOM)

Goirleseweg 15
P.O. Box 3240
Tilburg, Netherlands 5003 AE
Phone: 31-13-531-1120
Fax: 31-13-531-1121
E-mail: bom@bom.nl
Website: www.bom.nl

Type of Firm

Corporate PE/Venture

Association Membership

European Private Equity and Venture Capital Assoc.

Project Preferences

Type of Financing Preferred:
Balanced

Geographical Preferences

International Preferences:
Netherlands
Europe

Additional Information

Year Founded: 2000
Capital Under Management: $19,500,000
Current Activity Level : Actively seeking new investments

NV INDUSTRIEBANK LIOF

Boschstaat 76
P.O. Box 1310
Maastricht, Netherlands 6201 BH
Phone: 31-43-328-0280
Fax: 31-43-328-0200
E-mail: info@liof.nl
Website: www.liof.nl

Other Offices

Noorderpoort 63
Postbus 1122
Venlo, Netherlands 5900 BC
Phone: 31-77-320-8108
Fax: 31-77-320-8100

Type of Firm

Government Affiliated Program

Association Membership

European Private Equity and Venture Capital Assoc.

Project Preferences

Type of Financing Preferred:
Early Stage
Expansion
Startup

Geographical Preferences

International Preferences:
Netherlands

Industry Preferences

In Communications prefer:
Communications and Media

In Semiconductor/Electr prefer:
Electronics

In Medical/Health prefer:
Medical/Health

In Consumer Related prefer:
Consumer

In Industrial/Energy prefer:
Industrial Products

Additional Information
Name of Most Recent Fund: ICT START 25
Most Recent Fund Was Raised: 02/29/2000
Year Founded: 1935
Capital Under Management: $89,100,000
Current Activity Level : Actively seeking new investments

NV NOM
Postbus 424
Groningen, Netherlands 9700 AK
Phone: 31-50-521-44-08
Fax: 31-50-521-44-00
E-mail: info@nom.nl
Website: www.nom.nl

Type of Firm
Private Equity Firm

Additional Information
Current Activity Level : Actively seeking new investments

NWD NORD-WEST-DEUTSCHE UNTERNEHMENSBETEILIGUNGSGESELLSCHAFT
Wittekindstrasse 17 - 19
Osnabrueck, Germany 49074
Phone: 49-541-3243050
Fax: 49-541-3244037

Type of Firm
Bank Affiliated

Association Membership
German Venture Capital Association (BVK)

Project Preferences

Type of Financing Preferred:
Balanced

Geographical Preferences

International Preferences:
Germany

Additional Information
Year Founded: 2004
Current Activity Level : Actively seeking new investments

NWK KAPITALBETEILIGUNGSGESELLSCHAFT DER SPARKASSE BREMEN
Am Brill 1-3
Bremen, Germany 28195
Phone: 49-421-1792043
Fax: 49-421-1792043
E-mail: nwk-nwu@t-online.de
Website: www.sparkasse-bremen.de

Management and Staff
Ralf Kubitz, Managing Director
Ralf Paslack, Managing Director

Type of Firm
Bank Affiliated

Association Membership
German Venture Capital Association (BVK)

Project Preferences

Type of Financing Preferred:
Balanced

Geographical Preferences

International Preferences:
Germany

Additional Information
Year Founded: 2005
Current Activity Level : Actively seeking new investments

NYSTAR (FKA: SBTIF)
30 South Pearl Street
11th Floor
Albany, NY USA 12207
Phone: 518-292-5700
Fax: 518-292-5798
Website: www.nystar.state.ny.us

Management and Staff
Divjot Narang, Managing Director

Type of Firm
Government Affiliated Program

Project Preferences

Role in Financing:
Will function either as deal originator or investor in deals created by others

Type of Financing Preferred:
Second Stage Financing
Early Stage
First Stage Financing

Size of Investments Considered:
Min Size of Investment Considered (000s): $100
Max Size of Investment Considered (000s): $500

Geographical Preferences

United States Preferences:
New York

Industry Preferences

In Communications prefer:
Telecommunications
Wireless Communications
Satellite Microwave Comm.
Other Communication Prod.

In Computer Hardware prefer:
Computer Graphics and Dig
Terminals
Disk Relat. Memory Device

In Computer Software prefer:
Software
Systems Software
Applications Software
Artificial Intelligence

In Internet Specific prefer:
E-Commerce Technology

In Semiconductor/Electr prefer:
Electronic Components
Semiconductor
Micro-Processing
Controllers and Sensors
Sensors
Circuit Boards
Component Testing Equipmt
Laser Related
Fiber Optics
Analytic/Scientific
Optoelectronics

In Biotechnology prefer:
Human Biotechnology
Genetic Engineering
Agricultural/Animal Bio.
Industrial Biotechnology
Biosensors
Biotech Related Research

In Medical/Health prefer:
Medical Diagnostics
Diagnostic Test Products
Medical Therapeutics
Drug/Equipmt Delivery
Medical Products

Disposable Med. Products
Pharmaceuticals

In Consumer Related prefer:
Consumer

In Industrial/Energy prefer:
Energy
Industrial Products
Factory Automation
Robotics
Machinery

In Transportation prefer:
Aerospace

In Manufact. prefer:
Manufacturing

In Other prefer:
Environment Responsible

Additional Information
Year Founded: 1981
Capital Under Management: $25,000,000
Current Activity Level : Actively seeking new investments
Method of Compensation: Return on invest. most important, but chg. closing fees, service fees, etc.

- O -

111 CONVENTURING GMBH
Hauptplatz
Sackstrasse 2
Graz, Austria 8010
Phone: 43-31-681601110
Fax: 43-316-81601119
E-mail: office@conventuring.at
Website: www.conventuring.at

Management and Staff
Robert Prattes, Partner
Werner Grobl, Partner

Type of Firm
Private Equity Firm

Association Membership
Austrian PE and Venture Capital Association (AVCO)

Project Preferences

Type of Financing Preferred:
Early Stage
Startup

Geographical Preferences

International Preferences:
Europe
Austria

Additional Information
Year Founded: 2003
Current Activity Level : Actively seeking new investments

123VENTURE
41 boulevard des Capucines
Paris, France 75002
Phone: 33-1-4926-9800
Fax: 33-1-4926-9819
E-mail: info@123venture.com
Website: www.123venture.com

Other Offices
31 Oriole Avenue
Providence, RI USA 02906
Phone: 401-421-9240

Management and Staff
Eric Philippon, Partner
Paul De Freminville, Partner
Richard Allanic, General Director
Xavier Anthonioz, General Director

Type of Firm
Private Equity Firm

Association Membership
French Venture Capital Association (AFIC)

Project Preferences

Type of Financing Preferred:
Fund of Funds
Leveraged Buyout
Early Stage
Expansion
Research and Development
Balanced
Later Stage
Seed
Startup

Size of Investments Considered:
Min Size of Investment Considered (000s): $2,741
Max Size of Investment Considered (000s): $4,569

Geographical Preferences

International Preferences:
Europe
France

Industry Preferences

In Biotechnology prefer:
Biotechnology

In Industrial/Energy prefer:
Alternative Energy

Additional Information
Year Founded: 2001
Capital Under Management: $16,200,000
Current Activity Level : Actively seeking new investments

180 CAPITAL FUND, LLC
19819 Redbeam Avenue
Torrance, CA USA 90503
Phone: 310-600-3692

Type of Firm
Private Equity Firm

Project Preferences

Type of Financing Preferred:
Balanced

Geographical Preferences

United States Preferences:
All U.S.

Additional Information
Year Founded: 2004
Capital Under Management: $3,000,000
Current Activity Level : Actively seeking new investments

O'MELVENY & MYERS LLP

400 South Hope Street
Los Angeles, CA USA 90071
Phone: 213-430-6000
Fax: 213-430-6407
E-mail: omminfo@omm.com
Website: www.omm.com

Other Offices

Seven Times Square
Times Square Tower
New York, NY USA 10036
Phone: 212-326-2000
Fax: 212-326-2061

275 Battery Street
Embarcadero Center West
San Francisco, CA USA 94111
Phone: 415-984-8700
Fax: 415-984-8701

1999 Avenue of the Stars
Seventh Floor
Los Angeles, CA USA 90067
Phone: 310-553-6700
Fax: 310-246-6779

610 Newport Center Drive
17th Floor
Newport Beach, CA USA 92660
Phone: 949-760-9600
Fax: 949-823-6994

1266 Nanjing Road West
Plaza 66, Tower 1, 37th Floor
Shanghai, China 200040
Phone: 86-21-2307-7000
Fax: 86-21-2307-7300

1 Connaught Road Central
31st Floor, AIG Tower
Central, Hong Kong
Phone: 852-2523-8266
Fax: 852-2522-1760

2-1-1, Marunouchi, Chiyoda-ku
Meiji Yasuda Seimei Bldg., 11th Floor
Tokyo, Japan
Phone: 81-3-5293-2700
Fax: 81-3-5293-2780

No.2 Jianguomenwai Avenue
Yin Tai Center, Office Tower, 37th Floor
Beijing, China 100022
Phone: 86-10-6563-4200
Fax: 86-10-6563-4201

1625 Eye Street Northwest
Washington, DC USA 20006
Phone: 202-383-5300
Fax: 202-383-5414

5 Paternoster Square
Warwick Court
London, United Kingdom EC4M 7DX
Phone: 44-20-7088-0000
Fax: 44-20-7088-0001

2765 Sand Hill Road
Menlo Park, CA USA 94025
Phone: 650-473-2600
Fax: 650-473-2601

9 Temasek Boulevard
Suite 09-01 Suntec Tower Two
Singapore, Singapore 038989
Phone: 65-6407-1525
Fax: 65-6407-1526

Avenue Louise 326
Blue Tower
Brussels, Belgium 1050
Phone: 32-2-642-4100
Fax: 32-2-642-4190

Management and Staff

Howard Bergtraum, General Partner

Type of Firm

Service Provider

Project Preferences

Role in Financing:
Other

Type of Financing Preferred:
Fund of Funds

Geographical Preferences

United States Preferences:
All U.S.

Additional Information

Year Founded: 1885
Capital Under Management: $5,000,000
Current Activity Level : Actively seeking new investments
Method of Compensation: Return on investment is of primary concern, do not charge fees

O'REILLY ALPHA TECH VENTURES, LLC

One Lombard Street
Suite 303
San Francisco, CA USA 94111
Phone: 415-693-0203
Website: www.oatv.com

Management and Staff

Bryce Roberts, Managing General Partner
Mark Jacobsen, Managing General Partner

Type of Firm

Corporate PE/Venture

Project Preferences

Role in Financing:
Will function either as deal originator or investor in deals created by others

Additional Information

Name of Most Recent Fund: OATV, L.P.
Most Recent Fund Was Raised: 09/28/2006
Year Founded: 2006
Capital Under Management: $51,000,000
Current Activity Level : Actively seeking new investments

O.S.S. CAPITAL MANAGEMENT LP

598 Madison Avenue
New York, NY USA 10022
Phone: 212-756-8700

Management and Staff

Anthony Cimini, Chief Financial Officer

Type of Firm

Private Equity Advisor or Fund of Funds

Additional Information

Year Founded: 2009
Current Activity Level : Actively seeking new investments

O3 CAPITAL ADVISORS PVT., LTD.

#5367, Grand Hyatt Mumbai
Off Western Express Highway
Mumbai, India 400 055
Phone: 91-22-3262-6294
E-mail: mumbai@o3capital.com
Website: www.o3capital.com

Other Offices

#3, Lavelle Road,
Bangalore, India 560 001
Phone: 91-80-4112-8111

#4511, Singer Court
Suite 201
Chantilly, VA USA 20151
Phone: 774-922-2667

Management and Staff

Shyam Shenthar, Managing Director

Type of Firm

Bank Affiliated

Project Preferences

Type of Financing Preferred:
Expansion
Balanced

Geographical Preferences

International Preferences:
India

Industry Preferences

In Communications prefer:
Communications and Media
Radio & TV Broadcasting
Other Communication Prod.

Additional Information

Year Founded: 2008
Current Activity Level : Actively seeking new investments

OAK CAPITAL CORPORATION

6/F, Sumitomo Fudosan Akasaka
8-10-24 Akasaka, Minato-ku
Tokyo, Japan 107-0052
Phone: 81-3-5412-7700
Fax: 81-3-5412-8811
E-mail: irinfo2@oakcapital.jp
Website: www.oakcapital.jp

Management and Staff

Hiroyasu Takei, Chairman & CEO
Koichi Shinada, Managing Director
Tsutomu Akita, Managing Director

Type of Firm

Bank Affiliated

Project Preferences

Type of Financing Preferred:
Early Stage
Expansion
Public Companies
Later Stage
Private Placement

Geographical Preferences

International Preferences:
Asia
Japan

Additional Information

Year Founded: 1868
Capital Under Management: $86,000,000
Current Activity Level : Actively seeking new investments

OAK HILL CAPITAL MANAGEMENT, INC.

One Stamford Plaza; 15th Floor
263 Tresser Boulevard
Stamford, CT USA 06901
Phone: 203-328-1600
Fax: 203-328-1650
Website: www.oakhillcapital.com

Other Offices

65 East 55th Street
32nd Floor
New York, NY USA 10022
Phone: 212-527-8400

2775 Sand Hill Road
Suite 220
Menlo Park, CA USA 94025
Phone: 650-234-0500

Management and Staff

Benjamin Diesbach, Partner
Charles Patton, Partner
Denis Nayden, Managing Partner
Douglas Kaden, Partner
J. Taylor Crandall, Managing Director
John Malfettone, Partner
John Rachwalski, Vice President
John Monsky, Partner
Jonathan Friesel, Partner
Mark Wolfson, Managing Director
Michael Green, Partner
Ray Pinson, Chief Financial Officer
Robert Morse, Partner
Rowan Taylor, Partner
Steven Gruber, Managing Partner
Ted Dardani, Partner
Tyler Wolfram, Partner
William Pade, Partner

Type of Firm

Private Equity Firm

Project Preferences

Role in Financing:
Prefer role as deal originator but will also invest in deals created by others

Type of Financing Preferred:
Leveraged Buyout
Turnaround
Management Buyouts
Acquisition
Special Situation
Distressed Debt
Recapitalizations

Size of Investments Considered:
Min Size of Investment Considered (000s): $75,000
Max Size of Investment Considered (000s): $125,000

Geographical Preferences

International Preferences:
Western Europe
All International

Industry Focus

(% based on actual investment)	
Consumer Related	51.1%
Industrial/Energy	18.3%
Other Products	13.4%
Communications and Media	9.4%
Medical/Health	3.8%
Internet Specific	3.5%
Computer Hardware	0.5%

Additional Information

Name of Most Recent Fund: Oak Hill Capital Management Partners II, L.P.
Most Recent Fund Was Raised: 01/04/2005
Year Founded: 1992
Capital Under Management: $4,600,000,000
Current Activity Level : Actively seeking new investments
Method of Compensation: Return on invest. most important, but chg. closing fees, service fees, etc.

OAK HILL INVESTMENT MANAGEMENT (OHIM)

2775 Sand Hill Road
Suite 240
Menlo Park, CA USA 94025
Phone: 650-234-0500
E-mail: info@oakhillinvestments.com
Website: www.oakhillinvestments.com

Other Offices

3721 Douglas Boulevard
Suite 340
Roseville, CA USA 95661
Phone: 916-789-0600

Type of Firm

Private Equity Advisor or Fund of Funds

Project Preferences

Type of Financing Preferred:
Fund of Funds

Additional Information

Year Founded: 2006
Capital Under Management: $500,000,000
Current Activity Level : Actively seeking new investments

OAK HILL VENTURE PARTNERS (OHVP)

2775 Sand Hill Road
Suite 220
Menlo Park, CA USA 94025
Phone: 650-234-0500
Fax: 650-234-0590
E-mail: info@ohvp.com
Website: www.ohvp.com

Management and Staff

David Brown, Managing Partner
Michael Spence, Partner

Type of Firm

Private Equity Firm

Project Preferences

Role in Financing:
Prefer role as deal originator but will also invest in deals created by others

Type of Financing Preferred:
Balanced

Size of Investments Considered:
Min Size of Investment Considered (000s): $1,000
Max Size of Investment Considered (000s): $15,000

Geographical Preferences

United States Preferences:
Northern California
Northeast
All U.S.

Industry Preferences

In Communications prefer:
Commercial Communications
CATV & Pay TV Systems
Radio & TV Broadcasting
Telecommunications
Wireless Communications
Data Communications
Satellite Microwave Comm.

In Computer Hardware prefer:
Mainframes / Scientific
Mini and Personal/Desktop
Computer Graphics and Dig
Integrated Turnkey System
Terminals
Disk Relat. Memory Device

In Computer Software prefer:
Computer Services
Data Processing
Software
Systems Software
Applications Software
Artificial Intelligence

In Internet Specific prefer:
E-Commerce Technology
Internet
Web Aggregration/Portals

In Semiconductor/Electr prefer:
Electronic Components
Semiconductor
Micro-Processing
Controllers and Sensors
Sensors
Circuit Boards
Component Testing Equipmt
Laser Related
Fiber Optics
Analytic/Scientific

In Industrial/Energy prefer:
Energy
Superconductivity
Factory Automation
Process Control
Robotics

In Transportation prefer:
Transportation
Aerospace

In Financial Services prefer:
Financial Services
Insurance

Additional Information
Year Founded: 1997
Capital Under Management: $500,000,000
Current Activity Level : Actively seeking new investments
Method of Compensation: Return on investment is of primary concern, do not charge fees

---

OAK INVESTMENT PARTNERS

One Gorham Island
Westport, CT USA 06880
Phone: 203-226-8346
Fax: 203-227-0372
Website: www.oakvc.com

Other Offices
4550 Wells Fargo Center
90 South Seventh Street
Minneapolis, MN USA 55402
Phone: 612-339-9322
Fax: 612-337-8017

525 University Avenue
Suite 1300
Palo Alto, CA USA 94301
Phone: 650-614-3700
Fax: 650-328-6345

Management and Staff
Allan Kwan, Venture Partner
Anne Lamont, Managing Partner
Bandel Carano, Managing Partner
Brian Hinman, Venture Partner
Edward Glassmeyer, Managing Partner
Fredric Harman, Managing Partner
H. Eugene Lockhart, Venture Partner
Iftikar Ahmed, General Partner
Jerry Gallagher, General Partner
John Beletic, Venture Partner
Ranjan Chak, Venture Partner
Ren Riley, General Partner
Scot Jarvis, Venture Partner
Thomas Huseby, Venture Partner
Tony Downer, Venture Partner

Type of Firm
Private Equity Firm

Association Membership
National Venture Capital Association - USA (NVCA)

Project Preferences

Role in Financing:
Will function either as deal originator or investor in deals created by others

Type of Financing Preferred:
Expansion
Balanced
Later Stage
Management Buyouts
Private Placement
Special Situation

Size of Investments Considered:
Min Size of Investment Considered (000s): $1,000
Max Size of Investment Considered (000s): $60,000

Geographical Preferences

United States Preferences:
All U.S.

Industry Focus
(% based on actual investment)

Internet Specific	20.4%
Communications and Media	19.1%
Computer Software and Services	16.7%
Semiconductors/Other Elect.	11.7%
Other Products	11.4%
Medical/Health	7.5%
Computer Hardware	4.8%
Consumer Related	4.3%
Industrial/Energy	2.4%
Biotechnology	1.6%

Additional Information
Year Founded: 1978
Capital Under Management: $8,400,000,000
Current Activity Level : Actively seeking new investments
Method of Compensation: Return on investment is of primary concern, do not charge fees

---

OAKCREST CAPITAL PARTNERS LLC

600 13th Street Northeast
Suite 790
Washington, DC USA 20005
Phone: 202-315-4250
Fax: 202-315-4251
Website: www.oakcrestcapital.com

Management and Staff
Linda Roach, Partner
Michael Bluestein, Partner

Type of Firm
Private Equity Firm

Project Preferences

Type of Financing Preferred:
Expansion
Management Buyouts
Acquisition
Recapitalizations

Geographical Preferences

United States Preferences:
All U.S.

Industry Preferences

In Medical/Health prefer:
Health Services

In Consumer Related prefer:
Consumer Products
Consumer Services

In Industrial/Energy prefer:
Industrial Products

In Transportation prefer:
Transportation

In Business Serv. prefer:
Services
Media

In Manufact. prefer:
Manufacturing

Additional Information
Year Founded: 2006
Current Activity Level : Actively seeking new investments

OAKLEY CAPITAL INVESTMENT LIMITED (AKA: OCI)
11 Harbour Road
Paget, Bermuda PG01
Website: www.oakleycapitalinvestments.com

Type of Firm
Private Equity Firm

Project Preferences

Type of Financing Preferred:
Leveraged Buyout
Generalist PE
Later Stage

Size of Investments Considered:
Min Size of Investment Considered (000s): $40,268
Max Size of Investment Considered (000s): $201,340

Geographical Preferences

International Preferences:
United Kingdom
Europe

Additional Information
Year Founded: 2007
Capital Under Management: $198,000,000
Current Activity Level : Actively seeking new investments

OAKSTONE VENTURE PARTNERS
260 Sheridan Avenue
Suite 400
Palo Alto, CA USA 94306
Phone: 925-937-3307
Fax: 925-937-3303
E-mail: info@oakstoneventures.com
Website: www.oakstoneventures.com

Other Offices
100 Sopris Drive
P.O. Box 4358
Basalt, CO USA 81621
Phone: 970-927-8761
Fax: 775-259-0254

Management and Staff
Peter Hawkins, General Partner

Type of Firm
Private Equity Firm

Project Preferences

Type of Financing Preferred:
Balanced

Geographical Preferences

United States Preferences:
All U.S.

Additional Information
Year Founded: 1999
Capital Under Management: $4,000,000
Current Activity Level : Actively seeking new investments

OAKTREE CAPITAL MANAGEMENT LLC
333 South Grand Avenue
28th Floor
Los Angeles, CA USA 90071
Phone: 213-830-6300
Fax: 213-830-6293
E-mail: info@oaktreecapital.com
Website: www.oaktreecapital.com

Other Offices
27 Knightsbridge
London, United Kingdom SW1X 7LY
Phone: 44-207-201-4600
Fax: 44-207-201-4601

Atago Green Hills, Mori Tower 37th Floor
2-5-1 Atago Minato-ku
Tokyo, Japan 105-6237
Phone: 813-5776-6760
Fax: 813-5776-6761

680 Washington Boulevard
Sixth Floor
Stamford, CT USA 06901
Phone: 203-363-3200
Fax: 203-363-3210

46th Floor, Plaza 66
1266 Nanjing Road West, Suite 4609
Shanghai, China 200040
Phone: 8621-6288-6679

1301 Avenue of the Americas
34th Floor
New York, NY USA 10019
Phone: 212-284-1900
Fax: 212-284-1901

15 rue Louvigny
Luxembourg L-1946
Phone: 352-264-582-9210
Fax: 352-264-582-8294

31/F Maybank Tower
2 Battery Road
Singapore, Singapore 049907
Phone: 65-6438-8864
Fax: 65-6438-8869

Frankfurter Welle
An der Welle 4, 4. Stock
Frankfurt, Germany 60322
Phone: 49-69-7593-8529
Fax: 49-69-7593-8368

AIG Tower, 1 Connaught Road
Suite 2001
Central, Hong Kong
Phone: 852-3655-6800
Fax: 852-3655-6900

44, rue de Lisbonne
Paris, France 75008
Phone: 331-4299-1515
Fax: 331-4299-1511

67-8 Yangiae I-dong, Seocho-gu
6th Floor
Seoul, South Korea 137-889
Phone: 822-2191-8000

Ste 2522-2524, 25th Fl, Kerry Centre
S. Tower, No. 1 Guanghua Road
Beijing, Chaoyang District, China 100020
Phone: 8610-6587-7800
Fax: 8610-6587-7900

80 Raffles Place
51-03 UOB Plaza 1
Singapore 048624

Jan van Goyenkade 8
Amsterdam, Netherlands 1075 HP
Phone: 20-579-2138

Management and Staff
Abraham Ofer, Managing Director
Alexander Popov, Vice President
Andrew Watts, Managing Director
B. James Ford, Managing Director
Bharat Lakhanpal, Managing Director
Bill Moores, Managing Director
Caleb Kramer, Managing Director
Dennis Zhu, Managing Director
Frank Carroll, Managing Director
Gary Trabka, Managing Director
George Leiva, Managing Director
Jackie Nooner, Vice President

Jean-Paul Nedelec, Managing Director
Jeffrey Arnold, Managing Director
Karim Khairallah, Managing Director
Kenneth Liang, Managing Director
Kevin Clayton, Principal
Larry Keele, Principal
Linda Weiss, Managing Director
Lowell Hill, Managing Director
Mel Carlisle, Managing Director
Melissa Obegi, Managing Director
Michael Harmon, Managing Director
Nazar Sharif, Managing Director
Richard Goldstein, Managing Director
Richard Masson, Principal
Ronald Beck, Managing Director
Scott Beltz, Vice President
Scott Graves, Managing Director
Sheldon Stone, Principal
Stephen Kaplan, Principal
Timothy Jensen, Managing Director
Timothy Andrews, Managing Director
Vincent Cebula, Managing Director
William Kerins, Managing Director
William Sacher, Managing Director

Type of Firm

Investment Management Firm

Project Preferences

Role in Financing:

Will function either as deal originator or investor in deals created by others

Type of Financing Preferred:

Control-block Purchases
Mezzanine
Generalist PE
Other
Special Situation
Distressed Debt

Geographical Preferences

United States Preferences:

All U.S.

Canadian Preferences:

All Canada

International Preferences:

United Kingdom
Netherlands
Taiwan
Europe
China
Hong Kong
Austria
Australia
Asia
Japan
All International

Additional Information

Name of Most Recent Fund: OCM Opportunities Fund VIIb, L.P.
Most Recent Fund Was Raised: 03/21/2007
Year Founded: 1995
Capital Under Management: $40,281,000,000
Current Activity Level : Actively seeking new investments
Method of Compensation: Other

OAKWOOD MEDICAL INVESTORS

10411 Clayton Road
Suite 302
Saint Louis, MO USA 63131
Phone: 314-991-7979
Fax: 314-991-7914
E-mail: info@oakwoodmedical.com
Website: www.oakwoodmedical.com

Management and Staff

Daniel Burkhardt, Partner
James Nouss, Partner
Raul Perez, President

Type of Firm

Private Equity Firm

Project Preferences

Role in Financing:

Will function either as deal originator or investor in deals created by others

Type of Financing Preferred:

Balanced

Size of Investments Considered:

Min Size of Investment Considered (000s): $1,000
Max Size of Investment Considered (000s): $3,000

Industry Preferences

In Biotechnology prefer:

Biotechnology
Human Biotechnology

In Medical/Health prefer:

Medical Diagnostics
Diagnostic Test Products
Medical Therapeutics
Drug/Equipmt Delivery
Medical Products
Disposable Med. Products
Pharmaceuticals

Additional Information

Year Founded: 1997
Capital Under Management: $77,000,000
Current Activity Level : Actively seeking new investments
Method of Compensation: Return on investment is of primary concern, do not charge fees

---

OASIS CAPITAL PARTNERS LLC

1001 Avenue of the Americas
Fourth Floor
New York, NY USA 10001
Phone: 212-302-4525
Fax: 212-279-1804
Website: www.oasiscapital.com

Management and Staff

Cathy Ross, Managing Director
Joseph Lucchese, Managing Director
Wilford Adkins, Managing Director

Type of Firm

Bank Affiliated

Project Preferences

Role in Financing:

Prefer role as deal originator but will also invest in deals created by others

Type of Financing Preferred:

Leveraged Buyout
Expansion
Turnaround
Management Buyouts
Industry Rollups
Recapitalizations

Geographical Preferences

United States Preferences:

All U.S.

International Preferences:

Latin America

Additional Information

Year Founded: 1997
Current Activity Level : Actively seeking new investments
Method of Compensation: Return on invest. most important, but chg. closing fees, service fees, etc.

OBERBANK OPPORTUNITY INVEST MANAGEMENT GMBH

Hofgasse 1
Linz, Austria A-4020
Phone: 43-73-278-020
Fax: 43-73-780-221
E-mail: office@oberbank.at
Website: www.oberbank.at

Type of Firm

Bank Affiliated

Association Membership

European Private Equity and Venture Capital Assoc.

Project Preferences

Type of Financing Preferred:

Balanced

Geographical Preferences

International Preferences:

Europe

Additional Information
Year Founded: 2006
Capital Under Management: $198,000,000
Current Activity Level : Actively seeking new investments

OBEROSTERREICHISCHE UNTERNEHMENSBETEILIGUNGS GMBH
Dinghoferstrasse 21
Linz, Austria 4010
Phone: 43-732-7800-285
Fax: 43-707-7780-040
E-mail: info@kgg-ubg.at
Website: www.kgg-ubg.at

Type of Firm
Bank Affiliated

Additional Information
Year Founded: 2004
Current Activity Level : Actively seeking new investments

OBSIDIAN FINANCE GROUP LLC
10260 South West Greenburg Rd.
Suite 1150
Portland, OR USA 97223
Phone: 503-245-8800
Fax: 503-245-8804
Website: www.obsidianfinance.com

Management and Staff
F. Michael Nugent, Managing Director
J. Franklin Cable, Managing Director
Patricia Whittington, Vice President

Type of Firm
Private Equity Firm

Project Preferences
Type of Financing Preferred:
Balanced

Geographical Preferences
United States Preferences:
All U.S.

Additional Information
Year Founded: 2007
Current Activity Level : Actively seeking new investments

OCA VENTURE PARTNERS
141 W. Jackson
39th Floor
Chicago, IL USA 60604
Phone: 312-542-8954
Fax: 312-542-8952
Website: www.ocaventures.com

Management and Staff
Edward Lou, General Partner
Jason Heltzer, Principal
John Dugan, General Partner
Peter Ianello, General Partner

Type of Firm
Private Equity Firm

Association Membership
National Venture Capital Association - USA (NVCA)

Project Preferences
Role in Financing:
Prefer role as deal originator but will also invest in deals created by others

Type of Financing Preferred:
Second Stage Financing
Early Stage
Expansion
Mezzanine
Start-up Financing
Balanced
Seed
First Stage Financing

Size of Investments Considered:
Min Size of Investment Considered (000s): $1,000
Max Size of Investment Considered (000s): $10,000

Geographical Preferences
United States Preferences:
Mid Atlantic
Midwest
Southeast
Northeast
Rocky Mountain

Industry Preferences
In Computer Software prefer:
Software

In Internet Specific prefer:
Internet

In Consumer Related prefer:
Consumer Services
Education Related

In Financial Services prefer:
Financial Services

Additional Information
Year Founded: 1999
Capital Under Management: $70,400,000
Current Activity Level : Actively seeking new investments
Method of Compensation: Return on investment is of primary concern, do not charge fees

OCCAM CAPITAL
5 rue Daunou
Paris, France 75002
Phone: 33-1-4458-9210
Fax: 33-1-4458-9238
Website: www.occamcapital.net

Other Offices
35 Park Lane
London, United Kingdom W1K 1RB
Phone: 44-207-355-7777
Fax: 44-207-409-2304

Management and Staff
Guillaume Dry, Partner
Jeff Clavier, Partner

Type of Firm
Private Equity Firm

Association Membership
French Venture Capital Association (AFIC)

Project Preferences
Type of Financing Preferred:
Early Stage
Expansion

Geographical Preferences
International Preferences:
Europe
Israel

Industry Preferences
In Communications prefer:
Communications and Media
Telecommunications

In Industrial/Energy prefer:
Energy

In Financial Services prefer:
Financial Services

Additional Information
Year Founded: 2004
Capital Under Management: $67,000,000
Current Activity Level : Actively seeking new investments

OCEAN PARTICIPATIONS
34 rue Leandre Merlet
BP 19
La Roche-sur-Yon, France 85001
Phone: 33-2-5147-5475
Fax: 33-2-5147-5245
E-mail: ocean.participations@cmocean.fr

Type of Firm
Private Equity Firm

Project Preferences

Type of Financing Preferred:
Leveraged Buyout
Early Stage
Expansion

Geographical Preferences

International Preferences:
France

Additional Information
Year Founded: 1988
Capital Under Management: $8,600,000
Current Activity Level : Actively seeking new investments

OCEAN TOMO, LLC
200 West Madison
37th Floor
Chicago, IL USA 60606
Phone: 312-327-4400
Fax: 312-327-4401
Website: www.oceantomo.com

Other Offices
126 Sea View Avenue
Palm Beach, FL USA 33480
Phone: 561-309-0011
Fax: 561-835-0003

19990 MacArthur Blvd
Suite 1150
Irvine, CA USA 92612
Phone: 888-295-7007
Fax: 949-222-1265

125 Summer Street
7th Floor
Boston, MA USA 02110
Phone: 617-345-3824
Fax: 617-812-3077

101 Montgomery Street
Suite 2100
San Francisco, CA USA 94104
Phone: 415-946-2600

4630 Montgomery Ave
3rd Floor
Bethesda, MD USA 20814
7475 Wisconsin Avenue
Suite 525
Bethesda, MD USA 20814
Phone: 240-482-8200

251 Kearny Street
8th Floor
San Francisco, CA USA 94108
Phone: 415-946-2600
Fax: 415-946-2601

19200 Von Karman Avenue
Suite 600
Irvine, CA USA 92612
Phone: 949-648-7340

340 Royal Poinciana Way
Suite 317
Palm Beach, FL USA 33480
Phone: 786-266-8989

Two Sound View Drive
Greenwich, CT USA 06830
Phone: 203-602-3901
Fax: 203-602-3902

Management and Staff
Andrew Carter, Managing Director

Type of Firm
Bank Affiliated

Association Membership
Illinois Venture Capital Association

Project Preferences

Type of Financing Preferred:
Leveraged Buyout
Mezzanine

Additional Information
Year Founded: 2005
Current Activity Level : Actively seeking new investments

OCH-ZIFF CAPITAL MANAGEMENT GROUP (AKA: OZ ADVISORS, LLC)
Nine West 57th Street
39th Floor
New York, NY USA 10019
Phone: 212-790-0000
Website: www.ozcap.com

Other Offices
Cheung Kong Center, Suite 2003A
2 Queens Road Central
Hong Kong
Phone: 852-2297-2595

7 Clifford Street
1st Floor
London, United Kingdom W1S 2FT
Phone: 44-20-7758-4400
Unit 1901, Level 19, Tower E2, Oriental
1 East Chang An Avenue, Dong Cheng Dist
Beijing, China 100738
Phone: 86-10-8520-0500

#58, 2nd Floor, 100 Ft. Road
Indirangar, Defence Colony
Bangalore, India 560 038
Phone: 91-80-2521-0123

Management and Staff
Daniel Och, Chief Executive Officer
Joel Frank, Chief Financial Officer

Type of Firm
Bank Affiliated

Project Preferences

Type of Financing Preferred:
Other
Distressed Debt

Geographical Preferences

United States Preferences:
All U.S.

Industry Preferences

In Financial Services prefer:
Real Estate

Additional Information
Year Founded: 2001
Capital Under Management: $22,300,000
Current Activity Level : Actively seeking new investments

OCTANE CAPITAL MANAGEMENT
800 West El Camino Real
Suite 180
Mountain View, CA USA 94040
Phone: 650-316-3663
Fax: 650-316-3667
Website: www.octanecapital.com

Management and Staff
Alex Monte-Sano, Principal
David Golob, Principal
Emeric McDonald, Principal
George Lee, Principal
Laura Paradis, Principal
Timothy Murphy, Principal

Type of Firm
Private Equity Firm

Project Preferences

Type of Financing Preferred:
Later Stage

Additional Information
Year Founded: 2000
Current Activity Level : Making few, if any, new investments

OCTOPUS ASSET MANAGEMENT, LTD.
8 Angel Court
London, United Kingdom EC2R 7HP
Phone: 44-20-7710-2800
Fax: 44-84-5671-7273
E-mail: info@octopusinvestments.com
Website: www.octopusinvestments.com

Management and Staff

Alex Macpherson, Chief Executive Officer
Chris Hulatt, Founder
Paul Latham, Chief Operating Officer
Simon Rogerson, Chief Executive Officer

Type of Firm

Private Equity Firm

Project Preferences

Type of Financing Preferred:
Fund of Funds
Early Stage
Expansion
Mezzanine
Balanced
Public Companies
Later Stage

Geographical Preferences

International Preferences:
United Kingdom
Europe

Industry Preferences

In Biotechnology prefer:
Biotechnology

In Medical/Health prefer:
Pharmaceuticals

Additional Information

Name of Most Recent Fund: Eclipse VCT
Most Recent Fund Was Raised: 12/31/2004
Year Founded: 2000
Capital Under Management: $61,900,000
Current Activity Level : Actively seeking new investments

OCV INVESTORS, LLC

525 West Monroe Street
Suite 1600
Chicago, IL USA 60661
Phone: 312-902-5254

Type of Firm

Private Equity Firm

Additional Information

Year Founded: 2002
Capital Under Management: $4,000,000
Current Activity Level : Actively seeking new investments

ODDO ASSET MANAGEMENT

12 Boulevard de la Madeleine
Paris, France 75440
Phone: 33-1-4451-8500
Fax: 33-1-4451-8510
Website: www.oddoam.fr

Type of Firm

Investment Management Firm

Association Membership

French Venture Capital Association (AFIC)

Project Preferences

Type of Financing Preferred:
Fund of Funds
Early Stage
Expansion

Geographical Preferences

International Preferences:
Europe
France

Industry Preferences

In Medical/Health prefer:
Medical/Health

In Industrial/Energy prefer:
Environmental Related

Additional Information

Year Founded: 2009
Current Activity Level : Actively seeking new investments

ODEON CAPITAL PARTNERS, L.P.

825 3rd Avenue
32nd Floor
New York, NY USA 10022
Phone: 212-785-1300
Fax: 212-785-3159
Website: www.odeoncapital.com

Other Offices

10050 North Wolfe Road
Cupertino, CA USA 95014
Phone: 408-343-0253
Fax: 603-947-9552

Management and Staff

Jeffrey Finkle, Managing Director
Marc Aronstein, Partner
Matthew Smith, Managing Partner
Qayyum Hafeez, Principal

Type of Firm

Private Equity Firm

Industry Focus

(% based on actual investment)

Internet Specific	59.6%
Computer Software and Services	36.4%
Other Products	4.0%

Additional Information

Year Founded: 1998
Capital Under Management: $115,000,000
Current Activity Level : Actively seeking new investments

ODEWALD & COMPAGNIE GMBH (AKA : OCIE)

Franzoesische Strasse 8
Berlin, Germany D-10117
Phone: 49-30-2017-230
Fax: 49-30-2017-2360
E-mail: info@ocie.de
Website: www.ocie.de

Management and Staff

Andreas Fetting, Partner
August Von Joest, Partner
Ernst-Moritz Lipp, Partner
Frank Gerhold, Partner
Guenther Niethammer, Partner
Jens Odewald, Founding Partner
Joachim Von Ribbentrop, Partner
Klaus Eierhoff, Partner
Norbert Nelles, Partner
Oliver Schoenknecht, Partner

Type of Firm

Private Equity Firm

Project Preferences

Role in Financing:
Prefer role as deal originator

Type of Financing Preferred:
Leveraged Buyout
Expansion
Management Buyouts

Size of Investments Considered:
Min Size of Investment Considered (000s): $7,061
Max Size of Investment Considered (000s): $127,101

Geographical Preferences

International Preferences:
Switzerland
Europe
Western Europe
Austria
Germany

Industry Preferences

In Computer Other prefer:
Computer Related

In Industrial/Energy prefer:
Industrial Products

Additional Information

Year Founded: 1997
Capital Under Management: $1,590,200,000
Current Activity Level : Actively seeking new investments

ODIEN GROUP

Loretanske nam. 3
Praha 1
Prague, Czech Republic 110 00
Phone: 420-233-085-490
Fax: 420-233-085-492
E-mail: odien@odiengroup.com
Website: www.odiengroup.com

Other Offices

Haciosman Bayiri No: 65
Sariyer
Istanbul, Turkey 34453

Management and Staff

Michael Saran, Managing Partner
Omer Muftuler, Partner
R. Brian Wilson, Partner

Type of Firm

Private Equity Firm

Project Preferences

Type of Financing Preferred:
Leveraged Buyout
Acquisition

Geographical Preferences

International Preferences:
Central Europe
Eastern Europe

Additional Information

Year Founded: 2001
Current Activity Level : Actively seeking new investments

ODIN CAPITAL GROUP

1625 Farnam Street
Suite 700
Omaha, NE USA 68102
Phone: 402-827-9900
Fax: 402-408-6354
Website: www.odincapital.com

Management and Staff

David McLeese, Partner
Donna Walsh, Managing Director
John Gustafson, Venture Partner
Thompson Rogers, Partner

Type of Firm

Private Equity Firm

Project Preferences

Role in Financing:
Will function either as deal originator or investor in deals created by others

Type of Financing Preferred:
Second Stage Financing
Early Stage
Expansion
First Stage Financing

Size of Investments Considered:
Min Size of Investment Considered (000s): $500
Max Size of Investment Considered (000s): $3,000

Geographical Preferences

United States Preferences:
Midwest
Rocky Mountain
Southwest

Industry Preferences

In Communications prefer:
Wireless Communications

In Computer Software prefer:
Systems Software
Applications Software

In Internet Specific prefer:
E-Commerce Technology
Internet
Ecommerce

In Medical/Health prefer:
Medical Products
Health Services

In Industrial/Energy prefer:
Factory Automation

In Financial Services prefer:
Financial Services
Insurance

In Business Serv. prefer:
Services
Distribution

Additional Information

Name of Most Recent Fund: Odin Fund I, LP
Most Recent Fund Was Raised: 10/31/2000
Year Founded: 1999
Capital Under Management: $40,600,000
Current Activity Level : Actively seeking new investments
Method of Compensation: Return on investment is of primary concern, do not charge fees

ODIN EQUITY PARTNERS

Helsingorsvej 38B
Fredensborg, Denmark 3480
Phone: 45-48401200
Fax: 45-84841213
Website: www.odinequity.dk

Management and Staff

Bernd Petersen, Founder
Esben Bay Jorgensen, Partner
Jesper Wadum Nielsen, Partner

Type of Firm

Private Equity Firm

Project Preferences

Type of Financing Preferred:
Leveraged Buyout
Turnaround
Recapitalizations

Geographical Preferences

International Preferences:
Sweden
Germany
Denmark

Additional Information

Year Founded: 2005
Capital Under Management: $472,700,000
Current Activity Level : Actively seeking new investments

ODIN INVESTMENTS

The Museum Tower, 18th Floor
4 Berkovich Street
Tel Aviv, Israel 64238
Phone: 972-3693-5155
Fax: 972-3693-5160
E-mail: info@odin-invest.com
Website: www.odin-invest.com

Management and Staff

Avner Ben Yeshaya, Principal
Gabriel Perel, Managing Director
Ronen Melnik, Managing Partner

Type of Firm

Private Equity Firm

Project Preferences

Type of Financing Preferred:
Early Stage
Balanced

Geographical Preferences

International Preferences:
Israel

Industry Preferences

In Financial Services prefer:
Real Estate

Additional Information

Year Founded: 2006
Capital Under Management: $50,000,000
Current Activity Level : Actively seeking new investments

ODLANDER, FREDRIKSON & CO. AB (AKA: HEALTHCAP)

Strandvagen 5B
Stockholm, Sweden SE-114 51
Phone: 46-8-442-5850
Fax: 46-8-442-5879
Website: www.healthcap.se

Other Offices

18 Avenue D'Ouchy
Lausanne, Switzerland CH-1006
Phone: 41-21-614-3500
Fax: 41-21-601-5544

Management and Staff

Anki Forsberg, Partner
Bjorn Odlander, Founding Partner
Carl-Johan Dalsgaard, Partner
Eugen Steiner, Partner
Johan Christenson, Partner
Magnus Persson, Partner
Peder Fredrikson, Founding Partner
Per Samuelsson, Partner
Staffan Lindstrand, Partner

Type of Firm

Private Equity Advisor or Fund of Funds

Association Membership

Swedish Venture Capital Association (SVCA)
European Private Equity and Venture Capital Assoc.

Project Preferences

Type of Financing Preferred:
Early Stage
Balanced
Later Stage

Geographical Preferences

International Preferences:
Europe
Scandanavia/Nordic Region

Industry Preferences

In Biotechnology prefer:
Biotechnology

In Medical/Health prefer:
Medical/Health
Medical Products

Additional Information

Name of Most Recent Fund: HealthCap IV Bis, L.P.
Most Recent Fund Was Raised: 07/01/2002
Year Founded: 1996
Capital Under Management: $1,177,300,000
Current Activity Level : Actively seeking new investments

ODYSSEE VENTURE

12 Boulevard de la Madeleine
Paris, France 75009
Phone: 33-1-4451-8135
Fax: 33-1-4451-8146
E-mail: entrepreneurs@odyssee-venture.com
Website: www.odyssee-venture.com

Management and Staff

Mathieu Boillet, Co-Founder
Sebastien Sassolas, Co-Founder

Type of Firm

Bank Affiliated

Association Membership

French Venture Capital Association (AFIC)

Project Preferences

Type of Financing Preferred:
Early Stage
Expansion
Startup

Size of Investments Considered:
Min Size of Investment Considered (000s): $994
Max Size of Investment Considered (000s): $4,968

Geographical Preferences

International Preferences:
Europe
France

Industry Preferences

In Computer Software prefer:
Software

In Biotechnology prefer:
Biotechnology

In Medical/Health prefer:
Medical/Health

Additional Information

Year Founded: 1999
Capital Under Management: $134,100,000
Current Activity Level : Actively seeking new investments

ODYSSEY INVESTMENT PARTNERS, LLC

280 Park Avenue
38th Floor, West Tower
New York, NY USA 10017
Phone: 212-351-7900
Fax: 212-351-7925
E-mail: info@odysseyinvestment.com
Website: www.odysseyinvestment.com

Other Offices

21650 Oxnard Street
Suite 1650
Woodland Hills, CA USA 91367
Phone: 818-737-1111
Fax: 818-737-1101

Management and Staff

David Mait, Principal
Dennis Moore, Vice President
Matthew Satnick, Vice President
Muzzafar Mirza, Partner
Paul Barnett, Partner
Robert Aikman, Principal
Ross Rodrigues, Principal
Vincent Sarullo, Chief Financial Officer

Type of Firm

Private Equity Firm

Project Preferences

Type of Financing Preferred:
Leveraged Buyout
Expansion
Generalist PE
Management Buyouts
Acquisition
Recapitalizations

Geographical Preferences

United States Preferences:
All U.S.

Industry Focus

(% based on actual investment)	
Industrial/Energy	34.3%
Consumer Related	32.4%
Other Products	15.7%
Semiconductors/Other Elect.	8.1%
Computer Hardware	7.7%
Communications and Media	1.5%
Computer Software and Services	0.1%

Additional Information

Name of Most Recent Fund: Odyssey Investment Partners Fund III, L.P.
Most Recent Fund Was Raised: 07/12/2004
Year Founded: 1982
Capital Under Management: $760,000,000
Current Activity Level : Actively seeking new investments

ODYSSEY VENTURE PARTNERS

600 Anton Boulevard
Suite 1750
Costa Mesa, CA USA 92626
Phone: 714-241-7500
Fax: 815-642-0271
E-mail: info@2odyssey.com
Website: www.2odyssey.com

Management and Staff

Alan Sellers, Partner
David Jones, General Partner
Hank Babicht, Managing Partner
Jeffrey Brady, Partner
Mark Czepiel, Partner

Meir Arnon, Venture Partner
Thomas Cain, General Partner
Walter Schindler, Managing Partner
William Maya, Venture Partner

Type of Firm

Private Equity Firm

Additional Information

Year Founded: 2000
Current Activity Level : Actively seeking new investments

OFER HI-TECH

Ramat Aviv Towers, Sixth Floor
40 Einstein St., Ramat Aviv
Tel Aviv, Israel
Phone: 972-03-745-6000
Fax: 972-03-760-4355
Website: www.oferhitech.com

Management and Staff

Assif Stoffman, Chief Executive Officer
Daniel Plotkin, Venture Partner
Shay Dubi, Vice President
Yoav Sebba, Vice President
Yoav Doppelt, Chief Executive Officer

Type of Firm

Private Equity Firm

Project Preferences

Type of Financing Preferred:

Early Stage
Balanced
Public Companies
Seed

Geographical Preferences

International Preferences:

Israel

Industry Preferences

In Communications prefer:

Communications and Media

In Computer Software prefer:

Software

In Semiconductor/Electr prefer:

Electronics

In Biotechnology prefer:

Biotechnology

In Medical/Health prefer:

Medical Products

Additional Information

Year Founded: 1997
Current Activity Level : Actively seeking new investments

OFI PRIVATE EQUITY CAPITAL

1 rue Vernier
Paris, France 75017
Phone: 33-140-686-044
Fax: 33-140-686-791
Website: www.ofi-pecapital.com

Type of Firm

Private Equity Firm

Association Membership

French Venture Capital Association (AFIC)

Project Preferences

Type of Financing Preferred:

Leveraged Buyout
Mezzanine
Management Buyouts

Size of Investments Considered:

Min Size of Investment Considered (000s): $20,973
Max Size of Investment Considered (000s): $104,866

Geographical Preferences

International Preferences:

France

Additional Information

Year Founded: 2007
Current Activity Level : Actively seeking new investments

OFIVALMO (AKA : OMNIUM FINANCIER DE VALEURS MOBILIERS)

1 rue Vernier
Paris, France 75017
Phone: 33-1-4068-1717
Fax: 33-1-4068-1718
E-mail: contact@ofivalmo.fr
Website: www.ofivalmo.fr

Management and Staff

Gerard Bourret, President

Type of Firm

Bank Affiliated

Project Preferences

Type of Financing Preferred:

Leveraged Buyout
Early Stage
Expansion
Generalist PE

Geographical Preferences

International Preferences:

Europe
France

Additional Information

Name of Most Recent Fund: Oficap FCPR
Most Recent Fund Was Raised: 12/31/2001
Year Founded: 1971
Current Activity Level : Actively seeking new investments

OHIO INNOVATION FUND (OIF)

1120 Chester Avenue
Suite 418
Cleveland, OH USA 44114
Phone: 216-533-2351
Fax: 330-659-3270
Website: www.oifventures.com

Management and Staff

Jeff Hanson, Partner
Timothy Biro, Managing Partner

Type of Firm

Private Equity Firm

Project Preferences

Role in Financing:

Prefer role as deal originator but will also invest in deals created by others

Type of Financing Preferred:

Early Stage

Size of Investments Considered:

Min Size of Investment Considered (000s): $250
Max Size of Investment Considered (000s): $1,000

Geographical Preferences

United States Preferences:

Midwest

Industry Preferences

In Communications prefer:

Telecommunications

In Computer Software prefer:

Software
Systems Software
Applications Software

In Internet Specific prefer:

E-Commerce Technology

In Semiconductor/Electr prefer:

Semiconductor
Micro-Processing
Sensors
Analytic/Scientific

In Biotechnology prefer:

Human Biotechnology

In Medical/Health prefer:
Medical Diagnostics
Medical Therapeutics
Pharmaceuticals

Additional Information
Year Founded: 1997
Capital Under Management: $12,600,000
Current Activity Level : Actively seeking new investments
Method of Compensation: Return on investment is of primary concern, do not charge fees

---

OIKOCREDIT INTERNATIONAL
Tesselschadelaan 4
Amersfoort, Netherlands 3817 HN
Phone: 31-31-334224040
Fax: 31-33-4650336
E-mail: info@oikocredit.org
Website: www.oikocredit.org

Management and Staff
Tor G. Gull, Managing Director

Type of Firm
Private Equity Firm

Project Preferences

Size of Investments Considered:
Min Size of Investment Considered (000s): $500
Max Size of Investment Considered (000s): $2,000

Geographical Preferences

International Preferences:
Latin America
Central Europe
Eastern Europe
Asia
Africa

Industry Preferences

In Financial Services prefer:
Financial Services

In Manufact. prefer:
Manufacturing

In Agr/Forestr/Fish prefer:
Agribusiness

Additional Information
Year Founded: 1975
Capital Under Management: $200,000,000
Current Activity Level : Actively seeking new investments

OJAS VENTURE PARTNERS
#772, 3rd Floor, 80 Ft. Road
4th Block, Koramangala
Bangalore, India 560 034
Phone: 91-80-4061-0300
Fax: 91-80-4061-0301
E-mail: pingus@ojasventures.com
Website: www.ojasventures.com

Management and Staff
Gautam Balijepalli, Principal
Pavan Krishnamurthy, Partner
Raghu Batta, Partner
Rajesh Srivathsa, Managing Partner

Type of Firm
Private Equity Firm

Project Preferences

Type of Financing Preferred:
Early Stage
Seed

Size of Investments Considered:
Min Size of Investment Considered (000s): $750
Max Size of Investment Considered (000s): $3,000

Geographical Preferences

International Preferences:
India

Additional Information
Year Founded: 2007
Capital Under Management: $35,000,000
Current Activity Level : Actively seeking new investments

OKANAGAN INNOVATION FUND
1708 Dolphin Avenue
Suite 406
Kelowna, Canada V1Y9S4
Phone: 250-762-6850
Fax: 250-762-6870
E-mail: info@oifund.ca
Website: www.oifund.ca

Management and Staff
John Drope, Managing Director

Type of Firm
Private Equity Firm

Additional Information
Year Founded: 2009
Current Activity Level : Actively seeking new investments

OKAPI VENTURE CAPITAL LLC
1590 South Coast Highway
Suite Ten
Laguna Beach, CA USA 92651
Phone: 949-715-5557
Fax: 949-715-5556
Website: www.okapivc.com

Management and Staff
B. Marc Averitt, Managing Director
Sharon Stevenson, Managing Director

Type of Firm
Private Equity Firm

Association Membership
National Venture Capital Association - USA (NVCA)

Project Preferences

Role in Financing:
Prefer role as deal originator

Type of Financing Preferred:
Early Stage
Seed

Size of Investments Considered:
Min Size of Investment Considered (000s): $500
Max Size of Investment Considered (000s): $4,000

Geographical Preferences

United States Preferences:
California

Additional Information
Name of Most Recent Fund: Okapi Ventures, L.P.
Most Recent Fund Was Raised: 06/05/2006
Year Founded: 2005
Capital Under Management: $27,500,000
Current Activity Level : Actively seeking new investments
Method of Compensation: Return on investment is of primary concern, do not charge fees

---

OKASAN VENTURE CAPITAL CO., LTD.
9-9 Koamicho
Nihonbashi,Chuo-ku
Tokyo, Japan 103-0016
Phone: 81-3-3665-1011
Website: www.okasan-holding.co.jp

Management and Staff
Yoshida Takashi, President

Type of Firm
Bank Affiliated

Additional Information
Year Founded: 1983
Current Activity Level : Actively seeking new investments

OKLAHOMA EQUITY PARTNERS

415 S Boston Avenue
Suite 702
Tulsa, OK USA 74103
Phone: 918-382-0395
Website: www.oepvc.com

Management and Staff

David Humphrey, Chief Operating Officer

Type of Firm

Private Equity Firm

Project Preferences

Type of Financing Preferred:
Balanced

Geographical Preferences

United States Preferences:
All U.S.

Additional Information

Year Founded: 2006
Current Activity Level : Actively seeking new investments

OLD CITY PARTNERS, LLC (OCP)

5200 Town Center Circle
Suite 525
Boca Raton, FL USA 33486
Phone: 561-395-3534
Fax: 561-395-2464
Website: www.oldcitypartners.com

Other Offices

Ayalon Tower
11 Menachem Begin Street
Ramat Gan, Israel 52521
Phone: 972-3-575-7553
Fax: 972-3-575-7543

515 Enterprise Drive
Suite 202
Lowell, AR USA 72745
Phone: 479-725-2155
Fax: 479-725-2160

Management and Staff

Bram Portnoy, Vice President
Shai Bazak, Managing Director

Type of Firm

Private Equity Firm

Project Preferences

Type of Financing Preferred:
Expansion

Size of Investments Considered:
Min Size of Investment Considered (000s): $1,000
Max Size of Investment Considered (000s): $10,000

Geographical Preferences

United States Preferences:
All U.S.

International Preferences:
Israel

Industry Preferences

In Computer Software prefer:
Software

In Consumer Related prefer:
Consumer

In Transportation prefer:
Transportation

Additional Information

Year Founded: 2004
Current Activity Level : Actively seeking new investments

OLD MUTUAL PLC

5th Floor, Old Mutual Place
2 Lambeth Hill
London, United Kingdom EC4V 4GG
Phone: 44-20-7002-7000
Fax: 44-20-7002-7200
E-mail: contact@oldmutual.com
Website: www.oldmutual.com

Other Offices

OMAM Building, West Campus
Mutualpark, John Smuts Drive, Pinelands
Cape Town, South Africa 7405
Phone: 27-21-509-2400

Type of Firm

Bank Affiliated

Association Membership

South African Venture Capital Association (SAVCA)

Project Preferences

Type of Financing Preferred:
Generalist PE
Balanced

Geographical Preferences

International Preferences:
Europe
South Africa

Industry Preferences

In Medical/Health prefer:
Medical/Health

In Industrial/Energy prefer:
Energy
Oil and Gas Exploration
Oil & Gas Drilling,Explor
Industrial Products
Environmental Related

In Manufact. prefer:
Manufacturing

Additional Information

Year Founded: 2001
Current Activity Level : Actively seeking new investments

OLTENIA FINANCIAL INVESTMENT CY

BL. 313 Tufanele Street
Craiova, Romania 1100
Phone: 40-251-419-397
Fax: 40-251-419-340
E-mail: public@sifolt.ro
Website: www.sifolt.ro

Management and Staff

Despina Cirstea, Partner
Tudor Ciurezu, Partner
Vasile Salapa, Partner

Type of Firm

Private Equity Firm

Association Membership

European Private Equity and Venture Capital Assoc.

Project Preferences

Type of Financing Preferred:
Expansion
Turnaround
Startup

Geographical Preferences

International Preferences:
Europe
All International

Industry Preferences

In Semiconductor/Electr prefer:
Electronics

In Medical/Health prefer:
Medical/Health

In Financial Services prefer:
Real Estate

In Business Serv. prefer:
Services

Additional Information

Year Founded: 1999
Capital Under Management: $31,800,000
Current Activity Level : Actively seeking new investments

OLYMPUS CAPITAL HOLDINGS ASIA

One Exchange Square
Suite 3406
Central, Hong Kong
Phone: 852-2140-0500
Fax: 852-2140-0555
E-mail: info@olympuscap.com
Website: www.olympuscap.com

Other Offices

485 Madison Avenue
18th Floor
New York, NY USA 10022
Phone: 212-201-8533
Fax: 212-201-8534

17/F The Tokyo Ginko Kyokai Building
1-3-1 Marunouchi, Chiyoda-ku
Tokyo, Japan 100-0005
Phone: 813-5288-6721
Fax: 813-5288-6722

Unit 4101, Grand Gateway Tower 2
No.3 Hongqiao Road
Shanghai, China 200030
Phone: 86-21-6447-0066
Fax: 86-21-6447-6299

Level 12, Tower 08, Block C
DLF Cyber City, Phase II, Gurgaon
New Delhi, India 122 002
Phone: 91-124-469-6900
Fax: 91-124-469-6950

14/F, Young Poong Building
33 Suhrin-Dong, Jongro-Ku
Seoul, South Korea 110-752
Phone: 822-399-5100
Fax: 822-399-5555

Management and Staff

Dilip Kothari, Managing Director
Edan Lee, Managing Director
Gaurav Malik, Managing Director
Lawrence Miao, Managing Director

Type of Firm

Private Equity Firm

Project Preferences

Type of Financing Preferred:
Leveraged Buyout
Early Stage
Expansion
Mezzanine
Balanced
Turnaround
Seed
Management Buyouts
Startup

Geographical Preferences

International Preferences:
Vietnam
Indonesia
India
China
Hong Kong
Thailand
Philippines
Australia
Singapore
Korea, South
Asia
Japan
Malaysia

Industry Preferences

In Communications prefer:
Telecommunications

In Semiconductor/Electr prefer:
Electronics

In Consumer Related prefer:
Consumer Products
Consumer Services

In Industrial/Energy prefer:
Alternative Energy
Energy Conservation Relat
Environmental Related

In Financial Services prefer:
Financial Services

In Business Serv. prefer:
Services
Media

Additional Information

Year Founded: 1997
Capital Under Management: $500,000,000
Current Activity Level : Actively seeking new investments

OLYMPUS CAPITAL INVESTMENTS LLC

67 Park Place East
Morristown, NJ USA 07960
Phone: 973-889-9100
Fax: 973-889-0020
E-mail: info@olympuscapinv.com
Website: www.olympuscapinv.com

Management and Staff

Dean Vanech, Chairman & CEO

Type of Firm

Private Equity Firm

Project Preferences

Type of Financing Preferred:
Leveraged Buyout
Mezzanine
Later Stage

Additional Information

Year Founded: 2008
Current Activity Level : Actively seeking new investments

OMAN INVESTMENT CORPORATION (AKA: OIC)

P.O.Box 299
Jawharat Al-Shatti, Oman 134
Phone: 968-2448-8867
Fax: 968-2448-8857
Website: www.omaninvcorp.com

Type of Firm

Bank Affiliated

Project Preferences

Type of Financing Preferred:
Leveraged Buyout
Acquisition

Geographical Preferences

International Preferences:
Oman

Additional Information

Year Founded: 2008
Current Activity Level : Actively seeking new investments

OMANI CENTER FOR INVESTMENT PROMOTION AND EXPORT DEVELOPMENT

P.O. Box 25
Wadi Kabir P.C. 117
Sultanate of Oman, Oman
Phone: 968-2481-2344
Fax: 968-2481-0890
E-mail: info@ociped.com
Website: www.ociped.com

Type of Firm

Government Affiliated Program

Project Preferences

Type of Financing Preferred:
Balanced

Geographical Preferences

International Preferences:
Oman

Additional Information

Year Founded: 1996
Capital Under Management: $135,000,000

Current Activity Level : Actively seeking new investments

OMEGA CAPITAL SL

Paseo de la Castellana, 28
Madrid, Spain 28046
Phone: 34-917-027-991

Management and Staff

Alicia Koplowitz, Founder
Oscar Fanjul, Vice President

Type of Firm

Private Equity Firm

Project Preferences

Type of Financing Preferred:
Balanced

Geographical Preferences

International Preferences:
Spain

Additional Information

Year Founded: 2003
Current Activity Level : Actively seeking new investments

OMERS PRIVATE EQUITY

One University Avenue
Suite 800
Toronto, Canada M5J 2P1
Phone: 416-369-2400
Fax: 416-360-0217
E-mail: contactus@omerspe.com
Website: www.omerspe.com

Other Offices

Royal Bank Plaza, South Tower
Suite 2010, 200 Bay Street
Toronto, Canada M5J 2J2
Phone: 416-864-3200
Fax: 416-864-3255

Management and Staff

Don Morrison, Senior Managing Director
Francois Houde, Managing Director
Jim Orlando, Managing Director
John Young, Managing Director
Lisa Melchior, Managing Director
Mark Redman, Managing Director
Martin Day, Managing Director
Michael Graham, Senior Managing Director
Michael Lank, Managing Director
Phil Mauchel, Managing Director
Robert Hedges, Chief Financial Officer

Type of Firm

Private Equity Firm

Association Membership

Canadian Venture Capital Association

Project Preferences

Role in Financing:
Will function either as deal originator or investor in deals created by others

Type of Financing Preferred:
Fund of Funds
Leveraged Buyout
Mezzanine
Generalist PE
Special Situation

Size of Investments Considered:
Min Size of Investment Considered (000s): $50,000
Max Size of Investment Considered (000s): $500,000

Geographical Preferences

Canadian Preferences:
All Canada

International Preferences:
All International

Industry Preferences

In Communications prefer:
Communications and Media
Wireless Communications

In Computer Software prefer:
Software

In Consumer Related prefer:
Retail
Food/Beverage
Consumer Products
Education Related

In Industrial/Energy prefer:
Industrial Products

In Transportation prefer:
Transportation

In Financial Services prefer:
Financial Services

In Manufact. prefer:
Manufacturing

Additional Information

Year Founded: 1962
Current Activity Level : Actively seeking new investments

OMIDYAR NETWORK

1991 Broadway
Suite 200
Redwood City, CA USA 94063
Phone: 650-482-2500
Fax: 650-482-2525
E-mail: info@omidyar.net
Website: www.omidyar.net

Management and Staff

Matt Halprin, Partner
Matthew Bannick, Managing Partner
Pam Omidyar, Co-Founder
Sal Giambanco, Partner

Type of Firm

Private Equity Firm

Association Membership

National Venture Capital Association - USA (NVCA)

Project Preferences

Type of Financing Preferred:
Fund of Funds
Second Stage Financing
Balanced
Seed
First Stage Financing

Geographical Preferences

United States Preferences:
All U.S.

Industry Preferences

In Computer Software prefer:
Software

In Internet Specific prefer:
Internet

Additional Information

Name of Most Recent Fund: Omidyar Network Fund, LLC
Most Recent Fund Was Raised: 06/30/2004
Year Founded: 2004
Capital Under Management: $200,000,000
Current Activity Level : Actively seeking new investments

OMNI CAPITAL GROUP LLC

675 Route One South
New Jersey Technology Centre
North Brunswick, NJ USA 08902
Phone: 908-497-6807
Fax: 908-502-0424
E-mail: info@omnivc.com
Website: www.omnivc.com

Management and Staff

Arun Netravali, President
Bidyut Sen, Venture Partner
David Stahl, Partner
James Zucco, Venture Partner
Jon Harrington, Venture Partner

Type of Firm

Private Equity Firm

Association Membership

National Venture Capital Association - USA (NVCA)

Project Preferences

Type of Financing Preferred:
Startup

Additional Information

Name of Most Recent Fund: OmniCapital Fund, L.P.
Most Recent Fund Was Raised: 05/10/2006
Year Founded: 2003
Capital Under Management: $15,900,000
Current Activity Level : Actively seeking new investments

OMRON SILICON VALLEY (FKA: OMRON ADVANCED SYSTEMS, INC.)

3945 Freedom Circle
Suite 1070
Santa Clara, CA USA 95054
Phone: 408-970-1150
Fax: 408-727-5540
E-mail: info@oas.net
Website: www.oas.net

Management and Staff

Kimihiko Iwamura, President

Type of Firm

Corporate PE/Venture

Association Membership

National Venture Capital Association - USA (NVCA)

Additional Information

Year Founded: 2002
Current Activity Level : Actively seeking new investments

ONCAP INVESTMENT PARTNERS

161 Bay Street
48th Floor
Toronto, Canada MSJ 2S1
Phone: 416-214-4300
Fax: 416-214-6106
E-mail: info@oncap.com
Website: www.oncap.com

Management and Staff

Bethlehem Shiferaw, Vice President
Ed Rieckelman, Partner
Gregory Baylin, Partner
Jeremy Thompson, Partner
Mark MacTavish, Managing Director
Mark Gordon, Partner
Michael Lay, Managing Partner

Type of Firm

Corporate PE/Venture

Association Membership

Canadian Venture Capital Association

Project Preferences

Type of Financing Preferred:
Leveraged Buyout
Balanced
Management Buyouts
Acquisition

Size of Investments Considered:
Min Size of Investment Considered (000s): $20,000
Max Size of Investment Considered (000s): $80,000

Geographical Preferences

Canadian Preferences:
All Canada

Industry Preferences

In Semiconductor/Electr prefer:
Electronic Components

In Industrial/Energy prefer:
Environmental Related

In Manufact. prefer:
Manufacturing

Additional Information

Name of Most Recent Fund: ONCAP (US) II-A L.P.
Most Recent Fund Was Raised: 06/02/2006
Year Founded: 1999
Capital Under Management: $567,700,000
Current Activity Level : Actively seeking new investments
Method of Compensation: Return on invest. most important, but chg. closing fees, service fees, etc.

ONDERNEMEND TWENTE BV

Postbus 5504
Enschede, Netherlands 7500 GM
Phone: 31-53-484-9840
Fax: 31-53-484-9838
E-mail: info@tib-advies.nl
Website: info@tib-advies.nl

Type of Firm

Private Equity Firm

Additional Information

Current Activity Level : Actively seeking new investments

ONE ASSET MANAGEMENT, LTD.

24/F Siam Tower
989 Rama I Road, Patumwan
Bangkok, Thailand 10330
Phone: 66-2-659-8888
Fax: 66-2-6598-8601
Website: www.one-asset.com

Other Offices

3/F Central Pinklao
Bangkok, Thailand
Phone: 66-2-884-8340
Fax: 66-2-884-8164

Management and Staff

Wiwan Tharahirunchote, President

Type of Firm

Investment Management Firm

Project Preferences

Role in Financing:
Will function either as deal originator or investor in deals created by others

Type of Financing Preferred:
Early Stage
Balanced

Geographical Preferences

International Preferences:
Thailand
Asia

Industry Preferences

In Business Serv. prefer:
Services

In Manufact. prefer:
Manufacturing

Additional Information

Year Founded: 1992
Capital Under Management: $120,000,000
Current Activity Level : Actively seeking new investments
Method of Compensation: Return on invest. most important, but chg. closing fees, service fees, etc.

ONE EQUITY PARTNERS (FKA: BANC ONE VENTURE PARTNERS)

320 Park Avenue
18th Floor
New York, NY USA 10022
Phone: 212-277-1500
Fax: 212-277-1533
E-mail: oep.info@oneequity.com
Website: www.oneequity.com

Other Offices

Chase Tower, 21 South Clark Street
14th Floor
Chicago, IL USA 60670
Phone: 312-732-6281
Fax: 312-732-7495

One Equity Partners Europe
Taunusanlage 21

Frankfurt am Main, Germany 60325
Phone: 49-69-5060-747-0
Fax: 49-69-5060-747-40

Management and Staff

Andrew Dunn, Vice President
Christian Ahrens, Partner
Christoph Giulini, Partner
Christopher Von Hugo, Partner
Chuck Auster, Partner
Daniel Selmonosky, Partner
David Walsh, Managing Director
David Robakidze, Managing Director
Erin Hill, Chief Financial Officer
Ethan Ayer, Partner
Hans-Dieter Von Meibom, Partner
James Koven, Managing Director
Jamie Rubin, Partner
Jaques Nasser, Partner
Johann-Melchior Von Peter, Partner
Joseph Huffsmith, Vice President
Ken Brown, Partner
Lee Gardner, Partner
Michael O'Hara, Managing Director
Richard Cashin, Managing Partner
Rick Smith, Partner
Tarek Shoeb, Partner
Thomas Kichler, Partner
Tobias Reich, Vice President
William Wangerin, Partner

Type of Firm

Bank Affiliated

Project Preferences

Type of Financing Preferred:

Expansion
Early Stage
Mezzanine
Later Stage
Acquisition

Geographical Preferences

International Preferences:

All International

Industry Focus

(% based on actual investment)

Consumer Related	22.4%
Medical/Health	18.0%
Communications and Media	15.3%
Industrial/Energy	13.2%
Internet Specific	11.3%
Other Products	10.4%
Computer Software and Services	4.6%
Biotechnology	3.5%
Computer Hardware	1.2%

Additional Information

Year Founded: 2001
Capital Under Management: $5,000,000,000
Current Activity Level : Actively seeking new investments

ONEX CORPORATION

161 Bay Street, 49th Floor
P.O. Box 700
Toronto, Canada M5J 2S1
Phone: 416-362-7711
Fax: 416-362-5765
Website: www.onex.com

Other Offices

712 Fifth Avenue
40th Floor
New York, NY USA 10019
Phone: 212-582-2211

Management and Staff

Andrew Sheiner, Managing Director
Anthony Munk, Managing Director
Christopher Govan, Vice President
Gerald Schwartz, Chairman & CEO
Mark Hilson, Managing Director
Nigel Wright, Managing Director
Robert Le Blanc, Managing Director
Seth Mersky, Managing Director
Timothy Duncanson, Managing Director

Type of Firm

Corporate PE/Venture

Project Preferences

Role in Financing:

Prefer role as deal originator but will also invest in deals created by others

Type of Financing Preferred:

Leveraged Buyout
Control-block Purchases
Special Situation

Size of Investments Considered:

Min Size of Investment Considered (000s): $10,000
Max Size of Investment Considered: No Limit

Geographical Preferences

United States Preferences:

All U.S.

Canadian Preferences:

All Canada

International Preferences:

Italy
United Kingdom
China
Mexico
Spain
Australia
Germany
France

Industry Preferences

In Medical/Health prefer:

Health Services

In Industrial/Energy prefer:

Environmental Related

In Manufact. prefer:

Manufacturing

Additional Information

Name of Most Recent Fund: Onex Corporation
Most Recent Fund Was Raised: 06/01/1986
Year Founded: 1983
Capital Under Management: $420,000,000
Current Activity Level : Actively seeking new investments
Method of Compensation: Return on invest. most important, but chg. closing fees, service fees, etc.

ONONDAGA VENTURE CAPITAL FUND, INC.

241 West Fayette Street
Syracuse, NY USA 13202
Phone: 315-478-0157
Fax: 315-478-0158
Website: www.ovcfund.com

Management and Staff

Michael Schattner, President

Type of Firm

Private Equity Firm

Project Preferences

Role in Financing:

Will function either as deal originator or investor in deals created by others

Type of Financing Preferred:

Second Stage Financing
Early Stage
Expansion

Size of Investments Considered:

Min Size of Investment Considered (000s): $50
Max Size of Investment Considered (000s): $300

Geographical Preferences

United States Preferences:

Northeast

Industry Preferences

In Communications prefer:

Commercial Communications
Wireless Communications

In Computer Software prefer:

Software

In Semiconductor/Electr prefer:

Electronic Components
Sensors

In Biotechnology prefer:

Industrial Biotechnology
Biosensors

In Medical/Health prefer:

Medical Diagnostics
Drug/Equipmt Delivery
Medical Products

Disposable Med. Products
Health Services

In Consumer Related prefer:
Consumer

In Manufact. prefer:
Manufacturing

In Agr/Forestr/Fish prefer:
Agriculture related

Additional Information
Name of Most Recent Fund: Onondaga Venture Capital
Most Recent Fund Was Raised: 06/01/1985
Year Founded: 1985
Capital Under Management: $2,500,000
Current Activity Level : Actively seeking new investments
Method of Compensation: Return on invest. most important, but chg. closing fees, service fees, etc.

ONPOINT TECHNOLOGIES
485 North Keller Road
Suite 100
Maitland, FL USA 32751
Phone: 407-838-1400
Fax: 407-659-0447
E-mail: info@onpoint.us
Website: www.onpoint.us

Management and Staff
Dennis Behm, Principal
Henry Huey, Principal
Jason Rottenberg, Managing Director
John Trbovich, Principal

Type of Firm
Government Affiliated Program

Project Preferences

Role in Financing:
Will function either as deal originator or investor in deals created by others

Type of Financing Preferred:
Early Stage

Size of Investments Considered:
Min Size of Investment Considered (000s): $500
Max Size of Investment Considered (000s): $2,500

Industry Preferences

In Semiconductor/Electr prefer:
Electronic Components

Industrial/Energy prefer:
Energy
Alternative Energy

Additional Information
Year Founded: 2003
Capital Under Management: $48,000,000
Current Activity Level : Actively seeking new investments
Method of Compensation: Return on investment is of primary concern, do not charge fees

---

ONSET VENTURES
2400 Sand Hill Road
Suite 150
Menlo Park, CA USA 94025
Phone: 650-529-0700
Fax: 650-529-0777
E-mail: menlopark@onset.com
Website: www.onset.com

Management and Staff
David Lane, General Partner
John Ryan, Partner
Leslie Bottorff, General Partner
Raman Khanna, General Partner
Richard Schell, Venture Partner
Robert Kuhling, General Partner
Shomit Ghose, Venture Partner
Stephen Bernardez, Principal
Steve LaPorte, Venture Partner
Susan Mason, General Partner
Terry Opdendyk, General Partner

Type of Firm
Private Equity Firm

Association Membership
Western Association of Venture Capitalists (WAVC)
National Venture Capital Association - USA (NVCA)

Project Preferences

Role in Financing:
Prefer role as deal originator but will also invest in deals created by others

Type of Financing Preferred:
Early Stage
Seed

Size of Investments Considered:
Min Size of Investment Considered (000s): $1,000
Max Size of Investment Considered (000s): $12,000

Geographical Preferences

United States Preferences:
West Coast
All U.S.

Industry Focus
(% based on actual investment)

Medical/Health	32.4%
Computer Software and Services	26.2%
Communications and Media	11.8%
Internet Specific	9.7%
Biotechnology	5.9%
Other Products	5.7%
Semiconductors/Other Elect.	3.3%
Computer Hardware	3.1%
Industrial/Energy	1.7%

Additional Information
Name of Most Recent Fund: ONSET VI, L.P.
Most Recent Fund Was Raised: 10/27/2008
Year Founded: 1984
Capital Under Management: $700,000,000
Current Activity Level : Actively seeking new investments
Method of Compensation: Return on investment is of primary concern, do not charge fees

---

ONTARIO CAPITAL GROWTH CORPORATION
56 Wellesley Street West
18th Floor
Toronto, Canada M7A 2E7
Phone: 416-325-6874
Fax: 416-326-9654
Website: www.ocgc.gov.on.ca

Type of Firm
Government Affiliated Program

Project Preferences

Type of Financing Preferred:
Early Stage

Geographical Preferences

Canadian Preferences:
Ontario

Industry Preferences

In Other prefer:
Environment Responsible

Additional Information
Year Founded: 2008
Capital Under Management: $200,800,000
Current Activity Level : Actively seeking new investments

ONTARIO CENTRES OF EXCELLENCE
156 Front Street West
Suite 200
Toronto, Canada M5J2L6
Phone: 416-861-1092
Fax: 416-971-7164
Website: www.oce-ontario.org

Management and Staff
Bryan Kanarens, Managing Director

Type of Firm
Private Equity Firm

Project Preferences

Type of Financing Preferred:
Early Stage
Seed
Startup

Geographical Preferences

Canadian Preferences:
Ontario

Additional Information

Year Founded: 2009
Current Activity Level : Actively seeking new investments

ONTARIO TEACHERS' PENSION PLAN

5650 Yonge Street
Suite 500
North York Ontario, Canada M2M 4H5
Phone: 416-228-5900
Fax: 416-730-5349
E-mail: inquiry@otpp.com
Website: www.otpp.com
Other Offices
Curzon Street
4th Floor, Leconfield house
London, United Kingdom W1J 5JA
Phone: 44 20 7659 4450

Management and Staff

Barbara Zvan, Vice President
Dan Houle, Vice President
David McGraw, Chief Financial Officer
Dean Metcalf, Vice President
John Brennan, Vice President
Lee Sienna, Vice President
Peter Maher, Vice President
Phil Nichols, Vice President
Ron Lepin, Vice President
Ronald Mock, Vice President
Rosemary Zigrossi, Vice President
Wayne Kozun, Vice President
Zev Frishman, Vice President

Type of Firm

Endowment, Foundation or Pension Fund
Association Membership
Canadian Venture Capital Association

Project Preferences

Type of Financing Preferred:
Leveraged Buyout
Expansion
Balanced
Later Stage
Seed
Other
Management Buyouts
Acquisition
Startup

Size of Investments Considered:
Min Size of Investment Considered (000s): $5,000
Max Size of Investment Considered (000s): $30,000

Geographical Preferences

United States Preferences:
All U.S.

Canadian Preferences:
All Canada
Quebec
Ontario

International Preferences:
Europe
Asia

Industry Preferences

In Communications prefer:
Telecommunications

In Computer Other prefer:
Computer Related

In Biotechnology prefer:
Biotechnology

Additional Information

Year Founded: 1917
Current Activity Level : Actively seeking new investments

ONTARIO VENTURE CAPITAL FUND INC.

TD Waterhouse Tower
79 Wellington Strt. W, 6th Flr
Toronto, Canada M5K 1A2
Phone: 866-831-2343
Fax: 416-983-9763
E-mail: ovcf@tdcapital.com
Website: www.ovcf.com

Type of Firm

Private Equity Firm

Additional Information

Year Founded: 2008
Current Activity Level : Actively seeking new investments

ONYX CAPITAL ADVISORS LLC

660 Woodward
Suite 2400
Detroit, MI USA 48226
Phone: 313-965-0186
Fax: 313-965-0173
E-mail: info@onyxcapitaladvisors.com
Website: www.onyxcapitaladvisors.com

Management and Staff

LaRoy Williams, Principal
Roy Dixon, Founding Partner

Type of Firm

Private Equity Firm

Project Preferences

Type of Financing Preferred:
Leveraged Buyout

Geographical Preferences

United States Preferences:
Midwest
Southeast

Canadian Preferences:
All Canada

Industry Preferences

In Consumer Related prefer:
Consumer

In Business Serv. prefer:
Services
Distribution

In Manufact. prefer:
Manufacturing

Additional Information

Year Founded: 2009
Current Activity Level : Actively seeking new investments

OOST EUROPA PARTICIPATIES BV (AKA MIDDLE EUROPE INVESTMENTS)

Zwiepseweg 27
GM Lochem, Netherlands 7241
Phone: 31-573-289888
Fax: 31-573-289899
E-mail: info@mei.nl
Website: www.mei.nl

Type of Firm

Private Equity Firm

Additional Information

Year Founded: 2005
Capital Under Management: $42,900,000
Current Activity Level : Actively seeking new investments

OPEN PRAIRIE VENTURES

400 East Jefferson
Effingham, IL USA 62401
Phone: 217-347-1000
Fax: 217-347-1001
E-mail: inquire@openprairie.com
Website: www.openprairie.com

Other Offices

18001 West 100th Street
Suite 125

Olathe, KS USA 66061
Phone: 913-317-1548
Fax: 913-317-1505

2001 South First Street
Suite 209A
Champaign, IL USA 61820
Phone: 217-337-7700
Fax: 217-347-1001

Management and Staff

Michael Peck, General Partner

Type of Firm

Private Equity Firm

Association Membership

National Venture Capital Association - USA (NVCA)

Project Preferences

Role in Financing:

Will function either as deal originator or investor in deals created by others

Type of Financing Preferred:

Early Stage
Seed
Later Stage

Geographical Preferences

United States Preferences:

Midwest

Industry Preferences

In Communications prefer:

Telecommunications
Wireless Communications
Data Communications

In Computer Software prefer:

Applications Software

In Semiconductor/Electr prefer:

Electronics
Semiconductor
Micro-Processing
Circuit Boards
Component Testing Equipmt
Fiber Optics

In Biotechnology prefer:

Biotechnology
Human Biotechnology
Agricultural/Animal Bio.
Biosensors

In Medical/Health prefer:

Drug/Equipmt Delivery
Medical Products
Pharmaceuticals

Additional Information

Name of Most Recent Fund: Open Prairie Ventures II, L.P.
Most Recent Fund Was Raised: 01/04/2008
Year Founded: 2000
Capital Under Management: $63,000,000
Current Activity Level : Actively seeking new investments
Method of Compensation: Return on invest. most important, but chg. closing fees, service fees, etc.

OPENGATE CAPITAL

8383 Wilshire Boulevard
Suite 950
Beverly Hills, CA USA 90211
Phone: 310-432-7000
Fax: 310-691-2119
Website: www.opengatecapital.com

Other Offices

41 rue boissy d'anglas
Paris, France 75008
Phone: 33-1-40-06-0158
Fax: 33-1-40-06-0389

Management and Staff

Jay Yook, Partner
Julien Lagreze, Partner

Type of Firm

Private Equity Firm

Project Preferences

Type of Financing Preferred:

Leveraged Buyout
Management Buyouts
Special Situation

Geographical Preferences

International Preferences:

All International

Additional Information

Year Founded: 2005
Current Activity Level : Actively seeking new investments

OPENVIEW VENTURE PARTNERS

303 Congress Street
Seventh Floor
Boston, MA USA 02210
Phone: 617-478-7500
Fax: 617-478-7501
Website: www.openviewpartners.com

Management and Staff

Adam Marcus, Principal
Bonnie Lewis, Chief Financial Officer
Brian Zimmerman, Principal
Cynthia Mignogna, Principal
Firas Raouf, Venture Partner
George Roberts, Venture Partner
Kamal Arafeh, Venture Partner
Mark Barry, Venture Partner
Thomas Charlton, Venture Partner

Type of Firm

Private Equity Firm

Project Preferences

Role in Financing:

Prefer role as deal originator

Type of Financing Preferred:

Expansion

Geographical Preferences

United States Preferences:

All U.S.

International Preferences:

Latin America
Europe
Pacific
Asia

Industry Preferences

In Computer Software prefer:

Software
Systems Software
Applications Software

In Internet Specific prefer:

E-Commerce Technology
Internet

Additional Information

Name of Most Recent Fund: OpenView Venture Partners II, L.P.
Most Recent Fund Was Raised: 09/29/2008
Year Founded: 2006
Capital Under Management: $227,800,000
Current Activity Level : Actively seeking new investments
Method of Compensation: Return on investment is of primary concern, do not charge fees

---

OPERA MANAGEMENT SA (AKA: OPERA SGR)

10 Corso Matteotti
Milan, Italy 20121
Phone: 39-2-3030-0300
Fax: 39-02-3030-0303
E-mail: t.dadda@lucens.it
Website: www.opera-privatequity.lu

Other Offices

Lucens - Adamas
10 Corso Matteotti
Milan, Italy
Phone: 39-2-3030-0300
Fax: 39-02-3030-0303

Type of Firm

Corporate PE/Venture

Project Preferences

Type of Financing Preferred:

Expansion

Geographical Preferences

International Preferences:
Italy
Europe

Industry Preferences

In Consumer Related prefer:
Consumer
Retail
Food/Beverage
Consumer Products
Consumer Services

In Business Serv. prefer:
Services

Additional Information

Year Founded: 2000
Current Activity Level : Actively seeking new investments

OPM BV

Postbus 241
Enschede, Netherlands 7500 AE
Phone: 53-480-5858
Fax: 53-432-3437
E-mail: informatie@opm.nl
Website: www.opm.nl

Type of Firm

Bank Affiliated

Project Preferences

Type of Financing Preferred:
Expansion

Geographical Preferences

International Preferences:
Netherlands
Europe

Additional Information

Year Founded: 2000
Current Activity Level : Actively seeking new investments

OPPENHEIMER

125 Broad Street
New York, NY USA 10004
Phone: 212-668-8000
Fax: 800-221-5588
E-mail: info@opco.com
Website: www.opco.com

Type of Firm

Private Equity Firm

Additional Information

Year Founded: 1950
Current Activity Level : Actively seeking new investments

OPPORTUNITY CAPITAL PARTNERS

12201 Walnut Avenue
Suite 210
Fremont, CA USA 94538
Phone: 510-795-7000
Fax: 510-494-5439
E-mail: info@opportunitycapitalpartners.com
Website: www.ocpcapital.com

Management and Staff

Anita Stephens, General Partner
J. Peter Thompson, Managing Partner
Lewis Byrd, General Partner

Type of Firm

SBIC

Association Membership

Natl Assoc of Investment Cos. (NAIC)
Natl Assoc of Small Bus. Inv. Co (NASBIC)

Project Preferences

Role in Financing:
Prefer role as deal originator but will also invest in deals created by others

Type of Financing Preferred:
Second Stage Financing
Leveraged Buyout
Mezzanine
Balanced
Later Stage
Industry Rollups

Size of Investments Considered:
Min Size of Investment Considered (000s): $2,000
Max Size of Investment Considered (000s): $8,000

Geographical Preferences

United States Preferences:
West Coast
California

Industry Focus

(% based on actual investment)	
Communications and Media	46.4%
Internet Specific	26.6%
Computer Software and Services	12.4%
Consumer Related	4.2%
Medical/Health	3.5%
Industrial/Energy	3.5%
Other Products	1.5%
Computer Hardware	1.3%
Semiconductors/Other Elect.	0.6%

Additional Information

Name of Most Recent Fund: Opportunity Capital Partners IV, L.P.
Most Recent Fund Was Raised: 06/01/2000
Year Founded: 1970
Capital Under Management: $135,000,000
Current Activity Level : Actively seeking new investments
Method of Compensation: Return on invest. most important, but chg. closing fees, service fees, etc.

OPUS CAPITAL

2730 Sand Hill Road
Suite 150
Menlo Park, CA USA 94025
Phone: 650-543-2900
Fax: 650-561-9570
E-mail: contact@opuscapital.com
Website: www.opuscapital.com

Management and Staff

Bob Borchers, General Partner
Carl Showalter, General Partner
Carol Pereira, Chief Financial Officer
Dan Avida, General Partner
Daniel Phelps, General Partner
Gill Cogan, General Partner
Isaac Applbaum, Partner
Ken Elefant, General Partner
Serge Plotkin, Venture Partner

Type of Firm

Private Equity Firm

Association Membership

Illinois Venture Capital Association

Project Preferences

Type of Financing Preferred:
Early Stage
Seed

Geographical Preferences

United States Preferences:
All U.S.

International Preferences:
Israel

Additional Information

Name of Most Recent Fund: Opus Capital Venture Partners, L.P.
Most Recent Fund Was Raised: 06/06/2006
Year Founded: 1963
Capital Under Management: $287,500,000
Current Activity Level : Actively seeking new investments

OPUS ELECTRA & PARTNERS

Dr. Eduardo S. Aranha 387/102
Sao Paulo, Brazil 04543-121
Phone: 55-11-3323-8000
Fax: 55-11-3323-8040
Website: www.opuselectra.com

Other Offices

405 Park Avenue
Suite 1104

New York, NY USA 10022
Phone: 212-871-8500
Fax: 212-871-8505

Management and Staff

Eduardo Plass, President, Founder
Fred Vinton, Partner
Randolph Freiberg, Managing Director

Type of Firm

Private Equity Firm

Association Membership

Brazilian Venture Capital Association (ABCR)

Project Preferences

Type of Financing Preferred:
Leveraged Buyout
Later Stage

Geographical Preferences

International Preferences:
Latin America

Additional Information

Year Founded: 1998
Capital Under Management: $220,000,000
Current Activity Level : Actively seeking new investments

ORADELL CAPITAL

9-b, Dmitrovskoe shosse
Moscow, Russia 127434
Phone: 7-495-967-8000
Fax: 7-495-967-8099
Website: www.oradellcapital.com

Management and Staff

Mikhail Luyanchuk, Managing Director

Type of Firm

Private Equity Firm

Project Preferences

Type of Financing Preferred:
Start-up Financing
Balanced

Geographical Preferences

International Preferences:
Europe

Industry Preferences

In Communications prefer:
Communications and Media

In Internet Specific prefer:
Internet

In Computer Other prefer:
Computer Related

In Semiconductor/Electr prefer:
Sensors

Additional Information

Year Founded: 1999
Current Activity Level : Actively seeking new investments

ORANGE VENTURES

50 George Street
London, United Kingdom W1U 7DZ
Phone: 44-870-376-8888
Fax: 44-207-984-1601
Website: www.orangeventures.com

Other Offices

51 JFK Parkway
1st Floor West
Short Hills, NJ USA 07078
Phone: 917-414-0021
Fax: 928-244-0379

One Market Plaza
Spear Tower, 35th Floor
San Francisco, CA USA 94105
Phone: 415-293-8300
Fax: 415-293-7719

175 Second Street
Cambridge, MA USA 02142
Phone: 617-995-8000
Fax: 617-995-8001

Management and Staff

Mateusz (Mati) Szeszkowski, Principal
Michael Dolbec, General Partner
Rich Miner, Venture Partner

Type of Firm

Corporate PE/Venture

Project Preferences

Type of Financing Preferred:
Early Stage
Balanced
Startup

Size of Investments Considered:
Min Size of Investment Considered (000s): $707
Max Size of Investment Considered (000s): $14,147

Geographical Preferences

International Preferences:
Ireland
United Kingdom
Scandanavia/Nordic Region
Israel

Industry Preferences

In Communications prefer:
Communications and Media

Additional Information

Year Founded: 2000
Capital Under Management: $225,000,000
Current Activity Level : Actively seeking new investments

ORANJE-NASSAU PARTICIPATIES BV

Postbus 22885
Amsterdam, Netherlands 1100 DJ
Phone: 31-20- 567-7111
Fax: 31-20-567-7170
E-mail: ong@oranje-nassau.com
Website: www.oranje-nassau.com

Type of Firm

Private Equity Firm

Project Preferences

Type of Financing Preferred:
Expansion
Balanced
Acquisition

Geographical Preferences

International Preferences:
Netherlands
Europe
Middle East
Belgium
Africa

Industry Preferences

In Industrial/Energy prefer:
Energy
Oil and Gas Exploration
Oil & Gas Drilling,Explor

In Financial Services prefer:
Real Estate

Additional Information

Year Founded: 1893
Current Activity Level : Actively seeking new investments

ORBE INVESTIMENTOS E PARTICIPACOES LTDA.

R. Wisard, 308 / sala 4
Vila Madalena
Sao Paulo, Brazil 05434-000
Phone: 11-3819-1828
Fax: 11-3819-5082
E-mail: orbe@orbeinvestimentos.com
Website: www.orbeinvestimentos.com

Type of Firm

Private Equity Firm

Association Membership

Brazilian Venture Capital Association (ABCR)

Project Preferences

Type of Financing Preferred:

Startup

Geographical Preferences

International Preferences:

Brazil

Industry Preferences

In Biotechnology prefer:

Agricultural/Animal Bio.

In Agr/Forestr/Fish prefer:

Agribusiness
Agriculture related

Additional Information

Year Founded: 2002
Current Activity Level : Actively seeking new investments

ORBIMED ADVISORS LLC

767 Third Avenue
30th Floor
New York, NY USA 10017
Phone: 212-739-6400
Fax: 212-739-6444
E-mail: info@orbimed.com
Website: www.orbimed.com

Other Offices

One Market Street
Spear Tower, Suite 3611
San Francisco, CA USA 94105
Phone: 415-293-8238
Fax: 415-373-9200

Management and Staff

Carl Gordon, General Partner
Jonathan Silverstein, General Partner
Klaus Veitinger, Venture Partner
Michael Sheffery, General Partner
Rishi Gupta, Principal
Robert Glassman, Partner
Samuel Isaly, Managing Partner
Samuel Wertheimer, Partner
Sven Borho, General Partner
Thomas Schuetz, Venture Partner
W. Carter Neild, General Partner

Type of Firm

Private Equity Firm

Project Preferences

Role in Financing:

Prefer role as deal originator but will also invest in deals created by others

Type of Financing Preferred:

Second Stage Financing
Generalist PE
Expansion
Mezzanine
Research and Development
Public Companies
Turnaround
Later Stage
Open Market
Management Buyouts
First Stage Financing
Acquisition
Private Placement
Industry Rollups
Special Situation
Startup
Recapitalizations
Distressed Debt

Size of Investments Considered:

Min Size of Investment Considered (000s): $2,000
Max Size of Investment Considered (000s): $50,000

Geographical Preferences

United States Preferences:

Mid Atlantic
Northwest
Southeast
Hawaii
Southern California
Northern California
Alaska
New York
Southwest

International Preferences:

India
Europe
Israel
Asia

Industry Focus

(% based on actual investment)

Medical/Health	50.0%
Biotechnology	44.1%
Computer Software and Services	5.9%

Additional Information

Name of Most Recent Fund: Caduceus Private Investments III, L.P.
Most Recent Fund Was Raised: 04/27/2006
Year Founded: 1989
Capital Under Management: $5,000,000,000
Current Activity Level : Actively seeking new investments
Method of Compensation: Return on investment is of primary concern, do not charge fees

---

ORBITEX INC.

Freigutstrasse 27
P.O. Box 452
Zurich, Switzerland 8027
Phone: 411-208-9010
Fax: 411-208-1711
E-mail: marketing@orbitex.ch
Website: www.orbitex.ch

Type of Firm

Private Equity Firm

Additional Information

Year Founded: 2009
Current Activity Level : Actively seeking new investments

ORCHARD FIRST SOURCE

2850 West Golf Road
5th Floor
Rolling Meadows, IL USA 60008
Phone: 847-734-2000
Fax: 847-734-7910
Website: www.fsfi.com

Management and Staff

David Quon, Managing Director
Kathi Inorio, Senior Managing Director

Type of Firm

Private Equity Advisor or Fund of Funds

Project Preferences

Size of Investments Considered:

Min Size of Investment Considered (000s): $10,000
Max Size of Investment Considered (000s): $86,000

Additional Information

Year Founded: 2000
Current Activity Level : Actively seeking new investments

ORCHID ASIA GROUP MANAGEMENT, LTD.

Suite 6110, 61/F, The Center
99 Queen's Road
Central, Hong Kong
Phone: 852-2115-8810
Fax: 852-2115-8120
E-mail: info@orchidasia.com
Website: www.orchidasia.com

Other Offices

3-15 Linhexi Road, Tianhe District
Suite 1002, China Shine Plaza
Guangzhou, China 510610
Phone: 86-20-3839-6155
Fax: 86-20-3839-6126

25/F, Tower 2, China Cntrl Place Office
No. 79 Jianguo Road, Chaoyang District
Beijing, China 100025
Phone: 86-10-6598-9160
Fax: 86-10-6598-9166

Suite 2706, Shanghai Kerry Centre
1515 Nanjing Road West
Shanghai, China 200040
Phone: 86-21-5298-6222
Fax: 86-21-5298-5210

555 California Street
Suite 5180
San Francisco, CA USA 94104
Phone: 1-415-875-5600
Fax: 1-415-875-5609

Management and Staff

Aaron Wen, Vice President
Gabriel Li, Managing Director
Peter Joost, President, Founder
Steven Kwok, Partner

Type of Firm

Private Equity Firm

Project Preferences

Role in Financing:
Prefer role as deal originator

Financing Preferred:
Expansion

Geographical Preferences

International Preferences:
China
Asia

Industry Preferences

In Consumer Related prefer:
Consumer
Consumer Products
Consumer Services

Additional Information

Name of Most Recent Fund: Orchid Asia III, LP
Most Recent Fund Was Raised: 01/11/2006
Year Founded: 1997
Capital Under Management: $700,000,000
Current Activity Level : Actively seeking new investments

ORESA VENTURES, S.A.

Al. Ujazdowskie 41
Warsaw, Poland 00-540
Phone: 48-22-3195-360
Fax: 48-22-3195-633
Website: www.oresaventures.com

Other Offices

Waterloo Office Park
Building O, Dreve Richelle 161
Waterloo, Belgium B-1410
Phone: 32-2-357-5577
Fax: 32-2-357-5505

Union International Center
11 Ion Campineanu St
Bucharest 1, Romania 010031
Phone: 40-21-312-2606
Fax: 40-21-312-2679
Management and Staff
Erik Hallgren, Partner

Type of Firm

Private Equity Firm

Association Membership

European Private Equity and Venture Capital Assoc.

Project Preferences

Role in Financing:
Prefer role as deal originator but will also invest in deals created by others

Type of Financing Preferred:
Second Stage Financing
Start-up Financing
First Stage Financing
Startup

Size of Investments Considered:
Min Size of Investment Considered (000s): $4,800
Max Size of Investment Considered: No Limit

Geographical Preferences

International Preferences:
Central Europe
Poland
Eastern Europe
Romania

Industry Preferences

In Biotechnology prefer:
Biotechnology

In Medical/Health prefer:
Medical/Health
Medical Diagnostics

In Consumer Related prefer:
Consumer
Consumer Products
Education Related

In Financial Services prefer:
Financial Services

In Business Serv. prefer:
Distribution

Additional Information

Year Founded: 1996
Capital Under Management: $75,000,000
Current Activity Level : Actively seeking new investments
Method of Compensation: Return on investment is of primary concern, do not charge fees

---

ORESUND-HEALTHCARE A/S

Science Park Scion-DTU
Diplomvej
Kgs. Lingby, Denmark 2800
Phone: 45-3314-9066
Fax: 45-3314-6705
E-mail: info@oresund-healthcare.com
Website: www.oresund-healthcare.com

Other Offices

Ideon
Lund, Sweden 223 70
Phone: 46-46-286-3760

Management and Staff

Ejvind Sandal, Partner
Hakan Nelson, Partner
Jorgen Gronlund Nielsen, Partner
Lars Vedin, Partner
Niels Mengel, Chief Executive Officer
Thomas Gronberg, Chief Operating Officer

Type of Firm

Private Equity Firm

Project Preferences

Type of Financing Preferred:
Early Stage
Expansion
Startup

Geographical Preferences

International Preferences:
Europe

Industry Preferences

In Biotechnology prefer:
Biotechnology

In Medical/Health prefer:
Medical/Health
Medical Diagnostics
Medical Products
Pharmaceuticals

Additional Information

Year Founded: 2000
Capital Under Management: $14,600,000
Current Activity Level : Actively seeking new investments

ORFIMAR

59, avenue Marceau
Paris, France 75116
Phone: 33-1-4723-0020
Fax: 33-1-4720-3978
E-mail: orfim@free.fr

Management and Staff

Sebastien Picciotto, President

Type of Firm

Private Equity Firm

Association Membership

French Venture Capital Association (AFIC)

Project Preferences

Type of Financing Preferred:
Balanced

Geographical Preferences

International Preferences:
France

Additional Information

Year Founded: 2002
Current Activity Level : Actively seeking new investments

ORGONE CAPITAL

1140 Edmer Avenue
Oak Park, IL USA 60302
Phone: 773-858-9263
Website: www.orgonecapital.com

Other Offices

Bosque de Acacias 61-B
Bosques de las Lomas, Mexico DF- 11700
Phone: 52-55-3098-2908

Management and Staff

Rafael Escobar, Founder

Type of Firm

Private Equity Firm

Project Preferences

Type of Financing Preferred:
Later Stage

Additional Information

Year Founded: 2009
Current Activity Level : Actively seeking new investments

ORICA CAPITAL CO., LTD.

Room 1708, Rongchao Jinmao
Jintian Road, Futian District
Shenzhen, China
Phone: 86-755-83515166
Fax: 86-755-82789371
Website: www.orica.com.cn

Management and Staff

Zhidong Kan, President

Type of Firm

Private Equity Firm

Association Membership

Shenzhen Venture Capital Association

Project Preferences

Type of Financing Preferred:
Balanced

Geographical Preferences

International Preferences:
China

Industry Preferences

In Biotechnology prefer:
Biotechnology

In Medical/Health prefer:
Medical/Health
Pharmaceuticals

In Industrial/Energy prefer:
Alternative Energy
Coal Related
Machinery

In Transportation prefer:
Transportation

In Business Serv. prefer:
Media

In Agr/Forestr/Fish prefer:
Mining and Minerals

Additional Information

Year Founded: 2005
Capital Under Management: $85,400,000
Current Activity Level : Actively seeking new investments

ORIENT GLOBAL

Level 46, UOB Plaza 1
80 Raffles Place
Singapore, Singapore 048624
Phone: 65-6210-5555
Fax: 65-6210-5556
E-mail: info@orientglobal.com
Website: www.orientglobal.com

Other Offices

Level 30
30 Street Mary Axe
London, United Kingdom EC3A 8BF
Phone: 44-207-2200600
Fax: 44-207-220-0601

Type of Firm

Investment Management Firm

Project Preferences

Type of Financing Preferred:
Balanced

Geographical Preferences

International Preferences:
Latin America
Eastern Europe
Asia
Africa

Additional Information

Year Founded: 2006
Current Activity Level : Actively seeking new investments

ORIENTEQ CAPITAL

Fabianinkatu 4 B
Helsinki, Finland 00130
Phone: 358-9-6124-0060
Website: www.orienteq.com

Type of Firm

Private Equity Firm

Association Membership

European Private Equity and Venture Capital Assoc.

Project Preferences

Type of Financing Preferred:
Balanced

Geographical Preferences

International Preferences:
Thailand
Finland

Industry Preferences

In Internet Specific prefer:
E-Commerce Technology

Additional Information

Year Founded: 2005
Capital Under Management: $24,000,000
Current Activity Level : Actively seeking new investments

ORIGIN PARTNERS

1200 Route 22 East
Suite 2000
Bridgewater, NJ USA 08807
Phone: 908-595-9100
Fax: 908-595-9763
E-mail: origin@originpartners.com
Website: www.originpartners.com

Other Offices

8007 Two Coves
Austin, TX USA 78730
Phone: 512-343-0484
Fax: 512-343-1740

One Apple Hill
Suite 316
Natick, MA USA 01760
Phone: 508-655-9977
Fax: 508-655-8955

Management and Staff

James Hutchens, Managing Director
Marc Yagjian, Managing Director

Type of Firm

Private Equity Firm

Project Preferences

Role in Financing:
Prefer role as deal originator but will also invest in deals created by others

Type of Financing Preferred:
Early Stage
Start-up Financing
Seed
First Stage Financing
Startup

Size of Investments Considered:
Min Size of Investment Considered (000s): $500
Max Size of Investment Considered (000s): $2,000

Geographical Preferences

United States Preferences:
Northeast
Southwest

Industry Preferences

In Communications prefer:
Communications and Media
Commercial Communications
Telecommunications
Wireless Communications
Data Communications

In Computer Software prefer:
Software
Systems Software
Applications Software

In Internet Specific prefer:
Internet

In Semiconductor/Electr prefer:
Semiconductor
Sensors

In Medical/Health prefer:
Medical Products

Additional Information
Name of Most Recent Fund: Origin Partners II, Limited Partnership
Most Recent Fund Was Raised: 03/03/2005
Year Founded: 1999
Capital Under Management: $55,000,000
Current Activity Level : Actively seeking new investments
Method of Compensation: Return on investment is of primary concern, do not charge fees

---

ORIGIN VENTURES, LLC
1033 Skokie Boulevard
Suite 430
Northbrook, IL USA 60062
Phone: 847-919-3546
Fax: 847-919-3547
E-mail: inquire@originventures.com
Website: www.originventures.com

Management and Staff
Bruce Barron, Principal
Steven Miller, Principal

Type of Firm
Private Equity Firm

Association Membership
Illinois Venture Capital Association

Project Preferences

Role in Financing:
Will function either as deal originator or investor in deals created by others

Type of Financing Preferred:
Early Stage

Size of Investments Considered:
Min Size of Investment Considered (000s): $250
Max Size of Investment Considered (000s): $1,000

Geographical Preferences

United States Preferences:
Midwest

Industry Preferences

In Internet Specific prefer:
Internet
Ecommerce
Web Aggregration/Portals

In Biotechnology prefer:
Human Biotechnology

In Medical/Health prefer:
Medical Diagnostics

In Financial Services prefer:
Insurance

Additional Information
Name of Most Recent Fund: Origin Ventures II, L.P.
Most Recent Fund Was Raised: 02/11/2005
Year Founded: 1999
Capital Under Management: $15,200,000
Current Activity Level : Actively seeking new investments
Method of Compensation: Return on investment is of primary concern, do not charge fees

---

ORIGINATE VENTURES
205 Webster Street
Bethlehem, PA USA 18015
Phone: 610-866-5588
Fax: 610-866-5688
Website: www.originateventures.com

Management and Staff
Eric Arnson, Partner
Mike Gausling, Managing Partner

Type of Firm
Private Equity Firm

Association Membership
National Venture Capital Association - USA (NVCA)

Project Preferences

Type of Financing Preferred:
Second Stage Financing
Early Stage
Expansion
Turnaround
Management Buyouts
Special Situation
Private Placement

Geographical Preferences

United States Preferences:
Mid Atlantic
Pennsylvania
Northeast

Industry Preferences

In Communications prefer:
Telecommunications

In Computer Software prefer:
Software
Systems Software
Applications Software

In Internet Specific prefer:
E-Commerce Technology
Internet
Web Aggregration/Portals

In Semiconductor/Electr prefer:
Fiber Optics

In Medical/Health prefer:
Medical/Health
Medical Diagnostics
Diagnostic Services
Diagnostic Test Products
Medical Therapeutics
Drug/Equipmt Delivery
Medical Products
Disposable Med. Products
Health Services

In Consumer Related prefer:
Consumer
Consumer Products

In Business Serv. prefer:
Distribution

Additional Information
Name of Most Recent Fund: Originate Growth Fund I
Most Recent Fund Was Raised: 02/01/2007
Year Founded: 2007
Capital Under Management: $46,200,000
Current Activity Level : Actively seeking new investments

ORIGO SINO-INDIA PLC
26F, Building A, SOHO Shangdu
No. 9 Dongdaqiao Road
Beijing, China 100020

Phone: 86-10-5900-2770
Fax: 86-10-5900-2760
E-mail: contact@origoplc.com
Website: www.origoplc.com

Management and Staff

Alan Matthews, Managing Director
Lin Lou, Chief Financial Officer
Michael Signorelli, Managing Director
Sig Dugal, Managing Director
Vinay Ganga, Managing Director

Type of Firm

Private Equity Firm

Project Preferences

Type of Financing Preferred:
Expansion
Later Stage
Startup

Geographical Preferences

International Preferences:
India
China

Additional Information

Year Founded: 2007
Current Activity Level : Actively seeking new investments

ORIUM

280, boulevard Saint-Germain
Paris, France 75007
Phone: 33-1-4411-7020
Fax: 33-1-4411-7029
E-mail: orium@orium.fr
Website: www.orium.fr

Management and Staff

Guy Van Der Mersbrugghe, President

Type of Firm

Private Equity Firm

Association Membership

French Venture Capital Association (AFIC)

Project Preferences

Type of Financing Preferred:
Balanced

Geographical Preferences

International Preferences:
France

Industry Preferences

In Internet Specific prefer:
Internet

Additional Information

Year Founded: 2000
Current Activity Level : Actively seeking new investments

ORIX ASIA LIMITED

30/F United Centre
95 Queensway
Central, Hong Kong
Phone: 852-2862-9268
Fax: 852-2527-9688
E-mail: enquiry@orix.com.hk
Website: www.orix.com.hk

Management and Staff

Kotaro Takamori, Managing Director

Type of Firm

Bank Affiliated

Project Preferences

Type of Financing Preferred:
Mezzanine

Geographical Preferences

International Preferences:
China
Hong Kong

Additional Information

Year Founded: 1972
Current Activity Level : Actively seeking new investments

ORIX CAPITAL CORPORATION

7/F World Trade Center Bldg.
2-4-1 Hamamatsu-cho, Minato-ku
Tokyo, Japan 105-6135
Phone: 81-3-3435-3341
Fax: 81-3-3435-3349
E-mail: info@orixcapital.co.jp
Website: www.orixcapital.co.jp

Other Offices

30/F, United Centre
95 Queensway
Hong Kong, Hong Kong
Phone: 852-2862-9268
Fax: 852-2527-9688

19/F Yasuda Life Osaka Building
3-3-20 Umeda, Kita-ku
Osaka, Japan 530-0001
Phone: 81-6-4799-5250
Fax: 81-6-4799-5984

Management and Staff

Kazutaka Shimoura, President

Type of Firm

Bank Affiliated

Project Preferences

Type of Financing Preferred:
Early Stage
Mezzanine
Balanced

Geographical Preferences

International Preferences:
Indonesia
India
Hong Kong
Thailand
Philippines
Australia
Asia
Japan
Malaysia
All International

Industry Preferences

In Semiconductor/Electr prefer:
Electronics

In Biotechnology prefer:
Biotechnology

In Other prefer:
Environment Responsible

Additional Information

Year Founded: 1983
Capital Under Management: $230,100,000
Current Activity Level : Actively seeking new investments

ORIX VENTURE FINANCE

1177 Avenue of the Americas
Tenth Floor
New York, NY USA 10036-2714
Phone: 212-739-1600
Fax: 212-739-1705
Website: www.orixventure.com

Management and Staff

Kevin Sheehan, Chief Executive Officer
Michael David, Managing Director

Type of Firm

Private Equity Firm

Additional Information

Year Founded: 2009
Current Activity Level : Actively seeking new investments

ORKOS CAPITAL

15 rue Auber
Paris, France 75009
Phone: 33-1-7544-2250
E-mail: info@orkoscapital.com
Website: www.orkoscapital.com

Management and Staff

Christian Borie, Partner
Dominique Rencurel, Partner
Jean-Jacques Bertrand, Partner
Pierre-Eric Leibovici, Partner
Pierre-Yves Meerschman, Partner

Type of Firm

Private Equity Firm

Association Membership

French Venture Capital Association (AFIC)

Project Preferences

Type of Financing Preferred:
Leveraged Buyout
Expansion
Later Stage
Acquisition

Industry Preferences

In Communications prefer:
Commercial Communications
Data Communications

In Computer Hardware prefer:
Computers

In Computer Software prefer:
Data Processing
Software

In Internet Specific prefer:
Ecommerce

In Business Serv. prefer:
Services

Additional Information

Year Founded: 2006
Current Activity Level : Actively seeking new investments

ORLANDO CAPITAL MANAGEMENT GMBH

Am Platzl 4
Munich, Germany 80331
Phone: 49-89-2900-4850
Fax: 49-89-2900-4899
E-mail: info@orlandofund.com
Website: www.orlandofund.com

Management and Staff

Enrico Ceccato, Managing Partner
Florian Pape, Managing Partner
Georg Madersbacher, Managing Partner
Gianni Mion, Managing Partner
Hans Gottwald, Managing Partner
Hendrik Fastrich, Managing Partner
Paolo Scarlatti, Managing Partner
Pier Domenico Gallo, Managing Partner

Type of Firm

Private Equity Firm

Project Preferences

Type of Financing Preferred:
Special Situation
Recapitalizations

Geographical Preferences

International Preferences:
Italy
Switzerland
Central Europe
Austria
Germany

Industry Preferences

In Consumer Related prefer:
Retail

In Industrial/Energy prefer:
Industrial Products

In Financial Services prefer:
Financial Services
Real Estate

In Business Serv. prefer:
Services

In Manufact. prefer:
Manufacturing

Additional Information

Year Founded: 2005
Capital Under Management: $835,800,000
Current Activity Level : Actively seeking new investments

ORLANDO VENTURE CAPITAL INC.

P.O.Box 1529
Daytona Beach, FL USA 32115
Phone: 407-234-1336
Website: www.orlandoventurecapital.com

Management and Staff

Gerry Nolan, President & Chairman

Type of Firm

Private Equity Firm

Project Preferences

Type of Financing Preferred:
Early Stage

Geographical Preferences

United States Preferences:
Florida

Industry Preferences

In Semiconductor/Electr prefer:
Laser Related
Fiber Optics

Additional Information

Year Founded: 2001
Current Activity Level : Actively seeking new investments

ORTHOGONAL PARTNERS LLP.

Regus Business Centre
90 Long Acre
London, United Kingdom WC2E 9RZ
Phone: 44-20-7716-5811
Fax: 44-20-7716-5378
Website: www.orthogonalpartners.com

Management and Staff

Ahmet Ismael, Founding Partner
Daniel Gore, Founding Partner
Romek Pawlowicz, Founding Partner

Type of Firm

Private Equity Firm

Project Preferences

Type of Financing Preferred:
Fund of Funds

Geographical Preferences

International Preferences:
Europe

Additional Information

Year Founded: 2006
Current Activity Level : Actively seeking new investments

ORYX PARTNER SAS

34, quai Charles de Gaulle
Lyon, France 69006
Phone: 33-4-7282-3737
Fax: 33-4-72823739
E-mail: info@oryxpartner.fr
Website: www.oryxpartner.fr

Management and Staff

Jerome Pignard, President

Type of Firm

Private Equity Firm

Additional Information

Year Founded: 2009
Current Activity Level : Actively seeking new investments

OSAGE INVESTMENTS

50 Monument Road
Suite 201
Bala Cynwyd, PA USA 19004

Phone: 484-434-2255
Fax: 484-434-2256
Website: www.osageventures.com

Management and Staff

David Drahms, Vice President
Robert Adelson, President

Type of Firm

Private Equity Firm

Association Membership

National Venture Capital Association - USA (NVCA)

Project Preferences

Role in Financing:

Prefer role as deal originator but will also invest in deals created by others

Type of Financing Preferred:

Early Stage

Size of Investments Considered:

Min Size of Investment Considered (000s): $1,000
Max Size of Investment Considered (000s): $3,000

Geographical Preferences

United States Preferences:

All U.S.

Additional Information

Year Founded: 2005
Capital Under Management: $21,000,000
Current Activity Level : Actively seeking new investments
Method of Compensation: Return on investment is of primary concern, do not charge fees

---

OSK VENTURES INTERNATIONAL BHD (AKA: OSK VENTURES EQUITIES)

15/F Plaza OSK
Jalan Ampang
Kuala Lumpur, Malaysia 50450
Phone: 603-2333-8333
Fax: 603-2175-3333
E-mail: corp.finance@osk.com.my
Website: www.osk.com.my

Management and Staff

Choo Chee Beng, Chief Financial Officer
Eddie Yap, Chief Operating Officer

Type of Firm

Bank Affiliated

Project Preferences

Role in Financing:

Prefer role as deal originator

Type of Financing Preferred:

Leveraged Buyout
Early Stage
Expansion
Mezzanine
Balanced
Startup

Geographical Preferences

International Preferences:

China
Hong Kong
Thailand
Singapore
Asia
Malaysia

Industry Preferences

In Communications prefer:

Telecommunications

In Computer Other prefer:

Computer Related

In Semiconductor/Electr prefer:

Electronics

In Biotechnology prefer:

Biotechnology

In Consumer Related prefer:

Entertainment and Leisure
Hotels and Resorts

In Transportation prefer:

Transportation

In Financial Services prefer:

Financial Services

In Business Serv. prefer:

Distribution

In Manufact. prefer:

Manufacturing

Additional Information

Year Founded: 2000
Capital Under Management: $26,000,000
Current Activity Level : Actively seeking new investments

OSPREY VENTURES, L.P.

203 Redwood Shores Parkway
Suite 610
Redwood City, CA USA 94065
Phone: 650-620-9450
Fax: 650-620-9458
E-mail: admin@ospreyventures.com
Website: www.ospreyventures.com

Management and Staff

David Stastny, Managing Director
Jerry Brown, Venture Partner
John Slitz, Venture Partner
Paul Sherer, Venture Partner
Ralph Eschenbach, Venture Partner
Ravi Chiruvolu, Venture Partner

Type of Firm

Private Equity Firm

Association Membership

Western Association of Venture Capitalists (WAVC)

Project Preferences

Role in Financing:

Will function either as deal originator or investor in deals created by others

Type of Financing Preferred:

Expansion
Later Stage

Size of Investments Considered:

Min Size of Investment Considered (000s): $500
Max Size of Investment Considered (000s): $5,000

Geographical Preferences

United States Preferences:

Rocky Mountain
West Coast

Industry Focus

(% based on actual investment)

Internet Specific	37.9%
Computer Software and Services	26.7%
Semiconductors/Other Elect.	13.5%
Communications and Media	13.4%
Computer Hardware	4.5%
Consumer Related	4.0%

Additional Information

Year Founded: 1999
Capital Under Management: $92,000,000
Current Activity Level : Actively seeking new investments
Method of Compensation: Function primarily in service area, receive contingent fee in cash or equity

---

OSTBELGIENINVEST AG

Hauptstrasse 54
St. Vith, Belgium B-4780
Phone: 32-8-028-0012
Fax: 32-8-022-9522
E-mail: info@obi.be
Website: www.obi.be

Other Offices

Hutte 79
Box 20
Eupen, Belgium
Phone: 32-87-56-8205
Fax: 32-87-74-3350

Type of Firm

Private Equity Firm

Association Membership

Belgium Venturing Association

Project Preferences

Type of Financing Preferred:
Balanced

Geographical Preferences

International Preferences:
Belgium

Additional Information

Year Founded: 2003
Current Activity Level : Actively seeking new investments

OTC ASSET MANAGEMENT

8 rue Lamennais
Paris, France 75008
Phone: 33-1-5396-5250
Fax: 33-1-5396-5251
E-mail: infos@otcam.com
Website: www.otcam.com

Management and Staff

Jean-Marc Palhon, Chief Executive Officer

Type of Firm

Private Equity Firm

Association Membership

French Venture Capital Association (AFIC)

Project Preferences

Type of Financing Preferred:
Early Stage
Generalist PE
Balanced
Later Stage

Geographical Preferences

International Preferences:
Europe
Western Europe
France

Additional Information

Year Founded: 2002
Capital Under Management: $437,900,000
Current Activity Level : Actively seeking new investments

OTTER CAPITAL, LLC

755 Page Mill Road
Suite A200
Palo Alto, CA USA 94304
Phone: 650-493-5263
E-mail: marion@ottercapital.com
Website: www.ottercapital.com

Management and Staff

John Pasquesi, Founder

Type of Firm

Private Equity Firm

Project Preferences

Type of Financing Preferred:
Balanced

Industry Preferences

In Internet Specific prefer:
Ecommerce

In Consumer Related prefer:
Food/Beverage

In Financial Services prefer:
Financial Services

Additional Information

Year Founded: 2000
Current Activity Level : Actively seeking new investments

OTTO CAPITAL PARTNERS

18-20 Place de la Madeleine
Paris, France 75008
Phone: 33-1-5305-9565
Fax: 33-1-5305-9570
E-mail: info@ottocapitalpartners.com

Management and Staff

Chun Li, Partner
Daniel Zenaty, Partner
Luc Muller, Partner

Type of Firm

Bank Affiliated

Association Membership

European Private Equity and Venture Capital Assoc.

Project Preferences

Type of Financing Preferred:
Leveraged Buyout
Expansion
Recapitalizations

Size of Investments Considered:
Min Size of Investment Considered (000s): $471
Max Size of Investment Considered (000s): $4,708

Geographical Preferences

International Preferences:
Europe
Israel
Germany
Asia
France

Additional Information

Year Founded: 2000
Capital Under Management: $89,100,000
Current Activity Level : Actively seeking new investments

OU BALTCAP (FKA: BALTCAP MANAGEMENT OY)

Ulmana gatve 86F
Riga, Latvia
Phone: 371-6735-6399
Fax: 371-6735-6395
Website: www.baltcap.com

Other Offices

J. Jasinskio 16B, 1112
Vilnius, Lithuania LT-01112
Phone: 370-5254-6713
Fax: 370-5254-6978

Ulmana gatve 86F
Riga, Latvia LV-1046
Phone: 371-6735-6399
Fax: 371-6735-6395

Tartu mnt. 2
Tallinn, Estonia 10145
Phone: 372-6-650-280
Fax: 372-6-650-281

Management and Staff

Dagnis Dreimanis, Partner
Kristjan Kalda, Partner
Martin Kodar, Partner
Matts Andersson, Partner
Peeter Saks, Managing Partner
Simonas Gustainis, Partner

Type of Firm

Private Equity Firm

Association Membership

Finnish Venture Capital Association (FVCA)
European Private Equity and Venture Capital Assoc.

Project Preferences

Type of Financing Preferred:
Leveraged Buyout
Early Stage
Expansion
Later Stage

Size of Investments Considered:
Min Size of Investment Considered (000s): $500
Max Size of Investment Considered (000s): $500,000

Geographical Preferences

International Preferences:
Central Europe
Eastern Europe
Estonia
Latvia
Lithuania

Industry Preferences

In Communications prefer:
Commercial Communications

In Consumer Related prefer:
Consumer Products

In Business Serv. prefer:
Distribution

In Manufact. prefer:
Manufacturing

Additional Information
Name of Most Recent Fund: BaltCap Private Equity Fund
Most Recent Fund Was Raised: 12/14/2007
Year Founded: 1995
Capital Under Management: $86,600,000
Current Activity Level : Actively seeking new investments

OUEST CROISSANCE S.A.
Immeuble L'Atalante
Avenue Marcelin Berthelot
Saint-Herblain Cedex, France 44812
Phone: 33-2-4058-6219
Fax: 33-2-4058-6203
Website: www.ouest-croissance.fr

Management and Staff
Gerard Bodiguel, General Director

Type of Firm
Bank Affiliated

Association Membership
French Venture Capital Association (AFIC)

Project Preferences

Type of Financing Preferred:
Leveraged Buyout
Early Stage
Expansion

Geographical Preferences

International Preferences:
France

Additional Information
Year Founded: 2000
Current Activity Level : Actively seeking new investments

OUEST VENTURES (FKA: GRAND OUEST GESTION)
18 Place de la Gare
Rennes, France 35000
Phone: 33-2-9935-0400
Fax: 33-2-9935-0022
E-mail: contact@ouestventures.com
Website: www.ouestventures.com

Management and Staff
Eric Cozanet, Managing Director
Thao Lane, Venture Partner
Thomas Gubler, Partner

Type of Firm
Private Equity Firm

Project Preferences

Type of Financing Preferred:
Early Stage
Expansion
Seed
Startup

Size of Investments Considered:
Min Size of Investment Considered (000s): $372
Max Size of Investment Considered (000s): $3,718

Geographical Preferences

International Preferences:
Europe
France

Industry Preferences

In Computer Software prefer:
Software

Additional Information
Year Founded: 2003
Capital Under Management: $37,300,000
Current Activity Level : Actively seeking new investments

OUTLOOK VENTURES (FKA: IMINDS, INTERACTIVE MINDS)
912 Cole Street
Suite 144
San Francisco, CA USA 94105
Phone: 415-547-0000
Fax: 415-547-0010
E-mail: info@outlookventures.com
Website: www.outlookventures.com

Management and Staff
Carl Nichols, Managing Director
Randy Haykin, Managing Director
Sandeep Aneja, Principal

Type of Firm
Private Equity Firm

Project Preferences

Role in Financing:
Prefer role as deal originator but will also invest in deals created by others

Type of Financing Preferred:
Early Stage
Seed
First Stage Financing
Startup

Size of Investments Considered:
Min Size of Investment Considered (000s): $500
Max Size of Investment Considered (000s): $10,000

Geographical Preferences

United States Preferences:
Northern California
West Coast

Industry Focus
(% based on actual investment)

Internet Specific	50.8%
Computer Software and Services	48.2%
Computer Hardware	0.8%
Other Products	0.2%

Additional Information
Name of Most Recent Fund: Outlook Ventures III
Most Recent Fund Was Raised: 10/10/2002
Year Founded: 1995
Capital Under Management: $225,000,000
Current Activity Level : Actively seeking new investments
Method of Compensation: Return on investment is of primary concern, do not charge fees

---

OVATION CAPITAL PARTNERS
800 3rd Ave
21st Floor
New York, NY USA 10022
Phone: 212-209-3036
Fax: 212-209-3039
E-mail: proposal@icentennial.com
Website: www.ovationcapital.com

Management and Staff
David Frankel, Partner
Greg Frank, Managing General Partner
Todd Squilanti, Partner

Type of Firm
Private Equity Firm

Project Preferences

Role in Financing:
Prefer role as deal originator but will also invest in deals created by others

Type of Financing Preferred:
Leveraged Buyout
Early Stage

Size of Investments Considered:
Min Size of Investment Considered (000s): $500
Max Size of Investment Considered (000s): $2,000

Geographical Preferences

United States Preferences:
Northeast

Industry Preferences

In Computer Software prefer:
Software

In Semiconductor/Electr prefer:
Semiconductor

Additional Information

Year Founded: 1997
Capital Under Management: $50,000,000
Current Activity Level : Actively seeking new investments

OVERSEAS PARTNERS ITALIA SRL (AKA: OPI)

Corso Matteotti 3
Milan, Italy 20121
Phone: 39-02-7601-3897
Fax: 39-02-7601-4250
E-mail: opi@overseas-partners.com

Type of Firm

Private Equity Firm

Association Membership

Italian Venture Capital Association (AIFI)

Project Preferences

Type of Financing Preferred:
Leveraged Buyout

Geographical Preferences

International Preferences:
Europe

Additional Information

Year Founded: 2000
Current Activity Level : Actively seeking new investments

OVERSEAS PRIVATE INVESTMENT CORP. (AKA: OPIC)

1100 New York Avenue
Washington, DC USA 20527
Phone: 202-336-8400
Fax: 202-336-7949
E-mail: info@opic.gov
Website: www.opic.gov

Management and Staff

Cynthia Hostetler, Vice President

Type of Firm

Private Equity Advisor or Fund of Funds

Association Membership

African Venture Capital Association (AVCA)

Project Preferences

Type of Financing Preferred:
Fund of Funds
Balanced

Size of Investments Considered:
Min Size of Investment Considered (000s): $25
Max Size of Investment Considered (000s): $100

Geographical Preferences

United States Preferences:
All U.S.

International Preferences:
Pakistan
Eastern Europe
Africa
All International

Industry Preferences

In Biotechnology prefer:
Agricultural/Animal Bio.

In Medical/Health prefer:
Medical/Health

In Other prefer:
Socially Responsible

Additional Information

Year Founded: 1987
Capital Under Management: $3,500,000,000
Current Activity Level : Actively seeking new investments

OVERTURE CAPITAL PARTNERS (AKA: OVERTURE)

205 - 5th Avenue Southwest
Ste 3400, Bow Valley Square II
Calgary, Canada T2P 2V7
Phone: 403-770-4800
Fax: 403-770-4850
Website: www.overlordfinancial.com

Type of Firm

Bank Affiliated

Project Preferences

Type of Financing Preferred:
Early Stage

Geographical Preferences

Canadian Preferences:
All Canada

Industry Preferences

In Industrial/Energy prefer:
Energy
Oil and Gas Exploration

Additional Information

Year Founded: 2003
Current Activity Level : Actively seeking new investments

OVP VENTURE PARTNERS (FKA: OLYMPIC VENTURE PARTNERS)

1010 Market Street
Kirkland, WA USA 98033
Phone: 425-889-9192
Fax: 425-889-0152
E-mail: info@ovp.com
Website: www.ovp.com

Other Offices

5550 Southwest Macadam Avenue
Suite 300
Portland, OR USA 97239
Phone: 503-697-8766
Fax: 503-697-8863

Management and Staff

Bill Funcannon, Managing Director & CFO
Carl Weissman, Managing Director
Charles Waite, Managing Director
Gerard Langeler, Managing Director
Lucinda Stewart, Managing Director
Mark Ashida, Managing Director
Rick LeFaivre, Venture Partner

Type of Firm

Private Equity Firm

Association Membership

National Venture Capital Association - USA (NVCA)

Project Preferences

Role in Financing:
Prefer role as deal originator but will also invest in deals created by others

Type of Financing Preferred:
Early Stage
Seed
First Stage Financing
Startup

Size of Investments Considered:
Min Size of Investment Considered (000s): $1,000
Max Size of Investment Considered (000s): $10,000

Geographical Preferences

United States Preferences:
Northwest
Southern California
Northern California
West Coast
Southwest

Canadian Preferences:
Western Canada

Industry Focus

(% based on actual investment)

Computer Software and Services	32.5%
Internet Specific	19.4%
Biotechnology	10.3%
Semiconductors/Other Elect.	10.3%
Communications and Media	8.8%
Computer Hardware	6.8%
Medical/Health	6.4%
Industrial/Energy	3.2%
Consumer Related	2.0%
Other Products	0.4%

Additional Information

Name of Most Recent Fund: OVP Venture Partners VII, L.P.
Most Recent Fund Was Raised: 05/15/2006
Year Founded: 1983
Capital Under Management: $757,500,000
Current Activity Level : Actively seeking new investments
Method of Compensation: Return on investment is of primary concern, do not charge fees

---

OXFORD BIOSCIENCE PARTNERS

222 Berkeley Street
Suite 1650
Boston, MA USA 02116
Phone: 617-357-7474
Fax: 617-357-7476
Website: www.oxbio.com

Other Offices

30765 Pacific Coast Highway
Suite 427
Malibu, CA USA 90265
Phone: 310-457-0010
Fax: 310-589-0099

191 Post Road West
Suite 69
Westport, CT USA 06880
Phone: 203-341-3300
Fax: 203-341-3309

Management and Staff

Alan Walton, General Partner
Cornelius Ryan, General Partner
Douglas Fambrough, General Partner
Edmund Olivier, General Partner
Ellen Baron, Partner
Jonathan Fleming, Managing Partner
Lisa Jordan, Principal
Matthew Gibbs, General Partner
Michael Lytton, General Partner
Ray Charest, Chief Financial Officer

Type of Firm

Private Equity Firm

Association Membership

National Venture Capital Association - USA (NVCA)

Project Preferences

Role in Financing:

Prefer role as deal originator but will also invest in deals created by others

Type of Financing Preferred:

Early Stage
Research and Development
Balanced
First Stage Financing
Startup

Size of Investments Considered:

Min Size of Investment Considered (000s): $25
Max Size of Investment Considered (000s): $20,000

Geographical Preferences

Canadian Preferences:

All Canada

International Preferences:

United Kingdom
Bermuda
Germany
France
Japan

Industry Focus

(% based on actual investment)

Biotechnology	52.0%
Medical/Health	40.5%
Computer Software and Services	1.8%
Internet Specific	1.7%
Semiconductors/Other Elect.	1.6%
Industrial/Energy	1.4%
Consumer Related	1.0%

Additional Information

Year Founded: 1992
Capital Under Management: $1,020,000,000
Current Activity Level : Actively seeking new investments
Method of Compensation: Return on investment is of primary concern, do not charge fees

---

OXFORD CAPITAL PARTNERS (FKA : EMSA CAPITAL)

201 Cumnor Hill
Oxford, United Kingdom OX2 9PJ
Phone: 44-1865-860-760
Fax: 44-1865-860-761
E-mail: info@oxcp.com
Website: www.oxcp.com

Management and Staff

Edward Mott, Chief Executive Officer
Ted Mott, Chief Executive Officer

Type of Firm

Bank Affiliated

Association Membership

British Venture Capital Association (BVCA)
European Private Equity and Venture Capital Assoc.

Project Preferences

Type of Financing Preferred:

Early Stage
Expansion
Balanced
Seed
Startup

Geographical Preferences

International Preferences:

United Kingdom
Europe

Industry Preferences

In Communications prefer:

Telecommunications
Wireless Communications
Data Communications

In Computer Software prefer:

Software

In Internet Specific prefer:

Internet

In Biotechnology prefer:

Biotechnology

In Medical/Health prefer:

Medical/Health
Pharmaceuticals

In Industrial/Energy prefer:

Advanced Materials

Additional Information

Year Founded: 1999
Capital Under Management: $73,400,000
Current Activity Level : Actively seeking new investments

OXFORDSHIRE INVESTMENT OPPORTUNITY NETWORK (AKA: OION)

Mill Street
Oxford, United Kingdom OX2 0JX
Phone: 44-186-581-1143
Fax: 44-186-520-9044
Website: www.oion.co.uk

Type of Firm

Private Equity Firm

Project Preferences

Type of Financing Preferred:

Early Stage

Geographical Preferences

International Preferences:
United Kingdom
Europe

Additional Information

Year Founded: 1995
Current Activity Level : Actively seeking new investments

OZORA TOSHI JIGYO YUGEN SEKININ KUMIAI

3-9-23, Kotobashi
Sumida-Ku
Tokyo, Japan
Phone: 816-4797-1102

Type of Firm

Private Equity Firm

Project Preferences

Type of Financing Preferred:
Balanced

Geographical Preferences

International Preferences:
Asia

Additional Information

Year Founded: 2008
Current Activity Level : Actively seeking new investments

P. SCHOENFELD ASSET MANAGEMENT LLC

1330 Avenue of the Americas
34th Floor
New York, NY USA 10019
Phone: 212-649-9509
Fax: 212-649-9540
E-mail: info@psamllc.com
Website: www.psam.com

Management and Staff

Louis Friedman, President

Type of Firm

Bank Affiliated

Additional Information

Name of Most Recent Fund: WSCI Limited Partnership
Most Recent Fund Was Raised: 01/01/1997
Capital Under Management: $300,000,000
Current Activity Level : Actively seeking new investments

P.A.G. CAPITAL PARTNERS

150 North Wacker Drive
Suite 2500
Chicago, IL USA 60606
Phone: 312-275-5758
Fax: 312-275-5768
E-mail: info@pagacapital.com
Website: www.pagcapital.com

Management and Staff

Alex Fridman, Partner
David Anderson, Partner
Jeff Temple, Partner
Stephen Sleigh, Partner
Timothy Van Mieghem, Partner

Type of Firm

Private Equity Firm

Project Preferences

Type of Financing Preferred:
Leveraged Buyout
Expansion
Acquisition
Recapitalizations

Geographical Preferences

United States Preferences:
All U.S.

Industry Preferences

In Consumer Related prefer:
Consumer Products
Consumer Services

In Business Serv. prefer:
Distribution

In Manufact. prefer:
Manufacturing

Additional Information

Year Founded: 2009
Current Activity Level : Actively seeking new investments

P.T. PAMA VENTURA INDONESIA

Wisma GKBI, Suite 3901
lantai 39 J . Jend. Sudirman
Jakarta, Indonesia 10210
Phone: 62-21-5799-8173
Fax: 62-21-5799-8174

Management and Staff

Nang Yong Tan, President

Type of Firm

Private Equity Firm

Project Preferences

Type of Financing Preferred:
Balanced

Geographical Preferences

International Preferences:
Asia

Additional Information

Year Founded: 2000
Current Activity Level : Actively seeking new investments

PAC-LINK MANAGEMENT CORPORATION

13&16/F, No 2 Tun-Hwa South Rd
Section 2
Taipei, Taiwan
Phone: 886-2-2755-5000
Fax: 886-2-2755-2000
E-mail: info@paclink.com.tw
Website: www.paclink.com.tw

Other Offices

20/F 8 Xingyi Road
Shanghai Maxdo Center
Shanghai, China
Phone: 86-21-5208-2929
Fax: 86-21-5208-1369

2445 Faber Place
Suite 102
Palo Alto, CA USA 94303
Phone: 650-857-0686
Fax: 650-857-0682

Management and Staff

Allen Hsu, General Partner
Ben Feng, General Partner
Irene Shih, Vice President
Jessica Wang, Vice President
Le-Chun Wang, Vice President
Ming Hsu, General Partner
Minyi Tang, Vice President
Neil Wu, Vice President
Toni Hong, Vice President

Type of Firm

Private Equity Firm

Association Membership

Taiwan Venture Capital Association(TVCA)

Project Preferences

Type of Financing Preferred:

Expansion
Mezzanine
Balanced
Seed
Startup

Geographical Preferences

International Preferences:

Taiwan
Asia

Industry Preferences

In Communications prefer:

Telecommunications

In Computer Software prefer:

Software

In Semiconductor/Electr prefer:

Semiconductor
Optoelectronics

In Biotechnology prefer:

Biotechnology

In Industrial/Energy prefer:

Advanced Materials
Factory Automation
Process Control
Machinery
Environmental Related

Additional Information

Name of Most Recent Fund: FuYu Venture Capital Investment Corporation
Most Recent Fund Was Raised: 01/24/2000
Year Founded: 1998
Capital Under Management: $205,700,000
Current Activity Level : Actively seeking new investments

PACESETTER CAPITAL GROUP (FKA: MESBIC VENTURES HOLDING CO.)

2435 North Central Expressway
Suite 200
Richardson, TX USA 75080
Phone: 972-991-1597
Fax: 972-991-4770
E-mail: info@pacesettercapital.com
Website: www.pacesettercapital.com

Management and Staff

Donald Lawhorne, Managing General Partner
Felix Villalba, Chief Financial Officer
Giovanni Capriglione, Vice President
Patrick Pullman, Vice President
Rahul Vaid, General Partner

Type of Firm

SBIC

Association Membership

Natl Assoc of Investment Cos. (NAIC)
Natl Assoc of Small Bus. Inv. Co (NASBIC)

Project Preferences

Role in Financing:

Will function either as deal originator or investor in deals created by others

Type of Financing Preferred:

Expansion
Mezzanine
Later Stage
Acquisition
Recapitalizations

Size of Investments Considered:

Min Size of Investment Considered (000s): $1,000
Max Size of Investment Considered (000s): $5,000

Geographical Preferences

United States Preferences:

West Coast
Southwest

Industry Focus

(% based on actual investment)

Communications and Media	47.7%
Computer Software and Services	13.6%
Consumer Related	13.1%
Medical/Health	12.5%
Semiconductors/Other Elect.	6.2%
Computer Hardware	1.9%
Internet Specific	1.9%
Other Products	1.8%
Industrial/Energy	1.2%

Additional Information

Year Founded: 1970
Capital Under Management: $174,700,000
Current Activity Level : Actively seeking new investments
Method of Compensation: Return on invest. most important, but chg. closing fees, service fees, etc.

PACIFIC ALLIANCE CAPITAL GROUP

Suite 2501, 25th Floor
9 Queens Road, Central
Honk Kong, Hong Kong
Phone: 852-2810-1399
Fax: 852-2524-1280
Website: www.pacgrp.com

Management and Staff

Cecilia Mak, Managing Director
Jacky Soong, Chief Operating Officer
Kevin Murphy, Managing Director
Wen Zhang, Managing Director

Type of Firm

Private Equity Firm

Project Preferences

Type of Financing Preferred:

Balanced

Geographical Preferences

International Preferences:

Pacific
Asia

Additional Information

Year Founded: 1991
Current Activity Level : Actively seeking new investments

PACIFIC ASSET PARTNERS

Two Embarcadero Center
Suite 1340
San Francisco, CA USA 94111
Phone: 415-362-6120
Fax: 415-362-3048
E-mail: info@pacificassetpartners.com
Website: www.pacificassetpartners.com

Type of Firm

Private Equity Firm

Association Membership

Western Association of Venture Capitalists (WAVC)

Project Preferences

Type of Financing Preferred:

Leveraged Buyout
Later Stage

Geographical Preferences

United States Preferences:

West Coast

Additional Information

Year Founded: 1983
Capital Under Management: $25,000,000
Current Activity Level : Actively seeking new investments

PACIFIC COMMUNITY VENTURES (FKA: SVCV)

539 Bryant
Suite 302
San Francisco, CA USA 94107
Phone: 415-442-4300
Fax: 415-442-4313
E-mail: info@pcvmail.org
Website: www.pcvfund.com

Other Offices

5010 North Woodrow
WC142
Fresno, CA USA 93710
Phone: 559-347-3910
Fax: 559-294-6655

410 B Street
Suite 304-A
San Diego, CA USA 92101
Phone: 858-663-1639
Fax: 619-699-3045

4060 South Figueroa Street
Los Angeles, CA USA 90037
Phone: 323-235-7001
Fax: 323-235-1686

Management and Staff

David Rosen, Chief Financial Officer
Eduardo Rallo, Managing Director
John Thornton, Managing Director
Penelope Douglas, President
Pete November, Managing Director

Type of Firm

Private Equity Firm

Association Membership

Community Development Venture Capital Alliance

Project Preferences

Role in Financing:

Will function either as deal originator or investor in deals created by others

Type of Financing Preferred:

Expansion
Generalist PE
Balanced
Management Buyouts
Industry Rollups

Size of Investments Considered:

Min Size of Investment Considered (000s): $500
Max Size of Investment Considered (000s): $1,000

Geographical Preferences

United States Preferences:

California

Industry Preferences

In Communications prefer:

Radio & TV Broadcasting

In Consumer Related prefer:

Consumer

In Business Serv. prefer:

Services
Distribution

In Manufact. prefer:

Manufacturing

In Other prefer:

Socially Responsible
Women/Minority-Owned Bus.

Additional Information

Name of Most Recent Fund: Pacific Community Ventures III, LLC
Most Recent Fund Was Raised: 01/09/2007
Year Founded: 1999
Capital Under Management: $60,000,000
Current Activity Level : Actively seeking new investments
Method of Compensation: Return on invest. most important, but chg. closing fees, service fees, etc.

PACIFIC CORPORATE GROUP

1200 Prospect Street
Suite 200
La Jolla, CA USA 92037
Phone: 858-456-6000
Fax: 858-456-6018
E-mail: info@pcgfunds.com
Website: www.pcgfunds.com

Management and Staff

Bernard McGuire, Managing Director
Brandon Park, Vice President
Charles Toy, Managing Director
Doug Meltzer, Managing Director
Gene Pohren, Managing Director
Jennifer Faust, Vice President
John Coughlin, Managing Director
Jose Fernandez, Managing Director
Kenn Lee, Vice President
Mark Oemcke, Chief Operating Officer
Michelle Davidson, Managing Director
Mike Taylor, Vice President
Mike Krems, Vice President
Oren Monhite Yahav, Vice President
Stephen O Neill, Managing Director
Steve Cowan, Managing Director
Timothy Kelleher, Managing Director

Type of Firm

Private Equity Advisor or Fund of Funds

Association Membership

European Private Equity and Venture Capital Assoc.

Project Preferences

Role in Financing:

Prefer role as deal originator but will also invest in deals created by others

Type of Financing Preferred:

Fund of Funds
Second Stage Financing
Leveraged Buyout
Early Stage
Expansion
Mezzanine
Generalist PE
Turnaround
Later Stage
Other
Seed
Management Buyouts
Joint Ventures
Private Placement
Special Situation
Distressed Debt
Recapitalizations

Size of Investments Considered:

Min Size of Investment Considered (000s): $5,000
Max Size of Investment Considered (000s): $500,000

Geographical Preferences

United States Preferences:

All U.S.

Canadian Preferences:

All Canada

International Preferences:

Italy
United Kingdom
Latin America
Luxembourg
Netherlands
Portugal
Eastern Europe
Spain
Belgium
Germany
Asia
France
All International

Industry Preferences

In Communications prefer:

Telecommunications

In Semiconductor/Electr prefer:

Semiconductor
Controllers and Sensors

In Biotechnology prefer:

Biotech Related Research

In Medical/Health prefer:

Medical/Health

In Consumer Related prefer:

Consumer
Retail
Hotels and Resorts
Education Related

In Industrial/Energy prefer:

Energy
Industrial Products

Superconductivity
Machinery

In Financial Services prefer:
Insurance
Real Estate

In Business Serv. prefer:
Services
Distribution
Media

In Manufact. prefer:
Manufacturing

In Utilities prefer:
Utilities

Additional Information
Name of Most Recent Fund: CALPERS/PCG Corporate Partners Fund, L.P.
Most Recent Fund Was Raised: 03/01/2001
Year Founded: 1979
Capital Under Management: $15,000,000,000
Current Activity Level : Actively seeking new investments
Method of Compensation: Return on invest. most important, but chg. closing fees, service fees, etc.

PACIFIC EQUITY PARTNERS
126 Phillip Street
Level 31
Sydney, Australia 2000
Phone: 612-8238-2600
Fax: 612-8238-2690
E-mail: information@pep.com.au
Website: www.pep.com.au

Management and Staff
Anthony Kerwick, Managing Director
Paul McCullagh, Managing Director
Rickard Gardell, Managing Director
Rob Koczkar, Managing Director
Sam Kong, Chief Financial Officer
Simon Pillar, Managing Director
Tim Sims, Managing Director

Type of Firm
Private Equity Firm

Association Membership
Australian Venture Capital Association (AVCAL)

Project Preferences

Role in Financing:
Will function either as deal originator or investor in deals created by others

Type of Financing Preferred:
Leveraged Buyout

Geographical Preferences

International Preferences:
New Zealand
Asia
Australia

Additional Information
Year Founded: 1998
Capital Under Management: $4,834,800,000
Current Activity Level : Actively seeking new investments
Method of Compensation: Return on invest. most important, but chg. closing fees, service fees, etc.

PACIFIC GROWTH EQUITIES LLC
One Bush Street
San Francisco, CA USA 94104
Phone: 415-274-6800
Fax: 415 274-6824
Website: www.pacgrow.com

Other Offices
225 Franklin Street
17th Floor
Boston, MA USA 02110
Phone: 617-695-7200
Fax: 617-695-7202

Type of Firm
Private Equity Firm

Additional Information
Year Founded: 1991
Current Activity Level : Actively seeking new investments

PACIFIC HORIZON VENTURES LLC
701 Fifth Avenue
Suite 4970
Seattle, WA USA 98104
Phone: 206-682-1181
Fax: 206-682-8077
E-mail: phv@pacifichorizon.com
Website: www.pacifichorizon.com

Management and Staff
David Krekel, Principal
Donald Elmer, Managing General Partner
Gene Rowland, Chief Financial Officer
Jean-Pierre Laurent, Principal
William Robbins, Principal

Type of Firm
Private Equity Firm

Association Membership
National Venture Capital Association - USA (NVCA)

Project Preferences

Role in Financing:
Will function either as deal originator or investor in deals created by others

Type of Financing Preferred:
Early Stage
Balanced
Seed

Size of Investments Considered:
Min Size of Investment Considered (000s): $250
Max Size of Investment Considered (000s): $2,000

Geographical Preferences

United States Preferences:
Northwest
California
Washington
All U.S.

Canadian Preferences:
Western Canada

Industry Focus
(% based on actual investment)

Biotechnology	67.4%
Medical/Health	20.5%
Industrial/Energy	4.5%
Computer Software and Services	3.7%
Internet Specific	2.1%
Communications and Media	1.2%
Computer Hardware	0.5%

Additional Information
Year Founded: 1993
Capital Under Management: $73,000,000
Current Activity Level : Actively seeking new investments
Method of Compensation: Return on investment is of primary concern, do not charge fees

---

PACIFIC INVESTMENTS
124 Sloane Street
London, United Kingdom SW1X 9BW
Phone: 44-207-225-2250
Fax: 44-207-591-1650
E-mail: bvca@beckwithlondon.com
Website: www.pacificinvestments.com

Type of Firm
Bank Affiliated

Association Membership
British Venture Capital Association (BVCA)

Project Preferences

Type of Financing Preferred:
Fund of Funds
Second Stage Financing
Leveraged Buyout
Early Stage
Expansion
Mezzanine
Generalist PE
Balanced
Seed
Startup

Geographical Preferences

International Preferences:
United Kingdom
All International

Industry Preferences

In Medical/Health prefer:
Medical/Health

In Consumer Related prefer:
Entertainment and Leisure

In Financial Services prefer:
Financial Services

In Business Serv. prefer:
Media

Additional Information

Year Founded: 1999
Current Activity Level : Actively seeking new investments

PACIFIC MEZZANINE FUND, L.P. (PMF)

2200 Powell Street
Suite 1250
Emeryville, CA USA 94608
Phone: 510-595-9800
Fax: 510-595-9801
E-mail: info@pacmezz.com
Website: www.pacmezz.com

Management and Staff

Brad Winegar, Managing Director
Nathan Bell, Managing Director

Type of Firm

SBIC

Association Membership

Natl Assoc of Small Bus. Inv. Co (NASBIC)

Project Preferences

Type of Financing Preferred:
Mezzanine

Size of Investments Considered:
Min Size of Investment Considered (000s): $2,000
Max Size of Investment Considered (000s): $4,000

Geographical Preferences

United States Preferences:
West Coast

Industry Focus

(% based on actual investment)

Other Products	41.5%
Consumer Related	31.3%
Computer Software and Services	15.3%
Medical/Health	7.7%
Computer Hardware	2.0%
Internet Specific	1.8%
Semiconductors/Other Elect.	0.5%

Additional Information

Name of Most Recent Fund: Pacific Mezzanine Fund, L.P.
Most Recent Fund Was Raised: 01/01/1994
Year Founded: 1994
Capital Under Management: $82,000,000
Current Activity Level : Actively seeking new investments

PACIFIC PARTNERS

601 Montgomery Street
Suite 1207
San Francisco, CA USA 94111
Phone: 415-217-0052
Fax: 415-217-0053
E-mail: info@PacificPartnersLP.com
Website: www.pacificpartnerslp.com

Management and Staff

Gordon Rubenstein, Managing Director
Max Kay, Vice President
Travis Nelson, Managing Director

Type of Firm

Private Equity Firm

Project Preferences

Type of Financing Preferred:
Early Stage
Balanced

Size of Investments Considered:
Min Size of Investment Considered (000s): $1,000
Max Size of Investment Considered (000s): $4,000

Industry Preferences

In Computer Software prefer:
Software
Systems Software
Applications Software

In Consumer Related prefer:
Consumer Services

Additional Information

Year Founded: 2000
Capital Under Management: $35,000,000
Current Activity Level : Actively seeking new investments

PACIFIC RIM VENTURES COMPANY, LTD.

Second Floor, Green Plaza
3-7-20, Komazawa, Setagaya-ku
Tokyo, Japan 154-0012
Phone: 81-3-5779-6752
Fax: 81-3-5779-6753
Website: www.pacificrim-ventures.com

Other Offices

1059A Canterbury Lane
Chapel Hill, NC USA 27517
Phone: 919-942-4547
Fax: 919-942-4501

180 Centennial Drive
Estes Park, CO USA 80517
Phone: 970-215-5700
Fax: 603-853-9202

129 Franklin Street
Suite 207
Cambridge, MA USA 02139
Phone: 617-252-0699

Management and Staff

Daisuke Takahashi, Vice President
Masahiro Michishita, Partner

Type of Firm

Private Equity Firm

Project Preferences

Type of Financing Preferred:
Balanced

Geographical Preferences

International Preferences:
Europe
Asia

Industry Preferences

In Biotechnology prefer:
Biotechnology

Additional Information

Year Founded: 2000
Current Activity Level : Actively seeking new investments

PACIFIC ROAD CAPITAL MANAGEMENT PTY, LTD. (AKA: PRCM)

1 Alfred Street
Level 23
Sydney, Australia 2000
Phone: 612-9241-1000
Fax: 612-9241-2255
Website: www.pacroad.com.au

Other Offices

422 Cedar Hill Drive
San Rafael, CA USA 94903
Phone: 415-785-8676
Fax: 415-479-5302

48 Shortland Street
Level 34, The Vero Centre
Auckland, New Zealand
Phone: 64-9976-6450
Fax: 64-9976-6499

Management and Staff

Paul Espie, Managing Director

Type of Firm

Investment Management Firm

Association Membership

Australian Venture Capital Association (AVCAL)

Project Preferences

Role in Financing:

Will function either as deal originator or investor in deals created by others

Type of Financing Preferred:

Leveraged Buyout
Expansion
Generalist PE

Size of Investments Considered:

Min Size of Investment Considered (000s): $10,000
Max Size of Investment Considered (000s): $60,000

Geographical Preferences

United States Preferences:

All U.S.

Canadian Preferences:

All Canada

International Preferences:

Australia
Asia
Africa

Industry Preferences

In Business Serv. prefer:

Services

In Agr/Forestr/Fish prefer:

Mining and Minerals

Additional Information

Year Founded: 2006
Capital Under Management: $325,900,000
Current Activity Level : Actively seeking new investments

PACIFIC VENTURE CAPITAL COMPANY, LTD.

13/F, No 169 Jen-Ai Road
Section Four
Taipei, Taiwan 106
Phone: 886-2-2751-0055
Fax: 886-2-2740-0005
E-mail: pvccinfo@psmc-tw.com

Type of Firm

Private Equity Firm

Association Membership

Taiwan Venture Capital Association(TVCA)

Project Preferences

Type of Financing Preferred:

Expansion
Mezzanine
Seed
Startup

Geographical Preferences

International Preferences:

Taiwan

Industry Preferences

In Communications prefer:

Telecommunications

In Computer Software prefer:

Software

In Internet Specific prefer:

Internet

In Semiconductor/Electr prefer:

Electronics
Semiconductor
Optoelectronics

In Biotechnology prefer:

Biotechnology

Additional Information

Name of Most Recent Fund: Pan-Pacific Venture Capital Company, Ltd.
Most Recent Fund Was Raised: 12/31/1998
Year Founded: 1998
Capital Under Management: $18,600,000
Current Activity Level : Actively seeking new investments

PACIFIC VENTURE GROUP

16830 Ventura Boulevard
Suite 244
Encino, CA USA 91436
Phone: 818-990-4141
Fax: 818-990-6556
Website: www.pacven.com

Other Offices

114 Pacifica Street
Suite 270
Irvine, CA USA 92618
Phone: 949-753-0490
Fax: 949-753-8932

303 Twin Dolphin Drive
Suite 400
Redwood City, CA USA 94065
Phone: 650-610-7930
Fax: 650-610-7931

Management and Staff

David Dennis, Managing Partner
Eve Kurtin, Managing Director
Layton Crouch, Managing Director
Ralph Sabin, Managing Director
William West, Chief Financial Officer

Type of Firm

Private Equity Firm

Project Preferences

Role in Financing:

Will function either as deal originator or investor in deals created by others

Type of Financing Preferred:

Second Stage Financing
Balanced
Seed
First Stage Financing

Size of Investments Considered:

Min Size of Investment Considered (000s): $1,000
Max Size of Investment Considered (000s): $10,000

Geographical Preferences

Canadian Preferences:

All Canada

International Preferences:

United Kingdom

Industry Focus

(% based on actual investment)

Medical/Health	46.6%
Internet Specific	13.8%
Computer Software and Services	11.3%
Consumer Related	5.5%
Industrial/Energy	5.4%
Other Products	4.7%
Semiconductors/Other Elect.	4.5%
Computer Hardware	3.7%
Biotechnology	2.6%
Communications and Media	1.9%

Additional Information

Name of Most Recent Fund: PVG Associates II
Most Recent Fund Was Raised: 11/01/1996
Year Founded: 1995
Capital Under Management: $209,700,000
Current Activity Level : Actively seeking new investments
Method of Compensation: Return on investment is of primary concern, do not charge fees

---

PACIFIC VENTURE PARTNERS

8/F, No. 351, Yangguang St.
Neihu District
Taipei, Taiwan
Phone: 886-2-2797-9877
Fax: 886-2-2797-0377
Website: www.pacificventurepartners.com

Other Offices

6/F, No. 26 Xinghai Street
Suzhou Industrial Park
Jiangsu, China 215021
Phone: 86-512-6762-3400
Fax: 65-512-6762-3466

38C, No.7, Lane 500
Chang De Road
Shanghai, China 200041
Phone: 86-21-5292-5811
Fax: 86-21-5292-5822

Management and Staff

Arthur Wang, Vice President
Ben Yang, General Partner
Christopher Chu, Partner
Cynthia Hsiue, Principal
David Chow, Managing Director
James Wang, Venture Partner
Jay Deng, Managing Director
Mick Chang, Principal
Paul Wang, Managing General Partner
Suzie Wu, Partner
Tan Chong Hee, Vice President

Type of Firm

Private Equity Firm

Association Membership

Taiwan Venture Capital Association(TVCA)

Project Preferences

Type of Financing Preferred:

Early Stage
Expansion
Balanced
Turnaround
Later Stage
Startup

Size of Investments Considered:

Min Size of Investment Considered (000s): $3,000
Max Size of Investment Considered (000s): $50,000

Geographical Preferences

International Preferences:

Taiwan
Pacific Rim
Asia

Industry Preferences

In Communications prefer:

Telecommunications

In Computer Software prefer:

Software

In Internet Specific prefer:

Internet

In Semiconductor/Electr prefer:

Electronics
Semiconductor
Optoelectronics

In Biotechnology prefer:

Biotechnology

In Industrial/Energy prefer:

Machinery

In Manufact. prefer:

Manufacturing

Additional Information

Name of Most Recent Fund: Pacific Technology Partners
Most Recent Fund Was Raised: 03/24/2000
Year Founded: 1990
Capital Under Management: $800,000,000
Current Activity Level : Actively seeking new investments

PACIFICA FUND

5150 El Camino Real
Suite A-32
Los Altos, CA USA 94022
Phone: 650-318-0063
Fax: 650-318-0290
E-mail: info@pacificafund.com
Website: www.pacificafund.com

Management and Staff

Himanshu Choksi, Managing Director
Mochio Umeda, Managing Director
Timothy Oren, Managing Director
Yukio Okamoto, Managing Director

Type of Firm

Private Equity Firm

Project Preferences

Role in Financing:

Will function either as deal originator or investor in deals created by others

Type of Financing Preferred:

Early Stage
Expansion

Size of Investments Considered:

Min Size of Investment Considered (000s): $250
Max Size of Investment Considered (000s): $1,500

Geographical Preferences

United States Preferences:

All U.S.

Industry Preferences

In Communications prefer:

Telecommunications
Wireless Communications
Data Communications
Satellite Microwave Comm.

In Computer Hardware prefer:

Computer Graphics and Dig
Terminals
Disk Relat. Memory Device

In Computer Software prefer:

Software
Systems Software
Applications Software

In Internet Specific prefer:

Internet
Ecommerce

In Semiconductor/Electr prefer:

Electronic Components
Semiconductor
Micro-Processing
Controllers and Sensors
Sensors

In Industrial/Energy prefer:

Energy
Advanced Materials

Additional Information

Year Founded: 2000
Capital Under Management: $25,000,000
Current Activity Level : Actively seeking new investments
Method of Compensation: Return on investment is of primary concern, do not charge fees

---

PACIFICAP GROUP LLC

1132 Bishop Street
Suite 1810
Honolulu, HI USA 96813
Phone: 808-440-2727

Management and Staff

Jeffrey Au, Managing Director

Type of Firm

Private Equity Firm

Project Preferences

Type of Financing Preferred:

Balanced

Geographical Preferences

United States Preferences:

All U.S.

International Preferences:

Pacific
Asia

Additional Information

Name of Most Recent Fund: Hawaii Innovation Growth Fund LLC
Most Recent Fund Was Raised: 02/08/2008
Year Founded: 2000
Capital Under Management: $6,400,000
Current Activity Level : Actively seeking new investments

PACRIM VENTURE MANAGEMENT

535 Middlefield Road
Suite 280
Menlo Park, CA USA 94025
Phone: 650-330-0880
Fax: 650-330-0785
E-mail: info@pacrimpartners.com
Website: www.pacrimpartners.com

Management and Staff

Glen Anderson, Venture Partner
Joe Hage, Venture Partner
Nisa Leung, Venture Partner
Thomas Toy, Managing Director

Type of Firm

Private Equity Firm

Association Membership

Western Association of Venture Capitalists (WAVC)

Project Preferences

Role in Financing:

Will function either as deal originator or investor in deals created by others

Type of Financing Preferred:

Early Stage
Start-up Financing
Seed
First Stage Financing

Size of Investments Considered:

Min Size of Investment Considered (000s): $100
Max Size of Investment Considered (000s): $2,000

Geographical Preferences

United States Preferences:

West Coast

Industry Preferences

In Communications prefer:

Telecommunications
Wireless Communications
Data Communications

In Computer Hardware prefer:

Computer Graphics and Dig
Integrated Turnkey System
Disk Relat. Memory Device

In Computer Software prefer:

Computer Services
Software
Systems Software
Applications Software
Artificial Intelligence

In Internet Specific prefer:

Internet

In Semiconductor/Electr prefer:

Semiconductor
Component Testing Equipmt
Laser Related
Fiber Optics

Additional Information

Name of Most Recent Fund: PacRim Venture Partners I, L.P.
Most Recent Fund Was Raised: 12/03/1999
Year Founded: 1999
Capital Under Management: $25,000,000
Current Activity Level : Actively seeking new investments
Method of Compensation: Return on investment is of primary concern, do not charge fees

---

PACT RESEARCH FUND

855-2nd Street, South West
Suite 1220
Calgary, Canada T2P 4J7
Phone: 403-303-1583
Fax: 403-294-1196

Management and Staff

Maury Parsons, Managing Partner

Type of Firm

Private Equity Firm

Additional Information

Year Founded: 2009
Current Activity Level : Actively seeking new investments

PACTUAL CAPITAL PARTNERS GESTAO DE RECURSOS LTDA.

Praia de Botafogo
no 300, 10 andar
Rio de Janeiro, Brazil
Website: www.pactual.com

Type of Firm

Private Equity Firm

Project Preferences

Type of Financing Preferred:

Balanced

Geographical Preferences

International Preferences:

Brazil

Additional Information

Year Founded: 2007
Current Activity Level : Actively seeking new investments

PAI PARTNERS (FKA: PAI MANAGEMENT)

43, avenue de l'Opera
Paris, France 75002
Phone: 33-1-5577-9100
Fax: 33-1-5577-9143
E-mail: pai.paris@paipartners.com
Website: www.paipartners.com

Other Offices

Piazza del Duomo, 17
Milan, Italy 20121
Phone: 39-2-854-5151
Fax: 39-2-867-300

26 Boulevard Royal
Luxembourg, Luxembourg L2449
Phone: 352-22-9999-5113
Fax: 352-22-9999-5404

22 Conduit Street
London, United Kingdom W1S 2XR
Phone: 44-20-7355-0890
Fax: 44-20-7495-1687

Calle Jose Ortega y Gasset
21, 3 Derecha
Madrid, Spain 28006
Phone: 34-91-590-2250
Fax: 34-91-590-2258

Luisenstrasse 14
Munich, Germany D-80333
Phone: 49-89-5151-4650
Fax: 49-89-5151-46510

Nyhavn 63A, 1st floor
Copenhagen, Denmark 1051
Phone: 45-3330-0630
Fax: 44-3311-1102

Management and Staff

Alex Kessler, Principal
Amaury De Seze, Chairman & CEO
Christilla De Moustier, Principal
Colm O'Sullivan, Partner
Eric Bouchez, Partner
Frederic Stevenin, Partner
Hamish Mackenzie, Partner
Jean D'Arthuys, Partner
Jean-Michel Dalmasso, Principal
Lise Nobre, Partner
Olivier De Vregille, Partner
Raffaele Vitale, Managing Director
Ricardo De Serdio, Partner
Sophie Lombard, Principal
Ziad Joseph Sarkis, Partner

Type of Firm

Private Equity Firm

Association Membership

Italian Venture Capital Association (AIFI)
French Venture Capital Association (AFIC)
European Private Equity and Venture Capital Assoc.
Spanish Venture Capital Association (ASCRI)

Project Preferences

Type of Financing Preferred:

Leveraged Buyout
Expansion

Size of Investments Considered:

Min Size of Investment Considered (000s): $9,416
Max Size of Investment Considered (000s): $188,320

Geographical Preferences

International Preferences:

Europe

Western Europe
France

Industry Focus

(% based on actual investment)

Consumer Related	48.0%
Other Products	25.9%
Biotechnology	11.0%
Communications and Media	5.3%
Internet Specific	3.8%
Industrial/Energy	3.3%
Semiconductors/Other Elect.	1.5%
Computer Software and Services	1.0%
Medical/Health	0.2%

Additional Information

Name of Most Recent Fund: PAI Europe IV
Most Recent Fund Was Raised: 04/22/2005
Year Founded: 1990
Capital Under Management: $12,050,500,000
Current Activity Level : Actively seeking new investments

PAINE & PARTNERS LLC (FKA: FOX PAINE MANAGEMENT III LLC)

950 Tower Lane
Suite 1150
Foster City, CA USA 94404
Phone: 650-525-1200
Fax: 650-525-1240
E-mail: info@painepartners.com
Website: www.painepartners.com

Other Offices

461 Fifth Avenue
17th Floor
New York, NY USA 10017
Phone: 212-379-7200
Fax: 212-379-7235

71 South Wacker Drive
Suite 1875
Chicago, IL USA 60606
Phone: 312-564-5300
Fax: 312-564-5400

Management and Staff

Amy Ghisletta, Chief Operating Officer
Justin Reyna, Principal
Kevin Schwartz, Partner
Mitchell Presser, Partner
Robert Meyer, Chief Financial Officer
Troy Thacker, Partner
W.Dexter Paine, Partner

Type of Firm

Private Equity Firm

Project Preferences

Type of Financing Preferred:
Leveraged Buyout
Expansion
Management Buyouts
Acquisition
Special Situation

Geographical Preferences

United States Preferences:
All U.S.

Additional Information

Name of Most Recent Fund: Paine & Partners Fund III, L.P. (Fox Paine Capital Fund III)
Most Recent Fund Was Raised: 04/17/2006
Year Founded: 2008
Capital Under Management: $1,200,000,000
Current Activity Level : Actively seeking new investments

PAK OMAN INVESTMENT COMPANY

1F, Tower A, Finace & Trade
Shahra-e-Faisal
Karachi, Pakistan
Phone: 92-21-566-0472
Fax: 92-21-566-0483
E-mail: info@pakoman.com
Website: www.pakoman.com

Management and Staff

Mohammad Jamal Nasir, Chief Financial Officer
Zafar Iqbal, CEO & Managing Director

Type of Firm

Bank Affiliated

Project Preferences

Type of Financing Preferred:
Balanced

Additional Information

Year Founded: 2001
Current Activity Level : Actively seeking new investments

PALACE VENTURES LTD

311 Great Guildford BusinessSq
30 Great Guildford Street
London, United Kingdom SE1 0HS
Phone: 44-20-7631-2158
Fax: 44-20-7803-0555
E-mail: enquiries@palaceventures.com
Website: www.palaceventures.com

Management and Staff

Andrew Halsall, Managing Director

Type of Firm

Private Equity Firm

Project Preferences

Type of Financing Preferred:
Balanced

Geographical Preferences

International Preferences:
United Kingdom
Europe
Middle East
Saudi Arabia

Industry Preferences

In Communications prefer:
Communications and Media
Telecommunications

Additional Information

Year Founded: 2004
Current Activity Level : Actively seeking new investments

PALADIN CAPITAL MANAGEMENT LLC

2001 Pennsylvania Avenue, NW
Suite 400
Washington, DC USA 20006
Phone: 202-293-5590
Fax: 202-293-5597
E-mail: info@paladincapgroup.com
Website: www.paladincapgroup.com

Management and Staff

Alf Andreassen, Managing Director
Colin Bryant, Principal
E. Kenneth Pentimonti, Principal
H. Lee Buchanan, Venture Partner
Kenneth Minihan, Managing Director
Michael Lyons, Venture Partner
Michael Moniz, Managing Director
Niloofar Howe, Managing Director
Paul Conley, Vice President
Philip Eliot, Principal
William Mulrow, Managing Director

Type of Firm

Private Equity Firm

Association Membership

National Venture Capital Association - USA (NVCA)

Project Preferences

Type of Financing Preferred:
Expansion
Balanced

Geographical Preferences

United States Preferences:
New York
All U.S.

Industry Preferences

In Computer Software prefer:
Systems Software

In Industrial/Energy prefer:
Alternative Energy

Additional Information
Name of Most Recent Fund: Paladin III, L.P.
Most Recent Fund Was Raised: 08/20/2007
Year Founded: 2000
Capital Under Management: $654,700,000
Current Activity Level : Actively seeking new investments

PALADIN PARTNERS
838 Kirkland Avenue
Kirkland, WA USA 98033
Phone: 425-739-0978
Fax: 425-739-0980
Website: www.paladinpartners.com

Other Offices
6916 SouthWest Tierra Del Mar Drive
Beaverton, OR USA 97007
Phone: 503-643-8214

Management and Staff
Cheryl Bachman, Partner

Type of Firm
Service Provider

Association Membership
National Venture Capital Association - USA (NVCA)

Project Preferences

Role in Financing:
Will function either as deal originator or investor in deals created by others

Type of Financing Preferred:
Early Stage
Seed
First Stage Financing
Startup

Geographical Preferences

United States Preferences:
West Coast

Industry Preferences

In Communications prefer:
Wireless Communications

In Computer Software prefer:
Software
Systems Software
Applications Software

In Internet Specific prefer:
E-Commerce Technology
Internet
Web Aggregration/Portals

In Business Serv. prefer:
Consulting Services
Media

Additional Information
Year Founded: 1995
Current Activity Level : Actively seeking new investments
Method of Compensation: Professional fee required whether or not deal closes

---

PALAMON CAPITAL PARTNERS (FKA: AMPHION CAPITAL PARTNERS)
Cleveland House
33 King Street
London, United Kingdom SW1Y 6RJ
Phone: 44-20-7766-2000
Fax: 44-20-7766-2002
Website: www.palamon.com

Management and Staff
Alexis de Dietrich, Vice President
Braam Verster, Vice President
Daniel Mytnik, Principal
Fabio Massimo Giuseppetti, Partner
Gary Pritchard, Chief Financial Officer
Holger Kleingarn, Partner
Jaime-Enrique Hugas, Principal
Jean Bonnavion, Vice President
Jonathan Heathcote, Partner
Owen Wilson, Vice President
Pascal Noth, Vice President
Ricardo Caupers, Vice President
Stefano Bacci, Partner
Valerio Boccardi, Vice President

Type of Firm
Private Equity Firm

Association Membership
British Venture Capital Association (BVCA)
European Private Equity and Venture Capital Assoc.

Project Preferences

Type of Financing Preferred:
Second Stage Financing
Leveraged Buyout
Expansion
Turnaround

Size of Investments Considered:
Min Size of Investment Considered (000s): $12,552
Max Size of Investment Considered (000s): $62,759

Geographical Preferences

International Preferences:
Italy
United Kingdom
Portugal
Europe
Western Europe
Spain
Scandanavia/Nordic Region

Industry Preferences

In Communications prefer:
Telecommunications

In Medical/Health prefer:
Medical/Health

In Financial Services prefer:
Financial Services

In Business Serv. prefer:
Services
Media

Additional Information
Year Founded: 1999
Capital Under Management: $1,487,700,000
Current Activity Level : Actively seeking new investments

PALISADE CAPITAL MANAGEMENT
One Bridge Plaza
Suite 695
Fort Lee, NJ USA 07024
Phone: 201-585-7733
Fax: 201-585-9798
E-mail: INFO@PALCAP.COM
Website: www.palisadecapital.com

Management and Staff
James Jahnke, Vice President
Sergey Dubin, Vice President

Type of Firm
Private Equity Advisor or Fund of Funds

Additional Information
Year Founded: 2000
Capital Under Management: $140,000,000
Current Activity Level : Actively seeking new investments

PALISADES VENTURES (FKA: CENTRE PALISADES VENTURES)
11766 Wilshire Boulevard
Suite 890
Los Angeles, CA USA 90025
Phone: 310-996-7696
Fax: 310-575-9504
E-mail: info@centrepalisades.com
Website: www.palisadesventures.com

Management and Staff
Anders Richardson, Managing Director
Bruce Pollack, Senior Managing Director
David Jaffe, Managing Director
Henry Lichstein, Venture Partner
Michael Banks, Managing Director
Michael Darby, Venture Partner

Paul D Addario, Senior Managing Director
Robert Bergmann, Managing Director

Type of Firm

Private Equity Firm

Project Preferences

Type of Financing Preferred:

Balanced

Size of Investments Considered:

Min Size of Investment Considered (000s): $2,500
Max Size of Investment Considered (000s): $7,000

Industry Preferences

In Communications prefer:

Wireless Communications

Additional Information

Year Founded: 2003
Capital Under Management: $75,000,000
Current Activity Level : Actively seeking new investments

PALL MALL PARTNERS LIMITED

52a Cromwell Road
London, United Kingdom SW7 5BE
Phone: 44-20-7590-1340
Fax: 44-20-7590-1345
E-mail: info@pallmallpartners.com
Website: www.pallmallpartners.com

Management and Staff

Michael Bauer, Founder

Type of Firm

Private Equity Firm

Project Preferences

Type of Financing Preferred:

Early Stage

Geographical Preferences

International Preferences:

Europe

Industry Preferences

In Internet Specific prefer:

Internet

Additional Information

Year Founded: 2002
Capital Under Management: $818,700,000
Current Activity Level : Actively seeking new investments

PALLADIO FINANZIARIA

23 Via Larga
Milan, Italy 20122
Phone: 39-2-5832-1020
Fax: 39-2-5830-1514
Website: www.palladiofinanziaria.it

Type of Firm

Investment Management Firm

Association Membership

Italian Venture Capital Association (AIFI)

Project Preferences

Type of Financing Preferred:

Leveraged Buyout
Early Stage
Expansion
Later Stage

Geographical Preferences

International Preferences:

Italy

Additional Information

Year Founded: 2000
Current Activity Level : Actively seeking new investments

PALLADIUM EQUITY PARTNERS LLC

1270 Avenue of the Americas
Rockefeller Center, Suite 2200
New York, NY USA 10020
Phone: 212-218-5150
Fax: 212-218-5155
E-mail: palladium@palladiumequity.com
Website: www.palladiumequity.com

Other Offices

11726 San Vicente Boulevard
Suite 300
Brentwood, CA USA 90049
Phone: 310-820-4009
Fax: 310-820-4055

Management and Staff

Alex Ventosa, Managing Director
Daniel Ilundain, Vice President
David Perez, Managing Director
Erik Scott, Principal
Gary Nusbaum, Managing Director
Ivelisse Rodriguez-Simon, Vice President
Kevin Reymond, Chief Financial Officer
Luis Zaldivar, Principal
Luis Francisco Lora, Vice President
Maria Del Pilar Avila, Vice President
Peter Joseph, Managing Director

Type of Firm

Private Equity Firm

Project Preferences

Role in Financing:

Prefer role as deal originator but will also invest in deals created by others

Type of Financing Preferred:

Leveraged Buyout
Mezzanine
Generalist PE
Management Buyouts

Size of Investments Considered:

Min Size of Investment Considered (000s): $10,000
Max Size of Investment Considered (000s): $50,000

Industry Focus

(% based on actual investment)	
Consumer Related	41.7%
Other Products	25.8%
Industrial/Energy	14.3%
Internet Specific	12.0%
Medical/Health	4.6%
Biotechnology	1.5%

Additional Information

Name of Most Recent Fund: Palladium Equity Partners III, L.P.
Most Recent Fund Was Raised: 11/01/2004
Year Founded: 1997
Capital Under Management: $936,000,000
Current Activity Level : Actively seeking new investments

PALM BEACH CAPITAL PARTNERS

180 Royal Palm Way
Suite 203
Palm Beach, FL USA 33480
Phone: 561-659-9022
Fax: 561-659-9055
Website: www.pbcap.com

Management and Staff

Adam Klein, Vice President
Michael Schmickle, Partner
Nathan Ward, Partner
Richard Schlanger, Partner
Robert Boyd, Vice President
Shaun McGruder, Partner

Type of Firm

Private Equity Firm

Project Preferences

Type of Financing Preferred:

Leveraged Buyout
Expansion

Size of Investments Considered:

Min Size of Investment Considered (000s): $100
Max Size of Investment Considered (000s): $10,000

Geographical Preferences

United States Preferences:

Florida

Additional Information

Year Founded: 2001
Capital Under Management: $170,000,000

Current Activity Level : Actively seeking new investments

PALMFUND MANAGEMENT LLC

Carrera 9 N 80-45
Of. 801
Bogota, Colombia
Phone: 57-1-742-0707
Fax: 57-1-742-1930
E-mail: info@palmfund.com
Website: www.palmfund.com

Other Offices

445 Hamilton Avenue
Suite 1102
White Plains, NY USA 10601
Phone: 914-220-5462
Fax: 914-220-5472

Montes Urales 723, P. O. Box 1
Lomas DE Chapultepec
Mexico, Mexico 11000
Phone: 52-55-5202-2598

Management and Staff

Carlos Gomez, Managing Partner
Cipriano Santisteban, Partner
Diego Acevedo, Principal

Type of Firm

Private Equity Firm

Project Preferences

Type of Financing Preferred:
Leveraged Buyout
Mezzanine
Distressed Debt

Geographical Preferences

International Preferences:
Latin America

Additional Information

Year Founded: 2008
Capital Under Management: $90,000,000
Current Activity Level : Actively seeking new investments

PALO ALTO INVESTORS

470 University Avenue
Palo Alto, CA USA 94301
Phone: 650-325-0772
Fax: 650-325-5028
E-mail: pai@pa-investors.com
Website: www.pa-investors.com

Management and Staff

Anthony Joon Yun, President
David Anderson, Partner
Paul Zweng, Partner
Ray Conley, Partner
Ted Janus, Partner

Type of Firm

Investment Management Firm

Project Preferences

Type of Financing Preferred:
Balanced

Geographical Preferences

United States Preferences:
California

Industry Preferences

In Medical/Health prefer:
Medical/Health

Additional Information

Year Founded: 1989
Capital Under Management: $1,200,000,000
Current Activity Level : Actively seeking new investments

PALO ALTO VENTURE PARTNERS (FKA: 21VC PARTNERS)

555 Bryant Street
Suite 558
Palo Alto, CA USA 94301
Phone: 650-462-1221
Fax: 650-462-1227
Website: www.pavp.com

Management and Staff

Neil Weintraut, Partner
Peter Ziebelman, Partner

Type of Firm

Private Equity Firm

Association Membership

Western Association of Venture Capitalists (WAVC)

Project Preferences

Role in Financing:
Prefer role as deal originator but will also invest in deals created by others

Type of Financing Preferred:
Early Stage
Seed
First Stage Financing
Startup

Size of Investments Considered:
Min Size of Investment Considered (000s): $1,000
Max Size of Investment Considered (000s): $10,000

Geographical Preferences

United States Preferences:
All U.S.

Industry Focus

(% based on actual investment)

Internet Specific	48.7%
Computer Software and Services	35.3%
Communications and Media	6.6%
Consumer Related	4.9%
Semiconductors/Other Elect.	2.4%
Other Products	2.3%

Additional Information

Name of Most Recent Fund: 21VC Fund II
Most Recent Fund Was Raised: 10/02/1999
Year Founded: 1996
Capital Under Management: $150,000,000
Current Activity Level : Actively seeking new investments
Method of Compensation: Return on investment is of primary concern, do not charge fees

PALOMAR VENTURES

100 Wilshire Boulevard
Suite 1700
Santa Monica, CA USA 90401
Phone: 310-260-6050
Fax: 310-656-4150
Website: www.palomarventures.com

Other Offices

555 Bryant Street
Suite 470
Palo Alto, CA USA 94301
Phone: 650-566-1100
Fax: 650-566-1110

18881 Von Karman Avenue
Suite 960
Irvine, CA USA 92612
Phone: 949-475-9455
Fax: 949-475-9456

Management and Staff

Amanda Reed, Partner
James Gauer, Managing Director
Kevin Jacques, Partner
Randall Lunn, Managing Director
Robert Obuch, Partner
Scott Walters, Chief Financial Officer

Type of Firm

Private Equity Firm

Association Membership

Western Association of Venture Capitalists (WAVC)
National Venture Capital Association - USA (NVCA)

Project Preferences

Role in Financing:
Prefer role as deal originator but will also invest in deals created by others

Type of Financing Preferred:
Early Stage
Seed
First Stage Financing
Startup

Size of Investments Considered:
Min Size of Investment Considered (000s): $250
Max Size of Investment Considered (000s): $15,000

Geographical Preferences

United States Preferences:
Northern California
West Coast
Southwest
All U.S.

Industry Focus

(% based on actual investment)

Computer Software and Services	38.1%
Communications and Media	28.2%
Internet Specific	19.7%
Semiconductors/Other Elect.	9.5%
Computer Hardware	4.1%
Other Products	0.4%

Additional Information

Name of Most Recent Fund: Palomar Ventures III Principals Fund
Most Recent Fund Was Raised: 11/30/2004
Year Founded: 1999
Capital Under Management: $525,000,000
Current Activity Level : Actively seeking new investments
Method of Compensation: Return on investment is of primary concern, do not charge fees

---

PALUEL-MARMONT CAPITAL

24, rue Murillo
Paris, France 75008
Phone: 33-1-4429-9823
Fax: 33-1-4429-9850
E-mail: info@paluel-marmont-capital.fr
Website: www.paluel-marmont-capital.fr

Type of Firm

Bank Affiliated

Association Membership

French Venture Capital Association (AFIC)

Project Preferences

Role in Financing:
Unknown

Type of Financing Preferred:
Leveraged Buyout

Size of Investments Considered:
Min Size of Investment Considered (000s): $1,225
Max Size of Investment Considered (000s): $6,276

Geographical Preferences

International Preferences:
France

Additional Information

Year Founded: 1999
Current Activity Level : Actively seeking new investments
Method of Compensation: Unknown

PAMODZI INVESTMENT HOLDINGS

Pamodzi House, 3rd Floor
5 Willowbrook close
Melrose North, South Africa
Phone: 27-11-912-7500
Fax: 27-11-912-7599
Website: www.pamodzi.co.za

Management and Staff

Ndaba Ntsele, Chief Executive Officer

Type of Firm

Private Equity Firm

Project Preferences

Type of Financing Preferred:
Balanced

Geographical Preferences

International Preferences:
South Africa

Industry Preferences

In Industrial/Energy prefer:
Energy

Additional Information

Year Founded: 2007
Capital Under Management: $1,300,000,000
Current Activity Level : Actively seeking new investments

PAMPLONA CAPITAL MANAGEMENT LLP

25 Park Lane
London, United Kingdom W1K 1RA
Phone: 44-20-7079-8000
Fax: 44-20-7495-3909
E-mail: info@pamplonafunds.com
Website: www.pamplonafunds.com

Other Offices

40th floor
3 Azrieli Center
Tel-Aviv, Israel 67023
Phone: 972-3769-6000
Fax: 972-3769-6001

Poststrasse 30
Zug, Switzerland 6300
Phone: 41-41-726-0700
Fax: 41-41-726-0701

Management and Staff

David Lang, Vice President
Eric Bidinger, Vice President
Henry Gregson, Partner
John Halsted, Managing Partner
Kevin O'Flaherty, Chief Financial Officer
Markku Lonnqvist, Partner
Markus Noe-Nordberg, Partner
Martin Schwab, Partner
Michael Rosen, Vice President
Paul Thompson, Partner
Selahattin Zoralioglu, Vice President

Type of Firm

Private Equity Firm

Project Preferences

Type of Financing Preferred:
Leveraged Buyout
Management Buyouts

Geographical Preferences

International Preferences:
United Kingdom
Europe

Additional Information

Year Founded: 2005
Capital Under Management: $1,807,600,000
Current Activity Level : Actively seeking new investments

PAN AFRICAN RESOURCES PLC (FKA:WHITE KNIGHT INVESTMENTS PLC)

6 Saint James's Place
London, United Kingdom SW1A 1NP
Phone: 44-20-7499-3916
Fax: 44-20-7491-1989
Website: www.panafricanresources.com

Type of Firm

Investment Management Firm

Project Preferences

Type of Financing Preferred:
Early Stage
Expansion
Later Stage
Seed
Startup

Geographical Preferences

International Preferences:
Scandanavia/Nordic Region

Industry Preferences

In Communications prefer:
Telecommunications

In Internet Specific prefer:
Internet

Additional Information

Year Founded: 2000
Capital Under Management: $1,800,000
Current Activity Level : Actively seeking new investments

PANASONIC VENTURES

550 South Winchester Boulevard
Suite 400
San Jose, CA USA 95128
Phone: 408-861-3900
Fax: 408-861-3990
Website: www.vcpanasonic.com

Other Offices

1207 Indiana Street
Suite 9
San Francisco, CA USA 94107

3-1-1 Yagumo-nakamachi
Moriguichi
Osaka, Japan 570-8501
Phone: 81-6-6906-9051
Fax: 81-6-6906-6026

Management and Staff

Dilip Sampath, Venture Partner
Patrick Suel, Venture Partner

Type of Firm

Corporate PE/Venture

Project Preferences

Type of Financing Preferred:
Balanced
Later Stage

Geographical Preferences

International Preferences:
Europe
Asia
All International

Industry Preferences

In Communications prefer:
CATV & Pay TV Systems
Wireless Communications

In Computer Software prefer:
Software

Additional Information

Year Founded: 1998
Capital Under Management: $100,000,000
Current Activity Level : Actively seeking new investments

PANDA CAPITAL ASIA, LTD.

Unit 706, Lu Plaza
2 Wing Yip Street, Kowloon
Hong Kong, Hong Kong
Phone: 852-2799-3733
Fax: 852-2798-6254
Website: www.pandacapital.cn

Other Offices

Huafu Tiandi, Room1602, Building 3
222 Ma Dang Road
Shanghai, China 200020
Phone: 86-21-5306-7202
Fax: 86-21-5306-7251

7, Lane 333, DunHua North Road
Taipei, Taiwan
Phone: 886-2-2718-9908
Fax: 886-2-2719-4765

222 Yan An Road (East)
Suite 4104, Bund Center
Shanghai, China
Phone: 86-21-6335-0305
Fax: 86-21-6335-0306

Management and Staff

Andreas Schwyn, Managing Partner
Arfen Hsu, Managing Partner
Harry Sprecher, Partner

Type of Firm

Private Equity Firm

Project Preferences

Type of Financing Preferred:
Expansion

Geographical Preferences

International Preferences:
China

Additional Information

Year Founded: 2007
Current Activity Level : Actively seeking new investments

PANGAEA VENTURES

1151 West 8th Avenue
Suite 1
Vancouver, Canada V6H 1C5
Phone: 604-738-0225
Fax: 413-751-2371
Website: www.pangaeaventures.com

Other Offices

101 Scarborough Road
Briarcliff Manor, NY USA 10510
Phone: 914-944-0858
Fax: 914-944-0858

Management and Staff

Calvin Yee, Partner
Christopher Erickson, Partner
Panos Kyriacou, Partner
Purnesh Seegopaul, Partner

Type of Firm

Private Equity Firm

Project Preferences

Type of Financing Preferred:
Seed
Startup

Geographical Preferences

Canadian Preferences:
Alberta
Central Canada
British Columbia
Eastern Canada
Western Canada

Industry Preferences

In Communications prefer:
Telecommunications

In Industrial/Energy prefer:
Energy

Additional Information

Year Founded: 2000
Capital Under Management: $50,000,000
Current Activity Level : Actively seeking new investments

PANORAMA CAPITAL

2440 Sand Hill Road
Suite 302
Menlo Park, CA USA 94025
Phone: 650-234-1420
Fax: 650-234-1437
E-mail: info@panoramacapital.com
Website: www.panoramacapital.com

Management and Staff

Allan Leinwand, Venture Partner
Audrey Vallen, Chief Financial Officer
Christopher Albinson, Managing Director
Damion Wicker, Managing Director
Gaurav Aggarwal, Principal
Michael Jung, Partner
Rodney Ferguson, Managing Director
Shahan Soghikian, Managing Director
Shankar Chandran, Principal

Type of Firm

Private Equity Firm

Association Membership

National Venture Capital Association - USA (NVCA)

Project Preferences

Type of Financing Preferred:
Early Stage
Balanced

Geographical Preferences

United States Preferences:
All U.S.

Industry Preferences

In Internet Specific prefer:
Internet

In Computer Other prefer:
Computer Related

In Semiconductor/Electr prefer:
Semiconductor

Additional Information

Year Founded: 2005
Capital Under Management: $240,000,000
Current Activity Level : Actively seeking new investments

PANTHEON VENTURES, LTD.

Norfolk House
31 Street James's Square
London, United Kingdom SW1Y 4JR
Phone: 44-20-7484-6200
Fax: 44-20-7484-6201
E-mail: contactus@pantheon.com.hk
Website: www.pantheonventures.com

Other Offices

12 Avenue des Buissons
Rhode St. Genese, Belgium B-1640
Phone: 32-2-380-9970
Fax: 32-2-290-2021

Transamerica Center
23rd Floor, 600 Montgomery Street
San Francisco, CA USA 94111
Phone: 415-249-6200
Fax: 415-249-6299

One Exchange Square, 8 Connaught Place
Suite 908, 9th Floor
Central, Hong Kong
Phone: 852-2810-8063
Fax: 852-2526-0218

One Market Street
Level 23
Sydney, Australia NSW 2000
Phone: 61-2-9285-1393
Fax: 61-2-9261-1227

590 Madison Avenue
40th Floor
New York, NY USA 10022
Phone: 212-702-7805
Fax: 212-702-7901

Management and Staff

Alastair Bruce, Managing Partner
Alex Scott, Principal
Alex Wilmerding, Principal
Andrew Lebus, Managing Partner
Brett Johnson, Principal
Brian Buenneke, Partner
Brian Lim, Principal
Carol Foster, Principal
Carola Mauer, Vice President
Carsten Huwendiek, Principal
Charlotte Westley, Vice President
Chris Meads, Partner
Colin Wimsett, Managing Partner
Daniela Konrath, Partner
Dennis McCrary, Partner
Dushy Sivanithy, Vice President
Elly Livingstone, Partner
Erik Wong, Vice President
Francesco Di Valmarana, Principal
Gary Hiatt, Managing Partner
Gina Lee, Principal
Graeme Keenan, Principal
Graham Read, Vice President
Hannah Malone, Vice President
Helen Steers, Partner
Ian Deas, Partner
J. Jay Pierrepont, Managing Partner
Jeff Ganung, Partner
Jeffrey Reed, Principal
Jennie Jury, Vice President
John Lance, Partner
John Morgan, Partner
Jonathan Spalter, Vice President
Josephine Defty, Vice President
Kathryn Leaf Wilmes, Principal
Laurence Jonkler, Vice President
Leon Hadass, Principal
Lily Wong, Partner
Lisa Wong, Vice President
Marcus Alexis, Principal
Matt Curran, Vice President
Matt Garfunkle, Principal
Matthew Jones, Vice President
Mattias Berntsson, Principal
Maureen Downey, Principal
Monica McGuire, Principal
Monica Rupan, Vice President
Nik Morandi, Vice President
Paul Ward, Partner
Peter Flynn, Partner
Rebeca Ehrnrooth, Vice President
Roar Storebaug, Vice President
Rob Barr, Partner
Rob Wright, Partner
Rudy Scarpa, Partner
Sally Collier, Partner
Saverio Costa, Principal
Serge Raicher, Partner
Steve Scarff, Principal
Susan Long McAndrews, Partner
Vincent Huang, Partner

Type of Firm

Private Equity Advisor or Fund of Funds

Association Membership

Hong Kong Venture Capital Association (HKVCA)
National Venture Capital Association - USA (NVCA)
European Private Equity and Venture Capital Assoc.

Project Preferences

Role in Financing:
Prefer role in deals created by others

Type of Financing Preferred:
Fund of Funds
Fund of Funds of Second

Geographical Preferences

United States Preferences:
All U.S.

International Preferences:
Europe
Asia
All International

Additional Information

Name of Most Recent Fund: Pantheon Global Secondary Fund III B, L.P.
Most Recent Fund Was Raised: 07/24/2006
Year Founded: 1982
Capital Under Management: $5,700,000,000
Current Activity Level : Actively seeking new investments
Method of Compensation: Return on investment is of primary concern, do not charge fees

---

PANTHERA CAPITAL GROUP

34 Fuxingxi Lu
Shanghai, China 200031
Phone: 86-21-6431-9126
Fax: 86-21-6431-9709
Website: www.panthera.cn

Management and Staff

Fu Zhong, Venture Partner
Jim Preissier, Managing Partner
Richard Hui, Managing Partner
San Eng, Managing Partner

Type of Firm

Private Equity Firm

Project Preferences

Type of Financing Preferred:
Expansion
Balanced
Later Stage

Geographical Preferences

International Preferences:
Asia

Industry Preferences

In Semiconductor/Electr prefer:
Electronics

In Consumer Related prefer:
Retail
Food/Beverage
Consumer Products
Other Restaurants
Hotels and Resorts
Education Related

In Industrial/Energy prefer:
Energy

In Financial Services prefer:
Real Estate
Financial Services

In Business Serv. prefer:
Distribution

Additional Information
Year Founded: 2007
Current Activity Level : Actively seeking new investments

PAPERBOY VENTURES, LLC
1875 K Street Northwest
Suite 700
Washington, DC USA 20006
Phone: 202-496-9220
Fax: 202-496-1748
E-mail: info@paperboyventures.com
Website: www.paperboyventures.com

Management and Staff
Anthony Garland, Managing Director & CFO
Jaime Lewis, Principal
Kay Perry, Principal

Type of Firm
Private Equity Firm

Association Membership
National Venture Capital Association - USA (NVCA)

Project Preferences

Type of Financing Preferred:
Early Stage

Industry Preferences

In Biotechnology prefer:
Biotechnology

Additional Information
Year Founded: 2003
Current Activity Level : Actively seeking new investments

PAPPAS VENTURES
2520 Meridian Parkway
Suite 400
Durham, NC USA 27713
Phone: 919-998-3300
Fax: 919-998-3301
E-mail: info@pappasventures.com
Website: www.pappasventures.com

Management and Staff
Arthur Pappas, Managing Partner
Eric Linsley, Managing Partner
Ernest Mario, Venture Partner
Ford Worthy, Partner
Rosina Maar Pavia, Partner
Scott Weiner, Principal

Type of Firm
Service Provider

Association Membership
National Venture Capital Association - USA (NVCA)

Project Preferences

Role in Financing:
Will function either as deal originator or investor in deals created by others

Type of Financing Preferred:
Second Stage Financing
Early Stage
Mezzanine
Balanced
Later Stage
First Stage Financing

Size of Investments Considered:
Min Size of Investment Considered (000s): $100
Max Size of Investment Considered (000s): $7,000

Geographical Preferences

Canadian Preferences:
All Canada

Industry Focus
(% based on actual investment)

Biotechnology	53.3%
Medical/Health	44.8%
Computer Software and Services	1.8%
Internet Specific	0.1%

Additional Information
Name of Most Recent Fund: A.M. Pappas Life Science Ventures IV, L.P.
Most Recent Fund Was Raised: 11/21/2008
Year Founded: 1994
Capital Under Management: $312,000,000
Current Activity Level : Actively seeking new investments
Method of Compensation: Return on investment is of primary concern, do not charge fees

PARACOR CAPITAL ADVISORS PVT., LTD.
704, 7th Floor, Dev Plaza
68, S.V. Road, Andheri West
Mumbai, India 400 058
Phone: 91-99-6705-9432
Fax: 91-22-2625-2667
Website: www.pca-in.com

Other Offices
Old #9A, New #12, Jeevanandan Street
Sriram Nagar, Thiruvanmiyur
Chennai, India 600 041
Phone: 91-44-4558-7362
Fax: 91-44-4558-7361

Mars Restaurant Complex
Off International Airport
Mumbai, India 400 059
Phone: 91-22-2825-1702
Fax: 91-22-2825-1704

208 Orchid Square
Block B, Sushant Lok 1
Gurgaon, India 122 002
Phone: 91-124-5049361
Fax: 91-124-504-9365

Management and Staff
Anil Pathak, Managing Director
Charles Garrard, Principal
John Lynch, Chairman & Managing Director
P.C. Sasikumar, Vice President
V. Ravindran, Principal

Type of Firm
Private Equity Advisor or Fund of Funds

Association Membership
Indian Venture Capital Association (IVCA)

Project Preferences

Role in Financing:
Prefer role as deal originator but will also invest in deals created by others

Type of Financing Preferred:
Generalist PE
Expansion
Acquisition
Joint Ventures

Size of Investments Considered:
Min Size of Investment Considered (000s): $5,000
Max Size of Investment Considered (000s): $10,000

Geographical Preferences

International Preferences:
India

Industry Preferences

In Consumer Related prefer:
Consumer
Food/Beverage

In Transportation prefer:
Transportation

In Financial Services prefer:
Financial Services

Additional Information

Year Founded: 1994
Capital Under Management: $200,000,000
Current Activity Level : Actively seeking new investments

PARADIGM MEDIA INVESTMENTS PLC

c/o Lipworth Capital Limited
65 Sloane Street
London, United Kingdom W1X 9SH
Phone: 44-207-235-1005
Fax: 44-207-235-1008
E-mail: info@paradigmmedia.co.uk

Type of Firm

Private Equity Firm

Project Preferences

Type of Financing Preferred:
Early Stage
Later Stage

Geographical Preferences

International Preferences:
United Kingdom
Europe
Eastern Europe

Industry Preferences

In Communications prefer:
Commercial Communications

In Internet Specific prefer:
Internet

In Business Serv. prefer:
Media

Additional Information

Year Founded: 2000
Capital Under Management: $32,800,000
Current Activity Level : Actively seeking new investments

PARAGON ADVISORS

20820 Chagrin Boulevard
Chagrin Corporate Center
Cleveland, OH USA 44122
Phone: 216-491-3990
Fax: 216-495-3995
E-mail: paragon@paragonadvisors.net
Website: www.paragonadvisors.net

Type of Firm

Private Equity Firm

Additional Information

Current Activity Level : Making few, if any, new investments

PARAGON ADVISORY PTY LTD. (FKA: PWR MANAGEMENT PTY LTD.)

121 Greenhill Road
Level 1, Unley
Adelaide, Australia 5061
Phone: 618-8271-0160
Fax: 618-8373-5075
E-mail: enquiry@paragonadvisory.com.au
Website: www.paragonadvisory.com.au

Management and Staff

Geoff Thomas, Chief Executive Officer

Type of Firm

Private Equity Advisor or Fund of Funds

Association Membership

Australian Venture Capital Association (AVCAL)

Project Preferences

Role in Financing:
Prefer role as deal originator but will also invest in deals created by others

Type of Financing Preferred:
Leveraged Buyout
Expansion
Management Buyouts

Size of Investments Considered:
Min Size of Investment Considered (000s): $958
Max Size of Investment Considered (000s): $4,791

Geographical Preferences

International Preferences:
Pacific
Australia

Industry Preferences

In Medical/Health prefer:
Medical/Health

In Manufact. prefer:
Manufacturing

In Agr/Forestr/Fish prefer:
Agribusiness

Additional Information

Year Founded: 2004
Capital Under Management: $26,800,000
Current Activity Level : Actively seeking new investments
Method of Compensation: Return on investment is of primary concern, do not charge fees

PARAGON INVESTMENT HOLDINGS

40 Eros Road
Windhoek, Namibia
Phone: 264-61-387-130
Fax: 264-61-387-143
E-mail: info@paragonnamibia.com
Website: www.paragonnamibia.com

Type of Firm

Private Equity Firm

Project Preferences

Type of Financing Preferred:
Leveraged Buyout

Additional Information

Year Founded: 2003
Current Activity Level : Actively seeking new investments

PARAGON PARTNERS GMBH

Leopoldstrasse 12
Munich, Germany 80802
Phone: 49-89-3888-7020
Fax: 49-89-3888-7015
E-mail: info@paragon-partners.de
Website: www.paragon-partners.de

Management and Staff

Edin Hadzic, Co-Founder
Krischan Von Moeller, Co-Founder
Stefan Winterling, Co-Founder

Type of Firm

Private Equity Firm

Project Preferences

Role in Financing:
Prefer role as deal originator

Type of Financing Preferred:
Leveraged Buyout
Management Buyouts

Geographical Preferences

International Preferences:
Switzerland
Austria
Germany

Industry Preferences

In Communications prefer:
Communications and Media

In Consumer Related prefer:
Education Related

In Financial Services prefer:
Financial Services

In Business Serv. prefer:
Services

Additional Information

Year Founded: 2004
Capital Under Management: $56,000,000
Current Activity Level : Actively seeking new investments

PARAKLETOS@VENTURES

175 Nortech Parkway
Suite 200
San Jose, CA USA 95134
Phone: 408-941-7000
Fax: 408-941-7001
E-mail: info@parakletos.com
Website: www.parakletos.com

Management and Staff

Paul Kim, Managing Partner

Type of Firm

Private Equity Firm

Project Preferences

Type of Financing Preferred:
Early Stage
Balanced

Geographical Preferences

United States Preferences:
California

Industry Preferences

In Communications prefer:
Communications and Media

In Financial Services prefer:
Financial Services

Additional Information

Year Founded: 1999
Capital Under Management: $30,000,000
Current Activity Level : Actively seeking new investments

PARALLAX CAPITAL PARTNERS LLC

18103 Sky Park South
Suite E2
Irvine, CA USA 92614
Phone: 949-863-3131
Fax: 949-863-3136
E-mail: info@parallaxcap.com
Website: www.parallaxcap.com

Management and Staff

James Hale, Managing Partner
Linda Michelman, Chief Financial Officer
Lisa Hale, Managing Partner
Michael Hale, Chief Operating Officer
Pam Wood, Vice President
Scott Lencz, Partner
William Koneval, Partner

Type of Firm

Private Equity Firm

Project Preferences

Type of Financing Preferred:
Leveraged Buyout
Turnaround
Management Buyouts
Acquisition

Industry Preferences

In Communications prefer:
Telecommunications
Wireless Communications

In Computer Hardware prefer:
Computers

In Computer Software prefer:
Software

In Financial Services prefer:
Financial Services

In Manufact. prefer:
Manufacturing

Additional Information

Year Founded: 2003
Current Activity Level : Actively seeking new investments

PARALLEL INVESMENT PARTNERS (FKA: SKM GROWTH INVESTORS)

2100 McKinney
Suite 1200
Dallas, TX USA 75201
Phone: 214-740-3600
Fax: 214-740-3630
E-mail: info@parallelip.com
Website: www.parallelip.com

Other Offices

1801 Century Park East
Suite 2505
Los Angeles, CA USA 90067
Phone: 310-556-9626
Fax: 310-556-9627

Management and Staff

Barron Fletcher, Managing Director
Clark Crosnoe, Managing Director
Ellery Roberts, Managing Director
Evan Karp, Vice President
Jared Johnson, Principal

Type of Firm

Private Equity Firm

Project Preferences

Type of Financing Preferred:
Leveraged Buyout
Expansion
Recapitalizations

Size of Investments Considered:
Min Size of Investment Considered (000s): $5,000
Max Size of Investment Considered (000s): $15,000

Geographical Preferences

United States Preferences:
All U.S.

Canadian Preferences:
All Canada

Additional Information

Year Founded: 1999
Capital Under Management: $150,000,000
Current Activity Level : Actively seeking new investments

PARAS VENTURES LLC

4545 Connecticut Avenue NW
Suite 26
Washington, DC USA 20008
Phone: 877-505-6317
Fax: 877-505-6317
E-mail: info@parasventures.com
Website: www.parasventures.com

Type of Firm

Private Equity Firm

Project Preferences

Type of Financing Preferred:
Early Stage

Industry Preferences

In Computer Software prefer:
Software

In Internet Specific prefer:
Internet

In Biotechnology prefer:
Biotechnology

Additional Information

Year Founded: 2001
Current Activity Level : Actively seeking new investments

PARAWIN VENTURE CAPITAL CORPORATION

1F, No.91, Sung-Jen Road
Taipei, Taiwan
Phone: 886-8-788-3998
Fax: 886-8-789-1830

Type of Firm
Private Equity Firm

Project Preferences

Type of Financing Preferred:
Balanced

Geographical Preferences

International Preferences:
All International

Additional Information
Year Founded: 2002
Current Activity Level : Actively seeking new investments

PARCOM CAPITAL (FKA: PARCOM VENTURES BV)
Olympia 4c
P.O. Box 434
Hilversum, Netherlands 1213 NT
Phone: 31-35-646-4440
Fax: 31-35-685-8585
E-mail: info@parcomcapital.com
Website: www.parcomcapital.com

Other Offices
55 bd Haussmann
Paris, France 75008
Phone: 33-1-5818-6050
Fax: 33-1-5818-6058

Ludwigstrasse 7
Munich, Georgia 80539
Phone: 49-89-200-0380
Fax: 49-89-2000-38111

Management and Staff
Jan Willem Doeksen, Partner

Type of Firm
Corporate PE/Venture

Association Membership
European Private Equity and Venture Capital Assoc.

Project Preferences

Type of Financing Preferred:
Fund of Funds
Leveraged Buyout
Expansion
Generalist PE
Management Buyouts

Size of Investments Considered:
Min Size of Investment Considered (000s): $2,000
Max Size of Investment Considered: No Limit

Geographical Preferences

International Preferences:
Netherlands
Europe

Industry Preferences

In Computer Software prefer:
Software

In Consumer Related prefer:
Consumer

In Industrial/Energy prefer:
Industrial Products

In Business Serv. prefer:
Services

Additional Information
Year Founded: 1982
Capital Under Management: $1,489,900,000
Current Activity Level : Actively seeking new investments

PARIS BUSINESS ANGELS
16, rue de Turbigo
Paris, France 75002
Phone: 33-1-4482-7773
Fax: 33-1-4482-7776
E-mail: contact@parisbusinessangels.com
Website: www.parisbusinessangels.com

Management and Staff
Jacques Collin, Vice President
Philippe Gluntz, President

Type of Firm
Private Equity Firm

Project Preferences

Type of Financing Preferred:
Early Stage
Seed
Startup

Geographical Preferences

International Preferences:
France

Additional Information
Year Founded: 2003
Current Activity Level : Actively seeking new investments

PARIS ORLEANS (FRANCAREP SA)
50 Avenue des Champs Elysees
Paris, France 75008
Phone: 33-1-5377-6510
Fax: 33-1-4563-8528
E-mail: contact@paris-orleans.com
Website: www.francarep.com

Management and Staff
David De Rothschild, Vice President
Eric De Rothschild, President
Georges Babinet, Managing Director

Type of Firm
Private Equity Firm

Association Membership
French Venture Capital Association (AFIC)

Project Preferences

Role in Financing:
Will function either as deal originator or investor in deals created by others

Type of Financing Preferred:
Balanced

Geographical Preferences

International Preferences:
Europe
France

Additional Information
Year Founded: 1838
Current Activity Level : Actively seeking new investments

PARISH CAPITAL ADVISORS LLC
5915 Farrington Road
Suite 202
Chapel Hill, NC USA 27517
Phone: 919-401-4949
Fax: 919-489-9500
E-mail: info@parishcapital.com
Website: www.parishcapital.com

Other Offices
Eleven Saint James' Place
London, United Kingdom SW1A 1NP
Phone: 44-20-7009-1055
Fax: 44-20-7009-1064

1500 Broadway
14th Floor
New York, NY USA 10036
Phone: 212-324-2203
Fax: 212-324-2230

Management and Staff
Bonnie McCullough, Chief Financial Officer
Catherine Lewis La Torre, Partner
Charles Merritt, Principal
David Jeffrey, Managing Partner
James Mason, Partner
Wendell McCain, Partner

Type of Firm
Private Equity Advisor or Fund of Funds

Association Membership
National Venture Capital Association - USA (NVCA)

Project Preferences

Type of Financing Preferred:
Fund of Funds
Leveraged Buyout
Early Stage

Geographical Preferences

United States Preferences:
All U.S.

Additional Information

Name of Most Recent Fund: Parish Capital Buyout Fund II, L.P.
Most Recent Fund Was Raised: 07/14/2006
Year Founded: 2003
Capital Under Management: $1,575,300,000
Current Activity Level : Actively seeking new investments

PARK AVENUE EQUITY PARTNERS, L.P.

399 Park Avenue
Suite 3204
New York, NY USA 10022
Phone: 212-758-4446
Fax: 212-430-0170
E-mail: PAEPinfo@pkave.com
Website: www.pkave.com

Other Offices

1720 N Street, NW
Washington, DC USA 20036-2907
Phone: 202-467-2070
Fax: 202-467-2074

Management and Staff

Daniel Kinder, Principal
J. Douglas Holladay, Partner
James Maher, Partner
Lex Leeming, Principal
Russel Peppet, Partner
William Mayer, Partner

Type of Firm

Private Equity Firm

Project Preferences

Role in Financing:
Prefer role as deal originator but will also invest in deals created by others

Type of Financing Preferred:
Leveraged Buyout

Size of Investments Considered:
Min Size of Investment Considered (000s): $7,000
Max Size of Investment Considered (000s): $22,000

Geographical Preferences

United States Preferences:
All U.S.

Canadian Preferences:
All Canada

International Preferences:
Mexico

Industry Preferences

In Communications prefer:
Wireless Communications

In Semiconductor/Electr prefer:
Controllers and Sensors

In Medical/Health prefer:
Medical Diagnostics
Diagnostic Test Products

In Industrial/Energy prefer:
Industrial Products

In Business Serv. prefer:
Services

In Manufact. prefer:
Manufacturing

Additional Information

Year Founded: 1999
Capital Under Management: $110,000,000
Current Activity Level : Actively seeking new investments
Method of Compensation: Return on invest. most important, but chg. closing fees, service fees, etc.

PARK HIGH APARTMENTS

300 River Place
Suite 6600
Detroit, MI USA 48207
Phone: 313-446-6900
Management and Staff
Carl Grenadier, Managing Partner
Herbert Strather, Managing Partner

Type of Firm

Private Equity Firm

Project Preferences

Type of Financing Preferred:
Other

Industry Preferences

In Financial Services prefer:
Real Estate

Additional Information

Year Founded: 2002
Capital Under Management: $2,900,000
Current Activity Level : Actively seeking new investments

PARK SQUARE CAPITAL, LLP

6th Floor, Devonshire House
Mayfair Place
London, United Kingdom W1J 8AJ
Phone: 44-20-7529-1800
Fax: 44-20-7529-1810
Website: www.parksquarecapital.com

Other Offices

50, Avenue de la Liberte
5th Floor
Luxembourg, Luxembourg L-1930
Phone: 352-268-974-418

P.O. Box 543, East Wing
Trafalgar Court, Admiral Park
Guernsey, United Kingdom GY1 6HJ
Phone: 44-1481-715-601
Fax: 44-1481-715-602

Management and Staff

Brandon Bradkin, Principal
David Cottam, Partner
Franck Duhamel, Principal
Klaus Petersen, Principal
Michael Small, Partner
Michael Thomas, Principal
Nikola Sutherland, Chief Financial Officer
Robin Doumar, Managing Partner

Type of Firm

Private Equity Firm

Project Preferences

Type of Financing Preferred:
Mezzanine
Balanced

Geographical Preferences

International Preferences:
Europe

Additional Information

Year Founded: 2005
Capital Under Management: $3,055,400,000
Current Activity Level : Actively seeking new investments

PARK STREET CAPITAL (FKA: TUCKER ANTHONY PRIVATE EQUITY)

One Federal Street
24th Floor
Boston, MA USA 02110
Phone: 617-897-9200
Fax: 617-897-9201
E-mail: info@parkstreetcapital.com
Website: www.parkstreetcapital.com

Other Offices

662 Sanchez Street
San Francisco, CA USA 94111
Phone: 415-273-4208
Fax: 415-391-7262

Management and Staff

Dorr Begnal, Managing Director
Heather Foley, Chief Financial Officer
Kristine Dailey, Managing Director
Robert Segel, Managing Director

Type of Firm

Private Equity Advisor or Fund of Funds

Project Preferences

Type of Financing Preferred:
Fund of Funds

Size of Investments Considered:
Min Size of Investment Considered (000s): $500
Max Size of Investment Considered (000s): $50,000

Geographical Preferences

United States Preferences:
All U.S.

Industry Preferences

In Financial Services prefer:
Investment Groups

Additional Information

Name of Most Recent Fund: Park Street Capital Natural Resources Fund III, L.P.
Most Recent Fund Was Raised: 09/01/2006
Year Founded: 1997
Capital Under Management: $2,798,000,000
Current Activity Level : Actively seeking new investments
Method of Compensation: Other

PARKER PRICE VENTURE CAPITAL INC.(FKA: ALLEGRO CAPITAL, INC)

101 California Street
Suite 2830
San Francisco, CA USA 94111
Phone: 415-623-2000
Fax: 415-617-0066
E-mail: info@parkerpricevc.com
Website: www.parkerpricevc.com

Management and Staff

Kent Price, President
Yachien Fu, Vice President

Type of Firm

Private Equity Firm

Project Preferences

Role in Financing:
Prefer role in deals created by others

Type of Financing Preferred:
Second Stage Financing
Early Stage
Expansion
First Stage Financing

Size of Investments Considered:
Min Size of Investment Considered (000s): $1,000
Max Size of Investment Considered (000s): $4,000

Geographical Preferences

United States Preferences:
West Coast
Texas

Industry Preferences

In Communications prefer:
Telecommunications
Wireless Communications
Data Communications
Satellite Microwave Comm.

In Computer Software prefer:
Software
Systems Software
Applications Software

In Semiconductor/Electr prefer:
Electronic Components
Semiconductor
Micro-Processing
Controllers and Sensors
Sensors
Circuit Boards
Component Testing Equipmt
Laser Related
Fiber Optics
Analytic/Scientific

In Industrial/Energy prefer:
Energy

Additional Information

Year Founded: 1998
Current Activity Level : Actively seeking new investments
Method of Compensation: Return on investment is of primary concern, do not charge fees

---

PARKLANE CAPITAL BETEILIGUNGSBERATUNG GMBH

Rathausmarkt 5
Hamburg, Germany 20095
Phone: 49-40-8199-1290
Fax: 49-40-8199-1295
E-mail: plc@parklane-capital.de
Website: www.parklanecapital.de

Management and Staff

Bjorn Soder, Managing Director

Type of Firm

Private Equity Firm

Project Preferences

Type of Financing Preferred:
Early Stage

Geographical Preferences

International Preferences:
Europe

Industry Preferences

In Business Serv. prefer:
Media

Additional Information

Year Founded: 2005
Current Activity Level : Actively seeking new investments

PARKMEAD GROUP PLC, THE (FKA: INTERREGNUM PLC)

2nd Floor
1-4 Vigo Street
London, United Kingdom W1S 3HT
Phone: 44-20-7494-5770
Fax: 44-20-7494-5780
E-mail: enquiries@parkmeadgroup.com
Website: www.interregnum.com

Management and Staff

David Poor, Managing Director
Gordon Ashworth, Chief Financial Officer
Niall Doran, Chief Executive Officer

Type of Firm

Bank Affiliated

Association Membership

European Private Equity and Venture Capital Assoc.

Project Preferences

Role in Financing:
Will function either as deal originator or investor in deals created by others

Type of Financing Preferred:
Early Stage
Public Companies
Turnaround
Balanced
Open Market
Seed
Management Buyouts
Acquisition
Private Placement
Industry Rollups
Startup

Size of Investments Considered:
Min Size of Investment Considered (000s): $300
Max Size of Investment Considered (000s): $300,000

Geographical Preferences

International Preferences:
Europe

Industry Preferences

In Computer Software prefer:
Software
Applications Software

In Internet Specific prefer:
Internet
Additional Information
Year Founded: 1992
Capital Under Management: $28,700,000
Current Activity Level : Actively seeking new investments

PARKVIEW VENTURES LLC

708 Third Avenue
Suite 1610
New York, NY USA 10017
Phone: 212-832-1263
Fax: 212-832-1240
Website: www.parkviewventures.com

Management and Staff
Laurent Ohana, Principal
Singari Seshadri, Principal
T.Raj Singh, Principal

Type of Firm
Bank Affiliated

Project Preferences

Type of Financing Preferred:
Leveraged Buyout
Generalist PE
Public Companies
Turnaround
Special Situation
Recapitalizations

Size of Investments Considered:
Min Size of Investment Considered (000s): $250
Max Size of Investment Considered (000s): $5,000

Industry Preferences

In Communications prefer:
Media and Entertainment

In Internet Specific prefer:
Ecommerce
Web Aggregration/Portals

In Financial Services prefer:
Financial Services

Additional Information
Year Founded: 2008
Current Activity Level : Actively seeking new investments

PARKWAY CAPITAL INVESTORS LLC

501 Fairmount Avenue
Suite 303
Towson, MD USA 21286
Phone: 410-616-1200
Fax: 410-616-1210
Website: www.parkwaycapital.com

Management and Staff
Christopher Pope, Principal
J. Drexel Knight, Principal
Noel Lassise, Vice President

Type of Firm
Private Equity Advisor or Fund of Funds

Association Membership
Mid-Atlantic Venture Association

Project Preferences

Type of Financing Preferred:
Leveraged Buyout
Mezzanine
Acquisition
Recapitalizations

Size of Investments Considered:
Min Size of Investment Considered (000s): $2,000
Max Size of Investment Considered (000s): $10,000

Industry Focus
(% based on actual investment)

Other Products	71.8%
Consumer Related	20.7%
Industrial/Energy	7.5%

Additional Information
Year Founded: 2000
Capital Under Management: $50,000,000
Current Activity Level : Actively seeking new investments

PARTECH INTERNATIONAL

50 California Street
Suite 3200
San Francisco, CA USA 94111
Phone: 415-788-2929
Fax: 415-788-6763
E-mail: bizplan@partechvc.com
Website: www.partechvc.com

Other Offices
Seven Ha-Ogen Street
Suite 405
Herzliyah Marina, Israel 46764
Phone: 972-99-573-444
Fax: 972-99-560-099

12 rue de Penthievre
Paris, France 75008
Phone: 33-1-5365-6553
Fax: 33-1-5365-6555

Dormi No.2 Yoyogi 301
1-57-4, Yoyogi, Shibuya-ku
Tokyo, Japan 105-0001
Phone: 813-5333-4618
Fax: 813-5412-0717

Management and Staff
Ami Amir, Partner
Andreas Schlenker, Principal
Gadi Toren, Principal
Jai Choi, Principal
Jean-Marc Patouillaud, Partner
Nicolas El Baze, Partner
Philippe Collombel, Partner
Philippe Cases, Partner
Philippe Crochet, Principal
Scott Matson, Chief Financial Officer
Thomas McKinley, Managing Partner
Timothy Wilson, Partner
Vincent Worms, Managing Partner

Type of Firm
Private Equity Firm

Association Membership
French Venture Capital Association (AFIC)
Western Association of Venture Capitalists (WAVC)
European Private Equity and Venture Capital Assoc.

Project Preferences

Role in Financing:
Will function either as deal originator or investor in deals created by others

Type of Financing Preferred:
Early Stage
Public Companies
Later Stage
Seed
First Stage Financing

Size of Investments Considered:
Min Size of Investment Considered (000s): $1,000
Max Size of Investment Considered (000s): $20,000

Geographical Preferences

Canadian Preferences:
All Canada

International Preferences:
Europe
Israel

Industry Focus
(% based on actual investment)

Computer Software and Services	28.5%
Internet Specific	23.7%
Consumer Related	16.8%
Semiconductors/Other Elect.	10.8%

Communications and Media	8.5%
Computer Hardware	4.3%
Medical/Health	3.9%
Industrial/Energy	1.6%
Other Products	1.1%
Biotechnology	0.8%

Additional Information

Name of Most Recent Fund: Partech International Ventures V, L.P.
Most Recent Fund Was Raised: 08/16/2006
Year Founded: 1982
Capital Under Management: $880,000,000
Current Activity Level : Actively seeking new investments
Method of Compensation: Return on investment is of primary concern, do not charge fees

---

PARTER CAPITAL GROUP GMBH

Wiesenau 36
Frankfurt am Main, Germany 60323
Phone: 49-6977-0619990
Fax: 49-6977-0619992
E-mail: info@parter-capital.de
Website: www.parter-capital.de

Type of Firm

Private Equity Firm

Project Preferences

Type of Financing Preferred:

Turnaround

Geographical Preferences

International Preferences:

Germany

Additional Information

Year Founded: 2008
Current Activity Level : Actively seeking new investments

PARTHENON CAPITAL LLC

265 Franklin Street
18th Floor
Boston, MA USA 02110
Phone: 617-960-4000
Fax: 617-960-4010
E-mail: info@parthenoncapital.com
Website: www.parthenoncapital.com

Other Offices

Four Embarcadero Center
Suite 3610
San Francisco, CA USA 94111
Phone: 415-913-3900
Fax: 415-913-3913

Management and Staff

Andrew Dodson, Principal
Benjamin Krick, Vice President
Brian Golson, Managing Partner
Casey Lynch, Principal
David Ament, Managing Partner
Ernest Jacquet, Managing Partner
Gerri Grossman, Chief Financial Officer
Greg Why, Partner
H. Bradley Sloan, Vice President
John Rutherford, Managing Partner
Jonathan Grad, Managing Partner
Marc Rubin, Principal
William Winterer, Managing Partner
Zachary Sadek, Vice President

Type of Firm

Private Equity Firm

Project Preferences

Role in Financing:

Prefer role as deal originator but will also invest in deals created by others

Type of Financing Preferred:

Leveraged Buyout
Early Stage
Expansion
Generalist PE
Later Stage
Management Buyouts
Acquisition
Recapitalizations

Size of Investments Considered:

Min Size of Investment Considered (000s): $10,000
Max Size of Investment Considered (000s): $75,000

Geographical Preferences

International Preferences:

United Kingdom

Industry Focus

(% based on actual investment)

Other Products	42.9%
Consumer Related	27.6%
Semiconductors/Other Elect.	8.6%
Industrial/Energy	8.1%
Computer Hardware	4.0%
Internet Specific	3.5%
Medical/Health	2.9%
Computer Software and Services	2.5%

Additional Information

Name of Most Recent Fund: Parthenon Investors III, L.P.
Most Recent Fund Was Raised: 08/19/2005
Year Founded: 1998
Capital Under Management: $1,100,000,000
Current Activity Level : Actively seeking new investments

PARTHENON TRUST SA

32 Amalias Avenue
Athens, Greece 10558
Phone: 30-210-331-3000
Fax: 30-210-331-3800

Management and Staff

Zaharias Palexas, Co-Founder

Type of Firm

Bank Affiliated

Additional Information

Year Founded: 2004
Current Activity Level : Actively seeking new investments

PARTICI-PATIEMAATSCHAPPIJ VLAANDEREN (AKA: VINNOF)

Hooikaai 55
Brussels, Belgium 1000
Phone: 32-2-229-5230
Fax: 32-2-229-5231
E-mail: info@pmvlaanderen.be
Website: www.pmvlaanderen.be

Type of Firm

Private Equity Firm

Association Membership

Belgium Venturing Association
European Private Equity and Venture Capital Assoc.

Project Preferences

Type of Financing Preferred:

Balanced

Geographical Preferences

International Preferences:

Europe

Additional Information

Year Founded: 2004
Current Activity Level : Actively seeking new investments

PARTICIPATION COMPANY EAST NETHERLANDS NV (AKA : PPM OOST)

Bedrijvenpark IJsseloord 2
Meander 601
Arnhem, Netherlands 6825 ME
Phone: 31-26-384-4044
Fax: 31-26-384-4040
E-mail: info@ppmoost.nl
Website: www.ppmoost.nl

Other Offices

Ondernemingshuis Zwole
Govert Flinckstraat 1
Zwolle, Netherlands 8021 ET
Phone: 31-38-456-1456
Fax: 31-38-454-6869

Keulenstraat 11a
Deventer, Netherlands 7418 ET
Phone: 31-570-855-917
Fax: 31-570-855-866

Ondernemingshuis Twente
Hengelosestraat 585
Enschede, Netherlands 7521 AG
Phone: 31-53-484-9649
Fax: 31-53-484-9678

Management and Staff

Marius Prins, President
Willem Van den Berg, President

Type of Firm

Government Affiliated Program

Project Preferences

Type of Financing Preferred:
Early Stage
Later Stage

Geographical Preferences

International Preferences:
Netherlands
Europe

Additional Information

Year Founded: 1996
Capital Under Management: $67,500,000
Current Activity Level : Actively seeking new investments

PARTICIPEX

1 rue Esquermoise
Grand Place - BP 112
Lille Cedex, France 59027
Phone: 33-3-2021-9380
Fax: 33-3-2021-9389
E-mail: participex@participex.fr
Website: www.participex.fr

Management and Staff

Felix Bonduelle, President

Type of Firm

Private Equity Firm

Association Membership

French Venture Capital Association (AFIC)

Project Preferences

Type of Financing Preferred:
Leveraged Buyout
Expansion

Size of Investments Considered:
Min Size of Investment Considered (000s): $137
Max Size of Investment Considered (000s): $3,430

Geographical Preferences

International Preferences:
Belgium
France

Additional Information

Year Founded: 1980
Capital Under Management: $41,200,000
Current Activity Level : Actively seeking new investments

PARTISAN MANAGEMENT GROUP

293 Pearl Street
Boulder, CO USA 80302
Phone: 303-444-8983
Fax: 303-444-0038
Website: www.partisanmgmt.com

Management and Staff

Karen Cassidy, Principal
Norman Weldon, Principal

Type of Firm

Private Equity Firm

Project Preferences

Role in Financing:
Prefer role as deal originator

Type of Financing Preferred:
Early Stage
Start-up Financing
Seed

Size of Investments Considered:
Min Size of Investment Considered (000s): $100
Max Size of Investment Considered (000s): $1,000

Geographical Preferences

United States Preferences:
Midwest
Southeast
Rocky Mountain

Industry Preferences

In Medical/Health prefer:
Medical Therapeutics
Disposable Med. Products

Additional Information

Year Founded: 1987
Capital Under Management: $10,000,000
Current Activity Level : Actively seeking new investments
Method of Compensation: Return on investment is of primary concern, do not charge fees

---

PARTNERS CAPITAL INVESTMENT GROUP, LLC

50 Rowes Wharf
Fourth Floor
Boston, MA USA 02110
Phone: 617-292-2570
Fax: 617-292-2571
Website: www.partners-cap.com

Other Offices

5 Young Street
London, United Kingdom W8 5EH
Phone: 44-20-7938-5200
Fax: 44-20-7938-5201

Management and Staff

Stan Miranda, Chief Executive Officer

Type of Firm

Private Equity Firm

Project Preferences

Type of Financing Preferred:
Balanced
Other

Additional Information

Name of Most Recent Fund: Partners Capital Condor Fund III, L.P.
Most Recent Fund Was Raised: 12/20/2007
Year Founded: 2004
Capital Under Management: $9,300,000
Current Activity Level : Actively seeking new investments

PARTNERS GROUP AG

Zugerstrasse 57
Baar-Zug, Switzerland 6341
Phone: 41-41-768-8585
Fax: 41-41-768-8558
E-mail: partnersgroup@partnersgroup.ch
Website: www.partnersgroup.net

Other Offices

3 Church Street
Samsung Hub, #28-06
Singapore, Singapore 049483
Phone: 65-6544-6565
Fax: 65-6544-6566

First Angel Court
19th Floor
London, United Kingdom EC2R 7HJ
Phone: 44-20-7260-1700
Fax: 44-20-7260-1701

Number 6 Wudinghou Street
Suite 1261 Excel Center
Beijing, China 100032
Phone: 8610-8800-3771
Fax: 8610-8800-3803

150 Spear Street
18th Floor
San Francisco, CA USA 94105
Phone: 415-537-8585
Fax: 415-537-8558

Tudor House
Third Floor, Le Bordage
Guernsey, United Kingdom GY1 1BT
Phone: 44-1481-711-690
Fax: 44-1481-730-947

55 avenue de la gare
Luxembourg, Luxembourg 1611
Phone: 352-274-8281
Fax: 352-2748-2828

450 Lexington Avenue
39th Floor
New York, NY USA 10017
Phone: 212-763-4700
Fax: 212-763-4701

Otemachi First Square East Tower 4F
1-5-1 Otemachi, Chiyoda-ku
Tokyo, Japan 100-0004
Phone: 81-3-5219-1321
Fax: 81-3-5219-1201

AMP Center
L34, 50 Bridg Street
Sydney, Australia 2000
Phone: 61-2-8216-0885
Fax: 61-2-8216-0883

Management and Staff

Alfred Gantner, Partner
Andrei Frei, Principal
Brooks Lindberg, Principal
Christoph Rubeli, Partner
Claude Angeloz, Partner
Cyrill Wipfli, Principal
Erik Kaas, Partner
Felix Haldner, Partner
Hans-Ulrich Muller, Partner
Henning Eckermann, Partner
Jochen Weirich, Partner
Josef Bieri, Partner
Jurg Wenger, Chief Operating Officer
Kurt Birchler, Chief Financial Officer
Lars Jaeger, Partner
Manuel Martiny, Partner
Marc Weiss, Principal
Marcel Wieduwilt, Partner
Marcel Erni, Partner
Mark Rowe, Principal
Michael Barben, Partner
Michel Jacquemai, Partner
Nan Leake, Principal
Nori Gerardo Lietz, Partner
Pam Alsterlind, Partner
Philipp Gysler, Partner
Rene Biner, Partner
Reto Schwager, Principal
Roland Roffler, Partner
Sandra Pajarola, Partner
Scott Higbee, Partner
Steffen Meister, Chief Executive Officer
Stephan Schaeli, Partner
Thomas Staubli, Partner
Tilman Trommsdorff, Partner
Urs Wietlisbach, Partner
Walter Keller, Partner

Type of Firm

Investment Management Firm

Association Membership

Swiss Venture Capital Association (SECA)
European Private Equity and Venture Capital Assoc.

Project Preferences

Type of Financing Preferred:

Fund of Funds
Leveraged Buyout
Early Stage
Expansion
Mezzanine
Generalist PE
Management Buyouts
Fund of Funds of Second

Size of Investments Considered:

Min Size of Investment Considered (000s): $5,000
Max Size of Investment Considered (000s): $20,000

Geographical Preferences

United States Preferences:

All U.S.

International Preferences:

Switzerland
Europe
Western Europe
Germany
Asia
All International

Industry Preferences

In Communications prefer:

Communications and Media

In Internet Specific prefer:

E-Commerce Technology

In Biotechnology prefer:

Biotechnology

In Consumer Related prefer:

Consumer

In Industrial/Energy prefer:

Materials
Machinery

Additional Information

Year Founded: 1996
Capital Under Management: $16,511,900,000
Current Activity Level : Actively seeking new investments

PARTNERS VENTURE CAPITAL CO., LTD.

11th Floor, Eunseong Building
53-8 Cheongdam-dong Gangnam-gu
Seoul, South Korea 135-763
Phone: 822-6248-7600
Fax: 822-6248-7612
E-mail: partners@partners.com
Website: www.partnersventure.com

Management and Staff

Gisik Kim, Vice President
Seunggwon Paik, Managing Director

Type of Firm

Private Equity Firm

Project Preferences

Type of Financing Preferred:

Balanced

Geographical Preferences

International Preferences:

Korea, South

Additional Information

Year Founded: 2000
Capital Under Management: $46,900,000
Current Activity Level : Actively seeking new investments

PARTNERS@VENTURE NV

Heilig Hartplein 10
Oostende, Belgium 8400
Phone: 32-59-513-032
Fax: 32-59-235-316
E-mail: info-b@online.be
Website: www.partnersatventure.be

Type of Firm

Private Equity Firm

Association Membership

European Private Equity and Venture Capital Assoc.

Project Preferences

Type of Financing Preferred:

Early Stage

Geographical Preferences

International Preferences:

Europe

Industry Focus

(% based on actual investment)

Computer Hardware	51.9%
Biotechnology	30.9%
Semiconductors/Other Elect.	8.7%
Medical/Health	8.4%

Additional Information

Year Founded: 1997
Capital Under Management: $25,200,000
Current Activity Level : Actively seeking new investments

PARTNERSHIPS UK PLC

10 Great George Street
London, United Kingdom SW1P 3AE
Phone: 44-20-7273-8383
Fax: 44-20-7273-8368
Website: www.partnershipsuk.org.uk

Type of Firm

Government Affiliated Program

Association Membership

British Venture Capital Association (BVCA)

Project Preferences

Type of Financing Preferred:
Early Stage
Expansion

Geographical Preferences

International Preferences:
United Kingdom
Europe
Western Europe

Industry Preferences

In Communications prefer:
Communications and Media

In Medical/Health prefer:
Medical/Health
Health Services

In Consumer Related prefer:
Education Related

In Industrial/Energy prefer:
Energy Conservation Relat

In Transportation prefer:
Transportation

In Business Serv. prefer:
Services

In Other prefer:
Environment Responsible

Additional Information

Year Founded: 2000
Current Activity Level : Actively seeking new investments

PARVILLA SAS

42, Avenue Montaigne
Paris, France 75008
E-mail: office@parvilla.com
Website: www.parvilla.com

Type of Firm

Private Equity Firm

Association Membership

French Venture Capital Association (AFIC)

Project Preferences

Type of Financing Preferred:
Fund of Funds
Leveraged Buyout

Geographical Preferences

International Preferences:
United Kingdom
Sweden
Netherlands
Luxembourg
Iceland
Spain
Belgium
Norway
Finland
France
Denmark

Additional Information

Year Founded: 2006
Current Activity Level : Actively seeking new investments

PASADENA CAPITAL PARTNERS

800 East Colorado Boulevard
Suite 820
Pasadena, CA USA 91101
Phone: 626-432-7070
Fax: 626-432-7470
Website: www.pasadenacapital.com

Management and Staff

Charles Woo, Vice President

Type of Firm

Private Equity Firm

Project Preferences

Type of Financing Preferred:
Leveraged Buyout
Turnaround
Management Buyouts
Acquisition
Private Placement
Recapitalizations

Size of Investments Considered:
Min Size of Investment Considered (000s): $10,000
Max Size of Investment Considered (000s): $25,000

Geographical Preferences

United States Preferences:
Southern California

Industry Preferences

In Consumer Related prefer:
Consumer
Retail
Consumer Products
Consumer Services

In Financial Services prefer:
Financial Services

In Manufact. prefer:
Manufacturing

Additional Information

Year Founded: 2002
Current Activity Level : Actively seeking new investments

PATH4 VENTURES, LLC

4030 West Braker Lane
Suite 360
Austin, TX USA 78759
Phone: 512-344-3300
Fax: 512-344-3350
Website: www.path4.com

Management and Staff

Brian Burkinshaw, Principal
James Rogan, Principal
Jerry DeVries, Principal
Steven Whitlock, Principal

Type of Firm

Private Equity Firm

Association Membership

National Venture Capital Association - USA (NVCA)

Project Preferences

Type of Financing Preferred:
Early Stage
Balanced
Seed

Industry Preferences

In Medical/Health prefer:
Medical/Health

Additional Information

Year Founded: 2004
Capital Under Management: $15,000,000
Current Activity Level : Actively seeking new investments

PATHFINDER INVESTMENT CO., LTD.

2/F, Varun Complex
153 A Law College Road
Pune, India 411004
Phone: 91-20-2565-1851

Fax: 91-20-2565-1846
E-mail: pathfind@vsnl.com

Management and Staff

N.K. Prasad, Chairman & Managing Director

Type of Firm

Private Equity Firm

Association Membership

Indian Venture Capital Association (IVCA)

Project Preferences

Role in Financing:

Prefer role as deal originator but will also invest in deals created by others

Type of Financing Preferred:

Second Stage Financing
Expansion
Mezzanine
Special Situation

Geographical Preferences

International Preferences:

India

Industry Preferences

In Communications prefer:

Commercial Communications
Telecommunications

In Computer Hardware prefer:

Integrated Turnkey System

In Computer Software prefer:

Computer Services
Systems Software
Applications Software

In Computer Other prefer:

Computer Related

In Semiconductor/Electr prefer:

Electronic Components
Analytic/Scientific

In Medical/Health prefer:

Medical/Health
Diagnostic Services
Medical Products
Disposable Med. Products
Hospital/Other Instit.
Pharmaceuticals

In Consumer Related prefer:

Consumer
Franchises(NEC)
Food/Beverage
Consumer Products
Consumer Services
Hotels and Resorts
Education Related

In Industrial/Energy prefer:

Alternative Energy
Energy Conservation Relat
Industrial Products
Materials
Factory Automation
Machinery
Environmental Related

In Financial Services prefer:

Financial Services

In Business Serv. prefer:

Services
Consulting Services

In Manufact. prefer:

Manufacturing
Publishing

Additional Information

Year Founded: 1993
Current Activity Level : Actively seeking new investments
Method of Compensation: Return on investment is of primary concern, do not charge fees

---

PATRIARCH PARTNERS LLC

32 Avenue of the Americas
17th Floor
New York, NY USA 10013
Phone: 212-825-0550
Fax: 212-825-2038
E-mail: info@patriarchpartners.com
Website: www.patriarchpartners.com

Management and Staff

Bill Hinz, Managing Director
Chad Clawson, Managing Director
Edward Ricci, Managing Director
Emil Giliotti, Managing Director
Gideon Agar, Chief Operating Officer
John Harrington, Managing Director
Lynn Tilton, Chief Executive Officer

Type of Firm

Private Equity Firm

Project Preferences

Type of Financing Preferred:

Leveraged Buyout
Acquisition
Distressed Debt

Industry Preferences

In Communications prefer:

Media and Entertainment

In Medical/Health prefer:

Medical/Health
Health Services

In Consumer Related prefer:

Consumer Products

In Transportation prefer:

Aerospace

In Business Serv. prefer:

Services

In Manufact. prefer:

Manufacturing

Additional Information

Year Founded: 2000
Capital Under Management: $1,200,000,000
Current Activity Level : Actively seeking new investments

PATRIOT CAPITAL FUNDING, INC. (AKA: PATRIOT CAPITAL)

61 Wilton Road
Second Floor
Westport, CT USA 06880
Phone: 203-227-7778
Fax: 203-221-8253
Website: www.pat-cap.com

Management and Staff

Richard Buckanavage, Managing Director

Type of Firm

Private Equity Firm

Project Preferences

Type of Financing Preferred:

Mezzanine
Acquisition
Recapitalizations

Industry Preferences

In Business Serv. prefer:

Services
Distribution

In Manufact. prefer:

Manufacturing

Additional Information

Year Founded: 2003
Capital Under Management: $150,000,000
Current Activity Level : Actively seeking new investments

PATRON CAPITAL, LTD.

16 Berkeley Street
London, United Kingdom W1J 8DZ
Phone: 44-20-7629-9417
Fax: 44-20-7629-9418
Website: www.patroncapital.com

Other Offices

285 West Broadway
Suite 500
New York, NY USA 10013
Phone: 212-461-4466

Via Santo Spirito, 5
Milan, Italy 20121

Phone: 39-2-798-416
Fax: 39-2-7601-2090

Passeig de Gracia 74
Barcelona, Spain 08007
Phone: 34-93-467-9100
Fax: 34-93-467-9101

6, Rue Adolphe
Luxembourg, Luxembourg L-1116
Phone: 352-222-1151
Fax: 352-22-2117

Management and Staff

Bertrand Schwab, Partner
Jason Meads, Managing Director
Johannes Kalker, Vice President
Keith Breslaur, Managing Director
Shane Law, Chief Operating Officer

Type of Firm

Private Equity Firm

Project Preferences

Type of Financing Preferred:

Leveraged Buyout
Expansion
Acquisition
Joint Ventures

Geographical Preferences

International Preferences:

United Kingdom
Europe
Western Europe

Industry Focus

(% based on actual investment)

Consumer Related	80.6%
Industrial/Energy	19.4%

Additional Information

Name of Most Recent Fund: Patron Capital, L.P. 1
Most Recent Fund Was Raised: 04/19/2001
Year Founded: 1999
Capital Under Management: $85,000,000
Current Activity Level : Actively seeking new investments

PAUL CAPITAL PARTNERS

50 California Street
Suite 3000
San Francisco, CA USA 94111
Phone: 415-283-4300
Fax: 415-283-4301
E-mail: info@paulcap.com
Website: www.paulcap.com

Other Offices

28 Avenue de Messine
2nd Floor
Paris, France 75008
Phone: 331-5353-0606
Fax: 33-1-5353-0607

Fourth Floor, Mellier House
26a Albermarle Street
London, United Kingdom W1S 4HY
Phone: 44-20-7514-0750
Fax: 44-20-7514-0751

3 Garden Road
Citibank Tower, Suite 3208
Central, Hong Kong
Phone: 852-3521-2200
Fax: 852-3521-2201

140 East 45th Street
44th Floor Two Grand Central Tower
New York, NY USA 10017
Phone: 646-264-1100
Fax: 646-264-1101

Rua Samuel Morse
120 Cj. 83
Sao Paolo, Brazil 04576

2 St. Clair Avenue East
Suite 800
Toronto, Canada M4T 2T5
Phone: 416-644-4930
Fax: 416-513-0348

Management and Staff

Andrew Rubinstein, Principal
Ann Watson, Principal
Brian Sullivan, Partner
Bryon Sheets, General Partner
Dana O'Brien, Managing Director
Daniel Mulderry, Principal
David York, General Partner
David Lippman, Principal
David deWeese, General Partner
Duncan Littlejohn, Principal
Elaine Small, Managing Director
Elizabeth Orzano Coleon, Principal
Guillaume Partiot, Principal
Guy Rico, General Partner
Jamie Johnson, Managing Director
Jean-Pierre Naegeli, Partner
John Leone, Partner
Ken MacLeod, Partner
Lara Sullivan, Principal
Lionel Leventhal, General Partner
Lucian Wu, Managing Director
Philip Paul, Managing Director
Simon Guenzl, Partner
Walter Flamenbaum, General Partner

Type of Firm

Private Equity Advisor or Fund of Funds
Association Membership
Hong Kong Venture Capital Association (HKVCA)
French Venture Capital Association (AFIC)
Western Association of Venture Capitalists (WAVC)

Project Preferences

Role in Financing:

Prefer role as deal originator

Type of Financing Preferred:

Fund of Funds
Leveraged Buyout
Mezzanine
Expansion
Balanced
Fund of Funds of Second

Size of Investments Considered:

Min Size of Investment Considered (000s): $1,000
Max Size of Investment Considered: No Limit

Geographical Preferences

United States Preferences:

All U.S.

International Preferences:

Europe
All International

Industry Preferences

In Communications prefer:

Communications and Media

In Computer Software prefer:

Software

In Computer Other prefer:

Computer Related

In Biotechnology prefer:

Biotechnology
Agricultural/Animal Bio.

In Medical/Health prefer:

Medical/Health

In Consumer Related prefer:

Retail

In Industrial/Energy prefer:

Energy
Industrial Products

In Transportation prefer:

Transportation

In Financial Services prefer:

Financial Services

In Manufact. prefer:

Manufacturing

In Agr/Forestr/Fish prefer:

Agribusiness

Additional Information

Name of Most Recent Fund: Paul Capital Top Tier Investments III, L.P.
Most Recent Fund Was Raised: 01/19/2005
Year Founded: 1981
Capital Under Management: $288,000,000
Current Activity Level : Actively seeking new investments
Method of Compensation: Return on investment is of primary concern, do not charge fees

PCGI LLC (AKA: PCG INTERNATIONAL)

616 High Street, North West
Suite 450
Washington, DC USA 20001
Phone: 202-824-1600
Fax: 202-824-4300
E-mail: info@pcgi.net
Website: www.pcgi.net

Management and Staff

Bernard McGuire, Managing Director
Charles Toy, Managing Director
Gene Pohren, Managing Director
Stephen O'Neill, Managing Director
Steve Cowan, Managing Director

Type of Firm

Private Equity Advisor or Fund of Funds
Association Membership

Brazilian Venture Capital Association (ABCR)

Japan Venture Capital Association
South African Venture Capital Association (SAVCA)
Emerging Markets Private Equity Association
European Private Equity and Venture Capital Assoc.

Geographical Preferences

International Preferences:
All International

Additional Information

Year Founded: 2005
Current Activity Level : Actively seeking new investments

PEACHTREE EQUITY PARTNERS

1170 Peachtree Street
Suite 1610
Atlanta, GA USA 30309
Phone: 404-253-6388
Fax: 404-253-6377
E-mail: info@peachtreeequity.com
Website: www.peachtreeequity.com

Management and Staff

David Christopher, Partner
John McCarty, Vice President
Matthew Sullivan, Partner

Type of Firm

Private Equity Firm

Project Preferences

Role in Financing:
Prefer role as deal originator

Type of Financing Preferred:
Expansion
Later Stage
Management Buyouts
Acquisition
Recapitalizations

Size of Investments Considered:
Min Size of Investment Considered (000s): $3,000
Max Size of Investment Considered (000s): $15,000

Geographical Preferences

United States Preferences:
Southeast

Industry Preferences

In Medical/Health prefer:
Health Services

In Industrial/Energy prefer:
Industrial Products

In Financial Services prefer:
Financial Services

In Business Serv. prefer:
Services
Distribution

In Manufact. prefer:
Manufacturing

Additional Information

Name of Most Recent Fund: Peachtree Equity Partners Fund I
Most Recent Fund Was Raised: 04/12/2002
Year Founded: 1997
Capital Under Management: $110,000,000
Current Activity Level : Actively seeking new investments
Method of Compensation: Return on investment is of primary concern, do not charge fees

PEARL STREET GROUP, LTD.

1401 Pearl Street
Suite 400
Boulder, CO USA 80302
Phone: 720-406-1100
Fax: 720-406-1101
E-mail: info@pearlstreetgroup.com
Website: www.pearlstreetgroup.com

Type of Firm

Private Equity Firm

Geographical Preferences

United States Preferences:
Colorado

Additional Information

Year Founded: 2002
Current Activity Level : Actively seeking new investments

PECHEL INDUSTRIES

162, rue du Faubourg
Saint Honore
Paris, France 75008
Phone: 33-1-5659-7959
Fax: 33-1-5659-7956
E-mail: pechel@pechel.com
Website: www.pechel.com

Management and Staff

Helene Ploix, President

Type of Firm

Private Equity Firm

Association Membership

French Venture Capital Association (AFIC)

Project Preferences

Type of Financing Preferred:
Leveraged Buyout
Expansion
Balanced

Geographical Preferences

International Preferences:
Luxembourg
Switzerland
Europe
Belgium
France

Additional Information

Year Founded: 1997
Capital Under Management: $364,100,000
Current Activity Level : Actively seeking new investments

PEEPUL CAPITAL LLC (FKA:ILABS CAPITAL, PVT. LTD.)

Manor House, 1st Floor
Cnr St George, Chazal Streets
Port Louis, Mauritius
Phone: 230-203-6600
Fax: 230-203-6650
E-mail: contact@peepulcapital.com
Website: www.peepulcapital.com

Other Offices

62/14, ABM Avenue
Boat Club, R.A. Puram
Chennai, India 600 028
Phone: 91-44-4502-6440
Fax: 91-44-4507-0404

Building No.3, # 18
Software Units Layout, Madhabpur
Hydrabad, India
Phone: 91-40-3048-4444

Management and Staff

Sandeep Reddy, Co-Founder
Srini Raju, Co-Founder
Venu Chittoory, Managing Director

Type of Firm

Private Equity Firm

Association Membership

Indian Venture Capital Association (IVCA)

Project Preferences

Type of Financing Preferred:
Early Stage
Expansion
Balanced
Recapitalizations

Size of Investments Considered:
Min Size of Investment Considered (000s): $5,000
Max Size of Investment Considered (000s): $30,000

Geographical Preferences

International Preferences:
India

Industry Preferences

In Communications prefer:
Telecommunications

In Consumer Related prefer:
Consumer
Consumer Services

In Financial Services prefer:
Financial Services

In Business Serv. prefer:
Media

Additional Information

Year Founded: 2000
Capital Under Management: $325,000,000
Current Activity Level : Actively seeking new investments

PEGASUS CAPITAL ADVISORS, L.P.

99 River Road
Cos Cob, CT USA 06807
Phone: 203-869-4400
Fax: 203-869-6940
E-mail: info@pegasusinvestors.com
Website: www.pcalp.com

Other Offices

505 Park Avenue
21st Floor
New York, NY USA 10022
Phone: 212-710-2500
Fax: 212-355-2303

Management and Staff

Alec Machiels, Partner
Andrew Cooper, Vice President
Craig Cogut, Founding Partner
Daniel Stencel, Chief Financial Officer
David Cunningham, Partner
Eric Gribetz, Partner
Richard Weinberg, Partner
Rodney Cohen, Managing Partner
Steven Wacaster, Vice President

Type of Firm

Private Equity Firm

Project Preferences

Role in Financing:
Prefer role as deal originator

Type of Financing Preferred:
Generalist PE
Special Situation
Distressed Debt

Size of Investments Considered:
Min Size of Investment Considered (000s): $10,000
Max Size of Investment Considered: No Limit

Geographical Preferences

United States Preferences:
All U.S.

Industry Focus

(% based on actual investment)	
Other Products	33.1%
Industrial/Energy	23.9%
Consumer Related	23.1%
Communications and Media	10.1%
Internet Specific	4.5%
Medical/Health	3.3%
Semiconductors/Other Elect.	1.6%
Computer Software and Services	0.4%

Additional Information

Name of Most Recent Fund: Pegasus Partners II, L.P.
Most Recent Fund Was Raised: 06/30/1999
Year Founded: 1996
Capital Under Management: $1,800,000,000
Current Activity Level : Actively seeking new investments
Method of Compensation: Return on invest. most important, but chg. closing fees, service fees, etc.

PEGASUS VENTURE CAPITAL

Av. del Libertador 602
Piso 18
Buenos Aires, Argentina C1001ABT
Phone: 54-11-4891-0770
Fax: 54-11-4891-0750
E-mail: contact@pegasusvc.com
Website: www.pegasusvc.com

Other Offices

Paragon Towers
233 Needham Street, Suite 300
Newton, MA USA 02464
Phone: 617-454-1020
Fax: 617-454-1025

Avenida Paulista, 1728
5th Andar, Edificio Ouroinvest
San Paulo, SP, Brazil 01310-200
Phone: 55-11-5088-1177
Fax: 55-11-289-8931

Ortiz de Ocampo 3050
PB of.002
Buenos Aires, Argentina C1425DSS
Phone: 54-11-4806-1750
Fax: 54-11-4809-3223

Management and Staff

Dirk Donath, Managing Director
Jeronimo Bosch, Principal
Juan Marrone, Principal
Mario Quintana, Managing Partner
Michael Chu, Managing Director
Richard Gluzman, Managing Director
Woods Staton, Managing Director

Type of Firm

Private Equity Firm

Project Preferences

Type of Financing Preferred:
Expansion
Balanced
Turnaround

Geographical Preferences

International Preferences:
Latin America
Brazil

Industry Preferences

In Communications prefer:
Telecommunications

In Computer Software prefer:
Software

In Biotechnology prefer:
Biotechnology

In Medical/Health prefer:
Health Services

In Consumer Related prefer:
Retail
Consumer Products

In Transportation prefer:
Transportation

Additional Information

Year Founded: 2000
Current Activity Level : Actively seeking new investments

PEMBANGUNAN EKUITI SDN BHD

Level 11, Menara SME Bank
Jalan Sultan Ismail
Kuala Lumpur, Malaysia 50250
Phone: 60-326-973-324
Fax: 60-326-073-343
Website: www.pekuiti.com

Management and Staff

Jasmani Abbas, Chief Executive Officer
Tairuddin Yusoff, Chief Operating Officer

Type of Firm

Private Equity Firm

Association Membership

Malaysian Venture Capital Association

Project Preferences

Type of Financing Preferred:
Balanced

Geographical Preferences

International Preferences:
Asia
Malaysia

Industry Preferences

In Communications prefer:
Communications and Media
Wireless Communications

In Consumer Related prefer:
Food/Beverage
Consumer Services

In Industrial/Energy prefer:
Oil and Gas Exploration
Oil & Gas Drilling,Explor
Industrial Products

Additional Information

Year Founded: 2009
Current Activity Level : Actively seeking new investments

PEMBRIDGE PARTNERS LLP

32-34 Great Titchfield Street
1st Floor
London, United Kingdom W1W 8BG
Phone: 44-20-7631-3145
Fax: 44-20-7631-3011
E-mail: info@pembridge.net
Website: www.pembridge.net

Management and Staff

David Prais, Managing Partner
Hugh Mason, Partner
Mark Adams, Partner
Rebecca Caroe, Partner
Rose Lewis, Partner
Tony McGuinness, Partner

Type of Firm

Service Provider

Project Preferences

Type of Financing Preferred:
Leveraged Buyout
Expansion
Management Buyouts
Acquisition

Geographical Preferences

International Preferences:
United Kingdom

Industry Preferences

In Communications prefer:
Media and Entertainment

In Business Serv. prefer:
Services
Consulting Services
Media

Additional Information

Year Founded: 2001
Current Activity Level : Actively seeking new investments

PENCARROW PRIVATE EQUITY, LTD.

1-3 Willeston Street
Level 14 Axon House
Wellington, New Zealand
Phone: 644-499-9190
Fax: 644-472-7687
Website: www.pencarrowpe.co.nz

Type of Firm

Private Equity Firm

Association Membership

Australian Venture Capital Association (AVCAL)

Project Preferences

Role in Financing:
Prefer role as deal originator

Type of Financing Preferred:
Second Stage Financing
Leveraged Buyout
Expansion
Later Stage
Management Buyouts

Size of Investments Considered:
Min Size of Investment Considered (000s): $8,046
Max Size of Investment Considered (000s): $24,139

Geographical Preferences

International Preferences:
New Zealand

Industry Focus

(% based on actual investment)

Consumer Related	35.8%
Industrial/Energy	34.1%
Other Products	30.1%

Additional Information

Name of Most Recent Fund: AMP Pencarrow JV Fund
Most Recent Fund Was Raised: 06/22/2005
Year Founded: 1993
Capital Under Management: $38,700,000
Current Activity Level : Actively seeking new investments

PENDER WEST CAPITAL PARTNERS, INC.

1111 West Hastings Street
Suite 200
Vancouver, Canada V6E 2J3
Phone: 604-669-1500
Website: www.penderwest.com

Management and Staff

Bruce Hodge, Managing Director
John Zaplatynsky, Managing Director
Wade Flemons, Managing Director

Type of Firm

Private Equity Firm

Additional Information

Year Founded: 2009
Current Activity Level : Actively seeking new investments

PENFUND PARTNERS, INC.

Munich Re Center
390 Bay Street, Suite 1720
Toronto, Canada M5H 2Y2
Phone: 416-865-0707
Fax: 416-364-4149
Website: www.penfund.com

Management and Staff

Adam Breslin, Partner
Barry Yontef, Partner
John Bradlow, Partner
Richard Bradlow, Partner

Type of Firm

Bank Affiliated

Association Membership

Canadian Venture Capital Association

Project Preferences

Role in Financing:
Will function either as deal originator or investor in deals created by others

Type of Financing Preferred:
Leveraged Buyout
Mezzanine
Generalist PE
Management Buyouts

Size of Investments Considered:
Min Size of Investment Considered (000s): $667
Max Size of Investment Considered (000s): $4,670

Geographical Preferences

Canadian Preferences:
Alberta
All Canada
Manitoba
Ontario
British Columbia
Saskatchewan

Industry Focus

(% based on actual investment)	
Consumer Related	92.1%
Industrial/Energy	4.3%
Other Products	3.6%

Additional Information
Year Founded: 1979
Capital Under Management: $308,400,000
Current Activity Level : Actively seeking new investments
Method of Compensation: Return on investment is of primary concern, do not charge fees

---

PENINSULA CAPITAL PARTNERS LLC

The Buhl Building
535 Griswold St, Suite 2050
Detroit, MI USA 48226
Phone: 313-237-5100
Fax: 313-237-5111
Website: www.peninsulafunds.com

Management and Staff
Daniel Scanlan, Vice President
Hector Bultynck, Partner
James Illikman, Partner
Jon Krempel, Vice President
Karl LaPeer, Partner
Scott Reilly, President
Steven Beckett, Partner

Type of Firm
Private Equity Firm

Project Preferences

Role in Financing:
Prefer role in deals created by others

Type of Financing Preferred:
Mezzanine

Size of Investments Considered:
Min Size of Investment Considered (000s): $3,000
Max Size of Investment Considered (000s): $25,000

Geographical Preferences

Canadian Preferences:
All Canada

Industry Focus

(% based on actual investment)	
Other Products	30.4%
Industrial/Energy	30.0%
Consumer Related	16.4%
Internet Specific	10.3%
Semiconductors/Other Elect.	9.8%
Communications and Media	1.7%
Computer Software and Services	1.0%
Medical/Health	0.4%

Additional Information
Name of Most Recent Fund: Peninsula Fund IV, L.P.
Most Recent Fund Was Raised: 10/01/2005
Year Founded: 1995
Capital Under Management: $467,000,000
Current Activity Level : Actively seeking new investments
Method of Compensation: Return on invest. most important, but chg. closing fees, service fees, etc.

PENINSULA VENTURES

3000 Sand Hill Road
Building Two, Suite 100
Menlo Park, CA USA 94025
Phone: 650-854-0314
Fax: 650-854-0670
E-mail: info@peninsulaventures.com
Website: www.peninsulaventures.com

Management and Staff
Bob Patterson, Managing Director
Brian Smith, Managing Director
Greg Ennis, Managing Director
Gregory Robinson, Managing Director
Sam Lee, Managing Director

Type of Firm
Private Equity Firm

Association Membership
National Venture Capital Association - USA (NVCA)

Project Preferences

Role in Financing:
Will function either as deal originator or investor in deals created by others

Type of Financing Preferred:
Second Stage Financing
Early Stage
First Stage Financing

Size of Investments Considered:
Min Size of Investment Considered (000s): $1,000
Max Size of Investment Considered (000s): $6,000

Industry Preferences

In Computer Software prefer:
Software

In Medical/Health prefer:
Health Services

Additional Information
Name of Most Recent Fund: Peninsula Technology Ventures, L.P.
Most Recent Fund Was Raised: 12/15/2006
Year Founded: 2002
Capital Under Management: $100,000,000
Current Activity Level : Actively seeking new investments

PENN VALLEY GROUP

435 Devon Park Drive
Building 700
Wayne, PA USA 19087
Phone: 610-977-2770
Fax: 610-977-2769
Website: www.pennvalleygroup.com

Management and Staff
Bruce Luehrs, Co-Founder

Type of Firm
Bank Affiliated

Project Preferences

Type of Financing Preferred:
Expansion
Management Buyouts
Recapitalizations

Size of Investments Considered:
Min Size of Investment Considered (000s): $1,000
Max Size of Investment Considered (000s): $25,000

Geographical Preferences

United States Preferences:
Mid Atlantic
All U.S.

Industry Preferences

In Communications prefer:
Communications and Media

In Internet Specific prefer:
Ecommerce
Web Aggregration/Portals

In Financial Services prefer:
Financial Services

In Business Serv. prefer:
Services
Distribution

In Manufact. prefer:
Manufacturing

Additional Information

Year Founded: 2006
Capital Under Management: $10,000,000
Current Activity Level : Actively seeking new investments
Method of Compensation: Return on invest. most important, but chg. closing fees, service fees, etc.

PENN VENTURE PARTNERS, LP

132 State Street
Suite 200
Harrisburg, PA USA 17101
Phone: 717-236-2300
Fax: 717-236-2350
Website: www.pennventures.com

Management and Staff

Dean Kline, Managing Director
Mary Vovokes, Vice President
Thomas Penn, Managing Director

Type of Firm

Private Equity Firm

Association Membership

National Venture Capital Association - USA (NVCA)

Project Preferences

Role in Financing:
Will function either as deal originator or investor in deals created by others

Type of Financing Preferred:
Leveraged Buyout
Early Stage
Expansion
Management Buyouts
Recapitalizations

Size of Investments Considered:
Min Size of Investment Considered (000s): $500
Max Size of Investment Considered (000s): $2,000

Geographical Preferences

United States Preferences:
Pennsylvania

Industry Preferences

In Communications prefer:
Telecommunications
Data Communications

In Computer Hardware prefer:
Computers

In Computer Software prefer:
Software

In Computer Other prefer:
Computer Related

In Biotechnology prefer:
Biotechnology

In Consumer Related prefer:
Education Related

In Industrial/Energy prefer:
Energy
Materials
Factory Automation

In Manufact. prefer:
Manufacturing

In Agr/Forestr/Fish prefer:
Agribusiness

Additional Information

Name of Most Recent Fund: Penn Venture Partners, LP
Most Recent Fund Was Raised: 12/01/2002
Year Founded: 2003
Capital Under Management: $25,000,000
Current Activity Level : Actively seeking new investments
Method of Compensation: Return on investment is of primary concern, do not charge fees

---

PENNELL VENTURE PARTNERS

332 Bleecker Street
K-67
New York, NY USA 10014
Phone: 212-206-1295
Fax: 646-365-3195
E-mail: plans@pennell.com
Website: www.pennell.com

Management and Staff

Thomas Pennell, Managing Partner

Type of Firm

Private Equity Firm

Association Membership

National Venture Capital Association - USA (NVCA)

Project Preferences

Role in Financing:
Prefer role as deal originator but will also invest in deals created by others

Type of Financing Preferred:
Early Stage

Size of Investments Considered:
Min Size of Investment Considered (000s): $300
Max Size of Investment Considered (000s): $1,500

Geographical Preferences

United States Preferences:
New York

Industry Preferences

In Computer Software prefer:
Software

Additional Information

Year Founded: 1996
Capital Under Management: $18,000,000
Current Activity Level : Actively seeking new investments

PENNINGTON ALLEN CAPITAL PARTNERS

401 South Boston Avenue
Mid-Continent Tower, Ste 2400
Tulsa, OK USA 74103
Phone: 918-749-6811
E-mail: info@penningtonallen.com
Website: www.penningtonallen.com

Type of Firm

Private Equity Firm

Project Preferences

Type of Financing Preferred:
Early Stage
Management Buyouts
Acquisition
Recapitalizations

Industry Preferences

In Communications prefer:
Communications and Media
Telecommunications

In Business Serv. prefer:
Services
Distribution

In Manufact. prefer:
Manufacturing

Additional Information

Year Founded: 2003
Current Activity Level : Actively seeking new investments

PENTA CAPITAL LLP (FKA: PENTA CAPITAL PARTNERS, LTD.)

150 Saint Vincent Street
Glasgow, United Kingdom G2 5NE
Phone: 44-141-572-7300
Fax: 44-141-572-7310
E-mail: info@pentacapital.com
Website: www.pentacapital.com

Other Offices

53 Chandos Place
London, United Kingdom WC2N 4HS
Phone: 44-20-7812-6555
Fax: 44-20-7812-6556

Management and Staff

David Calder, Founder
Mark Phillips, Partner
Steven Scott, Partner
Torquil MacNaughton, Partner

Type of Firm

Private Equity Firm

Association Membership

British Venture Capital Association (BVCA)

Project Preferences

Type of Financing Preferred:

Leveraged Buyout
Mezzanine
Later Stage
Management Buyouts
Recapitalizations

Size of Investments Considered:

Min Size of Investment Considered (000s): $5,800
Max Size of Investment Considered (000s): $29,001

Geographical Preferences

International Preferences:

Ireland
United Kingdom

Industry Preferences

In Communications prefer:

Communications and Media
Telecommunications

In Computer Software prefer:

Software

In Consumer Related prefer:

Entertainment and Leisure

In Business Serv. prefer:

Services

In Manufact. prefer:

Publishing

Additional Information

Name of Most Recent Fund: Penta Fund 1
Most Recent Fund Was Raised: 05/04/2000
Year Founded: 1999
Capital Under Management: $324,100,000
Current Activity Level : Actively seeking new investments

PENTA INVESTMENTS, LTD.

Agias Fylaxeos & Polygnostou,
212, C&I CENTER
Limassol, Cyprus 3803
Phone: 357-257-3310-4
Fax: 357-257-3313-5
E-mail: penta@pentainvestments.com.cy
Website: www.pentainvestments.com

Other Offices

Krizkova 9
Bratislava, Slovakia 81104
Phone: 421-257-788-111
Fax: 421-257-788-055

Na Prikope 15
Praha 1, Czech Republic 110 00
Phone: 420-210-083-111
Fax: 420-210-083-160

Nowogrodzka 21
Warsaw, Poland 00-511
Phone: 48-22-502-3233
Fax: 48-22-502-3223

M. Sukharevskaya pl. 12
Business Center Sadovaya Gallery
Moscow, Russia 125047
Phone: 7-495-937-8573
Fax: 7-495-937-8571

Management and Staff

Eduard Matak, Managing Partner
Jaroslav Hascak, Managing Partner
Jozef Oravkin, Partner
Jozef Janov, Managing Partner
Marek Dospiva, Founding Partner
Martin Kusik, Partner

Type of Firm

Private Equity Firm

Project Preferences

Type of Financing Preferred:

Leveraged Buyout
Other
Acquisition
Recapitalizations

Geographical Preferences

International Preferences:

Europe

Industry Preferences

In Communications prefer:

Telecommunications

In Medical/Health prefer:

Medical/Health

In Consumer Related prefer:

Retail

In Industrial/Energy prefer:

Industrial Products

In Financial Services prefer:

Financial Services

In Agr/Forestr/Fish prefer:

Mining and Minerals

In Utilities prefer:

Utilities

Additional Information

Year Founded: 1977
Capital Under Management: $607,500,000
Current Activity Level : Actively seeking new investments

PENTAR

2, Via Niorne
Milan, Italy 20123
Phone: 39-02882-3251
Fax: 39-02805-7647
E-mail: s.rocca@pentar-investments.com
Website: www.pentar-investments.com

Type of Firm

Private Equity Firm

Association Membership

Italian Venture Capital Association (AIFI)

Project Preferences

Type of Financing Preferred:

Expansion

Size of Investments Considered:

Min Size of Investment Considered (000s): $6,351
Max Size of Investment Considered (000s): $25,404

Geographical Preferences

International Preferences:

Italy
Europe

Industry Preferences

In Consumer Related prefer:

Food/Beverage
Consumer Products
Hotels and Resorts

In Manufact. prefer:

Manufacturing

Additional Information

Year Founded: 2006
Capital Under Management: $44,400,000
Current Activity Level : Actively seeking new investments

PENTECH VENTURES, LLP

39, Melville Street
Edinburgh, United Kingdom EH3 7JF
Phone: 44-131-516-4100
E-mail: info@pentechvc.com
Website: www.pentechvc.com

Management and Staff

David Armour, Partner
Eddie Anderson, Founding Partner
Marc Moens, Partner
Sandy McKinnon, Partner

Type of Firm

Private Equity Firm

Project Preferences

Type of Financing Preferred:
Early Stage

Geographical Preferences

International Preferences:
United Kingdom
Ireland

Industry Preferences

In Communications prefer:
Communications and Media
Telecommunications
Wireless Communications

In Computer Software prefer:
Software
Systems Software
Applications Software

In Internet Specific prefer:
Internet

In Business Serv. prefer:
Media

Additional Information

Name of Most Recent Fund: Pentech Fund I
Most Recent Fund Was Raised: 11/06/2001
Year Founded: 2001
Capital Under Management: $78,800,000
Current Activity Level : Actively seeking new investments

PENTON CONSULTING SP. K. (AKA: PENTON PARTNERS)

Wisniowa 40B
Suite 13
Warsaw, Poland 02520
Phone: 48-22-542-4280
Fax: 48-22-542-4281
E-mail: office@pentonpartners.com
Website: www.pentonpartners.com

Management and Staff

Adam Domzalski, Partner
Bartosz Janikowski, Partner
Jaroslaw Witczak, Partner
Marek Chlopek, Partner
Robert Niziol, Partner

Type of Firm

Private Equity Firm

Association Membership

Emerging Markets Private Equity Association
Polish Venture Capital Association (PSIC/PPEA)

Project Preferences

Type of Financing Preferred:
Expansion

Size of Investments Considered:
Min Size of Investment Considered (000s): $3,000
Max Size of Investment Considered (000s): $12,000

Geographical Preferences

International Preferences:
Central Europe
Poland
Eastern Europe

Industry Preferences

In Manufact. prefer:
Manufacturing

Additional Information

Year Founded: 2007
Current Activity Level : Actively seeking new investments

PEPPERMINT. FINANCIAL PARTNERS (FKA SCHRODER + PARTNER)

Neues Kranzler Eck
Kurfurstendamm 21
Berlin, Germany 10719
Phone: 49-30-590064400
Fax: 49-30-590064401
E-mail: info@peppermint-vc.de
Website: www.peppermint-vc.de

Management and Staff

Frank Albrecht, Managing Director
Ingeborg Neumann, Chief Executive Officer
Stefan Kahe, Partner

Type of Firm

Private Equity Firm

Project Preferences

Type of Financing Preferred:
Early Stage
Expansion
Turnaround
Startup

Geographical Preferences

International Preferences:
Europe

Industry Preferences

In Computer Software prefer:
Software

In Internet Specific prefer:
Internet

In Semiconductor/Electr prefer:
Electronics
Micro-Processing

In Biotechnology prefer:
Biotechnology

In Medical/Health prefer:
Medical/Health

In Industrial/Energy prefer:
Materials

Additional Information

Year Founded: 1996
Capital Under Management: $22,300,000
Current Activity Level : Actively seeking new investments

PEPPERTREE CAPITAL MANAGEMENT, INC.

3550 Lander Road
Suite 300
Cleveland, OH USA 44124
Phone: 216-514-4949
Fax: 216-514-4959
E-mail: info@peppertreefund.com
Website: www.peppertreefund.com

Other Offices

3713 Greenbrier Drive
Dallas, TX USA 75225
Phone: 214-207-3992
Fax: 214-987-4824

Management and Staff

Carl Tippit, Managing Director
Joseph Michael, Managing Director
Kevin McGinty, Managing Director

Type of Firm

Private Equity Advisor or Fund of Funds

Project Preferences

Role in Financing:
Prefer role in deals created by others

Type of Financing Preferred:
Fund of Funds
Leveraged Buyout
Early Stage
Expansion
Balanced
Later Stage
Seed
Management Buyouts
Recapitalizations

Size of Investments Considered:
Min Size of Investment Considered (000s): $1,000
Max Size of Investment Considered (000s): $20,000

Geographical Preferences

United States Preferences:
All U.S.

Industry Preferences

In Communications prefer:
Communications and Media
Radio & TV Broadcasting
Telecommunications

Media and Entertainment

In Business Serv. prefer:
Services
Media

Additional Information
Year Founded: 2000
Capital Under Management: $183,000,000
Current Activity Level : Actively seeking new investments
Method of Compensation: Return on investment is of primary concern, do not charge fees

---

PEQ AB
Stureplan 2
Stockholm, Sweden 10388
Phone: 46-84-076-408
Fax: 46-84-076-424
Website: www.peqab.se

Management and Staff
Lars Carlbom, Chief Executive Officer

Type of Firm
Private Equity Firm

Project Preferences

Type of Financing Preferred:
Balanced

Geographical Preferences

International Preferences:
Europe

Additional Information
Year Founded: 2008
Current Activity Level : Actively seeking new investments

PEQUOT CAPITAL MANAGEMENT, INC.
500 Nyala Farm Road
Westport, CT USA 06880
Phone: 203-429-2200
Fax: 203-429-2420
E-mail: investor_relations@pequotcap.com
Website: www.pequotcap.com

Other Offices
11111 Santa Monica Boulevard
Suite 1210
Los Angeles, CA USA 90025
Phone: 310-689-5100
Fax: 310-689-5199

One Market Plaza
Steuart Tower, 23rd Floor
San Francisco, CA USA 94105
Phone: 415-848-5000
Fax: 415-848-5049

33 Street James Square
London, United Kingdom SW1Y4JS
Phone: 44-20-7661-9374
Fax: 44-20-766-19893

1901 Assembly Street
Suite 390
Columbia, SC USA 29201
Phone: 803-251-7994
Fax: 803-251-7995

153 East 53rd Street
35th Floor
New York, NY USA 10022
Phone: 212-702-4400
Fax: 212-702-2730

Management and Staff
Arthur Samberg, Chairman & CEO
Barry Bycoff, Venture Partner
Brian Kempner, Chief Operating Officer
Carlos Rodriguez, Chief Financial Officer
Danielle Hootnick, Vice President
Deborah Bernstein, General Partner
Divya Gugnani, Vice President
Gerald Poch, Senior Managing Director
Gregory Rossmann, Managing Director
Jennifer Verina, Vice President
Juliet Bakker, Managing Director
Larry Wilson, Venture Partner
Lawrence Lenihan, Senior Managing Director
Martin Hale, Managing Director
Patrick Enright, Managing Director
Sterling Philips, Venture Partner

Type of Firm
Private Equity Firm

Project Preferences

Role in Financing:
Prefer role as deal originator but will also invest in deals created by others

Type of Financing Preferred:
Second Stage Financing
Leveraged Buyout
Early Stage
Expansion
Mezzanine
Balanced
Open Market
Seed
Later Stage
First Stage Financing
Private Placement
Startup
Recapitalizations
Distressed Debt

Size of Investments Considered:
Min Size of Investment Considered (000s): $100
Max Size of Investment Considered (000s): $10,000

Geographical Preferences

United States Preferences:
All U.S.

Canadian Preferences:
All Canada

International Preferences:
Italy
United Kingdom
Luxembourg
Netherlands
Middle East
Eastern Europe
Spain
Belgium
Germany
All International
France

Industry Focus
(% based on actual investment)	
Computer Software and Services	28.7%
Biotechnology	15.1%
Communications and Media	14.2%
Medical/Health	14.2%
Semiconductors/Other Elect.	8.8%
Internet Specific	7.5%
Industrial/Energy	5.6%
Other Products	4.7%
Computer Hardware	1.2%

Additional Information
Year Founded: 1999
Capital Under Management: $1,987,500,000
Current Activity Level : Actively seeking new investments

PEQUOT SPECIAL OPPORTUNITIES PARTNERS LLC
c/o Pequot Capital Management
500 Nyala Farm Road
Westport, CT USA 06880
Phone: 203-429-2200

Management and Staff
Arthur Samberg, Managing Director
Kevin O'Brien, Managing Director
Paul Mellinger, Principal
Peter Dartley, Managing Director
Robert Webster, Principal
Sheila Clancy, Managing Director

Type of Firm
Private Equity Firm

Project Preferences

Type of Financing Preferred:
Distressed Debt

Additional Information
Name of Most Recent Fund: Pequot Special Opportunities Fund, L.P.
Most Recent Fund Was Raised: 05/01/2002
Year Founded: 2002
Capital Under Management: $100,000,000
Current Activity Level : Actively seeking new investments

PERCEVA CAPITAL

164 rue de Rivoli
Paris, France 75001
Phone: 33-1-4297-1990
Fax: 33-1-4297-1991
E-mail: perceva@percevacapital.com
Website: www.percevacapital.com

Type of Firm

Private Equity Firm

Association Membership

French Venture Capital Association (AFIC)

Project Preferences

Type of Financing Preferred:
Leveraged Buyout
Generalist PE
Turnaround

Additional Information

Year Founded: 2009
Current Activity Level : Actively seeking new investments

PEREGRINE VENTURES

6 Yoni Netanyahu Street
Or Yehuda, Israel 60376
Phone: 972-3-6349-990
Fax: 972-3-6349-910
E-mail: contact@peregrinevc.com
Website: www.peregrinevc.com

Management and Staff

Eyal Lifshitz, Chief Executive Officer

Type of Firm

Private Equity Firm

Project Preferences

Type of Financing Preferred:
Early Stage
Seed
Startup

Geographical Preferences

International Preferences:
Israel

Industry Preferences

In Communications prefer:
Commercial Communications

In Medical/Health prefer:
Medical Products

Additional Information

Year Founded: 1995
Capital Under Management: $23,500,000
Current Activity Level : Actively seeking new investments

PEREGRINE VENTURES, LP

20833 Stevens Creek Boulevard
Suite 102
Cupertino, CA USA 95014
Phone: 408-996-7212
Fax: 408-996-7232

Management and Staff

Frank LaHaye, General Partner
Gene Miller, General Partner
Helen Smith-MacKenzie, Chief Financial Officer

Type of Firm

Private Equity Firm

Association Membership

Western Association of Venture Capitalists (WAVC)
Natl Assoc of Small Bus. Inv. Co (NASBIC)

Project Preferences

Role in Financing:
Will function either as deal originator or investor in deals created by others

Type of Financing Preferred:
Leveraged Buyout
Start-up Financing
First Stage Financing

Size of Investments Considered:
Min Size of Investment Considered (000s): $1,000
Max Size of Investment Considered: No Limit

Additional Information

Name of Most Recent Fund: Peregrine Ventures II
Most Recent Fund Was Raised: 03/30/1984
Year Founded: 1981
Capital Under Management: $50,000,000
Current Activity Level : Making few, if any, new investments
Method of Compensation: Return on investment is of primary concern, do not charge fees

PERFECTIS PRIVATE EQUITY

27 Boulevard Malesherbes
Paris, France 75008
Phone: 33-1-5305-9444
Fax: 33-1-5305-9445
Website: www.perfectis.fr

Management and Staff

Gabriel Fossorier, Partner
Jean-Marie Lavirotte, Partner

Type of Firm

Insurance Firm Affiliate

Association Membership

French Venture Capital Association (AFIC)

Project Preferences

Type of Financing Preferred:
Leveraged Buyout
Expansion
Management Buyouts

Size of Investments Considered:
Min Size of Investment Considered (000s): $2,194
Max Size of Investment Considered (000s): $10,529

Geographical Preferences

International Preferences:
France

Industry Focus

(% based on actual investment)

Industrial/Energy	40.7%
Other Products	38.5%
Internet Specific	20.7%

Additional Information

Year Founded: 2000
Capital Under Management: $95,800,000
Current Activity Level : Actively seeking new investments

PERFORMA INVESTIMENTOS

Avenida Paulista 2001
8 Andar cj 809
Sao Paolo, Brazil
Phone: 55-11-3263-0577
Website: www.performainvestimentos.com

Management and Staff

Eduardo Grytz, Partner
Felipe Teixeira Favaro, Partner
Humberto Matsuda, Founder

Type of Firm

Private Equity Firm

Project Preferences

Type of Financing Preferred:
Early Stage
Seed

Geographical Preferences

International Preferences:
Latin America
Brazil

Additional Information

Year Founded: 2009
Current Activity Level : Actively seeking new investments

PERFORMANCE EQUITY MANAGEMENT, LLC

Two Pickwick Plaza
Suite 310
Greenwich, CT USA 06830
Phone: 203-742-2400
Fax: 203-742-2340
Website: www.peqm.com

Other Offices

33-35 Cornhill
London, United Kingdom EC3V 3ND
Phone: 44-0-207-626-0461
Fax: 44-0-207-397-4398

Management and Staff

Charles Froland, Chief Executive Officer

Type of Firm

Private Equity Advisor or Fund of Funds

Association Membership

European Private Equity and Venture Capital Assoc.

Project Preferences

Type of Financing Preferred:
Fund of Funds
Expansion
Generalist PE

Geographical Preferences

United States Preferences:
All U.S.

International Preferences:
Europe
Asia

Additional Information

Name of Most Recent Fund: Performance Venture Capital, L.P.
Most Recent Fund Was Raised: 07/05/2005
Year Founded: 2005
Capital Under Management: $11,000,000,000
Current Activity Level : Actively seeking new investments

PERMIRA ADVISERS LLP (FKA: SCHRODER VENTURES EUROPE)

80 Pall Mall
London, United Kingdom SW1Y 5ES
Phone: 44-20-7632-1000
Fax: 44-20-7930-3185
Website: www.permira.com

Other Offices

PO Box 503, Trafalgar Court
Les Banques, St. Peter Port
Guernsey, United Kingdom GY1 6DJ
Phone: 44-1481-743-200
Fax: 44-1481-743-201

64 Willow Place
Suite 101
Menlo Park, CA USA 94025
Phone: 650-681-4701
Fax: 650-853-0180

Clemensstrasse 9 / Falkstrasse 5
Frankfurt am Main, Germany 60487
Phone: 49-69-971-4660
Fax: 49-69-9714-6699

Plaza del Marques de Salamanca, 10
Primero Izquierda
Madrid, Spain 28006
Phone: 34-91-418-2499
Fax: 34-91-426-1193

Birger Jarlsgatan 12
Stockholm, Sweden 114 34
Phone: 46-8-5031-2200
Fax: 46-8-5031-2299

Akasaka Intercity Building 3F
1-11-44 Akasaka, Minato-ku
Tokyo, Japan 107-0052
Phone: 81-3-6230-2051
Fax: 81-3-6230-2052

Unit 2806-2807, 28th Floor
One Exchange Square
Central, Hong Kong
Phone: 852-3972-0800
Fax: 852-2111-1148

Via San Paolo, 10
Milano, Italy 20121
Phone: 39-02-7600-4740
Fax: 39-02-7600-4706

374 rue St. Honore
Paris, France 75001

320 Park Avenue
33rd Floor
New York, NY USA 10022
Phone: 212-386-7480
Fax: 212-386-7481

282, route de Longwy
Luxembourg, Luxembourg L-1940
Phone: 352-26-86-811
Fax: 352-26-86-8181

Management and Staff

Alexandre Emery, Principal
Allen Haight, Partner
Brian Ruder, Partner
Carl Parker, Partner
Charles Sherwood, Partner
Evelyn Ehlert, Partner
Gianluca Andena, Partner
Goetz Maeuser, Partner
Graham Wrigley, Partner
Guido Paolo Gamucci, Managing Director
Guy Davies, Partner
Ian Sellers, Partner
John Coyle, Partner
Kurt Bjorklund, Managing Partner
Martin Clarke, Partner
Martin Weckwerth, Partner
Mike Garland, Partner
Nicola Volpi, Partner
Ole Oftedal, Partner
Paolo Colonna, Managing Partner
Peter Smitham, Managing Partner
Philip Bassett, Partner
Philippe Robert, Managing Director
Thomas Krenz, Managing Director
Thomas Jetter, Partner
Tom Lister, Managing Partner
Uwe Kolb, Partner
Veronica Eng, Partner
Wolfgang Reuther, Partner

Type of Firm

Private Equity Firm

Association Membership

Italian Venture Capital Association (AIFI)
British Venture Capital Association (BVCA)
European Private Equity and Venture Capital Assoc.

Project Preferences

Type of Financing Preferred:
Leveraged Buyout
Research and Development
Balanced
Turnaround
Management Buyouts
Acquisition

Size of Investments Considered:
Min Size of Investment Considered (000s): $14,564
Max Size of Investment Considered (000s): $87,384

Geographical Preferences

International Preferences:
Italy
United Kingdom
Europe
Germany
France

Industry Focus

(% based on actual investment)

Other Products	45.3%
Industrial/Energy	20.1%
Medical/Health	18.2%
Consumer Related	7.7%
Communications and Media	6.7%
Internet Specific	1.2%
Semiconductors/Other Elect.	0.4%
Biotechnology	0.3%
Computer Software and Services	0.1%

Additional Information

Year Founded: 1985
Capital Under Management: $12,000,000,000
Current Activity Level : Actively seeking new investments

PEROT INVESTMENTS, INC.

2300 W. Plano Parkway
Plano, TX USA 75075
Phone: 214-788-3000
Fax: 214-788-3097
Website: www.ps.net

Management and Staff

Brian Maloney, Chief Operating Officer
John King, Vice President

Type of Firm

Corporate PE/Venture

Project Preferences

Role in Financing:

Will function either as deal originator or investor in deals created by others

Type of Financing Preferred:

Second Stage Financing
First Stage Financing
Special Situation

Size of Investments Considered:

Min Size of Investment Considered (000s): $1,000
Max Size of Investment Considered: No Limit

Additional Information

Year Founded: 2001
Current Activity Level : Actively seeking new investments
Method of Compensation: Return on investment is of primary concern, do not charge fees

PERSEUS LLC

2099 Pennsylvania Avenue, NW
Ninth Floor
Washington, DC USA 20006
Phone: 202-452-0101
Fax: 202-429-0588
E-mail: info@perseusllc.com
Website: www.perseusllc.com

Other Offices

1325 Avenue of the Americas
25th Floor
New York, NY USA 10019
Phone: 212-651-6400
Fax: 212-651-6399

Schumannstrasse 4
Munich, Germany D-81679
Phone: 49-1890-8810
Fax: 49-1890-8850

Management and Staff

Anjali Jolly, Vice President
Brian Leitch, Senior Managing Director
Dave Davis, Senior Managing Director
Frank Pearl, Chairman & CEO
J.T. Mauk, Vice President
John Fox, Senior Managing Director
John Glazer, Managing Director
Kenneth Socha, Senior Managing Director
Kimberly Foerster, Managing Director
Lisa Schule, Vice President
Michael Rapport, Vice President
Michael Miller, Managing Director
Norman Selby, Senior Managing Director

Type of Firm

Private Equity Firm

Project Preferences

Role in Financing:

Prefer role as deal originator

Type of Financing Preferred:

Leveraged Buyout
Expansion
Mezzanine
Generalist PE
Later Stage
Acquisition
Private Placement
Recapitalizations

Size of Investments Considered:

Min Size of Investment Considered (000s): $10,000
Max Size of Investment Considered (000s): $50,000

Geographical Preferences

United States Preferences:

All U.S.

Industry Focus

(% based on actual investment)

Consumer Related	23.7%
Biotechnology	15.2%
Other Products	15.0%
Industrial/Energy	14.6%
Internet Specific	10.1%
Communications and Media	7.3%
Semiconductors/Other Elect.	6.5%
Computer Software and Services	5.4%
Computer Hardware	1.2%
Medical/Health	1.0%

Additional Information

Name of Most Recent Fund: Perseus VII Cayman, L.P.
Most Recent Fund Was Raised: 08/10/2006
Year Founded: 1995
Capital Under Management: $1,283,500,000
Current Activity Level : Actively seeking new investments
Method of Compensation: Return on invest. most important, but chg. closing fees, service fees, etc.

PERSIMMON CAPITAL, LTD.

12/F, On Lan Centre
11-15 On Lan Street
Central, Hong Kong
Phone: 852-3105-1580
Fax: 852-2140-6725
E-mail: info@persimmoncapital.com.hk
Website: www.persimmoncapital.com.hk

Management and Staff

Roger Marshall, Managing Director

Type of Firm

Private Equity Firm

Association Membership

Hong Kong Venture Capital Association (HKVCA)

Project Preferences

Type of Financing Preferred:

Balanced

Geographical Preferences

International Preferences:

China
Hong Kong
Thailand
Asia

Industry Preferences

In Medical/Health prefer:

Medical/Health

In Consumer Related prefer:

Consumer
Retail
Consumer Services
Hotels and Resorts

Additional Information

Year Founded: 1999
Current Activity Level : Actively seeking new investments

PERSIMMON TREE CAPITAL, L.P.

2100 Pennsylvania Avenue NW
Suite 545
Washington, DC USA 20037
Phone: 202-379-3113
E-mail: info@persimmontreecapital.com
Website: www.persimmontreecapital.com

Management and Staff

Jason Hicks, Managing Director
Lex Sant, Managing Director

Type of Firm

Private Equity Firm

Project Preferences

Type of Financing Preferred:

Early Stage
Expansion

Industry Preferences

In Industrial/Energy prefer:
Energy
Alternative Energy
Environmental Related

Additional Information
Year Founded: 2008
Current Activity Level : Actively seeking new investments

PERSISTENCE CAPITAL PARTNERS
500 Sherbrooke Street West
Suite 500
Montreal, Canada H3A 3C6
Phone: 514-843-2345
Fax: 514-845-9178
Website: www.pcpartners.ca

Management and Staff
Phillippe Couillard, Partner
Sheldon Elman, Managing Partner

Type of Firm
Private Equity Firm

Additional Information
Year Founded: 2008
Current Activity Level : Actively seeking new investments

PERUSA PARTNERS GMBH
Theatinerstrasse 40
Munich, Germany 80333
Phone: 49-89-238-87890
Fax: 49-89-238878950
Website: www.perusa-partners.de

Management and Staff
Christian Hollenberg, Co-Founder
Christopher Hofener, Co-Founder
Hanno Schmidt-Gothan, Co-Founder

Type of Firm
Private Equity Firm

Project Preferences

Type of Financing Preferred:
Leveraged Buyout

Geographical Preferences

International Preferences:
Europe
Germany

Additional Information
Year Founded: 2007
Current Activity Level : Actively seeking new investments

PETERSON PARTNERS (FKA: PETERSON CAPITAL)
2825 East Cottonwood Parkway
Suite 400
Salt Lake City, UT USA 84121
Phone: 801-359-8880
Fax: 801-359-8840
E-mail: info@petersonpartnerslp.com
Website: www.petersonpartnerslp.com

Type of Firm
Private Equity Firm

Project Preferences

Type of Financing Preferred:
Leveraged Buyout
Management Buyouts
Recapitalizations

Size of Investments Considered:
Min Size of Investment Considered (000s): $500
Max Size of Investment Considered (000s): $10,000

Industry Preferences

In Consumer Related prefer:
Consumer Products
Consumer Services

In Financial Services prefer:
Real Estate

In Business Serv. prefer:
Services

In Manufact. prefer:
Manufacturing

Additional Information
Year Founded: 1995
Capital Under Management: $100,000,000
Current Activity Level : Actively seeking new investments

PETIT POUCET PARTICIPATION
9 rue guyton de morveau
Paris, France 75013
Phone: 33-1-4565-9228
Fax: 33-1-4565-2588
E-mail: info@petitpoucet.fr
Website: www.petitpoucet.fr

Management and Staff
Mathias Monribot, Founder

Type of Firm
Private Equity Firm

Project Preferences

Type of Financing Preferred:
Balanced

Geographical Preferences

International Preferences:
Europe

Additional Information
Year Founded: 2002
Current Activity Level : Actively seeking new investments

PETRA CAPITAL PARTNERS, LLC
3825 Bedford Avenue
Suite 101
Nashville, TN USA 37215
Phone: 615-313-5999
Fax: 615-313-5990
Website: www.petracapital.com

Management and Staff
David Fitzgerald, Venture Partner
Doug Owen, Vice President
Michael Blackburn, Managing Partner
Robert Smith, Partner

Type of Firm
Private Equity Firm

Association Membership
Mid-Atlantic Venture Association
Natl Assoc of Small Bus. Inv. Co (NASBIC)

Project Preferences

Role in Financing:
Prefer role as deal originator but will also invest in deals created by others

Type of Financing Preferred:
Leveraged Buyout
Expansion
Mezzanine
Generalist PE
Later Stage
Acquisition
Recapitalizations

Size of Investments Considered:
Min Size of Investment Considered (000s): $4,000
Max Size of Investment Considered (000s): $15,000

Industry Focus
(% based on actual investment)

Computer Software and Services	36.2%
Other Products	28.7%
Medical/Health	11.7%
Communications and Media	11.6%
Internet Specific	4.7%
Consumer Related	3.6%
Computer Hardware	3.5%

Additional Information

Name of Most Recent Fund: Petra Growth Fund II, LP
Most Recent Fund Was Raised: 06/30/2007
Year Founded: 1996
Capital Under Management: $290,000,000
Current Activity Level : Actively seeking new investments
Method of Compensation: Return on investment is of primary concern, do not charge fees

PFINGSTEN PARTNERS, L.P.

300 North LaSalle Street
Suite 5400
Chicago, IL USA 60654
Phone: 312-222-8707
Fax: 312-222-8708
E-mail: pfingstenpartners@pfingsten.com
Website: www.pfingstenpartners.com

Other Offices

1 Trademark Drive
Hong Kong International Trade & Ex. Ctr.
Kowloon Bay, Hong Kong
Phone: 852-3100-0081
Fax: 852-2111-1140

Management and Staff

Alex Gregor, Vice President
Amy Lincoln, Vice President
Brenda Lee Lally, Vice President
Craig Tompkins, Vice President
David Johnston, Vice President
Denio Bolzan, Managing Director
James Norton, Senior Managing Director
Jeffrey Cote, Chief Financial Officer
John Starcevich, Managing Director
John Underwood, Senior Managing Director
Lawrence Taylor, Vice President
Lori Cunningham, Vice President
Robert Gladden, Vice President
Scott Finegan, Managing Director
Thomas Byrne, Vice President
Thomas Bagley, Senior Managing Director

Type of Firm

Private Equity Firm

Project Preferences

Role in Financing:
Prefer role as deal originator

Type of Financing Preferred:
Leveraged Buyout
Later Stage
Management Buyouts
Industry Rollups

Size of Investments Considered:
Min Size of Investment Considered (000s): $15,000
Max Size of Investment Considered: No Limit

Geographical Preferences

United States Preferences:
Mid Atlantic
Midwest

Industry Preferences

In Semiconductor/Electr prefer:
Electronic Components
Controllers and Sensors
Component Testing Equipmt
Analytic/Scientific

In Consumer Related prefer:
Food/Beverage
Consumer Products
Education Related

In Industrial/Energy prefer:
Industrial Products

In Business Serv. prefer:
Distribution

In Manufact. prefer:
Manufacturing
Publishing

Additional Information

Name of Most Recent Fund: Pfingsten Executive Fund III, L.P.
Most Recent Fund Was Raised: 04/11/2003
Year Founded: 1989
Capital Under Management: $590,300,000
Current Activity Level : Actively seeking new investments
Method of Compensation: Return on investment is of primary concern, do not charge fees

PFIZER STRATEGIC INVESTMENTS GROUP (PSIG)

235 East 42nd Street
New York, NY USA 10017
Phone: 212-733-7034
Fax: 212-883-4873
E-mail: PSIG-info@pfizer.com
Website: www.pfizer.com/psig

Management and Staff

Ilya Oshman, Vice President

Type of Firm

Corporate PE/Venture

Association Membership

National Venture Capital Association - USA (NVCA)

Additional Information

Year Founded: 2004
Current Activity Level : Actively seeking new investments

PFM CAPITAL

1925 Victoria Avenue
2nd Floor, The Assiniboia Club
Regina, Canada S4P 0R3
Phone: 306-791-4855
Fax: 306-791-4848
E-mail: pfm@pfm.ca
Website: www.pfm.ca

Type of Firm

Private Equity Firm

Project Preferences

Type of Financing Preferred:
Early Stage
Expansion
Startup

Geographical Preferences

Canadian Preferences:
Saskatchewan

Additional Information

Year Founded: 1989
Current Activity Level : Actively seeking new investments

PHARMA CAPITAL VENTURES (AKA: PCV)

600 East Crescent Avenue
Suite 205
Upper Saddle River, NJ USA 07458
Phone: 973-629-3777
E-mail: PCV@pharmacapitalventures.com
Website: www.pharmacapitalventures.com

Management and Staff

Gary Lubin, Managing Director
Jeff Tarlowe, Managing Director

Type of Firm

Private Equity Firm

Project Preferences

Type of Financing Preferred:
Balanced

Industry Preferences

In Biotechnology prefer:
Biotechnology

In Medical/Health prefer:
Medical/Health

Additional Information

Year Founded: 2009
Current Activity Level : Actively seeking new investments

PHARMAVENT PARTNERS

33 Avenue du Maine
Paris, France 75015
Phone: 33-1-5850-7173
Fax: 33-1-5850-7274
Website: www.pharmaventures.com

Other Offices

4555 Lake Forest Drive
Suite 650, Westlake Center
Cincinnati, OH USA 45242
Phone: 513-563-3555
Fax: 513-563-3557

425 Market Street
Suite 220
San Francisco, CA USA 94105
Phone: 415-512-6488
Fax: 415-397-6309

Management and Staff

Laurent Arthaud, President

Type of Firm

Private Equity Firm

Project Preferences

Type of Financing Preferred:
Balanced

Geographical Preferences

International Preferences:
Europe
France

Industry Preferences

In Biotechnology prefer:
Biotechnology
Human Biotechnology

In Medical/Health prefer:
Medical/Health

Additional Information

Name of Most Recent Fund: Pharmavent
Most Recent Fund Was Raised: 11/23/2004
Year Founded: 2004
Capital Under Management: $102,000,000
Current Activity Level : Actively seeking new investments

PHAROS CAPITAL GROUP LLC

300 Crescent Court
Suite 1380
Dallas, TX USA 75201
Phone: 214-855-0194
Fax: 214-855-1230
E-mail: info@pharosfunds.com
Website: www.pharosfunds.com

Other Offices

One Burton Hills Boulevard
Suite 180
Nashville, TN USA 37215
Phone: 615-234-5522
Fax: 615-263-0234

Management and Staff

Anna Kovalkova, Vice President
Jim Phillips, Partner
Joel Goldberg, Principal
Joseph Acevedo, Vice President
Kimberly Davis-Moody, Chief Financial Officer

Type of Firm

Private Equity Firm

Association Membership

Natl Assoc of Small Bus. Inv. Co (NASBIC)

Project Preferences

Role in Financing:
Prefer role as deal originator

Type of Financing Preferred:
Second Stage Financing
Leveraged Buyout
Expansion
Later Stage
Management Buyouts
Acquisition
Recapitalizations

Size of Investments Considered:
Min Size of Investment Considered (000s): $10,000
Max Size of Investment Considered (000s): $30,000

Geographical Preferences

United States Preferences:
All U.S.

Industry Preferences

In Communications prefer:
Wireless Communications

In Computer Software prefer:
Software

In Semiconductor/Electr prefer:
Semiconductor

In Medical/Health prefer:
Medical Diagnostics
Diagnostic Services
Diagnostic Test Products
Medical Products
Disposable Med. Products
Health Services
Hospitals/Clinics/Primary
Hospital/Other Instit.

In Consumer Related prefer:
Education Related

In Business Serv. prefer:
Services

In Other prefer:
Women/Minority-Owned Bus.

Additional Information

Year Founded: 1998
Capital Under Management: $450,000,000
Current Activity Level : Actively seeking new investments
Method of Compensation: Return on investment is of primary concern, do not charge fees

PHD EQUITY PARTNERS LLP

7700 Daresbury Park
Daresbury
Cheshire, United Kingdom WA4 4BS
Phone: 44-19-2871-5700
Fax: 44-19-2875-1839
Website: www.phdequitypartners.com

Management and Staff

Andy Dodd, Partner
Craig Richardson, Partner
Frank Herlihy, Partner
James Dow, Partner
Jon Schofield, Partner
Mark Watts, Partner
Philip Price, Partner

Type of Firm

Private Equity Firm

Project Preferences

Type of Financing Preferred:
Expansion
Turnaround
Management Buyouts
Acquisition
Recapitalizations

Geographical Preferences

International Preferences:
United Kingdom

Industry Preferences

In Medical/Health prefer:
Health Services

In Consumer Related prefer:
Consumer

In Financial Services prefer:
Financial Services

In Manufact. prefer:
Manufacturing

Additional Information

Year Founded: 2008
Capital Under Management: $6,000,000
Current Activity Level : Actively seeking new investments

PHILIPS VENTURE CAPITAL FUND B.V. (AKA: CORPORATE VENTURING)

Amstelplein 2
Breitner Center, HBT-11
Amsterdam, Netherlands 1070 MX
Phone: 31-20-59-77-288
Fax: 31-20-59-77-299
Website: www.venturing.philips.com

Other Offices

Philips Silicon Valley Center
1000 West Maude Avenue
Sunnyvale, CA USA 94085
Phone: 408-617-7700
Fax: 408-617-4795

Philips Electronics Rep Office Israel
8 Hasadnaot Street, P.O. Box 2079
Herzliya, Israel 46120
Phone: 972-9-956-4004
Fax: 972-9-956-9690

Type of Firm

Corporate PE/Venture

Association Membership

European Private Equity and Venture Capital Assoc.

Project Preferences

Role in Financing:
Prefer role in deals created by others

Type of Financing Preferred:
Second Stage Financing
Early Stage
Expansion
Later Stage
Private Placement
Startup

Geographical Preferences

United States Preferences:
All U.S.

International Preferences:
Luxembourg
Netherlands
Europe
Scandanavia/Nordic Region
Belgium

Industry Preferences

In Communications prefer:
Wireless Communications
Data Communications
Other Communication Prod.

In Computer Hardware prefer:
Computer Graphics and Dig
Disk Relat. Memory Device

In Internet Specific prefer:
Internet

In Semiconductor/Electr prefer:
Electronic Components
Semiconductor
Micro-Processing
Controllers and Sensors
Sensors
Circuit Boards
Component Testing Equipmt

Additional Information

Year Founded: 1998
Capital Under Management: $130,000,000
Current Activity Level : Actively seeking new investments
Method of Compensation: Return on investment is of primary concern, do not charge fees

PHILLIMORE INVESTISSEMENT

3, place des Pyramides
Paris, France 75001
Phone: 33-1-4703-0813
Fax: 33-1-4703-0817
E-mail: contact@phillimore.fr
Website: www.phillimore.fr

Management and Staff

Cyril Tramon, President
Frederic Arnaud, Partner

Type of Firm

Private Equity Firm

Association Membership

French Venture Capital Association (AFIC)

Project Preferences

Type of Financing Preferred:
Balanced

Size of Investments Considered:
Min Size of Investment Considered (000s): $618
Max Size of Investment Considered (000s): $2,472

Geographical Preferences

International Preferences:
Europe
France

Industry Preferences

In Communications prefer:
Communications and Media

In Business Serv. prefer:
Distribution

Additional Information

Year Founded: 2003
Current Activity Level : Actively seeking new investments

PHILLIP PRIVATE EQUITY PTE, LTD. (FKA: ECICS MGT. PTE, LTD.)

250 North Bridge Road
06-00 Raffles City Tower
Singapore, Singapore 179 101
Phone: 65-6533-6001
Website: www.phillip.com.sg/eqfinance2.htm

Management and Staff

Timothy Chan, Vice President

Type of Firm

Insurance Firm Affiliate

Project Preferences

Role in Financing:
Prefer role in deals created by others

Type of Financing Preferred:
Second Stage Financing
Expansion
Mezzanine
Research and Development
Balanced
Seed
First Stage Financing
Special Situation
Startup

Size of Investments Considered:
Min Size of Investment Considered (000s): $500
Max Size of Investment Considered (000s): $1,500

Geographical Preferences

United States Preferences:
California
All U.S.

International Preferences:
Pacific Rim
Eastern Europe
Singapore
Asia
All International

Industry Preferences

In Communications prefer:
Communications and Media
Radio & TV Broadcasting
Telecommunications

In Internet Specific prefer:
Internet

In Computer Other prefer:
Computer Related

In Semiconductor/Electr prefer:
Electronic Components

In Biotechnology prefer:
Biotechnology

In Medical/Health prefer:
Medical/Health
Pharmaceuticals

In Consumer Related prefer:
Entertainment and Leisure
Food/Beverage
Consumer Services

In Transportation prefer:
Transportation

In Financial Services prefer:
Financial Services

Additional Information
Year Founded: 1993
Capital Under Management: $30,200,000
Current Activity Level : Actively seeking new investments
Method of Compensation: Return on investment is of primary concern, do not charge fees

---

PHOENIX CAPITAL CO., LTD.

9F Kishimoto Bldg.
2-2-1 Marunouchi, Chiyoda-ku
Tokyo, Japan 100-0005
Phone: 813-3215-3260
Fax: 81-3-3215-3261
Website: www.phoenixcapital.co.jp

Type of Firm
Private Equity Firm

Project Preferences

Type of Financing Preferred:
Leveraged Buyout
Balanced
Management Buyouts

Geographical Preferences

International Preferences:
Japan

Additional Information
Year Founded: 2002
Capital Under Management: $637,000,000
Current Activity Level : Actively seeking new investments

PHOENIX EQUITY PARTNERS (FKA: DLJ EUROPEAN PRIVATE EQUITY)

33 Glasshouse Street
London, United Kingdom W1B 5DG
Phone: 44-20-7434-6999
Fax: 44-20-7434-6998
E-mail: enquiries@phoenix-equity.com
Website: www.phoenix-equity.com

Management and Staff
Andrew Deakin, Partner
Chris Hanna, Partner
David Burns, Partner
Hugh Lenon, Managing Partner
James Thomas, Managing Director
James Booth, Principal
John Rastrick, Partner
Kevin Keck, Partner
Phillip Seers, Managing Partner
Richard Daw, Partner
Sandy Muirhead, Managing Partner
Tim Dunn, Principal

Type of Firm
Private Equity Firm

Association Membership
British Venture Capital Association (BVCA)
European Private Equity and Venture Capital Assoc.

Project Preferences

Role in Financing:
Prefer role as deal originator but will also invest in deals created by others

Type of Financing Preferred:
Second Stage Financing
Leveraged Buyout
Expansion
Mezzanine
Turnaround
Special Situation

Size of Investments Considered:
Min Size of Investment Considered (000s): $16,200
Max Size of Investment Considered (000s): $151,100

Geographical Preferences

International Preferences:
Italy
United Kingdom
Europe
Bermuda
Spain
Germany
France

Industry Focus
(% based on actual investment)

Other Products	40.4%
Consumer Related	31.5%
Communications and Media	7.6%
Industrial/Energy	7.2%
Medical/Health	5.2%
Internet Specific	4.6%
Biotechnology	2.2%
Computer Software and Services	1.4%

Additional Information
Name of Most Recent Fund: Phoenix Equity Partners IV
Most Recent Fund Was Raised: 05/22/2001
Year Founded: 1991
Capital Under Management: $714,200,000
Current Activity Level : Actively seeking new investments
Method of Compensation: Return on invest. most important, but chg. closing fees, service fees, etc.

PHOENIX PARTNERS, THE

1000 Second Avenue
Suite 3950
Seattle, WA USA 98104
Phone: 206-624-8968
Fax: 206-624-1907
Website: www.phoenixvc.com

Management and Staff
Will Horne, Chief Financial Officer

Type of Firm
Private Equity Firm

Project Preferences

Role in Financing:
Prefer role as deal originator but will also invest in deals created by others

Type of Financing Preferred:
Second Stage Financing
Mezzanine
Research and Development
Start-up Financing
Seed
First Stage Financing

Size of Investments Considered:
Min Size of Investment Considered (000s): $2,000
Max Size of Investment Considered (000s): $3,000

Industry Focus
(% based on actual investment)

Biotechnology	36.2%
Internet Specific	33.8%
Computer Software and Services	20.1%
Computer Hardware	4.9%
Medical/Health	2.9%
Semiconductors/Other Elect.	1.0%
Consumer Related	0.5%
Communications and Media	0.5%
Other Products	0.2%

Additional Information
Name of Most Recent Fund: Phoenix Partners, The
Most Recent Fund Was Raised: 01/01/1996
Year Founded: 1982
Current Activity Level : Actively seeking new investments
Method of Compensation: Return on investment is of primary concern, do not charge fees

---

PHOENIX VENTURE FUND LLC

135 East 57th Street
12th floor
New York, NY USA 10022

Management and Staff

Andrea Goran, Managing Director

Type of Firm

Private Equity Firm

Additional Information

Year Founded: 2009
Current Activity Level : Actively seeking new investments

PHYSIC VENTURES

200 California Street
5th Floor
San Francisco, CA USA 94111
Phone: 415-354-4901
Fax: 415-354-4915
E-mail: info@physicventures.com
Website: www.physicventures.com

Management and Staff

Dion Madsen, Managing Director
Jean Frechet, Venture Partner
Patty O'Malley, Chief Financial Officer
William Rosenzweig, Managing Director

Type of Firm

Private Equity Firm

Association Membership

National Venture Capital Association - USA (NVCA)

Project Preferences

Type of Financing Preferred:

Early Stage

Geographical Preferences

United States Preferences:

All U.S.

Industry Preferences

In Medical/Health prefer:

Medical Products
Health Services
Pharmaceuticals

In Consumer Related prefer:

Food/Beverage

In Industrial/Energy prefer:

Alternative Energy

In Agr/Forestr/Fish prefer:

Agriculture related

In Other prefer:

Environment Responsible

Additional Information

Name of Most Recent Fund: Physic Ventures, L.P.
Most Recent Fund Was Raised: 03/28/2007
Year Founded: 2007
Capital Under Management: $205,000,000
Current Activity Level : Actively seeking new investments

PI CAPITAL

Berger House
38 Berkeley Square
London, United Kingdom W1J 5AE
Phone: 44-20-7529-5656
Fax: 44-20-7529-5657
E-mail: contact@picapital.co.uk
Website: www.picapital.co.uk

Management and Staff

David Giampaolo, Chief Executive Officer
Paul Thomas, Managing Director
Peter Brooks, Managing Director
Stephen Geddes, Chief Operating Officer

Type of Firm

Private Equity Firm

Project Preferences

Type of Financing Preferred:

Leveraged Buyout
Management Buyouts
Recapitalizations

Size of Investments Considered:

Min Size of Investment Considered (000s): $3,863
Max Size of Investment Considered (000s): $9,659

Geographical Preferences

International Preferences:

United Kingdom

Industry Preferences

In Communications prefer:

Communications and Media
Commercial Communications

In Computer Hardware prefer:

Computers

In Computer Other prefer:

Computer Related

In Semiconductor/Electr prefer:

Electronics

In Biotechnology prefer:

Biotechnology

In Medical/Health prefer:

Medical/Health

In Consumer Related prefer:

Consumer

In Industrial/Energy prefer:

Industrial Products
Materials
Factory Automation

In Transportation prefer:

Transportation

In Business Serv. prefer:

Services

In Manufact. prefer:

Manufacturing

In Agr/Forestr/Fish prefer:

Agriculture related
Mining and Minerals

In Utilities prefer:

Utilities

Additional Information

Name of Most Recent Fund: Pi Capital Co-investment Fund
Most Recent Fund Was Raised: 04/04/1998
Year Founded: 1998
Capital Under Management: $31,000,000
Current Activity Level : Actively seeking new investments

PIBORUS INC.

357 Sir Georges Etienne Cartie
Montreal, Canada H4C 3A3
Phone: 514-483-0871
Fax: 514-221-3190
Website: www.piborus.com

Type of Firm

Private Equity Firm

Additional Information

Year Founded: 2001
Current Activity Level : Actively seeking new investments

PICA (M) CORPORATION BERHAD

Level 25, Wisma KiaPeng
3 Jalan Kia Peng
Kuala Lumpur, Malaysia 50450
Phone: 603-2161-8800
Fax: 603-2161-1714

Management and Staff

Phui Fatt Ong, Chief Operating Officer

Type of Firm

Private Equity Firm

Project Preferences

Type of Financing Preferred:

Mezzanine

Geographical Preferences

International Preferences:

Malaysia

Industry Preferences

In Internet Specific prefer:

Internet

Additional Information

Year Founded: 1973
Capital Under Management: $44,000,000

Current Activity Level : Actively seeking new investments

PICARDIE INVESTISSEMENT (AKA: PICARDIE AVENIR)

67 Mail Albert 1er - BP 533
Amiens, France 80000
Phone: 33-3-2291-7020
Fax: 33-3-2291-6670
E-mail: contacts@picardie-investissement.fr
Website: www.picardie-investissement.fr

Management and Staff

Jean Pierre Dumas, President

Type of Firm

Private Equity Firm

Association Membership

French Venture Capital Association (AFIC)

Project Preferences

Type of Financing Preferred:
Leveraged Buyout
Early Stage
Expansion

Size of Investments Considered:
Min Size of Investment Considered (000s): $19
Max Size of Investment Considered (000s): $189

Geographical Preferences

International Preferences:
France

Additional Information

Year Founded: 1984
Current Activity Level : Actively seeking new investments

PIEMONTE HIGH TECHNOLOGY

64, Corso Galileo Ferraris
Torino, Italy 10129
Phone: 39-11-1950-1401
Fax: 39-11-509-7323
E-mail: info@piemontech.it
Website: www.piemontech.it

Management and Staff

Marco Natoli, Managing Director

Type of Firm

Endowment, Foundation or Pension Fund
Association Membership
Italian Venture Capital Association (AIFI)

Project Preferences

Type of Financing Preferred:
Early Stage
Startup

Geographical Preferences

International Preferences:
Italy
Europe

Industry Preferences

In Biotechnology prefer:
Biotechnology

Additional Information

Year Founded: 2005
Capital Under Management: $3,000,000
Current Activity Level : Actively seeking new investments

PILOT GROUP LLC

75 Rockefeller Plaza
23rd Floor
New York, NY USA 10019
Phone: 212-486-4446

Management and Staff

Marshall Cohen, Partner
Mayo Stuntz, Principal
Paul McNichol, Principal
Robert Pittman, Principal

Type of Firm

Private Equity Firm

Project Preferences

Type of Financing Preferred:
Turnaround
Later Stage

Geographical Preferences

United States Preferences:
All U.S.

Industry Preferences

In Communications prefer:
Communications and Media

In Consumer Related prefer:
Consumer

In Business Serv. prefer:
Services

Additional Information

Year Founded: 2003
Current Activity Level : Actively seeking new investments

PILOT HOUSE VENTURES GROUP, LLC

The Pilot House
Lewis Wharf
Boston, MA USA 02110
Phone: 617-742-9500
Website: www.pilothouseventures.com

Management and Staff

P. Eric Krauss, Principal
Stephen Van Beaver, Principal

Type of Firm

Private Equity Firm

Project Preferences

Role in Financing:
Prefer role in deals created by others

Type of Financing Preferred:
Early Stage
Seed

Size of Investments Considered:
Min Size of Investment Considered (000s): $2,000
Max Size of Investment Considered (000s): $10,000

Geographical Preferences

United States Preferences:
All U.S.

Industry Preferences

In Communications prefer:
Communications and Media
Telecommunications
Wireless Communications
Data Communications

In Computer Software prefer:
Software

Additional Information

Year Founded: 2000
Current Activity Level : Actively seeking new investments

PINE BROOK ROAD PARTNERS LLC

100 Park Avenue
Suite 2100
New York, NY USA 10017
Phone: 212-661-9175
Fax: 212-661-9178
Website: www.pinebrookpartners.com

Management and Staff

Arnold Chavkin, Managing Director
Craig Jarchow, Managing Director
Eric Leathers, Managing Director
Michael McMahon, Managing Director
Oliver Goldstein, Managing Director

Robert Jackowitz, Chief Financial Officer
Robert Glanville, Managing Director
William Spiegel, Managing Director

Type of Firm

Private Equity Firm

Project Preferences

Type of Financing Preferred:

Leveraged Buyout
Expansion
Management Buyouts
Acquisition

Industry Preferences

In Industrial/Energy prefer:

Oil and Gas Exploration
Oil & Gas Drilling,Explor
Alternative Energy

In Transportation prefer:

Transportation

In Financial Services prefer:

Financial Services
Insurance

In Business Serv. prefer:

Distribution

Additional Information

Year Founded: 2006
Capital Under Management: $1,430,000,000
Current Activity Level : Actively seeking new investments

PINE CREEK PARTNERS

1055 Thomas Jefferson St., NW
Suite 218
Washington, DC USA 20007
Phone: 202-333-7780
Fax: 202-333-7786
Website: www.pinecreekpartners.com

Management and Staff

George McCabe, Managing Partner
Rick Rickertsen, Managing Partner
Scott Bryant, Principal
Shannon Delany, Principal

Type of Firm

Private Equity Firm

Project Preferences

Type of Financing Preferred:

Leveraged Buyout
Management Buyouts
Recapitalizations

Size of Investments Considered:

Min Size of Investment Considered (000s): $3,000
Max Size of Investment Considered (000s): $7,000

Geographical Preferences

United States Preferences:

All U.S.

Industry Preferences

In Business Serv. prefer:

Services
Distribution

In Manufact. prefer:

Manufacturing

Additional Information

Year Founded: 2006
Capital Under Management: $53,000,000
Current Activity Level : Actively seeking new investments

PINE STREET CAPITAL PARTNERS LLC

99 Pine Street
Albany, NY USA 12207
Phone: 518-449-5131
E-mail: Info@pinecap.com
Website: www.pinecap.com

Other Offices

45 Broadway
26th Floor
New York, NY USA 10006
Phone: 212-785-4377

Management and Staff

David Smith, Managing Director
Timothy Welles, Managing Director
Tony Schmitz, Managing Director

Type of Firm

Bank Affiliated

Project Preferences

Type of Financing Preferred:

Leveraged Buyout
Expansion
Mezzanine
Recapitalizations

Size of Investments Considered:

Min Size of Investment Considered (000s): $1,000
Max Size of Investment Considered (000s): $8,000

Geographical Preferences

United States Preferences:

Mid Atlantic
Northeast

Additional Information

Year Founded: 2004
Capital Under Management: $25,000,000
Current Activity Level : Actively seeking new investments

PINETREE CAPITAL, LTD.

130 King Street West
Suite 2500
Toronto, Canada M5X 1A9
Phone: 416-941-9600
Fax: 416-941-1090
E-mail: info@pinetreecapital.com
Website: www.pinetreecapital.com

Management and Staff

Sheldon Inwentash, Chairman & CEO

Type of Firm

Bank Affiliated

Project Preferences

Type of Financing Preferred:

Early Stage
Expansion
Startup

Geographical Preferences

Canadian Preferences:

All Canada

Industry Preferences

In Communications prefer:

Telecommunications

In Computer Software prefer:

Software

In Internet Specific prefer:

Internet

Additional Information

Year Founded: 1992
Current Activity Level : Actively seeking new investments

PING AN CAPITAL

c/o Ping An Insurance Group
Ba Gua No. 3 Road
Shenzhen, China 518029
Phone: 86-755-82262888
Fax: 86-755-82414817

Management and Staff

Mingzhe Ma, Chairman & CEO

Type of Firm

Insurance Firm Affiliate

Additional Information

Year Founded: 2009
Current Activity Level : Actively seeking new investments

PINNACLE GROUP
145 Northfield Drive
Waterloo, Canada N2L 5J3
Phone: 519-746-3080
Fax: 519-888-6183

Type of Firm
Private Equity Firm

Additional Information
Year Founded: 1983
Current Activity Level : Actively seeking new investments

PINNACLE PRIVATE EQUITY, LTD.
Level 26, Governor Philip Twr.
1 Farrer Place
Sydney, Australia 2000
Phone: 612-8247-3109
Fax: 612-8247-6659
E-mail: enquiries@pinnacleinvestment.com.au
Website: www.pinnacleinvestment.com.au

Management and Staff
Bill Cook, Managing Director
Peter Ludemann, Managing Director

Type of Firm
Investment Management Firm

Geographical Preferences
International Preferences:
Australia

Additional Information
Year Founded: 2009
Current Activity Level : Actively seeking new investments

PINNACLE VENTURES
130 Lytton Avenue
Suite 220
Palo Alto, CA USA 94301
Phone: 650-926-7800
Fax: 650-926-7801
E-mail: info@pinnacleven.com
Website: www.pinnacleven.com

Management and Staff
Bob Savoie, Chief Financial Officer
Kenneth Pelowski, Managing Director
Robert Curley, Managing Director

Type of Firm
Private Equity Firm

Project Preferences
Type of Financing Preferred:
Early Stage
Expansion

Geographical Preferences
United States Preferences:
All U.S.

Additional Information
Name of Most Recent Fund: Pinnacle Ventures Equity Fund I, L.P.
Most Recent Fund Was Raised: 04/04/2007
Year Founded: 2002
Capital Under Management: $125,600,000
Current Activity Level : Actively seeking new investments

PINOVA CAPITAL GMBH
Tal 16
Munich, Germany 80331
Phone: 49-89189-425440
Fax: 49-89189-425469
Website: www.pinovacapital.com

Management and Staff
Joern Pelzer, Partner
Katrin Brokelmann, Partner
Marko Maschek, Partner
Martin Olbort, Partner

Type of Firm
Private Equity Firm

Project Preferences
Type of Financing Preferred:
Leveraged Buyout
Acquisition

Size of Investments Considered:
Min Size of Investment Considered (000s): $3,873
Max Size of Investment Considered (000s): $19,367

Geographical Preferences
International Preferences:
Europe
Germany

Industry Preferences
In Industrial/Energy prefer:
Industrial Products
Materials

In Transportation prefer:
Transportation

In Business Serv. prefer:
Services

In Other prefer:
Environment Responsible

Additional Information
Year Founded: 2008
Capital Under Management: $123,900,000
Current Activity Level : Actively seeking new investments

PINPOINT VENTURES
One Embarcadero Center
Suite 500
San Francisco, CA USA 94111
Phone: 415-294-4000
E-mail: mail@pinpointventures.com
Website: www.pinpointventures.com

Management and Staff
David Quinn, Founding Partner
Michael Pfeffer, Founding Partner
Samuel Long, Managing Director

Type of Firm
Private Equity Firm

Project Preferences
Type of Financing Preferred:
Seed

Geographical Preferences
United States Preferences:
Northwest
Southern California
Northern California

Industry Preferences
In Computer Software prefer:
Software

Additional Information
Name of Most Recent Fund: Pinpoint Venture Group III, LLC
Most Recent Fund Was Raised: 10/10/2000
Year Founded: 2000
Capital Under Management: $400,000
Current Activity Level : Actively seeking new investments

PIONEER CAPITAL PARTNERS
Level 27, PWC Tower
188 Quay Street
Auckland, New Zealand
Phone: 64-9-363-2966
Fax: 64-9-363-2967
Website: www.pioneercapital.co.nz

Other Offices
Level 14 Forsyth Barr House
764 Colombo Street
Christchurch, New Zealand

Type of Firm
Private Equity Firm

Project Preferences
Type of Financing Preferred:
Early Stage
Expansion

Geographical Preferences
International Preferences:
New Zealand

Industry Preferences
In Manufact. prefer:
Manufacturing

Additional Information
Year Founded: 2005
Current Activity Level : Actively seeking new investments

PIONEER VENTURE PARTNERS, LLC
520 Pike Street
Suite 2200
Seattle, WA USA 98101
E-mail: info@pvpartners.com
Website: www.pvpartners.com

Management and Staff
Ben Goux, Chief Financial Officer

Type of Firm
Private Equity Firm

Project Preferences
Type of Financing Preferred:
Early Stage

Geographical Preferences
United States Preferences:
Northwest

Industry Preferences
In Internet Specific prefer:
Web Aggregration/Portals

Additional Information
Year Founded: 2007
Current Activity Level : Actively seeking new investments

PIPER JAFFRAY PRIVATE CAPITAL LLC
800 Nicollet Mall
Suite 800
Minneapolis, MN USA 55402
Phone: 612-303-6000
Fax: 612-303-1350
Website: www.piperjaffray.com

Other Offices
233 South Wacker Drive
Suite 3620
Chicago, IL USA 60606
Phone: 312-775-3200

Management and Staff
Andrew Duff, Chairman & CEO
Thomas Schnettler, President & COO

Type of Firm
Bank Affiliated

Project Preferences
Type of Financing Preferred:
Fund of Funds
Leveraged Buyout
Generalist PE
Distressed Debt

Geographical Preferences
United States Preferences:
All U.S.

Additional Information
Year Founded: 2000
Capital Under Management: $537,200,000
Current Activity Level : Actively seeking new investments

PIPER JAFFRAY VENTURES
800 Nicollet Mall
Suite 800
Minneapolis, MN USA 55402
Phone: 612-303-6000
Fax: 612-303-1350
Website: www.piperjaffray.com

Other Offices
345 California Street
Suite 2400
San Francisco, CA USA 94104

1235 Hermosa Avenue
Suite 300
Hermosa Beach, CA USA 90254

8235 Forsyth Boulevard
Suite 700, Pierre Laclede Center II
Clayton, MO USA 63105

1950 University Avenue
Suite 200
Palo Alto, CA USA 94303

260 Newport Center Drive
Suite 100
Newport Beach, CA USA 92660

One South Place
5th Floor
London, United Kingdom EC2M 2RB
Phone: 44-20-3142-8700

89 Queensway
39/F, Tower 1, Lippo Centre
Admiralty, Hong Kong
Phone: 852-3189-3222

1414 Knight Street
Helena, MT USA 59601

11150 Overbrook Road
Suite 310, One Hallbrook Place
Leawood, KS USA 66211

1200 17th Street
Suite 1250
Denver, CO USA 80202

150 East 42nd Street
35th Floor
New York, NY USA 10017

265 Franklin Street
Suite 710
Boston, MA USA 02110

3900 Ingersoll Avenue
Suite 110
Des Moines, IA USA 50312

601 Union Street
Suite 5010, Two Union Square
Seattle, WA USA 98101

111 Southwest Fifth Avenue
Suite 1900
Portland, OR USA 97204

201 South College Street
Suite 1500
Charlotte, NC USA 28244

2525 East Camelback Road
Suite 925
Phoenix, AZ USA 85016

233 South 13th Street
Suite 1023
Lincoln, NE USA 68508

233 Tai Cang Road
9/F, Platinum Building
Shanghai, China 200020

71 South Wacker Drive
24th Floor, Hyatt Center
Chicago, IL USA 60606

1100 Louisiana Avenue
Suite 2750
Houston, TX USA 77002

100 Pearl Street
14th Floor
Hartford, CT USA 06103

3245 Maidens Road
Powhatan, VA USA 23139

222 East Erie Street
Suite 320
Milwaukee, WI USA 53202

245 Park Avenue
33rd Floor
New York, NY USA 10167

770 L Street
Suite 950, Pacific Business Centers
Sacramento, CA USA 95814
Phone: Pacific Business C

3333 Lee Parkway
Suite 600
Dallas, TX USA 75219

Management and Staff

Alex Ko, Chief Executive Officer
Andrew Duff, Chairman & CEO
David Wilson, Chief Executive Officer
David Windnam, Managing Director
Debbra Schoneman, Chief Financial Officer
Larry Zimmerman, Managing Director
Matt Traina, Managing Director
Terry McCabe, Managing Director
Thomas Schnettler, President & COO
Victor Caruso, Managing Director

Type of Firm

Bank Affiliated

Association Membership

Natl Assoc of Small Bus. Inv. Co (NASBIC)

Project Preferences

Role in Financing:

Prefer role as deal originator but will also invest in deals created by others

Type of Financing Preferred:

Fund of Funds
Leveraged Buyout
Early Stage
Expansion
Generalist PE
Balanced
Later Stage

Size of Investments Considered:

Min Size of Investment Considered (000s): $400
Max Size of Investment Considered: No Limit

Industry Focus

(% based on actual investment)

Medical/Health	46.4%
Internet Specific	14.1%
Computer Software and Services	13.8%
Industrial/Energy	8.2%
Semiconductors/Other Elect.	6.4%
Other Products	5.1%
Consumer Related	3.0%
Biotechnology	1.9%
Computer Hardware	1.1%

Additional Information

Name of Most Recent Fund: Piper Jaffray Venture Fund IV, L.P.
Most Recent Fund Was Raised: 03/10/2009
Year Founded: 1895
Capital Under Management: $245,000,000
Current Activity Level : Actively seeking new investments
Method of Compensation: Return on investment is of primary concern, do not charge fees

PIPER PRIVATE EQUITY LIMITED

Eardley House
182-184 Campden Hill Road
London, United Kingdom W8 7AS
Phone: 44-20-7727-3842
Fax: 44-20-7727-8969
E-mail: info@piperprivateequity.com
Website: www.piperprivateequity.com

Management and Staff

Crispin Tweddell, Founder
Libby Gibson, Co-Founder

Type of Firm

Private Equity Firm

Association Membership

British Venture Capital Association (BVCA)

Project Preferences

Type of Financing Preferred:

Second Stage Financing
Leveraged Buyout
Expansion

Size of Investments Considered:

Min Size of Investment Considered (000s): $700
Max Size of Investment Considered: No Limit

Geographical Preferences

International Preferences:

United Kingdom
Europe

Industry Focus

(% based on actual investment)

Consumer Related	100.0%

Additional Information

Year Founded: 1988
Capital Under Management: $14,300,000
Current Activity Level : Actively seeking new investments

PITANGO VENTURE CAPITAL (FKA:POLARIS VENTURE CAPITAL ISRAEL)

11 HaMenofim Street
Building B
Herzliya, Israel 46725
Phone: 972-9-971-8100
Fax: 972-9-971-8102
E-mail: pitango@pitango.com
Website: www.pitango.com

Other Offices

14 Hays Mews
London, United Kingdom W1J5PT
Phone: 44-20-7408-5450

2929 Campus Drive
Suite 410
San Mateo, CA USA 94403
Phone: 650-357-9080
Fax: 650-357-9088

Management and Staff

Aaron Mankovski, Managing General Partner
Bruce Crocker, General Partner
Chemi Peres, Managing General Partner
Eitan Bek, Partner
Isaac Hillel, Managing General Partner
Ittai Harel, Venture Partner
Joseph Vardi, Venture Partner
Micha Laor, Venture Partner
Nissim Darvish, Partner
Rami Kalish, Managing General Partner
Rami Beracha, Managing General Partner
Rona Segev-Gal, Partner
Ruti Alon, Partner
Tammy Mahn, Principal
Thomas Langer, Venture Partner
Yuri Shoshan, Principal
Zur Feldman, Venture Partner

Type of Firm

Private Equity Firm

Association Membership

Israel Venture Association
National Venture Capital Association - USA (NVCA)

Project Preferences

Role in Financing:

Prefer role as deal originator but will also invest in deals created by others

Type of Financing Preferred:

Early Stage
Expansion
Balanced
Later Stage
Seed
Startup

Size of Investments Considered:

Min Size of Investment Considered (000s): $100
Max Size of Investment Considered (000s): $10,000

Geographical Preferences

International Preferences:

Europe
Israel
All International

Industry Focus

(% based on actual investment)

Computer Software and Services	23.7%
Communications and Media	20.5%
Semiconductors/Other Elect.	16.2%
Internet Specific	16.2%
Medical/Health	14.7%
Biotechnology	3.8%
Industrial/Energy	3.1%
Other Products	1.1%
Computer Hardware	0.7%

Additional Information

Name of Most Recent Fund: Pitango Venture Capital Fund V, L.P.
Most Recent Fund Was Raised: 11/19/2007
Year Founded: 1993
Capital Under Management: $720,000,000
Current Activity Level : Actively seeking new investments

PITT CAPITAL PARTNERS, LTD. (AKA: SOULS PRIVATE EQUITY)

160 Pitt Street Mall
Level 2
Sydney, Australia 2000
Phone: 612-9210-7000
Fax: 612-9210-7099
E-mail: info@pittcapitalpartners.com.au
Website: www.pittcapitalpartners.com.au

Other Offices

459 Collins Street
Level 11
Melbourne, Australia 3000
Phone: 61-3-8669-0260
Fax: 61-3-8669-0264

Management and Staff

David Fairfull, Managing Director

Type of Firm

Bank Affiliated

Association Membership

Australian Venture Capital Association (AVCAL)

Project Preferences

Role in Financing:

Will function either as deal originator or investor in deals created by others

Type of Financing Preferred:

Leveraged Buyout
Generalist PE
Expansion
Balanced
Recapitalizations

Size of Investments Considered:

Min Size of Investment Considered (000s): $381
Max Size of Investment Considered (000s): $15,254

Geographical Preferences

International Preferences:

Australia
New Zealand
Asia

Additional Information

Year Founded: 2004
Capital Under Management: $112,600,000
Current Activity Level : Actively seeking new investments
Method of Compensation: Return on invest. most important, but chg. closing fees, service fees, etc.

PITTSBURGH LIFE SCIENCES GREENHOUSE

100 Technology Drive
Suite 400
Pittsburgh, PA USA 15219
Phone: 412-201-7370
Fax: 412-770-1276
E-mail: info@plsg.com
Website: www.plsg.com

Type of Firm

Private Equity Firm

Association Membership

National Venture Capital Association - USA (NVCA)

Project Preferences

Type of Financing Preferred:

Early Stage
Seed
Startup

Size of Investments Considered:

Min Size of Investment Considered (000s): $100
Max Size of Investment Considered (000s): $500

Geographical Preferences

United States Preferences:

Pennsylvania

Industry Preferences

In Semiconductor/Electr prefer:

Semiconductor
Fiber Optics

In Biotechnology prefer:

Human Biotechnology
Genetic Engineering
Industrial Biotechnology
Biosensors
Biotech Related Research

In Medical/Health prefer:

Medical/Health
Medical Diagnostics
Diagnostic Services
Diagnostic Test Products
Medical Therapeutics
Drug/Equipmt Delivery
Other Therapeutic
Health Services
Pharmaceuticals

Additional Information

Year Founded: 2002
Capital Under Management: $25,000,000
Current Activity Level : Actively seeking new investments

PIVOTAL INVESTMENTS

433 NorthWest Fourth Avenue
Suite 200
Portland, OR USA 97209
Phone: 503-341-0004
Fax: 503-295-2720
Website: www.pivotal-investments.com

Management and Staff

Bradley Zenger, Managing Director
Gregory Semler, Managing Director
John Miner, Managing Director

Type of Firm

Private Equity Firm

Project Preferences

Type of Financing Preferred:

Early Stage
Expansion
Seed

Geographical Preferences

United States Preferences:

Oregon
Idaho
Washington
Montana

Canadian Preferences:

Western Canada

Industry Preferences

In Consumer Related prefer:

Food/Beverage

In Industrial/Energy prefer:

Materials

In Other prefer:

Environment Responsible

Additional Information

Year Founded: 2008
Capital Under Management: $5,000,000
Current Activity Level : Actively seeking new investments

PLANTERSBANK VENTURE CAPITAL CORPORATION

314 Sen. Gil Puyat Avenue
Makati, Philippines
Phone: 632-884-7600
E-mail: info@plantersbank.com.ph
Website: www.plantersbank.com.ph

Management and Staff

Jesus Tambunting, Chairman & CEO

Type of Firm

Bank Affiliated

Project Preferences

Type of Financing Preferred:
Expansion
Management Buyouts

Geographical Preferences

International Preferences:
Philippines

Additional Information

Year Founded: 2005
Capital Under Management: $25,000,000
Current Activity Level : Actively seeking new investments

PLATAFORMA CAPITAL PARTNERS

Ave. Dr. Cardoso de Melo, 1460
12th Floor
Sao Paulo, SP, Brazil 04548-005
Phone: 5511-3047-4647
Fax: 5511-3047-4646
Website: www.pcapital.com.br

Management and Staff

Anibal Messa, Managing Partner
Antonio Henrique Prado, Partner
Franco Pontillo, Partner

Type of Firm

Private Equity Firm

Association Membership

Brazilian Venture Capital Association (ABCR)

Project Preferences

Type of Financing Preferred:
Seed
Startup

Geographical Preferences

International Preferences:
Brazil

Industry Preferences

In Communications prefer:
Communications and Media

In Computer Software prefer:
Software

In Semiconductor/Electr prefer:
Electronics

Additional Information

Year Founded: 1999
Current Activity Level : Actively seeking new investments

PLATINA PARTNERS LLP (FKA: PLATINA FINANCE, LTD.)

40 George Street
London, United Kingdom W1U 7DW
Phone: 44-20-7467-3190
Fax: 44-20-7467-3195
E-mail: info@platinafinance.com
Website: www.platinafinance.com

Other Offices

69, rue La Boetie
Paris, France 75008
Phone: 33-1-7674-9300
Fax: 33-1-7674-9310

Management and Staff

Alexandre Labouret, Partner
Emma Collins, Partner
Fabien Castello, Managing Partner
Joseph Muthu, Partner
Mikael Schoultz, Partner
Thomas Rottner, Managing Partner

Type of Firm

Private Equity Firm

Association Membership

British Venture Capital Association (BVCA)
French Venture Capital Association (AFIC)
European Private Equity and Venture Capital Assoc.

Project Preferences

Type of Financing Preferred:
Leveraged Buyout
Early Stage
Expansion
Balanced
Turnaround
Other
Management Buyouts

Size of Investments Considered:
Min Size of Investment Considered (000s): $6,394
Max Size of Investment Considered (000s): $12,788

Geographical Preferences

International Preferences:
United Kingdom
Luxembourg
Central Europe
Europe
Germany
Denmark
France

Industry Preferences

In Communications prefer:
Communications and Media

In Computer Hardware prefer:
Computers

In Computer Software prefer:
Software

In Internet Specific prefer:
E-Commerce Technology
Internet

In Consumer Related prefer:
Entertainment and Leisure

In Industrial/Energy prefer:
Energy
Alternative Energy

In Financial Services prefer:
Real Estate

In Business Serv. prefer:
Services

Additional Information

Year Founded: 2002
Capital Under Management: $452,500,000
Current Activity Level : Actively seeking new investments

PLATINUM EQUITY LLC

360 North Crescent Drive
Beverly Hills, CA USA 90210
Phone: 310-712-1850
Fax: 310-712-1848
Website: www.platinumequity.com

Other Offices

Berkeley Square House
2nd Floor
London, United Kingdom W1J 6BD
Phone: 44-20-7887-7877

250 Park Avenue
Third Floor
New York, NY USA 10177
Phone: 212-856-7500
Fax: 917-368-3444

Management and Staff

Brian Wall, Partner
David Anglin, Partner
Jacok Kotzubei, Partner

John Diggins, Partner
Johnny Lopez, Partner
Mark Barnhill, Principal
Mary Ann Sigler, Chief Financial Officer
Matt Young, Principal
Michael Scott, Principal
Phil Norment, Partner
Rob Archambault, Partner
Robert Joubran, Partner
Robert Wentworth, Partner
Robert Wymbs, Principal
Roger House, Principal
Steve Zollo, Principal

Type of Firm

Private Equity Firm

Project Preferences

Type of Financing Preferred:

Leveraged Buyout
Acquisition

Geographical Preferences

United States Preferences:

All U.S.

Industry Focus

(% based on actual investment)

Communications and Media	92.4%
Computer Software and Services	5.4%
Computer Hardware	1.3%
Other Products	0.7%
Internet Specific	0.2%

Additional Information

Name of Most Recent Fund: Platinum Equity Capital Partners II, L.P.
Most Recent Fund Was Raised: 09/26/2007
Year Founded: 1995
Capital Under Management: $3,450,000,000
Current Activity Level : Actively seeking new investments

PLATINUM-NEURONE VENTURES

21 Ha'arba'ah Street
15th Floor
Tel Aviv, Israel 64739
Phone: 972-3-684-5730
Fax: 972-3-686-9535
E-mail: info@pn-vc.com
Website: www.pn-vc.com

Management and Staff

Amiram Dotan, Managing Partner
Asi Metser, Partner
Ornit Avidar, Partner
Regina Ungar, Chief Financial Officer
Shuki Gleitman, Managing Partner
Yigal Livne, Managing Partner

Type of Firm

Private Equity Firm

Association Membership

Israel Venture Association

Project Preferences

Type of Financing Preferred:

Second Stage Financing
Early Stage
Expansion
Later Stage
Seed

Geographical Preferences

International Preferences:

Israel
All International

Industry Preferences

In Communications prefer:

Commercial Communications
Telecommunications

In Internet Specific prefer:

Internet

In Semiconductor/Electr prefer:

Semiconductor

In Medical/Health prefer:

Medical/Health

Additional Information

Year Founded: 2002
Capital Under Management: $110,000,000
Current Activity Level : Actively seeking new investments

PLATTE RIVER VENTURES

200 Fillmore Street
Suite 200
Denver, CO USA 80206
Phone: 303-292-7300
Fax: 303-292-7310
E-mail: info@platteriverventures.com
Website: www.platteriverventures.com

Management and Staff

Edward Hutcheson, Managing Director
Greg Sissel, Managing Director
J. Landis Martin, Managing Director
William Robb, Managing Director

Type of Firm

Private Equity Firm

Project Preferences

Type of Financing Preferred:

Leveraged Buyout
Expansion
Mezzanine
Management Buyouts
Acquisition
Recapitalizations

Size of Investments Considered:

Min Size of Investment Considered (000s): $5,000
Max Size of Investment Considered (000s): $30,000

Geographical Preferences

United States Preferences:

All U.S.

Industry Preferences

In Communications prefer:

Communications and Media

In Industrial/Energy prefer:

Energy
Industrial Products
Advanced Materials
Machinery
Environmental Related

In Transportation prefer:

Transportation
Aerospace

In Financial Services prefer:

Financial Services

In Manufact. prefer:

Manufacturing

Additional Information

Name of Most Recent Fund: Platte River Ventures I, L.P.
Most Recent Fund Was Raised: 08/25/2006
Year Founded: 2005
Capital Under Management: $75,000,000
Current Activity Level : Actively seeking new investments

PLAYA HOTELS & RESORTS, S.L.

Edificio Barcelo
C/O Jose Rover Motta
Palma De Mallorca Baleares, Spain 07006

Type of Firm

Private Equity Firm

Project Preferences

Type of Financing Preferred:

Balanced

Geographical Preferences

International Preferences:

All International

Industry Preferences

In Consumer Related prefer:

Hotels and Resorts

Additional Information

Year Founded: 2006
Current Activity Level : Actively seeking new investments

PLAYFORD CAPITAL PTY LTD. (FKA: SA.BITS)

108 North Terrace
Ground Floor, EDS Center
Adelaide, Australia 5000
Phone: 618-8110-1555
Fax: 618-8212-3809
E-mail: mail@playford.com.au
Website: www.playford.com.au

Management and Staff

Amanda Heyworth, Chief Executive Officer

Type of Firm

Incubator/Development Program

Association Membership

Australian Venture Capital Association (AVCAL)

Project Preferences

Role in Financing:
Will function either as deal originator or investor in deals created by others

Type of Financing Preferred:
Early Stage
Seed
Startup

Size of Investments Considered:
Min Size of Investment Considered (000s): $50
Max Size of Investment Considered (000s): $500

Geographical Preferences

International Preferences:
Australia

Industry Preferences

In Communications prefer:
Communications and Media
Telecommunications
Wireless Communications

In Computer Software prefer:
Applications Software

In Internet Specific prefer:
E-Commerce Technology
Internet
Ecommerce

In Computer Other prefer:
Computer Related

In Semiconductor/Electr prefer:
Electronics
Electronic Components
Controllers and Sensors

In Agr/Forestr/Fish prefer:
Agribusiness

Additional Information

Name of Most Recent Fund: Playford Capital (Fund #2)
Most Recent Fund Was Raised: 07/31/2001
Year Founded: 1997
Capital Under Management: $13,000,000
Current Activity Level : Actively seeking new investments
Method of Compensation: Return on investment is of primary concern, do not charge fees

PLEXUS CAPITAL LLC (FKA: PLEXUS FUND)

200 Providence Road
2nd Floor, Suite 210
Charlotte, NC USA 28207
Phone: 704-927-6245
Fax: 704-927-6255
Website: www.plexuscap.com

Other Offices

4601 Six Forks Road
Suite 528
Raleigh, NC USA 27609
Phone: 919-256-6340
Fax: 919-256-6350

Management and Staff

Bob Anders, Principal
Kel Landis, Principal
Michael Painter, Principal
Robert Gefaell, Principal

Type of Firm

Private Equity Firm

Project Preferences

Type of Financing Preferred:
Leveraged Buyout
Management Buyouts
Acquisition
Recapitalizations

Geographical Preferences

United States Preferences:
Mid Atlantic
Southeast

Industry Preferences

In Consumer Related prefer:
Consumer Services

In Business Serv. prefer:
Distribution

In Manufact. prefer:
Manufacturing

Additional Information

Name of Most Recent Fund: Plexus Fund I, L.P.
Most Recent Fund Was Raised: 12/29/2005
Year Founded: 2005
Capital Under Management: $26,900,000
Current Activity Level : Actively seeking new investments

PLUM CAPITAL LLC

209 West Chestnut Hill Avenue
Philadelphia, PA USA 19118
Phone: 215-247-4300
Fax: 215-247-3500
Website: www.plumcapital.com

Management and Staff

Charles Peebler, Managing Director
James Cutie, Managing Director
Paul Gruenberg, Managing Director

Type of Firm

Private Equity Firm

Association Membership

Mid-Atlantic Venture Association

Project Preferences

Role in Financing:
Prefer role as deal originator but will also invest in deals created by others

Type of Financing Preferred:
Early Stage

Size of Investments Considered:
Min Size of Investment Considered (000s): $3,000
Max Size of Investment Considered (000s): $5,000

Geographical Preferences

United States Preferences:
Mid Atlantic
Northeast

Industry Preferences

In Business Serv. prefer:
Media

Additional Information

Year Founded: 2000
Capital Under Management: $30,000,000
Current Activity Level : Actively seeking new investments
Method of Compensation: Return on investment is of primary concern, do not charge fees

PLUMTREE PARTNERS LLC

2911 Turtle Creek Boulevard
Suite 820
Dallas, TX USA 75219
Phone: 214-615-8680
Fax: 214-615-8683
E-mail: info@plumtreepartners.com
Website: www.plumtreepartners.com

Management and Staff

Jeffrey Rich, Managing Director
Todd Furniss, Managing Director

Type of Firm

Private Equity Firm

Project Preferences

Type of Financing Preferred:

Generalist PE

Industry Preferences

In Medical/Health prefer:

Health Services

In Financial Services prefer:

Financial Services

In Manufact. prefer:

Manufacturing

Additional Information

Year Founded: 2009
Current Activity Level : Actively seeking new investments

PLYMOUTH VENTURE PARTNERS

220 East Huron Street
3rd Floor
Ann Arbor, MI USA 48104
Phone: 734-747-9401
Fax: 747-929-1811
E-mail: info@plymouthventurepartners.com
Website: www.plymouthvc.com

Management and Staff

Dana Sutton, Vice President
Jeffery Barry, Partner
Mark Horne, Chief Executive Officer

Type of Firm

Private Equity Firm

Project Preferences

Role in Financing:

Will function either as deal originator or investor in deals created by others

Type of Financing Preferred:

Second Stage Financing
Generalist PE
Early Stage

Size of Investments Considered:

Min Size of Investment Considered (000s): $500
Max Size of Investment Considered (000s): $2,500

Geographical Preferences

United States Preferences:

Illinois
Michigan
Ohio
Wisconsin
All U.S.
Indiana

International Preferences:

Australia

Additional Information

Year Founded: 2002
Capital Under Management: $23,000,000
Current Activity Level : Actively seeking new investments
Method of Compensation: Return on invest. most important, but chg. closing fees, service fees, etc.

PM & PARTNERS SPA

via San Damiano, n 11
Milano, Italy 20122
Phone: 39-2-7601-1887
Fax: 39-2-7631-6202
E-mail: pmp@pm-partners.it
Website: www.pm-partners.it

Other Offices

via Campania, n 59
Roma, Italy 00187
Phone: 39-6-420-3621
Fax: 39-6-4203-6240

Management and Staff

Andrea Mugnai, Founding Partner
Francesco Panfilo, Founding Partner
Massimo Grasselli, Partner

Type of Firm

Private Equity Firm

Association Membership

Italian Venture Capital Association (AIFI)
European Private Equity and Venture Capital Assoc.

Project Preferences

Type of Financing Preferred:

Leveraged Buyout
Acquisition

Geographical Preferences

International Preferences:

Italy

Industry Focus

(% based on actual investment)

Other Products	66.1%
Computer Software and Services	30.4%
Medical/Health	3.4%

Additional Information

Year Founded: 2000
Capital Under Management: $291,900,000
Current Activity Level : Actively seeking new investments

PME INVESTIMENTOS - SOCIEDADE DE INVESTIMENTO SA

Rua Ivone Silva
n6, 14
Lisboa, Portugal 1050-124
Phone: 351-21-799-4260
Fax: 351-21-796-7284
E-mail: adm@pmeinvestimentos.pt
Website: www.pmeinvestimentos.pt

Type of Firm

Private Equity Firm

Association Membership

Portuguese Venture Capital Association (APCRI)
European Private Equity and Venture Capital Assoc.

Project Preferences

Type of Financing Preferred:

Second Stage Financing
Leveraged Buyout
Expansion
Mezzanine
Balanced

Size of Investments Considered:

Min Size of Investment Considered (000s): $100
Max Size of Investment Considered (000s): $100,000

Geographical Preferences

International Preferences:

Portugal
Europe

Industry Preferences

In Financial Services prefer:

Financial Services

Additional Information

Year Founded: 1989
Capital Under Management: $206,600,000
Current Activity Level : Actively seeking new investments

PNC EQUITY MANAGEMENT CORP. (PNC FINANCIAL SERVICES GROUP)

620 Liberty Avenue
22nd Floor, Two PNC Plaza
Pittsburgh, PA USA 15222
Phone: 412-762-2289
Fax: 412-705-3669
Website: www.pncequity.com

Management and Staff

David McI. Hillman, Partner
Deanna Barry, Chief Financial Officer

Jack Glover, Partner
Jonathan Lewis, Vice President
Justin Bertram, Vice President
Michael Hand, Vice President
Peter Del Presto, Partner
Wali Bacdayan, Partner

Type of Firm

Bank Affiliated

Project Preferences

Role in Financing:

Will function either as deal originator or investor in deals created by others

Type of Financing Preferred:

Second Stage Financing
Leveraged Buyout
Mezzanine
Generalist PE
Balanced
Later Stage
Special Situation

Size of Investments Considered:

Min Size of Investment Considered (000s): $10,000
Max Size of Investment Considered (000s): $30,000

Geographical Preferences

United States Preferences:

Midwest
Northeast

Industry Focus

(% based on actual investment)

Other Products	29.3%
Industrial/Energy	20.1%
Communications and Media	16.5%
Medical/Health	13.5%
Consumer Related	11.2%
Internet Specific	5.9%
Computer Software and Services	2.4%
Semiconductors/Other Elect.	0.8%
Biotechnology	0.2%
Computer Hardware	0.1%

Additional Information

Name of Most Recent Fund: PNC Equity Partners II, L.P.
Most Recent Fund Was Raised: 06/26/2006
Year Founded: 1982
Capital Under Management: $1,300,000,000
Current Activity Level : Actively seeking new investments

POALIM CAPITAL MARKETS TECHNOLOGIES LTD

Al-Rov Tower
46 Rothschild Blvd.
Tel Aviv, Israel 66883
Phone: 972-3-567-5333
Fax: 972-3-567-5740
E-mail: info@pcm.co.il
Website: www.pcm.co.il

Management and Staff

Amir Aviv, Managing Director
Eran Gersht, Managing Director
Rinat Gazit, Vice President

Type of Firm

Bank Affiliated

Association Membership

Israel Venture Association

Project Preferences

Type of Financing Preferred:

Fund of Funds
Expansion
Later Stage
Startup

Geographical Preferences

International Preferences:

Israel

Industry Preferences

In Communications prefer:

Telecommunications

In Computer Software prefer:

Software

In Internet Specific prefer:

Internet

Additional Information

Year Founded: 1990
Capital Under Management: $64,000,000
Current Activity Level : Actively seeking new investments

POD VENTURE PARTNERS INC.

One Financial Centre
40th Floor
Boston, MA USA 02111
Phone: 617-236-6380
Fax: 617-236-6390
E-mail: info@podventurepartners.com
Website: www.podventurepartners.com

Other Offices

Nybrogatan 3
P.O. Box 7550
Stockholm, Sweden SE 103 93
Phone: 46-8-5450-6460
Fax: 46-8-5450-6469

Management and Staff

Axel Roos, Managing Partner
Eric Douglas, Partner
Johan Pontin, Partner
Tom Nyman, Partner

Type of Firm

Private Equity Firm

Association Membership

National Venture Capital Association - USA (NVCA)
Swedish Venture Capital Association (SVCA)

Project Preferences

Type of Financing Preferred:

Expansion
Early Stage

Size of Investments Considered:

Min Size of Investment Considered (000s): $1,500
Max Size of Investment Considered (000s): $8,000

Geographical Preferences

United States Preferences:

Northeast

International Preferences:

Scandanavia/Nordic Region

Industry Preferences

In Communications prefer:

Telecommunications

In Computer Software prefer:

Computer Services
Software
Artificial Intelligence

In Internet Specific prefer:

Internet

Additional Information

Name of Most Recent Fund: POD Holding, L.P.
Most Recent Fund Was Raised: 11/01/2000
Year Founded: 2000
Capital Under Management: $74,700,000
Current Activity Level : Actively seeking new investments

POHJOLA CAPITAL PARTNERS, LTD. (FKA: OKO VENTURE CAPITAL OY)

Etelaesplanadi 12
Helsinki, Finland FI-00013
Phone: 358-10-252-011
Fax: 358-10-252-3652
Website: www.pohjola.fi

Management and Staff

Ilkka Hietala, Partner
Ilkka Pentikainen, Partner
Juha Peltola, Managing Director
Mikko Kumpulainen, Partner
Panu Vuorela, Partner

Type of Firm

Bank Affiliated

Association Membership

Finnish Venture Capital Association (FVCA)
European Private Equity and Venture Capital Assoc.

Project Preferences

Type of Financing Preferred:
Leveraged Buyout
Expansion
Mezzanine
Balanced
Later Stage
Management Buyouts

Size of Investments Considered:
Min Size of Investment Considered (000s): $300
Max Size of Investment Considered (000s): $300,000

Geographical Preferences

International Preferences:
Scandanavia/Nordic Region
Finland

Industry Preferences

In Semiconductor/Electr prefer:
Electronics

In Biotechnology prefer:
Biotechnology

In Consumer Related prefer:
Consumer

In Industrial/Energy prefer:
Industrial Products

Additional Information

Name of Most Recent Fund: Suomi Yritysjarjestelyrahasto I Ky
Most Recent Fund Was Raised: 01/01/2008
Year Founded: 1991
Capital Under Management: $246,500,000
Current Activity Level : Actively seeking new investments

POHJOLA PRIVATE EQUITY FUNDS OY

Etelaesplanadi 12
Helsinki, Finland
Phone: 358-10-252-011
Fax: 358-10-252-7201
Website: www.pohjola.fi

Management and Staff

Samuli Sipila, Managing Director
Ulla Niemela, Chief Operating Officer

Type of Firm

Private Equity Advisor or Fund of Funds

Association Membership

Finnish Venture Capital Association (FVCA)

Project Preferences

Type of Financing Preferred:
Fund of Funds
Leveraged Buyout
Mezzanine

Geographical Preferences

International Preferences:
Europe

Additional Information

Year Founded: 2007
Capital Under Management: $1,425,900,000
Current Activity Level : Actively seeking new investments

POIBOS VENTURE CAPITAL

7/F Shinhan Building
Yeoido-dong, Yeongdeungpo-ku
Seoul, South Korea 150-716
Phone: 822-783-3533
Fax: 822-783-3523
Website: www.poibosvc.com

Management and Staff

Kyung-Bae Kim, President

Type of Firm

Corporate PE/Venture

Project Preferences

Type of Financing Preferred:
Balanced

Geographical Preferences

International Preferences:
Asia

Industry Preferences

In Communications prefer:
Entertainment

Additional Information

Year Founded: 1999
Capital Under Management: $10,800,000
Current Activity Level : Actively seeking new investments

POINT JUDITH CAPITAL

50 Park Row West
Suite 107
Providence, RI USA 02903
Phone: 401-648-7360
Fax: 401-223-3130
E-mail: info@pointjudithcapital.com
Website: www.pointjudithcapital.com

Management and Staff

Brad Waugh, Venture Partner
David Mixer, Founding Partner
David Martirano, General Partner
Gina Raimondo, General Partner
Jeffrey Weiss, Venture Partner
Lee Hower, Principal
Martin Clifford, Venture Partner
Paul Mraz, Venture Partner
Sean Marsh, General Partner

Type of Firm

Private Equity Firm

Association Membership

New England Venture Capital Association

Project Preferences

Role in Financing:
Prefer role as deal originator but will also invest in deals created by others

Type of Financing Preferred:
Early Stage
Seed
First Stage Financing

Size of Investments Considered:
Min Size of Investment Considered (000s): $500
Max Size of Investment Considered (000s): $5,000

Geographical Preferences

United States Preferences:
All U.S.

Industry Preferences

In Communications prefer:
Telecommunications
Wireless Communications
Data Communications

In Computer Software prefer:
Data Processing
Software
Systems Software
Applications Software

In Internet Specific prefer:
E-Commerce Technology
Internet

In Semiconductor/Electr prefer:
Laser Related
Fiber Optics
Analytic/Scientific

In Medical/Health prefer:
Medical/Health
Medical Diagnostics
Diagnostic Services
Diagnostic Test Products
Medical Therapeutics
Medical Products
Health Services
Hospitals/Clinics/Primary
Hospital/Other Instit.

In Financial Services prefer:
Insurance

Additional Information

Name of Most Recent Fund: Point Judith Venture Fund II
Most Recent Fund Was Raised: 06/02/2006
Year Founded: 2001

Capital Under Management: $100,000,000
Current Activity Level : Actively seeking new investments
Method of Compensation: Return on investment is of primary concern, do not charge fees

POINT LOOKOUT CAPITAL PARTNERS, L.P.

275 Madison Avenue
39th Floor
New York, NY USA 10016
Phone: 212-774-5917
Fax: 212-774-5919
Website: www.pointlookoutcapital.com

Management and Staff

James Cesare, Managing Partner
Michael Monteleone, Managing Partner

Type of Firm

Private Equity Firm

Project Preferences

Type of Financing Preferred:
Leveraged Buyout
Management Buyouts

Size of Investments Considered:
Min Size of Investment Considered (000s): $5,000
Max Size of Investment Considered (000s): $20,000

Geographical Preferences

United States Preferences:
All U.S.

Industry Preferences

In Consumer Related prefer:
Consumer Products

In Manufact. prefer:
Manufacturing

Additional Information

Year Founded: 2005
Current Activity Level : Actively seeking new investments

POINTBREAK PRIVATE EQUITY

East Wing, Mettle Building
Willie van Schoor Avenue
Capetown, South Africa 7530
Phone: 27-21-949-3450
Fax: 27-21-949-3455
E-mail: info@pointbreak.co.za
Website: www.pointbreak.co.za

Type of Firm

Private Equity Firm

Association Membership

South African Venture Capital Association (SAVCA)

Project Preferences

Type of Financing Preferred:
Leveraged Buyout
Early Stage
Seed
Startup

Size of Investments Considered:
Min Size of Investment Considered (000s): $37
Max Size of Investment Considered (000s): $622

Geographical Preferences

International Preferences:
South Africa

Additional Information

Year Founded: 2000
Current Activity Level : Actively seeking new investments

POITOU-CHARENTES EXPANSION

15, rue de l'Ancienne Comedie
BP 575
Poitiers, France 86021
Phone: 33-5-4952-5809
Fax: 33-5-4950-4895
E-mail: P.C.E@wanadoo.fr
Website: www.poitou-charentes.fr

Type of Firm

Private Equity Firm

Project Preferences

Type of Financing Preferred:
Leveraged Buyout
Early Stage
Expansion

Geographical Preferences

International Preferences:
France

Additional Information

Year Founded: 1994
Capital Under Management: $8,200,000
Current Activity Level : Actively seeking new investments

POLAR CAPITAL INVESTMENTS, INC.

372 Bay Street
21st Floor
Toronto, Canada M5H 2W9
Phone: 416-367-4364
E-mail: info@polarcapital.com
Website: www.polarcapital.com

Other Offices

333 - 5th Avenue
Suite 200
Calgary, Canada T2P 3B6
Phone: 403-705-7300

Management and Staff

Andrew Gutman, Principal
David Lurie, Principal
Douglass McDougall, Principal
Glenn Phelps, Partner
Jerry Jackson, Partner
Pat Ross, Principal
Richard Vaughan, Principal
Steve Mulherin, Partner
Todd McDougall, Principal
Tom Sabourin, Partner

Type of Firm

Private Equity Firm

Project Preferences

Type of Financing Preferred:
Leveraged Buyout
Acquisition

Geographical Preferences

United States Preferences:
All U.S.

Canadian Preferences:
All Canada

International Preferences:
United Kingdom

Industry Preferences

In Medical/Health prefer:
Health Services

In Industrial/Energy prefer:
Alternative Energy
Industrial Products

In Manufact. prefer:
Manufacturing

Additional Information

Year Founded: 1995
Capital Under Management: $7,400,000
Current Activity Level : Actively seeking new investments

POLAR CAPITAL PARTNERS

30 Buckingham Gate
London, United Kingdom SW1E 6NN
Phone: 020-7592-1508-9
Fax: 020-7592-1599
Website: www.polarcapitaltechnologytrust.co.uk/

Management and Staff

James Brandt, General Partner
Kate Haslett, General Partner

Type of Firm
Private Equity Firm

Additional Information
Year Founded: 2009
Current Activity Level : Actively seeking new investments

POLARIS MANAGEMENT A/S

Malmoegade 3
Copenhagen, Denmark DK-2100
Phone: 45-3526-3574
Fax: 45-3526-3594
E-mail: polaris@polarisequity.dk
Website: www.polarisequity.com

Management and Staff
Jan Dahlquist, Partner
Jan Johan Kuhl, Managing Partner
Niels Worning, Partner
Peter Ankerst, Partner
Viggo Nedergaard Jensen, Managing Partner

Type of Firm
Private Equity Firm

Association Membership
European Private Equity and Venture Capital Assoc.

Project Preferences

Role in Financing:
Prefer role as deal originator but will also invest in deals created by others

Type of Financing Preferred:
Leveraged Buyout
Turnaround
Balanced
Management Buyouts
Recapitalizations

Size of Investments Considered:
Min Size of Investment Considered (000s): $60
Max Size of Investment Considered (000s): $140

Geographical Preferences

International Preferences:
Sweden
Scandanavia/Nordic Region
Denmark

Industry Focus
(% based on actual investment)

Communications and Media	62.0%
Medical/Health	27.9%
Consumer Related	7.6%
Internet Specific	2.5%

Additional Information
Name of Most Recent Fund: Polaris Private Equity II
Most Recent Fund Was Raised: 02/07/2005
Year Founded: 1998
Capital Under Management: $629,100,000
Current Activity Level : Actively seeking new investments

POLARIS PRINCIPAL FINANCE CO., LTD.

Otemachi Nomura Bldg. 20F
2-1-1, Otemachi, Chiyoda-ku
Tokyo, Japan 100-0004
Phone: 813-6225-5040
Website: www.polaris-pf.com

Management and Staff
Akira Iinuma, Partner
Hideo Mitsuda, Principal
Kaori Yagi, Partner
Ryoichi Ogawa, Principal
Tomohiro Isaji, Principal
Tomoji Asano, Managing Director
Toru Kajimura, Principal
Yuji Kimura, President
Yuka Katsuki, Managing Director

Type of Firm
Private Equity Firm

Project Preferences

Type of Financing Preferred:
Leveraged Buyout
Expansion
Generalist PE

Geographical Preferences

International Preferences:
Japan

Industry Preferences

In Communications prefer:
Entertainment

In Consumer Related prefer:
Retail
Consumer Products

In Transportation prefer:
Transportation

In Financial Services prefer:
Financial Services

In Business Serv. prefer:
Media

In Manufact. prefer:
Manufacturing

Additional Information
Year Founded: 2004
Capital Under Management: $1,700,000
Current Activity Level : Actively seeking new investments

POLARIS VENTURE PARTNERS

1000 Winter Street
Suite 3350
Waltham, MA USA 02451
Phone: 781-290-0770
Fax: 781-290-0880
Website: www.polarisventures.com

Other Offices
1000 Second Avenue
Suite 3100
Seattle, WA USA 98104
Phone: 206-652-4555
Fax: 206-652-4666

Management and Staff
Alan Crane, General Partner
Alan Spoon, Managing General Partner
Amir Nashat, General Partner
Brian Chee, General Partner
Bryce Youngren, General Partner
David Barrett, General Partner
Jason Trevisan, Principal
John Gannon, General Partner
Jonathan Flint, General Partner
Kevin Bitterman, Principal
Michael Hirshland, General Partner
Peter Flint, General Partner
Robert Metcalfe, General Partner
Robert Geiman, General Partner
Ryan Woodley, Principal
Stephen Arnold, Venture Partner
Terrance McGuire, General Partner

Type of Firm
Private Equity Firm

Association Membership
National Venture Capital Association - USA (NVCA)

Project Preferences

Role in Financing:
Prefer role as deal originator but will also invest in deals created by others

Type of Financing Preferred:
Second Stage Financing
Early Stage
Expansion
Research and Development
Balanced
Seed
First Stage Financing
Startup

Size of Investments Considered:
Min Size of Investment Considered (000s): $250
Max Size of Investment Considered (000s): $15,000

Geographical Preferences

United States Preferences:
All U.S.

Industry Focus

(% based on actual investment)

Internet Specific	31.1%
Computer Software and Services	22.5%
Medical/Health	17.4%
Biotechnology	11.3%
Communications and Media	5.6%
Semiconductors/Other Elect.	3.6%
Computer Hardware	3.4%
Consumer Related	3.3%
Industrial/Energy	1.1%
Other Products	0.7%

Additional Information

Name of Most Recent Fund: Polaris Venture Partners Entrepreneurs' Fund V, L.P.
Most Recent Fund Was Raised: 07/13/2006
Year Founded: 1996
Capital Under Management: $2,003,000,000
Current Activity Level : Actively seeking new investments
Method of Compensation: Return on investment is of primary concern, do not charge fees

---

POLYTECHNOS VENTURE-PARTNERS

Promenadeplatz 12
Munich, Germany D-80333
Phone: 49-89-2422-620
Fax: 49-89-2422-6221
E-mail: info@polytechnos.com
Website: www.polytechnos.com

Management and Staff

Dirk Lupberger, Venture Partner
Eric Achtmann, Venture Partner
Hasso Von Falkenhausen, Founding Partner
Knut Heitmann, Founding Partner
Oliver Haeggberg, Partner
Peter Weber, Partner
Tonio Barlage, Partner

Type of Firm

Private Equity Firm

Association Membership

German Venture Capital Association (BVK)
European Private Equity and Venture Capital Assoc.

Project Preferences

Role in Financing:

Prefer role as deal originator but will also invest in deals created by others

Type of Financing Preferred:

Early Stage
Expansion
Generalist PE
Later Stage
Startup
Acquisition

Size of Investments Considered:

Min Size of Investment Considered (000s): $6,399
Max Size of Investment Considered (000s): $19,196

Geographical Preferences

International Preferences:

Switzerland
Europe
Austria
Germany

Industry Focus

(% based on actual investment)

Semiconductors/Other Elect.	32.9%
Biotechnology	26.1%
Internet Specific	14.9%
Medical/Health	13.6%
Communications and Media	10.5%
Computer Software and Services	2.1%

Additional Information

Name of Most Recent Fund: PolyTechnos Venture Fund II (AKA: PTVF II)
Most Recent Fund Was Raised: 10/04/2001
Year Founded: 1998
Capital Under Management: $253,600,000
Current Activity Level : Actively seeking new investments
Method of Compensation: Return on investment is of primary concern, do not charge fees

---

POND VENTURE PARTNERS, LTD.

Wey Court West
Union Road
Farnham, United Kingdom GU9 7PT
Phone: 44-20-8940-1001
Fax: 44-20-8940-6792
E-mail: office@pondventures.com
Website: www.pondventures.com

Other Offices

32 Curzon Street
London, United Kingdom W1
Phone: 44-20-8940-1001

2033 Gateway Place
Suite 600
San Jose, CA USA 95110
Phone: 408-467-3806

Management and Staff

Charles Irving, Co-Founder
Jamie Urquhart, Venture Partner
Kent Godfrey, Partner
Michael Gera, Partner
Richard Irving, Co-Founder

Type of Firm

Private Equity Firm

Association Membership

British Venture Capital Association (BVCA)

Project Preferences

Type of Financing Preferred:

Early Stage
Balanced
Seed
Startup

Size of Investments Considered:

Min Size of Investment Considered (000s): $1,200
Max Size of Investment Considered: No Limit

Geographical Preferences

International Preferences:

Ireland
Sweden
United Kingdom
Europe
Finland

Industry Preferences

In Communications prefer:

Telecommunications
Wireless Communications

In Computer Software prefer:

Software

In Internet Specific prefer:

Internet

In Semiconductor/Electr prefer:

Semiconductor

In Medical/Health prefer:

Medical/Health

In Industrial/Energy prefer:

Energy

Additional Information

Year Founded: 1998
Capital Under Management: $70,000,000
Current Activity Level : Actively seeking new investments

PONTIFAX LTD.

8 Openheimer Street
Tel Aviv, Israel 69395
Management and Staff
Tomer Kariv, Managing Partner

Type of Firm

Private Equity Firm

Association Membership

Israel Venture Association

Project Preferences

Type of Financing Preferred:

Balanced

Geographical Preferences

International Preferences:

Israel

Additional Information

Year Founded: 2003
Capital Under Management: $35,000,000
Current Activity Level : Actively seeking new investments

PONTIS VENTURE PARTNERS

Loewelstrasse 12
Vienna, Austria 1010
Phone: 43-1-5333233-0
Fax: 43-1-5333233-30
E-mail: office@pontisventure.at
Website: www.pontisventure.at

Management and Staff

Gerhard Fiala, Managing Partner
Thomas Moser, Partner

Type of Firm

Private Equity Firm

Association Membership

Austrian PE and Venture Capital Association (AVCO)
European Private Equity and Venture Capital Assoc.

Project Preferences

Role in Financing:
Unknown

Type of Financing Preferred:
Expansion

Geographical Preferences

International Preferences:
Hungary
Slovenia
Czech Republic
Austria

Industry Preferences

In Industrial/Energy prefer:
Environmental Related

Additional Information

Name of Most Recent Fund: PVP I
Most Recent Fund Was Raised: 06/01/2005
Year Founded: 2005
Capital Under Management: $36,900,000
Current Activity Level : Actively seeking new investments
Method of Compensation: Unknown

POPULAR DE PARTICIPACIONES FINANCIERAS S.C.R. S.A.

Velazquez, 34-6
Madrid, Spain 28001
Phone: 34-91520-6946
Fax: 34-91435-5886
Website: www.bancopopular.es

Type of Firm

Private Equity Firm

Association Membership

Spanish Venture Capital Association (ASCRI)

Project Preferences

Type of Financing Preferred:
Expansion
Management Buyouts
Recapitalizations

Geographical Preferences

International Preferences:
Europe
Spain

Industry Preferences

In Consumer Related prefer:
Food/Beverage

In Financial Services prefer:
Real Estate

In Agr/Forestr/Fish prefer:
Agriculture related

Additional Information

Year Founded: 2001
Current Activity Level : Actively seeking new investments

PORTAGE VENTURE PARTNERS (AKA: GRAYSTONE VENTURE PARTNERS)

One Northfield Plaza
Suite 530
Northfield, IL USA 60093
Phone: 847-446-9460
Fax: 847-446-9470
E-mail: info@portageventures.com
Website: www.portageventures.com

Management and Staff

Edward Chandler, Managing Director
Judith Meyer, Managing Director
Judy Dorr, Chief Financial Officer
Matthew McCall, Managing Director
Stephen Kennedy, Managing Director

Type of Firm

Private Equity Firm

Association Membership

Illinois Venture Capital Association

Project Preferences

Role in Financing:
Will function either as deal originator or investor in deals created by others

Type of Financing Preferred:
Early Stage

Size of Investments Considered:

Min Size of Investment Considered (000s): $1,000
Max Size of Investment Considered (000s): $4,000

Industry Focus

(% based on actual investment)	
Internet Specific	36.8%
Computer Software and Services	20.1%
Semiconductors/Other Elect.	15.4%
Biotechnology	8.1%
Medical/Health	7.9%
Communications and Media	4.9%
Other Products	3.9%
Consumer Related	3.0%

Additional Information

Name of Most Recent Fund: Draper Fisher Jurvetson Portage Fund
Most Recent Fund Was Raised: 01/01/2003
Year Founded: 1997
Capital Under Management: $171,000,000
Current Activity Level : Actively seeking new investments
Method of Compensation: Return on investment is of primary concern, do not charge fees

PORTFOLIO ADVISORS LLC

Nine Old Kings Highway South
Darien, CT USA 06820
Phone: 203-662-3456
Fax: 203-662-0013
E-mail: info@portad.com
Website: www.portad.com

Other Offices

Seefeldstrasse 35
Zurich, Switzerland 8008
Phone: 41-44-200-3500
Fax: 41-44-200-3501

Management and Staff

Brian Murphy, Managing Director
Christopher Ruder, Managing Director
Donna Smolens, Managing Director
Harry Pierandri, Managing Director
Jonathan Murphy, Senior Managing Director
Kenneth Jarvis, Vice President
Kenneth Wisdom, Managing Director
Michael Galbreath, Managing Director
Michael Trinkaus, Chief Financial Officer
Paul Crotty, Managing Director
Ryan Butler, Vice President
William Indelicato, Managing Director
William Walsh, Managing Director

Type of Firm

Private Equity Advisor or Fund of Funds

Project Preferences

Type of Financing Preferred:
Fund of Funds

Geographical Preferences

International Preferences:
Europe
Western Europe
Asia
All International

Additional Information

Name of Most Recent Fund: Portfolio Advisors Private Equity Fund IV (Offshore), L.P.
Most Recent Fund Was Raised: 05/11/2006
Year Founded: 1994
Capital Under Management: $145,000,000
Current Activity Level : Actively seeking new investments

PORTVIEW COMMUNICATIONS LTD

CIBC Financial Cntr, 3rd Floor
11 Jennet St., PO Box 694GT
Grand Cayman, Cayman Islands
Phone: 345-914-9456
Fax: 345-945-2639
E-mail: hk@hkcatalyst.com
Website: www.portviewcommunications.com

Other Offices

1825 'I' Street NW
Suite 400
Washington, DC USA 20006
Phone: 202-857-8060
Fax: 202-775-4195

10 Hayetsira Street
POB 2197
Ra'anana, Israel 43650
Phone: 972-9-741-3140
Fax: 972-9-741-3240

Management and Staff

Julie Kunstler, Founder
Robin Hacke, Founder

Type of Firm

Private Equity Firm

Association Membership

Mid-Atlantic Venture Association

Project Preferences

Role in Financing:
Will function either as deal originator or investor in deals created by others

Type of Financing Preferred:
Early Stage
Balanced

Size of Investments Considered:
Min Size of Investment Considered (000s): $1,000
Max Size of Investment Considered (000s): $6,000

Geographical Preferences

United States Preferences:
All U.S.

International Preferences:
Sweden
United Kingdom
Finland
Israel

Industry Preferences

In Communications prefer:
Communications and Media

In Semiconductor/Electr prefer:
Optoelectronics

Additional Information

Name of Most Recent Fund: Portview Communications Partners, L.P.
Most Recent Fund Was Raised: 03/01/2000
Year Founded: 2000
Capital Under Management: $61,100,000
Current Activity Level : Actively seeking new investments
Method of Compensation: Return on investment is of primary concern, do not charge fees

---

POSCO BIOVENTURES

2121 Palomar Airport Road
Suite 300
Carlsbad, CA USA 92009
Phone: 760-448-2848
Fax: 760-448-2840
E-mail: jgoag@poscobioventures.com
Website: www.poscobioventures.com

Management and Staff

Leo Kim, Managing Director

Type of Firm

Corporate PE/Venture

Project Preferences

Role in Financing:
Will function either as deal originator or investor in deals created by others

Type of Financing Preferred:
Second Stage Financing
Early Stage
Mezzanine
Research and Development
Start-up Financing
Later Stage
Seed
First Stage Financing

Size of Investments Considered:
Min Size of Investment Considered (000s): $250
Max Size of Investment Considered (000s): $5,000

Geographical Preferences

Canadian Preferences:
All Canada

International Preferences:
Italy
United Kingdom
Luxembourg
Netherlands
Portugal
Spain
Belgium
Germany
France

Industry Preferences

In Biotechnology prefer:
Biotechnology

In Medical/Health prefer:
Medical Products

Additional Information

Year Founded: 2002
Capital Under Management: $50,000,000
Current Activity Level : Actively seeking new investments
Method of Compensation: Return on investment is of primary concern, do not charge fees

---

POST CAPITAL PARTNERS LLC

805 Third Avenue
8th Floor
New York, NY USA 10022
Phone: 212-888-5700
Fax: 206-222-2518
Website: www.postcp.com

Other Offices

410 Park Avenue
Suite 820
New York, NY USA 10022
Phone: 212-303-2710
Fax: 206-222-2518

Management and Staff

Michael Pfeffer, Managing Director
Mitchell Davidson, Managing Director
Stephen Lamberton, Vice President

Type of Firm

Private Equity Firm

Project Preferences

Type of Financing Preferred:
Generalist PE
Management Buyouts
Recapitalizations

Size of Investments Considered:
Min Size of Investment Considered (000s): $5,000
Max Size of Investment Considered (000s): $15,000

Geographical Preferences

United States Preferences:
All U.S.

Canadian Preferences:
All Canada

Industry Preferences

In Medical/Health prefer:
Health Services

In Consumer Related prefer:
Consumer Products

In Industrial/Energy prefer:
Industrial Products

In Financial Services prefer:
Financial Services

In Business Serv. prefer:
Services

In Manufact. prefer:
Manufacturing
Publishing

Additional Information

Year Founded: 2006
Capital Under Management: $25,000,000
Current Activity Level : Actively seeking new investments

POTEZA PARTNERS D.O.O.

Zelezna Cesta 18
Ljubljana, Slovenia SI-1000
Phone: 386-1-307-0700
Fax: 386-1-307-0701
E-mail: info@poteza.si
Website: www.poteza.si

Management and Staff

Leon Batagelj, Chief Executive Officer

Type of Firm

Bank Affiliated

Association Membership

European Private Equity and Venture Capital Assoc.

Project Preferences

Type of Financing Preferred:
Leveraged Buyout
Expansion
Generalist PE
Early Stage
Turnaround
Recapitalizations

Size of Investments Considered:
Min Size of Investment Considered (000s): $623
Max Size of Investment Considered (000s): $12,466

Geographical Preferences

International Preferences:
Slovenia
Europe
Macedonia
Croatia
Eastern Europe
Bulgaria
Moldova
Bosnia
Romania

Industry Preferences

In Communications prefer:
Telecommunications

In Internet Specific prefer:
Internet

In Medical/Health prefer:
Medical/Health
Pharmaceuticals

In Consumer Related prefer:
Retail
Food/Beverage

In Industrial/Energy prefer:
Energy

In Transportation prefer:
Transportation
Aerospace

In Financial Services prefer:
Real Estate
Financial Services

In Business Serv. prefer:
Services

Additional Information

Name of Most Recent Fund: Poteza Innovation and Growth Fund B.V.
Most Recent Fund Was Raised: 11/05/2007
Year Founded: 2003
Capital Under Management: $88,100,000
Current Activity Level : Actively seeking new investments

POUSCHINE COOK CAPITAL MANAGEMENT, LLC

375 Park Avenue
Suite 3408
New York, NY USA 10152
Phone: 212-784-0620
Fax: 212-784-0621
Website: www.pouschinecook.com

Management and Staff

Everett Cook, Managing Director
Geoffrey Teillon, Vice President
John Pouschine, Managing Director
Robert Jenkins, Principal
Ryan Gabel, Vice President

Type of Firm

Private Equity Firm

Project Preferences

Role in Financing:
Prefer role as deal originator

Type of Financing Preferred:
Expansion
Generalist PE
Management Buyouts
Acquisition
Recapitalizations

Size of Investments Considered:
Min Size of Investment Considered (000s): $5,000
Max Size of Investment Considered (000s): $10,000

Industry Preferences

In Computer Software prefer:
Data Processing

In Medical/Health prefer:
Medical/Health
Health Services
Hospitals/Clinics/Primary
Hospital/Other Instit.

In Consumer Related prefer:
Retail
Franchises(NEC)
Consumer Services
Education Related

In Industrial/Energy prefer:
Industrial Products

In Transportation prefer:
Transportation

In Financial Services prefer:
Financial Services
Insurance

In Business Serv. prefer:
Services
Distribution
Media

In Manufact. prefer:
Manufacturing

Additional Information

Name of Most Recent Fund: Pouschine Cook Capital Partners II, LP
Most Recent Fund Was Raised: 04/25/2005
Year Founded: 1999
Capital Under Management: $261,500,000
Current Activity Level : Actively seeking new investments
Method of Compensation: Return on invest. most important, but chg. closing fees, service fees, etc.

POWER CAPITAL CO., LTD.

No. 12 Zhaowai Street
1007 Kuntai Int'l Building
Beijing, China 100020

Phone: 86-10-5879-7997
Fax: 86-10-5879-7369
E-mail: power@powercapital.cn
Website: www.0101go.com

Other Offices

No. 189 Xiahe Road
Room 1201 Bank Center
Xiamen, China 361003
Phone: 86-592-2682-688
Fax: 86-592-2683-335

No. 296 Xinhua Road
Changning
Shanghai, China 200052
Phone: 86-21-5230-2266
Fax: 86-21-5230-3377

Management and Staff

Fan Liu, Partner
James Xu, Partner
Kemin Yang, Chief Executive Officer
Ken Wang, Partner
Lixin Zheng, Partner
Shi Chen, Chief Operating Officer

Type of Firm

Private Equity Firm

Project Preferences

Type of Financing Preferred:

Balanced

Geographical Preferences

International Preferences:

China

Additional Information

Year Founded: 2008
Current Activity Level : Actively seeking new investments

POWER CORPORATION OF CANADA

751 Victoria Square
Montreal, Canada H2Y 2J3
Phone: 514-286-7400
Fax: 514-286-7424
Website: www.powercorp.ca

Other Offices

Richardson Building, 1 Lombard Place
Suite 2600
Winnipeg, Canada R3B 0X5

1 rond-point des Champs Elysees
Paris, France 75008

Management and Staff

Michel Plessis-Belair, Chief Financial Officer

Type of Firm

Private Equity Firm

Geographical Preferences

International Preferences:

Europe

Industry Preferences

In Communications prefer:

Communications and Media

In Financial Services prefer:

Financial Services

Additional Information

Year Founded: 1925
Capital Under Management: $5,000,000
Current Activity Level : Actively seeking new investments

POWER FINANCE CORPORATION, LTD.

Urjanidhi, 1 Barakhamba Lane
Connaught Place
New Delhi, India 110 001
Phone: 91-11-2345-6000
Website: www.pfc.gov.in

Other Offices

1st Floor (Rear Side), SPS Building
New No.185, Old No.137, Anna Salai
Chennai, India 600 002
Phone: 91-44-2860-2431

Ground Floor, Moonlight Building
158 Maharishi Karve Rd, Churchgate
Mumbai, India 400 020
Phone: 91-22-2288-2440

Management and Staff

V.K. Garg, Chairman & Managing Director

Type of Firm

Government Affiliated Program

Project Preferences

Type of Financing Preferred:

Balanced
Other

Geographical Preferences

International Preferences:

India

Industry Preferences

In Industrial/Energy prefer:

Energy

Additional Information

Year Founded: 1986
Current Activity Level : Actively seeking new investments

PPF INVESTMENTS, LTD.

Whiteley Chambers
Don Street, Saint Helier
Jersey, United Kingdom JE4 9WG
E-mail: info@ppfinvestments.com
Website: www.ppfinvestments.com

Other Offices

72 (A), Chervonoarmiyska Strasse
(Veluka Vasylkivska), off. 157
Kyiv, Ukraine 03150
Phone: 380-442-068-401
Fax: 380-442-068-403

33 Chester Stree
London, United Kingdom SW1X7BH
Phone: 44-20-7259-5810
Fax: 44-20-7259-5801

Na Pankraci 1658/121
Praha 4, Czech Republic 140 21
Phone: 420-266-055-000
Fax: 420-266-055-090

Beijing Lufthansa Center, C 312A
50 Liangmaqiao Road, Chaoyang District
Beijing, China 100016
Phone: 86-10-6463-8682
Fax: 86-10-6264-2448

8 Pravda Street
Building 1
Moscow, Russia 125124
Phone: 7-495-648-9932
Fax: 7-495-648-9934

Management and Staff

Miroslav Nosal, Chief Executive Officer
Pavel Kuta, Managing Director

Type of Firm

Private Equity Firm

Project Preferences

Type of Financing Preferred:

Balanced

Geographical Preferences

International Preferences:

Central Europe
Eastern Europe
Asia

Additional Information

Year Founded: 2006
Current Activity Level : Actively seeking new investments

PPM AMERICA CAPITAL PARTNERS LLC

225 West Wacker Drive
Suite 1200
Chicago, IL USA 60606
Phone: 312-634-2500
Fax: 312-634-0050
Website: www.ppmamerica.com

Other Offices

750 Lexington Avenue
Tenth Floor
New York, NY USA 10022
Phone: 212-583-7300
Fax: 212-583-7311

300 North Martingale Road
Suite 440
Schaumburg, IL USA 60173
Phone: 847-413-8500
Fax: 847-413-3240

Management and Staff

Austin Krumpfes, Partner
Brian Gallagher, Partner
Bruce Gorchow, President
Champ Raju, Partner
Claudia Baron, Partner
Craig Radis, Principal
Craig Waslin, Principal
Guy Petrelli, Partner
Harisha Koneru, Principal
Joseph Dimberio, Principal
Kevin Keefe, Principal
Mark Staub, Principal
Patrick Lanigan, Principal
Robert O Rourke, Partner

Type of Firm

Bank Affiliated

Association Membership

Illinois Venture Capital Association

Project Preferences

Role in Financing:
Will function either as deal originator or investor in deals created by others

Type of Financing Preferred:
Leveraged Buyout
Mezzanine
Management Buyouts
Acquisition
Recapitalizations

Size of Investments Considered:
Min Size of Investment Considered (000s): $5,000
Max Size of Investment Considered (000s): $80,000

Industry Focus

(% based on actual investment)

Consumer Related	52.0%
Other Products	28.7%
Internet Specific	13.3%
Computer Software and Services	2.8%
Medical/Health	2.5%
Communications and Media	0.7%

Additional Information

Year Founded: 1990
Current Activity Level : Actively seeking new investments
Method of Compensation: Return on investment is of primary concern, do not charge fees

PPM MANAGERS

1 New Fetter Lane
London, United Kingdom EC4A 1HH
Phone: 44-20-7822-1000
Fax: 44-20-7822-1001
E-mail: info@ppmmanagers.com
Website: www.ppmmanagers.com

Type of Firm

Private Equity Advisor or Fund of Funds

Project Preferences

Type of Financing Preferred:
Fund of Funds

Geographical Preferences

International Preferences:
Europe
Asia

Additional Information

Year Founded: 2000
Current Activity Level : Actively seeking new investments

PPM STIMULANS

Van der Does de Willeboissinge
Den Bosch, Netherlands 5211 CA
Phone: 31-73-614-4249
Fax: 31-73-614-3656
E-mail: info@ppm.stimulans.nl
Website: www.ppmstimulans.nl

Type of Firm

Private Equity Firm

Association Membership

Dutch Venture Capital Associaton (NVP)

Project Preferences

Type of Financing Preferred:
Leveraged Buyout
Expansion

Size of Investments Considered:
Min Size of Investment Considered (000s): $247
Max Size of Investment Considered (000s): $1,975

Geographical Preferences

International Preferences:
Netherlands

Additional Information

Year Founded: 1980
Current Activity Level : Actively seeking new investments

PRADO FINANCE

Avenue Brugmann, 205
Brussels, Belgium 1050
Phone: 32-498-979-632
Fax: 32-2-732-1281
E-mail: info@pradofinance.com
Website: www.pradofinance.com

Other Offices

49, avenue de l'Opera
Paris, France 75002
Phone: 33-1-4312-9104
Fax: 33-1-5818-3153

Management and Staff

Patrice Pierron, Founder

Type of Firm

Private Equity Firm

Additional Information

Year Founded: 1999
Current Activity Level : Actively seeking new investments

PRAESIDIAN CAPITAL, LLC

419 Park Avenue South
New York, NY USA 10016
Phone: 212-520-2600
Fax: 212-520-2601
E-mail: info@praesidian.com
Website: www.praesidian.com

Management and Staff

Edward Koch, Managing Partner
James Fisher, Managing Partner
Jason Drattell, Managing General Partner
John Utendahl, Partner
Neil Marks, Managing Partner

Type of Firm

Private Equity Firm

Project Preferences

Type of Financing Preferred:
Mezzanine
Generalist PE
Distressed Debt
Recapitalizations

Size of Investments Considered:
Min Size of Investment Considered (000s): $4,000
Max Size of Investment Considered (000s): $15,000

Geographical Preferences

United States Preferences:
All U.S.

Industry Preferences

In Business Serv. prefer:
Services
Distribution

In Manufact. prefer:
Manufacturing

Additional Information

Year Founded: 2003
Capital Under Management: $392,000,000
Current Activity Level : Actively seeking new investments

PRAGMA CAPITAL

13 Avenue Hoche
Paris, France 75008
Phone: 33-1-5836-4950
Fax: 33-1-5836-4951
E-mail: pragma@pragma-capital.com
Website: www.pragma-capital.com

Type of Firm

Private Equity Firm

Association Membership

French Venture Capital Association (AFIC)
European Private Equity and Venture Capital Assoc.

Project Preferences

Type of Financing Preferred:
Leveraged Buyout
Management Buyouts

Geographical Preferences

International Preferences:
Europe
France

Industry Preferences

In Industrial/Energy prefer:
Industrial Products

In Business Serv. prefer:
Services

In Manufact. prefer:
Manufacturing

Additional Information

Year Founded: 2002
Capital Under Management: $370,300,000
Current Activity Level : Actively seeking new investments

PRAIRIE CAPITAL

191 North Wacker Drive
Suite 800
Chicago, IL USA 60606
Phone: 312-360-1133
Fax: 312-360-1193
Website: www.prairie-capital.com

Management and Staff

Bryan Daniels, Principal
Christopher Killackey, Managing Director
Darren Snyder, Managing Director
Holly Lane, Chief Financial Officer
Stephen King, Principal
Steven Groya, Managing Director

Type of Firm

Private Equity Firm

Association Membership

Natl Assoc of Small Bus. Inv. Co (NASBIC)
Illinois Venture Capital Association

Project Preferences

Role in Financing:
Will function either as deal originator or investor in deals created by others

Type of Financing Preferred:
Leveraged Buyout
Mezzanine
Later Stage
Management Buyouts
Acquisition
Recapitalizations

Size of Investments Considered:
Min Size of Investment Considered (000s): $3,000
Max Size of Investment Considered (000s): $15,000

Geographical Preferences

United States Preferences:
All U.S.

Industry Focus

(% based on actual investment)

Other Products	56.3%
Consumer Related	37.6%
Communications and Media	5.6%
Medical/Health	0.6%

Additional Information

Name of Most Recent Fund: Prairie Capital III, L.P.
Most Recent Fund Was Raised: 09/15/2003
Year Founded: 1997
Capital Under Management: $390,000,000
Current Activity Level : Actively seeking new investments
Method of Compensation: Return on invest. most important, but chg. closing fees, service fees, etc.

PRAIRIE OAK CAPITAL LLC

5465 Mills Civic Parkway
Suite 400
West Des Moines, IA USA 50266
Phone: 515-564-7603
Website: www.prairieoakcapital.com

Management and Staff

Jim Kurtenbach, General Partner

Type of Firm

Private Equity Firm

Industry Preferences

In Medical/Health prefer:
Medical/Health

In Manufact. prefer:
Manufacturing

Additional Information

Year Founded: 2007
Capital Under Management: $7,500,000
Current Activity Level : Actively seeking new investments

PRAIRIEGOLD VENTURE PARTNERS

2329 North Career Avenue
Suite 225
Sioux Falls, SD USA 57107
Phone: 605-275-2999
Website: www.pgvp.com

Management and Staff

Christine Hamilton, Founder

Type of Firm

Private Equity Firm

Project Preferences

Type of Financing Preferred:
Early Stage
Expansion
Balanced

Size of Investments Considered:
Min Size of Investment Considered (000s): $250
Max Size of Investment Considered (000s): $1,000

Geographical Preferences

United States Preferences:
Midwest
South Dakota

Industry Preferences

In Consumer Related prefer:
Food/Beverage

In Agr/Forestr/Fish prefer:
Agriculture related

Additional Information
Name of Most Recent Fund: PrairieGold VenCap Fund II, LP
Most Recent Fund Was Raised: 04/14/2008
Year Founded: 2003
Capital Under Management: $19,500,000
Current Activity Level : Actively seeking new investments

PRAX CAPITAL
Suite 1701, Shui On Plaza
333 Huai Hai Zhong Road
Shanghai, China 200021
Phone: 86-21-6385-0606
Fax: 86-21-6237-6709
E-mail: www.praxcapital.com
Website: www.praxcapital.com

Other Offices
1001 Brickell Bay Drive
Suite 2402
Miami, FL USA 33131
Phone: 305-358-9696
Fax: 305-358-9797

Diagonal 605, 7 - 3
Barcelona, Spain 08028
Phone: 34-93-363-3320
Fax: 34-93-419-1042

Level 25, Bank Of China Tower
1 Garden Road
Central Hong Kong, Hong Kong
Phone: 852-2251-8652
Fax: 852-2251-8656

Management and Staff
Alex Liao, Principal
Anselm Adams, Partner
Fernando Vila, Chief Financial Officer
Gonzalo Rodriguez-Fraile, Partner
Jeff Jie-Ping Yao, Managing Partner
Meilan Gan, Partner
Michael Xu, Partner

Type of Firm
Private Equity Firm

Project Preferences

Type of Financing Preferred:
Expansion
Balanced
Other

Size of Investments Considered:
Min Size of Investment Considered (000s): $10,000
Max Size of Investment Considered (000s): $30,000

Geographical Preferences

International Preferences:
China

Industry Preferences

In Industrial/Energy prefer:
Industrial Products

In Financial Services prefer:
Real Estate

In Business Serv. prefer:
Services

Additional Information
Year Founded: 2005
Current Activity Level : Actively seeking new investments

PRAXIS CAPITAL
Postnet Suite No. 241
P/Bag X30500
Houghton, South Africa 2041
Phone: 27-11-484-2255
Fax: 27-11-484-2223
Website: www.praxiscapital.co.za

Type of Firm
Private Equity Advisor or Fund of Funds

Association Membership
South African Venture Capital Association (SAVCA)

Project Preferences

Type of Financing Preferred:
Early Stage
Expansion
Balanced
Later Stage
Startup

Size of Investments Considered:
Min Size of Investment Considered (000s): $3,143
Max Size of Investment Considered (000s): $3,771

Geographical Preferences

International Preferences:
United Kingdom
South Africa

Industry Preferences

In Medical/Health prefer:
Medical/Health

In Consumer Related prefer:
Education Related

Additional Information
Year Founded: 1997
Capital Under Management: $24,900,000
Current Activity Level : Actively seeking new investments

PRE IPO INVEST (AKA: PRE-IPO.NET)
5 bis rue du Cirque
Paris, France 75008
Phone: 33-1-4435-7777
Fax: 33-1-4563-6525

Type of Firm
Private Equity Firm

Project Preferences

Type of Financing Preferred:
Early Stage
Expansion

Geographical Preferences

International Preferences:
Europe
Germany
France

Additional Information
Year Founded: 2000
Capital Under Management: $36,100,000
Current Activity Level : Actively seeking new investments

PREIPO CAPITAL PARTNERS
No. 832 Huamu Road
3rd Floor
Shanghai, China 201204
Phone: 86-21-5059-1378
Fax: 86-21-5045-3554
E-mail: info@preipo.cn
Website: www.preipo.cn

Management and Staff
Scott Zheng, Partner

Type of Firm
Private Equity Firm

Project Preferences

Role in Financing:
Will function either as deal originator or investor in deals created by others

Type of Financing Preferred:
Expansion
Later Stage

Size of Investments Considered:
Min Size of Investment Considered (000s): $1,000
Max Size of Investment Considered (000s): $50,000

Geographical Preferences

International Preferences:
China

Industry Preferences

In Computer Other prefer:
Computer Related

In Biotechnology prefer:
Biotechnology

In Medical/Health prefer:
Health Services

In Consumer Related prefer:
Retail
Consumer Products

In Transportation prefer:
Transportation

In Financial Services prefer:
Financial Services

In Business Serv. prefer:
Media

Additional Information

Year Founded: 1999
Current Activity Level : Actively seeking new investments

PREMIER VENTURE PARTNERS LLC

5F, Kosmo Tower
1002 Daichi-dong, Kangman-ku
Seoul, South Korea
Phone: 822-554-0030
Fax: 822-554-6442
E-mail: premier@premiervp.co.kr
Website: www.premiervp.co.kr

Management and Staff

Hyuk Jin Song, Managing Director
Seung-Wook Cheon, Managing Director
Tae Sung Oh, Partner

Type of Firm

Private Equity Firm

Association Membership

Korean Venture Capital Association (KVCA)

Project Preferences

Type of Financing Preferred:
Balanced

Geographical Preferences

International Preferences:
Korea, South

Industry Preferences

In Semiconductor/Electr prefer:
Electronics

Additional Information

Year Founded: 2005
Capital Under Management: $54,600,000
Current Activity Level : Actively seeking new investments

PREMIERS PAS

Rue de Franche-Comte
BP 311
Cherbourg, France F - 50103
Phone: 33-2-3344-1733
Fax: 33-2-3388-7809
E-mail: info@premierspas.com

Management and Staff

Patrick Le Granche, Founding Partner

Type of Firm

Incubator/Development Program

Project Preferences

Type of Financing Preferred:
Seed
Startup

Geographical Preferences

International Preferences:
Europe

Industry Preferences

In Internet Specific prefer:
Internet

Additional Information

Year Founded: 2000
Capital Under Management: $900,000
Current Activity Level : Actively seeking new investments

PRESIDIO INVESTORS LLC

101 California Street
Suite 1200
San Francisco, CA USA 94111
Phone: 415-449-1000
Fax: 415-449-2592
Website: www.presidiofp.com

Other Offices

9533 West Pico Boulevard
Second Floor, Suite A
Los Angeles, CA USA 90035
Phone: 310-407-7901
Fax: 310-407-7906

100 Crescent Court
Suite 550
Dallas, TX USA 75201
Phone: 214-855-2200
Fax: 214-855-2219

Management and Staff

Barry Rudolph, Managing Director
Brodie Cobb, CEO & Managing Director
James Student, Managing Director
Karl Schade, Managing Director

Type of Firm

Bank Affiliated

Project Preferences

Type of Financing Preferred:
Leveraged Buyout
Expansion

Size of Investments Considered:
Min Size of Investment Considered (000s): $3,000
Max Size of Investment Considered (000s): $10,000

Additional Information

Year Founded: 2008
Capital Under Management: $44,500,000
Current Activity Level : Actively seeking new investments

PRESIDIO STX (FKA: PRESIDIO VENTURE PARTNERS, LLC)

3979 Freedom Circle
Suite 340
Santa Clara, CA USA 95054
Phone: 408-845-9458
Fax: 408-845-9365
E-mail: investment-info@presidiostx.com
Website: www.presidiostx.com

Other Offices

24 New England Executive Park
Burlington, MA USA 01803
Phone: 781-229-8977
Fax: 781-229-8931

Type of Firm

Bank Affiliated

Project Preferences

Role in Financing:
Will function either as deal originator or investor in deals created by others

Type of Financing Preferred:
Early Stage

Size of Investments Considered:
Min Size of Investment Considered (000s): $500
Max Size of Investment Considered (000s): $5,000

Geographical Preferences

United States Preferences:
All U.S.

Industry Preferences

In Communications prefer:
Commercial Communications
CATV & Pay TV Systems
Radio & TV Broadcasting
Telecommunications

Wireless Communications
Data Communications
Satellite Microwave Comm.
Other Communication Prod.

In Computer Hardware prefer:
Mainframes / Scientific
Computer Graphics and Dig

In Computer Software prefer:
Data Processing
Software
Systems Software

In Internet Specific prefer:
E-Commerce Technology
Internet
Ecommerce

In Semiconductor/Electr prefer:
Electronic Components
Semiconductor
Micro-Processing
Controllers and Sensors
Sensors
Circuit Boards
Optoelectronics

In Biotechnology prefer:
Biotech Related Research

In Medical/Health prefer:
Drug/Equipmt Delivery

Additional Information
Year Founded: 1997
Current Activity Level : Actively seeking new investments
Method of Compensation: Return on investment is of primary concern, do not charge fees

PRICOA CAPITAL GROUP, LTD.
47 King William Street
5th Floor
London, United Kingdom EC4R 9JD
Phone: 44-20-7621-8448
Fax: 44-207-287-5702
E-mail: marketing@pricoacapital.com
Website: www.pricoacapital.com

Other Offices
Justinianstrasse 22
Frankfurt am Main, Germany 60322
Phone: 49 69 955 2870
Fax: 49 68 955 28799

9 Avenue Matignon
Paris, France 75008
Phone: 33 156 59 98 51
Fax: 33 156 59 98 54

Management and Staff
Bruno Wanske, Managing Partner

Type of Firm
Insurance Firm Affiliate

Association Membership
European Private Equity and Venture Capital Assoc.

Project Preferences

Type of Financing Preferred:
Leveraged Buyout
Expansion
Mezzanine
Management Buyouts
Recapitalizations

Size of Investments Considered:
Min Size of Investment Considered (000s): $7,300
Max Size of Investment Considered (000s): $146,400

Geographical Preferences

International Preferences:
Europe

Industry Focus
(% based on actual investment)

Consumer Related	47.9%
Internet Specific	35.7%
Computer Software and Services	14.4%
Communications and Media	2.0%

Additional Information
Name of Most Recent Fund: PRICOA Private Capital Partners II
Most Recent Fund Was Raised: 10/03/2000
Year Founded: 1985
Capital Under Management: $800,000,000
Current Activity Level : Actively seeking new investments

PRIDE INVESTMENTS GROUP, LTD., THE (AKA: PRIDE GROUP, THE)
99 Queen's Road
3606, The Center
Central, Hong Kong
Phone: 852-2110-3129
Fax: 852-2110-0616
E-mail: info@prideinvestmentsgroup.com
Website: www.prideinvestmentsgroup.com

Other Offices
2702, 2 Grand Gateway
No. 3 Hongqiao Road
Shanghai, China
Phone: 86-21-3353-0081
Fax: 86-21-6227-0239

Management and Staff
BoBo Tang, Chief Executive Officer
Jue Qi, Managing Director

Type of Firm
Investment Management Firm

Association Membership
Hong Kong Venture Capital Association (HKVCA)

Project Preferences

Type of Financing Preferred:
Early Stage
Expansion
Balanced
Later Stage

Geographical Preferences

International Preferences:
China
Hong Kong

Industry Preferences

In Consumer Related prefer:
Consumer

In Industrial/Energy prefer:
Environmental Related

In Financial Services prefer:
Financial Services

Additional Information
Year Founded: 2007
Current Activity Level : Actively seeking new investments

PRIMARY CAPITAL, LTD.
Augustine House
Austin Friars
London, United Kingdom EC2N 2HA
Phone: 44-20-7920-4800
Fax: 44-20-7920-4801
E-mail: primary@primaryeurope.com
Website: www.primaryeurope.com

Management and Staff
Charles Gonszor, Chief Executive Officer

Type of Firm
Private Equity Firm

Association Membership
British Venture Capital Association (BVCA)
European Private Equity and Venture Capital Assoc.

Project Preferences

Type of Financing Preferred:
Leveraged Buyout
Expansion
Turnaround
Later Stage
Management Buyouts

Size of Investments Considered:
Min Size of Investment Considered (000s): $19,984
Max Size of Investment Considered (000s): $199,840

Geographical Preferences

International Preferences:
United Kingdom
Western Europe
Germany

Industry Focus
(% based on actual investment)

Consumer Related	46.7%
Other Products	45.7%
Computer Hardware	7.6%

Additional Information
Year Founded: 1995
Capital Under Management: $707,000,000
Current Activity Level : Actively seeking new investments

PRIME CAPITAL MANAGEMENT CO., INC.

107 John Street
Southport, CT USA 06890
Phone: 203-259-8287
Fax: 203-964-0862

Type of Firm
Private Equity Firm

Project Preferences

Role in Financing:
Prefer role as deal originator but will also invest in deals created by others

Type of Financing Preferred:
Expansion
Mezzanine
Turnaround
Acquisition

Size of Investments Considered:
Min Size of Investment Considered (000s): $500
Max Size of Investment Considered (000s): $1,500

Geographical Preferences

United States Preferences:
Southeast
Northeast

Industry Focus
(% based on actual investment)

Consumer Related	29.3%
Communications and Media	26.0%
Other Products	11.3%
Computer Hardware	11.0%
Computer Software and Services	9.0%
Semiconductors/Other Elect.	6.6%
Industrial/Energy	3.7%
Internet Specific	1.8%
Biotechnology	1.2%

Additional Information

Year Founded: 1981
Capital Under Management: $12,000,000
Current Activity Level : Actively seeking new investments
Method of Compensation: Return on investment is of primary concern, do not charge fees

---

PRIME TECHNOLOGY VENTURES NV

Stroombaan 6-8
P.O. Box 260, 1180 AG
Amstelveen, Netherlands 1181 VX
Phone: 31-20-330-0650
Fax: 31-20-330-0651
E-mail: info@ptv.com
Website: www.ptv.com

Other Offices
Wellington House, East Road
Suite 217
Cambridge, United Kingdom CB1 1BH
Phone: 44-1223-451-294
Fax: 44-1223-451-100

Management and Staff
Jelto Smits, General Partner
Joost Holleman, General Partner
Monish Suri, General Partner
Pekka Roine, General Partner
Roel De Hoop, General Partner
Sake Bosch, Managing Partner
Sandeep Kapadia, General Partner

Type of Firm
Private Equity Firm

Association Membership
Swedish Venture Capital Association (SVCA)
European Private Equity and Venture Capital Assoc.
Dutch Venture Capital Associaton (NVP)

Project Preferences

Type of Financing Preferred:
Early Stage
Expansion
Balanced
Seed
Later Stage
Startup

Size of Investments Considered:
Min Size of Investment Considered (000s): $471
Max Size of Investment Considered (000s): $6,591

Geographical Preferences

International Preferences:
United Kingdom
Europe
Western Europe
Scandanavia/Nordic Region

Industry Preferences

In Communications prefer:
Telecommunications
Data Communications

In Internet Specific prefer:
Internet

In Computer Other prefer:
Computer Related

In Semiconductor/Electr prefer:
Electronics
Semiconductor

Additional Information
Year Founded: 1999
Capital Under Management: $260,100,000
Current Activity Level : Actively seeking new investments

PRIMUS CAPITAL FUNDS (FKA: PRIMUS VENTURE PARTNERS, INC.)

5900 Landerbrook Drive
Suite 200
Cleveland, OH USA 44124
Phone: 440-684-7300
Fax: 440-684-7342
E-mail: info@primuscapital.com
Website: www.primuscapital.com

Management and Staff
Jonathan Dick, Managing Director
Keith Kerman, Managing Director
Loyal Wilson, Managing Director
Phillip Molner, Managing Director
Scott Harper, Managing Director
Steven Rothman, Managing Director & CFO
William Mulligan, Managing Director
William McMaster, Principal

Type of Firm
Private Equity Firm

Association Membership
National Venture Capital Association - USA (NVCA)

Project Preferences

Role in Financing:
Prefer role as deal originator but will also invest in deals created by others

Type of Financing Preferred:
Leveraged Buyout
Early Stage
Expansion
Later Stage
Management Buyouts
Acquisition
Recapitalizations

Size of Investments Considered:
Min Size of Investment Considered (000s): $5,000
Max Size of Investment Considered (000s): $20,000

Geographical Preferences

United States Preferences:
Midwest

Northeast
All U.S.

Industry Focus

(% based on actual investment)

Computer Software and Services	21.3%
Other Products	19.3%
Communications and Media	18.8%
Medical/Health	13.3%
Consumer Related	9.5%
Internet Specific	7.6%
Industrial/Energy	3.9%
Biotechnology	3.9%
Computer Hardware	1.6%
Semiconductors/Other Elect.	0.9%

Additional Information

Name of Most Recent Fund: Primus Capital Fund VI, L.P.
Most Recent Fund Was Raised: 11/01/2007
Year Founded: 1983
Capital Under Management: $625,000,000
Current Activity Level : Actively seeking new investments
Method of Compensation: Return on investment is of primary concern, do not charge fees

---

PRIMUS CAPITAL PARTNERS LLC

Balzac u. 35
Budapest, Hungary 1136
Phone: 36-20-365-0868
Fax: 36-1-320-3311
E-mail: info@primuscapitalpartners.com
Website: www.primuscapitalpartners.com

Management and Staff

Zoltan Bruckner, Managing Director

Type of Firm

Private Equity Firm

Association Membership

Hungarian Venture Capital Association (HVCA)

Project Preferences

Type of Financing Preferred:
Early Stage

Size of Investments Considered:
Min Size of Investment Considered (000s): $50
Max Size of Investment Considered (000s): $250

Geographical Preferences

International Preferences:
Hungary
Slovak Repub.
Czech Republic
Central Europe

Industry Preferences

In Communications prefer:
Telecommunications

In Computer Software prefer:
Software

In Semiconductor/Electr prefer:
Electronics

In Biotechnology prefer:
Biotechnology

In Medical/Health prefer:
Pharmaceuticals

In Financial Services prefer:
Real Estate

Additional Information

Year Founded: 2004
Current Activity Level : Actively seeking new investments

PRIMUS PACIFIC PARTNERS

34th Floor Queen's Road
Central, Hong Kong

Management and Staff

Guocang Huan, Chief Executive Officer
Wing-Fai Ng, Managing Director

Type of Firm

Private Equity Firm

Project Preferences

Type of Financing Preferred:
Balanced

Geographical Preferences

International Preferences:
China
Asia

Industry Preferences

In Financial Services prefer:
Financial Services

Additional Information

Year Founded: 2005
Capital Under Management: $26,700,000
Current Activity Level : Actively seeking new investments

PRINCIPLE CAPITAL, LTD.

360 Pudong Nan Road
Suite 26C
Shanghai, China 200120
Phone: 86-21-6886-2466
Fax: 86-21-6886-2467
Website: www.principle-capital.com

Management and Staff

Jessica Miao, Vice President
Lin Lin Zhou, Chief Executive Officer
Zhong Ren Jing, Managing Director

Type of Firm

Private Equity Firm

Project Preferences

Type of Financing Preferred:
Leveraged Buyout

Geographical Preferences

International Preferences:
China

Industry Preferences

In Biotechnology prefer:
Biotechnology

In Medical/Health prefer:
Pharmaceuticals

In Consumer Related prefer:
Food/Beverage
Consumer Products

In Industrial/Energy prefer:
Energy
Materials

Additional Information

Year Founded: 1999
Current Activity Level : Actively seeking new investments

PRISM CAPITAL

444 North Michigan Avenue
Suite 1910
Chicago, IL USA 60611
Phone: 312-464-7900
Fax: 312-464-7915
E-mail: info@prismfund.com
Website: www.prismfund.com

Management and Staff

Bill Harlan, Partner
Bill Lump, Chief Financial Officer
Blaine Crissman, Partner
John Hoesley, Partner
Mark Finkel, Venture Partner
Robert Finkel, Managing Partner
Stephen Vivian, Partner

Type of Firm

Private Equity Firm

Association Membership

Illinois Venture Capital Association
Natl Assoc of Small Bus. Inv. Co (NASBIC)

Project Preferences

Role in Financing:
Prefer role as deal originator but will also invest in deals created by others

Type of Financing Preferred:
Leveraged Buyout
Expansion

Mezzanine
Later Stage
Acquisition

Size of Investments Considered:

Min Size of Investment Considered (000s): $2,000
Max Size of Investment Considered (000s): $8,000

Geographical Preferences

United States Preferences:

All U.S.

Industry Focus

(% based on actual investment)

Other Products	26.2%
Computer Software and Services	24.4%
Consumer Related	14.8%
Industrial/Energy	12.6%
Medical/Health	9.9%
Internet Specific	8.5%
Computer Hardware	3.0%
Semiconductors/Other Elect.	0.7%

Additional Information

Year Founded: 1999
Capital Under Management: $190,000,000
Current Activity Level : Actively seeking new investments
Method of Compensation: Return on investment is of primary concern, do not charge fees

PRISM VENTUREWORKS (FKA:PRISM VENTURE PARTNERS)

117 Kendrick Street
Suite 200
Needham, MA USA 02494
Phone: 781-302-4000
Fax: 781-302-4040
Website: www.prismventure.com

Other Offices

1212 Abbot Kinney Boulevard
Unit B
Venice, CA USA 90291
Phone: 310-396-9464
Fax: 310-775-9792

Management and Staff

Anthony Natale, Venture Partner
Brendan O'Leary, General Partner
Gordie Nye, General Partner
James Counihan, General Partner
John Brooks, Founder
Robert Fleming, Founder
William Kohler, Principal
William Seifert, General Partner
Woody Benson, General Partner

Type of Firm

Private Equity Firm

Association Membership

National Venture Capital Association - USA (NVCA)

Project Preferences

Role in Financing:

Prefer role as deal originator but will also invest in deals created by others

Type of Financing Preferred:

Early Stage

Size of Investments Considered:

Min Size of Investment Considered (000s): $5,000
Max Size of Investment Considered (000s): $15,000

Geographical Preferences

United States Preferences:

Mid Atlantic
Northwest
Northeast
West Coast
All U.S.

Canadian Preferences:

All Canada

Industry Focus

(% based on actual investment)

Medical/Health	28.8%
Internet Specific	21.9%
Communications and Media	15.8%
Computer Software and Services	12.8%
Biotechnology	7.4%
Computer Hardware	6.6%
Semiconductors/Other Elect.	6.3%
Consumer Related	0.3%

Additional Information

Year Founded: 1996
Capital Under Management: $1,250,000,000
Current Activity Level : Actively seeking new investments
Method of Compensation: Return on investment is of primary concern, do not charge fees

PRIVAST CAPITAL PARTNERS

Leopolstraat 39
Mechelen, Belgium B - 2800
Phone: 32-15-28-78-80
Fax: 32-15-28-78-89
E-mail: privast@privast.com
Website: www.privast.com

Other Offices

Keltenlaan 20
avenue des Celtes
Brussels, Belgium B - 1040
Phone: 32-2-740-28-60
Fax: 32-2-740-28-69

Management and Staff

Guido Stubbe, Founding Partner
Robert Van den Broeck, Founding Partner
Willem Prinselaar, Founding Partner

Type of Firm

Private Equity Firm

Association Membership

European Private Equity and Venture Capital Assoc.

Project Preferences

Type of Financing Preferred:

Early Stage
Expansion
Startup

Geographical Preferences

International Preferences:

United Kingdom
Europe
Belgium
Germany
France

Industry Preferences

In Communications prefer:

Telecommunications

In Computer Software prefer:

Software

In Internet Specific prefer:

Internet

In Biotechnology prefer:

Biotechnology

In Business Serv. prefer:

Media

Additional Information

Year Founded: 2001
Capital Under Management: $13,000,000
Current Activity Level : Actively seeking new investments

PRIVATE ADVISORS LLC

1800 Bayberry Court
Suite 300
Richmond, VA USA 23226
Phone: 804-289-6000
Fax: 804-289-6001
Website: www.privateadvisors.com

Other Offices

4/5 Grosvenor Place
Ground Floor A (Front South)
London, United Kingdom SW1X 7HJ
Phone: 44-779-556-0525

Management and Staff

Amy Gray, Chief Financial Officer
Charles Johnson, Partner
E. Macon Clarkson, Vice President
James Shannon, Chief Operating Officer
Jennifer Buckley, Managing Director
Jens Bisgaard-Frantzen, Partner
Laura Baird, Vice President

Louis Moelchert, Partner
Matthew Baker, Managing Director
Rafael Astruc, Founding Partner
Rickard Fischerstrom, Managing Director
Robert Voeks, Partner
Scott Crenshaw, Vice President
Timothy Berry, Partner
Todd Milligan, Vice President

Type of Firm
Private Equity Advisor or Fund of Funds

Project Preferences
Type of Financing Preferred:
Fund of Funds
Distressed Debt

Geographical Preferences
International Preferences:
Europe

Additional Information
Year Founded: 1997
Capital Under Management: $1,000,000,000
Current Activity Level : Actively seeking new investments

PRIVATE EQUITY INVESTORS, INC.
505 Park Avenue
Fourth Floor
New York, NY USA 10022
Phone: 212-750-1228
Fax: 212-750-2685
E-mail: info@peifunds.com
Website: www.peifunds.com

Management and Staff
Charles Stetson, Managing Director
David Parshall, Managing Director
Gunnar Fremuth, Vice President
Lucien Ruby, Managing Director

Type of Firm
Private Equity Advisor or Fund of Funds

Association Membership
National Venture Capital Association - USA (NVCA)

Project Preferences
Role in Financing:
Prefer role as deal originator but will also invest in deals created by others

Type of Financing Preferred:
Fund of Funds
Fund of Funds of Second

Industry Focus
(% based on actual investment)

Biotechnology	84.4%
Computer Software and Services	15.6%

Additional Information
Name of Most Recent Fund: Private Equity Investment Fund IV, L.P.
Most Recent Fund Was Raised: 03/21/2005
Year Founded: 1992
Capital Under Management: $110,000,000
Current Activity Level : Actively seeking new investments
Method of Compensation: Return on investment is of primary concern, do not charge fees

PRIVATE EQUITY JAPAN CO., LTD.
Dutch Hills Forest Tower
Minato-ku, Toranomon 5
Tokyo, Japan
Phone: 813-5733-2611
Fax: 813-5733-2612
Website: www.pej.co.jp

Management and Staff
Shinji Kimura, Managing Director

Type of Firm
Private Equity Firm

Project Preferences
Type of Financing Preferred:
Balanced

Geographical Preferences
International Preferences:
Japan

Additional Information
Year Founded: 2005
Current Activity Level : Actively seeking new investments

PRIVATE EQUITY MANAGEMENT CORPORATION
70 University Avenue
Suite 1400
Toronto, Canada
Phone: 416-977-3131
Fax: 514-977-3122

Type of Firm
Private Equity Firm

Additional Information
Year Founded: 2009
Current Activity Level : Actively seeking new investments

PRIVATE EQUITY PARTNERS
301 Commerce Street
Suite 1300
Fort Worth, TX USA 76102
Phone: 817-332-1600
Fax: 817-336-7523
Website: www.pepartners.net

Management and Staff
Jeff Alexander, Principal
Scott Kleberg, Principal

Type of Firm
Private Equity Firm

Project Preferences
Role in Financing:
Will function either as deal originator or investor in deals created by others

Type of Financing Preferred:
Leveraged Buyout
Later Stage
Management Buyouts
Acquisition
Recapitalizations

Size of Investments Considered:
Min Size of Investment Considered (000s): $1,000
Max Size of Investment Considered (000s): $10,000

Industry Focus
(% based on actual investment)

Consumer Related	37.4%
Other Products	26.9%
Communications and Media	15.2%
Internet Specific	11.2%
Computer Software and Services	7.9%
Industrial/Energy	1.5%

Additional Information
Name of Most Recent Fund: Private Equity Partners I, L.P.
Most Recent Fund Was Raised: 07/01/1997
Year Founded: 1996
Capital Under Management: $65,000,000
Current Activity Level : Actively seeking new investments
Method of Compensation: Return on investment is of primary concern, do not charge fees

PRIVATE EQUITY PARTNERS SPA (FKA: CHASE GEMINA ITALIA)
Via degli Omenoni, 2
Milan, Italy 20121
Phone: 39-2-805-2171
Fax: 39-2-805-2321
E-mail: info@privateequitypartners.com
Website: www.privateequitypartners.com

Other Offices

Wielicka Street 36
Suite 9
Warsaw, Poland 02-657
Phone: 48-22-853-1085

ul. S. Makeeva, 7a
Moscow, Russia 123100
Phone: 7-495-725-3203

Fairlink Centre, C.T.S. No. 701
Village Oshiwara, Off New Link Road
Mumbai, India 400 053
Phone: 91-022-2673-3369
Fax: 91-022-2673-3368

2809 China insurance Building
166 Lu Jia Zui East Road
Shanghai, China 200120
Phone: 86-21-5879-5600
Fax: 86-21-5879-5699

Management and Staff

Fabio Lorenzo Sattin, Founding Partner
Giovanni Campolo, Managing Director
Leonardo Bruzzichesi, Partner

Type of Firm

Bank Affiliated

Association Membership

Italian Venture Capital Association (AIFI)
European Private Equity and Venture Capital Assoc.

Project Preferences

Role in Financing:

Prefer role as deal originator but will also invest in deals created by others

Type of Financing Preferred:

Leveraged Buyout
Expansion
Management Buyouts
Acquisition

Size of Investments Considered:

Min Size of Investment Considered (000s): $900
Max Size of Investment Considered: No Limit

Geographical Preferences

International Preferences:

Italy
India
China
Russia

Industry Focus

(% based on actual investment)

Industrial/Energy	48.5%
Other Products	25.5%
Computer Software and Services	22.9%
Consumer Related	2.7%
Internet Specific	0.4%

Additional Information

Year Founded: 1989
Capital Under Management: $397,600,000
Current Activity Level : Actively seeking new investments

PRIVEE INVESTMENT HOLDINGS CO., LTD.

Kasumigaseki Building, 36F
3-2-5, Kasumigaseki
Tokyo, Japan 100-6036
Website: www.prvz.com

Management and Staff

Kazuhide Fujii, Chief Financial Officer
Kenzo Matsumura, Chief Executive Officer
Seiji Himuro, Chairman & CEO

Type of Firm

Private Equity Firm

Project Preferences

Type of Financing Preferred:

Turnaround

Geographical Preferences

International Preferences:

Japan

Additional Information

Year Founded: 2005
Current Activity Level : Actively seeking new investments

PRIVEQ CAPITAL FUNDS

1500 Don Mills Road
Suite 711
Toronto, Canada M3B 3K4
Phone: 416-447-3330
Fax: 416-447-3331
Website: www.priveq.ca

Management and Staff

Brad Ashley, Managing Partner
Kevin B. Melnyk, Partner

Type of Firm

Private Equity Firm

Association Membership

Canadian Venture Capital Association

Project Preferences

Role in Financing:

Prefer role as deal originator but will also invest in deals created by others

Type of Financing Preferred:

Leveraged Buyout
Expansion
Later Stage
Management Buyouts
Acquisition

Size of Investments Considered:

Min Size of Investment Considered (000s): $1,661
Max Size of Investment Considered (000s): $8,307

Geographical Preferences

United States Preferences:

Midwest
Northeast
Southwest

Canadian Preferences:

All Canada
Ontario

Industry Preferences

In Semiconductor/Electr prefer:

Electronic Components
Controllers and Sensors
Sensors
Component Testing Equipmt

In Consumer Related prefer:

Consumer

In Industrial/Energy prefer:

Industrial Products
Factory Automation
Robotics
Machinery

In Business Serv. prefer:

Services

In Manufact. prefer:

Manufacturing

Additional Information

Year Founded: 1994
Capital Under Management: $37,000,000
Current Activity Level : Actively seeking new investments
Method of Compensation: Return on investment is of primary concern, do not charge fees

---

PRIVEQ PARTNERS (AKA: SKANDIA INVESTMENTS)

Riddargatan 17
P.O. Box 5295
Stockholm, Sweden SE-102 46
Phone: 46-8-459-6774
Fax: 46-8-203-566
E-mail: info@priveq.se
Website: www.priveq.se

Management and Staff

Helena Ekstrand, Chief Financial Officer
Magnus Hardmeier, Chief Executive Officer

Type of Firm

Private Equity Firm

Association Membership

Swedish Venture Capital Association (SVCA)
European Private Equity and Venture Capital Assoc.

Project Preferences

Type of Financing Preferred:

Leveraged Buyout
Expansion

Size of Investments Considered:

Min Size of Investment Considered (000s): $2,900
Max Size of Investment Considered (000s): $17,399

Geographical Preferences

International Preferences:

Sweden
Europe

Additional Information

Name of Most Recent Fund: Priveq Investment Fund III
Most Recent Fund Was Raised: 04/29/2005
Year Founded: 1983
Capital Under Management: $191,000,000
Current Activity Level : Actively seeking new investments

PROBITAS PARTNERS, INC.

425 California Street
Suite 2300
San Francisco, CA USA 94104
Phone: 415-402-0700
Fax: 415-402-0052
E-mail: info@probitaspartners.com
Website: www.probitaspartners.com

Other Offices

3 Garden Road
21/F ICBC Tower Citibank Plaza
Central, Hong Kong
Phone: 852-2273-5143
Fax: 852-2273-5999

1251 Avenue of the Americas, 44th Floor
Suite 2390
New York, NY USA 10020
Phone: 212-403-3662
Fax: 212-403-3537

36-38 Southampton Street
1st Floor Dudley House
London, United Kingdom WC2E 7HF
Phone: 44-20-7845-5400
Fax: 44-20-7240-3339

Management and Staff

Adam Frieman, Partner
Alan Bear, Principal
Charles Phillips, Vice President
Christopher Mayo, Vice President
Craig Marmer, Partner
Dale Meyer, Partner
David Dinerman, Chief Financial Officer
Greg Hausler, Partner
Jack Wills, Principal
James Coleman, Managing Director
Jeffrey Mills, Principal
Jonathan Jameson, Principal
Kelly DePonte, Partner
Michael Hoffmann, President, Founder
Nam Hoang, Vice President
Reidan Cruz, Partner
Robert Hofeditz, Partner
Stacy Kincaid, Vice President
Stephen Salyer, Vice President
Sumit Jussal, Vice President

Type of Firm

Service Provider

Additional Information

Year Founded: 2001
Current Activity Level : Actively seeking new investments

PROCOM VENTURE AS

P.O. Box 360
Forusbeen 78
Stavanger, Norway 4067
Phone: 47-51-57-9000
Fax: 47-51-57-9005
Website: www.procomventure.no

Management and Staff

Jorn Bergeland, Managing Director

Type of Firm

Private Equity Firm

Additional Information

Current Activity Level : Actively seeking new investments

PROCTER & GAMBLE COMPANY, THE

P.O. Box 599
Cincinnati, OH USA 45201
Phone: 513-945-9990
Fax: 513-983-2744
Website: www.pg.com

Management and Staff

A Lafley, Chief Executive Officer

Type of Firm

Corporate PE/Venture

Association Membership

National Venture Capital Association - USA (NVCA)

Additional Information

Year Founded: 1837
Current Activity Level : Actively seeking new investments

PROCURITAS PARTNERS KB

Skeppsbron 20
Stockholm, Sweden SE-111 30
Phone: 46-8-5061-4300
Fax: 46-8-5061-4344
E-mail: procuritas@procuritas.se
Website: www.procuritas.com

Other Offices

Amaliegade 8
Copenhagen, Denmark DK-1256
Phone: 45-3391-8700
Fax: 45-3391-8786

Management and Staff

Erik Fougner, Partner
John Dare, Partner
Mattias Olson, Partner
Mikael Ahlstrom, Founding Partner
Peter Toyberg, Chief Financial Officer
Philippe Haspeslagh, Partner
Tomas Johansson, Partner

Type of Firm

Private Equity Firm

Association Membership

European Private Equity and Venture Capital Assoc.

Project Preferences

Role in Financing:

Prefer role as deal originator

Type of Financing Preferred:

Leveraged Buyout
Expansion
Management Buyouts

Size of Investments Considered:

Min Size of Investment Considered (000s): $5,000
Max Size of Investment Considered (000s): $250,000

Geographical Preferences

International Preferences:

Sweden
Scandanavia/Nordic Region
Finland
Denmark

Additional Information

Year Founded: 1986
Capital Under Management: $100,000,000
Current Activity Level : Actively seeking new investments
Method of Compensation: Return on invest. most important, but chg. closing fees, service fees, etc.

PROFITA MANAGEMENT OY (FKA: NORDEA CAPITAL; MERITA CAPITAL)

Korkeavuorenkatu 47 B 3.kerros
Helsinki, Finland 00130
Phone: 358-207-798-620
Fax: 358-9-625-878
E-mail: profita@profitagroup.fi
Website: www.profitagroup.fi

Management and Staff

Jouko Helomaa, Managing Director

Type of Firm

Bank Affiliated

Association Membership

Finnish Venture Capital Association (FVCA)
European Private Equity and Venture Capital Assoc.

Project Preferences

Type of Financing Preferred:
Leveraged Buyout
Expansion
Mezzanine
Management Buyouts

Geographical Preferences

International Preferences:
Scandanavia/Nordic Region
Finland

Industry Focus

(% based on actual investment)

Industrial/Energy	70.3%
Computer Software and Services	14.5%
Communications and Media	6.9%
Semiconductors/Other Elect.	2.7%
Biotechnology	2.6%
Computer Hardware	1.8%
Other Products	1.2%

Additional Information

Year Founded: 1994
Capital Under Management: $53,600,000
Current Activity Level : Actively seeking new investments

PROGRESS EQUITY PARTNERS, LTD.

2200 Ross Avenue
Suite 3838
Dallas, TX USA 75201
Phone: 214-978-3838
Fax: 214-978-3848
E-mail: contact_us@progressequity.com
Website: www.progressequity.com

Other Offices

7887 East Belleview Avenue
Suite 1100
Englewood, CO USA 80111
Phone: 303-297-1701
Fax: 303-557-0677

Management and Staff

Melanie Barton, Vice President
Michael Bailey, Founding Partner
Paul Yeoham, Founding Partner
Ralph Manning, Founding Partner
Stephen Sangalis, Founding Partner

Type of Firm

Private Equity Firm

Project Preferences

Role in Financing:
Prefer role as deal originator

Type of Financing Preferred:
Management Buyouts
Recapitalizations

Industry Preferences

In Communications prefer:
Communications and Media

In Medical/Health prefer:
Health Services
Pharmaceuticals

In Consumer Related prefer:
Franchises(NEC)
Food/Beverage

Additional Information

Year Founded: 2006
Current Activity Level : Actively seeking new investments

PROGRESS INVESTMENT MANAGEMENT COMPANY

71 Stevenson Street
Suite 1620
San Francisco, CA USA 94105-2962
Phone: 415-512-3480
Fax: 415-512-3475
E-mail: marketing@progressinvestment.com
Website: www.progressinvestment.com

Management and Staff

Samuel Molinaro, President

Type of Firm

Private Equity Firm

Project Preferences

Type of Financing Preferred:
Fund of Funds

Additional Information

Name of Most Recent Fund: Discovery Fund II, L.P.
Most Recent Fund Was Raised: 06/30/2002
Year Founded: 1990
Capital Under Management: $65,000,000
Current Activity Level : Actively seeking new investments

PROGRESSIO SGR

Via Grazioli 25
Trento, Italy 20123
Phone: 39-2-7214-1242
Fax: 39-2-7214-1299
E-mail: segreteria@progressiosgr.it
Website: www.progressiosgr.it

Management and Staff

Mario Marangoni, President

Type of Firm

Private Equity Firm

Project Preferences

Type of Financing Preferred:
Balanced

Geographical Preferences

International Preferences:
Italy
Europe

Additional Information

Year Founded: 2004
Current Activity Level : Actively seeking new investments

PROGRESSIVE INVESTMENT TRUST

29 President Steyn Avenue
Westdein
Bloemfontein, South Africa 9310
Phone: 27-51-400-7000
Fax: 27-51-448-9693

Type of Firm

Private Equity Firm

Association Membership

South African Venture Capital Association (SAVCA)

Project Preferences

Type of Financing Preferred:
Balanced

Geographical Preferences

International Preferences:
South Africa

Additional Information

Year Founded: 2004
Current Activity Level : Actively seeking new investments

PROKOM INVESTMENTS SA

Aleje Jerozolimskie 65/79
Warsaw, Poland 02-511
Phone: 48-22-630-3990
Fax: 48-22-630-3994

Type of Firm

Private Equity Firm

Geographical Preferences

International Preferences:
All International

Industry Preferences

In Biotechnology prefer:
Biotechnology

In Industrial/Energy prefer:
Oil & Gas Drilling,Explor

In Financial Services prefer:
Real Estate

Additional Information

Year Founded: 1997
Current Activity Level : Actively seeking new investments

PROLOG VENTURES LLC

7733 Forsyth Boulevard
Suite 1440
Saint Louis, MO USA 63105
Phone: 314-743-2400
Fax: 314-743-2403
E-mail: info@prologventures.com
Website: www.prologventures.com

Management and Staff

Brian Clevinger, Managing Director
Daniel Broderick, Partner
Gregory Johnson, Managing Director
Ilya Nykin, Managing Director
Michelle Murray, Chief Financial Officer

Type of Firm

Private Equity Firm

Association Membership

National Venture Capital Association - USA (NVCA)

Project Preferences

Role in Financing:
Will function either as deal originator or investor in deals created by others

Type of Financing Preferred:
Second Stage Financing
Early Stage
Expansion
Seed
First Stage Financing
Startup

Size of Investments Considered:
Min Size of Investment Considered (000s): $250
Max Size of Investment Considered (000s): $3,000

Geographical Preferences

United States Preferences:
All U.S.

Industry Preferences

In Biotechnology prefer:
Biotechnology
Biotech Related Research

In Medical/Health prefer:
Medical/Health
Medical Diagnostics
Medical Therapeutics
Drug/Equipmt Delivery
Medical Products
Pharmaceuticals

In Consumer Related prefer:
Food/Beverage

In Agr/Forestr/Fish prefer:
Agriculture related

Additional Information

Name of Most Recent Fund: Prolog Fund II
Most Recent Fund Was Raised: 06/28/2004
Year Founded: 2001
Capital Under Management: $100,000,000
Current Activity Level : Actively seeking new investments

PROLOGIS

4F Shiodome City Center, 1-5-2
Higashi-Shimbashi, Minato-ku
Tokyo, Japan 105-7104
Phone: 81-3-6215-9099
Fax: 81-3-6215-8490
Website: www.prologis.co.jp

Other Offices

4F Hakata-ekimae Business Center
3-25-21 Hakata-ekimae, Hakata-ku
Fukuoka, Japan 812-0011
Phone: 81-092-432-7105
Fax: 81-092-432-7104

11F Nakanoshima Mitsui Bldg.
3-3-3 Nakanoshima, Kita-ku
Osaka, Japan 530-0005
Phone: 81-06-6447-2525
Fax: 81-06-6447-2455

Type of Firm

Corporate PE/Venture

Project Preferences

Type of Financing Preferred:
Balanced

Geographical Preferences

International Preferences:
Japan

Industry Preferences

In Financial Services prefer:
Real Estate

Additional Information

Year Founded: 1999
Capital Under Management: $600,000,000
Current Activity Level : Actively seeking new investments

PROMETHEAN INVESTMENTS

23A Conduit Street
London, United Kingdom W1S 2XS
Phone: 44-20-7016-5110
Fax: 44-20-7493-1706
Website: www.prometheaninvestments.com

Management and Staff

Gaurav Burman, Principal
Michael Burt, Principal
Mike Biddulph, Principal
Sebastian McKinlay, Principal

Type of Firm

Private Equity Firm

Project Preferences

Type of Financing Preferred:
Balanced
Special Situation

Geographical Preferences

International Preferences:
India
United Kingdom

Industry Preferences

In Medical/Health prefer:
Medical/Health

In Consumer Related prefer:
Retail
Consumer Products

In Industrial/Energy prefer:
Industrial Products

In Financial Services prefer:
Financial Services

In Business Serv. prefer:
Media

Additional Information

Year Founded: 2005
Current Activity Level : Actively seeking new investments

PROMETHEUS V, LLC

Two Concourse Parkway
Suite 155
Atlanta, GA USA 30328
Phone: 770-395-9091
Fax: 770-395-9668
E-mail: info@prometheuspartners.com
Website: www.prometheuspartners.com

Management and Staff

Wayne Stabile, Managing Director

Type of Firm

Private Equity Firm

Project Preferences

Role in Financing:
Prefer role as deal originator

Type of Financing Preferred:
Leveraged Buyout
Management Buyouts
Acquisition
Recapitalizations

Size of Investments Considered:
Min Size of Investment Considered (000s): $5,000
Max Size of Investment Considered (000s): $10,000

Geographical Preferences

United States Preferences:
All U.S.

Additional Information

Name of Most Recent Fund: Windward V
Most Recent Fund Was Raised: 08/31/2005
Year Founded: 1996
Capital Under Management: $100,000,000
Current Activity Level : Actively seeking new investments

PROMON VENTURES

Ave. Pres. J. Kubitschek, 1830
Sao Paulo, Brazil 04543-900
Phone: 55-11-5213-4410
Website: www.promon.com.br

Other Offices

Rod. SP - 340 (Campinas-Mogi), km 118,5
Building 9A
Campinas, Brazil 13086-902
Phone: 55-19-3707-3400

Av. Abiurana, 449 - Block 1
Manaus, Brazil 69075-010
Phone: 55-92-3616-9201

Praia do Flamengo, 154
Rio de Janeiro, Brazil 22210-906
Phone: 55-21-3235-1200

Type of Firm

Private Equity Firm

Association Membership

Brazilian Venture Capital Association (ABCR)

Project Preferences

Type of Financing Preferred:
Balanced

Geographical Preferences

International Preferences:
Brazil

Additional Information

Year Founded: 2000
Current Activity Level : Actively seeking new investments

PROMSVYAZCAPITAL GROUP

7, Building 4 Derbenevskaya
Moscow, Russia
Phone: 7-49-5649-7010
Fax: 7-49-5649-7013

Type of Firm

Private Equity Firm

Project Preferences

Type of Financing Preferred:
Leveraged Buyout

Geographical Preferences

International Preferences:
Russia

Additional Information

Year Founded: 2008
Current Activity Level : Actively seeking new investments

PROPARCO

5 rue Roland Barthes
Paris, Cedex 12, France 755958
Phone: 33-1-5344-3737
Fax: 33-1-5344-3838
Website: www.proparco.fr

Management and Staff

Claude Periou, Chief Executive Officer

Type of Firm

Private Equity Firm

Association Membership

African Venture Capital Association (AVCA)

Project Preferences

Type of Financing Preferred:
Early Stage
Expansion
Balanced
Management Buyouts

Size of Investments Considered:
Min Size of Investment Considered (000s): $1,184
Max Size of Investment Considered (000s): $11,840

Geographical Preferences

International Preferences:
Africa

Industry Preferences

In Communications prefer:
Communications and Media

In Industrial/Energy prefer:
Industrial Products

In Financial Services prefer:
Financial Services

In Manufact. prefer:
Manufacturing

In Agr/Forestr/Fish prefer:
Agribusiness

Additional Information

Year Founded: 1977
Capital Under Management: $118,400,000
Current Activity Level : Actively seeking new investments

PROPEL INVESTMENTS (FKA: DB CAPITAL PARTNERS AUSTRALIA)

Level 12
201 Kent Street
Sydney, Australia 2000
Phone: 612-8272-5200
Fax: 612-8272-5222
E-mail: info@propelinvestments.com.au
Website: www.propelinvestments.com.au

Management and Staff

Albin Kurti, Managing Director
Fraser Henderson, Managing Director
Jo Anne Maher, Chief Financial Officer
Peter Dowding, Managing Director
Sam Winter, Vice President
Victoria Rohrsheim, Vice President

Type of Firm

Private Equity Firm

Association Membership

Australian Venture Capital Association (AVCAL)

Project Preferences

Role in Financing:
Will function either as deal originator or investor in deals created by others

Type of Financing Preferred:
Leveraged Buyout
Expansion
Balanced
Later Stage
Management Buyouts
Acquisition
Industry Rollups

Size of Investments Considered:
Min Size of Investment Considered (000s): $9,582
Max Size of Investment Considered (000s): $114,984

Geographical Preferences

International Preferences:
Australia
New Zealand

Industry Focus

(% based on actual investment)

Other Products	58.0%
Consumer Related	27.1%
Medical/Health	5.4%
Computer Software and Services	3.1%
Internet Specific	2.8%
Communications and Media	2.1%
Industrial/Energy	1.6%

Additional Information

Year Founded: 1994
Capital Under Management: $423,000,000
Current Activity Level : Actively seeking new investments
Method of Compensation: Return on invest. most important, but chg. closing fees, service fees, etc.

PROPHET EQUITY LLC

181 Grand Avenue
Suite 201
Southlake, TX USA 76092
Phone: 817-898-1500
Fax: 817-898-1509
E-mail: investors@prophetequity.com
Website: www.prophetequity.com

Type of Firm

Private Equity Firm

Project Preferences

Type of Financing Preferred:
Leveraged Buyout
Turnaround
Management Buyouts
Acquisition
Special Situation

Size of Investments Considered:
Min Size of Investment Considered (000s): $5,000
Max Size of Investment Considered (000s): $50,000

Geographical Preferences

United States Preferences:
All U.S.

Industry Preferences

In Medical/Health prefer:
Medical/Health

In Consumer Related prefer:
Consumer Products
Consumer Services

In Industrial/Energy prefer:
Energy
Environmental Related

In Transportation prefer:
Transportation
Aerospace

In Financial Services prefer:
Financial Services

In Business Serv. prefer:
Services
Distribution

In Manufact. prefer:
Manufacturing

Additional Information

Year Founded: 2007
Capital Under Management: $215,000,000
Current Activity Level : Actively seeking new investments

PROPHETES INC.

Trzaska 132
Ljubljana, Slovenia 1000
Phone: 386-1-244-2820
Fax: 386-1-423-1815
E-mail: info@prophetes.com
Website: www.prophetes.com

Type of Firm

Private Equity Firm

Project Preferences

Type of Financing Preferred:
Early Stage

Geographical Preferences

International Preferences:
Slovenia
Europe

Industry Preferences

In Medical/Health prefer:
Medical Products

In Consumer Related prefer:
Consumer Products

Additional Information

Year Founded: 1999
Current Activity Level : Actively seeking new investments

PROPULSION VENTURES, INC. (FKA: TELSOFT VENTURES)

1250 Rene-Levesque Boulevard W
38th Floor
Montreal, Canada H3B4W
Phone: 514-397-8450
Fax: 514-397-8451
E-mail: info@propulsionventures.com
Website: www.propulsionventures.com

Management and Staff

Benoit Hogue, Co-Founder
Charles Sirois, President, CEO, Chairman
David Bernardi, Venture Partner
Francois Gaouette, Co-Founder
Robert Talbot, Co-Founder
Thomas Birch, Managing Partner

Type of Firm

Private Equity Firm

Project Preferences

Type of Financing Preferred:
Early Stage
Expansion
Startup

Size of Investments Considered:
Min Size of Investment Considered (000s): $1,000
Max Size of Investment Considered (000s): $3,000

Geographical Preferences

United States Preferences:
All U.S.

Canadian Preferences:
All Canada
Quebec
Ontario

Industry Preferences

In Computer Software prefer:
Software

In Internet Specific prefer:
Internet

Additional Information

Name of Most Recent Fund: Propulsion Ventures III, L.P.
Most Recent Fund Was Raised: 12/31/2005
Year Founded: 1995
Capital Under Management: $200,000,000
Current Activity Level : Actively seeking new investments

PROQUEST INVESTMENTS

90 Nassau Street
Fifth Floor
Princeton, NJ USA 08542
Phone: 609-919-3560
Fax: 609-919-3570
Website: www.proquestvc.com

Other Offices

12626 High Bluff Drive
Suite 325
San Diego, CA USA 92130
Phone: 858-847-0315
Fax: 858-847-0316

380 Rue St-Antoine Ouest
Bureau 2020
Montreal, Canada H2Y 3X7
Phone: 514-842-1625
Fax: 514-842-1379

Management and Staff

Alain Schreiber, Partner
Jee Shin, Principal
Joyce Tsang, Partner
Karen Hong, Principal
Pasquale DeAngelis, Chief Financial Officer
Steven Ratoff, Venture Partner
Wendy Johnson, Venture Partner

Type of Firm

Private Equity Firm

Association Membership

National Venture Capital Association - USA (NVCA)

Project Preferences

Role in Financing:
Will function either as deal originator or investor in deals created by others

Type of Financing Preferred:
Second Stage Financing
Early Stage
Expansion
Mezzanine
Research and Development
Balanced
Start-up Financing
Later Stage
Seed
First Stage Financing
Private Placement

Size of Investments Considered:
Min Size of Investment Considered (000s): $250
Max Size of Investment Considered (000s): $250,000

Geographical Preferences

United States Preferences:
All U.S.

Canadian Preferences:
All Canada

International Preferences:
United Kingdom

Industry Focus

(% based on actual investment)

Medical/Health	50.5%
Biotechnology	47.2%
Internet Specific	2.3%

Additional Information

Name of Most Recent Fund: ProQuest Investments IV, L.P.
Most Recent Fund Was Raised: 12/08/2006
Year Founded: 1998
Capital Under Management: $885,000,000
Current Activity Level : Actively seeking new investments
Method of Compensation: Return on invest. most important, but chg. closing fees, service fees, etc.

PROREGIO MITTELSTANDSFINANZIERUNGS AG

Robert-Stoltz Strasse 7
Linz, Austria A-4020
Phone: 43-732-609-6910
Fax: 43-732-60969120
E-mail: office@proregio.at
Website: www.proregio.at

Type of Firm

Private Equity Firm

Association Membership

European Private Equity and Venture Capital Assoc.

Project Preferences

Type of Financing Preferred:
Balanced

Geographical Preferences

International Preferences:
Europe

Additional Information

Year Founded: 2003
Capital Under Management: $10,600,000
Current Activity Level : Actively seeking new investments

PROSEED VENTURE CAPITAL FUND

85 Yehuda Halevi St.
Tel Aviv, Israel 65796
Phone: 972-3-566-1284
Fax: 972-3-566-1285
E-mail: mail@proseed.co.il
Website: www.proseed.co.il

Management and Staff

Efrat Boker-Ferri, Vice President
Eyal Pahima, Chief Executive Officer

Type of Firm

Private Equity Firm

Project Preferences

Type of Financing Preferred:
Early Stage
Seed

Geographical Preferences

International Preferences:
Israel

Industry Preferences

In Communications prefer:
Communications and Media

In Computer Software prefer:
Software

In Internet Specific prefer:
Internet

In Medical/Health prefer:
Medical Products

Additional Information

Year Founded: 2000
Capital Under Management: $10,000,000
Current Activity Level : Actively seeking new investments

PROSPECT PARTNERS LLC

200 West Madison Street
Suite 2710
Chicago, IL USA 60606
Phone: 312-782-7400
Fax: 312-782-7410
Website: www.prospect-partners.com

Management and Staff

David Choe, Vice President
Douglas Smith, Vice President
Erik Maurer, Principal
Louis Kenter, Principal
Maneesh Chawla, Principal
Richard Tuttle, Principal
Suken Shah, Vice President
William Glastris, Principal

Type of Firm

Private Equity Firm

Association Membership

Illinois Venture Capital Association

Project Preferences

Role in Financing:
Prefer role as deal originator

Type of Financing Preferred:
Leveraged Buyout
Management Buyouts
Industry Rollups
Special Situation

Size of Investments Considered:
Min Size of Investment Considered (000s): $1,000
Max Size of Investment Considered (000s): $15,000

Geographical Preferences

United States Preferences:
All U.S.

Canadian Preferences:
All Canada

Industry Focus

(% based on actual investment)

Other Products	48.1%
Consumer Related	37.1%
Computer Hardware	14.8%

Additional Information

Name of Most Recent Fund: Prospect Partners II, L.P.
Most Recent Fund Was Raised: 06/01/2004
Year Founded: 1998
Capital Under Management: $105,000,000
Current Activity Level : Actively seeking new investments
Method of Compensation: Return on invest. most important, but chg. closing fees, service fees, etc.

PROSPECT STREET VENTURES

10 East 40th Street
44th Floor
New York, NY USA 10016
Phone: 212-448-0702
Fax: 212-448-9652
E-mail: info@prospectstreet.com
Website: www.prospectstreet.com

Other Offices

Exchange Place
37th Floor
Boston, MA USA 02109
Phone: 617-742-3800
Fax: 617-742-9455

Management and Staff

Bart de Bie, Managing Director
Brian Oswald, Chief Financial Officer
Daria Becker, Managing Director
David Belzer, Managing Director
Gautam Shirhattikar, Vice President
Jason Wilson, Vice President
Jay Schiff, Managing Director
John Hopley, Managing Director
John Barry, Chairman & CEO
M.Grier Eliasek, President & COO
Mark Hull, Vice President
Simon Marom, Vice President
W.Montgomery Cook, Managing Director
William Vastardis, Chief Financial Officer

Type of Firm

Private Equity Firm

Association Membership

Natl Assoc of Small Bus. Inv. Co (NASBIC)

Project Preferences

Role in Financing:
Prefer role as deal originator but will also invest in deals created by others

Type of Financing Preferred:
Expansion
Mezzanine
Acquisition

Size of Investments Considered:
Min Size of Investment Considered (000s): $5,000
Max Size of Investment Considered (000s): $100,000

Geographical Preferences

Canadian Preferences:
All Canada

Industry Focus

(% based on actual investment)

Computer Software and Services	65.1%
Industrial/Energy	13.1%
Internet Specific	12.4%
Medical/Health	4.0%
Other Products	3.5%
Communications and Media	1.9%

Additional Information

Year Founded: 1988
Capital Under Management: $206,000,000
Current Activity Level : Actively seeking new investments
Method of Compensation: Return on invest. most important, but chg. closing fees, service fees, etc.

PROSPECT VENTURE PARTNERS (FKA: PROSPECT MANAGEMENT LLC)

435 Tasso Street
Suite 200
Palo Alto, CA USA 94301
Phone: 650-327-8800
Fax: 650-324-8838
E-mail: info@prospectventures.com
Website: www.prospectventures.com

Management and Staff

Alexander Barkas, Managing Director
Dave Markland, Chief Financial Officer
David Schnell, Managing Director
Dorothy Margolskee, Partner
Ilan Zipkin, Partner
James Tananbaum, Managing Director
Philip Needleman, Partner
Russell Hirsch, Managing Director
Scott Wolf, Partner

Type of Firm

Private Equity Firm

Association Membership

Western Association of Venture Capitalists (WAVC)
National Venture Capital Association - USA (NVCA)

Project Preferences

Role in Financing:
Prefer role as deal originator but will also invest in deals created by others

Type of Financing Preferred:
Second Stage Financing
Early Stage
Expansion
Later Stage
Seed
First Stage Financing
Special Situation

Size of Investments Considered:
Min Size of Investment Considered (000s): $1,000
Max Size of Investment Considered (000s): $50,000

Geographical Preferences

United States Preferences:
All U.S.

Industry Focus

(% based on actual investment)

Medical/Health	60.6%
Biotechnology	34.3%
Other Products	1.7%
Computer Software and Services	1.4%
Consumer Related	1.2%
Semiconductors/Other Elect.	0.7%

Additional Information

Name of Most Recent Fund: Prospect Venture Partners III, L.P.
Most Recent Fund Was Raised: 12/09/2004
Year Founded: 1997
Capital Under Management: $1,000,000,000
Current Activity Level : Actively seeking new investments
Method of Compensation: Return on invest. most important, but chg. closing fees, service fees, etc.

PROSPECTOR EQUITY CAPITAL, L.P.

136 Heber Avenue, Suite 304
P.O. Box 682500
Park City, UT USA 84060
Phone: 435-647-3835
Fax: 435-647-5614
E-mail: info@pecinvestors.com
Website: www.pecinvestors.com

Management and Staff
Alison Wistner, Vice President
David Eastman, General Partner
Larry Griffin, General Partner

Type of Firm
Private Equity Firm

Project Preferences

Role in Financing:
Will function either as deal originator or investor in deals created by others

Type of Financing Preferred:
Leveraged Buyout
Balanced
Later Stage
Management Buyouts
Recapitalizations

Size of Investments Considered:
Min Size of Investment Considered (000s): $500
Max Size of Investment Considered (000s): $4,000

Geographical Preferences

United States Preferences:
Rocky Mountain
West Coast
Southwest

Industry Preferences

In Communications prefer:
Communications and Media

In Computer Software prefer:
Software

In Internet Specific prefer:
Internet

In Medical/Health prefer:
Health Services

In Manufact. prefer:
Manufacturing

Additional Information
Year Founded: 2002
Capital Under Management: $27,000,000
Current Activity Level : Actively seeking new investments

PROSPER CAPITAL
Kungsgatan 12-14
Box 3356
Stockholm, Sweden 103 67
Phone: 46-8-454-0650
Fax: 46-8-454-0671
E-mail: info@prospercapital.com
Website: www.prospercapital.com

Type of Firm
Private Equity Firm

Association Membership
Swedish Venture Capital Association (SVCA)

Project Preferences

Type of Financing Preferred:
Early Stage

Geographical Preferences

International Preferences:
Sweden

Additional Information
Year Founded: 2002
Current Activity Level : Actively seeking new investments

PROSPERITAS CAPITAL PARTNERS
Rambla Armenia 3871
Montevideo, Uruguay 11-300
Phone: 598-2-628-4724
Fax: 598-2-628-4724
E-mail: info@prosperitascp.com
Website: www.prosperitascp.com

Management and Staff
Carlos Lecueder, Partner
Nicolas Herrera, Partner
Pablo Brenner, Partner
Rodolfo Oppenheimer, Partner
Ruben Ordoqui, Partner
Thomas Kossmann, Partner
Victor Zerbino, Partner

Type of Firm
Private Equity Firm

Project Preferences

Type of Financing Preferred:
Seed

Size of Investments Considered:
Min Size of Investment Considered (000s): $300
Max Size of Investment Considered (000s): $1,000

Geographical Preferences

International Preferences:
Uruguay

Industry Preferences

In Computer Software prefer:
Software

In Biotechnology prefer:
Biotechnology

In Business Serv. prefer:
Services

In Agr/Forestr/Fish prefer:
Agribusiness

Additional Information
Year Founded: 2005
Capital Under Management: $10,000,000
Current Activity Level : Actively seeking new investments

PROTOSTAR PARTNERS, LLC
13 West 54th Street
Fourth Floor
New York, NY USA 10019
Phone: 646-273-5200
Fax: 646-273-5210

Type of Firm
Private Equity Advisor or Fund of Funds

Project Preferences

Role in Financing:
Prefer role as deal originator but will also invest in deals created by others

Type of Financing Preferred:
Fund of Funds of Second

Size of Investments Considered:
Min Size of Investment Considered (000s): $50,000
Max Size of Investment Considered (000s): $250,000

Industry Preferences

In Consumer Related prefer:
Consumer
Retail
Food/Beverage

In Industrial/Energy prefer:
Industrial Products
Machinery

In Manufact. prefer:
Manufacturing

Additional Information
Year Founded: 2001
Capital Under Management: $300,000,000
Current Activity Level : Actively seeking new investments

PROVENANCE VENTURES
10864 Savona Road
Los Angeles, CA USA 90077
Phone: 310-562-2660
Fax: 310-472-9968
Website: www.provenanceventures.com

Management and Staff
Bryan Biniak, Managing Director

Type of Firm
Private Equity Firm

Project Preferences

Type of Financing Preferred:
Early Stage
Seed

Size of Investments Considered:
Min Size of Investment Considered (000s): $250
Max Size of Investment Considered (000s): $500

Geographical Preferences

United States Preferences:
All U.S.

Industry Preferences

In Communications prefer:
Communications and Media
Media and Entertainment

Additional Information

Name of Most Recent Fund: Provenance Ventures I
Most Recent Fund Was Raised: 08/14/2006
Year Founded: 2006
Capital Under Management: $10,000,000
Current Activity Level : Actively seeking new investments

PROVENTIS GMBH

Brienner Strasse 7
Munich, Germany 80333
Phone: 49-89-388-881-0
Fax: 49-89-388-88177
E-mail: info@proventis.com
Website: www.proventis.biz

Management and Staff

Elke Gerauer, Partner
Jan Porschmann, Partner
Lutz Deyerling, Partner
Markus Kaiser, Partner
Rainer Wieser, Partner
Walter Oberhorner, Partner

Type of Firm

Private Equity Firm

Project Preferences

Type of Financing Preferred:
Early Stage

Geographical Preferences

International Preferences:
Germany

Industry Preferences

In Communications prefer:
Communications and Media

In Computer Other prefer:
Computer Related

Additional Information

Year Founded: 2000
Capital Under Management: $9,000,000
Current Activity Level : Actively seeking new investments

PROVENTURE AS

P.O. Box 1290
Pirsenteret
Trondheim, Norway N-7462
Phone: 47-73-5450
E-mail: post@proventure.no
Website: www.proventure.no

Management and Staff

Hans Olav Torsen, Partner
Herbjorn Skjervold, Managing Partner
Thor Five, Partner

Type of Firm

Private Equity Firm

Association Membership

Norwegian Venture Capital Association

Project Preferences

Type of Financing Preferred:
Early Stage
Seed
Startup

Geographical Preferences

International Preferences:
Norway

Industry Preferences

In Industrial/Energy prefer:
Energy
Materials

In Transportation prefer:
Transportation

Additional Information

Year Founded: 2009
Current Activity Level : Actively seeking new investments

PROVENTUS AB

Birger Jarlsgatan 25
P.O. Box 1719
Stockholm, Sweden 111 87
Phone: 46-8-723-3100
Fax: 46-8-205-725
E-mail: info@proventus.se
Website: www.proventus.se

Management and Staff

Daniel Sachs, Chief Executive Officer

Type of Firm

Private Equity Firm

Project Preferences

Type of Financing Preferred:
Expansion

Geographical Preferences

International Preferences:
Sweden
Europe

Additional Information

Year Founded: 1980
Current Activity Level : Actively seeking new investments

PROVIDENCE EQUITY PARTNERS, INC. (FKA: PROVIDENCE VENTURES)

50 Kennedy Plaza
18th Floor
Providence, RI USA 02903
Phone: 401-751-1700
Fax: 401-751-1790
E-mail: contact@provequity.com
Website: www.provequity.com

Other Offices

390 Park Avenue
Fourth Floor
New York, NY USA 10022
Phone: 212-644-1200
Fax: 212-521-0845

10250 Constellation Boulevard
Suite 2062
Los Angeles, CA USA 90067
Phone: 310-449-3755
Fax: 310-449-3752

18th Floor, York House
15 Queen's Road
Central, Hong Kong
Phone: 852-3653-3800
Fax: 852-3653-3900

25 Barakhamba Road
6th Floor, Birla Tower
New Delhi, India 110 001
Phone: 91-11-3041-9000
Fax: 91-11-3041-9090

28 St.George Street
London, United Kingdom W1S 2FA
Phone: 44-207-514-8800
Fax: 44-207-629-2778

Management and Staff

Albert Dobron, Managing Director
Alexander Evans, Managing Director
Andrew Tisdale, Managing Director
Biswajit Subramanian, Managing Director
Bruno Mourgue d Algue, Vice President
Chris Ragona, Principal

Christopher Gunther, Principal
Craig Stern, Vice President
Gary Weinstein, Chief Operating Officer
Gaurav Sharma, Vice President
Glenn Creamer, Senior Managing Director
Gustavo Schwed, Managing Director
J. David Phillips, Vice President
Jesse Du Bey, Vice President
John Hahn, Managing Director
Jonathan Nelson, Chief Executive Officer
Julie Richardson, Managing Director
Julie Fisher, Managing Director
Lindsey Mead, Vice President
Manish Kheterpal, Vice President
Maria Ganong, Vice President
Mark Noble, Principal
Mark Masiello, Managing Director
Matthew Nelson, Vice President
Michael Gray, Vice President
Michael Dominguez, Managing Director
Michelle Guthrie, Managing Director
Nadim Nsouli, Managing Director
Osvaldo Pereira, Vice President
Paul Salem, Senior Managing Director
Peter Wilde, Managing Director
R. Davis Noell, Vice President
Raymond Mathieu, Chief Financial Officer
Richard Essex, Principal
Ronald Collins, Principal
Sean Tong, Managing Director
Spencer Neumann, Principal
Thura Ko, Vice President
Xunyoung Wang, Vice President

Type of Firm

Private Equity Firm

Association Membership

Private Equity Council (PEC)

Project Preferences

Role in Financing:

Prefer role as deal originator

Type of Financing Preferred:

Leveraged Buyout
Mezzanine
Management Buyouts
Acquisition
Industry Rollups
Recapitalizations
Distressed Debt

Size of Investments Considered:

Min Size of Investment Considered (000s): $250,000
Max Size of Investment Considered: No Limit

Geographical Preferences

United States Preferences:

All U.S.

Canadian Preferences:

All Canada

International Preferences:

Italy
United Kingdom
Luxembourg
Netherlands
Portugal
Turkey
Western Europe
Eastern Europe
Spain
Belgium
Germany
Asia
France
All International

Industry Focus

(% based on actual investment)

Communications and Media	59.3%
Consumer Related	10.2%
Computer Hardware	8.4%
Internet Specific	7.9%
Other Products	7.1%
Computer Software and Services	4.2%
Semiconductors/Other Elect.	3.0%

Additional Information

Name of Most Recent Fund: Providence Equity Partners VI, L.P.
Most Recent Fund Was Raised: 12/04/2006
Year Founded: 1989
Capital Under Management: $21,000,000,000
Current Activity Level : Actively seeking new investments

PROVIDENTIAL CAPITAL

17011 Beach Boulevard
Suite 1230
Huntington Beach, CA USA 92647
Phone: 714-843-5450
Fax: 714-843-5452
Website: www.phiglobal.com

Management and Staff

Benjamin Tran, Managing Director
Tan Phuong, Chief Operating Officer

Type of Firm

Bank Affiliated

Project Preferences

Type of Financing Preferred:

Expansion
Later Stage
Acquisition
Industry Rollups

Geographical Preferences

International Preferences:

Vietnam

Additional Information

Year Founded: 2000
Current Activity Level : Actively seeking new investments

PROVIDER VENTURE PARTNERS AB (FKA: IT PROVIDER ADVISOR 1 AB)

Master Samuelsgatan 42, 17tr
Stockholm, Sweden 111 57
Phone: 46-8-614-0000
Fax: 46-8-611-3959
E-mail: info@providerventure.com
Website: www.it-provider.com

Management and Staff

Anders Lindqvist, Partner
Asa Sundberg, Partner
Gosta Johannesson, Partner
Hakan Ramsin, Partner
Johan Hernmarck, Founding Partner
Jonas Nygren, Chief Executive Officer
Richard Hellekant, Partner
Tony Kylberg, Partner

Type of Firm

Private Equity Firm

Association Membership

Swedish Venture Capital Association (SVCA)
European Private Equity and Venture Capital Assoc.

Project Preferences

Type of Financing Preferred:

Early Stage
Expansion
Seed
Startup

Size of Investments Considered:

Min Size of Investment Considered (000s): $975
Max Size of Investment Considered (000s): $4,873

Geographical Preferences

International Preferences:

Sweden
Europe
Scandanavia/Nordic Region
Finland

Industry Preferences

In Communications prefer:

Telecommunications

In Computer Hardware prefer:

Computers

In Computer Software prefer:

Software

Additional Information

Year Founded: 1998
Capital Under Management: $244,600,000
Current Activity Level : Actively seeking new investments

PRUDENT CAPITAL

1120 Connecticut Avenue, NW
Suite 1200
Washington, DC USA 20036
Phone: 202-828-9041
Fax: 202-296-6293
Website: www.prudentcapital.com

Management and Staff

Steven Schwartz, Partner

Type of Firm

Private Equity Firm

Project Preferences

Role in Financing:

Prefer role as deal originator

Type of Financing Preferred:

Leveraged Buyout
Expansion
Mezzanine
Later Stage
Management Buyouts
Recapitalizations

Size of Investments Considered:

Min Size of Investment Considered (000s): $1,000
Max Size of Investment Considered (000s): $10,000

Geographical Preferences

United States Preferences:

Mid Atlantic

Additional Information

Year Founded: 1999
Capital Under Management: $50,000,000
Current Activity Level : Actively seeking new investments
Method of Compensation: Return on invest. most important, but chg. closing fees, service fees, etc.

PRUDENTIAL CAPITAL GROUP

Two Prudential Plaza
180 North Stetson, Suite 5600
Chicago, IL USA 60601
Phone: 312-540-4235
Fax: 312-540-4219
E-mail: prudentialcapitalgroup@prudential.com
Website:
www3.prudential.com/pcg/main/pru_cap_grp_main.html

Management and Staff

Albert Trank, Managing Director
Allen Weaver, Senior Managing Director
Charles King, Managing Director
Jeffrey Dickson, Managing Director
Marie Fioramonti, Managing Director
Mark Hoffmeister, Managing Director
Matthew Chanin, Principal
Paul Meiring, Managing Director
Paul Price, Managing Director
Randall Kob, Managing Director
Ric Abel, Managing Director
Robert Penfold, Managing Director
Robert Derrick, Managing Director
Scott Von Fischer, Managing Director
Stephen DeMartini, Managing Director

Type of Firm

Insurance Firm Affiliate

Project Preferences

Role in Financing:

Will function either as deal originator or investor in deals created by others

Type of Financing Preferred:

Fund of Funds
Leveraged Buyout
Mezzanine
Management Buyouts
Acquisition
Recapitalizations

Size of Investments Considered:

Min Size of Investment Considered (000s): $10,000
Max Size of Investment Considered (000s): $30,000

Industry Focus

(% based on actual investment)

Industrial/Energy	30.2%
Other Products	21.4%
Communications and Media	17.5%
Internet Specific	8.7%
Computer Hardware	7.7%
Consumer Related	6.6%
Semiconductors/Other Elect.	4.8%
Medical/Health	3.1%

Additional Information

Name of Most Recent Fund: Prudential Capital Partners II, L.P.
Most Recent Fund Was Raised: 12/17/2004
Year Founded: 1969
Capital Under Management: $31,000,000,000
Current Activity Level : Actively seeking new investments
Method of Compensation: Return on invest. most important, but chg. closing fees, service fees, etc.

PS SEED II, LLC

101 California Street
36th Floor
San Francisco, CA USA 94111
Phone: 415-352-7100

Type of Firm

Private Equity Firm

Project Preferences

Type of Financing Preferred:

Seed

Geographical Preferences

United States Preferences:

All U.S.

Additional Information

Year Founded: 2004
Capital Under Management: $8,900,000
Current Activity Level : Actively seeking new investments

PSG CAPITAL LIMITED

1st Floor, Ou Kollege
35 Kerk Street
Stellenbosch, South Africa 7600
Phone: 27-21-887-9602
Fax: 27-27-887-9624
Website: www.psg-online.co.za

Type of Firm

Private Equity Firm

Association Membership

South African Venture Capital Association (SAVCA)

Project Preferences

Type of Financing Preferred:

Balanced

Geographical Preferences

International Preferences:

South Africa
Additional Information
Year Founded: 1996
Current Activity Level : Actively seeking new investments

PSI, INC.

Nine East, 38th Street
12th Floor
New York, NY USA 10016
Phone: 212-813-3112
Fax: 866-734-0593
E-mail: ny@psi-world.com
Website: www.psi-world.com

Other Offices

204 Global Business Park
Tower-B
Gurgaon, India 122 002
Phone: 91-124-280-3035

Type of Firm

Bank Affiliated

Association Membership

Indian Venture Capital Association (IVCA)

Project Preferences

Type of Financing Preferred:

Expansion
Early Stage
Balanced
Seed

Geographical Preferences

International Preferences:
India

Industry Preferences

In Medical/Health prefer:
Pharmaceuticals

Additional Information

Year Founded: 2007
Current Activity Level : Actively seeking new investments

PSILOS GROUP MANAGERS, LLC

140 Broadway
51st Floor
New York, NY USA 10005
Phone: 212-242-8844
Fax: 212-242-8855
Website: www.psilos.com

Other Offices

21 Tamal Vista Boulevard
Suite 194
Corte Madera, CA USA 94925
Phone: 415-945-7010
Fax: 415-945-7011

100 North Guadalupe Street
Suite 203
Santa Fe, NM USA 87501
Phone: 505-995-8500
Fax: 505-995-8501

Management and Staff

Albert Waxman, Senior Managing Director
Darlene Collins, Managing Director

Type of Firm

Private Equity Firm

Association Membership

National Venture Capital Association - USA (NVCA)

Project Preferences

Type of Financing Preferred:
Second Stage Financing
Early Stage
Balanced
First Stage Financing
Startup

Geographical Preferences

United States Preferences:
All U.S.

Industry Focus

(% based on actual investment)

Medical/Health	41.7%
Computer Software and Services	31.4%
Internet Specific	17.9%
Biotechnology	4.4%
Other Products	3.6%
Computer Hardware	0.9%

Additional Information

Name of Most Recent Fund: Psilos Group Partners IIIA, L.P.
Most Recent Fund Was Raised: 10/12/2005
Year Founded: 1998
Capital Under Management: $550,000,000
Current Activity Level : Actively seeking new investments

PTV SCIENCES

211 West Sith Street
Suite 700
Austin, TX USA 78701
Phone: 512-542-0010
Fax: 512-542-0062
E-mail: ptv@ptvsciences.com
Website: www.ptvsciences.com

Other Offices

1000 Main
Suite 3250
Houston, TX USA 77002
Phone: 713-209-7555
Fax: 713-209-7599

Management and Staff

Evan Melrose, Managing Director
Matt Crawford, Managing Director
Rick Anderson, Managing Director

Type of Firm

Private Equity Firm

Association Membership

National Venture Capital Association - USA (NVCA)

Project Preferences

Type of Financing Preferred:
Second Stage Financing
Early Stage
Seed
Later Stage
First Stage Financing

Geographical Preferences

United States Preferences:
All U.S.

Industry Preferences

In Communications prefer:
Wireless Communications

In Semiconductor/Electr prefer:
Electronic Components
Semiconductor

In Biotechnology prefer:
Human Biotechnology

In Medical/Health prefer:
Medical Diagnostics
Medical Therapeutics
Medical Products
Health Services
Pharmaceuticals

Additional Information

Name of Most Recent Fund: Pinto TV Annex Fund, L.P.
Most Recent Fund Was Raised: 10/31/2007
Year Founded: 2003
Capital Under Management: $257,000,000
Current Activity Level : Actively seeking new investments

PUBLIC INVESTMENT COMMISSIONERS

cor Oberon Ave & Glenwood Road
Faerie Glen
Pretoria, South Africa 0001
Phone: 27-12-369-3327
Fax: 27-12-348-5852
Website: www.pic.gov.za

Type of Firm

Private Equity Firm

Association Membership

South African Venture Capital Association (SAVCA)

Project Preferences

Type of Financing Preferred:
Balanced

Geographical Preferences

International Preferences:
South Africa

Additional Information

Year Founded: 1984
Current Activity Level : Actively seeking new investments

PUNJAB VENTURE CAPITAL, LTD.

Udyog Bhawan, 18-Himalaya Marg
Sector 17
Chandigarh, India 160017
Phone: 91-172-270-3693
Fax: 91-172-704-145
Website: www.pvcl.org

Other Offices

2nd Florr, Udyog Bhawan
18, Himalaya Marg, Sector - 17
Chandigarh, India 160017
Phone: 91-172-2703-963

Management and Staff

R.K. Bhandari, Chief Executive Officer

Type of Firm
Private Equity Firm

Association Membership
Indian Venture Capital Association (IVCA)

Project Preferences
Type of Financing Preferred:
Early Stage
Expansion
Mezzanine
Seed
Management Buyouts
Startup

Size of Investments Considered:
Min Size of Investment Considered (000s): $51
Max Size of Investment Considered (000s): $508

Geographical Preferences
International Preferences:
India

Industry Preferences
In Computer Hardware prefer:
Computers

In Computer Software prefer:
Software

Additional Information
Year Founded: 2000
Capital Under Management: $2,200,000
Current Activity Level : Actively seeking new investments

PUREPAY
15800 Crabbs Branch Way
Suite 210
Rockville, MD USA 20855
Phone: 614-944-5788
Fax: 614-944-5789
E-mail: information@pure-pay.com
Website: www.pure-pay.com

Type of Firm
Private Equity Firm

Additional Information
Year Founded: 2007
Current Activity Level : Actively seeking new investments

PURETECH VENTURES
222 Berkeley Street
Suite 1040
Boston, MA USA 02116
Phone: 617-482-2333
Fax: 617-482-3337
E-mail: info@puretechventures.com
Website: www.puretechventures.com

Management and Staff
Bennett Shapiro, Venture Partner
Daphne Zohar, Managing General Partner
Francis Bullock, Venture Partner
Frank Douglas, Partner
John Zabriskie, General Partner
Todd Dagres, Venture Partner
Yishai Zohar, General Partner

Type of Firm
Private Equity Firm

Association Membership
National Venture Capital Association - USA (NVCA)

Project Preferences
Type of Financing Preferred:
Early Stage
Seed

Geographical Preferences
International Preferences:
Israel

Additional Information
Year Founded: 2001
Current Activity Level : Actively seeking new investments

PUTNAM INVESTMENTS
P.O. Box 8383
Boston, MA USA 02266
Phone: 888-478-8626
Website: www.putnam.com

Type of Firm
Private Equity Firm

Additional Information
Year Founded: 1937
Current Activity Level : Actively seeking new investments

PYMBLE HOLDINGS INC.
Box 1239
Lambeth, Canada N0L 1S0
Phone: 519-652-5675
Fax: 519-652- 6450

Type of Firm
Private Equity Firm

Additional Information
Year Founded: 1983
Current Activity Level : Actively seeking new investments

- Q -

Q1 CAPITAL PARTNERS
144 Front Street West
Suite 725
Toronto, Canada M5B 1B3
Phone: 416-850-7474
Fax: 416-850-7476
Website: www.q1capital.com

Other Offices
144 Front Street West
Suite 725
Toronto, Canada M5B 1B3
Phone: 416-850-7474
Fax: 416-850-7476

Management and Staff
Mike Middleton, Managing Director

Type of Firm
Private Equity Firm

Additional Information
Year Founded: 2009
Current Activity Level : Actively seeking new investments

QAT INVESTMENTS SA (AKA: QUERCUS AIMER TRUST)
8, Bd Royal
Luxembourg, Luxembourg L-2449
Phone: 352-26-262652
Fax: 352-26-26265252
E-mail: info@qatinvestments.lu
Website: www.qatinvestments.com

Other Offices
World Trade Center Schiphol
Schiphol Boulevard 249
BH Luchthaven Schiphol, Netherlands NL-1118

Louizalaan 109
Brussel, Belgium B1050
Phone: 32-2567-17-88
Fax: 32-2567-17-89

Type of Firm
Private Equity Firm

Project Preferences
Type of Financing Preferred:
Early Stage
Balanced

Geographical Preferences
International Preferences:
Europe

Belgium

Industry Preferences

In Communications prefer:
Telecommunications
Entertainment

In Medical/Health prefer:
Medical/Health

In Industrial/Energy prefer:
Environmental Related

In Other prefer:
Environment Responsible

Additional Information

Year Founded: 2006
Capital Under Management: $54,300,000
Current Activity Level : Actively seeking new investments

QCAPITAL PARTNERS CO, LTD. (FKA: TG VENTURES, INC.)

10th Floor, Hiliving Building
890-16 Daechi-Dong Kangnam-Gu
Seoul, South Korea
Phone: 822-538-2411
Fax: 822-538-1583
E-mail: qcp1@qcapital.co.kr
Website: www.qcapital.co.kr

Type of Firm

Private Equity Firm

Project Preferences

Role in Financing:
Prefer role as deal originator but will also invest in deals created by others

Type of Financing Preferred:
Second Stage Financing
Leveraged Buyout
Early Stage
Expansion
Mezzanine
Turnaround
Balanced
Later Stage
Management Buyouts
First Stage Financing
Recapitalizations

Size of Investments Considered:
Min Size of Investment Considered (000s): $500
Max Size of Investment Considered (000s): $5,000

Geographical Preferences

United States Preferences:
All U.S.

International Preferences:
Korea, South
Japan

Industry Preferences

In Communications prefer:
Communications and Media

In Computer Other prefer:
Computer Related

In Semiconductor/Electr prefer:
Electronic Components

In Biotechnology prefer:
Biotechnology

In Medical/Health prefer:
Medical/Health

In Consumer Related prefer:
Consumer

In Industrial/Energy prefer:
Energy
Industrial Products
Materials
Factory Automation
Machinery

In Business Serv. prefer:
Services
Distribution

In Manufact. prefer:
Manufacturing

In Utilities prefer:
Utilities

Additional Information

Year Founded: 1982
Capital Under Management: $96,000,000
Current Activity Level : Actively seeking new investments
Method of Compensation: Return on investment is of primary concern, do not charge fees

---

QED GLOBAL, LTD.

17/F China Hong Kong Tower
8-12 Hennessy Road
Hennesy, Hong Kong
Phone: 852-3102-8700
Fax: 852-3102-9010
E-mail: info@qedglobal.com
Website: www.qedglobal.com

Management and Staff

Helen Wong, Co-Founder
Patrick Cheung, Co-Founder

Type of Firm

Private Equity Firm

Project Preferences

Type of Financing Preferred:
Balanced

Geographical Preferences

International Preferences:
Indonesia
India
China
Asia

Industry Preferences

In Internet Specific prefer:
Internet

Additional Information

Year Founded: 2000
Current Activity Level : Actively seeking new investments

QIFUND

Sphere Business Park Doornveld
Industrie Asse 3 nr.11
Box 10 Zellik, Belgium B - 1731
Phone: 32-478-31-8840
Fax: 32-2-256-4302
Website: www.qifund.com

Management and Staff

Carlo Van Dyck, Partner
Dirk Deceuninck, Partner

Type of Firm

Private Equity Firm

Project Preferences

Type of Financing Preferred:
Early Stage
Startup

Geographical Preferences

International Preferences:
Europe
Belgium

Industry Preferences

In Communications prefer:
Communications and Media

In Business Serv. prefer:
Services

Additional Information

Year Founded: 2001
Current Activity Level : Actively seeking new investments

QIMING VENTURE PARTNERS

Rm.3906 Jinmao Tower
88 Century Boulevard
Shanghai, China 200121
Phone: 86-21-6101-6522
Fax: 86-21-6101-6512
E-mail: info@qimingventures.com
Website: www.qimingventures.com

Management and Staff

Chivas Lam, Venture Partner
Duane Kuang, Managing Director
Gary Rieschel, Managing Director
Hans Tung, Partner
JP Gan, Managing Director
John Zagula, Managing Director
Nisa Leung, Partner
Richard Tong, Managing Director
Richard Chen, Venture Partner
Robert Headley, Managing Director
Steven Hu, Vice President
William Hu, Principal
Zhang Yong, Partner

Type of Firm

Private Equity Firm

Project Preferences

Type of Financing Preferred:
Early Stage
Expansion
Balanced

Geographical Preferences

International Preferences:
China
Asia

Additional Information

Year Founded: 2006
Capital Under Management: $524,200,000
Current Activity Level : Actively seeking new investments

QINETIQ VENTURES LTD

85 Buckingham Gate
London, United Kingdom SW1E 6PD
Phone: 44-8700-100-942
Website: www.qinetiq.com

Management and Staff

Doug Webb, Chief Financial Officer
Hal Kruth, Chief Executive Officer

Type of Firm

Government Affiliated Program

Project Preferences

Type of Financing Preferred:
Seed
Startup

Geographical Preferences

International Preferences:
United Kingdom

Industry Preferences

In Communications prefer:
Wireless Communications

In Industrial/Energy prefer:
Materials

Additional Information

Year Founded: 2001
Capital Under Management: $35,400,000
Current Activity Level : Actively seeking new investments

QINGDAO U-ONE ASSET MANAGEMENT CO., LTD.

10/F, 7 Qingdao Software Park
288 Ningxia Road
Qingdao, China 266071
Phone: 86-532-85710050
Fax: 86-532-85739676
E-mail: info@uonemanagement.com
Website: www.uonemanagement.com

Type of Firm

Private Equity Firm

Project Preferences

Type of Financing Preferred:
Early Stage
Expansion
Later Stage

Geographical Preferences

International Preferences:
China
Asia

Industry Preferences

In Communications prefer:
Telecommunications

In Biotechnology prefer:
Biotechnology
Agricultural/Animal Bio.

In Medical/Health prefer:
Pharmaceuticals

In Industrial/Energy prefer:
Alternative Energy
Materials

In Business Serv. prefer:
Services
Media

Additional Information

Year Founded: 2009
Capital Under Management: $14,600,000
Current Activity Level : Actively seeking new investments

QLEAP ACCELERATORS, LTD.

Suite 1204, 12F, Wing On House
71 Des Voeux Road Central
Hong Kong, Hong Kong
Phone: 852-2116-3218
Fax: 852-2116-9186
E-mail: business@qleap.com.hk
Website: www.qleap.com.hk

Management and Staff

Wilton Chau, Managing Director
Yaw-Nam Yong, Partner

Type of Firm

Private Equity Firm

Project Preferences

Type of Financing Preferred:
Expansion
Balanced

Geographical Preferences

International Preferences:
Asia

Industry Preferences

In Communications prefer:
Communications and Media

In Semiconductor/Electr prefer:
Semiconductor

In Industrial/Energy prefer:
Advanced Materials

Additional Information

Year Founded: 2007
Current Activity Level : Actively seeking new investments

QUAD VENTURES

21 Penn Plaza
Suite 1501
New York, NY USA 10001
Phone: 212-724-2200
Fax: 212-758-0608
E-mail: quad@quadpartners.com
Website: www.quadventures.com

Other Offices

895 Dove Street
3rd Floor
Newport Beach, CA USA 92660
Phone: 949-851-6450

Management and Staff

Andrew Kaplan, Partner
Daniel Neuwirth, Partner
Lincoln Frank, Founder
Stephen Spahn, Partner

Strauss Zelnick, Partner
Thomas Kean, Partner

Type of Firm

Private Equity Firm

Project Preferences

Type of Financing Preferred:

Generalist PE

Industry Focus

(% based on actual investment)

Consumer Related	89.1%
Computer Software and Services	8.6%
Internet Specific	2.3%

Additional Information

Year Founded: 2000
Capital Under Management: $47,200,000
Current Activity Level : Actively seeking new investments

QUAD-C MANAGEMENT, INC.

230 East High Street
Charlottesville, VA USA 22902
Phone: 434-979-9122
Fax: 434-979-1145
Website: www.quadcmanagement.com

Other Offices

156 West 56th Street
Suite 1702
New York, NY USA 10019
Phone: 212-333-3813
Fax: 212-333-3816

Management and Staff

Anthony Ignaczak, Partner
Frank Winslow, Principal
Gary Binning, Partner
Matthew Engel, Vice President
Robert Haswell, Principal
Stephen Burns, Partner
Terrence Daniels, Managing Partner
Thad Jones, Principal

Type of Firm

Private Equity Firm

Project Preferences

Role in Financing:

Prefer role as deal originator

Type of Financing Preferred:

Leveraged Buyout
Acquisition
Recapitalizations

Size of Investments Considered:

Min Size of Investment Considered (000s): $10,000
Max Size of Investment Considered (000s): $130,000

Geographical Preferences

Canadian Preferences:

All Canada

Industry Focus

(% based on actual investment)

Consumer Related	62.8%
Medical/Health	18.1%
Industrial/Energy	11.9%
Internet Specific	6.0%
Communications and Media	1.2%

Additional Information

Year Founded: 1989
Capital Under Management: $650,000,000
Current Activity Level : Actively seeking new investments
Method of Compensation: Return on invest. most important, but chg. closing fees, service fees, etc.

QUADRANGLE GROUP LLC

375 Park Avenue
New York, NY USA 10152
Phone: 212-418-1700
Fax: 212-218-1701
E-mail: info@quadranglegroup.com
Website: www.quadranglegroup.com

Other Offices

525 University Avenue
Suite 605
Palo Alto, CA USA 94301
Phone: 650-646-6400
Fax: 650-646-6441

15 Conduit Street
London, United Kingdom W1S 2XJ
Phone: 44-20-7317-3800
Fax: 44-20-7317-3801

16/F, One Exchange Square
8 Connaught Place
Central, Hong Kong
Phone: 852-3656-6300
Fax: 852-3656-6301

Management and Staff

Alex Hocherman, Vice President
Amanda Siegel, Principal
Andrew Frey, Principal
Daniel Fine, Vice President
David Crosby, Principal
Henry Ormond, Principal
John Hill, Vice President
Kevin Dugan, Vice President
Mark Brennan, Vice President
Michael Minars, Vice President
Michelle Stoneburn, Vice President
Patrick Bartels, Vice President
Ryan Brown, Vice President
Sachin Khajuria, Principal
Sebastien Briens, Vice President
Stacey Harris, Vice President
Steven Davidson, Chief Financial Officer
Thomas Vigliotta, Principal

Type of Firm

Private Equity Firm

Association Membership

Hong Kong Venture Capital Association (HKVCA)

Project Preferences

Role in Financing:

Prefer role as deal originator but will also invest in deals created by others

Type of Financing Preferred:

Leveraged Buyout
Expansion
Generalist PE
Later Stage
Acquisition
Distressed Debt

Size of Investments Considered:

Min Size of Investment Considered (000s): $20,000
Max Size of Investment Considered (000s): $150,000

Geographical Preferences

United States Preferences:

All U.S.

International Preferences:

Western Europe

Industry Focus

(% based on actual investment)

Communications and Media	70.1%
Consumer Related	17.8%
Internet Specific	8.3%
Other Products	3.9%

Additional Information

Year Founded: 2000
Capital Under Management: $920,000,000
Current Activity Level : Actively seeking new investments
Method of Compensation: Return on invest. most important, but chg. closing fees, service fees, etc.

QUADRANT PRIVATE EQUITY PTY, LTD.

126 Phillip Street
Level 30
Sydney, Australia 2000
Phone: 612-9221-3044
Fax: 612-9221-8447
E-mail: quadrant@quadrantpe.com.au
Website: www.quadrantpe.com.au

Management and Staff

Chris Hadley, Managing Director

Type of Firm
Bank Affiliated

Association Membership
Australian Venture Capital Association (AVCAL)

Project Preferences
Type of Financing Preferred:
Leveraged Buyout
Expansion
Mezzanine
Generalist PE
Later Stage
Management Buyouts

Geographical Preferences
International Preferences:
Pacific
Australia

Additional Information
Name of Most Recent Fund: Quadrant Private Equity Fund No.2
Most Recent Fund Was Raised: 04/30/2007
Year Founded: 1995
Capital Under Management: $586,400,000
Current Activity Level : Actively seeking new investments

QUADRIGA CAPITAL EIGENKAPITAL BERATUNG GMBH
Hamburger Allee 2-10
Frankfurt, Germany 60486
Phone: 49-69-795-0000
Fax: 49-69-795000-60
E-mail: contact@quadriga-capital.de
Website: www.quadriga-capital.de

Other Offices
Deputatskay St. 1
Yarozlavl, Russia RF-150000
Phone: 7-0852-328789
Fax: 7-0852-329183

Osharskaya St. 52
Nizhny Novgorod, Russia RF-603600
Phone: 7-8312-773-255
Fax: 7-8312-773-252

Nevski Prospekt
30 - Office No. 3.3
St. Petersburg, Russia RF-191011
Phone: 7-812-325-8474
Fax: 7-812/325-84-77

Management and Staff
Andreas Fendel, Partner
Burkhard Bonsels, Partner
Christoph Weise, Partner
Max Romer, Partner
Peter Besthof, Partner
Philipp Jacobi, Partner
Reinhard Kohleick, Partner

Type of Firm
Private Equity Advisor or Fund of Funds

Association Membership
German Venture Capital Association (BVK)
Russian Venture Capital Association (RVCA)
European Private Equity and Venture Capital Assoc.

Project Preferences
Role in Financing:
Prefer role as deal originator

Type of Financing Preferred:
Leveraged Buyout
Expansion
Balanced
Management Buyouts
Recapitalizations

Size of Investments Considered:
Min Size of Investment Considered (000s): $15,000
Max Size of Investment Considered: No Limit

Geographical Preferences
International Preferences:
Luxembourg
Netherlands
Europe
Scandanavia/Nordic Region
Belgium
Germany
France

Industry Focus
(% based on actual investment)

Industrial/Energy	100.0%

Additional Information
Year Founded: 1994
Capital Under Management: $329,800,000
Current Activity Level : Actively seeking new investments
Method of Compensation: Return on invest. most important, but chg. closing fees, service fees, etc.

QUADRIVIO SGR
17/a Viale Majno
Milan, Italy 20122
Phone: 39-02-7631-7693
Fax: 39-02-7639-4658
E-mail: info@quadriviosgr.it
Website: www.quadriviosgr.it

Type of Firm
Incubator/Development Program

Association Membership
Italian Venture Capital Association (AIFI)

Project Preferences
Type of Financing Preferred:
Second Stage Financing
Leveraged Buyout
Early Stage
Expansion

Geographical Preferences
International Preferences:
Italy
Europe

Additional Information
Year Founded: 2001
Capital Under Management: $68,600,000
Current Activity Level : Actively seeking new investments

QUAESTUS PRIVATE EQUITY, LTD.
Ilica 1a
Zagreb, Croatia 10000
Phone: 385-1-488-0900
Fax: 385-1-487-0159
E-mail: quaestus@quaestus.hr
Website: www.quaestus.hr

Management and Staff
Ante Ramljak, Partner
Borislav Skegro, Partner
Tomislav Matic, Partner
Zeljko Lukac, Partner

Type of Firm
Investment Management Firm

Association Membership
European Private Equity and Venture Capital Assoc.

Project Preferences
Type of Financing Preferred:
Generalist PE

Size of Investments Considered:
Min Size of Investment Considered (000s): $500
Max Size of Investment Considered (000s): $16,417

Geographical Preferences
International Preferences:
Macedonia
Eastern Europe
Croatia
Bosnia

Industry Preferences
In Communications prefer:
Communications and Media

In Medical/Health prefer:
Medical/Health
Health Services

In Consumer Related prefer:
Food/Beverage

In Industrial/Energy prefer:
Alternative Energy

Additional Information
Name of Most Recent Fund: Quaestus Private Equity Kapital
Most Recent Fund Was Raised: 03/07/2006
Year Founded: 2006
Capital Under Management: $46,400,000
Current Activity Level : Actively seeking new investments

QUAKER BIOVENTURES, INC.
Cira Centre
2929 Arch Street
Philadelphia, PA USA 19104
Phone: 215-988-6800
Fax: 215-988-6801
E-mail: info@quakerbio.com
Website: www.quakerbio.com

Other Offices
C/O Pittsburgh Life Sciences Greenhouse
100 Technology Drive, Suite 400
Pittsburgh, PA USA 15219
Phone: 412-201-7370
Fax: 412-770-1276

Management and Staff
Adele Oliva, Partner
Brenda Gavin, Partner
David King, Venture Partner
Eric Emrich, Chief Financial Officer
Geeta Vemuri, Partner
Ira Lubert, Managing Partner
Matthew Rieke, Partner
P. Sherrill Neff, Partner
Peter Sears, Venture Partner
Richard Kollender, Partner

Type of Firm
Private Equity Firm

Association Membership
Mid-Atlantic Venture Association
National Venture Capital Association - USA (NVCA)

Project Preferences

Role in Financing:
Will function either as deal originator or investor in deals created by others

Type of Financing Preferred:
Early Stage
Balanced
Public Companies
Later Stage

Size of Investments Considered:
Min Size of Investment Considered (000s): $2,500
Max Size of Investment Considered (000s): $20,000

Geographical Preferences

United States Preferences:
Mid Atlantic
Pennsylvania
Southeast
New Jersey
East Coast

Industry Preferences

In Biotechnology prefer:
Biotechnology

In Medical/Health prefer:
Medical/Health
Medical Diagnostics
Medical Therapeutics
Medical Products
Health Services
Pharmaceuticals

Additional Information
Name of Most Recent Fund: Quaker BioVentures II, L.P.
Most Recent Fund Was Raised: 04/02/2007
Year Founded: 2001
Capital Under Management: $280,000,000
Current Activity Level : Actively seeking new investments

QUALITAS EQUITY PARTNERS
Juan Bravo 38
1st Floor
Madrid, Spain 28006
Phone: 34-91-423-8270
Fax: 34-91-423-8275
E-mail: info@qualitasequity.com
Website: www.qualitasequity.com

Management and Staff
Eric Halverson, Founding Partner
Gonzalo Hinojosa, Partner
Inigo Olaguibel, Founding Partner
Jose Machuca, Partner
Sergio Perez, Partner

Type of Firm
Private Equity Firm

Project Preferences

Type of Financing Preferred:
Leveraged Buyout
Expansion
Mezzanine

Size of Investments Considered:
Min Size of Investment Considered (000s): $1,776
Max Size of Investment Considered (000s): $10,656

Geographical Preferences

International Preferences:
Spain

Additional Information
Year Founded: 2001
Current Activity Level : Actively seeking new investments

QUAN VENTURES
39 Winchester Drive
Atherton, CA USA 94027
Phone: 650-483-9638
Fax: 650-329-0479
E-mail: info@quanvc.com
Website: www.quanvc.com

Other Offices
8, Avenue Peschier
Geneva, Switzerland 1206
Phone: 41-22-789-4008
Fax: 41-22-789-4041

Management and Staff
Edward Schneider, General Partner
Magnus Ryde, General Partner
Robert Kalman, Partner

Type of Firm
Private Equity Firm

Association Membership
European Private Equity and Venture Capital Assoc.

Project Preferences

Role in Financing:
Will function either as deal originator or investor in deals created by others

Type of Financing Preferred:
Balanced

Size of Investments Considered:
Min Size of Investment Considered (000s): $50
Max Size of Investment Considered (000s): $5,000

Geographical Preferences

United States Preferences:
All U.S.

International Preferences:
Europe

Industry Preferences

In Communications prefer:
Commercial Communications
Telecommunications
Wireless Communications
Data Communications
Satellite Microwave Comm.

In Computer Hardware prefer:
Computer Graphics and Dig

In Internet Specific prefer:
E-Commerce Technology

In Semiconductor/Electr prefer:
Electronics
Semiconductor

Laser Related
Fiber Optics
Optoelectronics

Additional Information

Year Founded: 1996
Capital Under Management: $1,500,000
Current Activity Level : Actively seeking new investments
Method of Compensation: Return on investment is of primary concern, do not charge fees

---

QUANTICA SGR SPA

Via Broletto 37
Milan, Italy 20121
Phone: 39-2-3656-7070
Fax: 39-2-3656-7071
Website: www.quanticasgr.it

Type of Firm

Private Equity Firm

Project Preferences

Type of Financing Preferred:

Early Stage
Expansion
Balanced

Geographical Preferences

International Preferences:

Italy

Additional Information

Year Founded: 2007
Capital Under Management: $88,300,000
Current Activity Level : Actively seeking new investments

QUANTUM CAPITAL PARTNERS

140 Fountain Parkway
Suite 420
Saint Petersburg, FL USA 33716
Phone: 727-456-2020
Fax: 727-456-2021
E-mail: information@qcpventures.com
Website: www.qcpventures.com

Management and Staff

N.John Simmons, President

Type of Firm

Private Equity Firm

Project Preferences

Role in Financing:

Will function either as deal originator or investor in deals created by others

Type of Financing Preferred:

Expansion
Later Stage

Size of Investments Considered:

Min Size of Investment Considered (000s): $500
Max Size of Investment Considered (000s): $7,500

Geographical Preferences

United States Preferences:

Southeast
Florida

Industry Preferences

In Communications prefer:

Commercial Communications

In Computer Software prefer:

Computer Services
Data Processing
Software
Systems Software
Applications Software

In Internet Specific prefer:

E-Commerce Technology
Internet
Ecommerce
Web Aggregration/Portals

In Semiconductor/Electr prefer:

Electronic Components
Controllers and Sensors
Sensors

In Medical/Health prefer:

Medical Diagnostics
Diagnostic Services
Diagnostic Test Products
Medical Products
Disposable Med. Products
Health Services

In Consumer Related prefer:

Consumer
Retail
Franchises(NEC)
Food/Beverage
Education Related

In Industrial/Energy prefer:

Industrial Products
Machinery

In Financial Services prefer:

Financial Services

In Business Serv. prefer:

Services
Distribution
Consulting Services

In Manufact. prefer:

Manufacturing

Additional Information

Year Founded: 1999
Capital Under Management: $30,000,000
Current Activity Level : Actively seeking new investments
Method of Compensation: Return on invest. most important, but chg. closing fees, service fees, etc.

QUANTUM EQUITY PARTNERS LLC

1420 Spring Hill Road
Suite 205
McLean, VA USA 22102
Phone: 703-970-2250
Fax: 703-970-2251
E-mail: info@quantumequity.com
Website: www.quantumequity.com

Management and Staff

Charles Citrin, Partner
David Wechsler, Co-Founder
Dominick Carducci, Co-Founder
Evan Wechsler, Co-Founder
Richard Fried, Co-Founder
Steven Blumenfeld, Co-Founder

Type of Firm

Private Equity Firm

Project Preferences

Type of Financing Preferred:

Leveraged Buyout
Acquisition

Geographical Preferences

United States Preferences:

Midwest
Mid Atlantic
Southeast
Northeast

Additional Information

Year Founded: 2005
Current Activity Level : Actively seeking new investments

QUANTUM TECHNOLOGY PARTNERS

1072 De Anza Boulevard
Suite A107-538
San Jose, CA USA 95129
Phone: 408-241-2311
Fax: 408-273-6397
Website: www.quantumtp.com

Management and Staff

Barry Dickman, Managing Director

Type of Firm

Private Equity Firm

Project Preferences

Type of Financing Preferred:

Early Stage

Additional Information
Year Founded: 2000
Current Activity Level : Actively seeking new investments

QUARRY CAPITAL MANAGEMENT LLC
Two Pleasant Street
Natick, MA USA 01760
Phone: 508-655-3540
Website: www.quarrycapital.com

Management and Staff
Brent Johnstone, Managing Director
Darren Bonnstetter, Managing Director

Type of Firm
Private Equity Firm

Project Preferences

Type of Financing Preferred:
Leveraged Buyout
Public Companies
Acquisition
Special Situation

Industry Preferences

In Medical/Health prefer:
Health Services

In Consumer Related prefer:
Retail

In Business Serv. prefer:
Services
Distribution

In Manufact. prefer:
Manufacturing

Additional Information
Year Founded: 2009
Current Activity Level : Actively seeking new investments

QUARTERDECK INVESTMENT PARTNERS INC
11111 Santa Monica Boulevard
Suite 1800
West Los Angeles, CA USA 90025
Phone: 310-481-0070
Fax: 310-481-0075
E-mail: info@qtrdeck.com
Website: www.qtrdeck.com

Type of Firm
Bank Affiliated

Project Preferences

Role in Financing:
Prefer role as deal originator but will also invest in deals created by others

Type of Financing Preferred:
Leveraged Buyout
Start-up Financing
First Stage Financing
Special Situation

Industry Focus
(% based on actual investment)

Other Products	52.3%
Internet Specific	47.7%

Additional Information
Year Founded: 1992
Current Activity Level : Actively seeking new investments
Method of Compensation: Return on invest. most important, but chg. closing fees, service fees, etc.

QUARTUS GESTION
28 rue de Berri
Paris, France 75008
Phone: 33-1-4495-7383
Fax: 33-1-4495-7384
E-mail: quartus@quartus.fr
Website: www.quartus.fr

Management and Staff
Frederic Crot, Managing Director
Patrick Jemelen, Chairman & CEO

Type of Firm
Private Equity Firm

Association Membership
European Private Equity and Venture Capital Assoc.

Project Preferences

Type of Financing Preferred:
Leveraged Buyout
Expansion
Management Buyouts
Acquisition

Size of Investments Considered:
Min Size of Investment Considered (000s): $7,138
Max Size of Investment Considered (000s): $24,268

Geographical Preferences

International Preferences:
Switzerland
Belgium
France

Industry Focus
(% based on actual investment)

Other Products	89.5%
Industrial/Energy	10.5%

Additional Information
Year Founded: 1998
Capital Under Management: $129,300,000
Current Activity Level : Reducing investment activity

QUATRIS FUND
120 South 6th Street
Suite 2005
Minneapolis, MN USA 55402
Phone: 612-376-7333
Fax: 612-376-7334
Website: www.quatrisfund.com

Management and Staff
Erwin Kelen, Principal
Gary Smaby, Principal
John Rollwagen, Principal
Steve Goldstein, Principal

Type of Firm
Bank Affiliated

Project Preferences

Role in Financing:
Prefer role as deal originator

Type of Financing Preferred:
Seed
Startup

Size of Investments Considered:
Min Size of Investment Considered (000s): $222
Max Size of Investment Considered (000s): $2,000

Geographical Preferences

United States Preferences:
Midwest
Minnesota

Industry Preferences

In Communications prefer:
Communications and Media

In Computer Software prefer:
Software

In Biotechnology prefer:
Biotechnology

Additional Information
Name of Most Recent Fund: Quatris Fund I, L.P.
Most Recent Fund Was Raised: 07/01/2000
Year Founded: 2000
Capital Under Management: $15,000,000
Current Activity Level : Actively seeking new investments

QUAY PARTNERS PTY., LTD.
Suite 303B
55 Harrington Street
Sydney, Australia 2000
Phone: 612-9252-9788
Fax: 612-9251-8077
E-mail: quaypartners@quaypartners.com.au
Website: www.quaypartners.com.au

Management and Staff
Dominic Tayco, Chief Executive Officer
Jake Burgess, Partner
Stephen White, Managing Partner

Type of Firm
Private Equity Firm

Project Preferences

Type of Financing Preferred:
Fund of Funds
Leveraged Buyout
Early Stage
Expansion
Mezzanine
Balanced
Management Buyouts

Geographical Preferences

International Preferences:
Pacific
Australia
All International

Additional Information
Year Founded: 2000
Capital Under Management: $38,000,000
Current Activity Level : Actively seeking new investments

QUBIS LTD
Lanyon North
Queen's University of Belfast
Belfast, United Kingdom BT7 1NN
Phone: 44-28-9068-2321
Fax: 44-28-9066-3015
E-mail: info@qubis.co.uk
Website: www.qubis.co.uk

Other Offices
10 Malone Road
Belfast, United Kingdom BT9 5BN
Phone: 44-28-9066-2321
Fax: 44-28-9066-3015

Management and Staff
Panos Lioulias, Chief Executive Officer

Type of Firm
University Program

Association Membership
British Venture Capital Association (BVCA)

Project Preferences

Type of Financing Preferred:
Early Stage
Seed
Startup

Geographical Preferences

International Preferences:
United Kingdom

Industry Preferences

In Communications prefer:
Commercial Communications

In Computer Software prefer:
Software

In Internet Specific prefer:
Internet

In Computer Other prefer:
Computer Related

In Semiconductor/Electr prefer:
Electronics

In Biotechnology prefer:
Biotechnology

In Industrial/Energy prefer:
Industrial Products

Additional Information
Year Founded: 1984
Capital Under Management: $6,700,000
Current Activity Level : Actively seeking new investments

QUEBEC EQUITY
1010 Rue Sherbrooke Ouest
Suite 2210
Montreal, Canada H3A 2R7

Type of Firm
Private Equity Firm

Additional Information
Year Founded: 1988
Current Activity Level : Actively seeking new investments

QUEENSLAND INVESTMENT CORPORATION (QIC)
66 Eagle Street
Level 6 Central Plaza II
Brisbane, Australia 4000
Phone: 617-3009-6850
Fax: 617-3009-6851
E-mail: info@qbf.qic.com
Website: www.qbf.qic.com.au

Management and Staff
Andrew Michell, Chief Financial Officer
Neill Colledge, Chief Executive Officer

Type of Firm
Government Affiliated Program

Association Membership
Australian Venture Capital Association (AVCAL)

Project Preferences

Type of Financing Preferred:
Second Stage Financing
Early Stage
Balanced
First Stage Financing

Size of Investments Considered:
Min Size of Investment Considered (000s): $2,417
Max Size of Investment Considered (000s): $12,087

Geographical Preferences

International Preferences:
Pacific
Australia
All International

Industry Preferences

In Biotechnology prefer:
Biotechnology

In Medical/Health prefer:
Medical/Health
Pharmaceuticals

Additional Information
Year Founded: 2002
Capital Under Management: $96,700,000
Current Activity Level : Actively seeking new investments

QUERCUS EQUITY
Felipe IV, 8 2l
Madrid, Spain 28014
Phone: 34-91369-1329
Fax: 34-91420-2864
E-mail: info@quercusequity.com
Website: www.quercusequity.com

Type of Firm
Corporate PE/Venture

Project Preferences

Type of Financing Preferred:
Balanced

Geographical Preferences

International Preferences:
Spain

Additional Information
Year Founded: 2005
Capital Under Management: $241,000,000
Current Activity Level : Actively seeking new investments

QUEST CAPITAL, INC.

2344 Washington Street
Newton, MA USA 02462
Phone: 617-332-7227
Fax: 617-332-3113
Website: www.questcapcorp.com

Management and Staff

Ed Slade, Co-Founder
John Bello, Co-Founder

Type of Firm

Private Equity Firm

Project Preferences

Type of Financing Preferred:
Early Stage

Industry Preferences

In Consumer Related prefer:
Consumer
Retail
Food/Beverage

Additional Information

Year Founded: 2003
Current Activity Level : Actively seeking new investments

QUEST MANAGEMENT NV

Lei 19, bus 2
Leuven, Belgium B-3000
Phone: 32-16-284-128
Fax: 32-16-284-129
E-mail: quest@questmanagement.com
Website: www.questmanagement.com

Management and Staff

Rene Avonts, Managing Director

Type of Firm

Private Equity Advisor or Fund of Funds

Association Membership

Belgium Venturing Association
European Private Equity and Venture Capital Assoc.

Project Preferences

Type of Financing Preferred:
Early Stage
Expansion
Balanced
Public Companies

Size of Investments Considered:
Min Size of Investment Considered (000s): $220
Max Size of Investment Considered (000s): $2,198

Geographical Preferences

International Preferences:
Latin America
Europe
Asia

Industry Preferences

In Communications prefer:
Telecommunications

In Computer Software prefer:
Software

In Semiconductor/Electr prefer:
Electronics
Semiconductor

In Biotechnology prefer:
Biotechnology

In Medical/Health prefer:
Medical/Health

In Industrial/Energy prefer:
Advanced Materials

Additional Information

Year Founded: 1998
Current Activity Level : Actively seeking new investments

QUEST TECHNOLOGY VENTURES

9707 South 76th Avenue
Bridgeview, IL USA 60455
Phone: 847-318-8200
Website: www.questtechventures.com

Management and Staff

Jeff Hart, Principal

Type of Firm

Private Equity Firm

Project Preferences

Type of Financing Preferred:
Early Stage

Industry Preferences

In Computer Software prefer:
Software

In Industrial/Energy prefer:
Energy

Additional Information

Year Founded: 2005
Current Activity Level : Actively seeking new investments

QUEST VENTURES

601 Montgomery
Suite 700
San Francisco, CA USA 94111
Phone: 415-782-1414
Fax: 415-782-1415

Type of Firm

Private Equity Firm

Association Membership

National Venture Capital Association - USA (NVCA)

Project Preferences

Role in Financing:
Prefer role as deal originator but will also invest in deals created by others

Type of Financing Preferred:
Second Stage Financing
Early Stage
Start-up Financing
Seed
First Stage Financing
Special Situation

Size of Investments Considered:
Min Size of Investment Considered (000s): $300
Max Size of Investment Considered (000s): $1,000

Geographical Preferences

United States Preferences:
West Coast
Southwest

Industry Preferences

In Communications prefer:
Commercial Communications
Radio & TV Broadcasting
Telecommunications
Data Communications
Satellite Microwave Comm.
Other Communication Prod.

In Computer Hardware prefer:
Computers

In Computer Other prefer:
Computer Related

In Semiconductor/Electr prefer:
Electronics
Electronic Components
Semiconductor
Controllers and Sensors
Circuit Boards
Component Testing Equipmt
Laser Related
Analytic/Scientific

In Biotechnology prefer:
Biotechnology

In Medical/Health prefer:
Medical/Health
Medical Products

In Consumer Related prefer:
Entertainment and Leisure
Retail
Computer Stores
Food/Beverage
Consumer Products
Consumer Services
Education Related

In Industrial/Energy prefer:
Alternative Energy
Energy Conservation Relat
Industrial Products

In Financial Services prefer:
Financial Services

In Manufact. prefer:
Publishing

Additional Information

Year Founded: 1986
Capital Under Management: $12,100,000
Current Activity Level : Actively seeking new investments
Method of Compensation: Return on invest. most important, but chg. closing fees, service fees, etc.

QUESTER CAPITAL MANAGEMENT

29 Queen Anne's Gate
London, United Kingdom SW1H 9BU
Website: www.quester.co.uk

Other Offices

29 Queen Anne's Gate
London, United Kingdom SW1H 9BU

Management and Staff

Andrew Holmes, Managing Director

Type of Firm

Private Equity Firm

Additional Information

Year Founded: 1894
Current Activity Level : Actively seeking new investments

QUESTMARK PARTNERS, L.P.

One South Street
Suite 800
Baltimore, MD USA 21202
Phone: 410-895-5800
Fax: 410-895-5808
Website: www.questmarkpartners.com

Management and Staff

Benjamin Schapiro, Partner
Jason Sydow, Principal
Michael Ward, Partner
Timothy Krongard, Partner

Type of Firm

Private Equity Firm

Association Membership

National Venture Capital Association - USA (NVCA)

Project Preferences

Role in Financing:
Prefer role as deal originator but will also invest in deals created by others

Type of Financing Preferred:
Expansion
Mezzanine
Later Stage
Private Placement

Size of Investments Considered:
Min Size of Investment Considered (000s): $5,000
Max Size of Investment Considered (000s): $15,000

Geographical Preferences

United States Preferences:
All U.S.

Canadian Preferences:
All Canada
Quebec
Central Canada
Ontario

Industry Focus

(% based on actual investment)

Computer Software and Services	38.5%
Medical/Health	19.6%
Semiconductors/Other Elect.	12.6%
Internet Specific	12.6%
Communications and Media	11.3%
Biotechnology	5.4%

Additional Information

Name of Most Recent Fund: QuestMark Partners III, L.P.
Most Recent Fund Was Raised: 06/01/2007
Year Founded: 1998
Capital Under Management: $755,000,000
Current Activity Level : Actively seeking new investments
Method of Compensation: Return on investment is of primary concern, do not charge fees

---

QUESTOR MANAGEMENT COMPANY LLC

700 East Maple Road
4th Floor
Birmingham, MI USA 48009
Phone: 248—593-1930
Fax: 248-723-3907
E-mail: postmaster@questorfund.com
Website: www.questorfund.com

Other Offices

Nine West 57th Street
34th Floor
New York, NY USA 10019
Phone: 212-297-1599
Fax: 212-297-1588

Management and Staff

Albert Koch, Managing Director
David Wathen, Principal
Dean Anderson, Managing Director
Dominick Schiano, Managing Director
Henry Druker, Principal
Kevin Prokop, Vice President
Robert Shields, Chief Operating Officer
Robert Denious, Managing Director
Terry Theodore, Managing Director
Wallace Rueckel, Principal

Type of Firm

Private Equity Firm

Project Preferences

Type of Financing Preferred:
Leveraged Buyout
Turnaround
Management Buyouts
Special Situation
Distressed Debt
Recapitalizations

Size of Investments Considered:
Min Size of Investment Considered (000s): $25,000
Max Size of Investment Considered (000s): $125,000

Industry Focus

(% based on actual investment)

Other Products	45.1%
Industrial/Energy	21.6%
Communications and Media	18.4%
Consumer Related	6.7%
Medical/Health	5.8%
Computer Software and Services	2.0%
Semiconductors/Other Elect.	0.5%

Additional Information

Name of Most Recent Fund: Questor Partners Fund II, L.P.
Most Recent Fund Was Raised: 01/20/1999
Year Founded: 1995
Capital Under Management: $1,200,000,000
Current Activity Level : Actively seeking new investments

QUICKSILVER VENTURES (FKA: QTV CAPITAL)

12930 Saratoga Avenue
Suite D-8
Saratoga, CA USA 95070
Phone: 408-647-1246
Fax: 408-865-1055
E-mail: info@qtvcapital.com
Website: www.quicksilverventures.com

Management and Staff

Maury Domengeaux, Managing Director
Randall Meals, Managing Director
Steve Schlossareck, Managing Director

Type of Firm

Private Equity Firm

Project Preferences

Type of Financing Preferred:
Balanced

Industry Preferences

In Computer Software prefer:
Software
Applications Software

Additional Information
Year Founded: 1997
Current Activity Level : Actively seeking new investments

QUILVEST CAPITAL
598 Madison Avenue
Eighth Floor
New York, NY USA 10022
Phone: 212-920-3800
Fax: 212-920-3850
E-mail: WagnerW@tcr-ny.com
Website: www.quilvest.com

Management and Staff
Ali Al-Husseini, Managing Partner

Type of Firm
Private Equity Firm

Additional Information
Year Founded: 1983
Current Activity Level : Actively seeking new investments

QUILVEST PRIVATE EQUITY
84, Grand-Rue
Luxembourg, Luxembourg 1660
Phone: 352-473-885
Fax: 352-226-056
Website: www.quilvest.com

Other Offices
598 Madison Avenue
8th Floor
New York, NY USA 10022
Phone: 212-920-3830
Fax: 212-920-3850

Stockerstrasse 23
Zurich, Switzerland 8002
Phone: 41-1-224-4444
Fax: 41-1-224-4400

243, boulevard Saint-Germain
Paris, France 75007
Phone: 33-1-4062-0754
Fax: 33-1-4705-2471

Management and Staff
F. Michel Abouchalache, Chief Executive Officer
Jerome Chevalier, Managing Partner

Type of Firm
Private Equity Firm

Association Membership
French Venture Capital Association (AFIC)

Project Preferences

Type of Financing Preferred:
Fund of Funds
Leveraged Buyout
Expansion
Balanced

Geographical Preferences

United States Preferences:
All U.S.

International Preferences:
Western Europe
Asia

Industry Preferences

In Medical/Health prefer:
Medical/Health

Additional Information
Year Founded: 1972
Current Activity Level : Actively seeking new investments

QUINTILES TRANSNATIONAL CORPORATION
4709 Creekstone Drive
Riverbirch Building Suite 200
Durham, NC USA 27703
Phone: 919-998-2000
Fax: 919-998-9113
Website: www.qtrn.com

Management and Staff
Dennis Gillings, Chairman & CEO

Type of Firm
Corporate PE/Venture

Project Preferences

Type of Financing Preferred:
Balanced

Additional Information
Year Founded: 2003
Current Activity Level : Actively seeking new investments

QVENTURES AG
Am Pilgerrain 17
Bad Homburg, Germany 61352
Phone: 49-6172-402-197
Fax: 49-6172-402-119
E-mail: qventures@quandt.de
Website: www.qventures.de

Type of Firm
Bank Affiliated

Project Preferences

Type of Financing Preferred:
Early Stage
Expansion
Later Stage

Geographical Preferences

International Preferences:
Europe
Germany

Industry Preferences

In Communications prefer:
Telecommunications
Wireless Communications

In Computer Software prefer:
Software

Additional Information
Year Founded: 2000
Current Activity Level : Actively seeking new investments

- R -

R CAPITAL LTD

15 Whitcomb Street
London, United Kingdom WC2H7HA
Phone: 44-870-444-0613
Fax: 44-870-444-1784
E-mail: info@rcapital.co.uk
Website: www.rcapital.co.uk

Type of Firm

Private Equity Firm

Project Preferences

Type of Financing Preferred:
Turnaround

Geographical Preferences

International Preferences:
United Kingdom

Additional Information

Year Founded: 2004
Current Activity Level : Actively seeking new investments

R&D ADVISORY

3, Via Brera
Milano, Italy 20121
Phone: 39-02-80-9401
Fax: 39-028-699-8148
Website: www.rdadvisory.com

Management and Staff

Alberto Camaggi, Partner
Enrico Ricotta, Managing Director

Type of Firm

Private Equity Advisor or Fund of Funds

Association Membership

Italian Venture Capital Association (AIFI)

Project Preferences

Type of Financing Preferred:
Leveraged Buyout
Expansion
Recapitalizations

Geographical Preferences

International Preferences:
Italy
Europe

Additional Information

Year Founded: 2005
Capital Under Management: $118,400,000
Current Activity Level : Actively seeking new investments

R.G. SHONIKER & ASSOCIATES

95 Wellington St. West
Suite 900
Toronto, Canada M5J 2N7
Phone: 416-863-6096
Fax: 416-865-9550

Other Offices

145 King Street West
Toronto, Canada M5H1J8
Phone: 604-659-8000
Fax: 604-659-8099

Management and Staff

Bob Shoniker, Partner

Type of Firm

Private Equity Firm

Additional Information

Year Founded: 2009
Current Activity Level : Actively seeking new investments

RA CAPITAL MANAGEMENT, LLC

800 Boylston Street
Suite 1500
Boston, MA USA 02199
Phone: 617-778-2509
Fax: 617-778-2510
Website: www.racap.com

Type of Firm

Private Equity Firm

Project Preferences

Type of Financing Preferred:
Early Stage

Geographical Preferences

United States Preferences:
All U.S.

Industry Preferences

In Biotechnology prefer:
Biotechnology

In Medical/Health prefer:
Medical/Health
Pharmaceuticals

Additional Information

Name of Most Recent Fund: RA Capital Healthcare Fund, L.P.
Most Recent Fund Was Raised: 08/06/2008
Year Founded: 2005
Capital Under Management: $250,000,000
Current Activity Level : Actively seeking new investments

RABO INDIA FINANCE, LTD.

GF/A-03B, Ground Floor
DLF Cyber City Phase - III
Gurgaon, India 122 022
Phone: 91-124-271-3000
Fax: 91-124-271-3004
E-mail: india@rabobank.com
Website: www.rabobank.com

Other Offices

Forbes Building, 2nd Floor
Charanjit Rai Marg
Mumbai, India 400 001
Phone: 91-22-2203-4567
Fax: 91-22-2203-5544

Management and Staff

Rajesh Srivastava, Managing Director
Sanjiv Bhasin, CEO & Managing Director

Type of Firm

Bank Affiliated

Association Membership

Indian Venture Capital Association (IVCA)

Project Preferences

Type of Financing Preferred:
Balanced

Geographical Preferences

International Preferences:
India

Industry Preferences

In Medical/Health prefer:
Pharmaceuticals

In Consumer Related prefer:
Food/Beverage

In Industrial/Energy prefer:
Alternative Energy

In Agr/Forestr/Fish prefer:
Agribusiness
Agriculture related

Additional Information

Year Founded: 2003
Capital Under Management: $95,000,000
Current Activity Level : Actively seeking new investments

RABO PARTICIPATIES BV

Mondriaantoren, 3e etage
Amstelplein 6-8
Amsterdam, Netherlands 1096 BC
Phone: 31-88-720-0100
Fax: 31-88-720-0117
E-mail: info@raboprivateequity.nl

Website: www.raboparticipaties.nl

Other Offices

Rubens 2000 Blok D
Uitbreidingsstraat 86 bus 3
Berchem, Belgium 2600
Phone: 32-3-290-1719
Fax: 32-3-290-1798

Management and Staff

Joost Verbeek, Managing Director

Type of Firm

Bank Affiliated

Association Membership

Dutch Venture Capital Associaton (NVP)
European Private Equity and Venture Capital Assoc.

Project Preferences

Type of Financing Preferred:
Fund of Funds
Leveraged Buyout
Early Stage
Expansion
Balanced
Turnaround
Management Buyouts
Startup
Acquisition

Geographical Preferences

International Preferences:
Sweden
Netherlands
Europe
Belgium

Additional Information

Year Founded: 1989
Capital Under Management: $224,400,000
Current Activity Level : Actively seeking new investments

RABO VENTURES

Mondriaantoren, 3e etage
Amstelplein 6-8, AM 3046
Amsterdam, Netherlands 1096 BC
Phone: 31-0-88-7200100
Fax: 31-0-88-7200117
E-mail: info@raboprivateequity.nl
Website: www.raboprivateequity.nl

Type of Firm

Private Equity Firm

Additional Information

Year Founded: 2009
Current Activity Level : Actively seeking new investments

RADAR PARTNERS

737 Bryant Street
Palo Alto, CA USA 94301
Phone: 650-566-3300

Management and Staff

Douglas Mackenzie, Founder
J. Andrew Bugas, Partner
Kevin Compton, Founder

Type of Firm

Private Equity Firm

Project Preferences

Type of Financing Preferred:
Seed
Startup

Additional Information

Year Founded: 2005
Current Activity Level : Actively seeking new investments

RADIUS VENTURES LLC (FKA: NPV CAPITAL PARTNERS LLC)

400 Madison Avenue
Eighth Floor
New York, NY USA 10017
Phone: 212-897-7778
Fax: 212-397-2656
E-mail: info@radiusventures.com
Website: www.radiusventures.com

Management and Staff

Daniel Lubin, Managing Partner
Dilip Mehta, Venture Partner
Floyd Loop, Venture Partner
George Milne, Venture Partner
James Mead, Venture Partner
Jordan Davis, Managing Partner
Sanuj Ravindran, Principal

Type of Firm

Private Equity Firm

Association Membership

National Venture Capital Association - USA (NVCA)
Natl Assoc of Small Bus. Inv. Co (NASBIC)

Project Preferences

Role in Financing:
Prefer role as deal originator but will also invest in deals created by others

Type of Financing Preferred:
Expansion
Later Stage

Size of Investments Considered:
Min Size of Investment Considered (000s): $100
Max Size of Investment Considered (000s): $5,000

Industry Preferences

In Medical/Health prefer:
Medical/Health
Medical Diagnostics
Diagnostic Services
Diagnostic Test Products
Medical Therapeutics
Drug/Equipmt Delivery
Medical Products
Disposable Med. Products
Health Services
Pharmaceuticals

Additional Information

Name of Most Recent Fund: Radius Venture Partners III, L.P.
Most Recent Fund Was Raised: 01/08/2007
Year Founded: 1997
Capital Under Management: $200,000,000
Current Activity Level : Actively seeking new investments
Method of Compensation: Return on investment is of primary concern, do not charge fees

RAIFFEISEN MEZZANIN PARTNERS

Am Stadtpark 9
Vienna, Austria A-1090
Phone: 43-171-707-3236
Fax: 43-171707763236
Website: www.mezzanin.info

Type of Firm

Private Equity Firm

Association Membership

European Private Equity and Venture Capital Assoc.

Project Preferences

Type of Financing Preferred:
Mezzanine
Balanced

Geographical Preferences

International Preferences:
Austria

Additional Information

Year Founded: 2007
Current Activity Level : Actively seeking new investments

RAIFFEISEN UNTERNEHMENS BETEILIGUNGS GMBH

Rheinstrasse 11
Bregenz, Austria A-6900
Phone: 43-73-2780-0261
Fax: 43-55744059564

Type of Firm
Bank Affiliated

Project Preferences

Type of Financing Preferred:
Early Stage

Geographical Preferences

International Preferences:
Austria

Additional Information
Year Founded: 2003
Current Activity Level : Actively seeking new investments

RAIN SOURCE CAPITAL, INC. (FKA:MINNESOTA INVESTMENT NETWORK)

1600 University Avenue West
Suite 401
Saint Paul, MN USA 55104
Phone: 651-632-2140
Fax: 651-632-2145
E-mail: info@rainsourcecapital.com
Website: www.rainsourcecapital.com

Management and Staff
Peter Birkeland, Chief Financial Officer

Type of Firm
Private Equity Firm

Association Membership
National Venture Capital Association - USA (NVCA)

Project Preferences

Role in Financing:
Will function either as deal originator or investor in deals created by others

Type of Financing Preferred:
Second Stage Financing
Leveraged Buyout
Generalist PE
Early Stage
Expansion
Mezzanine
Balanced
Turnaround
Later Stage
Management Buyouts
First Stage Financing
Private Placement
Special Situation
Startup
Recapitalizations

Size of Investments Considered:
Min Size of Investment Considered (000s): $250
Max Size of Investment Considered (000s): $2,000

Geographical Preferences

United States Preferences:
South Dakota
Iowa
North Dakota
Oregon
Idaho
Washington
Minnesota
Montana
All U.S.

Industry Preferences

In Communications prefer:
Communications and Media

In Computer Hardware prefer:
Computers

In Semiconductor/Electr prefer:
Electronics

In Biotechnology prefer:
Biotechnology

In Medical/Health prefer:
Medical/Health

In Consumer Related prefer:
Consumer
Food/Beverage
Education Related

In Industrial/Energy prefer:
Energy
Industrial Products
Superconductivity
Process Control
Robotics
Machinery

In Transportation prefer:
Transportation

In Business Serv. prefer:
Distribution

In Manufact. prefer:
Manufacturing

In Agr/Forestr/Fish prefer:
Agriculture related

In Other prefer:
Socially Responsible
Environment Responsible
Women/Minority-Owned Bus.

Additional Information
Year Founded: 1998
Capital Under Management: $16,000,000
Current Activity Level : Actively seeking new investments
Method of Compensation: Return on invest. most important, but chg. closing fees, service fees, etc.

RAINTREE VENTURES PTE., LTD.

5 Shenton Way
09-07, UIC Building
Singapore, Singapore 068808
Phone: 65-6319-4999
Fax: 65-6226-5206
E-mail: enquiries@westcombfinancial.com
Website: www.westcombfinancial.com

Management and Staff
Aw Soon Beng, Chief Executive Officer

Type of Firm
Bank Affiliated

Association Membership
Singapore Venture Capital Association (SVCA)

Project Preferences

Type of Financing Preferred:
Leveraged Buyout
Expansion

Additional Information
Year Founded: 2004
Current Activity Level : Actively seeking new investments

RAJASTHAN ASSET MANAGEMENT COMPANY PVT., LTD.

Room No-414,III Flr,RIICO Wing
Udyog Bhavan, Tilak Marg
Jaipur, India 302 005
Phone: 91-141-510-1225
Fax: 91-141-510-1226
E-mail: rvcf@rvcf.org
Website: www.rvcf.org

Management and Staff
Girish Gupta, Chief Executive Officer

Type of Firm
Government Affiliated Program

Association Membership
Indian Venture Capital Association (IVCA)

Project Preferences

Type of Financing Preferred:
Early Stage
Expansion
Mezzanine
Seed
Management Buyouts
Startup

Size of Investments Considered:
Min Size of Investment Considered (000s): $250

Max Size of Investment Considered (000s): $250,000

Geographical Preferences

International Preferences:
India

Industry Preferences

In Computer Other prefer:
Computer Related

In Biotechnology prefer:
Biotechnology

In Consumer Related prefer:
Entertainment and Leisure
Retail
Hotels and Resorts

In Transportation prefer:
Transportation

In Business Serv. prefer:
Services

Additional Information
Year Founded: 2002
Capital Under Management: $1,800,000
Current Activity Level : Actively seeking new investments

RANCH CAPITAL LLC
12275 El Camino Real
Suite 110
San Diego, CA USA 92130
Phone: 858-523-1799
Fax: 858-523-1899
Website: www.ranchcapital.com

Management and Staff
Dustin Gillman, Vice President
Lawrence Hershfield, Chief Executive Officer
Michael Smith, Vice President
Nathan Birchall, Chief Financial Officer
Randall Jenson, Managing Director

Type of Firm
Private Equity Firm

Project Preferences

Type of Financing Preferred:
Leveraged Buyout
Acquisition
Recapitalizations

Industry Preferences

In Consumer Related prefer:
Entertainment and Leisure

In Industrial/Energy prefer:
Energy

In Transportation prefer:
Transportation

In Financial Services prefer:
Financial Services
Real Estate
Financial Services

Additional Information
Year Founded: 2002
Current Activity Level : Actively seeking new investments

RAND CAPITAL CORPORATION
2200 Rand Building
Buffalo, NY USA 14203
Phone: 716-853-0802
Fax: 716-854-8480
Website: www.randcapital.com

Management and Staff
Allen Grum, President, CEO, Director

Type of Firm
Private Equity Firm

Association Membership
Natl Assoc of Small Bus. Inv. Co (NASBIC)

Project Preferences

Role in Financing:
Will function either as deal originator or investor in deals created by others

Type of Financing Preferred:
Early Stage
Expansion

Size of Investments Considered:
Min Size of Investment Considered (000s): $50
Max Size of Investment Considered (000s): $5,000

Geographical Preferences

United States Preferences:
Northeast

Industry Focus
(% based on actual investment)

Industrial/Energy	17.5%
Other Products	15.8%
Consumer Related	14.4%
Internet Specific	13.2%
Communications and Media	9.4%
Computer Software and Services	8.8%
Medical/Health	7.4%
Semiconductors/Other Elect.	7.1%
Computer Hardware	6.3%
Biotechnology	0.1%

Additional Information
Name of Most Recent Fund: Rand Capital Corporation
Most Recent Fund Was Raised: 06/01/1969
Year Founded: 1969
Capital Under Management: $20,000,000
Current Activity Level : Actively seeking new investments

Method of Compensation: Return on invest. most important, but chg. closing fees, service fees, etc.

RAPS FINANCE (PTY) LTD
224 Loristo Street
Pretorius Park
Pretoria, South Africa 0010
Phone: 27-12-998-8280
Fax: 27-12-998-8401
E-mail: info@raps.co.za
Website: www.raps.co.za

Type of Firm
Private Equity Firm

Association Membership
South African Venture Capital Association (SAVCA)

Project Preferences

Type of Financing Preferred:
Balanced

Geographical Preferences

International Preferences:
South Africa

Industry Preferences

In Industrial/Energy prefer:
Energy

Additional Information
Year Founded: 2003
Capital Under Management: $2,000,000
Current Activity Level : Actively seeking new investments

RAS ASSET MANAGEMENT SGR
23, Corso Italia
Milan, Italy 20122
Phone: 39-02721-64099
Fax: 39-02725-48905
E-mail: infoweb@rasfin.it
Website: www.rasfin.it

Type of Firm
Private Equity Firm

Association Membership
Italian Venture Capital Association (AIFI)

Project Preferences

Type of Financing Preferred:
Leveraged Buyout
Expansion

Size of Investments Considered:
Min Size of Investment Considered (000s): $3,811
Max Size of Investment Considered (000s): $15,242

Geographical Preferences

International Preferences:
Italy
Europe

Additional Information

Year Founded: 1981
Capital Under Management: $249,000,000
Current Activity Level : Actively seeking new investments

RASMALA PARTNERS, LTD.

The Gate Village
Building 10, Level 1
Dubai, Utd. Arab Em.
Phone: 971-4-363-5600
Fax: 971-4-363-5635
E-mail: info@rasmala.com
Website: www.rasmala.com

Management and Staff

Arif Masood Naqvi, Managing Partner
Hani Helou, Chief Financial Officer
Humayun Shahryar, Vice President
Tamer Bazzari, Chief Executive Officer

Type of Firm

Private Equity Firm

Project Preferences

Type of Financing Preferred:
Second Stage Financing
Leveraged Buyout
Early Stage
Expansion
Startup

Geographical Preferences

International Preferences:
India
Middle East
Asia
Africa

Industry Preferences

In Consumer Related prefer:
Consumer Products

In Industrial/Energy prefer:
Energy

In Financial Services prefer:
Financial Services

In Business Serv. prefer:
Media

In Manufact. prefer:
Manufacturing

Additional Information

Year Founded: 1999
Capital Under Management: $120,000,000
Current Activity Level : Actively seeking new investments

RATIONAL EQUITY LLC

760 Stillwater Road
Suite B
Mahtomedi, MN USA 55115
Phone: 651-407-0126
Fax: 651-407-0127
E-mail: info@rationalequity.com
Website: www.rationalequity.com

Management and Staff

Doug McGregor, Managing Partner

Type of Firm

Private Equity Firm

Project Preferences

Type of Financing Preferred:
Balanced

Geographical Preferences

United States Preferences:
All U.S.

Industry Preferences

In Communications prefer:
Media and Entertainment

In Medical/Health prefer:
Health Services

In Consumer Related prefer:
Retail

In Financial Services prefer:
Financial Services

In Business Serv. prefer:
Services

In Manufact. prefer:
Manufacturing

In Utilities prefer:
Utilities

Additional Information

Year Founded: 2008
Current Activity Level : Actively seeking new investments

RATOS AB

Drottninggatan 2
P.O. Box 1661
Stockholm, Sweden 111 96
Phone: 46-8-700-1700
Fax: 46-8-102-559
E-mail: info@ratos.se
Website: www.ratos.se

Other Offices

DLA Piper
P.O. Box 1364 Vika
Oslo, Norway 0114
Phone: 47-2-413-1550
Fax: 47-2-413-1501

Management and Staff

Arne Karlsson, Chief Executive Officer
Carina Strid, Chief Financial Officer

Type of Firm

Private Equity Firm

Association Membership

Swedish Venture Capital Association (SVCA)
European Private Equity and Venture Capital Assoc.

Project Preferences

Type of Financing Preferred:
Leveraged Buyout
Expansion
Later Stage
Acquisition

Size of Investments Considered:
Min Size of Investment Considered (000s): $25,428
Max Size of Investment Considered (000s): $152,564

Geographical Preferences

International Preferences:
Sweden
Scandanavia/Nordic Region

Industry Focus

(% based on actual investment)

Other Products	37.4%
Internet Specific	27.4%
Medical/Health	16.9%
Biotechnology	7.5%
Computer Software and Services	5.2%
Communications and Media	5.1%
Consumer Related	0.3%
Computer Hardware	0.2%

Additional Information

Year Founded: 1995
Capital Under Management: $1,198,500,000
Current Activity Level : Actively seeking new investments

RAY & VENTURE INVESTMENT CO., LTD.

1412 High Brand Living Bldg.
215 Yangjae-dong Seocho-ku
Seoul, South Korea
Phone: 822-2155-3611
Fax: 822-2155-3655

Management and Staff

Hakkyun Kim, President

Type of Firm
Private Equity Firm

Project Preferences

Type of Financing Preferred:
Balanced

Geographical Preferences

International Preferences:
Korea, South

Additional Information
Year Founded: 2000
Capital Under Management: $32,500,000
Current Activity Level : Actively seeking new investments

RAYMOND JAMES, LTD.
925 West Georgia Street
Suite 2100
Vancouver, Canada V6C 3L2
Phone: 604-659-8000
Fax: 604-659-8099
Website: www.raymondjames.ca

Other Offices
707 Eighth Avenue South West
Suite 2300
Calgary, Canada T2P 1H5
Phone: 403-221-0333
Fax: 403-221-0350

925 West Georgia Street
Suite 2100
Vancouver, Canada V6C 3L2
Phone: 604-659-8000
Fax: 604-659-8099

Management and Staff
Darren Martin, Senior Managing Director
Ian Brown, Senior Managing Director
Mark Kennedy, Senior Managing Director
Roland Cardy, Senior Managing Director

Type of Firm
Investment Management Firm

Additional Information
Year Founded: 1929
Current Activity Level : Actively seeking new investments

RB WEBBER & COMPANY
2637 Marine Way
Suite 100
Mountain View, CA USA 94043
Phone: 650-903-7500
Fax: 650-903-7575
E-mail: info@rbwebber.com
Website: www.rbwebber.com

Management and Staff
Jeffrey Webber, Partner
Joseph Brilando, Partner
Katharine Boshkoff, Partner
Mark Hamilton, Principal
Rob Meinhardt, Principal
Robert Lauridsen, Partner
Stephen Plume, Partner
Stephen Jordan, Partner
Todd Keleher, Principal

Type of Firm
Private Equity Firm

Project Preferences

Type of Financing Preferred:
Early Stage

Geographical Preferences

United States Preferences:
All U.S.

Industry Preferences

In Communications prefer:
Wireless Communications

In Computer Software prefer:
Software

In Internet Specific prefer:
E-Commerce Technology

Additional Information
Name of Most Recent Fund: Entrepreneurs' Fund III, The (AKA: TEF3)
Most Recent Fund Was Raised: 08/23/2007
Year Founded: 1991
Capital Under Management: $9,700,000
Current Activity Level : Actively seeking new investments

RBC CAPITAL PARTNERS/ RBC TECHNOLOGY VENTURES
200 Bay Street
4th Floor, North Tower
Toronto, Canada M5J 2W7
Phone: 416-842-2000
Fax: 416-842-4060
E-mail: rbcpact@rbcds.com
Website: www.rbcap.com

Other Offices
One East Weaver Street
3rd Floor
Greenwich, CT USA 06831
Phone: 212-428-6902
Fax: 212-428-3069

Suite 1340 - B.C. Gas Building
1111 West Georgia Street
Vancouver, Canada V6C 2X8
Phone: 604-665-0460
Fax: 604-665-8699

One Place Ville Marie
Fourth Floor, North Wing
Montreal, Canada H3C 3A9
Phone: 514-874-5081
Fax: 514-874-2294

Two Embarcadero Center
Suite 1200
San Francisco, CA USA 94111
Phone: 415-633-8619

75 Fifth Street, NW
Suite 900
Atlanta, GA USA 30308
Phone: 404-495-6060

Management and Staff
Alan Hibben, Chief Executive Officer
Bruce Rothstein, Managing Partner
Darin Booth, Partner
Doug McGregor, Managing Director
Euclid Sarjoo, Partner
Greg Connor, Partner
Howard Steinberg, Partner
John Coady, Partner
Louis Draper, Managing Director
Marc Daniel, Managing Director
Paul McDermott, Managing Partner
Peter Diedrich, Managing Partner
Robert Antoniades, Managing Director
Tony Manastersky, Managing Partner
Troy Maxwell, Chief Financial Officer
Wally Hunter, Partner

Type of Firm
Bank Affiliated

Association Membership
National Venture Capital Association - USA (NVCA)
Canadian Venture Capital Association

Project Preferences

Role in Financing:
Prefer role as deal originator but will also invest in deals created by others

Type of Financing Preferred:
Second Stage Financing
Leveraged Buyout
Early Stage
Mezzanine
Expansion
Balanced
Seed
First Stage Financing
Startup
Acquisition

Size of Investments Considered:
Min Size of Investment Considered (000s): $3,000
Max Size of Investment Considered (000s): $20,000

Geographical Preferences

Canadian Preferences:
All Canada

Industry Focus

(% based on actual investment)

Computer Software and Services	22.4%
Communications and Media	16.2%
Biotechnology	16.1%
Industrial/Energy	14.3%
Medical/Health	13.4%
Internet Specific	10.1%
Semiconductors/Other Elect.	4.3%
Other Products	2.8%
Consumer Related	0.3%

Additional Information

Year Founded: 1969
Capital Under Management: $800,000,000
Current Activity Level : Actively seeking new investments
Method of Compensation: Return on invest. most important, but chg. closing fees, service fees, etc.

RBC DAIN RAUSCHER

Dain Rauscher Plaza
60 South Sixth Street
Minneapolis, MN USA 55402-4422
Phone: 612-371-7676
Fax: 612-371-2763
Website: www.rbcdain.com

Management and Staff

Ian Berman, Managing Director
Jeffrey Greiner, Managing Director
Mary Zimmer, Managing Director
Peter Grant, Managing Director
Robert Reynolds, Managing Director
Suzanne Bookstein, Managing Director

Type of Firm

Bank Affiliated

Industry Focus

(% based on actual investment)

Computer Software and Services	30.0%
Internet Specific	26.5%
Communications and Media	19.9%
Semiconductors/Other Elect.	14.9%
Computer Hardware	4.5%
Medical/Health	2.8%
Consumer Related	1.5%

Additional Information

Year Founded: 1999
Capital Under Management: $23,000,000
Current Activity Level : Actively seeking new investments

RBK HANNOVER MBH & CO. KG

Osterstrasse 60
Hannover, Germany 30159
Phone: 49-511353995-40
Fax: 49-511353995-43
Website: www.bk-hannover.de

Management and Staff

Hans-Georg Martensen, Managing Director
Stephanie Breiter, Managing Director

Type of Firm

Bank Affiliated

Association Membership

German Venture Capital Association (BVK)

Project Preferences

Type of Financing Preferred:
Expansion
Later Stage
Management Buyouts
Startup
Recapitalizations

Geographical Preferences

International Preferences:
Germany

Additional Information

Year Founded: 2001
Current Activity Level : Actively seeking new investments

RBS MEZZANINE LTD

42 St Andrew Street
Edinburgh, United Kingdom EH2 2YE
Phone: 44-207-375-5000
Fax: 44-207-375-5392
E-mail: leveragedfinance@rbs.co.uk
Website: www.rbs.co.uk

Management and Staff

Leith Robertson, Managing Director

Type of Firm

Bank Affiliated

Association Membership

British Venture Capital Association (BVCA)

Project Preferences

Type of Financing Preferred:
Leveraged Buyout
Expansion
Mezzanine
Public Companies
Turnaround
Management Buyouts
Private Placement
Recapitalizations

Geographical Preferences

International Preferences:
United Kingdom
Europe

Industry Focus

(% based on actual investment)

Other Products	68.5%
Semiconductors/Other Elect.	24.7%
Industrial/Energy	6.8%

Additional Information

Year Founded: 1996
Capital Under Management: $704,700,000
Current Activity Level : Actively seeking new investments

RCP ADVISORS LLC

100 North Riverside Plaza
Suite 2400
Chicago, IL USA 60606
Phone: 312-266-7300
Fax: 312-266-7433
E-mail: info@rcpadvisors.com
Website: www.rcpadvisors.com

Other Offices

8235 Forsyth Boulevard
Suite 1101
Saint Louis, MO USA 63105
Phone: 314-678-1200
Fax: 314-678-1212

949 South Coast Drive
Suite 550
Costa Mesa, CA USA 92626
Phone: 949-335-5000
Fax: 714-754-1492

Management and Staff

Jon Madorsky, Principal
Michael Feinglass, Principal
Nell Blatherwick, Principal

Type of Firm

Private Equity Advisor or Fund of Funds

Project Preferences

Role in Financing:
Other

Type of Financing Preferred:
Fund of Funds
Leveraged Buyout
Fund of Funds of Second

Geographical Preferences

United States Preferences:
All U.S.

Additional Information

Name of Most Recent Fund: RCP Fund IV, L.P.
Most Recent Fund Was Raised: 07/05/2006
Year Founded: 2001
Capital Under Management: $1,500,000,000
Current Activity Level : Actively seeking new investments

REALZA CAPITAL SGECR SA

Paseo de la Castellana, 50 - 4
Madrid, Spain 28046
Phone: 34-91-782-0982
Fax: 34-91-782-0983
E-mail: bv@realzacapital.com
Website: www.realzacapital.com

Management and Staff

Alfredo Zavala, Founder
Martin Gonzalez del Valle, Founder
Sonsoles Manglano, Chief Financial Officer

Type of Firm

Private Equity Firm

Project Preferences

Role in Financing:

Prefer role as deal originator but will also invest in deals created by others

Type of Financing Preferred:

Leveraged Buyout

Size of Investments Considered:

Min Size of Investment Considered (000s): $14,665
Max Size of Investment Considered (000s): $36,662

Geographical Preferences

International Preferences:

Spain

Additional Information

Name of Most Recent Fund: Realza Capital Fondo FCR
Most Recent Fund Was Raised: 09/19/2007
Year Founded: 2007
Capital Under Management: $236,900,000
Current Activity Level : Actively seeking new investments

RECAP MANAGEMENT GMBH

Spittelwiese 7-9
Linz, Austria 4020
Phone: 43-70-651789-15
Fax: 43-70-651789-20
E-mail: office@recap.cc
Website: www.recap.cc

Other Offices

Zurcherstrasse 202
St. Gallen, Switzerland 9014
Phone: 41-71-272-23-00
Fax: 41-71-272-23-19

Turkenstrasse 104
Munchen, Germany 80799
Phone: 49-89-3838-91-23
Fax: 48-89-3838-91-22

Management and Staff

Anton Stumpf, Managing Partner
Fred Duswald, Managing Partner

Type of Firm

Private Equity Firm

Association Membership

Austrian PE and Venture Capital Association (AVCO)

Project Preferences

Type of Financing Preferred:

Acquisition

Geographical Preferences

International Preferences:

Switzerland
Europe
Austria
Germany

Additional Information

Year Founded: 2007
Current Activity Level : Actively seeking new investments

RECOGNITION GROUP, THE

40 Broad Street
Suite 500
New York, NY USA 10004
Phone: 212-774-3700
Fax: 212-480-8805

Other Offices

473 Pine Street
5th Floor
San Francisco, CA USA 94104
Phone: 415-743-0050
Fax: 707-929-8357

Management and Staff

John Fisher, Partner
Juan-Carlos Garcia, Managing Director
Kaleil D. Isaza Tuzman, Managing Director

Type of Firm

Bank Affiliated

Project Preferences

Type of Financing Preferred:

Leveraged Buyout
Distressed Debt

Geographical Preferences

United States Preferences:

Northeast
New York

International Preferences:

Latin America

Additional Information

Year Founded: 2001
Capital Under Management: $15,000,000
Current Activity Level : Actively seeking new investments

RED ABBEY VENTURE PARTNERS, LLC

2330 West Joppa Road
Suite 330
Timonium, MD USA 21093
Phone: 410-494-7401
Website: www.redabbey.com

Management and Staff

David U Prichard, Venture Partner
Jigar Raythatha, Principal
Matt Zuga, Managing Director

Type of Firm

Private Equity Firm

Project Preferences

Role in Financing:

Prefer role in deals created by others

Type of Financing Preferred:

Early Stage

Industry Preferences

In Biotechnology prefer:

Biotechnology

In Medical/Health prefer:

Medical Diagnostics
Drug/Equipmt Delivery
Medical Products
Pharmaceuticals

Additional Information

Name of Most Recent Fund: Red Abbey CEO's Fund, LP
Most Recent Fund Was Raised: 08/18/2004
Year Founded: 2003
Capital Under Management: $50,000,000
Current Activity Level : Actively seeking new investments

RED ACRE CAPITAL LLC

217 Deerfield Drive
Berlin, CT USA 06037
Phone: 978-944-2672
Fax: 978-236-7228
E-mail: acquisitions@redacrecapital.com
Website: www.redacre.com

Type of Firm
Private Equity Firm

Project Preferences

Type of Financing Preferred:
Leveraged Buyout

Geographical Preferences

United States Preferences:
Mid Atlantic
West Virginia

Industry Preferences

In Consumer Related prefer:
Retail

In Business Serv. prefer:
Services

In Manufact. prefer:
Manufacturing

Additional Information
Year Founded: 2008
Current Activity Level : Actively seeking new investments

RED BARN INVESTMENTS LLC

1101 Skokie Boulevard
Suite 245
Northbrook, IL USA 60062
Phone: 847-498-0890
Fax: 847-498-0891
E-mail: info@redbarnllc.com
Website: www.redbarnllc.com

Management and Staff
Patrick Pollard, General Partner
Terrance Holt, General Partner

Type of Firm
Private Equity Firm

Project Preferences

Type of Financing Preferred:
Expansion
Acquisition
Recapitalizations

Size of Investments Considered:
Min Size of Investment Considered (000s): $1,000
Max Size of Investment Considered (000s): $5,000

Industry Preferences

In Communications prefer:
Media and Entertainment

In Computer Software prefer:
Software

In Medical/Health prefer:
Health Services

In Consumer Related prefer:
Consumer
Retail

In Industrial/Energy prefer:
Energy

In Transportation prefer:
Transportation

In Business Serv. prefer:
Services
Distribution

In Manufact. prefer:
Manufacturing

Additional Information
Year Founded: 2009
Current Activity Level : Actively seeking new investments

RED OAK CAPITAL

5057 Keller Springs Road
Suite 100
Dallas, TX USA 75371
Phone: 214-545-3474
Fax: 214-545-3469
Website: www.redoakcapital.com

Management and Staff
Alan Moore, Founder

Type of Firm
Private Equity Firm

Project Preferences

Role in Financing:
Prefer role as deal originator but will also invest in deals created by others

Type of Financing Preferred:
Expansion
Later Stage
Acquisition

Size of Investments Considered:
Min Size of Investment Considered (000s): $500
Max Size of Investment Considered (000s): $5,000

Geographical Preferences

United States Preferences:
Southwest

Industry Preferences

In Financial Services prefer:
Real Estate

Additional Information
Year Founded: 2000
Capital Under Management: $35,000,000
Current Activity Level : Actively seeking new investments
Method of Compensation: Return on invest. most important, but chg. closing fees, service fees, etc.

RED RIVER VENTURES

6860 North Dallas Parkway
Suite 200
Plano, TX USA 75024
Phone: 972-265-7946
Fax: 972-265-7995
Website: www.redriverventures.com

Other Offices
1155 University Boulevard SE
Albuquerque, NM USA 87106
Phone: 505-843-4275
Fax: 505-843-4273

Management and Staff
J. Bruce Duty, Partner
James Wolfe, Partner
Scott Letier, Chief Financial Officer

Type of Firm
Private Equity Firm

Association Membership
Natl Assoc of Small Bus. Inv. Co (NASBIC)

Project Preferences

Role in Financing:
Will function either as deal originator or investor in deals created by others

Type of Financing Preferred:
Expansion
Later Stage
Management Buyouts
Recapitalizations

Size of Investments Considered:
Min Size of Investment Considered (000s): $3,000
Max Size of Investment Considered (000s): $6,000

Geographical Preferences

United States Preferences:
Southwest
Texas

Industry Preferences

In Semiconductor/Electr prefer:
Electronic Components
Controllers and Sensors
Component Testing Equipmt

In Medical/Health prefer:
Medical/Health
Medical Products
Health Services

In Consumer Related prefer:
Education Related

In Industrial/Energy prefer:
Industrial Products

In Financial Services prefer:
Financial Services

In Business Serv. prefer:
Services

In Manufact. prefer:
Manufacturing

Additional Information

Name of Most Recent Fund: Red River Ventures I, LP
Most Recent Fund Was Raised: 06/30/2000
Year Founded: 2000
Capital Under Management: $86,000,000
Current Activity Level : Actively seeking new investments
Method of Compensation: Return on investment is of primary concern, do not charge fees

---

RED ROCK VENTURES

180 Lytton Avenue
Palo Alto, CA USA 94301
Phone: 650-325-3111
Fax: 650-853-7044
E-mail: info@redrockventures.com
Website: www.redrockventures.com

Management and Staff

Curtis Myers, General Partner
Laura Brege, General Partner
Laura Gwosden, Chief Financial Officer
Peter Dumanian, General Partner
Robert Marsh, General Partner
Robert Todd, General Partner

Type of Firm

Private Equity Firm

Association Membership

Western Association of Venture Capitalists (WAVC)
Natl Assoc of Small Bus. Inv. Co (NASBIC)

Project Preferences

Role in Financing:
Will function either as deal originator or investor in deals created by others

Type of Financing Preferred:
Seed
First Stage Financing

Size of Investments Considered:
Min Size of Investment Considered (000s): $500
Max Size of Investment Considered (000s): $5,000

Geographical Preferences

United States Preferences:
West Coast

Industry Focus

(% based on actual investment)

Computer Software and Services	51.1%
Internet Specific	35.8%
Computer Hardware	7.9%
Communications and Media	4.6%
Medical/Health	0.5%

Additional Information

Name of Most Recent Fund: Red Rock Ventures III, L.P.
Most Recent Fund Was Raised: 10/01/2000
Year Founded: 1997
Capital Under Management: $223,000,000
Current Activity Level : Actively seeking new investments

RED TOP CAPITAL LLC (FKA: CRIMSON CAPITAL COMPANY)

6192 Old Ironworks Road
Greensboro, NC USA 27455
Phone: 336-643-5133
Fax: 336-855-8588
E-mail: Partners@Redtopcapital.com
Website: www.redtopcapital.com

Other Offices

625 Walnut Ridge Drive
Suite 109
Hartland, WI USA 53029
Phone: 262-369-5175
Fax: 262-369-5174

Management and Staff

David Parker, Partner
Theodore Rolfs, Partner
Thomas Rolfs, Partner

Type of Firm

Private Equity Firm

Project Preferences

Type of Financing Preferred:
Leveraged Buyout
Management Buyouts

Industry Focus

(% based on actual investment)

Internet Specific	100.0%

Additional Information

Name of Most Recent Fund: Crimson Capital Company
Most Recent Fund Was Raised: 12/01/1990
Year Founded: 1993
Current Activity Level : Actively seeking new investments

RED ZONE CAPITAL PARTNERS

1800 Tysons Boulevard
Suite 550
McLean, VA USA 22102
Phone: 301-765-5345

Management and Staff

Dwight Schar, Partner

Type of Firm

Private Equity Firm

Project Preferences

Type of Financing Preferred:
Leveraged Buyout

Geographical Preferences

United States Preferences:
All U.S.

Additional Information

Name of Most Recent Fund: Red Zone Capital Partners II, L.P.
Most Recent Fund Was Raised: 11/07/2006
Year Founded: 2006
Capital Under Management: $126,000,000
Current Activity Level : Actively seeking new investments

REDBACK NETWORKS, INC.

300 Holger Way
San Jose, CA USA 95134
Phone: 408-750-5000
Fax: 408-750-5599
Website: www.redback.com

Other Offices

300 Holger Way
San Jose, CA USA 95134
Phone: 408-750-5000
Fax: 408-750-5599

Management and Staff

Kevin DeNuccio, Chief Executive Officer

Type of Firm

Private Equity Firm

Additional Information

Year Founded: 2002
Current Activity Level : Actively seeking new investments

REDBUS INVESTMENTS, LTD. (AKA: REDBUS GROUP)

Ariel House
74A Charlotte Street
London, United Kingdom W1T 4QJ
Phone: 44-207-299-8844
Fax: 44-207-299-8840
E-mail: info@redbus.co.uk
Website: www.invest.redbus.co.uk

Management and Staff

Dean Dorrell, Chief Executive Officer

Type of Firm

Private Equity Firm

Project Preferences

Type of Financing Preferred:
Balanced
Recapitalizations

Geographical Preferences

International Preferences:
United Kingdom

Additional Information

Year Founded: 1998
Capital Under Management: $24,700,000
Current Activity Level : Actively seeking new investments

REDFIRE INVESTMENTS PTY, LTD.

Level 2, 217 Queen Street
Melbourne, Australia 3000
Phone: 613-8610-2527
Fax: 613-9670-6495
E-mail: info@redfireinvestments.com.au
Website: www.redfireinvestments.com.au

Management and Staff

Geoff Drucker, Co-Founder
Gordon Crosbie-Walsh, Co-Founder

Type of Firm

Private Equity Firm

Project Preferences

Type of Financing Preferred:
Early Stage
Expansion

Geographical Preferences

International Preferences:
Australia
Asia

Industry Preferences

In Industrial/Energy prefer:
Environmental Related

Additional Information

Year Founded: 2008
Capital Under Management: $10,000,000
Current Activity Level : Actively seeking new investments

REDHILLS VENTURES LLC

2620 Regatta Drive
Suite 208
Las Vegas, NV USA 89128
Phone: 702-233-2160
Fax: 702-233-2167
E-mail: info@redhillsventures.com
Website: www.redhillsventures.com

Type of Firm

Private Equity Firm

Association Membership

National Venture Capital Association - USA (NVCA)

Project Preferences

Size of Investments Considered:
Min Size of Investment Considered (000s): $125
Max Size of Investment Considered (000s): $7,000

Industry Preferences

In Medical/Health prefer:
Health Services

Additional Information

Year Founded: 2002
Current Activity Level : Actively seeking new investments

REDHORSE CO., LTD.

3-6-16 Kita Aoyama
Minato-ku
Tokyo, Japan 107-0061
Phone: 813-5766-5111
Fax: 813-5766-4029
Website: www.redhorse.co.jp

Management and Staff

Shin Iijima, Chief Financial Officer
Takashi Onozawa, Chief Executive Officer
Takashi Murakoshi, Chief Operating Officer

Type of Firm

Private Equity Advisor or Fund of Funds

Project Preferences

Type of Financing Preferred:
Early Stage
Expansion
Balanced

Geographical Preferences

International Preferences:
Japan

Additional Information

Year Founded: 1974
Current Activity Level : Actively seeking new investments

REDLEAF GROUP, INC

14395 Saratoga Avenue
Suite 130
Saratoga, CA USA 95070
Phone: 408-868-0800
Fax: 408-868-0810
Website: www.redleaf.com

Other Offices

100 First Avenue
Suite 1100
Pittsburgh, PA USA 15222
Phone: 412-201-5600
Fax: 412-201-5650

555 West Fifth Street
30th Floor
Los Angeles, CA USA 90013
Phone: 213-996-8397
Fax: 213-996-8564

2100 Reston Parkway
Suite 204
Reston, VA USA 20191
Phone: 703-860-3000
Fax: 703-860-3100

999 Third Avenue
Suite 2424
Seattle, WA USA 98104
Phone: 206-447-1350
Fax: 206-4471351

Management and Staff

Charles Sum, Managing Director
George Hoyem, Managing Director
Michael Nelson, Managing Director

Type of Firm

Private Equity Firm

Association Membership

Mid-Atlantic Venture Association

Project Preferences

Role in Financing:
Prefer role as deal originator

Type of Financing Preferred:
Seed
First Stage Financing

Size of Investments Considered:
Min Size of Investment Considered (000s): $1,000
Max Size of Investment Considered (000s): $20,000

Geographical Preferences

United States Preferences:
California

Industry Focus

(% based on actual investment)

Computer Software and Services	44.2%
Internet Specific	25.4%
Other Products	10.4%
Communications and Media	9.3%
Medical/Health	8.2%
Consumer Related	2.4%

Additional Information

Name of Most Recent Fund: Redleaf Group Inc. (FKA: Redleaf Venture II, L.P.)
Most Recent Fund Was Raised: 05/01/2000
Year Founded: 1996
Capital Under Management: $250,000,000
Current Activity Level : Actively seeking new investments
Method of Compensation: Return on investment is of primary concern, do not charge fees

---

REDMONT VENTURE PARTNERS

500 Beacon Parkway West
Birmingham, AL USA 35209
Phone: 205-943-5646
Fax: 205-943-4748
Website: www.redmontvp.com

Management and Staff

Philip Hodges, Managing Director
Roddy Clark, Managing Director

Type of Firm

Private Equity Firm

Association Membership

National Venture Capital Association - USA (NVCA)

Project Preferences

Role in Financing:
Will function either as deal originator or investor in deals created by others

Type of Financing Preferred:
Second Stage Financing
Early Stage
Expansion
First Stage Financing
Startup
Recapitalizations

Size of Investments Considered:
Min Size of Investment Considered (000s): $500
Max Size of Investment Considered (000s): $3,000

Geographical Preferences

United States Preferences:
Southeast
Alabama

Industry Preferences

In Computer Software prefer:
Computer Services
Software
Systems Software
Applications Software

In Biotechnology prefer:
Human Biotechnology
Genetic Engineering
Agricultural/Animal Bio.
Industrial Biotechnology
Biosensors
Biotech Related Research

In Medical/Health prefer:
Medical Diagnostics
Diagnostic Services
Diagnostic Test Products
Medical Therapeutics
Medical Products
Disposable Med. Products
Pharmaceuticals

In Industrial/Energy prefer:
Industrial Products

In Manufact. prefer:
Manufacturing

In Agr/Forestr/Fish prefer:
Agriculture related

Additional Information

Name of Most Recent Fund: Enhanced Alabama Issuer II LLC
Most Recent Fund Was Raised: 06/24/2008
Year Founded: 1997
Capital Under Management: $33,700,000
Current Activity Level : Actively seeking new investments
Method of Compensation: Return on investment is of primary concern, do not charge fees

---

REDPOINT VENTURES

3000 Sand Hill Road
Building Two, Suite 290
Menlo Park, CA USA 94025
Phone: 650-926-5600
Fax: 650-854-5762
E-mail: ideas@redpoint.com
Website: www.redpoint.com

Other Offices

11150 Santa Monica Boulevard
Suite 1200
Los Angeles, CA USA 90025
Phone: 310-477-7678
Fax: 310-312-1868

1366 Nanjin Road West
Plaza 66, Tower 2, Suite 2904
Shanghai, China 200040
Phone: 86-21-6288-7757
Fax: 86-21-6288-7797

Management and Staff

Allen Beasley, Partner
Chris Moore, Partner
David Yuan, Partner
Fouad ElNaggar, Principal
G. Bradford Jones, Founding Partner
Geoff Yang, Founding Partner
Greg Martin, Partner
Jeffrey Brody, Founding Partner
John Walecka, Founding Partner
Lars Pedersen, Chief Financial Officer
Nety Krishna, Venture Partner
Pueo Keffer, Vice President
R. Thomas Dyal, Founding Partner
Satish Dharmaraj, Partner
Scott Raney, Partner
Tim Haley, Founding Partner

Type of Firm

Private Equity Firm

Association Membership

National Venture Capital Association - USA (NVCA)

Project Preferences

Type of Financing Preferred:
Early Stage
Balanced
Later Stage

Geographical Preferences

United States Preferences:
All U.S.

Industry Focus

(% based on actual investment)

Internet Specific	33.1%
Communications and Media	29.9%
Semiconductors/Other Elect.	12.7%
Computer Software and Services	11.1%
Industrial/Energy	7.5%
Other Products	2.4%
Computer Hardware	1.9%
Consumer Related	0.9%
Medical/Health	0.6%

Additional Information

Name of Most Recent Fund: Redpoint Omega, L.P.
Most Recent Fund Was Raised: 02/26/2007
Year Founded: 1999
Capital Under Management: $2,000,000,000
Current Activity Level : Actively seeking new investments

REDSHIFT VENTURES (FKA: SPACEVEST CAPITAL)

5425 Wisconsin Avenue
Suite 704
Chevy Chase, MD USA 20815
Phone: 703-904-9800
Fax: 703-904-0571

E-mail: spacevest@spacevest.com
Website: www.redshiftventures.com

Other Offices

3057 Nutley Street
Suite 562
Fairfax, VA USA 22031
Phone: 703-904-9800

Management and Staff

Mark Frantz, Venture Partner
Richard Harris, Managing General Partner
Srinivas Mirmira, Venture Partner

Type of Firm

Private Equity Firm

Association Membership

Mid-Atlantic Venture Association
National Venture Capital Association - USA (NVCA)

Project Preferences

Role in Financing:

Will function either as deal originator or investor in deals created by others

Type of Financing Preferred:

Early Stage
Expansion

Size of Investments Considered:

Min Size of Investment Considered (000s): $1,000
Max Size of Investment Considered (000s): $5,000

Industry Focus

(% based on actual investment)

Communications and Media	36.4%
Computer Software and Services	28.2%
Semiconductors/Other Elect.	17.2%
Internet Specific	15.5%
Industrial/Energy	1.8%
Other Products	0.9%

Additional Information

Name of Most Recent Fund: RedShift Ventures III, L.P. (FKA: SpaceVest III)
Most Recent Fund Was Raised: 04/18/2001
Year Founded: 1991
Capital Under Management: $222,000,000
Current Activity Level : Actively seeking new investments
Method of Compensation: Return on invest. most important, but chg. closing fees, service fees, etc.

REDWOOD VENTURE PARTNERS

4984 El Camino Real
Suite 200
Los Altos, CA USA 94022
Phone: 650-335-1111
Fax: 650-335-1110
E-mail: info@redwoodvp.com
Website: www.redwoodvp.com

Management and Staff

Jeffrey Yasuda, Chief Financial Officer
Karim Walji, Managing Director
Raj Parekh, Founding Partner
Raj Singh, Founding Partner
Sanjiv Ahuja, Partner

Type of Firm

Private Equity Firm

Project Preferences

Role in Financing:

Will function either as deal originator or investor in deals created by others

Type of Financing Preferred:

Second Stage Financing
Early Stage
First Stage Financing

Size of Investments Considered:

Min Size of Investment Considered (000s): $1,000
Max Size of Investment Considered (000s): $10,000

Industry Preferences

In Communications prefer:

Telecommunications
Wireless Communications
Data Communications
Other Communication Prod.

In Biotechnology prefer:

Biotechnology

Additional Information

Name of Most Recent Fund: Redwood Ventures IV, LP
Most Recent Fund Was Raised: 09/29/2000
Year Founded: 1999
Capital Under Management: $150,000,000
Current Activity Level : Actively seeking new investments
Method of Compensation: Return on investment is of primary concern, do not charge fees

---

REED ELSEVIER VENTURES

1-3 Strand
London, United Kingdom WC2N 5JR
Phone: 44-20-7930-7077
Fax: 44-20-7166-5799
E-mail: ventures@reedelsevier.co.uk
Website: www.reedelsevier.com

Other Offices

Radarweg 29
Amsterdam, Netherlands 1043 NX
Phone: 31-20-485-2222
Fax: 31-20-618-0325

125 Park Avenue
23rd Floor
New York, NY USA 10017
Phone: 212-309-5498
Fax: 212-309-5480

Management and Staff

Ian Smith, Chief Executive Officer
Kevin Brown, Partner
Mark Armour, Chief Financial Officer
Tony Askew, Managing Director

Type of Firm

Corporate PE/Venture

Project Preferences

Type of Financing Preferred:

Early Stage
Expansion
Later Stage
Startup

Size of Investments Considered:

Min Size of Investment Considered (000s): $2,000
Max Size of Investment Considered (000s): $10,000

Geographical Preferences

United States Preferences:

All U.S.

International Preferences:

Europe
Israel

Industry Preferences

In Computer Software prefer:

Applications Software

In Semiconductor/Electr prefer:

Electronics

In Medical/Health prefer:

Medical/Health

In Business Serv. prefer:

Media

Additional Information

Year Founded: 2000
Capital Under Management: $200,000,000
Current Activity Level : Actively seeking new investments

REFERENCE CAPITAL MANAGEMENT LLC (FKA: CASCADIA PARTNERS)

7128 Southwest Gonzaga Street
Suite 150
Portland, OR USA 97223
Phone: 503-282-2885
Fax: 503-282-2976
E-mail: info@cascadia-partners.com
Website: www.cascadia-partners.com

Management and Staff

John Metcalf, Managing Partner
Wayne Embree, Managing Partner

Type of Firm

Private Equity Firm

Project Preferences

Type of Financing Preferred:
Early Stage

Geographical Preferences

United States Preferences:
Northwest

International Preferences:
Pacific

Industry Preferences

In Industrial/Energy prefer:
Energy

Additional Information

Year Founded: 1986
Current Activity Level : Actively seeking new investments

REGAL INVESTMENT

18 Queen's Road
21/F New World Tower 1
Central, China
Phone: 852-2583-2400
Fax: 852-3020-4990
E-mail: info@chinaapo.com.cn
Website: www.chinaapo.com.cn

Other Offices

No. 12 ChaoWai Street
Room 1509 KunTai Int'l Mansion
Beijing, China
Phone: 86-10-5905-1049
Fax: 86-10-5905-1046

27/F Int'l Chamber of Commerce Tower
Fuhua Road, Futian District
Shenzhen, China
Phone: 86-755-83024518
Fax: 86-75583024137

49 Showers Drive
Suite W102
Mountain View, CA USA 94040
Phone: 650-281-8375

Management and Staff

Jian Wu, President & Chairman
Jianhua Lu, Chief Financial Officer

Type of Firm

Bank Affiliated

Project Preferences

Type of Financing Preferred:
Balanced

Geographical Preferences

International Preferences:
China

Industry Preferences

In Computer Software prefer:
Software

In Internet Specific prefer:
Internet

In Semiconductor/Electr prefer:
Semiconductor

In Medical/Health prefer:
Medical/Health

In Business Serv. prefer:
Media

Additional Information

Year Founded: 2004
Current Activity Level : Actively seeking new investments

REGIONALIS FEJLESZTESI HOLDING RT.

Baross u. 22-26.
Budapest, Hungary 1085
Phone: 36-1-486-3120
Fax: 36-1-486-3176
E-mail: rfh-rt@rfh-rt.hu
Website: www.rfh-rt.hu

Management and Staff

Zoltan Kis, Chief Executive Officer

Type of Firm

Private Equity Firm

Association Membership

Hungarian Venture Capital Association (HVCA)
European Private Equity and Venture Capital Assoc.

Project Preferences

Type of Financing Preferred:
Balanced

Geographical Preferences

International Preferences:
Hungary
Eastern Europe

Additional Information

Year Founded: 2000
Current Activity Level : Actively seeking new investments

REGIONALNE FUNDUSZE INWESTYCJI SP. Z O.O.

Wroblewskiego 18
Lodz, Poland 93-578
Phone: 48-42-685-53-10
Fax: 48-42-685-53-13
E-mail: biuro@rfi.pl
Website: www.rfi.pl

Other Offices

ul. Graniczna 29
Katowice, Poland 40-017
Phone: 48-32-209-0497
Fax: 48-32-255-2274

Management and Staff

Edward Sieranski, Chief Executive Officer

Type of Firm

Incubator/Development Program

Association Membership

Polish Venture Capital Association (PSIC/PPEA)
European Private Equity and Venture Capital Assoc.

Project Preferences

Type of Financing Preferred:
Early Stage
Expansion
Startup

Size of Investments Considered:
Min Size of Investment Considered (000s): $100
Max Size of Investment Considered (000s): $100,000

Geographical Preferences

International Preferences:
Poland

Industry Preferences

In Computer Other prefer:
Computer Related

In Medical/Health prefer:
Medical/Health

In Industrial/Energy prefer:
Industrial Products
Materials

In Business Serv. prefer:
Services

In Manufact. prefer:
Manufacturing

Additional Information

Year Founded: 1997
Capital Under Management: $3,300,000
Current Activity Level : Actively seeking new investments

REICHMANNHAUER CAPITAL PARTNERS

One First Canadian Place
Suite 3300, P.O. Box 72
Toronto, Canada M5X 1B1
Phone: 416-862-6040
Fax: 416-862-6908
E-mail: info@rhcapitalpartners.com
Website: www.rhcp.ca

Management and Staff

Andrew Cockwell, Principal
Frank Hauer, Co-Founder
John Kelleher, Principal
Pashant Pathak, Managing Partner
Phillip Reichmann, Co-Founder

Type of Firm

Private Equity Firm

Additional Information

Year Founded: 2009
Current Activity Level : Actively seeking new investments

REINVESTMENT FUND, THE (AKA: TRF)

718 Arch Street
Suite 300 North
Philadelphia, PA USA 19106
Phone: 215-574-5800
Fax: 215-574-5900
E-mail: Info@trfund.com
Website: www.trfund.com

Other Offices

1025 Connecticut Avenue Northwest
Suite 901
Washington, DC USA 20036
Phone: 202-223-3361
Fax: 202-223-3363

1120 North Charles Street
Suite 102
Baltimore, MD USA 21201
Phone: 410-637-8268
Fax: 410-637-8265

Management and Staff

C. Sean Closkey, President
Donald Hinkle-Brown, President
Nancy Wagner-Hislip, Managing Director
Robert Sanders, Managing Director
Sara Vernon Sterman, Managing Director

Type of Firm

Incubator/Development Program

Association Membership

Mid-Atlantic Venture Association
Community Development Venture Capital Alliance

Project Preferences

Role in Financing:

Will function either as deal originator or investor in deals created by others

Type of Financing Preferred:

Mezzanine
Later Stage

Size of Investments Considered:

Min Size of Investment Considered (000s): $1,000
Max Size of Investment Considered (000s): $5,000

Geographical Preferences

United States Preferences:

Mid Atlantic

Industry Focus

(% based on actual investment)

Industrial/Energy	57.8%
Other Products	21.1%
Consumer Related	8.6%
Internet Specific	6.5%
Medical/Health	5.5%
Computer Software and Services	0.6%

Additional Information

Name of Most Recent Fund: Sustainable Development Fund
Most Recent Fund Was Raised: 06/01/1999
Year Founded: 1985
Capital Under Management: $60,000,000
Current Activity Level : Actively seeking new investments
Method of Compensation: Function primarily in service area, receive contingent fee in cash or equity

---

REITEN & CO STRATEGIC INVESTMENTS AS

Haakon VIIs gt. 1, 3rd floor
P.O. Box 1531
Oslo, Norway 0117
Phone: 47-23-113-700
Fax: 47-23-113-721
E-mail: post@reitenco.no
Website: www.reitenco.no

Management and Staff

Bard Brath Ingero, Partner
Christian Melby, Partner
John Bjerkan, Partner
Kathryn Baker, Partner
Narve Reiten, Partner
Per Anders Wien, Chief Financial Officer
Terje Bakken, Partner

Type of Firm

Private Equity Firm

Association Membership

Norwegian Venture Capital Association
European Private Equity and Venture Capital Assoc.

Project Preferences

Type of Financing Preferred:

Second Stage Financing
Leveraged Buyout
Expansion
Balanced
Management Buyouts

Size of Investments Considered:

Min Size of Investment Considered (000s): $13,980
Max Size of Investment Considered (000s): $83,881

Geographical Preferences

United States Preferences:

All U.S.

International Preferences:

Sweden
Europe
Scandanavia/Nordic Region
Finland
Norway
Denmark

Industry Preferences

In Computer Other prefer:

Computer Related

In Medical/Health prefer:

Medical/Health

In Consumer Related prefer:

Consumer
Consumer Products
Consumer Services

In Industrial/Energy prefer:

Energy

In Transportation prefer:

Transportation

In Financial Services prefer:

Financial Services
Insurance
Real Estate

In Business Serv. prefer:

Services

Additional Information

Year Founded: 1996
Capital Under Management: $615,100,000
Current Activity Level : Actively seeking new investments

REL

63, rue Pierre Charron
Paris, France 75008
Phone: 33-1-5383-8620
Fax: 33-1-4225-0632
E-mail: informations@rel.fr
Website: www.rel.fr

Type of Firm

Private Equity Firm

Association Membership

French Venture Capital Association (AFIC)

Project Preferences

Type of Financing Preferred:

Leveraged Buyout
Management Buyouts

Geographical Preferences

International Preferences:

Europe

Additional Information

Year Founded: 1997
Capital Under Management: $67,000,000
Current Activity Level : Actively seeking new investments

RELATIVITY CAPITAL LLC

1300 17th Street, North
Eleventh Floor
Arlington, VA USA 22209
Phone: 703-812-3020
E-mail: info@relativitycapitalllc.com
Website: www.relativitycapitalllc.com

Other Offices

909 Third Avenue
Suite 2931
New York, NY USA 10022
Phone: 212-350-1540

Management and Staff

Andrew Lodge, Principal
James Riepe, Vice President
Jennifer Versaw, Chief Financial Officer
Joyce Johnson-Miller, Senior Managing Director
Leslie Armitage, Senior Managing Director
Ralph Cacci, Principal

Type of Firm

Private Equity Firm

Project Preferences

Type of Financing Preferred:

Leveraged Buyout
Acquisition
Distressed Debt

Size of Investments Considered:

Min Size of Investment Considered (000s): $5,000
Max Size of Investment Considered (000s): $30,000

Industry Preferences

In Medical/Health prefer:

Medical/Health

In Consumer Related prefer:

Consumer

In Transportation prefer:

Aerospace

In Business Serv. prefer:

Services

In Manufact. prefer:

Manufacturing

Additional Information

Year Founded: 2005
Capital Under Management: $168,500,000
Current Activity Level : Actively seeking new investments

RELIANCE BANK

142 Ahmadu Bello Way
Victoria Island
Lagos, Nigeria
Phone: 803-306-1226
Website: www.reliancebanklimited.com

Management and Staff

Abayomi Majekodunmi, Chief Executive Officer
George Irechukwu, Managing Director

Type of Firm

Bank Affiliated

Project Preferences

Type of Financing Preferred:

Balanced

Geographical Preferences

International Preferences:

Nigeria

Additional Information

Year Founded: 2000
Current Activity Level : Actively seeking new investments

RELIANT EQUITY INVESTORS

401 North Michigan Avenue
Suite 550
Chicago, IL USA 60611
Phone: 312-494-0300
Fax: 312-494-0317
E-mail: info@reliantequity.com
Website: www.reliantequity.com

Management and Staff

Carr Preston, Managing Director
Gordon Liao, Vice President
Ivelisse Rodriguez, Vice President
Omar Simmons, Managing Director
Qian Elmore, Vice President
Roy Roberts, Managing Director
Thomas Darden, Managing Director

Type of Firm

Private Equity Firm

Additional Information

Year Founded: 2001
Capital Under Management: $30,000,000
Current Activity Level : Actively seeking new investments

RELIGARE ENTERPRISES, LTD.

19, Nehru Place
New Delhi, India 110 019
Phone: 91-11-3081-5100
Fax: 91-11-3081-5711
E-mail: info@religare.in
Website: www.religare.in

Other Offices

301/302, Viraj Tower, Gundavali
Andheri East, Mumbai
Mumbai, India 400093
Phone: 91-22-5655-0000
Fax: 91-22-2207-3190

4th Floor, Ideal Plaza
11/1, Sarat Bose Road
Kolkata, India 700020
Phone: 91-33-2213-5057
Fax: 91-33-2213-5058

2nd Floor, Dev Complex
Opp Parimal Garden, C.G. Road
Ahmedabad, India 380006

Amar Calibre, C.T.S. No. 911
Grd. Flr., BMCC Road, Shivajinagar
Pune, India 411004

G-16, Marina Arcade
Connaught Place
New Delhi, India 110001

No. 117, Theagaraya Road
4th Flr., City Tower, T. Nagar
Chennai, India 600017
Phone: 91-44-5203-7217
Fax: 91-44-5204-0334

Management and Staff

Anil Saxena, Chief Financial Officer
Shachindra Nath, Chief Operating Officer
Sunil Godhwani, CEO & Managing Director

Type of Firm

Bank Affiliated

Project Preferences

Type of Financing Preferred:

Expansion
Balanced
Open Market
Acquisition

Geographical Preferences

International Preferences:

India

Industry Preferences

In Medical/Health prefer:

Medical/Health

Health Services

In Consumer Related prefer:
Retail
Education Related

In Financial Services prefer:
Insurance
Financial Services

In Manufact. prefer:
Manufacturing

Additional Information
Year Founded: 2006
Current Activity Level : Actively seeking new investments

REMACO MERGER AG
Centralbahnstrasse 7
Postfach 3945
Basel, Switzerland 4002
Phone: 41-61-206-9966
Fax: 41-61-271-1950
E-mail: office.basel@remaco.com
Website: www.remaco.com

Management and Staff
Georg Fankhauser, Partner
Pascal Boni, Partner

Type of Firm
Private Equity Firm

Association Membership
Swiss Venture Capital Association (SECA)

Project Preferences

Type of Financing Preferred:
Leveraged Buyout
Early Stage
Expansion
Mezzanine
Recapitalizations

Geographical Preferences

United States Preferences:
All U.S.

International Preferences:
United Kingdom
Switzerland
Austria
Germany

Industry Preferences

In Industrial/Energy prefer:
Alternative Energy
Energy Conservation Relat
Environmental Related

Additional Information
Year Founded: 1969
Current Activity Level : Actively seeking new investments

REMBRANDT VENTURE PARTNERS
2200 Sand Hill Road
Suite 160
Menlo Park, CA USA 94025
Phone: 650-326-7070
Fax: 650-326-3780
E-mail: inquiries@rembrandtvc.com
Website: www.rembrandtvc.com

Management and Staff
Clara Yee, Chief Financial Officer
Douglas Schrier, Managing Director
Gerald Casilli, Managing Director
Gregory Eaton, Managing Director
In Sik Rhee, General Partner
Richard Ling, Managing Director

Type of Firm
Private Equity Firm

Association Membership
National Venture Capital Association - USA (NVCA)

Project Preferences

Type of Financing Preferred:
Early Stage
Expansion
Balanced
Later Stage

Geographical Preferences

United States Preferences:
California
All U.S.

Industry Preferences

In Communications prefer:
Communications and Media
Telecommunications
Wireless Communications

In Internet Specific prefer:
E-Commerce Technology
Internet

Additional Information
Name of Most Recent Fund: Rembrandt Venture Partners Fund Two, L.P.
Most Recent Fund Was Raised: 06/05/2008
Year Founded: 2004
Capital Under Management: $192,600,000
Current Activity Level : Actively seeking new investments

RENAISSANCE CAPITAL
Naberezhnaya Tower, Block C
Krasnopresnenskaya nab, 18
Moscow, Russia 123317
Phone: 7-495-258-7777
Fax: 7-495-258-7778
E-mail: info@rencap.com
Website: www.rencap.com

Other Offices
780 Third Avenue
15th Floor
New York, NY USA 10017
Phone: 212-824-1099
Fax: 212-824-1098

Suite 810, Seventh Floor
Purshottam Place, Chiromo Road
Nairobi, Kenya 40560
Phone: 254-20-360-1822
Fax: 254-20-360-1100

Samal-Tower
Zholdasbekova str., 97
Almaty, Kazakhstan 050051
Phone: 7-727-244-1544
Fax: 7-727-244-1545

Palais D'Ivoire
12 Them Dervis Street, Office 402
Nicosia, Cyprus 1066
Phone: 357-22-445-600
Fax: 357-22-676-755

One Angel Court
CoptHall Avenue
London, United Kingdom EC2R 7 HJ
Phone: 44-20-7367-7777
Fax: 44-20-7367-7778

Fourth Floor, Fortune Towers
27 Adeyemo Alakija Street
Victoria Island, Lagos, Nigeria
Phone: 234-1-271-9129-30
Fax: 234-1-261-0456

77-A, Velyka Vasylkivska Street
Kyiv, Ukraine 03150
Phone: 38-44-492-7383
Fax: 38-44-492-7393

Management and Staff
Alexander Pertsovsky, Chief Executive Officer
Anna Vyshlova, Managing Director
Brian Lazell, Managing Director
Gordon McCulloch, Managing Director
Gregory Gurtovoy, CEO & Managing Director
Hans Jochum Horn, Chief Operating Officer
Igor Sagiryan, President
Richard Bruens, Managing Director
Stephen Jennings, Chief Executive Officer
Steven Wootton, Managing Director

Type of Firm
Bank Affiliated

Project Preferences

Type of Financing Preferred:
Leveraged Buyout
Expansion

Geographical Preferences

International Preferences:
Russia

Additional Information
Year Founded: 2007
Capital Under Management: $660,000,000
Current Activity Level : Actively seeking new investments

RENAISSANCE CAPITAL MANITOBA VENTURES FUND
3106 201 Portage Avenue
Winnipeg, Canada R3B 3K6
Phone: 204-925-2250

Type of Firm
Private Equity Firm

Additional Information
Year Founded: 2009
Current Activity Level : Actively seeking new investments

RENDERA
Platensgatan 29
Box 1224
Linkoping, Sweden 581 12
Phone: 46-13-203-293
E-mail: info@rendera.se
Website: www.rendera.se

Management and Staff
Mikael Karlsson, Chief Executive Officer

Type of Firm
Government Affiliated Program

Association Membership
Swedish Venture Capital Association (SVCA)
European Private Equity and Venture Capital Assoc.

Project Preferences

Type of Financing Preferred:
Early Stage

Geographical Preferences

International Preferences:
Sweden

Additional Information
Year Founded: 2003
Current Activity Level : Actively seeking new investments

RENDEX PARTNERS
Straalstraat 2
Antwerp, Belgium 2170
Phone: 32-3-640-3400
Fax: 32-3-640-3405
E-mail: info@rendex.com
Website: www.rendex.com

Management and Staff
Cedric Van Cauwenberghe, Partner

Type of Firm
Private Equity Firm

Association Membership
Dutch Venture Capital Associaton (NVP)

Project Preferences

Type of Financing Preferred:
Leveraged Buyout
Early Stage
Expansion

Size of Investments Considered:
Min Size of Investment Considered (000s): $900
Max Size of Investment Considered (000s): $4,600

Geographical Preferences

International Preferences:
Europe
Belgium

Industry Focus
(% based on actual investment)

Biotechnology	38.9%
Semiconductors/Other Elect.	28.1%
Computer Software and Services	20.7%
Computer Hardware	12.3%

Additional Information
Year Founded: 1998
Capital Under Management: $44,700,000
Current Activity Level : Actively seeking new investments

RENEWAGY A/S (FKA: ITH INDUSTRI INVEST A/S)
Kongevejen 153
Virum, Denmark 2830
Phone: 45-4333-1343
Fax: 45-4333-1344
E-mail: renewagy@renewagy.com
Website: www.renewagy.com

Type of Firm
Private Equity Firm

Project Preferences

Type of Financing Preferred:
Leveraged Buyout
Expansion

Geographical Preferences

International Preferences:
Denmark

Industry Preferences

In Industrial/Energy prefer:
Industrial Products

Additional Information
Year Founded: 2004
Current Activity Level : Actively seeking new investments

RENOVA CAPITAL ADVISORS
40 Buiding 4
Bolshaya Ordynka Street
Moscow, Russia 119017
Phone: 7-495-745-5757
Fax: 7-495-981-2921
Website: www.renovacapital.com

Management and Staff
Alexei Perekhojev, Chief Financial Officer
Dmitry Levonian, Partner
Oleg Tsarkov, Managing Partner

Type of Firm
Private Equity Firm

Association Membership
Russian Venture Capital Association (RVCA)

Project Preferences

Role in Financing:
Prefer role as deal originator but will also invest in deals created by others

Type of Financing Preferred:
Expansion
Later Stage

Size of Investments Considered:
Min Size of Investment Considered (000s): $20,000
Max Size of Investment Considered (000s): $50,000

Geographical Preferences

International Preferences:
Kazakhstan
Ukraine
Russia

Industry Preferences

In Communications prefer:
Communications and Media
Commercial Communications
Telecommunications
Wireless Communications

In Computer Hardware prefer:
Computers

In Semiconductor/Electr prefer:
Electronics

In Biotechnology prefer:
Biotechnology

In Medical/Health prefer:
Medical/Health
Pharmaceuticals

In Consumer Related prefer:
Consumer
Consumer Services

In Industrial/Energy prefer:
Materials

In Business Serv. prefer:
Services

In Agr/Forestr/Fish prefer:
Mining and Minerals

Additional Information
Name of Most Recent Fund: Earlier Stage Alternative Fund L.P.
Most Recent Fund Was Raised: 04/17/2008
Year Founded: 2004
Capital Under Management: $400,000,000
Current Activity Level : Actively seeking new investments

RENPART PARTICIPATIE HOLDING NV
Rivium Quadrant 81
Rotterdam, Netherlands 2909 LC
Phone: 31-10-288-1446
Fax: 31-10-447-1718
E-mail: participaties@renpart.nl
Website: www.renpart.nl

Type of Firm
Private Equity Firm

Association Membership
Dutch Venture Capital Associaton (NVP)

Project Preferences

Type of Financing Preferred:
Leveraged Buyout
Early Stage
Expansion
Mezzanine
Turnaround
Management Buyouts

Size of Investments Considered:
Min Size of Investment Considered (000s): $247
Max Size of Investment Considered (000s): $1,979

Geographical Preferences

International Preferences:
Netherlands

Industry Preferences

In Communications prefer:
Communications and Media

In Industrial/Energy prefer:
Energy
Industrial Products
Materials

Additional Information
Year Founded: 1999
Current Activity Level : Actively seeking new investments

REPUBLIC FINANCIAL CORPORATION
3300 South Parker Road
Suite 500
Aurora, CO USA 80014
Phone: 303-751-3501
Fax: 303-751-4777
E-mail: info@republic-financial.com
Website: www.republic-financial.com

Management and Staff
Paul Morrison, Managing Director
Thomas McCarthy, Managing Director

Type of Firm
Private Equity Firm

Project Preferences

Type of Financing Preferred:
Leveraged Buyout
Expansion

Size of Investments Considered:
Min Size of Investment Considered (000s): $2,000
Max Size of Investment Considered (000s): $8,000

Geographical Preferences

United States Preferences:
All U.S.

Industry Preferences

In Industrial/Energy prefer:
Industrial Products

In Business Serv. prefer:
Services
Distribution

In Manufact. prefer:
Manufacturing

Additional Information
Year Founded: 2006
Capital Under Management: $5,800,000
Current Activity Level : Actively seeking new investments

RESEARCH CORPORATION TECHNOLOGIES
101 North Wilmot Road
Suite 600
Tucson, AZ USA 85711
Phone: 520-748-4400
Fax: 520-748-0025
E-mail: attention@rctech.com
Website: www.rctech.com

Management and Staff
Christopher Martin, Chief Financial Officer

Type of Firm
Incubator/Development Program

Association Membership
National Venture Capital Association - USA (NVCA)

Project Preferences

Type of Financing Preferred:
Early Stage
Startup

Geographical Preferences

United States Preferences:
All U.S.

Canadian Preferences:
All Canada

International Preferences:
United Kingdom
Australia

Industry Preferences

In Biotechnology prefer:
Biotechnology

In Medical/Health prefer:
Medical/Health
Medical Therapeutics
Pharmaceuticals

Additional Information
Year Founded: 1987
Current Activity Level : Actively seeking new investments

RESEARCH PARTNERS, LTD.
17 State Street
Seventh Floor
New York, NY USA 10004
Phone: 212-785-3611
Fax: 212-785-3616
E-mail: info@researchpartnersltd.com
Website: www.researchpartnersltd.com

Management and Staff
Antal Foldi, Chief Financial Officer

Arie Abecassis, Managing Director
Arthur Rosenzweig, Founder
Lisa Warren, Managing Director
Peter Arnold, Managing Director

Type of Firm

Private Equity Firm

Industry Preferences

In Computer Other prefer:
Computer Related

In Financial Services prefer:
Financial Services

Additional Information

Year Founded: 1994
Current Activity Level : Actively seeking new investments

RESEARCH TRIANGLE VENTURES (RTV)

1500 Sunday Drive
Suite 300A
Raleigh, NC USA 27607
Phone: 919-571-8819
Fax: 919-571-8631
Website: www.rtventures.com

Management and Staff

Bud Whitmeyer, General Partner
Fred Hutchison, General Partner
Sam Tetlow, Partner
Timothy Gupton, General Partner

Type of Firm

Private Equity Firm

Association Membership

National Venture Capital Association - USA (NVCA)

Project Preferences

Role in Financing:
Will function either as deal originator or investor in deals created by others

Type of Financing Preferred:
Early Stage
Seed

Size of Investments Considered:
Min Size of Investment Considered (000s): $100
Max Size of Investment Considered (000s): $500

Geographical Preferences

United States Preferences:
Southeast

Industry Preferences

In Communications prefer:
Telecommunications
Wireless Communications

In Computer Hardware prefer:
Computer Graphics and Dig

In Computer Software prefer:
Systems Software
Applications Software
Artificial Intelligence

In Internet Specific prefer:
Internet

In Semiconductor/Electr prefer:
Electronics

In Biotechnology prefer:
Human Biotechnology
Agricultural/Animal Bio.

In Medical/Health prefer:
Medical Diagnostics
Diagnostic Services
Diagnostic Test Products
Medical Therapeutics
Drug/Equipmt Delivery

Additional Information

Name of Most Recent Fund: Research Triangle Ventures, L.P.
Most Recent Fund Was Raised: 12/01/2000
Year Founded: 2000
Capital Under Management: $10,300,000
Current Activity Level : Actively seeking new investments
Method of Compensation: Return on investment is of primary concern, do not charge fees

RESERVOIR VENTURE PARTNERS

500 West Wilson Bridge Road
Suite 310
Columbus, OH USA 43085
Phone: 614-846-7241
Fax: 614-846-7267
E-mail: info@reservoirvp.com
Website: www.reservoirvp.com

Management and Staff

Curtis Crocker, Managing Partner
Steven Jaffee, General Partner
Timothy Biro, General Partner
William Tanner, Chief Financial Officer

Type of Firm

Private Equity Firm

Project Preferences

Type of Financing Preferred:
Early Stage
Seed

Size of Investments Considered:
Min Size of Investment Considered (000s): $500
Max Size of Investment Considered (000s): $1,000

Geographical Preferences

United States Preferences:
Midwest

Industry Preferences

In Communications prefer:
Wireless Communications

In Computer Software prefer:
Software

In Biotechnology prefer:
Biotechnology

In Medical/Health prefer:
Medical/Health
Medical Diagnostics
Drug/Equipmt Delivery
Medical Products

In Industrial/Energy prefer:
Advanced Materials

Additional Information

Name of Most Recent Fund: Reservoir Venture Partners (FKA: Battelle Technology Fund)
Most Recent Fund Was Raised: 11/01/2001
Year Founded: 2003
Capital Under Management: $28,000,000
Current Activity Level : Actively seeking new investments

RESIDEX VENTURES B.V.

Kosterijland 70-78
Bunnik, Netherlands 3981 AJ
Phone: 31-30-659-5500
Fax: 31-30-659-5511
E-mail: info@residexventures.com
Website: www.residexventures.com

Management and Staff

Cees Van Luijk, Partner
De Heer Tom Paffen, Partner
Greg Brown, Partner
Paul Schroeder, Partner

Type of Firm

Private Equity Firm

Project Preferences

Type of Financing Preferred:
Early Stage
Later Stage
Startup

Geographical Preferences

United States Preferences:
All U.S.

Canadian Preferences:
All Canada

International Preferences:
Europe

Industry Preferences

In Communications prefer:
Communications and Media
Telecommunications

Additional Information
Year Founded: 2003
Current Activity Level : Actively seeking new investments

RESILIENCE CAPITAL PARTNERS LLC
25201 Chagrin Boulevard
Suite 360
Beachwood, OH USA 44122
Phone: 216-292-0200
Fax: 216-292-4750
E-mail: info@resiliencecapital.com
Website: www.resiliencecapital.com

Other Offices
39555 Orchard Place
Suite 600
Novi, MI USA 48375

Management and Staff
Doug Campbell, Vice President
Malachi Mixon, Principal
Michael Cavanaugh, Vice President
Rose Frysinger, Chief Financial Officer
William Wildern, Principal
Ziv Sarag, Chief Operating Officer

Type of Firm
Private Equity Firm

Project Preferences

Type of Financing Preferred:
Leveraged Buyout
Turnaround
Management Buyouts
Acquisition
Special Situation
Distressed Debt
Recapitalizations

Size of Investments Considered:
Min Size of Investment Considered (000s): $5,000
Max Size of Investment Considered (000s): $20,000

Geographical Preferences

United States Preferences:
All U.S.

Industry Preferences

In Communications prefer:
Commercial Communications
Satellite Microwave Comm.

In Semiconductor/Electr prefer:
Component Testing Equipmt

In Industrial/Energy prefer:
Industrial Products
Advanced Materials
Superconductivity
Process Control

In Transportation prefer:
Transportation
Aerospace

In Business Serv. prefer:
Distribution

In Manufact. prefer:
Manufacturing

Additional Information
Year Founded: 2001
Capital Under Management: $75,000,000
Current Activity Level : Actively seeking new investments

RESO INVESTMENT, INC.
1751 Richardson Avenue
Suite 6509
Montreal, Canada H3K 1G6
Phone: 514-931-5737
Fax: 514-931-4317
Website: www.resoinvest.com

Management and Staff
Moustafa Magar, Managing Director

Type of Firm
Private Equity Firm

Additional Information
Year Founded: 2009
Current Activity Level : Actively seeking new investments

RESONA CAPITAL CO., LTD.
1-3-1 Kyobashi
Chuo-ku
Tokyo, Japan 104-0031
Phone: 81-3-3270-3311
Website: www.resonacapital.co.jp

Other Offices
ResonaBnak Osakahonbu bldg
2-2-1 Bigocho, Chuo-ku
Osaka-shi, Japan 541-0051

Management and Staff
Hirohide Takahashi, President

Type of Firm
Bank Affiliated

Additional Information
Year Founded: 1988
Current Activity Level : Actively seeking new investments

RESOURCE FINANCIAL CORP
550 West Van Buren Street
Suite 1410
Chicago, IL USA 60607
Phone: 312-525-2600
Fax: 312-525-2610
Website: www.resource-financial.com

Other Offices
111 East Kilbourn
Suite 1725
Milwaukee, WI USA 53202
Phone: 414-224-7000
Fax: 414-224-7015

Management and Staff
Mark Teufel, Managing Director

Type of Firm
Bank Affiliated

Project Preferences

Role in Financing:
Prefer role as deal originator but will also invest in deals created by others

Type of Financing Preferred:
Leveraged Buyout
Early Stage
Expansion
Generalist PE
Turnaround
Management Buyouts
Acquisition
Special Situation
Distressed Debt
Recapitalizations

Size of Investments Considered:
Min Size of Investment Considered (000s): $5,000
Max Size of Investment Considered: No Limit

Geographical Preferences

Canadian Preferences:
All Canada

International Preferences:
Italy
India
United Kingdom
Latin America
Luxembourg
Netherlands
Portugal
Mexico
Spain
Australia
Belgium
New Zealand
Germany
France

Additional Information
Year Founded: 2001

Current Activity Level : Actively seeking new investments
Method of Compensation: Professional fee required whether or not deal closes

RESOURCE PATNERS SP. Z.O.O.

Aleje Jerozolimskie 56c
Warsaw, Poland 00-803
Phone: 48-6012-50101

Type of Firm

Private Equity Firm
Additional Information
Year Founded: 2009
Current Activity Level : Actively seeking new investments

RESULT VENTURE KNOWLEDGE INTERNATIONAL

Grev Turegatan 11A, 5 tr
Stockholm, Sweden 114 86
Phone: 46-850-650-300
Fax: 46-850-650-310
E-mail: info.se@result.com
Website: www.result.com

Other Offices

33 Glasshouse Street
London, United Kingdom W1R 5RG
Phone: 44-207-851 7750
Fax: 44 207 851 7770

Associated partner Palo Alto
105/107, Avenue de la Republique
Paris, France 75002
Phone: 33-155-340-939
Fax: 33-155-340-930

Stadhausbruecke 3
Hamburg, Germany 20355
Phone: 44-40-376 44 652
Fax: 44-40-376 44 500

Sarkiniementie 5
Helsinki, Finland 00210
Phone: 358 9 622 9000
Fax: 358 9 6824 2627

160 Mercer Street
New York, NY USA 10012
Phone: 1-212 979 1700
Fax: 1-212 979 1773
Bygdoy Alle 23
Oslo, Norway 0262

Cinca
21 El Viso
Madrid, Spain 28002
Phone: 34-91-745-0545
Fax: 34-91-745-0549

Willemsparkweg 66
Amsterdam, Netherlands 1071 HK
Phone: 31-20-573 0890
Fax: 31-20-672-3373

c/o Synoco Asia Pacific Ltd
Unit 1113, 11F, Tower II,
833 Cheung Sha Wan Rd, Kowloon, Hong Kong

Bredgade 25 G, 4
Copenhagen K, Denmark 1260
Phone: 45-7025-3501
Fax: 45-7025-3502

Management and Staff

Abdallah Hitti, Managing Partner
Bob Stumpel, Managing Partner
Charles Levison, Managing Partner
Felicio De Costa, Partner
Gonzalo De la Cierva, Managing Partner
Niklas Flisberg, Venture Partner
Urban Pettersson, Managing Partner
Willie Wilenius, Managing Partner

Type of Firm

Private Equity Firm

Project Preferences

Type of Financing Preferred:
Early Stage
Expansion

Geographical Preferences

International Preferences:
Europe
Asia

Industry Preferences

In Internet Specific prefer:
Internet

Additional Information

Current Activity Level : Actively seeking new investments

RETRO VENTURE MANAGEMENT LLC

3000 Sand Hill Road
Building 2, Suite 150
Menlo Park, CA USA 94025
Phone: 650-543-8999
Website: www.retrovp.com

Type of Firm

Private Equity Firm

Project Preferences

Type of Financing Preferred:
Balanced

Additional Information

Name of Most Recent Fund: Retro Venture Partners, L.P.
Most Recent Fund Was Raised: 05/13/2008
Year Founded: 2008
Capital Under Management: $30,000,000
Current Activity Level : Actively seeking new investments

RETROCOM GROWTH FUND INC.

89 The Queensway West
Suite 400
Mississauga, Canada L5B 2V2
Phone: 905-848-2430
Fax: 905-848-2869

Other Offices

2892 South Sheridan Way
Suite 301
Oakville, Canada L6J 7G9

Type of Firm

Private Equity Firm

Additional Information

Year Founded: 1997
Current Activity Level : Actively seeking new investments

REUS CAPITAL DE NEGOCIS SCR, SA

Centre Internat. de Negocis
Cami de Valls, 81-87
Reus, Spain 43205
Phone: 34-97730-0313
Fax: 34-97775-4097
E-mail: rcn@reuscn.com
Website: www.reuscn.com

Type of Firm

Incubator/Development Program

Project Preferences

Type of Financing Preferred:
Generalist PE

Geographical Preferences

International Preferences:
Spain

Industry Preferences

In Biotechnology prefer:
Biotechnology

In Consumer Related prefer:
Consumer Services

In Agr/Forestr/Fish prefer:
Agriculture related

In Other prefer:
Environment Responsible

Additional Information
Year Founded: 2006
Current Activity Level : Actively seeking new investments

REVOLUTION VENTURES, LLC
11682 El Camino Real
Suite 100
San Diego, CA USA 92130
Phone: 858-450-2842
Fax: 877-881-9192
Website: www.revolutionventures.com

Management and Staff
Greg Mauro, Managing Partner
Robert Hutter, Venture Partner

Type of Firm
Private Equity Firm

Project Preferences
Type of Financing Preferred:
Early Stage

Geographical Preferences
United States Preferences:
All U.S.

Industry Preferences
In Communications prefer:
Communications and Media

In Business Serv. prefer:
Media

Additional Information
Name of Most Recent Fund: Revolution Community Ventures 1, LLC
Most Recent Fund Was Raised: 02/28/2007
Year Founded: 2000
Capital Under Management: $7,500,000
Current Activity Level : Actively seeking new investments

REXITER CAPITAL MANAGEMENT LTD.
One International Place
25th Floor
Boston, MA USA 02110
Phone: 617-664-6005
Fax: 617-664-2939
E-mail: wporter@rexiter.com
Website: www.rexiter.com

Other Offices
Kwanghwamun Bldg., 13/F
64-8 Taepyung-ro 1 ka, Chung-ku
Seoul, South Korea
Phone: 822-399-3736
Fax: 822-399-3749

21 St. James's Square
London, United Kingdom SW1Y 4SS
Phone: 44-20-7698-6401
Fax: 44-20-7698-6410

Management and Staff
Christopher Vale, Managing Director

Type of Firm
Bank Affiliated

Project Preferences
Type of Financing Preferred:
Early Stage
Expansion
Mezzanine
Private Placement

Geographical Preferences
International Preferences:
Korea, South
All International

Additional Information
Year Founded: 1997
Current Activity Level : Actively seeking new investments

REYNOLDS, DEWITT & CO.
300 Main Street
Cincinnati, OH USA 45202
Phone: 513-241-8716
Fax: 513-421-3602

Management and Staff
Grant Troja, Vice President
James Dealy, Managing Director
John Kern, Managing Director

Type of Firm
Private Equity Firm

Project Preferences
Role in Financing:
Prefer role as deal originator but will also invest in deals created by others

Type of Financing Preferred:
Leveraged Buyout
Control-block Purchases
Expansion
Generalist PE
Later Stage
Management Buyouts
Acquisition
Private Placement
Special Situation

Size of Investments Considered:
Min Size of Investment Considered (000s): $2,500
Max Size of Investment Considered (000s): $25,000

Geographical Preferences
United States Preferences:
Midwest
Southeast
All U.S.

Additional Information
Year Founded: 1979
Current Activity Level : Actively seeking new investments
Method of Compensation: Return on invest. most important, but chg. closing fees, service fees, etc.

RFE INVESTMENT PARTNERS
36 Grove Street
New Canaan, CT USA 06840
Phone: 203-966-2800
Fax: 203-966-3109
E-mail: info@freip.com
Website: www.rfeip.com

Management and Staff
Don Juricic, Chief Financial Officer
Howard Landis, Managing Director
James Parsons, Managing Director
Michael Rubel, Principal
Michael Foster, Managing Director
Ned Truslow, Principal
Thomas Burger, Managing Director

Type of Firm
Private Equity Firm

Association Membership
Natl Assoc of Small Bus. Inv. Co (NASBIC)

Project Preferences
Role in Financing:
Will function either as deal originator or investor in deals created by others

Type of Financing Preferred:
Leveraged Buyout
Balanced
Later Stage
Management Buyouts
Acquisition
Recapitalizations

Size of Investments Considered:
Min Size of Investment Considered (000s): $5,000
Max Size of Investment Considered (000s): $24,000

Geographical Preferences
United States Preferences:
All U.S.

Industry Focus

(% based on actual investment)

Other Products	29.0%
Medical/Health	20.0%
Industrial/Energy	19.6%
Consumer Related	11.1%
Computer Software and Services	6.9%
Computer Hardware	5.9%
Communications and Media	4.1%
Semiconductors/Other Elect.	3.1%
Biotechnology	0.2%

Additional Information

Name of Most Recent Fund: RFE Investment Partners VII, L.P.
Most Recent Fund Was Raised: 03/20/2008
Year Founded: 1979
Capital Under Management: $600,000,000
Current Activity Level : Actively seeking new investments
Method of Compensation: Return on invest. most important, but chg. closing fees, service fees, etc.

RHJ INTERNATIONAL JAPAN

Daiwa Seimei Building
1-1-7 Uchisaiwaicho, Chiyodaku
Tokyo, Japan
Website: www.rhji.com

Management and Staff

Hiroshi Nonomiya, Managing Director

Type of Firm

Private Equity Firm

Additional Information

Year Founded: 1999
Current Activity Level : Actively seeking new investments

RHO VENTURES (AKA: RHO MANAGEMENT)

152 West 57th Street
23rd Floor
New York, NY USA 10019
Phone: 212-751-6677
Fax: 212-751-3613
E-mail: businessplans@rho.com
Website: www.rho.com

Other Offices

525 University Avenue
Suite 1350
Palo Alto, CA USA 94301
Phone: 650-463-0300
Fax: 650-463-0311

1800 McGill College Avenue
Suite 840
Montreal, Canada H3A 3J6
Phone: 514-844-5605
Fax: 514-844-9004

Management and Staff

Benjamin Terk, Partner
Gordon Hargraves, Partner
Habib Kairouz, Managing Partner
John Parker, Venture Partner
John Sculley, Venture Partner
Joshua Ruch, Managing Partner
Mark Leschly, Managing Partner
Martin Vogelbaum, Partner
Neetesh Kumar, Partner
Paul Bartlett, Partner
Peter Kalkanis, Chief Financial Officer

Type of Firm

Bank Affiliated

Project Preferences

Type of Financing Preferred:
Second Stage Financing
Early Stage
Mezzanine
Balanced
Later Stage
Seed
First Stage Financing
Fund of Funds of Second

Size of Investments Considered:
Min Size of Investment Considered (000s): $275
Max Size of Investment Considered (000s): $25,000

Geographical Preferences

Canadian Preferences:
All Canada

Industry Focus

(% based on actual investment)

Internet Specific	27.9%
Communications and Media	15.8%
Biotechnology	12.6%
Medical/Health	10.4%
Computer Software and Services	9.2%
Semiconductors/Other Elect.	7.7%
Industrial/Energy	6.5%
Other Products	6.1%
Computer Hardware	3.8%

Additional Information

Name of Most Recent Fund: Rho Ventures VI, L.P.
Most Recent Fund Was Raised: 11/16/2007
Year Founded: 1981
Capital Under Management: $2,500,000,000
Current Activity Level : Actively seeking new investments

RHONE CAPITAL LLC

630 Fifth Avenue
27th Floor
New York, NY USA 10111
Phone: 212-218-6770
Fax: 212-218-6789

Other Offices

5 Princes Gate
3rd Floor
London, United Kingdom SW7 1QJ
Phone: 44-20-77611100
Fax: 44-20-77611111

Management and Staff

Andrew Sweet, Managing Director
Colin Hall, Partner
Elaine Eng, Chief Financial Officer
Ferdinand Groos, Partner
M. Steven Langman, Managing Director
Nancy Cooper, Partner
Robert Agostinelli, Partner

Type of Firm

Private Equity Firm

Association Membership

European Private Equity and Venture Capital Assoc.

Project Preferences

Type of Financing Preferred:
Leveraged Buyout

Geographical Preferences

International Preferences:
Italy
Sweden
United Kingdom
Netherlands
Western Europe
Spain
Germany
France

Industry Focus

(% based on actual investment)

Industrial/Energy	57.2%
Other Products	19.8%
Consumer Related	12.4%
Communications and Media	5.7%
Biotechnology	4.9%

Additional Information

Name of Most Recent Fund: Rhone Partners II L.P.
Most Recent Fund Was Raised: 06/11/2002
Year Founded: 1996
Capital Under Management: $350,000,000
Current Activity Level : Actively seeking new investments

RHONE DAUPHINE DEVELOPPEMENT

2 chemin du Vieux Chene
BP 38242
Meylan Cedex, France 38240
Phone: 33-4-7641-4949
Fax: 33-4-7690-8257
E-mail: info@rhone-dauphine-developpement.fr

Type of Firm
Private Equity Firm

Project Preferences

Type of Financing Preferred:
Leveraged Buyout
Early Stage
Expansion

Geographical Preferences

International Preferences:
France

Industry Preferences

In Industrial/Energy prefer:
Industrial Products

In Business Serv. prefer:
Services

Additional Information
Year Founded: 1988
Current Activity Level : Actively seeking new investments

RICARDO, INC.
7850 Grant Street
Burr Ridge, IL USA 60527-5852
Phone: 630-789-0003
Fax: 630-789-0127
Website: www.ricardo.com

Type of Firm
Private Equity Firm

Additional Information
Year Founded: 2009
Current Activity Level : Actively seeking new investments

RICHARDSON CAPITAL LIMITED
3000 One Lombard Place
Winnipeg, Canada R3B 0Y1
Phone: 204-953-7969
Fax: 204-949-0731
E-mail: info@richardsoncapital.com
Website: www.rfgpe.ca

Other Offices
BCE Place, 181 Bay Street
Suite 3800
Toronto, Canada M5J 2T3
Phone: 416-969-3049
Fax: 416-969-3034

1250 Rene-Levesque Boulevard West
Suite 1900
Montreal, Canada H3B 4W8
Phone: 514-9894860
Fax: 514-989-4877

Management and Staff
David Brown, Managing Director
Gourdeau Jean-Guy, Managing Director
Hartley Richardson, Managing Director
Robert Puchniak, Managing Director
Sandy Riley, Managing Director
William Biggar, Managing Director

Type of Firm
Private Equity Firm

Association Membership
Canadian Venture Capital Association

Project Preferences

Type of Financing Preferred:
Leveraged Buyout
Expansion
Balanced
Management Buyouts
Acquisition

Size of Investments Considered:
Min Size of Investment Considered (000s): $10,000
Max Size of Investment Considered (000s): $50,000

Geographical Preferences

United States Preferences:
All U.S.

Canadian Preferences:
All Canada

Industry Preferences

In Biotechnology prefer:
Biotechnology

In Medical/Health prefer:
Medical Products

In Industrial/Energy prefer:
Energy
Alternative Energy

Additional Information
Year Founded: 2003
Capital Under Management: $1,045,000,000
Current Activity Level : Actively seeking new investments

RICHLAND VENTURES
1201 16th Avenue South
Nashville, TN USA 37212
Phone: 615-383-8030
Fax: 615-269-0463
E-mail: mail@richven.com
Website: www.richlandventures.com

Other Offices
3100 West End Avenue
Suite 400
Nashville, TN USA

Management and Staff
David Fitzgerald, Principal
Jack Tyrell, Managing Partner
W. Patrick Ortale, Managing Partner

Type of Firm
Private Equity Firm

Project Preferences

Role in Financing:
Prefer role as deal originator but will also invest in deals created by others

Type of Financing Preferred:
Expansion

Size of Investments Considered:
Min Size of Investment Considered (000s): $5,000
Max Size of Investment Considered (000s): $15,000

Industry Focus
(% based on actual investment)

Medical/Health	31.7%
Internet Specific	25.6%
Computer Software and Services	10.0%
Communications and Media	8.8%
Other Products	7.6%
Industrial/Energy	6.8%
Consumer Related	5.1%
Computer Hardware	3.2%
Biotechnology	0.6%
Semiconductors/Other Elect.	0.6%

Additional Information
Name of Most Recent Fund: Richland Ventures III
Most Recent Fund Was Raised: 01/01/1999
Year Founded: 1985
Capital Under Management: $456,000,000
Current Activity Level : Actively seeking new investments
Method of Compensation: Return on investment is of primary concern, do not charge fees

---

RICHLINK INTERNATIONAL CAPITAL CO., LTD.
13th Floor, Shum Tower
268 Des Voeux Road
Central, Hong Kong
Phone: 852-2851-4722
Fax: 852-3545-6693
E-mail: info@richlink.com.cn
Website: www.richlink.com.cn

Other Offices
East 4th Ring Center Road
62 Ocean Int'l Center D
Beijing, China 100025
Phone: 86-10-5964-8704
Fax: 86-10-5964-8703

No. 17 Santaiyun House
Hangzhou, China 310000
Phone: 86-571-8798-0837
Fax: 86-571-8798-0839

No. 933 Tiantong North Road
Room 3003 Hebang Building
Ningbo, China 315100
Phone: 86-574-8741-1771
Fax: 86-574-8741-1769

30 Sturdee Road #06-05
Kerrisdale
Singapore, Singapore 207852
Phone: 65-9668-9187
Fax: 65-6618-0597

No. 49 Central Business District
23/F Jincheng East International
Zhengzhou, China
Phone: 86-371-6808-0166
Fax: 86-371-6808-0066

Management and Staff

Changyong Zhang, Partner
Hong Zhou, Partner
Hongwei Sun, Partner
Jason Zheng, President, CEO, Chairman

Type of Firm

Investment Management Firm

Project Preferences

Type of Financing Preferred:
Early Stage
Expansion
Later Stage

Size of Investments Considered:
Min Size of Investment Considered (000s): $732
Max Size of Investment Considered (000s): $4,390

Geographical Preferences

International Preferences:
Hong Kong
China
Asia

Industry Preferences

In Biotechnology prefer:
Biotechnology

In Medical/Health prefer:
Medical/Health

In Consumer Related prefer:
Consumer

In Industrial/Energy prefer:
Environmental Related

In Business Serv. prefer:
Services
Media

Additional Information

Year Founded: 2006
Current Activity Level : Actively seeking new investments

RIDGELIFT VENTURES

P.O. Box 620405
Woodside, CA USA 94062
Phone: 650-331-0092
Fax: 650-529-1788
E-mail: info@ridgelift.com
Website: www.ridgelift.com

Other Offices

155 Constitution Drive
Menlo Park, CA USA 94025
Phone: 650-331-0092
Fax: 650-529-1788

Management and Staff

David Newman, Managing Director
Kendall Cooper, Chief Financial Officer
Robert Goldberg, Managing Director
Stuart Phillips, Managing Director

Type of Firm

Private Equity Firm

Project Preferences

Type of Financing Preferred:
Early Stage
Seed

Geographical Preferences

United States Preferences:
All U.S.

Additional Information

Year Founded: 2006
Current Activity Level : Actively seeking new investments

RIDGEWAY CAPITAL PARTNERS, LTD. (FKA:OPE PARTNERS LTD.)

6F Kioicho Building
3-12 Kioicho, Chiyoda-ku
Tokyo, Japan 102-0094
Phone: 81-3-3511-7530
Fax: 81-3-3511-7550
Website: www.ridgewaycapital.co.jp

Management and Staff

Hidetoshi Mine, President
Isao Nishimuta, Partner
Kiyoyuki Katsumata, Partner
Koji Abe, Partner
Mitsunaga Tada, Managing Partner
Nao Watanabe, Principal
Shiniji Uga, Principal
Takumi Sakagami, Partner
Toshiki Kano, Principal

Type of Firm

Private Equity Firm

Project Preferences

Type of Financing Preferred:
Balanced

Additional Information

Year Founded: 2001
Current Activity Level : Actively seeking new investments

RIDGEWOOD CAPITAL MANAGEMENT, LLC

Ridgewood Commons
947 Linwood Avenue
Ridgewood, NJ USA 07450
Phone: 201-447-9000
Fax: 201-447-0474
Website: www.ridgewoodcapital.com

Other Offices

540 Cowper Street
Palo Alto, CA USA 94301
Phone: 650-614-9030

Management and Staff

Cathy Wong, Vice President
Elton Sherwin, Senior Managing Director
Joerg Sperling, Managing Director
Lou Mazzucchelli, Venture Partner
Mary Louise Olin, Vice President
Warren Majek, Chief Financial Officer

Type of Firm

Private Equity Firm

Association Membership

Mid-Atlantic Venture Association
National Venture Capital Association - USA (NVCA)

Project Preferences

Role in Financing:
Will function either as deal originator or investor in deals created by others

Type of Financing Preferred:
Early Stage
Expansion
Later Stage

Size of Investments Considered:
Min Size of Investment Considered (000s): $3,000
Max Size of Investment Considered (000s): $7,000

Geographical Preferences

United States Preferences:
Mid Atlantic
Northeast
West Coast
All U.S.

Industry Focus

(% based on actual investment)	
Internet Specific	30.5%
Semiconductors/Other Elect.	21.4%

Computer Software and Services	18.4%
Communications and Media	15.5%
Industrial/Energy	6.6%
Other Products	3.5%
Computer Hardware	3.4%
Biotechnology	0.8%

Additional Information

Year Founded: 1998
Capital Under Management: $290,000,000
Current Activity Level : Actively seeking new investments
Method of Compensation: Return on investment is of primary concern, do not charge fees

RIELLO INVESTIMENTI SPA

Via E. Filiberto
Padova, Italy 35100
Phone: 39-049-877-4824
Fax: 39-049-876-4466
E-mail: info@rielloinvestimenti.it
Website: www.rielloinvestimenti.it

Type of Firm

Private Equity Firm

Project Preferences

Type of Financing Preferred:
Balanced

Geographical Preferences

International Preferences:
Europe

Additional Information

Year Founded: 2004
Current Activity Level : Actively seeking new investments

RIGEL ASSOCIATES LLC

1875 South Grant Street
Suite 960
San Mateo, CA USA 94402
Phone: 650-292-7681
Website: www.rigelassociates.com

Management and Staff

Harold Robinson, Managing Partner
Jonathan Firestein, Vice President
Michael Mitgang, Managing Partner

Type of Firm

Private Equity Firm

Project Preferences

Type of Financing Preferred:
Leveraged Buyout
Turnaround
Management Buyouts
Acquisition
Recapitalizations

Geographical Preferences

United States Preferences:
All U.S.

Canadian Preferences:
All Canada

Industry Preferences

In Business Serv. prefer:
Services

Additional Information

Year Founded: 2004
Current Activity Level : Actively seeking new investments

RIMASIA CAPITAL PARTNERS

1808 Hutchison House
10 Harcourt Road
Admiralty, Hong Kong
Phone: 852-2524-6100
Fax: 852-2970-0078
E-mail: info@RimAsiaCapital.com
Website: www.rimasiacapital.com

Other Offices

14 Robinson Road
#06-02 Far East Finanace Building
Singapore, Singapore 048545
Phone: 65-6227-3033
Fax: 65-6227-3533

800 Shang Cheng Road, Pudong
Room 1225, CIMIC Tower
Shanghai, China 200120
Phone: 86-21-5835-6080
Fax: 86-21-5835-7208

Management and Staff

Eric Lin, Partner
Eric Wei, Managing Partner
Gavin Caudle, Partner
Lester Lim, Principal
Rose Siow, Managing Director
Synthia Hillberry, Chief Financial Officer

Type of Firm

Private Equity Firm

Project Preferences

Type of Financing Preferred:
Balanced

Geographical Preferences

International Preferences:
Asia

Additional Information

Year Founded: 2004
Current Activity Level : Actively seeking new investments

RINCON VENTURE PARTNERS

101 West Anapamu Street
4th Floor
Santa Barbara, CA USA 93101
Phone: 805-899-2616
Fax: 805-899-2617
Website: www.rinconvp.com

Management and Staff

Brian Kelly, Founding Partner
James Andelman, Founding Partner

Type of Firm

Private Equity Firm

Project Preferences

Type of Financing Preferred:
Early Stage
Seed

Size of Investments Considered:
Min Size of Investment Considered (000s): $500
Max Size of Investment Considered (000s): $1,500

Geographical Preferences

United States Preferences:
Southern California

Industry Preferences

In Communications prefer:
Communications and Media

In Internet Specific prefer:
Internet

In Industrial/Energy prefer:
Alternative Energy

Additional Information

Name of Most Recent Fund: Rincon Venture Partners, L.P.
Most Recent Fund Was Raised: 05/03/2007
Year Founded: 2005
Capital Under Management: $6,000,000
Current Activity Level : Actively seeking new investments

RIOBRAVO INVESTIMENTOS

Av. Chedid Jaffet, 222
Bloco B - 3 Andar Vila Olimpia
Sao Paulo, Brazil 04551-065
Phone: 55-11-2107-6600
Fax: 55-11-2107-6699
E-mail: contato@riobravo.com.br
Website: www.riobravo.com.br

Other Offices

Av. Presidente Wilson, 231
Grupo 1602
Rio de Janeiro, Brazil 20030-021
Phone: 55-21-2173-6650
Fax: 55-21-2173-6651

Rua Francisco da Cunha
392 - 6 andar
Recife, Brazil 51020-040
Phone: 55-81-2122-6600
Fax: 55-81-2122-6605

Libertad 1133 - 5 Piso
Buenos Aires, Argentina 1012
Phone: 54-11-4814-0162
Fax: 54-11-4814-0166

Rua Dona Laura, 414 - cj . 601
6 andar
Porto Alegre, Brazil 90430-090
Phone: 55-51-3333-3777
Fax: 55-51-3333-3777

Management and Staff

Carlos Kawall, Partner
Luiz Eugenio, Partner

Type of Firm

Private Equity Firm

Association Membership

Brazilian Venture Capital Association (ABCR)

Project Preferences

Type of Financing Preferred:

Expansion
Balanced

Geographical Preferences

International Preferences:

Brazil

Industry Preferences

In Communications prefer:

Communications and Media
Telecommunications

In Computer Software prefer:

Software

In Internet Specific prefer:

Internet

In Biotechnology prefer:

Biotechnology
Agricultural/Animal Bio.

In Industrial/Energy prefer:

Energy

In Transportation prefer:

Transportation

In Business Serv. prefer:

Services
Consulting Services

Additional Information

Year Founded: 2000
Capital Under Management: $6,900,000
Current Activity Level : Actively seeking new investments

RIOJANA DE CAPITAL RIESGO S.A. (AKA: RICARI)

C/ Vara del Rey, 41 bis 7o
Logrono, Spain 26002
Phone: 34-941-259-688
Fax: 34-941-259-803
Website: www.ricari.es

Type of Firm

Bank Affiliated

Project Preferences

Type of Financing Preferred:

Second Stage Financing
Early Stage
Expansion

Geographical Preferences

International Preferences:

Spain

Additional Information

Year Founded: 1990
Current Activity Level : Actively seeking new investments

RIORDAN, LEWIS & HADEN

300 South Grand Avenue
27th Floor
Los Angeles, CA USA 90071
Phone: 213-229-8500
Fax: 213-229-8597
Website: rlhinvestors.com

Other Offices

19200 Von Karman
Suite 500
Irvine, CA USA 92612
Phone: 949-475-9458
Fax: 949-861-6392

Type of Firm

Private Equity Firm

Project Preferences

Role in Financing:

Prefer role as deal originator but will also invest in deals created by others

Type of Financing Preferred:

Second Stage Financing
Leveraged Buyout
Start-up Financing
First Stage Financing
Special Situation

Size of Investments Considered:

Min Size of Investment Considered (000s): $2,000
Max Size of Investment Considered: No Limit

Geographical Preferences

United States Preferences:

West Coast

Industry Preferences

In Computer Software prefer:

Computer Services

In Medical/Health prefer:

Medical Diagnostics
Medical Therapeutics
Medical Products
Hospital/Other Instit.

In Consumer Related prefer:

Food/Beverage
Consumer Products
Consumer Services
Other Restaurants
Education Related

In Industrial/Energy prefer:

Industrial Products
Environmental Related

In Transportation prefer:

Transportation

In Business Serv. prefer:

Consulting Services

In Manufact. prefer:

Publishing

Additional Information

Year Founded: 1974
Capital Under Management: $200,000,000
Current Activity Level : Actively seeking new investments
Method of Compensation: Return on investment is of primary concern, do not charge fees

RIPPLEWOOD HOLDINGS LLC

1 Rockefeller Plaza
32nd Floor
New York, NY USA 10020
Phone: 212-582-6700
Fax: 212-582-4110

Management and Staff

Jeffrey Hendren, Managing Director
Masamoto Yashiro, Partner
Paul Liska, Partner
Peter Berger, Chief Financial Officer
Robert Berner, Managing Director
Tim Collins, Chief Executive Officer

Type of Firm
Private Equity Firm

Project Preferences

Type of Financing Preferred:
Leveraged Buyout
Turnaround
Management Buyouts

Geographical Preferences

International Preferences:
Japan

Industry Focus
(% based on actual investment)

Other Products	68.3%
Consumer Related	27.4%
Internet Specific	3.3%
Communications and Media	1.0%
Industrial/Energy	0.1%

Additional Information
Name of Most Recent Fund: Ripplewood Partners II, L.P.
Most Recent Fund Was Raised: 12/22/2000
Year Founded: 1996
Current Activity Level : Actively seeking new investments

RISA PARTNERS INC.
5F Akasaka Inter City
1-11-44 Akasaka, Minato-ku
Tokyo, Japan 107-0052
Phone: 81-3-5573-8011
Fax: 81-3-5573-8012
Website: www.risa-p.com

Management and Staff
Atsushi Imuta, President

Type of Firm
Private Equity Firm

Additional Information
Year Founded: 1998
Capital Under Management: $26,000,000
Current Activity Level : Actively seeking new investments

RISING STAR MANAGEMENT GMBH
Seestrasse 46
Bottighofen, Switzerland CH 8598
Phone: 41-71-686-9400
Fax: 41-71-686-9415
E-mail: info@risingstar.ch
Website: www.risingstar.ch

Type of Firm
Private Equity Firm

Project Preferences

Type of Financing Preferred:
Balanced

Geographical Preferences

International Preferences:
Europe

Additional Information
Year Founded: 2007
Current Activity Level : Actively seeking new investments

RISING TIDE FUND
255 Shoreline Drive
Suite 520
Redwood City, CA USA 94065
Phone: 650-486-2444
Fax: 650-595-2442
Website: www.risingtidefund.com

Other Offices
350 Terry Fox Drive
Suite 350
Kanata, Canada K2K 2W5
Phone: 613-271-1005
Fax: 613-271-0066

90 Avenue Henri Martin
Paris, France 75016
Phone: 33-8-70-38-2467
Fax: 33-1-45-04-9616

Management and Staff
Bruce Bauer, Managing Partner
David Kapnick, Managing Director & CFO
Jay Morrison, Managing Partner
Jean-Noel Mereur, Venture Partner
Ken Wigglesworth, Venture Partner
Ossama Hassanein, General Partner
Trevor Kienzle, General Partner

Type of Firm
Private Equity Firm

Project Preferences

Role in Financing:
Prefer role as deal originator

Type of Financing Preferred:
Second Stage Financing
First Stage Financing

Size of Investments Considered:
Min Size of Investment Considered (000s): $10,000
Max Size of Investment Considered (000s): $10,000

Geographical Preferences

United States Preferences:
Northwest

Canadian Preferences:
Eastern Canada

International Preferences:
Sweden
United Kingdom
France

Industry Focus
(% based on actual investment)

Computer Software and Services	31.0%
Semiconductors/Other Elect.	23.6%
Communications and Media	20.2%
Internet Specific	15.0%
Medical/Health	5.4%
Computer Hardware	4.9%

Additional Information
Name of Most Recent Fund: Newbury Ventures III, LP
Most Recent Fund Was Raised: 04/05/2001
Year Founded: 1992
Capital Under Management: $300,000,000
Current Activity Level : Actively seeking new investments
Method of Compensation: Return on investment is of primary concern, do not charge fees

RISK CAPITAL PARTNERS, LTD.
9 Grafton Mews
Fitzrovia
London, United Kingdom W1T 5HZ
Phone: 44-20-7554-9740
Fax: 44-20-7388-4737
Website: www.riskcapitalpartners.co.uk

Management and Staff
Ben Redmond, Managing Director
Luke Johnson, Managing Director

Type of Firm
Private Equity Firm

Association Membership
British Venture Capital Association (BVCA)

Project Preferences

Type of Financing Preferred:
Generalist PE
Mezzanine
Expansion
Turnaround

Size of Investments Considered:
Min Size of Investment Considered (000s): $5,876
Max Size of Investment Considered (000s): $97,930

Geographical Preferences

International Preferences:
United Kingdom

Industry Preferences

In Medical/Health prefer:
Medical/Health

In Consumer Related prefer:
Consumer
Retail
Food/Beverage

In Transportation prefer:
Transportation

In Financial Services prefer:
Financial Services

In Business Serv. prefer:
Services

Additional Information

Year Founded: 2001
Capital Under Management: $107,000,000
Current Activity Level : Actively seeking new investments

RISQUE ET SERENITE

184, rue de la Pompe
Paris, France 75116
Phone: 33-1-5370-7777
Fax: 33-1-5370-7778
Website: www.risqueetsernite.fr

Management and Staff

Guy De Soucy, President

Type of Firm

Private Equity Firm

Association Membership

French Venture Capital Association (AFIC)

Project Preferences

Type of Financing Preferred:
Expansion
Generalist PE

Geographical Preferences

International Preferences:
Europe
France

Additional Information

Year Founded: 2000
Current Activity Level : Actively seeking new investments

RIT CAPITAL PARTNERS PLC

Spencer House
27 St. James Place
London, United Kingdom SW1A 1NR
Phone: 020-7493-8111
Fax: 020-7493-5765
Website: www.ritcap.co.uk

Management and Staff

Duncan Budge, Chief Operating Officer

Type of Firm

Private Equity Firm

Project Preferences

Type of Financing Preferred:
Expansion
Balanced

Geographical Preferences

International Preferences:
United Kingdom
China

Industry Preferences

In Internet Specific prefer:
Ecommerce

In Consumer Related prefer:
Consumer
Entertainment and Leisure

Additional Information

Year Founded: 1988
Current Activity Level : Actively seeking new investments

RITCHIE CAPITAL

801 Warrenville Road
Suite 650
Lisle, IL USA 60532
Phone: 630-786-4000
E-mail: inquiries@ritchiecapital.com
Website: www.ritchiecapital.com

Other Offices

747 Third Avenue
38th Floor
New York, NY USA 10017

3000 Sand Hill Road
Building One, Suite 205
Menlo Park, CA USA 94025

Management and Staff

Douglas Rothschild, Senior Managing Director
Duncan Goldie-Morrison, Senior Managing Director
John Stocchetti, Chief Financial Officer
Paul Wolfe, Senior Managing Director
Tom Juterbock, Senior Managing Director
Warren DeMaio, Senior Managing Director

Type of Firm

Private Equity Firm

Project Preferences

Type of Financing Preferred:
Balanced

Geographical Preferences

International Preferences:
All International

Additional Information

Year Founded: 1997
Current Activity Level : Actively seeking new investments

RITE INTERNET VENTURES AB

Malmskillnadsgatan 39
Stockholm, Sweden 111 38
Fax: 46-8-611-7715
Website: www.riteventures.com

Management and Staff

Anders Strom, Partner
Christoffer Haggblom, Managing Director
Peter Lindell, Partner
Staffan Persson, Partner
Tommy Jacobson, Partner

Type of Firm

Private Equity Firm

Project Preferences

Type of Financing Preferred:
Early Stage
Start-up Financing

Geographical Preferences

International Preferences:
Sweden
Switzerland
Scandanavia/Nordic Region
Norway

Additional Information

Year Founded: 2008
Current Activity Level : Actively seeking new investments

RIVA Y GARCIA PRIVATE EQUITY

Casa Berenguer
Diputacion, 246 principal
Barcelona, Spain 08007
Phone: 34-93-445-7644
Fax: 34-93-270-1213
E-mail: bcn@rivaygarcia.es
Website: www.rivaygarcia.es

Management and Staff

Borja Garcia-Nieto Portabella, Founding Partner

Type of Firm

Investment Management Firm

Project Preferences

Type of Financing Preferred:
Second Stage Financing
Leveraged Buyout
Early Stage
Expansion
Balanced
Seed
Startup

Geographical Preferences

International Preferences:
Spain

Industry Preferences

In Communications prefer:
Wireless Communications

In Computer Software prefer:
Applications Software

In Internet Specific prefer:
Internet

In Business Serv. prefer:
Media

Additional Information
Year Founded: 1999
Capital Under Management: $69,000,000
Current Activity Level : Actively seeking new investments

RIVENROCK CAPITAL LLC
915 Wilshire Boulevard
Suite 1760
Los Angeles, CA USA 90017
Phone: 213-489-4660
E-mail: contacts@rivenrockcapital.com
Website: www.rivenrockcapital.com

Type of Firm
Private Equity Firm

Project Preferences

Type of Financing Preferred:
Balanced

Geographical Preferences

United States Preferences:
All U.S.

Industry Preferences

In Consumer Related prefer:
Food/Beverage
Consumer Products
Education Related

In Industrial/Energy prefer:
Industrial Products

In Transportation prefer:
Transportation

In Manufact. prefer:
Manufacturing

Additional Information
Year Founded: 2004
Current Activity Level : Actively seeking new investments

RIVER ASSOCIATES, LLC
633 Chestnut Street
Suite 1640
Chattanooga, TN USA 37450
Phone: 423-755-0888
Fax: 423-755-0870
Website: www.riverassociatesllc.com

Management and Staff
G.H. Patten Pettway, Partner
J. Mark Jones, Partner
James Baker, Partner
Mike Brookshire, Partner
W. Craig Baker, Principal

Type of Firm
Private Equity Firm

Project Preferences

Role in Financing:
Will function either as deal originator or investor in deals created by others

Type of Financing Preferred:
Leveraged Buyout
Management Buyouts
Acquisition
Recapitalizations

Size of Investments Considered:
Min Size of Investment Considered (000s): $10,000
Max Size of Investment Considered (000s): $50,000

Geographical Preferences

Canadian Preferences:
All Canada

International Preferences:
Mexico

Industry Preferences

In Semiconductor/Electr prefer:
Electronic Components
Controllers and Sensors
Sensors
Component Testing Equipmt
Analytic/Scientific

In Medical/Health prefer:
Medical Products
Disposable Med. Products

In Consumer Related prefer:
Consumer
Food/Beverage

In Industrial/Energy prefer:
Industrial Products
Machinery

In Transportation prefer:
Aerospace

In Business Serv. prefer:
Services
Distribution

In Manufact. prefer:
Manufacturing

Additional Information
Name of Most Recent Fund: River V, L.P.
Most Recent Fund Was Raised: 07/08/2005
Year Founded: 1990
Capital Under Management: $100,000,000
Current Activity Level : Actively seeking new investments
Method of Compensation: Return on invest. most important, but chg. closing fees, service fees, etc.

RIVER CAPITAL
4200 Northside Parkway
Building 14, Suite 250
Atlanta, GA USA 30327
Phone: 404-873-2166
Fax: 404-873-2158
E-mail: info@river-capital.com
Website: www.river-capital.com

Management and Staff
Jon Van Tuin, Vice President

Type of Firm
Private Equity Firm

Project Preferences

Role in Financing:
Prefer role as deal originator but will also invest in deals created by others

Type of Financing Preferred:
Leveraged Buyout
Mezzanine
Recapitalizations

Size of Investments Considered:
Min Size of Investment Considered (000s): $3,000
Max Size of Investment Considered: No Limit

Geographical Preferences

United States Preferences:
Mid Atlantic
Midwest
Southeast
Southwest

Industry Preferences

In Semiconductor/Electr prefer:
Circuit Boards

In Medical/Health prefer:
Medical Products
Disposable Med. Products

In Consumer Related prefer:
Entertainment and Leisure
Franchises(NEC)
Food/Beverage
Consumer Products
Education Related

In Industrial/Energy prefer:
Industrial Products

In Transportation prefer:
Transportation

In Manufact. prefer:
Publishing

Additional Information
Name of Most Recent Fund: River Capital Fund V, L.P.
Most Recent Fund Was Raised: 06/07/2006
Year Founded: 1983
Capital Under Management: $50,000,000
Current Activity Level : Actively seeking new investments
Method of Compensation: Return on invest. most important, but chg. closing fees, service fees, etc.

RIVER CITIES CAPITAL FUNDS
221 East Fourth Street
Suite 2400
Cincinnati, OH USA 45202
Phone: 513-621-9700
Fax: 513-579-8939
E-mail: info@rccf.com
Website: www.rccf.com

Other Offices
3737 Glenwood Avenue
Suite 100
Raleigh, NC USA 27612
Phone: 919-573-6111
Fax: 919-573-6050

Management and Staff
Daniel Fleming, Managing Director
Edward McCarthy, Managing Director
Edwin Robinson, Managing Director
J. Carter McNabb, Managing Director
J. Eric Lenning, Principal
Murray Wilson, Managing Director
R. Glen Mayfield, Managing Director
Robert Heimann, Principal
Rurik Vandevenne, Principal

Type of Firm
Private Equity Firm

Association Membership
Illinois Venture Capital Association
Natl Assoc of Small Bus. Inv. Co (NASBIC)

Project Preferences

Role in Financing:
Will function either as deal originator or investor in deals created by others

Type of Financing Preferred:
Early Stage
Expansion
Balanced

Size of Investments Considered:
Min Size of Investment Considered (000s): $1,500
Max Size of Investment Considered (000s): $6,000

Geographical Preferences

United States Preferences:
Midwest
Southeast

Industry Preferences

In Communications prefer:
Radio & TV Broadcasting
Telecommunications
Wireless Communications
Data Communications

In Computer Software prefer:
Software
Systems Software
Applications Software
Artificial Intelligence

In Internet Specific prefer:
Internet
Ecommerce
Web Aggregration/Portals

In Medical/Health prefer:
Medical/Health
Medical Diagnostics
Diagnostic Test Products
Medical Therapeutics
Drug/Equipmt Delivery
Medical Products
Disposable Med. Products
Health Services
Hospitals/Clinics/Primary
Hospital/Other Instit.

In Industrial/Energy prefer:
Industrial Products
Factory Automation
Process Control
Robotics

In Financial Services prefer:
Financial Services

In Manufact. prefer:
Manufacturing

Additional Information
Name of Most Recent Fund: River Cities Capital Fund IV (NQP), L.P.
Most Recent Fund Was Raised: 01/03/2007
Year Founded: 1994
Capital Under Management: $290,000,000
Current Activity Level : Actively seeking new investments
Method of Compensation: Return on investment is of primary concern, do not charge fees

---

RIVERLAKE PARTNERS LLC
1000 Southwest Broadway
Suite 1010
Portland, OR USA 97205
Phone: 503-228-7100
Fax: 503-228-7105
Website: www.riverlakepartners.com

Other Offices
29911 South West Boones Ferry Road
Suite Three
Wilsonville, OR USA 97070
Phone: 503-682-3073

Management and Staff
Charles Grant, Partner
Erik Krieger, Managing Partner
Greg Tansey, Vice President
Thomas Zupan, Chief Financial Officer
Victor Petroff, Partner

Type of Firm
Private Equity Firm

Project Preferences

Role in Financing:
Prefer role as deal originator

Type of Financing Preferred:
Control-block Purchases
Leveraged Buyout
Later Stage
Management Buyouts
Acquisition
Recapitalizations

Size of Investments Considered:
Min Size of Investment Considered (000s): $2,500
Max Size of Investment Considered (000s): $10,000

Geographical Preferences

United States Preferences:
All U.S.

Industry Preferences

In Semiconductor/Electr prefer:
Electronics

In Industrial/Energy prefer:
Industrial Products
Factory Automation
Machinery

In Transportation prefer:
Transportation
Aerospace

In Business Serv. prefer:
Services
Distribution

In Manufact. prefer:
Manufacturing

Additional Information

Year Founded: 2003
Capital Under Management: $23,900,000
Current Activity Level : Actively seeking new investments
Method of Compensation: Return on invest. most important, but chg. closing fees, service fees, etc.

RIVERROCK HOLDINGS LLC

15851 Dallas Parkway
Suite 600
Addison, TX USA 75001
Phone: 214-561-8728
Fax: 214-561-8729
E-mail: info@riverrockholdings.com
Website: www.riverrockholdings.com

Management and Staff

Amy Brown, Partner
Barbara Hill, Partner
Geoff Kearney, Partner

Type of Firm

Private Equity Firm

Project Preferences

Type of Financing Preferred:

Leveraged Buyout
Mezzanine
Management Buyouts

Industry Preferences

In Business Serv. prefer:

Services

Additional Information

Year Founded: 2008
Current Activity Level : Actively seeking new investments

RIVERSIDE COMPANY

45 Rockefeller Center
630 Fifth Avenue, Suite 2400
New York, NY USA 10111
Phone: 212-265-6575
Fax: 212-265-6478
E-mail: riverside@riversidecompany.com
Website: www.riversidecompany.com

Other Offices

21 Flr., Seoul Finance Center
Taepyeongro 1-ga, Jung-gu
Seoul, South Korea 100-768
Phone: 82-2-3782-6821
Fax: 82-2-3782-6824

Terminal Tower
50 Public Square, 29th Floor
Cleveland, OH USA 44113
Phone: 216-344-1040
Fax: 216-344-1330

Blasieholmsgatan 4A
Suite 160
Stockholm, Sweden 114 48
Phone: 46-8-5450-3030
Fax: 46-8-5450-3035

ul. Zielna 37/c
Warszaw, Poland 00-108
Phone: 48-22-320-4820
Fax: 48-22-320-4828

Serrano 120-3 dcha
Madrid, Spain 28006
Phone: 34-91-590-1337
Fax: 34-91-561-1606

10 Hagestraat 5-B
Eindhoven, Netherlands 5611 EG
Phone: 31-40-203-4710
Fax: 31-40-203-4715

c/o Horvat Capital Corporation
3400-666 Burrard Street
Vancouver, Canada V6C 2X8
Phone: 604-639-3139
Fax: 604-688-1320

630 Fifth Avenue
Suite 2400
New York, NY USA 10111
Phone: 212-265-6575
Fax: 212-265-6478

561 Vinings Estates Drive
Atlanta, GA USA 30126
Phone: 770-948-4256
Fax: 770-948-6881

7, Avenue Lloyd George
Brussels
, Belgium B-1000
Phone: 32-2-626-2121
Fax: 32-2-626-2122

Tokyo Sankei Building 27th Floor
1-7-2 Otemachi
Tokyo, Japan 107-0052
Phone: 81-3-3242-6198
Fax: 81-3-3242-6336

3131 McKinney Avenue
Suite 540
Dallas, TX USA 75204
Phone: 214-871-9640
Fax: 214-871-9620

Batthyany u. 49
Budapest, Hungary 1015
Phone: 36-1-224-9050
Fax: 36-1-224-9051

455 Market Street
Suite 1520
San Francisco, CA USA 94105
Phone: 415-348-9560
Fax: 415-348-9561

4545 North Hermitage Avenue
Chicago, IL USA 60640
Phone: 773-334-7518
Fax: 310-374-1858

Vaclavske nam. 832/19
Praha 1
Prague, Czech Republic 110 00
Phone: 420-224-890-166
Fax: 420-224-890-164

Alter Hof 5
Munich, Germany 80331
Phone: 49-89-2422-4890
Fax: 49-89-2422-4899

Management and Staff

Bela Schwartz, Chief Financial Officer
Brian Bunker, Managing Director
Joseph Lee, Principal
Kai Koeppen, Partner
Martha Anders, Vice President
Pam Hendrickson, Chief Operating Officer
Simon Feiglin, Principal
Trey Vincent, Principal
Volker Schmidt, Partner

Type of Firm

Private Equity Firm

Association Membership

European Private Equity and Venture Capital Assoc.

Project Preferences

Role in Financing:

Prefer role as deal originator but will also invest in deals created by others

Type of Financing Preferred:

Generalist PE

Size of Investments Considered:

Min Size of Investment Considered (000s): $1,000
Max Size of Investment Considered (000s): $100,000

Geographical Preferences

United States Preferences:

All U.S.

International Preferences:

Europe
Central Europe
Western Europe
China
Korea, South
Singapore
Australia
Japan

Industry Focus

(% based on actual investment)

Other Products	33.5%
Consumer Related	30.3%
Medical/Health	14.7%
Industrial/Energy	10.8%
Semiconductors/Other Elect.	4.0%
Communications and Media	3.0%
Internet Specific	2.2%
Computer Software and Services	1.5%

Additional Information

Name of Most Recent Fund: Riverside Europe Fund III, L.P.
Most Recent Fund Was Raised: 06/12/2005
Year Founded: 1988
Capital Under Management: $2,650,400,000
Current Activity Level : Actively seeking new investments
Method of Compensation: Return on invest. most important, but chg. closing fees, service fees, etc.

RIVERSIDE MANAGEMENT GROUP

335 Madison Avenue
Suite 1602
New York, NY USA 10017
Phone: 212-230-1880
Fax: 212-230-1057
Website: www.rmginvestments.com

Management and Staff

Christopher Wood, General Partner
D. Jim Carpenter, Managing Partner
Mark Bernegger, General Partner
Robert Hoguet, General Partner

Type of Firm

Private Equity Firm

Geographical Preferences

International Preferences:

Europe

Industry Focus

(% based on actual investment)

Internet Specific	46.9%
Communications and Media	20.5%
Computer Software and Services	19.2%
Industrial/Energy	12.3%
Other Products	0.6%
Semiconductors/Other Elect.	0.5%

Additional Information

Name of Most Recent Fund: Riverside Holdings II
Most Recent Fund Was Raised: 05/19/2000
Year Founded: 1996
Current Activity Level : Actively seeking new investments

RIVERSTONE LLC

712 Fifth Avenue
51st Floor
New York, NY USA 10019
Phone: 212-993-0076
Fax: 212-993-0077
Website: www.riverstonellc.com

Management and Staff

Ralph Alexander, Managing Director

Type of Firm

Private Equity Firm

Additional Information

Year Founded: 2009
Current Activity Level : Actively seeking new investments

RIVERVEST VENTURE PARTNERS

7733 Forsyth Boulevard
Suite 1650
Saint Louis, MO USA 63105
Phone: 314-726-6700
Fax: 314-726-6715
Website: www.rivervest.com

Other Offices

11000 Cedar Avenue
Suite 100
Cleveland, OH USA 44106
Phone: 216-658-3982

Management and Staff

Andrew Craig, Managing Director
Dennis Wahr, Venture Partner
J. Gordon Foulkes, Managing Director
Jay Schmelter, Managing Director
John McKearn, Venture Partner
Karen Spilizewski, Vice President
Thomas Melzer, Managing Director

Type of Firm

Private Equity Firm

Association Membership

National Venture Capital Association - USA (NVCA)

Project Preferences

Role in Financing:

Will function either as deal originator or investor in deals created by others

Type of Financing Preferred:

Early stage
Expansion
Later Stage
Seed
Startup

Size of Investments Considered:

Min Size of Investment Considered (000s): $500
Max Size of Investment Considered (000s): $6,000

Industry Preferences

In Biotechnology prefer:

Biotechnology
Human Biotechnology

In Medical/Health prefer:

Medical Therapeutics
Drug/Equipmt Delivery
Medical Products
Disposable Med. Products
Pharmaceuticals

Additional Information

Name of Most Recent Fund: RiverVest Venture Fund II, L.P.
Most Recent Fund Was Raised: 08/29/2006
Year Founded: 2000
Capital Under Management: $164,000,000
Current Activity Level : Actively seeking new investments
Method of Compensation: Return on investment is of primary concern, do not charge fees

RIVERWOOD CAPITAL LLC (FKA: BIGWOOD CAPITAL LLC)

245 Lytton Avenue
Suite 250
Palo Alto, CA USA 94301-1465
Phone: 650-473-5465

Management and Staff

Michael Marks, Founder

Type of Firm

Private Equity Firm

Project Preferences

Type of Financing Preferred:

Leveraged Buyout
Expansion
Balanced

Geographical Preferences

United States Preferences:

All U.S.

International Preferences:

China

Additional Information

Year Founded: 2007
Capital Under Management: $200,000,000
Current Activity Level : Actively seeking new investments

RIZVI TRAVERSE MANAGEMENT, LLC

401 South Old Woodward
Suite 426
Birmingham, MI USA 48009
Phone: 248-594-4751
Fax: 248-594-4754
Website: www.rizvitraverse.com

Other Offices

9000 Sunset Boulevard
Suite 1560
West Hollywood, CA USA 90069

Management and Staff

Ben Kohn, Partner
Chris Hopkins, Partner
John Giampetroni, Chief Operating Officer
Karen Blanchard, Vice President
Viq Shariff, Partner

Type of Firm

Private Equity Firm

Project Preferences

Type of Financing Preferred:
Leveraged Buyout
Generalist PE
Expansion
Turnaround
Management Buyouts
Acquisition
Recapitalizations

Geographical Preferences

United States Preferences:
All U.S.

Additional Information

Year Founded: 2005
Current Activity Level : Actively seeking new investments

RJD PARTNERS LIMITED (FKA: ROYAL LONDON PRIVATE EQUITY)

8-9 Well Court
Bow Lane
London, United Kingdom EC4M 9DN
Phone: 44-20-7050-6868
Fax: 44-20-7050-6869
Website: www.rjdpartners.com

Other Offices

19 St. Andrew Square
Edinburgh, United Kingdom EH2 1YE
Phone: 44-870-606-2000

P.O. Box 9428
Dublin, Ireland

Alderley Road
Wilmslow
Cheshire, United Kingdom SK9 1PF

Management and Staff

David MacLellan, Chairman & CEO
John Dillon, Partner
Richard Caston, Partner

Type of Firm

Bank Affiliated

Association Membership

British Venture Capital Association (BVCA)

Project Preferences

Type of Financing Preferred:
Leveraged Buyout
Expansion
Balanced

Size of Investments Considered:
Min Size of Investment Considered (000s): $28,656
Max Size of Investment Considered (000s): $143,280

Geographical Preferences

International Preferences:
United Kingdom
Europe

Industry Focus

(% based on actual investment)

Other Products	50.0%
Consumer Related	14.6%
Industrial/Energy	13.2%
Medical/Health	12.1%
Internet Specific	10.1%

Additional Information

Name of Most Recent Fund: Royal London Private Equity (RLPE)
Most Recent Fund Was Raised: 04/28/2003
Year Founded: 2001
Capital Under Management: $469,600,000
Current Activity Level : Actively seeking new investments

RLJ EQUITY PARTNERS LLC

Three Bethesda Metro Center
Suite 1000
Bethesda, MD USA 20814
Phone: 240-744-7856
Fax: 301-280-7798
E-mail: epteam@rljequity.com
Website: www.rljequitypartners.com

Management and Staff

Daphne Dufresne, Managing Director
Jerry Johnson, Vice President
Nigel Howard, Vice President
R. Kenneth Bryant, Managing Director
Rufus Rivers, Managing Director
T. Otey Smith, Vice President

Type of Firm

Bank Affiliated

Project Preferences

Type of Financing Preferred:
Leveraged Buyout
Expansion

Industry Preferences

In Financial Services prefer:
Financial Services

In Business Serv. prefer:
Services
Media

Additional Information

Year Founded: 2008
Capital Under Management: $225,000,000
Current Activity Level : Actively seeking new investments

RMB CAPITAL PARTNERS LTD. (FKA: RMB VENTURES LTD.)

60 Castlereagh Street
Level 13
Sydney, Australia 2000
Phone: 612-9256-6245
Fax: 612-9256-6293
E-mail: info@rmbcapital.com.au
Website: www.rmbcapital.com.au

Management and Staff

Mark Summerhayes, Partner
Nicholas Batchelor, Partner

Type of Firm

Bank Affiliated

Association Membership

Australian Venture Capital Association (AVCAL)

Project Preferences

Type of Financing Preferred:
Leveraged Buyout
Expansion
Management Buyouts
Acquisition
Industry Rollups

Size of Investments Considered:
Min Size of Investment Considered (000s): $12,087
Max Size of Investment Considered (000s): $40,290

Geographical Preferences

International Preferences:
Pacific

Additional Information

Year Founded: 1998
Capital Under Management: $241,700,000
Current Activity Level : Actively seeking new investments

RMB PRIVATE EQUITY

1 Merchant Place
Sandton
Johannesburg, South Africa 2146
Phone: 27-11-282-8000
Fax: 27-11-282-8008
E-mail: Info@rmb.co.za
Website: www.rmbcorvest.co.za

Management and Staff

Neil Page, Managing Director

Type of Firm

Bank Affiliated

Association Membership

South African Venture Capital Association (SAVCA)

Project Preferences

Type of Financing Preferred:

Leveraged Buyout
Expansion

Geographical Preferences

International Preferences:

Africa

Industry Focus

(% based on actual investment)

Other Products	100.0%

Additional Information

Year Founded: 1999
Current Activity Level : Actively seeking new investments

ROARK CAPITAL GROUP

1180 Peachtree Street NE
Suite 2500
Atlanta, GA USA 30309
Phone: 404-591-5200
Fax: 404-591-5201
E-mail: info@roarkcapital.com
Website: www.roarkcapital.com

Management and Staff

Anthony Scotto, Managing Director
David Lee, Vice President
Erik Morris, Managing Director
Ezra Field, Managing Director
Jeffrey Keenan, Chief Operating Officer
Lawrence DeAngelo, Managing Director
Neal Aronson, President, Founder
Robert Chambers, Managing Director
Robert Sheft, Managing Director
Robert Bryant, Vice President

Type of Firm

Private Equity Firm

Project Preferences

Type of Financing Preferred:

Leveraged Buyout
Management Buyouts
Acquisition
Recapitalizations

Size of Investments Considered:

Min Size of Investment Considered (000s): $20,000
Max Size of Investment Considered: No Limit

Geographical Preferences

United States Preferences:

All U.S.

Industry Preferences

In Consumer Related prefer:

Retail
Franchises(NEC)
Food/Beverage

In Financial Services prefer:

Financial Services

In Business Serv. prefer:

Distribution

Additional Information

Name of Most Recent Fund: Roark Capital Partners Parallel, L.P.
Most Recent Fund Was Raised: 12/27/2004
Year Founded: 2001
Capital Under Management: $1,500,000,000
Current Activity Level : Actively seeking new investments

ROBECO PRIVATE EQUITY

Coolsingel 120
Rotterdam, Netherlands 3011 AG
Phone: 31-10-224-1224
Fax: 31-10-411-5288
E-mail: private.equity@robeco.nl
Website: www.robeco.com

Other Offices

909 Third Avenue
New York, NY USA 10022
Phone: 212-908-9576
Fax: 212-908-9672

21, Boulevard de la Madeleine
Paris Cedex 01, France 75039
Phone: 33-1-5535-4500
Fax: 33-1-5535-4501

Taunusanlage 17
Frankfurt am Main, Germany 60325
Phone: 49-69-959-0858
Fax: 49-69-959-0850

Paseo de la Castellana 41-6B
Madrid, Spain 28046
Phone: 34-91-702-0705
Fax: 34-91-702-0671

Uraniastrasse 12
Zurich, Switzerland 8001
Phone: 41-44-227-7272
Fax: 41-44-227-7222

6-12, Place d' Armes
Luxembourg, Luxembourg 1136

ul. Grzybowska 12/14
office B-3
Warszawa, Poland 00-132
Phone: 48-22-374-7666
Fax: 48-22-405-2750

Thames Court One Queenhithe
London, United Kingdom EC4V 3RL
Phone: 44-207-334-9199
Fax: 44-207-334-9187

Avenue de Tervuren, 273
Brussels, Belgium 1150
Phone: 32-2-761-1040
Fax: 32-2-762-5140

Management and Staff

Ad Van den Ouweland, Managing Director
Constant Korthout, Chief Financial Officer
George Moller, Chief Executive Officer
Harrie Meijers, Managing Partner
Leni Boeren, Chief Operating Officer

Type of Firm

Bank Affiliated

Association Membership

European Private Equity and Venture Capital Assoc.

Project Preferences

Type of Financing Preferred:

Fund of Funds
Leveraged Buyout
Early Stage
Expansion
Balanced

Geographical Preferences

United States Preferences:

All U.S.

International Preferences:

Europe
Western Europe
Eastern Europe
Israel
Asia
Japan
All International

Industry Focus

(% based on actual investment)

Industrial/Energy	34.0%
Other Products	26.5%
Consumer Related	12.1%
Communications and Media	8.5%
Computer Hardware	6.2%
Computer Software and Services	5.1%
Medical/Health	4.4%
Biotechnology	1.3%
Semiconductors/Other Elect.	1.3%
Internet Specific	0.6%

Additional Information

Name of Most Recent Fund: WPG Corporate Development Associates V, L.P.
Most Recent Fund Was Raised: 04/16/1997
Year Founded: 1983
Capital Under Management: $88,800,000
Current Activity Level : Actively seeking new investments

ROBECO TEDA (TIANJIN) INVESTMENT MANAGEMENT COMPANY

Tianjin Economic Tech Dev'l
Binhai New Area
Tianjin, China

Type of Firm

Bank Affiliated

Project Preferences

Type of Financing Preferred:

Balanced

Geographical Preferences

International Preferences:

China

Industry Preferences

In Industrial/Energy prefer:

Energy Conservation Relat
Environmental Related

Additional Information

Year Founded: 2009
Current Activity Level : Actively seeking new investments

ROBIN HOOD VENTURES

200 Musket Lane
Wayne, PA USA 19087
Phone: 610-993-9060
Fax: 484-214-0114
E-mail: info@robinhoodventures.com
Website: www.robinhoodventures.com

Management and Staff

George Marks, Co-Founder
John Moore, Managing Partner
Lawrence Brotzge, Managing Partner

Type of Firm

Angel Group

Project Preferences

Role in Financing:

Prefer role as deal originator but will also invest in deals created by others

Type of Financing Preferred:

Second Stage Financing
Early Stage
First Stage Financing

Size of Investments Considered:

Min Size of Investment Considered (000s): $200
Max Size of Investment Considered (000s): $500

Geographical Preferences

United States Preferences:

Mid Atlantic

Industry Preferences

In Communications prefer:

Wireless Communications

In Computer Software prefer:

Software
Systems Software
Applications Software

In Internet Specific prefer:

Internet
Ecommerce

In Semiconductor/Electr prefer:

Electronic Components
Semiconductor
Micro-Processing

In Medical/Health prefer:

Medical Diagnostics
Diagnostic Test Products
Medical Therapeutics
Medical Products

In Industrial/Energy prefer:

Factory Automation

In Financial Services prefer:

Financial Services

Additional Information

Year Founded: 1999
Capital Under Management: $9,800,000
Current Activity Level : Actively seeking new investments
Method of Compensation: Return on investment is of primary concern, do not charge fees

ROCK HILL CAPITAL GROUP LLC

2777 Allen Parkway
Suite 850
Houston, TX USA 77019
Phone: 713-715-7510
Fax: 713-715-7520
E-mail: info@rockhillcap.com
Website: www.rockhillcap.com

Management and Staff

Randall Hale, Managing Director

Type of Firm

Private Equity Firm

Project Preferences

Type of Financing Preferred:

Leveraged Buyout
Expansion
Management Buyouts
Recapitalizations

Additional Information

Year Founded: 2008
Current Activity Level : Actively seeking new investments

ROCK MAPLE VENTURES, L.P.

38 Newbury Street
Seventh Floor
Boston, MA USA 02116
Phone: 617-262-8501
Fax: 617-687-0050
E-mail: info@rockmapleventures.com
Website: www.rockmapleventures.com

Other Offices

711 5th Avenue
Fifth Floor
New York, NY USA 10022
Phone: 212-813-2720
Fax: 212-813-2730

Management and Staff

Aris Hatch, Principal
David Freelove, Managing Director
Dennis Costello, Managing Director
Jason Henrichs, Managing Director

Type of Firm

Private Equity Firm

Association Membership

Mid-Atlantic Venture Association

Project Preferences

Role in Financing:

Will function either as deal originator or investor in

deals created by others

Type of Financing Preferred:
Early Stage
Balanced

Size of Investments Considered:
Min Size of Investment Considered (000s): $1,000
Max Size of Investment Considered (000s): $5,000

Geographical Preferences

United States Preferences:
All U.S.

Industry Preferences

In Computer Software prefer:
Software
Systems Software
Applications Software

In Semiconductor/Electr prefer:
Semiconductor
Component Testing Equipmt
Analytic/Scientific

In Biotechnology prefer:
Human Biotechnology

In Medical/Health prefer:
Medical Diagnostics
Drug/Equipmt Delivery
Medical Products
Health Services

Additional Information

Year Founded: 2001
Capital Under Management: $62,000,000
Current Activity Level : Actively seeking new investments
Method of Compensation: Return on invest. most important, but chg. closing fees, service fees, etc.

ROCK RIVER CAPITAL

1302 South Union
Rock Rapids, IA USA 51246
Phone: 712-472-2531
E-mail: info@rockrivercapital.com
Website: www.rockrivercapital.com

Type of Firm

Private Equity Firm

Project Preferences

Type of Financing Preferred:
Startup

Geographical Preferences

United States Preferences:
Iowa

Additional Information

Year Founded: 2005
Capital Under Management: $500,000
Current Activity Level : Actively seeking new investments

ROCKBRIDGE EQUITY PARTNERS LLC

20555 Victor Parkway
Livonia, MI USA 48152
Phone: 734-805-1800
E-mail: info@rbequity.com
Website: www.rbequity.com

Management and Staff

Brian Hermelin, Founding Partner
Daniel Gilbert, Founding Partner
Kevin Prokop, Founding Partner
Robert Kramer, Founding Partner

Type of Firm

Private Equity Firm

Project Preferences

Type of Financing Preferred:
Leveraged Buyout
Expansion
Acquisition

Size of Investments Considered:
Min Size of Investment Considered (000s): $20,000
Max Size of Investment Considered (000s): $30,000

Geographical Preferences

United States Preferences:
All U.S.

Industry Preferences

In Consumer Related prefer:
Entertainment and Leisure
Sports

In Financial Services prefer:
Financial Services

In Business Serv. prefer:
Services
Media

Additional Information

Year Founded: 2007
Current Activity Level : Actively seeking new investments

ROCKBROOK ADVISORS LLC

10730 Pacific Street
Suite 247
Omaha, NE USA 68114
Phone: 402-614-2731
Fax: 866-463-4874
Website: www.rockbrookadvisors.com

Management and Staff

Kristina Castle, Vice President

Type of Firm

Private Equity Firm

Project Preferences

Type of Financing Preferred:
Leveraged Buyout
Balanced
Acquisition

Geographical Preferences

United States Preferences:
Midwest
All U.S.

Industry Preferences

In Financial Services prefer:
Insurance

Additional Information

Year Founded: 2008
Current Activity Level : Actively seeking new investments

ROCKET VENTURES

2200 Sand Hill Road
Suite 240
Menlo Park, CA USA 94025
Phone: 650-561-9100
Fax: 650-561-9183
Website: www.rocketventures.com

Management and Staff

Bob Evans, Partner
David Adams, Managing Director
Jeff Allen, Managing Director
Larry Roberts, Partner
Nigel Backwith, Partner

Type of Firm

Private Equity Firm

Association Membership

National Venture Capital Association - USA (NVCA)

Project Preferences

Type of Financing Preferred:
Early Stage
Start-up Financing
Seed

Size of Investments Considered:
Min Size of Investment Considered (000s): $1,000
Max Size of Investment Considered (000s): $8,000

Geographical Preferences

United States Preferences:
West Coast
California

Industry Preferences

In Communications prefer:
Communications and Media

In Computer Software prefer:
Software

In Internet Specific prefer:
Internet

Additional Information

Name of Most Recent Fund: Rocket Ventures II, L.P.
Most Recent Fund Was Raised: 03/01/2000
Year Founded: 1998
Capital Under Management: $40,000,000
Current Activity Level : Actively seeking new investments

ROCKET VENTURES

300 Madison Avenue
Suite 270
Toledo, OH USA 43604
Phone: 419-252-2700
Fax: 419-252-2724
E-mail: info@rocketventures.org
Website: www.rocketventures.org

Management and Staff

Greg Knudson, Vice President

Type of Firm

Private Equity Firm

Project Preferences

Role in Financing:
Will function either as deal originator or investor in deals created by others

Type of Financing Preferred:
Early Stage
Seed

Size of Investments Considered:
Min Size of Investment Considered (000s): $250,000
Max Size of Investment Considered (000s): $750,000

Geographical Preferences

United States Preferences:
Midwest
Ohio

Industry Preferences

In Semiconductor/Electr prefer:
Electronic Components
Semiconductor
Micro-Processing
Controllers and Sensors
Sensors
Circuit Boards
Laser Related
Optoelectronics

In Biotechnology prefer:
Human Biotechnology
Genetic Engineering
Agricultural/Animal Bio.
Industrial Biotechnology
Biosensors

In Medical/Health prefer:
Medical Diagnostics
Diagnostic Services
Diagnostic Test Products
Medical Therapeutics
Drug/Equipmt Delivery
Medical Products
Disposable Med. Products
Health Services
Pharmaceuticals

In Industrial/Energy prefer:
Energy
Industrial Products
Factory Automation
Robotics

In Transportation prefer:
Aerospace

In Manufact. prefer:
Manufacturing

Additional Information

Name of Most Recent Fund: Rocket Venture Fund, LLC
Most Recent Fund Was Raised: 06/17/2008
Year Founded: 2008
Capital Under Management: $13,500,000
Current Activity Level : Actively seeking new investments

ROCKLEY GROUP, THE

P.O. Box 793
Oxford, United Kingdom OX19HH
Phone: 44-1-6725-11022
Fax: 44-1-6725-11002
Website: www.rockleygroup.com

Management and Staff

Robert Rickman, Managing Partner

Type of Firm

Private Equity Firm

Project Preferences

Type of Financing Preferred:
Balanced

Geographical Preferences

International Preferences:
United Kingdom
Industry Preferences

In Communications prefer:
Communications and Media

In Computer Hardware prefer:
Computers

In Computer Software prefer:
Data Processing

In Medical/Health prefer:
Medical/Health

In Industrial/Energy prefer:
Energy

In Other prefer:
Environment Responsible

Additional Information

Year Founded: 2009
Current Activity Level : Actively seeking new investments

ROCKPORT CAPITAL PARTNERS

160 Federal Street
18th Floor
Boston, MA USA 02110
Phone: 617-912-1420
Fax: 617-912-1449
E-mail: businessplans@rockportcap.com
Website: www.rockportcap.com

Other Offices

3000 Sand Hill Road
Building Two, Suite 110
Menlo Park, CA USA 94025
Phone: 650-854-93000
Fax: 650-845-9302

Management and Staff

Abe Yokell, Principal
Alexander Ellis, General Partner
Charles McDermott, General Partner
Daniel Hullah, Principal
David Prend, Managing General Partner
Dhiraj Malkani, Principal
Janet James, Managing General Partner
Stoddard Wilson, General Partner
Victor Westerlind, General Partner
William James, Managing General Partner

Type of Firm

Private Equity Firm

Association Membership

Natl Assoc of Small Bus. Inv. Co (NASBIC)
National Venture Capital Association - USA (NVCA)

Project Preferences

Role in Financing:
Will function either as deal originator or investor in deals created by others

Type of Financing Preferred:
Second Stage Financing
Early Stage
Expansion
Mezzanine
Research and Development
Start-up Financing

Balanced
Later Stage
Seed
First Stage Financing
Startup
Recapitalizations

Size of Investments Considered:
Min Size of Investment Considered (000s): $1,000
Max Size of Investment Considered (000s): $10,000

Geographical Preferences

United States Preferences:
All U.S.

Canadian Preferences:
All Canada

Industry Preferences

In Semiconductor/Electr prefer:
Controllers and Sensors
Sensors
Laser Related
Optoelectronics

In Industrial/Energy prefer:
Energy
Oil and Gas Exploration
Oil & Gas Drilling,Explor
Alternative Energy
Energy Conservation Relat
Industrial Products
Materials
Advanced Materials
Superconductivity
Process Control
Environmental Related

In Business Serv. prefer:
Distribution

In Utilities prefer:
Utilities

In Other prefer:
Environment Responsible

Additional Information

Name of Most Recent Fund: RockPort Capital Partners III, L.P.
Most Recent Fund Was Raised: 06/17/2008
Year Founded: 2000
Capital Under Management: $850,000,000
Current Activity Level : Actively seeking new investments
Method of Compensation: Return on investment is of primary concern, do not charge fees

---

ROCKPORT VENTURE PARTNERS

275 Cabot Street
#10
Beverly, MA USA 01915
Phone: 978-969-3500
Website: www.rockportventure.com

Type of Firm

Private Equity Firm

Project Preferences

Type of Financing Preferred:
Second Stage Financing
Public Companies
Later Stage
First Stage Financing

Geographical Preferences

United States Preferences:
All U.S.

Industry Preferences

In Medical/Health prefer:
Medical Therapeutics
Drug/Equipmt Delivery
Disposable Med. Products
Pharmaceuticals

Additional Information

Name of Most Recent Fund: Rockport Venture Fund I, L.P.
Most Recent Fund Was Raised: 06/01/2005
Year Founded: 2001
Capital Under Management: $6,000,000
Current Activity Level : Actively seeking new investments

ROCKRIDGE CAPITAL PARTNERS, INC.

One Stamford Landing
Suite 201
Stamford, CT USA 06902
Phone: 203-969-2000
Website: www.rrcap.com

Management and Staff

Erik Jansen, Managing Partner
Jeff Marshall, Managing Partner

Type of Firm

Private Equity Firm

Project Preferences

Size of Investments Considered:
Min Size of Investment Considered (000s): $10,000
Max Size of Investment Considered (000s): $12,000

Industry Preferences

In Computer Software prefer:
Software

Additional Information

Year Founded: 2002
Current Activity Level : Actively seeking new investments

ROCKWOOD EQUITY PARTNERS LLC

600 Fifth Avenue
25th Floor
New York, NY USA 10020
Phone: 212-218-8284
Fax: 212-218-8207
Website: www.rockwoodequity.com

Other Offices

925 Euclid Avenue
Suite 647
Cleveland, OH USA 44115
Phone: 216-622-2666
Fax: 216-622-2667

Management and Staff

Brett Keith, Principal
Owen Colligan, Principal

Type of Firm

Private Equity Firm

Project Preferences

Type of Financing Preferred:
Leveraged Buyout

Geographical Preferences

United States Preferences:
All U.S.

Industry Preferences

In Business Serv. prefer:
Services
Distribution
Consulting Services
Media

In Manufact. prefer:
Manufacturing
Office Automation Equipmt

Additional Information

Year Founded: 1999
Capital Under Management: $33,000,000
Current Activity Level : Actively seeking new investments

ROCKY MOUNTAIN CAPITAL PARTNERS (FKA:HANIFEN IMHOFF CAPITAL)

1125 17th Street
Suite 2260
Denver, CO USA 80202
Phone: 303-297-1701
Fax: 303-297-1702
E-mail: info@rockycapital.com
Website: www.rockymountaincapital.com

Management and Staff
Edward Brown, Managing Partner
Paul Lyons, Partner
Stephen Sangalis, Partner

Type of Firm
SBIC

Association Membership
Natl Assoc of Small Bus. Inv. Co (NASBIC)

Project Preferences
Role in Financing:
Prefer role in deals created by others

Type of Financing Preferred:
Mezzanine
Management Buyouts
Acquisition
Recapitalizations

Size of Investments Considered:
Min Size of Investment Considered (000s): $3,000
Max Size of Investment Considered (000s): $7,000

Geographical Preferences
United States Preferences:
Midwest
Northwest
Rocky Mountain
West Coast
California
Southwest

Industry Focus
(% based on actual investment)

Communications and Media	35.6%
Other Products	25.8%
Industrial/Energy	15.8%
Medical/Health	9.7%
Consumer Related	9.5%
Semiconductors/Other Elect.	2.2%
Computer Hardware	0.9%
Internet Specific	0.7%

Additional Information
Year Founded: 1994
Capital Under Management: $210,000,000
Current Activity Level : Actively seeking new investments
Method of Compensation: Return on invest. most important, but chg. closing fees, service fees, etc.

RODMAN & RENSHAW
330 Madison Avenue
27th Floor
New York, NY USA 10017
Phone: 212-356-0500
Fax: 212-356-0532
E-mail: tpapp@rodmanandrenshaw.com
Website: www.rodmanandrenshaw.com

Management and Staff
John Borer, Founder
Thomas Pinou, Chief Financial Officer

Type of Firm
Bank Affiliated

Project Preferences
Type of Financing Preferred:
Early Stage

Additional Information
Year Founded: 2002
Current Activity Level : Actively seeking new investments

ROGERS CASEY
One Parklands Drive
Darien, CT USA 06820
Phone: 203-656-5992
Fax: 203-656-2233
Website: www.rogerscasey.com

Management and Staff
David Katz, Managing Director

Type of Firm
Private Equity Firm

Additional Information
Year Founded: 2009
Current Activity Level : Actively seeking new investments

ROHER CAPITAL GROUP LLC
105 Linwood Court
Little Rock, AR USA 72205
Phone: 504-239-3331
Fax: 501-421-1865

Management and Staff
Michael Roher, Managing Director

Type of Firm
Private Equity Firm

Project Preferences
Role in Financing:
Prefer role as deal originator but will also invest in deals created by others

Type of Financing Preferred:
Leveraged Buyout
Control-block Purchases
Expansion
Mezzanine
Later Stage
Management Buyouts
Acquisition
Special Situation
Recapitalizations

Size of Investments Considered:
Min Size of Investment Considered (000s): $500
Max Size of Investment Considered (000s): $15,000

Geographical Preferences
United States Preferences:
All U.S.

Canadian Preferences:
All Canada

Industry Focus
(% based on actual investment)

Industrial/Energy	53.6%
Other Products	46.4%

Additional Information
Year Founded: 1998
Current Activity Level : Actively seeking new investments
Method of Compensation: Return on invest. most important, but chg. closing fees, service fees, etc.

ROLLS ROYCE CORPORATE VENTURE
Post Office Box 420
Indianapolis, IN USA 46206
Phone: 317-230-4793
Fax: 317-230-6572
Website: www.rolls-royce.com

Other Offices
227 Rue de la Loi
Brussels, Belgium
Phone: 32-2-230-8652
Fax: 32-2-230-0872

14850 Conference Center Drive
Chantilly, VA USA 20151
Phone: 703-834-1700
Fax: 703-709-6087

9500 Cote De Liesse Road
Quebec, Canada
Phone: 514-636-0964
Fax: 514-636-9969

Bangbae 4-dong
3rd Floor, Seil Building, 882-33
Seoul, South Korea
Phone: 82-2-3476-7750
Fax: 82-2-3476-0122

6 Nha Tho Street, Hoan Kiem District
Unit 402, 4th Floor Asia Tower Building
Hanoi, Vietnam
Phone: 84-4-9380-228
Fax: 84-4-9380-230

Pobrezni 3
IBC Building
Prague, Czech Republic
Phone: 420-2-248-35069
Fax: 420-2-248-35013

Av. Almirante Barroso 52
Rio de Janeiro, Brazil 20031
Phone: 55-21-2277-0100
Fax: 55-21-2277-0186

16 Chaoyangmenwai Street
2109 China Life Tower
Beijing, China
Phone: 86-10-8525-2288
Fax: 86-10-8525-2213

Office 26, B. Sadovaya Street, 10
Moscow, Russia
Phone: 7-495-651-9330
Fax: 7-495-651-9332

25 Barakhambha Road
2nd Floor, West Tower, Birla House
New Delhi, India
Phone: 91-11-2335-7118
Fax: 91-11-2335-7117

UBN Tower
32nd Floor
Kuala Lumpur, Malaysia
Phone: 60-3-2026-1990
Fax: 60-3-2031-7990

Lyonpark Road, Macquarie Park
Suite 102, 2-4
New South Wales, Australia
Phone: 61-2-9325-1333
Fax: 61-2-9325-1300

Jagerstrasse 59
Berlin, Germany
Phone: 49-30-2094-2501
Fax: 49-30-2094-2508

Dubai Airport Free Zone
Dubai, Utd. Arab Em.
Phone: 971-4-2994-343
Fax: 971-4-2994-344

Jln Jendral Sudirman Kav 10-11
16th Floor, Mid Plaza II Building
Jakarta, Indonesia
Phone: 62-21-570-3888
Fax: 62-21-570-6286

3-2-5 Kasumigaseki
3124A Kasumigaseki Building
Tokyo, Japan
Phone: 81-3-3592-0966
Fax: 81-3-3592-0969

16 International Business Park #03-01
Singapore, Singapore
Phone: 65-734-5031
Fax: 65-734-5038

900 Tonson Tower, 11th Floor
Ploenchit Road
Bangkok, Thailand
Phone: 66-2-263-0500
Fax: 66-2-263-0505

122 Avenue Charles de Gaulle
Neuilly-sur-Seine Cedex, France
Phone: 33-1-4722-1440
Fax: 33-1-4745-7738

6-8 Harbour Road
Room 1008B Shui-on-Centre
Wanchai, Hong Kong
Phone: 852-2802-4843
Fax: 852-2511-0461

40 Marcus Clarke Street
Canberra, Australia
Phone: 61-2-6257-0861
Fax: 61-2-6257-0862

65 Buckingham Gate
London, United Kingdom
Phone: 44-20-7222-9020
Fax: 44-20-7227-9170

PO Box 88215
Riyadh, Saudi Arabia
Phone: 966-1240-1712
Fax: 966-1240-1713

Via IV Novembre 114
Rome, Italy
Phone: 39-06-6976-671
Fax: 39-06-6791-755

Management and Staff

John Rose, Chief Executive Officer
Michael Terrett, Chief Operating Officer

Type of Firm

Corporate PE/Venture

Additional Information

Year Founded: 2005
Current Activity Level : Actively seeking new investments

ROMANIAN - AMERICAN ASSET MANAGEMENT COMPANY

91-111, Calea Floreasca
BL.F1, Apt.45
Bucharest, Romania 71401
Phone: 40-21-230-1427
Fax: 40-21-230-1427
E-mail: fcex@eln.ro
Website: www.fcex.fx.ro

Type of Firm

Private Equity Firm

Project Preferences

Type of Financing Preferred:
Balanced

Geographical Preferences

International Preferences:
Europe
Romania

Additional Information

Year Founded: 1996
Current Activity Level : Actively seeking new investments

ROMANIAN ENERGY EFFICIENCY FUND (AKA: EFICIENTA ENERGIEI)

Str. Johann Strauss nr. 2A
Sector 2
Bucharest, Romania 020312
Phone: 40-21-233-8801
Fax: 40-21-233-8802
E-mail: office@free.org.ro
Website: www.free.org.ro

Type of Firm

Private Equity Firm

Project Preferences

Type of Financing Preferred:
Balanced

Geographical Preferences

International Preferences:
Europe
Romania

Additional Information

Year Founded: 2005
Current Activity Level : Actively seeking new investments

ROMULUS CAPITAL

362 Memorial Drive
Cambridge, MA USA 02139
Phone: 630-930-8828
Website: www.romuluscap.com

Type of Firm

Private Equity Firm

Project Preferences

Type of Financing Preferred:
Seed
Startup

Geographical Preferences

United States Preferences:
Massachusetts

Additional Information

Name of Most Recent Fund: Romulus Capital I, L.P.

Most Recent Fund Was Raised: 11/04/2008
Year Founded: 2008
Current Activity Level : Actively seeking new investments

RONG INTERNATIONAL INVESTMENT MANAGEMENT CO. LTD.

Rm. 1607, Tower B
No. 88 Jianguo Rd., Chaoyang
Beijing, China 10002
Phone: 86-10-8589-8662
Fax: 86-10-8589-8667
E-mail: beijing@rongqin.com
Website: www.rongqin.com

Management and Staff

Ann Huang, Partner

Type of Firm

Private Equity Firm

Project Preferences

Type of Financing Preferred:
Balanced

Geographical Preferences

International Preferences:
China

Additional Information

Year Founded: 2000
Current Activity Level : Actively seeking new investments

RONGZHONG INVESTMENTS GROUP CO., LTD.

568 Xinshe Dadao
50/F New World Trade Building
Wuhan, China 430022
Phone: 86-27-8555-8008
Fax: 86-27-8555-8190
Website: www.rongzhong.cn

Management and Staff

Hai Tao Zhang, Vice President

Type of Firm

Bank Affiliated

Project Preferences

Type of Financing Preferred:
Mezzanine
Generalist PE
Balanced

Geographical Preferences

International Preferences:
China

Industry Preferences

In Medical/Health prefer:
Medical/Health

In Industrial/Energy prefer:
Energy

In Transportation prefer:
Transportation

In Financial Services prefer:
Financial Services
Real Estate

In Business Serv. prefer:
Media

In Manufact. prefer:
Manufacturing

Additional Information

Year Founded: 2005
Capital Under Management: $16,200,000
Current Activity Level : Actively seeking new investments

ROOT CAPITAL

2 Wardrobe Place
London, United Kingdom EC4V 5AH
Phone: 44-207236-7011
Fax: 44-207248-2693
Website: www.rootcapital.co.uk

Management and Staff

Simon Phillips, Founder

Type of Firm

Private Equity Firm

Association Membership

British Venture Capital Association (BVCA)

Project Preferences

Type of Financing Preferred:
Start-up Financing
Turnaround
Startup

Geographical Preferences

International Preferences:
United Kingdom
Europe

Industry Preferences

In Communications prefer:
Telecommunications

In Computer Software prefer:
Software

In Business Serv. prefer:
Services
Consulting Services

Additional Information

Year Founded: 2002
Current Activity Level : Actively seeking new investments
Method of Compensation: Return on invest. most important, but chg. closing fees, service fees, etc.

ROPART GROUP

One East Weaver Street
Greenwich, CT USA 06831
Phone: 203-552-6659
Fax: 203-661-1965
Website: www.ropart.com

Management and Staff

Jonathan Shapiro, Partner
Todd Goergen, Managing Partner
William Schlueter, Partner

Type of Firm

Private Equity Firm

Project Preferences

Type of Financing Preferred:
Leveraged Buyout
Mezzanine
Expansion

Size of Investments Considered:
Min Size of Investment Considered (000s): $3,000
Max Size of Investment Considered (000s): $10,000

Industry Focus

(% based on actual investment)

Computer Software and Services	75.5%
Semiconductors/Other Elect.	16.8%
Internet Specific	7.8%

Additional Information

Name of Most Recent Fund: Ropart Partners II
Most Recent Fund Was Raised: 01/01/1995
Year Founded: 1995
Current Activity Level : Actively seeking new investments

ROSE CORPORATION, THE

156 Duncan Mill Road
Suite 12
Toronto, Canada M3B 3N2
Phone: 416-449-3535
Fax: 416-449-9887
Website: www.rosecorp.com

Management and Staff

Lana Sherman, Chief Financial Officer
Martin Simon, Chief Operating Officer
Sam Reisman, Chief Executive Officer

Type of Firm

Investment Management Firm

Additional Information

Year Founded: 1982
Current Activity Level : Actively seeking new investments

ROSE TECH VENTURES, LLC

30 East 23rd Street
8th Floor
New York, NY USA 10010
Phone: 212-228-8770
Fax: 212-228-9911
Website: www.rosetechven.com

Management and Staff

David Rose, Principal

Type of Firm

Private Equity Firm

Association Membership

National Venture Capital Association - USA (NVCA)

Project Preferences

Type of Financing Preferred:

Early Stage
Seed

Additional Information

Year Founded: 2007
Capital Under Management: $10,000,000
Current Activity Level : Actively seeking new investments

ROSEMONT INVESTMENT PARTNERS LLC

300 Conshohocken State Road
Suite 680
West Conshohocken, PA USA 19428
Phone: 610-834-1370
Fax: 610-832-1265
E-mail: info@rosemontpartnersllc.com
Website: www.rosemontpartnersllc.com

Management and Staff

Charles Burkhart, Founder
David Silvera, Managing Director
Genie Logue, Principal
Sam Schecter, Chief Financial Officer
Thomas Balderston, Principal

Type of Firm

Bank Affiliated

Project Preferences

Role in Financing:

Prefer role as deal originator

Type of Financing Preferred:

Leveraged Buyout
Expansion
Start-up Financing
Management Buyouts
First Stage Financing
Recapitalizations

Size of Investments Considered:

Min Size of Investment Considered (000s): $3,000
Max Size of Investment Considered (000s): $15,000

Industry Focus

(% based on actual investment)

Other Products	74.0%
Computer Software and Services	26.0%

Additional Information

Year Founded: 2000
Capital Under Management: $168,000,000
Current Activity Level : Actively seeking new investments
Method of Compensation: Return on investment is of primary concern, do not charge fees

ROSEMONT SOLEBURY CAPITAL MANAGEMENT LLC

401 Greenwich Street
Fourth Floor
New York, NY USA 10013
Phone: 212-933-9965
E-mail: info@rosemontsolebury.com
Website: www.rosemontsolebury.com

Management and Staff

Alan Sheriff, Managing Director
Christopher Heinz, Managing Director
Daniel Senor, Managing Director
David Fife, Managing Director
Devon Archer, Chief Operating Officer
Victor Cohn, Managing Director

Type of Firm

Private Equity Firm

Project Preferences

Type of Financing Preferred:

Leveraged Buyout
Expansion
Recapitalizations

Size of Investments Considered:

Min Size of Investment Considered (000s): $5,000
Max Size of Investment Considered (000s): $50,000

Additional Information

Year Founded: 2008
Capital Under Management: $99,300,000
Current Activity Level : Actively seeking new investments

ROSER VENTURES LLC

1105 Spruce Street
Boulder, CO USA 80302
Phone: 303-443-6436
Fax: 303-443-1885
E-mail: roserventures@roserventures.com
Website: www.roserventures.com

Management and Staff

Alan Valenti, Chief Financial Officer
Christopher Roser, Partner
James Roser, Partner

Type of Firm

Private Equity Firm

Association Membership

Natl Assoc of Small Bus. Inv. Co (NASBIC)

Project Preferences

Role in Financing:

Prefer role as deal originator but will also invest in deals created by others

Type of Financing Preferred:

Early Stage
Expansion

Size of Investments Considered:

Min Size of Investment Considered (000s): $250
Max Size of Investment Considered (000s): $3,000

Geographical Preferences

United States Preferences:

Rocky Mountain

Industry Focus

(% based on actual investment)

Industrial/Energy	23.4%
Internet Specific	17.2%
Communications and Media	15.4%
Semiconductors/Other Elect.	13.3%
Computer Software and Services	11.9%
Other Products	9.1%
Computer Hardware	4.4%
Medical/Health	3.7%
Biotechnology	1.5%
Consumer Related	0.2%

Additional Information

Name of Most Recent Fund: Roser Partnership III SBIC
Most Recent Fund Was Raised: 06/01/1999
Year Founded: 1987
Capital Under Management: $75,000,000
Current Activity Level : Actively seeking new investments
Method of Compensation: Return on investment is of primary concern, do not charge fees

ROSETTA CAPITAL CORPORATION

1121 Boyce Road
Pittsburgh, PA USA 15241
Phone: 724-969-0730
Fax: 724-969-0733
Website: www.rosetta-capital.com

Management and Staff

Lee Welgs, Vice President
Thomas Wright, Chief Executive Officer, President

Type of Firm

Private Equity Firm

Project Preferences

Type of Financing Preferred:
Leveraged Buyout
Balanced
Acquisition

Size of Investments Considered:
Min Size of Investment Considered (000s): $1,000
Max Size of Investment Considered (000s): $10,000

Geographical Preferences

United States Preferences:
Pennsylvania
Ohio
Maryland
Virginia
New Jersey
West Virginia
New York

Industry Preferences

In Medical/Health prefer:
Medical/Health

In Industrial/Energy prefer:
Industrial Products

In Business Serv. prefer:
Services

In Manufact. prefer:
Manufacturing

Additional Information

Year Founded: 2009
Current Activity Level : Actively seeking new investments

ROSETTA CAPITAL, LTD.

New Broad Street House
35 New Broad Street
London, United Kingdom EC2M 1NH
Phone: 44-20-7194-8080
Fax: 44-1462-896-781
E-mail: info@rosettacapital.com
Website: www.rosettacapital.com

Other Offices

MaRS Centre, Heritage Building
101 College Street, Suite 140
Toronto, Canada M5G 1L7
Phone: 416-673-8443
Fax: 416-977-9332

Management and Staff

Julian Feneley, Managing Director
Michael Forer, Managing Director

Type of Firm

Private Equity Firm

Project Preferences

Type of Financing Preferred:
Leveraged Buyout
Early Stage
Expansion
Seed
Startup

Geographical Preferences

International Preferences:
United Kingdom
Europe

Industry Preferences

In Biotechnology prefer:
Biotechnology

Additional Information

Year Founded: 2001
Current Activity Level : Actively seeking new investments

ROSEWOOD CAPITAL, L.P.

One Maritime Plaza
Suite 1575
San Francisco, CA USA 94111-3503
Phone: 415-362-5526
Fax: 415-362-1192
E-mail: info@rosewoodvc.com
Website: www.rosewoodcap.com

Management and Staff

Blythe Jack, Managing Director
Chip Adams, Managing Director
Kevin Reily, Managing Director
Kyle Anderson, Managing Director
Peter Breck, Managing Director
Tim Burke, Managing Director
Trevor Ashley, Vice President

Type of Firm

Private Equity Firm

Association Membership

Western Association of Venture Capitalists (WAVC)

Project Preferences

Role in Financing:
Prefer role as deal originator but will also invest in deals created by others

Type of Financing Preferred:
Second Stage Financing
Leveraged Buyout
Control-block Purchases
Special Situation

Size of Investments Considered:
Min Size of Investment Considered (000s): $5,000
Max Size of Investment Considered (000s): $20,000

Industry Focus

(% based on actual investment)

Consumer Related	50.5%
Internet Specific	24.0%
Computer Software and Services	11.7%
Other Products	5.8%
Communications and Media	4.9%
Biotechnology	3.2%

Additional Information

Name of Most Recent Fund: Rosewood Capital V, L.P.
Most Recent Fund Was Raised: 10/31/2005
Year Founded: 1985
Capital Under Management: $120,000,000
Current Activity Level : Actively seeking new investments
Method of Compensation: Return on investment is of primary concern, do not charge fees

ROSSLYN CAPITAL PARTNERS

13 Slavyanska Street
Sofia, Bulgaria 1000
Website: www.rosslyncp.com
Management and Staff
Daniel Alexandrov, Managing Director

Type of Firm

Private Equity Firm

Project Preferences

Type of Financing Preferred:
Leveraged Buyout

Industry Preferences

In Communications prefer:
Telecommunications

In Consumer Related prefer:
Food/Beverage

In Industrial/Energy prefer:
Alternative Energy

In Financial Services prefer:
Real Estate

In Manufact. prefer:
Manufacturing

In Agr/Forestr/Fish prefer:
Agriculture related

Additional Information

Year Founded: 2008
Current Activity Level : Actively seeking new investments

ROSWELL CAPITAL PARTNERS, LLC

1120 Sanctuary Parkway
Suite 325
Alpharetta, GA USA 30004
Phone: 770-640-8130
Fax: 770-777-5844
Website: www.roswellcapitalpartners.com

Management and Staff

Eric Swartz, Principal
Michael Kendrick, Principal

Type of Firm

Private Equity Firm

Project Preferences

Type of Financing Preferred:
Balanced

Size of Investments Considered:
Min Size of Investment Considered (000s): $2,000
Max Size of Investment Considered (000s): $5,000

Geographical Preferences

United States Preferences:
All U.S.

Additional Information

Year Founded: 1994
Current Activity Level : Actively seeking new investments

ROTHSCHILD ASSET MANAGEMENT LIMITED

1 Toronto Street
Suite 200
Toronto, Canada M5C 2V6
Phone: 416-955-4606
Fax: 416-955-1899

Type of Firm

Private Equity Firm

Additional Information

Year Founded: 2009
Current Activity Level : Actively seeking new investments

ROTHSCHILD GESTION

42, rue d'Anjou
Paris, France 75008
Phone: 33-1-4074-8810
Fax: 33-1-4074-8820
Website: www.rothschild-cie.fr

Management and Staff

Pierre Remy, Vice President

Type of Firm

Private Equity Firm

Project Preferences

Type of Financing Preferred:
Expansion

Geographical Preferences

International Preferences:
Europe
France

Industry Preferences

In Communications prefer:
Telecommunications

In Computer Software prefer:
Software

In Semiconductor/Electr prefer:
Semiconductor

Additional Information

Year Founded: 2001
Current Activity Level : Actively seeking new investments

ROUNDTABLE HEALTH CARE PARTNERS

272 East Deerpath Road
Suite 350
Lake Forest, IL USA 60045
Phone: 847-739-3200
Fax: 847-482-9215
E-mail: brasbid@roundtablehp.com
Website: www.roundtablehp.com

Management and Staff

David Koo, Partner
Jack McGinley, Founding Partner
James Stauner, Principal
Joseph Damico, Founding Partner
Lester Knight, Founding Partner
R. Craig Collister, Principal
Todd Warnock, Founding Partner

Type of Firm

Private Equity Firm

Association Membership

Illinois Venture Capital Association

Project Preferences

Type of Financing Preferred:
Leveraged Buyout

Size of Investments Considered:
Min Size of Investment Considered (000s): $5
Max Size of Investment Considered (000s): $50

Industry Focus

(% based on actual investment)
Medical/Health 100.0%

Additional Information

Year Founded: 2001
Capital Under Management: $500,000,000
Current Activity Level : Actively seeking new investments

ROYAL DUTCH SHELL GROUP

30, Carel van Bylandtlaan
Hague, Netherlands 2596
Fax: 31-70-377-3115
Website: www.shell.com

Type of Firm

Corporate PE/Venture

Additional Information

Year Founded: 2009
Current Activity Level : Actively seeking new investments

ROYAL PALM CAPITAL PARTNERS, LLP

595 South Federal Highway
Suite 600
Boca Raton, FL USA 33432
Phone: 561-955-7300
E-mail: info@rpcp.com
Website: www.rpcp.com

Management and Staff

Beau Ferrari, Vice President
Jack Ruff, Principal
Phillip Harlow, Principal
Stephen Roddenberry, Principal
Tuyen Do, Vice President
William Pierce, Principal

Type of Firm

Private Equity Firm

Project Preferences

Size of Investments Considered:
Min Size of Investment Considered (000s): $15,000
Max Size of Investment Considered (000s): $75,000

Additional Information

Year Founded: 2002
Current Activity Level : Actively seeking new investments

ROYALTON PARTNERS (FKA : EUROPEAN DIRECT CAPITAL MANAGEMENT)

Millennium Plaza
V Celnici 10
Prague, Czech Republic 117 21
Phone: 420-2-2103-3024
Fax: 420-2-2103-3025
Website: www.royalton-partners.com

Other Offices

Regus, World Trade Centre Bucharest
10 Montreal Square, Entr. F
Bucharest 1, Romania 011469
Phone: 40-21202-3197
Fax: 40-21202-3100

Regus EMKE Building
Rakoczi ut 42
Budapest, Hungary 1072
Phone: 36-1327-4521
Fax: 36-1267-9100

ul. Domaniewska 37
Zepter Business Centre
Warsaw, Poland 02-657
Phone: 48-22-337-8250
Fax: 48-22-337-8251

Seefeldstrasse 69
Zurich, Switzerland 8008
Phone: 41-43-488-3661
Fax: 41-43-488-3521

Management and Staff

Gabriella Huber, Chief Financial Officer
Ivan Vohlmuth, Managing Director
Nigel Williams, Chairman & CEO
Roman Babka, Managing Director

Type of Firm

Private Equity Firm

Association Membership

Polish Venture Capital Association (PSIC/PPEA)
European Private Equity and Venture Capital Assoc.

Project Preferences

Type of Financing Preferred:

Second Stage Financing
Leveraged Buyout
Expansion
Turnaround

Size of Investments Considered:

Min Size of Investment Considered (000s): $10,120
Max Size of Investment Considered (000s): $23,920

Geographical Preferences

International Preferences:

Hungary
Czech Republic
Poland
Eastern Europe
Estonia

Industry Preferences

In Communications prefer:

Commercial Communications
Telecommunications

In Business Serv. prefer:

Services

Additional Information

Name of Most Recent Fund: Royalton Capital Investors II, L.P.
Most Recent Fund Was Raised: 11/07/2007
Year Founded: 1997
Capital Under Management: $74,600,000
Current Activity Level : Actively seeking new investments

ROYALTY CAPITAL MANAGEMENT LLC

Five Downing Road
Lexington, MA USA 02421-6918
Phone: 781-861-8490
Fax: 781-674-2363
E-mail: info@royaltycapitalmanagement.com
Website: www.royaltycapitalmanagement.com

Management and Staff

Arthur Fox, President & Chairman

Type of Firm

Private Equity Firm

Association Membership

Natl Assoc of Small Bus. Inv. Co (NASBIC)

Project Preferences

Role in Financing:

Prefer role as deal originator but will also invest in deals created by others

Type of Financing Preferred:

Second Stage Financing
Leveraged Buyout
Start-up Financing
Seed
First Stage Financing
Special Situation

Size of Investments Considered:

Min Size of Investment Considered (000s): $57,000
Max Size of Investment Considered (000s): $300,000

Geographical Preferences

United States Preferences:

Northeast

Industry Preferences

In Communications prefer:

Telecommunications
Data Communications
Satellite Microwave Comm.

In Computer Hardware prefer:

Computer Graphics and Dig
Integrated Turnkey System

In Computer Software prefer:

Systems Software
Applications Software
Artificial Intelligence

In Internet Specific prefer:

Internet

In Semiconductor/Electr prefer:

Semiconductor
Sensors
Laser Related
Fiber Optics
Analytic/Scientific

In Biotechnology prefer:

Industrial Biotechnology
Biosensors
Biotech Related Research

In Medical/Health prefer:

Medical Diagnostics
Diagnostic Services
Diagnostic Test Products
Medical Therapeutics
Other Therapeutic
Disposable Med. Products
Pharmaceuticals

In Consumer Related prefer:

Retail
Food/Beverage
Education Related

In Industrial/Energy prefer:

Alternative Energy
Factory Automation
Robotics
Machinery
Environmental Related

In Manufact. prefer:

Office Automation Equipmt

Additional Information

Name of Most Recent Fund: Eureka Partners I, LLC
Most Recent Fund Was Raised: 09/19/2005
Year Founded: 1994
Capital Under Management: $190,000,000
Current Activity Level : Actively seeking new investments
Method of Compensation: Return on investment is of primary concern, do not charge fees

ROYNAT CAPITAL CORP. (AKA: ROYNAT VENTURES)

40 King Street West
26th Floor
Toronto, Canada M5H 1H1
Phone: 416-933-2730

Fax: 416-933-2783
Website: www.roynatcapital.com

Other Offices

Canterra Tower
400 Third Avenue
Calgary, Canada T2P 4H2
Phone: 403-269-7755
Fax: 403-269-7701

Purdy's Wharf Tower II
1969 Upper Water Street
Halifax, Canada B3J 3R7
Phone: 902-429-3500
Fax: 902-423-5607

1800 McGill College
Suite 1800
Montreal, Canada H8A 3J6
Phone: 514-987-4900
Fax: 514-987-4905

Type of Firm

Bank Affiliated

Association Membership

Canadian Venture Capital Association

Project Preferences

Role in Financing:
Prefer role as deal originator but will also invest in deals created by others

Type of Financing Preferred:
Early Stage
Expansion
Balanced

Size of Investments Considered:
Min Size of Investment Considered (000s): $3,000
Max Size of Investment Considered: No Limit

Geographical Preferences

Canadian Preferences:
All Canada

Additional Information

Year Founded: 1962
Capital Under Management: $78,000,000
Current Activity Level : Actively seeking new investments
Method of Compensation: Return on invest. most important, but chg. closing fees, service fees, etc.

ROZVOJOVY FOND PRE MALE A STREDNE PODNIKANIE, A.S.

Nevadzova 5
Bratislava, Slovakia

Type of Firm

Private Equity Firm

Project Preferences

Type of Financing Preferred:
Seed

Geographical Preferences

International Preferences:
Europe

Additional Information

Year Founded: 2004
Current Activity Level : Actively seeking new investments

RPE CAPITAL MANAGEMENT (AKA: RETAIL PRIVATE EQUITY)

Stadsgarden 10
12 tr
Stockholm, Sweden 116 55
Phone: 46-8-5451-1600
E-mail: info@rpe.se
Website: www.rpe.se

Management and Staff

Christel Kinning, Co-Founder
Nils Tunebjer, Founding Partner

Type of Firm

Private Equity Firm

Project Preferences

Type of Financing Preferred:
Expansion
Balanced

Geographical Preferences

International Preferences:
Sweden
Europe
Iceland
Finland
Norway
Denmark

Industry Preferences

In Consumer Related prefer:
Retail

Additional Information

Year Founded: 2006
Current Activity Level : Actively seeking new investments

RPM VENTURES (FKA: WAYPOINT VENTURES)

320 North Main Street
Suite 400
Ann Arbor, MI USA 48104
Phone: 734-332-1700
Fax: 734-332-1900
E-mail: info@rpmvc.com
Website: www.rpmvc.com

Management and Staff

Marc Weiser, Managing Director
Tony Grover, Managing Director

Type of Firm

Private Equity Firm

Project Preferences

Role in Financing:
Will function either as deal originator or investor in deals created by others

Type of Financing Preferred:
Early Stage
Balanced
Seed

Size of Investments Considered:
Min Size of Investment Considered (000s): $40
Max Size of Investment Considered (000s): $300

Geographical Preferences

United States Preferences:
Midwest
All U.S.

International Preferences:
All International

Industry Preferences

In Communications prefer:
Telecommunications

In Computer Software prefer:
Software

In Internet Specific prefer:
Internet
Ecommerce

In Industrial/Energy prefer:
Alternative Energy

Additional Information

Name of Most Recent Fund: RPM Ventures II, L.P.
Most Recent Fund Was Raised: 02/08/2008
Year Founded: 2000
Capital Under Management: $15,000,000
Current Activity Level : Actively seeking new investments

RR CAPITAL GMBH

Berliner Allee 52
Zossen, Germany 15806

Type of Firm

Private Equity Firm

Project Preferences

Type of Financing Preferred:
Balanced

Geographical Preferences

International Preferences:
Germany

Industry Preferences

In Communications prefer:
Media and Entertainment

Additional Information

Year Founded: 2008
Current Activity Level : Actively seeking new investments

RRE VENTURES LLC

126 East 56th Street
New York, NY USA 10022
Phone: 212-418-5100
Fax: 212-980-1870
E-mail: info@rre.com
Website: www.rre.com

Management and Staff

Eric Wiesen, Principal
Harsh Patel, General Partner
M. Michel Orban, Founding Partner
Richard McGinn, General Partner
William Porteous, General Partner

Type of Firm

Private Equity Firm

Association Membership

National Venture Capital Association - USA (NVCA)

Project Preferences

Role in Financing:
Will function either as deal originator or investor in deals created by others

Type of Financing Preferred:
Second Stage Financing
Early Stage
Expansion
Balanced
Seed
First Stage Financing
Private Placement
Startup

Size of Investments Considered:
Min Size of Investment Considered (000s): $5,000
Max Size of Investment Considered (000s): $10,000

Geographical Preferences

United States Preferences:
Southeast
Northeast
Virginia
West Coast
California
New York

Industry Focus

(% based on actual investment)

Internet Specific	37.7%
Computer Software and Services	28.5%
Communications and Media	16.4%
Computer Hardware	5.3%
Other Products	4.8%
Semiconductors/Other Elect.	3.6%
Industrial/Energy	3.1%
Consumer Related	0.7%

Additional Information

Name of Most Recent Fund: RRE Venture IV, L.P.
Most Recent Fund Was Raised: 06/30/2006
Year Founded: 1994
Capital Under Management: $600,000,000
Current Activity Level : Actively seeking new investments
Method of Compensation: Return on invest. most important, but chg. closing fees, service fees, etc.

RSG CAPITAL D.O.O.

Tehnoloski park 21
Ljubljana, Slovenia 1125
Phone: 386-1-620-3300
Fax: 386-1-620-3305
E-mail: info@rsg-capital.si
Website: www.rsg-capital.si

Management and Staff

Jure Mikuz, Managing Partner
Mateja Mesl, Partner

Type of Firm

Private Equity Firm

Project Preferences

Type of Financing Preferred:
Early Stage
Balanced
Startup
Acquisition

Size of Investments Considered:
Min Size of Investment Considered (000s): $385
Max Size of Investment Considered (000s): $1,928

Geographical Preferences

International Preferences:
Central Europe
Europe

Industry Preferences

In Communications prefer:
Communications and Media

In Computer Other prefer:
Computer Related

In Biotechnology prefer:
Biotechnology

In Medical/Health prefer:
Medical/Health

In Consumer Related prefer:
Consumer

In Industrial/Energy prefer:
Energy
Industrial Products
Materials

Additional Information

Name of Most Recent Fund: Prvi sklad
Most Recent Fund Was Raised: 03/25/2008
Year Founded: 2006
Capital Under Management: $15,600,000
Current Activity Level : Actively seeking new investments

RSS INVESTORS

66 Church Street
Cambridge, MA USA 02138
Phone: 617-495-7513

Management and Staff

John Palfrey, Principal
Steve Smith, Managing Director
Tom Cowley, Managing Director

Type of Firm

Private Equity Firm

Project Preferences

Type of Financing Preferred:
Early Stage
Balanced

Industry Preferences

In Communications prefer:
Data Communications

Additional Information

Name of Most Recent Fund: RSS Investors, L.P.
Most Recent Fund Was Raised: 07/15/2005
Year Founded: 2005
Capital Under Management: $20,000,000
Current Activity Level : Actively seeking new investments

RUSHEEN CAPITAL PARTNERS, LLC

2332 Mandeville Canyon Road
Suite 1000
Brentwood, CA USA 90049

Type of Firm

Private Equity Firm

Project Preferences

Type of Financing Preferred:
Early Stage

Industry Preferences

In Industrial/Energy prefer:
Alternative Energy

In Other prefer:
Environment Responsible

Additional Information

Year Founded: 2007
Current Activity Level : Actively seeking new investments

RUSSIAN TECHNOLOGIES JSC

Tower 2000
T. Shevchenko 23A - B
Moscow, Russia 121151
Phone: 7-095-255-8364
E-mail: info@ru-tech.ru
Website: www.ru-tech.ru

Management and Staff

Mikhail Gamzin, General Director

Type of Firm

Bank Affiliated

Association Membership

Russian Venture Capital Association (RVCA)

Project Preferences

Type of Financing Preferred:
Early Stage

Geographical Preferences

International Preferences:
Russia

Industry Preferences

In Semiconductor/Electr prefer:
Sensors
Laser Related

In Biotechnology prefer:
Biotechnology

In Industrial/Energy prefer:
Alternative Energy
Advanced Materials

Additional Information

Year Founded: 2003
Current Activity Level : Actively seeking new investments

RUSSIAN TECHNOLOGY FUND MANAGEMENT, LTD.

27, Engelsa pr.
St. Petersburg, Russia 194156
Phone: 7-812-244-2506
Fax: 7-812-326-6191
E-mail: rtf@fi.ru

Type of Firm

Private Equity Firm

Association Membership

Russian Venture Capital Association (RVCA)

Project Preferences

Type of Financing Preferred:
Balanced

Geographical Preferences

International Preferences:
Russia

Additional Information

Year Founded: 2005
Current Activity Level : Actively seeking new investments

RUSSIAN VENTURE COMPANY

Kapranova Street
3/4
Moscow, Russia 123242
Phone: 7-495-777-0104
Fax: 7-495-777-0106
Website: www.rusventure.ru

Management and Staff

Alexei Korobov, Chief Executive Officer

Type of Firm

Private Equity Advisor or Fund of Funds

Project Preferences

Type of Financing Preferred:
Fund of Funds
Seed

Geographical Preferences

International Preferences:
Russia

Additional Information

Year Founded: 2007
Capital Under Management: $1,250,000,000
Current Activity Level : Actively seeking new investments

RUSTIC CANYON PARTNERS

2425 Olympic Boulevard
Suite 6050 West
Santa Monica, CA USA 90404
Phone: 310-998-8000
Fax: 310-998-8001
E-mail: info@rusticcanyon.com
Website: www.rusticcanyon.com

Other Offices

719 Second Avenue
Suite 900
Seattle, WA USA 98104
Phone: 310-998-8000
Fax: 310-998-8001

203 Redwood Shores Parkway
Suite 450
Redwood City, CA USA 94065
Phone: 650-654-8500
Fax: 650-654-8520

Management and Staff

John Babcock, Partner
Mark Menell, Partner
Michael Song, Partner
Michael Kim, Partner
Nathan Redmond, Partner
Renee LaBran, Partner
Thomas Unterman, Managing Partner

Type of Firm

Private Equity Firm

Association Membership

National Venture Capital Association - USA (NVCA)

Project Preferences

Role in Financing:
Prefer role as deal originator but will also invest in deals created by others

Type of Financing Preferred:
Early Stage
Balanced
Other

Size of Investments Considered:
Min Size of Investment Considered (000s): $2,000
Max Size of Investment Considered (000s): $10,000

Geographical Preferences

United States Preferences:
West Coast
Southwest
All U.S.

Industry Focus

(% based on actual investment)

Internet Specific	41.1%
Computer Software and Services	17.9%
Other Products	12.1%
Communications and Media	10.3%

Semiconductors/Other Elect.	9.1%
Consumer Related	5.3%
Industrial/Energy	2.8%
Computer Hardware	1.2%
Medical/Health	0.2%

Additional Information

Name of Most Recent Fund: Rustic Canyon Ventures III, L.P.
Most Recent Fund Was Raised: 06/06/2007
Year Founded: 1999
Capital Under Management: $972,000,000
Current Activity Level : Actively seeking new investments

RUTBERG & COMPANY, LLC

351 California Street
Suite 1100
San Francisco, CA USA 94104
Phone: 415-371-1186
Fax: 415-317-1187
E-mail: info@rutbergco.com
Website: www.rutbergco.com

Management and Staff

Bryan Rutberg, Chief Executive Officer
Christopher Greer, Senior Managing Director
Eric Risley, Senior Managing Director
John Mecklenburg, Managing Director
Justin Behar, Managing Director

Type of Firm

Bank Affiliated

Project Preferences

Type of Financing Preferred:

Second Stage Financing
Later Stage

Additional Information

Year Founded: 2001
Current Activity Level : Actively seeking new investments

RUTLAND FUND MANAGEMENT, LTD. (AKA: RUTLAND PARTNERS LLP)

Cunard House
15 Regent Street
London, United Kingdom SW1 4LR
Phone: 44-20-7451-0700
Fax: 44-20-7451-0701
E-mail: info@rutlandpartners.com
Website: www.rutlandpartners.com

Management and Staff

Ben Slatter, Partner
Chris Dowling, Chief Executive Officer
Jonathan Brooks, Partner
Mike Harris, Partner
Nicholas Morrill, Managing Partner
Paul Cartwright, Managing Partner

Type of Firm

Private Equity Firm

Association Membership

British Venture Capital Association (BVCA)

Project Preferences

Type of Financing Preferred:

Leveraged Buyout
Turnaround
Management Buyouts

Size of Investments Considered:

Min Size of Investment Considered (000s): $19,622
Max Size of Investment Considered (000s): $78,488

Geographical Preferences

International Preferences:

United Kingdom

Industry Preferences

In Consumer Related prefer:

Food/Beverage
Consumer Products

In Industrial/Energy prefer:

Industrial Products

In Transportation prefer:

Transportation

Additional Information

Name of Most Recent Fund: Rutland Fund
Most Recent Fund Was Raised: 11/02/2000
Year Founded: 1986
Capital Under Management: $363,000,000
Current Activity Level : Actively seeking new investments

RVC EUROPE LIMITED (FKA: THE GREENHOUSE FUND)

11 Upper Grosvenor Street
London, United Kingdom W1K 2NB
Phone: 44-20-7355-5700
Fax: 44-20-7355-5701
E-mail: enquiries@rvc.com
Website: www.rvc.com

Other Offices

3375 Hillview Avenue
Palo Alto, CA USA 94304
Phone: 650 461 3290
Fax: 650 461 3824

1 Sansome Street, 30th Floor
San Francisco, CA USA CA 94104
Phone: 415 677 2521
Fax: 415 677 2585

Type of Firm

Private Equity Firm

Association Membership

British Venture Capital Association (BVCA)

Project Preferences

Type of Financing Preferred:

Early Stage
Expansion
Balanced
Seed
Startup

Geographical Preferences

United States Preferences:

All U.S.

International Preferences:

Europe
Asia

Industry Preferences

In Communications prefer:

Communications and Media
Commercial Communications

In Computer Software prefer:

Software

In Internet Specific prefer:

Internet

Additional Information

Year Founded: 1995
Capital Under Management: $400,000,000
Current Activity Level : Actively seeking new investments

RWB RENDITEWERT-BETEILIGUNGEN AG

Keltenring 5
Oberhaching, Germany 82041
Phone: 49-8966-6694-0
Fax: 49-8966-6694-20
E-mail: info@rwb-ag.de
Website: www.rwb-ag.de

Type of Firm

Private Equity Firm

Project Preferences

Type of Financing Preferred:

Fund of Funds
Leveraged Buyout
Generalist PE
Expansion
Mezzanine
Later Stage
Startup

Geographical Preferences

International Preferences:
India
Europe
China
Western Europe
Austria
Germany
Asia
All International

Industry Focus

(% based on actual investment)

Other Products	100.0%

Additional Information

Year Founded: 1999
Capital Under Management: $75,600,000
Current Activity Level : Actively seeking new investments

RWI VENTURES

2440 Sand Hill Road
Suite 100
Menlo Park, CA USA 94025
Phone: 650-543-3300
Fax: 650-543-3339
E-mail: plans@rwigroup.com
Website: www.rwiventures.com

Management and Staff

Alexis Lakes, Chief Financial Officer
Donald Lucas, Managing Director
Mark Foley, Managing Director
William Baumel, Managing Director

Type of Firm

Private Equity Firm

Association Membership

Western Association of Venture Capitalists (WAVC)

Project Preferences

Role in Financing:
Will function either as deal originator or investor in deals created by others

Type of Financing Preferred:
Second Stage Financing
Early Stage
Expansion
Later Stage
First Stage Financing
Startup

Size of Investments Considered:
Min Size of Investment Considered (000s): $500
Max Size of Investment Considered (000s): $8,000

Industry Focus

(% based on actual investment)

Medical/Health	34.7%
Semiconductors/Other Elect.	21.8%
Computer Software and Services	21.5%
Communications and Media	16.0%
Internet Specific	4.8%
Consumer Related	1.2%

Additional Information

Name of Most Recent Fund: RWI Ventures II, L.P.
Most Recent Fund Was Raised: 06/06/2006
Year Founded: 1995
Capital Under Management: $168,000,000
Current Activity Level : Actively seeking new investments
Method of Compensation: Return on invest. most important, but chg. closing fees, service fees, etc.

- S -

---

698 CAPITAL

Chinachem Centre, 22F
One Hollywood Road
Central, Hong Kong
Phone: 852-2231-8600
Fax: 852-2231-8601
E-mail: mailbox@698capital.com

Management and Staff

Arthur Wang, General Partner
Thomas Liu, General Partner

Type of Firm

Private Equity Firm

Project Preferences

Type of Financing Preferred:
Early Stage
Balanced

Size of Investments Considered:
Min Size of Investment Considered (000s): $250
Max Size of Investment Considered (000s): $3,000

Geographical Preferences

International Preferences:
Pacific

Additional Information

Year Founded: 2000
Current Activity Level : Actively seeking new investments

---

7 HEALTH VENTURES

Shenkar 16/b, P.O.Box 12327
Herzeliya Pituach, Israel 46733
Phone: 972-9-952-0214
Fax: 972-9-952-0201
E-mail: Info@7HealthVentures.com
Website: www.7healthventures.com

Management and Staff

Amir Zaidman, Principal
Dalia Megiddo, Managing Partner
Ephraim Heller, Partner
Limor Sandach, Partner

Type of Firm

Private Equity Firm

Project Preferences

Type of Financing Preferred:
Expansion
Balanced
Seed
Startup

Geographical Preferences

International Preferences:
Israel

Additional Information
Year Founded: 2007
Capital Under Management: $70,000,000
Current Activity Level : Actively seeking new investments

---

7 L CAPITAL PARTNERS (AKA: 7LCP)
75 Marathonodromou Street
Maroussi, Greece 11634
Phone: 30-210-614-7344
Fax: 30-210-614-7431
Website: www.7lcp.com

Management and Staff
Aristides C. Fronistas, Managing Partner
Costin Florin Donoaica, Principal
Markus Pedriks, Principal
Salvator I. Levis, Principal

Type of Firm
Private Equity Firm

Project Preferences

Role in Financing:
Prefer role as deal originator but will also invest in deals created by others

Type of Financing Preferred:
Early Stage
Expansion
Balanced
Start-up Financing
First Stage Financing
Management Buyouts

Size of Investments Considered:
Min Size of Investment Considered (000s): $1,412
Max Size of Investment Considered (000s): $9,886

Geographical Preferences

International Preferences:
Greece
Turkey
Czech Republic
Bulgaria
Romania
Cyprus

Industry Preferences

In Communications prefer:
Media and Entertainment
Entertainment

In Computer Hardware prefer:
Computers

In Computer Software prefer:
Computer Services
Software

In Internet Specific prefer:
E-Commerce Technology
Internet
Ecommerce

In Biotechnology prefer:
Biotechnology

In Medical/Health prefer:
Medical/Health

Additional Information
Year Founded: 2002
Capital Under Management: $119,200,000
Current Activity Level : Actively seeking new investments

---

755 CAPITAL PARTNERS, LLC
23270 Mora Heights Way
Los Altos, CA USA 94024
Phone: 650-465-6711

Management and Staff
Ravi Chiruvolu, Founder

Type of Firm
Private Equity Firm

Project Preferences

Type of Financing Preferred:
Balanced

Additional Information
Name of Most Recent Fund: 755 Capital Partners I, LLC
Most Recent Fund Was Raised: 04/27/2007
Year Founded: 2007
Capital Under Management: $2,800,000
Current Activity Level : Actively seeking new investments

7BRIDGE CAPITAL PARTNERS, LTD.
10 Chater Road
Suite 1524, Prince's Building
Central, Hong Kong
Phone: 852-2110-9200
Fax: 852-2110-9983
E-mail: hongkong@7bridge.com
Website: www.7bridge.com

Other Offices
1662 West Petunia
Tucson, AZ USA 85737

616 - 1489 Marine Drive
West Vancouver, Canada V7T 1B8
Phone: 604-725-8022
Fax: 778-737-4775

Management and Staff
Alan Chan, Vice President
Cherry Lim, Partner
Richard Clarke, Partner

Type of Firm
Private Equity Firm

Project Preferences

Type of Financing Preferred:
Leveraged Buyout
Early Stage
Generalist PE

Geographical Preferences

United States Preferences:
All U.S.

Canadian Preferences:
All Canada

International Preferences:
India
Taiwan
Hong Kong
Malaysia

Industry Preferences

In Communications prefer:
Telecommunications

In Computer Hardware prefer:
Computers

In Internet Specific prefer:
Internet

In Biotechnology prefer:
Biotechnology

Additional Information
Year Founded: 2007
Current Activity Level : Actively seeking new investments

S & C INVESTMENT ADVISORS BV
Herengracht 468
Amsterdam, Netherlands 1017 CA
Phone: 31-20-489-08-80
Fax: 31-20-489-14-69

Type of Firm
Private Equity Firm

Additional Information
Current Activity Level : Actively seeking new investments

S&R INVESTIMENTI E GESTIONI

Via Armorari 14
Milan, Italy 20123
Phone: 39-02-805-3753
Fax: 39-02-805-2415
Website: www.unicredit.it

Type of Firm

Bank Affiliated

Project Preferences

Type of Financing Preferred:
Balanced

Additional Information

Year Founded: 2007
Current Activity Level : Actively seeking new investments

S-BETEILIGUNGSGE-SELLSCHAFT DER KREIS-PARKASSE MUNCHEN

Sendlinger- Tor- Platz 1
Munich, Germany 80336
Phone: 49-8923-8010
E-mail: s-beges@sparkasse-starnberg.de
Website: www.kskms.de

Type of Firm

Bank Affiliated

Association Membership

German Venture Capital Association (BVK)

Project Preferences

Type of Financing Preferred:
Expansion
Seed
Management Buyouts
Startup

Geographical Preferences

International Preferences:
Germany

Additional Information

Year Founded: 2001
Current Activity Level : Actively seeking new investments

S-PARTNER KAPITAL AG

Promenadenplatz 1
Munich, Germany
Phone: 49-89-55256350
Fax: 49-89-55256390
E-mail: info@PartnerKapital-AG.de
Website: www.PartnerKapital-AG.de

Management and Staff

Klaus Michael Holtershinken, Managing Director
Werner Stockner, Managing Director

Type of Firm

Bank Affiliated

Association Membership

German Venture Capital Association (BVK)

Project Preferences

Type of Financing Preferred:
Balanced

Geographical Preferences

International Preferences:
Germany

Additional Information

Year Founded: 2002
Current Activity Level : Actively seeking new investments

S-REFIT AG

Sedanstrasse 15
Regensburg, Germany 93055
Phone: 49-941-695-560
Fax: 49-941-695-5613
E-mail: info@s-refit.de
Website: www.s-refit.de

Management and Staff

Peter Terhardt, Chief Executive Officer

Type of Firm

Bank Affiliated

Association Membership

German Venture Capital Association (BVK)

Project Preferences

Type of Financing Preferred:
Leveraged Buyout
Expansion
Balanced
Start-up Financing
Seed
Startup

Geographical Preferences

International Preferences:
Germany

Industry Preferences

In Medical/Health prefer:
Medical/Health

Additional Information

Year Founded: 1990
Capital Under Management: $35,500,000
Current Activity Level : Actively seeking new investments

S-SIEGERLANDFONDS 1 GMBH & CO.

Siechhausweg 1a
Siegen, Germany 57072
Phone: 49-271-596-150
Fax: 49-271-596-155
E-mail: s@siegerlandfonds.de
Website: www.siegerlandfonds.de

Management and Staff

Marion Bangard, Managing Director
Peter Topfer, Managing Director

Type of Firm

Bank Affiliated

Association Membership

German Venture Capital Association (BVK)

Project Preferences

Type of Financing Preferred:
Expansion
Management Buyouts
Startup
Recapitalizations

Geographical Preferences

International Preferences:
Germany

Additional Information

Year Founded: 2001
Current Activity Level : Actively seeking new investments

S-UBG AG

Markt 45-47
Aachen, Germany 52062
Phone: 49-241-47056-0
Fax: 49-241-47056-20
E-mail: info@s-ubg.de
Website: www.s-ubg.de

Management and Staff

Dorit Dittmann, Chief Executive Officer

Type of Firm

Bank Affiliated

Association Membership

German Venture Capital Association (BVK)

Project Preferences

Type of Financing Preferred:
Expansion
Balanced
Later Stage
Seed
Management Buyouts
Startup
Recapitalizations

Size of Investments Considered:
Min Size of Investment Considered (000s): $481
Max Size of Investment Considered (000s): $2,407

Geographical Preferences

International Preferences:
Germany

Industry Preferences

In Semiconductor/Electr prefer:
Electronics

In Biotechnology prefer:
Biotechnology

In Industrial/Energy prefer:
Environmental Related

In Manufact. prefer:
Manufacturing

Additional Information
Year Founded: 1988
Capital Under Management: $43,600,000
Current Activity Level : Actively seeking new investments

S-UNTERNEHMENS-BETEILIGUNGSGE-SELLSCHAFT DER SPARKASSE LEIPZIG
Humboldtstrasse 25
Leipzig, Germany 04105
Phone: 49-341-986-7242
Fax: 49-341-986-3809
E-mail: info@s-beteiligungen.de
Website: www.s-beteiligungen.de

Type of Firm
Bank Affiliated

Association Membership
German Venture Capital Association (BVK)

Project Preferences

Type of Financing Preferred:
Expansion
Startup

Geographical Preferences

International Preferences:
Germany
Africa

Additional Information
Year Founded: 2001
Current Activity Level : Actively seeking new investments

S-VENTURE CAPITAL DORTMUND GMBH
Freistuhl 2
Dortmund, Germany 44137
Phone: 49-231-18334211
Fax: 49-231-18334299
E-mail: info@svc-do.de
Website: www.svc-do.de

Type of Firm
Bank Affiliated

Project Preferences

Type of Financing Preferred:
Balanced

Geographical Preferences

International Preferences:
Germany

Industry Preferences

In Communications prefer:
Communications and Media
Commercial Communications
Telecommunications
Wireless Communications

In Computer Other prefer:
Computer Related

In Semiconductor/Electr prefer:
Electronics

In Biotechnology prefer:
Biotechnology

In Medical/Health prefer:
Medical/Health
Pharmaceuticals

In Industrial/Energy prefer:
Alternative Energy

Additional Information
Year Founded: 2006
Current Activity Level : Actively seeking new investments

S.I. TECHNOLOGY VENTURE CAPITAL, LTD.
26/F, Harcourt House
39 Gloucester Road, Wanchai
Hong Kong, Hong Kong
Phone: 852-2529-5652
Fax: 852-2520-0128
Website: www.sihl.com.hk

Type of Firm
Private Equity Firm

Project Preferences

Type of Financing Preferred:
Balanced

Geographical Preferences

International Preferences:
Asia

Additional Information
Year Founded: 2000
Current Activity Level : Actively seeking new investments

S.R. ONE, LTD.
161 Washington Street
Suite 500, Eight Tower Bridge
Conshohocken, PA USA 19428
Phone: 610-567-1000
Fax: 610-567-1039
E-mail: info@srone.com
Website: www.srone.com

Management and Staff
Carol Ashe, Partner
David Phillips, Partner
Deborah Harland, Partner
John Keller, Partner
Kent Gossett, Partner
Mathieu Lane, Partner
Michael Diem, Partner
Philip Smith, General Partner
Rajeev Dadoo, Partner
Russell Greig, President
Simeon George, Partner

Type of Firm
Corporate PE/Venture

Association Membership
Mid-Atlantic Venture Association
National Venture Capital Association - USA (NVCA)

Project Preferences

Role in Financing:
Prefer role as deal originator but will also invest in deals created by others

Type of Financing Preferred:
Early Stage
Later Stage

Size of Investments Considered:
Min Size of Investment Considered (000s): $500
Max Size of Investment Considered (000s): $5,000

Industry Focus
(% based on actual investment)

Medical/Health	48.4%
Biotechnology	45.4%
Computer Software and Services	3.8%
Internet Specific	1.7%
Consumer Related	0.7%

Additional Information

Name of Most Recent Fund: S.R. One Limited
Most Recent Fund Was Raised: 01/01/1985
Year Founded: 1985
Capital Under Management: $500,000,000
Current Activity Level : Actively seeking new investments
Method of Compensation: Return on investment is of primary concern, do not charge fees

---

S3 VENTURES

11910 Volente Road
Suite Two
Austin, TX USA 78726
Phone: 512-258-1759
Fax: 512-853-9303
Website: www.s3vc.com

Management and Staff

Brian Smith, Managing Director
Stephen Banks, Venture Partner

Type of Firm

Private Equity Firm

Association Membership

National Venture Capital Association - USA (NVCA)

Project Preferences

Type of Financing Preferred:

Early Stage

Geographical Preferences

United States Preferences:

Southwest
Texas
All U.S.

Additional Information

Name of Most Recent Fund: S3 Ventures I, L.P.
Most Recent Fund Was Raised: 02/07/2007
Year Founded: 2007
Capital Under Management: $20,000,000
Current Activity Level : Actively seeking new investments

SAAB IC

Box 70392
Stockholm, Sweden 107 24
Phone: 46-8-787-7228
Fax: 46-8-787-7232
Website: www.saab.se

Type of Firm

Corporate PE/Venture

Project Preferences

Type of Financing Preferred:

Balanced

Geographical Preferences

International Preferences:

Sweden
Europe

Additional Information

Year Founded: 2006
Capital Under Management: $34,100,000
Current Activity Level : Actively seeking new investments

SAAD INVESTMENTS COMPANY, LTD.

Salahuddin Al-Ayoubi Street
Golden Belt Area, P.O. Box3250
Al-Khobar, Saudi Arabia 31952
Phone: 966-3-882-2220
Fax: 966-3-882-7989
E-mail: info@saad.com.sa
Website: www.saadgroup.com

Type of Firm

Private Equity Firm

Additional Information

Year Founded: 2009
Current Activity Level : Actively seeking new investments

SAARLANDISCHE WAGNISFINANZIERUNGS-GESELLSCHAFT MBH (AKA SWG)

Johannisstrasse 2
Saarbruecken, Germany 66111
Phone: 49-0681-379580
Fax: 49-0681-3795829
E-mail: info@swgmbh.de
Website: www.swgmbh.de

Management and Staff

Andre Doll, Managing Director
Lutz Schroter, Partner

Type of Firm

Bank Affiliated

Association Membership

German Venture Capital Association (BVK)

Project Preferences

Type of Financing Preferred:

Early Stage
Expansion
Startup

Geographical Preferences

International Preferences:

Germany

Industry Preferences

In Communications prefer:

Communications and Media

In Biotechnology prefer:

Biotechnology

In Medical/Health prefer:

Medical/Health

In Industrial/Energy prefer:

Materials

Additional Information

Year Founded: 1998
Current Activity Level : Actively seeking new investments

SABAN VENTURES

c/o Saban Capital Group
10100 Santa Monica Boulevard
Los Angeles, CA USA 90067
Phone: 310-557-5100
Website: www.sabanventures.com

Management and Staff

Craig Cooper, Managing Director

Type of Firm

Investment Management Firm

Project Preferences

Role in Financing:

Will function either as deal originator or investor in deals created by others

Type of Financing Preferred:

Early Stage
Expansion

Size of Investments Considered:

Min Size of Investment Considered (000s): $1,000
Max Size of Investment Considered (000s): $5,000

Geographical Preferences

United States Preferences:

All U.S.

Industry Preferences

In Communications prefer:

Communications and Media
Telecommunications
Media and Entertainment

In Internet Specific prefer:

E-Commerce Technology
Internet

Additional Information

Year Founded: 2008

Current Activity Level : Actively seeking new investments

SABVEST, LTD.

Four Commerce Square
39 Rivonia Road
Sandhurst, South Africa
Phone: 27-11-268-2400
Fax: 27-11-268-2422
E-mail: ho@sabvest.com
Website: www.sabvest.com

Management and Staff

Christopher Seabrooke, Chief Executive Officer

Type of Firm

Private Equity Firm

Association Membership

South African Venture Capital Association (SAVCA)

Project Preferences

Type of Financing Preferred:
Balanced

Geographical Preferences

International Preferences:
South Africa

Additional Information

Year Founded: 1998
Current Activity Level : Actively seeking new investments

SACHSEN LB CORPORATE FINANCE HOLDING GMBH

Lohrstrasse 16
Leipzig, Germany 04105
Phone: 49-341-22038802
Fax: 49-341-22038809
E-mail: cf@cfh.de
Website: www.cfh.de

Management and Staff

Gisbert Enkel, Partner
Hans Jorg Schwarz, Partner
Harald Rehberg, Partner
Michael M Theis, Partner

Type of Firm

Bank Affiliated

Association Membership

German Venture Capital Association (BVK)

Project Preferences

Type of Financing Preferred:
Early Stage
Expansion
Balanced
Seed
Later Stage
Startup

Geographical Preferences

International Preferences:
Germany

Industry Preferences

In Semiconductor/Electr prefer:
Semiconductor

In Medical/Health prefer:
Medical/Health

In Industrial/Energy prefer:
Energy
Environmental Related

In Business Serv. prefer:
Media

Additional Information

Year Founded: 1995
Capital Under Management: $130,100,000
Current Activity Level : Actively seeking new investments

SADEPAR

24, Rue du Palais
Metz, France 57000
Phone: 33-387-75-9358
Fax: 33-387-75-9351
E-mail: sadepar@i-l-p.com.fr
Website: www.i-l-p.com.fr/sadepar.html

Type of Firm

Private Equity Firm

Project Preferences

Type of Financing Preferred:
Early Stage
Seed
Startup

Size of Investments Considered:
Min Size of Investment Considered (000s): $37
Max Size of Investment Considered (000s): $154

Geographical Preferences

International Preferences:
Europe
France

Additional Information

Year Founded: 1989
Current Activity Level : Actively seeking new investments

SAEHAN VENTURE CAPITAL (FKA: WOOSUNG VENTURE CAPITAL)

2/F, Donghoon Tower, 702-19
Yeoksam dong, Kangnam-gu
Seoul, South Korea 135-080
Phone: 822-565-4111
Fax: 822-501-0630

Management and Staff

Jongrim Lee, President

Type of Firm

Private Equity Firm

Association Membership

Korean Venture Capital Association (KVCA)

Project Preferences

Type of Financing Preferred:
Balanced

Geographical Preferences

International Preferences:
Korea, South

Industry Preferences

In Communications prefer:
Communications and Media

In Computer Other prefer:
Computer Related

Additional Information

Year Founded: 1989
Capital Under Management: $100,000
Current Activity Level : Actively seeking new investments

SAFEGUARD SCIENTIFICS, INC.

435 Devon Park Drive
Building 800
Wayne, PA USA 19087
Phone: 610-293-0600
Fax: 610-293-0601
E-mail: IR@safeguard.com
Website: www.safeguard.com

Management and Staff

Gary Kurtzman, Vice President
Kevin Kemmerer, Managing Director

Type of Firm

Private Equity Firm

Association Membership

Mid-Atlantic Venture Association
National Venture Capital Association - USA (NVCA)

Project Preferences

Role in Financing:
Prefer role as deal originator but will also invest in deals created by others

Type of Financing Preferred:
Second Stage Financing
Early Stage
Expansion
Turnaround
Later Stage
Management Buyouts
Acquisition
Joint Ventures
Recapitalizations

Size of Investments Considered:
Min Size of Investment Considered (000s): $5,000
Max Size of Investment Considered (000s): $50,000

Geographical Preferences

United States Preferences:
Mid Atlantic
Southeast
Northeast
West Coast

Industry Focus

(% based on actual investment)	
Computer Software and Services	35.2%
Internet Specific	30.2%
Communications and Media	9.6%
Medical/Health	9.1%
Biotechnology	8.4%
Other Products	6.4%
Semiconductors/Other Elect.	1.2%

Additional Information
Year Founded: 1953
Capital Under Management: $350,000,000
Current Activity Level : Actively seeking new investments
Method of Compensation: Return on invest. most important, but chg. closing fees, service fees, etc.

SAFFRON HILL VENTURES
52 Upper Brook Street
London, United Kingdom W1K 2BU
Phone: 44-207-693-8300
Fax: 44-20-7693-8346
E-mail: Information@saffronhill.com
Website: www.saffronhill.com

Management and Staff
Martin Blindheim, Principal
Ranjeet Bhatia, Managing Director
Shawn Luetchens, Managing Director

Type of Firm
Private Equity Firm

Project Preferences

Type of Financing Preferred:
Early Stage
Seed
First Stage Financing
Startup

Size of Investments Considered:
Min Size of Investment Considered (000s): $966
Max Size of Investment Considered (000s): $3,863

Geographical Preferences

International Preferences:
United Kingdom
Europe

Industry Preferences

In Computer Software prefer:
Software

In Internet Specific prefer:
Internet

In Business Serv. prefer:
Media

Additional Information
Year Founded: 2000
Capital Under Management: $20,000,000
Current Activity Level : Actively seeking new investments

SAGARD
24-32 rue Jean Goujon
Paris, France 75008
Phone: 33-1-5383-3000
Fax: 33-1-5383-3030
E-mail: contact@sagard.com
Website: www.sagard.com

Management and Staff
Antoine Ernoult-Dairaine, Partner
Chris Spencer, Partner
Frederic Stolar, Founding Partner
Jocelyn Lefebvre, Founding Partner
Mariane Le Bourdiec, Chief Financial Officer

Type of Firm
Private Equity Firm

Association Membership
French Venture Capital Association (AFIC)
European Private Equity and Venture Capital Assoc.

Project Preferences

Type of Financing Preferred:
Leveraged Buyout
Balanced
Management Buyouts

Geographical Preferences

International Preferences:
Switzerland
Europe
Belgium
France

Additional Information
Name of Most Recent Fund: Sagard II-A FCPR
Most Recent Fund Was Raised: 08/01/2006
Year Founded: 2001
Capital Under Management: $1,048,900,000
Current Activity Level : Actively seeking new investments

SAGE CAPITAL, LLC
8025 Forsyth Boulevard
Saint Louis, MO USA 63105
Phone: 314-754-1118
Fax: 314-721-7238
E-mail: info@sagecapitalllc.com
Website: www.sagecapitalllc.com

Management and Staff
John Lemkemeier, Managing Partner
Wesley McAfee Jones, Managing Partner

Type of Firm
Private Equity Firm

Project Preferences

Type of Financing Preferred:
Leveraged Buyout
Expansion
Mezzanine
Generalist PE
Acquisition

Size of Investments Considered:
Min Size of Investment Considered (000s): $2,000
Max Size of Investment Considered (000s): $10,000

Geographical Preferences

United States Preferences:
Southeast

Industry Preferences

In Financial Services prefer:
Real Estate

In Business Serv. prefer:
Services
Distribution

In Manufact. prefer:
Manufacturing

Additional Information
Year Founded: 2003
Current Activity Level : Actively seeking new investments

SAGE HILL PARTNERS
210 Broadway
Fourth Floor
Cambridge, MA USA 02139

Phone: 617-498-7800
Fax: 617-621-6780
E-mail: info@sagehillpartners.com
Website: www.sagehillpartners.com

Management and Staff

Steve Johnson, Managing Partner

Type of Firm

Private Equity Firm

Additional Information

Year Founded: 2000
Current Activity Level : Actively seeking new investments

SAGEVIEW CAPITAL LLC

245 Lytton Avenue
Suite 250
Palo Alto, CA USA 94301
Phone: 650-473-5400
Fax: 650-473-5401
E-mail: investorservices@sageviewcapital.com
Website: www.sageviewcapital.com

Other Offices

55 Railroad Avenue
Greenwich, CT USA 06830
Phone: 203-625-4200
Fax: 203-625-4201

Management and Staff

Barbara Parker, Chief Financial Officer

Type of Firm

Private Equity Firm

Additional Information

Year Founded: 2009
Current Activity Level : Actively seeking new investments

SAGIN VENTURE CAPITAL CO., LTD.

7-17 Aikei machi
Saga shi, Japan 840-0812
Phone: 81-95-229-7658
Fax: 81-95-229-8052
Website: www.sagin-vc.co.jp

Type of Firm

Private Equity Firm

Project Preferences

Type of Financing Preferred:

Balanced

Geographical Preferences

International Preferences:

Japan

Additional Information

Year Founded: 2000
Capital Under Management: $14,700,000
Current Activity Level : Actively seeking new investments

SAGIPAR (AKA: SOCIETE ANTILLES-GUYANE D INVESTISSEMENT)

Morne Vergain / Abymes
BP 14 - Imm. Caducee
Pointe a Pitre, France 97165
Phone: 33-590-83-4897
Fax: 33-590-82-0709
E-mail: sagipar@apriga.com

Type of Firm

Private Equity Firm

Project Preferences

Type of Financing Preferred:

Balanced

Size of Investments Considered:

Min Size of Investment Considered (000s): $15
Max Size of Investment Considered (000s): $95

Geographical Preferences

International Preferences:

Martinque
France

Additional Information

Year Founded: 2000
Current Activity Level : Actively seeking new investments

SAGRI DEVELOPMENT AB

Hovslagargatan 5B
2nd Floor
Stockholm, Sweden SE-11148
Phone: 46-8-5450-4410
Fax: 46-8-678-4730
E-mail: info@grimaldi.se
Website: www.grimaldi.se

Type of Firm

Private Equity Firm

Association Membership

European Private Equity and Venture Capital Assoc.

Project Preferences

Type of Financing Preferred:

Balanced

Geographical Preferences

International Preferences:

Sweden

Additional Information

Year Founded: 2006
Current Activity Level : Actively seeking new investments

SAIC VENTURE CAPITAL CORPORATION

7455 West Washington Avenue
Suite 290
Las Vegas, NV USA 89128
Phone: 702-328-8495
Fax: 702-839-5630
E-mail: Investments@saic-vcc.com
Website: www.saic-vcc.com

Management and Staff

Kenneth Dahlberg, Chairman & CEO

Type of Firm

Corporate PE/Venture

Project Preferences

Type of Financing Preferred:

Balanced

Geographical Preferences

United States Preferences:

All U.S.

Industry Preferences

In Communications prefer:

Telecommunications

In Internet Specific prefer:

Internet

Additional Information

Year Founded: 2000
Current Activity Level : Actively seeking new investments

SAIF PARTNERS

Suites 2115-2118
2 Pacific Place, 88 Queensway
Central, Hong Kong
Phone: 852-2918-2200
Fax: 852-2234-9116
E-mail: info@sbaif.com
Website: www.sbaif.com

Other Offices

18F Tower C Central Int'l Trade Center
6A Jianguomenwai Avenue
Beijing, China 100005
Phone: 86-10-6563-0202
Fax: 86-10-6563-0252

DBS Business Center
Raheja Chambers, 213, Nariman Point
Mumbai, India 400021

Shanghai Hong Qiao State Guest Hotel
1591 Hong Qiao Road, Villa +16
Shanghai, China 200336

5F, 1 Labs Ctr, Plot No. 18
Software Units Layout, Madhapu
Hyderabad, India 500081
Phone: 91-98-6646-1770
Fax: 91-22-6645-9581

C/O One97 Communications (P) Limited
1st Floor, Devika Tower, Nehru Place
New Delhi, India 110 019
Phone: 91-98-1019-4624

Management and Staff

Andy Yan, Managing Partner
Babar Khan, Vice President
Ben Yam, Vice President
Ben Ng, Partner
Daniel Yang, Partner
Derek Chen, Principal
Don Han, Partner
Eric Xu, Vice President
Hang Xu, Partner
Janson Law, Chief Financial Officer
Jason So, Partner
Joe Zhou, Partner
JooDong Yu, Vice President
Lynda Lau, Principal
Ravi Adusumalli, General Partner
Shirley Yuan, Vice President
Vibhor Mehra, Principal
Yanchao Zhao, Vice President

Type of Firm

Private Equity Firm

Project Preferences

Type of Financing Preferred:
Expansion
Balanced

Geographical Preferences

International Preferences:
India
Taiwan
China
Hong Kong
Korea, South
Asia

Industry Preferences

In Communications prefer:
Telecommunications

In Business Serv. prefer:
Media

Additional Information

Year Founded: 2001
Capital Under Management: $1,977,900,000
Current Activity Level : Actively seeking new investments

SAIL VENTURE PARTNERS

600 Anton Boulevard
Suite 1010
Costa Mesa, CA USA 92626
Phone: 714-241-7500
Fax: 714-241-7505
Website: www.sailvc.com

Other Offices

2900 South Quincy Street
Suite 410
Arlington, VA USA 22206
Phone: 703-379-2713
Fax: 703-802-6168

Management and Staff

Alan Sellers, Partner
Dave Jones, Partner
F. Henry Habicht, Managing Partner
Tom Cain, Partner
Walter Schindler, Partner

Type of Firm

Private Equity Firm

Association Membership

National Venture Capital Association - USA (NVCA)

Project Preferences

Type of Financing Preferred:
Early Stage

Geographical Preferences

United States Preferences:
All U.S.

Industry Preferences

In Industrial/Energy prefer:
Alternative Energy
Energy Conservation Relat
Environmental Related

In Other prefer:
Environment Responsible

Additional Information

Name of Most Recent Fund: Sail Venture Partners, L.P.
Most Recent Fund Was Raised: 02/09/2009
Year Founded: 2006
Capital Under Management: $108,200,000
Current Activity Level : Actively seeking new investments

SAINTS VENTURES (AKA: SAINTS CAPITAL)

475 Sansome Street
Suite 1850
San Francisco, CA USA 94111
Phone: 415-773-2080
Fax: 415-835-5970
E-mail: info@saintsvc.com
Website: www.saintsvc.com

Management and Staff

Amar Senan, Managing Director
Anthony Tsao, Vice President
Chris Edge, Venture Partner
David Quinlivan, Managing Director
Emmanuel Roubinowitz, Vice President
Jane Crawford, Venture Partner
Kenneth Sawyer, Managing Director
Lilian Shackleford Murray, Managing Director
Robert Keppler, Chief Financial Officer
Scott Halsted, Managing Director

Type of Firm

Private Equity Firm

Association Membership

National Venture Capital Association - USA (NVCA)

Project Preferences

Role in Financing:
Will function either as deal originator or investor in deals created by others

Type of Financing Preferred:
Early Stage
Generalist PE

Geographical Preferences

United States Preferences:
All U.S.

Industry Preferences

In Communications prefer:
Wireless Communications

In Computer Software prefer:
Software
Systems Software

In Internet Specific prefer:
Internet

Additional Information

Name of Most Recent Fund: Saints Capital V, L.P.
Most Recent Fund Was Raised: 09/12/2005
Year Founded: 2000
Capital Under Management: $22,000,000
Current Activity Level : Actively seeking new investments

SAKORN INVEST AS

Petroleumsveien 8
P.O. Box 263
Stavanger, Norway 4066
Phone: 47-5195-8575
Fax: 47-5195-8501
Website: www.sakorn.no

Type of Firm

Private Equity Firm

Project Preferences

Type of Financing Preferred:
Seed

Geographical Preferences

International Preferences:
Norway

Additional Information

Year Founded: 2003
Current Activity Level : Actively seeking new investments

SAKORN SYD

Televeien 5
Grimstad, Norway 4879
Phone: 47-3729-5165
Fax: 47-3729-5166
Website: www.saakorn.no

Type of Firm

Private Equity Firm

Project Preferences

Type of Financing Preferred:
Seed

Geographical Preferences

International Preferences:
Norway

Industry Preferences

In Internet Specific prefer:
Internet

In Industrial/Energy prefer:
Energy
Industrial Products

Additional Information

Year Founded: 2003
Current Activity Level : Actively seeking new investments

SAKORNINVEST INNLANDET AS

Torggaten 22
Hamar, Norway 2317
Phone: 47-62-511-874
Fax: 47-62-511-871

Type of Firm

Bank Affiliated

Association Membership

European Private Equity and Venture Capital Assoc.

Project Preferences

Type of Financing Preferred:
Early Stage
Expansion
Startup

Geographical Preferences

International Preferences:
Norway

Industry Preferences

In Internet Specific prefer:
Internet

In Medical/Health prefer:
Medical/Health

In Industrial/Energy prefer:
Industrial Products

Additional Information

Year Founded: 2003
Current Activity Level : Actively seeking new investments

SAKORNINVEST NORD AS

Sandgata SA
PO Box 521
Bodo, Norway 8001
Phone: 47-7540-2530
Fax: 47-7540-2501
Website: www.sinas.no

Type of Firm

Private Equity Firm

Project Preferences

Type of Financing Preferred:
Seed

Geographical Preferences

International Preferences:
Norway

Additional Information

Year Founded: 2003
Current Activity Level : Actively seeking new investments

SAL. OPPENHEIM PRIVATE EQUITY PARTNERS

412F route d'Esch
Luxembourg, Luxembourg L-2086
E-mail: info@sopep.eu
Website: www.sopep.eu

Other Offices

Max-Joseph-Strasse 7
Munich, Germany 80333
Phone: 49-89-5490-8580
Fax: 49-89-549-085-845

Zeppelinstrasse 4-8
Cologne, Germany 50667
Phone: 49-221-9370-850
Fax: 49-221-9370-8519

Management and Staff

Andreas Schmidt, Partner
Andreas Wilde, Partner
Daniel Schmidt, Managing Director
Egbert Von Cramm, Partner
Egbert Freiherr Von Cramm, Partner
Frank Albrecht, Managing Director
Jan Graf Von Bassewitz, Managing Director
Jens Rowohlt, Managing Director
Juergen Borchers, Managing Director
Klaus-Peter Marek, Managing Director
Marco Yanar, Managing Director
Matthias Unser, Partner
Pascal Feucher, Managing Director
Rolf Enders, Partner
Rolf Wickenkamp, Partner
Stefan Herzog, Partner
Ulrich Eilers, Managing Director
Volker Beckmann, Partner

Type of Firm

Private Equity Advisor or Fund of Funds

Project Preferences

Type of Financing Preferred:
Fund of Funds
Leveraged Buyout
Mezzanine
Unknown
Balanced
Turnaround
Distressed Debt

Geographical Preferences

International Preferences:
Europe
Asia

Additional Information

Year Founded: 1995
Capital Under Management: $1,461,000,000
Current Activity Level : Actively seeking new investments

SALEM CAPITAL PARTNERS, LP (FKA: VENTURE CAPITAL SOLUTIONS)

112 Cambridge Plaza Drive
Winston-Salem, NC USA 27104
Phone: 336-768-9343
Fax: 336-768-6471
E-mail: inquiry@salemcapital.com
Website: www.salemcapital.com

Other Offices

600 Paces Summit
2410 Paces Ferry Road

Atlanta, GA USA 30339
Phone: 770-805-2320
Fax: 770-805-2185

Management and Staff

Phillip Martin, Principal

Type of Firm

Bank Affiliated

Project Preferences

Type of Financing Preferred:

Leveraged Buyout
Expansion
Mezzanine
Later Stage
Management Buyouts
Acquisition
Recapitalizations

Size of Investments Considered:

Min Size of Investment Considered (000s): $750
Max Size of Investment Considered (000s): $2,000

Geographical Preferences

United States Preferences:

Tennessee
Southeast
Alabama
North Carolina
South Carolina
Maryland
Virginia
Florida
Georgia

Industry Preferences

In Business Serv. prefer:

Services
Distribution

In Manufact. prefer:

Manufacturing

Additional Information

Year Founded: 1999
Capital Under Management: $40,000,000
Current Activity Level : Actively seeking new investments

SALFORD (UK), LTD.

78 Pall Mall
London, United Kingdom SW1Y 5ES
Phone: 44-20-3178-4850
Fax: 44-20-3178-4851
E-mail: info@salford.co.uk
Website: www.salfordcapital.com

Other Offices

Bulevar Zorana Djindjica 8a
Belgrade, Serbia and Montenegro 11070
Phone: 381-11-2222-500
Fax: 381-11-2222-533

2-ya Magistralnaya Street
8A, 4th Floor
Moscow, Russia 123290
Phone: 7-495-787-5314
Fax: 7-495-787-5316

44 Leselidze Str.
Tbilisi, Georgia 0105
Phone: 995-32-505-400
Fax: 995-32-505-406

Type of Firm

Private Equity Firm

Project Preferences

Type of Financing Preferred:

Leveraged Buyout

Geographical Preferences

International Preferences:

Central Europe
Eastern Europe
Russia

Additional Information

Year Founded: 2001
Capital Under Management: $450,000,000
Current Activity Level : Actively seeking new investments

SALIDA CAPITAL CORP.

2200 Yonge Street
Toronto, Canada M4S 2C6
Phone: 416-322-7607
Fax: 416-322-7610
Website: www.salidacapital.com

Type of Firm

Private Equity Firm

Additional Information

Year Founded: 2001
Current Activity Level : Actively seeking new investments

SALIX VENTURES

30 Burton Hills Boulevard
Suite 370
Nashville, TN USA 37215
Phone: 615-665-1409
Fax: 615-665-2912
E-mail: plans@salixventures.com
Website: www.salixventures.com

Other Offices

300 Brickstone Square
10th Floor
Andover, MA USA 01810
Phone: 978-470-2500
Fax: 978-470-2512

Management and Staff

Christopher Grant, General Partner
David Ward, General Partner
Mark Donovan, Venture Partner
Robert Ivy, Chief Financial Officer

Type of Firm

Private Equity Firm

Project Preferences

Role in Financing:

Will function either as deal originator or investor in deals created by others

Type of Financing Preferred:

Early Stage
Expansion
Later Stage

Size of Investments Considered:

Min Size of Investment Considered (000s): $5,000
Max Size of Investment Considered (000s): $7,000

Industry Focus

(% based on actual investment)

Medical/Health	61.2%
Computer Software and Services	16.2%
Internet Specific	8.4%
Biotechnology	4.1%
Consumer Related	2.8%
Industrial/Energy	2.5%
Other Products	2.4%
Communications and Media	2.3%

Additional Information

Name of Most Recent Fund: Salix Ventures II, L.P.
Most Recent Fund Was Raised: 04/03/2000
Year Founded: 1997
Capital Under Management: $190,000,000
Current Activity Level : Actively seeking new investments
Method of Compensation: Return on investment is of primary concern, do not charge fees

---

SALMON RIVER CAPITAL

680 Fifth Avenue
8th Floor
New York, NY USA 10019
Phone: 212-9315300
Website: www.salmonrivercapital.com

Management and Staff

Matthew Evans, Principal
S. Joshua Lewis, Principal

Type of Firm

Private Equity Firm

Project Preferences

Type of Financing Preferred:

Balanced

Industry Preferences

In Computer Software prefer:
Software
Applications Software

In Financial Services prefer:
Financial Services

Additional Information

Year Founded: 2005
Capital Under Management: $20,000,000
Current Activity Level : Actively seeking new investments

SALOMON SMITH BARNEY PRIVATE MANAGEMENT LLC

388 Greenwich Street
16th Floor
New York, NY USA 10013
Phone: 212-816-4999

Type of Firm

Bank Affiliated

Project Preferences

Type of Financing Preferred:
Distressed Debt

Additional Information

Year Founded: 2001
Capital Under Management: $113,400,000
Current Activity Level : Actively seeking new investments

SALZBURGER UNTERNEHMENSBETEILIGUNGSGESELLSCHAFT M.B.H.

Julius-Raab-Platz 1
Salzburg, Austria 5027
Phone: 43-662-888-8558
Fax: 43-662-888-8678
E-mail: office@subg-skgg.at
Website: www.subg-skgg.at

Management and Staff

Guido Piekarz, Managing Director
Manfred Werndl, Managing Director

Type of Firm

Private Equity Firm

Association Membership

European Private Equity and Venture Capital Assoc.

Project Preferences

Type of Financing Preferred:
Balanced

Geographical Preferences

International Preferences:
Europe

Additional Information

Year Founded: 2005
Capital Under Management: $5,300,000
Current Activity Level : Actively seeking new investments

SAM GROUP

481 Brazil Street
Sonoma, CA USA 95476
Phone: 1-707-996-6500
Fax: 1-707-996-0909
E-mail: hugo.steensma@sam-group.com
Website: www.sam-group.com

Type of Firm

Private Equity Firm

Additional Information

Year Founded: 2009
Current Activity Level : Actively seeking new investments

SAMARA CAPITAL PARTNERS, LTD.

IFS Court
Twenty Eight, Cybercity
Ebene, Mauritius
Phone: 230-467-3000
E-mail: ifs@samaracapital.com
Website: www.samaracapital.com

Other Offices

Eros Corporate Tower, 15th Floor
Nehru Place
New Delhi, India 110 019
Phone: 91-11-4223-5091

413 Maker Chambers V
Nariman Point
Mumbai, India 400 021
Phone: 91-22-2288-6661

Management and Staff

Gautam Gode, Managing Director
Radhika Dubash, Managing Director

Type of Firm

Private Equity Firm

Project Preferences

Type of Financing Preferred:
Balanced

Geographical Preferences

International Preferences:
India

Industry Preferences

In Communications prefer:
Telecommunications

In Medical/Health prefer:
Pharmaceuticals

In Financial Services prefer:
Financial Services

In Business Serv. prefer:
Media

In Manufact. prefer:
Manufacturing

Additional Information

Year Founded: 2006
Capital Under Management: $263,000,000
Current Activity Level : Actively seeking new investments

SAMBRINVEST S.A.

Avenue Georges Lemaitre
62 Aeropole
Gosselies, Belgium 6041
Phone: 32 71 25 94 94
Fax: 32 71 25 94 99
E-mail: sambrinvest@sambrinvest.be
Website: www.sambrinvest.be

Management and Staff

Claude Dewolf, Partner
Dennis Tillier, Partner
Guy Preaux, Partner

Type of Firm

Private Equity Firm

Association Membership

European Private Equity and Venture Capital Assoc.

Project Preferences

Type of Financing Preferred:
Leveraged Buyout
Early Stage
Expansion
Mezzanine
Start-up Financing
Seed

Geographical Preferences

International Preferences:
Belgium

Industry Preferences

In Computer Software prefer:
Software

In Computer Other prefer:
Computer Related

In Biotechnology prefer:
Biotechnology

In Industrial/Energy prefer:
Factory Automation

In Other prefer:
Environment Responsible

Additional Information

Year Founded: 1985
Capital Under Management: $5,000,000
Current Activity Level : Actively seeking new investments

SAMINVEST MITT AB

P.O. Box 87
Harnosand, Sweden 871 22
Phone: 46-70-269-2710
Website: www.saminvest.se

Type of Firm

Private Equity Firm

Association Membership

European Private Equity and Venture Capital Assoc.

Project Preferences

Type of Financing Preferred:
Early Stage
Generalist PE

Geographical Preferences

International Preferences:
Sweden

Additional Information

Year Founded: 2006
Capital Under Management: $9,200,000
Current Activity Level : Actively seeking new investments

SAMSUNG VENTURE INVESTMENT CORPORATION (SVIC)

16/F, Korea Knowledge Center
647-9 Yeoksam-Dong, Kangnam-Gu
Seoul, South Korea 135-980
Phone: 822-3430-5555
Fax: 822-3430-5566
Website: www.samsungventure.co.kr

Other Offices

85 West Tasman Drive
San Jose, CA USA 95134
Phone: 408-544-4470
Fax: 409-544-4976

Management and Staff

Bill Byun, Managing Director
Brian Kang, Managing Director
Eugene Hong, Vice President
Jong-Won Kim, Vice President
Yang-Jin Kim, Vice President

Type of Firm

Corporate PE/Venture

Association Membership

Korean Venture Capital Association (KVCA)

Project Preferences

Role in Financing:
Will function either as deal originator or investor in deals created by others

Type of Financing Preferred:
Early Stage
Balanced
Later Stage

Geographical Preferences

United States Preferences:
All U.S.

International Preferences:
Korea, South

Industry Preferences

In Communications prefer:
Communications and Media

In Internet Specific prefer:
Internet

In Semiconductor/Electr prefer:
Electronics
Electronic Components
Semiconductor

In Biotechnology prefer:
Biotechnology

In Medical/Health prefer:
Medical/Health

In Consumer Related prefer:
Entertainment and Leisure

In Business Serv. prefer:
Media

Additional Information

Year Founded: 1999
Capital Under Management: $249,000,000
Current Activity Level : Actively seeking new investments
Method of Compensation: Return on investment is of primary concern, do not charge fees

---

SAMURAI INCUBATE, INC.

2-66-7, Kotake-Cho
Nerima-ku
Tokyo, Japan
Website: www.samurai-incubate.asia

Type of Firm

Incubator/Development Program

Project Preferences

Type of Financing Preferred:
Early Stage
Seed

Geographical Preferences

International Preferences:
Japan

Additional Information

Year Founded: 2008
Current Activity Level : Actively seeking new investments

SAN FRANCISCO EQUITY PARTNERS

575 Market Street
Suite 1975
San Francisco, CA USA 94105
Phone: 415-738-1200
Fax: 415-738-3085
E-mail: info@sfequitypartners.com
Website: www.sfequitypartners.com

Management and Staff

Cameron Steele, Partner
Scott Potter, Managing Partner

Type of Firm

Private Equity Firm

Project Preferences

Type of Financing Preferred:
Leveraged Buyout
Expansion
Public Companies
Fund of Funds of Second
Recapitalizations

Size of Investments Considered:
Min Size of Investment Considered (000s): $5,000
Max Size of Investment Considered (000s): $20,000

Industry Preferences

In Consumer Related prefer:
Consumer

In Business Serv. prefer:
Services
Media

Additional Information

Name of Most Recent Fund: San Francisco Equity Partners II, L.P.
Most Recent Fund Was Raised: 10/22/2007
Year Founded: 2005
Capital Under Management: $80,000,000
Current Activity Level : Actively seeking new investments

SAND AIRE PRIVATE EQUITY, LTD. (AKA: SAND AIRE, LTD.)

101 Wigmore Street
London, United Kingdom W1U 1QU
Phone: 44-20-7290-5200
Fax: 44-20-7495-0240
E-mail: info@sandaire.com
Website: www.sandaire.com

Type of Firm

Private Equity Firm

Association Membership

European Private Equity and Venture Capital Assoc.

Project Preferences

Type of Financing Preferred:

Leveraged Buyout
Expansion
Mezzanine
Generalist PE
Turnaround

Size of Investments Considered:

Min Size of Investment Considered (000s): $1,500
Max Size of Investment Considered: No Limit

Geographical Preferences

International Preferences:

United Kingdom

Industry Preferences

In Communications prefer:

Communications and Media

In Computer Other prefer:

Computer Related

In Semiconductor/Electr prefer:

Electronics

In Biotechnology prefer:

Biotechnology

In Medical/Health prefer:

Medical/Health

In Industrial/Energy prefer:

Energy
Industrial Products

Additional Information

Name of Most Recent Fund: Equity Harvest Fund
Most Recent Fund Was Raised: 12/19/2003
Year Founded: 1997
Capital Under Management: $75,000,000
Current Activity Level : Actively seeking new investments

SAND HILL CAPITAL

3000 Sand Hill Road
Building One, Suite 240
Menlo Park, CA USA 94025
Phone: 650-926-7000
Fax: 650-926-7001
E-mail: info@sandhillcapital.com
Website: www.sandhillcapital.com

Management and Staff

Christopher Barber, General Partner
Franklin Loffer, Chief Financial Officer
Paul Sestili, General Partner
William Stewart, General Partner

Type of Firm

Private Equity Firm

Project Preferences

Role in Financing:

Prefer role as deal originator but will also invest in deals created by others

Type of Financing Preferred:

Expansion
Mezzanine
Later Stage

Size of Investments Considered:

Min Size of Investment Considered (000s): $2,000
Max Size of Investment Considered (000s): $10,000

Geographical Preferences

United States Preferences:

All U.S.

Industry Preferences

In Communications prefer:

Telecommunications
Wireless Communications
Data Communications
Satellite Microwave Comm.

In Computer Software prefer:

Software
Systems Software
Applications Software

In Internet Specific prefer:

Internet
Ecommerce

In Computer Other prefer:

Computer Related

In Semiconductor/Electr prefer:

Semiconductor
Fiber Optics

Additional Information

Name of Most Recent Fund: Sand Hill Capital IV, L.P.
Most Recent Fund Was Raised: 06/04/2007
Year Founded: 1996
Capital Under Management: $300,000,000
Current Activity Level : Actively seeking new investments
Method of Compensation: Return on invest. most important, but chg. closing fees, service fees, etc.

SAND HILL GROUP, LLC

3450 Sacramento Street
Suite 615
San Francisco, CA USA 94118
Phone: 415-922-9802
Fax: 415-922-9806
Website: www.sandhill.com

Management and Staff

Constatin Delivanis, Co-Founder
Madhavan Rangaswami, Co-Founder

Type of Firm

Private Equity Firm

Additional Information

Year Founded: 2005
Current Activity Level : Actively seeking new investments

SANDALWOOD CAPITAL PARTNERS

No. 401, Embassy Square
No.148, Infantry Road
Bangalore, India 560 001
Website: www.sandalwoodpartners.com

Other Offices

3561 Homestead Road
Suite 532
Santa Clara, CA USA 95051
Phone: 408-859-7801

No. 5327, Four Seasons Place
Central, Hong Kong

Management and Staff

Ajay Jalan, Chief Financial Officer
Bob Kondamoori, Managing Director
Hari Iyengar, Managing Director
V.R. Ranganath, Managing Director

Type of Firm

Private Equity Firm

Project Preferences

Type of Financing Preferred:

Early Stage
Expansion

Geographical Preferences

United States Preferences:

All U.S.

International Preferences:

India
China
Hong Kong

Industry Preferences

In Communications prefer:

Telecommunications

In Internet Specific prefer:

Internet

In Semiconductor/Electr prefer:

Semiconductor

In Industrial/Energy prefer:

Alternative Energy

Additional Information

Year Founded: 2006
Capital Under Management: $17,500,000
Current Activity Level : Actively seeking new investments

SANDERLING VENTURES

400 South El Camino Real
Suite 1200
San Mateo, CA USA 94402
Phone: 650-401-2000
Fax: 650-375-7077
E-mail: info@sanderling.com
Website: www.sanderling.com

Other Offices

4410 Eastgate Mall
San Diego, CA USA 92121
Phone: 858-677-0828
Fax: 858-677-0800

Management and Staff

Fred Middleton, Managing Director
Peter McWilliams, Principal
Robert McNeil, Managing Director
Roger Flugel, Principal
Timothy Mills, Managing Director
Timothy Wollaeger, Managing Director

Type of Firm

Private Equity Firm

Association Membership

Western Association of Venture Capitalists (WAVC)
National Venture Capital Association - USA (NVCA)

Project Preferences

Role in Financing:

Prefer role as deal originator but will also invest in deals created by others

Type of Financing Preferred:

Early Stage
Balanced
Later Stage
Seed
Startup

Size of Investments Considered:

Min Size of Investment Considered (000s): $2,000
Max Size of Investment Considered (000s): $15,000

Geographical Preferences

United States Preferences:

All U.S.

Canadian Preferences:

All Canada

Industry Focus

(% based on actual investment)

Medical/Health	45.1%
Biotechnology	42.7%
Industrial/Energy	7.2%
Computer Software and Services	2.5%
Internet Specific	1.5%
Communications and Media	0.6%
Other Products	0.3%
Computer Hardware	0.1%
Semiconductors/Other Elect.	0.1%

Additional Information

Name of Most Recent Fund: Sanderling Venture Partners VI Co-Investment, L.P.
Most Recent Fund Was Raised: 10/19/2004
Year Founded: 1979
Capital Under Management: $881,000,000
Current Activity Level : Actively seeking new investments
Method of Compensation: Return on invest. most important, but chg. closing fees, service fees, etc.

SANDERS & WIKLUND KAPITALPARTNER

Norrlandsgatan 7
Stockholm, Sweden 111 48
Phone: 46-8-5661-3300
Fax: 46-8-5554-4449

Type of Firm

Private Equity Firm

Project Preferences

Type of Financing Preferred:

Balanced

Geographical Preferences

International Preferences:

Sweden
Europe

Additional Information

Year Founded: 2004
Current Activity Level : Actively seeking new investments

SANDLER CAPITAL MANAGEMENT

711 Fifth Avenue
15th Floor
New York, NY USA 10153
Phone: 212-754-8100
Fax: 212-826-0280
E-mail: webmaster@sandlercap.com
Website: www.sandlercap.com

Other Offices

Bennet House, 4th Floor
54 St. James's Street
London, United Kingdom SW1A SJT
Phone: 44-207-409-0049
Fax: 44-207-409-1071

Management and Staff

Andrew Sandler, Managing Director
Bradley Burde, Vice President
Brent Benkovic, Vice President
Carese Gillespie, Vice President
David Powers, Managing Director
Douglas Schimmel, Managing Director
Eric Lewis, Managing Director
Hannah Craven, Managing Director
Harvey Sandler, Founder
Jae Kim, Vice President
John Kornreich, Managing Director
Joshua Kornreich, Vice President
Kevin Putt, Managing Director
Michael Marocco, Managing Director
Richard Keller, Managing Director
Samantha McCuen, Managing Director
Stacey Wruble Seewald, Vice President
Steven Warshavsky, Chief Financial Officer
William Bianco, Managing Director

Type of Firm

Private Equity Firm

Project Preferences

Role in Financing:

Prefer role as deal originator but will also invest in deals created by others

Type of Financing Preferred:

Second Stage Financing
Leveraged Buyout
Control-block Purchases
Mezzanine
Research and Development
Start-up Financing
Seed
First Stage Financing
Special Situation

Size of Investments Considered:

Min Size of Investment Considered (000s): $20,000
Max Size of Investment Considered: No Limit

Geographical Preferences

United States Preferences:

All U.S.

Canadian Preferences:
All Canada

International Preferences:
Italy
United Kingdom
Bermuda
Middle East
Spain
Australia
South Africa
Germany
France

Industry Focus
(% based on actual investment)

Internet Specific	33.0%
Communications and Media	32.5%
Other Products	23.2%
Computer Software and Services	5.7%
Consumer Related	2.6%
Medical/Health	1.6%
Semiconductors/Other Elect.	1.4%

Additional Information
Year Founded: 1980
Capital Under Management: $1,500,000,000
Current Activity Level : Actively seeking new investments
Method of Compensation: Return on investment is of primary concern, do not charge fees

SANDS BROTHERS & CO., LTD.
90 Park Avenue
New York, NY USA 10016
Phone: 212-697-5200
Fax: 212-297-1096
Website: www.sandsbros.com

Other Offices
Canadian Pacific Tower, Suite 2100
100 Wellington Street
Toronto, Canada M5K 1A1
Phone: 416-363-0046
Fax: 416-363-5543

319 Congress Avenue
Austin, TX USA 78701
Phone: 512-236-6980
Fax: 512-236-8276

2801 Ocean Drive
Suite 102
Vero Beach, FL USA 32963
Phone: 772-234-9995
Fax: 772-234-1245

35 Dover Street
Mayfair
London, United Kingdom W1X 3GB
Phone: 011-44207-262-4460
Fax: 011-44207-402-3416

519 Arthur Godfrey Boulevard
Vero Beach, FL USA 32963
Phone: 305-534-5111
Fax: 305-534-7511

3700 East Alameda Avenue
Suite 500
Denver, CO USA 80209
Phone: 303-388-5531
Fax: 303-388-9623

2351 East Hallandale Beach Boulevard
Hallandale, FL USA 33009
Phone: 954-454-0304
Fax: 954-454-3360

505 Sansome Street
Transamerica Center Two
San Francisco, CA USA 94111
Phone: 415-836-6000
Fax: 415-543-5581

Management and Staff
Howard Sterling, Managing Director
Lawrence Kass, Vice President

Type of Firm
Bank Affiliated

Project Preferences

Role in Financing:
Will function either as deal originator or investor in deals created by others

Type of Financing Preferred:
Expansion
Mezzanine
Later Stage
Distressed Debt

Size of Investments Considered:
Min Size of Investment Considered (000s): $250
Max Size of Investment Considered (000s): $5,000

Industry Preferences

In Communications prefer:
Wireless Communications
Data Communications

In Computer Software prefer:
Software
Applications Software

In Internet Specific prefer:
Internet

In Semiconductor/Electr prefer:
Electronic Components
Semiconductor

In Biotechnology prefer:
Human Biotechnology

In Medical/Health prefer:
Drug/Equipmt Delivery
Health Services
Pharmaceuticals

Additional Information
Name of Most Recent Fund: Sands Brothers Venture Capital Fund IV, L.P.
Most Recent Fund Was Raised: 06/01/2001
Year Founded: 1990
Current Activity Level : Actively seeking new investments

SANGAMON INDUSTRIES LLC
520 Lake Cook Road
Suite 375
Deerfield, IL USA 60015
Phone: 847-374-9140
Fax: 847-347-9150
Website: www.sangamonindustries.com

Type of Firm
Private Equity Firm

Project Preferences

Type of Financing Preferred:
Management Buyouts
Recapitalizations
Distressed Debt

Geographical Preferences

United States Preferences:
All U.S.

Industry Preferences

In Business Serv. prefer:
Distribution

In Manufact. prefer:
Manufacturing

Additional Information
Year Founded: 2009
Current Activity Level : Actively seeking new investments

SANLAM PRIVATE EQUITY
55 Willie van Schoor Avenue
Bellville, South Africa 7530
Phone: 27-21-950-2500
Fax: 27-21-950-2552
Website: www.spe.sanlam.com

Management and Staff
Thando Mhlambiso, Chief Executive Officer

Type of Firm
Private Equity Firm

Association Membership
South African Venture Capital Association (SAVCA)

Project Preferences

Type of Financing Preferred:
Expansion
Balanced

Geographical Preferences

International Preferences:
South Africa
Africa

Industry Preferences

In Agr/Forestr/Fish prefer:
Agribusiness
Agriculture related

Additional Information
Year Founded: 2004
Capital Under Management: $42,000,000
Current Activity Level : Actively seeking new investments

SANPAOLO IMI FONDI CHUISI SGR SPA
Via Zamboni, 2
Bologna, Italy 40126
Phone: 39-51-275-8330
Fax: 39-51-23-7936
Website: www.sanpaolope.com

Type of Firm
Bank Affiliated

Association Membership
Italian Venture Capital Association (AIFI)

Project Preferences

Type of Financing Preferred:
Expansion
Early Stage
Generalist PE
Balanced
Seed
Startup
Recapitalizations

Geographical Preferences

International Preferences:
Italy
Europe
Israel
All International

Industry Preferences

In Communications prefer:
Commercial Communications

In Computer Other prefer:
Computer Related

In Semiconductor/Electr prefer:
Electronics

In Biotechnology prefer:
Biotechnology

In Medical/Health prefer:
Medical/Health

In Consumer Related prefer:
Consumer

In Industrial/Energy prefer:
Energy
Industrial Products
Materials

Additional Information
Year Founded: 1988
Capital Under Management: $270,300,000
Current Activity Level : Actively seeking new investments

SANPAOLO IMI INVESTMENTI PER LO SVILUPPO SGR
177 Via Toledo
Naples, Italy 80132
Phone: 39-081-792-3610
Fax: 39-081-580-1492
Website: www.imi-investimenti.it

Type of Firm
Private Equity Firm

Association Membership
Italian Venture Capital Association (AIFI)

Project Preferences

Type of Financing Preferred:
Leveraged Buyout
Early Stage
Expansion
Recapitalizations

Geographical Preferences

International Preferences:
Italy
Europe

Additional Information
Year Founded: 1988
Current Activity Level : Actively seeking new investments

SANPAOLO IMI PRIVATE EQUITY SPA
Via Farini, 12
Bologna, Italy 40124
Phone: 39-051-275-8330
E-mail: infomedia@sanpaoloimi.com
Website: www.sanpaoloimi.com

Other Offices
Viale dell'Arte, 25
Rome, Italy 00144
Phone: 39-06-5959-3864
Fax: 39-06-5959-2238

Via Brera, 19
Milan, Italy 20121
Phone: 39-272-383-150
Fax: 39-272-383-169

Management and Staff
Carlo Viola, Managing Director
Claudio Montanari, Managing Director

Type of Firm
Bank Affiliated

Project Preferences

Role in Financing:
Prefer role as deal originator but will also invest in deals created by others

Type of Financing Preferred:
Leveraged Buyout
Early Stage
Expansion
Management Buyouts

Size of Investments Considered:
Min Size of Investment Considered (000s): $2,000
Max Size of Investment Considered (000s): $20,000

Geographical Preferences

International Preferences:
Italy
United Kingdom
Europe

Industry Preferences

In Communications prefer:
Radio & TV Broadcasting
Wireless Communications

In Computer Software prefer:
Software

In Internet Specific prefer:
E-Commerce Technology
Internet
Web Aggregration/Portals

In Semiconductor/Electr prefer:
Electronic Components
Fiber Optics

In Medical/Health prefer:
Medical Products
Pharmaceuticals

In Consumer Related prefer:
Consumer
Entertainment and Leisure
Retail
Food/Beverage

In Industrial/Energy prefer:
Industrial Products
Machinery

In Business Serv. prefer:
Services
Media

In Manufact. prefer:
Manufacturing

Additional Information
Year Founded: 1987
Capital Under Management: $172,800,000
Current Activity Level : Actively seeking new investments
Method of Compensation: Return on investment is of primary concern, do not charge fees

---

SANSEI CAPITAL INVESTMENT CO., LTD.
Mitsui Seimei Bldg.
1-2-3 Ote-machi, Chiyoda-ku
Tokyo, Japan
Phone: 81-3-3211-1541
Fax: 81-3-3211-1564
E-mail: info@sanseicapital.com
Website: www.sanseicapital.com

Type of Firm
Private Equity Firm

Project Preferences

Type of Financing Preferred:
Balanced

Geographical Preferences

International Preferences:
Japan

Additional Information
Year Founded: 2000
Capital Under Management: $27,400,000
Current Activity Level : Actively seeking new investments

SANTE VENTURES
Frost Bank Tower, 401 Congress
Suite 2950
Austin, TX USA 78701
Phone: 512-721-1200
Fax: 512-607-6235
Website: www.santeventures.com

Other Offices
5123 Virginia Way
Suite C22
Brentwood, TN USA 37027

Management and Staff
Brad Wolfe, Chief Financial Officer
Douglas French, Managing Director
Joe Cunningham, Managing Director
Kevin Lalande, Managing Director

Type of Firm
Private Equity Firm

Association Membership
National Venture Capital Association - USA (NVCA)

Project Preferences

Type of Financing Preferred:
Second Stage Financing
Early Stage
Expansion
Seed
First Stage Financing
Startup

Size of Investments Considered:
Min Size of Investment Considered (000s): $200
Max Size of Investment Considered (000s): $20,000

Geographical Preferences

United States Preferences:
All U.S.

Industry Preferences

In Medical/Health prefer:
Medical/Health
Medical Products
Health Services

Additional Information
Name of Most Recent Fund: Sante Health Ventures I, L.P.
Most Recent Fund Was Raised: 06/30/2007
Year Founded: 2007
Capital Under Management: $130,000,000
Current Activity Level : Actively seeking new investments

SANTIS INVESTMENT AG
Platz 12
Herisau, Switzerland 9100
Phone: 41-71-352-72-40
Fax: 41-71-352-72-41
Website: www.saentis-investment.ch

Type of Firm
Private Equity Firm

Association Membership
Swiss Venture Capital Association (SECA)

Additional Information
Current Activity Level : Actively seeking new investments

SAP VENTURES
3410 Hillview Avenue
Palo Alto, CA USA 94304
Phone: 650-461-2970
Fax: 650-847-3433
Website: www.sapventures.com

Other Offices
Dietmar-Hopp-Allee 16
Walldorf, Germany 69190
Phone: 49-6227-7-47474
Fax: 49-6227-7-61663

Management and Staff
Andreas Weiskam, Partner
David Hartwig, Partner
Doug Higgins, Partner
Jai Das, Partner
Jennifer Scholze, Partner
Joerg Sievert, Partner

Type of Firm
Corporate PE/Venture

Association Membership
National Venture Capital Association - USA (NVCA)
European Private Equity and Venture Capital Assoc.

Project Preferences

Type of Financing Preferred:
Expansion
Later Stage

Geographical Preferences

International Preferences:
All International

Industry Preferences

In Internet Specific prefer:
Internet

In Computer Other prefer:
Computer Related

In Medical/Health prefer:
Medical/Health

In Consumer Related prefer:
Consumer

In Industrial/Energy prefer:
Oil and Gas Exploration
Machinery

In Transportation prefer:
Aerospace

In Financial Services prefer:
Insurance

Additional Information
Year Founded: 1996
Capital Under Management: $47,100,000
Current Activity Level : Actively seeking new investments

SAPIENT CAPITAL MANAGEMENT LLC
4020 West Lake Creek Drive
P.O. Box 3404
Wilson, WY USA 83014

Phone: 307-733-3806
Fax: 307-733-4630
E-mail: contact@sapientcapital.com
Website: www.sapientcapital.com

Management and Staff

Mitchell Dann, Principal

Type of Firm

Private Equity Firm

Association Membership

National Venture Capital Association - USA (NVCA)

Project Preferences

Role in Financing:
Will function either as deal originator or investor in deals created by others

Type of Financing Preferred:
Second Stage Financing
Early Stage
Seed
First Stage Financing

Geographical Preferences

United States Preferences:
Midwest
Southern California
Northern California
Rocky Mountain
West Coast

Industry Preferences

In Biotechnology prefer:
Human Biotechnology
Biotech Related Research

In Medical/Health prefer:
Medical Diagnostics
Diagnostic Services
Diagnostic Test Products
Medical Therapeutics
Drug/Equipmt Delivery
Medical Products
Disposable Med. Products
Health Services

Additional Information

Year Founded: 2000
Capital Under Management: $26,000,000
Current Activity Level : Actively seeking new investments
Method of Compensation: Return on investment is of primary concern, do not charge fees

---

SAPPORO HOKUYO LEASE CO., LTD.

3/F Hokuyo Sapporo South Bldg.
8 West 3 South 2, Chuo-ku
Sapporo-shi, Japan 060-0062
Phone: 81-11-231-7135
Website: www.shls.co.jp

Management and Staff

Toshihiko Aoyama, President

Type of Firm

Private Equity Firm

Additional Information

Year Founded: 2006
Current Activity Level : Actively seeking new investments

SARATOGA PARTNERS, LP

535 Madison Avenue
4th Floor
New York, NY USA 10022
Phone: 212-906-7800
Fax: 212-750-3343
E-mail: saratoga@saratogapartners.com
Website: www.saratogapartners.com

Management and Staff

Alan Wilkinson, Managing Director
Christian Oberbeck, President

Type of Firm

Private Equity Firm

Project Preferences

Type of Financing Preferred:
Leveraged Buyout
Public Companies
Acquisition
Recapitalizations

Industry Focus

(% based on actual investment)	
Communications and Media	35.5%
Industrial/Energy	27.5%
Other Products	26.0%
Consumer Related	8.2%
Medical/Health	2.9%

Additional Information

Name of Most Recent Fund: Saratoga Partners IV, L.P.
Most Recent Fund Was Raised: 11/01/1998
Year Founded: 1984
Current Activity Level : Actively seeking new investments

SARATOGA VENTURES, L.P.

19361 San Marcos Road
Saratoga, CA USA 95070
Phone: 408-439-3334
Fax: 408-867-4323
E-mail: info@saratogaventureslp.com
Website: www.saratogaventureslp.com

Management and Staff

Foster Hendrix, General Partner
Richard Ferrari, General Partner

Type of Firm

Private Equity Firm

Project Preferences

Role in Financing:
Prefer role in deals created by others

Type of Financing Preferred:
Early Stage
Startup

Size of Investments Considered:
Min Size of Investment Considered (000s): $100
Max Size of Investment Considered (000s): $1,000

Geographical Preferences

United States Preferences:
All U.S.

Industry Preferences

In Medical/Health prefer:
Medical Diagnostics
Medical Products

Additional Information

Name of Most Recent Fund: Saratoga Ventures VI, L.P.
Most Recent Fund Was Raised: 03/27/2007
Year Founded: 1997
Capital Under Management: $18,500,000
Current Activity Level : Actively seeking new investments
Method of Compensation: Return on invest. most important, but chg. closing fees, service fees, etc.

SARSIA INNOVATION AS

Thormohlensgate 55
Bergen High Technology Centre
Bergen, Norway N-5008
Phone: 47-5554-3835
Fax: 47-5554-3836
E-mail: postmaster@sarsia.com
Website: www.sarsia.no

Management and Staff

Erlend Skagseth, Partner
Hans Hekland, Venture Partner
Johannes Hellevang, Chief Financial Officer
Nils Vogt, Partner
Thomas Grunfeld, Venture Partner

Type of Firm

Private Equity Firm

Association Membership

Norwegian Venture Capital Association
European Private Equity and Venture Capital Assoc.

Project Preferences

Type of Financing Preferred:
Early Stage
Seed
Startup

Geographical Preferences

International Preferences:
Europe
Norway

Industry Preferences

In Biotechnology prefer:
Biotechnology

In Medical/Health prefer:
Medical/Health

In Other prefer:
Environment Responsible

Additional Information

Year Founded: 2001
Current Activity Level : Actively seeking new investments

SAS INVESTORS

800 Third Avenue
21th Floor
New York, NY USA 10022
Phone: 212-367-7676
E-mail: info@sasinvestors.com
Website: www.sasinvestors.com

Management and Staff

George Abraham, Partner
Josh Grotstein, Partner
Ramana Jampala, Partner

Type of Firm

Private Equity Firm

Project Preferences

Role in Financing:
Prefer role as deal originator but will also invest in deals created by others

Type of Financing Preferred:
Early Stage
Seed

Size of Investments Considered:
Min Size of Investment Considered (000s): $250
Max Size of Investment Considered (000s): $1,500

Geographical Preferences

United States Preferences:
Northeast
New York

Industry Preferences

In Communications prefer:
Data Communications

In Computer Software prefer:
Software

In Semiconductor/Electr prefer:
Semiconductor

In Industrial/Energy prefer:
Alternative Energy
Materials

Additional Information

Name of Most Recent Fund: Silicon Alley Seed Investors Fund I
Most Recent Fund Was Raised: 01/31/2001
Year Founded: 2001
Capital Under Management: $40,000,000
Current Activity Level : Actively seeking new investments

SASKTEL

SaskTel Corporate
7th Flr, 2121 Saskatchewan Dr.
Regina, Canada S4P 3Y2
Phone: 877-337-2445
Fax: 306-359-0305
Website: www.sasktel.com

Type of Firm

Government Affiliated Program

Additional Information

Year Founded: 2009
Current Activity Level : Actively seeking new investments

SATILA HOLDING AB

Vastra Hamngatan 9
Goteborg, Sweden 411 17
Phone: 46-31-132-420
Fax: 46-31-132-479
Website: www.satila.net

Management and Staff

Lennart Grebelius, Managing Director

Type of Firm

Private Equity Firm

Association Membership

Swedish Venture Capital Association (SVCA)

Project Preferences

Type of Financing Preferred:
Balanced

Geographical Preferences

>International Preferences:
Sweden
Europe

Additional Information

Year Founded: 2003
Capital Under Management: $102,500,000
Current Activity Level : Actively seeking new investments

SATURN MANAGEMENT LLC

75 Federal Street
Suite 1320
Boston, MA USA 02110
Phone: 617-574-3330
Fax: 617-574-3331
Website: www.saturnasset.com

Management and Staff

Susan Antonio, General Partner

Type of Firm

Private Equity Firm

Project Preferences

Type of Financing Preferred:
Early Stage

Industry Preferences

In Computer Software prefer:
Software

In Medical/Health prefer:
Other Therapeutic

In Financial Services prefer:
Financial Services

Additional Information

Year Founded: 2001
Current Activity Level : Actively seeking new investments

SAUGATUCK CAPITAL COMPANY

One Canterbury Green
Stamford, CT USA 06901
Phone: 203-348-6669
Fax: 203-324-6995
E-mail: saugatuck@saugatuckcapital.com
Website: www.saugatuckcapital.com

Management and Staff

DeVer Warner, Managing Director
F. Jared Sprole, Principal
Frank Hawley, Managing Director
Gary Goldberg, Managing Director
Stuart Hawley, Managing Director
Thomas Berardino, Managing Director

Type of Firm

Private Equity Firm

Association Membership

Natl Assoc of Small Bus. Inv. Co (NASBIC)

Project Preferences

Role in Financing:
Prefer role as deal originator

Type of Financing Preferred:
Leveraged Buyout
Later Stage
Management Buyouts

Size of Investments Considered:
Min Size of Investment Considered (000s): $4,000
Max Size of Investment Considered (000s): $200,000

Industry Focus

(% based on actual investment)

Other Products	36.9%
Medical/Health	16.7%
Consumer Related	14.8%
Communications and Media	11.4%
Industrial/Energy	9.0%
Computer Hardware	3.6%
Semiconductors/Other Elect.	3.3%
Computer Software and Services	2.8%
Internet Specific	1.4%

Additional Information

Name of Most Recent Fund: Saugatuck Capital Company L.P. IV
Most Recent Fund Was Raised: 09/15/1999
Year Founded: 1982
Capital Under Management: $125,000,000
Current Activity Level : Actively seeking new investments
Method of Compensation: Return on invest. most important, but chg. closing fees, service fees, etc.

SAVIA CAPITAL INVERSION S.A.

C/ Joaquin Costa, 4, 4a
Zaragoza, Spain 50001
Phone: 34-976-797-909
Fax: 34-976-218-974
E-mail: info@saviacapital.com
Website: www.saviacapital.com

Type of Firm
Government Affiliated Program

Project Preferences

Type of Financing Preferred:
Expansion
Balanced
Startup

Geographical Preferences

International Preferences:
Spain

Additional Information
Year Founded: 2007
Current Activity Level : Actively seeking new investments

SAVVIS, INC. (FKA: SAVVIS COMMUNICATIONS)

1 Savvis Parkway
Town & Country
Chesterfield, MO USA 63017
Phone: 314-628-7000
Fax: 314-719-2499
E-mail: info@savvis.net
Website: www.savvis.net

Management and Staff
Jeffrey Von Deylen, Chief Financial Officer
Philip Koen, Chief Executive Officer

Type of Firm
Corporate PE/Venture

Additional Information
Year Founded: 2002
Current Activity Level : Actively seeking new investments

SAW MILL CAPITAL, LLC

555 Pleasantville Road
South Building, Suite 220
Briarcliff Manor, NY USA 10510
Phone: 914-741-1300
Fax: 914-741-9099
E-mail: info@sawmillcapital.com
Website: www.sawmillcapital.com

Management and Staff
Blinn Cirella, Chief Financial Officer
Howard Unger, Managing Partner
Jason Mueller, Vice President
John Shaia, Principal
Scott Budoff, Partner
Scott Rivard, Vice President
Timothy Nelson, Vice President
William Gerstner, Principal

Type of Firm
Private Equity Firm

Project Preferences

Role in Financing:
Prefer role as deal originator but will also invest in deals created by others

Type of Financing Preferred:
Leveraged Buyout
Expansion
Management Buyouts
Acquisition
Recapitalizations

Size of Investments Considered:
Min Size of Investment Considered (000s): $10,000
Max Size of Investment Considered (000s): $75,000

Geographical Preferences

United States Preferences:
All U.S.

Industry Focus

(% based on actual investment)

Other Products	53.6%
Industrial/Energy	46.4%

Additional Information
Name of Most Recent Fund: Saw Mill Capital Partners, L.P.
Most Recent Fund Was Raised: 12/22/2006
Year Founded: 1997
Capital Under Management: $100,000,000
Current Activity Level : Actively seeking new investments
Method of Compensation: Return on invest. most important, but chg. closing fees, service fees, etc.

SB CAPITAL CORPORATION

2 Bloor Street East
Suite 3304
Toronto, Canada M4W 1A7
Phone: 416-967-5439

Management and Staff
Mitch Kostuch, President

Type of Firm
Private Equity Firm

Additional Information
Year Founded: 2009
Current Activity Level : Actively seeking new investments

SB ENERGY PARTNERS

1225 17th Street
Suite 2575
Denver, CO USA 80202
Phone: 303-893-5007
Fax: 303-893-5011
E-mail: info@sbepartners.com
Website: www.sbepartners.com

Management and Staff
Geoff Solich, Managing Director
Grant Carnie, Vice President
John Cleveland, Managing Director
Kenneth Friedman, Vice President
Mitchell Solich, Senior Managing Director
Patrick Galuska, Vice President
Roger Flahive, Managing Director
Todd Hattenbach, Vice President

Type of Firm
Private Equity Firm

Project Preferences

Type of Financing Preferred:
Balanced

Geographical Preferences

United States Preferences:
All U.S.

Industry Preferences

In Industrial/Energy prefer:
Energy
Oil and Gas Exploration

Additional Information

Year Founded: 2007
Capital Under Management: $415,000,000
Current Activity Level : Actively seeking new investments

SB LIFE SCIENCE EQUITY MANAGEMENT LLC

203 Redwood Shores Parkway
Suite 610
Redwood City, CA USA 94065
Phone: 650-233-8838
Fax: 650-508-1890
E-mail: info@sblifescience.com
Website: www.sblifescience.com

Management and Staff

Joseph Chow, Managing Director
Toshi Nakada, Managing Director

Type of Firm

Private Equity Firm

Project Preferences

Role in Financing:
Will function either as deal originator or investor in deals created by others

Type of Financing Preferred:
Second Stage Financing
Early Stage
Expansion
Mezzanine
Balanced
First Stage Financing
Startup

Size of Investments Considered:
Min Size of Investment Considered (000s): $500
Max Size of Investment Considered (000s): $10,000

Geographical Preferences

United States Preferences:
All U.S.

Canadian Preferences:
All Canada

International Preferences:
United Kingdom
France
Japan

Industry Preferences

In Biotechnology prefer:
Biotechnology

In Medical/Health prefer:
Medical Diagnostics
Medical Therapeutics
Drug/Equipmt Delivery
Medical Products
Pharmaceuticals

Additional Information

Name of Most Recent Fund: SB Life Science Ventures I, L.P.
Most Recent Fund Was Raised: 08/01/2001
Year Founded: 2001
Capital Under Management: $100,000,000
Current Activity Level : Actively seeking new investments
Method of Compensation: Return on investment is of primary concern, do not charge fees

---

SBG SPARKASSEN-BETEILIGUNGSGE-SELLSCHAFT SACHSEN-ANHALT MBH

IGZ Barleben
Steinfeldstrasse 3
Barleben, Germany 39179
Phone: 49-3-920396680
Fax: 49-3-9203966819
Website: www.SBG-Sachsen-Anhalt.de

Management and Staff

Christian Heimann, Chief Executive Officer

Type of Firm

Bank Affiliated

Association Membership

German Venture Capital Association (BVK)

Project Preferences

Type of Financing Preferred:
Balanced

Geographical Preferences

International Preferences:
Germany

Additional Information

Year Founded: 2003
Current Activity Level : Actively seeking new investments

SBI & TH VENTURE CAPITAL ENTERPRISE

Tsinghua Science Park
Suite 601 S.P. Tower A
Beijing, China 100084
Phone: 86-1-8215-8855
Fax: 86-1-8215-8841
E-mail: hhtvc@bjhhtvc.com
Website: www.bjhhtvc.com

Management and Staff

Jianwei Zheng, Managing Director

Type of Firm

Bank Affiliated

Project Preferences

Type of Financing Preferred:
Early Stage
Expansion
Startup

Geographical Preferences

International Preferences:
China

Industry Preferences

In Communications prefer:
Telecommunications

In Computer Software prefer:
Software

In Internet Specific prefer:
Internet

In Biotechnology prefer:
Biotechnology

In Consumer Related prefer:
Consumer

In Industrial/Energy prefer:
Energy
Environmental Related

In Business Serv. prefer:
Media

Additional Information

Year Founded: 2007
Current Activity Level : Actively seeking new investments

SBI CAPITAL COMPANY, LTD.

Izumi Garden Tower 1-6-1
Roppongi, Minato-ku
Tokyo, Japan 106-6019
Phone: 813-6229-0100
Fax: 813-3224-1970
E-mail: inq-all@sbigroup.co.jp
Website: www.sbigroup.co.jp

Management and Staff

Kentaro Azuma, Chief Operating Officer
Yoshitaka Kitao, Chief Executive Officer

Type of Firm

Bank Affiliated

Project Preferences

Type of Financing Preferred:

Leveraged Buyout
Balanced
Later Stage
Management Buyouts

Geographical Preferences

International Preferences:

Asia
Japan

Industry Preferences

In Communications prefer:

Communications and Media
Telecommunications

Additional Information

Year Founded: 2001
Capital Under Management: $275,000,000
Current Activity Level : Actively seeking new investments

SBI CAPITAL VENTURES (AKA: SBI CAPITAL MARKETS, LTD.)

202, Maker Tower E
Cuffe Parade
Mumbai, India 400 005
Phone: 91-22-2218-2883
Fax: 91-22-2218-8832
E-mail: corporate.office@sbicaps.com
Website: www.sbicaps.com

Management and Staff

A. Verma, CEO & Managing Director

Type of Firm

Bank Affiliated

Project Preferences

Type of Financing Preferred:

Early Stage
Expansion
Balanced
Startup

Geographical Preferences

International Preferences:

India

Industry Preferences

In Biotechnology prefer:

Biotechnology

In Medical/Health prefer:

Pharmaceuticals

In Business Serv. prefer:

Services

In Manufact. prefer:

Manufacturing

Additional Information

Year Founded: 2006
Capital Under Management: $100,000,000
Current Activity Level : Actively seeking new investments

SBI E2-CAPITAL ASIA SECURITIES LTD.

43/F Jardine House
1 Connaught Place
Central, Hong Kong
Phone: 852-2768-3700
Fax: 852-2768-3733
E-mail: info@e2capital.com
Website: www.sbie2capital.com

Management and Staff

Kenny Wong, Chief Financial Officer

Type of Firm

Bank Affiliated

Project Preferences

Type of Financing Preferred:

Leveraged Buyout
Mezzanine
Later Stage

Geographical Preferences

International Preferences:

China
Hong Kong

Additional Information

Year Founded: 2001
Current Activity Level : Actively seeking new investments

SBI INVESTMENT COMPANY, LTD. (FKA:SOFTBANK INVESTMENT CORP)

19F Izumi Garden Tower
1-6-1, Roppongi, Minato-ku
Tokyo, Japan 105-0003
Phone: 81-3-5501-2711
Fax: 81-3-5501-2718
E-mail: info@sbinvestment.co.jp
Website: www.sbinvestment.co.jp

Management and Staff

Yoshiaki Hasegawa, Managing Director

Type of Firm

Private Equity Firm

Project Preferences

Type of Financing Preferred:

Leveraged Buyout
Balanced
Turnaround
Management Buyouts

Geographical Preferences

United States Preferences:

All U.S.

International Preferences:

India
China
Hong Kong
Asia
Japan
All International

Industry Preferences

In Computer Software prefer:

Data Processing

In Internet Specific prefer:

Internet

In Industrial/Energy prefer:

Environmental Related

Additional Information

Name of Most Recent Fund: Restructuring Fund No. 1 Limited Partnership
Most Recent Fund Was Raised: 02/15/2002
Year Founded: 1996
Capital Under Management: $1,513,700,000
Current Activity Level : Actively seeking new investments

SBV VENTURE PARTNERS (AKA: SIGEFI, BURNETTE & VALLEE)

100 Hamilton Avenue
Suite 250
Palo Alto, CA USA 94301
Phone: 650-522-0085
Fax: 650-522-0087
E-mail: info@sbvpartners.com
Website: www.sbvpartners.com

Management and Staff

Graham Burnette, General Partner
Jacques Vallee, General Partner

Type of Firm

Private Equity Firm

Association Membership
Western Association of Venture Capitalists (WAVC)

Project Preferences

Role in Financing:
Prefer role as deal originator but will also invest in deals created by others

Type of Financing Preferred:
Early Stage
Research and Development
Seed
First Stage Financing
Startup

Size of Investments Considered:
Min Size of Investment Considered (000s): $500
Max Size of Investment Considered (000s): $2,500

Geographical Preferences

United States Preferences:
West Coast

Industry Preferences

In Communications prefer:
Telecommunications
Wireless Communications
Data Communications
Other Communication Prod.

In Computer Hardware prefer:
Mini and Personal/Desktop
Computer Graphics and Dig
Disk Relat. Memory Device

In Computer Software prefer:
Computer Services
Data Processing
Software
Systems Software
Applications Software
Artificial Intelligence

In Internet Specific prefer:
E-Commerce Technology
Internet
Web Aggregration/Portals

In Semiconductor/Electr prefer:
Electronic Components
Laser Related
Fiber Optics

In Biotechnology prefer:
Human Biotechnology
Industrial Biotechnology
Biotech Related Research

In Medical/Health prefer:
Medical/Health
Medical Diagnostics

Additional Information
Year Founded: 2000
Capital Under Management: $50,000,000
Current Activity Level : Actively seeking new investments
Method of Compensation: Return on investment is of primary concern, do not charge fees

---

SC CAPITAL MANAGEMENT LLC
712 Fifith Avenue
11th Floor
New York, NY USA 10019
Phone: 212-245-1719
E-mail: info@sccapitalmanagement.com
Website: www.sccapitalmanagement.com

Management and Staff
Srini Conjeevaram, Managing Director

Type of Firm
Private Equity Firm

Project Preferences

Type of Financing Preferred:
Balanced

Additional Information
Year Founded: 2008
Capital Under Management: $5,800,000
Current Activity Level : Actively seeking new investments

SCALE VENTURE PARTNERS (FKA: BA VENTURE PARTNERS)
950 Tower Lane
Suite 700
Foster City, CA USA 94404
Phone: 650-378-6000
Fax: 650-378-6040
Website: www.scalevp.com

Management and Staff
Andy Vitus, Principal
James Jones, Managing Director
Jeff Calcagno, Principal
Kate Mitchell, Managing Director
Louis Bock, Managing Director
Mark Brooks, Managing Director
Mary Denten, Chief Financial Officer
Nancy Lynch, Principal
Robert Herb, Venture Partner
Robert Theis, Managing Director
Rory O'Driscoll, Managing Director
Sharon Wienbar, Managing Director
Stacey Curry Bishop, Principal

Type of Firm
Private Equity Firm

Association Membership
Western Association of Venture Capitalists (WAVC)
National Venture Capital Association - USA (NVCA)
Natl Assoc of Small Bus. Inv. Co (NASBIC)

Project Preferences

Role in Financing:
Prefer role as deal originator

Type of Financing Preferred:
Second Stage Financing
Early Stage
Expansion
Balanced
Later Stage
First Stage Financing

Size of Investments Considered:
Min Size of Investment Considered (000s): $5,000
Max Size of Investment Considered (000s): $30,000

Geographical Preferences

United States Preferences:
All U.S.

Industry Focus
(% based on actual investment)

Computer Software and Services	22.1%
Internet Specific	22.0%
Medical/Health	15.2%
Biotechnology	10.6%
Semiconductors/Other Elect.	9.5%
Communications and Media	8.0%
Other Products	4.7%
Computer Hardware	3.8%
Industrial/Energy	2.8%
Consumer Related	1.3%

Additional Information
Name of Most Recent Fund: Scale Venture Partners III
Most Recent Fund Was Raised: 06/26/2008
Year Founded: 1995
Capital Under Management: $950,000,000
Current Activity Level : Actively seeking new investments
Method of Compensation: Return on investment is of primary concern, do not charge fees

---

SCANDI-LATIN CORPORATE FINANCE AB
Nybrokajen 7
Stockholm, Sweden 111 48
Phone: 46-8-5661-3300
Fax: 46-8-678-6521

Type of Firm
Private Equity Firm

Project Preferences

Type of Financing Preferred:
Balanced

Geographical Preferences

International Preferences:
Sweden
Europe

Additional Information

Year Founded: 2005
Current Activity Level : Actively seeking new investments

SCANDINAVIAN BALTIC DEVELOPMENT, LTD.

Gostauto 40 A
Sermuksniu Street 1
Vilnius, Lithuania 2001
Phone: 370-5-249-7077
Fax: 370-5-249-7078
Website: www.sc-baltic.com

Other Offices

Liivalaia 14
Tallinn, Estonia 10118
Phone: 372-6-461-172
Fax: 372-6-462-234

Strandvagen 5B
Stockholm, Sweden SE 114 51
Phone: 46-8-679-5025
Fax: 46-8-679 5026

Management and Staff

Arvydas Strumskis, Partner
Hanno Riismaa, Partner

Type of Firm

Government Affiliated Program

Project Preferences

Type of Financing Preferred:
Leveraged Buyout
Expansion
Balanced

Size of Investments Considered:
Min Size of Investment Considered (000s): $2,596
Max Size of Investment Considered (000s): $7,138

Geographical Preferences

International Preferences:
Sweden
Europe
Estonia
Latvia
Lithuania

Additional Information

Year Founded: 1996
Current Activity Level : Actively seeking new investments

SCANDINAVIAN FINANCIAL MANAGEMENT AB

Lyckans Vag 4
Goteborg, Sweden 412 56
Phone: 46-31-708-1780
Fax: 46-31-708-1785
Website: www.sfmab.com

Management and Staff

Anders Carlryd, Partner
Anders Bjurstrom, Partner
Jesper Kahr, Partner
Martin Skoglund, Partner
Mats Lind, Partner
Michael Koch, Partner
Staffan Hillberg, Partner

Type of Firm

Private Equity Firm

Association Membership

Swedish Venture Capital Association (SVCA)

Project Preferences

Type of Financing Preferred:
Expansion
Balanced
Seed
Management Buyouts
Startup
Recapitalizations

Geographical Preferences

International Preferences:
Sweden
Europe

Industry Preferences

In Communications prefer:
Communications and Media
Telecommunications

In Computer Hardware prefer:
Computers

In Computer Software prefer:
Software

In Semiconductor/Electr prefer:
Electronics
Semiconductor

In Biotechnology prefer:
Biotechnology

In Medical/Health prefer:
Medical/Health

In Industrial/Energy prefer:
Industrial Products
Factory Automation

In Financial Services prefer:
Financial Services

Additional Information

Year Founded: 2005
Current Activity Level : Actively seeking new investments

SCANDINAVIAN LIFE SCIENCE VENTURE (AKA: SLS VENTURE)

Birger Jarlsgatan 10
Stockholm, Sweden 114 34
Phone: 46-8-5450-7030
Fax: 46-8-5450-7039
E-mail: info@slsinvest.com
Website: www.slsventure.com

Other Offices

2nd Floor
Vester Vold Gade 106
Copenhagen V, Denmark DK-1552
Phone: 45-3264-8181
Fax: 45-3264-8191

Management and Staff

Henrik Lawaetz, Founding Partner
Jonas Frick, Chief Executive Officer
Mikael Mortensen, Chief Financial Officer

Type of Firm

Private Equity Firm

Association Membership

Swedish Venture Capital Association (SVCA)
European Private Equity and Venture Capital Assoc.

Project Preferences

Type of Financing Preferred:
Second Stage Financing
Early Stage
Expansion
Balanced
Startup

Size of Investments Considered:
Min Size of Investment Considered (000s): $1,049
Max Size of Investment Considered (000s): $8,392

Geographical Preferences

International Preferences:
Sweden
Europe
Scandanavia/Nordic Region
Norway
Denmark

Industry Preferences

In Biotechnology prefer:
Biotechnology

In Medical/Health prefer:
Medical/Health
Pharmaceuticals

Additional Information

Year Founded: 2000
Capital Under Management: $209,800,000
Current Activity Level : Actively seeking new investments

SCF PARTNERS

600 Travis
Suite 6600
Houston, TX USA 77002
Phone: 713-227-7888
Fax: 713-227-7850
E-mail: info@scfpartners.com
Website: www.scfpartners.com

Other Offices

3430 Canterra Tower
400-3rd Avenue South West
Calgary, Canada T2P 4H2
Phone: 403-244-7888
Fax: 403-234-7829

15 Rubislaw Terrace
Aberdeen
Scotland, United Kingdom AB10 IXE
Phone: 44-11-4465-6930
Fax: 44-11-4465-6931

Management and Staff

Adam Zylman, Vice President
Amy Nelson, Vice President
Andrew Waite, Managing Director
Anthony Deluca, Managing Director & CFO
Cindy Taylor, Chief Financial Officer
David Baldwin, Managing Director
John Geddes, President
Kevin Nugent, Vice President
Kevin Binnie, Vice President
L. Simmons, President, Founder
Logan Walters, Vice President

Type of Firm

Private Equity Firm

Project Preferences

Type of Financing Preferred:
Leveraged Buyout

Size of Investments Considered:
Min Size of Investment Considered (000s): $50
Max Size of Investment Considered (000s): $500

Geographical Preferences

United States Preferences:
All U.S.

Canadian Preferences:
All Canada

Industry Preferences

In Industrial/Energy prefer:
Energy

Additional Information

Name of Most Recent Fund: SCF-VI, L.P.
Most Recent Fund Was Raised: 07/20/2005
Year Founded: 1989
Capital Under Management: $1,000,000,000
Current Activity Level : Actively seeking new investments

SCHEER & COMPANY

The Maritime Center
555 Long Wharf Drive
New Haven, CT USA 06511
Phone: 203-773-1195
E-mail: info@scheerandcompany.com
Website: www.scheerandcompany.com

Management and Staff

David Scheer, President

Type of Firm

Investment Management Firm

Project Preferences

Type of Financing Preferred:
Early Stage
Seed
Startup

Geographical Preferences

United States Preferences:
All U.S.

Industry Preferences

In Medical/Health prefer:
Medical/Health

Additional Information

Year Founded: 1981
Current Activity Level : Actively seeking new investments

SCHILLING - SAMINVEST

Erdbergstrasse 8
Wien, Austria 1030
Phone: 43-1-24-280
Fax: 43-1-1242-80209
E-mail: office@saminvest.at
Website: www.saminvest.at

Type of Firm

Private Equity Firm

Association Membership

European Private Equity and Venture Capital Assoc.

Project Preferences

Type of Financing Preferred:
Balanced

Geographical Preferences

International Preferences:
Austria

Additional Information

Year Founded: 2004
Current Activity Level : Actively seeking new investments

SCHNEIDER ELECTRIC VENTURES

7 rue de Caumartin
5th Floor
Paris, France 75009
Phone: 33-1-4561-3095
Fax: 33-1-4561-3450
E-mail: contact@se-ventures.com
Website: www.se-ventures.com

Other Offices

3rd Floor, Mitsui Sumitomo Bank
Nihonbashi Odemma-cho, Chuo-ku
Tokyo, Japan 103-0011
Phone: 81-3-5643-7875
Fax: 81-3-5641-1474

6th Floor, Shneider Building
No. 2 Jiang Tai Road, Chao Yang District
Beijing, China 100016
Phone: 86-10-8434-6699
Fax: 86-10-8450-1079

Management and Staff

Jean-Marc Bally, General Partner

Type of Firm

Corporate PE/Venture

Association Membership

French Venture Capital Association (AFIC)

Project Preferences

Type of Financing Preferred:
Second Stage Financing
First Stage Financing
Startup

Size of Investments Considered:
Min Size of Investment Considered (000s): $506
Max Size of Investment Considered (000s): $4,047

Geographical Preferences

United States Preferences:
All U.S.

International Preferences:
Europe
All International

Industry Preferences

In Communications prefer:
Communications and Media

In Internet Specific prefer:
Internet

In Semiconductor/Electr prefer:
Electronics

In Industrial/Energy prefer:
Industrial Products
Factory Automation

Additional Information

Year Founded: 2000
Capital Under Management: $46,900,000
Current Activity Level : Actively seeking new investments

SCHOFFSTALL VENTURES

5790 Devnonshire Road
Harrisburg, PA USA 17112
Phone: 717-671-3208
Fax: 717-671-3221
E-mail: sv-info@schoffstall.com
Website: www.schoffstallventures.com

Management and Staff

Martin Schoffstall, Managing Partner
Marvin Schoffstall, General Partner

Type of Firm

Private Equity Firm

Association Membership

Mid-Atlantic Venture Association

Project Preferences

Type of Financing Preferred:

Early Stage
Expansion

Industry Preferences

In Communications prefer:

Communications and Media

In Internet Specific prefer:

Internet

Additional Information

Year Founded: 2000
Current Activity Level : Actively seeking new investments

SCHOTT AG (FKA:SCHOTT GLAS)

Hattenbergstrasse 10
Mainz, Germany 55122
Phone: 49-61-3166-7240
Fax: 49-41-2888-9033
Website: www.schott.com/vc

Type of Firm

Corporate PE/Venture

Association Membership

European Private Equity and Venture Capital Assoc.

Project Preferences

Type of Financing Preferred:

Early Stage
Startup

Geographical Preferences

United States Preferences:

All U.S.

Canadian Preferences:

All Canada

International Preferences:

Europe
China
Singapore
Japan

Industry Preferences

In Communications prefer:

Telecommunications

In Semiconductor/Electr prefer:

Electronics

In Biotechnology prefer:

Biotechnology

In Medical/Health prefer:

Medical/Health

In Industrial/Energy prefer:

Industrial Products
Materials
Environmental Related

Additional Information

Year Founded: 2002
Current Activity Level : Actively seeking new investments

SCHRODER VENTURES LIFE SCIENCES

60 State Street
Suite 3650
Boston, MA USA 02109 - 28
Phone: 617-367-8100
Fax: 617-367-1590
E-mail: info@svlifesciences.com
Website: www.svlifesciences.com

Management and Staff

Michael Ross, Managing Partner

Type of Firm

Private Equity Firm

Additional Information

Year Founded: 1993
Current Activity Level : Actively seeking new investments

SCHRODERS PLC

31 Gresham Street
London, United Kingdom EC2V 7QA
Phone: 44-207-658-6000
Fax: 44-207-658-6965
Website: www.schroders.com

Other Offices

Ing. Enrique Butty 220, Piso 12
Representative Office
Buenos Aires, Argentina C1001AFB
Phone: 54-11-4317-1300
Fax: 54-11-4317-1313

Av. Paseo de las Palmas 425
Piso 11, Col. Lomas de Chapultepec
Mexico City, Mexico 11000
Phone: 52-55-1100-1030
Fax: 52-55-1100-1039

Independence Square West
Suite L60, The Curtis Center
Philadelphia, PA USA 19106
Phone: 215-861-0997
Fax: 215-861-0989

7 Finance Street
Room 926, Winland Int'l Finance Center
Beijing, China 100140
Phone: 86-10-6655-5388
Fax: 86-10-6655-5398

131 Front Street
Hamilton, Bermuda HM 12
Phone: 441-292-4995
Fax: 441-292-2437

P.O. Box 1040GT
Harbour Center
Grand Cayman, Cayman Islands BWI
Phone: 345-949-2849
Fax: 345-949-5409

1000 Lujiazui Ring Road
18/F, HSBC Building
Shanghai, China 200120
Phone: 86-21-6841-1988
Fax: 86-21-6841-0668

77, Dr. Annie Besant Road
Ground Floor, Ramnord House
Mumbai, India 400018

1-11-1 Marunouchi, Chiyoda-ku
Pacific Century Place Marunouchi
Tokyo, Japan 100-6224
Phone: 81-3-5293-1500
Fax: 81-3-5293-1505

65 Chulia Street
#47-01, OCBC Center
Singapore, Singapore 049513
Phone: 65-6535-3411
Fax: 65-6535-3486

875 Third Avenue
22nd Floor
New York, NY USA 10022-6225
Phone: 212-641-3830
Fax: 212-641-3985

Rua Joaquim Floriano
100 - Cjtos 141/142, Itaim Bibi

Sao Paulo, Brazil 04534-000
Phone: 55-11-3054-5155
Fax: 55-11-3054-5173

88 Queensway
Suite 3301, Level 33, Two Pacific Place
Central, Hong Kong
Phone: 852-2521-1633
Fax: 852-2530-9095

123 Pitt Street
Level, Angel Place
Sydney, Australia 2000
Phone: 61-2-9210-9200
Fax: 61-2-9231-1119

Type of Firm

Bank Affiliated

Project Preferences

Type of Financing Preferred:

Fund of Funds
Balanced

Geographical Preferences

United States Preferences:

All U.S.

International Preferences:

Europe
All International

Additional Information

Name of Most Recent Fund: Schroder Private Equity Fund of Funds III
Most Recent Fund Was Raised: 10/10/2005
Year Founded: 1970
Capital Under Management: $36,000,000,000
Current Activity Level : Actively seeking new investments
Method of Compensation: Return on invest. most important, but chg. closing fees, service fees, etc.

SCHULTZE ASSET MANAGEMENT LLC

3000 Westchester Avenue
Purchase, NY USA 10577
Phone: 914-701-5260
Fax: 914-701-5269
E-mail: info@samco.net
Website: www.samco.net

Management and Staff

Edward Petit, Managing Director
George Schultze, Managing Director

Type of Firm

Private Equity Firm

Project Preferences

Type of Financing Preferred:

Mezzanine
Distressed Debt

Industry Focus

(% based on actual investment)

Medical/Health	100.0%

Additional Information

Year Founded: 1998
Current Activity Level : Actively seeking new investments

SCIENCE CENTER, THE

3701 Market Street
Third Floor
Philadelphia, PA USA 19104
Phone: 215-966-6295
Fax: 215-966-6001
E-mail: info@sciencecenter.org
Website: www.sciencecenter.org

Management and Staff

Richard Miller, Vice President
Tom Greenwood, Vice President

Type of Firm

Incubator/Development Program

Project Preferences

Type of Financing Preferred:

Early Stage

Geographical Preferences

United States Preferences:

All U.S.

Additional Information

Year Founded: 1963
Capital Under Management: $1,000,000
Current Activity Level : Actively seeking new investments

SCIENS CAPITAL PARTNERS (FKA: ZILKHA VENTURE PARTNERS)

667 Madison Avenue
New York, NY USA 10021
Phone: 212-471-6100
Fax: 212-471-6199
E-mail: info@scienscapital.com
Website: www.scienscapital.com

Management and Staff

Daniel Standen, General Partner
Donald Young, Principal
Gordon Buchanan, Partner
James Larmett, Partner
John Rigas, Managing Partner

Type of Firm

Private Equity Firm

Project Preferences

Type of Financing Preferred:

Leveraged Buyout
Early Stage
Expansion
Seed
Recapitalizations

Size of Investments Considered:

Min Size of Investment Considered (000s): $1,000
Max Size of Investment Considered (000s): $5,000

Geographical Preferences

United States Preferences:

All U.S.

Industry Preferences

In Communications prefer:

Telecommunications

In Internet Specific prefer:

Internet

In Financial Services prefer:

Financial Services

Additional Information

Year Founded: 1994
Capital Under Management: $20,000,000
Current Activity Level : Actively seeking new investments

SCIMITAR GLOBAL VENTURES

Capricorn Tower, 9th Floor
Sheikh Zayed Road
Dubai, Utd. Arab Em.
Phone: 971-4-403-7100
Website: www.scimitar.net

Other Offices

Two Penn Center
Suite 200
Philadelphia, PA USA 19102
Phone: 610-768-8098
Fax: 610-337-0997

Management and Staff

Scott Ogur, Partner
Zachary Venegas, Partner

Type of Firm

Private Equity Firm

Project Preferences

Type of Financing Preferred:

Generalist PE

Geographical Preferences

International Preferences:

Morocco
Romania
Iraq

Industry Preferences

In Industrial/Energy prefer:
Energy

In Financial Services prefer:
Financial Services

In Business Serv. prefer:
Services

Additional Information

Year Founded: 2006
Current Activity Level : Actively seeking new investments

SCIVENTURES INVESTMENTS PTY., LTD.

159 Dorcas Street
Level 1
South Melbourne, Australia 3205
Phone: 613-8606-3400
Fax: 613-9686-9866
E-mail: info@sciventures.com.au
Website: www.sciventures.com.au

Management and Staff

Gregory Smith, Co-Founder
Ross Chessari, Co-Founder

Type of Firm

Private Equity Firm

Project Preferences

Type of Financing Preferred:
Seed
Startup

Size of Investments Considered:
Min Size of Investment Considered (000s): $7
Max Size of Investment Considered (000s): $742

Geographical Preferences

International Preferences:
Pacific

Industry Preferences

In Biotechnology prefer:
Biotechnology

Additional Information

Name of Most Recent Fund: SciVentures Pre-Seed Fund
Most Recent Fund Was Raised: 12/18/2002
Year Founded: 2002
Capital Under Management: $21,700,000
Current Activity Level : Actively seeking new investments

SCM STRATEGIC CAPITAL MANAGEMENT AG

Kasernenstrasse 77b
Zurich, Switzerland CH-8004
Phone: 41-43-499-4949
Fax: 41-43-499-4950
E-mail: scm@scmag.com
Website: www.scmag.com

Other Offices

29th Floor, One Canada Square
Canary Wharf
London, United Kingdom E14 5DY
Phone: 44-207-712-1696

3rd Floor, Three Pacific Place
1 Queen's Road East
Central, Hong Kong
Phone: 852-2855-6930

Management and Staff

Mark Engler, Vice President

Type of Firm

Private Equity Firm

Project Preferences

Type of Financing Preferred:
Fund of Funds
Generalist PE

Geographical Preferences

International Preferences:
Europe
Asia

Additional Information

Year Founded: 1996
Capital Under Management: $6,600,000,000
Current Activity Level : Actively seeking new investments

SCOPE CAPITAL ADVISORY AB

Kungsgatan 30
Stockholm, Sweden 111 35
Phone: 46-8-5060-6200
Fax: 46-8-5060-6210
E-mail: contact@scope.se
Website: www.scope.se

Other Offices

Place de la Taconnerie 3
Geneva, Switzerland CH-1204
Phone: 41-22-318-6039

Management and Staff

Anders Rundgren, Partner
Andreas Ossmark, Partner
Frederik Oweson, Partner
Jonas Palmquist, Partner
Kristina Patek, Partner
Monalotte Theorell, CFO, CEO
Svante Andreen, Partner

Type of Firm

Private Equity Firm

Association Membership

Swedish Venture Capital Association (SVCA)

Project Preferences

Type of Financing Preferred:
Expansion
Balanced
Seed
Startup

Size of Investments Considered:
Min Size of Investment Considered (000s): $3,098
Max Size of Investment Considered (000s): $15,484

Geographical Preferences

International Preferences:
Sweden
Iceland
Scandanavia/Nordic Region
Finland
Norway
Denmark

Additional Information

Year Founded: 2001
Capital Under Management: $189,200,000
Current Activity Level : Actively seeking new investments

SCORPION CAPITAL PARTNERS, L.P.

245 5th Avenue
25th Floor
New York, NY USA 10016
Phone: 212-207-9020
E-mail: info@scorpioncap.com
Website: www.scorpionholdings.com

Management and Staff

Kevin McCarthy, General Partner
Nuno Brandolini, Co-Founder
Robert Schoff, Chief Financial Officer

Type of Firm

Private Equity Firm

Project Preferences

Type of Financing Preferred:
Leveraged Buyout
Later Stage
Recapitalizations

Size of Investments Considered:
Min Size of Investment Considered (000s): $2,000
Max Size of Investment Considered (000s): $8,000

Geographical Preferences

United States Preferences:
All U.S.

Additional Information

Year Founded: 2004
Capital Under Management: $18,300,000
Current Activity Level : Actively seeking new investments

SCOTIABANK PRIVATE EQUITY

44 King Street West
64th Floor
Toronto, Canada M5H 3Y2
Phone: 416-945-4888
Fax: 416-945-4588
Website: www.scotiacapital.com

Management and Staff

Peter Adamek, Managing Director
Tony Cestra, Managing Director

Type of Firm

Investment Management Firm

Project Preferences

Type of Financing Preferred:
Expansion
Startup

Geographical Preferences

United States Preferences:
All U.S.

Canadian Preferences:
All Canada

Additional Information

Year Founded: 2000
Current Activity Level : Actively seeking new investments

SCOTTISH ENTERPRISE

5 Atlantic Quay
150 Broomielaw
Glasgow, United Kingdom G2 8LU
Phone: 44-141-248-2700
Fax: 44-141-221-3217
Website: www.scottish-enterprise.com

Other Offices

Apex House
99 Haymarket Terrace
Edinburgh, United Kingdom EH12 5HD
Phone: 44-131-313-4000
Fax: 44-131-313-4231

17-19 Hill Street
Kilmarnock, United Kingdom KA3 1HA
Phone: 44-1563-526-623
Fax: 44-1563-543-636

27 Albyn Place
Aberdeen, United Kingdom AB10 1DB
Phone: 44-1224-252-000
Fax: 44-1224-213-417

Enterprise House
3 Greenmarket
Dundee, United Kingdom DD1 4QB
Phone: 44-1382-223-100
Fax: 44-1382-201-319

Laurel House
Laurelhill Business Park
Stirling, United Kingdom FK7 9JQ
Phone: 44-1786-451-919
Fax: 44-1786-478-123

Dumfries Enterprise Park
Tinwald Downs Road
Dumfries, United Kingdom DG1 3SJ
Phone: 44-1387-245-000
Fax: 44-1387-246-224

New Lanarkshire House
Dove Wynd, Strathclyde Business Park
Bellshill, United Kingdom ML4 3AD
Phone: 44-1698-745-454
Fax: 44-1698-842-211

Bridge Street
Galashiels, United Kingdom TD1 1SW
Phone: 44-1896-758-991
Fax: 44-1896-758-625

Kingdom House
Saltire Centre, Glenrothes
Fife, United Kingdom KY6 2AQ
Phone: 44-1592-623-000
Fax: 44-1592-623-149

Atrium Court
50 Waterloo Street
Glasglow, United Kingdom G2 6HQ
Phone: 44-141-204-1111
Fax: 44-141-248-1600

27 Causeyside Street
Paisley, United Kingdom PA1 1UL
Phone: 44-141-848-0101
Fax: 44-141-848-6930

2nd Floor, Spectrum House
Clydebank Business Park, Clydebank
Glasglow, United Kingdom G81 2DR
Phone: 44-141-951-2121
Fax: 44-141-951-1907

Management and Staff

Jack Perry, Chief Executive Officer
Janet Brown, Managing Director
John Phillips, Managing Director
Lena Wilson, Chief Operating Officer

Type of Firm

Government Affiliated Program

Project Preferences

Type of Financing Preferred:
Early Stage
Balanced
Seed
Startup

Size of Investments Considered:
Min Size of Investment Considered (000s): $39
Max Size of Investment Considered (000s): $9,816

Geographical Preferences

International Preferences:
United Kingdom

Industry Preferences

In Semiconductor/Electr prefer:
Electronics

In Biotechnology prefer:
Biotechnology

In Medical/Health prefer:
Health Services
Pharmaceuticals

In Consumer Related prefer:
Retail
Hotels and Resorts

In Financial Services prefer:
Real Estate
Financial Services

In Business Serv. prefer:
Consulting Services

In Manufact. prefer:
Manufacturing

In Agr/Forestr/Fish prefer:
Agriculture related

Additional Information

Year Founded: 2006
Capital Under Management: $8,300,000
Current Activity Level : Actively seeking new investments

SCOTTISH EQUITY PARTNERS (AKA: SEP)

17 Blythswood Square
Glasgow, United Kingdom G2 4AD
Phone: 44-141-273-4000
Fax: 44-141-273-4001
E-mail: enquiries@sep.co.uk
Website: www.sep.co.uk

Other Offices

29 St. George Street
London, United Kingdom W1S 2FA
Phone: 44-207-758-5900
Fax: 44-207-758-5901

Management and Staff

Andrew Davison, Partner
Brian Kerr, Partner
Calum Paterson, Managing Partner
David Sneddon, Partner
Fearghal O'Riordain, Partner
Gary Le Sueur, Partner
Gordon Beveridge, Principal
Jan Rutherford, Principal
Julie Curran, Principal
Richard Sparrow, Partner
Stuart Paterson, Partner

Type of Firm

Private Equity Firm

Association Membership

British Venture Capital Association (BVCA)
European Private Equity and Venture Capital Assoc.

Project Preferences

Role in Financing:

Prefer role as deal originator but will also invest in deals created by others

Type of Financing Preferred:

Second Stage Financing
Early Stage
Expansion
Balanced
Seed
Later Stage
First Stage Financing
Startup

Size of Investments Considered:

Min Size of Investment Considered (000s): $1,783
Max Size of Investment Considered (000s): $17,833

Geographical Preferences

International Preferences:

United Kingdom
Europe

Industry Focus

(% based on actual investment)

Semiconductors/Other Elect.	23.2%
Computer Software and Services	21.6%
Communications and Media	11.5%
Biotechnology	11.4%
Other Products	10.8%
Industrial/Energy	7.3%
Medical/Health	6.6%
Internet Specific	3.9%
Consumer Related	2.2%
Computer Hardware	1.5%

Additional Information

Year Founded: 1996
Capital Under Management: $494,000,000
Current Activity Level : Actively seeking new investments

SCOTTWOOD CAPITAL, LLC

230 Park Avenue
7th Floor
New York, NY USA 10169
Phone: 212-499-2450

Type of Firm

Private Equity Firm

Additional Information

Year Founded: 2002
Capital Under Management: $21,700,000
Current Activity Level : Actively seeking new investments

SCP PRIVATE EQUITY PARTNERS

1200 Liberty Ridge Drive
Suite 300
Wayne, PA USA 19087
Phone: 610-995-2900
Fax: 610-975-9546
E-mail: webmaster@scppartners.com
Website: www.scppartners.com

Other Offices

One Rockefeller Plaza
Suite 2301
New York, NY USA 10020
Phone: 212-586-3800

74 Grand Avenue
Englewood, NJ USA 07631
Phone: 201-541-1080
Fax: 201-541-1084

Management and Staff

Amit Avnet, Principal
Christopher Doherty, Principal
Dennis Ferry, Chief Financial Officer
Doron Cohen, Venture Partner
Edmundo Gonzalez, Principal
James Brown, Partner
Jim Evans, Venture Partner
Richard Sherman, Venture Partner
Robert Yablunsky, Venture Partner
Roger Carolin, Venture Partner
Salman Farmanfarmaian, Principal
Thomas Rebar, Partner
Wayne Weisman, Partner
Winston Churchill, Managing General Partner
Yaron Eitan, Partner
Yossi Shachak, Venture Partner

Type of Firm

Private Equity Firm

Project Preferences

Type of Financing Preferred:

Leveraged Buyout
Early Stage
Later Stage

Geographical Preferences

International Preferences:

All International

Industry Focus

(% based on actual investment)

Internet Specific	39.3%
Computer Software and Services	29.8%
Medical/Health	9.1%
Other Products	7.5%
Biotechnology	3.7%
Communications and Media	3.7%
Consumer Related	3.2%
Semiconductors/Other Elect.	3.1%
Computer Hardware	0.6%

Additional Information

Name of Most Recent Fund: SCP Vitalife Partners II, L.P.
Most Recent Fund Was Raised: 04/23/2007
Year Founded: 1996
Capital Under Management: $828,300,000
Current Activity Level : Actively seeking new investments

SCS CAPITAL SDN. BHD.

Level 40 Petronas Twin Towers
Twr. 2, Kuala Lumpur City Ctr.
Kuala Lumpur, Malaysia 50088
Phone: 603-2168-4740
Fax: 603-2168-4201
Website: www.scscapital.com

Other Offices

30th Floor Shinjuku Park Tower
3-7-1 Nishi-Shinjuku
Shinjuku-ku, Tokyo, Japan 163-1030
Phone: 813-5326-3625
Fax: 813-5326-3001

29th Floor One Canada Square
Canary Wharf
London, United Kingdom E14 5DY
Phone: 44-207-712-1591
Fax: 44-207-712-1501

14 Wall Street
20th Floor, New York
New York, NY USA 100050
Phone: 212-618-1255
Fax: 212-618-1705

Type of Firm

Private Equity Firm

Project Preferences

Type of Financing Preferred:

Balanced

Geographical Preferences

International Preferences:
Malaysia

Additional Information

Year Founded: 2005
Current Activity Level : Actively seeking new investments

SCSI CAPITAL

Six Jantar Mantar Road
Connaught Place
New Delhi, India 110 001
Phone: 91-11-2336-7917
Fax: 91-11-2336-7961
Website: www.scsicapital.com

Management and Staff

Joseph Fowler, General Partner
Satish Mehta, General Partner
Steve Rogerson, General Partner
Yogesh Shah, General Partner

Type of Firm

Private Equity Firm

Project Preferences

Type of Financing Preferred:
Early Stage
Seed

Geographical Preferences

International Preferences:
India
China

Industry Preferences

in Semiconductor/Electr prefer:
Semiconductor
Fiber Optics

In Industrial/Energy prefer:
Energy

Additional Information

Year Founded: 2005
Current Activity Level : Actively seeking new investments

SDEM-MADEIRA CORPORATE DEVELOPMENT COMPANY, SGPS SA

Rua da Mouraria, 9
3 Andar, Sala A
Funchal, Portugal 9000-047
Phone: 351-291-201-380
Fax: 351-291-201-389
E-mail: sdem@sdem.pt
Website: www.sdem.pt

Management and Staff

Joao Lara, Chief Executive Officer

Type of Firm

Private Equity Firm

Association Membership

European Private Equity and Venture Capital Assoc.

Project Preferences

Role in Financing:
Prefer role in deals created by others

Type of Financing Preferred:
Expansion
Balanced
Startup

Size of Investments Considered:
Min Size of Investment Considered (000s): $636
Max Size of Investment Considered (000s): $1,908

Geographical Preferences

International Preferences:
Portugal
Europe

Additional Information

Year Founded: 2002
Capital Under Management: $6,600,000
Current Activity Level : Actively seeking new investments

SDL VENTURES, LLC

One First Street
Suite 14
Los Altos, CA USA 94022
Phone: 650-559-9355
Fax: 650-559-9353
Website: www.sdlventures.com

Management and Staff

Donald Scifres, Managing Director

Type of Firm

Private Equity Firm

Project Preferences

Type of Financing Preferred:
Early Stage

Industry Preferences

In Internet Specific prefer:
Internet

In Semiconductor/Electr prefer:
Fiber Optics

In Medical/Health prefer:
Medical/Health

In Industrial/Energy prefer:
Energy

Additional Information

Year Founded: 2003
Current Activity Level : Actively seeking new investments

SEABURY VENTURE PARTNERS

345 Lorton Avenue
Suite 401
Burlingame, CA USA 94010
Phone: 650-373-1030
Fax: 650-373-1031
E-mail: info@seaburypartners.com
Website: www.seaburypartners.com

Management and Staff

Mark Olhoeft, Chief Financial Officer
Michael Fitzpatrick, General Partner
Patricia Fitzpatrick, General Partner

Type of Firm

Private Equity Firm

Industry Preferences

In Communications prefer:
Telecommunications

In Semiconductor/Electr prefer:
Optoelectronics

Additional Information

Year Founded: 2000
Current Activity Level : Actively seeking new investments

SEACOAST CAPITAL

55 Ferncroft Road
Suite 110
Danvers, MA USA 01923
Phone: 978-750-1300
Fax: 978-750-1301
Website: www.seacoastcapital.com

Other Offices

455 Market Street
Suite 2000
San Francisco, CA USA 94105
Phone: 415-956-1400
Fax: 415-956-1459

Management and Staff

Eben Moulton, Managing Director
Jeffrey Holland, Managing Director
Thomas Gorman, Managing Director
Walter Leonard, Managing Director & CFO

Type of Firm

Private Equity Firm

Association Membership

Natl Assoc of Small Bus. Inv. Co (NASBIC)

Project Preferences

Role in Financing:
Prefer role as deal originator but will also invest in deals created by others

Type of Financing Preferred:
Mezzanine

Size of Investments Considered:
Min Size of Investment Considered (000s): $2,000
Max Size of Investment Considered (000s): $10,000

Industry Focus
(% based on actual investment)

Other Products	33.3%
Consumer Related	15.3%
Internet Specific	12.3%
Computer Software and Services	10.9%
Semiconductors/Other Elect.	10.7%
Industrial/Energy	9.0%
Medical/Health	8.5%

Additional Information
Year Founded: 1989
Capital Under Management: $200,000,000
Current Activity Level : Actively seeking new investments
Method of Compensation: Return on invest. most important, but chg. closing fees, service fees, etc.

SEAFLOWER VENTURES

Bay Colony Corporate Center
1000 Winter Street, Suite 1000
Waltham, MA USA 02451
Phone: 781-466-9552
Fax: 781-466-9553
E-mail: info@seaflower.com
Website: www.seaflower.com

Management and Staff
Alex Moot, General Partner
Amin Ladak, Principal
James Sherblom, Managing General Partner
Zach Jonasson, Principal

Type of Firm
Private Equity Firm

Association Membership
National Venture Capital Association - USA (NVCA)

Project Preferences

Role in Financing:
Prefer role as deal originator but will also invest in deals created by others

Type of Financing Preferred:
Second Stage Financing
Early Stage
Start-up Financing
First Stage Financing

Size of Investments Considered:
Min Size of Investment Considered (000s): $200
Max Size of Investment Considered (000s): $3,000

Geographical Preferences

United States Preferences:
Mid Atlantic
Midwest
Illinois
Southeast
Michigan
Northeast
Wisconsin
West Coast

Canadian Preferences:
All Canada
Quebec
Central Canada
Ontario

Industry Focus
(% based on actual investment)

Biotechnology	61.1%
Medical/Health	24.9%
Internet Specific	9.2%
Computer Hardware	2.9%
Industrial/Energy	1.9%

Additional Information
Name of Most Recent Fund: Seaflower Health Ventures III, L.P.
Most Recent Fund Was Raised: 03/29/2001
Year Founded: 1993
Capital Under Management: $50,000,000
Current Activity Level : Actively seeking new investments
Method of Compensation: Return on investment is of primary concern, do not charge fees

SEAGROVE, LLC

1801 Century Park East
Suite 1080
Los Angeles, CA USA 90067
Phone: 310-552-4900
Fax: 310-552-2026

Management and Staff
Rick Edwards, Partner

Type of Firm
Private Equity Firm

Additional Information
Year Founded: 1994
Current Activity Level : Actively seeking new investments

SEAPOINT VENTURES

719 Second Avenue
Suite 1405
Seattle, WA USA 98104
Phone: 206-438-1880
Fax: 206-438-1880
E-mail: info@seapointventures.com
Website: www.seapointventures.com

Management and Staff
Debbie Beatenbough, Chief Financial Officer
Melissa Widner, General Partner
Susan Sigl, General Partner
Thomas Huseby, Managing Partner

Type of Firm
Private Equity Firm

Project Preferences

Role in Financing:
Prefer role as deal originator but will also invest in deals created by others

Type of Financing Preferred:
Second Stage Financing
Early Stage
Seed
First Stage Financing

Size of Investments Considered:
Min Size of Investment Considered (000s): $300
Max Size of Investment Considered (000s): $4,000

Geographical Preferences

United States Preferences:
Northwest
West Coast

Industry Focus
(% based on actual investment)

Computer Software and Services	35.4%
Communications and Media	30.1%
Computer Hardware	19.2%
Internet Specific	14.1%
Biotechnology	1.2%

Additional Information
Name of Most Recent Fund: Seapoint Ventures II, L.P.
Most Recent Fund Was Raised: 03/31/2001
Year Founded: 1997
Capital Under Management: $68,000,000
Current Activity Level : Actively seeking new investments
Method of Compensation: Return on investment is of primary concern, do not charge fees

SEAPORT CAPITAL, LLC

199 Water Street, 20th Floor
One Seaport Plaza
New York, NY USA 10038
Phone: 212-847-8900
Fax: 212-425-1420
E-mail: info@seaportcapital.com
Website: www.seaportcapital.com

Management and Staff
Alison Mulhern, Partner
Drew Meyers, Principal
James Collis, Partner
Robert Tamashunas, Principal

Scott McCormack, Partner
William Luby, Partner

Type of Firm

Private Equity Firm

Project Preferences

Role in Financing:

Prefer role as deal originator but will also invest in deals created by others

Type of Financing Preferred:

Leveraged Buyout
Control-block Purchases
Early Stage
Expansion
Later Stage
Management Buyouts
Acquisition
Industry Rollups

Size of Investments Considered:

Min Size of Investment Considered (000s): $5,000
Max Size of Investment Considered (000s): $50,000

Geographical Preferences

United States Preferences:

All U.S.

Canadian Preferences:

All Canada

Industry Focus

(% based on actual investment)

Communications and Media	48.9%
Internet Specific	31.0%
Other Products	18.9%
Computer Software and Services	1.1%
Computer Hardware	0.1%

Additional Information

Name of Most Recent Fund: Seaport Capital Partners III-A, L.P.
Most Recent Fund Was Raised: 03/08/2007
Year Founded: 1997
Capital Under Management: $410,000,000
Current Activity Level : Actively seeking new investments
Method of Compensation: Return on investment is of primary concern, do not charge fees

---

SEARS CAPITAL MANAGEMENT, INC.

300 Third Street, Second Floor
Suite Six
Los Altos, CA USA 94022
Phone: 650-947-9167
Fax: 650-947-9111
E-mail: info@searscapital.net
Website: www.searscapital.net

Type of Firm

Private Equity Firm

Project Preferences

Type of Financing Preferred:

Early Stage
Seed

Industry Preferences

In Medical/Health prefer:

Medical Products
Pharmaceuticals

Additional Information

Year Founded: 1994
Current Activity Level : Actively seeking new investments

SEAVI ADVENT CORPORATION, LTD. (AKA: SEAVI ADVENT)

331 North Bridge Road
#05-04/05 Odeon Towers
Singapore, Singapore 188720
Phone: 65-6339-9090
Fax: 65-6339-8247
E-mail: info@seavi.com.sg
Website: www.seavi.com.sg

Other Offices

Suite 1520, 15F, One Corporate Avenue
222 Hubin Road, Luwan District
Shanghai, China 200021
Phone: 86-21-6122-1136
Fax: 86-21-6122-2418

Room 1312, 13th Floor, Ocean Centre
5 Canton Road, Tsimshatsui West
Kowloon, Hong Kong
Phone: 852-2376-0606
Fax: 852-2375-9666

Central International Trade Center
6A Jian Guo Men Wai St., Chaoyang Dist.
Beijing, China 100022
Phone: 86-10-6563-9815
Fax: 86-10-6563-9833

Management and Staff

Derrick Lee, Managing Partner
Francis L.F. Ng, Partner
Harold Chan, Partner
Henry Yao Wei Min, Partner
Hoe Boon Kwee, Chief Financial Officer
Keng Boon Tan, Managing Partner
Tan Keng Boon, Managing Partner
Teo Yi-Dar, Partner

Type of Firm

Private Equity Firm

Association Membership

Hong Kong Venture Capital Association (HKVCA)

Project Preferences

Role in Financing:

Prefer role as deal originator but will also invest in deals created by others

Type of Financing Preferred:

Leveraged Buyout
Early Stage
Expansion
Mezzanine
Generalist PE
Later Stage
Management Buyouts
Recapitalizations

Size of Investments Considered:

Min Size of Investment Considered (000s): $1,000
Max Size of Investment Considered (000s): $15,000

Geographical Preferences

International Preferences:

China
Hong Kong
Singapore
Asia
Malaysia

Industry Preferences

In Communications prefer:

Telecommunications

In Semiconductor/Electr prefer:

Electronics

In Consumer Related prefer:

Retail

In Industrial/Energy prefer:

Energy
Materials
Environmental Related

In Business Serv. prefer:

Services

Additional Information

Year Founded: 1984
Capital Under Management: $50,000,000
Current Activity Level : Actively seeking new investments

SEAVIEW CAPITAL ADVISORS, LLC

509 Madison Avenue
Suite 1510
New York, NY USA 10022
Phone: 212-774-3655
Fax: 646-278-0813
Website: www.seaviewcapitaladvisors.com

Management and Staff

David Montoya, Partner
Scott Hartman, Partner

Type of Firm

Private Equity Firm

Project Preferences

Role in Financing:

Prefer role as deal originator but will also invest in deals created by others

Type of Financing Preferred:

Control-block Purchases
Mezzanine
Public Companies
Later Stage
Management Buyouts
Industry Rollups

Size of Investments Considered:

Min Size of Investment Considered (000s): $1,000
Max Size of Investment Considered (000s): $30,000

Additional Information

Year Founded: 2004
Capital Under Management: $150,000,000
Current Activity Level : Actively seeking new investments
Method of Compensation: Return on invest. most important, but chg. closing fees, service fees, etc.

SEAWAY PRIVATE EQUITY CORPORATION (AKA: SPEC)

65 Main Street
Suite 101
Potsdam, NY USA 13676
Phone: 315-268-3778
Website: www.specinvest.org

Management and Staff

Anthony Collins, President
Ronald McDougall, Vice President

Type of Firm

Private Equity Firm

Project Preferences

Type of Financing Preferred:

Early Stage
Balanced

Geographical Preferences

United States Preferences:

All U.S.

Industry Preferences

In Industrial/Energy prefer:

Energy
Environmental Related

Additional Information

Year Founded: 2007
Current Activity Level : Actively seeking new investments

SEB VENTURE CAPITAL (FKA: SEB FORETAGSINVEST)

Kungstradgardsgatan 8
Stockholm, Sweden 10640
Phone: 46-8-763-7900
Fax: 46-8-763-7909
E-mail: foretagsinvest@seb.se
Website: www.foretagsinvest.seb.se

Management and Staff

Dan Peterson, Partner
Frederick Johansson, Partner
Thomas Sjostrom, Partner

Type of Firm

Bank Affiliated

Association Membership

Swedish Venture Capital Association (SVCA)
European Private Equity and Venture Capital Assoc.

Project Preferences

Type of Financing Preferred:

Leveraged Buyout
Early Stage
Expansion
Balanced
Startup

Size of Investments Considered:

Min Size of Investment Considered (000s): $200
Max Size of Investment Considered (000s): $200,000

Geographical Preferences

International Preferences:

Eastern Europe
Scandanavia/Nordic Region

Industry Focus

(% based on actual investment)

Medical/Health	29.9%
Other Products	26.6%
Biotechnology	14.5%
Computer Software and Services	13.2%
Internet Specific	7.3%
Semiconductors/Other Elect.	4.4%
Industrial/Energy	2.9%
Consumer Related	1.2%
Computer Hardware	0.1%

Additional Information

Year Founded: 1972
Capital Under Management: $52,000,000
Current Activity Level : Actively seeking new investments

SECOND AVENUE PARTNERS

1000 Second Avenue
Suite 1200
Seattle, WA USA 98104
Phone: 206-332-1200
Fax: 206-322-1201
Website: www.secondave.com

Management and Staff

Keith Grinstein, Partner
Michael Slade, Partner
Nicholas Hanauer, Partner
Pete Higgins, Partner

Type of Firm

Private Equity Firm

Additional Information

Year Founded: 2000
Current Activity Level : Actively seeking new investments

SECOND CITY CAPITAL PARTNERS

1075 West Georgia Street
Suite 2600
Vancouver, Canada V6E 3C9
Phone: 604-806-3350
Fax: 604-661-4873
Website: www.secondcitycapital.com

Management and Staff

Chris Wallace, Partner
David Huberman, Partner
Richard Osborn, Partner
Sam Belzberg, Partner

Type of Firm

Private Equity Firm

Geographical Preferences

Canadian Preferences:

All Canada

Additional Information

Year Founded: 2004
Current Activity Level : Actively seeking new investments

SECURITY GROWTH PARTNERS

450 Seventh Avenue
Suite 2100
New York, NY USA 10123
Phone: 212-875-1210
E-mail: info@securitygrowth.com
Website: www.securitygrowth.com

Type of Firm
Private Equity Firm

Project Preferences
Type of Financing Preferred:
Early Stage

Geographical Preferences
United States Preferences:
All U.S.

Industry Preferences
In Communications prefer:
Wireless Communications

In Computer Software prefer:
Software

Additional Information
Year Founded: 2006
Current Activity Level : Actively seeking new investments

SED VENTURES
62, rue de la Boitie
Paris, France 75008
Phone: 33-01-4289-8397
Fax: 33-01-4289-8452
E-mail: sed@artinternet.fr

Type of Firm
Private Equity Firm

Project Preferences
Type of Financing Preferred:
Balanced

Geographical Preferences
International Preferences:
United Kingdom
Netherlands
France

Industry Preferences
In Biotechnology prefer:
Biotechnology

In Medical/Health prefer:
Medical/Health

Additional Information
Name of Most Recent Fund: FCPR Ven Sed I
Most Recent Fund Was Raised: 06/30/1990
Year Founded: 1990
Current Activity Level : Actively seeking new investments

SEDCO DIRECT INVESTMENT GROUP
Zumrat Al Saleheen St. (122)
Al-Khaldiah District
Jeddah, Saudi Arabia
Phone: 966-2-606-6556
Fax: 966-2—606-0931
E-mail: info@sedco.com
Website: www.sedco.com

Management and Staff
Chee Yuen Ng, Vice President
Yousuf Khayat, Managing Director

Type of Firm
Private Equity Advisor or Fund of Funds

Project Preferences
Type of Financing Preferred:
Fund of Funds

Geographical Preferences
International Preferences:
Middle East
Asia

Additional Information
Year Founded: 2009
Current Activity Level : Actively seeking new investments

SEDONA CAPITAL, INC.
3F, BYGS Shinkuku Bldg.
2-19-1 Shinjuku-ku
Tokyo, Japan 160-0022
Phone: 81-3-5367-1661
Fax: 81-3-5367-1689
E-mail: info@sedona-capital.com
Website: www.sedona-capital.com

Management and Staff
Hiroshi Nakata, Managing Director

Type of Firm
Private Equity Firm

Project Preferences
Type of Financing Preferred:
Balanced

Geographical Preferences
International Preferences:
Japan
All International

Industry Preferences
In Communications prefer:
Communications and Media
Media and Entertainment

Additional Information
Year Founded: 2005
Capital Under Management: $100,000
Current Activity Level : Actively seeking new investments

SEED CAPITAL COMPANY, S.R.O. (FKA: FOND FONDOV, S.R.O.)
Nevadzova 5
82101
Bratislava, Slovakia 821 01
Phone: 421-2-4333-1873
Fax: 421-2-4828-7645
E-mail: seedcapital@seedcapital.sk
Website: www.seedcapital.sk

Other Offices
Rudohorska 33
Banska Bystrica, Slovakia 974 11
Phone: 421-48-471-6489
Fax: 421-48-471-6414

Type of Firm
Private Equity Firm

Association Membership
European Private Equity and Venture Capital Assoc.

Project Preferences
Type of Financing Preferred:
Expansion
Early Stage
Seed
Startup

Geographical Preferences
International Preferences:
Slovak Repub.

Industry Preferences
In Consumer Related prefer:
Consumer
Hotels and Resorts

In Industrial/Energy prefer:
Industrial Products

In Transportation prefer:
Transportation

In Business Serv. prefer:
Services

Additional Information
Year Founded: 1995
Capital Under Management: $3,500,000
Current Activity Level : Actively seeking new investments

SEED CAPITAL DENMARK

SCION-DTU Forskerpark
Diplomvej 381 (DTU)
Lyngby, Denmark DK 2800
Phone: 45-8818-4100
Fax: 45-8818-4120
E-mail: info@seedcapital.dk
Website: www.seedcapital.dk

Management and Staff

Carsten Schou, Partner
Jakob Fuglede Nielsen, Chief Financial Officer
Lars Andersen, Managing Director
Peter Tottrup, Partner

Type of Firm

Investment Management Firm

Project Preferences

Type of Financing Preferred:

Early Stage
Expansion
Seed
Startup

Size of Investments Considered:

Min Size of Investment Considered (000s): $9
Max Size of Investment Considered (000s): $38

Geographical Preferences

International Preferences:

Denmark

Additional Information

Year Founded: 2004
Capital Under Management: $94,500,000
Current Activity Level : Actively seeking new investments

SEED CAPITAL LTD.

The Magdalen Centre
The Oxford Science Park
Oxford, United Kingdom OX4 4GA
Phone: 44-1865-784-466
Fax: 44-1865-784-430
Website: www.oxfordtechnology.com

Management and Staff

Lucius Cary, Managing Director

Type of Firm

Private Equity Firm

Project Preferences

Role in Financing:

Prefer role as deal originator but will also invest in deals created by others

Type of Financing Preferred:

Fund of Funds
Early Stage
Seed
Startup

Geographical Preferences

International Preferences:

United Kingdom
Europe

Industry Focus

(% based on actual investment)

Medical/Health	43.5%
Biotechnology	25.9%
Internet Specific	9.7%
Industrial/Energy	6.9%
Computer Software and Services	6.8%
Semiconductors/Other Elect.	3.5%
Communications and Media	2.2%
Computer Hardware	1.5%

Additional Information

Name of Most Recent Fund: Oxford Technology 4 VCT
Most Recent Fund Was Raised: 08/31/2004
Year Founded: 1983
Capital Under Management: $18,100,000
Current Activity Level : Actively seeking new investments
Method of Compensation: Return on invest. most important, but chg. closing fees, service fees, etc.

SEED CAPITAL PARTNERS

50 Fountain Plaza
Suite 1320
Buffalo, NY USA 14202
Phone: 716-845-7520
Fax: 716-845-7539
E-mail: info@seedcp.com
Website: www.seedcp.com

Other Offices

585 Massachusetts Avenue
Fourth Floor
Cambridge, MA USA 02139
Phone: 617-299-2740
Fax: 617-299-2749

Management and Staff

Ashok Kalelkar, Venture Partner
Jordan Levy, Managing General Partner

Type of Firm

Bank Affiliated

Project Preferences

Role in Financing:

Prefer role as deal originator

Type of Financing Preferred:

Early Stage
Seed

Size of Investments Considered:

Min Size of Investment Considered (000s): $250
Max Size of Investment Considered (000s): $2,500

Geographical Preferences

United States Preferences:

Northeast

Canadian Preferences:

Quebec
Ontario

International Preferences:

Israel

Industry Focus

(% based on actual investment)

Internet Specific	33.7%
Computer Software and Services	29.1%
Communications and Media	21.6%
Industrial/Energy	9.6%
Semiconductors/Other Elect.	4.3%
Computer Hardware	1.8%

Additional Information

Year Founded: 1999
Capital Under Management: $58,000,000
Current Activity Level : Actively seeking new investments
Method of Compensation: Return on investment is of primary concern, do not charge fees

SEED GMBH

Schlossplatz 10
Karlsruhe, Germany 76113
Phone: 49-721-150-1819
E-mail: info@seed-gmbh.de
Website: www.seed-gmbh.de

Other Offices

Etterschlagerstrasse 4
Woerthsee
Munich, Germany D-82237
Phone: 49-8153-8811-990

Pfalzhaldenweg 10
Tuebingen, Germany 72070
Phone: 49-7071-938-7710

Management and Staff

J.Peter Ruppersberg, Managing Director
Werner Zoellner, Managing Director

Type of Firm

Private Equity Firm

Association Membership

German Venture Capital Association (BVK)
European Private Equity and Venture Capital Assoc.

Project Preferences

Type of Financing Preferred:

Early Stage
Seed
Startup

Geographical Preferences

International Preferences:
Europe
Germany

Industry Preferences

In Communications prefer:
Communications and Media

In Computer Software prefer:
Software

In Internet Specific prefer:
Internet

In Computer Other prefer:
Computer Related

In Biotechnology prefer:
Biotechnology

In Medical/Health prefer:
Medical/Health

In Business Serv. prefer:
Media

Additional Information

Name of Most Recent Fund: L-Seed Fonds
Most Recent Fund Was Raised: 07/25/2001
Year Founded: 1999
Capital Under Management: $8,800,000
Current Activity Level : Actively seeking new investments

SEED VENTURE FINANCE LLC

80 Dean Street
Taunton, MA USA 02780
Phone: 508-822-1020
Fax: 508-880-7869
E-mail: info@seedvf.com
Website: www.seedvf.com

Type of Firm

Private Equity Firm

Association Membership

Natl Assoc of Small Bus. Inv. Co (NASBIC)

Project Preferences

Role in Financing:
Will function either as deal originator or investor in deals created by others

Type of Financing Preferred:
Leveraged Buyout
Early Stage
Expansion
Mezzanine
Generalist PE
Later Stage
Management Buyouts
Special Situation
Recapitalizations

Size of Investments Considered:
Min Size of Investment Considered (000s): $250
Max Size of Investment Considered (000s): $1,300

Geographical Preferences

United States Preferences:
Northeast
All U.S.

Additional Information

Year Founded: 2004
Capital Under Management: $20,000,000
Current Activity Level : Actively seeking new investments
Method of Compensation: Return on invest. most important, but chg. closing fees, service fees, etc.

SEEDFUND

001, Turf Estate
Shakti Mills Lane, Mahalakshmi
Mumbai, India 400 011
Phone: 91-22-2490-2201
Fax: 91-22-2490-2205
E-mail: info@seedfund.in
Website: www.seedfund.in

Management and Staff

Anand Lunia, Chief Financial Officer
Bharati Jacob, General Partner
Mahesh Murthy, General Partner
Pravin Gandhi, General Partner

Type of Firm

Private Equity Firm

Association Membership

Indian Venture Capital Association (IVCA)

Project Preferences

Type of Financing Preferred:
Early Stage
Seed

Geographical Preferences

International Preferences:
India

Industry Preferences

In Communications prefer:
Wireless Communications

In Internet Specific prefer:
Internet

In Consumer Related prefer:
Retail

In Business Serv. prefer:
Media

Additional Information

Year Founded: 2006
Capital Under Management: $10,000,000
Current Activity Level : Actively seeking new investments

SEEFT MANAGEMENT

8 Avenue Franklin Roosvelt
Paris, France 75008
Phone: 33-1-4225-6485
E-mail: contact@seeft.com
Website: www.seeft.com

Management and Staff

Christian Toulouse, Partner
Francois Poirier, Partner
Jean-Michel Renck, Partner
Laurent Vernier, Partner
Maximilien Oursel, Partner

Type of Firm

Private Equity Firm

Association Membership

French Venture Capital Association (AFIC)

Project Preferences

Type of Financing Preferred:
Seed
Startup

Size of Investments Considered:
Min Size of Investment Considered (000s): $100
Max Size of Investment Considered (000s): $2,200

Geographical Preferences

International Preferences:
Western Europe

Industry Preferences

In Computer Software prefer:
Software

In Internet Specific prefer:
Internet

In Semiconductor/Electr prefer:
Electronics

Additional Information

Year Founded: 1999
Capital Under Management: $21,900,000
Current Activity Level : Actively seeking new investments

SEGUIN PARTNERS LLC

444 Washington Street
Suite 308
Woburn, MA USA 01801
Phone: 781-935-5711
Fax: 781-935-5720
Website: www.seguinpartners.com

Management and Staff

Kirk Blanchette, Partner

Type of Firm

Private Equity Firm

Project Preferences

Type of Financing Preferred:
Leveraged Buyout
Mezzanine
Management Buyouts
Acquisition
Recapitalizations

Size of Investments Considered:
Min Size of Investment Considered (000s): $5,000
Max Size of Investment Considered (000s): $20,000

Geographical Preferences

United States Preferences:
All U.S.

Industry Preferences

In Computer Software prefer:
Data Processing

In Medical/Health prefer:
Health Services

In Business Serv. prefer:
Services
Media

In Manufact. prefer:
Manufacturing
Publishing

Additional Information
Year Founded: 2007
Capital Under Management: $3,000,000
Current Activity Level : Actively seeking new investments

SEGULAH ADVISOR AB
Styrmansgatan 2
Stockholm, Sweden 114 84
Phone: 46-8-442-8950
Fax: 46-8-442-8960
E-mail: info@segulah.se
Website: www.segulah.se

Management and Staff
Anders Claesson, Partner
Christian Sievert, Managing Partner
Hakan Dahlin, Chief Financial Officer
Jorgen Centerman, Partner
Lennart Kalen, Partner
Marcus Jansson, Partner
Percy Calissendorff, Partner
Peter Elving, Partner
Sebastian Ehrnrooth, Partner

Type of Firm
Private Equity Advisor or Fund of Funds

Association Membership
Swedish Venture Capital Association (SVCA)
European Private Equity and Venture Capital Assoc.

Project Preferences

Role in Financing:
Prefer role as deal originator

Type of Financing Preferred:
Leveraged Buyout
Generalist PE
Management Buyouts

Size of Investments Considered:
Min Size of Investment Considered (000s): $63,905
Max Size of Investment Considered (000s): $383,430

Geographical Preferences

International Preferences:
Sweden
Norway
Finland
Denmark

Industry Focus
(% based on actual investment)

Consumer Related	83.7%
Other Products	15.8%
Internet Specific	0.5%

Additional Information
Name of Most Recent Fund: Segulah IV, L.P.
Most Recent Fund Was Raised: 10/23/2007
Year Founded: 1994
Capital Under Management: $1,073,500,000
Current Activity Level : Actively seeking new investments

SEIDLER EQUITY PARTNERS
4640 Admiralty Way
Suite 1200
Marina del Rey, CA USA 90292
Phone: 213-683-4622
Fax: 213-624-0691
E-mail: info@sepfunds.com
Website: www.sepfunds.com

Management and Staff
Eric Kutsenda, Partner
Peter Seidler, Partner
Robert Seidler, Partner

Type of Firm
Private Equity Firm

Project Preferences

Type of Financing Preferred:
Expansion
Generalist PE
Management Buyouts
Recapitalizations

Geographical Preferences

United States Preferences:
All U.S.

Additional Information
Name of Most Recent Fund: Seidler Equity Partners III, L.P.
Most Recent Fund Was Raised: 02/15/2006
Year Founded: 2000
Capital Under Management: $477,000,000
Current Activity Level : Actively seeking new investments

SEIR VENTURE CAPITAL
2/F, 12-20 Jamwon-dong
Seocho-ku
Seoul, South Korea 137-903
Phone: 82-2-547-2300
Fax: 82-2-547-8477
Website: www.seir.co.kr

Management and Staff
Hyun Joo Choi, President

Type of Firm
Private Equity Firm

Project Preferences

Type of Financing Preferred:
Balanced

Geographical Preferences

International Preferences:
Korea, South

Additional Information
Year Founded: 2007
Current Activity Level : Actively seeking new investments

SEJIN T.S CO., LTD. (FKA: SEJIN VENTURE CAPITAL CO., LTD.)
#561-1 Jimoon-Ri, Wongok-Myun
Kyungki-Do
Ansung, South Korea 456-810
Phone: 82-31-650-3700
Fax: 82-31-692-3700
E-mail: thpark@sejints.co.kr
Website: www.sejints.co.kr

Management and Staff
Dal-je Kim, President

Type of Firm
Private Equity Firm

Project Preferences

Type of Financing Preferred:
Balanced

Geographical Preferences

International Preferences:
Korea, South

Additional Information
Year Founded: 1990
Current Activity Level : Actively seeking new investments

SELBY VENTURE PARTNERS
3500 Alameda de las Pulgas
Suite 200
Menlo Park, CA USA 94025
Phone: 650-854-7399
Fax: 650-854-7039
E-mail: info@selbyventures.com
Website: www.selbyventures.com

Management and Staff
Anthony Matusich, Chief Financial Officer
Doug Barry, Managing Director
Jim Marshall, Managing Director
Robert Marshall, Chairman & Managing Director

Type of Firm
Private Equity Firm

Association Membership
Western Association of Venture Capitalists (WAVC)
National Venture Capital Association - USA (NVCA)

Project Preferences

Role in Financing:
Prefer role as deal originator but will also invest in deals created by others

Type of Financing Preferred:
Second Stage Financing
Early Stage
Start-up Financing
Seed

Size of Investments Considered:
Min Size of Investment Considered (000s): $250
Max Size of Investment Considered (000s): $7,000

Geographical Preferences

United States Preferences:
Southern California
Northern California
West Coast

Industry Focus
(% based on actual investment)

Internet Specific	37.5%
Communications and Media	17.2%
Computer Software and Services	16.2%
Semiconductors/Other Elect.	8.8%
Computer Hardware	7.8%
Other Products	7.6%
Consumer Related	4.8%

Additional Information
Name of Most Recent Fund: Selby Venture Partners II, L.P.
Most Recent Fund Was Raised: 05/16/2000
Year Founded: 1998
Capital Under Management: $135,000,000
Current Activity Level : Actively seeking new investments
Method of Compensation: Return on investment is of primary concern, do not charge fees

---

SELECT CAPITAL VENTURES
4718 Old Gettysburg Road
Suite 405
Mechanicsburg, PA USA 17055
Phone: 717-972-1314
Fax: 717-972-1050
E-mail: general@selectcapitalventures.com
Website: www.selectcapitalventures.com

Management and Staff
Debra Hellyer, Chief Financial Officer
Robert Ortenzio, Co-Founder
Rocco Ortenzio, Co-Founder

Type of Firm
Private Equity Firm

Project Preferences

Role in Financing:
Will function either as deal originator or investor in deals created by others

Type of Financing Preferred:
Early Stage
Expansion
Seed

Size of Investments Considered:
Min Size of Investment Considered (000s): $500
Max Size of Investment Considered (000s): $2,700

Geographical Preferences

United States Preferences:
Mid Atlantic

Industry Preferences

In Computer Software prefer:
Software

In Medical/Health prefer:
Medical/Health
Medical Products
Pharmaceuticals

In Consumer Related prefer:
Consumer Services

In Financial Services prefer:
Financial Services

Additional Information
Name of Most Recent Fund: Select Capital Ventures I, L.P.
Most Recent Fund Was Raised: 06/30/2002
Year Founded: 2002
Capital Under Management: $14,000,000
Current Activity Level : Actively seeking new investments

SELVAAG INVEST AS
Lorenvangen 22
P.O. Box, Okern
Oslo, Norway 0512
Phone: 47-23-137-000
Fax: 47-22-492-469
E-mail: selvaag.invest@selvaag.no
Website: www.selvaag-invest.no

Management and Staff
Asgeir Nord, Partner
Erik Sandersen, Partner
Jacob Svendsen, Partner
Jens Petter Falck, Partner

Type of Firm
Private Equity Firm

Association Membership
Norwegian Venture Capital Association
European Private Equity and Venture Capital Assoc.

Project Preferences

Type of Financing Preferred:
Early Stage

Geographical Preferences

International Preferences:
Norway

Industry Preferences

In Biotechnology prefer:
Biotechnology

In Industrial/Energy prefer:
Energy

Additional Information
Year Founded: 2000
Current Activity Level : Actively seeking new investments

SEMBAWANG CAPITAL PTE., LTD.
No. 143 Cecil Street
09-01
Singapore, Singapore 069542
Phone: 65-6226-3383
Fax: 65-6221-9789

Management and Staff
Boon Wah Tan, Vice President

Type of Firm
Corporate PE/Venture

Project Preferences

Type of Financing Preferred:
Expansion
Start-up Financing

Geographical Preferences

International Preferences:
Asia

Industry Preferences

In Medical/Health prefer:
Medical/Health

Additional Information
Year Founded: 1997
Current Activity Level : Actively seeking new investments

SEMCO VENTURES
Rua Dom Aguirre 348
Jardim Marajoara
Sao Paulo, Brazil 04671-390
Phone: 55-11-5681-2000
Fax: 55-11-5548-4834
E-mail: semcoventures@semcoventures.com.br
Website: www.semco.com.br

Type of Firm
Corporate PE/Venture

Project Preferences

Type of Financing Preferred:
Balanced
Startup

Geographical Preferences

International Preferences:
Brazil

Additional Information
Year Founded: 2006
Current Activity Level : Actively seeking new investments

SENECA PARTNERS, INC.
300 Park Street
Suite 400
Birmingham, MI USA 48009
Phone: 248-723-6650
Fax: 248-723-6651
E-mail: info@senecapartners.com
Website: www.senecapartners.com

Other Offices
2201 Waukegan Road
Suite 245
Bannockburn, IL USA 60015
Phone: 847-282-7040
Fax: 847-282-7043

122 Main Street
Suite 200
Ann Arbor, MI USA 48104
Phone: 734-996-4434
Fax: 734-996-4434

Management and Staff
Alfred Robertson, Vice President
Anthony Zambelli, Managing Director
Kirk Ziehm, Vice President
Michael Skaff, Managing Director
Rajesh Kothari, Managing Director
Ron Reed, Managing Director
Thomas Cox, Managing Director

Type of Firm
Private Equity Firm

Association Membership
Illinois Venture Capital Association

Project Preferences

Role in Financing:
Will function either as deal originator or investor in deals created by others

Type of Financing Preferred:
Second Stage Financing
Early Stage
Expansion
Balanced
Later Stage

Size of Investments Considered:
Min Size of Investment Considered (000s): $500
Max Size of Investment Considered (000s): $2,500

Geographical Preferences

United States Preferences:
Southeast
Rocky Mountain
Southwest
All U.S.

Industry Preferences

In Biotechnology prefer:
Industrial Biotechnology
Biosensors
Biotech Related Research
Biotech Related Research

In Medical/Health prefer:
Medical/Health
Medical Diagnostics
Diagnostic Services
Diagnostic Test Products
Medical Therapeutics
Drug/Equipmt Delivery
Medical Products
Disposable Med. Products
Health Services
Hospitals/Clinics/Primary
Hospital/Other Instit.
Pharmaceuticals

Additional Information
Name of Most Recent Fund: Seneca Health Partners, L.P.
Most Recent Fund Was Raised: 01/01/2004
Year Founded: 2005
Capital Under Management: $20,000,000
Current Activity Level : Actively seeking new investments
Method of Compensation: Return on investment is of primary concern, do not charge fees

---

SENTICA PARTNERS OY
Bulevardi 1
Helsinki, Finland 00100
Phone: 358-207-529-610
Fax: 358-207-529-637
Website: www.sentica.fi

Other Offices
Kelloportinkatu 1 B
Tampere, Finland 33100
Phone: 358-207-529-610
Fax: 358-207-529-639

TietoTeknia House
PL 1750, Savilahdentie 6
Kuopio, Finland 70211
Phone: 358-207-529-610
Fax: 358-207-529-638

Management and Staff
Mika Uotila, Managing Director

Type of Firm
Private Equity Firm

Association Membership
Finnish Venture Capital Association (FVCA)
European Private Equity and Venture Capital Assoc.

Project Preferences

Type of Financing Preferred:
Leveraged Buyout
Early Stage
Expansion
Balanced
Seed
Management Buyouts
Startup

Size of Investments Considered:
Min Size of Investment Considered (000s): $1,295
Max Size of Investment Considered (000s): $12,950

Geographical Preferences

International Preferences:
Europe
Finland

Industry Preferences

In Computer Software prefer:
Software

In Medical/Health prefer:
Medical/Health
Health Services

In Industrial/Energy prefer:
Industrial Products
Materials

In Business Serv. prefer:
Services
Consulting Services

In Manufact. prefer:
Manufacturing

Additional Information

Name of Most Recent Fund: Sention Elektronukkarahasto Ky
Most Recent Fund Was Raised: 12/27/2001
Year Founded: 1998
Capital Under Management: $18,600,000
Current Activity Level : Actively seeking new investments

SENTIENT GROUP, THE

3/F, The Harbour Centre
George Town
Gran Cayman, Cayman Islands
Website: www.thesentientgroup.com

Other Offices

264 George Street, Suite 2401
Level 24 Australia Square Tower
Sydney, Australia 2000
Phone: 612-8243-2900
Fax: 612-8243-2990

1010 Sherbrooke Street West
Suite 1512
Montreal, Canada H3A 2R7

Management and Staff

Colin Maclean, Partner
Ian Hume, Partner
Mark Jackson, Principal
Mei Yao, Partner
Peter William Cassidy, Partner

Type of Firm

Private Equity Firm

Project Preferences

Type of Financing Preferred:
Expansion

Geographical Preferences

International Preferences:
All International

Industry Preferences

In Industrial/Energy prefer:
Energy
Environmental Related

In Agr/Forestr/Fish prefer:
Mining and Minerals

Additional Information

Year Founded: 2001
Capital Under Management: $449,000,000
Current Activity Level : Actively seeking new investments

SENTINEL CAPITAL PARTNERS

330 Madison Avenue
27th Floor
New York, NY USA 10017
Phone: 212-688-3100
Fax: 212-688-6513
E-mail: info@sentinelpartners.com
Website: www.sentinelpartners.com

Management and Staff

David Lobel, Managing Partner
Eric Bommer, Principal
James Coady, Principal
Paul Murphy, Principal

Type of Firm

Private Equity Firm

Project Preferences

Role in Financing:
Prefer role as deal originator but will also invest in deals created by others

Type of Financing Preferred:
Leveraged Buyout
Control-block Purchases
Turnaround
Management Buyouts
Acquisition
Special Situation
Distressed Debt
Recapitalizations

Size of Investments Considered:
Min Size of Investment Considered (000s): $7,500
Max Size of Investment Considered (000s): $25,000

Geographical Preferences

United States Preferences:
All U.S.

Canadian Preferences:
All Canada

Industry Focus

(% based on actual investment)

Medical/Health	44.3%
Other Products	19.0%
Internet Specific	15.1%
Consumer Related	13.5%
Industrial/Energy	6.3%
Communications and Media	1.7%

Additional Information

Name of Most Recent Fund: Sentinel Capital Partners III, L.P.
Most Recent Fund Was Raised: 11/01/2004
Year Founded: 1995
Capital Under Management: $500,000,000
Current Activity Level : Actively seeking new investments
Method of Compensation: Return on investment is of primary concern, do not charge fees

---

SEPIDES

C/ Velazquez, 134 bis
Madrid, Spain 28006
Phone: 34-91-396-1494
Fax: 34-91-396-1593
E-mail: sepides@sepides.es
Website: www.sepides.es

Management and Staff

Javier Goizueta, President

Type of Firm

Private Equity Firm

Project Preferences

Type of Financing Preferred:
Expansion
Balanced
Startup

Geographical Preferences

International Preferences:
Europe
Spain

Additional Information

Year Founded: 2002
Capital Under Management: $6,000,000
Current Activity Level : Actively seeking new investments

SEQUEL VENTURE PARTNERS

4430 Arapahoe Avenue
Suite 220
Boulder, CO USA 80303
Phone: 303-546-0400
Fax: 303-546-9728
E-mail: info@sequelvc.com
Website: www.sequelvc.com

Management and Staff

Christopher Scoggins, Venture Partner
Daniel Mitchell, Partner
Kinney Johnson, Partner

Ronald Bernal, Partner
Thomas Washing, Partner
Tim Connor, Partner

Type of Firm

Private Equity Firm

Association Membership

National Venture Capital Association - USA (NVCA)

Project Preferences

Role in Financing:

Prefer role as deal originator but will also invest in deals created by others

Type of Financing Preferred:

Early Stage
Seed
First Stage Financing

Size of Investments Considered:

Min Size of Investment Considered (000s): $2,000
Max Size of Investment Considered (000s): $12,000

Geographical Preferences

United States Preferences:

Rocky Mountain
Colorado

Industry Focus

(% based on actual investment)	
Computer Software and Services	33.3%
Internet Specific	30.1%
Medical/Health	11.5%
Biotechnology	10.1%
Other Products	3.5%
Semiconductors/Other Elect.	3.1%
Communications and Media	3.1%
Industrial/Energy	2.8%
Computer Hardware	2.3%

Additional Information

Name of Most Recent Fund: Sequel Co-Investment Fund, L.P. II (AKA: SeqCo2)
Most Recent Fund Was Raised: 06/04/2001
Year Founded: 1997
Capital Under Management: $400,000,000
Current Activity Level : Actively seeking new investments

SEQUOIA CAPITAL

3000 Sand Hill Road
Building Four, Suite 180
Menlo Park, CA USA 94025
Phone: 650-854-3927
Fax: 650-854-2977
Website: www.sequoiacap.com

Other Offices

2408 Air China Plaza
No. 36 Xiaoyun Road, Chaoyang District
Beijing, China 100027
Phone: 86-10-84475668
Fax: 86-10-84475669

50 Ramat-Yam Street
Oceanos Hotel
Herzelia, Israel 46851
Phone: 972-9-957-9440
Fax: 972-9-957-9443

Suite 235, Hyatt Regency
Bhikaji Cama Place
New Delhi, India 110067
Phone: 91-11-4165-8040
Fax: 91-11-4165-8046

88 Queensway Road
Two Pacific Place Suite 2215, 22nd Floor
Hong Kong, Hong Kong
Phone: 852-2501-8989
Fax: 852-2501-5249

1366 Nanjing West Road
Suite 2808, Plaza 66, Tower 2
Shanghai, China 200040
Phone: 86-21-6288-4222
Fax: 86-21-6288-4350

Doctor Annie Besant Road, Worli
Suite 404 Ceejay House, Shivsagar Estate
Mumbai, India 400018
Phone: 91-22-407-47272
Fax: 91-22-407-47271

One and Two Murphy Road, Ulsoor
The Millenia Tower A, 11th Floor
Bangalore, India 560025
Phone: 91-80-4124-5880
Fax: 91-80-4124-5884

Management and Staff

Alexander Harrison, Partner
Benny Hanigal, General Partner
Christopher Olsen, Partner
Donald Valentine, Founder
Gaurav Garg, General Partner
Gil Raanan, General Partner
Greg McAdoo, Partner
Haim Sadger, General Partner
James Goetz, Partner
KP Balaraj, Managing Director
Kui Zhou, Principal
Mark Kvamme, General Partner
Melinda Dunn, Chief Financial Officer
Michael Goguen, General Partner
Michael Moritz, General Partner
Patrick Grady, Partner
Randy Ditzler, Partner
Roelof Botha, General Partner
Sameer Gandhi, General Partner
Scott Carter, Partner
Shmil Levy, General Partner
Steven Ji, Vice President
Thomas Stephenson, General Partner
Warren Hogarth, General Partner
Yuval Baharav, Partner
Zheng Xu, Vice President

Type of Firm

Private Equity Firm

Association Membership

Western Association of Venture Capitalists (WAVC)
National Venture Capital Association - USA (NVCA)

Project Preferences

Role in Financing:

Will function either as deal originator or investor in deals created by others

Type of Financing Preferred:

Second Stage Financing
Early Stage
Expansion
Start-up Financing
Balanced
Later Stage
Seed
First Stage Financing
Startup

Size of Investments Considered:

Min Size of Investment Considered (000s): $50
Max Size of Investment Considered (000s): $10,000

Geographical Preferences

United States Preferences:

West Coast

International Preferences:

India
China
Israel

Industry Focus

(% based on actual investment)	
Internet Specific	30.2%
Computer Software and Services	19.0%
Communications and Media	16.1%
Semiconductors/Other Elect.	12.0%
Consumer Related	6.2%
Other Products	5.1%
Computer Hardware	5.0%
Medical/Health	3.8%
Biotechnology	1.3%
Industrial/Energy	1.3%

Additional Information

Year Founded: 1972
Capital Under Management: $4,000,000,000
Current Activity Level : Actively seeking new investments
Method of Compensation: Return on investment is of primary concern, do not charge fees

SEQUOIA CAPITAL INDIA (FKA: WESTBRIDGE CAPITAL PARTNERS)

The Millenia, Tower A, 11F
No. 1 & 2 Murphy Road, Ulsoor
Bangalore, India 560008
Phone: 91-80-4124-5880
Fax: 91-80-4124-5884
Website: www.sequoiacap.com/india

Other Offices

Room 2808, Plaza 66, Tower 2
1366 Nanjing West Road
Shanghai, China 200040
Phone: 86-21-6288-4222
Fax: 86-21-6288-4350

50 Ramat-Yam Street
Oceanos Hotel
Herzelia, Israel 46851
Phone: 972-9-957-9440
Fax: 972-9-957-9443

404, Ceejay House
Dr. Annie Besant Road, Worli
Mumbai, India 400018
Phone: 91-22-4074-7272
Fax: 91-22-4074-7271

3000 Sand Hill Road
Building 4, Suite 180
Menlo Park, CA USA 94025
Phone: 650-854-3927
Fax: 650-854-2977

Ste 2215, 22nd floor, Two Pacific Place
88 Queensway Road
Central, Hong Kong
Phone: 852-2501-8989
Fax: 852-2501-5249

2408 Air China Plaza
No. 36 Xiaoyun Road
Beijing, China 100027
Phone: 86-10-8447-5668
Fax: 86-10-8447-5669

Management and Staff

Gautam Mago, Vice President
K.P. Balaraj, Managing Director
Naresh Malhotra, Partner
Ravi Shankar GV, Vice President
Sandeep Singhal, Managing Director
Shailendra Jit Singh, Vice President
Sumir Chadha, Senior Managing Director
Surendra Jain, Managing Director

Type of Firm

Private Equity Firm

Association Membership

National Venture Capital Association - USA (NVCA)
Indian Venture Capital Association (IVCA)

Project Preferences

Role in Financing:

Prefer role as deal originator but will also invest in deals created by others

Type of Financing Preferred:

Early Stage
Expansion
Mezzanine
Balanced
Public Companies
Later Stage
Management Buyouts
Startup

Size of Investments Considered:

Min Size of Investment Considered (000s): $100
Max Size of Investment Considered (000s): $7,000

Geographical Preferences

International Preferences:

India

Industry Preferences

In Communications prefer:

Communications and Media
Telecommunications

In Computer Software prefer:

Software

In Internet Specific prefer:

Internet

In Computer Other prefer:

Computer Related

In Semiconductor/Electr prefer:

Semiconductor

In Medical/Health prefer:

Health Services

In Consumer Related prefer:

Retail

In Financial Services prefer:

Financial Services

In Business Serv. prefer:

Services

Additional Information

Name of Most Recent Fund: Sequoia Capital India Growth Fund 1, L.P.
Most Recent Fund Was Raised: 07/14/2006
Year Founded: 2000
Capital Under Management: $350,000,000
Current Activity Level : Actively seeking new investments
Method of Compensation: Return on investment is of primary concern, do not charge fees

---

SERAPH GROUP

530 Piedmont Avenue, Northeast
Suite 209
Atlanta, GA USA 30308
Phone: 678-919-7191
Fax: 678-919-7242
Website: www.seraphgroup.net

Other Offices

2000 University Avenue
East Palo Alto, CA USA 94303
Phone: 650-292-0893
Fax: 678-919-7242

Management and Staff

Tuff Yen, President

Type of Firm

Private Equity Firm

Project Preferences

Type of Financing Preferred:

Early Stage
Seed

Additional Information

Name of Most Recent Fund: Seraph Partners IV, L.P.
Most Recent Fund Was Raised: 09/09/2008
Year Founded: 2008
Capital Under Management: $700,000
Current Activity Level : Actively seeking new investments

SERAPHIM CAPITAL

New City Court
20 St. Thomas Street
London, United Kingdom SE1 9RS
Phone: 44-20-7089-2318
Fax: 44-20-7089-2301
E-mail: info@seraphimcapital.co.uk
Website: www.seraphimcapital.co.uk

Management and Staff

John May, Managing Partner
Mark Boggett, Managing Partner
Paul Thomas, Managing Partner

Type of Firm

Private Equity Firm

Association Membership

British Venture Capital Association (BVCA)

Project Preferences

Type of Financing Preferred:

Expansion
Early Stage
Balanced
Start-up Financing
Turnaround
Seed

Geographical Preferences

International Preferences:

Europe

Additional Information

Year Founded: 2006
Capital Under Management: $57,300,000
Current Activity Level : Actively seeking new investments

SERAPHIM PARTNERS

3340 Peachtree Road NE
Suite 2270
Atlanta, GA USA 30326

Phone: 404-262-2352
Fax: 208-693-9431
E-mail: sanford@seraphimpartners.com
Website: www.seraphimpartners.com

Management and Staff

David McDaniel, Partner
Harold Solomon, Partner
Sanford Levings, Partner

Type of Firm

Private Equity Firm

Project Preferences

Role in Financing:
Prefer role in deals created by others

Type of Financing Preferred:
Early Stage

Size of Investments Considered:
Min Size of Investment Considered (000s): $100
Max Size of Investment Considered (000s): $300

Geographical Preferences

United States Preferences:
Southeast

Industry Preferences

In Communications prefer:
Telecommunications
Wireless Communications
Data Communications

In Computer Hardware prefer:
Computer Graphics and Dig

In Computer Software prefer:
Data Processing
Software
Systems Software
Applications Software
Artificial Intelligence

In Internet Specific prefer:
Internet
Ecommerce
Web Aggregration/Portals

In Semiconductor/Electr prefer:
Electronic Components
Semiconductor
Micro-Processing

In Consumer Related prefer:
Education Related

Additional Information

Year Founded: 2000
Current Activity Level : Actively seeking new investments
Method of Compensation: Return on investment is of primary concern, do not charge fees

SERAPHIMA VENTURES

410 Park Avenue
15th Floor
New York, NY USA 10022
Phone: 212-380-1818
Fax: 212-656-1481
E-mail: info@seraphimaventures.com
Website: www.seraphimaventures.com

Other Offices

401 Centre, Langham House
302 Regents Street
London, United Kingdom W1B 2HH
Phone: 44 20 7993 2914
Fax: 44 20 7681 2390

Management and Staff

Chris Montano, General Partner
Pearl Chin, Managing General Partner
Randal Leeb-du Toit, General Partner

Type of Firm

Private Equity Firm

Project Preferences

Role in Financing:
Will function either as deal originator or investor in deals created by others

Type of Financing Preferred:
Early Stage
Later Stage

Size of Investments Considered:
Min Size of Investment Considered (000s): $1,000
Max Size of Investment Considered (000s): $40,000

Geographical Preferences

International Preferences:
All International

Industry Preferences

In Biotechnology prefer:
Biotechnology
Biosensors

In Medical/Health prefer:
Medical/Health

In Industrial/Energy prefer:
Advanced Materials

Additional Information

Year Founded: 2003
Capital Under Management: $100,000,000
Current Activity Level : Actively seeking new investments
Method of Compensation: Return on invest. most important, but chg. closing fees, service fees, etc.

SERENA CAPITAL

21 rue Auber
Paris, France 75009
Phone: 33-1-7737-3030
Fax: 33-1-7735-2515
E-mail: ibrambilla@serenacapital.com
Website: www.serenacapital.com

Management and Staff

Marc Fournier, Founding Partner
Philippe Hayat, Founding Partner
Xavier Lorphelin, Founding Partner

Type of Firm

Government Affiliated Program

Association Membership

French Venture Capital Association (AFIC)

Project Preferences

Type of Financing Preferred:
Early Stage

Geographical Preferences

International Preferences:
France

Additional Information

Year Founded: 2009
Current Activity Level : Actively seeking new investments

SERENT CAPITAL LLC

600 Montgomery Street
37th Floor
San Francisco, CA USA 94111
Phone: 415-343-1050
Fax: 415-343-1051
E-mail: info@serentcapital.com
Website: www.serentcapital.com

Management and Staff

David Kennedy, Partner
Kevin Frick, Partner
Mark Shang, Chief Financial Officer

Type of Firm

Private Equity Firm

Project Preferences

Type of Financing Preferred:
Leveraged Buyout
Expansion
Management Buyouts
Recapitalizations

Size of Investments Considered:
Min Size of Investment Considered (000s): $5,000
Max Size of Investment Considered (000s): $100,000

Additional Information

Year Founded: 2008
Capital Under Management: $250,000,000
Current Activity Level : Actively seeking new investments

SEROBA BIOVENTURES LIMITED

Alma House
Alma Place, Monkstown
Co. Dublin, Ireland
Phone: 353-1-214-0400
Fax: 353-1-214-0432
E-mail: contact@seroba.ie
Website: www.seroba.ie

Management and Staff

Alan O Connell, Partner
Peter Sandys, Partner
Seamus O'Hara, Partner

Type of Firm

Private Equity Firm

Association Membership

Irish Venture Capital Association

Project Preferences

Role in Financing:
Prefer role as deal originator but will also invest in deals created by others

Type of Financing Preferred:
Early Stage
Expansion
Public Companies
Seed

Geographical Preferences

International Preferences:
Ireland
United Kingdom

Industry Preferences

In Medical/Health prefer:
Medical Diagnostics
Medical Therapeutics
Medical Products

Additional Information

Year Founded: 2001
Capital Under Management: $26,400,000
Current Activity Level : Actively seeking new investments

SEROBA KERNEL LIFE SCIENCES, LTD. (AKA: SEROBA KERNEL)

15 Molesworth Street
Dublin 2, Ireland
Phone: 353-1-633-4028
Fax: 353-1-214-0432
E-mail: contactireland@seroba-kernel.com
Website: www.seroba-kernel.com

Management and Staff

Alan O Connell, Partner
Daniel O Mahony, Partner
Graham Fagg, Partner
Jonathan Hepple, Partner
Niall Olden, Managing Director
Peter Sandys, Managing Partner
Seamus O'Hara, Partner

Type of Firm

Private Equity Firm

Project Preferences

Type of Financing Preferred:
Early Stage
Expansion
Public Companies

Size of Investments Considered:
Min Size of Investment Considered (000s): $3,899
Max Size of Investment Considered (000s): $9,097

Geographical Preferences

International Preferences:
Ireland
United Kingdom

Industry Preferences

In Medical/Health prefer:
Medical Diagnostics
Medical Therapeutics
Medical Products
Pharmaceuticals

Additional Information

Year Founded: 2009
Capital Under Management: $75,000,000
Current Activity Level : Actively seeking new investments

SERVISEN INVESTMENT MANAGEMENT AB

Linnegatan 6
P.O. Box 5712
Stockholm, Sweden 114 87
Phone: 46-8-701-0900
Fax: 46-8-679-7722
Website: www.servisen.se

Management and Staff

Greger Ericsson, Chief Executive Officer

Type of Firm

Private Equity Firm

Association Membership

Swedish Venture Capital Association (SVCA)
European Private Equity and Venture Capital Assoc.

Project Preferences

Type of Financing Preferred:
Leveraged Buyout
Balanced
Seed
Startup

Size of Investments Considered:
Min Size of Investment Considered (000s): $106
Max Size of Investment Considered (000s): $2,655

Geographical Preferences

International Preferences:
Scandanavia/Nordic Region

Additional Information

Year Founded: 1997
Capital Under Management: $34,800,000
Current Activity Level : Actively seeking new investments

SET VENTURE PARTNERS

Keizersgracht 756-I
Amsterdam, Netherlands 1017 EZ
Phone: 31-20-320-0104
Fax: 31-20-320-0107
E-mail: info@setvp.com
Website: www.setvp.com

Management and Staff

Rene Savelsberg, CEO & Managing Director
Wouter Jonk, Managing Director

Type of Firm

Bank Affiliated

Project Preferences

Type of Financing Preferred:
Early Stage
Later Stage

Geographical Preferences

International Preferences:
Europe

Industry Preferences

In Industrial/Energy prefer:
Alternative Energy
Energy Conservation Relat
Environmental Related

Additional Information

Year Founded: 2007
Capital Under Management: $73,200,000
Current Activity Level : Actively seeking new investments

SEVENTURE PARTNERS (FKA: SPEF VENTURE)

5-7 rue de Monttessuy
Paris, France 75340
Phone: 33-1-5819-2270
Fax: 33-1-5819-2280

E-mail: contact@Seventure.fr
Website: www.seventure.fr

Management and Staff

Anne Costaseque, Partner
Bruno Rivet, Partner
Didier Piccino, Partner
Emmanuel Fiessinger, Partner
Fadwa Sube, Venture Partner
Ioana Simionescu, Partner
Isabelle de Cremoux, Partner
Marion Aubry, Partner
Olivier Protard, Venture Partner
Thi Than Vu, Chief Financial Officer
Valerie Gombart, Partner

Type of Firm

Bank Affiliated

Association Membership

French Venture Capital Association (AFIC)

Project Preferences

Type of Financing Preferred:

Early Stage
Expansion
Mezzanine
Balanced
Seed
Startup

Size of Investments Considered:

Min Size of Investment Considered (000s): $1,212
Max Size of Investment Considered (000s): $9,694

Geographical Preferences

International Preferences:

Europe
France

Industry Preferences

In Communications prefer:

Communications and Media
Telecommunications
Data Communications

In Computer Software prefer:

Software

In Internet Specific prefer:

Internet

In Semiconductor/Electr prefer:

Micro-Processing

In Biotechnology prefer:

Biotechnology

In Medical/Health prefer:

Medical/Health

In Industrial/Energy prefer:

Alternative Energy

Additional Information

Year Founded: 1997
Capital Under Management: $662,600,000
Current Activity Level : Actively seeking new investments

SEVIN ROSEN FUNDS (AKA: SEVIN ROSEN MANAGEMENT CO.)

Two Galleria Tower
13455 Noel Road, Suite 1670
Dallas, TX USA 75240
Phone: 972-702-1100
Fax: 972-702-1103
E-mail: info@srfunds.com
Website: www.srfunds.com

Other Offices

421 Kipling Street
Palo Alto, CA USA 94301
Phone: 650-326-0550
Fax: 650-326-0707

6300 Bridgepoint Parkway
Building One, Suite 500
Austin, TX USA 78730
Phone: 512-795-5810
Fax: 512-795-5849

Management and Staff

Al Schuele, General Partner
Alan Buehler, Chief Financial Officer
Charles Phipps, General Partner
Dan Meyer, Partner
David McLean, General Partner
Jackie Kimzey, General Partner
John Oxaal, Partner
John Jaggers, General Partner
Jon Bayless, General Partner
Nick Sturiale, General Partner
Stephen Dow, General Partner
Stephen Domenik, General Partner
William Paiva, Venture Partner

Type of Firm

Private Equity Firm

Association Membership

Western Association of Venture Capitalists (WAVC)
National Venture Capital Association - USA (NVCA)

Project Preferences

Role in Financing:

Prefer role as deal originator

Type of Financing Preferred:

Second Stage Financing
Early Stage
Start-up Financing
First Stage Financing

Size of Investments Considered:

Min Size of Investment Considered (000s): $100
Max Size of Investment Considered (000s): $10,000

Geographical Preferences

United States Preferences:

All U.S.

Industry Focus

(% based on actual investment)

Communications and Media	29.6%
Computer Software and Services	21.3%
Internet Specific	16.9%
Semiconductors/Other Elect.	15.6%
Computer Hardware	7.8%
Biotechnology	3.9%
Industrial/Energy	2.2%
Medical/Health	1.2%
Consumer Related	1.1%
Other Products	0.4%

Additional Information

Name of Most Recent Fund: Sevin Rosen Fund IX
Most Recent Fund Was Raised: 07/19/2004
Year Founded: 1981
Capital Under Management: $1,600,000,000
Current Activity Level : Making few, if any, new investments
Method of Compensation: Return on investment is of primary concern, do not charge fees

---

SFIRS SPA

4, Via S. Margherita
Cagliari, Italy 09124
Phone: 39-070-679-791
Fax: 39-070-663-213
E-mail: sfirs@tin.it
Website: www.sfirs.it

Type of Firm

Government Affiliated Program

Association Membership

Italian Venture Capital Association (AIFI)

Project Preferences

Type of Financing Preferred:

Second Stage Financing
Leveraged Buyout
Expansion
Startup

Geographical Preferences

International Preferences:

Italy

Additional Information

Year Founded: 2002
Current Activity Level : Actively seeking new investments

SFW CAPITAL PARTNERS, LLC

22 Elm Place
Rye, NY USA 10580
Phone: 914-510-8910
Fax: 914-510-8911
E-mail: info@sfwcap.com
Website: www.sfwcap.com

Other Offices

571 Boston Mills Road
Suite 300
Hudson, OH USA 44236
Phone: 330-655-8850
Fax: 330-655-8851

Management and Staff

David Webb, Principal
Norman Wells, Principal
Roger Freeman, Principal
Terry Smith, Chief Financial Officer
Thomas Salice, Principal

Type of Firm

Private Equity Firm

Project Preferences

Type of Financing Preferred:
Leveraged Buyout

Geographical Preferences

United States Preferences:
All U.S.

Industry Preferences

In Semiconductor/Electr prefer:
Component Testing Equipmt

In Industrial/Energy prefer:
Industrial Products

Additional Information

Year Founded: 2005
Capital Under Management: $300,000,000
Current Activity Level : Actively seeking new investments

SG CAPITAL EUROPE, LTD. (AKA: SG PRIVATE EQUITY CAPITAL MGT)

Exchange House
Primrose Street
London, United Kingdom EC2A 2EF
Phone: 44-20-7762-5134
Fax: 44-20-7509-2809
E-mail: infouk@sgce.com
Website: www.sgce.com

Other Offices

Via Panzacchi, 6
Milan, Italy 20123
Phone: 39-02-855-0151

Barckhausstr 1
Frankfurt, Germany 60325
Phone: 49-69-7171-29840

170 place Henri Regnault
Paris La Defense Cedex, France 92043
Phone: 33-1-5637-8223
Fax: 33-1-5637-7968

Management and Staff

Bruno Lambert, Partner
Philip Percival, Partner
Philippe Renie, Partner
Philippe Sevin, Partner

Type of Firm

Bank Affiliated

Association Membership

French Venture Capital Association (AFIC)
European Private Equity and Venture Capital Assoc.

Project Preferences

Role in Financing:
Will function either as deal originator or investor in deals created by others

Type of Financing Preferred:
Leveraged Buyout
Early Stage
Expansion
Turnaround
Management Buyouts
Special Situation

Size of Investments Considered:
Min Size of Investment Considered (000s): $20,664
Max Size of Investment Considered (000s): $206,640

Geographical Preferences

International Preferences:
Italy
Netherlands
Switzerland
Austria
Belgium
Germany
France

Additional Information

Year Founded: 1997
Capital Under Management: $658,100,000
Current Activity Level : Actively seeking new investments
Method of Compensation: Return on investment is of primary concern, do not charge fees

---

SG COWEN VENTURES

1221 Avenue of the Americas
New York, NY USA 10020
Phone: 212-278-6000
Fax: 212-278-6789
Website: www.sgcowen.com

Management and Staff

Mark Grossman, Managing Director

Type of Firm

Private Equity Firm

Additional Information

Year Founded: 2009
Current Activity Level : Actively seeking new investments

SG PRIVATE EQUITY

Tour Societe Generale
17 Cours Valmy
Paris La Defense Cedex, France 92972
Phone: 33-1-4214-7724
Fax: 33-1-4214-8853
E-mail: philippe.fabre@sgcib.com
Website: www.sgcib.com

Other Offices

41 Tower Hill
SG House
London, United Kingdom
Phone: 44.207.676.6000
Fax: 44.207.702.4424

Type of Firm

Bank Affiliated

Project Preferences

Role in Financing:
Unknown

Type of Financing Preferred:
Unknown

Geographical Preferences

International Preferences:
Europe

Additional Information

Year Founded: 2003
Current Activity Level : Actively seeking new investments
Method of Compensation: Unknown

SGAM PRIVATE EQUITY

170, Place Henri Regnault
Paris La Defense 6, France 92043
Phone: 33-1-5637-8000
Fax: 33-1-5637-8647
E-mail: info.privateequity@sgam.com
Website: www.sgam-ai.com

Other Offices

32-A Pictor Negulici St.
Bd Ion Mihalache Nr 1-7
Bucharest, Romania 71289
Phone: 40-21-301-4150
Fax: 40-21-301-4159

ul. Wspolna 47/49
Warsaw, Poland 00-684
Phone: 48-22-627-4000
Fax: 48-22-627-4001

5-1, Kabuto-Cho Nihonbashi Chuo-ku
Tokyo, Japan 103-0026

Phone: 81-3-3660-5185
Fax: 81-3-3669-8269

9th Floor-Exchange House
Primrose Street
London, United Kingdom EC2A 2EF
Phone: 44-20-7090-2500
Fax: 44-20-7329-5602

Mainzer Landstrasse 36
Frankfurt, Germany 60325
Phone: 49-69-71042-80812
Fax: 49-69-717-4249

Management and Staff

Alain Clos, General Director
Olivier Leclerc, Chief Executive Officer
Philippe Collas, President

Type of Firm

Bank Affiliated

Association Membership

French Venture Capital Association (AFIC)
European Private Equity and Venture Capital Assoc.

Project Preferences

Type of Financing Preferred:

Fund of Funds
Leveraged Buyout
Early Stage
Expansion
Balanced
Turnaround
Other
Seed
Acquisition
Startup

Geographical Preferences

International Preferences:

Europe
Western Europe
Eastern Europe
Romania
France

Industry Preferences

In Communications prefer:

Communications and Media

In Computer Software prefer:

Computer Services
Software

In Internet Specific prefer:

Internet

In Semiconductor/Electr prefer:

Semiconductor

In Biotechnology prefer:

Biotechnology

In Medical/Health prefer:

Medical/Health

In Industrial/Energy prefer:

Industrial Products

Additional Information

Year Founded: 1998
Capital Under Management: $2,370,300,000
Current Activity Level : Actively seeking new investments

SGPME - SOCIEDADE CAPITAL DE RISCO, S.A.

Av. Joao XXI
775 - 1 Esq.
Braga, Portugal 4715-035
Phone: 351-707-501-234
Fax: 351-707-501-235
E-mail: info@pmeportugal.com.pt

Type of Firm

Private Equity Firm

Association Membership

European Private Equity and Venture Capital Assoc.

Project Preferences

Type of Financing Preferred:

Balanced

Geographical Preferences

International Preferences:

Portugal

Additional Information

Year Founded: 2006
Current Activity Level : Actively seeking new investments

SHAANXI HAISHI VENTURE INVESTMENT CO., LTD.

Xiaozhai Shizi Trade Building
10th Floor
Xian, China
Phone: 86-29-8538-1677
Fax: 86-29-8538-1676
Website: www.sxhstz.com

Type of Firm

Private Equity Firm

Project Preferences

Type of Financing Preferred:

Early Stage
Expansion
Balanced
Later Stage

Geographical Preferences

International Preferences:

China

Industry Preferences

In Communications prefer:

Wireless Communications

In Internet Specific prefer:

Internet

In Biotechnology prefer:

Biotechnology

In Consumer Related prefer:

Retail

In Industrial/Energy prefer:

Energy

In Financial Services prefer:

Real Estate

In Business Serv. prefer:

Services

Additional Information

Year Founded: 2003
Current Activity Level : Actively seeking new investments

SHACKLETON ADVISORS

9440 Little Santa Monica Blvd.
Suite 401
Beverly Hills, CA USA 90210
Phone: 310-988-2816
E-mail: investors@shackletonadvisors.com
Website: www.shackletonadvisors.com

Management and Staff

Cyrus Maghami, Vice President
Mark Schelbert, Managing Partner

Type of Firm

Private Equity Firm

Project Preferences

Type of Financing Preferred:

Leveraged Buyout
Acquisition

Geographical Preferences

Canadian Preferences:

All Canada

International Preferences:

Mexico

Industry Preferences

In Communications prefer:

Telecommunications

In Computer Hardware prefer:

Computers

In Computer Software prefer:
Software

In Industrial/Energy prefer:
Industrial Products

In Business Serv. prefer:
Media

In Manufact. prefer:
Manufacturing

Additional Information

Year Founded: 2009
Current Activity Level : Actively seeking new investments

SHACKLETON VENTURES, LTD.

14-15 Jewry Street
Winchester
Hampshire, United Kingdom SO23 8RZ
Phone: 44-1962-842621
Fax: 44-870-3836626
E-mail: info@shackletonventures.com
Website: www.shackletonventures.com

Management and Staff

Dominic Marinelli, Partner
Hugh Stewart, Managing Partner
Michael Low, Managing Partner

Type of Firm

Private Equity Advisor or Fund of Funds

Association Membership

British Venture Capital Association (BVCA)

Project Preferences

Type of Financing Preferred:
Fund of Funds

Geographical Preferences

International Preferences:
United Kingdom
Europe
All International

Industry Preferences

In Communications prefer:
Communications and Media

In Medical/Health prefer:
Medical/Health
Health Services

In Industrial/Energy prefer:
Energy

In Financial Services prefer:
Financial Services

Additional Information

Year Founded: 2006
Capital Under Management: $50,000,000
Current Activity Level : Actively seeking new investments

SHAH MANAGEMENT PARTNERS, LLC

5201 Great America Parkway
Suite 532
Santa Clara, CA USA 95054
Phone: 408-982-0200
Fax: 408-982-0207
E-mail: info@shahcap.com
Website: www.shahcap.com

Management and Staff

Ajay Shah, Founder
Gerald Hwasta, Vice President
Kyle Ryland, Partner
Lata Krishnan, Chief Financial Officer

Type of Firm

Private Equity Firm

Project Preferences

Role in Financing:
Prefer role as deal originator but will also invest in deals created by others

Type of Financing Preferred:
Leveraged Buyout
Expansion
Management Buyouts
Acquisition
Recapitalizations

Industry Preferences

In Semiconductor/Electr prefer:
Semiconductor
Sensors

In Manufact. prefer:
Manufacturing

Additional Information

Year Founded: 2004
Capital Under Management: $27,500,000
Current Activity Level : Actively seeking new investments
Method of Compensation: Return on invest. most important, but chg. closing fees, service fees, etc.

SHAKED GLOBAL GROUP LTD.

85A Medinat Hayehudim Street
Herzliya Pituach, Israel 46140
Phone: 972-732-565-555
Fax: 972-792-565-551
E-mail: info@shaked-global.com
Website: www.shaked-global.com

Management and Staff

Guy Regev, Chief Financial Officer
Ohad Shaked, Founder
Shai Onn, Chief Executive Officer

Type of Firm

Private Equity Firm

Project Preferences

Type of Financing Preferred:
Expansion
Later Stage

Geographical Preferences

International Preferences:
All International

Industry Preferences

In Industrial/Energy prefer:
Alternative Energy
Environmental Related

In Other prefer:
Environment Responsible

Additional Information

Year Founded: 2007
Current Activity Level : Actively seeking new investments

SHALON VENTURES

532 Emerson Street
Palo Alto, CA USA 94301
Phone: 650-566-8200
Fax: 650-473-9196
E-mail: contact@shalon.com
Website: www.shalon.com

Type of Firm

Private Equity Firm

Project Preferences

Type of Financing Preferred:
Early Stage
Startup

Geographical Preferences

United States Preferences:
Northwest
Northern California

Industry Preferences

In Biotechnology prefer:
Biotechnology

In Medical/Health prefer:
Medical/Health

Additional Information

Year Founded: 2003
Current Activity Level : Actively seeking new investments

SHAMROCK HOLDINGS, INC.

4444 Lakeside Drive
Burbank, CA USA 91505
Phone: 818-845-4444
Fax: 818-845-9718
E-mail: info@shamrock.com
Website: www.shamrock.com

Management and Staff

Andrew Howard, Vice President
Arie Ovadia, Managing Director
Arik Ahitov, Vice President
Bruce Stein, Managing Director
Christopher Kiper, Vice President
Dan Beaney, Managing Director
Dennis Johnson, Managing Director
George Buchler, Managing Director
Gregory Martin, Chief Financial Officer
Igal Litovsky, Vice President
Mark Schaffer, Managing Director
Michael McConnell, Managing Director
Michael Geiger, Managing Director
Michael LaSalle, Vice President
Robert Perille, Managing Director
Robert Moskowitz, Managing Director
Ron Stern, Vice President
Stephen Royer, Managing Director
William Wynperle, Managing Director

Type of Firm

Private Equity Firm

Project Preferences

Role in Financing:

Prefer role as deal originator but will also invest in deals created by others

Type of Financing Preferred:

Second Stage Financing
Leveraged Buyout
Control-block Purchases
Early Stage
Expansion
Mezzanine
Generalist PE
Public Companies
Recapitalizations

Size of Investments Considered:

Min Size of Investment Considered (000s): $5,000
Max Size of Investment Considered (000s): $75,000

Geographical Preferences

United States Preferences:

Southern California

International Preferences:

Guam
Australia
Israel
New Zealand

Industry Focus

(% based on actual investment)

Communications and Media	40.1%
Computer Hardware	14.8%
Industrial/Energy	11.8%
Other Products	9.9%
Internet Specific	9.8%
Computer Software and Services	6.3%
Semiconductors/Other Elect.	3.4%
Consumer Related	1.9%
Medical/Health	1.7%
Biotechnology	0.3%

Additional Information

Name of Most Recent Fund: Shamrock Capital Growth Fund II, L.P.
Most Recent Fund Was Raised: 09/30/2005
Year Founded: 1978
Capital Under Management: $2,000,000,000
Current Activity Level : Actively seeking new investments
Method of Compensation: Return on invest. most important, but chg. closing fees, service fees, etc.

SHANDUKA FUND MANGERS (PTY) LTD.

18 Acacia Road
Chislehurston
Sandton, South Africa
Phone: 27-11-305-8900
Fax: 27-11-305-8999
E-mail: info@shanduka.co.za
Website: www.shanduka.co.za

Management and Staff

Kojo Mills, Chief Executive Officer
Phuti Malabie, Managing Director
Rowan Smith, Managing Director
Rute Moyo, Managing Director

Type of Firm

Private Equity Firm

Association Membership

South African Venture Capital Association (SAVCA)

Project Preferences

Type of Financing Preferred:

Balanced

Geographical Preferences

International Preferences:

South Africa

Industry Preferences

In Consumer Related prefer:

Food/Beverage

In Industrial/Energy prefer:

Oil and Gas Exploration
Oil & Gas Drilling,Explor
Alternative Energy
Coal Related

In Financial Services prefer:

Financial Services
Real Estate

In Agr/Forestr/Fish prefer:

Mining and Minerals

Additional Information

Year Founded: 2004
Current Activity Level : Actively seeking new investments

SHANGHAI CHONGYANG INVESTMENT CO., LTD.

No. 33 Shiqiao Huayuan Road
8th Floor Huaqi Group Building
Shanghai, China 200120
Phone: 86-21-6887-3533
Fax: 86-21-6887-3500
E-mail: chongyang@chongyang.net
Website: www.chongyang.net

Type of Firm

Private Equity Firm

Project Preferences

Type of Financing Preferred:

Balanced

Additional Information

Year Founded: 2001
Current Activity Level : Actively seeking new investments

SHANGHAI DINGJIA VENTURES CO., LTD.

No. 350 Chunxiao Road
Zhangjiang Gaokeji Park
Shanghai, China 201203
Phone: 86-21-5080-0508
Fax: 86-21-5080-1918
E-mail: zj-vc@zj-vc.com
Website: www.zj-vc.com

Management and Staff

Jiwei Hu, Partner
Kang Gu, Partner
Xiaohua Yang, Partner
Yongxiang Jiang, Partner

Type of Firm

Private Equity Firm

Project Preferences

Type of Financing Preferred:

Expansion
Early Stage
Startup

Geographical Preferences

International Preferences:
China

Industry Preferences

In Communications prefer:
Telecommunications

In Biotechnology prefer:
Biotechnology

In Industrial/Energy prefer:
Alternative Energy
Materials

In Business Serv. prefer:
Services
Media

Additional Information

Year Founded: 2003
Current Activity Level : Actively seeking new investments

SHANGHAI HUITONG TIANXIA EQUITY INVESTMENT CO., LTD.

c/o Greater China Int'l Group
Greater China International
Shenzhen, China
Management and Staff
Donglin Zhong, Managing Partner

Type of Firm

Private Equity Firm

Project Preferences

Type of Financing Preferred:
Balanced
Later Stage

Geographical Preferences

International Preferences:
China
Asia

Additional Information

Year Founded: 2009
Capital Under Management: $292,800,000
Current Activity Level : Actively seeking new investments

SHANGHAI INDUSTRIAL HOLDINGS, LTD.

26/F Harcourt House
39 Gloucester Rd.
Wanchai, Hong Kong
Phone: 852-2529-5652
Fax: 852-2529-5067
E-mail: enquiry@sihl.com.hk
Website: www.sihl.com.hk

Type of Firm

Corporate PE/Venture

Project Preferences

Type of Financing Preferred:
Balanced

Additional Information

Year Founded: 1996
Current Activity Level : Actively seeking new investments

SHANGHAI JIASHI INVESTMENT CO., LTD.

No. 1591 Hongqiao Road
Yingbin Guan B-1Bieye
Changning, Shanghai, China 200336
Phone: 86-21-6275-8228
Fax: 86-21-6275-9996
E-mail: shgsi@shgsi.com.cn
Website: www.shgsi.com.cn

Type of Firm

Bank Affiliated

Project Preferences

Type of Financing Preferred:
Balanced
Later Stage

Size of Investments Considered:
Min Size of Investment Considered (000s): $1,466
Max Size of Investment Considered (000s): $73,317

Geographical Preferences

International Preferences:
China

Industry Preferences

In Consumer Related prefer:
Consumer Products

In Industrial/Energy prefer:
Energy

In Business Serv. prefer:
Services

In Manufact. prefer:
Manufacturing

Additional Information

Year Founded: 2008
Capital Under Management: $73,000,000
Current Activity Level : Actively seeking new investments

SHANGHAI LONYER INVESTMENT CO., LTD.

No. 710 Tomson Commercial Bldg
Dongfang Road
Shanghai, China 200122
Phone: 86-21-5830-1681
Fax: 86-21-5830-1682
E-mail: invest@lonyer.com
Website: www.lonyer.com

Type of Firm

Corporate PE/Venture

Project Preferences

Type of Financing Preferred:
Balanced

Geographical Preferences

International Preferences:
China

Industry Preferences

In Biotechnology prefer:
Biotechnology

In Industrial/Energy prefer:
Advanced Materials

In Other prefer:
Environment Responsible

Additional Information

Year Founded: 1999
Current Activity Level : Actively seeking new investments

SHANGHAI PUDONG SCIENCE AND TECHNOLOGY INVESTMENT CO., LTD.

No. 439 Chunxiao Road
13/F Changjiang High-tech Dist
Shanghai, China 201203
Phone: 86-21-5027-6328
Fax: 86-21-5027-6385
E-mail: info@pdsti.com
Website: www.pdsti.com

Type of Firm

Government Affiliated Program

Project Preferences

Type of Financing Preferred:
Fund of Funds
Expansion
Later Stage

Geographical Preferences

International Preferences:
China

Industry Preferences

In Computer Software prefer:
Software

In Semiconductor/Electr prefer:
Semiconductor

In Biotechnology prefer:
Biotechnology

In Industrial/Energy prefer:
Energy
Materials

In Agr/Forestr/Fish prefer:
Agriculture related

Additional Information

Year Founded: 1999
Current Activity Level : Actively seeking new investments

SHANGHAI VENTURE CAPITAL CO., LTD.

2/F, No.1634, Huaihai Road (M)
Shanghai, China 200031
Phone: 86-21-6431-1988
Fax: 86-21-6433-6311
E-mail: infos@shvc.com.cn
Website: www.shvc.com.cn

Management and Staff

Peijun Wang, Vice President
Pingao Wang, President

Type of Firm

Private Equity Firm

Project Preferences

Type of Financing Preferred:
Early Stage

Geographical Preferences

International Preferences:
China

Industry Preferences

In Communications prefer:
Telecommunications

In Computer Software prefer:
Software

In Biotechnology prefer:
Biotechnology

In Industrial/Energy prefer:
Advanced Materials

In Manufact. prefer:
Manufacturing

Additional Information

Year Founded: 1999
Current Activity Level : Actively seeking new investments

SHANGHAI WIN CAPITAL PTE., LTD.

855 South Pudong Road
10th Floor, World Plaza
Shanghai, China
Phone: 86-21-5840-3608
Fax: 86-21-6859-8125
Website: www.venturestar.cn

Type of Firm

Private Equity Firm

Project Preferences

Type of Financing Preferred:
Balanced

Industry Preferences

In Industrial/Energy prefer:
Energy
Environmental Related

Additional Information

Year Founded: 2008
Capital Under Management: $146,000,000
Current Activity Level : Actively seeking new investments

SHANGHAI ZHONGZHI VENTURE CAPITAL CO., LTD.

16/F World Plaza A
855 South Pudong Road
Shanghai, China 200120
Phone: 86-21-6887-3258
Fax: 86-21-6887-3257
Website: www.chdhvc.com

Management and Staff

Michael Lee, Managing Director

Type of Firm

Private Equity Firm

Project Preferences

Type of Financing Preferred:
Early Stage
Expansion
Seed

Geographical Preferences

International Preferences:
Macau
Taiwan
China
Hong Kong

Industry Preferences

In Biotechnology prefer:
Biotechnology

In Medical/Health prefer:
Pharmaceuticals

In Industrial/Energy prefer:
Energy Conservation Relat
Environmental Related

Additional Information

Year Founded: 2007
Current Activity Level : Actively seeking new investments

SHANGHAI ZIJIANG VENTURE CAPITAL CORPORATION LIMITED

4/F Hongqiao Business Center
2272 Hongqiao Road
Shanghai, China 200336
Phone: 86-21-6237-6111
Fax: 86-21-6237-6110
E-mail: info@zjvc.com.cn
Website: www.zjvc.com.cn

Type of Firm

Private Equity Firm

Project Preferences

Type of Financing Preferred:
Balanced

Geographical Preferences

International Preferences:
China

Industry Preferences

In Biotechnology prefer:
Biotechnology

In Industrial/Energy prefer:
Energy
Materials

In Other prefer:
Environment Responsible

Additional Information

Year Founded: 2000
Current Activity Level : Actively seeking new investments

SHANNON DEVELOPMENT COMPANY

Park House
National Technology Park
Castleroy, Limerick, Ireland
Phone: 353 61/33.65.55

Fax: 353 61/33.65.45
E-mail: investments@shannon-dev.ie
Website: www.shannon-dev.ie/investments

Management and Staff

Geoff McMullen, Partner
Michael Halpin, Partner
Michelle O'Grady, Partner

Type of Firm

SBIC

Association Membership

European Private Equity and Venture Capital Assoc.

Project Preferences

Role in Financing:

Prefer role as deal originator but will also invest in deals created by others

Type of Financing Preferred:

Second Stage Financing
Start-up Financing
Seed
First Stage Financing

Size of Investments Considered:

Min Size of Investment Considered (000s): $100
Max Size of Investment Considered (000s): $5,000

Geographical Preferences

International Preferences:

Ireland

Industry Preferences

In Communications prefer:

Telecommunications
Wireless Communications

In Computer Hardware prefer:

Integrated Turnkey System

In Computer Software prefer:

Computer Services
Systems Software
Applications Software

In Internet Specific prefer:

Internet

In Semiconductor/Electr prefer:

Electronic Components
Component Testing Equipmt
Analytic/Scientific

In Biotechnology prefer:

Agricultural/Animal Bio.

In Medical/Health prefer:

Medical Products
Pharmaceuticals

In Consumer Related prefer:

Consumer
Food/Beverage

In Transportation prefer:

Aerospace

In Agr/Forestr/Fish prefer:

Agriculture related

Additional Information

Year Founded: 1959
Capital Under Management: $17,000,000
Current Activity Level : Actively seeking new investments
Method of Compensation: Return on invest. most important, but chg. closing fees, service fees, etc.

SHASTA VENTURES MANAGEMENT LLC

2440 Sand Hill Road
Suite 300
Menlo Park, CA USA 94025
Phone: 650-543-1700
Fax: 650-543-1799
Website: www.shastaventures.com

Management and Staff

Austin Grose, Chief Financial Officer
Jason Pressman, Partner
Ravi Mohan, Managing Director
Robert Coneybeer, Managing Director
Tod Francis, Managing Director

Type of Firm

Private Equity Firm

Association Membership

National Venture Capital Association - USA (NVCA)

Project Preferences

Type of Financing Preferred:

Early Stage

Industry Preferences

In Computer Software prefer:

Software

Additional Information

Name of Most Recent Fund: Shasta Ventures II, L.P.
Most Recent Fund Was Raised: 11/12/2007
Year Founded: 2004
Capital Under Management: $457,500,000
Current Activity Level : Actively seeking new investments

SHATTUCK HAMMOND PARTNERS

3414 Peachtree Road NE
Suite 420
Atlanta, GA USA 30326
Phone: 404-848-9190
Fax: 404-848-9192
Website: www.shattuckhammond.com

Other Offices

630 Fifth Avenue
New York, NY USA 10111
Phone: 212-314-0400
Fax: 212-314-0444

601 California Street
San Francisco, CA USA 94108
Phone: 415-788-6900
Fax: 415-788-0822

123 North Wacker Drive
Chicago, IL USA 60606
Phone: 312-541-6400
Fax: 312-541-6444

Type of Firm

Bank Affiliated

Additional Information

Year Founded: 2002
Current Activity Level : Actively seeking new investments

SHAW KWEI & PARTNERS

1101 Chuang's Tower
32 Connaught Road
Central, Hong Kong
Phone: 852-2868-5883
Fax: 852-3162-8499
E-mail: info@shawkwei.com
Website: www.shawkwei.com

Management and Staff

Christoph Mueller, Managing Director
John Pinkel, Partner
Kyle Shaw, Chairman & Managing Director
Randy Kwei, Partner
Sung Tsui, Partner
Tsui Sung Lam, Partner

Type of Firm

Private Equity Advisor or Fund of Funds

Project Preferences

Role in Financing:

Prefer role as deal originator but will also invest in deals created by others

Type of Financing Preferred:

Early Stage
Expansion
Mezzanine
Balanced
Later Stage
Management Buyouts

Geographical Preferences

International Preferences:

Indonesia
Taiwan
China
Hong Kong
Thailand
Philippines
Singapore
Korea, South
Malaysia

Industry Preferences

In Consumer Related prefer:
Food/Beverage

In Business Serv. prefer:
Distribution

In Manufact. prefer:
Manufacturing

Additional Information

Name of Most Recent Fund: Asian Value Investment Fund
Most Recent Fund Was Raised: 04/01/2000
Year Founded: 1999
Capital Under Management: $100,000,000
Current Activity Level : Actively seeking new investments

SHELL INTERNET VENTURES

Shell Center
2 York Road
London, United Kingdom SE1 7NA
Phone: 4420-7934-4914
Fax: 44207-934-7797
E-mail: internetventures@si.shell.com
Website: www.shell.com/internetventures

Other Offices

c/o Shell Internet Services, Inc.
1600 Smith Street, Room 5009A
Houston, TX USA 77002
Fax: 713-241-0633

Management and Staff

Doug Watson, Principal
Petra Koselka, Vice President

Type of Firm

Corporate PE/Venture

Project Preferences

Type of Financing Preferred:
Early Stage
Expansion
Mezzanine
Balanced

Size of Investments Considered:
Min Size of Investment Considered (000s): $2,000
Max Size of Investment Considered (000s): $1,000

Geographical Preferences

International Preferences:
Europe

Industry Preferences

In Communications prefer:
Communications and Media
Commercial Communications

In Computer Software prefer:
Software

In Internet Specific prefer:
Internet

Additional Information

Year Founded: 2000
Capital Under Management: $200,000,000
Current Activity Level : Actively seeking new investments

SHELTER CAPITAL PARTNERS LLC

10880 Wilshire Boulevard
Suite 1850
Los Angeles, CA USA 90024
Phone: 310-234-2300
Fax: 310-234-2329
Website: www.sheltercap.com

Management and Staff

Arthur Bilger, Principal
Bahram Nour-Omid, Principal
Kevin Wall, Founder
Michael Rotgin, Principal

Type of Firm

Private Equity Firm

Project Preferences

Type of Financing Preferred:
Early Stage
Expansion
Balanced
Later Stage
Seed

Size of Investments Considered:
Min Size of Investment Considered (000s): $750
Max Size of Investment Considered (000s): $20,000

Geographical Preferences

United States Preferences:
West Coast
California

Industry Preferences

In Communications prefer:
Wireless Communications

In Computer Software prefer:
Software
Applications Software

In Semiconductor/Electr prefer:
Semiconductor

In Business Serv. prefer:
Media

Additional Information

Year Founded: 2000
Current Activity Level : Actively seeking new investments

SHENZHEN CAPITAL GROUP CO., LTD.

11/F, Investment Building
No. 4009, Shennan Road
Shenzhen, China
Phone: 86-755-82912888
Fax: 86-755-82912880
E-mail: master@szvc.com.cn
Website: www.szvc.com.cn

Management and Staff

Cheng Houbo, Vice President
Jiang Weiping, Vice President
Kan Zhi Dong, President
Li Wanshou, Vice President
Wei Chen, President

Type of Firm

Government Affiliated Program

Project Preferences

Type of Financing Preferred:
Expansion
Balanced
Later Stage
Seed
Startup

Geographical Preferences

International Preferences:
China

Industry Preferences

In Communications prefer:
Communications and Media

In Computer Software prefer:
Software

In Semiconductor/Electr prefer:
Semiconductor

Additional Information

Year Founded: 1999
Capital Under Management: $363,000,000
Current Activity Level : Actively seeking new investments

SHENZHEN CDF-CAPITAL CO., LTD.

Shennan Zhong Road, Futian
Room 1209 West Qiushi Building
Shenzhen, China 518040
Phone: 86-755-83189608
Fax: 86-755-83021830
Website: www.cdf-capital.com

Management and Staff

Hui Xian Zhang, President
Wei Wu, Vice President

Type of Firm
Private Equity Firm

Project Preferences
Type of Financing Preferred:
Balanced

Geographical Preferences
International Preferences:
China

Industry Preferences
In Internet Specific prefer:
E-Commerce Technology
Internet

Additional Information
Year Founded: 2007
Capital Under Management: $29,200,000
Current Activity Level : Actively seeking new investments

SHENZHEN CO-POWER VENTURE CAPITAL CO., LTD.

Overseas Chinese Town, Nanshan
Suite 1104, Hantang Plaza
Shenzhen, China 518053
Phone: 86-755-26935145
Fax: 86-755-26935815
E-mail: vc@chinacopower.com
Website: www.chinacopower.com

Type of Firm
Private Equity Firm

Association Membership
Shenzhen Venture Capital Association

Project Preferences
Type of Financing Preferred:
Expansion

Geographical Preferences
International Preferences:
China
Asia

Industry Preferences
In Consumer Related prefer:
Consumer Products

In Industrial/Energy prefer:
Alternative Energy
Machinery

In Financial Services prefer:
Insurance
Financial Services

Additional Information
Year Founded: 2008
Current Activity Level : Actively seeking new investments

SHENZHEN FORTUNE VENTURE CAPITAL CO., LTD.

23/F, East Area, Baoye Plaza
6008 Shennan Dadao
Shenzhen, China 518034
Phone: 86-755-83515108
Fax: 86-755-83515115
E-mail: Fortune@fortunevc.com
Website: www.fortunevc.com

Management and Staff
Bing Xiao, Vice President
Dehua Hu, Vice President
Margaret Xiao, Vice President
Zhou Liu, President & Chairman

Type of Firm
Corporate PE/Venture

Project Preferences
Type of Financing Preferred:
Mezzanine
Expansion
Balanced
Seed

Size of Investments Considered:
Min Size of Investment Considered (000s): $734
Max Size of Investment Considered (000s): $14,685

Geographical Preferences
International Preferences:
China

Industry Preferences
In Communications prefer:
Telecommunications
Media and Entertainment

In Consumer Related prefer:
Consumer
Food/Beverage

In Industrial/Energy prefer:
Energy Conservation Relat
Advanced Materials
Environmental Related

In Manufact. prefer:
Manufacturing

In Agr/Forestr/Fish prefer:
Agriculture related

Additional Information
Year Founded: 2000
Capital Under Management: $102,700,000
Current Activity Level : Actively seeking new investments

SHENZHEN GREEN PINE CAPITAL PARTNERS CO., LTD.

No. 3039 Shennan Zhong Road
Rm. 2805 Int'l Culture Bldg.
Shenzhen, China 518033
Phone: 86-755-83290633
Fax: 86-755-83290622
E-mail: pinevc@pinevc.com.cn
Website: www.pinevc.com.cn

Management and Staff
Fei Luo, Chairman & Managing Director
Hao Liu, Managing Director
Shijun Chen, Managing Director
Wei Li, Managing Director
Yong Wang, Managing Partner

Type of Firm
Private Equity Firm

Project Preferences
Type of Financing Preferred:
Balanced

Geographical Preferences
International Preferences:
China

Industry Preferences
In Communications prefer:
Communications and Media
Telecommunications

In Internet Specific prefer:
Internet

In Semiconductor/Electr prefer:
Electronics

In Medical/Health prefer:
Pharmaceuticals

In Industrial/Energy prefer:
Materials
Machinery

In Business Serv. prefer:
Media

Additional Information
Year Founded: 2006
Current Activity Level : Actively seeking new investments

SHENZHEN GTJA INVESTMENT GROUP CO., LTD.

No. 3 Hai De Road
15 Floor Tiley Center Plaza
Shenzhen, China 518054
Phone: 86-755-86332999
Fax: 86-755-86332710

E-mail: master@szgig.com
Website: www.szgig.com

Management and Staff

Dajian Cai, President & Chairman
Qing Huang, Partner
Yanfu Liang, Vice President
Yu Huang, Vice President

Type of Firm

Private Equity Firm

Project Preferences

Type of Financing Preferred:
Early Stage
Start-up Financing
Later Stage

Geographical Preferences

International Preferences:
China

Industry Preferences

In Communications prefer:
Telecommunications

In Computer Software prefer:
Software

In Biotechnology prefer:
Biotechnology

In Medical/Health prefer:
Medical/Health

In Consumer Related prefer:
Consumer

In Industrial/Energy prefer:
Energy
Environmental Related

Additional Information

Year Founded: 2001
Capital Under Management: $30,000,000
Current Activity Level : Actively seeking new investments

SHENZHEN INNOVATION CENTER CO. LTD.

5/F, Block 2, Cybercity
Hi-tech Industry Park
Shenzhen, China
Phone: 86-755-671-6698
E-mail: sic@sicvc.com
Website: www.sicvc.com

Type of Firm

Bank Affiliated

Project Preferences

Type of Financing Preferred:
Balanced
Seed
Startup

Geographical Preferences

International Preferences:
China

Industry Preferences

In Computer Software prefer:
Software

In Semiconductor/Electr prefer:
Electronics

In Biotechnology prefer:
Biotechnology

In Industrial/Energy prefer:
Energy
Advanced Materials
Environmental Related

Additional Information

Year Founded: 2003
Current Activity Level : Actively seeking new investments

SHENZHEN LEAGUER VENTURE CAPITAL CO., LTD.

3rd Flr., Tsinghua University
High-Tech Industrial Park
Shenzhen, China 518057
Phone: 86-755-26551416
Fax: 86-755-26551372
E-mail: info@leaguer.com.cn
Website: www.leaguer.com.cn

Type of Firm

University Program

Association Membership

Shenzhen Venture Capital Association

Project Preferences

Type of Financing Preferred:
Early Stage
Seed

Geographical Preferences

International Preferences:
China

Industry Preferences

In Communications prefer:
Data Communications

In Semiconductor/Electr prefer:
Electronics

Additional Information

Year Founded: 1999
Current Activity Level : Actively seeking new investments

SHENZHEN OFC INVESTMENT MANAGEMENT, LTD.

Tianan Cyber Park
Room 2602 Cybertimes Tower A
Shenzhen, China 518040
Phone: 86-755-88836399
Fax: 86-755-83475799
E-mail: ofc@ofcapital.com
Website: www.ofcapital.com

Management and Staff

Houbo Cheng, President
Jian Mei, Partner
Jun Huan Diao, Partner
Qing Liu, Partner
Wun Qing Tan, Partner

Type of Firm

Bank Affiliated

Project Preferences

Type of Financing Preferred:
Balanced

Geographical Preferences

International Preferences:
China

Industry Preferences

In Medical/Health prefer:
Medical/Health

In Consumer Related prefer:
Consumer

In Industrial/Energy prefer:
Energy

In Business Serv. prefer:
Services

Additional Information

Year Founded: 2006
Capital Under Management: $181,000,000
Current Activity Level : Actively seeking new investments

SHENZHEN ZHONGAN VENTURE CAPITAL CO., LTD. (AKA: ZA CAPITAL)

2018 Shen Nan Zhong Road
Room 10218 Xing Hua Building
Shenzhen, China 518031
Phone: 86-755-83678503
Fax: 86-755-83696922
E-mail: manager@zavcfund.com
Website: www.zavcfund.com

Management and Staff

Guo Xian Zhu, Chief Financial Officer

Type of Firm
Private Equity Firm

Project Preferences

Type of Financing Preferred:
Balanced

Geographical Preferences

International Preferences:
China

Industry Preferences

In Computer Software prefer:
Software

In Medical/Health prefer:
Pharmaceuticals

In Consumer Related prefer:
Retail
Consumer Products

In Financial Services prefer:
Financial Services

Additional Information
Year Founded: 2008
Current Activity Level : Actively seeking new investments

SHEPHERD VENTURES
12250 El Camino Real
Suite 116
San Diego, CA USA 92130
Phone: 858-509-4744
Fax: 858-509-3662
E-mail: info@shepherdventures.com
Website: www.shepherdventures.com

Management and Staff
Frederick Lawrence, Venture Partner
George Kenney, Managing Director
John Nelson, Venture Partner
Richard Kuntz, Managing Director
Tom Siegel, Managing Director

Type of Firm
Private Equity Firm

Association Membership
National Venture Capital Association - USA (NVCA)

Project Preferences

Role in Financing:
Will function either as deal originator or investor in deals created by others

Type of Financing Preferred:
Expansion
Later Stage
First Stage Financing

Size of Investments Considered:
Min Size of Investment Considered (000s): $500
Max Size of Investment Considered (000s): $3,000

Geographical Preferences

United States Preferences:
Southern California
Northern California
West Coast
Southwest

Industry Preferences

In Communications prefer:
Commercial Communications
Wireless Communications
Data Communications

In Computer Hardware prefer:
Computer Graphics and Dig

In Computer Software prefer:
Computer Services
Software
Applications Software

In Biotechnology prefer:
Biotechnology

In Medical/Health prefer:
Medical/Health
Medical Diagnostics
Medical Therapeutics
Medical Products

Additional Information
Year Founded: 2001
Capital Under Management: $80,500,000
Current Activity Level : Actively seeking new investments
Method of Compensation: Return on investment is of primary concern, do not charge fees

---

SHERBROOKE CAPITAL
2344 Washington Street
Newton Lower Falls, MA USA 02462
Phone: 617-332-7227
Fax: 617-332-3113
E-mail: info@sherbrookecapital.com
Website: www.sherbrookecapital.com

Management and Staff
Cory Comstock, General Partner
John Giannuzzi, Managing General Partner
John Bello, General Partner

Type of Firm
Private Equity Firm

Association Membership
New England Venture Capital Association

Project Preferences

Role in Financing:
Will function either as deal originator or investor in deals created by others

Type of Financing Preferred:
Second Stage Financing
Expansion
Balanced
First Stage Financing

Size of Investments Considered:
Min Size of Investment Considered (000s): $2,000
Max Size of Investment Considered (000s): $10,000

Geographical Preferences

United States Preferences:
All U.S.

Canadian Preferences:
All Canada

Industry Preferences

In Biotechnology prefer:
Agricultural/Animal Bio.

In Medical/Health prefer:
Medical Diagnostics
Diagnostic Services
Diagnostic Test Products
Drug/Equipmt Delivery
Medical Products
Disposable Med. Products
Health Services

In Consumer Related prefer:
Consumer
Food/Beverage
Consumer Products
Consumer Services

In Other prefer:
Environment Responsible

Additional Information
Name of Most Recent Fund: Sherbrooke Health And Wellness Fund II, L.P.
Most Recent Fund Was Raised: 02/26/2007
Year Founded: 1998
Capital Under Management: $183,000,000
Current Activity Level : Actively seeking new investments
Method of Compensation: Return on investment is of primary concern, do not charge fees

---

SHERPA PARTNERS LLC
5050 Lincoln Drive
Suite 490
Edina, MN USA 55436
Phone: 952-942-1070
Fax: 952-942-1071
E-mail: info@sherpapartners.com
Website: www.sherpapartners.com

Management and Staff
C. McKenzie Lewis, Partner
Richard Brimacomb, Partner
Steven Pederson, Partner

Type of Firm
Private Equity Firm

Project Preferences

Role in Financing:
Will function either as deal originator or investor in deals created by others

Type of Financing Preferred:
Early Stage
Start-up Financing
Seed
First Stage Financing

Size of Investments Considered:
Min Size of Investment Considered (000s): $250
Max Size of Investment Considered (000s): $2,000

Geographical Preferences

United States Preferences:
Midwest
Minnesota

Industry Preferences

In Communications prefer:
Telecommunications
Wireless Communications

In Computer Software prefer:
Software
Systems Software
Applications Software

In Semiconductor/Electr prefer:
Semiconductor

Additional Information

Name of Most Recent Fund: Sherpa Trek Fund I
Most Recent Fund Was Raised: 01/14/2001
Year Founded: 1997
Capital Under Management: $13,000,000
Current Activity Level : Actively seeking new investments
Method of Compensation: Return on investment is of primary concern, do not charge fees

SHERPALO VENTURES

P.O. Box 2627
Saratoga, CA USA 95070
Phone: 415-441-4344
E-mail: info@sherpalo.com
Website: www.sherpalo.com

Management and Staff

Ram Shriram, Founder
Sandeep Murthy, Partner

Type of Firm

Private Equity Firm

Project Preferences

Type of Financing Preferred:
Early Stage

Geographical Preferences

United States Preferences:
All U.S.

Industry Preferences

In Consumer Related prefer:
Consumer

Additional Information

Year Founded: 2000
Current Activity Level : Actively seeking new investments

SHIGIN CAPITAL RESEARCH CO., LTD

3F Shikoku Sogo Bldg.
1-21 Saienbamachi
Kochi-shi, Kochi-ken, Japan
Phone: 81-88-883-1152
Website: www.shikokubank.co.jp

Type of Firm

Private Equity Firm

Additional Information

Year Founded: 2007
Current Activity Level : Actively seeking new investments

SHIKATA VENTURE FUND

19F Hilton Plaza West Office
2-2-2 Umeda, Kita-ku
Osaka, Japan 530-0001

Management and Staff

Osamu Shikata, President

Type of Firm

Private Equity Firm

Additional Information

Year Founded: 2005
Current Activity Level : Reducing investment activity

SHIN POONG VENTURE CAPITAL CORP.

1/F Shinpoong Building, 733-23
Yeongsam-2-dong, Kangnam-gu
Seoul, South Korea
Phone: 822-563-3121
Fax: 822-563-3124

Management and Staff

Yong Taek Chang, President

Type of Firm

Private Equity Firm

Project Preferences

Type of Financing Preferred:
Balanced

Geographical Preferences

International Preferences:
Korea, South

Additional Information

Year Founded: 2000
Current Activity Level : Actively seeking new investments

SHINBO INVESTMENT CORPORATION

8F, Dabong Tower
890-12, Daechi-Dong, Gangnam-G
Seoul, South Korea 135-280
Phone: 822-563-2010
Fax: 822-563-0045
E-mail: shinbo@venturecapital.co.kr
Website: www.venturecapital.co.kr

Management and Staff

In Wook Kong, Chief Executive Officer

Type of Firm

Private Equity Firm

Project Preferences

Type of Financing Preferred:
Balanced

Geographical Preferences

International Preferences:
Korea, South

Industry Preferences

In Biotechnology prefer:
Biotechnology

In Industrial/Energy prefer:
Environmental Related

Additional Information

Year Founded: 1987
Capital Under Management: $11,100,000
Current Activity Level : Actively seeking new investments

SHINHAN PRIVATE EQUITY CO., LTD.

c/o Shinhan Financial Group
120 2Ga Taepyungro
Seoul, South Korea
Phone: 822-6360-3000

Type of Firm

Bank Affiliated

Project Preferences

Type of Financing Preferred:
Balanced

Geographical Preferences

International Preferences:
Korea, South

Additional Information

Year Founded: 2004
Current Activity Level : Actively seeking new investments

SHINKIN CAPITAL CO., LTD

3-4-15 Nihonbashi
Chuo-ku
Tokyo, Japan 103-0027
Phone: 81-3-5299-4356

Type of Firm

Private Equity Firm

Additional Information

Year Founded: 2001
Current Activity Level : Actively seeking new investments

SHINKO PRINCIPAL INVESTMENT CO., LTD.

6/F Yaesu Chuo Building
2-8-1 Kyobashi, Chuo-ku
Tokyo, Japan 104-0031
Phone: 81-3-5203-2280

Management and Staff

Hiroo Kanbe, Managing Director
Naoki Maruyama, President

Type of Firm

Private Equity Firm

Project Preferences

Type of Financing Preferred:
Balanced

Geographical Preferences

International Preferences:
Japan

Additional Information

Year Founded: 2005
Capital Under Management: $900,000
Current Activity Level : Actively seeking new investments

SHINSEI BANK LTD.

2-1-8 Uchisaiwaicho
Chiyoda-ku
Tokyo, Japan 100-8501
Phone: 81-3-5511-5111
Website: www.shinseibank.com

Type of Firm

Bank Affiliated

Project Preferences

Type of Financing Preferred:
Balanced

Additional Information

Year Founded: 1952
Current Activity Level : Actively seeking new investments

SHINWA VENTURE CAPITAL CO., LTD

6F Shinwa Bank Bldg. Annex
10-12 Shimanose-cho
Nagasaki, Japan 857-0806
Phone: 81-956-24-6165
Fax: 81-956-24-6165
Website: www.shinwavc.co.jp

Management and Staff

Mitsukazu Iwasa, President

Type of Firm

Bank Affiliated

Additional Information

Year Founded: 1996
Current Activity Level : Actively seeking new investments

SHINWON VENTURE CAPITAL (A.K.A. SHINYON VENTURE CAPITAL)

532 Tohwa-dong Mapo-ku
Seoul, South Korea
Phone: 822-3274-7474
Fax: 822-3274-7479

Management and Staff

Ki Han Song, President

Type of Firm

Private Equity Firm

Project Preferences

Type of Financing Preferred:
Balanced

Geographical Preferences

International Preferences:
Korea, South

Additional Information

Year Founded: 2000
Current Activity Level : Actively seeking new investments

SHIPROCK CAPITAL LLC

Suite 148
396 Washington Street
Wellesley, MA USA 02481
Phone: 781-772-1229
Fax: 781-772-1172
E-mail: info@shiprock.com
Website: www.shiprock.com

Management and Staff

Richard Shipley, Senior Managing Director

Type of Firm

Private Equity Firm

Project Preferences

Type of Financing Preferred:
Early Stage
Expansion
Balanced

Additional Information

Year Founded: 1957
Current Activity Level : Actively seeking new investments

SHK FUND MANAGEMENT, LTD.

902-905, Bank of America Tower
12 Harcourt Road
Hong Kong, Hong Kong
Phone: 852-3667-8306
E-mail: funds@shkf.com
Website: www.SHKFunds.com

Other Offices

77A Amoy Street
Singapore, Singapore 069896
Phone: 65-6513-1428

Management and Staff

Christophe Lee, Chief Executive Officer
Ken Wong, Managing Director
Rizal Wijono, Managing Director

Type of Firm

Bank Affiliated

Project Preferences

Type of Financing Preferred:
Balanced

Geographical Preferences

International Preferences:
Asia

Additional Information

Year Founded: 2007
Capital Under Management: $100,000,000
Current Activity Level : Actively seeking new investments

SHOGIN VENTURE CAPITAL CO., LTD

2F Shogin Yamagata Bldg.
1-4-21 Honcho
Yamagata-shi, Japan 990-0043
Phone: 81-23-635-5030
Fax: 81-23-625-2626
Website: www.shogin-venture.com

Type of Firm

Bank Affiliated

Additional Information

Year Founded: 1995
Current Activity Level : Actively seeking new investments

SHORE CAPITAL PARTNERS LLC

70 East Lake Street
Suite 520
Chicago, IL USA 60601
Phone: 312-348-7580
Fax: 312-348-7669
E-mail: info@shorecp.com
Website: www.shorecp.com

Management and Staff

John Hennegan, Vice President
Justin Ishbia, Managing Partner
Michael Cooper, Vice President
Ryan Kelley, Partner

Type of Firm

Private Equity Firm

Project Preferences

Type of Financing Preferred:
Leveraged Buyout
Expansion
Later Stage
Management Buyouts
Recapitalizations

Size of Investments Considered:
Min Size of Investment Considered (000s): $500
Max Size of Investment Considered (000s): $8,000

Geographical Preferences

United States Preferences:
All U.S.

Industry Preferences

In Medical/Health prefer:
Health Services

In Consumer Related prefer:
Consumer Services

In Financial Services prefer:
Financial Services

In Business Serv. prefer:
Services

Additional Information

Year Founded: 2009
Capital Under Management: $15,000,000
Current Activity Level : Actively seeking new investments

SHORE CAPITAL, LTD.

Bond Street House
14 Clifford Street
London, United Kingdom W1S 4JU
Phone: 44-20-7408-4090
Fax: 44-20-7408-4081
E-mail: info@shorecap.co.uk
Website: www.shorecap.co.uk

Other Offices

The Corn Exchange
Fenwick Street
Liverpool, United Kingdom L2 7RB
Phone: 44-151-600-3700
Fax: 44-151-600-3727

Mellier House
26a Albemarle Street
London, United Kingdom W1S 4HY

Management and Staff

Alex Abadie, Chief Executive Officer
Graham Shore, Managing Director
Thomas Marlinghaus, Chief Operating Officer

Type of Firm

Bank Affiliated

Project Preferences

Role in Financing:
Prefer role as deal originator but will also invest in deals created by others

Type of Financing Preferred:
Expansion
Mezzanine
Later Stage
Other

Geographical Preferences

International Preferences:
United Kingdom
Europe
Utd. Arab Em.
Israel

Industry Preferences

In Communications prefer:
Telecommunications

In Computer Software prefer:
Software

In Semiconductor/Electr prefer:
Electronics

In Consumer Related prefer:
Retail

In Financial Services prefer:
Real Estate

In Business Serv. prefer:
Media

Additional Information

Name of Most Recent Fund: Puma Property Fund LP
Most Recent Fund Was Raised: 08/14/2002
Year Founded: 1985
Capital Under Management: $30,700,000
Current Activity Level : Actively seeking new investments

SHOREBANK CAPITAL CORP.

7936 S. Cottage Grove
Chicago, IL USA 60619
Phone: 773-371-7060
Fax: 773-371-7035

Management and Staff

David Shryock, Chief Executive Officer

Type of Firm

SBIC

Association Membership

Natl Assoc of Small Bus. Inv. Co (NASBIC)

Additional Information

Year Founded: 1978
Capital Under Management: $4,300,000
Current Activity Level : Actively seeking new investments

SHORELINE VENTURE MANAGEMENT, LLC

675 Mariners Island Boulevard
Suite 109
San Mateo, CA USA 94404

Phone: 650-854-6685
Fax: 415-389-6757
E-mail: info@shorelineventures.com
Website: www.shorelineventures.com

Management and Staff

Peter Craddock, Managing Director

Type of Firm

Private Equity Firm

Project Preferences

Type of Financing Preferred:
Early Stage
Seed

Geographical Preferences

International Preferences:
Europe
Asia

Industry Preferences

In Consumer Related prefer:
Food/Beverage

Additional Information

Year Founded: 1998
Capital Under Management: $8,100,000
Current Activity Level : Actively seeking new investments

SHORENSTEIN COMPANY LLC

235 Montgomery Street
Russ Building, 16th Floor
San Francisco, CA USA 94104
Phone: 415-772-7000
Website: www.shorenstein.com

Other Offices

450 Lexington Avenue
Suite 3200
New York, NY USA 10017
Phone: 212-986-2100

Management and Staff

Andrew Friedman, Managing Director
Christine Kwak, Managing Director
Douglas Shorenstein, Chairman & CEO
Glenn Shannon, President
Mark McCarthy, Managing Director
Mark Portner, Managing Director
Richard Chicotel, Managing Director & CFO
Robert Underhill, Managing Director

Type of Firm

Private Equity Firm

Project Preferences

Type of Financing Preferred:
Other

Industry Preferences

In Financial Services prefer:
Real Estate

Additional Information

Year Founded: 1999
Capital Under Management: $494,900,000
Current Activity Level : Actively seeking new investments

SHOREVIEW INDUSTRIES

222 South Ninth Street
Suite 3230
Minneapolis, MN USA 55402
Phone: 612-436-0575
Fax: 612-436-0576
E-mail: info@shoreviewindustries.com
Website: www.shoreviewindustries.com

Management and Staff

Brett Habstritt, Vice President
Daniel Kubes, Principal
David Wakefield, Principal
Jeffrey Mudge, Principal
Robert Davis, Principal

Type of Firm

Private Equity Firm

Project Preferences

Type of Financing Preferred:
Leveraged Buyout
Management Buyouts
Acquisition
Recapitalizations

Geographical Preferences

United States Preferences:
All U.S.

Canadian Preferences:
All Canada

International Preferences:
Mexico

Industry Preferences

In Industrial/Energy prefer:
Industrial Products

In Business Serv. prefer:
Services

In Manufact. prefer:
Manufacturing

Additional Information

Name of Most Recent Fund: ShoreView Parallel Partners II, L.P.
Most Recent Fund Was Raised: 02/03/2007
Year Founded: 2003
Capital Under Management: $300,000,000
Current Activity Level : Actively seeking new investments

SHREM FUDIM KELNER TECHNOLOGIES, LTD.

21 Haarbah St.
Tel Aviv, Israel 64739
Phone: 972-3684-5555
Fax: 972-3684-5554
E-mail: info@sfk.co.il
Website: www.sfk.co.il

Management and Staff

Yair Fudim, Chief Executive Officer

Type of Firm

Bank Affiliated

Project Preferences

Type of Financing Preferred:
Fund of Funds
Seed

Geographical Preferences

International Preferences:
Israel

Industry Preferences

In Communications prefer:
Telecommunications

In Internet Specific prefer:
Internet

Additional Information

Year Founded: 1991
Current Activity Level : Actively seeking new investments

SHS GESELLSCHAFT FUER BETEILIGUNGSMANAGEMENT MBH

Bismarckstrasse 12
Tuebingen, Germany D-72072
Phone: 49-7071-9169-0
Fax: 49-7071-9169190
E-mail: tuebingen@shsvc.net
Website: www.shsvc.net

Management and Staff

Bernhard Schirmers, Founding Partner
Hubertus Leonhardt, Partner
Rainer Miller, Partner
Reinhilde Spatscheck, Founding Partner

Type of Firm

Private Equity Firm

Association Membership

German Venture Capital Association (BVK)
European Private Equity and Venture Capital Assoc.

Project Preferences

Role in Financing:
Prefer role as deal originator

Type of Financing Preferred:
Expansion
Later Stage

Size of Investments Considered:
Min Size of Investment Considered (000s): $1,412
Max Size of Investment Considered (000s): $7,061

Geographical Preferences

International Preferences:
Switzerland
Austria
Germany

Industry Preferences

In Biotechnology prefer:
Human Biotechnology

In Medical/Health prefer:
Medical/Health
Medical Diagnostics
Pharmaceuticals

Additional Information
Year Founded: 1993
Capital Under Management: $120,800,000
Current Activity Level : Actively seeking new investments

SHUAA PARTNERS
DIFC, Gate Precinct Building 1
P.O. Box 31045
Dubai, Utd. Arab Em.
Phone: 971-4-319-9499
Fax: 971-4-319-9707
E-mail: info@shuaapartners.com
Website: www.shuaapartners.com

Management and Staff
Iyad Duwaji, Chief Executive Officer
Kerim Mitri, Chief Operating Officer

Type of Firm
Bank Affiliated

Project Preferences

Type of Financing Preferred:
Leveraged Buyout
Expansion
Generalist PE
Balanced
Public Companies
Later Stage
Management Buyouts
Startup
Recapitalizations

Geographical Preferences

International Preferences:
Oman
Jordan
Qatar
Lebanon
Egypt
Utd. Arab Em.
Middle East
Saudi Arabia
Syria
All International
Africa

Industry Preferences

In Communications prefer:
Telecommunications

In Medical/Health prefer:
Hospital/Other Instit.

In Consumer Related prefer:
Hotels and Resorts

In Financial Services prefer:
Financial Services

Additional Information
Name of Most Recent Fund: Shuaa Partners Fund I, LP
Most Recent Fund Was Raised: 06/30/2005
Year Founded: 1979
Capital Under Management: $1,200,000,000
Current Activity Level : Actively seeking new investments

SI VENTURES
12600 Gateway Boulevard
Ft. Myers, FL USA 33913
Phone: 239-561-4760
Fax: 239-561-4916
E-mail: info@siventures.com
Website: www.siventures.com

Management and Staff
Brian Beach, Managing Director
John Halligan, Managing Director
Manny Fernandez, Managing Director
Minette LaCroix, Chief Financial Officer

Type of Firm
Corporate PE/Venture

Project Preferences

Role in Financing:
Will function either as deal originator or investor in deals created by others

Type of Financing Preferred:
Early Stage
Expansion
Balanced

Size of Investments Considered:
Min Size of Investment Considered (000s): $4,000
Max Size of Investment Considered (000s): $10,000

Geographical Preferences

United States Preferences:
East Coast

Industry Focus
(% based on actual investment)

Internet Specific	48.2%
Computer Software and Services	37.1%
Communications and Media	5.9%
Biotechnology	3.5%
Semiconductors/Other Elect.	2.4%
Other Products	1.4%
Computer Hardware	0.8%
Medical/Health	0.8%

Additional Information
Year Founded: 1996
Capital Under Management: $132,900,000
Current Activity Level : Actively seeking new investments

SIBL
Blvd. Emile de Laveleye 191
Liege, Belgium 4020
Phone: 32-4-340-3594
Fax: 32-4-343-9895
Website: www.sibl.be

Type of Firm
Corporate PE/Venture

Association Membership
Belgium Venturing Association

Project Preferences

Type of Financing Preferred:
Expansion

Geographical Preferences

International Preferences:
Belgium

Additional Information
Year Founded: 1998
Current Activity Level : Actively seeking new investments

SICAR HORIZON
3, rue 8601 Zone
Industrielle la Charguia
Tunis, Tunisia 2035
Phone: 216-71-791-313
Fax: 216-71-785-030
E-mail: chimap@planet.tn

Type of Firm
Private Equity Firm

Association Membership
Tunisian Venture Capital Association

Project Preferences
Type of Financing Preferred:
Balanced

Geographical Preferences
International Preferences:
Tunisia

Additional Information
Year Founded: 2004
Current Activity Level : Actively seeking new investments

SICAR INVEST
67, Rue Jugurtha
Tunis, Tunisia 1002
Phone: 216-71-891-070
Fax: 216-71-890-669
E-mail: sicar.invest@planet.tn

Type of Firm
Private Equity Firm

Project Preferences
Type of Financing Preferred:
Balanced

Geographical Preferences
International Preferences:
Tunisia

Additional Information
Year Founded: 2004
Current Activity Level : Actively seeking new investments

SICAR L AVENIR
Siege de la BIAT
Av. Habib Bourguiba
Tunis, Tunisia 1000
Phone: 216-71-340-733
Fax: 216-71-348-324
E-mail: moez.jabeur@biat.com.tn

Type of Firm
Private Equity Firm

Project Preferences
Type of Financing Preferred:
Balanced

Geographical Preferences
International Preferences:
Tunisia

Additional Information
Year Founded: 2004
Current Activity Level : Actively seeking new investments

SICAR STB
52 bis Avenue 1er juin
Mutuelleville
Tunis, Tunisia 1082
Phone: 216-71-286-873
Fax: 216-71-286-297
E-mail: nmaaoui@planet.tn

Type of Firm
Private Equity Firm

Association Membership
Tunisian Venture Capital Association

Project Preferences
Type of Financing Preferred:
Balanced

Geographical Preferences
International Preferences:
Tunisia

Additional Information
Year Founded: 1998
Current Activity Level : Actively seeking new investments

SICHUAN SHIZHI INVESTMENT CO., LTD.
7F, Great Wall Financial Bldg.
1 East Road, Gaosheng Bridge
Chengdu, China 610041
Phone: 86-28-6601-6455
Fax: 86-28-6601-6477
E-mail: ceff2007@126.com
Website: www.china-eff.com

Management and Staff
Guohua Qiu, Partner
Guoliang Luo, Partner

Type of Firm
Service Provider

Project Preferences
Type of Financing Preferred:
Leveraged Buyout
Early Stage
Expansion
Mezzanine
Startup

Geographical Preferences
International Preferences:
China

Industry Preferences
In Industrial/Energy prefer:
Environmental Related

Additional Information
Year Founded: 2007
Capital Under Management: $4,000,000
Current Activity Level : Actively seeking new investments

SICI SGR SPA
47 Via Scialoia
Firenze, Italy 50136
Phone: 39-055-249-8505
Fax: 3955 -234-5018
E-mail: info@fondisici.it
Website: www.sicisgr.it

Type of Firm
Private Equity Firm

Project Preferences
Type of Financing Preferred:
Balanced

Geographical Preferences
International Preferences:
All International

Additional Information
Year Founded: 1999
Current Activity Level : Actively seeking new investments

SID R. BASS ASSOCIATES, LP
201 Main Street
32nd Floor
Fort Worth, TX USA 76102
Phone: 817-390-8820
Fax: 817-390-8821

Type of Firm
Private Equity Firm

Association Membership
National Venture Capital Association - USA (NVCA)

Project Preferences
Role in Financing:
Will function either as deal originator or investor in deals created by others

Type of Financing Preferred:
Second Stage Financing

Leveraged Buyout
Control-block Purchases
Early Stage
Expansion
Balanced
Turnaround
Later Stage
Seed
Management Buyouts
First Stage Financing
Acquisition
Industry Rollups
Special Situation
Startup
Recapitalizations

Size of Investments Considered:
Min Size of Investment Considered (000s): $1,000
Max Size of Investment Considered (000s): $10,000

Geographical Preferences

United States Preferences:
All U.S.

Additional Information
Year Founded: 2004
Capital Under Management: $300,000,000
Current Activity Level : Actively seeking new investments
Method of Compensation: Return on investment is of primary concern, do not charge fees

---

SIDBI VENTURE CAPITAL, LTD. (SVCL)
SME Development Centre, C-11
G Block, Bandra Kurla Complex
Mumbai, India 400 051
Phone: 91-22-2652-7124
Fax: 91-22-2652-7126
E-mail: info@sidbiventure.co.in
Website: www.sidbiventure.co.in

Other Offices
Jolly Maker Chambers II, 107, 10th Floor
Nariman Point
Mumbai, India 400 021
Phone: 91-22-2204-3065
Fax: 91-22-2204-3078

Management and Staff
Ajay Kumar Kapur, Chief Executive Officer
Rakesh Rewari, Chief Executive Officer
Sailendra Narain, Managing Director
Vipul Mankad, President

Type of Firm
Bank Affiliated

Association Membership
Indian Venture Capital Association (IVCA)

Project Preferences

Type of Financing Preferred:
Early Stage
Expansion
Balanced
Startup

Size of Investments Considered:
Min Size of Investment Considered (000s): $111
Max Size of Investment Considered (000s): $1,110

Geographical Preferences

International Preferences:
India
Asia

Industry Preferences

In Computer Software prefer:
Software

In Internet Specific prefer:
Internet

In Computer Other prefer:
Computer Related

In Semiconductor/Electr prefer:
Electronics
Semiconductor

In Biotechnology prefer:
Agricultural/Animal Bio.

In Medical/Health prefer:
Medical/Health

In Consumer Related prefer:
Retail
Food/Beverage

In Industrial/Energy prefer:
Environmental Related

In Manufact. prefer:
Manufacturing

In Agr/Forestr/Fish prefer:
Agribusiness
Agriculture related

Additional Information
Name of Most Recent Fund: National Venture Fund for Software and Information Tech.
Most Recent Fund Was Raised: 07/29/1999
Year Founded: 1999
Capital Under Management: $33,300,000
Current Activity Level : Actively seeking new investments

SIDCO
70 Avenue de la liberte
Tunis, Tunisia 1002
Phone: 216-71-797-004
Fax: 216-71-799-750
E-mail: sidco.sicar@gnet.tn

Type of Firm
Private Equity Firm

Association Membership
Tunisian Venture Capital Association

Project Preferences

Type of Financing Preferred:
Balanced

Geographical Preferences

International Preferences:
Tunisia

Additional Information
Year Founded: 2004
Current Activity Level : Actively seeking new investments

SIEMENS TECHNOLOGY ACCELERATOR (STA)
Otto-Hahn-Ring 6
Munich, Germany D-81739
Phone: 49-89-6363-5853
Fax: 49-89-6363-5856
Website: www.sta.siemens.com

Management and Staff
Andreas Brinkrolf, Chief Executive Officer
Christian Wiesinger, Chief Financial Officer

Type of Firm
Corporate PE/Venture

Project Preferences

Type of Financing Preferred:
Seed

Geographical Preferences

International Preferences:
Europe
Germany

Industry Preferences

In Computer Software prefer:
Software

In Medical/Health prefer:
Medical/Health

In Industrial/Energy prefer:
Energy
Materials
Environmental Related

In Manufact. prefer:
Manufacturing

Additional Information
Year Founded: 2000
Current Activity Level : Actively seeking new investments

SIEMENS VENTURE CAPITAL GMBH (AKA: SVC)

Otto-Hahn-Ring 6
Munich, Germany D-81739
Phone: 49-89-6363-6040
Fax: 49-89-6363-4884
Website: www.siemensventurecapital.com

Other Offices

801 Boylston Street
5th Floor
Boston, MA USA 02116
Phone: 617-531-2901
Fax: 617-531-2908

5th Floor, Electric Mansion
1086, Appasaheb Marathe Marg Prabhadevi
Mumbai, India 400 025
Phone: 91-22-6757-2203
Fax: 91-22-6757-2260

435 Tasso Street
Suite 315
Palo Alto, CA USA 94301
Phone: 650-463-1700
Fax: 650-289-9108

13 Hamelacha Street
Afeq Industrial Park
Rosh Ha'ayin, Israel 48091
Phone: 972-3-915-1536
Fax: 972-3-915-1551

No.7 Wangjing Zhonghuan Nanlu
Chaoyang District
Beijing, China 100102
Phone: 86-10-6476-8890
Fax: 86-10-6476-4984

Management and Staff

Andrew Jay, Managing Partner
Gerd Goette, Managing Partner
Madeline Song, Managing Director
Thomas Kolbinger, Chief Financial Officer

Type of Firm

Corporate PE/Venture

Association Membership

Israel Venture Association
German Venture Capital Association (BVK)
National Venture Capital Association - USA (NVCA)
European Private Equity and Venture Capital Assoc.
Indian Venture Capital Association (IVCA)

Project Preferences

Role in Financing:

Will function either as deal originator or investor in deals created by others

Type of Financing Preferred:

Fund of Funds
Second Stage Financing
Early Stage
Expansion
Balanced
Start-up Financing
Later Stage
First Stage Financing
Startup

Size of Investments Considered:

Min Size of Investment Considered (000s): $1,000
Max Size of Investment Considered (000s): $10,000

Geographical Preferences

United States Preferences:

All U.S.

International Preferences:

India
Europe
China
Israel
Germany
Asia

Industry Focus

(% based on actual investment)	
Computer Software and Services	21.3%
Communications and Media	20.8%
Internet Specific	18.5%
Semiconductors/Other Elect.	12.8%
Medical/Health	7.8%
Industrial/Energy	7.7%
Other Products	4.3%
Biotechnology	4.3%
Computer Hardware	2.4%

Additional Information

Year Founded: 1999
Capital Under Management: $1,137,500,000
Current Activity Level : Actively seeking new investments
Method of Compensation: Return on investment is of primary concern, do not charge fees

SIENNA VENTURES (FKA: SIENNA HOLDINGS INC.)

2330 Marinship Way
Suite 130
Sausalito, CA USA 94965
Phone: 415-339-2800
Fax: 415-339-2808
E-mail: info@siennaventures.com
Website: www.siennaventures.com

Management and Staff

Daniel Skaff, Managing Partner
Virginia Breen, General Partner

Type of Firm

Private Equity Firm

Association Membership

National Venture Capital Association - USA (NVCA)

Project Preferences

Role in Financing:

Prefer role as deal originator but will also invest in deals created by others

Type of Financing Preferred:

Second Stage Financing
Early Stage
Balanced
Start-up Financing
First Stage Financing

Size of Investments Considered:

Min Size of Investment Considered (000s): $35,000
Max Size of Investment Considered: No Limit

Geographical Preferences

Canadian Preferences:

All Canada

Industry Focus

(% based on actual investment)	
Internet Specific	29.3%
Communications and Media	22.9%
Computer Software and Services	18.2%
Consumer Related	11.0%
Other Products	7.0%
Semiconductors/Other Elect.	6.8%
Computer Hardware	4.7%

Additional Information

Name of Most Recent Fund: Sienna III, LP
Most Recent Fund Was Raised: 06/20/2000
Year Founded: 1990
Capital Under Management: $180,000,000
Current Activity Level : Actively seeking new investments
Method of Compensation: Return on investment is of primary concern, do not charge fees

SIERRA VENTURES

2884 Sand Hill Road
Suite 100
Menlo Park, CA USA 94025
Phone: 650-854-1000
Fax: 650-854-5593
E-mail: info@sierraventures.com
Website: www.sierraventures.com

Management and Staff

Ben Yu, Managing Director
David Schwab, Managing Director
Gamiel Gran, Vice President
Jeffrey Drazan, Managing Director
Jeffrey Loomans, Venture Partner
Mark Fernandes, Managing Director
Martha Clarke Adamson, Chief Financial Officer
Peter Wendell, Managing Director
Robert Walker, Principal
Steven Williams, Managing Director
Tim Guleri, Managing Director
Vimal Patel, Principal
Vispi Daver, Partner

Type of Firm
Private Equity Firm

Association Membership
Western Association of Venture Capitalists (WAVC)
National Venture Capital Association - USA (NVCA)

Project Preferences

Role in Financing:
Prefer role as deal originator but will also invest in deals created by others

Type of Financing Preferred:
Second Stage Financing
Early Stage
Seed
First Stage Financing
Startup

Size of Investments Considered:
Min Size of Investment Considered (000s): $10,000
Max Size of Investment Considered (000s): $15,000

Geographical Preferences

United States Preferences:
West Coast
All U.S.

International Preferences:
India
China

Industry Focus
(% based on actual investment)

Computer Software and Services	30.5%
Internet Specific	16.0%
Communications and Media	12.3%
Semiconductors/Other Elect.	11.5%
Computer Hardware	8.8%
Biotechnology	7.4%
Other Products	5.5%
Medical/Health	4.4%
Industrial/Energy	2.0%
Consumer Related	1.6%

Additional Information
Name of Most Recent Fund: Sierra Ventures IX, L.P.
Most Recent Fund Was Raised: 07/17/2006
Year Founded: 1979
Capital Under Management: $1,100,000,000
Current Activity Level : Actively seeking new investments
Method of Compensation: Return on investment is of primary concern, do not charge fees

---

SIF - BANAT - CRISANA SA
Calea Victoriei
Nr. 35A
Arad, Romania 2900
Phone: 40-257-234-167
Fax: 40-57-250-165
E-mail: sifbc@banat-crisana.com
Website: www.banat-crisana.com

Management and Staff
Emil Cazan, Vice President
Ioan Cuzman, President

Type of Firm
Private Equity Firm

Project Preferences

Type of Financing Preferred:
Balanced

Geographical Preferences

International Preferences:
Europe
Romania

Additional Information
Year Founded: 2006
Current Activity Level : Actively seeking new investments

SIF MOLDOVA
94 C, Pictor Aman St
Bacau, Romania 5500
Phone: 40-234-576-740
Fax: 40-234-570-062
E-mail: sifm@sifm.ro
Website: www.sifm.ro

Type of Firm
Private Equity Firm

Project Preferences

Type of Financing Preferred:
Balanced

Geographical Preferences

International Preferences:
Europe
Romania

Additional Information
Year Founded: 2005
Current Activity Level : Actively seeking new investments

SIF TRANSILVANIA
2, Nicolae Iorga Street
Brasov, Romania RO - 2200
Phone: 40-268-413-752
Fax: 40-268-473-215
Website: www.transif.ro

Management and Staff
Mihai Fercala, President

Type of Firm
Investment Management Firm

Association Membership
European Private Equity and Venture Capital Assoc.

Project Preferences

Role in Financing:
Prefer role as deal originator but will also invest in deals created by others

Type of Financing Preferred:
Second Stage Financing
Expansion
Startup

Geographical Preferences

International Preferences:
Romania

Industry Preferences

In Communications prefer:
Commercial Communications
Telecommunications
Other Communication Prod.

In Computer Software prefer:
Computer Services
Applications Software

In Internet Specific prefer:
Internet

In Semiconductor/Electr prefer:
Electronics

In Consumer Related prefer:
Food/Beverage
Consumer Products
Consumer Services
Hotels and Resorts

In Industrial/Energy prefer:
Oil & Gas Drilling,Explor
Materials
Machinery

In Transportation prefer:
Transportation

In Financial Services prefer:
Financial Services
Insurance
Real Estate

In Business Serv. prefer:
Consulting Services

In Agr/Forestr/Fish prefer:
Mining and Minerals

Additional Information
Year Founded: 1996
Current Activity Level : Actively seeking new investments
Method of Compensation: Return on investment is of primary concern, do not charge fees

SIFEM AG (AKA: SWISS INVESTMENT FUND FOR EMERGING MARKETS)

Bubenbergplatz 11
Bern, Switzerland 3011
Phone: 41-31-310-0930
Fax: 41-31-310-0939
Website: www.sifem.ch

Management and Staff

Claude Barras, Managing Director

Type of Firm

Private Equity Firm

Association Membership

African Venture Capital Association (AVCA)

Project Preferences

Type of Financing Preferred:
Balanced

Geographical Preferences

International Preferences:
Latin America
Asia
All International

Additional Information

Year Founded: 2005
Capital Under Management: $196,000,000
Current Activity Level : Actively seeking new investments

SIG ASIA INVESTMENTS, LLLP

222 Hu Bin Road
Suite 1504-05, Corporate Ave.
Shanghai, China 200021
Phone: 86-21-5122-2888
Fax: 86-21-6122-3488
E-mail: Info@sig-china.com
Website: www.sig-china.com

Other Offices

101 California Street
Suite 3250
San Francisco, CA USA 94111
Phone: 415-403-6510
Fax: 610-617-3896

Suite 1908, Twin Towers
B12 Jianguomenwai Da Jie
Beijing, China 100022
Phone: 86-10-6566-6882
Fax: 86-10-6566-6881

Management and Staff

Ryan Weidenmiller, Founder

Type of Firm

Bank Affiliated

Project Preferences

Type of Financing Preferred:
Early Stage
Expansion
Balanced
Later Stage

Geographical Preferences

International Preferences:
China

Industry Preferences

In Internet Specific prefer:
Internet

In Consumer Related prefer:
Consumer

In Business Serv. prefer:
Services
Media

Additional Information

Year Founded: 2004
Current Activity Level : Actively seeking new investments

SIGHTLINE PARTNERS

50 South Sixth Street
Suite 1390
Minneapolis, MN USA 55402
Phone: 612-465-0600
Fax: 612-465-0620
Website: www.sightlinepartners.com

Other Offices

505 Hamilton Avenue
Suite 300
Palo Alto, CA USA 94301
Phone: 650-851-6865
Fax: 253-323-3520

Management and Staff

Archie Smith, Managing Director
Buzz Benson, Managing Director

Type of Firm

Private Equity Firm

Project Preferences

Role in Financing:
Will function either as deal originator or investor in deals created by others

Type of Financing Preferred:
Early Stage
Balanced
Later Stage

Size of Investments Considered:
Min Size of Investment Considered (000s): $2,000
Max Size of Investment Considered (000s): $6,000

Geographical Preferences

United States Preferences:
All U.S.

Industry Preferences

In Medical/Health prefer:
Medical Diagnostics
Diagnostic Test Products
Medical Therapeutics
Drug/Equipmt Delivery
Medical Products
Disposable Med. Products

Additional Information

Name of Most Recent Fund: SightLine Healthcare Vintage Fund
Most Recent Fund Was Raised: 04/13/2006
Year Founded: 1992
Capital Under Management: $248,000,000
Current Activity Level : Actively seeking new investments

SIGMA CAPITAL CORP.

22668 Caravelle Circle
Boca Raton, FL USA 33433
Phone: 561-368-9783

Management and Staff

Alvin Schwartz, President

Type of Firm

Private Equity Firm

Project Preferences

Role in Financing:
Prefer role as deal originator but will also invest in deals created by others

Type of Financing Preferred:
Second Stage Financing

Size of Investments Considered:
Min Size of Investment Considered (000s): $100
Max Size of Investment Considered (000s): $300

Geographical Preferences

United States Preferences:
Southeast

Industry Preferences

In Communications prefer:
CATV & Pay TV Systems
Telecommunications
Data Communications
Other Communication Prod.

In Computer Hardware prefer:
Mini and Personal/Desktop
Computer Graphics and Dig

In Computer Software prefer:
Computer Services

In Semiconductor/Electr prefer:
Electronics
Electronic Components
Sensors
Circuit Boards
Component Testing Equipmt
Laser Related
Fiber Optics
Analytic/Scientific

In Biotechnology prefer:
Industrial Biotechnology
Biotech Related Research

In Medical/Health prefer:
Medical Diagnostics
Diagnostic Test Products
Medical Therapeutics
Drug/Equipmt Delivery
Medical Products
Disposable Med. Products

In Consumer Related prefer:
Food/Beverage
Consumer Products
Consumer Services
Hotels and Resorts

In Industrial/Energy prefer:
Industrial Products
Materials
Factory Automation
Robotics
Machinery

In Financial Services prefer:
Financial Services
Real Estate

In Manufact. prefer:
Office Automation Equipmt

Additional Information
Year Founded: 1998
Capital Under Management: $1,000,000,000
Current Activity Level : Actively seeking new investments
Method of Compensation: Other

SIGMA CAPITAL GROUP PLC
Northwest Wing, Bush House
Aldwych
London, United Kingdom WC2B 4EZ
Phone: 44-131-220-9444
Fax: 44-131-220-9445
E-mail: london@sigmacapital.co.uk
Website: www.sigmacapital.co.uk

Other Offices
41 Charlotte Square
Edinburgh, United Kingdom EH2 4HQ
Phone: 44-131-220-9444
Fax: 44-131-220-9445

Management and Staff
Graham Barnet, Chief Executive Officer
Gregor Clark, Chief Operating Officer
Neil Crabb, Managing Director

Type of Firm
Investment Management Firm

Association Membership
British Venture Capital Association (BVCA)

Project Preferences

Type of Financing Preferred:
Expansion
Early Stage
Seed
Fund of Funds of Second

Geographical Preferences

International Preferences:
United Kingdom
Europe

Industry Preferences

In Communications prefer:
Communications and Media
Telecommunications

In Industrial/Energy prefer:
Alternative Energy
Energy Conservation Relat
Environmental Related

In Business Serv. prefer:
Media

Additional Information
Year Founded: 1996
Capital Under Management: $119,000,000
Current Activity Level : Actively seeking new investments

SIGMA CAPITAL MANAGEMENT
Grueneburgweg 18
Frankfurt am Main, Germany 60322
Phone: 49-69719-159660
Fax: 49-69-713758811
E-mail: info@altira-ag.de
Website: www.altira-ag.de

Other Offices
Maximiliansstrasse 35
Munich, Germany D-80539
Phone: 49-89-24218-221
Fax: 49-89-24218-200

Friedrichstrasse 15
Frankfurt / Main, Germany D-60323
Phone: 49-69-7137588-20
Fax: 49-69-7137588-11

Management and Staff
Andreas Lange, Managing Partner
Christian Angermayer, Partner
Frank Ebbing, Partner
Lutz Michalski, Partner
Lutz Schroeder, Managing Partner
Michael Gruner, Partner
Michael H Schulz, Partner
Peter Brumm, Partner

Type of Firm
Private Equity Firm

Association Membership
German Venture Capital Association (BVK)
European Private Equity and Venture Capital Assoc.

Project Preferences

Type of Financing Preferred:
Fund of Funds
Early Stage
Expansion
Mezzanine
Startup

Size of Investments Considered:
Min Size of Investment Considered (000s): $471
Max Size of Investment Considered (000s): $2,825

Geographical Preferences

International Preferences:
Europe
Germany

Industry Preferences

In Communications prefer:
Communications and Media
Telecommunications

In Computer Software prefer:
Software

In Internet Specific prefer:
E-Commerce Technology
Internet

In Computer Other prefer:
Computer Related

In Semiconductor/Electr prefer:
Electronics
Semiconductor
Laser Related
Fiber Optics

In Biotechnology prefer:
Biotechnology

In Medical/Health prefer:
Medical/Health
Pharmaceuticals

In Industrial/Energy prefer:
Energy
Alternative Energy
Environmental Related

In Business Serv. prefer:
Media

Additional Information

Year Founded: 1998
Capital Under Management: $35,700,000
Current Activity Level : Actively seeking new investments

SIGMA CAPITAL PARTNERS, LLC

800 Third Avenue
Suite 1701
New York, NY USA 10022
Phone: 212-201-6612
Fax: 212-937-3558
E-mail: info@sigmacp.com
Website: www.sigmacp.com

Management and Staff

Gary Marks, Chief Financial Officer
Maydan Rothblum, Principal
Thom Waye, Managing Partner

Type of Firm

Private Equity Firm

Project Preferences

Role in Financing:

Prefer role as deal originator but will also invest in deals created by others

Type of Financing Preferred:

Turnaround

Size of Investments Considered:

Min Size of Investment Considered (000s): $3,000
Max Size of Investment Considered (000s): $15,000

Industry Preferences

In Communications prefer:

Telecommunications

In Computer Software prefer:

Computer Services
Software

In Medical/Health prefer:

Health Services

Additional Information

Name of Most Recent Fund: Sigma Opportunity Fund, The
Most Recent Fund Was Raised: 05/12/2005
Year Founded: 2004
Capital Under Management: $15,600,000
Current Activity Level : Actively seeking new investments
Method of Compensation: Return on invest. most important, but chg. closing fees, service fees, etc.

SIGMA GESTION

9 rue Saint Florentin
Paris, France 75008
Phone: 33-1-4703-9842
Fax: 33-1-4926-9111
E-mail: info@groupesigma.com
Website: www.groupesigma.com

Management and Staff

Phillippe Cholet, Managing Director

Type of Firm

Private Equity Firm

Association Membership

French Venture Capital Association (AFIC)

Project Preferences

Type of Financing Preferred:

Research and Development
Expansion
Early Stage
Balanced

Geographical Preferences

International Preferences:

Europe
France

Additional Information

Year Founded: 2004
Capital Under Management: $30,800,000
Current Activity Level : Actively seeking new investments

SIGMA PARTNERS

1600 El Camino Real
Suite 280
Menlo Park, CA USA 94025
Phone: 650-853-1700
Fax: 650-853-1717
E-mail: info@sigmapartners.com
Website: www.sigmapartners.com

Other Offices

20 Custom House Street
Suite 830
Boston, MA USA 02110
Phone: 617-330-7872
Fax: 617-323-7975

4000 Executive Parkway
Suite 530
San Ramon, CA USA 94583
Phone: 925-904-0222
Fax: 925-904-0221

Management and Staff

C. Bradford Jeffries, Co-Founder
Clifford Haas, Managing Director
Fahri Diner, Managing Director
Gregory Gretsch, Managing Director
J. Burgess Jamieson, Co-Founder
John Mandile, Managing Director
Kevin Laracey, Venture Partner
Lawrence Finch, Managing Director
Melissa Alves, Chief Financial Officer
Paul Flanagan, Managing Director
Peter Solvik, Managing Director
Richard Dale, Principal
Robert Davoli, Managing Director
Robert Spinner, Managing Director
Wade Woodson, Managing Director

Type of Firm

Private Equity Firm

Association Membership

Western Association of Venture Capitalists (WAVC)
National Venture Capital Association - USA (NVCA)

Project Preferences

Role in Financing:

Prefer role as deal originator but will also invest in deals created by others

Type of Financing Preferred:

Early Stage
Expansion
Balanced
Start-up Financing

Size of Investments Considered:

Min Size of Investment Considered (000s): $1,000
Max Size of Investment Considered: No Limit

Industry Focus

(% based on actual investment)	
Computer Software and Services	47.6%
Internet Specific	23.7%
Semiconductors/Other Elect.	8.9%
Communications and Media	8.5%
Computer Hardware	5.9%
Industrial/Energy	3.5%
Other Products	0.8%
Biotechnology	0.7%
Consumer Related	0.3%
Medical/Health	0.2%

Additional Information

Name of Most Recent Fund: Sigma Partners 8, L.P.
Most Recent Fund Was Raised: 08/14/2007
Year Founded: 1984
Capital Under Management: $2,229,000,000
Current Activity Level : Actively seeking new investments
Method of Compensation: Return on investment is of primary concern, do not charge fees

---

SIGMABLEYZER

4A Baseyna Street
8th Floor Mandarin Plaza
Kyiv, Ukraine 01004
Phone: 380-44-284-1289
Fax: 380-44-284-1283
E-mail: kyiv.office@sigmaleyzer.com.ua
Website: www.sigmableyzer.com

Other Offices

12 Samal City District
Office 20-III
Astana, Kazakhstan 010000

Phone: 8-3172-59-2577

Meytin House
49 Sumaskaya Street, Office 4
Kharkov, Ukraine 61022
Phone: 380-577-141-180
Fax: 380-577-141-188

123 North Post Oak Ln.
Suite 410
Houston, TX USA 77024
Phone: 713-621-3111
Fax: 713-621-4666
22 Zlaten Rog Street
8th Floor, Office 20
Sofia, Bulgaria 1407
Phone: 359-2-868-1868
Fax: 359-2-868-7868

12Bis, Dr. Draghiescu Street
Section 5
Bucharest, Romania 050579
Phone: 40-21-410-1000
Fax: 40-21-410-2222

Management and Staff

Neal Sigda, Partner
Sergey Bulavin, Vice President
Victor Gekker, Vice President

Type of Firm

Private Equity Firm

Association Membership

European Private Equity and Venture Capital Assoc.

Project Preferences

Type of Financing Preferred:
Leveraged Buyout
Expansion
Mezzanine
Turnaround
Management Buyouts

Geographical Preferences

International Preferences:
Eastern Europe
Bulgaria
Ukraine
Romania

Industry Preferences

In Communications prefer:
Telecommunications

In Computer Software prefer:
Software

In Consumer Related prefer:
Retail

In Industrial/Energy prefer:
Industrial Products

In Transportation prefer:
Transportation

In Manufact. prefer:
Manufacturing

Additional Information

Year Founded: 1993
Capital Under Management: $365,900,000
Current Activity Level : Actively seeking new investments

SIGNAL HILL EQUITY PARTNERS, INC.

Four King Street West
Suite 1000
Toronto, Canada M5H 1B6
Phone: 416-847-1170
Fax: 416-203-1713
Website: www.signalhillequity.com

Management and Staff

James Johnson, Managing Partner

Type of Firm

Private Equity Firm

Geographical Preferences

Canadian Preferences:
All Canada

Additional Information

Year Founded: 2009
Current Activity Level : Actively seeking new investments

SIGNAL IDUNA PRIVATE EQUITY FONDS GMBH

Joseph-Scherer-Str. 3
Dortmund, Germany D-44139
Phone: 49-231-135-0
Fax: 49-231-135-4638
Website: www.signal-iduna.com

Other Offices

Neue Rabenstr. 15-19
Hamburg, Germany D-20354
Phone: 49-40-4124-0
Fax: 49-40-4124-2958

Type of Firm

Insurance Firm Affiliate

Project Preferences

Type of Financing Preferred:
Balanced

Geographical Preferences

International Preferences:
Europe

Additional Information

Year Founded: 1999
Current Activity Level : Actively seeking new investments

SIGNAL LAKE MANAGEMENT LLC

606 Post Road East
Suite 667
Westport, CT USA 06880
Phone: 203-454-1133
Fax: 203-454-7142
E-mail: info@signallake.com
Website: www.signallake.com

Other Offices

50 Commonwealth Avenue
Suite 504
Boston, MA USA 02116
Phone: 617-267-5205
Fax: 617-262-7037

Management and Staff

Anna Brady-Estevez, Principal
Avery Lyford, Managing Director
Bart Stuck, Managing Director
Cheryl Smith, Venture Partner
Mark Stahlman, Venture Partner
Michael Weingarten, Managing Director
Werner Stapela, Venture Partner
William Chu, Principal

Type of Firm

Private Equity Firm

Association Membership

National Venture Capital Association - USA (NVCA)

Project Preferences

Role in Financing:
Will function either as deal originator or investor in deals created by others

Type of Financing Preferred:
Leveraged Buyout
Early Stage
Expansion
Mezzanine
Balanced
Seed
Later Stage
Acquisition

Size of Investments Considered:
Min Size of Investment Considered (000s): $100
Max Size of Investment Considered (000s): $25,000

Geographical Preferences

International Preferences:
Latin America
Europe
Eastern Europe
Pacific

Asia
All International

Industry Focus

(% based on actual investment)

Communications and Media	41.7%
Internet Specific	21.7%
Computer Hardware	16.2%
Semiconductors/Other Elect.	13.7%
Computer Software and Services	6.7%

Additional Information

Year Founded: 1998
Capital Under Management: $200,000,000
Current Activity Level : Actively seeking new investments
Method of Compensation: Return on investment is of primary concern, do not charge fees

---

SIGNATURE CAPITAL LLC

780 Fifth Avenue South
Suite 200
Naples, FL USA 34102
Phone: 877-845-2774
Fax: 239-963-3699
Website: www.signaturecapital.com

Management and Staff

Stephen Shea, President
William Turner, Managing Director

Type of Firm

Private Equity Firm

Association Membership

National Venture Capital Association - USA (NVCA)

Project Preferences

Role in Financing:

Prefer role as deal originator

Type of Financing Preferred:

Early Stage

Geographical Preferences

United States Preferences:

Mid Atlantic
Midwest
Southeast
Northeast
Southwest

Industry Preferences

In Communications prefer:

Telecommunications
Wireless Communications

In Computer Software prefer:

Computer Services
Software

In Internet Specific prefer:

Internet
Ecommerce

In Semiconductor/Electr prefer:

Electronic Components
Semiconductor
Micro-Processing
Circuit Boards

In Biotechnology prefer:

Human Biotechnology

In Medical/Health prefer:

Medical Products

In Business Serv. prefer:

Services
Distribution

Additional Information

Year Founded: 1997
Current Activity Level : Actively seeking new investments
Method of Compensation: Return on invest. most important, but chg. closing fees, service fees, etc.

SIGNATURE FINANCIAL MANAGMENT, INC.

150 West Main Street
Suite 1550
Norfolk, VA USA 23510
Phone: 757-625-7670
Fax: 757-625-7673
E-mail: info@sigfin.com
Website: www.sigfin.com

Management and Staff

Anne Shumadine, President

Type of Firm

Private Equity Advisor or Fund of Funds

Project Preferences

Type of Financing Preferred:

Fund of Funds
Expansion

Geographical Preferences

United States Preferences:

All U.S.

Additional Information

Year Founded: 2006
Capital Under Management: $181,000,000
Current Activity Level : Actively seeking new investments

SIGNET HEALTHCARE PARTNERS (FKA: SANDERS MORRIS HARRIS)

152 West 57th Street
19th Floor
New York, NY USA 10019
Phone: 646-840-4990
Fax: 212-419-3956
Website: www.signethealthcarepartners.com

Other Offices

3100 Chase Tower
Houston, TX USA 77002
Phone: 713-993-4690
Fax: 713-993-4699

Management and Staff

Al Hansen, Managing Director
Ben Morris, Chief Executive Officer
Bruce McMaken, Managing Director
Charles Davis, Managing Director
James Gale, Managing Director
Jerald Cobbs, Managing Director
Rick Berry, Chief Financial Officer
Robert Garrison, President
Stephen Bonebrake, Managing Director

Type of Firm

Bank Affiliated

Project Preferences

Role in Financing:

Prefer role as deal originator but will also invest in deals created by others

Type of Financing Preferred:

Leveraged Buyout
Early Stage
Expansion
Balanced
Public Companies
Later Stage
Acquisition
Private Placement

Geographical Preferences

United States Preferences:

All U.S.

Industry Preferences

In Communications prefer:

Telecommunications

In Medical/Health prefer:

Medical/Health
Drug/Equipmt Delivery
Medical Products
Health Services
Pharmaceuticals

In Consumer Related prefer:

Consumer Products

In Other prefer:

Environment Responsible

Additional Information

Name of Most Recent Fund: SMH Private Equity Fund
Most Recent Fund Was Raised: 12/31/2005
Year Founded: 1998
Capital Under Management: $200,000,000

Current Activity Level : Actively seeking new investments

SIGULER GUFF & COMPANY

825 Third Avenue
Tenth Floor
New York, NY USA 10022
Phone: 212-332-5100
Fax: 212-332-5120
E-mail: info@sigulerguff.com
Website: www.sigulerguff.com

Other Offices

Russia Pastress
Stoleshnikov Pes. 14, 2nd Floor
Moscow, Russia 107031
Phone: 7-495-234-3095
Fax: 7-495-234-3099

12100 Wilshire Boulevard
Suite 1090
West Los Angeles, CA USA 90025
Phone: 310-954-0151
Fax: 212-634-5954

Level 8 Rajeha Building
Bandra Kurla Complex
Mumbai, India 400051
Phone: 91-22-4090-7044

100 North Riverside Plaza
Suite 2450
Chicago, IL USA 60606
Phone: 312-279-9300
Fax: 312-575-0222

2205 Citic Square
1168 West Nanjing Road
Shanghai, China 200040
Phone: 86-21-5292-5256
Fax: 86-21-5292-5575

One Post Office Square
36th Floor
Boston, MA USA 02109
Phone: 617-338-1140
Fax: 617-338-1371

Management and Staff

Anthony Corriggio, Principal
Avinash Amin, Managing Director
Christopher Pace, Principal
Christopher Brandely, Vice President
Clifford Yonce, Managing Director
David Lee, Vice President
Dmitry Piskulov, Vice President
Donald Spencer, Managing Director
Drew Guff, Managing Director
George Siguler, Managing Director
James Corl, Managing Director
James Gereghty, Managing Director
Jason Mundt, Vice President
Jonathan Wilson, Vice President
Kenneth Burns, Managing Director
Kevin Kester, Managing Director
Maria Boyazny, Managing Director
Marianna Fassinotti, Vice President
Michael Kenough, Managing Director
Natalie Geissler, Vice President
Patricia Dinneen, Managing Director
Praneet Singh, Managing Director
Ross Goodhart, Vice President
Tereza Trivell, Vice President
Terri Ambron Liftin, Principal
Thomas McGowan, Managing Director
Vladimir Andrienko, Managing Director

Type of Firm

Private Equity Advisor or Fund of Funds

Association Membership

Emerging Markets Private Equity Association
European Private Equity and Venture Capital Assoc.

Project Preferences

Role in Financing:

Prefer role as deal originator but will also invest in deals created by others

Type of Financing Preferred:

Fund of Funds
Expansion
Balanced
Turnaround
Management Buyouts
Special Situation
Industry Rollups
Distressed Debt
Recapitalizations
Fund of Funds of Second

Size of Investments Considered:

Min Size of Investment Considered (000s): $1,000
Max Size of Investment Considered (000s): $50,000

Geographical Preferences

United States Preferences:

All U.S.

International Preferences:

India
Europe
China
Utd. Arab Em.
Brazil
Ukraine
Asia
Russia

Industry Preferences

In Communications prefer:

Radio & TV Broadcasting
Telecommunications
Media and Entertainment

In Computer Software prefer:

Software

In Medical/Health prefer:

Health Services
Pharmaceuticals

In Consumer Related prefer:

Retail
Food/Beverage
Consumer Products
Consumer Services

In Industrial/Energy prefer:

Energy
Oil & Gas Drilling,Explor
Materials

In Financial Services prefer:

Financial Services

In Business Serv. prefer:

Media

Additional Information

Name of Most Recent Fund: Russia Partners III, L.P.
Most Recent Fund Was Raised: 11/30/2007
Year Founded: 1991
Capital Under Management: $7,000,000,000
Current Activity Level : Actively seeking new investments
Method of Compensation: Return on investment is of primary concern, do not charge fees

SIGVION CAPITAL

806 West Washington Street
Suite 204
Chicago, IL USA 60607
Phone: 312-226-6373
Fax: 312-226-6343
E-mail: sigvion@sigvion.com
Website: www.sigvion.com

Type of Firm

Private Equity Firm

Project Preferences

Type of Financing Preferred:

Early Stage

Geographical Preferences

United States Preferences:

All U.S.

Industry Preferences

In Medical/Health prefer:

Medical Therapeutics
Drug/Equipmt Delivery
Pharmaceuticals

Additional Information

Name of Most Recent Fund: Sigvion Fund I, LP
Most Recent Fund Was Raised: 03/08/2006
Year Founded: 2006
Capital Under Management: $4,700,000
Current Activity Level : Actively seeking new investments

SILICOM VENTURES

1442 Fowler Lane
Los Altos, CA USA 94024
Phone: 650-961-8877
Fax: 650-988-1888
E-mail: info@silicomventures.com
Website: www.silicomventures.com

Management and Staff

Gadi Behar, Managing Director

Type of Firm

Private Equity Firm

Project Preferences

Type of Financing Preferred:
Early Stage
Seed

Industry Preferences

In Communications prefer:
Telecommunications
Wireless Communications

In Computer Software prefer:
Software

In Semiconductor/Electr prefer:
Semiconductor

Additional Information

Year Founded: 1999
Current Activity Level : Actively seeking new investments

SILICON VALLEY INNOVATION CAPITAL (SVIC)

P.O. Box 209
Palo Alto, CA USA 94302
Phone: 650-289-5600
Fax: 650-324-1999
E-mail: info@svic.com
Website: www.svic.com

Management and Staff

Alexander Hern, General Partner
Matthew Bigge, General Partner
Patricia Gutierrez, Venture Partner
Robert Shaw, Chief Executive Officer

Type of Firm

Private Equity Firm

Project Preferences

Type of Financing Preferred:
Early Stage
Seed

Industry Preferences

In Communications prefer:
Communications and Media

In Computer Software prefer:
Software

In Industrial/Energy prefer:
Advanced Materials

Additional Information

Year Founded: 2000
Current Activity Level : Actively seeking new investments

SILKROAD EQUITY, LLC

111 North Chestnut Street
Suite 200
Winston-Salem, NC USA 27101
Phone: 336-201-5100
Fax: 336-201-5141
E-mail: info@silkroadequity.com
Website: www.silkroadequity.com

Management and Staff

Matthew Roszak, Managing Partner

Type of Firm

Private Equity Firm

Association Membership

Illinois Venture Capital Association

Project Preferences

Type of Financing Preferred:
Leveraged Buyout
Early Stage
Acquisition

Size of Investments Considered:
Min Size of Investment Considered (000s): $1,000
Max Size of Investment Considered (000s): $20,000

Geographical Preferences

United States Preferences:
All U.S.

Industry Preferences

In Communications prefer:
Telecommunications
Media and Entertainment

In Consumer Related prefer:
Retail

In Business Serv. prefer:
Services

In Manufact. prefer:
Manufacturing

Additional Information

Year Founded: 2003
Current Activity Level : Actively seeking new investments

SILVER CREEK VENTURES

5949 Sherry Lane
Suite 1450
Dallas, TX USA 75225
Phone: 214-265-2020
Fax: 214-692-6233
E-mail: plans@silvercreekfund.com
Website: www.silvercreekfund.com

Management and Staff

Felipe Mendoza, Chief Financial Officer
John Adler, General Partner
Mark Masur, General Partner
Michael Segrest, General Partner

Type of Firm

Private Equity Firm

Association Membership

National Venture Capital Association - USA (NVCA)

Project Preferences

Role in Financing:
Prefer role as deal originator but will also invest in deals created by others

Type of Financing Preferred:
Second Stage Financing
Early Stage
Balanced
Seed
First Stage Financing

Size of Investments Considered:
Min Size of Investment Considered (000s): $500
Max Size of Investment Considered (000s): $10,000

Geographical Preferences

United States Preferences:
Rocky Mountain
West Coast
California
Colorado
Southwest
Texas

Industry Focus

(% based on actual investment)

Communications and Media	59.1%
Computer Software and Services	16.3%
Semiconductors/Other Elect.	9.6%
Computer Hardware	9.4%
Internet Specific	2.9%
Consumer Related	2.0%
Other Products	0.7%

Additional Information

Year Founded: 1989
Capital Under Management: $140,000,000
Current Activity Level : Actively seeking new investments
Method of Compensation: Return on investment is of primary concern, do not charge fees

SILVER LAKE SUMERU

Nine West 57th Street
25th Floor
New York, NY USA 10019
Phone: 212-981-5600
Fax: 212-981-3535
E-mail: info@slpartners.com
Website: www.silverlake.com

Other Offices

10080 North Wolfe Road
Suite SW3-190
Cupertino, CA USA 95014
Phone: 408-454-4732
Fax: 408-454-4734

Steuart Tower
One Market Plaza, Suite 1000
San Francisco, CA USA 94105
Phone: 415-293-4355
Fax: 415-293-4365

33rd Floor Two IFC
8 Finance Street
Central, Hong Kong
Phone: 852-3664-3300
Fax: 852-3664-3456

2775 Sand Hill Road
Suite 100
Menlo Park, CA USA 94025
Phone: 650-233-8120
Fax: 650-233-8125

Broadbent House
65 Grosvenor Street
London, United Kingdom W1K 3JH
Phone: 44-20-3205-8400
Fax: 44-20-3205-8401

Management and Staff

Ajay Shah, Managing Director
Andrew Wagner, Chief Financial Officer
Egon Durban, Managing Director
Gerald Hwasta, Principal
Greg Mondre, Managing Director
Hollie Moore Haynes, Managing Director
James Davidson, Co-Founder
Joe Osnoss, Principal
John Wright, Principal
John Joyce, Managing Director
Kenneth Hao, Managing Director
Kyle Ryland, Managing Director
Mike Bingle, Managing Director
Paul Mercadante, Managing Director
Prashant Mehrotra, Principal
Roger Wittlin, Managing Director
Sean Delehanty, Principal
Stephanie Staub, Principal
Todd Morgenfeld, Principal
Tony Ling, Principal
Yolande Jun, Chief Financial Officer

Type of Firm

Private Equity Firm

Association Membership

Private Equity Council (PEC)

Project Preferences

Type of Financing Preferred:
Leveraged Buyout
Recapitalizations

Size of Investments Considered:
Min Size of Investment Considered (000s): $100,000
Max Size of Investment Considered (000s): $500,000

Geographical Preferences

United States Preferences:
All U.S.

Industry Focus

(% based on actual investment)

Computer Software and Services	36.6%
Computer Hardware	27.7%
Internet Specific	16.2%
Other Products	12.7%
Communications and Media	4.5%
Industrial/Energy	2.2%

Additional Information

Name of Most Recent Fund: Silver Lake Partners III, L.P.
Most Recent Fund Was Raised: 01/05/2007
Year Founded: 1999
Capital Under Management: $5,900,000,000
Current Activity Level : Actively seeking new investments

SILVER OAK MANAGEMENT

1603 Orrington Avenue
Suite 2050
Evanston, IL USA 60201
Phone: 847-332-0400
Fax: 847-492-1717
E-mail: info@silveroaksp.com
Website: www.silveroaksp.com

Management and Staff

Adam Waldo, Managing Director
Bradley O'Dell, Vice President
Daniel Gill, Managing Partner
Dave Bornhoeft, Vice President
Gregory Barr, Managing Partner
Jeffrey Mann, Managing Director & CFO
M. Scott Donaldson, Vice President

Type of Firm

Private Equity Firm

Project Preferences

Type of Financing Preferred:
Leveraged Buyout
Recapitalizations

Size of Investments Considered:
Min Size of Investment Considered (000s): $15,000
Max Size of Investment Considered (000s): $50,000

Geographical Preferences

United States Preferences:
All U.S.

Industry Preferences

In Computer Software prefer:
Software

In Medical/Health prefer:
Health Services

In Consumer Related prefer:
Entertainment and Leisure
Consumer Services

In Business Serv. prefer:
Services
Distribution

Additional Information

Year Founded: 2006
Current Activity Level : Actively seeking new investments

SILVER POINT CAPITAL LLC

600 Steamboat Road
Greenwich, CT USA 06830
Phone: 203-618-2660
Fax: 203-618-2669

Type of Firm

Private Equity Firm

Project Preferences

Type of Financing Preferred:
Turnaround
Distressed Debt

Additional Information

Year Founded: 2001
Current Activity Level : Actively seeking new investments

SILVERFERN GROUP, INC., THE

150 East 52nd Street
32nd Floor
New York, NY USA 10022
Phone: 212-209-8860
Fax: 212-209-8861
Website: www.silfern.com

Other Offices

1 Farrer Place
Level 46, Governor Phillip Tower
Sydney, Australia 2000
Phone: 612-9960-5883
Fax: 612-9960-5884

555 California Street
Suite 300
San Francisco, CA USA 94104
Phone: 415-568-2230
Fax: 415-568-2104

Management and Staff

Alfredo Barreto, Managing Director
Antonio Memmo, Managing Director
Brett Chenoweth, Managing Director
Christopher Marlowe, Managing Director
Edward Rimland, Managing Director
George Holder, Managing Director
Kevin Murphy, Managing Director
Kevin Smith, Managing Director
Lawrence Nathanson, Managing Director
Mitch Scherzer, Managing Director
Reeta Kapani, Managing Director
Thomas Remien, Managing Director
Thomas Burchill, Managing Director
William Harrison, Managing Director

Type of Firm

Bank Affiliated

Project Preferences

Type of Financing Preferred:

Leveraged Buyout
Acquisition
Recapitalizations

Additional Information

Year Founded: 2005
Current Activity Level : Actively seeking new investments

SILVERFLEET CAPITAL (FKA: PPM CAPITAL PARTNERS)

1 New Fetter Lane
2nd Floor
London, United Kingdom EC4A 1HH
Phone: 44-20-7822-1000
Fax: 44-20-7822-1001
E-mail: info@ppmcapital.com
Website: www.silverfleetcapital.com

Other Offices

225 West Wacker Drive
Suite 1200
Chicago, IL USA 60606
Phone: 312-634-2561
Fax: 312-634-0044

Oberanger 28
Munich, Germany D-80331
Phone: 49-89-238-8960
Fax: 49-89-2388-9699

46 avenue Kleber
Paris, France 75116
Phone: 33-1-5689-1414
Fax: 33-1-5689-1429

Management and Staff

Adrian Yurkwich, Partner
Chris Kelly, Partner
Gareth Whiley, Partner
Geraldine Kennell, Partner
Guido May, Partner
Ian Oxley, Partner
James Barton, Partner
Jean-Lou Rihon, Partner
Kay Ashton, Partner
Keith Haslett, Partner
Maire Deslandes, Partner
Neil MacDougall, Managing Director
Paul Pruss, Partner
Sebastian Kern, Partner

Type of Firm

Insurance Firm Affiliate

Association Membership

Hong Kong Venture Capital Association (HKVCA)
British Venture Capital Association (BVCA)
French Venture Capital Association (AFIC)
Singapore Venture Capital Association (SVCA)
European Private Equity and Venture Capital Assoc.

Project Preferences

Role in Financing:

Prefer role as deal originator but will also invest in deals created by others

Type of Financing Preferred:

Leveraged Buyout
Expansion
Balanced
Turnaround
Management Buyouts
Special Situation

Size of Investments Considered:

Min Size of Investment Considered (000s): $50,000
Max Size of Investment Considered (000s): $500,000

Geographical Preferences

International Preferences:

Vietnam
India
United Kingdom
Luxembourg
Netherlands
China
Hong Kong
Thailand
Philippines
Australia
Belgium
Singapore
Korea, South
Germany
Asia
France
Japan

Industry Focus

(% based on actual investment)

Consumer Related	49.7%
Other Products	37.3%
Medical/Health	6.0%
Communications and Media	2.6%
Industrial/Energy	2.3%
Computer Software and Services	1.9%
Computer Hardware	0.3%

Additional Information

Year Founded: 1986
Capital Under Management: $2,183,600,000
Current Activity Level : Actively seeking new investments
Method of Compensation: Return on invest. most important, but chg. closing fees, service fees, etc.

SILVERHAWK CAPITAL PARTNERS LLC

140 Greenwich Avenue
Second Floor
Greenwich, CT USA 06830
Phone: 203-861-2905
Fax: 203-861-2903
E-mail: info@silverhawkcp.com
Website: www.silverhawkcapitalpartners.com

Other Offices

1901 Roxborough Road
Suite 200
Charlotte, NC USA 28211
Phone: 704-366-6666
Fax: 704-366-6777

Management and Staff

David Scanlan, Managing Partner
James Cook, Managing Partner
Ted Gardner, Managing Partner

Type of Firm

Private Equity Firm

Project Preferences

Type of Financing Preferred:

Mezzanine
Management Buyouts

Size of Investments Considered:

Min Size of Investment Considered (000s): $10,000
Max Size of Investment Considered (000s): $35,000

Geographical Preferences

United States Preferences:

All U.S.

International Preferences:
Europe
Eastern Europe

Industry Preferences

In Medical/Health prefer:
Medical/Health

In Consumer Related prefer:
Consumer Services

In Industrial/Energy prefer:
Energy
Oil and Gas Exploration
Industrial Products

In Business Serv. prefer:
Services
Distribution

In Manufact. prefer:
Manufacturing

Additional Information

Year Founded: 2005
Capital Under Management: $150,000,000
Current Activity Level : Actively seeking new investments

SILVERTON FOUNDATION

1000 Rio Grande Street
Austin, TX USA 78701
Phone: 512-477-6262
Fax: 512-477-0025
E-mail: info@silvertonfoundation.com
Website: www.silvertonfoundation.com

Type of Firm

Endowment, Foundation or Pension Fund

Additional Information

Name of Most Recent Fund: Silverton Partners III, L.P.
Most Recent Fund Was Raised: 06/02/2006
Year Founded: 2002
Capital Under Management: $74,500,000
Current Activity Level : Actively seeking new investments

SIM SICAR (AKA: SOCIETE DE L INVESTISSEMENT MODERNE)

67, Rue Alain Savary
cite jardin II Bloc B 3 etage
Tunis, Tunisia 1002
Phone: 216-71-845-267
Fax: 216-71-846-675
E-mail: simsicar@wanadoo.tn
Website: www.sim-sicar.com

Type of Firm

Private Equity Firm

Association Membership

Tunisian Venture Capital Association

Project Preferences

Role in Financing:
Will function either as deal originator or investor in deals created by others

Type of Financing Preferred:
Balanced

Size of Investments Considered:
Min Size of Investment Considered (000s): $12
Max Size of Investment Considered (000s): $3,753

Geographical Preferences

International Preferences:
Tunisia

Additional Information

Year Founded: 1997
Capital Under Management: $66,100,000
Current Activity Level : Actively seeking new investments

SIMBIOSIS VENTURE CAPITAL S.L.

Paseo de la Castellana, 95
Edificio Torre Europa, Pl 15A
Madrid, Spain 28046
Phone: 34-91-418-6913
Fax: 34-91-418-6999
E-mail: info@simbiosis.biz
Website: www.simbiosis.biz

Management and Staff

Carlos Perreau de Pinnick, Co-Founder
Ken Douglas, Co-Founder

Type of Firm

Private Equity Firm

Association Membership

Spanish Venture Capital Association (ASCRI)

Project Preferences

Type of Financing Preferred:
Early Stage

Geographical Preferences

United States Preferences:
All U.S.

International Preferences:
Europe
Spain

Additional Information

Year Founded: 2003
Current Activity Level : Actively seeking new investments

SIMFONEC

Cass Business School
106 Bunhill Row
London, United Kingdom EC1Y 8TZ
Phone: 44-20-7040-8726
Fax: 44-20-7040-8882
E-mail: info@simfonec.co.uk
Website: www.simfonec.co.uk

Type of Firm

University Program

Project Preferences

Type of Financing Preferred:
Early Stage
Seed
Startup

Geographical Preferences

International Preferences:
United Kingdom
Europe

Industry Preferences

In Biotechnology prefer:
Biotechnology

In Medical/Health prefer:
Medical/Health
Pharmaceuticals

Additional Information

Year Founded: 2003
Current Activity Level : Actively seeking new investments

SINCLAIR VENTURES, INC.

10706 Beaver Dam Road
Hunt Valley, MD USA 21030
Phone: 410-568-1500
Fax: 410-568-1591
Website: www.sbgi.net/business/ventures.shtml

Management and Staff

David Amy, Chief Financial Officer

Type of Firm

Corporate PE/Venture

Association Membership

Mid-Atlantic Venture Association

Project Preferences

Type of Financing Preferred:
Second Stage Financing
Early Stage
First Stage Financing

Size of Investments Considered:
Min Size of Investment Considered (000s): $500
Max Size of Investment Considered (000s): $5,000

Industry Preferences

In Communications prefer:
Radio & TV Broadcasting
Wireless Communications
Media and Entertainment

In Computer Software prefer:
Software

In Internet Specific prefer:
Internet

In Consumer Related prefer:
Consumer Services

In Financial Services prefer:
Investment Groups

In Business Serv. prefer:
Media

Additional Information
Year Founded: 1999
Capital Under Management: $40,000,000
Current Activity Level : Actively seeking new investments

SINDICATUM CARBON CAPITAL, LTD.

5th Floor
18 Hanover Square
London, United Kingdom W1S 1HX
Phone: 44-20-3008-8602
Fax: 44-20-3008-4752
E-mail: info@sindicatum.com
Website: www.sindicatum.com

Other Offices
69 Road 161
PO box 2
Cairo, Egypt 11431
Phone: 2-2-528-3693

Rua Sao Tome
86-11th floor
Sao Paulo, Brazil 04551-080
Phone: 55-11-3055-2050
Fax: 55-11-3055-2050

Culiacan 123 Col.
Hipodromo Condesa C.P
Mexico, Mexico
Phone: 52-55-5265-1230
Fax: 52-55-5265-1246

Tengda Building No 168
Xiwai Street
Beijing, China 100044
Phone: 86-10-8857-6830

Wisma 46 Kota BNI
Jalan Jendral Sudirman Kav. 1
Jakarta, Indonesia 10220
Phone: 62-817-076-9030
Fax: 62-21-251-4719

598 Madison Avenue
9th floor
New York, NY USA 10022
Phone: 212-508-3620
Fax: 212-508-3629

138 Rue du Faubourg St. Honore
Paris, France 75008
Phone: 33-1-5353-0808
Fax: 33-1-5353-0800

IBC Building F
Seimyniskiu g. 3
Vilnius, Lithuania 09312
Phone: 370-5-263-8787
Fax: 370-5-263-6242

6 Duke Street
London, United Kingdom W1U 3EN
Phone: 44-20-7224-7555
Fax: 44-20-7224-7333

Management and Staff
Assaad Razzouk, Chief Executive Officer
Greg Coleman, President

Type of Firm
Bank Affiliated

Project Preferences

Type of Financing Preferred:
Balanced

Geographical Preferences

International Preferences:
Europe

Additional Information
Year Founded: 2002
Current Activity Level : Actively seeking new investments

SINO H & B PRIVATE EQUITY FUND CO., LTD.

Nanxin Chuang Guoji Building
Room 806-A
Beijing, China 100007
Phone: 86-1-6409-6283
Fax: 86-1-6409-6927

Type of Firm
Private Equity Firm

Project Preferences

Type of Financing Preferred:
Balanced

Geographical Preferences

International Preferences:
Asia

Additional Information
Year Founded: 2008
Current Activity Level : Actively seeking new investments

SINO-CAN HARVEST CAPITAL CO., LTD.

No. 91 Jianguo Road, Chaoyang
Room 1508-1512 Gemdale Plaza B
Beijing, China 100022
Phone: 86-1-5825-2247
Fax: 86-5825-2336
Website: www.scharvestcap.com

Type of Firm
Private Equity Advisor or Fund of Funds

Project Preferences

Type of Financing Preferred:
Balanced

Geographical Preferences

International Preferences:
China

Industry Preferences

In Semiconductor/Electr prefer:
Electronics

In Medical/Health prefer:
Medical/Health

In Consumer Related prefer:
Entertainment and Leisure
Food/Beverage
Consumer Products
Education Related

In Industrial/Energy prefer:
Energy
Materials
Machinery
Environmental Related

In Business Serv. prefer:
Media

In Agr/Forestr/Fish prefer:
Agriculture related

Additional Information
Year Founded: 2008
Capital Under Management: $91,300,000
Current Activity Level : Actively seeking new investments

SINOHEAD CAPITAL INVESTMENT, LTD.

877 Dongfang Road
Room 2001 Jiaxing Building
Shanghai, China
Phone: 86-21-6867-1258
E-mail: SH@sinohead.com
Website: www.sinohead.com

Type of Firm

Private Equity Firm

Project Preferences

Type of Financing Preferred:
Generalist PE
Early Stage
Expansion
Balanced
Later Stage

Geographical Preferences

International Preferences:
China

Industry Preferences

In Internet Specific prefer:
Internet

In Biotechnology prefer:
Biotechnology

In Medical/Health prefer:
Medical/Health

In Industrial/Energy prefer:
Energy
Energy Conservation Relat
Environmental Related

In Financial Services prefer:
Financial Services

In Manufact. prefer:
Manufacturing

Additional Information

Year Founded: 2007
Current Activity Level : Actively seeking new investments

SINOWISDOM INVESTMENT MANAGEMENT CO., LTD.

#3 Building, Zhejiang Hotel
278 Santai Mountain Road
Hangzhou, China
Phone: 86-571-88163182
Fax: 86-571-88163180
E-mail: sam806@sina.com
Website: www.sinowisdom.cn

Management and Staff

Peimin Zong, President

Type of Firm

Investment Management Firm

Project Preferences

Type of Financing Preferred:
Balanced

Geographical Preferences

International Preferences:
China

Additional Information

Year Founded: 2002
Current Activity Level : Actively seeking new investments

SINVENT

S P Andersens vei 5
Trondheim, Norway 7465
Phone: 47-73-59-3000
Fax: 47-73-59-3350
E-mail: webmaster@sintef.no
Website: www.sintef.no

Type of Firm

Private Equity Firm

Association Membership

Norwegian Venture Capital Association

Project Preferences

Type of Financing Preferred:
Balanced

Geographical Preferences

International Preferences:
Europe
Norway

Additional Information

Year Founded: 2005
Current Activity Level : Actively seeking new investments

SIP SICAR

30 rue Tarak Ibn Zied
Mutuelleville
Tunis, Tunisia 1082
Phone: 216-71-796-654
Fax: 216-894-330
E-mail: simpar@planet.tn

Type of Firm

Private Equity Firm

Association Membership

Tunisian Venture Capital Association

Project Preferences

Role in Financing:
Will function either as deal originator or investor in deals created by others

Type of Financing Preferred:
Balanced

Geographical Preferences

International Preferences:
Tunisia

Additional Information

Year Founded: 2004
Current Activity Level : Actively seeking new investments

SIPAREX GROUP

139, rue Vendome
Lyon, France 69477
Phone: 33-4-7283-2323
Fax: 33-4-7283-2300
E-mail: siparex@siparex.com
Website: www.siparex.com

Other Offices

37/41, rue de la Barre
Lille, France 59005
Phone: 33-3-2017-6600
Fax: 33-3-2014-2131

28, rue de la republique
BP 56087
Besancon, France 25013
Phone: 33-3-8125-0614
Fax: 33-3-2125-0613

Via Molino delle Armi, 4
Milan, Italy 20123
Phone: 39-02-8909-6427
Fax: 39-02-805-5252

15, rue de Belleville
Nantes, France 44100
Phone: 33-2-4069-3838
Fax: 33-2-4069-0150

27, rue Marbeuf
Paris, France 75008
Phone: 33-1-5393-0220
Fax: 33-1-5393-0230

1400 Fashion Island Boulevard
Suite 600
San Mateo, CA USA 94404
Phone: 650-522-0085
Fax: 650-522-0087

Calle Serrano 88
Madrid, Spain 28006
Phone: 34-91-400-5464
Fax: 39-41-435-3593

Management and Staff

Francois Pontet, Managing Director
Jacques Vallee, General Partner
Jean-Francois Puech, Managing Director
Michel Faure, Partner
Pierre Bordeaux, Managing Director
Rene Maury, Senior Managing Director
Tanguy Hoffmann, Managing Director
William Higgons, Managing Director

Type of Firm

Private Equity Firm

Association Membership

French Venture Capital Association (AFIC)
European Private Equity and Venture Capital Assoc.

Project Preferences

Type of Financing Preferred:

Second Stage Financing
Leveraged Buyout
Early Stage
Expansion
Balanced
Later Stage
Acquisition
Startup
Recapitalizations

Geographical Preferences

International Preferences:

Italy
Portugal
Europe
Western Europe
Spain
Belgium
France

Industry Focus

(% based on actual investment)

Other Products	25.6%
Internet Specific	19.4%
Consumer Related	12.2%
Semiconductors/Other Elect.	9.4%
Computer Software and Services	8.8%
Medical/Health	7.1%
Industrial/Energy	6.4%
Biotechnology	5.2%
Communications and Media	3.5%
Computer Hardware	2.3%

Additional Information

Name of Most Recent Fund: FIP Bourgogne Franche-Comte Rhone-Alpes PME 3
Most Recent Fund Was Raised: 02/03/2006
Year Founded: 1977
Capital Under Management: $1,113,100,000
Current Activity Level : Actively seeking new investments

SIPPL MACDONALD VENTURES

1422 El Camino Real
Menlo Park, CA USA 94025
Phone: 650-566-6860
Fax: 650-326-4404
Website: www.sipmac.com

Management and Staff

Glenn Myers, Chief Financial Officer
Jacqueline Macdonald, Founding Partner
Roger Sippl, Founding Partner

Type of Firm

Private Equity Firm

Project Preferences

Type of Financing Preferred:

Early Stage

Size of Investments Considered:

Min Size of Investment Considered (000s): $200
Max Size of Investment Considered (000s): $750

Geographical Preferences

United States Preferences:

West Coast
California

Industry Focus

(% based on actual investment)

Computer Software and Services	77.1%
Internet Specific	21.9%
Communications and Media	0.5%
Other Products	0.4%

Additional Information

Year Founded: 1995
Capital Under Management: $18,000,000
Current Activity Level : Actively seeking new investments

SIRIUS VENTURE CONSULTING PTE, LTD.

30 Cecil Street
Prudential Tower Level 15
Singapore, Singapore 049712
Phone: 65-6232-2742
Fax: 65-6232-2888
E-mail: general@sirius.com.sg
Website: www.sirius.com.sg

Other Offices

555 Bryant Street
Suite 190
Palo Alto, CA USA 94301

Kamiyacho MT Building, 14th Floor
4-3-20 Toranomon Minato-ku
Tokyo, Japan 105-0001
Phone: 813-4496-4481
Fax: 813-4496-4481

Room 1708 Dominon Centre
43-59 Queen's Road East
Wanchai, Hong Kong
Phone: 852-9468-8525

Management and Staff

Eugene Wong, Managing Director
Ivan Hajadi, Partner
Shigeru Fukunaga, Managing Director

Type of Firm

Service Provider

Project Preferences

Role in Financing:

Prefer role as deal originator but will also invest in deals created by others

Type of Financing Preferred:

Early Stage
Expansion
Seed
Later Stage
Startup
Recapitalizations

Size of Investments Considered:

Min Size of Investment Considered (000s): $69
Max Size of Investment Considered (000s): $2,085

Geographical Preferences

United States Preferences:

All U.S.

International Preferences:

Indonesia
China
Singapore
Japan

Industry Preferences

In Semiconductor/Electr prefer:

Electronics

In Consumer Related prefer:

Consumer
Food/Beverage

In Industrial/Energy prefer:

Energy
Environmental Related

In Transportation prefer:

Transportation

In Business Serv. prefer:

Services

In Manufact. prefer:

Manufacturing

Additional Information

Year Founded: 2002
Capital Under Management: $28,200,000
Current Activity Level : Actively seeking new investments

SIRIUS VENTURE PARTNERS GMBH

Viktoriastr. 3
Wiesbaden, Germany 65189
Phone: 49-61169-66990
Fax: 49-61169-669990
E-mail: info@sirius-venture.com
Website: www.sirius-venture.com

Other Offices

Merowingerplatz 1
Dusseldorf, Germany 40225

Management and Staff

Ernst G. Mayer, Managing Partner
Friedrich von Diest, Managing Partner
Wolfram Glock, Founder

Type of Firm

Private Equity Firm

Project Preferences

Type of Financing Preferred:
Seed
Startup

Geographical Preferences

International Preferences:
Switzerland
Austria
Germany

Industry Preferences

In Medical/Health prefer:
Medical/Health

In Industrial/Energy prefer:
Materials

Additional Information

Year Founded: 2004
Current Activity Level : Actively seeking new investments

SITRA (AKA: FINNISH NATIONAL FUND FOR R&D, THE)

Itamerentori 2
P.O. Box 160
Helsinki, Finland FI-00181
Phone: 358-9-618-991
Fax: 358-9-645-072
Website: www.sitra.fi

Management and Staff

Kari Tolvanen, Vice President
Mikko Kosonen, President

Type of Firm

Endowment, Foundation or Pension Fund

Association Membership

Finnish Venture Capital Association (FVCA)
European Private Equity and Venture Capital Assoc.

Project Preferences

Role in Financing:
Will function either as deal originator or investor in deals created by others

Type of Financing Preferred:
Fund of Funds
Early Stage
Research and Development
Balanced
Seed
First Stage Financing
Startup

Size of Investments Considered:
Min Size of Investment Considered (000s): $100
Max Size of Investment Considered (000s): $5,000

Geographical Preferences

International Preferences:
Europe
Finland

Industry Focus

(% based on actual investment)	
Medical/Health	40.7%
Internet Specific	16.3%
Biotechnology	14.1%
Other Products	8.2%
Semiconductors/Other Elect.	8.1%
Computer Software and Services	4.6%
Industrial/Energy	3.9%
Communications and Media	1.9%
Computer Hardware	1.2%
Consumer Related	1.1%

Additional Information

Year Founded: 1967
Capital Under Management: $131,000,000
Current Activity Level : Actively seeking new investments
Method of Compensation: Return on investment is of primary concern, do not charge fees

SIXTH SWEDISH NATIONAL PENSION FUND (AKA: SJATTE AP-FONDEN)

Ostra Hamngatan 18
Gothenborg, Sweden S - 411 09
Phone: 46-31-741-1000
Fax: 46-31-741-1098
E-mail: info@apfond6.se
Website: www.apfond6.se

Management and Staff

Erling Gustafsson, President

Type of Firm

Endowment, Foundation or Pension Fund

Association Membership

Swedish Venture Capital Association (SVCA)
European Private Equity and Venture Capital Assoc.

Project Preferences

Type of Financing Preferred:
Second Stage Financing
Leveraged Buyout
Early Stage
Expansion
Balanced

Geographical Preferences

International Preferences:
Sweden
Scandanavia/Nordic Region

Industry Preferences

In Industrial/Energy prefer:
Industrial Products

Additional Information

Year Founded: 1996
Capital Under Management: $1,325,900,000
Current Activity Level : Actively seeking new investments

SJF VENTURES

200 North Magnum Street
Suite 203
Durham, NC USA 27701
Phone: 919-530-1177
Fax: 919-530-1178
Website: www.sjfund.com

Other Offices

101 California Street
Suite 2450
San Francisco, CA USA 94111
Phone: 415-659-8277

800 Third Avenue
21st Floor
New York, NY USA 10022
Phone: 212-209-3042
Fax: 212-371-5500

Management and Staff

Alan Kelley, Managing Director
David Griest, Managing Director
David Kirkpatrick, Managing Director
Richard Defieux, Co-Founder

Type of Firm

Private Equity Firm

Association Membership

Community Development Venture Capital Alliance
Natl Assoc of Small Bus. Inv. Co (NASBIC)
National Venture Capital Association - USA (NVCA)

Project Preferences

Role in Financing:
Will function either as deal originator or investor in deals created by others

Type of Financing Preferred:
Second Stage Financing
Expansion
Later Stage
First Stage Financing

Size of Investments Considered:
Min Size of Investment Considered (000s): $500
Max Size of Investment Considered (000s): $4,000

Geographical Preferences

United States Preferences:
Mid Atlantic
Midwest
Southeast
Northeast
All U.S.

Industry Preferences

In Computer Software prefer:
Computer Services

In Consumer Related prefer:
Consumer
Food/Beverage
Consumer Products

In Industrial/Energy prefer:
Energy
Alternative Energy
Energy Conservation Relat
Environmental Related

In Business Serv. prefer:
Services

In Utilities prefer:
Utilities

In Other prefer:
Socially Responsible
Environment Responsible
Women/Minority-Owned Bus.

Additional Information
Name of Most Recent Fund: SJF Ventures II, L.P.
Most Recent Fund Was Raised: 10/27/2004
Year Founded: 1999
Capital Under Management: $43,000,000
Current Activity Level : Actively seeking new investments
Method of Compensation: Return on investment is of primary concern, do not charge fees

---

SK VENTURES
1-11-2 Heiwadori
Shunan-shi, Japan 745-0015
Phone: 81-834-33-2661
Fax: 81-834-33-2662
E-mail: info@skv.jp
Website: net-bs.co.jp/skv/

Type of Firm
Bank Affiliated

Additional Information
Year Founded: 2000
Current Activity Level : Actively seeking new investments

SKAGERAK VENTURE CAPITAL
Markensgate 9
Kristiansand, Norway 4610
Phone: 47-417-48-000
E-mail: post@svc.no
Website: www.saakorn.no

Other Offices
Storgata 8
Kongsberg, Norway 3611

Karenslyst Alle 10
Oslo, Norway 0278

Management and Staff
Andre Edvardsen, Chief Financial Officer
Erik Toennesen, Managing Partner
Joern Lindtvedt, Partner
Trym Skeie, Partner

Type of Firm
Private Equity Firm

Project Preferences

Type of Financing Preferred:
Early Stage
Seed
Later Stage

Geographical Preferences

International Preferences:
Europe
Norway

Industry Preferences

In Consumer Related prefer:
Entertainment and Leisure

In Industrial/Energy prefer:
Oil and Gas Exploration
Alternative Energy

Additional Information
Year Founded: 2006
Capital Under Management: $61,200,000
Current Activity Level : Actively seeking new investments

SKANDIA INNOVATION AB
Sveavagen 44
Stockholm, Sweden 103 50
Phone: 46-8-788-1000
Fax: 46-8-788-3080
E-mail: newventures@skandia.se
Website: www.skandia.com

Other Offices
Bosque de Ciruelos 162
1er piso Col.
Bosques de las Lomas, Mexico
Phone: 52-55-5093-0200
Fax: 52-55-5245-1272

Flat C-1, Floor 24, JiuShi FuXing Mansio
No. 918, Huai Hai Road (M)
Shanghai, China 200020
Phone: 86-21-6415-8145
Fax: 86-21-6415-8146

Postfach 10
Wildpretmarkt 2-4
Vienna, Austria 1013
Phone: 43-1-536-640
Fax: 43-1-535-1662

Via Fatebenefratelli 3
Milan, Italy I-20121
Phone: 39-02-623-1161
Fax: 39-02-655-4576

PL 1129 FIN-00101
Bulevardi 2-4A
Helsinki, Finland FIN-00120
Phone: 358-9-680-3260
Fax: 358-9-644-194

One Corporate Drive
PO Box 883
Shelton, CT USA 06484-0883
Phone: 203-926-1888

C/. Ruiz de Alarcon 11
Madrid, Spain E-28014
Phone: 34-91-524-3400
Fax: 34-91-524-3401

Office 102, Alastor Building
23 Armenias Avenue
Nicosia, Cyprus
Phone: 357-22-315-380
Fax: 357-22-315-254

Level 18
1 Castlereagh Street
Sydney, Australia 2000
Phone: 61-2-8226-8900
Fax: 61-2-9232-1433

Av. da Liberdade
180 E 1 dto
Lisbon, Portugal
Phone: 351-211-210-000
Fax: 351-211-210-009

Stenersgt. 2
Postboks 731 Sentrum
Oslo, Norway
Phone: 47-23-15-9800

Fax: 47-23-15-9801

Tour Areva
1, place de la Coupole
Paris, France 92084
Phone: 33-1-479-667-00
Fax: 33-1-479-667-01

Centro Skandia Avenida 19, 113-30
Apartado Aereo 103 970
Bogota D.C., Colombia
Phone: 57-1-620-5566
Fax: 57-1-612-9105

Migdalowa 4
Warsaw, Poland
Phone: 48-22-332-1700
Fax: 48-22-332-1701

Magdalena 121
Las Condes
Santiago, Chile
Phone: 56-428-7000
Fax: 56-374-2137

Stamholmen 151
Hvidovre, Denmark
Phone: 45-70-12-4747
Fax: 45-70-12-4748

Kaiserin-Augusta-Allee 108
Berlin, Germany 10553
Phone: 49-30-31-0070
Fax: 49-30-31-007-2888

Management and Staff

Jenny Rosberg, Vice President

Type of Firm

Bank Affiliated

Association Membership

Swedish Venture Capital Association (SVCA)

Project Preferences

Type of Financing Preferred:

Leveraged Buyout
Early Stage
Expansion
Seed
Startup

Geographical Preferences

International Preferences:

Europe
Scandanavia/Nordic Region

Industry Preferences

In Financial Services prefer:

Financial Services

Additional Information

Year Founded: 2000
Current Activity Level : Actively seeking new investments

SKANDITEK INDUSTRI-FORVALTNING AB (PUBL)

Kungstradgardsgatan 18
Stockholm, Sweden 111 47
Phone: 46-8-614-0020
Fax: 46-8-614-0038
E-mail: info@skanditek.se
Website: www.skanditek.se

Management and Staff

Hakan Dahlin, Chief Financial Officer

Type of Firm

Private Equity Firm

Association Membership

Swedish Venture Capital Association (SVCA)

Project Preferences

Type of Financing Preferred:

Early Stage

Geographical Preferences

International Preferences:

Sweden

Industry Preferences

In Semiconductor/Electr prefer:

Electronics

In Biotechnology prefer:

Biotechnology

In Business Serv. prefer:

Services

Additional Information

Year Founded: 1984
Capital Under Management: $318,600,000
Current Activity Level : Actively seeking new investments

SKYLAKE INCUVEST & COMPANY

4th Floor, Dae-dong Building
517-10 Dogok-dong Gangnam-gu
Seoul, South Korea 135-270
Phone: 822-579-5511
Fax: 822-579-5441
E-mail: info@skylakeincuvest.com
Website: www.skylakeincuvest.com

Other Offices

1801 Page Mill
Suite 270
Palo Alto, CA USA 94304

Management and Staff

David Lee, Managing Director
Don Suh, Managing Director
Harry Kim, Managing Director
Jin Gyu Kim, Managing Director
Kangsuk Lee, Managing Director
Kevin Choi Seungwoo, Managing Director
Sang-il Park, Managing Director

Type of Firm

Private Equity Firm

Project Preferences

Type of Financing Preferred:

Early Stage
Expansion
Balanced
Later Stage
Seed

Geographical Preferences

International Preferences:

Korea, South
Asia

Industry Preferences

In Communications prefer:

Communications and Media
Commercial Communications
Telecommunications
Wireless Communications
Data Communications

Additional Information

Year Founded: 2006
Capital Under Management: $80,000,000
Current Activity Level : Actively seeking new investments

SKYLAND CAPITAL LLC

8514 Skyland Drive
Niwot, CO USA 80503
Phone: 303-588-1432
Website: www.skylandcapital.com

Management and Staff

Robert Di Scipio, Founder

Type of Firm

Private Equity Firm

Project Preferences

Type of Financing Preferred:

Later Stage

Geographical Preferences

United States Preferences:

All U.S.

Additional Information

Year Founded: 2005
Current Activity Level : Actively seeking new investments

SKYLIGHT CAPITAL

Three Embarcadero Center
Suite 2330
San Francisco, CA USA 94111
Phone: 415-591-1325
Fax: 415-358-9977
E-mail: info@skylight-capital.com
Website: www.skylight-capital.com

Management and Staff

Collin Hathaway, Partner

Type of Firm

Private Equity Firm

Project Preferences

Type of Financing Preferred:
Leveraged Buyout
Later Stage
Acquisition
Recapitalizations

Geographical Preferences

United States Preferences:
West Coast

Industry Preferences

In Consumer Related prefer:
Publishing-Retail
Consumer Products
Consumer Services
Education Related

In Financial Services prefer:
Financial Services

In Business Serv. prefer:
Services
Consulting Services

Additional Information

Year Founded: 2008
Current Activity Level : Actively seeking new investments

SKYLINE VENTURES

525 University Avenue
Suite 520
Palo Alto, CA USA 94301
Phone: 650-462-5800
Fax: 650-329-1090
Website: www.skylineventures.com

Other Offices

1050 Winter Street
Suite 1000
Waltham, MA USA 02451
Phone: 781-530-3616
Fax: 781-530-6805

Management and Staff

David Lowe, Managing Director
Eric Gordon, Partner
Glenn Reicin, Managing Director
John Freund, Managing Director
Stephen Sullivan, Managing Director
Stephen Hoffman, Managing Director
Yasumori Kaneko, Managing Director

Type of Firm

Private Equity Firm

Association Membership

Western Association of Venture Capitalists (WAVC)

Project Preferences

Type of Financing Preferred:
Early Stage
Expansion
Later Stage

Geographical Preferences

United States Preferences:
All U.S.

Industry Focus

(% based on actual investment)

Biotechnology	48.9%
Medical/Health	43.0%
Computer Software and Services	6.0%
Internet Specific	2.0%

Additional Information

Name of Most Recent Fund: Skyline Venture Partners V, L.P.
Most Recent Fund Was Raised: 11/12/2007
Year Founded: 1997
Capital Under Management: $800,000,000
Current Activity Level : Actively seeking new investments

SKYMOON VENTURES

3350 Scott Boulevard
Building One
Santa Clara, CA USA 95054
Phone: 408-327-6610
Fax: 408-484-0580
E-mail: info@skymoonventures.com
Website: www.skymoonventures.com

Management and Staff

Barbara Paldus, Principal
Mark Holtzman, Chief Financial Officer
Michael Farmwald, General Partner

Type of Firm

Private Equity Firm

Project Preferences

Role in Financing:
Will function either as deal originator or investor in deals created by others

Type of Financing Preferred:
Second Stage Financing
Early Stage
Research and Development
Balanced
Startup

Size of Investments Considered:
Min Size of Investment Considered (000s): $50
Max Size of Investment Considered (000s): $15,000

Industry Preferences

In Computer Software prefer:
Computer Services
Software

In Semiconductor/Electr prefer:
Electronic Components
Semiconductor
Sensors
Analytic/Scientific

In Biotechnology prefer:
Biotech Related Research

In Industrial/Energy prefer:
Industrial Products

In Business Serv. prefer:
Services

Additional Information

Name of Most Recent Fund: Skymoon Ventures I
Most Recent Fund Was Raised: 03/19/2001
Year Founded: 2001
Capital Under Management: $85,000,000
Current Activity Level : Actively seeking new investments
Method of Compensation: Return on investment is of primary concern, do not charge fees

SKYPOINT CAPITAL CORPORATION

555 Legget Drive, Tower B
Suite 830
Ottawa, Canada K2K 2X3
Phone: 613-271-1500
Fax: 613-271-1505
E-mail: info@skypointcorp.com
Website: www.skypointcorp.com

Other Offices

1501 McGill College Avenue
Suite 2240
Montreal, Canada H3B 3N2
Phone: 514-878-1400
Fax: 514-878-2446

Management and Staff

Andrew Katz, General Partner
Ann Gordon, Chief Financial Officer
Claude Haw, General Partner
Donna Cowan, Venture Partner
Larry Perron, Partner
Leo Lax, Partner
Louis Desmarais, Partner
Peter Diedrich, Partner
Peter Charbonneau, General Partner

Stefan Opalski, Venture Partner

Type of Firm
Private Equity Firm

Project Preferences
Type of Financing Preferred:
Early Stage

Geographical Preferences
Canadian Preferences:
All Canada

International Preferences:
United Kingdom
Israel

Industry Preferences
In Communications prefer:
Telecommunications

Additional Information
Name of Most Recent Fund: Skypoint Telecom Fund II
Most Recent Fund Was Raised: 05/16/2001
Year Founded: 1998
Capital Under Management: $185,000,000
Current Activity Level : Actively seeking new investments

SKYVEN ASSET MANAGEMENT PTE, LTD.
2 Alexandra Road
#06-02 Delta House
Singapore, Singapore 159919
Phone: 65-6371-7088
Fax: 65-6272-0602
E-mail: info@skyven.com
Website: www.skyven.com

Management and Staff
Peter Tan, Managing Partner

Type of Firm
Private Equity Firm

Project Preferences
Type of Financing Preferred:
Expansion
Later Stage

Size of Investments Considered:
Min Size of Investment Considered (000s): $1,000
Max Size of Investment Considered (000s): $5,000

Geographical Preferences
United States Preferences:
All U.S.

International Preferences:
India
China
Asia
Singapore

Industry Preferences
In Medical/Health prefer:
Medical/Health

In Consumer Related prefer:
Consumer
Retail
Food/Beverage

In Industrial/Energy prefer:
Energy
Environmental Related

In Business Serv. prefer:
Services

In Manufact. prefer:
Manufacturing

In Other prefer:
Environment Responsible

Additional Information
Year Founded: 2000
Current Activity Level : Actively seeking new investments

SKYVIEW CAPITAL
9777 Wilshire Boulevard
7th Floor
Beverly Hills, CA USA 90210
Phone: 310-273-6000
Fax: 310-273-6006
E-mail: info@skyviewcapital.com
Website: www.skyviewcapital.com

Type of Firm
Private Equity Firm

Project Preferences
Type of Financing Preferred:
Leveraged Buyout
Acquisition

Geographical Preferences
United States Preferences:
All U.S.

International Preferences:
Latin America
Europe

Industry Preferences
In Communications prefer:
Telecommunications

In Computer Software prefer:
Software
Systems Software

Additional Information
Year Founded: 2005
Current Activity Level : Actively seeking new investments

SL CAPITAL PARTNERS LLP
2nd Floor
1 George Street
Edinburgh, United Kingdom EH2 2LL
Phone: 44-131-245-0055
Fax: 44-131-245-6105
E-mail: private_equity@standardlife.com
Website: www.privateequity.standardlifeinvestments.com

Other Offices
One Beacon Street
34th Floor
Boston, MA USA 02108
Phone: 617-720-7900

Management and Staff
Craig Williamson, Partner
Dan Cahill, Managing Director
David Currie, Chief Executive Officer
Graeme Faulds, Partner
Graeme Gunn, Partner
Graham Paterson, Partner
Roger Pim, Partner
Roland Brinkman, Partner
Stewart Hay, Partner
Vicente Miguel Ramos, Vice President

Type of Firm
Private Equity Advisor or Fund of Funds
Association Membership
European Private Equity and Venture Capital Assoc.

Project Preferences
Role in Financing:
Prefer role as deal originator but will also invest in deals created by others

Type of Financing Preferred:
Fund of Funds
Leveraged Buyout
Balanced
Management Buyouts

Size of Investments Considered:
Min Size of Investment Considered (000s): $13,980
Max Size of Investment Considered (000s): $104,851

Geographical Preferences
Canadian Preferences:
All Canada

International Preferences:
Italy
Ireland
United Kingdom
Portugal
Europe
Western Europe
Bermuda
Eastern Europe
Spain
Belgium

Germany
France

Industry Focus

(% based on actual investment)

Other Products	41.6%
Consumer Related	23.5%
Medical/Health	13.9%
Industrial/Energy	13.9%
Communications and Media	4.0%
Computer Software and Services	3.1%

Additional Information

Year Founded: 1998
Capital Under Management: $8,711,000,000
Current Activity Level : Actively seeking new investments
Method of Compensation: Return on investment is of primary concern, do not charge fees

SL INVESTMENT COMPANY, LTD.

25/F, Gangnam Finance Center
737 Yeoksam 1-dong, Gangnam-gu
Seoul, South Korea 135-984
Phone: 82-2-6241-5400
Fax: 82-2-6241-5412
Website: www.slinvestment.com

Other Offices

501 Orchard Road
Wheelock Place, 13-02
Singapore, Singapore 238880
Phone: 65-6820-9665
Fax: 65-6820-9700

Type of Firm

Private Equity Firm

Association Membership

Korean Venture Capital Association (KVCA)

Project Preferences

Type of Financing Preferred:
Early Stage
Expansion
Mezzanine
Balanced
Turnaround
Recapitalizations

Size of Investments Considered:
Min Size of Investment Considered (000s): $500
Max Size of Investment Considered (000s): $2,500

Geographical Preferences

International Preferences:
Korea, South

Industry Preferences

In Communications prefer:
Telecommunications

In Computer Software prefer:
Software

In Computer Other prefer:
Computer Related

In Semiconductor/Electr prefer:
Electronics
Semiconductor

In Biotechnology prefer:
Biotechnology

In Industrial/Energy prefer:
Energy

In Manufact. prefer:
Manufacturing

Additional Information

Year Founded: 2000
Capital Under Management: $30,800,000
Current Activity Level : Actively seeking new investments

SLATE VENTURE GROUP

2201 Old Court Road
Baltimore, MD USA 21208
Phone: 410-560-3572
Fax: 630-214-8572
Website: www.slateventuregroup.com

Management and Staff

Erik Ginsberg, Partner
Rick Corcoran, Partner

Type of Firm

Private Equity Firm

Project Preferences

Type of Financing Preferred:
Leveraged Buyout
Generalist PE
Expansion

Geographical Preferences

United States Preferences:
Mid Atlantic

Industry Preferences

In Consumer Related prefer:
Consumer
Retail

In Business Serv. prefer:
Services

Additional Information

Year Founded: 2007
Current Activity Level : Actively seeking new investments

SLATER TECHNOLOGY FUND

Three Davol Square
Suite A301, MB 175
Providence, RI USA 02903
Phone: 401-831-9700
Fax: 401-521-9850
Website: www.slaterfund.com

Management and Staff

Richard Horan, Senior Managing Director

Type of Firm

Government Affiliated Program

Association Membership

National Venture Capital Association - USA (NVCA)

Project Preferences

Type of Financing Preferred:
Early Stage
Seed
Startup

Size of Investments Considered:
Min Size of Investment Considered (000s): $100
Max Size of Investment Considered (000s): $500

Geographical Preferences

United States Preferences:
Rhode Island

Industry Preferences

In Biotechnology prefer:
Biotechnology

In Other prefer:
Environment Responsible

Additional Information

Year Founded: 1997
Capital Under Management: $28,000,000
Current Activity Level : Actively seeking new investments

SLAVIA CAPITAL

Heydukova 6
P.O. Box 29
Bratislava, Slovakia 81499
Phone: 421-2-5931-7110
Fax: 421-2-5931-7155
E-mail: slavia@slaviacapital.com
Website: www.slaviacapital.com

Other Offices

Ul. Svetozara Markovica 19
Belgrade, Serbia and Montenegro 11000
Phone: 381-11-323-3291
Fax: 381-11-323-3291

Rytirska 13
Prague, Czech Republic 11000
Phone: 420-221-181-060
Fax: 420-221-181-068

Management and Staff

Adrian Corba, Partner
Erik Cebik, Partner
Magda Halandova, Partner
Peter Kusnir, Partner

Type of Firm

Bank Affiliated

Project Preferences

Type of Financing Preferred:
Balanced

Geographical Preferences

International Preferences:
Central Europe

Industry Preferences

In Biotechnology prefer:
Biotechnology

In Industrial/Energy prefer:
Energy
Alternative Energy

In Financial Services prefer:
Financial Services

Additional Information

Year Founded: 2007
Current Activity Level : Actively seeking new investments

SLOAN VENTURES

430 North Old Woodword
Birmingham, MI USA 48009
Phone: 248-540-9660
Fax: 248-540-5461
E-mail: info@sloanventures.com
Website: www.sloanventures.com

Management and Staff

Christopher Cameron, Partner
Jeffrey Sloan, CEO & Managing Director
John Siverling, Partner
Richard Sloan, Managing Director

Type of Firm

Private Equity Firm

Project Preferences

Type of Financing Preferred:
Early Stage
Later Stage
Seed

Size of Investments Considered:
Min Size of Investment Considered (000s): $200
Max Size of Investment Considered (000s): $2,000

Geographical Preferences

United States Preferences:
Midwest
Michigan

International Preferences:
All International

Industry Preferences

In Internet Specific prefer:
Internet

In Biotechnology prefer:
Biotechnology

In Business Serv. prefer:
Services

Additional Information

Name of Most Recent Fund: MLSC Catalyst Fund
Most Recent Fund Was Raised: 09/30/2001
Year Founded: 1995
Capital Under Management: $9,000,000
Current Activity Level : Actively seeking new investments

SLOVAK AMERICAN ENTERPRISE FUND (AKA: SAEF)

Obchodna 58
P.O. Box 100
Bratislava, Slovakia 810 06
Phone: 421-2-5710-0200
Fax: 421-2-5273-1323
E-mail: office@saef.sk
Website: www.saef.sk

Management and Staff

Peter Srpon, Chief Financial Officer

Type of Firm

Private Equity Firm

Association Membership

European Private Equity and Venture Capital Assoc.

Project Preferences

Type of Financing Preferred:
Leveraged Buyout
Expansion
Joint Ventures
Distressed Debt

Size of Investments Considered:
Min Size of Investment Considered (000s): $350
Max Size of Investment Considered (000s): $2,500

Geographical Preferences

International Preferences:
Slovak Repub.

Industry Focus

(% based on actual investment)

Other Products	36.4%
Computer Software and Services	30.6%
Industrial/Energy	30.1%
Communications and Media	2.9%

Additional Information

Year Founded: 1991
Capital Under Management: $24,500,000
Current Activity Level : Actively seeking new investments

SMAC PARTNERS (FKA: SIEMENS ACCELERATION IN COMMUNICATION)

Ottobrunner Str. 41
Unterhaching, Germany 82008
Phone: 49-89-550-6880
Fax: 49-89-5506-8850
E-mail: info@smacpartners.com
Website: www.smacpartners.com

Management and Staff

Ingo Potthof, Founding Partner

Type of Firm

Private Equity Advisor or Fund of Funds

Association Membership

Swedish Venture Capital Association (SVCA)
European Private Equity and Venture Capital Assoc.

Project Preferences

Role in Financing:
Prefer role as deal originator but will also invest in deals created by others

Type of Financing Preferred:
Early Stage
Balanced
Start-up Financing
Later Stage
First Stage Financing
Startup
Fund of Funds of Second

Size of Investments Considered:
Min Size of Investment Considered (000s): $706
Max Size of Investment Considered (000s): $14,110

Geographical Preferences

United States Preferences:
All U.S.

International Preferences:
Europe
Israel
Asia
Finland
All International

Industry Preferences

In Communications prefer:
Communications and Media
Commercial Communications
Telecommunications
Wireless Communications
Data Communications
Other Communication Prod.

In Computer Other prefer:
Computer Related

In Semiconductor/Electr prefer:
Electronics

Additional Information
Name of Most Recent Fund: SMAC Partners Fund II, L.P.
Most Recent Fund Was Raised: 12/17/2007
Year Founded: 2001
Capital Under Management: $90,100,000
Current Activity Level : Actively seeking new investments

SMAFORETAGSINVEST AB
Vasagatan 11
11 Tr
Stockholm, Sweden 11120
Phone: 46-8-5879-1970
Fax: 46-46-8587-9197
Type of Firm
Bank Affiliated

Project Preferences

Type of Financing Preferred:
Balanced

Geographical Preferences

International Preferences:
Sweden

Industry Preferences

In Manufact. prefer:
Manufacturing

Additional Information
Year Founded: 2007
Current Activity Level : Actively seeking new investments

SMALL BUSINESS GUARANTEE AND FINANCE CORPORATION
17 & 18F, 139 Corporate Center
139 Valero St, Salcedo Village
Makati, Philippines 1227
Phone: 63-2-751-1888
Fax: 63-2-813-5726
Website: www.sbgfc.org.ph

Other Offices
Unit 76, 7F, Landco Corporate Center
JP Laurel Avenue, Bajada
Davao, Philippines
Phone: 63-82-221-1488
Fax: 63-82-221-0858

Unit 802-B, Keppel Center
Cebu Business Park
Cebu City, Philippines
Phone: 63-32-232-1200
Fax: 63-32-234-4500

Management and Staff
Alfredo Dimaculangan, Vice President
Alice Sy, Vice President
Daniel Gonzales, Vice President
Hector Olmedillo, Vice President
Melvin Abanto, Vice President
Modesto Butalid, Vice President
Peter Pizarro, Vice President
Virgilio Angelo, Chairman & CEO

Type of Firm
Government Affiliated Program

Project Preferences

Type of Financing Preferred:
Balanced

Geographical Preferences

International Preferences:
Philippines

Additional Information
Year Founded: 1991
Current Activity Level : Actively seeking new investments

SMALL ENTERPRISE ASSISTANCE FUND (SEAF)
1050 17th Street NW
Suite 1150
Washington, DC USA 20036
Phone: 202-737-8463
Fax: 202-737-5536
E-mail: seafhq@seafweb.org
Website: www.seafweb.org

Other Offices
Baltic Small Equity Fund
29-2 Lacplesa St., Suite 9
Riga, Latvia 1011
Phone: 371-728-9500
Fax: 371-728-9547

Trans-Balkan Bulgaria Fund
22 Zlaten Rog St, 8th Floor
Sofia, Bulgaria 1407
Phone: 359-2-917-4950
Fax: 359-2-917-4951

Sichuan Small Investment Fund
Building Office 2307, 45 Zhongfu Road
Chengdu, China 610016
Phone: 86-28-8290-3508
Fax: 86-28-8625-5325

CASEF
Kabanbai Batyr 76
Almaty, Kazakhstan 050012
Phone: 7-3272-587-593
Fax: 7-3272-587-595

TBRF, Strada Octavian Goga 4,
Bloc M26, Parter, Sector 3
Bucharest, Romania 030982
Phone: 4021-326-7340
Fax: 4021-326 7337

Baltic Small Equity Fund/CEE Growth Fund
Parnu mnt 142, 6th Floor
Tallinn, Estonia 11317
Phone: 372-651-2690
Fax: 372-651-2693

SEAF-Croatia
Britanski trg 5/11
Zagreb, Croatia 10000
Phone: 385-1-481-1912
Fax: 385-1-482-3558

CASEF
Rakatboshi Street #27
Tashkent, Uzbekistan 70031
Phone: 998-71-139-1620
Fax: 998-71-139-1680

Ed. Eduardo Abaroa, Planta Baja,
Sanchez Lima esq. Belisario
Salinas, La Paz, Bolivia
Phone: 591-2-242-4788
Fax: 591-2-242-4788

SEAF-Macedonia
Metropolit Teodosij Gologanov 28
Skopje, Macedonia 1000
Phone: 389-2-3079-611
Fax: 389-2-3079-612

CARESBAC
ul. Polna 40
Warsaw, Poland 00-635
Phone: 48-22-825-6205
Fax: 48-22-825-4650

Stichting-SEAF
Valeriusstraat 124-boven
Amsterdam, Netherlands 1075 GD
Phone: 31-641-385-111
Fax: 31-348-424-652

Equipetrol Calle 7
Oeste #16
Santa Cruz, Bolivia
Phone: 591-3-332-5392
Fax: 591-3-332-5392

Transandian Fund
Calle Martir Olaya 129, Miraflores
Lima, Peru 18
Phone: 51-1-444-2020
Fax: 51-1-444-2009

Management and Staff

Jose Garcia Herz, General Director

Type of Firm

Incubator/Development Program

Project Preferences

Type of Financing Preferred:

Early Stage
Expansion
Balanced
Strategic Alliances

Size of Investments Considered:

Min Size of Investment Considered (000s): $100
Max Size of Investment Considered (000s): $100,000

Geographical Preferences

International Preferences:

Slovenia
Vietnam
India
Slovak Repub.
Czech Republic
Kazakhstan
Central Europe
Bolivia
China
Macedonia
Peru
Poland
Croatia
Kyrgyzstan
Tajikistan
Turkmenistan
Eastern Europe
Bulgaria
Estonia
Colombia
Romania
Uzbekistan
Latvia
Lithuania

Industry Preferences

In Communications prefer:

CATV & Pay TV Systems
Telecommunications
Media and Entertainment

In Computer Software prefer:

Software

In Internet Specific prefer:

Internet

In Semiconductor/Electr prefer:

Electronics

In Medical/Health prefer:

Pharmaceuticals

In Consumer Related prefer:

Retail
Food/Beverage
Consumer Products

In Industrial/Energy prefer:

Industrial Products

In Business Serv. prefer:

Services
Distribution
Media

In Agr/Forestr/Fish prefer:

Agriculture related

Additional Information

Year Founded: 1992
Capital Under Management: $130,000,000
Current Activity Level : Actively seeking new investments

SMALL VENTURES USA, L.P.

3050 Post Oak Boulevard
Suite 460
Houston, TX USA 77056
Phone: 713-341-7916
Fax: 713-583-9206
E-mail: info@smallventuresusa.com
Website: www.smallventuresusa.com

Management and Staff

Eddie Hernandez, Partner
Kayla Bruzzese, Chief Financial Officer
Mathew Johnson, Partner
William Perkins, President, Founder

Type of Firm

Private Equity Firm

Project Preferences

Type of Financing Preferred:

Early Stage
Balanced

Additional Information

Year Founded: 2008
Current Activity Level : Actively seeking new investments

SMART TECHNOLOGY VENTURES

1801 Century Park West
Fifth Floor
Los Angeles, CA USA 90067
Phone: 310-203-3800
Fax: 310-203-3801
Website: www.stv.com

Management and Staff

Michael Holton, Principal
Paula Robins, Chief Financial Officer

Type of Firm

Private Equity Firm

Association Membership

Natl Assoc of Small Bus. Inv. Co (NASBIC)

Project Preferences

Role in Financing:

Will function either as deal originator or investor in deals created by others

Type of Financing Preferred:

Second Stage Financing
Early Stage
Later Stage
Seed
First Stage Financing

Size of Investments Considered:

Min Size of Investment Considered (000s): $3,000
Max Size of Investment Considered (000s): $8,000

Geographical Preferences

United States Preferences:

Southern California
West Coast

Industry Preferences

In Communications prefer:

Wireless Communications

In Semiconductor/Electr prefer:

Electronic Components
Semiconductor
Micro-Processing
Laser Related
Fiber Optics

Additional Information

Year Founded: 1997
Capital Under Management: $175,000,000
Current Activity Level : Actively seeking new investments
Method of Compensation: Return on investment is of primary concern, do not charge fees

---

SMARTFOREST VENTURES

319 Southwest Washington St.
Suite 720
Portland, OR USA 97204
Phone: 503-222-2552
Fax: 503-222-2834
E-mail: contactus@smartforest.com
Website: www.smartforest.com

Other Offices

535 Middlefield Road
Suite 280

Menlo Park, CA USA 94025
Phone: 650-330-0880
Fax: 650-330-0785

Management and Staff

Debi Coleman, Managing Partner
Hans Lundin, Chief Financial Officer
Hugh Mackworth, Managing Partner
Huoy-Ming Yeh, Partner
Peter Gardner, Venture Partner
Thomas Toy, General Partner

Type of Firm

SBIC

Association Membership

Natl Assoc of Small Bus. Inv. Co (NASBIC)

Project Preferences

Role in Financing:
Prefer role as deal originator but will also invest in deals created by others

Type of Financing Preferred:
Early Stage
Seed
First Stage Financing
Startup

Size of Investments Considered:
Min Size of Investment Considered (000s): $250
Max Size of Investment Considered (000s): $2,000

Geographical Preferences

United States Preferences:
Northwest

Industry Preferences

In Communications prefer:
Communications and Media

In Computer Hardware prefer:
Computers

In Internet Specific prefer:
Internet

Additional Information

Year Founded: 2000
Capital Under Management: $75,000,000
Current Activity Level : Actively seeking new investments
Method of Compensation: Return on investment is of primary concern, do not charge fees

---

SMEDVIG CAPITAL, LTD. (FKA: PEDER SMEDVIG CAPITAL LTD)

20 St. James's Street
London, United Kingdom SW1A 1ES
Phone: 44-20-7451-2100
Fax: 44-20-7451-2101
E-mail: enquiries@smedvigcapital.com
Website: www.smedvigcapital.com

Other Offices

Finnestadveien 28
PO Box 110
Stavanger, Norway 4001
Phone: 47 5150 9900
Fax: 47 5150 9688

Management and Staff

Alistair Cairns, Managing Director
Rob Toms, Managing Director

Type of Firm

Private Equity Firm

Association Membership

British Venture Capital Association (BVCA)

Project Preferences

Type of Financing Preferred:
Early Stage
Expansion
Management Buyouts
Startup

Size of Investments Considered:
Min Size of Investment Considered (000s): $2,706
Max Size of Investment Considered (000s): $13,531

Geographical Preferences

International Preferences:
United Kingdom
Europe

Additional Information

Year Founded: 1996
Capital Under Management: $250,000,000
Current Activity Level : Actively seeking new investments

SMITH DEFIEUX CAPITAL PARTNERS

1850 K Street, North West
Suite 1075
Washington, DC USA 20006
Phone: 202-223-7574
Fax: 202-293-8850
E-mail: info@smithdefieux.com
Website: www.smithdefieux.com

Management and Staff

Gustav Koven, General Partner
Richard Defieux, General Partner
Tom Smith, General Partner

Type of Firm

Private Equity Firm

Project Preferences

Type of Financing Preferred:
Balanced

Additional Information

Year Founded: 2007
Current Activity Level : Actively seeking new investments

SNOW PHIPPS GROUP LLC (FKA: SPG PARTNERS, LLC)

667 Madison Avenue
18th Floor
New York, NY USA 10021
Phone: 212-508-3300
Fax: 212-508-3301

Management and Staff

Ian Snow, Co-Founder
Ogden Phipps, Co-Founder
Steven Schwinger, Chief Financial Officer

Type of Firm

Private Equity Firm

Project Preferences

Type of Financing Preferred:
Leveraged Buyout
Acquisition

Geographical Preferences

United States Preferences:
All U.S.

Additional Information

Year Founded: 2005
Capital Under Management: $620,000,000
Current Activity Level : Actively seeking new investments

SNVB PARTICIPATIONS

4 place Andre Maginot
Nancy, France 54000
Phone: 33-3-8334-5563
Fax: 33-3-8334-5325
E-mail: snvbpart@snvb.cic.fr
Website: www.snvb.fr

Management and Staff

Henri Jaron, President
Luc Dymarski, General Director
Philippe Vidal, President
Thierry Marois, Vice President

Type of Firm

Private Equity Firm

Project Preferences

Type of Financing Preferred:
Leveraged Buyout
Early Stage
Expansion

Geographical Preferences

International Preferences:
France

Additional Information

Year Founded: 1987
Current Activity Level : Actively seeking new investments

SOCADIF

26 quai de la Rapee
Paris, France 75012
Phone: 33-1-4473-2638
Fax: 33-1-4473-1523
E-mail: socadif@ca-socadif.fr
Website: www.socadif.fr

Type of Firm

Private Equity Firm

Association Membership

French Venture Capital Association (AFIC)

Project Preferences

Type of Financing Preferred:
Leveraged Buyout
Early Stage
Expansion

Geographical Preferences

International Preferences:
France

Additional Information

Year Founded: 1990
Current Activity Level : Actively seeking new investments

SOCCRENT

2455, rue Cantin
C.P. 933
Jonquiere, Canada G7X 8S7
Phone: 418-546-1155
Fax: 418-546-1150

Management and Staff

Marc Lalancette, Vice President

Type of Firm

Private Equity Firm

Additional Information

Year Founded: 1986
Current Activity Level : Actively seeking new investments

SOCIEDAD REGIONAL DE PROMOCION DEL PRINCIPADO DE ASTURIAS

Parque Tecnologico de Asturias
Llanera, Spain 33428
Phone: 34-985-980-096
Fax: 34-985-980-222
E-mail: srp@srp.es
Website: www.srp.es

Type of Firm

Private Equity Firm

Project Preferences

Type of Financing Preferred:
Early Stage
Expansion
Balanced
Other

Geographical Preferences

International Preferences:
Spain

Additional Information

Year Founded: 2004
Current Activity Level : Actively seeking new investments

SOCIETE AFRICAINE DE PARTICIPATION (SAPA)

P.O. Box 11834 Yaounde
Yaounde, Cameroon
Phone: 237-23-220-6732
Fax: 237-23-220-6650

Type of Firm

Private Equity Firm

Association Membership

African Venture Capital Association (AVCA)

Project Preferences

Type of Financing Preferred:
Early Stage
Expansion

Size of Investments Considered:
Min Size of Investment Considered (000s): $22
Max Size of Investment Considered (000s): $324

Geographical Preferences

International Preferences:
Cameroon
Africa

Industry Preferences

In Communications prefer:
Telecommunications

In Financial Services prefer:
Financial Services
Insurance

Additional Information

Year Founded: 1990
Current Activity Level : Actively seeking new investments

SOCIETE D INVESTISSEMENT EN PARTICIPATION INC.

100-1155, boulevard
Rene-Levesque Ouest
Montreal, Canada H3B 4P7
Phone: 514-861-9252

Type of Firm

Investment Management Firm

Geographical Preferences

Canadian Preferences:
Quebec

Additional Information

Year Founded: 1993
Current Activity Level : Actively seeking new investments

SOCIETE FONCIERE ET FINANCIERE DE PARTICIPATION (AKA: SFFP)

75, Avenue de la Grande
Paris, France 33680
Phone: 33-1-4066-4211
Fax: 33-1-4066-5992
Website: www.societe-ffp.fr

Management and Staff

Robert Peugeot, Chief Executive Officer

Type of Firm

Bank Affiliated

Project Preferences

Type of Financing Preferred:
Acquisition

Geographical Preferences

International Preferences:
France

Additional Information

Year Founded: 2001
Current Activity Level : Actively seeking new investments

SOCIETE GENERALE DE FINANCEMENT DU QUEBEC (SGF)

600 de la Gauchetiere West
Suite 1700
Montreal, Canada H3B 4L8
Phone: 514-876-9290
Fax: 514-395-8055
E-mail: info@sgfqc.com
Website: www.sgfqc.com

Management and Staff

Henri Roy, President
Jean-Yves Duthel, Vice President
Richard Fredette, Vice President

Type of Firm

Bank Affiliated

Project Preferences

Type of Financing Preferred:
Balanced

Geographical Preferences

Canadian Preferences:
All Canada

Industry Preferences

In Medical/Health prefer:
Medical/Health

In Industrial/Energy prefer:
Energy

In Transportation prefer:
Transportation

In Agr/Forestr/Fish prefer:
Agriculture related

Additional Information

Year Founded: 2001
Current Activity Level : Actively seeking new investments

SOCIETE REGIONALE D INVESTISSEMENT DE WALLONIE SA (SRIW)

Avenue Destenay, 13
Liege, Belgium B-40000
Phone: 32-41-21-9811
Fax: 32-41-21-9999
E-mail: sriw@sriw.be
Website: www.sriw.be

Type of Firm

Private Equity Firm

Project Preferences

Type of Financing Preferred:
Second Stage Financing
Early Stage
Expansion
Startup

Geographical Preferences

International Preferences:
Europe
Belgium

Industry Preferences

In Communications prefer:
Telecommunications

In Financial Services prefer:
Real Estate

In Other prefer:
Environment Responsible

Additional Information

Year Founded: 1978
Current Activity Level : Actively seeking new investments

SOCIT D INVESTISSEMENT TREMPLIN 2000 INC.

2, Complexe Desjardins
bureau 1717
Montreal, Canada H5B 1B8
Phone: 514-281-7131
Fax: 514-281-7808

Type of Firm

Private Equity Advisor or Fund of Funds

Additional Information

Year Founded: 1987
Current Activity Level : Actively seeking new investments

SOCO

114-15 Innovation Boulevard
Saskatoon, Canada S7N 2X8
Phone: 306-933-6295
Fax: 306-933-8215
E-mail: saskatoon@innovationplace.com
Website: www.soco.sk.ca

Management and Staff

Austin Beggs, Vice President
Lorne Vinish, Vice President

Type of Firm

Government Affiliated Program

Additional Information

Year Founded: 1994
Current Activity Level : Actively seeking new investments

SODECO (AKA: SOC. DESAR. COMARCAS MINERAS)

C/La Union, 21
La Felguera (Asturias), Spain 33930
Phone: 34-985-691-446
Fax: 34-985-682-962
E-mail: sodeco@las.es
Website: www.sodeco.es

Management and Staff

Jose Mier Albert, General Director

Type of Firm

Private Equity Firm

Association Membership

Spanish Venture Capital Association (ASCRI)

Project Preferences

Role in Financing:
Prefer role in deals created by others

Type of Financing Preferred:
Second Stage Financing
Start-up Financing
First Stage Financing
Startup

Geographical Preferences

International Preferences:
Spain

Additional Information

Year Founded: 1988
Capital Under Management: $40,000,000
Current Activity Level : Actively seeking new investments
Method of Compensation: Return on invest. most important, but chg. closing fees, service fees, etc.

SODEK

70 Avenue de la liberte
Tunis, Tunisia 1002
Phone: 216-71-798-932
Fax: 216-71-799-750
E-mail: sidco.sicar@gnet.tn

Type of Firm

Private Equity Firm

Project Preferences

Role in Financing:
Will function either as deal originator or investor in deals created by others

Type of Financing Preferred:
Balanced

Geographical Preferences

International Preferences:
Tunisia

Additional Information

Year Founded: 2004
Current Activity Level : Actively seeking new investments

SODENA - SOCIEDAD DE DESARROLLO DE NAVARRA

Avenida Carlos III el Noble
36, 1 Dcha.
Pamplona, Spain 31003
Phone: 34-848-421-942
Fax: 34-848-421-943
E-mail: info@sodena.com
Website: www.sodena.com

Management and Staff

Jose Javier Armendariz, President
Jose Maria Yoldi, Chief Executive Officer

Type of Firm

Incubator/Development Program

Association Membership

European Private Equity and Venture Capital Assoc.
Spanish Venture Capital Association (ASCRI)

Project Preferences

Type of Financing Preferred:
Leveraged Buyout
Expansion
Balanced
Turnaround
Seed
Startup

Geographical Preferences

International Preferences:
Spain

Industry Preferences

In Communications prefer:
Telecommunications

In Computer Other prefer:
Computer Related

In Biotechnology prefer:
Biotechnology

In Consumer Related prefer:
Entertainment and Leisure

In Industrial/Energy prefer:
Alternative Energy
Environmental Related

In Business Serv. prefer:
Services

Additional Information

Year Founded: 1984
Capital Under Management: $450,000,000
Current Activity Level : Actively seeking new investments

SODERHAMN INVEST AB

P.O. Box 141
Soderhamn, Sweden 82 623
Phone: 46-270-18-000
Fax: 46-270-14-900
E-mail: info@soderhamn-invest.se
Website: www.soderhamn-invest.se

Management and Staff

Bo Nyman, Managing Director

Type of Firm

Private Equity Firm

Association Membership

Swedish Venture Capital Association (SVCA)

Project Preferences

Type of Financing Preferred:
Leveraged Buyout
Expansion
Seed
Startup

Geographical Preferences

International Preferences:
Scandanavia/Nordic Region

Additional Information

Year Founded: 2000
Capital Under Management: $6,400,000
Current Activity Level : Actively seeking new investments

SODERLIND & CO AB

Birger Jarlsgatan 41A
Stockholm, Sweden 111 45
Phone: 46-8-402-1060
Fax: 46-8-402-1061
E-mail: info@soderlind.se
Website: www.soderlind.se

Type of Firm

Private Equity Firm

Project Preferences

Type of Financing Preferred:
Balanced

Geographical Preferences

International Preferences:
Sweden
Europe

Additional Information

Year Founded: 2005
Current Activity Level : Actively seeking new investments

SODERO PARTICIPATIONS

13 rue la Perouse
Nantes, France BP 31715
Phone: 33-2-4041-5216
Fax: 33-2-4048-5987
Website: www.gpe-sodero.com

Type of Firm

Corporate PE/Venture

Association Membership

French Venture Capital Association (AFIC)

Project Preferences

Type of Financing Preferred:
Leveraged Buyout
Early Stage
Expansion
Recapitalizations

Size of Investments Considered:
Min Size of Investment Considered (000s): $71
Max Size of Investment Considered (000s): $706

Geographical Preferences

International Preferences:
France

Additional Information

Year Founded: 1999
Capital Under Management: $9,300,000
Current Activity Level : Actively seeking new investments

SODIAR - SOCIEDAD PARA EL DESARROLLO INDUSTRIAL DE ARAGON

Pl. Roma f-1, oficina 12
Zaragoza, Spain 50010
Phone: 34-976-320-000
Fax: 34-976-535-220
E-mail: sodiar@sodiar.com
Website: www.sodiar.com

Type of Firm

Private Equity Firm

Association Membership

Spanish Venture Capital Association (ASCRI)

Project Preferences

Type of Financing Preferred:
Expansion

Size of Investments Considered:
Min Size of Investment Considered (000s): $105
Max Size of Investment Considered (000s): $474

Geographical Preferences

International Preferences:
Spain

Additional Information

Year Founded: 1983
Current Activity Level : Actively seeking new investments

SODICAB - SICAR S.A.

Place 7 Novembre
Imm. de la Jarre, BP 160
Nabeul, Tunisia 8000
Phone: 216-72-230-240
Fax: 216-72-230-161
E-mail: sodicab@planet.tn
Website: www.sodicab.com.tn

Type of Firm

Private Equity Firm

Association Membership

African Venture Capital Association (AVCA)

Project Preferences

Type of Financing Preferred:
Early Stage
Expansion

Size of Investments Considered:
Min Size of Investment Considered (000s): $53
Max Size of Investment Considered (000s): $531

Geographical Preferences

International Preferences:
Tunisia

Industry Preferences

In Industrial/Energy prefer:
Industrial Products

Additional Information

Year Founded: 1999
Capital Under Management: $4,600,000
Current Activity Level : Actively seeking new investments

SODICAL - SOC.IND. DE CASTILLA Y LEON

Doctrinos, 6 - 4o
Valladolid, Spain 47001
Phone: 34-98-334-3811
Fax: 34-98-333-0702
E-mail: sodical@sodical.es
Website: www.sodical.es

Management and Staff

Manuel Fernandez Diez, General Director
Matias Pedruelo Diez, President

Type of Firm

Private Equity Firm

Association Membership

Spanish Venture Capital Association (ASCRI)

Project Preferences

Type of Financing Preferred:
Second Stage Financing
Expansion
Balanced
Startup

Size of Investments Considered:
Min Size of Investment Considered (000s): $158
Max Size of Investment Considered (000s): $1,052

Geographical Preferences

International Preferences:
Europe
Spain

Industry Preferences

In Industrial/Energy prefer:
Materials

In Agr/Forestr/Fish prefer:
Agribusiness
Agriculture related

In Other prefer:
Environment Responsible

Additional Information

Year Founded: 1994
Current Activity Level : Actively seeking new investments

SODICAMAN

Avda. De Castilla, 12-1
Guadalajara, Spain 19002
Phone: 34-949-229-121
Fax: 34-949-215-555
E-mail: sodicaman@sodicaman.com
Website: www.sodicaman.com

Type of Firm

Private Equity Firm

Association Membership

Spanish Venture Capital Association (ASCRI)

Project Preferences

Type of Financing Preferred:
Balanced

Geographical Preferences

International Preferences:
Spain

Additional Information

Year Founded: 1999
Capital Under Management: $14,600,000
Current Activity Level : Actively seeking new investments

SODIEX SOCIEDAD PARA EL DESARROLLO INDUSTRIAL DE EXTREMADURA

Avda. Virgen de Guadalupe
Caceres, Spain 10001
Phone: 34-92422-4878
E-mail: sodiex@sodiex.es
Website: www.sodiex.es

Management and Staff

Pablo Gonzalez, President

Type of Firm

Private Equity Firm

Association Membership

Spanish Venture Capital Association (ASCRI)

Project Preferences

Type of Financing Preferred:
Expansion
Startup

Geographical Preferences

International Preferences:
Europe
Spain

Additional Information

Year Founded: 2004
Current Activity Level : Actively seeking new investments

SODIGA - SOC. IND. DE GALICIA

Orense 6
La Rosaleda
Santiago de Compostela, Spain
Phone: 34-981-566-100
Fax: 34-981-566-183

Type of Firm

Private Equity Advisor or Fund of Funds

Association Membership

Spanish Venture Capital Association (ASCRI)

Project Preferences

Type of Financing Preferred:
Balanced

Geographical Preferences

International Preferences:
Spain

Additional Information

Year Founded: 2006
Current Activity Level : Actively seeking new investments

SODINO

70 Avenue de la liberte
Tunis, Tunisia 1002
Phone: 216-71-795-688
Fax: 216-71-797-513
E-mail: sodino.sicar@hexabyte.tn

Type of Firm

Private Equity Firm

Project Preferences

Type of Financing Preferred:
Balanced

Geographical Preferences

International Preferences:
Tunisia

Additional Information

Year Founded: 2004
Current Activity Level : Actively seeking new investments

SODIS

70 Avenue de la liberte
Tunis, Tunisia 1002
Phone: 216-71-801-113
Fax: 216-75-643-000
E-mail: sodis.sicar@planet.tn

Type of Firm

Private Equity Firm

Project Preferences

Type of Financing Preferred:
Balanced

Geographical Preferences

International Preferences:
Tunisia

Additional Information

Year Founded: 2004
Current Activity Level : Actively seeking new investments

SOFIEX (AKA: SOCIEDAD DE FOMENTO INDUSTRIAL DE EXTREMADURA)

Avda. Jose Fernandez Lopez, 4
Merida, Spain 06800
Phone: 34-924-319-159
Fax: 34-924-319-212
E-mail: informacion@sofiex.es
Website: www.sofiex.es

Type of Firm

Private Equity Firm

Association Membership

Spanish Venture Capital Association (ASCRI)

Project Preferences

Type of Financing Preferred:
Expansion
Balanced
Startup

Geographical Preferences

International Preferences:
Europe
Spain

Industry Preferences

In Computer Software prefer:
Computer Services

In Biotechnology prefer:
Agricultural/Animal Bio.

In Consumer Related prefer:
Food/Beverage

In Industrial/Energy prefer:
Industrial Products
Machinery

In Business Serv. prefer:
Services

In Agr/Forestr/Fish prefer:
Agriculture related

Additional Information

Year Founded: 1987
Current Activity Level : Actively seeking new investments

SOFINANCE

32 Ave Mohamed, Belkacemi
Les Anasses
Alger, Algeria
Phone: 213-21-47-66-00
Fax: 213-21-47-66-30
E-mail: sofinance@djazair-connect.com
Website: www.sofinance-dz.com

Type of Firm

Private Equity Firm

Association Membership

African Venture Capital Association (AVCA)

Project Preferences

Type of Financing Preferred:
Expansion
Management Buyouts

Size of Investments Considered:
Min Size of Investment Considered (000s): $133
Max Size of Investment Considered (000s): $1,327

Geographical Preferences

International Preferences:
Tunisia
Algeria
Morocco

Additional Information

Year Founded: 2004
Capital Under Management: $78,300,000
Current Activity Level : Actively seeking new investments

SOFINDEV MANAGEMENT N.V.

Green Square
Lambroekstraat 5 D
Diegem, Belgium 1831
Phone: 32-2-720-7007
Fax: 32-2-721-4352
E-mail: info@sofindev.be
Website: www.sofindev.be

Management and Staff

Eric Van Droogenbroeck, Partner
Ghislain Thijs, Partner
Lieven Cuvelier, Managing Partner

Type of Firm

Private Equity Firm

Association Membership

Belgium Venturing Association
European Private Equity and Venture Capital Assoc.

Project Preferences

Role in Financing:
Prefer role as deal originator but will also invest in deals created by others

Type of Financing Preferred:
Generalist PE
Mezzanine
Expansion
Management Buyouts

Size of Investments Considered:
Min Size of Investment Considered (000s): $2,735
Max Size of Investment Considered (000s): $14,937

Geographical Preferences

International Preferences:

Belgium
France

Industry Focus

(% based on actual investment)

Biotechnology	57.3%
Other Products	33.2%
Computer Software and Services	9.5%

Additional Information

Year Founded: 1982
Capital Under Management: $96,700,000
Current Activity Level : Actively seeking new investments
Method of Compensation: Return on investment is of primary concern, do not charge fees

SOFINIM NV

Begijnenvest 113
Antwerpen, Belgium B-2000
Phone: 32-3-897-9230
Fax: 32-3-225-2533
E-mail: info@sofinim.be
Website: www.sofinim.be

Other Offices

Avenue de Tervueren 72
Brussels, Belgium B-1040
Phone: 32-2-237-0701
Fax: 32-2-237-0800

Management and Staff

Andre-Xavier Cooreman, Chief Operating Officer
Jan Suykens, Chief Financial Officer
Leo Thielemans, Partner
Luc Bertrand, Partner
Marc De Pauw, Managing Director

Type of Firm

Corporate PE/Venture

Association Membership

European Private Equity and Venture Capital Assoc.
Indian Venture Capital Association (IVCA)

Project Preferences

Role in Financing:

Prefer role as deal originator but will also invest in deals created by others

Type of Financing Preferred:

Fund of Funds
Leveraged Buyout
Control-block Purchases
Mezzanine
Turnaround
Balanced
Public Companies
Later Stage
Management Buyouts
Acquisition
Industry Rollups
Private Placement
Recapitalizations

Size of Investments Considered:

Min Size of Investment Considered (000s): $3,000
Max Size of Investment Considered (000s): $146,007

Geographical Preferences

International Preferences:

Luxembourg
Netherlands
Belgium
France

Industry Focus

(% based on actual investment)

Consumer Related	92.3%
Internet Specific	7.7%

Additional Information

Year Founded: 1988
Capital Under Management: $463,100,000
Current Activity Level : Actively seeking new investments
Method of Compensation: Return on invest. most important, but chg. closing fees, service fees, etc.

SOFINNOVA PARTNERS

17, rue de Surene
Paris, France 75008
Phone: 33-1-5305-4100
Fax: 33-1-5305-4129
E-mail: info@sofinnova.fr
Website: www.sofinnova.fr

Management and Staff

Alain Rodermann, General Partner
Antoine Papiernik, General Partner
Denis Lucquin, General Partner
Graziano Seghezzi, Partner
Jean Schmitt, Partner
Jean-Bernard Schmidt, Managing Partner
Olivier Sichel, Partner
Olivier Protard, General Partner
Rafaele Tordjman, Partner

Type of Firm

Private Equity Firm

Association Membership

French Venture Capital Association (AFIC)
European Private Equity and Venture Capital Assoc.

Project Preferences

Type of Financing Preferred:

Early Stage
Balanced
Startup

Size of Investments Considered:

Min Size of Investment Considered (000s): $2,824
Max Size of Investment Considered (000s): $28,245

Geographical Preferences

International Preferences:

Europe
France

Industry Preferences

In Communications prefer:

Commercial Communications
Telecommunications

In Semiconductor/Electr prefer:

Semiconductor

In Biotechnology prefer:

Human Biotechnology
Industrial Biotechnology

In Medical/Health prefer:

Medical Therapeutics

In Industrial/Energy prefer:

Alternative Energy

Additional Information

Name of Most Recent Fund: Sofinnova Capital V FCPR
Most Recent Fund Was Raised: 02/07/2005
Year Founded: 1972
Capital Under Management: $1,553,500,000
Current Activity Level : Actively seeking new investments

SOFINNOVA VENTURES

140 Geary Street
Tenth Floor
San Francisco, CA USA 94108
Phone: 415-228-3380
Fax: 415-228-3390
E-mail: info@sofinnova.com
Website: www.sofinnova.com

Other Offices

850 Oak Grove Avenue
Menlo Park, CA USA 94025
Phone: 415-228-3380
Fax: 650-322-2037

4510 Executive Drive
Suite 206
San Diego, CA USA 92121
Phone: 858-550-0959
Fax: 415-228-3390

Management and Staff

Alain Azan, General Partner
Anand Mehra, Principal
Brian Wilcove, Partner
Eric Buatois, General Partner
Goro Takeda, Venture Partner
James Healy, General Partner
Jeffrey Stein, Venture Partner
Michael Powell, General Partner
Nathalie Auber, Chief Financial Officer

Type of Firm

Private Equity Firm

Association Membership

French Venture Capital Association (AFIC)
Western Association of Venture Capitalists (WAVC)
National Venture Capital Association - USA (NVCA)
European Private Equity and Venture Capital Assoc.

Project Preferences

Role in Financing:

Prefer role as deal originator but will also invest in deals created by others

Type of Financing Preferred:

Early Stage

Size of Investments Considered:

Min Size of Investment Considered (000s): $5,000
Max Size of Investment Considered (000s): $15,000

Geographical Preferences

International Preferences:

Europe

Industry Focus

(% based on actual investment)

Biotechnology	45.8%
Medical/Health	14.5%
Internet Specific	14.4%
Computer Software and Services	10.5%
Communications and Media	7.8%
Semiconductors/Other Elect.	4.2%
Computer Hardware	2.6%

Additional Information

Name of Most Recent Fund: Sofinnova Venture Partners VII, L.P.
Most Recent Fund Was Raised: 10/31/2006
Year Founded: 1974
Capital Under Management: $564,000,000
Current Activity Level : Actively seeking new investments
Method of Compensation: Return on investment is of primary concern, do not charge fees

---

SOFIPACA SA

Esplanade des Lices
C/O Credit Agricole
Arles, France 13200
Phone: 33 4 9049 2504
Fax: 33 4 9093 7060
E-mail: sofipaca@wanadoo.fr

Type of Firm

Bank Affiliated

Project Preferences

Type of Financing Preferred:

Expansion
Balanced

Geographical Preferences

International Preferences:

France

Additional Information

Year Founded: 1983
Current Activity Level : Actively seeking new investments

SOFIREM

4 rue des Grandes Terres
BP 220
Rueil-Malmaison Cedex, France 92503
Phone: 33-1-4752-3820
Fax: 33-1-4749-6493
Website: www.sofirem.fr

Management and Staff

Claude Trink, Chairman & Managing Director

Type of Firm

Private Equity Firm

Project Preferences

Type of Financing Preferred:

Balanced

Geographical Preferences

International Preferences:

France

Additional Information

Current Activity Level : Actively seeking new investments

SOFTBANK CAPITAL

1188 Centre Street
Newton Center, MA USA 02459
Phone: 617-928-9300
Fax: 617-928-9304
E-mail: contactsbcapital@softbank.com
Website: www.softbank.com

Other Offices

Key Center
One HSBC, Suite 3850
Buffalo, NY USA 14203
Phone: 716-845-7520
Fax: 716-845-7539

461 Sixth Avenue
15th Floor
New York, NY USA 10017
Phone: 212-503-5800
Fax: 212-503-5855

Management and Staff

Frederick Singer, Venture Partner
Jordan Levy, Partner
Joseph Medved, Principal
Karin Klein, Vice President
Michael Perlis, Partner
Ronald Fisher, Managing Partner
Ronald Schreiber, Partner
Steve Murray, Partner

Type of Firm

Corporate PE/Venture

Association Membership

National Venture Capital Association - USA (NVCA)

Project Preferences

Role in Financing:

Prefer role as deal originator but will also invest in deals created by others

Type of Financing Preferred:

Second Stage Financing
Leveraged Buyout
Early Stage
Expansion
Mezzanine
Balanced
Start-up Financing
Later Stage
Seed
First Stage Financing
Special Situation

Size of Investments Considered:

Min Size of Investment Considered (000s): $500
Max Size of Investment Considered (000s): $20,000

Geographical Preferences

United States Preferences:

All U.S.

Industry Focus

(% based on actual investment)

Internet Specific	61.6%
Consumer Related	15.3%
Communications and Media	10.4%
Computer Software and Services	9.0%
Computer Hardware	2.9%
Semiconductors/Other Elect.	0.5%
Other Products	0.3%
Industrial/Energy	0.1%

Additional Information

Name of Most Recent Fund: SoftBank Capital Technology Fund 2009, L.P.
Most Recent Fund Was Raised: 09/12/2008
Year Founded: 1994
Capital Under Management: $275,000,000
Current Activity Level : Actively seeking new investments
Method of Compensation: Return on investment is of primary concern, do not charge fees

---

SOFTBANK CHINA VENTURE CAPITAL

15A-C, HuanMin Empire Plaza
728 YanAn Road
Shanghai, China 200050

Phone: 86-21-5253-4888
Fax: 86-21-5240-0366
E-mail: contact@sbcvc.com
Website: www.sbcvc.com

Management and Staff

Alan Song, Managing Partner
Masayoshi Son, Founder
Peter Hua, Managing Partner

Type of Firm

Private Equity Firm

Project Preferences

Type of Financing Preferred:

Early Stage
Expansion
Balanced
Seed
Later Stage

Size of Investments Considered:

Min Size of Investment Considered (000s): $500
Max Size of Investment Considered (000s): $500,000

Geographical Preferences

International Preferences:

Macau
Taiwan
China
Hong Kong
Asia

Industry Preferences

In Communications prefer:

Wireless Communications

In Computer Software prefer:

Software

In Internet Specific prefer:

Internet

In Semiconductor/Electr prefer:

Electronic Components

In Medical/Health prefer:

Medical/Health
Medical Products

In Consumer Related prefer:

Consumer
Retail

In Industrial/Energy prefer:

Energy
Materials
Environmental Related

In Manufact. prefer:

Manufacturing

Additional Information

Name of Most Recent Fund: SOFTBANK China Venture Capital Fund II, LP (SBCVC II)
Most Recent Fund Was Raised: 03/17/2006
Year Founded: 2000
Capital Under Management: $498,000,000
Current Activity Level : Actively seeking new investments

SOFTBANK CORP.

Tokyo Shiodome Building
1-9-1, Higashi-shimbashi
Tokyo, Japan 105-7303
Phone: 81-3-5642-8005
Fax: 81-3-5641-3401
Website: www.softbank.co.jp

Other Offices

Suites 2115-2118, Two Pacific Place
88 Queensway
Admiralty, Hong Kong
Phone: 852-2918-2206
Fax: 852-2234-9116

Type of Firm

Corporate PE/Venture

Project Preferences

Type of Financing Preferred:

Early Stage
Unknown
Balanced
Startup

Geographical Preferences

International Preferences:

Ireland
United Kingdom
Latin America
Europe
China
Korea, South
Asia
Japan
All International

Industry Focus

(% based on actual investment)

Other Products	65.2%
Internet Specific	15.5%
Communications and Media	11.0%
Computer Software and Services	5.3%
Medical/Health	2.2%
Biotechnology	0.8%

Additional Information

Year Founded: 1981
Capital Under Management: $20,000,000
Current Activity Level : Actively seeking new investments

SOFTBANK VENTURES KOREA, INC.

8th Floor, Shinyoung Building
68-5 Chungdam-dong, Gangnam-gu
Seoul, South Korea 135-100
Phone: 822-3484-9115
Fax: 822-3484-9010
Website: www.softbank.co.kr

Other Offices

1050 Walnut Street
Suite 210
Boulder, CO USA 80302
Phone: 303-642-4000

Management and Staff

Greg Moon, Chief Executive Officer
Steve Lee, Managing Director
Sungwoon Yu, Principal

Type of Firm

Bank Affiliated

Project Preferences

Type of Financing Preferred:

Balanced

Geographical Preferences

International Preferences:

Korea, South
Asia

Industry Preferences

In Biotechnology prefer:

Biotechnology

Additional Information

Year Founded: 2000
Capital Under Management: $95,400,000
Current Activity Level : Actively seeking new investments

SOFTRONIC VENTURES AB

Ringvagen 100
Stockholm, Sweden 118 60
Phone: 46-8-51-90-9000
Fax: 46-8-51-90-9100
E-mail: info@softronic.se
Website: www.softronic.se

Type of Firm

Private Equity Firm

Additional Information

Current Activity Level : Actively seeking new investments

SOFTTECH VC

654 High Street
Suite 200
Palo Alto, CA USA 94301
Phone: 650-688-1801
Fax: 650-475-3937
E-mail: contact@softtechvc.com
Website: www.softtechvc.com

Management and Staff

Jean-Francois Clavier, Managing Partner

Type of Firm

Private Equity Firm

Project Preferences

Type of Financing Preferred:
Early Stage
Seed
Startup

Size of Investments Considered:
Min Size of Investment Considered (000s): $100
Max Size of Investment Considered (000s): $500

Geographical Preferences

United States Preferences:
All U.S.

Industry Preferences

In Internet Specific prefer:
Ecommerce
Web Aggregration/Portals

Additional Information

Name of Most Recent Fund: SoftTech VC II, L.P.
Most Recent Fund Was Raised: 09/18/2007
Year Founded: 2004
Capital Under Management: $12,000,000
Current Activity Level : Actively seeking new investments

SOFTWARE HOLDING & FINANCE (AKA: SHF)

Nieuwlandlaan 9
Aarschot, Belgium 3200
Phone: 32-16-56-00-00
Fax: 32-16-56-66-60
E-mail: info@shf.be
Website: www.shf.be

Type of Firm

Private Equity Firm

Project Preferences

Type of Financing Preferred:
Early Stage
Seed

Geographical Preferences

International Preferences:
Europe
Belgium

Industry Preferences

In Communications prefer:
Telecommunications

In Computer Software prefer:
Software

In Biotechnology prefer:
Biotechnology

In Medical/Health prefer:
Pharmaceuticals

Additional Information

Year Founded: 1995
Current Activity Level : Actively seeking new investments

SOGINNOVE

Tour Societe Generale 17
Cours Valmy
Paris, France 92972
Phone: 33-1-4214-7724
Fax: 33-1-4214-8853

Type of Firm

Private Equity Firm

Project Preferences

Type of Financing Preferred:
Balanced

Geographical Preferences

International Preferences:
France

Additional Information

Year Founded: 2005
Current Activity Level : Actively seeking new investments

SOLAMERE CAPITAL

585 Commercial Street
Boston, MA USA 02114
Phone: 617-997-1798

Management and Staff

Eric Scheuermann, Founder
John Miller, Founder
Spencer Zwick, Founder
Tagg Romney, Founder

Type of Firm

Private Equity Firm

Project Preferences

Type of Financing Preferred:
Fund of Funds
Leveraged Buyout

Additional Information

Year Founded: 2008
Current Activity Level : Actively seeking new investments

SOLAR VENTURE PARTNERS

2575 Augustine Drive
Santa Clara, CA USA 95054
Phone: 408-855-4900
Fax: 408-855-4999

Management and Staff

V.R. Ranganath, General Partner

Type of Firm

Private Equity Firm

Project Preferences

Role in Financing:
Prefer role in deals created by others

Type of Financing Preferred:
Early Stage

Size of Investments Considered:
Min Size of Investment Considered (000s): $100
Max Size of Investment Considered (000s): $1,000

Geographical Preferences

United States Preferences:
Northern California

Industry Preferences

In Communications prefer:
Telecommunications
Wireless Communications
Data Communications

In Computer Software prefer:
Applications Software

In Semiconductor/Electr prefer:
Semiconductor

Additional Information

Year Founded: 2000
Capital Under Management: $17,100,000
Current Activity Level : Actively seeking new investments
Method of Compensation: Return on invest. most important, but chg. closing fees, service fees, etc.

SOLBORN VENTURE INVESTMENT, INC.

1549-7 Seocho-dong
Seocho-gu
Seoul, South Korea 137-070
Phone: 822-580-2840
Fax: 822-587-9281
Website: www.solbornvi.com

Type of Firm

Corporate PE/Venture

Project Preferences

Type of Financing Preferred:
Balanced

Geographical Preferences

International Preferences:
Korea, South

Industry Preferences

In Biotechnology prefer:
Biotechnology

Additional Information
Year Founded: 2000
Capital Under Management: $8,100,000
Current Activity Level : Actively seeking new investments

SOLERA CAPITAL, LLC
625 Madison Avenue
3rd Floor
New York, NY USA 10022
Phone: 212-833-1440
Fax: 212-833-1460
E-mail: businessplans@soleracapital.com
Website: www.soleracapital.com

Management and Staff
Brian Murphy, Managing Director
C.J. Kettler, Managing Director
Karen Mills, Managing Director
Lori Koffman, Managing Director
Mary Hennessy-Jones, Managing Director
Molly Ashby, Chief Executive Officer

Type of Firm
Private Equity Firm

Project Preferences

Type of Financing Preferred:
Mezzanine
Later Stage

Size of Investments Considered:
Min Size of Investment Considered (000s): $10,000
Max Size of Investment Considered (000s): $40,000

Geographical Preferences

United States Preferences:
All U.S.

Additional Information
Name of Most Recent Fund: Solera Partners, L.P.
Most Recent Fund Was Raised: 05/26/2000
Year Founded: 1999
Capital Under Management: $250,000,000
Current Activity Level : Actively seeking new investments

SOLID CAPITAL BV
PO Box 8530
Utrecht, Netherlands 3503 RM
Phone: 31-30-248-1030
Fax: 31-30-248-1031
E-mail: info@solidcapital.com
Website: www.solidcapital.com

Management and Staff
Floris Van Alkemade, Founder
Herman DeLatte, Partner

Type of Firm
Private Equity Firm

Project Preferences

Type of Financing Preferred:
Early Stage
Expansion

Geographical Preferences

International Preferences:
Luxembourg
Netherlands
Belgium

Additional Information
Year Founded: 2004
Capital Under Management: $97,000,000
Current Activity Level : Actively seeking new investments

SOLIDUS PARTNERS LLP
54, boulevard Napoleon 1er
Luxembourg, Luxembourg L-2210
Website: www.soliduspartners.com

Other Offices
Thames Wharf Studios
2/F, Block 1, Rainville Road
London, United Kingdom W6 9HA
Phone: 44-20-7471-2670
Fax: 44-20-7471-2679

Type of Firm
Private Equity Firm

Project Preferences

Type of Financing Preferred:
Leveraged Buyout
Management Buyouts

Geographical Preferences

International Preferences:
Europe

Additional Information
Year Founded: 2004
Current Activity Level : Actively seeking new investments

SOLIS CAPITAL PARTNERS, LLC
24 Corporate Plaza
Suite 180
Newport Beach, CA USA 92660
Phone: 949-720-4672
Fax: 949-720-4675
Website: www.soliscapital.com

Other Offices
2890 Rancho Cortes
Suite 100
Carlsbad, CA USA 92009
Phone: 760-309-9436

Management and Staff
Craig Dupper, Principal

Type of Firm
Private Equity Firm

Project Preferences

Type of Financing Preferred:
Management Buyouts
Recapitalizations

Geographical Preferences

United States Preferences:
All U.S.

Additional Information
Year Founded: 2006
Current Activity Level : Actively seeking new investments

SOLITAIRE CAPITAL ADVISORS PVT. LTD.
112, 113 Charmwood Plaza
Suraj Kund Road, Eros Garden
Faridabad, India 121 009
Phone: 91-29-411-8193
Fax: 91-29-411-8194
E-mail: solitaire@solitairecapital.com
Website: www.solitairecapital.com

Other Offices
491B, River Valley Road
#08-03 Valley Point
Singapore, Singapore 248373
Phone: 65-6536-8915
Fax: 65-6536-8914

241, Okhla Industrial Estate
Phase III
New Delhi, India 110 019
Phone: 91-11-4100-0861

Management and Staff
Sanjiv Ahuja, Chief Executive Officer

Type of Firm
Private Equity Firm

Project Preferences
Type of Financing Preferred:
Balanced

Geographical Preferences
International Preferences:
India

Additional Information
Year Founded: 2005
Current Activity Level : Actively seeking new investments

SOLOMON CAPITAL PARTNERS, LTD. (AKA: SCP)
United Building, Level 1
107 Customhouse Quay
Wellington, New Zealand 6004
Website: www.scp.co.nz

Type of Firm
Private Equity Firm

Project Preferences
Type of Financing Preferred:
Early Stage

Additional Information
Year Founded: 2009
Current Activity Level : Actively seeking new investments

SOLON VENTURES, LTD.
24 Old Bond Street
London, United Kingdom W1S 4AW
Phone: 44-20-7535-4913
Fax: 44-20-7493-9172
E-mail: contact@solonventures.com
Website: www.solonventures.com

Management and Staff
Angus Whiteley, Managing Director

Type of Firm
Private Equity Firm

Project Preferences
Type of Financing Preferred:
Balanced

Geographical Preferences
International Preferences:
United Kingdom

Industry Preferences
In Medical/Health prefer:
Medical/Health

Additional Information
Year Founded: 2007
Current Activity Level : Actively seeking new investments

SOLSTICE CAPITAL
15 Broad Street
Third Floor
Boston, MA USA 02109
Phone: 617-523-7733
Fax: 617-523-5827
E-mail: info@solcap.com
Website: www.solcap.com

Other Offices
6245 East Broadway Boulevard
Suite 620
Tucson, AZ USA 85711
Phone: 520-514-8000
Fax: 520-514-8001

Management and Staff
Frederick Bamber, General Partner
Harry George, Managing General Partner
Henry Newman, General Partner

Type of Firm
Investment Management Firm

Association Membership
National Venture Capital Association - USA (NVCA)

Project Preferences
Role in Financing:
Will function either as deal originator or investor in deals created by others

Type of Financing Preferred:
Early Stage
Seed
First Stage Financing

Size of Investments Considered:
Min Size of Investment Considered (000s): $500
Max Size of Investment Considered (000s): $1,500

Geographical Preferences
United States Preferences:
Northeast
Southwest

Industry Focus
(% based on actual investment)

Computer Software and Services	36.5%
Biotechnology	19.7%
Industrial/Energy	13.2%
Medical/Health	12.8%
Internet Specific	8.0%
Computer Hardware	5.8%
Semiconductors/Other Elect.	2.3%
Communications and Media	1.4%
Consumer Related	0.3%

Additional Information
Name of Most Recent Fund: Solstice Capital II, L.P.
Most Recent Fund Was Raised: 05/22/2001
Year Founded: 1995
Capital Under Management: $80,000,000
Current Activity Level : Actively seeking new investments
Method of Compensation: Professional fee required whether or not deal closes

---

SONY CORPORATION
6-7-35 Kitagashinagawa
Shinagawa-ku,
Tokyo, Japan 141-0001
Phone: 81-3-5448-2303
Fax: 81-3-5448-4551
Website: www.sonyvc.com

Other Offices
Kemperplatz 1
Berlin, Germany 10785
Phone: 49 30 2575 5144
Fax: 49 30 2575 5144

3300 Zanker Road
MS SJ2J11
San Jose, CA USA 95134
Phone: 408-955-5346
Fax: 408-955-5030

550 Madison Avenue
Room 906
New York, NY USA 10022
Phone: 212-833-8671
Fax: 212-833-5441

Type of Firm
Corporate PE/Venture

Project Preferences
Type of Financing Preferred:
Early Stage
Balanced

Geographical Preferences
United States Preferences:
All U.S.

International Preferences:
Asia
All International

Industry Preferences
In Computer Software prefer:
Systems Software

In Internet Specific prefer:
Internet

In Semiconductor/Electr prefer:
Electronics

Additional Information

Name of Most Recent Fund: Sony Corporation
Most Recent Fund Was Raised: 07/01/1985
Year Founded: 1985
Current Activity Level : Actively seeking new investments

SOPAF SPA

39, via S. Vittore
Milan, Italy 20123
Phone: 39-2439-211
Website: www.sopafgroup.it

Type of Firm

Investment Management Firm

Project Preferences

Type of Financing Preferred:
Expansion

Geographical Preferences

International Preferences:
China

Additional Information

Year Founded: 2006
Capital Under Management: $45,000,000
Current Activity Level : Actively seeking new investments

SOPARTEC SA (AKA: VIVES)

Chemin du Cyclotron 6
Louvain-la-Neuve, Belgium 1348
Phone: 32-10-390-021
Fax: 32-10-390-029
E-mail: secretariat@sopartec.com
Website: www.sopartec.com

Management and Staff

F Lagae, Partner
Gilles Capart, Managing Director
H Bultot, Partner
O Witmeur, Partner

Type of Firm

University Program

Association Membership

European Private Equity and Venture Capital Assoc.

Project Preferences

Type of Financing Preferred:
Early Stage
Expansion
Start-up Financing
Seed

Size of Investments Considered:
Min Size of Investment Considered (000s): $100
Max Size of Investment Considered (000s): $100,000

Geographical Preferences

United States Preferences:
All U.S.

International Preferences:
Europe

Industry Preferences

In Communications prefer:
Communications and Media

In Computer Other prefer:
Computer Related

In Biotechnology prefer:
Biotechnology

In Medical/Health prefer:
Medical/Health

In Industrial/Energy prefer:
Energy
Materials

Additional Information

Year Founded: 1990
Capital Under Management: $34,000,000
Current Activity Level : Actively seeking new investments

SOPHIA EURO LAB SAS

905 Rue Albert Einstein
BP 60247
Sophia Antipolis Cedex, France 06905
Phone: 33-4-9365-3530
Fax: 33-4-9296-0087
E-mail: info@sophiaeurolab.com
Website: www.sophiaeurolab.com

Management and Staff

Guillame Girard, Partner
Pierre Laffitte, Founder

Type of Firm

Incubator/Development Program

Project Preferences

Type of Financing Preferred:
Early Stage
Seed
First Stage Financing
Startup

Geographical Preferences

International Preferences:
France

Industry Preferences

In Communications prefer:
Communications and Media
Commercial Communications

Additional Information

Year Founded: 2001
Capital Under Management: $9,600,000
Current Activity Level : Actively seeking new investments

SOPROMEC PARTICIPATIONS

5-7 rue de Monttessuy
Paris Cedex 07, France 75340
Phone: 33-15819-1318
Fax: 33-15819-2230
E-mail: contact@sopromec.fr
Website: www.sopromec.fr

Type of Firm

Private Equity Firm

Project Preferences

Type of Financing Preferred:
Balanced

Geographical Preferences

International Preferences:
Europe
France

Industry Preferences

In Industrial/Energy prefer:
Industrial Products

In Business Serv. prefer:
Services

Additional Information

Year Founded: 2003
Current Activity Level : Actively seeking new investments

SORENSON CAPITAL PARTNERS

3098 West Executive Parkway
Suite 200
Lehi, UT USA 84043
Phone: 801-407-8400
Fax: 801-407-8411
E-mail: info@sorensoncap.com
Website: www.sorensoncap.com

Other Offices

1424 South Stanley Drive
Mesa, AZ USA 85204
Phone: 602-317-1400
Fax: 602-296-0146

3300 Hillview Avenue
Suite 190
Palo Alto, CA USA 94304
Phone: 650-354-1888
Fax: 650-354-1803

Management and Staff

Curtis Toone, Principal
D. Fraser Bullock, Managing Director
Luke Sorenson, Principal
Matt Lehman, Principal
Rhett Neuenschwander, Principal
Richard Lawson, Managing Director
Ronald Mika, Managing Director
Steve Young, Managing Director
Tim Layton, Managing Director

Type of Firm

Private Equity Firm

Project Preferences

Type of Financing Preferred:
Leveraged Buyout
Generalist PE
Early Stage
Balanced

Geographical Preferences

United States Preferences:
Rocky Mountain
California
All U.S.

Additional Information

Name of Most Recent Fund: Sorenson Capital Partners II
Most Recent Fund Was Raised: 01/07/2008
Year Founded: 2004
Capital Under Management: $650,000,000
Current Activity Level : Actively seeking new investments

SORIDEC

Alco 4 - 248, Rue Michel Teule
Montpellier, France 34080
Phone: 33-499-23-3240
Fax: 33-499-23-3241
E-mail: contact@soridec.fr
Website: www.soridec.fr

Management and Staff

Andre Moulin, President
Bernard Olivier, General Director

Type of Firm

Private Equity Firm

Project Preferences

Type of Financing Preferred:
Expansion
Balanced
Startup

Geographical Preferences

International Preferences:
France

Industry Preferences

In Computer Software prefer:
Data Processing

In Consumer Related prefer:
Food/Beverage

In Business Serv. prefer:
Services

In Agr/Forestr/Fish prefer:
Agriculture related

Additional Information

Year Founded: 1983
Current Activity Level : Actively seeking new investments

SOROS STRATEGIC PARTNERS

888 Seventh Avenue
33rd Floor
New York, NY USA 10106
Phone: 212-262-6300
Fax: 212-245-5154

Management and Staff

Abbas Zuaiter, Chief Financial Officer

Type of Firm

Private Equity Firm

Additional Information

Year Founded: 2009
Current Activity Level : Actively seeking new investments

SOUTH ATLANTIC VENTURE FUNDS, L.P.

614 West Bay Street
Tampa, FL USA 33606-2704
Phone: 813-253-2500
Fax: 813-253-2360
Website: www.southatlantic.com

Other Offices

102 Marseille Place
Cary, NC USA 27511
Phone: 919-461-0803
Fax: 919-319-0026

1239 O.G. Skinner Drive
West Point, GA USA 31833
Phone: 706-645-8758
Fax: 706-643-5067

2601 South Bayshore Drive
Suite 1147
Miami, FL USA 33133
Phone: 305-250-4681
Fax: 305-250-4682

Management and Staff

Sandra Barber, Managing Director

Type of Firm

Private Equity Firm

Project Preferences

Role in Financing:
Will function either as deal originator or investor in deals created by others

Type of Financing Preferred:
Second Stage Financing
Expansion
Later Stage
Management Buyouts
First Stage Financing
Acquisition
Recapitalizations

Size of Investments Considered:
Min Size of Investment Considered (000s): $1,500
Max Size of Investment Considered (000s): $7,500

Geographical Preferences

United States Preferences:
Southeast
Florida
Texas

Industry Focus

(% based on actual investment)

Communications and Media	32.3%
Medical/Health	22.8%
Other Products	15.4%
Internet Specific	10.7%
Consumer Related	6.0%
Semiconductors/Other Elect.	5.6%
Computer Software and Services	4.4%
Computer Hardware	2.5%
Industrial/Energy	0.4%

Additional Information

Name of Most Recent Fund: South Atlantic Private Equity Fund IV, L.P.
Most Recent Fund Was Raised: 07/01/1997
Year Founded: 1983
Capital Under Management: $115,400,000
Current Activity Level : Reducing investment activity
Method of Compensation: Return on investment is of primary concern, do not charge fees

---

SOUTHBRIDGE CAPITAL

50 Water Street South
Cambridge, Canada N1R 3E2
Phone: 519-621-8886
Fax: 519-621-8144
Website: www.southbridgeinc.com

Management and Staff

Bob Yoanidis, Partner
Linda King, Partner
Mike Petersen, Managing Partner

Type of Firm

Private Equity Firm

Additional Information

Year Founded: 1997
Current Activity Level : Actively seeking new investments

SOUTHEAST EUROPE EQUITY FUND

C/O 45, Oborishte Street
P.O. Box 147
Sofia, Bulgaria 1504
Phone: 359-2-943-4417
Fax: 359-2-943-4979

Type of Firm

Private Equity Firm

Project Preferences

Type of Financing Preferred:

Balanced

Geographical Preferences

International Preferences:

Europe

Additional Information

Year Founded: 2005
Current Activity Level : Actively seeking new investments

SOUTHEAST INTERACTIVE TECHNOLOGY FUNDS

3800 Paramount Parkway
Suite 115
Morrisville, NC USA 27560
Phone: 919-558-8324
Fax: 919-558-2025
E-mail: info@seinteractive.com
Website: www.seinteractive.com

Other Offices

303 Twin Dolphin Road
Suite 600
Redwood City, CA USA 94065
Phone: 650-632-4314

Management and Staff

Norvell Miller, Managing General Partner
Rami Elkhatib, General Partner
Ravi Trivedi, Principal
Steve Rakes, General Partner

Type of Firm

Private Equity Firm

Association Membership

Mid-Atlantic Venture Association
National Venture Capital Association - USA (NVCA)

Project Preferences

Role in Financing:

Prefer role as deal originator

Type of Financing Preferred:

Early Stage
Seed
First Stage Financing

Size of Investments Considered:

Min Size of Investment Considered (000s): $2,000
Max Size of Investment Considered (000s): $4,000

Geographical Preferences

United States Preferences:

Southeast
Southwest

Industry Focus

(% based on actual investment)

Internet Specific	45.8%
Computer Software and Services	29.3%
Computer Hardware	9.0%
Semiconductors/Other Elect.	6.2%
Other Products	5.7%
Communications and Media	4.1%

Additional Information

Year Founded: 1995
Capital Under Management: $185,000,000
Current Activity Level : Actively seeking new investments
Method of Compensation: Return on investment is of primary concern, do not charge fees

---

SOUTHERN AFRICA ENTERPRISE DEVELOPMENT FUND, THE (SAEDF)

First Floor, 32 Fricker Road
Illovo
Sandton, South Africa 2169
Phone: 27-11-283-1630
Fax: 27-11-442-9824
E-mail: info@saedf.org.za
Website: www.saedf.com

Management and Staff

Cecil Callahan, Chief Executive Officer
Richard Swai, Vice President

Type of Firm

Government Affiliated Program

Association Membership

South African Venture Capital Association (SAVCA)
African Venture Capital Association (AVCA)

Project Preferences

Type of Financing Preferred:

Fund of Funds
Early Stage
Expansion
Mezzanine
Management Buyouts
Acquisition

Size of Investments Considered:

Min Size of Investment Considered (000s): $1,000
Max Size of Investment Considered (000s): $5,000

Geographical Preferences

International Preferences:

Angola
Malawi
Swaziland
Zambia
Tanzania
Botswana
Namibia
Lesotho
Mozambique
South Africa
Zimbabwe

Additional Information

Year Founded: 1994
Capital Under Management: $100,000,000
Current Activity Level : Actively seeking new investments

SOUTHERN APPALACHIAN MANAGEMENT COMPANY LLC

362 Old Whitley Road
P.O. Box 1738
London, KY USA 40743-1738
Phone: 606-864-5175
Fax: 606-864-5194
E-mail: info@SouthAppFund.com
Website: www.southappfund.com

Other Offices

1020 Commerce Park Drive
Oak Ridge, TN USA 37830
Phone: 865-220-2020
Fax: 865-220-2030

Management and Staff

Brenda McDaniel, Chief Financial Officer
L. Ray Moncrief, President

Type of Firm

Government Affiliated Program

Association Membership

Community Development Venture Capital Alliance

Project Preferences

Role in Financing:
Prefer role as deal originator but will also invest in deals created by others

Type of Financing Preferred:
Early Stage
Expansion
Balanced

Size of Investments Considered:
Min Size of Investment Considered (000s): $200
Max Size of Investment Considered (000s): $600

Geographical Preferences

United States Preferences:
Tennessee
Mississippi
Alabama
Georgia
Kentucky

Industry Preferences

In Computer Software prefer:
Software

In Manufact. prefer:
Manufacturing

Additional Information
Year Founded: 2003
Capital Under Management: $12,500,000
Current Activity Level : Actively seeking new investments

SOUTHERN CAPITAL GROUP PRIVATE LTD. (FKA: MULBERRY PARTNERS)
501 Orchard Road
17-01 Wheelock Place
Singapore, Singapore 238880
Phone: 65-6836-8600
Fax: 65-6836-8601
E-mail: information@southerncapitalgroup.com
Website: www.southerncapitalgroup.com

Type of Firm
Private Equity Firm

Project Preferences

Type of Financing Preferred:
Leveraged Buyout
Management Buyouts

Geographical Preferences

International Preferences:
Laos
Vietnam
Indonesia
Brunei
China
Thailand
Cambodia
Philippines
Singapore
Korea, South
Asia
Malaysia

Industry Preferences

In Medical/Health prefer:
Medical/Health

In Consumer Related prefer:
Food/Beverage

In Financial Services prefer:
Financial Services

In Manufact. prefer:
Manufacturing

Additional Information
Year Founded: 2007
Capital Under Management: $78,200,000
Current Activity Level : Actively seeking new investments

SOUTHERN CAPITOL VENTURES
21 Glenwood Avenue
Suite 105
Raleigh, NC USA 27603
Phone: 919-858-7580
Fax: 919-863-2394
E-mail: info@southerncapitolventures.com
Website: www.southerncapitolventures.com

Management and Staff
Al Childers, Venture Partner
Benjamin Brooks, Founding Partner
Dave Murray, General Partner
David Jones, Partner
Jason Caplain, General Partner

Type of Firm
Private Equity Firm

Project Preferences

Role in Financing:
Will function either as deal originator or investor in deals created by others

Type of Financing Preferred:
Early Stage
Seed

Size of Investments Considered:
Min Size of Investment Considered (000s): $100
Max Size of Investment Considered (000s): $1,000

Geographical Preferences

United States Preferences:
Mid Atlantic
Southeast
North Carolina

Additional Information
Year Founded: 2000
Capital Under Management: $20,000,000
Current Activity Level : Actively seeking new investments
Method of Compensation: Return on investment is of primary concern, do not charge fees

SOUTHERN CROSS GROUP (AKA: SCG)
Cerrito 1294 Piso 8
Buenos Aires, Argentina C 1010AAZ
Phone: 54-11-4816-5054
Fax: 54-11-4816-2469
Website: www.southerncrossgroup.com

Other Offices
El Regidor 66 Piso 16
Las Condes
Santiago, Chile
Phone: 562-582-5715
Fax: 562-582-5180

Manuel Avila Camacho Boulevard, N 40
Edificio Esmeralda I. Piso 18 - 1802
Col. Lomas de Chapultepec, Mexico 11000
Phone: 52-55-2623-7167
Fax: 52-55-2623-7167

Brigadeiro Faria Lima Avenue, 3729-5
andar Itaim Bibi - CEP 04538-905 -
Sao Paolo, Brazil
Phone: 55-11-3443-6215
Fax: 55-11-3443-6201

41 West Putnam Avenue
Second Floor
Greenwich, CT USA 06830
Phone: 203-629-8272
Fax: 203-629-8370

Management and Staff
Angel Uribe, Managing Director
Cesar Perez Barnes, Managing Director
Gonzalo Dulanto, Managing Director
Horacio Reyser, Partner
Raul Sotomayor, Partner
Ricardo Rodriguez, President
Sebastian Villa, Partner

Type of Firm
Private Equity Firm

Project Preferences

Type of Financing Preferred:
Leveraged Buyout

Geographical Preferences

International Preferences:
Latin America
Uruguay
Argentina

Peru
Paraguay
Bolivia
Brazil
Mexico
Chile

Additional Information

Year Founded: 1998
Current Activity Level : Actively seeking new investments

SOUTHERN CROSS LATIN AMERICA PRIVATE EQUITY FUND, L.P.

P.O. Box 31106 SMB
Corporate Centre, West Bay Rd.
George Town, Cayman Islands
Phone: 345-949-3977

Type of Firm

Private Equity Firm

Project Preferences

Type of Financing Preferred:
Leveraged Buyout

Geographical Preferences

International Preferences:
Latin America

Additional Information

Name of Most Recent Fund: Southern Cross Latin America Private Equity Fund II, L.P.
Most Recent Fund Was Raised: 08/06/2003
Year Founded: 1998
Capital Under Management: $968,100,000
Current Activity Level : Actively seeking new investments

SOUTHERN CROSS VENTURE PARTNERS

80 Mount Street
Level 5
Sydney, Australia 2060
Phone: 612-8314-7400
Fax: 612-9957-6399
E-mail: info@sxvp.com
Website: www.sxvp.com

Other Offices

285 Hamilton Avenue
Suite 240
Palo Alto, CA USA 94303
Phone: 650-561-7150

545 Queen Street
Level 9
Brisbane, Australia 4000
Phone: 617-3831-6757
Fax: 617-3009-0414

Management and Staff

Anneliese Bisson, Chief Financial Officer
Frank Foster, Venture Partner
Gareth Dando, Managing Director
John Scull, Managing Director
Larry Marshall, Managing Director
Robert Christiansen, Managing Director
William Bartee, Managing Director

Type of Firm

Private Equity Firm

Association Membership

Australian Venture Capital Association (AVCAL)

Project Preferences

Type of Financing Preferred:
Early Stage
Expansion

Size of Investments Considered:
Min Size of Investment Considered (000s): $81
Max Size of Investment Considered (000s): $8,058

Geographical Preferences

International Preferences:
Pacific

Industry Preferences

In Communications prefer:
Telecommunications

In Computer Software prefer:
Software
Systems Software

In Semiconductor/Electr prefer:
Electronics

In Industrial/Energy prefer:
Energy
Advanced Materials
Environmental Related

Additional Information

Year Founded: 2006
Capital Under Management: $137,100,000
Current Activity Level : Actively seeking new investments

SOUTHLAKE EQUITY GROUP (FKA: CHALLENGER EQUITY PARTNERS LLC)

180 State Street
Suite 230
Grapevine, TX USA 76092
Phone: 817-328-3600
Fax: 817-328-3601
Website: www.southlakeequity.com

Type of Firm

Bank Affiliated

Project Preferences

Type of Financing Preferred:
Leveraged Buyout
Management Buyouts
Industry Rollups
Recapitalizations

Size of Investments Considered:
Min Size of Investment Considered (000s): $10,000
Max Size of Investment Considered (000s): $50,000

Geographical Preferences

United States Preferences:
All U.S.
Texas
Southwest

Industry Preferences

In Medical/Health prefer:
Health Services

In Industrial/Energy prefer:
Industrial Products
Advanced Materials

In Business Serv. prefer:
Services

In Manufact. prefer:
Manufacturing
Publishing

Additional Information

Year Founded: 2007
Current Activity Level : Actively seeking new investments

SOUTHVENTURE BETEILIGUNGSBERATUNG & VERWALTUNGS GMBH

Robert-Koch-Strasse 1
Munich, Germany 80538
Phone: 49-8924-21160
Fax: 49-8924-211699
E-mail: info@southventure.com
Website: www.southventure.com

Type of Firm

Private Equity Firm

Project Preferences

Type of Financing Preferred:
Fund of Funds
Leveraged Buyout
Expansion

Geographical Preferences

International Preferences:
Europe

All International

Industry Preferences

In Biotechnology prefer:
Biotechnology

In Medical/Health prefer:
Medical/Health

In Industrial/Energy prefer:
Energy
Alternative Energy

Additional Information

Year Founded: 1998
Capital Under Management: $54,000,000
Current Activity Level : Actively seeking new investments

SOVAR

2750, rue Einstein
Bureau 130
Sainte-Foy, Canada G1P 4R1
Phone: 418-650-2829
Fax: 418-656-1981
E-mail: info@sovar.com
Website: www.cvar.qc.ca

Type of Firm

Government Affiliated Program

Additional Information

Year Founded: 2009
Current Activity Level : Actively seeking new investments

SOVEREIGN CAPITAL LLP (FKA:SOVEREIGN CAPITAL, LTD.)

25 Buckingham Gate
London, United Kingdom SW1E 6LD
Phone: 44-20-7828-6944
Fax: 44-20-7828-9958
E-mail: info@sovereigncapital.co.uk
Website: www.sovereigncapital.co.uk

Management and Staff

Andrew Hayden, Partner
David Myers, Partner
Dominic Dalli, Partner
Kevin Whittle, Partner
Ryan Robson, Partner

Type of Firm

Private Equity Firm

Association Membership

British Venture Capital Association (BVCA)
European Private Equity and Venture Capital Assoc.

Project Preferences

Role in Financing:
Prefer role as deal originator but will also invest in deals created by others

Type of Financing Preferred:
Leveraged Buyout
Other
Management Buyouts
Acquisition
Joint Ventures

Size of Investments Considered:
Min Size of Investment Considered (000s): $9,897
Max Size of Investment Considered (000s): $39,588

Geographical Preferences

International Preferences:
United Kingdom
Europe

Industry Preferences

In Medical/Health prefer:
Health Services

In Consumer Related prefer:
Entertainment and Leisure
Education Related

In Financial Services prefer:
Financial Services

In Business Serv. prefer:
Services

In Other prefer:
Environment Responsible

Additional Information

Name of Most Recent Fund: Sovereign Capital Limited Partnership II (AKA: SCLP II)
Most Recent Fund Was Raised: 05/11/2005
Year Founded: 1988
Capital Under Management: $2,806,800,000
Current Activity Level : Actively seeking new investments
Method of Compensation: Return on invest. most important, but chg. closing fees, service fees, etc.

SOVIK VENTURE CAPITAL COMPANY, LTD.

6/F, Dongyang Bldg., 764-19
Bangbaebon-dong, Seocho-ku
Seoul, South Korea 137-069
Phone: 822-594-8470
Fax: 822-594-8471

Management and Staff

Hyung Tae Park, President

Type of Firm

Investment Management Firm

Project Preferences

Type of Financing Preferred:
Balanced

Geographical Preferences

International Preferences:
Korea, South

Industry Preferences

In Communications prefer:
Media and Entertainment
Entertainment

Additional Information

Year Founded: 2000
Capital Under Management: $79,300,000
Current Activity Level : Actively seeking new investments

SP ADMINISTRADORA DE FUNDOS

Av. Brig. Faria Lima, 2391
fourth floor
Sao Paulo, SP, Brazil 01452-002
Phone: 5511-3031-1731
E-mail: sptec@sptec.com.br
Website: www.sptec.com.br

Type of Firm

Private Equity Firm

Project Preferences

Type of Financing Preferred:
Balanced

Geographical Preferences

International Preferences:
Brazil

Additional Information

Year Founded: 2001
Current Activity Level : Actively seeking new investments

SPACE CENTER VENTURES, INC.

2501 Rosegate
Roseville, MN USA 55113
Phone: 651-604-4204
Fax: 651-604-4250
E-mail: businessplan@scvinc.com
Website: www.scvinc.com

Type of Firm

Private Equity Firm

Project Preferences

Role in Financing:
Will function either as deal originator or investor in deals created by others

Type of Financing Preferred:
Early Stage
Expansion

Size of Investments Considered:
Min Size of Investment Considered (000s): $1,000
Max Size of Investment Considered (000s): $5,000

Geographical Preferences

United States Preferences:
Midwest
Minnesota

Industry Preferences

In Communications prefer:
Telecommunications

In Computer Software prefer:
Software

In Semiconductor/Electr prefer:
Electronics
Semiconductor

In Biotechnology prefer:
Biotechnology

In Medical/Health prefer:
Medical Products
Health Services

In Financial Services prefer:
Financial Services

In Business Serv. prefer:
Media

Additional Information

Year Founded: 1999
Capital Under Management: $11,000,000
Current Activity Level : Actively seeking new investments
Method of Compensation: Return on investment is of primary concern, do not charge fees

---

SPANGLER VENTURES, LLC

2802 10th Avenue East
Seattle, WA USA 98102
Phone: 206-720-6114
E-mail: info@spanglerventures.net
Website: www.spanglerventures.net

Management and Staff

Mark Spangler, President, Founder
William Carleton, Principal

Type of Firm

Bank Affiliated

Project Preferences

Type of Financing Preferred:
Early Stage
Later Stage
Seed
Startup

Industry Preferences

In Communications prefer:
Wireless Communications

In Internet Specific prefer:
Internet

Additional Information

Year Founded: 1999
Current Activity Level : Actively seeking new investments

SPARK CAPITAL

137 Newbury Street
Eighth Floor
Boston, MA USA 02116
Phone: 617-830-2000
Fax: 617-830-2001
E-mail: spark@sparkcapital.com
Website: www.sparkcapital.com

Management and Staff

Alex Finkelstein, General Partner
Bijan Sabet, General Partner
Dennis Miller, General Partner
Mo Koyfman, Principal
Santo Politi, General Partner
Todd Dagres, General Partner

Type of Firm

Private Equity Firm

Project Preferences

Type of Financing Preferred:
Balanced

Geographical Preferences

United States Preferences:
All U.S.

Industry Preferences

In Communications prefer:
Data Communications
Media and Entertainment

Additional Information

Name of Most Recent Fund: Spark Capital Founders' Fund II, L.P.
Most Recent Fund Was Raised: 03/18/2008
Year Founded: 2005
Capital Under Management: $260,000,000
Current Activity Level : Actively seeking new investments

SPARK VENTURES PLC (FKA: NEWMEDIA SPARK PLC)

33 Glasshouse Street
4th Floor
London, United Kingdom W1B 5DG
Phone: 44-20-7851-7777
Fax: 44-20-7851-7770
E-mail: enquiries@sparkventures.com
Website: www.sparkventures.com

Management and Staff

Andrew Carruthers, Chief Executive Officer
Martin Williams, Managing Director

Type of Firm

Private Equity Firm

Association Membership

British Venture Capital Association (BVCA)
European Private Equity and Venture Capital Assoc.

Project Preferences

Role in Financing:
Prefer role as deal originator but will also invest in deals created by others

Type of Financing Preferred:
Second Stage Financing
Leveraged Buyout
Expansion
Early Stage
Balanced
Start-up Financing
Seed
First Stage Financing
Special Situation
Startup

Size of Investments Considered:
Min Size of Investment Considered (000s): $700
Max Size of Investment Considered: No Limit

Geographical Preferences

International Preferences:
United Kingdom
Europe

Industry Focus

(% based on actual investment)

Internet Specific	23.7%
Communications and Media	16.8%
Computer Software and Services	15.9%
Biotechnology	15.7%
Semiconductors/Other Elect.	10.1%
Other Products	7.1%
Medical/Health	5.6%
Industrial/Energy	2.8%
Computer Hardware	1.2%
Consumer Related	1.1%

Additional Information

Year Founded: 1984
Capital Under Management: $478,400,000

Current Activity Level : Actively seeking new investments
Method of Compensation: Return on invest. most important, but chg. closing fees, service fees, etc.

SPARKASSEN- BETEILIGUNGSGESELLSCHAFT HEILBRONN-FRANKEN MBH

Am Wollhaus 14
Heilbronn, Germany 74072
Phone: 49-7131-6381700
Fax: 49-7131-6381314
E-mail: info@sparkassen-beteiligung.de
Website: www.sparkassen-beteiligung.de

Type of Firm

Bank Affiliated

Association Membership

German Venture Capital Association (BVK)

Project Preferences

Type of Financing Preferred:
Balanced

Geographical Preferences

International Preferences:
Germany

Additional Information

Year Founded: 2000
Current Activity Level : Actively seeking new investments

SPARKASSENKAPITAL ULM GMBH

Neue Str. 66
Ulm, Germany D-89073
Phone: 49-731-101-511
E-mail: stefanie.foesinger@sparkasse-ulm.de
Website: www.sparkasse-ulm.de

Management and Staff

Gunter Guthan, Chief Executive Officer
Klaus Hopner, Chief Executive Officer

Type of Firm

Bank Affiliated

Project Preferences

Role in Financing:
Will function either as deal originator or investor in deals created by others

Type of Financing Preferred:
Early Stage
Expansion

Geographical Preferences

International Preferences:
Germany

Additional Information

Year Founded: 2006
Current Activity Level : Actively seeking new investments

SPARKVENTURES, LLC

10 Wilson Road
Suite 3
Cambridge, MA USA 02138

Management and Staff

Andrew Robbins, Managing Director
Matt D Arbeloff, Managing Director

Type of Firm

Private Equity Firm

Project Preferences

Type of Financing Preferred:
Early Stage

Geographical Preferences

United States Preferences:
Northeast

Industry Preferences

In Computer Software prefer:
Software

In Internet Specific prefer:
Internet

Additional Information

Year Founded: 1998
Current Activity Level : Actively seeking new investments

SPARX CAPITAL PARTNERS CO., LTD.

16F East TW. Gate City Ohsaki
1-11-12 Ohsaki, Shinagawa-ku
Tokyo, Japan 141-0032
Phone: 81-3-54357-9800
Fax: 81-3-54357-9801
Website: www.sparxgroup.com

Management and Staff

Shinji Naito, Senior Managing Director
Shuhei Abe, Founder

Type of Firm

Private Equity Firm

Additional Information

Year Founded: 2006
Current Activity Level : Actively seeking new investments

SPB CAPITAL PARTNERS, L.P.

10091 Park Run Drive
Suite 190
Las Vegas, NV USA 89145
Phone: 702-471-0030

Management and Staff

Roger Bulloch, Managing Director

Type of Firm

Private Equity Firm

Project Preferences

Type of Financing Preferred:
Leveraged Buyout

Additional Information

Year Founded: 2006
Capital Under Management: $44,500,000
Current Activity Level : Actively seeking new investments

SPECIAL SITUATIONS FUNDS

153 East 53rd Street
55th Floor
New York, NY USA 10022
Phone: 212-207-6500
Fax: 212-207-6515

Type of Firm

Private Equity Firm

Project Preferences

Type of Financing Preferred:
Generalist PE
Other

Additional Information

Year Founded: 2002
Capital Under Management: $162,200,000
Current Activity Level : Actively seeking new investments

SPECTRUM EQUITY INVESTORS

One International Place
29th Floor
Boston, MA USA 02110
Phone: 617-464-4600
Fax: 617-464-4601
Website: www.spectrumequity.com

Other Offices

333 Middlefield Road
Suite 200
Menlo Park, CA USA 94025

Phone: 415-464-4600
Fax: 415-464-4601

Management and Staff

Adam Margolin, Vice President
Benjamin Spero, Principal
Benjamin Coughlin, Managing Director
Brion Applegate, Senior Managing Director
Christopher Mitchell, Managing Director
Jim Quagliaroli, Principal
Kevin Maroni, Senior Managing Director
Michael Kennealy, Managing Director
Nicolas Massard, Principal
Steven LeSieur, Vice President
Victor Parker, Managing Director
William Collatos, Senior Managing Director

Type of Firm

Private Equity Firm

Association Membership

Western Association of Venture Capitalists (WAVC)

Project Preferences

Role in Financing:

Prefer role as deal originator but will also invest in deals created by others

Type of Financing Preferred:

Second Stage Financing
Leveraged Buyout
Early Stage
Expansion
Mezzanine
Balanced
Later Stage
Seed
First Stage Financing
Acquisition
Startup
Recapitalizations

Size of Investments Considered:

Min Size of Investment Considered (000s): $5,000
Max Size of Investment Considered: No Limit

Geographical Preferences

Canadian Preferences:

All Canada

International Preferences:

Italy
United Kingdom
Luxembourg
Netherlands
Portugal
Europe
Eastern Europe
Spain
Belgium
Germany
France

Industry Focus

(% based on actual investment)

Communications and Media	30.7%
Other Products	21.9%
Internet Specific	19.4%
Computer Software and Services	16.6%
Consumer Related	5.1%
Medical/Health	3.3%
Semiconductors/Other Elect.	2.0%
Computer Hardware	1.1%

Additional Information

Name of Most Recent Fund: Spectrum Equity Investors V, LP
Most Recent Fund Was Raised: 03/02/2005
Year Founded: 1994
Capital Under Management: $4,019,100,000
Current Activity Level : Actively seeking new investments
Method of Compensation: Return on investment is of primary concern, do not charge fees

SPELL CAPITAL PARTNERS LLC

222 South Ninth Street
Suite 2880
Minneapolis, MN USA 55402
Phone: 612-371-9650
Fax: 612-371-9651
Website: www.spellcapital.com

Management and Staff

Andrea Nelson, Vice President
Bruce Richard, Managing Director
Dobson West, Senior Managing Director
Jim Rikkers, Managing Director
Steve Jones, Managing Director
William Spell, President

Type of Firm

Private Equity Firm

Project Preferences

Role in Financing:

Prefer role as deal originator but will also invest in deals created by others

Type of Financing Preferred:

Leveraged Buyout
Mezzanine
Acquisition

Size of Investments Considered:

Min Size of Investment Considered (000s): $4,000
Max Size of Investment Considered (000s): $12,000

Geographical Preferences

United States Preferences:

Midwest

Industry Focus

(% based on actual investment)

Semiconductors/Other Elect.	56.7%
Industrial/Energy	43.3%

Additional Information

Name of Most Recent Fund: Spell Capital Partners Fund III, L.P.
Most Recent Fund Was Raised: 02/15/2006
Year Founded: 1988
Capital Under Management: $110,000,000
Current Activity Level : Actively seeking new investments
Method of Compensation: Return on invest. most important, but chg. closing fees, service fees, etc.

SPENCER TRASK VENTURES, INC. (FKA: SPENCER TRASK SECURITIES)

535 Madison Avenue
New York, NY USA 10022
Phone: 312-326-9000
Fax: 212-751-3362
E-mail: inquiries@spencertrask.com
Website: www.spencertrask.com

Other Offices

12310 Pinecrest Road
Suite 302
Reston, VA USA 20191
Phone: 703-262-7900
Fax: 703-262-0115

1299 Ocean Avenue
Suite 900
Santa Monica, CA USA 90401
Phone: 310-395-5960

Management and Staff

William Dioguardi, President

Type of Firm

Private Equity Firm

Association Membership

Mid-Atlantic Venture Association

Project Preferences

Role in Financing:

Prefer role as deal originator

Type of Financing Preferred:

Second Stage Financing
Early Stage
Start-up Financing
First Stage Financing

Size of Investments Considered:

Min Size of Investment Considered (000s): $1,000
Max Size of Investment Considered (000s): $20,000

Geographical Preferences

United States Preferences:

All U.S.

Industry Preferences

In Communications prefer:

Communications and Media
Telecommunications

In Computer Hardware prefer:
Computer Graphics and Dig
Disk Relat. Memory Device

In Computer Software prefer:
Computer Services
Systems Software
Applications Software

In Internet Specific prefer:
Internet

In Semiconductor/Electr prefer:
Electronic Components
Semiconductor
Controllers and Sensors
Circuit Boards
Fiber Optics

In Biotechnology prefer:
Biotechnology
Biosensors
Biotech Related Research

In Medical/Health prefer:
Diagnostic Services
Diagnostic Test Products
Drug/Equipmt Delivery
Hospitals/Clinics/Primary
Hospital/Other Instit.
Pharmaceuticals

In Consumer Related prefer:
Consumer Products
Other Restaurants
Education Related

In Industrial/Energy prefer:
Alternative Energy
Materials
Robotics
Machinery

In Financial Services prefer:
Financial Services

In Manufact. prefer:
Office Automation Equipmt
Publishing

Additional Information
Name of Most Recent Fund: Spencer Trask Private Equity Fund I
Most Recent Fund Was Raised: 03/31/2001
Year Founded: 1991
Current Activity Level : Actively seeking new investments
Method of Compensation: Function primarily in service area, receive contingent fee in cash or equity

---

SPEYSIDE EQUITY LLC
1741 Tomlinson Road
Philadelphia, PA USA 19116
Website: www.speysideequity.com

Type of Firm
Private Equity Firm

Project Preferences

Type of Financing Preferred:
Leveraged Buyout
Acquisition

Additional Information
Year Founded: 2004
Current Activity Level : Actively seeking new investments

SPHERE PRIVATE EQUITY
The Place, Third Floor
1 Sandton Drive
Sandton, South Africa 2196
Phone: 27-11-944-7800
Fax: 27-11-944-7801
E-mail: info@sphereholdings.co.za
Website: www.sphereholdings.co.za

Management and Staff
Itumeleng Kgaboesele, Chief Executive Officer

Type of Firm
Private Equity Advisor or Fund of Funds

Project Preferences

Type of Financing Preferred:
Acquisition

Geographical Preferences

International Preferences:
South Africa
Africa

Industry Preferences

In Consumer Related prefer:
Retail

In Industrial/Energy prefer:
Industrial Products
Machinery

In Business Serv. prefer:
Services
Distribution

In Manufact. prefer:
Manufacturing

Additional Information
Year Founded: 2005
Capital Under Management: $40,500,000
Current Activity Level : Actively seeking new investments

SPINN INVESTMENT
Grev Turegatan 21, 3 tr
Stockholm, Sweden 114 38
Phone: 46-70-253-913
Website: www.spinninvestment.se

Other Offices
Kungsgatan 8, 4 vn
Helsingborg, Sweden 252 21

Vastra Hamngatan 11, 1 van
Goteborg, Sweden 411 17

Management and Staff
Bjorn Holmqvist, Partner
Bosse Larsson, Partner
Urban Trolle, Partner

Type of Firm
Private Equity Firm

Association Membership
Swedish Venture Capital Association (SVCA)
European Private Equity and Venture Capital Assoc.

Project Preferences

Type of Financing Preferred:
Balanced

Geographical Preferences

International Preferences:
Sweden
Europe

Additional Information
Year Founded: 2005
Current Activity Level : Actively seeking new investments

SPINNAKER TRUST
Five Milk Street
P.O. Box 7160
Portland, ME USA 04112
Phone: 207-553-7160
Fax: 207-553-7162
E-mail: Spinnakerinfo@spinnakertrust.com
Website: www.spinnakertrust.com

Management and Staff
Amanda Rand, Vice President
Anne Wood, Vice President
David Carter, Vice President
Kimberly Volk, Chief Financial Officer
Sarah Lewis, Vice President

Type of Firm
Investment Management Firm

Project Preferences

Type of Financing Preferred:
Early Stage
Generalist PE

Geographical Preferences

United States Preferences:
Northeast

Additional Information

Name of Most Recent Fund: Spinnaker Private Equity Fund, LLC
Most Recent Fund Was Raised: 08/29/2006
Year Founded: 2001
Capital Under Management: $3,000,000
Current Activity Level : Actively seeking new investments

SPINNAKER VENTURES

582 Market Street
Suite 307
San Francisco, CA USA 94104
Phone: 415-374-2700
Fax: 415-374-2707
E-mail: information@spinnakerventures.com
Website: www.spinnakerventures.com

Other Offices

Al Santos, 1940-2o
Sao Paulo, SP, Brazil 01418-200
Phone: 55-11-3253-2255
Fax: 55-11-3253-2437

Management and Staff

Claude Pomper, General Partner
Gregorio Schneider, General Partner
Pete Patterson, Chief Financial Officer

Type of Firm

Private Equity Firm

Project Preferences

Role in Financing:

Prefer role in deals created by others

Type of Financing Preferred:

Expansion
Later Stage

Size of Investments Considered:

Min Size of Investment Considered (000s): $200
Max Size of Investment Considered (000s): $200

Geographical Preferences

International Preferences:

Latin America

Industry Preferences

In Communications prefer:

Telecommunications
Wireless Communications
Data Communications

In Computer Software prefer:

Software
Applications Software

In Internet Specific prefer:

Internet

In Semiconductor/Electr prefer:

Semiconductor
Micro-Processing
Fiber Optics

In Medical/Health prefer:

Diagnostic Test Products
Medical Products
Disposable Med. Products

In Industrial/Energy prefer:

Energy

In Financial Services prefer:

Financial Services

Additional Information

Year Founded: 1997
Capital Under Management: $53,500,000
Current Activity Level : Actively seeking new investments
Method of Compensation: Return on investment is of primary concern, do not charge fees

---

SPIRE CAPITAL

1500 Broadway
Suite 1811
New York, NY USA 10036
Phone: 212-218-5454
Fax: 212-218-5455
E-mail: info@spirecapital.com
Website: www.spirecapital.com

Other Offices

10 Town Square
Chatham, NJ USA 07928
Phone: 973-701-7711
Fax: 973-701-7772

Five Tower Bridge
300 Barr Harbor Drive, Suite 720
West Conshohocken, PA USA 19428
Phone: 610-397-1700
Fax: 610-397-1014

Management and Staff

Andrew Armstrong, Partner
Bruce Hernandez, Partner
Joel Goldblatt, Partner
Richard Patterson, Partner
Sean White, Principal
Thomas Savage, Principal

Type of Firm

Private Equity Firm

Project Preferences

Role in Financing:

Prefer role as deal originator but will also invest in deals created by others

Type of Financing Preferred:

Second Stage Financing
Leveraged Buyout
Expansion
Later Stage

Size of Investments Considered:

Min Size of Investment Considered (000s): $15,000
Max Size of Investment Considered (000s): $25,000

Geographical Preferences

United States Preferences:

All U.S.

International Preferences:

Europe

Industry Focus

(% based on actual investment)

Communications and Media	53.3%
Consumer Related	16.7%
Other Products	10.6%
Semiconductors/Other Elect.	8.9%
Computer Software and Services	8.0%
Internet Specific	2.6%

Additional Information

Name of Most Recent Fund: Spire Capital Partners II, L.P.
Most Recent Fund Was Raised: 12/08/2006
Year Founded: 2000
Capital Under Management: $260,000,000
Current Activity Level : Actively seeking new investments
Method of Compensation: Return on investment is of primary concern, do not charge fees

---

SPIRIT CAPITAL PARTNERS (FKA: ABERDEEN ASSET MANAGERS PE)

One Bow Churchyard
London, United Kingdom EC4M 9HH
Phone: 44-20-7463-6136
Fax: 44-20-7463-6452
E-mail: private.equity@aberdeen-asset.com
Website: www.aberdeen-asset.com/privateequity

Other Offices

3 The Embankment
Sovereign Street
Leeds, United Kingdom LS1 4BJ
Phone: 44-113-242-2644

10 Queens Terrace
Aberdeen, United Kingdom AB10 1YG
Phone: 44-1224-631-999

Second Floor
28/29 Threadneedle Street
London, United Kingdom EC2R 8AY
Phone: 44-207-448-9680

Sutherland House
149 St. Vincent Street
Glasgow, United Kingdom G2 5NW
Phone: 44-41-306-7400

1 Cornwall Street
Birmingham, United Kingdom B3 2JN
Phone: 44-121-236-1222

Ballantyne House
84 Academy Street

Inverness, United Kingdom IV1 1LU
Phone: 44-1463-717-214

St. James House
7 Charlotte Street
Manchester, United Kingdom M1 4DZ
Phone: 44-161-233-3500

Type of Firm

Bank Affiliated

Association Membership

British Venture Capital Association (BVCA)
European Private Equity and Venture Capital Assoc.

Project Preferences

Role in Financing:

Prefer role as deal originator but will also invest in deals created by others

Type of Financing Preferred:

Second Stage Financing
Leveraged Buyout
Generalist PE
Expansion
Turnaround
Balanced
Management Buyouts
Acquisition
Recapitalizations

Size of Investments Considered:

Min Size of Investment Considered (000s): $2,068
Max Size of Investment Considered (000s): $41,352

Geographical Preferences

International Preferences:

United Kingdom

Industry Focus

(% based on actual investment)

Other Products	55.1%
Industrial/Energy	32.4%
Computer Hardware	12.4%

Additional Information

Year Founded: 1986
Capital Under Management: $477,300,000
Current Activity Level : Actively seeking new investments

SPLIT ROCK PARTNERS LLC

10400 Viking Drive
Suite 550
Minneapolis, MN USA 55344
Phone: 952-995-7474
Fax: 952-995-7475
Website: www.splitrock.com

Other Offices

1600 El Camino Real
Suite 290
Menlo Park, CA USA 94025
Phone: 650-617-1500
Fax: 650-617-1510

Management and Staff

Allan Will, Managing Director
David Stassen, Managing Director
James Simons, Managing Director
Michael Gorman, Managing Director
Steve Schwen, Chief Financial Officer

Type of Firm

Private Equity Firm

Association Membership

National Venture Capital Association - USA (NVCA)

Project Preferences

Type of Financing Preferred:

Early Stage
Startup

Size of Investments Considered:

Min Size of Investment Considered (000s): $500
Max Size of Investment Considered (000s): $8,000

Geographical Preferences

United States Preferences:

Midwest
West Coast

Industry Preferences

In Computer Software prefer:

Software

In Internet Specific prefer:

Internet

In Medical/Health prefer:

Medical/Health
Medical Products
Pharmaceuticals

In Consumer Related prefer:

Consumer Services

Additional Information

Name of Most Recent Fund: Split Rock Partners II, L.P.
Most Recent Fund Was Raised: 05/07/2008
Year Founded: 2004
Capital Under Management: $575,000,000
Current Activity Level : Actively seeking new investments

SPMO

Carel van Bylandtlaan 30
Postbus 444
Den Haag, Netherlands 2501 CK
Phone: 31-70-377-8787
Fax: 31-70-377-8789
Website: www.shell.com

Type of Firm

Corporate PE/Venture

Association Membership

Dutch Venture Capital Associaton (NVP)

Project Preferences

Type of Financing Preferred:

Early Stage

Geographical Preferences

International Preferences:

Netherlands

Additional Information

Year Founded: 2003
Current Activity Level : Actively seeking new investments

SPO PARTNERS & CO

591 Redwood Highway
Suite 3215
Mill Valley, CA USA 94941
Phone: 415-383-6600

Type of Firm

Private Equity Advisor or Fund of Funds

Project Preferences

Type of Financing Preferred:

Leveraged Buyout

Additional Information

Name of Most Recent Fund: SPO Partners II, L.P.
Most Recent Fund Was Raised: 12/26/2001
Year Founded: 1991
Capital Under Management: $2,340,200,000
Current Activity Level : Actively seeking new investments

SPONSOR CAPITAL OY

Mannerheimintie 4
Helsinki, Finland 00100
Phone: 358-9-680-3300
Fax: 358-9-643-252
Website: www.sponsor.fi

Management and Staff

Ari Jokelainen, Partner
Juuso Kivinen, Partner
Kaj Hagglund, Partner
Matti Suutarinen, Managing Director
Olli Anttila, Partner
Sami Heikkila, Partner

Type of Firm

Private Equity Firm

Association Membership

Finnish Venture Capital Association (FVCA)

Project Preferences

Type of Financing Preferred:
Leveraged Buyout
Expansion
Turnaround
Management Buyouts

Size of Investments Considered:
Min Size of Investment Considered (000s): $6,132
Max Size of Investment Considered (000s): $22,995

Geographical Preferences

International Preferences:
Finland

Industry Focus
(% based on actual investment)

Consumer Related	59.0%
Communications and Media	22.3%
Other Products	18.8%

Additional Information
Year Founded: 1997
Capital Under Management: $67,800,000
Current Activity Level : Actively seeking new investments

SPRAY VENTURE PARTNERS
2330 Washington Street
Newton, MA USA 02462
Phone: 617-332-6060
Fax: 617-332-6070
E-mail: info@spraypartners.com
Website: www.spraypartners.com

Management and Staff
J. Daniel Cole, General Partner
Kevin Connors, General Partner

Type of Firm
Private Equity Firm

Project Preferences

Role in Financing:
Will function either as deal originator or investor in deals created by others

Type of Financing Preferred:
Second Stage Financing
Start-up Financing
Seed
First Stage Financing

Size of Investments Considered:
Min Size of Investment Considered (000s): $50
Max Size of Investment Considered (000s): $6,000

Industry Focus
(% based on actual investment)

Medical/Health	87.5%
Biotechnology	10.5%
Internet Specific	2.0%

Additional Information
Name of Most Recent Fund: Spray Venture Partners II, L.P.
Most Recent Fund Was Raised: 12/01/2003
Year Founded: 1996
Capital Under Management: $52,000,000
Current Activity Level : Actively seeking new investments
Method of Compensation: Return on investment is of primary concern, do not charge fees

---

SPRING BAY COMPANIES, THE (AKA: SPRING BAY VENTURES)
816 A1A North
Suite 201
Ponte Vedra Beach, FL USA 32082
Phone: 904-273-8755
Fax: 904-273-8745
Website: www.spring-bay.com

Management and Staff
Charles Gregory, Chief Financial Officer
Daniel Ryan, Vice President
Frederick Sontag, President

Type of Firm
Private Equity Firm

Project Preferences

Type of Financing Preferred:
Leveraged Buyout
Generalist PE
Expansion
Acquisition
Recapitalizations

Size of Investments Considered:
Min Size of Investment Considered (000s): $1,000
Max Size of Investment Considered (000s): $10,000

Additional Information
Year Founded: 2009
Current Activity Level : Actively seeking new investments

SPRING CAPITAL ASIA, LTD.
27/F Entertainment Building
30 Queen's Road
Central, Hong Kong
Phone: 852-3667-7787
Fax: 852-3667-7789
Website: www.springcapasia.com

Other Offices
Suite 2605, Tian An Center
338 Nanjing West Road
Shanghai, China 200003
Phone: 86-21-5375-2063
Fax: 86-21-5375-2070

Management and Staff
Louis Choy, Managing Director
Thomas Xue, Managing Director

Type of Firm
Private Equity Firm

Association Membership
Hong Kong Venture Capital Association (HKVCA)

Project Preferences

Type of Financing Preferred:
Early Stage
Expansion
Acquisition

Size of Investments Considered:
Min Size of Investment Considered (000s): $5,000
Max Size of Investment Considered (000s): $12,000

Geographical Preferences

International Preferences:
China
Hong Kong

Industry Preferences

In Communications prefer:
Wireless Communications

In Medical/Health prefer:
Medical Diagnostics
Health Services

In Consumer Related prefer:
Consumer
Entertainment and Leisure
Education Related

In Industrial/Energy prefer:
Environmental Related

In Business Serv. prefer:
Services

In Manufact. prefer:
Manufacturing

Additional Information
Year Founded: 2007
Capital Under Management: $103,000,000
Current Activity Level : Actively seeking new investments

SPRING CAPITAL PARTNERS (FKA: SPRING CAPITAL INVESTORS LLC)
Latrobe Building, Fifth Floor
Two East Read Street
Baltimore, MD USA 21202
Phone: 410-685-8000
Fax: 410-545-0015
E-mail: mailbox@springcap.com
Website: www.springcap.com

Other Offices

Five Radnor Corporate Center, Suite 520
100 Matsonford Road
Radnor, PA USA 19087
Phone: 610-964-7972
Fax: 610-977-0119

Management and Staff

Brian McDaid, Vice President
F. Stuart Knott, Vice President
John Acker, General Partner
Michael Donoghue, General Partner
Peter Orthwein, Vice President
Robert Stewart, General Partner

Type of Firm

Private Equity Firm

Association Membership

Mid-Atlantic Venture Association
Natl Assoc of Small Bus. Inv. Co (NASBIC)

Project Preferences

Role in Financing:

Will function either as deal originator or investor in deals created by others

Type of Financing Preferred:

Leveraged Buyout
Expansion
Mezzanine
Later Stage
Management Buyouts
Acquisition
Industry Rollups
Recapitalizations

Size of Investments Considered:

Min Size of Investment Considered (000s): $4,000
Max Size of Investment Considered (000s): $10,000

Geographical Preferences

United States Preferences:

Mid Atlantic

Industry Preferences

In Communications prefer:

Commercial Communications
CATV & Pay TV Systems
Radio & TV Broadcasting
Telecommunications
Wireless Communications
Data Communications
Satellite Microwave Comm.
Other Communication Prod.

In Computer Hardware prefer:

Mainframes / Scientific
Mini and Personal/Desktop
Computer Graphics and Dig
Integrated Turnkey System
Terminals
Disk Relat. Memory Device

In Computer Software prefer:

Computer Services
Data Processing
Software
Systems Software
Applications Software
Artificial Intelligence

In Internet Specific prefer:

E-Commerce Technology
Internet
Ecommerce
Web Aggregration/Portals

In Semiconductor/Electr prefer:

Electronic Components
Semiconductor
Micro-Processing
Controllers and Sensors
Sensors
Circuit Boards
Component Testing Equipmt
Laser Related
Fiber Optics
Analytic/Scientific
Optoelectronics

In Medical/Health prefer:

Medical Diagnostics
Diagnostic Services
Diagnostic Test Products
Medical Therapeutics
Drug/Equipmt Delivery
Medical Products
Disposable Med. Products
Health Services
Hospitals/Clinics/Primary
Hospital/Other Instit.
Pharmaceuticals

In Consumer Related prefer:

Consumer
Entertainment and Leisure
Sports
Retail
Franchises(NEC)
Food/Beverage
Education Related

In Industrial/Energy prefer:

Energy
Industrial Products
Factory Automation
Robotics
Machinery

In Transportation prefer:

Transportation
Aerospace

In Business Serv. prefer:

Services
Distribution
Consulting Services
Media

In Manufact. prefer:

Manufacturing

In Agr/Forestr/Fish prefer:

Agriculture related

In Utilities prefer:

Utilities

In Other prefer:

Women/Minority-Owned Bus.

Additional Information

Year Founded: 1999
Capital Under Management: $187,000,000
Current Activity Level : Actively seeking new investments
Method of Compensation: Return on invest. most important, but chg. closing fees, service fees, etc.

SPRING MILL VENTURE PARTNERS

11611 North Meridian Street
Suite 310
Carmel, IN USA 46032-6153
Phone: 317-713-7550
E-mail: info@springmillvp.com
Website: www.springmillvp.com

Other Offices

Historic Hirons Building
555 N. Morton Street
Bloomington, IN USA 47404

Management and Staff

David Mann, General Partner
Jane Martin, Co-Founder
Ken Green, Managing Partner

Type of Firm

Private Equity Firm

Project Preferences

Type of Financing Preferred:

Early Stage

Geographical Preferences

United States Preferences:

Indiana

Additional Information

Year Founded: 2000
Current Activity Level : Actively seeking new investments

SPRING RIDGE VENTURES

800 El Camino Real
Suite 220
Menlo Park, CA USA 94025
Phone: 650-566-9100
Fax: 650-566-9200
Website: www.springridgeventures.com

Management and Staff

Andrew Thompson, General Partner
David Apfelberg, Venture Partner
George Savage, General Partner
William LaFayette, Chief Financial Officer

Type of Firm
Private Equity Firm

Project Preferences

Type of Financing Preferred:
Early Stage
Expansion

Geographical Preferences

United States Preferences:
All U.S.

Industry Preferences

In Biotechnology prefer:
Human Biotechnology

Additional Information
Year Founded: 2000
Capital Under Management: $11,700,000
Current Activity Level : Actively seeking new investments

SPRING SEEDS CAPITAL PTE, LTD.

2 Bukit Merah Central
Singapore, Singapore 159835
Phone: 65-6278-6666
Fax: 65-6278-6667
E-mail: SEEDS@spring.gov.sg
Website: www.spring.gov.sg

Management and Staff
Chew Mok Lee, Chief Executive Officer

Type of Firm
Government Affiliated Program

Project Preferences

Type of Financing Preferred:
Seed

Geographical Preferences

International Preferences:
Singapore

Additional Information
Year Founded: 2007
Current Activity Level : Actively seeking new investments

SPRINGBANK TECHVENTURES

Suite 200, 1301
10th Ave. S.W.
Calgary, Canada T3C 0J4
Phone: 403-685-8001
Fax: 403-685-8002
E-mail: email@sbtechventures.com
Website: www.sbtechventures.com

Management and Staff
Andrew Kyle, General Partner
Barb Richardson, General Partner
Barry Poffenroth, General Partner
Shawn Abbott, General Partner

Type of Firm
Private Equity Firm

Project Preferences

Type of Financing Preferred:
Early Stage
Startup

Geographical Preferences

Canadian Preferences:
All Canada

Industry Preferences

In Communications prefer:
Telecommunications
Wireless Communications

In Internet Specific prefer:
Internet

Additional Information
Year Founded: 2000
Current Activity Level : Actively seeking new investments

SPRINGHILL MANAGEMENT SDN BHD (FKA: IKATAN MENAWAN SDN BHD)

Suite 12.08 12/F Plaza 138
Jalan Ampang
Kuala Lumpur, Malaysia 50450
Phone: 603-2732-0588
Fax: 603-2732-1988

Management and Staff
Kim Tan, General Partner

Type of Firm
Private Equity Firm

Project Preferences

Type of Financing Preferred:
Early Stage
Expansion
Mezzanine
Balanced
Startup

Geographical Preferences

United States Preferences:
All U.S.

International Preferences:
Europe
Asia
Malaysia

Industry Preferences

In Biotechnology prefer:
Biotechnology

Additional Information
Year Founded: 2003
Capital Under Management: $30,000,000
Current Activity Level : Actively seeking new investments

SPRINGWORKS, LLC

4400 Baker Road
Minnetonka, MN USA 55343
Phone: 952-934-9918
Fax: 952-936-5048
E-mail: pginfo@pettersgroup.com
Website: www.pettersgroup.com

Management and Staff
George Danko, Chief Executive Officer

Type of Firm
Corporate PE/Venture

Additional Information
Year Founded: 2005
Current Activity Level : Actively seeking new investments

SPROUT GROUP

Eleven Madison Avenue
13th Floor
New York, NY USA 10010
Phone: 212-538-3600
Fax: 212-538-8245
E-mail: info@sproutgroup.com
Website: www.sproutgroup.com

Other Offices
3000 Sand Hill Road
Building 3, Suite 170
Menlo Park, CA USA 94025
Phone: 650-234-2700
Fax: 650-234-2779

Management and Staff
Amy Yeung, Chief Financial Officer
Janet Hickey, General Partner
Robert Finzi, General Partner
Wayne Nemeth, Partner

Type of Firm
Bank Affiliated

Association Membership
Western Association of Venture Capitalists (WAVC)

National Venture Capital Association - USA (NVCA)

Project Preferences

Role in Financing:
Will function either as deal originator or investor in deals created by others

Type of Financing Preferred:
Leveraged Buyout
Early Stage
Expansion
Later Stage
Management Buyouts
Startup

Size of Investments Considered:
Min Size of Investment Considered (000s): $5,000
Max Size of Investment Considered (000s): $50,000

Geographical Preferences

International Preferences:
Italy
United Kingdom
Spain
Germany
France

Industry Focus

(% based on actual investment)

Medical/Health	22.6%
Biotechnology	17.3%
Internet Specific	16.0%
Communications and Media	11.9%
Computer Software and Services	11.6%
Consumer Related	6.5%
Other Products	5.0%
Computer Hardware	3.9%
Semiconductors/Other Elect.	3.4%
Industrial/Energy	1.8%

Additional Information

Name of Most Recent Fund: Sprout Capital IX
Most Recent Fund Was Raised: 08/09/2000
Year Founded: 1969
Capital Under Management: $3,500,000,000
Current Activity Level : Actively seeking new investments

SPUR CAPITAL PARTNERS LLC

2370 Nowata Place
Bartlesville, OK USA 74006
Phone: 918-331-3800
Fax: 918-331-3848
Website: www.spurcap.com

Management and Staff

C. Bradford Kelly, Managing Director
Joan Heidorn, Managing Director
Paul Gompers, Managing Director
Paul Fetsch, Managing Director
Teri Hightower, Chief Financial Officer

Type of Firm

Private Equity Advisor or Fund of Funds

Project Preferences

Type of Financing Preferred:
Fund of Funds
Early Stage

Size of Investments Considered:
Min Size of Investment Considered (000s): $5,000
Max Size of Investment Considered (000s): $10,000

Geographical Preferences

International Preferences:
India
China
Israel

Industry Preferences

In Communications prefer:
Communications and Media
Telecommunications

In Internet Specific prefer:
Internet

In Computer Other prefer:
Computer Related

In Semiconductor/Electr prefer:
Electronic Components
Semiconductor

In Biotechnology prefer:
Biotechnology

In Medical/Health prefer:
Medical/Health

Additional Information

Name of Most Recent Fund: Spur Ventures II, L.P.
Most Recent Fund Was Raised: 11/03/2005
Year Founded: 2001
Capital Under Management: $342,000,000
Current Activity Level : Actively seeking new investments

SQUADRON CAPITAL ADVISORS, LTD.

46th Floor, Cheung Kong Center
2 Queen's Road
Central, Hong Kong
Phone: 852-2826-2000
Fax: 852-2297-0880
E-mail: info@squadroncapital.com
Website: www.squadroncapital.com

Management and Staff

Alice Chow, Managing Director
Boris Bong, Managing Director
David Pierce, Chief Executive Officer
Jacob Chiu, Managing Director
Wen Tan, Managing Director

Type of Firm

Private Equity Advisor or Fund of Funds

Association Membership

Hong Kong Venture Capital Association (HKVCA)

Project Preferences

Role in Financing:
Will function either as deal originator or investor in deals created by others

Type of Financing Preferred:
Fund of Funds

Geographical Preferences

United States Preferences:
All U.S.

International Preferences:
Vietnam
India
Indonesia
Taiwan
China
Hong Kong
Thailand
Philippines
Australia
Korea, South
Singapore
Japan
Malaysia

Industry Preferences

In Communications prefer:
Commercial Communications
Telecommunications

In Computer Hardware prefer:
Computers

In Computer Software prefer:
Software

In Internet Specific prefer:
Internet

In Semiconductor/Electr prefer:
Electronics

In Biotechnology prefer:
Biotech Related Research

In Medical/Health prefer:
Medical/Health
Pharmaceuticals

In Consumer Related prefer:
Retail
Consumer Products
Consumer Services

In Industrial/Energy prefer:
Energy
Environmental Related

In Transportation prefer:
Transportation

In Financial Services prefer:
Financial Services

In Manufact. prefer:
Manufacturing

In Agr/Forestr/Fish prefer:
Agriculture related

Additional Information

Year Founded: 2006
Capital Under Management: $1,500,000,000
Current Activity Level : Actively seeking new investments

SQUARE 1 VENTURES LLC

406 Blackwell Street
Suite 240
Durham, NC USA 27701
Phone: 919-354-1275
Fax: 919-314-3080
E-mail: info@square1ventures.com
Website: www.square1financial.com

Other Offices

701 Fifth Avenue
Suite 7170
Seattle, WA USA 98104
Phone: 206-812-4254
Fax: 206-812-4253

8902 Winter Street
Suite 220
North Waltham, MA USA 02451
Phone: 781-547-0847
Fax: 781-547-0848

1801 13th Street
Suite 204
Boulder, CO USA 80302
Phone: 303-938-3094
Fax: 303-938-3099

2425 Olympic Boulevard
Suite 6040W
Santa Monica, CA USA 90404
Phone: 310-961-0576

1950 University Avenue
Suite 150
East Palo Alto, CA USA 94303
Phone: 650-543-2700
Fax: 650-543-2780

12481 High Bluff Drive
Suite 350
San Diego, CA USA 92130
Phone: 858-436-3500
Fax: 858-436-3501

501 Kings Highway East
Rm.108, Suite E210
Fairfield, CT USA 06825
Phone: 203-610-8257
Fax: 203-610-8102

600 Congress Avenue
Suite 1200
Austin, TX USA 78701
Phone: 512-439-2830
Fax: 512-439-2829

1420 Beverly Road
Suite 300
McLean, VA USA 22101
Phone: 703-962-6630
Fax: 703-448-1849

Management and Staff

Adrian Wilson, President
Chris Woolley, President, Founder
Richard Gorczynski, Chief Financial Officer
Susan Casey, Chief Operating Officer
Will Kelly, President, Founder

Type of Firm

Bank Affiliated

Association Membership

National Venture Capital Association - USA (NVCA)

Project Preferences

Type of Financing Preferred:
Fund of Funds

Additional Information

Year Founded: 2005
Capital Under Management: $35,500,000
Current Activity Level : Actively seeking new investments

SQUARE FOUR INVESTMENTS GMBH

Eschersheimer Landstr. 121
Frankfurt am Main, Germany 60-322
Phone: 49-69-905503780
Fax: 49-69-905503789
E-mail: info@squarefour.de
Website: www.squarefour.de

Management and Staff

Gabriela Kroll, Partner

Type of Firm

Private Equity Firm

Project Preferences

Type of Financing Preferred:
Distressed Debt

Geographical Preferences

International Preferences:
Europe

Industry Preferences

In Consumer Related prefer:
Consumer

In Industrial/Energy prefer:
Industrial Products

In Manufact. prefer:
Manufacturing

Additional Information

Year Founded: 2009
Current Activity Level : Actively seeking new investments

SREI VENTURE CAPITAL LTD. (FKA: SREI GLOBAL ASSET MGT.)

Vishwakarma, 86C
Topsia Road (South)
Calcutta, India 700 046
Phone: 91-33-2285-0112
Fax: 91-33-2285-7542
E-mail: corporate@srei.com
Website: www.srei.com

Other Offices

21-23, T.V.I.Estate, Gr.Floor, 248
S.K.Ahire Marg, Behind Door Darshan
Mumbai, India 400 030
Phone: 022-2492-3904
Fax: 022-2497-3709

Parishram, 5 Rashmi Society
Meethakhali Circle, Opp. L G Show Room
Ahmedabad, India 380 009
Phone: 079-2658-0860
Fax: 079-2658-6634

A-162 Sahid Nagar
Bhubaneswar, India
Phone: 91-674-3018-715
Fax: 91-674-3018-721

D-2, 5th Floor, Southern Park
Saket Place, Saket
New Delhi, India 110017
Phone: 91-11-3061-5700
Fax: 91-11-3061-5799

7/2, Brunton Road
Off. M.G.Road, Behind Ajantha Hotel
India 560 025
Phone: 080-3058-4300
Fax: 080-3058-4318

6A Kiran Shankar Roy Road
Kolkata, India 700 001
Phone: 91-33-3022-9123
Fax: 91-33-3022-9173

202 & 203 Saptagiri Towers
2nd Floor, Begumpet, S. P. Road
Hyderabad, India 500 016
Phone: 91-40-5549-6600
Fax: 91-40-5549-4400

Mahalaxmi, 1st Floor
290 Peters Road, Gopalapuram
Chennai, India 600 086
Phone: 91-44-2855-5470
Fax: 91-44-2855-5584

Shradha Complex, F-7
1st Floor, Kingsway
Nagpur, India 440 001
Phone: 91-712-3018-600
Fax: 91-712-3018-602

Management and Staff

Devendra Vyas, Chief Financial Officer
Kaushik Chaudhuri, Chief Operating Officer
Naveen Bansal, Vice President
Sanjeeve Sancheti, Vice President

Type of Firm

Bank Affiliated

Project Preferences

Type of Financing Preferred:
Balanced

Size of Investments Considered:
Min Size of Investment Considered (000s): $5,000
Max Size of Investment Considered (000s): $100,000

Geographical Preferences

International Preferences:
India

Additional Information

Year Founded: 2005
Capital Under Management: $190,000,000
Current Activity Level : Actively seeking new investments

SRK (AKA: SVENSKT REKONSTRUKTIONSKAPITAL AB)

Kungsgatan 30, 10th flr
Stockholm, Sweden 111 35
Phone: 46-8-5464-9840
Fax: 46-8-5464-9849
E-mail: info@rekonstruktionskapital.se
Website: www.rekonstruktionskapital.se

Management and Staff

Robert Rehbinder, Chief Executive Officer

Type of Firm

Private Equity Firm

Project Preferences

Type of Financing Preferred:
Leveraged Buyout
Expansion
Balanced

Geographical Preferences

International Preferences:
Sweden
Switzerland
Europe

Industry Preferences

In Industrial/Energy prefer:
Industrial Products

Additional Information

Year Founded: 2003
Capital Under Management: $15,800,000
Current Activity Level : Actively seeking new investments

SSM PARTNERS

6075 Poplar Avenue
Suite 335
Memphis, TN USA 38119
Phone: 901-767-1131
Fax: 901-767-1135
Website: www.ssmpartners.com

Management and Staff

Casey West, Partner
David Swenson, Venture Partner
Hunter Witherington, Vice President
James Witherington, Managing General Partner
Larry Coleman, Venture Partner
R. Wilson Orr, Managing Partner
William Harrison, Partner

Type of Firm

Private Equity Firm

Project Preferences

Role in Financing:
Prefer role as deal originator but will also invest in deals created by others

Type of Financing Preferred:
Second Stage Financing
Early Stage
Expansion
Balanced
Later Stage
First Stage Financing

Size of Investments Considered:
Min Size of Investment Considered (000s): $3,000
Max Size of Investment Considered (000s): $10,000

Geographical Preferences

United States Preferences:
Southeast
Texas

Industry Focus

(% based on actual investment)

Computer Software and Services	26.5%
Internet Specific	24.3%
Medical/Health	15.2%
Communications and Media	14.2%
Consumer Related	6.2%
Computer Hardware	5.6%
Other Products	5.1%
Semiconductors/Other Elect.	2.9%

Additional Information

Name of Most Recent Fund: SSM Partners IV, L.P.
Most Recent Fund Was Raised: 09/11/2009
Year Founded: 1973
Capital Under Management: $215,500,000
Current Activity Level : Actively seeking new investments
Method of Compensation: Return on investment is of primary concern, do not charge fees

---

ST ASSET MANAGEMENT LTD.

51 Cuppage Road
10-03 StarHub Centre
Singapore, Singapore 229469
Phone: 65-6828-8133
Fax: 65-6720-2990
E-mail: contact@stassetmgt.com
Website: www.stam.stassetmgt.sg

Management and Staff

Patrick Kuan Chow Ng, Managing Director

Type of Firm

Investment Management Firm

Project Preferences

Type of Financing Preferred:
Balanced
Later Stage

Geographical Preferences

International Preferences:
India
China
Singapore

Additional Information

Year Founded: 2002
Capital Under Management: $30,000,000
Current Activity Level : Actively seeking new investments

ST. CLOUD CAPITAL, LLC

10866 Wilshire Boulevard
Suite 1450
Los Angeles, CA USA 90024
Phone: 310-475-2700
Fax: 310-475-0550
Website: www.stcloudcapital.com

Management and Staff

Benjamin Horn, Principal
Kacy Rozelle, Managing Director

Marshall Geller, Senior Managing Director
Robert Lautz, Managing Director

Type of Firm

Private Equity Firm

Project Preferences

Type of Financing Preferred:

Leveraged Buyout
Mezzanine
Acquisition
Recapitalizations

Size of Investments Considered:

Min Size of Investment Considered (000s): $1
Max Size of Investment Considered (000s): $20

Geographical Preferences

United States Preferences:

All U.S.

Additional Information

Year Founded: 2001
Capital Under Management: $125,000,000
Current Activity Level : Actively seeking new investments

ST. GEORGE BANK - VENTURE CAPITAL

Level 11
55 Market Street
Sydney, Australia
Phone: 612-9320-5715
Fax: 612-9320-5604
Website: www.stgeorge.com.au

Type of Firm

Bank Affiliated

Project Preferences

Type of Financing Preferred:

Balanced

Geographical Preferences

International Preferences:

Pacific

Additional Information

Year Founded: 1996
Current Activity Level : Actively seeking new investments

ST. PAUL VENTURE CAPITAL, INC.

10400 Viking Drive
Suite 550
Eden Prairie, MN USA 55344
Phone: 952-995-7474
Fax: 952-995-7475
Website: www.spvc.com

Other Offices

1600 El Camino Real
Suite 290
Menlo Park, CA USA 94025
Phone: 650-617-1500
Fax: 650-617-1510

601 Edgewater Drive
Suite 345
Wakefield, MA USA 01880
Phone: 508-475-2300
Fax: 508-475-2399

Management and Staff

Steve Schwen, Chief Financial Officer

Type of Firm

Private Equity Firm

Project Preferences

Role in Financing:

Prefer role as deal originator but will also invest in deals created by others

Type of Financing Preferred:

Early Stage

Size of Investments Considered:

Min Size of Investment Considered (000s): $2,000
Max Size of Investment Considered (000s): $40,000

Geographical Preferences

United States Preferences:

Massachusetts
California
Minnesota

Industry Focus

(% based on actual investment)

Internet Specific	20.4%
Computer Software and Services	20.1%
Communications and Media	18.7%
Medical/Health	18.2%
Semiconductors/Other Elect.	8.7%
Consumer Related	7.1%
Computer Hardware	3.3%
Other Products	1.3%
Biotechnology	1.2%
Industrial/Energy	1.1%

Additional Information

Year Founded: 1988
Capital Under Management: $3,000,000,000
Current Activity Level : Actively seeking new investments
Method of Compensation: Return on investment is of primary concern, do not charge fees

STAENBERG VENTURE PARTNERS (FKA: STAENBERG PRIVATE CAPITAL)

100 4th Avenue North
Suite 550
Seattle, WA USA 98109
Phone: 206-404-7777
Fax: 206-404-7105
E-mail: info@staenberg.com
Website: www.staenberg.com

Management and Staff

Jon Staenberg, Managing Partner
Paul Notaras, Chief Financial Officer

Type of Firm

Private Equity Firm

Project Preferences

Type of Financing Preferred:

Balanced

Size of Investments Considered:

Min Size of Investment Considered (000s): $100
Max Size of Investment Considered (000s): $3,000

Geographical Preferences

United States Preferences:

Northwest
Northern California

Industry Focus

(% based on actual investment)

Internet Specific	61.3%
Computer Software and Services	18.6%
Other Products	13.6%
Consumer Related	3.0%
Medical/Health	2.8%
Semiconductors/Other Elect.	0.7%

Additional Information

Name of Most Recent Fund: Staenberg Venture Partners II, L.P.
Most Recent Fund Was Raised: 05/23/2000
Year Founded: 1998
Capital Under Management: $100,000,000
Current Activity Level : Actively seeking new investments

STAFFORD TIMBERLAND, LTD.

49/50 Eagle Wharf Road
London, United Kingdom N1 7ED
Phone: 44-20-7336-8899
Fax: 44-20-7336-8877
E-mail: thestaffordteam@staffordtimberland.net
Website: www.staffordtimberland.net

Other Offices

One Main Street
Suite Five
Lyme, NH USA 03768
Phone: 603-795-4460
Fax: 603-795-4465

Suite 303b, 55 Harrington Street
The Rocks
Sydney, Australia 2000
Phone: 61-2-9241-5188

Management and Staff
Geoff Norman, Principal
Richard Bowley, Principal
Tom Goodrich, Principal

Type of Firm
Private Equity Advisor or Fund of Funds

Project Preferences
Type of Financing Preferred:
Fund of Funds

Geographical Preferences
United States Preferences:
All U.S.

International Preferences:
Europe
Western Europe
Pacific

Industry Preferences
In Agr/Forestr/Fish prefer:
Agribusiness

Additional Information
Year Founded: 2002
Capital Under Management: $250,000,000
Current Activity Level : Actively seeking new investments

STAGE 1 VENTURES, LLC
1000 Winter Street
Suite 2000
Waltham, MA USA 02451
Phone: 781-772-1010
Fax: 941-847-7121
E-mail: info@stage1ventures.com
Website: www.stage1ventures.com

Management and Staff
David William Baum, Partner
Ed Hamilton, Chief Financial Officer
Jonathan Gordon, Partner

Type of Firm
Private Equity Firm

Project Preferences
Type of Financing Preferred:
Early Stage

Geographical Preferences
United States Preferences:
All U.S.

Industry Preferences
In Communications prefer:
Commercial Communications
Wireless Communications

In Computer Software prefer:
Software

In Internet Specific prefer:
Internet

Additional Information
Year Founded: 2007
Current Activity Level : Actively seeking new investments

STAGE ONE VENTURES
6 Ha-nechoshet St
Tel Aviv, Israel 69710
Phone: 972-36-49-4000
Fax: 972-36-49-5000
E-mail: contact@stageonevc.com
Website: www.stageonevc.com

Management and Staff
Adoram Ga ash, Managing Partner
Gur Shomron, Venture Partner
Moshe Katzenelson, Principal
Tal Jacobi, Chief Financial Officer
Yuval Cohen, Managing Partner

Type of Firm
Corporate PE/Venture

Project Preferences
Type of Financing Preferred:
Early Stage

Geographical Preferences
International Preferences:
Israel

Industry Preferences
In Communications prefer:
Telecommunications

Additional Information
Year Founded: 2001
Current Activity Level : Actively seeking new investments

STAIRWAY CAPITAL MANAGEMENT
519 RXR Plaza
Uniondale, NY USA 11556
Phone: 516-629-3478
Fax: 516-629-3481
Website: www.stariwaycapital.com

Management and Staff
Alex Verba, Vice President
Chris Leheny, Chief Operating Officer
John Rijo, Principal

Type of Firm
Private Equity Firm

Project Preferences
Type of Financing Preferred:
Leveraged Buyout

Additional Information
Name of Most Recent Fund: Stairway Capital Management II, L.P.
Most Recent Fund Was Raised: 06/23/2005
Year Founded: 2005
Capital Under Management: $90,300,000
Current Activity Level : Actively seeking new investments

STANDARD BANK CAPITAL INVESTMENTS
Standard Bank Centre
3 Simmonds Street
Johannesburg, South Africa 2001
Phone: 27-11-631-5342
Fax: 27-11-631-0801
Website: www.scmb.co.za

Type of Firm
Bank Affiliated

Project Preferences
Type of Financing Preferred:
Generalist PE

Geographical Preferences
International Preferences:
South Africa

Additional Information
Year Founded: 1999
Current Activity Level : Actively seeking new investments

STANDARD CHARTERED PRIVATE EQUITY, LTD. (AKA: FINVENTURES)
20/F Henley Building
5 Queens Road
Central, Hong Kong
Phone: 852-2841-0275
Fax: 852-2868-5430
Website: www.standardchartered.com

Other Offices
12th Floor Henley Building
5 Queen's Road
Central, Hong Kong
Phone: 852-2841-0275
Fax: 852-2868-5430

90 Mahatma Gandhi Road
Mumbai, India 400 001
Phone: 91-22-2267-0162
Fax: 91-22-2267-0163

DIFC Building 1
Dubai, Utd. Arab Em. 189554
Phone: 97-14-508-3609
Fax: 97-14-428-2560

1F, Augusta Hse., Inanda Green Ofc Park
Alberyn Road, Wierda Valley West
Sandton, South Africa 2146
Phone: 27-11-217-6887
Fax: 27-11-217-6801

Management and Staff

Alastair Morrison, Managing Director
Andrew Dawson, Chief Financial Officer
Nainesh Jaisingh, Managing Director
Rajiv Maliwal, Managing Director

Type of Firm

Bank Affiliated

Association Membership

Hong Kong Venture Capital Association (HKVCA)
Singapore Venture Capital Association (SVCA)

Project Preferences

Type of Financing Preferred:

Expansion
Generalist PE
Balanced
Later Stage
Management Buyouts
Acquisition

Size of Investments Considered:

Min Size of Investment Considered (000s): $10,000
Max Size of Investment Considered (000s): $50,000

Geographical Preferences

International Preferences:

India
China
Hong Kong
Thailand
Singapore
Korea, South
Asia
Malaysia

Industry Preferences

In Communications prefer:

Communications and Media

In Semiconductor/Electr prefer:

Electronics

In Medical/Health prefer:

Medical/Health
Health Services

In Consumer Related prefer:

Consumer Products
Consumer Services

In Financial Services prefer:

Financial Services

Additional Information

Year Founded: 2002
Capital Under Management: $1,000,000,000
Current Activity Level : Actively seeking new investments

STANFORD INVESTMENT GROUP

629 Grove Street
Suite 100
Ridgewood, NJ USA 07450
Phone: 201-652-8529
Fax: 201-652-1212
E-mail: DSR@StanfordInvGroup.com
Website: www.StanfordInvGroup.com

Management and Staff

Bart Klim, Chief Financial Officer
Bruce Campbell, Principal
David Rajpurohit, Managing Director
M. LaRobordier, Principal

Type of Firm

Private Equity Firm

Project Preferences

Role in Financing:

Prefer role as deal originator

Type of Financing Preferred:

Leveraged Buyout
Turnaround
Management Buyouts
Special Situation
Recapitalizations

Size of Investments Considered:

Min Size of Investment Considered (000s): $1,000
Max Size of Investment Considered (000s): $10,000

Geographical Preferences

United States Preferences:

Mid Atlantic
Northeast
All U.S.

Canadian Preferences:

All Canada

International Preferences:

India
China

Additional Information

Year Founded: 1992
Capital Under Management: $200,000,000
Current Activity Level : Actively seeking new investments
Method of Compensation: Return on invest. most important, but chg. closing fees, service fees, etc.

STANLEY MEDICAL RESEARCH INSTITUTE

8401 Connecticut Avenue
Suite 200
Chevy Chase, MD USA 20815
Phone: 301-571-0760
Fax: 301-571-0769
E-mail: info@stanleyresearch.org
Website: www.stanleyresearch.org

Type of Firm

Private Equity Advisor or Fund of Funds

Additional Information

Year Founded: 2009
Current Activity Level : Actively seeking new investments

STAR CAPITAL PARTNERS, LTD.

33 Cavendish Square
6th Floor
London, United Kingdom W1G 0PW
Phone: 44-20-7016-8500
Fax: 44-20-7016-8501
E-mail: mail@star-capital.com
Website: www.star-capital.com

Management and Staff

Mark Coxall, Partner
Martina Lyons, Chief Financial Officer
Mike Williams, Chief Financial Officer
Paul Gough, Partner
Rick Haythornthwaite, Managing Director
Roy Mani, Partner
Stephen Wright, Partner
Tony Mallin, Chief Executive Officer
Uniti Bhalla, Partner

Type of Firm

Bank Affiliated

Association Membership

British Venture Capital Association (BVCA)
European Private Equity and Venture Capital Assoc.

Project Preferences

Type of Financing Preferred:

Fund of Funds
Leveraged Buyout
Expansion
Balanced
Management Buyouts
Acquisition

Size of Investments Considered:

Min Size of Investment Considered (000s): $21,719
Max Size of Investment Considered (000s): $108,593

Geographical Preferences

International Preferences:

United Kingdom
Europe
Western Europe
Germany
France

Industry Preferences

In Communications prefer:

Communications and Media
Telecommunications

In Medical/Health prefer:

Medical/Health

In Consumer Related prefer:

Consumer Products

In Industrial/Energy prefer:

Energy
Oil & Gas Drilling,Explor
Industrial Products
Materials

In Transportation prefer:

Transportation

In Utilities prefer:

Utilities

Additional Information

Name of Most Recent Fund: STAR II
Most Recent Fund Was Raised: 12/23/2005
Year Founded: 2001
Capital Under Management: $1,813,400,000
Current Activity Level : Actively seeking new investments

STAR VENTURES MANAGEMENT GMBH & CO. KG

Possartstrasse 9
Munich, Germany 81679
Phone: 49-89-419-4300
Fax: 49-89-4194-3030
E-mail: mail@star-ventures.de
Website: www.star-ventures.com

Other Offices

Two Galleria Tower
13455 Noel Road; Suite 1670
Dallas, TX USA 75240
Phone: 972-776-1516
Fax: 972-702-1103

11 Galgaley Haplada Street
P.O.Box 12600
Herzliya Pituach, Israel 46733
Phone: 972-9-961-7111
Fax: 972-9-961-7100

Management and Staff

Anthony Maher, Partner
Christina Moehrle, Partner
Jeanne Bayless, Managing Partner
Limor Radoshitzky, Partner
Meir Barel, Managing Partner
Ran Shahor, Managing Partner
Yaffa Krindel, Partner

Type of Firm

Private Equity Firm

Association Membership

European Private Equity and Venture Capital Assoc.

Project Preferences

Role in Financing:

Prefer role as deal originator but will also invest in deals created by others

Type of Financing Preferred:

Early Stage
Expansion
Balanced
Later Stage
Seed
Startup

Size of Investments Considered:

Min Size of Investment Considered (000s): $500
Max Size of Investment Considered (000s): $10,000

Geographical Preferences

United States Preferences:

All U.S.

International Preferences:

Europe
Israel
Germany

Industry Focus

(% based on actual investment)

Communications and Media	33.7%
Computer Software and Services	21.6%
Internet Specific	14.2%
Semiconductors/Other Elect.	13.9%
Medical/Health	6.5%
Computer Hardware	5.1%
Biotechnology	2.0%
Industrial/Energy	1.7%
Other Products	1.3%

Additional Information

Year Founded: 1992
Capital Under Management: $960,000,000
Current Activity Level : Actively seeking new investments
Method of Compensation: Return on investment is of primary concern, do not charge fees

---

STARFISH VENTURES PTY., LTD.

120 Jolimont Street
Level 1
East Melbourne, Australia 3002
Phone: 613-9654-2121
Fax: 613-9654-2922
Website: www.starfishventures.com.au

Management and Staff

Eve Burgess, Chief Financial Officer
John Dyson, Principal
Michael Panaccio, Principal

Type of Firm

Private Equity Firm

Association Membership

Australian Venture Capital Association (AVCAL)

Project Preferences

Role in Financing:

Prefer role as deal originator but will also invest in deals created by others

Type of Financing Preferred:

Early Stage
Expansion
Later Stage
Seed
Startup

Size of Investments Considered:

Min Size of Investment Considered (000s): $81
Max Size of Investment Considered (000s): $8,058

Geographical Preferences

International Preferences:

Pacific
Australia
New Zealand

Industry Preferences

In Communications prefer:

Commercial Communications
Telecommunications

In Computer Software prefer:

Software

In Biotechnology prefer:

Biotechnology

In Industrial/Energy prefer:

Energy
Alternative Energy

In Other prefer:

Environment Responsible

Additional Information

Year Founded: 2001
Capital Under Management: $325,700,000
Current Activity Level : Actively seeking new investments

STARGATE CAPITAL MANAGEMENT LIMITED

62-65 Trafalgar Square
London, United Kingdom WC2N 5DY
Phone: 44-20-7024-9740
E-mail: info@trapeziacapital.co.uk
Website: www.trapeziacapital.co.uk

Type of Firm
Private Equity Firm

Project Preferences

Type of Financing Preferred:
Generalist PE

Geographical Preferences

International Preferences:
Europe

Additional Information
Year Founded: 2005
Capital Under Management: $9,000,000
Current Activity Level : Actively seeking new investments

START INVEST AB
Maskingatan 5
Box 8794
Goteborg, Sweden 402 76
Phone: 46-31-779-7925
Fax: 46-31-779-0685
Website: www.startinvest.se

Management and Staff
Mats Enegren, Managing Director

Type of Firm
Private Equity Firm

Association Membership
Swedish Venture Capital Association (SVCA)

Project Preferences

Type of Financing Preferred:
Expansion
Seed
Startup

Size of Investments Considered:
Min Size of Investment Considered (000s): $106
Max Size of Investment Considered (000s): $531

Geographical Preferences

International Preferences:
Sweden

Additional Information
Year Founded: 1994
Current Activity Level : Actively seeking new investments

START-IT
Liege Science Park - Centre
Socran-Ctr., Pre-Aily
Angleur, Belgium 4031
Phone: 32-4-367-8920
Fax: 32-4-367-8921
Website: www.start-it.be

Type of Firm
Bank Affiliated

Association Membership
European Private Equity and Venture Capital Assoc.

Project Preferences

Type of Financing Preferred:
Early Stage
Startup

Size of Investments Considered:
Min Size of Investment Considered (000s): $200
Max Size of Investment Considered (000s): $200,000

Geographical Preferences

International Preferences:
Europe
Belgium

Industry Preferences

In Computer Other prefer:
Computer Related

Additional Information
Year Founded: 1999
Capital Under Management: $9,800,000
Current Activity Level : Actively seeking new investments

START-UP AUSTRALIA PTY, LTD.
Three Spring Street
Sydney, Australia 2000
Phone: 612-8249-4029
Fax: 612-9233-8129
E-mail: start-up@start-up.com.au
Website: www.start-up.com.au

Management and Staff
George Jessup, Managing Director

Type of Firm
Investment Management Firm

Project Preferences

Role in Financing:
Prefer role as deal originator but will also invest in deals created by others

Type of Financing Preferred:
Early Stage
Seed
Startup

Size of Investments Considered:
Min Size of Investment Considered (000s): $381
Max Size of Investment Considered (000s): $2,288

Geographical Preferences

International Preferences:
Australia

Industry Preferences

In Medical/Health prefer:
Medical/Health
Pharmaceuticals

In Consumer Related prefer:
Food/Beverage

In Agr/Forestr/Fish prefer:
Agribusiness

In Other prefer:
Environment Responsible

Additional Information
Name of Most Recent Fund: BioVentures Australia Partnership
Most Recent Fund Was Raised: 02/01/2001
Year Founded: 1996
Capital Under Management: $21,000,000
Current Activity Level : Actively seeking new investments
Method of Compensation: Return on investment is of primary concern, do not charge fees

---

STARTECH EARLY VENTURES
1302 East Collins Boulevard
Richardson, TX USA 75081
Phone: 214-576-9800
Fax: 214-576-9849
Website: www.startechev.com

Other Offices
6300 Bridgepoint Parkway
Building One, Suite 500
Austin, TX USA 78730
Phone: 512-795-5851
Fax: 512-795-5849

Management and Staff
Frank Gerome, Partner

Type of Firm
University Program

Project Preferences

Type of Financing Preferred:
Early Stage
Seed
Strategic Alliances
Startup

Size of Investments Considered:
Min Size of Investment Considered (000s): $500
Max Size of Investment Considered (000s): $900

Geographical Preferences

United States Preferences:
Texas
All U.S.

Industry Preferences

In Communications prefer:
Telecommunications

In Computer Software prefer:
Software

In Internet Specific prefer:
Internet

In Medical/Health prefer:
Medical/Health

Additional Information
Name of Most Recent Fund: STARTech Seed Fund II
Most Recent Fund Was Raised: 04/30/2000
Year Founded: 1997
Capital Under Management: $36,000,000
Current Activity Level : Actively seeking new investments

STARTUP CAPITAL VENTURES L.P.
100 Hamilton Avenue
Suite 100
Palo Alto, CA USA 94301
Phone: 650-461-8100
Fax: 650-461-8101
E-mail: administrator@startupcv.com
Website: www.startupcv.com

Other Offices
Chamber of Commerce Tower No. 168
Fuhua Rd. 3 CBD Futian District
Shenzhen, China 518048

Room 2101, 21/F, Westlands Centre
20 Westland Road, Quarry Bay
Hong Kong, Hong Kong
Phone: 852-2960-4611
Fax: 852-2960-0185

Management and Staff
A. Catherine Ngo, General Partner
Danny Lui, Managing General Partner
John Dean, Managing General Partner
Pia Camenzind, Chief Financial Officer
Robert Rees, General Partner
Timohy Dick, General Partner

Type of Firm
Private Equity Advisor or Fund of Funds

Project Preferences

Role in Financing:
Will function either as deal originator or investor in deals created by others

Type of Financing Preferred:
Balanced
Seed
Startup

Size of Investments Considered:
Min Size of Investment Considered (000s): $250
Max Size of Investment Considered (000s): $1,500

Geographical Preferences

United States Preferences:
Oklahoma
Hawaii
Texas
All U.S.

International Preferences:
China

Additional Information
Name of Most Recent Fund: Startup Capital Ventures, L.P.
Most Recent Fund Was Raised: 04/27/2005
Year Founded: 2005
Capital Under Management: $25,500,000
Current Activity Level : Actively seeking new investments

STARVEST PARTNERS, L.P.
750 Lexington Avenue
15th Floor
New York, NY USA 10022
Phone: 212-863-2500
Fax: 212-863-2520
E-mail: info@starvestpartners.com
Website: www.starvestpartners.com

Management and Staff
Deborah Farrington, General Partner
Jeanne Sullivan, General Partner
Larry Bettino, General Partner
Laura Sachar, General Partner
Robert Kelly, Chief Financial Officer

Type of Firm
Private Equity Firm

Project Preferences

Role in Financing:
Prefer role as deal originator but will also invest in deals created by others

Type of Financing Preferred:
Second Stage Financing
Early Stage
Expansion
Balanced
Private Placement
Industry Rollups

Size of Investments Considered:
Min Size of Investment Considered (000s): $2,000
Max Size of Investment Considered (000s): $8,000

Geographical Preferences

United States Preferences:
All U.S.

Industry Preferences

In Computer Software prefer:
Software
Applications Software

In Internet Specific prefer:
E-Commerce Technology
Internet
Ecommerce
Web Aggregration/Portals

In Computer Other prefer:
Computer Related

In Financial Services prefer:
Financial Services

Additional Information
Year Founded: 1999
Capital Under Management: $150,000,000
Current Activity Level : Actively seeking new investments
Method of Compensation: Return on investment is of primary concern, do not charge fees

---

STARWOOD CAPITAL GROUP
591 West Putnam Avenue
Greenwich, CT USA 06830
Phone: 203-422-7700
Fax: 203-422-7784
E-mail: starwood@starwood.com
Website: www.starwoodcapital.com

Management and Staff
Christopher Graham, Managing Director
Jeffrey Dishner, Senior Managing Director
Jerome Silvey, Chief Financial Officer
Karl Frey, Managing Director
Madison Grose, Senior Managing Director
Maria D Avanzo, Vice President
Merrick Kleeman, Senior Managing Director
Richard Gomel, Managing Director

Type of Firm
Private Equity Firm

Project Preferences

Type of Financing Preferred:
Mezzanine

Industry Preferences

In Financial Services prefer:
Real Estate

Additional Information
Year Founded: 1991
Current Activity Level : Actively seeking new investments

STATE OF WISCONSIN INVESTMENT BOARD

121 E. Wilson Street
Madison, WI USA 53702
Phone: 608-266-2381
E-mail: info@swib.state.wi.us
Website: www.swib.state.wi.us

Management and Staff

Kenneth Johnson, Chief Operating Officer

Type of Firm

Government Affiliated Program

Project Preferences

Type of Financing Preferred:
Balanced

Geographical Preferences

United States Preferences:
Wisconsin

Additional Information

Year Founded: 1999
Current Activity Level : Actively seeking new investments

STATOIL INNOVATION AS (AKA: STATOILHYDRO)

Forusbeen 50
Stavanger, Norway 4035
Phone: 47-51-990-000
Fax: 47-51-990-050
E-mail: statoil@statoil.com
Website: www.statoilhydro.com

Other Offices

1A Bourdillon Road
P.O. Box 56190
Lagos, Nigeria
Phone: 234-1-269-0491
Fax: 234-1-269-1245

Tornimae Two
Tallinn, Estonia 10145
Phone: 372-665-77-00
Fax: 372-665-77-01

International Financial Services Centre
Six George's Dock
Dublin, Ireland 1
Phone: 353-16-368-100
Fax: 353-18-180-100

20/F Times Plaza, No.1
Taizi Road
Shenzen, China 518067
Phone: 86-755-2685-5335
Fax: 86-755-2685-5331

A. Gostauto 12a
Vilnius, Lithuania 2000
Phone: 370-5-268-6500
Fax: 370-2-220-456

The Landmark Building
96 Nizami Str.
Baku, Azerbaijan 370010
Phone: 994-12-977-340
Fax: 994-12-977-944

12 Samal Micordistrict
Astana Tower, 13-I
Astana, Kazakhstan 473000
Phone: 7-3172-580-086
Fax: 7-3172-580-087

255, Mirdamad Boulevard
Teheran, Iran 1918933931
Phone: 98-21-225-6330
Fax: 98-21-225-6335

Postfach 2262
Emden, Germany 26702
Phone: 49-49-279-140
Fax: 49-49-2791-4160

Borgmester Christiansens Gade 50
Postboks 120
Copenhagen, Denmark 0900
Phone: 45-70-101-101
Fax: 45-70-101-401

Praia de Botafogo 501
Bloco Corcovado, Two andar
Rio de Janeiro, Brazil 22250-040
Phone: 55-21-2586-6000
Fax: 55-21-2586-6233

Barlenhuisstraat One
Kaai 524
Zeebrugge, Belgium 8380
Phone: 32-50-461-611
Fax: 32-50-599-004

Hotel Sheraton Club des Pins
Alger, Algeria 16000
Phone: 213-21-377-777
Fax: 213-21-376-601

Rua de Benguela No. 17
Luanda, Angola
Phone: 244-2-640-900
Fax: 244-2-640-999

Blv. Manuel Avila Camacho 24, 18th floor
Lomas de Chapultepec C.P.
Mexico City, Mexico 11000
Phone: 52-55-5540-6273
Fax: 52-55-5520-7076

Citadeles 12
Riga, Latvia 1010
Phone: 371-7-088-100
Fax: 371-7-088-150

One place de la Pyramide
La Defense Nine
Paris La Defense cedex, France 92911
Phone: 33-1-4967-0530
Fax: 33-1-4967-0531

Type of Firm

Corporate PE/Venture

Association Membership

Norwegian Venture Capital Association
European Private Equity and Venture Capital Assoc.

Project Preferences

Type of Financing Preferred:
Balanced

Geographical Preferences

International Preferences:
Europe

Additional Information

Year Founded: 1972
Current Activity Level : Actively seeking new investments

STB INVESTMENT CORP.

6F Tokyo Bank Association Bldg
1-3-1 Marunouchi, Chiyoda-ku
Tokyo, Japan
Phone: 81-3-6212-2720
Fax: 81-3-6212-2730
E-mail: info@stb-ifund.co.jp

Management and Staff

Atsuhiko Mizukawa, Chief Executive Officer
David Seu, Managing Director
Hiroki Kawakami, Principal
Toshihiko Tsuji, Managing Director

Type of Firm

Private Equity Firm

Additional Information

Year Founded: 2000
Capital Under Management: $300,000
Current Activity Level : Actively seeking new investments

STEADFAST CAPITAL GMBH (FKA: BHF PRIVATE EQUITY GMBH)

Myliusstrasse 47
Frankfurt am Main, Germany 60323
Phone: 49-69-506-850
Fax: 49-69-506-85100
E-mail: info@steadfastcapital.de
Website: www.steadfastcapital.de

Management and Staff

Clemens Busch, Partner
James Homer, Chief Financial Officer
Nicholas Money-Kyrle, Managing Partner
Thomas Rubahn, Partner

Type of Firm

Private Equity Firm

Association Membership

German Venture Capital Association (BVK)
European Private Equity and Venture Capital Assoc.

Project Preferences

Type of Financing Preferred:

Fund of Funds
Leveraged Buyout
Management Buyouts

Size of Investments Considered:

Min Size of Investment Considered (000s): $1,412
Max Size of Investment Considered (000s): $141,223

Geographical Preferences

International Preferences:

Switzerland
Europe
Luxembourg
Netherlands
Austria
Germany
Belgium

Additional Information

Name of Most Recent Fund: Steadfast Capital Fund II
Most Recent Fund Was Raised: 02/13/2006
Year Founded: 2001
Capital Under Management: $435,000,000
Current Activity Level : Actively seeking new investments

STEAMBOAT VENTURES

3601 West Olive Avenue
Suite 650
Burbank, CA USA 91505
Phone: 818-566-7400
Fax: 818-566-7490
E-mail: svmail@steamboatvc.com
Website: www.steamboatvc.com

Other Offices

222 Hu Bin Road
Unit 1002-1004, One Corporate Avenue
Shanghai, China 200021
Phone: 86-21-2308-1800
Fax: 86-21-2308-1999

One Matheson Street
20th Floor, Shell Tower, Times Square
Causeway Bay, Hong Kong
Phone: 852-2203-2300
Fax: 852-2203-18000

Management and Staff

Alex Hartigan, Managing Director
Beau Laskey, Managing Director
Daniel Beldy, Managing Director
David Min, Principal
Greg Schneider, Managing Director
Jennifer Yan, Principal
John Ball, Managing Director
Liping Fan, Chief Financial Officer
Olivier Glauser, Managing Director
Scott Hilleboe, Managing Director

Type of Firm

Corporate PE/Venture
Association Membership
Hong Kong Venture Capital Association (HKVCA)
National Venture Capital Association - USA (NVCA)

Project Preferences

Role in Financing:

Will function either as deal originator or investor in deals created by others

Type of Financing Preferred:

Fund of Funds
Early Stage
Expansion
Mezzanine
Later Stage
First Stage Financing
Startup

Size of Investments Considered:

Min Size of Investment Considered (000s): $2,000
Max Size of Investment Considered (000s): $20,000

Geographical Preferences

United States Preferences:

All U.S.

International Preferences:

China

Industry Preferences

In Communications prefer:

Communications and Media
Media and Entertainment

In Internet Specific prefer:

Internet

Additional Information

Year Founded: 2000
Capital Under Management: $575,000,000
Current Activity Level : Actively seeking new investments

STEELPOINT CAPITAL PARTNERS

One Penn Palaza
Suite 2207
New York, NY USA 10119
Phone: 212-912-3800
E-mail: contact@steelpointcp.com
Website: www.steelpointcp.com

Management and Staff

Adam Dell, Managing Director
Charlie Kemper, Principal
Roy Thiele-Sardina, Managing Director

Type of Firm

Private Equity Advisor or Fund of Funds

Project Preferences

Type of Financing Preferred:

Later Stage

Size of Investments Considered:

Min Size of Investment Considered (000s): $5,000
Max Size of Investment Considered (000s): $30,000

Geographical Preferences

United States Preferences:

All U.S.

Industry Preferences

In Communications prefer:

Telecommunications

In Medical/Health prefer:

Health Services

In Business Serv. prefer:

Media

Additional Information

Year Founded: 2003
Current Activity Level : Actively seeking new investments

STENA ADACTUM AB

Box 2181
Rosenlundsgatan 3
Goteborg, Sweden SE-403 13
Phone: 46-31774-3570
Fax: 46-31774-3575
E-mail: info@adactum@stena.com
Website: www.stenaadactum.com

Management and Staff

Anders Jansson, Chief Executive Officer
Bert-Ake Eriksson, Chief Executive Officer
Dan Sten Olsson, Chairman & CEO
Hakan Johansson, Partner
Martin Svalstedt, Managing Director
Svante Carlsson, Chief Financial Officer

Type of Firm

Private Equity Firm

Association Membership

Swedish Venture Capital Association (SVCA)

Project Preferences

Type of Financing Preferred:

Leveraged Buyout

Geographical Preferences

International Preferences:

Sweden
All International

Additional Information

Year Founded: 2007
Current Activity Level : Actively seeking new investments

STENTON LEIGH GROUP, INC.

102 Northeast Second Street
Suite 416
Boca Raton, FL USA 33432
Phone: 561-361-1866
Fax: 561-361-1867
E-mail: info@stentonleighgroup.com
Website: www.stentonleighgroup.com

Management and Staff

Milton Barbarosh, Chief Executive Officer

Type of Firm

Bank Affiliated

Project Preferences

Role in Financing:

Will function either as deal originator or investor in deals created by others

Type of Financing Preferred:

Leveraged Buyout
Control-block Purchases
Expansion
Mezzanine
Later Stage
Management Buyouts
Acquisition
Recapitalizations

Size of Investments Considered:

Min Size of Investment Considered (000s): $500
Max Size of Investment Considered (000s): $100,000

Geographical Preferences

Canadian Preferences:

All Canada
Quebec
Ontario

Additional Information

Year Founded: 1989
Capital Under Management: $20,000,000
Current Activity Level : Actively seeking new investments
Method of Compensation: Return on invest. most important, but chg. closing fees, service fees, etc.

STEPHENS GROUP, INC.

111 Center Street
Suite 2400
Little Rock, AR USA 72201
Phone: 501-377-2000
Website: www.stephens.com

Other Offices

3700 Buffalo Speedway
Suite 900
Houston, TX USA 77098
Phone: 713-993-4200

65 East 55th Street
22nd Floor
New York, NY USA 10022
Phone: 212-891-1700
Fax: 212-891-1750

601 Pennsylvania Avenue North West
Suite 720 South Building
Washington, DC USA 20004
Phone: 202-628-6668

Crescent Boulevard
Suite 203
Ridgeland, MS USA 39157
Phone: 601-605-5660
Fax: 601-605-5670

161 Television Hill Road
Hot Springs, AR USA 71913
Phone: 501-609-4100
Fax: 501-609-4115

100 North Broadway
Suite 1850
Oklahoma City, OK USA 73102
Phone: 405-231-4445
Fax: 405-231-4466

100 Congress Avenue
Suite 750
Austin, TX USA 78701
Phone: 512-542-3200
Fax: 512-542-3275

175 Federal Street
Ninth Floor
Boston, MA USA 02110
Phone: 617-237-7500
Fax: 617-239-7546

703 Chestnut
Conway, AR USA 72032
Phone: 501-328-4000
Fax: 501-328-4090

909 Davis Street
Suite 260
Evanston, IL USA 60201
Phone: 847-563-5500
Fax: 847-563-5507

9100 South Dadeland Boulevard
Suite 1500
Miami, FL USA 33156
Phone: 786-497-7233

3100 West End Avenue
Suite 630
Nashville, TN USA 37203
Phone: 615-279-4300
Fax: 615-279-4365

195 Church Street
15th Floor
New Haven, CT USA 06510
Phone: 203-747-3600
Fax: 203-747-3610

Westerre III Building
3900 Westerre Parkway, Suite 204
Richmond, VA USA 23233
Phone: 804-727-6200
Fax: 804-727-6250

950 East Paces Ferry Road
Suite 2850
Atlanta, GA USA 30326
Phone: 404-461-5100
Fax: 404-461-5135

445 North Boulevard
City Plaza, Suite 802
Baton Rouge, LA USA 70802
Phone: 225-214-4883
Fax: 225-214-4898

3425 North Futrall Drive
Suite 201
Fayetteville, AR USA 72703
Phone: 479-718-7400
Fax: 479-718-7490

1320 Main Street
Suite 550
Columbia, SC USA 29201
Phone: 803-343-0100
Fax: 803-343-0110

300 Crescent Court
Suite 600
Dallas, TX USA 75201
Phone: 214-258-2700
Fax: 214-258-2740

6075 Poplar Avenue
Suite 200
Memphis, TN USA 38119
Phone: 901-681-1300
Fax: 901-681-1375

4521 Sharon Road
Suite 200
Charlotte, NC USA 28211
Phone: 704-442-5000
Fax: 704-442-5055

63 Saint James' Street
London, United Kingdom

150 Second Avenue North
Suite 700
Saint Petersburg, FL USA 33701
Phone: 727-502-3500
Fax: 727-502-3550

Management and Staff

Doug Martin, Managing Director
Jennifer Bishop, Managing Director
Jon E.M. Jacoby, Managing Director
Kerry North, Managing Director
Michael Stuart, Managing Director
Phyllis Riggins, Managing Director
Rick Turner, Managing Director
Ryan Murphy, Vice President
Warren Stephens, President, CEO, Chairman

Type of Firm

Bank Affiliated

Association Membership

Mid-Atlantic Venture Association

Project Preferences

Role in Financing:

Will function either as deal originator or investor in deals created by others

Type of Financing Preferred:

Leveraged Buyout
Control-block Purchases
Mezzanine
Generalist PE
Later Stage
Management Buyouts
Private Placement
Special Situation
Acquisition

Size of Investments Considered:

Min Size of Investment Considered (000s): $1,000
Max Size of Investment Considered (000s): $100,000

Industry Focus

(% based on actual investment)

Industrial/Energy	35.2%
Consumer Related	24.9%
Computer Software and Services	10.0%
Medical/Health	9.2%
Communications and Media	8.6%
Biotechnology	7.7%
Internet Specific	3.1%
Semiconductors/Other Elect.	1.4%

Additional Information

Name of Most Recent Fund: Center Street Capital Partners
Most Recent Fund Was Raised: 08/12/1994
Year Founded: 1933
Current Activity Level : Actively seeking new investments
Method of Compensation: Return on investment is of primary concern, do not charge fees

STERLING GRACE CAPITAL MANAGEMENT, L.P.

55 Brookville Road
Glen Head, NY USA 11545
Phone: 516-686-2201
Website: www.sterlinggrace.com

Type of Firm

Private Equity Firm

Project Preferences

Role in Financing:

Prefer role as deal originator but will also invest in deals created by others

Type of Financing Preferred:

Second Stage Financing
Leveraged Buyout
Control-block Purchases
Mezzanine
First Stage Financing
Special Situation

Size of Investments Considered:

Min Size of Investment Considered (000s): $300
Max Size of Investment Considered: No Limit

Geographical Preferences

United States Preferences:

All U.S.

International Preferences:

United Kingdom
Australia
Germany
France

Industry Preferences

In Communications prefer:

CATV & Pay TV Systems
Radio & TV Broadcasting
Telecommunications
Data Communications

In Computer Software prefer:

Applications Software

In Internet Specific prefer:

Internet

In Consumer Related prefer:

Entertainment and Leisure
Food/Beverage
Consumer Products
Consumer Services
Hotels and Resorts

In Industrial/Energy prefer:

Oil & Gas Drilling,Explor
Alternative Energy

In Financial Services prefer:

Financial Services
Real Estate

In Agr/Forestr/Fish prefer:

Agriculture related

Additional Information

Year Founded: 1983
Capital Under Management: $100,000,000
Current Activity Level : Actively seeking new investments
Method of Compensation: Return on investment is of primary concern, do not charge fees

STERLING INVESTMENT PARTNERS

285 Riverside Avenue
Westport, CT USA 06880
Phone: 203-226-8711
Fax: 203-454-5780
Website: www.sterlinglp.com

Management and Staff

Amy Weisman, Vice President
Charles Santoro, Managing Partner
Douglas Newhouse, Managing Partner
M. William Macey, Managing Partner
Michael Barr, Vice President
William Selden, Managing Partner

Type of Firm

Private Equity Firm

Project Preferences

Role in Financing:

Prefer role as deal originator but will also invest in deals created by others

Type of Financing Preferred:

Leveraged Buyout
Later Stage
Recapitalizations

Size of Investments Considered:

Min Size of Investment Considered (000s): $50,000
Max Size of Investment Considered (000s): $500,000

Geographical Preferences

Canadian Preferences:

All Canada

Industry Focus

(% based on actual investment)

Other Products	88.4%
Computer Software and Services	11.6%

Additional Information

Name of Most Recent Fund: Sterling Investment Partners II, L.P.
Most Recent Fund Was Raised: 07/11/2005
Year Founded: 1991
Capital Under Management: $1,000,000,000
Current Activity Level : Actively seeking new investments
Method of Compensation: Return on invest. most important, but chg. closing fees, service fees, etc.

STERLING PARTNERS

650 South Exeter Street
Suite 1000
Baltimore, MD USA 21202
Phone: 443-703-1700
Fax: 443-703-1750
Website: www.sterlingpartners.us

Other Offices

1033 Skokie Boulevard
Suite 600
Northbrook, IL USA 60062
Phone: 847-480-4000
Fax: 847-480-0199

Management and Staff

B. Lee McGee, Principal
Daniel Hosler, Vice President
Daniel Rosenberg, Managing Director
Eric Becker, Senior Managing Director
Eugene Yeh, Vice President
Garrick Rice, Principal
George Watson, Vice President
Jack Slye, Vice President
James Waller, Principal
Jeffrey Schechter, Chief Financial Officer
Jeffrey Moss, Vice President
Jenny Morgan, Principal
Juan Pablo Reyes, Vice President
Kimberly Moffat, Principal
Michael Bronfein, Senior Managing Director
Philip Alphonse, Principal
R. Alan Macksey, Managing Director
Richard Federico, Managing Director
Rick Inatome, Managing Director
Rick Elfman, Senior Managing Director
Robert Polston, Vice President
Shoshana Vernick, Principal
Stephen Thompson, Principal
Steven Taslitz, Senior Managing Director
Timothy Boswell, Vice President
Todd Wilson, Principal
Tom Wippman, Managing Director

Type of Firm

Private Equity Firm

Association Membership

Mid-Atlantic Venture Association
Illinois Venture Capital Association
National Venture Capital Association - USA (NVCA)

Project Preferences

Role in Financing:
Will function either as deal originator or investor in deals created by others

Type of Financing Preferred:
Leveraged Buyout
Expansion
Generalist PE
Later Stage
Management Buyouts
Industry Rollups

Size of Investments Considered:
Min Size of Investment Considered (000s): $500
Max Size of Investment Considered (000s): $19,000

Geographical Preferences

United States Preferences:
All U.S.

Canadian Preferences:
All Canada

Industry Preferences

In Communications prefer:
Radio & TV Broadcasting

In Computer Software prefer:
Software
Applications Software

In Medical/Health prefer:
Medical/Health
Medical Diagnostics
Diagnostic Services
Diagnostic Test Products
Medical Therapeutics
Drug/Equipmt Delivery
Medical Products
Disposable Med. Products
Health Services
Hospitals/Clinics/Primary
Hospital/Other Instit.
Pharmaceuticals

In Consumer Related prefer:
Franchises(NEC)
Education Related

In Industrial/Energy prefer:
Industrial Products

In Transportation prefer:
Transportation

In Financial Services prefer:
Financial Services
Insurance

In Business Serv. prefer:
Services
Distribution

In Manufact. prefer:
Manufacturing

Additional Information

Name of Most Recent Fund: Sterling Venture Partners II, L.P.
Most Recent Fund Was Raised: 05/03/2005
Year Founded: 1983
Capital Under Management: $1,200,000,000
Current Activity Level : Actively seeking new investments
Method of Compensation: Return on invest. most important, but chg. closing fees, service fees, etc.

STERN PARTNERS INC.

650 West Georgia Street
Suite 2900 - P.O Box 11583
Vancouver, Canada V6B 4N8
Phone: 604-681-8817
Fax: 604-681-8861
E-mail: info@sternpartners.com
Website: www.sternpartners.com

Type of Firm

Private Equity Advisor or Fund of Funds

Additional Information

Year Founded: 2009
Current Activity Level : Actively seeking new investments

STERNHILL PARTNERS

777 Post Oak Boulevard
Suite 250
Houston, TX USA 77056
Phone: 713-622-2727
Fax: 713-622-3529
Website: www.sternhillpartners.com

Other Offices

8911 Capital of Texas Highway
Suite 2310
Austin, TX USA 78759
Phone: 512-349-0240
Fax: 512-349-2888

Management and Staff

Marc Geller, Managing Director
Mary Helen O'Leary, Chief Financial Officer
Robert Stearns, Managing Director

Type of Firm

Service Provider

Project Preferences

Role in Financing:
Prefer role as deal originator but will also invest in deals created by others

Type of Financing Preferred:
Second Stage Financing
Early Stage
Start-up Financing
Seed
First Stage Financing

Size of Investments Considered:
Min Size of Investment Considered (000s): $500
Max Size of Investment Considered (000s): $6,000

Geographical Preferences

United States Preferences:
West Coast
Southwest

Industry Focus

(% based on actual investment)

Internet Specific	47.0%
Computer Software and Services	25.1%
Communications and Media	19.0%
Computer Hardware	5.7%
Semiconductors/Other Elect.	3.3%

Additional Information

Name of Most Recent Fund: Sternhill Partners I, L.P.
Most Recent Fund Was Raised: 12/20/1999
Year Founded: 1999
Capital Under Management: $100,000,000
Current Activity Level : Actively seeking new investments

STEVE NORRIS PARTNERS

399 Park Avenue
36th Floor
New York, NY USA 10022
Phone: 202-468-6793
Fax: 212-980-1695
Website: www.snpartners.com

Management and Staff

Stewart Paperin, Chief Operating Officer

Type of Firm

Private Equity Firm

Project Preferences

Type of Financing Preferred:

Leveraged Buyout

Geographical Preferences

United States Preferences:

All U.S.

International Preferences:

Western Europe
Asia

Additional Information

Year Founded: 2008
Current Activity Level : Actively seeking new investments

STG CAPITAL, LLC

780 Third Avenue
45th Floor
New York, NY USA 10017
Phone: 212-833-9975

Management and Staff

Steven Glass, Managing Partner

Type of Firm

Other

Industry Preferences

In Communications prefer:

Telecommunications
Media and Entertainment

Additional Information

Year Founded: 2002
Capital Under Management: $3,600,000
Current Activity Level : Actively seeking new investments

STI VENTURES

Haaksbergweg 59
Amsterdam, Netherlands 1101 BR
Phone: 31-20-564-0480
Fax: 31-20-691-5329
E-mail: info@stiventures.com
Website: www.stiventures.com

Other Offices

85 Medinat Hayehudim St.
Herzliya Business Park
Herzliya Pituach, Israel
Phone: 972-9-9710710
Fax: 972-9-9710711

535 5th Av.
17th Floor
New York, NY USA 10017
Phone: 212-931-6312
Fax: 646-435-0681

Management and Staff

Beny Steinmetz, Founder
Erez Aluf, Managing Director
Peter Blauw, Chief Financial Officer
Roy Kadir, Chief Financial Officer
Stanley Stern, Managing Director

Type of Firm

Private Equity Firm

Project Preferences

Type of Financing Preferred:

Early Stage
Startup

Geographical Preferences

International Preferences:

Israel
All International

Industry Preferences

In Communications prefer:

Communications and Media

In Computer Software prefer:

Software

In Internet Specific prefer:

Internet

Additional Information

Year Founded: 1997
Current Activity Level : Making few, if any, new investments

STIC INVESTMENTS, INC. (AKA: STIC IT VENTURE CAPITAL)

10F, MSA Bldg. No.891-43
Daechi-dong, Kangnam-gu
Seoul, South Korea 135-280
Phone: 82-2-3404-7800
Fax: 82-2-3453-5188
E-mail: info@stic.co.kr
Website: www.stic.co.kr

Other Offices

228 Hamilton Avenue
Suite 210
Palo Alto, CA USA 94301
Phone: 650-330-7350
Fax: 650-330-7351

Level 17, Unit 1704, Corp. Ave. Tower
222 Hu Bin Road
Shanghai, China 200021
Phone: 86-21-6340-6660
Fax: 86-21-6340-6670

Suite 908, 9Fl, Sun Wah Tower
115 Nguyen Hue Blvd. Dist. 1
Ho Chi Minh, Vietnam
Phone: 84-8-3827-8491
Fax: 84-8-3827-8492

402 Centun Venure Town
No. 1475 U-dong, Haeundae-gu
Busan, South Korea 612-020
Phone: 82-51-731-2195
Fax: 82-51-731-2197

7th Floor, No. 69 Chowtze Street
Neihu District
Taipei, Taiwan
Phone: 886-2-7720-1180
Fax: 886-2-7720-1186

Suite 2002, Nexxus Building
41 Connaught Road
Central, Hong Kong
Phone: 852-2901-2300
Fax: 852-2973-0013

Management and Staff

Andy Chang, Principal
Chul Ho Ghim, Managing Director
DG Kwak, Managing Partner
DH Lee, Principal
Daniel Lee, Principal
David Lee, Principal
Dongguel Kwak, Managing Partner
Hans Jung, Managing Partner
Hoang Duy Ly, Principal
Hugh Shin, Managing Director
Jason Kook, Principal
Jungkang Im, Chief Executive Officer
Junsuk Hwang, Principal
KC Gu, Managing Director

Minho Cho, Managing Partner
Richard Yang, Venture Partner
SK Lee, Managing Director
Sam Lee, Managing Director
Sean Kim, Principal
Steven Lee, Partner
Sung Kyu Lee, Managing Director
Trevor Chan, Principal
Wanshik Kim, Principal
Wung Kim, Principal

Type of Firm
Private Equity Firm

Association Membership
Hong Kong Venture Capital Association (HKVCA)
Korean Venture Capital Association (KVCA)

Project Preferences

Type of Financing Preferred:
Leveraged Buyout
Early Stage
Expansion
Mezzanine
Generalist PE
Balanced
Start-up Financing
Later Stage
Acquisition
Startup
Fund of Funds of Second

Size of Investments Considered:
Min Size of Investment Considered (000s): $3,000
Max Size of Investment Considered (000s): $15,000

Geographical Preferences

United States Preferences:
All U.S.

International Preferences:
Vietnam
India
Taiwan
China
Hong Kong
Korea, South
Singapore
Asia

Industry Preferences

In Communications prefer:
Telecommunications

In Computer Other prefer:
Computer Related

In Semiconductor/Electr prefer:
Electronics

In Medical/Health prefer:
Medical Products
Hospitals/Clinics/Primary

In Consumer Related prefer:
Entertainment and Leisure
Retail
Consumer Products
Consumer Services

In Transportation prefer:
Transportation

In Financial Services prefer:
Financial Services

In Business Serv. prefer:
Services
Media

In Manufact. prefer:
Manufacturing

Additional Information
Name of Most Recent Fund: STIC Job Creation Fund
Most Recent Fund Was Raised: 06/30/2004
Year Founded: 1999
Capital Under Management: $247,900,000
Current Activity Level : Actively seeking new investments

STILL RIVER FUND, THE
1601 Trapelo Road
Suite 289
North Waltham, MA USA 02451
Phone: 781-290-5363
Fax: 781-290-0606
Website: www.stillriverfund.com

Management and Staff
James Saalfield, General Partner
Mary Ellen Brayton, Vice President

Type of Firm
Private Equity Firm

Association Membership
Natl Assoc of Small Bus. Inv. Co (NASBIC)

Project Preferences

Role in Financing:
Prefer role as deal originator but will also invest in deals created by others

Type of Financing Preferred:
Early Stage
Balanced
Seed

Size of Investments Considered:
Min Size of Investment Considered (000s): $500
Max Size of Investment Considered (000s): $3,000

Geographical Preferences

United States Preferences:
Northeast
All U.S.

Industry Focus
(% based on actual investment)

Biotechnology	30.5%
Other Products	23.6%
Semiconductors/Other Elect.	16.1%
Communications and Media	11.3%
Internet Specific	10.9%
Computer Software and Services	4.7%
Consumer Related	2.8%

Additional Information
Name of Most Recent Fund: Still River Fund III, L.P.
Most Recent Fund Was Raised: 01/23/2004
Year Founded: 1996
Capital Under Management: $55,000,000
Current Activity Level : Actively seeking new investments
Method of Compensation: Return on investment is of primary concern, do not charge fees

---

STING CAPITAL
Isafjordsg 22
elev. B, 5th floor
Kista, Sweden 164 40
Phone: 46-8-5000-5090
Fax: 46-8-751-6062
Website: www.stingcapital.com

Management and Staff
Par Hedberg, Chief Executive Officer

Type of Firm
Private Equity Firm

Association Membership
Swedish Venture Capital Association (SVCA)

Project Preferences

Type of Financing Preferred:
Early Stage
Seed
Startup

Geographical Preferences

International Preferences:
Sweden
Europe

Additional Information
Year Founded: 2002
Capital Under Management: $5,900,000
Current Activity Level : Actively seeking new investments

STIRLING SQUARE CAPITAL PARTNERS
Liscarton House, 4th Floor
127-131 Sloane Street
London, United Kingdom SW1X 9AS
Phone: 44-20-7808-4130
Fax: 44-20-7808-4131
E-mail: info@stirlingsquare.com
Website: www.stirlingsquare.com

Other Offices

11 - 15 Seaton Place
St. Helier
Jersey, Channel Islands JE4 0QH
Phone: 44-1534-7808-4130
Fax: 44-1534-7808-4131

Management and Staff

Bolaji Odunsi, Partner
Gregorio Napoleone, Partner
Jakob Forschner, Partner
Martin Calderbank, Partner
Stefano Bonfiglio, Partner
Stuyvie Comfort, Partner

Type of Firm

Private Equity Firm

Project Preferences

Type of Financing Preferred:
Leveraged Buyout
Expansion
Acquisition

Geographical Preferences

International Preferences:
Italy
United Kingdom
Europe
Scandanavia/Nordic Region
Germany
France

Industry Preferences

In Communications prefer:
Communications and Media

In Medical/Health prefer:
Medical Products

In Consumer Related prefer:
Consumer
Food/Beverage
Consumer Products
Education Related

In Industrial/Energy prefer:
Industrial Products

In Business Serv. prefer:
Services

Additional Information

Year Founded: 1988
Current Activity Level : Actively seeking new investments

STMICROELECTRONICS

39, Chemin du Champ des Filles
Plan-Les-Ouates
Geneva, Switzerland CH 1228
Phone: 41-22-929-2929
Fax: 41-22-929-2928

Management and Staff

Alain Dutheil, Chief Operating Officer
Alisia Grenville, Vice President
Carlo Ferro, Chief Financial Officer
Francois Guibert, Vice President

Type of Firm

Corporate PE/Venture

Project Preferences

Type of Financing Preferred:
Generalist PE

Geographical Preferences

International Preferences:
Switzerland

Industry Preferences

In Semiconductor/Electr prefer:
Semiconductor

Additional Information

Year Founded: 2003
Current Activity Level : Actively seeking new investments

STOCKTON PARTNERS

410 Park Avenue
Suite 930
New York, NY USA 10022
Phone: 212-433-1117
Fax: 212-319-4874
E-mail: info@stocktonpartners.com
Website: www.stocktonpartners.com

Management and Staff

Faruk Amin, Vice President
Harvey Krueger, Chief Executive Officer
Kenneth Goldman, Managing Director

Type of Firm

Private Equity Firm

Project Preferences

Type of Financing Preferred:
Balanced

Industry Preferences

In Medical/Health prefer:
Medical/Health

Additional Information

Year Founded: 2001
Current Activity Level : Actively seeking new investments

STOCKWELL CAPITAL LLC

222 West Adams Street
Suite 1000
Chicago, IL USA 60606
Phone: 312-870-1369
Fax: 312-795-0455
Website: www.stockwellcapital.com

Management and Staff

Christopher Collins, Managing Director
Matthew Klinger, Principal
Maurice Gordon, Principal
Seth Weis, Vice President
Thomas Hufnagel, Principal

Type of Firm

Private Equity Firm

Project Preferences

Role in Financing:
Prefer role in deals created by others

Type of Financing Preferred:
Later Stage

Geographical Preferences

International Preferences:
Europe

Additional Information

Year Founded: 2002
Capital Under Management: $235,200,000
Current Activity Level : Actively seeking new investments

STOLBERG EQUITY PARTNERS LLC

370 17th Street
Suite 3650
Denver, CO USA 80202
Phone: 303-592-4900
Fax: 303-592-4912
E-mail: contact@stolbergep.com
Website: www.stolbergep.com

Management and Staff

Diana Crabtree, Chief Financial Officer
E. Theodore Stolberg, Partner

Type of Firm

Private Equity Firm

Project Preferences

Role in Financing:
Prefer role as deal originator

Type of Financing Preferred:
Leveraged Buyout
Acquisition

Size of Investments Considered:
Min Size of Investment Considered (000s): $1,000
Max Size of Investment Considered (000s): $15,000

Geographical Preferences

United States Preferences:
All U.S.

Industry Focus

(% based on actual investment)

Internet Specific	38.1%
Communications and Media	23.6%
Semiconductors/Other Elect.	11.7%
Consumer Related	8.4%
Medical/Health	7.7%
Other Products	7.6%
Computer Software and Services	3.0%

Additional Information

Name of Most Recent Fund: SMS II-A, L.P.
Most Recent Fund Was Raised: 03/15/2002
Year Founded: 1993
Capital Under Management: $183,000,000
Current Activity Level : Actively seeking new investments
Method of Compensation: Return on invest. most important, but chg. closing fees, service fees, etc.

STONE ARCH CAPITAL LLC

800 Nicollet Mall
Suite 1150
Minneapolis, MN USA 55402
Phone: 612-317-2980
Fax: 612-317-2988
E-mail: info@stonearchcapital.com
Website: www.stonearchcapital.com

Management and Staff

Charlie Lannin, Partner
F. Clayton Miller, Partner
Kelly Horner, Chief Financial Officer
Peter Offenhauser, Vice President
Peter Grant, Partner

Type of Firm

Private Equity Firm

Project Preferences

Role in Financing:

Prefer role as deal originator

Type of Financing Preferred:

Leveraged Buyout
Acquisition

Size of Investments Considered:

Min Size of Investment Considered (000s): $20,000
Max Size of Investment Considered (000s): $100,000

Geographical Preferences

United States Preferences:

Midwest
Illinois
Michigan
Nebraska
South Dakota
Iowa
North Dakota
Kansas
Ohio
Wisconsin
Missouri
Indiana
Minnesota

Industry Preferences

In Semiconductor/Electr prefer:

Component Testing Equipmt

In Medical/Health prefer:

Disposable Med. Products
Health Services

In Consumer Related prefer:

Consumer
Sports
Food/Beverage
Consumer Products
Consumer Services
Education Related

In Industrial/Energy prefer:

Energy
Industrial Products
Factory Automation
Process Control
Machinery

In Financial Services prefer:

Financial Services

In Business Serv. prefer:

Services
Distribution

In Manufact. prefer:

Manufacturing
Publishing

In Agr/Forestr/Fish prefer:

Agribusiness
Agriculture related

Additional Information

Year Founded: 2004
Capital Under Management: $150,000,000
Current Activity Level : Actively seeking new investments
Method of Compensation: Return on invest. most important, but chg. closing fees, service fees, etc.

STONE CANYON VENTURE PARTNERS (SCVP)

301 North Canon Drive
Suite 302
Beverly Hills, CA USA 90210
Phone: 310-432-5180
Fax: 310-432-5181
E-mail: info@scvp.com
Website: www.scvp.com

Management and Staff

John Matise, Managing Director
John Davis, Managing Director
Kenneth Kilroy, Managing Director
Michael Seibert, Managing Director
Philip Smith, Managing Director
Wendy Seretan, Chief Financial Officer

Type of Firm

Private Equity Firm

Association Membership

Natl Assoc of Small Bus. Inv. Co (NASBIC)

Project Preferences

Role in Financing:

Will function either as deal originator or investor in deals created by others

Type of Financing Preferred:

Second Stage Financing
Expansion
Management Buyouts

Size of Investments Considered:

Min Size of Investment Considered (000s): $1,500
Max Size of Investment Considered (000s): $5,500

Geographical Preferences

United States Preferences:

Southern California
Northern California
West Coast

Industry Preferences

In Communications prefer:

CATV & Pay TV Systems
Radio & TV Broadcasting
Other Communication Prod.

In Internet Specific prefer:

E-Commerce Technology

In Medical/Health prefer:

Diagnostic Services
Medical Therapeutics
Medical Products
Health Services
Hospitals/Clinics/Primary

In Consumer Related prefer:

Consumer
Entertainment and Leisure
Retail
Franchises(NEC)
Food/Beverage
Hotels and Resorts

In Business Serv. prefer:

Media

Additional Information

Name of Most Recent Fund: Stone Canyon Venture Partners SBIC Fund
Most Recent Fund Was Raised: 01/09/2001
Year Founded: 2002
Capital Under Management: $85,000,000
Current Activity Level : Actively seeking new investments
Method of Compensation: Return on investment is of primary concern, do not charge fees

STONE POINT CAPITAL LLC (FKA: MMC CAPITAL, INC.)

20 Horseneck Lane
Greenwich, CT USA 06830
Phone: 203-862-2900
Fax: 203-625-8357
E-mail: Trident@StonePointCapital.com
Website: www.mmccapital.com

Other Offices

919 Third Avenue
New York, NY USA 10022

Management and Staff

Agha Khan, Principal
Charles Davis, Chief Executive Officer
Christopher Doody, Principal
Darran Baird, Principal
Emanuel Citron, Vice President
Fayez Muhtadie, Vice President
James Carey, Principal
Peter Mundheim, Principal
Richard Goldman, Chief Financial Officer

Type of Firm

Bank Affiliated

Association Membership

Mid-Atlantic Venture Association

Project Preferences

Type of Financing Preferred:
Second Stage Financing
Leveraged Buyout
Early Stage
Generalist PE
Balanced
Later Stage
Acquisition

Size of Investments Considered:
Min Size of Investment Considered (000s): $5,000
Max Size of Investment Considered (000s): $10,000

Geographical Preferences

International Preferences:
Western Europe
All International

Industry Focus

(% based on actual investment)

Other Products	75.2%
Computer Software and Services	17.5%
Internet Specific	4.7%
Semiconductors/Other Elect.	1.1%
Computer Hardware	0.7%
Communications and Media	0.6%
Medical/Health	0.1%

Additional Information

Name of Most Recent Fund: Trident IV, L.P.
Most Recent Fund Was Raised: 12/28/2006
Year Founded: 1994
Capital Under Management: $3,316,000,000
Current Activity Level : Actively seeking new investments

STONE RIDGE VENTURES

P.O. Box Z5350
Perth, Australia 6831
Phone: 619-9322-2360
Fax: 619-9325-8837
Website: www.stoneridgeventures.com

Type of Firm

Private Equity Firm

Project Preferences

Type of Financing Preferred:
Early Stage
Expansion
Later Stage
Seed

Geographical Preferences

International Preferences:
Australia

Industry Preferences

In Communications prefer:
Communications and Media
Telecommunications

In Computer Software prefer:
Software

In Computer Other prefer:
Computer Related

In Biotechnology prefer:
Biotechnology

Additional Information

Year Founded: 2001
Capital Under Management: $54,500,000
Current Activity Level : Actively seeking new investments

STONEBRIDGE MERCHANT CAPITAL CORPORATION

2370, 255 - 5th Ave South West
Bow Valley Square 3
Calgary, Canada T2P 3G6
Phone: 403-216-2168
Fax: 403-216-2169
Website: www.stonebridge.net

Management and Staff

Gary Lang, Managing Director
Rod Maxwell, Managing Director

Type of Firm

Private Equity Firm

Additional Information

Year Founded: 1996
Current Activity Level : Actively seeking new investments

STONEBRIDGE PARTNERS

81 Main Street
Suite 505
White Plains, NY USA 10601
Phone: 914-682-2700
Fax: 914-682-0834
Website: www.stonebridgepartners.com

Management and Staff

Andrew Thomas, Partner
Harrison Wilson, Partner
Michael Bruno, Partner
Robert Raziano, Partner
William Connors, Principal

Type of Firm

Private Equity Firm

Project Preferences

Role in Financing:
Prefer role as deal originator

Type of Financing Preferred:
Leveraged Buyout
Management Buyouts

Size of Investments Considered:
Min Size of Investment Considered (000s): $20,000
Max Size of Investment Considered: No Limit

Industry Focus

(% based on actual investment)

Other Products	63.8%
Industrial/Energy	21.5%
Communications and Media	12.4%
Consumer Related	2.0%
Internet Specific	0.4%

Additional Information

Year Founded: 1986
Capital Under Management: $350,000,000
Current Activity Level : Actively seeking new investments
Method of Compensation: Return on invest. most important, but chg. closing fees, service fees, etc.

STONEFUND N.V.

Oudenaardse steenweg 285 b2
Erpe Mere, Belgium BE-9420
Phone: 32-1630-1720
Fax: 32-53-60-64-20
E-mail: stonefund@stonefund.com
Website: www.stonefund.com

Management and Staff

Anthony Theys, Chief Executive Officer
Dirk Creado, Partner
Patrick Lemmens, Partner

Type of Firm

Private Equity Firm

Association Membership

Belgium Venturing Association
European Private Equity and Venture Capital Assoc.

Project Preferences

Type of Financing Preferred:
Leveraged Buyout
Early Stage
Expansion
Mezzanine
Seed
Startup

Size of Investments Considered:
Min Size of Investment Considered (000s): $212
Max Size of Investment Considered (000s): $12,743

Geographical Preferences

United States Preferences:
All U.S.

International Preferences:
Europe
Belgium

Industry Preferences

In Communications prefer:
Communications and Media
Telecommunications

In Internet Specific prefer:
Internet

In Computer Other prefer:
Computer Related

Additional Information

Year Founded: 2000
Capital Under Management: $34,500,000
Current Activity Level : Actively seeking new investments

STONEGATE CAPITAL GROUP LLC

CityPlace II, 17th Floor
185 Asylum Street
Hartford, CT USA 06103
Phone: 860-678-7800
Fax: 860-899-1491
Website: www.stonegatecapitalgroup.com

Management and Staff

Claudia Horn, Vice President
Joel Hartstone, Managing Director

Type of Firm

Private Equity Firm

Project Preferences

Role in Financing:
Unknown

Type of Financing Preferred:
Leveraged Buyout
Turnaround
Management Buyouts
Recapitalizations

Geographical Preferences

United States Preferences:
All U.S.

Additional Information

Year Founded: 1982
Current Activity Level : Actively seeking new investments
Method of Compensation: Unknown

STONEHENGE CAPITAL COMPANY

236 Third Street
Baton Rouge, LA USA 70801
Phone: 225-408-3000
Fax: 225-408-3090
E-mail: info@stonehengeholdings.com
Website: www.stonehengecapital.com

Other Offices

8000 Maryland Avenue
Suite 1190
Saint Louis, MO USA 63105
Phone: 314-721-5707
Fax: 314-721-5135

7887 East Belleview Avenue
Suite 1100
Englewood, CO USA 80111
Phone: 720-956-0235
Fax: 720-956-0209

152 West 57th Street
20th Floor
New York, NY USA 10019
Phone: 212-265-9380
Fax: 212-656-1344

191 West Nationwide Boulevard
Suite 600
Columbus, OH USA 43215
Phone: 614-246-2456
Fax: 614-246-2461

3424 North Shepard Avenue
Milwaukee, WI USA 53211
Phone: 414-906-1702
Fax: 414-906-1703

2001 Park Place
Suite 320
Birmingham, AL USA 35203
Phone: 205-458-2778
Fax: 866-539-9881

3625 North Hall Street
Suite 615
Dallas, TX USA 75219
Phone: 214-599-8850
Fax: 214-442-5626

707 West Azeele Street
Tampa, FL USA 33606
Phone: 813-221-4413
Fax: 813-221-6453

Management and Staff

Andrew Aye, Managing Director
Ari David Kocen, Managing Director
Brian Model, Managing Director
Charles Haberkorn, Managing Director
David Webber, Managing Director
Lucinda Temuru, Vice President
Michael Kirby, Managing Director
Michael Craven, Vice President
Nemesio Viso, Managing Director
Stephen Bennett, Managing Director
Steven Lux, Managing Director
Thomas Adamek, President
Travis Milks, Vice President
Whitney LaNasa, Vice President
William Owens, Vice President
William Lay, Vice President

Type of Firm

Private Equity Firm

Project Preferences

Role in Financing:
Will function either as deal originator or investor in deals created by others

Type of Financing Preferred:
Leveraged Buyout
Early Stage
Expansion
Mezzanine
Generalist PE
Balanced
Management Buyouts
First Stage Financing
Acquisition
Recapitalizations

Size of Investments Considered:
Min Size of Investment Considered (000s): $1,000
Max Size of Investment Considered (000s): $25,000

Geographical Preferences

United States Preferences:
Midwest
Wisconsin
Colorado
Florida
Louisiana

Missouri
All U.S.
New York
Texas

Industry Focus

(% based on actual investment)

Other Products	21.8%
Industrial/Energy	18.2%
Internet Specific	12.6%
Computer Software and Services	12.3%
Communications and Media	10.6%
Consumer Related	9.5%
Semiconductors/Other Elect.	5.8%
Medical/Health	4.6%
Biotechnology	4.4%
Computer Hardware	0.3%

Additional Information

Name of Most Recent Fund: Stonehenge Capital Fund Texas II, L.P.
Most Recent Fund Was Raised: 02/06/2008
Year Founded: 1999
Capital Under Management: $500,000,000
Current Activity Level : Actively seeking new investments
Method of Compensation: Return on invest. most important, but chg. closing fees, service fees, etc.

STONEHILL CAPITAL MANAGEMENT

885 Third Avenue
30th Floor
New York, NY USA 10022
Phone: 212-739-7474
Fax: 212-838-2291

Management and Staff

Christopher Wilson, General Partner
John Motulsky, General Partner
Wayne Teetsel, General Partner

Type of Firm

Private Equity Firm

Project Preferences

Type of Financing Preferred:

Distressed Debt

Additional Information

Year Founded: 1997
Capital Under Management: $279,800,000
Current Activity Level : Actively seeking new investments

STONEWOOD CAPITAL MANAGEMENT, INC.

Three Gateway Center
13 East
Pittsburgh, PA USA 15222
Phone: 412-391-0300
Fax: 412-391-0500
E-mail: info@stonewoodcapital.com
Website: www.stonewoodcapital.com

Management and Staff

George Knapp, Chief Executive Officer
J. Kenneth Moritz, Vice President

Type of Firm

Private Equity Firm

Project Preferences

Type of Financing Preferred:

Second Stage Financing
Leveraged Buyout
Early Stage
Expansion
Research and Development
Generalist PE
Later Stage
Management Buyouts
Acquisition
Industry Rollups

Size of Investments Considered:

Min Size of Investment Considered (000s): $1,000
Max Size of Investment Considered (000s): $5,000

Geographical Preferences

United States Preferences:

Midwest
Northeast

Canadian Preferences:

Eastern Canada

Industry Focus

(% based on actual investment)

Computer Software and Services	65.0%
Medical/Health	22.0%
Semiconductors/Other Elect.	13.0%

Additional Information

Year Founded: 1993
Current Activity Level : Actively seeking new investments

STONEY RIVER CAPITAL PARTNERS LLC

300 Colonial Center Parkway
Suite 100
Roswell, GA USA 30076
Phone: 770-587-2166
Fax: 770-649-5639
E-mail: info@stoneyrivercapital.com
Website: www.stoneyrivercapital.com

Other Offices

1250 Market Street
Suite 3020
Chattanooga, TN USA 37402
Phone: 678-520-9989
Fax: 770-549-5639

Management and Staff

Alan Urech, Managing Partner

Type of Firm

Private Equity Firm

Project Preferences

Role in Financing:

Prefer role as deal originator

Type of Financing Preferred:

Early Stage
Expansion
Seed
Distressed Debt

Size of Investments Considered:

Min Size of Investment Considered (000s): $100,000
Max Size of Investment Considered: No Limit

Geographical Preferences

United States Preferences:

Mid Atlantic
Southeast
All U.S.

Industry Preferences

In Communications prefer:

Communications and Media
Entertainment

In Medical/Health prefer:

Health Services

In Consumer Related prefer:

Consumer Products

In Industrial/Energy prefer:

Energy

In Financial Services prefer:

Financial Services

In Manufact. prefer:

Manufacturing

In Other prefer:

Environment Responsible

Additional Information

Year Founded: 2007
Current Activity Level : Actively seeking new investments
Method of Compensation: Professional fee required whether or not deal closes

STONINGTON PARTNERS, INC.

540 Madison Avenue
25th Floor
New York, NY USA 10022
Phone: 212-339-8500
Fax: 212-339-8585
Website: www.stonington.com

Management and Staff

Albert Fitzgibbons, Partner
Alexis Michas, Managing Partner
Bradley Hoecker, Partner
Frank Bartoletti, Chief Financial Officer
J. Joe Adorjan, Managing Partner
James Burke, Partner
John Bartholdson, Partner

Type of Firm

Private Equity Firm

Project Preferences

Role in Financing:
Prefer role as deal originator

Type of Financing Preferred:
Leveraged Buyout
Expansion
Management Buyouts
Acquisition

Size of Investments Considered:
Min Size of Investment Considered (000s): $50,000
Max Size of Investment Considered: No Limit

Geographical Preferences

Canadian Preferences:
All Canada

Industry Focus

(% based on actual investment)

Other Products	41.4%
Computer Software and Services	19.0%
Computer Hardware	14.8%
Biotechnology	11.1%
Consumer Related	10.2%
Medical/Health	3.5%

Additional Information

Year Founded: 1993
Capital Under Management: $1,000,000,000
Current Activity Level : Actively seeking new investments
Method of Compensation: Return on invest. most important, but chg. closing fees, service fees, etc.

STORA ENSO VENTURES

Kanavaranta 1
P.O. Box 309
Helsinki, Finland 00101
Phone: 358-2046-21-497
Website: www.storaenso.com/venturing

Other Offices

Postfach 10 10 14
Dusseldorf, Germany DE-40227
Phone: 49-211-581-2364

Type of Firm

Private Equity Firm

Association Membership

Swedish Venture Capital Association (SVCA)

Project Preferences

Type of Financing Preferred:
Early Stage
Expansion
Seed
Startup

Geographical Preferences

International Preferences:
Europe
Finland

Additional Information

Year Founded: 1998
Current Activity Level : Actively seeking new investments

STOREBRAND ALTERNATIVE INVESTMENTS ASA

Filipstad Brygge 1
P.O.Box 1380 Vika
Oslo, Norway 0114
Phone: 47-2231-5050
Fax: 47-2231-1030
Website: www.storebrand.no

Other Offices

Storebrand Kapitalforvaltning Sverige
Engelbrektsplan 2 Box 5541
Stockholm, Sweden 114 85
Phone: 08-614 24 00

Management and Staff

Ivar Waage, Partner
Ove Christian Norheim, Managing Director
Rune Holen, Partner

Type of Firm

Private Equity Advisor or Fund of Funds

Association Membership

European Private Equity and Venture Capital Assoc.

Project Preferences

Type of Financing Preferred:
Fund of Funds
Leveraged Buyout
Early Stage
Expansion
Turnaround

Geographical Preferences

United States Preferences:
All U.S.

International Preferences:
Europe
Japan
All International

Additional Information

Name of Most Recent Fund: Storebrand International Private Equity II
Most Recent Fund Was Raised: 08/12/2000
Year Founded: 1990
Capital Under Management: $315,200,000
Current Activity Level : Actively seeking new investments

STORM VENTURES LLC

2440 Sand Hill Road
Suite 301
Menlo Park, CA USA 94025
Phone: 650-926-8800
Fax: 650-926-8888
E-mail: generalinfo@stormventures.com
Website: www.stormventures.com

Management and Staff

Alex Mendez, Managing Director
Ben Choi, Principal
Josef Friedman, Principal
Richard Moley, Venture Partner
Ryan Floyd, Managing Director
Sanjay Subhedar, Managing Director
Tae Hea Nahm, Managing Director
Timothy Danford, Managing Director

Type of Firm

Private Equity Firm

Association Membership

National Venture Capital Association - USA (NVCA)

Project Preferences

Role in Financing:
Prefer role as deal originator but will also invest in deals created by others

Type of Financing Preferred:
Early Stage
Seed
Startup

Geographical Preferences

United States Preferences:
West Coast

Industry Preferences

In Communications prefer:
Telecommunications
Wireless Communications
Data Communications
Other Communication Prod.

n Computer Hardware prefer:
Mainframes / Scientific
Computer Graphics and Dig

In Computer Software prefer:
Software
Systems Software

In Internet Specific prefer:
Internet

Additional Information

Name of Most Recent Fund: Storm Ventures Affiliates Fund III, L.P.
Most Recent Fund Was Raised: 04/28/2005
Year Founded: 1997
Capital Under Management: $538,000,000
Current Activity Level : Actively seeking new investments
Method of Compensation: Return on investment is of primary concern, do not charge fees

---

STRATEGIA ITALIA

88, Corso Vittorio Emanuele II
Torino, Italy 10121
Phone: 39-011557-5201
Fax: 39-011557-3888
E-mail: mmondini@strategiaitalia.it
Website: www.strategiaitalia.it

Type of Firm

Private Equity Firm

Association Membership

Italian Venture Capital Association (AIFI)

Project Preferences

Type of Financing Preferred:

Leveraged Buyout
Expansion
Recapitalizations

Geographical Preferences

International Preferences:

Italy
Europe

Additional Information

Year Founded: 2005
Current Activity Level : Actively seeking new investments

STRATEGIC ADVISORY GROUP, INC.

253 Main Street
P.O. Box 773
Sag Harbor, NY USA 11963
Phone: 631-725-7746
Fax: 631-725-7739
Website: www.strategicadvisorygroup.com

Other Offices

94 Mohegan Drive
West Hartford, CT USA 06117
Phone: 203-523-4257
Fax: 203-523-4530

Management and Staff

Carol Hance, Managing Director
Pierce Hance, Managing Director

Type of Firm

Service Provider

Project Preferences

Role in Financing:

Prefer role as deal originator

Type of Financing Preferred:

Second Stage Financing
Early Stage
Expansion
Mezzanine
Management Buyouts
Industry Rollups
Private Placement

Size of Investments Considered:

Min Size of Investment Considered (000s): $500
Max Size of Investment Considered (000s): $50,000

Geographical Preferences

United States Preferences:

All U.S.

Canadian Preferences:

All Canada

Industry Preferences

In Computer Software prefer:

Software
Applications Software

In Consumer Related prefer:

Consumer
Retail
Franchises(NEC)
Food/Beverage
Hotels and Resorts

In Business Serv. prefer:

Services
Distribution

Additional Information

Year Founded: 1992
Current Activity Level : Actively seeking new investments
Method of Compensation: Professional fee required whether or not deal closes

---

STRATEGIC CAPITAL CORPORATION

1st Floor, Marshall Building
Shoorji Vallabhdhas Marg
Mumbai, India 400 038
Phone: 91-22-6634-9946
Fax: 91-22-2264-2393
E-mail: info@strategicindia.net
Website: www.strategicindia.net

Other Offices

Marshall Building, 1st Floor
Shoorji Vallabhdhas Marg, Ballard Estate
Mumbai, India 400 038

Management and Staff
Atul Sud, Managing Director

Type of Firm

Bank Affiliated

Project Preferences

Type of Financing Preferred:

Balanced

Geographical Preferences

International Preferences:

India

Industry Preferences

In Financial Services prefer:

Insurance
Real Estate
Investment Groups

In Business Serv. prefer:

Services

Additional Information

Year Founded: 1995
Current Activity Level : Actively seeking new investments

STRATEGIC CAPITAL PARTNERS CO., LTD.

1-6-15 Nishi-Shinbashi
Nishishimbashi, Minato-ku
Tokyo, Japan 105-0

Type of Firm

SBIC

Additional Information

Year Founded: 2006
Current Activity Level : Actively seeking new investments

STRATEGIC VENTURE MGMT. ADVISORS (FKA: MENTORTECH VENTURES)

3624 Market Street
Suite 300
Philadelphia, PA USA 19104
Phone: 215-382-4200
Fax: 215-382-5567
E-mail: mba@mentortechventures.com
Website: www.mentortechventures.com

Management and Staff

Boris Kalandar, Managing Director
Michael Aronson, Managing Director

Type of Firm

Private Equity Firm

Project Preferences

Type of Financing Preferred:
Early Stage

Size of Investments Considered:
Min Size of Investment Considered (000s): $250
Max Size of Investment Considered (000s): $1,000

Geographical Preferences

United States Preferences:
Pennsylvania

International Preferences:
Israel

Additional Information

Year Founded: 2006
Capital Under Management: $10,000,000
Current Activity Level : Actively seeking new investments

STRATHDON INVESTMENT PLC (FKA: STRATHDON INVESTMENTS, LTD.)

Canister House
Jewry Street, Winchester
Hampshire, United Kingdom SO23 8RY
Phone: 44-1962-870-492
Fax: 44-1962-844-064
E-mail: info@strathdon.com
Website: www.strathdon.com

Other Offices

5385 Eldorado Parkway
Frisco, TX USA 75034
Phone: 972-668-9700
Fax: 972-668-9701

Type of Firm

Private Equity Firm

Association Membership

European Private Equity and Venture Capital Assoc.

Project Preferences

Type of Financing Preferred:
Fund of Funds
Early Stage
Expansion
Turnaround
Seed
Startup

Size of Investments Considered:
Min Size of Investment Considered (000s): $100
Max Size of Investment Considered (000s): $100,000

Geographical Preferences

International Preferences:
United Kingdom

Industry Preferences

In Communications prefer:
Communications and Media

In Computer Other prefer:
Computer Related

In Semiconductor/Electr prefer:
Electronics

In Medical/Health prefer:
Medical/Health

In Industrial/Energy prefer:
Energy

In Financial Services prefer:
Financial Services

Additional Information

Year Founded: 1997
Capital Under Management: $25,100,000
Current Activity Level : Actively seeking new investments

STRATTECH PARTNERS LLC

225 Bala Avenue
Suite 200
Bala Cynwyd, PA USA 19004
Phone: 610-668-2200
Fax: 610-664-5529
E-mail: info@strattechpartners.com
Website: www.strattechpartners.com

Management and Staff

Britton Murdoch, Managing Director
Steve Holstad, Managing Director

Type of Firm

Private Equity Firm

Project Preferences

Type of Financing Preferred:
Early Stage

Geographical Preferences

United States Preferences:
Northeast

Industry Preferences

In Internet Specific prefer:
Internet

In Biotechnology prefer:
Biotechnology

Additional Information

Year Founded: 2000
Capital Under Management: $12,000,000
Current Activity Level : Actively seeking new investments

STRATUS BANCO DE NEGOCIOS

Rua Funchal, 129
13 Andar
Sao Paulo, Brazil 04551-060
Phone: 5511-2166-8800
Fax: 5511-2166-8801
Website: www.stratusbr.com

Management and Staff

Alvaro Goncalves, Managing Partner
Jorge Zapata, Principal
Luiz Recchia, Managing Partner
Philippe Lisbona, Principal
Wagner Duduch, Principal

Type of Firm

Private Equity Firm

Association Membership

Brazilian Venture Capital Association (ABCR)

Project Preferences

Type of Financing Preferred:
Second Stage Financing
Expansion
Mezzanine
Generalist PE
Later Stage
Startup

Geographical Preferences

International Preferences:
Brazil

Industry Preferences

In Communications prefer:
Communications and Media

In Computer Software prefer:
Software

In Semiconductor/Electr prefer:
Electronics
Component Testing Equipmt

In Biotechnology prefer:
Biotechnology

In Consumer Related prefer:
Consumer

In Industrial/Energy prefer:
Materials
Machinery
Environmental Related

In Transportation prefer:
Aerospace

In Business Serv. prefer:
Services

Additional Information

Year Founded: 1999
Capital Under Management: $6,800,000

Current Activity Level : Actively seeking new investments

STRENGTH CAPITAL PARTNERS

555 South Old Woodward
Suite 755
Birmingham, MI USA 48009
Phone: 248-593-5800
Fax: 248-593-6875
Website: www.strengthcapital.com

Management and Staff

Jeffrey Wigginton, Vice President
Mark McCammon, Managing Partner
Michael Bergeron, Managing Partner

Type of Firm

Private Equity Firm

Project Preferences

Type of Financing Preferred:
Leveraged Buyout
Later Stage

Size of Investments Considered:
Min Size of Investment Considered (000s): $5,000
Max Size of Investment Considered (000s): $60,000

Geographical Preferences

United States Preferences:
Mid Atlantic
Midwest

Industry Focus

(% based on actual investment)

Industrial/Energy	58.4%
Consumer Related	41.6%

Additional Information

Name of Most Recent Fund: Strength Capital Partners II, LP
Most Recent Fund Was Raised: 06/30/2005
Year Founded: 2000
Capital Under Management: $100,000,000
Current Activity Level : Actively seeking new investments

STRIPES GROUP

70 East 55th Street
15th Floor
New York, NY USA 10022
Phone: 212-207-3455
Fax: 212-207-3459
Website: www.stripesgroup.com

Management and Staff

Eric Weiss, Partner
Kenneth Fox, President
Richard Pan, Partner
William Patty, Partner

Type of Firm

Bank Affiliated

Project Preferences

Type of Financing Preferred:
Expansion

Size of Investments Considered:
Min Size of Investment Considered (000s): $5,000
Max Size of Investment Considered (000s): $100,000

Geographical Preferences

United States Preferences:
All U.S.

Canadian Preferences:
All Canada

Industry Preferences

In Medical/Health prefer:
Health Services

In Consumer Related prefer:
Consumer Products

In Financial Services prefer:
Financial Services

In Business Serv. prefer:
Services

Additional Information

Year Founded: 2003
Current Activity Level : Actively seeking new investments

STUART MILL CAPITAL, INC.

252 North Washington Street
Falls Church, VA USA 22046
Phone: 703-533-2461
E-mail: contact@stuartmillcap.com
Website: www.stuartmillvp.com

Management and Staff

Jana Hernandes, Principal
Jeffrey Salinger, Principal
Walter Lubsen, Principal

Type of Firm

Private Equity Firm

Project Preferences

Type of Financing Preferred:
Expansion

Geographical Preferences

United States Preferences:
All U.S.

Industry Preferences

In Consumer Related prefer:
Hotels and Resorts

In Business Serv. prefer:
Services

Additional Information

Year Founded: 1997
Capital Under Management: $20,000,000
Current Activity Level : Actively seeking new investments

SUBHKAM VENTURES

1202, Maker Chambers V
Nariman Point
Mumbai, India 400 021
Phone: 91-22-2287-5863
Fax: 91-22-2287-6540
E-mail: info@subhkam.com
Website: www.subhkam.com

Other Offices

15, Onlooker Building
14 Sir P. M. Road, Fort
Mumbai, India 400 001
Phone: 91-22-4094-2000
Fax: 91-22-2270-4381

303, Jasmin Towers
31, Shakespeare Sarani
Calcutta, India 700 017
Phone: 91-33-4008-4770

Management and Staff

Manu Punnoose, Chief Executive Officer

Type of Firm

Private Equity Firm

Project Preferences

Type of Financing Preferred:
Expansion
Balanced
First Stage Financing
Acquisition

Geographical Preferences

International Preferences:
India

Industry Preferences

In Biotechnology prefer:
Biotechnology

In Medical/Health prefer:
Medical/Health
Pharmaceuticals

In Consumer Related prefer:
Entertainment and Leisure

In Industrial/Energy prefer:
Alternative Energy
Industrial Products

In Transportation prefer:
Transportation
Aerospace

In Financial Services prefer:
Financial Services
Real Estate

In Business Serv. prefer:
Services

In Manufact. prefer:
Manufacturing

In Agr/Forestr/Fish prefer:
Agribusiness
Agriculture related

Additional Information
Year Founded: 1999
Current Activity Level : Actively seeking new investments

SUCSY, FISCHER & CO.
799 Central Avenue
Suite 350
Highland Park, IL USA 60035
Phone: 312-554-7575
Fax: 312-554-7501
E-mail: sfco@sfco.com
Website: www.sfco.com

Type of Firm
Service Provider

Project Preferences

Role in Financing:
Prefer role as deal originator

Type of Financing Preferred:
Second Stage Financing
Leveraged Buyout
Mezzanine
Special Situation

Size of Investments Considered:
Min Size of Investment Considered (000s): $50,000
Max Size of Investment Considered: No Limit

Geographical Preferences

United States Preferences:
All U.S.

Industry Preferences

In Communications prefer:
Commercial Communications
CATV & Pay TV Systems
Radio & TV Broadcasting
Telecommunications
Data Communications
Satellite Microwave Comm.
Other Communication Prod.

In Computer Hardware prefer:
Mini and Personal/Desktop
Computer Graphics and Dig
Disk Relat. Memory Device

In Computer Software prefer:
Computer Services
Systems Software
Applications Software

In Internet Specific prefer:
Internet

In Semiconductor/Electr prefer:
Electronics
Electronic Components
Sensors
Circuit Boards
Laser Related
Analytic/Scientific

In Biotechnology prefer:
Biotechnology

In Medical/Health prefer:
Medical/Health
Medical Products

In Consumer Related prefer:
Food/Beverage
Consumer Products

In Industrial/Energy prefer:
Alternative Energy
Industrial Products
Robotics
Machinery
Environmental Related

In Financial Services prefer:
Financial Services
Real Estate

In Manufact. prefer:
Office Automation Equipmt
Publishing

Additional Information
Year Founded: 1972
Current Activity Level : Actively seeking new investments
Method of Compensation: Function primarily in service area, receive contingent fee in cash or equity

---

SUD SICAR
116 Avenue De La Liberte
Tunis, Tunisia 1002
Phone: 216-71-801-113
Fax: 216-75-643-000
E-mail: sudsicar@planet.tn
Website: www.sudsicar.com

Type of Firm
Private Equity Firm

Project Preferences

Type of Financing Preferred:
Balanced

Additional Information
Year Founded: 1997
Current Activity Level : Actively seeking new investments

SUDINNOVA
Espace Cordeliers
2, rue President Carnot
Lyon, France 69293
Phone: 33-4-7256-9100
Fax: 33-4-7277-5855

Type of Firm
Private Equity Firm

Project Preferences

Type of Financing Preferred:
Early Stage
Expansion
Startup

Geographical Preferences

International Preferences:
Europe
France

Additional Information
Name of Most Recent Fund: Sudinnova II
Most Recent Fund Was Raised: 09/04/2000
Year Founded: 1983
Current Activity Level : Actively seeking new investments

SUED PRIVATE EQUITY (FKA: SUED KB & SUED PE GMBH & CO. KGAA)
Fritz-Elsas-Str. 31
Stuttgart, Germany 70174
Phone: 49-711-1249812
Fax: 49-711-1249636
E-mail: information@suedpe.de
Website: www.suedpe.de

Type of Firm
Bank Affiliated

Association Membership
German Venture Capital Association (BVK)

Project Preferences

Type of Financing Preferred:
Early Stage
Expansion
Turnaround
Later Stage
Seed
Management Buyouts
Startup
Recapitalizations

Geographical Preferences

International Preferences:
Europe
Germany

Additional Information
Year Founded: 2001
Current Activity Level : Actively seeking new investments

SUEZ VENTURES (FKA: INDOSUEZ VENTURES)
1690 Woodside Road
Suite 103
Redwood City, CA USA 94061
Phone: 650-367-8300
Fax: 650-367-8301
E-mail: summary@indosuezventures.com
Website: www.suezventures.com

Type of Firm
Private Equity Firm

Association Membership
Western Association of Venture Capitalists (WAVC)

Project Preferences

Role in Financing:
Prefer role as deal originator but will also invest in deals created by others

Type of Financing Preferred:
Early Stage
Mezzanine
First Stage Financing
Startup

Size of Investments Considered:
Min Size of Investment Considered (000s): $250
Max Size of Investment Considered (000s): $4,000

Geographical Preferences

United States Preferences:
West Coast

Industry Focus
(% based on actual investment)

Biotechnology	22.5%
Consumer Related	21.6%
Computer Software and Services	19.7%
Medical/Health	12.9%
Computer Hardware	7.8%
Semiconductors/Other Elect.	5.9%
Internet Specific	4.0%
Communications and Media	3.1%
Industrial/Energy	1.8%
Other Products	0.7%

Additional Information
Name of Most Recent Fund: STF III, L.P.
Most Recent Fund Was Raised: 01/01/1997
Year Founded: 1985
Capital Under Management: $100,000,000
Current Activity Level : Making few, if any, new investments
Method of Compensation: Return on investment is of primary concern, do not charge fees

---

SUGAR MOUNTAIN CAPITAL
104 Pike Street
Suite 200
Seattle, WA USA 98101
Phone: 206-749-0270
Fax: 206-749-0269

Management and Staff
Ellen Gerber, Chief Financial Officer
Kurt Dammeier, Managing Partner

Type of Firm
Private Equity Firm

Additional Information
Year Founded: 1999
Current Activity Level : Actively seeking new investments

SUMA CAPITAL
Avda. Diagonal 464
Barcelona, Spain 08006
Phone: 34-93-368-0203
Fax: 34-93-368-7257
E-mail: suma@sumacapital.es
Website: www.sumacapital.es

Other Offices
Montalban 5
Madrid, Spain 28014

Management and Staff
Enrique Tombas, Chief Executive Officer
Marian Puig, Vice President
Miguel Gari, President

Type of Firm
Private Equity Firm

Project Preferences

Type of Financing Preferred:
Generalist PE
Management Buyouts

Size of Investments Considered:
Min Size of Investment Considered (000s): $4,773
Max Size of Investment Considered (000s): $15,903

Geographical Preferences

International Preferences:
Spain

Additional Information
Year Founded: 2006
Capital Under Management: $63,600,000
Current Activity Level : Actively seeking new investments

SUMMER STREET CAPITAL LLC
70 Chippewa Street
Suite 500
Buffalo, NY USA 14202
Phone: 716-566-2900
Fax: 716-566-2910
E-mail: info@summerstreetcapital.com
Website: www.summerstreetcapital.com

Management and Staff
Andrew Fors, Partner
Baris Civelek, Principal
Brian D Amico, Managing Partner
Jennifer Balbach, Partner
Michael Petri, Vice President
Micheal McQueeney, Managing Partner
Ronald Fleissner, Chief Financial Officer

Type of Firm
Private Equity Firm

Association Membership
Natl Assoc of Small Bus. Inv. Co (NASBIC)

Project Preferences

Role in Financing:
Prefer role as deal originator but will also invest in deals created by others

Type of Financing Preferred:
Leveraged Buyout
Control-block Purchases
Expansion
Generalist PE
Later Stage
Management Buyouts
Acquisition
Recapitalizations

Size of Investments Considered:
Min Size of Investment Considered (000s): $10,000
Max Size of Investment Considered (000s): $30,000

Geographical Preferences

United States Preferences:
Mid Atlantic
Midwest
Southeast
Northeast

Canadian Preferences:
Ontario
Eastern Canada

Industry Focus
(% based on actual investment)

Medical/Health	37.5%
Consumer Related	29.8%
Other Products	13.5%
Communications and Media	11.4%
Computer Hardware	3.7%

Computer Software and Services	2.3%
Semiconductors/Other Elect.	1.8%

Additional Information

Name of Most Recent Fund: Summer Street Capital II, L.P.
Most Recent Fund Was Raised: 09/11/2006
Year Founded: 1997
Capital Under Management: $250,000,000
Current Activity Level : Actively seeking new investments
Method of Compensation: Return on invest. most important, but chg. closing fees, service fees, etc.

SUMMERHILL VENTURE PARTNERS

21 St. Clair Avenue East
Suite 1400
Toronto, Canada M4T 1L8
Phone: 416-408-0700
Fax: 416-585-9749
Website: www.bcecapital.com

Other Offices

1050 Winter Street
Suite 1000
Waltham, MA USA 02451
Phone: 617-314-9196
Fax: 978-287-0146

555 Legget Drive
Tower B, Suite 610
Ottawa, Canada K2K 2X3
Phone: 613-725-1939
Fax: 613-599-4514

Management and Staff

David McCarthy, Managing Director
Gary Rubinoff, Managing Partner
George Cooney, Venture Partner
Joseph Catalfamo, Managing Director
Marc Faucher, Principal
Omner Chohan, Chief Financial Officer

Type of Firm

Investment Management Firm

Association Membership

Canadian Venture Capital Association

Project Preferences

Role in Financing:

Prefer role as deal originator but will also invest in deals created by others

Type of Financing Preferred:

Second Stage Financing
Early Stage
Expansion
Seed
First Stage Financing

Size of Investments Considered:

Min Size of Investment Considered (000s): $2,000
Max Size of Investment Considered (000s): $10,000

Geographical Preferences

United States Preferences:

All U.S.

Canadian Preferences:

All Canada

Industry Focus

(% based on actual investment)

Communications and Media	53.3%
Computer Software and Services	32.4%
Internet Specific	7.4%
Semiconductors/Other Elect.	7.0%

Additional Information

Year Founded: 1987
Capital Under Management: $250,000,000
Current Activity Level : Actively seeking new investments
Method of Compensation: Return on investment is of primary concern, do not charge fees

SUMMIT ACCELERATOR FUND

499 Hamilton Avenue
Suite 200
Palo Alto, CA USA 94301
Phone: 650-321-1166
Fax: 650-321-1188
Website: www.summitaccelerator.com

Other Offices

222 Berkeley Street
18th Floor
Boston, MA USA 02216
Phone: 617-824-1000
Fax: 617-824-1100

Berkeley Square House, Eight Floor
Berkeley Square
London, United Kingdom W1J 6DB
Phone: 44-20-7659-7500
Fax: 44-20-7659-7550

Management and Staff

Harrison Miller, General Partner
Isaac Kato, Vice President
John Partridge, Partner
Kip Sheeline, General Partner
Marc Friend, General Partner
Mark DeLaar, Principal
Michael Balmuth, General Partner
Robin Devereux, Chief Financial Officer

Type of Firm

Bank Affiliated

Project Preferences

Role in Financing:

Prefer role as deal originator

Type of Financing Preferred:

Early Stage
Expansion
Balanced
First Stage Financing

Size of Investments Considered:

Min Size of Investment Considered (000s): $2,000
Max Size of Investment Considered (000s): $15,000

Additional Information

Name of Most Recent Fund: Summit Accelerator Fund
Most Recent Fund Was Raised: 10/01/1999
Year Founded: 1999
Capital Under Management: $180,000,000
Current Activity Level : Actively seeking new investments

SUMMIT GROUP, LTD., THE

The Pavilion
3 Broadgate
London, United Kingdom EC2M 2QS
Phone: 44-20-7614-0000
Fax: 44-20-7614-0066
E-mail: proposals@summit-group.co.uk
Website: www.summit-group.co.uk

Type of Firm

Private Equity Firm

Association Membership

British Venture Capital Association (BVCA)

Project Preferences

Type of Financing Preferred:

Early Stage
Expansion
Seed
Startup

Geographical Preferences

Canadian Preferences:

All Canada

International Preferences:

United Kingdom
Europe

Industry Preferences

In Communications prefer:

Commercial Communications

In Computer Other prefer:

Computer Related

In Medical/Health prefer:

Medical/Health

In Industrial/Energy prefer:

Energy

In Financial Services prefer:

Financial Services

Additional Information

Year Founded: 2000
Capital Under Management: $30,000,000
Current Activity Level : Actively seeking new investments

SUMMIT PARTNERS

222 Berkeley Street
18th Floor
Boston, MA USA 02116
Phone: 617-824-1000
Fax: 617-824-1100
E-mail: mail_bos@summitpartners.com
Website: www.summitpartners.com

Other Offices

Queensberry House, 3rd Floor
3 Old Burlington Street
London, United Kingdom W1S 3AE
Phone: 44-20-7659-7500
Fax: 44-20-7659-7550

499 Hamilton Avenue
Suite 200
Palo Alto, CA USA 94301
Phone: 650-321-1166
Fax: 650-321-1188

Management and Staff

Adam Hennessey, Vice President
Amit Chaturvedy, Vice President
Andrew Doyle, Vice President
Brandon Roach, Vice President
Bruce Evans, Managing Director
Charles Fitzgerald, Managing Director
Chris Crawford, Vice President
Christian Strain, Principal
Christopher Dean, General Partner
Craig Frances, Managing Director
Greg Goldfarb, Principal
Han Sikkens, Vice President
Harrison Miller, General Partner
J.J. Kardwell, Principal
Jason Glass, Vice President
Jason Tan, Vice President
Jennifer Trickett, Vice President
John Carroll, Managing Director
Joseph Trustey, Managing Partner
Kevin Mohan, General Partner
Leslie Noonan, Vice President
Mark DeLaar, Vice President
Martin Mannion, Managing Partner
Matthew Hamilton, Vice President
Matthias Steinberg, Vice President
Michael Anderson, Vice President
Mood Rowghani, Vice President
Musab Balbale, Vice President
Oliver Thomas, Vice President
Peter Chung, Managing Director
Peter Connolly, Principal
Peter Rottier, Vice President
Robert Hall, Vice President
Robin Devereux, Chief Financial Officer
Rytis Vitkauskas, Vice President
Scott Collins, Managing Director
Sonya Brown, Principal
Sotiris Lyritzis, General Partner
Spencer Neumann, Principal
Thomas Roberts, Managing Partner
Thomas Jennings, General Partner
Walter Kortschak, Managing Partner

Type of Firm

Private Equity Firm

Association Membership

Western Association of Venture Capitalists (WAVC)
National Venture Capital Association - USA (NVCA)

Project Preferences

Role in Financing:

Prefer role as deal originator but will also invest in deals created by others

Type of Financing Preferred:

Leveraged Buyout
Mezzanine
Generalist PE
Expansion
Balanced
Later Stage
Management Buyouts
Special Situation
Recapitalizations

Size of Investments Considered:

Min Size of Investment Considered (000s): $5,000
Max Size of Investment Considered (000s): $800,000

Geographical Preferences

United States Preferences:

All U.S.

Canadian Preferences:

All Canada

International Preferences:

Italy
United Kingdom
Europe
Central Europe
Bermuda
Eastern Europe
Spain
Israel
Germany
Asia
France

Industry Focus

(% based on actual investment)

Other Products	31.3%
Computer Software and Services	16.7%
Medical/Health	10.3%
Communications and Media	9.7%
Internet Specific	9.6%
Computer Hardware	7.4%
Consumer Related	6.1%
Semiconductors/Other Elect.	4.9%
Industrial/Energy	2.4%
Biotechnology	1.6%

Additional Information

Name of Most Recent Fund: Summit Partners Venture Capital Fund II-A, L.P.
Most Recent Fund Was Raised: 12/13/2006
Year Founded: 1984
Capital Under Management: $9,000,000,000
Current Activity Level : Actively seeking new investments
Method of Compensation: Return on investment is of primary concern, do not charge fees

---

SUN CAPITAL PARTNERS JAPAN K.K.

5th Floor Toranomon
4 Chome MT Building
Tokyo, Japan
Phone: 81-3-6402-0900
Fax: 81-3-5472-8200
E-mail: www.suncappart.com

Management and Staff

Akio Sato, Managing Director
Akitoshi Nakamura, Chairman & CEO
Chisato Toyama, Vice President
Shigeru Utsugi, Managing Director

Type of Firm

Bank Affiliated

Project Preferences

Type of Financing Preferred:

Leveraged Buyout
Generalist PE
Balanced
Distressed Debt

Geographical Preferences

International Preferences:

Asia
Japan

Additional Information

Year Founded: 2007
Current Activity Level : Actively seeking new investments

SUN CAPITAL PARTNERS, INC.

5200 Town Center Circle
Suite 600
Boca Raton, FL USA 33486
Phone: 561-394-0550
Fax: 561-394-0540
Website: www.suncappart.com

Other Offices

100 Park Avenue
33rd Floor
New York, NY USA 10017
Phone: 212-588-9156
Fax: 212-588-1584

11111 Santa Monica Boulevard
Suite 1050
Los Angeles, CA USA 90025
Phone: 310-473-1116
Fax: 310-473-1119

36 Rue Beaujon
Paris, France 75008
Phone: 33-1-7225-6578
Fax: 33-1-7225-6579

Bockenheimer Anlage, Frankfurter Welle
An der Welle 4
Frankfurt, Germany 60322
Phone: 49-69-7593-8654
Fax: 49-69-7593-7311

6 Gracechurch Street
4th Floor
London, United Kingdom EC3V 0AT
Phone: 44-207-929-5906
Fax: 44-207-621-1856

Unit G & H, 42nd Flr., World Finance Rd.
4003 Shennan East Road, Luohu District
Shenzhen, China 518001
Phone: 86-755-2598-1628
Fax: 86-755-2598-1638

Management and Staff

Benjamin Emmons, Vice President
Clarence Terry, Managing Director
David Kreilein, Vice President
Erik Swimmer, Principal
Gary Talarico, Managing Director
James Allen, Vice President
Jason Neimark, Principal
Jason Leach, Vice President
Kevin Feinblum, Vice President
Lynn Skillen, Vice President
M. Steven Liff, Principal
Marc Leder, Managing Director
Matthew Garff, Vice President
Michael Fieldstone, Vice President
Michael Satzberg, Managing Director
Michael Kalb, Principal
Philip Dougall, Principal
Ralph Lynch, Managing Director
Rodger Krouse, Managing Director
Stephen Marble, Vice President
T. Scott King, Managing Director
Thomas Taylor, Managing Director

Type of Firm

Bank Affiliated

Project Preferences

Role in Financing:

Prefer role as deal originator

Type of Financing Preferred:

Leveraged Buyout
Mezzanine
Turnaround
Special Situation
Distressed Debt

Geographical Preferences

United States Preferences:

All U.S.

Industry Focus

(% based on actual investment)

Consumer Related	59.5%
Industrial/Energy	38.6%
Other Products	0.8%
Communications and Media	0.7%
Semiconductors/Other Elect.	0.3%
Computer Software and Services	0.1%

Additional Information

Year Founded: 1995
Capital Under Management: $700,000,000
Current Activity Level : Actively seeking new investments
Method of Compensation: Other

SUN MICROSYSTEMS, INC.

4150 Network Circle
Santa Clara, CA USA 95054
Phone: 650-336-7409
Fax: 650-336-0237
Website: www.sun.com

Management and Staff

Jonathan Schwartz, Chief Executive Officer
Robert Sproull, Vice President

Type of Firm

Corporate PE/Venture

Project Preferences

Type of Financing Preferred:

Early Stage
Seed
Startup

Geographical Preferences

United States Preferences:

All U.S.

Industry Preferences

In Internet Specific prefer:

Internet

Additional Information

Year Founded: 1999
Current Activity Level : Actively seeking new investments

SUN MOUNTAIN CAPITAL

301 Griffin Street
Santa Fe, NM USA 87501
Phone: 505-954-5474
Fax: 505-954-5497
E-mail: info@sunmountaincapital.com
Website: www.sunmountaincapital.com

Management and Staff

Brian Birk, Managing Partner
Lee Rand, Partner
Leslie Shaw, Chief Financial Officer
Sally Corning, Partner

Type of Firm

Private Equity Advisor or Fund of Funds

Project Preferences

ype of Financing Preferred:

Fund of Funds

Geographical Preferences

United States Preferences:

Arizona

Additional Information

Year Founded: 2006
Capital Under Management: $500,000,000
Current Activity Level : Actively seeking new investments

SUNAMERICA VENTURES

One SunAmerica Center
38th Floor
Los Angeles, CA USA 90067
Phone: 310-772-6000
Fax: 310-772-6705
E-mail: bp@sunamerica.com
Website: www.sunamericavc.com

Management and Staff

Marc Gamsin, President
Troy Fukumoto, Managing Director

Type of Firm

Insurance Firm Affiliate

Project Preferences

Role in Financing:

Prefer role as deal originator but will also invest in deals created by others

Type of Financing Preferred:

Leveraged Buyout
Early Stage
Expansion
Later Stage

Size of Investments Considered:

Min Size of Investment Considered (000s): $1,000
Max Size of Investment Considered (000s): $10,000

Geographical Preferences

United States Preferences:
West Coast

Industry Preferences

In Communications prefer:
Telecommunications
Wireless Communications
Data Communications
Satellite Microwave Comm.

In Computer Software prefer:
Software
Systems Software
Applications Software

In Internet Specific prefer:
E-Commerce Technology
Internet

In Semiconductor/Electr prefer:
Electronics
Electronic Components
Semiconductor
Sensors
Component Testing Equipmt
Laser Related
Fiber Optics

In Industrial/Energy prefer:
Alternative Energy

Additional Information
Name of Most Recent Fund: SunAmerica Ventures
Most Recent Fund Was Raised: 12/31/1997
Year Founded: 1997
Capital Under Management: $750,000,000
Current Activity Level : Actively seeking new investments
Method of Compensation: Return on investment is of primary concern, do not charge fees

---

SUNBRIDGE PARTNERS
3659 Green Road
Suite 118
Beachwood, OH USA 44122
Phone: 216-360-0151
E-mail: info@sunbridgepartners.com
Website: www.sunbridgepartners.com

Other Offices
440 North Wolfe Road
Suite 118
Sunnyvale, CA USA 94085
Phone: 650-353-5401

Management and Staff
Allen Miner, Chief Executive Officer
J. Paul Reilly Grim, General Partner
John Gannon, General Partner
Ken Ehrhart, General Partner
Kenji Uchida, Chief Financial Officer
Takaaki Nagayama, Chief Operating Officer

Type of Firm
Private Equity Firm

Association Membership
National Venture Capital Association - USA (NVCA)

Project Preferences

Role in Financing:
Prefer role as deal originator but will also invest in deals created by others

Type of Financing Preferred:
Early Stage
Expansion
Seed

Size of Investments Considered:
Min Size of Investment Considered (000s): $390
Max Size of Investment Considered (000s): $3,000

Geographical Preferences

United States Preferences:
All U.S.

International Preferences:
Japan

Industry Preferences

In Computer Software prefer:
Software

Additional Information
Name of Most Recent Fund: SunBridge Partners Technology Fund EF, L.P.
Most Recent Fund Was Raised: 09/30/2005
Year Founded: 1999
Capital Under Management: $95,000,000
Current Activity Level : Actively seeking new investments

SUNNYBROOK WORKING VENTURES MEDICAL BREAKTHROUGH FUND, INC.
3504 - 20 Queen Street W.
Toronto, Canada M5H 3R3
Phone: 416-934-7731
Fax: 416-929-0901
E-mail: swvmnf@hotmail.com

Type of Firm
Private Equity Firm

Project Preferences

Role in Financing:
Will function either as deal originator or investor in deals created by others

Type of Financing Preferred:
Early Stage
Research and Development
Balanced
Seed

Size of Investments Considered:
Min Size of Investment Considered (000s): $200
Max Size of Investment Considered (000s): $750

Geographical Preferences

Canadian Preferences:
Ontario

Industry Preferences

In Biotechnology prefer:
Human Biotechnology
Agricultural/Animal Bio.
Biosensors
Biotech Related Research

In Medical/Health prefer:
Medical Diagnostics
Diagnostic Test Products
Disposable Med. Products
Pharmaceuticals

Additional Information
Name of Most Recent Fund: MVF (AKA: Medical Venture Fund)
Most Recent Fund Was Raised: 12/20/2002
Year Founded: 1999
Capital Under Management: $6,000,000
Current Activity Level : Actively seeking new investments
Method of Compensation: Return on investment is of primary concern, do not charge fees

---

SUNPLUS VENTURE CAPITAL COMPANY, LTD.
No. 10, Lane 16
Chang-Chun Street
Hsin-Chu, Taiwan 300
Phone: 886-3-578-9145
Fax: 886-3-564-5100

Type of Firm
Private Equity Firm

Association Membership
Taiwan Venture Capital Association(TVCA)

Project Preferences

Type of Financing Preferred:
Balanced

Geographical Preferences

International Preferences:
Taiwan

Industry Preferences

In Semiconductor/Electr prefer:
Semiconductor
Optoelectronics

Additional Information

Year Founded: 1999
Capital Under Management: $29,400,000
Current Activity Level : Actively seeking new investments

SUNRISE FINANCIAL GROUP, INC.

641 Lexington Avenue
25th Floor
New York, NY USA 10022
Phone: 212-421-1616
Fax: 212-750-7277
Website: www.sunrisecorp.com

Management and Staff

Amnon Mandelbaum, Managing Director
Jay Rodin, Managing Director
Marcia Kucher, Chief Financial Officer
Marilyn Adler, General Partner
Nathan Low, President, Founder
Phillip Kassai, Managing Director
Richard Stone, Managing Director

Type of Firm

Bank Affiliated

Project Preferences

Type of Financing Preferred:
Balanced

Industry Preferences

In Communications prefer:
Telecommunications

In Internet Specific prefer:
Internet

In Medical/Health prefer:
Medical/Health

Additional Information

Year Founded: 1991
Capital Under Management: $10,700,000
Current Activity Level : Actively seeking new investments

SUNROCK VENTURES, INC.

201 East Kennedy Boulevard
Suite 950
Tampa, FL USA 33602
Phone: 813-990-0361
Fax: 813-936-4764
Website: www.sunrockventures.com

Other Offices

1205 Lincoln Road
Suite 216
Miami Beach, FL USA 33139
Phone: 305-432-4684
Fax: 305-503-8566

Management and Staff

Jeffrey Wolf, Managing Director
Matt Shaw, Managing Director
Tate Garrett, Managing Director

Type of Firm

Private Equity Firm

Project Preferences

Type of Financing Preferred:
Early Stage
Expansion
Balanced
Later Stage
Acquisition

Size of Investments Considered:
Min Size of Investment Considered (000s): $4,000
Max Size of Investment Considered (000s): $7,000

Geographical Preferences

United States Preferences:
Southeast
Florida
All U.S.

Industry Preferences

In Medical/Health prefer:
Health Services

In Business Serv. prefer:
Services

Additional Information

Year Founded: 2007
Current Activity Level : Actively seeking new investments

SUNSINO VENTURES GROUP (FKA: SUNSINO DEVELOPMENT ASSOCIATE)

6F-2 248 Nan King Rd.
Section 3
Taipei, Taiwan 105
Phone: 886-2-7706-3339
Fax: 886-2-7706-3338
E-mail: sunsino@tpts1.seed.net.tw
Website: www.sunsino.com.tw

Other Offices

Room F202, No.12 Nanke 2nd Road
Shanhua Township
Tainan, Taiwan 741
Phone: 886-6-505-3596
Fax: 886-505-3583

15/F-2 295 Kwang Fu Rd.
Sec. 2
Hsinchu, Taiwan 300
Phone: 886-3-572-0568
Fax: 886-3-574-5063

10/F 87 Po-kuan Rd.
Taichung, Taiwan 404
Phone: 886-4-2301-9387
Fax: 886-4-2301-5589

Management and Staff

Cheng Sang Huang, President
Freemand Chang, Vice President

Type of Firm

Private Equity Firm

Association Membership

Taiwan Venture Capital Association(TVCA)

Project Preferences

Role in Financing:
Prefer role as deal originator but will also invest in deals created by others

Type of Financing Preferred:
Expansion
Mezzanine
Startup

Geographical Preferences

United States Preferences:
All U.S.

International Preferences:
Taiwan

Industry Preferences

In Communications prefer:
Telecommunications

In Computer Software prefer:
Software

In Semiconductor/Electr prefer:
Electronics
Semiconductor
Optoelectronics

In Biotechnology prefer:
Biotechnology

In Medical/Health prefer:
Pharmaceuticals

In Industrial/Energy prefer:
Advanced Materials

Additional Information

Year Founded: 1994
Capital Under Management: $100,000,000
Current Activity Level : Actively seeking new investments

SUNSTONE CAPITAL A/S

Lautrupsgade 7, 5
Copenhagen, Denmark 2100
Phone: 45-2012-6000

Fax: 45-3920-9898
E-mail: reception@sunstonecapital.com
Website: www.sunstonecapital.com

Other Offices

Angelholmsvagen 28
Bastad, Sweden 26931
Phone: 46-43-131-1740

1370 Willow Road
Second Floor, Silicon Valley Office
Menlo Park, CA USA 94025
Phone: 650-587-1518

Management and Staff

Christer Fahraeus, Venture Partner
Eric-Alan Rapp, Partner
Jimmy Fussing Nielsen, Managing Partner
Jorgen Smidt, Partner
Merete Lundbye Moller, Partner
Pekka Vartiainen, Venture Partner
Peter Benson, Managing Partner
Soren Lemonius, Partner
Soren Christensen, Partner
Sten Verland, Partner
Yvonne Martensson, Venture Partner

Type of Firm

Private Equity Firm

Project Preferences

Type of Financing Preferred:

Early Stage

Geographical Preferences

International Preferences:

Sweden
Greenland
Iceland
Finland
Norway
Denmark
Faroe Islands

Industry Preferences

In Computer Software prefer:

Software

In Biotechnology prefer:

Biotechnology

In Medical/Health prefer:

Pharmaceuticals

Additional Information

Year Founded: 2005
Capital Under Management: $548,000,000
Current Activity Level : Actively seeking new investments

SUNTRUST BANK, INC.

Mail Code HDQ 4109
P.O. Box 85024
Richmond, VA USA 23285-502
Website: www.suntrust.com

Management and Staff

Phillip Humann, Chief Executive Officer

Type of Firm

Investment Management Firm

Additional Information

Year Founded: 2009
Current Activity Level : Actively seeking new investments

SUNTRUST EQUITY PARTNERS

424 Church Street
Suite 2600
Nashville, TN USA 37219
Phone: 615-748-5800
Fax: 615-748-5799
E-mail: step@suntrust.com
Website: www.suntrust.com/private_equity

Other Offices

303 Peachtree Street, Northeast
Fourth Floor
Atlanta, GA USA 30308
Phone: 404-827-6505
Fax: 404-588-7511

Management and Staff

F. Matthew Petronzio, Vice President
Ken Millar, Managing Director
Martin Mayden, Managing Director

Type of Firm

Bank Affiliated

Project Preferences

Role in Financing:

Prefer role in deals created by others

Type of Financing Preferred:

Expansion
Mezzanine
Later Stage
Management Buyouts
Acquisition
Recapitalizations

Size of Investments Considered:

Min Size of Investment Considered (000s): $2,000
Max Size of Investment Considered (000s): $20,000

Geographical Preferences

United States Preferences:

All U.S.

Industry Preferences

In Communications prefer:

Radio & TV Broadcasting
Telecommunications
Wireless Communications

In Medical/Health prefer:

Medical Diagnostics
Diagnostic Services
Diagnostic Test Products
Medical Therapeutics
Drug/Equipmt Delivery
Medical Products
Disposable Med. Products
Health Services
Hospitals/Clinics/Primary
Pharmaceuticals

In Consumer Related prefer:

Consumer
Food/Beverage

In Industrial/Energy prefer:

Energy

In Financial Services prefer:

Financial Services

In Business Serv. prefer:

Services
Media

Additional Information

Year Founded: 1995
Capital Under Management: $315,000,000
Current Activity Level : Actively seeking new investments
Method of Compensation: Return on invest. most important, but chg. closing fees, service fees, etc.

SUNTX CAPITAL PARTNERS

Two Lincoln Centre
5420 LBJ Freeway, Suite 1000
Dallas, TX USA 75240
Phone: 972-663-8900
Fax: 972-661-9977
Website: www.suntx.com

Management and Staff

Benjamin Eakes, Principal
Mark Matteson, Partner
Michael Ilagan, Principal
Ned Fleming, Managing Partner
Richard Boyle, Partner

Type of Firm

Private Equity Firm

Project Preferences

Type of Financing Preferred:

Leveraged Buyout
Early Stage
Expansion
Balanced
Turnaround
Later Stage
Management Buyouts
Acquisition
Startup
Recapitalizations

Geographical Preferences

United States Preferences:
New Mexico
Oklahoma
Tennessee
Arizona
Mississippi
Alabama
North Carolina
South Carolina
Virginia
Florida
Louisiana
Arkansas
Georgia
Kentucky
Texas
All U.S.

Industry Focus

(% based on actual investment)

Communications and Media	75.0%
Semiconductors/Other Elect.	15.0%
Other Products	10.0%

Additional Information

Year Founded: 2001
Capital Under Management: $164,300,000
Current Activity Level : Actively seeking new investments

SUPERIOR CAPITAL PARTNERS

500 Griswold Street
Suite 2320
Detroit, MI USA 48226
Phone: 315-596-9600
Fax: 313-596-9610
Website: www.superiorfund.com

Management and Staff

Andrew Wiegand, Vice President
Brian Demkowicz, Partner
Douglas Kearney, Principal
Mark Carroll, Managing Partner
Scott Hauncher, Managing Director
Scott Reilly, Partner

Type of Firm

Private Equity Firm

Project Preferences

Type of Financing Preferred:
Leveraged Buyout
Management Buyouts
Acquisition
Recapitalizations

Size of Investments Considered:
Min Size of Investment Considered (000s): $5,000
Max Size of Investment Considered (000s): $15,000

Geographical Preferences

United States Preferences:
All U.S.

Industry Preferences

In Industrial/Energy prefer:
Industrial Products

In Business Serv. prefer:
Services
Distribution

In Manufact. prefer:
Manufacturing

Additional Information

Year Founded: 2007
Capital Under Management: $60,200,000
Current Activity Level : Actively seeking new investments

SUPPLY CHAIN EQUITY PARTNERS

1300 East Ninth Street
Suite 600
Cleveland, OH USA 44114
Phone: 216-925-4184
Fax: 216-363-0135
E-mail: info@SupplyChainEquity.com
Website: www.supplychainequity.com

Management and Staff

Jay Greyson, Principal
Jim Miller, Principal
Nir Gabriely, Principal

Type of Firm

Private Equity Firm

Project Preferences

Type of Financing Preferred:
Leveraged Buyout
Acquisition

Size of Investments Considered:
Min Size of Investment Considered (000s): $2,000
Max Size of Investment Considered (000s): $20,000

Industry Preferences

In Business Serv. prefer:
Distribution

Additional Information

Year Founded: 2007
Capital Under Management: $25,000,000
Current Activity Level : Actively seeking new investments

SUSSEX PLACE INVESTMENT MANAGEMENT (SPIM), LTD.

18-20 Huntsworth Mews
London, United Kingdom NW1 6DD
Phone: 44-207-535-8805
Fax: 44-207-535-8804
E-mail: info@spventures.co.uk
Website: www.spventures.co.uk

Management and Staff

John Brimacombe, Venture Partner
Richard Gourlay, Managing Director

Type of Firm

University Program

Association Membership

British Venture Capital Association (BVCA)

Project Preferences

Type of Financing Preferred:
Early Stage
Seed
Startup

Size of Investments Considered:
Min Size of Investment Considered (000s): $100
Max Size of Investment Considered (000s): $100,000

Geographical Preferences

International Preferences:
United Kingdom

Industry Preferences

In Business Serv. prefer:
Services
Media

Additional Information

Name of Most Recent Fund: Sussex Place Partners II
Most Recent Fund Was Raised: 07/25/2000
Year Founded: 1998
Capital Under Management: $23,000,000
Current Activity Level : Actively seeking new investments

SUSTAINABLE DEVELOPMENT TECHNOLOGY CANADA

45 O?Connor Street
Suite 1850
Ottawa, Canada K1P 1A4
Phone: 613-234-6313
Fax: 613-234-0303
E-mail: info@sdtc.ca
Website: www.sdtc.ca

Type of Firm
Government Affiliated Program

Additional Information
Year Founded: 2001
Current Activity Level : Actively seeking new investments

SUSTAINABLE RESOURCE VENTURES
60 Thoreau Street
Suite 108
Concord, MA USA 01742
Phone: 978-369-5043
Website: www.sustainvc.com

Type of Firm
Private Equity Firm

Project Preferences
Type of Financing Preferred:
Early Stage
Expansion

Industry Preferences
In Medical/Health prefer:
Medical/Health

In Consumer Related prefer:
Food/Beverage
Education Related

In Industrial/Energy prefer:
Energy
Environmental Related

Additional Information
Year Founded: 2006
Current Activity Level : Actively seeking new investments

SUSTAINABLE TECHNOLOGY PARTNERS NORDIC AB
Amiralitetshuset
Stockholm, Sweden SE-111 49
Phone: 46-8650-7718
Fax: 46-8650-7713
E-mail: info@stechfund.com
Website: www.stechpartner.com

Other Offices
625 Liberty Ave.
3200 Dominion Tower
Pittsburgh, PA USA 15222
Phone: 412-497-5700
Fax: 412-497-5740

Management and Staff
Anders Frisk, Founding Partner
Andre Heinz, Founding Partner

Type of Firm
Private Equity Firm

Project Preferences
Type of Financing Preferred:
Expansion

Geographical Preferences
International Preferences:
Scandanavia/Nordic Region

Industry Preferences
In Biotechnology prefer:
Industrial Biotechnology

In Industrial/Energy prefer:
Energy
Materials
Environmental Related

Additional Information
Year Founded: 2007
Capital Under Management: $84,000,000
Current Activity Level : Actively seeking new investments

SUTTER HILL VENTURES
755 Page Mill Road
Suite A-200
Palo Alto, CA USA 94304
Phone: 650-493-5600
Fax: 650-858-1854
E-mail: shv@shv.com
Website: www.shv.com

Management and Staff
Andy Sheehan, Managing Director
David Anderson, Managing Director
David Sweet, Chief Financial Officer
George Leonard Baker, Managing Director
Gregory Sands, Managing Director
James Gaither, Managing Director
James White, Managing Director
Jeffrey Bird, Managing Director
Tench Coxe, Managing Director
William Younger, Managing Director

Type of Firm
Private Equity Firm

Association Membership
Western Association of Venture Capitalists (WAVC)
National Venture Capital Association - USA (NVCA)

Project Preferences
Role in Financing:
Prefer role as deal originator but will also invest in deals created by others

Type of Financing Preferred:
Early Stage
Seed
First Stage Financing
Startup

Size of Investments Considered:
Min Size of Investment Considered (000s): $100
Max Size of Investment Considered (000s): $10,000

Industry Focus
(% based on actual investment)

Internet Specific	21.7%
Computer Software and Services	17.6%
Medical/Health	17.2%
Communications and Media	12.9%
Biotechnology	8.2%
Computer Hardware	7.8%
Other Products	6.0%
Semiconductors/Other Elect.	3.8%
Consumer Related	3.1%
Industrial/Energy	1.6%

Additional Information
Year Founded: 1962
Capital Under Management: $400,000,000
Current Activity Level : Actively seeking new investments
Method of Compensation: Return on invest. most important, but chg. closing fees, service fees, etc.

SUZHOU VENTURES GROUP CO., LTD.
158 Wang Dun Road
Suzhou Industrial Park
Suzhou, China 215028
Phone: 86-512-66606971
Fax: 86-512-66606111

Type of Firm
Private Equity Firm

Project Preferences
Type of Financing Preferred:
Balanced

Geographical Preferences
International Preferences:
Asia

Additional Information
Year Founded: 2007
Capital Under Management: $439,800,000
Current Activity Level : Actively seeking new investments

SUZHOU WUZHONG GUOFA VENTURE CAPITAL
Wuzhong District
Suzhou, China
Type of Firm
Private Equity Firm

Geographical Preferences

International Preferences:
Asia

Additional Information
Year Founded: 2008
Current Activity Level : Actively seeking new investments

SV INVESTMENT PARTNERS (FKA: SCHRODER VENTURES US)

505 Fifth Avenue
Floor 28
New York, NY USA 10017
Phone: 212-735-0700
Fax: 212-735-0711
E-mail: info@svip.com
Website: www.svip.com

Management and Staff
Andrew Gaspar, Partner
John Cochran, Principal
Kathleen Stowe, Principal
Matt Rho, Partner
Nicholas Somers, Managing Partner
W. Montague Yort, Managing Partner

Type of Firm
Private Equity Firm

Project Preferences

Type of Financing Preferred:
Leveraged Buyout
Expansion

Size of Investments Considered:
Min Size of Investment Considered (000s): $10,000
Max Size of Investment Considered (000s): $500,000

Geographical Preferences

United States Preferences:
All U.S.

International Preferences:
United Kingdom

Industry Preferences

In Communications prefer:
Communications and Media
Telecommunications
Wireless Communications

In Computer Software prefer:
Computer Services
Software
Systems Software
Applications Software

In Business Serv. prefer:
Services
Media

Additional Information
Name of Most Recent Fund: SV Investments Fund I
Most Recent Fund Was Raised: 01/01/2000
Year Founded: 1999
Capital Under Management: $286,000,000
Current Activity Level : Actively seeking new investments

SV LIFE SCIENCES ADVISERS (SCHRODER VENTURES LIFE SCIENCES)

60 State Street
Suite 3650
Boston, MA USA 02109
Phone: 617-367-8100
Fax: 617-367-1590
E-mail: info@svlsa.com
Website: www.svlsa.com

Other Offices
950 Tower Lane, Metro Center
Suite 1725
Foster City, CA USA 94404
Phone: 650-571-8200
Fax: 650-571-8201

71 Kingsway
London, United Kingdom WC2 B6ST
Phone: 44-207-421-7070
Fax: 44-207-421-7077

Management and Staff
Bruce Peacock, Venture Partner
Bruce Cerullo, Venture Partner
Darren Black, Partner
David Guyer, Partner
David Milne, Managing Partner
Eugene Hill, Managing Partner
Gary Velasquez, Venture Partner
George Wallace, Venture Partner
Graham Boulnois, Partner
Hamish Cameron, Venture Partner
Henry Simon, Partner
Jeffery Vender, Venture Partner
Kate Bingham, Managing Partner
Lutz Giebel, Managing Partner
Michael Ross, Managing Partner
Michael Carter, Venture Partner
Nick Coleman, Partner
Paul LaViolette, Venture Partner
Robert Palmisano, Venture Partner
Samual Wu, Principal
Sarah Bodary, Venture Partner
Tillman Gerngross, Venture Partner

Type of Firm
Private Equity Firm

Association Membership
British Venture Capital Association (BVCA)
National Venture Capital Association - USA (NVCA)
European Private Equity and Venture Capital Assoc.

Project Preferences

Role in Financing:
Prefer role as deal originator but will also invest in deals created by others

Type of Financing Preferred:
Second Stage Financing
Leveraged Buyout
Mezzanine
Research and Development
Public Companies
Seed
Later Stage
Other
First Stage Financing
Special Situation
Startup
Recapitalizations

Size of Investments Considered:
Min Size of Investment Considered (000s): $1,000
Max Size of Investment Considered (000s): $50,000

Geographical Preferences

United States Preferences:
Mid Atlantic
Midwest
Northwest
Southeast
Southern California
Northeast
Massachusetts
California
West Coast
Texas
All U.S.

Canadian Preferences:
All Canada

International Preferences:
Italy
Sweden
United Kingdom
Europe
Central Europe
Western Europe
Israel
Germany
France

Industry Focus
(% based on actual investment)

Medical/Health	39.9%
Biotechnology	35.3%
Other Products	8.2%
Industrial/Energy	7.9%
Computer Software and Services	5.6%
Internet Specific	1.7%
Computer Hardware	1.2%
Semiconductors/Other Elect.	0.1%

Additional Information
Name of Most Recent Fund: SV Life Sciences IV Strategic Partners, L.P.
Most Recent Fund Was Raised: 02/22/2007
Year Founded: 1983

Capital Under Management: $1,537,000,000
Current Activity Level : Actively seeking new investments
Method of Compensation: Return on invest. most important, but chg. closing fees, service fees, etc.

SV VENTURE CAPITAL

10F, KTPF Building
27-2 Yeoidodong Yeungdeungpoku
Seoul, South Korea
Phone: 822-3775-1020
Fax: 822-3775-1021
E-mail: svvc@svvc.co.kr
Website: www.svvc.co.kr

Management and Staff

Sungho Park, President

Type of Firm

Private Equity Firm

Project Preferences

Type of Financing Preferred:

Balanced

Geographical Preferences

International Preferences:

Korea, South

Additional Information

Year Founded: 2006
Capital Under Management: $20,300,000
Current Activity Level : Actively seeking new investments

SVB CAPITAL

3005 Tasman Drive
Santa Clara, CA USA 95054
Phone: 408-654-7400
Website: www.svb.com/svbcapital

Other Offices

3000 Sand Hill Road
Building 3, Suite 150
Menlo Park, CA USA 94025
Phone: 650-233-7420
Fax: 650-233-6611

2221 Washington Street
Suite 200, One Newton Executive Park
Newton, MA USA 02462
Phone: 617-630-4100
Fax: 617-969-4395

380 Interlocken Crescent
Suite 600
Broomfield, CO USA 80021
Phone: 303-410-3400
Fax: 303-469-9088

185 Berry Street
Lobby One, Suite 3000
San Francisco, CA USA 94107
Phone: 415-512-4200
Fax: 415-856-0810

230 West Monroe
Suite 720
Chicago, IL USA 60606
Phone: 312-704-9510
Fax: 312-704-1530

8705 Southwest Nimbus
Suite 240
Beaverton, OR USA 97008
Phone: 503-574-3700
Fax: 503-526-0818

38 Technology Drive West
Suite 150
Irvine, CA USA 92618
Phone: 949-754-0800
Fax: 949-790-9007

3rd Floor, Prestige Loka
Brunton Road
Bangalore, India 560 025
Phone: 91-80-4112-8282
Fax: 91-80-4112-1616

34 Dover Street
5th Floor
London, United Kingdom W1S 4NG
Phone: 207-647-1280
Fax: 207-647-1281

2 Palo Alto Square
Suite 110
Palo Alto, CA USA 94306
Phone: 650-812-0682
Fax: 650-493-5859

3353 Peachtree Road. Northeast
North Tower, Suite M-10
Atlanta, GA USA 30326
Phone: 404-264-8333
Fax: 404-467-4467

100 Matsonford Road
Suite 555 Five Radnor Corporate Center
Radnor, PA USA 19087
Phone: 610-971-2065
Fax: 610-971-2063

333 Huai Hai Zhong Road
Unit 1604, Shui On Plaza
Shanghai, China 200021
Phone: 86-21-6120-8850
Fax: 86-21-6120-8835

5915 Farrington Road
Chapel Hill, NC USA 27517-9900
Phone: 919-442-2300
Fax: 919-442-2155

14185 North Dallas Parkway
Suite 780
Dallas, TX USA 75254
Phone: 972-455-0950
Fax: 972-387-0782

301 Carlson Parkway
Suite 255
Minnetonka, MN USA 55305
Phone: 952-745-1400
Fax: 952-475-8471

3979 Freedom Circle
Suite 600
Santa Clara, CA USA 95054
Phone: 408-654-5550
Fax: 408-654-1045

3700 Old Redwood Highway
Suite 220
Santa Rosa, CA USA 95403
Phone: 707-535-5060
Fax: 707-579-1004

11 Hamenofim Street
P.O. Box 2148
Herzilya Pituach, Israel 46725
Phone: 972-9-971-5910

5820 Canoga Avenue
Suite 210
Woodland Hills, CA USA 91367
Phone: 818-226-2040
Fax: 818-340-0395

2400 Hanover Street
Palo Alto, CA USA 94304
Phone: 650-320-1100
Fax: 650-320-0016

899 Adams Street
Suite G-2
St Helena, CA USA 94574
Phone: 707-967-4825
Fax: 707-967-4827

7000 North MoPac Expressway
Suite 360
Austin, TX USA 78731
Phone: 512-372-6750
Fax: 512-794-0855

8020 Towers Crescent Drive
Suite 475
Vienna, VA USA 22182
Phone: 703-448-5060
Fax: 703-356-7643

84 Free Press House 215
Nariman Point
Mumbai, India 400021
Phone: 91-22-6744-6510

901 Fifth Avenue
Suite 3900
Seattle, WA USA 98164
Phone: 206-342-7600
Fax: 206-624-0374

2151 East Broadway Road
Suite 117
Tempe, AZ USA 85282
Phone: 480-557-4900
Fax: 480-967-5022

4370 La Jolla Village Drive
Suite 860
San Diego, CA USA 92122
Phone: 858-784-330
Fax: 858-622-1424

535 Fifth Avenue
27th Floor
New York, NY USA 10017
Phone: 212-821-8960
Fax: 212-688-5994

Management and Staff

Aaron Gershenberg, Managing Partner
Anne Rockhold, Chief Financial Officer
Chuck Tedeschi, Principal
Daniel Quon, Managing Director
Farouk Ladha, Partner
Henry Chung, Partner
John Dominguez, Partner
John Norris, Managing Director
John Otterson, Partner
Katie Knepley, Principal
Ken Loveless, Managing Director
Larry Zahn, Partner
Mark MacLennan, President
Michael Devery, Managing Director
Min Berbon, Principal
Natalie Braun, Partner
Philip Korn, Managing Director
Sherer Brian, Managing Director
Sulaiman Mamdani, Principal
Suresh Shanmugham, Managing Director
Vincent Williams, Partner

Type of Firm

Bank Affiliated

Association Membership

National Venture Capital Association - USA (NVCA)
Indian Venture Capital Association (IVCA)

Project Preferences

Role in Financing:

Prefer role as deal originator but will also invest in deals created by others

Type of Financing Preferred:

Fund of Funds
Second Stage Financing
Early Stage
Mezzanine
Balanced
Start-up Financing
Later Stage
First Stage Financing
Strategic Alliances

Size of Investments Considered:

Min Size of Investment Considered (000s): $500
Max Size of Investment Considered (000s): $1,000

Geographical Preferences

United States Preferences:

All U.S.

International Preferences:

India
China

Industry Focus

(% based on actual investment)

Internet Specific	25.0%
Computer Software and Services	23.1%
Communications and Media	18.6%
Semiconductors/Other Elect.	12.5%
Other Products	11.4%
Computer Hardware	3.3%
Consumer Related	2.1%
Medical/Health	1.7%
Biotechnology	1.7%
Industrial/Energy	0.6%

Additional Information

Name of Most Recent Fund: SVB Capital China Councils Fund, L.P.
Most Recent Fund Was Raised: 08/21/2008
Year Founded: 1994
Capital Under Management: $1,000,000,000
Current Activity Level : Actively seeking new investments
Method of Compensation: Return on invest. most important, but chg. closing fees, service fees, etc.

SVERICA INTERNATIONAL

800 Boylston Street
Suite 3325
Boston, MA USA 02199
Phone: 617-695-0221
Fax: 617-507-5824
Website: www.sverica.com

Other Offices

1900 Crestwood Boulevard
Suite 301
Birmingham, AL USA 35210
Phone: 205-271-2149
Fax: 205-271-2148

44 Montgomery Street
Suite 3000
San Francisco, CA USA 94104
Phone: 415-249-4900
Fax: 415-249-4901

Management and Staff

Alessandro Mina, Managing Director
David Finley, Managing Director
Frank Young, Managing Director
Gunnar Bjorklund, Managing Director
John McLane, Principal

Type of Firm

Private Equity Firm

Project Preferences

Type of Financing Preferred:

Leveraged Buyout
Management Buyouts
Acquisition

Geographical Preferences

United States Preferences:

All U.S.

Canadian Preferences:

All Canada

Industry Preferences

In Business Serv. prefer:

Services
Distribution

In Manufact. prefer:

Manufacturing

Additional Information

Year Founded: 2001
Capital Under Management: $430,000,000
Current Activity Level : Actively seeking new investments

SVILUPPO IMPRESE CENTRO ITALIA S.P.A.

1728Via dei Della Robbia-5/r
Firenze, Italy 50132
Phone: 39-848-886-886
E-mail: info@sviluppoitalia.it
Website: www.sviluppoitalia.it

Management and Staff

Domenico Arcuri, Chief Executive Officer
Nicolo Piazza, President

Type of Firm

Corporate PE/Venture

Project Preferences

Type of Financing Preferred:

Balanced

Geographical Preferences

International Preferences:

Italy

Additional Information

Year Founded: 2004
Capital Under Management: $61,300,000
Current Activity Level : Actively seeking new investments

SVILUPPO ITALIA SPA

46, Via Calabria
Rome, Italy 00187
Phone: 39-06-421-601

Fax: 39-06-421-60975
E-mail: info@sviluppoitalia.it
Website: www.sviluppoitalia.it

Type of Firm

Government Affiliated Program

Association Membership

Italian Venture Capital Association (AIFI)

Project Preferences

Type of Financing Preferred:

Second Stage Financing
Expansion
Startup

Geographical Preferences

International Preferences:

Italy

Industry Preferences

In Consumer Related prefer:

Entertainment and Leisure

In Business Serv. prefer:

Services

In Manufact. prefer:

Manufacturing

In Agr/Forestr/Fish prefer:

Agribusiness
Agriculture related

Additional Information

Year Founded: 2000
Current Activity Level : Actively seeking new investments

SVOBODA CAPITAL PARTNERS (FKA: SVOBODA, COLLINS LLC)

One North Franklin Street
Suite 1500
Chicago, IL USA 60606
Phone: 312-267-8750
Fax: 312-267-6025
E-mail: info@svoco.com
Website: www.svoco.com

Management and Staff

Alex Miller, Managing Director
Andrew Albert, Managing Director
John Svoboda, Senior Managing Director

Type of Firm

Private Equity Firm

Association Membership

Natl Assoc of Small Bus. Inv. Co (NASBIC)
Illinois Venture Capital Association

Project Preferences

Role in Financing:

Prefer role as deal originator but will also invest in deals created by others

Type of Financing Preferred:

Leveraged Buyout
Expansion
Generalist PE
Later Stage
Management Buyouts
Acquisition
Private Placement
Recapitalizations

Size of Investments Considered:

Min Size of Investment Considered (000s): $10,000
Max Size of Investment Considered (000s): $25,000

Geographical Preferences

United States Preferences:

Mid Atlantic
Midwest
Southeast
Northeast
Rocky Mountain
All U.S.

Industry Focus

(% based on actual investment)

Internet Specific	52.4%
Other Products	29.8%
Computer Software and Services	17.8%

Additional Information

Year Founded: 1998
Capital Under Management: $150,000,000
Current Activity Level : Actively seeking new investments
Method of Compensation: Return on invest. most important, but chg. closing fees, service fees, etc.

SWANDER PACE CAPITAL

345 California Street
Suite 2550
San Francisco, CA USA 94104
Phone: 415-477-8500
Fax: 415-477-8510
E-mail: info@spcap.com
Website: www.spcap.com

Other Offices

1420 Routh 206 North
Suite 120
Bedminster, NJ USA 07921
Phone: 908-719-2322
Fax: 908-719-9311

Management and Staff

Andrew Richards, Managing Director
C. Morris Stout, Managing Director
Heather Fraser, Chief Financial Officer
J.B. Handley, Managing Director
John Novak, Vice President
Mark Poff, Vice President
Shawn Hecht, Managing Director
Valerie Scott, Principal

Type of Firm

Private Equity Firm

Project Preferences

Role in Financing:

Prefer role as deal originator but will also invest in deals created by others

Type of Financing Preferred:

Second Stage Financing
Leveraged Buyout

Size of Investments Considered:

Min Size of Investment Considered (000s): $5,000
Max Size of Investment Considered: No Limit

Geographical Preferences

United States Preferences:

All U.S.

Industry Focus

(% based on actual investment)

Consumer Related	48.4%
Medical/Health	33.5%
Internet Specific	13.0%
Computer Software and Services	4.5%
Communications and Media	0.6%

Additional Information

Year Founded: 1996
Capital Under Management: $85,000,000
Current Activity Level : Actively seeking new investments
Method of Compensation: Return on invest. most important, but chg. closing fees, service fees, etc.

SWARRATON PARTNERS LIMITED

79 Knightsbridge
London, United Kingdom SW1X 7RB
Phone: 44-20-7752-0860
Fax: 44-20-7752-0590
E-mail: ir@swarraton.com
Website: www.swarraton.com

Management and Staff

Christophe Jungels-Winkler, Partner
Stephen Brooke, Managing Partner

Type of Firm

Private Equity Firm

Project Preferences

Type of Financing Preferred:

Early Stage
Seed

Geographical Preferences

International Preferences:

United Kingdom
Europe
Switzerland
Germany

Additional Information

Year Founded: 2008
Current Activity Level : Actively seeking new investments

SWEDFUND INTERNATIONAL AB

Sveavagen 24-26
PO Box 3286
Stockholm, Sweden 103 65
Phone: 46-8-725-9400
Fax: 46-8-203-093
E-mail: info@swedfund.se
Website: www.swedfund.se

Management and Staff

Olle Arefalk, Managing Director

Type of Firm

Government Affiliated Program

Association Membership

Swedish Venture Capital Association (SVCA)

Project Preferences

Type of Financing Preferred:

Fund of Funds
Leveraged Buyout
Expansion
Seed
Startup

Size of Investments Considered:

Min Size of Investment Considered (000s): $106
Max Size of Investment Considered (000s): $5,310

Geographical Preferences

nternational Preferences:

Latin America
Central Europe
Eastern Europe
Asia
Africa

Industry Focus

(% based on actual investment)
Semiconductors/Other Elect. 100.0%

Additional Information

Year Founded: 1979
Current Activity Level : Actively seeking new investments

SWEDISH INDUSTRIAL DEVELOPMENT FUND (AKA: INDUSTRIFONDEN)

Vasagatan 11
P.O. Box 1163
Stockholm, Sweden SE-111 91
Phone: 46-8-5879-1900
Fax: 46-8-5879-1950
E-mail: info@industrifonden.se
Website: www.industrifonden.se

Management and Staff

Bjorn Ogenstam, Vice President
Claes De Neergaard, President
Lennart Samuelsson, Vice President

Type of Firm

Government Affiliated Program

Association Membership

Swedish Venture Capital Association (SVCA)
European Private Equity and Venture Capital Assoc.

Project Preferences

Type of Financing Preferred:

Early Stage
Expansion

Size of Investments Considered:

Min Size of Investment Considered (000s): $200
Max Size of Investment Considered (000s): $200,000

Geographical Preferences

International Preferences:

Sweden

Industry Preferences

In Semiconductor/Electr prefer:

Electronics

In Biotechnology prefer:

Biotechnology

In Medical/Health prefer:

Medical/Health

In Industrial/Energy prefer:

Industrial Products
Factory Automation

In Manufact. prefer:

Manufacturing

Additional Information

Year Founded: 1979
Capital Under Management: $539,200,000
Current Activity Level : Actively seeking new investments

SWEDOCEAN

Box 1279
Helsingborg, Sweden 251 12
Phone: 46-42-142-650
Fax: 46-42-124-710

Type of Firm

Private Equity Firm

Association Membership

Swedish Venture Capital Association (SVCA)

Project Preferences

Type of Financing Preferred:

Balanced

Geographical Preferences

International Preferences:

Sweden
Europe

Additional Information

Year Founded: 2005
Current Activity Level : Actively seeking new investments

SWICORP CAPITAL PARTNERS

Quai Gustave-Ador 8
P.O. Box 6404
Geneva, Switzerland 1211
Phone: 41-22-737-3737
Fax: 41-22-737-3700
E-mail: info@swicorp.com
Website: www.swicorp.com

Other Offices

Immeuble SUN
Rue du Lac Ontario
Les Berges du Lac, Tunisia 1053
Phone: 216-71-960-137
Fax: 216-71-960-237

c/o Saudi Business Center
Medina Road, 13th Floor (Office 10)
Jeddah, Saudi Arabia 21456
Phone: 966-2-657-4160
Fax: 966-2-652-6541

No 34/1, Shahid Haghani Highway
After Didar Shomali, Vanak Sq.
Tehran, Iran 15188
Phone: 98-21-8879-52394
Fax: 98-21-8866-2425

Management and Staff

Daniel Schenker, Partner
David Rey, Partner
Nabil Triki, Partner
Simon Rowe, Partner

Type of Firm
Bank Affiliated

Association Membership
Swiss Venture Capital Association (SECA)
European Private Equity and Venture Capital Assoc.

Project Preferences

Type of Financing Preferred:
Leveraged Buyout
Early Stage
Expansion
Generalist PE
Balanced
Management Buyouts
Startup

Geographical Preferences

International Preferences:
Bahrain
Oman
Tunisia
Jordan
Qatar
Turkey
Europe
Egypt
Iran
Utd. Arab Em.
Algeria
Middle East
Saudi Arabia
Morocco
South Africa
Kuwait
Sudan
Africa

Industry Preferences

In Communications prefer:
Communications and Media

In Consumer Related prefer:
Consumer
Consumer Products

In Industrial/Energy prefer:
Energy
Oil and Gas Exploration
Oil & Gas Drilling,Explor
Alternative Energy
Coal Related
Energy Conservation Relat

In Financial Services prefer:
Financial Services

Additional Information
Year Founded: 2003
Capital Under Management: $800,000,000
Current Activity Level : Actively seeking new investments

SWIFT CAPITAL PARTNERS GMBH
Lombard House
Pelzerstrasse 9-13
Hamburg, Germany 20095
Phone: 49-40-3060500
Website: www.scpartners.de

Type of Firm
Bank Affiliated

Project Preferences

Type of Financing Preferred:
Fund of Funds

Geographical Preferences

International Preferences:
Europe

Additional Information
Year Founded: 2005
Current Activity Level : Actively seeking new investments

SWISS LIFE PRIVATE EQUITY PARTNERS LTD
General Guisan-Quai 40
Zurich, Switzerland CH - 8022
Phone: 41-43-284-3311
Fax: 41-1-284-63-11
E-mail: info@slpep.com
Website: www.swisslife.ch

Management and Staff
Alexander Pfeifer, Partner
Andrea Gambazzi, Partner
David Salim, Partner

Type of Firm
Bank Affiliated

Association Membership
European Private Equity and Venture Capital Assoc.

Project Preferences

Type of Financing Preferred:
Fund of Funds
Leveraged Buyout
Early Stage
Expansion

Geographical Preferences

United States Preferences:
All U.S.

International Preferences:
Europe

Industry Preferences

In Communications prefer:
Communications and Media
Telecommunications

In Internet Specific prefer:
Internet

In Biotechnology prefer:
Biotechnology

In Medical/Health prefer:
Medical/Health

In Financial Services prefer:
Financial Services
Real Estate

Additional Information
Year Founded: 1999
Current Activity Level : Reducing investment activity

SWISS RE PRIVATE EQUITY ADVISERS
Genferstrasse 27
Zurich, Switzerland 8022
Phone: 41-43-285-6943
Fax: 41-43-282-6943
Website: www.swissre.com

Other Offices
55 East 52nd Street
New York, NY USA 10055
Phone: 1-917-368-4002
Fax: 1-917-368-4386

Management and Staff
Donat Auf der Maur, Vice President
Harold Weiss, Managing Director
Peter Von Lehe, Managing Director
Robert Nef, Managing Director
Vincenzo Narciso, Vice President

Type of Firm
Insurance Firm Affiliate

Project Preferences

Type of Financing Preferred:
Fund of Funds

Geographical Preferences

International Preferences:
Europe
All International

Additional Information
Year Founded: 1998
Capital Under Management: $2,000,000,000
Current Activity Level : Actively seeking new investments

SWISSCOM AG

Alte Tiefenaustrasse 6
Worblaufen, Switzerland 3048
Phone: 41-31-342-1696
Fax: 41-31-342-1270
Website: www.swisscom.com

Type of Firm

Corporate PE/Venture

Association Membership

European Private Equity and Venture Capital Assoc.

Project Preferences

Type of Financing Preferred:
Early Stage
Expansion
Startup

Geographical Preferences

nternational Preferences:
Europe

Industry Preferences

In Communications prefer:
Communications and Media
Telecommunications

In Internet Specific prefer:
Internet

Additional Information

Year Founded: 2004
Capital Under Management: $41,000,000
Current Activity Level : Actively seeking new investments

SWMF LIFE SCIENCE VENTURE FUND, L.P.

241 East Michigan Avenue
Kalamazoo, MI USA 49007
Phone: 269-553-9588
Fax: 269-553-6897
Website: www.southwestmichiganfirst.com

Management and Staff

Patrick Morand, Managing Director

Type of Firm

Government Affiliated Program

Project Preferences

ype of Financing Preferred:
Early Stage
Expansion
Seed

Geographical Preferences

United States Preferences:
Michigan

Additional Information

Name of Most Recent Fund: SWMF Life Science Venture Fund, L.P.
Most Recent Fund Was Raised: 06/09/2006
Year Founded: 2006
Capital Under Management: $50,000,000
Current Activity Level : Actively seeking new investments

SYCAMORE VENTURES PTE, LTD.

1 North Bridge Road
Suite 13-03 High Street Centre
Singapore, Singapore 179094
Phone: 65-6535-0112
Fax: 65-6532-5870
Website: www.sycamorevc.com

Other Offices

1st floor, 284 Anfu Road
Shanghai, China 200031
Phone: 86-21-5405-1313
Fax: 86-21-5404-5528

19925 Stevens Creek Boulevard
Cupertino, CA USA 95014
Phone: 408-973-7861
Fax: 408-973-7261

845 Alexander Road
Princeton, NJ USA 08540
Phone: 609-759-8888
Fax: 609-759-8900

1775 Broadway
New York, NY USA 10019
Phone: 212-247-4590
Fax: 212-247-4801

13Floor-1, 189, Keelung Road
Section 2
Taipei, Taiwan
Phone: 886-2-2528-3051
Fax: 886-2-2528-3985

Management and Staff

David Lichtenstein, Chief Financial Officer
Jerry Sze, Managing Partner
John Whitman, Managing Partner
Jonas Wang, Partner
Kilin To, Managing Partner
Peter Gerry, Managing Partner
Ravi Singh, Partner
Richard Chong, Partner
Seth Pierrepont, Managing Partner
Stephen Sun Chiao, Partner

Type of Firm

Private Equity Firm

Association Membership

Natl Assoc of Small Bus. Inv. Co (NASBIC)
Singapore Venture Capital Association (SVCA)

Project Preferences

Role in Financing:
Prefer role as deal originator but will also invest in deals created by others

Type of Financing Preferred:
Expansion
Balanced
Later Stage

Size of Investments Considered:
Min Size of Investment Considered (000s): $5,000
Max Size of Investment Considered (000s): $25,000

Geographical Preferences

International Preferences:
India
Taiwan
China
Hong Kong
Singapore

Industry Focus

(% based on actual investment)	
Medical/Health	25.1%
Communications and Media	20.4%
Internet Specific	20.2%
Semiconductors/Other Elect.	11.6%
Computer Software and Services	8.5%
Biotechnology	7.8%
Other Products	3.6%
Consumer Related	1.7%
Computer Hardware	1.1%

Additional Information

Name of Most Recent Fund: AsiaStar IT Fund
Most Recent Fund Was Raised: 05/31/2000
Year Founded: 1995
Capital Under Management: $550,000,000
Current Activity Level : Actively seeking new investments
Method of Compensation: Return on investment is of primary concern, do not charge fees

SYDDANSK INNOVATION A/S

Forskerparken 10
Odense M, Denmark 5230
Phone: 45-63-15-7100
Fax: 45-63-15-7300
Website: www.innofyn.dk

Type of Firm

Private Equity Firm

Project Preferences

Type of Financing Preferred:
Seed

Geographical Preferences

International Preferences:
Denmark

Additional Information

Year Founded: 1992
Capital Under Management: $4,000,000
Current Activity Level : Actively seeking new investments

SYDES

Gossetlaan 32
Grand-Bigard, Belgium 1702
Phone: 32-24-67-4912
Fax: 32-24-63-3706
E-mail: info@sydes.be
Website: www.sydes.be

Management and Staff

Jean-Christophe Massart, Chief Operating Officer
Marc Appel, Managing Director

Type of Firm

Private Equity Firm

Association Membership

Belgium Venturing Association

Project Preferences

Type of Financing Preferred:

Leveraged Buyout
Expansion

Geographical Preferences

International Preferences:

Europe
Belgium

Industry Preferences

In Communications prefer:

Communications and Media
Telecommunications
Media and Entertainment

Additional Information

Year Founded: 2005
Capital Under Management: $27,000,000
Current Activity Level : Actively seeking new investments

SYDVESTOR CORPORATE

P.O. Box 402
Ulsteinvik, Norway 6067
Phone: 47-70-01-9911
Website: www.kredittbanken.no

Type of Firm

Private Equity Firm

Association Membership

Norwegian Venture Capital Association

Additional Information

Current Activity Level : Actively seeking new investments

SYMBION CAPITAL A/S

Symbion Science Park
Fruebjergvej 3
Copenhagen, Denmark 2100
Phone: 45-3917-9999
Fax: 45-3917-9900
E-mail: info@symbion.dk
Website: www.symbion.dk

Management and Staff

Jakob Fuglede Nielsen, Chief Financial Officer

Type of Firm

Incubator/Development Program

Association Membership

Danish Venture Capital Association (DVCA)
European Private Equity and Venture Capital Assoc.

Project Preferences

Type of Financing Preferred:

Seed

Size of Investments Considered:

Min Size of Investment Considered (000s): $120
Max Size of Investment Considered (000s): $2,400

Geographical Preferences

International Preferences:

Denmark

Industry Preferences

In Communications prefer:

Telecommunications

In Computer Software prefer:

Software

In Internet Specific prefer:

Internet

In Biotechnology prefer:

Biotechnology

In Medical/Health prefer:

Medical/Health

In Financial Services prefer:

Financial Services

Additional Information

Year Founded: 2001
Capital Under Management: $36,700,000
Current Activity Level : Actively seeking new investments

SYMMETRIC CAPITAL LLC

950 Winter Street
Suite 2500
Waltham, MA USA 02451
Phone: 781-419-1100
Fax: 781-419-1101
E-mail: info@symmetriccapital.com
Website: www.symmetriccapital.com

Management and Staff

Daniel Doyle, Principal
Robert Walsh, Principal

Type of Firm

Private Equity Firm

Project Preferences

Type of Financing Preferred:

Balanced

Size of Investments Considered:

Min Size of Investment Considered (000s): $5,000
Max Size of Investment Considered (000s): $20,000

Geographical Preferences

United States Preferences:

All U.S.

Canadian Preferences:

All Canada

Industry Preferences

In Computer Software prefer:

Software

In Medical/Health prefer:

Health Services

In Consumer Related prefer:

Consumer Products

In Industrial/Energy prefer:

Industrial Products

In Financial Services prefer:

Financial Services

In Business Serv. prefer:

Services

Additional Information

Year Founded: 2007
Capital Under Management: $255,900,000
Current Activity Level : Actively seeking new investments

SYMMETRY CAPITAL MANAGEMENT LLC

One Montgomery Street
33rd Floor
San Francisco, CA USA 94104
Phone: 415-374-8122
Fax: 415-374-8124

Type of Firm

Private Equity Firm

Industry Preferences

In Medical/Health prefer:

Medical/Health

Additional Information

Year Founded: 2001
Capital Under Management: $8,100,000

Current Activity Level : Actively seeking new investments

SYMMETRY INVESTMENT ADVISORS, INC.

150 North Wacker Drive
Suite 2250
Chicago, IL USA 60606
Phone: 312-634-0900
Fax: 312-634-0920
Website: www.symmetryinvestmentadvisors.com

Other Offices

3460 Garland Street
Wheat Ridge, CO USA 80033
Fax: 303-756-0274

Management and Staff

Larry Wonnacott, Principal
Marshall Greenwald, Principal

Type of Firm

Private Equity Advisor or Fund of Funds

Project Preferences

Type of Financing Preferred:

Fund of Funds of Second

Geographical Preferences

United States Preferences:

Midwest
All U.S.

Industry Preferences

In Financial Services prefer:

Financial Services

Additional Information

Year Founded: 2003
Capital Under Management: $70,200,000
Current Activity Level : Actively seeking new investments

SYMPASIS INNOVATION CAPITAL GMBH

65a Zahringerstrasse
Karlsruhe, Germany D- 76133
Phone: 49-721-354-8040
E-mail: info@sympasis.com
Website: www.sympasis.com

Other Offices

Aussenstrasse 100
Munich, Germany D- 80469
Phone: 49-89-727-192-55
Fax: 49-89-727-192-43

Type of Firm

Private Equity Firm

Additional Information

Year Founded: 2009
Current Activity Level : Actively seeking new investments

SYMPHONY CAPITAL LLC

875 Third Avenue
Third Floor
New York, NY USA 10022
Phone: 212-632-5400
Fax: 212-632-5401
E-mail: info@symphonycapital.com
Website: www.symphonycapital.com

Management and Staff

Alastair Wood, Managing Director
Andrew Busser, Principal
Harri Taranto, Managing Director
Jeffrey Edelman, Principal
Mark Kessel, Managing Director
Neil Sandler, Managing Director
Zachary Sharon, Vice President

Type of Firm

Private Equity Firm

Project Preferences

Type of Financing Preferred:

Leveraged Buyout
Acquisition

Industry Preferences

In Biotechnology prefer:

Biotechnology

In Medical/Health prefer:

Pharmaceuticals

Additional Information

Name of Most Recent Fund: Symphony Strategic Partners, L.P.
Most Recent Fund Was Raised: 06/23/2004
Year Founded: 2002
Capital Under Management: $315,000,000
Current Activity Level : Actively seeking new investments

SYMPHONY CAPITAL PARTNERS ASIA, LTD.

9 Raffles Place #52-02
Republic Plaza Tower 1
Singapore, Singapore 048619
Phone: 65-6536-6177
Fax: 65-6536-6077
E-mail: info@symphonyasia.com
Website: www.scpal.com

Other Offices

Suite 1408, Two Exchange Sqaure
8 Connaught Place
Central, Hong Kong
Phone: 852-2801-6199
Fax: 852-2801-7979

C/O The Manor
77, Friends Colony
New Delhi, India 110 065
Phone: 91-11-4162-6883
Fax: 91-11-4162-7770

Management and Staff

David LaRue, Partner
Gautam Gulati, Principal
Raj Rajkumar, Partner
Ramon Lo, Partner
Ronald Ling, Principal
Sunil Chandiramani, Partner

Type of Firm

Service Provider

Association Membership

Hong Kong Venture Capital Association (HKVCA)
Singapore Venture Capital Association (SVCA)

Project Preferences

Role in Financing:

Prefer role as deal originator

Type of Financing Preferred:

Leveraged Buyout
Generalist PE
Expansion
Later Stage
Management Buyouts
Recapitalizations

Size of Investments Considered:

Min Size of Investment Considered (000s): $10,000
Max Size of Investment Considered (000s): $50,000

Geographical Preferences

International Preferences:

Vietnam
Indonesia
India
Taiwan
China
Hong Kong
Thailand
Philippines
Australia
Sri Lanka
New Zealand
Singapore
Korea, South
Asia
Malaysia

Industry Preferences

In Medical/Health prefer:

Medical/Health

In Consumer Related prefer:

Food/Beverage
Consumer Products

Consumer Services
Other Restaurants
Hotels and Resorts
Education Related

In Financial Services prefer:
Real Estate

In Manufact. prefer:
Manufacturing

Additional Information

Name of Most Recent Fund: Schroder Ventures Asia Pacific Fund
Most Recent Fund Was Raised: 08/01/1999
Year Founded: 1981
Capital Under Management: $870,000,000
Current Activity Level : Actively seeking new investments

SYNAPSIS ASSOCIATES

Chaussee de Louvain, 505
La Hulpe, Belgium 1380
Phone: 32-2-655-0000
Fax: 32-2-655-0001
E-mail: info@synapsis.be
Website: www.synapsis.be

Management and Staff

Bryan Whitnack, Partner
David Franeau, Partner
Jean-Francois Sidler, Partner

Type of Firm

Private Equity Firm

Project Preferences

Type of Financing Preferred:
Balanced

Geographical Preferences

International Preferences:
Western Europe

Industry Preferences

In Consumer Related prefer:
Food/Beverage

Additional Information

Year Founded: 2003
Current Activity Level : Actively seeking new investments

SYNCOM MANAGEMENT CO. INC.

8401 Colesville Road
Suite 300
Silver Spring, MD USA 20601
Phone: 301-608-3203
Fax: 301-608-3307
E-mail: contactus@syncomfunds.com
Website: www.syncomfunds.com

Management and Staff

Amiel Bent, Principal
Duane McKnight, General Partner
H. Michael Tesfamichael, Chief Financial Officer
Herb Wilkins, Managing Partner
Milford Thomas, General Partner
Robert Greene, Principal
Stanley Smith, Principal
Terry Jones, Managing General Partner

Type of Firm

Private Equity Firm

Project Preferences

Type of Financing Preferred:
Balanced

Geographical Preferences

United States Preferences:
All U.S.

Industry Preferences

In Communications prefer:
Communications and Media
Telecommunications

In Business Serv. prefer:
Media

Additional Information

Name of Most Recent Fund: Syndicated Communications Venture Partners V, L.P.
Most Recent Fund Was Raised: 10/18/2007
Year Founded: 1977
Capital Under Management: $275,400,000
Current Activity Level : Actively seeking new investments

SYNERGIA CAPITAL PARTNERS B.V.

Plesmanstraat 62
P.O. Box 514
Veenendaal, Netherlands 3905 KZ
Phone: 31-318-553-675
Fax: 31-318-554-084
E-mail: office@synergia.nl
Website: www.synergia.nl

Type of Firm

Private Equity Firm

Association Membership

European Private Equity and Venture Capital Assoc.

Project Preferences

Type of Financing Preferred:
Balanced

Geographical Preferences

International Preferences:
Netherlands
Europe

Industry Preferences

In Computer Software prefer:
Software

In Consumer Related prefer:
Consumer

In Industrial/Energy prefer:
Industrial Products

In Manufact. prefer:
Manufacturing

Additional Information

Year Founded: 1999
Capital Under Management: $65,700,000
Current Activity Level : Actively seeking new investments

SYNERGIE FINANCE SOBREPAR

1, rue Louis Lichou
Le Relecq-Kerhuon, France 29480
Phone: 33-2-9800-2224
Fax: 33-2-9800-3718
E-mail: contacts@synergie-finance.com

Management and Staff

Jacques Brisse, President

Type of Firm

Private Equity Firm

Association Membership

French Venture Capital Association (AFIC)

Project Preferences

Type of Financing Preferred:
Expansion

Size of Investments Considered:
Min Size of Investment Considered (000s): $312
Max Size of Investment Considered (000s): $7,799

Geographical Preferences

International Preferences:
France

Additional Information

Year Founded: 1992
Capital Under Management: $205,600,000
Current Activity Level : Actively seeking new investments

SYNERGIS TECHNOLOGIES, LTD.

23 Buckingham Gate
London, United Kingdom SW1E 6LB
Phone: 44-20-7932-0727
Fax: 44-20-7828-2713
E-mail: enquiries@synergistechnologies.com
Website: www.synergistechnologies.com

Management and Staff

Shimi Shah, Chief Executive Officer

Type of Firm

Private Equity Firm

Project Preferences

Type of Financing Preferred:
Early Stage
Seed

Geographical Preferences

International Preferences:
United Kingdom

Additional Information

Year Founded: 2007
Current Activity Level : Actively seeking new investments

SYNERGO SGR S.P.A.

Via Campo Lodigiano, 3
Milan, Italy 20122
Phone: 39-02-859-111
Fax: 39-02-7209-4122
E-mail: welcome@synergosgr.it
Website: www.synergosgr.it

Management and Staff

Flavio Abbondati, Partner
Matteo Cirla, Partner
Paolo Moro, Partner
Rossano Rufini, Partner

Type of Firm

Private Equity Firm

Association Membership

Italian Venture Capital Association (AIFI)

Project Preferences

Type of Financing Preferred:
Leveraged Buyout
Expansion

Size of Investments Considered:
Min Size of Investment Considered (000s): $20,297
Max Size of Investment Considered (000s): $67,655

Geographical Preferences

International Preferences:
Italy

Additional Information

Year Founded: 2004
Capital Under Management: $426,200,000
Current Activity Level : Actively seeking new investments

SYNERGY LIFE SCIENCE PARTNERS

3284 Alpine Road
Portola Valley, CA USA 94028
Phone: 650-854-7155
Website: www.synergylsp.com

Management and Staff

John Onopchenko, Managing Director
Mudit Jain, Principal
Richard Stack, Managing Director
Tracy Pappas, Chief Financial Officer
William Starling, Managing Director

Type of Firm

Private Equity Firm

Association Membership

National Venture Capital Association - USA (NVCA)

Project Preferences

Role in Financing:
Prefer role as deal originator but will also invest in deals created by others

Type of Financing Preferred:
Early Stage

Size of Investments Considered:
Min Size of Investment Considered (000s): $1,000
Max Size of Investment Considered (000s): $15,000

Geographical Preferences

United States Preferences:
All U.S.

Industry Preferences

In Medical/Health prefer:
Medical Therapeutics
Medical Products

Additional Information

Name of Most Recent Fund: Synergy Life Science Partners, L.P.
Most Recent Fund Was Raised: 12/08/2006
Year Founded: 2006
Capital Under Management: $143,000,000
Current Activity Level : Actively seeking new investments

SYNERGY PARTNERS

535 Middlefield Road
Suite 170
Menlo Park, CA USA 94025
Phone: 650-322-3475
Fax: 650-326-3735
Website: www.synergyventures.net

Management and Staff

Allan Johnston, General Partner
Robert Okun, General Partner

Type of Firm

Private Equity Firm

Project Preferences

Role in Financing:
Will function either as deal originator or investor in deals created by others

Type of Financing Preferred:
Early Stage
Seed
Startup

Size of Investments Considered:
Min Size of Investment Considered (000s): $50
Max Size of Investment Considered (000s): $2,000

Geographical Preferences

United States Preferences:
All U.S.

Industry Focus

(% based on actual investment)

Medical/Health	87.5%
Biotechnology	10.3%
Internet Specific	1.8%
Other Products	0.3%

Additional Information

Name of Most Recent Fund: Synergy Ventures II, L.P.
Most Recent Fund Was Raised: 03/10/2006
Year Founded: 1985
Capital Under Management: $15,000,000
Current Activity Level : Actively seeking new investments
Method of Compensation: Return on investment is of primary concern, do not charge fees

SYNETRO CAPITAL, LLC (FKA: EBLAST VENTURES, LLC)

Eleven South LaSalle
Fifth Floor
Chicago, IL USA 60603
Phone: 312-372-0840
Fax: 312-803-2035
E-mail: info@synetrocapital.com
Website: www.synetrocapital.com

Management and Staff

Pantelis (Pete) Georgiadis, Managing Partner

Type of Firm

Private Equity Firm

Project Preferences

Role in Financing:

Prefer role as deal originator but will also invest in deals created by others

Type of Financing Preferred:

Leveraged Buyout
Early Stage
Start-up Financing
Turnaround
Seed
Management Buyouts
Acquisition
Startup
Recapitalizations

Size of Investments Considered:

Min Size of Investment Considered (000s): $100
Max Size of Investment Considered (000s): $4,000

Geographical Preferences

United States Preferences:

Midwest

Industry Preferences

In Computer Software prefer:

Software

In Internet Specific prefer:

Internet
Ecommerce

In Medical/Health prefer:

Medical Products
Health Services

In Consumer Related prefer:

Consumer Products

In Industrial/Energy prefer:

Industrial Products

In Business Serv. prefer:

Services
Distribution
Consulting Services

In Manufact. prefer:

Manufacturing

Additional Information

Year Founded: 2000
Current Activity Level : Actively seeking new investments
Method of Compensation: Return on investment is of primary concern, do not charge fees

---

SYNOVA CAPITAL LLP

41 Dover Street
London, United Kingdom W1S 4NS
Phone: 44-20-7491-5705
Fax: 44-20-7491-5706
E-mail: info@synova-capital.com
Website: www.synova-capital.com

Management and Staff

David Menton, Managing Partner
Philip Shapiro, Managing Partner
Shirley Palmer, Chief Financial Officer

Type of Firm

Private Equity Firm

Project Preferences

Type of Financing Preferred:

Leveraged Buyout
Balanced

Size of Investments Considered:

Min Size of Investment Considered (000s): $19,933
Max Size of Investment Considered (000s): $99,665

Geographical Preferences

International Preferences:

United Kingdom

Industry Preferences

In Medical/Health prefer:

Medical/Health
Health Services

In Consumer Related prefer:

Entertainment and Leisure

In Financial Services prefer:

Financial Services

In Business Serv. prefer:

Services

Additional Information

Year Founded: 2007
Capital Under Management: $143,200,000
Current Activity Level : Actively seeking new investments

SYNTAXIS CAPITAL

Blumenstockgasse 5/7
Vienna, Austria A-1010
Phone: 43-1-513-4469
Fax: 43-1-513-4581
E-mail: office@syntaxis-capital.com
Website: www.syntaxis-capital.com

Other Offices

Warsaw Financial Center
Emilii Plater 53, 11th Floor
Warsaw, Poland 00-113
Phone: 48-22-528-6899
Fax: 48-22-528-4581

Management and Staff

Ben Edwards, Managing Partner
Przemek Szczepanski, Partner
Thomas Spring, Partner

Type of Firm

Private Equity Firm

Project Preferences

Type of Financing Preferred:

Mezzanine

Geographical Preferences

International Preferences:

Hungary
Slovenia
Slovak Repub.
Central Europe
Czech Republic
Albania
Turkey
Poland
Macedonia
Croatia
Eastern Europe
Bulgaria
Estonia
Ukraine
Romania
Bosnia
Latvia
Lithuania
Russia

Additional Information

Year Founded: 2006
Capital Under Management: $239,300,000
Current Activity Level : Actively seeking new investments

SYNTEK CAPITAL AG

Zugspitzstrasse 15
Pullach, Germany 82049
Phone: 49-89-55277400
Fax: 49-89-55277405
E-mail: info.munich@syntekcapital.com
Website: www.syntekcapital.com

Other Offices

423 West 55th Street
6th Floor
New York, NY USA 10019
Phone: 1-646-557-6553
Fax: 1-212-247-3223

85 Medinat Hayahudim
POB 4021
Herzlia, Israel 46140
Phone: 972-9-970-1828
Fax: 972-9-957-8206

11 Grosvenor Crescent
London, United Kingdom SW1X 7EE

Phone: 44-207-2010790
Fax: 44-207-2359181

Calle Orense
4-Planta 12
Madrid, Spain 28020
Phone: 34-91-5143633

41-30 Av. Alvares Cabral
Lisboa, Portugal 1250-015
Phone: 351-21-383-5550

Via Durini 28
Milano, Italy 20122
Phone: 39-02-7627-0303
Fax: 39-02-7627-0334

Management and Staff

Bruce Rigal, Chief Financial Officer
Christoph Shoeller, Chief Executive Officer
Georg Reisch, Chief Operating Officer
Sam Humphreys, Chief Executive Officer

Type of Firm

Private Equity Firm

Project Preferences

Type of Financing Preferred:
Early Stage

Geographical Preferences

nternational Preferences:
Europe
Israel

Industry Preferences

In Communications prefer:
Wireless Communications

Additional Information

Year Founded: 2000
Current Activity Level : Actively seeking new investments

- T -

21 CENTRALE PARTNERS

9 Avenue Hoche
Paris, France 75008
Phone: 33-1-5688-3300
Fax: 33-1-5688-3320
E-mail: info@21centralepartners.com
Website: www.21centralepartners.com

Other Offices

Via G. Felissent,90
Treviso, Italy 31100
Phone: 39-4223-166-11
Fax: 39-4223-166-00

Management and Staff

Antoine Pupin, Managing Partner
Dino Furlan, Managing Partner
Eustache Besancon, Principal
Francois Barbier, Managing Partner
Francois Tranie, Principal
Henry Huyghues-Despointes, Managing Partner
Jacques Rossignol, Partner
Marco Monis, Managing Partner
Regis Lamarche, Principal
Sebastien Peru, Chief Financial Officer
Stefano Tanzi, Managing Partner
Stephane Perriquet, Partner

Type of Firm

Bank Affiliated

Association Membership

French Venture Capital Association (AFIC)

Project Preferences

Type of Financing Preferred:
Leveraged Buyout
Research and Development
Early Stage
Expansion
Balanced
Management Buyouts

Geographical Preferences

International Preferences:
Europe
France

Additional Information

Name of Most Recent Fund: 21 Centrale Partners III
Most Recent Fund Was Raised: 07/06/2006
Year Founded: 1998
Capital Under Management: $668,200,000
Current Activity Level : Actively seeking new investments

21 INVESTIMENTI SPA

90 Viale G. Felissent
Villa Pavan
Treviso, Italy 31100
Phone: 39-422-31-6611
Fax: 39-422-31-6600
E-mail: info@21investimenti.it
Website: www.21investimenti.it

Other Offices

22 Grenville Street
St Helier
Jersey - Channel Islands, United Kingdom JE4 8PX
Phone: 44-1534-609-000

8 Via Monte Napoleone
Milan, Italy 20121
Phone: 39-2-7712-1311
Fax: 39-2-7712-1333

Management and Staff

Alessandro Benetton, Managing Director
Dino Furlan, Managing Director
Giovani Bonandini, Managing Partner
Marco Monis, Managing Partner
Stefano Tanzi, Managing Partner

Type of Firm

Investment Management Firm

Association Membership

Italian Venture Capital Association (AIFI)
European Private Equity and Venture Capital Assoc.
Spanish Venture Capital Association (ASCRI)

Project Preferences

Role in Financing:
Prefer role as deal originator

Type of Financing Preferred:
Leveraged Buyout
Expansion
Recapitalizations

Size of Investments Considered:
Min Size of Investment Considered (000s): $14,601
Max Size of Investment Considered (000s): $43,802

Geographical Preferences

International Preferences:
Italy

Additional Information

Year Founded: 1999
Capital Under Management: $584,000,000
Current Activity Level : Actively seeking new investments

21ST CENTURY GROUP, LLC

200 Crescent Court
Suite 1600
Dallas, TX USA 75201

Phone: 214-965-7999
Fax: 214-965-7993
E-mail: info@21stcenturygroupfund.com
Website: www.21stcenturygroupfund.com

Management and Staff

Francisco De Jesus, Partner
John Ware, Chief Executive Officer
W. Kelvin Walker, Partner

Type of Firm

Private Equity Firm

Project Preferences

Role in Financing:
Prefer role as deal originator

Type of Financing Preferred:
Later Stage
Acquisition

Size of Investments Considered:
Min Size of Investment Considered (000s): $10,000
Max Size of Investment Considered (000s): $25,000

Geographical Preferences

United States Preferences:
All U.S.

Industry Preferences

In Communications prefer:
Radio & TV Broadcasting

In Business Serv. prefer:
Services
Distribution
Media

In Manufact. prefer:
Manufacturing

Additional Information

Name of Most Recent Fund: 21st Century Group Fund II, L.P.
Most Recent Fund Was Raised: 02/05/2008
Year Founded: 1998
Capital Under Management: $80,000,000
Current Activity Level : Actively seeking new investments
Method of Compensation: Return on invest. most important, but chg. closing fees, service fees, etc.

21ST CENTURY VC INVESTMENT CO., LTD.

11/A Shennan Road, C
Shenzhen, China 518031
Phone: 86-755-83295527
Fax: 86-755-83295534

Type of Firm

Private Equity Firm

Project Preferences

Type of Financing Preferred:
Balanced

Geographical Preferences

International Preferences:
China

Industry Preferences

In Medical/Health prefer:
Medical/Health

In Industrial/Energy prefer:
Energy Conservation Relat
Materials
Environmental Related

Additional Information

Year Founded: 2000
Current Activity Level : Actively seeking new investments

21VENTURES LLC

The Chrysler Building
405 Lexington Avenue, 26/F
New York, NY USA 10174
Phone: 212-699-0842
E-mail: info@21Ventures.net
Website: www.21ventures.net

Management and Staff

David Anthony, Managing Partner
Dileep Agnihotri, Principal
Jessica Bloomgarden, Principal
Lyle Deitch, Principal
Sheldon Freedman, Principal

Type of Firm

Private Equity Firm

Project Preferences

Type of Financing Preferred:
Early Stage
Seed

Size of Investments Considered:
Min Size of Investment Considered (000s): $100
Max Size of Investment Considered (000s): $20,000

Industry Preferences

In Communications prefer:
Wireless Communications

In Computer Software prefer:
Applications Software
Artificial Intelligence

In Industrial/Energy prefer:
Energy Conservation Relat
Environmental Related

Additional Information

Year Founded: 2004
Capital Under Management: $250,000,000
Current Activity Level : Actively seeking new investments

---

280 CAPITAL PARTNERS

1560 Sunnyvale Saratoga Road
Suite 200
Sunnyvale, CA USA 94087
Phone: 408-718-9027
E-mail: info@280capitalpartners.com
Website: www.280capitalpartners.com

Type of Firm

Private Equity Firm

Project Preferences

Type of Financing Preferred:
Balanced

Additional Information

Year Founded: 2008
Current Activity Level : Actively seeking new investments

2I CAPITAL ASSET MANAGEMENT COMPANY, LTD.

IFS Court
28 Cybercity
Ebene, Mauritius
Phone: 230-467-3000
Fax: 230-467-4000
E-mail: info@2icapital.com
Website: www.2icapital.com

Other Offices

E-14/19,
1st Floor,Vasant Vihar
New Delhi, India 110057
Phone: 91-11-6565-7267

613 Oxford Towers
139 Airport Road,
Bangalore, India 560 008
Phone: 91-80-4115-1990
Fax: 91-80-4115-1994

Management and Staff

Shailesh Singh, Vice President
Sudhir Kamath, Managing Director

Type of Firm

Private Equity Firm

Association Membership

Indian Venture Capital Association (IVCA)

Project Preferences

Type of Financing Preferred:
Early Stage
Expansion

Mezzanine
Balanced

Size of Investments Considered:

Min Size of Investment Considered (000s): $1,000
Max Size of Investment Considered (000s): $20,000

Geographical Preferences

International Preferences:

India
Europe
Asia

Industry Preferences

In Communications prefer:

Communications and Media
Telecommunications

In Computer Software prefer:

Software

In Computer Other prefer:

Computer Related

In Semiconductor/Electr prefer:

Electronics

In Biotechnology prefer:

Biotechnology

In Medical/Health prefer:

Medical/Health
Health Services
Pharmaceuticals

In Consumer Related prefer:

Retail

In Business Serv. prefer:

Distribution

In Agr/Forestr/Fish prefer:

Agribusiness

Additional Information

Year Founded: 2000
Capital Under Management: $60,000,000
Current Activity Level : Actively seeking new investments

2X CONSUMER PRODUCTS GROWTH PARTNERS LP

205 West Randolph Street
Suite 1830
Chicago, IL USA 60606
Phone: 312-357-1800
Fax: 312-873-4509
E-mail: info@2xpartners.com
Website: www.2xpartners.com

Management and Staff

Andrew Whitman, Managing Partner
David Bauserman, Partner
Gary Sebek, Managing Partner

Type of Firm

Private Equity Firm

Project Preferences

Type of Financing Preferred:

Balanced

Geographical Preferences

United States Preferences:

All U.S.

Industry Preferences

In Consumer Related prefer:

Food/Beverage
Consumer Products
Consumer Services

Additional Information

Name of Most Recent Fund: 2x Consumer Products Growth Partners LP
Most Recent Fund Was Raised: 10/04/2007
Year Founded: 2007
Capital Under Management: $1,300,000
Current Activity Level : Actively seeking new investments

3 DEGREES ASSET MANAGEMENT PTE., LTD.

600 North Bridge Road 08-08
Parkview Square
Singapore, Singapore 188778
Phone: 65-6750-2260
Fax: 65-6534-5157
E-mail: ir@3degrees.com.sg
Website: www.theasiandebtfund.com

Management and Staff

Akanksha Sagar, Principal
Jeffrey Tolk, Principal

Type of Firm

Private Equity Firm

Project Preferences

Type of Financing Preferred:

Turnaround
Special Situation
Distressed Debt
Recapitalizations

Geographical Preferences

International Preferences:

India
Asia

Additional Information

Year Founded: 2002
Current Activity Level : Actively seeking new investments

32 DEGREES CAPITAL

633-Sixth Avenue South West
Suite 310
Calgary, Canada T2P2Y5
Phone: 403-695-1074
E-mail: info@32degrees.ca
Website: www.32degrees.ca

Management and Staff

D. David Ambedian, Partner
Gary Jones, Partner
Larry Evans, Partner
Mitch Putnam, Partner
Trent Baker, Partner

Type of Firm

Private Equity Firm

Additional Information

Year Founded: 2004
Current Activity Level : Actively seeking new investments

360 CAPITAL MANAGEMENT SA (AKA: 360 CAPITAL PARTNERS)

13-15 Avenue de la Liberte
Luxembourg, Luxembourg L-1931
Phone: 352-621-294-505
E-mail: info@360capitalpartners.com
Website: www.360capitalpartners.com

Other Offices

Via Brisa 3
Milan, Italy 20123
Phone: 39-02-3656-0950

68 Boulevard De Sebastopol
Paris, France 75003
Phone: 33-1-7118-2912

Management and Staff

Diana Saraceni, General Partner
Emanuele Levi, General Partner
Fausto Boni, General Partner
Francois Tison, General Partner
Paolo Gesess, General Partner

Type of Firm

Private Equity Firm

Association Membership

French Venture Capital Association (AFIC)
European Private Equity and Venture Capital Assoc.

Project Preferences

Type of Financing Preferred:

Early Stage
Expansion
Seed
Strategic Alliances

Startup

Size of Investments Considered:
Min Size of Investment Considered (000s): $1,200
Max Size of Investment Considered (000s): $5,998

Geographical Preferences

International Preferences:
Italy
Europe
France

Industry Preferences

In Communications prefer:
Wireless Communications

In Medical/Health prefer:
Medical/Health
Medical Diagnostics
Diagnostic Services

In Consumer Related prefer:
Retail

In Industrial/Energy prefer:
Energy

In Financial Services prefer:
Financial Services

In Other prefer:
Environment Responsible

Additional Information
Year Founded: 1997
Capital Under Management: $211,800,000
Current Activity Level : Actively seeking new investments

3I (US)
880 Winter Street
Suite 330
Waltham, MA USA 02451
Phone: 781-890-8300
Fax: 781-890-8301
E-mail: eastcoast@3i.com
Website: www.3i.com

Other Offices
275 Middlefield Road
Menlo Park, CA USA 94025
Phone: 650-470-3200
Fax: 650-470-3201

Management and Staff
David Silverman, Partner
James McLean, Partner
John Moore, Partner
Kevin Scott, Partner
Robin Murray, Partner

Type of Firm
Bank Affiliated

Association Membership
Western Association of Venture Capitalists (WAVC)
National Venture Capital Association - USA (NVCA)

Project Preferences

Role in Financing:
Will function either as deal originator or investor in deals created by others

Type of Financing Preferred:
Early Stage
Expansion
Later Stage
Seed
Startup
Recapitalizations

Size of Investments Considered:
Min Size of Investment Considered (000s): $1,000
Max Size of Investment Considered (000s): $75,000

Geographical Preferences

United States Preferences:
Southern California
Northern California
Northeast

Canadian Preferences:
All Canada

International Preferences:
Italy
India
United Kingdom
Latin America
Netherlands
Portugal
China
Hong Kong
Mexico
Middle East
Spain
Australia
Belgium
New Zealand
Germany
Japan
Africa

Industry Focus
(% based on actual investment)

Internet Specific	28.9%
Computer Software and Services	16.3%
Semiconductors/Other Elect.	13.2%
Medical/Health	10.7%
Communications and Media	10.0%
Other Products	9.7%
Industrial/Energy	4.5%
Consumer Related	2.6%
Biotechnology	2.1%
Computer Hardware	2.0%

Additional Information
Year Founded: 1982
Capital Under Management: $601,000,000
Current Activity Level : Actively seeking new investments
Method of Compensation: Return on investment is of primary concern, do not charge fees

---

3I GROUP PLC
16 Palace Street
London, United Kingdom SW1E 5JD
Phone: 44-20-7928-3131
Fax: 44-20-7928-0058
E-mail: enquiries@3igroup.com
Website: www.3i.com

Other Offices
The Observatory
Chapel Walks
Manchester, United Kingdom M2 1HL
Phone: 44-161-839-3131
Fax: 44-161-833-9182

Larsbjornsstraede 3
Copenhagen, Denmark 1454
Phone: 45-7027-1031
Fax: 45-7027-1030

Bockenheimer
Landstrasse 55
Frankfurt, Germany 60325
Phone: 49-69-710-0000
Fax: 49-69-7190-0039

3 rue Paul Cezanne
Paris, France 75008
Phone: 33-1-7315-1100

Avenida Diagonal
613 - 9a
Barcelona, Spain 08028
Phone: 34-934-391-991
Fax: 34-934-393-913

Birger Jarlsgatan 25
Stockholm, Sweden 103 99
Phone: 46-8-5061-0100
Fax: 46-8-5062-1100

Bickenhill
Birmingham, United Kingdom B37 7ES
Phone: 44-121-782-3131
Fax: 44-121-782-6161

375 Park Avenue
Suite 3001, Seagram Building
New York, NY USA 10152
Phone: 212-848-1400
Fax: 212-848-1401

2 Via Orefici
Milan, Italy 20123
Phone: 39-02-88-0841
Fax: 39-02-7200-3205

3/F, Nicholas Piraml Twr, Peninsula Prk
Ganpatrao Kadam Marg, Lower Parel (West)
Mumbai, India 400013
Phone: 91-22-6652-3131
Fax: 91-22-6652-3141

3 Temasek Avenue
#22-03 Centennial Tower Singapore
Singapore, Singapore 039190
Phone: 65-6438-3131
Fax: 65-6536-2429

Cornelis Schuytstraat 72
Amsterdam, Netherlands 1071 JL
Phone: 31-20-3057-444
Fax: 31-20-3057-455

ITC Maurya
Suite 1751
New Delhi, India 110021
Phone: 91-11-4166-8830
Fax: 91-11-4166-8831

70 Queens Road
Aberdeen, United Kingdom AB15 4YE
Phone: 44-1224-638-666
Fax: 44-1224-641-460

Calle Ruiz de Alarcon 12
Madrid, Spain 28014
Phone: 34-91-521-4419
Fax: 34-91-521-9819

Management and Staff

Alan Mackay, Managing Director
Alex Scherbakovsky, Vice President
Ali Erfan, Partner
Andrew Fraser, Partner
Bob Oreschnick, Chairman & Managing Director
Bob Stefanowski, Chairman & Managing Director
Brian Larcombe, Chief Executive Officer
Bruce Carnegie-Brown, Managing Partner
Bruno Deschamps, Managing Partner
Chris Rowlands, Managing Partner
Clement Cordier, Managing Director
Daizong Wang, Vice President
Girish Baliga, Partner
Gustav Bard, Managing Director
Guy Zarzavatdjian, Managing Director
Ian Nolan, Managing Partner
Jae Kim, Vice President
Jo Taylor, Managing Partner
Jonathan Russell, Managing Partner
Kevin Lyon, Managing Director
Mark Heappey, Partner
Markus Reich, Managing Partner
Michael Queen, Chief Executive Officer
Neil King, Partner
Nick Kingsbury, Partner
Ole Hauskov, Managing Director
Paul Grubic, Managing Director
Paul Waller, Managing Partner
Pietro Lifonti, Partner
Richard Relyea, Principal
Roberto Ranera, Partner
Rupert Lyle, Partner
Sergio Sambonet, Partner
Sundip Murthy, Principal
Wolfgang Kitza, Venture Partner

Type of Firm

Private Equity Firm

Association Membership

Italian Venture Capital Association (AIFI)
Finnish Venture Capital Association (FVCA)
Hong Kong Venture Capital Association (HKVCA)
China Venture Capital Association
British Venture Capital Association (BVCA)
French Venture Capital Association (AFIC)
Hungarian Venture Capital Association (HVCA)
German Venture Capital Association (BVK)
Singapore Venture Capital Association (SVCA)
European Private Equity and Venture Capital Assoc.
Spanish Venture Capital Association (ASCRI)

Project Preferences

Role in Financing:

Prefer role as deal originator but will also invest in deals created by others

Type of Financing Preferred:

Second Stage Financing
Leveraged Buyout
Early Stage
Expansion
Balanced
Other
Management Buyouts
First Stage Financing
Startup
Recapitalizations

Size of Investments Considered:

Min Size of Investment Considered (000s): $800
Max Size of Investment Considered (000s): $235,400

Geographical Preferences

International Preferences:

Italy
India
United Kingdom
Luxembourg
Netherlands
Europe
Spain
Belgium
Germany
France
Japan
All International

Industry Focus

(% based on actual investment)

Other Products	25.4%
Industrial/Energy	14.7%
Consumer Related	14.3%
Medical/Health	13.2%
Communications and Media	12.3%
Computer Software and Services	6.7%
Internet Specific	6.1%
Biotechnology	3.4%
Semiconductors/Other Elect.	3.0%
Computer Hardware	1.1%

Additional Information

Name of Most Recent Fund: 3i Eurofund V
Most Recent Fund Was Raised: 08/09/2006
Year Founded: 1945
Capital Under Management: $21,269,900,000
Current Activity Level : Actively seeking new investments
Method of Compensation: Return on invest. most important, but chg. closing fees, service fees, etc.

3I INFRASTRUCTURE PLC (FKA: 3I INFRASTRUCTURE, LTD.)

22 Grenville Street
St. Helier
Jersey, United Kingdom JE4 8PX
Website: www.3i-infrastructure.com

Type of Firm

Private Equity Firm

Project Preferences

Type of Financing Preferred:

Balanced

Geographical Preferences

United States Preferences:

All U.S.

International Preferences:

Europe
Asia

Additional Information

Year Founded: 2007
Current Activity Level : Actively seeking new investments

3M CORPORATION

3M General Offices
Building 220-13W-37
Saint Paul, MN USA 55144
Phone: 651-733-1110
Fax: 651-733-3110
E-mail: innovation.be@mmm.com
Website: www.3m.com

Management and Staff

Jan Yeomans, Vice President

Type of Firm

Corporate PE/Venture

Project Preferences

Type of Financing Preferred:

Balanced

Industry Preferences

In Communications prefer:

Communications and Media

In Computer Other prefer:

Computer Related

In Biotechnology prefer:
Biotechnology
Biotech Related Research

In Medical/Health prefer:
Medical/Health

In Consumer Related prefer:
Consumer

In Industrial/Energy prefer:
Industrial Products
Materials

Additional Information
Year Founded: 2001
Current Activity Level : Actively seeking new investments

3TS CAPITAL PARTNERS, LTD. (FKA: 3TS VENTURE PARTNERS AG)
Vaclavska 12
Prague, Czech Republic 120 00
Phone: 420-221-460-130
Fax: 420-221-460-137
E-mail: info@3tscapital.com
Website: www.3tscapital.com

Other Offices
ul. Ogrodowa 58
Warsaw, Poland 00-876
Phone: 48-22-520-2180
Fax: 48-22-520-2181

Brassai Samuel u. 16
Budapest, Hungary H-1126
Phone: 36-1-393-5060
Fax: 36-1-393-5069

TechGate Tower
Donau-City Strasse 1
Vienna, Austria A-1220
Phone: 43-660-313-3325
Fax: 43-1-718-7857-200

Management and Staff
Daniel Lynch, Managing Director
Hannu Piepponen, Chief Financial Officer
Pekka Santeri Makal, Managing Director
Pekka Santeri Maki, Managing Director

Type of Firm
Bank Affiliated
Association Membership
Hungarian Venture Capital Association (HVCA)
Czech Venture Capital Association (CVCA)
Polish Venture Capital Association (PSIC/PPEA)
European Private Equity and Venture Capital Assoc.

Project Preferences

Type of Financing Preferred:
Leveraged Buyout
Unknown
Expansion
Generalist PE

Size of Investments Considered:
Min Size of Investment Considered (000s): $437
Max Size of Investment Considered (000s): $5,682

Geographical Preferences

International Preferences:
Hungary
Slovak Repub.
Czech Republic
Central Europe
Turkey
Poland
Austria
Croatia
Eastern Europe
Bulgaria
Estonia
Ukraine
Romania
Latvia
Lithuania

Industry Preferences

In Communications prefer:
Communications and Media
Commercial Communications
Telecommunications
Media and Entertainment

In Computer Software prefer:
Software

In Internet Specific prefer:
Internet

In Computer Other prefer:
Computer Related

In Semiconductor/Electr prefer:
Electronics

In Business Serv. prefer:
Media

Additional Information
Name of Most Recent Fund: 3TS Central European Fund II
Most Recent Fund Was Raised: 05/17/2005
Year Founded: 2000
Capital Under Management: $224,300,000
Current Activity Level : Actively seeking new investments

3V SOURCEONE CAPITAL PTE, LTD. (AKA: 3VS1)
1 Coleman Street
#06-05 The Adelphi
Singapore, Singapore 179803
Phone: 65-6338-1880
Fax: 65-6338-0086
E-mail: asiainfo@3Vs1.com
Website: www.3vs1.com

Other Offices
13888 Trinity Avenue
Saratoga, CA USA 95070
Phone: 408-507-5135
Fax: 408-741-7009

5/G Hua Min Empire Plaza
726# Yan An Road West
Shanghai, China 200050
Phone: 86-21-6251-6032

Management and Staff
Jeffrey Khoo, General Partner
KK Ip, Venture Partner
Kim Seng Tan, General Partner
Lim Yew Seng, Venture Partner
Michael Ming-Yih Wu, General Partner

Type of Firm
Private Equity Firm

Association Membership
Singapore Venture Capital Association (SVCA)

Project Preferences

Type of Financing Preferred:
Leveraged Buyout
Early Stage
Mezzanine
Expansion
Balanced
Later Stage
Seed
Management Buyouts

Size of Investments Considered:
Min Size of Investment Considered (000s): $200
Max Size of Investment Considered (000s): $2,000

Geographical Preferences

United States Preferences:
All U.S.

International Preferences:
Laos
Vietnam
Indonesia
Taiwan
Brunei
China
Hong Kong
Thailand
Cambodia
Philippines
Singapore
Burma
Malaysia

Industry Preferences

In Communications prefer:
Communications and Media
Telecommunications

In Computer Software prefer:
Software

In Internet Specific prefer:
Internet

In Computer Other prefer:
Computer Related

In Semiconductor/Electr prefer:
Electronics
Electronic Components
Semiconductor

In Medical/Health prefer:
Medical/Health
Health Services

In Industrial/Energy prefer:
Industrial Products

In Financial Services prefer:
Financial Services

In Manufact. prefer:
Manufacturing

Additional Information
Year Founded: 2000
Current Activity Level : Actively seeking new investments

T SQUARED PARTNERS LLC
1325 Sixth Avenue
Floor 27
New York, NY USA 10019
Phone: 212-763-8615
Fax: 212-671-1403
E-mail: investor@tsquaredpartners.com
Website: www.tsquaredpartners.com

Management and Staff
Mark Jensen, Co-Founder
Thomas Sauve, Co-Founder

Type of Firm
Private Equity Firm

Project Preferences

Type of Financing Preferred:
Leveraged Buyout
Expansion
Public Companies
Acquisition
Recapitalizations

Size of Investments Considered:
Min Size of Investment Considered (000s): $750
Max Size of Investment Considered (000s): $2,000

Additional Information
Year Founded: 2009
Current Activity Level : Actively seeking new investments

T-VENTURE HOLDING GMBH (AKA: T-TELEMATIK VENTURE HOLDING)
Gotenstrasse 156
Bonn, Germany 53175
Phone: 49-228-308-4811
Fax: 49-228-308-4819
E-mail: t-venture@telekom.de
Website: www.t-venture.de

Other Offices
950 Tower Lane
Suite 1600
Foster City, CA USA 94404
Phone: 650-358-2011
Fax: 650-292-8353

Management and Staff
Axel Kolb, Managing Director
Georg Schwegler, CEO & Managing Director
Mark Von Lillienskiold, Managing Director & CFO

Type of Firm
Corporate PE/Venture

Association Membership
German Venture Capital Association (BVK)
European Private Equity and Venture Capital Assoc.

Project Preferences

Type of Financing Preferred:
Early Stage
Expansion
Balanced
Start-up Financing
Seed
Acquisition
Startup

Size of Investments Considered:
Min Size of Investment Considered (000s): $141
Max Size of Investment Considered (000s): $2,354

Geographical Preferences

United States Preferences:
All U.S.

International Preferences:
Europe
Israel
Germany
Asia

Industry Preferences

In Communications prefer:
Communications and Media
Telecommunications
Wireless Communications
Other Communication Prod.

In Internet Specific prefer:
Internet

Additional Information
Year Founded: 1997
Capital Under Management: $440,400,000
Current Activity Level : Actively seeking new investments

T. ROWE PRICE THRESHOLD PARTNERSHIPS
100 East Pratt Street
Baltimore, MD USA 21202
Phone: 410-345-2000
Fax: 410-345-2800
Website: www.troweprice.com

Other Offices
Yamato Seimei Building, 12th Floor
1-7, Uchisaiwai-cho 1-chome
Chiyoda-ku, Tokyo, Japan 100-0011
Phone: 81-3-3504-1863

Carlos Pellegrini 1149
piso 12
Buenos Aires, Argentina C1009 ABW

1 Connaught Place
8/F, Rm. 802-809, Jardine House
Central, Hong Kong

Strawinskylaan 3051
Atrium Gebouw
Amsterdam, Netherlands 1077 ZX
Phone: 31-20-301-2114

ATEAC Paris Champs Elysees
90, avenue de Champs Elysees
Paris, France 75008

2260 Briargate Parkway
Colorado Springs, CO USA 80920
Phone: 800-225-5132

4515 Painters Mill Road
Owings Mills, MD USA 21117-4903

Lautrupsgade 7
1st Floor
Copenhagen, Denmark 2100
Phone: 45-33-360-500

60 Queen Victoria Street
London, United Kingdom EC4N 4TZ
Phone: 44-20-7651-8200

No. 290 Orchard Road
#14-04 Paragon
Singapore, Singapore 238859

4211 West Boy Scout Boulevard
Tampa, FL USA 33607
Phone: 800-225-5132

Stureplan 4c
4th Floor

Stockholm, Sweden 114 35
Phone: 46-8-463-3212

333 Bush Street
Suite 2550
San Francisco, CA USA 94104-2833

Type of Firm

Bank Affiliated

Association Membership

Mid-Atlantic Venture Association

Project Preferences

Role in Financing:

Prefer role as deal originator but will also invest in deals created by others

Type of Financing Preferred:

Leveraged Buyout
Expansion
Mezzanine
Turnaround
Later Stage
Special Situation

Size of Investments Considered:

Min Size of Investment Considered (000s): $3,000
Max Size of Investment Considered (000s): $5,000

Geographical Preferences

United States Preferences:

All U.S.

Industry Focus

(% based on actual investment)

Industrial/Energy	41.8%
Internet Specific	13.9%
Computer Software and Services	8.9%
Biotechnology	7.5%
Consumer Related	7.2%
Medical/Health	6.4%
Other Products	4.4%
Semiconductors/Other Elect.	4.1%
Computer Hardware	3.4%
Communications and Media	2.5%

Additional Information

Name of Most Recent Fund: T. Rowe Price Recovery Fund II
Most Recent Fund Was Raised: 10/18/1996
Year Founded: 1983
Capital Under Management: $245,000,000
Current Activity Level : Actively seeking new investments
Method of Compensation: Return on investment is of primary concern, do not charge fees

---

T2C2 CAPITAL

1550 Metcalfe Street
Suite 502
Montreal, Canada H3A 1X6
Phone: 514-842-9849
Fax: 514-842-1505
Website: www.t2c2capital.com

Management and Staff

Bernard Coupal, President
Bertrand Cayrol, Vice President
Mario Thomas, Vice President

Type of Firm

Bank Affiliated

Project Preferences

Role in Financing:

Prefer role as deal originator

Type of Financing Preferred:

Early Stage
Startup

Geographical Preferences

Canadian Preferences:

All Canada
Quebec

Industry Preferences

In Computer Software prefer:

Software

In Internet Specific prefer:

Internet

In Medical/Health prefer:

Medical/Health

Additional Information

Year Founded: 1997
Current Activity Level : Actively seeking new investments

TA ASSOCIATES, INC.

200 Clarendon Street
John Hancock Tower, 56/F
Boston, MA USA 02116
Phone: 617-574-6700
Fax: 617-574-6728
E-mail: info@ta.com
Website: www.ta.com

Other Offices

114 Dr. E. Moses Road
Four Seasons Hotel, Suite 1406
Worli, Mumbai, India 400 018
Phone: 91-22-6144-3100
Fax: 91-22-6144-3101

64 Willow Place
Suite 100
Menlo Park, CA USA 94025
Phone: 650-473-2200
Fax: 650-473-2235

25 Knightsbridge
2nd Floor
London, United Kingdom SW1X 7RZ
Phone: 44-20-7823-0200
Fax: 44-20-7823-0201

Management and Staff

A. Bruce Johnston, Managing Director
Ajit Nedungadi, Managing Director
Brian Conway, Managing Director
C. Kevin Landry, Chairman & Managing Director
Christian Gruenwald, Principal
Christopher Parkin, Principal
Harry Taylor, Principal
J. Morgan Seigler, Vice President
Jason Werlin, Vice President
Jeffrey Barber, Managing Director
Jeffrey Chambers, Managing Director
Jonathan Goldstein, Managing Director
Jonathan Meeks, Managing Director
Kenneth Schiciano, Managing Director
Kurt Jaggers, Managing Director
Michael Berk, Managing Director
Michael Wilson, Managing Director
Michael Child, Managing Director
Naveen Wadhera, Vice President
Richard Tadler, Managing Director
Roger Kafker, Managing Director
Tad Yanagi, Vice President
Thomas Alber, Chief Financial Officer
Todd Crockett, Managing Director
Vivian Wu, Principal
William Christ, Vice President

Type of Firm

Private Equity Firm

Project Preferences

Role in Financing:

Prefer role as deal originator but will also invest in deals created by others

Type of Financing Preferred:

Leveraged Buyout
Expansion
Mezzanine
Balanced
Later Stage
Management Buyouts
Recapitalizations

Size of Investments Considered:

Min Size of Investment Considered (000s): $60,000
Max Size of Investment Considered (000s): $500,000

Geographical Preferences

United States Preferences:

All U.S.

Canadian Preferences:

All Canada

International Preferences:

Italy
United Kingdom
India
Luxembourg
Netherlands
Portugal
Europe
Spain
Belgium

Germany
Asia
France

Industry Focus

(% based on actual investment)

Computer Software and Services	24.0%
Communications and Media	22.0%
Medical/Health	15.2%
Other Products	13.5%
Internet Specific	11.9%
Semiconductors/Other Elect.	4.3%
Consumer Related	4.1%
Computer Hardware	2.5%
Biotechnology	1.3%
Industrial/Energy	1.2%

Additional Information

Year Founded: 1968
Capital Under Management: $12,000,000,000
Current Activity Level : Actively seeking new investments
Method of Compensation: Return on investment is of primary concern, do not charge fees

---

TAILWIND CAPITAL PARTNERS

485 Lexington Avenue
New York, NY USA 10017
Phone: 212-271-3800
Fax: 212-271-4911
E-mail: info@tailwindcapital.com
Website: www.tailwindcapital.com

Other Offices

88 Kearny Street
San Francisco, CA USA 94108
Phone: 415-364-7800
Fax: 415-364-7810

Management and Staff

Adam Stulberger, Managing Director
Cliff Moskowitz, Vice President
David Bauman, Managing Director
Douglas Karp, Managing Partner
Eric Haley, Principal
Frank Sica, Managing Partner
Gagan Verma, Managing Director
Geoffrey Raker, Managing Director
James Hoch, Managing Partner
Jeffrey Calhoun, Principal
Lawrence Sorrel, Managing Partner
Mark Epstein, Chief Financial Officer

Type of Firm

Private Equity Firm

Project Preferences

Role in Financing:

Prefer role as deal originator but will also invest in deals created by others

Type of Financing Preferred:

Leveraged Buyout
Control-block Purchases
Expansion
Generalist PE
Turnaround
Later Stage
Management Buyouts
Acquisition
Private Placement
Special Situation
Recapitalizations

Size of Investments Considered:

Min Size of Investment Considered (000s): $15,000
Max Size of Investment Considered (000s): $200,000

Geographical Preferences

United States Preferences:

All U.S.

Canadian Preferences:

All Canada

Industry Preferences

In Communications prefer:

Communications and Media

In Semiconductor/Electr prefer:

Electronic Components

In Medical/Health prefer:

Medical/Health

In Consumer Related prefer:

Consumer Services

In Industrial/Energy prefer:

Industrial Products

In Financial Services prefer:

Insurance

In Business Serv. prefer:

Consulting Services
Media

Additional Information

Year Founded: 2005
Capital Under Management: $2,000,000,000
Current Activity Level : Actively seeking new investments
Method of Compensation: Return on invest. most important, but chg. closing fees, service fees, etc.

TAISHAN INVEST AG

Dufourstrasse 121
Saint Gallen, Switzerland 9001
Phone: 41-44-783-8034
Fax: 41-44-783-8040
E-mail: contact@taishan-invest.com
Website: www.taishan-invest.com

Other Offices

504 Full Tower
9 Dongsanhuan Zhong Road
Beijing, China
Phone: 86-10-8591-1988
Fax: 86-10-8591-1986

Management and Staff

Chris Hong Wen, Venture Partner
Jackie Liang Chen, Vice President
Ocean Meng An, Venture Partner
Raymond Lei Yang, Founding Partner
Sebastian Kubler, Managing Director

Type of Firm

Private Equity Firm

Project Preferences

Type of Financing Preferred:

Early Stage
Expansion
Later Stage
Special Situation
Startup

Geographical Preferences

International Preferences:

Europe
China

Industry Preferences

In Communications prefer:

Communications and Media
Telecommunications
Data Communications

In Semiconductor/Electr prefer:

Micro-Processing

In Medical/Health prefer:

Medical/Health

In Industrial/Energy prefer:

Alternative Energy

In Business Serv. prefer:

Media

Additional Information

Year Founded: 2008
Current Activity Level : Actively seeking new investments

TAISHIN MANAGEMENT AND CONSULTING CO., LTD.

No. 46 Chung-Shan N. Road
Section 2, 10th Floor
Taipei, Taiwan
Phone: 886-2-2531-8678
Fax: 886-2-2531-8646

Management and Staff

Jerry Wu, President

Type of Firm

Private Equity Firm

Association Membership

Taiwan Venture Capital Association(TVCA)

Project Preferences

Type of Financing Preferred:
Expansion
Mezzanine
Balanced
Startup

Geographical Preferences

International Preferences:
Taiwan

Industry Preferences

In Communications prefer:
Telecommunications

In Computer Software prefer:
Software

In Internet Specific prefer:
Internet

In Semiconductor/Electr prefer:
Electronics
Semiconductor
Optoelectronics

In Medical/Health prefer:
Medical/Health
Pharmaceuticals

In Industrial/Energy prefer:
Advanced Materials

Additional Information

Name of Most Recent Fund: Taishin Venture Capital Investment Corporation, Ltd.
Most Recent Fund Was Raised: 12/17/1998
Year Founded: 1995
Capital Under Management: $44,100,000
Current Activity Level : Actively seeking new investments

TAKEDA RESEARCH INVESTMENT, INC.

435 Tasso Street
Suite 300
Palo Alto, CA USA 94301
Phone: 650-328-2900
Fax: 650-328-2922
E-mail: contact@tri-takeda.com
Website: www.tri-takeda.com

Management and Staff

Juan Harrison, Vice President

Type of Firm

Corporate PE/Venture

Project Preferences

Role in Financing:
Will function either as deal originator or investor in deals created by others

Type of Financing Preferred:
Second Stage Financing
Early Stage
Mezzanine
Start-up Financing
Later Stage
Seed

Size of Investments Considered:
Min Size of Investment Considered (000s): $250
Max Size of Investment Considered (000s): $3,000

Geographical Preferences

United States Preferences:
All U.S.

Canadian Preferences:
All Canada

International Preferences:
Europe

Industry Preferences

In Biotechnology prefer:
Biotechnology
Human Biotechnology

In Medical/Health prefer:
Medical/Health

Additional Information

Year Founded: 2002
Capital Under Management: $30,000,000
Current Activity Level : Actively seeking new investments

TAKEOFF VENTURE CAPITAL MANAGEMENT GMBH

Bleichstrasse 10
Mulheim an der Ruhr, Germany 45468
Phone: 49-208-300-0340
Fax: 49-208-300-0345
E-mail: info@takeoff-vc.de
Website: www.takeoff-vc.de

Management and Staff

Hans-Peter Dietz, Managing Director

Type of Firm

Private Equity Firm

Association Membership

German Venture Capital Association (BVK)

Project Preferences

Role in Financing:
Prefer role as deal originator but will also invest in deals created by others

Type of Financing Preferred:
Early Stage
Startup

Geographical Preferences

International Preferences:
Europe
Germany

Industry Preferences

In Communications prefer:
Communications and Media

In Computer Software prefer:
Software

In Internet Specific prefer:
Internet

In Computer Other prefer:
Computer Related

In Semiconductor/Electr prefer:
Electronics

Additional Information

Year Founded: 1999
Current Activity Level : Actively seeking new investments

TALDE GESTION SGECR SA

Rodriguez Arias Street 9, 1
Bilbao, Spain 48008
Phone: 34-94-435-5040
Fax: 34-94-435-5041
E-mail: info@talde.com
Website: www.talde.com

Type of Firm

Private Equity Firm

Association Membership

European Private Equity and Venture Capital Assoc.
Spanish Venture Capital Association (ASCRI)

Project Preferences

Role in Financing:
Will function either as deal originator or investor in deals created by others

Type of Financing Preferred:
Second Stage Financing
Leveraged Buyout
Early Stage
Expansion
Balanced
Later Stage
Management Buyouts
Startup
Recapitalizations

Size of Investments Considered:
Min Size of Investment Considered (000s): $920
Max Size of Investment Considered (000s): $4,600

Geographical Preferences

International Preferences:
Portugal
Europe
Western Europe
Spain
France

Industry Focus
(% based on actual investment)

Industrial/Energy	52.8%
Other Products	29.0%
Internet Specific	8.4%
Consumer Related	4.6%
Medical/Health	1.5%
Semiconductors/Other Elect.	1.4%
Biotechnology	1.0%
Communications and Media	1.0%
Computer Software and Services	0.3%

Additional Information
Year Founded: 1977
Capital Under Management: $65,000,000
Current Activity Level : Actively seeking new investments
Method of Compensation: Return on invest. most important, but chg. closing fees, service fees, etc.

TALISMAN CAPITAL
5200 Rings Road
Dublin, OH USA 43017
Phone: 614-210-5500
Fax: 614-210-5501
E-mail: info@talismancapital.com
Website: www.talismancapital.com

Management and Staff
George Bennett, Partner
Matthew Walter, Founding Partner
Michael Scott, Managing Partner

Type of Firm
Private Equity Firm

Project Preferences

Type of Financing Preferred:
Acquisition
Recapitalizations

Industry Preferences

In Medical/Health prefer:
Medical/Health

In Consumer Related prefer:
Consumer Products

In Financial Services prefer:
Financial Services

Additional Information
Year Founded: 2000
Current Activity Level : Actively seeking new investments

TALL OAKS CAPITAL PARTNERS LLC
315 Old Ivy Way
Suite 301
Charlottesville, VA USA 22903
Phone: 434-951-0440
Fax: 434-951-0478
E-mail: info@talloakscapital.com
Website: www.talloakscapital.com

Management and Staff
A. Reenst Lesemann, Managing Director
Colin Rolph, Managing Director
Hiram Ewald, Managing Director
Jim Farinholt, Managing Director
Kathryne Carr, Managing Director

Type of Firm
Private Equity Firm

Project Preferences

Role in Financing:
Will function either as deal originator or investor in deals created by others

Type of Financing Preferred:
Early Stage
Seed
First Stage Financing
Startup

Size of Investments Considered:
Min Size of Investment Considered (000s): $300
Max Size of Investment Considered (000s): $1,500

Geographical Preferences

United States Preferences:
Mid Atlantic
Southeast

Industry Preferences

In Communications prefer:
Telecommunications
Satellite Microwave Comm.

In Computer Software prefer:
Software
Systems Software
Applications Software

In Internet Specific prefer:
Internet

In Biotechnology prefer:
Human Biotechnology
Industrial Biotechnology

In Medical/Health prefer:
Medical Diagnostics
Medical Products

Additional Information
Name of Most Recent Fund: Tall Oaks Capital, L.P.
Most Recent Fund Was Raised: 11/01/2000
Year Founded: 2000
Capital Under Management: $12,500,000
Current Activity Level : Actively seeking new investments
Method of Compensation: Return on investment is of primary concern, do not charge fees

---

TALLWOOD VENTURE CAPITAL
400 Hamilton Avenue
Suite 230
Palo Alto, CA USA 94301
Phone: 650-473-6750
Fax: 650-473-6755
E-mail: information@tallwoodvc.com
Website: www.tallwoodvc.com

Management and Staff
Chen Tang, Chief Financial Officer
Diosdado Banatao, Managing Partner
Donna Young, Venture Partner
George Pavlov, General Partner
Luis Arzubi, General Partner
Natasha Skok, Venture Partner
Reza Kasnavi, Venture Partner

Type of Firm
Private Equity Firm

Project Preferences

Type of Financing Preferred:
Early Stage
Balanced
Startup

Geographical Preferences

United States Preferences:
All U.S.

Industry Preferences

In Communications prefer:
Communications and Media

In Semiconductor/Electr prefer:
Semiconductor

Additional Information
Name of Most Recent Fund: Tallwood III, L.P
Most Recent Fund Was Raised: 12/13/2005
Year Founded: 2000
Capital Under Management: $526,800,000
Current Activity Level : Actively seeking new investments

TAM CAPITAL MANAGEMENT
38 Miller Avenue
Suite 295
Mill Valley, CA USA 94941
E-mail: info@tamcapital.com
Website: www.tamcapital.com

Management and Staff

Thomas Cusick, Managing Director

Type of Firm

Private Equity Advisor or Fund of Funds

Project Preferences

Type of Financing Preferred:
Expansion

Geographical Preferences

United States Preferences:
All U.S.

Industry Preferences

In Computer Hardware prefer:
Terminals

In Computer Software prefer:
Software

In Internet Specific prefer:
Internet

Additional Information

Year Founded: 2007
Current Activity Level : Actively seeking new investments

TAMARACK CAPITAL ADVISORS, INC.

715 - Fifth Avenue South West
Seventh Floor
Calgary, Canada T2P 2X6
Phone: 403-269-1011
Fax: 403-269-1438
Website: www.tamarackgrp.ca

Other Offices

14310 - 111th Avenue
Suite 400
Edmonton, Canada T5M 3Z7
Phone: 780-451-4406
Fax: 780-454-1908

Type of Firm

Private Equity Firm

Project Preferences

Type of Financing Preferred:
Expansion

Geographical Preferences

Canadian Preferences:
Western Canada

Additional Information

Year Founded: 1992
Current Activity Level : Actively seeking new investments

TAMBURI INVESTMENT PARTNERS (AKA TAMBURI & ASSOCIATI SPA)

Via Pontaccio, 10
Milan, Italy 20121
Phone: 39-02-885-8801
Fax: 39-02-890-0421
Website: www.tamburi.it

Type of Firm

Private Equity Firm

Association Membership

Italian Venture Capital Association (AIFI)

Project Preferences

Type of Financing Preferred:
Expansion

Geographical Preferences

International Preferences:
Italy

Industry Preferences

In Computer Other prefer:
Computer Related

In Consumer Related prefer:
consumer

In Industrial/Energy prefer:
Industrial Products

Additional Information

Year Founded: 2000
Capital Under Management: $11,000,000
Current Activity Level : Actively seeking new investments

TAMIR FISHMAN VENTURES

21 Ha'arbaa St.
Platinum Tower
Tel Aviv, Israel 64739
Phone: 972-36-84-9333
Fax: 972-36-85-3393
E-mail: info@tfventures.com
Website: www.tfventures.com

Management and Staff

Benny Zeevi, Partner
Danny Fishman, Chief Executive Officer
Eldad Tamir, Chief Executive Officer
Michael Elias, General Partner
Oren Ahr, Partner
Shai Saul, Managing General Partner

Type of Firm

Bank Affiliated

Project Preferences

Type of Financing Preferred:
Early Stage
Later Stage
Seed
Startup

Geographical Preferences

International Preferences:
Israel
Russia

Industry Focus

(% based on actual investment)

Communications and Media	35.1%
Computer Software and Services	24.5%
Internet Specific	12.7%
Semiconductors/Other Elect.	11.1%
Biotechnology	6.9%
Industrial/Energy	3.7%
Medical/Health	3.6%
Other Products	2.3%

Additional Information

Year Founded: 1998
Capital Under Management: $70,000,000
Current Activity Level : Actively seeking new investments

TANDEM CAPITAL GESTION

Dr. Romagosa, 1-2
M. Edificio Lucini
Valencia, Spain 46002
Phone: 34-902-106-974
Fax: 34-963-942-400
E-mail: info@tandemcapital.es
Website: www.tandemcapital.es

Type of Firm

Private Equity Firm

Association Membership

Spanish Venture Capital Association (ASCRI)

Project Preferences

Type of Financing Preferred:
Management Buyouts

Geographical Preferences

International Preferences:
Gibraltar
Portugal
Andorra
China
Ghana
Spain
France

Industry Preferences

In Computer Software prefer:
Software

In Consumer Related prefer:
Food/Beverage
Consumer Products
Consumer Services

Additional Information
Year Founded: 2008
Capital Under Management: $78,000,000
Current Activity Level : Actively seeking new investments

TANO CAPITAL LLC
One Franklin Parkway
Building 970, Second Floor
San Mateo, CA USA 94403
Phone: 650-212-0330
Fax: 650-212-0006
E-mail: information@tanocapital.com
Website: www.tanocapital.com

Other Offices
c/o International Financial Services
IFS Court TwentyEight, Cybercity
Ebene, Mauritius
Phone: 230-467-3000
Fax: 230-467-4000

10F, No.87, Section 4
Chung Hsiao East Road
Taipei, Taiwan
Phone: 886-2-2771-7663
Fax: 886-2-8773-3987

Unit B2 (603), 6F, Bank of America
Tower, No.12, Harcourt Road
Hong Kong

189 Ly Thai To Street
Hoi An Town
Quang Nam Province, Vietnam

70, An Shang Boulevard
Tianjin, China 3000020
Phone: 86-22-5878-1053
Fax: 88-22-2721-9086

No.94, Lane 468, Urumqi Road North
Shanghai, China 200040
Phone: 86-21-6248-8877
Fax: 86-21-6249-5659

9 Nirlon House, Ground Floor
254-B Dr. Annie Besant Rd.
Mumbai, India 400025
Phone: 91-22-6746-8000
Fax: 91-22-6746-8002

Management and Staff
Amit Dand, Vice President
Carlton Pereira, Managing Director
Charles Johnson, Managing Director
Frank Liu, Managing Director
Hetal Gandhi, Managing Director
Piyush Goenka, Vice President
Richard Leider, Managing Director
Shruti Gupta, Vice President
William Knuff, Managing Director
Winston Lee, Managing Director

Type of Firm
Private Equity Firm

Project Preferences

Type of Financing Preferred:
Expansion
Balanced

Geographical Preferences

International Preferences:
India
China

Additional Information
Year Founded: 2006
Capital Under Management: $61,000,000
Current Activity Level : Actively seeking new investments

TAR HEEL
Foksal 3/5 Street
Warsaw, Poland 00-366
Website: www.tarheelcap.com

Management and Staff
Grzegorz Bielowicki, Partner
Marcin Wysocki, Partner

Type of Firm
Private Equity Firm

Project Preferences

Type of Financing Preferred:
Balanced

Geographical Preferences

International Preferences:
Sweden
Europe

Additional Information
Year Founded: 2005
Current Activity Level : Actively seeking new investments

TARAVAL ASSOCIATES LLC
845 Oak Grove Avenue
Suite 220
Menlo Park, CA USA 94025
Phone: 650-329-1044
Fax: 650-329-1043
E-mail: info@taraval.com
Website: www.taraval.com

Management and Staff
George Murphy, General Partner
Robert Balch, General Partner

Type of Firm
Private Equity Firm

Project Preferences

Role in Financing:
Will function either as deal originator or investor in deals created by others

Type of Financing Preferred:
Early Stage
Expansion
Research and Development
Start-up Financing
Seed

Size of Investments Considered:
Min Size of Investment Considered (000s): $100
Max Size of Investment Considered (000s): $1,000

Geographical Preferences

United States Preferences:
All U.S.

Canadian Preferences:
All Canada

International Preferences:
Australia
New Zealand

Industry Preferences

In Biotechnology prefer:
Human Biotechnology
Agricultural/Animal Bio.
Industrial Biotechnology
Biosensors
Biotech Related Research

In Medical/Health prefer:
Medical Diagnostics
Diagnostic Services
Diagnostic Test Products
Medical Therapeutics
Drug/Equipmt Delivery
Medical Products
Disposable Med. Products

In Consumer Related prefer:
Food/Beverage

In Agr/Forestr/Fish prefer:
Agriculture related

Additional Information

Year Founded: 1999
Capital Under Management: $7,500,000
Current Activity Level : Actively seeking new investments
Method of Compensation: Return on invest. most important, but chg. closing fees, service fees, etc.

TARGET PARTNERS GMBH

Kardinal-Faulhaber Strasse 10
Munich, Germany 80333
Phone: 49-89-2070-490
Fax: 49-89-2070-4999
E-mail: info@targetpartners.de
Website: www.targetpartners.de

Management and Staff

Berthold Von Freyberg, Partner
Dirk Uhlemann, Venture Partner
Joerg Sperling, Venture Partner
Kurt Mueller, Partner
Michael Birkel, Venture Partner
Olaf Jacobi, Partner
Waldemar Jantz, Partner

Type of Firm

Private Equity Firm

Association Membership

German Venture Capital Association (BVK)
European Private Equity and Venture Capital Assoc.

Project Preferences

Type of Financing Preferred:

Early Stage
Expansion
Seed
Startup

Geographical Preferences

United States Preferences:

All U.S.

International Preferences:

Europe
Germany

Industry Preferences

In Communications prefer:

Communications and Media
Telecommunications

In Computer Software prefer:

Software

In Internet Specific prefer:

Internet

In Semiconductor/Electr prefer:

Electronic Components

In Industrial/Energy prefer:

Energy
Environmental Related

Additional Information

Name of Most Recent Fund: Target Partners Fund I Gmbh & Company KG
Most Recent Fund Was Raised: 03/01/2000
Year Founded: 2000
Capital Under Management: $289,800,000
Current Activity Level : Actively seeking new investments

TAROS CAPITAL NETHERLANDS BV

Vinoly tower, 21th floor
Claude Debussylaan 46
Amsterdam, Netherlands 1082 MD
Phone: 31-20-404-1221
Fax: 31-20-404-4213
E-mail: amsterdam@taroscapital.com
Website: www.taroscapital.com

Other Offices

Friedrich-Ebert-Anlage 54
Frankfurt, Germany D-60325
Phone: 49-69-972-0830
Fax: 49-69-9720-8320

Uitbreidingstraat 10-16
Antwerp, Belgium B-2600
Phone: 32-3-286-9930
Fax: 32-3-286-9939

Management and Staff

Alexander Van Wassenaer, Managing Partner
Arnoud Oltmans, Principal
Christian Bachle, Managing Director
Hilde Famaey, Principal
Paul Lamers, Managing Partner
Theo Bot, Principal

Type of Firm

Private Equity Firm

Project Preferences

Type of Financing Preferred:

Leveraged Buyout
Expansion
Balanced
Acquisition

Size of Investments Considered:

Min Size of Investment Considered (000s): $33,289
Max Size of Investment Considered (000s): $466,045

Geographical Preferences

International Preferences:

Netherlands
Belgium
Germany

Additional Information

Year Founded: 2005
Capital Under Management: $732,400,000
Current Activity Level : Actively seeking new investments

TARPON INVESTMENT GROUP

Avenida Brigadeiro Faria Lima
3144 - cj. 52
Sao Paulo, Brazil 01451-000
Phone: 55-11-3074-5800
Fax: 55-11-3074-5801
Website: www.tarponinvest.com

Management and Staff

Fernando Shayer, Managing Partner
Jose Carlos Reis De Magalhaes, Chairman & CEO
Pedro Faria, Partner

Type of Firm

Private Equity Firm

Project Preferences

Type of Financing Preferred:

Generalist PE
Public Companies

Geographical Preferences

International Preferences:

Brazil

Additional Information

Year Founded: 2002
Current Activity Level : Actively seeking new investments

TASMAN CAPITAL PARTNERS (FKA:NIKKO PRINCIPAL INV. AUSTRALIA)

Chifley Tower, Level 34
Chifley Square
Sydney, Australia 2000
Phone: 61-2-8226-2200
Fax: 61-2-8226-2299
E-mail: info@tasmancapital.com.au
Website: www.tasmancapital.com.au

Management and Staff

Gene Lorenz, Managing Director
Janine Middleton, Managing Director
Rob Nichols, Managing Director
Victoria Rohrsheim, Chief Financial Officer

Type of Firm

Private Equity Firm

Association Membership

Australian Venture Capital Association (AVCAL)

Project Preferences

Type of Financing Preferred:

Leveraged Buyout
Expansion
Management Buyouts

Acquisition
Recapitalizations

Geographical Preferences

International Preferences:
Australia
New Zealand

Additional Information
Name of Most Recent Fund: Tasman Secondaries Trust
Most Recent Fund Was Raised: 09/30/2008
Year Founded: 2008
Capital Under Management: $4,000,000
Current Activity Level : Actively seeking new investments

TAT CAPITAL PARTNERS, LTD. (AKA: TRANS ATLANTIC TECHNOLOGY)
vorderi Boede 3
P.O. Box
Oberrohrdorf, Switzerland CH-5452
Phone: 41-56-485-8989
Fax: 41-56-485-8985
Website: www.tatcapital.com

Other Offices
Vikingavagen 17 D
Saltsjobaden, Sweden S-13334
Phone: 46-8717-4950
Fax: 46-8717-4955

P.O. Box 23326
San Jose, CA USA 95153-3326
Phone: 408-270-9200
Fax: 408-270-4140

Caracasbaaiweg 201
P.O. Box 6085
Curacao, Neth. Antilles
Phone: 599-9-4343569
Fax: 599-9-4343567

Management and Staff
Rolf Haegler, Partner
Thomas Egolf, Partner

Type of Firm
Private Equity Firm

Association Membership
Swiss Venture Capital Association (SECA)
Western Association of Venture Capitalists (WAVC)
National Venture Capital Association - USA (NVCA)
European Private Equity and Venture Capital Assoc.

Project Preferences

Type of Financing Preferred:
Second Stage Financing
Early Stage
Expansion
Start-up Financing
First Stage Financing

Size of Investments Considered:
Min Size of Investment Considered (000s): $1,000
Max Size of Investment Considered (000s): $5,000

Geographical Preferences

United States Preferences:
West Coast
All U.S.

Canadian Preferences:
All Canada

International Preferences:
Sweden
Switzerland
Western Europe
Israel
Germany

Industry Preferences

In Communications prefer:
Commercial Communications
Telecommunications

In Computer Hardware prefer:
Computers
Disk Relat. Memory Device

In Computer Other prefer:
Computer Related

In Semiconductor/Electr prefer:
Electronics
Semiconductor
Micro-Processing
Sensors
Circuit Boards
Component Testing Equipmt
Fiber Optics

In Medical/Health prefer:
Medical/Health
Medical Diagnostics
Diagnostic Services
Diagnostic Test Products
Medical Therapeutics
Drug/Equipmt Delivery
Medical Products
Disposable Med. Products

Additional Information
Name of Most Recent Fund: TAT Investments II L.P.
Most Recent Fund Was Raised: 07/01/1999
Year Founded: 1997
Capital Under Management: $45,000,000
Current Activity Level : Actively seeking new investments
Method of Compensation: Return on investment is of primary concern, do not charge fees

---

TATE & LYLE PLC
Sugar Quay
Lower Thames Street
London, United Kingdom EC3R 6DQ
Phone: 44-20-7626-6525
Fax: 44-20-7623-5213
Website: www.tateandlyle.com

Management and Staff
Simon Barnes, Managing Partner
Stanley Musesengwa, Chief Operating Officer

Type of Firm
Corporate PE/Venture

Project Preferences

Type of Financing Preferred:
Early Stage
Expansion
Startup

Industry Preferences

In Biotechnology prefer:
Biotechnology
Industrial Biotechnology

In Consumer Related prefer:
Food/Beverage

In Industrial/Energy prefer:
Materials

Additional Information
Year Founded: 2005
Capital Under Management: $47,400,000
Current Activity Level : Actively seeking new investments

TAURUS VENTURE CAPITAL COMPANY, LTD. (AKA: TVC)
4/F, Sandos Building, 82-3
Cheongdam-dong, Gangnam-gu
Seoul, South Korea 135-100
Phone: 822-541-0800
Fax: 822-541-0821
Website: www.taurus21.co.kr

Management and Staff
Hee Taek Lim, Chief Executive Officer

Type of Firm
Private Equity Firm

Project Preferences

Type of Financing Preferred:
Leveraged Buyout
Generalist PE
Early Stage
Expansion
Research and Development
Turnaround
Balanced
Management Buyouts
Startup
Acquisition

Geographical Preferences

International Preferences:
Korea, South

Industry Preferences

In Communications prefer:
Entertainment

In Computer Software prefer:
Software

In Internet Specific prefer:
Internet

Additional Information

Year Founded: 2000
Capital Under Management: $22,900,000
Current Activity Level : Actively seeking new investments

TAVISTOCK LIFE SCIENCES (AKA: TLS)

3030 Bunker Hill
Suite 214
San Diego, CA USA 92109
Phone: 858-270-5677
Fax: 858-274-5699
E-mail: contacts@tavistock.com
Website: www.tavistocklifesciences.com

Type of Firm

Corporate PE/Venture

Project Preferences

Type of Financing Preferred:
Early Stage

Industry Preferences

In Biotechnology prefer:
Biotechnology

Additional Information

Year Founded: 2003
Current Activity Level : Actively seeking new investments

TC CAPITAL PTE., LTD.

4 Shenton Way
#13-06 SGX Center 2
Singapore, Singapore 068807
Phone: 65-6511-0688
E-mail: info@tccapital.com
Website: www.tccapital.com

Other Offices

16/F Cheung Kong Center
2 Queen's Road
Central, Hong Kong
Phone: 852-2297-2386

Management and Staff

Ravi Chidambaram, President, Founder
Tommy Tan, Co-Founder

Type of Firm

Private Equity Firm

Project Preferences

Type of Financing Preferred:
Balanced

Additional Information

Year Founded: 2006
Current Activity Level : Actively seeking new investments

TCIB INVESTMENT CO., LTD.

Tower 1, China Central Place
No.81 Jianguo Road
Beijing, China 100025
Phone: 86-10-5969-5112
Fax: 86-10-5969-5119
E-mail: admin@tcib.com.cn
Website: www.tcib.com.cn

Other Offices

3660 South Valley View Boulevard
Las Vegas, NV USA 89103
Phone: 702-222-2250
Fax: 702-222-2251

Management and Staff

Andrew Ong, Managing Partner
Eric Gier, Managing Director
James Walsh, Managing Director
Michelle Yu, Managing Partner
Yen Wang, Chief Executive Officer

Type of Firm

Investment Management Firm

Project Preferences

Type of Financing Preferred:
Generalist PE
Mezzanine
Acquisition

Geographical Preferences

International Preferences:
China

Additional Information

Year Founded: 2000
Capital Under Management: $125,000,000
Current Activity Level : Actively seeking new investments

TCR INDUSTRIAL MANAGERS (AKA: INDUSTRIAL CAPITAL)

5, rue Paul Cezanne
Paris, France 75008
Phone: 33-1-5381-7781
Fax: 33-1-5381-7799
E-mail: info@tcrcapital.com
Website: www.tcrcapital.com

Management and Staff

Christian Dorleac, Partner
Marc Demicheli, Managing Partner
Marco De Alfaro, Partner
Roberta Nataf, Partner

Type of Firm

Private Equity Firm

Association Membership

French Venture Capital Association (AFIC)

Project Preferences

Role in Financing:
Prefer role as deal originator

Type of Financing Preferred:
Second Stage Financing
Leveraged Buyout

Size of Investments Considered:
Min Size of Investment Considered (000s): $10,000
Max Size of Investment Considered: No Limit

Geographical Preferences

International Preferences:
Italy
Spain
France

Industry Focus

(% based on actual investment)

Consumer Related	61.9%
Medical/Health	38.1%

Additional Information

Name of Most Recent Fund: TCR Industrial Partners
Most Recent Fund Was Raised: 06/26/2004
Year Founded: 1988
Capital Under Management: $100,000,000
Current Activity Level : Actively seeking new investments
Method of Compensation: Return on invest. most important, but chg. closing fees, service fees, etc.

TCS CAPITAL LLC

350 Park Avenue
4th Floor
New York, NY USA 10022
Phone: 212-259-2650
Fax: 212-259-2692

Management and Staff

Eamon Smith, Chief Financial Officer

Type of Firm

Private Equity Firm

Additional Information

Year Founded: 2001
Capital Under Management: $11,400,000
Current Activity Level : Actively seeking new investments

TCW CAPITAL

865 South Figueroa Street
Suite 1800
Los Angeles, CA USA 90017
Phone: 213-244-0000
Fax: 213-244-0489
E-mail: feedback@tcw.com
Website: www.tcwgroup.com

Other Offices

1251 Avenue of the Americas
Suite 4700
New York, NY USA 10020
Phone: 212-771-4000
Fax: 212-771-4079

11100 Santa Monica Boulevard
West Los Angeles, CA USA 90025
Phone: 310-235-5900

333 Clay Street
Suite 4150
Houston, TX USA 77002
Phone: 713-615-7400

Management and Staff

David DeVito, Chief Financial Officer
James Lewis, Vice President
Marc Stern, President
Robert Day, Chief Executive Officer

Type of Firm

Bank Affiliated

Project Preferences

Role in Financing:

Prefer role as deal originator

Type of Financing Preferred:

Leveraged Buyout
Expansion
Mezzanine
Balanced
Later Stage
Other
Special Situation
Distressed Debt

Size of Investments Considered:

Min Size of Investment Considered (000s): $5,000
Max Size of Investment Considered: No Limit

Geographical Preferences

United States Preferences:

All U.S.

International Preferences:

China
All International

Industry Focus

(% based on actual investment)

Industrial/Energy	47.6%
Other Products	26.6%
Consumer Related	12.8%
Communications and Media	7.0%
Medical/Health	3.7%
Computer Hardware	1.6%
Computer Software and Services	0.5%
Semiconductors/Other Elect.	0.2%

Additional Information

Name of Most Recent Fund: European Clean Energy Fund, L.P.
Most Recent Fund Was Raised: 06/12/2006
Year Founded: 1984
Capital Under Management: $750,000,000
Current Activity Level : Actively seeking new investments
Method of Compensation: Return on investment is of primary concern, do not charge fees

---

TCW CAPITAL VENTURES LLC (AKA: TCW HOLDINGS LLC)

3050 Coronado Drive
Santa Clara, CA USA 95050

Management and Staff

David Weng, General Partner
Michael Chiu, General Partner

Type of Firm

Private Equity Firm

Additional Information

Year Founded: 2006
Capital Under Management: $10,100,000
Current Activity Level : Actively seeking new investments

TD CAPITAL GROUP LTD. (AKA: TORONTO DOMINION CAPITAL)

111 Huntington Ave
Suite 1400
Boston, MA USA 02199
Phone: 617-425-0800
Fax: 617-425-0801
E-mail: info@tdcapital.com
Website: www.tdcapital.com

Other Offices

79 Wellington Street West
6th Floor
Toronto, Canada M5K 1A2
Phone: 866-831-2343
Fax: 416-983-9763

909 Fannin
Suite 1700
Houston, TX USA 77010
Phone: 713-653-8200
Fax: 713-652-2647

Management and Staff

Ian Kidson, Managing Director
John Greenwood, Managing Director
Mel Gabel, Chief Financial Officer
Robert MacLellan, President
Stuart Waugh, Managing Director
Tom Rashotte, Managing Director

Type of Firm

Bank Affiliated

Association Membership

Canadian Venture Capital Association

Project Preferences

Role in Financing:

Will function either as deal originator or investor in deals created by others

Type of Financing Preferred:

Fund of Funds
Leveraged Buyout
Early Stage
Expansion
Mezzanine
Generalist PE
Balanced
Management Buyouts
Recapitalizations

Size of Investments Considered:

Min Size of Investment Considered (000s): $500
Max Size of Investment Considered: No Limit

Geographical Preferences

United States Preferences:

All U.S.

Canadian Preferences:

All Canada

International Preferences:

Europe

Industry Focus

(% based on actual investment)

Other Products	24.1%
Communications and Media	23.4%
Internet Specific	19.4%
Medical/Health	12.8%
Industrial/Energy	9.1%
Consumer Related	6.8%
Computer Software and Services	3.2%

Semiconductors/Other Elect. 1.2%
Computer Hardware 0.1%

Additional Information

Year Founded: 1995
Capital Under Management: $120,000,000
Current Activity Level : Actively seeking new investments
Method of Compensation: Return on invest. most important, but chg. closing fees, service fees, etc.

TD CAPITAL PRIVATE EQUITY INVESTORS

79 Wellington Street West
Sixth Floor
Toronto, Canada M5K 1A2
Phone: 866-831-2343
Fax: 416-983-9763
E-mail: peinvestors@tdcapital.com
Website: www.tdcapital.com

Other Offices

Triton Court
14/18 Finsbury Square
London, United Kingdom EC2A 1DB
Phone: 44-20-7448-8385
Fax: 44-20-7588-8374

Management and Staff

David Austin, Vice President
Jeff Pentland, Vice President
John Greenwood, Managing Director
Melissa McJannet, Vice President
Stuart Waugh, Managing Director

Type of Firm

Private Equity Advisor or Fund of Funds

Project Preferences

Type of Financing Preferred:

Fund of Funds
Early Stage
Expansion

Size of Investments Considered:

Min Size of Investment Considered (000s): $1,000
Max Size of Investment Considered (000s): $10,000

Geographical Preferences

United States Preferences:

All U.S.

Canadian Preferences:

All Canada

International Preferences:

Europe
Asia
All International

Industry Preferences

In Communications prefer:

Wireless Communications

In Computer Software prefer:

Software

In Semiconductor/Electr prefer:

Semiconductor

Additional Information

Year Founded: 1969
Capital Under Management: $200,000,000
Current Activity Level : Actively seeking new investments

TDA CAPITAL PARTNERS, INC.

15 River Road
Suite 245
Wilton, CT USA 06897
Phone: 203-762-7637
Fax: 203-762-7972
E-mail: info@tdacapital.com
Website: www.tdacapital.com

Other Offices

156-157, Nariman Bhavan
15th Floor
Mumbai, India 400 021
Phone: 91-22-204-2635
Fax: 91-22-204-2637

Management and Staff

Girish Kulkarni, Partner

Type of Firm

Private Equity Firm

Association Membership

Polish Venture Capital Association (PSIC/PPEA)

Project Preferences

Type of Financing Preferred:

Balanced

Geographical Preferences

International Preferences:

India
All International

Additional Information

Year Founded: 1996
Current Activity Level : Actively seeking new investments

TDK CORPORATION

1-13-1 Nihonbashi
Chuo-ku
Tokyo, Japan 103
Phone: 81-3-5201-7100
Website: www.tdk.co.jp

Management and Staff

Hajime Sawabe, Chairman & CEO
Takehiro Kamigama, President & COO

Type of Firm

Corporate PE/Venture

Project Preferences

Type of Financing Preferred:

Balanced

Geographical Preferences

International Preferences:

All International

Additional Information

Year Founded: 2000
Current Activity Level : Actively seeking new investments

TDR CAPITAL LLP

One Stanhope Gate
London, United Kingdom W1K 1AF
Phone: 44-20-7399-4200
Fax: 44-20-7399-4242
E-mail: info@tdrcapital.com
Website: www.tdrcapital.com

Management and Staff

Jonathan Rosen, Partner
Manjit Dale, Founding Partner
Stephen Robertson, Founding Partner

Type of Firm

Private Equity Firm

Association Membership

British Venture Capital Association (BVCA)

Project Preferences

Type of Financing Preferred:

Leveraged Buyout
Management Buyouts

Geographical Preferences

International Preferences:

Europe

Additional Information

Name of Most Recent Fund: TDR Capital II
Most Recent Fund Was Raised: 07/03/2006
Year Founded: 2002
Capital Under Management: $2,815,000,000
Current Activity Level : Actively seeking new investments

TEACHERS INSURANCE & ANNUITY ASSOCIATION COLLEGE RETIREMENT

730 Third Avenue
New York, NY USA 10017-3206
Phone: 212-916-5244
Fax: 212-907-2454
Website: www.tiaa-cref.org

Management and Staff
Sheryl Schwartz, Managing Director

Type of Firm
Endowment, Foundation or Pension Fund

Project Preferences

Role in Financing:
Prefer role in deals created by others

Type of Financing Preferred:
Leveraged Buyout
Early Stage
Generalist PE
Balanced
Later Stage
Other
Distressed Debt

Size of Investments Considered:
Min Size of Investment Considered (000s): $25
Max Size of Investment Considered (000s): $200

Geographical Preferences

International Preferences:
Europe
Asia

Industry Preferences

In Communications prefer:
Telecommunications

In Medical/Health prefer:
Pharmaceuticals

In Consumer Related prefer:
Consumer Products
Consumer Services

In Industrial/Energy prefer:
Energy

In Financial Services prefer:
Financial Services
Insurance

In Manufact. prefer:
Manufacturing

Additional Information
Year Founded: 1918
Capital Under Management: $6,000,000,000
Current Activity Level : Actively seeking new investments
Method of Compensation: Return on investment is of primary concern, do not charge fees

---

TEACHIWORLD VENTURE INVESTMENT COMPANY, LTD.
5th Floor, KTMF Bldg., 35-3
Youido-dong, Youngdungpo-gu
Seoul, South Korea 150 010
Phone: 822-785-2996
Fax: 822-785-2535

Management and Staff
Seunghan Kim, President

Type of Firm
Government Affiliated Program

Project Preferences

Type of Financing Preferred:
Balanced

Geographical Preferences

International Preferences:
Korea, South

Industry Preferences

In Biotechnology prefer:
Biotechnology

Additional Information
Year Founded: 1990
Capital Under Management: $80,500,000
Current Activity Level : Actively seeking new investments

TEAKWOOD CAPITAL, L.P.
Douglas Plaza
8226 Douglas Avenue, Suite 355
Dallas, TX USA 75225
Phone: 214-750-1590
Fax: 214-750-1468
E-mail: contact@teakwoodcapital.com
Website: www.teakwoodcapital.com

Management and Staff
Daniel Shimer, Managing Director
Ed Olkkola, Managing Director
Richard Beckert, Managing Director
Shawn Kelly, Managing Director

Type of Firm
Private Equity Firm

Project Preferences

Type of Financing Preferred:
Mezzanine
Management Buyouts
Acquisition

Size of Investments Considered:
Min Size of Investment Considered (000s): $1,000
Max Size of Investment Considered (000s): $20,000

Geographical Preferences

United States Preferences:
Texas

Additional Information
Year Founded: 2009
Current Activity Level : Actively seeking new investments

TEASSES CAPITAL, LTD.
Teasses House
Teasses Estate, Ceres
Fife, United Kingdom KY8 5PG
Phone: 44-131-225-0911

Management and Staff
Andy Macfie, Managing Director

Type of Firm
Private Equity Firm

Project Preferences

Type of Financing Preferred:
Early Stage
Expansion
Balanced
Management Buyouts

Size of Investments Considered:
Min Size of Investment Considered (000s): $530
Max Size of Investment Considered (000s): $8,842

Geographical Preferences

International Preferences:
United Kingdom
Europe

Additional Information
Year Founded: 2001
Current Activity Level : Actively seeking new investments

TECH CAPITAL PARTNERS
8 Erb Street West
Waterloo, Canada N2L 1S7
Phone: 519-883-8255
Fax: 519-883-1265
Website: www.techcapital.com

Management and Staff
Andrew Abouchar, Partner
Jacqui Murphy, Vice President
Tim Jackson, Partner

Type of Firm
Private Equity Advisor or Fund of Funds

Association Membership
Canadian Venture Capital Association

Project Preferences

Role in Financing:
Prefer role as deal originator

Type of Financing Preferred:
Early Stage
Start-up Financing
Seed
First Stage Financing

Size of Investments Considered:
Min Size of Investment Considered (000s): $4,500
Max Size of Investment Considered (000s): $4,500

Geographical Preferences

Canadian Preferences:
All Canada
Ontario

Industry Preferences

In Communications prefer:
Commercial Communications
CATV & Pay TV Systems
Radio & TV Broadcasting
Telecommunications
Wireless Communications
Data Communications
Satellite Microwave Comm.
Other Communication Prod.

In Semiconductor/Electr prefer:
Electronic Components
Semiconductor
Micro-Processing
Controllers and Sensors
Sensors
Circuit Boards
Component Testing Equipmt
Laser Related
Fiber Optics
Analytic/Scientific

Additional Information
Year Founded: 2001
Capital Under Management: $35,000,000
Current Activity Level : Actively seeking new investments
Method of Compensation: Return on invest. most important, but chg. closing fees, service fees, etc.

TECH COAST ANGELS, INC. (AKA: TCA)
3720 Hughes Avenue
Suite 5
Los Angeles, CA USA 90034
Phone: 310-841-2345
Fax: 310-841-2346
Website: www.techcoastangels.com

Type of Firm
Angel Group

Project Preferences

Type of Financing Preferred:
Early Stage
Seed

Size of Investments Considered:
Min Size of Investment Considered (000s): $250
Max Size of Investment Considered (000s): $2,000

Geographical Preferences

United States Preferences:
Southern California

Additional Information
Year Founded: 1997
Current Activity Level : Actively seeking new investments

TECHBANC, INC.
121 King Street West
Suite 2525
Toronto, Canada M5H 3T9
Phone: 416-947-1492
Fax: 416-947-9673

Type of Firm
Private Equity Advisor or Fund of Funds

Additional Information
Year Founded: 2000
Current Activity Level : Actively seeking new investments

TECHFARM VENTURES (AKA:TECHFUND CAPITAL)
4750 Patrick Henry Drive
Santa Clara, CA USA 95054
Phone: 408-492-0142
Fax: 408-492-0182
E-mail: info@techfarm.com
Website: www.techfarm.com

Management and Staff
Gordon Campbell, Managing Director
Laura Onopchenko, Managing Director

Type of Firm
Private Equity Firm

Association Membership
National Venture Capital Association - USA (NVCA)

Project Preferences

Role in Financing:
Will function either as deal originator or investor in deals created by others

Type of Financing Preferred:
Early Stage
Later Stage
Seed
First Stage Financing

Size of Investments Considered:
Min Size of Investment Considered (000s): $1,500
Max Size of Investment Considered (000s): $10,000

Geographical Preferences

United States Preferences:
Northern California
All U.S.

Industry Focus
(% based on actual investment)

Semiconductors/Other Elect.	62.6%
Communications and Media	13.4%
Computer Hardware	11.8%
Computer Software and Services	9.6%
Internet Specific	2.7%

Additional Information
Name of Most Recent Fund: TechFarm Ventures
Most Recent Fund Was Raised: 12/18/2000
Year Founded: 1997
Capital Under Management: $73,000,000
Current Activity Level : Actively seeking new investments
Method of Compensation: Return on investment is of primary concern, do not charge fees

---

TECHFUND CAPITAL
200 West Evelyn Avenue
Suite 100
Mountain View, CA USA 94041
Phone: 650-934-0900
Fax: 650-934-0910
Website: www.techfarm.com

Other Offices
233 rue de la Croix Nivert, suite 10
Paris, France 75015
Phone: 44-1404-430-020

Management and Staff
Gordon Campbell, Managing Director
James Whims, Managing Director
Kurt Keilhockor, Managing Director

Type of Firm
Private Equity Firm

Additional Information
Year Founded: 1997
Capital Under Management: $95,000,000
Current Activity Level : Actively seeking new investments

TECHFUND CAPITAL EUROPE MANAGEMENT SAS
233, rue de la Croix-Nivert
Suite 10
Paris, France 75015
Phone: 33-1-4043-0020
Fax: 33-1-4043-0111
E-mail: contact@techfundcapitaleurope.com
Website: www.techfundcapitaleurope.com

Management and Staff
Francoise Lohezic, Partner
Jean-Michel Barbier, Managing Partner
Kurt Keilhacker, Partner

Type of Firm
Private Equity Firm

Association Membership
French Venture Capital Association (AFIC)

Project Preferences
Type of Financing Preferred:
Early Stage
Seed
Startup

Geographical Preferences
International Preferences:
Europe
Germany
France

Industry Preferences
In Communications prefer:
Telecommunications
Wireless Communications

In Computer Software prefer:
Software

In Business Serv. prefer:
Media

Additional Information
Year Founded: 2000
Capital Under Management: $22,600,000
Current Activity Level : Actively seeking new investments

TECHINA INVESTMENT MANAGEMENT LTD
Rm 2614, China Merchant Tower
161 Eastern Lu Jia Zui Road
Shanghai, China
Phone: 86-21-5882-8186
Fax: 86-21-5054-1122
Website: www.itechina.com

Management and Staff
Li Qi, Managing Partner

Type of Firm
Private Equity Firm

Project Preferences
Type of Financing Preferred:
Mezzanine
Balanced
Seed

Geographical Preferences
International Preferences:
China

Industry Preferences
In Communications prefer:
Commercial Communications
Wireless Communications

In Medical/Health prefer:
Medical Products

Additional Information
Year Founded: 2001
Capital Under Management: $40,000,000
Current Activity Level : Actively seeking new investments

TECHNIKOS
20 St. Dunstan's Hill
London, United Kingdom EC3R 8HL
Phone: 44-20-7929-8560
Fax: 44-20-7929-7934
E-mail: info@technikos.co.uk
Website: www.technikos.co.uk

Management and Staff
Anthony Colletta, Managing Partner

Type of Firm
Private Equity Firm

Project Preferences
Type of Financing Preferred:
Leveraged Buyout
Early Stage
Expansion
Balanced
Seed

Geographical Preferences
International Preferences:
United Kingdom

Industry Preferences
In Medical/Health prefer:
Medical/Health
Medical Therapeutics
Medical Products

Additional Information
Year Founded: 2006
Current Activity Level : Actively seeking new investments

TECHNOLOGY CROSSOVER VENTURES
528 Ramona Street
Palo Alto, CA USA 94301
Phone: 650-614-8200
Fax: 650-614-8222
E-mail: IR@tcv.com
Website: www.tcv.com

Other Offices
750 Third Avenue
Suite 2300
New York, NY USA 10017
Phone: 212—808-0200
Fax: 212-808-0259

56 Main Street
Suite 210
Millburn, NJ USA 07041
Phone: 973-467-5320
Fax: 973-467-5323

Management and Staff
Carla Newell, General Partner
Christopher Marshall, General Partner
David Yuan, Principal
Eric Liaw, Vice President
Gregory Stanger, Venture Partner
Henry Feinberg, Venture Partner
Jake Reynolds, General Partner
Jerome Hershey, Vice President
John Rosenberg, Principal
John Drew, General Partner
Peter Harding, Vice President
Rick Fenton, Principal
Robert Solomon, Venture Partner
Robert Trudeau, General Partner
William Griffith, General Partner
Yidrienne Lai, Vice President

Type of Firm
Private Equity Firm

Association Membership
Western Association of Venture Capitalists (WAVC)
National Venture Capital Association - USA (NVCA)

Project Preferences
Role in Financing:
Prefer role as deal originator but will also invest in deals created by others

Type of Financing Preferred:
Second Stage Financing
Leveraged Buyout
Expansion
Public Companies
Later Stage
Acquisition
Recapitalizations

Size of Investments Considered:
Min Size of Investment Considered (000s): $20,000
Max Size of Investment Considered (000s): $200,000

Geographical Preferences
United States Preferences:
All U.S.

Canadian Preferences:
All Canada

Industry Focus

(% based on actual investment)

Internet Specific	32.5%
Consumer Related	24.7%
Computer Software and Services	18.9%
Other Products	11.3%
Communications and Media	10.2%
Computer Hardware	1.7%
Semiconductors/Other Elect.	0.6%

Additional Information

Name of Most Recent Fund: Technology Crossover Ventures VII, L.P.
Most Recent Fund Was Raised: 11/06/2007
Year Founded: 1995
Capital Under Management: $7,716,000,000
Current Activity Level : Actively seeking new investments
Method of Compensation: Return on investment is of primary concern, do not charge fees

TECHNOLOGY FUNDING

460 St. Michael's Drive
Building 1000
Santa Fe, NM USA 87505
Phone: 505-982-2200
Fax: 505-820-6900
E-mail: businessplans@technologyfunding.com
Website: www.technologyfunding.com

Other Offices

1107 Investment Boulevard
Suite 180
El Dorado Hills, CA USA 95762
Phone: 916-941-1400
Fax: 916-941-7551

Management and Staff

Charles Kokesh, Managing General Partner

Type of Firm

Incubator/Development Program

Association Membership

Western Association of Venture Capitalists (WAVC)

Project Preferences

Role in Financing:

Prefer role in deals created by others

Type of Financing Preferred:

Early Stage
Expansion
Joint Ventures

Geographical Preferences

United States Preferences:

Northern California

Industry Focus

(% based on actual investment)

Biotechnology	18.4%
Medical/Health	16.5%
Industrial/Energy	15.3%
Computer Hardware	13.1%
Internet Specific	11.5%
Computer Software and Services	9.5%
Semiconductors/Other Elect.	6.8%
Communications and Media	5.4%
Other Products	3.1%
Consumer Related	0.5%

Additional Information

Year Founded: 1979
Capital Under Management: $315,000,000
Current Activity Level : Actively seeking new investments
Method of Compensation: Other

TECHNOLOGY INNOVATION (AKA: TEKNOLOGISK INNOVATION AS)

Gregersensvej 1A
P.O. Box 141
Taastrup, Denmark 2630
Phone: 45-7220-2800
Fax: 45-7220-2802
Website: www.teknologisk.dk

Type of Firm

Incubator/Development Program

Project Preferences

Type of Financing Preferred:

Seed

Geographical Preferences

International Preferences:

Denmark

Industry Preferences

In Communications prefer:

Wireless Communications

In Computer Software prefer:

Software

In Computer Other prefer:

Computer Related

In Utilities prefer:

Utilities

Additional Information

Year Founded: 1998
Capital Under Management: $17,700,000
Current Activity Level : Actively seeking new investments

TECHNOLOGY PARTNERS

550 University Avenue
Palo Alto, CA USA 94301
Phone: 650-289-9000
Fax: 650-289-9001
E-mail: admin@technologypartners.com
Website: www.technologypartners.com

Other Offices

100 Shoreline Highway
Suite 282, Building B
Mill Valley, CA USA 94941
Phone: 415-332-9999
Fax: 415-332-9998

Management and Staff

Ira Ehrenpreis, Partner
James Glasheen, General Partner
Roger Quy, General Partner
Ted Ardell, General Partner

Type of Firm

Private Equity Firm

Association Membership

Western Association of Venture Capitalists (WAVC)
National Venture Capital Association - USA (NVCA)

Project Preferences

Role in Financing:

Prefer role as deal originator but will also invest in deals created by others

Type of Financing Preferred:

Early Stage
Seed
First Stage Financing

Size of Investments Considered:

Min Size of Investment Considered (000s): $2,000
Max Size of Investment Considered (000s): $8,000

Geographical Preferences

United States Preferences:

Rocky Mountain
West Coast

Industry Focus

(% based on actual investment)

Medical/Health	18.6%
Industrial/Energy	16.6%
Computer Software and Services	15.6%
Biotechnology	14.5%
Internet Specific	8.6%
Communications and Media	7.4%
Semiconductors/Other Elect.	6.8%
Computer Hardware	4.2%
Other Products	4.1%
Consumer Related	3.7%

Additional Information

Name of Most Recent Fund: Technology Partners Fund VIII, LP
Most Recent Fund Was Raised: 08/03/2007
Year Founded: 1984
Capital Under Management: $400,000,000
Current Activity Level : Actively seeking new investments
Method of Compensation: Return on investment is of primary concern, do not charge fees

TECHNOLOGY VENTURE PARTNERS

8500 Normandale Lake Boulevard
Suite 2170
Minneapolis, MN USA 55437
Phone: 952-646-3000
Fax: 952-646-3010
E-mail: email@tvp.com
Website: www.tvp.com

Management and Staff

Bryson Hollimon, Managing General Partner
Mark Kunkel, Principal

Type of Firm

Private Equity Firm

Project Preferences

Role in Financing:
Will function either as deal originator or investor in deals created by others

Type of Financing Preferred:
Early Stage
Expansion

Size of Investments Considered:
Min Size of Investment Considered (000s): $2,000
Max Size of Investment Considered (000s): $10,000

Geographical Preferences

Canadian Preferences:
All Canada

Industry Preferences

In Communications prefer:
Telecommunications
Data Communications

In Computer Software prefer:
Software

In Semiconductor/Electr prefer:
Semiconductor
Fiber Optics

Additional Information

Year Founded: 2000
Capital Under Management: $85,000,000
Current Activity Level : Actively seeking new investments
Method of Compensation: Return on investment is of primary concern, do not charge fees

TECHNOLOGY VENTURE PARTNERS PTY LTD.

Suite 4, Jones Bay Wharf 19-21
26-32 Pirrama Road
Pyrmont, Australia 2009
Phone: 612-9562-9000
Fax: 612-9562-9001
E-mail: enquiries@tvp.com.au
Website: www.tvp.com.au

Other Offices

555 Bryant Street
#556
Palo Alto, CA USA 94301
Phone: 415-516-0618

Management and Staff

Allan Aaron, General Partner
John Murray, General Partner
Michael Zimmerman, Principal

Type of Firm

Private Equity Firm

Association Membership

Australian Venture Capital Association (AVCAL)

Project Preferences

Role in Financing:
Prefer role as deal originator

Type of Financing Preferred:
Second Stage Financing
Early Stage
Expansion
Seed
First Stage Financing
Startup

Size of Investments Considered:
Min Size of Investment Considered (000s): $403
Max Size of Investment Considered (000s): $8,058

Geographical Preferences

International Preferences:
Pacific
Australia
New Zealand
Asia

Industry Focus

(% based on actual investment)

Internet Specific	50.5%
Computer Software and Services	22.2%
Semiconductors/Other Elect.	9.2%
Computer Hardware	8.8%
Industrial/Energy	4.8%
Other Products	2.4%
Biotechnology	1.7%
Communications and Media	0.3%

Additional Information

Name of Most Recent Fund: TVP No.3 Fund
Most Recent Fund Was Raised: 02/07/2001
Year Founded: 1997
Capital Under Management: $141,800,000
Current Activity Level : Actively seeking new investments
Method of Compensation: Return on investment is of primary concern, do not charge fees

TECHNOPLUS VENTURES

24 Raul Wallenberg Street
Tel Aviv, Israel 69719
Phone: 972 3 766 6555
Fax: 972 3 766 6556
E-mail: info@technoplusvc.com
Website: www.technoplusvc.com

Management and Staff

Dror Gad, Chief Executive Officer

Type of Firm

Private Equity Firm

Project Preferences

Type of Financing Preferred:
Seed
Startup

Size of Investments Considered:
Min Size of Investment Considered (000s): $200
Max Size of Investment Considered (000s): $200,000

Geographical Preferences

International Preferences:
Israel

Industry Preferences

In Communications prefer:
Communications and Media
Telecommunications

In Medical/Health prefer:
Medical/Health

Additional Information

Year Founded: 1997
Capital Under Management: $50,000,000
Current Activity Level : Actively seeking new investments

TECHNOSTARS

BOM Starterscentrum
Eutechpark MMP 0.10, Horsten 1
Eindhoven, Netherlands 5612 AX
Phone: 40-29-399-55
Fax: 40-29-399-54
E-mail: starterscentrum@bom.nl
Website: www.technostars.nl

Type of Firm

Private Equity Firm

Additional Information

Current Activity Level : Actively seeking new investments

TECHNOSTART GMBH

Martin-Luther-Strasse 57
Ludwigsburg, Germany 71636
Phone: 49-7141-971-590
Fax: 49-7141-9715910
E-mail: office@technostart.com
Website: www.technostart.com

Management and Staff

Jochen Kohlhaas, Chief Financial Officer
Michael Mayer, Founder

Type of Firm

Private Equity Firm

Association Membership

German Venture Capital Association (BVK)
European Private Equity and Venture Capital Assoc.

Project Preferences

Type of Financing Preferred:
Early Stage
Seed
Startup

Size of Investments Considered:
Min Size of Investment Considered (000s): $300
Max Size of Investment Considered (000s): $300,000

Geographical Preferences

International Preferences:
Europe
Germany

Industry Focus

(% based on actual investment)

Biotechnology	42.4%
Medical/Health	23.1%
Semiconductors/Other Elect.	20.1%
Computer Software and Services	9.1%
Internet Specific	3.7%
Communications and Media	1.6%

Additional Information

Name of Most Recent Fund: Zweite TechnoStart Ventures Fond & Co. KG
Most Recent Fund Was Raised: 05/31/2001
Year Founded: 1991
Capital Under Management: $30,000,000
Current Activity Level : Actively seeking new investments

TECHOPERATORS LLC

75 Fifth Street NorthWest
Suite 422
Atlanta, GA USA 30327
Phone: 770-330-0812
E-mail: info@techoperators.com
Website: www.techoperators.com

Management and Staff

Glenn McGonnigle, General Partner
Said Mohammadioun, Managing Partner

Type of Firm

Private Equity Firm

Project Preferences

Type of Financing Preferred:
Early Stage

Industry Preferences

In Computer Software prefer:
Software

In Internet Specific prefer:
Internet

Additional Information

Year Founded: 2008
Current Activity Level : Actively seeking new investments

TECHSTARS

1756, 114th Avenue Southeast
Suite 110
Bellevue, WA USA 98004
Phone: 425-467-2272
Website: www.techstars.org

Management and Staff

Bradley Feld, Co-Founder
David Brown, Co-Founder
Jared Polis, Co-Founder

Type of Firm

Private Equity Firm

Project Preferences

Type of Financing Preferred:
Early Stage
Seed
Strategic Alliances
Startup

Geographical Preferences

United States Preferences:
All U.S.

Additional Information

Name of Most Recent Fund: Invention Development Fund I, LLC
Most Recent Fund Was Raised: 08/16/2007
Year Founded: 2007
Capital Under Management: $458,000,000
Current Activity Level : Actively seeking new investments

TECHXAS VENTURES LLC

4401 West Gate Boulevard
Suite 300
Austin, TX USA 78745
Phone: 512-334-3140
Fax: 512-334-3121
E-mail: ventures@techxas.com
Website: www.techxas.com

Management and Staff

Bruce Ezell, Managing Director

Type of Firm

Service Provider

Association Membership

National Venture Capital Association - USA (NVCA)

Project Preferences

Role in Financing:
Will function either as deal originator or investor in deals created by others

Type of Financing Preferred:
Second Stage Financing
Early Stage
Seed
First Stage Financing
Joint Ventures
Startup

Size of Investments Considered:
Min Size of Investment Considered (000s): $100
Max Size of Investment Considered (000s): $3,000

Geographical Preferences

United States Preferences:
Texas

Industry Focus

(% based on actual investment)

Computer Software and Services	37.7%
Internet Specific	25.1%
Computer Hardware	15.4%
Communications and Media	9.7%
Semiconductors/Other Elect.	6.5%
Industrial/Energy	2.9%
Medical/Health	2.7%

Additional Information

Name of Most Recent Fund: Techxas Fund II
Most Recent Fund Was Raised: 06/20/2007
Year Founded: 1998
Capital Under Management: $66,000,000
Current Activity Level : Actively seeking new investments
Method of Compensation: Return on investment is of primary concern, do not charge fees

TECNET EQUITY TECHNOLOGIEBETEILIGUNGS-INVEST AG

Bahnhofplatz 10
St. Poelten, Austria 3100
Phone: 43-2742-365-440
Fax: 43-274236544400
E-mail: office@tecnet.co.at
Website: www.tecnet.co.at

Type of Firm

Private Equity Firm

Association Membership

European Private Equity and Venture Capital Assoc.

Project Preferences

Type of Financing Preferred:
Early Stage
Expansion
Startup

Size of Investments Considered:
Min Size of Investment Considered (000s): $4,091
Max Size of Investment Considered (000s): $20,455

Geographical Preferences

International Preferences:
Europe
Austria

Industry Preferences

In Communications prefer:
Telecommunications

In Computer Other prefer:
Computer Related

In Semiconductor/Electr prefer:
Electronics

In Biotechnology prefer:
Biotechnology

In Medical/Health prefer:
Medical/Health

In Industrial/Energy prefer:
Energy
Industrial Products
Materials
Factory Automation
Environmental Related

Additional Information

Year Founded: 2002
Capital Under Management: $24,500,000
Current Activity Level : Actively seeking new investments

TECVENTURE PARTNERS GMBH

Maximilianstrasse 35 A
Munich, Germany 80539
Phone: 49-89-2421-8192
Fax: 49-89-2421-8200
E-mail: info@tec-venture.com
Website: www.tec-venture.com

Management and Staff

Edward M Stadum, Managing Partner
Klaus-Jurgen Werner, Chief Financial Officer

Type of Firm

Private Equity Firm

Association Membership

German Venture Capital Association (BVK)

Project Preferences

Type of Financing Preferred:
Early Stage
Expansion
Startup

Geographical Preferences

International Preferences:
Europe
Germany

Industry Preferences

In Communications prefer:
Telecommunications

In Computer Software prefer:
Software

In Internet Specific prefer:
E-Commerce Technology
Internet

In Biotechnology prefer:
Biotechnology

In Medical/Health prefer:
Medical/Health

In Industrial/Energy prefer:
Factory Automation

Additional Information

Year Founded: 2000
Capital Under Management: $65,300,000
Current Activity Level : Actively seeking new investments

TEKNOINVEST MANAGEMENT AS

Grev Wedels plass 5
Postboks 566 Sentrum
Oslo, Norway 0151
Phone: 47-22-979-000
Fax: 47-22-979-001
E-mail: teknoinvest@teknoinvest.com
Website: www.teknoinvest.com

Other Offices

Radhusgt 5B
Oslo, Norway N-0151
Phone: 47-2-2330020
Fax: 47-2-2421041

Management and Staff

Andreas Mollatt, Partner
Bjorn Bjora, Managing Partner
Christian Winther, Chief Financial Officer
Hadar Cars, Partner
Steinar Engelsen, Partner
Steven Morrell, Partner
Tore Mengshoel, Partner

Type of Firm

Private Equity Advisor or Fund of Funds

Association Membership

Norwegian Venture Capital Association

Project Preferences

Role in Financing:
Will function either as deal originator or investor in deals created by others

Type of Financing Preferred:
Second Stage Financing
Early Stage
Expansion
Start-up Financing
Balanced
First Stage Financing
Startup

Size of Investments Considered:
Min Size of Investment Considered (000s): $500
Max Size of Investment Considered (000s): $5,000

Geographical Preferences

United States Preferences:
All U.S.

International Preferences:
Europe
Scandanavia/Nordic Region

Industry Preferences

In Communications prefer:
Communications and Media

In Computer Hardware prefer:
Terminals

In Computer Other prefer:
Computer Related

In Semiconductor/Electr prefer:
Electronics

In Biotechnology prefer:
Biotechnology

In Medical/Health prefer:
Medical/Health

Medical Diagnostics
Diagnostic Services
Diagnostic Test Products
Medical Therapeutics
Drug/Equipmt Delivery
Medical Products

In Industrial/Energy prefer:
Energy

Additional Information

Name of Most Recent Fund: Teknoinvest VIII
Most Recent Fund Was Raised: 07/02/2002
Year Founded: 1984
Capital Under Management: $105,900,000
Current Activity Level : Actively seeking new investments
Method of Compensation: Return on investment is of primary concern, do not charge fees

---

TEKNOSEED AB

Ideon Innovation
Ideon
Lund, Sweden 223 70
Phone: 46-46-286-8756
Fax: 46-46-286-8755
E-mail: info@teknoseed.se
Website: www.teknoseed.se

Management and Staff

Adam Schatz, Managing Director

Type of Firm

Private Equity Firm

Association Membership

Swedish Venture Capital Association (SVCA)
European Private Equity and Venture Capital Assoc.

Project Preferences

Type of Financing Preferred:
Expansion
Balanced
Seed
Startup

Size of Investments Considered:
Min Size of Investment Considered (000s): $235
Max Size of Investment Considered (000s): $423

Geographical Preferences

International Preferences:
Sweden
Europe
Denmark

Industry Preferences

In Biotechnology prefer:
Biotechnology

In Industrial/Energy prefer:
Energy

Additional Information

Year Founded: 1997
Capital Under Management: $26,800,000
Current Activity Level : Actively seeking new investments

TEKNOVENTURE MANAGEMENT OY

Isokatu 32 B
Oulu, Finland 90100
Phone: 358-8-887-3300
Fax: 358-8-887-3310
E-mail: info@teknoventure.fi
Website: www.teknoventure.fi

Management and Staff

Ilkka Lukkariniemi, Partner
Kari Italahti, Partner
Mauri Visuri, Partner
Tuulikki Marjomaa, Partner

Type of Firm

Private Equity Advisor or Fund of Funds

Association Membership

Finnish Venture Capital Association (FVCA)

Project Preferences

Type of Financing Preferred:
Leveraged Buyout
Expansion
Balanced
Turnaround
Seed
Startup

Size of Investments Considered:
Min Size of Investment Considered (000s): $200
Max Size of Investment Considered (000s): $200,000

Geographical Preferences

International Preferences:
Finland

Industry Preferences

In Communications prefer:
Communications and Media

In Computer Other prefer:
Computer Related

In Biotechnology prefer:
Biotechnology

In Medical/Health prefer:
Medical/Health

In Industrial/Energy prefer:
Industrial Products

Additional Information

Name of Most Recent Fund: Teknoventure Rahasto II Ky
Most Recent Fund Was Raised: 05/30/2002
Year Founded: 1994
Capital Under Management: $46,400,000
Current Activity Level : Actively seeking new investments

TEL VENTURE CAPITAL, INC.

2953 Bunker Hill Lane
Suite 300
Santa Clara, CA USA 95054
Phone: 408-568-4400
Fax: 408-566-4410
E-mail: info@telusa.com
Website: www.telusa.com

Management and Staff

Mike Yamaguchi, President
Ruben Serrato, Venture Partner

Type of Firm

Corporate PE/Venture

Association Membership

National Venture Capital Association - USA (NVCA)

Project Preferences

Type of Financing Preferred:
Early Stage
Expansion
Later Stage
Startup

Industry Preferences

In Communications prefer:
Telecommunications
Wireless Communications
Data Communications

In Computer Software prefer:
Software

In Semiconductor/Electr prefer:
Semiconductor

In Biotechnology prefer:
Biotechnology

In Medical/Health prefer:
Medical/Health

In Manufact. prefer:
Manufacturing

In Other prefer:
Environment Responsible

Additional Information

Year Founded: 2006
Capital Under Management: $10,000,000
Current Activity Level : Actively seeking new investments

TELECOMMUNICATIONS DEVELOPMENT FUND (TDF)

1850 K Street Northwest
Suite 1075
Washington, DC USA 20006
Phone: 202-293-8840
Fax: 202-293-8850
E-mail: info@tdfund.com
Website: www.tdfund.com

Management and Staff

James Pastoriza, Managing Partner
Neal Douglas, Venture Partner

Type of Firm

Private Equity Firm

Association Membership

Natl Assoc of Investment Cos. (NAIC)
Mid-Atlantic Venture Association
Natl Assoc of Small Bus. Inv. Co (NASBIC)
National Venture Capital Association - USA (NVCA)

Project Preferences

Role in Financing:

Will function either as deal originator or investor in deals created by others

Type of Financing Preferred:

Second Stage Financing
Early Stage
Balanced
First Stage Financing

Size of Investments Considered:

Min Size of Investment Considered (000s): $500
Max Size of Investment Considered (000s): $5,000

Industry Focus

(% based on actual investment)

Communications and Media	48.2%
Computer Software and Services	26.8%
Internet Specific	12.1%
Semiconductors/Other Elect.	11.4%
Computer Hardware	1.5%

Additional Information

Name of Most Recent Fund: Telecommunications Development Fund II
Most Recent Fund Was Raised: 08/04/2004
Year Founded: 1996
Capital Under Management: $90,000,000
Current Activity Level : Actively seeking new investments
Method of Compensation: Return on investment is of primary concern, do not charge fees

TELEGRAPH HILL PARTNERS (AKA: THP)

360 Post Street
Suite 601
San Francisco, CA USA 94108
Phone: 415-765-6980
Fax: 415-765-6983
E-mail: info@thpartners.net
Website: www.thpartners.net

Management and Staff

J. Matthew Mackowski, Founder
Robert Shepler, Founder

Type of Firm

Private Equity Firm

Project Preferences

Type of Financing Preferred:

Leveraged Buyout
Early Stage

Size of Investments Considered:

Min Size of Investment Considered (000s): $2,000
Max Size of Investment Considered (000s): $8,000

Geographical Preferences

United States Preferences:

All U.S.

International Preferences:

Europe
Pacific Rim

Industry Preferences

In Communications prefer:

Communications and Media
Telecommunications

In Medical/Health prefer:

Medical Products
Health Services

Additional Information

Year Founded: 2001
Capital Under Management: $42,000,000
Current Activity Level : Actively seeking new investments

TELENOR MOBILE

Snaroyveien 30
P.O. Box Telenor
Fornebu, Norway 1331
Phone: 47-81-07-7000
Website: www.telenormobile.com

Type of Firm

Corporate PE/Venture

Association Membership

Norwegian Venture Capital Association

Additional Information

Current Activity Level : Actively seeking new investments

TELESOFT PARTNERS

950 Tower Lane
Suite 1600
Foster City, CA USA 94404
Phone: 650-358-2500
Fax: 650-358-2501
E-mail: investors@telesoftvc.com
Website: www.telesoftvc.com

Management and Staff

Al Howard, Chief Financial Officer
Alan Foster, Managing Director
Arjun Gupta, Managing Partner
Bill Magill, Managing Director
George Schmitt, Managing Director
Marcia Burkey, Managing Director

Type of Firm

Private Equity Firm

Association Membership

National Venture Capital Association - USA (NVCA)
Natl Assoc of Small Bus. Inv. Co (NASBIC)

Project Preferences

Role in Financing:

Will function either as deal originator or investor in deals created by others

Type of Financing Preferred:

Second Stage Financing
Early Stage
Expansion
Balanced
Seed
Later Stage
First Stage Financing
Private Placement
Special Situation
Startup
Recapitalizations

Size of Investments Considered:

Min Size of Investment Considered (000s): $1,000
Max Size of Investment Considered (000s): $15,000

Geographical Preferences

International Preferences:

Italy
United Kingdom
India
Spain
Israel
Germany
France

Industry Focus

(% based on actual investment)

Communications and Media	37.0%
Semiconductors/Other Elect.	24.9%

Internet Specific	17.3%
Computer Software and Services	13.2%
Computer Hardware	3.3%
Other Products	2.5%
Consumer Related	1.9%

Additional Information

Year Founded: 1997
Capital Under Management: $628,000,000
Current Activity Level : Actively seeking new investments
Method of Compensation: Return on investment is of primary concern, do not charge fees

TELESYSTEM-ARGO GLOBAL CAPITAL (AKA: ARGO GLOBAL CAPITAL)

601 Edgewater Drive
Suite 345
Wakefield, MA USA 01880
Phone: 781-213-9344
Fax: 781-213-9345
E-mail: info@argoglobal.com
Website: www.argoglobal.com

Other Offices

Gainsborough House
2 Sheen Road, Richmond-Upon-Thames
Surrey, United Kingdom TW9 1AE
Phone: 44-20-8973-2643
Fax: 44-20-8973-2641

28th Floor, EIB Center
40-44 Bonham Strand, Sheung Wan
Central, Hong Kong
Phone: 852-2295-2209
Fax: 852-2295-3111

1250 Rene-Levesque Boulevard West
38th Floor
Montreal, Canada H3B 4W8
Phone: 514-397-8444
Fax: 514-397-8445

Management and Staff

Christopher Legg, Partner
Simon Wong, General Partner
Tony Wing-Ming Tsang, Partner
William McHale, Partner

Type of Firm

Private Equity Firm
Association Membership
Hong Kong Venture Capital Association (HKVCA)

Project Preferences

Type of Financing Preferred:
Second Stage Financing
Early Stage
Later Stage

Size of Investments Considered:
Min Size of Investment Considered (000s): $3,000
Max Size of Investment Considered (000s): $12,000

Geographical Preferences

International Preferences:
All International

Industry Focus

(% based on actual investment)

Communications and Media	56.2%
Computer Software and Services	23.5%
Internet Specific	12.1%
Semiconductors/Other Elect.	6.3%
Other Products	2.0%

Additional Information

Year Founded: 1997
Capital Under Management: $437,000,000
Current Activity Level : Actively seeking new investments

TELEVENTURE MANAGEMENT AS (FKA: TELENOR VENTURE AS)

Tollbugaten 24
Oslo, Norway 0157
Phone: 47-22-779-910
Fax: 47-22-779-921
E-mail: info@televenture.com
Website: www.telenorventure.no

Management and Staff

Bente Loe, Partner
Patrick Sandahl, Partner

Type of Firm

Corporate PE/Venture

Association Membership

Norwegian Venture Capital Association

Project Preferences

Type of Financing Preferred:
Balanced

Geographical Preferences

International Preferences:
Europe
Scandanavia/Nordic Region

Industry Preferences

In Communications prefer:
Communications and Media
Commercial Communications
Telecommunications
Wireless Communications

Additional Information

Year Founded: 1993
Current Activity Level : Actively seeking new investments

TELUS VENTURES

3777 Kingsway
12th Floor
Vancouver, Canada V5H 3Z7
Phone: 604-432-2150
Fax: 604-438-0325
E-mail: ventureinfo@telus.com
Website: www.telus.com/ventures

Management and Staff

Mathew George, Vice President

Type of Firm

Corporate PE/Venture

Association Membership

Canadian Venture Capital Association

Project Preferences

Type of Financing Preferred:
Early Stage
Expansion
Seed
Startup

Geographical Preferences

Canadian Preferences:
All Canada

Industry Preferences

In Communications prefer:
Wireless Communications

In Internet Specific prefer:
Internet

Additional Information

Year Founded: 2001
Capital Under Management: $100,000,000
Current Activity Level : Actively seeking new investments

TEMASEK HOLDINGS PVT., LTD.

60B Orchard Road, 6-18 Tower 2
The Atrium, Orchard
Singapore, Singapore 238891
Phone: 65-6828-6828
Fax: 65-6821-1188
E-mail: enquire@temasek.com.sg
Website: www.temasekholdings.com.sg

Other Offices

Suite 1806, Two Pacific Place
88 Queensway
Central, Hong Kong
Phone: 852-3589-3200
Fax: 852-2156-1180

Unit 2201, Plaza 66
1266 Nan Jing Xi Road

Shanghai, China 200040
Phone: 86-21-6133-1900
Fax: 86-21-6133-1901

Unit 406, Level 4, Hanoi Towers
49 Hai Ba Trung Street
Hanoi, Vietnam
Phone: 84-4-3936-9069
Fax: 84-4-3936-9066

F705 Winland Int'l Finance Center
No. 7 Financial Street, Xicheng District
Beijing, China 100140
Phone: 86-10-5930-4900
Fax: 86-10-5930-4901

Ruben Dario 281-1301
Bosque de Chapultepec
Mexico D.F, Mexico 11580
Phone: 52-55-4335-3050
Fax: 55-4335-3099

Express Towers 12th Floor
Nariman Point
Mumbai, India 400 021
Phone: 91-22-6654-5500
Fax: 91-22-6654-5599

65 Le Loi Boulevard, Saigon Centre
5th Floor, Unit 2, District 1
Ho Chi Minh, Vietnam
Phone: 84-8-8212-789
Fax: 84-8-8212-767

ITC Park Sheraton & Towers
Suite 1240, T.T.K. Road
Chennai, India 600 018
Phone: 91-44-4225-5000
Fax: 91-44-4225-5099

Management and Staff

Cheo Hock Kuan, Senior Managing Director
Gan Chee Yen, Senior Managing Director
Hiew Yoon Khong, Senior Managing Director
Leong Wai Leng, Chief Financial Officer
Manish Kejriwal, Senior Managing Director
Michael Dee, Senior Managing Director
Rohit Sipahimalani, Managing Director
Vijay Parekh, Senior Managing Director

Type of Firm

Government Affiliated Program

Project Preferences

Type of Financing Preferred:

Early Stage
Expansion
Mezzanine
Balanced
Seed
Management Buyouts
Startup

Size of Investments Considered:

Min Size of Investment Considered (000s): $5,000
Max Size of Investment Considered: No Limit

Geographical Preferences

International Preferences:

Armenia
Belarus
Kazakhstan
Taiwan
China
Hong Kong
Kyrgyzstan
Tajikistan
Turkmenistan
Azerbaijan
Moldova
Ukraine
Singapore
Uzbekistan
Asia
Russia

Industry Preferences

In Communications prefer:

Telecommunications
Media and Entertainment

In Medical/Health prefer:

Medical/Health
Pharmaceuticals

In Consumer Related prefer:

Retail
Consumer Products

In Industrial/Energy prefer:

Energy

In Transportation prefer:

Transportation

In Financial Services prefer:

Real Estate
Financial Services

Additional Information

Year Founded: 1974
Capital Under Management: $150,000,000
Current Activity Level : Actively seeking new investments

TEMBUSU PARTNERS PTE., LTD.

151 Chin Swee Road
#04-08 Manhattan House
Singapore, Singapore 169876
Phone: 65-6238-7422
Fax: 65-6238-7237
E-mail: enquiry@tembusupartners.com
Website: www.tembusupartners.com

Other Offices

c/o Segitiga Emas Business Park
CBD B 01/01, Jl. Prof. Dr. Satrio Kav. 6
Jakarta, Indonesia 12940
Phone: 62-21-5790-2338

1121 Tongji Tech Plaza, 8F
Zhongshan No.2 (N) Road
Shanghai, China 200092
Phone: 86-21-6598-8632

1513 Zhejiang Dasha, Anzhen Xili
Chaoyang District
Beijing, China
Phone: 86-135-1105-6187

155 Queen Street
P.O. Box 105252
Auckland, New Zealand
Phone: 642-1282-8988

Fourth Floor Menara Multi Purpose
No. Eight Jalan Munshi Abdullah
Kuala Lumpur, Malaysia 50100
Phone: 60-1-6905-0709

87, Lyndhurst Gardens
London, United Kingdom N3 1TE
Phone: 44-7973-640043

Management and Staff

Kim Seng Tan, Co-Founder
Loo Cheng Guan, Managing Director
Peter Lai Hock Meng, Managing Director
Yap Pao Gin, Vice President

Type of Firm

Private Equity Firm

Project Preferences

Type of Financing Preferred:

Leveraged Buyout
Expansion
Later Stage
Acquisition

Geographical Preferences

International Preferences:

India
China
Singapore
Asia

Industry Preferences

In Consumer Related prefer:

Education Related

In Industrial/Energy prefer:

Oil and Gas Exploration
Oil & Gas Drilling,Explor
Industrial Products

Additional Information

Year Founded: 2007
Capital Under Management: $57,000,000
Current Activity Level : Actively seeking new investments

TEMBUSU VENTURES PTE., LTD.

80 Raffles Place
UOB Plaza 1 #51-02
Singapore, Singapore 048624
Phone: 65-6538-3345
Fax: 65-6536-8129
E-mail: contact@tembusuventures.com
Website: www.tembusuventures.com

Management and Staff

Nicholas Chua Hwee Song, Managing Director
Wong Yek Meng, Venture Partner

Type of Firm

Private Equity Firm

Project Preferences

Type of Financing Preferred:
Early Stage
Seed
Startup

Geographical Preferences

International Preferences:
Singapore

Additional Information

Year Founded: 2004
Current Activity Level : Actively seeking new investments

TEMPLETON ASSET MANAGEMENT, LTD.

Seven Temasek Boulevard
#38-03 Suntec Tower One
Singapore, Singapore 038987
Phone: 65-6241-2662
Fax: 65-6332-2295
E-mail: query@franklintempleton.com.sg
Website: www.templeton.com.sg

Other Offices

1st Floor, Empire Tower
26-28 Ham Nghi Boulevard, District 1
Ho Chi Minh City, Vietnam
Phone: 84-8-915-1800
Fax: 84-8-915-1787

P.O. Box 2258
Rancho Cordova, CA USA 95741-2258

2701 Shui On Centre
6-8 Harbour Rd.
Hong Kong, Hong Kong
Phone: 852-2829-0600
Fax: 852-2519-9482

Management and Staff

Fred Kam, Vice President
Thi Thu Lam Nguyen, Vice President

Type of Firm

Bank Affiliated

Project Preferences

Type of Financing Preferred:
Balanced

Geographical Preferences

International Preferences:
China
Singapore
All International

Additional Information

Year Founded: 1994
Capital Under Management: $138,500,000
Current Activity Level : Actively seeking new investments

TENAYA CAPITAL (FKA: LEHMAN BROTHERS VENTURE PARTNERS)

1271 Avenue of the Americas
45th Floor
New York, NY USA 10020
Phone: 212-526-2380
Website: www.lehmanbrothersestate.com

Management and Staff

Ben Boyer, Partner
Brian Melton, Partner
Brian Paul, Partner
Stewart Gollmer, Partner
Thomas Banahan, Managing Director

Type of Firm

Bank Affiliated

Project Preferences

Type of Financing Preferred:
Expansion
Balanced
Later Stage

Industry Preferences

In Computer Other prefer:
Computer Related

Additional Information

Name of Most Recent Fund: Lehman Brothers Venture Partners V, L.P.
Most Recent Fund Was Raised: 09/20/2007
Year Founded: 1995
Capital Under Management: $750,000,000
Current Activity Level : Actively seeking new investments

TENEX GREENHOUSE VENTURES

839 Mitten Road
Burlingame, CA USA 94010
Phone: 650-697-7120
Fax: 650-697-7119
Website: www.10xgreenhouse.com

Management and Staff

Frank Ruderman, Chief Executive Officer
Paul Quadros, Managing Partner
Robert Leach, President & COO
Timothy Mills, Managing Partner

Type of Firm

Private Equity Firm

Project Preferences

Type of Financing Preferred:
Early Stage
Seed
Startup

Geographical Preferences

United States Preferences:
California

Industry Preferences

In Biotechnology prefer:
Biotechnology

Additional Information

Year Founded: 2001
Current Activity Level : Actively seeking new investments

TENNANT CAPITAL PARTNERS LLC

99 Pratt Street
Suite 200
Hartford, CT USA 06103
Phone: 860-280-2140
E-mail: info@tennantcapital.com
Website: www.tennantcapital.com

Management and Staff

Joseph Sargent, Managing Partner
Robert Sargent, Managing Partner
Thomas Sargent, Managing Partner

Type of Firm

Private Equity Firm

Project Preferences

Type of Financing Preferred:
Balanced

Industry Preferences

In Financial Services prefer:
Insurance

In Business Serv. prefer:
Services
Distribution

Additional Information

Year Founded: 2007
Capital Under Management: $200,000
Current Activity Level : Actively seeking new investments

TENNANTS VENTURES

69 Grosvenor St
London, United Kingdom W1K 3BP

Type of Firm

Private Equity Firm

Project Preferences

Type of Financing Preferred:
Expansion

Geographical Preferences

United States Preferences:
All U.S.

Additional Information

Year Founded: 2004
Current Activity Level : Actively seeking new investments

TENNENBAUM CAPITAL PARTNERS, LLC (AKA: TCP)

2951 28th Street
Suite 1000
Santa Monica, CA USA 90405
Phone: 310-566-1000
Fax: 310-899-4950
E-mail: mailbox@tennenbaumcapital.com
Website: www.tennenbaumcapital.com

Management and Staff

Ameesh Shah, Principal
Brett Albert, Principal
Dan Worrell, Principal
David Hollander, Managing Director
Eric Pagel, Managing Partner
Jeevan Gore, Principal
Michael Leitner, Managing Partner
Rajneesh Vig, Managing Director
Steve Wilson, Managing Partner

Type of Firm

Bank Affiliated

Project Preferences

Type of Financing Preferred:
Mezzanine
Turnaround
Open Market
Special Situation
Distressed Debt
Recapitalizations

Size of Investments Considered:
Min Size of Investment Considered (000s): $25,000
Max Size of Investment Considered (000s): $250,000

Geographical Preferences

United States Preferences:
All U.S.

Industry Preferences

In Computer Software prefer:
Software

In Semiconductor/Electr prefer:
Electronics

In Medical/Health prefer:
Medical/Health

In Consumer Related prefer:
Retail
Food/Beverage
Consumer Products

In Industrial/Energy prefer:
Energy

In Transportation prefer:
Aerospace

In Financial Services prefer:
Financial Services

In Manufact. prefer:
Manufacturing

In Other prefer:
Environment Responsible

Additional Information

Year Founded: 1996
Capital Under Management: $7,000,000,000
Current Activity Level : Actively seeking new investments

TENTH STREET CAPITAL PARTNERS, LLC

901 Tallan Building
Two Union Square
Chattanooga, TN USA 37402
Phone: 423-266-5908
Fax: 423-266-7590
Website: www.tenthstreetcapital.com

Management and Staff

R. Alton Duke, Managing Director

Type of Firm

Private Equity Firm

Project Preferences

Type of Financing Preferred:
Mezzanine

Size of Investments Considered:
Min Size of Investment Considered (000s): $1,000
Max Size of Investment Considered (000s): $3,000

Geographical Preferences

United States Preferences:
All U.S.

Industry Preferences

In Business Serv. prefer:
Services
Distribution

In Manufact. prefer:
Manufacturing

Additional Information

Name of Most Recent Fund: Tenth Street Fund I, L.P.
Most Recent Fund Was Raised: 06/09/2005
Year Founded: 2005
Capital Under Management: $26,900,000
Current Activity Level : Actively seeking new investments

TERANET ENTERPRISES, INC.

One Adelaide Street East
Suite 1405
Toronto, Canada M5C 2V9
Phone: 416-360-5263
Website: www.teranet.ca

Type of Firm

Investment Management Firm

Additional Information

Year Founded: 1991
Current Activity Level : Actively seeking new investments

TERRA FIRMA CAPITAL PARTNERS, LTD.

2 More London Riverside
London, United Kingdom SE1 2AP
Phone: 44-20-7015-9500
Fax: 44-20-7015-9501
E-mail: info@terrafirma.com
Website: www.terrafirma.com

Other Offices

Garden Towers
Neue Mainzer - Strasse 46-50

Frankfurt am Main, Germany 60311
Phone: 49-69-3807-56000
Fax: 49-69-3807-56001

First Floor, Dorey Court
Admiral Park, Saint Peter Port
Guernsey, United Kingdom GY1 6HJ
Phone: 44-14-8171-5601

Management and Staff

Ashley Unwin, Managing Director
Cormac O'Haire, Managing Director
Fraser Duncan, Managing Director
Julie Williamson, Managing Director
Mayamiko Kachingwe, Managing Director
Mike Kinski, Managing Director
Pat O'Driscoll, Managing Director
Peter Cornell, Managing Director
Phillip Burns, Managing Director
Quentin Stewart, Managing Director
Tim Pryce, Chief Executive Officer

Type of Firm

Private Equity Advisor or Fund of Funds

Association Membership

British Venture Capital Association (BVCA)
European Private Equity and Venture Capital Assoc.

Project Preferences

Role in Financing:
Prefer role as deal originator

Type of Financing Preferred:
Leveraged Buyout
Turnaround
Balanced
Public Companies
Acquisition

Geographical Preferences

International Preferences:
Italy
United Kingdom
Ireland
Europe
Western Europe
Eastern Europe
Spain
Germany
France

Industry Focus

(% based on actual investment)	
Other Products	81.5%
Consumer Related	18.0%
Industrial/Energy	0.6%

Additional Information

Year Founded: 1994
Capital Under Management: $4,179,700,000
Current Activity Level : Actively seeking new investments

TERRA ROSSA CAPITAL, LTD.

33 King William Street
Level 15
Adelaide, Australia 5000
Phone: 618-8217-6450
Fax: 618-8217-6451
E-mail: info@terrarossacapital.com
Website: www.terrarossacapital.com

Type of Firm

Private Equity Firm

Association Membership

Australian Venture Capital Association (AVCAL)

Project Preferences

Type of Financing Preferred:
Early Stage

Size of Investments Considered:
Min Size of Investment Considered (000s): $201
Max Size of Investment Considered (000s): $2,015

Geographical Preferences

International Preferences:
Australia

Industry Preferences

In Biotechnology prefer:
Agricultural/Animal Bio.
Industrial Biotechnology

In Medical/Health prefer:
Medical/Health
Medical Products

Additional Information

Year Founded: 2006
Capital Under Management: $28,200,000
Current Activity Level : Actively seeking new investments

TERRAPIN PARTNERS LLC

540 Madison Avenue
17th Floor
New York, NY USA 10022
Phone: 212-710-4100
Fax: 212-710-4105
E-mail: info@terrapinpartners.com
Website: www.terrapinpartners.com

Other Offices

1001 Rivas Canyon Road
Pacific Palisades, CA USA 90272
Phone: 310-459-5132
Fax: 310-459-5822

Management and Staff

Jason Weiss, Partner
Nathan Leight, Partner

Type of Firm

Private Equity Firm

Project Preferences

Type of Financing Preferred:
Generalist PE
Seed

Geographical Preferences

United States Preferences:
All U.S.

Industry Preferences

In Medical/Health prefer:
Medical Products
Health Services

In Consumer Related prefer:
Retail
Food/Beverage

In Industrial/Energy prefer:
Energy

In Financial Services prefer:
Real Estate

In Business Serv. prefer:
Media

Additional Information

Year Founded: 1998
Current Activity Level : Actively seeking new investments

TERTIAIRE DEVELOPPEMENT (AKA: AWF FINANCIAL SERVICES)

47 rue de Chaillot
Paris, France 75016
Phone: 33-1-5662-2100
Fax: 33-1-4720-2858
E-mail: terdev@club-internet.fr

Management and Staff

Herve Debache, President

Type of Firm

Private Equity Firm

Association Membership

French Venture Capital Association (AFIC)

Project Preferences

Type of Financing Preferred:
Balanced

Geographical Preferences

International Preferences:
France

Additional Information

Year Founded: 2007

Current Activity Level : Actively seeking new investments

TFG CAPITAL AG UNTERNEHMENSBETEILIGUNGSGESELLSCHAFT

Mainstrasse 16
Marl, Germany 45768
Phone: 49-2365-97800
Fax: 49-2365-978033
E-mail: info@tfg.de
Website: www.tfg.de

Type of Firm

Private Equity Firm

Association Membership

German Venture Capital Association (BVK)
European Private Equity and Venture Capital Assoc.

Project Preferences

Type of Financing Preferred:
Early Stage
Expansion
Seed
Startup

Geographical Preferences

International Preferences:
Europe
Israel
Germany
Asia

Additional Information

Name of Most Recent Fund: TFG Technologie-Fonds II KG
Most Recent Fund Was Raised: 01/12/1998
Year Founded: 1994
Capital Under Management: $100,700,000
Current Activity Level : Actively seeking new investments

TGAP VENTURES LLC

259 East Michigan
Suite 208
Kalamazoo, MI USA 49007
Phone: 269-760-4570
Fax: 413-832-4838
E-mail: plans@tgapventures.com
Website: www.tgapventures.com

Management and Staff

Jack Ahrens, Managing Director
Peter Farner, Managing Director

Type of Firm

Private Equity Firm

Association Membership

National Venture Capital Association - USA (NVCA)

Project Preferences

Type of Financing Preferred:
Second Stage Financing
Early Stage
Expansion
First Stage Financing
Private Placement
Startup

Size of Investments Considered:
Min Size of Investment Considered (000s): $250
Max Size of Investment Considered (000s): $1,000

Geographical Preferences

United States Preferences:
Midwest

Industry Preferences

In Communications prefer:
Communications and Media
Commercial Communications
Telecommunications
Data Communications

In Computer Hardware prefer:
Computers
Computer Graphics and Dig

In Computer Software prefer:
Software
Systems Software
Applications Software

In Internet Specific prefer:
E-Commerce Technology
Internet

In Semiconductor/Electr prefer:
Electronics
Laser Related
Fiber Optics

In Biotechnology prefer:
Biosensors

In Medical/Health prefer:
Medical/Health
Medical Diagnostics
Medical Therapeutics
Drug/Equipmt Delivery
Medical Products
Disposable Med. Products
Health Services

In Industrial/Energy prefer:
Alternative Energy
Advanced Materials

In Manufact. prefer:
Manufacturing

Additional Information

Name of Most Recent Fund: TGap Venture Capital Fund, L.P.
Most Recent Fund Was Raised: 09/30/2003
Year Founded: 2002
Capital Under Management: $20,300,000
Current Activity Level : Actively seeking new investments

TGF MANAGEMENT CORP (FKA:TEXAS GROWTH FUND)

111 Congress Avenue
Suite 2900
Austin, TX USA 78701
Phone: 512-322-3100
Fax: 512-322-3101
E-mail: tgfmgmt@tgfmanagement.com
Website: www.tgfmanagement.com

Management and Staff

Antonio DiGesualdo, Principal
Barry Twomey, Principal
David Harr, Principal
James Kozlowski, Principal
Janet Waldeier, Chief Financial Officer
Ronald Duncan, Principal
Stephen Soileau, Principal
Vernon Bryant, Principal

Type of Firm

Private Equity Firm

Project Preferences

Role in Financing:
Will function either as deal originator or investor in deals created by others

Type of Financing Preferred:
Second Stage Financing
Leveraged Buyout
Expansion
Mezzanine
Later Stage
Management Buyouts
Acquisition
Industry Rollups

Size of Investments Considered:
Min Size of Investment Considered (000s): $10,000
Max Size of Investment Considered (000s): $40,000

Geographical Preferences

United States Preferences:
Southwest
Texas

Industry Focus

(% based on actual investment)

Other Products	45.4%
Communications and Media	15.0%
Industrial/Energy	14.3%
Computer Software and Services	12.5%
Internet Specific	5.2%
Semiconductors/Other Elect.	2.8%
Consumer Related	2.4%
Medical/Health	1.6%
Computer Hardware	0.7%

Additional Information

Name of Most Recent Fund: Texas Growth Fund II-1998 Trust
Most Recent Fund Was Raised: 12/22/1998
Year Founded: 1992
Capital Under Management: $677,000,000
Current Activity Level : Actively seeking new investments
Method of Compensation: Return on investment is of primary concern, do not charge fees

TH LEE PUTNAM VENTURES, L.P. (AKA: THOMAS H. LEE PUTNAM)

200 Madison Avenue
Suite 1900
New York, NY USA 10016
Phone: 212-951-8600
E-mail: dealsubmission@thlpv.com
Website: www.thlpv.com

Other Offices

P.O. Box 7396
Hook
London, United Kingdom RG27 7JP
Phone: 44-207-073-9401
Fax: 44-207-073-9424

Management and Staff

James Brown, Managing Director
Paul Licursi, Managing Director
Ramanan Raghavendran, Managing Director
Sharon Pipe, Managing Director
Warren Smith, Managing Director

Type of Firm

Bank Affiliated

Project Preferences

Role in Financing:

Prefer role as deal originator but will also invest in deals created by others

Type of Financing Preferred:

Second Stage Financing
Generalist PE
Later Stage
Management Buyouts
Special Situation
Recapitalizations

Size of Investments Considered:

Min Size of Investment Considered (000s): $10,000
Max Size of Investment Considered (000s): $50,000

Geographical Preferences

United States Preferences:

Northeast
All U.S.

Industry Focus

(% based on actual investment)	
Internet Specific	54.6%
Other Products	23.3%
Computer Software and Services	16.2%
Computer Hardware	4.0%
Consumer Related	1.2%
Communications and Media	0.7%

Additional Information

Name of Most Recent Fund: TH Lee Putnam Ventures (FKA:TH Lee Putnam Internet Partners)
Most Recent Fund Was Raised: 12/01/1999
Year Founded: 1999
Capital Under Management: $1,100,000,000
Current Activity Level : Actively seeking new investments

THAI DEVELOPMENT CAPITAL FUND LIMITED

3/F 36c Bermuda Tower
Dr. Roy's Drive, George Town
Grand Cayman, Cayman Islands
E-mail: tdcfthai@samart.co.th
Website: www.tdcf.com

Type of Firm

Private Equity Firm

Project Preferences

Role in Financing:

Will function either as deal originator or investor in deals created by others

Type of Financing Preferred:

Balanced

Geographical Preferences

International Preferences:

Thailand

Additional Information

Year Founded: 2000
Current Activity Level : Actively seeking new investments
Method of Compensation: Return on investment is of primary concern, do not charge fees

THAI INCUBATOR DOT COM CO., LTD.

10/F, Satorn Thani, 90/22-23
90/25 North Sathorn Road
Bangkok, Thailand 10500
Phone: 662-636-8282
Fax: 662-268-1483
E-mail: idea@thaiincubator.com
Website: www.thaiincubator.com

Type of Firm

Incubator/Development Program

Project Preferences

Type of Financing Preferred:

Startup

Geographical Preferences

International Preferences:

Thailand

Industry Preferences

In Computer Software prefer:

Software

In Internet Specific prefer:

Internet

Additional Information

Year Founded: 2000
Current Activity Level : Actively seeking new investments

THAI STRATEGIC CAPITAL MANAGEMENT CO., LTD.

22/F, Silom Complex Building
191 Silom Road, Bankrak
Bangkok, Thailand 10500
Phone: 662-231-3870
Fax: 662-231-3887
Website: www.thaistrategic.com

Management and Staff

Chittinan Palavatana, Principal
Peter Emblin, Principal
Sumalee Soontornwat, Principal

Type of Firm

Private Equity Firm

Project Preferences

Type of Financing Preferred:

Leveraged Buyout
Expansion
Balanced
Management Buyouts

Geographical Preferences

International Preferences:

Asia

Additional Information

Year Founded: 1999
Capital Under Management: $50,000,000
Current Activity Level : Actively seeking new investments

THALES CORPORATE VENTURES (FKA: THOMSON-CSF VENTURES)

56-58, rue de Ponthieu
Paris, France 75008
Phone: 33-1-5377-8420
Fax: 33-1-5377-8733
E-mail: info@ventures.thomson-csf.com

Other Offices

c/o Cetia, Inc.
350 Cambridge Avenue
Palo Alto, CA USA 94306
Phone: 415-325-5349
Fax: 415-325-6226

Management and Staff

Jean Dufour, Partner

Type of Firm

Corporate PE/Venture

Association Membership

European Private Equity and Venture Capital Assoc.

Project Preferences

Role in Financing:
Will function either as deal originator or investor in deals created by others

Type of Financing Preferred:
Second Stage Financing
Early Stage
Expansion
First Stage Financing
Startup

Size of Investments Considered:
Min Size of Investment Considered (000s): $283
Max Size of Investment Considered (000s): $2,825

Geographical Preferences

United States Preferences:
All U.S.

International Preferences:
Europe
Asia

Industry Preferences

In Communications prefer:
Telecommunications

In Computer Software prefer:
Software

In Computer Other prefer:
Computer Related

In Semiconductor/Electr prefer:
Electronics

Additional Information

Name of Most Recent Fund: THALES Corporate Ventures SA
Most Recent Fund Was Raised: 08/01/1981
Year Founded: 1986
Capital Under Management: $66,900,000
Current Activity Level : Actively seeking new investments

THAYER HIDDEN CREEK

1455 Pennsylvania Avenue NW
Suite 350
Washington, DC USA 20004
Phone: 202-371-0150
Fax: 202-371-0391
Website: www.thayerhiddencreek.com

Other Offices

4508 IDS Center
Minneapolis, MN USA 55402
Phone: 612-766-9150
Fax: 612-332-2012

Management and Staff

Carl Nelson, Managing Director
Dan Moorse, Managing Director
Daniel Dickinson, Managing Partner
Douglas McCormick, Managing Partner
Judy Vijums, Managing Director
Scott Rued, Managing Director
Scott Gibaratz, Vice President

Type of Firm

Private Equity Firm

Project Preferences

Role in Financing:
Prefer role as deal originator but will also invest in deals created by others

Type of Financing Preferred:
Leveraged Buyout
Control-block Purchases
Later Stage
Management Buyouts
Acquisition
Recapitalizations

Geographical Preferences

United States Preferences:
All U.S.

Industry Focus

(% based on actual investment)

Semiconductors/Other Elect.	28.0%
Consumer Related	26.6%
Other Products	20.3%
Industrial/Energy	13.7%
Communications and Media	5.9%
Computer Software and Services	3.8%
Internet Specific	1.7%

Additional Information

Name of Most Recent Fund: Thayer Equity Investors V, L.P.
Most Recent Fund Was Raised: 12/20/2001
Year Founded: 1996
Capital Under Management: $1,200,000,000
Current Activity Level : Actively seeking new investments
Method of Compensation: Return on invest. most important, but chg. closing fees, service fees, etc.

THAYER LODGING GROUP, INC.

1997 Annapolis Exchange Pkwy
Suite 550
Annapolis, MD USA 21401
Phone: 410-268-0515
Fax: 410-268-1582
E-mail: info@thayerlodging.com
Website: www.thayerlodging.com

Management and Staff

Carroll Warfield, Managing Director
David Weymer, Managing Director
George Dabney, Vice President
Jin Lee, Managing Director
Kim Gauthier, Vice President
Leland Pillsbury, Chairman & CEO
Martin Reid, Managing Director
Steve Neiman, Vice President
Sujan Patel, Vice President
Sun Do, Vice President
Thomas Kammerer, Managing Director

Type of Firm

Corporate PE/Venture

Project Preferences

Type of Financing Preferred:
Other
Acquisition

Geographical Preferences

United States Preferences:
All U.S.

Industry Focus

(% based on actual investment)

Consumer Related	100.0%

Additional Information

Name of Most Recent Fund: Thayer Hotel Investors IV, L.P.
Most Recent Fund Was Raised: 04/30/2004
Year Founded: 1991
Capital Under Management: $317,600,000
Current Activity Level : Actively seeking new investments

THESAN CAPITAL

Paseo de la Castellana, 40-5
Madrid, Spain 28046
Phone: 34-914-360-597
Fax: 34-915-763-656
E-mail: thesan@thesancapital.com

Website: www.thesancapital.com

Management and Staff

Jose Luis Machado, Founder
Santiago Corral, Founder

Type of Firm

Private Equity Firm

Project Preferences

Type of Financing Preferred:

Turnaround
Distressed Debt

Geographical Preferences

International Preferences:

Portugal
Spain

Industry Preferences

In Communications prefer:

Telecommunications

In Consumer Related prefer:

Food/Beverage

In Industrial/Energy prefer:

Materials

In Manufact. prefer:

Manufacturing

Additional Information

Year Founded: 2008
Current Activity Level : Actively seeking new investments

THIRD ROCK VENTURES LLC

29 Newbury Street
Third Floor
Boston, MA USA 02116
Phone: 617-585-2000
Fax: 617-859-2891
E-mail: info@thirdrockventures.com
Website: www.thirdrockventures.com

Management and Staff

Cary Pfeffer, Partner
Craig Muir, Partner
Gregory Verdine, Venture Partner
Kevin Starr, Partner
Lou Tartaglia, Partner
Mark Levin, Partner
Neil Exter, Partner
Nick Leschly, Partner
Philip Reilly, Venture Partner
Robert Tepper, Partner

Type of Firm

Private Equity Firm

Association Membership

National Venture Capital Association - USA (NVCA)

Project Preferences

Role in Financing:

Will function either as deal originator or investor in deals created by others

Type of Financing Preferred:

Early Stage

Size of Investments Considered:

Min Size of Investment Considered (000s): $10,000
Max Size of Investment Considered (000s): $30,000

Geographical Preferences

United States Preferences:

Northeast

Industry Preferences

In Biotechnology prefer:

Biotechnology

In Medical/Health prefer:

Medical Products
Pharmaceuticals

Additional Information

Name of Most Recent Fund: Third Rock Ventures Fund
Most Recent Fund Was Raised: 09/14/2007
Year Founded: 2007
Capital Under Management: $378,000,000
Current Activity Level : Actively seeking new investments
Method of Compensation: Return on investment is of primary concern, do not charge fees

THIRD SECURITY LLC

1881 Grove Avenue
The Governor Tyler
Radford, VA USA 24141
Phone: 540-633-7900
Fax: 540-633-7979
E-mail: investments@thirdsecurity.com
Website: www.thirdsecurity.com

Other Offices

735 Market Street
Third Floor
San Francisco, CA USA 94103
Phone: 415-644-5365

Management and Staff

Ankit Desai, Managing Director
Doit Koppler, Managing Director
Jeff Perez, Managing Director
Julian Kirk, Managing Director
Krish Krishnan, Senior Managing Director
Lisa Moose, Managing Director
Randal Kirk, Chief Executive Officer
Robert Patzig, Senior Managing Director
Sanjeev Balhara, Vice President
Tad Fisher, Managing Director

Type of Firm

Private Equity Firm

Project Preferences

Type of Financing Preferred:

Expansion
Balanced

Geographical Preferences

United States Preferences:

Virginia
Washington
All U.S.

Industry Preferences

In Business Serv. prefer:

Services

Additional Information

Year Founded: 1996
Capital Under Management: $800,000,000
Current Activity Level : Actively seeking new investments

THOMA BRAVO LLC

9200 Sears Tower
233 South Wacker Drive
Chicago, IL USA 60606
Phone: 312-777-4444
Website: www.thomabravo.com

Management and Staff

Carl Thoma, Managing Partner
Lee Mitchell, Managing Partner
Orlando Bravo, Managing Partner
Scott Crabill, Managing Partner

Type of Firm

Private Equity Firm

Project Preferences

Type of Financing Preferred:

Leveraged Buyout

Geographical Preferences

United States Preferences:

All U.S.

Industry Preferences

In Computer Software prefer:

Software

In Consumer Related prefer:

Consumer Products
Education Related

In Business Serv. prefer:

Services

Additional Information

Year Founded: 2008
Capital Under Management: $822,500,000
Current Activity Level : Actively seeking new investments

THOMA CRESSEY BRAVO

233 South Wacker Drive
Suite 9200, Sears Tower
Chicago, IL USA 60606
Phone: 312-777-4424
Fax: 312-777-4445
Website: www.tcb.com

Other Offices

2525 West End Avenue
Suite 1175
Nashville, TN USA 37203
Phone: 615-369-8400
Fax: 615-369-8444

600 Montgomery Street
32nd Floor
San Francisco, CA USA 94111
Phone: 415-263-3660
Fax: 415-392-6480

Management and Staff

Bryan Cressey, Managing Partner
Carl Thoma, Managing Partner
David Schuppan, Vice President
David Rogero, Vice President
Heather Smith Thorne, Vice President
Jane Kim, Vice President
Jeffrey Del Papa, Vice President
Katie Brennan, Chief Financial Officer
Lee Mitchell, Managing Partner
Merrick Axel, Principal
Orlando Bravo, Managing Partner
P. Holden Spaht, Principal
Peter Ehrich, Partner
Ralph Davis, Partner
Robert Sayle, Vice President
Scott Crabill, Partner
Seth Boro, Principal

Type of Firm

Private Equity Firm

Association Membership

Illinois Venture Capital Association
National Venture Capital Association - USA (NVCA)

Project Preferences

Role in Financing:
Prefer role as deal originator

Type of Financing Preferred:
Leveraged Buyout
Later Stage
Recapitalizations

Size of Investments Considered:
Min Size of Investment Considered (000s): $20,000
Max Size of Investment Considered (000s): $100,000

Geographical Preferences

United States Preferences:
All U.S.

Canadian Preferences:
All Canada

Industry Focus

(% based on actual investment)

Computer Software and Services	37.4%
Other Products	23.9%
Medical/Health	19.9%
Internet Specific	14.6%
Consumer Related	2.4%
Biotechnology	1.1%
Computer Hardware	0.7%

Additional Information

Name of Most Recent Fund: Thoma Cressey Fund VIII, L.P.
Most Recent Fund Was Raised: 10/27/2005
Year Founded: 1998
Capital Under Management: $1,017,400,000
Current Activity Level : Actively seeking new investments
Method of Compensation: Return on invest. most important, but chg. closing fees, service fees, etc.

THOMAS H. LEE PARTNERS (AKA: TH LEE PARTNERS)

100 Federal Street
35th Floor
Boston, MA USA 02110
Phone: 617-227-1050
Fax: 617-227-3514
Website: www.thlee.com

Management and Staff

Alex Alexandrov, Vice President
Alexandra DeLaite, Vice President
Anthony DiNovi, Managing Director
Charles Brizius, Managing Director
Charles Holden, Managing Director & CFO
Daniel Jones, Vice President
David Harkins, Managing Director
Dhruv Prasad, Vice President
Douglas Vandenberg, Vice President
Ganesh Rao, Principal
George Taylor, Managing Director
Gregory White, Managing Director
Hobart Cook, Vice President
J. Lucas Wimer, Principal
James Carlisle, Principal
Jeff Swenson, Principal
John McClellan, Managing Director
Joshua Bresler, Vice President
Kent Weldon, Managing Director
Margaret Covell, Managing Director
Richard Bressler, Managing Director
Scott Sperling, Managing Director
Scott Jaeckel, Managing Director
Scott Schoen, Managing Director
Seth Lawry, Managing Director
Shari Wolkon, Managing Director
Soren Oberg, Managing Director
Thomas Hagerty, Managing Director
Todd Abbrecht, Managing Director

Type of Firm

Private Equity Firm

Association Membership

Private Equity Council (PEC)

Project Preferences

Type of Financing Preferred:
Leveraged Buyout
Mezzanine

Geographical Preferences

International Preferences:
Europe
All International

Additional Information

Name of Most Recent Fund: Thomas H. Lee Equity Partners VI, L.P.
Most Recent Fund Was Raised: 07/14/2006
Year Founded: 1974
Capital Under Management: $20,000,000,000
Current Activity Level : Actively seeking new investments

THOMAS WEISEL PARTNERS GROUP, INC.

One Montgomery Tower
One Montgomery Street
San Francisco, CA USA 94104
Phone: 415-364-2500
Fax: 415-364-2695
E-mail: TWPInfo@tweisel.com
Website: www.tweisel.com

Other Offices

805 SouthWest Broadway
Suite 1150
Portland, OR USA 97205
Phone: 503-944-3240
Fax: 503-944-3255

390 Park Avenue, Lever House
Second Floor
New York, NY USA 10022
Phone: 212-271-3700
Fax: 212-271-3610

6100 Oak Tree Boulevard
Suite 200
Independence, OH USA 44131
Phone: 216-328-2095
Fax: 216-643-2901

10 Dominion Street
5th Floor
London, United Kingdom EC2M 2EE
Phone: 44-207-877-4300
Fax: 44-207-877-4440

190 South LaSalle Street
Suite 550

Chicago, IL USA 60603
Phone: 312-750-0606
Fax: 312-750-0649

1950 University Avenue
Suite 501
East Palo Alto, CA USA 94303
Phone: 650-688-5500
Fax: 650-688-5269

520-5th Avenue SouthWest
Suite 2400
Calgary, Canada T2P 3R7
Phone: 403-265-1939
Fax: 403-265-1935

Bellerivestrasse 17
Zurich, Switzerland CH-8008
Phone: 41-44-389-4343
Fax: 41-44-389-4444

300 East Lombard Street
Suite 840
Baltimore, MD USA 21202
Phone: 443-872-5897
Fax: 410-814-7539

3200 Cherry Creek South Drive
Suite 280
Denver, CO USA 80209
Phone: 720-479-2433
Fax: 720-479-2434

Two International Place
Boston, MA USA 02110
Phone: 617-488-4100
Fax: 617-488-4620

79 Wellington Street West
P.O. Box 37, 21st Floor
Toronto, Canada M5K 1B7
Phone: 416-815-0888
Fax: 416-815-1808

215 Free Press Journal Marg
Nariman Point
Mumbai, India 400 021
Phone: 91-22-3021-4500
Fax: 91-22-2283-4455

Management and Staff

Adam Stulberger, Principal
Alex Wylie, Managing Director
Alexander Chefetz, Managing Director
Andrew Sessions, General Partner
Arthur Kwan, Vice President
Bob West, Chief Financial Officer
Bowman Wingard, Partner
Caley Castelein, General Partner
Chris Hurst, Vice President
Chris Schaefer, Vice President
Christian Munafo, Principal
Christy Richardson, Principal
Clifford Meijer, Managing Partner
Curt Futch, Vice President
David Crowder, General Partner
David Beatty, Managing Director
David Bauman, Principal
Derek Lemke-von Ammon, Partner
Dorian Faust, Vice President
Douglas Karp, Managing Partner
Eamon Hurley, Managing Director
Eric Fitzgerald, Partner
Geoffrey Raker, Principal
Gregory White, Partner
James Streator, Partner
James Hoch, Partner
Jason Moran, Managing Director
Jeffrey Calhoun, Vice President
Jesse Meidl, Vice President
John Book, Managing Director
John Soden, Managing Director
Kimberly Ng, Vice President
Lawrence Sorrel, Partner
Lionel Conacher, President & COO
Mark Lieberman, Partner
Michelle Cherrick, Managing Director
Paul Colucci, Managing Director
Ralph Sutton, Managing Director
Richard Spalding, General Partner
Rob Steele, Managing Director
Rob Born, Vice President
Rob Magwood, Vice President
Robert Kaplan, Vice President
Robert Nabholz, Managing Director
Robert Kitts, Chief Executive Officer
Shaugn Stanley, Chief Financial Officer
Thomas Weisel, Chairman & CEO
William Bunting, Partner

Type of Firm

Bank Affiliated

Association Membership

National Venture Capital Association - USA (NVCA)

Project Preferences

Type of Financing Preferred:

Fund of Funds
Leveraged Buyout
Generalist PE
Early Stage
Seed
Later Stage
Fund of Funds of Second

Geographical Preferences

United States Preferences:

California

International Preferences:

India
All International

Industry Focus

(% based on actual investment)

Computer Software and Services	49.4%
Communications and Media	18.1%
Internet Specific	15.8%
Medical/Health	8.6%
Semiconductors/Other Elect.	8.1%

Additional Information

Name of Most Recent Fund: Thomas Weisel Strategic Opportunities Partners, L.P.
Most Recent Fund Was Raised: 07/01/2001
Year Founded: 1999
Capital Under Management: $2,000,000,000
Current Activity Level : Actively seeking new investments

THOMAS WEISEL VENTURE PARTNERS

1 Montgomery Street
37th Floor
San Francisco, CA USA 94104
Phone: 650-688-5500
Fax: 650-688-5620
E-mail: contact@twvp.com
Website: www.twvp.com

Management and Staff

Andrew Sessions, General Partner
David Crowder, General Partner
Mangesh Pimpalkhare, Venture Partner
Rob Born, Venture Partner

Type of Firm

Bank Affiliated

Association Membership

National Venture Capital Association - USA (NVCA)

Project Preferences

Role in Financing:

Prefer role as deal originator but will also invest in deals created by others

Type of Financing Preferred:

Second Stage Financing
Early Stage
Expansion
Seed
First Stage Financing

Size of Investments Considered:

Min Size of Investment Considered (000s): $2,000
Max Size of Investment Considered (000s): $10,000

Geographical Preferences

United States Preferences:

All U.S.

Industry Preferences

In Communications prefer:

CATV & Pay TV Systems
Radio & TV Broadcasting
Telecommunications
Wireless Communications
Media and Entertainment

In Computer Software prefer:

Software
Systems Software
Applications Software

In Internet Specific prefer:
Internet

In Semiconductor/Electr prefer:
Electronic Components
Semiconductor
Micro-Processing
Controllers and Sensors
Sensors
Laser Related
Fiber Optics

In Medical/Health prefer:
Health Services

In Consumer Related prefer:
Consumer
Entertainment and Leisure
Retail
Consumer Products

In Business Serv. prefer:
Services

Additional Information
Name of Most Recent Fund: Thomas Weisel Venture Partners, L.P.
Most Recent Fund Was Raised: 06/30/2001
Year Founded: 2000
Capital Under Management: $255,000,000
Current Activity Level : Actively seeking new investments

THOMAS, MCNERNEY & PARTNERS LLC
60 South Sixth Street
Suite 3620
Minneapolis, MN USA 55402
Phone: 612-465-8660
Fax: 612-465-8661
Website: www.tm-partners.com

Other Offices
One Stamford Plaza
263 Tresser Boulevard, Suite 1600
Stamford, CT USA 06901
Phone: 203-978-2000
Fax: 203-978-2005

150 Spear Street
Suite 1050
San Francisco, CA USA 94105
Phone: 415-541-8600
Fax: 415-541-8980

Management and Staff
Alex Zisson, Partner
Christine Siu, Vice President
Eric Aguiar, Partner
James Thomas, Partner
Jason Brown, Vice President
Kathleen Tune, Principal
Peter McNerney, Partner
Pratik Shah, Partner
Susan Haedt, Chief Financial Officer

Type of Firm
Private Equity Firm

Association Membership
National Venture Capital Association - USA (NVCA)

Project Preferences

Type of Financing Preferred:
Early Stage
Balanced
Later Stage
Seed

Size of Investments Considered:
Min Size of Investment Considered (000s): $100
Max Size of Investment Considered (000s): $20,000

Geographical Preferences

United States Preferences:
All U.S.

Canadian Preferences:
Alberta

Industry Preferences

In Biotechnology prefer:
Biotechnology

In Medical/Health prefer:
Medical Diagnostics
Medical Products
Pharmaceuticals

Additional Information
Name of Most Recent Fund: Thomas, McNerney & Partners II, L.P.
Most Recent Fund Was Raised: 09/30/2006
Year Founded: 2002
Capital Under Management: $591,000,000
Current Activity Level : Actively seeking new investments

THOMPSON CLIVE & PARTNERS, LTD.
24 Old Bond Street
London, United Kingdom W1S 4AW
Phone: 44-20-7535-4900
Fax: 44-20-7493-9172
E-mail: mail@tcvc.com
Website: www.tcvc.com

Other Offices
4620 White Chapel Way
Raleigh, NC USA 27615
Phone: 919-846-1061
Fax: 919-847-6124

20 Verissimo Drive
Novato, CA USA 94947
Phone: 415-897-4880
Fax: 707-769-9624

Management and Staff
Colin Clive, Co-Founder
Richard Thompson, Co-Founder

Type of Firm
Private Equity Firm

Association Membership
British Venture Capital Association (BVCA)
European Private Equity and Venture Capital Assoc.

Project Preferences

Type of Financing Preferred:
Early Stage
Expansion
Turnaround
Management Buyouts
Recapitalizations

Geographical Preferences

International Preferences:
Ireland
Sweden
United Kingdom
Netherlands
Switzerland
Austria
Belgium
Finland
Norway
Germany
Denmark
France

Industry Focus
(% based on actual investment)

Computer Software and Services	45.1%
Medical/Health	22.4%
Computer Hardware	13.2%
Internet Specific	6.7%
Semiconductors/Other Elect.	5.6%
Communications and Media	3.9%
Biotechnology	3.2%

Additional Information
Year Founded: 1977
Capital Under Management: $157,100,000
Current Activity Level : Actively seeking new investments

THOMPSON STREET CAPITAL PARTNERS
120 South Central Avenue
Suite 600
Saint Louis, MO USA 63105
Phone: 314-727-2112
Fax: 314-727-2118
E-mail: info@thompsonstreet.net
Website: www.thompsonstreet.net

Other Offices

Five Cascades Terrace
Branchburg, NJ USA 08876
Phone: 908-707-8587

2200 Renaissance Boulevard
King of Prussia, PA USA 19406
Phone: 610-275-7382

120 Grenville
Southampton, PA USA 18966

Management and Staff

Brian Kornmann, Vice President
Elizabeth Borow, Managing Director
Harry Holiday, Chief Operating Officer
James Cooper, Managing Partner
John Senneff, Vice President
Kevin Sullivan, Principal
Matthew Scherrer, Vice President
Neal Berman, Managing Director
Peter Villhard, Managing Director
Robert Hill, Vice President
Robert Dunn, Managing Director
Thomas D Ovidio, Principal
Timothy Spencer, Chief Financial Officer
Vincent Warrick, Managing Director

Type of Firm

Private Equity Advisor or Fund of Funds

Project Preferences

Role in Financing:

Prefer role as deal originator but will also invest in deals created by others

Type of Financing Preferred:

Second Stage Financing
Leveraged Buyout
Turnaround
Management Buyouts

Size of Investments Considered:

Min Size of Investment Considered (000s): $3,000
Max Size of Investment Considered (000s): $75,000

Geographical Preferences

United States Preferences:

All U.S.

Canadian Preferences:

All Canada

International Preferences:

Mexico

Industry Preferences

In Medical/Health prefer:

Medical Diagnostics
Drug/Equipmt Delivery
Medical Products
Disposable Med. Products

In Consumer Related prefer:

Food/Beverage

In Industrial/Energy prefer:

Industrial Products
Factory Automation
Process Control
Machinery

In Transportation prefer:

Transportation
Aerospace

In Business Serv. prefer:

Distribution

In Manufact. prefer:

Manufacturing

Additional Information

Year Founded: 2000
Capital Under Management: $140,000,000
Current Activity Level : Actively seeking new investments
Method of Compensation: Return on invest. most important, but chg. closing fees, service fees, etc.

THOMVEST VENTURES

65 Queen Street West
Suite 2400
Toronto, Canada M5H 2M8
Phone: 416-364-8700
Fax: 416-361-9129
E-mail: info@thomvest.com
Website: www.thomvest.com

Other Offices

222 Pine Street
Philadelphia, PA USA 19106
Phone: 242-356-9336
Fax: 650-618-1509

Management and Staff

William Dodds, Partner

Type of Firm

Bank Affiliated

Project Preferences

Type of Financing Preferred:

Second Stage Financing
Early Stage
Expansion
Balanced
Later Stage
First Stage Financing

Geographical Preferences

Canadian Preferences:

All Canada

Industry Preferences

In Communications prefer:

Telecommunications
Wireless Communications

In Computer Software prefer:

Software

In Internet Specific prefer:

E-Commerce Technology
Internet

In Semiconductor/Electr prefer:

Semiconductor

In Financial Services prefer:

Financial Services

Additional Information

Year Founded: 1996
Current Activity Level : Actively seeking new investments

THORNER VENTURES

P.O. Box 830
Larkspur, CA USA 94977-0830
Phone: 415-925-9304
Fax: 801-848-6098

Management and Staff

Tom Thorner, General Partner

Type of Firm

Private Equity Firm

Project Preferences

Role in Financing:

Prefer role in deals created by others

Type of Financing Preferred:

Second Stage Financing
Early Stage

Size of Investments Considered:

Min Size of Investment Considered (000s): $50
Max Size of Investment Considered (000s): $500

Geographical Preferences

United States Preferences:

Northern California
California

Industry Preferences

In Communications prefer:

Other Communication Prod.

In Computer Software prefer:

Software

In Internet Specific prefer:

Internet
Ecommerce
Web Aggregration/Portals

In Semiconductor/Electr prefer:

Semiconductor

In Biotechnology prefer:

Human Biotechnology

In Medical/Health prefer:

Medical Diagnostics
Diagnostic Services
Medical Therapeutics
Medical Products
Pharmaceuticals

Additional Information

Year Founded: 1981
Capital Under Management: $10,000,000
Current Activity Level : Actively seeking new investments
Method of Compensation: Return on investment is of primary concern, do not charge fees

THREE ARCH PARTNERS

3200 Alpine Road
Portola Valley, CA USA 94028
Phone: 650-529-8000
Fax: 650-529-8039
E-mail: info@threearchpartners.com
Website: www.threearchpartners.com

Management and Staff

Mark Wan, General Partner
Michael Ellwein, Venture Partner
Richard Lin, Partner
Roderick Young, Venture Partner
Steve Bonelli, Chief Financial Officer
Wilfred Jaeger, General Partner
William Harrington, Partner

Type of Firm

Private Equity Firm

Association Membership

National Venture Capital Association - USA (NVCA)

Project Preferences

Role in Financing:

Prefer role as deal originator but will also invest in deals created by others

Type of Financing Preferred:

Early Stage
Start-up Financing
Later Stage
Seed
First Stage Financing

Size of Investments Considered:

Min Size of Investment Considered (000s): $11
Max Size of Investment Considered (000s): $14,323

Industry Focus

(% based on actual investment)

Medical/Health	88.8%
Biotechnology	5.9%
Internet Specific	1.9%
Computer Software and Services	1.6%
Computer Hardware	1.6%
Other Products	0.1%

Additional Information

Year Founded: 1993
Capital Under Management: $999,000,000
Current Activity Level : Actively seeking new investments
Method of Compensation: Return on investment is of primary concern, do not charge fees

THUJA CAPITAL B.V.

Alexander Numan Building
Yalelaan 40
Utrecht, Netherlands 3584 CM
Phone: 31-30-253-9898
Fax: 31-30-253-9969
E-mail: info@thujacapital.com
Website: www.thujacapital.com

Management and Staff

Harrold Van Barlingen, Managing Director

Type of Firm

Private Equity Firm

Project Preferences

Type of Financing Preferred:

Early Stage

Geographical Preferences

International Preferences:

Luxembourg
Europe
Netherlands
Belgium

Industry Preferences

In Biotechnology prefer:

Human Biotechnology

In Medical/Health prefer:

Medical Products
Pharmaceuticals

Additional Information

Year Founded: 2007
Capital Under Management: $26,400,000
Current Activity Level : Actively seeking new investments

THULE INVESTMENTS (FKA: BRU VENTURE CAPITAL HF.)

Kringlunni 7
10th Floor
Reykjavik, Iceland 103
Phone: 354-545-5400
Fax: 354-545-5401
E-mail: thuleinvestments@thuleinvestments.is
Website: www.thuleinvestments.is

Management and Staff

Gisli Hjalmtysson, Chief Executive Officer
Linda Metusalemsdottir, Chief Financial Officer
Melanie Cary, Venture Partner
Sigurdur Saevarsson, Principal
Sigurdur Bjornsson, Partner
Skuli Valberg Olafsson, Partner

Type of Firm

Bank Affiliated

Association Membership

European Private Equity and Venture Capital Assoc.

Project Preferences

Type of Financing Preferred:

Leveraged Buyout
Expansion
Balanced
Turnaround

Geographical Preferences

International Preferences:

Europe
Iceland
All International

Industry Preferences

In Communications prefer:

Communications and Media

In Biotechnology prefer:

Biotechnology

In Industrial/Energy prefer:

Energy

Additional Information

Year Founded: 2003
Capital Under Management: $87,400,000
Current Activity Level : Actively seeking new investments

TI VENTURES (AKA: TEXAS INSTRUMENTS VENTURE CAPITAL PROGRAM)

7839 Churchill Way
MS 3995
Dallas, TX USA 75251
Phone: 972-917-3809
Fax: 972-917-3804
E-mail: tivc@ti.com
Website: www.ti.com/tiventures

Management and Staff

Mark Denissen, Vice President
Martin Izzard, Vice President

Type of Firm

Corporate PE/Venture

Association Membership

National Venture Capital Association - USA (NVCA)

Project Preferences

Role in Financing:

Will function either as deal originator or investor in deals created by others

Type of Financing Preferred:
Second Stage Financing
Early Stage
Balanced
First Stage Financing
Startup

Size of Investments Considered:
Min Size of Investment Considered (000s): $500
Max Size of Investment Considered (000s): $5,000

Geographical Preferences

United States Preferences:
All U.S.

Canadian Preferences:
All Canada

Industry Preferences

In Communications prefer:
Communications and Media
Commercial Communications
Telecommunications
Wireless Communications
Data Communications
Other Communication Prod.

In Computer Hardware prefer:
Mini and Personal/Desktop
Computer Graphics and Dig

In Computer Software prefer:
Software

In Semiconductor/Electr prefer:
Electronics
Electronic Components
Semiconductor
Controllers and Sensors
Sensors
Optoelectronics

In Biotechnology prefer:
Biosensors

In Industrial/Energy prefer:
Advanced Materials
Superconductivity

Additional Information
Name of Most Recent Fund: Texas Instruments, Inc.
Most Recent Fund Was Raised: 10/01/1984
Year Founded: 1984
Capital Under Management: $160,000,000
Current Activity Level : Actively seeking new investments
Method of Compensation: Return on investment is of primary concern, do not charge fees

---

TIANDE VENTURE
No. 796 Dong Road, Dongjiang
20th floor Chongguang Building
Ningbo, China
Phone: 86-574-27871855
Fax: 86-574-87873010
Website: www.tiandevc.com

Type of Firm
Private Equity Firm

Project Preferences

Type of Financing Preferred:
Balanced

Geographical Preferences

International Preferences:
China

Industry Preferences

In Communications prefer:
Communications and Media

In Computer Software prefer:
Systems Software

Additional Information
Year Founded: 2007
Current Activity Level : Actively seeking new investments

TIANDI GROWTH CAPITAL
930 Winter Street
Suite 2500
North Waltham, MA USA 02451
Phone: 781-478-6600
Fax: 781-478-6601
E-mail: info@tiandigrowth.com
Website: www.tiandigrowth.com

Other Offices
Shanghai Kerry Center, Suite 2606
1515 Nanjing West Road, Jing An District
Shanghai, China
Phone: 86-21-52985606
Fax: 86-21-52985601

Management and Staff
Oliver Curme, Founder

Type of Firm
Private Equity Firm

Project Preferences

Type of Financing Preferred:
Balanced

Geographical Preferences

United States Preferences:
All U.S.

International Preferences:
China

Industry Preferences

In Industrial/Energy prefer:
Alternative Energy
Environmental Related

In Manufact. prefer:
Manufacturing

Additional Information
Year Founded: 2007
Capital Under Management: $40,000,000
Current Activity Level : Actively seeking new investments

TIANGUIS, LTD.
5 Edwardes Place
London, United Kingdom W8 6LR
Phone: 44-20-7603-7788
Fax: 44-20-7603-7667
E-mail: info@tianguis-ltd.com
Website: www.tianguis-ltd.com

Type of Firm
Private Equity Firm

Association Membership
European Private Equity and Venture Capital Assoc.

Project Preferences

Role in Financing:
Prefer role as deal originator but will also invest in deals created by others

Type of Financing Preferred:
Second Stage Financing
Leveraged Buyout
Turnaround
Management Buyouts
First Stage Financing
Acquisition
Recapitalizations

Size of Investments Considered:
Min Size of Investment Considered (000s): $500
Max Size of Investment Considered (000s): $10,000

Geographical Preferences

United States Preferences:
All U.S.

Canadian Preferences:
All Canada

International Preferences:
Italy
United Kingdom
Spain
Australia
All International

Industry Preferences

In Biotechnology prefer:
Agricultural/Animal Bio.

In Industrial/Energy prefer:
Industrial Products

Additional Information
Year Founded: 1985
Capital Under Management: $10,100,000

Current Activity Level : Actively seeking new investments
Method of Compensation: Return on invest. most important, but chg. closing fees, service fees, etc.

TIANJIN TEDA VENTURE CAPITAL COMPANY, LTD. (AKA: TEDAVC)

3/F North Area, Software Bldg.
No. 80, Fourth Avenue, TEDA
Tianjin, China 300457
Phone: 86-22-6629-9990
Fax: 86-22-6629-7288
E-mail: public@tedavc.com.cn
Website: www.tedavc.com.cn

Type of Firm

Private Equity Firm

Project Preferences

Type of Financing Preferred:
Balanced

Geographical Preferences

International Preferences:
China

Industry Preferences

In Biotechnology prefer:
Biotechnology

In Medical/Health prefer:
Pharmaceuticals

In Industrial/Energy prefer:
Materials
Environmental Related

Additional Information

Year Founded: 2000
Capital Under Management: $80,000,000
Current Activity Level : Actively seeking new investments

TIANJIN VENTURE CAPITAL ASSOCIATION

No. 103-1 Qiongzhou St.
2nd Floor, Hexi District
Tianjin, China
Phone: 86-22-5879-2790
Fax: 86-22-5879-2791
E-mail: tjvc@tjvc.org
Website: www.tjvc.org

Type of Firm

Private Equity Firm

Project Preferences

Type of Financing Preferred:
Expansion
Balanced
Startup

Geographical Preferences

International Preferences:
China

Industry Preferences

In Communications prefer:
Wireless Communications

In Semiconductor/Electr prefer:
Electronics

Additional Information

Year Founded: 2000
Capital Under Management: $19,000,000
Current Activity Level : Actively seeking new investments

TIANTU CAPITAL CO., LTD.

8 Baihe Road, Shennan Avenue
Shenzhen Golf Club
Shenzhen, China 518034
Phone: 86-755-83586102
E-mail: tc@tiantu.com.cn
Website: www.tiantu.com.cn

Other Offices

3 South Street
Room 1501, Haidian Capital Center
Beijing, China 100081
Phone: 86-10-6894-2112

Type of Firm

Private Equity Firm

Association Membership

Shenzhen Venture Capital Association

Project Preferences

Type of Financing Preferred:
Balanced

Geographical Preferences

International Preferences:
China

Additional Information

Year Founded: 2002
Capital Under Management: $129,800,000
Current Activity Level : Actively seeking new investments

TIBURON PARTNERS AG

Nymphenburger Strasse 13
Munich, Germany 80335
Phone: 49-89-200005443
Fax: 49-89-200005445
E-mail: info@tiburon.de
Website: www.tiburon.de

Management and Staff

Andreas Brinkrolf, Chief Executive Officer
Daniel Wild, Chief Executive Officer

Type of Firm

Private Equity Firm

Project Preferences

Type of Financing Preferred:
Seed

Geographical Preferences

International Preferences:
Germany

Additional Information

Year Founded: 2007
Current Activity Level : Actively seeking new investments

TICONDEROGA CAPITAL, INC. (FKA: DILLON READ VENTURE CAPITAL)

230 Third Avenue
North Waltham, MA USA 02451
Phone: 781-416-3400
Fax: 781-416-9868
E-mail: info@ticonderogacap.com
Website: www.ticonderogacap.com

Other Offices

3000 Sand Hill Road
Building 3, Suite 105
Menlo Park, CA USA 94025
Phone: 650-234-9593
Fax: 650-234-9608

Management and Staff

Craig Jones, Managing Partner
James Vandervelden, Partner
Tyler Wick, Vice President

Type of Firm

Private Equity Firm

Project Preferences

Role in Financing:
Prefer role as deal originator

Type of Financing Preferred:
Leveraged Buyout
Generalist PE
Later Stage

Size of Investments Considered:
Min Size of Investment Considered (000s): $5,000
Max Size of Investment Considered (000s): $10,000

Geographical Preferences

United States Preferences:
All U.S.

Canadian Preferences:
All Canada

Industry Focus

(% based on actual investment)

Computer Software and Services	19.6%
Other Products	15.8%
Medical/Health	11.9%
Industrial/Energy	11.1%
Consumer Related	9.1%
Biotechnology	8.8%
Semiconductors/Other Elect.	7.7%
Communications and Media	5.8%
Internet Specific	5.3%
Computer Hardware	4.8%

Additional Information

Name of Most Recent Fund: Ticonderoga & Services Fund II, L.P.
Most Recent Fund Was Raised: 10/06/2000
Year Founded: 1982
Capital Under Management: $150,000,000
Current Activity Level : Actively seeking new investments
Method of Compensation: Return on investment is of primary concern, do not charge fees

---

TIF VENTURES PTE., LTD.

250 North Bridge Road
20-03 Raffles City Tower
Singapore, Singapore 179101
Phone: 65-6333-1221
Fax: 65-6337-8839
E-mail: fundadmin@tifventures.com
Website: www.tifventures.com

Management and Staff

Jimmy Hsu, Chief Executive Officer
Tan Kit Jong, Chief Operating Officer

Type of Firm

Government Affiliated Program

Association Membership

Singapore Venture Capital Association (SVCA)

Project Preferences

Type of Financing Preferred:
Fund of Funds
Early Stage
Balanced
Seed
Startup

Geographical Preferences

United States Preferences:
All U.S.

International Preferences:
Europe
Israel
Singapore
Asia

Industry Preferences

In Financial Services prefer:
Investment Groups

Additional Information

Year Founded: 2001
Current Activity Level : Actively seeking new investments

TIGER GLOBAL (FKA:TIGER TECHNOLOGY PERFORMANCE, LLC)

101 Park Avenue
48th Floor
New York, NY USA 10178
Phone: 212-984-2562

Type of Firm

Private Equity Firm

Project Preferences

Type of Financing Preferred:
Leveraged Buyout
Generalist PE
Balanced

Geographical Preferences

International Preferences:
All International

Additional Information

Name of Most Recent Fund: Tiger Technology Private Investment Partners, L.P.
Most Recent Fund Was Raised: 08/01/2003
Year Founded: 2001
Capital Under Management: $1,252,500,000
Current Activity Level : Actively seeking new investments

TILENIUS INVESTMENTS (FKA: TILENIUS VENTURES)

1900 South Norfolk Street
Suite 350
San Mateo, CA USA 94403
Phone: 650-577-2344
Fax: 650-745-7372
Website: www.tilenius.com

Management and Staff

Eric Tilenius, Partner

Type of Firm

Private Equity Firm

Project Preferences

Type of Financing Preferred:
Early Stage
Seed

Geographical Preferences

United States Preferences:
All U.S.

Industry Preferences

In Computer Software prefer:
Software

In Internet Specific prefer:
Internet

In Consumer Related prefer:
Entertainment and Leisure
Consumer Products

In Business Serv. prefer:
Media

Additional Information

Year Founded: 2005
Current Activity Level : Actively seeking new investments

TIM SPA - TRANSITION MANAGEMENT

30 Corso Vittorio
Emanuele II
Milan, Italy 20122
Phone: 3902-7631-8387
E-mail: info@tim-management.com
Website: www.tim-management.com

Management and Staff

Albino Collini, President, Founder
Domenico Costa, Managing Director

Type of Firm

Private Equity Firm

Project Preferences

Type of Financing Preferred:
Balanced

Geographical Preferences

International Preferences:
All International

Additional Information

Year Founded: 1987
Current Activity Level : Actively seeking new investments

TIME EQUITY PARTNERS

121 Avenue des Champs Elysees
Paris, France 75008
Phone: 33-1-7271-8523
E-mail: contact@time-ep.com
Website: www.timeequitypartners.com

Management and Staff

Henri De Bodinat, President
Jean-Luc Cyrot, Partner

Type of Firm
Private Equity Firm

Project Preferences

Type of Financing Preferred:
Balanced

Geographical Preferences

International Preferences:
Europe

Industry Preferences

In Communications prefer:
Telecommunications

In Consumer Related prefer:
Entertainment and Leisure

In Business Serv. prefer:
Media

Additional Information
Year Founded: 2009
Capital Under Management: $64,000,000
Current Activity Level : Actively seeking new investments

TIME WARNER INVESTMENTS (FKA: AOL TIME WARNER VENTURES)

22000 AOL Way
Dulles, VA USA 20166
Phone: 703-265-1000
Fax: 703-265-3925
Website: www.aoltwventures.com

Management and Staff
Chris Bolster, Vice President
Lennert Leader, President
Ron Peele, Vice President
Tige Savage, Vice President

Type of Firm
Corporate PE/Venture

Association Membership
Mid-Atlantic Venture Association

Project Preferences

Type of Financing Preferred:
Early Stage

Size of Investments Considered:
Min Size of Investment Considered (000s): $2,000
Max Size of Investment Considered (000s): $25,000

Geographical Preferences

United States Preferences:
All U.S.

Additional Information
Year Founded: 1996
Capital Under Management: $250,000,000
Current Activity Level : Actively seeking new investments

TIMELINE VENTURES LLC

6540 Lusk Boulevard
Suite C-115
San Diego, CA USA 92121
Phone: 858-550-1560
Fax: 858-550-1755
E-mail: tlv@timelineventures.com
Website: www.timelineventures.com

Management and Staff
Dev Purkayastha, Principal
Michael Kucha, Principal
Sangeet Chowfla, Principal

Type of Firm
Private Equity Firm

Project Preferences

Role in Financing:
Will function either as deal originator or investor in deals created by others

Type of Financing Preferred:
Early Stage
Expansion
Balanced
Later Stage

Size of Investments Considered:
Min Size of Investment Considered (000s): $250
Max Size of Investment Considered (000s): $5,000

Geographical Preferences

United States Preferences:
California
Southwest

Industry Preferences

In Communications prefer:
Wireless Communications
Data Communications

In Computer Hardware prefer:
Mainframes / Scientific
Mini and Personal/Desktop
Computer Graphics and Dig
Integrated Turnkey System
Terminals
Disk Relat. Memory Device

In Computer Software prefer:
Computer Services
Data Processing
Software
Systems Software
Applications Software
Artificial Intelligence

In Internet Specific prefer:
Internet
Web Aggregration/Portals

In Semiconductor/Electr prefer:
Electronic Components
Semiconductor
Micro-Processing
Controllers and Sensors
Sensors
Circuit Boards
Component Testing Equipmt
Laser Related
Fiber Optics
Analytic/Scientific

In Industrial/Energy prefer:
Robotics

In Financial Services prefer:
Financial Services

Additional Information
Year Founded: 2000
Capital Under Management: $50,000,000
Current Activity Level : Actively seeking new investments
Method of Compensation: Return on investment is of primary concern, do not charge fees

TINICUM CAPITAL PARTNERS

800 Third Avenue
40th Floor
New York, NY USA 10022
Phone: 212-446-9300
Website: www.tinicum.com

Management and Staff
Eric Ruttenberg, Principal
Putnam Crafts, Principal
Robert Kelly, Principal
Seth Hedon, Principal
Terence O'Toole, Managing Partner

Type of Firm
Private Equity Firm

Project Preferences

Type of Financing Preferred:
Leveraged Buyout
Acquisition

Size of Investments Considered:
Min Size of Investment Considered (000s): $25,000
Max Size of Investment Considered (000s): $75,000

Industry Preferences

In Communications prefer:
Media and Entertainment

In Medical/Health prefer:
Medical Products

In Industrial/Energy prefer:
Industrial Products
Machinery

In Transportation prefer:
Aerospace

In Financial Services prefer:
Financial Services

In Manufact. prefer:
Manufacturing

Additional Information
Name of Most Recent Fund: Tinicum Capital Partners II Parallel Fund, L.P.
Most Recent Fund Was Raised: 03/29/2004
Year Founded: 1999
Capital Under Management: $1,167,400,000
Current Activity Level : Actively seeking new investments

TISO GROUP
Abcon House, Fairway Office Pa
52 Grosvenor Road
Bryanston East, South Africa
Phone: 27-11-549-2400
E-mail: info@tiso.co.za
Website: www.tiso.co.za

Management and Staff
Fani Titi, CEO & Managing Director

Type of Firm
Private Equity Firm

Association Membership
South African Venture Capital Association (SAVCA)

Project Preferences

Type of Financing Preferred:
Balanced

Geographical Preferences

International Preferences:
Africa

Additional Information
Year Founded: 2000
Current Activity Level : Actively seeking new investments

TL VENTURES
435 Devon Park Drive
700 Building
Wayne, PA USA 19087-1990
Phone: 610-971-1515
Fax: 610-975-9330
E-mail: info@tlventures.com
Website: www.tlventures.com

Other Offices
555 California Street
Suite 300, Third Floor
San Francisco, CA USA 94104
Phone: 415-568-2100

Management and Staff
Anthony Chang, Managing Director
Mark DeNino, Managing Director
Pamela Strisofsky, Managing Director & CFO
Robert Keith, Managing Director
Robert McParland, Partner

Type of Firm
Private Equity Firm

Association Membership
Mid-Atlantic Venture Association
National Venture Capital Association - USA (NVCA)

Project Preferences

Role in Financing:
Prefer role as deal originator but will also invest in deals created by others

Type of Financing Preferred:
Early Stage

Size of Investments Considered:
Min Size of Investment Considered (000s): $1,000
Max Size of Investment Considered (000s): $6,000

Geographical Preferences

United States Preferences:
Mid Atlantic
Northwest
Northern California

Industry Focus
(% based on actual investment)

Internet Specific	23.5%
Computer Software and Services	22.9%
Semiconductors/Other Elect.	16.6%
Communications and Media	10.6%
Biotechnology	8.9%
Medical/Health	7.4%
Other Products	5.7%
Computer Hardware	1.7%
Consumer Related	1.4%
Industrial/Energy	1.3%

Additional Information
Name of Most Recent Fund: TL Ventures VII
Most Recent Fund Was Raised: 11/20/2008
Year Founded: 1988
Capital Under Management: $1,290,000,000
Current Activity Level : Actively seeking new investments
Method of Compensation: Return on investment is of primary concern, do not charge fees

---

TLCOM CAPITAL, LLP (FKA: TLCOM CAPITAL PARTNERS, LTD.)
Carrington House
Regent Street 126-130
London, United Kingdom W1B 5SE
Phone: 44-207-8516-930
Fax: 44-207-8516-931
E-mail: info@tlcom.co.uk
Website: www.tlcom.co.uk

Other Offices
Viale Liegi 42
Rome, Italy 00198
Phone: 39-06-844-0601
Fax: 39-06-844-060-40

Via Bianca di Savoia 17
Milan, Italy 20122
Phone: 39-02-582-0981
Fax: 39-02-582-09828

Management and Staff
Colin Watts, General Partner
Mauro Pretolani, General Partner

Type of Firm
Private Equity Firm

Association Membership
Italian Venture Capital Association (AIFI)
European Private Equity and Venture Capital Assoc.

Project Preferences

Type of Financing Preferred:
Early Stage
Expansion
Balanced

Geographical Preferences

International Preferences:
Europe

Industry Preferences

In Communications prefer:
Communications and Media

In Internet Specific prefer:
Internet

In Computer Other prefer:
Computer Related

Additional Information
Year Founded: 1999
Capital Under Management: $182,400,000
Current Activity Level : Actively seeking new investments

TMB INDUSTRIES INVESTMENTS
980 North Michigan Avenue
Suite 1900
Chicago, IL USA 60611
Phone: 312-280-2565
Fax: 312-280-4820
E-mail: info@tmbindustries.com
Website: www.tmbindustries.com

Management and Staff

Camillo Santomero, Managing Director
Chris Alford, Vice President
David Hoyte, Managing Director
James Cirar, Managing Director
Jeffrey Elmer, Managing Director
Joseph Ponteri, Managing Director
Keith Carpentier, Managing Director
Kelly Bodway, Managing Director
Michael Wilson, Managing Director
Timothy Masek, Managing Director

Type of Firm

Private Equity Firm

Project Preferences

Type of Financing Preferred:

Leveraged Buyout

Geographical Preferences

United States Preferences:

Northwest
Northeast

Industry Preferences

In Industrial/Energy prefer:

Industrial Products

In Transportation prefer:

Transportation

Additional Information

Year Founded: 1989
Current Activity Level : Actively seeking new investments

TMF PARTICIPATIONS MANAGEMENT

Parnassustoren
Locatellikade 1
Amsterdam, Netherlands 1076 AZ
Phone: 31-20-575-5600
Fax: 31-20-673-0016
E-mail: netherlands@tmf-group.com
Website: www.tmf-group.com

Other Offices

2 rue Dufrenoy
Paris, France 75116
Phone: 33-1-4503-6036
Fax: 33-1-4503-6377

85 Merrion Square
Dublin, Ireland
Phone: 353-1-614-6240
Fax: 353-1-614-6250

Rue de Hesse 16
Geneva, Switzerland 1204
Phone: 41-22-311-8978
Fax: 41-22-311-3309

Maipu 255 - 19 Floor
Buenos Aires, Argentina C1084ABE
Phone: 54-11-5031-5900
Fax: 54-11-5031-5901

34 91 426 07 00
Barcelona, Spain 08036
Phone: 34-93-414-3822
Fax: 34-93-414-6014

Turinina 5
Zagreb, Croatia 10010
Phone: 385-1-480-2050
Fax: 385-1-480-2051

Eschenheimer Anlage 1
Frankfurt, Germany 60316
Phone: 49-69-663-6980
Fax: 49-69-663-6988

13A Avenue de Tervuren
Brussels, Belgium 1040
Phone: 32-2-732-5695
Fax: 32-2-732-1281

Praha City Center
Klimentska 46
Prague, Czech Republic 110 02
Phone: 420-225-000-522
Fax: 420-225-000-555

Panenska 21
Bratislava, Slovakia 811 03
Phone: 421-2-5942-0000
Fax: 421-2-5942-0001

Grand Palais
Axenstrasse 17
Brunnen, Switzerland 6440
Phone: 41-41-82-565
Fax: 41-41-825-6566

Wesselenyi u. 16
Budapest, Hungary 1077
Phone: 36-6-1461-3100
Fax: 36-6-2253-4266

Foro Buonaparte 70
Milan, Italy 20121
Phone: 39-02-861-914
Fax: 39-02-862-495

Westblaak 89
Rotterdam, Netherlands 3012 KG
Phone: 31-10-271-1300
Fax: 31-10-271-1390

Bulevar AVNOJ-a 64a
Belgrade, Serbia and Montenegro 11070
Phone: 381-11-220-9300
Fax: 381-11-220-9310

Velazquez 17
Madrid, Spain 28001
Phone: 34-91-426-0700
Fax: 34-91-426-0701

2A, Paris Street
Timisoara, Romania 1900
Phone: 40-256-295-784
Fax: 40-256-295-785

133, Calea Serban Voda
Central Business Park
Bucharest, Romania 040205
Phone: 40-21-316-6848
Fax: 40-21-316-6838

Atlas House, Fourth Floor
1 King Street
London, United Kingdom EC2V 8AU
Phone: 44-20-7600-3000
Fax: 44-20-7776-7507

Mill Mall
Road Town
Tortola, Br. Virgin I.
Phone: 284-494-4997
Fax: 284-494-4999

2a Saborna Street
4th Floor
Sofia, Bulgaria 1000
Phone: 359-2-930-8940
Fax: 359-2-981-0482

1, Allee Scheffer
Luxembourg, Luxembourg L-2520
Phone: 352-241-4331
Fax: 352-241-433-300

Nieuwe Uitleg 10
Den Haag, Netherlands 2514 BP
Phone: 31-70-363-0223
Fax: 31-70-362-8614

Penstraat 35
Willemstad
Curacao, Neth. Antilles
Phone: 599-9-461-1317
Fax: 599-9-461-9117

Pl. Pilsudskiego 1
Warsaw, Poland 00-078
Phone: 48-22-456-4500
Fax: 48-22-456-4599

Ulica Gradnikove brigade 4
Ljubljana, Slovenia 1000
Phone: 386-1-586-2960
Fax: 386-1-541-4211

Type of Firm

Private Equity Firm

Association Membership

European Private Equity and Venture Capital Assoc.

Project Preferences

Type of Financing Preferred:

Balanced

Geographical Preferences

International Preferences:
Europe

Additional Information

Year Founded: 2005
Current Activity Level : Actively seeking new investments

TMG CAPITAL PARTNERS LTD.

Rua Joaquim Floriano, 72
9 Andar, Cj. 93, Itaim Bibi
Sao Paulo, Brazil 04534-000
Phone: 55-11-3079-5055
Fax: 55-11-829-6179
E-mail: tmg@tmg.com.br
Website: www.tmg.com.br

Management and Staff

Andre Guimaraes, Managing Director
Eduardo Augusto Buarque de Almeida, Partner
Pedro Paulo Teixeira, Managing Director
Sacha Lainovic, Managing Director

Type of Firm

Private Equity Firm

Association Membership

Brazilian Venture Capital Association (ABCR)

Project Preferences

Type of Financing Preferred:
Early Stage
Expansion
Balanced
Later Stage

Geographical Preferences

International Preferences:
Brazil

Industry Preferences

In Communications prefer:
Communications and Media

In Medical/Health prefer:
Medical/Health

In Consumer Related prefer:
Retail

In Business Serv. prefer:
Services

Additional Information

Name of Most Recent Fund: TMG Fund
Most Recent Fund Was Raised: 08/01/1998
Year Founded: 1997
Capital Under Management: $100,000,000
Current Activity Level : Actively seeking new investments

TOA CAPITAL CO., LTD

3F Marunouchi Mitsui Bldg.
2-2-2 Marunouchi, Chiyoda-ku
Tokyo, Japan 100-0005
Phone: 81-3-5288-5520
Fax: 81-3-5288-5521
E-mail: info@toa-capital.jp
Website: www.toa-capital.jp

Type of Firm

Private Equity Firm

Additional Information

Year Founded: 2004
Current Activity Level : Actively seeking new investments

TOBAT CAPITAL LLC

200 Crescent Court
Suite 880
Dallas, TX USA 75201
Phone: 214-855-2484
Fax: 214-855-2482
Website: www.tobatcapital.com

Management and Staff

Cory Moulton, Managing Partner
Ian Packer, Managing Partner
Scott Brock, Managing Partner

Type of Firm

Private Equity Firm

Project Preferences

Type of Financing Preferred:
Balanced

Industry Preferences

In Financial Services prefer:
Financial Services

Additional Information

Year Founded: 2000
Current Activity Level : Actively seeking new investments

TOHOKU INNOVATION CAPITAL CORP.

14F Mitsui Life Ins Honcho Bg.
1-1-1 Honcho, Aoba-ku
Sendai-shi, Japan 980-0014
Phone: 81-22-716-6401
Fax: 81-22-716-6420
E-mail: info@tohoku-innocapital.co.jp
Website: www.tohoku-innocapital.co.jp

Management and Staff

Koh Kumagai, President

Type of Firm

Private Equity Firm

Additional Information

Year Founded: 2003
Current Activity Level : Actively seeking new investments

TOKIO MARINE CAPITAL COMPANY, LTD.

6F Tokyo Marine Nichido Bldg.
1-2-1 Marunouchi, Chiyoda-ku
Tokyo, Japan 100-0005
Phone: 81-3-5223-3516
Fax: 81-3-5223-3547
E-mail: tmcinfo@tmcap.co.jp
Website: www.tmcap.co.jp

Management and Staff

Eisuke Shigemura, General Partner
Eriko Matsunawa, Vice President
Kazutaka Komori, Partner
Koji Sasaki, General Partner
Shigeru Matsumoto, Partner
Shunichiro Nakagawa, Partner
Takayuki Ohgishi, Vice President
Tomoko Inoue, Vice President
Yasushi Usami, Principal
Yoshihiro Osako, Vice President
Yuji Komiya, Managing Partner

Type of Firm

Private Equity Firm

Project Preferences

Type of Financing Preferred:
Leveraged Buyout
Expansion
Balanced
Turnaround
Management Buyouts

Geographical Preferences

International Preferences:
Jordan
Japan

Additional Information

Year Founded: 1991
Current Activity Level : Actively seeking new investments

TOKYO SMALL & MEDIUM BUSINESS INVESTMENT & CONSULTATION CO.

Toshi Ikusei Bldg.
Tokyo, Japan 150-0002
Phone: 81-3-5469-1811
Fax: 81-3-5469-5875

E-mail: iida@sbic.co.jp
Website: www.sbic.gr.jp

Other Offices

Asahi Seimei Sendai Honcho Bldg.
2-3-10 Hon-cho, Aoba-ku
Sendai, Japan 980-0014
Phone: 812-2213-7966
Fax: 812-2213-7997

1-2-6 Tajimahama
Kita-Ku
Osaka, Japan
Phone: 816-6341-5476
Fax: 816-6341-7687

Management and Staff

Akira Watanabe, Managing Director
Hideaki Kumano, President
Isao Usami, Managing Director

Type of Firm

Private Equity Firm

Project Preferences

Role in Financing:
Prefer role as deal originator

Type of Financing Preferred:
Second Stage Financing
Early Stage
Mezzanine
Balanced
Start-up Financing
First Stage Financing

Size of Investments Considered:
Min Size of Investment Considered (000s): $500
Max Size of Investment Considered (000s): $1,000

Geographical Preferences

International Preferences:
Asia
Japan

Industry Focus

(% based on actual investment)

Internet Specific	30.1%
Computer Software and Services	15.0%
Semiconductors/Other Elect.	14.9%
Biotechnology	12.1%
Other Products	9.9%
Medical/Health	6.7%
Industrial/Energy	4.3%
Communications and Media	3.6%
Computer Hardware	2.8%
Consumer Related	0.7%

Additional Information

Name of Most Recent Fund: Tokyo SBIC Limited Partnership
Most Recent Fund Was Raised: 09/01/2000
Year Founded: 1963
Capital Under Management: $350,000,000
Current Activity Level : Actively seeking new investments

Method of Compensation: Return on investment is of primary concern, do not charge fees

TOLOMEI PARTICIPATIONS

15 rue de Palestro
Paris, France 75002
Phone: 33-1-4508-1125
Fax: 33-1-4634-8640

Management and Staff

Eric Dailey, President

Type of Firm

Private Equity Advisor or Fund of Funds

Project Preferences

Type of Financing Preferred:
Balanced

Geographical Preferences

International Preferences:
Europe

Additional Information

Year Founded: 2005
Current Activity Level : Actively seeking new investments

TONG YANG VENTURE CAPITAL CORPORATION

19th Floor, Hiliving Building
890-16 Daechi-dong, Gangnam-gu
Seoul, South Korea 135-280
Phone: 822-561-0056
Fax: 822-561-9191
Website: www.tyvc.co.kr

Other Offices

6119-1-7 Asaka
Minato-ku
Tokyo, Japan 107-0052
Phone: 813-5474-3119
Fax: 813-5474-3202

2882 Sand Hill Road
Suite 100
Menlo Park, CA USA 94025
Phone: 650-233-9834
Fax: 650-233-9821

Management and Staff

Hyung Tae Park, President
Jinsuk Chung, President

Type of Firm

Bank Affiliated

Association Membership

Korean Venture Capital Association (KVCA)

Project Preferences

Type of Financing Preferred:
Early Stage
Balanced
Later Stage
Startup

Geographical Preferences

International Preferences:
Korea, South

Additional Information

Year Founded: 1989
Capital Under Management: $100,200,000
Current Activity Level : Actively seeking new investments

TONIC VENTURE CAPITAL, LTD.

10B, Summit Building
30 Man Yue St., Hunghom, Kl
Hong Kong, Hong Kong
Phone: 852-2364-9365
Fax: 852-2303-0471

Management and Staff

Gary Liu, Chief Executive Officer

Type of Firm

Corporate PE/Venture

Association Membership

Hong Kong Venture Capital Association (HKVCA)

Project Preferences

Type of Financing Preferred:
Turnaround
Recapitalizations

Geographical Preferences

International Preferences:
China

Industry Preferences

In Semiconductor/Electr prefer:
Electronics

Additional Information

Year Founded: 2006
Capital Under Management: $10,000,000
Current Activity Level : Actively seeking new investments

TONKA BAY EQUITY PARTNERS (AKA: BAYVIEW CAPITAL MANAGEMENT)

301 Carlson Parkway
Suite 325
Minnetonka, MN USA 55305

Phone: 952-345-2030
Fax: 952-345-2001
Website: www.tonkabayequity.com

Management and Staff

Michael Smiggen, Principal
Stephen Soderling, Principal

Type of Firm

Private Equity Firm

Association Membership

Natl Assoc of Small Bus. Inv. Co (NASBIC)

Project Preferences

Role in Financing:

Prefer role as deal originator but will also invest in deals created by others

Type of Financing Preferred:

Leveraged Buyout
Later Stage
Management Buyouts
Acquisition
Recapitalizations

Size of Investments Considered:

Min Size of Investment Considered (000s): $4,000
Max Size of Investment Considered (000s): $10,000

Geographical Preferences

United States Preferences:

Midwest
All U.S.

Industry Preferences

In Business Serv. prefer:

Services
Distribution

In Manufact. prefer:

Manufacturing

Additional Information

Name of Most Recent Fund: Bayview Capital Partners LP
Most Recent Fund Was Raised: 11/01/1999
Year Founded: 1997
Capital Under Management: $78,000,000
Current Activity Level : Actively seeking new investments
Method of Compensation: Return on invest. most important, but chg. closing fees, service fees, etc.

TOP TECHNOLOGY VENTURES, LTD.

Warwick Court
5 Paternoster Square
London, United Kingdom EC4M 7BP
Phone: 44-20-7489-5200
Fax: 44-20-7489-5201
E-mail: ttv@toptechnology.co.uk
Website: www.toptechnology.co.uk

Management and Staff

Harry Fitzgibbons, Managing Director

Type of Firm

Bank Affiliated

Association Membership

British Venture Capital Association (BVCA)

Project Preferences

Type of Financing Preferred:

Early Stage
Balanced
Later Stage
Startup

Size of Investments Considered:

Min Size of Investment Considered (000s): $500
Max Size of Investment Considered (000s): $500,000

Geographical Preferences

International Preferences:

United Kingdom
Europe

Industry Focus

(% based on actual investment)

Computer Software and Services	21.8%
Biotechnology	21.4%
Internet Specific	15.1%
Semiconductors/Other Elect.	11.0%
Other Products	11.0%
Communications and Media	10.2%
Computer Hardware	8.5%
Consumer Related	1.0%

Additional Information

Name of Most Recent Fund: Hambros Advanced Technology Trust III, L.P. (AKA: HATT)
Most Recent Fund Was Raised: 12/31/1997
Year Founded: 1982
Capital Under Management: $64,700,000
Current Activity Level : Actively seeking new investments

TOPSPIN PARTNERS

Three Expressway Plaza
Roslyn Heights, NY USA 11577
Phone: 516-625-9400
Fax: 516-625-9499
E-mail: info@topspinpartners.com
Website: www.topspinpartners.com

Management and Staff

Leigh Randall, Managing Director
Leo Guthart, Managing Director
Paul Lowell, Managing Director
Paul Wimer, Managing Director
Steve Winick, Principal
Steve Lebowitz, Managing Director
Walter Kissinger, Managing Director

Type of Firm

Private Equity Firm

Association Membership

National Venture Capital Association - USA (NVCA)

Project Preferences

Type of Financing Preferred:

Leveraged Buyout
Early Stage
Balanced
Later Stage

Geographical Preferences

United States Preferences:

Northeast
All U.S.

Industry Preferences

In Communications prefer:

Media and Entertainment
Publishing

In Biotechnology prefer:

Biotechnology

In Consumer Related prefer:

Consumer
Retail
Food/Beverage
Consumer Products
Other Restaurants

In Business Serv. prefer:

Media

In Manufact. prefer:

Manufacturing

Additional Information

Name of Most Recent Fund: Topspin Offshore LBO, L.P.
Most Recent Fund Was Raised: 06/08/2007
Year Founded: 2000
Capital Under Management: $215,000,000
Current Activity Level : Actively seeking new investments

TORCH HILL PARTNERS

655 Fifteenth Street Northwest
Suite 810
Washington, DC USA 20005
Phone: 202-536-1200
Website: www.torchhillpartners.com

Management and Staff

Gregory Newbold, Managing Partner

Type of Firm

Private Equity Firm

Project Preferences

Type of Financing Preferred:

Expansion
Later Stage

Geographical Preferences

United States Preferences:
All U.S.

Industry Preferences

In Medical/Health prefer:
Medical/Health

Additional Information

Name of Most Recent Fund: Torch Hill Fund, L.P.
Most Recent Fund Was Raised: 10/13/2005
Year Founded: 2005
Capital Under Management: $17,600,000
Current Activity Level : Actively seeking new investments

TORQUEST PARTNERS, INC.

BCE Place, 161 Bay Street
Suite 4240
Toronto, Canada M5J 2S1
Phone: 416-956-7022
Fax: 416-956-7001
E-mail: info@torquest.com
Website: www.torquest.com

Management and Staff

Alan Lever, Principal
Bogdan Cenanovic, Principal
Brent Belzberg, Managing Partner
Daniel Sonshine, Principal
Eric Berke, Managing Partner
George Rossolatos, Partner
Jeremy Busch, Principal
Kimberly Davis, Chief Financial Officer
Marc Lipton, Partner

Type of Firm

Private Equity Firm

Association Membership

Canadian Venture Capital Association

Project Preferences

Type of Financing Preferred:
Leveraged Buyout
Later Stage
Acquisition

Size of Investments Considered:
Min Size of Investment Considered (000s): $13,000
Max Size of Investment Considered (000s): $90,000

Geographical Preferences

United States Preferences:
All U.S.

Canadian Preferences:
All Canada

Industry Preferences

In Consumer Related prefer:
Consumer Products
Consumer Services

Additional Information

Name of Most Recent Fund: TorQuest II Co-investment Fund, L.P.
Most Recent Fund Was Raised: 10/26/2006
Year Founded: 2002
Capital Under Management: $673,500,000
Current Activity Level : Actively seeking new investments
Method of Compensation: Return on invest. most important, but chg. closing fees, service fees, etc.

TORREAL SCR SA

Paseo de la Castellana 40
Madrid, Spain 28046
Phone: 34-91-575-6622
Fax: 34-91-578-0397

Management and Staff

Jose Diaz-Rato Revuelta, Managing Director
Pedro Lomas, Managing Director

Type of Firm

Private Equity Firm

Association Membership

Spanish Venture Capital Association (ASCRI)

Project Preferences

Type of Financing Preferred:
Startup

Geographical Preferences

International Preferences:
Europe

Additional Information

Year Founded: 1999
Current Activity Level : Actively seeking new investments

TORYS LLP

79 Wellington Street W.
Toronto, Canada M5K 1N2
Phone: 416-865-7500
Fax: 416-865-7380
Website: www.torys.com

Management and Staff

Les Viner, Managing Partner
Sharon Geraphty, Partner
Wendy Del Mul, Partner

Type of Firm

Private Equity Firm

Additional Information

Year Founded: 2009
Current Activity Level : Actively seeking new investments

TOTAL TECHNOLOGY VENTURES LLC

1230 Peachtree Street
Suite 1150
Atlanta, GA USA 30309
Phone: 404-347-8400
Fax: 404-347-8420
Website: www.ttvatlanta.com

Management and Staff

Mark Johnson, Partner
Sean Banks, Chief Financial Officer

Type of Firm

Private Equity Firm

Project Preferences

Role in Financing:
Will function either as deal originator or investor in deals created by others

Type of Financing Preferred:
Second Stage Financing
Expansion
Balanced
Later Stage

Size of Investments Considered:
Min Size of Investment Considered (000s): $250
Max Size of Investment Considered (000s): $8,000

Geographical Preferences

United States Preferences:
Southeast
All U.S.

Industry Preferences

In Internet Specific prefer:
E-Commerce Technology
Ecommerce

In Financial Services prefer:
Financial Services

Additional Information

Year Founded: 2000
Capital Under Management: $111,000,000
Current Activity Level : Actively seeking new investments
Method of Compensation: Return on invest. most important, but chg. closing fees, service fees, etc.

TOTTA FINANCE

Av. Eng Duarte Pacheco
Amoreiras, Torre 1 6
Lisboa, Portugal 1099-024

Phone: 351-217-26-2125
Fax: 351-217-26-2134

Type of Firm

Private Equity Firm

Additional Information

Current Activity Level : Actively seeking new investments

TOTTORI CAPITAL CO., LTD.

2F Torigin Plaza Bldg
9-2 Oogi-cho
Tottori-shi, Japan 680-0846
Phone: 81-857-20-2733
Fax: 81-857-25-6193
E-mail: info@tottoricap.com
Website: www.tottoricap.com

Type of Firm

Bank Affiliated

Additional Information

Year Founded: 1997
Current Activity Level : Actively seeking new investments

TOUCAN CAPITAL

7600 Wisconsin Avenue
7th Floor
Bethesda, MD USA 20814
Phone: 240-497-4060
Fax: 240-497-4065
E-mail: info@toucancapital.com
Website: www.toucancapital.com

Management and Staff

Linda Powers, Managing Director
Robert Hemphill, Managing Director

Type of Firm

Private Equity Firm

Association Membership

Mid-Atlantic Venture Association

Project Preferences

Role in Financing:

Prefer role as deal originator

Type of Financing Preferred:

Early Stage
Start-up Financing
Seed
Startup

Size of Investments Considered:

Min Size of Investment Considered (000s): $100
Max Size of Investment Considered (000s): $5,000

Geographical Preferences

United States Preferences:

Mid Atlantic
Northeast
All U.S.

Industry Preferences

In Biotechnology prefer:

Biotechnology

In Industrial/Energy prefer:

Energy

Additional Information

Year Founded: 1998
Capital Under Management: $60,000,000
Current Activity Level : Actively seeking new investments

TOWARZYSTWO INWESTCYJI SPOTECZNO-EKONOMICZNYCH SA (TISE)

ul. Nalewki 8/27
Warsaw, Poland 00-158
Phone: 48-22-6360-740
Fax: 48-22-636-2902
E-mail: inwestycje@tise.com.pl
Website: www.tise.com.pl

Management and Staff

Karol Sachs, President

Type of Firm

Private Equity Firm

Association Membership

European Private Equity and Venture Capital Assoc.

Project Preferences

Type of Financing Preferred:

Expansion
Startup

Geographical Preferences

International Preferences:

Poland

Additional Information

Year Founded: 1991
Capital Under Management: $1,200,000
Current Activity Level : Actively seeking new investments

TOWER GATE CAPITAL (FKA: FAR BLUE PLC)

1 Marble Quay
London, United Kingdom E1W 1UH
Phone: 44-20-7481-8002
Fax: 44-20-7481-8003
E-mail: enquiries@farblue.com
Website: www.farblue.com

Other Offices

The Beacon
176 St Vincent Street
Glasgow, United Kingdom G2 5SG
Phone: 44-141-249-6630
Fax: 44-141-249-6634

Management and Staff

Matthew Hudson, Chief Executive Officer

Type of Firm

Private Equity Firm

Project Preferences

Type of Financing Preferred:

Early Stage
Seed

Geographical Preferences

International Preferences:

United Kingdom
Europe

Industry Preferences

In Medical/Health prefer:

Medical/Health

Additional Information

Year Founded: 2000
Capital Under Management: $15,000,000
Current Activity Level : Actively seeking new investments

TOWER GATE CAPITAL, LTD. (AKA:TGC)

New Broad Street House
35 New Broad Street
London, United Kingdom EC2 1NH
Phone: 44-845-056-8401
Fax: 44-870-9223-997
Website: www.tower-gate.com

Type of Firm

Private Equity Firm

Project Preferences

Type of Financing Preferred:

Expansion
Later Stage

Industry Preferences

In Communications prefer:

Telecommunications
Wireless Communications

In Business Serv. prefer:

Media

Additional Information

Year Founded: 1999
Current Activity Level : Actively seeking new investments

TOWERBROOK CAPITAL PARTNERS L.P. (FKA: SOROS PRIVATE EQUITY)

430 Park Avenue
New York, NY USA 10022
Phone: 212-699-2200
Fax: 917-591-9851
Website: www.towerbrook.com

Other Offices

Kinnaird House
1 Pall Mall East
London, United Kingdom SW1Y 5AU
Phone: 44-20-7451-2002
Fax: 44-20-7451-2022

555 California Street
18th Floor
San Francisco, CA USA 94104
Phone: 415-259-5001

Management and Staff

Axel Meyersiek, Principal
Evan Goldman, Principal
Filippo Cardini, Chief Operating Officer
Ian Sachs, Venture Partner
James Harrison, Managing Director
John Sinik, Managing Director
Jonathan Bilzin, Managing Director
Karim Saddi, Managing Director
Niclas Gabran, Managing Director
Patrick Smulders, Senior Managing Director
Richard Grimm, Principal
Winston Ginsberg, Managing Director

Type of Firm

Private Equity Firm

Association Membership

British Venture Capital Association (BVCA)

Project Preferences

Type of Financing Preferred:
Leveraged Buyout
Balanced

Geographical Preferences

United States Preferences:
Maryland
All U.S.

International Preferences:
Europe
All International

Industry Focus

(% based on actual investment)

Communications and Media	24.3%
Internet Specific	19.3%
Other Products	16.3%
Computer Software and Services	13.8%
Consumer Related	10.0%
Medical/Health	5.3%
Industrial/Energy	4.7%
Semiconductors/Other Elect.	3.0%
Biotechnology	2.0%
Computer Hardware	1.3%

Additional Information

Year Founded: 1995
Capital Under Management: $4,205,200,000
Current Activity Level : Actively seeking new investments

TOYO CAPITAL CO., LTD.

6F KyobashiFuji Bldg.
2-8-5 Kyobashi,Chuo-ku
Tokyo, Japan 104-0031
Phone: 81-3-3281-1040
Fax: 81-3-5524-1043
E-mail: info[toyocapital.co.jp
Website: www.toyocapital.co.jp

Management and Staff

Shiro Hashimoto, President

Type of Firm

Private Equity Firm

Project Preferences

Type of Financing Preferred:
Balanced

Geographical Preferences

International Preferences:
Asia

Additional Information

Year Founded: 1983
Capital Under Management: $36,700,000
Current Activity Level : Actively seeking new investments

TOZAI CAPITAL

6-10-1 Roppongi, Minato-ku
Roppongi Hills Mori Tower 28/F
Tokyo, Japan 106-6128
Phone: 81-3-5772-2701
Fax: 81-3-5772-2702
E-mail: info@tozaicapital.com
Website: www.tozaicapital.com

Other Offices

30 Finsbury Square
London, United Kingdom EC2P 2YU
Phone: 44-20-7184-4490
Fax: 44-20-7184-4491

Daechi-dong 942-1, Kangnam-gu
Pacific Tower 18th Floor
Seoul, South Korea 135-909
Phone: 82-2-2184-7778
Fax: 82-2-2184-7788

Management and Staff

Andrew Mankiewicz, Chief Executive Officer
Neil Crawford, Chief Operating Officer

Type of Firm

Private Equity Firm

Project Preferences

Type of Financing Preferred:
Balanced

Geographical Preferences

United States Preferences:
All U.S.

International Preferences:
Europe
Japan

Additional Information

Year Founded: 2004
Current Activity Level : Actively seeking new investments

TP INVEST

st. Stepinska 39
Warsaw, Poland 00-739
Phone: 48-22-559-1400
Fax: 48-22-627-1019
Website: www.tpinvest.pl

Management and Staff

Marek Jozefiak, President

Type of Firm

Corporate PE/Venture

Project Preferences

Type of Financing Preferred:
Early Stage

Geographical Preferences

International Preferences:
Poland

Industry Preferences

In Communications prefer:
Telecommunications

Additional Information

Year Founded: 1998
Current Activity Level : Actively seeking new investments

TPG (FKA:TEXAS PACIFIC GROUP)

301 Commerce Street
Suite 3300
Fort Worth, TX USA 76102
Phone: 817-871-4000
Fax: 817-871-4010
E-mail: info@texpac.com
Website: www.tpg.com

Other Offices

2nd Floor Stirling Square
5-7 Carlton Gardens
London, United Kingdom SW1Y 5AD
Phone: 44-20-7544-6500
Fax: 44-20-7544-6565

1133 Connecticut Avenue, NorthWest
Suite 700
Washington, DC USA 20036
Phone: 202-530-1400
Fax: 202-496-0051

12 Zhongshan Road
Suite 332
Shanghai, China
Phone: 86-21-3313-0203
Fax: 86-21-6329-9100

Atago Green Hills MORI Tower
36F, 2-5-1, Atago, Minato-ku
Tokyo, Japan
Phone: 81-3-5408-6900
Fax: 81-3-5408-0691

2882 Sand Hill Road
Suite 106
Menlo Park, CA USA 94025
Phone: 650-289-5800
Fax: 650-289-5801

153 Maker Chamber VI
Nariman Point
Mumbai, India 400 002
Phone: 91-22-4039-1000
Fax: 91-22-4039-1002

One George Street
#1401
Singapore, Singapore 049145
Phone: 65-6390-5000
Fax: 65-6390-5001

Znamenka 7
Building 3
Moscow, Russia 119019
Phone: 7-495-660-8600
Fax: 7-495-660-8601

888 7th Avenue
38th Floor
New York, NY USA 10019
Phone: 212-601-4700
Fax: 212-601-4701

8 Finance Street
57/F Two International Finance Centre
Central, Hong Kong
Phone: 852-3515-8888
Fax: 852-3515-8999

The Goldbell Centre
5 rue Eugene Ruppert
Luxembourg, Luxembourg L-2453
Phone: 352-2700-41251
Fax: 352-2700-412599

Level 31
101 Collins Street
Melbourne, Australia 3000
Phone: 61-3-9664-4444
Fax: 61-3-9663-7005

345 California Street
Suite 3300
San Francisco, CA USA 94104
Phone: 415-743-1500
Fax: 415-743-1501

Management and Staff

Abel Halpern, General Partner
Andrew Dechet, Partner
Cornel Riklin, Partner
David Bonderman, Founding Partner
Dick Boyce, Partner
Gates Jamie, Partner
Jacob Polny, Vice President
James Coulter, Founding Partner
John Marren, Partner
Jun Tsusaka, Partner
Kevin Burns, Partner
Mary Ma, Managing Director
Philippe Costeletos, Partner
Sing Wang, Partner
Steven Schneider, Partner
William Price, Founding Partner

Type of Firm

Private Equity Firm

Association Membership

Australian Venture Capital Association (AVCAL)
British Venture Capital Association (BVCA)
French Venture Capital Association (AFIC)
European Private Equity and Venture Capital Assoc.
Private Equity Council (PEC)

Project Preferences

Type of Financing Preferred:
Leveraged Buyout
Expansion
Mezzanine
Balanced
Turnaround

Geographical Preferences

United States Preferences:
All U.S.

International Preferences:
India
Europe
Western Europe
China
Bermuda
Asia
All International

Industry Focus

(% based on actual investment)

Industrial/Energy	28.2%
Other Products	19.3%
Medical/Health	16.1%
Consumer Related	10.3%
Computer Hardware	9.5%
Semiconductors/Other Elect.	5.6%
Internet Specific	4.6%
Communications and Media	4.0%
Computer Software and Services	1.3%
Biotechnology	1.0%

Additional Information

Year Founded: 1992
Capital Under Management: $30,000,000,000
Current Activity Level : Actively seeking new investments

TPG GROWTH

345 California Street
Suite 3300
San Francisco, CA USA 94104
Phone: 415-743-1635
Fax: 415-743-1685
Website: www.tpgventures.com

Other Offices

2882 Sand Hill Road
Suite 106
Menlo Park, CA USA 94025
Phone: 650-289-5800
Fax: 650-289-5801

153, Maker Chamber VI
15th Floor, Nariman Point
Mumbai, India 400 021
Phone: 91-22-4039-1000
Fax: 91-22-4039-1001

57th Floor, Suite 5704-13
8 Finance Street
Central, Hong Kong
Phone: 852-3515-8888
Fax: 852-2186-6208

301 Commerce Street
Suite 3300
Fort Worth, TX USA 76102
Phone: 817-871-4000
Fax: 817-871-4010

Management and Staff

Chad Herrin, Principal
David Levison, Venture Partner
Geoffrey Duyk, Managing Director
Heather Preston, Principal

Matt Hobart, Principal
Simba Gill, Venture Partner
Steve Foster, Managing Director

Type of Firm
Bank Affiliated

Association Membership
National Venture Capital Association - USA (NVCA)

Project Preferences

Role in Financing:
Will function either as deal originator or investor in deals created by others

Type of Financing Preferred:
Early Stage
Expansion
Balanced
Seed
Distressed Debt

Size of Investments Considered:
Min Size of Investment Considered (000s): $1,000
Max Size of Investment Considered (000s): $20,000

Geographical Preferences

International Preferences:
India
China
Hong Kong

Industry Preferences

In Communications prefer:
Telecommunications
Wireless Communications

In Computer Software prefer:
Computer Services
Software

In Semiconductor/Electr prefer:
Semiconductor

In Biotechnology prefer:
Biotechnology
Human Biotechnology

In Medical/Health prefer:
Medical Diagnostics
Drug/Equipmt Delivery
Medical Products
Pharmaceuticals

In Consumer Related prefer:
Consumer
Retail

Additional Information
Year Founded: 2000
Capital Under Management: $718,800,000
Current Activity Level : Actively seeking new investments
Method of Compensation: Return on investment is of primary concern, do not charge fees

---

TPH PARTNERS LLC
1111 Bagby
Suite 5100
Houston, TX USA 77002
Phone: 713-333-7100
Website: www.tphpartners.com

Management and Staff
Curt Schaefer, Vice President
George McCormick, Managing Director

Type of Firm
Bank Affiliated

Project Preferences

Type of Financing Preferred:
Leveraged Buyout
Management Buyouts

Size of Investments Considered:
Min Size of Investment Considered (000s): $10,000
Max Size of Investment Considered (000s): $25,000

Industry Preferences

In Industrial/Energy prefer:
Energy

Additional Information
Year Founded: 2009
Capital Under Management: $50,600,000
Current Activity Level : Actively seeking new investments

TR ADVISORS, LTD.
Unit C, 7/F, On Hing Building
On Hing Terrace
Central, Hong Kong
Phone: 852-2526-7080
Fax: 852-2526-9112
E-mail: Info@tr-capital.com
Website: www.tr-capital.com

Management and Staff
Antoine Flamarion, Founding Partner
Mathieu Chabran, Founding Partner
Paul Robine, Founder

Type of Firm
Private Equity Advisor or Fund of Funds

Association Membership
Hong Kong Venture Capital Association (HKVCA)

Project Preferences

Type of Financing Preferred:
Fund of Funds
Expansion
Balanced
Special Situation
Fund of Funds of Second

Geographical Preferences

International Preferences:
India
Pakistan
China
Asia

Additional Information
Year Founded: 2008
Current Activity Level : Actively seeking new investments

TRAFELET & COMPANY LLC
153 East 53rd Street
New York, NY USA 10022
Phone: 212-201-7800

Type of Firm
Private Equity Advisor or Fund of Funds

Additional Information
Year Founded: 2009
Current Activity Level : Actively seeking new investments

TRAMMELL-SHOTT CAPITAL MANAGEMENT LLC
350 Fifth Avenue
Room 5714
New York, NY USA 10118
Phone: 212-947-8610

Other Offices
1 International Place
31st Floor
Boston, MA USA 02211
Phone: 617-790-2960

601 California Street
Suite 80
San Francisco, CA USA 94108
Phone: 415-394-7271

Management and Staff
Webb Trammell, Partner

Type of Firm
Private Equity Firm

Project Preferences

Type of Financing Preferred:
Fund of Funds
Leveraged Buyout

Geographical Preferences

United States Preferences:
All U.S.

Canadian Preferences:
All Canada

Additional Information

Year Founded: 1996
Capital Under Management: $5,000,000
Current Activity Level : Actively seeking new investments
Method of Compensation: Return on investment is of primary concern, do not charge fees

TRANS COSMOS USA

12505 Bellevue Redmond Road
Suite 209
Bellevue, WA USA 98005
Phone: 425-468-3930
Fax: 425-468-3933
Website: www.transcosmos.com

Management and Staff

James Geddes, Senior Managing Director
Mark Kalow, Managing Director
Shinichi Nagakura, Managing Director
Steve Clemons, Managing Director

Type of Firm

Corporate PE/Venture

Additional Information

Year Founded: 1996
Current Activity Level : Actively seeking new investments

TRANS-SCIENCE, INC.

8/F Imperial Hotel Tower
1-1-1 Uchisaiwaicho, Chiyodaku
Tokyo, Japan 100-0011
Phone: 81-3-3500-3588
Fax: 81-3-3500-3589
Website: www.trans-science.co.jp

Type of Firm

Incubator/Development Program

Additional Information

Year Founded: 2001
Current Activity Level : Actively seeking new investments

TRANSLINK CAPITAL

228 Hamilton Avenue
3rd Floor
Palo Alto, CA USA 94301
Phone: 650-798-5415
Fax: 650-798-5416
E-mail: info@translinkcapital.com
Website: www.translinkcapital.com

Management and Staff

Jackie Yang, Managing Director
Jay Eum, Managing Director
Kazunori Ozaki, Venture Partner
Sung Park, Managing Director
Toshiya Otani, Managing Director

Type of Firm

Private Equity Firm

Association Membership

National Venture Capital Association - USA (NVCA)

Project Preferences

Role in Financing:
Will function either as deal originator or investor in deals created by others

Type of Financing Preferred:
Early Stage
Expansion

Size of Investments Considered:
Min Size of Investment Considered (000s): $1,000
Max Size of Investment Considered (000s): $5,000

Geographical Preferences

International Preferences:
China
Korea, South
Japan

Industry Preferences

In Communications prefer:
Commercial Communications
Telecommunications
Wireless Communications
Data Communications
Other Communication Prod.

In Computer Hardware prefer:
Mainframes / Scientific
Mini and Personal/Desktop
Computer Graphics and Dig
Integrated Turnkey System
Terminals
Disk Relat. Memory Device

In Computer Software prefer:
Computer Services
Data Processing
Software
Systems Software
Applications Software

In Internet Specific prefer:
E-Commerce Technology
Internet
Ecommerce
Web Aggregration/Portals

In Semiconductor/Electr prefer:
Electronic Components
Semiconductor

Additional Information

Name of Most Recent Fund: Translink Capital Partners I, L.P.
Most Recent Fund Was Raised: 05/03/2007
Year Founded: 2007
Capital Under Management: $50,000,000
Current Activity Level : Actively seeking new investments
Method of Compensation: Return on investment is of primary concern, do not charge fees

TRANSOM CAPITAL GROUP

1801 Century Park East
Suite 520
Los Angeles, CA USA 90067
Phone: 310-407-0929
Website: www.transomcap.com

Management and Staff

Adam Fraser, Principal
Brian Biggott, Principal
David Ascher, Managing Director
Ken Firtel, Managing Director
Russ Roenick, Managing Director

Type of Firm

Private Equity Firm

Project Preferences

Type of Financing Preferred:
Leveraged Buyout

Size of Investments Considered:
Min Size of Investment Considered (000s): $5,000
Max Size of Investment Considered (000s): $25,000

Geographical Preferences

United States Preferences:
All U.S.

Industry Preferences

In Consumer Related prefer:
Consumer
Entertainment and Leisure
Retail

In Industrial/Energy prefer:
Industrial Products

In Transportation prefer:
Aerospace

In Business Serv. prefer:
Media

In Manufact. prefer:
Manufacturing

Additional Information

Year Founded: 2008
Current Activity Level : Actively seeking new investments

TRANSPAC CAPITAL PTE, LTD.

Level 31, Bank of China Bldg.
4 Battery Road
Singapore, Singapore 049908
Phone: 65-6224-1211
Fax: 65-6225-5538
E-mail: corporate_inquiries@transpac-capital.com
Website: www.transpac-capital.com

Other Offices

33rd Floor, Two Pacific Place
Suite 3322, 88 Queensway
Central, Hong Kong
Phone: 852-2525-2661
Fax: 852-2877-6612

Management and Staff

Adrian Woo, Vice President
Christopher Leong, President, Founder

Type of Firm

Private Equity Firm

Association Membership

Venture Capital Association of Beijing (VCAB)
Hong Kong Venture Capital Association (HKVCA)
Singapore Venture Capital Association (SVCA)

Project Preferences

Role in Financing:

Prefer role as deal originator

Type of Financing Preferred:

Leveraged Buyout
Generalist PE
Expansion

Size of Investments Considered:

Min Size of Investment Considered (000s): $3,000
Max Size of Investment Considered (000s): $60,000

Geographical Preferences

International Preferences:

Indonesia
Taiwan
China
Hong Kong
Thailand
Philippines
Singapore
Asia
Malaysia

Industry Focus

(% based on actual investment)

Semiconductors/Other Elect.	23.4%
Computer Software and Services	22.0%
Other Products	21.2%
Internet Specific	12.5%
Consumer Related	7.8%
Communications and Media	3.9%
Medical/Health	3.7%
Computer Hardware	3.5%
Industrial/Energy	2.1%

Additional Information

Name of Most Recent Fund: Transpac Capital 1996 Investment Trust
Most Recent Fund Was Raised: 02/01/1997
Year Founded: 1989
Capital Under Management: $820,000,000
Current Activity Level : Actively seeking new investments

TRANSPORTATION RESOURCE PARTNERS (TRP) (FKA: PENSKE CAPITAL)

2555 Telegraph Road
Bloomfield Hills, MI USA 48302
Phone: 248-648-2101
Fax: 248-648-2105
Website: www.trpfund.com

Other Offices

One Harmon Plaza
9th Floor
Secaucus, NJ USA 07094
Phone: 201-325-3080
Fax: 201-325-8650

Management and Staff

David Mitchell, Managing Director
James Hislop, Managing Director
Richard Peters, Managing Director
Roger Penske, Managing Director
Steven Carrel, Vice President

Type of Firm

Private Equity Firm

Project Preferences

Type of Financing Preferred:

Leveraged Buyout

Industry Focus

(% based on actual investment)

Consumer Related	33.7%
Other Products	31.6%
Internet Specific	22.3%
Industrial/Energy	7.5%
Semiconductors/Other Elect.	4.9%

Additional Information
Name of Most Recent Fund: Penske Capital Partners
Most Recent Fund Was Raised: 06/01/1997
Year Founded: 1997
Capital Under Management: $386,300,000
Current Activity Level : Actively seeking new investments

TRAVANT CAPITAL PARTNERS

Eighth Floor, The Octagon
13A A.J. Marinho Drive
Lagos, Nigeria
Phone: 234-1-462-6832
E-mail: Info@travantcapital.com
Website: www.travantcapital.com

Other Offices

6B George Street
Ikoyi
Lagos, Nigeria
Phone: 234-1-280-6804
Fax: 234-1-462-6835

3rd Floor, Victoria Building
316 Rue Victoria, Bonanjo
Douala, Cameroon BP 1617
Phone: 237-3343-6600
Fax: 237-3343-6655

Management and Staff

Andrew Alli, Partner
Osaze Osifo, Chief Executive Officer

Type of Firm

Private Equity Firm

Association Membership

African Venture Capital Association (AVCA)

Project Preferences

Type of Financing Preferred:

Leveraged Buyout
Early Stage
Expansion
Balanced

Geographical Preferences

International Preferences:

Nigeria
Africa

Industry Preferences

In Consumer Related prefer:

Consumer

In Industrial/Energy prefer:

Energy

In Financial Services prefer:

Financial Services

Additional Information

Year Founded: 2007
Capital Under Management: $107,000,000
Current Activity Level : Actively seeking new investments

TREACLE VENTURE PARTNERS

Gleneagles Fairway Office Park
52 Grosvenor Road
Bryanston, South Africa
Phone: 27-11-463-7476
Fax: 27-11-463-1213
Website: www.treacle.co.za

Management and Staff

Christoff Botha, Founding Partner
Konrad Fleischhauer, Founding Partner
Rudolf Pretorius, Founding Partner

Type of Firm

Private Equity Firm

Association Membership

South African Venture Capital Association (SAVCA)

Project Preferences

Type of Financing Preferred:

Early Stage
Expansion
Balanced
Turnaround
Later Stage
Special Situation
Startup

Size of Investments Considered:

Min Size of Investment Considered (000s): $1,245
Max Size of Investment Considered (000s): $5,603

Geographical Preferences

International Preferences:

South Africa

Industry Preferences

In Communications prefer:

Telecommunications
Wireless Communications

In Semiconductor/Electr prefer:

Electronics

In Business Serv. prefer:

Media

Additional Information

Year Founded: 2001
Capital Under Management: $30,500,000
Current Activity Level : Actively seeking new investments

TREADSTONE GROUP INC., THE

717 North Harwood Street
Suite 2630
Dallas, TX USA 75201
Phone: 214-220-1030
Fax: 214-220-2180
E-mail: tsinfo@treadstone.com
Website: www.treadstone.com

Other Offices

Nisky Center
Suite 211
Charlotte Amalie, Am. Virgin Is. 00802
Phone: 340-777-5696
Fax: 340-777-5699

Management and Staff

Charlotte Hickey, Chief Financial Officer
Gary Thomason, Principal
Phillip Dixon, President

Type of Firm

Private Equity Firm

Project Preferences

Type of Financing Preferred:

Leveraged Buyout
Turnaround
Management Buyouts
Recapitalizations

Size of Investments Considered:

Min Size of Investment Considered (000s): $5,000
Max Size of Investment Considered (000s): $25,000

Geographical Preferences

United States Preferences:

All U.S.

Additional Information

Year Founded: 1993
Current Activity Level : Actively seeking new investments
Method of Compensation: Return on invest. most important, but chg. closing fees, service fees, etc.

TREGARON CAPITAL COMPANY LLC

540 University Avenue
Suite 250
Palo Alto, CA USA 94301
Phone: 650-618-2550
E-mail: info@tregaroncapital.com
Website: www.tregaroncapital.com

Management and Staff

JR Matthews, Principal
John Thornton, Managing Director
Todd Collins, Principal

Type of Firm

Private Equity Firm

Project Preferences

Role in Financing:

Prefer role as deal originator but will also invest in deals created by others

Type of Financing Preferred:

Leveraged Buyout
Control-block Purchases
Expansion
Public Companies
Acquisition

Industry Preferences

In Communications prefer:

Publishing

In Medical/Health prefer:

Medical/Health

In Financial Services prefer:

Financial Services

In Business Serv. prefer:

Services

In Manufact. prefer:

Publishing

Additional Information

Year Founded: 2005
Current Activity Level : Actively seeking new investments

TRELLIS CAPITAL CORPORATION

330 Bay Street
Suite 1302
Toronto, Canada M5H 2S8
Phone: 416-398-2299
Fax: 416-398-1799
Website: www.trelliscapital.com

Management and Staff

Sunil Selby, Managing Director

Type of Firm

Private Equity Firm

Association Membership

Canadian Venture Capital Association

Project Preferences

Role in Financing:

Will function either as deal originator or investor in deals created by others

Type of Financing Preferred:

Second Stage Financing
Early Stage
Expansion
First Stage Financing

Size of Investments Considered:

Min Size of Investment Considered (000s): $250
Max Size of Investment Considered (000s): $1,500

Geographical Preferences

Canadian Preferences:

All Canada

Industry Preferences

In Communications prefer:
Telecommunications
Wireless Communications
Data Communications
Satellite Microwave Comm.

In Internet Specific prefer:
Internet

In Semiconductor/Electr prefer:
Electronic Components
Semiconductor
Micro-Processing
Controllers and Sensors
Sensors
Circuit Boards
Component Testing Equipmt
Laser Related
Fiber Optics
Analytic/Scientific

In Industrial/Energy prefer:
Alternative Energy
Industrial Products
Superconductivity
Factory Automation
Process Control
Robotics
Machinery

In Manufact. prefer:
Manufacturing

Additional Information
Name of Most Recent Fund: Trellis Capital Corporation
Most Recent Fund Was Raised: 05/01/2000
Year Founded: 2000
Capital Under Management: $6,700,000
Current Activity Level : Actively seeking new investments
Method of Compensation: Return on invest. most important, but chg. closing fees, service fees, etc.

TRELLIS HEALTH VENTURES, L.P.

425 Market Street
Suite 2200
San Francisco, CA USA 94105
Phone: 415-951-4799
Fax: 415-951-4688

Type of Firm
Private Equity Advisor or Fund of Funds

Association Membership
Western Association of Venture Capitalists (WAVC)
National Venture Capital Association - USA (NVCA)

Project Preferences

Role in Financing:
Will function either as deal originator or investor in deals created by others

Type of Financing Preferred:
Second Stage Financing
Early Stage
Expansion
Mezzanine
Balanced
Later Stage
Private Placement
Special Situation
Recapitalizations

Size of Investments Considered:
Min Size of Investment Considered (000s): $100
Max Size of Investment Considered (000s): $1,000

Geographical Preferences

United States Preferences:
All U.S.

Industry Preferences

In Medical/Health prefer:
Medical/Health
Diagnostic Services
Medical Therapeutics
Medical Products
Disposable Med. Products
Health Services
Hospitals/Clinics/Primary
Hospital/Other Instit.

Additional Information
Year Founded: 1999
Capital Under Management: $23,000,000
Current Activity Level : Actively seeking new investments
Method of Compensation: Return on investment is of primary concern, do not charge fees

---

TRELLIS PARTNERS

2600 Via Fortuna
Suite 150
Austin, TX USA 78746
Phone: 512-330-9200
Fax: 512-330-9400
E-mail: businessplans@trellis.com
Website: www.trellis.com

Management and Staff
Alex Broeker, General Partner
John Long, General Partner
Leland Murphy, General Partner

Type of Firm
Private Equity Firm

Association Membership
National Venture Capital Association - USA (NVCA)

Project Preferences

Role in Financing:
Will function either as deal originator or investor in deals created by others

Type of Financing Preferred:
Early Stage
Start-up Financing
Seed
First Stage Financing

Geographical Preferences

United States Preferences:
Southwest
Texas

Industry Focus
(% based on actual investment)

Internet Specific	42.9%
Computer Software and Services	31.5%
Communications and Media	17.0%
Other Products	4.4%
Semiconductors/Other Elect.	4.3%

Additional Information
Name of Most Recent Fund: Trellis Partners II, L.P.
Most Recent Fund Was Raised: 02/02/2000
Year Founded: 1997
Capital Under Management: $67,000,000
Current Activity Level : Actively seeking new investments
Method of Compensation: Return on investment is of primary concern, do not charge fees

---

TRELYS FUNDS

2525 Meridian Parkway
Suite 225
Durham, NC USA 27713
Phone: 803-251-7990
Fax: 803-251-7995
Website: www.trelys.com

Management and Staff
Adrian Wilson, Managing General Partner
Mike Gorman, Chief Financial Officer

Type of Firm
Private Equity Firm

Association Membership
National Venture Capital Association - USA (NVCA)

Project Preferences

Role in Financing:
Will function either as deal originator or investor in deals created by others

Type of Financing Preferred:
Start-up Financing
Seed

Size of Investments Considered:
Min Size of Investment Considered (000s): $100
Max Size of Investment Considered (000s): $3,000

Geographical Preferences

United States Preferences:
Southeast

Industry Preferences

In Communications prefer:
Telecommunications
Wireless Communications

In Computer Hardware prefer:
Computer Graphics and Dig

In Computer Software prefer:
Data Processing
Software
Systems Software
Applications Software

In Semiconductor/Electr prefer:
Electronic Components
Fiber Optics

In Biotechnology prefer:
Biotechnology
Human Biotechnology

In Medical/Health prefer:
Medical Diagnostics
Drug/Equipmt Delivery
Medical Products

In Industrial/Energy prefer:
Energy

In Financial Services prefer:
Financial Services
Insurance

Additional Information
Name of Most Recent Fund: The Trelys Funds, L.P.
Most Recent Fund Was Raised: 02/25/2002
Year Founded: 2002
Capital Under Management: $22,000,000
Current Activity Level : Actively seeking new investments
Method of Compensation: Return on investment is of primary concern, do not charge fees

---

TRENDLINES GROUP, THE
Shorashim Western Galilee
D.N. Misgav, Israel 20164
Phone: 972-4-958-3323
Fax: 972-4-958-3325
E-mail: postmaster@trendlines.com
Website: www.trendlines.com

Other Offices
Asternweg 2
Friedrichsdorf, Germany D-61381
Phone: 49-6172-77150
Fax: 49-6172-737940

2940 West 123rd Terrace
Shawnee Mission, KS USA 66209
Phone: 913-317-8788
Fax: 913-317-8787

Migdal Shalom
26th floor
Tel Aviv, Israel 65251
Phone: 972-4-958-3323
Fax: 972-4-958-3325

Management and Staff
D. Todd Dollinger, Managing Director
Steve Rhodes, Managing Director

Type of Firm
Service Provider

Project Preferences

Type of Financing Preferred:
Early Stage

Geographical Preferences

International Preferences:
Israel

Industry Preferences

In Medical/Health prefer:
Medical/Health

Additional Information
Year Founded: 2003
Current Activity Level : Actively seeking new investments

TRENWITH SECURITIES LLC
3200 Bristol Street
Fourth Floor
Costa Mesa, CA USA 92626
Phone: 714-668-7333
Fax: 714-668-7377
Website: www.trenwith.com

Other Offices
360 Madison Avenue
Fourth Floor
New York, NY USA 10017
Phone: 212-885-8585

150 Federal Street
Suite 900
Boston, MA USA 02110
Phone: 617-422-7576

520 Kirkland Way
Suite 300
Kirkland, WA USA 98033
Phone: 425-896-4356

233 North Michigan
Suite 2500
Chicago, IL USA 60601
Phone: 312-233-1800

Spear Tower, One Market
Suite 1100
San Francisco, CA USA 94105
Phone: 415-337-9600

1900 Avenue Of The Stars
Eleventh Floor
Los Angeles, CA USA 90067
Phone: 310-557-8533

Management and Staff
Eric Gier, Managing Director
Leonard Brooks, Senior Managing Director
Luciane Roessler, Managing Director
Ron Ainsworth, Managing Director
Ulf Angelin, Vice President

Type of Firm
Bank Affiliated

Project Preferences

Role in Financing:
Prefer role as deal originator

Type of Financing Preferred:
Leveraged Buyout
Expansion
Management Buyouts
Industry Rollups
Recapitalizations

Size of Investments Considered:
Min Size of Investment Considered (000s): $3,000
Max Size of Investment Considered (000s): $10,000

Geographical Preferences

United States Preferences:
All U.S.

Additional Information
Year Founded: 1981
Capital Under Management: $100,000,000
Current Activity Level : Actively seeking new investments
Method of Compensation: Return on invest. most important, but chg. closing fees, service fees, etc.

TRESTLE VENTURES
760 Constitution Drive
Suite 106
Exton, PA USA 19341
Phone: 610-851-9950
Website: www.trestleventures.com

Management and Staff
Frank Lordi, Managing Partner
Jeff White, Managing Partner
Vincent Menichelli, Managing Partner

Type of Firm
Private Equity Firm

Project Preferences

Type of Financing Preferred:
Early Stage
Seed

Additional Information
Name of Most Recent Fund: Trestle Ventures, L.P.

Most Recent Fund Was Raised: 06/10/2008
Year Founded: 2008
Capital Under Management: $3,900,000
Current Activity Level : Actively seeking new investments

TREVI HEALTH VENTURES

110 East 59th Street
Suite 3300
New York, NY USA 10022
Phone: 212-813-9201
E-mail: info@trevihealth.com
Website: www.trevihealth.com

Management and Staff

Andrew Fink, Managing Director
David Robbins, Managing Director
Scott Cragg, Principal

Type of Firm

Private Equity Firm

Project Preferences

Type of Financing Preferred:
Early Stage
Expansion
Balanced
Seed
Startup

Size of Investments Considered:
Min Size of Investment Considered (000s): $5,000
Max Size of Investment Considered (000s): $10,000

Geographical Preferences

United States Preferences:
All U.S.

International Preferences:
United Kingdom

Industry Preferences

In Medical/Health prefer:
Medical/Health
Medical Products
Health Services
Pharmaceuticals

Additional Information

Year Founded: 2005
Current Activity Level : Actively seeking new investments

TRG ASSET MANAGEMENT GMBH

Wipplingerstrasse 25
Vienna, Austria A-1010
Phone: 43-532-0466-422
Fax: 43-532-0466-420
E-mail: rpem@rpem.at
Website: www.rpem.at

Other Offices

Two Atlantic Avenue
Boston, MA USA 02110
Phone: 617-482-4242
Fax: 617-482-4242

Management and Staff

Rolf Theuer, Chief Executive Officer
Witold Szymanski, Chief Executive Officer

Type of Firm

Bank Affiliated

Association Membership

Hungarian Venture Capital Association (HVCA)
Polish Venture Capital Association (PSIC/PPEA)
European Private Equity and Venture Capital Assoc.

Project Preferences

Type of Financing Preferred:
Second Stage Financing
Expansion

Size of Investments Considered:
Min Size of Investment Considered (000s): $2,801
Max Size of Investment Considered (000s): $13,073

Geographical Preferences

International Preferences:
Central Europe
Europe
Eastern Europe

Industry Preferences

In Communications prefer:
Communications and Media

In Consumer Related prefer:
Consumer

In Industrial/Energy prefer:
Industrial Products

In Business Serv. prefer:
Services

Additional Information

Year Founded: 1999
Capital Under Management: $85,900,000
Current Activity Level : Actively seeking new investments

TRIANGLE CAPITAL PARTNERS LLC

3600 Glenwood Avenue
Suite 104
Raleigh, NC USA 27612
Phone: 919-719-4770
Fax: 919-719-4777
Website: www.trianglecapitalpartners.com

Management and Staff

Aaron Shackelford, Vice President
David Parker, Managing Director
Garland Tucker, Managing Director
John Schramm, Managing Director
Michael Patterson, Managing Director
Sheri Colquitt, Vice President
Tarlton Long, Managing Director
William Wagner, Managing Director

Type of Firm

Private Equity Firm

Association Membership

Natl Assoc of Small Bus. Inv. Co (NASBIC)

Project Preferences

Role in Financing:
Will function either as deal originator or investor in deals created by others

Type of Financing Preferred:
Leveraged Buyout
Mezzanine
Later Stage
Management Buyouts
Acquisition
Recapitalizations

Size of Investments Considered:
Min Size of Investment Considered (000s): $1,500
Max Size of Investment Considered (000s): $10,000

Geographical Preferences

United States Preferences:
Mid Atlantic
Southeast

Industry Preferences

In Communications prefer:
Telecommunications

In Medical/Health prefer:
Medical Diagnostics
Diagnostic Services
Diagnostic Test Products
Medical Therapeutics
Drug/Equipmt Delivery
Health Services
Hospitals/Clinics/Primary
Hospital/Other Instit.

In Consumer Related prefer:
Consumer
Retail
Franchises(NEC)
Food/Beverage
Education Related

In Industrial/Energy prefer:
Industrial Products

In Business Serv. prefer:
Services
Distribution
Media

In Manufact. prefer:
Manufacturing

Additional Information

Year Founded: 2003

Capital Under Management: $80,000,000
Current Activity Level : Actively seeking new investments
Method of Compensation: Return on invest. most important, but chg. closing fees, service fees, etc.

TRIANGLE VENTURE CAPITAL GROUP MANAGEMENT GMBH

Markstrasse 65
St. Leon-Rot, Germany 68789
Phone: 49-700-87426453
Fax: 49-700-87426329
E-mail: info@triangle-venture.com
Website: www.triangle-venture.com

Other Offices

Talstrasse 27e
Bensheim-Auerbach, Germany D-64625

Management and Staff

Bernd Geiger, Managing Partner
Karl Ebetshuber, Managing Partner
Malte Kollner, Managing Partner
Soeren Schuster, Partner
Uli Fricke, Managing Partner

Type of Firm

Private Equity Firm

Association Membership

European Private Equity and Venture Capital Assoc.

Project Preferences

Type of Financing Preferred:
Early Stage
Seed
Startup

Size of Investments Considered:
Min Size of Investment Considered (000s): $220
Max Size of Investment Considered (000s): $880

Geographical Preferences

International Preferences:
Europe
Germany

Industry Preferences

In Communications prefer:
Communications and Media
Telecommunications

In Computer Other prefer:
Computer Related

In Semiconductor/Electr prefer:
Electronics

In Biotechnology prefer:
Biotechnology

In Medical/Health prefer:
Medical/Health

Additional Information

Year Founded: 1997
Capital Under Management: $66,000,000
Current Activity Level : Actively seeking new investments

TRIATHLON MEDICAL VENTURES LLC

250 East Fifth Street
1100 Chiquita Center
Cincinnati, OH USA 45202
Phone: 513-723-2600
Fax: 513-723-2615
E-mail: info@tmvp.com
Website: www.tmvp.com

Other Offices

201 East Jefferson
Suite 315A
Louisville, KY USA 40202
Phone: 502-569-1590
Fax: 502-657-1591

201 North Illinois Street
16th Floor
Indianapolis, IN USA 46204
Phone: 317-280-8233
Fax: 317-328-9743

231 South Bemiston
Suite 800
Saint Louis, MO USA 63105
Phone: 314-854-1332
Fax: 314-854-9118

Management and Staff

Carrie Bates, Managing Partner
George Emont, Partner
Mark Collar, Venture Partner
Randy Weiss, Partner
Suzette Dutch, Managing Partner

Type of Firm

Private Equity Firm

Association Membership

Natl Assoc of Small Bus. Inv. Co (NASBIC)
National Venture Capital Association - USA (NVCA)

Project Preferences

Type of Financing Preferred:
Early Stage
Expansion
Balanced
Later Stage
Seed

Size of Investments Considered:
Min Size of Investment Considered (000s): $500
Max Size of Investment Considered (000s): $8,000

Geographical Preferences

United States Preferences:
Midwest
All U.S.

Industry Preferences

In Biotechnology prefer:
Human Biotechnology

In Medical/Health prefer:
Medical Diagnostics
Medical Therapeutics
Drug/Equipmt Delivery
Medical Products
Disposable Med. Products
Pharmaceuticals

Additional Information

Year Founded: 2003
Capital Under Management: $105,000,000
Current Activity Level : Actively seeking new investments

TRIBECAPITAL PARTNERS S.A. (AKA: TRIBECA PARTNERS)

Avenida 82, No. 12-18
Oficina 401
Bogota, Colombia
Phone: 57-1-490-0040
Fax: 57-1-490-9955
Website: www.tribecapitalpartners.net

Management and Staff

Luc Gerard, President

Type of Firm

Private Equity Firm

Project Preferences

Type of Financing Preferred:
Leveraged Buyout
Turnaround
Acquisition

Geographical Preferences

International Preferences:
Latin America
Colombia

Industry Preferences

In Communications prefer:
Communications and Media

In Medical/Health prefer:
Medical/Health

In Consumer Related prefer:
Consumer
Other Restaurants

In Industrial/Energy prefer:
Energy

Industrial Products
Environmental Related

In Transportation prefer:
Transportation

In Financial Services prefer:
Real Estate

In Business Serv. prefer:
Services

Additional Information
Year Founded: 2007
Capital Under Management: $115,500,000
Current Activity Level : Actively seeking new investments

TRICOR PACIFIC CAPITAL, INC.
The Waterfront Centre
200 Burrard Street, Suite 1560
Vancouver, Canada V6C 3L6
Phone: 604-688-7669
Fax: 604-688-7649
Website: www.tricorpacific.com

Other Offices
One Westminster Place
Suite 100
Lake Forest, IL USA 60045
Phone: 847-295-4427
Fax: 847-295-4243

Management and Staff
Bradley Seaman, Managing Director
David Rowntree, Managing Director
J. Trevor Johnstone, Managing Director
Joseph Lucke, Vice President
Nicholas Peters, Vice President
Paola Yawney, Vice President
Roderick Senft, Managing Director
Scott Daum, Vice President

Type of Firm
Private Equity Firm

Project Preferences
Type of Financing Preferred:
Leveraged Buyout
Later Stage
Management Buyouts
Acquisition
Recapitalizations

Geographical Preferences
United States Preferences:
Midwest
Northwest
West Coast
Southwest

Canadian Preferences:
All Canada
Western Canada

Industry Preferences
In Consumer Related prefer:
Consumer Products
Consumer Services

In Industrial/Energy prefer:
Industrial Products

In Business Serv. prefer:
Services

In Manufact. prefer:
Manufacturing

Additional Information
Year Founded: 1996
Capital Under Management: $642,800,000
Current Activity Level : Actively seeking new investments

TRIDENT CAPITAL
505 Hamilton Avenue
Suite 200
Palo Alto, CA USA 94301
Phone: 650-289-4400
Fax: 650-289-4444
E-mail: info@tridentcap.com
Website: www.tridentcapital.com

Other Offices
325 Riverside Avenue
Westport, CT USA 06880
Phone: 203-222-4590
Fax: 203-222-4592

270 Westminster
Suite 300
Lake Forest, IL USA 60045
Phone: 847-283-9891
Fax: 847-283-9901

277 West 83rd Street
Suite B-2
Burr Ridge, IL USA 60527
Phone: 630-570-5750
Fax: 630-570-5780

Management and Staff
Arneek Multani, Principal
Brendan Reidy, Venture Partner
Chirag Patel, Venture Partner
Dipika Chopra, Venture Partner
Donald Dixon, Managing Director
Evangelos Simoudis, Managing Director
J. Alberto Yepez, Venture Partner
John Moragne, Managing Director
Mark Iwanowski, Venture Partner
Mark Platshon, Venture Partner
Matthew Chagan, Vice President
Michael Biggee, Principal
Nick Bellomo, Vice President
Peter Meekin, Managing Director
Sara England Bergeron, Venture Partner
Venetia Kontogouris, Managing Director

Type of Firm
Private Equity Firm

Association Membership
Mid-Atlantic Venture Association
National Venture Capital Association - USA (NVCA)

Project Preferences
Role in Financing:
Prefer role as deal originator but will also invest in deals created by others

Type of Financing Preferred:
Second Stage Financing
Early Stage
Expansion
Mezzanine
Start-up Financing
Later Stage
Seed
First Stage Financing
Acquisition

Size of Investments Considered:
Min Size of Investment Considered (000s): $5,000
Max Size of Investment Considered (000s): $20,000

Geographical Preferences
United States Preferences:
All U.S.

Canadian Preferences:
All Canada

International Preferences:
United Kingdom
India
China

Industry Focus
(% based on actual investment)

Internet Specific	36.6%
Computer Software and Services	29.6%
Other Products	8.7%
Communications and Media	8.0%
Medical/Health	6.7%
Industrial/Energy	3.5%
Computer Hardware	3.4%
Consumer Related	2.8%
Semiconductors/Other Elect.	0.8%

Additional Information
Name of Most Recent Fund: Trident Capital Fund - VI Principals Fund, L.L.C.
Most Recent Fund Was Raised: 12/17/2004
Year Founded: 1993
Capital Under Management: $1,300,000,000
Current Activity Level : Actively seeking new investments
Method of Compensation: Return on invest. most important, but chg. closing fees, service fees, etc.

TRIGINTA CAPITAL PARTNERS GMBH (FKA: AVIDA EQUITY PARTNERS)

Steinstrasse 20
Duesseldorf, Germany D-40212
Phone: 49-211-862-890
Fax: 49-211-86289455
E-mail: info@triginta-capital.com
Website: www.triginta-capital.com

Other Offices

Schiffgraben 13
Hannover, Germany D-30159
Phone: 49-511-357-9140
Fax: 49-511-3579-1414

Markgrafenstrasse 33
Berlin, Germany D-10117
Phone: 49-89-3069-2063040
Fax: 49-89-3069-2063049

Management and Staff

Anthony Bunker, Partner
Christian Von Oppen, Partner
Detlef Mackewicz, Partner
Johannes Rabini, Partner
Martin Heumann, Partner
Matthias Graat, Managing Partner
Stefan Beil, Partner

Type of Firm

Private Equity Firm

Project Preferences

Type of Financing Preferred:
Fund of Funds
Leveraged Buyout
Generalist PE
Start-up Financing
Later Stage
Other

Geographical Preferences

International Preferences:
Italy
United Kingdom
Netherlands
Switzerland
Europe
Germany
France

Industry Preferences

In Communications prefer:
Other Communication Prod.

In Internet Specific prefer:
Internet

In Computer Other prefer:
Computer Related

In Semiconductor/Electr prefer:
Semiconductor

In Biotechnology prefer:
Biotechnology

In Medical/Health prefer:
Medical/Health

In Transportation prefer:
Transportation

In Financial Services prefer:
Financial Services

Additional Information

Year Founded: 1999
Capital Under Management: $688,600,000
Current Activity Level : Actively seeking new investments

TRIGON ALTERNATIVE INVESTMENTS

ul. Wspolna 47/49
Warsaw, Poland 00-684
Phone: 48-22-627-4100
Fax: 48-22-627-4103
Website: www.trigon.ee

Other Offices

Kawe Plaza
Parnu mnt. 15
Tallinn, Estonia 10141
Phone: 372-6-679-200
Fax: 372-6-679-201

Torna Street 4
Section IIIc-303
Riga, Latvia 1050
Phone: 371-750-7335
Fax: 371-750-7336

Type of Firm

Bank Affiliated

Association Membership

European Private Equity and Venture Capital Assoc.

Project Preferences

Type of Financing Preferred:
Balanced
Startup

Geographical Preferences

International Preferences:
Central Europe
Europe
Eastern Europe

Industry Preferences

In Agr/Forestr/Fish prefer:
Agribusiness
Agriculture related

Additional Information

Year Founded: 1994
Current Activity Level : Actively seeking new investments

TRIKONA TRINITY CAPITAL PLC (AKA: TRIKONA TC)

IOMA House, Hope Street
Douglas
Isle of Man, United Kingdom IM1 1AP
E-mail: info@trikonacapital.com
Website: www.trinitycapitalplc.com

Other Offices

B-1, The Mira Corporate Suites
Old Iswar Nagar
New Delhi, India 110 065
Phone: 91-11-4659-6000
Fax: 91-11-4659-6060

Management and Staff

Rakshid Chugh, Managing Director

Type of Firm

Private Equity Firm

Project Preferences

Type of Financing Preferred:
Balanced

Geographical Preferences

International Preferences:
India

Industry Preferences

In Financial Services prefer:
Real Estate

Additional Information

Year Founded: 2006
Current Activity Level : Actively seeking new investments

TRILLIUM GROUP, LLC

1221 Pittsford-Victor Road
Pittsford, NY USA 14534
Phone: 585-383-5680
Fax: 585-383-0042
E-mail: info@trillium-group.com
Website: www.trillium-group.com

Management and Staff

Christopher O'Donnell, General Partner
Dennis DeLeo, General Partner
Frank Strong, General Partner
Jose Coronas, General Partner
Kevin Phelps, General Partner
Robert Frame, General Partner

Type of Firm

Private Equity Firm

Association Membership

Western Association of Venture Capitalists (WAVC)
National Venture Capital Association - USA (NVCA)

Project Preferences

Role in Financing:
Prefer role as deal originator but will also invest in deals created by others

Type of Financing Preferred:
Leveraged Buyout
Expansion
Early Stage
Mezzanine
Later Stage
Seed
Management Buyouts
Joint Ventures
Acquisition

Size of Investments Considered:
Min Size of Investment Considered (000s): $500
Max Size of Investment Considered (000s): $5,000

Geographical Preferences

United States Preferences:
Northeast

Industry Preferences

In Communications prefer:
Telecommunications
Wireless Communications

In Computer Software prefer:
Software
Systems Software

In Internet Specific prefer:
Internet

In Semiconductor/Electr prefer:
Semiconductor

In Biotechnology prefer:
Human Biotechnology
Industrial Biotechnology
Biotech Related Research

In Medical/Health prefer:
Medical Diagnostics
Diagnostic Services
Medical Therapeutics

In Consumer Related prefer:
Consumer

In Industrial/Energy prefer:
Energy
Industrial Products
Factory Automation
Machinery

In Business Serv. prefer:
Services
Distribution

In Manufact. prefer:
Manufacturing

Additional Information
Name of Most Recent Fund: Trillium Lakefront Partners III, L.P.
Most Recent Fund Was Raised: 06/01/2004
Year Founded: 1997
Capital Under Management: $63,200,000
Current Activity Level : Actively seeking new investments
Method of Compensation: Return on investment is of primary concern, do not charge fees

---

TRIMARAN CAPITAL PARTNERS, LLC

1325 Avenue of the Americas
34th Floor
New York, NY USA 10019
Phone: 212-616-3700
Fax: 212-616-3701
E-mail: info@trimarancapital.com
Website: www.trimarancapital.com

Management and Staff
Alberto Robaina, Managing Director
Andrew Heyer, Managing Partner
Dean Kehler, Managing Partner
Jay Levine, Managing Director
Jay Bloom, Managing Partner
Jon Erik Larson, Managing Director
Mark Dalton, Managing Director
Michael Maselli, Managing Director
Robert Fioretti, Managing Director
William Phoenix, Managing Director

Type of Firm
Private Equity Advisor or Fund of Funds

Project Preferences

Role in Financing:
Prefer role as deal originator but will also invest in deals created by others

Type of Financing Preferred:
Second Stage Financing
Leveraged Buyout
Expansion
Generalist PE
Later Stage
Management Buyouts
Acquisition

Size of Investments Considered:
Min Size of Investment Considered (000s): $5,000
Max Size of Investment Considered (000s): $150,000

Geographical Preferences

United States Preferences:
All U.S.

International Preferences:
Italy
United Kingdom
Europe
Luxembourg
Netherlands
Belgium
Germany
France

Industry Focus

(% based on actual investment)	
Other Products	53.0%
Consumer Related	32.7%
Medical/Health	4.9%
Communications and Media	4.5%
Internet Specific	3.8%
Semiconductors/Other Elect.	1.1%
Biotechnology	0.1%

Additional Information
Name of Most Recent Fund: Caravelle Investment Fund II, LLC
Most Recent Fund Was Raised: 11/01/2000
Year Founded: 1999
Capital Under Management: $3,900,000,000
Current Activity Level : Actively seeking new investments
Method of Compensation: Return on investment is of primary concern, do not charge fees

---

TRIMOTEUR HOLDING B.V.

Utrechtseweg 67-B
Zeist, Netherlands 3700 AJ
Phone: 31-30-6361-260
Fax: 31-30-6361-254
E-mail: info@trimoteur.nl
Website: www.trimoteur.nl

Type of Firm
Private Equity Firm

Project Preferences

Type of Financing Preferred:
Leveraged Buyout
Management Buyouts
Acquisition

Industry Preferences

In Business Serv. prefer:
Services

Additional Information
Year Founded: 1994
Current Activity Level : Actively seeking new investments

TRINITY HUNT PARTNERS

2001 Ross Avenue
Suite 4800
Dallas, TX USA 75201
Phone: 214-777-6600
Website: www.trinityhunt.com

Management and Staff
Daniel Dross, Partner
Hunter Peterson, Principal
Jim Holland, Partner
Scott Colvert, Partner
William Bixby, Partner

Type of Firm
Private Equity Firm

Project Preferences

Role in Financing:
Prefer role as deal originator

Type of Financing Preferred:
Leveraged Buyout
Later Stage
Recapitalizations

Size of Investments Considered:
Min Size of Investment Considered (000s): $5,000
Max Size of Investment Considered (000s): $30,000

Geographical Preferences

United States Preferences:
New Mexico
Nevada
Oklahoma
Arizona
Kansas
Colorado
Louisiana
Missouri
Utah
Southwest
Arkansas
Texas

Industry Preferences

In Communications prefer:
Entertainment

In Medical/Health prefer:
Medical/Health
Health Services

In Consumer Related prefer:
Consumer Products

In Transportation prefer:
Aerospace

In Business Serv. prefer:
Services
Distribution
Media

In Manufact. prefer:
Manufacturing

Additional Information
Year Founded: 2004
Capital Under Management: $215,000,000
Current Activity Level : Actively seeking new investments

TRINITY MANAGEMENT SP. Z O.O.
Nowogrodzka 47a
Warsaw, Poland 00-695
Phone: 48-22-525-9999
Fax: 48-22-525-9988
E-mail: trinity@trinity.com.pl
Website: www.trinity.com.pl

Type of Firm
Private Equity Advisor or Fund of Funds

Association Membership
European Private Equity and Venture Capital Assoc.

Project Preferences

Type of Financing Preferred:
Second Stage Financing
Early Stage
Expansion
Balanced
Startup

Geographical Preferences

International Preferences:
Poland

Industry Preferences

In Communications prefer:
Telecommunications

In Medical/Health prefer:
Pharmaceuticals

In Financial Services prefer:
Financial Services

In Manufact. prefer:
Publishing

Additional Information
Year Founded: 1995
Capital Under Management: $120,000,000
Current Activity Level : Actively seeking new investments

TRINITY VENTURES
3000 Sand Hill Road
Building Four, Suite 160
Menlo Park, CA USA 94025
Phone: 650-854-9500
Fax: 650-854-9501
E-mail: info@trinityventures.com
Website: www.trinityventures.com

Management and Staff
Ajay Chopra, General Partner
Alex Osadzinski, Venture Partner
Augustus Tai, General Partner
Fred Wang, General Partner
Jim Tybur, Principal
Kathy Murphy, Chief Financial Officer
Lawrence Orr, General Partner
Noel Fenton, General Partner
Patricia Nakache, General Partner
Timothy McAdam, General Partner
Tom Cole, General Partner

Type of Firm
Private Equity Firm

Association Membership
Western Association of Venture Capitalists (WAVC)
National Venture Capital Association - USA (NVCA)

Project Preferences

Role in Financing:
Will function either as deal originator or investor in deals created by others

Type of Financing Preferred:
Early Stage
Balanced

Size of Investments Considered:
Min Size of Investment Considered (000s): $5,000
Max Size of Investment Considered (000s): $20,000

Geographical Preferences

>United States Preferences:
All U.S.

Industry Focus
(% based on actual investment)

Internet Specific	33.6%
Computer Software and Services	26.3%
Communications and Media	13.9%
Other Products	10.3%
Semiconductors/Other Elect.	5.3%
Consumer Related	5.3%
Computer Hardware	4.1%
Medical/Health	1.0%
Industrial/Energy	0.2%

Additional Information
Name of Most Recent Fund: Trinity Ventures X, L.P.
Most Recent Fund Was Raised: 02/03/2009
Year Founded: 1986
Capital Under Management: $1,100,000,000
Current Activity Level : Actively seeking new investments
Method of Compensation: Return on invest. most important, but chg. closing fees, service fees, etc.

TRINORTH CAPITAL, INC.
220 Bay Street
Suite 1500
Toronto, Canada M5J 2W4
Phone: 416-362-4999
Fax: 416-362-0063
Website: www.trinorthcapital.com

Type of Firm
Private Equity Advisor or Fund of Funds

Additional Information
Year Founded: 2000
Current Activity Level : Actively seeking new investments

TRIO CAPITAL

1280 Avenue Bernard
Montreal, Canada H2V 1V9
Phone: 514-843-4730
E-mail: info@triocapital.ca
Website: www.triocapital.ca

Type of Firm

Private Equity Firm

Project Preferences

Type of Financing Preferred:
Acquisition

Geographical Preferences

United States Preferences:
All U.S.

Canadian Preferences:
All Canada

Industry Preferences

In Communications prefer:
Communications and Media

Additional Information

Year Founded: 2006
Capital Under Management: $200,000,000
Current Activity Level : Actively seeking new investments
Method of Compensation: Return on invest. most important, but chg. closing fees, service fees, etc.

TRIPLEPOINT CAPITAL

2500 Sand Hill Road
Suite 110
Menlo Park, CA USA 94025
Phone: 650-926-0630
Fax: 650-926-0629
E-mail: info@tpcp.com
Website: www.tpcp.com

Management and Staff

Jim Labe, Chief Executive Officer
Sajal Srivastava, Chief Operating Officer

Type of Firm

Private Equity Firm

Project Preferences

Type of Financing Preferred:
Mezzanine

Size of Investments Considered:
Min Size of Investment Considered (000s): $250
Max Size of Investment Considered (000s): $10,000

Additional Information

Name of Most Recent Fund: TriplePoint Capital, LLC
Most Recent Fund Was Raised: 07/13/2005
Year Founded: 2005
Capital Under Management: $52,800,000
Current Activity Level : Actively seeking new investments

TRIPOD CAPITAL

Tower A, Golden Eagle Mansion
1518 Min Sheng Road
Pudong, China 200135
Phone: 86-21-6104-2968
Fax: 86-21-6104-2969
E-mail: contact@tripodcapital.com
Website: www.tripodcapital.com

Management and Staff

Alec Chen, Managing Director
Guo Wang, Managing Director
Guo Hui, Managing Director
Michael Bruck, Managing Director
Xie Cheng, Managing Director
Zhao Xiangti, Managing Director

Type of Firm

Private Equity Firm

Project Preferences

Type of Financing Preferred:
Balanced

Geographical Preferences

International Preferences:
China
Asia

Industry Preferences

In Industrial/Energy prefer:
Alternative Energy
Environmental Related

In Financial Services prefer:
Financial Services

In Manufact. prefer:
Manufacturing

Additional Information

Year Founded: 2006
Capital Under Management: $30,000,000
Current Activity Level : Actively seeking new investments

TRISTATE INVESTMENT GROUP

6002 Meadow Run Court
Chapel Hill, NC USA 27516
Phone: 919-247-3769
E-mail: contact@tignc.com
Website: www.tignc.com

Type of Firm

Private Equity Firm

Project Preferences

Role in Financing:
Will function either as deal originator or investor in deals created by others

Type of Financing Preferred:
Early Stage
Expansion
Start-up Financing
Seed
First Stage Financing

Size of Investments Considered:
Min Size of Investment Considered (000s): $100
Max Size of Investment Considered (000s): $500

Geographical Preferences

United States Preferences:
North Carolina
South Carolina
Virginia

Industry Preferences

In Communications prefer:
Telecommunications
Wireless Communications

In Computer Hardware prefer:
Computers

In Computer Software prefer:
Software

In Biotechnology prefer:
Biotechnology

In Medical/Health prefer:
Medical Products

In Consumer Related prefer:
Consumer Products

In Manufact. prefer:
Manufacturing

Additional Information

Name of Most Recent Fund: TIG IV
Most Recent Fund Was Raised: 07/20/2000
Year Founded: 1995
Capital Under Management: $23,000,000
Current Activity Level : Actively seeking new investments
Method of Compensation: Return on investment is of primary concern, do not charge fees

TRITON MANAGEMENT CORPORATION

3F, No. 135, Sec. 2
Jianguo North Road
Taipei, Taiwan 110
Phone: 886-2-2503-1622
Fax: 886-2-2503-1506
E-mail: venture@triton.com.tw
Website: www.triton.com.tw

Management and Staff

Frank Jiang, Co-Founder
Frank Liang, Vice President
Michael Hung, General Partner
Richard Chiang, Co-Founder
Yahon Huang Chang, Co-Founder

Type of Firm

Private Equity Firm

Association Membership

Taiwan Venture Capital Association(TVCA)

Project Preferences

Type of Financing Preferred:
Expansion
Mezzanine
Seed
Startup

Geographical Preferences

United States Preferences:
All U.S.

International Preferences:
Taiwan
Singapore
Korea, South

Industry Preferences

In Communications prefer:
Telecommunications

In Computer Software prefer:
Software

In Internet Specific prefer:
Internet

In Semiconductor/Electr prefer:
Semiconductor
Optoelectronics

Additional Information

Year Founded: 1999
Capital Under Management: $76,400,000
Current Activity Level : Actively seeking new investments

TRITON PACIFIC CAPITAL PARTNERS LLC

2029 Century Park East
Suite 2910
Los Angeles, CA USA 90067
Phone: 310-300-0830
Fax: 310-300-0835
E-mail: info@tritonpacific.com
Website: www.tritonpacific.com

Management and Staff

Craig Faggen, Managing Partner
Fred Thiel, Managing Partner
Ivan Faggen, Managing Partner
Joe Davis, Managing Partner
Sean Gjos, Principal
Thomas Scott, Principal

Type of Firm

Private Equity Firm

Project Preferences

Type of Financing Preferred:
Generalist PE

Size of Investments Considered:
Min Size of Investment Considered (000s): $2,000
Max Size of Investment Considered (000s): $10,000

Geographical Preferences

United States Preferences:
All U.S.

Industry Preferences

In Computer Software prefer:
Software

In Medical/Health prefer:
Health Services

In Consumer Related prefer:
Consumer Products

In Transportation prefer:
Transportation

In Manufact. prefer:
Manufacturing

Additional Information

Year Founded: 2001
Capital Under Management: $150,000,000
Current Activity Level : Actively seeking new investments

TRITON PARTNERS (AKA: TRITON BETEILIGUNGS-BERATUNG GMBH)

Rathenauplatz 1
Frankfurt, Germany 60313
Phone: 49-699-21020
Fax: 49-69921020100
E-mail: info@triton-partners.com
Website: www.triton-partners.com

Other Offices

105 Piccadilly, 5th floor
London, United Kingdom W1J 7NJ
Phone: 44-207-2976150
Fax: 44-207-2976189

Master Samuelsgatan 3, 3rd floor
Stockholm, Sweden 11144
Phone: 46-8-50559600
Fax: 46-8-50559699

Management and Staff

Matthias Hillmann, Principal
Peder Prahl, Managing Director
Peter Sewing, Chief Executive Officer

Type of Firm

Private Equity Firm

Project Preferences

Type of Financing Preferred:
Leveraged Buyout
Acquisition

Geographical Preferences

International Preferences:
Europe
Scandanavia/Nordic Region
Germany

Additional Information

Year Founded: 1999
Capital Under Management: $607,000,000
Current Activity Level : Actively seeking new investments

TRITON VENTURES

6300 Bridge Point Parkway
Building 1, Suite 500
Austin, TX USA 78730
Phone: 512-795-5820
Fax: 512-795-5828
Website: www.tritonventures.com

Management and Staff

D. Scott Collier, Managing Director
Laura Kilcrease, Managing Director

Type of Firm

Private Equity Firm

Project Preferences

Type of Financing Preferred:
Early Stage
Seed
Startup

Size of Investments Considered:
Min Size of Investment Considered (000s): $500
Max Size of Investment Considered (000s): $6,000

Geographical Preferences

United States Preferences:
Texas
All U.S.

Industry Preferences

In Communications prefer:
Communications and Media

In Computer Software prefer:
Software

In Internet Specific prefer:
Internet

In Semiconductor/Electr prefer:
Electronics

In Industrial/Energy prefer:
Alternative Energy

Additional Information

Year Founded: 1999
Capital Under Management: $40,000,000
Current Activity Level : Actively seeking new investments

TRIVELLA INVESTIMENTOS LTDA.

Avenida Tiradentes, 451
Conjunto 64, Itu
Sao Paulo, Brazil 13309-320
Phone: 55-11-4025-1370
Fax: 55-11-4025-1378
E-mail: investimentos@trivella.net
Website: www.trivella.net

Other Offices

Avenida Paulista, 2073
H1, Conjunto 2124
Sao Paulo, Brazil 01311-300
Phone: 5511-289-1371

Type of Firm

Private Equity Firm

Association Membership

Brazilian Venture Capital Association (ABCR)

Project Preferences

>Type of Financing Preferred:
Balanced

Geographical Preferences

International Preferences:
Brazil

Additional Information

Year Founded: 2001
Current Activity Level : Actively seeking new investments

TRIVEST PARTNERS, L.P.

550 South Dixie Highway
Suite 300
Coral Gables, FL USA 33146
Phone: 305-858-2200
Fax: 305-285-0102
E-mail: info@trivest.com
Website: www.trivest.com

Management and Staff

David Gershman, Principal
Earl Powell, Founding Partner
Forest Wester, Principal
Jamie Elias, Partner
Jorge Gross, Vice President
Peter Vandenberg, Partner
Richard Moran, Chief Financial Officer
Russ Wilson, Principal
Todd Jerles, Vice President
Troy Templeton, Managing Partner

Type of Firm

Private Equity Firm

Project Preferences

Role in Financing:
Prefer role as deal originator but will also invest in deals created by others

Type of Financing Preferred:
Leveraged Buyout

Size of Investments Considered:
Min Size of Investment Considered (000s): $1,000
Max Size of Investment Considered (000s): $50,000

Geographical Preferences

United States Preferences:
Midwest
Southeast
All U.S.

Industry Focus

(% based on actual investment)

Industrial/Energy	43.8%
Medical/Health	22.3%
Consumer Related	19.4%
Semiconductors/Other Elect.	10.3%
Other Products	2.2%
Internet Specific	1.9%

Additional Information

Year Founded: 1981
Capital Under Management: $600,000,000
Current Activity Level : Actively seeking new investments
Method of Compensation: Return on invest. most important, but chg. closing fees, service fees, etc.

TRIWEST CAPITAL MANAGEMENT CORPORATION

150-6th Avenue SW
Suite 3210
Calgary, Canada T2P 3Y7
Phone: 403-225-1144
Fax: 403-225-3547
E-mail: info@triwest.ca
Website: www.triwest.ca

Management and Staff

Cody Church, Managing Director
Jeff Belford, Managing Director
Kevin Jenkins, Managing Director
Lorne Jacobson, Managing Director

Type of Firm

Private Equity Firm

Project Preferences

Type of Financing Preferred:
Leveraged Buyout
Expansion
Generalist PE
Management Buyouts
Acquisition
Private Placement
Industry Rollups
Special Situation
Recapitalizations

Geographical Preferences

Canadian Preferences:
All Canada

Industry Focus

(% based on actual investment)

Other Products	89.5%
Industrial/Energy	9.3%
Medical/Health	1.2%

Additional Information

Year Founded: 1998
Capital Under Management: $132,900,000
Current Activity Level : Actively seeking new investments

TROIKA CAPITAL PARTNERS

Romanov Center
4, Romanov Pereulok
Moscow, Russia 125009
Phone: 7-495-258-0500
Fax: 7-495-258-0547
E-mail: info_vc@troika.ru
Website: www.troika.ru

Management and Staff

Maria Korneeva, Chief Operating Officer
Serguei Skvortsov, President

Type of Firm

Bank Affiliated

Project Preferences

Role in Financing:
Prefer role as deal originator

Type of Financing Preferred:
Leveraged Buyout
Expansion
Generalist PE

Geographical Preferences

International Preferences:
Europe
Kazakhstan
Eastern Europe
Ukraine
Russia

Industry Preferences

In Communications prefer:
Communications and Media

In Medical/Health prefer:
Medical/Health
Medical Diagnostics
Diagnostic Services
Health Services

In Consumer Related prefer:
Consumer
Retail

In Financial Services prefer:
Financial Services

In Business Serv. prefer:
Media

In Manufact. prefer:
Manufacturing

Additional Information
Name of Most Recent Fund: Russia New Growth Fund, L.P.
Most Recent Fund Was Raised: 01/27/2006
Year Founded: 2005
Capital Under Management: $509,600,000
Current Activity Level : Actively seeking new investments

TRUE VENTURES
530 Lytton Avenue
Suite 303
Palo Alto, CA USA 94301
Phone: 650-319-2150
Fax: 650-319-7330
E-mail: info@trueventures.com
Website: www.trueventures.com

Other Offices
766-B Walker Road
Great Falls, VA USA 22066
Phone: 650-319-2163
Fax: 650-330-7330

Pier 38
The Embarcadero
San Francisco, CA USA 94107
Phone: 650-319-2150
Fax: 650-330-7330

Management and Staff
Anthony Conrad, Venture Partner
Braughm Ricke, Chief Financial Officer
John Burke, General Partner
Jon Callaghan, General Partner
Om Malik, Venture Partner
Philip Black, General Partner
Puneet Agarwal, Partner
Toni Schneider, Venture Partner

Type of Firm
Private Equity Firm

Project Preferences

Role in Financing:
Prefer role as deal originator

Type of Financing Preferred:
Early Stage
Seed

Size of Investments Considered:
Min Size of Investment Considered (000s): $50
Max Size of Investment Considered (000s): $4,000

Additional Information
Name of Most Recent Fund: True Ventures II, L.P.
Most Recent Fund Was Raised: 07/23/2008
Year Founded: 2006
Capital Under Management: $350,000,000
Current Activity Level : Actively seeking new investments

TRUEBRIDGE CAPITAL PARTNERS
1350 Environ Way
Chapel Hill, NC USA 27517
Phone: 919-442-5201
Fax: 919-869-1444
E-mail: info@truebridgecapital.com
Website: www.truebridgecapital.com

Management and Staff
Edwin Poston, General Partner
Mel Williams, General Partner

Type of Firm
Private Equity Advisor or Fund of Funds

Project Preferences

Type of Financing Preferred:
Fund of Funds

Additional Information
Year Founded: 2007
Capital Under Management: $310,000,000
Current Activity Level : Actively seeking new investments

TRUFFLE VENTURE
5 Rue De La Baume
Paris, France 75008
Phone: 33-1-4720-2220
Fax: 33-1-4720-1209
E-mail: info@truffle-venture.com
Website: www.truffle.com

Management and Staff
Bernard-Louis Roques, General Partner
Frederic Billet, Chief Financial Officer
Gwen Chapman, Chief Financial Officer
Jean Francois Fourt, General Partner
Jean-Jacques Bertrand, Venture Partner
Miguel Sieler, Venture Partner
Philippe Pouletty, General Partner
Ron Belt, Venture Partner

Type of Firm
Private Equity Firm

Association Membership
French Venture Capital Association (AFIC)

Project Preferences

Type of Financing Preferred:
Fund of Funds
Early Stage
Expansion
Balanced
Later Stage
Seed
Startup

Size of Investments Considered:
Min Size of Investment Considered (000s): $5,033
Max Size of Investment Considered (000s): $15,098

Geographical Preferences

International Preferences:
Luxembourg
Netherlands
Switzerland
Europe
Belgium
Germany
France
All International

Industry Preferences

In Computer Software prefer:
Software

In Medical/Health prefer:
Medical/Health

In Industrial/Energy prefer:
Energy

Additional Information
Year Founded: 2002
Capital Under Management: $51,200,000
Current Activity Level : Actively seeking new investments

TRUST AND INVESTMENT BANK (T&IB)
4/4 Kolpachny per.
Moscow, Russia 101990
Phone: 7-95-247-2583
Fax: 7-95-247-2581
E-mail: office@tibank.ru

Type of Firm
Bank Affiliated

Project Preferences

Type of Financing Preferred:
Early Stage
Expansion

Geographical Preferences

International Preferences:
Europe

Additional Information
Year Founded: 2001
Current Activity Level : Actively seeking new investments

TRUST COMPANY OF THE WEST (AKA: TCW/CRESCENT)
865 South Figueroa Street
Suite 1800
Los Angeles, CA USA 90017
Phone: 213-244-0000
Fax: 213-244-0489
E-mail: feedback@tcw.com
Website: www.tcwgroup.com

Other Offices
11100 Santa Monica Boulevard
West Los Angeles, CA USA 90025
Phone: 310-235-5900

333 Clay Street
Suite 4150
Houston, TX USA 77002
Phone: 713-615-7400

200 Park Avenue
New York, NY USA 10166
Phone: 212-771-4000

Management and Staff
Bill Soheborn, Chief Financial Officer
James Lewis, Vice President
John Rocchio, Managing Director

Type of Firm
Private Equity Firm

Project Preferences

Type of Financing Preferred:
Fund of Funds
Leveraged Buyout
Mezzanine
Other

Geographical Preferences

United States Preferences:
All U.S.

Canadian Preferences:
All Canada

International Preferences:
Latin America

Industry Focus
(% based on actual investment)

Industrial/Energy	53.3%
Medical/Health	14.7%
Internet Specific	12.9%
Other Products	12.3%
Consumer Related	3.9%
Communications and Media	1.1%
Semiconductors/Other Elect.	0.9%
Computer Software and Services	0.9%

Additional Information
Year Founded: 1985
Capital Under Management: $335,300,000
Current Activity Level : Actively seeking new investments

TRUSTCAPITAL PARTNERS NV
Ter Bede Center
Kapel Ter Bede 86
Kortrijk, Belgium 8500
Phone: 32-5-624-95-11
Fax: 32-5-622-86-99
E-mail: info@trustcapital.be
Website: www.trustcapital.be

Management and Staff
Katrien Mattelaer, Chief Financial Officer
Pascale Weber, Managing Director

Type of Firm
Private Equity Firm

Association Membership
Belgium Venturing Association

Project Preferences

Type of Financing Preferred:
Balanced
Later Stage
Seed

Geographical Preferences

International Preferences:
Belgium

Industry Focus
(% based on actual investment)

Internet Specific	42.6%
Medical/Health	22.8%
Computer Software and Services	12.5%
Consumer Related	8.7%
Biotechnology	7.1%
Other Products	3.8%
Computer Hardware	1.1%
Semiconductors/Other Elect.	0.7%
Industrial/Energy	0.6%

Additional Information
Year Founded: 1998
Capital Under Management: $142,700,000
Current Activity Level : Actively seeking new investments

TSG CONSUMER PARTNERS
600 Montgomery Street
Suite 2900
San Francisco, CA USA 94111
Phone: 415-217-2300
Fax: 415-217-2350
Website: www.tsgconsumer.com

Other Offices
712 Fifth Avenue
31st Floor
New York, NY USA 10019
Phone: 212-265-4111
Fax: 212-265-4845

Management and Staff
Alexander Panos, Managing Director
Brian Krumrei, Principal
J. Gary Shansby, President
James O'Hara, Managing Director
Jennifer Baxter, Vice President
John Kenney, Managing Director
M. Hadley Mullin, Managing Director
Pierre LeComte, Managing Director
Robyn Lawrie Rutledge, Principal
Yasser Toor, Managing Director

Type of Firm
Private Equity Firm

Project Preferences

Type of Financing Preferred:
Leveraged Buyout
Turnaround

Size of Investments Considered:
Min Size of Investment Considered (000s): $2,000
Max Size of Investment Considered: No Limit

Industry Focus
(% based on actual investment)

Consumer Related	94.2%
Medical/Health	5.8%

Additional Information
Year Founded: 1987
Capital Under Management: $1,375,000,000
Current Activity Level : Actively seeking new investments

TSG EQUITY PARTNERS, L.L.C.

636 Great Road
Stow, MA USA 01775
Phone: 978-461-9900
Fax: 978-461-9909
Website: www.tsgequity.com

Management and Staff

T. Nathanael Shepherd, President
William Woo, Managing Director

Type of Firm

Private Equity Firm

Project Preferences

Type of Financing Preferred:
Leveraged Buyout
Expansion
Later Stage
Acquisition
Special Situation
Recapitalizations

Size of Investments Considered:
Min Size of Investment Considered (000s): $2,000
Max Size of Investment Considered (000s): $4,000

Geographical Preferences

United States Preferences:
Northeast

Industry Focus

(% based on actual investment)

Computer Software and Services	56.4%
Medical/Health	21.4%
Communications and Media	12.0%
Industrial/Energy	6.4%
Internet Specific	3.8%

Additional Information

Year Founded: 1996
Current Activity Level : Actively seeking new investments

TSING CAPITAL (AKA: TSINGHUA VENTURE CAPITAL COMPANY, LTD.)

Room 2608 Huaye Building
Tsinghua University
Beijing, China 100084
Phone: 86-10-6279-1192
Fax: 86-10-6278-0287
E-mail: thvc@tsinghuavc.com
Website: www.tsinghuavc.com

Management and Staff

Hong-Ru Yang, President
Qirui Cao, Chief Financial Officer

Type of Firm

Private Equity Firm

Association Membership

Venture Capital Association of Beijing (VCAB)

Project Preferences

Type of Financing Preferred:
Early Stage
Expansion
Balanced
Seed
Startup

Geographical Preferences

International Preferences:
China

Industry Preferences

In Communications prefer:
Telecommunications

In Computer Software prefer:
Software

In Semiconductor/Electr prefer:
Electronics
Semiconductor

In Biotechnology prefer:
Biotechnology

In Medical/Health prefer:
Medical/Health

In Industrial/Energy prefer:
Energy
Energy Conservation Relat
Materials
Environmental Related

In Other prefer:
Environment Responsible

Additional Information

Year Founded: 2000
Capital Under Management: $24,100,000
Current Activity Level : Actively seeking new investments

TSING-TECH INNOVATIONS CO., LTD.

8/F Century Centre
44 - 46 Hung To Road
Kowloon, Hong Kong
Phone: 852-2723-8860
Fax: 852-2723-3821
E-mail: info@tsing-tech.com.hk
Website: www.tsing-tech.com

Other Offices

Room 806, Block B, Xue Yan Building
Tsinghua Science Park, Haidian District
Beijing, China 100084
Phone: 86-10-6279-7157
Fax: 86-10-6277-1053

Type of Firm

Private Equity Firm

Project Preferences

Type of Financing Preferred:
Balanced

Geographical Preferences

International Preferences:
China
Asia

Industry Preferences

In Communications prefer:
Wireless Communications

In Medical/Health prefer:
Health Services

In Industrial/Energy prefer:
Environmental Related

Additional Information

Year Founded: 2003
Current Activity Level : Actively seeking new investments

TSINGHUA UNISPLENDOUR HI-TECH VENTURE CAPITAL, INC.

1 Zhong Guangcun South Street
Suite 62528, Yiyuan Apartment
Beijing, China 100086
Phone: 86-10-6894-9919
Fax: 86-10-6894-7226
E-mail: thuvc@163.com
Website: www.thuvc.com

Type of Firm

Private Equity Firm

Association Membership

Venture Capital Association of Beijing (VCAB)

Project Preferences

Type of Financing Preferred:
Expansion

Geographical Preferences

International Preferences:
China

Industry Preferences

In Biotechnology prefer:
Biotechnology

In Medical/Health prefer:
Medical/Health

In Industrial/Energy prefer:
Energy

Additional Information

Year Founded: 2000
Current Activity Level : Actively seeking new investments

TSPP SICAR

32 Rue Hedi Karray
Tunis, Tunisia 1082
Phone: 216-71-716-550
Fax: 216-71-719-233
E-mail: stusid@gnet.tn

Type of Firm

Private Equity Firm

Project Preferences

Type of Financing Preferred:
Expansion
Balanced

Geographical Preferences

International Preferences:
Tunisia

Additional Information

Year Founded: 2004
Current Activity Level : Actively seeking new investments

TSUNAMI NETWORK PARTNERS CORP.

8F Shinyokohama SR Bldg
3-6-1 Shinyokohama, Kohoku-ku
Yokohama, Japan 222-0033
Phone: 81-45-470-8088
Fax: 81-45-470-8090
E-mail: info@tsunami2000.co.jp
Website: www.tsunami2000.co.jp

Type of Firm

Government Affiliated Program

Project Preferences

Type of Financing Preferred:
Balanced

Additional Information

Year Founded: 2000
Capital Under Management: $67,600,000
Current Activity Level : Actively seeking new investments

TTP VENTURE MANAGERS, LTD. (FKA: TECHNOLOGY PARTNERSHIP, THE)

Melbourn Science Park
Melbourn
Hertfordshire, United Kingdom SG8 6EE
Phone: 44-17-6326-2626
Fax: 44-17-6326-2265
E-mail: mailventures@ttpventures.com
Website: www.ttpventures.com

Management and Staff

David Gee, Chief Executive Officer
Gerry Fitzsimons, Chief Executive Officer

Type of Firm

Private Equity Firm

Association Membership

British Venture Capital Association (BVCA)
European Private Equity and Venture Capital Assoc.

Project Preferences

Type of Financing Preferred:
Early Stage
Expansion
Start-up Financing
Seed
Startup

Size of Investments Considered:
Min Size of Investment Considered (000s): $99
Max Size of Investment Considered (000s): $5,962

Geographical Preferences

United States Preferences:
All U.S.

International Preferences:
United Kingdom
Europe

Industry Preferences

In Communications prefer:
Communications and Media

In Computer Other prefer:
Computer Related

In Semiconductor/Electr prefer:
Electronics

In Medical/Health prefer:
Medical/Health

In Industrial/Energy prefer:
Industrial Products
Materials
Environmental Related

In Business Serv. prefer:
Services

In Other prefer:
Environment Responsible

Additional Information

Year Founded: 1998
Capital Under Management: $67,900,000
Current Activity Level : Actively seeking new investments

TUAREG CAPITAL, LTD.

Walker House, Mary Street
George Town, Cayman Islands
E-mail: info@tuaregcapital.com
Website: www.tuaregcapital.com

Other Offices

Al Matrook Building
Diplomatic Area, PO Box 11544
Manama, Bahrain
Phone: 973-1753-7277

Hafsa Arrakunia Street
Hay El-Andulus 2, PO Box 5521
Tripoli, Libya

Management and Staff

Adel Saudi, Chairman & CEO

Type of Firm

Private Equity Firm

Geographical Preferences

International Preferences:
Algeria
Africa
Libya

Additional Information

Year Founded: 2006
Capital Under Management: $100,000,000
Current Activity Level : Actively seeking new investments

TUBE INVESTMENT, INC.

5th Floor, HB Building
627-17, Sinsa-dong, Kangnam-Gu
Seoul, South Korea 135-895
Phone: 822-3448-5620
Fax: 822-3448-5630
Website: www.tubei.com

Management and Staff

Jungsoon Song, Managing Director

Type of Firm

Private Equity Firm

Association Membership

Korean Venture Capital Association (KVCA)

Project Preferences

Type of Financing Preferred:
Leveraged Buyout
Expansion
Early Stage
Balanced
Turnaround
Seed
Management Buyouts
Startup

Geographical Preferences

International Preferences:
Korea, South

Industry Preferences

In Communications prefer:
Communications and Media
Media and Entertainment

In Medical/Health prefer:
Medical/Health

In Consumer Related prefer:
Entertainment and Leisure

In Business Serv. prefer:
Services

In Manufact. prefer:
Manufacturing

Additional Information

Year Founded: 1999
Capital Under Management: $101,900,000
Current Activity Level : Actively seeking new investments

TUCKER PARTNERS

2821 Pebble Drive
Corona del Mar, CA USA 92625
Phone: 949-640-7997
Fax: 949-640-7829
Website: www.tuckerpartners.com

Management and Staff

James Tucker, Principal
Stewart Slykhous, Principal
William Blaney, Principal

Type of Firm

Private Equity Firm

Project Preferences

Type of Financing Preferred:
Leveraged Buyout
Acquisition

Size of Investments Considered:
Min Size of Investment Considered (000s): $5,000
Max Size of Investment Considered (000s): $50,000

Geographical Preferences

United States Preferences:
West Coast
California

Industry Preferences

In Semiconductor/Electr prefer:
Electronics

In Medical/Health prefer:
Medical/Health

In Consumer Related prefer:
Consumer
Food/Beverage

In Industrial/Energy prefer:
Industrial Products

In Business Serv. prefer:
Services

In Manufact. prefer:
Manufacturing

Additional Information

Year Founded: 2007
Current Activity Level : Actively seeking new investments

TUCKERMAN CAPITAL

80 South Main Street
Hanover, NH USA 03755
Phone: 603-640-2291
Fax: 603-640-2239
Website: www.tuckermancapital.com

Type of Firm

Private Equity Firm

Project Preferences

Type of Financing Preferred:
Acquisition

Geographical Preferences

United States Preferences:
All U.S.

Industry Preferences

In Manufact. prefer:
Manufacturing

Additional Information

Year Founded: 2001
Capital Under Management: $165,000,000
Current Activity Level : Actively seeking new investments

TUDOR VENTURES

50 Rowes Wharf
Sixth Floor
Boston, MA USA 02110
Phone: 617-772-4600
Fax: 617-737-0993
E-mail: info@tudorventures.com
Website: www.tudorventures.com

Management and Staff

Carmen Scarpa, Partner
Dan MacKeigan, Principal
Jeffrey Williams, Principal
John Danielsen, Principal
Richard Ganong, Partner
Robert Forlenza, Managing Partner

Type of Firm

Bank Affiliated

Project Preferences

Type of Financing Preferred:
Expansion

Industry Focus

(% based on actual investment)	
Communications and Media	18.8%
Computer Software and Services	18.3%
Internet Specific	17.6%
Other Products	17.4%
Medical/Health	6.6%
Computer Hardware	6.5%
Semiconductors/Other Elect.	6.0%
Industrial/Energy	5.6%
Consumer Related	3.4%

Additional Information

Name of Most Recent Fund: Tudor Ventures III L.P.
Most Recent Fund Was Raised: 02/07/2006
Year Founded: 1995
Capital Under Management: $262,300,000
Current Activity Level : Actively seeking new investments

TUFAN VENTURE PARTNERS

146 West Beaver Creek Road
Suite Three
Toronto, Canada L4B 1C2
Phone: 905-762-8770
Fax: 905-762-8799
Website: www.tufanvp.com

Other Offices

146 West Beaver Creek Road
Suite Three
Toronto, Canada L4B 1C2
Phone: 905-762-8770
Fax: 905-762-8799

Management and Staff

Hardev Arora, Managing Partner
Roy Pathak, Managing Partner
Zool Kassum, Managing Partner

Type of Firm

Private Equity Firm

Project Preferences

Type of Financing Preferred:
Seed

Additional Information

Year Founded: 2000
Current Activity Level : Actively seeking new investments

TUGBOAT VENTURES

325 Sharon Park Drive
Menlo Park, CA USA 94025
Phone: 650-470-1400
Website: www.tugboatventures.com

Management and Staff

David Whorton, Founder

Type of Firm

Private Equity Firm

Association Membership

National Venture Capital Association - USA (NVCA)

Project Preferences

Role in Financing:

Prefer role as deal originator but will also invest in deals created by others

Type of Financing Preferred:

Early Stage
Balanced
Seed
First Stage Financing
Startup

Size of Investments Considered:

Min Size of Investment Considered (000s): $100
Max Size of Investment Considered (000s): $5,000

Geographical Preferences

United States Preferences:

West Coast
All U.S.

Industry Preferences

In Computer Software prefer:

Software
Systems Software

In Internet Specific prefer:

Internet
Ecommerce
Web Aggregration/Portals

In Financial Services prefer:

Financial Services

In Business Serv. prefer:

Services
Media

Additional Information

Name of Most Recent Fund: Tugboat Strategic Limited Partners II, L.P.
Most Recent Fund Was Raised: 02/25/2009
Year Founded: 2006
Capital Under Management: $125,000,000
Current Activity Level : Actively seeking new investments

TULLIS HEALTH INVESTORS (FKA: TULLIS-DICKERSON & CO., INC.)

One Stamford Plaza
263 Tresser Boulevard
Stamford, CT USA 06901
Phone: 203-629-8700
Fax: 203-629-9293
E-mail: info@tullisdickerson.com
Website: www.thi-funds.com

Management and Staff

Curt LaBelle, Managing Director
Jim Tullis, Partner
Neil Ryan, Partner
Nora Mende, Chief Financial Officer

Type of Firm

Private Equity Firm

Association Membership

National Venture Capital Association - USA (NVCA)
Natl Assoc of Small Bus. Inv. Co (NASBIC)

Project Preferences

Role in Financing:

Prefer role as deal originator but will also invest in deals created by others

Type of Financing Preferred:

Second Stage Financing
Early Stage
Expansion
Seed
Later Stage
First Stage Financing

Size of Investments Considered:

Min Size of Investment Considered (000s): $1,000
Max Size of Investment Considered (000s): $20,000

Industry Preferences

In Biotechnology prefer:

Biotechnology
Human Biotechnology
Agricultural/Animal Bio.
Industrial Biotechnology
Biosensors
Biotech Related Research

In Medical/Health prefer:

Medical Diagnostics
Diagnostic Services
Medical Therapeutics
Drug/Equipmt Delivery
Medical Products
Disposable Med. Products
Health Services
Pharmaceuticals

Additional Information

Name of Most Recent Fund: Tullis-Dickerson Capital Focus III, L.P.
Most Recent Fund Was Raised: 06/13/2001
Year Founded: 1986
Capital Under Management: $350,000,000
Current Activity Level : Actively seeking new investments
Method of Compensation: Return on investment is of primary concern, do not charge fees

TULLY & HOLLAND, INC. (FKA: ULIN & HOLLAND, INC.)

60 William Street
Suite 100
Wellesley, MA USA 02481
Phone: 781-239-2900
Fax: 781-239-2901
E-mail: info@tullyandholland.com
Website: www.tullyandholland.com

Management and Staff

Alfred Rossow, Managing Director
Andrew Crain, Managing Director
Christopher Kampe, Managing Director
Donald O'Connor, Managing Director
Russell Robb, Managing Director
Stuart Rose, Managing Director
Timothy Tully, President

Type of Firm

Bank Affiliated

Project Preferences

Role in Financing:

Other

Type of Financing Preferred:

Second Stage Financing
Leveraged Buyout
Mezzanine
Recapitalizations

Size of Investments Considered:

Min Size of Investment Considered (000s): $5,000
Max Size of Investment Considered: No Limit

Geographical Preferences

United States Preferences:

Midwest
Southeast
Northeast

Industry Preferences

In Medical/Health prefer:

Diagnostic Services
Diagnostic Test Products
Other Therapeutic
Medical Products
Disposable Med. Products

In Consumer Related prefer:

Retail
Computer Stores
Food/Beverage
Consumer Products

Consumer Services
Other Restaurants

Additional Information

Year Founded: 1992
Current Activity Level : Actively seeking new investments
Method of Compensation: Other

TUNINVEST FINANCE GROUP (TFG)

Immeuble Iris
Les Berges du Lac
Tunis, Tunisia 1053
Phone: 216-71-862-311
Fax: 216-71-862-805
E-mail: tfg.mail@tuninvest.com
Website: www.tuninvest.com

Management and Staff

Ahmed Abdelkefi, President, Founder

Type of Firm

Private Equity Firm

Association Membership

Tunisian Venture Capital Association
African Venture Capital Association (AVCA)

Project Preferences

Type of Financing Preferred:

Leveraged Buyout
Early Stage
Expansion
Generalist PE
Balanced

Size of Investments Considered:

Min Size of Investment Considered (000s): $200
Max Size of Investment Considered (000s): $2,500

Geographical Preferences

International Preferences:

Tunisia
Nigeria
Algeria
Ghana
Morocco
Africa

Industry Preferences

In Communications prefer:

Telecommunications

In Medical/Health prefer:

Pharmaceuticals

In Consumer Related prefer:

Education Related

In Industrial/Energy prefer:

Energy

In Transportation prefer:

Transportation

In Financial Services prefer:

Financial Services

In Manufact. prefer:

Manufacturing

In Agr/Forestr/Fish prefer:

Agriculture related

Additional Information

Year Founded: 1994
Capital Under Management: $61,100,000
Current Activity Level : Actively seeking new investments

TURENNE CAPITAL

29 - 31 rue Saint Augustin
Paris, France 75002
Phone: 33-1-5343-0303
Fax: 33-1-5343-0304
E-mail: turenne@turennecapital.com
Website: www.turennecapital.com

Other Offices

31, rue Montgrand
BP 303
Marseille, France 13177
Phone: 33-4-9114-3135
Fax: 33-4-9155-6259

Management and Staff

Beatrice Vernet, Chief Operating Officer
Yves Guez, Partner

Type of Firm

Private Equity Firm

Association Membership

French Venture Capital Association (AFIC)

Project Preferences

Type of Financing Preferred:

Leveraged Buyout
Early Stage
Expansion
Generalist PE
Balanced
Startup

Geographical Preferences

International Preferences:

Europe
Western Europe
France

Industry Preferences

In Communications prefer:

Telecommunications

In Internet Specific prefer:

Internet

In Computer Other prefer:

Computer Related

In Semiconductor/Electr prefer:

Electronics

In Medical/Health prefer:

Medical/Health

In Consumer Related prefer:

Consumer

Additional Information

Year Founded: 1999
Capital Under Management: $269,800,000
Current Activity Level : Actively seeking new investments

TURK VENTURE PARTNERS LIMITED (TURKVEN)

Muallim Naci Cad. No. 40
Ortakoy
Istanbul, Turkey 34347
Phone: 90-212-326-8400
Fax: 90-212-326-8484
E-mail: info@turkven.com
Website: www.turkven.com

Type of Firm

Bank Affiliated

Project Preferences

Type of Financing Preferred:

Early Stage

Geographical Preferences

International Preferences:

Turkey
Europe

Additional Information

Year Founded: 2000
Capital Under Management: $41,000,000
Current Activity Level : Actively seeking new investments

TURNER BROADCASTING

One CNN Center
Atlanta, GA USA 30303
Phone: 404-827-1700
Website: www.turner.com

Type of Firm

Corporate PE/Venture

Association Membership

National Venture Capital Association - USA (NVCA)

Additional Information

Year Founded: 2005
Capital Under Management: $10,000,000
Current Activity Level : Actively seeking new investments

TURTLE CREEK PRIVATE EQUITY

Four King Street West
Suite 1300
Toronto, Canada M5H 1B6
Phone: 416-363-7400
Fax: 416-363-7511
Website: www.turtlecreek.ca

Other Offices

Four King Street West
Suite 1300
Toronto, Canada Toronto
Phone: 416-363-7400
Fax: 416-363-7511

Management and Staff

Andrew Brenton, Chief Executive Officer
Garth Davis, Managing Partner
Jeff Hebel, Managing Partner
Jeffrey Cole, Managing Partner
Todd Hryhorczuk, Managing Partner

Type of Firm

Private Equity Firm

Project Preferences

Type of Financing Preferred:
Early Stage
Turnaround
Other
Acquisition

Geographical Preferences

United States Preferences:
All U.S.

Canadian Preferences:
All Canada

Additional Information

Year Founded: 1997
Current Activity Level : Actively seeking new investments

TUSCAN VENTURES PVT., LTD.

501-E, Poonam Chambers
'A' Wing, Dr.Annie Besant Road
Mumbai, India 400 018
Phone: 91-22-4089-5151
Fax: 91-22-4089-5152
E-mail: info@tuscanventures.com
Website: www.tuscanventures.com

Other Offices

19, Boscombe Road
Near Tanjong Katong
Singapore, Singapore 439 759
Phone: 65-8163-33391

Management and Staff

Vishal Sharma, Founder

Type of Firm

Private Equity Firm

Project Preferences

Type of Financing Preferred:
Balanced

Geographical Preferences

International Preferences:
India
Singapore

Industry Preferences

In Transportation prefer:
Transportation

Additional Information

Year Founded: 2007
Current Activity Level : Actively seeking new investments

TUTOR INVEST OY, LTD

Hameenkatu 9
Tampere, Finland 33100
Phone: 358-1-0548-0800
Fax: 358-1-0548-0810
E-mail: info@tutorinvest.com
Website: www.tutorinvest.com

Other Offices

Nahkatehtaankatu 2
Oulu, Finland 90100
Keskuskatu 8
Helsinki, Finland 00100

Management and Staff

Pekka Haanmaki, Chief Financial Officer

Type of Firm

Private Equity Firm

Association Membership

Finnish Venture Capital Association (FVCA)

Project Preferences

Type of Financing Preferred:
Early Stage
Balanced

Geographical Preferences

International Preferences:
Finland

Additional Information

Year Founded: 2007
Current Activity Level : Actively seeking new investments

TVC CAPITAL, LLC (FKA: TVC VENTURES LLC)

853 Camino del Mar
Suite 200
Del Mar, CA USA 92014
Phone: 858-704-3261
Fax: 858-947-2801
Website: www.tvccapital.com

Management and Staff

Jeb Spencer, Managing Partner
Steven Hamerslag, Managing Partner

Type of Firm

Private Equity Firm

Project Preferences

Type of Financing Preferred:
Leveraged Buyout
Expansion
Later Stage
Recapitalizations

Size of Investments Considered:
Min Size of Investment Considered (000s): $2,000
Max Size of Investment Considered (000s): $5,000

Geographical Preferences

United States Preferences:
Southern California
West Coast

Industry Preferences

In Computer Hardware prefer:
Computer Graphics and Dig

In Computer Software prefer:
Software
Systems Software

In Internet Specific prefer:
Internet

Additional Information

Year Founded: 2002
Capital Under Management: $60,000,000
Current Activity Level : Actively seeking new investments

TVC HOLDINGS PLC (FKA: TRINITY VENTURE CAPITAL)

Beech House, Beech Hill Office
Clonskeagh
Dublin, Ireland
Phone: 353-1-205-7700
Fax: 353-1-205-7701
E-mail: info@tvc.com
Website: www.tvc.com

Other Offices

1 Lombard Street
Belfast, Ireland BT1 1BN
Phone: 353-2890-233-222
Fax: 353-2890-330-032

Management and Staff

John Fagan, Chief Financial Officer
John Tracey, Chief Executive Officer

Type of Firm

Corporate PE/Venture

Association Membership

British Venture Capital Association (BVCA)
European Private Equity and Venture Capital Assoc.

Project Preferences

Type of Financing Preferred:

Leveraged Buyout
Early Stage
Expansion
Start-up Financing

Size of Investments Considered:

Min Size of Investment Considered (000s): $1,308
Max Size of Investment Considered (000s): $19,621

Geographical Preferences

International Preferences:

Ireland
United Kingdom
Europe

Industry Preferences

In Communications prefer:

Communications and Media

In Computer Other prefer:

Computer Related

In Semiconductor/Electr prefer:

Electronics

In Industrial/Energy prefer:

Industrial Products
Factory Automation

Additional Information

Name of Most Recent Fund: Trinity Fund II
Most Recent Fund Was Raised: 03/28/2001
Year Founded: 1997
Capital Under Management: $215,700,000
Current Activity Level : Actively seeking new investments

TVG CAPITAL PARTNERS, LTD.

50 Stanley Street
Unit A, 8/F, World Trust Tower
Central, Hong Kong
Phone: 852-2147-2080
Fax: 852-2147-3320
E-mail: E.contact@tvglp.com
Website: www.tvgfunds.com

Other Offices

60 Pacific Highway
Level One, St. Leonards
Sydney, Australia 2065
Phone: 612-9315-2705
Fax: 612-9662-3311

Management and Staff

Dan Kiang, Vice President
John Troy, Managing Director
Stephen Choi, Vice President
Varun Bery, Managing Director

Type of Firm

Private Equity Firm

Project Preferences

Type of Financing Preferred:

Early Stage
Expansion
Balanced
Turnaround

Size of Investments Considered:

Min Size of Investment Considered (000s): $5,000
Max Size of Investment Considered: No Limit

Geographical Preferences

International Preferences:

Indonesia
India
Hong Kong
Philippines
Australia
Asia

Industry Focus

(% based on actual investment)

Communications and Media	58.1%
Internet Specific	32.6%
Industrial/Energy	3.2%
Computer Software and Services	3.1%
Semiconductors/Other Elect.	3.0%

Additional Information

Name of Most Recent Fund: TVG Asian Communications Fund II
Most Recent Fund Was Raised: 05/01/1999
Year Founded: 1998
Capital Under Management: $600,000,000
Current Activity Level : Actively seeking new investments

TVI INVESTMENTS BV

Kastanie Laan 4
P.O. Box 1030
Ridderkerk, Netherlands 2980 BA
Phone: 31-180-460412
Fax: 31-180-487218

Management and Staff

Chris Melisse, President

Type of Firm

Private Equity Firm

Project Preferences

Role in Financing:

Prefer role as deal originator but will also invest in deals created by others

Type of Financing Preferred:

Leveraged Buyout
Control-block Purchases
Turnaround

Size of Investments Considered:

Min Size of Investment Considered (000s): $100
Max Size of Investment Considered (000s): $1,000

Geographical Preferences

United States Preferences:

Northeast

International Preferences:

Luxembourg
Netherlands
Belgium

Additional Information

Year Founded: 1996
Capital Under Management: $20,000,000
Current Activity Level : Actively seeking new investments
Method of Compensation: Return on invest. most important, but chg. closing fees, service fees, etc.

TVM CAPITAL (AKA: TECHNO VENTURE MANAGEMENT) (FKA: TVM)

Maximilianstrasse 35
Entrance C
Munich, Germany 80539
Phone: 49-89-998-9920
Fax: 49-89-9989-9255
E-mail: info@tvm-capital.com
Website: www.tvm-capital.com

Other Offices

101 Arch Street
Suite 1950
Boston, MA USA 02110
Phone: 617-345-9320
Fax: 617-345-9377

Management and Staff

Alexandra Goll, General Partner
Annegret De Baey-Diepolder, Partner
Axel Polack, General Partner
Christoph Schroeder, General Partner
Christopher Cobbold, Partner
David Poltack, General Partner
Edward Braginsky, General Partner
Friedrich Bornikoel, Managing Partner
Hans Schreck, General Partner
Helmut Schuehsler, Managing Partner

Hsing Ma Hui, General Partner
Hubert Birner, General Partner
Hui Hsing Ma, General Partner
Irena Melnikova, Principal
Jens Eckstein, General Partner
Josef Moosholzer, Partner
Keiarasch Parssanedjad, Principal
Marios Fotiadis, General Partner
Mark Cipriano, General Partner
Peter Neubeck, Principal
Robert Lamkin, Venture Partner
Steffen Schuster, General Partner
Stephen Fischer, General Partner
Werner Wolf, Venture Partner

Type of Firm

Private Equity Firm

Association Membership

New England Venture Capital Association
German Venture Capital Association (BVK)
National Venture Capital Association - USA (NVCA)
European Private Equity and Venture Capital Assoc.

Project Preferences

Role in Financing:

Prefer role as deal originator but will also invest in deals created by others

Type of Financing Preferred:

Second Stage Financing
Early Stage
Balanced
Later Stage
Seed
First Stage Financing
Startup

Size of Investments Considered:

Min Size of Investment Considered (000s): $5,000
Max Size of Investment Considered (000s): $20,000

Geographical Preferences

International Preferences:

United Kingdom
Europe
Asia

Industry Focus

(% based on actual investment)

Biotechnology	42.0%
Medical/Health	25.0%
Computer Software and Services	9.3%
Semiconductors/Other Elect.	7.9%
Communications and Media	7.4%
Internet Specific	3.8%
Other Products	2.8%
Computer Hardware	1.3%
Consumer Related	0.2%
Industrial/Energy	0.2%

Additional Information

Name of Most Recent Fund: TVM Life Science Venture VI
Most Recent Fund Was Raised: 10/05/2005
Year Founded: 1983
Capital Under Management: $1,542,900,000
Current Activity Level : Actively seeking new investments
Method of Compensation: Return on investment is of primary concern, do not charge fees

---

TWILIGHT VENTURE PARTNERS

111 Monument Circle
Chase Tower, Suite 4700
Indianapolis, IN USA 46244
Phone: 317-423-3240
Fax: 317-423-3242
E-mail: info@twivp.com
Website: www.twivp.com

Management and Staff

August Watanabe, Partner
Harry Gonso, Partner
James Cornelius, Senior Managing Director
James Baumgardt, Partner
Kent Hawryluk, Partner
Richard DiMarchi, Partner

Type of Firm

Private Equity Firm

Project Preferences

Size of Investments Considered:

Min Size of Investment Considered (000s): $100
Max Size of Investment Considered (000s): $1,000

Geographical Preferences

United States Preferences:

Midwest

Additional Information

Year Founded: 2002
Capital Under Management: $15,000,000
Current Activity Level : Actively seeking new investments

TWIN BRIDGE CAPITAL PARTNERS

225 West Washington Street
Suite 1155
Chicago, IL USA 60606
Phone: 312-284-5600
Fax: 312-284-5599
Website: www.twinbridgecapital.com

Type of Firm

Private Equity Advisor or Fund of Funds

Project Preferences

Type of Financing Preferred:

Fund of Funds
Leveraged Buyout

Geographical Preferences

United States Preferences:

All U.S.

Additional Information

Year Founded: 2005
Capital Under Management: $500,000,000
Current Activity Level : Actively seeking new investments

TWINVENTURES AG

Wettsteinstrasse 1
Zurich, Switzerland 8038
Phone: 41-79-322-8246
Fax: 41-1-48-20919
E-mail: info@twinventures.com
Website: www.twinventures.com

Management and Staff

Fabrizio Verdiani, Co-Founder
Paul-Andre Casademont, Partner

Type of Firm

Private Equity Firm

Project Preferences

Type of Financing Preferred:

Leveraged Buyout
Early Stage
Startup

Geographical Preferences

International Preferences:

Switzerland

Industry Preferences

In Internet Specific prefer:

Internet

Additional Information

Year Founded: 2001
Current Activity Level : Actively seeking new investments

TWJ CAPITAL LLC

Six Landmark Square
Suite 404
Stamford, CT USA 06901
Phone: 203-359-5610
Fax: 203-359-5810
Website: www.twjcapital.com

Other Offices

Two Wisconsin Circle
Suite 702
Chevy Chase, MD USA 20815
Phone: 240-235-6022
Fax: 240-235-6023

Management and Staff

Nigel Jones, Partner

Type of Firm

Private Equity Firm

Project Preferences

Type of Financing Preferred:

Early Stage
Expansion

Size of Investments Considered:

Min Size of Investment Considered (000s): $250
Max Size of Investment Considered (000s): $5,000

Industry Preferences

In Communications prefer:

Telecommunications

In Internet Specific prefer:

Internet

In Consumer Related prefer:

Retail

Additional Information

Year Founded: 2005
Capital Under Management: $60,000,000
Current Activity Level : Actively seeking new investments

TWO RIVERS ASSOCIATES LLC (FKA: GATEWAY ASSOCIATES, L.P.)

8000 Maryland Avenue
Suite 330
St. Louis, MO USA 63105
Phone: 314-721-5707
Fax: 314-721-5135

Management and Staff

Charles Dill, General Partner
Gregory Johnson, General Partner
John McCarthy, General Partner
Mark Lewis, Partner
Richard Ford, General Partner

Type of Firm

Private Equity Firm

Project Preferences

Role in Financing:

Prefer role as deal originator but will also invest in deals created by others

Type of Financing Preferred:

Second Stage Financing
Leveraged Buyout
Expansion
Mezzanine
Special Situation
Acquisition

Size of Investments Considered:

Min Size of Investment Considered (000s): $500
Max Size of Investment Considered (000s): $2,000

Geographical Preferences

United States Preferences:

Midwest

Industry Focus

(% based on actual investment)

Computer Software and Services	16.8%
Internet Specific	16.0%
Communications and Media	15.3%
Biotechnology	13.2%
Medical/Health	13.1%
Semiconductors/Other Elect.	11.0%
Other Products	5.0%
Computer Hardware	4.9%
Industrial/Energy	4.7%

Additional Information

Name of Most Recent Fund: BOME Investors III, LLC
Most Recent Fund Was Raised: 12/22/2000
Year Founded: 1984
Capital Under Management: $112,300,000
Current Activity Level : Reducing investment activity
Method of Compensation: Return on investment is of primary concern, do not charge fees

---

TXU ENERGY CORPORATION

Energy Plaza
1601 Bryan Street
Dallas, TX USA 75201
Phone: 214-812-4600
Website: www.txucorp.com

Management and Staff

David Campbell, Chief Financial Officer

Type of Firm

Corporate PE/Venture

Industry Preferences

In Industrial/Energy prefer:

Energy
Alternative Energy

Additional Information

Year Founded: 2006
Capital Under Management: $200,000,000
Current Activity Level : Actively seeking new investments

TYCO CAPITAL (FKA: CIT GROUP)

505 Fifth Avenue
New York, NY USA 10017
Phone: 212-771-0505
E-mail: info@cit.com
Website: www.cit.com

Other Offices

1211 Avenue of the Americas
New York, NY USA 10036
Phone: 212-536-1211

One CIT Drive
Livingston, NJ USA 07039
Phone: 973-740-5000

Management and Staff

Eric Tozier, Managing Director
Jeffrey Peek, Chairman & CEO
Joseph Leone, Chief Financial Officer
Mark Affolter, Managing Director
Mitchell Drucker, Senior Managing Director
Peter White, Managing Director
Tim Eichenlaub, Senior Managing Director

Type of Firm

Corporate PE/Venture

Association Membership

Natl Assoc of Small Bus. Inv. Co (NASBIC)

Project Preferences

Role in Financing:

Prefer role as deal originator but will also invest in deals created by others

Type of Financing Preferred:

Second Stage Financing
Leveraged Buyout
Mezzanine
First Stage Financing

Size of Investments Considered:

Min Size of Investment Considered (000s): $3,000
Max Size of Investment Considered: No Limit

Geographical Preferences

United States Preferences:

All U.S.

International Preferences:

All International

Industry Focus

(% based on actual investment)

Consumer Related	40.1%
Internet Specific	14.9%
Communications and Media	11.1%
Computer Software and Services	9.7%
Other Products	6.7%
Semiconductors/Other Elect.	6.1%
Medical/Health	4.5%
Computer Hardware	3.4%
Industrial/Energy	1.7%
Biotechnology	1.7%

Additional Information

Year Founded: 1908
Capital Under Management: $15,000,000
Current Activity Level : Actively seeking new investments

Method of Compensation: Return on invest. most important, but chg. closing fees, service fees, etc.

TZP GROUP LLC

Seven Times Square
Suite 4307
New York, NY USA 10036
Phone: 212-398-0300
Website: www.tzpgroup.com

Management and Staff

Harris Newman, Principal
Nathan Chandrasekaran, Vice President
Samuel Abraham, Partner
Samuel Katz, Managing Partner
Sheera Michael, Chief Financial Officer
Vladimir Gutin, Partner

Type of Firm

Private Equity Firm

Project Preferences

Type of Financing Preferred:
Leveraged Buyout

Size of Investments Considered:
Min Size of Investment Considered (000s): $20,000
Max Size of Investment Considered (000s): $50,000

Geographical Preferences

United States Preferences:
All U.S.

Industry Preferences

In Medical/Health prefer:
Health Services

In Consumer Related prefer:
Consumer Services

In Financial Services prefer:
Financial Services
Real Estate

In Business Serv. prefer:
Services
Distribution
Media

Additional Information

Year Founded: 2007
Capital Under Management: $152,500,000
Current Activity Level : Actively seeking new investments

- U -

U.S. BANCORP

111 S.W. Fifth Avenue
Suite 1450
Portland, OR USA 97204
Phone: 503-275-5710
Fax: 503-275-7565
Website: www.usbancorp.com

Management and Staff

Gary Patterson, Vice President
Susan Lester, Chief Financial Officer

Type of Firm

SBIC

Additional Information

Year Founded: 1984
Current Activity Level : Actively seeking new investments

U.S. VENTURE PARTNERS

2735 Sand Hill Road
Menlo Park, CA USA 94025
Phone: 650-854-9080
Fax: 650-854-3018
Website: www.usvp.com

Other Offices

7900 Southeast 28th Street
Suite 250
Mercer Island, WA USA 98040
Phone: 206-236-5776
Fax: 206-236-5779

Unit 1605B, 16th Floor Shui On Plaza
No. 333 Huaihai Central Road
Shanghai, China 200020

Management and Staff

Alan Kaganov, Partner
Arati Prabhakar, General Partner
Casey Tansey, General Partner
Casper De clercq, Venture Partner
Christopher Rust, Partner
David Liddle, Venture Partner
Geoffrey Baehr, Venture Partner
Irwin Federman, General Partner
Jonathan Root, General Partner
Larry Lasky, Venture Partner
Mamoon Hamid, Principal
Paul Matteucci, General Partner
Philip Schlein, Venture Partner
Phillip Young, Venture Partner
Rick Lewis, Principal
Steven Krausz, General Partner
Ted Maidenberg, Principal
Timothy Connors, General Partner
Van Kwok, Principal
William Bowes, Founding Partner
Winston Fu, General Partner

Type of Firm

Private Equity Firm

Association Membership

Western Association of Venture Capitalists (WAVC)
National Venture Capital Association - USA (NVCA)

Project Preferences

Role in Financing:
Prefer role as deal originator but will also invest in deals created by others

Type of Financing Preferred:
Second Stage Financing
Early Stage
Expansion
Later Stage
Seed
First Stage Financing
Startup

Size of Investments Considered:
Min Size of Investment Considered (000s): $250
Max Size of Investment Considered (000s): $25,000

Geographical Preferences

United States Preferences:
All U.S.

International Preferences:
Italy

Industry Focus

(% based on actual investment)

Semiconductors/Other Elect.	19.2%
Computer Software and Services	17.1%
Internet Specific	16.7%
Communications and Media	16.2%
Medical/Health	9.3%
Biotechnology	7.2%
Computer Hardware	5.7%
Consumer Related	5.2%
Industrial/Energy	2.5%
Other Products	0.8%

Additional Information

Name of Most Recent Fund: U.S. Venture Partners X, L.P.
Most Recent Fund Was Raised: 07/07/2008
Year Founded: 1981
Capital Under Management: $3,200,000,000
Current Activity Level : Actively seeking new investments
Method of Compensation: Return on investment is of primary concern, do not charge fees

UAB LIGNUM CORDIS

Ateities g. 21
Vilnius, Lithuania 06326
Management and Staff
Andrius Nikitinas, Founder

Type of Firm
Private Equity Firm

Project Preferences

Type of Financing Preferred:
Balanced

Geographical Preferences

International Preferences:
Lithuania

Additional Information
Year Founded: 2007
Current Activity Level : Actively seeking new investments

UBA PRIVATE EQUITY LIMITED
UBA House
57 Marina
Lagos, Nigeria
Phone: 234-1-264-4651
Fax: 234-1-262-0371
Website: www.ubagroup.com

Type of Firm
Private Equity Firm

Association Membership
Nigerian Venture Capital Association
African Venture Capital Association (AVCA)

Project Preferences

Type of Financing Preferred:
Early Stage
Expansion
Generalist PE
Startup

Size of Investments Considered:
Min Size of Investment Considered (000s): $230
Max Size of Investment Considered (000s): $3,840

Geographical Preferences

International Preferences:
Nigeria

Industry Preferences

In Consumer Related prefer:
Other Restaurants
Hotels and Resorts

Additional Information
Year Founded: 2005
Capital Under Management: $26,500,000
Current Activity Level : Actively seeking new investments

UBS CAPITAL CORPORATION
299 Park Avenue
New York, NY USA 10171
Phone: 212-821 4301
Fax: 212-821 6366
Website: www.ubscapital.com

Other Offices
Via Santa Margherita 16
Milan, Italy I-20121
Phone: 39-2-7252-7789
Fax: 39-2-8901-3374

Five Temasek Boulevard
Suntec City Tower Five, #18-00
Singapore, Singapore 038895
Phone: 65-6431-8000
Fax: 65-6836-5145

East Tower, Otemachi First Square 5-1
Otemachi 1-chome
Chiyoda-ku, Tokyo, Japan 100-0004
Phone: 81-3-5208-6982
Fax: 81-3-5208-6989

Elias Canetti-Strasse 2
Zurich, Switzerland 8050
Phone: 41-1-237-2064
Fax: 41-1-237-2121

L25, Governor Phillip Tower
1 Farrer Place
Sydney, Australia 2000
Phone: 612-9324-2078
Fax: 612-9324-2331

25/F, One Exchange Square
8 Connaught Place
Central, Hong Kong
Phone: 852-2971-8618
Fax: 852-2971-6168

29, rue de Lisbonne
Paris, France 75008
Phone: 01-44-56-4343
Fax: 01-44-56-4300

St. Anna-Gasse 9
Zurich, Switzerland 8001
Phone: 41-1-234-91-06
Fax: 41-1-234-64-33

10th Floor, Young Poong Building 33
Seorin-dong, Chongru-ku
Seoul, South Korea 110-752
Phone: 822-3702-8770
Fax: 822-3702-8771

P.O. Box 350
24 Union Street
St. Helier, Jersey, United Kingdom JE4 8UJ
Phone: 44-1534-701-000
Fax: 44-1534-701-289

677 Washington Boulevard
Stamford, CT USA 06901
Phone: 203-719-3000
Fax: 203-719-4920

100 Liverpool Street
London, United Kingdom EC2M 2RH
Phone: 44-20-7567-2153
Fax: 44-20-7568-9890

Management and Staff
Andrew Evans, Partner
Antony Fraser, Partner
Blake Moore, Partner
David Lai, President
David Solo, Chairman & CEO
Derek Smith, Chief Financial Officer
Eric De la Bigne, Partner
Giulio Azzolini, Partner
Greg Lockwood, Partner
James Schaefer, Managing Director
Kevin Smith, Partner
Lawrence Handen, Partner
Malcolm Thomson, Partner
Maneksh Dattani, Partner
Maurizio Mauro, Partner
Nico Helling, Partner
Peter Hjelt, Partner
Richard Allsopp, Managing Director
Simon Jennings, Partner
Sylvia Barrecchia, Partner

Type of Firm
Bank Affiliated

Association Membership
Italian Venture Capital Association (AIFI)
British Venture Capital Association (BVCA)
European Private Equity and Venture Capital Assoc.
Singapore Venture Capital Association (SVCA)

Project Preferences

Type of Financing Preferred:
Fund of Funds
Second Stage Financing
Leveraged Buyout
Early Stage
Expansion
Mezzanine
Balanced
Turnaround
Later Stage
Seed
Management Buyouts
Acquisition

Size of Investments Considered:
Min Size of Investment Considered (000s): $16,905
Max Size of Investment Considered (000s): $56,350

Geographical Preferences

United States Preferences:
All U.S.

International Preferences:
Italy

Taiwan
Europe
Hong Kong
Pacific
Australia
New Zealand
Singapore
Korea, South
Asia
Japan

Industry Focus

(% based on actual investment)

Other Products	22.5%
Medical/Health	18.0%
Internet Specific	11.9%
Communications and Media	11.1%
Consumer Related	10.5%
Computer Software and Services	9.0%
Industrial/Energy	6.3%
Computer Hardware	5.1%
Semiconductors/Other Elect.	5.1%
Biotechnology	0.5%

Additional Information

Year Founded: 1994
Capital Under Management: $4,237,200,000
Current Activity Level : Actively seeking new investments

UBS CAPITAL MARKETS

111 Pavonia Avenue East
Newport Financial Center
Jersey City, NJ USA 07310
Phone: 212-713-3090
Website: www.ubscapitalmarkets.com

Management and Staff

Joseph Mecane, Managing Director
Ron Schwartz, Managing Director

Type of Firm

Private Equity Firm

Additional Information

Year Founded: 2009
Current Activity Level : Actively seeking new investments

UFG PRIVATE EQUITY (FKA: NORD EUROPE PRIVATE EQUITY)

173, boulevard Haussmann
Paris, France 75008
Phone: 33-1-4456-4180
Fax: 33-1-4456-4185
E-mail: contact-ufgpe@groupe-ufg.com
Website: www.ufg-pe.com

Management and Staff

Xavier Lepine, President

Type of Firm

Private Equity Firm

Association Membership

French Venture Capital Association (AFIC)

Project Preferences

Type of Financing Preferred:
Fund of Funds
Leveraged Buyout
Early Stage
Expansion
Generalist PE
Balanced
Other
Management Buyouts

Geographical Preferences

United States Preferences:
All U.S.

International Preferences:
Luxembourg
Europe
Belgium
Asia
France

Industry Preferences

In Consumer Related prefer:
Consumer Services

In Business Serv. prefer:
Services
Distribution

Additional Information

Year Founded: 2004
Capital Under Management: $253,400,000
Current Activity Level : Actively seeking new investments

UIB CAPITAL, INC.

200 South Wacker Drive
Suite 3020
Chicago, IL USA 60606
Phone: 312-334-0770
Fax: 312-334-0768
E-mail: info@uibcapital.com
Website: www.uibcapital.com

Other Offices

Dubai Intl. Financial Center (DIFC)
The Gate Precinct, Bldg. 3, Level 3
Dubai, Utd. Arab Em.
Phone: 971-4362-1833
Fax: 971-4363-7405

Ahli United Bank Bldg. 2495
Road 2832, Al-Seef District 428
Bahrain, Bahrain
Phone: 973-1756-6000
Fax: 973-1756-6001

Level 38, Menara Standard Chartered
Jalan Sultan Ismail
Kuala Lumpur, Malaysia 50250
Phone: 603-2711-1606
Fax: 603-2711-0787

Management and Staff

Christopher Freeburg, Vice President
Ross Christianson, Principal
Tariq Al-Rifai, Vice President
Tariq Malhance, President
Toni Pelaez, Vice President
Troy Monthye, Vice President

Type of Firm

Bank Affiliated

Project Preferences

Type of Financing Preferred:
Early Stage
Expansion
Management Buyouts
Recapitalizations

Size of Investments Considered:
Min Size of Investment Considered (000s): $10,000
Max Size of Investment Considered (000s): $25,000

Industry Preferences

In Medical/Health prefer:
Medical/Health

In Consumer Related prefer:
Consumer

In Business Serv. prefer:
Services

In Manufact. prefer:
Manufacturing

Additional Information

Year Founded: 2004
Current Activity Level : Actively seeking new investments

UK INFRASTRUKTURNYE INVESTITSII, ZAO

Partiynyi pereulok 1/1
Moscow, Russia 115093
Phone: 7-495-648-4708
Fax: 7-495-648-4708
E-mail: Info@infra-invest.ru
Website: www.infra-invest.ru

Type of Firm

Private Equity Firm

Association Membership

Russian Venture Capital Association (RVCA)

Project Preferences

Type of Financing Preferred:
Early Stage
Expansion

Geographical Preferences

International Preferences:
Russia

Additional Information

Year Founded: 2004
Capital Under Management: $1,000,000
Current Activity Level : Actively seeking new investments

UK STEEL ENTERPRISE, LTD. (FKA: BRITISH STEEL INDUSTRY,LTD.)

The Innovation Centre
217 Portobello
Sheffield, United Kingdom S1 4DP
Phone: 44-114-273-1612
Fax: 44-114-270-1390
E-mail: ho@uksteelenterprise.co.uk
Website: www.uksteelenterprise.co.uk

Other Offices

Cardiff Bay Business Centre
Lewis Road, Ocean Park
Cardiff, United Kingdom CF24 5BS
Phone: 44-29-2047-1122
Fax: 44-29-2049-2622

Grovewood Business Centre
Stathclyde Business Park, Bellshill
Lanarkshire, United Kingdom ML4 3NQ
Phone: 44-1698-845-045
Fax: 44-1698-845-123

The Innovation Centre
Vienna Court, Kirkleatham Business Park
Redcar, United Kingdom TS10 5SH
Phone: 44-1642-777-888
Fax: 44-1642-777-999

Management and Staff

Stuart Green, Managing Director

Type of Firm

Corporate PE/Venture

Association Membership

British Venture Capital Association (BVCA)

Project Preferences

Role in Financing:
Prefer role as deal originator but will also invest in deals created by others

Type of Financing Preferred:
Second Stage Financing
Leveraged Buyout
Start-up Financing
Turnaround
Later Stage
First Stage Financing
Startup

Geographical Preferences

International Preferences:
United Kingdom

Industry Preferences

In Business Serv. prefer:
Services

In Manufact. prefer:
Manufacturing

Additional Information

Year Founded: 1975
Capital Under Management: $17,000,000
Current Activity Level : Actively seeking new investments
Method of Compensation: Return on investment is of primary concern, do not charge fees

UMC CAPITAL

No. 3, Li-Hsin 2nd Road
Hsinchu Science Park
Hsinchu, Taiwan
Phone: 886-3-578-2258
Fax: 886-3-577-9392
Website: www.umc.com

Management and Staff

Shih-Wei Sun, Chief Executive Officer

Type of Firm

Corporate PE/Venture

Project Preferences

Type of Financing Preferred:
Balanced

Geographical Preferences

International Preferences:
All International

Additional Information

Year Founded: 2001
Current Activity Level : Actively seeking new investments

UMINOVA FORETAGSUTVECKLING AB (AKA: UMINOVA INVEST)

Tvistevagen 47
Box 7970
Umea, Sweden 907 19
Phone: 46-90-154-962
Fax: 46-90-154-961
Website: www.uminova-ab.com

Type of Firm

Private Equity Firm

Association Membership

Swedish Venture Capital Association (SVCA)
European Private Equity and Venture Capital Assoc.

Project Preferences

Type of Financing Preferred:
Balanced

Geographical Preferences

International Preferences:
Sweden
Europe

Additional Information

Year Founded: 2006
Current Activity Level : Actively seeking new investments

UMS PARTNERS

27 North 3rd Street
Philadelphia, PA USA 19106
Phone: 215-592-8880
Fax: 215-592-0389
Website: www.umspartners.com

Management and Staff

Mark Turnbull, General Partner

Type of Firm

Private Equity Firm

Project Preferences

Type of Financing Preferred:
Generalist PE

Industry Preferences

In Communications prefer:
Communications and Media

In Medical/Health prefer:
Medical/Health

In Financial Services prefer:
Real Estate

Additional Information

Year Founded: 2004
Capital Under Management: $12,800,000
Current Activity Level : Actively seeking new investments

UNDERDOG VENTURES LLC

625 Broadway
Suite 1001
New York, NY USA 10012
Phone: 212-777-7099
Fax: 212-777-0234
E-mail: info@underdogventures.com
Website: www.underdogventures.com

Management and Staff
David Berge, President

Type of Firm
Private Equity Firm

Association Membership
Community Development Venture Capital Alliance

Project Preferences

Type of Financing Preferred:
Early Stage
Expansion
Later Stage

Size of Investments Considered:
Min Size of Investment Considered (000s): $500
Max Size of Investment Considered (000s): $1,000

Geographical Preferences

Canadian Preferences:
All Canada

Industry Preferences

In Consumer Related prefer:
Food/Beverage
Consumer Products

In Industrial/Energy prefer:
Environmental Related

Additional Information
Year Founded: 2001
Capital Under Management: $5,500,000
Current Activity Level : Actively seeking new investments

UNI EXPANSION OUEST
7 bis bd de la Tour d'Auvergne
C.S. 86505
Rennes Cedex, France 35065
Phone: 33-2-9967-2014
Fax: 33-2-9967-0226
E-mail: contact@ueo.fr
Website: www.ueo.fr

Type of Firm
Private Equity Firm

Association Membership
French Venture Capital Association (AFIC)

Project Preferences

Type of Financing Preferred:
Generalist PE

Geographical Preferences

International Preferences:
France

Additional Information
Year Founded: 2000
Current Activity Level : Actively seeking new investments

UNIAO DE BANCOS BRASILEIROS S.A. (AKA: UNIBANCO)
Avenida Eusebio Matoso, 891
18 Andar, Pinheiros
Sao Paulo, Brazil 05423-901
Phone: 55-11-3584-1980
Fax: 55-11-3584-1585
E-mail: investor.relations@unibanco.com.br
Website: www.unibanco.com.br

Type of Firm
Bank Affiliated

Association Membership
Brazilian Venture Capital Association (ABCR)

Project Preferences

Type of Financing Preferred:
Balanced

Geographical Preferences

International Preferences:
Brazil

Additional Information
Year Founded: 2001
Current Activity Level : Actively seeking new investments

UNICORN INVESTMENT BANK B.S.C.
Ahli United Bank Building 2495
2/F Tenants Wing Road
Al-Seef District, Bahrain 2832
Phone: 973-1756-6000
Fax: 973-1756-6001
E-mail: contact@unicorninvestmentbank.com
Website: www.unicorninvestmentbank.com

Other Offices
200 South Wacker Drive
Suite 3020
Chicago, IL USA 60606
Phone: 312-334-0770
Fax: 312-334-0768

Muallim Naci Cad. No. 47
Ortakoy
Istanbul, Turkey 34347
Phone: 90-212-236-4141
Fax: 90-212-236-3918

Level 38, Menara Standard Chartered
Jalan Sultan Ismail
Kuala Lumpur, Malaysia 50250
Phone: 63-2711-1606
Fax: 63-2711-0787

Building 3, Level 3
Dubai International Financial Center
Dubai, Utd. Arab Em.
Phone: 971-4365-8123
Fax: 971-4367405

Management and Staff
Aamir Khan, Managing Director
Ayman Sejiny, Managing Director
David Pace, Chief Financial Officer
Falah Nasser Al-Falah, CEO & Managing Director
Frederick Stonehouse, Managing Director
Hadi Humaidan, Chief Operating Officer
Ikbal Daredia, Managing Director
Majid Al-Sayed Bader Al-Sefai, CEO & Managing Director
Najib Youssef Fayyad, Managing Director

Type of Firm
Bank Affiliated

Project Preferences

Type of Financing Preferred:
Leveraged Buyout
Expansion
Management Buyouts

Geographical Preferences

United States Preferences:
All U.S.

International Preferences:
Bahrain
Turkey
Jordan
Utd. Arab Em.
Malaysia
Kuwait

Industry Preferences

In Medical/Health prefer:
Health Services

In Consumer Related prefer:
Consumer

In Industrial/Energy prefer:
Industrial Products

Additional Information
Year Founded: 2004
Capital Under Management: $45,000,000
Current Activity Level : Actively seeking new investments

UNICREDIT BANCA D IMPRESA
Via Garibaldi 1
Verona, Italy 37121
Phone: 39-45-808-1140
Fax: 39-45-867-9769

Website: www.unicreditimpresa.it

Type of Firm
Bank Affiliated

Association Membership
Italian Venture Capital Association (AIFI)

Additional Information
Year Founded: 2004
Current Activity Level : Actively seeking new investments

UNIFIED GROWTH PARTNERS, L.P.

Two Greenwich Office Park
Greenwich, CT USA 06831
Phone: 203-422-0650
Fax: 203-422-0650
E-mail: info@unifiedgrowth.com
Website: www.unifiedgrowth.com

Type of Firm
Private Equity Firm

Geographical Preferences

Canadian Preferences:
All Canada

Industry Preferences

In Consumer Related prefer:
Consumer Services

In Business Serv. prefer:
Services

Additional Information
Year Founded: 2005
Capital Under Management: $20,300,000
Current Activity Level : Actively seeking new investments

UNIGESTION

8C, Avenue de Champel
P.O. Box 387
Geneva, Switzerland 1211
Phone: 41-22-704-4111
Fax: 41-22-704-4211
E-mail: info@unigestion.com
Website: www.unigestion.com

Other Offices
105 Piccadilly
London, United Kingdom W1J 7NJ
Phone: 44-207-529-4150

Plaza 10 Harborside Financial Center
Suite 203
Jersey City, NJ USA 07311
Phone: 201-714-2400

12 Avenue Matignon
Paris, France 75008
Phone: 33-14-359-7373

152 Beach Road, Suite #23-05/06
The Gateway East
Singapore, Singapore 189721
Phone: 65-64-96-0200

Farnley House, La Charroterie
St. Peter Port
Guernsey, Channel Islands GY1 1EJ
Phone: 44-1481-812-600

Management and Staff
Cedric Abitbol, Vice President
David Smith, Chief Operating Officer
Hanspeter Bader, Managing Director
Nicolas Barletta, Vice President
Patrick Fenal, Chief Executive Officer

Type of Firm
Private Equity Advisor or Fund of Funds

Association Membership
Swiss Venture Capital Association (SECA)
European Private Equity and Venture Capital Assoc.

Project Preferences

Type of Financing Preferred:
Fund of Funds
Leveraged Buyout
Early Stage
Expansion
Balanced
Fund of Funds of Second
Distressed Debt

Geographical Preferences

United States Preferences:
All U.S.

International Preferences:
Latin America
Switzerland
Europe
Asia

Industry Preferences

In Industrial/Energy prefer:
Alternative Energy
Environmental Related

Additional Information
Year Founded: 1971
Capital Under Management: $775,000,000
Current Activity Level : Actively seeking new investments

UNIGRAINS

23/25 avenue de Neuilly
BP 2120
Paris Cedex 16, France 75771
Phone: 33-1-4431-1000
Fax: 33-1-4431-1087
E-mail: contact@unigrains.fr
Website: www.unigrains.fr

Type of Firm
Incubator/Development Program

Association Membership
French Venture Capital Association (AFIC)

Project Preferences

Type of Financing Preferred:
Leveraged Buyout
Expansion
Mezzanine
Turnaround

Geographical Preferences

International Preferences:
France

Industry Preferences

In Biotechnology prefer:
Agricultural/Animal Bio.
Industrial Biotechnology

Additional Information
Year Founded: 1960
Current Activity Level : Actively seeking new investments

UNILEVER VENTURES, LTD. (AKA: UNILEVER NV)

1st Floor
16 Charles II Street
London, United Kingdom SW1Y 4QU
Phone: 44-20-7321-6199
Fax: 44-20-7321-6198
Website: www.unileverventures.com

Other Offices
Unilever Technology Ventures Advisory Co
812 Anacapa Street, Suite A
Santa Barbara, CA USA 93101
Phone: 805-963-0250
Fax: 805-963-0270

Management and Staff
John Coombs, Managing Director
Lisa Smith, Principal
Michael Lee, Principal

Type of Firm
Corporate PE/Venture

Association Membership
National Venture Capital Association - USA (NVCA)

Project Preferences

Type of Financing Preferred:
Fund of Funds
Early Stage

Expansion
Seed
Startup

Size of Investments Considered:
Min Size of Investment Considered (000s): $672
Max Size of Investment Considered (000s): $13,437

Geographical Preferences

International Preferences:
Europe

Industry Preferences

In Biotechnology prefer:
Biotechnology
Genetic Engineering

In Medical/Health prefer:
Health Services

In Consumer Related prefer:
Entertainment and Leisure
Consumer Products
Consumer Services

In Industrial/Energy prefer:
Materials

In Business Serv. prefer:
Media

Additional Information

Year Founded: 2002
Capital Under Management: $68,600,000
Current Activity Level : Actively seeking new investments

UNION BANCAIRE PRIVEE PRIVATE EQUITY

26 St. James's Square
London, United Kingdom SW1Y 4JH
Phone: 44-20-7663-1525
Fax: 44-20-7369-0461
Website: www.ubp.ch

Other Offices

30 Rockefeller Center
Suite 2800
New York, NY USA 10112
Phone: 212-218-6750
Fax: 212-218-6755

Emarut Atrium, Office 252
Sheikh Zayed Road
Dubai, Utd. Arab Em.
Phone: 97-14-343-2277
Fax: 97-14-343-9164

96-98, rue du Rhone
Switzerland, Switzerland CH-1204
Phone: 41-22-819-2111
Fax: 41-22-819-2200

Management and Staff

Kathleen Cira, Partner
Morten Thorsen, Partner
Vincenzo Narciso, Chief Executive Officer

Type of Firm

Bank Affiliated

Project Preferences

Type of Financing Preferred:
Fund of Funds

Geographical Preferences

International Preferences:
Europe

Additional Information

Year Founded: 2007
Current Activity Level : Actively seeking new investments

UNION CAPITAL CORPORATION

405 Park Avenue
Suite 1003
New York, NY USA 10022
Phone: 212-832-1141
Fax: 212-832-0554
Website: www.unioncapitalcorp.com

Management and Staff

Arthur Murray, Managing Director
Gregory Garville, President
Jay Landauer, Vice President
William Ogden, Managing Director

Type of Firm

Bank Affiliated

Project Preferences

Type of Financing Preferred:
Leveraged Buyout
Turnaround

Size of Investments Considered:
Min Size of Investment Considered (000s): $10,000
Max Size of Investment Considered (000s): $100,000

Geographical Preferences

United States Preferences:
Mid Atlantic
Southeast
Northeast

Additional Information

Year Founded: 1968
Current Activity Level : Actively seeking new investments
Method of Compensation: Return on investment is of primary concern, do not charge fees

---

UNION SQUARE VENTURES

915 Broadway
Suite 1408
New York, NY USA 10010
Phone: 212-994-7880
Fax: 212-994-7399
E-mail: info@unionsquareventures.com
Website: www.unionsquareventures.com

Management and Staff

Albert Wenger, Partner
Fred Wilson, Managing General Partner
R. Bradford Burnham, Managing General Partner

Type of Firm

Private Equity Advisor or Fund of Funds

Association Membership

National Venture Capital Association - USA (NVCA)

Project Preferences

Type of Financing Preferred:
Early Stage

Additional Information

Name of Most Recent Fund: Union Square Ventures 2008, L.P.
Most Recent Fund Was Raised: 03/03/2008
Year Founded: 2004
Capital Under Management: $125,000,000
Current Activity Level : Actively seeking new investments

UNIPOL MERCHANT SPA (FKA : FINEC MERCHANT SPA)

Via Stalingrado, 57
Bologna, Italy 40121
Phone: 39-51-631-8211
Fax: 39-51-631-8229
E-mail: info@unipolmerchant.it
Website: www.unipolmerchant.it

Type of Firm

Private Equity Firm

Association Membership

Italian Venture Capital Association (AIFI)

Project Preferences

Type of Financing Preferred:
Leveraged Buyout
Expansion
Management Buyouts

Geographical Preferences

International Preferences:
Italy
Europe

Industry Preferences

In Industrial/Energy prefer:
Industrial Products

In Financial Services prefer:
Financial Services

In Business Serv. prefer:
Services

Additional Information

Year Founded: 1999
Current Activity Level : Actively seeking new investments

UNIQUE INVESTMENT CORPORATION

500 North State College Blvd.
Suite 525
Orange, CA USA 92868
Phone: 714-780-5888
Fax: 714-780-5887
E-mail: info@uniquepartners.com
Website: www.uniquepartners.com

Management and Staff

David Hejl, Vice President
John Makoff, Managing Director
Joseph Phillips, Principal
Scott Hartman, Managing Director

Type of Firm

Private Equity Firm

Project Preferences

Type of Financing Preferred:
Leveraged Buyout
Management Buyouts

Industry Focus

(% based on actual investment)

Internet Specific	100.0%

Additional Information

Year Founded: 1994
Capital Under Management: $40,000,000
Current Activity Level : Actively seeking new investments

UNIQUEST

4350 West Cypress Street
Suite 450
Tampa, FL USA 33607
Phone: 813-387-1000
Fax: 813-387-3000
Website: www.uniquest.com

Type of Firm

Corporate PE/Venture

Additional Information

Year Founded: 2002
Current Activity Level : Actively seeking new investments

UNISEED MANAGEMENT PTY LTD.

Level 7, GP South Building 78
Staff House Road
St Lucia, Australia 4072
Phone: 617-3365-6937
Fax: 617-3365-4433
E-mail: enquiries@uniseed.com
Website: www.uniseed.com

Other Offices

New South Innovations
Rupert Myers Building, UNSW
Sydney, Australia 2052
Phone: 612-9385-6525
Fax: 612-9385-6600

205-211 Grattan Street
Parkville, Australia 3053
Phone: 613-8344-3193
Fax: 613-9347-5888

Management and Staff

Peter Devine, Chief Executive Officer

Type of Firm

University Program

Project Preferences

Type of Financing Preferred:
Early Stage
Seed

Size of Investments Considered:
Min Size of Investment Considered (000s): $40
Max Size of Investment Considered (000s): $403

Geographical Preferences

International Preferences:
Pacific

Industry Preferences

In Biotechnology prefer:
Biotechnology
Biotech Related Research

In Medical/Health prefer:
Medical/Health

In Manufact. prefer:
Manufacturing

Additional Information

Year Founded: 2000
Capital Under Management: $49,200,000
Current Activity Level : Actively seeking new investments

UNISON CAPITAL, INC.

Kioicho Kelton Building
4-5 Kioicho, Chiyoda-ku
Tokyo, Japan 102-0094
Phone: 81-3-3511-3901
Fax: 81-3-3511-3981
E-mail: uc@unisoncap.com
Website: www.unisoncap.com

Management and Staff

John Ehara, Co-Founder
Kenichi Kiso, Partner
Kiyoto Matsuda, Partner
Nobuo Sayama, Co-Founder
Nobuyoshi Ehara, Chief Executive Officer
Osamu Yamamoto, Partner
Tatsuo Kawasaki, Co-Founder
Tatsuya Hayashi, Co-Founder

Type of Firm

Private Equity Firm

Project Preferences

Type of Financing Preferred:
Leveraged Buyout
Mezzanine
Management Buyouts

Size of Investments Considered:
Min Size of Investment Considered (000s): $25,986
Max Size of Investment Considered (000s): $43,310

Geographical Preferences

International Preferences:
Japan

Industry Focus

(% based on actual investment)

Consumer Related	72.2%
Other Products	23.7%
Semiconductors/Other Elect.	4.1%

Additional Information

Name of Most Recent Fund: Unison Capital Partners II, L.P.
Most Recent Fund Was Raised: 07/30/2004
Year Founded: 1998
Capital Under Management: $385,000,000
Current Activity Level : Actively seeking new investments

UNITAS CAPITAL PTE, LTD. (FKA: CCMP CAPITAL ASIA PTE, LTD.)

1 Harbour View Street
30/F One Int'l Finance Center
Central, Hong Kong
Phone: 852-2533-1818
Fax: 852-2868-5551
Website: www.unitascapital.com

Other Offices

21F Seoul Finance Center
84 Taepyungro 1-ga Jung-gu
Seoul, South Korea 100-768
Phone: 822-319-8600
Fax: 822-319-8675

120 Collins Street
Level 41
Melbourne, Australia 3000
Phone: 613-9091-1088

1010 Huai Hai Zhong Road
Suite 3803, K. Wah Center
Shanghai, China 200031
Phone: 86-21-6103-2688
Fax: 86-21-6103-2633

Management and Staff

Ajeet Singh, Partner
Anurag Mathur, Partner
Atsushi Abe, Partner
Avi Gilboa, Managing Director
Eugene Zhao, Managing Director
Jim Tsao, Managing Director
John Lewis, Partner
Jonathan Kotler, Principal
Julian Buckley, Principal
Kei Chua, Partner
Leo Cheung, Managing Director
Phillip Bower, Managing Director
Sang Song, Principal
Sharon Lim, Chief Financial Officer
Stephen King, Partner
Steve Stewart, Managing Director
Xiaolu Lian, Managing Director
Yoon Sok Baek, Vice President
Young-Ho Hur, Managing Director

Type of Firm

Private Equity Firm

Association Membership

Australian Venture Capital Association (AVCAL)
Hong Kong Venture Capital Association (HKVCA)

Project Preferences

Type of Financing Preferred:
Leveraged Buyout
Management Buyouts

Geographical Preferences

International Preferences:
China
Australia
Singapore
Korea, South
Asia
Japan

Industry Preferences

In Consumer Related prefer:
Retail
Consumer Products
Consumer Services

In Industrial/Energy prefer:
Industrial Products

In Business Serv. prefer:
Services

In Manufact. prefer:
Manufacturing

Additional Information

Name of Most Recent Fund: Asia Opportunity Fund II, L.P.
Most Recent Fund Was Raised: 08/01/2005
Year Founded: 1999
Capital Under Management: $4,000,000,000
Current Activity Level : Actively seeking new investments

UNITED CAPITAL INVESTMENT GROUP (CHINA) LTD

28F Zhao Feng World Trade Bldg
369 Jiang Su Road
Shanghai, China 200050
Phone: 86-21-3212-4668
Fax: 86-21-5240-0958
E-mail: contact@ucigroup.org
Website: www.ucigroup.org

Management and Staff

Isaac Mao, Vice President

Type of Firm

Private Equity Firm

Project Preferences

Type of Financing Preferred:
Early Stage
Expansion
Seed
Startup

Geographical Preferences

International Preferences:
China

Industry Preferences

In Communications prefer:
Communications and Media
Telecommunications
Media and Entertainment

In Business Serv. prefer:
Media

Additional Information

Year Founded: 2003
Capital Under Management: $70,000,000
Current Activity Level : Actively seeking new investments

UNITED FINANCIAL GROUP ASSET MANAGEMENT (AKA: UFG)

5, Petrovka Street
Moscow, Russia 107031
Phone: 7-495-721-1212
Fax: 7-495-721-1210
E-mail: pe@ufgam.com
Website: www.ufgam.com

Other Offices

23 Gogolevsky Boulevard
Moscow, Russia

Management and Staff

Boris Fedorov, Founding Partner
Dimitri Elkin, Managing Director
Dmitry Khilov, Managing Director
Dominic Reed, Managing Director
Florian Fenner, Managing Partner

Type of Firm

Bank Affiliated

Project Preferences

Type of Financing Preferred:
Leveraged Buyout
Expansion
Balanced
Management Buyouts

Geographical Preferences

International Preferences:
Belarus
Kazakhstan
Europe
Ukraine
Russia

Industry Preferences

In Communications prefer:
Communications and Media

In Consumer Related prefer:
Consumer
Retail
Food/Beverage

In Industrial/Energy prefer:
Industrial Products
Materials

In Transportation prefer:
Transportation

In Financial Services prefer:
Financial Services
Insurance
Financial Services

In Business Serv. prefer:
Services
Media

Additional Information

Year Founded: 2002
Capital Under Management: $2,300,000,000
Current Activity Level : Actively seeking new investments

UNITED INVESTMENTS COMPANY

4/F-2, No 76 Tun-Hua South Rd
Section 2
Taipei, Taiwan
Phone: 886-2-2709-7078
Fax: 886-2-2709-7098
Website: www.venture.ui.com.tw

Type of Firm

Private Equity Firm

Association Membership

Taiwan Venture Capital Association(TVCA)

Project Preferences

Type of Financing Preferred:
Balanced

Geographical Preferences

International Preferences:
Taiwan

Industry Preferences

In Communications prefer:
Telecommunications

In Computer Software prefer:
Software

In Semiconductor/Electr prefer:
Electronics
Semiconductor
Optoelectronics

In Biotechnology prefer:
Biotechnology

Additional Information

Year Founded: 2000
Capital Under Management: $1,500,000
Current Activity Level : Actively seeking new investments

UNITEK CAPITAL CORPORATION

No. 25 Jen-Ai Road
Section 4, 9th Floor
Taipei, Taiwan
Phone: 886-2-8773-0501
Fax: 8862—8773-0502

Type of Firm

Private Equity Firm

Association Membership

Taiwan Venture Capital Association(TVCA)

Additional Information

Year Founded: 1998
Capital Under Management: $9,300,000
Current Activity Level : Actively seeking new investments

UNIVERS INVEST SICAR

10 Bis Ave.
Mohamed V BKTD
Tunis, Tunisia 1001
Phone: 216-7125- 9546
Fax: 216-7125- 9546
E-mail: univers.invest@planet.tn

Type of Firm

Private Equity Firm

Association Membership

African Venture Capital Association (AVCA)

Project Preferences

Type of Financing Preferred:
Expansion
Mezzanine

Size of Investments Considered:
Min Size of Investment Considered (000s): $27
Max Size of Investment Considered (000s): $464,499

Geographical Preferences

International Preferences:
Tunisia

Industry Preferences

In Communications prefer:
Telecommunications

In Semiconductor/Electr prefer:
Electronics

In Medical/Health prefer:
Medical Products

In Consumer Related prefer:
Food/Beverage

In Industrial/Energy prefer:
Industrial Products

Additional Information

Year Founded: 2004
Capital Under Management: $3,600,000
Current Activity Level : Actively seeking new investments

UNIVERSITY MEDICAL DISCOVERIES, INC.

100 International Blvd.
Toronto, Canada M9W 6J6
Phone: 416-213-4257
Fax: 416-213-4232
E-mail: info@umdi.net
Website: www.umdi.net

Type of Firm

Private Equity Firm

Project Preferences

Type of Financing Preferred:
Early Stage
Seed

Geographical Preferences

Canadian Preferences:
All Canada
Western Canada

Additional Information

Year Founded: 1996
Current Activity Level : Actively seeking new investments

UNIVERSITY OF CAMBRIDGE CHALLENGE FUND (AKA: UCF)

10 Trumpington Street
Cambridge, United Kingdom CB2 1QA
Phone: 44-1223-763-723
Fax: 44-1223-764-888
Website: www.challengefund.cam.ac.uk

Type of Firm

University Program

Project Preferences

Type of Financing Preferred:
Seed
Startup

Geographical Preferences

International Preferences:
United Kingdom

Additional Information

Year Founded: 1999
Capital Under Management: $6,500,000
Current Activity Level : Actively seeking new investments

UNIVERSITY OF MICHIGAN

701 Tappan Street
Ann Arbor, MI USA 48109
Phone: 734-615-4419

Fax: 734-615-4420
E-mail: zlicontact@umich.edu
Website: www.zli.bus.umich.edu

Type of Firm

University Program

Project Preferences

Type of Financing Preferred:
Early Stage
Start-up Financing

Geographical Preferences

United States Preferences:
Michigan

Additional Information

Year Founded: 1999
Current Activity Level : Actively seeking new investments

UNIVERSITY OF TOKYO EDGE CAPITAL CO., LTD., THE (AKA: UTEC)

7-3-1 Hongo, Bunkyo-ku
Tokyo, Japan 113-0033
Phone: 81-3-5841-1490
Fax: 81-3-5841-1491
E-mail: info@ut-ec.co.jp
Website: www.ut-ec.co.jp

Management and Staff

Hide Tsuji, General Partner
Maiko Katadae, Principal
Ted Yamamoto, General Partner
Teru Murakami, Principal
Tomotaka Goji, Managing Partner
Yumiko Nagatsuma, Partner

Type of Firm

University Program

Project Preferences

Type of Financing Preferred:
Early Stage
Start-up Financing
Seed
Startup

Geographical Preferences

International Preferences:
Japan

Industry Preferences

In Biotechnology prefer:
Biotechnology

In Medical/Health prefer:
Medical/Health

In Industrial/Energy prefer:
Environmental Related

Additional Information

Year Founded: 2004
Capital Under Management: $123,000,000
Current Activity Level : Actively seeking new investments

UNIVERSITY VENTURE FUND, THE

299 South Main Street
Eighth Floor
Salt Lake City, UT USA 84111
Phone: 801-246-1873
Fax: 801-961-8014
E-mail: info@uventurefund.com
Website: www.uventurefund.com

Management and Staff

Jared Hutchings, Managing Director
Michael Hennessey, Chief Financial Officer

Type of Firm

University Program

Project Preferences

Type of Financing Preferred:
Leveraged Buyout
Early Stage
Expansion

Geographical Preferences

United States Preferences:
Utah
All U.S.

Additional Information

Year Founded: 2005
Capital Under Management: $5,000,000
Current Activity Level : Actively seeking new investments

UNIVEST CAPITAL

2nd Floor, Dong-bo Building
718-33 Yeoksam-Dong, Kangnam-G
Seoul, South Korea 135-080
Phone: 82-2-564-1881
Fax: 82-2-565-1454
Website: www.univestcapital.co.kr

Management and Staff

Taeksu Kang, President

Type of Firm

Bank Affiliated

Project Preferences

Type of Financing Preferred:
Balanced

Geographical Preferences

International Preferences:
Korea, South

Additional Information

Year Founded: 2006
Current Activity Level : Actively seeking new investments

UNTERNEHMENS INVEST AG (AKA: UIAG)

Waehringer Strasse 3
Vienna, Austria A-1090
Phone: 43-1-4059-7710
Fax: 43-1-4059-7719
E-mail: office@uiag.at
Website: www.uiag.at

Management and Staff

Kurt Stiassny, Chief Executive Officer

Type of Firm

Private Equity Firm

Association Membership

European Private Equity and Venture Capital Assoc.

Project Preferences

Type of Financing Preferred:
Leveraged Buyout
Expansion

Geographical Preferences

International Preferences:
Austria

Industry Focus

(% based on actual investment)

Other Products	87.7%
Medical/Health	6.4%
Industrial/Energy	4.1%
Consumer Related	1.8%
Computer Software and Services	0.1%

Additional Information

Year Founded: 1990
Capital Under Management: $60,400,000
Current Activity Level : Actively seeking new investments

UOB BIOVENTURES MANAGEMENT PTE, LTD.

80 Raffles Place
Suite 30-20, UOB Plaza 2
Singapore, Singapore 048624
Phone: 65-6539-3533
Fax: 65-6538-2569

Type of Firm
Bank Affiliated

Project Preferences

Type of Financing Preferred:
Early Stage
Balanced
Later Stage

Geographical Preferences

United States Preferences:
All U.S.

International Preferences:
Singapore
Asia
Japan

Industry Preferences

In Biotechnology prefer:
Biotechnology

In Medical/Health prefer:
Medical/Health

Additional Information
Year Founded: 2001
Capital Under Management: $12,000,000
Current Activity Level : Actively seeking new investments

UOB VENTURE MANAGEMENT PTE, LTD.
80 Raffles Place
#30-20 UOB Plaza 2
Singapore, Singapore 048624
Phone: 65-6539-3044
Fax: 65-6538-2569
E-mail: info@uobvm.com.sg
Website: www.uobvm.com.sg

Other Offices
11/F Investment Building No. 4009
Shennan Road, Futian Centre District
Shenzhen, China 518026
Phone: 86-755-8291-2888
Fax: 86-755-8290-4093

8th Floor, TaiJi Building
No.211 Bei Si Huan Middle Road
Beijing, China 100083
Phone: 86-10-5161-6671
Fax: 86-10-5161-6700

Room 3307, United Plaza
1468 Nanjing Road West
Shanghai, China 200040
Phone: 86-21-6247-6228
Fax: 86-21-6289-8817

Management and Staff
Kian Wee Seah, Managing Director

Type of Firm
Bank Affiliated

Association Membership
Korean Venture Capital Association (KVCA)
Singapore Venture Capital Association (SVCA)

Project Preferences

Role in Financing:
Prefer role in deals created by others

Type of Financing Preferred:
Expansion
Mezzanine
Balanced

Size of Investments Considered:
Min Size of Investment Considered (000s): $3,000
Max Size of Investment Considered (000s): $10,000

Geographical Preferences

International Preferences:
Laos
Vietnam
Indonesia
Taiwan
Brunei
China
Hong Kong
Thailand
Philippines
Cambodia
Singapore
Korea, South
Asia
Malaysia
Burma

Industry Preferences

In Communications prefer:
Communications and Media
Telecommunications

In Semiconductor/Electr prefer:
Electronics
Semiconductor

In Biotechnology prefer:
Biotechnology

In Medical/Health prefer:
Medical/Health

In Consumer Related prefer:
Retail
Food/Beverage
Consumer Services
Education Related

In Industrial/Energy prefer:
Energy
Oil & Gas Drilling,Explor
Materials
Environmental Related

In Transportation prefer:
Transportation
Aerospace

In Business Serv. prefer:
Services
Distribution

In Manufact. prefer:
Manufacturing

In Agr/Forestr/Fish prefer:
Agribusiness

In Other prefer:
Socially Responsible

Additional Information
Name of Most Recent Fund: ASEAN China Investment Fund LP, The
Most Recent Fund Was Raised: 01/31/2003
Year Founded: 1992
Capital Under Management: $250,000,000
Current Activity Level : Actively seeking new investments
Method of Compensation: Return on investment is of primary concern, do not charge fees

---

UP CAPITAL, LTD.
111 Richmond Street West
Suite 1014
Toronto, Canada M5H 2G4
Phone: 416-360-3464
Fax: 416-360-8385
E-mail: contact@upcapital.com
Website: www.upcapital.com

Type of Firm
Private Equity Advisor or Fund of Funds

Additional Information
Year Founded: 2002
Current Activity Level : Actively seeking new investments

UPDATA PARTNERS
11955 Freedom Drive
Suite 7000
Reston, VA USA 20190
Phone: 703-736-0020
Fax: 703-736-0022
E-mail: info@updata.com
Website: www.updatapartners.com

Other Offices
379 Thornall Street
Tenth Floor
Edison, NJ USA 08837
Phone: 732-945-1000
Fax: 732-945-1001

Management and Staff
Barry Goldsmith, General Partner
Carter Griffin, Partner
Connor Mullett, General Partner
Ira Cohen, Chief Financial Officer
James Socas, General Partner

John Burton, Managing General Partner
Jon Seeber, Principal
Richard Erickson, General Partner

Type of Firm

Private Equity Firm

Association Membership

Mid-Atlantic Venture Association
National Venture Capital Association - USA (NVCA)

Project Preferences

Role in Financing:

Will function either as deal originator or investor in deals created by others

Type of Financing Preferred:

Leveraged Buyout
Early Stage
Expansion
Turnaround
Later Stage
Acquisition
Recapitalizations

Size of Investments Considered:

Min Size of Investment Considered (000s): $5,000
Max Size of Investment Considered (000s): $20,000

Geographical Preferences

United States Preferences:

All U.S.

International Preferences:

Europe

Industry Preferences

In Communications prefer:

Communications and Media

In Computer Software prefer:

Computer Services
Systems Software
Applications Software

In Internet Specific prefer:

E-Commerce Technology
Internet
Web Aggregration/Portals

Additional Information

Name of Most Recent Fund: Updata Partners IV, L.P.
Most Recent Fund Was Raised: 03/13/2007
Year Founded: 1998
Capital Under Management: $400,000,000
Current Activity Level : Actively seeking new investments
Method of Compensation: Return on investment is of primary concern, do not charge fees

---

UPLIFT EQUITY PARTNERS

100 Park Avenue
20th Floor
New York, NY USA 10017
Phone: 212-661-8111
Fax: 212-687-5392
Website: www.upliftequity.com

Other Offices

591 Redwood Highway
Suite 5280
Mill Valley, CA USA 94941
Phone: 415-389-9300
Fax: 415-383-1837

25 Upper Brook Street
London, United Kingdom W1K 7PT
Phone: 44-207629-2669
Fax: 44-207629-1348

Type of Firm

Private Equity Advisor or Fund of Funds

Project Preferences

Type of Financing Preferred:

Leveraged Buyout
Expansion
Public Companies
Acquisition

Geographical Preferences

United States Preferences:

All U.S.

Industry Preferences

In Medical/Health prefer:

Medical/Health

Additional Information

Year Founded: 2005
Current Activity Level : Actively seeking new investments

UPS STRATEGIC ENTERPRISE FUND

55 Glenlake Parkway, Northeast
Bldg One, Fourth Floor
Atlanta, GA USA 30328
Phone: 404-828-7352
Fax: 404-828-8088
E-mail: sef@ups.com
Website: www.ups.com/sef

Management and Staff

Bob Burman, Principal

Type of Firm

Corporate PE/Venture

Association Membership

National Venture Capital Association - USA (NVCA)

Project Preferences

Role in Financing:

Prefer role in deals created by others

Type of Financing Preferred:

Early Stage
Start-up Financing
First Stage Financing

Size of Investments Considered:

Min Size of Investment Considered (000s): $100
Max Size of Investment Considered (000s): $500

Geographical Preferences

Canadian Preferences:

All Canada

International Preferences:

Italy
United Kingdom
India
Netherlands
Portugal
China
Spain
Belgium
Germany
France

Industry Focus

(% based on actual investment)

Communications and Media	39.4%
Internet Specific	27.3%
Computer Software and Services	16.8%
Other Products	6.4%
Computer Hardware	6.2%
Semiconductors/Other Elect.	3.9%

Additional Information

Name of Most Recent Fund: SEF
Most Recent Fund Was Raised: 03/01/1998
Year Founded: 1997
Capital Under Management: $50,000,000
Current Activity Level : Actively seeking new investments
Method of Compensation: Return on investment is of primary concern, do not charge fees

---

UPSTART VENTURES MANAGEMENT

417 Wakara Way
Suite 3111
Salt Lake City, UT USA 84108
Phone: 801-585-6330
E-mail: info@upstartventures.com
Website: www.upstartventures.com

Management and Staff

Liz Hamburg, President, Founder

Type of Firm

Incubator/Development Program

Project Preferences

Type of Financing Preferred:

Early Stage
Seed

Industry Preferences

In Medical/Health prefer:
Diagnostic Services
Diagnostic Test Products
Drug/Equipmt Delivery
Pharmaceuticals

Additional Information
Year Founded: 2009
Capital Under Management: $7,100,000
Current Activity Level : Actively seeking new investments

UPSTREAM VENTURES PTE., LTD.
15 Queen Street #03-05
Singapore, Singapore 188537
Phone: 65-6536-7331
Fax: 65-6536-7301
E-mail: information@upstreamventures.com
Website: www.upstreamventures.com

Management and Staff
Carmelo Pistorio, Managing Partner
Pierre Hennes, Partner

Type of Firm
Private Equity Firm

Project Preferences

Role in Financing:
Prefer role as deal originator but will also invest in deals created by others

Type of Financing Preferred:
Early Stage

Size of Investments Considered:
Min Size of Investment Considered (000s): $500
Max Size of Investment Considered (000s): $3,000

Geographical Preferences

International Preferences:
India
China
Singapore

Industry Preferences

In Communications prefer:
Telecommunications
Wireless Communications

In Computer Software prefer:
Software

In Internet Specific prefer:
Internet

In Semiconductor/Electr prefer:
Semiconductor

In Business Serv. prefer:
Media

Additional Information
Year Founded: 2003
Current Activity Level : Actively seeking new investments

US TRUST PRIVATE EQUITY
225 High Ridge Road
Stamford, CT USA 06905
Phone: 203-352-4494
Fax: 203-352-4456
Website: www.ustrust.com

Other Offices
5 Palo Alto Square
9th Floor, 3000 Camino Real
Palo Alto, CA USA 94306
Phone: 650-213-4800
Fax: 650-813-6219

Management and Staff
David Fann, Managing Director
Douglas Lindgren, Managing Director

Type of Firm
Investment Management Firm

Project Preferences

Role in Financing:
Will function either as deal originator or investor in deals created by others

Type of Financing Preferred:
Fund of Funds
Leveraged Buyout
Balanced

Size of Investments Considered:
Min Size of Investment Considered (000s): $2,000
Max Size of Investment Considered (000s): $10,000

Industry Focus
(% based on actual investment)

Computer Software and Services	17.8%
Semiconductors/Other Elect.	16.3%
Internet Specific	16.0%
Communications and Media	13.1%
Other Products	9.1%
Computer Hardware	8.8%
Medical/Health	7.6%
Biotechnology	6.8%
Consumer Related	4.5%

Additional Information
Year Founded: 1995
Capital Under Management: $385,500,000
Current Activity Level : Actively seeking new investments
Method of Compensation: Return on invest. most important, but chg. closing fees, service fees, etc.

UTI VENTURE FUNDS MANAGEMENT COMPANY PVT., LTD. (AKA: UVF)
16th Floor, UB City
#24 Vittal Mallya Road
Bangalore, India 560 001
Phone: 91-80-3055-1200
Fax: 91-80-3055-1234
E-mail: info@utiventures.com
Website: www.utiventures.com

Other Offices
12th (M) Floor, East Wing
Raheja Towers, 26/27, M. G.Road
Bangalore, India 560001
Phone: 91-80-4112-3794
Fax: 91-80-2532-3127

Type of Firm
Bank Affiliated

Association Membership
Indian Venture Capital Association (IVCA)

Project Preferences

Type of Financing Preferred:
Expansion

Geographical Preferences

International Preferences:
India

Industry Preferences

In Communications prefer:
Telecommunications

In Internet Specific prefer:
Internet

In Semiconductor/Electr prefer:
Semiconductor

In Biotechnology prefer:
Biotechnology

In Medical/Health prefer:
Health Services
Pharmaceuticals

In Consumer Related prefer:
Entertainment and Leisure
Retail
Consumer Products

In Business Serv. prefer:
Consulting Services
Media

In Manufact. prefer:
Manufacturing

Additional Information
Name of Most Recent Fund: Ascent India Fund
Most Recent Fund Was Raised: 04/12/2005
Year Founded: 2000
Capital Under Management: $40,000,000

Current Activity Level : Actively seeking new investments

UUTECH LIMITED

University of Ulster
Cromore Road
Coleraine, United Kingdom BT52 1SA
Phone: 44-28-7028-0073
Fax: 44-28-7028-0050
E-mail: uutech@ulst.ac.uk
Website: www.ulst.ac.uk/uusrp

Other Offices

University Challenge Fund
Lanyon North, Queens University
Belfast, United Kingdom
Phone: 44-2890-682-321
Fax: 44-2890-273-899

Type of Firm

University Program

Project Preferences

Type of Financing Preferred:
Seed
Startup

Geographical Preferences

International Preferences:
United Kingdom

Industry Preferences

In Biotechnology prefer:
Biotechnology

In Medical/Health prefer:
Medical/Health
Medical Products

Additional Information

Year Founded: 2001
Current Activity Level : Actively seeking new investments

UV PARTNERS (AKA: UTAH VENTURES)

2755 East Cottonwood Parkway
Suite 520
Salt Lake City, UT USA 84121
Phone: 801-365-0262
Fax: 801-365-0233
E-mail: info@uvpartners.com
Website: www.uvpartners.com

Other Offices

720 31st Street
Manhattan Beach, CA USA 90266
Phone: 310-546-2777
Fax: 310-546-6757

Management and Staff

Allan Wolfe, Partner
Blake Modersitzki, Managing Partner
Carl Ledbetter, Managing Partner
Chris Cooper, Vice President
Heidi Huntsman, Partner
James Dreyfous, Managing Partner
Jaquie McKay, Chief Financial Officer

Type of Firm

Private Equity Firm

Association Membership

Natl Assoc of Small Bus. Inv. Co (NASBIC)
National Venture Capital Association - USA (NVCA)

Project Preferences

Role in Financing:
Will function either as deal originator or investor in deals created by others

Type of Financing Preferred:
Early Stage
Seed
First Stage Financing

Size of Investments Considered:
Min Size of Investment Considered (000s): $500
Max Size of Investment Considered (000s): $10,000

Geographical Preferences

United States Preferences:
Northwest
Southern California
Northern California
Rocky Mountain
West Coast
Southwest

Industry Focus

(% based on actual investment)

Internet Specific	28.0%
Computer Software and Services	22.5%
Medical/Health	19.2%
Communications and Media	14.3%
Biotechnology	12.7%
Computer Hardware	2.8%
Industrial/Energy	0.3%
Semiconductors/Other Elect.	0.1%

Additional Information

Name of Most Recent Fund: UV Partners IV, L.P.
Most Recent Fund Was Raised: 06/25/2007
Year Founded: 1986
Capital Under Management: $200,000,000
Current Activity Level : Actively seeking new investments
Method of Compensation: Return on investment is of primary concern, do not charge fees

- V -

V+ BETEILIGUNGS 2 GMBH

Loschwitzer Strasse 44
Dresden, Germany 01309
Phone: 871-43-06-08-0
Fax: 871-43-06-08-49
E-mail: info@venture-plus.de
Website: www.venture-plus.de

Type of Firm

Private Equity Firm

Project Preferences

Role in Financing:
Prefer role in deals created by others

Type of Financing Preferred:
Early Stage

Geographical Preferences

International Preferences:
Europe

Additional Information

Year Founded: 2008
Capital Under Management: $3,400,000
Current Activity Level : Actively seeking new investments

V4B - VENTURE FOR BUSINESS BETEILIGUNGS AG

Peregringasse
Vienna, Austria 1090
Phone: 43-1-3134-07010
Fax: 43-1-3134-07020
E-mail: info@v4b.at
Website: www.v4b.at

Type of Firm

Bank Affiliated

Project Preferences

Type of Financing Preferred:
Early Stage
Startup

Size of Investments Considered:
Min Size of Investment Considered (000s): $318
Max Size of Investment Considered (000s): $1,926

Geographical Preferences

International Preferences:
Austria

Industry Preferences

In Communications prefer:
Telecommunications
Wireless Communications

Additional Information
Year Founded: 2000
Capital Under Management: $19,300,000
Current Activity Level : Actively seeking new investments

VAEKSTFONDEN (AKA: DANISH GROWTH FUND, THE)
Strandvejen 104A
Hellerup, Denmark 2900
Phone: 45-3529-8600
Fax: 45-3529-8635
E-mail: vf@vf.dk
Website: www.vaekstfonden.dk

Other Offices
ul. Mokotowska 23/8
Warsaw, Poland 00-560
Phone: 48-22-621-1377
Fax: 48-22-621-8363

Management and Staff
Bent Kiemer, Managing Director
Christian Motzfeldt, Chief Executive Officer
Fussing Nielsen Jimmy, Partner
Kure Sussane, Chief Financial Officer
Martin Vang Hansen, Chief Operating Officer
Peter Benson, Partner
Sten Verland, Venture Partner
Sussane Kure, Chief Financial Officer

Type of Firm
Government Affiliated Program

Association Membership
European Private Equity and Venture Capital Assoc.

Project Preferences

Type of Financing Preferred:
Fund of Funds
Early Stage
Expansion
Mezzanine
Startup

Geographical Preferences

International Preferences:
Sweden
Iceland
Finland
Norway
Denmark

Industry Preferences

In Medical/Health prefer:
Medical/Health

Additional Information
Year Founded: 1992
Capital Under Management: $270,900,000
Current Activity Level : Actively seeking new investments

VALCAPITAL GESTION SGECR SA
C/Salva 10, Puerta 6
Valencia, Spain 46002
Phone: 34-96342-7245
Fax: 34-9634-2247
E-mail: valcapital@valcapital.com
Website: www.valcapital.com

Type of Firm
Private Equity Firm

Geographical Preferences

International Preferences:
Portugal
Spain

Industry Preferences

In Financial Services prefer:
Real Estate

Additional Information
Year Founded: 2004
Current Activity Level : Actively seeking new investments

VALCO CAPITAL PARTNERS LP (FKA: HILCO CAPITAL PARTNERS LP)
80 Bond Street
London, United Kingdom W1S 1SB

Type of Firm
Private Equity Firm

Project Preferences

Type of Financing Preferred:
Leveraged Buyout
Management Buyouts

Geographical Preferences

International Preferences:
United Kingdom

Additional Information
Year Founded: 2009
Current Activity Level : Actively seeking new investments

VALEDO PARTNERS (FKA: CREVAL PARTNERS)
Kungsgatan 2
Third Floor
Stockholm, Sweden 111 43
Phone: 46-8-678-0850
Fax: 46-8-678-0851
E-mail: info@crevalpartners.com
Website: www.crevalpartners.com

Management and Staff
Per Forsberg, Partner

Type of Firm
Private Equity Firm

Project Preferences

Type of Financing Preferred:
Leveraged Buyout
Management Buyouts
Acquisition

Geographical Preferences

International Preferences:
Sweden
Iceland
Norway
Finland
Denmark

Additional Information
Year Founded: 2006
Capital Under Management: $94,500,000
Current Activity Level : Actively seeking new investments

VALENCE CAPITAL MANAGEMENT, LP
1251 Avenue of the Americas
17th Floor
New York, NY USA 10020
Phone: 212-782-6036
Fax: 212-382-9845
Website: www.valencecapital.com

Management and Staff
James Caccavo, General Partner
Roy Thiele-Sardina, Venture Partner
Sharath Sury, Venture Partner

Type of Firm
Bank Affiliated

Project Preferences

Type of Financing Preferred:
Expansion
Later Stage

Industry Preferences

In Consumer Related prefer:

Consumer Products

In Business Serv. prefer:

Services
Media

Additional Information

Year Founded: 2000
Current Activity Level : Actively seeking new investments

VALHALLA PARTNERS

8000 Towers Crescent Drive
Suite 1050
Vienna, VA USA 22182
Phone: 703-448-1400
Fax: 703-448-1441
E-mail: info@valhallapartners.com
Website: www.valhallapartners.com

Management and Staff

Arthur Marks, General Partner
Charles Curran, General Partner
Gene Riechers, General Partner
Harry D Andrea, Chief Financial Officer
Hooks Johnston, General Partner
Kevin Greene, Principal
Kiran Hebbar, Partner
Saj Cherian, Principal
Scott Frederick, General Partner

Type of Firm

Private Equity Firm

Association Membership

Mid-Atlantic Venture Association
National Venture Capital Association - USA (NVCA)

Project Preferences

Role in Financing:

Prefer role as deal originator but will also invest in deals created by others

Type of Financing Preferred:

Early Stage
Start-up Financing
Seed
First Stage Financing

Size of Investments Considered:

Min Size of Investment Considered (000s): $1,000
Max Size of Investment Considered (000s): $10,000

Geographical Preferences

United States Preferences:

Mid Atlantic

Industry Preferences

In Communications prefer:

Communications and Media
Commercial Communications
CATV & Pay TV Systems
Radio & TV Broadcasting
Telecommunications
Wireless Communications
Data Communications
Satellite Microwave Comm.
Other Communication Prod.

In Computer Hardware prefer:

Mainframes / Scientific
Mini and Personal/Desktop
Computer Graphics and Dig
Integrated Turnkey System
Terminals
Disk Relat. Memory Device

In Computer Software prefer:

Computer Services
Data Processing
Software
Systems Software
Applications Software
Artificial Intelligence

In Internet Specific prefer:

E-Commerce Technology
Internet
Ecommerce
Web Aggregration/Portals

In Computer Other prefer:

Computer Related

In Semiconductor/Electr prefer:

Electronics
Semiconductor
Micro-Processing
Controllers and Sensors
Sensors
Circuit Boards
Component Testing Equipmt
Laser Related
Fiber Optics
Analytic/Scientific

Additional Information

Name of Most Recent Fund: Valhalla Partners II, L.P.
Most Recent Fund Was Raised: 10/31/2006
Year Founded: 2002
Capital Under Management: $440,900,000
Current Activity Level : Actively seeking new investments
Method of Compensation: Return on investment is of primary concern, do not charge fees

---

VALIANT PARTNERS CO. LTD.

Sanbancho Duplex B's
7-14 Sanbancho Chiyoda-ku
Tokyo, Japan 102-0075
Phone: 81-3-3288-6251
Fax: 81-3-3288-6276
Website: www.valiant-partners.com

Management and Staff

Akira Takagi, Principal
Ayumi Sakurai, Founding Partner
Daisuke Shintani, Principal
Ken Kato, Founding Partner

Type of Firm

Private Equity Firm

Project Preferences

Type of Financing Preferred:

Leveraged Buyout
Turnaround
Management Buyouts

Geographical Preferences

International Preferences:

Japan

Additional Information

Year Founded: 2006
Current Activity Level : Actively seeking new investments

VALLEY VENTURES (FKA: ARIZONA GROWTH PARTNERS, L.P.)

1275 W. Washington St
Suite 101
Tempe, AZ USA 85281
Phone: 480-661-6600
Fax: 602-286-5284
E-mail: businessplans@valleyventures.com
Website: www.valleyventures.com

Other Offices

6245 East Broadway Boulevard
Suite 620
Tucson, AZ USA 85711
Phone: 520-327-5556
Fax: 520-327-5665

One Technology Center
1155 University Blvd., SE, Suite N219
Albuquerque, NM USA 87106
Phone: 505-843-4054
Fax: 505-821-5210

Management and Staff

Gregg Adkin, General Partner
John Holliman, General Partner

Type of Firm

Private Equity Firm

Association Membership

Natl Assoc of Small Bus. Inv. Co (NASBIC)

Project Preferences

Role in Financing:

Prefer role as deal originator but will also invest in

deals created by others

Type of Financing Preferred:
Second Stage Financing
Leveraged Buyout
Early Stage
Expansion
Balanced
Seed
Private Placement
Recapitalizations

Size of Investments Considered:
Min Size of Investment Considered (000s): $500
Max Size of Investment Considered (000s): $2,000

Geographical Preferences

United States Preferences:
New Mexico
Nevada
Arizona
Southern California
Colorado
Utah
Southwest
Texas

Industry Preferences

In Computer Software prefer:
Computer Services
Software
Systems Software
Applications Software
Artificial Intelligence

In Internet Specific prefer:
E-Commerce Technology

In Semiconductor/Electr prefer:
Electronics
Semiconductor
Micro-Processing
Controllers and Sensors
Sensors
Laser Related
Fiber Optics

In Biotechnology prefer:
Biotechnology
Human Biotechnology
Agricultural/Animal Bio.
Industrial Biotechnology
Biosensors
Biotech Related Research

In Medical/Health prefer:
Medical/Health
Medical Diagnostics
Diagnostic Services
Diagnostic Test Products
Medical Therapeutics
Drug/Equipmt Delivery
Medical Products
Disposable Med. Products
Health Services
Pharmaceuticals

Additional Information
Name of Most Recent Fund: Valley Ventures III, L.P.
Most Recent Fund Was Raised: 09/17/2002
Year Founded: 1984
Capital Under Management: $73,000,000
Current Activity Level : Actively seeking new investments
Method of Compensation: Return on investment is of primary concern, do not charge fees

---

VALOR EQUITY PARTNERS
200 South Michigan Avenue
Suite 1020
Chicago, IL USA 60604
Phone: 312-683-1900
Fax: 312-683-1881
E-mail: info@valorep.comc
Website: www.valorep.com

Management and Staff
Antonio Gracias, Chief Executive Officer
Benjamin Rodman, Managing Director
Bradley Sheftel, Vice President
Daniel Barlow, Principal
David Heskett, Vice President
Jason Macatangay, Vice President
Jonathan Shulkin, Managing Director
Nelson Sun, Vice President
Peter Goldman, Vice President
Timothy Watkins, Managing Director

Type of Firm
Private Equity Firm

Project Preferences

Type of Financing Preferred:
Turnaround
Acquisition
Special Situation

Geographical Preferences

United States Preferences:
All U.S.

Additional Information
Year Founded: 2002
Capital Under Management: $19,100,000
Current Activity Level : Actively seeking new investments

VALORA
Rua Funchal 129/7B
Vila Olimpia
Sao Paulo, Brazil 04551-060
Phone: 55-11-3040-3300
Fax: 55-11-3040-3301
Website: www.valoranet.com.br

Other Offices
SHIS QI 9 Conjunto 17 Casa 16
Lago Sul
Brasilia, Brazil 71625-170
Phone: 55-61-248-3731
Fax: 55-61-248-0162

Rua Lauro Muller, 116/ Conjunto 1803
Torre de Rio Sul
Rio de Janeiro, Brazil
Phone: 55-21-2541-1550
Fax: 55-21-2275-3389

Type of Firm
Private Equity Firm

Association Membership
Brazilian Venture Capital Association (ABCR)

Project Preferences

Type of Financing Preferred:
Balanced

Geographical Preferences

International Preferences:
Brazil

Additional Information
Year Founded: 2006
Current Activity Level : Actively seeking new investments

VALSTONE PARTNERS LLC (FKA: TOUCHSTONE PARTNERS LLC)
260 East Brown Street
Suite 250
Birmingham, MI USA 48009
Phone: 248-646-9200
Fax: 248-646-3322
E-mail: inquiries@valstonepartners.com
Website: www.valstonepartners.com

Other Offices
300 East Lombard Street
Suite 1111
Baltimore, MD USA 21202
Phone: 410-244-0000
Fax: 410-244-0703

Management and Staff
Eric Abel, Managing Director
Gerald Timmis, Senior Managing Director
Hee-Jin Yi, Vice President
Jason Jarjosa, Vice President
Larry Jennings, Senior Managing Director

Type of Firm
Private Equity Firm

Project Preferences

Role in Financing:
Will function either as deal originator or investor in deals created by others

Type of Financing Preferred:
Leveraged Buyout
Turnaround
Special Situation
Acquisition
Distressed Debt

Size of Investments Considered:
Min Size of Investment Considered (000s): $2,000
Max Size of Investment Considered (000s): $100,000

Geographical Preferences

United States Preferences:
Mid Atlantic
All U.S.

Canadian Preferences:
All Canada

Industry Preferences

In Financial Services prefer:
Real Estate

Additional Information
Name of Most Recent Fund: ValStone Opportunity Fund IV LLC
Most Recent Fund Was Raised: 03/07/2008
Year Founded: 1998
Capital Under Management: $207,200,000
Current Activity Level : Actively seeking new investments
Method of Compensation: Other

VALUE ADDED CAPITAL, LLC

240 Oak Ridge Avenue
Summit, NJ USA 07901
Phone: 908-273-7750
Fax: 908-277-6024

Management and Staff
Robert Edgreen, Managing Director

Type of Firm
Private Equity Firm

Project Preferences

Role in Financing:
Prefer role as deal originator but will also invest in deals created by others

Type of Financing Preferred:
Leveraged Buyout
Turnaround
Management Buyouts

Size of Investments Considered:
Min Size of Investment Considered (000s): $5,000
Max Size of Investment Considered (000s): $20,000

Geographical Preferences

International Preferences:
United Kingdom

Additional Information
Year Founded: 1993
Capital Under Management: $46,000,000
Current Activity Level : Actively seeking new investments
Method of Compensation: Return on invest. most important, but chg. closing fees, service fees, etc.

VALUE INVESTMENTS PERU - SAFI

Manuel Olguin 571 Oficina 502
Santiago de Surco
Lima, Peru 33
Phone: 51-1-610-5600
Fax: 51-1-610-5610
E-mail: mail@valinvest.net
Website: www.valinvest.net

Type of Firm
Private Equity Firm

Project Preferences

Type of Financing Preferred:
Balanced

Geographical Preferences

International Preferences:
Peru

Industry Preferences

In Communications prefer:
Communications and Media

In Computer Software prefer:
Applications Software

In Medical/Health prefer:
Health Services

In Business Serv. prefer:
Services

Additional Information
Year Founded: 2007
Current Activity Level : Actively seeking new investments

VALUE MANAGEMENT SERVICES GMBH (AKA: VMS)

Garnisongasse 4/10
Vienna, Austria A-1090
Phone: 43-1-5120-5550
Fax: 43-1-5120-5555
E-mail: info@valuemanagement.at
Website: www.valuemanagement.at

Type of Firm
Private Equity Firm

Association Membership
European Private Equity and Venture Capital Assoc.

Project Preferences

Type of Financing Preferred:
Leveraged Buyout
Balanced

Geographical Preferences

International Preferences:
Switzerland
Europe
Austria
Germany

Industry Preferences

In Consumer Related prefer:
Consumer

In Industrial/Energy prefer:
Industrial Products

Additional Information
Name of Most Recent Fund: REB II
Most Recent Fund Was Raised: 01/18/2006
Year Founded: 2000
Capital Under Management: $36,400,000
Current Activity Level : Actively seeking new investments

VALUE PLUS VENTURES

5755 North Point Parkway
Suite 41
Alpharetta, GA USA 30022
Phone: 770-664-2774
Fax: 770-664-2775
Website: www.v-pventures.com

Management and Staff
Chris Demetree, Co-Founder
Steve Nussrallah, Partner

Type of Firm
Private Equity Firm

Project Preferences

Type of Financing Preferred:
Early Stage

Size of Investments Considered:
Min Size of Investment Considered (000s): $200
Max Size of Investment Considered (000s): $5,000

Industry Preferences

In Communications prefer:
Commercial Communications
CATV & Pay TV Systems

Telecommunications
Wireless Communications

In Computer Software prefer:
Software
Systems Software
Applications Software

In Internet Specific prefer:
Internet
Ecommerce
Web Aggregration/Portals

In Consumer Related prefer:
Consumer

In Business Serv. prefer:
Services

Additional Information
Year Founded: 2008
Capital Under Management: $10,000,000
Current Activity Level : Actively seeking new investments

VAN DEN ENDE & DEITMERS B.V.
Johannes Vermeerstraat 23
Amsterdam, Netherlands 1071 DK
Phone: 31-20-794-7777
Fax: 31-20-794-7700
E-mail: info@endeit.nl
Website: www.endeit.nl

Management and Staff
Hubert Deitmers, Managing Partner
Joop van den Ende, Founder
Martijn Hamann, Partner
Robert Wilhelm, Partner

Type of Firm
Private Equity Firm

Project Preferences

Type of Financing Preferred:
Expansion
Generalist PE
Management Buyouts
Acquisition
Recapitalizations

Geographical Preferences

International Preferences:
Europe
Western Europe

Industry Preferences

In Communications prefer:
Telecommunications

In Computer Software prefer:
Software
Systems Software

In Internet Specific prefer:
E-Commerce Technology
Internet
Web Aggregration/Portals

In Business Serv. prefer:
Media

In Manufact. prefer:
Publishing

Additional Information
Year Founded: 2006
Current Activity Level : Actively seeking new investments

VAN HERK INVESTMENTS
Lichtenauerlaan 32
Postbus 4068
Rotterdam, Netherlands 3006
Phone: 31-10-241-1555
Fax: 31-10-436-3640
E-mail: vanherkinvestments@vanherkgroep.nl
Website: www.vanherkgroep.nl

Management and Staff
Erik Esveld, Chief Financial Officer

Type of Firm
Private Equity Firm

Project Preferences

Type of Financing Preferred:
Generalist PE

Geographical Preferences

International Preferences:
Europe

Additional Information
Year Founded: 1972
Current Activity Level : Actively seeking new investments

VANCE STREET CAPITAL LLC
11150 Santa Monica Boulevard
Suite 750
Los Angeles, CA USA 90025
Phone: 310-231-7100
Fax: 310-478-8072
Website: www.vancest.com

Management and Staff
Jake Blumenthal, Principal
Leslie Shaw, Chief Financial Officer
Richard Crowell, Partner
Richard Roeder, Partner
William Kuntz, Principal

Type of Firm
Private Equity Firm

Project Preferences

Type of Financing Preferred:
Leveraged Buyout
Expansion
Recapitalizations

Size of Investments Considered:
Min Size of Investment Considered (000s): $50,000
Max Size of Investment Considered (000s): $200,000

Geographical Preferences

United States Preferences:
All U.S.

Additional Information
Year Founded: 2007
Current Activity Level : Actively seeking new investments

VANDERBILT UNIVERSITY OFFICE OF TRANSFER AND DEVELOPMENT
1207 17th Avenue South
Suite 105
Nashville, TN USA 37212
Phone: 615-343-2430
Fax: 615-343-4419
Website: www.vutc.net

Type of Firm
Endowment, Foundation or Pension Fund

Project Preferences

Type of Financing Preferred:
Early Stage

Additional Information
Year Founded: 1992
Capital Under Management: $10,000,000
Current Activity Level : Actively seeking new investments

VANGUARD ATLANTIC, LTD.
Post Office Box 1360
Saranac Lake, NY USA 12983
E-mail: Partner@VanguardAtlantic.com
Website: www.vanguardatlantic.com

Type of Firm
Private Equity Firm

Project Preferences

Type of Financing Preferred:
Leveraged Buyout

Early Stage
Seed
Startup

Size of Investments Considered:
Min Size of Investment Considered (000s): $150
Max Size of Investment Considered (000s): $6,000

Geographical Preferences

International Preferences:
Europe

Industry Preferences

In Computer Software prefer:
Software

In Internet Specific prefer:
E-Commerce Technology

Additional Information
Name of Most Recent Fund: Vanguard Atlantic, L.P.
Most Recent Fund Was Raised: 01/01/1990
Year Founded: 1984
Current Activity Level : Actively seeking new investments

VANGUARD VENTURES
560 South Winchester Boulevard
Suite 500
San Jose, CA USA 95128
Phone: 650-321-2900
Fax: 650-321-2902
E-mail: info@vanguardventures.com
Website: www.vanguardventures.com

Other Offices
1330 Post Oak Boulevard
Suite 2550
Houston, TX USA 77056
Phone: 713-877-1662
Fax: 713-877-8669

Management and Staff
Daniel Eilers, Managing Director
Donald Wood, Managing Director
Jack Gill, Managing Director
Ken Shilling, Chief Financial Officer
Robert Ulrich, Managing Director
Thomas McConnell, Managing Director

Type of Firm
Private Equity Firm

Association Membership
Western Association of Venture Capitalists (WAVC)

Project Preferences

Role in Financing:
Prefer role as deal originator but will also invest in deals created by others

Type of Financing Preferred:
Early Stage
Research and Development
Seed
First Stage Financing

Size of Investments Considered:
Min Size of Investment Considered (000s): $500
Max Size of Investment Considered (000s): $10,000

Geographical Preferences

United States Preferences:
All U.S.

Industry Focus
(% based on actual investment)

Communications and Media	25.3%
Medical/Health	19.1%
Computer Software and Services	13.8%
Internet Specific	10.9%
Semiconductors/Other Elect.	10.1%
Computer Hardware	5.9%
Biotechnology	5.8%
Other Products	4.0%
Consumer Related	3.3%
Industrial/Energy	2.0%

Additional Information
Year Founded: 1981
Capital Under Management: $500,000,000
Current Activity Level : Actively seeking new investments
Method of Compensation: Return on investment is of primary concern, do not charge fees

---

VANTAGE PARTNERS LLC
Brighton Landing West
10 Guest Street
Brighton, MA USA 02135
Phone: 617-354-6090
Fax: 617-354-4685
E-mail: info@vantagepartners.com
Website: www.vantagepartners.com

Type of Firm
Private Equity Firm

Association Membership
National Venture Capital Association - USA (NVCA)

Additional Information
Year Founded: 1999
Current Activity Level : Actively seeking new investments

VANTAGE VENTURE PARTNERS (AKA: VANTAGE CAPITAL)
Vantage Capital House
24 Hurlingham Road
Illovo Boulevard, South Africa 2196
Phone: 27-11-880-5730
Fax: 27-11-880-5731
E-mail: info@vantagecapital.co.za
Website: www.vantagecapital.co.za

Type of Firm
Private Equity Firm

Association Membership
South African Venture Capital Association (SAVCA)

Project Preferences

Type of Financing Preferred:
Early Stage
Expansion
Mezzanine
Later Stage

Geographical Preferences

International Preferences:
Europe
Africa

Industry Preferences

In Communications prefer:
Telecommunications

In Computer Software prefer:
Software

In Biotechnology prefer:
Biotechnology

In Business Serv. prefer:
Services
Distribution

Additional Information
Year Founded: 2000
Capital Under Management: $66,000,000
Current Activity Level : Actively seeking new investments

VANTAGEPOINT VENTURE PARTNERS
1001 Bayhill Drive
Suite 300
San Bruno, CA USA 94066
Phone: 650-866-3100
Fax: 650-869-6078
Website: www.vpvp.com

Other Offices
1200 McGill College
Suite 1240
Montreal, Canada H3B 4G7
Phone: 514-448-5790
Fax: 514-448-5796

6th Floor, Tower 3, China Central Place
No.79 Jan Guo Road
Beijing, China 100025
Phone: 86-10-5920-4270

Level 39, One Exchange Square
Eight Connaught Place
Central, Hong Kong

Phone: 852-3101-7150
Fax: 86-10-5920-4270

Management and Staff

Annette Bianchi, Managing Director
Bernard Bulkin, Venture Partner
Bill Green, Managing Director
Brad Matson, Partner
David Fries, Managing Director
Duncan Davidson, Venture Partner
E. Richard Prostko, Vice President
Eve Kurtin, Venture Partner
Harold Friedman, Chief Financial Officer
J. Stephan Dolezalek, Managing Director
James Marver, Managing Partner
Jim Mills, Managing Director
John Leggate, Venture Partner
Lee Burrows, Principal
Lei Yang, Principal
Lipkin Boris, Venture Partner
Marc Van Den Berg, Managing Director
Melissa Guzy, Managing Director
Neil Wolff, Managing Director
Pat Splinter, Managing Director
Patrick Gallagher, Principal
R. James Woolsey, Venture Partner
Rafael Simon, Partner
Richard Harroch, Managing Director
Terry Chen, Venture Partner
Thomas Huot, Principal
Tom Bevilacqua, Managing Director
William Harding, Managing Director
William McDonough, Venture Partner

Type of Firm

Private Equity Firm

Association Membership

Western Association of Venture Capitalists (WAVC)
National Venture Capital Association - USA (NVCA)

Project Preferences

Role in Financing:

Prefer role as deal originator

Type of Financing Preferred:

Second Stage Financing
Early Stage
Expansion
Mezzanine
Balanced
Public Companies
First Stage Financing
Private Placement
Startup
Recapitalizations

Size of Investments Considered:

Min Size of Investment Considered (000s): $5,000
Max Size of Investment Considered (000s): $50,000

Geographical Preferences

United States Preferences:

All U.S.

Canadian Preferences:

All Canada

International Preferences:

United Kingdom
Western Europe
Asia

Industry Focus

(% based on actual investment)	
Internet Specific	23.7%
Semiconductors/Other Elect.	19.9%
Communications and Media	15.2%
Computer Software and Services	13.4%
Industrial/Energy	9.1%
Computer Hardware	5.5%
Other Products	4.5%
Medical/Health	3.5%
Consumer Related	2.8%
Biotechnology	2.4%

Additional Information

Year Founded: 1996
Capital Under Management: $4,485,000,000
Current Activity Level : Actively seeking new investments
Method of Compensation: Other

VANTERRA CAPITAL, LTD.

40 West 57th Street
20th Floor
New York, NY USA 10019
Phone: 212-231-3930
Fax: 212-231-3939
E-mail: info@vanterra.com
Website: www.vanterra.com

Management and Staff

Alan Quasha, Partner
Jason Young, Partner
Shad Azimi, Founding Partner

Type of Firm

Private Equity Firm

Project Preferences

Type of Financing Preferred:

Fund of Funds
Expansion

Size of Investments Considered:

Min Size of Investment Considered (000s): $20,000
Max Size of Investment Considered (000s): $500,000

Geographical Preferences

International Preferences:

India
China
Eastern Europe
Middle East
Africa

Additional Information

Year Founded: 2008
Capital Under Management: $152,000,000
Current Activity Level : Actively seeking new investments

VARDE PARTNERS, INC.

8500 Normandale Lake Boulevard
Suite 1570
Minneapolis, MN USA 55437
Phone: 952-893-1554
Fax: 612-893-9613
Website: www.varde.com

Management and Staff

George Hicks, Managing Partner
Greg McMillan, Managing Partner
Jason Spaeth, Partner
Jeannie Sonstegard, Chief Financial Officer
Jeremy Hedberg, Partner
Marcia Page, Managing Partner

Type of Firm

Private Equity Firm

Project Preferences

Type of Financing Preferred:

Special Situation
Distressed Debt

Geographical Preferences

United States Preferences:

All U.S.

Canadian Preferences:

All Canada

International Preferences:

Western Europe
All International

Additional Information

Year Founded: 1993
Capital Under Management: $143,400,000
Current Activity Level : Actively seeking new investments

VARDY VENTURE CAPITAL

Venture House
Aykley Heads
Durham, United Kingdom DH1 5TS
Phone: 44-19-1374-4744
Website: www.vardygroup.com

Management and Staff

Peter Vardy, Founder

Type of Firm

Private Equity Firm

Project Preferences

Type of Financing Preferred:

Generalist PE
Balanced

Geographical Preferences

International Preferences:
United Kingdom

Industry Preferences

In Consumer Related prefer:
Consumer

In Financial Services prefer:
Real Estate

Additional Information

Year Founded: 2005
Capital Under Management: $95,000,000
Current Activity Level : Actively seeking new investments

VASDAQ INVESTMENT, LTD. (AKA: V-INVESTMENT)

9F Aiosu Meguroekimae Bldg.
2-15-19 Kami-Osaki,Shinagawaku
Tokyo, Japan 141-0021
Phone: 81-3-5772-8568
Fax: 81-3-5772-9581
E-mail: info@v-investment.jp
Website: www.v-investment.jp

Other Offices

IP Innovation Ltd Innovatioon House
139 Hillcrest, Weybridge
Surrey, United Kingdom KT13 8AS

Type of Firm

Angel Group

Additional Information

Year Founded: 2003
Current Activity Level : Actively seeking new investments

VAUBAN PARTENAIRES S.A. (AKA: VAUBAN FINANCE)

15, avenue Victor Hugo
Paris, France 75116
Phone: 33-1-4924-0707
Fax: 33-1-4924-0808
E-mail: courrier@vauban-sa.fr
Website: www.vauban-sa.fr

Other Offices

1, rue Esquermoise - BP 112
Lille Cedex, France 59027
Phone: 33-3-2021-9380
Fax: 33-3-2021-9389

Type of Firm

Private Equity Firm

Association Membership

French Venture Capital Association (AFIC)

Project Preferences

Type of Financing Preferred:
Leveraged Buyout
Expansion

Size of Investments Considered:
Min Size of Investment Considered (000s): $686
Max Size of Investment Considered (000s): $960

Geographical Preferences

International Preferences:
France

Additional Information

Year Founded: 1992
Capital Under Management: $30,200,000
Current Activity Level : Actively seeking new investments

VB RIZIKOS KAPITALO VALDYMAS (AKA: VB VENTURE CAPITAL MGMT)

Jogailos g. 10
Vilnius, Lithuania 01116
Phone: 370-5-268-2407
Fax: 370-5-268-2402
E-mail: kapitalas@seb.lt
Website: www.seb.lt

Type of Firm

Bank Affiliated
Association Membership
European Private Equity and Venture Capital Assoc.

Project Preferences

Type of Financing Preferred:
Expansion
Management Buyouts
Startup

Size of Investments Considered:
Min Size of Investment Considered (000s): $758
Max Size of Investment Considered (000s): $3,030

Geographical Preferences

International Preferences:
Europe
Lithuania

Additional Information

Year Founded: 2000
Capital Under Management: $10,300,000
Current Activity Level : Actively seeking new investments

VC ADVANTAGE FUND

365 Bay Street
10th Floor
Toronto, Canada M5H 2V2
Phone: 416-860-6130
Fax: 416-860-6355
Website: www.advantagefunds.net

Type of Firm

Private Equity Firm

Project Preferences

Type of Financing Preferred:
Early Stage
Other

Geographical Preferences

Canadian Preferences:
All Canada

Additional Information

Year Founded: 1999
Current Activity Level : Actively seeking new investments

VCCHINA, LTD.

Kuntai International Plaza
No. 12 Chaowai Street
Beijing, China 100028
Phone: 86-10-5879-7706
Fax: 86-10-5879-7705
E-mail: questions@vcchina.com
Website: www.vcchina.com

Other Offices

31/F, Room 3105 Panglin Square
2001 Jiabin Road, Luohu District
Shenzhen, China 518005
Phone: 86-755-5185-223
Fax: 86-755-5185-232

Unit 2106 Westgate Tower
No.1308 Nanjing Road(west)
Shanghai, China 200041
Phone: 86-21-6218-1888
Fax: 86-21-6217-3888

Management and Staff

Wayne Zhao, President
Wolfgang Yang, Vice President

Type of Firm

Private Equity Firm

Association Membership

Venture Capital Association of Beijing (VCAB)

Project Preferences

Type of Financing Preferred:
Seed
Startup

Geographical Preferences

International Preferences:
China

Industry Preferences

In Communications prefer:
Telecommunications

In Computer Software prefer:
Software

In Biotechnology prefer:
Biotechnology

In Medical/Health prefer:
Medical/Health

In Industrial/Energy prefer:
Energy
Materials

Additional Information
Year Founded: 1999
Current Activity Level : Actively seeking new investments

VCE CAPITAL
820 Garrett Drive
Bossier City, LA USA 71111
Phone: 318-746-8430
Fax: 318-746-3771
Website: www.vcecapital.com

Other Offices
29 Constitution Court
Tuxedo Park, NY USA 10987
Phone: 914-588-7200
Fax: 318-746-3771

201 St. Charles Avenue
Suite 3700
New Orleans, LA USA 70170
Phone: 504-569-7900
Fax: 504-569-7910

Management and Staff
Richard Montgomery, General Partner
Ross Barrett, Managing Partner
Russell Vernon, General Partner

Type of Firm
Private Equity Firm

Project Preferences

Role in Financing:
Will function either as deal originator or investor in deals created by others

Type of Financing Preferred:
Early Stage
Expansion
Generalist PE
Balanced

Size of Investments Considered:
Min Size of Investment Considered (000s): $250
Max Size of Investment Considered (000s): $3,000

Geographical Preferences

United States Preferences:
Southeast
Northeast
Louisiana
New York

Industry Preferences

In Biotechnology prefer:
Biotech Related Research

In Medical/Health prefer:
Health Services
Hospitals/Clinics/Primary

In Industrial/Energy prefer:
Energy

Additional Information
Name of Most Recent Fund: Themelios Ventures, LP
Most Recent Fund Was Raised: 03/01/2006
Year Founded: 2004
Capital Under Management: $36,000,000
Current Activity Level : Actively seeking new investments
Method of Compensation: Return on investment is of primary concern, do not charge fees

---

VCFA GROUP (AKA: VENTURE CAPITAL FUND OF AMERICA, INC.)
509 Madison Avenue
Suite 1400
New York, NY USA 10022
Phone: 212-838-5577
Fax: 212-838-7614
E-mail: mail@vcfa.com
Website: www.vcfa.com

Other Offices
100 Pine Street
Suite 2820
San Francisco, CA USA 94111
Phone: 415-296-0660
Fax: 415-296-0990

Management and Staff
Brett Byers, Managing Director
Deena Seelendfreund, Chief Financial Officer
Edward Hortick, Managing Director
Kevin Monroe, Managing Director
Steven Taubman, Managing Director

Type of Firm
Private Equity Advisor or Fund of Funds

Association Membership
Western Association of Venture Capitalists (WAVC)
National Venture Capital Association - USA (NVCA)

Project Preferences

Type of Financing Preferred:
Fund of Funds of Second

Size of Investments Considered:
Min Size of Investment Considered (000s): $2,000
Max Size of Investment Considered (000s): $100,000

Geographical Preferences

Canadian Preferences:
All Canada

International Preferences:
India
China
Middle East
Japan

Additional Information
Name of Most Recent Fund: VCFA Private Equity Partners IV, L.P.
Most Recent Fund Was Raised: 12/30/2003
Year Founded: 1982
Capital Under Management: $507,400,000
Current Activity Level : Actively seeking new investments
Method of Compensation: Return on investment is of primary concern, do not charge fees

---

VCH BETEILIGUNGS AG
Praterstrasse 38
Palais Rohan
Vienna, Austria A-1020
Phone: 43-1-2270-1400
Fax: 43-1-2270-1450
E-mail: info@vch-group.de
Website: www.vch-ag.com

Type of Firm
Private Equity Firm

Association Membership
European Private Equity and Venture Capital Assoc.

Project Preferences

Type of Financing Preferred:
Expansion

Geographical Preferences

International Preferences:
Austria

Additional Information
Year Founded: 2003
Capital Under Management: $26,400,000
Current Activity Level : Actively seeking new investments

VECATA A/S

Dandyvej 19
Vejle, Denmark 7100
Phone: 45-7215-1500
Fax: 45-7215-1909
Website: www.vecata.com

Management and Staff

Hans-Henrik Eriksen, Managing Director

Type of Firm

Private Equity Firm

Project Preferences

Type of Financing Preferred:
Leveraged Buyout
Expansion
Balanced
Management Buyouts
Startup

Geographical Preferences

International Preferences:
Europe

Additional Information

Year Founded: 2006
Current Activity Level : Actively seeking new investments

VECTIS CAPITAL SA

2-4 Mesogion Avenue
3rd floor
Athens, Greece 115 21
Phone: 30-210-747-4205
Fax: 30-210-642-8774
E-mail: mail@vectis.gr
Website: www.vectis.gr

Management and Staff

Dionissis Alissandratos, Managing Director

Type of Firm

Bank Affiliated

Association Membership

European Private Equity and Venture Capital Assoc.

Project Preferences

Type of Financing Preferred:
Early Stage
Expansion
Startup

Size of Investments Considered:
Min Size of Investment Considered (000s): $471
Max Size of Investment Considered (000s): $1,883

Geographical Preferences

International Preferences:
Greece
Nigeria
Western Europe
Africa

Industry Preferences

In Internet Specific prefer:
Internet

In Computer Other prefer:
Computer Related

In Biotechnology prefer:
Biotechnology

In Consumer Related prefer:
Consumer
Food/Beverage

In Industrial/Energy prefer:
Industrial Products

Additional Information

Year Founded: 2000
Capital Under Management: $36,200,000
Current Activity Level : Actively seeking new investments

VECTOR CAPITAL

One Market Street
Steuart Tower, 23rd Floor
San Francisco, CA USA 94105
Phone: 415-293-5000
Fax: 415-293-5100
Website: www.vectorcapital.com

Management and Staff

Amish Mehta, Partner
Andy Fishman, Vice President
Christopher Nicholson, Partner
David Baylor, Chief Operating Officer
David Fishman, Principal
Dewey Chambers, Chief Financial Officer
Jayee Xu, Vice President
Peter Krow, Vice President
Robert Hansen, Vice President
Robert Amen, Principal
Stephen Wolfe, Vice President

Type of Firm

Private Equity Firm

Association Membership

Western Association of Venture Capitalists (WAVC)

Project Preferences

Role in Financing:
Prefer role as deal originator

Type of Financing Preferred:
Early Stage
Expansion
Balanced
Public Companies
Later Stage
Management Buyouts
Acquisition
Special Situation
Recapitalizations

Size of Investments Considered:
Min Size of Investment Considered (000s): $10,000
Max Size of Investment Considered (000s): $100,000

Geographical Preferences

United States Preferences:
All U.S.

Canadian Preferences:
All Canada

Industry Focus

(% based on actual investment)

Computer Software and Services	71.9%
Internet Specific	22.5%
Computer Hardware	3.8%
Communications and Media	1.3%
Other Products	0.5%

Additional Information

Name of Most Recent Fund: Vector Capital IV, L.P.
Most Recent Fund Was Raised: 06/07/2007
Year Founded: 1997
Capital Under Management: $1,574,100,000
Current Activity Level : Actively seeking new investments
Method of Compensation: Return on invest. most important, but chg. closing fees, service fees, etc.

VEDANTA CAPITAL

540 Madison Avenue
38th Floor
New York, NY USA 10022
Phone: 212-710-5220
Fax: 212-710-5221
E-mail: info@vedacap.com
Website: www.vedacap.com

Management and Staff

Alessandro Piol, Managing Director
Howard Goldstein, Managing Director
Parag Saxena, Managing Director

Type of Firm

Private Equity Advisor or Fund of Funds

Project Preferences

Type of Financing Preferred:
Fund of Funds
Balanced

Geographical Preferences

United States Preferences:
All U.S.

Additional Information

Year Founded: 2006
Capital Under Management: $52,600,000
Current Activity Level : Actively seeking new investments

VEGAGEST SGR

Corso Giovecca, 3
Ferrara P.Iva, Italy 44100
Phone: 39-152-718-0362
E-mail: info@vegagest.it
Website: www.vegagest.it

Management and Staff

Alessandro Cameroni, Partner
Alessandro Betti, Partner
Francesco Conforti, Partner
Stefano Costagli, Partner

Type of Firm

Corporate PE/Venture

Project Preferences

Type of Financing Preferred:
Expansion
Balanced

Geographical Preferences

International Preferences:
Italy

Additional Information

Year Founded: 2007
Current Activity Level : Actively seeking new investments

VELOCITY EQUITY PARTNERS LLC

50 Salem Street
Building B
Lynnfield, MA USA 01940
Phone: 617-338-2545
Fax: 617-261-3864
E-mail: info@velocityep.com
Website: www.velocityep.com

Management and Staff

Barney Corning, Managing Director
David Vogel, Managing Director
Jeffrey Vogel, Managing Director
Samuel Foster, Managing Director

Type of Firm

Private Equity Firm

Association Membership

Natl Assoc of Small Bus. Inv. Co (NASBIC)

Project Preferences

Type of Financing Preferred:
Second Stage Financing
Early Stage
Expansion
First Stage Financing
Special Situation

Size of Investments Considered:
Min Size of Investment Considered (000s): $300
Max Size of Investment Considered (000s): $1,500

Geographical Preferences

United States Preferences:
Northeast
D. of Columbia
New York

Industry Preferences

In Communications prefer:
Communications and Media
Telecommunications
Wireless Communications
Data Communications

In Computer Software prefer:
Software
Systems Software
Applications Software

In Internet Specific prefer:
E-Commerce Technology
Internet

In Computer Other prefer:
Computer Related

In Semiconductor/Electr prefer:
Electronics
Semiconductor
Controllers and Sensors
Sensors

In Medical/Health prefer:
Diagnostic Test Products

In Industrial/Energy prefer:
Industrial Products
Advanced Materials
Factory Automation
Process Control

In Manufact. prefer:
Manufacturing

Additional Information

Year Founded: 2001
Capital Under Management: $15,600,000
Current Activity Level : Actively seeking new investments

VELOCITY VENTURE CAPITAL LLC

101 Parkshore Drive
Suite 100
Folsom, CA USA 95630
Phone: 916-608-7996
Fax: 916-404-5098
E-mail: info@velocityvc.com
Website: www.velocityvc.com

Management and Staff

Farid Dibachi, General Partner
Jacob Jorgensen, General Partner

Type of Firm

Private Equity Firm

Association Membership

National Venture Capital Association - USA (NVCA)

Project Preferences

Type of Financing Preferred:
Early Stage
Seed

Size of Investments Considered:
Min Size of Investment Considered (000s): $5,000
Max Size of Investment Considered (000s): $20,000

Geographical Preferences

United States Preferences:
Northern California
All U.S.

Industry Preferences

In Communications prefer:
Wireless Communications
Data Communications

In Computer Software prefer:
Software

In Internet Specific prefer:
Internet

In Semiconductor/Electr prefer:
Semiconductor

In Medical/Health prefer:
Medical Products

In Industrial/Energy prefer:
Energy

Additional Information

Name of Most Recent Fund: Velocity VC Partners III
Most Recent Fund Was Raised: 06/30/2008
Year Founded: 2005
Capital Under Management: $28,000,000
Current Activity Level : Actively seeking new investments

VENCAP INTERNATIONAL PLC

King Charles House
Park End Street
Oxford, United Kingdom OX1 1JD
Phone: 44-1865-799-300
Fax: 44-1865-799-301
E-mail: info@vencapintl.com
Website: www.vencapintl.com

Management and Staff

Michael Ashall, Chairman & CEO

Type of Firm

Private Equity Firm

Project Preferences

Type of Financing Preferred:
Fund of Funds
Balanced

Geographical Preferences

International Preferences:
Western Europe
All International

Additional Information

Year Founded: 1994
Current Activity Level : Making few, if any, new investments

VENDAGES

163 Willow Farm Lane
Aurora, Canada L4G 6K5
Phone: 905-726-1173

Management and Staff

Rod Munro, President

Type of Firm

Private Equity Firm

Additional Information

Year Founded: 2009
Current Activity Level : Actively seeking new investments

VENESIS LIMITED

Medius House
2 Sheraton Street
London, United Kingdom W1F 8BH
Phone: 44-870-366-5299
E-mail: info@venesis.com
Website: www.venesis.com

Type of Firm

Private Equity Firm

Project Preferences

Type of Financing Preferred:
Early Stage
Balanced
Seed
First Stage Financing
Startup

Geographical Preferences

International Preferences:
United Kingdom
Europe

Industry Preferences

In Communications prefer:
Wireless Communications

In Biotechnology prefer:
Biotechnology

Additional Information

Year Founded: 2005
Current Activity Level : Actively seeking new investments

VENFIN LIMITED

25 Quantum Street
Techno Park
Stellenbosch, South Africa 7600
Phone: 27-21-888-3200
Fax: 27-21-880-1397
E-mail: info@venfin.com
Website: www.venfin.com

Management and Staff

Josua Malherbe, Chief Executive Officer

Type of Firm

Private Equity Firm

Association Membership

South African Venture Capital Association (SAVCA)

Project Preferences

Type of Financing Preferred:
Early Stage

Geographical Preferences

International Preferences:
South Africa
Africa

Industry Preferences

In Communications prefer:
Commercial Communications

Additional Information

Year Founded: 2000
Capital Under Management: $7,000,000
Current Activity Level : Actively seeking new investments

VENGLOBAL CAPITAL

19450 Stevens Creek Boulevard
Suite 600
Cupertino, CA USA 95014
Phone: 408-861-1035
Fax: 408-861-1150
Website: www.venglobal.com

Management and Staff

Gary Cheng, General Partner
James Lung, General Partner
Phil Mak, General Partner

Type of Firm

Private Equity Firm

Project Preferences

Role in Financing:
Prefer role as deal originator but will also invest in deals created by others

Type of Financing Preferred:
Second Stage Financing
Early Stage
Seed
First Stage Financing

Geographical Preferences

United States Preferences:
West Coast

Industry Focus

(% based on actual investment)

Semiconductors/Other Elect.	38.0%
Computer Software and Services	27.7%
Communications and Media	20.7%
Medical/Health	6.1%
Internet Specific	4.8%
Computer Hardware	2.8%

Additional Information

Year Founded: 1997
Capital Under Management: $20,000,000
Current Activity Level : Actively seeking new investments
Method of Compensation: Return on investment is of primary concern, do not charge fees

---

VENGROW CORPORATE FINANCE AG

Hardstrasse 73
Wettingen, Switzerland 5430
Phone: 41-56-200-0850
Fax: 41-56-200-0859
E-mail: office@vengrow.com
Website: www.vengrow.com

Other Offices

4901 Tamiami Trail North
Naples, FL USA 34103

Institutstrasse 23
Munich, Germany 81241

Esplanade 6
Hamburg, Germany 20354

Leutschenstrasse 1
Freienbach, Switzerland 8807

Management and Staff

Andreas Buenter, Managing Partner
Hans-Peter Vogt, Principal

Type of Firm

Private Equity Firm

Project Preferences

Type of Financing Preferred:
Mezzanine
Balanced

Geographical Preferences

International Preferences:
Switzerland
Germany

Industry Preferences

In Industrial/Energy prefer:
Industrial Products

In Business Serv. prefer:
Services

Additional Information
Year Founded: 2004
Current Activity Level : Actively seeking new investments

VENGROWTH CAPITAL FUNDS
145 Wellington Street West
Suite 200
Toronto, Canada M5J 1H8
Phone: 416-971-6656
Fax: 416-971-6519
E-mail: info@vengrowth.com
Website: www.vengrowth.com

Management and Staff
Graham McBride, General Partner
Graham Matthews, General Partner
Jeffrey Courtney, General Partner
Luc E.J. Marengere, Managing General Partner
Patrick DiPietro, Managing General Partner
Peter Carrescia, General Partner
Timothy Lee, General Partner

Type of Firm
Private Equity Firm

Association Membership
Canadian Venture Capital Association

Project Preferences

Role in Financing:
Prefer role as deal originator but will also invest in deals created by others

Type of Financing Preferred:
Leveraged Buyout
Early Stage
Mezzanine
Balanced
Later Stage

Size of Investments Considered:
Min Size of Investment Considered (000s): $1,000
Max Size of Investment Considered: No Limit

Geographical Preferences

Canadian Preferences:
All Canada
Ontario

Industry Preferences

In Biotechnology prefer:
Biotechnology

In Medical/Health prefer:
Medical/Health

In Business Serv. prefer:
Services

In Manufact. prefer:
Manufacturing

Additional Information
Name of Most Recent Fund: VG Mezzanine I Limited Partnership
Most Recent Fund Was Raised: 02/01/2005
Year Founded: 1982
Capital Under Management: $700,000,000
Current Activity Level : Actively seeking new investments
Method of Compensation: Return on investment is of primary concern, do not charge fees

---

VENQUEST CAPITAL PARTNERS
2001 Bryan Street
Suite 1965
Dallas, TX USA 75201
Phone: 214-978-4640
Fax: 214-978-4646
Website: www.venquestcapital.com

Management and Staff
David Smartt, Managing Partner
Paul Bureau, Managing Partner

Type of Firm
Private Equity Firm

Project Preferences

Type of Financing Preferred:
Leveraged Buyout
Expansion
Balanced
Management Buyouts
Acquisition
Recapitalizations

Size of Investments Considered:
Min Size of Investment Considered (000s): $1,000
Max Size of Investment Considered (000s): $10,000

Geographical Preferences

United States Preferences:
All U.S.

Industry Preferences

In Business Serv. prefer:
Services
Distribution

In Manufact. prefer:
Manufacturing

Additional Information
Year Founded: 2003
Current Activity Level : Actively seeking new investments

VENROCK ASSOCIATES
3340 Hillview Avenue
Palo Alto, CA USA 94304
Phone: 650-561-9580
Fax: 650-561-9180
Website: www.venrock.com

Other Offices
530 Fifth Avenue
22nd Floor
New York, NY USA 10036
Phone: 212-444-4100
Fax: 212-444-4101

4 Hasadnaot Street
Herzelya Pituach, Israel 46733
Phone: 972-9951-1570
Fax: 972-9951-1578

55 Cambridge Parkway
Suite 100
Cambridge, MA USA 02142
Phone: 617-995-2000
Fax: 617-995-2001

Management and Staff
Anders Hove, Partner
Anthony Evnin, General Partner
Anthony Sun, General Partner
Brett Teele, Vice President
Brian Ascher, Partner
Bryan Roberts, Partner
Dafina Toncheva, Vice President
David Pakman, Partner
David Beisel, Vice President
David Shaw, Partner
Dev Khare, Vice President
Fred Aslan, Vice President
Gur Roshwalb, Vice President
Jocelyne Cooke, Vice President
Ken Song, Vice President
Matthew Nordan, Vice President
Matthew Trevithick, Partner
Michael Tyrrell, Partner
Michael Broooks, Partner
Modassir Choudhry, Vice President
Neeraj Choubey, Vice President
Ohad Finkelstein, Venture Partner
Ray Rothrock, Partner
Richard Bradshaw, Partner

Steven Goldby, Partner
William Rastetter, Partner

Type of Firm

Private Equity Firm

Association Membership

Western Association of Venture Capitalists (WAVC)
National Venture Capital Association - USA (NVCA)

Project Preferences

Role in Financing:

Prefer role as deal originator but will also invest in deals created by others

Type of Financing Preferred:

Second Stage Financing
Early Stage
Start-up Financing
Public Companies
Later Stage
Seed
Open Market
First Stage Financing
Startup
Private Placement

Size of Investments Considered:

Min Size of Investment Considered (000s): $1,000
Max Size of Investment Considered (000s): $25,000

Geographical Preferences

United States Preferences:

All U.S.

Industry Focus

(% based on actual investment)

Computer Software and Services	20.1%
Internet Specific	17.2%
Biotechnology	15.9%
Communications and Media	15.6%
Medical/Health	13.1%
Semiconductors/Other Elect.	10.0%
Industrial/Energy	3.1%
Computer Hardware	2.9%
Other Products	1.3%
Consumer Related	0.8%

Additional Information

Year Founded: 1969
Capital Under Management: $2,300,000,000
Current Activity Level : Actively seeking new investments
Method of Compensation: Return on investment is of primary concern, do not charge fees

VENTACC BETEILIGUNGS- UND BERATUNGS GMBH

Fischhof 3
Vienna, Austria 1010
Phone: 43-1537-030
Fax: 43-15370-3130
E-mail: contact@ventacc.com
Website: www.ventacc.com

Management and Staff

Florian Vitus Dietz, Partner
Stephan Schuster, Partner

Type of Firm

Private Equity Firm

Project Preferences

Type of Financing Preferred:

Expansion
Generalist PE
Seed
Startup

Geographical Preferences

International Preferences:

Europe
Austria

Additional Information

Year Founded: 2001
Current Activity Level : Actively seeking new investments

VENTANA BETEILIGUNGS-GESELLSCHAFT GMBH

Prinz Eugen Strasse 30/5
Vienna, Austria 1040
Phone: 431-512-99-58
Fax: 431-512-99-5822
Website: www.ventana.at

Type of Firm

Private Equity Firm

Additional Information

Year Founded: 2000
Current Activity Level : Actively seeking new investments

VENTANA CAPITAL MANAGEMENT, INC

31473 Rancho Viejo Road
Suite 203
San Juan Capistrano, CA USA 92675
Phone: 949-481-4200
Fax: 949-481-4440
E-mail: ventana@ventanaglobal.com
Website: www.ventanaglobal.com

Other Offices

Avenida Loma de la Palma 275
Suite Two
Mexico City, Mexico 05100
Phone: 52-5-259-4660
Fax: 52-5-259-5099

Rio Vista Towers
8880 Rio San Diego Drive
San Diego, CA USA 92108
Phone: 619-291-2757
Fax: 619-295-0189

Management and Staff

Allen Bah, Venture Partner
Barry Toyonaga, Managing Director
Brantley Haigh, Principal
C. Ian Sym-Smith, Venture Partner
Cyndi Abee, Chief Financial Officer
Ed Berkey, Managing Director
Fred Thiel, Venture Partner
Robert Tufts, Venture Partner

Type of Firm

Private Equity Firm

Association Membership

National Venture Capital Association - USA (NVCA)

Project Preferences

Role in Financing:

Will function either as deal originator or investor in deals created by others

Type of Financing Preferred:

Early Stage

Size of Investments Considered:

Min Size of Investment Considered (000s): $1,000
Max Size of Investment Considered: No Limit

Geographical Preferences

United States Preferences:

Southern California

Industry Preferences

In Communications prefer:

Telecommunications
Wireless Communications

In Semiconductor/Electr prefer:

Semiconductor
Micro-Processing
Controllers and Sensors
Sensors

In Biotechnology prefer:

Human Biotechnology
Biosensors

In Medical/Health prefer:

Pharmaceuticals

Additional Information

Name of Most Recent Fund: Technology Gateway Partnership II
Most Recent Fund Was Raised: 01/01/2002
Year Founded: 1984
Capital Under Management: $82,000,000
Current Activity Level : Actively seeking new investments
Method of Compensation: Return on investment is of primary concern, do not charge fees

VENTECH S.A.

5/7 rue de Monttessuy
Cedex 07
Paris, France 75007
Phone: 33-1-5819-2150
Fax: 33-1-5819-2160
E-mail: contact@ventechvc.com
Website: www.ventechvc.com

Management and Staff

Alain Maiore, General Partner
Eric Huet, General Partner
Jean Bourcereau, General Partner
Laurent Assaraf, Principal
Mounia Chaoui, General Partner

Type of Firm

Bank Affiliated

Association Membership

French Venture Capital Association (AFIC)
European Private Equity and Venture Capital Assoc.

Project Preferences

Role in Financing:
Prefer role as deal originator but will also invest in deals created by others

Type of Financing Preferred:
Fund of Funds
Early Stage
Seed
Startup

Size of Investments Considered:
Min Size of Investment Considered (000s): $1,150
Max Size of Investment Considered (000s): $9,200

Geographical Preferences

United States Preferences:
All U.S.

International Preferences:
Switzerland
Europe
Scandanavia/Nordic Region
Israel
Germany
Asia
France

Industry Preferences

In Communications prefer:
Telecommunications
Other Communication Prod.

In Computer Software prefer:
Software

In Internet Specific prefer:
Internet

In Computer Other prefer:
Computer Related

In Semiconductor/Electr prefer:
Electronics
Electronic Components

In Biotechnology prefer:
Biotechnology

In Business Serv. prefer:
Services

Additional Information

Year Founded: 1998
Capital Under Management: $455,100,000
Current Activity Level : Actively seeking new investments

VENTEGIS CAPITAL AG

Kurfuerstendamm 119
Berlin, Germany 10711
Phone: 49-30-890-21180
Fax: 49-30-890-21189
E-mail: info@ventegis-capital.de
Website: www.ventegis-capital.de

Type of Firm

Private Equity Firm

Project Preferences

Type of Financing Preferred:
Expansion
Seed
Startup

Geographical Preferences

International Preferences:
Europe
Germany

Industry Preferences

In Communications prefer:
Communications and Media

In Biotechnology prefer:
Biotechnology

In Medical/Health prefer:
Medical/Health

Additional Information

Year Founded: 1996
Capital Under Management: $31,500,000
Current Activity Level : Actively seeking new investments

VENTIZZ CAPITAL PARTNERS ADVISORY AG

Graf-Adolf-Strasse 18
Duesseldorf, Germany 40212
Phone: 49-211-86286910
Fax: 49-211-86286977
E-mail: info@ventizz.de
Website: www.ventizz.de

Management and Staff

Helmut Vorndran, General Partner
Peter Levin, Venture Partner
Reinhard Loechner, Managing Partner
Willi Mannheims, Managing Partner

Type of Firm

Private Equity Firm

Project Preferences

Type of Financing Preferred:
Leveraged Buyout
Early Stage
Expansion
Startup
Acquisition

Size of Investments Considered:
Min Size of Investment Considered (000s): $500
Max Size of Investment Considered (000s): $5,000

Geographical Preferences

International Preferences:
Europe
Switzerland
Austria
Germany

Industry Preferences

In Communications prefer:
Telecommunications

In Internet Specific prefer:
Internet

In Semiconductor/Electr prefer:
Electronics

In Biotechnology prefer:
Biotechnology

In Medical/Health prefer:
Medical/Health

In Industrial/Energy prefer:
Industrial Products

In Business Serv. prefer:
Media

Additional Information

Year Founded: 1999
Capital Under Management: $22,000,000
Current Activity Level : Actively seeking new investments

VENTURE ASSOCIATES PARTNERS LLC

355 Sweetbriar Road
Memphis, TN USA 38120
Phone: 901-763-1434
Fax: 901-763-1428
E-mail: email@venture-associates.com
Website: www.venture-associates.com

Management and Staff
Burton Weil, President, CEO, Chairman

Type of Firm
Private Equity Firm

Project Preferences

Role in Financing:
Prefer role as deal originator

Type of Financing Preferred:
Leveraged Buyout
Control-block Purchases
Generalist PE
Turnaround
Management Buyouts
Acquisition
Industry Rollups
Recapitalizations

Size of Investments Considered:
Min Size of Investment Considered (000s): $20,000
Max Size of Investment Considered (000s): $200,000

Geographical Preferences

International Preferences:
Mexico

Industry Preferences

In Semiconductor/Electr prefer:
Electronic Components

In Transportation prefer:
Aerospace

In Manufact. prefer:
Manufacturing

Additional Information
Year Founded: 1985
Current Activity Level : Actively seeking new investments
Method of Compensation: Return on investment is of primary concern, do not charge fees

---

VENTURE ASSOCIATES, LTD.

4950 East Evans Street
Suite 105
Denver, CO USA 80222
Phone: 303-758-8710
Fax: 303-758-8747
Website: www.venturea.com

Other Offices
4811 Trailwood Way
Springfield, MO USA 65804
Phone: 417-882-9218

Management and Staff
James Arkebauer, President

Type of Firm
Private Equity Firm

Project Preferences

Role in Financing:
Prefer role as deal originator but will also invest in deals created by others

Type of Financing Preferred:
Second Stage Financing
Leveraged Buyout
Early Stage
Expansion
Generalist PE
Turnaround
Seed
First Stage Financing
Acquisition
Private Placement
Startup
Recapitalizations

Size of Investments Considered:
Min Size of Investment Considered (000s): $100
Max Size of Investment Considered (000s): $10,000

Additional Information
Year Founded: 1982
Capital Under Management: $20,000,000
Current Activity Level : Actively seeking new investments
Method of Compensation: Return on invest. most important, but chg. closing fees, service fees, etc.

VENTURE CAPITAL BANK (VCBANK)

Building 247
Road 1704, Block 317
Bahrain, Utd. Arab Em.
Phone: 973-17-518-888
Fax: 973-17-518-880
E-mail: info@VC-Bank.com
Website: www.vc-bank.com

Type of Firm
Private Equity Firm

Project Preferences

Type of Financing Preferred:
Balanced
Startup

Geographical Preferences

International Preferences:
Bahrain
Oman
Qatar
Middle East
Saudi Arabia
Africa

Industry Preferences

In Financial Services prefer:
Real Estate

In Business Serv. prefer:
Consulting Services

Additional Information
Year Founded: 2005
Current Activity Level : Actively seeking new investments

VENTURE CAPITAL FUND OF NEW ENGLAND, THE

30 Washington Street
Wellesley, MA USA 02481
Phone: 781-431-8400
Fax: 781-237-6578
E-mail: inquiries@vcfne.com
Website: www.vcfne.com

Management and Staff
Carl Novotny, Managing Director
Edward Stewart, Managing Director
George Aggouras, Chief Financial Officer
Gordon Penman, Managing Director
Harry Healer, Managing Director
Kevin Dougherty, Managing Director

Type of Firm
Private Equity Firm

Association Membership
Natl Assoc of Small Bus. Inv. Co (NASBIC)

Project Preferences

Role in Financing:
Prefer role as deal originator

Type of Financing Preferred:
Early Stage
First Stage Financing
Startup

Size of Investments Considered:
Min Size of Investment Considered (000s): $1,000
Max Size of Investment Considered (000s): $3,500

Geographical Preferences

United States Preferences:
Mid Atlantic
Northeast

Industry Focus
(% based on actual investment)

Computer Software and Services	17.2%
Internet Specific	13.6%
Communications and Media	12.5%
Semiconductors/Other Elect.	12.0%
Industrial/Energy	11.4%
Medical/Health	10.0%
Other Products	7.7%
Computer Hardware	6.7%

Consumer Related 6.1%
Biotechnology 2.6%

Additional Information

Name of Most Recent Fund: Venture Capital Fund of New England IV, L.P.
Most Recent Fund Was Raised: 07/31/2001
Year Founded: 1981
Capital Under Management: $81,000,000
Current Activity Level : Actively seeking new investments
Method of Compensation: Return on investment is of primary concern, do not charge fees

---

VENTURE CAPITAL PARTNERS PTY., LTD.

Level 13
26, O'Connell Street
Sydney, Australia 2000
Phone: 612-8223-6400
Fax: 612-8223-6401
E-mail: vcp@vcp.com.au
Website: www.vcp.com.au

Management and Staff

David Gemmell, Managing Director
John O Farrell, Managing Director

Type of Firm

Bank Affiliated

Project Preferences

Role in Financing:

Will function either as deal originator or investor in deals created by others

Type of Financing Preferred:

Second Stage Financing
Leveraged Buyout
Generalist PE
Expansion
Management Buyouts
First Stage Financing
Acquisition
Special Situation
Distressed Debt
Recapitalizations

Size of Investments Considered:

Min Size of Investment Considered (000s): $349
Max Size of Investment Considered (000s): $3,142

Geographical Preferences

International Preferences:

Australia

Additional Information

Name of Most Recent Fund: Venture Capital Partners Number 1 Fund
Most Recent Fund Was Raised: 06/01/2000
Year Founded: 1997
Capital Under Management: $15,100,000
Current Activity Level : Actively seeking new investments
Method of Compensation: Return on investment is of primary concern, do not charge fees

---

VENTURE CORPORATION OF AUSTRALIA PTY LTD.

Unit 2, 92 Pacific Highway
Roseville, Australia 2069
Phone: 612-9413-1944
Fax: 612-9413-9618
E-mail: enquiries@venturecorp.com.au
Website: www.venturecorp.com.au

Management and Staff

John Paterson, Managing Director

Type of Firm

Private Equity Firm

Association Membership

Austrian PE and Venture Capital Association (AVCO)

Project Preferences

Role in Financing:

Prefer role as deal originator

Type of Financing Preferred:

Startup

Geographical Preferences

International Preferences:

Pacific Rim

Industry Preferences

In Computer Software prefer:

Computer Services
Software

In Manufact. prefer:

Manufacturing

Additional Information

Year Founded: 1984
Capital Under Management: $3,900,000
Current Activity Level : Actively seeking new investments

VENTURE INCUBATOR AG (AKA: VI PARTNERS AG)

Baarerstrasse 86
Postfach 2146
Zug, Switzerland 6302
Phone: 41-41-729-0000
Fax: 41-41-729-0001
E-mail: info@vipartners.ch
Website: www.vipartners.ch

Management and Staff

Alain Nicod, Managing Partner
Arnd Kaltofen, General Partner
Daniel Gutenberg, General Partner
Diego Braguglia, General Partner

Type of Firm

Private Equity Firm

Association Membership

Swiss Venture Capital Association (SECA)

Project Preferences

Type of Financing Preferred:

Early Stage
Startup

Size of Investments Considered:

Min Size of Investment Considered (000s): $602
Max Size of Investment Considered (000s): $1,805

Geographical Preferences

International Preferences:

Switzerland

Industry Preferences

In Communications prefer:

Communications and Media

In Medical/Health prefer:

Medical/Health

Additional Information

Year Founded: 2001
Current Activity Level : Actively seeking new investments

VENTURE INVESTMENT ASSOCIATES

88 Main Street
Peapack, NJ USA 07977
Phone: 908-532-0020
Fax: 908-532-0040
E-mail: office@viafunds.com
Website: www.viafunds.com

Management and Staff

Clifford Gilman, Managing Director
Jason Andris, Managing Director
Jennifer Ayer, Principal
Stathis Andris, President, Founder

Type of Firm

Private Equity Advisor or Fund of Funds

Project Preferences

Type of Financing Preferred:

Fund of Funds
Leveraged Buyout
Early Stage
Fund of Funds of Second

Size of Investments Considered:

Min Size of Investment Considered (000s): $5,000
Max Size of Investment Considered (000s): $30,000

Geographical Preferences

United States Preferences:
All U.S.

Industry Preferences

In Communications prefer:
Communications and Media

In Medical/Health prefer:
Medical/Health

In Industrial/Energy prefer:
Energy

Additional Information

Year Founded: 1993
Capital Under Management: $950,000,000
Current Activity Level : Actively seeking new investments

VENTURE INVESTORS LLC

University Research Park
505 South Rosa Road, Suite 201
Madison, WI USA 53719
Phone: 608-441-2700
Fax: 608-441-2727
E-mail: venture@ventureinvestors.com
Website: www.ventureinvestors.com

Other Offices

201 South Main Street
Suite 900
Ann Arbor, MI USA 48104
Phone: 734-274-2904

Management and Staff

George Arida, Managing Director
James Adox, Managing Director
John Neis, Managing Director
Kevin McPherson, Chief Financial Officer
Paul Weiss, Managing Director
Roger Ganser, Managing Partner
Scott Button, Managing Director
Winslow Sargeant, Managing Director

Type of Firm

Private Equity Firm

Association Membership

National Venture Capital Association - USA (NVCA)

Project Preferences

Role in Financing:
Will function either as deal originator or investor in deals created by others

Type of Financing Preferred:
Early Stage
Seed

Size of Investments Considered:
Min Size of Investment Considered (000s): $300
Max Size of Investment Considered (000s): $2,500

Geographical Preferences

United States Preferences:
Midwest
Wisconsin

Industry Focus

(% based on actual investment)

Medical/Health	36.7%
Biotechnology	29.2%
Other Products	11.0%
Industrial/Energy	8.4%
Computer Software and Services	4.3%
Semiconductors/Other Elect.	3.6%
Consumer Related	2.5%
Internet Specific	1.8%
Communications and Media	1.4%
Computer Hardware	1.1%

Additional Information

Name of Most Recent Fund: Venture Investors Early Stage Fund IV, L.P.
Most Recent Fund Was Raised: 06/02/2006
Year Founded: 1982
Capital Under Management: $200,000,000
Current Activity Level : Actively seeking new investments
Method of Compensation: Return on investment is of primary concern, do not charge fees

---

VENTURE MECHANICS, LLC

7250 92nd Avenue SE
Mercer Island, WA USA 98040
Website: www.venturemechanics.com

Management and Staff

Ron Wiener, Managing Director

Type of Firm

Private Equity Firm

Project Preferences

Type of Financing Preferred:
Early Stage
Balanced

Geographical Preferences

United States Preferences:
All U.S.

Additional Information

Year Founded: 2007
Current Activity Level : Actively seeking new investments

VENTURE PARTNERS AG

Bodmerstrasse 7
Zurich, Switzerland 8027
Phone: 41-1-206-5080
Fax: 41-1-206-5090
E-mail: info@venturepartners.ch
Website: www.venturepartners.ch

Management and Staff

Andrea Wikart, Partner
Massimo Lattmann, Partner

Type of Firm

Private Equity Firm

Association Membership

Swiss Venture Capital Association (SECA)
European Private Equity and Venture Capital Assoc.

Project Preferences

Type of Financing Preferred:
Early Stage
Expansion
Balanced
Start-up Financing
Seed

Size of Investments Considered:
Min Size of Investment Considered (000s): $471
Max Size of Investment Considered (000s): $9,416

Geographical Preferences

United States Preferences:
All U.S.

International Preferences:
Europe

Industry Focus

(% based on actual investment)

Internet Specific	40.8%
Computer Software and Services	25.7%
Communications and Media	10.2%
Biotechnology	7.3%
Medical/Health	5.1%
Computer Hardware	4.9%
Industrial/Energy	4.0%
Consumer Related	1.5%
Other Products	0.4%

Additional Information

Year Founded: 1997
Capital Under Management: $107,600,000
Current Activity Level : Actively seeking new investments

VENTURE PARTNERS BOTSWANA

1st Floor, Block B Lot 50676
Fairgrounds Office Park
Gaborone, Botswana 00304
Phone: 267-31-81-012
Fax: 267-31-81-038
E-mail: enquiries@venture-p.com
Website: www.venture-p.com

Type of Firm

Private Equity Firm

Association Membership
South African Venture Capital Association (SAVCA)
European Private Equity and Venture Capital Assoc.
African Venture Capital Association (AVCA)

Project Preferences

Type of Financing Preferred:
Generalist PE
Early Stage
Balanced

Size of Investments Considered:
Min Size of Investment Considered (000s): $92
Max Size of Investment Considered (000s): $5,505

Geographical Preferences

International Preferences:
Angola
Switzerland
Swaziland
Zambia
Botswana
Namibia
Lesotho
Mozambique
South Africa

Industry Preferences

In Communications prefer:
Communications and Media
Commercial Communications
Other Communication Prod.

In Biotechnology prefer:
Agricultural/Animal Bio.

In Medical/Health prefer:
Medical/Health

In Consumer Related prefer:
Consumer
Retail
Consumer Products
Consumer Services
Education Related

In Transportation prefer:
Transportation

In Financial Services prefer:
Financial Services

In Manufact. prefer:
Manufacturing

In Other prefer:
Women/Minority-Owned Bus.

Additional Information
Year Founded: 2003
Capital Under Management: $36,700,000
Current Activity Level : Actively seeking new investments

VENTURE TDF PTE LTD.
19A Ann Siang Road
Singapore, Singapore 069699
Phone: 65-6236-6920
Fax: 65-6887-0535
E-mail: info_enquiry@venturetdf.com
Website: www.venturetdf.com

Other Offices
Unit 2505, K.WAH Center
1010 Huaihai Zhong Road
Shanghai, China 200031
Phone: 86-21-5467-0500
Fax: 86-21-5404-7557

Management and Staff
Forrest Zhong, Partner

Type of Firm
Private Equity Firm

Project Preferences

Type of Financing Preferred:
Early Stage
Expansion
Balanced
Start-up Financing
Seed

Size of Investments Considered:
Min Size of Investment Considered (000s): $500
Max Size of Investment Considered (000s): $3,000

Geographical Preferences

United States Preferences:
All U.S.

International Preferences:
China
Hong Kong
Israel
Singapore
Asia

Industry Preferences

In Communications prefer:
Telecommunications

In Internet Specific prefer:
Internet

In Computer Other prefer:
Computer Related

In Semiconductor/Electr prefer:
Electronics
Semiconductor

In Medical/Health prefer:
Medical/Health

In Financial Services prefer:
Investment Groups
Financial Services

Additional Information
Year Founded: 1995
Capital Under Management: $350,000,000
Current Activity Level : Actively seeking new investments

VENTUREAST (FKA: APIDC VENTURE CAPITAL LIMITED)
20B ASCI College Park
Road No. 3, Banjara Hills
Hyderabad, India 500 034
Phone: 91-40-2355-0481
Fax: 91-40-2355-0487
E-mail: info@ventureast.net
Website: www.ventureast.net

Other Offices
5B, Ramachandra Ave,Seethammal Colony
First Main Road, Alwarpet
Chennai, India 600 018
Phone: 91-44-2432-9864
Fax: 91-44-2432-9865

Management and Staff
A. Ramesh, General Partner
Aditya Kapil, Principal
Anuradha Ramachandaran, Principal
Bobba Venkatadari, General Partner
C. Shekhar Kundur, General Partner
M. Krishna Meka, Principal
Ned Olivier, Venture Partner
Raghuveer Mendu, General Partner
Ramesh Alur, General Partner
Sarath Naru, Managing Partner
Siddhartha Das, General Partner

Type of Firm
Corporate PE/Venture

Association Membership
Indian Venture Capital Association (IVCA)

Project Preferences

Role in Financing:
Prefer role as deal originator but will also invest in deals created by others

Type of Financing Preferred:
Expansion
Early Stage
Seed

Size of Investments Considered:
Min Size of Investment Considered (000s): $1,000
Max Size of Investment Considered (000s): $10,000

Geographical Preferences

United States Preferences:
All U.S.

International Preferences:
India
Europe
Asia

Industry Preferences

In Communications prefer:
Communications and Media
Commercial Communications
Telecommunications
Wireless Communications

In Computer Software prefer:
Computer Services
Software

In Internet Specific prefer:
Internet

In Computer Other prefer:
Computer Related

In Semiconductor/Electr prefer:
Electronic Components

In Biotechnology prefer:
Biotechnology
Human Biotechnology
Agricultural/Animal Bio.
Industrial Biotechnology

In Medical/Health prefer:
Medical/Health
Health Services
Pharmaceuticals

In Consumer Related prefer:
Consumer
Retail
Food/Beverage

In Industrial/Energy prefer:
Energy
Alternative Energy
Energy Conservation Relat
Industrial Products
Materials
Environmental Related

In Transportation prefer:
Transportation

In Financial Services prefer:
Financial Services
Insurance

In Business Serv. prefer:
Services
Distribution

In Manufact. prefer:
Manufacturing

In Agr/Forestr/Fish prefer:
Agriculture related

Additional Information
Year Founded: 1990
Capital Under Management: $150,000,000
Current Activity Level : Actively seeking new investments
Method of Compensation: Return on invest. most important, but chg. closing fees, service fees, etc.

VENTUREBAY
Lambroekstraat 5
Diegem, Belgium 1831
Phone: 32-2-719-0033
Fax: 32-2-719-0035
E-mail: info@venturebay.com

Management and Staff
Danny Lein, Managing Partner
Paul Janssens, Managing Partner

Type of Firm
Incubator/Development Program

Project Preferences

Type of Financing Preferred:
Early Stage
Seed
Startup

Geographical Preferences

International Preferences:
Europe
Belgium

Industry Preferences

In Internet Specific prefer:
Internet

Additional Information
Year Founded: 1999
Capital Under Management: $1,200,000
Current Activity Level : Actively seeking new investments

VENTUREFONDET
Box 35 Lindeberg Gard
Oslo, Norway 1007
Phone: 47-90-912-409

Type of Firm
Private Equity Firm

Association Membership
Norwegian Venture Capital Association

Project Preferences

Type of Financing Preferred:
Balanced

Geographical Preferences

International Preferences:
Europe
Norway

Additional Information
Year Founded: 2004
Current Activity Level : Actively seeking new investments

VENTUREHOUSE GROUP
509 7th Street, NorthWest
Washington, DC USA 20004
Phone: 202-654-7001
Fax: 202-654-7070
E-mail: info@venturehousegroup.com
Website: www.venturehousegroup.com

Other Offices
1750 Tysons Boulevard
Suite 400
McLean, VA USA 22102
Phone: 703-883-9600
Fax: 703-744-1328

Management and Staff
Mark Ein, Chief Executive Officer

Type of Firm
Private Equity Firm

Association Membership
Mid-Atlantic Venture Association

Project Preferences

Role in Financing:
Prefer role as deal originator but will also invest in deals created by others

Type of Financing Preferred:
Second Stage Financing
Early Stage
Expansion
Balanced
Later Stage
Seed
Management Buyouts
First Stage Financing
Acquisition
Startup

Size of Investments Considered:
Min Size of Investment Considered (000s): $250
Max Size of Investment Considered (000s): $5,000

Geographical Preferences

United States Preferences:
All U.S.

Industry Preferences

In Communications prefer:
Commercial Communications
Telecommunications
Wireless Communications
Data Communications
Satellite Microwave Comm.

In Internet Specific prefer:
Internet
Ecommerce
Web Aggregration/Portals

In Semiconductor/Electr prefer:
Sensors
Laser Related

Fiber Optics

In Business Serv. prefer:
Media

Additional Information

Year Founded: 1999
Capital Under Management: $50,000,000
Current Activity Level : Actively seeking new investments
Method of Compensation: Return on investment is of primary concern, do not charge fees

---

VENTURELABOUR.COM

512 Woolwich Street
Guelph, Canada N1H 3X7
Phone: 514-763-9660
Fax: 514-837-9883
Website: www.venturelabour.com

Management and Staff

Graham Dyer, Chief Operating Officer

Type of Firm

Private Equity Firm

Additional Information

Year Founded: 1998
Current Activity Level : Actively seeking new investments

VENTURELINK FUNDS (FKA:VL ADVISORS LP, SKYLON CAPITAL)

801-1 Richmond Street West
Toronto, Canada M5J 2T3
Phone: 416-681-6676
Fax: 416-681-6661
E-mail: info@venturelinkfunds.com
Website: www.venturelinkfunds.com

Management and Staff

John Varghese, Managing Partner

Type of Firm

Private Equity Firm

Project Preferences

Type of Financing Preferred:
Balanced
Later Stage

Geographical Preferences

Canadian Preferences:
All Canada

Industry Preferences

In Communications prefer:
Telecommunications
Wireless Communications

In Computer Software prefer:
Software

In Semiconductor/Electr prefer:
Fiber Optics

In Biotechnology prefer:
Biotechnology

Additional Information

Year Founded: 2000
Capital Under Management: $49,800,000
Current Activity Level : Actively seeking new investments

VENTURES AND TRUSTS

5A Adeyemo Alakija
Victoria Island
Lagos, Nigeria
Phone: 234-1-461-6839
Fax: 234-1-461-6995
E-mail: vt@venturesandtrusts.com
Website: www.venturesandtrusts.com

Management and Staff

Femi Akingbe, CEO & Managing Director

Type of Firm

Private Equity Firm

Project Preferences

Type of Financing Preferred:
Balanced

Geographical Preferences

International Preferences:
Nigeria

Additional Information

Year Founded: 2004
Current Activity Level : Actively seeking new investments

VENTURES WEST MANAGEMENT, INC.

1066 West Hastings Street
Suite 2500
Vancouver, Canada V6E 3X1
Phone: 604-688-9495
Fax: 604-687-2145
E-mail: info@ventureswest.com
Website: www.ventureswest.com

Other Offices

20 Adelaide Street East
Suite 1200
Toronto, Canada M5C 2T6
Phone: 416-861-0700
Fax: 416-861-0866

300 March Road
Fourth Floor
Kanata, Canada K2K 2E2
Phone: 613-270-9911
Fax: 613-270-9552

410 22nd Street East
Suite 880
Saskatoon, Canada S7K 5T6
Phone: 306-653-8887
Fax: 306-653-8886

1155 Rene-Levesque Boulevard West
25th floor
Montreal, Canada H3B 2K4
Phone: 514-395-0777
Fax: 514-395-8757

Management and Staff

Barry Gekiere, General Partner
Chris Laird, Vice President
David Berkowitz, General Partner
Kenneth Galbraith, General Partner
Maha Katabi, Vice President
Marc Wickham, Vice President
Paul Kedrosky, Venture Partner
Robin Axon, Partner
Robin Louis, General Partner
Sam Znaimer, General Partner
Ted Anderson, Managing General Partner

Type of Firm

Bank Affiliated

Association Membership

Canadian Venture Capital Association

Project Preferences

Role in Financing:
Prefer role as deal originator but will also invest in deals created by others

Type of Financing Preferred:
Second Stage Financing
Early Stage
Research and Development
Balanced
Start-up Financing
Seed
First Stage Financing

Size of Investments Considered:
Min Size of Investment Considered (000s): $1,000
Max Size of Investment Considered (000s): $9,999

Geographical Preferences

Canadian Preferences:
All Canada

Industry Focus

(% based on actual investment)

Computer Software and Services	23.4%
Communications and Media	21.1%
Biotechnology	16.8%
Medical/Health	11.3%
Industrial/Energy	11.2%

Semiconductors/Other Elect.	8.6%
Internet Specific	5.7%
Other Products	1.7%
Computer Hardware	0.2%

Additional Information

Name of Most Recent Fund: Ventures West 8
Most Recent Fund Was Raised: 11/03/2003
Year Founded: 1968
Capital Under Management: $450,000,000
Current Activity Level : Actively seeking new investments
Method of Compensation: Return on investment is of primary concern, do not charge fees

---

VENTURETECH ALLIANCE LLC

2585 Junction Avenue
San Jose, CA USA 95134
Phone: 408-382-8000
Fax: 408-382-8004
E-mail: info@vtalliance.com
Website: www.vtalliance.com

Other Offices

2821 Second Avenue
Suite 1801
Seattle, WA USA 98121
Phone: 206-441-8080
Fax: 206-441-7373

Number 10, Li-Hsin 6th Road
Hsin-Chu Science-Based Industrial Park
Hsin-Chu, Taiwan 300
Phone: 886-3-666-9800
Fax: 886-3-666-9970

Type of Firm

Investment Management Firm

Project Preferences

Role in Financing:
Prefer role in deals created by others

Type of Financing Preferred:
Early Stage
Seed

Size of Investments Considered:
Min Size of Investment Considered (000s): $500
Max Size of Investment Considered (000s): $5,000

Geographical Preferences

United States Preferences:
All U.S.

Canadian Preferences:
All Canada

International Preferences:
Europe
Asia

Industry Preferences

In Semiconductor/Electr prefer:
Semiconductor

Additional Information

Name of Most Recent Fund: VentureTech Alliance Fund III, L.P.
Most Recent Fund Was Raised: 09/30/2006
Year Founded: 2001
Capital Under Management: $165,000,000
Current Activity Level : Actively seeking new investments
Method of Compensation: Return on investment is of primary concern, do not charge fees

---

VENTURION GROUP, INC.

25 King Street West
Suite 2902
Toronto, Canada M5L 1E2
Phone: 416-703-7800
Fax: 416-703-7039
Website: www.venturiongroup.com

Management and Staff

Douglas Steiner, Managing Director
Joanna Liczyk, Managing Director

Type of Firm

Private Equity Firm

Project Preferences

Type of Financing Preferred:
Expansion
Seed

Geographical Preferences

United States Preferences:
All U.S.

Canadian Preferences:
All Canada

Additional Information

Year Founded: 2002
Current Activity Level : Actively seeking new investments

VENTUROS VENTURES AS

Ruselokkveien 26
PO Box 1508 - Vika
Oslo, Norway N-0117
Phone: 47-23-308-400
Fax: 47-23-308-401
E-mail: mail@venturos.no
Website: www.venturos.no

Other Offices

Gaseholmen Brygge
PO Box 113
Farsund, Norway 4552
Phone: 47-38-399-770
Fax: 47-38-399-710

Management and Staff

Oddvar Aaserud, Chief Executive Officer
Rune Dybesland, Chief Financial Officer

Type of Firm

Private Equity Firm

Association Membership

Norwegian Venture Capital Association
European Private Equity and Venture Capital Assoc.

Project Preferences

Type of Financing Preferred:
Second Stage Financing
Early Stage
Expansion
Startup

Geographical Preferences

International Preferences:
Europe

Industry Preferences

In Communications prefer:
Telecommunications

In Other prefer:
Environment Responsible

Additional Information

Year Founded: 1999
Current Activity Level : Actively seeking new investments

VERAVENTURE AB

Haapaniemenkatu 40
Kuopio, Finland 70111
Phone: 358-20-460-3988
Fax: 358-20-460-3987
E-mail: feedback@veraventure.fi
Website: www.veraventure.fi

Other Offices

Etelaesplanadi 8
Helsinki, Finland 00101
Fax: 358-20-460-3587

Oulu, Asemakatu 37
Oulu, Finland 90100
Fax: 358-20-460-3967

Management and Staff

Leo Houtsonen, Managing Director

Type of Firm

Private Equity Advisor or Fund of Funds

Project Preferences

Type of Financing Preferred:
Fund of Funds

Geographical Preferences

International Preferences:
Finland

Additional Information
Year Founded: 2003
Current Activity Level : Actively seeking new investments

VERAX CAPITAL PARTNERS LLC

90 East Halsey Road
Suite 111
Parsippany, NJ USA 07054
Phone: 973-599-9400
Fax: 973-599-9450
Website: www.veraxcapital.com

Management and Staff
Donald Kelley, Partner
Eric Koza, Partner
Steven Hardek, Partner

Type of Firm
Private Equity Firm

Project Preferences

Type of Financing Preferred:
Leveraged Buyout
Management Buyouts
Special Situation
Recapitalizations

Size of Investments Considered:
Min Size of Investment Considered (000s): $2,000
Max Size of Investment Considered (000s): $15,000

Geographical Preferences

United States Preferences:
All U.S.

Industry Preferences

In Communications prefer:
Telecommunications

In Medical/Health prefer:
Health Services

In Consumer Related prefer:
Consumer Products
Education Related

In Industrial/Energy prefer:
Energy

In Transportation prefer:
Aerospace

In Business Serv. prefer:
Media

Additional Information
Year Founded: 2007
Capital Under Management: $15,500,000
Current Activity Level : Actively seeking new investments

VERDANE CAPITAL (FKA: FOUR SEASONS VENTURE CAPITAL AS)

Vika Atrium
Munkedamsveien 45F
Oslo, Norway NO-0250
Phone: 47-24-137-000
Fax: 47-24-137-001
E-mail: office@verdanecapital.com
Website: www.verdanecapital.com

Other Offices
Birger Jarlsgatan 32 B
Stockholm, Sweden SE-114 29
Phone: 46-8-407-4200
Fax: 46-8-407-4201

Management and Staff
Anders Thuve, Partner
Andreas Teilman, Partner
Arne Handeland, Partner
Arnstein Nordbotten, Partner
Atle Sovik, Partner
Birger Nergaard, Managing Partner
Bjarne Lie, Partner
Goran Strandberg, Partner
Henrik Aspen, Partner
Jorgen Morkved, Chief Financial Officer
Knut Frigaard, Partner
Lars Thoresen, Partner
Per Nordlander, Partner
Peter Gullander, Partner

Type of Firm
Private Equity Firm

Association Membership
Norwegian Venture Capital Association
Swedish Venture Capital Association (SVCA)
European Private Equity and Venture Capital Assoc.

Project Preferences

Role in Financing:
Prefer role as deal originator but will also invest in deals created by others

Type of Financing Preferred:
Second Stage Financing
Leveraged Buyout
Early Stage
Expansion
Balanced
Turnaround
Seed
Startup

Size of Investments Considered:
Min Size of Investment Considered (000s): $1,255
Max Size of Investment Considered (000s): $7,500

Geographical Preferences

International Preferences:
Sweden
Europe
Scandanavia/Nordic Region
Norway
Denmark
All International

Industry Preferences

In Communications prefer:
Telecommunications
Data Communications

In Internet Specific prefer:
Internet

In Computer Other prefer:
Computer Related

In Semiconductor/Electr prefer:
Electronics
Electronic Components

In Medical/Health prefer:
Medical/Health
Diagnostic Test Products

In Consumer Related prefer:
Retail

In Industrial/Energy prefer:
Factory Automation

In Business Serv. prefer:
Services
Media

Additional Information
Year Founded: 1985
Capital Under Management: $220,000,000
Current Activity Level : Actively seeking new investments

VERDEXUS

22 Frederick Street
Suite 800
Waterloo, Canada N2H 6M6
Phone: 519-957-2230
Fax: 519-957-2239
E-mail: canada@verdexus.com
Website: www.verdexus.com

Other Offices
157 Adelaide Street West
Suite 290
Toronto, Canada M5H 4E7
Phone: 416-548-4730
Fax: 416-548-4739

Type of Firm
Private Equity Firm

Additional Information

Year Founded: 2001
Current Activity Level : Actively seeking new investments

VERGE

317 Commercial St. NorthEast
Albuquerque, NM USA 87102
Phone: 505-247-1038
Fax: 505-244-8040
E-mail: info@vergefund.com
Website: www.vergefund.com

Management and Staff

David Durgin, General Partner
H.Ray Radosevich, General Partner
James Higdon, Partner
Ron McPhee, Partner
Thomas Stephenson, General Partner
William Bice, Partner

Type of Firm

Private Equity Firm

Association Membership

National Venture Capital Association - USA (NVCA)

Project Preferences

Type of Financing Preferred:

Start-up Financing
Seed

Size of Investments Considered:

Min Size of Investment Considered (000s): $100
Max Size of Investment Considered (000s): $1,000

Geographical Preferences

United States Preferences:

Rocky Mountain
Southwest

Industry Preferences

In Communications prefer:

Commercial Communications
Telecommunications
Wireless Communications
Data Communications
Other Communication Prod.

In Computer Hardware prefer:

Computer Graphics and Dig

In Computer Software prefer:

Computer Services
Software
Systems Software
Applications Software

In Internet Specific prefer:

E-Commerce Technology
Internet
Ecommerce
Web Aggregration/Portals

In Semiconductor/Electr prefer:

Electronic Components
Semiconductor
Controllers and Sensors
Laser Related
Fiber Optics
Optoelectronics

In Medical/Health prefer:

Medical Diagnostics
Medical Products

In Consumer Related prefer:

Entertainment and Leisure
Sports

In Industrial/Energy prefer:

Energy

In Other prefer:

Environment Responsible

Additional Information

Name of Most Recent Fund: Verge I.5, L.P.
Most Recent Fund Was Raised: 05/01/2006
Year Founded: 2003
Capital Under Management: $20,000,000
Current Activity Level : Actively seeking new investments

VERITAS CAPITAL

590 Madison Avenue
41st Floor
New York, NY USA 10022
Phone: 212-415-6700
Fax: 212-688-9411
E-mail: info@veritascapital.com
Website: www.veritascapital.com

Management and Staff

Brian Gorczynski, Principal
Gail Dady, Principal
James Griffin, Principal
Ramzi Musallam, Principal
Robert McKeon, President, Founder
Thomas Campbell, Partner

Type of Firm

Private Equity Firm

Project Preferences

Type of Financing Preferred:

Leveraged Buyout
Recapitalizations

Geographical Preferences

United States Preferences:

All U.S.

Industry Focus

(% based on actual investment)

Other Products	92.4%
Semiconductors/Other Elect.	4.8%
Industrial/Energy	2.2%
Internet Specific	0.6%

Additional Information

Name of Most Recent Fund: Veritas Capital Fund III, L.P.
Most Recent Fund Was Raised: 08/30/2005
Year Founded: 1992
Capital Under Management: $303,000,000
Current Activity Level : Actively seeking new investments

VERLINVEST SA

18 Place Flagey
Brussels, Belgium 1200
Phone: 32-2-6269-870
Fax: 32-2-6269-878
Website: www.verlinvest.be

Management and Staff

Frederic de Mevius, Managing Director

Type of Firm

Private Equity Firm

Project Preferences

Type of Financing Preferred:

Leveraged Buyout
Generalist PE
Mezzanine
Balanced
Acquisition
Distressed Debt

Size of Investments Considered:

Min Size of Investment Considered (000s): $69,435
Max Size of Investment Considered (000s): $694,348

Geographical Preferences

United States Preferences:

All U.S.

International Preferences:

Europe

Industry Preferences

In Medical/Health prefer:

Health Services

In Consumer Related prefer:

Consumer Products
Consumer Services

Additional Information

Year Founded: 2005
Current Activity Level : Actively seeking new investments

VERMEER CAPITAL PARTNERS

120 Avenue des Champs-Elysees
Paris, France 75008
Phone: 331-4420-0202

Fax: 331-4562-5909
E-mail: info@vermeercapital.fr
Website: www.vermeerprivateequity.com

Management and Staff

Jean-Louis Detry, President
Michel Bon, Partner
Olivier Elmalek, Partner
Pierre Khoury, Partner

Type of Firm

Private Equity Firm

Association Membership

French Venture Capital Association (AFIC)

Project Preferences

Type of Financing Preferred:
Leveraged Buyout
Turnaround

Size of Investments Considered:
Min Size of Investment Considered (000s): $4,684
Max Size of Investment Considered (000s): $23,419

Geographical Preferences

International Preferences:
Europe
France

Industry Preferences

In Consumer Related prefer:
Consumer Products

In Business Serv. prefer:
Services

Additional Information

Year Founded: 2008
Capital Under Management: $117,300,000
Current Activity Level : Actively seeking new investments

VERNON & PARK CAPITAL, L.P.

1751 Lake Cook Road
Suite 350
Deerfield, IL USA 60015
Phone: 847-374-3865
E-mail: contact@vernonpark.com
Website: www.vernonpark.com

Management and Staff

James Ginsburg, Managing Partner

Type of Firm

Private Equity Firm

Additional Information

Year Founded: 2001
Current Activity Level : Actively seeking new investments

VERON INTERNATIONAL

Top Floor
77 Mody Road; Tsimshatsui
Kowloon, Hong Kong

Type of Firm

Private Equity Firm

Project Preferences

Type of Financing Preferred:
Balanced

Geographical Preferences

International Preferences:
All International

Additional Information

Year Founded: 2002
Current Activity Level : Actively seeking new investments

VERONIS SUHLER STEVENSON (FKA: VERONIS, SUHLER & ASSOCIATES)

350 Park Avenue
Seventh Floor
New York, NY USA 10022
Phone: 212-935-4990
Fax: 212-381-8168
Website: www.vss.com

Other Offices

Buchanan House, 8th Floor
3 St. James Square
London, United Kingdom SW1Y 4JU
Phone: 44-207-484-4100
Fax: 44-207-484-1410

Management and Staff

Andrew Buchholtz, Managing Director
Chris Russell, Managing Director
David Holland, Managing Director
David Bainbridge, Managing Director
George Cole, Managing Director
Gerald Benford, Partner
Hal Greenberg, Managing Director
J. Morgan Callagy, Managing Director
Jack Clarke, Managing Director
Jeffrey Stevenson, Partner
Johannes Von Bismarck, Managing Director
John Sinatra, Chief Financial Officer
John Suhler, President
John Veronis, Managing Partner
Kevin Waldman, Managing Director
Lawrence Crutcher, Managing Director
Marco Sodi, Partner
Marvin Shapiro, Managing Director
Michael Kessler, Managing Director
Nick Veronis, Managing Director
R. Trent Hickman, Managing Director
Robert Broadwater, Managing Director
Scott Troeller, Partner
Thomas Kemp, Managing Director
Xiaohong Chen, Managing Director

Type of Firm

Bank Affiliated

Project Preferences

Type of Financing Preferred:
Leveraged Buyout
Expansion
Mezzanine
Acquisition
Recapitalizations

Size of Investments Considered:
Min Size of Investment Considered (000s): $5,000
Max Size of Investment Considered (000s): $200,000

Geographical Preferences

Canadian Preferences:
All Canada

International Preferences:
Latin America
Europe

Industry Focus

(% based on actual investment)

Other Products	42.1%
Communications and Media	26.0%
Internet Specific	22.6%
Consumer Related	7.3%
Computer Hardware	1.9%

Additional Information

Name of Most Recent Fund: VSS Communications Partners IV, L.P.
Most Recent Fund Was Raised: 10/07/2004
Year Founded: 1987
Capital Under Management: $1,150,000,000
Current Activity Level : Actively seeking new investments

VERSA CAPITAL MANAGEMENT (FKA: CHRYSALIS CAPITAL PARTNERS)

2929 Arch Street
Cira Centre
Philadelphia, PA USA 19104
Phone: 215-609-3400
Fax: 215-609-3499
E-mail: info@versafund.com
Website: www.versafund.com

Management and Staff

Alexander Popovich, Vice President
David Pichler, Vice President
Gregory Segall, Managing Partner
Jeffrey Armbrister, Vice President

Joel Biran, Vice President
Keith Polak, Principal
Lewis Aronson, Principal
Michael Koffler, Vice President
Randall Schultz, Principal
Raymond French, Partner
Seth Lemler, Principal
Stephen Dorman, Principal
William Quinn, Principal

Type of Firm

Private Equity Firm

Project Preferences

Type of Financing Preferred:

Leveraged Buyout
Turnaround
Special Situation
Distressed Debt
Recapitalizations

Size of Investments Considered:

Min Size of Investment Considered (000s): $5,000
Max Size of Investment Considered (000s): $30,000

Additional Information

Name of Most Recent Fund: Versa Capital Fund II, L.P.
Most Recent Fund Was Raised: 06/17/2008
Year Founded: 2005
Capital Under Management: $52,800,000
Current Activity Level : Actively seeking new investments

VERSANT VENTURES

3000 Sand Hill Road
Building Four, Suite 210
Menlo Park, CA USA 94025
Phone: 650-233-7877
Fax: 650-854-9513
Website: www.versantventures.com

Other Offices

1700 Owens Street
Suite 541
San Francisco, CA USA 94158
Phone: 650-233-7877
Fax: 650-854-9513

450 Newport Center Drive
Suite 600
Newport Beach, CA USA 92660
Phone: 949-729-4500
Fax: 949-729-4501

Management and Staff

Barbara Lubash, Managing Director
Bradley Bolzon, Managing Director
Brian Atwood, Managing Director
Camille Samuels, Managing Director
Charles Warden, Managing Director
Donald Milder, Managing Director
Kevin Wasserstein, Managing Director
Kirk Nielsen, Principal
Rebecca Robertson, Managing Director
Robin Praeger, Managing Director & CFO
Ross Jaffe, Managing Director
Samuel Colella, Managing Director
William Link, Managing Director

Type of Firm

Private Equity Firm

Association Membership

Western Association of Venture Capitalists (WAVC)
National Venture Capital Association - USA (NVCA)

Project Preferences

Role in Financing:

Prefer role as deal originator but will also invest in deals created by others

Type of Financing Preferred:

Second Stage Financing
Early Stage
Start-up Financing
Seed
First Stage Financing

Size of Investments Considered:

Min Size of Investment Considered (000s): $1,000
Max Size of Investment Considered (000s): $15,000

Geographical Preferences

United States Preferences:

All U.S.

Industry Focus

(% based on actual investment)

Medical/Health	64.8%
Biotechnology	27.8%
Computer Software and Services	2.8%
Other Products	2.3%
Internet Specific	2.0%
Semiconductors/Other Elect.	0.3%
Consumer Related	0.1%

Additional Information

Name of Most Recent Fund: Versant Venture Capital IV, L.P.
Most Recent Fund Was Raised: 07/31/2008
Year Founded: 1999
Capital Under Management: $1,585,000,000
Current Activity Level : Actively seeking new investments
Method of Compensation: Return on investment is of primary concern, do not charge fees

---

VERTEX MANAGEMENT ISRAEL (AKA: VERTEX VENTURE CAPITAL)

1 Hashikma Street
PO Box 89
Savyon, Israel 56530
Phone: 972-3-737-8888
Fax: 972-3-737-8889
E-mail: contact@VertexVC.com
Website: www.VertexVC.com

Other Offices

77 Science Park Drive
#02-15 Cintech III
Singapore, Singapore 118256
Phone: 65-6777-0122
Fax: 65-6777-1878

20 Berkeley Square
London, United Kingdom W1J 6EQ
Phone: 44-207-629-8838
Fax: 44-207-629-3338

Lyngbyvej 20
Copenhagen, Denmark 2100
Phone: 45-3915-8030
Fax: 45-3915-8031

210A Twin Dolphin Drive
Redwood City, CA USA 94065
Phone: 650-508-2400
Fax: 650-591-5926

570 av. du club hippique
Aix en Provence, France 13090
Phone: 33-4-4264-0645
Fax: 33-4-4228-1925

Management and Staff

David Heller, Partner
Ehud Levy, Partner
Elisheva Yakobovich, Partner
Emanuel Timor, Partner
Moshe Shahaf, Managing Partner
Moty Ben-Arie, Managing Partner
Ran Gartenberg, Chief Financial Officer
Robert Genieser, Managing Partner
Yifat Oron, Partner

Type of Firm

Bank Affiliated

Association Membership

Israel Venture Association

Project Preferences

Type of Financing Preferred:

Early Stage
Seed

Size of Investments Considered:

Min Size of Investment Considered (000s): $300
Max Size of Investment Considered (000s): $300,000

Geographical Preferences

International Preferences:

Europe
Israel
Asia
Japan

Industry Preferences

In Communications prefer:
Communications and Media

In Internet Specific prefer:
Internet

Additional Information

Year Founded: 1997
Capital Under Management: $250,000,000
Current Activity Level : Actively seeking new investments

VERTEX MANAGEMENT PTE, LTD. (AKA: VERTEX VENTURE HOLDINGS)

250 North Bridge Road
Suite 05-01 Raffles City Tower
Singapore, Singapore 179101
Phone: 65-6828-8088
Fax: 65-6828-8090
E-mail: contact@vertexmgt.com
Website: www.vertexmgt.com

Other Offices

1 HaShikma St.
P.O. Box 89
Savyon, Israel 56530
Phone: 972-3737-8888
Fax: 972-3737-8889

20 Berkeley Square
London, United Kingdom W1J 6EQ
Phone: 44-207-629-8838
Fax: 44-207-629-3338

8/F, No. 301, Section 2
Ti-ding Blvd.
Taipei, Taiwan
Phone: 886-2-8797-1887
Fax: 886-2-8797-4868

No. 1518 Minsheng Road
Unit 1202, A Building
Shanghai, China 200135
Phone: 86-21-6104-2718
Fax: 86-21-6104-2710

Lyngbyvej 20
Copenhagen, Denmark DK-2100
Phone: 45-3915-8030
Fax: 45-3915-8031

338 Kings Road, North Point
Unit 1803-18/F., Two Chinachem
Hong Kong, Hong Kong
Phone: 852-252-36133
Fax: 852-252-37233

Unit 2115, Level 21
China World Trade Tower 1
Beijing, China 100004
Phone: 86-10-6505-9555
Fax: 86-10-6505-2555

210A Twin Dolphin Drive
Redwood City, CA USA 94065
Phone: 650-508-2400
Fax: 650-591-5926

Management and Staff

Choon Chong Tay, Managing Director
Fu Min Zhuo, Chairman & CEO
Joo Hock Chua, Managing Director
Kum Tho Wan, Vice President
Robert Genieser, Managing Director
Steven Ji, Vice President
Yip Loi Lee, Vice President

Type of Firm

Corporate PE/Venture

Association Membership

Hong Kong Venture Capital Association (HKVCA)
Singapore Venture Capital Association (SVCA)

Project Preferences

Role in Financing:
Prefer role as deal originator but will also invest in deals created by others

Type of Financing Preferred:
Second Stage Financing
Early Stage
Expansion
Mezzanine
Balanced
Later Stage
Seed
First Stage Financing

Size of Investments Considered:
Min Size of Investment Considered (000s): $500
Max Size of Investment Considered (000s): $10,000

Geographical Preferences

International Preferences:
Taiwan
Europe
China
Hong Kong
Israel
Singapore
Asia
All International

Industry Focus

(% based on actual investment)

Computer Software and Services	27.9%
Internet Specific	24.5%
Other Products	17.7%
Communications and Media	15.9%
Semiconductors/Other Elect.	6.9%
Biotechnology	3.0%
Medical/Health	2.0%
Computer Hardware	2.0%
Consumer Related	0.1%

Additional Information

Year Founded: 1988
Capital Under Management: $1,000,000,000
Current Activity Level : Actively seeking new investments
Method of Compensation: Return on investment is of primary concern, do not charge fees

VERTEX VENTURE CAPITAL

1 HaShikma Street
P.O. Box 89
Savyon, Israel 56530
Phone: 972-3737-8888
Fax: 972-3737-8889
E-mail: contact@VertexVC.com
Website: www.VertexVC.com

Other Offices

20 Berkeley Square
London, United Kingdom W1J 6EQ
Phone: 44-207-629-8838
Fax: 44-207-629-3338

51 Cuppage Road
#10-08 Starhub Centre
Singapore, Singapore 229469
Phone: 65-6828-8088
Fax: 65-6720-8007

Management and Staff

David Heller, Partner
Ehud Levy, Partner
Elisheva Yakobovich, Partner
Emanuel Timor, Partner
Moshe Shahaf, Managing Partner
Moty Ben-Arie, Managing Partner
Ran Gartenberg, Chief Financial Officer
Robert Genieser, Managing Partner
Yifat Oron, Partner

Type of Firm

Private Equity Firm

Project Preferences

Role in Financing:
Will function either as deal originator or investor in deals created by others

Type of Financing Preferred:
Early Stage

Geographical Preferences

United States Preferences:
All U.S.

International Preferences:
Europe
Israel
Asia
Japan

Industry Preferences

In Communications prefer:
Communications and Media

In Computer Software prefer:
Software

Additional Information
Year Founded: 1996
Current Activity Level : Actively seeking new investments

VERTICAL GROUP, THE
25 DeForest Avenue
Summit, NJ USA 07901
Phone: 908-277-3737
Fax: 908-273-9434
E-mail: info@vertical-group.com
Website: www.vertical-group.com

Other Offices
530 Lytton Avenue
Suite 304
Palo Alto, CA USA 94301
Phone: 650-566-9060
Fax: 650-838-9383

Management and Staff
Jack Lasersohn, General Partner
John Slattery, Chief Financial Officer
John Runnells, General Partner
Richard Emmitt, General Partner
Stephen Baksa, General Partner
Tony Chou, Venture Partner
Yue-Teh Jang, General Partner

Type of Firm
Private Equity Firm

Association Membership
National Venture Capital Association - USA (NVCA)

Project Preferences

Role in Financing:
Prefer role as deal originator but will also invest in deals created by others

Type of Financing Preferred:
Leveraged Buyout
Control-block Purchases
Early Stage
Mezzanine
Balanced
Later Stage
Special Situation

Size of Investments Considered:
Min Size of Investment Considered (000s): $250
Max Size of Investment Considered (000s): $3,000

Industry Focus
(% based on actual investment)

Medical/Health	60.7%
Biotechnology	32.5%
Semiconductors/Other Elect.	3.1%
Internet Specific	3.1%
Communications and Media	0.4%
Computer Software and Services	0.3%

Additional Information
Year Founded: 1988
Capital Under Management: $100,000,000
Current Activity Level : Actively seeking new investments
Method of Compensation: Return on investment is of primary concern, do not charge fees

---

VESBRIDGE PARTNERS, LLC
1700 West Park Drive
Westborough, MA USA 01581
Phone: 508-475-2300
Fax: 508-475-2399
Website: www.vesbridge.com

Management and Staff
Jeffrey Hinck, Senior Managing Director
Mark Burns, Vice President
Martin Steinmann, Venture Partner
Raj Alur, Managing Director
Roderick Randall, Senior Managing Director
Staffan Ericsson, Venture Partner
Tom Rowbotham, Venture Partner
William Cadogan, Senior Managing Director
Zenas Hutcheson, Senior Managing Director

Type of Firm
Private Equity Firm

Association Membership
National Venture Capital Association - USA (NVCA)

Project Preferences

Type of Financing Preferred:
Early Stage
Balanced

Size of Investments Considered:
Min Size of Investment Considered (000s): $5,000
Max Size of Investment Considered (000s): $30,000

Industry Preferences

In Communications prefer:
Wireless Communications
Data Communications

In Computer Software prefer:
Applications Software

Additional Information
Year Founded: 2004
Current Activity Level : Actively seeking new investments

VESPA CAPITAL LLP
North Cottage, Langton Green
Tunbridge Wells
Kent, United Kingdom TN3 0BB
Phone: 44-1892-531373
E-mail: info@vespacapital.com
Website: www.vespacapital.com

Other Offices
25 rue Marbeuf
Paris, France 75008
Phone: 33-1-6825-67055

Amadeus House
27b Floral Street, Covent Garden
London, United Kingdom WC2E 9DP
Phone: 44-20-7812-7144
Fax: 44-20-7812-6495

Management and Staff
Nigel Hammond, Co-Founder

Type of Firm
Private Equity Firm

Project Preferences

Type of Financing Preferred:
Leveraged Buyout
Management Buyouts

Geographical Preferences

International Preferences:
United Kingdom
France

Additional Information
Year Founded: 2008
Capital Under Management: $69,900,000
Current Activity Level : Actively seeking new investments

VESTAR CAPITAL PARTNERS, INC.
245 Park Avenue
41st Floor
New York, NY USA 10167
Phone: 212-351-1600
Fax: 212-808-4922
Website: www.vestarcapital.com

Other Offices
Seventeenth Street Plaza
1225 17th Street, Suite 1660
Denver, CO USA 80202
Phone: 303-292-6300

1, Rond Point Des Champs Elysees
Paris, France 75008
Phone: 33-1-5856-6010

500 Boylston Street
17th Floor
Boston, MA USA 02116
Phone: 617-247-1200

Via Manzoni, 3
Milan, Italy 20121
Phone: 39-2-863-5911

23rd Floor, Yamato Seimei Building
1-1-7 Uchisaiwai-cho, Chiyoda-ku
Tokyo, Japan 100-0011
Phone: 81-3-5251-4300

Maximilianstrasse 34
Munich, Germany 80539
Phone: 49-89-2000-3410

Management and Staff

Anil Shrivastava, Managing Director
Arthur Nagle, Founding Partner
Brian Modesitt, Managing Director
Brian Ratzan, Managing Director
Brian Schwartz, Managing Director
Brian O'Connor, Principal
Chris Durbin, Managing Director
Erin Russell, Principal
Evan Marks, Principal
Garrick Bernstein, Vice President
J. Christopher Henderson, Managing Director
James Kelly, President
James Elrod, Managing Director
James Kelley, Founding Partner
Jean-Francois Felix, Managing Director
Jeffrey Long, Managing Director
Jens Tonn, Managing Director
Kenny O'Keefe, Managing Director
Kevin Mundt, Managing Director
Kristian Whalen, Managing Director
Marco Mantica, Managing Director
Norman Alpert, Managing Director
Patrick Shattenkirk, Managing Director
Peter Baumgartner, Managing Director
Prakash Melwani, Founder
Roger Holstein, Managing Director
Sander Levy, Founding Partner
Shinji Sunouchi, Managing Director
Taro Sumitani, Managing Director
Victor Cohen, Vice President

Type of Firm

Private Equity Firm

Association Membership

Italian Venture Capital Association (AIFI)

Project Preferences

Type of Financing Preferred:
Leveraged Buyout
Expansion
Mezzanine
Management Buyouts
Recapitalizations

Geographical Preferences

International Preferences:
Europe

Industry Focus

(% based on actual investment)

Consumer Related	58.5%
Other Products	19.7%
Industrial/Energy	11.7%
Medical/Health	6.2%
Communications and Media	3.4%
Computer Software and Services	0.4%
Internet Specific	0.2%

Additional Information

Year Founded: 1988
Capital Under Management: $4,318,000,000
Current Activity Level : Actively seeking new investments

VESTRA PARTNERINVEST AB

Kopmangatan 23-25
P.O. Box 8023
Orebro, Sweden 700 08
Phone: 46-19-174-804
E-mail: info@vestrapartner.se
Website: www.vestrapartner.se

Type of Firm

Private Equity Firm

Association Membership

European Private Equity and Venture Capital Assoc.

Project Preferences

Type of Financing Preferred:
Balanced

Geographical Preferences

International Preferences:
Sweden

Additional Information

Year Founded: 2006
Capital Under Management: $7,200,000
Current Activity Level : Actively seeking new investments

VF CAPITAL SDN BHD (AKA: VF CAPITAL)

Sublot 1187 & 1188, Lot 901
Block 9, MCLD, Miri Waterfront
Sarawak, Malaysia 98000
Phone: 603-8542-6000
Fax: 603-8542-0029
E-mail: enquiry@vfcapital.com.my
Website: www.vfcapital.com.my

Management and Staff

Chia Pheng, Chief Executive Officer

Type of Firm

Private Equity Firm

Association Membership

Malaysian Venture Capital Association

Project Preferences

Type of Financing Preferred:
Early Stage
Expansion
Start-up Financing

Geographical Preferences

International Preferences:
Malaysia

Industry Preferences

In Communications prefer:
Communications and Media

In Biotechnology prefer:
Biotechnology

Additional Information

Year Founded: 2004
Current Activity Level : Actively seeking new investments

VI PARTNERS

Beddingen 8
Trondheim, Norway 7014
Phone: 47-73-60-0290
Fax: 47-73-60-0291
Website: www.v-i.no

Management and Staff

Kjell Hagan, Partner

Type of Firm

Private Equity Firm

Project Preferences

Type of Financing Preferred:
Balanced

Additional Information

Year Founded: 2008
Current Activity Level : Actively seeking new investments

VIA VENTURE PARTNERS

ATP-huset
Kongens Vaenge 8
Hillerod, Denmark 3400
Phone: 45-3977-5060
Fax: 45-4820-4814
Website: www.viaventurepartners.com

Management and Staff

Jesper Horsholt, Chief Financial Officer
John Helmsoe-Zinck, Founder
Peter Thorlund Haahr, Partner

Type of Firm

Private Equity Firm

Project Preferences

Type of Financing Preferred:
Early Stage
Expansion
Seed

Geographical Preferences

International Preferences:
Scandanavia/Nordic Region

Industry Preferences

In Computer Software prefer:
Software

In Internet Specific prefer:
Internet

In Industrial/Energy prefer:
Industrial Products

Additional Information

Year Founded: 2006
Capital Under Management: $154,000,000
Current Activity Level : Actively seeking new investments

VIANOVA CAPITAL

100 Pall Mall
London, United Kingdom SW1Y 5HP
Phone: 44-20-7664-8695
Fax: 44-20-7664-8697
E-mail: info@vianova-capital.com
Website: www.vianova-capital.com

Other Offices

Waldmannstrasse 4
Zurich, Switzerland CH-8001
Phone: 41-43-243-6700
Fax: 41-43-243-6701

Management and Staff

Andrew Evans, Managing Partner
Martin Dreher, Managing Partner
Thomas Bischoff, Managing Partner

Type of Firm

Private Equity Advisor or Fund of Funds

Project Preferences

Type of Financing Preferred:
Fund of Funds

Geographical Preferences

International Preferences:
Europe

Additional Information

Year Founded: 2003
Current Activity Level : Actively seeking new investments
Method of Compensation: Other

VIAVAR CAPITAL

888 Sherbrooke Ouest
Montreal, Canada H3A 1G3
Phone: 514-849-4488
Fax: 514-849-2580
E-mail: info@viavar.com
Website: www.vianeva.com

Type of Firm

Private Equity Firm

Additional Information

Year Founded: 2002
Current Activity Level : Actively seeking new investments

VIBURNUM FUNDS PTY., LTD. (AKA: WYLLIE GROUP)

19/F, St. Georges Square
225 St. Georges Terrace
Perth, Australia 6000
Phone: 618-9322-6699
Fax: 618-9322-2075
E-mail: wyllie@wylliegroup.com
Website: www.wylliegroup.com.au

Management and Staff

Ben Bartholomaeus, Chief Operating Officer
David St Quintin, Chief Financial Officer
Melissa Karlson, Managing Director

Type of Firm

Private Equity Firm

Project Preferences

Type of Financing Preferred:
Generalist PE
Recapitalizations

Size of Investments Considered:
Min Size of Investment Considered (000s): $5,000
Max Size of Investment Considered (000s): $20,000

Geographical Preferences

International Preferences:
Asia
Australia

Additional Information

Year Founded: 2007
Capital Under Management: $25,800,000
Current Activity Level : Actively seeking new investments

VICENTE CAPITAL PARTNERS

11726 San Vicente Boulevard
Suite 300
Los Angeles, CA USA 90049
Phone: 310-826-2255
Fax: 310-826-2299
E-mail: info@vicentecapital.com
Website: www.vicentecapital.com

Management and Staff

Alain Rothstein, Principal
David Casares, Principal
Greg Arsenault, Chief Financial Officer
Jay Ferguson, Managing Partner
Klaus Koch, Managing Partner
Nicholas Memmo, Managing Partner

Type of Firm

Private Equity Firm

Project Preferences

Type of Financing Preferred:
Leveraged Buyout
Expansion
Acquisition
Recapitalizations

Size of Investments Considered:
Min Size of Investment Considered (000s): $8,000
Max Size of Investment Considered (000s): $16,000

Geographical Preferences

United States Preferences:
All U.S.

Industry Preferences

In Communications prefer:
Telecommunications
Wireless Communications
Data Communications

In Internet Specific prefer:
Internet

In Medical/Health prefer:
Health Services

In Consumer Related prefer:
Consumer Services

In Industrial/Energy prefer:
Environmental Related

In Transportation prefer:
Aerospace

In Business Serv. prefer:
Services

In Manufact. prefer:
Manufacturing

Additional Information

Name of Most Recent Fund: Vicente Capital Partners Growth Equity Fund, L.P.
Most Recent Fund Was Raised: 02/23/2007
Year Founded: 2007
Capital Under Management: $162,000,000
Current Activity Level : Actively seeking new investments
Method of Compensation: Return on investment is of primary concern, do not charge fees

---

VICKERS VENTURE PARTNERS

7 Temasek Boulevard
#26-01, Suntec Tower One
Singapore, Singapore 038987
Phone: 65-6339-0338
Fax: 65-6339-3380
E-mail: info@vickersventure.com
Website: www.vickerscapitalgroup.com

Other Offices

1266 Nanjing West Road
Plaza 66, Suite 1202
Shanghai, China 200040
Phone: 86-21-6288-2626
Fax: 86-21-6288-2825

Management and Staff

Damian Tan, Venture Partner
Finian Tan, Managing Director
Jeffrey Chi, Managing Director
Vincent Xu, Venture Partner

Type of Firm

Private Equity Firm

Project Preferences

Type of Financing Preferred:
Early Stage
Expansion
Mezzanine
Startup

Geographical Preferences

International Preferences:
China
Asia

Industry Preferences

In Communications prefer:
Communications and Media
Telecommunications

Additional Information

Year Founded: 2004
Current Activity Level : Actively seeking new investments

VICTORIA PARK CAPITAL

1850 - 1874 Scarth Street
Regina, Canada S4P 4B3
Phone: 306.566.4600
Fax: 306.566.4618
Website: www.victoriaparkcapital.com

Type of Firm

Government Affiliated Program

Association Membership

Canadian Venture Capital Association

Project Preferences

Role in Financing:
Will function either as deal originator or investor in deals created by others

Geographical Preferences

Canadian Preferences:
Saskatchewan

Additional Information

Name of Most Recent Fund: Investment Saskatchewan FKA:CIC Industrial Interests CIC III
Most Recent Fund Was Raised: 05/01/1989
Year Founded: 1989
Current Activity Level : Actively seeking new investments
Method of Compensation: Return on investment is of primary concern, do not charge fees

---

VIENNA CAPITAL PARTNERS

Tegetthoffstrasse 7
Vienna, Austria 1010
Phone: 43-1-514-17
Fax: 43-1-514-17-300
E-mail: office@vcpag.com
Website: www.vcpag.com

Other Offices

Vlaska 40/III
Zagreb, Croatia 10000
Phone: 385-1-4881-500
Fax: 385-1-4881-530

Rondo ONZ 1
Warsaw, Poland 00-124
Phone: 48-22-520-6600
Fax: 48-22-520-6601

Management and Staff

Christian Fischer, Partner
Gabriel Dielacher, Partner
Markus Basalka, Partner

Type of Firm

Investment Management Firm

Project Preferences

Type of Financing Preferred:
Leveraged Buyout
Expansion
Research and Development
Turnaround
Seed
Management Buyouts
Startup
Recapitalizations

Geographical Preferences

International Preferences:
Hungary
Central Europe
Poland
Austria
Eastern Europe
Romania

Industry Focus

(% based on actual investment)

Industrial/Energy	100.0%

Additional Information

Year Founded: 2001
Current Activity Level : Actively seeking new investments

VIETNAM PIONEER PARTNERS

Loyal Office Bldg., 9th Floor
151 Vo Thi Sau Street, Dist. 3
Ho Chi Minh, Vietnam
Phone: 84-8-820-8975
Fax: 84-8-820-8871
E-mail: info@vnpioneers.com
Website: www.vnpioneers.com

Other Offices

DMC Bldg., 5th Floor
535 Kim Ma Street, Ba Dinh District
Hanoi, Vietnam
Phone: 84-4-220-3127
Fax: 84-4-220-3128

Management and Staff

Hoa Thi Dinh, Co-Founder
Trung Ha Nguyen, Co-Founder
Viet Hung Do, Co-Founder

Type of Firm

Private Equity Firm

Project Preferences

Type of Financing Preferred:
Leveraged Buyout
Generalist PE
Expansion
Recapitalizations

Geographical Preferences

International Preferences:
Vietnam

Industry Preferences

In Communications prefer:
Media and Entertainment

In Medical/Health prefer:
Health Services

In Consumer Related prefer:
Retail
Consumer Products

In Industrial/Energy prefer:
Energy

In Financial Services prefer:
Financial Services

Additional Information

Year Founded: 2009
Capital Under Management: $20,000,000
Current Activity Level : Actively seeking new investments

VIEWPOINT CAPITAL PARTNERS GMBH

Bockenheimer Landstrasse 47
Frankfurt am Main, Germany 60323
Phone: 49-69-7191-800
Fax: 49-69-7191-8088
E-mail: info@viewpointpartners.com
Website: www.viewpointpartners.com

Other Offices

Seegartenstrasse 2
Zurich, Switzerland CH-8008
Phone: 41-44-210-4985
Fax: 41-44-210-4986

P.O. Box 22885
Atlas Office Complex Hoogoorddreef 7
Amsterdam, Netherlands NL-1100
Phone: 31-2056-77107

Management and Staff

Christian Janson-Euterneck, Managing Director
De heer De Wit, Partner
Dieter Giesbrecht, Venture Partner
Ulrich Seng, Venture Partner
Urs Ehrismann, Managing Director

Type of Firm

Private Equity Firm

Association Membership

European Private Equity and Venture Capital Assoc.

Project Preferences

Type of Financing Preferred:
Early Stage
Expansion
Balanced
Later Stage
Seed
Startup
Recapitalizations

Size of Investments Considered:
Min Size of Investment Considered (000s): $3,886
Max Size of Investment Considered (000s): $19,428

Geographical Preferences

International Preferences:
United Kingdom
Luxembourg
Netherlands
Switzerland
Europe
Austria
Belgium
Germany
France
Denmark

Industry Preferences

In Communications prefer:
Telecommunications
Other Communication Prod.

In Computer Software prefer:
Software

In Internet Specific prefer:
Internet

In Computer Other prefer:
Computer Related

In Financial Services prefer:
Financial Services

Additional Information

Year Founded: 2002
Capital Under Management: $259,000,000
Current Activity Level : Actively seeking new investments

VIGO ACTIVO SOCIEDAD DE CAPITAL RIESGO SA

Arenal 18-2
Oficina 7
Vigo, Spain 36210
Phone: 34-986-202-406
Fax: 34-986-203-105
E-mail: vigoactivo@vigoactivo.com
Website: www.vigoactivo.com

Type of Firm

Private Equity Firm

Association Membership

European Private Equity and Venture Capital Assoc.
Spanish Venture Capital Association (ASCRI)

Project Preferences

Role in Financing:
Prefer role in deals created by others

Type of Financing Preferred:
Second Stage Financing
Early Stage
Expansion
Balanced
Start-up Financing
Seed
First Stage Financing

Geographical Preferences

International Preferences:
Spain

Industry Preferences

In Communications prefer:
Communications and Media

In Computer Other prefer:
Computer Related

In Semiconductor/Electr prefer:
Electronic Components

In Biotechnology prefer:
Biotechnology

In Medical/Health prefer:
Medical/Health

In Consumer Related prefer:
Consumer

In Industrial/Energy prefer:
Energy
Industrial Products

In Financial Services prefer:
Real Estate

In Business Serv. prefer:
Distribution

In Agr/Forestr/Fish prefer:
Agriculture related

Additional Information

Year Founded: 1993
Capital Under Management: $12,600,000
Current Activity Level : Actively seeking new investments
Method of Compensation: Return on invest. most important, but chg. closing fees, service fees, etc.

VIKING FUND, THE

Metic House
Ripley Drive
Normanton, United Kingdom WF6 1QT
Website: www.vikingfund.com

Management and Staff

Andrew Burton, Managing Director

Type of Firm
Government Affiliated Program

Project Preferences

Type of Financing Preferred:
Early Stage
Seed
Startup

Size of Investments Considered:
Min Size of Investment Considered (000s): $90
Max Size of Investment Considered (000s): $180

Geographical Preferences

International Preferences:
United Kingdom
Europe

Additional Information
Name of Most Recent Fund: Viking Fund, The
Most Recent Fund Was Raised: 06/24/2004
Year Founded: 2002
Capital Under Management: $10,000,000
Current Activity Level : Actively seeking new investments
Method of Compensation: Return on invest. most important, but chg. closing fees, service fees, etc.

VIKING VENTURE MANAGEMENT AS

Beddingen 8
Trondheim, Norway 7014
Phone: 47-73-600-190
Fax: 47-73-600-195
E-mail: post@vikingventure.no
Website: www.vikingventure.com

Management and Staff
Erik Hagen, Managing Partner
Harald Jeremiassen, Partner
Joar Welde, Partner
Jostein Vik, Partner
Shane McElroy, Partner

Type of Firm
Private Equity Firm

Association Membership
Norwegian Venture Capital Association
European Private Equity and Venture Capital Assoc.

Project Preferences

Type of Financing Preferred:
Early Stage
Expansion
Seed
First Stage Financing
Startup

Geographical Preferences

International Preferences:
Norway

Industry Preferences

In Communications prefer:
Commercial Communications

In Computer Software prefer:
Software

In Semiconductor/Electr prefer:
Electronics

In Biotechnology prefer:
Biotechnology

In Medical/Health prefer:
Medical/Health

In Industrial/Energy prefer:
Energy
Oil and Gas Exploration
Oil & Gas Drilling,Explor
Environmental Related

Additional Information
Year Founded: 2001
Capital Under Management: $100,000,000
Current Activity Level : Actively seeking new investments

VILLAGE VENTURES

430 Main Street
Suite One
Williamstown, MA USA 01267
Phone: 413-458-1100
Fax: 413-458-0338
E-mail: info@villageventures.com
Website: www.villageventures.com

Other Offices
Historic Hirons Building
555 North Morton
Bloomington, IN USA 47404
Phone: 812-336-8841
Fax: 812-332-2352

10 East 53rd Street
31st Floor
New York, NY USA 10022

1512 Larimer Street
Suite 200
Denver, CO USA 80206
Phone: 303-339-7270

Management and Staff
Jane Martin, General Partner
Matthew Warta, Venture Partner
Matthew Harris, Managing General Partner
Michael Barach, Venture Partner
Thomas Davidson, Venture Partner
William Peabody, Managing General Partner

Type of Firm
Private Equity Firm

Association Membership
National Venture Capital Association - USA (NVCA)

Project Preferences

Role in Financing:
Will function either as deal originator or investor in deals created by others

Type of Financing Preferred:
Leveraged Buyout
Early Stage
Balanced
Later Stage
Seed
Startup

Size of Investments Considered:
Min Size of Investment Considered (000s): $500
Max Size of Investment Considered (000s): $2,000

Geographical Preferences

United States Preferences:
All U.S.

Industry Preferences

In Communications prefer:
Communications and Media
Wireless Communications
Satellite Microwave Comm.

In Computer Software prefer:
Software

In Internet Specific prefer:
Internet

In Medical/Health prefer:
Medical/Health
Health Services

In Financial Services prefer:
Financial Services

In Business Serv. prefer:
Media

Additional Information
Year Founded: 2000
Capital Under Management: $250,000,000
Current Activity Level : Actively seeking new investments
Method of Compensation: Return on investment is of primary concern, do not charge fees

---

VIMAC VENTURES LLC (FKA: VIMAC LLC)

177 Milk Street
Boston, MA USA 02109-3410
Phone: 617-350-9800
Fax: 617-350-9899
E-mail: info@vimac.com
Website: www.vimac.com

Management and Staff
David Marcus, Managing Director
Douglas Redding, Chief Operating Officer
John Evans, Managing Director
Keith Cooper, Managing Director

Praveen Sahay, Principal
R. Dana Ono, Managing Director
Robert Roeper, Managing Director
Sena Biswas, Managing Director

Type of Firm

Private Equity Firm

Association Membership

Canadian Venture Capital Association

Project Preferences

Role in Financing:

Prefer role as deal originator but will also invest in deals created by others

Type of Financing Preferred:

Early Stage

Size of Investments Considered:

Min Size of Investment Considered (000s): $1,000
Max Size of Investment Considered (000s): $5,000

Geographical Preferences

United States Preferences:

Northeast

Canadian Preferences:

Quebec
Ontario
Eastern Canada

Industry Focus

(% based on actual investment)

Internet Specific	36.4%
Computer Software and Services	25.0%
Medical/Health	13.4%
Communications and Media	10.0%
Semiconductors/Other Elect.	7.5%
Biotechnology	4.8%
Consumer Related	1.4%
Industrial/Energy	1.1%
Computer Hardware	0.1%
Other Products	0.1%

Additional Information

Year Founded: 1982
Capital Under Management: $155,000,000
Current Activity Level : Actively seeking new investments
Method of Compensation: Return on investment is of primary concern, do not charge fees

---

VINACAPITAL INVESTMENT MANAGEMENT COMPANY

Nguyen Hue Blvd. District 1
17th Floor Sun Wah Tower
Ho Chi Minh, Vietnam
Phone: 84-8-821-9930
Fax: 84-8-821-9931
E-mail: info@vinacapital.com
Website: www.vinacapital.com

Other Offices

5F, 13 Hai Ba Trung
Hai Ba Trung District
Hanoi, Vietnam
Phone: 84-4-3936-4630
Fax: 84-4-3936-4629

The Hearst Building
Market at Third St. Suite 810
San Francisco, CA USA 94103
Phone: 415-974-1000
Fax: 415-974-1150

13/F St. John Building
33 Garden Road
Central, Hong Kong
Phone: 852-2918-0088
Fax: 852-2918-0881

Management and Staff

Andy Ho, Managing Director
Chris Gradel, Partner
Don Lam, Chief Executive Officer
Stacy Kincaid, Managing Director

Type of Firm

Investment Management Firm

Project Preferences

Type of Financing Preferred:

Leveraged Buyout
Expansion
Balanced
Later Stage
Other
Management Buyouts
Acquisition
Startup
Distressed Debt

Geographical Preferences

International Preferences:

Vietnam
India
China
Asia

Industry Preferences

In Communications prefer:

Telecommunications
Wireless Communications

In Computer Software prefer:

Software

In Internet Specific prefer:

Internet

In Consumer Related prefer:

Retail
Consumer Products
Consumer Services

In Industrial/Energy prefer:

Energy

In Transportation prefer:

Transportation

In Financial Services prefer:

Real Estate
Investment Groups
Financial Services

In Business Serv. prefer:

Services
Media

In Utilities prefer:

Utilities

Additional Information

Year Founded: 2003
Capital Under Management: $1,663,000,000
Current Activity Level : Actively seeking new investments

VINCI CAPITAL

PSE, Batiment C
Lausanne, Switzerland CH-1051
Phone: 41-21-693-9234
Fax: 41-21-693-9230
E-mail: info@vincicapital.ch
Website: www.vincicapital.ch

Other Offices

Baarerstrasse 21
Zug, Germany CH-6304
Phone: 41-41-711-1081

Management and Staff

Christian Waldvogel, Managing Partner
Olivier Tavel, Managing Partner

Type of Firm

Private Equity Firm

Project Preferences

Type of Financing Preferred:

Generalist PE

Geographical Preferences

International Preferences:

Switzerland
Europe

Additional Information

Year Founded: 1998
Capital Under Management: $150,800,000
Current Activity Level : Actively seeking new investments

VINEYARD VENTURES

P.O. Box 1268
Edgartown, MA USA 02539
Phone: 508-292-1612
Fax: 508-627-9694
Website: www.vineyard-ventures.com

Other Offices

Level 40, Tower 2
Petronas Twin Towers
Kuala Lumpur, Malaysia
Phone: 603-2168-4311
Fax: 603-2168-4657

Management and Staff

Robb Fipp, Managing Partner
Warren Adams, Managing Partner

Type of Firm

Private Equity Firm

Project Preferences

Type of Financing Preferred:

Early Stage
Additional Information
Year Founded: 2000
Current Activity Level : Actively seeking new investments

VINTAGE CAPITAL PARTNERS

11611 San Vicente Boulevard
Suite 1000
Los Angeles, CA USA 90049
Phone: 310-979-9090
Fax: 310-207-0035
Website: www.vintage-vfm.com

Management and Staff

Fred Sands, Chairman & Managing Director
Henry Brandon, Managing Director
Jeremy Holland, Principal
Mark Sampson, Managing Director
Thomas Webster, Vice President

Type of Firm

Private Equity Firm

Project Preferences

Role in Financing:

Prefer role as deal originator

Type of Financing Preferred:

Leveraged Buyout
Expansion
Later Stage
Management Buyouts
Special Situation
Acquisition
Recapitalizations

Size of Investments Considered:

Min Size of Investment Considered (000s): $5,000
Max Size of Investment Considered (000s): $20,000

Geographical Preferences

United States Preferences:

All U.S.

Industry Preferences

In Business Serv. prefer:

Services

In Manufact. prefer:

Manufacturing

Additional Information

Name of Most Recent Fund: Vintage Capital Partners Side, L.P.
Most Recent Fund Was Raised: 09/14/2006
Year Founded: 2004
Capital Under Management: $162,500,000
Current Activity Level : Actively seeking new investments

VINTAGE VENTURE PARTNERS

16 Abba Eban Avenue
P.O.B. 2037
Herzliyah Pituach, Israel 46120
Phone: 972-9-954-8464
Fax: 972-9-954-1012
E-mail: info@vintageventures.com
Website: www.vintageventures.com

Management and Staff

Abe Finkelstein, Principal
Alan Feld, Managing General Partner
Amit Frenkel, Venture Partner
Hagai Goldhirsch, Chief Financial Officer

Type of Firm

Private Equity Advisor or Fund of Funds

Project Preferences

Type of Financing Preferred:

Fund of Funds
Early Stage
Seed
Fund of Funds of Second

Geographical Preferences

International Preferences:

Middle East
Israel
Asia

Additional Information

Name of Most Recent Fund: Vintage Ventures II
Most Recent Fund Was Raised: 12/09/2005
Year Founded: 2003
Capital Under Management: $234,000,000
Current Activity Level : Actively seeking new investments

VIOLA PRIVATE EQUITY

c/o Viola Group
16 Abba Eban Avenue
Herzeliya, Israel 46725
Phone: 972-9-972-0500
E-mail: gality@violape.com
Website: www.violaprivateequity.com

Management and Staff

Harel Beit-On, Partner
Jonathan Kolber, Partner
Osnat Ronen, Partner
Sami Totah, Partner

Type of Firm

Bank Affiliated

Project Preferences

Type of Financing Preferred:

Leveraged Buyout
Expansion

Geographical Preferences

International Preferences:

Israel

Additional Information

Year Founded: 2008
Capital Under Management: $150,000,000
Current Activity Level : Actively seeking new investments

VIRGIN GREEN FUND

512 Second Street
4th floor
San Francisco, CA USA 94107
Phone: 415-979-0280
E-mail: info@virgingreenfund.com
Website: www.virgingreenfund.com

Other Offices

Level 6
48 Leicester Square
London, United Kingdom WC2H 7LT

Management and Staff

Anup Jacob, Partner
Bakhrom Ibragimov, Principal
Dimitri Pauwels, Venture Partner
Evan Lovell, Partner
Mike Willis, Principal
Shai Weiss, Managing Partner
Victoria Newman, Principal

Type of Firm

Private Equity Firm

Project Preferences

Type of Financing Preferred:

Second Stage Financing
Expansion
First Stage Financing

Geographical Preferences

International Preferences:

United Kingdom

Industry Preferences

In Industrial/Energy prefer:
Alternative Energy
Energy Conservation Relat

Additional Information
Name of Most Recent Fund: Virgin Green Fund I, L.P.
Most Recent Fund Was Raised: 09/20/2007
Year Founded: 2007
Capital Under Management: $216,900,000
Current Activity Level : Actively seeking new investments

VIRGO CAPITAL

611 South Congress Avenue
Suite 420
Austin, TX USA 78704
Phone: 512-275-7840
Fax: 512-519-1656
E-mail: info@virgocapital.com
Website: www.virgocapital.com

Other Offices
12316-A North May Avenue
Suite 274
Oklahoma City, OK USA 73120
Phone: 405-227-9451
Fax: 512-519-1656

Management and Staff
Guhan Swaminathan, Managing Director
Hemanth Parasuram, Managing Director

Type of Firm
Private Equity Firm

Project Preferences

Role in Financing:
Prefer role as deal originator but will also invest in deals created by others

Type of Financing Preferred:
Leveraged Buyout
Later Stage
Acquisition

Size of Investments Considered:
Min Size of Investment Considered (000s): $2,000
Max Size of Investment Considered (000s): $15,000

Geographical Preferences

United States Preferences:
All U.S.

Industry Preferences

In Computer Software prefer:
Data Processing
Software
Applications Software

In Internet Specific prefer:
Web Aggregration/Portals

In Consumer Related prefer:
Education Related

In Financial Services prefer:
Financial Services
Insurance

In Business Serv. prefer:
Services

Additional Information
Name of Most Recent Fund: Virgo Capital Fund I
Most Recent Fund Was Raised: 02/01/2006
Year Founded: 2005
Capital Under Management: $50,000,000
Current Activity Level : Actively seeking new investments
Method of Compensation: Return on investment is of primary concern, do not charge fees

---

VIRTAA HAMEESEEN KY

Visamaentie 33 A-rakennus
Hameenlinna, Finland 13100
Phone: 358-3-621-5209
Fax: 358-3-621-5200

Type of Firm
Private Equity Firm

Association Membership
European Private Equity and Venture Capital Assoc.

Project Preferences

Type of Financing Preferred:
Balanced

Geographical Preferences

International Preferences:
Europe

Additional Information
Year Founded: 2000
Current Activity Level : Actively seeking new investments

VIRTUS CAPITAL PARTNERS

Via Bruno Buozzi 10
Torino, Italy 10123
Phone: 39-011-542384
Fax: 39-011-5069407
E-mail: info@vcp.it
Website: www.vcp.it

Management and Staff
Emanuele Di Gresy, President
Silvia Rovere, Partner
Walter Ricciotti, Partner

Type of Firm
Private Equity Advisor or Fund of Funds

Association Membership
European Private Equity and Venture Capital Assoc.

Project Preferences

Type of Financing Preferred:
Second Stage Financing
Leveraged Buyout
Expansion
Later Stage

Geographical Preferences

International Preferences:
Italy
United Kingdom
Switzerland

Industry Preferences

In Internet Specific prefer:
Internet

In Computer Other prefer:
Computer Related

In Medical/Health prefer:
Medical/Health

In Industrial/Energy prefer:
Energy
Industrial Products

In Business Serv. prefer:
Services

In Manufact. prefer:
Manufacturing
Additional Information
Year Founded: 2001
Capital Under Management: $26,400,000
Current Activity Level : Actively seeking new investments

VISA INC. (FKA: VISA INTERNATIONAL)

900 Metro Center Boulevard
Foster City, CA USA 94404
Phone: 650-432-7253
Fax: 650-4325788
Website: www.visa.com/sai

Management and Staff
Jay Reineman, Vice President

Type of Firm
Corporate PE/Venture

Association Membership
National Venture Capital Association - USA (NVCA)

Project Preferences

Role in Financing:
Prefer role in deals created by others

Type of Financing Preferred:
Second Stage Financing

Size of Investments Considered:
Min Size of Investment Considered (000s): $1,000
Max Size of Investment Considered (000s): $5,000

Geographical Preferences

International Preferences:
All International

Industry Preferences

In Communications prefer:
Wireless Communications

In Computer Software prefer:
Data Processing
Software
Applications Software
Artificial Intelligence

In Internet Specific prefer:
E-Commerce Technology
Internet
Ecommerce
Web Aggregration/Portals

In Financial Services prefer:
Financial Services

Additional Information

Year Founded: 1995
Capital Under Management: $10,000,000
Current Activity Level : Actively seeking new investments
Method of Compensation: Return on investment is of primary concern, do not charge fees

---

VISCOGLIOSI BROS LLC

505 Park Avenue
14th Floor
New York, NY USA 10022
Phone: 01-212-583-9700
Fax: 01-212-583-9707
Website: www.vbllc.com

Management and Staff

Anthony Viscogliosi, Founding Partner
John Viscogliosi, Founding Partner
Marc Viscogliosi, Founding Partner

Type of Firm

Private Equity Firm

Project Preferences

Type of Financing Preferred:
Balanced

Geographical Preferences

United States Preferences:
All U.S.

International Preferences:
Europe

Industry Preferences

In Medical/Health prefer:
Medical/Health
Medical Products

Additional Information

Name of Most Recent Fund: Viscogliosi Brothers, LLC
Most Recent Fund Was Raised: 05/09/2005
Year Founded: 1999
Capital Under Management: $6,000,000
Current Activity Level : Actively seeking new investments

VISION CAPITAL LLP

54 Jermyn Street
London, United Kingdom SW1Y 6LX
Phone: 44-20-7389-6410
Fax: 44-20-7389-6411
E-mail: info@visioncapital.com
Website: www.visioncapital.com

Management and Staff

Alistar Wormsley, Managing Partner
Andrew Hawkins, Managing Partner
David Robinson, Chief Operating Officer
Julian Mash, Chief Executive Officer
Lorenzo Russo, Partner
Matt Shafer, Principal
Paul Kilduff, Managing Director
Scott Greenhalgh, Managing Director
Tim Wright, Managing Director

Type of Firm

Private Equity Firm

Project Preferences

Type of Financing Preferred:
Fund of Funds
Leveraged Buyout
Balanced
Fund of Funds of Second

Geographical Preferences

United States Preferences:
All U.S.

International Preferences:
United Kingdom
Europe

Additional Information

Year Founded: 1997
Capital Under Management: $599,200,000
Current Activity Level : Actively seeking new investments

VISION CAPITAL MANAGEMENT

One Bayshore Plaza, Suite 360
1350 Old Bayshore Hwy
Burlingame, CA USA 94010
Phone: 650-373-2720
Fax: 650-373-2727
Website: www.visioncap.com

Other Offices

6 Rue de la Croix d'Or
Geneva, Switzerland 1204
Phone: 41-22-544-6000
Fax: 41-22-544-6006

Management and Staff

Brendan Richardson, Partner
Dag Syrrist, General Partner
Dominique Pitteloud, Principal
Herve Goguely, Venture Partner
Jacques Clay, Venture Partner
John Turner, General Partner
Linus Lundberg, Principal
Sven Lingjaerde, General Partner
William Wick, Chief Financial Officer

Type of Firm

Private Equity Firm

Association Membership

European Private Equity and Venture Capital Assoc.

Project Preferences

Role in Financing:
Will function either as deal originator or investor in deals created by others

Type of Financing Preferred:
Expansion

Size of Investments Considered:
Min Size of Investment Considered (000s): $1,000
Max Size of Investment Considered (000s): $3,500

Geographical Preferences

International Preferences:
Europe

Industry Focus

(% based on actual investment)

Internet Specific	28.9%
Semiconductors/Other Elect.	28.2%
Other Products	18.8%
Communications and Media	14.1%
Computer Software and Services	10.1%

Additional Information

Name of Most Recent Fund: Vision Capital III, L.P.
Most Recent Fund Was Raised: 03/31/2001
Year Founded: 1997
Capital Under Management: $163,000,000
Current Activity Level : Actively seeking new investments

Method of Compensation: Return on investment is of primary concern, do not charge fees

VISION INVESTMENT CORPORATION (AKA: DECHENG SHENGJING)

No. 32 Zhongguancun Street
20/F Hengsheng Tower
Haidian, Beijing, China 100086
Phone: 86-1-5292-6696
Fax: 86-1-5292-6613
E-mail: biz@vision-investment.com
Website: www.vision-investment.com

Type of Firm

Private Equity Firm

Project Preferences

Type of Financing Preferred:
Later Stage

Geographical Preferences

International Preferences:
Macau
Taiwan
China
Hong Kong

Industry Preferences

In Consumer Related prefer:
Consumer
Retail

In Industrial/Energy prefer:
Energy
Materials

Additional Information

Year Founded: 2007
Current Activity Level : Actively seeking new investments

VISION VENTURE CAPITAL LTD

Level 9, 500 Queen Street
Brisbane, Australia 4000
Phone: 1-800-666-262
Fax: 1-800-666-363
Website: www.vvcinternational.com/home

Type of Firm

Angel Group

Project Preferences

Type of Financing Preferred:
Seed

Geographical Preferences

International Preferences:
Pacific

Additional Information

Year Founded: 2000
Capital Under Management: $500,000
Current Activity Level : Actively seeking new investments

VISTA CAPITAL DE EXPANSION SA

Apartado de Correos 6009
Serrano 67-4
Madrid, Spain 28006
Phone: 34-914-426-2590
Fax: 34-91-431-3267

Type of Firm

Bank Affiliated

Association Membership

Spanish Venture Capital Association (ASCRI)

Project Preferences

Role in Financing:
Prefer role as deal originator

Type of Financing Preferred:
Second Stage Financing
Leveraged Buyout
Expansion

Size of Investments Considered:
Min Size of Investment Considered (000s): $5,000
Max Size of Investment Considered: No Limit

Geographical Preferences

International Preferences:
Spain

Industry Preferences

In Communications prefer:
Data Communications

In Consumer Related prefer:
Entertainment and Leisure
Retail
Food/Beverage
Consumer Products

In Industrial/Energy prefer:
Alternative Energy
Industrial Products
Environmental Related

Additional Information

Name of Most Recent Fund: Vista Expansion
Most Recent Fund Was Raised: 01/01/1989
Year Founded: 1990
Capital Under Management: $127,000,000
Current Activity Level : Actively seeking new investments
Method of Compensation: Return on invest. most important, but chg. closing fees, service fees, etc.

VISTA CAPITAL LLC (FKA: AO CAPITAL CORP.)

80 Field Point Road
Greenwich, CT USA 06830
Phone: 203-622-6600
Fax: 203-622-1292
E-mail: aocapital@aocapital.net
Website: www.aocapital.net

Management and Staff

Allen Skott, Managing Director
J.W. Van Dyke, Chief Financial Officer
William Cotter, Managing Director

Type of Firm

Private Equity Firm

Project Preferences

Type of Financing Preferred:
Leveraged Buyout
Turnaround
Management Buyouts
Acquisition

Size of Investments Considered:
Min Size of Investment Considered (000s): $3,000
Max Size of Investment Considered (000s): $25,000

Geographical Preferences

United States Preferences:
All U.S.

Canadian Preferences:
All Canada

International Preferences:
Italy
United Kingdom
Latin America
Luxembourg
Netherlands
Spain
Belgium
Germany
France

Industry Preferences

In Industrial/Energy prefer:
Industrial Products
Process Control
Machinery

In Financial Services prefer:
Financial Services

In Manufact. prefer:
Manufacturing

Additional Information

Year Founded: 1972
Capital Under Management: $135,000,000
Current Activity Level : Actively seeking new investments

Method of Compensation: Return on investment is of primary concern, do not charge fees

VISTA EQUITY PARTNERS

150 California Street
19th Floor
San Francisco, CA USA 94111
Phone: 415-765-6500
Fax: 415-765-6666
E-mail: vep@vistaequitypartners.com
Website: www.vistaequitypartners.com

Management and Staff

Betty Hung, Vice President
Brian Sheth, Principal
Christian Sowul, Vice President
James Ford, Vice President
James Hickey, Principal
John Warnken-Brill, Chief Financial Officer
Martin Taylor, Principal
Robert Rogers, Vice President
Stephen Davis, Principal

Type of Firm

Private Equity Firm

Project Preferences

Role in Financing:

Prefer role as deal originator but will also invest in deals created by others

Type of Financing Preferred:

Generalist PE

Size of Investments Considered:

Min Size of Investment Considered (000s): $10,000
Max Size of Investment Considered (000s): $200,000

Geographical Preferences

United States Preferences:

All U.S.

Canadian Preferences:

All Canada

International Preferences:

Italy
United Kingdom
Luxembourg
Netherlands
Portugal
Spain
Australia
Belgium
New Zealand
Germany
France

Industry Focus

(% based on actual investment)

Computer Software and Services	72.4%
Internet Specific	27.6%

Additional Information

Name of Most Recent Fund: Vista Equity Partners Fund III, L.P.
Most Recent Fund Was Raised: 08/13/2007
Year Founded: 2000
Capital Under Management: $1,200,000,000
Current Activity Level : Actively seeking new investments
Method of Compensation: Return on invest. most important, but chg. closing fees, service fees, etc.

VISTA VENTURES

1011 Walnut Street
Fourth Floor
Boulder, CO USA 80302
Phone: 303-543-5716
Fax: 303-543-5717
E-mail: info@vistavc.com
Website: www.vistavc.com

Other Offices

19 Old Town Square
Suite 238
Fort Collins, CO USA 80524
Phone: 970-495-1800
Fax: 970-482-0251

Management and Staff

Catharine Merigold, General Partner
David Dwyer, General Partner
Kirk Holland, General Partner
Lisa Reeves, General Partner
Molly Nasky, Chief Financial Officer

Type of Firm

Private Equity Firm

Association Membership

National Venture Capital Association - USA (NVCA)

Project Preferences

Role in Financing:

Prefer role as deal originator but will also invest in deals created by others

Type of Financing Preferred:

Early Stage
Expansion
Seed

Size of Investments Considered:

Min Size of Investment Considered (000s): $1,000
Max Size of Investment Considered (000s): $4,000

Geographical Preferences

United States Preferences:

Rocky Mountain
West Coast
Colorado

Industry Preferences

In Communications prefer:

Communications and Media
Wireless Communications

In Computer Software prefer:

Software
Systems Software
Applications Software

In Internet Specific prefer:

Internet
Ecommerce

Additional Information

Name of Most Recent Fund: Vista Ventures I
Most Recent Fund Was Raised: 04/15/2000
Year Founded: 2000
Capital Under Management: $75,000,000
Current Activity Level : Actively seeking new investments
Method of Compensation: Return on investment is of primary concern, do not charge fees

VISTECH CORP.

P.O. Box 510
Westport, CT USA 06881
Phone: 203-454-0300
Fax: 203-454-1054
E-mail: admin@vistechcorp.com
Website: www.vistechcorp.com

Management and Staff

E. Per Sorensen, Managing Director
Lincoln Rathman, Managing Director

Type of Firm

Private Equity Advisor or Fund of Funds

Project Preferences

Role in Financing:

Prefer role as deal originator

Type of Financing Preferred:

Joint Ventures
Private Placement

Geographical Preferences

International Preferences:

Latin America
Mexico

Industry Preferences

In Biotechnology prefer:

Human Biotechnology
Industrial Biotechnology
Biosensors

In Medical/Health prefer:

Drug/Equipmt Delivery

In Consumer Related prefer:

Food/Beverage
Hotels and Resorts

In Industrial/Energy prefer:

Energy
Industrial Products
Process Control

In Financial Services prefer:
Financial Services

In Business Serv. prefer:
Consulting Services

In Utilities prefer:
Utilities

Additional Information
Year Founded: 1980
Current Activity Level : Actively seeking new investments
Method of Compensation: Professional fee required whether or not deal closes

VITA NOVA VENTURES AB
Haraldsgatan 5
Gothenburg, Sweden 413 14
Phone: 46-31-703-1850
Fax: 46-31-703-1860
E-mail: information@vnv.se
Website: www.vnv.se

Management and Staff
Anders Sjogren, Chief Financial Officer

Type of Firm
Private Equity Firm

Association Membership
European Private Equity and Venture Capital Assoc.

Project Preferences
Type of Financing Preferred:
Balanced

Geographical Preferences
International Preferences:
Sweden

Additional Information
Year Founded: 2006
Capital Under Management: $20,500,000
Current Activity Level : Actively seeking new investments

VITRUVIAN PARTNERS LLP
53 Davies Street
London, United Kingdom W1K 5JH
Phone: 44-20-7152-6503
Fax: 44-20-7152-6504
Website: www.vitruvianpartners.com

Management and Staff
Ben Johnson, Principal
David Nahama, Partner
Ian Riley, Managing Partner
Jussi Wuoristo, Vice President
Leonard Clemens, Vice President
Mark Hartford, Partner
Michael Risman, Managing Partner
Stephen Byrne, Principal
Toby Wyles, Managing Partner

Type of Firm
Private Equity Firm

Project Preferences
Type of Financing Preferred:
Leveraged Buyout
Expansion
Management Buyouts
Private Placement
Recapitalizations

Size of Investments Considered:
Min Size of Investment Considered (000s): $75,075
Max Size of Investment Considered (000s): $225,225

Geographical Preferences
International Preferences:
United Kingdom
Ireland
Sweden
Netherlands
Luxembourg
Switzerland
Greenland
Austria
Iceland
Germany
Belgium
Finland
Norway
Denmark
Faroe Islands

Industry Preferences
In Communications prefer:
Communications and Media
Telecommunications
Media and Entertainment

In Consumer Related prefer:
Entertainment and Leisure

In Financial Services prefer:
Financial Services

In Business Serv. prefer:
Services

Additional Information
Year Founded: 2006
Capital Under Management: $1,388,900,000
Current Activity Level : Actively seeking new investments

VIVERIS MANAGEMENT S.A.S.
6, allees Turcat Mery
Marseille, France 13008
Phone: 33-4-9129-4150
Fax: 33-4-9129-4151
Website: www.innoveris.fr

Management and Staff
Eric Schettini, President

Type of Firm
Bank Affiliated

Association Membership
French Venture Capital Association (AFIC)

Project Preferences
Type of Financing Preferred:
Leveraged Buyout
Early Stage
Expansion
Balanced
Management Buyouts
Startup

Geographical Preferences
International Preferences:
Europe
Western Europe
France

Industry Preferences
In Communications prefer:
Telecommunications
Data Communications

In Computer Software prefer:
Software

In Industrial/Energy prefer:
Materials
Environmental Related

In Business Serv. prefer:
Services

Additional Information
Year Founded: 2000
Capital Under Management: $60,900,000
Current Activity Level : Actively seeking new investments

VIVO VENTURES
575 High Street
Suite 201
Palo Alto, CA USA 94301
Phone: 650-688-0818
Fax: 650-688-0815
E-mail: info@vivoventures.com
Website: www.vivoventures.com

Management and Staff
Albert Cha, Managing Partner
Chen Yu, Partner
Edgar Engleman, Managing Partner

Type of Firm
Private Equity Firm

Project Preferences

Role in Financing:
Prefer role as deal originator

Type of Financing Preferred:
Second Stage Financing
Mezzanine
Early Stage
Seed
First Stage Financing
Startup

Size of Investments Considered:
Min Size of Investment Considered (000s): $2,500
Max Size of Investment Considered (000s): $25,000

Geographical Preferences

United States Preferences:
All U.S.

Industry Focus

(% based on actual investment)

Biotechnology	52.5%
Medical/Health	40.1%
Consumer Related	4.1%
Communications and Media	1.2%
Computer Software and Services	1.2%
Internet Specific	0.8%

Additional Information

Year Founded: 1997
Capital Under Management: $383,000,000
Current Activity Level : Actively seeking new investments
Method of Compensation: Return on invest. most important, but chg. closing fees, service fees, etc.

VIZILLE CAPITAL INNOVATION

Espace Cordeliers
2, rue du President Carnot
Lyon, France 69002
Phone: 33-4-7256-9348
Fax: 33-4-7277-5855
Website: www.banquedevizille.fr

Management and Staff
Olivier Levy, Partner

Type of Firm
Bank Affiliated

Project Preferences

Type of Financing Preferred:
Early Stage
Expansion

Geographical Preferences

International Preferences:
Europe
France

Additional Information

Year Founded: 1990
Current Activity Level : Actively seeking new investments

VL NEUBERG

69 Jervois Street
Unit 2705-06
Sheung Wan, Hong Kong
Phone: 852-2919-5350
Fax: 852-2802-8229
E-mail: hkoffice@neuberg.com.hk
Website: www.neuberg.com.hk

Type of Firm
Private Equity Firm

Association Membership
Hong Kong Venture Capital Association (HKVCA)

Project Preferences

Type of Financing Preferred:
Early Stage
Balanced
Startup

Geographical Preferences

International Preferences:
China
Hong Kong

Industry Preferences

In Communications prefer:
Telecommunications

In Computer Software prefer:
Systems Software

In Internet Specific prefer:
Internet
Ecommerce

Additional Information

Year Founded: 1998
Current Activity Level : Actively seeking new investments

VMG EQUITY PARTNERS

55 Francisco Street
Suite 400
San Francisco, CA USA 94133
Phone: 415-632-4200
Fax: 415-632-4222
Website: www.vmgpartners.com

Other Offices

Two Park Plaza
Suite 770
Irvine, CA USA 92614
Phone: 949-428-0085
Fax: 949-428-0086

Management and Staff
David Baram, Co-Founder
Emmy Cattani, Partner
Kara Cissell-Roell, Managing Director
Michael Mauze, Managing Director
Robert Schult, Co-Founder
Scott Elaine Case, Co-Founder

Type of Firm
Private Equity Firm

Project Preferences

Type of Financing Preferred:
Leveraged Buyout
Expansion

Geographical Preferences

United States Preferences:
All U.S.

Industry Preferences

In Consumer Related prefer:
Consumer
Entertainment and Leisure
Food/Beverage
Consumer Products
Consumer Services

Additional Information

Year Founded: 2007
Capital Under Management: $325,000,000
Current Activity Level : Actively seeking new investments

VNT MANAGEMENT OY, LTD.

Yrittajankatu 15
5th floor
Vaasa, Finland 65380
Phone: 358-20-121-2560
Fax: 358-6-282-8945
Website: www.vntm.com

Other Offices

Teknobulevardi 3-5
Vantaa, Finland 01530
Fax: 358-9-2517-8480

Dachauerstrasse 37
Munich, Germany 80335
Phone: 49-89-5455-8311
Fax: 49-89-5455-8333

Management and Staff
Harri Ollila, Partner
Jarmo Saaranen, President
Jussi Palmroth, Partner
Torsten Wipiejewsk, Partner
Vesa Sadeharju, Partner

Type of Firm
Private Equity Firm

Association Membership
European Private Equity and Venture Capital Assoc.

Project Preferences

Type of Financing Preferred:
Early Stage

Size of Investments Considered:
Min Size of Investment Considered (000s): $702
Max Size of Investment Considered (000s): $7,017

Geographical Preferences

Canadian Preferences:
All Canada

International Preferences:
Europe
Finland

Industry Preferences

In Semiconductor/Electr prefer:
Electronics

In Industrial/Energy prefer:
Energy
Alternative Energy
Energy Conservation Relat
Environmental Related

Additional Information
Name of Most Recent Fund: Power Fund I
Most Recent Fund Was Raised: 02/26/2003
Year Founded: 2002
Capital Under Management: $112,300,000
Current Activity Level : Actively seeking new investments

VNU VENTURES
Ceylonpoort 5 - 25
Haarlem, Netherlands 2037 AA
Phone: 31-23-546-38-67
Fax: 31-23-546-39-04

Type of Firm
Private Equity Firm

Additional Information
Current Activity Level : Actively seeking new investments

VOGA CAPITAL S.A. (FKA: FR CAPITAL)
Av. Ataulfo de Paiva, 1251
s.307
Rio de Janeiro, RJ, Brazil 22440-031
Phone: 55-21-2294-1876
Fax: 55-21-2511-3721
E-mail: info@vogacapital.com.br
Website: www.vogacapital.com.br

Type of Firm
Other

Project Preferences

Type of Financing Preferred:
Balanced

Geographical Preferences

International Preferences:
Brazil

Additional Information
Year Founded: 2002
Current Activity Level : Actively seeking new investments

VOLATI INDUSTRI AB
Engelbrektsplan 1
Stockholm, Sweden 114 34
Phone: 46-8-216-840
Fax: 46-8-216-918
E-mail: volatiindustri@volati.com
Website: www.volati.com

Type of Firm
Private Equity Firm

Project Preferences

Type of Financing Preferred:
Balanced

Geographical Preferences

International Preferences:
Sweden
Europe

Additional Information
Year Founded: 2003
Capital Under Management: $60,600,000
Current Activity Level : Actively seeking new investments

VOLCANO CAPITAL, LTD.
1251 Avenue of the Americas
18th floor
New York, NY USA 10020
E-mail: info@volcanocap.com
Website: www.volcanocap.com

Type of Firm
Private Equity Firm

Project Preferences

Type of Financing Preferred:
Leveraged Buyout
Generalist PE
Early Stage
Expansion
Seed
Later Stage

Geographical Preferences

United States Preferences:
All U.S.

Industry Preferences

In Medical/Health prefer:
Medical/Health
Medical Products
Health Services

Additional Information
Year Founded: 2009
Current Activity Level : Actively seeking new investments

VOLGA RESOURCES SICAV-SIF
124, bd. de la Petrusse
Luxembourg, Luxembourg 2330
E-mail: info@volga.lu
Website: www.volga.lu

Type of Firm
Private Equity Firm

Project Preferences

Type of Financing Preferred:
Balanced
Public Companies

Geographical Preferences

International Preferences:
Central Europe
Turkey
Eastern Europe
Russia

Industry Preferences

In Industrial/Energy prefer:
Oil and Gas Exploration

In Financial Services prefer:
Financial Services
Real Estate

Additional Information
Year Founded: 2007
Current Activity Level : Actively seeking new investments

VOLIO CAPITAL, S.A.
Parque Empresarial Forum
Torre G, Piso 7
Santa Ana, Costa Rica
Phone: 506-204-7080
Fax: 506-204-7667
E-mail: info@voliocapital.com
Website: www.voliocapital.com

Other Offices

Bosques de Duraznos
No.61 Piso 1
Bosques de Las Lomas, Mexico 11 700
Phone: 5255-5245-8676
Fax: 5255-5245-1693

Edificio CAR, Piso 3
4 km Carretera a Masaya
Managua, Nicaragua
Phone: 505-270-2112
Fax: 505-270-5225

World Trade Center Building 89 North Ave
El Mirador Street, Tower 1, Level 2
San Salvador, El Salvador
Phone: 503-2500-0895
Fax: 503-2500-0851

Management and Staff

Jorge Volio, Founding Partner

Type of Firm

Bank Affiliated

Project Preferences

Type of Financing Preferred:

Balanced

Geographical Preferences

International Preferences:

El Salvador
Mexico
Costa Rica
Nicaragua

Additional Information

Year Founded: 2007
Current Activity Level : Actively seeking new investments

VOLVO TECHNOLOGY TRANSFER AB

Gotaverksgatan 2
P.O. Box 3300, VHK
Goteborg, Sweden 405 08
Phone: 46-31-669-160
Fax: 46-31-669-196
E-mail: vhk.vtt@memo.volvo.se
Website: www.volvo.com/veturetech

Management and Staff

Charlotta Modig, Chief Financial Officer

Type of Firm

Corporate PE/Venture

Association Membership

Swedish Venture Capital Association (SVCA)
European Private Equity and Venture Capital Assoc.

Project Preferences

Type of Financing Preferred:

Leveraged Buyout
Expansion
Seed
Startup

Geographical Preferences

International Preferences:

Europe
Scandanavia/Nordic Region

Industry Preferences

In Communications prefer:

Communications and Media

In Industrial/Energy prefer:

Energy
Industrial Products

In Business Serv. prefer:

Services
Consulting Services

Additional Information

Year Founded: 1927
Capital Under Management: $65,900,000
Current Activity Level : Actively seeking new investments

VON BRAUN & SCHREIBER PRIVATE EQUITY PARTNERS GMBH

Promenadeplatz 12
Munich, Germany 80333
Phone: 49-89-28695-20
Fax: 49-89-2869-5210
E-mail: private.equity@braunschreiber.com
Website: www.braunschreiber.com

Management and Staff

Alexander Binz, Managing Director
Emmeram Von Braun, Managing Director
Gottfried Schreiber, Managing Director
Timothy Reynolds, Managing Director

Type of Firm

Private Equity Firm

Association Membership

European Private Equity and Venture Capital Assoc.

Project Preferences

Type of Financing Preferred:

Fund of Funds

Geographical Preferences

International Preferences:

Europe
Israel

Additional Information

Year Founded: 1999
Capital Under Management: $1,600,000
Current Activity Level : Actively seeking new investments

VOOBON VENTURES, INC.

3020 Roswell Road North East
Suite # 200
Marietta, GA USA 30062
Phone: 678-265-3720
E-mail: investor@voobonventures.com
Website: www.voobonventures.com

Management and Staff

Curtis Fox, Chief Executive Officer
Mark Shariar, President

Type of Firm

Private Equity Firm

Project Preferences

Type of Financing Preferred:

Leveraged Buyout
Generalist PE
Early Stage
Expansion
Turnaround
Seed
Management Buyouts
Startup
Acquisition
Recapitalizations

Size of Investments Considered:

Min Size of Investment Considered (000s): $5,000
Max Size of Investment Considered (000s): $500,000

Industry Preferences

In Communications prefer:

Telecommunications
Media and Entertainment

In Biotechnology prefer:

Biotechnology

In Medical/Health prefer:

Medical/Health

In Industrial/Energy prefer:

Oil & Gas Drilling,Explor
Alternative Energy

In Transportation prefer:

Aerospace

In Financial Services prefer:

Real Estate

Additional Information

Year Founded: 2008
Current Activity Level : Actively seeking new investments

VORTEX PARTNERS, L.P.

14135 Midway Road
Suite 100
Addison, TX USA 75001
Phone: 214-849-9806
Fax: 214-849-9850
E-mail: info@vortexpartners.com
Website: www.vortexpartners.com

Management and Staff

Chris O'Neill, General Partner
John Scarisbrick, Venture Partner
Robert Miles, General Partner
Tom Hedrick, General Partner
Victor Liu, General Partner

Type of Firm

Private Equity Firm

Project Preferences

Role in Financing:
Prefer role as deal originator but will also invest in deals created by others

Type of Financing Preferred:
Seed
First Stage Financing
Startup

Size of Investments Considered:
Min Size of Investment Considered (000s): $500
Max Size of Investment Considered (000s): $5,000

Industry Preferences

In Communications prefer:
Telecommunications
Wireless Communications
Data Communications

In Computer Software prefer:
Computer Services
Data Processing
Software
Systems Software
Applications Software

In Internet Specific prefer:
Internet
Ecommerce

In Semiconductor/Electr prefer:
Semiconductor
Laser Related
Fiber Optics

In Business Serv. prefer:
Services

Additional Information

Name of Most Recent Fund: Vortex Corporate Development Fund
Most Recent Fund Was Raised: 03/01/2000
Year Founded: 1998
Capital Under Management: $50,000,000
Current Activity Level : Actively seeking new investments
Method of Compensation: Return on investment is of primary concern, do not charge fees

VOSTOK GAS, LTD. (FKA: VOSTOK NAFTA INVESTMENT)

2 Church Street
P.O. Box HM 666
Hamilton, Bermuda
E-mail: info@vostokgas.com
Website: www.vostokgas.com

Other Offices

Hovslagargatan 5
3rd floor
Stockholm, Sweden SE-111 48
Phone: 46-8-5450-1550
Fax: 46-8-5450-1554

Management and Staff

William Rand, Managing Director

Type of Firm

Investment Management Firm

Project Preferences

Type of Financing Preferred:
Leveraged Buyout
Expansion

Geographical Preferences

International Preferences:
Russia

Industry Preferences

In Industrial/Energy prefer:
Energy
Oil and Gas Exploration
Oil & Gas Drilling,Explor

In Agr/Forestr/Fish prefer:
Mining and Minerals

Additional Information

Year Founded: 2002
Capital Under Management: $20,000,000
Current Activity Level : Actively seeking new investments

VOTORANTIM VENTURE CAPITAL LTDA.

Rua Jeronimo da Veiga, 384
12 andar, Itaim Bibi
Sao Paulo, Brazil 04536-000
Phone: 55-11-3077-5050
Fax: 55-11-3077-5051
Website: www.vnnegocios.com.br

Management and Staff

Paulo Henrique De Oliveira Santos, President

Type of Firm

Corporate PE/Venture

Association Membership

Brazilian Venture Capital Association (ABCR)

Project Preferences

Type of Financing Preferred:
Expansion
Balanced
Seed
Startup

Size of Investments Considered:
Min Size of Investment Considered (000s): $1,000
Max Size of Investment Considered (000s): $15,000

Geographical Preferences

International Preferences:
Brazil

Industry Preferences

In Communications prefer:
Communications and Media

In Biotechnology prefer:
Biotechnology

In Consumer Related prefer:
Retail

In Industrial/Energy prefer:
Industrial Products

In Business Serv. prefer:
Services

Additional Information

Year Founded: 2000
Capital Under Management: $300,000,000
Current Activity Level : Actively seeking new investments

VOYAGER CAPITAL

719 Second Avenue
Suite 1400
Seattle, WA USA 98104
Phone: 206-438-1800
Fax: 206-438-1900
E-mail: info@voyagercapital.com
Website: www.voyagercapital.com

Other Offices

3000 Sand Hill Road
3-100
Menlo Park, CA USA 94025
Phone: 650-854-4300
Fax: 650-854-4399

34 North West First Avenue
Suite 400
Portland, OR USA 97209
Phone: 503-501-2615
Fax: 503-922-0131

Management and Staff

Bruce Chizen, Venture Partner
Curtis Feeny, Managing Director
Daniel Ahn, Managing Director
Diane Fraiman, Venture Partner
Enrique Godreau, Managing Director
Erik Benson, Managing Director
Geoff Entress, Venture Partner
Jodi Sherman Jahic, Venture Partner
Thomas Huseby, Venture Partner
Tom Kippola, Venture Partner
William McAleer, Managing Director

Type of Firm

Private Equity Firm

Association Membership

Western Association of Venture Capitalists (WAVC)
National Venture Capital Association - USA (NVCA)

Project Preferences

Role in Financing:

Prefer role as deal originator but will also invest in deals created by others

Type of Financing Preferred:

Early Stage
Balanced

Size of Investments Considered:

Min Size of Investment Considered (000s): $2,000
Max Size of Investment Considered (000s): $10,000

Geographical Preferences

United States Preferences:

Northwest
California

Industry Focus

(% based on actual investment)

Computer Software and Services	60.2%
Internet Specific	22.9%
Computer Hardware	10.0%
Other Products	2.6%
Semiconductors/Other Elect.	2.4%
Communications and Media	1.2%
Industrial/Energy	0.8%

Additional Information

Year Founded: 1997
Capital Under Management: $365,000,000
Current Activity Level : Actively seeking new investments
Method of Compensation: Return on investment is of primary concern, do not charge fees

VPSA (FKA: VIVENTURES PARTNERS)

21 Avenue Montaigne
Paris, France 75008
Phone: 33-1-5357-7700
Fax: 33-1-5357-7718
E-mail: info@viventures.com
Website: www.vpsa.com

Other Offices

Reading Thames Valley Park, Regus House
400 Thames Valley Park Drive
Reading, United Kingdom RG6 1PT
Phone: 44-118-963-7452
Fax: 44-118-963-7553

151 North Buona Vista Road
#02-25 Phase Z. Road
Singapore, Singapore 139347
Phone: 65-6311-9683
Fax: 65-6311-9682

169 University Avenue
Second Floor
Palo Alto, CA USA 94301
Phone: 650-566-8885
Fax: 650-566-8882

Type of Firm

Corporate PE/Venture

Association Membership

Singapore Venture Capital Association (SVCA)
European Private Equity and Venture Capital Assoc.

Project Preferences

Type of Financing Preferred:

Early Stage
Expansion
Mezzanine
Balanced
Seed
Startup

Size of Investments Considered:

Min Size of Investment Considered (000s): $891
Max Size of Investment Considered (000s): $13,371

Geographical Preferences

United States Preferences:

All U.S.

International Preferences:

Europe
Asia

Industry Focus

(% based on actual investment)

Internet Specific	34.2%
Computer Software and Services	34.1%
Communications and Media	14.9%
Semiconductors/Other Elect.	12.2%
Industrial/Energy	4.6%

Additional Information

Name of Most Recent Fund: Viventures II
Most Recent Fund Was Raised: 06/01/2000
Year Founded: 1998
Capital Under Management: $673,900,000
Current Activity Level : Actively seeking new investments

VSP CAPITAL (FKA: VENTURE STRATEGY PARTNERS)

201 Post Street
Suite 1100
San Francisco, CA USA 94118
Phone: 415-558-8600
Fax: 415-558-8686
E-mail: info@vspcapital.com
Website: www.vspcapital.com

Management and Staff

Dana Settle, Partner
Joanna Rees Gallanter, Managing Partner
John Hamm, General Partner

Type of Firm

Private Equity Firm

Association Membership

National Venture Capital Association - USA (NVCA)

Project Preferences

Role in Financing:

Prefer role as deal originator but will also invest in deals created by others

Type of Financing Preferred:

Early Stage
Start-up Financing
Seed
First Stage Financing

Size of Investments Considered:

Min Size of Investment Considered (000s): $1,000
Max Size of Investment Considered (000s): $10,000

Geographical Preferences

United States Preferences:

Northwest
Rocky Mountain
West Coast
Southwest

Industry Focus

(% based on actual investment)

Internet Specific	39.7%
Computer Software and Services	26.2%
Communications and Media	10.5%
Other Products	8.2%
Computer Hardware	5.3%
Semiconductors/Other Elect.	4.4%
Medical/Health	4.3%
Consumer Related	1.3%

Additional Information

Year Founded: 1996
Capital Under Management: $400,000,000
Current Activity Level : Actively seeking new investments
Method of Compensation: Return on invest. most important, but chg. closing fees, service fees, etc.

VSPRING CAPITAL

2795 East Cottonwood Parkway
Suite 360
Salt Lake City, UT USA 84121
Phone: 801-942-8999
Fax: 801-942-1636
E-mail: info@vspring.com
Website: www.vspring.com

Other Offices

317 Commercial Northeast
Albuquerque, NM USA 87102
Phone: 505-903-6740

Management and Staff

David Anderson, Chief Financial Officer
Dinesh Patel, Managing Director
Edward Ekstrom, Managing Director
Jeron Paul, Principal
Michael Connolly, Venture Partner
Michael Paul, Venture Partner
Paul Ahlstrom, Managing Director
Scott Petty, Managing Director

Type of Firm

Private Equity Firm

Association Membership

National Venture Capital Association - USA (NVCA)
Natl Assoc of Small Bus. Inv. Co (NASBIC)

Project Preferences

Role in Financing:
Prefer role as deal originator but will also invest in deals created by others

Type of Financing Preferred:
Second Stage Financing
Early Stage
Balanced
Seed
First Stage Financing

Size of Investments Considered:
Min Size of Investment Considered (000s): $250
Max Size of Investment Considered (000s): $5,000

Geographical Preferences

United States Preferences:
New Mexico
Nevada
Arizona
West Coast
California
Colorado
Idaho
Utah

Industry Preferences

In Communications prefer:
Communications and Media
Wireless Communications

In Computer Software prefer:
Software
Systems Software
Applications Software

In Internet Specific prefer:
Internet

In Computer Other prefer:
Computer Related

In Biotechnology prefer:
Biotechnology
Biotech Related Research

In Medical/Health prefer:
Drug/Equipmt Delivery
Pharmaceuticals

Additional Information

Name of Most Recent Fund: KickStart Seed Fund, L.P.
Most Recent Fund Was Raised: 07/23/2008
Year Founded: 2000
Capital Under Management: $180,000,000
Current Activity Level : Actively seeking new investments
Method of Compensation: Return on investment is of primary concern, do not charge fees

VTB CAPITAL

6, Lesnaya str.
Moscow, Russia 125047
Phone: 7-495-960-999
Fax: 7-495-663-470
E-mail: info@vtbcapital.com
Website: www.vtbcapital.com

Other Offices

50 Robinson Road
Westport, Singapore 068882
Phone: 65-6220-9422
Fax: 65-6225-0140

14 Cornhill
London, United Kingdom EC3V 3ND
Phone: 44-203-334-8000
Fax: 44-203-334-8900

Type of Firm

Investment Management Firm

Association Membership

Austrian PE and Venture Capital Association (AVCO)

Project Preferences

Type of Financing Preferred:
Early Stage
Generalist PE
Start-up Financing
Startup

Geographical Preferences

International Preferences:
Eastern Europe
Russia

Additional Information

Year Founded: 2009
Current Activity Level : Actively seeking new investments

VTC PARTNERS GMBH

Theatiner Strasse 8
Munich, Germany D-80333
Phone: 49-89-64-9490
Fax: 49-89-6494-9150
E-mail: info@vtc-venture.com
Website: www.vtc-partners.com

Management and Staff

Jurgen Max Leuze, Managing Director
Richard G. Ramsauer, Managing Director
Stefan Leuze, Managing Director
Stefan C. Heilmann, Managing Director
Thomas Robl, Managing Director
Ulrich Wolfrum, Managing Director

Type of Firm

Private Equity Firm

Project Preferences

Type of Financing Preferred:
Early Stage
Seed
Industry Rollups
Startup

Geographical Preferences

International Preferences:
Europe
Austria
Germany

Industry Preferences

In Computer Software prefer:
Software

In Internet Specific prefer:
Internet

Additional Information

Year Founded: 1992
Capital Under Management: $31,300,000
Current Activity Level : Actively seeking new investments

VULCAN CAPITAL

505 Fifth Avenue South
Suite 900
Seattle, WA USA 98104
Phone: 206-342-2000
Fax: 206-342-3000
E-mail: info@vulcan.com
Website: capital.vulcan.com

Management and Staff

Chris Temple, President
Daniel Kingston, Managing Director
Geoff McKay, Managing Director
Paul Allen, Founder
Steven Hall, Managing Director

Type of Firm

Private Equity Firm

Association Membership

National Venture Capital Association - USA (NVCA)

Project Preferences

Type of Financing Preferred:

Expansion
Balanced
Later Stage

Size of Investments Considered:

Min Size of Investment Considered (000s): $1,000
Max Size of Investment Considered (000s): $25,000

Industry Focus

(% based on actual investment)

Communications and Media	50.1%
Consumer Related	16.5%
Internet Specific	13.1%
Other Products	6.2%
Biotechnology	5.6%
Industrial/Energy	4.7%
Computer Software and Services	1.4%
Semiconductors/Other Elect.	1.4%
Computer Hardware	0.7%
Medical/Health	0.4%

Additional Information

Year Founded: 1986
Capital Under Management: $2,533,400,000
Current Activity Level : Actively seeking new investments

W CAPITAL PARTNERS

One East 52nd Street
Fifth Floor
New York, NY USA 10022
Phone: 212-561-5240
Fax: 212-561-5241
Website: www.wcapgroup.com

Management and Staff

David Wachter, Managing Director
Eugene Song, Vice President
John Kim, Vice President
Robert Migliorino, Managing Director
Stephen Wertheimer, Managing Director

Type of Firm

Private Equity Firm

Project Preferences

Role in Financing:

Prefer role as deal originator

Type of Financing Preferred:

Fund of Funds
Early Stage
Balanced
Later Stage
Fund of Funds of Second

Size of Investments Considered:

Min Size of Investment Considered (000s): $5,000
Max Size of Investment Considered (000s): $150,000

Geographical Preferences

United States Preferences:

All U.S.

International Preferences:

Europe

Industry Focus

(% based on actual investment)

Computer Software and Services	41.9%
Other Products	26.9%
Communications and Media	10.9%
Semiconductors/Other Elect.	9.8%
Medical/Health	9.7%
Internet Specific	0.5%
Computer Hardware	0.2%

Additional Information

Name of Most Recent Fund: W Capital Partners II (Cayman), L.P.
Most Recent Fund Was Raised: 05/09/2007
Year Founded: 2001
Capital Under Management: $1,100,000,000
Current Activity Level : Actively seeking new investments

W MEDIA VENTURES

1122 Mainland Street
Suite 590
Vancouver, Canada V6B 5L1
E-mail: info@wmediaventures.com
Website: www.wmediaventures.com

Management and Staff

Boris Wertz, Founder

Type of Firm

Private Equity Firm

Additional Information

Year Founded: 2009
Current Activity Level : Actively seeking new investments

W.L. ROSS & CO. LLC

Manhattan Tower
101 East 52nd Street, 19th Fl.
New York, NY USA 10022
Phone: 212-826-1100
Fax: 212-403-3578

Management and Staff

Harvey Tepner, Principal
Wilbur Ross, Chairman & CEO

Type of Firm

Private Equity Firm

Project Preferences

Type of Financing Preferred:

Leveraged Buyout
Turnaround
Acquisition
Special Situation
Distressed Debt

Geographical Preferences

International Preferences:

India
Latin America
Thailand
Korea, South
Asia
Japan

Industry Focus

(% based on actual investment)

Other Products	63.3%
Industrial/Energy	36.7%

Additional Information

Name of Most Recent Fund: WLR Recovery Fund IV, L.P.
Most Recent Fund Was Raised: 09/28/2007
Year Founded: 1998
Capital Under Management: $5,383,000,000
Current Activity Level : Actively seeking new investments

W.R. HAMBRECHT & CO., LLC

539 Bryant Street
Suite 100
San Francisco, CA USA 94107
Phone: 415-551-8600
Fax: 415-551-8686
E-mail: info@wrhambrecht.com
Website: www.wrhambrecht.com

Other Offices

555 Lancaster Avenue
Suite 200
Berwyn, PA USA 19312
Phone: 610-725-1150
Fax: 610-725-1167

45 Milk Street
Fifth Floor
Boston, MA USA 02109
Phone: 617-892-6100
Fax: 617-892-6130

60 Lombard Street
London, United Kingdom EC3V 9EA
Phone: 44-020-7083-0006
Fax: 44-020-7083-0007

420 Lexington Avenue
Suite 1825
New York, NY USA 10170
Phone: 212-313-5900
Fax: 212-313-5959

Five Stamford Landing
78 Southfield Avenue
Stamford, CT USA 06902
Phone: 203-975-6600
Fax: 203-975-6650

225 West Washington
Suite 2200
Chicago, IL USA 60606
Phone: 312-924-2843
Fax: 312-924-2844

One Place Ville Marie
Suite 2821
Montreal, Canada H3B 4R4
Phone: 514-448-4886
Fax: 514-448-4888

Management and Staff

Alan Katz, Managing Director
Barclay Corbus, Chief Executive Officer
Bob Hambrecht, Managing Director
Brian Bristol, Managing Director
Lee Ting, Managing Director
Michael Szeto, Senior Managing Director
Scott McLaughlin, Managing Director

Type of Firm

Bank Affiliated

Project Preferences

Type of Financing Preferred:
Early Stage

Industry Preferences

In Computer Software prefer:
Software

In Internet Specific prefer:
Internet

Additional Information

Name of Most Recent Fund: WR Hambrecht Ventures II, LP
Most Recent Fund Was Raised: 06/14/2007
Year Founded: 1998
Capital Under Management: $6,300,000
Current Activity Level : Actively seeking new investments

WACHOVIA CORPORATION (FKA:FIRST UNION CAPITAL PARTNERS)

301 South College Street
Suite 4000
Charlotte, NC USA 28288-0013
Phone: 704-374-6161
Fax: 704-374-6711
Website: www.wachovia.com

Other Offices

599 West Putnam Avenue
Suite 200
Greenwich, CT USA 06830
Phone: 203-862-5466
Fax: 203-661-1799

401 South Tyron Street
TH3
Charlotte, NC USA 28288
Phone: 704-383-5161
Fax: 704-383-9829

Management and Staff

David Zwiener, Chief Financial Officer
Frederick Eubank, Partner
James Cook, Partner
Kenneth Peppercorn, Vice President
L. Watts Hamrick, Partner
Neal Morrison, Partner
Robert Calton, Partner
Scott Perper, Managing Partner
Sean Smith, Principal
Ted Gardner, Managing Partner

Type of Firm

Bank Affiliated

Association Membership

Natl Assoc of Small Bus. Inv. Co (NASBIC)

Project Preferences

Role in Financing:
Will function either as deal originator or investor in deals created by others

Type of Financing Preferred:
Fund of Funds
Second Stage Financing
Leveraged Buyout
Early Stage
Expansion
Mezzanine
Generalist PE
Later Stage
Seed
Management Buyouts
First Stage Financing
Acquisition
Special Situation
Startup
Recapitalizations

Size of Investments Considered:
Min Size of Investment Considered (000s): $5,000
Max Size of Investment Considered (000s): $100,000

Geographical Preferences

International Preferences:
Latin America
Western Europe

Industry Focus

(% based on actual investment)

Other Products	30.4%
Internet Specific	29.6%
Communications and Media	17.8%
Consumer Related	7.4%
Medical/Health	6.2%
Computer Software and Services	5.8%
Industrial/Energy	2.4%
Semiconductors/Other Elect.	0.2%
Computer Hardware	0.1%

Additional Information

Year Founded: 1988
Capital Under Management: $900,000,000
Current Activity Level : Actively seeking new investments
Method of Compensation: Return on investment is of primary concern, do not charge fees

WADINKO CV

Postbus 445
Zwolle, Netherlands 8000 AK
Phone: 31-38-429-4206
Fax: 31-38-429-4228
E-mail: wadinko@hetnet.nl
Website: www.wadinko.nl

Type of Firm

Private Equity Firm

Association Membership
Dutch Venture Capital Associaton (NVP)

Project Preferences

Type of Financing Preferred:
Early Stage
Expansion
Turnaround
Startup

Geographical Preferences

International Preferences:
Netherlands

Industry Preferences

In Industrial/Energy prefer:
Industrial Products

Additional Information
Year Founded: 1993
Capital Under Management: $47,600,000
Current Activity Level : Actively seeking new investments

WAGNISKAPITAL GMBH DER KREISSPARKASSE REUTLINGEN
Marktplatz 6
Reutlingen, Germany 72764
Phone: 49-71-213312168
Fax: 49-71-213312499
E-mail: wagniskapital@ksk-reutlingen.de
Website: www.ksk-reutlingen.de

Type of Firm
Bank Affiliated

Association Membership
German Venture Capital Association (BVK)

Project Preferences

Type of Financing Preferred:
Expansion
Turnaround
Management Buyouts
Startup
Recapitalizations

Geographical Preferences

International Preferences:
Germany

Additional Information
Year Founded: 2001
Current Activity Level : Actively seeking new investments

WAKEFIELD GROUP
1110 East Morehead Street
Charlotte, NC USA 28204
Phone: 704-372-0355
Fax: 704-372-8216
Website: www.wakefieldgroup.com

Other Offices
5915 Farrington Road
Suite 201
Chapel Hill, NC USA 27517
Phone: 919-442-2160
Fax: 919-442-2162

Management and Staff
Anna Nelson, Partner
Steve Nelson, Partner
Thomas Nelson, Partner
Type of Firm
Private Equity Firm

Project Preferences

Role in Financing:
Prefer role as deal originator but will also invest in deals created by others

Type of Financing Preferred:
Early Stage

Size of Investments Considered:
Min Size of Investment Considered (000s): $1,000
Max Size of Investment Considered (000s): $5,000

Geographical Preferences

United States Preferences:
Southeast

Industry Focus
(% based on actual investment)

Communications and Media	24.3%
Computer Software and Services	23.9%
Internet Specific	15.6%
Medical/Health	12.7%
Computer Hardware	10.6%
Biotechnology	7.4%
Consumer Related	4.9%
Other Products	0.6%

Additional Information
Year Founded: 1988
Capital Under Management: $100,000,000
Current Activity Level : Actively seeking new investments
Method of Compensation: Return on investment is of primary concern, do not charge fees

---

WALDEN INTERNATIONAL
One California Street
Suite 2800
San Francisco, CA USA 94111
Phone: 415-765-7100
Fax: 415-765-7200
E-mail: usa@waldenintl.com
Website: www.waldenintl.com

Other Offices
18th Floor-2 Ruentex Banking Tower
No. 76, Tun Hua South Road, Section 2
Taipei, Taiwan
Phone: 8862-2704-8018
Fax: 8862-2704-2787

361 Lytton Avenue
Second Floor
Palo Alto, CA USA 94301-1431
Phone: 650-330-3500
Fax: 650-330-3535

2806A, Central Plaza
18 Harbour Road, Wanchai
Hong Kong, Hong Kong
Phone: 852-2523-0615
Fax: 852-2521-5778

Suite 320, Shanghai Centre
1376 Nanjing Xi Lu
Shanghai, China 200040
Phone: 86-21-6279-8200
Fax: 86-21-6279-8203

Unit 1416 Tower One and Exchange Plaza
Ayala Triangle, Ayala Avenue
Makati, Philippines 1226
Phone: 632-759-4170
Fax: 632-812-3996

Great World City West Tower
1 Kim Seng Promenade, #14-07
Singapore, Singapore 237994
Phone: 65-6272-3250
Fax: 65-6272-3251

#22-01, Menara Dion, No. 27
Jalan Sultan Ismail
Kuala Lumpur, Malaysia 50250
Phone: 60-3-2031-2202
Fax: 60-3-2031-2205

Prestige Omega, Regus, 2nd Floor
104 EPIP Zone, Whitefield
Bangalore, India 560 025
Phone: 91-80-4060-0719
Fax: 91-80-4060-0700

Suite 1806, Beijing China Resources Bldg
No. 8 Jiangoumenbei Ave., Dongcheng
Beijing, China 100005
Phone: 86-10-8519-2519
Fax: 86-10-8519-2520

Management and Staff
Andrew Kau, Managing Director
Bill Li, Managing Director
Brian Chiang, Managing Director
Carson Chen, Venture Partner
Clifford Higgerson, Venture Partner
Daniel Tsai, Vice President
Hing Wong, Managing Director

Hock Voon Loo, Managing Director
Kris Leong Seok Wan, Vice President
Mary Coleman, Managing Director
Rajesh Subramaniam, Managing Director
Soo Ping Yong, Vice President
Steve Ahn, Venture Partner
Stu Phillips, Venture Partner
Syrus Madavi, Venture Partner
Teresa Smith, Chief Financial Officer
Yimin Zimmerer, Managing Director

Type of Firm
Private Equity Firm

Association Membership
Hong Kong Venture Capital Association (HKVCA)
Western Association of Venture Capitalists (WAVC)
National Venture Capital Association - USA (NVCA)
Natl Assoc of Small Bus. Inv. Co (NASBIC)
Singapore Venture Capital Association (SVCA)
Indian Venture Capital Association (IVCA)

Project Preferences

Role in Financing:
Will function either as deal originator or investor in deals created by others

Type of Financing Preferred:
Early Stage
Expansion
Balanced
Seed
Startup

Size of Investments Considered:
Min Size of Investment Considered (000s): $10,000
Max Size of Investment Considered (000s): $10,000

Geographical Preferences

International Preferences:
India
Taiwan
China
Hong Kong
Philippines
Australia
Singapore
Korea, South
Asia
Japan
Malaysia

Industry Focus
(% based on actual investment)

Semiconductors/Other Elect.	26.5%
Internet Specific	17.9%
Communications and Media	17.9%
Computer Software and Services	12.7%
Other Products	12.3%
Computer Hardware	4.9%
Medical/Health	3.4%
Industrial/Energy	2.0%
Biotechnology	1.8%
Consumer Related	0.5%

Additional Information
Year Founded: 1987
Capital Under Management: $1,600,000,000
Current Activity Level : Actively seeking new investments
Method of Compensation: Other

WALDEN VENTURE CAPITAL
750 Battery Street
Suite 700
San Francisco, CA USA 94111
Phone: 415-391-7225
Fax: 415-391-7262
E-mail: info@waldenvc.com
Website: www.waldenvc.com

Management and Staff
Alex Gove, Principal
Arthur Berliner, Managing Director
George Sarlo, Managing Director
Larry Marcus, Managing Director
Matt Miller, Managing Director
Robert Raynard, Chief Financial Officer
William McDonagh, Venture Partner

Type of Firm
Bank Affiliated

Association Membership
Western Association of Venture Capitalists (WAVC)
National Venture Capital Association - USA (NVCA)

Project Preferences

Role in Financing:
Prefer role as deal originator but will also invest in deals created by others

Type of Financing Preferred:
Early Stage
Start-up Financing
Public Companies
Seed
First Stage Financing

Size of Investments Considered:
Min Size of Investment Considered (000s): $1,000
Max Size of Investment Considered (000s): $7,000

Geographical Preferences

United States Preferences:
Southern California
Northern California
West Coast

Industry Focus
(% based on actual investment)

Internet Specific	35.4%
Communications and Media	16.4%
Computer Software and Services	15.7%
Semiconductors/Other Elect.	10.3%
Computer Hardware	8.0%
Other Products	4.1%
Consumer Related	3.8%
Medical/Health	2.4%
Biotechnology	2.3%
Industrial/Energy	1.5%

Additional Information
Name of Most Recent Fund: WaldenVC II, L.P.
Most Recent Fund Was Raised: 06/15/2000
Year Founded: 1974
Capital Under Management: $400,000,000
Current Activity Level : Actively seeking new investments
Method of Compensation: Return on investment is of primary concern, do not charge fees

WALES FUND MANAGERS, LTD.
Cedar House, Greenwood Close
Cardiff Gate Business Park
Cardiff, United Kingdom CF23 8RD
Phone: 44-29-2054-6250
Fax: 44-29-2054-6251
E-mail: info@wfml.co.uk
Website: www.wfml.co.uk

Other Offices
400 Thames Valley Park Drive
Reading, United Kingdom RG6 1PT

Management and Staff
Guy Davies, Chief Executive Officer

Type of Firm
Private Equity Firm

Association Membership
British Venture Capital Association (BVCA)

Project Preferences

Type of Financing Preferred:
Second Stage Financing
Generalist PE
Early Stage
Balanced
Startup

Size of Investments Considered:
Min Size of Investment Considered (000s): $199
Max Size of Investment Considered (000s): $1,987

Geographical Preferences

International Preferences:
United Kingdom
Europe

Industry Focus
(% based on actual investment)

Semiconductors/Other Elect.	44.1%
Computer Hardware	29.8%
Consumer Related	10.5%
Other Products	5.9%
Computer Software and Services	5.3%
Internet Specific	3.4%
Industrial/Energy	1.0%

Additional Information

Year Founded: 1994
Capital Under Management: $21,900,000
Current Activity Level : Actively seeking new investments

WALKER VENTURES SBIC (AKA: WALKER VENTURES)

3060 Washington Road
Suite 200
Glenwood, MD USA 21738
Phone: 301-854-6850
Fax: 301-854-6235
E-mail: info@walkerventures.com
Website: www.walkerventures.com

Other Offices

114 East German Street
Suite 201
Shepherdstown, WV USA 25443

Management and Staff

Gina Dubbe, Managing Partner
Rusty Griffith, Principal
Stephen Walker, Managing Partner

Type of Firm

Private Equity Firm

Association Membership

Mid-Atlantic Venture Association
Natl Assoc of Small Bus. Inv. Co (NASBIC)

Project Preferences

Role in Financing:

Will function either as deal originator or investor in deals created by others

Type of Financing Preferred:

Early Stage

Size of Investments Considered:

Min Size of Investment Considered (000s): $250
Max Size of Investment Considered (000s): $3,000

Geographical Preferences

United States Preferences:

Mid Atlantic

Industry Focus

(% based on actual investment)

Computer Software and Services	56.4%
Internet Specific	25.9%
Medical/Health	11.3%
Communications and Media	2.8%
Other Products	2.6%
Semiconductors/Other Elect.	0.9%

Additional Information

Name of Most Recent Fund: Walker Investment Fund II
Most Recent Fund Was Raised: 03/31/2000
Year Founded: 1998
Capital Under Management: $100,000,000
Current Activity Level : Actively seeking new investments
Method of Compensation: Professional fee required whether or not deal closes

WALL STREET TECHNOLOGY PARTNERS

75 Wall Street
34th Floor
New York, NY USA 10005
Phone: 212-429-3083
Fax: 212-429-3099
Website: www.wallstreettp.com

Management and Staff

Adam Lichtenstein, Partner
Gaurav Burman, Partner
Richard Wolf, Managing Partner
Victoria Katsov, Partner

Type of Firm

Private Equity Firm

Additional Information

Year Founded: 2009
Current Activity Level : Actively seeking new investments

WALL STREET VENTURE CAPITAL

110 Wall Street
Eleventh Floor
New York, NY USA 10005
Phone: 877-748-4468
Fax: 860-599-3799
E-mail: wallstreetventurecapital@yahoo.com
Website: www.wallstreetventurecapital.net

Other Offices

28 East Jackson Building
Tenth Floor
Chicago, IL USA 60604
Phone: 877-748-4468

75 State Street
Boston, MA USA 02109
Phone: 877-748-4468

23 Nanjing East Road
Shanghai, China 200002
Phone: 8621-6329-5787
Fax: 8621-6329-5787

Management and Staff

Frank O'Connell, Partner
John Adair, Partner
John Meyer, Partner
Jonathan Morrone, Partner
Joseph DeMarco, Partner
Joseph McAndrew, CEO & Managing Director
Joseph Gill, Partner
Leo Nolan, Partner
Nico Eboma, Partner
T. Claycomb, Partner
William Nielson, Partner

Type of Firm

Private Equity Firm

Project Preferences

Type of Financing Preferred:

Generalist PE
Expansion
Mezzanine
Turnaround
Acquisition
Distressed Debt
Recapitalizations

Size of Investments Considered:

Min Size of Investment Considered (000s): $3,000
Max Size of Investment Considered (000s): $100,000

Industry Preferences

In Communications prefer:

Communications and Media

In Medical/Health prefer:

Medical Products
Health Services
Pharmaceuticals

In Consumer Related prefer:

Retail
Food/Beverage
Consumer Products

In Industrial/Energy prefer:

Energy

Additional Information

Year Founded: 2008
Current Activity Level : Actively seeking new investments

WALNUT GROUP, THE

312 Walnut Street
Suite 1151
Cincinnati, OH USA 45202
Phone: 513-651-3300
Fax: 513-651-1084
E-mail: info@thewalnutgroup.com
Website: www.thewalnutgroup.com

Other Offices

100 Park Avenue
Suite 2100
New York, NY USA 10017
Phone: 513-651-3300
Fax: 513-651-1084

Management and Staff

Daniel Staton, Managing General Partner

Frederic Mayerson, Managing Partner
James Gould, Managing General Partner
John Benloehr, President
Patrick McBride, Partner
R. Scott Barnes, Chief Financial Officer

Type of Firm

Private Equity Firm

Association Membership

National Venture Capital Association - USA (NVCA)
Natl Assoc of Small Bus. Inv. Co (NASBIC)

Project Preferences

Role in Financing:

Will function either as deal originator or investor in deals created by others

Type of Financing Preferred:

Second Stage Financing
Expansion
Generalist PE
Management Buyouts
First Stage Financing
Acquisition

Size of Investments Considered:

Min Size of Investment Considered (000s): $1,000
Max Size of Investment Considered (000s): $7,000

Geographical Preferences

United States Preferences:

All U.S.

Industry Preferences

In Communications prefer:

Media and Entertainment

In Medical/Health prefer:

Health Services
Pharmaceuticals

In Consumer Related prefer:

Consumer
Entertainment and Leisure
Sports
Retail
Consumer Products
Consumer Services
Education Related

In Financial Services prefer:

Financial Services
Insurance

In Business Serv. prefer:

Services
Distribution
Media

In Manufact. prefer:

Manufacturing

In Other prefer:

Socially Responsible

Additional Information

Year Founded: 1995
Capital Under Management: $400,000,000
Current Activity Level : Actively seeking new investments
Method of Compensation: Return on investment is of primary concern, do not charge fees

WALSINGHAM FUND, THE

4 King Street West
Suite 1300
Toronto, Canada M5H 1B6
Phone: 416-363-7400
Fax: 416-363-7511
E-mail: info@walsinghamfund.com
Website: www.walsinghamfund.com

Management and Staff

Alisha Hirsch, Partner

Type of Firm

Private Equity Firm

Project Preferences

Type of Financing Preferred:

Early Stage
Expansion
Later Stage

Geographical Preferences

Canadian Preferences:

All Canada

Additional Information

Year Founded: 2005
Capital Under Management: $58,400,000
Current Activity Level : Actively seeking new investments

WARBURG PINCUS LLC

450 Lexington Avenue
New York, NY USA 10017
Phone: 212-878-0600
Fax: 212-878-9351
E-mail: info@warburgpincus.com
Website: www.warburgpincus.com

Other Offices

Two International Finance Center
8 Finance Street
Centre, Hong Kong
Phone: 852-2536-6183
Fax: 852-2521-3869

Liebigstr. 53
Frankfurt, Germany D-60323
Phone: 49-69-7703-5500
Fax: 49-69-7703-5555

7th Floor, Express Towers
Nariman Point
Mumbai, India 400 021
Phone: 91-22-6650-0000
Fax: 91-22-6650-0001

Bund Center Office Tower
Unit 2201, No. 222 Yanan Road
Shanghai, China 200002
Phone: 86-21-6335-0308
Fax: 86-21-6335-0802

One Market Plaza
Spear Tower, Suite 1700
San Francisco, CA USA 94105
Phone: 415-796-5200
Fax: 415-796-1922

Almack House
28 King Street, St. James's
London, United Kingdom SW1Y 6QW
Phone: 44-207-306-0306
Fax: 44-207-321-0881

Hibiya Marine Bldg. 8th Floor
1-5-1 Yurakucho, Chiyoda-ku
Tokyo, Japan 100-0006
Phone: 81-3-5521-6830
Fax: 81-3-5521-0066

9th Floor, China World Tower 1
1 Jianguomenwai Avenue
Beijing, China 100004
Phone: 86-10-5923-2533
Fax: 86-10-6505-6683

Management and Staff

Alex Berzofsky, Managing Director
Barry Taylor, Managing Director
Bilge Ogut, Managing Director
Brian Spillane, Vice President
Cary Davis, Managing Director
Chansoo Joung, Managing Director
Dalip Pathak, Managing Director
David Krieger, Partner
David Li, Managing Director
David Coulter, Managing Director
David Barr, Managing Director
David Wenstrup, Managing Director
Elizabeth Weatherman, Managing Director
George Allen, Principal
Henry Makansi, Vice President
Henry Schacht, Partner
Henry Kressel, Managing Director
James Neary, Managing Director
Jeffrey Harris, Managing Director
Jeremy Young, Managing Director
Joe Schull, Managing Director
John Macintosh, Managing Director
Jonathan Leff, Managing Director
Jonathan Cosgrave, Principal
Julian Cheng, Managing Director
Julie Johnson Staples, Managing Director
Justin Sadrian, Partner
Kevin Kruse, Managing Director
Kewsong Lee, Managing Director
Mark Colodny, Managing Director
Miao Chi, Principal
Mimi Strouse, Managing Director
Nancy Martin, Managing Director
Nicholas Lowcock, Managing Director
Patrick Hackett, Managing Director

Paul Best, Principal
Pedro Aznar, Vice President
Peter Kagan, Managing Director
Peter Wilson, Managing Director
Qiang Chang Sun, Managing Director
Rajesh Khanna, Managing Director
Rajiv Gathalia, Managing Director
Reuben Leibowitz, Managing Director
Rodman Moorhead, Managing Director
Rosanne Zimmerman, Managing Director
Sean Carney, Managing Director
Sidney Lapidus, Managing Director
Simon Begg, Principal
Simon Turton, Managing Director
Stan Raatz, Managing Director
Steve Coates, Managing Director
Steven Schneider, Managing Director
Stewart Hen, Managing Director
Sung-Jin Hwang, Managing Director
Timothy Curt, Managing Director
W. Bowman Cutter, Managing Director

Type of Firm

Private Equity Firm

Association Membership

Hong Kong Venture Capital Association (HKVCA)
British Venture Capital Association (BVCA)
National Venture Capital Association - USA (NVCA)
European Private Equity and Venture Capital Assoc.
Singapore Venture Capital Association (SVCA)
Indian Venture Capital Association (IVCA)

Project Preferences

Role in Financing:

Prefer role as deal originator but will also invest in deals created by others

Type of Financing Preferred:

Second Stage Financing
Leveraged Buyout
Control-block Purchases
Early Stage
Expansion
Research and Development
Generalist PE
Balanced
Turnaround
Later Stage
Open Market
Seed
Management Buyouts
First Stage Financing
Acquisition
Private Placement
Special Situation
Startup
Recapitalizations

Size of Investments Considered:

Min Size of Investment Considered (000s): $1,000
Max Size of Investment Considered: No Limit

Geographical Preferences

United States Preferences:

All U.S.

Canadian Preferences:

All Canada

International Preferences:

Italy
India
United Kingdom
Europe
China
Spain
Korea, South
Germany
Asia
France
Japan

Industry Focus

(% based on actual investment)

Other Products	28.1%
Industrial/Energy	20.4%
Medical/Health	11.3%
Communications and Media	11.0%
Computer Software and Services	10.7%
Consumer Related	9.7%
Internet Specific	4.0%
Biotechnology	2.3%
Semiconductors/Other Elect.	1.5%
Computer Hardware	0.9%

Additional Information

Name of Most Recent Fund: Warburg Pincus Private Equity X, L.P.
Most Recent Fund Was Raised: 09/25/2007
Year Founded: 1971
Capital Under Management: $10,000,000,000
Current Activity Level : Actively seeking new investments
Method of Compensation: Return on investment is of primary concern, do not charge fees

---

WARWICK ADVISERS CORPORATION

1330 Post Oak Boulevard
16th Floor
Houston, TX USA 77056
Phone: 713-963-3610
Fax: 713-977-2966
E-mail: mgwirtz@warwickresources.com
Website: www.warwickresources.com

Management and Staff

Michael Wirtz, Managing Director

Type of Firm

Private Equity Firm

Project Preferences

Role in Financing:

Will function either as deal originator or investor in deals created by others

Type of Financing Preferred:

Leveraged Buyout
Control-block Purchases
Early Stage
Expansion
Turnaround
Management Buyouts
First Stage Financing
Acquisition
Special Situation
Distressed Debt
Recapitalizations

Size of Investments Considered:

Min Size of Investment Considered (000s): $2,000
Max Size of Investment Considered (000s): $500,000

Geographical Preferences

United States Preferences:

Southeast
Rocky Mountain
Southwest

International Preferences:

Latin America
Africa

Industry Focus

(% based on actual investment)

Medical/Health	100.0%

Additional Information

Year Founded: 2002
Capital Under Management: $130,000,000
Current Activity Level : Actively seeking new investments
Method of Compensation: Return on invest. most important, but chg. closing fees, service fees, etc.

WASHINGTON GAS

6801 Industrial Road
Springfield, VA USA 22151
Phone: 703-750-1000
Fax: 703-750-5922
Website: www.washgas.com

Type of Firm

Corporate PE/Venture

Association Membership

Mid-Atlantic Venture Association

Project Preferences

Type of Financing Preferred:

Balanced

Size of Investments Considered:

Min Size of Investment Considered (000s): $1,000
Max Size of Investment Considered (000s): $20,000

Industry Preferences

In Industrial/Energy prefer:

Energy
Oil and Gas Exploration
Oil & Gas Drilling,Explor

Additional Information

Year Founded: 2000
Current Activity Level : Actively seeking new investments

WASHINGTON TECHNOLOGY PARTNERS, INC. (AKA: WTP)

3130 Fairview Park Drive
Suite 500
Falls Church, VA USA 22042
Phone: 703-934-6922
Fax: 703-991-6581
E-mail: general@wtpcapital.com
Website: www.wtpcapital.com

Management and Staff

Abhi-Shek Jain, CEO & Managing Director
Arie Bernardo, Principal
Kshanika Ratnayaka, Principal
Neeraj Vohra, Vice President
Peter Tewksbury, Partner
Stephen Jones, Partner

Type of Firm

Private Equity Firm

Project Preferences

Type of Financing Preferred:

Startup

Additional Information

Year Founded: 1999
Current Activity Level : Actively seeking new investments

WASSERSTEIN VENTURES (FKA: WASSERSTEIN & CO.)

1301 Avenue of the Americas
44th Floor
New York, NY USA 10019
Phone: 212-702-5600
Fax: 212-702-5625
Website: www.wasserco.com

Other Offices

1999 Avenue of the Stars
Suite 2950
Los Angeles, CA USA 90067

101 California Street
42nd Floor
San Francisco, CA USA 94111
Phone: 415-677-4800
Fax: 415-288-3960

1705 El Camino Real
Palo Alto, CA USA 94306
Phone: 650-473-2300
Fax: 650-473-2332

Management and Staff

Ellis Jones, Chief Executive Officer
George Lauro, Managing Director
Thomas Huang, Vice President
Vijay Rajamani, Vice President
W. Townsend Ziebold, President

Type of Firm

Private Equity Firm

Project Preferences

Role in Financing:

Prefer role as deal originator but will also invest in deals created by others

Type of Financing Preferred:

Leveraged Buyout
Later Stage

Geographical Preferences

United States Preferences:

All U.S.

Industry Focus

(% based on actual investment)

Internet Specific	33.5%
Consumer Related	15.8%
Semiconductors/Other Elect.	9.2%
Communications and Media	9.0%
Other Products	8.4%
Medical/Health	8.1%
Computer Software and Services	6.6%
Computer Hardware	5.1%
Industrial/Energy	4.2%

Additional Information

Year Founded: 1988
Capital Under Management: $300,000,000
Current Activity Level : Actively seeking new investments
Method of Compensation: Return on investment is of primary concern, do not charge fees

---

WATER STREET HEALTHCARE PARTNERS (FKA: WATER STREET CAPITAL)

333 West Wacker Drive
Suite 2800
Chicago, IL USA 60606
Phone: 312-506-2900
Fax: 312-506-2901
E-mail: info@wshp.com
Website: www.wshp.com

Management and Staff

Chris Sweeney, Principal
Eric Lev, Principal
Harreld Kirkpatrick, Partner
James Connelly, Partner
Jeffrey Holway, Chief Financial Officer
Jim Connelly, Principal
Kevin Swan, Partner
Max Mishkin, Vice President
Ned Villers, Principal
Peter Strothman, Principal
Robert Womsley, Partner
Timothy Dugan, Managing Partner

Type of Firm

Private Equity Firm

Project Preferences

Type of Financing Preferred:

Leveraged Buyout
Management Buyouts

Size of Investments Considered:

Min Size of Investment Considered (000s): $50,000
Max Size of Investment Considered (000s): $500,000

Geographical Preferences

United States Preferences:

All U.S.

Industry Preferences

In Medical/Health prefer:

Medical Products
Health Services
Pharmaceuticals

In Business Serv. prefer:

Services

Additional Information

Name of Most Recent Fund: Water Street Healthcare Partners II, L.P.
Most Recent Fund Was Raised: 09/03/2008
Year Founded: 2005
Capital Under Management: $1,020,000,000
Current Activity Level : Actively seeking new investments

WATER TOWER CAPITAL LLC

218 North Jefferson Street
Suite 100
Chicago, IL USA 60661
Phone: 312-373-8000
Fax: 312-373-8025
Website: www.watertowercapital.com

Management and Staff

F. John Stark, Chief Executive Officer
Lewis Rieck, Principal
Melissa Stark, Vice President
Rob Woseth, Vice President
Terry Coleman, Vice President
Timothy Shanahan, Vice President

Type of Firm

Private Equity Firm

Project Preferences

Type of Financing Preferred:
Distressed Debt

Additional Information

Year Founded: 2001
Current Activity Level : Actively seeking new investments

WATERLAND PRIVATE EQUITY INVESTMENTS B.V.

Nieuwe's-Gravelandseweg 17
Bussum, Netherlands 1405 HK
Phone: 31-35-694-1680
Fax: 31-35-697-0972
E-mail: info@waterland.nu
Website: www.waterland.nu

Other Offices

Neuer Zollhof 1
Dusseldorf, Germany 40221
Phone: 49-211-6878-4010
Fax: 49-211-6878-4029

Uitbreidingstraat 10-16
Antwerpen-Berchem, Belgium 2600
Phone: 32-3-292-9660
Fax: 32-3-292-9661

Management and Staff

Frank Vlayen, Principal
Jorg Dreisow, Principal
Kai Lahmann, Principal
Lex Douze, Principal

Type of Firm

Private Equity Firm

Association Membership

Belgium Venturing Association
German Venture Capital Association (BVK)
Dutch Venture Capital Associaton (NVP)
European Private Equity and Venture Capital Assoc.

Project Preferences

Role in Financing:
Prefer role in deals created by others

Type of Financing Preferred:
Leveraged Buyout
Management Buyouts
Acquisition

Size of Investments Considered:
Min Size of Investment Considered (000s): $13,980
Max Size of Investment Considered (000s): $139,802

Geographical Preferences

International Preferences:
Netherlands
Europe
Luxembourg
Belgium
Germany

Industry Preferences

In Communications prefer:
Communications and Media

In Medical/Health prefer:
Medical/Health

In Consumer Related prefer:
Consumer
Entertainment and Leisure

In Industrial/Energy prefer:
Energy
Industrial Products

In Business Serv. prefer:
Services

Additional Information

Name of Most Recent Fund: Waterland Private Equity Fund II B.V.
Most Recent Fund Was Raised: 07/01/2003
Year Founded: 2000
Capital Under Management: $1,990,300,000
Current Activity Level : Actively seeking new investments

WATERMILL VENTURES, INC.

One Cranberrry Hill
750 Marrett Road, Suite 401
Lexington, MA USA 02421
Phone: 781-891-6660
Fax: 781-891-9712
E-mail: info@Watermill.com
Website: www.watermill.com

Management and Staff

Charles Stolper, Principal
Kitty Sahin, Partner
Robert Ackerman, Partner
Steve Kotler, Chief Financial Officer
Steven Karol, Managing Partner
Timothy Eburne, Partner

Type of Firm

Bank Affiliated

Project Preferences

Type of Financing Preferred:
Leveraged Buyout
Turnaround
Recapitalizations

Geographical Preferences

United States Preferences:
All U.S.

Additional Information

Year Founded: 2000
Current Activity Level : Actively seeking new investments

WATERVEIN PARTNERS CO., LTD.

4/F Smile Building
3-5-6 Kudan-minami, Chiyoda-ku
Tokyo, Japan 102-0074
Phone: 81-3-3264-5616
Fax: 81-3-3264-5617
E-mail: info@watervein.jp
Website: www.watervein.jp

Management and Staff

Masanori Ishikiwa, Partner
Tatsuzo Ishigami, Partner
Tetsuya Mishima, Partner

Type of Firm

Bank Affiliated

Project Preferences

Type of Financing Preferred:
Start-up Financing

Geographical Preferences

International Preferences:
Japan

Industry Preferences

In Biotechnology prefer:
Biotechnology

In Medical/Health prefer:
Medical/Health

Additional Information

Year Founded: 2004
Capital Under Management: $21,800,000
Current Activity Level : Actively seeking new investments

WAUD CAPITAL PARTNERS LLC

560 Oakwood Avenue
Suite 203
Lake Forest, IL USA 60045
Phone: 847-604-9550
Fax: 847-604-9554
E-mail: info@waudcapital.com
Website: www.waudcapital.com

Other Offices

321 North Clark Street
Suite 1465
Chicago, IL USA 60610
Phone: 312-676-8400
Fax: 312-676-8444

Management and Staff

Chuck Edwards, Vice President
David Neighbours, Principal
Gary Mecklenburg, Partner
Mark Flower, Chief Financial Officer
Matthew Clary, Partner
Peter Keehn, Principal
Reeve Waud, Managing Partner
Wendy Chronister, Partner

Type of Firm

Private Equity Firm

Project Preferences

Role in Financing:

Will function either as deal originator or investor in deals created by others

Type of Financing Preferred:

Leveraged Buyout
Mezzanine
Generalist PE
Later Stage
Management Buyouts
Acquisition
Recapitalizations

Size of Investments Considered:

Min Size of Investment Considered (000s): $5,000
Max Size of Investment Considered (000s): $25,000

Geographical Preferences

United States Preferences:

All U.S.

Canadian Preferences:

All Canada

International Preferences:

Mexico

Industry Focus

(% based on actual investment)

Other Products	47.5%
Medical/Health	34.4%
Internet Specific	18.1%

Additional Information

Name of Most Recent Fund: Waud Capital Partners FIF II, L.P.
Most Recent Fund Was Raised: 04/28/2005
Year Founded: 1993
Capital Under Management: $115,000,000
Current Activity Level : Actively seeking new investments
Method of Compensation: Return on invest. most important, but chg. closing fees, service fees, etc.

WAVE EQUITY PARTNERS

177 Milk Street
Boston, MA USA 02109
Phone: 617-350-9808
Fax: 617-350-9899
E-mail: info@waveep.com
Website: www.waveep.com

Management and Staff

Mark Robinson, Managing Director
Praveen Sahay, Managing Director
Robert Roeper, Managing Director

Type of Firm

Private Equity Firm

Project Preferences

Type of Financing Preferred:

Early Stage
Expansion
Seed
Startup

Size of Investments Considered:

Min Size of Investment Considered (000s): $2,000
Max Size of Investment Considered (000s): $15,000

Geographical Preferences

United States Preferences:

All U.S.

Canadian Preferences:

All Canada

International Preferences:

All International

Industry Preferences

In Industrial/Energy prefer:

Alternative Energy

In Other prefer:

Environment Responsible

Additional Information

Year Founded: 2009
Current Activity Level : Actively seeking new investments

WAVEPOINT VENTURES (FKA: CAPITAL VALLEY VENTURES LLC)

1107 Investment Boulevard
Suite 180
El Dorado Hills, CA USA 95762
Phone: 916-941-1400
Fax: 916-941-7551
E-mail: info@wavepointventures.com
Website: www.wavepointventures.com

Other Offices

535 Middlefield Road
Suite 280
Menlo Park, CA USA 94025
Phone: 650-331-7393
Fax: 650-331-7393

Management and Staff

Daniel Lankford, Managing Director
Peter Gardner, Managing Director
Peter Bernardoni, Managing Director

Type of Firm

Private Equity Firm

Project Preferences

Role in Financing:

Will function either as deal originator or investor in deals created by others

Type of Financing Preferred:

Early Stage
Seed

Size of Investments Considered:

Min Size of Investment Considered (000s): $100
Max Size of Investment Considered (000s): $250

Geographical Preferences

United States Preferences:

Southern California
Northern California
West Coast

Industry Preferences

In Communications prefer:

Telecommunications
Wireless Communications
Data Communications

In Computer Software prefer:

Software

In Internet Specific prefer:

E-Commerce Technology
Internet

In Semiconductor/Electr prefer:

Electronic Components
Micro-Processing

In Biotechnology prefer:

Biosensors

In Medical/Health prefer:

Medical Diagnostics
Diagnostic Services
Diagnostic Test Products
Pharmaceuticals

In Industrial/Energy prefer:

Energy
Robotics

In Other prefer:

Environment Responsible

Additional Information

Name of Most Recent Fund: CVV Partners, L.P.
Most Recent Fund Was Raised: 08/29/2003
Year Founded: 2003
Capital Under Management: $6,300,000
Current Activity Level : Actively seeking new investments

WAYGATE CAPITAL INDIA PVT., LTD.

201 A, Gagangiri
10 Carter Road, Khar
Mumbai, India 400 052
Phone: 91-22-2600-8606
Fax: 91-22-2600-8608

Management and Staff

Rajesh Jog, Managing Director

Type of Firm

Private Equity Firm

Association Membership

Indian Venture Capital Association (IVCA)

Project Preferences

Type of Financing Preferred:
Mezzanine
Management Buyouts

Size of Investments Considered:
Min Size of Investment Considered (000s): $100
Max Size of Investment Considered (000s): $200

Geographical Preferences

International Preferences:
India

Industry Preferences

In Communications prefer:
Media and Entertainment

In Computer Software prefer:
Computer Services
Systems Software

In Computer Other prefer:
Computer Related

Additional Information

Year Founded: 1994
Current Activity Level : Actively seeking new investments

WAYZATA INVESTMENT PARTNERS

701 East Lake Street
Suite 300
Wayzata, MN USA 55391
Phone: 952-345-0700
Fax: 952-345-8901
Website: www.wayzatainvestmentpartners.com

Other Offices

45 Fairfield Street
Fourth Floor
Boston, MA USA 02116
Phone: 617-375-5835
Fax: 617-375-5757

Management and Staff

Blake Carlson, Partner
John Foley, Partner
John McEvoy, Partner
Joseph Deignan, Partner
Mary Burns, Partner
Patrick Halloran, Managing Partner
Steven Adams, Partner

Type of Firm

Private Equity Firm

Project Preferences

Type of Financing Preferred:
Balanced
Distressed Debt

Geographical Preferences

United States Preferences:
All U.S.
Minnesota

Additional Information

Name of Most Recent Fund: Wayzata Opportunities Fund II, L.P.
Most Recent Fund Was Raised: 02/12/2008
Year Founded: 2004
Capital Under Management: $5,000,000,000
Current Activity Level : Actively seeking new investments

WEATHERGAGE VENTURE CAPITAL

201 Redwood Shores Parkway
Suite 295
Redwood City, CA USA 94065
Phone: 650-440-3630

Management and Staff

Courtney Russell McCrea, Managing Director
J. Bradford Hammond, General Partner
Judith Elsea, General Partner
Sandra Wallis, General Partner
Timothy Bliamptis, General Partner

Type of Firm

Private Equity Advisor or Fund of Funds

Additional Information

Name of Most Recent Fund: Weathergage Venture Capital (Parallel), LP
Most Recent Fund Was Raised: 07/05/2007
Year Founded: 2007
Capital Under Management: $65,000,000
Current Activity Level : Actively seeking new investments

WEBER CAPITAL MANAGEMENT LLC

340 Pine Street
Suite 300
San Francisco, CA USA 94104
Phone: 415-362-5007
Fax: 415-288-3323
Website: www.webercapital.com

Management and Staff

Colin Hillberg, Partner
Eugene Weber, Managing Partner

Type of Firm

Private Equity Firm

Association Membership

Western Association of Venture Capitalists (WAVC)

Project Preferences

Role in Financing:
Will function either as deal originator or investor in deals created by others

Type of Financing Preferred:
Second Stage Financing
Expansion
Mezzanine
Public Companies
Later Stage
Recapitalizations

Size of Investments Considered:
Min Size of Investment Considered (000s): $1,000
Max Size of Investment Considered (000s): $5,000

Geographical Preferences

United States Preferences:
Northeast
West Coast

Industry Preferences

In Communications prefer:
Commercial Communications
CATV & Pay TV Systems
Radio & TV Broadcasting
Telecommunications
Wireless Communications
Data Communications
Satellite Microwave Comm.
Other Communication Prod.

In Computer Hardware prefer:
Terminals

In Computer Software prefer:
Data Processing
Software
Systems Software
Applications Software
Artificial Intelligence

In Internet Specific prefer:
E-Commerce Technology
Internet

Ecommerce
Web Aggregration/Portals

In Semiconductor/Electr prefer:

Semiconductor

Additional Information

Year Founded: 1994
Capital Under Management: $125,000,000
Current Activity Level : Actively seeking new investments
Method of Compensation: Return on investment is of primary concern, do not charge fees

WEBSTER CAPITAL MANAGEMENT, L.L.C.

950 Winter Street
Sute 4200
North Waltham, MA USA 02451
Phone: 781-419-1515
Fax: 781-419-1516
E-mail: info@webstercapital.com
Website: www.webstercapital.com

Management and Staff

Andrew McKee, General Partner
Charles Larkin, General Partner
David Malm, General Partner
Donald Steiner, Managing Partner
Mark Greene, Chief Financial Officer

Type of Firm

Private Equity Firm

Project Preferences

Type of Financing Preferred:

Management Buyouts

Size of Investments Considered:

Min Size of Investment Considered (000s): $2,000
Max Size of Investment Considered (000s): $15,000

Geographical Preferences

United States Preferences:

All U.S.

Industry Preferences

In Consumer Related prefer:

Consumer

In Business Serv. prefer:

Services

In Manufact. prefer:

Manufacturing

Additional Information

Year Founded: 2002
Capital Under Management: $1,200,000
Current Activity Level : Actively seeking new investments

WEDBUSH CAPITAL PARTNERS

1000 Wilshire Boulevard
Suite 830
Los Angeles, CA USA 90017
Phone: 213-688-8018
Fax: 213-688-8095
E-mail: info@wedbushcapital.com
Website: www.wedbushcapital.com

Management and Staff

Ben Wu, Vice President
Eric Wedbush, Managing Director
Geoff Bland, Managing Director
Peter Shoemaker, Managing Director

Type of Firm

Private Equity Firm

Project Preferences

Role in Financing:

Prefer role as deal originator

Type of Financing Preferred:

Leveraged Buyout
Expansion
Generalist PE
Later Stage
Management Buyouts
Acquisition
Private Placement
Industry Rollups
Recapitalizations

Size of Investments Considered:

Min Size of Investment Considered (000s): $2,000
Max Size of Investment Considered (000s): $10,000

Geographical Preferences

United States Preferences:

Nevada
Arizona
Northwest
Nebraska
Southern California
Oregon
Northern California
Rocky Mountain
West Coast
California
Washington
Southwest
All U.S.

Industry Preferences

In Semiconductor/Electr prefer:

Sensors

In Medical/Health prefer:

Medical/Health
Medical Diagnostics
Diagnostic Services
Diagnostic Test Products
Medical Therapeutics
Drug/Equipmt Delivery
Medical Products
Disposable Med. Products
Health Services

In Consumer Related prefer:

Consumer
Entertainment and Leisure
Retail
Food/Beverage
Consumer Products
Consumer Services
Hotels and Resorts
Education Related

In Industrial/Energy prefer:

Energy
Oil and Gas Exploration
Oil & Gas Drilling,Explor
Alternative Energy
Industrial Products
Machinery
Environmental Related

In Transportation prefer:

Transportation
Aerospace

In Financial Services prefer:

Financial Services
Insurance

In Business Serv. prefer:

Services
Distribution

In Manufact. prefer:

Manufacturing

In Agr/Forestr/Fish prefer:

Agriculture related

In Other prefer:

Environment Responsible
Women/Minority-Owned Bus.

Additional Information

Year Founded: 2005
Capital Under Management: $120,000,000
Current Activity Level : Actively seeking new investments
Method of Compensation: Return on invest. most important, but chg. closing fees, service fees, etc.

WEDECO MANAGEMENT OY AB

Yrittajankatu 15
Vaasa, Finland 65380
Phone: 358-6-316-5800
Fax: 358-6-316-5801
E-mail: info@wedeco.fi
Website: www.wedeco.fi

Type of Firm

Private Equity Firm

Association Membership

Finnish Venture Capital Association (FVCA)

Project Preferences

Type of Financing Preferred:
Leveraged Buyout
Expansion
Balanced
Later Stage
Startup

Geographical Preferences

International Preferences:
Finland

Additional Information
Year Founded: 1987
Capital Under Management: $16,600,000
Current Activity Level : Actively seeking new investments

WEINBERG CAPITAL PARTNERS
40 rue La Boetie
Paris, France 75008
Phone: 33-1-5353-5500
Fax: 33-1-5353-5519
E-mail: contact@weinbergcapital.com
Website: www.weinbergcapital.com

Management and Staff
Benjamin Teszner, Chief Operating Officer
Guillaume D Angerville, Partner
Henri Gagnaire, Partner
Jerome Louvet, Vice President
Laurent Halimi, Partner
Nicolas Teboul, Vice President
Philippe Klocanas, Partner
Serge Weinberg, Partner
Wandrille Ract-Madoux, Vice President
Yann Ballan, Vice President

Type of Firm
Private Equity Advisor or Fund of Funds

Association Membership
French Venture Capital Association (AFIC)

Project Preferences

Type of Financing Preferred:
Leveraged Buyout

Size of Investments Considered:
Min Size of Investment Considered (000s): $13,359
Max Size of Investment Considered (000s): $80,154

Geographical Preferences

International Preferences:
Europe
France

Industry Preferences

In Consumer Related prefer:
Retail

In Business Serv. prefer:
Services
Distribution

In Manufact. prefer:
Manufacturing

Additional Information
Name of Most Recent Fund: WCP 1
Most Recent Fund Was Raised: 06/07/2005
Year Founded: 2005
Capital Under Management: $537,000,000
Current Activity Level : Actively seeking new investments

WELLINGTON FINANCIAL LP
161 Bay Street
BCE Place, Suite 2520
Toronto, Canada M5J 2S1
Phone: 416-682-6000
Fax: 416-682-1160
Website: www.wellingtonfund.com

Management and Staff
Kul Mani, Vice President
Mark Wilk, Vice President
Mark Usher, Partner

Type of Firm
Private Equity Firm

Association Membership
Canadian Venture Capital Association

Project Preferences

Type of Financing Preferred:
Mezzanine

Geographical Preferences

Canadian Preferences:
All Canada
Ontario
British Columbia

Industry Preferences

In Computer Software prefer:
Software

In Internet Specific prefer:
Internet

In Industrial/Energy prefer:
Energy

In Other prefer:
Environment Responsible

Additional Information
Name of Most Recent Fund: Wellington Financial Fund III
Most Recent Fund Was Raised: 08/01/2006
Year Founded: 2000
Capital Under Management: $171,800,000
Current Activity Level : Actively seeking new investments

WELLINGTON PARTNERS VENTURE CAPITAL GMBH
Theresienstrasse 6
Munich, Germany 80333
Phone: 49-89-219-9410
Fax: 49-89-2199-4198
E-mail: info@wellington-partners.com
Website: www.wellington-partners.com

Other Offices
Seidengasse 16
Zurich, Switzerland 8001
Phone: 41-44-567-27

42, Berkeley Square
London, United Kingdom W1J5AW

459 Hamilton Avenue
Suite 207
Palo Alto, CA USA 94301

Management and Staff
Bart Markus, General Partner
Boris Anderer, Venture Partner
Chandra Paul Leo, Principal
Christian Reitberger, General Partner
Daniel Waterhouse, Partner
Eberhard Plattfaut, Venture Partner
Eric Archambeau, General Partner
Eric Ly, Venture Partner
Erich Schlick, General Partner
Ernst Mannheimer, Partner
Frank Boehnke, General Partner
Fred Van Den Bosch, Venture Partner
George Colliat, Venture Partner
Gerrit Huy, Venture Partner
Johannes von Borries, Principal
Loic Le Meur, Venture Partner
Markus Bart, General Partner
Melvin Spigelman, Venture Partner
Michael Wolfle, Venture Partner
Neal Margulis, Venture Partner
Neil Richardson, Venture Partner
Olivier Schuepbach, Principal
Rainer Strohmenger, General Partner
Ram Srinivasan, Venture Partner
Rolf Dienst, General Partner
Royston Hoggarth, Venture Partner
Stephan Mohren, Venture Partner
Ulrich Granzer, Venture Partner

Type of Firm
Private Equity Firm

Association Membership
German Venture Capital Association (BVK)
European Private Equity and Venture Capital Assoc.

Project Preferences

Type of Financing Preferred:
Early Stage
Expansion
Seed
Startup

Size of Investments Considered:
Min Size of Investment Considered (000s): $900
Max Size of Investment Considered (000s): $900,000

Geographical Preferences

International Preferences:
United Kingdom
Netherlands
Switzerland
Europe
Austria
Germany
France

Industry Focus

(% based on actual investment)

Internet Specific	41.3%
Computer Software and Services	12.8%
Communications and Media	12.5%
Consumer Related	11.8%
Biotechnology	5.7%
Medical/Health	4.8%
Semiconductors/Other Elect.	4.5%
Industrial/Energy	4.0%
Computer Hardware	1.4%
Other Products	1.3%

Additional Information

Year Founded: 1991
Capital Under Management: $666,800,000
Current Activity Level : Actively seeking new investments

WELLSPRING CAPITAL MANAGEMENT LLC

Lever House
390 Park Avenue
New York, NY USA 10022
Phone: 212-318-9800
Fax: 212-332-7575
E-mail: info@wellspringcapital.com
Website: www.wellspringcapital.com

Management and Staff

Alexander Carles, Partner
Carl Stanton, Partner
Daniel Han, Vice President
David Kass, Chief Financial Officer
David Mariano, Partner
Greg Feldman, Partner
Jason Fortin, Principal
John Morningstar, Principal
Joshua Cascade, Partner
William Dawson, Partner

Type of Firm

Private Equity Firm

Project Preferences

Type of Financing Preferred:
Leveraged Buyout
Turnaround
Recapitalizations

Size of Investments Considered:
Min Size of Investment Considered (000s): $50,000
Max Size of Investment Considered: No Limit

Geographical Preferences

Canadian Preferences:
All Canada

Industry Focus

(% based on actual investment)

Industrial/Energy	60.3%
Consumer Related	22.9%
Other Products	14.1%
Internet Specific	2.7%

Additional Information

Year Founded: 1995
Capital Under Management: $350,000,000
Current Activity Level : Actively seeking new investments

WELSH, CARSON, ANDERSON & STOWE

320 Park Avenue
Suite 2500
New York, NY USA 10022
Phone: 212-893-9500
Fax: 212-893-9575
Website: www.welshcarson.com

Management and Staff

Brian Regan, Principal
Bruce Anderson, General Partner
D. Scott Mackesy, General Partner
Darren Battistoni, Vice President
David Caluori, Vice President
Eric Lee, General Partner
James Dimitri, Vice President
John Clark, General Partner
John Almeida, General Partner
Lucas Garman, Principal
Michael Donovan, Principal
Paul Queally, General Partner
Russell Carson, General Partner
Sanjay Swani, General Partner
Sean Traynor, General Partner
Thomas Scully, General Partner

Type of Firm

Private Equity Firm

Project Preferences

Role in Financing:
Prefer role as deal originator

Type of Financing Preferred:
Leveraged Buyout
Expansion
Mezzanine
Management Buyouts
Joint Ventures
Special Situation
Recapitalizations

Size of Investments Considered:
Min Size of Investment Considered (000s): $100,000
Max Size of Investment Considered (000s): $500,000

Industry Focus

(% based on actual investment)

Medical/Health	31.2%
Other Products	20.8%
Communications and Media	15.7%
Internet Specific	14.2%
Computer Software and Services	13.1%
Computer Hardware	2.8%
Consumer Related	1.7%
Semiconductors/Other Elect.	0.2%
Industrial/Energy	0.1%

Additional Information

Year Founded: 1979
Capital Under Management: $12,000,000,000
Current Activity Level : Actively seeking new investments
Method of Compensation: Return on invest. most important, but chg. closing fees, service fees, etc.

WENDEL (FKA: WENDEL INVESTISSEMENT) (FKA: MARINE WENDEL)

89, rue Taitbout
Paris, France 75009
Phone: 33-1-4285-3000
Fax: 33-1-4280-6867
Website: www.wendel-investissement.com

Management and Staff

Antoine Ernest Seilliere, President
Arnaud Fayet, Partner
Bernard Gautier, Partner
Bernard Renard, Partner
Fanny Picard, Managing Director
Oliver Chambriard, Partner
Philippe Donnet, Managing Director
Roland Lienau, Managing Director
Yves Moutran, Partner

Type of Firm

Private Equity Firm

Association Membership

French Venture Capital Association (AFIC)

Project Preferences

Type of Financing Preferred:
Expansion

Geographical Preferences

International Preferences:
France

Additional Information

Year Founded: 2002
Current Activity Level : Actively seeking new investments

WERU INVESTMENT CO., LTD.

3F Kasuya Bldg.
65 Kikuicho, Shinjuku-ku
Tokyo, Japan 162-0044
Phone: 81-3-5272-0471
Fax: 03-5272-0472
Website: www.weruinvest.com

Management and Staff

Takeo Asai, President

Type of Firm

Private Equity Firm

Project Preferences

Type of Financing Preferred:
Early Stage
Balanced

Geographical Preferences

International Preferences:
Japan

Additional Information

Year Founded: 1998
Capital Under Management: $8,400,000
Current Activity Level : Actively seeking new investments

WESLEY CLOVER, LTD.

The Manor House
Celtic Manor Resort
Newport, United Kingdom NP18 1HQ
Phone: 44-1633-410-383
Fax: 44-1633-410-384
Website: www.wesleyclover.com

Other Offices

157 Walker Street
Suite 3, Level 12
North Sydney, Australia 2060
Phone: 61-2-9023-9536
Fax: 61-2-9023-9501

555 Legget Drive
Suite 534 - Tower B
Kanata, Canada K2K 2X3
Phone: 613-271-6305
Fax: 613-271-9810

Management and Staff

Jose Medeiros, President & COO
Mark Colcomb, Vice President
Simon Gibson, Chief Executive Officer

Type of Firm

Private Equity Firm

Project Preferences

Type of Financing Preferred:
Early Stage
Seed
Startup

Geographical Preferences

International Preferences:
United Kingdom

Additional Information

Year Founded: 2001
Capital Under Management: $250,000,000
Current Activity Level : Actively seeking new investments

WEST COAST CAPITAL

Olympic Business Park
Dundonald
Kilmarnock, United Kingdom KA2 9AE
Phone: 44-1563-852-200
Fax: 44-1563-850-091
E-mail: info@westcoastcapital.co.uk
Website: www.westcoastcapital.co.uk

Management and Staff

Jim McMahon, Partner
Paul Davidson, Partner
Tom Hunter, Founding Partner

Type of Firm

Private Equity Firm

Project Preferences

Role in Financing:
Will function either as deal originator or investor in deals created by others

Type of Financing Preferred:
Balanced

Geographical Preferences

International Preferences:
United Kingdom
Europe

Industry Preferences

In Consumer Related prefer:
Retail

In Financial Services prefer:
Real Estate

Additional Information

Year Founded: 2001
Capital Under Management: $293,700,000
Current Activity Level : Actively seeking new investments

WEST HILL PARTNERS LLC

800 Boylston Street
45th Floor
Boston, MA USA 02199
Phone: 617-585-8000
Fax: 617-585-8001
E-mail: info@wh-partners.com
Website: www.wh-partners.com

Management and Staff

Dana Schmaltz, Managing Partner
James Rhee, Partner
Jeffrey Teschke, Partner
Mark Tricolli, Partner
Ted Yun, Managing Partner
William Altieri, Managing Director

Type of Firm

Private Equity Firm

Project Preferences

Type of Financing Preferred:
Leveraged Buyout
Recapitalizations

Industry Preferences

In Medical/Health prefer:
Medical/Health

In Consumer Related prefer:
Consumer Products

In Business Serv. prefer:
Services

Additional Information

Year Founded: 2007
Current Activity Level : Actively seeking new investments

WESTBRIDGE VENTURES LLC

One Maritime Plaza
Suite 1545
San Francisco, CA USA 94111
Phone: 415-277-1000
Fax: 415-277-1077

E-mail: info@westbridgevc.com
Website: www.westbridgevc.com

Management and Staff

Jason Breaux, Vice President
Steven Strandberg, Managing Director

Type of Firm

Private Equity Firm

Project Preferences

Type of Financing Preferred:

Leveraged Buyout
Mezzanine
Later Stage
Special Situation

Size of Investments Considered:

Min Size of Investment Considered (000s): $3,000
Max Size of Investment Considered (000s): $10,000

Geographical Preferences

Canadian Preferences:

All Canada

International Preferences:

United Kingdom

Industry Preferences

In Communications prefer:

Radio & TV Broadcasting
Telecommunications
Wireless Communications
Data Communications
Satellite Microwave Comm.

In Computer Software prefer:

Computer Services
Software
Systems Software
Applications Software

In Internet Specific prefer:

Internet
Ecommerce

In Semiconductor/Electr prefer:

Semiconductor

Additional Information

Year Founded: 1999
Capital Under Management: $100,000,000
Current Activity Level : Actively seeking new investments

WESTBURY PARTNERS

100 Motor Parkway
Suite 165
Hauppauge, NY USA 11788
Phone: 631-231-4121
Fax: 631-231-8121
E-mail: info@westburypartners.com
Website: www.westburypartners.com

Management and Staff

James Schubauer, President & COO
Joseph Fogg, Chairman & CEO
Richard Sicoli, Chief Financial Officer

Type of Firm

Bank Affiliated

Association Membership

Natl Assoc of Small Bus. Inv. Co (NASBIC)

Project Preferences

Role in Financing:

Prefer role as deal originator but will also invest in deals created by others

Type of Financing Preferred:

Second Stage Financing
Leveraged Buyout
Mezzanine
Special Situation

Size of Investments Considered:

Min Size of Investment Considered (000s): $3,000
Max Size of Investment Considered (000s): $9,000

Geographical Preferences

United States Preferences:

All U.S.

Canadian Preferences:

All Canada

Industry Focus

(% based on actual investment)

Computer Software and Services	34.9%
Communications and Media	32.6%
Internet Specific	16.7%
Other Products	7.3%
Computer Hardware	5.7%
Medical/Health	2.7%

Additional Information

Year Founded: 1994
Capital Under Management: $150,000,000
Current Activity Level : Actively seeking new investments
Method of Compensation: Return on investment is of primary concern, do not charge fees

---

WESTCAP MANAGEMENT, LTD.

1300-410 - 22nd Street East
Saskatoon, Canada S7K 5T6
Phone: 306-652-5557
Fax: 306-652-8186
Website: www.westcapmgt.ca

Management and Staff

Douglas Banzet, Vice President
Grant Kook, President, CEO, Director

Type of Firm

Private Equity Firm

Project Preferences

Type of Financing Preferred:

Balanced

Geographical Preferences

Canadian Preferences:

All Canada

Additional Information

Name of Most Recent Fund: Golden Opportunities Fund
Most Recent Fund Was Raised: 06/30/1999
Year Founded: 1999
Current Activity Level : Actively seeking new investments

WESTERKIRK CAPITAL, INC.

95 Wellington Street West
Suite 1410
Toronto, Canada M5J 2N7
Phone: 416-927-2232
Website: www.westerkirk.ca

Management and Staff

David Nowak, Managing Director
Douglas Bradley, Managing Director
Peter Winters, Managing Director

Type of Firm

Private Equity Firm

Additional Information

Year Founded: 2009
Current Activity Level : Actively seeking new investments

WESTERN DEVELOPMENT COMMISSION

Dillon House
Ballaghaderreen
Roscommon, Ireland
Phone: 353-94-9861441
Fax: 353-94-9861443
E-mail: info@wdc.ie
Website: www.wdc.ie

Type of Firm

Government Affiliated Program

Project Preferences

Type of Financing Preferred:

Balanced

Geographical Preferences

International Preferences:

Ireland

Additional Information

Year Founded: 2003
Capital Under Management: $39,800,000
Current Activity Level : Actively seeking new investments

WESTERN STATES INVESTMENT GROUP

6335 Ferris Square
Suite A
San Diego, CA USA 92121
Phone: 858-678-0800
Fax: 858-678-0900
Website: www.wsig.com

Management and Staff

William Patch, Vice President

Type of Firm

Private Equity Firm

Project Preferences

Role in Financing:

Prefer role as deal originator but will also invest in deals created by others

Type of Financing Preferred:

Leveraged Buyout
Research and Development
Start-up Financing
Seed
First Stage Financing

Size of Investments Considered:

Min Size of Investment Considered (000s): $1,000
Max Size of Investment Considered: No Limit

Geographical Preferences

United States Preferences:

West Coast
Southwest

Industry Focus

(% based on actual investment)

Computer Software and Services	28.7%
Industrial/Energy	19.8%
Medical/Health	16.9%
Communications and Media	13.2%
Semiconductors/Other Elect.	11.4%
Biotechnology	10.0%

Additional Information

Year Founded: 1976
Capital Under Management: $35,000,000
Current Activity Level : Making few, if any, new investments
Method of Compensation: Return on investment is of primary concern, do not charge fees

WESTERN TECHNOLOGY INVESTMENT

2010 North First Street
Suite 310
San Jose, CA USA 95131
Phone: 408-436-8577
Fax: 408-436-8625
E-mail: contact@westerntech.com
Website: www.westerntech.com

Type of Firm

Private Equity Firm

Association Membership

Western Association of Venture Capitalists (WAVC)
National Venture Capital Association - USA (NVCA)

Project Preferences

Role in Financing:

Prefer role as deal originator

Type of Financing Preferred:

Second Stage Financing
Mezzanine
Research and Development
Balanced
Start-up Financing
Other
Seed
First Stage Financing
Special Situation

Size of Investments Considered:

Min Size of Investment Considered (000s): $500
Max Size of Investment Considered (000s): $25,000

Geographical Preferences

United States Preferences:

All U.S.

International Preferences:

Ireland
United Kingdom
China

Industry Preferences

In Communications prefer:

Communications and Media

In Computer Software prefer:

Software

In Semiconductor/Electr prefer:

Electronics

In Biotechnology prefer:

Biotechnology

In Medical/Health prefer:

Medical Products

In Manufact. prefer:

Manufacturing

Additional Information

Name of Most Recent Fund: Venture Lending & Leasing V LLC
Most Recent Fund Was Raised: 02/21/2007
Year Founded: 1980
Capital Under Management: $767,000,000
Current Activity Level : Actively seeking new investments
Method of Compensation: Return on investment is of primary concern, do not charge fees

WESTFIELD CAPITAL MANAGEMENT

One Financial Center
24th Floor
Boston, MA USA 02111
Phone: 617-428-7100
Fax: 617-428-7190
Website: www.westfieldcapital.com

Management and Staff

Arthur Bauernfeind, Chairman & CEO
Karen Digravio, Chief Financial Officer

Type of Firm

Private Equity Firm

Project Preferences

Type of Financing Preferred:

Public Companies
Balanced

Additional Information

Year Founded: 2001
Current Activity Level : Actively seeking new investments

WESTLAKE GROUP (FKA: CAPITAL NETWORK, THE)

2700 Via Fortuna
Suite 450
Austin, TX USA 78746
Phone: 512-314-0711
Fax: 512-306-1651
Website: www.thecapitalnetwork.com

Management and Staff

Michael McAllister, Managing Director
Newt Hamlin, Chairman & CEO
Wilson Allen, Managing Director

Type of Firm

Service Provider

Project Preferences

Role in Financing:

Prefer role as deal originator but will also invest in deals created by others

Type of Financing Preferred:

Second Stage Financing
Leveraged Buyout
Mezzanine

Research and Development
Start-up Financing
Seed
First Stage Financing
Special Situation

Size of Investments Considered:

Min Size of Investment Considered (000s): $100
Max Size of Investment Considered (000s): $500

Geographical Preferences

United States Preferences:

All U.S.

Canadian Preferences:

All Canada

Industry Preferences

In Communications prefer:

Commercial Communications
CATV & Pay TV Systems
Telecommunications
Data Communications
Satellite Microwave Comm.

In Computer Other prefer:

Computer Related

In Semiconductor/Electr prefer:

Electronic Components

In Biotechnology prefer:

Biotechnology

In Medical/Health prefer:

Medical/Health

In Consumer Related prefer:

Entertainment and Leisure
Retail
Computer Stores
Food/Beverage
Consumer Products
Consumer Services
Education Related

In Industrial/Energy prefer:

Oil and Gas Exploration
Oil & Gas Drilling,Explor
Alternative Energy
Energy Conservation Relat
Industrial Products

In Financial Services prefer:

Financial Services

In Business Serv. prefer:

Distribution

In Manufact. prefer:

Publishing

In Agr/Forestr/Fish prefer:

Mining and Minerals

Additional Information

Year Founded: 1989
Capital Under Management: $100,000,000
Current Activity Level : Actively seeking new investments
Method of Compensation: Professional fee required whether or not deal closes

WESTLB AG EQUITY INVESTMENTS (AKA: WESTDEUTSCHE LANDESBANK)

Friedrichstrasse 62-80
Duesseldorf, Germany 40217
Phone: 49-211-8268255
Fax: 49-211-8266168
E-mail: equity_investments@westlb.de
Website: www.westlb.de

Other Offices

35 New Broad Street
London, United Kingdom EC2M 1SQ
Phone: 44-207-220-8434

38 Via Canova
Milan, Italy 20145
Phone: 39-234-97-4365
Fax: 39-234-97-4261

Friedrichstrasse 1
Munster, Germany 48145
Phone: 49-251-412-01
Fax: 49-251-412-2921

Management and Staff

Hans-Jurgen Niehaus, Chief Financial Officer
Heinz Hilgert, Chairman & CEO
Klemens Breuer, Managing Director
Thomas Gross, Managing Director
Werner Taiber, Managing Director
Wolfgang Nickels, Managing Director

Type of Firm

Bank Affiliated

Association Membership

Italian Venture Capital Association (AIFI)

Project Preferences

Type of Financing Preferred:

Leveraged Buyout
Early Stage
Expansion
Generalist PE
Later Stage
Management Buyouts
Acquisition
Recapitalizations

Geographical Preferences

International Preferences:

Europe
Germany

Industry Focus

(% based on actual investment)

Semiconductors/Other Elect.	82.8%
Biotechnology	7.9%
Internet Specific	5.2%
Computer Software and Services	4.1%

Additional Information

Year Founded: 1999
Capital Under Management: $251,400,000
Current Activity Level : Actively seeking new investments

WESTLB MELLON ASSET MANAGEMENT (USA) LLC

1211 Avenue of the Americas
25th Floor
New York, NY USA 10036
Phone: 212-597-1180
Fax: 212-597-1199
E-mail: peginfo@wmam.com
Website: www.wmam.com/peg

Other Offices

100 North Riverside Plaza
Suite 1700
Chicago, IL USA 60606
Phone: 312-279-9300
Fax: 312-575-0222

Friedrichstrasse 62-80
Dusseldorf, Germany 40217

12100 Wilshire Boulevard
Suite 1090
Los Angeles, CA USA 90025
Phone: 310-954-0150
Fax: 310-954-0160

Management and Staff

Christopher Pace, General Partner
Jens Winther, General Partner
John O'Malley, General Partner
Ravi Vish, Chief Executive Officer

Type of Firm

Private Equity Advisor or Fund of Funds

Project Preferences

Role in Financing:

Other

Type of Financing Preferred:

Fund of Funds
Leveraged Buyout
Early Stage
Expansion
Generalist PE
Mezzanine
Balanced
Turnaround
Later Stage
Management Buyouts
Special Situation
Distressed Debt

Geographical Preferences

United States Preferences:

All U.S.

International Preferences:
Europe
Middle East
Asia
Japan

Additional Information
Name of Most Recent Fund: COREplus Private Equity Partners II, L.P.
Most Recent Fund Was Raised: 09/20/2007
Year Founded: 1998
Capital Under Management: $1,003,000,000
Current Activity Level : Actively seeking new investments
Method of Compensation: Other

WESTLY GROUP, THE
2200 Sand Hill Road
Menlo Park, CA USA 94025
Phone: 650-233-3466
E-mail: wg@westlygroup.com
Website: www.westlygroup.com

Management and Staff
Dave Coglizer, Principal
Gary Dillabough, Principal
Isaac Applbaum, Venture Partner
Kenneth Goldman, Venture Partner
Michael Dorsey, Managing Partner

Type of Firm
Private Equity Firm

Association Membership
National Venture Capital Association - USA (NVCA)

Project Preferences

Role in Financing:
Prefer role as deal originator but will also invest in deals created by others

Type of Financing Preferred:
Expansion
Later Stage

Size of Investments Considered:
Min Size of Investment Considered (000s): $500
Max Size of Investment Considered (000s): $8,000

Geographical Preferences

Canadian Preferences:
All Canada

International Preferences:
All International

Industry Preferences

In Communications prefer:
Wireless Communications
Other Communication Prod.

In Computer Software prefer:
Data Processing
Systems Software
Applications Software

In Internet Specific prefer:
Internet
Ecommerce
Web Aggregration/Portals

In Semiconductor/Electr prefer:
Electronic Components
Laser Related

In Medical/Health prefer:
Medical/Health
Health Services

In Consumer Related prefer:
Consumer
Retail

In Industrial/Energy prefer:
Energy

In Transportation prefer:
Transportation

In Financial Services prefer:
Financial Services
Insurance

Additional Information
Name of Most Recent Fund: Westly Capital Partners, L.P.
Most Recent Fund Was Raised: 06/12/2008
Year Founded: 2007
Capital Under Management: $125,000,000
Current Activity Level : Actively seeking new investments
Method of Compensation: Return on invest. most important, but chg. closing fees, service fees, etc.

WESTON PRESIDIO (FKA: WESTON PRESIDIO CAPITAL MANAGEMENT)
200 Clarendon Street
50th Floor, John Hancock Tower
Boston, MA USA 02116
Phone: 617-988-2500
Fax: 617-988-2515
Website: www.westonpresidio.com

Other Offices
Pier 1, Bay 2
San Francisco, CA USA 94111
Phone: 415-398-0770
Fax: 415-398-0990

2460 Sand Hill Road
Suite 200
Menlo Park, CA USA 94025
Phone: 650-926-0500
Fax: 650-926-0504

Management and Staff
Charles Baird, Partner
David Ferguson, Partner
James McElwee, Partner
Jeffrey Mills, Partner
John Berg, Partner
John McKee, Principal
Josh McDowell, Principal
Kevin Hayes, Partner
Mark Bono, Partner
Michael Cronin, Managing Partner
Michael Lazarus, Managing Partner
Michelle Brooks, Principal
R. Sean Honey, Partner
Scott Bell, Principal
Therese Mrozek, Chief Operating Officer

Type of Firm
Private Equity Firm

Association Membership
Western Association of Venture Capitalists (WAVC)
National Venture Capital Association - USA (NVCA)

Project Preferences

Role in Financing:
Will function either as deal originator or investor in deals created by others

Type of Financing Preferred:
Leveraged Buyout
Early Stage
Generalist PE
Balanced
Later Stage

Size of Investments Considered:
Min Size of Investment Considered (000s): $10,000
Max Size of Investment Considered (000s): $75,000

Geographical Preferences

United States Preferences:
All U.S.

Canadian Preferences:
All Canada

International Preferences:
Europe

Industry Focus
(% based on actual investment)

Other Products	28.2%
Consumer Related	26.4%
Internet Specific	13.3%
Communications and Media	10.0%
Industrial/Energy	8.3%
Semiconductors/Other Elect.	4.7%
Computer Software and Services	4.1%
Medical/Health	3.6%
Biotechnology	1.1%
Computer Hardware	0.4%

Additional Information
Name of Most Recent Fund: Weston Presidio Capital V, L.P.
Most Recent Fund Was Raised: 03/03/2005
Year Founded: 1991
Capital Under Management: $3,278,000,000
Current Activity Level : Actively seeking new investments
Method of Compensation: Return on investment is of primary concern, do not charge fees

WESTSHORE CAPITAL PARTNERS

400 North Ashley Drive
Rivergate Tower, Suite 2610
Tampa, FL USA 33602
Phone: 813-223-3600
Fax: 813-223-3699
Website: www.westshorecapitalpartners.com

Management and Staff

David Malizia, Managing Partner
Earl Powell, Principal
P. Craig Sanford, Vice President
Ryan Cortner, Vice President
W. Andrew Krusen, Principal

Type of Firm

Private Equity Firm

Project Preferences

Role in Financing:
Prefer role as deal originator but will also invest in deals created by others

Type of Financing Preferred:
Leveraged Buyout
Management Buyouts
Recapitalizations

Size of Investments Considered:
Min Size of Investment Considered (000s): $1,000
Max Size of Investment Considered (000s): $7,000

Geographical Preferences

United States Preferences:
All U.S.

Canadian Preferences:
All Canada
Ontario

Industry Preferences

In Medical/Health prefer:
Medical Diagnostics
Diagnostic Services
Diagnostic Test Products
Drug/Equipmt Delivery
Disposable Med. Products

In Consumer Related prefer:
Consumer
Food/Beverage
Education Related

In Industrial/Energy prefer:
Industrial Products

In Business Serv. prefer:
Services
Distribution

In Manufact. prefer:
Manufacturing

Additional Information

Year Founded: 2006
Capital Under Management: $20,000,000
Current Activity Level : Actively seeking new investments
Method of Compensation: Return on invest. most important, but chg. closing fees, service fees, etc.

WESTVIEW CAPITAL PARTNERS

One International Place
Seventh Floor
Boston, MA USA 02110
Phone: 617-261-2050
Fax: 617-261-2060
Website: www.wvcapital.com

Management and Staff

Carlo Von Schroeter, Managing Partner
John Turner, General Partner
Jonathan Hunnicutt, General Partner
Matthew Carroll, General Partner
Richard Williams, Managing Partner
Thomas Reardon, Principal

Type of Firm

Private Equity Firm

Project Preferences

Type of Financing Preferred:
Leveraged Buyout
Later Stage
Acquisition
Distressed Debt
Recapitalizations

Size of Investments Considered:
Min Size of Investment Considered (000s): $8,000
Max Size of Investment Considered (000s): $30,000

Geographical Preferences

United States Preferences:
All U.S.

Canadian Preferences:
All Canada

Industry Preferences

In Communications prefer:
Media and Entertainment
Publishing

In Medical/Health prefer:
Medical/Health

In Consumer Related prefer:
Retail
Consumer Products
Consumer Services

In Industrial/Energy prefer:
Industrial Products

In Financial Services prefer:
Financial Services

In Business Serv. prefer:
Services
Distribution

In Manufact. prefer:
Manufacturing

Additional Information

Year Founded: 2004
Capital Under Management: $195,000,000
Current Activity Level : Actively seeking new investments

WFD VENTURES, LLC

Carnegie Hall Tower, 10th Flr
152 West 57th Street
New York, NY USA 10019
Phone: 212-767-7500
Fax: 212-767-7575
E-mail: info@wfdventures.com
Website: www.wfdventures.com

Management and Staff

Tim Langloss, Principal
William Doyle, Managing Director

Type of Firm

Private Equity Firm

Project Preferences

Type of Financing Preferred:
Balanced

Geographical Preferences

International Preferences:
All International

Industry Preferences

In Medical/Health prefer:
Medical/Health
Health Services

Additional Information

Year Founded: 2007
Current Activity Level : Actively seeking new investments

WHARTON BIOTECHNOLOGY ADVISORS, LLC

520 Madison Avenue
38th Floor
New York, NY USA 10022
Phone: 212-570-5959
Fax: 212-570-0777
Website: www.whartonequity.com

Management and Staff

Peter Lewis, President

Type of Firm

Private Equity Firm

Project Preferences

Type of Financing Preferred:
Early Stage
Expansion

Geographical Preferences

United States Preferences:
All U.S.

Industry Preferences

In Biotechnology prefer:
Biotechnology

Additional Information

Year Founded: 2004
Current Activity Level : Actively seeking new investments

WHEATLEY PARTNERS

80 Cuttermill Road
Suite 302
Great Neck, NY USA 11021
Phone: 516-773-1024
Fax: 516-773-0996
E-mail: bizplan@wheatleypartners.com
Website: www.wheatleypartners.com

Other Offices

825 Third Avenue
32nd Floor
New York, NY USA 10022
Phone: 212-918-0563
Fax: 212-486-4469

Management and Staff

Barry Rubenstein, General Partner
Barry Fingerhut, General Partner
David Dantzker, General Partner
Irwin Lieber, General Partner
Jonathan Lieber, General Partner
Lawrence Wagenberg, General Partner
Len Hirsch, Chief Financial Officer
Nancy Casey, General Partner
Seth Lieber, General Partner

Type of Firm

Private Equity Firm

Project Preferences

Role in Financing:
Will function either as deal originator or investor in deals created by others

Type of Financing Preferred:
Second Stage Financing
Balanced
First Stage Financing
Startup

Size of Investments Considered:
Min Size of Investment Considered (000s): $100
Max Size of Investment Considered (000s): $4,500

Geographical Preferences

United States Preferences:
All U.S.

Industry Focus

(% based on actual investment)	
Computer Software and Services	37.1%
Internet Specific	23.0%
Communications and Media	14.4%
Medical/Health	7.3%
Biotechnology	7.1%
Semiconductors/Other Elect.	5.7%
Other Products	5.3%
Industrial/Energy	0.1%

Additional Information

Year Founded: 1992
Capital Under Management: $200,000,000
Current Activity Level : Actively seeking new investments
Method of Compensation: Return on investment is of primary concern, do not charge fees

---

WHEB VENTURES, LTD.

34 Queen Anne Street
London, United Kingdom W1G 8HE
Phone: 44-20-7299-4141
Fax: 44-20-7299-4151
E-mail: info@whebventures.com
Website: www.whebventures.com

Other Offices

Lenbach-Palais
Lenbachplatz 3
Muenchen, Germany 80333
Phone: 49-89-5527-93410
Fax: 49-89-9218-5151

Management and Staff

Ben Goldsmith, Partner
James McNaught-Davis, Managing Partner
Joerg Sperling, Partner
Kim Heyworth, Partner
Mark Preston, Principal
Mike Mattner, Venture Partner
Rob Wylie, Partner
Thilo von Selchow, Venture Partner

Type of Firm

Private Equity Firm

Association Membership

British Venture Capital Association (BVCA)

Project Preferences

Type of Financing Preferred:
Early Stage
Expansion

Geographical Preferences

United States Preferences:
All U.S.

International Preferences:
United Kingdom
Asia

Industry Preferences

In Industrial/Energy prefer:
Alternative Energy

In Agr/Forestr/Fish prefer:
Agriculture related

In Other prefer:
Environment Responsible

Additional Information

Year Founded: 1995
Capital Under Management: $185,500,000
Current Activity Level : Actively seeking new investments

WHI CAPITAL PARTNERS

191 North Wacker Drive
Suite 1500
Chicago, IL USA 60606
Phone: 312-621-0590
Fax: 312-604-7900
Website: www.whicapital.com

Management and Staff

Adam Schecter, Managing Partner
Andy Baker, Vice President
Eric Cohen, Managing Partner
Michael Schopin, Vice President

Type of Firm

Bank Affiliated

Association Membership

Illinois Venture Capital Association

Project Preferences

Role in Financing:
Prefer role as deal originator but will also invest in deals created by others

Type of Financing Preferred:
Leveraged Buyout
Generalist PE
Management Buyouts
Acquisition
Recapitalizations

Size of Investments Considered:
Min Size of Investment Considered (000s): $5,000
Max Size of Investment Considered (000s): $15,000

Geographical Preferences

United States Preferences:
All U.S.

Canadian Preferences:
All Canada

Industry Preferences

In Semiconductor/Electr prefer:
Controllers and Sensors

In Medical/Health prefer:
Diagnostic Test Products
Medical Products

In Consumer Related prefer:
Consumer Products
Consumer Services
Education Related

In Industrial/Energy prefer:
Industrial Products
Materials
Factory Automation
Process Control
Machinery
Environmental Related

In Transportation prefer:
Aerospace

In Business Serv. prefer:
Distribution

In Manufact. prefer:
Manufacturing

Additional Information

Year Founded: 2004
Capital Under Management: $100,000,000
Current Activity Level : Actively seeking new investments
Method of Compensation: Return on investment is of primary concern, do not charge fees

WHITE ROSE GP I, LLC

625 Fouth Avenue, South
Minneapolis, MN USA 55415
Phone: 612-340-4249

Type of Firm

Private Equity Firm

Project Preferences

Type of Financing Preferred:
Fund of Funds
Mezzanine
Balanced

Additional Information

Name of Most Recent Fund: White Rose Fund I Equity, L.P.
Most Recent Fund Was Raised: 10/07/2007
Year Founded: 2007
Capital Under Management: $500,000,000
Current Activity Level : Actively seeking new investments

WHITECASTLE INVESTMENTS

22 St. Clair Avenue East
Suite 1010
Toronto, Canada M4T 2S3
Phone: 416-961-5355
Fax: 416-961-3232
Website: www.whitecapvp.com

Management and Staff

Elmer Kim, Managing Director
Michael Fricker, Vice President
Peter Chung, Chief Financial Officer

Type of Firm

Bank Affiliated

Association Membership

Canadian Venture Capital Association

Project Preferences

Role in Financing:
Prefer role in deals created by others

Type of Financing Preferred:
Leveraged Buyout
Early Stage
Management Buyouts
Acquisition

Geographical Preferences

Canadian Preferences:
All Canada

Industry Preferences

In Communications prefer:
Telecommunications

In Computer Software prefer:
Software

In Internet Specific prefer:
Internet

In Medical/Health prefer:
Medical/Health

In Other prefer:
Environment Responsible

Additional Information

Year Founded: 1959
Capital Under Management: $50,100,000
Current Activity Level : Actively seeking new investments

WHITECLIFF CAPITAL PARTNERS

7825 Washington Avenue North
Suite 500
Edina, MN USA 55439
Phone: 612-373-2000
Fax: 612-373-2020
E-mail: info@whitecliff.com
Website: www.whitecliff.com

Management and Staff

William Brown, Managing Director

Type of Firm

Bank Affiliated

Project Preferences

Role in Financing:
Prefer role as deal originator but will also invest in deals created by others

Type of Financing Preferred:
Leveraged Buyout
Turnaround
Management Buyouts
Industry Rollups
Recapitalizations

Size of Investments Considered:
Min Size of Investment Considered (000s): $1,000
Max Size of Investment Considered (000s): $8,000

Geographical Preferences

United States Preferences:
All U.S.

Industry Focus

(% based on actual investment)

Computer Software and Services	58.1%
Medical/Health	22.0%
Industrial/Energy	18.3%
Internet Specific	1.5%

Additional Information

Year Founded: 1991
Capital Under Management: $35,000,000
Current Activity Level : Actively seeking new investments

WHITESUN EQUITY PARTNERS

Sixth Floor, No. 76, Sec. 2
Tunhwa South Road
Taipei, Taiwan 106
Phone: 886-2-2755-0148
Fax: 886-2-2755-3308
E-mail: investors@we-partners.com
Website: www.we-partners.com

Other Offices

Room 1806-1807
No. 2299 Yan An West Road
Shanghai, China 200336
Phone: 86-21-6236-1670
Fax: 86-21-6236-1822

Management and Staff

David Lin, Managing General Partner
Gloria Wang, Chief Financial Officer
Jack Lee, Principal

Kevin Hsu, General Partner
Rick Lu, General Partner

Type of Firm

Private Equity Firm

Project Preferences

Type of Financing Preferred:

Balanced

Geographical Preferences

International Preferences:

China

Industry Preferences

In Internet Specific prefer:

E-Commerce Technology

In Consumer Related prefer:

Consumer

Additional Information

Year Founded: 2007
Current Activity Level : Actively seeking new investments

WHITMAN CAPITAL, LLC

525 University Avenue
Suite 701
Palo Alto, CA USA 94301
Phone: 650-325-9700
Fax: 650-325-9765
E-mail: whitcap@whitcap.com
Website: www.whitcap.com

Management and Staff

Douglas Whitman, President

Type of Firm

Private Equity Advisor or Fund of Funds

Project Preferences

Type of Financing Preferred:

Early Stage
Mezzanine
Public Companies
Later Stage
Seed
Startup

Industry Preferences

In Communications prefer:

Communications and Media

In Computer Software prefer:

Software

In Internet Specific prefer:

Internet

Additional Information

Year Founded: 1994
Capital Under Management: $100,000,000
Current Activity Level : Actively seeking new investments

WI HARPER GROUP

50 California Street
Suite 2920
San Francisco, CA USA 94111
Phone: 415-397-6200
Fax: 415-397-6280
E-mail: info@wiharper.com
Website: www.wiharper.com

Other Offices

10F-2 Ruentex Banking Tower
76 Tun Hua South Road, Sec. 2
Taipei, Taiwan
Phone: 886-2-2755-6033
Fax: 886-2-2709-2127

No. 63 Market Street
#09-02
Singapore, Singapore 048942
Phone: 65-6837-0568
Fax: 65-6837-2660

806 IBM Tower, Pacific Century Place
2A Gongti Bei Lu, Chao Yang District
Beijing, China 100027
Phone: 8610-6539-1366
Fax: 8610-6539-1367

Management and Staff

Ahmad Bahai, Venture Partner
Charles Jiggs Davis, Venture Partner
Cynthia Qiu, Managing Director
David Wang, Managing Director
David Lam, Managing Director
Ellen Gao, Principal
Eric Chen, Venture Partner
Jackson Hu, Venture Partner
James Lee, Venture Partner
Joseph Fan, Venture Partner
Kang Sun, Venture Partner
Lucas Wang, Partner
Paul Chau, Partner
Peter Peng, Principal
Schui Sche, Venture Partner
Sean Peng, Managing Director
Wayne Shiong, Partner
Winnie Hsu, Principal
YK Chu, Managing Director
Zirui Tian, Venture Partner

Type of Firm

Private Equity Firm

Association Membership

Venture Capital Association of Beijing (VCAB)
Taiwan Venture Capital Association(TVCA)
National Venture Capital Association - USA (NVCA)

Project Preferences

Role in Financing:

Will function either as deal originator or investor in deals created by others

Type of Financing Preferred:

Early Stage
Expansion
Seed

Size of Investments Considered:

Min Size of Investment Considered (000s): $1,000
Max Size of Investment Considered (000s): $5,000

Geographical Preferences

United States Preferences:

Southern California
Northern California

International Preferences:

Taiwan
China

Industry Focus

(% based on actual investment)

Internet Specific	44.5%
Semiconductors/Other Elect.	16.3%
Medical/Health	10.9%
Computer Software and Services	9.3%
Communications and Media	5.4%
Biotechnology	4.0%
Computer Hardware	3.2%
Industrial/Energy	3.1%
Other Products	1.6%
Consumer Related	1.6%

Additional Information

Name of Most Recent Fund: WI Harper Inc. Fund VI, Ltd.
Most Recent Fund Was Raised: 05/31/2005
Year Founded: 1993
Capital Under Management: $300,000,000
Current Activity Level : Actively seeking new investments
Method of Compensation: Return on invest. most important, but chg. closing fees, service fees, etc.

WICKS GROUP OF COMPANIES LLC, THE

405 Park Avenue
Suite 702
New York, NY USA 10022
Phone: 212-838-2100
Fax: 212-223-2109
E-mail: info@wicksgroup.com
Website: www.wicksgroup.com

Management and Staff

Adam Crider, Vice President
Daniel Black, Partner
Daniel Kortick, Managing Partner
E. Sue Cho, Principal
E.J. Sloboda, Principal
Jamie Weston, Partner

Matthew Gormly, Managing Partner
Max Von Zuben, Principal
Thomas Kearney, Vice President

Type of Firm

Private Equity Firm

Project Preferences

Role in Financing:

Prefer role as deal originator

Type of Financing Preferred:

Leveraged Buyout
Control-block Purchases
Management Buyouts

Size of Investments Considered:

Min Size of Investment Considered (000s): $5,000
Max Size of Investment Considered (000s): $200,000

Industry Focus

(% based on actual investment)

Communications and Media	43.2%
Other Products	41.4%
Consumer Related	15.4%

Additional Information

Name of Most Recent Fund: Wicks Communications & Media Partners III, L.P.
Most Recent Fund Was Raised: 10/12/2004
Year Founded: 1989
Capital Under Management: $450,000,000
Current Activity Level : Actively seeking new investments
Method of Compensation: Return on invest. most important, but chg. closing fees, service fees, etc.

WILDCAT ANGEL FUND, LLC

555 Main Street
Suite 250
Chico, CA USA 95928
Phone: 530-895-3111

Type of Firm

Private Equity Firm

Project Preferences

Type of Financing Preferred:

Balanced

Additional Information

Year Founded: 2004
Capital Under Management: $600,000
Current Activity Level : Actively seeking new investments

WILH. SONESSON AB

St Nygatan 61
Malmo, Sweden 211 37
Phone: 46-46-280-8100
Fax: 46-46-280-8101
E-mail: info@wilhsonesson.com
Website: www.wilhsonesson.com

Type of Firm

Private Equity Firm

Project Preferences

Type of Financing Preferred:

Balanced

Geographical Preferences

United States Preferences:

Alaska

International Preferences:

Africa

Additional Information

Year Founded: 2004
Current Activity Level : Actively seeking new investments

WILL CAPITAL MANAGEMENT CO., LTD.

1F Toda Kioicho Bldg.
1-11 Kioicho, Chiyoda-ku
Tokyo, Japan 102-0094
Phone: 813-5210-4200
Fax: 813-5216-2120
E-mail: secretary@willcapital.com
Website: www.willcapital.com

Type of Firm

Private Equity Firm

Project Preferences

Type of Financing Preferred:

Early Stage

Geographical Preferences

International Preferences:

Japan

Additional Information

Year Founded: 1997
Capital Under Management: $22,000,000
Current Activity Level : Actively seeking new investments

WILLIS STEIN & PARTNERS

One North Wacker Drive
Suite 4800
Chicago, IL USA 60606
Phone: 312-422-2400
Fax: 312-422-2424
E-mail: info@willisstein.com
Website: www.willisstein.com

Other Offices

12 East 49th Street
27th Floor
New York, NY USA 10017
Phone: 212-994-7300
Fax: 212-994-7301

Management and Staff

Avy Stein, Managing Partner
Bradley Shisler, Principal
Christopher Boehm, Principal
Daniel Blumenthal, Managing Partner
David Mills, Chief Financial Officer
Jeffrey Beyer, Principal
John Willis, Managing Partner
Julie Constas, Vice President
Paul Mayfield, Managing Director
Philip Pool, Managing Director
R. Jason Weller, Managing Director
Robert Froetscher, Managing Director

Type of Firm

Private Equity Firm

Association Membership

Illinois Venture Capital Association

Project Preferences

Role in Financing:

Prefer role as deal originator

Type of Financing Preferred:

Leveraged Buyout
Control-block Purchases
Industry Rollups
Special Situation

Geographical Preferences

United States Preferences:

Midwest

Industry Focus

(% based on actual investment)

Consumer Related	52.0%
Communications and Media	16.0%
Other Products	11.4%
Semiconductors/Other Elect.	9.7%
Internet Specific	6.0%
Medical/Health	2.2%
Industrial/Energy	1.7%
Computer Software and Services	0.9%

Additional Information

Name of Most Recent Fund: Willis Stein & Partners III, L.P.
Most Recent Fund Was Raised: 07/05/2000
Year Founded: 1995
Capital Under Management: $2,983,000,000
Current Activity Level : Actively seeking new investments
Method of Compensation: Return on investment is of primary concern, do not charge fees

WILSHIRE ASSOCIATES PRIVATE MARKETS GROUP

210 Sixth Avenue
Suite 3720
Pittsburgh, PA USA 15222
Phone: 412-434-1580
Fax: 412-434-5249
E-mail: contactpmg@wilshire.com
Website: www.wilshirepmg.com

Other Offices

4th flr. East Tower, Otemachi 1st Square
1-5-1 Otemachi, Chiyoda-ku
Tokyo, Japan 100-0004
Phone: 81-3-5219-1376
Fax: 81-3-5219-1201

1299 Ocean Avenue
Suite 700
Santa Monica, CA USA 90401
Phone: 310-451-3051
Fax: 310-458-0479

Wilshire Associates Europe B.V.
Prins Hendriklaan 43
Amsterdam, Netherlands 1075 BA
Phone: 31-20-305-7530
Fax: 31-20305-7539

101 East 52nd Street
20th Floor
New York, NY USA 10022
Phone: 212-308-9500
Fax: 212-308-3930

Level 6, AMP
1 Hobart Place
Canberra, Australia 2601
Phone: 612-6279-6000
Fax: 612-6230-5144

Management and Staff

David Webb, Managing Director
Derek Minno, Managing Director
Grant Harrison, Managing Director
Grant Fleming, Managing Director
Ilona Brom, Managing Director
Jeff Ennis, Managing Director
Kevin Nee, President
Laurie Coggan, Managing Director
Matt Westwood, Managing Director
Neville Page, Managing Director
Ovidio Iglesias, Managing Director
Thomas Lynch, Senior Managing Director
William Van Eesteren, Managing Director

Type of Firm

Investment Management Firm

Project Preferences

Type of Financing Preferred:
Fund of Funds
Leveraged Buyout
Balanced

Geographical Preferences

United States Preferences:
All U.S.

International Preferences:
Europe
Pacific
Australia
All International

Additional Information

Name of Most Recent Fund: Wilshire PMG Fund IV
Most Recent Fund Was Raised: 09/15/2000
Year Founded: 1984
Capital Under Management: $6,242,200,000
Current Activity Level : Actively seeking new investments

WINCHESTER CAPITAL TECHNOLOGY PARTNERS LLC

Winchester House
445 Orange Street
New Haven, CT USA 06511
Phone: 203-787-5029
Fax: 203-785-0018
E-mail: info@winchestercapital.com
Website: www.winchestercapital.com

Type of Firm

Bank Affiliated

Project Preferences

Type of Financing Preferred:
Early Stage
Generalist PE
Acquisition

Geographical Preferences

Canadian Preferences:
All Canada

International Preferences:
Europe

Industry Preferences

In Medical/Health prefer:
Health Services

Additional Information

Year Founded: 1986
Current Activity Level : Actively seeking new investments

WINCOVE CAPITAL

260 Madison Avenue
Eigth Floor
New York, NY USA 10016
Phone: 314-814-5278
Website: www.wincovecapital.com

Management and Staff

John McAlister, Partner
John Lenahan, Principal
Michael McGovern, Partner

Type of Firm

Private Equity Firm

Project Preferences

Type of Financing Preferred:
Leveraged Buyout
Management Buyouts
Acquisition
Recapitalizations

Geographical Preferences

United States Preferences:
All U.S.

Canadian Preferences:
All Canada

Industry Preferences

In Business Serv. prefer:
Services
Distribution

In Manufact. prefer:
Manufacturing

Additional Information

Year Founded: 2008
Current Activity Level : Actively seeking new investments

WIND POINT PARTNERS

One Town Square
Suite 780
Southfield, MI USA 48076
Phone: 248-945-7200
Fax: 248-945-7220
E-mail: info@wppartners.com
Website: www.wppartners.com

Other Offices

676 North Michigan Avenue
Suite 3700
Chicago, IL USA 60611
Phone: 312-255-4800
Fax: 312-255-4820

Management and Staff

Alex Washington, Managing Director
David Stott, Vice President
James TenBroek, Managing Director
LeAnn Kilarski, Chief Financial Officer
Mark Burgett, Managing Director
Michael Nelson, Principal
Nathaniel Brown, Principal
Paul Peterson, Principal
Richard Kracum, Managing Director

Robert Cummings, Managing Director
Salam Chaudhary, Principal

Type of Firm

Private Equity Firm

Association Membership

Illinois Venture Capital Association

Project Preferences

Role in Financing:

Prefer role as deal originator but will also invest in deals created by others

Type of Financing Preferred:

Leveraged Buyout
Expansion
Generalist PE
Balanced
Later Stage
Management Buyouts
Acquisition
Recapitalizations

Size of Investments Considered:

Min Size of Investment Considered (000s): $20,000
Max Size of Investment Considered (000s): $70,000

Geographical Preferences

United States Preferences:

All U.S.

Industry Focus

(% based on actual investment)

Other Products	43.5%
Consumer Related	22.7%
Medical/Health	8.1%
Internet Specific	8.1%
Communications and Media	7.8%
Industrial/Energy	6.3%
Biotechnology	1.2%
Semiconductors/Other Elect.	0.9%
Computer Hardware	0.8%
Computer Software and Services	0.5%

Additional Information

Year Founded: 1983
Capital Under Management: $2,500,000,000
Current Activity Level : Actively seeking new investments
Method of Compensation: Return on invest. most important, but chg. closing fees, service fees, etc.

WINDAMERE VENTURE PARTNERS, LLC

6402 Cardeno Drive
La Jolla, CA USA 92037
Phone: 858-350-7950
Fax: 858-350-7951
E-mail: information@windamerevp.com
Website: www.windamerevp.com

Management and Staff

Jack Goldstein, General Partner
John Burd, General Partner
Kenneth Widder, General Partner
Scott Glenn, Managing Partner

Type of Firm

Private Equity Firm

Project Preferences

Type of Financing Preferred:

Early Stage
Startup

Industry Preferences

In Medical/Health prefer:

Medical/Health
Medical Therapeutics
Pharmaceuticals

Additional Information

Year Founded: 1998
Current Activity Level : Actively seeking new investments

WINDJAMMER CAPITAL INVESTORS (FKA:PACIFIC MEZZANINE INV.)

610 Newport Center Drive
Suite 1100
Newport Beach, CA USA 92660
Phone: 949-721-9944
Fax: 949-720-4222
E-mail: info@windjammercapital.com
Website: www.windjammercapital.com

Other Offices

890 Winter Street
Suite 130
Waltham, MA USA 02451
Phone: 781-530-9100
Fax: 781-530-9200

Management and Staff

Greg Bondick, Principal
J. Derek Watson, Principal

Type of Firm

Private Equity Firm

Project Preferences

Role in Financing:

Prefer role as deal originator but will also invest in deals created by others

Type of Financing Preferred:

Leveraged Buyout
Mezzanine

Size of Investments Considered:

Min Size of Investment Considered (000s): $10,000
Max Size of Investment Considered (000s): $75,000

Geographical Preferences

United States Preferences:

All U.S.

Canadian Preferences:

All Canada

Industry Preferences

In Semiconductor/Electr prefer:

Sensors

In Medical/Health prefer:

Diagnostic Services
Other Therapeutic
Medical Products
Disposable Med. Products
Hospitals/Clinics/Primary
Hospital/Other Instit.
Pharmaceuticals

In Consumer Related prefer:

Food/Beverage
Consumer Products
Consumer Services

In Industrial/Energy prefer:

Industrial Products
Materials
Factory Automation
Machinery

In Financial Services prefer:

Financial Services
Real Estate

Additional Information

Name of Most Recent Fund: Windjammer Mezzanine & Equity Fund II, L.P.
Most Recent Fund Was Raised: 11/01/1999
Year Founded: 1990
Capital Under Management: $750,000,000
Current Activity Level : Actively seeking new investments
Method of Compensation: Return on invest. most important, but chg. closing fees, service fees, etc.

WINDSPEED VENTURES

52 Waltham Street
Lexington, MA USA 02421
Phone: 781-860-8888
Fax: 781-860-0493
E-mail: info@wsventures.com
Website: www.wsventures.com

Management and Staff

Bernard Haan, General Partner
Daniel Bathon, General Partner
David Safaii, Principal
John Bullock, Managing Partner
Steven Karlson, General Partner

Type of Firm

Private Equity Firm

Association Membership

National Venture Capital Association - USA (NVCA)

Project Preferences

Role in Financing:

Prefer role as deal originator but will also invest in deals created by others

Type of Financing Preferred:

Early Stage

Size of Investments Considered:

Min Size of Investment Considered (000s): $500
Max Size of Investment Considered (000s): $5,000

Geographical Preferences

United States Preferences:

Northeast

Industry Preferences

In Communications prefer:

Communications and Media

In Computer Software prefer:

Computer Services
Data Processing
Software
Systems Software
Applications Software

In Internet Specific prefer:

Internet
Ecommerce
Web Aggregration/Portals

Additional Information

Name of Most Recent Fund: Comdisco Ventures Fund A, LLC
Most Recent Fund Was Raised: 06/01/1992
Year Founded: 1999
Capital Under Management: $176,000,000
Current Activity Level : Actively seeking new investments
Method of Compensation: Return on investment is of primary concern, do not charge fees

---

WINDWARD VENTURES

600 B Street
Suite 2230
San Diego, CA USA 92101
Phone: 619-234-6800
Fax: 619-234-6886
E-mail: mailbox@windwardventures.com
Website: www.windwardventures.com

Other Offices

2660 Townsgate Road
Village Park, Bldg. 800, Ste. J
Westlake Village, CA USA 91361
Phone: 805-497-3222
Fax: 805-497-9331

Management and Staff

James Cole, Managing Partner
M. David Titus, Managing Partner
Paul Scott, Chief Financial Officer

Type of Firm

Private Equity Firm

Association Membership

Western Association of Venture Capitalists (WAVC)

Project Preferences

Role in Financing:

Will function either as deal originator or investor in deals created by others

Type of Financing Preferred:

Second Stage Financing
Early Stage
Start-up Financing
First Stage Financing
Startup

Size of Investments Considered:

Min Size of Investment Considered (000s): $25
Max Size of Investment Considered (000s): $5,000

Geographical Preferences

United States Preferences:

Southern California

Industry Focus

(% based on actual investment)

Medical/Health	47.1%
Computer Software and Services	20.6%
Communications and Media	19.5%
Internet Specific	7.6%
Semiconductors/Other Elect.	4.7%
Other Products	0.5%

Additional Information

Year Founded: 1997
Capital Under Management: $100,000,000
Current Activity Level : Actively seeking new investments
Method of Compensation: Return on investment is of primary concern, do not charge fees

---

WING EQUITY MANAGEMENT GMBH

Hainburger Strasse 15
Vienna, Austria 1030
Phone: 43-1-7169-0580
Fax: 43-1-7169-0589
E-mail: office@wingequity.com

Management and Staff

Christian Wimmer, Managing Partner

Type of Firm

Private Equity Firm

Project Preferences

Type of Financing Preferred:

Balanced

Geographical Preferences

International Preferences:

Czech Republic
Europe
Croatia
Bosnia

Industry Preferences

In Consumer Related prefer:

Food/Beverage

In Industrial/Energy prefer:

Industrial Products

Additional Information

Year Founded: 2006
Current Activity Level : Actively seeking new investments

WINONA CAPITAL MANAGEMENT

333 West Wacker Drive
Suite 1720
Chicago, IL USA 60606
Phone: 312-334-8800
Fax: 312-223-9484
E-mail: info@winonacapital.com
Website: www.winonacapital.com

Other Offices

801 Second Avenue
Suite 1300
Seattle, WA USA 98104
Phone: 206-464-3855
Fax: 206-464-5250

Management and Staff

Dan Kipp, Managing Director
Ian Jacobson, Vice President
Laird Koldyke, Managing Director
Luke Reese, Managing Director

Type of Firm

Private Equity Firm

Project Preferences

Size of Investments Considered:

Min Size of Investment Considered (000s): $5,000
Max Size of Investment Considered (000s): $15,000

Industry Preferences

In Consumer Related prefer:

Entertainment and Leisure
Sports
Consumer Products
Consumer Services
Education Related

In Business Serv. prefer:

Distribution

In Manufact. prefer:

Manufacturing

Additional Information

Year Founded: 2005
Current Activity Level : Actively seeking new investments

WINSTON PARTNERS

1750 Tysons Boulevard
Suite 200
McLean, VA USA 22101
Phone: 703-905-9555
E-mail: info@winstonpartners.com
Website: www.winstonpartners.com

Management and Staff

A. Scott Andrews, Managing Director
Douglas Gilbert, Managing Director
Marvin Bush, Managing Partner
Matthew Malone, Principal
Michael Bluestein, Principal

Type of Firm

Bank Affiliated

Association Membership

Mid-Atlantic Venture Association

Project Preferences

Type of Financing Preferred:

Leveraged Buyout

Industry Focus

(% based on actual investment)

Internet Specific	43.9%
Other Products	38.8%
Computer Software and Services	17.1%
Semiconductors/Other Elect.	0.1%

Additional Information

Name of Most Recent Fund: Winston/Thayer Partners
Most Recent Fund Was Raised: 08/01/1999
Year Founded: 1993
Capital Under Management: $100,000,000
Current Activity Level : Actively seeking new investments

WINTHROP, BROWN & COMPANY, INC. (DBA: WINTHROP VENTURES)

74 Trinity Place
Suite 600
New York, NY USA 10023-2666
Phone: 212-422-0100

Management and Staff

Cyrus Brown, President

Type of Firm

Bank Affiliated

Project Preferences

Role in Financing:

Prefer role as deal originator

Type of Financing Preferred:

Second Stage Financing
Leveraged Buyout
Start-up Financing
First Stage Financing

Size of Investments Considered:

Min Size of Investment Considered (000s): $1,000
Max Size of Investment Considered: No Limit

Industry Preferences

In Communications prefer:

Commercial Communications
CATV & Pay TV Systems
Telecommunications
Data Communications
Satellite Microwave Comm.
Other Communication Prod.

In Computer Hardware prefer:

Computers
Computer Graphics and Dig
Integrated Turnkey System
Terminals
Disk Relat. Memory Device

In Computer Software prefer:

Computer Services
Systems Software
Applications Software

In Semiconductor/Electr prefer:

Electronics
Electronic Components
Semiconductor
Laser Related
Analytic/Scientific

In Biotechnology prefer:

Industrial Biotechnology
Biosensors
Biotech Related Research

In Medical/Health prefer:

Medical Diagnostics
Diagnostic Test Products
Drug/Equipmt Delivery
Other Therapeutic
Medical Products
Disposable Med. Products
Hospitals/Clinics/Primary
Hospital/Other Instit.
Pharmaceuticals

In Consumer Related prefer:

Entertainment and Leisure
Retail
Computer Stores
Food/Beverage
Consumer Products
Consumer Services
Education Related

In Industrial/Energy prefer:

Alternative Energy
Energy Conservation Relat
Industrial Products

In Transportation prefer:

Transportation

In Financial Services prefer:

Financial Services

In Manufact. prefer:

Office Automation Equipmt
Publishing

Additional Information

Year Founded: 1972
Current Activity Level : Actively seeking new investments
Method of Compensation: Return on invest. most important, but chg. closing fees, service fees, etc.

WINVEST VENTURE INVESTMENT

7F, Yoongjeon Building
154-10 Samsung-Dong Gangnam-Gu
Seoul, South Korea
Phone: 822-565-3626
Fax: 822-565-3484

Management and Staff

Taeksu Lee, President

Type of Firm

Private Equity Firm

Project Preferences

Type of Financing Preferred:

Balanced

Geographical Preferences

International Preferences:

Korea, South

Additional Information

Year Founded: 2000
Capital Under Management: $7,000,000
Current Activity Level : Actively seeking new investments

WIPPRIVATE EQUITY

WIPHOLD House
61 Central Street
Houghton, South Africa 2198
Phone: 27-11-715-3500
Fax: 27-11-728-8891
Website: www.wipcapital.com

Management and Staff

Gloria Serobe, Chief Executive Officer
Lance Katz, Managing Director
Louisa Mojela, Chief Executive Officer

Type of Firm
Bank Affiliated

Association Membership
South African Venture Capital Association (SAVCA)

Project Preferences
Type of Financing Preferred:
Leveraged Buyout
Expansion

Geographical Preferences
International Preferences:
South Africa

Additional Information
Year Founded: 2001
Capital Under Management: $14,600,000
Current Activity Level : Actively seeking new investments

WISDOM CAPITAL GROUP
47th Floor, The Center
99 Queen's Road
Central, Hong Kong
Phone: 852-2312-7696
Fax: 852-2312-1515
E-mail: info@wisdomcapital.net
Website: www.wisdomcapital.com

Type of Firm
Private Equity Firm

Project Preferences
Type of Financing Preferred:
Balanced

Geographical Preferences
International Preferences:
China
Asia

Industry Preferences
In Computer Software prefer:
Data Processing

In Biotechnology prefer:
Biotechnology

In Consumer Related prefer:
Education Related

In Industrial/Energy prefer:
Energy

In Financial Services prefer:
Real Estate

Additional Information
Year Founded: 2005
Current Activity Level : Actively seeking new investments

WISE SRG S.P.A. (AKA: WISEQUITY)
Foro Buonaparte 76
Milan, Italy 20121
Phone: 39-02-854-5691
Fax: 39-02-8050-9485
E-mail: info@wisesgr.it
Website: www.wisequity.it

Management and Staff
Fabrizio Medea, Partner
Michele Semenzato, Partner
Paolo Gambarini, Partner
Roberto Saviane, Partner

Type of Firm
Private Equity Advisor or Fund of Funds

Association Membership
European Private Equity and Venture Capital Assoc.

Project Preferences
Type of Financing Preferred:
Leveraged Buyout
Expansion
Balanced

Geographical Preferences
International Preferences:
Italy
Europe

Industry Preferences
In Communications prefer:
Telecommunications
Wireless Communications

In Computer Software prefer:
Software

In Internet Specific prefer:
Internet

In Business Serv. prefer:
Media

Additional Information
Name of Most Recent Fund: Wisequity II & Macchine Italia
Most Recent Fund Was Raised: 07/22/2005
Year Founded: 2000
Capital Under Management: $115,200,000
Current Activity Level : Actively seeking new investments

WIT INVESTMENT PARTNERS, LTD.
No.169 Jen-Ai Road
16th Floor, Section 4
Taipei, Taiwan
Phone: 886-2-2711-3401
Fax: 886-2-2711-3403
E-mail: witip@mail.sysnet.net.tw

Management and Staff
C. H. Hsiao, President

Type of Firm
Private Equity Firm

Association Membership
Taiwan Venture Capital Association(TVCA)

Project Preferences
Type of Financing Preferred:
Expansion
Mezzanine
Balanced
Seed
Startup

Geographical Preferences
International Preferences:
Taiwan

Industry Preferences
In Communications prefer:
Telecommunications

In Semiconductor/Electr prefer:
Electronics
Semiconductor

Additional Information
Year Founded: 1997
Capital Under Management: $15,600,000
Current Activity Level : Actively seeking new investments

WIZARD PARTNERS SRL
30 Corso Vittorio Emanuele II
Milan, Italy 20122
Phone: 39-276-322-041
Fax: 39-276-015-183
E-mail: wizard@wizardpartners.com

Management and Staff
Francesco Noseda, Managing Partner
Jonathan Schwartz, Partner
Luigi Maniglio, Managing Partner

Type of Firm
Private Equity Firm

Association Membership
Italian Venture Capital Association (AIFI)

Project Preferences
Type of Financing Preferred:
Second Stage Financing
Leveraged Buyout
Expansion
Turnaround

Geographical Preferences

International Preferences:
Europe

Additional Information

Year Founded: 2000
Capital Under Management: $78,500,000
Current Activity Level : Actively seeking new investments

WK ASSOCIATES

6/F, No 15 TiDing Avenue
Section 2
Taipei, Taiwan
Fax: 886-2-8797-7999

Type of Firm
Private Equity Firm

Association Membership
Taiwan Venture Capital Association(TVCA)

Project Preferences

Type of Financing Preferred:
Expansion
Mezzanine
Balanced
Later Stage

Geographical Preferences

International Preferences:
Taiwan

Industry Focus

(% based on actual investment)

Semiconductors/Other Elect.	33.2%
Communications and Media	25.6%
Internet Specific	25.4%
Computer Software and Services	12.6%
Computer Hardware	2.5%
Consumer Related	0.6%

Additional Information

Name of Most Recent Fund: WK Technology Fund VIII
Most Recent Fund Was Raised: 01/19/2001
Year Founded: 1990
Capital Under Management: $352,800,000
Current Activity Level : Actively seeking new investments

WM ENTERPRISE (AKA: WEST MIDLANDS ENTERPRISE, LTD.)

Wellington House
31-34 Waterloo Street
Birmingham, United Kingdom B2 5TJ
Phone: 44-121-236-8855
Fax: 44-121-233-3942
E-mail: mail@wm-enterprise.co.uk
Website: www.wm-enterprise.co.uk

Other Offices

Antler House
Crouchley Lane
Lymm, United Kingdom WA13 0AN
Phone: 44-1925-759-246
Fax: 44-1925-759-692

2nd Floor Orbital House
85-87 Croydon Road
Caterham, United Kingdom CR3 6PD
Phone: 44-1883-337-111
Fax: 44-1883-337-112

Tulip House
70 Borough High Street, London Bridge
London, United Kingdom SE1 1XF

Type of Firm
Private Equity Firm

Association Membership
British Venture Capital Association (BVCA)

Project Preferences

Role in Financing:
Prefer role as deal originator but will also invest in deals created by others

Type of Financing Preferred:
Expansion
Generalist PE
Balanced
Later Stage
Seed
Management Buyouts
Recapitalizations

Size of Investments Considered:
Min Size of Investment Considered (000s): $746
Max Size of Investment Considered (000s): $11,942

Geographical Preferences

International Preferences:
United Kingdom

Industry Preferences

In Communications prefer:
Commercial Communications
Telecommunications
Data Communications
Other Communication Prod.

In Computer Hardware prefer:
Computers
Integrated Turnkey System

In Computer Software prefer:
Computer Services
Systems Software
Applications Software

In Computer Other prefer:
Computer Related

In Semiconductor/Electr prefer:
Electronics
Electronic Components

In Medical/Health prefer:
Medical/Health
Medical Diagnostics
Drug/Equipmt Delivery
Other Therapeutic
Disposable Med. Products

In Consumer Related prefer:
Entertainment and Leisure
Computer Stores
Food/Beverage
Consumer Products
Consumer Services
Education Related

In Industrial/Energy prefer:
Energy
Industrial Products
Environmental Related

In Transportation prefer:
Transportation

In Financial Services prefer:
Financial Services

In Business Serv. prefer:
Services

In Manufact. prefer:
Manufacturing
Office Automation Equipmt

Additional Information

Name of Most Recent Fund: South East Growth Fund (AKA: SEGF)
Most Recent Fund Was Raised: 06/03/2003
Year Founded: 1982
Capital Under Management: $60,000,000
Current Activity Level : Actively seeking new investments
Method of Compensation: Return on invest. most important, but chg. closing fees, service fees, etc.

WOLF VENTURES (AKA: WOLF ASSET MANAGEMENT CORP.)

1625 Broadway
Suite 930
Denver, CO USA 80202
Phone: 303-321-4800
Fax: 303-321-4848
Website: www.wolfventures.com

Management and Staff
David Wolf, Managing Partner
James Conboy, Partner

Type of Firm
Private Equity Firm

Association Membership
Natl Assoc of Small Bus. Inv. Co (NASBIC)

Project Preferences

Role in Financing:
Will function either as deal originator or investor in deals created by others

Type of Financing Preferred:
Second Stage Financing
Early Stage
Expansion
First Stage Financing

Size of Investments Considered:
Min Size of Investment Considered (000s): $250
Max Size of Investment Considered (000s): $3,000

Geographical Preferences

United States Preferences:
Rocky Mountain

Industry Focus

(% based on actual investment)

Semiconductors/Other Elect.	34.1%
Computer Software and Services	31.1%
Internet Specific	15.8%
Communications and Media	7.0%
Medical/Health	5.1%
Computer Hardware	3.9%
Other Products	1.7%
Industrial/Energy	0.7%
Consumer Related	0.6%

Additional Information

Name of Most Recent Fund: Wolf Ventures Aerie Fund LLC
Most Recent Fund Was Raised: 09/30/2000
Year Founded: 1995
Capital Under Management: $48,000,000
Current Activity Level : Actively seeking new investments
Method of Compensation: Return on investment is of primary concern, do not charge fees

---

WOLSELEY PARTNERS

2 Bulletin Place
Level 4
Sydney, Australia 2000
Phone: 612-8815-4200
Fax: 612-8815-4201
E-mail: info@wolseley.com.au
Website: www.wolseley.com.au

Management and Staff

Alan Lee, Chief Financial Officer
James Todd, Managing Director
Mark Richardson, Managing Director
Peter Hasko, Managing Director

Type of Firm

Private Equity Firm

Association Membership

Australian Venture Capital Association (AVCAL)

Project Preferences

Role in Financing:
Prefer role as deal originator but will also invest in deals created by others

Type of Financing Preferred:
Leveraged Buyout
Expansion
Generalist PE
Balanced
Turnaround
Later Stage
Management Buyouts
Industry Rollups
Acquisition

Size of Investments Considered:
Min Size of Investment Considered (000s): $8,058
Max Size of Investment Considered (000s): $40,290

Geographical Preferences

International Preferences:
Australia
New Zealand

Industry Preferences

In Business Serv. prefer:
Services
Distribution

In Manufact. prefer:
Manufacturing

Additional Information

Name of Most Recent Fund: Wolseley Partners Fund II
Most Recent Fund Was Raised: 12/17/2007
Year Founded: 1999
Capital Under Management: $327,700,000
Current Activity Level : Actively seeking new investments
Method of Compensation: Return on investment is of primary concern, do not charge fees

---

WONIK INVESTMENT PARTNERS (FKA: HANMI TECHNOLOGY INVESTMENT)

4/F Seowoo Building, 837-12
Yeoksam-dong, Kangnam-gu
Seoul, South Korea 135080
Phone: 822-6446-7114
Fax: 822-6446-7199
E-mail: skyblue71@hmtic.co.kr
Website: www.hmtic.co.kr

Management and Staff

Tae Kyu Lee, Partner
Yong Sung Lee, President

Type of Firm

Corporate PE/Venture

Association Membership

Korean Venture Capital Association (KVCA)

Project Preferences

Type of Financing Preferred:
Fund of Funds
Early Stage
Expansion
Balanced

Geographical Preferences

International Preferences:
Korea, South

Industry Preferences

In Semiconductor/Electr prefer:
Electronics

In Biotechnology prefer:
Biotechnology

In Business Serv. prefer:
Services

In Manufact. prefer:
Manufacturing

Additional Information

Year Founded: 1997
Capital Under Management: $39,800,000
Current Activity Level : Actively seeking new investments

WOODBOURNE CANADA PARTNES ADVISORS LLC

1919 14th Street
Suite 300
Boulder, CO USA 80302

Type of Firm

Private Equity Firm

Project Preferences

Type of Financing Preferred:
Balanced

Additional Information

Year Founded: 2007
Capital Under Management: $41,600,000
Current Activity Level : Actively seeking new investments

WOODBROOK CAPITAL, INC.

501 Fairmount Avenue
Suite 300
Towson, MD USA 21286
Phone: 410-769-6131
Fax: 410-321-4468
Website: www.woodbrookcapital.com

Type of Firm
Private Equity Advisor or Fund of Funds

Project Preferences

Role in Financing:
Prefer role as deal originator but will also invest in deals created by others

Type of Financing Preferred:
Expansion
Management Buyouts
Acquisition
Recapitalizations

Geographical Preferences

United States Preferences:
Mid Atlantic

Industry Preferences

In Medical/Health prefer:
Health Services

In Industrial/Energy prefer:
Materials

In Financial Services prefer:
Real Estate

Additional Information
Year Founded: 1988
Current Activity Level : Actively seeking new investments
Method of Compensation: Return on invest. most important, but chg. closing fees, service fees, etc.

WOODSIDE CAPITAL PARTNERS
20 Church Street
Suite 730
Hartford, CT USA 06103
Phone: 860- 547-1761
Fax: 860-547-1870
E-mail: info@woodsidemanagement.com
Website: www.woodsidemanagement.com

Management and Staff
Michael Niland, Chief Financial Officer

Type of Firm
Private Equity Firm

Additional Information
Year Founded: 1997
Current Activity Level : Actively seeking new investments

WOODSIDE FUND
350 Marine Parkway
Suite 300
Redwood City, CA USA 94065
Phone: 650-610-8050
Fax: 650-610-8051
E-mail: info@woodsidefund.com
Website: www.woodsidefund.com

Management and Staff
Gary Tyrrell, Chief Financial Officer
John Occhipinti, Managing Director
Mark Hoover, Venture Partner
Rick Shriner, Venture Partner
Robert Larson, Managing Director
Thomas Shields, Managing Director
Vincent Occhipinti, Managing Director

Type of Firm
Private Equity Firm

Association Membership
Western Association of Venture Capitalists (WAVC)

Project Preferences

Role in Financing:
Prefer role as deal originator but will also invest in deals created by others

Type of Financing Preferred:
Early Stage
Seed
First Stage Financing
Startup

Size of Investments Considered:
Min Size of Investment Considered (000s): $3,000
Max Size of Investment Considered (000s): $15,000

Geographical Preferences

United States Preferences:
Northern California
West Coast

Industry Focus
(% based on actual investment)

Communications and Media	30.7%
Semiconductors/Other Elect.	16.3%
Biotechnology	15.9%
Computer Software and Services	13.4%
Internet Specific	13.1%
Computer Hardware	6.2%
Other Products	1.9%
Industrial/Energy	1.6%
Consumer Related	0.6%
Medical/Health	0.3%

Additional Information
Year Founded: 1983
Capital Under Management: $209,200,000
Current Activity Level : Actively seeking new investments
Method of Compensation: Return on investment is of primary concern, do not charge fees

---

WOORI BANK LTD. (FKA: HANIL BANK)
606-1 Daechi-dong Kangnam
4/F Daehung Bldg.
Seoul, South Korea 135 280
Phone: 822-768-8000
Fax: 822-768-8059
Website: www.wooribank.com

Management and Staff
Kim Jong-wook, Vice President
Lee Duk-hoon, President
Min Jong-ku, Managing Director

Type of Firm
Bank Affiliated

Project Preferences

Type of Financing Preferred:
Leveraged Buyout
Turnaround
Management Buyouts
Recapitalizations

Geographical Preferences

International Preferences:
Korea, South
Asia

Additional Information
Year Founded: 2004
Capital Under Management: $200,000,000
Current Activity Level : Actively seeking new investments

WOORI PRIVATE EQUITY COMPANY
20/F 203 Hoehyeon-dong 1-ga
Chung-gu
Seoul, South Korea 100-792
Phone: 822-2125-2000
Fax: 822-2125-2291
E-mail: woorifg@woorifg.com
Website: www.woorifg.com

Type of Firm
Bank Affiliated

Project Preferences

Type of Financing Preferred:
Leveraged Buyout
Balanced

Geographical Preferences

International Preferences:
Korea, South

Additional Information
Year Founded: 2006
Current Activity Level : Actively seeking new investments

WOORI TECHNOLOGY INVESTMENT COMPANY, LTD.

12F, Hongwoo Building
945-1 Daechi-dong Kangnam-ku
Seoul, South Korea 305-348
Phone: 822-2008-3100
Fax: 822-2008-3123
Website: www.wooricapital.co.kr

Other Offices

59-4 Hwaam-dong
Yusung-gu
Taejeon, South Korea
Phone: 8242-861-1540

Management and Staff

Wan-Keun Lee, Chief Executive Officer

Type of Firm

Corporate PE/Venture

Association Membership

Korean Venture Capital Association (KVCA)

Project Preferences

Type of Financing Preferred:
Early Stage
Expansion
Balanced

Geographical Preferences

International Preferences:
Korea, South

Industry Preferences

In Communications prefer:
Telecommunications

In Computer Software prefer:
Software

In Internet Specific prefer:
Internet

In Semiconductor/Electr prefer:
Electronics
Semiconductor

In Biotechnology prefer:
Biotechnology

Additional Information

Year Founded: 1996
Capital Under Management: $7,300,000
Current Activity Level : Actively seeking new investments

WOORIDUL VENTURE CAPITAL CO., LTD.

4/F., SDA Building
635-9 Shinsa-Dong, Kangnam-Gu
Seoul, South Korea 135-892
Phone: 822-3448-1060
Fax: 822-3448-1065

Management and Staff

Jongwook Jung, President

Type of Firm

Private Equity Firm

Project Preferences

Type of Financing Preferred:
Balanced

Geographical Preferences

International Preferences:
Korea, South

Industry Preferences

In Communications prefer:
Communications and Media
Media and Entertainment

In Business Serv. prefer:
Media

Additional Information

Year Founded: 2006
Capital Under Management: $12,100,000
Current Activity Level : Actively seeking new investments

WORCESTER CAPITAL PARTNERS, LLC

446 Main Street
Worcester, MA USA 01608
Phone: 508-459-6251

Type of Firm

Private Equity Firm

Project Preferences

Type of Financing Preferred:
Early Stage

Size of Investments Considered:
Min Size of Investment Considered (000s): $500
Max Size of Investment Considered (000s): $5,000

Geographical Preferences

United States Preferences:
Northeast
Massachusetts

Industry Preferences

In Communications prefer:
Telecommunications

In Medical/Health prefer:
Health Services

Additional Information

Year Founded: 2000
Capital Under Management: $15,000,000
Current Activity Level : Actively seeking new investments

WORKERS INVESTMENT FUND INC.

1133 Regent Street
Suite 400
Fredericton, Canada E3B 3Z2
Phone: 506-444-0091
Fax: 506-444-0816

Type of Firm

Private Equity Firm

Additional Information

Year Founded: 2001
Current Activity Level : Actively seeking new investments

WORLD INVESTMENTS, INC.

World Herald Square
Omaha, NE USA 68102
Phone: 402-444-1172
Fax: 402-346-8804

Type of Firm

Bank Affiliated

Project Preferences

Role in Financing:
Prefer role as deal originator but will also invest in deals created by others

Type of Financing Preferred:
Second Stage Financing
Mezzanine
First Stage Financing

Geographical Preferences

United States Preferences:
Midwest
Rocky Mountain

Industry Preferences

In Communications prefer:
Communications and Media
Other Communication Prod.

In Computer Hardware prefer:
Computers

In Computer Other prefer:
Computer Related

In Semiconductor/Electr prefer:
Semiconductor
Component Testing Equipmt
Laser Related
Fiber Optics

In Medical/Health prefer:
Diagnostic Services

In Industrial/Energy prefer:
Robotics

In Manufact. prefer:
Publishing

Additional Information

Year Founded: 1987
Capital Under Management: $2,500,000
Current Activity Level : Actively seeking new investments
Method of Compensation: Return on investment is of primary concern, do not charge fees

WORLDVIEW TECHNOLOGY PARTNERS

435 Tasso Street
Suite 120
Palo Alto, CA USA 94301
Phone: 650-322-3800
Fax: 650-322-3880
Website: www.worldview.com

Other Offices

Fronwiesse 9
Roden, Germany 97849
Phone: 49-9391-81340

35/F CITIC Square
1168 Nanjing Road West
Shanghai, China 200041
Phone: 86-21-5111-9012
Fax: 86-21-5252-4616

16F, Shinjuku Mitsui #2 Bldg.
3-2-11 Nishi-Shinjuku, Shinjuku-ku
Tokyo, Japan 160-0023
Phone: 813-5339-6272
Fax: 813-5339-6274

Management and Staff

Colin Savage, General Partner
David Suzuki, Partner
Irwin Gross, General Partner
James Strawbridge, Chief Operating Officer
James Wei, General Partner
Lonnie Schilling, Managing Director
Michael Orsak, General Partner
Peter Goettner, General Partner
Stephen Eglash, Principal
Susumu Tanaka, General Partner
Tim Weingarten, General Partner
Yasuharu Watanabe, Partner

Type of Firm

Private Equity Firm

Association Membership

Western Association of Venture Capitalists (WAVC)

Project Preferences

Role in Financing:
Prefer role as deal originator but will also invest in deals created by others

Type of Financing Preferred:
Second Stage Financing
Mezzanine
Research and Development
Balanced
Start-up Financing
Seed
First Stage Financing

Industry Focus

(% based on actual investment)

Communications and Media	31.6%
Internet Specific	26.1%
Semiconductors/Other Elect.	21.7%
Computer Software and Services	12.5%
Computer Hardware	3.8%
Other Products	3.2%
Industrial/Energy	1.1%

Additional Information

Name of Most Recent Fund: Worldview Strategic Partners IV, L.P.
Most Recent Fund Was Raised: 06/20/2001
Year Founded: 1996
Capital Under Management: $1,743,100,000
Current Activity Level : Actively seeking new investments
Method of Compensation: Return on investment is of primary concern, do not charge fees

WORTHY CAPITAL, LTD.

355 Burrard 410
Vancouver, Canada V6C 2G8
Phone: 604-683-3161
Fax: 604-683-6859

Type of Firm

Private Equity Firm

Additional Information

Year Founded: 2003
Current Activity Level : Actively seeking new investments

WP GLOBAL PARTNERS INC.

155 North Wacker Drive
Suite 4400
Chicago, IL USA 60606
Phone: 312-277-1300
Fax: 312-377-2011
E-mail: info@wpglobalpartners.com
Website: www.wpglobalpartners.com

Other Offices

350 West Colorado Boulevard
Suite 215
Pasadena, CA USA 91105
Phone: 310-918-3346
Fax: 626-578-5710

590 Madison Avenue
Eighth Floor
New York, NY USA 10022
Phone: 212-558-2300
Fax: 212-558-2098

Management and Staff

Bassam Barazi, Vice President
Celia Chapman, Managing Director
Donald Phillips, Founder
Greg Jania, Partner
Greg Oberholtzer, Managing Director
J.F. Berry, Partner
Sharon Murphy, Chief Financial Officer
Tom Boudakian, Partner
Tom Thompson, Managing Director

Type of Firm

Private Equity Advisor or Fund of Funds

Project Preferences

Type of Financing Preferred:
Fund of Funds
Leveraged Buyout
Balanced
Acquisition
Special Situation

Geographical Preferences

United States Preferences:
All U.S.

Additional Information

Year Founded: 2008
Current Activity Level : Actively seeking new investments

WRF CAPITAL

2815 Eastlake Avenue E
Suite 300
Seattle, WA USA 98102
Phone: 206-336-5600
Fax: 206-336-5615
Website: www.wrfseattle.org

Management and Staff

John Reagh, Managing Director
Lortetta Little, Managing Director
Ronald Howell, Managing Director

Type of Firm

Government Affiliated Program

Association Membership

National Venture Capital Association - USA (NVCA)

Project Preferences

Type of Financing Preferred:
Seed

Size of Investments Considered:
Min Size of Investment Considered (000s): $1
Max Size of Investment Considered (000s): $2,000

Geographical Preferences

United States Preferences:
Washington

Industry Preferences

In Other prefer:
Socially Responsible

Additional Information

Year Founded: 1997
Current Activity Level : Actively seeking new investments

WUHAN EAST LAKE VENTURE CAPITAL CO., LTD.

No. 933 Jianshe Dadao
11/F Shangye Yinhang
Wuhan, China 430015
Phone: 86-27-8765-5827
Fax: 86-27-8765-5876
E-mail: wventure@whvcc.com
Website: www.whvcc.com

Type of Firm

Private Equity Firm

Project Preferences

Type of Financing Preferred:
Expansion
Later Stage

Geographical Preferences

International Preferences:
China

Industry Preferences

In Computer Software prefer:
Software

In Internet Specific prefer:
Ecommerce

In Biotechnology prefer:
Biotechnology

Additional Information
Year Founded: 1999
Current Activity Level : Actively seeking new investments

WUHAN HUAGONG VENTURE CAPITAL CO., LTD.

243 Luoyu Road
13/F Huagong SciTech & Ind'l
Wuhan, China 430074
Phone: 86-27-8752-2618
Fax: 86-27-8752-2800
E-mail: info@hustvc.com.cn
Website: www.hustvc.com.cn

Management and Staff

Bill Qian, Vice President
Joanna Li, President, CEO, Director
Robert Lu, Vice President

Type of Firm

Private Equity Firm

Project Preferences

Type of Financing Preferred:
Balanced

Geographical Preferences

International Preferences:
China

Industry Preferences

In Communications prefer:
Telecommunications
Wireless Communications

In Computer Software prefer:
Software
Systems Software

In Internet Specific prefer:
E-Commerce Technology

In Biotechnology prefer:
Biotechnology

In Medical/Health prefer:
Medical/Health

In Industrial/Energy prefer:
Materials

Additional Information

Year Founded: 2000
Capital Under Management: $161,400,000
Current Activity Level : Actively seeking new investments

WUHU JIANGDONG VENTURE CAPITAL CO., LTD.

c/o ShenZhen CDF-Capital
Shennan Zhong Road, Futian
Shenzhen, China 518040
Phone: 86-755-83189608
Fax: 86-755-83021830

Type of Firm

Private Equity Firm

Project Preferences

Type of Financing Preferred:
Balanced

Geographical Preferences

International Preferences:
China

Additional Information

Year Founded: 2009
Current Activity Level : Actively seeking new investments

WUNDERLICH & PARTNER WIRTSCHAFTSBERATUNG FUR DEN MITTELSTAND

Braeuhausstrasse 4b
Plannegg, Germany 82152
Phone: 49-89-89948860
Fax: 49-89-899488899
E-mail: info@wunderlich-partner.de
Website: www.wunderlich-partner.de

Management and Staff

Hans-Dieter Wunderlich, Managing Partner
Henning Diekmann, Chief Executive Officer

Type of Firm

Service Provider

Project Preferences

Type of Financing Preferred:
Expansion
Recapitalizations

Geographical Preferences

International Preferences:
Germany

Additional Information

Year Founded: 2005
Current Activity Level : Actively seeking new investments

WWC CAPITAL GROUP LLC

11911 Freedom Drive
Suite 1010
Reston, VA USA 20190
Phone: 703-736-9446
Fax: 703-736-9447
E-mail: reston@wwccapital.com
Website: www.wwcfirm.com

Management and Staff

David Galper, Vice President
Jonathan Wallace, Partner
Michael Cromwell, Partner

Type of Firm

Bank Affiliated

Project Preferences

Role in Financing:
Unknown

Type of Financing Preferred:
Balanced

Size of Investments Considered:
Min Size of Investment Considered (000s): $250
Max Size of Investment Considered (000s): $1,000

Industry Preferences

In Communications prefer:
Wireless Communications

In Computer Software prefer:
Software

In Internet Specific prefer:
Internet

Additional Information

Name of Most Recent Fund: WWC Capital Fund II, L.P.
Most Recent Fund Was Raised: 01/20/2005
Year Founded: 1998
Capital Under Management: $19,600,000
Current Activity Level : Actively seeking new investments
Method of Compensation: Unknown

WYNDCREST HOLDINGS, LLC

150 South US Highway One
Suite 500
Jupiter, FL USA 33477
Phone: 561-277-6410
Fax: 561-277-6446
Website: www.wyndcrest.com

Management and Staff

Carl Stork, Principal
Dan Marino, Principal
Jonathan Teaford, Principal
Michael Bay, Principal

Type of Firm

Private Equity Firm

Project Preferences

Type of Financing Preferred:
Leveraged Buyout
Acquisition

Geographical Preferences

United States Preferences:
All U.S.

Industry Preferences

In Communications prefer:
Telecommunications

In Internet Specific prefer:
Internet

In Consumer Related prefer:
Entertainment and Leisure

Additional Information

Year Founded: 1997
Current Activity Level : Actively seeking new investments

WYNNCHURCH CAPITAL, LTD.

6250 North River Road
Suite 10-100
Rosemont, IL USA 60018
Phone: 847-604-6100
Fax: 847-604-6105
E-mail: wynnchurch@wynnchurch.com
Website: www.wynnchurch.com

Other Offices

Brookfield Place - TD Canada Trust Tower
161 Bay Street, 25th Floor
Toronto, Canada M5J 2S1
Phone: 416-363-1423
Fax: 416-363-3905

39400 Woodward Avenue
Suite 185
Bloomfield, MI USA 48304
Phone: 248-593-3801
Fax: 248-593-5728

One Place Ville-Marie
Suite 2221
Montreal, Canada H3B3M4
Phone: 514-878-1800
Fax: 514-878-4541

Management and Staff

Charles Grace, Managing Director
Christopher O Brien, Vice President
Duncan Bourne, Managing Director
Frank Hayes, Partner
Ian Kirson, Managing Director
John Hatherly, Managing Partner
Jon Kleinke, Managing Director
Morty White, Managing Director
Roy Sroka, Chief Financial Officer
Steve Welborn, Managing Director
Terry Theodore, Partner

Type of Firm

Private Equity Firm

Association Membership

Illinois Venture Capital Association

Project Preferences

Role in Financing:
Prefer role as deal originator but will also invest in deals created by others

Type of Financing Preferred:
Leveraged Buyout
Public Companies
Turnaround
Management Buyouts
Acquisition
Industry Rollups
Special Situation
Recapitalizations

Size of Investments Considered:
Min Size of Investment Considered (000s): $5,000
Max Size of Investment Considered (000s): $75,000

Geographical Preferences

United States Preferences:
All U.S.

Canadian Preferences:
All Canada

Industry Focus

(% based on actual investment)

Other Products	57.4%
Industrial/Energy	31.1%
Computer Software and Services	5.5%
Consumer Related	3.2%
Communications and Media	2.9%

Additional Information

Name of Most Recent Fund: Wynnchurch Capital Partners II, L.P.
Most Recent Fund Was Raised: 11/23/2005
Year Founded: 1999
Capital Under Management: $513,000,000
Current Activity Level : Actively seeking new investments
Method of Compensation: Return on invest. most important, but chg. closing fees, service fees, etc.

WYNNEFIELD CAPITAL ADVISORS

1530 Chestnut Street
Suite 307
Philadelphia, PA USA 19102
Phone: 215-568-6883
Fax: 215-568-6884

Management and Staff

Andrea McFadden, Principal
Sam Katz, Principal

Type of Firm

Private Equity Firm

Project Preferences

Type of Financing Preferred:

Early Stage

Geographical Preferences

United States Preferences:

Mid Atlantic

Additional Information

Year Founded: 2001
Current Activity Level : Actively seeking new investments

- X -

XANGE PRIVATE EQUITY

12 rue Tronchet
Paris, France 75008
Phone: 33-1-5343-0530
Fax: 33-1-5330-0225
E-mail: contact@xange.fr
Website: www.xange.fr

Management and Staff

Francois Cavalie, Managing Director
Nicolas Rose, Partner
Thierry Lopez, Partner
Vincent Dron, Chief Financial Officer

Type of Firm

Private Equity Firm

Association Membership

French Venture Capital Association (AFIC)
European Private Equity and Venture Capital Assoc.

Project Preferences

Type of Financing Preferred:

Leveraged Buyout
Early Stage
Expansion
Generalist PE
Balanced
Acquisition

Geographical Preferences

International Preferences:

Europe
Israel
France

Industry Preferences

In Communications prefer:

Communications and Media
Data Communications

In Internet Specific prefer:

Ecommerce

In Computer Other prefer:

Computer Related

In Semiconductor/Electr prefer:

Electronics

In Biotechnology prefer:

Biotechnology

In Medical/Health prefer:

Medical/Health

In Consumer Related prefer:

Retail
Consumer Services

In Industrial/Energy prefer:

Energy
Industrial Products
Materials

In Financial Services prefer:

Financial Services

In Business Serv. prefer:

Services
Distribution

Additional Information

Year Founded: 2003
Capital Under Management: $455,400,000
Current Activity Level : Actively seeking new investments

XENIA VENTURE CAPITAL

1 Leshem Street
Kiryat Gat, Israel 82000
Phone: 972-8-681-1761
Fax: 972-8-681-1763
Website: www.xenia.co.il

Management and Staff

Anat Segal, Chief Executive Officer
Eli Sorzon, Chief Financial Officer

Type of Firm

Private Equity Firm

Project Preferences

Type of Financing Preferred:

Early Stage
Seed
Startup

Geographical Preferences

International Preferences:

Israel

Additional Information

Year Founded: 2003
Current Activity Level : Actively seeking new investments

XESGALICIA SGECR SA

Barrio de San Lazero s/n
Santiago de Compostela, Spain 15703
Phone: 34-981-541-621
Fax: 34-981-580-658
E-mail: xesgalicia@xesgalicia.org
Website: www.xesgalicia.org

Type of Firm

Private Equity Firm

Association Membership

Spanish Venture Capital Association (ASCRI)

Project Preferences

Type of Financing Preferred:
Expansion
Balanced

Geographical Preferences

International Preferences:
Europe
Spain

Additional Information

Year Founded: 1999
Current Activity Level : Actively seeking new investments

XI AN CAPITECH VENTURE CAPITAL CO., LTD. (AKA: CAPITECH)

No. 52 Gaoxin Road
21/F Gaoke Building
Xi'an, China 710075
Phone: 86-29-8831-4952
E-mail: capitech@capitech.com.cn
Website: www.capitech.com.cn

Type of Firm

Private Equity Firm

Project Preferences

Type of Financing Preferred:
Expansion
Early Stage
Startup

Geographical Preferences

International Preferences:
China

Industry Preferences

In Biotechnology prefer:
Biotechnology

Additional Information

Year Founded: 1996
Current Activity Level : Actively seeking new investments

XI AN PRUTENTION INVESTMENT & DEVELOPMENT CO., LTD.

13F, B Section, Century Plaza
93, Heping road
Xi'an, China 710001
Phone: 86-29-875-1407
Fax: 86-29-8742-7310
Website: www.prutention.com

Management and Staff

Xiang Jun Qu, President

Type of Firm

Private Equity Firm

Project Preferences

Type of Financing Preferred:
Balanced

Geographical Preferences

International Preferences:
China

Industry Preferences

In Semiconductor/Electr prefer:
Electronics

In Medical/Health prefer:
Medical/Health

In Consumer Related prefer:
Education Related

In Transportation prefer:
Transportation

In Financial Services prefer:
Real Estate
Financial Services

In Agr/Forestr/Fish prefer:
Agriculture related

In Other prefer:
Environment Responsible

Additional Information

Year Founded: 1998
Current Activity Level : Actively seeking new investments

XIANGCAI SECURITIES CO., LTD.

18/F Huaneng Union Tower
139 Yincheng Road East
Pudong, China 200120
Phone: 86-21-6863-4518
Fax: 86-21-5054-3470
E-mail: ibd@xcsc.com
Website: www.xcsc.com

Type of Firm

Investment Management Firm

Association Membership

Venture Capital Association of Beijing (VCAB)

Project Preferences

Type of Financing Preferred:
Expansion

Geographical Preferences

International Preferences:
China

Industry Preferences

In Communications prefer:
Telecommunications

In Computer Software prefer:
Software

In Semiconductor/Electr prefer:
Semiconductor

In Biotechnology prefer:
Biotechnology

In Medical/Health prefer:
Medical/Health

In Industrial/Energy prefer:
Energy
Materials

In Manufact. prefer:
Manufacturing

In Other prefer:
Environment Responsible

Additional Information

Year Founded: 1993
Current Activity Level : Actively seeking new investments

XPV CAPITAL CORPORATION

100 Adelaide Street West
Suite 1302
Toronto, Canada M5H 1S3
Phone: 416-864-0475
Fax: 416-864-0514
Website: www.xpvcapital.com

Management and Staff

David Henderson, Managing Director
John Coburn, Managing Director
Khalil Maalouf, Managing Director

Type of Firm

Private Equity Firm

Project Preferences

Type of Financing Preferred:
Early Stage

Geographical Preferences

Canadian Preferences:
All Canada

Industry Preferences

In Industrial/Energy prefer:
Alternative Energy
Energy Conservation Relat
Environmental Related

Additional Information

Year Founded: 2006
Current Activity Level : Actively seeking new investments

- Y -

Y COMBINATOR

320 Pioneer Way
Mountain View, CA USA 94041
Phone: 617-576-0695
E-mail: info@ycombinator.com
Website: www.ycombinator.com

Other Offices

135 Garden Street
Cambridge, MA USA 02138

Management and Staff

Jessica Livingston, Partner
Paul Graham, Partner
Robert Morris, Partner
Trevor Blackwell, Partner

Type of Firm

Private Equity Firm

Project Preferences

Type of Financing Preferred:
Early Stage
Startup

Industry Preferences

In Computer Software prefer:
Applications Software

In Internet Specific prefer:
Internet
Web Aggregration/Portals

Additional Information

Year Founded: 2005
Current Activity Level : Actively seeking new investments

YAHOO

701 First Avenue
Sunnyvale, CA USA 94089
Phone: 408-349-3300
Fax: 408-349-3301
Website: www.yahoo.com

Type of Firm

Corporate PE/Venture

Additional Information

Year Founded: 1997
Current Activity Level : Actively seeking new investments

YALETOWN VENTURE PARTNERS, INC.

1224 Hamilton Street
Suite 301
Vancouver, Canada V6B 2S2
Phone: 604-688-7807
Fax: 604-688-7031
E-mail: info@yaletown.com
Website: www.yaletown.com

Management and Staff

Hans Knapp, General Partner
Kirk Washington, General Partner
Mike Satterfield, General Partner
Steve Hnatiuk, General Partner

Type of Firm

Private Equity Firm

Association Membership

Canadian Venture Capital Association

Project Preferences

Role in Financing:
Prefer role as deal originator

Type of Financing Preferred:
Early Stage

Size of Investments Considered:
Min Size of Investment Considered (000s): $500
Max Size of Investment Considered (000s): $3,500

Geographical Preferences

United States Preferences:
Washington

Canadian Preferences:
Alberta
British Columbia
Western Canada

Industry Preferences

In Computer Software prefer:
Software

In Industrial/Energy prefer:
Energy
Alternative Energy

In Other prefer:
Environment Responsible

Additional Information

Year Founded: 2001
Capital Under Management: $27,000,000
Current Activity Level : Actively seeking new investments
Method of Compensation: Return on investment is of primary concern, do not charge fees

YAMAGUCHI CAPITAL CO., LTD

1-10 Nakaichi-machi
Yamaguchi-shi, Japan 753-0077
Phone: 81-83-922-9088
Fax: 81-83-922-9093
E-mail: info@yamaguchi-capital.co.jp
Website: www.yamaguchi-capital.co.jp

Management and Staff

Seiji Shibuya, President

Type of Firm

SBIC

Additional Information

Year Founded: 1996
Current Activity Level : Actively seeking new investments

YAMANASHI CHUGIN BUSINESS CONSULTING CO., LTD.

1-20-8 Marunouchi
Kofu-shi, Japan 400-0031
Phone: 81-55-224-1032
E-mail: consult@yamanashibank.co.jp
Website: www.yamanashibank.co.jp

Type of Firm

Bank Affiliated

Additional Information

Year Founded: 1996
Current Activity Level : Actively seeking new investments

YANKEE EQUITY SOLUTION (AKA: YES)

P.O. Box 630
Cotuit, MA USA 02635
Website: www.yankeeequitysolution.com

Management and Staff

John Williams, Managing Director

Type of Firm

Private Equity Firm

Project Preferences

Type of Financing Preferred:
Expansion

Geographical Preferences

United States Preferences:
Massachusetts

Industry Preferences

In Medical/Health prefer:

Medical/Health

Additional Information

Name of Most Recent Fund: YES Medical Technology Fund - DIF
Most Recent Fund Was Raised: 11/21/2008
Year Founded: 2008
Capital Under Management: $50,000,000
Current Activity Level : Actively seeking new investments

YANKEE HILL CAPITAL MANAGEMENT LLC

33 Riverside Avenue
Fourth Floor
Westport, CT USA 06880
Phone: 203-454-9654
Fax: 203-454-9657
Website: www.yankeehillcapital.com

Other Offices

300 East 42nd Street
Suite 1700
New York, NY USA 10017
Phone: 646-356-8450
Fax: 212-661-2601

Management and Staff

Lawrence Weinbach, Managing Director
Peter Weinbach, Managing Director

Type of Firm

Private Equity Firm

Project Preferences

Type of Financing Preferred:

Leveraged Buyout
Management Buyouts

Additional Information

Year Founded: 2008
Current Activity Level : Actively seeking new investments

YARRA CAPITAL PARTNERS

Level 4/164 Flinders Lane
Melbourne, Australia 3000
Phone: 613-9653-5300
E-mail: info@ycp.com.au
Website: www.ycp.com.au

Management and Staff

Alan Schwartz, Founding Partner
Huy Truong, Founding Partner

Type of Firm

Private Equity Firm

Association Membership

Australian Venture Capital Association (AVCAL)

Project Preferences

Type of Financing Preferred:

Leveraged Buyout
Expansion
Management Buyouts

Geographical Preferences

International Preferences:

Australia

Additional Information

Year Founded: 2008
Capital Under Management: $39,000,000
Current Activity Level : Actively seeking new investments

YASUDA ENTERPRISE DEVELOPMENT CO., LTD. (FKA: NIPPON ENT.DEV)

Kojimachi 4-chome Kyodo Bldg.
9F 4-2-7 Kojimachi, Chiyoda-ku
Tokyo, Japan 102-0083
Phone: 81-3-6811-7100
Fax: 81-3-5213-3405
E-mail: info@yedvc.co.jp
Website: www.yedvc.co.jp

Other Offices

435 Tasso Street
Suite 205
Palo Alto, CA USA 94301
Phone: 650-289-9733
Fax: 650-289-9145

Management and Staff

Takao Suzuki, Managing Director

Type of Firm

Insurance Firm Affiliate

Association Membership

Western Association of Venture Capitalists (WAVC)
National Venture Capital Association - USA (NVCA)

Project Preferences

Role in Financing:

Will function either as deal originator or investor in deals created by others

Type of Financing Preferred:

Second Stage Financing
Early Stage
Expansion
Mezzanine
Research and Development
Balanced
Later Stage
First Stage Financing
Startup

Size of Investments Considered:

Min Size of Investment Considered (000s): $500
Max Size of Investment Considered (000s): $5,000

Geographical Preferences

United States Preferences:

All U.S.

International Preferences:

United Kingdom
Japan

Industry Focus

(% based on actual investment)

Biotechnology	31.1%
Semiconductors/Other Elect.	22.0%
Medical/Health	11.0%
Computer Hardware	9.7%
Communications and Media	8.6%
Computer Software and Services	7.5%
Industrial/Energy	6.0%
Internet Specific	4.1%

Additional Information

Year Founded: 1983
Capital Under Management: $400,000,000
Current Activity Level : Actively seeking new investments
Method of Compensation: Return on investment is of primary concern, do not charge fees

---

YELLOW POINT EQUITY PARTNERS LP

1055 West Georgia Street
Suite 1700
Vancouver, Canada V6E 3P3
Phone: 604-659-1750
Fax: 604-659-1899
Website: www.ypoint.ca

Management and Staff

Brian Begert, Managing Partner
David Chapman, Managing Partner

Type of Firm

Private Equity Firm

Project Preferences

Type of Financing Preferred:

Expansion
Management Buyouts
Recapitalizations

Size of Investments Considered:

Min Size of Investment Considered (000s): $1,471
Max Size of Investment Considered (000s): $14,715

Geographical Preferences

Canadian Preferences:

Western Canada

Industry Preferences

In Communications prefer:
Communications and Media

In Medical/Health prefer:
Medical/Health

In Business Serv. prefer:
Services

In Manufact. prefer:
Manufacturing

Additional Information
Year Founded: 2004
Capital Under Management: $50,000,000
Current Activity Level : Actively seeking new investments
Method of Compensation: Return on invest. most important, but chg. closing fees, service fees, etc.

YELLOWSTONE CAPITAL, INC.
5555 San Felipe
Suite 1650
Houston, TX USA 77056
Phone: 713-650-0065
Fax: 713-650-0055
E-mail: info@yellowstonecapital.com
Website: www.yellowstonecapital.com

Management and Staff
Omar Sawaf, Chairman & CEO
Richard Owen, Chief Financial Officer
William Brewer, President

Type of Firm
Private Equity Firm

Project Preferences

Role in Financing:
Prefer role as deal originator but will also invest in deals created by others

Type of Financing Preferred:
Leveraged Buyout
Early Stage
Expansion
Mezzanine
Generalist PE
Other
Acquisition

Size of Investments Considered:
Min Size of Investment Considered (000s): $3,000
Max Size of Investment Considered: No Limit

Geographical Preferences

United States Preferences:
Southwest
All U.S.

Industry Focus
(% based on actual investment)

Industrial/Energy	81.2%
Medical/Health	10.0%
Semiconductors/Other Elect.	6.9%
Biotechnology	1.9%

Additional Information
Name of Most Recent Fund: Yellowstone Energy Ventures II, L.P.
Most Recent Fund Was Raised: 09/10/2008
Year Founded: 1993
Capital Under Management: $31,800,000
Current Activity Level : Actively seeking new investments

YES BANK, LTD.
Nehru Centre, Ninth Floor
Discovery of India, Dr. AB Rd
Mumbai, India 400 018
Phone: 91-22-6669-9000
Fax: 91-22-2490-0314
E-mail: contactus@yesbank.in
Website: www.yesbank.in

Other Offices
48, Nyaya Marg,
Chanakya Puri,
New Delhi, India 110021
Phone: 91-11-6656-9000
Fax: 91-11-5168-0144

Management and Staff
Vivek Ganguly, Vice President

Type of Firm
Bank Affiliated

Association Membership
Indian Venture Capital Association (IVCA)

Project Preferences

Type of Financing Preferred:
Expansion
Balanced

Size of Investments Considered:
Min Size of Investment Considered (000s): $5,000
Max Size of Investment Considered (000s): $7,500

Geographical Preferences

International Preferences:
India

Industry Preferences

In Consumer Related prefer:
Food/Beverage

In Agr/Forestr/Fish prefer:
Agribusiness

Additional Information
Year Founded: 2007
Current Activity Level : Actively seeking new investments

YEUROPE VENTURES
Rathausstrasse 6
Wien, Austria 1010
Phone: 43-699-10110863
Website: www.yeurope.net

Type of Firm
Private Equity Firm

Project Preferences

Type of Financing Preferred:
Startup

Geographical Preferences

International Preferences:
Europe

Industry Preferences

In Communications prefer:
Telecommunications
Wireless Communications
Data Communications
Other Communication Prod.

In Internet Specific prefer:
E-Commerce Technology

In Computer Other prefer:
Computer Related

Additional Information
Year Founded: 2009
Capital Under Management: $1,000,000,000
Current Activity Level : Actively seeking new investments

YL VENTURES GP, LTD.
P.O. Box 61
Grand Cayman, Cayman Islands KY1-1102
E-mail: info@ylventures.com
Website: www.ylventures.com

Other Offices
Ackerstein Towers
Hertzelia, Israel 46120
Phone: 972-9-971-6021
Fax: 972-9-777-0119

Herengracht 574
Amsterdam, Netherlands 1017 CJ
Phone: 31-20-521-9461
Fax: 31-20-890-7704

Management and Staff
Boaz Misholi, Partner
John Quigley, Partner
Robert Goldberg, Venture Partner

Type of Firm
Private Equity Firm

Project Preferences

Type of Financing Preferred:
Early Stage
Mezzanine
Startup

Geographical Preferences

International Preferences:
Europe
Israel

Industry Preferences

In Communications prefer:
Communications and Media
Telecommunications
Wireless Communications
Data Communications
Media and Entertainment

In Computer Software prefer:
Software

In Internet Specific prefer:
E-Commerce Technology
Internet
Ecommerce

Additional Information
Year Founded: 2008
Current Activity Level : Actively seeking new investments

YMER VENTURE CAPITAL ASIA
P.O. Box 5539
Central, Hong Kong
E-mail: yvc@ymerfund.com
Website: www.ymerfund.com

Management and Staff
Adam Bornstein, Managing Director

Type of Firm
Private Equity Firm

Project Preferences

Type of Financing Preferred:
Early Stage
Balanced

Geographical Preferences

International Preferences:
China

Additional Information
Year Founded: 2006
Current Activity Level : Actively seeking new investments

YMG CAPITAL MANAGEMENT
One Queen Street East
Suite 2300
Toronto, Canada M5C 2W5
Phone: 416-364-3711
Fax: 416-955-4877
Website: www.ymg.ca

Management and Staff
Eric A. Innes, President, CEO, Chairman
Jim Craven, Chief Operating Officer

Type of Firm
Endowment, Foundation or Pension Fund

Additional Information
Year Founded: 1983
Current Activity Level : Actively seeking new investments

YOKOHAMA CAPITAL CO., LTD
3-1-1 Minatomirai
Nishi-ku
Yokohama-shi, Japan
Phone: 81-45-225-2331
Fax: 81-45-225-2330
Website: www.boy.co.jp

Type of Firm
Bank Affiliated

Project Preferences

Type of Financing Preferred:
Balanced

Geographical Preferences

International Preferences:
Japan

Additional Information
Year Founded: 1984
Current Activity Level : Actively seeking new investments

YORK STREET CAPITAL PARTNERS, LLC
One Pluckemin Way
Bedminster, NJ USA 07921
Phone: 908-658-4700
Fax: 908-658-9933
E-mail: mail@yorkstreetcapital.com
Website: www.yorkstreetcapital.com

Management and Staff
Andreas Skibiel, Partner
Christopher Layden, Managing Partner
David Tahan, Principal
Robert Golding, Managing Partner

Type of Firm
Private Equity Firm

Project Preferences

Type of Financing Preferred:
Leveraged Buyout
Mezzanine
Acquisition

Additional Information
Year Founded: 2002
Capital Under Management: $950,000,000
Current Activity Level : Actively seeking new investments

YORKSHIRE FUND MANAGERS, LTD. (AKA: YFM GROUP)
Saint Martins House
210 - 212 Chapeltown Road
Leeds, United Kingdom LS7 4HZ
Phone: 44-113-294-5019
Fax: 44-113-294-5001
E-mail: info@yfmgroup.co.uk
Website: www.yhef.co.uk

Other Offices
Argentum, 510 Bristol Business Park
Coldharbour Lane
Bristol, United Kingdom BS16 1EJ
Phone: 44-117-906-3410
Fax: 44-117-906-3646

Brookmount House
62-65 Chandos Place
London, United Kingdom WC2N 4LP
Phone: 44-20-7812-6772
Fax: 44-20-7812-6773

The Quadrant, 99 Parkway Avenue
Parkway Business Park
Sheffield, United Kingdom S9 4WG
Phone: 44-114-227-0025
Fax: 44-114-227-0027

Reresby House, Bow Bridge Close
Temple Borough
Rotherham, United Kingdom S60 1BY
Phone: 44-1709-386-369
Fax: 44-1709-386-363

Unit 1, Silkwood Business Park
Fryers Way, Ossett
Wakefield, United Kingdom WF5 9TJ
Phone: 44-1924-237-850

City Business Park, Somerset Place
Stoke
Plymouth, United Kingdom PL3 4BB
Phone: 44-1752-609-230
Fax: 44-1752-609-240

Innovation Technology Centre
Advanced Manufacturing Park, Brunel Way
Catcliffe, United Kingdom S60 5WG
Phone: 44-114-254-1222
Fax: 44-114-254-1224

Delphian House, Riverside
New Bailey Street
Manchester, United Kingdom M3 5AP
Phone: 44-161-832-7603
Fax: 44-161-819-3192

St. George's House
1-5 St. George's Street
Hull, United Kingdom HU3 6ED
Phone: 44-1482-575-859
Fax: 44-1482-575-860

53 Chandos Place
Covent Garden
London, United Kingdom WC2 4HS
Phone: 44-20-7812-6470
Fax: 44-20-7812-6677

Management and Staff

David Best, Managing Director
David Hall, Managing Director
Miles Stanyard, Managing Director
Peter Garnham, Managing Director
Ray Lowe, Managing Director

Type of Firm

Bank Affiliated

Association Membership

British Venture Capital Association (BVCA)
European Private Equity and Venture Capital Assoc.

Project Preferences

Role in Financing:

Prefer role as deal originator but will also invest in deals created by others

Type of Financing Preferred:

Second Stage Financing
Leveraged Buyout
Early Stage
Expansion
Mezzanine
Generalist PE
Balanced
Start-up Financing
Later Stage
Seed
Management Buyouts
Special Situation
Startup

Size of Investments Considered:

Min Size of Investment Considered (000s): $250
Max Size of Investment Considered (000s): $9,862

Geographical Preferences

International Preferences:

United Kingdom
Europe

Industry Focus

(% based on actual investment)

Computer Software and Services	38.3%
Other Products	22.4%
Medical/Health	9.2%
Communications and Media	8.3%
Consumer Related	6.6%
Internet Specific	4.1%
Computer Hardware	4.0%
Industrial/Energy	2.7%
Biotechnology	2.6%
Semiconductors/Other Elect.	1.9%

Additional Information

Year Founded: 1987
Capital Under Management: $182,400,000
Current Activity Level : Actively seeking new investments
Method of Compensation: Return on invest. most important, but chg. closing fees, service fees, etc.

YORKTOWN PARTNERS LLC

410 Park Avenue
Suite 19
New York, NY USA 10022-4407
Phone: 212-515-2100
Fax: 212-515-2105

Type of Firm

Private Equity Firm

Project Preferences

Type of Financing Preferred:

Leveraged Buyout
Generalist PE
Other
Recapitalizations

Geographical Preferences

United States Preferences:

All U.S.

Industry Focus

(% based on actual investment)

Industrial/Energy	90.4%
Other Products	8.1%
Communications and Media	1.4%

Additional Information

Year Founded: 1983
Capital Under Management: $1,438,000,000
Current Activity Level : Actively seeking new investments

YORKVILLE ADVISORS LLC

101 Hudson Street
Suite 3700
Jersey City, NJ USA 07302
Phone: 201-985-8300
Fax: 201-985-8266
E-mail: info@yorkvilleadvisors.com
Website: www.yorkvilleadvisors.com

Management and Staff

Mark Angelo, Founder
Troy Rillo, Senior Managing Director

Type of Firm

Private Equity Firm

Additional Information

Year Founded: 2001
Current Activity Level : Actively seeking new investments

YOUNG ASSOCIATES LIMITED

Harcourt House
19 Cavendish Square
London, United Kingdom W1G 0PL
Phone: 44 20 7447 8800
Fax: 44 20 7447 8849
E-mail: info@youngassoc.com
Website: www.youngassoc.com

Type of Firm

Private Equity Firm

Association Membership

British Venture Capital Association (BVCA)

Project Preferences

Type of Financing Preferred:

Early Stage

Geographical Preferences

International Preferences:

United Kingdom
Europe
Israel

Industry Preferences

In Communications prefer:

Communications and Media

Additional Information

Year Founded: 1996
Current Activity Level : Actively seeking new investments

YOUNGSHIN VENTURE CAPITAL

1480-3 Yeonhang-dong
Sooncheon-si Jeollanamdo
Jeollanamdo, South Korea 540-951
Phone: 822-3424-1977
Fax: 822-3436-9127

Other Offices

2512 Technomart Building
546-4 Kooeui-dong Kwangjin-ku
Seoul, South Korea

Management and Staff

Mink Chang, Chief Executive Officer

Type of Firm

Private Equity Firm

Project Preferences

Type of Financing Preferred:
Balanced

Geographical Preferences

International Preferences:
Korea, South

Additional Information

Year Founded: 1999
Capital Under Management: $1,600,000
Current Activity Level : Actively seeking new investments

YOZMA VENTURE CAPITAL LTD

Ramat Aviv Tower
40 Einstein Street
Tel Aviv, Israel 69102
Phone: 972-3-643-7766
Fax: 972-3-643-7888
E-mail: mail@yozma.com
Website: www.yozma.com

Type of Firm

Private Equity Firm

Association Membership

Israel Venture Association

Project Preferences

Type of Financing Preferred:
Fund of Funds
Early Stage
Later Stage

Size of Investments Considered:
Min Size of Investment Considered (000s): $500
Max Size of Investment Considered (000s): $500,000

Geographical Preferences

International Preferences:
Israel

Industry Preferences

In Communications prefer:
Communications and Media

Additional Information

Year Founded: 1992
Capital Under Management: $200,000,000
Current Activity Level : Actively seeking new investments

YSIOS CAPITAL PARTNERS

Baldiri Reixac 10-12
Parc Cientific de Barcelona
Barcelona, Spain 08028
Phone: 34-93-517-3545
E-mail: ysios@ysioscapital.com
Website: www.ysioscapital.com

Other Offices

Mikeletegi, 56 1a planta
Parque Tecnologico De San Sebastian
Donostia-San Sebastian, Spain 20009
Phone: 34-93-517-3545

Management and Staff

Cristina Garmendia, Partner
Joel Jean-Mairet, Partner
Josep Ll. Sanfeliu, Partner
Julia Salaverria, Partner
Karen Wagner, Venture Partner
Marc Casellas, Chief Financial Officer

Type of Firm

Private Equity Firm

Project Preferences

Type of Financing Preferred:
Early Stage
Expansion
Balanced
Later Stage
Seed

Size of Investments Considered:
Min Size of Investment Considered (000s): $731
Max Size of Investment Considered (000s): $5,850

Geographical Preferences

International Preferences:
Europe
Spain

Industry Preferences

In Biotechnology prefer:
Biotechnology

In Medical/Health prefer:
Medical/Health
Medical Diagnostics
Pharmaceuticals

Additional Information

Year Founded: 2007
Capital Under Management: $95,600,000
Current Activity Level : Actively seeking new investments

YUCAIPA COMPANIES LLC, THE

9130 West Sunset Boulevard
West Hollywood, CA USA 90069
Phone: 310-789-7200
Fax: 310-228-2873
Website: www.yucaipaco.com

Management and Staff

Ira Tochner, Partner
Jeffrey Johnson, Principal
Ronald Burkle, Managing Partner

Type of Firm

Private Equity Firm

Project Preferences

Type of Financing Preferred:
Leveraged Buyout
Management Buyouts
Recapitalizations

Geographical Preferences

United States Preferences:
All U.S.

Industry Focus

(% based on actual investment)

Consumer Related	70.7%
Other Products	23.3%
Communications and Media	6.0%

Additional Information

Year Founded: 1986
Capital Under Management: $2,489,600,000
Current Activity Level : Actively seeking new investments

YUEN FOONG YU VENTURE CAPITAL INVESTMENT CORPORATION

No 17-3 Bo-Ai Rd.
Zhongzheng
Taipei, Taiwan 100
Phone: 886-2-2396-1166
Fax: 886-2-2396-6771
Website: www.yfy.com

Management and Staff

L. C. Hsiao, President

Type of Firm

Private Equity Firm

Association Membership

Taiwan Venture Capital Association(TVCA)

Project Preferences

Type of Financing Preferred:
Early Stage
Mezzanine
Startup

Geographical Preferences

International Preferences:
Taiwan

Industry Preferences

In Semiconductor/Electr prefer:
Electronics

In Financial Services prefer:
Financial Services

Additional Information

Name of Most Recent Fund: Yuen Foong Yu Venture Capital Investment Corporation
Most Recent Fund Was Raised: 10/01/1988
Year Founded: 1988
Capital Under Management: $6,200,000
Current Activity Level : Actively seeking new investments

YUKON VENTURE GROUP

409 Black Street
Whitehorse, Canada Y1A 2N2
Phone: 867-668-6925
Fax: 867-668-3127
E-mail: dnv@dananaye.com
Website: www.dananaye.yk.net

Type of Firm

Private Equity Firm

Geographical Preferences

Canadian Preferences:
Yukon
British Columbia

Additional Information

Year Founded: 2009
Current Activity Level : Actively seeking new investments

YUNNAN AGRICULTURE THROUGH VENTURE CAPITAL CO., LTD.

Beijing Road
Yanchangxian Jinsenianhua Bldg
Kunshan, Yunnan, China 650224
Phone: 86-871-5749-925
Website: www.168xn.com

Type of Firm

Private Equity Firm

Project Preferences

Type of Financing Preferred:
Expansion
Later Stage

Geographical Preferences

International Preferences:
China

Industry Preferences

In Business Serv. prefer:
Services

In Agr/Forestr/Fish prefer:
Agriculture related

Additional Information

Year Founded: 2008
Current Activity Level : Actively seeking new investments

- Z -

Z CAPITAL PARTNERS LLC

Two Conway Park
150 Field Drive, Suite 300
Lake Forest, IL USA 60045
Phone: 847-235-8100
Fax: 847-235-8111
E-mail: InvestorRelations@zcap.net
Website: www.zcap.net

Management and Staff

Bradley Eden, Managing Director
Christopher Kipley, Managing Director
Martin Auerbach, Managing Director
Rahul Sawhney, Managing Director

Type of Firm

Private Equity Firm

Project Preferences

Type of Financing Preferred:
Turnaround
Distressed Debt
Recapitalizations

Industry Preferences

In Communications prefer:
Entertainment

In Consumer Related prefer:
Consumer Products

In Financial Services prefer:
Financial Services

Additional Information

Year Founded: 2006
Capital Under Management: $109,300,000
Current Activity Level : Actively seeking new investments

Z-INVEST AB

Prastgatan 31 B
Ostersund, Sweden 831 31
Phone: 46-63-132-040
Fax: 46-63-131-881
E-mail: z-invest@swipnet.se
Website: www.z-invest.se

Management and Staff

Christer Thylin, Managing Director

Type of Firm

Private Equity Firm

Project Preferences

Type of Financing Preferred:
Expansion
Startup

Geographical Preferences

International Preferences:
Sweden
Scandanavia/Nordic Region

Additional Information
Year Founded: 1980
Current Activity Level : Actively seeking new investments

ZABEEL INVESTMENTS
DIFC Wing, Building 4
East, Level Seven
Dubai, Utd. Arab Em.
Phone: 971-4-365-7900
Fax: 971-4-363-7295
E-mail: info@zabeelinvestments.com
Website: www.zabeelinvestments.com

Type of Firm
Private Equity Firm

Project Preferences

Type of Financing Preferred:
Balanced

Additional Information
Year Founded: 2007
Current Activity Level : Actively seeking new investments

ZACHARY SCOTT & CO.
500 Union Street
Suite 1000
Seattle, WA USA 98101
Phone: 206-224-7380
Fax: 206-224-7384
E-mail: info@zacharyscott.com
Website: www.zacharyscott.com

Management and Staff
Frank Buhler, Principal
Mark Working, Principal
Michael Newsome, Vice President
Ray Rezab, Vice President
William Hanneman, Principal

Type of Firm
Bank Affiliated

Project Preferences

Type of Financing Preferred:
Leveraged Buyout
Expansion
Mezzanine
Turnaround
Management Buyouts
Acquisition
Recapitalizations

Geographical Preferences

United States Preferences:
Northwest
Rocky Mountain
West Coast
All U.S.

Additional Information
Year Founded: 1991
Current Activity Level : Actively seeking new investments

ZANKEL CAPITAL ADVISORS, LLC
535 Madison Avenue
26th Floor
New York, NY USA 10002
Phone: 212-421-7548

Management and Staff
Arthur Zankel, General Partner

Type of Firm
Other

Additional Information
Year Founded: 2002
Capital Under Management: $84,400,000
Current Activity Level : Actively seeking new investments

ZAP VENTURES
12335 Stonebrook Court
Los Altos, CA USA 94022
Phone: 650-559-0864
E-mail: plans@zapvc.com
Website: www.zapvc.com

Management and Staff
Kelly Porter, Managing General Partner
Mike Halloran, Managing Partner

Type of Firm
Private Equity Firm

Project Preferences

Type of Financing Preferred:
Early Stage

Geographical Preferences

United States Preferences:
All U.S.

Industry Preferences

In Communications prefer:
Telecommunications
Wireless Communications

Additional Information
Year Founded: 2001
Current Activity Level : Actively seeking new investments

ZELKOVA VENTURES
641 Lexington Avenue
15th Floor
New York, NY USA 10022
Phone: 212-750-3156
Fax: 212-750-3158
Website: www.zelkovavc.com

Management and Staff
Jay Levy, Principal

Type of Firm
Private Equity Firm

Project Preferences

Type of Financing Preferred:
Early Stage
Seed

Additional Information
Year Founded: 2008
Current Activity Level : Actively seeking new investments

ZENISON VENTURE CAPTIAL
12/F, Century Star Building
No.88, W/Block, South Er'huan
Xi'an, China
Phone: 86-29-8825-5097
Fax: 86-29-8836-0586
E-mail: 21-vc@163.com
Website: www.21-vc.com

Type of Firm
Private Equity Firm

Project Preferences

Type of Financing Preferred:
Balanced

Geographical Preferences

International Preferences:
China

Industry Preferences

In Internet Specific prefer:
Internet

In Biotechnology prefer:
Agricultural/Animal Bio.

In Industrial/Energy prefer:
Alternative Energy

In Business Serv. prefer:
Media

Additional Information
Year Founded: 2007
Current Activity Level : Actively seeking new investments

ZENSHIN CAPITAL MANAGEMENT

535 Middlefield Road
Suite 100
Menlo Park, CA USA 94025
Phone: 650-240-2734
Fax: 650-324-9101
E-mail: info@zenshincapital.com
Website: www.zenshincapital.com

Management and Staff
Takeshi Mori, Managing Director
Yoji Kawaguchi, Managing Director

Type of Firm
Private Equity Firm

Association Membership
National Venture Capital Association - USA (NVCA)

Project Preferences

Role in Financing:
Will function either as deal originator or investor in deals created by others

Type of Financing Preferred:
Early Stage
Balanced
Later Stage

Geographical Preferences

United States Preferences:
Northern California

International Preferences:
Asia
Japan

Industry Preferences

In Communications prefer:
Telecommunications
Wireless Communications

In Internet Specific prefer:
E-Commerce Technology
Internet
Web Aggregration/Portals

In Financial Services prefer:
Financial Services

Additional Information
Name of Most Recent Fund: ADS-ZenShin I-Investment L.P.
Most Recent Fund Was Raised: 04/29/2006
Year Founded: 2005
Capital Under Management: $15,000,000
Current Activity Level : Actively seeking new investments

ZEPHYR MANAGEMENT, L.P.

320 Park Avenue
New York, NY USA 10022
Phone: 212-508-9400
Fax: 212-508-9494
Website: www.zephyrmanagement.com

Other Offices
Unit 201, 2nd Floor, Embassy Classic
No11, Vittal Mallya Road
Bangalore, India 560 001
Phone: 91-80-4147-3300
Fax: 91-80-4147-3400

25 Hill Street
1st Floor
London, United Kingdom W1J 5LW
Phone: 44-207-907-2400
Fax: 44-207-907-2420

Avenida Paseo de la Reforma 2608-1812
Colonia Lomas Altas, Mexico D.F.
Mexico City, Mexico 11950
Phone: 52-55-2167-6999

81 Osu Badu Street
West Airport
Accra, Ghana
Phone: 233-21-769-725
Fax: 233-21-769-727

Management and Staff
Albert Bartosic, Managing Partner
Brian Kim, Managing Director
Charles Frischer, Principal
J.Kofi Bucknor, Managing Partner
Kartik Parija, Managing Director
Leo Corbett, Managing Partner
Mukul Gulati, Managing Director
Richard Corey, Managing Partner
Roy Kelvin, Chief Financial Officer
Runa Alam, Managing Partner
Sofiane Lahmar, Principal
Tina Keriazes, Partner

Type of Firm
Private Equity Firm

Project Preferences

Type of Financing Preferred:
Leveraged Buyout
Early Stage
Balanced
Acquisition

Geographical Preferences

International Preferences:
Latin America
India
Mexico
South Africa
Africa
All International

Industry Preferences

In Communications prefer:
Communications and Media
Entertainment

In Medical/Health prefer:
Medical/Health

In Consumer Related prefer:
Consumer
Consumer Products
Consumer Services
Education Related

In Industrial/Energy prefer:
Environmental Related

In Financial Services prefer:
Financial Services

In Business Serv. prefer:
Services
Distribution

In Manufact. prefer:
Manufacturing

Additional Information
Name of Most Recent Fund: Zephyr Peacock India Fund II, L.P.
Most Recent Fund Was Raised: 04/11/2008
Year Founded: 1994
Capital Under Management: $285,300,000
Current Activity Level : Actively seeking new investments

ZERO STAGE CAPITAL CO., INC.

101 Main Street
17th Floor
Cambridge, MA USA 02142-1519
Phone: 617-876-5355
Fax: 617-876-1248
Website: www.zerostage.com

Other Offices
195 Church Street
10th Floor
New Haven, CT USA 06510
Phone: 203-865-7986
Fax: 203-865-7987

40 Westminster Street
Suite 702
Providence, RI USA 02903
Phone: 401-351-3036
Fax: 401-351-3056

Management and Staff
Ben Bronstein, Managing Director

David Carmisciano, Chief Financial Officer
Edwin Wang, Managing General Partner
Frank Pinto, Managing Director
Gordon Baty, Co-Founder
Matt Kelley, Managing General Partner

Type of Firm
Private Equity Firm

Association Membership
Natl Assoc of Small Bus. Inv. Co (NASBIC)

Project Preferences

Role in Financing:
Prefer role as deal originator but will also invest in deals created by others

Type of Financing Preferred:
Fund of Funds
Second Stage Financing
Early Stage
Start-up Financing
Later Stage
Seed
First Stage Financing

Size of Investments Considered:
Min Size of Investment Considered (000s): $2,000
Max Size of Investment Considered (000s): $10,000

Geographical Preferences

United States Preferences:
Northeast
East Coast

Industry Focus
(% based on actual investment)

Computer Software and Services	26.8%
Internet Specific	18.4%
Communications and Media	9.8%
Industrial/Energy	9.2%
Medical/Health	9.1%
Biotechnology	8.8%
Computer Hardware	6.9%
Semiconductors/Other Elect.	5.7%
Consumer Related	3.5%
Other Products	1.7%

Additional Information
Name of Most Recent Fund: Zero Stage Capital VII, L.P.
Most Recent Fund Was Raised: 06/01/2001
Year Founded: 1981
Capital Under Management: $450,000,000
Current Activity Level : Actively seeking new investments
Method of Compensation: Return on investment is of primary concern, do not charge fees

ZEUS INFRAMANAGEMENT PVT, LTD.
1st Floor, NBCC Tower
15, Bhikaji Cama Place
New Delhi, India 110 066
Phone: 91-11-4659-8813
Fax: 91-11-4659-8847
E-mail: contact@zeusfund.in
Website: www.zeusfund.in

Other Offices
7-1-24, B-Block, 5th Floor, Roxana Tower
Greenlands, Begumpet
Hyderabad, India 500 016
Phone: 91-40-6657-0665
Fax: 91-40-6657-0666

Management and Staff
A. Mohan Menon, Principal

Type of Firm
Private Equity Firm

Project Preferences

Type of Financing Preferred:
Generalist PE

Geographical Preferences

International Preferences:
India

Industry Preferences

In Industrial/Energy prefer:
Energy
Alternative Energy

In Business Serv. prefer:
Services

Additional Information
Year Founded: 2007
Current Activity Level : Actively seeking new investments

ZEUS PRIVATE EQUITY
Eleventh Floor, Lowry House
17 Marble Street
Manchester, United Kingdom M2 3AW
Phone: 44-161-214-4730
Fax: 44-161-839-2816
E-mail: info@zeusprivateequity.co.uk
Website: www.zeusprivateequity.co.uk

Other Offices
Venturers House
King Street
Bristol, United Kingdom BS1 4PB
Phone: 44-0117-915-4017
Fax: 44-0117-915-4088

Four Park Place
London, United Kingdom SW1A 1LP
Phone: 44-20-7661-9196
Fax: 44-20-3178-4120

Management and Staff
Ed Fazakerley, Partner
Gary Tipper, Managing Partner
Tony Dickin, Partner

Type of Firm
Private Equity Firm

Association Membership
British Venture Capital Association (BVCA)

Project Preferences

Type of Financing Preferred:
Leveraged Buyout
Management Buyouts
Acquisition

Geographical Preferences

International Preferences:
Europe

Industry Preferences

In Medical/Health prefer:
Health Services

In Consumer Related prefer:
Retail
Consumer Products

In Industrial/Energy prefer:
Industrial Products

In Financial Services prefer:
Financial Services

Additional Information
Year Founded: 2007
Capital Under Management: $197,500,000
Current Activity Level : Actively seeking new investments

ZHEJIANG ANFENG VENTURE CAPITAL CO., LTD.
No. 8 Qiushi Road
Room 1605 Gongyuan Building
Hangzhou, China 310013
Phone: 86-571-87633598

Type of Firm
Private Equity Firm

Project Preferences

Type of Financing Preferred:
Balanced

Geographical Preferences

International Preferences:
China

Industry Preferences

In Communications prefer:
Wireless Communications

Additional Information
Year Founded: 2008
Current Activity Level : Actively seeking new investments

ZHEJIANG UNIVERSITY VENTURE CAPITAL CO., LTD.

No. 116 Yugu Road
Room 309 Fangyuan Building
Hangzhou, China 310013
Phone: 86-571-87952824
Fax: 86-571-87952825

Management and Staff

Guo Ying Zhu, President

Type of Firm

University Program

Project Preferences

Type of Financing Preferred:
Balanced

Geographical Preferences

International Preferences:
China

Industry Preferences

In Computer Software prefer:
Software

In Biotechnology prefer:
Biotechnology

In Industrial/Energy prefer:
Environmental Related

Additional Information

Year Founded: 2001
Current Activity Level : Actively seeking new investments

ZHEJIANG VENTURE CAPITAL CO., LTD.

16/F Gaoxin Building
No.212 Wen'er Road
Hangzhou, China 310012
Phone: 86-571-88869571
Fax: 86-571-88869550
E-mail: zhjvcc@mail.hz.zj.cn
Website: www.zvc-zj.com

Type of Firm

Private Equity Firm

Project Preferences

Type of Financing Preferred:
Balanced

Geographical Preferences

International Preferences:
China

Industry Preferences

In Medical/Health prefer:
Medical/Health

In Industrial/Energy prefer:
Energy

Additional Information

Year Founded: 1993
Current Activity Level : Actively seeking new investments

ZHEJIANG ZHESHANG VENTURE CAPITAL CO., LTD.

No. 8 Qiu Shi Road
10th Floor Gong Yuan Building
Hangzhou, China 310013
Phone: 86-571-89922222
Fax: 86-571-89922221
E-mail: invest@zsvc.com.cn
Website: www.zsvc.com.cn

Management and Staff

Yuemeng Chen, President

Type of Firm

Private Equity Firm

Project Preferences

Type of Financing Preferred:
Expansion
Mezzanine
Early Stage
Balanced
Later Stage
Seed

Geographical Preferences

International Preferences:
China

Industry Preferences

In Computer Software prefer:
Software

In Biotechnology prefer:
Biotechnology

In Medical/Health prefer:
Pharmaceuticals

In Consumer Related prefer:
Entertainment and Leisure
Education Related

In Industrial/Energy prefer:
Energy
Environmental Related

In Transportation prefer:
Transportation

In Financial Services prefer:
Financial Services

In Business Serv. prefer:
Services

In Manufact. prefer:
Manufacturing

Additional Information

Year Founded: 2007
Capital Under Management: $71,100,000
Current Activity Level : Actively seeking new investments

ZHENGZHOU BAIRUI INNOVATION INVESTMENT MANAGEMENT CO., LTD.

No. 24 Jinshui Road
4/F Runhua Shangwu Garden D
Zhengzhou, China 450012
Phone: 86-371-63577690
Fax: 86-371-63577692

Type of Firm

Bank Affiliated

Project Preferences

Type of Financing Preferred:
Balanced

Geographical Preferences

International Preferences:
China

Additional Information

Year Founded: 2007
Capital Under Management: $14,700,000
Current Activity Level : Actively seeking new investments

ZIEGLER HEALTHVEST MANAGEMENT LLC

250 East Wisconsin Avenue
Suite 2000
Milwaukee, WI USA 53202
Phone: 414-978-6400
Website: www.ziegler.com

Management and Staff

Charles O'Meara, Senior Managing Director
Jeffrey Rideout, Managing Director
Paul Kusserow, Managing Director

Type of Firm

Bank Affiliated

Association Membership

National Venture Capital Association - USA (NVCA)

Project Preferences

Type of Financing Preferred:
Leveraged Buyout

Geographical Preferences

United States Preferences:
All U.S.

Industry Preferences

In Medical/Health prefer:
Medical/Health
Health Services

Additional Information

Year Founded: 2008
Capital Under Management: $10,400,000
Current Activity Level : Actively seeking new investments

ZIEGLER MEDITECH PARTNERS

250 East Wisconsin Avenue
Suite 2000
Milwaukee, WI USA 53202
Phone: 414-978-6508
Fax: 414-978-6549
Website: www.zmep.com

Type of Firm

Private Equity Firm

Project Preferences

Type of Financing Preferred:
Later Stage

Geographical Preferences

United States Preferences:
All U.S.

International Preferences:
Israel

Industry Preferences

In Medical/Health prefer:
Medical Products

Additional Information

Year Founded: 2006
Capital Under Management: $52,700,000
Current Activity Level : Actively seeking new investments

ZIFF BROTHERS INVESTMENTS

153 East 53rd Street
New York, NY USA 10115
Phone: 212-292-6000

Management and Staff

Timothy Mitchell, Chief Financial Officer

Type of Firm

Private Equity Firm

Project Preferences

Type of Financing Preferred:
Expansion
Balanced

Additional Information

Name of Most Recent Fund: Asian Private Equity Fund
Most Recent Fund Was Raised: 01/01/1996
Year Founded: 1992
Current Activity Level : Actively seeking new investments

ZINDEL INVESTMENT PARTNERS

47-49 La Motte Street
P.O. Box 583
Jersey, United Kingdom JE4 8XR
Phone: 44-153-488-1209
E-mail: info@zindelfund.com
Website: www.zindelfund.com

Management and Staff

Alexander Abolmasov, Managing Director

Type of Firm

Private Equity Firm

Association Membership

Russian Venture Capital Association (RVCA)

Project Preferences

Type of Financing Preferred:
Balanced

Geographical Preferences

International Preferences:
Russia

Industry Preferences

In Communications prefer:
Media and Entertainment

In Consumer Related prefer:
Consumer

In Industrial/Energy prefer:
Alternative Energy
Industrial Products
Environmental Related

In Business Serv. prefer:
Media

In Other prefer:
Environment Responsible

Additional Information

Year Founded: 2004
Capital Under Management: $100,000,000
Current Activity Level : Actively seeking new investments

ZON CAPITAL PARTNERS

Five Vaughn Drive
Suite 302
Princeton, NJ USA 08540
Phone: 609-452-1653
Fax: 609-452-1693
E-mail: zonadmin@zoncapital.com
Website: www.zoncapital.com

Other Offices

100 Matsonford Road
3 Radnor Corporate Center, Suite 304
Radnor, PA USA 19087
Phone: 610-989-9282

Management and Staff

E. Michael Forgash, Managing Partner
H. Donald Perkins, Managing Partner
William Bridgers, Managing Partner

Type of Firm

Private Equity Firm

Association Membership

National Venture Capital Association - USA (NVCA)
Natl Assoc of Small Bus. Inv. Co (NASBIC)

Project Preferences

Type of Financing Preferred:
Second Stage Financing
Expansion
First Stage Financing

Size of Investments Considered:
Min Size of Investment Considered (000s): $1,000
Max Size of Investment Considered (000s): $2,000

Geographical Preferences

United States Preferences:
Mid Atlantic

Industry Preferences

In Communications prefer:
Telecommunications
Wireless Communications
Data Communications

In Computer Software prefer:
Software

Additional Information

Year Founded: 2002
Capital Under Management: $57,300,000
Current Activity Level : Actively seeking new investments

ZONE VENTURES

241 South Figueroa Street
Suite 340
Los Angeles, CA USA 90012
Phone: 213-628-2400
Fax: 213-628-2433
E-mail: moreinfo@zonevc.com
Website: www.zonevc.com

Management and Staff

Bill Lewis, Partner
Frank Creer, Managing Director
Mark Greenstein, Chief Financial Officer
N. Darius Sankey, Managing Director
Rick Barry, Partner
Timothy Draper, Managing Director

Type of Firm

Private Equity Firm

Project Preferences

Role in Financing:
Prefer role as deal originator

Type of Financing Preferred:
Early Stage
Seed
Startup

Size of Investments Considered:
Min Size of Investment Considered (000s): $500
Max Size of Investment Considered (000s): $3,000

Geographical Preferences

United States Preferences:
California
Southwest
All U.S.

Industry Focus

(% based on actual investment)

Internet Specific	72.7%
Computer Software and Services	14.9%
Semiconductors/Other Elect.	9.4%
Other Products	2.2%
Computer Hardware	0.8%

Additional Information

Year Founded: 1998
Capital Under Management: $135,000,000
Current Activity Level : Actively seeking new investments
Method of Compensation: Return on investment is of primary concern, do not charge fees

ZOUK VENTURES, LTD.

140 Brompton Road
London, United Kingdom SW3 1HY
Phone: 44-20-7947-3400
Fax: 44-20-7947-3449
E-mail: contact@zouk.com
Website: www.zouk.com

Management and Staff

Alois Flatz, Partner
Anthony Fox, Partner
Felix von Schubert, Founding Partner
Peter Zaboji, Partner
Samer Salty, Partner
Tom Singh, Venture Partner

Type of Firm

Private Equity Firm

Association Membership

European Private Equity and Venture Capital Assoc.

Project Preferences

Type of Financing Preferred:
Expansion
Seed
Startup

Geographical Preferences

International Preferences:
Europe
Western Europe
All International

Industry Preferences

In Communications prefer:
Telecommunications

In Internet Specific prefer:
Internet

In Computer Other prefer:
Computer Related

In Industrial/Energy prefer:
Energy
Energy Conservation Relat
Environmental Related

Additional Information

Year Founded: 1999
Capital Under Management: $79,700,000
Current Activity Level : Actively seeking new investments

ZS FUND L.P.

1133 Avenue of the Americas
New York, NY USA 10036
Phone: 212-398-6200
Fax: 212-398-1808
Website: www.zsfundlp.com

Management and Staff

Adam Lehrhoff, Partner
Douglas Brown, Partner
Ned Sherwood, Partner
Nick Burger, Partner
Robert Horne, Partner

Type of Firm

Private Equity Firm

Project Preferences

Role in Financing:
Prefer role as deal originator but will also invest in deals created by others

Type of Financing Preferred:
Leveraged Buyout
Recapitalizations

Size of Investments Considered:
Min Size of Investment Considered (000s): $90,000
Max Size of Investment Considered: No Limit

Geographical Preferences

United States Preferences:
All U.S.

Canadian Preferences:
All Canada

International Preferences:
United Kingdom
China
Bermuda
France

Industry Preferences

In Communications prefer:
Communications and Media

In Semiconductor/Electr prefer:
Electronics
Electronic Components
Sensors

In Medical/Health prefer:
Disposable Med. Products

In Consumer Related prefer:
Entertainment and Leisure
Retail
Food/Beverage
Consumer Products
Consumer Services
Other Restaurants
Education Related

In Industrial/Energy prefer:
Industrial Products
Materials
Factory Automation
Machinery

In Manufact. prefer:
Office Automation Equipmt
Publishing

Additional Information

Year Founded: 1985
Capital Under Management: $150,000,000
Current Activity Level : Actively seeking new investments
Method of Compensation: Return on invest. most important, but chg. closing fees, service fees, etc.

ZUKUNFT LAND SALZBURG AG

Schwarzstrasse 13-15
Salzburg, Austria 5020
Phone: 43-662-88862085
Fax: 43-662-88862089
E-mail: office@zls.at
Website: www.zukunftlandsalzburg.at

Type of Firm

Bank Affiliated

Association Membership

European Private Equity and Venture Capital Assoc.

Project Preferences

Type of Financing Preferred:
Leveraged Buyout
Early Stage
Expansion

Geographical Preferences

International Preferences:
Austria

Additional Information

Year Founded: 2003
Capital Under Management: $55,400,000
Current Activity Level : Actively seeking new investments

ZURCHER KANTONALBANK

Corporate Finance Postfach
Zurich, Switzerland 8010
Phone: 41-1-292-26-88
Fax: 41-1-292-39-67
Website: www.zkb.ch

Type of Firm

Bank Affiliated

Association Membership

Swiss Venture Capital Association (SECA)

Project Preferences

Type of Financing Preferred:
Leveraged Buyout
Expansion
Balanced
Startup

Geographical Preferences

International Preferences:
Switzerland
Eastern Europe

Additional Information

Year Founded: 1996
Current Activity Level : Actively seeking new investments

ZURICH ALTERNATIVE ASSET MANAGEMENT, LLC (ZAAM)

105 East 17th Street
New York, NY USA 10003
Phone: 212-871-1613
E-mail: zaam@zurichna.com
Website: www.zurichna.com

Management and Staff

James Kester, Managing Director
Louis Rubino, Chief Operating Officer

Type of Firm

Insurance Firm Affiliate

Additional Information

Year Founded: 2006
Current Activity Level : Actively seeking new investments

ZURMONT MADISON MANAGEMENT AG (FKA: ZURMONT MANAGEMENT AG)

Eisengasse 15
P.O. Box 272
Zurich, Switzerland 8034
Phone: 41-44267-5000
Fax: 41-44267-5001
E-mail: info@zurmontmadison.ch
Website: www.zurmontmadison.ch

Other Offices

Birkenstasse 49
Rotkreuz, Switzerland
Phone: 41-41-790-5355
Fax: 41-41-790-3515

Management and Staff

Bjoern Boeckenfoerde, Founding Partner
Guido Patroncini, Founding Partner

Type of Firm

Private Equity Firm

Association Membership

Swiss Venture Capital Association (SECA)

Project Preferences

Type of Financing Preferred:
Leveraged Buyout
Expansion

Geographical Preferences

International Preferences:
Switzerland
Europe
Austria
Germany

Industry Preferences

In Computer Software prefer:
Software

In Biotechnology prefer:
Biotechnology

In Consumer Related prefer:
Consumer
Consumer Products

In Industrial/Energy prefer:
Industrial Products

Additional Information

Year Founded: 1987
Capital Under Management: $112,000,000
Current Activity Level : Actively seeking new investment

U.S. Firm Cross Reference by State

For more comprehensive querying, searching, and referencing, Thomson Reuters supplies Pratt's Guide online at www.prattsguide.com. Annual subscriptions are available for USD$995 per user. For more information, please contact Greg Winterton at 001 646 223 6787 or email greg.winterton@thomsonreuters.com.

Buyout Firms—Alabama
Harbert Management Corporation
Stonehenge Capital Company
Sverica International

Buyout Firms—Arizona
Alerion Capital Group
Canal Partners LLC
Cave Creek Capital Management
DCA Partners, Inc.
Flagstone Capital LLC
Grayhawk Capital
Miller Capital Corporation
Piper Jaffray Ventures
7bridge Capital Partners, Ltd.
SVB Capital
Sorenson Capital Partners

Buyout Firms—Arkansas
Stephens Group, Inc.

Buyout Firms—California
Accel-KKR LLC
Acorn Ventures, Inc.
Aetos Capital LLC
Allied Capital Corporation
Alpine Investors, L.P.
American Capital, Ltd.
Angelo, Gordon & Company
Aqua International Partners, LP
Ares Management, Inc.
Atlantic-Pacific Capital, Inc.
Aurora Capital Group (FKA: Aurora Capital Partners)
Aurora Resurgence Management Partners LLC
BPEP International
Babson Capital Management LLC
Balmoral Advisors LLC
Banc of America Securities LLC
BancBoston Capital/BancBoston Ventures
Battery Ventures, L.P.
Behrman Capital
Belvedere Capital Partners LLC
Bertram Capital
BioMedical Innovations, Ltd.
Bison Capital Asset Management LLC
Black Canyon Capital
Blackstone Group, L.P.
Blue Horizon Equity
Brentwood Associates
Bruckmann, Rosser, Sherrill & Co.
Bunker Hill Capital
C.M. Capital Corporation
CIBC Capital Partners
CIBC Wood Gundy Capital
CRG Partners
Calera Capital (FKA: Fremont Partners)
Caltius Equity Partners
Cambria Group, The
Cameron Holdings Corporation
Canaan Partners
Capital Dynamics AG
Capital International Research, Inc.
Cappello Capital Corp.
Carlyle Group, The
Castle Creek Capital LLC
Celerity Partners
Centre Partners Management LLC
Century Park Capital Partners
Champlain Capital Management LLC
Clarey Capital LLC
Clarity Partners
Clearview Capital LLC
CoVestia Capital Partners
Colony Capital LLC
Compass Group International LLC, The
Compass Group, Inc
Corridor Capital, LLC
Cowen Capital Partners LLC (FKA: SG Capital Partners LLC)
Credit Suisse Private Equity
Creo Capital Partners, LLC
Crimson Investment, LLC
DCA Partners, Inc.
Dick Israel & Partners (FKA: Sponsored Consulting Services)
Duff Ackerman & Goodrich LLC (AKA: DAG Ventures)
Elevation Associates LLC
Encore Consumer Capital LLC
Evercore Partners
Evergreen Pacific Partners LLC
Fairmont Capital, Inc.
Fenway Partners, Inc.
Fog City Capital LLC
Forrest Binkley & Brown
Fortress Investment Group LLC
Fox Paine & Company LLC
Francisco Partners
Freeman Spogli & Co.
Friedman, Fleischer & Lowe, LLC
Fulcrum Venture Capital Corporation
Fundamental Capital LLC
GCP Capital Partners
GE Antares Capital Corporation
GESD Capital Partners, LLC
Garnett & Helfrich Capital
Gemini Partners, Inc.
General Atlantic LLC
Generation Capital Partners
Genstar Capital LLC
Gilbert Global Equity Capital, L.L.C.
Glenmount, LLC
Global Equity Capital LLC
Global Innovation Partners LLC
Global Technology Investment (GTI)
Golden Gate Capital
Goldman, Sachs & Co.
Goode Partners LLC
Gores Group LLC, The
Grayson & Associates, Inc.
Green Tree Capital
Gryphon Investors, Inc.
H&Q Asia Pacific
H.I.G. Capital LLC
Halifax Group, The
Hancock Park Associates
Hanover Partners, Inc
Harbert Management Corporation
Headwaters Merchant Bank
Health Evolution Partners LLC
Hellman & Friedman LLC
Hercules Technology Growth Capital, Inc.
Hispania Capital Partners (HCP)
Horizon Holdings, LLC
Houlihan, Lokey, Howard & Zukin
Housatonic Partners
Huntsman Gay Global Capital LLC
Imperial Capital, LLC
Industrial Growth Partners
Integral Capital Partners
Internet Capital Group
Inverness Graham Investments
Invesco Private Capital
Investor Growth Capital, Inc.
Invision Capital Management LLC
Irving Place Capital
J.H. Whitney & Co. LLC
J.P. Morgan Capital Corporation
J.P. Morgan H&Q (FKA: Chase H&Q)
J.P. Morgan Partners (FKA: Chase Capital Partners)
JH Partners, LLC (FKA: Jesse.Hansen & Co.)
JP Capital Partners, LLC
Jefferies Group, Inc.
KCA Partners, Ltd.
KRG Capital Partners LLC
Key Principal Partners LLC (AKA: KPP)
Knowledge Universe
Kohlberg & Company LLC
Kohlberg, Kravis, Roberts & Company, L.P.
LLM Capital Partners LLC
LRG Capital Group (FKA: Baystar Capital, LLC)
LaSalle Capital Group, Inc.
Laminar Direct Capital, L.P.
Lazard Capital Partners
Lehman Brothers, Inc.
Leonard Green & Partners
Levine Leichtman Capital Partners, Inc.
Lexington Commercial Holdings
Li & Fung Investments
Liberty Capital Management Corporation
Lincolnshire Management, Inc.
Lombard Investments, Inc.
Lovell Minnick Partners LLC
MTS Health Partners, L.P.
Mainsail Partners
Markstone Capital
Marlin Equity Partners, LLC
Marwit Capital, LLC
McCall Springer
Meriturn Partners LLC
Merrill Lynch Capital Partners
Morgan Stanley Private Equity
Morgenthaler Ventures
Morrison & Foerster
Nogales Investors Management, LLC
North Castle Partners
Northleaf Capital Partners
Nortia Capital Partners, Inc. (FKA: BF Acquisition Group I)
Norwest Venture Partners
Oak Hill Capital Management, Inc.
Oaktree Capital Management LLC
Odyssey Investment Partners, LLC
OpenGate Capital
Opportunity Capital Partners
OrbiMed Advisors LLC
Pacific Road Capital Management Pty, Ltd.
Paine & Partners LLC
Palladium Equity Partners LLC
Parallax Capital Partners LLC

Parallel Invesment Partners
Parthenon Capital LLC
Partners Group AG
Pasadena Capital Partners
Permira Advisers LLP
Piper Jaffray Ventures
Platinum Equity LLC
Providence Equity Partners LLC
Quad Ventures
Quadrangle Group LLC
RBC Capital Partners/RBC Technology Ventures
Ranch Capital LLC
Revolution Capital Group LLC
Rigel Associates LLC
Riordan, Lewis & Haden
Ritchie Capital
Riverside Company
Riverwood Capital LLC (FKA: Bigwood Capital LLC)
Rizvi Traverse Management, LLC
Rosewood Capital, L.P.
SPO Partners & Co
STIC Investments, Inc.
SVB Capital
Sageview Capital LLC
Saints Ventures
Seagrove, LLC
Seidler Equity Partners
Serent Capital LLC
Shackleton Equity Partners LLC
Shamrock Holdings, Inc.
Siguler Guff & Company
Silver Lake Sumeru
Silverfern Group, Inc., The
Siparex Group SAS
Skylight Capital
Skyview Capital
Socius Capital Group LLC
Solis Capital Partners, LLC
Sorenson Capital Partners
Spectrum Equity Investors
St. Cloud Capital, LLC
Summit Partners
Sun Capital Partners, Inc.
Sverica International
Swander Pace Capital
TA Associates, Inc.
TCW Capital
TPG Capital
TSG Consumer Partners
TVC Capital, LLC (FKA: TVC Ventures LLC)
Terrapin Partners LLC
Thoma Cressey Bravo
Thomas Weisel Partners Group, Inc.
Ticonderoga Capital, Inc. (FKA: Dillon Read Venture Capital)
TowerBrook Capital Partners L.P.
Trammell-Shott Capital Management LLC
Transom Capital Group
Tregaron Capital Company LLC
Trenwith Securities LLC
Triton Pacific Capital Partners LLC
Trust Company of the West (AKA: TCW/Crescent)
Tucker Partners
Unique Investment Corporation
VMG Equity Partners
Vance Street Capital LLC
Vicente Capital Partners
VinaCapital Investment Management Company
Vintage Capital Partners
Vista Equity Partners
Walden International
Wasserstein Ventures (FKA: Wasserstein & Co.)
Wedbush Capital Partners
Weston Presidio (FKA: Weston Presidio Capital Management)
Whitman Capital, LLC
Wilshire Private Markets
Windjammer Capital Investors (FKA:Pacific Mezzanine Inv.)
Yucaipa Companies LLC, The

Buyout Firms—Colorado

Axiom Equity Partners
Bard Capital Group, LLC
Bow River Capital Partners
Carlyle Group, The
Cheyenne Capital Fund, L.P.
Cowen Capital Partners LLC (FKA: SG Capital Partners LLC)
Excellere Capital Management
Global Equity Capital LLC
Gores Group LLC, The
Grayson & Associates, Inc.
Grey Mountain Partners
Headwaters Merchant Bank
Hercules Technology Growth Capital, Inc.
Iron Gate Capital, LLC
KRG Capital Partners LLC
KSL Capital Partners
Kachi Partners
Livingston Capital, Ltd.
Montis Capital, LLC
Morgenthaler Ventures
Morrison & Foerster
Piper Jaffray Ventures
Platte River Ventures
Progress Equity Partners, Ltd.
Republic Financial Corporation
SVB Capital
Socius Capital Group LLC
Stolberg Equity Partners LLC
Stonehenge Capital Company
Thomas Weisel Partners Group, Inc.
Venture Associates, Ltd.
Vestar Capital Partners, Inc.
Wilshire Private Markets
Yorkville Advisors LLC

Buyout Firms—Connecticut

AEA Investors LP
AeroEquity Partners, LLC
Altus Capital Partners
Atlantic Street Capital Management, LLC
Atlantic-Pacific Capital, Inc.
Atlas Holdings FRM LLC
BIBB Co. (FKA: NTC Group, The)
Beacon Partners, Inc.
Black Diamond Capital Management, LLC
Brynwood Partners L.P.
CCP Equity Partners
Canaan Partners
Capital Partners, Inc.
Catterton Partners
Centripetal Capital Partners, Inc.
Clearview Capital LLC
Compass Group International LLC, The
Crown Capital Corporation
DLB Capital LLC
Design Investors LLC
Equinox Capital, Inc.
First New England Capital, L.P.
First Reserve Corporation
Fort Hill Partners, Inc.
Fortress Investment Group LLC
GE Antares Capital Corporation
GE Commercial Finance - Equity
GarMark Partners
General Atlantic LLC
General Electric Equity
Generation Capital Partners
Gilbert Global Equity Capital, L.L.C.
Goff Moore Strategic Partners
Gridiron Capital LLC
India Value Fund Advisors Private Ltd. (FKA: GW Capital)
Industrial Renaissance Inc.
J.H. Whitney & Co. LLC
JHP Enterprises LLC
JM Galef & Co., Inc.
Jefferies Group, Inc.
KarpReilly LLC
Key Principal Partners LLC (AKA: KPP)
Littlejohn & Company LLC
Longroad Asset Management
MML Capital Partners
Main Street Resources (FKA: Colt Capital Group)
Med Opportunity Partners LLC
Mill Road Capital LLC
Millennium Equity
MissionPoint Capital Partners
Natural Gas Partners (NGP)
North Castle Partners
Nova Capital Management, Ltd.
Oak Hill Capital Management, Inc.
Oaktree Capital Management LLC
Pegasus Capital Advisors, L.P.
Piper Jaffray Ventures
Prime Capital Management Co., Inc.
RBC Capital Partners/RBC Technology Ventures
Red Acre Capital LLC
Ropart Group
Sageview Capital LLC
Saugatuck Capital Company
Siguler Guff & Company
Silver Point Capital LLC
Silverhawk Capital Partners LLC
Southern Cross Group (AKA: SCG)
Southfield Capital Advisors
Stephens Group, Inc.
Sterling Investment Partners
Stone Point Capital LLC
Stonegate Capital Group LLC
TSG Capital Group, L.L.C.
Turnstone Capital Management LLC
Twin Haven Capital Partners
UBS Capital Corporation
Vista Capital LLC (FKA: AO Capital Corp.)
Winchester Capital Technology Partners LLC
Woodside Capital Partners

Yankee Hill Capital Management LLC

Buyout Firms—D. of Columbia

Allied Capital Corporation
Arlington Capital Partners
BIDV Vietnam Partners Investment Management Co. (AKA: BVIM)
Carlyle Group, The
DC Capital Partners LLC
Darby Overseas Investments, Ltd.
EMP Africa Fund Management (AKA: Emerging Capital Partners)
Evercore Partners
Goldman, Sachs & Co.
Halifax Group, The
International Finance Corporation
Key Bridge Partners LLC
Kohlberg, Kravis, Roberts & Company, L.P.
Lehman Brothers, Inc.
Monument Capital Group LLC
Morrison & Foerster
Oakcrest Capital Partners LLC
Park Avenue Equity Partners, L.P.
Perseus LLC
Pine Creek Partners
Siva Ventures, LLC
Stephens Group, Inc.
TPG Capital
Thayer Hidden Creek
York Capital Management, LLC

Buyout Firms—Delaware

Lehman Brothers, Inc.
North American Financial Holdings, Inc.

Buyout Firms—Florida

AP Capital Partners
Accretive Exit Capital Partners LLC
AeroEquity Partners, LLC
Andlinger & Company, Inc.
Blackstreet Capital Management (FKA: MMP Capital Advisors)
Boyne Capital Partners LLC
Brockway Moran & Partners, Inc.
Brown Brothers Harriman & Company (AKA: BBH)
Comvest Investment Partners
Crown Capital Corporation
Darby Overseas Investments, Ltd.
ESP Equity Partners LLC
Empire Investment Holdings, LLC
FCP Investors
Fairholme Capital Management
Fireman Capital Partners
Goldman, Sachs & Co.
Gordon River Capital
GunnAllen Venture Partners
H.I.G. Capital LLC
Harren Equity Partners
HealthEdge Investment Partners
Hispania Capital Partners (HCP)
Horizon Partners, Ltd.
Huntsman Gay Global Capital LLC
LRG Capital Group (FKA: Baystar Capital, LLC)
Lehman Brothers, Inc.
Levco Group, Ltd.
MBF Healthcare Partners L.P.
Mangrove Equity Partners LLC
New River Capital Partners
Palm Beach Capital Partners
Royal Palm Capital Partners, LLP
Siguler Guff & Company
Spring Bay Companies, The (AKA: Spring Bay Ventures)
Stenton Leigh Group, Inc.
Stephens Group, Inc.
Stonehenge Capital Company
Sun Capital Partners, Inc.
Trivest Partners, L.P.
VenGrow Corporate Finance AG
Westshore Capital Partners
Wyndcrest Holdings, LLC
Yorkville Advisors LLC

Buyout Firms—Georgia

Accel-KKR LLC
AeroEquity Partners, LLC
Arbor Private Investment Company, LLC
Arcapita, Inc.
Atlanta Capital Partners LLC
Atlanta Equity Investors LLC
Blackstone Group, L.P.
Brighton Partners, LLC
C&B Capital
CGW Southeast Partners (AKA: Cravey, Green, & Wahlen)
CRG Partners
Cordova Ventures (FKA:Cordova Capital)
EDG Partners LLC
Fulcrum Ventures
Goldman, Sachs & Co.
H.I.G. Capital LLC
Harbert Management Corporation
Houlihan, Lokey, Howard & Zukin
Jefferies Group, Inc.
KT Capital Management LLC
Kurt Salmon Associates Capital Advisors
LINX Partners
Lazard Capital Partners
Lehman Brothers, Inc.
Lincolnshire Management, Inc.
MSouth Equity Partners
Nancy Creek Capital
Navigation Capital Partners
Noro-Moseley Partners
Nortia Capital Partners, Inc. (FKA: BF Acquisition Group I)
Peachtree Equity Partners
Prometheus V, LLC
RBC Capital Partners/RBC Technology Ventures
River Capital
Riverside Company
Roark Capital Group
SVB Capital
Stephens Group, Inc.
Vexiom Equity Partners, L.P.
Voobon Ventures, Inc.

Buyout Firms—Hawaii

Colony Capital LLC

Buyout Firms—Idaho

Imperial Capital, LLC

Buyout Firms—Illinois

Allied Capital Corporation
Altus Capital Partners
Angelo, Gordon & Company
Arbor Private Investment Company, LLC
Archbrook Capital Management LLC
Argo Management Partners LLC
Ascent Equity Capital (FKA: Pinnacle Equity Capital)
Atlantic-Pacific Capital, Inc.
Bain Capital
Baird Capital Partners
Beecken, Petty & Company LLC
Benford Capital Partners LLC
Bolder Capital LLC
Bridge Street Capital Partners LLC
Brown Brothers Harriman & Company (AKA: BBH)
Brown Gibbons Lang & Company LLC
CIVC Partners LP (FKA: Continental Illinois Venture Corp.)
CRG Partners
Capital Strategy Management Co., The
Chicago Growth Partners (William Blair Capital Partners)
Clearview Capital LLC
Cloquet Capital Partners
Code, Hennessy & Simmons LLC
Concentric Equity Partners, L.P.
Convergent Capital Management, Inc (AKA: CCM)
Corinthian Capital Group LLC
Cowen Capital Partners LLC (FKA: SG Capital Partners LLC)
Creation Investments Capital Management LLC
Cressey & Company, L.P.
Draupnir LLC
Dresner Partners (FKA: Dresner Capital Resources, Inc.)
Ellipse Capital LLC
Flexpoint Ford (FKA: Flexpoint Partners LLC)
Focus Equity Partners, LLC
Forest Hill Partners LLC
Forstmann Little & Company
Fortress Investment Group LLC
Frontenac Company
GE Antares Capital Corporation
GLL Investors, Inc.
GTCR Golder Rauner LLC
Gateway City Capital, Inc.
Glencoe Capital LLC (FKA: Glencoe Investment Corporation)
Goense Bounds & Partners, LP
Goldman, Sachs & Co.
GrowthPath Capital, LLC (FKA: Tangram Partners, Inc.)
Hadley Capital
Hall Capital Partners, L.P.
Hammond Kennedy Whitney & Co
Hercules Technology Growth Capital, Inc.
High Street Capital
Hilco Equity Management, LLC
Hispania Capital Partners (HCP)
Horizon Capital
Houlihan, Lokey, Howard & Zukin
Industrial Opportunity Partners, LLC
Invision Capital Management LLC
Jefferies Group, Inc.
Jordan Company, The
Kingsman Capital LLC
LaSalle Capital Group, Inc.
Lake Capital Partners, Inc.

Lake Pacific Partners, LLC
Lazard Capital Partners
Lehman Brothers, Inc.
Levine Leichtman Capital Partners, Inc.
Lincolnshire Management, Inc.
Linden LLC
MASI, Ltd.
MFC Capital Funding, Inc.
Madison Capital Funding LLC (AKA: Madison Capital)
Madison Capital Partners
Madison Dearborn Partners LLC
Mercantile Capital Group (MCG)
Mesirow Private Equity Investments, Inc.
Midwest Mezzanine Funds
Nicolet Capital Partners LLC
One Equity Partners (FKA: Banc One Venture Partners)
P.A.G. Capital Partners
PPM America Capital Partners LLC
PRICOA Capital Group, Ltd.
Paine & Partners LLC
Pfingsten Partners, L.P.
Piper Jaffray Private Capital LLC
Piper Jaffray Ventures
Prospect Partners LLC
Prudential Capital Group
Red Barn Investments LLC
Resource Financial Corp
Ritchie Capital
Riverside Company
RoundTable Health Care Partners
SVB Capital
Sangamon Industries LLC
Second Century Ventures LLC
Shore Capital Partners LLC
Siguler Guff & Company
Silver Oak Management
Silverfleet Capital (FKA: PPM Capital Partners)
Stephens Group, Inc.
Sterling Partners
Sucsy, Fischer & Co.
Svoboda Capital Partners (FKA: Svoboda, Collins LLC)
TMB Industries Investments
Thoma Bravo LLC
Thoma Cressey Bravo
Thomas Weisel Partners Group, Inc.
Trenwith Securities LLC
Tricor Pacific Capital, Inc.
UIB Capital, Inc.
Unicorn Investment Bank B.S.C.
Valor Equity Partners
Vernon & Park Capital, L.P.
WHI Capital Partners
Wall Street Venture Capital
Water Street Healthcare Partners
Water Tower Capital LLC
Waud Capital Partners LLC
Willis Stein & Partners
Wilshire Private Markets
Wind Point Partners
Winona Capital Management
Wynnchurch Capital, Ltd.
Z Capital Partners LLC

Buyout Firms—Indiana

BrightPath Capital, Inc.
Cardinal Equity Partners (FKA: Cardinal Ventures)
Hammond Kennedy Whitney & Co

Buyout Firms—Iowa

Piper Jaffray Ventures

Buyout Firms—Kansas

Catalyst Equity Group LLC
Mariner Capital Partners LLC
Piper Jaffray Ventures

Buyout Firms—Kentucky

Blue Equity, LLC
Southfield Capital Advisors

Buyout Firms—Louisiana

Jefferies Group, Inc.
Stephens Group, Inc.
Stonehenge Capital Company

Buyout Firms—Maine

Spinnaker Trust

Buyout Firms—Maryland

American Capital, Ltd.
Blackstreet Capital Management (FKA: MMP Capital Advisors)
CRG Partners
Calvert Street Capital Partners, Inc. (FKA: Legg Mason)
Dyad Partners
Global Environment Fund Management Corporation
Integral Capital Partners
Laminar Direct Capital, L.P.
Leading Ridge Capital Partners LLC
Purepay
RLJ Equity Partners LLC
Slate Capital Group
Spring Capital Partners (FKA: Spring Capital Investors LLC)
Sterling Partners
Thomas Weisel Partners Group, Inc.
ValStone Partners LLC
Vinco Capital, Inc.
Woodbrook Capital, Inc.

Buyout Firms—Massachusetts

ABRY Partners LLC
AMX Capital, Ltd.
Accretive Exit Capital Partners LLC
Advent International
American Capital, Ltd.
Argonaut Partners, LLC
Audax Group
Axia Capital
Babson Capital Management LLC
Bain Capital
BancBoston Capital/BancBoston Ventures
Bank of America Capital Advisors (BACA)
Barish Fund, The
Battery Ventures, L.P.
Berkshire Partners LLC
Bio Equity Risk Management LLC
Blackstone Group, L.P.
Boston Ventures Management, Inc.
Brown Brothers Harriman & Company (AKA: BBH)
Brown Gibbons Lang & Company LLC
Bunker Hill Capital
CIBC Capital Partners
CRG Capital
CRG Partners
Calera Capital (FKA: Fremont Partners)
Castanea Partners
Charlesbank Capital Partners LLC
Cherington Capital
Citizens Capital, Inc.
Colony Capital LLC
Coppermine Capital LLC
Cowen Capital Partners LLC (FKA: SG Capital Partners LLC)
Crescent Private Capital, L.P.
CrossHarbor Capital Partners LLC
DDJ Capital Management, LLC
Eastern Link Capital
Evercore Partners
Falcon Investment Advisors LLC
Fidelity Equity Partners
Fireman Capital Partners
Fulham & Company, Inc.
GB Merchant Partners, LLC (FKA: GB Palladin Capital LLC)
GE Antares Capital Corporation
GenNx360 Capital Partners
Generation Equity Investors
Goldman, Sachs & Co.
Great Hill Equity Partners LLC
H.I.G. Capital LLC
Halpern, Denny & Company
Hastings Equity Partners LLC
Headwaters Merchant Bank
Hercules Technology Growth Capital, Inc.
Heritage Partners
Housatonic Partners
Humphrey Enterprises, LLC
Huntsman Gay Global Capital LLC
IDP Industrial Development Partners GmbH & Co KG
Internet Capital Group
Intervale Capital
Islington Capital Partners
J.W. Childs Associates
JMH Capital
Jefferies Group, Inc.
Kairos Capital Partners
Kamylon Capital LLC
LLM Capital Partners LLC
Lehman Brothers, Inc.
Lincolnshire Management, Inc.
Lineage Capital LLC
Lionheart Ventures
Madison Parker Capital LLC
Monitor Clipper Partners LLC
Morgenthaler Ventures
Murphy & Partners, L.P.
Mustang Group LLC, The
New England Capital Partners
Parthenon Capital LLC
Piper Jaffray Ventures
Quarry Capital Management LLC
Riverside Partners
SVB Capital
Seguin Partners LLC
Siguler Guff & Company
Spectrum Equity Investors

Staley Capital Management LLC
Stephens Group, Inc.
Summit Partners
Sverica International
TA Associates, Inc.
TD Capital Group, Ltd.
TSG Equity Partners, L.L.C.
Thomas H. Lee Partners (AKA: TH Lee Partners)
Thomas Weisel Partners Group, Inc.
Ticonderoga Capital, Inc. (FKA: Dillon Read Venture Capital)
Trammell-Shott Capital Management LLC
Trenwith Securities LLC
Tully & Holland, Inc. (FKA: Ulin & Holland, Inc.)
Vestar Capital Partners, Inc.
Wall Street Venture Capital
Watermill Group, The
Wayzata Investment Partners
Webster Capital Management, L.L.C.
WestView Capital Partners
Weston Presidio (FKA: Weston Presidio Capital Management)
Windjammer Capital Investors (FKA:Pacific Mezzanine Inv.)

Buyout Firms—Michigan

BlackEagle Partners (FKA: Centurion Capital Partners)
Bridge Street Capital Partners LLC
DLJ Merchant Banking Partners
Forest Hill Partners LLC
Huron Capital Partners LLC
Long Point Capital Inc.
Onyx Capital Advisors LLC
Plymouth Venture Partners
Questor Management Company LLC
Resilience Capital Partners LLC
Rizvi Traverse Management, LLC
RockBridge Equity Partners LLC
Strength Capital Partners
Superior Capital Partners
Transportation Resource Partners (TRP) (FKA: Penske Capital)
ValStone Partners LLC
Wynnchurch Capital, Ltd.

Buyout Firms—Midi-Pyrenees

Naxicap Partners SA

Buyout Firms—Minnesota

Brass Ring Capital, Inc.
CFSC Wayland Advisers, Inc.
CarVal Investors LLC
Churchill Equity, Inc.
CoVestia Capital Partners
Convergent Capital Partners
Goldner Hawn Johnson & Morrison, Inc.
Granite Equity Partners
Houlihan, Lokey, Howard & Zukin
LFE Capital
Lazard Capital Partners
Northstar Capital, LLC (FKA: Seidler Capital, Ltd.)
Norwest Equity Partners
Piper Jaffray Private Capital LLC
Piper Jaffray Ventures
RAIN Source Capital, Inc.
SVB Capital
Shoreview Industries
Spell Capital Partners LLC
Stone Arch Capital LLC
Thayer Hidden Creek
Tonka Bay Equity Partners
Varde Partners, Inc.
Wayzata Investment Partners
White Rose GP I, LLC
Whitecliff Capital Partners

Buyout Firms—Mississippi

Stephens Group, Inc.

Buyout Firms—Missouri

B12 Capital Partners LLC
Bush O'Donnell Capital Partners
C3 Capital LLC
Cameron Holdings Corporation
Capital For Business, Inc.
Consumer Growth Partners
Crown Capital Corporation
Forsyth Capital Investors LLC
Harbour Group, Ltd.
Piper Jaffray Ventures
Sage Capital, LLC
Stonehenge Capital Company
Thompson Street Capital Partners
Venture Associates, Ltd.
Warson Capital Partners

Buyout Firms—Montana

Piper Jaffray Ventures

Buyout Firms—Nebraska

McCarthy Group, Inc.
Piper Jaffray Ventures
Rockbrook Advisors LLC

Buyout Firms—Nevada

Brookstone Capital, Inc.
KRG Capital Partners LLC
SPB Capital Partners, L.P.
TCIB Investment Co., Ltd.

Buyout Firms—New Hampshire

Barish Fund, The
Tuckerman Capital

Buyout Firms—New Jersey

Appaloosa Management, L.P.
Atlantic-Pacific Capital, Inc.
Aztec Equity Partners, LLC
Bedminster Capital LLC
Black Opal Equity
Blackstreet Capital Management (FKA: MMP Capital Advisors)
Brown Brothers Harriman & Company (AKA: BBH)
CIT Group Inc.
Crystal Ridge Partners, LLC
ESP Equity Partners LLC
Egis Capital Partners LLC
Equis Capital Partners
FFR Capital Partners
Friend Skoler & Co., L.L.C.
GSC Partners (FKA: Greenwich Street Capital Partners)
Goldman, Sachs & Co.
Hudson Capital Management, L.P.
Jefferies Group, Inc.
Jina Ventures, Inc.
Laud Collier & Company LLC (AKA: LC & Co.)
Lehman Brothers, Inc.
Morgenthaler Ventures
Northern Capital Management Group
Olympus Capital Investments LLC
Palisade Capital Management
SCP Private Equity Partners
Spire Capital
Stanford Investment Group
Swander Pace Capital
Thompson Street Capital Partners
Transportation Resource Partners (TRP) (FKA: Penske Capital)
Value Added Capital, LLC
Verax Capital Partners LLC
Wilshire Private Markets
Yorkville Advisors LLC

Buyout Firms—New Mexico

Blue Sage Capital, L.P.
Natural Gas Partners (NGP)

Buyout Firms—New York

ACI Capital Co., LLC
AEA Investors LP
AIG Capital Partners
ARCIS Finance SA
AXA Private Equity
Acacia Capital, Inc.
Admiral Capital Group
Advent International
Aetos Capital LLC
Aleutian Capital Partners LLC
Allied Capital Corporation
Allied Irish Investment (AKA: AIB Bank) (AKA: AIB Group)
Alothon Group LLC
AlpInvest Partners N.V.
Altaris Capital Partners LLC
Alumni Capital Network
American Capital, Ltd.
American Industrial Partners
American Securities Capital Partners LLC
Andlinger & Company, Inc.
Angelo, Gordon & Company
Angler Capital Management LLC
Apax Partners Worldwide
Apollo Management
Aquiline Capital Partners
Archbrook Capital Management LLC
Ares Management, Inc.
Arsenal Capital Partners
Audax Group
Avalon Equity Partners
Avenue Capital Group
Avista Capital Holdings, L.P.
Axxess Capital Partners S.A. (FKA: Enterprise Capital)
BC Partners Ltd
BIDV Vietnam Partners Investment Management Co. (AKA: BVIM)
BPEP International
Babson Capital Management LLC
Bain Capital
Baker Capital Corp.
Banc of America Securities LLC
Bangert Dawes Reade Davis & Thom
Barish Fund, The

Bear Growth Capital Partners
Bedford Funding
Beekman Group LLC, The
Behrman Capital
Bendigo Partners LLC
BlackEagle Partners (FKA: Centurion Capital Partners)
Blackstone Group, L.P.
Blue Wolf Capital Management LLC
Boston Ventures Management, Inc.
Bradford Equities Management LLC
Branford Castle, Inc.
Brookfield Asset Management
Brookstone Partners
Brown Brothers Harriman & Company (AKA: BBH)
Bruckmann, Rosser, Sherrill & Co.
Buckingham Capital Partners
Butler Capital Corporation
CAI Capital Management Company
CCMP Capital Advisors LLC
CI Capital Partners LLC (FKA: Caxton-Iseman Capital, Inc)
CIBC Capital Partners
CIMB Private Equity Sdn Bhd
CIT Group Inc.
CITIC Capital Partners, Ltd.
CLB Partners, LLC
CLSA Capital Partners (AKA: Credit Lyonnais Securities Asia)
CM Equity Partners (FKA; Lynx Investment Management, L.P.)
CN Private Equity Partners
CRG Capital
CRG Partners
CVC Capital Partners (Europe), Ltd.
CapGen Financial Group
Capital Dynamics AG
CapitalSpring LLC
Cappello Capital Corp.
Carlyle Group, The
Cartesian Capital Group, LLC
Castle Harlan, Inc.
Cavalry Investments LLC
Celtic Pharma Management, LP
Celtic Therapeutics Management, L.L.L.P.
Centenium-Pinetree China Private Equity
Centerbridge Partners
Centerview Partners Holdings LLC
Centre Partners Management LLC
Cerberus Capital Management, L.P.
Channelstone Partners LLC
Charlesbank Capital Partners LLC
Chart Capital Management LLC
Charterhouse Group International, Inc.
Circle Peak Capital LLC (AKA: CPC)
Citi Venture Capital International
Citigroup Private Bank
Citigroup Private Equity
Clarion Capital Partners LLC
Clayton, Dubilier & Rice, Inc.
Clearlake Capital Group
Clearwater Capital Partners, LLC
CoBe Capital LLC
CoVestia Capital Partners
Colony Capital LLC
Commonwealth Capital Partners LP
Comvest Investment Partners
Conduit Capital Partners, LLC
Consumer Growth Partners
Cordova, Smart & Williams, LLC
Corinthian Capital Group LLC
Cornestone Capital Partners
Corporate Fuel Partners
Corsair Capital LLC
Cortec Group, Inc.
Court Square Capital Partners
Cowen Capital Partners LLC (FKA: SG Capital Partners LLC)
Credit Suisse Private Equity
Crestview Partners L.P. (FKA: Crestview, LLC)
Croupier Prive Private Equity Partners LLC
Crown Capital Corporation
DLJ Merchant Banking Partners
DMC Capital Funding LLC
Darby Overseas Investments, Ltd.
Delany Capital Management Corporation (DCM)
DeltaPoint Capital Management LLC
Deutsche Banc Alex Brown (FKA: Bankers Trust New York Corp)
Diamond Castle Holdings LLC
Diamond Point Capital Management
Dominus Capital, L.P.
EG Capital Group LLC
EQT Funds management Limited
Elevation Associates LLC
Emigrant Capital
Enhanced Equity Fund, L.P.
Environmental Capital Partners LLC
Eos Partners, L.P.
Equifin Capital Partners
ErGo Media Capital
Evercore Partners
Evolvence Capital
Exeter Capital Partners
Falconhead Capital (FKA: Sports Capital Partners)
Fenway Partners, Inc.
Firebird Management LLC
First Atlantic Capital, Ltd.
FlatWorld Capital LLC
Forstmann Little & Company
Fortress Investment Group LLC
Founders Equity, Inc.
Freeman Spogli & Co.
FriedbergMilstein, LLC
Fulcrum Management, Inc.
G.L. Ohrstrom & Co., Inc. (AKA: GLO & Co.)
GB Merchant Partners, LLC (FKA: GB Palladin Capital LLC)
GCP Capital Partners
GE Antares Capital Corporation
GE Commercial Finance - Equity
GF Capital Management & Advisors LLC
GSC Partners (FKA: Greenwich Street Capital Partners)
GenNx360 Capital Partners
General Atlantic LLC
Generation Equity Investors
Genesis Capital, Inc.
Gilbert Global Equity Capital, L.L.C.
Giraffe Capital LP
Gleacher & Co.
Global Capital Finance
Global Emerging Markets
Global Technology Investment (GTI)
Goldfish Holdings, Inc.
Goldman Sachs JBWere Private Equity (FKA:JBWere Prv Equity)
Goldman Sachs Urban Investment Group
Goldman, Sachs & Co.
Goode Partners LLC
Gotham Private Equity Partners, L.P.
Grayson & Associates, Inc.
Green Brook Capital Management LLC
Greenbriar Equity Group LLC
Greenfield Capital Partners
Grey Mountain Partners
Gruss & Co.
Gustafson & Co., Inc.
H.I.G. Capital LLC
HARDT GROUP Capital Partners Limited
HB Equity Partners, L.P.
HSBC Capital (Canada)
HT Capital Advisors LLC
Hale Fund Management, L.P.
Hammond Kennedy Whitney & Co
Hampshire Equity Partners (FKA: ING Equity Partners)
Harbert Management Corporation
Harvest Partners LLC
Hastings Private Equity
Health Evolution Partners LLC
HealthpointCapital LLC
Hellman & Friedman LLC
High Road Capital Partners
Highland Capital Management, L.P.
Houlihan, Lokey, Howard & Zukin
Hudson Ferry Capital LLC
ICV Capital Partners LLC
Imperial Capital, LLC
Incyte Capital Holdings LLC
IndexAtlas Group
InterMedia Partners
Invesco Private Capital
Investcorp Bank B.S.C.
Investcorp Technology Investments Group
Investor Growth Capital, Inc.
Invus Group Ltd., The
Irving Place Capital
iEurope Capital LLC
J.C. Flowers & Co. LLC
J.F. Lehman & Company
J.H. Whitney & Co. LLC
J.P. Morgan Capital Corporation
J.P. Morgan Partners (FKA: Chase Capital Partners)
JC Asia Alpha Private Equity
JLL Partners (FKA: Joseph, Littlejohn & Levy, Inc.)
Jacobson Partners
Jefferies Group, Inc.
Jina Ventures, Inc.
Jordan Company, The
Jordan, Edmiston Group, Inc., The
KCPS Israel Private Equity Partners
KKR & Co. (Guernsey) L.P.
KPS Capital Partners, L.P.
Kairos Capital Partners
Kelso & Company
Kinderhook Industries
Kohlberg & Company LLC

Kohlberg, Kravis, Roberts & Company, L.P.
LINX Partners
LJH Linley Capital LLC
LNK Partners
LRG Capital Group (FKA: Baystar Capital, LLC)
Lazard Alternative Investment
Lazard Capital Partners
Leading Ridge Capital Partners LLC
Lee Equity Partners
Leeds Equity Partners
Lehman Brothers, Inc.
Levine Leichtman Capital Partners, Inc.
Liberty Partners
Lightyear Capital LLC
Lincolnshire Management, Inc.
Lindsay Goldberg LLC (FKA: Lindsay Goldberg & Bessemer GP)
Lion Chemical Capital
Long Point Capital Inc.
Lower Volga River Management Inc.
MHR Capital Partners
MSD Capital L.P.
MTN Capital Partners
MTS Health Partners, L.P.
MVC Capital (FKA: meVC)
MatlinPatterson Global Advisers LLC
Maverick Capital Ltd.
Mercantile Capital Group (MCG)
Mercury Capital Partners
Meriwether Capital
Merrill Lynch Capital Partners
Merrill Lynch Global Emerging Markets Group
Metalmark Capital LLC
MidOcean Partners
Mistral Equity Partners
Monomoy Capital Partners, LLC
Morgan Stanley Private Equity
Morrison & Foerster
Murphy & Partners, L.P.
NIBC Principal Investments (FKA: Parnib Holding NV)
NRDC Equity Partners
NYPC Capital
New Mountain Capital LLC
New Silk Route Partners LLC
New York Life Capital Partners (AKA: NYLCAP)
NewSmith Asset Management LLP
North Peak Capital, LLC
Northwood Ventures
Noson Lawen Partners LLC
O.S.S. Capital Management LP
Oak Hill Capital Management, Inc.
Oaktree Capital Management LLC
Oasis Capital Partners LLC
Odyssey Investment Partners, LLC
One Equity Partners (FKA: Banc One Venture Partners)
Onex Corporation
Ontario Teachers' Pension Plan
Opus Electra & Partners
OrbiMed Advisors LLC
P. Schoenfeld Asset Management LLC
PPM America Capital Partners LLC
Paine & Partners LLC
Palladium Equity Partners LLC
Palmfund Management LLC
Park Avenue Equity Partners, L.P.
Parkview Ventures LLC
Partners Group AG
Patriarch Partners LLC
Patron Capital, Ltd.
Pegasus Capital Advisors, L.P.
Permira Advisers LLP
Perseus LLC
Pine Brook Road Partners LLC
PineBridge Investments
Piper Jaffray Ventures
Platinum Equity LLC
Point Lookout Capital Partners, L.P.
Post Capital Partners LLC
Pouschine Cook Capital Management, LLC
Praesidian Capital, LLC
Protostar Partners, LLC
Providence Equity Partners LLC
Quad Ventures
Quad-C Management, Inc.
Quadrangle Group LLC
Questor Management Company LLC
Quilvest Private Equity
Red Diamond Capital
Relativity Capital LLC
Renaissance Capital
Reservoir Capital Group
Rhone Capital LLC
Ripplewood Holdings LLC
Ritchie Capital
Riverside Company
Riverstone LLC
Robeco Private Equity
RockWood Equity Partners LLC
Rosemont Solebury Capital Management LLC
SCP Private Equity Partners
SFW Capital Partners, LLC
SK Capital Partners
SV Investment Partners (FKA: Schroder Ventures US)
SVB Capital
Salomon Smith Barney Private Management LLC
Saratoga Partners, LP
Saw Mill Capital, LLC
Scorpion Capital Partners, L.P.
Seaport Capital, LLC
Searchlight Capital Partners LLC
Sentinel Capital Partners
Sigma Capital Partners, LLC
Signet Healthcare Partners (FKA: Sanders Morris Harris)
Siguler Guff & Company
Silver Lake Sumeru
Silverfern Group, Inc., The
Snow Phipps Group LLC (FKA: SPG Partners, LLC)
Spire Capital
Stairway Capital Management
Steelpoint Capital Partners
Stephens Group, Inc.
Steve Norris Partners
Stone Point Capital LLC
Stonebridge Partners
Stonehenge Capital Company
Stonehill Capital Management
Stonington Partners, Inc.
Stripes Group
Summer Street Capital LLC
Sun Capital Partners, Inc.
Symphony Capital LLC
3i Group PLC
T Squared Partners LLC
TCW Capital
TH Lee Putnam Ventures, L.P.
TPG Capital
TSG Consumer Partners
TZP Group LLC
Tailwind Capital Partners
Teachers Insurance & Annuity Association College Retirement
Terrapin Partners LLC
Thomas Weisel Partners Group, Inc.
Tiger Global (FKA:Tiger Technology Performance, LLC)
Tinicum Capital Partners
Tocqueville Finance SA
TowerBrook Capital Partners L.P.
Trafelet & Company LLC
Trammell-Shott Capital Management LLC
Trenwith Securities LLC
Trimaran Capital Partners, LLC
Trust Company of the West (AKA: TCW/Crescent)
UBS Capital Corporation
Union Capital Corporation
Vanguard Atlantic, Ltd.
Veritas Capital
Veronis Suhler Stevenson (FKA: Veronis, Suhler & Associates)
Vestar Capital Partners, Inc.
Viscogliosi Bros LLC
Volcano Capital, Ltd.
W.L. Ross & Co. LLC
Wall Street Venture Capital
Wasserstein Ventures (FKA: Wasserstein & Co.)
Wellspring Capital Management LLC
Welsh, Carson, Anderson & Stowe
Wicks Group of Companies LLC, The
Willis Stein & Partners
Wilshire Private Markets
Wincove Capital
Yankee Hill Capital Management LLC
York Capital Management, LLC
ZS Fund L.P.
Zelnick Media
Zephyr Management, L.P.
Zurich Alternative Asset Management, LLC (ZAAM)

Buyout Firms—North Carolina

Babson Capital Management LLC
Banc of America Securities LLC
Bison Capital Asset Management LLC
Blue Point Capital Partners (FKA: Key Equity Capital)
Brown Brothers Harriman & Company (AKA: BBH)
CRG Partners
CapitalSouth Partners, L.L.C.
Carlyle Group, The
Copeley Capital Partners
Falfurrias Capital Partners
Franklin Street Partners
Halifax Group, The
Jefferies Group, Inc.
Kendall Capital Associates LLC
Meriturn Partners LLC

Pamlico Capital
Piper Jaffray Ventures
Plexus Capital LLC (FKA: Plexus Fund)
Red Top Capital LLC (FKA: Crimson Capital Company)
Ridgemont Equity Partners
SVB Capital
SilkRoad Equity, LLC
Silverhawk Capital Partners LLC
Stephens Group, Inc.
UNC Kenan-Flagler Private Equity Fund

Buyout Firms—Ohio

Blue Point Capital Partners (FKA: Key Equity Capital)
Brantley Partners
Brown Gibbons Lang & Company LLC
CapitalWorks LLC
Capstone Capital Partners LLC
Cowen Capital Partners LLC (FKA: SG Capital Partners LLC)
Edgewater Capital Group, Inc.
Evolution Capital Partners, LLC
Excel Capital Partners, L.P.
HillStreet Capital, Inc.
Key Principal Partners LLC (AKA: KPP)
Kirtland Capital Partners
Lehman Brothers, Inc.
Linsalata Capital Partners
MCM Capital Partners, LP
Morgenthaler Ventures
NatCity Investments, Inc.
Portal Capital LLC
Primus Capital Funds
Resilience Capital Partners LLC
Reynolds, DeWitt & Co.
Riverside Company
RockWood Equity Partners LLC
SFW Capital Partners, LLC
Stonehenge Capital Company
Supply Chain Equity Partners
Thomas Weisel Partners Group, Inc.
US Equity LLC

Buyout Firms—Oklahoma

Acorn Growth Companies
Argonaut Private Equity
Hall Capital Partners, L.P.
Pennington Allen Capital Partners
Stephens Group, Inc.
Virgo Capital

Buyout Firms—Oregon

Adventure Funds LLC
Aequitas Capital Management, Inc.
Endeavour Capital
Hanover Partners, Inc
Piper Jaffray Ventures
Riverlake Partners LLC
SVB Capital
Thomas Weisel Partners Group, Inc.

Buyout Firms—Pennsylvania

Archbrook Capital Management LLC
Argosy Capital
Baird Capital Partners
Boathouse Capital
Brook Street Investments LLC
Brown Brothers Harriman & Company (AKA: BBH)
CD Ventures, LLC
CMS Companies
Cameron Capital Management
Clearwater Capital Management
Entrepreneur Partners, L.P.
Eureka Growth Capital
F.N.B. Capital Corporation LLC
Gatehouse Ventures, L.P.
Goldman, Sachs & Co.
Graham Partners, Inc.
Guardian Capital Partners
Hawthorne Group
Huron Capital Partners LLC
Internet Capital Group
Inverness Graham Investments
Investment Fund for Foundations
LLR Partners, Inc.
Lionheart Ventures
Lovell Minnick Partners LLC
Main Street Capital Holdings LLC
Mentor Capital Partners
Meridian Venture Partners (MVP)
Milestone Partners
Noson Lawen Partners LLC
PNC Equity Management Corp.
Penn Valley Group
Rosemont Investment Partners LLC
Rosetta Capital Corporation
SCP Private Equity Partners
SVB Capital
Safeguard Scientifics, Inc.
Scimitar Global Ventures
Speyside Equity LLC
Spire Capital
Spring Capital Partners (FKA: Spring Capital Investors LLC)
Stonewood Capital Management, Inc.
Thompson Street Capital Partners
UMS Partners
Versa Capital Management (FKA: Chrysalis Capital Partners)
Wilshire Private Markets

Buyout Firms—Puerto Rico

Lehman Brothers, Inc.

Buyout Firms—Rhode Island

American Capital, Ltd.
Bay Capital Advisors, LLC
Nautic Partners LLC
123Venture SA
Providence Equity Partners LLC

Buyout Firms—South Carolina

Azalea Capital LLC
Stephens Group, Inc.

Buyout Firms—South Dakota

Capitaline Advisors, LLC

Buyout Firms—Tennessee

Andrew W. Byrd & Co. LLC
Cressey & Company, L.P.
DesignWorks Investments
GEN CAP America, Inc.
Harbert Management Corporation
Jefferies Group, Inc.
Petra Capital Partners, LLC
River Associates, LLC
Stephens Group, Inc.
Thoma Cressey Bravo
Venture Associates Partners LLC

Buyout Firms—Texas

AIG Capital Partners
Admiral Capital Group
American Capital, Ltd.
Amerimark Capital Group
Ancor Capital Partners
Aqua International Partners, LP
Asparron Capital LLC
Atlantic-Pacific Capital, Inc.
Avista Capital Holdings, L.P.
B4 Ventures
Baymark Partners
Blue Sage Capital, L.P.
Brazos Private Equity Partners LLC
Brown Brothers Harriman & Company (AKA: BBH)
C3 Capital LLC
CCMP Capital Advisors LLC
CIC Partners, L.P. (FKA: Cardinal Investment Company, Inc.)
CRG Partners
CapStreet Group LLC, The (FKA: Summit Capital Group)
Cappello Capital Corp.
Caris, Ltd.
Comerica Bank
Compass Equity Partners LLC
Cowen Capital Partners LLC (FKA: SG Capital Partners LLC)
EFO Holdings, L.P.
Elm Creek Partners
Equus Total Return, Inc.
Evercore Partners
Evolve Capital
Ewing Management Group LLC
First Reserve Corporation
Fortress Investment Group LLC
G.A. Herrera & Co., LLC
GCP Capital Partners
GE Antares Capital Corporation
GTD Capital
Goff Moore Strategic Partners
Goldman, Sachs & Co.
HM Capital Partners LLC
Halifax Group, The
Hancock Park Associates
Hicks Equity Partners
Highland Capital Management, L.P.
HitecVision AS
Hoak & Co.
Houlihan, Lokey, Howard & Zukin
Hunt Private Equity Group, Inc. (FKA: Hunt Financial Corp.)
Hunt Special Situations Group
Incyte Capital Holdings LLC
Indofin
Insight Equity Holdings LLC
Intervale Capital
Jefferies Group, Inc.
Kahala Investments, Inc.
Kohlberg, Kravis, Roberts & Company, L.P.
Laminar Direct Capital, L.P.
Lazard Capital Partners

Lehman Brothers, Inc.
Levine Leichtman Capital Partners, Inc.
Lion Chemical Capital
Lone Star Funds
Lone Star Investment Advisors (AKA: Lewis Hollingsworth LP)
Longroad Asset Management
Magellan Capital Partners, Ltd.
Maverick Capital Ltd.
Medford Investments, L.P.
Mercury Capital Partners
NLM Capital Partners, L.P.
Natural Gas Partners (NGP)
Parallel Invesment Partners
Piper Jaffray Ventures
PlumTree Partners LLC
Private Equity Partners
Progress Equity Partners, Ltd.
Prophet Equity LLC
Revolution Learning
Ridgemont Equity Partners
RiverRock Holdings LLC
Riverside Company
Rock Hill Capital Group LLC
SCF Partners
SVB Capital
Satori Capital LLC
Sid R. Bass Associates, LP
SigmaBleyzer
Signet Healthcare Partners (FKA: Sanders Morris Harris)
Silverton Foundation
Small Ventures USA, L.P.
Southlake Equity Group
Stephens Group, Inc.
Stonehenge Capital Company
SunTx Capital Partners
TCW Capital
TD Capital Group, Ltd.
TGF Management Corp (FKA:Texas Growth Fund)
TPG Capital
TPH Partners LLC
Teakwood Capital, L.P.
Treadstone Group Inc., The
Trinity Hunt Partners
Trust Company of the West (AKA: TCW/Crescent)
Venquest Capital Partners
Virgo Capital
White Deer Energy
Yellowstone Capital, Inc.

Buyout Firms—Utah

Alerion Capital Group
DW Healthcare Partners
Goldman, Sachs & Co.
Granite Capital Partners
Ground Swell Equity Partners
Huntsman Gay Global Capital LLC
Peterson Partners (FKA: Peterson Capital)
Prospector Equity Capital, L.P.
Sorenson Capital Partners

Buyout Firms—Vermont

Headwaters Merchant Bank

Buyout Firms—Virginia

Acorn Growth Companies
BB&T Capital Markets
Boxwood Capital Partners, LLC
CrossHill Financial Group, Inc
DC Capital Partners LLC
FedCap Advisors LLC
Grindstone Partners LLC
Harbert Management Corporation
Harren Equity Partners
Houlihan, Lokey, Howard & Zukin
J.F. Lehman & Company
Leveraged Green Energy LLC
Longstreet Partners, LLC
Morrison & Foerster
Piper Jaffray Ventures
Quad-C Management, Inc.
Red Zone Capital Partners
Relativity Capital LLC
SVB Capital
Southfield Capital Advisors
Stephens Group, Inc.
3P International Energy Corporation
Winston Partners

Buyout Firms—Washington

Aequitas Capital Management, Inc.
Banyan Capital Partners
Blue Point Capital Partners (FKA: Key Equity Capital)
Broadmark Capital Corp.
Eagle River Holdings
Endeavour Capital
Evergreen Pacific Partners LLC
GenNx360 Capital Partners
Goldman, Sachs & Co.
Ignition Capital
Internet Capital Group
Lehman Brothers, Inc.
Meridian Capital (FKA: Olympic Capital Partners, LLC)
Piper Jaffray Ventures
Revolution Learning
SVB Capital
Trenwith Securities LLC
Winona Capital Management
Zachary Scott & Co.

Buyout Firms—Wisconsin

Baird Capital Partners
Brass Ring Capital, Inc.
Generation Growth Capital, Inc.
Horizon Partners, Ltd.
Lakeview Equity Partners, LLC
Mason Wells Private Equity (FKA: M&I Ventures)
Northwestern Mutual Capital
Piper Jaffray Ventures
Red Top Capital LLC (FKA: Crimson Capital Company)
Resource Financial Corp
Stonehenge Capital Company

Fund of Funds—California

Adams Street Partners LLC
Asia Alternatives Management LLC
Bay Hills Capital (FKA: Mansbridge Capital Management)
Centinela Capital Partners LLC
Commonfund Capital, Inc. (FKA: Common Fund)
Darwin Ventures LLC
FireStarter Partners LLC
Fisher Lynch Capital
Fondinvest Capital (Grp. Caisse de Depots)
GKM Newport Generation Funds
Golding Capital Partners GmbH
Greenspring Associates, Inc.
Grove Street Advisors LLC
Hall Capital Partners LLC (FKA: Offit Hall Capital Mgmt)
Hamilton Lane Advisors, Inc.
Horsley Bridge Partners
Keystone National Group LLC
Legacy Venture
Macquarie Investment Management, Ltd. (AKA: MIML)
Montauk TriGuard Management, Inc.
Northgate Capital Group
O'Melveny & Myers LLP
Oak Hill Investment Management (OHIM)
Pacific Corporate Group
Pantheon Ventures, Ltd.
Park Street Capital LLC
Paul Capital Partners
Progress Investment Management Company
RCP Advisors LLC
Square 1 Ventures
VCFA Group
WP Global Partners Inc.
Weathergage Venture Capital
WestLB Mellon Asset Management (USA) LLC

Fund of Funds—Colorado

Emerald Hill Capital Partners, Ltd.
GF Private Equity Group, LLC
Montauk TriGuard Management, Inc.
Square 1 Ventures
Symmetry Investment Advisors, Inc.

Fund of Funds—Connecticut

AXA Investment Managers
Allen Capital Partners LLC
BDC Capital (AKA: Massachusetts Business Development Corp.)
Commonfund Capital, Inc. (FKA: Common Fund)
Drum Capital Management
Landmark Partners, Inc.
Newbury Partners LLC
Performance Equity Management, LLC
Portfolio Advisors LLC
Square 1 Ventures

Fund of Funds—D. of Columbia

Accolade Capital Management
EMAlternatives LLC
O'Melveny & Myers LLP
Overseas Private Investment Corp. (AKA: OPIC)
PCGI LLC (AKA: PCG International)

Fund of Funds—Florida

Hamilton Lane Advisors, Inc.

Fund of Funds—Illinois
Adams Street Partners LLC
BAML Capital Access Funds
Frye-Louis Capital Advisors LLC
Granite Hall Partners (FKA: Sports Venture Partners, LLC)
Muller & Monroe Asset Management, LLC (AKA: M2)
RCP Advisors LLC
Symmetry Investment Advisors, Inc.
Twin Bridge Capital Partners
WP Global Partners Inc.
WestLB Mellon Asset Management (USA) LLC

Fund of Funds—Iowa
Great River Capital LLC

Fund of Funds—Maine
BDC Capital (AKA: Massachusetts Business Development Corp.)

Fund of Funds—Maryland
Greenspring Associates, Inc.

Fund of Funds—Massachusetts
BDC Capital (AKA: Massachusetts Business Development Corp.)
BlackRock Private Equity Partners
Brooke Private Equity Associates
Constitution Capital Partners, LLC
Fisher Lynch Capital
Grove Street Advisors LLC
HarbourVest Partners LLC
Kendall Investments
Landmark Partners, Inc.
Massachusetts Institute of Technology
Park Street Capital LLC
SL Capital Partners LLP
Solamere Capital
Square 1 Ventures

Fund of Funds—Michigan
Detroit Renaissance

Fund of Funds—Minnesota
Advantus Capital Management, Inc.
Mount Yale Asset Management

Fund of Funds—Missouri
RCP Advisors LLC

Fund of Funds—New Hampshire
Stafford Timberland, ltd.

Fund of Funds—New Jersey
BlackRock Private Equity Partners
Unigestion SA

Fund of Funds—New Mexico
Fort Washington Capital Partners Group
Sun Mountain Capital

Fund of Funds—New York
ATP Private Equity Partners
Adveq Management AG
Allianz Capital Partners GmbH
Arcano Capital
Auda Private Equity LLC
Bear Stearn Venture Partners LLC
Bessemer Trust Co. Funds of Funds Group
Bowside Capital, LLC
Bregal Investments
Capital E Group
Capital Z Investment Partners (FKA: Union Square Partners)
Capvent AG
Centinela Capital Partners LLC
Coller Capital
Frank Russell Capital
Hall Capital Partners LLC (FKA: Offit Hall Capital Mgmt)
Hamilton Lane Advisors, Inc.
Independence Holdings Partners (FKA: Newbrook Capital Mgmt)
Industry Funds Management
J.P. Morgan Asset Management
Knightsbridge Management, L.L.C.
LGT Capital Partners AG
Millennium Technology Ventures
Morgan Creek Capital Management LLC
Morgan Stanley Alternative Investment Partners
NB Alternatives - Fund of Funds
O'Melveny & Myers LLP
Pantheon Ventures, Ltd.
Parish Capital Advisors LLC
Paul Capital Partners
Private Equity Investors, Inc.
Square 1 Ventures
Swiss Re Private Equity Advisers
Union Bancaire Privee Private Equity
VCFA Group
Vanterra Capital, Ltd.
Vedanta Capital
W Capital Partners
WP Global Partners Inc.
WestLB Mellon Asset Management (USA) LLC

Fund of Funds—North Carolina
BlackRock Private Equity Partners
Morgan Creek Capital Management LLC
Parish Capital Advisors LLC
Square 1 Ventures
TrueBridge Capital Partners

Fund of Funds—Ohio
Fort Washington Capital Partners Group
Key Capital Corp.
Peppertree Capital Management, Inc.

Fund of Funds—Oklahoma
Spur Capital Partners LLC

Fund of Funds—Pennsylvania
Griffon Venture Partners
Hamilton Lane Advisors, Inc.
Mellon Bank, N.A.
MidCoast Capital, LLC

Fund of Funds—Texas
American Beacon Advisors, Inc. (FKA:AMR Investment Services)
Montauk TriGuard Management, Inc.
NB Alternatives - Fund of Funds
Peppertree Capital Management, Inc.
Square 1 Ventures

Fund of Funds—Utah
Fort Washington Capital Partners Group

Fund of Funds—Virginia
Private Advisors LLC
Signature Financial Managment, Inc.
Square 1 Ventures

Fund of Funds—Washington
Frank Russell Capital
Square 1 Ventures

Mezzanine Firms—Arizona
Merit Capital Partners (FKA:William Blair Mezzanine)

Mezzanine Firms—California
Avante Mezzanine Partners
Bacchus Capital Management LLC
Caltius Mezzanine
CapitalSource Holdings, Inc.
Central Valley Fund, L.P., The
Fifth Street Capital LLC
Greyrock Capital Group
Huntington Capital
Needham Asset Management
Newstone Capital Partners
Ocean Tomo, LLC
Pacific Mezzanine Fund, L.P. (PMF)
RW Capital Partners LLC
Sand Hill Capital
Seacoast Capital
Tennenbaum Capital Partners LLC
TriplePoint Capital

Mezzanine Firms—Colorado
NewWest Mezzanine Fund, L.P. (FKA:Touchstone Capital Group)

Mezzanine Firms—Connecticut
Brooks, Houghton & Company, Inc.
Greyrock Capital Group
Growth Capital Partners, L.P.
Ironwood Capital (AKA: Ironwood Capital Advisors LLC)
Ocean Tomo, LLC
Patriot Capital Funding, Inc. (AKA: Patriot Capital)

Mezzanine Firms—D. of Columbia
Capital Trust, Ltd.
Minority Broadcast Investment Corporation

Mezzanine Firms—Florida
Banyan Capital Advisors LLC
Florida Mezzanine Fund, The
Ocean Tomo, LLC

Mezzanine Firms—Georgia
Capstone Financial Partners LLC
Chatham Capital
Golub Capital
Salem Capital Partners, LP (FKA: Venture Capital Solutions)

Mezzanine Firms—Illinois
Banc One Mezzanine Corporation
Fidus Capital
Golub Capital
Greyrock Capital Group
Maranon Capital, L.P.
Marquette Capital Partners
Merit Capital Partners (FKA:William Blair Mezzanine)
Ocean Tomo, LLC
Orchard First Source
Prairie Capital

Mezzanine Firms—Indiana
Centerfield Capital Partners

Mezzanine Firms—Kansas
Kansas Venture Capital, Inc.
Mezzanine Firms—Maryland
CapitalSource Holdings, Inc.
Ocean Tomo, LLC
Parkway Capital Investors LLC

Mezzanine Firms—Massachusetts
Babson Capital Europe
Capital Resource Partners
Capstone Financial Partners LLC
Eastward Capital
Hancock Capital Management LLC
Ironwood Capital (AKA: Ironwood Capital Advisors LLC)
Needham Asset Management
Ocean Tomo, LLC
Prospect Street Ventures
Seacoast Capital

Mezzanine Firms—Michigan
Maranon Capital, L.P.
Peninsula Capital Partners LLC

Mezzanine Firms—Minnesota
GMB Mezzanine Capital, L.P.
Marquette Capital Partners
Norwest Mezzanine Partners
Yukon Partners Management LLC

Mezzanine Firms—New Jersey
York Street Capital Partners LLC

Mezzanine Firms—New York
Albion Investors, LLC (FKA: Albion Alliance, LLC)
BNP Paribas Principal, Inc.
Babson Capital Europe
Brooks, Houghton & Company, Inc.
CT Investment Management Co. (AKA: Capital Trust)
Capital Trust, Ltd.
Fidus Capital
Fifth Street Capital LLC
Golub Capital
Halyard Partners
Intermediate Capital Group Plc
Needham Asset Management
Pine Street Capital Partners LLC
Prospect Street Ventures
Schultze Asset Management LLC
SeaView Capital Advisors, LLC

Mezzanine Firms—North Carolina
Babson Capital Europe
Fidus Capital
Salem Capital Partners, LP (FKA: Venture Capital Solutions)
Triangle Capital Corporation

Mezzanine Firms—Ohio
Banc One Mezzanine Corporation
Laux Capital Partners
Northcreek Mezzanine

Mezzanine Firms—Pennsylvania
Merion Investment Partners, L.P.

Mezzanine Firms—Tennessee
Tenth Street Capital Partners, LLC

Mezzanine Firms—Texas
Banc One Mezzanine Corporation
Capital Point Partners
Growth Capital Partners, L.P.
Independent Bankers Capital Funds
Main Street Capital Corporation
Newstone Capital Partners

Mezzanine Firms—Virginia
BIA Digital Partners, L.P.

OPE—Arizona
Desert Cedars, LLC

OPE—California
Apollo Real Estate Advisors
Bancroft Capital, LLC
Canyon Capital
Cavalry Asset Management
GFI Energy Ventures
Lake Street Capital LLC
Mathematica Capital Management, LLC
Shorenstein Company LLC
Symmetry Capital Management LLC

OPE—Colorado
Capital Royalty Partners
Cirrus Investment Partners LLC
SB Energy Partners

OPE—Connecticut
Addison Clark Capital, LLC
Atlantic Asset Management, L.L.C.
Global Infrastructure Partners
Lime Rock Partners LLC
Starwood Capital Group

OPE—Illinois
Apollo Real Estate Advisors
OCV Investors, LLC

OPE—Kansas
Atlantic Asset Management, L.L.C.

OPE—Maryland
Calvert Funds
Maryland DBED (AKA:Dept. of Business & Economic Development)

OPE—Massachusetts
ArcLight Capital
Braemar Energy Ventures
Cabot Properties, Inc.
Hammerman Capital, LLC
Partners Capital Investment Group, LLC

OPE—Michigan
Park High Apartments
OPE—New Jersey
E+Co
Eagle Trading Systems, Inc.

OPE—New York
Apollo Real Estate Advisors
ArcLight Capital
Berens Capital Management LLC
Blue Ridge Capital
Braemar Energy Ventures
Brahman Management, LLC
Brickman, Bruce S & Associates, Inc.
CF Advisors, LLC
Capital Royalty Partners
Echo Street Capital Advisors
Global Infrastructure Partners
HFIC Partners, LLC
Healy Circle Capital, LLC
Hull Capital Management, LLC
Och-Ziff Capital Management Group
Scottwood Capital, LLC
Shorenstein Company LLC
Special Situations Funds
TCS Capital LLC
Yorktown Partners LLC
Zankel Capital Advisors, LLC

OPE—Pennsylvania
Henry Investment Trust, L.P.
Longboat Capital Management LLC
Mid Atlantic Financial Management, Inc.

OPE—Texas
ARGO Investors L.L.C.
Best, Patterson, Crothers & Yeoham, Ltd. (AKA: BPCY)
Capital Royalty Partners
Lime Rock Partners LLC

Venture Firms—Alabama
Adams and Reese LLP
Advantage Capital Partners
Aegis Capital Group LLC
Eastside Partners
Enhanced Capital Partners, LLC
Greer Capital Advisors LLC
Harbert Venture Partners
Jemison Investments
Murphree Venture Partners
New Capital Partners
Redmont Venture Partners

Venture Firms—Arizona
Air Products and Chemicals, Inc.
Biltmore Ventures, L.P.
Cornerstone Advisors, Inc.
Indigo Partners LLC
Initium Capital LLC
Intel Capital
Mayo Medical Ventures
Moshir Venture Partners
Nest Ventures
Research Corporation Technologies
Solstice Capital
Valley Ventures (FKA: Arizona Growth Partners, L.P.)

Venture Firms—Arkansas
Diamond State Ventures, L.P.
ECD Investments LLC/ECD Investments BIDCO
Old City Partners, LLC (OCP)

Venture Firms—California
@Ventures
ABS Capital Partners
ABS Ventures
ACA Ventures LLC
ARC China, Inc.
ARCH Venture Partners
ATA Ventures
ATEL Ventures, Inc.
Aavishkaar Venture Management Services Pvt, Ltd.
Aberdare Ventures
Abingworth Management, Ltd.
Acacia Venture Partners
Accel Partners
Accelerator Ventures
Accuitive Medical Ventures
Acorn Campus Ventures
Acuity Ventures
Adams Capital Management, Inc.
Adler & Co.
Advanced Technology Ventures
Affymetrix, Inc.
Agilent Ventures
Agility Capital LLC
Air Products and Chemicals, Inc.
Alacon Ventures LLC
Alafi Capital Co.
Alexandria Real Estate Equities, LLC
Allegis Capital (AKA: Media Technology Ventures)
Alloy Ventures
Almaz Capital Partners
Alsop Louie Partners
Alta Communications
Alta Partners
Altos Ventures

American River Ventures
Amgen, Inc.
Amicus Capital, LLC
AmidZad, LLC
Ampersand Ventures
Andreessen Horowitz
Angel Capital Network
Angel Investors, LP
Angeleno Group, LLC
Angels' Forum & the Halo Fund
Annex Venture Management, LLC
Anthem Venture Partners
Aphelion Capital, LLC
Applied Ventures, LLC
Aragon Ventures, Inc.
Arba Seed Investment Group
Arcturus Capital
Argon Venture Partners
ArrowPath Venture Capital (FKA: E*TRADE Group, Inc.)
Arsenal Venture Partners
Artiman Ventures
Asia Pacific Ventures
Asia Private Equity Capital (FKA: MediBIC Alliance)
AsiaTech Internet Group
AsiaTech Internet Group (ATIG) (FKA: AsiaTech Ventures)
AsiaTech Management LLC
Aspen Ventures
Asset Management Company Venture Capital
Astellas Venture Capital
Astrolabe Ventures
Athena Capital Partners LLC
Atherton Venture Partners, LLC
Atlas Capital Group, Inc., The
Atrium Capital
August Capital Management
Austral Capital
Avalon Ventures
Axiom Venture Partners, L.P.
Azure Capital Partners
BASF Venture Capital GmbH
BD Ventures (AKA: Becton, Dickinson & Co.)
BEA Systems
BSD Venture Capital LLC
BV Capital (FKA: Bertelsmann Ventures, LP)
Band of Angels
Baroda Ventures LLC
Baseline Ventures LLC
Bay City Capital LLC
Bay Partners
Bay Ventures, LLC
Benchmark Capital
Bessemer Venture Partners
Big Sky Partners
BioVeda Capital Private, Ltd.
Biofrontier Partners, Inc.
Blacksmith Capital
Blade Ventures
BlueCar Partners
BlueLine Partners LLC
BlueRun Ventures
Blumberg Capital Ventures
Brentwood Venture Capital
Bridgescale Partners
Burrill & Company
CDIB BioScience Venture Management
CDP Capital - Technology Ventures (FKA: CDP Sofinov)
CE Unterberg Towbin (FKA:Unterberg Harris Capital Partners)
CMEA Capital
CNET
CORAL Ventures Management, Inc.
CSV Capital Partners (FKA: China Seed Ventures)
CW Group, Inc.
California Technology Ventures LLC
Cambrian Ventures
CampVentures
Canaccord Genuity
Capricorn Investment Group LLC (AKA: Capricorn Management)
Cardinal Venture Capital
Catamount Ventures, L.P.
Ceyuan Ventures Management, LLC
Charles River Ventures
Charter Life Sciences
Charter Venture Capital (AKA: Charter Ventures)
Chengwei Ventures
Chess Ventures
Chevron Technology Ventures
ChinaVest, Ltd.
ChrysCapital Management Company
Cipio Partners
Cisco Systems, Inc.
Claremont Creek Ventures
Clarus Ventures
Clean Pacific Ventures
ClearLight Partners LLC
Clearstone Venture Partners
Club Auto Sport
Clydesdale Ventures LLC
Columbia Equity Partners
Column Group, The
Comerica Venture Capital Group
Compass Technology Partners
Concept Development Associates, Inc.
Concept Ventures Management LLC
Consor Capital LLC
Convergence Partners
Cooley Godward LLP
Copan, Inc
Copia Associates LLC
Coronis Medical Ventures
Costella Kirsch, Inc.
Craton Equity Partners
Crescendo Venture Management LLC
Crimson
Crocker Capital
CrossBridge Venture Partners
Crosscut Ventures
Crosslink Capital
Crosspoint Venture Partners
Crossroads Capital Partners, LLC
Crystal Capital
Cutlass Capital
Cycad Group LLC
Cypress Capital Corporation
D. E. Shaw Group, The
DBL Investors (AKA: Double Bottom Line Venture Capital)
DCM
DFJ Athena
DFJ Frontier
DFJ InCube Ventures
DN Capital, Ltd. (FKA: Digital Networks Global Ventures)
DT Capital Partners
Daiwa Corporate Investment Co., Ltd.
De Novo Ventures
Defta Partners
Delphi Ventures
Diamond TechVentures
Diamondhead Ventures, L.P.
Disney (AKA The Walt Disney Company)
DoCoMo Capital
Domain Associates LLC
Dominion Ventures, Inc.
Dorset Capital
Dot Edu Ventures
DragonVenture, Inc.
Draper Fisher Jurvetson
Draper Fisher Jurvetson ePlanet Ventures, L.P.
Draper Richards, L.P.
Duke Equity Partners
DynaFund Ventures LLC
EDB Investments Pte, Ltd.
East Gate Private Equity Partners LLC
Ecosystem Ventures LLC
El Dorado Ventures
Element Partners
Emergence Capital Partners LLC
Emergence Venture Partners LLC
Emergent Medical Ventures, LLP
Endeavour Ventures, Ltd.
Enterprise Partners Venture Capital
Entrepia Ventures, Inc.
Eos Asia Investments, Ltd. (FKA: JCAR Funds, Ltd.)
Equal Elements
Equip Ventures LLC
Escalate Capital
Essex Woodlands Health Ventures
EuroUs Ventures
Expansion Capital Partners LLC
eVenture Capital Partners GmbH
5AM Ventures
FTV Capital (FKA: FTVentures)
Felicis Ventures
Finaventures
Finistere Partners LLC
Finistere Ventures LLC
Firelake Capital Management
First Round Capital
Firsthand Capital Management
Fjord Ventures, LLC
Floodgate Fund, L.P.
Flywheel Ventures
Focus Ventures
Formative Ventures
Fortune Venture Investment Group (AKA:Fortune Consulting)
Forward Ventures
Foundation Capital
Founders Capital Partners
Founders Fund, The
Four Rivers Partners
Frazier Healthcare and Technology Ventures
Fremont Group

Fremont Ventures
Frontera Group LLC
Funk Ventures, Inc.
Fuse Capital
GC&H Partners
GGV Capital
GIC Special Investments Pte, Ltd.
GKM Ventures
GRP Partners
GSIM Corporation (AKA: Global Strategic Investment Mgmt.)
GSR Ventures
Gabriel Venture Partners
Garage Technology Ventures LLC (FKA: Garage.com)
Garon Financial Group, The
Gemini Israel Funds, Ltd.
Genentech Corporation
Gerken Capital Associates
Gideon Hixon Fund
Gilo Ventures
Global Asia Partners
Global Asset Capital LLC
Global Catalyst Partners
Globespan Capital Partners
Glynn Capital Management
Gold Hill Capital Management LLC
Good Capital
Granite Hill Capital Partners
Granite Ventures LLC
Great Pacific Capital, LLC
Greenhill SAVP
Greenhouse Capital Partners
Greycroft Partners
Greylock Partners
Guggenheim Venture Partners LLC
Guidant Corporation
H & S Capital (AKA: Heidrick & Struggles Capital)
HLM Venture Partners
Hamilton BioVentures
Harbert Venture Partners
Harbinger Venture Management
Harbor Pacific Capital LLC
Harris & Harris Group, Inc.
Harrison Metal Capital
Helix Ventures
HighBAR Ventures
Highland Capital Partners LLC
Hina Capital Partners
Honda Strategic Venturing (HSV)
Horizon Technology Finance Management LLC
Horizon Ventures
Hotung International Company, Ltd.
Hummer Winblad Venture Partners
Huntington Ventures
IDG Technology Venture Investment, Inc.
IDG Ventures SF
IGNITE Group, The (AKA: Ignite Associates, LLC)
INC3 Ventures, LLC
ITU Ventures
ITX International Holdings, Inc.
Idanta Partners, Ltd.
Illuminate Ventures
Incubic Venture Capital
Industry Ventures
Infinity Capital LLC
Inflection Partners, LLC
Infocomm Investments Pte., Ltd. (FKA: NCB Holdings Pte Ltd)
Infotech Pacific Ventures L.P. (FKA: Infotech Ventures Co.)
InnoCal Venture Capital
Innovacom SA
Institutional Venture Partners
Intel Capital
InterActive Partners
InterWest Partners
InveStar Capital, Inc.
Invencor, Inc.
Inventus Capital Partners
Investor Growth Capital AB
Iron Capital Partners
Itochu Technology, Inc.
iD Innovation, Inc.
iD Ventures America, LLC (AKA: Acer Technology Ventures)
iGlobe Partners, Ltd.
idealab!
J.F. Shea & Company
JAFCO Co., Ltd. (FKA: Japan Associated Finance Co. Ltd.)
JAFCO Ventures
JMI Equity
Jacobs Capital Group, LLC
Japan Asia Investment Company, Ltd. (AKA: JAIC)
Javelin Venture Partners
Johnson & Johnson Development Corporation
JumpStartUp Fund Advisors Pvt. Ltd.
Juniper Networks
K9 Ventures
KLM Capital Management, Inc.
KPG Ventures
KT Venture Group LLC
KTB Securities Co., Ltd. (FKA: KTB Network Co., Ltd.)
KTB Ventures
Kaiser Permanente Ventures
Kearny Venture Partners
Keiretsu Forum
Kennet Venture Partners, Ltd. (FKA: Kennet Capital, Ltd.)
Kern Whelan Capital, LLC
Keynote Ventures (FKA: Dali, Hook Partners)
Khosla Ventures
Kleiner Perkins Caufield & Byers
Kline Hawkes & Co.
Kohlberg Ventures LLC
Kolon Investment, Inc.
Korea Technology Investment Corporation (AKA: KTIC)
Labrador Ventures
Latterell Venture Partners
Lauder Partners
Lawrence Financial Group
Leapfrog Ventures
Leasing Technologies International, Inc.
Levensohn Venture Partners LLC (FKA: Levensohn Capital Mgmt)
Lighthouse Capital Partners
Lightspeed Venture Partners (FKA: Weiss, Peck & Greer)
Lincoln Funds
Longitude Capital Management Company LLC
Loudwater Investment Partners, Ltd.
Lucas Venture Group LLC
Lumira Capital Corporation.
M/C Venture Partners
MHS Capital Management, LLC
MMV Financial, Inc.
MPM Capital (FKA: MPM Asset Management LLC)
Mach Ventures, LP.
Madrone Capital Partners
Manoa Venture Partners
Marsman-Drysdale Corporation
Maton Venture
Matrix Partners
Maven Venture Partners
Maveron LLC
Mayfield Fund
MedFocus Fund LLC
MedVenture Associates
Media Venture Partners
Menlo Ventures
Mentor Capital Group
Meritech Capital Partners
Merus Capital Investment
Mesa Verde Venture Partners
Mingly Capital
Mirador Capital
Miramar Venture Partners
Mission Bay Capital LLC
Mission Ventures
Mitsui & Co. Venture Partners (MCVP)
Mitsui Comtek
Mitsui INCUBASE Corp.
Mohr Davidow Ventures
Momentum Venture Management LLC
Monitor Venture Management, L.L.C.
Monterey Venture Partners, LLC
Montgomery & Co. (FKA: Digital Coast Partners)
Montreux Equity Partners
Morgan Stanley Venture Partners (AKA: MSDW)
Motorola Ventures
Mustang Ventures
mc3 ventures (FKA: McKenna Venture Accelerator (MVA))
NEA-IndoUS Capital Advisors Pvt. Ltd.
NEC Corporation of America (FKA: NEC USA, Inc.)
NGEN Partners LLC (FKA: NextGen Partners LLC)
National Healthcare Services
Navigation Capital Partners (AKA: NCP)
Navitas Capital
NeoCarta Ventures, Inc.
NetService Ventures
New Cycle Capital LLC
New Enterprise Associates, Inc.
New Leaf Venture Partners LLC
New Millennium Partners, L.P.
New Venture Partners LLC
NewPath Ventures, LLC
NewSchools Venture Fund
Newbridge Capital, Ltd.
Newcap Partners, Inc.
Newton Technology Partners (NTP)
Nexit Ventures Oy
Nexos Capital Partners
Nexus Group LLC
Nexus Venture Partners

Nokia Growth Partners
North Bridge Venture Partners
Northern Light Venture Capital
Noventi
Novus Ventures
Nth Power
Nueva Ventures
Numenor Ventures LLC
180 Capital Fund, LLC
O'Reilly Alpha Tech Ventures, LLC
ONSET Ventures
Oak Hill Venture Partners (OHVP)
Oak Investment Partners
Oakstone Venture Partners
Octane Capital Management
Odeon Capital Partners, L.P.
Okapi Venture Capital LLC
Olympus Capital Partners
Omidyar Network
Omron Silicon Valley (FKA: Omron Advanced Systems, Inc.)
One Earth Capital LLC
Opus Capital
Orchid Asia Group Management, Ltd.
Osprey Ventures, L.P.
Otter Capital, LLC
Outlook Ventures (FKA: iMinds, Interactive Minds)
Oxford Bioscience Partners
POSCO BioVentures
PS Seed II, LLC
Pac-Link Management Corporation
PacRim Venture Management
Pacific Asset Partners
Pacific Community Ventures (FKA: SVCV)
Pacific Enterprise Capital, LLC
Pacific Growth Equities LLC
Pacific Lake Partners
Pacific Partners
Pacific Venture Group
Pacifica Fund
Palisades Ventures (FKA: Centre Palisades Ventures)
Palo Alto Investors
Palo Alto Venture Partners
Palomar Ventures
Panasonic Ventures
Panorama Capital
Parakletos@Ventures
Parker Price Venture Capital Inc.(FKA: Allegro Capital, Inc)
Partech International
Pasadena Angels
Pelion Venture Partners
Peninsula Ventures
Peregrine Ventures, LP
Pharmavent Partners
Philips Venture Capital Fund B.V. (AKA: Corporate Venturing)
Physic Ventures
Pinnacle Ventures
Pinpoint Ventures
Pitango Venture Capital (FKA:Polaris Venture Capital Israel)
Pond Venture Partners
Presidio Investors LLC
Presidio STX (FKA: Presidio Venture Partners, LLC)
ProQuest Investments
Probitas Partners, Inc.
Prospect Venture Partners (FKA: Prospect Management LLC)
Provenance Ventures
Providential Capital
Psilos Group Managers LLC
Quan Ventures
Quantum Technology Partners
Quest Ventures
Quicksilver Ventures (FKA: QTV Capital)
RB Webber & Company
RVC Europe Limited (FKA: The Greenhouse Fund)
RWI Ventures
Radar Partners
Rady School of Management
Red Rock Ventures
Redleaf Group, Inc
Redpoint Ventures
Redwood Capital, Inc.
Redwood Venture Partners
Regal Investment
Rembrandt Venture Partners
Retro Venture Management LLC
Revolution Ventures, LLC
Rho Capital Partners, Inc.
Ridgelift Ventures
Ridgewood Capital Management, LLC
Rincon Venture Partners
Rising Tide Fund
Rivenrock Capital LLC
Rocket Ventures
Rockport Capital Partners
Rusheen Capital Partners, LLC
Rustic Canyon Partners
Rutberg & Company, LLC
755 Capital Partners, LLC
SAIL Venture Partners
SAM Group
SAP Ventures
SB Life Science Equity Management LLC
SBV Venture Partners
SDL Ventures, LLC
SIG Asia Investments, LLLP
SJF Ventures
SV Life Sciences Advisers
Saban Ventures
Samsung Venture Investment Corporation (SVIC)
San Francisco Equity Partners
Sand Hill Group, LLC
Sandalwood Capital Partners
Sanderling Ventures
Sands Brothers & Co., Ltd.
Saratoga Ventures, L.P.
Scale Venture Partners
Sea Change Management LLC
Seabury Venture Partners
Sears Capital Management, Inc.
Selby Venture Partners
Sequoia Capital
Sequoia Capital India (FKA: WestBridge Capital Partners)
Seraph Group
Sevin Rosen Funds
Shasta Ventures Management LLC
Shattuck Hammond Partners
Shelter Capital Partners LLC
Shepherd Ventures
Sherpalo Ventures
Shoreline Venture Management, LLC
Siemens Venture Capital GmbH
Sienna Ventures (FKA: Sienna Holdings Inc.)
Sierra Ventures
SightLine Partners
Sigma Partners
Silicom Ventures
Silicon Valley Innovation Capital (SVIC)
Sippl Macdonald Ventures
Sirius Venture Consulting Pte, Ltd.
Skylake Incuvest & Company
Skyline Ventures
Skymoon Ventures
Smart Technology Ventures
SmartForest Ventures
Sofinnova Ventures
SoftTech VC
Solar Venture Partners
Sony Corporation
Southeast Interactive Technology Funds
Southern Cross Venture Partners
Spencer Trask Ventures, Inc. (FKA: Spencer Trask Securities)
Split Rock Partners LLC
Spring Ridge Ventures
Sprout Group
St. Paul Venture Capital, Inc.
Startup Capital Ventures L.P.
Steamboat Ventures
Stone Canyon Venture Partners (SCVP)
Storm Ventures LLC
Summit Accelerator Fund
Sun Microsystems, Inc.
SunAmerica Ventures
SunBridge Partners
Sunstone Capital A/S
Sutter Hill Ventures
Sycamore Ventures Pte, Ltd.
Synergy Life Science Partners
Synergy Partners
280 Capital Partners
3V SourceOne Capital Pte, Ltd.
3i (US)
T-Venture Holding GmbH
T. Rowe Price Threshold Partnerships
TBL Capital, L.P.
TCW Capital Ventures LLC (AKA: TCW Holdings LLC)
TEL Venture Capital, Inc.
TL Ventures
TPG Growth
Takeda Research Investment, Inc.
Tallwood Venture Capital
Tam Capital Management
Tano Capital LLC
Taraval Associates LLC
Tavistock Life Sciences (AKA: TLS)
Tech Coast Angels, Inc.
TechFarm Ventures (AKA:TechFund Capital)
TechFund Capital
Techfund Capital Europe Management SAS
Technology Crossover Ventures
Technology Funding

Technology Partners
Technology Venture Partners Pty Ltd.
TeleSoft Partners
Telegraph Hill Partners (AKA: THP)
Templeton Asset Management, Ltd.
Tenex Greenhouse Ventures
Thales Corporate Ventures (FKA:Thomson-CSF Ventures)
Third Security LLC
Thomas Weisel Venture Partners
Thomas, McNerney & Partners LLC
Thompson Clive & Partners, Ltd.
Thorner Ventures
Three Arch Partners
Tilenius Investments (FKA: Tilenius Ventures)
Timeline Ventures LLC
TomorrowVentures LLC
Tong Yang Venture Capital Corporation
TransLink Capital
Trellis Health Ventures, L.P.
Trident Capital
Trinity Ventures
True Ventures
Tugboat Ventures
U.S. Venture Partners
US Trust Private Equity
Undisclosed Firm
Unilever Ventures, Ltd. (AKA: Unilever NV)
VPSA (FKA: Viventures Partners)
VSP Capital (FKA: Venture Strategy Partners)
Vanguard Ventures
VantagePoint Venture Partners
Vector Capital
Velocity Venture Capital LLC
VenGlobal Capital
Venrock Associates
VentureTech Alliance LLC
Versant Ventures
Vertex Management Israel (AKA: Vertex Venture Capital)
Vertex Management Pte, Ltd. (AKA: Vertex Venture Holdings)
Vertical Group, The
Virgin Green Fund
Visa Inc. (FKA: Visa International)
Vision Capital Management
Vivo Ventures
Voyager Capital
W.R. Hambrecht & Co., LLC
WI Harper Group
Walden Venture Capital
Warburg Pincus LLC
Wavepoint Ventures
Weber Capital Management LLC
Wellington Partners Venture Capital GmbH
WestBridge Ventures LLC
Western Technology Investment
Westly Group, The
Wildcat Angel Fund, LLC
Windamere Venture Partners, LLC
Windward Ventures
Woodside Fund
Worldview Technology Partners
Y Combinator
Yahoo
Yasuda Enterprise Development Co., Ltd.(FKA: Nippon Ent.Dev)
ZAP Ventures
Zenshin Capital Management
Zone Ventures

Venture Firms—Colorado

Access Venture Partners
Advantage Capital Partners
Altamont Capital Partners
Altira Group LLC
Altitude Life Science Management, LLC
Appian Ventures
Aweida Capital Management LLP
BV-Cornerstone Ventures, L.P.
Boulder Ventures, Ltd.
Bullet Time Ventures
CHB Capital Partners
CSU Management Corporation
Calim Private Equity, LLC
Cascade Investment Group
Cascadia Capital LLC
Centennial Ventures
Colorado Venture Management (AKA: CVM Equity Funds)
Econergy International Corporation
Enhanced Capital Partners, LLC
eonBusiness Corporation
5280 Partners
Fisher Capital Partners
Foundry Group
GC&H Partners
Green Spark Ventures LLC
Greenmont Capital Partners
High Country Venture LLC
ITU Ventures
Infield Capital
iSherpa Capital
Keating Investments LLC
Lacuna, LLC
Media Venture Partners
Meritage Funds
Mobius Venture Capital, Inc.
Murphree Venture Partners
Novell Technology Capital
Oakstone Venture Partners
Pacific Rim Ventures Company, Ltd.
Partisan Management Group
Pearl Street Group, Ltd.
Primera Capital
Roser Ventures LLC
Sands Brothers & Co., Ltd.
Sequel Venture Partners
Skyland Capital LLC
SoftBank Ventures Korea, Inc.
T. Rowe Price Threshold Partnerships
TechStars
TomorrowVentures LLC
Vista Ventures
Woodbourne Canada Partnes Advisors LLC

Venture Firms—Connecticut

ASML Ventures
Adler & Co.
Alerion Partners
Asia West, LLC
Axiom Venture Partners, L.P.
BEV Capital (FKA: Brand Equity Ventures)
Balyasny Asset Management LP (AKA: BAM)
Blue Chip Venture Company
CHL Medical Partners
Capital Resource Co. of Connecticut
Commonfund Realty
Connecticut Innovations, Inc.
Consor Capital LLC
Digital Power Capital, LLC
Dolphin Capital Group, LLC
EGS Healthcare Capital Partners, LLC
Elm Street Ventures
Emerge Venture Capital (AKA: Emerge VC)
Endeavor Capital Management
Evaluation Associates
Foundation Medical Partners
GBP Capital (AKA: Greenwich Biotech Partners)
Galen Associates
Gartner Group, Inc.
Great Point Partners LLC
Greenwoods Capital Partners
Grosvenor Funds, The
Hartford Ventures
Horizon Technology Finance Management LLC
IT Matrix Ventures
L&L Capital Partners, LLC
Leasing Technologies International, Inc.
McGovern Capital LLC
Mirador Capital
NFR Energy LLC
NGN Capital LLC
Najeti Ventures
Next Generation Ventures, LLC
Next Wave Funds
Oak Investment Partners
Oxford Bioscience Partners
RFE Investment Partners
Rockridge Capital Partners, Inc.
Rogers Casey
Scheer & Company
Signal Lake
Skandia Innovation AB
Strategic Advisory Group, Inc.
TWJ Capital LLC
Tennant Capital Partners LLC
Thomas, McNerney & Partners LLC
Trident Capital
Tullis Health Investors (FKA: Tullis-Dickerson & Co., Inc.)
US Trust Private Equity
Unified Growth Partners, L.P.
Vistech Corp.
W.R. Hambrecht & Co., LLC
Zero Stage Capital Co., Inc.

Venture Firms—D. of Columbia

Adams and Reese LLP
Advanced Finance & Investment Group LLC (AKA: AFIG)
Advantage Capital Partners
Bancroft Group
Claritas Capital LLC
Climate Change Capital, Ltd.
Core Capital Partners
Darby Technology Ventures Group (AKA: DTV)
Digital Power Capital, LLC
Dunrath Capital, Inc.
Econergy International Corporation

Energy Ventures Group LLC
Grosvenor Funds, The
LaunchBox Digital
Lazard Technology Partners
MASA Life Science Ventures, L.P. (AKA: MLSV)
MedVest
Mid-Atlantic Venture Funds (FKA: NEPA Management Corp.)
National Corn Growers Association
New Enterprise East Investments (AKA: NEEI)
New Horizons Venture Capital
NewSchools Venture Fund
NewSpring Capital
Newbridge Capital, Ltd.
NextCom Ventures
NextPoint Partners, L.P.
Paladin Capital Management LLC
Paperboy Ventures, LLC
Paras Ventures LLC
Persimmon Tree Capital, L.P.
Portview Communications Ltd
Prudent Capital
Small Enterprise Assistance Fund (SEAF)
Smith Defieux Capital Partners
Telecommunications Development Fund (TDF)
Torch Hill Partners

Venture Firms—Delaware

Blue Rock Capital
Delaware Innovation Fund (AKA: DIF)
DuPont Ventures
Inflection Point Ventures

Venture Firms—Florida

Accuitive Medical Ventures
Adams and Reese LLP
Adler & Co.
Advantage Capital Partners
Alliance Technology Ventures
Antares Capital Corporation
Arsenal Venture Partners
Athenian Venture Partners
Avery Business Development Services
Ballast Point Venture Partners
Crossbow Ventures
Easton Hunt Capital Partners, L.P.
Fundamental Management Corporation
Gerrity Capital Partners, LLC (FKA: MultiChannel Ventures)
Grace Venture Partners
Grotech Ventures
Guggenheim Venture Partners LLC
LJH Global Investments
Lane Five Ventures LLC (FKA: Swan Holdings LLC)
Lovett Miller & Co. Incorporated
Lucor Holdings
Mayo Medical Ventures
Morgenthau Venture Partners, LLC
New World Angels, Inc.
North Bay Equity Partners
Old City Partners, LLC (OCP)
OnPoint Technologies
Orlando Venture Capital Inc.
Prax Capital
Quantum Capital Partners
SI Ventures
Sands Brothers & Co., Ltd.
Sigma Capital Corp.
Signature Capital LLC
Sunrock Ventures, Inc.
T. Rowe Price Threshold Partnerships
TECHinspirations, Inc.
Undisclosed Firm

Venture Firms—Georgia

Accuitive Medical Ventures
Acquisition Search Corp., The
Advanced Technology Development Center
Atlanta Technology Angels (AKA: ATA)
BlueCar Partners
Buckhead Investment Partners LLC
CDC Corporation (FKA: Chinadotcom Ventures)
CHB Capital Partners
GRA Venture Fund LLC
Georgia Venture Partners LLC
Gray Ghost Ventures
Harbert Venture Partners
HealthCare Capital Partners
Imlay Investments
Jerusalem Global Ventures
Kinetic Ventures LLC
Monolith Capital Partners
Navigation Capital Partners (AKA: NCP)
NextStart Capital
Roswell Capital Partners, LLC
Seraph Group
Seraphim Partners
Stoney River Capital Partners LLC
SunTrust Equity Partners
TechOperators LLC
Total Technology Ventures LLC
Turner Broadcasting
UPS Strategic Enterprise Fund
Value Plus Ventures
Venturelab

Venture Firms—Hawaii

DragonBridge Capital
Kolohala Ventures
Lava Management, LLC
Manoa Venture Partners
PacifiCap Group LLC

Venture Firms—Idaho

EPIC Ventures
Highway 12 Ventures
Montlake Capital

Venture Firms—Illinois

ARCH Development Partners LLC
ARCH Venture Partners
Adena Ventures
Advanced Equities Capital Partners LLC
Advantage Capital Partners
Alpha Capital Partners, Ltd.
Apex Venture Partners
Ardesta
BMO Capital Corporation
Baird Venture Partners
Balyasny Asset Management LP (AKA: BAM)
Batterson Venture Partners (AKA: BVP)
BlueStar Ventures L.P.
Bulgarian-American Enterprise Fund, The
CID Capital
Calyon (FKA: Credit Agricole Indosuez)
Catalyst Capital Managment
Ceres Venture Fund
Channel Medical Partners
Crystal Capital
Duchossois Technology Partners LLC (DTEC)
Dunrath Capital, Inc.
Edgewater Funds, The
First Analysis Corporation
Granite Creek Partners
Greenhill SAVP
Gryffindor Capital Partners LLC
Guggenheim Venture Partners LLC
H & S Capital (AKA: Heidrick & Struggles Capital)
Heartland Capital Network
Hopewell Ventures
Illinois Development Finance Authority
Illinois Innovation Accelerator Fund (i2A)
Illinois Partners, LLC
Illinois Ventures LLC
InDecatur Ventures LLC
JK&B Capital
KB Partners LLC
Kettle Partners
Leo Capital Holdings LLC
MK Capital
Marquette Venture Partners
Mitsubishi Corporation
Mosaix Ventures
Motorola Ventures
New World Ventures
Next Frontier Capital
OCA Venture Partners
Open Prairie Ventures
Orgone Capital
Origin Ventures, LLC
Platinum Venture Partners
Portage Venture Partners (AKA: Graystone Venture Partners)
Prism Capital
Quest Technology Ventures
Seneca Partners, Inc.
Shattuck Hammond Partners
Sigvion Capital
Stockwell Capital LLC
Synetro Group LLC
2x Consumer Products Growth Partners LP
Technology Crossover Ventures
Trident Capital
Undisclosed Firm
W.R. Hambrecht & Co., LLC

Venture Firms—Indiana

ARCH Development Partners LLC
Barnard Associates, Inc.
BioCrossroads, Inc.
Blue Chip Venture Company
Clarian Health Ventures, Inc.
Command Equity Group
Concept Development Associates, Inc.
Eos Asia Investments, Ltd. (FKA: JCAR Funds, Ltd.)
Gazelle TechVentures
Guidant Corporation
Heron Capital LLC
IN Partners LLC (AKA: Midpoint)
Lilly Ventures (FKA: e.Lilly Ventures)
Rolls Royce Corporate Venture
Spring Mill Venture Partners

Triathlon Medical Ventures LLC
Twilight Venture Partners

Venture Firms—Iowa

Aavin Equity Advisors LLC
Corridor Management Company LLC
InvestAmerica Venture Group, Inc.
Prairie Oak Capital LLC
Rock River Capital

Venture Firms—Kansas

Five Elms Capital
Kansas Technology Enterprise Corporation
Koch Genesis LLC
Midwest Venture Alliance
Open Prairie Ventures
Trendlines Group, The

Venture Firms—Kentucky

Chrysalis Ventures
Heron Capital LLC
Kentucky Seed Capital Fund
Meritus Ventures, L.P.
Mountain Ventures Inc.
Southern Appalachian Management Company LLC
Triathlon Medical Ventures LLC

Venture Firms—Louisiana

Adams and Reese LLP
Advantage Capital Partners
Air Products and Chemicals, Inc.
ECD Investments LLC/ECD Investments BIDCO
Enhanced Capital Partners, LLC
VCE Capital

Venture Firms—Maine

CEI Community Ventures, Inc. (AKA: CCVI)
CEI Ventures, Inc. (AKA: CVI)
Mousam Ventures LLC
North Atlantic Capital Corporation
Supply Chain Ventures LLC

Venture Firms—Maryland

ABS Capital Partners
Adler & Co.
Anthem Capital Management
Ashby Point Capital
Athlone Global Security, Inc.
Blue Rock Capital
BlueCar Partners
Boulder Ventures, Ltd.
CNF Investments, LLC
CS Capital Partners LLC
Camden Partners, Inc. (FKA: Cahill, Warnock & Co. LLC)
Chesapeake Emerging Opportunities Club LLC
Chord Capital, Ltd. (FKA: Generics Group, The)
Columbia Partners LLC
Corstone Corporation
Emerging Technology Partners, LLC
Grande Ventures
Grotech Ventures
IVS A/S (AKA: Internet Ventures Scandinavia A/S)
India Venture Partners
Inflection Point Ventures
JMI Equity
Kinetic Ventures LLC
Legend Ventures LLC
Legg Mason Capital Management
Maryland Technology Development Corporation
MedImmune Ventures
Meridian Management Group, Inc. (AKA: MMG)
MicroVest Capital Management LLC
Monuments Funds Group
NAC Ventures, LLC
New Enterprise Associates, Inc.
New Markets Venture Partners (AKA: New Markets Growth Fund)
New Venture Partners
Nobska Ventures
Novak Biddle Venture Partners, L.P.
QuestMark Partners, L.P.
Red Abbey Venture Partners, LLC
RedShift Ventures
Sinclair Ventures, Inc.
Syncom Management Co. Inc.
T. Rowe Price Threshold Partnerships
TWJ Capital LLC
Toucan Capital
Walker Ventures SBIC (AKA: Walker Ventures)

Venture Firms—Massachusetts

.406 Ventures (AKA: Point 406 Ventures)
@Ventures
ABS Capital Partners
ABS Ventures
AH Ventures (AKA: Adams Harkness & Hill Technology Ventures)
Abingworth Management, Ltd.
Accrue Sports and Entertainment Partners LLC
Adams Capital Management, Inc.
Advanced Technology Ventures
Alta Communications
Ampersand Ventures
Arcadia Management, LLC (AKA: Arcadia Partners)
Ascent Venture Partners
Atlas Venture, Ltd.
BT Venture Fund Management, LLC
Bain Capital Ventures
Barry Financial LLC
Beacon Bioventures
Bellevue Asset Management AG
Berkshires Capital Investors
Bessemer Venture Partners
BioVentures Investors
Biotechonomy Ventures, LLC
Black Coral Capital
Boston Capital Ventures
Boston Medical Investors
Boston Millennia Partners
Boston University Technology Development Fund
Breakaway Ventures
Brook Venture Partners LLC
Brookline Venture Partners
C.W. Downer & Company (FKA: Downer & Company)
CambridgeLight Partners
Canaccord Genuity
Castile Ventures
Catalyst Health and Technology Partners LLC
Century Capital Management, Inc.
Charles River Ventures
Chestnut Partners
Chord Capital, Ltd. (FKA: Generics Group, The)
Clarus Ventures
Clean Energy Venture Group
Collaborative Seed & Growth Partners LLC
Columbia Capital LLC
CommonAngels
Commons Capital, L.P.
Commonwealth Capital Ventures
Crystal Capital
Cue Ball Group, LLC, The
Cutlass Capital
CypressTree Investment Management Company, Inc.
Dace Ventures
Dominion Ventures, Inc.
Dragonvest Partners
Draper Fisher Jurvetson New England (AKA: DFJ/NE)
Dutchess Advisors LLC
EDB Investments Pte, Ltd.
East Hill Management
Echelon Ventures LLC
Edison Venture Fund
Egan-Managed Capital
Enterasys Networks (FKA: Cabletron Systems, Inc.)
EuroUs Ventures
Excel Venture Management
Expansion Capital Partners LLC
5AM Ventures
FA Technology Ventures
Fairhaven Capital Partners
Fidelity Investments
Fidelity Ventures
Flagship Ventures
Fletcher Spaght Associates
Flybridge Capital Partners
Founder Collective
GIV Venture Partners (AKA: Global Internet Ventures)
GSIM Corporation (AKA: Global Strategic Investment Mgmt.)
Garvin Hill Capital Partners LLC
Gemini Investors
Gen 3 Partners
General Catalyst Partners (FKA: General Catalyst Group LLC)
Globespan Capital Partners
Gold Hill Capital Management LLC
GrandBanks Capital
Greylock Partners
Guggenheim Venture Partners LLC
HLM Venture Partners
Hambrecht & Quist Capital Management (H&Q) LLC
Hartford Ventures
Harvard Management Company, Inc.
HealthCare Ventures LLC
Highland Capital Partners LLC
IDG Technology Venture Investment, Inc.
Inflection Point Ventures
Intel Capital
Ironside Capital Group (FKA:Ironside Ventures LLC)
incTANK Inc.
Jarvinian LLC
Kepha Partners
Kestrel Management LLC
Key Venture Partners
Kodiak Venture Partners
Kraft Group, The
LaunchCapital LLC

Leasing Technologies International, Inc.
Life Sciences Partners BV
Lighthouse Capital Partners
Link Ventures LLLP
Long River Capital Partners, LLC
Longworth Venture Partners, L.P.
Lumira Capital Corporation.
M/C Venture Partners
MP Healthcare Venture Management, Inc.
MPM Capital (FKA: MPM Asset Management LLC)
MTDC (Massachusetts Technology Development Corp.)
MTI Partners, Ltd.
MVM Life Science Partners LLP (AKA: MVM, Ltd.)
Makaira Venture Partners
Massachusetts Green Energy Fund
Massachusetts Mutual Life
Masthead Venture Partners
Matrix Partners
MedEquity Investors LLC
Media Venture Partners
Mediphase Venture Partners
Megunticook Management
Mi3 Venture Partners
Mithra Group, LLC
Nauta Capital
Navigator Technology Ventures (A.K.A. NTV)
NeoCarta Ventures, Inc.
NeoMed Management AS
New Atlantic Ventures
New England Partners
NextPoint Partners, L.P.
Nexus Medical Partners
North Bridge Venture Partners
North Hill Ventures
Norwich Ventures
Novartis Venture Fund (FKA: Novartis Corp.)
Novell Technology Capital
OpenView Venture Partners
Origin Partners
Oxford Bioscience Partners
POD Holdings
Pacific Growth Equities LLC
Pacific Rim Ventures Company, Ltd.
Peak Capital Group LLC
Pegasus Venture Capital
Pilot House Ventures Group, LLC
Pod Venture Partners Inc.
Polaris Venture Partners
Presidio STX (FKA: Presidio Venture Partners, LLC)
Prism VentureWorks
PureTech Ventures
Quest Capital, Inc.
RA Capital Management, LLC
RSS Investors
Rexiter Capital Management Ltd.
Rock Maple Ventures, L.P.
Rockport Capital Partners
Rockport Venture Partners
Romulus Capital
Royalty Capital Management LLC
SEED Venture Finance LLC
SV Life Sciences Advisers
Sage Hill Partners
Salix Ventures
Saturn Management LLC
Schroder Ventures Life Sciences
Seaflower Ventures
Seed Capital Partners
Sherbrooke Capital
Shiprock Capital LLC
Siemens Venture Capital GmbH
Sigma Partners
Signal Lake
Skyline Ventures
SoftBank Capital
Solstice Capital
Spark Capital
Sparkventures, LLC
Spray Venture Partners
Stage 1 Ventures, LLC
Still River Fund, The
Summerhill Venture Partners
Summit Accelerator Fund
Sustainable Resource Ventures
Symmetric Capital LLC
3i (US)
TVM Capital GmbH
TechStars
Telesystem-Argo Global Capital
Third Rock Ventures LLC
TianDi Growth Capital
Tudor Ventures
VIMAC Ventures LLC (FKA: VIMAC LLC)
Vantage Partners LLC
Velocity Equity Partners LLC
Venrock Associates
Venture Capital Fund of New England, The
Vesbridge Partners, LLC
Village Ventures
Vineyard Ventures
Volition Capital
W.R. Hambrecht & Co., LLC
Wave Equity Partners
Westfield Capital Management
WindSail Ventures LLC
Windspeed Ventures
Worcester Capital Partners, LLC
Y Combinator
Yankee Equity Solution (AKA: YES)
Zero Stage Capital Co., Inc.

Venture Firms—Michigan

ARCH Development Partners LLC
Alpha Capital Partners, Ltd.
Ann Arbor SPARK
Apjohn Ventures, LLC
Arbor Partners LLC
Arboretum Ventures
Ardesta
Beringea LLC
BioStar Ventures
Camelot Ventures
Chrysalis Ventures
EDF Ventures
Equity 11, Ltd.
Fontinalis Partners LLC
Innovation Capital Associates Pty, Ltd.
Michigan Economic Development Corporation
North Coast Technology Investors, L.P.
RPM Ventures (FKA: Waypoint Ventures)
SWMF Life Science Venture Fund, L.P.
Seneca Partners, Inc.
TGap Ventures LLC
The Charter Group
University of Michigan
Venture Investors LLC

Venture Firms—Minnesota

Accuitive Medical Ventures
Affinity Capital Management
BlueFire Partners Capital Markets
BlueStream Ventures
Brightstone Capital
CORAL Ventures Management, Inc.
Cargill Ventures
Coral Group LLC
El Dorado Ventures
Gemini Investors
Lemhi Ventures
Mayo Medical Ventures
Oak Investment Partners
Quatris Fund
RBC Dain Rauscher
Rational Equity LLC
Sherpa Partners LLC
SightLine Partners
Split Rock Partners LLC
Springworks, LLC
St. Paul Venture Capital, Inc.
3M Corporation
Technology Venture Partners
Thomas, McNerney & Partners LLC

Venture Firms—Mississippi

Adams and Reese LLP
CapSource Fund, L.P.
ECD Investments LLC/ECD Investments BIDCO
MAF of Mississippi, Inc.

Venture Firms—Missouri

Advantage Capital Partners
Ascension Health Ventures LLC
Bank of America Commercial Finance
Guggenheim Venture Partners LLC
InvestAmerica Venture Group, Inc.
K.C. Venture Group
Media Venture Partners
National Corn Growers Association
Oakwood Medical Investors
Pilgrim Baxter
Prolog Ventures LLC
RiverVest Venture Partners
Savvis, Inc. (FKA: Savvis Communications)
Triathlon Medical Ventures LLC
Two Rivers Associates LLC (FKA: Gateway Associates, L.P.)

Venture Firms—Montana

Montlake Capital

Venture Firms—Nebraska

First Capital Partners LLC
World Investments, Inc.

Venture Firms—Nevada

Nevada Ventures
Redhills Ventures LLC
SAIC Venture Capital Corporation

Venture Firms—New Hampshire

Arete Corporation
Borealis Ventures

MerchantBanc
New Energy Capital Corporation

Venture Firms—New Jersey

Aberlyn Capital Management Co., Inc.
Aegis Capital Group LLC
Alcatel-Lucent Ventures
BD Ventures (AKA: Becton, Dickinson & Co.)
BaseCamp Ventures
Battelle Ventures
Blue Rock Capital
CS Capital Partners LLC
Cahn Medical Technolgies, LLC (CMT)
Cardinal Partners
Care Capital, LLC
Celgene Corporation
Chart Venture Partners
Condor Capital Management, Inc.
Conexus Capital Management, Inc.
Cornell Capital Partners, LP
Craton Equity Partners
DFW Capital Partners (AKA:DeMuth, Folger & Wetherill)
Domain Associates LLC
Early Stage Enterprises, L.P.
Edelson Technology Partners
Edison Venture Fund
Endeavor Capital Management
Foundation Venture Capital Group LLC
ff Asset Management LLC
HealthCare Ventures LLC
Intel Capital
Ivy Capital Partners
Johnson & Johnson Development Corporation
Leasing Technologies International, Inc.
Merck Capital Ventures LLC
Momentum Technology Partners LLC
Nassau Capital LLC
New Jersey Economic Development Authority
New Jersey Technology Council (AKA: NJTC)
New Venture Partners LLC
New Vernon Private Equity (FKA: New Vernon Bharat Ltd.)
NewSpring Capital
Novitas Capital (FKA: PA Early Stage Partners)
Omni Capital Group LLC
Origin Partners
Pharma Capital Ventures (AKA: PCV)
ProQuest Investments
Ridgewood Capital Management, LLC
Sycamore Ventures Pte, Ltd.
Technology Crossover Ventures
UBS Capital Markets
Updata Partners
Vertical Group, The
Zon Capital Partners

Venture Firms—New Mexico

Cottonwood Technology Group
EPIC Ventures
Flywheel Ventures
ITU Ventures
Intel Capital
Invencor, Inc.
Jerome Capital LLC
Mesa Capital Partners
Murphree Venture Partners
New Mexico Community Capital
Psilos Group Managers LLC
Red River Ventures
Technology Funding
Valley Ventures (FKA: Arizona Growth Partners, L.P.)
Verge
vSpring Capital

Venture Firms—New York

ABS Ventures
Accretive LLC (FKA: Accretive Technology Partners LLC)
Accrue Sports and Entertainment Partners LLC
Acumen Fund
Adirondack Venture Fund, The
Adler & Co.
Advantage Capital Partners
Aegis Capital Group LLC
Aisling Capital
Allegra Partners (FKA: Lawrence, Smith & Horey)
Allen & Company
AllianceBernstein L.P. (FKA: Alliance Capital Management)
Altitude Capital Partners
American International Group, Inc.
Amphion Capital Management, LLC (FKA: Wolfensohn Associates)
Amphion Innovations PLC
Ankar Capital Management LLC
Aperture Venture Partners, LLC
Arcus Ventures Management LLC
ArrowPath Venture Capital (FKA: E*TRADE Group, Inc.)
Ascend Venture Group LLC
Ascent Biomedical Ventures
Asia Pacific Investment Partners
AvantaLion, LLC
BMO Capital Corporation
BR Ventures
BRM Capital
Venture Firms—New York
Baker Bros. Advisors, LLC
Balloch China Fund, The
Balyasny Asset Management LP (AKA: BAM)
Bessemer Venture Partners
Biotechvest
Black Coral Capital
BlueCar Partners
Boldcap Ventures LLC
Broadline Capital LLC.
Bushido Capital Partners, L.P.
CDP Capital Private Equity
CE Unterberg Towbin (FKA:Unterberg Harris Capital Partners)
CW Group, Inc.
Calgary Enterprises, Inc.
Calim Private Equity, LLC
Capitol Health Partners, L.P.
Carnegie Fund
Carrot Capital LLC
Cascadia Capital LLC
Catalyst Investors
Cayuga Venture Fund
Cephas Capital Partners, L.P.
Channel Group LLC, The (TCG)
Chart Venture Partners
Chazen Capital Partners
Citicorp Venture Capital, Ltd.
City Light Capital
Claret Capital, Ltd.
Coburn Ventures, LLC
Constellation Ventures (AKA: Constellation Growth Capital)
Contour Venture Partners
Coriolis Ventures LLC
Corning Innovation Ventures
Creation Capital LLC
Credit Suisse Asset Management
Critical Capital Growth Fund, LP
Cross Atlantic Partners, Inc.
Crossroads Capital Partners, LLC
Culbro, LLC
D. E. Shaw Group, The
Dawntreader Ventures
Delta Capital Management (AKA:Delta Private Equity Partners)
Dolphin Equity Partners
Double D Venture Fund LLC
Draper Fisher Jurvetson Gotham Venture Partners
Dubai Investment Group (AKA: DIG)
Dutchess Advisors LLC
EarlyBirdCapital, Inc.
Earthrise Capital Partners LLC
Eastman Kodak Company
Easton Hunt Capital Partners, L.P.
Edelweiss Capital, Ltd.
Edison Venture Fund
Enhanced Capital Partners, LLC
Eos Asia Investments, Ltd. (FKA: JCAR Funds, Ltd.)
Equip Ventures LLC
Ericsson Venture Partners
Essex Woodlands Health Ventures
Ethanol Capital Management, LLC
EuclidSR Partners
Expansion Capital Partners LLC
eIndia Venture Management
FA Technology Ventures
FTV Capital (FKA: FTVentures)
First Round Capital
FirstMark Capital LLC
Forum Capital Partners
GIC Special Investments Pte, Ltd.
GMG Capital Partners (FKA: GMS Capital Partners)
Galleon Group
Gefinor Ventures
Generation Investment Management LLP
Glenmont Partners, LLC
Goldman Sachs JBWere (NZ) Ltd. (FKA: JBWere (NZ) Ltd.)
Gotham Partners
Greenhill SAVP
Greenwoods Capital Partners
Greycroft Partners
Guggenheim Venture Partners LLC
Hamilton Investments
Harbert Venture Partners
Harris & Harris Group, Inc.
Hawkeye Capital
Health Enterprise Partners (AKA: HEP Fund)
HealthShares(TM), Inc.
Hearst Corporation
High Peaks Venture Partners, LLC

Himalaya Capital
Holding Capital Group, Inc.
Homeland Defense Ventures
Hudson Venture Partners
IA Venture Partners LLC
IBM Corporation
Impact Venture Partners
Inclusive Ventures, LLC
Infinity Venture Capital
Infinity Venture Capital Fund (AKA: Israel Infinity Fund)
InnovationsKapital
Insight Venture Partners
Inter-Atlantic Group
InvestBio, Inc.
Investor Growth Capital AB
Istithmar World Capital
Itochu Technology, Inc.
i-Hatch Ventures LLC
idealab!
J&W Seligman & Company
JVP
KBL Healthcare Ventures
Kaupthing Bank hf.
Kestrel Energy Partners LLC
Kodak External Alliances
Kubera Partners, LLC
L Capital Partners
Lambda Funds, The
Laurus Master Fund, Ltd.
Lazard Technology Partners
Leeward Fund Management
Lighthouse Funds LLC
Lux Capital
MC Capital, Inc.
MKW Capital, Ltd.
MMV Financial, Inc.
Masthead Venture Partners
McGovern Capital LLC
McGraw-Hill Ventures (FKA: McGraw-Hill Capital Corp.)
Merlin Nexus
Merrill Lynch Venture Capital
Metamorphic Ventures, LLC (FKA: Gersh Venture Partners)
Milestone Venture Partners
Mitsui & Co. Venture Partners (MCVP)
Mitsui INCUBASE Corp.
Montefiore, LLC
Morgan Stanley Venture Partners (AKA: MSDW)
NBT Capital Corporation
NCH Capital, Inc.
NGEN Partners LLC (FKA: NextGen Partners LLC)
NGN Capital LLC
NYSTAR (FKA: SBTIF)
Navigation Capital Partners (AKA: NCP)
Neuberger Berman LLC
New Leaf Venture Partners LLC
New Science Ventures, LLC
New York Business Development Corporation
New York City Investment Fund
New York Times Company,The
NewWorld Capital Group LLC
Newlight Associates
Nexos Capital Partners
NextLevel Group
NextPoint Partners, L.P.
Novartis Venture Fund (FKA: Novartis Corp.)
Odeon Capital Partners, L.P.
Olympus Capital Holdings Asia
Onondaga Venture Capital Fund, Inc.
Ovation Capital Partners
PSi, Inc.
Pangaea Ventures
Pennell Venture Partners
Pershing Square Capital Management
Pfizer Venture Investments
Phoenix Venture Fund LLC
Pilot Group LLC
Probitas Partners, Inc.
Psilos Group Managers LLC
Quilvest Capital
RRE Ventures LLC
Radius Ventures LLC
Rand Capital Corporation
Reed Elsevier Ventures
Research Partners, Ltd.
Result Venture Knowledge International
Rho Capital Partners, Inc.
Riverside Management Group
Rock Maple Ventures, L.P.
Rodman & Renshaw LLC
Rose Tech Ventures, LLC
SAIL Venture Partners
SAS Investors
SC Capital Management LLC
SCS Capital Sdn. Bhd.
SJF Ventures
STG Capital, LLC
Salmon River Capital
Sands Brothers & Co., Ltd.
Schroders PLC
Sciens Capital Partners (FKA: Zilkha Venture Partners)
Seaway Private Equity Corporation (AKA: SPEC)
Security Growth Partners
Seed Capital Partners
Seraphima Ventures
Shattuck Hammond Partners
Sindicatum Carbon Capital, Ltd.
SoftBank Capital
Solera Capital, LLC
Sony Corporation
Soros Strategic Partners
Spencer Trask Ventures, Inc. (FKA: Spencer Trask Securities)
Sprout Group
StarVest Partners, L.P.
Starr International Company, Inc
Sterling Grace Capital Management, L.P.
Stockton Partners
Strategic Advisory Group, Inc.
Sunrise Financial Group, Inc.
Sycamore Ventures Pte, Ltd.
Syntek Capital AG
21Ventures LLC
Technology Crossover Ventures
Tenaya Capital (FKA: Lehman Brothers Venture Partners)
TopSpin Partners
Trevi Health Ventures
Trillium Group LLC
Undisclosed Firm
Union Square Ventures
VCE Capital
Valence Capital Management, LP
Vencon Management, Inc.
Venrock Associates
Village Ventures
W.R. Hambrecht & Co., LLC
WFD Ventures, LLC
Wall Street Technology Partners
Walnut Group, The
Warburg Pincus LLC
Westbury Partners
Wheatley Partners
Wilton Capital Group
Winthrop, Brown & Company, Inc. (DBA: Winthrop Ventures)
Zelkova Ventures
Ziff Brothers Investments

Venture Firms—North Carolina

Academy Funds
Atlantis Group LLC, The
Aurora Funds, Inc.
Carousel Capital Partners
Charlotte Angel Partners
Dogwood Equity
Frontier Capital LLC
Hatteras Funds
Hatteras Venture Partners (FKA:Catalysta Partners)
IDEA Fund Partners
Intel Capital
Intersouth Partners
Kitty Hawk Capital
Massey Burch Capital Corp.
NovaQuest
Pacific Rim Ventures Company, Ltd.
Pappas Ventures
Quintiles Transnational Corporation
Research Triangle Ventures (RTV)
River Cities Capital Funds
SJF Ventures
Southeast Interactive Technology Funds
Southern Capitol Ventures
Technibilt
Thompson Clive & Partners, Ltd.
Trelys Funds
TriState Investment Group
Wakefield Group

Venture Firms—North Dakota

Arthur Ventures

Venture Firms—Ohio

Adena Ventures
Affymetrix, Inc.
Alpha Capital Partners, Ltd.
Arboretum Ventures
Athenian Venture Partners
Battelle Memorial Institute
BioEnterprise
Blue Chip Venture Company
Bridge Investment Fund
C&T Access Ventures
CID Capital
Capvest Venture Fund (FKA: Virgin Ventures Fund LP)
Case Technology Ventures

Charter Life Sciences
Chrysalis Ventures
CincyTech
Crystal Internet Venture Fund, L.P.
Custer Capital, Inc.
Danville Partners, LLC
Draper Triangle Ventures
Early Stage Partners, L.P.
Frantz Medical Ventures
Glengary LLC
Isabella Capital LLC
JumpStart, Inc.
Legend Partners, The
Luxemburg Capital LLC
Miami Valley Economic Development
Mutual Capital Partners
NCIC Capital Fund
NCT Ventures LLC
National City Equity Partners, Inc.
Nationwide Mutual Capital LLC
North Coast Angel Fund
Ohio Innovation Fund (OIF)
Paragon Advisors
Pharmavent Partners
Procter & Gamble Company, The
Reservoir Venture Partners
River Cities Capital Funds
RiverVest Venture Partners
Rocket Ventures
SunBridge Partners
Talisman Capital
Triathlon Medical Ventures LLC
Walnut Group, The

Venture Firms—Oklahoma

Altus Ventures, LLC
Bounty Equity Fund LLC
Chisholm Private Capital Partners, LC
Mesa Capital Partners
Oklahoma Equity Partners

Venture Firms—Oregon

Altien Ventures LLC
Capybara Ventures LLC
DFJ Frontier
Elliott Associates
Empire Ventures
Intel Capital
Marquam Hill Capital LLC
Montlake Capital
Mount Hood Equity Partners, L.P.
Northwest Technology Ventures
OVP Venture Partners
Obsidian Finance Group LLC
Paladin Partners
Pivotal Investments LLC
Reference Capital Management LLC (FKA: Cascadia Partners)
SmartForest Ventures
U.S. Bancorp
Voyager Capital

Venture Firms—Pennsylvania

Adams Capital Management, Inc.
Air Products and Chemicals, Inc.
Anthem Capital Management
BTG International (AKA: British Technology Group)
Baird Venture Partners
Ben Franklin Technology Partners Southeastern PA
Ben Franklin Technology Partners of Central and Northern PA
Ben Franklin Technology Partners of Northeastern PA
BioAdvance
Birchmere Ventures
Blue Hill Partners LLC
Cardinal Partners
Chrysalis Ventures
Comcast Interactive Capital
Cross Atlantic Capital Partners
Devon Park Bioventures
Draper Triangle Ventures
Edison Venture Fund
Element Partners
Emerald Stage2 Ventures (AKA: Stage2 Capital Ventures)
EnerTech Capital
First Round Capital
GIV Venture Partners (AKA: Global Internet Ventures)
Gamma Investors LLC
Garber Venture Capital Center, The
Guggenheim Venture Partners LLC
Innovation Philadelphia
Innovation Transfer Center - Carnegie Mellon University
Innovation Works, Inc.
iNetworks, LLC
Larsen MacColl Partners
LaunchCyte LLC
Leasing Technologies International, Inc.
Liberty Venture Partners, Inc.
Life Sciences Greenhouse of Central Pensylvania (LSGPA)
Lighthouse Funds LLC
Meakem Becker Venture Capital
Meidlinger Partners LLC
Mid-Atlantic Venture Funds (FKA: NEPA Management Corp.)
Murex Investments, Inc.
NewSpring Capital
NextStage Capital
Nittany Lion Venture Capital
Norwich Ventures
Novitas Capital (FKA: PA Early Stage Partners)
Originate Ventures
Osage Partners, LLC
Penn Venture Partners, LP
Pittsburgh Equity Partners
Pittsburgh Life Sciences Greenhouse
Quaker BioVentures, Inc.
Redleaf Group, Inc
Robin Hood Ventures
S.R. One, Ltd.
Schoffstall Ventures
Schroders PLC
Science Center, The
Select Capital Ventures
SeventySix Capital
Strategic Venture Mgmt. Advisors (FKA: MentorTech Ventures)
Strattech Partners LLC
Sustainable Technology Partners Nordic AB
TL Ventures
Thomvest Ventures
Trestle Ventures
W.R. Hambrecht & Co., LLC
Wynnefield Capital Advisors
Zon Capital Partners

Venture Firms—Puerto Rico

Advent-Morro Equity Partners
Miradero Capital Partners, Inc.

Venture Firms—Rhode Island

China Capital Management Company, Ltd.
Point Judith Capital
Slater Technology Fund
Zero Stage Capital Co., Inc.

Venture Firms—South Carolina

CF Investment Company (Carolina First)
Columbia Capital Group, Inc.
Companion Capital Management, Inc.
FirstMark Capital LLC

Venture Firms—South Dakota

Bluestem Capital Partners
Guggenheim Venture Partners LLC
McGowan Capital Group
PrairieGold Venture Partners

Venture Firms—Tennessee

Adams and Reese LLP
Capital Services & Resources, Inc.
Claritas Capital LLC
Clayton Associates LLC
Council Ventures
Delta Capital Management LLC
ECD Investments LLC/ECD Investments BIDCO
Eastman Ventures
First Avenue Partners, L.P.
Harbert Venture Partners
Innova Memphis, Inc.
MB Venture Partners, LLC
Massey Burch Capital Corp.
Meritus Ventures, L.P.
Morgan Keegan Merchant Banking
Pharos Capital Group LLC
Richland Ventures
SSM Partners
Salix Ventures
Sante Ventures
Solidus Company, L.P.
Southern Appalachian Management Company LLC
Stoney River Capital Partners LLC
SunTrust Equity Partners
Vanderbilt University Office of Transfer and Development

Venture Firms—Texas

ARCH Venture Partners
AV Labs
Accent Capital
Access Venture Partners
Adams Capital Management, Inc.
Adams and Reese LLP
Advantage Capital Partners
Aegis Capital Group LLC
Agility Capital LLC
Air Products and Chemicals, Inc.
Asia Capital Management (ACM) Limited (AKA: ACL Asia Ltd)
Austin Ventures, L.P.

BCM Technologies, Inc.
BankCap Partners
CCG Venture Partners, LLC
CT Holdings
Calyon (FKA: Credit Agricole Indosuez)
CapSource Fund, L.P.
Capital Southwest Corporation
Castletop Capital
Centennial Ventures
CenterPoint Venture Partners
Chevron Technology Ventures
Chisholm Private Capital Partners, LC
Cogene Ventures
ComStar Media
Cottonwood Technology Group
Covera Ventures
Crispian Venture Capital, LLC
DFJ Mercury
Duchossois Technology Partners LLC (DTEC)
ECT Merchant Investments Corp (Enron Corp.)
EIV Capital Management Company LLC
Energy Ventures AS
Escalate Capital
Essex Woodlands Health Ventures
First Capital Group Management Co. LLC (AKA: FCG)
Freebird Partners, LP
G-51 Capital LLC
GSIM Corporation (AKA: Global Strategic Investment Mgmt.)
Gefinor Ventures
Genesis Campus, L.P.
Genesis Park Ventures
Gideon Hixon Fund
Greenhill SAVP
Guggenheim Venture Partners LLC
GulfStar Group
HO2 Partners
Haddington Ventures, LLC
Harris Preston & Partners, LLC
Haynes and Boone LLC
Hunt BioVentures
Hunt Capital Group
Incyte Venture Partners LLC
Infrastructure Fund, The
Intel Capital
InterWest Partners
JatoTech Management LLC
Kenda Capital BV
Keynote Ventures (FKA: Dali, Hook Partners)
Lonestar CAPCO Fund LLC
MPower Ventures, L.P.
Markpoint Venture Partners
Maven Capital Management LLC
Millennium Ventures LLC
Mobility Ventures
Murphree Venture Partners
New Capital Partners
Newbridge Capital, Ltd.
Origin Partners
PTV Sciences
Pacesetter Capital Group (FKA: MESBIC Ventures Holding Co.)
Path4 Ventures, LLC
Perot Investments, Inc.
Pharos Capital Group LLC
Presidio Investors LLC
Red Oak Capital
Red River Ventures
S3 Ventures
STARTech Early Ventures
Sands Brothers & Co., Ltd.
Sante Ventures
Sevin Rosen Funds
Shell Internet Ventures
Silver Creek Ventures
Star Ventures Management GmbH & Co. KG
Sternhill Partners
Strathdon Investment plc (FKA: Strathdon Investments, Ltd.)
TEXO Ventures
TI Ventures
TPG Growth
TXU Energy Corporation
Techxas Ventures LLC
Texas Intrepid Ventures
Texas Women Ventures Fund
Trailblazer Capital
Trellis Partners
Triton Ventures
Undisclosed Firm
Vanguard Ventures

Venture Firms—Utah

Canopy Group
Cross Creek Capital, an affiliate of Wasatch Advisors
Dolphin Capital Group, LLC
EPIC Ventures
GMG Capital Partners (FKA: GMS Capital Partners)
Grow Utah Ventures
HealthRight Partners
InnoVentures Capital Partners
Intel Capital
JCP Capital LLC
Mercato Partners
Novell Technology Capital
Pelion Venture Partners
University Venture Fund, The
UpStart Ventures Management
vSpring Capital

Venture Firms—Vermont

FreshTracks Capital
Underdog Ventures LLC

Venture Firms—Virginia

ABS Ventures
Amplifier Venture Partners
Andover Group Pty, Ltd.
Avansis Ventures, LLC
BV-Cornerstone Ventures, L.P.
Blue Water Capital LLC
Brand Journey Capital LP
CIT GAP Funds
CSI (FKA: Virginia Community Development Loan Fund)
Calvert Social Venture Partners, L.P.
Columbia Capital LLC
Comerica Venture Capital Group
Comspace Development LLC
Court Square Ventures, LLC
DynaFund Ventures LLC
Dynamis Advisors LLC
EcoEnterprises Fund
Edison Venture Fund
Envest
Gabriel Venture Partners
Grotech Ventures
Harbert Venture Partners
In-Q-Tel, Inc.
Jefferson Capital Partners, Ltd.
Liquid Capital Management Group, LLC
MMV Financial, Inc.
Mid-Atlantic Venture Funds (FKA: NEPA Management Corp.)
Monumental Venture Partners LLC
NeuroVentures Capital
New Atlantic Ventures
New Vantage Group
Newbury Partners LLC
RedShift Ventures
Redleaf Group, Inc
Rolls Royce Corporate Venture
SAIL Venture Partners
Spencer Trask Ventures, Inc. (FKA: Spencer Trask Securities)
Stuart Mill Capital, Inc.
SunTrust Bank, Inc.
Tall Oaks Capital Partners LLC
Third Security LLC
Time Warner Investments (FKA: AOL Time Warner Ventures)
True Ventures
Undisclosed Firm
Updata Partners
Valhalla Partners
Virginia Capital
WWC Capital Group LLC
Washington Gas
Washington Technology Partners, Inc. (AKA: WTP)

Venture Firms—Washington

ARCH Venture Partners
Ackerley Partners LLC
Alexander Hutton Venture Partners
Benaroya Capital Company
Bezos Expeditions
Cascadia Capital LLC
Columbia Equity Partners
Compass Capital Fund Management LLC
Divergent Ventures
Elevar Equity Advisors Pvt., Ltd.
eFund, LLC
Fluke Venture Partners
Frazier Healthcare and Technology Ventures
Holding Capital Group, Inc.
Ignition Partners (FKA: Ignition Corporation)
Integra Ventures
Intel Capital
Kirlan Venture Capital, Inc.
Madrona Venture Group
Maveron LLC
Monster Venture Partners
Montgomery & Co. (FKA: Digital Coast Partners)
Montlake Capital
Northern Lights Ventures, LLC
Northwest Venture Associates, Inc.(FKA:Spokane Capital Mgmt)
OVP Venture Partners
Pacific Horizon Ventures LLC
Paladin Partners
Phoenix Partners, The

Pioneer Venture Partners, LLC
Polaris Venture Partners
Redleaf Group, Inc
Seapoint Ventures
Second Avenue Partners
Spangler Ventures, LLC
Staenberg Venture Partners (FKA: Staenberg Private Capital)
Sugar Mountain Capital
Trans Cosmos USA
U.S. Venture Partners
Venture Mechanics, LLC
Voyager Capital
Vulcan Capital
WRF Capital

Venture Firms—West Virginia

Adena Ventures
iNetworks, LLC
Mountaineer Capital, L.P.
Novitas Capital (FKA: PA Early Stage Partners)
Walker Ventures SBIC (AKA: Walker Ventures)

Venture Firms—Wisconsin

Advantage Capital Partners
Baird Capital Partners Europe
Baird Venture Partners
Capital Midwest Fund, L.P.
DaneVest Tech Fund Advisors
Diamond Capital Management
Dot Edu Ventures
Fisk Ventures, Inc. (AKA: FVI)
Future Value Ventures, Inc.
InvestAmerica Venture Group, Inc.
Kegonsa Capital Partners, LLC
Kimberly-Clark Ventures, LLC
NEW Capital Management, Inc.
Peak Capital Group LLC
Phenomenelle Angels Management
State of Wisconsin Investment Board
Venture Investors LLC
Ziegler HealthVest Management LLC
Ziegler Meditech Partners

Venture Firms—Wyoming

Sapient Capital Management LLC

Non-U.S. Firm Cross Reference by Nation

For more comprehensive querying, searching, and referencing, Thomson Reuters supplies Pratt's Guide online at www.prattsguide.com. Annual subscriptions are available for USD$995 per user. For more information, please contact Greg Winterton at 001 646 223 6787 or email greg.winterton@thomsonreuters.com.

Buyout Firms—Algeria
Citadel Capital S.A.E.

Buyout Firms—Am. Virgin Is.
Celtic Therapeutics Management, L.L.L.P.
Treadstone Group Inc., The

Buyout Firms—Angola
Angola Capital Partners

Buyout Firms—Argentina
AIG Capital Partners
Advent International
BancBoston Capital/BancBoston Ventures
GE Commercial Finance - Equity
Goldman, Sachs & Co.
HSBC Private Equity Latin America
J.P. Morgan Capital Corporation
J.P. Morgan Partners (FKA: Chase Capital Partners)
Lehman Brothers, Inc.
Linzor Capital Partners, L.P.
Southern Cross Group (AKA: SCG)

Buyout Firms—Australia
AMP Capital Investors
Accretion Investment Management Pty, Ltd.
Advent Private Capital
Affinity Equity Partners
Allco Equity Partners Management Pty Ltd.
Allegro Private Equity Pty, Ltd.
Anacacia Capital
Anchorage Capital Partners
Archer Capital
Arowana Capital Pty, Ltd.
Aureos Capital, Ltd.
Babson Capital Management LLC
Banksia Capital
Bayard Group (AKA: Landis+Gyr Holdings)
Blue Sky Private Equity
Bobcock & Brown
Business Management, Ltd.
CHAMP Private Equity Pty Ltd.
CHAMP Ventures Pty Ltd.
CVC Asia Pacific, Ltd.
CVC Capital Partners (Europe), Ltd.
Carlyle Group, The
Catalyst Investment Managers Pty, Ltd.
Credit Suisse Private Equity
Crescent Capital Partners
DIF Capital Partners, Ltd.
Equity Partners Management Pty Ltd.
Fortress Investment Group LLC
Fulcrum Capital Partners, Ltd.
GE Commercial Finance - Equity
Global Capital Finance
Goldman Sachs JBWere Private Equity (FKA:JBWere Prv Equity)
Greenstone Partners Private Capital Pty, Ltd.
Gresham Partners - Gresham Private Equity
Harbert Management Corporation
Hastings Private Equity
Hawkesbridge Private Equity
Helmsman Funds Management Pty Ltd.
Intersuisse Bioscience Managers Pty, Ltd. (IB Managers)
Investec Wentworth Private Equity Pty., Ltd.
Ironbridge Capital Pty., Ltd.
J.P. Morgan Capital Corporation
J.P. Morgan Partners (FKA: Chase Capital Partners)
Kestrel Capital (FKA: Nanyang Ventures Pty., Ltd.)
Kohlberg, Kravis, Roberts & Company, L.P.
Lazard Capital Partners
Macquarie Group Limited
Mariner Financial, Ltd. (AKA: Mariner Brand Capital, Ltd.)
Merrill Lynch Capital Partners
NBC Capital Pty., Ltd.
Navis Capital Partners, Ltd.
Navis Investment Partners (Asia), Ltd.
Next Capital Pty., Ltd.
Pacific Equity Partners
Pacific Road Capital Management Pty, Ltd.
Paragon Advisory Pty Ltd.
Partners Group AG
Pinnacle Investment Management Pty, Ltd.
Pitt Capital Partners, Ltd.
Propel Investments
Quadrant Private Equity Pty, Ltd.
RMB Capital Partners, Ltd.
Riverside Company
Silverfern Group, Inc., The
TPG Capital
Tasman Capital Partners
Telopea Capital Partners Pty, Ltd.
UBS Capital Corporation
Unitas Capital Pte, Ltd.
Venture Capital Partners Pty., Ltd.
Viburnum Funds Pty., Ltd. (AKA: Wyllie Group)
Wilshire Private Markets
Wolseley Private Equity
Yarra Capital Partners

Buyout Firms—Austria
AFINUM Management GmbH
AXA Private Equity
Andlinger & Company, Inc.
AvW Managment Beteiligungs AG
Buy-Out Central Europe
CRG Capital
CRG Partners
Credit Suisse Private Equity
Darby Overseas Investments, Ltd.
ECO Unternehmensbeteiligungs-AG
EK Mittelstandsfinanzierungs AG
Euro Capital Partners
Global Capital Finance
HANNOVER Finanz Austria GmbH
HANNOVER Finanz GmbH
HARDT GROUP Capital Partners Limited
HYPO-Unternehmensbeteiligungen AG
IB Industrie-Beteiligungen GmbH
IPO Beteiligungs-Management AG
IndexAtlas Group
Invest Equity Management Consulting GmbH
Invest Unternehmensbeteiligungs AG
MPC Capital Austria AG
Oberbank Opportunity Invest Management GmbH
RECAP Management GmbH
3TS Capital Partners, Ltd.
Unternehmens Invest AG
Value Management Services GmbH
Ventacc Beteiligungs- und Beratungs GmbH
Ventana Beteiligungsgesellschaft GmbH

Buyout Firms—Bahamas
Credit Suisse Private Equity

Buyout Firms—Bahrain
Arcapita, Inc.
BNP Paribas Asset Management SGR SpA (FKA: BNL Gestioni SGR)
CIMB Private Equity Sdn Bhd
Global Investment House
Investcorp Bank B.S.C.
Tadhamon Capital BSC
UIB Capital, Inc.
Unicorn Investment Bank B.S.C.

Buyout Firms—Bangladesh
Asian Tiger Capital Partners, Ltd. (AKA: AT Capital)

Buyout Firms—Belgium
AlpInvest Partners N.V.
Andlinger & Company, Inc.
Bencis Capital Partners
CVC Capital Partners (Europe), Ltd.
Gevaert N.V.
Halder Holdings BV
KBC Private Equity NV
Kenmore Private Equity, Ltd. (AKA: KPE)
Morrison & Foerster
NIBC Principal Investments (FKA: Parnib Holding NV)
NPM Capital NV
Rabo Private Equity
Riverside Company
Robeco Private Equity
Sofindev Management N.V.
Sydes
Synapsis Associates
3D Participaties NV
Verlinvest SA
Waterland Private Equity Investments B.V.

Buyout Firms—Bermuda
AIG Capital Partners
Celtic Pharma Management, LP
Oakley Capital Investment Limited (AKA: OCI)
Renaissance Capital
Vostok Gas, Ltd. (FKA: Vostok Nafta Investment)

Buyout Firms—Botswana
African Alliance Private Equity

Buyout Firms—Br. Virgin I.
ICAfrica Private Equity, Ltd.

Buyout Firms—Brazil
AIG Capital Partners
Actis Capital LLP
Advent International
BPEP International
BancBoston Capital/BancBoston Ventures
Carlyle Group, The
Credit Suisse Private Equity
Darby Overseas Investments, Ltd.
Espirito Santo Capital - Sociedade de Capital de Risco SA
FAMA Private Equity
GE Commercial Finance - Equity
GP Investimentos
General Atlantic LLC
Goldman, Sachs & Co.
J.P. Morgan Capital Corporation

J.P. Morgan Partners (FKA: Chase Capital Partners)
Novabase Capital
Opus Electra & Partners
Southern Cross Group (AKA: SCG)
Tarpon Investment Group
Temasek Holdings Pvt., Ltd.

Buyout Firms—Brunei

Aureos Capital, Ltd.
CIMB Private Equity Sdn Bhd

Buyout Firms—Bulgaria

Axxess Capital Partners S.A. (FKA: Enterprise Capital)
Charlemagne Capital (UK) Limited
Equest Partners, Ltd.
GED Group
GILD Bankers (FKA: LHV Ventures)
Rosslyn Capital Partners
SigmaBleyzer
Southeast Europe Equity Fund

Buyout Firms—Burma

CIMB Private Equity Sdn Bhd

Buyout Firms—Cambodia

Clavel Investissement SAS
Leopard Capital, Ltd.

Buyout Firms—Cameroon

EMP Africa Fund Management (AKA: Emerging Capital Partners)
Travant Capital Partners

Buyout Firms—Canada

AIG Capital Partners
Abacus Private Equity (ASA: Abacus Capital Corporation)
Aberdeen Gould
Acces Capital QuEbec
Artemis Investment Management Inc.
Balaton Group Inc.
Banyan Capital Partners
Bedford Capital
Bennett Jones
Birch Hill Equity Partners Management, Inc.
Bond Capital Partners, Ltd.
Brookfield Asset Management
C.A. Bancorp, Inc.
CAI Capital Management Company
CAPE Fund Management, Inc.
CIBC Capital Partners
CIBC Wood Gundy Capital
Callisto Capital
Canterbury Park Capital
Clarke, Inc.
Cordiant Capital
Corporate Growth Assistance, Ltd.
Counsel Corporation
Cowen Capital Partners LLC (FKA: SG Capital Partners LLC)
Credit Suisse Private Equity
Crocus Investment Fund
Dancap Private Equity Inc.
EdgeStone Capital Partners, Inc.
F.J. Stork Holdings
Fondaction
Fortress Investment Group LLC
Front Street Capital
GCP Capital Partners
GMP Securities, L.P.
Genesis Capital Corp.
Goldman, Sachs & Co.
Gran Retail Investments, Inc.
Granite Partners Corporation
HSBC Capital (Canada)
Hilco Consumer Capital Corporation
Huron Capital Partners LLC
Imperial Capital Corporation
Integrated Partners
Investissement Desjardins
Ironbridge Equity Partners
JOG Capital
KERN Partners
Ken Fowler Enterprises, Ltd.
Latitude Partners
Lazard Capital Partners
Lex Capital Management, Inc.
Longroad Asset Management
Macquarie Group Limited
Maxam Capital Corp.
Merrill Lynch Capital Partners
Moventis Capital, Inc. (FKA:Online Innovation, Inc.)
New Equity Capital
NorthRock Capital Partners
Northbridge Capital Partners
Northern Plains Capital, Ltd.
Northleaf Capital Partners
Northwater capital Management
OMERS Private Equity
ONCAP Investment Partners
Oak Bridge Holdings, Inc.
Onex Corporation
Ontario Teachers' Pension Plan
Pender West Capital Partners, Inc.
Perseis Private Equity
Persistence Capital Partners
Piborus Inc.
Priveq Capital Funds
RBC Capital Partners/RBC Technology Ventures
ReichmannHauer Capital Partners
Richardson Capital Limited
Riverside Company
7bridge Capital Partners, Ltd.
SCF Partners
Second City Capital Partners
Signal Hill Equity Partners, Inc.
Stern Partners Inc.
StoneBridge Merchant Capital Corporation
32 Degrees Capital
TD Capital Group, Ltd.
Thomas Weisel Partners Group, Inc.
TorQuest Partners, Inc.
TriNorth Capital, Inc.
TriWest Capital Management Corporation
Tricor Pacific Capital, Inc.
Trio Capital
Viavar Capital
Westerkirk Capital, Inc.
Wynnchurch Capital, Ltd.
Yellow Point Equity Partners LP

Buyout Firms—Cayman Islands

Brown Brothers Harriman & Company (AKA: BBH)
CDH China Management Co., Ltd.
Clayton, Dubilier & Rice, Inc.
Credit Suisse Private Equity
Ethemba Capital, Ltd.
Goldman, Sachs & Co.
Greater Pacific Capital LLP
Millennium Private Equity

Buyout Firms—Channel Islands

Alpha Group
BPEP International
IK Investment Partners, Ltd.
KKR & Co. (Guernsey) L.P.
Nordic Capital (AKA: NC Advisory)
Stirling Square Capital Partners

Buyout Firms—Chile

AIG Capital Partners
Larrain Vial SA
Linzor Capital Partners, L.P.
Southern Cross Group (AKA: SCG)

Buyout Firms—China

ADM Capital
AIG Capital Partners
AMP Capital Investors
Abax Global Capital Ltd.
Actis Capital LLP
Apax Partners Worldwide
Arsenal Capital Partners
Aureos Capital, Ltd.
BPEP International
Bain Capital
Baird Capital Partners
Beijing SME Venture Capital Fund of Funds
Blackstone Group, L.P.
Blue Oak Venture Capital Co., Ltd.
Blue Point Capital Partners (FKA: Key Equity Capital)
CAS Capital, Inc.
CDH China Management Co., Ltd.
CITIC Capital Partners, Ltd.
CITIC Private Equity Funds Management Co., Ltd.
CLSA Capital Partners (AKA: Credit Lyonnais Securities Asia)
CMIA Capital Partners (AKA: CM Investment Advisers Pte Ltd.)
CVC Asia Pacific, Ltd.
CVC Capital Partners (Europe), Ltd.
Cappello Capital Corp.
Capvis Equity Partners AG
Carlyle Group, The
Cathay Capital Private Equity SAS
Cathay Fortune Corporation
Centenium-Pinetree China Private Equity
Centurion Investment Management
China Everbright, Ltd.
China International Capital Corporation, Ltd.
China New Enterprise Investment (AKA: CNEI)
China OperVestors, Inc.
China Resources Investment Management, Co., Ltd,
Chongqing Yufu Assets Management Co., Ltd.
Clarity Partners
Clearwater Capital Partners, LLC
Colony Capital LLC
Crimson Capital China
Crimson Investment, LLC
EQT Funds management Limited
ESP Equity Partners LLC
Eastern Link Capital

Ewing Management Group LLC
FountainVest Partners (Asia), Ltd.
General Atlantic LLC
Goldman, Sachs & Co.
Guangdong Pacific Technology Venture Co., Ltd.
H&Q Asia Pacific
Hammond Kennedy Whitney & Co
Hollyhigh International Capital
Hony Capital Ltd.
Houlihan, Lokey, Howard & Zukin
Investor Growth Capital, Inc.
J.W. Childs Associates
JC Asia Alpha Private Equity
Jefferies Group, Inc.
Jordan Company, The
Key Principal Partners LLC (AKA: KPP)
Kohlberg, Kravis, Roberts & Company, L.P.
Lazard Capital Partners
Longreach Group, Ltd., The
MBK Partners
Mandarin Capital Partners
Milestone Capital Management, Ltd.
Morrison & Foerster
NYPC Capital
Navis Capital Partners, Ltd.
Northern Capital Management Group
Oaktree Capital Management LLC
OrbiMed Advisors LLC
Partners Group AG
PinPoint Fund
Piper Jaffray Ventures
Principle Capital, Ltd.
Private Equity Partners SpA
Quad-C Management, Inc.
Revolution Learning
Rongzhong Investments Group Co., Ltd.
SEAVI Advent Corporation, Ltd.
SIG Capital Partners Limited
STIC Investments, Inc.
SVB Capital
Shanghai Megasun Investment Co., Ltd.
Shanghai ZhongBo Capital Co., Ltd.
Shenzhen Right-Sun Investment Company, Ltd.
Sichuan Shizhi Investment Co., Ltd.
Siguler Guff & Company
Silicon-valley Paradise Venture Investment Co., Ltd.
SinoLatin Capital
Standard Chartered Private Equity, Ltd.
Sun Capital Partners, Inc.
TCIB Investment Co., Ltd.
TPG Capital
Telopea Capital Partners Pty, Ltd.
Temasek Holdings Pvt., Ltd.
Tembusu Partners Pte., Ltd.
Tripod Capital International, Ltd.
Unisun (Beijing) Investment Co., Ltd.
Unitas Capital Pte, Ltd.
Walden International
Wall Street Venture Capital
Whitesun Equity Partners

Buyout Firms—Colombia

Altra Investments
Aureos Capital, Ltd.
Larrain Vial SA
Palmfund Management LLC
Tribecapital Partners S.A. (AKA: Tribeca Partners)

Buyout Firms—Costa Rica

Aureos Capital, Ltd.
Norfund

Buyout Firms—Croatia

AIG Capital Partners
Nexus Private Equity Partneri d.o.o.
Quaestus Private Equity, Ltd.

Buyout Firms—Cuba

Actis Capital LLP

Buyout Firms—Cyprus

Cyprus Development Bank, The
Dolphin Capital Partners
Penta Investments, Ltd.
Renaissance Capital

Buyout Firms—Czech Republic

AIG Capital Partners
Advent International
Arx Equity Partners
Benson Oak Capital
Dragon Capital
EnerCap Capital Partners
Genesis Capital, s.r.o.
Invest Equity Management Consulting GmbH
JV Capital Management s.r.o.
Jet Investment A.S.
KBC Private Equity NV
Odien Group
Penta Investments, Ltd.
Riverside Company
Royalton Partners
3TS Capital Partners, Ltd.

Buyout Firms—Denmark

Altor Equity Partners AB
Axcel Industriinvestor AS
CVC Capital Partners (Europe), Ltd.
CapMan Plc
Capidea Management ApS
Dansk Erhvervsudvikling A/S
EQT Funds management Limited
EVO Holding A/S (AKA: EVO Management A/S)
FSN Capital Partners AS
JMI Invest A/S
Jysk Fynsk Kapitalanaeg AS
LD Invest A/S
Nordic Capital (AKA: NC Advisory)
NorthCap Partners ApS
Odin Equity Partners
PAI Partners (FKA: PAI Management)
Polaris Management A/S
Procuritas Partners KB
SR Private Brands A/S
3i Group PLC

Buyout Firms—Egypt

Actis Capital LLP
Beltone Private Equity
Carlyle Group, The
Citadel Capital S.A.E.
EFG-Hermes Private Equity
Global Investment House
Buyout Firms—El Salvador
Aureos Capital, Ltd.

Buyout Firms—Estonia

Alta Capital
Askembla Asset Management AB
Baltcap
GILD Bankers (FKA: LHV Ventures)
Pontos Oy
Trigon Alternative Investments

Buyout Firms—Finland

Aboa Venture Management Oy
Ahlstrom Capital Oy
Altor Equity Partners AB
Canelco Capital Oy
CapMan Plc
EQT Funds management Limited
Fenno Management Oy
Helmet Business Mentors Oy
Intera Equity Partners Oy
Karnell
MB Funds (AKA: MB Rahastot Oy)
Midinvest Management Oy
Nordia Management Oy
Nordic Capital (AKA: NC Advisory)
Pohjola Capital Partners Oy
Pontos Oy
Profita Management Oy
Sentica Partners Oy
Sponsor Capital Oy

Buyout Firms—France

ACE Management
AGF Private Equity
ALP Capital
ARCIS Finance SA
AXA Private Equity
Abenex Capital (FKA: ABN AMRO Capital France)
Acofi Gestion
Actem Partners SA (FKA: SPEF LBO)
Activa Capital SAS
Acute
Advent International
Agence Francaise de Developpement
Agro Invest SAS
Alliance Entreprendre SAS
Alpha Group
American Capital, Ltd.
Apax Partners Worldwide
Ardens & Associes SAS
Argan Capital (FKA: BA Capital Partners Europe, BACPE)
Argos Soditic SA
Astorg Partners SAS (FKA : Suez Capital Partenaires)
AtriA Capital Partenaires
Aurinvest SAS
Autonomie et Solidarite
Avenir Tourisme
Azulis Capital (FKA:Banexi Capital Partenaires)
BC Partners Ltd
BNP Paribas Asset Management SGR SpA (FKA: BNL Gestioni SGR)
BNP Paribas Private Equity SAS
Barclays Private Equity, Ltd.
Before SA
Blackstone Group, L.P.
Bridgepoint Capital, Ltd.
Bridgepoint Development Capital
Brockton Capital LLP
Butler Capital Partners SA

CIC LBO Partners SAS
CIC Mezzanine Gestion SAS
CICLAD SAS
CM-CIC Capital Prive
CVC Capital Partners (Europe), Ltd.
Candover Investments PLC
Canec International
Carlyle Group, The
Carvest (AKA: Credit Agricole Regions Investissement)
Cathay Capital Private Equity SAS
Centre Capital Developpement SA
Centre Loire Expansion SAS
Cerea Gestion SAS
Charterhouse Capital Partners LLP
Chequers Capital
Chevrillon & Associes SCA
Cinven, Ltd.
Citizen Capital SAS
Clavel Investissement SAS
Cobalt Capital SAS
Cognetas LLP
Colony Capital LLC
Cowen Capital Partners LLC (FKA: SG Capital Partners LLC)
Creadev SAS
Credit Agricole Private Equity SA (FKA: Credit Lyonnais PE)
Credit Suisse Private Equity
Developpement & Partenariat SAS
Doughty Hanson & Co., Ltd.
Duke Street Capital
ELAIA Partners
EURAZEO
EURIDI
East Capital Private Equity AB
Edmond de Rothschild Capital Partners SAS
Etoile ID
European Capital Financial Services Ltd.
Expansinvest SA
4D Global Energy Advisors
Finadvance SA
Fonds Partenaires Gestion
Franche-Comte PME Gestion
GCE Capital SAS
Gilde Buy Out Partners
Gilde Investment Management B.V.
Global Emerging Markets
Goldman, Sachs & Co.
Groupama Private Equity (FKA: Finama Private Equity SA)
Groupe Arnault SAS
Groupe Sofimac
H.I.G. Capital LLC
Harbert Management Corporation
Houlihan, Lokey, Howard & Zukin
IDI Asset Management SA
IK Investment Partners, Ltd.
IRDI
Industries et Finances Partenaires SA
Initiative & Finance Investissement SA
Internet Capital Group
Investisseur et partenaire pour le Developpement (AKA: I&P)
Investors In Private Equity (AKA : IPE)
Invus Group Ltd., The
Ixcore
iXEN Partners
iXO Private Equity
Jefferies Group, Inc.
KBC Private Equity NV
Kenmore Private Equity, Ltd. (AKA: KPE)
Kohlberg, Kravis, Roberts & Company, L.P.
LBO France SAS
LMO SAS
Lazard Capital Partners
M3 Investissements
MBO Partenaires
MML Capital Partners
Massena Capital Partners
Midi Capital
Milestone Capital Partners Ltd. (AKA: EAC Manager Ltd.)
Montagu Private Equity, Ltd.
Montefiore Investment
Multicroissance SAS
NBGI Private Equity
NCI Gestion
Natixis Private Equity SA
Naxicap Partners SA
Newfund Management SA
NextStage SAS
123Venture SA
OFI Private Equity Capital SCA
ORKOS Capital
OTC Asset Management
Oaktree Capital Management LLC
Ofivalmo (AKA : Omnium Financier De Valeurs Mobiliers)
OpenGate Capital
Oryx Partner SAS
Ouest Croissance SA
PAI Partners (FKA: PAI Management)
PRICOA Capital Group, Ltd.
Paluel-Marmont Capital SA
Parcom Capital
Paris Orleans (Francarep SA)
Parvilla SAS
Perceva Capital
Perfectis Private Equity
Permira Advisers LLP
Phillimore Investissement
Pragma Capital
Qualium Investissement
Quartus Gestion
Quilvest Private Equity
REL
Robeco Private Equity
SGAM Private Equity
Sagard SAS
Sagipar (AKA: Societe Antilles-Guyane d'Investissement)
Silverfleet Capital (FKA: PPM Capital Partners)
Siparex Group SAS
Societe Fonciere et Financiere de Participation (AKA: SFFP)
Societe Generale Capital Partenaires SAS
Sopromec Participations
Sun Capital Partners, Inc.
Syntegra Capital, Ltd.
21 Centrale Partners
21 Partners SpA
3i Group PLC
TCR CAPITAL SAS
Tocqueville Finance SA
Truffle Venture SAS
UBS Capital Corporation
UFG Private Equity SAS
Undisclosed Firm
Uni Expansion Ouest
Unigrains S.A.
Vermeer Capital Partners
Vespa Capital LLP
Vestar Capital Partners, Inc.
Viveris Management S.A.S.
Weinberg Capital Partners SAS
Wendel
Windhurst Participations SA
XAnge Private Equity

Buyout Firms—Georgia

Parcom Capital
Salford (UK), Ltd.

Buyout Firms—Germany

ADCURAM Group AG (FKA: Adcuram Industriekapital AG)
AEA Investors LP
AFINUM Management GmbH
ARCADIA Beteiligungen Bensel Tiefenbacher & Co GmbH
AUCTUS Capital Partners AG
AXA Private Equity
Advent International
AlpInvest Partners N.V.
Alpha Group
Ammer!Partners
Apax Partners Worldwide
Apollo Capital Partners
Argantis GmbH
Augur Capital Group
Aurelius AG
BC Brandenburg Capital GmbH
BC Partners Ltd
BGM Beteiligungsgesellschaft KS Ravensburg
BKK-Investitionsfonds GmbH
BLS Venture Capital GmbH
BPE Unternehmensbeteiligungen GmbH
BPEP International
BTG Beteiligungsgesellschaft Hamburg mbH
Baigo Capital GmbH
Bain Capital
Baird Capital Partners
Barclays Private Equity, Ltd.
BayBG Bayerische Beteiligungsgesellschaft mbH
Bridgepoint Capital, Ltd.
Brockhaus Private Equity GmbH
bm-t beteiligungsmanagement thueringen gmbh
CBPE Capital, LLP (AKA: Close Brothers Private Equity, Ltd.)
CFC Industriebeteiligungen GmbH & Co. KGaA
COREST AG
CVC Capital Partners (Europe), Ltd.
Capital Dynamics AG
Capital Stage AG
Capvis Equity Partners AG
Carlyle Group, The
Cinven, Ltd.
Climate Solutions Management GmbH

CoBe Capital LLC
Cognetas LLP
Conetwork Erneuerbare Energien Holding GmbH & Co. KGaA
CornerstoneCapital Verwaltungs AG
capiton AG
DIH Deutsche Industrie-Holding GmbH
DPE Deutsche Private Equity GmbH (AKA: Parcom Deutsche PE)
DZ Equity Partner GmbH
Deutsche Bank Corporate Investments
Deutsche Beteiligungs AG
Deutsche Investitions- und Entwicklungsgesellschaft mbH
Doughty Hanson & Co., Ltd.
ECM Equity Capital Management GmbH
EKK Dr. Engelhardt, Kaupp, Kiefer Beteiligungsberatung GmbH
EQT Funds management Limited
EiKaM GmbH & Co. KG
Equita Management GmbH
Equity Partners GmbH
European Capital Financial Services Ltd.
equitrust AG
FIDURA Capital Consult GmbH
Findos Investor GmbH
Fonterelli GmbH & Co KGaA
Fortress Investment Group LLC
Frankfurt CapitalPartners AG (AKA: FCP)
GCP Capital Partners
GE Commercial Finance - Equity
General Atlantic LLC
German Capital GmbH
Goldfish Holdings, Inc.
Goldman, Sachs & Co.
Gruenwald Equity Management GmbH
H.I.G. Capital LLC
HANNOVER Finanz GmbH
Halder Holdings BV
Heidelberg Capital Asset Management GmbH
Heliad Equity Partners GmbH & Co. KGaA
Henderson Equity Partners (AKA: Henderson Private Capital)
Houlihan, Lokey, Howard & Zukin
IB H Beteiligungs-Managementgesellschaft Hessen mbH (BM H)
IDP Industrial Development Partners GmbH & Co KG
IK Investment Partners, Ltd.
Internet Capital Group
J. Hirsch & Co. S.a.r.l.
J.C. Flowers & Co. LLC
J.P. Morgan Capital Corporation
J.P. Morgan Partners (FKA: Chase Capital Partners)
Jefferies Group, Inc.
KSH Capital Partners AG (FKA: UEG Beteiligungs AG)
Kenmore Private Equity, Ltd. (AKA: KPE)
LRP Capital GmbH
Lazard Capital Partners
MBG Schleswig-Holstein GmbH
MML Capital Partners
Mittelstandische Beteiligungsgesellschaft Thuringen mbH
Montagu Private Equity, Ltd.
NPM Capital NV
NWD Nord-West-Deutsche Unternehmensbeteiligungsgesellschaft
Nordic Capital (AKA: NC Advisory)
Nordwind Capital GmbH
nwk Kapitalbeteiligungsgesellschaft der Sparkasse Bremen
Oaktree Capital Management LLC
Odewald & Compagnie GmbH
One Equity Partners (FKA: Banc One Venture Partners)
Orlando Capital Management GmbH
PAI Partners (FKA: PAI Management)
PARTER Capital Group GmbH
PINOVA Capital GmbH
PRICOA Capital Group, Ltd.
Paragon Partners GmbH
Permira Advisers LLP
Perseus LLC
Perusa Partners GmbH
PolyTechnos Venture-Partners GmbH
Quadriga Capital
RECAP Management GmbH
Riverside Company
Robeco Private Equity
S-Beteiligungsgesellschaft der Kreisparkasse Munchen
S-Partner Kapital AG
S-Siegerlandfonds 1 GmbH & Co.
SBG Sparkassenbeteiligungsgesellschaft Sachsen-Anhalt mbH
SGAM Private Equity
Silverfleet Capital (FKA: PPM Capital Partners)
Sparkassenkapital Ulm GmbH
Square Four Investments GmbH
Steadfast Capital GmbH (FKA: BHF Private Equity GmbH)
Sued Private Equity (FKA: Sued KB & Sued PE GmbH & Co. KGaA)
Sun Capital Partners, Inc.
Syntegra Capital, Ltd.
3i Group PLC
Triton Partners
VENTIZZ Capital Partners Advisory AG
VenGrow Corporate Finance AG
Vestar Capital Partners, Inc.
Vinci Capital
WAMEX Private Equity Management
WagnisKapital GmbH der Kreissparkasse Reutlingen
Waterland Private Equity Investments B.V.
WestLB AG Equity Investments (AKA: Westdeutsche Landesbank)
XAnge Private Equity

Buyout Firms—Ghana

Aureos Capital, Ltd.
Fidelity Capital Partners Ltd.
Zephyr Management, L.P.

Buyout Firms—Greece

Dolphin Capital Partners
IBG Management

Buyout Firms—Hong Kong

ADM Capital
AEA Investors LP
AFINUM Management GmbH
AIF Capital Pvt, Ltd.
AIG Capital Partners
AMP Capital Investors
Abax Global Capital Ltd.
Aetos Capital LLC
Affinity Equity Partners
AlpInvest Partners N.V.
American Capital, Ltd.
Angelo, Gordon & Company
Apax Partners Worldwide
Asset Managers Holding Company, Ltd.
Atlantic-Pacific Capital, Inc.
Atlantis Investment Management (Hong Kong) Ltd.
Aureos Capital, Ltd.
BPEP International
Bain Capital
Baird Capital Partners
BancBoston Capital/BancBoston Ventures
Blackstone Group, L.P.
Brown Brothers Harriman & Company (AKA: BBH)
CDH China Management Co., Ltd.
CIMB Private Equity Sdn Bhd
CITIC Capital Partners, Ltd.
CITIC Securities International Partners, Ltd.
CLSA Capital Partners (AKA: Credit Lyonnais Securities Asia)
CMIA Capital Partners (AKA: CM Investment Advisers Pte Ltd.)
CNOOC , Ltd.
CVC Asia Pacific, Ltd.
CVC Capital Partners (Europe), Ltd.
Candover Investments PLC
Capital Dynamics AG
Capital International Research, Inc.
Carlyle Group, The
Centurion Investment Management
Cinven, Ltd.
Citi Venture Capital International
Colony Capital LLC
Credit Suisse Private Equity
DBS Private Equity
Darby Overseas Investments, Ltd.
EQT Funds management Limited
First Eastern Investment Group
Fortress Investment Group LLC
FountainVest Partners (Asia), Ltd.
GE Commercial Finance - Equity
General Atlantic LLC
Gilbert Global Equity Capital, L.L.C.
Goldman, Sachs & Co.
H&Q Asia Pacific
HSBC Private Equity (UK), Ltd.
HSBC Pte Equity (Asia), Ltd. (FKA: HSBC Private Equity Mgt.)
Henderson Equity Partners (AKA: Henderson Private Capital)
Hilco Equity Management, LLC
InterLeader Capital, Ltd.
International Finance Corporation
Internet Capital Group
Investor Growth Capital, Inc.
Invus Group Ltd., The
J.P. Morgan Capital Corporation
J.P. Morgan Partners (FKA: Chase Capital Partners)
J.W. Childs Associates
Kohlberg, Kravis, Roberts & Company, L.P.
LDC (FKA: Lloyds TSB Development Capital, Ltd.)
Lazard Capital Partners

Leopard Capital, Ltd.
Li & Fung Investments
Lombard Investments, Inc.
Longreach Group, Ltd., The
MBK Partners
MatlinPatterson Global Advisers LLC
Merrill Lynch Capital Partners
Morgan Stanley Private Equity
Morrison & Foerster
Myo Capital
Navis Investment Partners (Asia), Ltd.
NewSmith Asset Management LLP
Northern Capital Management Group
Oaktree Capital Management LLC
Permira Advisers LLP
Pfingsten Partners, L.P.
Piper Jaffray Ventures
Providence Equity Partners LLC
Quadrangle Group LLC
Quam Asset Management, Ltd.
Riverside Company
7bridge Capital Partners, Ltd.
SBI E2-Capital Asia Holdings, Ltd.
SCM Strategic Capital Management AG
SEAVI Advent Corporation, Ltd.
STIC Investments, Inc.
Silver Lake Sumeru
Simon Murray and Associates
Standard Chartered Private Equity, Ltd.
Symphony Asia Holdings Pte. Ltd.
TPG Capital
Temasek Holdings Pvt., Ltd.
Tonic Venture Capital, Ltd.
Transpac Capital Pte, Ltd.
UBS Capital Corporation
Unitas Capital Pte, Ltd.
VinaCapital Investment Management Company
Walden International
York Capital Management, LLC

Buyout Firms—Hungary

AIG Capital Partners
Arx Equity Partners
Darby Overseas Investments, Ltd.
Global Capital Finance
iEurope Capital LLC
Mid Europa Partners
Riverside Company
3TS Capital Partners, Ltd.

Buyout Firms—Iceland

Aftvinnuprounarsjoour Suourlands
Baugur-ID
Bunaoarbankinn Verobref
Fjarfestingafelag Suourlands ehf
Framtak Investment Bank (AKA: Albjooafjarfestingarfelag EFA)

Buyout Firms—India

ADM Capital
AIF Capital Pvt, Ltd.
AIG Capital Partners
AMP Capital Investors
Actis Capital LLP
Aditya Birla Capital Advisors Pvt., Ltd.
Advent International
Apax Partners Worldwide
Aquarius Investment Advisors Pte., Ltd.
Aureos Capital, Ltd.
Avigo Capital Partners
BPEP International
Baer Capital Partners, Ltd.
Bain Capital
Battery Ventures, L.P.
Blackstone Group, L.P.
Blackstreet Capital Management (FKA: MMP Capital Advisors)
CIMB Private Equity Sdn Bhd
CLSA Capital Partners (AKA: Credit Lyonnais Securities Asia)
Canaan Partners
Candover Investments PLC
Carlyle Group, The
Citi Venture Capital International
Citigroup Private Equity
Clearwater Capital Partners, LLC
Credit Suisse Private Equity
Darby Overseas Investments, Ltd.
Evolvence Capital
FlatWorld Capital LLC
GE Commercial Finance - Equity
GenNx360 Capital Partners
General Atlantic LLC
Global Investment House
Goldman, Sachs & Co.
Greater Pacific Capital LLP
HSBC Pte Equity (Asia), Ltd. (FKA: HSBC Private Equity Mgt.)
Henderson Equity Partners (AKA: Henderson Private Capital)
ICICI Venture Funds Management Co., Pvt. Ltd. (FKA: TDICI)
India Value Fund Advisors Private Ltd. (FKA: GW Capital)
International Finance Corporation
ic2 Capital LLP
Jefferies Group, Inc.
Jina Ventures, Inc.
Kohlberg, Kravis, Roberts & Company, L.P.
Kotak Investment Advisors, Ltd. (AKA: KPEG)
Lazard Capital Partners
Lumis Partners
Merrill Lynch Capital Partners
Multiples Alternate Asset Management
Navis Capital Partners, Ltd.
Navis Investment Partners (Asia), Ltd.
New Silk Route Partners LLC
Norwest Venture Partners
OrbiMed Advisors LLC
Power Finance Corporation, Ltd.
Private Equity Partners SpA
Providence Equity Partners LLC
SVB Capital
Siguler Guff & Company
Sonoma Management Partners
Standard Chartered Private Equity, Ltd.
Symphony Asia Holdings Pte. Ltd.
3i Group PLC
TA Associates, Inc.
TPG Capital
Temasek Holdings Pvt., Ltd.
Thomas Weisel Partners Group, Inc.
Walden International
Zephyr Management, L.P.
Zeus Inframanagement Pvt, Ltd.

Buyout Firms—Indonesia

Actis Capital LLP
Aureos Capital, Ltd.
CLSA Capital Partners (AKA: Credit Lyonnais Securities Asia)
Garuda Capital Partners
Tembusu Partners Pte., Ltd.

Buyout Firms—Ireland

AIG Capital Partners
Allied Irish Investment (AKA: AIB Bank) (AKA: AIB Group)
Anglo Irish Capital Partners Limited
Bowmark Capital (FKA: Sagitta Private Equity)
Brown Brothers Harriman & Company (AKA: BBH)
FL Partners
Goldman, Sachs & Co.
RJD Partners Limited (FKA: Royal London Private Equity)

Buyout Firms—Israel

Abraaj Capital
Apax Partners Worldwide
Battery Ventures, L.P.
Canaan Partners
GE Commercial Finance - Equity
Goldman, Sachs & Co.
KCPS Israel Private Equity Partners
Markstone Capital
Pamplona Capital Management LLP
SKY FUND
SVB Capital
Siraj Fund Management Company
Undisclosed Firm
Viola Private Equity

Buyout Firms—Italy

AAC Capital Partners
AVM Associati SpA
AXA Private Equity
Advanced Capital SGRpA
Advent International
Aksia Group SGR SpA
Alcedo SGR SpA
Aletti Private equity SGR
Alpha Group
Alto Partners SGR SpA
Ambienta SGR S.p.A.
Apax Partners Worldwide
Argan Capital (FKA: BA Capital Partners Europe, BACPE)
Argos Soditic SA
Atlantis Capital Special Situations SpA
BC Partners Ltd
BNP Paribas Asset Management SGR SpA (FKA: BNL Gestioni SGR)
BPEP International
BS Private Equity SpA (FKA: B&S Private Equity Group)
Banca Popolare Commercio e Industria (AKA: Group BPCI)
Barclays Private Equity, Ltd.
Bridgepoint Capital, Ltd.
CAPITALIA Sofipa SGR (FKA: MCC Sofipa)
CVC Capital Partners (Europe), Ltd.
Candover Investments PLC

Carlyle Group, The
Centrobanca
Cinven, Ltd.
Clessidra Capital
Clubinvest Private Equity
Cognetas LLP
Colony Capital LLC
Consilium SGR pA
Credit Suisse Private Equity
DGPA SGR Spa
Doughty Hanson & Co., Ltd.
Efibanca SpA
Foresight Group
Fortress Investment Group LLC
Friulia SpA Fin.Reg.Friuli-Venezia
GE Commercial Finance - Equity
Goldman, Sachs & Co.
Henderson Equity Partners (AKA: Henderson Private Capital)
IDeA Capital Funds Sgr SpA
IMI Fondi Chiusi SGR SpA
INTERBANCA SpA
Impresa e Finanza SGR
Industria & Finanza SGR S.p.A.
Industrial Assets SpA
Iniziativa Gestione Investimenti SGR
Investindustrial Partners, Ltd.
Investitori Associati SpA
Istituto Atesino SpA
J. Hirsch & Co. S.a.r.l.
Lazard Capital Partners
MVI Italia s.r.l.
Management & Capitali SpA
Mandarin Capital Partners
Mediolanum State Street SGRpA
NEM SGR SpA
Natixis-Cape SGR SpA
Overseas Partners Italia Srl (AKA: OPI)
PAI Partners (FKA: PAI Management)
PM & Partners SpA
Patron Capital, Ltd.
Pentar
Permira Advisers LLP
Private Equity Partners SpA
Progressio SGR
R&D Advisory
R72 Partners Srl
Ras Asset Management Sgr
S+R Investimenti e Gestioni
SANPAOLO IMI Fondi Chiusi SGR SpA
Sanpaolo IMI Private Equity SpA
Siparex Group SAS
Sopaf SpA
Strategia Italia
Synergo SGR S.p.A.
Syntegra Capital, Ltd.
21 Centrale Partners
21 Partners SpA
3i Group PLC
Tamburi Investment Partners (AKA Tamburi & Associati SpA)
UBS Capital Corporation
Unicredit Banca d'Impresa
Vestar Capital Partners, Inc.
WestLB AG Equity Investments (AKA: Westdeutsche Landesbank)

Buyout Firms—Ivory Coast

Actis Capital LLP
EMP Africa Fund Management (AKA: Emerging Capital Partners)

Buyout Firms—Jamaica

Caribbean Equity Partners Limited

Buyout Firms—Japan

AIG Capital Partners
AIG Japan Partners Inc.
AMP Capital Investors
Advantage Partners LLP
Advent International
Aetos Capital LLC
Arise Capital Partners, Inc.
Asset Managers Holding Company, Ltd.
BPEP International
Bain Capital
Blackstone Group, L.P.
Brown Brothers Harriman & Company (AKA: BBH)
CAS Capital, Inc.
CITIC Capital Partners, Ltd.
CLSA Capital Partners (AKA: Credit Lyonnais Securities Asia)
CVC Asia Pacific, Ltd.
CVC Capital Partners (Europe), Ltd.
Capital International Research, Inc.
Carlyle Group, The
Chuo Mitsui Capital Co., Ltd.
Colony Capital LLC
Credit Suisse Private Equity
DOGAN Investments, Inc.
Fortress Investment Group LLC
Fukuoka Capital Partners
Fund Creation Co., Ltd.
GE Commercial Finance - Equity
Global Fund 1 Go Toshi Jigyo Kumiai
Goldman, Sachs & Co.
H&Q Asia Pacific
Integral Investments, Inc.
Investor Growth Capital, Inc.
Iwakaze Capital, Inc.
J Bridge Corporation
J-Star Co., Ltd.
J-Will Partners Co., Ltd.
J.P. Morgan Capital Corporation
J.P. Morgan Partners (FKA: Chase Capital Partners)
JBF Partners
Japan Private Equity Co., Ltd
Jefferies Group, Inc.
Jina Ventures, Inc.
Kagawagin Capital Co., Ltd
Kohlberg, Kravis, Roberts & Company, L.P.
Lazard Capital Partners
Lehman Brothers, Inc.
Lone Star Funds
Longreach Group, Ltd., The
MBK Co.,Ltd.
MBK Partners
MKS Partners, Ltd. (FKA: Schroder Ventures K.K.)
Milestone Turnaround Management Co., Ltd.
Mizuho Capital Partners Co., Ltd.
Morrison & Foerster
Mushup Partners Godo Gaisha
New Horizon Capital Co., Ltd.
NewSmith Asset Management LLP
Nippon Mirai Capital Co., Ltd
Oaktree Capital Management LLC
Partners Group AG
Permira Advisers LLP
Phoenix Capital Co., Ltd.
Polaris Principal Finance Co., Ltd.
Privee Investment Holdings Co., Ltd.
RHJ International Japan
Ridgeway Capital Partners, Ltd. (FKA:OPE Partners Ltd.)
Riverside Company
SBI Capital Company, Ltd.
SGAM Private Equity
STB Investment Corporation
Sedona Capital, Inc.
Sun Capital Partners Japan K.K.
TPG Capital
Tokio Marine Capital Company, Ltd.
UBS Capital Corporation
Unison Capital, Inc.
Valiant Partners Co. Ltd.
Vestar Capital Partners, Inc.
Wilshire Private Markets

Buyout Firms—Jordan

Global Investment House

Buyout Firms—Kazakhstan

Aureos Capital, Ltd.
Renaissance Capital
SigmaBleyzer

Buyout Firms—Kenya

Actis Capital LLP
African Alliance Private Equity
Aureos Capital, Ltd.
Baraka Africa Fund, Ltd.
Centum Investment (FKA: ICDC Investment Co., Ltd.)
East Africa Capital Partners
Norfund
Renaissance Capital

Buyout Firms—Kuwait

Global Investment House
NBK Capital, Ltd.

Buyout Firms—Latvia

Alta Capital
Askembla Asset Management AB
Baltcap
GILD Bankers (FKA: LHV Ventures)
Trigon Alternative Investments

Buyout Firms—Lebanon

Carlyle Group, The
Colony Capital LLC

Buyout Firms—Lithuania

Alta Capital
Askembla Asset Management AB
Baltcap
GILD Bankers (FKA: LHV Ventures)
Hermis Capital, JSC

Buyout Firms—Luxembourg

AMP Capital Investors
Abacus Invest S.C.A. SICAR
Advanced Capital SGRpA
Audiolux

Augur Capital Group
BIP Investment Partners SA (FKA: BGL Investment Partners)
BLUO SICAV-SIF
BeCapital Private Equity SCA SICAR
Bridgepoint Capital, Ltd.
Brown Brothers Harriman & Company (AKA: BBH)
CVC Capital Partners (Europe), Ltd.
CapMan Plc
Carlyle Group, The
Doughty Hanson & Co., Ltd.
Firebird Management LLC
IK Investment Partners, Ltd.
Investindustrial Partners, Ltd.
J. Hirsch & Co. S.a.r.l.
Mandarin Capital Partners
Oaktree Capital Management LLC
PAI Partners (FKA: PAI Management)
Partners Group AG
Patron Capital, Ltd.
Permira Advisers LLP
Quilvest Private Equity
Robeco Private Equity
Solidus Partners LLP
TPG Capital
Triton Partners

Buyout Firms—Madagascar

I&P Management Ltd. (AKA: Indian Ocean)

Buyout Firms—Malaysia

AIG Capital Partners
Actis Capital LLP
Aureos Capital, Ltd.
CIMB Private Equity Sdn Bhd
CLSA Capital Partners (AKA: Credit Lyonnais Securities Asia)
Ingenious Haus Group
Musharaka Venture Management Sdn Bhd
Navis Investment Partners (Asia), Ltd.
Pica (M) Corporation Berhad
Tembusu Partners Pte., Ltd.
UIB Capital, Inc.
Unicorn Investment Bank B.S.C.
Walden International

Buyout Firms—Mauritius

AfriCap Microfinance Investment Company
Aureos Capital, Ltd.
Avigo Capital Partners
I&P Management Ltd. (AKA: Indian Ocean)

Buyout Firms—Mexico

Advent International
Aureos Capital, Ltd.
BPEP International
Carlyle Group, The
Credit Suisse Private Equity
Darby Overseas Investments, Ltd.
EMX Capital
Evercore Partners
GE Commercial Finance - Equity
Goldman, Sachs & Co.
Larrain Vial SA
Monterrey Capital Partners
Palmfund Management LLC
Promecap, S.C.
Southern Cross Group (AKA: SCG)
Temasek Holdings Pvt., Ltd.
WAMEX Private Equity Management
Zephyr Management, L.P.
Buyout Firms—Moldova
Horizon Capital

Buyout Firms—Monaco

Alpha Group
Goldman, Sachs & Co.

Buyout Firms—Morocco

Aureos Capital, Ltd.
Marocinvest Finance Group

Buyout Firms—Namibia

Paragon Investment Holdings

Buyout Firms—Neth. Antilles

Greenfield Capital Partners

Buyout Firms—Netherlands

AAC Capital Partners
ABN AMRO Participaties BV
Advent International
Albatros Investments
AlpInvest Partners N.V.
Antea Participaties Management BV
Astor Participaties BV
Atlantic Capital BV
Bencis Capital Partners
CVC Capital Partners (Europe), Ltd.
Concordia Fund
Cyrte Investments BV (FKA: Talpa Capital Beheer)
Dinvest B.V.
Dolfin Capital BV
Ecart Invest 1 BV
Egeria B.V.
European Hotel Capital
F. van Lanschot Participaties BV
fr2 Capital B.V.
Gilde Buy Out Partners
Gilde Equity Management Benelux B.V.
Gilde Investment Management B.V.
Greenfield Capital Partners
Halder Holdings BV
Holland Venture Partners BV
Indofin
Informal Capital Network (AKA: ICN)
Investor Growth Capital, Inc.
Janivo Investments BV
LDC (FKA: Lloyds TSB Development Capital, Ltd.)
Lazard Capital Partners
M2Group
Main Corporate Finance
Manaus Holding bv
NCB Participaties
NIBC Principal Investments (FKA: Parnib Holding NV)
NPM Capital NV
Netherlands Development Finance Company (AKA: FMO)
Newion Investments B.V.
NoorderHuys Participaties BV
OPM BV
Oaktree Capital Management LLC
Oikocredit International
Oost Europa Participaties BV (AKA Middle Europe Investments)
PPM Stimulans
Parcom Capital
Plain Vanilla Investments BV
Rabo Private Equity
Riverside Company
Robeco Private Equity
3i Group PLC
Tvi Investments Bv
Van Herk Investments
Van den Ende & Deitmers B.V.
Waterland Private Equity Investments B.V.
Wilshire Private Markets

Buyout Firms—New Zealand

AMP Capital Investors
Direct Capital Private Equity
Goldman Sachs JBWere Private Equity (FKA:JBWere Prv Equity)
Ironbridge Capital Pty., Ltd.
Knox Investment Partners, Ltd.
Murray Capital, Ltd.
Pencarrow Private Equity, Ltd.
Tembusu Partners Pte., Ltd.
Waterman Capital Ltd

Buyout Firms—Nigeria

Actis Capital LLP
Adlevo Capital Managers LLC
Aureos Capital, Ltd.
Avante Capital Partners
EMP Africa Fund Management (AKA: Emerging Capital Partners)
First Funds Ltd
Renaissance Capital
Travant Capital Partners
UBA Private Equity Limited

Buyout Firms—Norway

Altaria AS
Altor Equity Partners AB
Borea AS
CapMan Plc
Cardo Partners
Cinclus AS
Cubera Private Equity AS
EQT Funds management Limited
FSN Capital Partners AS
Herkules Capital AS
HitecVision AS
Jotunfjell Partners AS (AKA: JFP)
Nordic Capital (AKA: NC Advisory)
Norfund
Norvestor Equity AS (FKA: Norsk Vekst Forvaltning AS)
Venturefondet

Buyout Firms—Oman

Al Anwar Holdings SAOG
Oman Investment Co SAOC

Buyout Firms—Pakistan

Actis Capital LLP
JS Group

Buyout Firms—Peru

Aureos Capital, Ltd.
Enfoca Sociedad Administradora de Fondos de Inversion
Larrain Vial SA

Buyout Firms—Philippines

Aureos Capital, Ltd.
CAS Capital, Inc.
CLSA Capital Partners (AKA: Credit Lyonnais Securities Asia)
H&Q Asia Pacific
Walden International

Buyout Firms—Poland

AIG Capital Partners
AVALLON Sp. z o.o.
Abris Capital Partners
Advent International
Argan Capital (FKA: BA Capital Partners Europe, BACPE)
Arx Equity Partners
BPEP International
Bridgepoint Capital, Ltd.
Darby Overseas Investments, Ltd.
EQT Funds management Limited
Enterprise Investors Sp z oo
GE Commercial Finance - Equity
Investors Towarzystwo Funduszy Inwestycyjnych SA
KBC Private Equity NV
Krakowskie Centrum Inwestycyjne
Krokus Private Equity Sp. z o.o.
Mid Europa Partners
Penta Investments, Ltd.
Penton Consulting Sp. K. (AKA: Penton Partners)
Private Equity Partners SpA
Resource Partners sp. Z.o.o.
Riverside Company
Robeco Private Equity
Royalton Partners
SGAM Private Equity
3TS Capital Partners, Ltd.
Trigon Alternative Investments

Buyout Firms—Portugal

BPN Gestao de Activos, SGFIM, S.A.
Caixa Capital - Sociedade De Capital De Risco S.A.
Change Partners
Cofina, SGPS SA
ECS Capital, S.A.
Espirito Santo Capital - Sociedade de Capital de Risco SA
GED Group
ISQ, Sociedade Capital de Risco, SA
Magnum Capital Industrial Partners
New Capital - Sociedade de Capital de Risco, S.A.
Novabase Capital

Buyout Firms—Qatar

Global Investment House
Goldman, Sachs & Co.
QInvest LLC
Buyout Firms—Romania
AIG Capital Partners
Abris Capital Partners
Advent International
Arx Equity Partners
Axxess Capital Partners S.A. (FKA: Enterprise Capital)
BPEP International
Blackstreet Capital Management (FKA: MMP Capital Advisors)
Enterprise Investors Sp z oo
Finanziara Senese Di Sviluppo SpA
GED Group
Gemisa Investments
J.P. Morgan Partners (FKA: Chase Capital Partners)
Romanian - American Asset Management Company
Romanian Energy Efficiency Fund (AKA: Eficienta Energiei)
Royalton Partners
SGAM Private Equity
SIF Moldova
SigmaBleyzer

Buyout Firms—Russia

Alfa Capital Partners
BPEP International
Baring Vostok Capital Partners
Basic Element (AKA: Bazovy Element; FKA: Sibirsky Aluminium)
CapMan Plc
Credit Suisse Private Equity
Czura Thornton
Da Vinci Capital Management
Elbrus Capital
Goldman, Sachs & Co.
IndexAtlas Group
International Finance Corporation
Interros Holding
Lower Volga River Management Inc.
Marshall Capital Partners
Penta Investments, Ltd.
Private Equity Partners SpA
PromSvyazCapital Group
Quadriga Capital
Renaissance Capital
Salford (UK), Ltd.
Siguler Guff & Company
TPG Capital
Troika Capital Partners
VTB Capital
VTB Upravleniye Aktivami, ZAO

Buyout Firms—Saudi Arabia

Abraaj Capital
Global Investment House
Goldman, Sachs & Co.
HBG Holdings, Ltd.

Buyout Firms—Senegal

Aureos Capital, Ltd.

Buyout Firms—Serbia and Montenegro

Equest Partners, Ltd.
Salford (UK), Ltd.

Buyout Firms—Singapore

ADM Capital
AIG Capital Partners
AMP Capital Investors
AXA Private Equity
Actis Capital LLP
Affinity Equity Partners
Aquarius Investment Advisors Pte., Ltd.
Arcapita, Inc.
Aventures Capital Management Pte Ltd.
BPEP International
CDH China Management Co., Ltd.
CHAMP Private Equity Pty Ltd.
CIMB Private Equity Sdn Bhd
CLSA Capital Partners (AKA: Credit Lyonnais Securities Asia)
CMIA Capital Partners (AKA: CM Investment Advisers Pte Ltd.)
CVC Asia Pacific, Ltd.
CVC Capital Partners (Europe), Ltd.
Capital International Research, Inc.
Carlyle Group, The
Centurion Investment Management
Citi Venture Capital International
Clavel Investissement SAS
Clearwater Capital Partners, LLC
Credit Suisse Private Equity
DBS Private Equity
Darby Overseas Investments, Ltd.
Goldman, Sachs & Co.
Henderson Equity Partners (AKA: Henderson Private Capital)
Highland Capital Management, L.P.
Ingenious Haus Group
Jefferies Group, Inc.
Jina Ventures, Inc.
Lazard Capital Partners
Merrill Lynch Capital Partners
Morrison & Foerster
Nalanda Capital Pte, Ltd.
Navis Capital Partners, Ltd.
Navis Investment Partners (Asia), Ltd.
NewSmith Asset Management LLP
Oaktree Capital Management LLC
Orient Global
Partners Group AG
Raintree Ventures Pte., Ltd.
SEAVI Advent Corporation, Ltd.
Southern Capital Group Private Ltd.
Symphony Asia Holdings Pte. Ltd.
3 Degrees Asset Management Pte., Ltd.
3i Group PLC
TPG Capital
Temasek Holdings Pvt., Ltd.
Tembusu Partners Pte., Ltd.
Transpac Capital Pte, Ltd.
UBS Capital Corporation
VTB Capital
Walden International
Wilshire Private Markets

Buyout Firms—Slovakia

Across Private Equity - Health Care
Genesis Capital, s.r.o.
Penta Investments, Ltd.
Slovak American Enterprise Fund (AKA: SAEF)

Buyout Firms—Slovenia

KD Group
Poteza Partners d.o.o.

Buyout Firms—South Africa

AMB Private Equity Partners Limited (AKA: AMB Partners)
Absa Capital Private Equity (Pty) Ltd.
Actis Capital LLP
Adlevo Capital Managers LLC
AfriCap Microfinance Investment Company
Aureos Capital, Ltd.
EMP Africa Fund Management (AKA: Emerging Capital Partners)
EVI Capital Partners
Ethos Private Equity
Goldman, Sachs & Co.

Imbewu Capital Partners
International Finance Corporation
Investec Private Equity
Jala Capital (Pty) Ltd.
Kingdom Zephyr Africa Management (AKA: KZAM)
Lereko Invesments Property, Ltd.
Marlow Capital
New Africa Advisers
Norfund
Old Mutual PLC
RMB Private Equity
Southern Africa Enterprise Development Fund, The (SAEDF)
Sphere Private Equity
Spirit Capital Private Equity
Standard Bank Capital Investments
Tiso Group
Wipprivate Equity

Buyout Firms—South Korea

AIG Capital Partners
Affinity Equity Partners
Angelo, Gordon & Company
CLSA Capital Partners (AKA: Credit Lyonnais Securities Asia)
CVC Asia Pacific, Ltd.
CVC Capital Partners (Europe), Ltd.
Cappello Capital Corp.
Carlyle Group, The
Clearwater Capital Partners, LLC
Colony Capital LLC
Darby Overseas Investments, Ltd.
Global Capital Finance
Goldman, Sachs & Co.
H&Q Asia Pacific
IMM Private Equity, Inc.
KB Investment Co., Ltd. (FKA: Kookmin Investment Company)
Kohlberg, Kravis, Roberts & Company, L.P.
Korea Development Bank
Lazard Capital Partners
Lone Star Funds
MBK Partners
Oaktree Capital Management LLC
Riverside Company
STIC Investments, Inc.
Taurus Venture Capital Company, Ltd. (AKA: TVC)
Tube Investment, Inc.
UBS Capital Corporation
Unitas Capital Pte, Ltd.
Vogo Investment
Woongjin Capital Company

Buyout Firms—Spain

AAC Capital Partners
AC Desarrollo SGECR SA
Advent International
American Capital, Ltd.
Apax Partners Worldwide
Atlas Capital Close Brothers (FKA: Atlas Capital Investment)
Axon Capital
BPEP International
Banco Sabadell Capital Development
Bridgepoint Capital, Ltd.
CVC Capital Partners (Europe), Ltd.
Caixa Capital - Sociedade De Capital De Risco S.A.
Caixa Capital Desarrollo, SCR (AKA : CCD)
Candover Investments PLC
Carlyle Group, The
Colony Capital LLC
Corpfin Capital Asesores SA
Credit Suisse Private Equity
Doughty Hanson & Co., Ltd.
EIG Venture Capital, Ltd. (AKA: EVC)
Espiga Capital Gestion SCR SA
Espirito Santo Capital - Sociedade de Capital de Risco SA
European Capital Financial Services Ltd.
Excel Partners
GED Group
Gala Capital Partners (AKA: GCP)
Gala Fund Management
Goldman, Sachs & Co.
Harbert Management Corporation
Ibercaja Gestion SGICC SA
Impala Capital Partners (FKA; Suala Capital Advisors)
Inversiones Ibersuizas S.A.
Investindustrial Partners, Ltd.
Lazard Capital Partners
MCH Private Equity SA
Magnum Capital Industrial Partners
McCall Springer
Mercapital Servicios Financieros
Minerva Capital
Miura Private Equity SGECR, S.A.
N+1
Nazca Capital SGECR SA
Nmas1 Private Equity (FKA: Nmas1 Electra Capital Privado)
Novabase Capital
Omega Capital SL
PAI Partners (FKA: PAI Management)
Patron Capital, Ltd.
Permira Advisers LLP
Playa Hotels & Resorts, S.L.
Qualitas Equity Partners
Realza Capital SGECR SA
Reus Capital de Negocis SCR, SA
Riverside Company
Robeco Private Equity

Buyout Firms—Spain

Siparex Group SAS
Suma Capital
3i Group PLC
Tandem Capital Gestion
Valcapital Gestion SGECR SA

Buyout Firms—Sri Lanka

Aureos Capital, Ltd.
Lanka Ventures, Ltd.
Leopard Capital, Ltd.

Buyout Firms—Sudan

Global Investment House

Buyout Firms—Swaziland

African Alliance Private Equity

Buyout Firms—Sweden

AAC Capital Partners
Adrea i Malmo AB
Altor Equity Partners AB
Apax Partners Worldwide
Argan Capital (FKA: BA Capital Partners Europe, BACPE)
Askembla Asset Management AB
Axcel Industriinvestor AS
Bridgepoint Capital, Ltd.
Bridgepoint Development Capital
CVC Capital Partners (Europe), Ltd.
CapMan Plc
Capilon AB
Capital International Research, Inc.
Carlyle Group, The
Cevian Capital AB (FKA: Amaranth Capital)
Credelity Capital
Cubera Private Equity AS
Deseven Catalyst Group AB
Deva Group AB
Doughty Hanson & Co., Ltd.
EDP
EIG Venture Capital, Ltd. (AKA: EVC)
EQT Funds management Limited
East Capital Private Equity AB
FSN Capital Partners AS
Fagerberg & Dellby AB
Goldman, Sachs & Co.
IK Investment Partners, Ltd.
Industrial Development & Investment AB (AKA: IDI)
Investa Foretagskapital AB
Investor Growth Capital, Inc.
Jotunfjell Partners AS (AKA: JFP)
Karnell
Kenmore Private Equity, Ltd. (AKA: KPE)
Lazard Capital Partners
Litorina Capital Advisors AB
Montagu Private Equity, Ltd.
Nordic Capital (AKA: NC Advisory)
Nordstjernan
Norvestor Equity AS (FKA: Norsk Vekst Forvaltning AS)
PEQ AB
Paron Ventures AB
Permira Advisers LLP
Procuritas Partners KB
Qeep Ventures AB
Riverside Company
Sanders & Wiklund Kapitalpartner
Segulah Advisor AB
Stena Adactum AB
Swedfund International AB
3i Group PLC
Triton Partners
Valedo Partners (FKA: CreVal Partners)
Vostok Gas, Ltd. (FKA: Vostok Nafta Investment)
Wilh. Sonesson AB

Buyout Firms—Switzerland

AFINUM Management GmbH
AIG Capital Partners
AXA Private Equity
Advanced Capital SGRpA
Aralon AG
Argos Soditic SA
affentranger associates (FKA: Ultreia Capital, Ltd.)
BC Partners Ltd
BNP Paribas Private Equity SAS
BS Private Equity SpA (FKA: B&S Private Equity Group)
BV Holding AG

Baer Capital Partners, Ltd.
Bank Vontobel AG
Banque Cantonale de Geneve
Barclays Private Equity, Ltd.
Bax Capital Advisors AG
BioMedical Innovations, Ltd.
BlueOrchard Investments Sarl
Brown Brothers Harriman & Company (AKA: BBH)
CGS Management giesinger gloor lanz & co.
CLSA Capital Partners (AKA: Credit Lyonnais Securities Asia)
CVC Capital Partners (Europe), Ltd.
Capital Dynamics AG
Capvis Equity Partners AG
Co-Investor AG
Corporate Equity Partners AG
Cowen Capital Partners LLC (FKA: SG Capital Partners LLC)
Credit Suisse Private Equity
Cross Equity Partners AG
Czura Thornton
DEFI Gestion SA
DLJ Merchant Banking Partners
EGS Beteiligungen AG
EQT Funds management Limited
Ethemba Capital, Ltd.
Fortress Investment Group LLC
German Capital GmbH
Gilde Buy Out Partners
Gilde Investment Management B.V.
Good Energies, Inc.
HARDT GROUP Capital Partners Limited
Horizon 21 Private Equity
IDP Industrial Development Partners GmbH & Co KG
Indofin
Investindustrial Partners, Ltd.
Jefferies Group, Inc.
LODH Private Equity AG
Leman Capital
Lydian Capital Advisors S.A.
Lyrique SArl
M2 Capital Management AG
MCG Master Consulting AG
Massena Capital Partners
Matador Private Equity AG
Monitor Clipper Partners LLC
Mountain Partners AG
Muller-Mohl Group
Pamplona Capital Management LLP
Partners Group AG
Quilvest Private Equity
RECAP Management GmbH
Remaco Merger AG
Renaissance Capital
Robeco Private Equity
Royalton Partners
SCM Strategic Capital Management AG
Thomas Weisel Partners Group, Inc.
Tocqueville Finance SA
UBS Capital Corporation
VENTIZZ Capital Partners Advisory AG
VenGrow Corporate Finance AG
Vinci Capital
Zurmont Madison Management AG (FKA: Zurmont Management AG)

Buyout Firms—Taiwan

AIG Capital Partners
Alliance Management Consulting Co., Ltd.
CAS Capital, Inc.
CLSA Capital Partners (AKA: Credit Lyonnais Securities Asia)
Colony Capital LLC
Credit Suisse Private Equity
Crimson Investment, LLC
Goldman, Sachs & Co.
H&Q Asia Pacific
Lone Star Funds
STIC Investments, Inc.
Walden International
Whitesun Equity Partners

Buyout Firms—Tanzania

Actis Capital LLP
Aureos Capital, Ltd.

Buyout Firms—Thailand

Aureos Capital, Ltd.
CIMB Private Equity Sdn Bhd
CLSA Capital Partners (AKA: Credit Lyonnais Securities Asia)
ESP Equity Partners LLC
Goldman, Sachs & Co.
Jina Ventures, Inc.
Lombard Investments, Inc.
Navis Capital Partners, Ltd.
Navis Investment Partners (Asia), Ltd.

Buyout Firms—Tunisia

EMP Africa Fund Management (AKA: Emerging Capital Partners)
Invest Development Sicar (AKA: I.D. Sicar)
Sages Capital
Tuninvest Finance Group (TFG)
Viveris Management S.A.S.

Buyout Firms—Turkey

ADM Capital
AIG Capital Partners
AccessTurkey Private Equity
Actera Group
Advent International
Carlyle Group, The
Darby Overseas Investments, Ltd.
International Finance Corporation
Is Private Equity Investment Trust
NBK Capital, Ltd.
Odien Group
Unicorn Investment Bank B.S.C.

Buyout Firms—Uganda

African Alliance Private Equity
American Capital, Ltd.

Buyout Firms—Ukraine

Abris Capital Partners
Advent International
Credit Suisse Private Equity
Dragon Capital
GILD Bankers (FKA: LHV Ventures)
Horizon Capital
Ineko Capital Partners LLP
Kompaniya po upravleniyu aktivami TEKT
Renaissance Capital
SigmaBleyzer

Buyout Firms—United Kingdom

AAC Capital Partners
ACP Capital, Ltd.
ADM Capital
AEA Investors LP
AIG Capital Partners
AMP Capital Investors
ARCIS Finance SA
AXA Private Equity
Abbey Road Venture Ltd
Actis Capital LLP
Active Private Equity Advisory LLP
Acuity Capital LLP (FKA: Electra Partners LLP)
Advanced Capital SGRpA
Advantage Capital Limited
Advent International
Alchemy Partners LLP
Alcuin Capital
Aletheia Partners Ltd
Alliance Fund Managers, Ltd.
AlpInvest Partners N.V.
AnaCap Financial Partners LLP
Angelo, Gordon & Company
Apax Partners Worldwide
Apposite Capital LLP
Arcapita, Inc.
Ares Management, Inc.
Argan Capital (FKA: BA Capital Partners Europe, BACPE)
Ariya Capital Group, Ltd.
Ashmore Investment Management, Ltd.
Atlantic-Pacific Capital, Inc.
August Equity LLP
Aureos Capital, Ltd.
Avista Capital Holdings, L.P.
BC Partners Ltd
BPEP International
Baer Capital Partners, Ltd.
Bain Capital
Balmoral Capital
BancBoston Capital/BancBoston Ventures
Bank of Scotland Corporate
Barclays Private Equity, Ltd.
Better Capital LLP
Blackstone Group, L.P.
Blue Oak Venture Capital Co., Ltd.
BlueGem Capital Partners LLP
Bowmark Capital (FKA: Sagitta Private Equity)
Bridgepoint Capital, Ltd.
Bridgepoint Development Capital
Brown Brothers Harriman & Company (AKA: BBH)
CBPE Capital, LLP (AKA: Close Brothers Private Equity, Ltd.)
CCMP Capital Advisors LLC
CIBC Capital Partners
CIMB Private Equity Sdn Bhd
CLSA Capital Partners (AKA: Credit Lyonnais Securities Asia)
CVC Capital Partners (Europe), Ltd.
Candover Investments PLC
CapMan Plc
Capital Dynamics AG
Capital International Research, Inc.
Carlyle Group, The
Celtic Pharma Management, LP
Centurion Capital Ltd (FKA: Finartis Private Equity, Ltd.)

Change Capital Partners LLP
Charlemagne Capital (UK) Limited
Charterhouse Capital Partners LLP
Cinven, Ltd.
Citi Venture Capital International
Citigroup Private Bank
Citigroup Private Equity
Clayton, Dubilier & Rice, Inc.
Cognetas LLP
Colony Capital LLC
Continental Capital Partners, Ltd.
Core Growth Capital LLP
Cowen Capital Partners LLC (FKA: SG Capital Partners LLC)
Credit Suisse Private Equity
DLJ Merchant Banking Partners
Da Vinci Capital Management
Dar Capital (UK), Ltd.
Darwin Private Equity LLP
Dawnay Day Principal Investments
Doughty Hanson & Co., Ltd.
Dubai International Capital LLC
Duke Street Capital
Dunedin Capital Partners, Ltd. (FKA: Dunedin Ventures, Ltd.)
ECI Partners LLP
EDP
EPIC Investment Partners (AKA: EPIC Private Equity)
EQT Funds management Limited
EVI Capital Partners
Elysian Capital
Endless LLP
Englefield Capital
Equest Partners, Ltd.
Ethemba Capital, Ltd.
European Capital Financial Services Ltd.
European Islamic Investment Bank Plc
Evercore Partners
Exponent Private Equity LLP (FKA: Square Capital Management)
F&C Asset Management plc
Fidelity Equity Partners
First Reserve Corporation
Fleming Family & Partners, Ltd. (AKA: FF&P)
Foresight Group
Fortress Investment Group LLC
Francisco Partners
GCP Capital Partners
GE Commercial Finance - Equity
GILD Bankers (FKA: LHV Ventures)
GMT Communications Partners LLP
GSC Partners (FKA: Greenwich Street Capital Partners)
General Atlantic LLC
Gilbert Global Equity Capital, L.L.C.
Gleacher & Co.
Global Capital Finance
Global Emerging Markets
Global Innovation Partners LLC
Global Private Equity PLC
Goldman Sachs JBWere Private Equity (FKA:JBWere Prv Equity)
Goldman, Sachs & Co.
Gores Group LLC, The
Graphite Capital (FKA: F&C Ventures, Ltd.)
Greater Pacific Capital LLP
Gresham LLP
H.I.G. Capital LLC
HARDT GROUP Capital Partners Limited
HSBC Private Equity (UK), Ltd.
HSBC Private Equity Middle East
Hamilton Bradshaw
Harbert Management Corporation
Hastings Private Equity
Headway Capital Partners LLP
Helios Investment Partners LLP
Hellman & Friedman LLC
Henderson Equity Partners (AKA: Henderson Private Capital)
Highland Capital Management, L.P.
HitecVision AS
Houlihan, Lokey, Howard & Zukin
IK Investment Partners, Ltd.
IndexAtlas Group
Infinity Asset Management LLP
Internet Capital Group
Intersuisse Bioscience Managers Pty, Ltd. (IB Managers)
Invesco Private Capital
Investcorp Bank B.S.C.
Investcorp Technology Investments Group
Investec Private Equity
Investindustrial Partners, Ltd.
Invex Capital Partners
Invus Group Ltd., The
ic2 Capital LLP
J.C. Flowers & Co. LLC
J.F. Lehman & Company
J.P. Morgan Capital Corporation
J.P. Morgan Partners (FKA: Chase Capital Partners)
JS Group
Jefferies Group, Inc.
Kelso Place Asset Management Limited
Kenmore Private Equity, Ltd. (AKA: KPE)
Key Capital Partners
Klesch Capital Partners
Kohlberg, Kravis, Roberts & Company, L.P.
LDC (FKA: Lloyds TSB Development Capital, Ltd.)
LGV Capital, Ltd. (FKA: Legal & General Ventures, Ltd.)
Langholm Capital LLP
Lazard Capital Partners
Lehman Brothers, Inc.
Li & Fung Investments
Lion Capital (FKA: Hicks Muse (Europe))
Lionhart Investments Ltd.
Lone Star Funds
Lonsdale Capital Partners LLP
Lyceum Capital
MML Capital Partners
MST Capital, Ltd.
Magenta Partners LLP
Marwyn Investment Management, LLP
MatlinPatterson Global Advisers LLC
Media & Print Investments Plc
Merchant Equity Partners
Mid Europa Partners
MidOcean Partners
Milestone Capital Partners Ltd. (AKA: EAC Manager Ltd.)
Monitor Clipper Partners LLC
Montagu Private Equity, Ltd.
Monument Capital Group LLC
Morgan Stanley Private Equity
Morrison & Foerster
NBGI Private Equity
NEL Fund Managers (FKA: Northern Enterprise, Ltd.)
NIBC Principal Investments (FKA: Parnib Holding NV)
Naxos Capital Partners
Nevis Capital LLP
NewSmith Asset Management LLP
Next Wave Partners LLP
Nikko Principal Investments Ltd
Nordic Capital (AKA: NC Advisory)
Northleaf Capital Partners
Northwestern Mutual Capital
Nova Capital Management, Ltd.
Oaktree Capital Management LLC
Old Mutual PLC
Ontario Teachers' Pension Plan
Orient Global
Oxfordshire Investment Opportunity Network (AKA: OION)
PAI Partners (FKA: PAI Management)
PHD Equity Partners LLP
PRICOA Capital Group, Ltd.
Pacific Investments
Palace Ventures Ltd
Palamon Capital Partners (FKA: Amphion Capital Partners)
Pamplona Capital Management LLP
Partners Group AG
Patron Capital, Ltd.
Penta Capital LLP (FKA: Penta Capital Partners, Ltd.)
Permira Advisers LLP
Phoenix Equity Partners (FKA: DLJ European Private Equity)
Pi Capital
PineBridge Investments
Piper Jaffray Ventures
Piper Private Equity Limited
Platinum Equity LLC
Primary Capital, Ltd.
Privet Capital LLP
Providence Equity Partners LLC
Quadrangle Group LLC
RJD Partners Limited (FKA: Royal London Private Equity)
Renaissance Capital
Revolution Capital Group LLC
Rhone Capital LLC
Risk Capital Partners, Ltd.
Robeco Private Equity
Rutland Fund Management, Ltd. (AKA: Rutland Partners LLP)
SCF Partners
SCM Strategic Capital Management AG
SGAM Private Equity
SVB Capital
Saints Ventures
Salford (UK), Ltd.
Silver Lake Sumeru
Silverfleet Capital (FKA: PPM Capital Partners)
Solidus Partners LLP

Sovereign Capital LLP (FKA:Sovereign Capital, Ltd.)
Spirit Capital Partners (FKA: Aberdeen Asset Managers PE)
StarGate Capital Management Limited
Stephens Group, Inc.
Stirling Square Capital Partners
Summit Partners
Sun Capital Partners, Inc.
Synova Capital LLP
Syntegra Capital, Ltd.
21 Partners SpA
3i Group PLC
TA Associates, Inc.
TDR Capital LLP
TH Lee Putnam Ventures, L.P.
TPG Capital
Teasses Capital, Ltd.
Tembusu Partners Pte., Ltd.
Tennants Ventures
Thomas Weisel Partners Group, Inc.
Tokio Marine Capital Company, Ltd.
TowerBrook Capital Partners L.P.
Triton Partners
UBS Capital Corporation
Undisclosed Firm
VTB Capital
Valco Capital Partners LP (FKA: Hilco Capital Partners LP)
Vardy Venture Capital
Veronis Suhler Stevenson (FKA: Veronis, Suhler & Associates)
Vespa Capital LLP
Vision Capital LLP
WM Enterprise (AKA: West Midlands Enterprise, Ltd.)
WestLB AG Equity Investments (AKA: Westdeutsche Landesbank)
Wilshire Private Markets
York Capital Management, LLC
Zephyr Management, L.P.
Zeus Private Equity

Buyout Firms—Uruguay

Lehman Brothers, Inc.

Buyout Firms—Utd. Arab Em.

Abraaj Capital
Abu Dhabi Investment House
Algebra Capital
Avigo Capital Partners
Baer Capital Partners, Ltd.
Carlyle Group, The
Credit Suisse Private Equity
Dubai International Capital LLC
EFG-Hermes Private Equity
Evolvence Capital
GCC Energy Fund, The
Gala Fund Management
Global Investment House
Goldman, Sachs & Co.
GrowthGate Capital Corporation
Gulf Capital
HBG Holdings, Ltd.
Invest AD
JS Group
Jefferies Group, Inc.
Kenmore Private Equity, Ltd. (AKA: KPE)
Kohlberg, Kravis, Roberts & Company, L.P.
M'Sharie LLC
Millennium Private Equity
NBD Sana Capital
NBK Capital, Ltd.
New Silk Route Partners LLC
Partners Group AG
SHUAA Partners
Scimitar Global Ventures
Standard Chartered Private Equity, Ltd.
UIB Capital, Inc.
Unicorn Investment Bank B.S.C.

Buyout Firms—Vietnam

Aureos Capital, Ltd.
BIDV Vietnam Partners Investment Management Co. (AKA: BVIM)
STIC Investments, Inc.
Temasek Holdings Pvt., Ltd.
Vietnam Pioneer Partners
VinaCapital Investment Management Company

Buyout Firms—Yemen

Global Investment House

Buyout Firms—Zambia

Aureos Capital, Ltd.
INTERBANCA SpA

Buyout Firms—Zimbabwe

Batanai Capital Finance

Fund of Funds—Australia

Frank Russell Capital
ING Investment Management
Industry Funds Management
Jolimont Capital Pty, Ltd.
Macquarie Investment Management, Ltd. (AKA: MIML)
Pantheon Ventures, Ltd.
Stafford Timberland, ltd.

Fund of Funds—Austria

Global Private Equity Holding AG

Fund of Funds—Belgium

ARKimedes
AXA Investment Managers
BIO (Belgian Investment Company for Developing Countries)
Groupe Bruxelles Lambert S.A. (GBL)
O'Melveny & Myers LLP
Pantheon Ventures, Ltd.

Fund of Funds—Brazil

Paul Capital Partners

Fund of Funds—Canada

Frank Russell Capital
Kensington Capital Partners
Kirchner Private Capital Group
Paul Capital Partners

Fund of Funds—Channel Islands

Unigestion SA

Fund of Funds—China

Adveq Management AG
Asia Alternatives Management LLC
CDC Group PLC (FKA: Commonwealth Development Corporation)
CNSTONE
Chengdu Yinke Venture Capital Co., Ltd.
China Venture Capital Research Institute, Ltd.
EMAlternatives LLC
Horsley Bridge Partners
Jade Alternative Investment Advisors
Jade China Value Partners L.P.
Jilin Venture Capital Fund of Funds Management Co., Ltd.
Morgan Creek Capital Management LLC
O'Melveny & Myers LLP
Shanghai Pudong Science and Technology Investment Co., Ltd.

Fund of Funds—Denmark

ATP Private Equity Partners
Danske Private Equity A/S
Nordea Private Equity
Scandinavian Private Equity A/S

Fund of Funds—Egypt

Amundi Private Equity Funds SA

Fund of Funds—Finland

Amanda Capital Oyj
Nordea Private Equity

Fund of Funds—France

ACG Private Equity (FKA: Altium Capital Gestion)
Access Capital Partners
Amundi Private Equity Funds SA
Bex Capital

Fondinvest Capital (Grp. Caisse de Depots)
Fonds de Reserve pour les Retraites (AKA: FRR)
Frank Russell Capital
Gimar Capital Investissement
Paul Capital Partners
Unigestion SA

Fund of Funds—Germany

ACG Private Equity (FKA: Altium Capital Gestion)
AXA Investment Managers
Adveq Management AG
Allianz Capital Partners GmbH
Auda Private Equity LLC
CAM Private Equity Consulting & Verwaltungs - GmbH
Golding Capital Partners GmbH
HVB Russell Management GmbH
Kreditanstalt fuer Wiederaufbau (KfW)
Sal. Oppenheim Private Equity Partners
Swift Capital Partners GmbH
southventure Beteiligungsberatung & Verwaltungs GmbH
Terra Firma Capital Partners, Ltd.
von Braun & Schreiber Private Equity Partners GmbH
WealthCap Initiatoren GmbH
WestLB Mellon Asset Management (USA) LLC

Fund of Funds—Greece

ACG Private Equity (FKA: Altium Capital Gestion)
New Economy Development Fund, The (AKA : TANEO)

Fund of Funds—Hong Kong

Asia Alternatives Management LLC
Auda Private Equity LLC
Capital Z Investment Partners (FKA: Union Square Partners)
China Venture Capital Research Institute, Ltd.
Emerald Hill Capital Partners, Ltd.
Hamilton Lane Advisors, Inc.
HarbourVest Partners LLC
ING Investment Management
LESS Limited
LGT Capital Partners AG
Macquarie Investment Management, Ltd. (AKA: MIML)
Morgan Creek Capital Management LLC
Morgan Stanley Alternative Investment Partners
NB Alternatives - Fund of Funds
O'Melveny & Myers LLP
Pantheon Ventures, Ltd.
Paul Capital Partners
Portfolio Advisors LLC
Squadron Capital Advisors, Ltd.
TR Advisors, Ltd.

Fund of Funds—India

Capvent AG
ING Investment Management

Fund of Funds—Ireland

LGT Capital Partners AG

Fund of Funds—Israel

Hamilton Lane Advisors, Inc.
Vintage Venture Partners

Fund of Funds—Italy

ACG Private Equity (FKA: Altium Capital Gestion)
AXA Investment Managers

Fund of Funds—Japan

Alternative Investment Capital, Ltd.
Frank Russell Capital
Hamilton Lane Advisors, Inc.
HarbourVest Partners LLC
LGT Capital Partners AG
O'Melveny & Myers LLP

Fund of Funds—Kazakhstan

Kazyna Capital Management, AO

Fund of Funds—Luxembourg

European Investment Bank, The (AKA: EIB)
European Investment Fund (AKA: EIF)
Golding Capital Partners GmbH
Sal. Oppenheim Private Equity Partners

Fund of Funds—Malaysia

ING Investment Management

Fund of Funds—Morocco

Amundi Private Equity Funds SA

Fund of Funds—Netherlands

EMAlternatives LLC

Fund of Funds—New Zealand

Frank Russell Capital
New Zealand Venture Investment Fund, Ltd.

Fund of Funds—Norway

Anchor Capital Management Ltd
Argentum Fondsinvesteringer AS
Nordea Private Equity
Storebrand Alternative Investments ASA

Fund of Funds—Poland

Amundi Private Equity Funds SA

Fund of Funds—Portugal

AXA Investment Managers

Fund of Funds—Qatar

AXA Investment Managers

Fund of Funds—Romania

Amundi Private Equity Funds SA

Fund of Funds—Saudi Arabia

SEDCO Direct Investment Group

Fund of Funds—Singapore

Adams Street Partners LLC
Allianz Capital Partners GmbH
Axiom Asia Private Capital
CDC Group PLC (FKA: Commonwealth Development Corporation)
Frank Russell Capital
Hamilton Lane Advisors, Inc.
IDFC Capital (Singapore) Pte, Ltd.
ING Investment Management
O'Melveny & Myers LLP
TIF Ventures Pte., Ltd.
Unigestion SA

Fund of Funds—South Africa

Industrial Development Corporation of South Africa Ltd (IDC)
SP Aktif
Vunani Private Equity Partners (Pty), Ltd.

Fund of Funds—South Korea

Korea Venture Investment Corporation

Fund of Funds—Spain

ACG Private Equity (FKA: Altium Capital Gestion)
AXA Investment Managers
Altamar Private Equity
Arcano Capital

Fund of Funds—Sweden

Anchor Capital Management Ltd
Auda Private Equity LLC
Coeli Private Equity Management AB
NAXS Nordic Access Buyout Fund AB
Nordea Private Equity
Sixth Swedish National Pension Fund (AKA: Sjatte AP-fonden)
Storebrand Alternative Investments ASA

Fund of Funds—Switzerland

ACG Private Equity (FKA: Altium Capital Gestion)
Adveq Management AG
Alpha Associates AG
Capvent AG
LGT Capital Partners AG
Portfolio Advisors LLC
Swiss Re Private Equity Advisers
Unigestion SA
Union Bancaire Privee Private Equity
ViaNova Capital

Fund of Funds—Tunisia

Amundi Private Equity Funds SA

Fund of Funds—United Kingdom

ACG Private Equity (FKA: Altium Capital Gestion)
AXA Investment Managers
Access Capital Partners
Adams Street Partners LLC
Anchor Capital Management Ltd
Auda Private Equity LLC
Bex Capital
BlackRock Private Equity Partners
Bregal Investments
CDC Group PLC (FKA: Commonwealth Development Corporation)
Capital Z Investment Partners (FKA: Union Square Partners)
Capital for Enterprise, Ltd.
Coller Capital
Commonfund Capital, Inc. (FKA: Common Fund)
Crystal Partners & Co., LLP
Frank Russell Capital
Greenpark Capital, Ltd.
Greenspring Associates, Inc.
Hamilton Lane Advisors, Inc.
HarbourVest Partners LLC
Hermes Private Equity Management, Ltd.
Horsley Bridge Partners
Industry Funds Management
Innisfree Group
Keyhaven Capital Partners, Ltd.
LGT Capital Partners AG
Landmark Partners, Inc.
Macquarie Investment Management, Ltd. (AKA: MIML)
NB Alternatives - Fund of Funds
New Star Asset Management
Northgate Capital Group
O'Melveny & Myers LLP
Orthogonal Partners LLP.

PPM Managers
Pantheon Ventures, Ltd.
Parish Capital Advisors LLC
Paul Capital Partners
Performance Equity Management, LLC
Private Advisors LLC
SL Capital Partners LLP
Shackleton Ventures, Ltd.
Stafford Timberland, ltd.
Terra Firma Capital Partners, Ltd.
Unigestion SA
Union Bancaire Privee Private Equity
VenCap International plc
ViaNova Capital

Fund of Funds—Utd. Arab Em.
Jade China Value Partners L.P.
Union Bancaire Privee Private Equity

Mezzanine Firms—Australia
Intermediate Capital Group Plc

Mezzanine Firms—Austria
Invest Mezzanine Capital Management GmbH
Mezzanin Finanzierungs AG
Mezzanine Management Finanz- und Unternehmensberatungs GmbH
Raiffeisen Mezzanin Partners
Syntaxis Capital

Mezzanine Firms—Canada
Crown Capital Partners Inc.
Global Capital Partners
Penfund Partners, Inc.
Romspen Investment Corporation
Rose Corporation, The
Wellington Financial LP

Mezzanine Firms—Finland
Nordic Mezzanine Advisers Ltd

Mezzanine Firms—France
Capzanine
Euromezzanine Conseil (AKA: Euromezzanine Gestion)
IFE Mezzanine
Indigo Capital, Ltd.
Intermediate Capital Group Plc

Mezzanine Firms—Germany
IKB Private Equity GmbH
Intermediate Capital Group Plc
Mittelstaendische Beteiligungsgesellschaft Niedersachsen mbH

Mezzanine Firms—Greece
Capital Connect Venture Partners S.A.

Mezzanine Firms—Haiti
Darby Asia Investors, Ltd.

Mezzanine Firms—Hong Kong
Asia Mezzanine Capital Advisers, Ltd.
Darby Asia Investors, Ltd.
Intermediate Capital Group Plc

Mezzanine Firms—Hungary
Mezzanine Management Finanz- und Unternehmensberatungs GmbH

Mezzanine Firms—India
BanyanTree Finance Pvt. Ltd.
Waygate Capital India Pvt., Ltd.

Mezzanine Firms—Indonesia
Kendall Court Capital Partners, Ltd.

Mezzanine Firms—Israel
First Israel Mezzanine Investors, Ltd. (AKA: FIMI)

Mezzanine Firms—Italy
AF Mezzanine SGRpA

Mezzanine Firms—Lebanon
Capital Trust, Ltd.

Mezzanine Firms—Luxembourg
Park Square Capital, LLP

Mezzanine Firms—Malaysia
Kendall Court Capital Partners, Ltd.

Mezzanine Firms—Netherlands
Intermediate Capital Group Plc

Mezzanine Firms—Poland
Mezzanine Management Finanz- und Unternehmensberatungs GmbH
Syntaxis Capital

Mezzanine Firms—Qatar
Qatari Fortis Investment Management

Mezzanine Firms—Romania
Mezzanine Management Finanz- und Unternehmensberatungs GmbH

Mezzanine Firms—Singapore
Kendall Court Capital Partners, Ltd.

Mezzanine Firms—South Korea
Dream Venture Investment (FKA: Basic Venture Investment)

Mezzanine Firms—Spain
Intermediate Capital Group Plc

Mezzanine Firms—Sweden
Intermediate Capital Group Plc

Mezzanine Firms—Ukraine
Mezzanine Management Finanz- und Unternehmensberatungs GmbH

Mezzanine Firms—United Kingdom
Babson Capital Europe
Capital Trust, Ltd.
Growth Capital Partners (FKA: Close Brothers Growth Capital)
Hutton Collins & Company Limited
Indigo Capital, Ltd.
Intermediate Capital Group Plc
Nordic Mezzanine Advisers Ltd
Park Square Capital, LLP
RBS Mezzanine Ltd

OPE—Bolivia
E+Co
OPE—Brazil
Starwood Capital Group

OPE—Canada
ARC Financial Corporation
Borealis Infrastructure Management, Inc.
Power Corporation of Canada

OPE—China
Och-Ziff Capital Management Group

OPE—Costa Rica
E+Co
OPE—France
Power Corporation of Canada

OPE—Hong Kong
Global Infrastructure Partners
Och-Ziff Capital Management Group

OPE—India
DHFL Venture Capital India Pvt Ltd.
Och-Ziff Capital Management Group

OPE—Nepal
E+Co

OPE—Netherlands
Oranje-Nassau Participaties BV

OPE—Norway
Verdane Capital (FKA: Four Seasons Venture Capital AS)

OPE—South Africa
E+Co

OPE—Sweden
Verdane Capital (FKA: Four Seasons Venture Capital AS)

OPE—United Kingdom
Apollo Real Estate Advisors
Global Infrastructure Partners
Lime Rock Partners LLC
Och-Ziff Capital Management Group
Partners Capital Investment Group, LLC
STAR Capital Partners, Ltd.

OPE—Utd. Arab Em.
Lime Rock Partners LLC

OPE—Vietnam
E+Co

Venture Firms—Albania
NCH Capital, Inc.

Venture Firms—Algeria
Calyon (FKA: Credit Agricole Indosuez)
European Bank for Reconstruction and Development
Sofinance
Statoil Innovation AS (AKA: StatoilHydro)

Venture Firms—Angola
Statoil Innovation AS (AKA: StatoilHydro)

Venture Firms—Argentina
Axxon Group
Calyon (FKA: Credit Agricole Indosuez)
Exxel Group S.A.
Litexco Mediterranea
Modena Technologies Capital Partners
Pegasus Venture Capital
RioBravo Investimentos
Schroders PLC
T. Rowe Price Threshold Partnerships
TMF Participations Management

Venture Firms—Armenia
European Bank for Reconstruction and Development

Venture Firms—Australia
AMWIN Management Pty., Ltd.
ANU Connect Ventures Pty., Ltd.
Accede Capital
Accord Capital Investors Pty., Ltd.
Advance Asset Management, Ltd.
African Lion Management Ltd (AKA: AFL Management Ltd)
Allen & Buckeridge Pty, Ltd.
Andover Group Pty, Ltd.
Australian Capital Ventures, Ltd.
Brandon Capital Partners
C.W. Downer & Company (FKA: Downer & Company)
CVC Managers Pty Ltd (Continental Venture Capital)
Challenger International Ltd.
China Century Capital Limited
Cleantech Ventures Pty, Ltd.
Co-Investor Capital Partners Pty., Ltd.
Coates Myer & Co. Pty Ltd.
DB Capital Partners Australia
Divergent Capital Partners (FKA: Bluefire Innovation)
Exto Partners Pty, Ltd.
Falconer Bellomo and Co., Ltd.
Foundation Capital, Ltd.
Four Hats Capital Pty, Ltd.
GBS Venture Partners, Ltd.
Generation Investment Management LLP
Goldman Sachs JBWere (NZ) Ltd. (FKA: JBWere (NZ) Ltd.)
Gresham Rabo Management, Ltd.
Harbert Venture Partners
Imprimatur Capital, Ltd.
Innovation Capital Associates Pty, Ltd.
Intel Capital
Investment Capital Partners Pty., Ltd.
incite.Capital Management Pty, Ltd.
Macquarie Capital Alliance Management Ltd.
Macquarie Direct Investment Ltd.
MillhouseIAG
Neo Technology Ventures Pty, Ltd.
Neuberger Berman LLC
Newbridge Capital, Ltd.
OneVentures Pty, Ltd.
Playford Capital Pty Ltd. (FKA: SA.BITS)
Queensland BioCapital Fund
RedFire Investments Pty, Ltd.
Rolls Royce Corporate Venture
Schroders PLC
SciVentures Investments Pty., Ltd.
Sentient Group, The
Skandia Innovation AB
Southern Cross Venture Partners
St. George Bank - Venture Capital
Starfish Ventures Pty., Ltd.
Start-up Australia Pty, Ltd.
Stone Ridge Ventures
TVG Capital Partners, Ltd.
Technology Venture Partners Pty Ltd.
Templeton Asset Management, Ltd.
Terra Rossa Capital, Ltd.
Uniseed Management Pty Ltd.
Venture Corporation of Australia Pty Ltd.
Wesley Clover, Ltd.
Yuuwa Capital, L.P.

Venture Firms—Austria
"schilling" Unternehmensbeteiligung GmbH
ARAX Capital Partners GmbH
Atila Ventures
Austria Wirtschaftsservice Gesellschaft mbH
BA Private Equity GmbH
Baird Capital Partners Europe
Capexit Beteiligungsmanagement AG
Danube Equity Invest Management GmbH
ECOS Beteiligungsmanagement GmbH
Gasser+Partner Beteiligungs GmbH
Global Equity Partners Beteiligungs-Management GmbH
Gruenderfonds GmbH & Co KEG
gcp gamma capital partners Beratungs- & Beteiligungs AG
HKK Partners
Horizonte Venture Management GmbH
IK Investmentbank AG
Kapital-Beteiligungs AG (KABAG)
Lead Equities GmbH
MINAS GmbH
Mittelstandsbeteiligungs AG
NOE Beteiligungsfinanzierungen GmbH
111 conventuring - consulting und beteiligungs gmbh
Oberosterreichische Unternehmensbeteiligungs GmbH
PONTIS Capital GmbH
ProRegio Mittelstandsfinanzierungs AG
Salzburger Unternehmensbeteiligungsgesellschaft m.b.H.
Skandia Innovation AB
StemCell Holding AG
tecnet capital Technologiemanagement GmbH
Undisclosed Firm
V4B - Venture for Business Beteiligungs AG
VCH Beteiligungs GmbH
Vienna Capital Partners
Wing Equity Management GmbH
YEurope Ventures

Venture Firms—Azerbaijan
European Bank for Reconstruction and Development
Statoil Innovation AS (AKA: StatoilHydro)

Venture Firms—Bahamas
Bahamas Entrepreneurial Venture Fund, Ltd.
inventages venture capital S.A.
Leeward Fund Management

Venture Firms—Bahrain
Accelerator Management Company B.S.C
Bahrain Development Bank
Capinnova Investment Bank
Emerging Markets Partnership (Bahrain) E.C.
Islamic Development Bank, The
Khaleej Finance & Investment
Stratum W.L.L.
Tuareg Capital, Ltd.

Venture Firms—Bangladesh
Catalyst Microfinance Investment Company

Venture Firms—Belarus
European Bank for Reconstruction and Development

Venture Firms—Belgium
AXE Investments
Allegro Investment Fund NV
Aqua Alta NV/SA
BMI - SBI
Becap BVBA
Beluga NV
Big Bang Ventures CVA
Brussels I3 Fund NV (AKA:Vrije Universiteit Brussel)
CDP Capital - Technology Ventures (FKA: CDP Sofinov)
Calyon (FKA: Credit Agricole Indosuez)
Capital-e
Capricorn Venture Partners N.V.
Catella AB
Compagnie du Bois Sauvage
Creafund Management NV
Dor Ventures Management SA
E-Capital Management
Eagle Venture Partners
Fin.Co
Fortis Private Equity NV/SA (FKA: VIV NV)
Fundus
GIMV N.V.
ING Belgium
ITP Management NV (AKA: IT-Partners NV)
ITP-Management N.V.
Indufin
Intel Capital
Investsud
Johnson & Johnson Development Corporation
LRM Investeringsmaatschappij Voor Limburg
Merifin Capital Group
Meusinvest
Mitiska
NPM-CNP (AKA: Compagnie Nationale a Portefeuille)
Namur Invest
Net Partners
Ocas Ventures BVBA
Oresa Ventures Sp Z oo
Ostbelgieninvest AG
Participatiemaatschappij Vlaanderen (AKA: Vinnof)
Partners@Venture NV
Prado Finance
QAT investments SA (AKA: Quercus Aimer Trust)
QiFund
Quest Management NV
Rolls Royce Corporate Venture
Sambrinvest S.A.
Societe Regionale d'Investissement de Wallonie SA (SRIW)
Societe Regionale dInvestissement de Bruxelles (SRIB/GIMB)
Sofinim NV
Software Holding & Finance (AKA: SHF)
Sopartec SA (AKA: Vives)
Statoil Innovation AS (AKA: StatoilHydro)
StoneMan NV 2007
TMF Participations Management
TrustCapital Partners NV
VentureBay
Venture Firms—Bermuda
Atila Ventures
Continuum Group, Ltd. (AKA: Continuum Advisory, Ltd.)
Peak Capital Group LLC
Schroders PLC
Starr International Company, Inc

Venture Firms—Bolivia
Small Enterprise Assistance Fund (SEAF)

Venture Firms—Bosnia/Herz.
European Bank for Reconstruction and Development
Horizonte Venture Management GmbH

Venture Firms—Botswana
Venture Partners Botswana

Venture Firms—Br. Virgin I.
TMF Participations Management

Venture Firms—Brazil
AIG Capital Investments do Brasil S.A.
Ace Venture Capital
Albatroz Participacoes
Angra Partners
Ascet Investimentos
Axxon Group
BPE Investimentos
Banco Nacional de Desenvolvimento Economico e Social - BNDES
CRP (AKA: Companhia de Participacoes)
Calyon (FKA: Credit Agricole Indosuez)
Credit Suisse First Boston DVTM, Brasil
DML Invista
Decisao Gestao Financeira (AKA: DGF Investimentos)
Econergy International Corporation
FIR Capital Partners, Ltd.
Gavea Investimentos
Governanca & Gestao Investimentos
Imprimatur Capital, Ltd.
Intel Capital
Jardim Botanico Partners (FKA: Araujo Fontes Consultoria)
Latin America Equity Partners (FKA: LAEP)
Latinvalley
MultiCapital do Brasil Consultoria e Participacoes
Orbe Investimentos e Participacoes Ltda.
Pactual Capital Partners Gestao de Recursos Ltda.
Pegasus Venture Capital
Performa Investimentos
Plataforma Capital Partners
Promon Ventures
RioBravo Investimentos
Rolls Royce Corporate Venture
SP Administradora de Fundos
Schroders PLC
Semco Ventures
Sindicatum Carbon Capital, Ltd.
Spinnaker Capital Group
Statoil Innovation AS (AKA: StatoilHydro)
Stratus Banco de Negocios
TMG Capital Partners Ltd.
Trivella Investimentos Ltda.
Uniao de Bancos Brasileiros S.A. (AKA: UNIBANCO)
Valora
Voga Capital S.A. (FKA: FR Capital)

Venture Firms—Bulgaria
Bulgarian-American Enterprise Fund, The
ECM-Bulgarian Post-Privatisation Fund
European Bank for Reconstruction and Development
Global Finance SA
NCH Capital, Inc.
New Europe Venture Equity
Small Enterprise Assistance Fund (SEAF)
TMF Participations Management

Venture Firms—Cambodia
Frontier Investment & Development Partners

Venture Firms—Cameroon
Central African Investment Corporation (AKA: Cenainvest SA)

Venture Firms—Canada
@capital-enterprises
ACF Equity Atlantic, Inc
Acumen Capital Finance Partners Ltd.
Alberta Revenue
Ansera Ventures, Ltd.
Argon Venture Partners
Atlantic Canada Opportunity Agency
Avrio Ventures Management Corp.
BC Advantage Funds (VCC), Ltd. (FKA: Lions Capital Corp.)
BCE Capital
BDR Capital
BMO Capital Corporation
Balmoral Partners Ltd.
Betwin Investments, Inc.
Black Coral Capital
BlackBerry Partners Fund, The
Bradstone Equity Partners
Brightspark Ventures
British Columbia Investment Management Corporation (BCIMC)
British Columbia Ministry of Economic Development
Business Arts, Ltd.
Business Development Bank of Canada
CDP Capital - Technology Ventures (FKA: CDP Sofinov)
CDP Capital Private Equity
CFI Capital
CORE Partners, Inc.
CPP Investment Board
Calyon (FKA: Credit Agricole Indosuez)

Camelot Capital Corporation
Campbell Resources
Canaccord Genuity
Canadian Imperial Bank of Commerce (AKA: CIBC)
Canadian Medical Discoveries Fund
Cansbridge Capital Corporation
Capimont Inc
Capital Benoit, Inc.
Capital CGD
Capital Financiere agricole,, Inc.
Cassels Brock Lawyers
Celtic House Venture Partners
Centiva Capital
Centre QuEbEcois de valorisation des biotechnologies (CQVB)
CentreStone Ventures Inc.
China Select Capital Partners Corp.
Chrysalix Energy
Clarica
Clarity Capital
Cobalt Capital, Inc.
Coradin, Inc.
Covington Capital Corporation (FKA: C.I. Covington Fund)
Crescent Point Energy Trust
Cycle Capital Management
DIATEM Networks
Davies Ward Phillips & Vineberg
Discovery Capital
Dynex Capital Corporation
Echo Capital
Emerald Technology Ventures AG
Emerging ISV Capital Partners
EnerTech Capital
Enhanced Performance, Inc.
Entrepia Ventures, Inc.
Export Development Canada
Extreme Venture Partners, Inc.
eMedici Capital, Inc. (Accolade Capital, Inc.)
FCC Ventures
FIER CPVC Montreal S.E.C.
FIER Succes
Fairwater Growth Resources, Inc.
First Associates Investments, Inc.
First Canadian Title
First Energy Capital Corporation
First Nations Equity, Inc.
First Ontario Labour Sponsored Investment Fund, Ltd.
Flow Ventures
Fonds de Developpment Econom. Laprade Champlin Inc.
Foragen Technologies Management
Forbes Alliance Partners Inc.
Frontier Capital Partners (FCP)
GTI Capital Inc.
Garage Technology Ventures Canada
GeneChem Financial Corporation
Genesys Capital Partners, Inc.
Georgian Partners
Gibralt Capital Corporation
Greenhill SAVP
GrowthWorks
Hargan Ventures, Inc.
Headline Media Group (Web Capital Partners)
Hero Ventures
Hydro-Quebec CapiTech Inc.
ID Capital
IPS Industrial Promotion Services, Ltd.
InVivo Ventures
Innovatech Sud Du Quebec
Intrepid Equity Finance, Ltd.
Investeco Capital Corporation
Investissement Quebec
Invico Capital Corporation
iNovia Capital
JC Simmons & Associates
JLA Ventures (FKA: J.L. Albright Venture Partners)
Jefferson Partners
JovFunds
KPMG Corporate Finance
Kaofu Venture & Investment Corp.
Killick Capital
Kilmer Capital Partners
Kinetic Capital Partners
Kingsway Capital of Canada, Inc.
Knight's Bridge Capital Corporation
Kyoto Planet Capital Partners
LEvesque Beaubien Geoffrion (LBG)
Laurence Capital Corporation
Laurentian Bank
Le Groupe Forces
London Asia Capital Plc (FKA: netvest.com Plc)
Lumira Capital Corporation.
MMI Group Inc.
MMV Financial, Inc.
MSBi Valorisation
Manitoba Capital Fund
Maple Partners Financial Group, Inc.
McLean Watson Capital Inc.
MedTech Partners, Inc.
Medical Innovations Management, Inc.
Mercator Investments Limited
Meridius Capital
Miralta Capital, Inc.
Moneta Capital Partners, Ltd.
Montreal Start Up
Mosaic Venture Partners
Multiple Capital, Inc.
NDI Capital (FKA: Neuro Discovery, Inc.)
NSBI Venture Capital
National Bank Financial, Inc.
National Research Council of Canada
Native Venture Capital Co., Ltd.
New Brunswick Innovation Foundation
New Brunswick Investment Management Corporation (AKA: NBIMC)
New Media Innovation Centre
Niagara Growth Fund
Nibiru Capital
Norshield Capital Management Corp.
Okanagan Innovation Fund
Ontario Capital Growth Corporation
Ontario Centres of Excellence
Ontario Venture Capital Fund Inc.
Overture Capital Partners (AKA: Overture)
PARTEQ Innovations
PFM Capital
Pact Research Fund
Pangaea Ventures
Peak Capital Group LLC
Pinetree Capital, Ltd.
Pinnacle Group
ProQuest Investments
Propulsion Ventures, Inc.
Pymble Holdings Inc.
Quebec Equity
Quebecor Fund
Raymond James, Ltd.
Renewal Partners
Rho Capital Partners, Inc.
Rising Tide Fund
Rogers Ventures
Rolls Royce Corporate Venture
Rosetta Capital, Ltd.
Rothschild Asset Management Limited
RoyNat Capital Corp. (AKA: RoyNat Ventures)
SOCO
SOVAR
Sands Brothers & Co., Ltd.
Sentient Group, The
Shanghai Amara Equity Investment Management Co., Ltd.
Skypoint Capital Corporation
Societe Generale de Financement du Quebec (SGF)
SpringBank TechVentures
Summerhill Venture Partners
Sustainable Development Technology Canada
T2C2 Capital
TELUS Ventures
Tandem Expansion Fund, Inc.
Tech Capital Partners
Techbanc, Inc.
TechnoCap, Inc.
Telesystem-Argo Global Capital
Teranet Enterprises, Inc.
Thomvest Ventures
Torys LLP
Trellis Capital Corporation
Tufan Venture Partners
University Medical Discoveries, Inc.
Up Capital , Ltd.
Ursataur Capital Management
VERDEXUS
VanEdge Capital, Inc.
VantagePoint Venture Partners
VenGrowth Capital Funds
Vendages
VentureLabour.com
VentureLink Funds (FKA:VL Advisors LP, Skylon Capital)
Ventures West Management, Inc.
Victoria Park Capital
W Media Ventures
W.R. Hambrecht & Co., LLC
Walsingham Fund, The
Wesley Clover, Ltd.
Westcap Management, Ltd.
Whitecastle Investments
Worthy Capital, Ltd.
XPV Capital Corporation
Yaletown Venture Partners, Inc.
Yukon Venture Group

Venture Firms—Cayman Islands

Bull Capital Partners Ltd.
Entropy Ventures, Ltd.
HBM BioVentures AG (FKA: HBM Partners AG)
Infiniti Capital Limited

MerchantBridge & Co., Ltd.
NanoDimension Management Limited
Portview Communications Ltd
Schroders PLC
Sentient Group, The
Thai Development Capital Fund Limited
Tuareg Capital, Ltd.
YL Ventures GP, Ltd.
Yangtze China Investment Ltd.

Venture Firms—Channel Islands

Aurora Investment Advisors, Ltd.
NeoMed Management AS

Venture Firms—Chile

Austral Capital
Intel Capital
Skandia Innovation AB

Venture Firms—China

ABC Capital Management Co., Ltd.
AID Partners Capital, Ltd.
AIG Investment Corporation, (Asia) Ltd.
ARC Capital Partners, Ltd. (AKA: ARC Capital)
ARC China, Inc.
Accel Partners
Aloe Private Equity
Anhui Province Venture Capital Co., Ltd.
Asia Capital Management (ACM) Limited (AKA: ACL Asia Ltd)
Asia Private Equity Capital (FKA: MediBIC Alliance)
AsiaTech Internet Group (ATIG) (FKA: AsiaTech Ventures)
AsiaTech Management LLC
AsiaVest Partners, TCW/YFY Ltd. (FKA: TCW/YFY Investment)
Australian Capital Ventures, Ltd.
Avant Capital Group, Inc.
BOC International Holdings, Ltd.
BOCOM International Holdings Co., Ltd.
Baird Capital Partners Asia
Balloch China Fund, The
Beijing An Cai Technology Venture Capital Company, Ltd.
Beijing Ancai Venture Capital Co., Ltd.
Beijing Bingyuan Venture Capital Co., Ltd.
Beijing Blue Blood Science & Tech. Venture Capital Co., Ltd.
Beijing Broad Global Venture Capital Co., Ltd.
Beijing Capital Investment Co., Ltd.
Beijing College Venture Capital Company, Ltd.
Beijing Electricity Investment Company, Ltd.
Beijing GEM I&CC Company, Ltd.
Beijing Gui Gu Industry Investment Company, Ltd.
Beijing Guo Heng Technology Group Company, Ltd.
Beijing Guo Ke New Economy Investment Company, Ltd.
Beijing Industrial Developing Investment Management Co., Ltd
Beijing Ji Feng Industry Investment & Management Company
Beijing Jin Chang Investment & Consultation Company, Ltd.
Beijing Jin Gang Venture Capital Company, Ltd.
Beijing Jin Guan Investment Company, Ltd.
Beijing Redstone International Capital Management Co., Ltd.
Beijing SEEC Investment Management Co., Ltd.
Beijing Technology Yuan Portfolio Valuation Company, Ltd.
Beijing Tianyi Huirong Investment Management Co., Ltd.
Beijing Torch Cheng Xin Investment & Consultation
Beijing Zhengrun Investment Co., Ltd. (AKA: Prope)
Beringea LLC
Bessemer Venture Partners
Bizovo Capital
BlueRun Ventures
Bohai Sea Region Venture Capital Management Company, Ltd.
Bonanza Investment Co., Ltd.
Broadline Capital LLC.
Bull Capital Partners Ltd.
bScope Partners, Inc.
CAPI Venture Inc.
CBC Capital
CIAM Group Limited
CID Group, The
CMHJ Partners
CSV Capital Partners (FKA: China Seed Ventures)
Canton Venture Capital Co., Ltd.
Capital Today
Century Venture Capital
Ceyuan Ventures Management, LLC
Chang'an Capital
Changchun S&T Venture Capital Co., Ltd
Changsha High-Tech Venture Capital Co., Ltd.
Changsha Science & Technology Venture Capital Co., Ltd.
Changzhou Aoyang Venture Capital Company
Chengdu Beyond Capital Management Co., Ltd.
Chengdu Venture Capital Co., Ltd.
Chengwei Ventures
China Capital Management Company, Ltd.
China Century Venture Capital Company, Ltd.
China Development Finance Co., Ltd.
China Israel Value Capital (AKA: CIVC)
China KZ High Technology Co., Ltd.
China Merchants Securities Co., Ltd
China Mining United Fund
China Prosper Investment & Management (Tianjin) Co., Ltd.
China Renaissance Capital Investment
China Science & Merchants Capital Management Co., Ltd.
China Venture Capital Co., Ltd.
China Venture Labs Limited
China-Singapore Suzhou Industrial Park
ChinaEquity Group, Inc.
ChinaVest, Ltd.
Chongqing Keji Venture Capital Co., Ltd.
Climate Change Capital, Ltd.
Cnstar Capital Pte., Ltd
Comway Capital Limited
Conduit Ventures Limited
Conseco Global Investment
Conventional Wisdom Capital, Ltd.
Creation Power Capital
Crescent Point Group
Crest Capital Partners
Crimson
Cybernaut (China) Capital Management
DCM
DT Capital Partners
DaLian KaiDa Venture Capital Co., Ltd.
Daiwa Corporate Investment Co., Ltd.
Dehou Fund Management Co., Ltd. (AKA: Dohold Capital)
Development Principles Group, Ltd.
Diamond TechVentures
Dianlian Venture Capital Co., Ltd.
Dojane Capital
Dongguan Songshan Lake Venture Capital Management Co., Ltd.
DragonTech Ventures Management, Ltd.
DragonVenture, Inc.
Dragonvest Partners
Draper Fisher Jurvetson
Draper Fisher Jurvetson ePlanet Ventures, L.P.
Eos Asia Investments, Ltd. (FKA: JCAR Funds, Ltd.)
Everbright Guolian Capital Co., Ltd.
Export-Import Bank Of China, The
Fair Value Investment (AKA: Shanghai Anyi Investment)
Fidelity Growth Partners Asia
Fidelity Ventures
First Eastern (Shanghai) Investment Management, Ltd.
Fitch crown Venture Capital Management (Shenzhen) Co., Ltd.
Fortis Haitong Investment Management Co., Ltd.
Fortune Venture Investment Group (AKA:Fortune Consulting)
Foshan Kehai Venture Capital Co., Ltd.
Fudan Quantum Venture Capital Management Co., Ltd.
Fujian Investment & Development Co., Ltd.
Fujian Investment and Development Co., Ltd.
Fujian Venture Capital Co., Ltd.
GGV Capital
GIC Special Investments Pte, Ltd.
GIV Venture Partners (AKA: Global Internet Ventures)
GSR Ventures
Gao Sheng Asset Management Company, Ltd.
Genesis Capital Consulting & Management, Ltd.
Get Capital
Global Catalyst Partners
Gobi Partners, Inc.
Gold Stone Investment, Ltd.
Good Capital Group
Greatwall Securities Company, Ltd.
Guangdong Technology Venture Capital Group., Ltd
Guangzhou Venture Capital, Ltd.
Guigu Tiantang Venture Capital Co., Ltd.
GuoCheng Venture Capital Co., Ltd.
Guotai Junan Innovation Investment Co., Ltd.
Hangzhou Hi-Tech Venture Capital Co., Ltd.
Hangzhou Jinying Investment Management Co., Ltd.
Hangzhou Rigen Venture Capital Co., Ltd.
Harbin Israel Venture Capital Management Co., Ltd.
Harbinger Venture Management
Hebei Technology Venture Capital Co., Ltd.
Highland Capital Partners LLC
Hina Capital Partners
Holding Venture Capital, Ltd.
Hubei Aoxin Venture Capital Co., Ltd.
Hubei Hi-tech Industrial Investment Co., Ltd.
Hubei Kehua Insight Venturing Investment Co., Ltd.
Huinong Capital

Tangshan Hightech Venture Capital Co., Ltd.
Tano Capital LLC
TeChina Investment Management Ltd
TianDi Growth Capital
Tiande Venture
Tianjin Hitech Investment Management Co., Ltd.
Tianjin Huizhi Lianhe Private Equity
Tianjin Science & Technology Investment Company
Tianjin Shian Haitai Energy S&T VC Investment Enterprise
Tianjin TEDA Venture Capital Company, Ltd. (AKA: TEDAVC)
Tianjin Venture Capital Co., Ltd.
Tiantu Capital Co., Ltd.
Tonglian Venture Capital Co.,Ltd
Trust Bridge Partners
Tsing Capital
Tsing-Tech Innovations Co., Ltd.
Tsinghua Unisplendour Hi-Tech Venture Capital, Inc.
U.S. Venture Partners
UOB Venture Management Pte, Ltd.
United Capital Investment Group (China) Ltd
VCChina, Ltd.
VantagePoint Venture Partners
Ventech S.A.
Venture TDF Pte Ltd.
Vertex Management Pte, Ltd. (AKA: Vertex Venture Holdings)
Vickers Venture Partners
Vision Investment Corporation
WI Harper Group
Warburg Pincus LLC
Wenzhou Bozhi Investment Co., Ltd.
Worldview Technology Partners
Wuhan East Lake Venture Capital Co., Ltd.
Wuhan Good Insight Venturing Investment Co., Ltd.
Wuhan Huagong Tech Business Incubator Co., Ltd.
Wuhan Huagong Venture Capital Co., Ltd.
Wuhan KeyWin Venture Capital Co., Ltd.
Wuhan Optics-Valley Venture Capital Co.,Ltd.
Wuhan Puluodun Venture Capital Fund Management Co., Ltd.
Wuhu Jiangdong Venture Capital Co., Ltd.
Xi'an Capitech Venture Capital Co., Ltd. (AKA: CAPITECH)
Xi'an Prutention Investment & Development Co., Ltd.
Xiangcai Securities Co., Ltd.
Yilian Equity Fund
Yufeng Equity Investment Management Co., Ltd.
Yunnan Agriculture Through Venture Capital Co., Ltd.
Zenison Venture Captial
Zhejiang Anfeng Venture Capital Co., Ltd.
Zhejiang Huaou Venture Capital Co., Ltd.
Zhejiang University Venture Capital Co., Ltd.
Zhejiang Venture Capital Co., Ltd.
Zhejiang Zheshang Venture Capital Management Co., Ltd.
Zhengzhou Bairui Innovation Investment Management Co., Ltd.
Zhongshan Technology Innovation Invest. Management Co., Ltd.
Zhuhai Tsinghua Science Park Venture Capital Co., Ltd.
Zibo New & High-Tech Venture Capital Co., Ltd.

Venture Firms—Colombia

Skandia Innovation AB

Venture Firms—Costa Rica

EcoEnterprises Fund
Econergy International Corporation
Intel Capital
Volio Capital, S.A.

Venture Firms—Croatia

Eagle Ventures
European Bank for Reconstruction and Development
Small Enterprise Assistance Fund (SEAF)
TMF Participations Management
Vienna Capital Partners

Venture Firms—Cyprus

Athena High Technology Incubator, Ltd.
Diogenes Business Incubator
First Elements Ventures, Ltd. (FKA: SFS Corporate Analysis)
Skandia Innovation AB

Venture Firms—Czech Republic

Arca Capital
Argus Capital Group, Ltd.
Bancroft Group
Kilcullen Kapital Partners
MCI Management
PPF Investments, Ltd.
Rolls Royce Corporate Venture
Slavia Capital
TMF Participations Management

Venture Firms—Denmark

BankInvest Group A/S
Bio Fund Management Oy
CAT Seed A/S
Capital+ A/S
Catella AB
ComTech Invest A/S (FKA: AHEAD Enterprise SA)
DTU Innovation A/S
Danfoss Ventures A/S
Dania Capital K/S
Danisco Venture
Dansk Kapitalanlaeg Aktieselskab
Difko Venture A/S
East Jutland Innovation A/S (AKA: Ostjysk Innovation A/S)
Energi Invest Fyn A/S
Erhvervsinvest Management A/S
Firmainvest A/S
Global Life Science Ventures GmbH
HIH Development A/S
IVS A/S (AKA: Internet Ventures Scandinavia A/S)
Industri Udvikling A/S
InnoVenture A/S
Inventure Capital A/S
Kaupthing Bank hf.
LD Pensions
LMX Business Development A/S
Miljoudvikling A/S
Nordic Biotech Advisors APS
Nordic Growth Oy
Nordic Venture Partners (FKA: Danske Venture Partners)
Northzone Ventures AS (FKA: Venture Partners AS)
Norventum Capital A/S
Novo A/S
Oresund-Healthcare A/S
Result Venture Knowledge International
SEED Capital Denmark K/S
SLS Invest AB
Skandia Innovation AB
Statoil Innovation AS (AKA: StatoilHydro)
Sunstone Capital A/S
Syddansk Innovation A/S
T. Rowe Price Threshold Partnerships
Technology Innovation (AKA: Teknologisk Innovation AS)
VECATA A/S
Vaekstfonden (AKA: Danish Growth Fund, The)
Vertex Management Israel (AKA: Vertex Venture Capital)
Vertex Management Pte, Ltd. (AKA: Vertex Venture Holdings)
Via Venture Partners A/S

Venture Firms—Ecuador

MerchantBansa S.A.

Venture Firms—Egypt

Amwal AlKhaleej
Egypt Kuwait Holding Company
Nile Capital
Sindicatum Carbon Capital, Ltd.

Venture Firms—El Salvador

Volio Capital, S.A.

Venture Firms—Estonia

Estonian Development Fund
Martinson Trigon Venture Partners AS
Scandinavian Baltic Development, Ltd.
Small Enterprise Assistance Fund (SEAF)
Statoil Innovation AS (AKA: StatoilHydro)

Venture Firms—Faroe Islands

Kaupthing Bank hf.

Venture Firms—Finland

Aura Capital Oy
Bio Fund Management Oy
BlueRun Ventures
Calyon (FKA: Credit Agricole Indosuez)
Catella AB
Conor Venture Partners Oy
Creative Industries Management Oy (CIM)
Eqvitec Partners Oy
Finnish Fund for Industrial Cooperation, Ltd. (AKA:FINNFUND)
Head Industrial Partner Oy
Innofinance Oy (FKA: Culminatum Oy)
Inveni Capital
Inventure Oy
Kaupthing Bank hf.
Korona Invest Oy
Miraimon Oy
Neomarkka Oyj
Nexit Ventures Oy
Nokia (AKA: NEST Managment)
Nokia Growth Partners
Nordic Growth Oy
Nordic Venture Partners (FKA: Danske Venture Partners)
Orienteq Capital
Oy Wedeco Management Oy
Result Venture Knowledge International

Sitra
Skandia Innovation AB
Stora Enso Ventures Oy
Suomen Teollisuussijoitus Oy
Taito Capital Partners Oy
TeknoVenture Management Oy
Tutor Invest Oy, Ltd
VNT Management Oy
Veraventure Oy
Virtaa Hameeseen Oy

Venture Firms—France

A Plus Finance SA
Actidev
Agregator Gestion SAS
Aloe Private Equity
Alpes Developpement Durable Investissement SAS
Alternative Ventures
Althera Capital
Alto Invest
Alven Capital Partners SA
Amorcage Rhone-Alpes
Aquasourca Societe d' Investissement
Aquitaine Creation Innovation
Astrolabe Ventures
Auriga Partners S.A.
Auxitex
Avenir Entreprises SA
Avesta
BNP Paribas Developpement SA
Baird Capital Partners Europe
Banexi Ventures Partners
Banque De Vizille
BioGestion S.A. (AKA: Bioam Gestion - Fonds Bioam)
Biotek Partenaires
Bretagne Participations
Brittany Ventures
C.W. Downer & Company (FKA: Downer & Company)
CAP ISF SA
CDC Entreprises SAS
CDC Innovation SAS (FKA: CDC IXIS Innovation)
CDP Capital - Technology Ventures (FKA: CDP Sofinov)
CEA Valorisation SA
CIC Finance SA
CIC Regions Expansion
CITA Gestion SA
Calliode II
Calyon (FKA: Credit Agricole Indosuez)
Cap Decisif Management SAS
Catella AB
Cavipar SASU
Champagne Ardenne Croissance
China Equity Links
Convergent Capital SAS
Croissance Nord - Pas de Calais SAS
Dassault Developpement
Demeter Partners S.A.
EPF Partners
Edmond de Rothschild Investment Partners
EmerTec Gestion
Emergences
Entrepreneur Venture Gestion
Equitis
Esfin Gestion
Esperante BV
Euro Capital
European Equity Partners
Evolem SA
FINORPA
Femu Qui SA
Filtarn
Fin'Active
Financiere Galliera
Financiere Saint Merri
Financiere Vecteur
Finimmo
Fondations Capital SAS
Fontainebleau Ventures
Fortis Private Equity France (FKA: Robertsau Gestion)
Fortis Private Equity NV/SA (FKA: VIV NV)
GIMV N.V.
GSO Investissements
Galia Gestion
Galileo Partners
Garibaldi Participations SCR
Gemplus SCA
Generis Capital Partners
Genopole 1er Jour (AKA: G1J)
Grand Sud Ouest Capital
Green Recovery
Harbert Venture Partners
I-Source Gestion
IDIA Agricapital
IPO (Institut de Participations de L'Ouest)
IRPAC (Institut regional de participation Ardenne-Champagne)
Ile de France Developpement (AKA: IDFD)
InnovaFonds
InnovaFrance
Innovacom SA
Innoven Partenaires S.A.
Inocap S.A.
Inserm-Transfert Initiative
Institut Lorrain de Participation - ILP
Intel Capital
Iris Capital Management (FKA: Part'Com Management S.A.)
L Capital Management SAS
LC Capital
La Financiere Patrimoniale D'Investissment
La Financiere de Brienne
Limousin Participations
Matignon Investissement et Gestion
Midi-Pyrenees Creation
Milk Capital
Montefiore Investment SAS
Najeti France
Najeti Ventures
Nem Partners (AKA: Natexis Equity Management)
Nord Capital Partenaires SAS
Nord Creation SAS
Occam Capital
Ocean Participations
Octalfa SAS
Oddo Asset Management SA
Odyssee Venture
Orfimar
Orium SAS
Otto Capital Partners
Ouest Angels Developpement SA
Ouest Ventures (FKA: Grand Ouest Gestion)
Paris Business Angels
Partech International
Participex
Pechel Industries
Petit Poucet Participation
Pharmavent Partners
Picardie Investissement
Platina Partners LLP
Prado Finance
Pre Ipo Invest (AKA: PRE-IPO.net)
Premiers Pas
Promelys Participations SA
Proparco
Result Venture Knowledge International
Rhone Dauphine Developpement
Rhone-Alpes Creation SA
Rising Tide Fund
Rolls Royce Corporate Venture
Rothschild Gestion
SED Ventures
SEEFT Management SAS
SIGMA Gestion SA
SNVB Participations
SORIDEC
Sadepar
Schneider Electric Ventures
Serena Capital SAS
Seventure Partners SA (FKA: SPEF Venture)
Sindicatum Carbon Capital, Ltd.
Skandia Innovation AB
Socadif SA
Sodero Participations
Sofinnova Partners
Sofipaca SA
Sofirem
Sophia Euro Lab SAS
Starquest ISF SAS
Statoil Innovation AS (AKA: StatoilHydro)
Sud Rhone-Alpes Capital SAS
Sudinnova
Synergie Finance Sobrepar
360 Capital Management SA (AKA: 360 Capital Partners)
T. Rowe Price Threshold Partnerships
TIME Equity Partners SAS
TMF Participations Management
TechFund Capital
Techfund Capital Europe Management SAS
Tertiaire Developpement
Thales Corporate Ventures (FKA:Thomson-CSF Ventures)
Tolomei Participations SAS
Turenne Capital SA
Undisclosed Firm
VPSA (FKA: Viventures Partners)
Vatel Capital SAS
Vauban Partenaires S.A. (AKA: Vauban Finance)
Ventech S.A.
Vertex Management Israel (AKA: Vertex Venture Capital)
Vizille Capital Innovation SAS

Venture Firms—Georgia

European Bank for Reconstruction and Development
Greenhill SAVP

Venture Firms—Germany

ACA Equity-Partners GmbH
Accera Venture Partners AG
Acceres Beteiligungsmanagement GmbH & Co KG
Access Microfinance Holding AG
Acton Capital Partners GmbH
AdCapital AG
Aheim Capital GmbH (FKA: Buchanan Capital Partners GmbH)
Astutia Ventures GmbH
Atila Ventures
Aurelia Private Equity GmbH
BAG Aktiengesellschaft fuEr Industriebeteiligungen
BALTIK AG fur Kapitalbeteiligungen
BASF Future Business GmbH
BASF Venture Capital GmbH
BHF-Bank
BTV Beteiligungsverwaltung GmbH & Co. KG
BV Capital (FKA: Bertelsmann Ventures, LP)
BWK GmbH Unternehmensbeteiligungsgesellschaft
Baird Capital Partners Europe
BankInvest Group A/S
BayTech Venture Capital Beratungs GmbH
Bayern Kapital GmbH
BayernLB Private Equity Management GmbH
Beaufort Capital GmbH
Beteiligungsgesellschaft fur die deutsche Wirtschaft mbH
BioM AG
BonVenture Management GmbH
Burda Digital Ventures GmbH
bmp AG
C.W. Downer & Company (FKA: Downer & Company)
Carmel Ventures
ChancenKapitalfonds der Kreissparkasse Biberach GmbH
Chord Capital, Ltd. (FKA: Generics Group, The)
Cipio Partners
Conmit Invest GmbH
Copan, Inc
Creathor Venture Management GmbH
Crespi GmbH
DKB Wagniskapital Unternehmensbeteiligungsgesellschaft mbH
DVC Deutsche Venture Capital
Demeter Partners S.A.
Deutsche Effecten- und Wechsel-Beteiligungsgesellschaft AG
Die Protektus AG (FKA: AAFORTUNA Venture Capital & Mgmt AG)
Dr Schmidt Biotech GmbH
DuMont Venture Holding GmbH & Co. KG
Dynamics Venture Management GmbH
EMBL Ventures GmbH
EVP Capital Management AG
Earlybird Venture Capital GmbH & Co. KG
EquiVest GmbH & Co
Erimed Beteiligungsgesellschaft mbH
Estag Capital AG
European Founders Fund GmbH
eCAPITAL entrepreneurial Partners AG
eVenture Capital Partners GmbH
Finatem GmbH
Foo Brains&Capital, The
Freudenberg Venture Capital GmbH
Fronteris Business Development GmbH
Fronteris Energy Fund GmbH
Fronteris Private Equity AG
Future Capital AG
GCI Management
GENIUS Venture Capital GmbH
GIMV N.V.
Glenalta Capital LLP
Global Life Science Ventures GmbH
Goldman Sachs JBWere (NZ) Ltd. (FKA: JBWere (NZ) Ltd.)
Grazia Equity GmbH
Greenwich Beteiligungen AG (FKA: PEGASUS Beteiligungen AG)
gcp gamma capital partners Beratungs- & Beteiligungs AG
HSH Nordbank Kapital (FKA: Schleswig-Holsteinische)
Handwerk Consult Mittelstandsberatung e.K.
Haspa BGM
Hasso Plattner Ventures Management GmbH
Heidelberg Innovation Fonds Management GmbH
Heidelberg Innovation GmbH
HgCapital
High Tech Venture Partners GmbH
High-Tech Gruenderfonds Management GmbH
HighTech Private Equity GmbH
Holland Private Equity B.V.
Holtzbrinck Ventures GmbH
IBB Beteiligungsgesellschaft mbH
IBG Beteiligungsgesellschaft Sachsen-Anhalt mbH
INTRO-Verwaltungs GmbH
Impera Total Return AG
Industrieberatung Dr. h.c. Harald Eggers
Ingenium Capital GmbH & Co KG
Innovations-Capital Gottingen GmbH
Intel Capital
Intelligent Venture Capital Management GmbH
Inveni Capital
Investitions- und Strukturbank Rheinland-Pfalz (ISB) GmbH
iGlobe Partners, Ltd.
independent capital Unternehmensbeteiligungen AG
JCMB Beteiligungs GmbH
Kliegel & Hafner AG
L-EigenkapitalAgentur
LBBW Venture Capital GmbH
LEIFINA GmbH & Co. KG
Leonardo Venture GmbH & Co. KGaA
Life Science Fonds Esslingen Verwaltungs-GmbH
Life Sciences Partners BV
London Asia Capital Plc (FKA: netvest.com Plc)
MAZ level one GmbH
MBG Baden-Wuertemberg GmbH
MBG H Mittelstaendische Beteiligungsgesellschaft Hessen mbH
MBMV Mecklenburg-Vorpommern mbH
MIG Verwaltungs AG
MVC Unternehmensbeteiligungsgesellschaft mbH (AKA: MVC GmbH)
MVP Munich Venture Partners Managementgesellschaft mbH
Media Ventures GmbH
Medicis AG
MillhouseIAG
Mittelstaendische Beteiligungsgesellschaft Thueringen mbH
Mulligan BioCapital AG
mic AG
NGN Capital LLC
NRW Bank
Nanostart AG
Neuhaus Partners GmbH
Next Wave Funds
Nord Holding Unternehmensbeteiligungsgesellschaft mbH
new commercial room GmbH
PEPPERMINT. Financial Partners (FKA schroder + partner)
Parklane Capital Beteiligungsberatung GmbH
RBK Hannover mbH & Co. KG
RR Capital GmbH
RWB RenditeWertBeteiligungen AG
Result Venture Knowledge International
Rocket Internet GmbH
Rolls Royce Corporate Venture
S-Kap Unternehmensbeteiligungs GmbH & Co. KG
S-Refit AG
S-UBG AG
S-Unternehmensbeteiligungsgesellschaft der Sparkasse Leipzig
S-Venture Capital Dortmund GmbH
SAP Ventures
SHS Gesellschaft fuer Beteiligungsmanagement mbH
Saarlandische Wagnisfinanzierungsgesellschaft mbH (AKA SWG)
Sachsen LB Corporate Finance Holding GmbH
Schott AG (FKA:Schott Glas)
Seed GmbH
Seventure Partners SA (FKA: SPEF Venture)
Siemens Mobile Acceleration
Siemens Technology Accelerator (STA)
Siemens Venture Capital GmbH
Sigma Capital Management
Signal Iduna Private Equity Fonds GmbH
Sirius Venture Partners GmbH
Skandia Innovation AB
Sony Corporation
Sparkassen- Beteiligungsgesellschaft Heilbronn-Franken mbH
Star Ventures Management GmbH & Co. KG
Statoil Innovation AS (AKA: StatoilHydro)
Sympasis innovation capital GmbH
Syntek Capital AG
smac partners GmbH
T-Venture Holding GmbH
TIBURON Partners AG
TMF Participations Management
TVM Capital GmbH
TakeOff Venture Capital Management GmbH
Target Partners GmbH
Team Europe Ventures Management GmbH
TechnoStart GmbH
Trendlines Group, The
Triangle Venture Capital Group Management GmbH
Triginta Capital Partners GmbH (FKA: Avida Equity Partners)
V+ Beteiligungs 2 GmbH
VNT Management Oy
VTC Partners GmbH
Ventegis Capital AG

Vestcorp AG
ViewPoint Capital Partners GmbH
WHEB Ventures, Ltd.
Warburg Pincus LLC
Wellington Partners Venture Capital GmbH
Worldview Technology Partners
Wunderlich & Partner Wirtschaftsberatung fur den Mittelstand
ZFHN Zukunftsfonds Heilbronn GmbH & Co. KG

Venture Firms—Ghana

Databank Financial Services Ltd
National Investment Bank Ltd.

Venture Firms—Greece

AVC Venture Capital S.A.
Alpha Ventures SA
Global Finance SA
InQLab
Incubation For Growth
Innovative Ventures S.A. (iVen)
Notos Associates S.A.
Parthenon Trust SA
7 L Capital Partners
Thermi Venture S.A.
Vectis Capital SA

Venture Firms—Hong Kong

AID Partners Capital, Ltd.
AIG Investment Corporation, (Asia) Ltd.
ARC Capital Partners, Ltd. (AKA: ARC Capital)
Air Products and Chemicals, Inc.
Aquitaine Investment Advisors, Ltd.
Asia Capital Management (ACM) Limited (AKA: ACL Asia Ltd)
Asia Pacific Investment Partners
AsiaTech Internet Group (ATIG) (FKA: AsiaTech Ventures)
Atila Ventures
Authosis Ventures
Avanta Investment (International)
BASF Venture Capital GmbH
BOC International Holdings, Ltd.
BOCOM International Holdings Co., Ltd.
Baird Capital Partners Asia
Beijing Ji Feng Industry Investment & Management Company
Bizovo Capital
Boyer Allan Investment Management, LLP.
Broadline Capital LLC.
Bull Capital Partners Ltd.
CBC Capital
CCB International (Holdings), Ltd.
CDC Corporation (FKA: Chinadotcom Ventures)
CDP Capital - Technology Ventures (FKA: CDP Sofinov)
CIAM Group Limited
CSV Capital Partners (FKA: China Seed Ventures)
Calyon (FKA: Credit Agricole Indosuez)
China Capital Management Company, Ltd.
China Merchants China Investments, Ltd.
China Merchants Securities Co., Ltd
China Renaissance Capital Investment
ChinaVest, Ltd.
Chord Capital, Ltd. (FKA: Generics Group, The)
Crosby Capital, Ltd.
DSE Investment Services, Ltd.
DT Capital Partners
Daiwa Corporate Investment Co., Ltd.
Daiwa PI Partners Co., Ltd.
Development Principles Group, Ltd.
DragonTech Ventures Management, Ltd.
Draper Fisher Jurvetson ePlanet Ventures, L.P.
Dubai Investment Group (AKA: DIG)
Entrepreneur Venture Gestion
Entropy Ventures, Ltd.
eGarden Ventures Hong Kong, Ltd.
Fidelity Growth Partners Asia
Fidelity Ventures
General Enterprise Management Services Ltd (AKA: GEMS)
Genesis Capital Consulting & Management, Ltd.
Guangdong Investment (FKA: Guangdong Investment Management)
Guggenheim Venture Partners LLC
Hua Yu Investment Management Limited
HuaMei Capital Company, Inc.
IDG Technology Venture Investment, Inc.
Imprimatur Capital, Ltd.
Indochina Capital Management
Infiniti Capital Limited
Infinity Venture Capital Fund (AKA: Israel Infinity Fund)
Intel Capital
Inter-Asia Venture Management
Investor Growth Capital AB
iTM Ventures, Inc.
JAFCO Investment (Hong Kong), Ltd.
JAFCO Investment [FKA: Nomura/JAFCO Investment (Asia), Ltd.]
JAIC-Crosby Investment Management Co., Ltd.
Japan Asia Investment Company, Ltd. (AKA: JAIC)
KLM Capital Management, Inc.
London Asia Capital Plc (FKA: netvest.com Plc)
Lunar Capital Management, Ltd.
MKW Capital, Ltd.
MetLife Investments Asia, Ltd.
Mingly Capital
Mizuho Securities Asia, Ltd. (FKA: IBJ Asia Securities Ltd.)
Neuberger Berman LLC
New Asia Partners, Ltd.
Newbridge Capital, Ltd.
Newport Private Equity Asia
ORIX Asia Limited
Olympus Capital Holdings Asia
Orchid Asia Group Management, Ltd.
Orix Capital Corporation
Pacific Alliance Capital Group
Panda Capital Asia, Ltd.
Persimmon Capital, Ltd.
Prax Capital
Pride Investments Group, Ltd., The
PrimePartners Asset Management Pte, Ltd.
Primus Pacific Partners
Probitas Partners, Inc.
QED Global, Ltd.
Qleap Accelerators, Ltd.
Result Venture Knowledge International
Richlink International Capital Co., Ltd.
RimAsia Capital Partners
Rolls Royce Corporate Venture
S.I. Technology Venture Capital, Ltd.
SAIF Partners
SHK Fund Management, Ltd.
SOFTBANK Corp.
San Shan Capital Partners
Sandalwood Capital Partners
Schroders PLC
Sequoia Capital
Sequoia Capital India (FKA: WestBridge Capital Partners)
Shanghai Amara Equity Investment Management Co., Ltd.
Shanghai Industrial Holdings, Ltd.
Shaw Kwei & Partners
Sirius Venture Consulting Pte, Ltd.
Spinnaker Capital Group
Spring Capital Asia, Ltd.
Starr International Company, Inc
Startup Capital Ventures L.P.
Steamboat Ventures
T. Rowe Price Threshold Partnerships
TC Capital Pte., Ltd.
TPG Growth
TVG Capital Partners, Ltd.
Tano Capital LLC
Telesystem-Argo Global Capital
Templeton Asset Management, Ltd.
Tsing-Tech Innovations Co., Ltd.
VL Neuberg
VantagePoint Venture Partners
Veron International
Vertex Management Pte, Ltd. (AKA: Vertex Venture Holdings)
Warburg Pincus LLC
Wisdom Capital Group
Ymer Venture Capital Asia

Venture Firms—Hungary

Argus Capital Group, Ltd.
Bancroft Group
CDP Capital - Technology Ventures (FKA: CDP Sofinov)
CWC Capital Management LLC
Corvinus International Investment Rt
Covent rial Capital Investment Co., Ltd.
DBH Group
Eclipse Rt.
European Bank for Reconstruction and Development
Euroventures Capital Kft.
Gripen International
Kisvallalkozas-fejleszto Penzugyi Rt.
Litexco Mediterranea
M&A Capital, Ltd.
Magyar Fejlesztesi Bank (AKA: Hungarian Development Bank)
Primus Capital Partners LLC
TMF Participations Management

Venture Firms—Iceland

Audur Capital
Burdaras hf
Islensk Verobrefastofan hf
Kaupthing Bank hf.
MP Investment Bank
New Business Venture Fund
Thule Investments

Venture Firms—India

AIG Investment Corporation, (Asia) Ltd.
ASK Group

Aavishkaar Venture Management Services Pvt, Ltd.
Accel India Venture Fund (FKA: Erasmic Venture Fund Pvt)
Accel Partners
Acumen Fund
Aloe Private Equity
Ambit Pragma Ventures Pvt., Ltd.
Artiman Ventures
Ascent Capital Advisors India Pvt., Ltd.
Axis Holdings Pvt., Ltd.
Axis Private Equity, Ltd.
BTS Investment Advisors, Ltd.
Balyasny Asset Management LP (AKA: BAM)
Bessemer Venture Partners
Blue River Capital India Advisory Services Pvt., Ltd.
BlueRun Ventures
CDP Capital - Technology Ventures (FKA: CDP Sofinov)
Canbank Venture Capital Fund Limited
Caspian Advisors Pvt. Ltd.
ChrysCapital Management Company
Cisco Systems, Inc.
Citibank Venture Capital India
Clearstone Venture Partners
Crossover Advisors Pvt., Ltd. (FKA: Meta Crossover Advisors)
Draper Fisher Jurvetson
Draper Fisher Jurvetson ePlanet Ventures, L.P.
Duke Equity Partners
Edelweiss Capital, Ltd.
Elevar Equity Advisors Pvt., Ltd.
Everstone Capital
eIndia Venture Management
Fidelity Ventures
Fire Capital
Footprint Ventures
Fountainhead Capital Ltd
Frontline Strategy Pte. Ltd.
Fuse Capital
GIV Venture Partners (AKA: Global Internet Ventures)
GVFL Limited (FKA: Gujarat Venture Finance Limited)
Gaja Capital Partners
Greylock Partners
Guggenheim Venture Partners LLC
HDFC Venture Capital, Ltd.
HSBC Private Equity Management (Mauritius) Limited
Helion Venture Partners
Hexagram Investment Advisors Pvt, Ltd.
Hyderabad Information Technology Venture Enterprises, Ltd.
IDFC Private Equity
IDG Ventures India
IFCI Venture Capital Funds, Ltd. (FKA: Risk Capital & Tech.)
IL&FS Investment Managers Ltd (FKA: IL&FS Venture Corp)
India Infoline Ventures Capital (AKA: IIFL Capital)
IndiaCo
IndiaCo Ventures, Ltd.
Indian STEP's and Business Incubator's Association, The
Infinity Venture Capital
Infocomm Investments Pte., Ltd. (FKA: NCB Holdings Pte Ltd)
Intel Capital
Inventus Capital Partners
JM Financial Investment Managers, Ltd.
Jacob Ballas Capital India Pvt, Ltd. (AKA:JBC)
JumpStartUp Fund Advisors Pvt. Ltd.
Kaizen Private Equity
Karnataka Information Technology Venture Capital Fund
Kubera Partners, LLC
Lighthouse Funds LLC
Lightspeed Venture Partners (FKA: Weiss, Peck & Greer)
Lok Capital Group
Matrix Partners
Milestone Religare Investment Advisors Pvt., Ltd.
Motilal Oswal Private Equity Advisors Pvt., Ltd.
NEA-IndoUS Capital Advisors Pvt. Ltd.
Nadathur Holdings and Investments Pvt., Ltd.
New Enterprise Associates, Inc.
New Vernon Private Equity (FKA: New Vernon Bharat Ltd.)
NewPath Ventures, LLC
Newbridge Capital, Ltd.
Nexus Venture Partners
Nine Rivers Capital Management, Ltd. (AKA: NRCM)
Nokia Growth Partners
Ojas Venture Partners
Olympus Capital Holdings Asia
PSi, Inc.
Paracor Capital Advisors Pvt., Ltd.
Pathfinder Investment Co., Ltd.
Peepul Capital LLC
Punjab Venture Capital, Ltd.
Rabo India Finance, Ltd.
Rajasthan Asset Management Company Pvt., Ltd.
Reliance Equity Private Advisors (India), Ltd.
Religare Enterprises, Ltd.
Rolls Royce Corporate Venture
SAIF Partners
SBI Capital Ventures (AKA: SBI Capital Markets, Ltd.)
SIDBI Venture Capital, Ltd. (SVCL)
SREI Venture Capital Ltd. (FKA: SREI Global Asset Mgt.)
Samara Capital Partners, Ltd.
Sandalwood Capital Partners
Schroders PLC
Scsi Capital
Seedfund
Sequoia Capital
Sequoia Capital India (FKA: WestBridge Capital Partners)
Siemens Venture Capital GmbH
Small Enterprise Assistance Fund (SEAF)
Solitaire Capital Advisors Pvt. Ltd.
Spinnaker Capital Group
Strategic Capital Corporation
Subhkam Ventures
2i Capital Asset Management Company, Ltd.
TPG Growth
Tano Capital LLC
Trinity Capital PLC
Tuscan Ventures Pvt., Ltd.
VenturEast (FKA: APIDC Venture Capital Limited)
Warburg Pincus LLC
YES BANK, Ltd.

Venture Firms—Indonesia

AIG Investment Corporation, (Asia) Ltd.
Crest Capital Partners
Crosby Capital, Ltd.
JAFCO Investment (Hong Kong), Ltd.
P.T. Pama Ventura Indonesia
PrimePartners Asset Management Pte, Ltd.
Rolls Royce Corporate Venture
Sindicatum Carbon Capital, Ltd.
Spinnaker Capital Group

Venture Firms—Iran

Statoil Innovation AS (AKA: StatoilHydro)
Swicorp Capital Partners

Venture Firms—Iraq

MerchantBridge & Co., Ltd.

Venture Firms—Ireland

ACT Venture Capital, Ltd.
AIB Equity
Atlantic Bridge
BOI Venture Capital Limited
Bank of Scotland Venture Capital (FKA: ICC Venture Capital)
C.W. Downer & Company (FKA: Downer & Company)
Claret Capital, Ltd.
Cross Atlantic Capital Partners
Delta Partners, Ltd.
Dublin Business Innovation Centre
EBT Venture Fund, Ltd.
Enterprise 2000 Fund
Enterprise Equity Venture Capital Group
Enterprise Ireland
First Step Ltd.
Fourth Level Ventures (AKA : 4th Level Ventures)
Gensec Ireland Ltd
Growcorp Group, Ltd.
ION Equity, Ltd.
Intel Capital
International Investment and Underwriting
Kernel Capital Partners
Kerten Capital
Kilcullen Kapital Partners
Mianach Venture Capital
NCB Ventures, Ltd.
novusmodus LLP
Seroba BioVentures Limited
Seroba Kernel Life Sciences, Ltd. (AKA: Seroba Kernel)
Statoil Innovation AS (AKA: StatoilHydro)
TMF Participations Management
TVC Holdings plc (FKA: Trinity Venture Capital)
Western Development Commission

Venture Firms—Israel

Alice Ventures Srl
Ascend Technology Ventures
Athlone Global Security, Inc.
Aviv Venture Capital (FKA: Fantine Group, The)
BRM Capital
Benchmark Capital
Bessemer Venture Partners
Biomedix Incubator, Ltd.
Bridge Investment Fund
CE Unterberg Towbin (FKA:Unterberg Harris Capital Partners)

Capital Point, Ltd. (FKA: Archiquest Technologies)
Carmel Ventures
Cedar Fund
Challenge Fund - Etgar LP
China Israel Value Capital (AKA: CIVC)
Clal Venture Capital Management, Ltd. (AKA: CVC Management)
Concord Ventures (FKA: Nitzanim)
Defta Partners
Docor International B.V.
Edmond de Rothschild Venture Capital Management
Elron Electronic Industries
Eurofund LP
Evergreen Venture Partners
Evolution Venture Capital
Gemini Israel Funds, Ltd.
Genesis Partners
Gilo Ventures
Giza Venture Capital (FKA: Giza Investment Management)
GlenRock Israel, Ltd.
Gmul Investment Company, Ltd.
Greylock Partners
Infinity Venture Capital Fund (AKA: Israel Infinity Fund)
Intel Capital
Israel Cleantech Ventures
Israel Healthcare Ventures
Israel Seed Partners
JVP
Jerusalem Capital (AKA: JCP)
Jerusalem Global Ventures
Johnson & Johnson Development Corporation
Kinrot Technology Ventures
Kreos Capital (FKA: European Venture Partners)
L Capital Partners
Lab-One Innovations
LightSpeed Gemini Internet Lab
Lightspeed Venture Partners (FKA: Weiss, Peck & Greer)
Maayan Ventures
Magma Venture Partners
Medica Venture Partners
Mofet B-Yehuda Technological and Business Incubator
Motorola Ventures
Odin Investments
Ofer Hi-Tech
Old City Partners, LLC (OCP)
Partech International
Peregrine Ventures
Philips Venture Capital Fund B.V. (AKA: Corporate Venturing)
Pitango Venture Capital (FKA:Polaris Venture Capital Israel)
Platinum-Neurone Ventures
Poalim Capital Markets Technologies Ltd
Pontifax Ltd.
Portview Communications Ltd
ProSeed Venture Capital Fund
7 Health Ventures
Sequoia Capital
Sequoia Capital India (FKA: WestBridge Capital Partners)
Shaked Global Group Ltd.
Shrem Fudim Kelner Technologies, Ltd.
Siemens Venture Capital GmbH
Stage One Ventures
Star Ventures Management GmbH & Co. KG
Syntek Capital AG
Tamir Fishman Ventures
TechnoPlus Ventures
Trendlines Group, The
TriVentures
Venrock Associates
Vertex Management Israel (AKA: Vertex Venture Capital)
Vertex Management Pte, Ltd. (AKA: Vertex Venture Holdings)
Vertex Venture Capital
Xenia Venture Capital
YL Ventures GP, Ltd.
Yozma Venture Capital Ltd

Venture Firms—Italy

AME Ventures srl
AVM Italia
Abruzzo Capital SpA
Aliante Partners Srl
Alice Ventures Srl
Argy Venture Capital
BCC Private Equity SGR
BPB Investimenti
Banca Intesa SpA - Direzione Private Equity
Banca Popolare di Milano SpA (AKA: BPM Private Equity SGR)
Banca Profilo (Fondo Spinnaker)
BlueCar Partners
Centrobanca Sviluppo Impresa SGR
Cofiri
Compagnia Finanziaria Industriale (CFI)
Cooperazione Finanza Impresa scpa
Coopfond SpA
Credem Venture Capital
dPixel Srl
E-venture.it
Efibanca Palladio Finanziaria SGR
Endeavor Capital Management
FILAS - Finanziaria Laziale di Sviluppo SpA
FONDACO Societa di Gestione Risparmio SpA
Fidi Toscana SpA
Fincalabra SpA
Finint & Partners SpA
Finlombarda Gestioni SGR SpA
Finpiemonte SpA
Focus Gestioni SGR
Fondamenta SGR SpA
Friulia SGR SpA
Gepafin SpA
Glenalta Capital LLP
Hat Holding All Together SpA
Iniziativa Piemonte SpA
Innogest
Iritech SpA
L Capital Management SAS
Litexco Mediterranea
M.P.S. Merchant SpA- Ducato Gestioni SGR P.A.
MITTEL SpA
MPS VENTURE Societa di Gestione del Risparmio SpA
Market Capital Italia Srl
Net Partners
New Venture Development Srl
Nordest Merchant SpA
Opera Management SA (AKA: Opera SGR)
Palladio Finanziaria
Piemonte High Technology
Quadrivio SGR
Quantica SGR SpA
Riello Investimenti SpA
Rolls Royce Corporate Venture
SFIRS SpA
SICI SGR SpA
Sigefi Italia Private Equity SpA
Skandia Innovation AB
Sviluppo Imprese Centro Italia S.p.A.
Sviluppo Italia SpA
Syntek Capital AG
360 Capital Management SA (AKA: 360 Capital Partners)
TIM SpA - Transition Management
TLcom Capital LLP
TMF Participations Management
Undisclosed Firm
Unipol Merchant SpA (FKA : Finec Merchant SpA)
Vegagest Sgr
Vertis SGR SpA
Virtus Capital Partners
Wise SRG S.p.A. (AKA: Wisequity)
Wizard Partners Srl

Venture Firms—Japan

AC Ventures Co., Ltd.
AIFG
AIG Investment Corporation, (Asia) Ltd.
Advanced Science and Technology Enterprise Corporation
Affymetrix, Inc.
Angel Securities Inc.
Ant Capital Partners Co., Ltd.
Aozora Investment Co,. Ltd.
Aquitaine Investment Advisors, Ltd.
Asia Private Equity Capital (FKA: MediBIC Alliance)
Biofrontier Partners, Inc.
Bizovo Capital
Bugin Capital Co., Ltd.
CDP Capital - Technology Ventures (FKA: CDP Sofinov)
CSK Venture Capital Co., Ltd.
CSV Capital Partners (FKA: China Seed Ventures)
CUBIC Venture Capital Co.,Ltd (FKA Daiichi Mutual Life Capi)
Challenge Japan Investment Co., Ltd.
Chibagin Capital Company, Ltd.
Chugin Lease Co., Ltd.
Citigroup Principal Investment Japan Co., Ltd.
Constellation Ventures (AKA: Constellation Growth Capital)
CrossBridge Venture Partners
DCM
Daiwa Corporate Investment Co., Ltd.
Daiwa PI Partners Co., Ltd.
Daiwa Quantum Capital, Ltd.
Daiwa Securities SMBC Principal Investments Co., Ltd.
Defta Partners
Dentsu.com, Inc.
Draper Fisher Jurvetson ePlanet Ventures, L.P.
Entrepia Ventures, Inc.
Fukui JAFCO Company, Ltd.

Funai Capital Co., Ltd
Future International Co., Ltd.
Future Venture Capital Co., Ltd.
GIC Special Investments Pte, Ltd.
Gifushin Finance Co., Ltd.
Global Catalyst Partners
Global Venture Capital, Inc.
Globespan Capital Partners
Globis Capital Partners & Co. (FKS:Apax Globis Partners)
Gogin Capital Company, Ltd., The
Goldman Sachs JBWere (NZ) Ltd. (FKA: JBWere (NZ) Ltd.)
Greenhill SAVP
HIKARI private equity, Inc.
Hachijuni Capital Company, Ltd.
Hirogin Capital Company, Ltd.
Hiroshima Venture Capital Co., Ltd.
Hokkaido Venture Capital, Inc.
Hokuriku Capital Co., Ltd
Honda Strategic Venturing (HSV)
Hoya Corporation
Hurray Inc.
IDA Capital Company Limited
IGNITE Group, The (AKA: Ignite Associates, LLC)
Ikegin Capital Co., Ltd.
Information Technology Farm Corporation (AKA: IT Farm)
Intec IT Capital, Inc.
Intel Capital
Investor Growth Capital AB
Itochu Corporation
Iyogin Capital Co., Ltd.
incTANK Inc.
J-Seed Ventures, Inc.
JAFCO Co., Ltd. (FKA: Japan Associated Finance Co. Ltd.)
JVIC Venture Capital Co., Ltd.
Japan Asia Investment Company, Ltd. (AKA: JAIC)
Japan Industrial Partners, Inc.
Juroku Capital Company, Ltd., The
KSP (Kanagawa Science Park)
KTB Securities Co., Ltd. (FKA: KTB Network Co., Ltd.)
KTB Ventures
Kankaku Investment Co., Ltd.
Kyushu Venture Capital Co., Ltd.
MBL Venture Capital Co., Ltd.
MITSUI SUMITOMO INSURANCE Venture Capital Co., Ltd.
MU Hands-on Capital Ltd. (FKA:Tsubasa Hands-On Capital, Ltd)
MVC Corporation
Marubeni Corporation
Meiji Capital Co., Ltd.
Minato Capital Co., Ltd.
Minato Mirai Capital Co., Ltd.
Mitsubishi Corporation
Mitsubishi International Corp.
Mitsubishi Tanabe Pharma Corporation
Mitsubishi UFJ Capital Co., Ltd.
Mitsui & Co. Venture Partners (MCVP)
Mitsui INCUBASE Corp.
Miyagin Venture Capital Co., Ltd.
Mizuho Capital Company, Ltd.
Mobile Internet Capital Corporation
NEC Corporation of America (FKA: NEC USA, Inc.)
NGI Group (AKA: Netage Capital Partners, Inc.)
NTT Finance Corpration
NTT Leasing Co., Ltd.
Nagoya Small & Medium Business Investment & Consultation Co.
NetService Ventures
Neuberger Berman LLC
New Business Investment Co., Ltd.
New Frontier Partners Co., Ltd
Newbridge Capital, Ltd.
Nikko Principal Investments Japan, Ltd.
Nippon Angels Investment Co., Ltd
Nippon Monozukuri Capital Co., Ltd.
Nippon Venture Capital Co., Ltd.
Nissay Capital Co., Ltd.
Nomura Research & Advisory Co., Ltd.
Oak Capital Corporation
Okasan Venture Capital Co., Ltd.
Olympus Capital Holdings Asia
Orix Capital Corporation
Ozora Toshi Jigyo Yugen Sekinin Kumiai
Pacific Rim Ventures Company, Ltd.
Panasonic Ventures
Partech International
Private Equity Japan Co., Ltd.
Prologis
Resona Capital Co., Ltd.
Risa Partners, Inc.
Rolls Royce Corporate Venture
SBI Investment Company, Ltd. (FKA:Softbank Investment Corp)
SCS Capital Sdn. Bhd.
SK Ventures
SOFTBANK Corp.
SPARX Capital Partners Co., Ltd.
Sagin Venture Capital Co., Ltd.
Samurai Incubate, Inc.
Sansei Capital Investment Co., Ltd.
Sapporo Hokuyo Lease Co., Ltd.
Schneider Electric Ventures
Schroders PLC
Shigin Capital Research Co., Ltd
Shikata Venture Fund
Shinkin Capital Co., Ltd
Shinsei Bank Ltd.
Shinwa Venture Capital Co., Ltd
Shogin Venture Capital Co., Ltd
Sirius Venture Consulting Pte, Ltd.
Sofinnova Ventures
Sony Corporation
Strategic Capital Partners Co., Ltd.
T. Rowe Price Threshold Partnerships
TSUNAMI Network Partners Corp.
Toa Capital Co., Ltd
Tohoku Innovation Capital Corp.
Tokyo Small & Medium Business Investment & Consultation Co.
Tong Yang Venture Capital Corporation
Tottori Capital Co., Ltd.
Toyo Capital Co., Ltd.
Trans-Science, Inc.
University of Tokyo Edge Capital Co., Ltd., The (AKA: UTEC)
VASDAQ Investment, Ltd. (AKA: V-Investment)
Warburg Pincus LLC
Watervein Partners Co., Ltd.
Weru Investment Co., Ltd.
Will Capital Management Co., Ltd.
Worldview Technology Partners
Yamaguchi Capital Co., Ltd
Yamanashi Chugin Business Consulting Co., Ltd.
Yasuda Enterprise Development Co., Ltd.(FKA: Nippon Ent.Dev)
Yokohama Capital Co., Ltd

Venture Firms—Jordan

Accelerator Management Company B.S.C
Catalyst Private Equity
Foursan Group
IV Holdings

Venture Firms—Kazakhstan

Centras Capital Partners
Eagle Venture Partners
European Bank for Reconstruction and Development
Small Enterprise Assistance Fund (SEAF)
Statoil Innovation AS (AKA: StatoilHydro)

Venture Firms—Kenya

Acumen Fund
Fanisi Capital Ltd

Venture Firms—Kuwait

KIPCO Asset Management Company
Khazaen Venture Capital
National Technology Enterprises Company (AKA: NTEC)

Venture Firms—Kyrgyzstan

European Bank for Reconstruction and Development

Venture Firms—Latvia

Catella AB
European Bank for Reconstruction and Development
Imprimatur Capital, Ltd.
NCH Capital, Inc.
Norway - Latvia Business Support Fund, The
SIA "Zalas gaismas investicijas"
Small Enterprise Assistance Fund (SEAF)
Statoil Innovation AS (AKA: StatoilHydro)

Venture Firms—Lebanon

BADER Young Entrepreneurs Program

Venture Firms—Libya

Tuareg Capital, Ltd.

Venture Firms—Lithuania

Corecap Limited
European Bank for Reconstruction and Development
SEB Venture Capital
Scandinavian Baltic Development, Ltd.
Sindicatum Carbon Capital, Ltd.
Statoil Innovation AS (AKA: StatoilHydro)
UAB Lignum Cordis
VB Rizikos kapitalo valdymas (AKA: VB Venture Capital Mgmt)

Venture Firms—Luxembourg

Advans S.A., SICAR (FKA: La Fayette Investissement)
Aquasourca Societe d' Investissement
BankInvest Group A/S
Brait Capital Partners
Calyon (FKA: Credit Agricole Indosuez)
EonTech Ventures (FKA: Triton Ventures)

Equinox S.A.
Fanisi Capital Ltd
Fondations Capital SAS
Hunza Management SARL
Kaupthing Bank hf.
Leeward Fund Management
Mangrove Capital Partners SA
Newbridge Capital, Ltd.
Nexus Medical Partners
QAT investments SA (AKA: Quercus Aimer Trust)
360 Capital Management SA (AKA: 360 Capital Partners)
TMF Participations Management
Volga Resources SICAV-SIF

Venture Firms—Macau

MKW Capital, Ltd.

Venture Firms—Macedonia

European Bank for Reconstruction and Development
Small Enterprise Assistance Fund (SEAF)

Venture Firms—Madagascar

Undisclosed Firm

Venture Firms—Malaysia

AIG Investment Corporation, (Asia) Ltd.
Abundance Venture Capital
Banyan Ventures Sdn Bhd
CMS Opus Private Equity Sdn Bhd
Crest Capital Partners
DTA Capital
Dubai Investment Group (AKA: DIG)
Fajr Capital Ltd
First Floor Capital Sdn. Bhd.
Global Maritime Ventures Bhd
Goldis Berhad (FKA: Gold IS Bhd)
iCapital (M) Sdn Bhd
iSpringCapital Sdn Bhd (FKA: Productive Ideas Sdn Bhd)
Japan Asia Investment Company, Ltd. (AKA: JAIC)
Khazanah Nasional Berhad
London Asia Capital Plc (FKA: netvest.com Plc)
MIDF Amanah Ventures Sdn Bhd
Malaysian Technology Development Corp Sdn Bhd
Malaysian Venture Capital Management (MAVCAP)
Malaysian Ventures Management Incorporated Sdn Bhd
Mayban-JAIC Capital Management Sdn. Bhd.
OSK Ventures International Bhd (AKA: OSK Ventures Equities)
Pembangunan Ekuiti Sdn Bhd
Rolls Royce Corporate Venture
SCS Capital Sdn. Bhd.
SpringHill Management Sdn Bhd (FKA: Ikatan Menawan Sdn Bhd)
VF Capital Sdn Bhd (AKA: VF Capital)
Vineyard Ventures

Venture Firms—Mauritius

Advanced Finance & Investment Group LLC (AKA: AFIG)
Basil Growth Corporation
Blue River Capital India Advisory Services Pvt., Ltd.
Brait Capital Partners
ChrysCapital Management Company
Clearstone Venture Partners
HSBC Private Equity Management (Mauritius) Limited
Helion Venture Partners
IDG Ventures India
Jacob Ballas Capital India Pvt, Ltd. (AKA:JBC)
Matrix Partners
Nine Rivers Capital Management, Ltd. (AKA: NRCM)
Peepul Capital LLC
Samara Capital Partners, Ltd.
2i Capital Asset Management Company, Ltd.
Tano Capital LLC

Venture Firms—Mexico

Alta Growth Capital
CDP Capital - Technology Ventures (FKA: CDP Sofinov)
Calyon (FKA: Credit Agricole Indosuez)
IGNIA Partners LLC
Intel Capital
Latin Idea Ventures, LLC
NAFTA Fund of Mexico, LP
Nexxus Capital, S.C.
Orgone Capital
Schroders PLC
Sindicatum Carbon Capital, Ltd.
Skandia Innovation AB
Statoil Innovation AS (AKA: StatoilHydro)
Volio Capital, S.A.

Venture Firms—Moldova

European Bank for Reconstruction and Development
NCH Capital, Inc.

Venture Firms—Mongolia

Asia Pacific Investment Partners
European Bank for Reconstruction and Development
London Asia Capital Plc (FKA: netvest.com Plc)

Venture Firms—Morocco

CDP Capital - Technology Ventures (FKA: CDP Sofinov)

Venture Firms—Mozambique

Banco Efisa SA

Venture Firms—Neth. Antilles

DBH Group
Oresa Ventures Sp Z oo
TAT Capital Partners Ltd
TMF Participations Management

Venture Firms—Netherlands

Acorn (Netherlands) Z B.V.
Aescap Venture
Air Products and Chemicals, Inc.
BV Management MKB Fondsen
BV Venture Capital Investors (VCI)
Beheer Flevoland Participaties BV
Berk Management B.V.
BioGeneration Ventures
Biotech Turnaround Fund B.V.
Capital-C Ventures B.V.
Catalyst Microfinance Investment Company
DOEN Participaties BV
DSM
DSM Corporate Venturing
De Kruijff Venture Partners
Dragon Fund China-Europe
Eagle Venture Partners
Erasmus MC
Esperante BV
Favonius Ventures
Forbion Capital Partners
Fortis Private Equity NV/SA (FKA: VIV NV)
Freshwater Venture Partners
Friesland Bank Investments BV
GIMV N.V.
Gilde Healthcare Partners B.V.
H2 Equity Partners BV
HAL Investments BV
HENQ Invest
Holland Private Equity B.V.
Holland Venture III B.V. (FKA: Holland Venture B.V.)
ICOS Capital
INKEF Capital BV
Investor Growth Capital AB
K+ Venture Partners
Kenda Capital BV
Life Sciences Partners BV
Lowland Capital Partners BV (AKA: LCP)
Mentha Capital BV
Mercurius Beleggingsmaatschappij B.V.
Movipart BV
NV Brabantse Ontwikkelings Maatschappij (AKA: NV BOM)
NV Industriebank Liof
NV NOM
Netherlands Development Finance Company
New Venture Partners LLC
Nimbus
Ondernemend Twente BV
Participation Company East Netherlands NV (AKA : PPM Oost)
Philips Venture Capital Fund B.V. (AKA: Corporate Venturing)
Prime Technology Ventures NV
QAT investments SA (AKA: Quercus Aimer Trust)
Quest for Growth
Rabo Ventures
Reed Elsevier Ventures
Renpart Participatie Holding NV
Residex BV
Result Venture Knowledge International
Royal Dutch Shell Group
S & C Investment Advisors BV
SET Venture Partners
SPMO
Small Enterprise Assistance Fund (SEAF)
Solid Capital BV
Start Green Venture Capital
Synergia Capital Partners B.V.
T. Rowe Price Threshold Partnerships
TMF Participations Management
TechnoStars
Thuja Capital B.V.
Triodos International Fund Management BV
Undisclosed Firm
VNU Ventures
ViewPoint Capital Partners GmbH
Wadinko CV
YL Ventures GP, Ltd.
Yellow & Blue Investment Management BV

Venture Firms—New Zealand

Dragon Capital
Endeavour Capital, Ltd.
Far Pacific Capital Limited
Goldman Sachs JBWere (NZ) Ltd. (FKA: JBWere (NZ) Ltd.)

Imprimatur Capital, Ltd.
Infiniti Capital Limited
iGlobe Treasury Management, Ltd.
inventages venture capital S.A.
Kiwi Growth Partners Ltd.
Milestone Capital
No. 8 Ventures Management Ltd (FKA: Morel Ventures Ltd)
Pioneer Capital Partners
Solomon Capital Partners, Ltd. (AKA: SCP)

Venture Firms—Nicaragua

Volio Capital, S.A.

Venture Firms—Nigeria

HEIRS Capital Ltd
Reliance Bank
Statoil Innovation AS (AKA: StatoilHydro)
Vectis Capital SA

Venture Firms—Norway

Alliance Venture AS
BTV Invest
Bergen Venture AS
Campus Kjeller AS
Convexa Capital AS
Creo Ventures As
Energy Capital Management AS
Energy Ventures AS
Ferd Venture
Fjord Invest Management AS
Gezina AS
Glastad Invest AS
Hafslund Venture AS
IT Fornebu Inkubator AS
Icon Capital Group AS
Indo-Nordic Private Equity AS
Investinor AS
Investra ASA
Joto Investering
Kaupthing Bank hf.
Kentra AS
Kistefos Venture Capital AS
Kongsberg Innovasjon AS
Leiv Eiriksson Nyfotek AS (FKA: Sakorn Midt Norge)
Mallin AS
NeoMed Management AS
Nordika Asset Management
NorgesInvestor Management AS
Norinnova Forvaltning AS
Norinvest Management AS (AKA: Norinvest Forvaltning AS)
Norsk Hydro ASA (AKA: Norsk Hydro Technology Ventures)
Northzone Ventures AS (FKA: Venture Partners AS)
PRE Management
ProVenture AS
Procom Venture AS
Progressus Management AS
Reiten & Co Strategic Investments AS
Result Venture Knowledge International
Sakorn Invest AS
Sakorn Syd
Sakorninvest Innlandet AS
Sakorninvest Nord AS
Sarsia Innovation AS
Sarsia Seed Management AS
Selvaag Invest AS
Sinvent
Skagerak Venture Capital AS
Skandia Innovation AB
Smedvig Capital, Ltd. (FKA: Peder Smedvig Capital Ltd)
Statoil Innovation AS (AKA: StatoilHydro)
Sydvestor Corporate
Teknoinvest AS
TeleVenture Management AS (FKA: Telenor Venture AS)
Telenor Mobile
VI Partners
Viking Venture Management AS

Venture Firms—Oman

Omani Center for Investment Promotion and Export Development

Venture Firms—Pakistan

Acumen Fund
Crosby Capital, Ltd.
Jahangir Siddiqui Group (AKA: JS Group)
Pak Oman Investment Company

Venture Firms—Peru

Small Enterprise Assistance Fund (SEAF)
Value Investments Peru - SAFI

Venture Firms—Philippines

AB Capital & Investment Corporation
AIG Investment Corporation, (Asia) Ltd.
Advent Capital & Finance Corporation
Asia Capital Management (ACM) Limited (AKA: ACL Asia Ltd)
ICCP Venture Partners, Inc.
JAFCO Investment (Hong Kong), Ltd.
Japan Asia Investment Company, Ltd. (AKA: JAIC)
Marsman-Drysdale Corporation
Metrobank Venture Capital Corp.
Narra Venture Capital
Plantersbank Venture Capital Corporation
Small Business Guarantee and Finance Corporation

Venture Firms—Poland

AKJ Investments SA
Argus Capital Group, Ltd.
BBI Capital SA
Business Angel Seedfund Sp. z o.o. S.K.A.
bmp AG
CDP Capital - Technology Ventures (FKA: CDP Sofinov)
CWC Capital Management LLC
European Bank for Reconstruction and Development
e-Katalyst
Innova Capital
Intel Capital
Kerten Capital
Litexco Mediterranea
MCI Management
NFI Management Sp. z o.o. (AKA: Grupa CA-IB)
Oresa Ventures Sp Z oo
Prokom Investments SA
Regionalne Fundusze Inwestycji Sp. z o.o.
Secus Asset Management SA
Skandia Innovation AB
Small Enterprise Assistance Fund (SEAF)
TMF Participations Management
TP Invest
Tar Heel
Towarzystwo Inwestcyji Spoteczno-Ekonomicznych SA (TISE)
Trinity Management Sp. z o.o.
Vaekstfonden (AKA: Danish Growth Fund, The)
Vienna Capital Partners

Venture Firms—Portugal

AICEP Capital Global - Sociedade de Capital de Risco, S.A.
AITEC, SGPS, SA
BANIF - Banco de Investimentos SA
BCP Capital, Sociedade de Capital de Risco SA
BES.com, SGPS SA
BIG Capital, SA
BPI Private Equity
Banco Efisa SA
Beta, Sociedade Capital de Risco, SA
Centro Venture - Sociedade Capital Risco, S.A.
DRIVE Sociedade de Capital de Risco, SA
Espirito Santo (ES) Ventures - Sociedade de Capital de Risco
Espirito Santo Tech Ventures
Explorer Investments SCR, S.A.
FINPRO, SGPS SA
Fundo para a Internacionalizacao das Empresas Portuguesas
Inovcapital (AKA: PME Capital)
PME Investimentos - Sociedade de Investimento SA
SDEM-Madeira Corporate Development Company, SGPS SA
SGPME - Sociedade Capital de Risco, S.A.
Skandia Innovation AB
Syntek Capital AG
TC-Turismo Capital - SCR, S.A.
Totta Finance

Venture Firms—Qatar

Al Rayan Investment LLC

Venture Firms—Romania

DBH Group
European Bank for Reconstruction and Development
Foundation for Assistance to Small Innovative Enterprises
Global Finance SA
HKK Partners
K+ Venture Partners
Kerten Capital
Litexco Mediterranea
MCI Management
Mackenzie Capital srl
NCH Capital, Inc.
Oltenia Financial Investment Cy
Oresa Ventures Sp Z oo
SIF - Banat - Crisana SA
SIF Transilvania
Small Enterprise Assistance Fund (SEAF)
TMF Participations Management

Venture Firms—Russia

ABRT Venture Fund
Al'yans ROSNO Upravleniye Aktivami, OAO
Almaz Capital Partners
Aurora Investment Advisors, Ltd.
Delta Capital Management (AKA:Delta Private Equity Partners)
Eagle Venture Partners
European Bank for Reconstruction and Development

e-Trust Investment Group
GK Rossiyskaya Korporatsiya Nanotekhnologiy
I2BF
Innovative Technopark IDEA
Intel Capital
League of Management Companies
Mint Capital, Ltd.
NCH Capital, Inc.
Newbridge Capital, Ltd.
Oradell Capital
PPF Investments, Ltd.
Renova Capital Advisors
Roel Group
Rolls Royce Corporate Venture
Russian Technology Fund Management, Ltd.
Trust and Investment Bank (T&IB)
UK Infrastrukturnye investitsii, ZAO
UK NIKOR, OAO
United Financial Group Asset Management (AKA: UFG)

Venture Firms—Saudi Arabia

Amwal AlKhaleej
Arbah Global
Crescent Point Group
Islamic Development Bank, The
Malaz Group
MerchantBridge & Co., Ltd.
Rolls Royce Corporate Venture
Saad Investments Company , Ltd.
Swicorp Capital Partners

Venture Firms—Senegal

Advanced Finance & Investment Group LLC (AKA: AFIG)

Venture Firms—Serbia and Montenegro

Eagle Ventures
Global Finance SA
Slavia Capital
TMF Participations Management

Venture Firms—Sierra Leone

ManoCap, Ltd.

Venture Firms—Singapore

AIG Investment Corporation, (Asia) Ltd.
Aavishkaar Venture Management Services Pvt, Ltd.
Active Capital Asia, Ltd.
Air Products and Chemicals, Inc.
Arisaig Partners (Asia) Pte., Ltd.
AsiaTech Internet Group (ATIG) (FKA: AsiaTech Ventures)
Basil Growth Corporation
Bio*One Capital
BioVeda Capital Private, Ltd.
Cnstar Capital Pte., Ltd
Crescent Point Group
Crest Capital Partners
Crosby Capital, Ltd.
Crossover Advisors Pvt., Ltd. (FKA: Meta Crossover Advisors)
Daiwa Corporate Investment Co., Ltd.
Draper Fisher Jurvetson ePlanet Ventures, L.P.
EDB Investments Pte, Ltd.
East West Capital Partners Pte, Ltd.
Enspire Capital Pte Ltd.
Exploit Technologies Pte, Ltd.
Extream Ventures Pte, Ltd.
FEO Ventures Pte., Ltd.
Flextronics International, Ltd.
Fortune Venture Investment Group (AKA:Fortune Consulting)
Frontier Investment & Development Partners
Frontline Strategy Pte. Ltd.
GGV Capital
GIC Special Investments Pte, Ltd.
GIMV Asia Management Pte., Ltd.
Gemplus SCA
Giza Venture Capital (FKA: Giza Investment Management)
Goldman Sachs JBWere (NZ) Ltd. (FKA: JBWere (NZ) Ltd.)
Hina Capital Partners
Hupomone Capital Partners Pte, Ltd.
Imprimatur Capital, Ltd.
Infocomm Investments Pte., Ltd. (FKA: NCB Holdings Pte Ltd)
Intel Capital
Inter-Asia Venture Management
InterVest Co., Ltd.
iGlobe Partners, Ltd.
iGlobe Treasury Management, Ltd.
JAFCO Co., Ltd. (FKA: Japan Associated Finance Co. Ltd.)
JAFCO Investment (Hong Kong), Ltd.
JAFCO Investment [FKA: Nomura/JAFCO Investment (Asia), Ltd.]
Japan Asia Investment Company, Ltd. (AKA: JAIC)
Juniper Capital Ventures Pte, Ltd.
KTB Ventures
London Asia Capital Plc (FKA: netvest.com Plc)
McLean Watson Capital Inc.
MillhouseIAG
Nadathur Holdings and Investments Pvt., Ltd.
Neuberger Berman LLC
Newbridge Capital, Ltd.
Peepul Capital LLC
Phillip Private Equity Pte, Ltd. (FKA: ECICS Mgt. Pte, Ltd.)
PrimePartners Asset Management Pte, Ltd.
Richlink International Capital Co., Ltd.
RimAsia Capital Partners
Rolls Royce Corporate Venture
SBI Ven Capital Pte., Ltd.
SHK Fund Management, Ltd.
SL Investment Company, Ltd.
SPRING SEEDS Capital Pte, Ltd.
Schroders PLC
Sembawang Capital Pte., Ltd.
Singapore Power Group
Singapore Technologies Kinetics, Ltd.
Sirius Venture Consulting Pte, Ltd.
SkyVen Asset Management Pte, Ltd.
Solitaire Capital Advisors Pvt. Ltd.
Spinnaker Capital Group
Sycamore Ventures Pte, Ltd.
3V SourceOne Capital Pte, Ltd.
T. Rowe Price Threshold Partnerships
TC Capital Pte., Ltd.
Tembusu Ventures Pte., Ltd.
Templeton Asset Management, Ltd.
Tuscan Ventures Pvt., Ltd.
UOB Bioventures Management Pte, Ltd.
UOB Venture Management Pte, Ltd.
Undisclosed Firm
Upstream Ventures Pte., Ltd.
VPSA (FKA: Viventures Partners)
Value Capital Asset Management Pte. Ltd.
Venture TDF Pte Ltd.
Vertex Management Israel (AKA: Vertex Venture Capital)
Vertex Management Pte, Ltd. (AKA: Vertex Venture Holdings)
Vertex Venture Capital
Vickers Venture Partners
WI Harper Group

Venture Firms—Slovakia

Arca Capital
DBH Group
European Bank for Reconstruction and Development
gcp gamma capital partners Beratungs- & Beteiligungs AG
HKK Partners
Rozvojovy Fond pre male a stredne podnikanie, a.s.
Seed Capital Company, s.r.o. (FKA: Fond fondov, s.r.o.)
Slavia Capital
TMF Participations Management

Venture Firms—Slovenia

Eagle Ventures
Horizonte Venture Management GmbH
Prophetes Inc.
RSG Capital d.o.o.
TMF Participations Management

Venture Firms—South Africa

Advanced Finance & Investment Group LLC (AKA: AFIG)
Argil Venture Capital (Pty) Ltd
Bioventures (AKA: Biotech Venture Partners)
Brait Capital Partners
Business Partners
Calyon (FKA: Credit Agricole Indosuez)
Capricorn Capital Partners (Pty) Ltd
Decorum Capital Partners (Pty) Ltd
Delta Partners FZ LLC
Ellerine Bros. (Pty) Ltd
Equity Africa Trust
Export Venture Capital Corporation (Pty) Ltd.
First South Investment Managers
GKA Bayete
Glenhove Fund Managers (Pty) Ltd
Global Capital Private Equity Ltd
Hasso Plattner Ventures Africa
Here Be Dragons (HBD) Mgt Services (AKA:HBD Venture Capital)
Inspired Evolution Investment Management
Intrepid Venture Capital (Pty) Ltd
Investec Asset Management, Ltd
Kagiso Ventures
Khula Enterprise Finance Ltd
Lireas Holdings (Pty) Ltd
Modern Africa Fund Managers
NIB-MDM Fund Managers (Pty) Ltd
Nedbank Corporate Private Equity
Newfarmers Developement Company
PSG Capital Limited
Pamodzi Investment Holdings
PointBreak Private Equity

Praxis Capital
Progressive Investment Trust
Public Investment Commissioners
RAPS Finance (Pty) Ltd
Sabvest, Ltd.
Sanlam Private Equity
Shanduka Fund Mangers (Pty) Ltd.
Treacle Venture Partners
Trinitas Private Equity
Undisclosed Firm
Vantage Venture Partners (AKA: Vantage Capital)
VenFin DD Holdings Ltd.

Venture Firms—South Korea

AIG Investment Corporation, (Asia) Ltd.
ATVentures, Inc. (FKA: August Tiger Ventures, Inc.)
Aju IB Invesment Co., Ltd.
Albatross Investment Capital Co., Ltd.

Venture Firms—South Korea

Alpine Technology Investment Co., Ltd.
Asia Culture Technology Investment Co., Ltd.
Atinum Investment Co., Ltd.
Benex Investment, Inc.
BlueRun Ventures
Boston Investment Company, Ltd.
CBF Technology Investment Corporation
CDP Capital - Technology Ventures (FKA: CDP Sofinov)
Choongnam Venture Capital (FKA:Choongnam KI Venture Capital)
Crest Capital Partners
DFJ Athena
Daegyeong Venture Capital Corporation
Daesung Private Equity, Inc.
Daeyang Venture Capital Co., Ltd.
Darwin Venture Capital Co., Ltd.
Draper Fisher Jurvetson ePlanet Ventures, L.P.
E Trust Venture Capital
Fitech Venture Partners Company, Ltd.
Green Busan Investment Co., Ltd.
HST Venture Capital
Hanju Investment Corp.
Hanwha Venture Capital Corporation
Heungkook Venture Capital Company, Ltd.
Hyundai Venture Investment Corporation
IDG Ventures Korea
Ilshin Investment Co., Ltd. (AKA:Ilshin Venture Capital)
Industrial Bank of Korea Capital
Intel Capital
InterVest Co., Ltd.
Isu Venture Capital Co., Ltd. (FKA: Peta Capital)
i Venture Investment Co., Ltd.
JAFCO Co., Ltd. (FKA: Japan Associated Finance Co. Ltd.)
JAFCO Investment [FKA: Nomura/JAFCO Investment (Asia), Ltd.]
K-Net Investment
KTB Securities Co., Ltd. (FKA: KTB Network Co., Ltd.)
KTB Ventures
KTIC Global Investment Advisory Co., Ltd.
Kiwoom Investment Company, Ltd.
Kolon Investment, Inc.
Korea Biotech Investment Company, Ltd.
Korea Investment Partners Co., Ltd.
Korea Technology Investment Corporation (AKA: KTIC)
Korea Venture Creative Investment Co., Ltd. (AKA: KVCI)
Korea Venture Fund Management
Kunyoung Investment Co., Ltd.
L&S Venture Capital Corporation
LB Investment, Inc.
LTI Investments
Lee & Company Investments
Lindeman Asia Investment
M-Venture Investment, Inc. (FKA: Shinyoung Venture Capital)
MK Venture Capital
MVP Capital Company, Ltd.
Macquarie Shinhan Infrastructure Management Co., Ltd.
Michigan Venture Capital Co., Ltd.
Mirae Asset Venture Investment Co., Ltd. (FKA:Korean Dream)
Muhan Investment Co. (FKA: TeraSource Venture Capital Co.)
Munhwa Investment Corporation (AKA: Comet Investment)
Myventure Partners, Inc.
NEXUS Investment Corp. (FKA: Pusan Venture Tech. Capital)
Neoplux Company, Ltd.
Newton Technology Partners (NTP)
Next Venture Investment
Olympus Capital Holdings Asia
Partners Venture Capital Co., Ltd.
Poibos Venture Capital
Premier Venture Partners LLC
Qcapital Partners Co, Ltd. (FKA: TG Ventures, Inc.)
Ray & Venture Investment Co., Ltd.
Rexiter Capital Management Ltd.
Rolls Royce Corporate Venture
SK Telecom
SL Investment Company, Ltd.
SV Venture Capital
Saehan Venture Capital
Samsung Venture Investment Corporation (SVIC)
Seir Venture Capital
Sejin T.S Co., Ltd. (FKA: Sejin Venture Capital Co., Ltd.)
Shin Poong Venture Capital Corp.
Shinbo Investment Corporation
Shinhan Private Equity Co., Ltd.
Shinwon Venture Capital (a.k.a. Shinyon Venture Capital)
Sky Venture Capital
Skylake Incuvest & Company
SoftBank Ventures Korea, Inc.
Solborn Venture Investment, Inc.
Sovik Venture Capital Company, Ltd.
Teachiworld Venture Investment Company, Ltd.
Tong Yang Venture Capital Corporation
Undisclosed Firm
Univest Capital
Winvest Venture Investment
Wonik Investment Partners
Woori Private Equity Company
Woori Technology Investment Co., Ltd.
Wooridul Venture Capital Co., Ltd.
Youngshin Venture Capital

Venture Firms—Spain

Active Capital Partners S.L.
Adara Venture Partners
Agencia de Innovacion y Desarrollo de Andalucia (AKA: IDEA)
Arta Capital, S.A.
Aser Capital SCR
Axis ParticIpaCiones Empresariales SGECR SA
Baird Capital Partners Europe
Banco Espanol de Credito SA (AKA: Banesto)
Banco Santander SA (FKA: Banco Santander Central Hispano)
Bonsai Venture Capital
Bullnet Capital SCR SA
CAI Desarrollo Empresarial S.C.R. S.A.
COFIDES - Compania Espanola De Financiacion Del Desarrolo SA
Caja de Ahorros y Monte de Piedad de Navarra
Cantabria Capital
Capital Alianza Private Equity Investment SA
Capital Stock SCR SA
Catalana D'Iniciatives CR SA
Clave Mayor S.A.
Climate Change Capital, Ltd.
Corporacion Sant Bernat SA (AKA:CORSABE)
Cross Road Biotech S.C.R.
Debaeque Venture Capital
Demeter Partners S.A.
Diana Capital SGECR SA
EBM Sociedad Gestora de Entidades de Capital Riesgo SA
Empreserial Caja De Madrid, S.A.
Fortis Private Equity NV/SA (FKA: VIV NV)
Genera Navarra Iniciativas Empresariales SA
Gescaixa Galicia SGECR SA
Gestion De Capital Riesgo Del Pais Vasco
Harbert Venture Partners
Highgrowth Partners SGECR SA (AKA: bcnHighgrowth)
ICF Capital
Iame Capital Riesgo SGECR SA
Instituto Aragones de Fomento
Inveralia Group
Invereddy Seed Capital
Inverjaen S.C.R. SA
Inverpyme SA
Inversiones Progranada SA
Invertec
iNova Capital SCR SA
Landon Investments, SCR, SA
Litexco Mediterranea
M-Capital S.A.
Madrigal Participaciones, S.A.
Mobius Corporate Venture Capital SGECR SA
Murcia Emprende Sociedad de Capital Riesgo
Najeti Ventures
Nauta Capital
Nordkapp Gestion S.G.I.I.C., S.A.
Popular de Participaciones Financieras S.C.R. S.A.
Prax Capital
Quercus Equity
Result Venture Knowledge International
Riojana De Capital Riesgo S.A. (AKA: Ricari)
Riva y Garcia Private Equity
SODECO (AKA: Soc. Desar. Comarcas Mineras)
SODENA - Sociedad de Desarrollo de Navarra

SODIAR - Sociedad Para El Desarrollo Industrial De Aragon
SODICAMAN
SODIGA - Soc. Ind. de Galicia
SOFIEX (AKA: Sociedad de Fomento Industrial de EXTREMADURA)
Savia Capital Inversion S.A.
Sepides
Simbiosis Venture Capital S.L.
Skandia Innovation AB
Sociedad Regional de Promocion del Principado de Asturias
Sodiex Sociedad para el Desarrollo Industrial de Extremadura
Syntek Capital AG
TMF Participations Management
Talde Gestion SGECR SA
Thesan Capital
Torreal SCR SA
Vigo Activo Sociedad De Capital Riesgo SA
Vista Capital de Expansion SA
XesGalicia SGECR SA
Ysios Capital Partners

Venture Firms—Sri Lanka

Capital Development & Investment Co., Ltd.
Litexco Mediterranea

Venture Firms—St Kitts/Nevis

Leeward Fund Management

Venture Firms—Sweden

AB Chalmersinvest
AB Possessor
AB Traction
AH Smaforetagsinvest AB
Accent Equity Partners AB
Ackra Invest AB
Affarsstrategerna AB
Aktiva Invest Jamtland & Harjedalen AB
Allba Invest AB
Aloe Private Equity
AmberTank
Amplico Kapital AB
Amymone AB
Augmenta Venture Partners AB
BBE Business Development AB
Biolin Medical AB
Boforsstiftelsen
Borevind AB
BrainHeart Capital AB
Bure Equity
Catella AB
Chalmers Innovation
Chord Capital, Ltd. (FKA: Generics Group, The)
Coach & Capital Nordic 1 AB
Creandum KB
D. Carnegie & Co AB
Department of Ventures AB
Ekonord Invest AB
Emano AB
Eqvitec Partners Oy
European Equity Partners
Fairford Holdings Scandinavia AB (AKA: Fairford Holdings)
Fianchetto Venture Capital AB (FVC)
Firm Factory Network
Fore C Investment AB
ForetagsByggarna AB (AKA: Business Builders)
Forsta Entreprenorsfonden i Norden AB
Fouriertransform AB
GKL Growth Capital AB
GLD Invest AB
GZ Group
Gylling Invest AB
Hakon Invest AB (FKA: ICA Forbundet Invest)
Holdingbolaget vid Goteborgs universitet AB
Huvudkontoret i Kristinehamn AB
IDG International Data Group AB
ITP Invest AB (AKA: I Teknisk Partner Invest AB)
Initium AB
Innovacom SA
InnovationsKapital
Innovationsbron AB
Intel Capital
Investment AB Latour
Investment AB Spiltan
Investor Growth Capital AB
Iteksa Venture AB
KTH-Chalmers Capital KB
Karolinska Development AB
Karolinska Investment Management AB
Kaupthing Bank hf.
Konceptkapital AB
Kreos Capital (FKA: European Venture Partners)
Ledstiernan AB
LinkMed AB
LinkTech AB
Lumitec
Lund University Bioscience AB
Lunova AB
Malmohus Invest AB
Maxus Capital AB
MedCap AB (FKA: New Science Svenska AB)
Midway Holding AB
Mobyson AB (FKA: Extended Capital Group ECG AB)
Newcap Partners, Inc.
Nexit Ventures Oy
Nordic Growth Oy
Nordic Venture Partners (FKA: Danske Venture Partners)
NorgesInvestor Management AS
Norrlandsfonden
Norrskenet AB (AKA: Bothnia)
Northzone Ventures AS (FKA: Venture Partners AS)
Nostrum Ventures
Novax AB
Novestra AB
Odlander, Fredrikson & Co. AB (AKA: HealthCap)
Oresund-Healthcare A/S
PNP Venture Capital AB
Pod Venture Partners Inc.
Priveq Investment AB
Prosper Capital
Proventus AB
Provider Venture Partners AB (FKA: IT Provider Advisor 1 AB)
RPE Capital Management (AKA: Retail Private Equity)
Ratos AB
Result Venture Knowledge International
Rite Internet Ventures AB
Rosengard Invest AB
SEB Venture Capital
SLS Invest AB
Saab Ventures AB
Sagri Development AB
SamInvest Mitt AB
Satila Holding AB
Scandi-Latin Corporate Finance AB
Scandinavian Baltic Development, Ltd.
Scandinavian Financial Management AB
Scope Capital Advisory AB
Servisen Investment Management AB
Skandia Innovation AB
Skanditek Industriforvaltning AB (publ)
Smaforetagsinvest AB
Softronic Ventures AB
Spinn Investment AB
Start Invest AB
Stiftelsen Industrifonden
Sting Capital
Stora Enso Ventures Oy
Sunstone Capital A/S
Sustainable Technology Partners Nordic AB
Svenskt Rekonstruktionskapital AB
Swedocean
T. Rowe Price Threshold Partnerships
TeknoSeed AB
Uminova Foretagsutveckling AB
Vestra Partnerinvest AB
Vita Nova Ventures AB
Volati AB
Volvo Technology Transfer AB
Z-Invest AB

Venture Firms—Switzerland

Adinvest AG
Alta Berkeley Venture Partners
Aravis SA
Armada Venture Group LLC
Atila Ventures
Avendis Capital S.A.
adbodmer AG
BTS Investment Advisors, Ltd.
Bellevue Asset Management AG
BioMedPartners
Brait Capital Partners
Business Creation Management AG
Calyon (FKA: Credit Agricole Indosuez)
Creathor Venture Management GmbH
Credit Suisse Asset Management
Crossbow Ventures
Draper Investment Company
EPS Finanz AG
ETeCH Management GmbH
EVA - the Basel Life Sciences Agency
Ecosystem Ventures LLC
Emerald Technology Ventures AG
Endeavour Vision SA
Equatis AG
Equinox S.A.
EuroUs Ventures
F. Hoffmann - La Roche, Ltd.
Fabrel Lotos (AKA: Fabrel AG)
Fischer Investment Group (Holding) AG
Fongit
Friedli Corporate Finance AG
firstVentury GmbH
GEDEFI Technology Venture Services SA

Gemplus SCA
Genevest Consulting Group, S.A.
Grey Corporate Investments AG
Guggenheim Venture Partners LLC
HBM BioVentures AG (FKA: HBM Partners AG)
Helvetic Capital Ventures AG
Highland Capital Partners LLC
IVS A/S (AKA: Internet Ventures Scandinavia A/S)
Index Ventures
Initiative Capital SA
International BM Biomedicine Holdings, Ltd.
Invision Private Equity AG
iGlobe Partners, Ltd.
inventages venture capital S.A.
Jade Invest SA
Kaupthing Bank hf.
Leading Hedge SA
Litexco Mediterranea
LogiSpring Management Company S.a.r.l.
MerchantBridge & Co., Ltd.
Merifin Capital Group
Mountain Super Angel AG
NeoMed Management AS
Neuberger Berman LLC
Nextech Venture AG
Novartis Venture Fund (FKA: Novartis Corp.)
Odlander, Fredrikson & Co. AB (AKA: HealthCap)
Orbitex Inc.
Oxford Capital Partners
Quan Ventures
Rising Star Management GmbH
SANTIS Investment AG
STMicroelectronics
Scope Capital Advisory AB
Sifem AG (AKA: Swiss Investment Fund for Emerging Markets)
Swicorp Capital Partners
Swiss Life Private Equity Partners Ltd
Swisscom AG
TAT Capital Partners Ltd
TMF Participations Management
Taishan Invest AG
twinventures ag
Venture Incubator AG (AKA: VI Partners AG)
Venture Partners AG
ViewPoint Capital Partners GmbH
Vision Capital Management
Wellington Partners Venture Capital GmbH
Zurcher Kantonalbank

Venture Firms—Taiwan

AIG Investment Corporation, (Asia) Ltd.
Agora Investment Management, Ltd.
AsiaTech Internet Group (ATIG) (FKA: AsiaTech Ventures)
AsiaTech Management LLC
AsiaVest Partners, TCW/YFY Ltd. (FKA: TCW/YFY Investment)
Atlas Capital Group, Inc., The
Beijing Ji Feng Industry Investment & Management Company
Birch Venture Capital, Inc.
CDIB BioScience Venture Management
CID Group, The
CIDC Consultants, Inc. (AKA: China Investment & Development)
Cathay Financial Holdings Co., Ltd.
Cheng Xin Technology Development Corp. (FKA: Fidelity VC)
China Development Financial Holding Corporation
China Development Industrial Bank (CDIB)
China Venture Management, Inc.
Cnstar Capital Pte., Ltd
Crimson
Eminent Venture Capital Corporation
Fortune Venture Capital, Inc.
Fortune Venture Investment Group (AKA:Fortune Consulting)
GSIM Corporation (AKA: Global Strategic Investment Mgmt.)
Global Tech Management Consulting Corporation
Harbinger Venture Management
Hotung International Company, Ltd.
Hua Nan Venture Capital Co., Ltd.
Hyield Consulting Group
Industrial Bank of Taiwan
Intel Capital
InveStar Capital, Inc.
iD Innovation, Inc.
iD TechVentures, Inc. (FKA: Acer Technology Ventures)
iD Ventures America, LLC (AKA: Acer Technology Ventures)
JAFCO Co., Ltd. (FKA: Japan Associated Finance Co. Ltd.)
JAFCO Investment (Hong Kong), Ltd.
JAFCO Investment [FKA: Nomura/JAFCO Investment (Asia), Ltd.]
Kuo-Chun Financial Management, Inc.
Maxima Capital Management, Inc.
Mentor Consulting Corporation
Pac-Link Management Corporation
Pacific Venture Capital Company, Ltd.
Pacific Venture Partners
Panda Capital Asia, Ltd.
Parawin Venture Capital Corporation
Sunplus Venture Capital Company, Ltd.
Sunsino Ventures Group (FKA: Sunsino Development Associate)
Sycamore Ventures Pte, Ltd.
Taishin Management and Consulting Co., Ltd.
Tano Capital LLC
Triton Management Corporation
UMC Capital
United Investments Company
Unitek Capital Corporation
VentureTech Alliance LLC
Vertex Management Pte, Ltd. (AKA: Vertex Venture Holdings)
WI Harper Group
WIT Investment Partners, Ltd.
WK Associates
Yuanta Venture Capital
Yuen Foong Yu Venture Capital Investment Corporation

Venture Firms—Tajikistan

European Bank for Reconstruction and Development

Venture Firms—Thailand

AIG Investment Corporation, (Asia) Ltd.
CDP Capital - Technology Ventures (FKA: CDP Sofinov)
Dragon Capital
JAFCO Investment (Hong Kong), Ltd.
Japan Asia Investment Company, Ltd. (AKA: JAIC)
Khao Kla Venture Capital Management Co., Ltd.
One Asset Management, Ltd.
Rolls Royce Corporate Venture
Thai Incubator Dot Com Co., Ltd.
Thai Strategic Capital Management Co., Ltd.

Venture Firms—Togo

Cauris Management

Venture Firms—Trinidad/Tob.

Caribbean Development Capital, Ltd. (AKA: DEV-CAP)
Dynamic Equity, Ltd.

Venture Firms—Tunisia

Calyon (FKA: Credit Agricole Indosuez)
FRDCM SICAR
Gabes Invest Sicar
International Maghreb Merchant Bank (AKA: IMBank)
International Sicar
LE PROMOTEUR
Maghrebia Financiere
SICAR Horizon
SICAR Invest
SICAR L'Avenir
SICAR STB
SIDCO
SIM SICAR (AKA: Societe de l'Investissement Moderne)
SIP Sicar
SODEK SICAR
SODINO
SODIS SICAR
Sud Sicar
Swicorp Capital Partners
TSPP Sicar
Univers Invest SICAR

Venture Firms—Turkey

European Bank for Reconstruction and Development
iLab Holding AS
Rhea Venture Capital Investment Trust Inc
Turk Venture Partners Limited (Turkven)

Venture Firms—Turkmenistan

European Bank for Reconstruction and Development

Venture Firms—Uganda

African Agricultural Capital Ltd

Venture Firms—Ukraine

AVentures
Arca Capital
eVenture Capital Partners GmbH
Imprimatur Capital, Ltd.
KUA Fozzi Kapital, TOV
KUA Svarog Asset Management, TOV
Kompaniia z Upravlinnia Aktyvamy Dan, TOV
NCH Capital, Inc.
PPF Investments, Ltd.

Venture Firms—United Kingdom

AXM Venture Capital, Ltd.
Abingworth Management, Ltd.
Acacia Capital Partners
Accel Partners
Accelerator Media (UK) Ltd

Acorn Capital Partners
Add Partners, Ltd.
Advent Venture Partners LLP
Affymetrix, Inc.
Air Products and Chemicals, Inc.
Akara, Ltd. (DBA: IDG Ventures Europe)
Albany Venture Managers, Ltd.
Albion Ventures LLP (FKA: Close Venture Management)
Alliance Trust Equity Partners
Aloe Private Equity
Alta Berkeley Venture Partners
Amadeus Capital Partners, Ltd.
Amphion Innovations PLC
Aquarius Equity Partners, Ltd.
Arca Capital
Archangel Informal Investments Limited
Argus Capital Group, Ltd.
Ariadne Capital, Ltd.
Arts Alliance Advisors
Asia Pacific Investment Partners
Athlone International, Ltd
Atila Ventures
Atlantic Bridge
Atlas Venture, Ltd.
Atomico Ventures
Augmentum Capital LLP
AutoVision GmbH
Avlar BioVentures, Ltd.
B.P. Marsh & Partners, Ltd.
BNFL Enterprise (Investment Management) Limited
BTG International (AKA: British Technology Group)
Baird Capital Partners Europe
Balderton Capital (FKA: Benchmark Capital Europe)
Balyasny Asset Management LP (AKA: BAM)
Banco Efisa SA
Bancroft Group
BankInvest Group A/S
Barclays Ventures
Beringea LLC
Berkeley Mineral Resources PLC (FKA: Tecteon PLC)
Birmingham Technology (Venture Capital) Ltd
Bracken Partners Limited
Bramdean Asset Management
Braveheart Ventures, Ltd.
Bridges Community Ventures, Ltd.
CT Investment Partners LLP
Cabot Square Capital, Ltd.
Calyon (FKA: Credit Agricole Indosuez)
Canbank Venture Capital Fund Limited
CapVest Management Ltd
Capital Ideas PLC (FKA:Leisure Ventures PLC)
Cardiff University
Catalyst BioMedica Ltd
Catapult Venture Managers, Ltd.
Celtic House Venture Partners
Centurion Capital Ltd
Charmex Ventures Limited
Chess Ventures
Chord Capital, Ltd. (FKA: Generics Group, The)
Chrysalis VCT
Climate Change Capital, Ltd.
Clydesdale Bank PLC
Company Guides, Ltd. (AKA: Company Guides Venture Partners)
Compound Semiconductor Technologies Ltd
Conduit Ventures Limited
Connection Capital LLP
Continuum Group, Ltd. (AKA: Continuum Advisory, Ltd.)
Copan, Inc
Create Partners Ltd
Crescent Capital (NI) Ltd
Crosby Capital, Ltd.
Cross Atlantic Capital Partners
Curzon Park Capital, Ltd.
DC Thomson & Co
DFJ Esprit
DN Capital, Ltd. (FKA: Digital Networks Global Ventures)
Dawn Capital
Defta Partners
Delta Partners, Ltd.
Derbyshire First Investments Limited (DFI)
Derwent London PLC
Development Partners International
Dragon Capital
Draper Fisher Jurvetson
Draper Fisher Jurvetson ePlanet Ventures, L.P.
Dubai Investment Group (AKA: DIG)
Duet Capital
Duke Equity Partners
E-Synergy
ETF Manager LLP
East Hill Management
Econergy International Corporation
Eden Ventures (UK), Ltd.
Elderstreet Investments Limited
Elephant Capital
Endeavour Ventures, Ltd.
Energy Ventures AS
Enterprise Private Capital GP
Enterprise Ventures, Ltd. (FKA:Lancashire Enterprises PLC)
Entrepreneurs Fund Management LLP
Epi-V LLP
Equinox Securities Limited (AKA: FastVentures)
Essex Woodlands Health Ventures
European Bank for Reconstruction and Development
European Equity Partners
European Technology Ventures SA (AKA: ETV Capital SA)
Eurovestech PLC
Evolution Group (FKA: EVC Christows PLC)
Excalibur Fund Managers, Ltd.
e-Launcher
Facilities Corporate Management
Fajr Capital Ltd
Favonius Ventures
Fidelity Ventures
Finance South East, Ltd.
Finance Wales PLC
Finsbury Life Sciences Investment Trust
FirstVentures
Foursan Group
Frog Capital, Ltd.
Frontiers Capital, Ltd.
GATX European Technology Ventures
GIC Special Investments Pte, Ltd.
GIMV N.V.
Gartmore Investment Limited
Gateway Global (FKA:NW Brown Capital Partners)
Generation Investment Management LLP
Georgetown Venture Partners (AKA: GVP)
Glenalta Capital LLP
Global Leisure Partners LLP
GoEast Ventures, Ltd.
Goldman Sachs JBWere (NZ) Ltd. (FKA: JBWere (NZ) Ltd.)
Greenhill SAVP
Guggenheim Venture Partners LLC
Harbert Venture Partners
Hemisphere Capital LLC
Herald Investment Management Ltd (HIML)
HgCapital
Hotbed, Ltd.
I2BF
IBIS Capital, Ltd.
ION Equity, Ltd.
IP2IPO, Ltd. (AKA: IP Group plc)
ISIS Equity Partners PLC
IVS A/S (AKA: Internet Ventures Scandinavia A/S)
Impax Asset Management
Imperial Innovations (AKA: Imperial College Innovations)
Imprimatur Capital, Ltd.
Index Ventures
Inflexion plc (AKA: Inflexion Private Equity)
Ingenious Ventures
Innvotec, Ltd.
Inspired Evolution Investment Management
Intel Capital
Invest Northern Ireland
Investec Asset Management, Ltd
Isis Innovation Ltd
idealab!
JAFCO Co., Ltd. (FKA: Japan Associated Finance Co. Ltd.)
JAFCO Investment (Hong Kong), Ltd.
JO Hambro Capital Management
Jahangir Siddiqui Group (AKA: JS Group)
Javelin Ventures, Ltd.
Johnson & Johnson Development Corporation
Katalyst Ventures Limited
Kaupthing Bank hf.
Kennet Venture Partners, Ltd. (FKA: Kennet Capital, Ltd.)
Kings Park Capital LLP
Klarius Group, Ltd.
Kreos Capital (FKA: European Venture Partners)
LTG Development Capital Ltd
Lago Partners Ltd
Leasing & Equity Investments Ltd.
Ledstiernan AB
Lion Capital Advisers Ltd (FKA: Lion Capital Partners Plc)
London Asia Capital Plc (FKA: netvest.com Plc)
London Seed Capital, Ltd.
Longbow Capital
Loudwater Investment Partners, Ltd.
Low Carbon Accelerator
Loxko Venture Managers, Ltd.
Ludgate Investments, Ltd.
M/C Venture Partners
MCI Management
MMC Ventures, Ltd.
MTI Partners, Ltd.

MTM Capital Partners
MVM Life Science Partners LLP (AKA: MVM, Ltd.)
MacQuarie's Infrastructure and Specialised Funds Division
Manchester Technology Fund Ltd, The
Market Capital Italia Srl
Matrix Private Equity Partners LLP
Maven Capital Partners
MerchantBridge & Co., Ltd.
Midven, Ltd. (AKA: Midlands Venture Fund Managers, Ltd.)
Modus Private Equity
Momentum Capital Limited
Moorfield Investment Management Ltd
Motorola Ventures
NCB Ventures, Ltd.
National Endowment for Science, Technology & the Arts NESTA
Net Partners
Neuberger Berman LLC
New Venture Partners LLC
Newbridge Capital, Ltd.
Nichimen Europe plc
Noble Fund Managers, Ltd.
Nomura International PLC
Nomura New Energy & Clean Technology Ventures
Nomura Phase4 Ventures, Ltd.
North East Finance
North West Development Agency
Northern Venture Managers Limited (AKA: NVM)
Nova Technology Management Limited (NTML)
Novotech Investment
novusmodus LLP
Occam Capital
Octopus Asset Management, Ltd.
Oxford Capital Partners
PPF Investments, Ltd.
PROfounders Capital
Pall Mall Partners Limited
Pan African Resources PLC (FKA:White Knight Investments PLC)
Panoramic Growth Equity (Fund Management) LLP
Paradigm Media Investments PLC
Parkmead Group PLC, The (FKA: Interregnum PLC)
Partnerships UK plc
Pembridge Partners LLP
Pentech Ventures, LLP
Pitango Venture Capital (FKA:Polaris Venture Capital Israel)
Platina Partners LLP
Pond Venture Partners
Prime Technology Ventures NV
Probitas Partners, Inc.
Promethean Investments
QinetiQ Ventures Ltd
Qubis Ltd
R Capital Ltd
RIT Capital Partners plc
RVC Europe Limited (FKA: The Greenhouse Fund)
Redbus Investments, Ltd. (AKA: Redbus Group)
Reed Elsevier Ventures
Result Venture Knowledge International
Rexiter Capital Management Ltd.
Rockley Group, The
Rolls Royce Corporate Venture
Rosetta Capital, Ltd.
SCS Capital Sdn. Bhd.
SEB Venture Capital
SOFTBANK Corp.
SPARK Ventures Plc (FKA: NewMedia Spark Plc)
SV Life Sciences Advisers
Saffron Hill Ventures
Sands Brothers & Co., Ltd.
Schroders PLC
Scottish Enterprise
Scottish Equity Partners
Seed Capital Ltd.
Seraphim Capital
Seraphima Ventures
Seroba Kernel Life Sciences, Ltd. (AKA: Seroba Kernel)
Shanghai Amara Equity Investment Management Co., Ltd.
Shell Internet Ventures
Shore Capital, Ltd.
Sigma Capital Group Plc
Simfonec
Sindicatum Carbon Capital, Ltd.
Smedvig Capital, Ltd. (FKA: Peder Smedvig Capital Ltd)
Solon Ventures, Ltd.
Spinnaker Capital Group
Starr International Company, Inc
Strathdon Investment plc (FKA: Strathdon Investments, Ltd.)
Summit Accelerator Fund
Summit Group, Ltd., The
Sussex Place Investment Management (SPIM), Ltd.
Swarraton Partners Limited
Synergis Technologies, Ltd.
Syntek Capital AG
3i Infrastructure PLC (FKA: 3i Infrastructure, Ltd.)
T. Rowe Price Threshold Partnerships
TLcom Capital LLP
TMF Participations Management
TTP Venture Managers, Ltd. (FKA:Technology Partnership, The)
Tate & Lyle PLC
Technikos
Telesystem-Argo Global Capital
Thompson Clive & Partners, Ltd.
Tianguis, Ltd.
Top Technology Ventures, Ltd.
Tower Gate Capital, Ltd. (AKA:TGC)
Trinity Capital PLC
Triodos International Fund Management BV
UK Steel Enterprise, Ltd. (FKA: British Steel Industry,Ltd.)
UUTech Limited
Undisclosed Firm
Unilever Ventures, Ltd. (AKA: Unilever NV)
University of Cambridge Challenge Fund (AKA: UCF)
VASDAQ Investment, Ltd. (AKA: V-Investment)
VPSA (FKA: Viventures Partners)
Venesis Limited
Vertex Management Israel (AKA: Vertex Venture Capital)
Vertex Management Pte, Ltd. (AKA: Vertex Venture Holdings)
Vertex Venture Capital
Viking Fund, The
Virgin Green Fund
Vitruvian Partners LLP
W.R. Hambrecht & Co., LLC
WHEB Ventures, Ltd.
Warburg Pincus LLC
Wellington Partners Venture Capital GmbH
Wesley Clover, Ltd.
West Coast Capital
WestBridge Fund Managers, Ltd.
YFM Group, Ltd.
Yangtze China Investment Ltd.
Young Associates Limited
Zindel Investment Partners
Zouk Ventures, Ltd.

Venture Firms—Uruguay

Calyon (FKA: Credit Agricole Indosuez)
Prosperitas Capital Partners

Venture Firms—Utd. Arab Em.

Al Mal Capital
Alf Yad Limited
Alf Yad, Ltd.
Amwal AlKhaleej
Corecap Limited
Delta Partners FZ LLC
Dubai Investment Group (AKA: DIG)
Duke Equity Partners
Fajr Capital Ltd
Istithmar World Capital
Ithmar Capital
Jahangir Siddiqui Group (AKA: JS Group)
Legatum Capital
Masdar Venture Capital
MerchantBridge & Co., Ltd.
Mulverhill Associates
National Investor, The
New Enterprise East Investments (AKA: NEEI)
Rasmala Partners, Ltd.
Rolls Royce Corporate Venture
Saffar Capital, Ltd.
Shanghai Amara Equity Investment Management Co., Ltd.
Spinnaker Capital Group
TVM Capital GmbH
Venture Capital Bank (VCBank)
Zabeel Investments

Venture Firms—Uzbekistan

European Bank for Reconstruction and Development
Small Enterprise Assistance Fund (SEAF)

Venture Firms—Venezuela

Calyon (FKA: Credit Agricole Indosuez)

Venture Firms—Vietnam

BankInvest Group A/S
Dragon Capital
IDG Ventures Vietnam
Indochina Capital Management
JACCAR Investment
Mekong Capital, Ltd.
Rolls Royce Corporate Venture
Saigon Asset Management
Tano Capital LLC
Templeton Asset Management, Ltd.

Executive Cross Reference by Firm Name

For more comprehensive querying, searching, and referencing, Thomson Reuters supplies Pratt's Guide online at www.prattsguide.com. Annual subscriptions are available for USD$995 per user. For more information, please contact Greg Winterton at 001 646 223 6787 or email greg.winterton@thomson-reuters.com.

Ahlqvist, Rolf—Procom Venture AS
Ahlsand, Torleif—Northzone Ventures AS (FKA: Venture Partners AS)
Ahlstrom, Carl-Johan—Paron Ventures AB
Ahlstrom, Lars—Mainsail Partners
Ahlstrom, Mikael—Procuritas Partners KB
Ahmad, Amjad—NBK Capital, Ltd.
Ahmadi, Masoud—Berkeley Mineral Resources PLC (FKA: Tecteon PLC)
Ahmed, Iftikar—Oak Investment Partners
Ahmed, Javed—Fajr Capital Ltd
Ahn, Daniel—Voyager Capital
Ahn, Garrick—Caltius Equity Partners
Ahn, Hyo Moon—NEXUS Investment Corp. (FKA: Pusan Venture Tech. Capital)
Ahn, Keunyoung—LB Investment, Inc.
Ahn, Sang—Dawntreader Ventures
Ahn, Steve—Walden International
Ahonen, Seppo—Helmet Business Mentors Oy
Ahr, Oren—Tamir Fishman Ventures
Ahrens, Brent—Canaan Partners
Ahrens, Christian—One Equity Partners (FKA: Banc One Venture Partners)
Ahrens, Jack—TGap Ventures LLC
Ahuja, A.C.—IFCI Venture Capital Funds, Ltd. (FKA: Risk Capital & Tech.)
Ahuja, Gaurav—ChrysCapital Management Company
Ahuja, Sanjiv—Redwood Venture Partners
Ahuja, Sanjiv—Solitaire Capital Advisors Pvt. Ltd.
Ahvenniemi, Sami—Conor Venture Partners Oy
Ai, Bob—Merlin Nexus
Aida, Ryutaro—MKS Partners, Ltd. (FKA: Schroder Ventures K.K.)
Aier, Vignesh—New Mountain Capital LLC
Aikman, Robert—Odyssey Investment Partners, LLC
Ainslie, Lee—Maverick Capital Ltd.
Ainsworth, Ron—Trenwith Securities LLC
Aitchison, Carolyn—Blackstone Group, L.P.
Aitken, Brian—Nevis Capital LLP
Aitken-Davies, George—Altaris Capital Partners LLC
Aizenberg, Salo—Westbury Partners
Ajila, Rohan—Capvent AG
Ajouz, Michael—New Mountain Capital LLC
Akamatsu, Kazuhiko—Daiwa Securities SMBC Principal Investments Co., Ltd.
Akansu, Ali—Aztec Equity Partners, LLC
Akasaka, Naoko—J.P. Morgan Asset Management
Akers, Jeffrey—Adams Street Partners LLC
Akerson, Daniel—Carlyle Group, The
Akerson, Daniel—Forstmann Little & Company
Akhavan, Amir—Jordan, Edmiston Group, Inc., The
Akita, Tsutomu—Oak Capital Corporation
Akkaraju, Srinivas—J.P. Morgan Partners (FKA: Chase Capital Partners)
Akkaraju, Srinivas—New Leaf Venture Partners LLC
Akright, Richard—Axiom Equity Partners
Al Ansari, Sameer—SHUAA Partners
Al Bulooshi, Kalat Ghuloom—Oman Investment Co SAOC
Al Kudsi, Nazem Fawwaz—Invest AD
Al Rumaihi, Fouad—New Enterprise East Investments (AKA: NEEI)
Al Saifi, Samer—Dubai International Capital LLC
Al Sari, Ahmad—Malaz Group
Al Sonbaty, Hany—EFG-Hermes Private Equity
Al-Alfi, Moataz—Egypt Kuwait Holding Company
Al-Deweesh, Fahad—Amwal AlKhaleej
Al-Falah, Falah Nasser—Unicorn Investment Bank B.S.C.
Al-Foraih, Haitham—Amwal AlKhaleej
Al-Ghunaim, Maha—Global Investment House
Al-Khuzam, Mansour—Khazaen Venture Capital
Al-Rifai, Tariq—UIB Capital, Inc.
Al-Sabah al-Binali, Sabah Hamad—Saffar Capital, Ltd.
Al-Sefai, Majid Al-Sayed Bader—Unicorn Investment Bank B.S.C.
Al-Shroogi, Mohammed—Investcorp Bank B.S.C.
Al-Sultan, Adnan—National Technology Enterprises Company (AKA: NTEC)
Al-Usaimi, Mishaal Mussaid—Saffar Capital, Ltd.
AlKhudairy, Ammar—Amwal AlKhaleej
Alafi, Christopher—Alafi Capital Co.
Alafi, Moshe—Alafi Capital Co.
Alam, Runa—Development Partners International
Alam, Runa—Zephyr Management, L.P.
Alarie, Mark—CrossHill Financial Group, Inc
Alba, Glenn—Blackstone Group, L.P.
Albanell, Manuel—Catalana D'Iniciatives CR SA
Albanese, Glen—Needham Asset Management
Alber, Thomas—TA Associates, Inc.
Alberg, Tom—Madrona Venture Group
Alberici, Gilles—Octalfa SAS
Albert, Andrew—Svoboda Capital Partners (FKA: Svoboda, Collins LLC)
Albert, Brett—Tennenbaum Capital Partners LLC
Albert, Christian H.M.—Bowside Capital, LLC
Albert, Kevin—Elevation Associates LLC
Albert, M. Scott—Aurora Funds, Inc.
Alberti, C. Christopher—Colony Capital LLC
Alberts, Scott—DCM
Albertsen, Henrik—Nordic Venture Partners (FKA: Danske Venture Partners)
Albin, David—Natural Gas Partners (NGP)
Albinson, Christopher—J.P. Morgan Partners (FKA: Chase Capital Partners)
Albinson, Christopher—Panorama Capital
Albion, Peter—Cobalt Capital, Inc.
Albrecht, Cyril—Langholm Capital LLP
Albrecht, Frank—PEPPERMINT. Financial Partners (FKA schroder + partner)
Albrecht, Frank—Sal. Oppenheim Private Equity Partners
Albrecht, Hans—Nordwind Capital GmbH
Albrecht, Laura—Maranon Capital, L.P.
Albright, John—JLA Ventures (FKA: J.L. Albright Venture Partners)
Albright, Raymond—Carlyle Group, The
Alcon, Andy—Crosspoint Venture Partners
Alderson-Smith, Martin—Blackstone Group, L.P.
Aldridge, Mark—Better Capital LLP
Aleotti, Filippo—Investindustrial Partners, Ltd.
Ales, Alberto—GED Group
Alexander, Ben—CBPE Capital, LLP (AKA: Close Brothers Private Equity, Ltd.)
Alexander, Bradley—GulfStar Group
Alexander, Daniel—CambridgeLight Partners
Alexander, Douglas—Internet Capital Group
Alexander, Edward—Mission Ventures
Alexander, Geoff—Comvest Investment Partners
Alexander, Jeff—Private Equity Partners
Alexander, Patrick—Garuda Capital Partners
Alexander, Ralph—Riverstone LLC
Alexander, Seth—Massachusetts Institute of Technology
Alexander, Steven—BNP Paribas Principal, Inc.
Alexandrov, Alex—Thomas H. Lee Partners (AKA: TH Lee Partners)
Alexandrov, Daniel—Rosslyn Capital Partners
Alexis, Marcus—Pantheon Ventures, Ltd.
Alexos, Nicholas—Madison Dearborn Partners LLC
Alfano, Steven—Century Capital Management, Inc.
Alfaro, Alfredo—Advent International
Alfeld, Chad—Landmark Partners, Inc.
Alfonso, David—Empire Investment Holdings, LLC
Alford, Chris—TMB Industries Investments
Alger, Kevin—J.P. Morgan Capital Corporation
Algranti, Sol—Northbridge Capital Partners
Ali, Ahmad Mohamed—Islamic Development Bank, The
Ali, Mohd Nizar—First Floor Capital Sdn. Bhd.
Ali, Nur Baidzurah—Malaysian Venture Capital Management (MAVCAP)
Ali, Samiya—Ithmar Capital
Alias, Geraldine—Volition Capital
Aliberti, Giancarlo—Apax Partners Worldwide
Alipbayev, Dauren—Centras Capital Partners
Aliprandi, Paul—Credit Suisse Private Equity
Alissandratos, Dionissis—Vectis Capital SA
Allan, Shane—Allen & Buckeridge Pty, Ltd.
Allanic, Richard—123Venture SA
Allegaert, Hans—Fenway Partners, Inc.
Allegot, Laurent—Actem Partners SA (FKA: SPEF LBO)
Allegra, Joseph—Edison Venture Fund
Allen, Caroline—Creation Investments Capital Management LLC
Allen, Daniel—Bain Capital Ventures
Allen, George—Warburg Pincus LLC
Allen, James—Sun Capital Partners, Inc.
Allen, Jeff—Rocket Ventures
Allen, Kevin—5280 Partners
Allen, Mark—Formative Ventures
Allen, Paul—Vulcan Capital
Allen, Peter—Mercator Investments Limited
Allen, Rodney—Clarey Capital LLC
Allen, Roger—Allen & Buckeridge Pty, Ltd.
Allen, William—Carlyle Group, The
Allen, William—Houlihan, Lokey, Howard & Zukin
Allesch, Juergen—MillhouseIAG
Allgaier, Matthias—Favonius Ventures
Allgaier, Matthias—H.I.G. Capital LLC
Alli, Andrew—Travant Capital Partners
Allison, Robert—Edgewater Funds, The
Allison, Thomas—Mesirow Private Equity Investments, Inc.
Allsopp, Richard—UBS Capital Corporation
Allwin, James—Aetos Capital LLC
Almeida, Cristina—DRIVE Sociedade de Capital de Risco, SA
Almeida, John—Welsh, Carson, Anderson & Stowe
Almog, Yuval—CORAL Ventures Management, Inc.
Almog, Yuval—Coral Group LLC
Almojel, Mohammad—Atlantic-Pacific Capital, Inc.
Almstedt, Leif—NorgesInvestor Management AS
Aloisi, Federico—CAPITALIA Sofipa SGR (FKA: MCC Sofipa)

Antwi-Asimeng, Stephen—Fidelity Capital Partners Ltd.
Aoki, Yoshihisa—Itochu Corporation
Aoyama, Toshihiko—Sapporo Hokuyo Lease Co., Ltd.
Apfelberg, David—Spring Ridge Ventures
Aplin, Jennifer—Texas Women Ventures Fund
Aplin, John—CID Capital
Apostolo, Juan Carlos—Axxon Group
Appel, John—Emigrant Capital
Appel, Lloyd—Aisling Capital
Appel, Marc—Sydes
Appendino, Michele—Net Partners
Applbaum, Isaac—Carmel Ventures
Applbaum, Isaac—Opus Capital
Apple, David—Archbrook Capital Management LLC
Apple, Jason—Houlihan, Lokey, Howard & Zukin
Applegate, Brion—Spectrum Equity Investors
Applewhite, Jarrett—New Mexico Community Capital
Appleyard, Jean—Add Partners, Ltd.
Aquilano, Don—Blue Chip Venture Company
Aquilano, Don—Gazelle TechVentures
Arafeh, Kamal—OpenView Venture Partners
Aragona, Joseph—Austin Ventures, L.P.
Arai, Akiyo—New Horizon Capital Co., Ltd.
Arakawa, Satoru—J-Star Co., Ltd.
Araki, Hideki—Daiwa PI Partners Co., Ltd.
Aram, Ashok—Abraaj Capital
Arangala, Sumith—Lanka Ventures, Ltd.
Arato, Krisztina—Kisvallalkozas-fejleszto Penzugyi Rt.
Aravind, MJ—Artiman Ventures
Archambault, Rob—Platinum Equity LLC
Archambeau, Eric—Wellington Partners Venture Capital GmbH
Archer, Devon—Rosemont Solebury Capital Management LLC
Archer, Nick—CVC Capital Partners (Europe), Ltd.
Archibald, Jared—Huntsman Gay Global Capital LLC
Archibald, Jessica—Paul Capital Partners
Arcos Moya, Jose Antonio—Inverjaen S.C.R. SA
Arcuri, Domenico—Sviluppo Imprese Centro Italia S.p.A.
Ardell, Ted—Technology Partners
Ardi, Dana—CCMP Capital Advisors LLC
Arena, Paul—Atlantic-Pacific Capital, Inc.
Arenare, Scott—Warburg Pincus LLC
Arenberg, Daniel—NewWest Mezzanine Fund, L.P. (FKA:Touchstone Capital Group)
Arenz, Thomas—Harvest Partners LLC
Argyris, Marios—First Elements Ventures, Ltd. (FKA: SFS Corporate Analysis)
Ariake, Kazuo—Daiwa Corporate Investment Co., Ltd.
Arida, George—Venture Investors LLC
Arietta, Ignacio—Investindustrial Partners, Ltd.
Aristidou, Aris—HVB Russell Management GmbH
Ariz, Ricardo—Aureos Capital, Ltd.
Arkebauer, James—Venture Associates, Ltd.
Arland, Thomas—GF Private Equity Group, LLC
Armbrister, Jeffrey—Versa Capital Management (FKA: Chrysalis Capital Partners)
Armendariz, Jose Javier—SODENA - Sociedad de Desarrollo de Navarra
Armitage, Leslie—Relativity Capital LLC
Armony, Izhar—Charles River Ventures
Armour, David—Pentech Ventures, LLP
Armour, Mark—Reed Elsevier Ventures
Armstrong, Andrew—Spire Capital
Armstrong, Clayton—Clayton, Dubilier & Rice, Inc.
Armstrong, Curtis—Lex Capital Management, Inc.
Armstrong, James—Clearstone Venture Partners
Armstrong, Jim—Canal Partners LLC
Armstrong, Ronald—E-Synergy
Armstrong, Timothy—Apax Partners Worldwide
Armstrong, Timothy—H.I.G. Capital LLC
Armstrong, Tom—Cartesian Capital Group, LLC
Arnaboldi, Nicole—DLJ Merchant Banking Partners
Arnaud, Frederic—Phillimore Investissement
Arnell, Christian—Eos Asia Investments, Ltd. (FKA: JCAR Funds, Ltd.)
Arney, John—Candover Investments PLC
Arno, Andrew—CE Unterberg Towbin (FKA:Unterberg Harris Capital Partners)
Arnold, Bill—Neuberger Berman LLC
Arnold, Charlotte—Meridian Venture Partners (MVP)
Arnold, Jeffrey—Oaktree Capital Management LLC
Arnold, John—HBM BioVentures AG (FKA: HBM Partners AG)
Arnold, Mark—Albion Investors, LLC (FKA: Albion Alliance, LLC)
Arnold, Markus—EiKaM GmbH & Co. KG
Arnold, Peter—Research Partners, Ltd.
Arnold, R.T.—Channelstone Partners LLC
Arnold, Stephen—Polaris Venture Partners
Arnone, Miles—American Capital, Ltd.
Arnould, Emmanuel—InnovaFonds
Arnson, Eric—Originate Ventures
Arntz, Jorg—Mountain Super Angel AG
Aron, Jean-Francois—J. Hirsch & Co. S.a.r.l.
Aronoff, David—Flybridge Capital Partners
Aronson, Jeffrey—Centerbridge Partners
Aronson, Lewis—Versa Capital Management (FKA: Chrysalis Capital Partners)
Aronson, Michael—Strategic Venture Mgmt. Advisors (FKA: MentorTech Ventures)
Aronson, Neal—Roark Capital Group
Aronstein, Marc—Beekman Group LLC, The
Aronstein, Marc—Odeon Capital Partners, L.P.
Arora, Anup—Easton Hunt Capital Partners, L.P.
Arora, Hardev—Tufan Venture Partners
Arora, Manik—IDG Ventures India
Arora, Sanjiv—Cargill Ventures
Arougheti, Michael—Ares Management, Inc.
Arpey, Michael—Credit Suisse Private Equity
Arra, Phillip—Hunt Special Situations Group
Arrache, Jennifer—Colony Capital LLC
Arrechea, Javier—Sterling Partners
Arrequi, Alvaro Rodriguez—IGNIA Partners LLC
Arrington, Lloyd—Columbia Capital Group, Inc.
Arrowsmith, Peter—JMI Equity
Arscott, David—Compass Technology Partners
Arscott, Martha—Compass Technology Partners
Arsenault, Chris—iNovia Capital
Arsenault, Greg—Kline Hawkes & Co.
Arsenault, Greg—Vicente Capital Partners
Arthaud, Laurent—Pharmavent Partners
Arthur, Gillian—Actis Capital LLP
Arts, Anton—New Venture Partners LLC
Artunkal, Ali—Argus Capital Group, Ltd.
Arya, Ved Prakash—Milestone Religare Investment Advisors Pvt., Ltd.
Arya, Vikas—Gaja Capital Partners
Arzubi, Luis—Tallwood Venture Capital
Asahara, Tomohiko—Asia Private Equity Capital (FKA: MediBIC Alliance)
Asai, Takeo—Weru Investment Co., Ltd.
Asam, Alexander—DVC Deutsche Venture Capital
Asano, Tomoji—Polaris Principal Finance Co., Ltd.
Asanuma, Sakae—Yasuda Enterprise Development Co., Ltd.(FKA: Nippon Ent.Dev)
Asarnoj, Samuel—Firm Factory Network
Asarnow, Elliot—BlackRock Private Equity Partners
Ascani, Agostino—Balmoral Capital
Ascher, Brian—Venrock Associates
Ascher, David—Transom Capital Group
Ascione, Michael—Berkshire Partners LLC
Asel, Paul—Nokia Growth Partners
Ashai, Zaid—Point Judith Capital
Ashall, Michael—VenCap International plc
Ashby, Molly—Solera Capital, LLC
Ashe, Prescott—Golden Gate Capital
Asher, Jacqueline—Dubai Investment Group (AKA: DIG)
Ashida, Koichi—Advantage Partners LLP
Ashida, Mark—OVP Venture Partners
Ashley, Brad—Priveq Capital Funds
Ashley, Trevor—Rosewood Capital, L.P.
Ashmore, Bill—Ethos Private Equity
Ashton, Kay—Silverfleet Capital (FKA: PPM Capital Partners)
Ashworth, Gordon—Parkmead Group PLC, The (FKA: Interregnum PLC)
Askew, Glenn—Brazos Private Equity Partners LLC
Askew, Tony—Reed Elsevier Ventures
Aslan, Fred—Venrock Associates
Aslin, David—Nexit Ventures Oy
Asling, Per—Ekonord Invest AB
Aspemar, Per—TeknoSeed AB
Aspen, Henrik—Verdane Capital (FKA: Four Seasons Venture Capital AS)
Aspergren, Lindsay—North Coast Technology Investors, L.P.
Aspinwall, Michael—CCP Equity Partners
Assaad, Wassim—Gulf Capital
Assant, Lionel Yves—Blackstone Group, L.P.
Assaraf, Laurent—Ventech S.A.
Assaraf, Laurent—Ventech S.A.
Assulin, Vered—Genesis Partners
Astier, Jean-Francois—Continuum Group, Ltd. (AKA: Continuum Advisory, Ltd.)
Astruc, Rafael—Private Advisors LLC
Atherton, Paul—FirstVentures
Atherton, W. Clifford—GulfStar Group
Atkins, Colin—Carlyle Group, The
Atkins, Lee—Econergy International Corporation
Atkinson, Gordon—Cooley Godward LLP
Atkinson, Justin—Dar Capital (UK), Ltd.
Atluru, Rajesh—Draper Fisher Jurvetson
Atluru, Rajesh—Draper Fisher Jurvetson ePlanet Ventures, L.P.
Atre, Nisha—Navigation Capital Partners (AKA: NCP)
Atsuhiko, Mizukawa—STB Investment Corporation
Atsuumi, Daisuke—Arise Capital Partners, Inc.
Attanasio, Antonio—Hat Holding All Together SpA
Atterbury, David—HarbourVest Partners LLC

Atting, Fredrik—EQT Funds management Limited
Attwood, James—Carlyle Group, The
Attwood, Tom—Intermediate Capital Group Plc
Atwood, Brian—Brentwood Venture Capital
Atwood, Brian—Versant Ventures
Au, Jeffrey—PacifiCap Group LLC
Auber, Nathalie—Sofinnova Ventures
Aubert, Andre—LGT Capital Partners AG
Aubert, Philippe—Fortis Private Equity France (FKA: Robertsau Gestion)
Aubin, Guillaume—Alven Capital Partners SA
Aubrey, Alan—Aquarius Equity Partners, Ltd.
Aubrey, Alan—IP2IPO, Ltd. (AKA: IP Group plc)
Aubry, Marion—Seventure Partners SA (FKA: SPEF Venture)
Aucamp, Thomas—New River Capital Partners
Auclair, Pascale—UFG Private Equity SAS
Audagna, Guido—Carlyle Group, The
Auerbach, Daniel—Fidelity Growth Partners Asia
Auerbach, Jon—Charles River Ventures
Auerbach, Martin—Z Capital Partners LLC
Auerbach, Stuart—Ampersand Ventures
Auf der Maur, Donat—Swiss Re Private Equity Advisers
Aughterson, Peter—Lyceum Capital
Augustin, Larry—Azure Capital Partners
Augustyniak, Piotr—Enterprise Investors Sp z oo
Ault, Ben—Grey Mountain Partners
Aurelio, Louis—Kinderhook Industries
Auritt, Robert—Meridian Venture Partners (MVP)
Auspitz, Ben—Beacon Bioventures
Aust, R. Wade—C.W. Downer & Company (FKA: Downer & Company)
Austen, Christopher—Brooke Private Equity Associates
Auster, Chuck—One Equity Partners (FKA: Banc One Venture Partners)
Austin, David—Northleaf Capital Partners
Austin, Matt—Virginia Capital
Austin, Randolph—i-Hatch Ventures LLC
Austin, Robert—Lake Capital Partners, Inc.
Auth, Thomas—ACI Capital Co., LLC
Averitt, B. Marc—Okapi Venture Capital LLC
Averpil, Benny—Bure Equity
Avery, Henry—Avery Business Development Services
Avice, Edwige—La Financiere de Brienne
Avida, Dan—Opus Capital
Avidar, Ornit—China Israel Value Capital (AKA: CIVC)
Avidar, Ornit—Platinum-Neurone Ventures
Avidor, Itzik—Carmel Ventures
Avila, Joaquin—Carlyle Group, The
Avila, T. Scott—CRG Partners
Avnet, Amit—SCP Private Equity Partners
Avni, Micah—Jerusalem Global Ventures
Avonts, Rene—Quest Management NV
Awad, Dewey—Bain Capital
Awad, Sary—CM Equity Partners (FKA; Lynx Investment Management, L.P.)
Aweida, Daniel—Aweida Capital Management LLP
Aweida, Jesse—Aweida Capital Management LLP
Axel, Andrew—Great River Capital LLC
Axel, Merrick—Cressey & Company, L.P.
Axel, Merrick—Thoma Cressey Bravo
Axel, Steven—Calvert Street Capital Partners, Inc. (FKA: Legg Mason)
Axel, Steven—Southfield Capital Advisors
Axelsson, Lars Hylling—JMI Invest A/S
Axelsson, Yvonne—LinkMed AB
Axon, Robin—Ventures West Management, Inc.
Ayala, Alfredo—Crimson
Ayanz Guillen, Emilio—Minerva Capital
Ayars, Mike—Concentric Equity Partners, L.P.
Aye, Andrew—Stonehenge Capital Company
Ayed, Hanen Feki-Ben—Nem Partners (AKA: Natexis Equity Management)
Ayeni, Kayode—First Funds Ltd
Ayer, Ethan—One Equity Partners (FKA: Banc One Venture Partners)
Ayles, Ronald—Advent International
Ayling, Rob—Finistere Partners LLC
Aylwin, Andrew—Lyceum Capital
Ayub, Elena—Global Investment House
Azad, David—Galen Associates
Azan, Alain—Sofinnova Ventures
Azar, Makram—Kohlberg, Kravis, Roberts & Company, L.P.
Azimi, Shad—Vanterra Capital, Ltd.
Aziz, Dato Noor—Fajr Capital Ltd
Aziz, Luis Alberto—NAFTA Fund of Mexico, LP
Azmon, Barak—Accuitive Medical Ventures
Aznar, Pedro—Warburg Pincus LLC
Azulai, Sharon—Blumberg Capital Ventures
Azuma, Kentaro—SBI Capital Company, Ltd.
Azzam, Fouad—Eastman Ventures
Azzam, Fouad—Life Sciences Partners BV
Azzolini, Giulio—UBS Capital Corporation
B. Wang, Charles—AvantaLion, LLC
Baba, Katsuya—Advantage Partners LLP
Babcock, John—Rustic Canyon Partners
Babiarz, Michael—Clayton, Dubilier & Rice, Inc.
Babinet, Georges—Paris Orleans (Francarep SA)
Babitt, Cindy—Key Principal Partners LLC (AKA: KPP)
Babka, Roman—Royalton Partners
Babson, Stephen—Endeavour Capital
Babu, Arvin—Greylock Partners
Babu, Atish—Nexus Venture Partners
Bacas, Andrew—Key Principal Partners LLC (AKA: KPP)
Bacci, Stefano—Palamon Capital Partners (FKA: Amphion Capital Partners)
Bacci, Timothy—BlueLine Partners LLC
Bacdayan, Wali—PNC Equity Management Corp.
Bacevich, Mike—Capvest Venture Fund (FKA: Virgin Ventures Fund LP)
Bach, Anne-Valerie—Banexi Ventures Partners
Bachle, Christian M.—AlpInvest Partners N.V.
Bachli, Ronald—Belvedere Capital Partners LLC
Bachman, Cheryl—Paladin Partners
Bachmann, Andrin—M/C Venture Partners
Bachrach, Ernest—Advent International
Backer, Patrice—Advanced Finance & Investment Group LLC (AKA: AFIG)
Backlund, Marcus—Deseven Catalyst Group AB
Backman, Joel—Meritech Capital Partners
Backus, John—New Atlantic Ventures
Backwith, Nigel—Rocket Ventures
Bacon, Eric—Linsalata Capital Partners
Bacon, Kathleen—HarbourVest Partners LLC
Bacquaert, Stephane—Wendel
Bader, Hanspeter—Unigestion SA
Badr, Karim—Citadel Capital S.A.E.
Bae, Joseph—Kohlberg, Kravis, Roberts & Company, L.P.
Bae, Sung-Il—Lee & Company Investments
Bae, Young Soo—Korea Venture Investment Corporation
Baehr, Geoffrey—U.S. Venture Partners
Baek, Yoon Sok—Unitas Capital Pte, Ltd.
Baertschi, Urs—Cutlass Capital
Bagatelas, Paul—Carlyle Group, The
Bagin, Douglas—Lincolnshire Management, Inc.
Bagla, Prakash—Motilal Oswal Private Equity Advisors Pvt., Ltd.
Bagley, Thomas—Pfingsten Partners, L.P.
Bagusch, Thomas—Nord Holding Unternehmensbeteiligungsgesellschaft mbH
Bahai, Ahmad—WI Harper Group
Baharav, Yuval—Sequoia Capital
Bahl, Ravi—ChrysCapital Management Company
Bahnfleth, Andrew—GrowthPath Capital, LLC (FKA: Tangram Partners, Inc.)
Bahnsen, Birker—TA Associates, Inc.
Bai, Ru Guang—Harbinger Venture Management
Baiada, Mel—BaseCamp Ventures
Baier, Jerome—Northwestern Mutual Capital
Baijal, Shishir—Everstone Capital
Bailey, Brian—Carousel Capital Partners
Bailey, Christian—incTANK Inc.
Bailey, Elizabeth—Commons Capital, L.P.
Bailey, Michael—Argosy Capital
Bailey, Michael—Progress Equity Partners, Ltd.
Bailey, Stephen—Carlyle Group, The
Bailey, Steve—Frazier Healthcare and Technology Ventures
Bain, Thomas—Columbia Partners LLC
Bain, Tom—Columbia Capital LLC
Bainbridge, David—Veronis Suhler Stevenson (FKA: Veronis, Suhler & Associates)
Baines, Peter—Advent Venture Partners LLP
Baines, Simon—Exponent Private Equity LLP (FKA: Square Capital Management)
Baird, Charles—North Castle Partners
Baird, Charles—Weston Presidio (FKA: Weston Presidio Capital Management)
Baird, Darran—Stone Point Capital LLC
Baird, Laura—Private Advisors LLC
Baitman, Franklin—Nobska Ventures
Bajaj, Avnish—Matrix Partners
Bajc, Lea—Northzone Ventures AS (FKA: Venture Partners AS)
Bakal, Boris—Citi Venture Capital International
Bakatin, Vadim—Baring Vostok Capital Partners
Baker, Barry—Boston Ventures Management, Inc.
Baker, Douglas—Monument Capital Group LLC
Baker, Erik—GF Capital Management & Advisors LLC
Baker, Felix—Baker Bros. Advisors, LLC
Baker, George Leonard—Sutter Hill Ventures
Baker, Griffith—Chengwei Ventures
Baker, Henry—Baker Capital Corp.
Baker, James—Investcorp Bank B.S.C.
Baker, James—River Associates, LLC
Baker, John—Baker Capital Corp.
Baker, Julian—Baker Bros. Advisors, LLC
Baker, Kathryn—Reiten & Co Strategic Investments AS

Baker, Matthew—Private Advisors LLC
Baker, Nicola—GE Commercial Finance - Equity
Baker, Robert—NRDC Equity Partners
Baker, Stephen—Fort Washington Capital Partners Group
Baker, Trent—32 Degrees Capital
Baker, W. Craig—River Associates, LLC
Bakhshi, Bharat—Jacob Ballas Capital India Pvt, Ltd. (AKA:JBC)
Bakke, Even—Aravis SA
Bakken, Terje—Reiten & Co Strategic Investments AS
Bakker, Juliet—Longitude Capital Management Company LLC
Bakker, Ruud—Truffle Venture SAS
Baksa, Stephen—Vertical Group, The
Bakshi, Rajeev—ICICI Venture Funds Management Co., Pvt. Ltd. (FKA: TDICI)
Bal, Jasvinder—Henderson Equity Partners (AKA: Henderson Private Capital)
Balagopal, C.—Hyderabad Information Technology Venture Enterprises, Ltd.
Balaji, Anita—Carlyle Group, The
Balakrishnan, Karthik—Jina Ventures, Inc.
Balaraj, K.P.—Sequoia Capital India (FKA: WestBridge Capital Partners)
Balaraj, KP—Sequoia Capital
Balasco, Cynthia—Nautic Partners LLC
Balasubrahmanyan, Anand—Carlyle Group, The
Balbach, C. Teo—Mercury Capital Partners
Balbach, Jennifer—Summer Street Capital LLC
Balch, Robert—Cycad Group LLC
Balch, Robert—Taraval Associates LLC
Baldassarre, Carl—National City Equity Partners, Inc.
Baldassarro, Mallindi—Argus Capital Group, Ltd.
Balderston, Thomas—Rosemont Investment Partners LLC
Baldeschwieler, John—Arcturus Capital
Baldino, Frank—MPM Capital (FKA: MPM Asset Management LLC)
Baldwin, Chris—Charles River Ventures
Baldwin, David—SCF Partners
Baldwin, Ken—Capinnova Investment Bank
Baldwin, Thomas—Bruckmann, Rosser, Sherrill & Co.
Balen, John—Canaan Partners
Balevi, Marc—TechnoCap, Inc.
Balfour, Carter—Norwest Mezzanine Partners
Balhara, Sanjeev—Third Security LLC
Baliga, Girish—3i Group PLC
Baliga, Subhash—BTS Investment Advisors, Ltd.
Balijepalli, Gautam—Ojas Venture Partners
Baliotti, Marc—Blackstone Group, L.P.
Balkanski, Alexandre—Benchmark Capital
Balkin, Marc—Hasso Plattner Ventures Africa
Ball, Andrew—LDC (FKA: Lloyds TSB Development Capital, Ltd.)
Ball, Benjamin—Francisco Partners
Ball, Brian—Advent Private Capital
Ball, C. Thomas—Austin Ventures, L.P.
Ball, Charles—Andlinger & Company, Inc.
Ball, Damon—AEA Investors LP
Ball, John—Steamboat Ventures
Ball, Michael—Brandon Capital Partners
Balladur, Jerome—La Financiere Patrimoniale D'Investissment
Ballan, Yann—Weinberg Capital Partners SAS
Ballard, C. Andrew—Hellman & Friedman LLC
Ballard, Michael—Aragon Ventures, Inc.
Ballein, Valarie—JCP Capital LLC
Ballen, Maxine—New Jersey Technology Council (AKA: NJTC)
Ballew, M. Lee—Claritas Capital LLC
Balloch, Hugh—Goff Moore Strategic Partners
Ballta, Andi—NCH Capital, Inc.
Bally, Jean-Marc—Schneider Electric Ventures
Balmisse, Daniel—CDC Innovation SAS (FKA: CDC IXIS Innovation)
Balmuth, Michael—Edison Venture Fund
Balmuth, Michael—Summit Accelerator Fund
Baloff, Steve—Advanced Technology Ventures
Balogh, Edward—Ridgemont Equity Partners
Balsam, Ira—Avenue Capital Group
Balson, Andrew—Bain Capital
Bamber, Frederick—Solstice Capital
Banahan, Thomas—Tenaya Capital (FKA: Lehman Brothers Venture Partners)
Banas, Christopher—Incyte Venture Partners LLC
Banatao, Diosdado—Narra Venture Capital
Banatao, Diosdado—Tallwood Venture Capital
Bancroft, Charles—Capital Services & Resources, Inc.
Bandak, Mark—Blackstone Group, L.P.
Banerjee, Chiranjit—Fountainhead Capital Ltd
Banerjee, Sujit—Element Partners
Banga, Franceska—New Zealand Venture Investment Fund, Ltd.
Bangard, Marion—S-Siegerlandfonds 1 GmbH & Co.
Bank, Keith—KB Partners LLC
Banka, Bharat—Aditya Birla Capital Advisors Pvt., Ltd.
Banks, Michael—Palisades Ventures (FKA: Centre Palisades Ventures)
Banks, Peter—Astrolabe Ventures
Banks, Sean—Total Technology Ventures LLC
Banks, Stephen—S3 Ventures
Banner, Georg—MBG Schleswig-Holstein GmbH
Bannick, Matthew—Omidyar Network
Bannister-Parker, William—Capital International Research, Inc.
Bannon, Anne—Bank of Scotland Venture Capital (FKA: ICC Venture Capital)
Bannon, Wayne—Carlyle Group, The
Bansal, Naveen—SREI Venture Capital Ltd. (FKA: SREI Global Asset Mgt.)
Banta, Charles—Mercury Capital Partners
Banta, John—Illinois Ventures LLC
Banta, Neil—GCP Capital Partners
Banzet, Douglas—Westcap Management, Ltd.
Banzhof, Carl—CT Holdings
Bao, Daniel—ChinaVest, Ltd.
Bao, Xuming—Blackstone Group, L.P.
Bao, Yue—Guigu Tiantang Venture Capital Co., Ltd.
Bar-Niv, Moshe—Ascend Technology Ventures
Barach, Michael—Village Ventures
Barallobre, Carlos—Mercapital Servicios Financieros
Baram, David—VMG Equity Partners
Baranov, Eugene—Ineko Capital Partners LLP
Baranski, Lynn—BlackRock Private Equity Partners
Barasch, Robert—Infinity Venture Capital Fund (AKA: Israel Infinity Fund)
Barashi, Shmoulik—Undisclosed Firm
Baratta, Joseph—Blackstone Group, L.P.
Barazi, Bassam—WP Global Partners Inc.
Barbarosh, Milton—Stenton Leigh Group, Inc.
Barbashev, Sergey—Interros Holding
Barbeau, Mark—CRG Partners
Barbeau, Mark—Crossroads Capital Partners, LLC
Barben, Michael—Partners Group AG
Barber, Christopher—Sand Hill Capital
Barber, Jeffrey—TA Associates, Inc.
Barber, Paul—JMI Equity
Barber, Tom—Black Canyon Capital
Barberio, Caroline—Mission Ventures
Barbier, Francois—21 Centrale Partners
Barbier, Francois—21 Partners SpA
Barbieux, Manuel—Arcapita, Inc.
Barbour-Smith, James—Gresham LLP
Barchilon, Julie—Alven Capital Partners SA
Barclay, Bruce—Advent International
Bard, Gustav—3i Group PLC
Bard, Richard—Bard Capital Group, LLC
Bardakjy, Gene—Empire Investment Holdings, LLC
Bardinet, Yves—Galia Gestion
Barel, Meir—Star Ventures Management GmbH & Co. KG
Barer, Sol—Celgene Corporation
Bares, Keith—Convergent Capital Partners
Baret, Matthieu—AGF Private Equity
Baretta, Paolo—BS Private Equity SpA (FKA: B&S Private Equity Group)
Bargach, Saad—Lime Rock Partners LLC
Barger, Gregory—Calvert Street Capital Partners, Inc. (FKA: Legg Mason)
Barger, Gregory—NewSpring Capital
Baris, Brett—Inter-Atlantic Group
Barish, Keith—Barish Fund, The
Barkas, Alexander—Prospect Venture Partners (FKA: Prospect Management LLC)
Barkat, Eli—BRM Capital
Barker, David—Cinven, Ltd.
Barker, Karey—Cross Creek Capital, an affiliate of Wasatch Advisors
Barker, Nicholas—Huron Capital Partners LLC
Barker, Quint—New York Life Capital Partners (AKA: NYLCAP)
Barker, Richard—Homeland Defense Ventures
Barket, Keith—Angelo, Gordon & Company
Barkin, Michael—KRG Capital Partners LLC
Barkoff, Stuart—Global Environment Fund Management Corporation
Barlage, Tonio—PolyTechnos Venture-Partners GmbH
Barletta, Nicolas—Unigestion SA
Barlow, Charles—GCP Capital Partners
Barlow, Daniel—Valor Equity Partners
Barmeier, Bill—iGlobe Partners, Ltd.
Barnard, John—Barnard Associates, Inc.
Barnavon, Erez—Clarity Partners
Barnds, Thomas—Accel-KKR LLC
Barnea, Daniel—Aviv Venture Capital (FKA: Fantine Group, The)
Barnes, Cristy—Lighthouse Capital Partners
Barnes, Jeff—Clean Pacific Ventures
Barnes, Jonathan—Halyard Partners
Barnes, Phin—First Round Capital
Barnes, R. Scott—Legend Partners, The
Barnes, R. Scott—Walnut Group, The

Barnes, Simon—Tate & Lyle PLC
Barnes, Stephen—Novitas Capital (FKA: PA Early Stage Partners)
Barnes, Steven—Bain Capital
Barnet, Graham—Sigma Capital Group Plc
Barnet, Roland—Seventure Partners SA (FKA: SPEF Venture)
Barnett, Paul—Odyssey Investment Partners, LLC
Barnett, Troy—Adams Street Partners LLC
Barnhill, Mark—Platinum Equity LLC
Barnum, William—Brentwood Associates
Baron, Claudia—PPM America Capital Partners LLC
Baron, Ellen—Oxford Bioscience Partners
Baronav, Andrei—ABRT Venture Fund
Baroyan, Eric—American Industrial Partners
Barozzi, Mario—IDeA Capital Funds Sgr SpA
Barr, David—Warburg Pincus LLC
Barr, Gregory—Silver Oak Management
Barr, Katherine—Mohr Davidow Ventures
Barr, Michael—Sterling Investment Partners
Barr, Rob—Pantheon Ventures, Ltd.
Barr, Robbie—Terra Firma Capital Partners, Ltd.
Barra, James—Ironwood Capital (AKA: Ironwood Capital Advisors LLC)
Barrack, Robert—Blackstone Group, L.P.
Barrack, Robert—New York Life Capital Partners (AKA: NYLCAP)
Barrage, Khalil—Invus Group Ltd., The
Barraquias, Socorro—Credit Suisse Private Equity
Barras, Claude—Sifem AG (AKA: Swiss Investment Fund for Emerging Markets)
Barratt, Henry—Blue Water Capital LLC
Barrecchia, Sylvia—UBS Capital Corporation
Barreda, Jorge—SinoLatin Capital
Barreto, Alfredo—Silverfern Group, Inc., The
Barrett, David—Polaris Venture Partners
Barrett, M. James—New Enterprise Associates, Inc.
Barrett, Michael—Mesirow Private Equity Investments, Inc.
Barrett, Peter—Atlas Venture, Ltd.
Barrett, Robert—FTV Capital (FKA: FTVentures)
Barrett, Ross—VCE Capital
Barrier, Denis—Innovacom SA
Barris, Peter—New Enterprise Associates, Inc.
Barron, Adam—Englefield Capital
Barron, Bruce—Origin Ventures, LLC
Barron, Lisbeth—Centerview Partners Holdings LLC
Barrows, Tim—Matrix Partners
Barry, Brendan—Kenda Capital BV
Barry, Daniel—GE Antares Capital Corporation
Barry, Deanna—PNC Equity Management Corp.
Barry, Doug—Selby Venture Partners
Barry, Jeffery—Plymouth Venture Partners
Barry, John—Prospect Street Ventures
Barry, Mark—OpenView Venture Partners
Barry, R.Scott—Essex Woodlands Health Ventures
Barsby, Goran—CapMan Plc
Barsily, Brad—Atlantic-Pacific Capital, Inc.
Bart, Markus—Wellington Partners Venture Capital GmbH
Bartee, William—Southern Cross Venture Partners
Bartell, Mark—Guidant Corporation
Bartels, Patrick—Quadrangle Group LLC
Barth, R. Michael—Netherlands Development Finance Company
Barth, Thomas—Freudenberg Venture Capital GmbH
Barthelemy, Brennan—Sterling Partners
Bartholdson, John—Stonington Partners, Inc.
Bartholomaeus, Ben—Viburnum Funds Pty., Ltd. (AKA: Wyllie Group)
Bartkiewicz, Jakub—Investors Towarzystwo Funduszy Inwestycyjnych SA
Bartkowsk, William—BlueFire Partners Capital Markets
Bartlett, Marshall—Fisher Lynch Capital
Bartlett, Paul—Rho Capital Partners, Inc.
Bartlett, Sam—Charlesbank Capital Partners LLC
Bartlett, Thomas—GulfStar Group
Bartlett, Tom—Compass Equity Partners LLC
Bartok, Jared—Ampersand Ventures
Bartoletti, Frank—Stonington Partners, Inc.
Bartoli, Jeffrey—Centre Partners Management LLC
Barton, Brad—Natural Gas Partners (NGP)
Barton, Harris—Capital Dynamics AG
Barton, Melanie—Progress Equity Partners, Ltd.
Barton, Richard—Benchmark Capital
Bartos, Andrzej—Innova Capital
Bartosic, Albert—Zephyr Management, L.P.
Barua, Rajat—Lime Rock Partners LLC
Baruch, Adiv—Infinity Venture Capital Fund (AKA: Israel Infinity Fund)
Baruch, Thomas—CMEA Capital
Basadre, Jorge—Enfoca Sociedad Administradora de Fondos de Inversion
Basak, Amit—Staley Capital Management LLC
Basalka, Markus—Vienna Capital Partners
Bascur, Enrique—Citi Venture Capital International
Bashir, Imran—Extreme Venture Partners, Inc.
Bashour, Fouad—CIC Partners, L.P. (FKA: Cardinal Investment Company, Inc.)
Basile, Donald—Iron Capital Partners
Baskett, Forest—New Enterprise Associates, Inc.
Baskin, Pat—Blue Sage Capital, L.P.
Basner, David—GF Capital Management & Advisors LLC
Bass, Daniel—Fortress Investment Group LLC
Bassal, Omar—NBK Capital, Ltd.
Bassett, Philip—Permira Advisers LLP
Bassford, Stephen—Diamond Castle Holdings LLC
Bassi, Benoit—Bridgepoint Capital, Ltd.
Bassichis, Daniel—Admiral Capital Group
Basthdaw, Norman—Absa Capital Private Equity (Pty) Ltd.
Bastien, Ernest—CDP Capital - Technology Ventures (FKA: CDP Sofinov)
Basto, David—MidOcean Partners
Basu, Joy—Citibank Venture Capital India
Basu, Upal—Nokia Growth Partners
Batagelj, Leon—Poteza Partners d.o.o.
Batchelor, Joshua—Behrman Capital
Batchelor, Nicholas—RMB Capital Partners, Ltd.
Bates, Carrie—Triathlon Medical Ventures LLC
Bates, Gavin—Caltius Mezzanine
Bates, John—Arlington Capital Partners
Bathon, Daniel—Windspeed Ventures
Batlivala, Rustom—Matrix Partners
Batra, Rajeev—Mayfield Fund
Batta, Raghu—Ojas Venture Partners
Battaglia, Blake—ABRY Partners LLC
Battcock, Humphrey—Advent International
Battenfeld, Marc—Capvis Equity Partners AG
Batterson, Leonard—Batterson Venture Partners (AKA: BVP)
Battistoni, Darren—Welsh, Carson, Anderson & Stowe
Baty, Gordon—Zero Stage Capital Co., Inc.
Baty, Gregory—Hamilton Lane Advisors, Inc.
Baubeau, Francois—Natixis Private Equity SA
Bauchet, Pierrick—Inocap S.A.
Baucom, Christopher—Fort Washington Capital Partners Group
Baud, Jan Willem—NPM Capital NV
Baudon, Thierry—Mid Europa Partners
Bauer, Bruce—Rising Tide Fund
Bauer, Michael—Pall Mall Partners Limited
Bauer, Stacey—Galen Associates
Bauerly, Rick—Granite Equity Partners
Bauernfeind, Arthur—Westfield Capital Management
Baum, David William—Stage 1 Ventures, LLC
Baum, Richard—Consumer Growth Partners
Bauman, David—Tailwind Capital Partners
Bauman, David—Thomas Weisel Partners Group, Inc.
Bauman, Janet—Hamilton Lane Advisors, Inc.
Baumann, Jochen—Deutsche Beteiligungs AG
Baumann, Julie—Avenue Capital Group
Baumel, William—RWI Ventures
Baumer, John—Leonard Green & Partners
Baumgardt, James—Twilight Venture Partners
Baumgartner, Peter—Vestar Capital Partners, Inc.
Bauserman, David—2x Consumer Products Growth Partners LP
Baviere, Christophe—AGF Private Equity
Baxter, Jeff—Column Group, The
Baxter, Jennifer—TSG Consumer Partners
Bay, Michael—Wyndcrest Holdings, LLC
Bayazid, Wael—Carlyle Group, The
Bayhan, Burak—Is Private Equity Investment Trust
Bayless, Jeanne—Star Ventures Management GmbH & Co. KG
Bayless, Jon—Sevin Rosen Funds
Baylin, Gregory—ONCAP Investment Partners
Bayliss, Mark—Anchorage Capital Partners
Baylor, David—Vector Capital
Baynes, Brian—Flagship Ventures
Bazak, Shai—Old City Partners, LLC (OCP)
Bazin, Sebastien—Colony Capital LLC
Bazzari, Tamer—Rasmala Partners, Ltd.
Bazzocchi, Benoit—Nem Partners (AKA: Natexis Equity Management)
Beach, Brian—SI Ventures
Beach, Kenneth—Cascade Investment Group
Beakey, Jim—Nautic Partners LLC
Bean, Brian—Montgomery & Co. (FKA: Digital Coast Partners)
Beaney, Dan—Shamrock Holdings, Inc.
Bear, Alan—Probitas Partners, Inc.
Beard, F.Russell—Brazos Private Equity Partners LLC
Beare, Chris—Accede Capital
Beasley, Allen—Redpoint Ventures
Beasley, Michael—Nobska Ventures
Beatenbough, Debbie—Seapoint Ventures
Beaton, Andrew—Glenalta Capital LLP
Beatty, David—Thomas Weisel Partners Group, Inc.
Beaty, Derek—Global Environment Fund Management Corporation
Beaudette, Edna—NCH Capital, Inc.
Beaudoin, Mark—Adler & Co.

Beaudreault, Mary Ellen—Commonfund Capital, Inc. (FKA: Common Fund)
Beaulieu, Nathalie Faure—American Capital, Ltd.
Beaulieu, Nathalie Faure—European Capital Financial Services Ltd.
Beaumont, Michael—Industrial Growth Partners
Beauregard, Michael—Huron Capital Partners LLC
Bechard, Mark—Cabot Properties, Inc.
Bechtel, Karen—Carlyle Group, The
Beck, James—Mayfield Fund
Beck, Joseph—Shattuck Hammond Partners
Beck, Ronald—Oaktree Capital Management LLC
Beck, Thomas—Beacon Bioventures
Becker, Daria—Prospect Street Ventures
Becker, David—Meakem Becker Venture Capital
Becker, Douglas—Sterling Partners
Becker, Eric—Sterling Partners
Becker, Frank—Invision Private Equity AG
Becker, John—American Industrial Partners
Becker, Joost—Bregal Investments
Becker, Josh—New Cycle Capital LLC
Becker, Kai—Pontos Oy
Becker, Scott—Northstar Capital, LLC (FKA: Seidler Capital, Ltd.)
Becker, Todd—Next Generation Ventures, LLC
Beckers, Jan—Team Europe Ventures Management GmbH
Beckert, Richard—Teakwood Capital, L.P.
Beckett, Edward—Longbow Capital
Beckett, Steven—Peninsula Capital Partners LLC
Beckett, William—Future Value Ventures, Inc.
Beckett, William—Gefinor Ventures
Beckman, Eric—Ares Management, Inc.
Beckman, Joel—Greenbriar Equity Group LLC
Beckman, Robert—Channel Group LLC, The (TCG)
Beckmann, Marco—Nanostart AG
Beckmann, Volker—Sal. Oppenheim Private Equity Partners
Bedard, Jean—BDR Capital
Bednar, Horst—Austria Wirtschaftsservice Gesellschaft mbH
Bednar, Leopold—ECO Unternehmensbeteiligungs-AG
Bednarski, Eric—MVM Life Science Partners LLP (AKA: MVM, Ltd.)
Beebe, Joshua—Arbor Partners LLC
Beebe, Joshua—Blue Chip Venture Company
Beecken, Dave—Beecken, Petty & Company LLC
Beegle, Ron—DLJ Merchant Banking Partners
Beegle, Ron—Goode Partners LLC
Beekman, Doug—Advantage Capital Partners
Beeler, Charles—El Dorado Ventures
Beeney, Marisa—Blackstone Group, L.P.
Beg, Murad—Linsalata Capital Partners
Begert, Brian—Yellow Point Equity Partners LP
Begg, John—HarbourVest Partners LLC
Begg, Simon—Warburg Pincus LLC
Beggs, Austin—SOCO
Beghin, Jean-Michel—Rothschild Gestion
Begley, Lawrence—.406 Ventures (AKA: Point 406 Ventures)
Begnal, Dorr—Park Street Capital LLC
Begun, Michael—Coates Myer & Co. Pty Ltd.
Behar, Gadi—Silicom Ventures
Behar, Justin—Rutberg & Company, LLC
Behbahani, Ali—New Enterprise Associates, Inc.
Behm, Dennis—OnPoint Technologies
Behm, Denny—Arsenal Venture Partners
Behnam, Reza—IDG Ventures Vietnam
Behnke, Linda—Golding Capital Partners GmbH
Behrendt, Peter—New Enterprise Associates, Inc.
Behrens, Christopher—CCMP Capital Advisors LLC
Behrens, Christopher—J.P. Morgan Partners (FKA: Chase Capital Partners)
Behrens-Ramberg, Wolfgang—EquiVest GmbH & Co
Behrman, Grant—Behrman Capital
Bei, Duoguang—Jinpu Industrial Investment Fund Management Company
Beil, Stefan—Triginta Capital Partners GmbH (FKA: Avida Equity Partners)
Beim, Nicholas—Matrix Partners
Beinecke, Walter—Brook Venture Partners LLC
Beirne, David—Benchmark Capital
Beisel, David—Venrock Associates
Beit-On, Harel—Carmel Ventures
Beit-On, Harel—Viola Private Equity
Beitler, Stephen—Dunrath Capital, Inc.
Beitmann, Beatrice—AXA Private Equity
Bejjani, Ghassan—Morgan Stanley Private Equity
Bejjani, Ghassan—Morgan Stanley Venture Partners (AKA: MSDW)
Bek, Eitan—Pitango Venture Capital (FKA:Polaris Venture Capital Israel)
Bekenstein, Joshua—Bain Capital
Beker, Limor—Hamilton Lane Advisors, Inc.
Bekx, Paul A.—Gilde Buy Out Partners
Bekx, Paul A.—Gilde Investment Management B.V.
Bela, Marquez—Capital Southwest Corporation
Belard, Andre—Azulis Capital (FKA:Banexi Capital Partenaires)
Belardi, Ugo—Clessidra Capital
Belcastro, Luke—Jefferies Group, Inc.
Beldy, Daniel—Steamboat Ventures
Beletic, John—Oak Investment Partners
Belfer, Todd—Canal Partners LLC
Belford, Jeff—TriWest Capital Management Corporation
Belgrad, Stephen—HarbourVest Partners LLC
Belke, Robert—Lovell Minnick Partners LLC
Bell, David—CFI Capital
Bell, David—Nevis Capital LLP
Bell, George—General Catalyst Partners (FKA: General Catalyst Group LLC)
Bell, Michael—Monitor Clipper Partners LLC
Bell, Nathan—Pacific Mezzanine Fund, L.P. (PMF)
Bell, Peter—Highland Capital Partners LLC
Bell, Robert—Intersouth Partners
Bell, Ryan—Capital Partners, Inc.
Bell, Scott—Weston Presidio (FKA: Weston Presidio Capital Management)
Bell, Thatcher—Draper Fisher Jurvetson Gotham Venture Partners
Bell-Jones, Robin—Permira Advisers LLP
Bellas, Robert—Morgenthaler Ventures
Beller, Laura—Meritage Funds
Bellissimo, Barbara—Monterey Venture Partners, LLC
Bello, John—Quest Capital, Inc.
Bello, John—Sherbrooke Capital
Bello, Richard—Blue Ridge Capital
Belloir, Xavier—AXA Private Equity
Bellomo, Nick—Trident Capital
Belluck, David—Riverside Partners
Beloussov, Serguei—Almaz Capital Partners
Belt, Ron—Truffle Venture SAS
Belthoff, Thomas—PineBridge Investments
Beltramino, Danilo—IDeA Capital Funds Sgr SpA
Beltz, Scott—Oaktree Capital Management LLC
Belzberg, Brent—TorQuest Partners, Inc.
Belzberg, Sam—Second City Capital Partners
Belzer, David—Prospect Street Ventures
Bemis, Rob—Highland Capital Partners LLC
Ben-Arie, Moty—Vertex Management Israel (AKA: Vertex Venture Capital)
Ben-Arie, Moty—Vertex Venture Capital
Ben-Eliahu, Eitan—Giza Venture Capital (FKA: Giza Investment Management)
Ben-Haim, Ron—First Israel Mezzanine Investors, Ltd. (AKA: FIMI)
Ben-Porat, Tsvika—Maayan Ventures
Ben-Zvi, Gideon—Aviv Venture Capital (FKA: Fantine Group, The)
Benacerraf, Ari—Diamond Castle Holdings LLC
Benbow, Robert—Alta Communications
Benchimol, Didier—CDP Capital - Technology Ventures (FKA: CDP Sofinov)
Bendel, David—Excel Partners
Bendel, David—Minerva Capital
Bender, Michael—Churchill Equity, Inc.
Bender, Theodore—C&B Capital
Bendori, Ori—Carmel Ventures
Bendre, Dhananjay—IndiaCo
Bendre, Dhananjay—IndiaCo Ventures, Ltd.
Benear, John—DW Healthcare Partners
Benelbas, Leon—Atlas Capital Close Brothers (FKA: Atlas Capital Investment)
Beneski, Ted—Insight Equity Holdings LLC
Benetton, Alessandro—21 Partners SpA
Benevento, Steven—New York Life Capital Partners (AKA: NYLCAP)
Benford, Edward—Benford Capital Partners LLC
Benford, Gerald—Veronis Suhler Stevenson (FKA: Veronis, Suhler & Associates)
Beng, Aw Soon—Raintree Ventures Pte., Ltd.
Beng, Choo Chee—OSK Ventures International Bhd (AKA: OSK Ventures Equities)
Bengtsson, Carin—Capilon AB
Bengtsson, Jonas—Nostrum Ventures
Bengtsson, Nils—Novestra AB
Benham, Mark—Celerity Partners
Benik, Alexander—Battery Ventures, L.P.
Benin, David—CBPE Capital, LLP (AKA: Close Brothers Private Equity, Ltd.)
Beninga, Cheryl—American River Ventures
Benjamin, Bill—Apollo Real Estate Advisors
Benjamin, Gerald—Atlanta Equity Investors LLC
Benke, Akos—Corvinus International Investment Rt
Benkovic, Stephen—Rho Capital Partners, Inc.
Benloehr, John—Walnut Group, The
Benn, Mark—Lydian Capital Advisors S.A.
Benner, Christoph—ACA Equity-Partners GmbH
Bennett, George—Talisman Capital
Bennett, Peter—Consumer Growth Partners
Bennett, Peter—Liberty Partners
Bennett, Robert—Ground Swell Equity Partners
Bennett, Stephen—Stonehenge Capital Company
Bennis, Jeffrey—5280 Partners

Benoit, Michael—Makaira Venture Partners
Benoni Meurer, Clovis—CRP (AKA: Companhia de Participacoes)
Bensel, Wolfgang—ARCADIA Beteiligungen Bensel Tiefenbacher & Co GmbH
Benson, Buzz—SightLine Partners
Benson, Erik—Voyager Capital
Benson, Gregory—Huntsman Gay Global Capital LLC
Benson, Marc—Mid-Atlantic Venture Funds (FKA: NEPA Management Corp.)
Benson, Peter—Sunstone Capital A/S
Benson, Peter—Vaekstfonden (AKA: Danish Growth Fund, The)
Benson, Woody—Prism VentureWorks
Bensouda, Abdou—Finaventures
Bent, Amiel—Syncom Management Co. Inc.
Bent, Don—Latitude Partners
Bentley, Pam—Carlyle Group, The
Bentsen, Lloyd—Cogene Ventures
Bentz, Julien—IDI Asset Management SA
Benvenuti, Raynard—Greenbriar Equity Group LLC
Benway, Aaron—Carlyle Group, The
Benyamini, Liat—SKY FUND
Benzie, Patrick—Lunar Capital Management, Ltd.
Benzie, Sulger—Lunar Capital Management, Ltd.
Beracha, Rami—Pitango Venture Capital (FKA:Polaris Venture Capital Israel)
Beran, Bob—Momentum Technology Partners LLC
Berardino, Thomas—Saugatuck Capital Company
Berendes, Birger—GCP Capital Partners
Berendsen, Caspar—Cinven, Ltd.
Berg, Christian—Hafslund Venture AS
Berg, Ian—SeventySix Capital
Berg, John—Dorset Capital
Berg, John—Weston Presidio (FKA: Weston Presidio Capital Management)
Berg, Jon Trygve—Sarsia Seed Management AS
Berg, Steven—Castanea Partners
Berg, Thomas—Anchor Capital Management Ltd
Berge, David—Underdog Ventures LLC
Bergel, Jaime—Gala Capital Partners (AKA: GCP)
Bergeland, Jorn—Procom Venture AS
Bergen, Charles—Kilcullen Kapital Partners
Berger, Adam—Advanced Technology Ventures
Berger, Anders Are—Procom Venture AS
Berger, Ariella—Eurovestech PLC
Berger, Geoffrey—Atlantic-Pacific Capital, Inc.
Berger, Gideon—Blackstone Group, L.P.
Berger, Jacques—DEFI Gestion SA
Berger, Lawrence—Blackstreet Capital Management (FKA: MMP Capital Advisors)
Berger, Peter—Ripplewood Holdings LLC
Bergeron, Christine—Chrysalix Energy
Bergeron, Michael—Strength Capital Partners
Bergeron, Sara England—Trident Capital
Berges, James—Clayton, Dubilier & Rice, Inc.
Berggren, Per—Paron Ventures AB
Bergman, James—Brantley Partners
Bergmann, Oliver—Capital Z Investment Partners (FKA: Union Square Partners)
Bergmann, Robert—Palisades Ventures (FKA: Centre Palisades Ventures)
Bergquist, Kurt—Exeter Capital Partners
Bergsmyr, Eivind—Viking Venture Management AS
Bergstein, Bart—Forbion Capital Partners
Bergtraum, Howard—O'Melveny & Myers LLP
Beringsmith, Alan—Altos Ventures
Berk, Eli—KBL Healthcare Ventures
Berk, Howard—MSD Capital L.P.
Berk, Ted—Bain Capital
Berk, Zachary—KBL Healthcare Ventures
Berke, Eric—TorQuest Partners, Inc.
Berkeley, Richard—Camden Partners, Inc. (FKA: Cahill, Warnock & Co. LLC)
Berkery, Dermot—Delta Partners, Ltd.
Berkes, Mary Beth—Linden LLC
Berkner, Chris—One Earth Capital LLC
Berkowitz, David—Ventures West Management, Inc.
Berkowitz, Fred—Horsley Bridge Partners
Berkowitz, Mortimer—HealthpointCapital LLC
Berlin, Scott—Brown Gibbons Lang & Company LLC
Berliner, Arthur—Walden Venture Capital
Berman, Beverly—Advent International
Berman, Douglas—H.I.G. Capital LLC
Berman, Ian—RBC Dain Rauscher
Berman, Michael—Israel Seed Partners
Berman, Neal—Thompson Street Capital Partners
Berman, Ron—Carmel Ventures
Berman, Thomas—Adams Street Partners LLC
Berment, Olivier—AXA Private Equity
Bernal, Ron—New Enterprise Associates, Inc.
Bernard, Olivia—Massena Capital Partners
Bernard, Veronique—iXEN Partners
Bernard-Brunel, Ivan—AXA Private Equity
Bernardez, Stephen—ONSET Ventures
Bernardez, Timothy—Evergreen Pacific Partners LLC
Bernardi, David—ID Capital
Bernardi, David—Propulsion Ventures, Inc.
Bernardo, Allen—Cedar Fund
Bernardo, Arie—Washington Technology Partners, Inc. (AKA: WTP)
Bernardon, Roland—Capital Z Investment Partners (FKA: Union Square Partners)
Bernardoni, Peter—Wavepoint Ventures
Bernards, James—Brightstone Capital
Bernasek, Brian—Carlyle Group, The
Bernat, Viktor—K+ Venture Partners
Bernegger, Mark—Riverside Management Group
Berner, Robert—Ripplewood Holdings LLC
Berney, Philip—Kelso & Company
Bernier, Roger—Foragen Technologies Management
Bernloehr, John—Legend Partners, The
Bernstein, Adam—New Energy Capital Corporation
Bernstein, Brad—FTV Capital (FKA: FTVentures)
Bernstein, Garrick—Vestar Capital Partners, Inc.
Bernstein, Jay—KPS Capital Partners, L.P.
Bernstein, John—General Atlantic LLC
Bernstein, Richard—Eurovestech PLC
Bernstein, Robert—Leeds Equity Partners
Berntsson, Mattias—Pantheon Ventures, Ltd.
Bero, Bret—American Capital, Ltd.
Berrard, Steven—New River Capital Partners
Berry, David—Flagship Ventures
Berry, Harry—New Venture Partners LLC
Berry, J.F.—WP Global Partners Inc.
Berry, Orna—Gemini Israel Funds, Ltd.
Berry, Rick—Signet Healthcare Partners (FKA: Sanders Morris Harris)
Berry, Savinay—Granite Ventures LLC
Berry, Timothy—Private Advisors LLC
Berstein, Beth—Eos Partners, L.P.
Berterretche, Jackie—Granite Ventures LLC
Berthie, Marie-Laure—Banexi Ventures Partners
Bertin, Philippe—Equitis
Bertocci, Louis—Boston Ventures Management, Inc.
Bertoldi, Robert—Amphion Capital Management, LLC (FKA: Wolfensohn Associates)
Berton, John—Georgian Partners
Bertram, Justin—PNC Equity Management Corp.
Bertrand, Cyril—DVC Deutsche Venture Capital
Bertrand, Jean-Jacques—BNP Paribas Private Equity SAS
Bertrand, Jean-Jacques—ORKOS Capital
Bertrand, Jean-Jacques—Truffle Venture SAS
Bertrand, Luc—Sofinim NV
Bertrand, Marc—UFG Private Equity SAS
Bertrand, Sylvain—Multiple Capital, Inc.
Bery, Varun—J.P. Morgan Partners (FKA: Chase Capital Partners)
Bery, Varun—TVG Capital Partners, Ltd.
Berzofsky, Alex—Warburg Pincus LLC
Besancon, Eustache—21 Centrale Partners
Besancon, Eustache—21 Partners SpA
Bess, Stephanie—Investcorp Bank B.S.C.
Bessone, John—Fort Washington Capital Partners Group
Best, Brian—Dragon Capital
Best, Paul—Warburg Pincus LLC
Beste, Frederick—Mid-Atlantic Venture Funds (FKA: NEPA Management Corp.)
Besthof, Peter—Quadriga Capital
Besthoff, Skip—Castile Ventures
Betcher, Kurt—Norwest Venture Partners
Bethea, Brandon—Insight Equity Holdings LLC
Bethel, Erik—SinoLatin Capital
Bethell, Melissa—Bain Capital
Beti, Jea-Paul—Alto Invest
Betlach, Doug—Morgenthau Venture Partners, LLC
Betschart, Auguste—Leman Capital
Betten, Elizabeth—Madison Dearborn Partners LLC
Betti, Alessandro—Vegagest Sgr
Bettigole, Rob—Elm Street Ventures
Bettino, Larry—StarVest Partners, L.P.
Bettio, Nicola—EonTech Ventures (FKA: Triton Ventures)
Betts, Alex—Climate Change Capital, Ltd.
Betts, Julie—GCP Capital Partners
Bettum, Ole—Undisclosed Firm
Beuque, Bruno—Clearwater Capital Partners, LLC
Bevacqua, Michael—Bain Capital
Bevan, Michael—Element Partners
Bevelock, Mary—Globespan Capital Partners
Beveridge, Gordon—Scottish Equity Partners
Beverina, Alessio—Sofinnova Partners
Bevilacqua, Tom—VantagePoint Venture Partners
Beyda, Gil—Comcast Interactive Capital
Beyer, Jeffrey—Willis Stein & Partners
Bezprozvanna, Svitlana—AVentures
Bezugly, Alexander—Alfa Capital Partners
Bhadkamkar, Neal—Monitor Venture Management, L.L.C.
Bhalla, Uniti—STAR Capital Partners, Ltd.
Bhandari, R.K.—Punjab Venture Capital, Ltd.
Bharadwaj, Neeraj—Accel Partners
Bhargava, Sameer—Carlyle Group, The
Bhasin, Rahul—BPEP International

Bhasin, Sanjiv—Rabo India Finance, Ltd.
Bhat, Sandeep—Aditya Birla Capital Advisors Pvt., Ltd.
Bhatacharjee, Jishnu—Nexus Venture Partners
Bhatia, Harjit—Credit Suisse Private Equity
Bhatia, Harjit—GE Commercial Finance - Equity
Bhatia, Ranjeet—Saffron Hill Ventures
Bhatia, Sunny—Global Investment House
Bhatnagar, Amit—Mercantile Capital Group (MCG)
Bhattacharya, Sanjay—Frontline Strategy Pte. Ltd.
Bhattacharya, Sanjay—Infinity Venture Capital
Bhattacharyya, Pinaki—IDFC Private Equity
Bhaumik, Sam—Hercules Technology Growth Capital, Inc.
Bhayani, Dhimant—INC3 Ventures, LLC
Bhonsle, Ranjit—Enhanced Capital Partners, LLC
Bhonsle, Ranjit—Ithmar Capital
Bhora, Faiz—Gemini Partners, Inc.
Bhowmik, Nilanjana—Longworth Venture Partners, L.P.
Bhushan, Ajit—Citi Venture Capital International
Bhusri, Aneel—Greylock Partners
Biagioni, Ettore—Alothon Group LLC
Biagosch, Maximilian—Permira Advisers LLP
Bialas, Edward—First Reserve Corporation
Bialek, Paul—Frazier Healthcare and Technology Ventures
Bianchi, Annette—VantagePoint Venture Partners
Bianchinotti, Alberto—Merlin Nexus
Bianco, Andrew—Main Street Capital Holdings LLC
Bianco, Maurizio—Cognetas LLP
Bianco, William—Diamond Point Capital Management
Bibow, Robert—Atlantic-Pacific Capital, Inc.
Bice, William—Verge
Bichara, Axel—Atlas Venture, Ltd.
Bick, Mayer—Evercore Partners
Bickel, Jim—Redwood Capital, Inc.
Bicknell, Gene—Midwest Venture Alliance
Bicknell, Martin—Mariner Capital Partners LLC
Biddelman, Paul—Undisclosed Firm
Biddle, A.G.W (Jack)—Novak Biddle Venture Partners, L.P.
Biddulph, Mike—Promethean Investments
Bidinger, Eric—Pamplona Capital Management LLP
Bieber, Matt—Originate Ventures
Biederman, Carson—Mustang Group LLC, The
Biedermann, Wolfgang—H.I.G. Capital LLC
Bielowicki, Grzegorz—Tar Heel
Bienfait, Fabrice—ETF Manager LLP
Bieri, Josef—Partners Group AG
Bierman, Ben—Business Partners
Bierman, Julie—Apollo Real Estate Advisors
Bierman, Mike—Hunt BioVentures
Bifano, Tony—SeventySix Capital
Biffar, Ulrich—Bain Capital
Bigelow, Rick—Revolution Capital Group LLC
Biggar, William—Richardson Capital Limited
Bigge, Matthew—American Capital, Ltd.
Bigge, Matthew—Silicon Valley Innovation Capital (SVIC)
Biggee, Michael—Trident Capital
Biggott, Brian—Transom Capital Group
Bigham, Michael—Abingworth Management, Ltd.
Biglieri, Susan—Kleiner Perkins Caufield & Byers
Bilden, Philip—HarbourVest Partners LLC
Bildsten, Pelle—Energy Ventures AS
Bilek, Zdenek—Eagle Ventures
Bilenker, Josh—Aisling Capital
Bilger, Arthur—Shelter Capital Partners LLC
Bilimer, Evren—Invus Group Ltd., The
Billerbeck, Chuck—Navigation Capital Partners (AKA: NCP)
Billet, Frederic—Truffle Venture SAS
Billings, Timothy—MidOcean Partners
Bilnoski, Brian—Crossbow Ventures
Bilzin, Jonathan—TowerBrook Capital Partners L.P.
Bin Md Shariff, Norulhadi—Global Maritime Ventures Bhd
Binch, James—Lincolnshire Management, Inc.
Binder, Scott—Allied Capital Corporation
Binderow, Alex—Crestview Partners L.P. (FKA: Crestview, LLC)
Biner, Rene—Partners Group AG
Bingham, Hugh—Atlantic-Pacific Capital, Inc.
Bingham, Kate—SV Life Sciences Advisers
Bingham-Walker, Megan—WHEB Ventures, Ltd.
Bingle, Mike—Silver Lake Sumeru
Biniak, Bryan—Provenance Ventures
Binkevicius, Marius—Alta Capital
Binkley, Jay—Andrew W. Byrd & Co. LLC
Binkley, Nicholas—Forrest Binkley & Brown
Binnenbruecker, Joerg—DuMont Venture Holding GmbH & Co. KG
Binnie, Kevin—SCF Partners
Binning, Gary—Dominus Capital, L.P.
Binning, Gary—Quad-C Management, Inc.
Binz, Alexander—von Braun & Schreiber Private Equity Partners GmbH
Biotti, Jon—Charlesbank Capital Partners LLC
Biral, Alessandro—Keynote Ventures (FKA: Dali, Hook Partners)
Biran, Joel—Versa Capital Management (FKA: Chrysalis Capital Partners)
Birch, Thomas—Propulsion Ventures, Inc.
Birchall, Nathan—Ranch Capital LLC
Birchler, Kurt—Partners Group AG
Bird, Catherine—Boston Ventures Management, Inc.
Bird, Jeffrey—Sutter Hill Ventures
Bird, Jerry—MTDC (Massachusetts Technology Development Corp.)
Bird, Matthew—GarMark Partners
Bird, Steven—Focus Ventures
Birk, Brian—Sun Mountain Capital
Birke, Jason—Jordan, Edmiston Group, Inc., The
Birkel, Michael—Target Partners GmbH
Birkeland, Peter—RAIN Source Capital, Inc.
Birnbaum, Cynthia—Link Ventures LLLP
Birnbaum, Stevan—Arcturus Capital
Birner, Hubert—TVM Capital GmbH
Biro, Timothy—Ohio Innovation Fund (OIF)
Biro, Timothy—Reservoir Venture Partners
Birss, Edward—Advanced Technology Ventures
Bischof, George—Meritech Capital Partners
Bischoff, Thomas—ViaNova Capital
Bisconti, Ben—Accel-KKR LLC
Bisgaard, Peter Tuxen—Novo A/S
Bisgaard-Frantzen, Jens—Private Advisors LLC
Bishop, Anthony Paul—iGlobe Treasury Management, Ltd.
Bishop, Jennifer—Stephens Group, Inc.
Bishop, Nathan—HarbourVest Partners LLC
Bishop, Norman—BB&T Capital Markets
Bishop, Stephen—Global Emerging Markets
Bismuth, Didier—Duke Street Capital
Bismuth, Eric—Montefiore Investment
Bismuth, Eric—Montefiore Investment SAS
Bisner, Kerri—J.P. Morgan H&Q (FKA: Chase H&Q)
Bissette, Louis—Bison Capital Asset Management LLC
Bisson, Anneliese—Southern Cross Venture Partners
Bisson, Cedric—iNovia Capital
Biswas, Sena—VIMAC Ventures LLC (FKA: VIMAC LLC)
Bittelman, Eric—OrbiMed Advisors LLC
Bitterman, Kevin—Polaris Venture Partners
Bixby, William—Trinity Hunt Partners
Bixel, Kim—Greenmont Capital Partners
Bjerkan, John—Reiten & Co Strategic Investments AS
Bjorklund, Gunnar—Sverica International
Bjorklund, Johan—Catella AB
Bjorklund, Kurt—Permira Advisers LLP
Bjornoy, Trond—Norvestor Equity AS (FKA: Norsk Vekst Forvaltning AS)
Bjornsson, Sigurdur—Thule Investments
Bjursten, Oskar—Firm Factory Network
Bjurstrom, Anders—Scandinavian Financial Management AB
Bjurstrom, Johan—AAC Capital Partners
Blabey, Robert—LJH Global Investments
Blabey, Robert—LJH Linley Capital LLC
Black, Adam—Comcast Interactive Capital
Black, Benjamin—New Cycle Capital LLC
Black, Daniel—Wicks Group of Companies LLC, The
Black, Darren—SV Life Sciences Advisers
Black, John—H.I.G. Capital LLC
Black, Jonathan—Jefferson Partners
Black, Louis—Aleutian Capital Partners LLC
Black, Michael—Bridgepoint Capital, Ltd.
Black, Philip—Blacksmith Capital
Black, Philip—True Ventures
Black, Tim—Integra Ventures
Black, William—Castle Creek Capital LLC
Blackburn, Alan—GulfStar Group
Blackburn, Michael—Petra Capital Partners, LLC
Blackburn, Tara—Hamilton Lane Advisors, Inc.
Blackburn, Thomas—Kansas Venture Capital, Inc.
Blackwell, Trevor—Y Combinator
Blades, Geoff—Carlyle Group, The
Bladh, Jorgen—Northzone Ventures AS (FKA: Venture Partners AS)
Blain, David—Moneta Capital Partners, Ltd.
Blair, James—Domain Associates LLC
Blais, Alain—Campbell Resources
Blaisdell, Thomas—DCM
Blake, James—Growth Capital Partners (FKA: Close Brothers Growth Capital)
Blaker, Frank—Procom Venture AS
Blanchard, Jeffrey—First Capital Group Management Co. LLC (AKA: FCG)
Blanchard, Karen—Rizvi Traverse Management, LLC
Blanche, Christophe—Iris Capital Management (FKA: Part'Com Management S.A.)
Blanchette, Kirk—Seguin Partners LLC
Blanco, Jose—Central Valley Fund, L.P., The

Bland, Geoff—Wedbush Capital Partners
Blaney, Peter—Dynex Capital Corporation
Blaney, William—Tucker Partners
Blank, Esana—CCMP Capital Advisors LLC
Blank, Robert—Chicago Growth Partners (William Blair Capital Partners)
Blankfein, Lloyd—Goldman, Sachs & Co.
Blanks, Cameron—Pacific Equity Partners
Blasco, Ian—Bain Capital
Blasco, Ian—Fidelity Equity Partners
Blasselle, Patrick—Franche-Comte PME Gestion
Blatherwick, Nell—RCP Advisors LLC
Blatt, Eli—Undisclosed Firm
Blatte, David—Centre Partners Management LLC
Blatteis, Angela—Global Equity Capital LLC
Blazensky, Derek—Cardinal Venture Capital
Blecker, Joerg—AutoVision GmbH
Bleiberg, Gary—Carlyle Group, The
Bleijendaal, Martin—Greenfield Capital Partners
Bley, Christopher—Bridgepoint Capital, Ltd.
Bleyleben, Maximilian—Kennet Venture Partners, Ltd. (FKA: Kennet Capital, Ltd.)
Bliamptis, Timothy—Weathergage Venture Capital
Blindheim, Martin—Saffron Hill Ventures
Blinten, Tom—Agility Capital LLC
Bliska, Thomas—Crosslink Capital
Bliss, Simon—Nova Capital Management, Ltd.
Blitzer, David—Blackstone Group, L.P.
Blizzard, Peter—Business Management, Ltd.
Bloch, Bruno—Milk Capital
Bloch, Jonathan—GKM Newport Generation Funds
Bloch, Jonathan—GKM Ventures
Bloch, Stephen—Canaan Partners
Block, Martin—HgCapital
Block, Sam—Carlyle Group, The
Blodgett, Matthew—Alta Communications
Bloise, Christopher—Court Square Capital Partners
Blom, Peter—Triodos International Fund Management BV
Blomberg, Hans—European Equity Partners
Blomberg, Lars—BBE Business Development AB
Blomquist, Daniel—Creandum KB
Blomqvist, Berndt—Helmet Business Mentors Oy
Bloodworth, Jon—Mesa Capital Partners
Bloom, Bradley—Berkshire Partners LLC
Bloom, Jay—Trimaran Capital Partners, LLC
Bloom, Lucinda—Credit Suisse Private Equity
Bloomberg, Ken—AlpInvest Partners N.V.
Bloomgarden, Jessica—21Ventures LLC
Blower, Mark—Gresham Partners - Gresham Private Equity
Bloy, Nicholas—Navis Investment Partners (Asia), Ltd.
Blue, Harold—HealthEdge Investment Partners
Blue, Jonathan—Blue Equity, LLC
Bluestein, Michael—Grindstone Partners LLC
Bluestein, Michael—Oakcrest Capital Partners LLC
Bluestein, Michael—Winston Partners
Blum, Adi—High Road Capital Partners
Blum, Jason—Iron Capital Partners
Blumberg, David—Blumberg Capital Ventures
Blume, Frederick—Excel Venture Management
Blumenreich, Stephen—Shattuck Hammond Partners
Blumenthal, Daniel—Willis Stein & Partners
Blumenthal, Jake—Vance Street Capital LLC
Blumenwitz, Peter—Aheim Capital GmbH (FKA: Buchanan Capital Partners GmbH)
Blumstock, Judy—Genesys Capital Partners, Inc.
Blythe, Christopher—Brockway Moran & Partners, Inc.
Boasson, Maarten—Favonius Ventures
Boccardi, Valerio—Palamon Capital Partners (FKA: Amphion Capital Partners)
Bochnowski, James—Delphi Ventures
Bock, Christopher—KRG Capital Partners LLC
Bock, Kjeld—Dansk Kapitalanlaeg Aktieselskab
Bock, Lawrence—CW Group, Inc.
Bock, Louis—Scale Venture Partners
Bocker, Magnus—Huvudkontoret i Kristinehamn AB
Bockius, Ted—Insight Venture Partners
Bodary, Sarah—SV Life Sciences Advisers
Bode, Brian—Atlantic-Pacific Capital, Inc.
Bode, Joerg—Capital Dynamics AG
Bodenham, Martin—Advantage Capital Limited
Bodepudi, Raj—MASI, Ltd.
Bodine, Pete—Allegis Capital (AKA: Media Technology Ventures)
Bodnar, Kevin—Corporate Fuel Partners
Bodnick, Marc—Elevation Associates LLC
Bodor, Danielle—Net Partners
Bodway, Kelly—TMB Industries Investments
Boeckenfoerde, Bjoern—Zurmont Madison Management AG (FKA: Zurmont Management AG)
Boehler, Adam—Accretive LLC (FKA: Accretive Technology Partners LLC)
Boehm, Ami—First Israel Mezzanine Investors, Ltd. (AKA: FIMI)
Boehm, Christopher—Willis Stein & Partners
Boehnke, Frank—Wellington Partners Venture Capital GmbH
Boenisch, Michael—AFINUM Management GmbH
Boeren, Leni—Robeco Private Equity
Boesl, Alois—BayBG Bayerische Beteiligungsgesellschaft mbH
Boettcher, James—Focus Ventures
Boettcher, Jim—Mingly Capital
Boezi, Karen—CORAL Ventures Management, Inc.
Bogaerts, Joris—Plain Vanilla Investments BV
Bogdanov, Pavel—Almaz Capital Partners
Bogentoft, Conny—Karolinska Development AB
Boget, Franck—Azulis Capital (FKA:Banexi Capital Partenaires)
Boggett, Mark—Seraphim Capital
Boghossian, Thierry—Initiative & Finance Investissement SA
Bognar, Zoltan—Capital Stage AG
Bognar, Zoltan—H.I.G. Capital LLC
Bohart, Stuart—Fortress Investment Group LLC
Bohlen, Greg—Cross Creek Capital, an affiliate of Wasatch Advisors
Bohm, Bernhard—BLS Venture Capital GmbH
Bohm, Gregor—Carlyle Group, The
Bohm, Jan-Eric—Initium AB
Bohmert, Andrea—Hasso Plattner Ventures Africa
Bohn, Larry—General Catalyst Partners (FKA: General Catalyst Group LLC)
Bohnenkamp, Guido—bm-t beteiligungsmanagement thueringen gmbh
Bohnett, David—Baroda Ventures LLC
Bohorquez, Eduardo—Nexos Capital Partners
Bohr, Ryan—Hilco Equity Management, LLC
Bohrer, Scott—SeventySix Capital
Bohrmann, Braden—Masthead Venture Partners
Boich, Michael—Formative Ventures
Boillet, Mathieu—Odyssee Venture
Boker-Ferri, Efrat—ProSeed Venture Capital Fund
Bolander, Frederick—Gabriel Venture Partners
Bolandrina, Marco—Jotunfjell Partners AS (AKA: JFP)
Bolduc, John—H.I.G. Capital LLC
Bolg, John—Arbor Partners LLC
Bolland, Anthony—Boston Ventures Management, Inc.
Bollyky, Andrea—Aetos Capital LLC
Bolner, Michael—Capital Z Investment Partners (FKA: Union Square Partners)
Bolster, Chris—Time Warner Investments (FKA: AOL Time Warner Ventures)
Bolton, Michael—Novitas Capital (FKA: PA Early Stage Partners)
Boltz, Michael—Cognetas LLP
Bolyan, Gerry—Long Point Capital Inc.
Bolyky, Janos—Covent rial Capital Investment Co., Ltd.
Bolzan, Denio—Pfingsten Partners, L.P.
Bolzon, Bradley—Versant Ventures
Bommer, Eric—Sentinel Capital Partners
Boms, Elon—LaunchCapital LLC
Bon, Michel—Vermeer Capital Partners
Bonandini, Giovani—21 Partners SpA
Bonanni, Berthold—Beteiligungsgesellschaft fur die deutsche Wirtschaft mbH
Bonanno, Andrew—American Capital, Ltd.
Bonanno, Andrew—GE Commercial Finance - Equity
Bonanzinga, Roberto—Balderton Capital (FKA: Benchmark Capital Europe)
Bond, Jonathon—Actis Capital LLP
Bond, Joseph—NCH Capital, Inc.
Bond, Patrick—Mountaineer Capital, L.P.
Bonderman, David—TPG Capital
Bondick, Greg—Windjammer Capital Investors (FKA:Pacific Mezzanine Inv.)
Bonduelle, Felix—Participex
Bondy, Craig—GTCR Golder Rauner LLC
Bonebrake, Stephen—Signet Healthcare Partners (FKA: Sanders Morris Harris)
Bonelli, Steve—Three Arch Partners
Boneparth, John—Hall Capital Partners LLC (FKA: Offit Hall Capital Mgmt)
Boner, Frank—Global Capital Private Equity Ltd
Bonfiglio, Stefano—Stirling Square Capital Partners
Bong, Boris—Squadron Capital Advisors, Ltd.
Bonham, Scott—GGV Capital
Boni, Fausto—360 Capital Management SA (AKA: 360 Capital Partners)
Boni, Fausto—Net Partners
Boni, Pascal—Remaco Merger AG
Bonifacio, Dominique—Investissement Quebec
Bonita, David—OrbiMed Advisors LLC
Bonker, Virginia—Blue Rock Capital
Bonnavion, Jean—Palamon Capital Partners (FKA: Amphion Capital Partners)
Bonnecuelle, Alexandre—Montefiore Investment
Bonnet, Michael—HB Equity Partners, L.P.
Bonneton, Jean-Stephane—TIME Equity Partners SAS

Bonnstetter, Darren—Quarry Capital Management LLC
Bono, Mark—Weston Presidio (FKA: Weston Presidio Capital Management)
Bonomi, Carlo—Investindustrial Partners, Ltd.
Bonsal, Frank—Boulder Ventures, Ltd.
Bonsal, Frank—New Enterprise Associates, Inc.
Bonsal, Frank—New Markets Venture Partners (AKA: New Markets Growth Fund)
Bonsels, Burkhard—Quadriga Capital
Bonsels, Volker—Deutsche Beteiligungs AG
Bonugli, Mauro—General Atlantic LLC
Book, John—Thomas Weisel Partners Group, Inc.
Bookbinder, David—Tandem Expansion Fund, Inc.
Booker, Charles—Advantage Capital Partners
Booker, Niall—HSBC Private Equity Middle East
Bookstein, Suzanne—RBC Dain Rauscher
Booma, Jason—Columbia Capital LLC
Boon, Emily—Blue Sage Capital, L.P.
Boon, Tan Keng—SEAVI Advent Corporation, Ltd.
Boon, Zachhaeus—McLean Watson Capital Inc.
Boone, Brigitte—Fortis Private Equity NV/SA (FKA: VIV NV)
Boorstein, Brian—Granite Creek Partners
Boot, Gijsbert Maarten—K+ Venture Partners
Boot, Gijsbert—JV Capital Management s.r.o.
Booth, Bruce—Atlas Venture, Ltd.
Booth, Darin—RBC Capital Partners/RBC Technology Ventures
Booth, James—Phoenix Equity Partners (FKA: DLJ European Private Equity)
Booth, Jeffrey—Morgan Stanley Private Equity
Booth, Michael—Calvert Street Capital Partners, Inc. (FKA: Legg Mason)
Booth, Ralph—Fontinalis Partners LLC
Booysen, Steve—Absa Capital Private Equity (Pty) Ltd.
Borcher, Christian—Cardinal Venture Capital
Borchers, Bob—Opus Capital
Borchers, John—Crescendo Venture Management LLC
Borchers, Juergen—CAM Private Equity Consulting & Verwaltungs - GmbH
Borchers, Juergen—Sal. Oppenheim Private Equity Partners
Borda, Guillermo—BAML Capital Access Funds
Bordeau, David—Berkshire Partners LLC
Bordeaux, Pierre—Siparex Group SAS
Borden, Philip—Riverside Partners
Borelli, Ralph—Club Auto Sport
Borer, John—Rodman & Renshaw LLC
Borg, Alex—NBGI Private Equity
Borgdorff, Wim—AlpInvest Partners N.V.
Borges, Joao Coelho—Magnum Capital Industrial Partners
Borho, Sven—OrbiMed Advisors LLC
Borie, Christian—ORKOS Capital
Boris, Lipkin—VantagePoint Venture Partners
Borjesson, Per—Investment AB Spiltan
Bork, Jeff—NAXS Nordic Access Buyout Fund AB
Bork, Michael—Barclays Private Equity, Ltd.
Borkar, Manoj—IL&FS Investment Managers Ltd (FKA: IL&FS Venture Corp)
Borkowski, Patricia—Invision Capital Management LLC
Born, Rob—Thomas Weisel Partners Group, Inc.
Born, Rob—Thomas Weisel Venture Partners
Bornhoeft, Dave—Silver Oak Management
Bornikoel, Friedrich—TVM Capital GmbH
Bornstein, Adam—Ymer Venture Capital Asia
Boro, Seth—Thoma Cressey Bravo
Boroian, Patrick—Brockway Moran & Partners, Inc.
Borok, Daniel—Millennium Technology Ventures
Borow, Elizabeth—Thompson Street Capital Partners
Borries, Johannes von—Wellington Partners Venture Capital GmbH
Borrows, Simon—GCP Capital Partners
Borsa, Roberto—Aksia Group SGR SpA
Bort, Randy—CoVestia Capital Partners
Bortz, Gregory—Creo Capital Partners, LLC
Borud, Brad—Highland Capital Management, L.P.
Bosch, Jeronimo—Pegasus Venture Capital
Bosch, Sake—Prime Technology Ventures NV
Bosch, Willem—Business Partners
Boschetto, Charles—MidOcean Partners
Bosela, Sandra—EdgeStone Capital Partners, Inc.
Boshkoff, Katharine—RB Webber & Company
Bosman, Eric—AlpInvest Partners N.V.
Boss, Andrew—Fulcrum Capital Partners, Ltd.
Bosselin, Felipe—Larrain Vial SA
Bosso, William—Nortia Capital Partners, Inc. (FKA: BF Acquisition Group I)
Bosson, Anthony—Atlantic-Pacific Capital, Inc.
Boswell, T. Andrew—Brockway Moran & Partners, Inc.
Boswell, Timothy—Sterling Partners
Bot, Theo—AlpInvest Partners N.V.
Both, Ludovic Edward—Aloe Private Equity
Botha, Christoff—Treacle Venture Partners
Botha, Roelof—Sequoia Capital
Bothway, Colin—Longbow Capital
Botman, Gijs—Mentha Capital BV
Botsford, Christopher—ADM Capital
Bottega, Christophe—Ixcore
Bottger, Craig—Investcorp Bank B.S.C.
Bottomley, Rick—Gilo Ventures
Bottorff, Dennis—Council Ventures
Bottorff, Jennifer—Council Ventures
Bottorff, Leslie—ONSET Ventures
Boucheron, Philippe—BioGestion S.A. (AKA: Bioam Gestion - Fonds Bioam)
Bouchez, Eric—PAI Partners (FKA: PAI Management)
Boudakian, Tom—WP Global Partners Inc.
Boudo, David—Metalmark Capital LLC
Boughner, Hank—H.I.G. Capital LLC
Boughton, Neil—European Equity Partners
Bougrov, Andrei—Interros Holding
Bouillier, Valerie—Initiative & Finance Investissement SA
Bouissou, Michel—BNP Paribas Private Equity SAS
Boulais, Wayne—Apex Venture Partners
Boulau, Jacques—Bretagne Participations
Boulay, Nicolas—I-Source Gestion
Boullion, Elliott—Murphree Venture Partners
Boulnois, Graham—SV Life Sciences Advisers
Bounds, Mark—Goense Bounds & Partners, LP
Bourbonnais, Andre—CPP Investment Board
Bourcereau, Jean—Ventech S.A.
Bourdelas, Olivier—Inocap S.A.
Bourgeois, Mark—Lehman Brothers, Inc.
Bourn, Jonathan—AAC Capital Partners
Bourne, Duncan—Wynnchurch Capital, Ltd.
Bourque, Janice—Hercules Technology Growth Capital, Inc.
Bourquin, Robert—Harbert Venture Partners
Bourret, Gerard—Ofivalmo (AKA : Omnium Financier De Valeurs Mobiliers)
Bousek, Helmut—Invest Equity Management Consulting GmbH
Bousquette, Kevin—GCP Capital Partners
Bouten, Jan—Aurora Funds, Inc.
Bouten, Pieter-Jan—GCP Capital Partners
Boutros-Ghali, Teymour—Monitor Venture Management, L.L.C.
Bouw, Paula—Plain Vanilla Investments BV
Bouwers, Ward—Halder Holdings BV
Bouyea, Lee—FreshTracks Capital
Bouyoux, Laurent—Aquiline Capital Partners
Bowden, Roger—Mount Yale Asset Management
Bowen, David—Ascend Venture Group LLC
Bowen, Louis—Asia Capital Management (ACM) Limited (AKA: ACL Asia Ltd)
Bower, Phillip—Unitas Capital Pte, Ltd.
Bowerman, Bonnie—Romspen Investment Corporation
Bowes, William—U.S. Venture Partners
Bowker, Neil—CORE Partners, Inc.
Bowles, Erskine—Carousel Capital Partners
Bowles, Guy—Ingenious Ventures
Bowley, Richard—Stafford Timberland, ltd.
Bowman, Tim—Bedford Capital
Boyacigiller, Ziya—Formative Ventures
Boyadjian, Olivier—H.I.G. Capital LLC
Boyano Martinez, Jose—Inverjaen S.C.R. SA
Boyazny, Maria—Siguler Guff & Company
Boyce, Dick—TPG Capital
Boyce, Jack—PineBridge Investments
Boyd, Cheryl—Chatham Capital
Boyd, Garry—Ethos Private Equity
Boyd, Jamie—Cascadia Capital LLC
Boyd, Liza—Constellation Ventures (AKA: Constellation Growth Capital)
Boyd, Parris—GarMark Partners
Boyd, Robert—Palm Beach Capital Partners
Boyer, Ben—Tenaya Capital (FKA: Lehman Brothers Venture Partners)
Boyle, Chris—CLSA Capital Partners (AKA: Credit Lyonnais Securities Asia)
Boyle, Richard—SunTx Capital Partners
Bozarth, Michael—Alumni Capital Network
Bozeman, Bob—Angel Investors, LP
Bozjak, Ivana—Global Finance SA
Bozyk, Robert—Krokus Private Equity Sp. z o.o.
Braccini, Giovanni—CAPITALIA Sofipa SGR (FKA: MCC Sofipa)
Brach, Matthew—CD Ventures, LLC
Brackett, David—GE Antares Capital Corporation
Brackett, Gregory—Caltius Equity Partners
Brackett, Gregory—Caltius Mezzanine
Brackett, Steven—Ironside Capital Group (FKA:Ironside Ventures LLC)
Bracklo, Marcus—Baigo Capital GmbH
Bradbury, Nicole—Renewal Partners
Braddock, Richard—MidOcean Partners
Bradford, Kyle—American Capital, Ltd.
Bradkin, Brandon—Park Square Capital, LLP

Bradley, David—Blackstone Group, L.P.
Bradley, Douglas—Westerkirk Capital, Inc.
Bradley, Sarah—Investcorp Bank B.S.C.
Bradley, Timothy—Gryphon Investors, Inc.
Bradley, Tom—DFJ Esprit
Bradley, Tom—DN Capital, Ltd. (FKA: Digital Networks Global Ventures)
Bradley, Wade—Empire Ventures
Bradley, William—Allen & Company
Bradlow, John—Penfund Partners, Inc.
Bradlow, Richard—Penfund Partners, Inc.
Bradshaw, Larry—Escalate Capital
Brady, Christopher—Chart Capital Management LLC
Brady, Pat—GrowthWorks
Brady, Todd—Domain Associates LLC
Brady-Estevez, Anna—Signal Lake
Brag, Fredrik—Draper Fisher Jurvetson ePlanet Ventures, L.P.
Braga, Pedro—DRIVE Sociedade de Capital de Risco, SA
Braginsky, Edward—TVM Capital GmbH
Braguglia, Diego—Venture Incubator AG (AKA: VI Partners AG)
Braguglia, Federico—Advanced Capital SGRpA
Brakeman, Ed—Bain Capital
Bram, Jonathan—Global Infrastructure Partners
Brambilla, Fabio—Advanced Capital SGRpA
Brambring, Dominik—Blackstone Group, L.P.
Bramley, Donald—Audax Group
Branagan, Kieron—ACT Venture Capital, Ltd.
Branch, Barrington—Nancy Creek Capital
Brand, Giles—EPIC Investment Partners (AKA: EPIC Private Equity)
Brand, Martin—Blackstone Group, L.P.
Brandely, Christopher—Siguler Guff & Company
Brandes, Benjamin—Avalon Equity Partners
Brandewie, Richard—Ballast Point Venture Partners
Brandhuber, Walter—Millennium Private Equity
Brandis, Dirk—Lead Equities GmbH
Brandkamp, Michael—High-Tech Gruenderfonds Management GmbH
Brandolini, Nuno—Scorpion Capital Partners, L.P.
Brandon, Henry—Vintage Capital Partners
Brandtzag, Svein Richard—Norsk Hydro ASA (AKA: Norsk Hydro Technology Ventures)
Brannan, Stan—Midwest Venture Alliance
Branson, Alan—ECD Investments LLC/ECD Investments BIDCO
Brasch, Sam—Frazier Healthcare and Technology Ventures
Brass, Jason—Goldner Hawn Johnson & Morrison, Inc.
Brasted, Patricia—Midwest Venture Alliance
Brath Ingero, Bard—Reiten & Co Strategic Investments AS
Brauer, Henry—Colony Capital LLC
Braun, Christoph—Acton Capital Partners GmbH
Braun, Christoph—Burda Digital Ventures GmbH
Braun, Hugo—North Coast Technology Investors, L.P.
Braun, Rebecca—JumpStart, Inc.
Braun, Rudiger—Freudenberg Venture Capital GmbH
Brauns, Ryan—American Capital, Ltd.
Bravo, Alain—Techfund Capital Europe Management SAS
Bravo, Orlando—Thoma Bravo LLC
Bravo, Orlando—Thoma Cressey Bravo
Brayton, Mary Ellen—Still River Fund, The
Breaux, Jason—WestBridge Ventures LLC
Breck, Peter—Rosewood Capital, L.P.
Breckenridge, James—Med Opportunity Partners LLC
Bredt, Thomas—Menlo Ventures
Breece, R. William—Crown Capital Corporation
Breen, John—CPP Investment Board
Breen, Michael—CFI Capital
Breen, Virginia—Sienna Ventures (FKA: Sienna Holdings Inc.)
Brege, Laura—Red Rock Ventures
Brehm, Michael—Target Partners GmbH
Breidert, Christoph—PONTIS Capital GmbH
Breiner, Klaus—Bellevue Asset Management AG
Breiter, Stephanie—RBK Hannover mbH & Co. KG
Breitman, Alan—Corporate Fuel Partners
Breitner, Cameron—CVC Capital Partners (Europe), Ltd.
Brekka, Richard—Dolphin Equity Partners
Brenan, Coley—KSL Capital Partners
Brennan, Daniel—Humphrey Enterprises, LLC
Brennan, John—Coates Myer & Co. Pty Ltd.
Brennan, John—Ontario Teachers' Pension Plan
Brennan, Katie—Thoma Cressey Bravo
Brennan, Len—Frank Russell Capital
Brennan, Mark—Quadrangle Group LLC
Brennan, Martin—Excalibur Fund Managers, Ltd.
Brennan, Matthew—Key Principal Partners LLC (AKA: KPP)
Brennan, Ryan—Advantage Capital Partners
Brennan, Stephen—Hamilton Lane Advisors, Inc.
Brenner, Hans—East West Capital Partners Pte, Ltd.
Brenner, Joel—Fireman Capital Partners
Brenner, Johan—Balderton Capital (FKA: Benchmark Capital Europe)
Brenner, Pablo—Prosperitas Capital Partners
Brenninkmeijer, Bernard—Bregal Investments
Brenninkmeijer, Wolter—Bregal Investments
Breslaur, Keith—Patron Capital, Ltd.
Bresler, Joshua—Thomas H. Lee Partners (AKA: TH Lee Partners)
Breslin, Adam—Penfund Partners, Inc.
Bressler, Richard—Thomas H. Lee Partners (AKA: TH Lee Partners)
Bressner, Glen—Mid-Atlantic Venture Funds (FKA: NEPA Management Corp.)
Brett, David—Adams Street Partners LLC
Breuer, Klemens—WestLB AG Equity Investments (AKA: Westdeutsche Landesbank)
Breuil, Claude—AVM Associati SpA
Breukelman, W. David—Business Arts, Ltd.
Breward, Alastair—Amadeus Capital Partners, Ltd.
Brewer, Sam—Merion Investment Partners, L.P.
Brewer, William—Yellowstone Capital, Inc.
Brewitt, Tony—Absa Capital Private Equity (Pty) Ltd.
Breyer, James—Accel Partners
Brian, Douglas—Eastward Capital
Briant, Kate—CapVest Management Ltd
Brice, John—CarVal Investors LLC
Brickman, Bruce—Brickman, Bruce S & Associates, Inc.
Brickman, C. Andrew—Baird Capital Partners
Bridge, Charles—Boston Capital Ventures
Bridge, Gary—Horsley Bridge Partners
Bridgers, William—Zon Capital Partners
Bridges, Paul—Alchemy Partners LLP
Briens, Sebastien—Quadrangle Group LLC
Briggs, Frank—C&B Capital
Briggs, Hugh—CVC Capital Partners (Europe), Ltd.
Briggs, Hugh—MidOcean Partners
Briggs, Mark—GESD Capital Partners, LLC
Briggs, Michael—Anchorage Capital Partners
Brightfield, Steven—CampVentures
Brilando, Joseph—RB Webber & Company
Brill, Robert—Newlight Associates
Brillon, Tim—Evergreen Pacific Partners LLC
Brimacomb, Richard—Sherpa Partners LLC
Brimacombe, John—Sussex Place Investment Management (SPIM), Ltd.
Briner, Brad—Morgan Creek Capital Management LLC
Bring, Kenneth—Berkshire Partners LLC
Brinkman, Roland—SL Capital Partners LLP
Brinkrolf, Andreas—Siemens Technology Accelerator (STA)
Brinkrolf, Andreas—TIBURON Partners AG
Brisbourne, Nic—DFJ Esprit
Briscoe, Zuri—Navigation Capital Partners
Briseno, Monica—MFC Capital Funding, Inc.
Brisse, Jacques—Synergie Finance Sobrepar
Bristol, Brian—W.R. Hambrecht & Co., LLC
Britain, Lane—Highland Capital Management, L.P.
Brito e Abreu, Frederico—Advent International
Britt, Chris—Marwit Capital, LLC
Britts, David—Fuse Capital
Brizius, Charles—Thomas H. Lee Partners (AKA: TH Lee Partners)
Bro Nielsen, Morten—Bio Fund Management Oy
Broadhurst, Austin—NGN Capital LLC
Broadwater, Robert—Veronis Suhler Stevenson (FKA: Veronis, Suhler & Associates)
Broberg, P. Christian—Clayton, Dubilier & Rice, Inc.
Broche, Richard—MBO Partenaires
Brock, Clay—Hadley Capital
Brock, Peter—EquiVest GmbH & Co
Brock-Wilson, Jane—Berkshire Partners LLC
Brockenhuus-Schack, Ulla—DTU Innovation A/S
Brockenhuus-Schack, Ulla—SEED Capital Denmark K/S
Brocklebank, James—Advent International
Brockman, Ivan—Blackstone Group, L.P.
Brockway, Peter—Brockway Moran & Partners, Inc.
Brockwell, Christine—Global Capital Finance
Brod, Jonathan—Next Wave Partners LLP
Broderick, Daniel—Prolog Ventures LLC
Broderick, James—Morgenthaler Ventures
Brodersen, Gunnar—LMX Business Development A/S
Brodlieb, Jeffrey—Centripetal Capital Partners, Inc.
Brodsky, Julian—Comcast Interactive Capital
Brodsky, Peter—HM Capital Partners LLC
Brody, Jeffrey—Brentwood Venture Capital
Brody, Jeffrey—Redpoint Ventures
Brody, Timothy—Auda Private Equity LLC
Broe-Andersen, Thomas—FSN Capital Partners AS
Broeker, Alexander—Trellis Partners
Broekhuizen, Neil—Ironbridge Capital Pty., Ltd.
Brogdon, Todd—Diamond State Ventures, L.P.
Broglio, Anthony—Lake Capital Partners, Inc.

Brokaw, Clifford—Corsair Capital LLC
Brokelmann, Katrin—PINOVA Capital GmbH
Broker, Neel—Sterling Partners
Brom, Ilona—Wilshire Private Markets
Bromberg, Mark—Maven Capital Management LLC
Bronckers, Maurice—AAC Capital Partners
Bronfin, Barry—Axiom Venture Partners, L.P.
Bronfin, Kenneth—Hearst Corporation
Bronfman, Edgar—Accretive LLC (FKA: Accretive Technology Partners LLC)
Bronfman, Matthew—ACI Capital Co., LLC
Bronfman, Samuel—Bacchus Capital Management LLC
Bronner, Beth—Mistral Equity Partners
Bronner, Maximilian—LGT Capital Partners AG
Bronner, Philip—Novak Biddle Venture Partners, L.P.
Bronstein, Ben—Zero Stage Capital Co., Inc.
Brook, Robert—E-Synergy
Brooke, Geoffrey—GBS Venture Partners, Ltd.
Brooke, Graham—CVC Asia Pacific, Ltd.
Brooke, Graham—CVC Capital Partners (Europe), Ltd.
Brooke, John—Brooke Private Equity Associates
Brooke, Stephen—Swarraton Partners Limited
Brooke, W. Anthony—JMH Capital
Brooke, William—Harbert Venture Partners
Brooks, Ben—Southern Capitol Ventures
Brooks, Erik—ABRY Partners LLC
Brooks, Jason—Invico Capital Corporation
Brooks, John—Prism VentureWorks
Brooks, Jonathan—Rutland Fund Management, Ltd. (AKA: Rutland Partners LLP)
Brooks, Leonard—Trenwith Securities LLC
Brooks, Mark—Scale Venture Partners
Brooks, Michelle—Weston Presidio (FKA: Weston Presidio Capital Management)
Brooks, Peter—LDC (FKA: Lloyds TSB Development Capital, Ltd.)
Brooks, Peter—Pi Capital
Brooks, Robert—American Capital, Ltd.
Brooks, Rory—MML Capital Partners
Brooks, Simon—European Investment Bank, The (AKA: EIB)
Brooks, Stephen—J.F. Lehman & Company
Brooks, Steven—Brooks, Houghton & Company, Inc.
Brookshire, Mike—River Associates, LLC
Broomberg, Ashley—Matrix Private Equity Partners LLP
Broomhead, Steven—North West Development Agency
Broooks, Michael—Venrock Associates
Brophy, Kevin—Meidlinger Partners LLC
Brosnan, Denis—Lydian Capital Advisors S.A.
Bross, Jason—Argon Venture Partners
Brossier, Amelie—Cinven, Ltd.
Brotman, Stephen—GCP Capital Partners
Brotman, Stephen—Greenhill SAVP
Brotzge, Lawrence—Robin Hood Ventures
Brougham, Robert—Newstone Capital Partners
Broun, Jean Michel—Baring Vostok Capital Partners
Brous, Michael—Jerusalem Global Ventures
Brown, Amy—RiverRock Holdings LLC
Brown, Crichton—Advantage Capital Partners
Brown, Cyrus—Winthrop, Brown & Company, Inc. (DBA: Winthrop Ventures)
Brown, Dave—GCP Capital Partners
Brown, David—Oak Hill Venture Partners (OHVP)
Brown, David—Richardson Capital Limited
Brown, David—TechStars
Brown, Douglas—DLB Capital LLC
Brown, Douglas—ZS Fund L.P.
Brown, Grant—Covington Capital Corporation (FKA: C.I. Covington Fund)
Brown, Ian—Raymond James, Ltd.
Brown, J. David—Jemison Investments
Brown, James—SCP Private Equity Partners
Brown, James—TH Lee Putnam Ventures, L.P.
Brown, Janet—Scottish Enterprise
Brown, Jason—Thomas, McNerney & Partners LLC
Brown, Jeff—Forrest Binkley & Brown
Brown, Jerry—Osprey Ventures, L.P.
Brown, Ken—One Equity Partners (FKA: Banc One Venture Partners)
Brown, Kevin—ARC Financial Corporation
Brown, Kevin—Court Square Capital Partners
Brown, Kevin—Reed Elsevier Ventures
Brown, Leslie—Huntsman Gay Global Capital LLC
Brown, Malcolm—Climate Change Capital, Ltd.
Brown, Maud—Investcorp Bank B.S.C.
Brown, Michael—Battery Ventures, L.P.
Brown, Mike—Foundation Capital
Brown, Nathaniel—Wind Point Partners
Brown, Nick—PineBridge Investments
Brown, Pauline—Carlyle Group, The
Brown, Randolph—Brentwood Associates
Brown, Robert—Advent International
Brown, Robert—Catalyst Equity Group LLC
Brown, Robert—Encore Consumer Capital LLC
Brown, Robert—Meridian Venture Partners (MVP)
Brown, Ryan—Quadrangle Group LLC
Brown, Scott—New Energy Capital Corporation
Brown, Simon—Cognetas LLP
Brown, Sonya—Summit Partners
Brown, Steven—Code, Hennessy & Simmons LLC
Brown, Tim—Alta Berkeley Venture Partners
Brown, Timothy—Halyard Partners
Brown, William—Whitecliff Capital Partners
Browne, David—Compass Group International LLC, The
Browne, David—Marwit Capital, LLC
Brownell, Robert—Emergent Medical Ventures, LLP
Brownstein, Chad—ITU Ventures
Brownstein, Linda—Footprint Ventures
Brownstein, Neill—Footprint Ventures
Broyhill, Hunt—CapitalSouth Partners, L.L.C.
Broyles, Douglas—Huntington Ventures
Bru, Jean-Francois—CDC Innovation SAS (FKA: CDC IXIS Innovation)
Brubaker, Patrick—Alta Communications
Brucato, C.J.—ABRY Partners LLC
Bruce, Alastair—Pantheon Ventures, Ltd.
Bruck, Michael—ARC China, Inc.
Bruck, Michael—Tripod Capital International, Ltd.
Bruckmann, Bruce—Bruckmann, Rosser, Sherrill & Co.
Bruckner, Zoltan—Primus Capital Partners LLC
Bruens, Richard—Renaissance Capital
Bruix, Cedric—Argos Soditic SA
Brumfield, Bruce—Finistere Ventures LLC
Brumm, Peter—Sigma Capital Management
Bruning, Christian—Gresham LLP
Brunk, Gerry—Lumira Capital Corporation.
Bruno, Michael—Stonebridge Partners
Brusco, Martin—Azure Capital Partners
Bruss, Adam—Biltmore Ventures, L.P.
Brutocao, Brad—Freeman Spogli & Co.
Bruzzese, Kayla—Small Ventures USA, L.P.
Bruzzichesi, Leonardo—Private Equity Partners SpA
Bryant, Colin—Paladin Capital Management LLC
Bryant, R. Kenneth—RLJ Equity Partners LLC
Bryant, Richard—Dar Capital (UK), Ltd.
Bryant, Robert—Roark Capital Group
Bryant, Scott—Pine Creek Partners
Bryant, Vernon—TGF Management Corp (FKA:Texas Growth Fund)
Bryant, William—Draper Fisher Jurvetson
Bryson, Nancy—Evercore Partners
Brzezinski, Roberta—Abris Capital Partners
Buarque de Almeida, Eduardo Augusto—TMG Capital Partners Ltd.
Buatois, Eric—Sofinnova Ventures
Bublitz, Axel—DKB Wagniskapital Unternehmensbeteiligungsgesellschaft mbH
Bublitz, Axel—MVC Unternehmensbeteiligungsgesellschaft mbH (AKA: MVC GmbH)
Bubnack, Tim—Huntington Capital
Buch, Wally—Atherton Venture Partners, LLC
Buch, Wally—MedVenture Associates
Buchanan, Cameron—CHAMP Private Equity Pty Ltd.
Buchanan, Doug—Granite Partners Corporation
Buchanan, Gordon—Sciens Capital Partners (FKA: Zilkha Venture Partners)
Buchanan, H. Lee—Paladin Capital Management LLC
Buchanan, Stephen—Dogwood Equity
Buchanan, William—Lazard Capital Partners
Bucher, Philippe—Adveq Management AG
Bucher, Rudiger—Investitions- und Strukturbank Rheinland-Pfalz (ISB) GmbH
Buchet, Jean-Marc—NCI Gestion
Buchheim, Constanze—Team Europe Ventures Management GmbH
Buchholtz, Andrew—Veronis Suhler Stevenson (FKA: Veronis, Suhler & Associates)
Buchignani, Michele—CIBC Capital Partners
Buchler, George—Shamrock Holdings, Inc.
Buchwald, Adam—Carlyle Group, The
Buckalew, Jeffrey—GCP Capital Partners
Buckanavage, Richard—Patriot Capital Funding, Inc. (AKA: Patriot Capital)
Buckeridge, Roger—Allen & Buckeridge Pty, Ltd.
Buckland, Michael—Genesis Campus, L.P.
Buckland, Michael—Mobility Ventures
Buckle, Chris—Mezzanine Management Finanz- und Unternehmensberatungs GmbH
Buckley, Jennifer—Private Advisors LLC
Buckley, Julian—Unitas Capital Pte, Ltd.
Buckley, Matthew—Arlington Capital Partners
Buckley, Mike—Intel Capital
Buckley, Steven—Innova Capital
Buckner, Karen—MK Capital
Bucknor, J.Kofi—Kingdom Zephyr Africa Management (AKA: KZAM)
Bucknor, J.Kofi—Zephyr Management, L.P.
Budge, Duncan—RIT Capital Partners plc
Budgen, Lisa—NSBI Venture Capital

Budin, Ethan—Flexpoint Ford (FKA: Flexpoint Partners LLC)
Budinscak, Kyle—Summit Partners
Budnick, Victor—Ironwood Capital (AKA: Ironwood Capital Advisors LLC)
Budoff, Scott—Saw Mill Capital, LLC
Budzynski, James—BrightPath Capital, Inc.
Buechele, Alice—Madison Capital Partners
Buehler, Alan—Sevin Rosen Funds
Buehlmann, Beat—Horizon 21 Private Equity
Buenneke, Brian—Pantheon Ventures, Ltd.
Buenter, Andreas—VenGrow Corporate Finance AG
Buerk, Arthur—Montlake Capital
Buettell, Ben—Houlihan, Lokey, Howard & Zukin
Buettner, Jan—BV Capital (FKA: Bertelsmann Ventures, LP)
Buettner, Karl—Gatehouse Ventures, L.P.
Buffa, Anthony—Endeavor Capital Management
Buffington, Mark—Buckhead Investment Partners LLC
Bugas, J. Andrew—Radar Partners
Bugge Norman Pran, Adele—Herkules Capital AS
Buhl, W. Peter—BlueRun Ventures
Buhler, Frank—Zachary Scott & Co.
Bujake, Bill—American Capital, Ltd.
Bujnowski, Dave—Coburn Ventures, LLC
Bulavin, Sergey—SigmaBleyzer
Bulkin, Bernard—VantagePoint Venture Partners
Bull, David—Archer Capital
Bullitt, Christian—LLR Partners, Inc.
Bulloch, Roger—SPB Capital Partners, L.P.
Bullock, D. Fraser—Sorenson Capital Partners
Bullock, Francis—PureTech Ventures
Bullock, John—Windspeed Ventures
Bulmer, Patrick—AAC Capital Partners
Bultot, H—Sopartec SA (AKA: Vives)
Bultynck, Hector—Peninsula Capital Partners LLC
Bund, Ian—Innovation Capital Associates Pty, Ltd.
Bunker, Anthony—Triginta Capital Partners GmbH (FKA: Avida Equity Partners)
Bunker, Brian—Riverside Company
Bunting, Eric—Gilbert Global Equity Capital, L.L.C.
Bunting, Martin—CORE Partners, Inc.
Bunting, Stephen—Abingworth Management, Ltd.
Bunting, Tim—Balderton Capital (FKA: Benchmark Capital Europe)
Bunting, William—Thomas Weisel Partners Group, Inc.
Buonanno, Bernie—Nautic Partners LLC
Buono, Thomas—BIA Digital Partners, L.P.
Buotros, Naji—Colony Capital LLC
Buoymaster, John—Hall Capital Partners LLC (FKA: Offit Hall Capital Mgmt)
Buranakanonda, Anusorn—Aureos Capital, Ltd.
Burch, Lucius—Massey Burch Capital Corp.
Burch, Mark—ARCIS Finance SA
Burchardt, Michael—Mittelstaendische Beteiligungsgesellschaft Thueringen mbH
Burchill, Thomas—Silverfern Group, Inc., The
Burciaga, Gil—Accent Capital
Burd, John—Windamere Venture Partners, LLC
Burdel, Sebastien—Coller Capital
Burden, Bryan—Boxwood Capital Partners, LLC
Burden, Justin—Industry Ventures
Bureau, Paul—Venquest Capital Partners
Burgel, Oliver—Babson Capital Europe
Burger, Andre—CRP (AKA: Companhia de Participacoes)
Burger, Bill—Formative Ventures
Burger, Nick—ZS Fund L.P.
Burger, Thomas—RFE Investment Partners
Burgermeister, Patrick—BioMedPartners
Burgers, Gerard—NIBC Principal Investments (FKA: Parnib Holding NV)
Burgess, Andrew—Carlyle Group, The
Burgess, Bill—ABS Ventures
Burgess, Elizabeth—Altus Capital Partners
Burgess, Eve—Starfish Ventures Pty., Ltd.
Burgess, Trevor—Lime Rock Partners LLC
Burgett, Mark—Wind Point Partners
Burgis, Jeffery—Adams Street Partners LLC
Burgstahler, David—Avista Capital Holdings, L.P.
Burgum, James—Arthur Ventures
Burkart, Frazer—Carlyle Group, The
Burke, James—Formative Ventures
Burke, James—Stonington Partners, Inc.
Burke, John—True Ventures
Burke, Patrick—Change Capital Partners LLP
Burke, Richard—Jefferies Group, Inc.
Burke, Rugger—Satori Capital LLC
Burke, Tim—Rosewood Capital, L.P.
Burkett, Catharine—Camden Partners, Inc. (FKA: Cahill, Warnock & Co. LLC)
Burkett, J. Doyl—Aurora Capital Group (FKA: Aurora Capital Partners)
Burkey, Marcia—TeleSoft Partners
Burkhardt, C.A.—HT Capital Advisors LLC
Burkhardt, Daniel—Oakwood Medical Investors
Burkhart, Charles—Rosemont Investment Partners LLC
Burkinshaw, Brian—Path4 Ventures, LLC
Burkle, Ronald—Yucaipa Companies LLC, The
Burman, Bob—UPS Strategic Enterprise Fund
Burman, Gaurav—Promethean Investments
Burman, Gaurav—Wall Street Technology Partners
Burnes, Richard—Charles River Ventures
Burnette, Graham—Astrolabe Ventures
Burnette, Graham—SBV Venture Partners
Burnham, Ciara—Evercore Partners
Burnham, R. Bradford—Union Square Ventures
Burns, Brian—Grayhawk Capital
Burns, David—GCP Capital Partners
Burns, David—Phoenix Equity Partners (FKA: DLJ European Private Equity)
Burns, Edward—Emigrant Capital
Burns, John—Highland Capital Partners LLC
Burns, Kenneth—Siguler Guff & Company
Burns, Kevin—TPG Capital
Burns, M. Roy—TA Associates, Inc.
Burns, Mark—Vesbridge Partners, LLC
Burns, Mary—Wayzata Investment Partners
Burns, Michael—Guggenheim Venture Partners LLC
Burns, Phillip—Terra Firma Capital Partners, Ltd.
Burns, Stephen—Quad-C Management, Inc.
Burow, Kristina—ARCH Venture Partners
Burr, James—Carlyle Group, The
Burri, Scott—Huntington Ventures
Burrill, G. Steven—Burrill & Company
Burrows, David—First Associates Investments, Inc.
Burrows, Lee—VantagePoint Venture Partners
Bursky, Andrew—Atlas Holdings FRM LLC
Burson, Craig—H.I.G. Capital LLC
Burstein, Daniel—Millennium Technology Ventures
Burt, Katrin—Intersouth Partners
Burt, Michael—Promethean Investments
Burton, Andrew—Viking Fund, The
Burton, David—Haynes and Boone LLC
Burton, Donald—Ballast Point Venture Partners
Burton, John—Updata Partners
Burton, Mark—Evercore Partners
Bury, Christopher—Jefferies Group, Inc.
Busby, Christopher—Great Hill Equity Partners LLC
Busch, Brady—American Capital, Ltd.
Busch, Clemens—Steadfast Capital GmbH (FKA: BHF Private Equity GmbH)
Busch, Jeremy—Huron Capital Partners LLC
Busch, Jeremy—TorQuest Partners, Inc.
Buschmann, Mark—Blackstone Group, L.P.
Buschmann, Scott—Arcapita, Inc.
Buser, Curt—Carlyle Group, The
Buser, John—NB Alternatives - Fund of Funds
Bush, Marvin—Winston Partners
Bush, Michael—New River Capital Partners
Bush, William—Bush O'Donnell Capital Partners
Bushery, Glen—Falconhead Capital (FKA: Sports Capital Partners)
Bushner, Erica—GKM Newport Generation Funds
Busscher, Brad—Mesirow Private Equity Investments, Inc.
Busser, Andrew—Symphony Capital LLC
Bussgang, Jeffrey—Flybridge Capital Partners
Bussman, David—Asia Mezzanine Capital Advisers, Ltd.
Butalid, Modesto—Small Business Guarantee and Finance Corporation
Butkevich, Katherine—Emigrant Capital
Butler, David—Jordan Company, The
Butler, Duncan—Centennial Ventures
Butler, Michael—Cascadia Capital LLC
Butler, Ryan—Portfolio Advisors LLC
Butler, Sarah—Infinity Asset Management LLP
Butt, John—Conduit Ventures Limited
Button, Scott—Venture Investors LLC
Buyle, Johan—AlpInvest Partners N.V.
Buyon, Ethan—CRG Partners
Buyse, Steven—CVC Capital Partners (Europe), Ltd.
Buzik, Alexander—MTS Health Partners, L.P.
Bybee, Clinton—ARCH Venture Partners
Bye, Mark—Morgan Stanley Private Equity
Byers, Brett—VCFA Group
Byers, Brook—Kleiner Perkins Caufield & Byers
Bylin, Jonathan—Carlyle Group, The
Bynum, Frank—Kelso & Company
Byrd, Andrew—Andrew W. Byrd & Co. LLC
Byrd, Lewis—Opportunity Capital Partners
Byrne, Sara—Bessemer Venture Partners
Byrne, Stephen—Vitruvian Partners LLP
Byrne, Thomas—New River Capital Partners
Byrne, Thomas—Pfingsten Partners, L.P.
Byrnes, John—Mason Wells Private Equity (FKA: M&I Ventures)
Byrom, J. Thomas—Belvedere Capital Partners LLC
Byun, Bill—Samsung Venture Investment Corporation (SVIC)
Byunn, Eric—FTV Capital (FKA: FTVentures)
Caballero, Lou—Bison Capital Asset Management LLC
Cabes, Robert—Avista Capital Holdings, L.P.

Cabessa, Sydney—CIC Finance SA
Cable, J. Franklin—Obsidian Finance Group LLC
Cabo, Daniel—Care Capital, LLC
Cabral, Paul—Hampshire Equity Partners (FKA: ING Equity Partners)
Cabrera, Marcio—MBF Healthcare Partners L.P.
Caccavo, James—Valence Capital Management, LP
Cacci, Ralph—Relativity Capital LLC
Cadeddu, John—Duff Ackerman & Goodrich LLC (AKA: DAG Ventures)
Cader, Ainadin—Aureos Capital, Ltd.
Cadogan, William—Vesbridge Partners, LLC
Cahane, Olivier—CAP ISF SA
Cahill, Dan—Constitution Capital Partners, LLC
Cahill, Dan—SL Capital Partners LLP
Cahill, Edward—HLM Venture Partners
Cahr, Michael—Focus Equity Partners, LLC
Cai, Dajian—Shenzhen GTJA Investment Group Co., Ltd.
Cai, Leo—Kunwu Jiuding Capital Co., Ltd.
Cai, Ming-Po—Cathay Capital Private Equity SAS
Cai, Xiaoyun—Dojane Capital
Caillaux, Gabriel—General Atlantic LLC
Cain, Daniel—Health Enterprise Partners (AKA: HEP Fund)
Cain, Tom—SAIL Venture Partners
Caine, Shlomo—Jerusalem Global Ventures
Cairns, Alistair—Smedvig Capital, Ltd. (FKA: Peder Smedvig Capital Ltd)
Cairns, Niall—Kestrel Capital (FKA: Nanyang Ventures Pty., Ltd.)
Cairns, Patrick—Grotech Ventures
Cairo, Alberto—CapVest Management Ltd
Cairo, Emanuele—Barclays Private Equity, Ltd.
Cakala, Artur—NFI Management Sp. z o.o. (AKA: Grupa CA-IB)
Calcagno, Jeff—Scale Venture Partners
Caldbeck, Justin—Bain Capital Ventures
Caldbeck, Ryan—Encore Consumer Capital LLC
Caldeira, Paulo—Citi Venture Capital International
Calder, David—Penta Capital LLP (FKA: Penta Capital Partners, Ltd.)
Calder, Donald—G.L. Ohrstrom & Co., Inc. (AKA: GLO & Co.)
Calderbank, Martin—Stirling Square Capital Partners
Calderini, Mario—Finpiemonte SpA
Calderon, Jorge—iNova Capital SCR SA
Calhoun, Hal—Menlo Ventures
Calhoun, Jeffrey—Tailwind Capital Partners
Calhoun, Jeffrey—Thomas Weisel Partners Group, Inc.
Calibeo, Thomas—Eureka Growth Capital
Calice, Matthias—TPG Capital
Caliento, Paul—Clearview Capital LLC
Calise, Gianluca—Alcedo SGR SpA
Calissendorff, Percy—Segulah Advisor AB
Callaghan, Jon—True Ventures
Callaghan, Kevin—Berkshire Partners LLC
Callaghan, Mark—Andlinger & Company, Inc.
Callagy, J. Morgan—Veronis Suhler Stevenson (FKA: Veronis, Suhler & Associates)
Callahan, Cecil—Southern Africa Enterprise Development Fund, The (SAEDF)
Callahan, Ed—Momentum Technology Partners LLC
Callahan, Kevin—Adams Street Partners LLC
Callahan, Kevin—Century Capital Management, Inc.
Callahan, Morris—Biltmore Ventures, L.P.
Callahan, Robert—Catterton Partners
Callahan, Thomas—Lincolnshire Management, Inc.
Callaway, Thomas—Georgia Venture Partners LLC
Callerstrom, Caspar—EQT Funds management Limited
Callow, A. Dana—Boston Millennia Partners
Calmels, Didier—Developpement & Partenariat SAS
Caluori, David—Welsh, Carson, Anderson & Stowe
Calvet, Jorge—iNova Capital SCR SA
Calvey, Michael—BPEP International
Calvey, Mike—Baring Vostok Capital Partners
Camaggi, Alberto—R&D Advisory
Camenzind, Pia—Illuminate Ventures
Camenzind, Pia—Startup Capital Ventures L.P.
Cameron, Charles—DFJ Esprit
Cameron, Dennis—Eastward Capital
Cameron, Hamish—SV Life Sciences Advisers
Cameron, Hazel—Cross Atlantic Capital Partners
Cameron, Mark—Global Emerging Markets
Cameroni, Alessandro—Vegagest Sgr
Camp III, John—Lincolnshire Management, Inc.
Camp, Elizabeth Varley—HealthpointCapital LLC
Camp, Jerome—CampVentures
Camp, John—Southfield Capital Advisors
Camp, Justin—CampVentures
Camp, Keith—Lone Star Investment Advisors (AKA: Lewis Hollingsworth LP)
Camp, Philip—Shattuck Hammond Partners
Campbell, Brent—Madison Capital Partners
Campbell, Bruce—Ken Fowler Enterprises, Ltd.
Campbell, Bruce—Stanford Investment Group
Campbell, Dave—Costella Kirsch, Inc.
Campbell, David—Capital for Enterprise, Ltd.
Campbell, David—TXU Energy Corporation
Campbell, Doug—Resilience Capital Partners LLC
Campbell, Gordon—TechFarm Ventures (AKA:TechFund Capital)
Campbell, Gordon—TechFund Capital
Campbell, Gregory—Lone Star Investment Advisors (AKA: Lewis Hollingsworth LP)
Campbell, Jason—American Capital, Ltd.
Campbell, Kevin—Greenspring Associates, Inc.
Campbell, Mary—EDF Ventures
Campbell, Neil—Endeavour Capital, Ltd.
Campbell, Peter—Generation Capital Partners
Campbell, Thomas—DC Capital Partners LLC
Campbell, Thomas—Veritas Capital
Campe, Stephen—Investor Growth Capital AB
Campe, Stephen—Investor Growth Capital, Inc.
Campin, Richard—Exponent Private Equity LLP (FKA: Square Capital Management)
Campion, Jay—Access Venture Partners
Campion, Thomas—Merit Capital Partners (FKA:William Blair Mezzanine)
Campolo, Giovanni—Private Equity Partners SpA
Campolo, Joseph—Arbor Private Investment Company, LLC
Camposano, Felipe—Austral Capital
Camus, Philippe—Evercore Partners
Can, Stephen—Credit Suisse Private Equity
Canann, Brian—Carlyle Group, The
Canarick, Jonathan—North Castle Partners
Canderle, Sebastien—GMT Communications Partners LLP
Canellas, Marcelo—GED Group
Canfield, Philip—GTCR Golder Rauner LLC
Canin, Jeff—eFund, LLC
Cannestra, Tony—IGNITE Group, The (AKA: Ignite Associates, LLC)
Canning, Paul—H.I.G. Capital LLC
Canning, Tony—Lion Capital Advisers Ltd (FKA: Lion Capital Partners Plc)
Cantell, Aaro—Fenno Management Oy
Cantu, James—GTCR Golder Rauner LLC
Cantwell, Andrew—Norwest Equity Partners
Cantwell, Sean—Volition Capital
Cantwell, Wayne—Crescendo Venture Management LLC
Canty, Ed—Band of Angels
Cao, Catherine—LESS Limited
Cao, Qirui—Tsing Capital
Cao, Ron—Lightspeed Venture Partners (FKA: Weiss, Peck & Greer)
Cao, Sheng—Huinong Capital
Capart, Gilles—Sopartec SA (AKA: Vives)
Caplain, Jason—Southern Capitol Ventures
Caplan, Kenneth—Blackstone Group, L.P.
Caple, John—Comvest Investment Partners
Cappellari, John—Brooks, Houghton & Company, Inc.
Cappello, Alexander—Cappello Capital Corp.
Capperella, John—American Capital, Ltd.
Capriglione, Giovanni—Pacesetter Capital Group (FKA: MESBIC Ventures Holding Co.)
Caprioli, Brian—Vexiom Equity Partners, L.P.
Capsay, Terry—Madison Capital Funding LLC (AKA: Madison Capital)
Caputo, Paulo Sergio—DML Invista
Carano, Bandel—Oak Investment Partners
Carballo, Juan-Antonio—Argon Venture Partners
Carbery, Paul—Frontenac Company
Carbo, Carlos—Nazca Capital SGECR SA
Carbonara, Peter—Jordan Company, The
Carbone, Paul—Baird Venture Partners
Carbonell, Joan—Catalana D'Iniciatives CR SA
Carbonetti, Lidia—BS Private Equity SpA (FKA: B&S Private Equity Group)
Cardini, Filippo—TowerBrook Capital Partners L.P.
Cardito, Michael—Harvest Partners LLC
Cardwell, Jack—Blue Sage Capital, L.P.
Cardy, Roland—Raymond James, Ltd.
Carendi, Per—SLS Invest AB
Carey, Bryan—Vestar Capital Partners, Inc.
Carey, Chris—American Capital, Ltd.
Carey, Ray—Azure Capital Partners
Carifa, John—AllianceBernstein L.P. (FKA: Alliance Capital Management)
Caringi, Anthony—Merion Investment Partners, L.P.
Carlberg, Erik—Alta Growth Capital
Carlberg, Erik—BPEP International
Carlbom, Lars—PEQ AB
Carlborg, W. Eric—August Capital Management
Carles, Alexander—Wellspring Capital Management LLC
Carleton, William—Spangler Ventures, LLC
Carlick, David—Rho Capital Partners, Inc.
Carlisle, Douglas—Menlo Ventures
Carlisle, Greg—Gefinor Ventures
Carlisle, James—Thomas H. Lee Partners (AKA: TH Lee Partners)

Catania, Bruce—Citi Venture Capital International
Catapano, Salvatore—Investindustrial Partners, Ltd.
Cater, Todd—Global Environment Fund Management Corporation
Catherman, Gary—Kurt Salmon Associates Capital Advisors
Catoire, Stephan—Equitis
Cattaneo, Valerio—Finpiemonte SpA
Cattani, Emmy—VMG Equity Partners
Cattaruzza, Giovanna—Advanced Capital SGRpA
Catterall, Peter—Cinven, Ltd.
Cattet, Romain—Houlihan, Lokey, Howard & Zukin
Caudle, Gavin—RimAsia Capital Partners
Caufield, Frank—Darwin Ventures LLC
Caulier, Thibaud—H.I.G. Capital LLC
Caupers, Ricardo—Palamon Capital Partners (FKA: Amphion Capital Partners)
Causgrove, Tanya—ARC Financial Corporation
Cavalier, John—Hudson Capital Management, L.P.
Cavanaugh, James—HealthCare Ventures LLC
Cavanaugh, Michael—Resilience Capital Partners LLC
Cavanaugh, Wayne—KRG Capital Partners LLC
Cavanna, Andrew—Vestar Capital Partners, Inc.
Cave, Philip—Anchorage Capital Partners
Cavusoglu, Murat—Actera Group
Cayce, Brian—Gray Ghost Ventures
Cayer, Nicholas—Great Hill Equity Partners LLC
Cayrol, Bertrand—T2C2 Capital
Cazabon, Charles—Business Development Bank of Canada
Cazan, Emil—SIF - Banat - Crisana SA
Cebik, Erik—Slavia Capital
Cebula, Vincent—Oaktree Capital Management LLC
Ceccato, Enrico—Orlando Capital Management GmbH
Celestin, Thierry—Activa Capital SAS
Celestin, Thierry—Cinven, Ltd.
Celier, Nicolas—Alven Capital Partners SA
Cenanovic, Bogdan—TorQuest Partners, Inc.
Centelles, Enrique—GED Group
Centerman, Jorgen—Segulah Advisor AB
Centrella, Michael—Momentum Technology Partners LLC
Cerdeiras, Ramon—Inversiones Ibersuizas S.A.
Cerf, Monty—J.P. Morgan Capital Corporation
Cerrudo, Shirley—Novus Ventures
Cerullo, Bruce—SV Life Sciences Advisers
Cerullo, Michael—American Capital, Ltd.
Cervin, Johan—Altor Equity Partners AB
Cervone, Margarita—MTS Health Partners, L.P.
Cesare, James—Point Lookout Capital Partners, L.P.
Cesarek, Tim—Koch Genesis LLC
Cesarz, Joseph—Lakeview Equity Partners, LLC
Cesnavicius, Martynas—Firebird Management LLC
Cetingok, Alper—Morgan Keegan Merchant Banking
Ceva, Valerie—Homeland Defense Ventures
Cha, Albert—Vivo Ventures
Cha, Johnson—Charter Venture Capital (AKA: Charter Ventures)
Chabanel, Michel—Pragma Capital
Chabra, Roger—Rho Capital Partners, Inc.
Chabran, Mathieu—TR Advisors, Ltd.
Chace, Jayne—MTI Partners, Ltd.
Chaddha, Navin—Mayfield Fund
Chadehumbe, Wellington—Undisclosed Firm
Chadha, Sumir—Sequoia Capital India (FKA: WestBridge Capital Partners)
Chadwick, John—Claritas Capital LLC
Chae, DooSeok—LB Investment, Inc.
Chae, Michael—Blackstone Group, L.P.
Chae, Yoon—Isu Venture Capital Co., Ltd. (FKA: Peta Capital)
Chaffee, Darren McKenzie—CoBe Capital LLC
Chaffee, Todd—Institutional Venture Partners
Chaffin, Tracey—Pamlico Capital
Chagan, Matthew—Trident Capital
Chai, Nelson—Merrill Lynch Capital Partners
Chaikin, Chip—Blue Point Capital Partners (FKA: Key Equity Capital)
Chait, Jonathan—Dace Ventures
Chaiyakool, Patamaporn—Khao Kla Venture Capital Management Co., Ltd.
Chak, Ranjan—Oak Investment Partners
Chakrabarty, Sanjay—Columbia Capital LLC
Chakravarthy, Rohini—New Enterprise Associates, Inc.
Chalfen, Mike—Advent Venture Partners LLP
Chalk, Gilbert—BPEP International
Chalstrom, Brownell—Avansis Ventures, LLC
Cham, James—Bessemer Venture Partners
Chamberlain, Alex—Investeco Capital Corporation
Chamberlain, Grant—Shattuck Hammond Partners
Chambers, Brian—Beecken, Petty & Company LLC
Chambers, Dewey—Emergence Capital Partners LLC
Chambers, Dewey—Vector Capital
Chambers, Jeffrey—TA Associates, Inc.
Chambers, Robert—Roark Capital Group
Chambon, Philippe—New Leaf Venture Partners LLC
Chamboredon, Jean-David—DFJ Esprit
Chambriard, Oliver—Wendel
Chambriard, Olivier—Wendel
Chameh, Sidney—Decisao Gestao Financeira (AKA: DGF Investimentos)
Champenois, Denis—Innovacom SA
Champion, Richard—New York Business Development Corporation
Champsi, Farah—Alta Partners
Chan, Alan—7bridge Capital Partners, Ltd.
Chan, Alice—Carlyle Group, The
Chan, Eric—CITIC Capital Partners, Ltd.
Chan, Garrett—C.M. Capital Corporation
Chan, Harold—SEAVI Advent Corporation, Ltd.
Chan, Jackson—Hamilton Lane Advisors, Inc.
Chan, Johnny—Crosby Capital, Ltd.
Chan, Joseph—CID Group, The
Chan, KK—Climate Change Capital, Ltd.
Chan, Lily—Bio*One Capital
Chan, Lisa—Investor Growth Capital AB
Chan, Peter—BPEP International
Chan, Peter—Crest Capital Partners
Chan, Phillip—New Jersey Technology Council (AKA: NJTC)
Chan, Stanley Pui-Ling—McLean Watson Capital Inc.
Chan, Timothy—Phillip Private Equity Pte, Ltd. (FKA: ECICS Mgt. Pte, Ltd.)
Chan, Trevor—STIC Investments, Inc.
Chand, Sohil—Norwest Venture Partners
Chander, Satish—India Value Fund Advisors Private Ltd. (FKA: GW Capital)
Chandiramani, Sunil—Symphony Asia Holdings Pte. Ltd.
Chandler, David—Chicago Growth Partners (William Blair Capital Partners)
Chandler, Edward—Portage Venture Partners (AKA: Graystone Venture Partners)
Chandna, Asheem—Greylock Partners
Chandra, Amit—Bain Capital
Chandra, Anurag—Lighthouse Capital Partners
Chandra, Praveena—IndiaCo Ventures, Ltd.
Chandra, Rob—Bessemer Venture Partners
Chandran, Shankar—Panorama Capital
Chandrasekaran, Nathan—TZP Group LLC
Chandrasekaran, S—Crossover Advisors Pvt., Ltd. (FKA: Meta Crossover Advisors)
Chang, Andrew—New Mountain Capital LLC
Chang, Andy—STIC Investments, Inc.
Chang, Anthony—TL Ventures
Chang, Ben—Hotung International Company, Ltd.
Chang, Catherine—Carlyle Group, The
Chang, Dongshik—L&S Venture Capital Corporation
Chang, Edward—CIDC Consultants, Inc. (AKA: China Investment & Development)
Chang, Freemand—Sunsino Ventures Group (FKA: Sunsino Development Associate)
Chang, Herbert—InveStar Capital, Inc.
Chang, Herman—Carlyle Group, The
Chang, Ivan—ARC China, Inc.
Chang, James—Newbridge Capital, Ltd.
Chang, Julia—KPG Ventures
Chang, Justin—Colony Capital LLC
Chang, Lily—Leonard Green & Partners
Chang, Mick—Pacific Venture Partners
Chang, Milton—Incubic Venture Capital
Chang, Mink—Youngshin Venture Capital
Chang, Nancy—OrbiMed Advisors LLC
Chang, Richard—Carlyle Group, The
Chang, Roland—AsiaVest Partners, TCW/YFY Ltd. (FKA: TCW/YFY Investment)
Chang, Steve—Sterling Partners
Chang, Steven—Clearlake Capital Group
Chang, Tat Joel—AID Partners Capital, Ltd.
Chang, Timothy—Norwest Venture Partners
Chang, Victor—Hina Capital Partners
Chang, Vincent—Hotung International Company, Ltd.
Chang, Yahon Huang—Triton Management Corporation
Chang, Yong Taek—Shin Poong Venture Capital Corp.
Chang, Young—Altaris Capital Partners LLC
Chanin, Matthew—Prudential Capital Group
Channing, Walter—CW Group, Inc.
Chao, Chaoming—Raystone Capital, Ltd.
Chao, Clint—Formative Ventures
Chao, David—DCM
Chaoui, Mounia—Ventech S.A.
Chapekar, Manish—Montreux Equity Partners
Chapin II, Aldus—Blackstreet Capital Management (FKA: MMP Capital Advisors)
Chaplinsky, Robert—Bridgescale Partners
Chapman, Celia—WP Global Partners Inc.
Chapman, David—Yellow Point Equity Partners LP
Chapman, Gwen—Truffle Venture SAS

Chapman, Kyle—Forsyth Capital Investors LLC
Chapman, Rowan—Mohr Davidow Ventures
Chapman, Stuart—DFJ Esprit
Chapman, Tannaz—GTCR Golder Rauner LLC
Chappel, J. Randall—NLM Capital Partners, L.P.
Chappell, Scott—BIA Digital Partners, L.P.
Charalambides, Pierre—Dolphin Capital Partners
Charbonneau, Kevin—Perseis Private Equity
Charbonneau, Peter—Skypoint Capital Corporation
Charest, Ray—Oxford Bioscience Partners
Charlebois, Richard—GrowthWorks
Charles, Ian—Landmark Partners, Inc.
Charlton, Harry—MillhouseIAG
Charnock, David—Kingsway Capital of Canada, Inc.
Charon, Jean-Louis—Clavel Investissement SAS
Charpie, Richard—Ampersand Ventures
Chase, John—Atlantic-Pacific Capital, Inc.
Chattopadhyay, Somak—Greenhill SAVP
Chaturvedy, Amit—Summit Partners
Chau, Paul—WI Harper Group
Chau, Wilton—Qleap Accelerators, Ltd.
Chaudhary, Kapil—Illinois Innovation Accelerator Fund (i2A)
Chaudhary, Salam—Wind Point Partners
Chaudhry, Om—Fire Capital
Chaudhuri, Kaushik—SREI Venture Capital Ltd. (FKA: SREI Global Asset Mgt.)
Chaudron, Nicolas—AGF Private Equity
Chauffier, Frederic—Duke Street Capital
Chaung, Roy—CID Group, The
Chauvet, Jean-Marie—Dassault Developpement
Chavez, Lawrence—Flywheel Ventures
Chavez, Martin—Goldman Sachs Urban Investment Group
Chavkin, Arnold—Pine Brook Road Partners LLC
Chawla, Kuldeep—IL&FS Investment Managers Ltd (FKA: IL&FS Venture Corp)
Chawla, Maneesh—Prospect Partners LLC
Chawla, Muneesh—Blue River Capital India Advisory Services Pvt., Ltd.
Chawla, Muneesh—IL&FS Investment Managers Ltd (FKA: IL&FS Venture Corp)
Chawla, Rakesh—GCP Capital Partners
Chawla, Sunil—Jacob Ballas Capital India Pvt, Ltd. (AKA:JBC)
Chaya, Dina—NeoMed Management AS
Cheah, Hanson—AsiaTech Internet Group (ATIG) (FKA: AsiaTech Ventures)
Chee, Brian—Polaris Venture Partners
Chee, Christopher—Blackstone Group, L.P.
Chee, Jonathan—China Israel Value Capital (AKA: CIVC)
Chee, Max—Millennium Technology Ventures
Chee, Max—Navigation Capital Partners (AKA: NCP)
Cheek, John—Fidus Capital
Cheesman, David—Advent Venture Partners LLP
Cheever, Chris—Fontinalis Partners LLC
Chefetz, Alexander—Thomas Weisel Partners Group, Inc.
Chefitz, Robert—Egis Capital Partners LLC
Chefitz, Robert—New Jersey Technology Council (AKA: NJTC)
Chehime, Hasan—Investcorp Bank B.S.C.
Cheifetz, Yoni—Lightspeed Venture Partners (FKA: Weiss, Peck & Greer)
Chelouche, Yoav—Aviv Venture Capital (FKA: Fantine Group, The)
Chen, Aggie—CID Group, The
Chen, Alan—ARC China, Inc.
Chen, Alec—Tripod Capital International, Ltd.
Chen, Alice—CIDC Consultants, Inc. (AKA: China Investment & Development)
Chen, Andrew—BlueRun Ventures
Chen, Benjamin—Burrill & Company
Chen, Carson—Walden International
Chen, Celine—BioVeda Capital Private, Ltd.
Chen, Cliff—Crimson
Chen, Cory—CID Group, The
Chen, Dar—BPEP International
Chen, Datong—Northern Light Venture Capital
Chen, David—EQT Funds management Limited
Chen, David—Ground Swell Equity Partners
Chen, Derek—SAIF Partners
Chen, Deyin—NYPC Capital
Chen, Eric—WI Harper Group
Chen, Gongmen—China Venture Capital Research Institute, Ltd.
Chen, Han—Carlyle Group, The
Chen, Hao—Legend Capital
Chen, Hong—Hina Capital Partners
Chen, James—Hollyhigh International Capital
Chen, Jason—Fortune Venture Investment Group (AKA:Fortune Consulting)
Chen, Jerry—Cheng Xin Technology Development Corp. (FKA: Fidelity VC)
Chen, Jesse—Maton Venture
Chen, Jun—BPEP International
Chen, Kevin—AsiaVest Partners, TCW/YFY Ltd. (FKA: TCW/YFY Investment)
Chen, Leon—BioVeda Capital Private, Ltd.
Chen, Mark—Easton Hunt Capital Partners, L.P.
Chen, Mark—GE Commercial Finance - Equity
Chen, Norman—Fidelity Growth Partners Asia
Chen, Paul—Cybernaut (China) Capital Management
Chen, Richard—Qiming Venture Partners
Chen, Sherwin—Elevation Associates LLC
Chen, Shi—Power Capital Co., Ltd.
Chen, Shijun—Shenzhen Green Pine Capital Partners Co., Ltd.
Chen, Shuang—China Everbright, Ltd.
Chen, Terry—VantagePoint Venture Partners
Chen, Tom—Cybernaut (China) Capital Management
Chen, Vivian—CDH China Management Co., Ltd.
Chen, Wei—Shenzhen Capital Group Co., Ltd.
Chen, William—DT Capital Partners
Chen, Wu-Fu—Genesis Campus, L.P.
Chen, Wu-fu—Acorn Campus Ventures
Chen, Wu-fu—iD Innovation, Inc.
Chen, Xiaohong—Veronis Suhler Stevenson (FKA: Veronis, Suhler & Associates)
Chen, Yan—Nature Elements Capital
Chen, Yi-ju—iD Innovation, Inc.
Chen, York—iD TechVentures, Inc. (FKA: Acer Technology Ventures)
Chendo, John—Housatonic Partners
Cheng, Albert—Fidelity Growth Partners Asia
Cheng, Chih-Kai—Harbinger Venture Management
Cheng, Gary—VenGlobal Capital
Cheng, Houbo—Shenzhen OFC Investment Management, Ltd.
Cheng, Jose—Li & Fung Investments
Cheng, Julian—Warburg Pincus LLC
Cheng, Larry—Volition Capital
Cheng, Lawrence—Capital Z Investment Partners (FKA: Union Square Partners)
Cheng, Lawrence—Fidelity Ventures
Cheng, Tan Lei—Goldis Berhad (FKA: Gold IS Bhd)
Cheng, Xie—Tripod Capital International, Ltd.
Chennareddy, Praveen—Gaja Capital Partners
Chenoweth, Brett—Silverfern Group, Inc., The
Cheon, Seung-Wook—Premier Venture Partners LLC
Cheong, Kenneth—BPEP International
Chereskin, Benjamin—Madison Dearborn Partners LLC
Cherian, Saj—Valhalla Partners
Cherington, Charles—Cherington Capital
Cherington, Charles—Intervale Capital
Cherrick, Michelle—Thomas Weisel Partners Group, Inc.
Cherry, Brian—J.H. Whitney & Co. LLC
Chertok, Doug—Dace Ventures
Chesnoff, Adam—Saban Ventures
Chessari, Ross—SciVentures Investments Pty., Ltd.
Chestnut, Edward—Atlantic-Pacific Capital, Inc.
Chetrit, Alain—Colony Capital LLC
Cheuck, John—General Enterprise Management Services Ltd (AKA: GEMS)
Cheung, Cliff—InterLeader Capital, Ltd.
Cheung, David—Aetos Capital LLC
Cheung, David—CLSA Capital Partners (AKA: Credit Lyonnais Securities Asia)
Cheung, Emil—CITIC Capital Partners, Ltd.
Cheung, Leo—Unitas Capital Pte, Ltd.
Cheung, Patrick—QED Global, Ltd.
Cheung, Richard—Cinven, Ltd.
Cheung, Savio—Asset Managers Holding Company, Ltd.
Chevalier, Jerome—Quilvest Private Equity
Chew, James—Fortune Venture Investment Group (AKA:Fortune Consulting)
Chhachhi, Vivek—Citibank Venture Capital India
Chi, Jeffrey—Vickers Venture Partners
Chi, Miao—Warburg Pincus LLC
Chia, Chris—Kendall Court Capital Partners, Ltd.
Chiang, Albert—Bay Hills Capital (FKA: Mansbridge Capital Management)
Chiang, Brian—Walden International
Chiang, David—Wilshire Private Markets
Chiang, H.Eric—Invus Group Ltd., The
Chiang, Rachel—ARC Capital Partners, Ltd. (AKA: ARC Capital)
Chiang, Richard—Redwood Capital, Inc.
Chiang, Richard—Triton Management Corporation
Chiang, Rick—H&Q Asia Pacific
Chiang, Yao-Chye—Clearwater Capital Partners, LLC
Chiao, Stephen Sun—Sycamore Ventures Pte, Ltd.
Chiate, Gregory—Behrman Capital
Chico Pardo, Fernando—Promecap, S.C.
Chicotel, Richard—Shorenstein Company LLC
Chidambaram, Ravi—TC Capital Pte., Ltd.
Chidambaram, Srinivas—Jacob Ballas Capital India Pvt, Ltd. (AKA:JBC)
Chiecchio, Paola—4D Global Energy Advisors

Chien, Chi-Hua—Kleiner Perkins Caufield & Byers
Chien, Michael—Avant Capital Group, Inc.
Chilcott, James—Evolution Group (FKA: EVC Christows PLC)
Child, Michael—TA Associates, Inc.
Childers, Al—Southern Capitol Ventures
Childres, Chris—Edgewater Capital Group, Inc.
Childres, Nathaniel—CHAMP Private Equity Pty Ltd.
Childs, John—J.W. Childs Associates
Chillura, Joseph—Concentric Equity Partners, L.P.
Chin, Bay Chong—Actis Capital LLP
Chin, David—Harbinger Venture Management
Chin, Gordon—ARC China, Inc.
Chin, Kevin—Arowana Capital Pty, Ltd.
Chin, Pearl—Seraphima Ventures
Chin, Tahn-Joo—Hina Capital Partners
Chinchurreta, Fernando—Inversiones Ibersuizas S.A.
Ching, Stanley—CITIC Capital Partners, Ltd.
Chingwende, Marlon—Standard Chartered Private Equity, Ltd.
Chinn, Adam—Centerview Partners Holdings LLC
Chinn, Michael—Israel Seed Partners
Chirikos, Anthony—Gores Group LLC, The
Chirillo, Michael—GE Antares Capital Corporation
Chiruvolu, Ravi—755 Capital Partners, LLC
Chiruvolu, Ravi—GKM Ventures
Chiruvolu, Ravi—Osprey Ventures, L.P.
Chiu, Jacob—Squadron Capital Advisors, Ltd.
Chiu, Michael—TCW Capital Ventures LLC (AKA: TCW Holdings LLC)
Chizen, Bruce—Voyager Capital
Chladek, Melanie—Institutional Venture Partners
Chlopek, Marek—Penton Consulting Sp. K. (AKA: Penton Partners)
Cho, E. Sue—Wicks Group of Companies LLC, The
Cho, Il Hyung—Michigan Venture Capital Co., Ltd.
Cho, Jerry Ilhyun—Draper Fisher Jurvetson ePlanet Ventures, L.P.
Cho, Minho—STIC Investments, Inc.
Cho, Nam-Chun—Aju IB Invesment Co., Ltd.
Cho, Ralph—iD TechVentures, Inc. (FKA: Acer Technology Ventures)
Chock, Carty—Arsenal Capital Partners
Choe, Anthony—Brentwood Associates
Choe, Bill—Morrison & Foerster
Choe, David—Prospect Partners LLC
Choe, Michael—Charlesbank Capital Partners LLC
Chohan, Ommer—Summerhill Venture Partners
Choi, Ben—Maveron LLC
Choi, Ben—Storm Ventures LLC
Choi, Chris—Serent Capital LLC
Choi, Dong-Jo—IDG Ventures Korea
Choi, Hyun Joo—Seir Venture Capital
Choi, Hyung-Kew—LB Investment, Inc.
Choi, Jai—Partech International
Choi, Kenneth—East Gate Private Equity Partners LLC
Choi, Stephen—TVG Capital Partners, Ltd.
Choi, Wonyun—LB Investment, Inc.
Choi, Young-Soo—KTB Securities Co., Ltd. (FKA: KTB Network Co., Ltd.)
Choix, Didier—Massena Capital Partners
Choksi, Himanshu—Pacifica Fund
Cholet, Phillippe—SIGMA Gestion SA
Chong Hee, Tan—Pacific Venture Partners
Chong, F.T—PineBridge Investments
Chong, Richard—Sycamore Ventures Pte, Ltd.
Chong, Simon—Georgian Partners
Choo, Paul—Investor Growth Capital, Inc.
Chopova, Tatiana—AlpInvest Partners N.V.
Chopp, Joseph—First Analysis Corporation
Chopra, Ajay—Trinity Ventures
Chopra, Dipika—Trident Capital
Chopra, Vinodkumar—GVFL Limited (FKA: Gujarat Venture Finance Limited)
Chorpa, Hannes—Al'yans ROSNO Upravleniye Aktivami, OAO
Chotai, Beena—ICICI Venture Funds Management Co., Pvt. Ltd. (FKA: TDICI)
Chotai, Yagnish—Cinven, Ltd.
Chou, April—NewSchools Venture Fund
Chou, Cheng-Nan—Hotung International Company, Ltd.
Chou, H. Chin—Morgan Stanley Private Equity
Chou, Jonathan—Eureka Growth Capital
Chou, Scott—Gabriel Venture Partners
Chou, Thomas—Morrison & Foerster
Chou, Tony—Vertical Group, The
Chough, HS Richard—LTI Investments
Choung, S. Eugene—Emerald Hill Capital Partners, Ltd.
Chovanec, Patrick—Asia Mezzanine Capital Advisers, Ltd.
Chovatia, Vamesh—Kotak Investment Advisors, Ltd. (AKA: KPEG)
Chow Ching Ning, Michael—JAFCO Investment [FKA: Nomura/JAFCO Investment (Asia), Ltd.]
Chow, Alice—Squadron Capital Advisors, Ltd.
Chow, David—Pacific Venture Partners
Chow, Joseph—SB Life Science Equity Management LLC
Chow, Lon—Apex Venture Partners
Chow, Richard—Paul Capital Partners
Chowdhri, Rahul—Helion Venture Partners
Chowdhury, Ajay—Acacia Capital Partners
Chowdhury, Ajay—Akara, Ltd. (DBA: IDG Ventures Europe)
Chowfla, Sangeet—Timeline Ventures LLC
Choy, Chris—Quam Asset Management, Ltd.
Choy, Louis—Spring Capital Asia, Ltd.
Choy, Stephanie—AsiaTech Internet Group (ATIG) (FKA: AsiaTech Ventures)
Christensen, Bjorn—Alliance Venture AS
Christensen, Carlos—Latin America Equity Partners (FKA: LAEP)
Christensen, Carol—Northgate Capital Group
Christensen, Per—Axcel Industriinvestor AS
Christensen, Soren—Cinven, Ltd.
Christensen, Soren—Sunstone Capital A/S
Christensen, Steven—Nittany Lion Venture Capital
Christensen, Thorkil Kastberg—Novo A/S
Christenson, Johan—Odlander, Fredrikson & Co. AB (AKA: HealthCap)
Christensson, Magnus—Atlantic-Pacific Capital, Inc.
Christensson, Magnus—Jefferies Group, Inc.
Christhilf, Stuart—Pamlico Capital
Christian, Chenier—FCP Investors
Christiansen, Dean—Acacia Capital, Inc.
Christiansen, Robert—Southern Cross Venture Partners
Christianson, Ross—UIB Capital, Inc.
Christoffersen, Ralph—Morgenthaler Ventures
Christofferson, Monalotte Theorell—Scope Capital Advisory AB
Christophe, Cleveland—TSG Capital Group, L.L.C.
Christopher, David—Peachtree Equity Partners
Christopher, James—Blackstone Group, L.P.
Christopher, Michael—ArcLight Capital
Christopher, Nicholas—LaSalle Capital Group, Inc.
Christopoulos, James—Investcorp Bank B.S.C.
Chronister, Wendy—Waud Capital Partners LLC
Chronos, Nicolas—Essex Woodlands Health Ventures
Chu, Chinh—Blackstone Group, L.P.
Chu, Christopher—Pacific Venture Partners
Chu, Michael—IGNIA Partners LLC
Chu, Michael—Pegasus Venture Capital
Chu, Nelson—Kinetic Ventures LLC
Chu, Peter—AsiaTech Internet Group (ATIG) (FKA: AsiaTech Ventures)
Chu, Quentin—Crestview Partners L.P. (FKA: Crestview, LLC)
Chu, Shelley—Frazier Healthcare and Technology Ventures
Chu, Sherman—Grayhawk Capital
Chu, Steve—GGV Capital
Chu, Swee-Yeok—Bio*One Capital
Chu, Swee-Yeok—EDB Investments Pte, Ltd.
Chu, William—Signal Lake
Chu, YK—WI Harper Group
Chu, Yee-Ping—Bison Capital Asset Management LLC
Chua Hwee Song, Nicholas—Tembusu Ventures Pte., Ltd.
Chua, Joo Hock—Vertex Management Pte, Ltd. (AKA: Vertex Venture Holdings)
Chua, Kei—Unitas Capital Pte, Ltd.
Chua, Ted—Fidelity Growth Partners Asia
Chuang, George—FountainVest Partners (Asia), Ltd.
Chubais, Anatoly—GK Rossiyskaya Korporatsiya Nanotekhnologiy
Chubb, John—Leeds Equity Partners
Chudzinski, Pawel—Team Europe Ventures Management GmbH
Chueri, Paulo—BPE Investimentos
Chugg, Brett—Koch Genesis LLC
Chugh, Rakshid—Trinity Capital PLC
Chulack, Alexander—General Atlantic LLC
Chung, Andrew—Carlyle Group, The
Chung, Andrew—Lightspeed Venture Partners (FKA: Weiss, Peck & Greer)
Chung, Henry—DFJ Athena
Chung, Hong-Jen—Hyield Consulting Group
Chung, Hwan-Yoon—Metalmark Capital LLC
Chung, Jinsuk—Tong Yang Venture Capital Corporation
Chung, Joyce—Garage Technology Ventures LLC (FKA: Garage.com)
Chung, Katherine—Blackstone Group, L.P.
Chung, Mong-il—Hyundai Venture Investment Corporation
Chung, Patrick—New Enterprise Associates, Inc.
Chung, Peter—Summit Partners
Chung, Peter—Whitecastle Investments
Chung, Suk Geun—IDG Ventures Korea
Chung, Young—Duff Ackerman & Goodrich LLC (AKA: DAG Ventures)

Chuphi, Ngalaah—Ethos Private Equity
Church, Cody—TriWest Capital Management Corporation
Church, Scott—Lazard Capital Partners
Churchill, Winston—SCP Private Equity Partners
Churchwell, Thomas—ARCH Development Partners LLC
Chwang, Ronald—iD Ventures America, LLC (AKA: Acer Technology Ventures)
Ciampi, Johnny—Maxam Capital Corp.
Ciancimino, Marc—GSC Partners (FKA: Greenwich Street Capital Partners)
Ciannamea, John—Academy Funds
Ciechanover, Isaac—Kleiner Perkins Caufield & Byers
Ciechanover, Joseph—Challenge Fund - Etgar LP
Cifelli, Paul—Global Emerging Markets
Cifelli, Paul—Kinderhook Industries
Cifre, Juan Ignacio—Delta Partners FZ LLC
Cihak, Donald—Gridiron Capital LLC
Cilento, Alexander—Aspen Ventures
Cimini, Anthony—O.S.S. Capital Management LP
Cimino, Thomas—DeltaPoint Capital Management LLC
Ciofalo, Mario—New Venture Development Srl
Cioffi, Robert—Alerion Partners
Cioffi, Robert—GE Commercial Finance - Equity
Ciporin, Daniel—Canaan Partners
Cipriani, Andrea—Monomoy Capital Partners, LLC
Cipriano, Mark—TVM Capital GmbH
Cira, Kathleen—Union Bancaire Privee Private Equity
Cirar, James—TMB Industries Investments
Cirella, Blinn—Saw Mill Capital, LLC
Ciriello, Paul—Fairhaven Capital Partners
Cirilli, Mark—MissionPoint Capital Partners
Cirino, Maria—.406 Ventures (AKA: Point 406 Ventures)
Cirla, Giorgio—Iniziativa Gestione Investimenti SGR
Cirla, Matteo—Synergo SGR S.p.A.
Cirstea, Despina—Oltenia Financial Investment Cy
Cissell-Roell, Kara—VMG Equity Partners
Citrino, Mary Anne—Blackstone Group, L.P.
Citron, Emanuel—Stone Point Capital LLC
Ciurezu, Tudor—Oltenia Financial Investment Cy
Civantos, John—Court Square Capital Partners
Civelek, Baris—Summer Street Capital LLC
Claesson, Anders—Segulah Advisor AB
Claeys, Frank—Fortis Private Equity NV/SA (FKA: VIV NV)
Clair, Kuldip—ic2 Capital LLP
Clamagirand, Laurent—AXA Investment Managers
Clancy, Sheila—Twin Haven Capital Partners
Claquin, Herve—AAC Capital Partners
Claquin, Herve—Abenex Capital (FKA: ABN AMRO Capital France)
Clare, Daniel—Diamond Castle Holdings LLC
Clare, Peter—Carlyle Group, The
Clarey, John—Clarey Capital LLC
Clark, B. Jefferson—Aurora Funds, Inc.
Clark, Brett—Absa Capital Private Equity (Pty) Ltd.
Clark, Brian—M/C Venture Partners
Clark, David—Jordan, Edmiston Group, Inc., The
Clark, Dwight—New Asia Partners, Ltd.
Clark, Greg—Horizon Technology Finance Management LLC
Clark, Gregor—Sigma Capital Group Plc
Clark, J. Ryan—Genstar Capital LLC
Clark, James—Cabot Square Capital, Ltd.
Clark, John—Welsh, Carson, Anderson & Stowe
Clark, Kristin—GE Antares Capital Corporation
Clark, Mayree—Aetos Capital LLC
Clark, Piers—Frog Capital, Ltd.
Clark, Rachel—GCP Capital Partners
Clark, Ralph—Ascend Venture Group LLC
Clark, Reg—Loxko Venture Managers, Ltd.
Clark, Rena—GenNx360 Capital Partners
Clark, Robert—Leveraged Green Energy LLC
Clark, Roddy—Redmont Venture Partners
Clark, Rufus—Bunker Hill Capital
Clark, Sarah—Commonfund Capital, Inc. (FKA: Common Fund)
Clark, Simon—Fidelity Ventures
Clark, Timothy—Gridiron Capital LLC
Clark, Trevor—Madison Capital Funding LLC (AKA: Madison Capital)
Clark, William—Care Capital, LLC
Clarke Adamson, Martha—Sierra Ventures
Clarke, Anthony—London Seed Capital, Ltd.
Clarke, H. Glen—Brown Gibbons Lang & Company LLC
Clarke, Jack—Veronis Suhler Stevenson (FKA: Veronis, Suhler & Associates)
Clarke, John—Cardinal Partners
Clarke, Jonathan—Cinven, Ltd.
Clarke, Lisa—Kinderhook Industries
Clarke, Martin—Permira Advisers LLP
Clarke, Nigel—Caribbean Equity Partners Limited
Clarke, Owen—Barclays Private Equity, Ltd.
Clarke, Richard—7bridge Capital Partners, Ltd.
Clarke, Tim—August Equity LLP
Clarkson, Macon—Private Advisors LLC
Clarry, Nick—CVC Capital Partners (Europe), Ltd.
Clary, Matthew—Waud Capital Partners LLC
Clavier, Jean-Francois—SoftTech VC
Clavier, Jeff—Occam Capital
Clavijo, Jesus Olmos—Kohlberg, Kravis, Roberts & Company, L.P.
Clawson, Chad—Patriarch Partners LLC
Claxton, John—Catalyst Equity Group LLC
Clay, C. Kenneth—Corinthian Capital Group LLC
Clay, Jacques—Vision Capital Management
Clay, Kevin—Latitude Partners
Claycomb, T.—Wall Street Venture Capital
Clayton, David—Blackstone Group, L.P.
Clayton, Douglas—Leopard Capital, Ltd.
Clayton, Grant—CHB Capital Partners
Clayton, Kevin—Oaktree Capital Management LLC
Clemens, Adam—Portfolio Advisors LLC
Clemens, Leonard—Vitruvian Partners LLP
Clement, Mark—Excalibur Fund Managers, Ltd.
Clemins, Archie—Highway 12 Ventures
Clemons, Steve—Trans Cosmos USA
Clempson, Graham—MidOcean Partners
Cleveland, Bruce—InterWest Partners
Cleveland, John—SB Energy Partners
Clevers, Hans—Life Sciences Partners BV
Clevinger, Brian—Prolog Ventures LLC
Clifford, Kenneth—Metalmark Capital LLC
Clifford, Kenneth—Morgan Stanley Private Equity
Clifford, Martin—Point Judith Capital
Climan, Richard—Cooley Godward LLP
Cline, Alan—Accretive LLC (FKA: Accretive Technology Partners LLC)
Cline, J. Michael—Accretive LLC (FKA: Accretive Technology Partners LLC)
Cline, Roland—American Capital, Ltd.
Cline, Roland—European Capital Financial Services Ltd.
Clinton, John—CCP Equity Partners
Clippard, James—Circle Peak Capital LLC (AKA: CPC)
Clive, Colin—Thompson Clive & Partners, Ltd.
Cloherty, Patricia—Delta Capital Management (AKA:Delta Private Equity Partners)
Clos, Alain—SGAM Private Equity
Cloud, Sanford—Ironwood Capital (AKA: Ironwood Capital Advisors LLC)
Clough, Phillip—ABS Capital Partners
Clouth, Gundel—Deutsche Beteiligungs AG
Clow, Eric—Hina Capital Partners
Clute, George—Banyan Capital Partners
Coady, James—Sentinel Capital Partners
Coady, John—RBC Capital Partners/RBC Technology Ventures
Coates, Steve—Warburg Pincus LLC
Cobb, Brodie—Presidio Investors LLC
Cobbold, Christopher—TVM Capital GmbH
Cobbs, Jerald—Signet Healthcare Partners (FKA: Sanders Morris Harris)
Cobleigh, Jennifer—GCP Capital Partners
Cobo, Inaki—CVC Capital Partners (Europe), Ltd.
Coburn, Brooke—Carlyle Group, The
Coburn, Eric—Shattuck Hammond Partners
Coburn, John—XPV Capital Corporation
Coburn, Pip—Coburn Ventures, LLC
Cochais-Widmer, Veronique—Carlyle Group, The
Cochran, John—Lovell Minnick Partners LLC
Cochran, John—SV Investment Partners (FKA: Schroder Ventures US)
Cockell, Allen—MMC Ventures, Ltd.
Cockrell, Ross—Escalate Capital
Cockshutt, Timothy—Advantage Capital Partners
Cockwell, Andrew—Ursataur Capital Management
Cococcia, John—FA Technology Ventures
Code, Andrew—Code, Hennessy & Simmons LLC
Coers, Dirk—AutoVision GmbH
Coes, Ben—Mustang Group LLC, The
Coffey, Steven—Covera Ventures
Cogan, Gill—Opus Capital
Coggill, Christopher—Chord Capital, Ltd. (FKA: Generics Group, The)
Coglizer, Dave—Westly Group, The
Cogut, Craig—Pegasus Capital Advisors, L.P.
Cohen, Aaron—GTCR Golder Rauner LLC
Cohen, Allan—First Analysis Corporation
Cohen, Andrew—Apollo Real Estate Advisors
Cohen, Daniel—Gemini Israel Funds, Ltd.
Cohen, David—Centerview Partners Holdings LLC
Cohen, Doron—SCP Private Equity Partners
Cohen, Frank—Blackstone Group, L.P.
Cohen, Josh—City Light Capital
Cohen, Marshall—Pilot Group LLC
Cohen, Matt—City Light Capital
Cohen, Neal—CoBe Capital LLC
Cohen, Robert—Iron Gate Capital, LLC
Cohen, Rodney—Behrman Capital
Cohen, Rodney—Pegasus Capital Advisors, L.P.

Cohen, Tomer—Markstone Capital
Cohen, Victor—Vestar Capital Partners, Inc.
Cohen, Yuval—Stage One Ventures
Cohler, Matt—Benchmark Capital
Cohn, Gary—Goldman, Sachs & Co.
Cohn, Greg—Atlanta Equity Investors LLC
Cohn, Paul—Fort Washington Capital Partners Group
Cohn, Victor—Rosemont Solebury Capital Management LLC
Cohn-Sfetcu, Dan—American Capital, Ltd.
Coia, Anthony—BioVentures Investors
Coit, David—North Atlantic Capital Corporation
Colaianne, John—Industrial Opportunity Partners, LLC
Colas, Benoit—Carlyle Group, The
Colasson, Pierre—Bridgepoint Development Capital
Colato, Michael—Bain Capital
Colby, Jonathan—Carlyle Group, The
Colcomb, Mark—Wesley Clover, Ltd.
Cole, Allison—CCMP Capital Advisors LLC
Cole, C.Taylor—Charterhouse Group International, Inc.
Cole, Cali—Citigroup Private Equity
Cole, Dan—Oxford Bioscience Partners
Cole, Douglas—Flagship Ventures
Cole, George—Veronis Suhler Stevenson (FKA: Veronis, Suhler & Associates)
Cole, J. Daniel—Spray Venture Partners
Cole, James—Windward Ventures
Cole, Marc—Hamilton Investments
Cole, Matthew—North Bay Equity Partners
Cole, Michael—Madison Dearborn Partners LLC
Colella, Mark—5AM Ventures
Colella, Nicholas—Incubic Venture Capital
Coleman, Debi—SmartForest Ventures
Coleman, Greg—Sindicatum Carbon Capital, Ltd.
Coleman, James—Probitas Partners, Inc.
Coleman, Larry—SSM Partners
Coleman, Mary—Walden International
Coleman, Nick—SV Life Sciences Advisers
Coleman, Sean—Golub Capital
Coleman, Terry—Water Tower Capital LLC
Coleman, Timothy—Dresner Partners (FKA: Dresner Capital Resources, Inc.)
Coleman, Warren—CapitalWorks LLC
Coleman, Will—Mohr Davidow Ventures
Coleon, Elizabeth Orzano—Paul Capital Partners
Colette, Monique—Atlantic Canada Opportunity Agency
Colin, Patrick—Picardie Investissement
Colins, Morton—Battelle Ventures
Collan, Matias—Earlybird Venture Capital GmbH & Co. KG
Collar, Mark—Triathlon Medical Ventures LLC
Collard, Frederic—AXA Private Equity
Collas, Philippe—SGAM Private Equity
Collatos, William—Spectrum Equity Investors
Colledge, Neill—Queensland BioCapital Fund
Collet, James—NLM Capital Partners, L.P.
Collet, Pierre—Actidev
Colletta, Anthony—Technikos
Colliat, George—Wellington Partners Venture Capital GmbH
Collier, Colby—Laud Collier & Company LLC (AKA: LC & Co.)
Collier, D. Scott—Triton Ventures
Collier, David—CMEA Capital
Collier, David—Chart Capital Management LLC
Collier, Ian—Perseis Private Equity
Collier, Sally—Pantheon Ventures, Ltd.
Colligan, Owen—RockWood Equity Partners LLC
Collignon, Yann—Azulis Capital (FKA:Banexi Capital Partenaires)
Collin, David—Monomoy Capital Partners, LLC
Collin, Jacques—Paris Business Angels
Collina, Andrew—Castanea Partners
Collini, Albino—TIM SpA - Transition Management
Collins, Adam—New Mountain Capital LLC
Collins, Anthony—Seaway Private Equity Corporation (AKA: SPEC)
Collins, Chris—Cognetas LLP
Collins, Christopher—Glencoe Capital LLC (FKA: Glencoe Investment Corporation)
Collins, Christopher—Stockwell Capital LLC
Collins, Darlene—Psilos Group Managers LLC
Collins, Emma—Platina Partners LLP
Collins, James—Bruckmann, Rosser, Sherrill & Co.
Collins, Jarrett—NeoCarta Ventures, Inc.
Collins, Matthew—Hutton Collins & Company Limited
Collins, Morton—Battelle Memorial Institute
Collins, Rick—Capstone Capital Partners LLC
Collins, Scott—Summit Partners
Collins, Steven—Advent International
Collins, Tim—Ripplewood Holdings LLC
Collins, Todd—Tregaron Capital Company LLC
Collinson, Jeffrey—CHL Medical Partners
Collinson, Stuart—Forward Ventures
Collis, James—Seaport Capital, LLC
Collison, Terry—Blue Rock Capital
Collister, R. Craig—RoundTable Health Care Partners
Collombel, Philippe—Partech International
Colloredo-Mansfeld, Ferdinand—Cabot Properties, Inc.
Colloredo-Mansfeld, Franz—Cabot Properties, Inc.
Colloton, J. Edmund—Bessemer Venture Partners
Colmie, Anita—Idanta Partners, Ltd.
Colodny, Mark—Warburg Pincus LLC
Colon, Daniel—CM Equity Partners (FKA; Lynx Investment Management, L.P.)
Colone, Paul—C.W. Downer & Company (FKA: Downer & Company)
Colonna, Paolo—Permira Advisers LLP
Colonnetta, Joe—HM Capital Partners LLC
Colosimo, Louis—Comvest Investment Partners
Colquitt, Sheri—Triangle Capital Corporation
Colton, Brian—Generation Equity Investors
Colucci, Paul—Thomas Weisel Partners Group, Inc.
Colvert, Scott—Hunt Capital Group
Colvert, Scott—Trinity Hunt Partners
Colvin, Jeff—Basil Growth Corporation
Coly, Jean- Marc—UFG Private Equity SAS
Colyer, James—Huntsman Gay Global Capital LLC
Comaford Lynch, Christine—Novus Ventures
Combe, Bruno—Astrolabe Ventures
Comer, B. Bragg—Fidus Capital
Comfort, Stuyvie—Stirling Square Capital Partners
Comfort, William—Court Square Capital Partners
Comolli, Kevin—Accel Partners
Compall, John—CIVC Partners LP (FKA: Continental Illinois Venture Corp.)
Compton, Kevin—Kleiner Perkins Caufield & Byers
Compton, Kevin—Radar Partners
Compton, Matt—Madrona Venture Group
Comstock, Cory—Sherbrooke Capital
Conacher, Lionel—Thomas Weisel Partners Group, Inc.
Conard, Edward—Bain Capital
Conaton, Michael—Key Principal Partners LLC (AKA: KPP)
Concina, Stefano—KT Venture Group LLC
Coneybeer, Robert—Shasta Ventures Management LLC
Conforti, Francesco—Vegagest Sgr
Conjeevaram, Srini—SC Capital Management LLC
Conley, Paul—Paladin Capital Management LLC
Conley, Ray—Palo Alto Investors
Conn, Alastair—Northern Venture Managers Limited (AKA: NVM)
Conn, Robert—Innova Capital
Connaughton, John—Bain Capital
Conneely, Tom—Lighthouse Capital Partners
Connel, William—High Road Capital Partners
Connelly, James—Water Street Healthcare Partners
Connelly, Jim—Water Street Healthcare Partners
Conner, Charles—Climate Change Capital, Ltd.
Conner, Douglas—BrightPath Capital, Inc.
Conner, Patrick—Highland Capital Management, L.P.
Conners, Scott—Landmark Partners, Inc.
Connolly, Michael—Leonard Green & Partners
Connolly, Michael—vSpring Capital
Connolly, Peter—Summit Partners
Connor, Greg—RBC Capital Partners/RBC Technology Ventures
Connor, John—ABRY Partners LLC
Connor, Tim—Sequel Venture Partners
Connors, Brian—Formative Ventures
Connors, James—Kelso & Company
Connors, John—Ignition Partners (FKA: Ignition Corporation)
Connors, Kevin—Spray Venture Partners
Connors, Travis—Egan-Managed Capital
Connors, William—Stonebridge Partners
Conrad, Anthony—True Ventures
Conroy, Joe—Cooley Godward LLP
Conroy, Thomas—Next Generation Ventures, LLC
Constantino, Kevin—GCP Capital Partners
Constas, Julie—Willis Stein & Partners
Conte, Jean-Pierre—Genstar Capital LLC
Conte, Kathy—Hercules Technology Growth Capital, Inc.
Contractor, Ashish—GCP Capital Partners
Contro, Jerome—Crosslink Capital
Conway, Brian—TA Associates, Inc.
Conway, Edwin—Blackstone Group, L.P.
Conway, Jude—Hopewell Ventures
Conway, Kevin—Clayton, Dubilier & Rice, Inc.
Conway, Reid—Aetos Capital LLC
Conway, Ronald—Angel Investors, LP
Conway, Ronald—Baseline Ventures LLC
Conway, William—Carlyle Group, The
Cook, Andrew—Southfield Capital Advisors
Cook, Bill—Pinnacle Investment Management Pty, Ltd.
Cook, Everett—Pouschine Cook Capital Management, LLC

Cook, Hobart—Thomas H. Lee Partners (AKA: TH Lee Partners)
Cook, James—Aurora Investment Advisors, Ltd.
Cook, James—Silverhawk Capital Partners LLC
Cook, John—Investeco Capital Corporation
Cook, Kevin—Brantley Partners
Cook, Michael—Macquarie Capital Alliance Management Ltd.
Cook, Simon—DFJ Esprit
Cook, Todd—Bain Capital
Cook, W.Montgomery—Prospect Street Ventures
Cooke, Christopher—GCP Capital Partners
Cooke, J. Francis—Ursataur Capital Management
Cooke, Jocelyne—Venrock Associates
Cooke, Kim—Blue Water Capital LLC
Coombe, Chris—Invest AD
Coombs, John—Unilever Ventures, Ltd. (AKA: Unilever NV)
Coombs, Ron—Navigation Capital Partners (AKA: NCP)
Cooney, David—Beecken, Petty & Company LLC
Cooney, George—Summerhill Venture Partners
Coons, Ted—Blackstone Group, L.P.
Cooper, Andrew—Pegasus Capital Advisors, L.P.
Cooper, Bradley—Capital Z Investment Partners (FKA: Union Square Partners)
Cooper, Brian—GB Merchant Partners, LLC (FKA: GB Palladin Capital LLC)
Cooper, Chris—Pelion Venture Partners
Cooper, Douglas—American Capital, Ltd.
Cooper, James—Merck Capital Ventures LLC
Cooper, James—Thompson Street Capital Partners
Cooper, John—Montgomery & Co. (FKA: Digital Coast Partners)
Cooper, Joli—Cordova, Smart & Williams, LLC
Cooper, Keith—VIMAC Ventures LLC (FKA: VIMAC LLC)
Cooper, Ken—Capital for Enterprise, Ltd.
Cooper, Kendall—Allegis Capital (AKA: Media Technology Ventures)
Cooper, Kendall—Mayfield Fund
Cooper, Kendall—Ridgelift Ventures
Cooper, Michael—Shore Capital Partners LLC
Cooper, Nancy—Rhone Capital LLC
Cooper, Piers—mc3 ventures (FKA: McKenna Venture Accelerator (MVA))
Cooper, Thomas—Aperture Venture Partners, LLC
Coopersmith, Warren—Leading Ridge Capital Partners LLC
Coopersmith, Zach—Leading Ridge Capital Partners LLC
Cooreman, Andre-Xavier—Sofinim NV
Copans, Richard—Madison Dearborn Partners LLC
Cope, Brandon—JCP Capital LLC
Coppedge, Roy—Boston Ventures Management, Inc.
Coppel, Toby—Virgin Green Fund
Corba, Adrian—Slavia Capital
Corbani, Antonio—AAC Capital Partners
Corbett, Bryan—Carlyle Group, The
Corbett, Leo—Zephyr Management, L.P.
Corbus, Barclay—W.R. Hambrecht & Co., LLC
Corcoran, Rick—Slate Capital Group
Corcostegui, Angel—Magnum Capital Industrial Partners
Cordell, Gary—Clayton Associates LLC
Cordier, Clement—3i Group PLC
Cordova, Carl—Cordova, Smart & Williams, LLC
Cordt, Olaf—DuMont Venture Holding GmbH & Co. KG
Corey, Chris—Nautic Partners LLC
Corey, Richard—Zephyr Management, L.P.
Corl, James—Siguler Guff & Company
Corley, Tina—Eastside Partners
Corliss, Robert—Kairos Capital Partners
Cormack, Mike—Renewal Partners
Cormier, Lionel—Demeter Partners S.A.
Cornelis, Kelly—LaSalle Capital Group, Inc.
Cornelius, Craig—Hudson Capital Management, L.P.
Cornelius, James—Twilight Venture Partners
Cornelius, Ronn—Montauk TriGuard Management, Inc.
Cornell, John—Global Asia Partners
Cornell, Peter—Terra Firma Capital Partners, Ltd.
Cornetta, Peter—H.I.G. Capital LLC
Corning, Barney—Velocity Equity Partners LLC
Corning, Sally—Sun Mountain Capital
Cornwall, G. Rick—Business Development Bank of Canada
Cornwell, Simon—Amadeus Capital Partners, Ltd.
Corr, Peter—Celtic Therapeutics Management, L.L.L.P.
Corral, Santiago—CapVest Management Ltd
Corral, Santiago—Thesan Capital
Correal Marin, Francisco—Inverjaen S.C.R. SA
Corriggio, Anthony—Siguler Guff & Company
Corrodi, Brad—LogiSpring Management Company S.a.r.l.
Corscadden, Jay—AH Ventures (AKA: Adams Harkness & Hill Technology Ventures)
Corsellis, James—Marwyn Investment Management, LLP
Cortas, Usama—Leonard Green & Partners
Cortis, Christian—Advanced Technology Ventures
Cortner, Ryan—Westshore Capital Partners
Coseriff, Robert—Allen & Company
Cosgrave, Jonathan—Warburg Pincus LLC
Coskunturk, Cenk—Is Private Equity Investment Trust
Cosson, Nicolas—Azulis Capital (FKA:Banexi Capital Partenaires)
Costa, Domenico—TIM SpA - Transition Management
Costa, Saverio—Pantheon Ventures, Ltd.
Costabile, Steven—AIG Capital Partners
Costabile, Steven—PineBridge Investments
Costagli, Stefano—Vegagest Sgr
Costales, Carlos Puente—Mercapital Servicios Financieros
Costantino, John—NGN Capital LLC
Costaseque, Anne—Seventure Partners SA (FKA: SPEF Venture)
Costello, Dennis—Braemar Energy Ventures
Costello, Dennis—Rock Maple Ventures, L.P.
Costello, Jonathan—Brook Street Investments LLC
Costello, Neal—AlpInvest Partners N.V.
Costello, Timothy—Newstone Capital Partners
Costello, Tom—Baird Capital Partners
Cote, Andre—Investissement Quebec
Cote, Cathleen—Corporate Fuel Partners
Cote, Jeffrey—Pfingsten Partners, L.P.
Coticchia, Mark—Case Technology Ventures
Cottam, David—Park Square Capital, LLP
Cotter, Cian—Insight Venture Partners
Cotter, William—Vista Capital LLC (FKA: AO Capital Corp.)
Cotton, Tanguy—Atlantic-Pacific Capital, Inc.
Cottrill, Lance—Horsley Bridge Partners
Couch, John—C.M. Capital Corporation
Couet, Catherine—Astorg Partners SAS (FKA : Suez Capital Partenaires)
Coughlan, Elaine—Atlantic Bridge
Coughlin, John—Pacific Corporate Group
Coughlin, Paul—Longroad Asset Management
Coughlin, William—Aurora Capital Group (FKA: Aurora Capital Partners)
Coughlon, Jay—KRG Capital Partners LLC
Couillard, Phillippe—Persistence Capital Partners
Coull, Gary—CLSA Capital Partners (AKA: Credit Lyonnais Securities Asia)
Coulson, Fred—Five Elms Capital
Coulter, David—Warburg Pincus LLC
Coulter, James—TPG Capital
Counihan, James—Prism VentureWorks
Coupal, Bernard—T2C2 Capital
Coursey, Court—TomorrowVentures LLC
Court, Frederic—Advent Venture Partners LLP
Courtadon, Georges—GSC Partners (FKA: Greenwich Street Capital Partners)
Courtney, Jeffrey—VenGrowth Capital Funds
Couturier, Christian—Astorg Partners SAS (FKA : Suez Capital Partenaires)
Couturier, Jean-Francois—GTI Capital Inc.
Covell, Margaret—Thomas H. Lee Partners (AKA: TH Lee Partners)
Covello, Alexandre—Bex Capital
Covello, Alexandre—LGT Capital Partners AG
Covert, Kevin—Montgomery & Co. (FKA: Digital Coast Partners)
Covington, Howard—New Star Asset Management
Covington, Richard—Natural Gas Partners (NGP)
Cowan, David—Bessemer Venture Partners
Cowan, Donna—Skypoint Capital Corporation
Cowan, Matthew—Bridgescale Partners
Cowan, Sandra—EdgeStone Capital Partners, Inc.
Cowan, Steve—PCGI LLC (AKA: PCG International)
Cowan, Steve—Pacific Corporate Group
Cowen, William—Long River Capital Partners, LLC
Cowie, Donald—JOG Capital
Cowie, James—Frontenac Company
Cowley, Tom—RSS Investors
Cox, David—Dogwood Equity
Cox, Keith—Hercules Technology Growth Capital, Inc.
Cox, Thomas—Seneca Partners, Inc.
Coxall, Mark—STAR Capital Partners, Ltd.
Coxe, Tench—Sutter Hill Ventures
Coy, Bob—CincyTech
Coyle, John—Permira Advisers LLP
Coyne, J. Peter—Saw Mill Capital, LLC
Coyne, Patrick—Lincolnshire Management, Inc.
Cozanet, Eric—Ouest Ventures (FKA: Grand Ouest Gestion)
Cozzi, John—AEA Investors LP
Crabb, Neil—Sigma Capital Group Plc
Crabill, Scott—Thoma Bravo LLC
Crabill, Scott—Thoma Cressey Bravo
Crabtree, Diana—Stolberg Equity Partners LLC

Craddock, Peter—Shoreline Venture Management, LLC
Crafts, Putnam—Tinicum Capital Partners
Cragg, Scott—Trevi Health Ventures
Craig, Jackson—DDJ Capital Management, LLC
Craig, Ryan—Bertram Capital
Craig, William—Fifth Street Capital LLC
Crain, Andrew—Tully & Holland, Inc. (FKA: Ulin & Holland, Inc.)
Crain, Eberhard—EquiVest GmbH & Co
Cramer, Michael—GCP Capital Partners
Crandall, Duke—NBT Capital Corporation
Crandall, J. Taylor—Oak Hill Capital Management, Inc.
Crandall, Richard—Arbor Partners LLC
Crandell, Keith—ARCH Venture Partners
Crane, Alan—Polaris Venture Partners
Crary, Robert—Fulcrum Management, Inc.
Craven, Michael—Stonehenge Capital Company
Craver, Jeffrey—Advantage Capital Partners
Craves, Frederick—Bay City Capital LLC
Cravey, Richard—CGW Southeast Partners (AKA: Cravey, Green, & Wahlen)
Crawford, Chris—Summit Partners
Crawford, Gil—MicroVest Capital Management LLC
Crawford, Jane—Saints Ventures
Crawford, Matt—PTV Sciences
Crawford, Ryan—JOG Capital
Crawford, Stephen—Centerview Partners Holdings LLC
Crayford, Ian—Formative Ventures
Creado, Dirk—StoneMan NV 2007
Creamer, Glenn—Providence Equity Partners LLC
Creange, Jean-Pierre—Pragma Capital
Creer, Frank—Zone Ventures
Cremin, David—DFJ Frontier
Crenshaw, Scott—Private Advisors LLC
Crequit, Jean-Claude—GCE Capital SAS
Cressall, Justin—American Capital, Ltd.
Cressey, Bryan—Cressey & Company, L.P.
Cressey, Bryan—Thoma Cressey Bravo
Cresswell-Turner, Miles—Duke Street Capital
Crews, Brian—Lighthouse Capital Partners
Crews, Kenneth—GCP Capital Partners
Criares, Dean—Blackstone Group, L.P.
Crick, Charles—Longbow Capital
Crider, Adam—Wicks Group of Companies LLC, The
Crisan, Jeffrey—Bain Capital
Crisman, Forrest—Hammond Kennedy Whitney & Co
Crisp, David—Accel-KKR LLC
Crispino, Francis—Greater Pacific Capital LLP
Crisses, Alex—Insight Venture Partners
Crissman, Blaine—Prism Capital
Crist, Jason—Columbia Partners LLC
Crittenden, Gary—Huntsman Gay Global Capital LLC
Croce, Robert—New Enterprise Associates, Inc.
Crochet, Philippe—Partech International
Crocker, Bruce—J.P. Morgan H&Q (FKA: Chase H&Q)
Crocker, Bruce—Pitango Venture Capital (FKA:Polaris Venture Capital Israel)
Crocker, Curtis—Reservoir Venture Partners
Crocker, John—Atlantic-Pacific Capital, Inc.
Crocker, John—Capital Z Investment Partners (FKA: Union Square Partners)
Crockett, Cameron—GCP Capital Partners
Crockett, Catherine—Grove Street Advisors LLC
Crockett, Charles—Ascend Venture Group LLC
Crockett, E. David—Aspen Ventures
Crockett, Todd—TA Associates, Inc.
Croft, Edward—C&B Capital
Croker, Roger—Co-Investor Capital Partners Pty., Ltd.
Croll, David—M/C Venture Partners
Cromie, Daniel—Atlas Holdings FRM LLC
Crompton, Brad—GCP Capital Partners
Cromwell, Michael—WWC Capital Group LLC
Cronel, Arnaud—DEFI Gestion SA
Cronin, Michael—Weston Presidio (FKA: Weston Presidio Capital Management)
Crooke, Graham—Asset Management Company Venture Capital
Crooke, Graham—Helix Ventures
Cropper, Colin—American Capital, Ltd.
Crosbie-Walsh, Gordon—RedFire Investments Pty, Ltd.
Crosby, Brian—Falconhead Capital (FKA: Sports Capital Partners)
Crosby, Chris—Global Emerging Markets
Crosby, Chris—Nautic Partners LLC
Crosby, David—Quadrangle Group LLC
Crosby, Kevin—ArcLight Capital
Crosby, Richard—Hamilton BioVentures
Crosetto, Carl—GSC Partners (FKA: Greenwich Street Capital Partners)
Crosland, David—Atlanta Equity Investors LLC
Crosnoe, Clark—Parallel Invesment Partners
Cross, Cairn—FreshTracks Capital
Cross, Colin—Crystal Capital
Cross, Shawn—Burrill & Company
Crossan, Bill—Growth Capital Partners (FKA: Close Brothers Growth Capital)
Crot, Frederic—Quartus Gestion
Crotty, Paul—Portfolio Advisors LLC
Crotty, Thomas—Battery Ventures, L.P.
Crouch, Layton—Pacific Venture Group
Crouse, Dan—Grey Mountain Partners
Crowder, David—Thomas Weisel Partners Group, Inc.
Crowder, David—Thomas Weisel Venture Partners
Crowder, Randall—TEXO Ventures
Crowe, Jeffrey—Norwest Venture Partners
Crowe, Michael—Mesirow Private Equity Investments, Inc.
Crowell, Richard—Aurora Capital Group (FKA: Aurora Capital Partners)
Crowell, Richard—Vance Street Capital LLC
Crowley, Bob—Mustang Group LLC, The
Crowley, Kevin—FL Partners
Crowley, Robert—MTDC (Massachusetts Technology Development Corp.)
Crozier, Christopher—Permira Advisers LLP
Crumpler, John—Hatteras Venture Partners (FKA:Catalysta Partners)
Crupi, Anthony—Andlinger & Company, Inc.
Crutcher, Lawrence—Veronis Suhler Stevenson (FKA: Veronis, Suhler & Associates)
Crutchfield, Robert—Harbert Venture Partners
Cruz, Reidan—Probitas Partners, Inc.
Crystal, Jay—Staley Capital Management LLC
Cubac, Samuel—GE Commercial Finance - Equity
Cubeisy, Emile—IV Holdings
Cuddy, Brooke—J.P. Morgan Partners (FKA: Chase Capital Partners)
Cuesta, Juan—Corpfin Capital Asesores SA
Cuff, Michael—J.F. Lehman & Company
Cui, Jenny—Hina Capital Partners
Cui, Jianguo—Gold Stone Investment, Ltd.
Cui, Min—Bay City Capital LLC
Cukier, Benjamin—FTV Capital (FKA: FTVentures)
Cukierman, Francis—Invus Group Ltd., The
Cullerton, Scott—Morgan Stanley Private Equity
Cullinane, John—Islington Capital Partners
Culliss, Gary—New Capital Partners
Cully, Liam—Aureos Capital, Ltd.
Culver, David—CAI Capital Management Company
Cummings, Benton—Allied Capital Corporation
Cummings, Paul—Honda Strategic Venturing (HSV)
Cummings, Robert—GSC Partners (FKA: Greenwich Street Capital Partners)
Cummings, Robert—Wind Point Partners
Cummings, Stephen—Lumira Capital Corporation.
Cummins, Diarmuid—MidOcean Partners
Cunicelli, Jeanne—Birchmere Ventures
Cunningham, David—Pegasus Capital Advisors, L.P.
Cunningham, Emmett—Clarus Ventures
Cunningham, Joe—Sante Ventures
Cunningham, Lori—Pfingsten Partners, L.P.
Cunningham, Lyle—CMS Companies
Cunningham, Sean—GTCR Golder Rauner LLC
Cunningham, Steve—E+Co
Cupit, Dwight—Englefield Capital
Curatilo, Philip—Key Principal Partners LLC (AKA: KPP)
Curci, Rossella—CCMP Capital Advisors LLC
Cureton, Peter—Irving Place Capital
Cureton, Stewart—GulfStar Group
Curis, Duran—Drum Capital Management
Curl, Gregory—Temasek Holdings Pvt., Ltd.
Curley, Bruce—KPS Capital Partners, L.P.
Curley, Robert—Pinnacle Ventures
Curme, Oliver—Battery Ventures, L.P.
Curme, Oliver—TianDi Growth Capital
Curnock Cook, Jeremy—Intersuisse Bioscience Managers Pty, Ltd. (IB Managers)
Curran, Charles—Valhalla Partners
Curran, D. Patrick—C3 Capital LLC
Curran, Garrett—Growth Capital Partners (FKA: Close Brothers Growth Capital)
Curran, Julie—Scottish Equity Partners
Curran, Matt—Pantheon Ventures, Ltd.
Currie, David—SL Capital Partners LLP
Currie, James—Essex Woodlands Health Ventures
Currie, Lauchlan—ARC Financial Corporation
Curry Bishop, Stacey—Scale Venture Partners
Curry, Michael—Investeco Capital Corporation
Curry, Robert—Alliance Technology Ventures
Curt, Timothy—Warburg Pincus LLC
Curtin, Adam—Milestone Partners
Curtis Osorovitz, Karine—C.W. Downer & Company (FKA: Downer & Company)
Curtis, Dominic—AlpInvest Partners N.V.
Curvey, Colin—Duke Street Capital
Cusenza, Mary—NGEN Partners LLC (FKA: NextGen Partners LLC)
Cushing, Sara—Adams Street Partners LLC
Cusick, Thomas—CIBC Capital Partners

Cusick, Thomas—Tam Capital Management
Cusumano, Dino—American Industrial Partners
Cutler, Joel—General Catalyst Partners (FKA: General Catalyst Group LLC)
Cutler, Lucas—Brazos Private Equity Partners LLC
Cutter, W. Bowman—Warburg Pincus LLC
Cuvelier, Lieven—Sofindev Management N.V.
Cuzman, Ioan—SIF - Banat - Crisana SA
Cynn, David—Lightyear Capital LLC
Cyr, Daniel—ID Capital
Cyriac, Matthew—Blackstone Group, L.P.
Cyrot, Jean-Luc—TIME Equity Partners SAS
Czapski, Piotr—EQT Funds management Limited
Czechowisz, Tomasz—MCI Management
Czirjak, Laszlo—iEurope Capital LLC
D'Addario, Paul—Palisades Ventures (FKA: Centre Palisades Ventures)
D'Agrain, Corrine—Galileo Partners
D'Amico, Brian—Summer Street Capital LLC
D'Amore, Richard—North Bridge Venture Partners
D'Andrea, Harry—Valhalla Partners
D'Aniello, Daniel—Carlyle Group, The
D'Aquila, Jim—CoVestia Capital Partners
D'Arbeloff, Matt—Sparkventures, LLC
D'Argoubet, Christian—EPF Partners
D'Arthuys, Jean—PAI Partners (FKA: PAI Management)
D'Avanzo, Maria—Starwood Capital Group
D'Herouville, Baudouin—AXA Private Equity
D'Huart, Michel—Paluel-Marmont Capital SA
D'Janoeff, Alec—Balmoral Capital
D'Onofrio, Edward—Hamilton Lane Advisors, Inc.
D'Ovidio, Thomas—Thompson Street Capital Partners
D'Souza, Darryl—Investcorp Bank B.S.C.
D'Souza, Trevor—Mason Wells Private Equity (FKA: M&I Ventures)
D' agostino, Stephane—Groupama Private Equity (FKA: Finama Private Equity SA)
D. Sachs, Kylie—Ascend Venture Group LLC
DP Kelly, Sean—Cappello Capital Corp.
Da Silva Costa, Carlos—European Investment Bank, The (AKA: EIB)
Da Silva, Duarte—First South Investment Managers
DaValle, Albert—JK&B Capital
Daavsvand, Axel Hovo—Cubera Private Equity AS
Dabertin, Judy—Concentric Equity Partners, L.P.
Dabrowski, Kenneth—American Industrial Partners
Dadoo, Rajeev—S.R. One, Ltd.
Dady, Gail—DC Capital Partners LLC
Dady, Gail—Veritas Capital
Daems, Herman—GIMV N.V.
Dagi, Teo Forcht—Capstone Financial Partners LLC
Dagi, Teo Forcht—HLM Venture Partners
Dagres, Todd—PureTech Ventures
Dagres, Todd—Spark Capital
Dahan, Michel—Banexi Ventures Partners
Daher, Oussama—Carlyle Group, The
Dahl, Alan—EDG Partners LLC
Dahl, Erik—PRE Management
Dahl, Mikael—EQT Funds management Limited
Dahlberg, Bob—Horizon Ventures
Dahlberg, Johnny—Qeep Ventures AB
Dahlberg, Kenneth—SAIC Venture Capital Corporation
Dahlfors, Johan—Bridgepoint Development Capital
Dahlgaard, Finn—LMX Business Development A/S
Dahlin, Hakan—Segulah Advisor AB
Dahlin, Hakan—Skanditek Industriforvaltning AB (publ)
Dahlquist, Jan—Polaris Management A/S
Dahms, Peter—American Capital, Ltd.
Dahnke, Scott—Catterton Partners
Dahod, Shabbir—FirstMark Capital LLC
Dahong, Xie—CMIA Capital Partners (AKA: CM Investment Advisers Pte Ltd.)
Daileader, John—Greenbriar Equity Group LLC
Dailey, Eric—Tolomei Participations SAS
Dailey, Kristine—Park Street Capital LLC
Daitch, Joshua—Mesirow Private Equity Investments, Inc.
Dalal, Anupam—Kearny Venture Partners
Dalal, Shahzaad—IL&FS Investment Managers Ltd (FKA: IL&FS Venture Corp)
Dalal, Yogen—Mayfield Fund
Dalbello, Michael—Blackstone Group, L.P.
Dale, Andrew—Montlake Capital
Dale, Bernard—Connection Capital LLP
Dale, Manjit—TDR Capital LLP
Dale, Michael—Eastward Capital
Dale, Richard—Sigma Partners
Dalenson, Theodor—Novestra AB
Daley, George—MPM Capital (FKA: MPM Asset Management LLC)
Dali, Paul—Keynote Ventures (FKA: Dali, Hook Partners)
Dalle, Bernard—Index Ventures
Dalli, Dominic—Sovereign Capital LLP (FKA:Sovereign Capital, Ltd.)
Dalmasso, Jean-Michel—PAI Partners (FKA: PAI Management)
Dalmia, Gaurav—eIndia Venture Management
Dalsgaard, Carl-Johan—Odlander, Fredrikson & Co. AB (AKA: HealthCap)
Dalton, Barbara—EuclidSR Partners
Dalton, Barbara—Pfizer Venture Investments
Dalton, Frank—Cordova Ventures (FKA:Cordova Capital)
Dalton, Frank—Fulcrum Ventures
Dalton, Mark—Trimaran Capital Partners, LLC
Dalton, Sean—Highland Capital Partners LLC
Dalton-Hunt, Michelle—Newbury Partners LLC
Dalvey, David—Brightstone Capital
Dalvie, Shivanandan—AEA Investors LP
Daly, Paige—LNK Partners
Dames, Greg—Marquette Capital Partners
Damico, Joseph—RoundTable Health Care Partners
Damisch, Hans E—Beteiligungsgesellschaft fur die deutsche Wirtschaft mbH
Damm, Christopher—BioAdvance
Dammeier, Kurt—Sugar Mountain Capital
Damsgaard, Jens Kr.—Energi Invest Fyn A/S
Dan, Aubrey—Dancap Private Equity Inc.
Dancaster, David—Core Growth Capital LLP
Dance, Kerry—Hamilton BioVentures
Dand, Amit—Tano Capital LLC
Dando, Gareth—Southern Cross Venture Partners
Danella, Brian—DFJ Frontier
Danes, Elizabeth—Capital Z Investment Partners (FKA: Union Square Partners)
Daneshzadeh, Neda—Catterton Partners
Danford, Timothy—Storm Ventures LLC
Danhakl, John—Leonard Green & Partners
Daniel, Anand—Accel Partners
Daniel, David—Carlyle Group, The
Daniel, Marc—RBC Capital Partners/RBC Technology Ventures
Daniels, Bryan—Prairie Capital
Daniels, Leslie—CAI Capital Management Company
Daniels, Melissa—Morgan Stanley Venture Partners (AKA: MSDW)
Daniels, Terrence—Quad-C Management, Inc.
Danielsen, John—Danske Private Equity A/S
Danielson, Jon—Tudor Ventures
Danielsson, Hans—PineBridge Investments
Danko, George—Springworks, LLC
Dann, Mitchell—Sapient Capital Management LLC
Dannis, James—Berens Capital Management LLC
Dantas, Ana Siqueira—Jardim Botanico Partners (FKA: Araujo Fontes Consultoria)
Dantzker, David—Wheatley Partners
Daras, D. James—Inter-Atlantic Group
Darbon, Guillaume—Advent International
Darby, Christopher—In-Q-Tel, Inc.
Darby, Michael—Palisades Ventures (FKA: Centre Palisades Ventures)
Dardani, Ted—Oak Hill Capital Management, Inc.
Dare, John—Procuritas Partners KB
Daredia, Ikbal—Unicorn Investment Bank B.S.C.
Dargan, Alan—Lonsdale Capital Partners LLP
Darling, Scott—Frazier Healthcare and Technology Ventures
Darman, William—Carlyle Group, The
Darmon, David—Wendel
Darre, Bruno—Bow River Capital Partners
Dartley, Peter—Twin Haven Capital Partners
Darvish, Nissim—Pitango Venture Capital (FKA:Polaris Venture Capital Israel)
Darwent, Robert—Lion Capital (FKA: Hicks Muse (Europe))
Das, Jai—SAP Ventures
Das, Santanu—Signal Lake
Das, Siddhartha—VenturEast (FKA: APIDC Venture Capital Limited)
Dash, Somesh—Institutional Venture Partners
Dashiff, Duncan—Shattuck Hammond Partners
Daswani, Mohit—FTV Capital (FKA: FTVentures)
Daswani, Mohit—JMI Equity
Dattani, Maneksh—UBS Capital Corporation
Daudt, Robert—ChinaVest, Ltd.
Daugherty, F. Joseph—Grayson & Associates, Inc.
Daugherty, Patrick—Highland Capital Management, L.P.
Daum, Scott—Tricor Pacific Capital, Inc.
Daumet, Jean—Amundi Private Equity Funds SA
Dauphin, Steve—Murphree Venture Partners
Daussun, Robert—LBO France SAS
Dauvillaire, Pierre—Gimar Capital Investissement
Davenport, Aaron—Arsenal Capital Partners
Davenport, Aaron—SK Capital Partners
Davenport, Peter—Axxon Group
Daver, Vispi—Sierra Ventures
Daverman, Benjamin—GTCR Golder Rauner LLC
Daves, Jamie—City Light Capital
Davey, Brian—First Nations Equity, Inc.
Davey, Lynda—Kairos Capital Partners
David, Roy—Poalim Capital Markets Technologies Ltd

Davidow, William—Mohr Davidow Ventures
Davidson, Aaron—H.I.G. Capital LLC
Davidson, Duncan—VantagePoint Venture Partners
Davidson, Eran—Hasso Plattner Ventures Management GmbH
Davidson, George—MML Capital Partners
Davidson, James—Banyan Capital Advisors LLC
Davidson, James—Silver Lake Sumeru
Davidson, Mel—New Atlantic Ventures
Davidson, Michelle—Pacific Corporate Group
Davidson, Mitchell—Post Capital Partners LLC
Davidson, Paul—Facilities Corporate Management
Davidson, Paul—West Coast Capital
Davidson, Steven—Quadrangle Group LLC
Davidson, Stuart—Labrador Ventures
Davidson, Thomas—Enhanced Capital Partners, LLC
Davidson, Thomas—Village Ventures
Davidyuk, Gleb—Mint Capital, Ltd.
Davies, Gavyn—Active Private Equity Advisory LLP
Davies, Godfrey—CDC Group PLC (FKA: Commonwealth Development Corporation)
Davies, Guy—Permira Advisers LLP
Davies, Guy—WestBridge Fund Managers, Ltd.
Davies, Lord Mervyn—Corsair Capital LLC
Davies, Rhian—Acuity Capital LLP (FKA: Electra Partners LLP)
Davies, Robert—MML Capital Partners
Davies, Simon—Blackstone Group, L.P.
Davies, Stuart—Bain Capital
Davis, Andrew—Boston Ventures Management, Inc.
Davis, Anthony—Linden LLC
Davis, Cary—Warburg Pincus LLC
Davis, Charles Jiggs—WI Harper Group
Davis, Charles—Signet Healthcare Partners (FKA: Sanders Morris Harris)
Davis, Charles—Stone Point Capital LLC
Davis, Dave—Perseus LLC
Davis, Denise—Clean Pacific Ventures
Davis, Elliott—Next Wave Funds
Davis, Gregory—Key Principal Partners LLC (AKA: KPP)
Davis, James—Brockway Moran & Partners, Inc.
Davis, Jeff—Acorn Growth Companies
Davis, John—Club Auto Sport
Davis, John—Stone Canyon Venture Partners (SCVP)
Davis, Jordan—Radius Ventures LLC
Davis, Joseph—Triton Pacific Capital Partners LLC
Davis, K.Rodger—Northcreek Mezzanine
Davis, Kim—Charlesbank Capital Partners LLC
Davis, Kimberly—TorQuest Partners, Inc.
Davis, Mark—Balloch China Fund, The
Davis, Niall—firstVentury GmbH
Davis, Ralph—Cressey & Company, L.P.
Davis, Ralph—Thoma Cressey Bravo
Davis, Ray—Natural Gas Partners (NGP)
Davis, Richard—GarMark Partners
Davis, Rick—CCG Venture Partners, LLC
Davis, Robert—Highland Capital Partners LLC
Davis, Robert—Littlejohn & Company LLC
Davis, Robert—Shoreview Industries
Davis, Roy—Johnson & Johnson Development Corporation
Davis, Ryan—EPIC Ventures
Davis, Stacey—Johnson & Johnson Development Corporation
Davis, Stephen—Vista Equity Partners
Davis, Timothy—FreshTracks Capital
Davis, Tony—Brightspark Ventures
Davis-Moody, Kimberly—Pharos Capital Group LLC
Davison, Andrew—Scottish Equity Partners
Davison, Chris—Permira Advisers LLP
Davison, Guy—Cinven, Ltd.
Davison, Jeffrey—Inflection Point Ventures
Davison, Kristina—iEurope Capital LLC
Davoli, Bob—Sigma Partners
Davoody, Harry—American Capital, Ltd.
Davy, Michael—Bridgepoint Capital, Ltd.
Daw, Richard—Phoenix Equity Partners (FKA: DLJ European Private Equity)
Dawson, Andrew—Standard Chartered Private Equity, Ltd.
Dawson, Mark—Peak Capital Group LLC
Dawson, William—Wellspring Capital Management LLC
Day, Benson—London Asia Capital Plc (FKA: netvest.com Plc)
Day, Martin—OMERS Private Equity
Day, Matthew—Black Opal Equity
Day, Rob—@Ventures
Day, Rob—Black Coral Capital
Day, Robert—TCW Capital
Day, Timothy—First Reserve Corporation
Dayan, Jean-Marc—Duke Street Capital
Dayton, Sky—Evercore Partners
De Alfaro, Marco—IDI Asset Management SA
De Almeida, Abel Cubal—AICEP Capital Global - Sociedade de Capital de Risco, S.A.
De Baey-Diepolder, Annegret—TVM Capital GmbH
De Beer, Anthonie—Ethos Private Equity
De Bellefonds, Philippe—Convergent Capital SAS
De Benedetti, Marco—Carlyle Group, The
De Benedetti, Mario—J. Hirsch & Co. S.a.r.l.
De Bernardy, Jean-Louis—Activa Capital SAS
De Beublain, Herve—NextStage SAS
De Bodinat, Henri—TIME Equity Partners SAS
De Boer, Klaas—Entrepreneurs Fund Management LLP
De Boer, Mark—Index Ventures
De Boever, Dirk—Ocas Ventures BVBA
De Bruin, Belle—Indofin
De Bruin, C.J.—Indofin
De Bure, Frederic—IDG Ventures Vietnam
De Calan, Mael—Butler Capital Partners SA
De Cambiaire, Bruno—iXO Private Equity
De Carvalho, Jose Augusto—Axxon Group
De Cecco, Enrico—CAPITALIA Sofipa SGR (FKA: MCC Sofipa)
De Chassey, Thibaut—AtriA Capital Partenaires
De Costa, Felicio—Result Venture Knowledge International
De Courten, Raffaele—Alto Partners SGR SpA
De Esteban, Pedro—Carlyle Group, The
De Fontaine Vive Curtaz, Philippe—European Investment Bank, The (AKA: EIB)
De Fouquet, Pierre—Iris Capital Management (FKA: Part'Com Management S.A.)
De Freminville, Paul—123Venture SA
De Gabriel, Jaime—iNova Capital SCR SA
De Geer, Gerard—IK Investment Partners, Ltd.
De Gheest, Anne—Concept Ventures Management LLC
De Giglio, Francesco—Advent International
De Graeve, Wim—Capital-e
De Groot, Mark—iNovia Capital
De Hoop, Roel—Prime Technology Ventures NV
De Jaime, Javier—CVC Capital Partners (Europe), Ltd.
De Jong, Jan—Favonius Ventures
De Jong, Peter H. J.—Undisclosed Firm
De Jong, Rob—AlpInvest Partners N.V.
De Kerdaniel, Domnin—CVC Capital Partners (Europe), Ltd.
De Kergrohen, Herve—CDC Innovation SAS (FKA: CDC IXIS Innovation)
De Klerk, Paul—AlpInvest Partners N.V.
De Klerk, Paul—NIBC Principal Investments (FKA: Parnib Holding NV)
De Kruif, J.D.—Indofin
De Kruijff, Gepco—Freshwater Venture Partners
De La Riviere, Erik—Iris Capital Management (FKA: Part'Com Management S.A.)
De Leeuw, David—Lion Chemical Capital
De Leeuw, Peter—Lion Chemical Capital
De Letona, Jose—Excel Partners
De Liagre Bohl, Cathrien—Freshwater Venture Partners
De Lint, Christiaan—Headway Capital Partners LLP
De Lisi, Paul—CapStreet Group LLC, The (FKA: Summit Capital Group)
De Luarca, Ramon Menendez—Excel Partners
De Magalhaes, Jose Carlos Reis—Tarpon Investment Group
De Marzio, Alfredo—Cofiri
De Meester, Joris—AlpInvest Partners N.V.
De Meester, Joris—NIBC Principal Investments (FKA: Parnib Holding NV)
De Mello, Michael E.S.—Espirito Santo Tech Ventures
De Metz, Jerome—MBO Partenaires
De Mitry, Francois—Intermediate Capital Group Plc
De Monico, A. Nicholas—Commonfund Capital, Inc. (FKA: Common Fund)
De Moraes, Eduardo Aguinaga—Latin America Equity Partners (FKA: LAEP)
De Moustier, Christilla—PAI Partners (FKA: PAI Management)
De Neergaard, Claes—Stiftelsen Indusstrifonden
De Pablo, Javier—Carlyle Group, The
De Pauw, Marc—Sofinim NV
De Remedios, Alvaro—Arcano Capital
De Ridder, Paul—Halder Holdings BV
De Rivera, Gonzalo—Impala Capital Partners (FKA; Suala Capital Advisors)
De Romanet, Augustin—Fonds de Reserve pour les Retraites (AKA: FRR)
De Rossi, Roberto—Consilium SGR pA
De Rothschild, David—Paris Orleans (Francarep SA)
De Roux, Thibaut—Generis Capital Partners
De Rubertis, Francesco—Index Ventures
De Rudder, Thierry—Groupe Bruxelles Lambert S.A. (GBL)
De Rycker, Sonali—Accel Partners
De Saint-Malo, Roberto—Adara Venture Partners
De Schrevel, Jean-Philippe—BlueOrchard Investments Sarl
De Serdio, Ricardo—PAI Partners (FKA: PAI Management)

De Seze, Amaury—PAI Partners (FKA: PAI Management)
De Silva, Nirosh—Leopard Capital, Ltd.
De Silva, Richard—Highland Capital Partners LLC
De Smedt, Patrick—Big Bang Ventures CVA
De Smet, Fitz—bScope Partners, Inc.
De Vaugelas, Francois—Grand Sud Ouest Capital
De Vecchi, Filippo—Advent International
De Vecchi, Guido—Natixis-Cape SGR SpA
De Verdalle, Philippe—Finimmo
De Vick, Philippe—KBC Private Equity NV
De Villiers, Etienne—Englefield Capital
De Vregille, Olivier—PAI Partners (FKA: PAI Management)
De Vries, Coenraad—Start Green Venture Capital
De Vries, Gilad—Carmel Ventures
De Vries, Harm—Erasmus MC
De Winter, Alex—Mohr Davidow Ventures
De Wit, De heer—ViewPoint Capital Partners GmbH
De clercq, Casper—U.S. Venture Partners
De la Bigne, Eric—UBS Capital Corporation
De la Brosse, Bernard—Access Capital Partners
De la Chapelle, Philippe—Equitis
De la Cierva, Gonzalo—Result Venture Knowledge International
De la Martiniere, Dominique—CITA Gestion SA
De la Serna, Nora—Corinthian Capital Group LLC
DeAngelis, Kenneth—Austin Ventures, L.P.
DeAngelis, Pasquale—ProQuest Investments
DeAngelis, Robert—Crystal Capital
DeAngelo, Lawrence—Roark Capital Group
DeAvila, Ricardo—Alerion Capital Group
DeBlois, Mark—Bunker Hill Capital
DeBolt, Robert—Mesirow Private Equity Investments, Inc.
DeBroux, Michel—Hydro-Quebec CapiTech Inc.
DeCarlo, Michele—Longboat Capital Management LLC
DeFlorio, Michael—Harvest Partners LLC
DeGrassi, W. Duke—Hamilton Lane Advisors, Inc.
DeHart, John—Meridius Capital
DeJesus, Jeffrey—Midwest Mezzanine Funds
DeLaar, Mark—Summit Accelerator Fund
DeLaar, Mark—Summit Partners
DeLaite, Alexandra—Thomas H. Lee Partners (AKA: TH Lee Partners)
DeLatte, Herman—Big Bang Ventures CVA
DeLatte, Herman—Solid Capital BV
DeLaughter, Ray—UNC Kenan-Flagler Private Equity Fund
DeLeo, Dennis—Trillium Group LLC
DeLeon, Kevin—Bracken Partners Limited
DeLoche, John—Bridgescale Partners
DeMaio, Warren—Ritchie Capital
DeMarco, Joseph—Wall Street Venture Capital
DeMartini, Stephen—Prudential Capital Group
DeMuth, Donald—DFW Capital Partners (AKA:DeMuth, Folger & Wetherill)
DeNino, Mark—TL Ventures
DeNunzio, David—Credit Suisse Private Equity
DePasquale, Scott—Braemar Energy Ventures
DePonte, Kelly—Probitas Partners, Inc.
DeRegt, Kenneth—Aetos Capital LLC
DeRosa, Michael—Element Partners
DeSantis, Daniel—Linsalata Capital Partners
DeVeer, Kipp—Ares Management, Inc.
DeVito, David—TCW Capital
DeVito, Jerry—Blackstone Group, L.P.
DeVore, David—Alpha Capital Partners, Ltd.
DeVries, Jerry—Path4 Ventures, LLC
DeVries, Jerry—TEXO Ventures
DeVries, Lawson—Grotech Ventures
DeVries, Michael—EDF Ventures
DeVries, Timothy—Norwest Equity Partners
DeVries, Timothy—Norwest Mezzanine Partners
DeWolf, Daniel—Dawntreader Ventures
Deadman, Davis—Highland Capital Management, L.P.
Deaker, Michelle—OneVentures Pty, Ltd.
Deakin, Andrew—Phoenix Equity Partners (FKA: DLJ European Private Equity)
Dealy, James—Reynolds, DeWitt & Co.
Dean, Allan—Incyte Venture Partners LLC
Dean, Christopher—Summit Partners
Dean, John—Startup Capital Ventures L.P.
Deane, Will—Exto Partners Pty, Ltd.
Deardorff, Tom—Virginia Capital
Deas, Ian—Pantheon Ventures, Ltd.
Debache, Herve—Tertiaire Developpement
Debbas, Christopher—CD Ventures, LLC
Decanniere, Olivier—AXA Private Equity
Deceuninck, Dirk—QiFund
Dechet, Andrew—TPG Capital
Decker, Robert L.—Global Leisure Partners LLP
Deckers, Floris G.—F. van Lanschot Participaties BV
Deckoff, Stephen—Black Diamond Capital Management, LLC
Dederick, Clint—IN Partners LLC (AKA: Midpoint)
Dee, Michael—Lindsay Goldberg LLC (FKA: Lindsay Goldberg & Bessemer GP)
Dee, Michael—Temasek Holdings Pvt., Ltd.
Deedrick, John—Accuitive Medical Ventures
Deel, Chris—Boxwood Capital Partners, LLC
Deeney, Daniel—New Venture Partners LLC
Deeter, Byron—Bessemer Venture Partners
Defforey-Crepet, Sophie—Aquasourca Societe d' Investissement
Defieux, Richard—Allegra Partners (FKA: Lawrence, Smith & Horey)
Defieux, Richard—SJF Ventures
Defieux, Richard—Smith Defieux Capital Partners
Defty, Josephine—Pantheon Ventures, Ltd.
Degenhart, Jeremy—Advantage Capital Partners
Degrassi, Michele—Friulia SpA Fin.Reg.Friuli-Venezia
Dehejia, Adi—Diamond Point Capital Management
Deignan, Joseph—Wayzata Investment Partners
Deitch, Lyle—21Ventures LLC
Deitmers, Hubert—Van den Ende & Deitmers B.V.
Dejoie, Eric—MBO Partenaires
Dekel, Eitan—Magma Venture Partners
Dekel, Elie—Saban Ventures
Dekker, Jan—Cleantech Ventures Pty, Ltd.
Dekleer, Rolf—GrowthWorks
Del Biaggio, William—MVC Capital (FKA: meVC)
Del Guercio, Joseph—CNF Investments, LLC
Del Mul, Wendy—Torys LLP
Del Papa, Jeffrey—Thoma Cressey Bravo
Del Presto, Peter—PNC Equity Management Corp.
Del Rosario, Ramon—AB Capital & Investment Corporation
Del Valle, Alejandro reynoso—Evercore Partners
Del Valle, Martin—Investindustrial Partners, Ltd.
DelBene, Gerard—Investcorp Bank B.S.C.
DelDonna, Christina—Allied Capital Corporation
Delachaume, Herve—IDIA Agricapital
Delagardelle, Jeani—New Leaf Venture Partners LLC
Delaney, Daniel—Industrial Growth Partners
Delaney, John—CapitalSource Holdings, Inc.
Delaney, Michael—Court Square Capital Partners
Delangle, Eric—Balmoral Capital
Delany, Logan—Delany Capital Management Corporation (DCM)
Delany, Robert—Sciens Capital Partners (FKA: Zilkha Venture Partners)
Delany, Shannon—Pine Creek Partners
Delaporte, Antoine—I&P Management Ltd. (AKA: Indian Ocean)
Delarosa, Steven—Highland Capital Management, L.P.
Delavenne, Francois—Acofi Gestion
Delclaux, Jorge—Inversiones Ibersuizas S.A.
Deldag, Can—Carlyle Group, The
Deleage, Jean—Alta Partners
Delehanty, Sean—Silver Lake Sumeru
Deleray, Michael—Bendigo Partners LLC
Delgado, Bruno—Mercapital Servicios Financieros
Delgado, Joe—CCMP Capital Advisors LLC
Delgado, Lister—IDEA Fund Partners
Delgado-Moreira, Juan—Hamilton Lane Advisors, Inc.
Delistathis, Thanasis—New Atlantic Ventures
Delivanis, Constatin—Sand Hill Group, LLC
Dell Aquila, Richard—Southfield Capital Advisors
Dell, Adam—Austin Ventures, L.P.
Dell, Adam—Impact Venture Partners
Dell, Adam—Steelpoint Capital Partners
Dell, Michael—MSD Capital L.P.
Dell, Steven—Impact Venture Partners
Della Rocca, Steven—Vestar Capital Partners, Inc.
Della Valentina, Francesco—Mandarin Capital Partners
Dellby, Ulrika—Fagerberg & Dellby AB
Dellenbach, Hans—Emerald Technology Ventures AG
Dellgren, Bjorn—BankInvest Group A/S
Delman, Scott—Capital Z Investment Partners (FKA: Union Square Partners)
Deloire, Monique—Indigo Capital, Ltd.
Delos, Alexandre—Access Capital Partners
Deluca, Anthony—SCF Partners
Delvaux, Jean-Louis—Natixis Private Equity SA
Demetree, Chris—Value Plus Ventures
Demicheli, Marc—TCR CAPITAL SAS
Demkowicz, Brian—Superior Capital Partners
Demont, Michel—Aurinvest SAS
Dempsey, Jill—Dolphin Capital Group, LLC
Dempsey, Neal—Bay Partners
Dempsey, Sean—Merus Capital Investment
Dempsey, Simon—Kenmore Private Equity, Ltd. (AKA: KPE)
Dempsey, Steve—Greyrock Capital Group
Demuynck, Pieter—Fortis Private Equity NV/SA (FKA: VIV NV)
Den Besten, Ron—Aureos Capital, Ltd.
Denegri, Michele—Iniziativa Piemonte SpA
Denenberg, Byron—KB Partners LLC

Deng, Feng—Northern Light Venture Capital
Deng, Jay—Pacific Venture Partners
Deng, Xihong—Hony Capital Ltd.
Dengla, Manoj—Carlyle Group, The
Denicola, Greg—Grande Ventures
Denious, Robert—Questor Management Company LLC
Denis, Bruno—Naxicap Partners SA
Denison, Thomas—Brown Gibbons Lang & Company LLC
Denissen, Mark—TI Ventures
Deniz, Melissa—Henderson Equity Partners (AKA: Henderson Private Capital)
Denker, Soren—MAZ level one GmbH
Denkmann, Andreas—capiton AG
Dennen, Brian—Iron Capital Partners
Dennen, Robert—Enhanced Capital Partners, LLC
Dennert, Roland—Cipio Partners
Dennis, David—Pacific Venture Group
Dennis, Reid—Institutional Venture Partners
Dennison, Piers—Candover Investments PLC
Denniston, John—Kleiner Perkins Caufield & Byers
Denny, George—Halpern, Denny & Company
Denomme, Mark—Hercules Technology Growth Capital, Inc.
Dent, Steve—Birch Hill Equity Partners Management, Inc.
Denten, Mary—Scale Venture Partners
Denvir, Michael—Jordan Company, The
Der Megreditchian, Philippe—Baring Vostok Capital Partners
Derendinger, Peter—Alpha Associates AG
Derrick, Robert—Prudential Capital Group
Derricks, Alma—BlueCar Partners
Derungs, Bruno—Climate Change Capital, Ltd.
Desaedeleer, Marc—Citi Venture Capital International
Desai, Ankit—Third Security LLC
Desai, Nick—Shackleton Equity Partners LLC
Desai, Rick—Madison Dearborn Partners LLC
Desbard, Michel—CDC Innovation SAS (FKA: CDC IXIS Innovation)
Desbois, Alain-Oliver—Cycle Capital Management
Descarpentries, Sebastien—Auriga Partners S.A.
Deschamps, Bernard—Capital Benoit, Inc.
Deschamps, Bruno—3i Group PLC
Deshmukh, Nitin—Kotak Investment Advisors, Ltd. (AKA: KPEG)
Deshpande, Bala—New Enterprise Associates, Inc.
Deshpande, Salil—Bay Partners
Desjardins, Jean—GTI Capital Inc.
Deslandes, Maire—Silverfleet Capital (FKA: PPM Capital Partners)
Desmarais, Louis—Garage Technology Ventures Canada
Desmarais, Louis—Skypoint Capital Corporation
Destin, Fred—Atlas Venture, Ltd.
Detlefs, Paul—Alumni Capital Network
Detry, Jean-Louis—Vermeer Capital Partners
Dettmar, Christopher—Monumental Venture Partners LLC
Dettmar, Christopher—NAC Ventures, LLC
Dettori, Gianluca—dPixel Srl
Deturck, Michiel—Mitiska
Deupree, A. Reed—Carlyle Group, The
Deuticke, Paul—Gilbert Global Equity Capital, L.L.C.
Deutsch, Bob—GCP Capital Partners
Deutschman, Rob—Cappello Capital Corp.
Deutschmann, Robert—Borealis Infrastructure Management, Inc.
Deuzeman, Leo—Greenfield Capital Partners
Devenny, John—Invision Capital Management LLC
Devereux, Robin—Summit Accelerator Fund
Devereux, Robin—Summit Partners
Deves, E—Holland Venture III B.V. (FKA: Holland Venture B.V.)
Devine, Joe—ION Equity, Ltd.
Devine, Peter—Uniseed Management Pty Ltd.
Devitte, Jesse—Borealis Ventures
Devloo, Steven—American Capital, Ltd.
Dewar, Andrew—Absa Capital Private Equity (Pty) Ltd.
Dewijngaert, Jan—Eagle Venture Partners
Dewitt, Gregory—CrossHarbor Capital Partners LLC
Dewolf, Claude—Sambrinvest S.A.
Dexheimer, John—First Analysis Corporation
Dey, Sudip—Investcorp Bank B.S.C.
Dhaliwal, Sunil—Battery Ventures, L.P.
Dhamelincourt, Philippe—Matignon Investissement et Gestion
Dhar, Ash—Horizon Ventures
Dharmaraj, Satish—Redpoint Ventures
Dhawan, Ashish—ChrysCapital Management Company
Dhawan, Prateek—Accel Partners
Dhawan, Rajeev—Equity Partners Management Pty Ltd.
Dhinsa, Jojar Singh—Athlone International, Ltd
Dhondge, Mukund—Nalanda Capital Pte, Ltd.
Dhondiyal, Siddharth—India Value Fund Advisors Private Ltd. (FKA: GW Capital)
Di Benedetto, Jean-Pierre—Argos Soditic SA
Di Bona, Tony—Alloy Ventures
Di Gresy, Emanuele—Virtus Capital Partners
Di Scipio, Robert—Skyland Capital LLC
Di Sciullo, Gino—Charter Life Sciences
Di Spiezio Sardo, Emilio—BlueGem Capital Partners LLP
Di Valmarana, Francesco—Pantheon Ventures, Ltd.
DiBella, Paul—Cordova Ventures (FKA:Cordova Capital)
DiBenedetto, Eric—Convergence Partners
DiDomenico, David—New Mountain Capital LLC
DiFranco, Dave—Blue Point Capital Partners (FKA: Key Equity Capital)
DiGesualdo, Antonio—TGF Management Corp (FKA:Texas Growth Fund)
DiMaio, Jack—Credit Suisse Asset Management
DiMarchi, Richard—Twilight Venture Partners
DiMartile, Michael—Hamilton Lane Advisors, Inc.
DiNardo, Lou—Crosslink Capital
DiNovi, Anthony—Thomas H. Lee Partners (AKA: TH Lee Partners)
DiPaolo, David—Brooks, Houghton & Company, Inc.
DiPaolo, Edward—Growth Capital Partners, L.P.
DiPiano, Michael—NewSpring Capital
DiPietro, Patrick—VenGrowth Capital Funds
DiPoto, Kenneth—North Bridge Venture Partners
DiRoma, Jill—Alcatel-Lucent Ventures
DiSimone, Anthony—Aurora Resurgence Management Partners LLC
Diab, Mohammed—DEFI Gestion SA
Diao, Jun Huan—Shenzhen OFC Investment Management, Ltd.
Diaz, Gonzalo—iNova Capital SCR SA
Diaz, Reinaldo—Celtic Pharma Management, LP
Diaz, Reinaldo—Celtic Therapeutics Management, L.L.L.P.
Diaz-Laviada, Juan—Advent International
Diaz-Rato, Gonzalo—Impala Capital Partners (FKA; Suala Capital Advisors)
Dibble, Timothy—Alta Communications
Dibner, Gil—Gemini Israel Funds, Ltd.
Dick, Christopher—Ascent Venture Partners
Dick, Timohy—Startup Capital Ventures L.P.
Dicker, Thomas—Innoven Partenaires S.A.
Dickerson, Melissa—Genstar Capital LLC
Dickes, Scott—Hadley Capital
Dickey, Keith—Shattuck Hammond Partners
Dickie, Brian—Investcorp Bank B.S.C.
Dickie, John—Berkshire Partners LLC
Dickin, Tony—Zeus Private Equity
Dickinson, Daniel—Thayer Hidden Creek
Dickinson, Mark—Candover Investments PLC
Dickman, Barry—Quantum Technology Partners
Dickson, Frank—Maryland DBED (AKA:Dept. of Business & Economic Development)
Dickson, Jeffrey—Prudential Capital Group
Didden, James—Blackstone Group, L.P.
Didier, Jean-Marie—Autonomie et Solidarite
Dieber, Gary—Behrman Capital
Diedrich, Peter—RBC Capital Partners/RBC Technology Ventures
Diedrich, Peter—Skypoint Capital Corporation
Diegruber, Jurgen—German Capital GmbH
Diehl, Bowen—American Capital, Ltd.
Diehl, Charles—Activa Capital SAS
Diehl, Jeffrey—Adams Street Partners LLC
Diehl, Michael—Activa Capital SAS
Diekmann, Henning—Wunderlich & Partner Wirtschaftsberatung fur den Mittelstand
Diekroeger, Kenneth—Golden Gate Capital
Dielacher, Gabriel—Vienna Capital Partners
Diem, Michael—S.R. One, Ltd.
Dien, Marc—Columbia Equity Partners
Dienst, Rolf—Wellington Partners Venture Capital GmbH
Dienst, Sedge—KCA Partners, Ltd.
Dierckx, Filip—Fortis Private Equity NV/SA (FKA: VIV NV)
Diesbach, Benjamin—Oak Hill Capital Management, Inc.
Diest, Friedrich von—Sirius Venture Partners GmbH
Dietz, Florian Vitus—Ventacc Beteiligungs- und Beratungs GmbH
Dietz, Hans-Peter—TakeOff Venture Capital Management GmbH
Dietz, Steven—GRP Partners
Dietz, William—Yukon Partners Management LLC
Dietze, Jane—NextPoint Partners, L.P.
Diggines, Jonathan—Enterprise Ventures, Ltd. (FKA:Lancashire Enterprises PLC)
Diggins, John—Platinum Equity LLC
Dighe, Bharat—BTS Investment Advisors, Ltd.
Dighton, Simon—Catalyst Investment Managers Pty, Ltd.
Digravio, Karen—Westfield Capital Management
Dilda, Mirco—Argos Soditic SA

Dill, Charles—Two Rivers Associates LLC (FKA: Gateway Associates, L.P.)
Dillabough, Gary—Westly Group, The
Dillard, Lauren—Carlyle Group, The
Diller, Christian—Capital Dynamics AG
Dillon, John—Emergence Capital Partners LLC
Dillon, John—Evercore Partners
Dillon, John—RJD Partners Limited (FKA: Royal London Private Equity)
Dillon, Kevin—Atlantic Bridge
Dimaculangan, Alfredo—Small Business Guarantee and Finance Corporation
Dimberio, Joseph—PPM America Capital Partners LLC
Diment, Tony—Company Guides, Ltd. (AKA: Company Guides Venture Partners)
Dimitri, James—Welsh, Carson, Anderson & Stowe
Dimitrov, Ivelin—Fifth Street Capital LLC
Dimmitt, Elizabeth—IndexAtlas Group
Diner, Fahri—Sigma Partners
Dinerman, David—Probitas Partners, Inc.
Ding, James—GSR Ventures
Dingle, Phillip—HealthEdge Investment Partners
Dingreville, Sophie—Iris Capital Management (FKA: Part'Com Management S.A.)
Dinh, Hoa Thi—Vietnam Pioneer Partners
Dinneen, Patricia—Siguler Guff & Company
Dinnen, Sean—CBPE Capital, LLP (AKA: Close Brothers Private Equity, Ltd.)
Dinsel, Detlef—IK Investment Partners, Ltd.
Dinte, Boaz—Evergreen Venture Partners
Dintersmith, Ted—Charles River Ventures
Dinur, Arnon—Greylock Partners
Dioguardi, William—Spencer Trask Ventures, Inc. (FKA: Spencer Trask Securities)
Dionne, Denis—CDP Capital - Technology Ventures (FKA: CDP Sofinov)
Dionne, John—Blackstone Group, L.P.
Dios, Jose—Sciens Capital Partners (FKA: Zilkha Venture Partners)
Diouf, Wagane—AfriCap Microfinance Investment Company
Dircks, Thomas—Charterhouse Group International, Inc.
Dirk, Posner—BPEP International
Dirvin, John—Austin Ventures, L.P.
Dishman, Robert—Mediphase Venture Partners
Dishner, Jeffrey—Starwood Capital Group
Ditlevsen, Mads—EQT Funds management Limited
Dittmann, Dorit—S-UBG AG
Dittmar, Christofer—Accera Venture Partners AG
Ditzler, Randy—Sequoia Capital
Diwakar, Sunil V.—IL&FS Investment Managers Ltd (FKA: IL&FS Venture Corp)
Diwan, Ajay—J&W Seligman & Company
Dixit, Amit—Blackstone Group, L.P.
Dixon, Donald—Trident Capital
Dixon, John—Endeavour Capital
Dixon, Phillip—Treadstone Group Inc., The
Dixon, Roy—Onyx Capital Advisors LLC
Dizengremel, Bruno—Innovacom SA
Do Amaral, Luis Manoel—Latin America Equity Partners (FKA: LAEP)
Do, Frank—American Capital, Ltd.
Do, Hiep—IDG Ventures Vietnam
Do, Tuyen—Royal Palm Capital Partners, LLP
Do, Viet Hung—Vietnam Pioneer Partners
Dobron, Albert—Providence Equity Partners LLC
Dockery, J. Stephen—Fidus Capital
Doctoroff, Adam—Monitor Clipper Partners LLC
Dodd, Andy—PHD Equity Partners LLP
Dodd, Mike—Austin Ventures, L.P.
Dodds, William—Thomvest Ventures
Doddy, Hurley—EMP Africa Fund Management (AKA: Emerging Capital Partners)
Dodge, Sherwood—GE Commercial Finance - Equity
Dodson, Andrew—Parthenon Capital LLC
Dodson, David—Headwaters Merchant Bank
Doeksen, Jan Willem—Parcom Capital
Doeksen, Volkert—AlpInvest Partners N.V.
Doering, Mark—Natural Gas Partners (NGP)
Doerr, Cynthia—Essex Woodlands Health Ventures
Doerr, John—Kleiner Perkins Caufield & Byers
Doherty, Christopher—Columbia Partners LLC
Doherty, Christopher—SCP Private Equity Partners
Doherty, Nora—BioCrossroads, Inc.
Doherty, Patrick—Mariner Capital Partners LLC
Doig, Michelle—Abingworth Management, Ltd.
Dokas, Elias—MidOcean Partners
Dolan, A. Barr—Charter Life Sciences
Dolan, A. Barr—Charter Venture Capital (AKA: Charter Ventures)
Dolan, David—GrowthPath Capital, LLC (FKA: Tangram Partners, Inc.)
Dolan, Mike—Media & Print Investments Plc
Dolanski, Anthony—Internet Capital Group
Dolder, Adam—Great Point Partners LLC
Dolezalek, J. Stephan—VantagePoint Venture Partners
Dolfato, Mark—Goode Partners LLC
Doll, Andre—Saarlandische Wagnisfinanzierungsgesellschaft mbH (AKA SWG)
Doll, Dixon—DCM
Doll, Norbert—Lead Equities GmbH
Dolla, Estelle—123Venture SA
Dolle, Bruce—BSD Venture Capital LLC
Dollhopf, Thomas—Marwit Capital, LLC
Dollinger, D. Todd—Trendlines Group, The
Dollinger, Steve—Crimson
Dolman, Clive—Candover Investments PLC
Dolphin, Geoff—Innovation Capital Associates Pty, Ltd.
Domach, Jim—Mason Wells Private Equity (FKA: M&I Ventures)
Domanig, Gina—Emerald Technology Ventures AG
Dombcik, Jeffrey—Triangle Capital Corporation
Domdey, Horst—BioM AG
Domengeaux, Maury—Quicksilver Ventures (FKA: QTV Capital)
Domenik, Stephen—Sevin Rosen Funds
Domin, Alex—WHEB Ventures, Ltd.
Dominguez, John—SVB Capital
Dominguez, Michael—Providence Equity Partners LLC
Dominik, David—Golden Gate Capital
Domolky, Randolph—Liquid Capital Management Group, LLC
Domoshevizki, Avi—Battery Ventures, L.P.
Domoshevizki, Avi—Concord Ventures (FKA: Nitzanim)
Domzalski, Adam—Penton Consulting Sp. K. (AKA: Penton Partners)
Donahue, Thomas—Alumni Capital Network
Donaldson, M. Scott—Silver Oak Management
Donaldson, Pierre—JLA Ventures (FKA: J.L. Albright Venture Partners)
Donatelli, Jerry—Cornestone Capital Partners
Donath, Dirk—Pegasus Venture Capital
Donck, Frank—3D Participaties NV
Dondero, James—Highland Capital Management, L.P.
Dondero, Stephen—Aegis Capital Group LLC
Donelan, Brett—American Capital, Ltd.
Dong, Guixin—Huinong Capital
Dong, Jonathan—Milestone Capital Management, Ltd.
Dong, Kan Zhi—Shenzhen Capital Group Co., Ltd.
Donigan, Meg—Monitor Clipper Partners LLC
Donnellan, Patrick—Equinox Capital, Inc.
Donnelly, David—Fleming Family & Partners, Ltd. (AKA: FF&P)
Donner, Michael—Abacus Private Equity (ASA: Abacus Capital Corporation)
Donner, Richard—HgCapital
Donnini, David—GTCR Golder Rauner LLC
Donnon, Jeffrey—First Round Capital
Donoaica, Costin Florin—7 L Capital Partners
Donoghue, Michael—Spring Capital Partners (FKA: Spring Capital Investors LLC)
Donohoe, Kevin—Liberty Capital Management Corporation
Donohoe, Robin—Draper Richards, L.P.
Donohoe, Suzanne—Kohlberg, Kravis, Roberts & Company, L.P.
Donohue, James—Keyhaven Capital Partners, Ltd.
Donohue, Liam—.406 Ventures (AKA: Point 406 Ventures)
Donohue, Liam—Arcadia Management, LLC (AKA: Arcadia Partners)
Donohue, Lilly—Fortress Investment Group LLC
Donovan, Alvin—Kiwi Growth Partners Ltd.
Donovan, Mark—Salix Ventures
Donovan, Michael—Welsh, Carson, Anderson & Stowe
Donovan, William—Columbia Equity Partners
Doo-Hoon, Kim—M-Venture Investment, Inc. (FKA: Shinyoung Venture Capital)
Doody, Christopher—Stone Point Capital LLC
Doogan, Declan—Beacon Bioventures
Dooley, John—Jarvinian LLC
Doolittle, H.F.—Clearview Capital LLC
Doomany, George—Andlinger & Company, Inc.
Doose, Jeff—Adena Ventures
Doppelt, Michael—Irving Place Capital
Doppelt, Yoav—Ofer Hi-Tech
Dorairaj, Anand—New Silk Route Partners LLC
Doran, John—Summit Partners
Doran, Mark—Freeman Spogli & Co.
Doran, Niall—Parkmead Group PLC, The (FKA: Interregnum PLC)
Dore, Guillaume-Olivier—Agregator Gestion SAS
Doren, Kevin—Divergent Ventures
Dorleac, Christian—TCR CAPITAL SAS
Dorman, D. Mark—Endeavour Capital
Dorman, Stephen—Versa Capital Management (FKA: Chrysalis Capital Partners)
Dorr, Judy—Portage Venture Partners (AKA: Graystone Venture Partners)

Dorrell, Dean—Redbus Investments, Ltd. (AKA: Redbus Group)
Dorrell, Michael—Blackstone Group, L.P.
Dorrian, James—Crosspoint Venture Partners
Dorsey, Michael—DBL Investors (AKA: Double Bottom Line Venture Capital)
Dorsey, Michael—Westly Group, The
Dorsey, Sean—NatCity Investments, Inc.
Dortch, Elyn—CapitalSouth Partners, L.L.C.
Dorton, Stephen—Invision Capital Management LLC
Dosch, Christian—Cinven, Ltd.
Dospiva, Marek—Penta Investments, Ltd.
Dossena, Giovanna—AVM Associati SpA
Dossett, Corey—Chicago Growth Partners (William Blair Capital Partners)
Dotan, Ami—China Israel Value Capital (AKA: CIVC)
Dotan, Amiram—Platinum-Neurone Ventures
Dotzler, Frederick—De Novo Ventures
Doub, Robb—New Markets Venture Partners (AKA: New Markets Growth Fund)
Douchet, Matthieu—Initiative & Finance Investissement SA
Dougall, Philip—Sun Capital Partners, Inc.
Dougery, John—Inventus Capital Partners
Dougherty, Dennis—Intersouth Partners
Dougherty, James—Arcus Ventures Management LLC
Dougherty, James—Cross Atlantic Partners, Inc.
Dougherty, Joe—Highland Capital Management, L.P.
Dougherty, Kevin—Venture Capital Fund of New England, The
Doughty, Nigel—Doughty Hanson & Co., Ltd.
Douglas, Cindy—Michigan Economic Development Corporation
Douglas, Eric—Pod Venture Partners Inc.
Douglas, Frank—PureTech Ventures
Douglas, Ken—Simbiosis Venture Capital S.L.
Douglas, Neal—Telecommunications Development Fund (TDF)
Douglas, Penelope—Pacific Community Ventures (FKA: SVCV)
Douglass, David—Delphi Ventures
Doumani, Ahmed—GrowthGate Capital Corporation
Doumani, Roy—Fulcrum Venture Capital Corporation
Doumar, Robin—Park Square Capital, LLP
Douville, Elizabeth—GeneChem Financial Corporation
Douze, Lex—Waterland Private Equity Investments B.V.
Dove, Robert—Carlyle Group, The
Dovey, Brian—Domain Associates LLC
Dovi, Damien—BIA Digital Partners, L.P.
Dovrat, Shlomo—Carmel Ventures
Dow, James—PHD Equity Partners LLP
Dow, Steve—Sevin Rosen Funds
Dowding, Peter—Propel Investments
Dowdle, Robin—Affinity Capital Management
Dowds, Allan—Solamere Capital
Dowling, Chris—Rutland Fund Management, Ltd. (AKA: Rutland Partners LLP)
Dowling, Patrick—GE Commercial Finance - Equity
Downer, Tony—Oak Investment Partners
Downey, Bruce—NewSpring Capital
Downey, Maureen—Pantheon Ventures, Ltd.
Downie, Jason—HM Capital Partners LLC
Downing, Joseph—C.W. Downer & Company (FKA: Downer & Company)
Downing, Timothy—Fulcrum Capital Partners, Ltd.
Downs, Mark—Navigation Capital Partners
Dowse, Peter—Ironbridge Equity Partners
Dowuona, NanaAma—Kingdom Zephyr Africa Management (AKA: KZAM)
Doxiadis, Aristos—Notos Associates S.A.
Doyle, Daniel—Symmetric Capital LLC
Doyle, Kenneth—Halifax Group, The
Doyle, Kevin—Longbow Capital
Doyle, Maurice—Advantage Capital Partners
Doyle, Noah—Javelin Venture Partners
Doyle, William—WFD Ventures, LLC
Dozier, William—GESD Capital Partners, LLC
Dracon, Greg—.406 Ventures (AKA: Point 406 Ventures)
Dragan, Kevin—Aegis Capital Group LLC
Drahms, David—Osage Partners, LLC
Drai, Michael—Sterling Partners
Drake, Nathan—Kachi Partners
Drakeman, Donald—Advent Venture Partners LLP
Drant, Ryan—New Enterprise Associates, Inc.
Draper III, William H.—Draper Investment Company
Draper, Louis—RBC Capital Partners/RBC Technology Ventures
Draper, Martin—LDC (FKA: Lloyds TSB Development Capital, Ltd.)
Draper, Timothy—Draper Fisher Jurvetson
Draper, Timothy—Draper Fisher Jurvetson Gotham Venture Partners
Draper, Timothy—Zone Ventures
Draper, William—Draper Richards, L.P.
Dratch, Dana—American Capital, Ltd.
Drattell, Jason—Praesidian Capital, LLC
Drazan, Jeffrey—Bertram Capital
Drazan, Jeffrey—Sierra Ventures
Drazan, Kenneth—Bertram Capital
Dreesen, David—Battery Ventures, L.P.
Dreher, Martin—ViaNova Capital
Drehkoff, William—Linden LLC
Dreimanis, Dagnis—Baltcap
Dreisow, Jorg—Waterland Private Equity Investments B.V.
Drennan, John—American Capital, Ltd.
Dresdale, Richard—Fenway Partners, Inc.
Dresner, Edward—Eastward Capital
Dresner, Steven—Dresner Partners (FKA: Dresner Capital Resources, Inc.)
Drew, John—Technology Crossover Ventures
Dreyer, Craig—Ethos Private Equity
Dreyfous, James—Pelion Venture Partners
Drinkwater, John—Kelso Place Asset Management Limited
Driscoll, Deane—Brooks, Houghton & Company, Inc.
Driscoll, Eileen—Mediphase Venture Partners
Driscoll, Eileen—Mi3 Venture Partners
Driscoll, John—C.A. Bancorp, Inc.
Driscoll, John—New Mexico Community Capital
Driscoll, Ted—Claremont Creek Ventures
Drope, John—Okanagan Innovation Fund
Dross, Daniel—Trinity Hunt Partners
Druce, Gareth—Absa Capital Private Equity (Pty) Ltd.
Drucker, Geoff—RedFire Investments Pty, Ltd.
Drucker, Mitchell—CIT Group Inc.
Druker, Henry—Questor Management Company LLC
Drury, Simon—Climate Change Capital, Ltd.
Drury, Tom—BaseCamp Ventures
Druyan, Lara—Allegis Capital (AKA: Media Technology Ventures)
Dry, Guillaume—Occam Capital
Drysdale, George—Marsman-Drysdale Corporation
Du Pelloux, Dominique—Chequers Capital
Du Preez, Jacques—Mid Europa Partners
Du Roy, Corentin—HarbourVest Partners LLC
Du, Yongzhong—Fitch crown Venture Capital Management (Shenzhen) Co., Ltd.
DuFour, Justin—American Capital, Ltd.
Dubash, Radhika—Samara Capital Partners, Ltd.
Dubbe, Gina—Walker Ventures SBIC (AKA: Walker Ventures)
Dubi, Shay—Ofer Hi-Tech
Dubin, Bennett—Asset Management Company Venture Capital
Dubin, Deborah—Advantage Capital Partners
Dubin, Sergey—Palisade Capital Management
Dubin, Steve—Chesapeake Emerging Opportunities Club LLC
Duboc, Samuel—EdgeStone Capital Partners, Inc.
Dubois, Alain—Net Partners
Dubois, Michel—Biotek Partenaires
Dubovoy, Mark—Leapfrog Ventures
Dubrova, Aleksandra—Colony Capital LLC
Dubuque, Louis—Advantage Capital Partners
Duchesne, Yann—Doughty Hanson & Co., Ltd.
Duckett, Stephen—Favonius Ventures
Duckett, Stephen—Hellman & Friedman LLC
Duckworth, Claire—Signal Hill Equity Partners, Inc.
Duckworth, Justin—Nomura Phase4 Ventures, Ltd.
Duduch, Wagner—Stratus Banco de Negocios
Dudzinski, Anthony—HealthShares(TM), Inc.
Due, Christopher—iGlobe Treasury Management, Ltd.
Dueholm, Kim—Novo A/S
Duerr, David—Focus Equity Partners, LLC
Dufer, Arnaud—AXA Private Equity
Duff, Andrew—Piper Jaffray Private Capital LLC
Duff, Andrew—Piper Jaffray Ventures
Duff, Declan—International Finance Corporation
Duff, John—Duff Ackerman & Goodrich LLC (AKA: DAG Ventures)
Duffner, Frank—Baigo Capital GmbH
Duffy, Carolyn—Ignition Partners (FKA: Ignition Corporation)
Dufour, Jean—Thales Corporate Ventures (FKA:Thomson-CSF Ventures)
Dufresne, Daphne—RLJ Equity Partners LLC
Dugal, Sig—Origo Partners PLC
Dugan, John—OCA Venture Partners
Dugan, Kevin—Quadrangle Group LLC
Dugan, Timothy—Water Street Healthcare Partners
Duhamel, Franck—Park Square Capital, LLP
Duhau de Berenx, Jean—Natixis Private Equity SA
Duimich, David—Asia Pacific Ventures
Dujardain, Thierry—Croissance Nord - Pas de Calais SAS
Dujic, Neven—KBC Private Equity NV
Duke, R. Alton—Tenth Street Capital Partners, LLC
Duker, Ekow—Absa Capital Private Equity (Pty) Ltd.

Dukes, Larry—Morgenthau Venture Partners, LLC
Dukic, Vesna—Hamilton Lane Advisors, Inc.
Dulac, Alex—Kubera Partners, LLC
Dulanto, Gonzalo—Southern Cross Group (AKA: SCG)
Dulberg, Ronit—JVP
Dullum, David—New England Partners
Dulude, Marc—Ampersand Ventures
Dumanian, Peter—Red Rock Ventures
Dumanis, Alon—Docor International B.V.
Dumler, Richard—Milestone Venture Partners
Dunbar, George—Arboretum Ventures
Dunbar, William—Core Capital Partners
Duncan, Alan—DFJ Esprit
Duncan, Patrick—Azalea Capital LLC
Duncan, Ronald—TGF Management Corp (FKA:Texas Growth Fund)
Duncan, Townes—Solidus Company, L.P.
Duncanson, Timothy—Onex Corporation
Dunleavy, Patrick—GCP Capital Partners
Dunlevie, Bruce—Benchmark Capital
Dunlop, Janet—Lion Capital (FKA: Hicks Muse (Europe))
Dunn, Andrew—One Equity Partners (FKA: Banc One Venture Partners)
Dunn, Barry—GTCR Golder Rauner LLC
Dunn, Brian—Sorenson Capital Partners
Dunn, David—Idanta Partners, Ltd.
Dunn, Eric—Cardinal Venture Capital
Dunn, Gordon—NewSmith Asset Management LLP
Dunn, Melinda—Sequoia Capital
Dunn, Robert—Monument Capital Group LLC
Dunn, Robert—Thompson Street Capital Partners
Dunn, Tim—Phoenix Equity Partners (FKA: DLJ European Private Equity)
Dunnan, Bruce—Grosvenor Funds, The
Dunnan, Douglas—Grosvenor Funds, The
Dunne, Stephen—AMP Capital Investors
Dunnett, Martin—Warburg Pincus LLC
Dunning, James—ARC China, Inc.
Dunnivant, Bryan—Lilly Ventures (FKA: e.Lilly Ventures)
Dunstan, Jenny—3i Group PLC
Dunster, Ashley—Capital International Research, Inc.
Dupper, Craig—Solis Capital Partners, LLC
Dupree, David—Halifax Group, The
Dupuis, Aaron—Serent Capital LLC
Dur, Philip—Investor Growth Capital AB
Dur, Philip—Investor Growth Capital, Inc.
Duran, Mike—Alpine Investors, L.P.
Duranti, Enrico—CAPITALIA Sofipa SGR (FKA: MCC Sofipa)
Durban, Egon—Silver Lake Sumeru
Durbin, Chris—Vestar Capital Partners, Inc.
Durden, Robert—Morgan Creek Capital Management LLC
Durfee, Mark—Global Emerging Markets
Durgin, David—Verge
Durkin, David—Avista Capital Holdings, L.P.
Durrett, Adam—Hellman & Friedman LLC
Durrett, Park—CapStreet Group LLC, The (FKA: Summit Capital Group)
Dury, David—Mentor Capital Group
Duster, Luke—Capital Royalty Partners
Duswald, Fred—RECAP Management GmbH
Dutch, Suzette—Triathlon Medical Ventures LLC
Dutheil, Alain—STMicroelectronics
Duthel, Jean-Yves—Societe Generale de Financement du Quebec (SGF)
Duthie, Tony—Pacific Equity Partners
Dutta, Barun—Alta Berkeley Venture Partners
Dutta, Rajiv—Elevation Associates LLC
Dutton, Lauren—NewSchools Venture Fund
Dutton, Mike—Dolphin Capital Group, LLC
Duty, J. Bruce—Red River Ventures
Duvall, Sharon—GESD Capital Partners, LLC
Duvivier, Jean-Marie—FINORPA
Duwaji, Iyad—SHUAA Partners
Duyck, Geert—CVC Capital Partners (Europe), Ltd.
Duyk, Geoffrey—TPG Growth
Duzan, Jason—Glencoe Capital LLC (FKA: Glencoe Investment Corporation)
Dvivedi, Deval—DLB Capital LLC
Dwaram, Srikrishna—India Value Fund Advisors Private Ltd. (FKA: GW Capital)
Dworkin, James—GB Merchant Partners, LLC (FKA: GB Palladin Capital LLC)
Dwyer, David—Vista Ventures
Dyal, R. Thomas—Redpoint Ventures
Dybkjaer, Lars—Danisco Venture
Dybkjaer, Lars—Dansk Kapitalanlaeg Aktieselskab
Dyer, Campbell—Carlyle Group, The
Dyer, Graham—VentureLabour.com
Dyer, William—American Capital, Ltd.
Dyer, William—Boathouse Capital
Dyke, Philip—Acuity Capital LLP (FKA: Electra Partners LLP)
Dykes, Robert—Flextronics International, Ltd.
Dymarski, Luc—SNVB Participations
Dyson, John—Starfish Ventures Pty., Ltd.
Dyvig, Christian Peter—Nordic Capital (AKA: NC Advisory)
Dywremose, Thomas—Dania Capital K/S
Dzeng, Simon—China Development Financial Holding Corporation
Dzialga, Mark—General Atlantic LLC
Dziembowski, Constantin von—CAM Private Equity Consulting & Verwaltungs - GmbH
Eagle, Sean—American Capital, Ltd.
Eakes, Benjamin—SunTx Capital Partners
Eakes, John—KRG Capital Partners LLC
Eales, Darryl—LDC (FKA: Lloyds TSB Development Capital, Ltd.)
Earl, Joshua—GTCR Golder Rauner LLC
Earle, Ralph—Clean Energy Venture Group
Earley, Richard—Dunrath Capital, Inc.
Earley, Rory—Capital for Enterprise, Ltd.
Earls, Alexander—Gryphon Investors, Inc.
Earnhardt, Jonathan—Harren Equity Partners
Earthman, William—Massey Burch Capital Corp.
Eastman, Barbara—Halpern, Denny & Company
Eastman, David—Prospector Equity Capital, L.P.
Eastman, Jay—EG Capital Group LLC
Eastman, Ronald—Essex Woodlands Health Ventures
Easton, Robert—Carlyle Group, The
Easwaran, Eyob—Conduit Capital Partners, LLC
Easwaran, Nithya—Multiples Alternate Asset Management
Eaton, Gregory—Rembrandt Venture Partners
Eaton, J. Stephen—EDG Partners LLC
Eatroff, Bruce—Halyard Partners
Ebbing, Frank—Sigma Capital Management
Eberly, David—Beringea LLC
Ebert, Sean—Altira Group LLC
Ebhardt, Andres—CAM Private Equity Consulting & Verwaltungs - GmbH
Ebinger, Jonathan—BlueRun Ventures
Eboma, Nico—Wall Street Venture Capital
Ebrahimi, Sasha—Mithra Group, LLC
Eburne, Timothy—Watermill Group, The
Echarri, Jose Luis—Iame Capital Riesgo SGECR SA
Echarri, Josep Maria—Inveready Seed Capital
Echave, Inaki—Magnum Capital Industrial Partners
Eckermann, Henning—Partners Group AG
Eckert, Alfred—GSC Partners (FKA: Greenwich Street Capital Partners)
Eckert, John—McLean Watson Capital Inc.
Eckhardt, Juerg—Bellevue Asset Management AG
Eckhardt, Ueli—Capvis Equity Partners AG
Eckhart, Adam—Gemini Partners, Inc.
Eckl, Nancy—American Beacon Advisors, Inc. (FKA:AMR Investment Services)
Eckman, Harald—Column Group, The
Eckstein, Jens—TVM Capital GmbH
Eddy, Thomas—Jarvinian LLC
Edeburn, Patrick—Granite Equity Partners
Edelman, Jeffrey—Symphony Capital LLC
Edelman, Thomas—White Deer Energy
Edelson, Harry—Edelson Technology Partners
Edelson, Jon—Ascent Biomedical Ventures
Edelson, Steven—Mercantile Capital Group (MCG)
Edelstein, Dick—M2Group
Eden, Bradley—Z Capital Partners LLC
Edfeldt, Johan—ForetagsByggarna AB (AKA: Business Builders)
Edgar, Lisa—Paul Capital Partners
Edgar, Raymond—Natural Gas Partners (NGP)
Edge, Chris—Saints Ventures
Edge, Gordon—Chord Capital, Ltd. (FKA: Generics Group, The)
Edgerley, Paul—Bain Capital
Edgreen, Robert—Value Added Capital, LLC
Edlinger, Werner—ECOS Beteiligungsmanagement GmbH
Edmands, Benjamin—CCMP Capital Advisors LLC
Edmonds, Brendan—Atlantic-Pacific Capital, Inc.
Edmonds, J. Rice—Bruckmann, Rosser, Sherrill & Co.
Edmonds, Susan—GMB Mezzanine Capital, L.P.
Edvardsen, Andre—Skagerak Venture Capital AS
Edwards, Ben—Syntaxis Capital
Edwards, Chuck—Waud Capital Partners LLC
Edwards, Douglas—Doughty Hanson & Co., Ltd.
Edwards, Gregory—Mesa Capital Partners
Edwards, Joe Bob—First Reserve Corporation
Edwards, Michael—AnaCap Financial Partners LLP
Edwards, Paul—Latterell Venture Partners
Edwards, Rick—Seagrove, LLC
Edwards, Robert—Ridgemont Equity Partners
Edwards, Stephen—Core Growth Capital LLP
Ee, Edward—Inter-Asia Venture Management
Effron, Blair—Centerview Partners Holdings LLC
Efrusy, Kevin—Accel Partners
Efstratis, Nicholaus—EPIC Ventures
Egan, Chris—Advent International
Egan, Francis—Draper Fisher Jurvetson ePlanet Ventures, L.P.

Eng, San—Panthera Capital Group
Eng, Veronica—Permira Advisers LLP
Engebretsen, Erik—Gezina AS
Engel, Matthew—Quad-C Management, Inc.
Engel, Robert A.—Gleacher & Co.
Engelhard, Teresa—Jolimont Capital Pty, Ltd.
Engelhardt, Tobias—EKK Dr. Engelhardt, Kaupp, Kiefer Beteiligungsberatung GmbH
Engelsen, Steinar—Teknoinvest AS
Enger, Oivind—Sarsia Seed Management AS
Englander, Peter—Apax Partners Worldwide
Engleman, Edgar—Vivo Ventures
Engler, Edward—Pittsburgh Equity Partners
Engler, Mark—SCM Strategic Capital Management AG
English, Peter—Foresight Group
English, Scott—Hearst Corporation
Enkel, Gisbert—Sachsen LB Corporate Finance Holding GmbH
Ennis, Greg—Peninsula Ventures
Enrico, Aaron—CIC Partners, L.P. (FKA: Cardinal Investment Company, Inc.)
Enright, Patrick—Longitude Capital Management Company LLC
Enriquez, Juan—Biotechonomy Ventures, LLC
Enriquez, Juan—Excel Venture Management
Entrecanales, Bruno—Bullnet Capital SCR SA
Entress, Geoff—Voyager Capital
Epstein, Jason—CN Private Equity Partners
Epstein, M. Avi—Sterling Partners
Epstein, Mark—MTS Health Partners, L.P.
Epstein, Mark—Tailwind Capital Partners
Epstein, Michael—CRG Partners
Erben, Amir—SKY FUND
Erbmann, Clement—First Analysis Corporation
Erdei, Sandor—DBH Group
Erez, Roy—Cedar Fund
Erfan, Ali—3i Group PLC
Ergul, Emmanuel—Accent Equity Partners AB
Erhard, Jake—ArcLight Capital
Erickson, Christopher—Pangaea Ventures
Erickson, Elaine—Nth Power
Erickson, Richard—Updata Partners
Erickson, Thomas—BlueStream Ventures
Ericson, Bill—Mohr Davidow Ventures
Ericson, Mikael—D. Carnegie & Co AB
Ericsson, Greger—Servisen Investment Management AB
Ericsson, Per—ETF Manager LLP
Ericsson, Staffan—Vesbridge Partners, LLC
Eriksen, Hans-Henrik—VECATA A/S
Eriksson, Bert-Ake—Stena Adactum AB
Erlandsson, Bo—Qeep Ventures AB
Erni, Marcel—Partners Group AG
Ernoult-Dairaine, Antoine—Sagard SAS
Ernst, Eric-Joost—Candover Investments PLC
Ernst, Manfred—Noventi
Errett, Amy—Maveron LLC
Erskine, Richard—Energy Capital Management AS
Erskine, Richard—Norsk Hydro ASA (AKA: Norsk Hydro Technology Ventures)
Esan, Folabi—Adlevo Capital Managers LLC
Esbin, Sheldon—Romspen Investment Corporation
Eschenbach, Ralph—GKM Ventures
Eschenbach, Ralph—Osprey Ventures, L.P.
Escobar, Rafael—Orgone Capital
Eshelman, Rodney—Crystal Ridge Partners, LLC
Esmeraldo, Fernando—ECS Capital, S.A.
Espander, Annika—Catella AB
Esparbes, Edouard—Calyon (FKA: Credit Agricole Indosuez)
Espie, Paul—Pacific Road Capital Management Pty, Ltd.
Espinal De Carulla, L. Carolina—HarbourVest Partners LLC
Espinal de Carulla, L. Carolina—HarbourVest Partners LLC
Esping, William—EFO Holdings, L.P.
Esposito, Gerry—BNP Paribas Principal, Inc.
Esposito, Gerry—Newbury Partners LLC
Esquenazi, Michael—Brickman, Bruce S & Associates, Inc.
Esser, Teresa—Capital Midwest Fund, L.P.
Estefanell, David—Mercapital Servicios Financieros
Estela, Juan Miguel—American Capital, Ltd.
Estense, Umberto Selvatico—Industrial Assets SpA
Estes, Derrick—Corsair Capital LLC
Estes, Phillip—Horizon Holdings, LLC
Estey, George—GCP Capital Partners
Esveld, Erik—Van Herk Investments
Etcharry, Eric—Fin'Active
Etlin, Patrice—Advent International
Etrillard, Gilles—Fonds Partenaires Gestion
Etrillard, Gilles—La Financiere Patrimoniale D'Investissment
Etrillard, Gilles—Lazard Capital Partners
Etter, Stephen—Greyrock Capital Group
Etzioni, Oren—Madrona Venture Group
Etzkorn, Kevin—Heron Capital LLC
Eubank, Frederick—Pamlico Capital
Eugenio, Luiz—RioBravo Investimentos
Eum, Jay—TransLink Capital
Eustace, Cheryl—J.P. Morgan Capital Corporation
Evain, Christophe—Intermediate Capital Group Plc
Evangelista, Tenio—Borealis Infrastructure Management, Inc.
Evans, Andrew—UBS Capital Corporation
Evans, Andrew—ViaNova Capital
Evans, Bob—Rocket Ventures
Evans, Bruce—Summit Partners
Evans, David—Glencoe Capital LLC (FKA: Glencoe Investment Corporation)
Evans, Doug—CapVest Management Ltd
Evans, Greg—Avista Capital Holdings, L.P.
Evans, Jim—SCP Private Equity Partners
Evans, John—Invesco Private Capital
Evans, John—VIMAC Ventures LLC (FKA: VIMAC LLC)
Evans, Larry—32 Degrees Capital
Evans, Mark—Balderton Capital (FKA: Benchmark Capital Europe)
Evans, Matthew—Salmon River Capital
Evans, Michael—Ancor Capital Partners
Evans, Paul—Adirondack Venture Fund, The
Evans, Paul—Ironbridge Capital Pty., Ltd.
Evans, Roger—Greylock Partners
Evans, Scott—Guardian Capital Partners
Evans, Thomas—American Capital, Ltd.
Evans-Freke, Stephen—Celtic Pharma Management, LP
Evans-Freke, Stephen—Celtic Therapeutics Management, L.L.L.P.
Eveloff, Adam Garcia—Castanea Partners
Evensen, R. Christian—Canyon Capital
Ever, Dennis—AlpInvest Partners N.V.
Everett, Carl—Accel Partners
Everett, Giselle—Citi Venture Capital International
Evers, Elliot—Media Venture Partners
Evers, Mark—MML Capital Partners
Every, Nathan—Frazier Healthcare and Technology Ventures
Evgeniev, Ivo—New Europe Venture Equity
Evnin, Anthony—Venrock Associates
Evseev, Boris—AIG Capital Partners
Ewald, Frank—IVS A/S (AKA: Internet Ventures Scandinavia A/S)
Ewald, Hiram—Tall Oaks Capital Partners LLC
Ewald, Oliver—Audax Group
Ewart, Donna—IBM Corporation
Exter, Diane—Bain Capital
Exter, Neil—Third Rock Ventures LLC
Eyers, Simon—4D Global Energy Advisors
Eyre, Chris—Legacy Venture
Ezekiev, Pavel—New Europe Venture Equity
Ezell, Bruce—Techxas Ventures LLC
Ezequelle, David—Alloy Ventures
Ezoe, Hisanori—Biofrontier Partners, Inc.
Ezra, Menashe—Gemini Israel Funds, Ltd.
Ezzeddine, Samer—Monitor Clipper Partners LLC
Faber, Barton—Atrium Capital
Faber, Jan—Bregal Investments
Faber, Michael—NextPoint Partners, L.P.
Fabritius, Guy—Euromezzanine Conseil (AKA: Euromezzanine Gestion)
Facca, Horacio—Headwaters Merchant Bank
Fachetti, David—Globespan Capital Partners
Facoetti, Matteo—BS Private Equity SpA (FKA: B&S Private Equity Group)
Fade, Richard—Ignition Partners (FKA: Ignition Corporation)
Fagan, John—TVC Holdings plc (FKA: Trinity Venture Capital)
Fagerberg, Christina—Fagerberg & Dellby AB
Fagerlund, Markku—Inveni Capital
Fagg, Graham—Catalyst BioMedica Ltd
Fagg, Graham—Seroba Kernel Life Sciences, Ltd. (AKA: Seroba Kernel)
Faggen, Craig—Triton Pacific Capital Partners LLC
Faggen, Ivan—Triton Pacific Capital Partners LLC
Fagnan, Jeffrey—Atlas Venture, Ltd.
Fahlberg, Mark—NextCom Ventures
Fahoury, Douglas—Iron Gate Capital, LLC
Fahraeus, Christer—Sunstone Capital A/S
Failing, Bruce—Alerion Partners
Fairfax, Cydonii—American Capital, Ltd.
Fairfull, David—Pitt Capital Partners, Ltd.
Fairman, Bernard—Foresight Group
Faison, Lane—Copeley Capital Partners
Fait, Igor—Jet Investment A.S.
Fajgenbaum, Jonas—Invus Group Ltd., The
Fakhry, Walid—Core Growth Capital LLP
Falakshahi, Katya—New Enterprise Associates, Inc.
Falck, Jens Petter—Selvaag Invest AS
Falezan, Franck—Carlyle Group, The
Falk, Karl-Anders—Coeli Private Equity Management AB
Falk, Michael—Comvest Investment Partners
Falkenstein, Joseph—Egis Capital Partners LLC

Falkenstein, Joseph—New Jersey Technology Council (AKA: NJTC)
Falkson, Joseph—NAC Ventures, LLC
Fallace, David—GF Private Equity Group, LLC
Fallen, Malcolm—Candover Investments PLC
Fallon, Julie—Celtic House Venture Partners
Fallon, Patrick—Gryphon Investors, Inc.
Famaey, Hilde—AlpInvest Partners N.V.
Famaey, Hilde—NIBC Principal Investments (FKA: Parnib Holding NV)
Fambrough, Douglas—Oxford Bioscience Partners
Fan, Anthony—AsiaTech Internet Group (ATIG) (FKA: AsiaTech Ventures)
Fan, Bruce—Gold Stone Investment, Ltd.
Fan, George—Blackstone Group, L.P.
Fan, Joseph—WI Harper Group
Fan, Liping—Steamboat Ventures
Fan, Vincent—Capital Z Investment Partners (FKA: Union Square Partners)
Fang, Karen—ChinaVest, Ltd.
Fang, Max—Maxima Capital Management, Inc.
Fang, Penny—China Capital Management Company, Ltd.
Fang, Wei—Wuhan Huagong Tech Business Incubator Co., Ltd.
Fanjul, Oscar—Omega Capital SL
Fankhauser, Georg—Remaco Merger AG
Fann, David—US Trust Private Equity
Fann, Emerson—Eastside Partners
Fanner, Helmut—BioMedPartners
Fanning, Steve—Monolith Capital Partners
Fanzilli, Frank—Allegis Capital (AKA: Media Technology Ventures)
Farazmand, Tim—LDC (FKA: Lloyds TSB Development Capital, Ltd.)
Farber, Jonathan—Lime Rock Partners LLC
Farello, Michael—Catterton Partners
Faremouth, Michael—Linsalata Capital Partners
Farhat, Eduardo—Darby Overseas Investments, Ltd.
Faria, Eduardo—Jardim Botanico Partners (FKA: Araujo Fontes Consultoria)
Faria, Pedro—Tarpon Investment Group
Faridi, Kamran—Fajr Capital Ltd
Farinholt, Jim—Tall Oaks Capital Partners LLC
Farkas, Benjamin—Hellman & Friedman LLC
Farkas, Bradford—i-Hatch Ventures LLC
Farley, Thomas—AIG Capital Partners
Farmanfarmaian, Salman—SCP Private Equity Partners
Farmer, Christopher—Bessemer Venture Partners
Farmwald, Michael—Skymoon Ventures
Farner, Peter—TGap Ventures LLC
Farnsworth, Craig—Citigroup Private Equity
Farnsworth, Tara—Focus Ventures
Farquharson, Andrew—DFJ InCube Ventures
Farrell, James—Calera Capital (FKA: Fremont Partners)
Farrell, Paul—CIBC Capital Partners
Farrell, Todd—GrowthWorks
Farrington, Deborah—StarVest Partners, L.P.
Farron, Matthew—Gryphon Investors, Inc.
Farscht, Russell—Carlyle Group, The
Fasano, JIm—Persistence Capital Partners
Fassbender, David—Bank of Scotland Venture Capital (FKA: ICC Venture Capital)
Fassinotti, Marianna—Siguler Guff & Company
Fastrich, Hendrik—Orlando Capital Management GmbH
Fates, Matt—Ascent Venture Partners
Faucher, Cornel—Battery Ventures, L.P.
Fauconnier, Lise—AXA Private Equity
Faughnan, R. Thomas—New York Business Development Corporation
Faught, George—Athlone Global Security, Inc.
Faulds, Graeme—SL Capital Partners LLP
Faulkner, Mitch—US Equity LLC
Faure, Michel—Siparex Group SAS
Faust, Dorian—Gryphon Investors, Inc.
Faust, Dorian—Thomas Weisel Partners Group, Inc.
Faust, Halley—Jerome Capital LLC
Faust, Jennifer—Pacific Corporate Group
Favreau, Frederic—Butler Capital Partners SA
Fay, Timothy—Key Principal Partners LLC (AKA: KPP)
Fayyad, Najib Youssef—Unicorn Investment Bank B.S.C.
Fazakerley, Ed—Zeus Private Equity
Fazio, Timothy—Atlas Holdings FRM LLC
Fealy, Robert—Duchossois Technology Partners LLC (DTEC)
Fechtmeyer, G. Kevin—Cave Creek Capital Management
Fecker, Betina—EKK Dr. Engelhardt, Kaupp, Kiefer Beteiligungsberatung GmbH
Feder, Ben—Zelnick Media
Federico, Richard—Sterling Partners
Federman, Irwin—U.S. Venture Partners
Federmann, Gidi—Eurofund LP
Fedorov, Boris—United Financial Group Asset Management (AKA: UFG)
Fedorowich, Richard—Beacon Bioventures
Feeley, Edmund—Littlejohn & Company LLC
Feeley, James—FriedbergMilstein, LLC
Feeney, Kathryn—Landmark Partners, Inc.
Feeney, Shane—Bridgepoint Development Capital
Feeny, Curtis—Voyager Capital
Fehrenbach, Isaac—Greylock Partners
Fei, Zhang—Ceyuan Ventures Management, LLC
Feiber, Jonathan—Mohr Davidow Ventures
Feiglin, Simon—Riverside Company
Fein, Russ—Corporate Fuel Partners
Feinblum, Barnet—Greenmont Capital Partners
Feinblum, Kevin—Sun Capital Partners, Inc.
Feinglass, Michael—RCP Advisors LLC
Feinleib, David—Mohr Davidow Ventures
Feinstein, Paul—Crystal Capital
Feinstein, Peter—BioVentures Investors
Fejer, Lars—Dania Capital K/S
Feld, Alan—Vintage Venture Partners
Feld, Bradley—Foundry Group
Feld, Bradley—Mobius Venture Capital, Inc.
Feld, Bradley—TechStars
Feldberg, Warren—Champlain Capital Management LLC
Feldman, Greg—Wellspring Capital Management LLC
Feldman, Jesse—Battery Ventures, L.P.
Feldman, Scott—Broadmark Capital Corp.
Feldman, Zur—Pitango Venture Capital (FKA:Polaris Venture Capital Israel)
Felgenhauer, Carsten—Leonardo Venture GmbH & Co. KGaA
Feliciano, Jose—Clearlake Capital Group
Felix, Jean-Francois—Vestar Capital Partners, Inc.
Felker, Tom—Investment Fund for Foundations
Feller, Andrew—Metalmark Capital LLC
Felsenthal, Martin—HLM Venture Partners
Fenal, Patrick—Unigestion SA
Fendel, Andreas—Quadriga Capital
Fender, Stacy—Undisclosed Firm
Feneley, Julian—Rosetta Capital, Ltd.
Feng, Ben—Pac-Link Management Corporation
Feng, Bo—Ceyuan Ventures Management, LLC
Feng, Eric—Kleiner Perkins Caufield & Byers
Feng, Janine—Carlyle Group, The
Fenner, Florian—United Financial Group Asset Management (AKA: UFG)
Fenton, Lance—Serent Capital LLC
Fenton, Noel—Trinity Ventures
Fenton, Peter—Benchmark Capital
Fenton, Rick—Technology Crossover Ventures
Fercala, Mihai—SIF Transilvania
Fercocq, Christophe—Cobalt Capital SAS
Ferenbach, Carl—Berkshire Partners LLC
Ferguson, Andrew—Baird Capital Partners Europe
Ferguson, David—Weston Presidio (FKA: Weston Presidio Capital Management)
Ferguson, Dennis—Juniper Networks
Ferguson, Jay—Kline Hawkes & Co.
Ferguson, Jay—Vicente Capital Partners
Ferguson, Jeff—Carlyle Group, The
Ferguson, Rodney—J.P. Morgan Partners (FKA: Chase Capital Partners)
Ferguson, Rodney—Panorama Capital
Ferguson, Thomas—FFR Capital Partners
Fernandes, Mark—Sierra Ventures
Fernandes, Paulo—Cofina, SGPS SA
Fernandez Lopez, Antonio—AC Desarrollo SGECR SA
Fernandez, Cora—Sanlam Private Equity
Fernandez, Edward—Mobility Ventures
Fernandez, Jose—Pacific Corporate Group
Fernandez, Manny—SI Ventures
Ferneau, Philip—Borealis Ventures
Ferran, Javier—Lion Capital (FKA: Hicks Muse (Europe))
Ferrante, Domenic—Bain Capital
Ferranti, Roberto—Baird Capital Partners
Ferrara, Alex—Bessemer Venture Partners
Ferrara, David—Greenhouse Capital Partners
Ferrara, Giovanni—Burrill & Company
Ferrari, Beau—Royal Palm Capital Partners, LLP
Ferrari, Ben—Imprimatur Capital, Ltd.
Ferrari, Marco—Boston Ventures Management, Inc.
Ferrari, Richard—De Novo Ventures
Ferrari, Richard—Saratoga Ventures, L.P.
Ferras, Ignacio—Compass Capital Fund Management LLC
Ferreira, Jose—Goode Partners LLC
Ferrero, Marc—Debaeque Venture Capital
Ferrero, Pierluigi—Noventi
Ferri, Paul—Matrix Partners
Ferrigno, Joseph—Asia Mezzanine Capital Advisers, Ltd.
Ferrington, Leonard—Summit Partners
Ferris, George—Allied Capital Corporation
Ferris, Joyce—Blue Hill Partners LLC
Ferris, Paul—Azure Capital Partners

Ferris, Robert—CI Capital Partners LLC (FKA: Caxton-Iseman Capital, Inc)
Ferro, Carlo—STMicroelectronics
Ferry, Dennis—SCP Private Equity Partners
Ferry, Jack—Ignition Partners (FKA: Ignition Corporation)
Fesler, Scott—Bush O'Donnell Capital Partners
Fesneau, Florence—Alpha Group
Fetsch, Paul—Spur Capital Partners LLC
Fetting, Andreas—Odewald & Compagnie GmbH
Feucher, Pascal—Sal. Oppenheim Private Equity Partners
Feuer, Hannah—Poalim Capital Markets Technologies Ltd
Feuer, Jonathan—CVC Capital Partners (Europe), Ltd.
Feuerabendt, Stefan—Blackstone Group, L.P.
Feuersenger, Uwe R.—firstVentury GmbH
Feuerstein, Edward—Audax Group
Feuille, James—Crosslink Capital
Fey, Lawrence—GTCR Golder Rauner LLC
Fiala, Tomas—Dragon Capital
Fialkow, David—General Catalyst Partners (FKA: General Catalyst Group LLC)
Fiato, John—HarbourVest Partners LLC
Ficheur, Benoit—Cinven, Ltd.
Fichtner, Martin—Elevation Associates LLC
Ficken, Jason—Headwaters Merchant Bank
Fidelman, Barry—Atlas Venture, Ltd.
Fidler, Josh—Boulder Ventures, Ltd.
Field, Ezra—Roark Capital Group
Fielding, Kevin—Alta Berkeley Venture Partners
Fields, Howard—Capital Dynamics AG
Fields, Steven—Excel Capital Partners, L.P.
Fieldstone, Michael—Sun Capital Partners, Inc.
Fiessinger, Emmanuel—Seventure Partners SA (FKA: SPEF Venture)
Fife, David—Rosemont Solebury Capital Management LLC
Figeac, Alexis—Entrepreneurs Fund Management LLP
Fihlani, Zola—EVI Capital Partners
Fikse, Mark—American Capital, Ltd.
Filip, William—Baird Venture Partners
Filippi, Charles-Henri—Weinberg Capital Partners SAS
Filippini, Stefano—AVM Associati SpA
Filippone, David—Gilbert Global Equity Capital, L.L.C.
Finch, David—Northwater capital Management
Finch, Lawrence—Sigma Partners
Findlay, Stephen—Fidelity Equity Partners
Fine, Daniel—Quadrangle Group LLC
Finegan, Ross—Lonsdale Capital Partners LLP
Finegan, Scott—Pfingsten Partners, L.P.
Finelli, Francis—Carlyle Group, The
Fines, Robert—Kirtland Capital Partners
Finestein, Daniel—Infinity Asset Management LLP
Fingerhut, Barry—Wheatley Partners
Fingerle, Linda—EDF Ventures
Fink, Andrew—Trevi Health Ventures
Fink, Jesse—MissionPoint Capital Partners
Fink, Laurence—BlackRock Private Equity Partners
Fink, Rick—Miramar Venture Partners
Finkel, Mark—Prism Capital
Finkel, Robert—Prism Capital
Finkelstein, Abe—Vintage Venture Partners
Finkelstein, Alex—Spark Capital
Finkelstein, Brian—Fifth Street Capital LLC
Finkelstein, James—Avista Capital Holdings, L.P.
Finkelstein, Ohad—Venrock Associates
Finkle, Jeffrey—Odeon Capital Partners, L.P.
Finlayson, Robin—Longbow Capital
Finley, David—Sverica International
Finley, John—Blackstone Group, L.P.
Finley, Michael—Court Square Capital Partners
Finn, Christopher—Carlyle Group, The
Finnegan, Ed—Crescent Capital (NI) Ltd
Finney, Mike—Ann Arbor SPARK
Finocchio, Robert—Advanced Technology Ventures
Finser, Mark—TBL Capital, L.P.
Finzi, Robert—Sprout Group
Fioramonti, Marie—Prudential Capital Group
Fiorentino, David—J.W. Childs Associates
Fioretti, Robert—Trimaran Capital Partners, LLC
Fiorini, Pierre—I-Source Gestion
Fioux, Isabelle—Montefiore Investment
Fipp, Robb—Vineyard Ventures
Fireman, Dan—Fireman Capital Partners
Firestein, Jonathan—Rigel Associates LLC
Firlik, Andrew—Foundation Medical Partners
First, Mark—Eos Partners, L.P.
Firtel, Ken—Transom Capital Group
Firth, Denys—ADM Capital
Firth, Peter—GSC Partners (FKA: Greenwich Street Capital Partners)
Fischer, Albert—Yellow & Blue Investment Management BV
Fischer, Avi—Clal Venture Capital Management, Ltd. (AKA: CVC Management)
Fischer, Carrie—SK Capital Partners
Fischer, Christian—Vienna Capital Partners
Fischer, Dave—Gold Hill Capital Management LLC
Fischer, Donald—Greylock Partners
Fischer, Glenn—AEA Investors LP
Fischer, Niccolo—Aliante Partners Srl
Fischer, Reinhard—Global Equity Partners Beteiligungs-Management GmbH
Fischer, Stephen—TVM Capital GmbH
Fischerstrom, Rickard—Private Advisors LLC
Fish, Guy—Fletcher Spaght Associates
Fishbein, Richard—Cortec Group, Inc.
Fisher, Adam—Bessemer Venture Partners
Fisher, Bill—Fisher Capital Partners
Fisher, Brett—Fisher Lynch Capital
Fisher, David—Brandon Capital Partners
Fisher, Don—Fisher Capital Partners
Fisher, Doug—InterWest Partners
Fisher, James—Praesidian Capital, LLC
Fisher, John—August Equity LLP
Fisher, John—CBPE Capital, LLP (AKA: Close Brothers Private Equity, Ltd.)
Fisher, John—Draper Fisher Jurvetson
Fisher, Julie—Providence Equity Partners LLC
Fisher, Michael—GE Commercial Finance - Equity
Fisher, Ronald—SoftBank Capital
Fisher, Scott—Vexiom Equity Partners, L.P.
Fisher, Stephen—Liberty Partners
Fisher, Stewart—KRG Capital Partners LLC
Fisher, Tad—Third Security LLC
Fishman, Andy—Vector Capital
Fishman, Danny—Tamir Fishman Ventures
Fishman, David—Vector Capital
Fiske, Jay—Massachusetts Green Energy Fund
FitzPatrick, Seamus—CapVest Management Ltd
Fitzgerald, Brian—Capital Partners, Inc.
Fitzgerald, Charles—Summit Partners
Fitzgerald, David—Carlyle Group, The
Fitzgerald, David—Petra Capital Partners, LLC
Fitzgerald, David—Richland Ventures
Fitzgerald, Eric—Thomas Weisel Partners Group, Inc.
Fitzgerald, John—Cheyenne Capital Fund, L.P.
Fitzgerald, Michael—Commonwealth Capital Ventures
Fitzgerald, Peter—Latterell Venture Partners
Fitzgerald, William—General Catalyst Partners (FKA: General Catalyst Group LLC)
Fitzgibbons, Albert—Stonington Partners, Inc.
Fitzgibbons, Harry—Top Technology Ventures, Ltd.
Fitzpatrick, Joseph—HealthpointCapital LLC
Fitzpatrick, Michael—Seabury Venture Partners
Fitzpatrick, Patricia—Seabury Venture Partners
Fitzpatrick, Todd—New England Partners
Fitzsimmons, Robert—High Road Capital Partners
Fitzsimons, Gerry—TTP Venture Managers, Ltd. (FKA:Technology Partnership, The)
Fitzsimons, Paul—Apax Partners Worldwide
Five, Thor Egil—ProVenture AS
Flagtvedt, Harald-Ingve—Argentum Fondsinvesteringer AS
Flaherman, Michael—New Mountain Capital LLC
Flaherty, John—Carlyle Group, The
Flahive, Roger—SB Energy Partners
Flaig, Daniel—Capvis Equity Partners AG
Flamarion, Antoine—TR Advisors, Ltd.
Flamenbaum, Walter—Paul Capital Partners
Flanagan, David—Intel Capital
Flanagan, Lauren—Phenomenelle Angels Management
Flanagan, Paul—Sigma Partners
Flanagan, Robert—CNF Investments, LLC
Flanagan, Sally—Permira Advisers LLP
Flanagan, Tom—Jefferies Group, Inc.
Flanigan, James—Granite Hall Partners (FKA: Sports Venture Partners, LLC)
Flanigan, John—CHB Capital Partners
Flaschen, David—Castanea Partners
Flashner, Lisa—New World Ventures
Flaskjer, Sverre—Herkules Capital AS
Flaster, Andrew—Fidelity Equity Partners
Flaster, Andrew—Volition Capital
Flatley, Daniel—Masthead Venture Partners
Flatz, Alois—Zouk Ventures, Ltd.
Fleck, Roman—Index Ventures
Fleischhauer, Konrad—Treacle Venture Partners
Fleischmann, Charles—Investcorp Bank B.S.C.
Fleissner, Ronald—Summer Street Capital LLC
Fleming, Daniel—River Cities Capital Funds
Fleming, Grant—Wilshire Private Markets
Fleming, Gregory—Merrill Lynch Capital Partners
Fleming, James—Columbia Capital LLC
Fleming, Jonathan—Medica Venture Partners
Fleming, Jonathan—Oxford Bioscience Partners
Fleming, Ned—SunTx Capital Partners
Fleming, Robert—Prism VentureWorks
Fleming, Susan—Capital Z Investment Partners (FKA: Union Square Partners)

Flemons, Wade—Pender West Capital Partners, Inc.
Fleshman, Skip—Asset Management Company Venture Capital
Fletcher, Barron—Parallel Invesment Partners
Fletcher, Edward—Atlas Holdings FRM LLC
Fletcher, Jim—Chrysalix Energy
Fletcher, Steve—Crosby Capital, Ltd.
Flichy, Joel—Galileo Partners
Flicker, Blair—Insight Venture Partners
Flicker, James—GCP Capital Partners
Fliegler, Brett—Enhanced Equity Fund, L.P.
Fligor, Andrew—Barish Fund, The
Flint, Jonathan—Polaris Venture Partners
Flint, Juliet—Kleiner Perkins Caufield & Byers
Flint, Peter—Polaris Venture Partners
Flisberg, Niklas—Result Venture Knowledge International
Flisser, Elizabeth—Capital Z Investment Partners (FKA: Union Square Partners)
Flitti, Karim—HarbourVest Partners LLC
Floersch, Jamie—Adams Street Partners LLC
Flood, Michael—Northleaf Capital Partners
Flore, Ralf—Heliad Equity Partners GmbH & Co. KGaA
Florence, Anthony—New Enterprise Associates, Inc.
Florence, Walter—Frontenac Company
Florian, Mark—First Reserve Corporation
Florman, Mark—Doughty Hanson & Co., Ltd.
Flower, Mark—Waud Capital Partners LLC
Flower, Tim—HarbourVest Partners LLC
Floyd, Nancy—Nth Power
Floyd, Ryan—Storm Ventures LLC
Flucht, Brian—Blade Ventures
Flugel, Roger—Sanderling Ventures
Flynn, Brian—Columbia Equity Partners
Flynn, Charles—Bregal Investments
Flynn, Gregory—Hampshire Equity Partners (FKA: ING Equity Partners)
Flynn, John—ACT Venture Capital, Ltd.
Flynn, Peter—Pantheon Ventures, Ltd.
Flynn, Richard—BlueStar Ventures L.P.
Flynn, Sean—Shasta Ventures Management LLC
Flynn, Terence—Houlihan, Lokey, Howard & Zukin
Flynn, Timothy—Leonard Green & Partners
Flynn, Tony—Medical Innovations Management, Inc.
Fodor, Stephen—Affymetrix, Inc.
Foerster, Kimberly—Perseus LLC
Fogarty, Thomas—Emergent Medical Ventures, LLP
Fogel, Rafael—Falcon Investment Advisors LLC
Fogelsong, Norman—Institutional Venture Partners
Fogg, Joseph—Westbury Partners
Foglio, Alfred—Global Innovation Partners LLC
Fogtdal, Soren—IVS A/S (AKA: Internet Ventures Scandinavia A/S)
Foin, Daniel—Naxicap Partners SA
Foist, Brian—Global Environment Fund Management Corporation
Fojtasek, Randall—Brazos Private Equity Partners LLC
Fok, Winnie—Investor Growth Capital AB
Foldi, Antal—Research Partners, Ltd.
Foley, David—Blackstone Group, L.P.
Foley, Heather—Park Street Capital LLC
Foley, James—Kirtland Capital Partners
Foley, John—Wayzata Investment Partners
Foley, Mark—RWI Ventures
Foley, Patrick—Delaware Innovation Fund (AKA: DIF)
Foley, Paul—CypressTree Investment Management Company, Inc.
Foley, Todd—MPM Capital (FKA: MPM Asset Management LLC)
Folger, Thomas—DFW Capital Partners (AKA:DeMuth, Folger & Wetherill)
Folino, Anthony—Graham Partners, Inc.
Folk, David—Jefferson Partners
Folkesson, Mans—Nordic Capital (AKA: NC Advisory)
Folle, Peter—HighTech Private Equity GmbH
Folsom, Richard—Advantage Partners LLP
Fong, Bryant—Burrill & Company
Fong, David—iSpringCapital Sdn Bhd (FKA: Productive Ideas Sdn Bhd)
Fong, Felix—BPEP International
Fong, William P.—Investor Growth Capital AB
Fong, William—Investor Growth Capital, Inc.
Fonseca, Rodrigo—Carlyle Group, The
Fonseca, Vitor—Romspen Investment Corporation
Fonstad, Jennifer—Draper Fisher Jurvetson
Font, Victor—Delta Partners FZ LLC
Fonta, Herve—Edmond de Rothschild Capital Partners SAS
Fontenot, Joel—Trailblazer Capital
Fontes, Evaldo—Jardim Botanico Partners (FKA: Araujo Fontes Consultoria)
Foo, Gavin—Northleaf Capital Partners
Foo, Jixun—GGV Capital
Foo, Peng Mun—London Asia Capital Plc (FKA: netvest.com Plc)
Foote, Sean—Labrador Ventures
Foote, Virginia—BIDV Vietnam Partners Investment Management Co. (AKA: BVIM)
Foran, Michael—Eureka Growth Capital
Forbes, John—eFund, LLC
Forbes, Robert—Glenmount, LLC
Force, Ding—Wuhan Good Insight Venturing Investment Co., Ltd.
Force, Jill—Chrysalis Ventures
Forchielli, Alberto—Mandarin Capital Partners
Ford, Andrew—Hanover Partners, Inc
Ford, B. James—Oaktree Capital Management LLC
Ford, James—Vista Equity Partners
Ford, Richard—Two Rivers Associates LLC (FKA: Gateway Associates, L.P.)
Ford, William Clay—Fontinalis Partners LLC
Ford, William—General Atlantic LLC
Fordyce, James—J.H. Whitney & Co. LLC
Forer, Michael—Celtic Therapeutics Management, L.L.L.P.
Forer, Michael—Rosetta Capital, Ltd.
Forest, Sophie—Brightspark Ventures
Forgash, E. Michael—Zon Capital Partners
Forlenza, Michael—Lincolnshire Management, Inc.
Forlenza, Robert—Tudor Ventures
Formandl, George—EnerCap Capital Partners
Formela, Jean-Francois—Atlas Venture, Ltd.
Formolo, Thomas—Code, Hennessy & Simmons LLC
Forrest, Gregory—Forrest Binkley & Brown
Forrest, Kevin—5AM Ventures
Forrest, William—Gleacher & Co.
Fors, Andrew—Summer Street Capital LLC
Forsberg, Anki—Odlander, Fredrikson & Co. AB (AKA: HealthCap)
Forsberg, Per—Valedo Partners (FKA: CreVal Partners)
Forsberg, Per-Ola—Lund University Bioscience AB
Forschner, Jakob—Stirling Square Capital Partners
Forshaw, Darren—Endless LLP
Forsingdal, Susanne—ATP Private Equity Partners
Forster, Bret—Serent Capital LLC
Forster, David—IBIS Capital, Ltd.
Forster, Frank—Blackstone Group, L.P.
Forster, Michael—Internet Capital Group
Forster, R. Patrick—Industrial Growth Partners
Forster, Shane—Babson Capital Management LLC
Forth, J. Bradford—GFI Energy Ventures
Fortier, Michelle—Megunticook Management
Fortin, Jason—Wellspring Capital Management LLC
Forton, Peter—CAPE Fund Management, Inc.
Fortune, Patrick—Boston Millennia Partners
Forusz, Holbrook—Circle Peak Capital LLC (AKA: CPC)
Forwood, Edward—Loudwater Investment Partners, Ltd.
Foskey, Andy—Hunt Private Equity Group, Inc. (FKA: Hunt Financial Corp.)
Foss, Stine—Northzone Ventures AS (FKA: Venture Partners AS)
Fossorier, Gabriel—Perfectis Private Equity
Foster, Alan—TeleSoft Partners
Foster, C. Michael—Midwest Mezzanine Funds
Foster, Carol—Pantheon Ventures, Ltd.
Foster, Douglas—Longitude Capital Management Company LLC
Foster, Frank—DFJ Frontier
Foster, Frank—Southern Cross Venture Partners
Foster, Franklin—Audax Group
Foster, J. David—Arbor Private Investment Company, LLC
Foster, John—HealthpointCapital LLC
Foster, John—Natural Gas Partners (NGP)
Foster, Michael—RFE Investment Partners
Foster, Samuel—Velocity Equity Partners LLC
Foster, Steve—Altira Group LLC
Foster, Steve—TPG Growth
Foster, Vincent—Main Street Capital Corporation
Fotiadis, Marios—TVM Capital GmbH
Fotteler, Thomas—Halder Holdings BV
Fougner, Erik—Procuritas Partners KB
Foulkes, J. Gordon—RiverVest Venture Partners
Fountain, Tom—Mayfield Fund
Fountas, Christopher—Arsenal Venture Partners
Fouque, Erick—Edmond de Rothschild Venture Capital Management
Fouquoire, Dominique—IFE Mezzanine
Fournage, Christophe—Colony Capital LLC
Fournier, Marc—Serena Capital SAS
Fournier, Marcel—Castle Harlan, Inc.
Fourt, Jean Francois—Truffle Venture SAS
Fourticq, Michael—Hancock Park Associates
Fourticq, Michael—Hancock Park Associates
Foushee, Scott—AIG Capital Partners
Fousse, Thomas—Carlyle Group, The
Fowler, Craig—BAML Capital Access Funds
Fowler, Joseph—Scsi Capital
Fowlkes, Dana—Hatteras Venture Partners (FKA:Catalysta Partners)

Fox, Anthony—Zouk Ventures, Ltd.
Fox, Arthur—Royalty Capital Management LLC
Fox, Curtis—Voobon Ventures, Inc.
Fox, Douglas—Nueva Ventures
Fox, Jeff—Harbour Group, Ltd.
Fox, John—Perseus LLC
Fox, Keith—Exeter Capital Partners
Fox, Kenneth—Stripes Group
Fox, Natasha—American Capital, Ltd.
Fox, Natasha—Avante Mezzanine Partners
Fox, Richard—Cross Atlantic Capital Partners
Fox, Saul—Fox Paine & Company LLC
Fox, Thomas—Alumni Capital Network
Fraiman, Diane—Voyager Capital
Fralic, Christopher—First Round Capital
Fram, Jonathan—Maveron LLC
Frame, Robert—Trillium Group LLC
Franca, Mauricio—Delta Partners FZ LLC
France, Michael—First Reserve Corporation
France, Robert—High Street Capital
Frances, Craig—Summit Partners
Franchino, Alberto—Industria & Finanza SGR S.p.A.
Francis, Tod—Shasta Ventures Management LLC
Franco Frazao, Emilia—Espirito Santo Capital - Sociedade de Capital de Risco SA
Franco, Thomas—Clayton, Dubilier & Rice, Inc.
Francoeur, Gregory—Convergent Capital Management, Inc (AKA: CCM)
Franeau, David—Synapsis Associates
Frank, Anthony—Belvedere Capital Partners LLC
Frank, Edward—Advanced Technology Ventures
Frank, Greg—Ovation Capital Partners
Frank, Joel—Och-Ziff Capital Management Group
Frank, Lincoln—Quad Ventures
Frank, Marshall—Monterey Venture Partners, LLC
Frank, Peter—GSC Partners (FKA: Greenwich Street Capital Partners)
Frank, Ramsey—JLL Partners (FKA: Joseph, Littlejohn & Levy, Inc.)
Frank, Richard—Darby Asia Investors, Ltd.
Frank, Richard—Darby Overseas Investments, Ltd.
Frank, Richard—Darby Overseas Investments, Ltd.
Frank, Richard—Darby Technology Ventures Group (AKA: DTV)
Frank, Theodore—JumpStart, Inc.
Franke, Willam—Indigo Partners LLC
Frankel, Adam—Evercore Partners
Frankel, Christopher—GunnAllen Venture Partners
Frankel, David—Ovation Capital Partners
Frankel, John—ff Asset Management LLC
Frankel, Mathew—American Capital, Ltd.
Frankel, Stuart—Grotech Ventures
Franken, Arthur—Gilde Healthcare Partners B.V.
Franklin, Cody—Leonard Green & Partners
Franklin, Will—Lime Rock Partners LLC
Franks, Paul—Gresham LLP
Franks, Timothy—Advent International
Frans, W. Douglas—Mesa Capital Partners
Fransen, Filip—Ocas Ventures BVBA
Franssen, Stefan—Cinven, Ltd.
Franssen, Stefan—GMT Communications Partners LLP
Frantz, Jerry—JumpStart, Inc.
Frantz, Mark—RedShift Ventures
Frantz, Stuart—Franklin Street Partners
Franz, Ingo—Creathor Venture Management GmbH
Franz, Peter—FCP Investors
Franzi, Joseph—Cornerstone Advisors, Inc.
Franzini, Caren—New Jersey Economic Development Authority
Franzke, Ekkehard—Ingenium Capital GmbH & Co KG
Franzone, James—General Atlantic LLC
Fraser, Adam—Transom Capital Group
Fraser, Andrew—3i Group PLC
Fraser, Antony—UBS Capital Corporation
Fraser, Heather—Swander Pace Capital
Frecchiami, Andrea—BS Private Equity SpA (FKA: B&S Private Equity Group)
Frechet, Jean—NGEN Partners LLC (FKA: NextGen Partners LLC)
Frechet, Jean—Physic Ventures
Frederick, Alisa—Caltius Mezzanine
Frederick, Scott—Valhalla Partners
Fredette, Richard—Societe Generale de Financement du Quebec (SGF)
Fredrick, Stephen—Grotech Ventures
Fredrikson, Peder—Odlander, Fredrikson & Co. AB (AKA: HealthCap)
Freeburg, Christopher—UIB Capital, Inc.
Freed, Jeffrey—Arlington Capital Partners
Freed, Tom—Allen & Buckeridge Pty, Ltd.
Freedman, Constance—Second Century Ventures LLC
Freedman, Sheldon—21Ventures LLC
Freel, Douglas—ARC Financial Corporation
Freeland, Peter—Great Hill Equity Partners LLC
Freelove, David—Rock Maple Ventures, L.P.
Freeman, Barry—ARC China, Inc.
Freeman, Barry—Summer Street Capital LLC
Freeman, Brad—Freeman Spogli & Co.
Freeman, Jonathon—Coller Capital
Freeman, Joseph—GE Commercial Finance - Equity
Freeman, Josh—Horsley Bridge Partners
Freeman, Keith—Hilco Equity Management, LLC
Freeman, Mason—5AM Ventures
Freeman, Ralph—Millennium Ventures LLC
Freeman, Roger—SFW Capital Partners, LLC
Freeman, Scott—Colony Capital LLC
Freeman, Terry—Northern Plains Capital, Ltd.
Freeman, Valerie—Texas Women Ventures Fund
Freeman, Varel—European Bank for Reconstruction and Development
Frege, Rodolphe—Butler Capital Partners SA
Frehner, Jacques—Lydian Capital Advisors S.A.
Frei, Andrei—Partners Group AG
Freiberg, Randolph—Opus Electra & Partners
Freifeld, Jed—Boldcap Ventures LLC
Freiherr von Cramm, Egbert—CAM Private Equity Consulting & Verwaltungs - GmbH
Freiherr von Tettau, Diethard—DIH Deutsche Industrie-Holding GmbH
Fremd, Thomas—Montreux Equity Partners
Fremuth, Gunnar—Private Equity Investors, Inc.
French, Douglas—Sante Ventures
French, Heather—American Capital, Ltd.
French, Mark—Greyrock Capital Group
French, Raymond—Versa Capital Management (FKA: Chrysalis Capital Partners)
French, T. Bondurant—Adams Street Partners LLC
Frenkel, Amit—Carmel Ventures
Frenkel, Amit—Vintage Venture Partners
Frere, Gerald—Groupe Bruxelles Lambert S.A. (GBL)
Freudenberg, Hans—Bain Capital
Freudenberg, Hans—Findos Investor GmbH
Freudenthal, Peter—Darwin Ventures LLC
Freund, Chris—Mekong Capital, Ltd.
Freund, Jay—National City Equity Partners, Inc.
Freund, John—Skyline Ventures
Freundlich, Tim—Good Capital
Frew, Paul—Elderstreet Investments Limited
Frey, Andrew—Continuum Group, Ltd. (AKA: Continuum Advisory, Ltd.)
Frey, Andrew—Quadrangle Group LLC
Frey, Karl—Starwood Capital Group
Frey, Oliver—AEA Investors LP
Frey, Ulrich—Foo Brains&Capital, The
Freyman, Daniel—Lightyear Capital LLC
Frezza, William—Adams Capital Management, Inc.
Friant, Todd—American Capital, Ltd.
Frias, Justo—Nexos Capital Partners
Frick, John—Chisholm Private Capital Partners, LC
Frick, Kevin—Serent Capital LLC
Fricke, Uli—Triangle Venture Capital Group Management GmbH
Fricker, Michael—Whitecastle Investments
Fridman, Alex—P.A.G. Capital Partners
Friedberg, Jared—Cortec Group, Inc.
Friedli, Peter—Friedli Corporate Finance AG
Friedli, Rolf—Capvis Equity Partners AG
Friedlich, Jim—Allegis Capital (AKA: Media Technology Ventures)
Friedman, Andrew—Shorenstein Company LLC
Friedman, Ashley—Investor Growth Capital AB
Friedman, Ashley—Investor Growth Capital, Inc.
Friedman, Clifford—Constellation Ventures (AKA: Constellation Growth Capital)
Friedman, Darren—Citigroup Private Equity
Friedman, Harold—VantagePoint Venture Partners
Friedman, Jeff—Monumental Venture Partners LLC
Friedman, Jeff—NAC Ventures, LLC
Friedman, John—Easton Hunt Capital Partners, L.P.
Friedman, Josef—Storm Ventures LLC
Friedman, Joshua—Canyon Capital
Friedman, Kenneth—SB Energy Partners
Friedman, Louis—P. Schoenfeld Asset Management LLC
Friedman, Mark—Evercore Partners
Friedman, Richard—Goldman, Sachs & Co.
Friedman, Robert—Blackstone Group, L.P.
Friedman, Tully—Friedman, Fleischer & Lowe, LLC
Frieman, Adam—Probitas Partners, Inc.
Friend, Alexander—Friend Skoler & Co., L.L.C.
Friend, Marc—Summit Accelerator Fund
Friend, Scott—Bain Capital Ventures
Friendly, Andrew—Advanced Technology Ventures
Frient, Jeffrey—Bolder Capital LLC
Frient, Jeffrey—Edgewater Funds, The
Fries, Alexander—Ecosystem Ventures LLC
Fries, David—VantagePoint Venture Partners
Friese, Stefan—Beaufort Capital GmbH
Friesel, Jonathan—Oak Hill Capital Management, Inc.
Friesen, Albert—CentreStone Ventures Inc.
Frigast, Christian—Axcel Industriinvestor AS
Friis, Janus—Atomico Ventures
Friis, Klaus—Danske Private Equity A/S

Frisbie, Richard—Battery Ventures, L.P.
Frischer, Charles—Zephyr Management, L.P.
Frishman, Marc—Conduit Capital Partners, LLC
Frishman, Zev—Ontario Teachers' Pension Plan
Frisk, Anders—Sustainable Technology Partners Nordic AB
Frist, William—Cressey & Company, L.P.
Fritz, Ben—Global Environment Fund Management Corporation
Fritz, Peter—Balloch China Fund, The
Fritzmeyer, Kevin—Cameron Holdings Corporation
Frodigh, Judy—Huntsman Gay Global Capital LLC
Froetscher, Robert—Willis Stein & Partners
Frohnhofen, Wilfried—Intelligent Venture Capital Management GmbH
Froiland, Arne—Energy Capital Management AS
Froland, Charles—Performance Equity Management, LLC
Fromson, John—Generis Capital Partners
Fronistas, Aristides C.—7 L Capital Partners
Fronterhouse, Jeff—Brazos Private Equity Partners LLC
Frost, Martin—Chord Capital, Ltd. (FKA: Generics Group, The)
Frost, Zac—UNC Kenan-Flagler Private Equity Fund
Fruehan, Mark—Mobility Ventures
Fruehwirth, John—Allied Capital Corporation
Fry, Eric—Metalmark Capital LLC
Fry, Eric—Morgan Stanley Private Equity
Fry, Stephen—BioMedical Innovations, Ltd.
Fu, Juanita—BioVeda Capital Private, Ltd.
Fu, Lei—Ivy Capital
Fu, Miao—Creation Power Capital
Fu, Qiang—New Enterprise Associates, Inc.
Fu, Shan—Blackstone Group, L.P.
Fu, Winston—U.S. Venture Partners
Fu, Yachien—Parker Price Venture Capital Inc.(FKA: Allegro Capital, Inc)
Fuchikami, Kinji—MVC Corporation
Fuchs, Harald—LBBW Venture Capital GmbH
Fuchs, Stuart—Gryffindor Capital Partners LLC
Fudim, Yair—Shrem Fudim Kelner Technologies, Ltd.
Fuglede Nielsen, Jakob—SEED Capital Denmark K/S
Fuhrman, Glenn—MSD Capital L.P.
Fujii, Daniel—Blackstone Group, L.P.
Fujii, Kazuhide—Privee Investment Holdings Co., Ltd.
Fujii, Tsuneo—Yasuda Enterprise Development Co., Ltd.(FKA: Nippon Ent.Dev)
Fujikawa, Koichi—Arise Capital Partners, Inc.
Fujimura, Michio—ATA Ventures
Fujinami, Mitsuo—Biofrontier Partners, Inc.
Fujiyama, Ian—Carlyle Group, The
Fukumoto, Troy—SunAmerica Ventures
Fukunaga, Shigeru—Sirius Venture Consulting Pte, Ltd.
Fukuzawa, Hidetaka—Japan Asia Investment Company, Ltd. (AKA: JAIC)
Fuld, Richard—Lehman Brothers, Inc.
Fulham, John—Fulham & Company, Inc.
Fulham, John—Fulham & Company, Inc.
Fulham, Timothy—Fulham & Company, Inc.
Fulk, Matthew—Golub Capital
Fulkerson, Davis—Century Capital Management, Inc.
Fuller, Mark—Alliance Fund Managers, Ltd.
Fuller, Ross—American Capital, Ltd.
Fuller, Thomas—Angelo, Gordon & Company
Fultz, Charles—Brown Gibbons Lang & Company LLC
Fumagalli, Laurence—Climate Change Capital, Ltd.
Fumin, Zhuo—GGV Capital
Funcannon, Bill—OVP Venture Partners
Fung, Annie—CITIC Capital Partners, Ltd.
Fung, Annie—Citigroup Private Bank
Fung, Ching- Ho—New Enterprise Associates, Inc.
Fung, James—Affinity Equity Partners
Fung, May—Inter-Asia Venture Management
Funk, Andy—Funk Ventures, Inc.
Funk, Jonathan—Allegis Capital (AKA: Media Technology Ventures)
Funk, R. Clayton—Media Venture Partners
Furey, Michael—Halyard Partners
Furia, Patrice—Alto Invest
Furlan, Dino—21 Centrale Partners
Furlan, Dino—21 Partners SpA
Furlong, Tom—Granite Ventures LLC
Furneaux, David—Kodiak Venture Partners
Furniss, Todd—PlumTree Partners LLC
Furnivall, James—Canaan Partners
Furst, Allen—Morgenthau Venture Partners, LLC
Furst, Gary—Generation Equity Investors
Furstenbach, Carl—Accent Equity Partners AB
Furukawa, Ryoji—Asset Managers Holding Company, Ltd.
Fussell, Tannis—Cordova, Smart & Williams, LLC
Fuster, Jose Miguel—Darby Overseas Investments, Ltd.
Futch, Curt—Thomas Weisel Partners Group, Inc.
Futterknecht, James—Hammond Kennedy Whitney & Co
Fyfe, Gordon—CDP Capital - Technology Ventures (FKA: CDP Sofinov)
Fymat, Isabelle—Crosslink Capital
GV, Ravi Shankar—Sequoia Capital India (FKA: WestBridge Capital Partners)
Ga ash, Adoram—Stage One Ventures
Gabbard, O. Gene—Ballast Point Venture Partners
Gabbita, Sam—Element Partners
Gabel, Mel—TD Capital Group, Ltd.
Gabelein, Kevin—Fluke Venture Partners
Gabelier, Philippe—CDP Capital - Technology Ventures (FKA: CDP Sofinov)
Gable, Scott—Hercules Technology Growth Capital, Inc.
Gabler, Ursula—Mittelstandische Beteiligungsgesellschaft Thuringen mbH
Gabran, Niclas—TowerBrook Capital Partners L.P.
Gabriel, Jean-Michel—BNP Paribas Developpement SA
Gabrieli, Christopher—Ironwood Capital (AKA: Ironwood Capital Advisors LLC)
Gabriely, Nir—Supply Chain Equity Partners
Gad, Dror—TechnoPlus Ventures
Gadicke, Ansbert—MPM Capital (FKA: MPM Asset Management LLC)
Gadkari, Prasad—IDFC Private Equity
Gadowski, Lukasz—Team Europe Ventures Management GmbH
Gadwal, Suresh—Canbank Venture Capital Fund Limited
Gaeddert, Gregory—B12 Capital Partners LLC
Gaede, Mary—GE Antares Capital Corporation
Gaenzle, Richard—Gilbert Global Equity Capital, L.L.C.
Gaffney, Christopher—Great Hill Equity Partners LLC
Gaffney, Michael—EDG Partners LLC
Gagalis, Robert—Enterasys Networks (FKA: Cabletron Systems, Inc.)
Gage, John—Kleiner Perkins Caufield & Byers
Gaggini, Filippo—Investitori Associati SpA
Gagna, Pascal—Pragma Capital
Gailar, Steve—Kentucky Seed Capital Fund
Gailar, Steven—Compass Capital Fund Management LLC
Gaillard, Dominique—AXA Private Equity
Gaitanos, Stephen—Telopea Capital Partners Pty, Ltd.
Gaither, James—Sutter Hill Ventures
Gajecka, Marta—European Investment Bank, The (AKA: EIB)
Gajo, Giovanni—Alcedo SGR SpA
Gajria, Narendra—Al Mal Capital
Gal-Or, Amir—Infinity Venture Capital Fund (AKA: Israel Infinity Fund)
Galakatos, Nicholas—Clarus Ventures
Galambos, Nicholas—Industrial Opportunity Partners, LLC
Galante, Jacques—Leeds Equity Partners
Galantini, Eugene—Dolphin Equity Partners
Galashan, J. Kristopher—Leonard Green & Partners
Galbraith, Kenneth—Ventures West Management, Inc.
Galbreath, Michael—Portfolio Advisors LLC
Gale, James—Signet Healthcare Partners (FKA: Sanders Morris Harris)
Galef, James—JM Galef & Co., Inc.
Galiette, Carolyn—Ironwood Capital (AKA: Ironwood Capital Advisors LLC)
Galitsky, Alexandr—Almaz Capital Partners
Gallagher, Brian—PPM America Capital Partners LLC
Gallagher, Brian—S.R. One, Ltd.
Gallagher, Evan—IDFC Capital (Singapore) Pte, Ltd.
Gallagher, Jerry—Oak Investment Partners
Gallagher, Patrick—Morgan Stanley Venture Partners (AKA: MSDW)
Gallagher, Patrick—VantagePoint Venture Partners
Gallagi, Frank—Greenwoods Capital Partners
Gallaher, Brendan—American Capital, Ltd.
Gallanter, Joanna Rees—VSP Capital (FKA: Venture Strategy Partners)
Galleher, Patrick—Boxwood Capital Partners, LLC
Galles, Daniel—HLM Venture Partners
Galletti, Marc-Henri—Longitude Capital Management Company LLC
Galligan, Joseph—Forrest Binkley & Brown
Gallinson, Evan—Merit Capital Partners (FKA:William Blair Mezzanine)
Gallivan, Gerry—Mediphase Venture Partners
Gallo, Michele—Alcedo SGR SpA
Gallo, Pier Domenico—Orlando Capital Management GmbH
Gallogly, Mark—Centerbridge Partners
Gallot, Jerome—CDC Entreprises SAS
Gallouin, Jean-Francois—AGF Private Equity

Galper, David—WWC Capital Group LLC
Galuhn, Thomas—Mesirow Private Equity Investments, Inc.
Galuska, Patrick—SB Energy Partners
Gambarini, Paolo—Wise SRG S.p.A. (AKA: Wisequity)
Gambazzi, Andrea—Swiss Life Private Equity Partners Ltd
Gambill, Katie—Council Ventures
Gamman, Einar—Energy Ventures AS
Gamsin, Marc—SunAmerica Ventures
Gan, Adi—Evergreen Venture Partners
Gan, JP—Qiming Venture Partners
Gan, Meilan—Prax Capital
Gandarias, Patrick—Corpfin Capital Asesores SA
Gandesha, Parag—MML Capital Partners
Gandhi, Hetal—IL&FS Investment Managers Ltd (FKA: IL&FS Venture Corp)
Gandhi, Hetal—Tano Capital LLC
Gandhi, Meena—J.P. Morgan Asset Management
Gandhi, Parth—ICICI Venture Funds Management Co., Pvt. Ltd. (FKA: TDICI)
Gandhi, Pravin—Infinity Venture Capital
Gandhi, Pravin—Seedfund
Gandhi, Pravin—eIndia Venture Management
Gandhi, Sameer—Accel Partners
Gandhi, Sameer—Sequoia Capital
Gandolfo, Carolynn—BioVeda Capital Private, Ltd.
Ganesan, N.—iGlobe Treasury Management, Ltd.
Ganesan, Venky—Globespan Capital Partners
Ganesh, Ghaitrie—Exeter Capital Partners
Ganga, Vinay—Origo Partners PLC
Ganguly, Vivek—YES BANK, Ltd.
Gani, Marcel—Juniper Networks
Gannon, Brian—Dunrath Capital, Inc.
Gannon, John—Polaris Venture Partners
Gannon, John—SunBridge Partners
Gannot, Gary—Genesis Partners
Ganong, Richard—Tudor Ventures
Gans, Helene—Alto Invest
Ganser, Roger—Venture Investors LLC
Gantar, Matjaz—KD Group
Gantner, Alfred—Partners Group AG
Ganung, Jeff—Pantheon Ventures, Ltd.
Gao, Ellen—WI Harper Group
Gao, Megan—Gold Stone Investment, Ltd.
Gaouette, Francois—Propulsion Ventures, Inc.
Garaialde, Jacques—Kohlberg, Kravis, Roberts & Company, L.P.
Garavelli, Giovanni—Advanced Capital SGRpA
Garber, Peni—ABRY Partners LLC
Garber, Robert—KB Partners LLC
Garbers, Grant—Headwaters Merchant Bank
Garcia, Alex—Aztec Equity Partners, LLC
Garcia, Francisco—Easton Hunt Capital Partners, L.P.
Garcia-Nieto Portabella, Borja—Riva y Garcia Private Equity
Gardell, Rickard—Pacific Equity Partners
Gardella, Lee—Adveq Management AG
Gardhouse, Mark—C.A. Bancorp, Inc.
Gardi, Paul—Liberty Capital Management Corporation
Gardiner, Alexandra—EMAlternatives LLC
Gardiner, Gregory—Elm Street Ventures
Gardner, Alston—Fulcrum Ventures
Gardner, Graham—Highland Capital Partners LLC
Gardner, John—Nokia Growth Partners
Gardner, Lee—One Equity Partners (FKA: Banc One Venture Partners)
Gardner, Peter—SmartForest Ventures
Gardner, Peter—Wavepoint Ventures
Gardner, Phyllis—Essex Woodlands Health Ventures
Gardner, Ted—Silverhawk Capital Partners LLC
Garel, John—Envest
Garff, Matthew—Sun Capital Partners, Inc.
Garfinkel, Neil—Francisco Partners
Garfinkle, Jan—Arboretum Ventures
Garfunkle, Matt—Pantheon Ventures, Ltd.
Garg, Ashu—Foundation Capital
Garg, Devesh—Bessemer Venture Partners
Garg, Gaurav—Sequoia Capital
Garg, Nikhil—Black Coral Capital
Garg, V.K.—Power Finance Corporation, Ltd.
Gargash, Shehab—Alf Yad, Ltd.
Gari, Miguel—Suma Capital
Garland, Anthony—Paperboy Ventures, LLC
Garland, Mike—Permira Advisers LLP
Garland, Robert—New Enterprise Associates, Inc.
Garman, Andrew—New Venture Partners LLC
Garman, Lucas—Welsh, Carson, Anderson & Stowe
Garman, Richard—FTV Capital (FKA: FTVentures)
Garmendia, Cristina—Ysios Capital Partners
Garnett, Terence—Garnett & Helfrich Capital
Garnier, Bernard—Socadif SA
Garofolo, John—Gemini Partners, Inc.
Garran, Peter—Great Hill Equity Partners LLC
Garrard, Charles—Paracor Capital Advisors Pvt., Ltd.
Garret, Ron—Funk Ventures, Inc.
Garrett, Brian—Crosscut Ventures
Garrett, Gregory—Portfolio Advisors LLC
Garrett, John—Meritage Funds
Garrett, Lester—Yorkville Advisors LLC
Garrett, Tate—Sunrock Ventures, Inc.
Garrido, Jose Miguel—Thesan Capital
Garrigan, Thomas—Carlyle Group, The
Garrigues, Antoine—Iris Capital Management (FKA: Part'Com Management S.A.)
Garrison, Robert—Signet Healthcare Partners (FKA: Sanders Morris Harris)
Garrou, Blair—DFJ Mercury
Garson, Palmer—Jefferson Capital Partners, Ltd.
Gartenberg, Ran—Vertex Management Israel (AKA: Vertex Venture Capital)
Gartenberg, Ran—Vertex Venture Capital
Garton, Anthony—Cinven, Ltd.
Garulli, Michele—Investindustrial Partners, Ltd.
Garvey, Shay—Delta Partners, Ltd.
Garville, Gregory—Union Capital Corporation
Garza, N. Rudy—G-51 Capital LLC
Garza, Theresa—G-51 Capital LLC
Gaspar, Andrew—SV Investment Partners (FKA: Schroder Ventures US)
Gaspar, Daniel—Gotham Private Equity Partners, L.P.
Gasparro, David—Lonsdale Capital Partners LLP
Gassee, Jean-Louis—Allegis Capital (AKA: Media Technology Ventures)
Gasset Loring, Jose—COFIDES - Compania Espanola De Financiacion Del Desarrolo SA
Gasull, Philippe—La Financiere de Brienne
Gates, Jay—Charterhouse Group International, Inc.
Gates, Peter—MedEquity Investors LLC
Gathalia, Rajiv—Warburg Pincus LLC
Gatlin, Ross—Insight Equity Holdings LLC
Gatto, Vic—Massey Burch Capital Corp.
Gatto, Vic—Solidus Company, L.P.
Gaudiani, Michael—Danville Partners, LLC
Gaudreau, Michel—Dubai International Capital LLC
Gauer, James—Palomar Ventures
Gaus, Wesley—CM Equity Partners (FKA; Lynx Investment Management, L.P.)
Gausling, Mike—Originate Ventures
Gauthier, Andre—Tandem Expansion Fund, Inc.
Gauthier, David—Foragen Technologies Management
Gavin, Brenda—Quaker BioVentures, Inc.
Gavin, Brian—Blackstone Group, L.P.
Gavirati, Alessandra—BS Private Equity SpA (FKA: B&S Private Equity Group)
Gaw, Arakin—Gilbert Global Equity Capital, L.L.C.
Gaw, Benjamin—Brazos Private Equity Partners LLC
Gay, Bob—Bain Capital
Gay, Mary Price—Gleacher & Co.
Gay, Robert—Huntsman Gay Global Capital LLC
Gay, Susan—Corecap Limited
Gazit, Rinat—Poalim Capital Markets Technologies Ltd
Geahchan, Marie-Luce—Colony Capital LLC
Geary, William—North Bridge Venture Partners
Gebauer, A. George—Capital Partners, Inc.
Geddes, James—Trans Cosmos USA
Geddes, John—SCF Partners
Geddes, Stephen—Pi Capital
Gee, David—TTP Venture Managers, Ltd. (FKA:Technology Partnership, The)
Geerolf, Pierre—Cerea Gestion SAS
Geerts, Harmen—H2 Equity Partners BV
Geeslin, Keith—Francisco Partners
Gefaell, Robert—Plexus Capital LLC (FKA: Plexus Fund)
Gehorsam, Robert—JVP
Geiger, Bernd—Triangle Venture Capital Group Management GmbH
Geiger, Michael—Shamrock Holdings, Inc.
Geiman, Robert—Polaris Venture Partners
Geis, Benjamin—Bush O'Donnell Capital Partners
Geis, Larry—Madison Capital Partners
Geisler, John—Golub Capital
Geismar, Xavier—Cinven, Ltd.
Geiss, William—Vexiom Equity Partners, L.P.
Geissler, Natalie—Siguler Guff & Company
Geist, William—CDC Corporation (FKA: Chinadotcom Ventures)
Gekiere, Barry—Ventures West Management, Inc.
Gekker, Victor—SigmaBleyzer
Gelfand, Jeffrey—Centerbridge Partners
Geliebter, David—Carrot Capital LLC
Geller, Marc—Sternhill Partners
Geller, Marshall—St. Cloud Capital, LLC
Gellermann, Lynn—Adena Ventures
Gemmell, David—Venture Capital Partners Pty., Ltd.
Gemvik, Martin—ForetagsByggarna AB (AKA: Business Builders)
Genda, Kevin—Cerberus Capital Management, L.P.
Genender, Mark—Carlyle Group, The

Genereux, Michael—Blackstone Group, L.P.
Geneser, Christopher—CIVC Partners LP (FKA: Continental Illinois Venture Corp.)
Genest, Jack—Charles River Ventures
Geng, Zhongqi—Sinovo Growth Capital Management Co., Ltd.
Genieser, Robert—ETF Manager LLP
Genieser, Robert—Vertex Management Israel (AKA: Vertex Venture Capital)
Genieser, Robert—Vertex Management Pte, Ltd. (AKA: Vertex Venture Holdings)
Genieser, Robert—Vertex Venture Capital
Gennarelli, Phillip—Millennium Ventures LLC
Gentil, Fernando—Darby Overseas Investments, Ltd.
Georgacacos, Aki—Avrio Ventures Management Corp.
George, Harry—Solstice Capital
George, Jean—Advanced Technology Ventures
George, Marcus—Code, Hennessy & Simmons LLC
George, Mathew—TELUS Ventures
George, Patrick—Gordon River Capital
George, Ross—Direct Capital Private Equity
George, Simeon—S.R. One, Ltd.
George, Timothy—GCP Capital Partners
Georges, Edouard—Golding Capital Partners GmbH
Georgiadis, Pantelis (Pete)—Synetro Group LLC
Gera, Michael—Pond Venture Partners
Geraphty, Sharon—Torys LLP
Gerard, Emanuel—GKM Ventures
Gerard, Luc—Tribecapital Partners S.A. (AKA: Tribeca Partners)
Gerbaldi, Alain—UFG Private Equity SAS
Gerber, David—Great Point Partners LLC
Gerber, Ellen—Sugar Mountain Capital
Gerber, Francois—Vatel Capital SAS
Gerber, Hal—Burrill & Company
Gerber, Laurie—Great Hill Equity Partners LLC
Gerbet, Valerie—Siparex Group SAS
Gereghty, James—Siguler Guff & Company
Gerhold, Frank—Odewald & Compagnie GmbH
Gerlach, Jurgen—DVC Deutsche Venture Capital
Gerlach, Mac—Hercules Technology Growth Capital, Inc.
Germain, Ann St.—Grove Street Advisors LLC
Gerngross, Tillman—SV Life Sciences Advisers
Gerome, Frank—STARTech Early Ventures
Gerry, Peter—Sycamore Ventures Pte, Ltd.
Gersch, Seth—Fox Paine & Company LLC
Gersfelt, Torsten—European Investment Bank, The (AKA: EIB)
Gersh, Lewis—Metamorphic Ventures, LLC (FKA: Gersh Venture Partners)
Gershenberg, Aaron—SVB Capital
Gershenson, Michael—Carlyle Group, The
Gershman, David—Trivest Partners, L.P.
Gersten, Richard—Catterton Partners
Gerstner, Franz—Mittelstandische Beteiligungsgesellschaft Thuringen mbH
Gerstner, Thomas—BTV Beteiligungsverwaltung GmbH & Co. KG
Gerstner, William—Saw Mill Capital, LLC
Gertner, Michael—Essex Woodlands Health Ventures
Gesell, Andrew—Court Square Capital Partners
Gesess, Paolo—360 Capital Management SA (AKA: 360 Capital Partners)
Geshwiler, James—CommonAngels
Geske, David—CAM Private Equity Consulting & Verwaltungs - GmbH
Gessel, David—American Capital, Ltd.
Geszti, Andras—Euroventures Capital Kft.
Gettleson, Harvey—Lexington Commercial Holdings
Geva, Michal—TriVentures
Geyr, Florian—Intelligent Venture Capital Management GmbH
Gezon, David—Midwest Mezzanine Funds
Gfoeller, Joachim—GMG Capital Partners (FKA: GMS Capital Partners)
Ghai, Achal—Avigo Capital Partners
Ghandour, Imad—Gulf Capital
Ghausi, Massy—MSD Capital L.P.
Ghegan, Thomas—Founders Equity, Inc.
Gherghina, Leo—BPEP International
Ghidirim, Patrick—NCH Capital, Inc.
Ghim, Chul Ho—STIC Investments, Inc.
Ghose, Shomit—ONSET Ventures
Ghosheh, Mayas—Gulf Capital
Giacometti, Luca—GE Commercial Finance - Equity
Giacometti, Luca—Glenalta Capital LLP
Giacometti, Paolo—Syntek Capital AG
Giacomotto, Lionel—Gimar Capital Investissement
Giallorenzo, David—Naxicap Partners SA
Giambanco, Sal—Omidyar Network
Giampaolo, David—Pi Capital
Giampetroni, John—Rizvi Traverse Management, LLC
Gianfriddo, Mary—Romspen Investment Corporation
Giannini, Mario—Hamilton Lane Advisors, Inc.
Giannuzzi, John—Sherbrooke Capital
Gianola, Andrea—Investitori Associati SpA
Gianos, Philip—InterWest Partners
Giaquinto, Michael—GCP Capital Partners
Gibaratz, Scott—Thayer Hidden Creek
Gibb, Ewan—EnerCap Capital Partners
Gibbons, Alastair—Bridgepoint Capital, Ltd.
Gibbons, James—Aetos Capital LLC
Gibbons, Michael—Brown Gibbons Lang & Company LLC
Gibbons, Michael—Fairmont Capital, Inc.
Gibbons, Michael—Invesco Private Capital
Gibbons, Paul—Castanea Partners
Gibbs, Ker—Hina Capital Partners
Gibbs, Matthew—Oxford Bioscience Partners
Gibian, Thomas—EMP Africa Fund Management (AKA: Emerging Capital Partners)
Gibson, Jim—CORE Partners, Inc.
Gibson, Jonathan—Ambienta SGR S.p.A.
Gibson, Libby—Piper Private Equity Limited
Gibson, Peter—Next Capital Pty., Ltd.
Gibson, Rebecca—Cinven, Ltd.
Gibson, Simon—Wesley Clover, Ltd.
Gibson, Stewart—Capital International Research, Inc.
Giebel, Lutz—SV Life Sciences Advisers
Gier, Eric—TCIB Investment Co., Ltd.
Gier, Eric—Trenwith Securities LLC
Gierosky, Paul—Evolution Capital Partners, LLC
Gierynski, Pawel—Abris Capital Partners
Giesbrecht, Dieter—ViewPoint Capital Partners GmbH
Gieselman, Scott—Natural Gas Partners (NGP)
Gieselman, Thomas—BV Capital (FKA: Bertelsmann Ventures, LP)
Giesinger, Peter—CGS Management giesinger gloor lanz & co.
Gifford, Charles—Heritage Partners
Giger, Corinne—Capital Dynamics AG
Gil, Manuel—Nmas1 Private Equity (FKA: Nmas1 Electra Capital Privado)
Gilbard, Marc—Moorfield Investment Management Ltd
Gilbert, Avrom—Jerusalem Global Ventures
Gilbert, Daniel—Camelot Ventures
Gilbert, Daniel—RockBridge Equity Partners LLC
Gilbert, Daryl—JOG Capital
Gilbert, Douglas—Winston Partners
Gilbert, Karen Derr—FTV Capital (FKA: FTVentures)
Gilbert, Myles—Ironside Capital Group (FKA:Ironside Ventures LLC)
Gilbert, Walter—BioVentures Investors
Gilbey, Hannah—Henderson Equity Partners (AKA: Henderson Private Capital)
Gilboa, Avi—Unitas Capital Pte, Ltd.
Gilchrest, Eric—Satori Capital LLC
Gildea, Brian—Hamilton Lane Advisors, Inc.
Giles, Eerik—Navigation Capital Partners
Giles, Eerik—Navigation Capital Partners (AKA: NCP)
Giles, J. Michael—Allegis Capital (AKA: Media Technology Ventures)
Gilfix, Jeffrey—GMG Capital Partners (FKA: GMS Capital Partners)
Gilhuly, Edward—Kohlberg, Kravis, Roberts & Company, L.P.
Giliotti, Emil—Patriarch Partners LLC
Gill, Daniel—Silver Oak Management
Gill, Jack—Vanguard Ventures
Gill, Joseph—Wall Street Venture Capital
Gill, Mark—Coates Myer & Co. Pty Ltd.
Gill, Mark—Fairmont Capital, Inc.
Gill, Simba—TPG Growth
Gill-Roberts, Jennifer—Maven Venture Partners
Gillbanks, Jonathan—GMT Communications Partners LLP
Gillespie, Robert—Evercore Partners
Gillette, James—Gryphon Investors, Inc.
Gillfillan, Michael—Meritum Partners LLC
Gilliard, Lukim—Incyte Venture Partners LLC
Gillies, Charles—Jolimont Capital Pty, Ltd.
Gilligan, Michael—Heritage Partners
Gillings, Dennis—Quintiles Transnational Corporation
Gillis, Steven—ARCH Venture Partners
Gillman, Dustin—Ranch Capital LLC
Gilmer, Barrett—MidOcean Partners
Gilmour, Robert—Finistere Partners LLC
Gilpin, Winston—DFJ Mercury
Gimbel, Jonathan—Gores Group LLC, The
Gin, Yap Pao—Tembusu Partners Pte., Ltd.
Ginader, Barbara—Boston Ventures Management, Inc.
Ginsberg, Erik—Slate Capital Group
Ginsberg, Winston—TowerBrook Capital Partners L.P.
Ginsburg, James—Vernon & Park Capital, L.P.
Gionfriddo, Julie—Landmark Partners, Inc.
Giordano, Gary—Berkshire Partners LLC
Giovacchini, Paul—Landmark Partners, Inc.
Girard, Cliff—Acorn Ventures, Inc.
Girard, Guillame—Sophia Euro Lab SAS

Girard, Guillaume—Astrolabe Ventures
Giraudo, Louis—GESD Capital Partners, LLC
Gire, Philippe—ELAIA Partners
Girgenti, Christopher—New World Ventures
Giri, Vinod—IDFC Private Equity
Giron, Thierry—Initiative & Finance Investissement SA
Gissauer, Oliver—PONTIS Capital GmbH
Gissel, Peter—Bridgepoint Development Capital
Gitig, Liron—FTV Capital (FKA: FTVentures)
Giuffrida, Alfred—Horsley Bridge Partners
Giugliano, Anthony—New York City Investment Fund
Giuliano, Claudio—Innogest
Giulini, Christoph—One Equity Partners (FKA: Banc One Venture Partners)
Giuriceo, Kenneth—Clayton, Dubilier & Rice, Inc.
Giuseppetti, Fabio Massimo—Palamon Capital Partners (FKA: Amphion Capital Partners)
Giusti, Margot—Blumberg Capital Ventures
Giusti, Margot—DFJ Athena
Given, David—Blue Point Capital Partners (FKA: Key Equity Capital)
Givens, C. Sage—Acacia Venture Partners
Gjos, Sean—Triton Pacific Capital Partners LLC
Gladden, Robert—Pfingsten Partners, L.P.
Gladden, Thomas—Adams Street Partners LLC
Glaeser, Larry—Footprint Ventures
Glanville, Robert—Pine Brook Road Partners LLC
Glarey, Luigi—Friulia SpA Fin.Reg.Friuli-Venezia
Glaser, Gregg—Advanced Equities Capital Partners LLC
Glaser, Rob—Accel Partners
Glaser, Robert—Accel Partners
Glasheen, Jim—Technology Partners
Glass, Charlie—ACT Venture Capital, Ltd.
Glass, Jason—Summit Partners
Glass, Jeffrey—Bain Capital
Glass, Jeffrey—Bain Capital Ventures
Glass, Jonathan—GE Commercial Finance - Equity
Glass, Jonathan—Millennium Technology Ventures
Glass, Steven—STG Capital, LLC
Glassmeyer, Edward—Oak Investment Partners
Glastris, William—Prospect Partners LLC
Glatman, Mark—Lyceum Capital
Glauninger, Mat—Hercules Technology Growth Capital, Inc.
Glauser, Olivier—Steamboat Ventures
Glausser, Gary—Birchmere Ventures
Glavas, Kostis—Global Finance SA
Glazer, John—Perseus LLC
Gleacher, Eric—Gleacher & Co.
Gleitman, Shuki—Platinum-Neurone Ventures
Glenn, David—Lightyear Capital LLC
Glenn, Scott—Windamere Venture Partners, LLC
Glennon, Jennifer—Nordic Biotech Advisors APS
Glew, Charles—Flexpoint Ford (FKA: Flexpoint Partners LLC)
Glick, Craig—Natural Gas Partners (NGP)
Glick, Peter—Ampersand Ventures
Glickman, Daniel—GE Antares Capital Corporation
Glickman, David—Apollo Real Estate Advisors
Glickman, Donald—J.F. Lehman & Company
Glickman, Richard—Kearny Venture Partners
Gline, Jean-Michel—InnovaFonds
Glock, Wolfram—Sirius Venture Partners GmbH
Glorfield, Joe—TBL Capital, L.P.
Glorioso, Antonio—Consilium SGR pA
Glouchevitch, Michael—Riordan, Lewis & Haden
Glover, Erik—Fox Paine & Company LLC
Glover, Jack—PNC Equity Management Corp.
Glovier, Curtis—Nassau Capital LLC
Gluck, Scott—Markstone Capital
Gluntz, Philippe—Paris Business Angels
Glushik, John—Intersouth Partners
Gluzman, Richard—Pegasus Venture Capital
Glynn Brandin, Jacqueline—Glynn Capital Management
Glynn, John—Glynn Capital Management
Gnodde, John—Brait Capital Partners
Goc, Wojciech—Argan Capital (FKA: BA Capital Partners Europe, BACPE)
Godbersen, Fabian—Blackstone Group, L.P.
Goddu, Roger—Brentwood Associates
Gode, Gautam—Samara Capital Partners, Ltd.
Godefroid, Bert—Bencis Capital Partners
Godfrey, Adam—Lindsay Goldberg LLC (FKA: Lindsay Goldberg & Bessemer GP)
Godfrey, Kent—Pond Venture Partners
Godfrey, Richard—Sarsia Innovation AS
Godhwani, Sunil—Religare Enterprises, Ltd.
Godner, Michael—Cavalry Investments LLC
Godreau, Enrique—Voyager Capital
Godron, Louis—Argos Soditic SA
Godwin, Kevin—Birch Hill Equity Partners Management, Inc.
Goebel, Markus—Novartis Venture Fund (FKA: Novartis Corp.)
Goebel, Thomas—NeoMed Management AS
Goeddel, David—Column Group, The
Goedhart, Felix—Capital Stage AG
Goel, Arun—DHFL Venture Capital India Pvt Ltd.
Goel, Vab—Norwest Venture Partners
Goenka, Piyush—Tano Capital LLC
Goense, John—Goense Bounds & Partners, LP
Goergen, Todd—Ropart Group
Goette, Gerd—Siemens Venture Capital GmbH
Goettner, Peter—Worldview Technology Partners
Goetz, Jim—Sequoia Capital
Goff, Charles—NEW Capital Management, Inc.
Goff, John—Goff Moore Strategic Partners
Goff, Laurens—Hampshire Equity Partners (FKA: ING Equity Partners)
Goff, Richard—Alpha Capital Partners, Ltd.
Gogel, Robert—CAP ISF SA
Goguely, Herve—Vision Capital Management
Goguen, Michael—Sequoia Capital
Goh, Andress—Allianz Capital Partners GmbH
Goh, Bernard—Eos Asia Investments, Ltd. (FKA: JCAR Funds, Ltd.)
Goh, Hock—Baird Capital Partners Asia
Goh, Ian—Matrix Partners
Goh, Kim—Hudson Venture Partners
Goh, Yewhong—Axiom Asia Private Capital
Goizueta, Javier—Sepides
Goji, Tomotaka—University of Tokyo Edge Capital Co., Ltd., The (AKA: UTEC)
Gold, Barry—Bracken Partners Limited
Gold, Barry—Carlyle Group, The
Gold, Darren—Genstar Capital LLC
Gold, Irwin—Houlihan, Lokey, Howard & Zukin
Gold, Jeffrey—Longitude Capital Management Company LLC
Gold, Jonathan—North East Finance
Gold, Peter—Archer Capital
Gold, Rick—InnoCal Venture Capital
Goldberg, Alan—Lindsay Goldberg LLC (FKA: Lindsay Goldberg & Bessemer GP)
Goldberg, Allan—Channel Group LLC, The (TCG)
Goldberg, Garrett—Blackstone Group, L.P.
Goldberg, Gary—Saugatuck Capital Company
Goldberg, Jay—Hudson Venture Partners
Goldberg, Joel—Pharos Capital Group LLC
Goldberg, Jon—GunnAllen Venture Partners
Goldberg, Marc—BioVentures Investors
Goldberg, Michael—Mohr Davidow Ventures
Goldberg, Michelle—Ignition Partners (FKA: Ignition Corporation)
Goldberg, Robert—Ridgelift Ventures
Goldberg, Robert—YL Ventures GP, Ltd.
Goldblatt, Joel—Spire Capital
Goldby, Steven—Venrock Associates
Golden, Bruce—Accel Partners
Golden, Michael—Exeter Capital Partners
Golden, Richard—Alumni Capital Network
Goldenberg, Irena—Highland Capital Partners LLC
Goldfarb, Alan—Carlyle Group, The
Goldfarb, Arnon—Israel Cleantech Ventures
Goldfarb, Greg—Summit Partners
Goldfarb, Lawrence—LRG Capital Group (FKA: Baystar Capital, LLC)
Goldfischer, Carl—Bay City Capital LLC
Goldhaber, Nathaniel—Claremont Creek Ventures
Goldhirsch, Hagai—Vintage Venture Partners
Goldie-Morrison, Duncan—Ritchie Capital
Golding, Gary—Edison Venture Fund
Golding, Jeremy P.—Golding Capital Partners GmbH
Golding, Robert—York Street Capital Partners LLC
Goldinger, James—Fairhaven Capital Partners
Goldman, Aaron—General Atlantic LLC
Goldman, Charles—Mill Road Capital LLC
Goldman, Daniel—Clean Energy Venture Group
Goldman, Evan—TowerBrook Capital Partners L.P.
Goldman, Joshua—Norwest Venture Partners
Goldman, Kenneth—Stockton Partners
Goldman, Kenneth—Westly Group, The
Goldman, Kent—First Round Capital
Goldman, Neal—Goode Partners LLC
Goldman, Peter—Valor Equity Partners
Goldman, Richard—Stone Point Capital LLC
Goldman, Ronald—C&B Capital
Goldsmith, Barry—Updata Partners
Goldsmith, Ben—WHEB Ventures, Ltd.
Goldstein, Dov—Aisling Capital
Goldstein, Edward—Coller Capital
Goldstein, Elizabeth—Highland Capital Management, L.P.
Goldstein, Hal—MHR Capital Partners
Goldstein, Howard—Vedanta Capital
Goldstein, Jack—Windamere Venture Partners, LLC
Goldstein, James—North Bridge Venture Partners
Goldstein, Jeffrey—Hellman & Friedman LLC
Goldstein, Jonathan—Advantage Capital Partners
Goldstein, Jonathan—TA Associates, Inc.
Goldstein, Mitchell—Ares Management, Inc.
Goldstein, Oliver—Pine Brook Road Partners LLC
Goldstein, Richard—Oaktree Capital Management LLC

Goldstein, Robert—CapGen Financial Group
Goldstein, Rodney—Frontenac Company
Goldstein, Ross—Draper Fisher Jurvetson Gotham Venture Partners
Goldstein, Steve—Quatris Fund
Goll, Alexandra—TVM Capital GmbH
Gollamudi, Raj—BlueStream Ventures
Gollmer, Stewart—Tenaya Capital (FKA: Lehman Brothers Venture Partners)
Gollner, Michael—Court Square Capital Partners
Golob, David—Francisco Partners
Golob, David—Octane Capital Management
Golomb, Michael—Marshall Capital Partners
Golson, Brian—Parthenon Capital LLC
Golub, Lawrence—Golub Capital
Golub, Steve—Lazard Alternative Investment
Golubieski, James—Foundation Venture Capital Group LLC
Golubovich, Ilya—I2BF
Gombart, Valerie—Seventure Partners SA (FKA: SPEF Venture)
Gombault, Vincent—AXA Private Equity
Gombert, Peter—Neuhaus Partners GmbH
Gomel, Richard—Starwood Capital Group
Gomes, Gene—Abacus Private Equity (ASA: Abacus Capital Corporation)
Gomez Cobo, Luis—SinoLatin Capital
Gomez Garcia, Daniel—Aser Capital SCR
Gomez, Alberto—Adara Venture Partners
Gomez, Carlos—Palmfund Management LLC
Gomez, Constantino—Arcano Capital
Gomez, Gabriel—Advent International
Gomez, Gabriel—DEFI Gestion SA
Gomez, Samuel—Conduit Capital Partners, LLC
Gomez-Zubeldia, Francisco—Diana Capital SGECR SA
Gompers, Paul—Spur Capital Partners LLC
Goncalves, Alvaro—Stratus Banco de Negocios
Gonda, Louis—Lexington Commercial Holdings
Gondek, Marc—Houlihan, Lokey, Howard & Zukin
Gonder, Barry—Grove Street Advisors LLC
Gonella, Franco—dPixel Srl
Gong, Henry—Infinity Venture Capital Fund (AKA: Israel Infinity Fund)
Gong, Li—Bessemer Venture Partners
Goni, Fernando—Gores Group LLC, The
Gonso, Harry—Twilight Venture Partners
Gonszor, Charles—Primary Capital, Ltd.
Gonzales, Daniel—Small Business Guarantee and Finance Corporation
Gonzales, Gilbert—Essex Woodlands Health Ventures
Gonzalez del Valle, Martin—Realza Capital SGECR SA
Gonzalez, Edmundo—SCP Private Equity Partners
Gonzalez, John—Alice Ventures Srl
Gonzalez, Pablo—Sodiex Sociedad para el Desarrollo Industrial de Extremadura
Good, Chris—Cinven, Ltd.
Goodacre, Glenn—Accord Capital Investors Pty., Ltd.
Goodell, Bill—Maverick Capital Ltd.
Goodhart, Ross—Siguler Guff & Company
Gooding, Douglas—Aurora Funds, Inc.
Goodlad, Magnus—IP2IPO, Ltd. (AKA: IP Group plc)
Goodman, Alan—Avlar BioVentures, Ltd.
Goodman, Bennett—Blackstone Group, L.P.
Goodman, Douglas—Equifin Capital Partners
Goodman, Edwin—Milestone Venture Partners
Goodman, James—Gemini Investors
Goodman, Jonathan—Bain Capital
Goodman, Mark—Brookline Venture Partners
Goodman, Robert—Bessemer Venture Partners
Goodrich, Jeffrey—High Road Capital Partners
Goodrich, Paul—Madrona Venture Group
Goodrich, Thomas—Duff Ackerman & Goodrich LLC (AKA: DAG Ventures)
Goodrich, Tom—Stafford Timberland, ltd.
Goodsell, Sally—Finance South East, Ltd.
Goodson, Ethan—JP Capital Partners, LLC
Goodson, Paul—Barclays Private Equity, Ltd.
Goodstein, Marcia—idealab!
Googel, Daniel—Easton Hunt Capital Partners, L.P.
Gooss, Henry—Investor Growth Capital AB
Gooss, Henry—Investor Growth Capital, Inc.
Goovaerts, Raf—CCMP Capital Advisors LLC
Gopal, Patwardhan—Duke Equity Partners
Goran, Andrea—Phoenix Venture Fund LLC
Gorbach, Eugene—Arsenal Capital Partners
Gorchow, Bruce—PPM America Capital Partners LLC
Gorczynski, Brian—Veritas Capital
Gorczynski, Richard—Square 1 Ventures
Gord, Steve—American Capital, Ltd.
Gord, Steven—Boathouse Capital
Gordon, Ann—Skypoint Capital Corporation
Gordon, Brett—HarbourVest Partners LLC
Gordon, Carl—OrbiMed Advisors LLC
Gordon, Chris—Bain Capital
Gordon, Eric—Skyline Ventures
Gordon, James—Bolder Capital LLC
Gordon, James—Edgewater Funds, The
Gordon, Jonathan—Stage 1 Ventures, LLC
Gordon, Mark—ONCAP Investment Partners
Gordon, Maurice—Stockwell Capital LLC
Gordon, Michael—Angelo, Gordon & Company
Gordon, Michael—Meritech Capital Partners
Gordon, Peter—Brookfield Asset Management
Gordon, Steve—Coral Group LLC
Gore, Al—Kleiner Perkins Caufield & Byers
Gore, Arun—Gray Ghost Ventures
Gore, Daniel—Orthogonal Partners LLP.
Gore, Jean—Pechel Industries
Gore, Jeevan—Tennenbaum Capital Partners LLC
Gorelick, Kenneth—NGN Capital LLC
Gorenberg, Mark—Hummer Winblad Venture Partners
Goret, David—GSC Partners (FKA: Greenwich Street Capital Partners)
Gorgi, Habib—Nautic Partners LLC
Gorin, Matthew—Contour Venture Partners
Gorkov, Evgeney—Lower Volga River Management Inc.
Gorman, Michael—Split Rock Partners LLC
Gorman, Michael—St. Paul Venture Capital, Inc.
Gorman, Mike—Aurora Funds, Inc.
Gorman, Mike—Trelys Funds
Gorman, Thomas—Seacoast Capital
Gormin, Jonathan—HB Equity Partners, L.P.
Gormley, Mark—Capital Z Investment Partners (FKA: Union Square Partners)
Gormley, Stephen—Great Hill Equity Partners LLC
Gormley, Steve—Equal Elements
Gormly, Matthew—Wicks Group of Companies LLC, The
Goros, Mark—Equip Ventures LLC
Gorton, Robert—Herald Investment Management Ltd (HIML)
Gosher, Hilary—Insight Venture Partners
Goss, Horst—BTV Beteiligungsverwaltung GmbH & Co. KG
Goss, Michael—Bain Capital
Gossels, Daniel—Montgomery & Co. (FKA: Digital Coast Partners)
Gossett, Kent—S.R. One, Ltd.
Goswami, Bobby—ABS Capital Partners
Gotsch, Peter—Code, Hennessy & Simmons LLC
Gotsch, Peter—Ellipse Capital LLC
Gottdiener, Charles—Providence Equity Partners LLC
Gotte, Benedict—Armada Venture Group LLC
Gottesman, Greg—Madrona Venture Group
Gottlieb, Adam—Industrial Opportunity Partners, LLC
Gottlieb, Scott—New Enterprise Associates, Inc.
Gottschalk, Gary—Churchill Equity, Inc.
Gottschalk, Jennifer—EIV Capital Management Company LLC
Gottsegen, Peter—CAI Capital Management Company
Gottwald, Hans—Orlando Capital Management GmbH
Gotzinger, Alexander—HARDT GROUP Capital Partners Limited
Goudreau, Nancy—BDR Capital
Gough, Jeremy—Graphite Capital (FKA: F&C Ventures, Ltd.)
Gough, Paul—STAR Capital Partners, Ltd.
Gouk, Warren—Cascadia Capital LLC
Gould, David—Merlin Nexus
Gould, James—Legend Partners, The
Gould, James—Walnut Group, The
Gould, Paul—Allen & Company
Goulet, Nicolas—Adara Venture Partners
Gounongbe, Felicia—Innovacom SA
Gourlay, Richard—Sussex Place Investment Management (SPIM), Ltd.
Goux, Ben—Pioneer Venture Partners, LLC
Govan, Christopher—Onex Corporation
Gove, Alex—Walden Venture Capital
Gowda, Umesh—Jina Ventures, Inc.
Gowdey, George—LJH Global Investments
Goyal, Maneesh—Miramar Venture Partners
Graat, Matthias—Triginta Capital Partners GmbH (FKA: Avida Equity Partners)
Grabe, William—General Atlantic LLC
Grabel, Jonathan—Baker Capital Corp.
Graber, Shani—Norwest Mezzanine Partners
Grabherr, Oliver—gcp gamma capital partners Beratungs- & Beteiligungs AG
Grabowski, Mark—Catterton Partners
Grace, Charles—Wynnchurch Capital, Ltd.
Grace, Edward—Grace Venture Partners
Gracias, Antonio—Valor Equity Partners
Grad, Jonathan—Parthenon Capital LLC
Gradel, Chris—VinaCapital Investment Management Company
Grady, Patrick—Sequoia Capital

Grady, Prisca—Bank of Scotland Venture Capital (FKA: ICC Venture Capital)
Graf von Bassewitz, Jan—CAM Private Equity Consulting & Verwaltungs - GmbH
Graf von der Schulenburg, Fritz—Argantis GmbH
Graf, A. Jay—New Enterprise Associates, Inc.
Graf, Harald—AlpInvest Partners N.V.
Graff, Brian—American Capital, Ltd.
Graffam, Robert—Darby Overseas Investments, Ltd.
Grafman, Allan—Mercury Capital Partners
Graham, Bruce—Infinity Capital LLC
Graham, C. Nichols—Shattuck Hammond Partners
Graham, Chris—Exponent Private Equity LLP (FKA: Square Capital Management)
Graham, Christopher—Starwood Capital Group
Graham, Dean—CapitalSource Holdings, Inc.
Graham, Drew—Ballast Point Venture Partners
Graham, Hatch—ATA Ventures
Graham, Kenneth—Inverness Graham Investments
Graham, Michael—OMERS Private Equity
Graham, Paul—Y Combinator
Graham, Rod—Northern Plains Capital, Ltd.
Graham, Steven—Graham Partners, Inc.
Graham, Stuart—CrossHill Financial Group, Inc
Grais, Linda—InterWest Partners
Gramat, Gilles—Pragma Capital
Grammer, Jeffery—Rho Capital Partners, Inc.
Gran, Gamiel—Sierra Ventures
Grangaard, Paul—Goldner Hawn Johnson & Morrison, Inc.
Granger, Philippe—Auriga Partners S.A.
Granick, Lisa—Fletcher Spaght Associates
Gransoe, Jorgen—Norventum Capital A/S
Grant, Alan—Blue Hill Partners LLC
Grant, Charles—Riverlake Partners LLC
Grant, Christopher—Salix Ventures
Grant, David—Perseis Private Equity
Grant, Ian—August Equity LLP
Grant, Murray—Actis Capital LLP
Grant, Peter—Aureos Capital, Ltd.
Grant, Peter—RBC Dain Rauscher
Grant, Peter—Stone Arch Capital LLC
Grant, Stuart—Blackstone Group, L.P.
Grantham, Larry—East Hill Management
Granville-Smith, Elizabeth—Boston Ventures Management, Inc.
Granzer, Ulrich—Wellington Partners Venture Capital GmbH
Grasselli, Massimo—PM & Partners SpA
Grassl, Walter—Carmel Ventures
Grassl, Walter—MVP Munich Venture Partners Managementgesellschaft mbH
Gratry, Oliver—Needham Asset Management
Grau, Alex—American Capital, Ltd.
Graulich, Benoit—Bencis Capital Partners
Graves, Ron—Maveron LLC
Graves, Scott—Oaktree Capital Management LLC
Gray, Amy—Private Advisors LLC
Gray, Andrew—Archer Capital
Gray, Daniel—KPS Capital Partners, L.P.
Gray, Ian—Candover Investments PLC
Gray, Jonathan—Blackstone Group, L.P.
Gray, Sam—Apposite Capital LLP
Gray, Stephen—CRG Partners
Grayce, David—Pacific Equity Partners
Grayson, Bruns—ABS Ventures
Grayson, Dayna—North Bridge Venture Partners
Grayson, Gerald—Grayson & Associates, Inc.
Grayson, Matthew—Aquiline Capital Partners
Greaves, Karen—Industrial Growth Partners
Grebelius, Lennart—Satila Holding AB
Grec, Alain—UFG Private Equity SAS
Greck, Scott—Archer Capital
Greck, Scott—Henderson Equity Partners (AKA: Henderson Private Capital)
Greeley, Michael—Flybridge Capital Partners
Green, Bill—VantagePoint Venture Partners
Green, Charlie—Candover Investments PLC
Green, Darrell—Granite Hall Partners (FKA: Sports Venture Partners, LLC)
Green, James—Humphrey Enterprises, LLC
Green, Jason—Emergence Capital Partners LLC
Green, Joshua—Arts Alliance Advisors
Green, Joshua—Mohr Davidow Ventures
Green, Justin—Palladium Equity Partners LLC
Green, Ken—Spring Mill Venture Partners
Green, Michael—Oak Hill Capital Management, Inc.
Green, Mitchell—Ancor Capital Partners
Green, Robert—Catalyst Equity Group LLC
Green, Stephen—Apax Partners Worldwide
Green, Stephen—Bridgepoint Capital, Ltd.
Green, Stephen—Canaan Partners
Green, Stuart—UK Steel Enterprise, Ltd. (FKA: British Steel Industry,Ltd.)
Green, Timothy—GMT Communications Partners LLP
Greenbarg, Todd—Avenue Capital Group
Greenberg, Frederic—EGS Healthcare Capital Partners, LLC
Greenberg, Gregory—Altus Capital Partners
Greenberg, Hal—Veronis Suhler Stevenson (FKA: Veronis, Suhler & Associates)
Greenberg, Jeffrey—Aquiline Capital Partners
Greenberg, Kenneth—MPM Capital (FKA: MPM Asset Management LLC)
Greenberg, Martin—iGlobe Treasury Management, Ltd.
Greenberg, Maurice—Starr International Company, Inc
Greenberg, Michael—Vexiom Equity Partners, L.P.
Greenberg, Myles—CHL Medical Partners
Greenberg, Russell—Altus Capital Partners
Greene, Adam—Dolphin Equity Partners
Greene, James—Kohlberg, Kravis, Roberts & Company, L.P.
Greene, Kevin—Valhalla Partners
Greene, Mark—Halpern, Denny & Company
Greene, Mark—Webster Capital Management, L.L.C.
Greene, Robert—Contour Venture Partners
Greene, Robert—Syncom Management Co. Inc.
Greenhalgh, Scott—Vision Capital LLP
Greenhill, Robert—GCP Capital Partners
Greenleaf, Timothy—Fairmont Capital, Inc.
Greenstein, Mark—Draper Fisher Jurvetson
Greenstein, Mark—Zone Ventures
Greenthal, Jill—Blackstone Group, L.P.
Greenwald, Gerald—Greenbriar Equity Group LLC
Greenwald, L. Spencer—Capital Z Investment Partners (FKA: Union Square Partners)
Greenwald, Marshall—Symmetry Investment Advisors, Inc.
Greenwood, Alyson—Leman Capital
Greenwood, John—Northleaf Capital Partners
Greenwood, John—TD Capital Group, Ltd.
Greenwood, Paul—Northern Lights Ventures, LLC
Greenwood, Tom—Science Center, The
Greer, Christopher—Rutberg & Company, LLC
Greer, Lawrence—Greer Capital Advisors LLC
Greer, Michelle—Numenor Ventures LLC
Greer, R. Scott—Numenor Ventures LLC
Greer, Thomas—Fulcrum Ventures
Gregg, Terrance—Galen Associates
Gregor, Alex—Pfingsten Partners, L.P.
Gregory, Charles—Spring Bay Companies, The (AKA: Spring Bay Ventures)
Gregory, Jonathan—Matrix Private Equity Partners LLP
Gregory, Tom—Maranon Capital, L.P.
Gregson, Henry—Pamplona Capital Management LLP
Gregson, Richard—Equity Partners Management Pty Ltd.
Greig, Thomas—Liberty Partners
Greiner, Jeffrey—RBC Dain Rauscher
Greitl, Robert—AFINUM Management GmbH
Grenadier, Carl—Park High Apartments
Grenville, Alisia—STMicroelectronics
Gresh, Lemy—CapVest Management Ltd
Gretland, Bjorge—Convexa Capital AS
Gretsch, Gregory—Sigma Partners
Greve, Frederico—Decisao Gestao Financeira (AKA: DGF Investimentos)
Grevet, Jean-Louis—Butler Capital Partners SA
Greville, Roger—Henderson Equity Partners (AKA: Henderson Private Capital)
Grey, Michael—Pappas Ventures
Greyson, Jay—Supply Chain Equity Partners
Gribetz, Eric—Pegasus Capital Advisors, L.P.
Gridley, Michael—Industry Ventures
Grierson, Nigel—Doughty Hanson & Co., Ltd.
Griest, David—SJF Ventures
Griffin, Carter—Updata Partners
Griffin, James—Veritas Capital
Griffin, Kevin—The Charter Group
Griffin, Larry—Prospector Equity Capital, L.P.
Griffin, Michael—Golub Capital
Griffin, T. Leo—Clarity Partners
Griffith, H. Tom—Convergent Capital Management, Inc (AKA: CCM)
Griffith, Rusty—Walker Ventures SBIC (AKA: Walker Ventures)
Griffith, William—Technology Crossover Ventures
Griffiths, Barry—Landmark Partners, Inc.
Griffiths, James—CD Ventures, LLC
Griffor, Jeff—Lighthouse Capital Partners
Grigg, Charles—Carousel Capital Partners
Grigolli, Sandro—EonTech Ventures (FKA: Triton Ventures)
Grim, J. Paul Reilly—SunBridge Partners
Grimes, John—Growth Capital Partners, L.P.
Grimes, Mark—Behrman Capital
Grimm, Richard—TowerBrook Capital Partners L.P.
Grimonprez, Eric—Nord Creation SAS
Grinde, Lars—Norvestor Equity AS (FKA: Norsk Vekst Forvaltning AS)
Grindheim, Trygve—IK Investment Partners, Ltd.
Grinnell, Richard—Fairhaven Capital Partners

Grinstein, Keith—Second Avenue Partners
Grippo, Sandy—Bessemer Venture Partners
Grisius, Michael—Allied Capital Corporation
Grissom, Douglas—Madison Dearborn Partners LLC
Grist, Walter—Brown Brothers Harriman & Company (AKA: BBH)
Griswold, E. Bulkeley—L&L Capital Partners, LLC
Griswold, Kirk—Argosy Capital
Gritsch, Richard—ECM Equity Capital Management GmbH
Groberg, Eric—Allied Capital Corporation
Grobl, Werner—111 conventuring - consulting und beteiligungs gmbh
Grobman, Ranan—Jerusalem Global Ventures
Grodem, Adne—Progressus Management AS
Groenke, Robert—Industrial Growth Partners
Grogan, Dale—The Charter Group
Grogan, Linda—Diamond Castle Holdings LLC
Gronberg, Thomas—Oresund-Healthcare A/S
Gronholm, Reijo—Pohjola Capital Partners Oy
Gronlund Nielsen, Jorgen—Oresund-Healthcare A/S
Groos, Ferdinand—Rhone Capital LLC
Groos, Tom—City Light Capital
Gros, Florent—Novartis Venture Fund (FKA: Novartis Corp.)
Groschopp, Maria—Firm Factory Network
Grose, Austin—Shasta Ventures Management LLC
Grose, Madison—Starwood Capital Group
Grosman, Doron—Court Square Capital Partners
Gross, Adam—Jordan, Edmiston Group, Inc., The
Gross, Arnie—Kilmer Capital Partners
Gross, Dana—Carmel Ventures
Gross, David—Great Pacific Capital, LLC
Gross, Diane—CIC Partners, L.P. (FKA: Cardinal Investment Company, Inc.)
Gross, Diane—HO2 Partners
Gross, Irwin—Worldview Technology Partners
Gross, Jorge—Trivest Partners, L.P.
Gross, Michael—BC Brandenburg Capital GmbH
Gross, Michael—Beringea LLC
Gross, Stewart—Lightyear Capital LLC
Gross, Thomas—WestLB AG Equity Investments (AKA: Westdeutsche Landesbank)
Gross, William—idealab!
Gross-Loh, David—Bain Capital
Grossberg, Erik—Jerusalem Global Ventures
Grosser, Adam—Foundation Capital
Grossi, Robert—CPP Investment Board
Grossi, Thomas—New Enterprise Associates, Inc.
Grossman, Adam—Health Evolution Partners LLC
Grossman, Gerri—Parthenon Capital LLC
Grossman, Jay—ABRY Partners LLC
Grossman, Kevin—Hercules Technology Growth Capital, Inc.
Grossmann, Benoist—AGF Private Equity
Grossmann, Susanne—BTS Investment Advisors, Ltd.
Grotenfelt, Martin—Intera Equity Partners Oy
Grotstein, Joshua—SAS Investors
Grove, Hilary—ABRY Partners LLC
Grover, Anthony—RPM Ventures (FKA: Waypoint Ventures)
Groves, Thomas—AEA Investors LP
Grovic, Mark—New Markets Venture Partners (AKA: New Markets Growth Fund)
Growney, Robert—Bolder Capital LLC
Growney, Robert—Edgewater Funds, The
Groya, Steven—Prairie Capital
Grua, Peter—HLM Venture Partners
Gruber, Axel—HVB Russell Management GmbH
Gruber, Sascha—LGT Capital Partners AG
Gruber, Steven—Oak Hill Capital Management, Inc.
Grubic, Paul—3i Group PLC
Grubstein, Peter—NGEN Partners LLC (FKA: NextGen Partners LLC)
Grum, Allen—Rand Capital Corporation
Grunberg, Gregory—Rho Capital Partners, Inc.
Gruner, Harry—JMI Equity
Gruner, Michael—Sigma Capital Management
Grunewald, Robert—American Capital, Ltd.
Grunfeld, Thomas—Sarsia Innovation AS
Gruss, Ralf—Apax Partners Worldwide
Grychta, Matthias—Neuhaus Partners GmbH
Grytz, Eduardo—Performa Investimentos
Grzybowski, Wojciech—NFI Management Sp. z o.o. (AKA: Grupa CA-IB)
Gu, Allen—Candover Investments PLC
Gu, Boncheon—LB Investment, Inc.
Gu, Huaming—Baird Capital Partners Asia
Gu, KC—STIC Investments, Inc.
Gu, Kang—Shanghai Dingjia Ventures Co., Ltd.
Gu, Yan—Cybernaut (China) Capital Management
Guan, Yue—Palladium Equity Partners LLC
Guanghua, Xu—China KZ High Technology Co., Ltd.
Gubbay, David—Falconhead Capital (FKA: Sports Capital Partners)
Gubler, Thomas—Ouest Ventures (FKA: Grand Ouest Gestion)
Gudgeon, Martin—Blackstone Group, L.P.
Gudibande, Anil—AIG Investment Corporation, (Asia) Ltd.
Guedes, J. Paul—Kyoto Planet Capital Partners
Guefor, Abdul—Intel Capital
Guemez, Eduardo—GE Commercial Finance - Equity
Guenther, Matthew—GenNx360 Capital Partners
Guenzl, Simon—Paul Capital Partners
Guerin Beresini, Debra—Invencor, Inc.
Guerin, Brian—Calvert Street Capital Partners, Inc. (FKA: Legg Mason)
Guernier, Michael—Shattuck Hammond Partners
Guerreiro de Sousa, Jose—Espirito Santo (ES) Ventures - Sociedade de Capital de Risco
Guerrero Igea, Felix—GED Group
Gueth, Anton—Burrill & Company
Guez, Arie—Aviv Venture Capital (FKA: Fantine Group, The)
Guez, Yves—Turenne Capital SA
Guff, Drew—Siguler Guff & Company
Guffey, Lawrence—Blackstone Group, L.P.
Guggenheimer, Randy—Burrill & Company
Guibert, Francois—STMicroelectronics
Guichard, Anne—Ouest Croissance SA
Guidi, Roger—Johnson & Johnson Development Corporation
Guidotti, Stefano—Aksia Group SGR SpA
Guilfoile, Thomas—Highland Capital Partners LLC
Guilford, Mark—Headwaters Merchant Bank
Guill, Benjamin—White Deer Energy
Guimaraes, Alfalo—Invus Group Ltd., The
Guimaraes, Andre—TMG Capital Partners Ltd.
Guimaraes, Rodrigo—Explorer Investments SCR, S.A.
Guinee, John—Constitution Capital Partners, LLC
Guise, Jonathan—Houlihan, Lokey, Howard & Zukin
Guitton, Anne-Cecile—NCI Gestion
Gulati, Gautam—Symphony Asia Holdings Pte. Ltd.
Gulati, Mukul—Zephyr Management, L.P.
Guld, Benny—IVS A/S (AKA: Internet Ventures Scandinavia A/S)
Guldstrand, Lars—GKL Growth Capital AB
Guleri, Tim—Sierra Ventures
Gull, Jason—Adams Street Partners LLC
Gull, Tor G.—Oikocredit International
Gullander, Peter—Verdane Capital (FKA: Four Seasons Venture Capital AS)
Gullans, Steve—Excel Venture Management
Gullicksen, Ken—Morgenthaler Ventures
Gumina, Buddy—Apax Partners Worldwide
Gummert, Stephan—BPE Unternehmensbeteiligungen GmbH
Gummeson, Peter—Audax Group
Gund, Grant—Coppermine Capital LLC
Gund, Zachary—Coppermine Capital LLC
Gundersen, Jarle—Norvestor Equity AS (FKA: Norsk Vekst Forvaltning AS)
Guney, Izzet—Millennium Private Equity
Gunn, Graeme—SL Capital Partners LLP
Gunnarsson, Gunnar Oern—New Business Venture Fund
Gunnlaugsson, Gordon—Lakeview Equity Partners, LLC
Gunsagar, Neeraj—Matrix Partners
Gunsenheimer, Curt—Iris Capital Management (FKA: Part'Com Management S.A.)
Gunst, Jeff—Avista Capital Holdings, L.P.
Gunterberg, Jacob—Odlander, Fredrikson & Co. AB (AKA: HealthCap)
Gunther, Craig—Blade Ventures
Gunther, Ralph—bmp AG
Gunther, Ryan—HarbourVest Partners LLC
Gunton, James—New Jersey Technology Council (AKA: NJTC)
Gunty, Murry—Blackstreet Capital Management (FKA: MMP Capital Advisors)
Gunty, Murry—Jacobson Partners
Guo, Cindy—Ventech S.A.
Guo, Owen—Hony Capital Ltd.
Guo, Shungen—Jiangsu High-Tech Investment Group (AKA: Govtor Capital)
Guo, Young—IDG Technology Venture Investment, Inc.
Gupta, Akhilesh—Blackstone Group, L.P.
Gupta, Alok—Axis Private Equity, Ltd.
Gupta, Amit—Clearwater Capital Partners, LLC
Gupta, Anup—Nexus Venture Partners
Gupta, Arjun—TeleSoft Partners
Gupta, Arun—Columbia Capital LLC
Gupta, Girish—Rajasthan Asset Management Company Pvt., Ltd.
Gupta, Krishna Kumar—Al Anwar Holdings SAOG
Gupta, Manoj—Nexus Venture Partners
Gupta, Naren—Nexus Venture Partners
Gupta, Pankaj—American Capital, Ltd.
Gupta, Rahul—Sonoma Management Partners
Gupta, Raj—FlatWorld Capital LLC
Gupta, Ramneek—Battery Ventures, L.P.
Gupta, Rishi—OrbiMed Advisors LLC
Gupta, Shruti—Tano Capital LLC

Gupta, Suneet—BTS Investment Advisors, Ltd.
Gupta, Vikram—J.P. Morgan Partners (FKA: Chase Capital Partners)
Gupta, Vishal—Bessemer Venture Partners
Gupton, Timothy—Research Triangle Ventures (RTV)
Gur, Saar—Charles River Ventures
Gurau, Michael—CEI Community Ventures, Inc. (AKA: CCVI)
Gurgiolo, Glenn—ComStar Media
Gurley, Bill—Benchmark Capital
Gurtler, Henrik—Novo A/S
Gurtovoy, Gregory—Renaissance Capital
Gushima, Hiroshi—Biofrontier Partners, Inc.
Gussarsky, David—Lightspeed Venture Partners (FKA: Weiss, Peck & Greer)
Gust, William—Anthem Capital Management
Gustafson, Mark—Gustafson & Co., Inc.
Gustafsson, Erling—Sixth Swedish National Pension Fund (AKA: Sjatte AP-fonden)
Gustainis, Simonas—Baltcap
Gustavson, Eric—First Capital Partners LLC
Gutenberg, Daniel—Venture Incubator AG (AKA: VI Partners AG)
Guterman, Steven—PineBridge Investments
Gutfreund, Joshua—Clarity Partners
Guthan, Gunter—Sparkassenkapital Ulm GmbH
Guthart, Leo—TopSpin Partners
Guthrie, Brian—Riverside Partners
Gutierrez, Alfredo—North Bay Equity Partners
Gutierrez, Eduardo—Development Partners International
Gutierrez, Matias—Linzor Capital Partners, L.P.
Gutierrez, Patricia—Silicon Valley Innovation Capital (SVIC)
Gutin, Boris—GCP Capital Partners
Gutin, Vladimir—TZP Group LLC
Gutmanis, Greg—Maxam Capital Corp.
Gutshall, Thomas—CampVentures
Gutstein, Jonathan—Coller Capital
Gutu, Taffy—Hilco Equity Management, LLC
Gutzen, Tim—Cubera Private Equity AS
Guy, Jack—Chatham Capital
Guyer, David—SV Life Sciences Advisers
Guyon, Nicolas—ALP Capital
Guyonnet, Sylvianne—AGF Private Equity
Guzy, Melissa—VantagePoint Venture Partners
Gwagwa, Lulu—Lereko Invesments Property, Ltd.
Gwilliam, Vince—Bridgepoint Capital, Ltd.
Gwin, Howard—Bridgescale Partners
Gwirtsman, Charles—KRG Capital Partners LLC
Gwosden, Laura—Maven Venture Partners
Gwosden, Laura—Red Rock Ventures
Gyani, Mohan—Primera Capital
Gygax, Rudolf—Nextech Venture AG
Gyimah, Daniel Charles—National Investment Bank Ltd.
Gylling, Bertil—Gylling Invest AB
Gysler, Philipp—Partners Group AG
Ha, Perry—DFJ Athena
Ha, Ryun—Undisclosed Firm
Haab, Larry—InDecatur Ventures LLC
Haabestad, Peter—Guardian Capital Partners
Haan, Bernard—Windspeed Ventures
Haan, Thomas—The Charter Group
Haanmaki, Pekka—Tutor Invest Oy, Ltd
Haar, Nancy—Endeavor Capital Management
Haarmann, Oliver—Searchlight Capital Partners LLC
Haas, Clifford—Sigma Partners
Haas, David—FCP Investors
Haas, Jean-David—NextStage SAS
Haas, Ken—Abingworth Management, Ltd.
Haas, Roland—HKK Partners
Haataja, Kari—Equest Partners, Ltd.
Haavel, Tonis—GILD Bankers (FKA: LHV Ventures)
Haber, Warren—Founders Equity, Inc.
Haber, Warren—Navigation Capital Partners (AKA: NCP)
Haberkorn, Charles—Stonehenge Capital Company
Habert, Benoit—Dassault Developpement
Haberzettl, Klaus—BA Private Equity GmbH
Habicht, F. Henry—SAIL Venture Partners
Habstritt, Brett—Shoreview Industries
Hacke, Robin—Portview Communications Ltd
Hacker, Erich—HighTech Private Equity GmbH
Hacker, Michael—AlpInvest Partners N.V.
Hackett, John—BDC Capital (AKA: Massachusetts Business Development Corp.)
Hackett, Patrick—Warburg Pincus LLC
Hackl, Berthold—Heidelberg Innovation GmbH
Hacohen, Yochai—Undisclosed Firm
Hadass, Leon—Pantheon Ventures, Ltd.
Haden, Patrick—Riordan, Lewis & Haden
Hadi, Nabil Mohammed—Khaleej Finance & Investment
Hadl, John—U.S. Venture Partners
Hadley, Charles—Cardinal Partners
Hadley, Chris—Quadrant Private Equity Pty, Ltd.
Hadley, Christopher—Berkshire Partners LLC
Hadley, Michael—Carlyle Group, The
Hadlock, Mark—CE Unterberg Towbin (FKA:Unterberg Harris Capital Partners)
Hadsell, Christopher—Cardinal Venture Capital
Hadzic, Edin—Paragon Partners GmbH
Haedt, Susan—Thomas, McNerney & Partners LLC
Haeger, Kent—High Street Capital
Haegg, Lars—Investcorp Bank B.S.C.
Haegler, Rolf—TAT Capital Partners Ltd
Hafeez, Qayyum—Odeon Capital Partners, L.P.
Haft, Ian—ACI Capital Co., LLC
Haft, Jay—CN Private Equity Partners
Hagan, Kjell—VI Partners
Hagander, Bengt—Gylling Invest AB
Hage, Joe—PacRim Venture Management
Hagedorn, John—Formative Ventures
Hagen, Erik—Viking Venture Management AS
Hagenah, Pamela—Integral Capital Partners
Hagenberg, Jasper—MillhouseIAG
Hagenbucher, Carsten—Investcorp Bank B.S.C.
Hagerty, Thomas—Thomas H. Lee Partners (AKA: TH Lee Partners)
Haggblom, Christoffer—Rite Internet Ventures AB
Haggerty, William—NatCity Investments, Inc.
Hagglund, Kaj—Sponsor Capital Oy
Hahn, James—JC Asia Alpha Private Equity
Hahn, John—Providence Equity Partners LLC
Hahn, Maria—Liberty Venture Partners, Inc.
Hahn, Ronald—Battelle Memorial Institute
Hahn, Ronald—Battelle Ventures
Hahn, Ronald—Early Stage Enterprises, L.P.
Hahn, Scott Sang-Won—Morgan Stanley Private Equity
Hahn-Petersen, Vilhelm—Axcel Industriinvestor AS
Haight, Allen—Permira Advisers LLP
Haikio, Marko—Suomen Teollisuussijoitus Oy
Haile, Don—Fidelity Ventures
Haile, Don—Volition Capital
Haim, Debbie—Genesis Partners
Hain, J. Travis—Ridgemont Equity Partners
Haines, Marshall—Bain Capital
Haines, Timothy—Abingworth Management, Ltd.
Hainguerlot, Bertrand—Pechel Industries
Hains, Ginette—CDP Capital - Technology Ventures (FKA: CDP Sofinov)
Hairston, Peter—New World Angels, Inc.
Haisch, Robert—Charterhouse Group International, Inc.
Haitao, Jin—China Israel Value Capital (AKA: CIVC)
Haitao, Jin—Shenzhen Venture Capital Association
Haiz, Patrick—ClearLight Partners LLC
Hajadi, Ivan—Sirius Venture Consulting Pte, Ltd.
Haji-Touma, Raja—Corsair Capital LLC
Hakim, Ben—Blackstone Group, L.P.
Halak, Brian—Domain Associates LLC
Halandova, Magda—Slavia Capital
Halasz, Ivan—Euroventures Capital Kft.
Halbout, Jerome—4D Global Energy Advisors
Haldner, Felix—Partners Group AG
Hale, James—FTV Capital (FKA: FTVentures)
Hale, James—Parallax Capital Partners LLC
Hale, Lisa—Parallax Capital Partners LLC
Hale, Martin—Hale Fund Management, L.P.
Hale, Michael—Parallax Capital Partners LLC
Hale, Randall—Rock Hill Capital Group LLC
Haley, Eric—Tailwind Capital Partners
Haley, Timothy—Redpoint Ventures
Halfen, Patty—Elevation Associates LLC
Halimi, Laurent—Weinberg Capital Partners SAS
Hall, Alan—Mercato Partners
Hall, Colin—Rhone Capital LLC
Hall, David—Innvotec, Ltd.
Hall, David—YFM Group, Ltd.
Hall, Donald—Arcturus Capital
Hall, Eric—mc3 ventures (FKA: McKenna Venture Accelerator (MVA))
Hall, Fred—Hall Capital Partners, L.P.
Hall, Jeffrey—Caribbean Equity Partners Limited
Hall, John—Fort Hill Partners, Inc.
Hall, John—Horizon Ventures
Hall, John—New River Capital Partners
Hall, Jonathan—Mulverhill Associates
Hall, Kathryn—Hall Capital Partners LLC (FKA: Offit Hall Capital Mgmt)
Hall, Michael—Yukon Partners Management LLC
Hall, Russell—Legacy Venture
Hall, Steven—Vulcan Capital
Hall, Timothy—CI Capital Partners LLC (FKA: Caxton-Iseman Capital, Inc)
Hall, W. Bradley—Headwaters Merchant Bank
Hall, William—Lincolnshire Management, Inc.
Hallberg, Anna—Start Invest AB
Hallerberg, Peter A.—LRP Capital GmbH
Hallett, Bruce—Miramar Venture Partners
Halley, Philippe—CDP Capital - Technology Ventures (FKA: CDP Sofinov)
Hallgren, Erik—Oresa Ventures Sp Z oo
Halliday, Sarah—New York Business Development Corporation

Halligan, John—SI Ventures
Halligan, Tony—Actis Capital LLP
Hallisey, Bill—NewWorld Capital Group LLC
Halloran, Mike—ZAP Ventures
Halloran, Patrick—Wayzata Investment Partners
Halloran, Todd—Freeman Spogli & Co.
Hallowell, Andrew—Arcadia Management, LLC (AKA: Arcadia Partners)
Halper, James—Leonard Green & Partners
Halperin, Ken—American Capital, Ltd.
Halpern, Abel—TPG Capital
Halpern, John—Halpern, Denny & Company
Halpin, Christopher—Providence Equity Partners LLC
Halpin, Kevin—DeltaPoint Capital Management LLC
Halprin, Matt—Omidyar Network
Halsall, Andrew—Palace Ventures Ltd
Halstead, David—Kirtland Capital Partners
Halsted, John—Pamplona Capital Management LLP
Halsted, Scott—Morgan Stanley Private Equity
Halsted, Scott—Morgan Stanley Venture Partners (AKA: MSDW)
Halsted, Scott—Saints Ventures
Halstedt, Steven—Centennial Ventures
Halstenberg, Dominik—Lion Capital (FKA: Hicks Muse (Europe))
Halusa, Martin—Apax Partners Worldwide
Halverson, Eric—Qualitas Equity Partners
Halvorsen, Jon—Colony Capital LLC
Ham, Ji—CN Private Equity Partners
Hamachek, Mark—Mainsail Partners
Hamada, Hiroaki—New Frontier Partners Co., Ltd
Hamade, Sami—Aberdare Ventures
Hamann, Martijn—Van den Ende & Deitmers B.V.
Hambrecht, Bob—W.R. Hambrecht & Co., LLC
Hamburg, Eric—Industrial Renaissance Inc.
Hamburg, Liz—UpStart Ventures Management
Hamel, John—Cue Ball Group, LLC, The
Hamelsky, Lawrence—Berkshire Partners LLC
Hamer, John—Burrill & Company
Hamerslag, Steven—TVC Capital, LLC (FKA: TVC Ventures LLC)
Hamid, Mamoon—U.S. Venture Partners
Hamilton, Charles—KRG Capital Partners LLC
Hamilton, Christine—PrairieGold Venture Partners
Hamilton, Douglas—Hamilton Investments
Hamilton, Ed—Stage 1 Ventures, LLC
Hamilton, Fred—Cirrus Investment Partners LLC
Hamilton, Jennifer—Nomura Phase4 Ventures, Ltd.
Hamilton, Mark—RB Webber & Company
Hamilton, Matthew—Summit Partners
Hamilton, Sandy—Axiom Equity Partners
Hamilton, Thomas—Cirrus Investment Partners LLC
Hamilton, Todd—Bolder Capital LLC
Hamlin, Geoffrey—Cartesian Capital Group, LLC
Hamm, John—VSP Capital (FKA: Venture Strategy Partners)
Hammack, Elizabeth—C.M. Capital Corporation
Hammarskjold, Philip—Hellman & Friedman LLC
Hammer, Amichai—Evergreen Venture Partners
Hammer, Jan—General Atlantic LLC
Hammond, Alastair—EnerCap Capital Partners
Hammond, Brian—Capital Trust, Ltd.
Hammond, Christopher—Calvert Street Capital Partners, Inc. (FKA: Legg Mason)
Hammond, Christopher—GEN CAP America, Inc.
Hammond, J. Bradford—Weathergage Venture Capital
Hammond, Kevin—JLL Partners (FKA: Joseph, Littlejohn & Levy, Inc.)
Hammond, Michael—Shattuck Hammond Partners
Hammond, Nigel—Vespa Capital LLP
Hammond, Peter—Exto Partners Pty, Ltd.
Hammons, Michael—SAIL Venture Partners
Hampp, Wes—Capital For Business, Inc.
Hampp, Wes—First Capital Partners LLC
Hampton, David—ING Investment Management
Hamrick, L. Watts—Pamlico Capital
Hamwee, Robert—GSC Partners (FKA: Greenwich Street Capital Partners)
Hamwee, Robert—New Mountain Capital LLC
Han, Allen—CVC Asia Pacific, Ltd.
Han, Cheol-Ho—Korea Venture Investment Corporation
Han, Daniel—Wellspring Capital Management LLC
Han, Don—SAIF Partners
Han, Jenhao—AXA Private Equity
Han, Ronald—Harbinger Venture Management
Hanabergh, Gerard—GE Antares Capital Corporation
Hanabusa, Dave—Aragon Ventures, Inc.
Hanafi, Ammar—Alloy Ventures
Hanauer, Linda—Paine & Partners LLC
Hanauer, Nicholas—Second Avenue Partners
Hance, Carol—Strategic Advisory Group, Inc.
Hance, Pierce—Strategic Advisory Group, Inc.
Hancock, Thomas—New England Partners
Hancock, Thomas—Nexus Medical Partners
Hand, Jeremy—Lyceum Capital
Hand, Michael—PNC Equity Management Corp.
Handal, Valerie—HarbourVest Partners LLC
Handeland, Arne—Verdane Capital (FKA: Four Seasons Venture Capital AS)
Handelsman, Karl—CMEA Capital
Handen, Lawrence—Insight Venture Partners
Handen, Lawrence—UBS Capital Corporation
Handler, Aaron—Elm Creek Partners
Handler, David—Centerview Partners Holdings LLC
Handler, Richard—Jefferies Group, Inc.
Handley, J.B.—Swander Pace Capital
Handy, Peter—Mercury Capital Partners
Haneef, Rafe—Fajr Capital Ltd
Hanemann, Charles—H.I.G. Capital LLC
Haney, Gail—Foundation Capital
Hanham, Ann—Burrill & Company
Hanigal, Benny—Sequoia Capital
Hanjie, Xu—NewMargin Ventures
Hanks, Robert—New England Partners
Hanley, Dermot—Claret Capital, Ltd.
Hanley, Mark—Capital Z Investment Partners (FKA: Union Square Partners)
Hanlon, William—Shattuck Hammond Partners
Hann, Eugene—JLL Partners (FKA: Joseph, Littlejohn & Levy, Inc.)
Hanna, Chris—Phoenix Equity Partners (FKA: DLJ European Private Equity)
Hanna, William—California Technology Ventures LLC
Hanna, William—Jacobs Capital Group, LLC
Hannah, Josh—Matrix Partners
Hanneman, William—Zachary Scott & Co.
Hannon, Michael—CCMP Capital Advisors LLC
Hanover, Alain—Navigator Technology Ventures (A.K.A. NTV)
Hanrahan, Chris—Key Capital Corp.
Hanrieder, Wolfgang—Carlyle Group, The
Hans, Jack—Dyad Partners
Hans, Kurt—Gores Group LLC, The
Hansch, Neal—Rustic Canyon Partners
Hansen, Al—Signet Healthcare Partners (FKA: Sanders Morris Harris)
Hansen, Christian—Nordic Biotech Advisors APS
Hansen, David—Lake Capital Partners, Inc.
Hansen, Eric—GE Antares Capital Corporation
Hansen, George—Corporate Fuel Partners
Hansen, Hakan—Amplico Kapital AB
Hansen, Jens Thoger—Capidea Management ApS
Hansen, John—JH Partners, LLC (FKA: Jesse.Hansen & Co.)
Hansen, Kent—CAM Private Equity Consulting & Verwaltungs - GmbH
Hansen, Lee—Meriturn Partners LLC
Hansen, Robert—Vector Capital
Hansing, Axel—Coller Capital
Hansjee, Anil—Akara, Ltd. (DBA: IDG Ventures Europe)
Hanson, Chris—Battery Ventures, L.P.
Hanson, Craig—FTV Capital (FKA: FTVentures)
Hanson, Jeff—Ohio Innovation Fund (OIF)
Hanson, Karen—Moneta Capital Partners, Ltd.
Hanson, Mark—Genstar Capital LLC
Hanson, Richard—Doughty Hanson & Co., Ltd.
Hanson, Rowland—Equal Elements
Hanssens, Christopher—Eureka Growth Capital
Hao, Fan—Shaanxi Zenisun Venture Capital Co.,Ltd
Hao, Kenneth—Silver Lake Sumeru
Haque, Ayaz ul—Draper Fisher Jurvetson ePlanet Ventures, L.P.
Haque, Promod—Norwest Venture Partners
Hara, George—Defta Partners
Harada, Kenichi—J-Star Co., Ltd.
Harada, Kenji—Hiroshima Venture Capital Co., Ltd.
Harari, Omer—Markstone Capital
Hardek, Steven—Verax Capital Partners LLC
Harder, Tom—Nordwind Capital GmbH
Harding, Peter—Technology Crossover Ventures
Harding, Richard—Invencor, Inc.
Harding, William—Morgan Stanley Venture Partners (AKA: MSDW)
Harding, William—VantagePoint Venture Partners
Hardy, Mark—Aurora Capital Group (FKA: Aurora Capital Partners)
Hardy, Stephen—Australian Capital Ventures, Ltd.
Hareid, Jan-Erik—Alliance Venture AS
Harel, Ittai—Pitango Venture Capital (FKA:Polaris Venture Capital Israel)
Hargraves, Gordon—Rho Capital Partners, Inc.
Hargrove, Thomas—GulfStar Group
Harinarayan, Venkatesh—Cambrian Ventures
Harkins, David—Thomas H. Lee Partners (AKA: TH Lee Partners)
Harlan, Bill—Prism Capital
Harland, Deborah—S.R. One, Ltd.
Harle, Emmanuel—Industries et Finances Partenaires SA
Harleaux, Antoine—FINORPA
Harley, Rob—NewSmith Asset Management LLP
Harlow, Phillip—Royal Palm Capital Partners, LLP

Harman, Fredric—Oak Investment Partners
Harman, Jeri—Allied Capital Corporation
Harman, Jeri—Avante Mezzanine Partners
Harmeling, Mark—Colony Capital LLC
Harmon, Michael—Oaktree Capital Management LLC
Harms, W.B.—Global Leisure Partners LLP
Harned, Carter—Leeds Equity Partners
Harnett, Matt—F.N.B. Capital Corporation LLC
Harper, John—Duke Street Capital
Harper, Julie—Balmoral Capital
Harper, Rob—Blackstone Group, L.P.
Harper, Ryan—Summit Partners
Harper, Scott—Primus Capital Funds
Harr, David—TGF Management Corp (FKA:Texas Growth Fund)
Harrick, Stephen—Institutional Venture Partners
Harrington, John—Patriarch Partners LLC
Harrington, Jon—Omni Capital Group LLC
Harrington, Rupert—Advent Private Capital
Harrington, William—Three Arch Partners
Harris, Bill—Buckhead Investment Partners LLC
Harris, Clinton—Grove Street Advisors LLC
Harris, Derek—Birmingham Technology (Venture Capital) Ltd
Harris, Douglas—Integrated Partners
Harris, Duane—Northstar Capital, LLC (FKA: Seidler Capital, Ltd.)
Harris, Jeffrey—Warburg Pincus LLC
Harris, Kathy—Noro-Moseley Partners
Harris, Kim—Bain Capital
Harris, Lisa—DCM
Harris, Mark—Avenue Capital Group
Harris, Mark—Northgate Capital Group
Harris, Matthew—Berkshires Capital Investors
Harris, Matthew—Global Infrastructure Partners
Harris, Matthew—Village Ventures
Harris, Mike—Rutland Fund Management, Ltd. (AKA: Rutland Partners LLP)
Harris, Peter—Generation Investment Management LLP
Harris, Richard—RedShift Ventures
Harris, Robert—e-Launcher
Harris, Ron—Harris Preston & Partners, LLC
Harris, Stacey—Quadrangle Group LLC
Harris, Vicki—GE Commercial Finance - Equity
Harrison, Alexander—FTV Capital (FKA: FTVentures)
Harrison, Alexander—Sequoia Capital
Harrison, Christopher—Highland Capital Management, L.P.
Harrison, Donald—Charter Life Sciences
Harrison, Donald—Ridgemont Equity Partners
Harrison, Eric—Global Innovation Partners LLC
Harrison, Grant—Wilshire Private Markets
Harrison, James—TowerBrook Capital Partners L.P.
Harrison, John—Harbert Venture Partners
Harrison, Juan—Takeda Research Investment, Inc.
Harrison, Justin—Boston Ventures Management, Inc.
Harrison, Matthew—Wellspring Capital Management LLC
Harrison, Seth—Undisclosed Firm
Harrison, Thomas—Colony Capital LLC
Harrison, Thomas—Invision Capital Management LLC
Harrison, William—SSM Partners
Harrison, William—Silverfern Group, Inc., The
Harroch, Richard—VantagePoint Venture Partners
Harrod, Kimberly—Arbor Private Investment Company, LLC
Harrus, Alain—Compass Technology Partners
Harrus, Alain—Crosslink Capital
Hart, Jason—Carlyle Group, The
Hart, Jeff—Quest Technology Ventures
Hartenbaum, Howard—August Capital Management
Hartfield, Tom—Houlihan, Lokey, Howard & Zukin
Hartford, David—firstVentury GmbH
Hartford, Mark—Vitruvian Partners LLP
Hartigan, Alex—Steamboat Ventures
Hartman, Alan—Centerview Partners Holdings LLC
Hartman, Curtis—Main Street Capital Corporation
Hartman, Karsten—HgCapital
Hartman, Scott—SeaView Capital Advisors, LLC
Hartman, Scott—Unique Investment Corporation
Hartman, Steven—Levine Leichtman Capital Partners, Inc.
Hartmann, Arne—General Atlantic LLC
Hartmann, Olaf—Cinven, Ltd.
Hartnett, John—Atlantic Bridge
Hartnett, Kevin—Brynwood Partners L.P.
Hartong, Hendrik—Brynwood Partners L.P.
Hartong, Hendrik—Brynwood Partners L.P.
Hartpence, Jean-Rene—Canec International
Hartstone, Joel—Stonegate Capital Group LLC
Hartvig, Jan G.—NorgesInvestor Management AS
Hartwig, David—SAP Ventures
Hartz, John—Inflexion plc (AKA: Inflexion Private Equity)
Harvey, Colin—iGlobe Treasury Management, Ltd.
Harvey, David—Coburn Ventures, LLC
Harvey, Ian—BTG International (AKA: British Technology Group)
Harvey, Kevin—Benchmark Capital
Harvey, Luis—Nexxus Capital, S.C.
Harvey, Mark—Coates Myer & Co. Pty Ltd.
Harvey, Nick—Ingenious Ventures
Harvey, Paul—Abbey Road Venture Ltd
Harvey, Paul—Atlantic Bridge
Harvey, R. Burton—Claritas Capital LLC
Hasan, Kamil—Granite Hill Capital Partners
Hasan, Talat—Granite Hill Capital Partners
Hascak, Jaroslav—Penta Investments, Ltd.
Hascoet, Gerard—Sofinnova Partners
Hasegawa, Hirokazu—Global Venture Capital, Inc.
Hasegawa, Tomohiko—Global Venture Capital, Inc.
Hasegawa, Yoshiaki—SBI Investment Company, Ltd. (FKA:Softbank Investment Corp)
Hashemi, Shahram—Ithmar Capital
Hashimi, Saud—Fajr Capital Ltd
Hashimoto, Hiroyuki—Advanced Science and Technology Enterprise Corporation
Hashimoto, Masako—Yasuda Enterprise Development Co., Ltd.(FKA: Nippon Ent.Dev)
Hashimoto, Mikio—Fund Creation Co., Ltd.
Hashimoto, Shiro—Toyo Capital Co., Ltd.
Hashimoto, Yasuhiro—Asia Private Equity Capital (FKA: MediBIC Alliance)
Hashkes, Yoni—Jerusalem Global Ventures
Hasko, Peter—Wolseley Private Equity
Haslett, Keith—Silverfleet Capital (FKA: PPM Capital Partners)
Haspeslagh, Philippe—Procuritas Partners KB
Hassan, Aatif—August Equity LLP
Hassan, S.M.—Greenmont Capital Partners
Hassanein, Ossama—Rising Tide Fund
Hasse, Joseph—Calvert Street Capital Partners, Inc. (FKA: Legg Mason)
Hassid, Mony—Motorola Ventures
Hasson, Avi—Gemini Israel Funds, Ltd.
Hastings, Mark—CIBC Capital Partners
Hastings, Mark—Garvin Hill Capital Partners LLC
Haswell, Robert—Dominus Capital, L.P.
Haswell, Robert—Quad-C Management, Inc.
Hata, Takaaki—Globis Capital Partners & Co. (FKS:Apax Globis Partners)
Hatakeyama, Naoko—New Horizon Capital Co., Ltd.
Hatch, Aris—HarbourVest Partners LLC
Hatch, Aris—Rock Maple Ventures, L.P.
Hatch, Robert—Constitution Capital Partners, LLC
Hatcher, Krista—Code, Hennessy & Simmons LLC
Hathaway, Collin—Skylight Capital
Hatherly, John—Wynnchurch Capital, Ltd.
Hatlem, Per—HitecVision AS
Hattenbach, Todd—SB Energy Partners
Haubold, Etienne—European Capital Financial Services Ltd.
Hauenstein, Daniela—Alpha Associates AG
Hauer, Frank—ReichmannHauer Capital Partners
Hauge, Martin—Creandum KB
Hauncher, Scott—Superior Capital Partners
Hauptmeier, Dietrich—Palamon Capital Partners (FKA: Amphion Capital Partners)
Hausberger, Jorgen—Invest Equity Management Consulting GmbH
Hausen, Jan zur—Mulligan BioCapital AG
Hauser, Hermann—Amadeus Capital Partners, Ltd.
Hauser, Mark—Legend Partners, The
Hauskov, Ole—3i Group PLC
Hausler, Greg—Probitas Partners, Inc.
Hausman, Ken—Darwin Ventures LLC
Hausman, Ken—Mirador Capital
Haussler, Jakki—Adena Ventures
Haussler, Jakki—Capvest Venture Fund (FKA: Virgin Ventures Fund LP)
Hautanen, Osmo—Mobility Ventures
Hautin, Herve—Alpha Group
Havaldar, Abhay—General Atlantic LLC
Havers, Simon—Baird Capital Partners Europe
Haw, Claude—Skypoint Capital Corporation
Hawes, Dudley—Yellow & Blue Investment Management BV
Hawes, James—Inter-Asia Venture Management
Hawk, Bob—DCM
Hawke, Joseph—Meridian Venture Partners (MVP)
Hawkins, Andrew—Vision Capital LLP
Hawkins, David—Code, Hennessy & Simmons LLC
Hawkins, John—Generation Capital Partners
Hawkins, Peter—Oakstone Venture Partners
Hawkins, Russ—Generation Capital Partners
Hawkins, Steve—JovFunds
Hawkins, Thomas—New River Capital Partners
Hawks, Randy—Claremont Creek Ventures
Hawley, Frank—Saugatuck Capital Company
Hawley, Stuart—Saugatuck Capital Company
Hawn, Van Zandt—Goldner Hawn Johnson & Morrison, Inc.
Hawryluk, Kent—Jordan, Edmiston Group, Inc., The

Hawryluk, Kent—Twilight Venture Partners
Hay, Andrew—Derbyshire First Investments Limited (DFI)
Hay, Stewart—SL Capital Partners LLP
Hayaly, Tarek—Citadel Capital S.A.E.
Hayama, Paul—Avante Mezzanine Partners
Hayano, Toshihito—New Frontier Partners Co., Ltd
Hayashi, Satoru—Carlyle Group, The
Hayashi, Shunsa—Ant Capital Partners Co., Ltd.
Hayashi, Tatsuya—Unison Capital, Inc.
Hayashida, Masaru—Fukui JAFCO Company, Ltd.
Hayat, Philippe—Serena Capital SAS
Hayden, Andrew—Sovereign Capital LLP (FKA:Sovereign Capital, Ltd.)
Hayes, Brooke—Milestone Partners
Hayes, David—Natural Gas Partners (NGP)
Hayes, Frank—Wynnchurch Capital, Ltd.
Hayes, James—Convergent Capital Management, Inc (AKA: CCM)
Hayes, John—Great Hill Equity Partners LLC
Hayes, Kevin—Weston Presidio (FKA: Weston Presidio Capital Management)
Hayes, Michael—Lake Capital Partners, Inc.
Hayes, Robert—First Round Capital
Hayes, Timothy—CSI (FKA: Virginia Community Development Loan Fund)
Hayes, Tom—GrowthWorks
Hayhurst, Brian—Carlyle Group, The
Haykin, Randy—Outlook Ventures (FKA: iMinds, Interactive Minds)
Haynes, David—FTV Capital (FKA: FTVentures)
Haynes, David—Greenmont Capital Partners
Haynes, Douglas—Metamorphic Ventures, LLC (FKA: Gersh Venture Partners)
Haynes, Stephen—Glengary LLC
Hays, Andrew—Main Street Capital Holdings LLC
Hays, Joe—Diamond State Ventures, L.P.
Haythornthwaite, Rick—STAR Capital Partners, Ltd.
Hayward, James—Double D Venture Fund LLC
Haza, Christopher—Fidus Capital
Hazard, Chip—Flybridge Capital Partners
Hazas Guerra, Carlos—Cantabria Capital
Hazelton, Ian—Babson Capital Europe
Hazen, Ned—Lighthouse Capital Partners
Hazenberg, Wil—BioGeneration Ventures
He, Kong—Beijing Bingyuan Venture Capital Co., Ltd.
He, Sean—Carlyle Group, The
He, Simon—Development Principles Group, Ltd.
He, Wei-Wu—Emerging Technology Partners, LLC
He, Xiaoqiu—SOVA Capital
Headley, Robert—Ignition Capital
Headley, Robert—Ignition Partners (FKA: Ignition Corporation)
Headley, Robert—Qiming Venture Partners
Headrick, Mark—Coral Group LLC
Healer, Harry—Venture Capital Fund of New England, The
Healey, Glenn—Housatonic Partners
Healey, Russell—Foresight Group
Healy, J J—GrandBanks Capital
Healy, James—Sofinnova Ventures
Healy, Michael—Goldner Hawn Johnson & Morrison, Inc.
Healy, Patrick—C3 Capital LLC
Healy, Robert—Chicago Growth Partners (William Blair Capital Partners)
Healy, Susan—Global Infrastructure Partners
Healy, Timothy—Linsalata Capital Partners
Heappey, Mark—3i Group PLC
Heard, Sue—Connection Capital LLP
Hearn, Christopher—First Reserve Corporation
Hearst, William—Kleiner Perkins Caufield & Byers
Heartfield, Brenda—GTD Capital
Heaston, Roger—Axiom Equity Partners
Heath, Chad—Endeavour Capital
Heath, Larry—Flagstone Capital LLC
Heathcote, Jonathan—Palamon Capital Partners (FKA: Amphion Capital Partners)
Hebbar, Kiran—Valhalla Partners
Hebel, Davor—Fidelity Ventures
Hebenstreit, Kolja—Team Europe Ventures Management GmbH
Heberling, Pascal—Cinven, Ltd.
Hebert, Peter—Lux Capital
Hebert, Victor—Burrill & Company
Hecht, Shawn—Swander Pace Capital
Hedberg, Jeremy—Varde Partners, Inc.
Hedberg, Par—Sting Capital
Hedges, Robert—OMERS Private Equity
Hedin, Earl—Bear Stearn Venture Partners LLC
Hedon, Seth—Tinicum Capital Partners
Heeger, Alan—NGEN Partners LLC (FKA: NextGen Partners LLC)
Heer, David—Acacia Venture Partners
Heffernan, Peter—CFI Capital
Heflin, William—Kinetic Ventures LLC
Hegele, W. Chris—Intersouth Partners
Hegele, W. Chris—Kitty Hawk Capital
Hehn, Michael—Morgan Stanley Private Equity
Heide, Harold—GrowthWorks
Heidecorn, David—Catterton Partners
Heiden, Thomas—EKK Dr. Engelhardt, Kaupp, Kiefer Beteiligungsberatung GmbH
Heidl, Christian—MML Capital Partners
Heidorn, Joan—Spur Capital Partners LLC
Heijbel, Johan—Novestra AB
Heijsteeg, Casper—Eagle Venture Partners
Heikkila, Sami—Sponsor Capital Oy
Heilbronner, Rob—Headwaters Merchant Bank
Heilmann, Stefan C.—VTC Partners GmbH
Heimann, Christian—SBG Sparkassenbeteiligungsgesellschaft Sachsen-Anhalt mbH
Heimann, Robert—River Cities Capital Funds
Hein, Kevin—Emerging ISV Capital Partners
Heinen, Joseph—Goldner Hawn Johnson & Morrison, Inc.
Heinen, Steven—Marquette Capital Partners
Heining, Matthias—BWK GmbH Unternehmensbeteiligungsgesellschaft
Heintzman, Andrew—Investeco Capital Corporation
Heinz Messer, Karl—Eagle Ventures
Heinz, Andre—Sustainable Technology Partners Nordic AB
Heinz, Christopher—Rosemont Solebury Capital Management LLC
Heinz, Ronald—Canopy Group
Heirshberg, Jay—American Capital, Ltd.
Heise, Brant—National Healthcare Services
Heith, Eric—American Capital, Ltd.
Heitmann, Knut—PolyTechnos Venture-Partners GmbH
Heitmann, York—Haspa BGM
Heivly, Chris—Atrium Capital
Heivly, Chris—LaunchBox Digital
Hejazi, Shahram—BioAdvance
Hejl, David—Unique Investment Corporation
Hekland, Hans—Sarsia Innovation AS
Hektor, Tjarko—AlpInvest Partners N.V.
Helenius, Joakim—Martinson Trigon Venture Partners AS
Helfrich, David—Garnett & Helfrich Capital
Helfrich, Matthias—Accera Venture Partners AG
Helgason, Ingolfur—Kaupthing Bank hf.
Helgerson, David—Hamilton Lane Advisors, Inc.
Helgesson, Staffan—Creandum KB
Hellberg, Niklas—Initium AB
Helle, Daniel—CIVC Partners LP (FKA: Continental Illinois Venture Corp.)
Hellebust, Helge—Ferd Venture
Heller, David—Goldman, Sachs & Co.
Heller, David—Vertex Management Israel (AKA: Vertex Venture Capital)
Heller, David—Vertex Venture Capital
Heller, Ephraim—7 Health Ventures
Heller, Joe—NextLevel Group
Hellevang, Johannes—Sarsia Innovation AS
Helling, Nico—UBS Capital Corporation
Hellman, F. Warren—Hellman & Friedman LLC
Hellman, Todd—Headwaters Merchant Bank
Hellstrom, Bengt—EQT Funds management Limited
Hellyer, Debra—Select Capital Ventures
Helm, Rob—Gold Hill Capital Management LLC
Helman, William—Greylock Partners
Helmers, Leo—Carlyle Group, The
Helmersen, Tor—Investinor AS
Helmsoe-Zinck, John—Via Venture Partners A/S
Helomaa, Jouko—Profita Management Oy
Helon, Ryan—Nationwide Mutual Capital LLC
Helou, Hani—Rasmala Partners, Ltd.
Helson, John—Kachi Partners
Helson, Patrick—Actis Capital LLP
Heltzer, Jason—OCA Venture Partners
Hemberger, Judith—Nomura Phase4 Ventures, Ltd.
Hemiadan, Daniel—GMB Mezzanine Capital, L.P.
Hemley, Simon—Gresham LLP
Hemmerle, Christophe—Finatem GmbH
Hemminga, Michael—Plain Vanilla Investments BV
Hemphill, Robert—Toucan Capital
Hen, Stewart—Warburg Pincus LLC
Henagan, Barbara—LINX Partners
Hendawi, Hatem Saad—Corecap Limited
Henderson, David—XPV Capital Corporation
Henderson, Fraser—Propel Investments
Henderson, J. Christopher—Vestar Capital Partners, Inc.
Hendren, David—Catalyst Health and Technology Partners LLC
Hendren, Jeffrey—Ripplewood Holdings LLC
Hendrickson, Pam—Riverside Company
Hendrie, Michael—Code, Hennessy & Simmons LLC
Hendriks, Michel—K+ Venture Partners
Hendrix, Foster—Saratoga Ventures, L.P.
Hendy, Patrick—Columbia Capital LLC
Henebery, Mike—Gresham LLP
Heneghan, Amy—Avenue Capital Group
Heng, Genevieve—CLSA Capital Partners (AKA: Credit Lyonnais Securities Asia)

Henig, Peter—Greenhouse Capital Partners
Henkelmann, Frank—Aheim Capital GmbH (FKA: Buchanan Capital Partners GmbH)
Henley, J. Rudy—Mountaineer Capital, L.P.
Hennegan, John—Shore Capital Partners LLC
Henner, Dennis—Clarus Ventures
Hennes, Pierre—Extream Ventures Pte, Ltd.
Hennes, Pierre—Upstream Ventures Pte., Ltd.
Hennessey, Michael—University Venture Fund, The
Hennessy, Daniel—Code, Hennessy & Simmons LLC
Hennessy, Jack—BPEP International
Hennessy, Janet—Advent International
Hennessy-Jones, Mary—Solera Capital, LLC
Hennigs, Robert—Finatem GmbH
Henninger, Matthew—Nortia Capital Partners, Inc. (FKA: BF Acquisition Group I)
Hennique, Gilbert—Nord Creation SAS
Henrich, Guenther—BayBG Bayerische Beteiligungsgesellschaft mbH
Henrichs, Jason—Rock Maple Ventures, L.P.
Henrion, Denis—Equitis
Henritze, Tyler—Blackstone Group, L.P.
Henry, Bob—Matrix Private Equity Partners LLP
Henry, David—NewWest Mezzanine Fund, L.P. (FKA:Touchstone Capital Group)
Henry, Desmond—Black Canyon Capital
Henry, Emil—Gleacher & Co.
Henry, George—Lincolnshire Management, Inc.
Henry, Joanne—BlueFire Partners Capital Markets
Henry, Larry—Hudson Capital Management, L.P.
Henry, Paul—Birch Hill Equity Partners Management, Inc.
Hens, Lars—Markstone Capital
Hensby, Barrie—NEL Fund Managers (FKA: Northern Enterprise, Ltd.)
Henshaw, Nathaniel—CEI Ventures, Inc. (AKA: CVI)
Henske, Robert—Hellman & Friedman LLC
Henson, Michael—MedFocus Fund LLC
Heppe, Jurgen—Millennium Private Equity
Hepple, Jonathan—Seroba Kernel Life Sciences, Ltd. (AKA: Seroba Kernel)
Heravi, Kayvan—LNK Partners
Herb, Robert—Scale Venture Partners
Herbelshimer, Larry—Comway Capital Limited
Herberg, Erica—Carlyle Group, The
Herberlein, Scott—FCP Investors
Herbinet, Antoine—Vatel Capital SAS
Herchel, Marek—AlpInvest Partners N.V.
Herger, Ivan—Capital Dynamics AG
Hergert, Ken—Moneta Capital Partners, Ltd.
Herget, Phil—Columbia Capital LLC
Herlihy, Frank—PHD Equity Partners LLP
Herman, Joseph—Atlantic-Pacific Capital, Inc.
Herman, Joseph—Blackstone Group, L.P.
Hermann, Frank—Cognetas LLP
Hermann, Klaus—AIG Capital Partners
Hermann, Matthew—Ascension Health Ventures LLC
Hermann, Peter—Heritage Partners
Hermelin, Brian—RockBridge Equity Partners LLC
Hermsen, Michael—Babson Capital Management LLC
Hern, Alexander—Silicon Valley Innovation Capital (SVIC)
Hernandes, Jana—Stuart Mill Capital, Inc.
Hernandez, Bruce—Spire Capital
Hernandez, Eddie—Small Ventures USA, L.P.
Herndon, James—CapSource Fund, L.P.
Hernmarck, Johan—Provider Venture Partners AB (FKA: IT Provider Advisor 1 AB)
Hernon, Martin—Boston Millennia Partners
Heron, Patrick—Frazier Healthcare and Technology Ventures
Herr, Stefan—EMBL Ventures GmbH
Herrera, Greg—Energy Ventures AS
Herrera, Nicolas—Prosperitas Capital Partners
Herrero, Javier—MCH Private Equity SA
Herrin, Chad—TPG Growth
Herring, Edward—HM Capital Partners LLC
Herron, Christine—First Round Capital
Herron, Dave—Clean Pacific Ventures
Hersh, Kenneth—Natural Gas Partners (NGP)
Hershenson, Gregg—Axon Capital
Hershey, Jerome—Technology Crossover Ventures
Hershfield, Lawrence—Ranch Capital LLC
Hersman, Brian—JMI Equity
Herstatt, Johann David—Beaufort Capital GmbH
Hertweck, Manuel—capiton AG
Hertzmark, Andrew—Generation Capital Partners
Herz, Jose Garcia—Small Enterprise Assistance Fund (SEAF)
Herzog, Joe—Northwest Venture Associates, Inc.(FKA:Spokane Capital Mgmt)
Herzog, Stefan—Sal. Oppenheim Private Equity Partners
Hesketh, Roberto—MultiCapital do Brasil Consultoria e Participacoes
Heskett, David—Valor Equity Partners
Hess, Alexandra—Cinven, Ltd.
Hesseborn, Goran—Hakon Invest AB (FKA: ICA Forbundet Invest)
Hessing, Michael—EquiVest GmbH & Co
Hetherington, Bruce—Perseis Private Equity
Hetu, Daniel—Lumira Capital Corporation.
Heumann, Martin—Triginta Capital Partners GmbH (FKA: Avida Equity Partners)
Hewett, Greg—Blackstone Group, L.P.
Hewett, Michael—Atlantic-Pacific Capital, Inc.
Hewitt, Paul—Lyceum Capital
Hewson, Paul David—Elevation Associates LLC
Heyer, Andrew—Mistral Equity Partners
Heyer, Andrew—Trimaran Capital Partners, LLC
Heyke, Christoph—KSH Capital Partners AG (FKA: UEG Beteiligungs AG)
Heywood, Ivan—LGV Capital, Ltd. (FKA: Legal & General Ventures, Ltd.)
Heyworth, Amanda—Playford Capital Pty Ltd. (FKA: SA.BITS)
Heyworth, Kim—WHEB Ventures, Ltd.
Hiatt, Gary—Pantheon Ventures, Ltd.
Hiatt, Thomas—Centerfield Capital Partners
Hibben, Alan—RBC Capital Partners/RBC Technology Ventures
Hichert, Volker—DPE Deutsche Private Equity GmbH (AKA: Parcom Deutsche PE)
Hickey, Brett—Aegis Capital Group LLC
Hickey, Charlotte—Treadstone Group Inc., The
Hickey, Douglas—Hummer Winblad Venture Partners
Hickey, James—Vista Equity Partners
Hickey, Janet—Sprout Group
Hickey, Kyle—Aegis Capital Group LLC
Hickey, Thomas—Castle Harlan, Inc.
Hickman, R. Trent—Veronis Suhler Stevenson (FKA: Veronis, Suhler & Associates)
Hickman-Smith, Dean—Juniper Networks
Hicks, George—Varde Partners, Inc.
Hicks, Jason—Persimmon Tree Capital, L.P.
Hicks, Larry—CapSource Fund, L.P.
Hicks, Matthew—Excellere Capital Management
Hicks, Peter—LINX Partners
Hicks, Randy—KPS Capital Partners, L.P.
Hicks, Robert—Allied Capital Corporation
Hicks, Terrence—Ben Franklin Technology Partners Southeastern PA
Hierro Lopes, Joaquim—GED Group
Hietala, Ilkka—Pohjola Capital Partners Oy
Higbee, Scott—Partners Group AG
Higdon, James—Verge
Higgerson, Clifford—Walden International
Higgins, Brian—Jordan Company, The
Higgins, Doug—SAP Ventures
Higgins, James—Golub Capital
Higgins, Kevin—Montgomery & Co. (FKA: Digital Coast Partners)
Higgins, Pete—Second Avenue Partners
Higgins, Robert—Highland Capital Partners LLC
Higgins, Thomas—Axxess Capital Partners S.A. (FKA: Enterprise Capital)
Higgins, Thomas—Bulgarian-American Enterprise Fund, The
Higgons, William—Siparex Group SAS
Highet, Ian—Court Square Capital Partners
Hightower, Teri—Spur Capital Partners LLC
Hijres, Jamal—Capinnova Investment Bank
Hildebrandt, Joseph—DaneVest Tech Fund Advisors
Hildebrandt, Joseph—Phenomenelle Angels Management
Hilderbrand, Mark—Housatonic Partners
Hildingsson, Magnus—Cinven, Ltd.
Hildisch, Michael—AFINUM Management GmbH
Hildisch, Michael—Argantis GmbH
Hilgert, Heinz—WestLB AG Equity Investments (AKA: Westdeutsche Landesbank)
Hilinski, Scott—Nautic Partners LLC
Hill, Alexandra—Blackstone Group, L.P.
Hill, Alexandra—Colony Capital LLC
Hill, Barbara—RiverRock Holdings LLC
Hill, Douglas—Nautic Partners LLC
Hill, Erin—One Equity Partners (FKA: Banc One Venture Partners)
Hill, Eugene—SV Life Sciences Advisers
Hill, Frederick—Allied Capital Corporation
Hill, James—Vexiom Equity Partners, L.P.
Hill, Jason—Media Venture Partners
Hill, John—Quadrangle Group LLC
Hill, Juan Marcos—Castanea Partners
Hill, Lowell—Oaktree Capital Management LLC
Hill, Ned—DFJ Mercury
Hill, Robert—Thompson Street Capital Partners
Hill, Shaun—Investcorp Bank B.S.C.
Hill, Steve—Millennium Ventures LLC
Hillabrant, Walter—NAC Ventures, LLC
Hillberg, Colin—Weber Capital Management LLC
Hillberg, Staffan—Scandinavian Financial Management AB
Hillberry, Synthia—RimAsia Capital Partners

Hilleboe, Scott—Steamboat Ventures
Hillel, Isaac—Pitango Venture Capital (FKA:Polaris Venture Capital Israel)
Hillelson, Fredrik—Investor Growth Capital AB
Hillenbrand, C. Justin—Monomoy Capital Partners, LLC
Hilliam, Mark—New Star Asset Management
Hillman, David McI.—PNC Equity Management Corp.
Hillmann, Matthias—Triton Partners
Hills, Dave—KPG Ventures
Hills, Matthew—LLM Capital Partners LLC
Hillyard, Carrie—Coates Myer & Co. Pty Ltd.
Hillyer, Cameron—Clearwater Capital Partners, LLC
Hilson, Mark—Onex Corporation
Hilson, Mark—Romspen Investment Corporation
Hilverkus, Gregor—CVC Capital Partners (Europe), Ltd.
Hilzinger, Kurt—Court Square Capital Partners
Himawan, Jeff—Essex Woodlands Health Ventures
Himmelmann, Nicolas—AUCTUS Capital Partners AG
Himmelreich, Karin—Cinven, Ltd.
Himuro, Seiji—Privee Investment Holdings Co., Ltd.
Hinck, Jeffrey—El Dorado Ventures
Hinck, Jeffrey—Vesbridge Partners, LLC
Hindery, Leo—Allegis Capital (AKA: Media Technology Ventures)
Hindery, Leo—InterMedia Partners
Hinkle, Ryan—Insight Venture Partners
Hinman, Brian—Oak Investment Partners
Hinojosa, Gonzalo—Qualitas Equity Partners
Hintikka, Martti—Innofinance Oy (FKA: Culminatum Oy)
Hinz, Bill—Patriarch Partners LLC
Hiram, Ron—Eurofund LP
Hirano, Masanobu—MVC Corporation
Hirano, Masao—Carlyle Group, The
Hiratsuka, Koji—DoCoMo Capital
Hirche, Lars—H.I.G. Capital LLC
Hirji, Nadim—BMO Capital Corporation
Hirn, Karine—East Capital Private Equity AB
Hirsch, Alisha—Walsingham Fund, The
Hirsch, Brian—GCP Capital Partners
Hirsch, Brian—Greenhill SAVP
Hirsch, David—Longitude Capital Management Company LLC
Hirsch, David—Metamorphic Ventures, LLC (FKA: Gersh Venture Partners)
Hirsch, Len—Wheatley Partners
Hirsch, Leonard—NGN Capital LLC
Hirsch, Russell—Prospect Venture Partners (FKA: Prospect Management LLC)
Hirsh, David—Blackstone Group, L.P.
Hirshland, Michael—Polaris Venture Partners
Hirst, Tim—ANU Connect Ventures Pty., Ltd.
Hirt, Dietmar—Conexus Capital Management, Inc.
Hirt, Lance—Lindsay Goldberg LLC (FKA: Lindsay Goldberg & Bessemer GP)
Hirtzel, Simon—Kreos Capital (FKA: European Venture Partners)
Hislop, James—Transportation Resource Partners (TRP) (FKA: Penske Capital)
Hitch, Jordan—Bain Capital
Hitchcock, Simon—Lyceum Capital
Hitti, Abdallah—Result Venture Knowledge International
Hitzig, William—Jordan, Edmiston Group, Inc., The
Hixon, Todd—Draper Fisher Jurvetson New England (AKA: DFJ/NE)
Hixon, Todd—New Atlantic Ventures
Hjalmtysson, Gisli—Thule Investments
Hjelt, Peter—UBS Capital Corporation
Hjerpe, Eric—Kepha Partners
Ho, Alvin—CLSA Capital Partners (AKA: Credit Lyonnais Securities Asia)
Ho, Andy—VinaCapital Investment Management Company
Ho, Charles—Olympus Capital Partners
Ho, Danny—CMIA Capital Partners (AKA: CM Investment Advisers Pte Ltd.)
Ho, Darren—CMHJ Partners
Ho, James—Capital International Research, Inc.
Ho, John-Paul—Crimson
Ho, Kent—Harbor Pacific Capital LLC
Ho, Michael—American Capital, Ltd.
Ho, Paul—Hudson Capital Management, L.P.
Ho, Philip—Yorkville Advisors LLC
Ho, Simmy—Global Private Equity PLC
Ho, Simon—IDG Technology Venture Investment, Inc.
Ho, Stephanie—Bertram Capital
Ho, Thierry—Lightyear Capital LLC
Ho, William—CVC Asia Pacific, Ltd.
Ho, William—CVC Capital Partners (Europe), Ltd.
Hoak, J.Hale—Hoak & Co.
Hoang, Nam—Probitas Partners, Inc.
Hobart, Matt—TPG Growth
Hobart, Ted—Chart Venture Partners
Hobbs, Jeremy—Draupnir LLC
Hobbs, Walter—ACT Venture Capital, Ltd.
Hobbs, William—Carousel Capital Partners
Hobbs, William—High Road Capital Partners
Hobby, Paul—Genesis Park Ventures
Hobman, Steven—NewSpring Capital
Hobo, Christoph—Cinven, Ltd.
Hoch, James—Tailwind Capital Partners
Hoch, James—Thomas Weisel Partners Group, Inc.
Hoch, Thomas—EVP Capital Management AG
Hochberg, Steve—Ascent Biomedical Ventures
Hocherman, Alex—Quadrangle Group LLC
Hochfelder, Peter—Brahman Management, LLC
Hock, Frank—AFINUM Management GmbH
Hockman, Kathleen—GE Antares Capital Corporation
Hodge, Bruce—Pender West Capital Partners, Inc.
Hodge, John—Blackstone Group, L.P.
Hodge, Mark—Andover Group Pty, Ltd.
Hodges, Deborah—MidOcean Partners
Hodges, Michael—ATA Ventures
Hodges, Philip—Redmont Venture Partners
Hodges, Robert—Carlyle Group, The
Hodgman, Jacob—Huntsman Gay Global Capital LLC
Hodgson, David—General Atlantic LLC
Hodgson, Ryan—American Industrial Partners
Hodits, Regina—Atlas Venture, Ltd.
Hodt, Niels Kr.—Kistefos Venture Capital AS
Hoecker, Bradley—Stonington Partners, Inc.
Hoegh, Thomas—Arts Alliance Advisors
Hoegh-Krohn, Joachim—Argentum Fondsinvesteringer AS
Hoellinger, Steffen—Team Europe Ventures Management GmbH
Hoelscher, Jens—Deutsche Beteiligungs AG
Hoenig, Michael—Equita Management GmbH
Hoerle, Hans-Jurgen—MBMV Mecklenburg-Vorpommern mbH
Hoesterey, Brian—AEA Investors LP
Hofeditz, Robert—Probitas Partners, Inc.
Hofener, Christopher—Perusa Partners GmbH
Hoff, Nikolaj—SR Private Brands A/S
Hoff, Robert—Crosspoint Venture Partners
Hoffen, Howard—Metalmark Capital LLC
Hoffman, Bill—Atlas Capital Group, Inc., The
Hoffman, David—Charterhouse Group International, Inc.
Hoffman, Elizabeth—Berkshire Partners LLC
Hoffman, Gordon—Northwest Technology Ventures
Hoffman, John—Silver Lake Sumeru
Hoffman, Mark—Monolith Capital Partners
Hoffman, Michael—Metalmark Capital LLC
Hoffman, Paul—Dresner Partners (FKA: Dresner Capital Resources, Inc.)
Hoffman, Reid—Greylock Partners
Hoffman, Spencer—Lovell Minnick Partners LLC
Hoffman, Stephen—Skyline Ventures
Hoffmann, Andrew—Capricorn Investment Group LLC (AKA: Capricorn Management)
Hoffmann, Anne—Graphite Capital (FKA: F&C Ventures, Ltd.)
Hoffmann, Michael—Probitas Partners, Inc.
Hoffmann, Tanguy—Siparex Group SAS
Hoffmeister, Mark—Prudential Capital Group
Hoffmeister, Stephen—Advent International
Hoffstroem, Petter—Amanda Capital Oyj
Hofmann, John—GTCR Golder Rauner LLC
Hogan, John—Norwest Mezzanine Partners
Hogan, Robert—Code, Hennessy & Simmons LLC
Hogan, Stephen—Levine Leichtman Capital Partners, Inc.
Hogan, Tracy—Elevation Associates LLC
HoganBruen, Matt—BAML Capital Access Funds
Hogarth, Warren—Sequoia Capital
Hoggarth, Royston—Wellington Partners Venture Capital GmbH
Hoglund, Oscar—BBE Business Development AB
Hogue, Benoit—Propulsion Ventures, Inc.
Hoguet, Robert—Riverside Management Group
Hojlo, Christopher—Court Square Capital Partners
Hokin, Daniel—HM Capital Partners LLC
Holbrook, David—MTI Partners, Ltd.
Holbrooke, David—MedVenture Associates
Holcomb, Richard—Aurora Funds, Inc.
Holden, Bradley—H & S Capital (AKA: Heidrick & Struggles Capital)
Holden, Charles—Thomas H. Lee Partners (AKA: TH Lee Partners)
Holden, Christopher—Court Square Ventures, LLC
Holden, Greg—Adams Street Partners LLC
Holden, Peter—Coller Capital
Holder, George—Silverfern Group, Inc., The
Holdsberg, Jeffrey—Caltius Equity Partners
Hole, Sveinung—Sarsia Seed Management AS
Holiday, Harry—Thompson Street Capital Partners
Holladay, J. Douglas—Park Avenue Equity Partners, L.P.
Holland, David—Veronis Suhler Stevenson (FKA: Veronis, Suhler & Associates)
Holland, George—Hull Capital Management, LLC

Holland, Jeffrey—Seacoast Capital
Holland, Jeremy—Vintage Capital Partners
Holland, Jim—Trinity Hunt Partners
Holland, Kirk—Vista Ventures
Holland, Paul—Foundation Capital
Holland, Rob—Creo Capital Partners, LLC
Holland, Robert—Cordova, Smart & Williams, LLC
Holland, Sean—Hercules Technology Growth Capital, Inc.
Hollander, Age—H2 Equity Partners BV
Hollander, David—Tennenbaum Capital Partners LLC
Hollander, Michael—GTCR Golder Rauner LLC
Holleman, Joost—Prime Technology Ventures NV
Hollenbeck, Chris—Granite Ventures LLC
Hollenberg, Christian—Perusa Partners GmbH
Holler, Frank—BC Advantage Funds (VCC), Ltd. (FKA: Lions Capital Corp.)
Holleran, Matt—Emergence Capital Partners LLC
Hollick, Clive—Kohlberg, Kravis, Roberts & Company, L.P.
Holliman, John—Valley Ventures (FKA: Arizona Growth Partners, L.P.)
Hollimon, Bryson—Technology Venture Partners
Hollin, Mitchell—LLR Partners, Inc.
Hollingsworth, Arthur—Lone Star Investment Advisors (AKA: Lewis Hollingsworth LP)
Hollmen, Harri—Intera Equity Partners Oy
Hollowood, Christopher—Apposite Capital LLP
Holm-Ovren, David—AAC Capital Partners
Holman, Albert—Chestnut Partners
Holman, Kelly—Genesys Capital Partners, Inc.
Holme, Catrina—DFJ Esprit
Holmen, Bob—Miramar Venture Partners
Holmes, Ben—Index Ventures
Holmes, John (Jack)—Natural Gas Partners (NGP)
Holmqvist, Bjorn—Spinn Investment AB
Holstad, Steve—Strattech Partners LLC
Holsted, David—Hall Capital Partners, L.P.
Holstein, Roger—Vestar Capital Partners, Inc.
Holsten, Heinz—CCMP Capital Advisors LLC
Holt, Allan—Carlyle Group, The
Holt, Terrance—Red Barn Investments LLC
Holtershinken, Klaus Michael—S-Partner Kapital AG
Holton, Michael—Smart Technology Ventures
Holtzman, Mark—Skymoon Ventures
Holway, Jeffrey—Water Street Healthcare Partners
Holzbaur, Ines—GeneChem Financial Corporation
Holzinger-Boecskoer, Dietmar—Oberbank Opportunity Invest Management GmbH
Holzman, Ben—Bain Capital Ventures
Holzman-Graziano, Glori—Carlyle Group, The
Homassel, Nicolas—Natixis Private Equity SA
Homer, James—Steadfast Capital GmbH (FKA: BHF Private Equity GmbH)
Homer, Paul—Northwood Ventures
Homler, Stewart—AIG Investment Corporation, (Asia) Ltd.
Homler, Stewart—PineBridge Investments
Homme, Matt—Aurora Resurgence Management Partners LLC
Hommels, Klaus—Balderton Capital (FKA: Benchmark Capital Europe)
Hommeyer, John—Blue Horizon Equity
Hon, Johnny—Global Private Equity PLC
Honda, Osuke—DCM
Honey, R. Sean—Weston Presidio (FKA: Weston Presidio Capital Management)
Honeybourne, Will—First Reserve Corporation
Hong Wen, Chris—Taishan Invest AG
Hong, Brian—CVC Asia Pacific, Ltd.
Hong, Brian—CVC Capital Partners (Europe), Ltd.
Hong, Eugene—Samsung Venture Investment Corporation (SVIC)
Hong, Jing—General Atlantic LLC
Hong, Karen—ProQuest Investments
Hong, Sunghyuk—M-Venture Investment, Inc. (FKA: Shinyoung Venture Capital)
Hong, Toni—Pac-Link Management Corporation
Hong, Young Chul—Heungkook Venture Capital Company, Ltd.
Hongzhi, Gan—Shenzhen Careall Capital Investment Co., Ltd. Kangwo
Honigblum, Gregg—Creation Capital LLC
Honis, John—Highland Capital Management, L.P.
Honney, John—BMO Capital Corporation
Honore, Jan—BankInvest Group A/S
Honos, Edward—Coppermine Capital LLC
Honour, Scott—Gores Group LLC, The
Hontebeyrie, Gerard—Alto Invest
Honzawa, Minoru—Nippon Mirai Capital Co., Ltd
Hood, Leroy—InterWest Partners
Hoogduin, Hein—Plain Vanilla Investments BV
Hoogheem, Timothy—Boulder Ventures, Ltd.
Hook, David—Baymark Partners
Hook, David—Keynote Ventures (FKA: Dali, Hook Partners)
Hook, Martin—Indigo Capital, Ltd.
Hook, Matt—Centerfield Capital Partners
Hooker, John—American Capital, Ltd.
Hooks, Michael—Black Canyon Capital
Hooper, Christopher—Welsh, Carson, Anderson & Stowe
Hooper, David—Centerview Partners Holdings LLC
Hooper, Herbert—Ampersand Ventures
Hooper, Pev—CVC Capital Partners (Europe), Ltd.
Hooper, Steven—Ignition Partners (FKA: Ignition Corporation)
Hooper, Suzanne—Cooley Godward LLP
Hooten, Kenneth—Concentric Equity Partners, L.P.
Hoover, Aaron—GCP Capital Partners
Hoover, Mark—Woodside Fund
Hopkins, Adam—Elevation Associates LLC
Hopkins, Chris—Rizvi Traverse Management, LLC
Hopkins, Daniel—HM Capital Partners LLC
Hopkins, Robert—CM Equity Partners (FKA; Lynx Investment Management, L.P.)
Hopkins, Tom—Active Private Equity Advisory LLP
Hopkinson, John—Adirondack Venture Fund, The
Hopley, John—Prospect Street Ventures
Hopner, Klaus—Sparkassenkapital Ulm GmbH
Hopp, Daniel—High Tech Venture Partners GmbH
Hopper, Harry—Columbia Capital LLC
Horak, Jaroslav—Arx Equity Partners
Horan, Avshalom—Bridge Investment Fund
Horan, Christine—HarbourVest Partners LLC
Horan, Harrison—Jacobson Partners
Horan, Richard—Slater Technology Fund
Horangic, Basil—North Bridge Venture Partners
Horbach, Sandra—Carlyle Group, The
Horelli-Rosenlew, Maria—ITP Invest AB (AKA: I Teknisk Partner Invest AB)
Horgan, Mark—Atlantic Bridge
Horgan, Michael—G.L. Ohrstrom & Co., Inc. (AKA: GLO & Co.)
Horing, David—American Securities Capital Partners LLC
Horing, Jeffrey—Insight Venture Partners
Horlick, Nicola—Bramdean Asset Management
Horlick, Tim—Frontiers Capital, Ltd.
Horn, Benjamin—St. Cloud Capital, LLC
Horn, Claudia—Stonegate Capital Group LLC
Horn, David—Montgomery & Co. (FKA: Digital Coast Partners)
Horn, Hans Jochum—Renaissance Capital
Horn, James—Noventi
Horn, Mark—Comerica Venture Capital Group
Horne, Mark—Plymouth Venture Partners
Horne, Robert—ZS Fund L.P.
Horne, Will—Phoenix Partners, The
Horner, Kelly—Stone Arch Capital LLC
Hornig, George—Credit Suisse Private Equity
Horning, Robert—Nexus Group LLC
Hornthal, James—Atrium Capital
Hornthal, James—CMEA Capital
Horowitz, Benjamin—Andreessen Horowitz
Horowitz, David—Comcast Interactive Capital
Horowitz, Joseph—JAFCO Ventures
Horsburgh, Peter—ETF Manager LLP
Horsholt, Jesper—Via Venture Partners A/S
Horsley, Erich—Intervale Capital
Horsley, Phillip—Horsley Bridge Partners
Horst, Sandy—Bluestem Capital Partners
Horst, Volker—EKK Dr. Engelhardt, Kaupp, Kiefer Beteiligungsberatung GmbH
Hortick, Edward—VCFA Group
Horton, Frederick—GSC Partners (FKA: Greenwich Street Capital Partners)
Horton, Matt—@Ventures
Horvath, Karoly—Estag Capital AG
Horvath, Nathan—American Capital, Ltd.
Horvitz, H.Robert—MPM Capital (FKA: MPM Asset Management LLC)
Hosang, Markus—BioMedPartners
Hoshino, Ryu—IGNITE Group, The (AKA: Ignite Associates, LLC)
Hoshino, Yo—Itochu Technology, Inc.
Hoskins, Richard—Genstar Capital LLC
Hosler, Daniel—Sterling Partners
Hosokawa, Chris Kosuke—Jina Ventures, Inc.
Hosokawa, Masnao—Angel Securities Inc.
Hoss, Moty—Evergreen Venture Partners
Hostetler, Cynthia—Overseas Private Investment Corp. (AKA: OPIC)
Hotta, Shinichi—Japan Private Equity Co., Ltd
Hotz, Robert—Houlihan, Lokey, Howard & Zukin
Hou, Faye—Coburn Ventures, LLC
Hou, Vincent—CID Group, The
Hou, Yudong—Eastern Link Capital
Houbo, Cheng—Shenzhen Capital Group Co., Ltd.
Houck, Joel—American Capital, Ltd.
Houde, Francois—OMERS Private Equity
Houette, Bruno—Abenex Capital (FKA: ABN AMRO Capital France)
Houghton, Gerald—Brooks, Houghton & Company, Inc.
Houk, Steve—Caris, Ltd.
Houle, Dan—Ontario Teachers' Pension Plan

Houlihan, James—InnoCal Venture Capital
Houry, Claire—Ventech S.A.
House, Roger—Platinum Equity LLC
Houtsonen, Leo—Veraventure Oy
Hove, Anders—Bellevue Asset Management AG
Hove, Anders—Venrock Associates
Howard, Al—TeleSoft Partners
Howard, Alan—Greenbriar Equity Group LLC
Howard, Andrew—Shamrock Holdings, Inc.
Howard, Christopher—Nevada Ventures
Howard, Grant—eMedici Capital, Inc. (Accolade Capital, Inc.)
Howard, John—Irving Place Capital
Howard, Lawrence—Hudson Venture Partners
Howard, Matthew—Norwest Venture Partners
Howard, Nigel—RLJ Equity Partners LLC
Howard, Paul—Mediphase Venture Partners
Howard, Robert—Houlihan, Lokey, Howard & Zukin
Howard, Russell—Berkshires Capital Investors
Howard, Russell—High Peaks Venture Partners, LLC
Howe, David—Enhanced Equity Fund, L.P.
Howe, David—Lightyear Capital LLC
Howe, Niloofar—Paladin Capital Management LLC
Howe, Timothy—CHL Medical Partners
Howell, Daniel—Mesirow Private Equity Investments, Inc.
Howell, Michael—C.W. Downer & Company (FKA: Downer & Company)
Howell, Ronald—WRF Capital
Howells, Thomas—Euroventures Capital Kft.
Hower, Lee—Point Judith Capital
Hower, Robert—Advanced Technology Ventures
Howery, Ken—Founders Fund, The
Howland, James—Morgan Stanley Private Equity
Howorth, Greg—Caltius Mezzanine
Hoy, Michael—Syntegra Capital, Ltd.
Hoyem, George—Redleaf Group, Inc
Hoyle, Richard—GCP Capital Partners
Hoyle, Roger—Enterprise Ventures, Ltd. (FKA:Lancashire Enterprises PLC)
Hoyte, David—TMB Industries Investments
Hromadko, Gary—Crosslink Capital
Hsiang, Yong Ho—CMIA Capital Partners (AKA: CM Investment Advisers Pte Ltd.)
Hsiao, C. H.—WIT Investment Partners, Ltd.
Hsiao, L. C.—Yuen Foong Yu Venture Capital Investment Corporation
Hsiao, Paul—New Enterprise Associates, Inc.
Hsieh, Jason—CID Group, The
Hsieh, Wen—Kleiner Perkins Caufield & Byers
Hsin, John—Crystal Internet Venture Fund, L.P.
Hsin, John—Highland Capital Partners LLC
Hsing, Peter—Merus Capital Investment
Hsiue, Cynthia—Pacific Venture Partners
Hsiung, Nancy—GeneChem Financial Corporation
Hsu, Allen—Pac-Link Management Corporation
Hsu, Arfen—Panda Capital Asia, Ltd.
Hsu, Geoffrey—OrbiMed Advisors LLC
Hsu, Henry—Blackstone Group, L.P.
Hsu, Hingge—Beacon Bioventures
Hsu, Jimmy—TIF Ventures Pte., Ltd.
Hsu, Kevin—Whitesun Equity Partners
Hsu, Mark—H&Q Asia Pacific
Hsu, Ming—Pac-Link Management Corporation
Hsu, Paul—NeoCarta Ventures, Inc.
Hsu, R. Rachel—Hall Capital Partners LLC (FKA: Offit Hall Capital Mgmt)
Hsu, Richard—Intel Capital
Hsu, Winnie—WI Harper Group
Hsui, Jenny—ChinaVest, Ltd.
Hu, Dehua—Shenzhen Fortune Venture Capital Co., Ltd.
Hu, Eion—Jordan Company, The
Hu, Ethan—Lilly Asian Ventures
Hu, Jackson—WI Harper Group
Hu, Jiwei—Shanghai Dingjia Ventures Co., Ltd.
Hu, Steven—Qiming Venture Partners
Hu, Terry Yongmin—FountainVest Partners (Asia), Ltd.
Hu, William—Qiming Venture Partners
Hu, XiaoBao—iGlobe Partners, Ltd.
Hua, Hsieh Fu—Temasek Holdings Pvt., Ltd.
Hua, Peter—SOFTBANK China Venture Capital
Hua, Yeyu—Zhejiang Zheshang Venture Capital Management Co., Ltd.
Huag, Andreas—eVenture Capital Partners GmbH
Huan, Guocang—Primus Pacific Partners
Huang, Andrew—Capital Z Investment Partners (FKA: Union Square Partners)
Huang, Ann—Rong International Investment Management Co. Ltd.
Huang, Biqiang—Eos Asia Investments, Ltd. (FKA: JCAR Funds, Ltd.)
Huang, Cheng Sang—Sunsino Ventures Group (FKA: Sunsino Development Associate)
Huang, Chih-Chien—Comway Capital Limited
Huang, Conrad—Atlas Capital Group, Inc., The
Huang, Darren—AsiaVest Partners, TCW/YFY Ltd. (FKA: TCW/YFY Investment)
Huang, Elise—AsiaTech Management LLC
Huang, George—Hotung International Company, Ltd.
Huang, Jingsheng—Bain Capital
Huang, Qing—Mingly Capital
Huang, Qing—Shenzhen GTJA Investment Group Co., Ltd.
Huang, Ricky—CSV Capital Partners (FKA: China Seed Ventures)
Huang, Shaobing—Fujian Venture Capital Co., Ltd.
Huang, Steven—Hotung International Company, Ltd.
Huang, Terry—Birch Venture Capital, Inc.
Huang, Thomas—Wasserstein Ventures (FKA: Wasserstein & Co.)
Huang, Tsong-Jen—AsiaVest Partners, TCW/YFY Ltd. (FKA: TCW/YFY Investment)
Huang, Tsui Hui—Hotung International Company, Ltd.
Huang, Vincent—Pantheon Ventures, Ltd.
Huang, Wayne—ChinaEquity Group, Inc.
Huang, Xiaojie—Kunwu Jiuding Capital Co., Ltd.
Huang, Xinmao—Navi Capital
Huang, Yu—Shenzhen GTJA Investment Group Co., Ltd.
Huber, Andres—BioMedPartners
Huber, Christoph—Alpha Associates AG
Huber, David—Grande Ventures
Huber, Gabriella—Royalton Partners
Huber, Jim—MASI, Ltd.
Huber, Markus—IndexAtlas Group
Huber, Peter—Digital Power Capital, LLC
Huber, Roman—Bayern Kapital GmbH
Huber, Stephan—Deutsche Beteiligungs AG
Huberman, David—Second City Capital Partners
Huberman, Jonathan—Idanta Partners, Ltd.
Hubers, Gert Jan—Nimbus
Hubler, Jodi—Lemhi Ventures
Hubregsen, Andrew—HB Equity Partners, L.P.
Huckfield, David—BPEP International
Huddie, Patrick—Chesapeake Emerging Opportunities Club LLC
Hudson, David—Darby Asia Investors, Ltd.
Hudson, David—Darby Overseas Investments, Ltd.
Hudson, Jacob—Atlas Holdings FRM LLC
Hudson, Jamie—Fireman Capital Partners
Hudson, Joe—One Earth Capital LLC
Hudson, L Sheryl—Equus Total Return, Inc.
Hudson, Mark—Graphite Capital (FKA: F&C Ventures, Ltd.)
Huebner, Charles—iEurope Capital LLC
Huebner, Matt—Headwaters Merchant Bank
Huechel, Shelley—Allied Capital Corporation
Huet, Eric—Ventech S.A.
Huey, Henry—Arsenal Venture Partners
Huey, Henry—OnPoint Technologies
Huff, Craig—Reservoir Capital Group
Huff, Curtis—Intervale Capital
Huff, Henry—Cambrian Ventures
Huff, Peter—Blue Sage Capital, L.P.
Huffard, Flip—Blackstone Group, L.P.
Huffsmith, Joseph—One Equity Partners (FKA: Banc One Venture Partners)
Hufnagel, Thomas—Stockwell Capital LLC
Hufnugel, Robert—IK Investmentbank AG
Hugas, Jaime-Enrique—Palamon Capital Partners (FKA: Amphion Capital Partners)
Hugenholtz, Paul—AAC Capital Partners
Hugger, Thomas—Leopard Capital, Ltd.
Hughes, Brent—Crown Capital Partners Inc.
Hughes, Charles—Easton Hunt Capital Partners, L.P.
Hughes, Christine—Avansis Ventures, LLC
Hughes, David—Foresight Group
Hughes, Donald—Camden Partners, Inc. (FKA: Cahill, Warnock & Co. LLC)
Hughes, F. Mackey—Camden Partners, Inc. (FKA: Cahill, Warnock & Co. LLC)
Hughes, Gayle—Merion Investment Partners, L.P.
Hughes, Neill—FL Partners
Hughes, Raoul—Bridgepoint Capital, Ltd.
Hughes, Travis—JMI Equity
Hugin, Robert—Celgene Corporation
Huh, Charles—Standard Chartered Private Equity, Ltd.
Hui, Daniel—AIF Capital Pvt, Ltd.
Hui, Guo—Tripod Capital International, Ltd.
Hui, Hsing Ma—TVM Capital GmbH
Hui, Kersten—Infinity Venture Capital Fund (AKA: Israel Infinity Fund)
Hui, Rao—Raystone Capital, Ltd.
Hui, Richard—Panthera Capital Group
Hukill, Nathan—Capital Royalty Partners
Hulatt, Chris—Octopus Asset Management, Ltd.
Hulecki, Gregory—FA Technology Ventures
Hulileh, Samir—Siraj Fund Management Company
Hull, Brandon—Cardinal Partners
Hull, Christina—GF Capital Management & Advisors LLC

Hull, David—Centennial Ventures
Hull, Hewes—Greer Capital Advisors LLC
Hull, James Mitchell—Hull Capital Management, LLC
Hull, John—Marquam Hill Capital LLC
Hull, Mark—Prospect Street Ventures
Hull, Robert—Providence Equity Partners LLC
Hullah, Daniel—Rockport Capital Partners
Hultin, Anders—Nordic Capital (AKA: NC Advisory)
Humaidan, Hadi—Unicorn Investment Bank B.S.C.
Humann, Phillip—SunTrust Bank, Inc.
Humber, Scott—Landmark Partners, Inc.
Hume, Ian—Sentient Group, The
Hume, Parker—General Atlantic LLC
Humer, Franz—F. Hoffmann - La Roche, Ltd.
Humes, Robert—JK&B Capital
Hummer, James—Luxemburg Capital LLC
Hummer, John—Hummer Winblad Venture Partners
Humphrey, David—Oklahoma Equity Partners
Humphrey, James—Humphrey Enterprises, LLC
Humphrey, Todd—Monster Venture Partners
Humphreys, Michael—Matrix Partners
Humphreyson, Charles—HO2 Partners
Humphries, Nic—HgCapital
Huneault, Philippe—Echo Capital
Hunecke, Jannick—Deutsche Beteiligungs AG
Hung, Betty—Vista Equity Partners
Hung, Frank—CDC Corporation (FKA: Chinadotcom Ventures)
Hung, Michael—Triton Management Corporation
Hung, Tony—DynaFund Ventures LLC
Hunkapiller, Michael—Alloy Ventures
Hunkin, John—Canadian Imperial Bank of Commerce (AKA: CIBC)
Hunnicutt, Jonathan—WestView Capital Partners
Hunt, Andrew—Marlow Capital
Hunt, John—ABRY Partners LLC
Hunt, Jon—Convergent Capital Management, Inc (AKA: CCM)
Hunt, Ronald—New Leaf Venture Partners LLC
Hunter, Brian—Northbridge Capital Partners
Hunter, Michael—H & S Capital (AKA: Heidrick & Struggles Capital)
Hunter, Peter—Axia Capital
Hunter, Sue—Frog Capital, Ltd.
Hunter, Tom—West Coast Capital
Hunter, Wally—EnerTech Capital
Hunter, Wally—RBC Capital Partners/RBC Technology Ventures
Hunter, Wayne—Harbert Venture Partners
Huntsman, Heidi—Pelion Venture Partners
Huntsman, Jon—Huntsman Gay Global Capital LLC
Hunziker, Erich—F. Hoffmann - La Roche, Ltd.
Hunzinger, Alexander—Perseus LLC
Huo, Richard—Lincolnshire Management, Inc.
Huot, Jacques—CFI Capital
Huot, Thomas—VantagePoint Venture Partners
Huot, Valery—CDC Innovation SAS (FKA: CDC IXIS Innovation)
Hupp, William—Adams Street Partners LLC
Huquan, Yan—Shenzhen High Tech Investment & Guaranty Co., Ltd.
Hurd, Jason—Bunker Hill Capital
Hurd, Timothy—Madison Dearborn Partners LLC
Huret, Robert—FTV Capital (FKA: FTVentures)
Hurley, Eamon—Thomas Weisel Partners Group, Inc.
Hursever, Umur—CCMP Capital Advisors LLC
Hurst, Chris—Thomas Weisel Partners Group, Inc.
Hurst, Jeffrey—Commonwealth Capital Ventures
Hurst, Patrick—Houlihan, Lokey, Howard & Zukin
Hurwitz, Peter—BMO Capital Corporation
Hurwitz, Roger—Fidelity Ventures
Hurwitz, Roger—Volition Capital
Husain, Fazle—Metalmark Capital LLC
Husain, Fazle—Morgan Stanley Private Equity
Husain, Fazle—Morgan Stanley Venture Partners (AKA: MSDW)
Huse, Del—Endless LLP
Huse, Del—Oakley Capital Investment Limited (AKA: OCI)
Huseby, Thomas—Oak Investment Partners
Huseby, Thomas—Seapoint Ventures
Huseby, Thomas—Voyager Capital
Huseby, Tom—Covera Ventures
Hussain Ebrahim, Ebrahim—Investcorp Bank B.S.C.
Husselby, Bill—Longbow Capital
Hutchens, James—Origin Partners
Hutcheson, Edward—Platte River Ventures
Hutcheson, Zenas—Vesbridge Partners, LLC
Hutchings, Jared—University Venture Fund, The
Hutchins, Winston—Forstmann Little & Company
Hutchinson, Mathew—CBPE Capital, LLP (AKA: Close Brothers Private Equity, Ltd.)
Hutchison, Fred—Research Triangle Ventures (RTV)
Hutt, Joseph—Formative Ventures
Hutter, Robert—Revolution Learning
Hutter, Robert—Revolution Ventures, LLC
Hutton, Graham—Hutton Collins & Company Limited
Hutton, Wende—Canaan Partners
Huwendiek, Carsten—Pantheon Ventures, Ltd.
Huwiler, John—Gleacher & Co.
Huy, Gerrit—Wellington Partners Venture Capital GmbH
Huyghues Despointes, Henry—21 Partners SpA
Huyghues-Despointes, Henry—21 Centrale Partners
Hwa, Erh-Cheng—GSIM Corporation (AKA: Global Strategic Investment Mgmt.)
Hwang, Jun Suk—Darby Overseas Investments, Ltd.
Hwang, Junsuk—STIC Investments, Inc.
Hwang, Sung-Jin—Warburg Pincus LLC
Hwang, Tien-Lai—Acorn Campus Ventures
Hwang, Tony—CID Group, The
Hwasta, Gerald—Silver Lake Sumeru
Hway, Gerry—CFI Capital
Hydari, Imtiaz—HBG Holdings, Ltd.
Hydari, Zulfi—HBG Holdings, Ltd.
Hyde, J.R.—MB Venture Partners, LLC
Hyde, Peter—Chord Capital, Ltd. (FKA: Generics Group, The)
Hyer, Robert—GCP Capital Partners
Hylton, Kevin—Ackerley Partners LLC
Hyndman, Stephen—GGV Capital
Hynes, Michael—GE Antares Capital Corporation
Hyvonen, Timo—Helmet Business Mentors Oy
Hyzak, Dwayne—Main Street Capital Corporation
Iacovone, Jack—Needham Asset Management
Iamoni, Stefano—Consilium SGR pA
Ianello, Peter—OCA Venture Partners
Ianni, Marino—Cooperazione Finanza Impresa scpa
Ianssen, Kine Buroy—Cubera Private Equity AS
Ibragimov, Bakhrom—Virgin Green Fund
Ibrahim, Maha—Canaan Partners
Ibrahim, Munaf—Jahangir Siddiqui Group (AKA: JS Group)
Ibscher, Karl—RECAP Management GmbH
Icaza, Alexandre—Albatroz Participacoes
Icaza, Gabriella—Albatroz Participacoes
Ide, Takeyoshi—Itochu Corporation
Ideguchi, Akihiro—Globis Capital Partners & Co. (FKS:Apax Globis Partners)
Iglesias, Ovidio—Wilshire Private Markets
Ignacio Moreno Garabito, Rafael—Vista Capital de Expansion SA
Ignaczak, Anthony—Quad-C Management, Inc.
Igram, Ab—GE Commercial Finance - Equity
Iinuma, Akira—Polaris Principal Finance Co., Ltd.
Iinuma, Ryosuke—Ant Capital Partners Co., Ltd.
Ikebuchi, Shohei—Gogin Capital Company, Ltd., The
Ikeda, Hogen—Nagoya Small & Medium Business Investment & Consultation Co.
Ilagan, Michael—SunTx Capital Partners
Illenberger, Stephan—AXA Private Equity
Illikman, James—Peninsula Capital Partners LLC
Ilsoe, Bo—Nokia Growth Partners
Ilundain, Daniel—Palladium Equity Partners LLC
Im, Jungkang—STIC Investments, Inc.
Imaizumi, Tomoyuki—Ant Capital Partners Co., Ltd.
Imbach, Scott—Levine Leichtman Capital Partners, Inc.
Imene, Maharzi—Butler Capital Partners SA
Imershein, Robert—ARC China, Inc.
Imeson, Patrick—Calim Private Equity, LLC
Imran, Mir—DFJ InCube Ventures
Imran, Mir—Draper Fisher Jurvetson ePlanet Ventures, L.P.
Imsieke, Gerrit—EVP Capital Management AG
Imuta, Atsushi—Risa Partners, Inc.
Inatome, Rick—Sterling Partners
Inbar, Doron—Carmel Ventures
Inchley, Simon—Gresham LLP
Ind, Charles—Bowmark Capital (FKA: Sagitta Private Equity)
Indahl, Reynir—Altor Equity Partners AB
Indelicato, William—Portfolio Advisors LLC
Ingero, Bard Brath—Reiten & Co Strategic Investments AS
Ingersoll, W. Brandon—MedEquity Investors LLC
Ingestrom, Anders—Coach & Capital Nordic 1 AB
Ingham, Carlos—Linzor Capital Partners, L.P.
Inglesby, Thomas—GSC Partners (FKA: Greenwich Street Capital Partners)
Inglese, Robert—Business Development Bank of Canada
Inglis, Mark—TSG Capital Group, L.L.C.
Ingraham, David—M/C Venture Partners
Ingram, Robert—Hatteras Venture Partners (FKA:Catalysta Partners)
Ingster, Mike—Formative Ventures
Inman, Bobby—Gefinor Ventures
Inman, Thomas—Gefinor Ventures
Innes, Mike—Graphite Capital (FKA: F&C Ventures, Ltd.)
Inorio, Kathi—Orchard First Source
Inoue, Akira—Daiwa Securities SMBC Principal Investments Co., Ltd.
Inoue, Hiroo—Itochu Corporation
Inoue, Takuo—Globis Capital Partners & Co. (FKS:Apax Globis Partners)

Inoue, Tomoko—Tokio Marine Capital Company, Ltd.
Insalaco, Steven—Calgary Enterprises, Inc.
Inui, Nicole—Darby Overseas Investments, Ltd.
Inwentash, Sheldon—Pinetree Capital, Ltd.
Ionescu, Val—AIG Capital Partners
Ip, KK—3V SourceOne Capital Pte, Ltd.
Ippolito, John—Headwaters Merchant Bank
Iqbal, Zafar—Pak Oman Investment Company
Iranzo, Juan—Iame Capital Riesgo SGECR SA
Irechukwu, George—Reliance Bank
Ireland, Bill—Mariner Financial, Ltd. (AKA: Mariner Brand Capital, Ltd.)
Ireland, Carolyn—GBS Venture Partners, Ltd.
Ireland, Elisabeth—Cirrus Investment Partners LLC
Ireland, James—Early Stage Partners, L.P.
Irigoin, Alfred—J.P. Morgan Partners (FKA: Chase Capital Partners)
Irigoin, Alfred—Linzor Capital Partners, L.P.
Irpola, Kimmo—GILD Bankers (FKA: LHV Ventures)
Irving, Charles—Pond Venture Partners
Irving, Richard—Pond Venture Partners
Irwin, Michael Scott—El Dorado Ventures
Irwin, Russel—Convergence Partners
Isaacs, Mark—First Avenue Partners, L.P.
Isaacs, Mark—GEN CAP America, Inc.
Isaacson, Andrew—Galen Associates
Isaacson, Jon—American Capital, Ltd.
Isaji, Tomohiro—Polaris Principal Finance Co., Ltd.
Isaly, Samuel—OrbiMed Advisors LLC
Isayama, Gen—DCM
Iseman, Frederick—CI Capital Partners LLC (FKA: Caxton-Iseman Capital, Inc)
Ishag, David—ARC China, Inc.
Ishbia, Justin—Shore Capital Partners LLC
Ishigami, Tatsuzo—Watervein Partners Co., Ltd.
Ishii, Makoto—Chuo Mitsui Capital Co., Ltd.
Ishii, Masazumi—Noventi
Ishii, Yoshiyuki—Mitsui & Co. Venture Partners (MCVP)
Ishikiwa, Masanori—Watervein Partners Co., Ltd.
Ishmael, Tokunboh—Aureos Capital, Ltd.
Ismael, Ahmet—Orthogonal Partners LLP.
Ismail, Rahmat—Malaysian Venture Capital Management (MAVCAP)
Isnard, Arnaud—ARCIS Finance SA
Isnard, Henri—ARCIS Finance SA
Isotamm, Lauri—GILD Bankers (FKA: LHV Ventures)
Israel, Michael—Goldner Hawn Johnson & Morrison, Inc.
Israel, Moises—Atlas Capital Close Brothers (FKA: Atlas Capital Investment)
Israel, Simon—Temasek Holdings Pvt., Ltd.
Israely, Gal—Cedar Fund
Israely, Ori—Giza Venture Capital (FKA: Giza Investment Management)
Isshi, Makoto—Japan Asia Investment Company, Ltd. (AKA: JAIC)
Italia, Roberto—Cinven, Ltd.
Ivankovich, Ivan—Revolution Capital Group LLC
Ivanov, Mikhail—Baring Vostok Capital Partners
Ivanova, Natalia—Da Vinci Capital Management
Ivanyi, Thomas—Brooks, Houghton & Company, Inc.
Ivashentseva, Elena—Baring Vostok Capital Partners
Ivey, Grahame—Investcorp Bank B.S.C.
Ivy, Robert—Salix Ventures
Iwamoto, Akira—Advantage Partners LLP
Iwamura, Kimihiko—Omron Silicon Valley (FKA: Omron Advanced Systems, Inc.)
Iwanowski, Mark—Trident Capital
Iwasa, Mitsukazu—Shinwa Venture Capital Co., Ltd
Iwasaki, Kenji—Asset Managers Holding Company, Ltd.
Iwashko, Mark—Horizon Capital
Iwata, Emiko—J-Star Co., Ltd.
Iyengar, Hari—Sandalwood Capital Partners
Iyer, Mohan—Burrill & Company
Iyer, Shriram—Edelweiss Capital, Ltd.
Iz, Ali—NewWorld Capital Group LLC
Izzard, Martin—TI Ventures
Izzo, Frank—Allied Capital Corporation
Jablon, Michael—MTS Health Partners, L.P.
Jabre, Jean-Marc—Morgan Stanley Private Equity
Jachet, Vincent—Bain Capital
Jack, Blythe—Rosewood Capital, L.P.
Jack, Eva—MedImmune Ventures
Jackowitz, Robert—Pine Brook Road Partners LLC
Jacks, Joel—CM Equity Partners (FKA; Lynx Investment Management, L.P.)
Jackson, Bret—Knox Investment Partners, Ltd.
Jackson, Chad—incTANK Inc.
Jackson, Christopher—American Capital, Ltd.
Jackson, Grant—Council Ventures
Jackson, John—Celgene Corporation
Jackson, Kevin—Gridiron Capital LLC
Jackson, Margaret—NeoCarta Ventures, Inc.
Jackson, Mark—Sentient Group, The
Jackson, Michael—Housatonic Partners
Jackson, Richard—NextStart Capital
Jackson, Shane—NextStart Capital
Jackson, Tim—Tech Capital Partners
Jackson, William—Bridgepoint Capital, Ltd.
Jacob, Anup—Virgin Green Fund
Jacob, Bharati—Seedfund
Jacob, Ravi—Intel Capital
Jacobi, Olaf—Target Partners GmbH
Jacobi, Philipp—Quadriga Capital
Jacobi, Tal—Stage One Ventures
Jacobs, Brian—Emergence Capital Partners LLC
Jacobs, Brian—Hatteras Funds
Jacobs, Jeff—Corning Innovation Ventures
Jacobsen, Eric—Dolphin Capital Group, LLC
Jacobsen, Kjell—Energy Ventures AS
Jacobsen, Mark—O'Reilly Alpha Tech Ventures, LLC
Jacobsen, Richard—GCP Capital Partners
Jacobson, Ben—Jacobson Partners
Jacobson, Daniel—CrossHarbor Capital Partners LLC
Jacobson, Dean—Accel-KKR LLC
Jacobson, Lorne—TriWest Capital Management Corporation
Jacobson, Mark—Ethemba Capital, Ltd.
Jacobson, Matthew—LaunchBox Digital
Jacobson, Perry—Brookstone Partners
Jacobson, Scott—Madrona Venture Group
Jacobson, Tommy—Rite Internet Ventures AB
Jacobsson, John—Apollo Real Estate Advisors
Jacoby, Jon E.M.—Stephens Group, Inc.
Jacqueau, Guillaume—Barclays Private Equity, Ltd.
Jacquemai, Michel—Partners Group AG
Jacquemart-Pernod, Karine—Butler Capital Partners SA
Jacques, Kevin—Palomar Ventures
Jacquin, Ken—Dolphin Capital Group, LLC
Jadeja, Asha—Dot Edu Ventures
Jadot, Bryan—Hercules Technology Growth Capital, Inc.
Jaeckel, Scott—Thomas H. Lee Partners (AKA: TH Lee Partners)
Jaeger, Lars—Partners Group AG
Jaeger, Mike—Bacchus Capital Management LLC
Jaeger, Wilfred—Three Arch Partners
Jaeggi, Andre—Adveq Management AG
Jafar, Imran—Gaja Capital Partners
Jaffe, David—Centre Partners Management LLC
Jaffe, David—Palisades Ventures (FKA: Centre Palisades Ventures)
Jaffe, James—Murex Investments, Inc.
Jaffe, Michael—Henderson Equity Partners (AKA: Henderson Private Capital)
Jaffe, Ross—Brentwood Venture Capital
Jaffe, Ross—Versant Ventures
Jaffe, Yitz—Infinity Asset Management LLP
Jaffee, Steven—Reservoir Venture Partners
Jagannathan, Anand—GCP Capital Partners
Jager, Remko—Gilde Equity Management Benelux B.V.
Jaggers, John—Sevin Rosen Funds
Jaggers, Kurt—TA Associates, Inc.
Jahn, Clemens—IKB Private Equity GmbH
Jahnke, James—Palisade Capital Management
Jahns, David—Galen Associates
Jain, Aalok—Diamond Castle Holdings LLC
Jain, Abhi-Shek—Washington Technology Partners, Inc. (AKA: WTP)
Jain, Akash—ICICI Venture Funds Management Co., Pvt. Ltd. (FKA: TDICI)
Jain, Arvind—BanyanTree Finance Pvt. Ltd.
Jain, Gopal—Gaja Capital Partners
Jain, Manish—Axis Holdings Pvt., Ltd.
Jain, Mitin—BanyanTree Finance Pvt. Ltd.
Jain, Mudit—Synergy Life Science Partners
Jain, Pravin—Sonoma Management Partners
Jain, Pushpam—Darby Overseas Investments, Ltd.
Jain, Sanjay—J.P. Morgan Capital Corporation
Jain, Sarita—Johnson & Johnson Development Corporation
Jain, Surendra—Sequoia Capital India (FKA: WestBridge Capital Partners)
Jain, Vishal—Nadathur Holdings and Investments Pvt., Ltd.
Jaisingh, Nainesh—Standard Chartered Private Equity, Ltd.
Jakola, Karl-Johan—Norinnova Forvaltning AS
Jalan, Ajay—Sandalwood Capital Partners
Jalba, Mircea—Abris Capital Partners
James, Brent—Jerusalem Capital (AKA: JCP)
James, Hamilton—Blackstone Group, L.P.
James, Janet—Rockport Capital Partners
James, Joanna—Advent International
James, Robert—DFJ Esprit
James, William—Rockport Capital Partners
Jameson, Jonathan—Probitas Partners, Inc.
Jamie, Gates—TPG Capital
Jamieson, Don—Caltius Mezzanine
Jamieson, J. Burgess—Sigma Partners
Jamp, Ray—Genesis Campus, L.P.
Jamp, Ray—Mobility Ventures

Joy, Andrew—Cinven, Ltd.
Joy, Bill—Kleiner Perkins Caufield & Byers
Jozefak, Paul—Neuhaus Partners GmbH
Jozefiak, Marek—TP Invest
Jrolf, Mark—Heritage Partners
Ju, Sunglin—L&S Venture Capital Corporation
Jubeir, T.J.—New Horizons Venture Capital
Jud, Thomas—Invest Equity Management Consulting GmbH
Judd, Damon—KRG Capital Partners LLC
Judson, K. Leonard—Cycad Group LLC
Julich, Chris—Escalate Capital
Julina, Radomir—Celtic Pharma Management, LP
Julis, Mitchell—Canyon Capital
Jullien, Thierry—Developpement & Partenariat SAS
Jun, Yolande—Silver Lake Sumeru
Junco, Pilar—Blackstone Group, L.P.
Juneja, Robert—Irving Place Capital
Jung, Christoph—Holtzbrinck Ventures GmbH
Jung, Hans—STIC Investments, Inc.
Jung, Jongwook—Wooridul Venture Capital Co., Ltd.
Jung, Kwang Myung—i Venture Investment Co., Ltd.
Jung, Marion—Earlybird Venture Capital GmbH & Co. KG
Jung, Michael—J.P. Morgan Partners (FKA: Chase Capital Partners)
Jung, Michael—Panorama Capital
Jung, Sokho—Credit Suisse Private Equity
Jungebloed, Ralf—Climate Solutions Management GmbH
Jungels-Winkler, Christophe—Swarraton Partners Limited
Jungersen, Nicolai—Capidea Management ApS
Junoy, Sebastian—Headway Capital Partners LLP
Juricic, Don—RFE Investment Partners
Jurish, Mark—HFIC Partners, LLC
Juristo, Tarmo—GILD Bankers (FKA: LHV Ventures)
Jurvetson, Steven—Draper Fisher Jurvetson
Jury, Jennie—Pantheon Ventures, Ltd.
Jussal, Sumit—Probitas Partners, Inc.
Juterbock, Tom—Ritchie Capital
K. Cappello, Gerard—Cappello Capital Corp.
Kaas, Erik—Partners Group AG
Kabcenell, Nicholas—Darby Overseas Investments, Ltd.
Kabra, Atim—Frontline Strategy Pte. Ltd.
Kacani, Timothy—Lightyear Capital LLC
Kacer, Peter—KT Capital Management LLC
Kacergis, Joseph—Dresner Partners (FKA: Dresner Capital Resources, Inc.)
Kachalia, Nirav—Morgan Creek Capital Management LLC
Kachanov, Oleg—UK NIKOR, OAO
Kacher, Glen—Integral Capital Partners
Kachingwe, Mayamiko—Terra Firma Capital Partners, Ltd.
Kaczynski, William—Bridge Street Capital Partners LLC
Kaden, Douglas—Oak Hill Capital Management, Inc.
Kadhiresan, V. Kadir—Johnson & Johnson Development Corporation
Kadlic, Jeffrey—Evolution Capital Partners, LLC
Kafker, Roger—TA Associates, Inc.
Kagan, Peter—Warburg Pincus LLC
Kaganov, Alan—U.S. Venture Partners
Kaganovich, Oleg—DFJ Frontier
Kagle, Robert—Benchmark Capital
Kagunye, Peter—Capital Resource Partners
Kahan, Michael—North Peak Capital, LLC
Kahana, Arie—Defta Partners
Kahe, Stefan—PEPPERMINT. Financial Partners (FKA schroder + partner)
Kahle, G. Kent—GulfStar Group
Kahn, Joshua—Hamilton Lane Advisors, Inc.
Kahn, Matthew—GB Merchant Partners, LLC (FKA: GB Palladin Capital LLC)
Kahn, Paul—Himalaya Capital
Kahr, Jesper—Scandinavian Financial Management AB
Kahr, Julia—Blackstone Group, L.P.
Kailian, Vaughn—MPM Capital (FKA: MPM Asset Management LLC)
Kairouz, Habib—Rho Capital Partners, Inc.
Kaiser, Harold—Litorina Capital Advisors AB
Kaiser, Nicholas—Marlin Equity Partners, LLC
Kaiser, Stefan—Askembla Asset Management AB
Kaiser, William—Greylock Partners
Kajimura, Toru—Polaris Principal Finance Co., Ltd.
Kalandar, Boris—Strategic Venture Mgmt. Advisors (FKA: MentorTech Ventures)
Kalb, Michael—Sun Capital Partners, Inc.
Kalbach, Gary—El Dorado Ventures
Kalbe, Jochen—HighTech Private Equity GmbH
Kalelkar, Ashok—Seed Capital Partners
Kalen, Lennart—Segulah Advisor AB
Kalender, Burcu—Is Private Equity Investment Trust
Kalinin, Alexei—BPEP International
Kalinin, Alexei—Baring Vostok Capital Partners
Kalish, Geoffrey—Aquiline Capital Partners
Kalish, Rami—Pitango Venture Capital (FKA:Polaris Venture Capital Israel)
Kalish, Shlomo—Jerusalem Global Ventures
Kalkanis, Peter—Rho Capital Partners, Inc.
Kalker, Johannes—Patron Capital, Ltd.
Kallen, Paul-Bernhard—Acton Capital Partners GmbH
Kalliovaara, Juhani—Sponsor Capital Oy
Kallmeyer, M. Neil—CapStreet Group LLC, The (FKA: Summit Capital Group)
Kallu, Heikki—GILD Bankers (FKA: LHV Ventures)
Kalman, Robert—Quan Ventures
Kalnow, Andrew—Alpha Capital Partners, Ltd.
Kalow, Mark—Trans Cosmos USA
Kalra, Rajeev—AIF Capital Pvt, Ltd.
Kalra, Vivek—Capital International Research, Inc.
Kaltofen, Arnd—Venture Incubator AG (AKA: VI Partners AG)
Kalverboer, Patrick—H2 Equity Partners BV
Kam, Fred—Templeton Asset Management, Ltd.
Kamath, Sudhir—2i Capital Asset Management Company, Ltd.
Kambourides, Miltos—Dolphin Capital Partners
Kamdar, Kim—Domain Associates LLC
Kameda, Takashi—Itochu Technology, Inc.
Kamei, Yasushi—Carlyle Group, The
Kaminski, Paul—Bruckmann, Rosser, Sherrill & Co.
Kaminsky, Howard—Appaloosa Management, L.P.
Kammar, Colleen—Calvert Street Capital Partners, Inc. (FKA: Legg Mason)
Kampe, Christopher—Tully & Holland, Inc. (FKA: Ulin & Holland, Inc.)
Kamperman, Gustav—Fianchetto Venture Capital AB (FVC)
Kampus, Miha—Gasser+Partner Beteiligungs GmbH
Kamra, Deepak—Canaan Partners
Kamtsios, Chris—Ineko Capital Partners LLP
Kan, Elisabeth—First Eastern Investment Group
Kan, Zhidong—Orica Capital Co., Ltd.
Kanai, Mayumi—Asia Private Equity Capital (FKA: MediBIC Alliance)
Kanakia, Hemant—Columbia Capital LLC
Kanani, Bharat—GVFL Limited (FKA: Gujarat Venture Finance Limited)
Kanarens, Bryan—Ontario Centres of Excellence
Kandasamy, Chandrasekar—Draper Fisher Jurvetson ePlanet Ventures, L.P.
Kandrac, Martin—Blackstone Group, L.P.
Kane, Joshua—GSC Partners (FKA: Greenwich Street Capital Partners)
Kane, Michael—Caltius Mezzanine
Kane, Neil—Illinois Partners, LLC
Kane, William—MTS Health Partners, L.P.
Kanehann, Garrett—BlackEagle Partners (FKA: Centurion Capital Partners)
Kaneko, Tomikazu—JAFCO Co., Ltd. (FKA: Japan Associated Finance Co. Ltd.)
Kaneko, Yasumori—Skyline Ventures
Kaneko, Yozo—NGI Group (AKA: Netage Capital Partners, Inc.)
Kang, Brian—Samsung Venture Investment Corporation (SVIC)
Kang, Daniel—Lovell Minnick Partners LLC
Kang, Moo-Gyung—KTB Securities Co., Ltd. (FKA: KTB Network Co., Ltd.)
Kang, Pei—Chengwei Ventures
Kang, Taeksu—Univest Capital
Kang, Younggeun—Fitech Venture Partners Company, Ltd.
Kangasniemi, Jaakko—Finnish Fund for Industrial Cooperation, Ltd. (AKA:FINNFUND)
Kanji, Azra—ABRY Partners LLC
Kanji, Shamez—North Hill Ventures
Kano, Toshiki—Ridgeway Capital Partners, Ltd. (FKA:OPE Partners Ltd.)
Kanter, Eric—Morgan Stanley Private Equity
Kantesaria, Devang—Devon Park Bioventures
Kao, Dan—China Century Capital Limited
Kao, Hsiao-wen—East Gate Private Equity Partners LLC
Kap, Noga—BRM Capital
Kapadia, Atul—Bay Partners
Kapadia, Sandeep—Prime Technology Ventures NV
Kapani, Reeta—Silverfern Group, Inc., The
Kapil, Aditya—VenturEast (FKA: APIDC Venture Capital Limited)
Kaplan, Andrew—Quad Ventures
Kaplan, Daniel—Firm Factory Network
Kaplan, Effram—Brown Gibbons Lang & Company LLC
Kaplan, Larry—Bedford Funding
Kaplan, Mark—CEI Ventures, Inc. (AKA: CVI)
Kaplan, Michael—Littlejohn & Company LLC
Kaplan, Robert—Thomas Weisel Partners Group, Inc.
Kaplan, Stephen—Oaktree Capital Management LLC
Kapler, A. William—Alumni Capital Network
Kapnick, David—Rising Tide Fund
Kapoor, Arrun—SJF Ventures

Kapoor, Raj—Mayfield Fund
Kapoor, Rana—YES BANK, Ltd.
Kapoor, Rishi—Investcorp Bank B.S.C.
Kapur, Gagan—Argonaut Private Equity
Kapur, Kip—Barclays Ventures
Karabelas, Argeris—Care Capital, LLC
Karadogan, Baris—Fuse Capital
Karadogan, Yalin—Cinven, Ltd.
Karal, Eva—Campus Kjeller AS
Karam, Assad—Amwal AlKhaleej
Karamouzis, Michael—GTCR Golder Rauner LLC
Karbenk, Christoph—capiton AG
Kardwell, J.J.—Summit Partners
Karimov, Albert—Innovative Technopark IDEA
Karimov, Maxim—e-Trust Investment Group
Karitihi, Kibuga—Baraka Africa Fund, Ltd.
Kariv, Tomer—Pontifax Ltd.
Kariyazono, Soichi—Globis Capital Partners & Co. (FKS:Apax Globis Partners)
Karjalainen, Petri—Equest Partners, Ltd.
Karkkainen, Pentti—KERN Partners
Karlander, Hans—Karnell
Karle, Thomas—MFC Capital Funding, Inc.
Karlen, John—Flybridge Capital Partners
Karleski, Koleman—Chrysalis Ventures
Karlson, Melissa—Viburnum Funds Pty., Ltd. (AKA: Wyllie Group)
Karlson, Steven—Windspeed Ventures
Karlsson, Joachim—KTH-Chalmers Capital KB
Karlsson, Karl-Magnus—GKL Growth Capital AB
Karnani, Nitin—Apollo Real Estate Advisors
Karnani, Nitin—Blackstone Group, L.P.
Karnes, Carl—B4 Ventures
Karol, Steven—Watermill Group, The
Karp, Douglas—Tailwind Capital Partners
Karp, Douglas—Thomas Weisel Partners Group, Inc.
Karp, Evan—Parallel Invesment Partners
Karp, Matty—Concord Ventures (FKA: Nitzanim)
Karras, Jeff—Levensohn Venture Partners LLC (FKA: Levensohn Capital Mgmt)
Kary, Rex—Moneta Capital Partners, Ltd.
Karyakin, Anatoliy—Baring Vostok Capital Partners
Kasdin, Kef—Battelle Memorial Institute
Kasdin, Kef—Battelle Ventures
Kasdin, Kef—Early Stage Enterprises, L.P.
Kase, George—Marlin Equity Partners, LLC
Kasela, Indrek—Firebird Management LLC
Kasher, Marc—AIG Capital Partners
Kasliwal, Sumant—ICICI Venture Funds Management Co., Pvt. Ltd. (FKA: TDICI)
Kasnavi, Reza—Tallwood Venture Capital
Kass, David—Wellspring Capital Management LLC
Kass, Lawrence—Sands Brothers & Co., Ltd.
Kassai, Phillip—Sunrise Financial Group, Inc.
Kasser, Susan—Carlyle Group, The
Kassin, Philip—Evercore Partners
Kassum, Zool—Tufan Venture Partners
Kaster, Christopher—MedVenture Associates
Kaswan, Mike—KBL Healthcare Ventures
Katabi, Maha—Ventures West Management, Inc.
Katadae, Maiko—University of Tokyo Edge Capital Co., Ltd., The (AKA: UTEC)
Katarincic, Jay—Draper Triangle Ventures
Katcha, Joseph—High Street Capital
Kathoke, Rusi—BTG International (AKA: British Technology Group)
Kato, Haru—Keynote Ventures (FKA: Dali, Hook Partners)
Kato, Isaac—General Catalyst Partners (FKA: General Catalyst Group LLC)
Kato, Isaac—Summit Accelerator Fund
Kato, Ken—MKS Partners, Ltd. (FKA: Schroder Ventures K.K.)
Kato, Ken—Valiant Partners Co. Ltd.
Kato, Shin—Arise Capital Partners, Inc.
Katsov, Victoria—Wall Street Technology Partners
Katsukawa, Kohei—Daiwa Corporate Investment Co., Ltd.
Katsuki, Yuka—Polaris Principal Finance Co., Ltd.
Katsumata, Kiyoyuki—Ridgeway Capital Partners, Ltd. (FKA:OPE Partners Ltd.)
Katsuta, Hisao—Daiwa Corporate Investment Co., Ltd.
Katsuya, Hisashi—IBM Corporation
Katz, Alan—W.R. Hambrecht & Co., LLC
Katz, Alex—ff Asset Management LLC
Katz, Andrew—Skypoint Capital Corporation
Katz, Daniel—Ares Management, Inc.
Katz, Daniel—Tailwind Capital Partners
Katz, David—GTCR Golder Rauner LLC
Katz, David—Rogers Casey
Katz, Jed—Draper Fisher Jurvetson Gotham Venture Partners
Katz, Jed—Javelin Venture Partners
Katz, Jordan—Gores Group LLC, The
Katz, Lance—Wipprivate Equity
Katz, Sam—Wynnefield Capital Advisors
Katz, Samuel—Edmond de Rothschild Venture Capital Management
Katz, Samuel—TZP Group LLC
Katzenelson, Moshe—Stage One Ventures
Katzenstein, Seth—GSC Partners (FKA: Greenwich Street Capital Partners)
Katzman, David—Camelot Ventures
Katzman, Elliot—Commonwealth Capital Ventures
Katzwer, Norman—Reservoir Capital Group
Kau, Andrew—Walden International
Kauffman, Paul—Highland Capital Management, L.P.
Kauffmann, David—European Equity Partners
Kauffmann, David—Generis Capital Partners
Kaufman, Andrea—Novak Biddle Venture Partners, L.P.
Kaufman, Anita—NextLevel Group
Kaufman, David—Envest
Kaufman, Glenn—American Securities Capital Partners LLC
Kaufman, Matthew—GSC Partners (FKA: Greenwich Street Capital Partners)
Kaufman, Michael—Westly Group, The
Kaufman, Peter—Bacchus Capital Management LLC
Kaufman, Sy—Crosslink Capital
Kaufmann, Eric—In-Q-Tel, Inc.
Kaul, Anjana—Footprint Ventures
Kaul, Ashish—Forrest Binkley & Brown
Kaul, Harsh—SIDBI Venture Capital, Ltd. (SVCL)
Kaul, Mike—Techfund Capital Europe Management SAS
Kaul, Samir—Khosla Ventures
Kaul, Sanjiv—ChrysCapital Management Company
Kaull, Kurtis—Gryphon Investors, Inc.
Kaupp, Karl Friedrich—EKK Dr. Engelhardt, Kaupp, Kiefer Beteiligungsberatung GmbH
Kauppi, Terhi—Pontos Oy
Kawada, Makoto—Wendel
Kawaguchi, Tetsushi—Globis Capital Partners & Co. (FKS:Apax Globis Partners)
Kawaguchi, Yoji—Zenshin Capital Management
Kawakami, Hiroki—STB Investment Corporation
Kawakami, Hiroo—Integral Investments, Inc.
Kawall, Carlos—RioBravo Investimentos
Kawano, Hiroshi—Biofrontier Partners, Inc.
Kawasaki, Guy—Garage Technology Ventures LLC (FKA: Garage.com)
Kawasaki, Tatsuo—Unison Capital, Inc.
Kawkabani, Joe—Algebra Capital
Kay, Chris—Chrysalis VCT
Kay, Max—Pacific Partners
Kay, Robert—Global Technology Investment (GTI)
Kayama, Yukihiro—CSV Capital Partners (FKA: China Seed Ventures)
Kayama, Yukihiro—CSV Capital Partners (FKA: China Seed Ventures)
Kayden, Joelle—Accolade Capital Management
Kaye, Jonathan—Darwin Private Equity LLP
Kaye, Michael—ClearLight Partners LLC
Kayes, Neal—Cortec Group, Inc.
Kayler, J. Allan—Midwest Mezzanine Funds
Kazandjian, Raffy—Equitis
Kaziewicz, Phil—Global Innovation Partners LLC
Ke, Hong—Centenium-Pinetree China Private Equity
Ke, Yan—Northern Light Venture Capital
Kealy, Tom—Montlake Capital
Kean, Thomas—Quad Ventures
Keane, Patrick—Cobalt Capital, Inc.
Keane, Roger—GE Commercial Finance - Equity
Keane, Thomas—Murphy & Partners, L.P.
Kearney, Douglas—Superior Capital Partners
Kearney, Geoff—RiverRock Holdings LLC
Kearney, Thomas—Wicks Group of Companies LLC, The
Keating, Stephen—Privet Capital LLP
Keay, Jeffrey—HarbourVest Partners LLC
Keck, Kevin—Phoenix Equity Partners (FKA: DLJ European Private Equity)
Kedrosky, Paul—Ventures West Management, Inc.
Keeble, Ben—CVC Asia Pacific, Ltd.
Keeble, Ben—CVC Capital Partners (Europe), Ltd.
Keefe, Edward—M/C Venture Partners
Keefe, Kevin—PPM America Capital Partners LLC
Keehn, Peter—Waud Capital Partners LLC
Keele, Larry—Oaktree Capital Management LLC
Keeley, Sabrina—Detroit Renaissance
Keenan, Graeme—Pantheon Ventures, Ltd.
Keenan, Jeffrey—Roark Capital Group
Keene, J. Randall—Ancor Capital Partners
Keene, Sean—Atlantic-Pacific Capital, Inc.
Keene, Sean—Blackstone Group, L.P.
Keene, Thomas—Ewing Management Group LLC
Keesey, Mike—Code, Hennessy & Simmons LLC
Keffer, Pueo—Redpoint Ventures
Kehaya, Mark—Meritum Partners LLC
Kehler, Dean—Trimaran Capital Partners, LLC
Keiko, Iwaisako—Entrepia Ventures, Inc.
Keil, Brian—GE Commercial Finance - Equity
Keilhacker, Kurt—Techfund Capital Europe Management SAS
Keilhockor, Kurt—TechFund Capital

Khayat, Yousuf—SEDCO Direct Investment Group
Kher, Renuka—NewSchools Venture Fund
Kherati, Rizwan—Fajr Capital Ltd
Khilov, Dmitry—United Financial Group Asset Management (AKA: UFG)
Kholi, Jacob—Aureos Capital, Ltd.
Khong, Hiew Yoon—Temasek Holdings Pvt., Ltd.
Khoo, Jeffrey—3V SourceOne Capital Pte, Ltd.
Khosla, Vinod—Khosla Ventures
Khosla, Vinod—Kleiner Perkins Caufield & Byers
Khouri, George—Growth Capital Partners, L.P.
Khoury, Karl—Columbia Capital LLC
Khoury, Pierre—Vermeer Capital Partners
Khuong, Chau—OrbiMed Advisors LLC
Khurana, Shivani—MVC Capital (FKA: meVC)
Kiakidis, Theodore—Global Finance SA
Kiam, Victor—CT Holdings
Kiang, Dan—TVG Capital Partners, Ltd.
Kiarie, Key—Saban Ventures
Kibayashi, Yasuji—CAS Capital, Inc.
Kichler, Thomas—One Equity Partners (FKA: Banc One Venture Partners)
Kidson, Ian—TD Capital Group, Ltd.
Kiefer, Georg—EKK Dr. Engelhardt, Kaupp, Kiefer Beteiligungsberatung GmbH
Kiemer, Bent—Vaekstfonden (AKA: Danish Growth Fund, The)
Kienzle, Trevor—GE Commercial Finance - Equity
Kienzle, Trevor—Rising Tide Fund
Kiep, Mathias—GCP Capital Partners
Kiervin, Jack—Jefferson Partners
Kiesel, Robert—Fifth Street Capital LLC
Kiev, Marshall—Main Street Resources (FKA: Colt Capital Group)
Kiggen, James—Blackstone Group, L.P.
Kight, Pete—Comvest Investment Partners
Kikta, Roman—Genesis Campus, L.P.
Kikta, Roman—Mobility Ventures
Kikuchi, Masato—IGNITE Group, The (AKA: Ignite Associates, LLC)
Kilarski, LeAnn—Wind Point Partners
Kilcrease, Laura—Triton Ventures
Kilduff, Paul—Vision Capital LLP
Kiley, Richard—Blue Chip Venture Company
Kilgore, Thomas—ArcLight Capital
Kilgour, P. Kenneth—CIBC Wood Gundy Capital
Kilicaslan, Erkan—Iris Capital Management (FKA: Part'Com Management S.A.)
Killackey, Christopher—Prairie Capital
Killen, Heather—Hemisphere Capital LLC
Killilea, Alison—W Capital Partners
Kilroy, Kenneth—Stone Canyon Venture Partners (SCVP)
Kilroy, William—Portal Capital LLC
Kilts, James—Centerview Partners Holdings LLC
Kim, Albert—Investor Growth Capital AB
Kim, Albert—Investor Growth Capital, Inc.
Kim, Anthony—Centerview Partners Holdings LLC
Kim, Brendon—Altos Ventures
Kim, Brian—Zephyr Management, L.P.
Kim, Chang-Ho—CBF Technology Investment Corporation
Kim, Chul-Joo—Myventure Partners, Inc.
Kim, Dal-je—Sejin T.S Co., Ltd. (FKA: Sejin Venture Capital Co., Ltd.)
Kim, David Younghoon—Daesung Private Equity, Inc.
Kim, David—Apax Partners Worldwide
Kim, David—Morgan Creek Capital Management LLC
Kim, Duksoo—Korea Venture Creative Investment Co., Ltd. (AKA: KVCI)
Kim, Edmund—M/C Venture Partners
Kim, Elmer—Whitecastle Investments
Kim, Eung-Suk—Mirae Asset Venture Investment Co., Ltd. (FKA:Korean Dream)
Kim, Gisik—Partners Venture Capital Co., Ltd.
Kim, Hakkyoon—LB Investment, Inc.
Kim, Hakkyun—Ray & Venture Investment Co., Ltd.
Kim, Han Seung—Myventure Partners, Inc.
Kim, Han—Altos Ventures
Kim, Harry—Skylake Incuvest & Company
Kim, Hee Chang—Boston Investment Company, Ltd.
Kim, Hong-Chae—LB Investment, Inc.
Kim, Hyun Woo—Boston Investment Company, Ltd.
Kim, Hyung-Kie—Lee & Company Investments
Kim, Jae—3i Group PLC
Kim, James—Carlyle Group, The
Kim, Jane—Thoma Cressey Bravo
Kim, Jang Yeon—Darby Overseas Investments, Ltd.
Kim, Jay—Myventure Partners, Inc.
Kim, Jeong-sik—Woongjin Capital Company
Kim, Ji Hoon—Korea Technology Investment Corporation (AKA: KTIC)
Kim, Jin Gyu—Skylake Incuvest & Company
Kim, Jinha—Lindeman Asia Investment
Kim, John—Burrill & Company
Kim, John—Capital Z Investment Partners (FKA: Union Square Partners)
Kim, John—Court Square Capital Partners
Kim, John—H.I.G. Capital LLC
Kim, John—MSD Capital L.P.
Kim, John—W Capital Partners
Kim, Jong-Won—Samsung Venture Investment Corporation (SVIC)
Kim, Jongpil—Korea Investment Partners Co., Ltd.
Kim, Jun Hong—Benex Investment, Inc.
Kim, Juyeon—Korea Biotech Investment Company, Ltd.
Kim, Kwangsoo—Sky Venture Capital
Kim, Kyu—KTB Ventures
Kim, Kyu-Tae—KTB Securities Co., Ltd. (FKA: KTB Network Co., Ltd.)
Kim, Kyung-Bae—Poibos Venture Capital
Kim, Leo—POSCO BioVentures
Kim, Leonard—Capital International Research, Inc.
Kim, Lisa—Development Principles Group, Ltd.
Kim, Mickey—Canaan Partners
Kim, Myengki—InterVest Co., Ltd.
Kim, Oh Jin—Hanju Investment Corp.
Kim, Paul—Parakletos@Ventures
Kim, Philip—Lincolnshire Management, Inc.
Kim, Sarah—Clayton, Dubilier & Rice, Inc.
Kim, Sarah—Halyard Partners
Kim, Se-Hyeon—Korea Technology Investment Corporation (AKA: KTIC)
Kim, Sean—STIC Investments, Inc.
Kim, Seunghan—Teachiworld Venture Investment Company, Ltd.
Kim, Shane—Camden Partners, Inc. (FKA: Cahill, Warnock & Co. LLC)
Kim, Shincheon—L&S Venture Capital Corporation
Kim, Tae-won—Neoplux Company, Ltd.
Kim, Timothy—AIG Investment Corporation, (Asia) Ltd.
Kim, Un Tae—Munhwa Investment Corporation (AKA: Comet Investment)
Kim, Wanshik—STIC Investments, Inc.
Kim, Woo-Han—Myventure Partners, Inc.
Kim, Wung—STIC Investments, Inc.
Kim, Y.Vincent—Aberdare Ventures
Kim, Yang-Jin—Samsung Venture Investment Corporation (SVIC)
Kim, Yong-Moon—Mirae Asset Venture Investment Co., Ltd. (FKA:Korean Dream)
Kim, Yoo Jin—Bain Capital
Kim, Young Ho—IMM Private Equity, Inc.
Kim, Young—LB Investment, Inc.
Kimberly, Adam—Montis Capital, LLC
Kimmel, Todd—Advanced Technology Ventures
Kimmel, Todd—Mayfield Fund
Kimmel, Wayne—SeventySix Capital
Kimura, Mikuni—Future Venture Capital Co., Ltd.
Kimura, Shinji—Private Equity Japan Co., Ltd.
Kimura, Yuji—Polaris Principal Finance Co., Ltd.
Kimzey, Jackie—Sevin Rosen Funds
Kincaid, Stacy—Probitas Partners, Inc.
Kincaid, Stacy—VinaCapital Investment Management Company
Kinder, Daniel—Park Avenue Equity Partners, L.P.
Kindle, Fred—Clayton, Dubilier & Rice, Inc.
Kindorf, William—Madison Capital Funding LLC (AKA: Madison Capital)
Kindtler, Jens W.—BankInvest Group A/S
King, Charles—Prudential Capital Group
King, David—Irving Place Capital
King, David—Quaker BioVentures, Inc.
King, Jason—Castile Ventures
King, Jennifer—Greer Capital Advisors LLC
King, John—New York Business Development Corporation
King, John—Perot Investments, Inc.
King, Mark—KRG Capital Partners LLC
King, Matthew—Clayton Associates LLC
King, Michael—GE Antares Capital Corporation
King, Neil—3i Group PLC
King, Stephen—Prairie Capital
King, Stephen—Unitas Capital Pte, Ltd.
King, Suzanne—New Enterprise Associates, Inc.
King, T. Scott—Sun Capital Partners, Inc.
Kingery, David—Carlyle Group, The
Kingsbury, Nick—3i Group PLC
Kingsbury, Raymond—Ancor Capital Partners
Kingsbury, Shaun—Hudson Capital Management, L.P.
Kingsland, Samuel—Granite Ventures LLC
Kingsley, Bill—EnerTech Capital
Kingston, Daniel—Vulcan Capital
Kinnear, Thomas—Arboretum Ventures
Kinnemann, Stephan—Deutsche Investitions- und Entwicklungsgesellschaft mbH
Kinning, Christel—RPE Capital Management (AKA: Retail Private Equity)
Kinsella, Kevin—Avalon Ventures
Kinserdal, Finn—Borea AS
Kinsey, Matthew—Boston Ventures Management, Inc.
Kinski, Mike—Terra Firma Capital Partners, Ltd.
Kinsman, Brian—Bunker Hill Capital

Kiper, Christopher—Shamrock Holdings, Inc.
Kipley, Christopher—Z Capital Partners LLC
Kipp, Dan—Winona Capital Management
Kippola, Tom—Voyager Capital
Kirby, Dennis—American Capital, Ltd.
Kirby, John—Blue Point Capital Partners (FKA: Key Equity Capital)
Kirby, Michael—Stonehenge Capital Company
Kirby, Steve—Bluestem Capital Partners
Kirchen, Christopher—BEV Capital (FKA: Brand Equity Ventures)
Kircher, Demian—Maranon Capital, L.P.
Kirchner, W.B.—Avrio Ventures Management Corp.
Kirdar, Nemir—Investcorp Bank B.S.C.
Kireker, Charles—FreshTracks Capital
Kirk, James—Corsair Capital LLC
Kirk, Julian—Third Security LLC
Kirk, Randal—Third Security LLC
Kirkbride, Brian—Health Evolution Partners LLC
Kirkman, Douglas—Blackstone Group, L.P.
Kirkman, Stuart—Here Be Dragons (HBD) Mgt Services (AKA:HBD Venture Capital)
Kirkpatrick, David—Abingworth Management, Ltd.
Kirkpatrick, David—SJF Ventures
Kirkpatrick, Doug—VantagePoint Venture Partners
Kirkpatrick, Harreld—Water Street Healthcare Partners
Kirkpatrick, Norm—Nibiru Capital
Kirova, Bistra—Axxess Capital Partners S.A. (FKA: Enterprise Capital)
Kirsch, Bill—Costella Kirsch, Inc.
Kirshner, Ori—Giza Venture Capital (FKA: Giza Investment Management)
Kirson, Ian—Wynnchurch Capital, Ltd.
Kirsten, Christopher—GCP Capital Partners
Kirsten, Rudo—GKA Bayete
Kirwan, Tom—Bank of Scotland Venture Capital (FKA: ICC Venture Capital)
Kirwin, John—Argosy Capital
Kishon, Eyal—Genesis Partners
Kislak, Jonathan—Antares Capital Corporation
Kisner, Daniel—Aberdare Ventures
Kissinger, Walter—TopSpin Partners
Kitao, Yoshitaka—SBI Capital Company, Ltd.
Kitchen, Garrison—CGW Southeast Partners (AKA: Cravey, Green, & Wahlen)
Kitterman, Roger—Mi3 Venture Partners
Kittler, Fred—Firelake Capital Management
Kitts, Robert—Thomas Weisel Partners Group, Inc.
Kitza, Wolfgang—3i Group PLC
Kivinen, Jaakko—Altor Equity Partners AB
Kivinen, Juuso—Sponsor Capital Oy
Kivinen, Juuso—Sponsor Capital Oy
Kiyohara, Akira—Mizuho Capital Company, Ltd.
Kjaergaard, Kent—ATP Private Equity Partners
Kjaergaard, Leif—Danisco Venture
Kjaernes, Jorgen—Cubera Private Equity AS
Kjellson, Nina—InterWest Partners
Kjerulf, Dan—Danske Private Equity A/S
Kjesbu, Geir Ove—Investinor AS
Klaassen, Merijin—Life Sciences Partners BV
Klaff, Larry—GB Merchant Partners, LLC (FKA: GB Palladin Capital LLC)
Klammer, Ronald—IT Matrix Ventures
Klapper, Paul—Clydesdale Ventures LLC
Klatsky, Bruce—LNK Partners
Klatt, Andrew—Charter Life Sciences
Klausner, Richard—Column Group, The
Klebanoff, Mark—Alexander Hutton Venture Partners
Kleberg, Scott—Private Equity Partners
Klebes, Daniel—Aetos Capital LLC
Kleeman, Merrick—Starwood Capital Group
Kleijwegt, Martijn—Life Sciences Partners BV
Klein, Adam—Crestview Partners L.P. (FKA: Crestview, LLC)
Klein, Adam—Palm Beach Capital Partners
Klein, Charles—American Securities Capital Partners LLC
Klein, Hans-Dieter—ACA Equity-Partners GmbH
Klein, Jason—Accel-KKR LLC
Klein, Justin—New Enterprise Associates, Inc.
Klein, Michael—Aetos Capital LLC
Klein, Michael—Littlejohn & Company LLC
Klein, Peter—Brockway Moran & Partners, Inc.
Klein, Robert—American Capital, Ltd.
Klein, Saul—Index Ventures
Klein, Todd—Legend Ventures LLC
Kleingarn, Holger—Palamon Capital Partners (FKA: Amphion Capital Partners)
Kleinhenz, Peter—CID Capital
Kleinke, Jon—Wynnchurch Capital, Ltd.
Kleinman, Ira—Harvest Partners LLC
Kleinman, Scott—Apollo Management
Kleiterp, Nanno—Netherlands Development Finance Company (AKA: FMO)
Klemmer, Jochen—AFINUM Management GmbH
Klepits, Thomas—IB Industrie-Beteiligungen GmbH
Klesch, Gary—Klesch Capital Partners
Klevens, Josh—Charlesbank Capital Partners LLC
Klim, Bart—Stanford Investment Group
Kliman, Gilbert—InterWest Partners
Klimczak, Sean—Blackstone Group, L.P.
Klimmeck, K. Thomas—Madison Capital Funding LLC (AKA: Madison Capital)
Kline, Charles—Century Capital Management, Inc.
Kline, Dean—Penn Venture Partners, LP
Kline, Frank—Kline Hawkes & Co.
Kline, Glenn—Battelle Ventures
Klinefelter, Josh—Aurora Capital Group (FKA: Aurora Capital Partners)
Klinge, John—Levine Leichtman Capital Partners, Inc.
Klingenstein, Paul—Aberdare Ventures
Klinger, Matthew—Stockwell Capital LLC
Klinsky, Steven—Forstmann Little & Company
Klintworth, William—DW Healthcare Partners
Klocanas, Philippe—Weinberg Capital Partners SAS
Klopfenstein, Gary—Mesirow Private Equity Investments, Inc.
Klopp, John—CT Investment Management Co. (AKA: Capital Trust)
Klopp, Mark—Coronis Medical Ventures
Klueger, Randy—Core Capital Partners
Kluger, Michael—Altaris Capital Partners LLC
Kluppel, Jochen—Grazia Equity GmbH
Kluzik, Janet—Gryphon Investors, Inc.
Klyce, Harvey—New Enterprise East Investments (AKA: NEEI)
Knapp, George—Stonewood Capital Management, Inc.
Knapp, Hans—Yaletown Venture Partners, Inc.
Knechtle, Tobias—Cinven, Ltd.
Kneen, John—Beecken, Petty & Company LLC
Knepley, Katie—SVB Capital
Knez, Brian—Castanea Partners
Knibb, Robert—Arlington Capital Partners
Knickel, Dave—HM Capital Partners LLC
Knight, J. Drexel—Parkway Capital Investors LLC
Knight, Lester—RoundTable Health Care Partners
Knight, Stephen—Beacon Bioventures
Knights, Julian—Ironbridge Capital Pty., Ltd.
Knoch, Douglas—Code, Hennessy & Simmons LLC
Knoff, S. Thomas—New York Life Capital Partners (AKA: NYLCAP)
Knorr, Robert—Mid Europa Partners
Knott, F. Stuart—Spring Capital Partners (FKA: Spring Capital Investors LLC)
Knott, Julian—Cognetas LLP
Knowles, Steve—Astellas Venture Capital
Knox, Elliott—Bedford Capital
Knox, Robert—Triangle Capital Corporation
Knudsen, Thomas Weilby—IVS A/S (AKA: Internet Ventures Scandinavia A/S)
Knudsen, Thomas Weilby—NorthCap Partners ApS
Knuff, William—Tano Capital LLC
Knutsson, Carl—Adrea i Malmo AB
Ko, Alex—Piper Jaffray Ventures
Ko, Peter Pil Jae—H&Q Asia Pacific
Kob, Randall—Prudential Capital Group
Kobayashi, Eizo—Itochu Corporation
Kobayashi, Kaoru—Yasuda Enterprise Development Co., Ltd.(FKA: Nippon Ent.Dev)
Kobayashi, Kazuo—Biofrontier Partners, Inc.
Kobayashi, Naomi—Capital International Research, Inc.
Kobrin, Shaun—Dancap Private Equity Inc.
Koby, Michael—Galen Associates
Kobza, John—Hall Capital Partners, L.P.
Kocen, Ari David—Stonehenge Capital Company
Koch, Albert—Questor Management Company LLC
Koch, Edward—Praesidian Capital, LLC
Koch, Klaus—Vicente Capital Partners
Koch, Michael—Scandinavian Financial Management AB
Koch, Robert—NGEN Partners LLC (FKA: NextGen Partners LLC)
Kochhaeuser, Andreas—EiKaM GmbH & Co. KG
Kocsi, Patrick—GE Commercial Finance - Equity
Koczkar, Rob—Pacific Equity Partners
Kodar, Martin—Baltcap
Kodde, Pieter—Lincolnshire Management, Inc.
Koehler, Gert—Creathor Venture Management GmbH
Koehler, Stephen—Barclays Private Equity, Ltd.
Koen, Philip—Savvis, Inc. (FKA: Savvis Communications)
Koeneman, Keith—Dresner Partners (FKA: Dresner Capital Resources, Inc.)
Koeneman, Keith—Kingsman Capital LLC
Koenig, Anja—Novartis Venture Fund (FKA: Novartis Corp.)
Koenig, Michael—Hamilton Lane Advisors, Inc.
Koenig, Olav—Capital Dynamics AG
Koenig, Peggy—ABRY Partners LLC
Koenig, Stuart—Apollo Real Estate Advisors
Koenigsberger, Rick—Apollo Real Estate Advisors
Koeppen, Kai—Riverside Company

Koertge, Matthew—Accede Capital
Koffler, Michael—Versa Capital Management (FKA: Chrysalis Capital Partners)
Koffler, Peter—Blackstone Group, L.P.
Koffman, Lori—Solera Capital, LLC
Kofler, Sebastian—Mountain Super Angel AG
Koga, Max—Entrepia Ventures, Inc.
Koga, Shigeaki—H&Q Asia Pacific
Kogan, Sam—Gen 3 Partners
Koh, Eng Hong—Aventures Capital Management Pte Ltd.
Koh, Judy—Bay City Capital LLC
Koh, Soo Boon—iGlobe Partners, Ltd.
Kohara, Takayuki—Daiwa Quantum Capital, Ltd.
Kohlberg, Jerome—Kohlberg & Company LLC
Kohleick, Reinhard—Quadriga Capital
Kohler, Will—Summerhill Venture Partners
Kohler, William—Prism VentureWorks
Kohlhaas, Jochen—TechnoStart GmbH
Kohn, Ben—Rizvi Traverse Management, LLC
Koike, Michael—Angelo, Gordon & Company
Koike, Satoshi—NGI Group (AKA: Netage Capital Partners, Inc.)
Koit, Carl-Henrik—Iteksa Venture AB
Koivisto, Heikki—Helmet Business Mentors Oy
Kojima, Akio—Information Technology Farm Corporation (AKA: IT Farm)
Kok, Wendy—Longreach Group, Ltd., The
Kokesh, Charles—Technology Funding
Kokkinen, Antti—BlueRun Ventures
Kokorotsikos, Paris—Incubation For Growth
Kola, Vani—NEA-IndoUS Capital Advisors Pvt. Ltd.
Kolada, David Harris—Jefferson Partners
Kolade, Wol—ISIS Equity Partners PLC
Kolb, Uwe—Bridgepoint Capital, Ltd.
Kolb, Uwe—Permira Advisers LLP
Kolber, Jonathan—Viola Private Equity
Kolbinger, Thomas—Siemens Venture Capital GmbH
Koldyke, Laird—Winona Capital Management
Koldyke, Martin—Frontenac Company
Kolesza, Olga Maria—CRP (AKA: Companhia de Participacoes)
Kollatz-Ahnen, Matthias—European Investment Bank, The (AKA: EIB)
Kollender, Richard—Quaker BioVentures, Inc.
Koller, Hans-Peter—M2 Capital Management AG
Kolln, Thies—Aavin Equity Advisors LLC
Kolluri, Krishna—New Enterprise Associates, Inc.
Kolodyuk, Andriy—AVentures
Kolodziejcyk, Richard—Essex Woodlands Health Ventures
Koltes, Steve—CVC Capital Partners (Europe), Ltd.
Koltin, Yigal—Concord Ventures (FKA: Nitzanim)
Koman, Juraj—HKK Partners
Kometz, Avi—Ascent Biomedical Ventures
Komisar, Randy—Kleiner Perkins Caufield & Byers
Komiya, Kazuyoshi—CAS Capital, Inc.
Komiya, Yuji—Tokio Marine Capital Company, Ltd.
Komori, Kazutaka—Tokio Marine Capital Company, Ltd.
Kondamoori, Bob—Sandalwood Capital Partners
Koneru, Harisha—PPM America Capital Partners LLC
Koneval, William—Parallax Capital Partners LLC
Kong, Garheng—Intersouth Partners
Kong, In Wook—Shinbo Investment Corporation
Kong, Qiang—Beijing Bingyuan Venture Capital Co., Ltd.
Kong, Sam—Pacific Equity Partners
Kong, Yani—Nature Elements Capital
Kongsted, Paul-Christian—Inventure Capital A/S
Konno, Takaaki—Yasuda Enterprise Development Co., Ltd.(FKA: Nippon Ent.Dev)
Konopka, Kathleen—GE Commercial Finance - Equity
Konrad, Robert—KT Capital Management LLC
Konrath, Daniela—Pantheon Ventures, Ltd.
Kontogouris, Venetia—Trident Capital
Koo, Angelo—China Development Industrial Bank (CDIB)
Koo, Bo-Hoi—Lee & Company Investments
Koo, Bon-Yong—KTB Securities Co., Ltd. (FKA: KTB Network Co., Ltd.)
Koo, Bonwan—LB Investment, Inc.
Koo, Bonwoong—Harbor Pacific Capital LLC
Koo, Brian—LB Investment, Inc.
Koo, David—RoundTable Health Care Partners
Koo, Jason—LB Investment, Inc.
Kooijman, Mark—Development Principles Group, Ltd.
Kook, Grant—Westcap Management, Ltd.
Kook, Jason—STIC Investments, Inc.
Koontz, Paul—Foundation Capital
Koop, Hans Jochen—Leonardo Venture GmbH & Co. KGaA
Koopman, Edward—Cognetas LLP
Kopans, Haim—JVP
Kopchinsky, Gregory—Canaan Partners
Kopeikin, Michael—UNC Kenan-Flagler Private Equity Fund
Kopelman, Joshua—First Round Capital
Kopelman, Michael—Edison Venture Fund
Koplovitz, Jonathan—Blackstone Group, L.P.
Koplovitz, Kay—Boldcap Ventures LLC
Koplowitz, Alicia—Omega Capital SL
Kopple, Elizabeth—Bounty Equity Fund LLC
Koppler, Doit—Third Security LLC
Kopylov, Denis—Ineko Capital Partners LLP
Korangy, Shervin—Blackstone Group, L.P.
Korati, Arun Prakash—IL&FS Investment Managers Ltd (FKA: IL&FS Venture Corp)
Korczak, James—Adams Street Partners LLC
Kordes, Olaf—Alpha Group
Korff, Campbell—Avenue Capital Group
Korn, Douglas—Irving Place Capital
Kornblit, Mitchell—Shattuck Hammond Partners
Kornelus, Chelutka—Martinson Trigon Venture Partners AS
Korngold, Jonathan—General Atlantic LLC
Kornmann, Brian—Thompson Street Capital Partners
Korpala, Jacek—Arx Equity Partners
Korsholm, Peter—EQT Funds management Limited
Korsvold, Age—Kistefos Venture Capital AS
Kortela, Risto—Helmet Business Mentors Oy
Korthout, Constant—Robeco Private Equity
Kortick, Daniel—Wicks Group of Companies LLC, The
Kortschak, Walter—Summit Partners
Korver, Clint—Crescendo Venture Management LLC
Korver, Michael—Global Venture Capital, Inc.
Koselka, Petra—Shell Internet Ventures
Koskinas, Ellen—InterWest Partners
Kosloff, David—Frazier Healthcare and Technology Ventures
Koslow, Michael—Desert Cedars, LLC
Koslow, Patricia—Desert Cedars, LLC
Kosofsky, Kristen—Horizon Technology Finance Management LLC
Kosonen, Mikko—Sitra
Kosoy, Daniel—Athenian Venture Partners
Kossmann, Thomas—Prosperitas Capital Partners
Koster, Matthew—Bush O'Donnell Capital Partners
Kostuchenko, Malcolm—Enhanced Equity Fund, L.P.
Kostyashkin, Andrey—Baring Vostok Capital Partners
Kotak, Uday—Kotak Investment Advisors, Ltd. (AKA: KPEG)
Kothari, Dilip—Olympus Capital Holdings Asia
Kothari, Nikhil—DTA Capital
Kothari, Rajesh—Seneca Partners, Inc.
Kotler, Steve—Watermill Group, The
Kotush, Brad—Canaccord Genuity
Kotynski, Dan—Concentric Equity Partners, L.P.
Kotz, Peter—Gridiron Capital LLC
Kotzubei, Jacok—Platinum Equity LLC
Koulogeorge, Mark—MK Capital
Kourtis, George—Global Finance SA
Koutoupes, Nikitas—Insight Venture Partners
Kovac, Caroline—Burrill & Company
Kovach, Jeffrey—Arsenal Capital Partners
Kovalkova, Anna—Pharos Capital Group LLC
Kovas, Edward—Lake Capital Partners, Inc.
Koven, Gustav—Smith Defieux Capital Partners
Koven, James—One Equity Partners (FKA: Banc One Venture Partners)
Kowal, Andrew—Francisco Partners
Kowalska, Agnieszka—Enterprise Investors Sp z oo
Kox, Georg—Intelligent Venture Capital Management GmbH
Koyfman, Mo—Spark Capital
Koza, Eric—Verax Capital Partners LLC
Kozina, Anna—Baring Vostok Capital Partners
Kozlowski, James—TGF Management Corp (FKA:Texas Growth Fund)
Kozun, Wayne—Ontario Teachers' Pension Plan
Kracum, Richard—Wind Point Partners
Kraemer, Andreas—Cognetas LLP
Kraft Le Marec, Catherine—Centre Capital Developpement SA
Kraft Le Marec, Catherine—Groupe Sofimac
Kraft, Jonathan—Kraft Group, The
Kraft, Robert—Kraft Group, The
Krahwinkler, Johannes—Capexit Beteiligungsmanagement AG
Krall, Phillip—Gleacher & Co.
Kramer, Andrea—Hamilton Lane Advisors, Inc.
Kramer, Bob—AAC Capital Partners
Kramer, Caleb—Oaktree Capital Management LLC
Kramer, Edward—NGEN Partners LLC (FKA: NextGen Partners LLC)
Kramer, Jordan—Kaiser Permanente Ventures
Kramer, Manfred—Investitions- und Strukturbank Rheinland-Pfalz (ISB) GmbH
Kramer, Marc—Fenway Partners, Inc.
Kramer, Nathaniel—Mercantile Capital Group (MCG)
Kramer, Robert—Altitude Capital Partners

Kramer, Robert—RockBridge Equity Partners LLC
Kramer, Ted—Hammond Kennedy Whitney & Co
Kramlich, C. Richard—New Enterprise Associates, Inc.
Kranz, Michael—Leapfrog Ventures
Kranzler, Daniel—eFund, LLC
Krasnov, Gregory—Innova Capital
Krasnow, David—Funk Ventures, Inc.
Kratus, Patrick—Montgomery & Co. (FKA: Digital Coast Partners)
Kraus, Laura—MFC Capital Funding, Inc.
Kraus, Matthew—Celerity Partners
Kraus, Stephen—Bessemer Venture Partners
Krause, Peter—GCP Capital Partners
Krause, Wolfgang—Seventure Partners SA (FKA: SPEF Venture)
Krauss, Marlene—KBL Healthcare Ventures
Krauss, P. Eric—Pilot House Ventures Group, LLC
Krausz, Steven—U.S. Venture Partners
Kravis, Henry—Kohlberg, Kravis, Roberts & Company, L.P.
Krawchuk, Stephen—Crystal Capital
Krawczyk, Krzysztof—Innova Capital
Kreager, JT—NCT Ventures LLC
Krebs, Alexander—Capvis Equity Partners AG
Kreher, Daniel—Warson Capital Partners
Kreidler, Robert—Fidus Capital
Kreie, Paul—Midwest Mezzanine Funds
Kreilein, David—Sun Capital Partners, Inc.
Kreimer, Thomas—GMB Mezzanine Capital, L.P.
Kreindl, Torsten—Grazia Equity GmbH
Krekel, David—Pacific Horizon Ventures LLC
Kremer, Kai—High Tech Venture Partners GmbH
Kremer, William—CrossHarbor Capital Partners LLC
Krempel, Jon—Peninsula Capital Partners LLC
Krems, Mike—Pacific Corporate Group
Krentz, Jeff—Critical Capital Growth Fund, LP
Krenz, Thomas—Permira Advisers LLP
Kressel, Henry—Warburg Pincus LLC
Kretz, Nikolaus—ProRegio Mittelstandsfinanzierungs AG
Kreutzer, Idar—Storebrand Alternative Investments ASA
Krichevsky, Eugene—American Capital, Ltd.
Krieger, David—Warburg Pincus LLC
Krieger, Erik—Riverlake Partners LLC
Krieger, Sanford—AEA Investors LP
Krieglstein, Stefan—Andlinger & Company, Inc.
Kriens, Scott—Juniper Networks
Krikorian, Jason—DCM
Krindel, Yaffa—Star Ventures Management GmbH & Co. KG
Krishna, Nety—Redpoint Ventures
Krishna, Vikram—GMT Communications Partners LLP
Krishnamurthy, Balaji—QInvest LLC
Krishnamurthy, K. G.—HDFC Venture Capital, Ltd.
Krishnamurthy, Pavan—Ojas Venture Partners
Krishnan, Anand—Dubai International Capital LLC
Krishnan, Krish—Third Security LLC
Krishnan, Sanjeev—Global Environment Fund Management Corporation
Krista, Karl—gcp gamma capital partners Beratungs- & Beteiligungs AG
Kristoffersen, Jan—Norinnova Forvaltning AS
Krna, Matt—Investor Growth Capital, Inc.
Kro, Lisa—Goldner Hawn Johnson & Morrison, Inc.
Krocke, Ingo—AUCTUS Capital Partners AG
Kroeger, Christopher—Aurora Funds, Inc.
Kroeze, Peter—H2 Equity Partners BV
Krogh, Lars—Convexa Capital AS
Kroin, David—Great Point Partners LLC
Kroizer, Israel—Israel Cleantech Ventures
Krol, Sebastian—Enterprise Investors Sp z oo
Kroll, Gabriela—Square Four Investments GmbH
Kronabel, Cristoph—Heidelberg Innovation GmbH
Kronborg, Gregers—Northzone Ventures AS (FKA: Venture Partners AS)
Kronfol, Mohieddine—Algebra Capital
Krongard, Cheryl—Apollo Management
Krongard, Timothy—QuestMark Partners, L.P.
Krouse, Rodger—Sun Capital Partners, Inc.
Krow, Peter—Vector Capital
Krueger, Alex—First Reserve Corporation
Krueger, Harvey—Stockton Partners
Kruetten, Rainer—WealthCap Initiatoren GmbH
Krug, Antonie—Siparex Group SAS
Kruger, Gert—GKA Bayete
Krugler, Bill—Mason Wells Private Equity (FKA: M&I Ventures)
Krull, Ken—Mercato Partners
Krumov, George—Equest Partners, Ltd.
Krumpfes, Austin—PPM America Capital Partners LLC
Krumrei, Brian—TSG Consumer Partners
Krupka, Michael—Bain Capital
Krupka, Michael—Bain Capital Ventures
Kruse, Jon—Intel Capital
Kruse, Kevin—Warburg Pincus LLC
Krusen, W. Andrew—Westshore Capital Partners
Kruth, Hal—QinetiQ Ventures Ltd
Kuan Yew, Lee—China-Singapore Suzhou Industrial Park
Kuan, Cheo Hock—Temasek Holdings Pvt., Ltd.
Kuan, Leon—Fisher Lynch Capital
Kuan, Michael—GGV Capital
Kuan, Roy—CVC Asia Pacific, Ltd.
Kuan, Roy—CVC Capital Partners (Europe), Ltd.
Kuang, Duane—Qiming Venture Partners
Kuang, Lan—Beijing Tianyi Huirong Investment Management Co., Ltd.
Kubal, Larry—Labrador Ventures
Kubes, Daniel—Shoreview Industries
Kubitz, Ralf—nwk Kapitalbeteiligungsgesellschaft der Sparkasse Bremen
Kubler, Sebastian—Taishan Invest AG
Kubo, Tatsuya—HarbourVest Partners LLC
Kubr, Thomas—Capital Dynamics AG
Kucha, Michael—Timeline Ventures LLC
Kucher, Marcia—Sunrise Financial Group, Inc.
Kuczek, David—Holtzbrinck Ventures GmbH
Kuder, Joshua—FCP Investors
Kudsi, Khaled—Blackstone Group, L.P.
Kuehl, Ronald—Frontenac Company
Kuehl, Timothy—Norwest Equity Partners
Kuehni, Christian—WealthCap Initiatoren GmbH
Kues, Matthias—Nord Holding Unternehmensbeteiligungsgesellschaft mbH
Kuflik, Mitchell—Brahman Management, LLC
Kuhling, Robert—ONSET Ventures
Kuhlmann, Frederic—Nord Capital Partenaires SAS
Kuijten, Rene—Life Sciences Partners BV
Kukenov, Talgat—Aureos Capital, Ltd.
Kukutai, Arama—Finistere Ventures LLC
Kulakofsky, David—Madison Capital Funding LLC (AKA: Madison Capital)
Kulawik, Maryline—ELAIA Partners
Kulig, Krzysztof—Innova Capital
Kulmala, Pentti—Helmet Business Mentors Oy
Kulvik, Pauli—Helmet Business Mentors Oy
Kumada, Tsuneo—Japan Asia Investment Company, Ltd. (AKA: JAIC)
Kumagai, Koh—Tohoku Innovation Capital Corp.
Kumano, Hideaki—Tokyo Small & Medium Business Investment & Consultation Co.
Kumar, Anurag—Jacob Ballas Capital India Pvt, Ltd. (AKA:JBC)
Kumar, Ashish—AIG Investment Corporation, (Asia) Ltd.
Kumar, Manu—K9 Ventures
Kumar, Neetesh—Rho Capital Partners, Inc.
Kumar, Samir—Inventus Capital Partners
Kumar, Suketu—ICICI Venture Funds Management Co., Pvt. Ltd. (FKA: TDICI)
Kumar-Sinha, Punita—Blackstone Group, L.P.
Kumble, Steven—Corinthian Capital Group LLC
Kumin, Michael—Great Hill Equity Partners LLC
Kummerer, Kenneth—Milestone Partners
Kump, Eric—Carlyle Group, The
Kump, Eric—Dubai International Capital LLC
Kumpulainen, Mikko—Pohjola Capital Partners Oy
Kumthekar, Kunal—Nine Rivers Capital Management, Ltd. (AKA: NRCM)
Kuncl, Jim—MFC Capital Funding, Inc.
Kunder, Thomas—Heliad Equity Partners GmbH & Co. KGaA
Kundra, Monish—Columbia Capital LLC
Kundur, C. Shekhar—VenturEast (FKA: APIDC Venture Capital Limited)
Kung, Bill—General Catalyst Partners (FKA: General Catalyst Group LLC)
Kung, Hsing—Acorn Campus Ventures
Kung, Kuo-Chuan—MBK Partners
Kunhart, John—American River Ventures
Kunica, Matt—Birch Hill Equity Partners Management, Inc.
Kunkel, Mark—Technology Venture Partners
Kunse, Jim—El Dorado Ventures
Kunstler, Julie—Portview Communications Ltd
Kuntz, Richard—Shepherd Ventures
Kuntz, William—Vance Street Capital LLC
Kunz, Kevin—AV Labs
Kunz, Kevin—Austin Ventures, L.P.
Kuo, Andrew—Blackstone Group, L.P.
Kuo, Frank—Yuanta Venture Capital
Kuo, Steve—Hercules Technology Growth Capital, Inc.
Kuo, Tom—Berkshire Partners LLC
Kuparinen, Mikko—Canelco Capital Oy
Kupor, Scott—Andreessen Horowitz
Kuppam, Sudheer—Intel Capital
Kupper, Hans A.—Global Life Science Ventures GmbH
Kuprasov, Alexander—Horizon Capital
Kurdziel, Michael—ARC China, Inc.
Kure, Sussane—Vaekstfonden (AKA: Danish Growth Fund, The)
Kurian, Jacob—New Silk Route Partners LLC

Kurimoto, Kiichiro—Chuo Mitsui Capital Co., Ltd.
Kurkijarvi, Kalevi—Bio Fund Management Oy
Kurkilahti, Lasse—Helmet Business Mentors Oy
Kurkure, Sunil—Darwin Ventures LLC
Kuroda, Keigo—Blackstone Group, L.P.
Kuroda, Yoshito—Mitsui & Co. Venture Partners (MCVP)
Kurosaki, Morio—Information Technology Farm Corporation (AKA: IT Farm)
Kurosawa, Yoichiro—New Horizon Capital Co., Ltd.
Kurpatow, Christoffer—Askembla Asset Management AB
Kurtenbach, Jim—Prairie Oak Capital LLC
Kurti, Albin—Propel Investments
Kurtin, Eve—Pacific Venture Group
Kurtin, Eve—VantagePoint Venture Partners
Kurtz, Evan—American Capital, Ltd.
Kurtz, Karl-Rudolf—BASF Future Business GmbH
Kurtzman, Gary—Safeguard Scientifics, Inc.
Kuruvilla, Finny—Clarus Ventures
Kurylo, Steve—Ironside Capital Group (FKA:Ironside Ventures LLC)
Kurz, Karl—CCMP Capital Advisors LLC
Kusik, Martin—Penta Investments, Ltd.
Kusio, Daniel—BV Holding AG
Kusnir, Peter—Slavia Capital
Kusserow, Paul—Ziegler HealthVest Management LLC
Kuta, Pavel—PPF Investments, Ltd.
Kutner, Asher—Carmel Ventures
Kutsenda, Eric—Seidler Equity Partners
Kuwahara, Michio—Marubeni Corporation
Kuykendall, Kevin—American Capital, Ltd.
Kvamme, Mark—Sequoia Capital
Kvistsand, Hege Kristine—Viking Venture Management AS
Kwak, Christine—Shorenstein Company LLC
Kwak, DG—STIC Investments, Inc.
Kwak, Dongguel—STIC Investments, Inc.
Kwan, Allan—Oak Investment Partners
Kwan, Arthur—Thomas Weisel Partners Group, Inc.
Kwan, Dick—BPEP International
Kwatinetz, Michael—Azure Capital Partners
Kwee, Andrew—LGT Capital Partners AG
Kwee, Hoe Boon—SEAVI Advent Corporation, Ltd.
Kwei, Randy—Shaw Kwei & Partners
Kwiecien, Tomasz—Mezzanine Management Finanz- und Unternehmensberatungs GmbH
Kwik, Derek—AsiaTech Internet Group (ATIG) (FKA: AsiaTech Ventures)
Kwok, Steven—Credit Suisse Private Equity
Kwok, Steven—Orchid Asia Group Management, Ltd.
Kwok, Stuart—Harbor Pacific Capital LLC
Kwok, Van—U.S. Venture Partners
Kwon, Don—Michigan Venture Capital Co., Ltd.
Kwon, Myoung-Ok—Nextech Venture AG
Kwon, OhSang—Avista Capital Holdings, L.P.
Kwon, Sungcheol—Korea Venture Investment Corporation
Kwon, Yongwon—Kiwoom Investment Company, Ltd.
Kwong William Chan, Chein—CIAM Group Limited
Kwong, Clement—ARC Capital Partners, Ltd. (AKA: ARC Capital)
Kyle, Andrew—SpringBank TechVentures
Kypriano, Robert—AXA Investment Managers
Kyriacou, Panos—Pangaea Ventures
Kyriopoulos, Christopher—Clayton Associates LLC
L Her, Jean-Francois—CDP Capital - Technology Ventures (FKA: CDP Sofinov)
L Heureux, Alexandre—Celtic Therapeutics Management, L.L.L.P.
La Voun, Veronica—Hamilton Investments
LaBelle, Curt—Tullis Health Investors (FKA: Tullis-Dickerson & Co., Inc.)
LaBran, Renee—Rustic Canyon Partners
LaCroix, Minette—SI Ventures
LaFayette, Justin—Georgian Partners
LaFayette, William—Asia Alternatives Management LLC
LaFayette, William—Spring Ridge Ventures
LaHaye, Frank—Peregrine Ventures, LP
LaNasa, Whitney—Stonehenge Capital Company
LaPeer, Karl—Peninsula Capital Partners LLC
LaPoint, William—Halpern, Denny & Company
LaPorte, Kathleen—New Leaf Venture Partners LLC
LaPorte, Steve—ONSET Ventures
LaRobordier, M.—Stanford Investment Group
LaRowe, James—Nautic Partners LLC
LaRue, David—Symphony Asia Holdings Pte. Ltd.
LaRussa, Benny—Azalea Capital LLC
LaSalle, Michael—Shamrock Holdings, Inc.
LaViolette, Paul—SV Life Sciences Advisers
Laats, Alex—Commonwealth Capital Ventures
Labatt, Nina—Health Evolution Partners LLC
Labe, Jim—TriplePoint Capital
Label, Justin—Bessemer Venture Partners
Labib, Taimoor—Standard Chartered Private Equity, Ltd.
Labouret, Alexandre—Platina Partners LLP
Labrum, Brandon—Sterling Partners
Labrunie, Guy—CEA Valorisation SA
Lacasse, Louis—GeneChem Financial Corporation
Lacenere, Anthony—iNetworks, LLC
Lachance, JP—KCA Partners, Ltd.
Lachman, Charles—Corporate Fuel Partners
Lack, David—Austin Ventures, L.P.
Lackler, Rick—Houlihan, Lokey, Howard & Zukin
Lacob, Joseph—Kleiner Perkins Caufield & Byers
Lacourte, Joel—Astorg Partners SAS (FKA : Suez Capital Partenaires)
Lacroix, Jacques—Echo Capital
Lacroix, Martial—GeneChem Financial Corporation
Lacy, Craig—Madison Capital Funding LLC (AKA: Madison Capital)
Ladak, Amin—Seaflower Ventures
Ladak, Zuher—Falconhead Capital (FKA: Sports Capital Partners)
Ladd, David—Mayfield Fund
Ladd, Robert—Laminar Direct Capital, L.P.
Ladha, Farouk—Four Rivers Partners
Ladriere, Bruno—AXA Private Equity
Lafaurie, Philippe—Franche-Comte PME Gestion
Laffitte, Pierre—Sophia Euro Lab SAS
Laffy, Laurent—Arts Alliance Advisors
Laflamme, Karen—CDP Capital - Technology Ventures (FKA: CDP Sofinov)
Lafley, A—Procter & Gamble Company, The
Lafreniere, Pierre—Investissement Quebec
Lagae, F—Sopartec SA (AKA: Vives)
Lagarde, Jean-Yves—Boston Millennia Partners
Lagarde, Michael—JLL Partners (FKA: Joseph, Littlejohn & Levy, Inc.)
Lagerlof, Ingemar—LinkMed AB
Lagerlund, Karin—HarbourVest Partners LLC
Lagod, Martin—Firelake Capital Management
Lagreze, Julien—OpenGate Capital
Lague, Come—Nueva Ventures
Laguerre, Kristen—Atlas Venture, Ltd.
Lahann, Greg—Novus Ventures
Lahmann, Kai—Waterland Private Equity Investments B.V.
Lahmar, Sofiane—Development Partners International
Lahmar, Sofiane—Kingdom Zephyr Africa Management (AKA: KZAM)
Lahmar, Sofiane—Zephyr Management, L.P.
Lahoty, Ruchir—ICICI Venture Funds Management Co., Pvt. Ltd. (FKA: TDICI)
Lahoty, Ruchir—New Enterprise Associates, Inc.
Lahoud, Abdallah—MerchantBridge & Co., Ltd.
Lai, Carey—Institutional Venture Partners
Lai, David—UBS Capital Corporation
Lai, Juanita—Mingly Capital
Lai, Pak-Seng—Auda Private Equity LLC
Lai, Ted—iD Ventures America, LLC (AKA: Acer Technology Ventures)
Lai, Yidrienne—Technology Crossover Ventures
Laine, Markus—Eqvitec Partners Oy
Lainee, Francois—Auriga Partners S.A.
Laino, Peter—Monitor Clipper Partners LLC
Lainovic, Sacha—TMG Capital Partners Ltd.
Laird, Chris—Ventures West Management, Inc.
Laird, Doug—Formative Ventures
Lais, Helen—AlpInvest Partners N.V.
Laitala, Chris—H.I.G. Capital LLC
Laitala, Christopher—Great Point Partners LLC
Lajous, Rene—Cambria Group, The
Lake, Barry—Vinco Capital, Inc.
Lake, Fred—New Media Innovation Centre
Lakes, Alexis—RWI Ventures
Lakhanpal, Bharat—Oaktree Capital Management LLC
Lal, Nityen—ICOS Capital
Lal, Ranjan—Mosaix Ventures
Lalande, Kevin—Sante Ventures
Lalley, John—Kirtland Capital Partners
Lally, Brenda Lee—Pfingsten Partners, L.P.
Lalonde, Chris—Century Capital Management, Inc.
Lalude, Yemi—Adlevo Capital Managers LLC
Lam, Alvin—CVC Asia Pacific, Ltd.
Lam, Alvin—CVC Capital Partners (Europe), Ltd.
Lam, Chihtsung—Axiom Asia Private Capital
Lam, Chivas—Qiming Venture Partners
Lam, Cynthia—Draper Richards, L.P.
Lam, David—DynaFund Ventures LLC
Lam, David—WI Harper Group
Lam, Don—VinaCapital Investment Management Company
Lam, Gordon—Citi Venture Capital International
Lam, Michelle—Bain Capital Ventures
Lam, Rachel—Undisclosed Firm
Lam, Tsui Sung—Shaw Kwei & Partners
Lam, Van—Merit Capital Partners (FKA:William Blair Mezzanine)
Lamarche, Regis—21 Centrale Partners
Lamarche, Regis—21 Partners SpA

Lavirotte, Jean-Marie—Perfectis Private Equity
Lavoie, Armand—Foragen Technologies Management
Lavolle, Bruno—Azulis Capital (FKA:Banexi Capital Partenaires)
Law, Janson—SAIF Partners
Law, Shane—Patron Capital, Ltd.
Law, Warren—China OperVestors, Inc.
Lawaetz, Henrik—SLS Invest AB
Lawani, Tope—Helios Investment Partners LLP
Lawhorne, Donald—Pacesetter Capital Group (FKA: MESBIC Ventures Holding Co.)
Lawler, Christopher—Graham Partners, Inc.
Lawler, Kenneth—Battery Ventures, L.P.
Lawlor, Augustine—HealthCare Ventures LLC
Lawrence, Frederick—Shepherd Ventures
Lawrence, Ken—Gresham LLP
Lawrence, Larry—Allegra Partners (FKA: Lawrence, Smith & Horey)
Lawrence, Peter—Pod Venture Partners Inc.
Lawrence, Shane—NBC Capital Pty., Ltd.
Lawry, Seth—Thomas H. Lee Partners (AKA: TH Lee Partners)
Lawson, Peter—NBC Capital Pty., Ltd.
Lawson, Richard—Huntsman Gay Global Capital LLC
Lawson, Richard—Sorenson Capital Partners
Lax Banon, Enrique—Clayton, Dubilier & Rice, Inc.
Lax, Andrew—Blackstone Group, L.P.
Lax, Charles—GrandBanks Capital
Lax, Leo—Skypoint Capital Corporation
Lax, Solomon—CS Capital Partners LLC
Lay, Michael—ONCAP Investment Partners
Lay, William—Stonehenge Capital Company
Layden, Christopher—York Street Capital Partners LLC
Layman, Bonnie—Intersouth Partners
Layther, Mark—Colony Capital LLC
Layton, Casey—DCA Partners, Inc.
Layton, Tim—Sorenson Capital Partners
Lazaro, Delfin—Narra Venture Capital
Lazarus, Edmund—Englefield Capital
Lazarus, Michael—Weston Presidio (FKA: Weston Presidio Capital Management)
Lazarus, Steven—ARCH Venture Partners
Lazarus, Xavier—ELAIA Partners
Lazell, Brian—Renaissance Capital
Le Blanc, Robert—Onex Corporation
Le Bourdiec, Mariane—Sagard SAS
Le Chevallier, Denis—Undisclosed Firm
Le Granche, Patrick—Premiers Pas
Le Guennou, Vincent—EMP Africa Fund Management (AKA: Emerging Capital Partners)
Le Marie, Alexis—Cinven, Ltd.
Le Merle, Matthew—Monitor Venture Management, L.L.C.
Le Meur, Loic—Wellington Partners Venture Capital GmbH
Le Roux, JP—Newfarmers Developement Company
Le Sueur, Gary—Scottish Equity Partners
LeBaron, Matthew—American Securities Capital Partners LLC
LeBlanc, Matthew—ArcLight Capital
LeComte, Pierre—TSG Consumer Partners
LeFaivre, Rick—OVP Venture Partners
LeFlore, Maggie—MedImmune Ventures
LeMay, John—Blue Point Capital Partners (FKA: Key Equity Capital)
LeSage Krause, Jacqueline—Hartford Ventures
LeSieur, Jean-Marc—HBM BioVentures AG (FKA: HBM Partners AG)
LeSieur, Steven—Spectrum Equity Investors
Lea, Lyndon—Lion Capital (FKA: Hicks Muse (Europe))
Leach, Jason—Sun Capital Partners, Inc.
Leach, Juan—Miura Private Equity SGECR, S.A.
Leach, Ray—JumpStart, Inc.
Leach, Robert—Tenex Greenhouse Ventures
Leader, Lennert—Time Warner Investments (FKA: AOL Time Warner Ventures)
Leake, Nan—Partners Group AG
Leary, Dennis—Champlain Capital Management LLC
Leary, Dominic—Hastings Private Equity
Leathers, David—Abingworth Management, Ltd.
Leathers, Eric—Pine Brook Road Partners LLC
Leblanc, Bertrand—Innoven Partenaires S.A.
Lebowitz, Steve—TopSpin Partners
Lebret, Herve—Index Ventures
Lebreton, Valerie—MML Capital Partners
Lebus, Andrew—Pantheon Ventures, Ltd.
Lebus, Timothy—Duke Street Capital
Lecaldano, Edoardo—Alice Ventures Srl
Lechelle, Luc—Dassault Developpement
Leck, Derek—American Industrial Partners
Leckie, Lars—Hummer Winblad Venture Partners
Leclerc, Olivier—SGAM Private Equity
Leclercq, Arnaud—Actem Partners SA (FKA: SPEF LBO)
Lecoeur, Jerome—Innovacom SA
Leconte, Didier—MSBi Valorisation
Lecueder, Carlos—Prosperitas Capital Partners
Ledbetter, Carl—Pelion Venture Partners
Leder, Marc—Sun Capital Partners, Inc.
Lederman, Marc—NewSpring Capital
Ledford, Gregory—Carlyle Group, The
Lee Jae, Woo—Vogo Investment
Lee, Aileen—Kleiner Perkins Caufield & Byers
Lee, Alan You—Macquarie Direct Investment Ltd.
Lee, Alan—Wolseley Private Equity
Lee, Andrew—Battery Ventures, L.P.
Lee, Andrew—Good Energies, Inc.
Lee, Angela—Cardinal Venture Capital
Lee, Anthony—Altos Ventures
Lee, Carol—Entropy Ventures, Ltd.
Lee, Chew Mok—SPRING SEEDS Capital Pte, Ltd.
Lee, Christophe—SHK Fund Management, Ltd.
Lee, Christopher—PineBridge Investments
Lee, Chul-Joo—Affinity Equity Partners
Lee, DH—STIC Investments, Inc.
Lee, Daniel—STIC Investments, Inc.
Lee, David—Baseline Ventures LLC
Lee, David—Clarity Partners
Lee, David—Roark Capital Group
Lee, David—STIC Investments, Inc.
Lee, David—Siguler Guff & Company
Lee, David—Skylake Incuvest & Company
Lee, Derrick Meow Chan—Advent International
Lee, Derrick Meow Chan—SEAVI Advent Corporation, Ltd.
Lee, Derrick—Bessemer Venture Partners
Lee, Desmond—Telopea Capital Partners Pty, Ltd.
Lee, Dorothy—Carlyle Group, The
Lee, Edan—Olympus Capital Holdings Asia
Lee, Eric—Welsh, Carson, Anderson & Stowe
Lee, Franny—AsiaVest Partners, TCW/YFY Ltd. (FKA: TCW/YFY Investment)
Lee, George—Octane Capital Management
Lee, Georgia—Hellman & Friedman LLC
Lee, Gina—Pantheon Ventures, Ltd.
Lee, Grace—JAFCO Investment (Hong Kong), Ltd.
Lee, Griffith—American Capital, Ltd.
Lee, Hak-Hyun—M-Venture Investment, Inc. (FKA: Shinyoung Venture Capital)
Lee, Hee-gyoo—LB Investment, Inc.
Lee, Ho Chan—KTB Ventures
Lee, Hyunkeun—LB Investment, Inc.
Lee, Jack—Whitesun Equity Partners
Lee, James—Blackstone Group, L.P.
Lee, James—Hunt Special Situations Group
Lee, James—WI Harper Group
Lee, Jane—Blackstone Group, L.P.
Lee, Janet—Invus Group Ltd., The
Lee, Jason Jeongseok—LB Investment, Inc.
Lee, Jason—Carlyle Group, The
Lee, Jeffrey—Northern Light Venture Capital
Lee, Jenny—GGV Capital
Lee, Jenny—Global Catalyst Partners
Lee, John—Blackstone Group, L.P.
Lee, Jong Gap—Neoplux Company, Ltd.
Lee, Jong Won (John)—H&Q Asia Pacific
Lee, Jongrim—Saehan Venture Capital
Lee, Jongsu—Fitech Venture Partners Company, Ltd.
Lee, Joong Suk—ATVentures, Inc. (FKA: August Tiger Ventures, Inc.)
Lee, Joseph—Riverside Company
Lee, Jung-Jin—H&Q Asia Pacific
Lee, Kai-Fu—Innovation Works
Lee, Kangsuk—Skylake Incuvest & Company
Lee, Kenn—Pacific Corporate Group
Lee, Kenneth—Hatteras Venture Partners (FKA:Catalysta Partners)
Lee, Kewsong—Warburg Pincus LLC
Lee, Kheng Nam—GGV Capital
Lee, Larry—Equity 11, Ltd.
Lee, Matthew—IDG Ventures Korea
Lee, Michael—Dominion Ventures, Inc.
Lee, Michael—Shanghai ZhongZhi Venture Capital Co., Ltd.
Lee, Michael—Unilever Ventures, Ltd. (AKA: Unilever NV)
Lee, Min-Hwa—Muhan Investment Co. (FKA: TeraSource Venture Capital Co.)
Lee, Nancy—Alsop Louie Partners
Lee, Patrick—Advent Venture Partners LLP
Lee, Peter—Baroda Ventures LLC
Lee, Peter—DynaFund Ventures LLC
Lee, Randall—CVC Capital Partners (Europe), Ltd.
Lee, Rene—3V SourceOne Capital Pte, Ltd.
Lee, Robert Y.C.—Inter-Asia Venture Management
Lee, Robert—KT Venture Group LLC
Lee, Roger—Battery Ventures, L.P.
Lee, SK—STIC Investments, Inc.
Lee, Sam—Finaventures
Lee, Sam—Infinity Capital LLC
Lee, Sam—Peninsula Ventures
Lee, Sam—STIC Investments, Inc.

Liu, Jesse—Arlington Capital Partners
Liu, Jian—Zhongshan Technology Innovation Invest. Management Co., Ltd.
Liu, Johnson—CSV Capital Partners (FKA: China Seed Ventures)
Liu, Lawrence—China Development Industrial Bank (CDIB)
Liu, Louie—AsiaTech Management LLC
Liu, Peigu—Get Capital
Liu, Pyramyth—iD Ventures America, LLC (AKA: Acer Technology Ventures)
Liu, Qing—Shenzhen OFC Investment Management, Ltd.
Liu, Roy—Hercules Technology Growth Capital, Inc.
Liu, Sheldon—Clarity Partners
Liu, Speed—Unitas Capital Pte, Ltd.
Liu, Tim—SOFTBANK China Venture Capital
Liu, Tingru—Infotech Pacific Ventures L.P. (FKA: Infotech Ventures Co.)
Liu, Weihan—Nokia Growth Partners
Liu, Weijin—Infotech Pacific Ventures L.P. (FKA: Infotech Ventures Co.)
Liu, Xiaoping—CITIC Capital Partners, Ltd.
Liu, Xiaoren—Holding Venture Capital, Ltd.
Liu, Yangxin—Milestone Capital Management, Ltd.
Liu, Yao—Chengdu Beyond Capital Management Co., Ltd.
Liu, Zhou—Shenzhen Fortune Venture Capital Co., Ltd.
Lium, Gretchen—Headwaters Merchant Bank
Livingston, Jessica—Y Combinator
Livingston, Richard—Leasing Technologies International, Inc.
Livingstone, Elly—Pantheon Ventures, Ltd.
Livnat, Zvi—Clal Venture Capital Management, Ltd. (AKA: CVC Management)
Livne, Yigal—China Israel Value Capital (AKA: CIVC)
Livne, Yigal—Platinum-Neurone Ventures
Lizotte, Pierre—Coradin, Inc.
Ljungman, Mattias—Atomico Ventures
Llewellyn-Lloyd, John—Noble Fund Managers, Ltd.
Llovera, Bernardo—Expansion Capital Partners LLC
Lloyd, Alexander—Accelerator Ventures
Lloyd, Ronald—Romspen Investment Corporation
Lloyd-Harris, Genghis—Abingworth Management, Ltd.
Lo, Lisa—CID Group, The
Lo, Ramon—Symphony Asia Holdings Pte. Ltd.
Lo, Wayne—China Venture Management, Inc.
LoGerfo, James—Earthrise Capital Partners LLC
LoRusso, Matthew—Carlyle Group, The
Loader, Adrian—Allegro Private Equity Pty, Ltd.
Loarie, Robert—Morgan Stanley Venture Partners (AKA: MSDW)
Lobel, David—Sentinel Capital Partners
Lobo, Richard—Code, Hennessy & Simmons LLC
Lobo, Vernon—Mosaic Venture Partners
Lobstein, Romain—Massena Capital Partners
Locher, Erwin—BioMedPartners
Locke, Ian—Jefferson Partners
Lockhart, H. Eugene—Oak Investment Partners
Lockhart, James—Greenhill SAVP
Lockhart, Sandy—Next Capital Pty., Ltd.
Lockwood, Greg—UBS Capital Corporation
Lockwood, Jeffrey—Brown Brothers Harriman & Company (AKA: BBH)
Lodewijk, Enneus—Greenfield Capital Partners
Lodge, Andrew—Relativity Capital LLC
Loe, Bente—TeleVenture Management AS (FKA: Telenor Venture AS)
Loechner, Reinhard—VENTIZZ Capital Partners Advisory AG
Loew, Guenther Paul—Impera Total Return AG
Loffer, Franklin—Sand Hill Capital
Logan, Jeffrey—J.P. Morgan Partners (FKA: Chase Capital Partners)
Logan, Mary—Capital Royalty Partners
Logan, William—Apax Partners Worldwide
Logsdon, Jason—Gateway City Capital, Inc.
Logue, Genie—Rosemont Investment Partners LLC
Loh Nahmias, Vivian—Glynn Capital Management
Loh, John—Birch Hill Equity Partners Management, Inc.
Loh, Leslie—Extream Ventures Pte, Ltd.
Loh, Terry—AIG Investment Corporation, (Asia) Ltd.
Lohezic, Francoise—Techfund Capital Europe Management SAS
Lohmus, Rain—GILD Bankers (FKA: LHV Ventures)
Lohrasbpour, Esfandiar—Invesco Private Capital
Lohser, Marc—Auda Private Equity LLC
Loke, Wai San—BPEP International
Lokey, O. Kit—Houlihan, Lokey, Howard & Zukin
Lomas, Eric—HT Capital Advisors LLC
Lomas, Pedro—Torreal SCR SA
Lomasky, Jeffrey—Cerberus Capital Management, L.P.
Lombard, Sophie—PAI Partners (FKA: PAI Management)
Lombard, Stuart—JLA Ventures (FKA: J.L. Albright Venture Partners)
Lombardi, Gregory—Landmark Partners, Inc.
Lomtadze, Michael—Baring Vostok Capital Partners
Londal, Douglas—New Mountain Capital LLC
Lonergan, Simon—Behrman Capital
Long McAndrews, Susan—Pantheon Ventures, Ltd.
Long, Ashley—GMT Communications Partners LLP
Long, Brian—Atlantic Bridge
Long, Elizabeth—ARCH Development Partners LLC
Long, Greg—Maranon Capital, L.P.
Long, Jeffrey—Commonfund Capital, Inc. (FKA: Common Fund)
Long, Jeffrey—Vestar Capital Partners, Inc.
Long, Jim—Gabriel Venture Partners
Long, John—Trellis Partners
Long, Julia—Here Be Dragons (HBD) Mgt Services (AKA:HBD Venture Capital)
Long, Michael—CGW Southeast Partners (AKA: Cravey, Green, & Wahlen)
Long, Michael—GIV Venture Partners (AKA: Global Internet Ventures)
Long, Robert—Allied Capital Corporation
Long, Samuel—Pinpoint Ventures
Long, T. Michael—Brown Brothers Harriman & Company (AKA: BBH)
Long, Tim—Lionheart Ventures
Longbottom, Wayne—Kestrel Capital (FKA: Nanyang Ventures Pty., Ltd.)
Longosz, Joseph—Golub Capital
Lonnevig, Jonas-Graff—LinkMed AB
Lonnqvist, Anders—Huvudkontoret i Kristinehamn AB
Lonnqvist, Markku—Pamplona Capital Management LLP
Loo, Hock Voon—Walden International
Look, Blair—Al Mal Capital
Loomans, Jeffrey—Sierra Ventures
Loomes, Ben—GCP Capital Partners
Loop, Floyd—Radius Ventures LLC
Loose, Steven—Audax Group
Lopez del Hierro, Ignacio—Thesan Capital
Lopez, Johnny—Platinum Equity LLC
Lopez-Cruz, Daniel—Investcorp Bank B.S.C.
Lopez-Figueroa, Manuel—Bay City Capital LLC
Lopez-Quesada, Alfonso—Minerva Capital
Lopez-Quesada, Juan—Bridgepoint Capital, Ltd.
Lora, Luis Francisco—Palladium Equity Partners LLC
Lorang, Gilles—Argos Soditic SA
Lordi, Frank—Trestle Ventures
Lorente, Pilar—Arsenal Capital Partners
Lorenti, Richard—Shattuck Hammond Partners
Lorentz, Jorgen—Borea AS
Lorenz, Gene—Tasman Capital Partners
Lorenzen, Christian—Langholm Capital LLP
Lorenzet, Sonia—Alcedo SGR SpA
Lorenzini, Robert—NGEN Partners LLC (FKA: NextGen Partners LLC)
Lorenzotti, Lorenzo—ACG Private Equity (FKA: Altium Capital Gestion)
Lori, Mathew—New Mountain Capital LLC
Loring, Ian—Bain Capital
Lorphelin, Xavier—Serena Capital SAS
Lorraine, Peter—Brown Brothers Harriman & Company (AKA: BBH)
Lorsch, David—Calera Capital (FKA: Fremont Partners)
Loschner, Klaus—Bayern Kapital GmbH
Losorelli, Lou—Freeman Spogli & Co.
Lothrop, Donald—Delphi Ventures
Lou, Edward—OCA Venture Partners
Lou, Lin—Origo Partners PLC
Lou, Samuel—China Capital Management Company, Ltd.
Lou, Yunli—Milestone Capital Management, Ltd.
Loudon, Mclean Owen—McLean Watson Capital Inc.
Loughlin, Philip—Bain Capital
Loughlin, Sam—CCG Venture Partners, LLC
Loughrey, Gavin—Alchemy Partners LLP
Loughridge, Mark—IBM Corporation
Louie, Gilman—Alsop Louie Partners
Louie, Mark—C.M. Capital Corporation
Louie, Mark—Mingly Capital
Louis, Robin—Ventures West Management, Inc.
Loukianoff, Peter—Almaz Capital Partners
Louren da Rosa, Wilson—Advent International
Louv, Robert—Montgomery & Co. (FKA: Digital Coast Partners)
Loux, Jacques—Alto Invest
Love, Colleen—Castanea Partners
Lovejoy, William—Bain Capital
Lovell, Evan—Virgin Green Fund
Loven, Paul A.—F. van Lanschot Participaties BV
Loverro, Frank—Kelso & Company
Loveys, Harry—Capital Royalty Partners
Low, Jeff—Ericsson Venture Partners
Low, Michael—Shackleton Ventures, Ltd.
Low, Nathan—Sunrise Financial Group, Inc.
Lowcock, Nicholas—Warburg Pincus LLC

Lowder, Maya—Hall Capital Partners, L.P.
Lowe, David—Skyline Ventures
Lowe, Esme—Climate Change Capital, Ltd.
Lowell, Paul—TopSpin Partners
Lowery, Jim—Eastman Ventures
Lowery, Stephen—Frog Capital, Ltd.
Lowinger, Andrew—DMC Capital Funding LLC
Lowitt, Ian—Lehman Brothers, Inc.
Loy, Trevor—Flywheel Ventures
Loyd, Lamar—Millennium Ventures LLC
Lozow, Matthew—Behrman Capital
Lozowick, Pini—Alta Berkeley Venture Partners
Lu, Allen—Fudan Quantum Venture Capital Management Co., Ltd.
Lu, Chunwei—Beijing Zhengrun Investment Co., Ltd. (AKA: Prope)
Lu, Frank—iD TechVentures, Inc. (FKA: Acer Technology Ventures)
Lu, James—iD Ventures America, LLC (AKA: Acer Technology Ventures)
Lu, Jianhua—Regal Investment
Lu, Li—Himalaya Capital
Lu, Luke—Fortune Venture Investment Group (AKA:Fortune Consulting)
Lu, Mei—SinoLatin Capital
Lu, Ming—J.P. Morgan Partners (FKA: Chase Capital Partners)
Lu, Ming—Kohlberg, Kravis, Roberts & Company, L.P.
Lu, Peter—Infinity Venture Capital Fund (AKA: Israel Infinity Fund)
Lu, Rick—Whitesun Equity Partners
Lu, Robert—Wuhan Huagong Venture Capital Co., Ltd.
Lu, Ruby—DCM
Lu, Teddy—iD Innovation, Inc.
Lu, Vincent—Blackstone Group, L.P.
Lu, Wei—Cybernaut (China) Capital Management
Lu, Wenyi—Beijing Capital Investment Co., Ltd.
Lu, Yuebing—Climate Change Capital, Ltd.
Lubash, Barbara—Versant Ventures
Lubash, Ron—Markstone Capital
Lubbehusen, Michael—MAZ level one GmbH
Lubert, Ira—LLR Partners, Inc.
Lubert, Ira—Quaker BioVentures, Inc.
Lubin, Daniel—Radius Ventures LLC
Lubin, Gary—Pharma Capital Ventures (AKA: PCV)
Lubin, Richard—Berkshire Partners LLC
Lubsen, Walter—Stuart Mill Capital, Inc.
Luby, William—Seaport Capital, LLC
Lucas, Donald—Lucas Venture Group LLC
Lucas, Ken—GF Private Equity Group, LLC
Lucas, Rob—CVC Capital Partners (Europe), Ltd.
Lucas, Stuart—Bracken Partners Limited
Lucchese, Joseph—Oasis Capital Partners LLC
Luce, Michael—Harbert Management Corporation
Luce, Michael—Harbert Venture Partners
Lucey, Kevin—Hamilton Lane Advisors, Inc.
Luck, Pascal—Core Capital Partners
Lucke, Joseph—Tricor Pacific Capital, Inc.
Ludemann, Peter—Pinnacle Investment Management Pty, Ltd.
Ludlow, Anthony—Baymark Partners
Ludwig, Georg—HighTech Private Equity GmbH
Ludwig, John—Ignition Partners (FKA: Ignition Corporation)
Ludwig, Mark—Sorenson Capital Partners
Ludwig, Thomas—Francisco Partners
Luedde, F.W.—GulfStar Group
Luehrs, Bruce—Emerald Stage2 Ventures (AKA: Stage2 Capital Ventures)
Luehrs, Bruce—Penn Valley Group
Luetchens, Shawn—Saffron Hill Ventures
Luh, Jenchyn—C.M. Capital Corporation
Luh, Tony—DragonVenture, Inc.
Lui, Danny—Authosis Ventures
Lui, Danny—Startup Capital Ventures L.P.
Luk, Raymond—Flow Ventures
Lukac, Zeljko—Quaestus Private Equity, Ltd.
Lukaczyk, Laura—Avansis Ventures, LLC
Lukas, Daniel—GSC Partners (FKA: Greenwich Street Capital Partners)
Lukatch, Heath—Novo A/S
Luke, Robert—GED Group
Lukkariniemi, Ilkka—TeknoVenture Management Oy
Lum, Philip—iGlobe Treasury Management, Ltd.
Lump, Bill—Prism Capital
Lunati, Thierry—Agregator Gestion SAS
Lund, David—Hercules Technology Growth Capital, Inc.
Lund, Morten—Draper Fisher Jurvetson ePlanet Ventures, L.P.
Lund, Ray—Dyad Partners
Lund, Simon—HarbourVest Partners LLC
Lundberg, Linus—Vision Capital Management
Lundblom, Stefan—Lunova AB
Lundefaret, Helge—Borea AS
Lundgren, Gosta—NAXS Nordic Access Buyout Fund AB
Lundgren, Petter—Deseven Catalyst Group AB
Lundin, Hans—Integra Ventures
Lundin, Hans—SmartForest Ventures
Lundstrom, Bill—Arcapita, Inc.
Lung, Friedrich—Bull Capital Partners Ltd.
Lung, James—VenGlobal Capital
Lung, Wendy—IBM Corporation
Lunia, Anand—Seedfund
Lunn, Randall—Palomar Ventures
Lunsford, William—Copeley Capital Partners
Luo, Angela—Centenium-Pinetree China Private Equity
Luo, Fei—Shenzhen Green Pine Capital Partners Co., Ltd.
Luo, Guoliang—Sichuan Shizhi Investment Co., Ltd.
Luo, Michael—Hony Capital Ltd.
Luo, Wei Hong—Fair Value Investment (AKA: Shanghai Anyi Investment)
Luo, Yi—Carlyle Group, The
Lupa, Mark—High Country Venture LLC
Lupton, James—GCP Capital Partners
Luscombe, Roger C.—Continental Capital Partners, Ltd.
Lusser, Harald—HVB Russell Management GmbH
Lussier, James—Norwest Venture Partners
Lustbader, Michael—Arlington Capital Partners
Luthria, Avinash—Gaja Capital Partners
Lutsi, John—Morgenthaler Ventures
Lutz, Christian—gcp gamma capital partners Beratungs- & Beteiligungs AG
Lutz, Claude—Massena Capital Partners
Lutzenberger, Hermann—Andlinger & Company, Inc.
Lutzke, Scott—Centerfield Capital Partners
Lutzker, Joshua—Berkshire Partners LLC
Lux, Steven—Stonehenge Capital Company
Luyanchuk, Mikhail—Oradell Capital
Lv, Gangzheng—Zhongshan Technology Innovation Invest. Management Co., Ltd.
Ly, Eric—Wellington Partners Venture Capital GmbH
Ly, Hoang Duy—STIC Investments, Inc.
Lyall, Les—GrowthWorks
Lyall, Les—Kirchner Private Capital Group
Lyford, Avery—Signal Lake
Lyle, Nick—Blackstone Group, L.P.
Lyle, Rupert—3i Group PLC
Lyman, Art—MASI, Ltd.
Lynch, Christopher—Ascent Venture Partners
Lynch, Daniel—3TS Capital Partners, Ltd.
Lynch, John—Paracor Capital Advisors Pvt., Ltd.
Lynch, Jonathan—CCMP Capital Advisors LLC
Lynch, Jonathan—J.P. Morgan Partners (FKA: Chase Capital Partners)
Lynch, Kevin—Emerge Venture Capital (AKA: Emerge VC)
Lynch, Kevin—Equinox Capital, Inc.
Lynch, Linda—Fisher Lynch Capital
Lynch, Michael—GSC Partners (FKA: Greenwich Street Capital Partners)
Lynch, Nancy—Scale Venture Partners
Lynch, Ralph—Sun Capital Partners, Inc.
Lynden, Sean—Gold Hill Capital Management LLC
Lyne, Timothy—GE Antares Capital Corporation
Lynett, Patty—Blackstone Group, L.P.
Lynn, Michael—Adams Street Partners LLC
Lynn, Rebecca—Morgenthaler Ventures
Lynn, Williard—Gryphon Investors, Inc.
Lyon, Adam—Canaccord Genuity
Lyon, Cliff—Avante Mezzanine Partners
Lyon, Clifford—Celerity Partners
Lyon, Kevin—3i Group PLC
Lyon-Mercado, Peter—Crescent Capital Partners
Lyons, Martina—STAR Capital Partners, Ltd.
Lyons, Michael—Lincolnshire Management, Inc.
Lyons, Michael—Paladin Capital Management LLC
Lyons, Nicholas—Longbow Capital
Lyons, Peter—Leeds Equity Partners
Lyritzis, Sotiris—Summit Partners
Lyttleton, Stephen—Lion Chemical Capital
Lytton, Michael—Oxford Bioscience Partners
MIller, James—Brown Gibbons Lang & Company LLC
Ma, Adrianna—General Atlantic LLC
Ma, Christine—Unitas Capital Pte, Ltd.
Ma, Connie—American Securities Capital Partners LLC
Ma, Dong Bing—Fair Value Investment (AKA: Shanghai Anyi Investment)
Ma, Feihong—Hina Capital Partners
Ma, Huateng—Draper Fisher Jurvetson ePlanet Ventures, L.P.
Ma, Hui Hsing—TVM Capital GmbH
Ma, Jiong—Braemar Energy Ventures
Ma, Larry—Jade Alternative Investment Advisors
Ma, Mary—TPG Capital
Ma, Melissa—Asia Alternatives Management LLC
Ma, Mingzhe—Ping An Bright Fortune Investment Management Company
Maalouf, Khalil—XPV Capital Corporation
Maar Pavia, Rosina—Pappas Ventures

Maartman-Moe, Erling—Alliance Venture AS
Mabbs, Kenneth—FA Technology Ventures
Mabuza, Busi—Ethos Private Equity
MacAllister, Neil—Galen Associates
MacBean, Mick—TriWest Capital Management Corporation
MacColl, Tim—Larsen MacColl Partners
MacCormack, Suzanne—Ampersand Ventures
MacDonald, Jeffrey—First Reserve Corporation
MacDonald, Lane—Alta Communications
MacDonald, Mark—C.A. Bancorp, Inc.
MacDonald, Scott—Emerald Technology Ventures AG
MacDonnell, Robert—Kohlberg, Kravis, Roberts & Company, L.P.
MacDougall, Neil—Silverfleet Capital (FKA: PPM Capital Partners)
MacDowell, Jeffrey—American Capital, Ltd.
MacFarlane, Bruce—Aquiline Capital Partners
MacInnis, Robert—ABRY Partners LLC
MacIntyre, James—NextPoint Partners, L.P.
MacIntyre, John—Birch Hill Equity Partners Management, Inc.
MacKeigan, Dan—Tudor Ventures
MacKenzie, Adrian—CVC Asia Pacific, Ltd.
MacKenzie, Adrian—CVC Capital Partners (Europe), Ltd.
MacKenzie, Helen—Gabriel Venture Partners
MacKenzie, Stuart—Carlyle Group, The
MacKenzie, Timothy—Merit Capital Partners (FKA:William Blair Mezzanine)
MacLean, Todd—Bain Capital
MacLellan, David—RJD Partners Limited (FKA: Royal London Private Equity)
MacLellan, Robert—TD Capital Group, Ltd.
MacLennan, Donald—Foresight Group
MacLennan, Mark—SVB Capital
MacLeod, Ken—Paul Capital Partners
MacLeod, Scott—Global Environment Fund Management Corporation
MacMillan, Charles—Early Stage Partners, L.P.
MacNaughton, Bruce—Crosslink Capital
MacNaughton, Torquil—Penta Capital LLP (FKA: Penta Capital Partners, Ltd.)
MacNay, Nick—CBPE Capital, LLP (AKA: Close Brothers Private Equity, Ltd.)
MacQuitty, Jonathan—Abingworth Management, Ltd.
MacRae, Bruce—Hastings Equity Partners LLC
MacTaggart, Ian—Brynwood Partners L.P.
MacTavish, Mark—ONCAP Investment Partners
Macatangay, Jason—Valor Equity Partners
Macaulay, William—First Reserve Corporation
Maccarone, Justin—Allied Capital Corporation
Macdonald, Andy—FirstMark Capital LLC
Macdonald, Jacqueline—Sippl Macdonald Ventures
Macdonald, James—First Analysis Corporation
Macdonald, Kevin—Morgenthaler Ventures
Macedo, Evangeline—Aravis SA
Macejko, Thomas—Madison Dearborn Partners LLC
Macey, M. William—Sterling Investment Partners
Macfarlane, Bruce—MMC Ventures, Ltd.
Macfie, Andy—Teasses Capital, Ltd.
Machado, Eduardo—Carlyle Group, The
Machado, Joseph—Morgenthaler Ventures
Machemehl, David—Crispian Venture Capital, LLC
Machiels, Alec—Pegasus Capital Advisors, L.P.
Macho, Jose Luis—Thesan Capital
Machuca, Jose—Qualitas Equity Partners
Macintosh, John—Warburg Pincus LLC
Mack, John—Egis Capital Partners LLC
Mack, John—Morgan Stanley Private Equity
Mack, Richard—Apollo Real Estate Advisors
Mack, Roszell—Ascend Venture Group LLC
Mack, Wayne—Alta Communications
Mackay, Alan—3i Group PLC
Mackay, Martin—Add Partners, Ltd.
Mackenzie, Davin—Telopea Capital Partners Pty, Ltd.
Mackenzie, Donald—CVC Capital Partners (Europe), Ltd.
Mackenzie, Douglas—Kleiner Perkins Caufield & Byers
Mackenzie, Douglas—Radar Partners
Mackenzie, Hamish—PAI Partners (FKA: PAI Management)
Mackenzie, Stuart—Ethos Private Equity
Mackesy, D. Scott—Welsh, Carson, Anderson & Stowe
Mackewicz, Detlef—Triginta Capital Partners GmbH (FKA: Avida Equity Partners)
Mackey, Jason—Canadian Medical Discoveries Fund
Macki, Haythem—GrowthGate Capital Corporation
Mackie, George—Noro-Moseley Partners
Mackin, John—Highland Capital Management, L.P.
Mackintosh, Alistair—Actis Capital LLP
Macklin, Chris—NBD Sana Capital
Macklin, Rodd—American Capital, Ltd.
Mackowski, J. Matthew—Telegraph Hill Partners (AKA: THP)
Macks, Lawrence—Boulder Ventures, Ltd.
Macksey, R. Alan—Sterling Partners
Mackworth, Hugh—SmartForest Ventures
Maclean, Colin—Sentient Group, The
Maclean, Ken—CORE Partners, Inc.
Maclean, Richard—Frontier Capital LLC
Macleod, Mark—Climate Change Capital, Ltd.
Macomber, Earl—Noson Lawen Partners LLC
Macpherson, Alex—Octopus Asset Management, Ltd.
Macpherson, Alexander—Katalyst Ventures Limited
Macpherson, Angus—Noble Fund Managers, Ltd.
Macquin, Nicolas—Alpha Group
Mactaggart, Terry—Fairwater Growth Resources, Inc.
Macuga, Daniel—Invencor, Inc.
Macy, Rick—Czura Thornton
Madan, Arunesh—Global Investment House
Madavi, Syrus—Walden International
Madden, Claire—Connection Capital LLP
Madden, Jim—Accretive LLC (FKA: Accretive Technology Partners LLC)
Maddin, Keith—Cabot Square Capital, Ltd.
Mader, Martin—Fabrel Lotos (AKA: Fabrel AG)
Madera, Paul—Meritech Capital Partners
Madersbacher, Georg—Orlando Capital Management GmbH
Madi, Khalid—Al Mal Capital
Madianos, Mihalis—Global Finance SA
Madorsky, Jon—RCP Advisors LLC
Madrid, Christopher—New Mexico Community Capital
Madridejos, Lorenzo—Arcano Capital
Madsen, Cora—Nordic Biotech Advisors APS
Madsen, Dion—Physic Ventures
Madsen, Kent—EPIC Ventures
Maeder, Paul—Highland Capital Partners LLC
Maene, Frank—Big Bang Ventures CVA
Maenhout, Peter—GIMV N.V.
Maerkle, Rainer—Holtzbrinck Ventures GmbH
Maestroni, Roberto—Investindustrial Partners, Ltd.
Maeuser, Goetz—Permira Advisers LLP
Magami, Steven—ARC China, Inc.
Magana, Daryl—Cybernaut (China) Capital Management
Magas, Pete—Beecken, Petty & Company LLC
Magdol, David—Main Street Capital Corporation
Magee, Wilson—Colony Capital LLC
Maggs, Roger—Celtic House Venture Partners
Maghami, Cyrus—Shackleton Equity Partners LLC
Magid, Kevin—Audax Group
Magida, Stephen—Andlinger & Company, Inc.
Magill, Bill—TeleSoft Partners
Magliacano, Marc—Catterton Partners
Magliano, John—Blackstone Group, L.P.
Magnano, Ben—Frazier Healthcare and Technology Ventures
Magnoni, Roberto—MPS VENTURE Societa di Gestione del Risparmio SpA
Magnus, Brian—Morgan Stanley Private Equity
Magnus, Edward—Madison Dearborn Partners LLC
Magnussen, Espen—Icon Capital Group AS
Mago, Gautam—Sequoia Capital India (FKA: WestBridge Capital Partners)
Magowan, Peter—Alta Berkeley Venture Partners
Maguire, Gerry—Atlantic Bridge
Maguy, Billy—Alpine Investors, L.P.
Magwood, Rob—Thomas Weisel Partners Group, Inc.
Mahadeva, Kumar—Kubera Partners, LLC
Mahan, Christopher—AEA Investors LP
Maharzi, Imene—Butler Capital Partners SA
Maher, Anthony—Star Ventures Management GmbH & Co. KG
Maher, Dan—ACT Venture Capital, Ltd.
Maher, Fintan—Growcorp Group, Ltd.
Maher, James—Park Avenue Equity Partners, L.P.
Maher, Jo Anne—Propel Investments
Maher, Peter—Ontario Teachers' Pension Plan
Maheshwari, Abhishek—Kubera Partners, LLC
Maheshwari, Sachin—Draper Fisher Jurvetson
Maheshwari, Sanjiv—Basil Growth Corporation
Mahn, Tammy—Pitango Venture Capital (FKA:Polaris Venture Capital Israel)
Mahomey, James—Huron Capital Partners LLC
Mahon, David—GE Antares Capital Corporation
Mahoney, James—Investcorp Bank B.S.C.
Mahoney, Pamela—Mohr Davidow Ventures
Mai, Vanessa—Lionheart Ventures
Maidenberg, Ted—U.S. Venture Partners
Maidment, Adam—GCP Capital Partners
Maigaard, Michael—Danske Private Equity A/S
Maila, Michel—International Finance Corporation
Mait, David—Odyssey Investment Partners, LLC
Majekodunmi, Abayomi—Reliance Bank
Majors, Michael—BEV Capital (FKA: Brand Equity Ventures)
Mak, Cecilia—Pacific Alliance Capital Group

Mak, Phil—VenGlobal Capital
Makadia, Jay—Berkshire Partners LLC
Makansi, Henry—Warburg Pincus LLC
Makela, Manu—Conor Venture Partners Oy
Makhlouf, Magellan—Gulf Capital
Makhzoumi, Mohamad—New Enterprise Associates, Inc.
Maki, David—Altitude Life Science Management, LLC
Maki, Pekka Santeri—3TS Capital Partners, Ltd.
Makinen, Jukka—Eqvitec Partners Oy
Makoff, John—Unique Investment Corporation
Makower, Joshua—New Enterprise Associates, Inc.
Malabie, Phuti—Shanduka Fund Mangers (Pty) Ltd.
Malahieude, Eric—ACG Private Equity (FKA: Altium Capital Gestion)
Malcolm, Scott—Greenstone Partners Private Capital Pty, Ltd.
Maldonado, John—Advent International
Maldonado, Jose Maria—Bridgepoint Capital, Ltd.
Malfettone, John—Oak Hill Capital Management, Inc.
Malhance, Tariq—UIB Capital, Inc.
Malherbe, Josua—VenFin DD Holdings Ltd.
Malherbe, Paul—Business Partners
Malhotra, Arwind—Firm Factory Network
Malhotra, Naresh—Sequoia Capital India (FKA: WestBridge Capital Partners)
Malick, Joseph—NB Alternatives - Fund of Funds
Malik, Andrea—Arcapita, Inc.
Malik, Deepak—Cargill Ventures
Malik, Gaurav—Olympus Capital Holdings Asia
Malik, Om—True Ventures
Malik, Shahzad—Advent Venture Partners LLP
Maliszewski, Stanislaw—GSC Partners (FKA: Greenwich Street Capital Partners)
Maliwal, Rajiv—Standard Chartered Private Equity, Ltd.
Malizia, David—Westshore Capital Partners
Malka, Benjamin—North Hill Ventures
Malkani, Dhiraj—Rockport Capital Partners
Mallement, Harvey—Harvest Partners LLC
Mallet, Jacques—Auriga Partners S.A.
Mallin, Tony—STAR Capital Partners, Ltd.
Malling, Nicolai—Convexa Capital AS
Mallory, Joy—Colony Capital LLC
Malloy, Frederick—Intervale Capital
Malloy, John—BlueRun Ventures
Malm, David—Halpern, Denny & Company
Malm, David—Webster Capital Management, L.L.C.
Malofeev, Konstantin—Marshall Capital Partners
Malone, Hannah—Pantheon Ventures, Ltd.
Malone, James—Boyne Capital Partners LLC
Malone, Matt—Hunt Private Equity Group, Inc. (FKA: Hunt Financial Corp.)
Malone, Matthew—Winston Partners
Malone, Stephanie—Growth Capital Partners, L.P.
Maloney, Barry—Balderton Capital (FKA: Benchmark Capital Europe)
Maloney, Brian—Perot Investments, Inc.
Maloney, T.J.—Lincolnshire Management, Inc.
Maloney, Tim—Frye-Louis Capital Advisors LLC
Maltz, Jules—Institutional Venture Partners
Maluth, Elliot—H.I.G. Capital LLC
Mamdani, Sulaiman—SVB Capital
Mamlet, Geoff—New Atlantic Ventures
Mammola, Carlo—Argan Capital (FKA: BA Capital Partners Europe, BACPE)
Mamoulkine, Vladislav—Alfa Capital Partners
Mampuru, Cedrick—Lereko Invesments Property, Ltd.
Man, Harry—Matrix Partners
Man, Zaidi Che—Malaysian Technology Development Corp Sdn Bhd
Manastersky, Tony—RBC Capital Partners/RBC Technology Ventures
Manby, William—Monterey Venture Partners, LLC
Mancuso, Salvatore—Equinox S.A.
Mandahl, Michael—BrainHeart Capital AB
Mandahl, Michael—Nexit Ventures Oy
Mandal, Sumant—Clearstone Venture Partners
Mandaric, Milan—Behrman Capital
Mandato, Joseph—De Novo Ventures
Mandel, David—Equal Elements
Mandelbaum, Amnon—Sunrise Financial Group, Inc.
Mandelbaum, Fern—Monitor Venture Management, L.L.C.
Mandell, Lloyd—Generation Capital Partners
Mandhana, Satish—IDFC Private Equity
Mandile, John—Sigma Partners
Mandon, Thierry—Genopole 1er Jour (AKA: G1J)
Maness, Samuel—BB&T Capital Markets
Mangiola, Mark—Canaan Partners
Manglano, Sonsoles—Realza Capital SGECR SA
Mani, Dariusch—Baigo Capital GmbH
Mani, Kul—Wellington Financial LP
Mani, Roy—STAR Capital Partners, Ltd.
Mani, Sitaraman—Citigroup Private Bank
Maniar, Imran—Millennium Ventures LLC
Manigbas, Luzile—Blackstone Group, L.P.
Maniglio, Luigi—Wizard Partners Srl
Manish, Gupta—Draper Fisher Jurvetson ePlanet Ventures, L.P.
Mankad, Vipul—SIDBI Venture Capital, Ltd. (SVCL)
Mankekar, Ranjit—Keating Investments LLC
Mankodi, Hiren—Audax Group
Mankovski, Aaron—Pitango Venture Capital (FKA:Polaris Venture Capital Israel)
Mankwitz, Brian—Brand Journey Capital LP
Manley, James—Atlantic-Pacific Capital, Inc.
Manlunas, Eric—Frontera Group LLC
Mann, David—Brazos Private Equity Partners LLC
Mann, David—Spring Mill Venture Partners
Mann, Jeffrey—Silver Oak Management
Mann, Laura—Glenmont Partners, LLC
Mann, Timothy—Armada Venture Group LLC
Mannaioni, Duilio—Fidi Toscana SpA
Mannetti, Peter—iSherpa Capital
Mannheimer, Ernst—Wellington Partners Venture Capital GmbH
Mannheims, Willi—VENTIZZ Capital Partners Advisory AG
Manning, Ralph—Progress Equity Partners, Ltd.
Manning, Robert—Baker Capital Corp.
Mannion, Martin—Summit Partners
Manos, Peter—Arlington Capital Partners
Manrique, Jose—Magnum Capital Industrial Partners
Mansbridge, Lance—Bay Hills Capital (FKA: Mansbridge Capital Management)
Manseau, Hubert—Multiple Capital, Inc.
Mansour, Mark—MCM Capital Partners, LP
Mansukhani, Jeff—Bay Hills Capital (FKA: Mansbridge Capital Management)
Mansur, Amit—Rho Capital Partners, Inc.
Mantica, Marco—Vestar Capital Partners, Inc.
Manuel, Victor—Atlantic-Pacific Capital, Inc.
Manukian, Edward—Leveraged Green Energy LLC
Manz, Robert—Enterprise Investors Sp z oo
Mao, Isaac—United Capital Investment Group (China) Ltd
Mao, Michael—IDG Technology Venture Investment, Inc.
Mao, Tianjiao—Gold Stone Investment, Ltd.
Maoz, Barak—Amadeus Capital Partners, Ltd.
Mapes, John—Aurora Capital Group (FKA: Aurora Capital Partners)
Maples, Michael—Floodgate Fund, L.P.
Marangoni, Mario—Progressio SGR
Maranhao, Fabio—Axxon Group
Marble, Stephen—Sun Capital Partners, Inc.
Marc, Simon—Permira Advisers LLP
Marcarelli, Edmund—Brown Brothers Harriman & Company (AKA: BBH)
Marcelli, Roberto—Cooperazione Finanza Impresa scpa
Marchand, Christophe—Edmond de Rothschild Capital Partners SAS
Marchesano, Michael—Jordan, Edmiston Group, Inc., The
Marchington, Allan—Apposite Capital LLP
Marcinkus, Tomas—GILD Bankers (FKA: LHV Ventures)
Marcus, Adam—OpenView Venture Partners
Marcus, David—VIMAC Ventures LLC (FKA: VIMAC LLC)
Marcus, G. Robert—Conexus Capital Management, Inc.
Marcus, Jerome—GE Commercial Finance - Equity
Marcus, Joel—Alexandria Real Estate Equities, LLC
Marcus, Larry—Walden Venture Capital
Marcus, Stephen—New Atlantic Ventures
Marden, James—SK Capital Partners
Mardirossian, Shant—Kohlberg & Company LLC
Marek, David—Arx Equity Partners
Marek, Klaus-Peter—Sal. Oppenheim Private Equity Partners
Marengere, Luc E.J.—VenGrowth Capital Funds
Marengi, Joseph—Austin Ventures, L.P.
Marescotti, Federico—Friulia SGR SpA
Marescotti, Federico—Friulia SpA Fin.Reg.Friuli-Venezia
Margolin, Adam—Spectrum Equity Investors
Margolis, Paul—Longworth Venture Partners, L.P.
Margolskee, Dorothy—Prospect Venture Partners (FKA: Prospect Management LLC)
Margulis, Neal—Wellington Partners Venture Capital GmbH
Margve, Dario—Brynwood Partners L.P.
Mariani, Paul—ABS Capital Partners
Mariani, Paul—Brown Gibbons Lang & Company LLC
Mariano, David—Wellspring Capital Management LLC
Mariategui, Alvaro—Nazca Capital SGECR SA
Marichalar, Amalio—Iame Capital Riesgo SGECR SA
Mariette, Christine—Azulis Capital (FKA:Banexi Capital Partenaires)

Marinaccio, Louis—North Castle Partners
Marineau, Philip—LNK Partners
Marinelli, Dominic—Shackleton Ventures, Ltd.
Marini, Giacomo—Noventi
Marini, Michele—Investitori Associati SpA
Marino, Andrew—Carlyle Group, The
Marino, Carol—Johnson & Johnson Development Corporation
Marino, Dan—Wyndcrest Holdings, LLC
Marino, Gabe—AAC Capital Partners
Mario, Ernest—Pappas Ventures
Marion, Herve—Avesta
Markaity, Daniel—Jefferies Group, Inc.
Markarov, Alexandre—Millennium Private Equity
Marker, Todd—Montlake Capital
Markham, Richard—Care Capital, LLC
Markland, Dave—Prospect Venture Partners (FKA: Prospect Management LLC)
Markley, Jay—Columbia Capital LLC
Markowitz, Jeff—H & S Capital (AKA: Heidrick & Struggles Capital)
Markowitz, Marcia—Muller & Monroe Asset Management, LLC (AKA: M2)
Marks, Arthur—Valhalla Partners
Marks, Chris—High Country Venture LLC
Marks, David—Brockton Capital LLP
Marks, Evan—Vestar Capital Partners, Inc.
Marks, Gary—Sigma Capital Partners, LLC
Marks, George—Robin Hood Ventures
Marks, Joel—Advanced Equities Capital Partners LLC
Marks, Joseph—Coller Capital
Marks, Michael—Riverwood Capital LLC (FKA: Bigwood Capital LLC)
Marks, Neil—Praesidian Capital, LLC
Markus, Bart—Wellington Partners Venture Capital GmbH
Markvoort, Hans—LGT Capital Partners AG
Marley, Julianne—Blue Point Capital Partners (FKA: Key Equity Capital)
Marlinghaus, Thomas—Shore Capital, Ltd.
Marlowe, Christopher—Silverfern Group, Inc., The
Marmer, Craig—Probitas Partners, Inc.
Marocco, Michael—Diamond Point Capital Management
Marois, Thierry—SNVB Participations
Marolda, Andrew—Beekman Group LLC, The
Marom, Simon—Prospect Street Ventures
Maroney, John—Delphi Ventures
Maroni, Kevin—Spectrum Equity Investors
Maroo, Mehul—Aditya Birla Capital Advisors Pvt., Ltd.
Maroof, Nabil—NBK Capital, Ltd.
Marovac, Nenad—DN Capital, Ltd. (FKA: Digital Networks Global Ventures)
Marquardt, David—August Capital Management
Marquardt, Rainer—High Tech Venture Partners GmbH
Marquez, Julio—Global Emerging Markets
Marquis, Joelle—Arsenal Capital Partners
Marren, John—TPG Capital
Marrero, Roger—ABRY Partners LLC
Marrero, Roger—Comvest Investment Partners
Marron, Donald—Lightyear Capital LLC
Marrone, Juan—Pegasus Venture Capital
Marsh, Andrew—Gresham LLP
Marsh, Nick—FirstMark Capital LLC
Marsh, Robert—Red Rock Ventures
Marsh, Rupert—B.P. Marsh & Partners, Ltd.
Marsh, Sean—Point Judith Capital
Marsh, Yvonne—Liberty Partners
Marshall, Christopher—North American Financial Holdings, Inc.
Marshall, Christopher—Technology Crossover Ventures
Marshall, Dana—Warson Capital Partners
Marshall, Harry—Armada Venture Group LLC
Marshall, Jeff—Rockridge Capital Partners, Inc.
Marshall, Jim—Selby Venture Partners
Marshall, Keith—Montgomery & Co. (FKA: Digital Coast Partners)
Marshall, Larry—Southern Cross Venture Partners
Marshall, Marcy—Arboretum Ventures
Marshall, Margaret Peggy—Jefferies Group, Inc.
Marshall, Michael—Halifax Group, The
Marshall, Robert—Selby Venture Partners
Marshall, Roger—AAC Capital Partners
Marshall, Roger—Persimmon Capital, Ltd.
Marshall, Ross—Dunedin Capital Partners, Ltd. (FKA: Dunedin Ventures, Ltd.)
Marshall, Stephen—EdgeStone Capital Partners, Inc.
Marshall, Stuart—Investcorp Bank B.S.C.
Marshbanks, Tracy—First Analysis Corporation
Marson-Smith, Paul—Gresham LLP
Marstrand, Thomas—Erhvervsinvest Management A/S
Martelli, Marco—Invision Private Equity AG
Martelli, Vincent—New England Capital Partners
Martens, Herbert—NatCity Investments, Inc.
Martens, Samuel—Neomarkka Oyj
Martensen, Hans-Georg—RBK Hannover mbH & Co. KG
Martensson, Yvonne—Sunstone Capital A/S
Marti Pena, Jorge—Miradero Capital Partners, Inc.
Martin, Allan—Concentric Equity Partners, L.P.
Martin, Brian—American Capital, Ltd.
Martin, Charles—Amerimark Capital Group
Martin, Charles—CapSource Fund, L.P.
Martin, Christopher—Research Corporation Technologies
Martin, Darren—Raymond James, Ltd.
Martin, Doug—Stephens Group, Inc.
Martin, Gregory—Shamrock Holdings, Inc.
Martin, J. Landis—Platte River Ventures
Martin, James—Boyne Capital Partners LLC
Martin, Jane—Spring Mill Venture Partners
Martin, Jane—Village Ventures
Martin, Jason—Argonaut Private Equity
Martin, Jim—Add Partners, Ltd.
Martin, Jochen—EQT Funds management Limited
Martin, John—GE Antares Capital Corporation
Martin, Lars—LinkMed AB
Martin, Nancy—Warburg Pincus LLC
Martin, Nick—Fidelity Equity Partners
Martin, Pamela—Audax Group
Martin, Phillip—Salem Capital Partners, LP (FKA: Venture Capital Solutions)
Martin, Robert—Excellere Capital Management
Martin, W. Todd—CapitalWorks LLC
Martinez, Andres—Marlin Equity Partners, LLC
Martinez, Laura—Atlas Capital Close Brothers (FKA: Atlas Capital Investment)
Martinez, Steven—Apollo Management
Martinez, Steven—Aurora Resurgence Management Partners LLC
Martino, Marcus Marques—GP Investimentos
Martino, Rocco—LaSalle Capital Group, Inc.
Martins, Jose—Foundation Capital, Ltd.
Martinson, Allan—Martinson Trigon Venture Partners AS
Martinson, John—Edison Venture Fund
Martinson, Ross—Edison Venture Fund
Martiny, Manuel—Partners Group AG
Martirano, David—Point Judith Capital
Martis, Mark—Imperial Capital, LLC
Marty, Alan—Legacy Venture
Marty, Andreas—VENTIZZ Capital Partners Advisory AG
Maruenda, Luc—AGF Private Equity
Maruhashi, Michael—Cascadia Capital LLC
Marumo, Masato—Carlyle Group, The
Maruri, Victor—Hispania Capital Partners (HCP)
Maruszewski, Robert—Key Bridge Partners LLC
Marver, James—VantagePoint Venture Partners
Marvin, Kim—American Industrial Partners
Marwaha, Vishal—Henderson Equity Partners (AKA: Henderson Private Capital)
Marx, Danie—European Islamic Investment Bank Plc
Mary, Bernard—Carvest (AKA: Credit Agricole Regions Investissement)
Marzen, Allan—Golub Capital
Marzio Soso, Tito—Investcorp Bank B.S.C.
Masaki, Shunsuke—MVC Corporation
Masalin, Heikki—Creative Industries Management Oy (CIM)
Maschek, Marko—PINOVA Capital GmbH
Masek, Christopher—IK Investment Partners, Ltd.
Masek, Timothy—TMB Industries Investments
Maselli, Michael—Trimaran Capital Partners, LLC
Masetti, Maurizio—Alcedo SGR SpA
Mash, Julian—Vision Capital LLP
Mashita, Hirokazu—HIKARI private equity, Inc.
Masiello, Mark—Providence Equity Partners LLC
Maskalunas, Scott—Cressey & Company, L.P.
Mason, Etsuko—Alexandria Real Estate Equities, LLC
Mason, Hugh—Pembridge Partners LLP
Mason, James—Parish Capital Advisors LLC
Mason, John—Convergent Capital Partners
Mason, Susan—ONSET Ventures
Masri, Bashar—Siraj Fund Management Company
Masri, Edgar—Matrix Partners
Massara, Paul—Genesis Capital Corp.
Massard, Nicolas—Continuum Group, Ltd. (AKA: Continuum Advisory, Ltd.)
Massart, Jean-Christophe—Sydes
Massey, Jim—Houlihan, Lokey, Howard & Zukin
Massey, Tim—Band of Angels
Massimo, Valerio—Cinven, Ltd.
Masson, Richard—Oaktree Capital Management LLC
Massoud, I. Joseph—Compass Group International LLC, The
Massy, John—Capital Z Investment Partners (FKA: Union Square Partners)
Master, Neel—ITU Ventures
Masters, Julian—Bowmark Capital (FKA: Sagitta Private Equity)

Masterson, Chris—Fajr Capital Ltd
Masto, Christopher—Friedman, Fleischer & Lowe, LLC
Masui, Toshio—Colony Capital LLC
Masur, Mark—Silver Creek Ventures
Mataix, Jorge—Cognetas LLP
Mataix, Jorge—Nmas1 Private Equity (FKA: Nmas1 Electra Capital Privado)
Matak, Eduard—Penta Investments, Ltd.
Mataki, Tateo—Dentsu.com, Inc.
Matelich, George—Kelso & Company
Mathers, Edward—New Enterprise Associates, Inc.
Matheson, James—Flagship Ventures
Mathews, Tom—Magenta Partners LLP
Mathewson, David—Bedminster Capital LLC
Mathias, Ben—New Enterprise Associates, Inc.
Mathias, Edward—Carlyle Group, The
Mathias, Franco Ottavio—Handwerk Consult Mittelstandsberatung e.K.
Mathieu, Bruno—Balmoral Capital
Mathieu, Didier—Grand Sud Ouest Capital
Mathieu, Raymond—Providence Equity Partners LLC
Mathieu, Romen—Capital Trust, Ltd.
Mathis, Scott—InvestBio, Inc.
Mathur, Anurag—Unitas Capital Pte, Ltd.
Matic, Tomislav—Quaestus Private Equity, Ltd.
Matise, John—Stone Canyon Venture Partners (SCVP)
Matkiwsky, Roman—MCI Management
Matlack, Thomas—Megunticook Management
Matlin, David—MatlinPatterson Global Advisers LLC
Matlin, Howard—Kelso & Company
Matlof, Jason—Battery Ventures, L.P.
Matson, Scott—Partech International
Matsubara, Yoshitaka—Global Venture Capital, Inc.
Matsuda, Humberto—Performa Investimentos
Matsuda, Ikkei—Hokkaido Venture Capital, Inc.
Matsuda, Kiyoto—Unison Capital, Inc.
Matsukawa, Rikizo—CITIC Capital Partners, Ltd.
Matsumoto, Hiroshi—Advent International
Matsumoto, Shigeru—Tokio Marine Capital Company, Ltd.
Matsumoto, Takashi—Aozora Investment Co,. Ltd.
Matsumura, Kenzo—Privee Investment Holdings Co., Ltd.
Matsunawa, Eriko—Tokio Marine Capital Company, Ltd.
Matsuo, Masatoshi—DOGAN Investments, Inc.
Mattelaer, Katrien—TrustCapital Partners NV
Matteson, Mark—SunTx Capital Partners
Matteucci, Paul—U.S. Venture Partners
Matthes, William—Behrman Capital
Matthew, Jim—Angel Capital Network
Matthews, Alan—Origo Partners PLC
Matthews, David—Trailblazer Capital
Matthews, Devin—Chicago Growth Partners (William Blair Capital Partners)
Matthews, Gary—Morgan Stanley Private Equity
Matthews, Graham—VenGrowth Capital Funds
Matthews, JR—Tregaron Capital Company LLC
Matthews, James—Evercore Partners
Matthews, Les—Mesa Capital Partners
Matthews, Richard—Augmentum Capital LLP
Mattner, Mike—WHEB Ventures, Ltd.
Mattson, Brad—VantagePoint Venture Partners
Matusich, Anthony—Selby Venture Partners
Matzka, Alfred—Horizonte Venture Management GmbH
Matzka, Klaus—gcp gamma capital partners Beratungs- & Beteiligungs AG
Mauchel, Phil—OMERS Private Equity
Mauer, Carola—Pantheon Ventures, Ltd.
Maughan, Deryck—Kohlberg, Kravis, Roberts & Company, L.P.
Maughan, Spencer—Venrock Associates
Mauk, J.T.—Perseus LLC
Maulle, Guillaume—Iris Capital Management (FKA: Part'Com Management S.A.)
Mauney, David—De Novo Ventures
Maunsbach, Bengt—Altor Equity Partners AB
Maurer, Erik—Prospect Partners LLC
Maurer, Greg—Heron Capital LLC
Mauro, Greg—Revolution Learning
Mauro, Greg—Revolution Ventures, LLC
Mauro, Maurizio—UBS Capital Corporation
Maurstad, Hugo—Altor Equity Partners AB
Maury, Rene—Siparex Group SAS
Mautz, Charles—Aequitas Capital Management, Inc.
Mauze, Michael—VMG Equity Partners
Mavredakais, John—Houlihan, Lokey, Howard & Zukin
Maw, Rory—Bridges Community Ventures, Ltd.
Mawhinney, Tom—JAFCO Ventures
Maxwell, Bret—MK Capital
Maxwell, Ian—Allen & Buckeridge Pty, Ltd.
Maxwell, Paul—Monitor Clipper Partners LLC
Maxwell, Ray—Invesco Private Capital
Maxwell, Rod—StoneBridge Merchant Capital Corporation
Maxwell, Troy—RBC Capital Partners/RBC Technology Ventures
May, Allan—Emergent Medical Ventures, LLP
May, Fergie—Entropy Ventures, Ltd.
May, Graham—Conexus Capital Management, Inc.
May, Guido—Silverfleet Capital (FKA: PPM Capital Partners)
May, John—Calvert Social Venture Partners, L.P.
May, John—Chesapeake Emerging Opportunities Club LLC
May, John—New Vantage Group
May, John—Seraphim Capital
May, Kevin—Horizon Technology Finance Management LLC
May, Timothy—Boyne Capital Partners LLC
Maybank, Mark—Canaccord Genuity
Maybaum, Richard—Littlejohn & Company LLC
Maybell, Mark—Ericsson Venture Partners
Mayden, Martin—SunTrust Equity Partners
Mayer, David—Abingworth Management, Ltd.
Mayer, Ernst G.—Sirius Venture Partners GmbH
Mayer, John—J.P. Morgan Capital Corporation
Mayer, Kelly—Lion Capital (FKA: Hicks Muse (Europe))
Mayer, Michael—TechnoStart GmbH
Mayer, Steven—Cerberus Capital Management, L.P.
Mayer, Susan—Allied Capital Corporation
Mayer, William—Park Avenue Equity Partners, L.P.
Mayer-Levi, Cecile—AXA Private Equity
Mayerson, Frederic—Walnut Group, The
Mayert, Christian—Allianz Capital Partners GmbH
Mayfield, Paul—Willis Stein & Partners
Mayfield, R. Glen—River Cities Capital Funds
Mayhew, Nicholas—DSE Investment Services, Ltd.
Mayhew, Timothy—Fenway Partners, Inc.
Mayn, Robert—Leading Ridge Capital Partners LLC
Maynard, Frederick—HarbourVest Partners LLC
Mayo, Christopher—Probitas Partners, Inc.
Mayo, John—Celtic Pharma Management, LP
Mayor, Hedley—BPEP International
Mayr, Rudolf—Bayern Kapital GmbH
Mays, Shaun—Climate Change Capital, Ltd.
Maystadt, Philippe—European Investment Bank, The (AKA: EIB)
Mazan, Michael—Birch Hill Equity Partners Management, Inc.
Mazard, Laurent—Grand Sud Ouest Capital
Mazza, Giampiero—MidOcean Partners
Mazzucchelli, Lou—Ridgewood Capital Management, LLC
McAdam, Timothy—Technology Crossover Ventures
McAdoo, Gregory—Sequoia Capital
McAfee Jones, Wesley—Sage Capital, LLC
McAleer, William—Voyager Capital
McAleese, Tom—Claret Capital, Ltd.
McAlister, John—Wincove Capital
McAllister, Kevin—American Capital, Ltd.
McAllister, Kevin—Sterling Partners
McAlpine, Stuart—Cinven, Ltd.
McAndrew, Joseph—Wall Street Venture Capital
McAndrews, Brian—Madrona Venture Group
McAndrews, Mark—Ericsson Venture Partners
McArthur, Lex—Jolimont Capital Pty, Ltd.
McBlain, John—Winona Capital Management
McBride, Graham—VenGrowth Capital Funds
McBride, James—Blue Sage Capital, L.P.
McBride, Patrick—Legend Partners, The
McBride, Patrick—Walnut Group, The
McCabe, George—Pine Creek Partners
McCabe, Joan—Brynwood Partners L.P.
McCabe, Michael—Hamilton Lane Advisors, Inc.
McCabe, Terry—Piper Jaffray Ventures
McCafferty, Kevin—Catalyst Health and Technology Partners LLC
McCain, Wendell—Parish Capital Advisors LLC
McCall, Bill—Lyceum Capital
McCall, Edward—Brentwood Associates
McCall, Jim—Intel Capital
McCall, Mark—Lime Rock Partners LLC
McCall, Matthew—New World Ventures
McCall, Matthew—Portage Venture Partners (AKA: Graystone Venture Partners)
McCammon, Mark—Strength Capital Partners
McCann, John—Jefferies Group, Inc.
McCarthy, Courtney—Pamlico Capital
McCarthy, Edward—River Cities Capital Funds
McCarthy, Eileen—Alta Communications
McCarthy, Jeffrey—North Bridge Venture Partners
McCarthy, John—Two Rivers Associates LLC (FKA: Gateway Associates, L.P.)
McCarthy, Kevin—Scorpion Capital Partners, L.P.
McCarthy, Laurence—Ampersand Ventures
McCarthy, Mark—Shorenstein Company LLC
McCarthy, Ryan—Aurora Resurgence Management Partners LLC
McCarthy, Sean—Pappas Ventures
McCarthy, Thomas—Republic Financial Corporation
McCarty, John—Peachtree Equity Partners

McCarty, Michiel—Gleacher & Co.
McCarty, Tammy—New Mexico Community Capital
McCauley, Gerard—Brown Brothers Harriman & Company (AKA: BBH)
McCauley, Gordon—NDI Capital (FKA: Neuro Discovery, Inc.)
McClain, Richard—High Street Capital
McClatchy, David—ING Investment Management
McCleary, Christopher—Blue Chip Venture Company
McClellan, John—Thomas H. Lee Partners (AKA: TH Lee Partners)
McClelland, Carter—Banc of America Securities LLC
McClelland, Spence—Noro-Moseley Partners
McClelland, Spence—Noro-Moseley Partners
McClenaghan, Sean—CHB Capital Partners
McCloskey, Thomas—BV-Cornerstone Ventures, L.P.
McCloy, Rush—Channelstone Partners LLC
McColl, Milton—New Leaf Venture Partners LLC
McCollum, Christian—Investcorp Bank B.S.C.
McComiskey, Mark—First Reserve Corporation
McConahey, Steve—Iron Gate Capital, LLC
McConnell, James—Landmark Partners, Inc.
McConnell, Michael—Shamrock Holdings, Inc.
McConnell, Nigel—Cognetas LLP
McConnell, Thomas—Vanguard Ventures
McCordick, Evan—BPEP International
McCormack, Chris—American Capital, Ltd.
McCormack, R. Stephen—Commonwealth Capital Ventures
McCormack, Robert—Mustang Ventures
McCormack, Scott—Seaport Capital, LLC
McCormick, Alan—Legatum Capital
McCormick, Douglas—Rho Capital Partners, Inc.
McCormick, Douglas—Thayer Hidden Creek
McCormick, George—TPH Partners LLC
McCormick, John—HealthpointCapital LLC
McCormick, Margaret—Integra Ventures
McCoy, David—National City Equity Partners, Inc.
McCoy, Michael—Dresner Partners (FKA: Dresner Capital Resources, Inc.)
McCrary, Dennis—Pantheon Ventures, Ltd.
McCrea, Courtney—Weathergage Venture Capital
McCreadie, Paul—Arboretum Ventures
McCrory, Gerry—Cross Atlantic Capital Partners
McCroskey, Nancy—ATA Ventures
McCrum, A Bliss—EuclidSR Partners
McCrystal, Amanda—HarbourVest Partners LLC
McCue, Matthew—Hopewell Ventures
McCullagh, Paul—Pacific Equity Partners
McCulloch, A. Donald—Liberty Capital Management Corporation
McCulloch, Gordon—Renaissance Capital
McCullough, Bonnie—Parish Capital Advisors LLC
McDade, Herbert—Lehman Brothers, Inc.
McDaid, Brian—Spring Capital Partners (FKA: Spring Capital Investors LLC)
McDanell, Philip—Accelerator Media (UK) Ltd
McDaniel, Brenda—Meritus Ventures, L.P.
McDaniel, Brenda—Mountain Ventures Inc.
McDaniel, Brenda—Southern Appalachian Management Company LLC
McDaniel, David—Seraphim Partners
McDaniel, Teresa—ArrowPath Venture Capital (FKA: E*TRADE Group, Inc.)
McDermott, Brian—Hancock Park Associates
McDermott, Charles—Rockport Capital Partners
McDermott, Dirk—Altira Group LLC
McDermott, Paul—RBC Capital Partners/RBC Technology Ventures
McDermott, Peter—KSL Capital Partners
McDonagh, Dennis—Blackstone Group, L.P.
McDonagh, Nicholas—Accede Capital
McDonagh, Vicky—Henderson Equity Partners (AKA: Henderson Private Capital)
McDonagh, William—Walden Venture Capital
McDonald, Don—First Ontario Labour Sponsored Investment Fund, Ltd.
McDonald, Emeric—Octane Capital Management
McDonald, John—MPM Capital (FKA: MPM Asset Management LLC)
McDonald, Robert—Craton Equity Partners
McDonnell, David—mc3 ventures (FKA: McKenna Venture Accelerator (MVA))
McDonough, Scott—Alta Growth Capital
McDonough, Tim—Gold Hill Capital Management LLC
McDonough, Tim—Hercules Technology Growth Capital, Inc.
McDonough, William—VantagePoint Venture Partners
McDougall, Ronald—Seaway Private Equity Corporation (AKA: SPEC)
McDowell, Derek—Boyne Capital Partners LLC
McDowell, Josh—Weston Presidio (FKA: Weston Presidio Capital Management)
McDowell, Mark—LaunchBox Digital
McElhattan, Matt—Chevron Technology Ventures
McElroy, Shane—Viking Venture Management AS
McElwee, James—Weston Presidio (FKA: Weston Presidio Capital Management)
McEvoy, John—Wayzata Investment Partners
McFadden, Andrea—Wynnefield Capital Advisors
McFadden, Barclay—Envest
McFadden, Christopher—Health Evolution Partners LLC
McFadden, Mark—CCMP Capital Advisors LLC
McFadyen, Finlay—AnaCap Financial Partners LLP
McGarth, John Paul—Growth Capital Partners (FKA: Close Brothers Growth Capital)
McGee, James—Carlyle Group, The
McGee, Patrick—Brazos Private Equity Partners LLC
McGhee, Michael—Global Infrastructure Partners
McGill, T.J.—Evergreen Pacific Partners LLC
McGillivray, Burton—Cloquet Capital Partners
McGinley, Jack—RoundTable Health Care Partners
McGinn, Richard—RRE Ventures LLC
McGinnis, Patrick—AIG Capital Partners
McGinty, Elissa—Weston Presidio (FKA: Weston Presidio Capital Management)
McGinty, Kevin—Peppertree Capital Management, Inc.
McGlinn, John—Archbrook Capital Management LLC
McGlynn, J. Casey—Angel Investors, LP
McGlynn, J. Casey—Dot Edu Ventures
McGonegal, Jeff—Livingston Capital, Ltd.
McGonigle, Michael—Audax Group
McGonnigle, Glenn—TechOperators LLC
McGovern, David—Marlin Equity Partners, LLC
McGovern, Kevin—McGovern Capital LLC
McGovern, Lisa—Nassau Capital LLC
McGovern, Michael—Hampshire Equity Partners (FKA: ING Equity Partners)
McGovern, Michael—Wincove Capital
McGovern, Patrick—Akara, Ltd. (DBA: IDG Ventures Europe)
McGovern, Robert—New Enterprise Associates, Inc.
McGowan, Christopher—Madison Dearborn Partners LLC
McGowan, Thomas—Siguler Guff & Company
McGowan-Smyth, Bob—Enterprise Equity Venture Capital Group
McGrane, Nicholas—MidOcean Partners
McGrath, Gerry—Perseis Private Equity
McGrath, Pat—Bank of Scotland Venture Capital (FKA: ICC Venture Capital)
McGrath, Steve—mc3 ventures (FKA: McKenna Venture Accelerator (MVA))
McGraw, David—Ontario Teachers' Pension Plan
McGregor, Doug—RBC Capital Partners/RBC Technology Ventures
McGregor, Doug—Rational Equity LLC
McGruder, Shaun—Palm Beach Capital Partners
McGuigan, James—Capital International Research, Inc.
McGuinness, Tony—Pembridge Partners LLP
McGuire, Bernard—PCGI LLC (AKA: PCG International)
McGuire, Bernard—Pacific Corporate Group
McGuire, Monica—Pantheon Ventures, Ltd.
McGuire, Terrance—Polaris Venture Partners
McHale, Bill—GIV Venture Partners (AKA: Global Internet Ventures)
McHale, William—Telesystem-Argo Global Capital
McHenry, Maurice—Bank of Scotland Venture Capital (FKA: ICC Venture Capital)
McIlwain, Matthew—Madrona Venture Group
McIlwraith, John—Blue Chip Venture Company
McIntire, John—Nexos Capital Partners
McIntosh, Robert—ArrowPath Venture Capital (FKA: E*TRADE Group, Inc.)
McIntyre, Charles—IBIS Capital, Ltd.
McIntyre, Ryan—Foundry Group
McIntyre, Ryan—Mobius Venture Capital, Inc.
McJannet, Melissa—Northleaf Capital Partners
McKay, Chris—Granite Ventures LLC
McKay, Ellen—Needham Asset Management
McKay, Geoff—Vulcan Capital
McKay, Jaquie—Pelion Venture Partners
McKay, Samuel—Axiom Venture Partners, L.P.
McKearn, John—RiverVest Venture Partners
McKee, Andrew—Webster Capital Management, L.L.C.
McKee, John—Weston Presidio (FKA: Weston Presidio Capital Management)
McKee, William—Graham Partners, Inc.
McKelvie, Roy—Gresham Partners - Gresham Private Equity
McKenna, David—Advent International
McKenna, Stephen—CCMP Capital Advisors LLC
McKenzie, Stuart—Endeavour Capital, Ltd.
McKeon, Robert—Veritas Capital
McKibben, Timothy—Ancor Capital Partners
McKiernan, John—novusmodus LLP
McKinlay, Sebastian—Fidelity Equity Partners

McKinlay, Sebastian—Promethean Investments
McKinley, John—LaunchBox Digital
McKinley, Thomas—Cardinal Partners
McKinley, Thomas—Partech International
McKinnon, Hull—Altira Group LLC
McKinnon, Sandy—Pentech Ventures, LLP
McKittrick, Stacey—Appian Ventures
McKnight, Duane—Syncom Management Co. Inc.
McLain, Hardy—CVC Capital Partners (Europe), Ltd.
McLane, J.—Lime Rock Partners LLC
McLane, John—Sverica International
McLaren, Bruce—Noble Fund Managers, Ltd.
McLarty, Robb—NGEN Partners LLC (FKA: NextGen Partners LLC)
McLaughlin, Christopher—CIVC Partners LP (FKA: Continental Illinois Venture Corp.)
McLaughlin, James—Lincolnshire Management, Inc.
McLaughlin, Scott—W.R. Hambrecht & Co., LLC
McLean, Bart—CGW Southeast Partners (AKA: Cravey, Green, & Wahlen)
McLean, Brian—Mount Yale Asset Management
McLean, David—Sevin Rosen Funds
McLean, James—3i (US)
McLean, Stephen—Arsenal Capital Partners
McLeese, David—First Capital Partners LLC
McLemore, J. Donald—Claritas Capital LLC
McLoone, Brian—PineBridge Investments
McLoughlin, Brian—GRP Partners
McLravy, R. Charles—MASI, Ltd.
McMahan, Ed—Falfurrias Capital Partners
McMahon, Jim—West Coast Capital
McMahon, Michael—Houlihan, Lokey, Howard & Zukin
McMahon, Michael—Pine Brook Road Partners LLC
McMaken, Bruce—Signet Healthcare Partners (FKA: Sanders Morris Harris)
McManamon, Peter—Atlantic Bridge
McManus, Joe—Duet Capital
McManus, Mark—CIVC Partners LP (FKA: Continental Illinois Venture Corp.)
McMartin, Cameron—CenterPoint Venture Partners
McMillan, Andrew—5AM Ventures
McMillan, Greg—Varde Partners, Inc.
McMonigall, John—Apax Partners Worldwide
McMorris, Marc—General Atlantic LLC
McMorrow, Michael—Newlight Associates
McMullan, Robert—Blackstone Group, L.P.
McMullen, Daniel—Blackstone Group, L.P.
McMurtrey, Thomas—Concentric Equity Partners, L.P.
McNabb, J. Carter—River Cities Capital Funds
McNair, James—Corinthian Capital Group LLC
McNair, Martin—Advent Venture Partners LLP
McNally, Andrew—Hammond Kennedy Whitney & Co
McNally, D. Ryan—Catalyst Investors
McNally, Ward—Edgewater Funds, The
McNamee, George—FA Technology Ventures
McNamee, Roger—Elevation Associates LLC
McNamee, Roger—Integral Capital Partners
McNaught-Davis, James—WHEB Ventures, Ltd.
McNeil, Robert—Sanderling Ventures
McNeill, Brian—Alta Communications
McNerney, Peter—CORAL Ventures Management, Inc.
McNerney, Peter—Thomas, McNerney & Partners LLC
McNichol, Paul—Pilot Group LLC
McNulty, Anthony—General Atlantic LLC
McNulty, Edward—Central Valley Fund, L.P., The
McNulty, Peter—Renaissance Capital
McParland, Robert—TL Ventures
McPhee, Ron—Verge
McPhee, William—Mi3 Venture Partners
McPherron, Matthew—Bain Capital
McPherson, George—Global Environment Fund Management Corporation
McPherson, Grant—No. 8 Ventures Management Ltd (FKA: Morel Ventures Ltd)
McPherson, Kevin—Venture Investors LLC
McPherson, Neil—Aegis Capital Group LLC
McQueeney, Micheal—Summer Street Capital LLC
McQuilkin, David—Asia Pacific Ventures
McQuillan, Kevin—Focus Ventures
McRae, Jeff—First Ontario Labour Sponsored Investment Fund, Ltd.
McReynolds, David—American Capital, Ltd.
McRoberts, John—Aurora Investment Advisors, Ltd.
McVeigh, Sean—Kilcullen Kapital Partners
McVey, George—Dynamis Advisors LLC
McVicar, Tracey—CAI Capital Management Company
McWhorter, Stuart—Clayton Associates LLC
McWilliams, Peter—Sanderling Ventures
McWilliams, Thomas—Citicorp Venture Capital, Ltd.
McWilliams, Thomas—Court Square Capital Partners
Mccrossin, Hunter—Friend Skoler & Co., L.L.C.
Mead, Dana—Kleiner Perkins Caufield & Byers
Mead, James—Radius Ventures LLC
Mead, Kevin—Ingenious Ventures
Mead, Matthew—National Endowment for Science, Technology & the Arts NESTA
Mead, Richard—Jordan, Edmiston Group, Inc., The
Meads, Chris—Pantheon Ventures, Ltd.
Meads, Jason—Patron Capital, Ltd.
Meakem, Chip—Kodiak Venture Partners
Meakem, Glen—Meakem Becker Venture Capital
Meals, Randall—Quicksilver Ventures (FKA: QTV Capital)
Means, Brad—Highland Capital Management, L.P.
Means, William—Merion Investment Partners, L.P.
Meany, Ryan—Edgewater Capital Group, Inc.
Mecane, Joseph—UBS Capital Markets
Mecham, Mark—Northwest Venture Associates, Inc.(FKA:Spokane Capital Mgmt)
Mecklenburg, Gary—Waud Capital Partners LLC
Mecklenburg, John—Rutberg & Company, LLC
Medea, Fabrizio—Wise SRG S.p.A. (AKA: Wisequity)
Medeiros, Jose—Wesley Clover, Ltd.
Medhekar, Ajit—ARCH Venture Partners
Medici, Michael—Summit Partners
Meduna, Cyril—Advent-Morro Equity Partners
Medved, Jonathan—Israel Seed Partners
Medved, Joseph—SoftBank Capital
Meehan, Jennifer—Aavishkaar Venture Management Services Pvt, Ltd.
Meeker, Jeffrey—Hamilton Lane Advisors, Inc.
Meekin, Peter—Trident Capital
Meeks, Jonathan—TA Associates, Inc.
Meenakshisundaram, T.C.—IDG Ventures India
Meerschman, Pierre-Yves—ORKOS Capital
Meeting, Liu Wen—Shaanxi Zenisun Venture Capital Co.,Ltd
Meeusen, Ronald—IN Partners LLC (AKA: Midpoint)
Megiddo, Dalia—7 Health Ventures
Megiddo, Dalia—Jerusalem Global Ventures
Mehaignerie, Laurence—Citizen Capital SAS
Mehall, Todd—GulfStar Group
Meheut, Jacques—Innovacom SA
Mehl, Randall—Baird Capital Partners
Mehlman, Ken—Kohlberg, Kravis, Roberts & Company, L.P.
Mehra, Anand—Sofinnova Ventures
Mehra, Avnish—Advent International
Mehra, Nadimeh—Alf Yad Limited
Mehra, Nadimeh—Alf Yad, Ltd.
Mehra, Pawan—mc3 ventures (FKA: McKenna Venture Accelerator (MVA))
Mehra, Rajan—Clearstone Venture Partners
Mehra, Vibhor—SAIF Partners
Mehra, Vivek—August Capital Management
Mehrgardt, Sonke—MVP Munich Venture Partners Managementgesellschaft mbH
Mehrotra, Prashant—Silver Lake Sumeru
Mehta, Amish—Vector Capital
Mehta, Dilip—Radius Ventures LLC
Mehta, Hitesh—Acacia Capital Partners
Mehta, Hitesh—Akara, Ltd. (DBA: IDG Ventures Europe)
Mehta, Mit—CCMP Capital Advisors LLC
Mehta, Nilesh—Aureos Capital, Ltd.
Mehta, Nilesh—eIndia Venture Management
Mehta, Paras—Black Canyon Capital
Mehta, Rahul—Blue River Capital India Advisory Services Pvt., Ltd.
Mehta, Sameet—Granite Hill Capital Partners
Mehta, Satish—Scsi Capital
Mehta, Shailesh—Clearstone Venture Partners
Mehta, Shailesh—Granite Hill Capital Partners
Mehta, Viral—Yorkville Advisors LLC
Mehta, Virat—UNC Kenan-Flagler Private Equity Fund
Mehta, Vishal—Lok Capital Group
Mei, Jian—Shenzhen OFC Investment Management, Ltd.
Meidl, Jesse—Thomas Weisel Partners Group, Inc.
Meier, Henri—BioMedPartners
Meijer, Clifford—Thomas Weisel Partners Group, Inc.
Meijers, Harrie—Robeco Private Equity
Meiler, Martin—Aravis SA
Meilner, John—Bridge Street Capital Partners LLC
Meinel, Wulf—Carlyle Group, The
Meinhardt, Rob—RB Webber & Company
Meininger, Christian—HillStreet Capital, Inc.
Meiring, Paul—Prudential Capital Group
Meise, Florian—ADCURAM Group AG (FKA: Adcuram Industriekapital AG)
Meisenzahl, Greg—Brookstone Partners
Meister, Steffen—Partners Group AG
Mejer, Preben—IVS A/S (AKA: Internet Ventures Scandinavia A/S)
Meka, M. Krishna—VenturEast (FKA: APIDC Venture Capital Limited)
Melander, Magnus—BrainHeart Capital AB
Melberg, Ole—Energy Ventures AS
Melby, Christian—Reiten & Co Strategic Investments AS

Melbye, Hans Kristian—Jotunfjell Partners AS (AKA: JFP)
Melchior, Lisa—OMERS Private Equity
Meldrum, Kelly—Adams Street Partners LLC
Melia Christiansen, Carlos—Inventure Capital A/S
Melisse, Chris—Tvi Investments Bv
Melka, Eric—Forbes Alliance Partners Inc.
Mellegers, Jan—Biotech Turnaround Fund B.V.
Meller, Alain—Convergent Capital SAS
Mellinger, Larry—PineBridge Investments
Mellinger, Paul—Twin Haven Capital Partners
Mellinger, Pierre Francois—AIG Capital Partners
Mello, Kevin—Bridgescale Partners
Mello, Kirsten—Menlo Ventures
Melloni, Paolo—Investitori Associati SpA
Melnick, Michael—CMEA Capital
Melnik, Ronen—Odin Investments
Melnikova, Irena—TVM Capital GmbH
Melnyk, Kevin B.—Priveq Capital Funds
Melo, Glen—Hercules Technology Growth Capital, Inc.
Melrose, Evan—PTV Sciences
Melton, Brian—Tenaya Capital (FKA: Lehman Brothers Venture Partners)
Melton, Emily—Mayfield Fund
Meltzer, Doug—Pacific Corporate Group
Melvin, Colin—Hermes Private Equity Management, Ltd.
Melwani, Prakash—Blackstone Group, L.P.
Melwani, Prakash—Vestar Capital Partners, Inc.
Melzer, Jon—Houlihan, Lokey, Howard & Zukin
Melzer, Thomas—RiverVest Venture Partners
Membrillera, Federico—Delta Partners FZ LLC
Memmo, Antonio—Silverfern Group, Inc., The
Memmo, Nicholas—Kline Hawkes & Co.
Memmo, Nicholas—Vicente Capital Partners
Menachem, Avraham—Jerusalem Global Ventures
Menary, Corrine—Kirtland Capital Partners
Mende, Manfred—DKB Wagniskapital Unternehmensbeteiligungsgesellschaft mbH
Mende, Manfred—MVC Unternehmensbeteiligungsgesellschaft mbH (AKA: MVC GmbH)
Mende, Nora—Tullis Health Investors (FKA: Tullis-Dickerson & Co., Inc.)
Mendelsohn, Fred—AXM Venture Capital, Ltd.
Mendelsohn, Fred—MST Capital, Ltd.
Mendelsohn, Kevin—JumpStart, Inc.
Mendelson, Alan—Axiom Venture Partners, L.P.
Mendelson, Jason—Foundry Group
Mendelson, Jason—Mobius Venture Capital, Inc.
Mendez, Alex—Storm Ventures LLC
Mendez, Zoilo—Miradero Capital Partners, Inc.
Mendicino, II. Frank—Access Venture Partners
Mendicino, III. Frank—Access Venture Partners
Mendoza, Felipe—Silver Creek Ventures
Mendoza, Orlando—Edison Venture Fund
Mendu, Raghuveer—VenturEast (FKA: APIDC Venture Capital Limited)
Meneau, Marc—Vatel Capital SAS
Menezes, Ashley—ChrysCapital Management Company
Meng An, Ocean—Taishan Invest AG
Meng, Peter Lai Hock—Tembusu Partners Pte., Ltd.
Meng, Rock—Vector Capital
Meng, Viktor—bScope Partners, Inc.
Mengel, Niels—Oresund-Healthcare A/S
Menichelli, Vincent—Trestle Ventures
Menke, Eric—Champlain Capital Management LLC
Menton, David—Synova Capital LLP
Meran, Johannes—Cognetas LLP
Mercadante, Paul—Silver Lake Sumeru
Mere, Philippe—Banexi Ventures Partners
Meredith, Debby—JAFCO Ventures
Meretta, Michael—American Capital, Ltd.
Mereur, Jean-Noel—Rising Tide Fund
Meric, Cem—LGT Capital Partners AG
Merieux, Henry-Louis—MML Capital Partners
Merigold, Catharine—Vista Ventures
Merindol, Nicolas—GCE Capital SAS
Mermoud, J. Frank—Monument Capital Group LLC
Merritt, Charles—Parish Capital Advisors LLC
Mersky, Seth—Onex Corporation
Mertsola, Matti—MB Funds (AKA: MB Rahastot Oy)
Merves, Jay—GSC Partners (FKA: Greenwich Street Capital Partners)
Mes, David—Cipio Partners
Mesbah, Bardia—Brookstone Partners
Mesgar, Eugene—Francisco Partners
Mesic, Brian—Anthem Venture Partners
Meskin, Jeffrey—Brown Brothers Harriman & Company (AKA: BBH)
Mesl, Mateja—RSG Capital d.o.o.
Messa, Anibal—Plataforma Capital Partners
Messersmith, Michael—American Capital, Ltd.
Messick, Diane—Inflection Point Ventures
Messman, Jack—Novell Technology Capital
Messmer, Ernst—affentranger associates (FKA: Ultreia Capital, Ltd.)
Metcalf, Chris—GF Private Equity Group, LLC
Metcalf, Dean—Ontario Teachers' Pension Plan
Metcalf, James—Shattuck Hammond Partners
Metcalf, John—Reference Capital Management LLC (FKA: Cascadia Partners)
Metcalfe, Robert—Polaris Venture Partners
Methot, Andree-lise—Cycle Capital Management
Metrick, Maryfrances—Blackstone Group, L.P.
Metser, Asi—Platinum-Neurone Ventures
Metter, David—Innisfree Group
Metternich, Hans-Joachim—Investitions- und Strukturbank Rheinland-Pfalz (ISB) GmbH
Metusalemsdottir, Linda—Thule Investments
Metz, Lloyd—ICV Capital Partners LLC
Metz, Travis—Monitor Clipper Partners LLC
Metzger, Denis—Chequers Capital
Metzger, Donald—Cameron Holdings Corporation
Meunier, Pierre-Andre—Celtic House Venture Partners
Meurer, William—BEV Capital (FKA: Brand Equity Ventures)
Meurisse, Jean-Bernard—Initiative & Finance Investissement SA
Meyer, Dale—Probitas Partners, Inc.
Meyer, Dan—Sevin Rosen Funds
Meyer, Edward—Easton Hunt Capital Partners, L.P.
Meyer, H. Conrad—Gleacher & Co.
Meyer, Jason—Hampshire Equity Partners (FKA: ING Equity Partners)
Meyer, John—Wall Street Venture Capital
Meyer, Judith—Portage Venture Partners (AKA: Graystone Venture Partners)
Meyer, Robert—Paine & Partners LLC
Meyer, Thomas—European Investment Fund (AKA: EIF)
Meyer, Urs—BioMedPartners
Meyer-Horn, Phillip—GCP Capital Partners
Meyers, Melissa—Heritage Partners
Meyersiek, Axel—TowerBrook Capital Partners L.P.
Mhatre, Ravi—Lightspeed Venture Partners (FKA: Weiss, Peck & Greer)
Mi, James—Lightspeed Venture Partners (FKA: Weiss, Peck & Greer)
Mi, Jamies—Conduit Ventures Limited
Mi, John—London Asia Capital Plc (FKA: netvest.com Plc)
Mian, Arslan—BlackRock Private Equity Partners
Miao, Eugene—Highland Capital Management, L.P.
Miao, Jessica—Principle Capital, Ltd.
Miao, Lawrence—Olympus Capital Holdings Asia
Michael, Berk—TA Associates, Inc.
Michael, Glenn—Highway 12 Ventures
Michael, Joseph—Fort Washington Capital Partners Group
Michael, Joseph—Peppertree Capital Management, Inc.
Michael, Marks—Flextronics International, Ltd.
Michael, Sheera—TZP Group LLC
Michael, Wrede—Future Capital AG
Michaeli, Tomer—Carmel Ventures
Michaels, David—Montgomery & Co. (FKA: Digital Coast Partners)
Michaelson, Bob—Bowmark Capital (FKA: Sagitta Private Equity)
Michalik, Christian—Kinderhook Industries
Michalik, Robert—Kinderhook Industries
Michalski, Karen—BDC Capital (AKA: Massachusetts Business Development Corp.)
Michalski, Lutz—Sigma Capital Management
Michas, Alexis—Stonington Partners, Inc.
Michat, Gilles—ACG Private Equity (FKA: Altium Capital Gestion)
Michaud, Jerry—Horizon Technology Finance Management LLC
Michel, Marc—Metamorphic Ventures, LLC (FKA: Gersh Venture Partners)
Michel-Weltert, Louis-Eric—AtriA Capital Partenaires
Michell, Andrew—Queensland BioCapital Fund
Michelman, Jenny—Graphite Capital (FKA: F&C Ventures, Ltd.)
Michelman, Linda—Parallax Capital Partners LLC
Michelsen, Marianne—FSN Capital Partners AS
Michienzi, Mike—American Capital, Ltd.
Michishita, Masahiro—Pacific Rim Ventures Company, Ltd.
Michotey, Nadine—Naxicap Partners SA
Mickelson, Mark—Nogales Investors Management, LLC
Middelthon, Hans—Energy Capital Management AS
Middlemas, George—Apex Venture Partners
Middleton, Fred—Sanderling Ventures
Middleton, Janine—Tasman Capital Partners
Middleton, Shaun—Dunedin Capital Partners, Ltd. (FKA: Dunedin Ventures, Ltd.)
Middleton, Thomas—Blackstone Group, L.P.
Miele, Cameron—Brown Gibbons Lang & Company LLC
Miele, Jay—Shattuck Hammond Partners
Mier Albert, Jose—SODECO (AKA: Soc. Desar. Comarcas Mineras)

Mieskonen, Jari—Conor Venture Partners Oy
Migliero, Steve—Crystal Capital
Migliorino, Robert—W Capital Partners
Mignano, Nick—Crosslink Capital
Mignogna, Cynthia—OpenView Venture Partners
Mihas, Constantine (Dean)—GTCR Golder Rauner LLC
Mii, Nobuo—IGNITE Group, The (AKA: Ignite Associates, LLC)
Mika, Ronald—Huntsman Gay Global Capital LLC
Mika, Ronald—Sorenson Capital Partners
Mikkelsen, Ole—Scandinavian Private Equity A/S
Mikola, Juhani—EQT Funds management Limited
Mikolajczyk, Michael—Catalyst Capital Managment
Mikula, Benn—Frontiers Capital, Ltd.
Mikulowski, Stan—LinkMed AB
Mikuz, Jure—RSG Capital d.o.o.
Milavsky, Gregory—Canterbury Park Capital
Milburn, John—Newton Technology Partners (NTP)
Milder, Donald—Crosspoint Venture Partners
Milder, Donald—Versant Ventures
Miles, Randall—Meridian Capital (FKA: Olympic Capital Partners, LLC)
Miles, Reid—BV-Cornerstone Ventures, L.P.
Miles, Vincent—Abingworth Management, Ltd.
Milgrim, Brett—JLL Partners (FKA: Joseph, Littlejohn & Levy, Inc.)
Milius, Craig—Austin Ventures, L.P.
Milks, Travis—Stonehenge Capital Company
Millar, James—Battelle Ventures
Millar, James—Early Stage Enterprises, L.P.
Millar, Jim—Battelle Memorial Institute
Millar, Ken—SunTrust Equity Partners
Milledge, Eric—Endeavour Vision SA
Miller, Aaron—Great Hill Equity Partners LLC
Miller, Alex—Athlone International, Ltd
Miller, Alex—Svoboda Capital Partners (FKA: Svoboda, Collins LLC)
Miller, Barry—AXA Investment Managers
Miller, Benjamin—Compass Technology Partners
Miller, Brian—Linden LLC
Miller, Chris—BioStar Ventures
Miller, Christian—Eureka Growth Capital
Miller, Cyril—Actem Partners SA (FKA: SPEF LBO)
Miller, David—CIVC Partners LP (FKA: Continental Illinois Venture Corp.)
Miller, Dean—Novitas Capital (FKA: PA Early Stage Partners)
Miller, Dennis—Spark Capital
Miller, Dorin—Cedar Fund
Miller, F. Clayton—Stone Arch Capital LLC
Miller, Gene—Peregrine Ventures, LP
Miller, Gerhard—Cipio Partners
Miller, Greg—Magellan Capital Partners, Ltd.
Miller, Gregory—Blackstone Group, L.P.
Miller, Gregory—GCP Capital Partners
Miller, Harrison—Summit Accelerator Fund
Miller, Harrison—Summit Partners
Miller, J. Sanford—Institutional Venture Partners
Miller, James—NDI Capital (FKA: Neuro Discovery, Inc.)
Miller, Jeb—JAFCO Ventures
Miller, Jeffrey—Alumni Capital Network
Miller, Jim—Haynes and Boone LLC
Miller, Jim—Supply Chain Equity Partners
Miller, John—Banyan Capital Advisors LLC
Miller, Keith—Goode Partners LLC
Miller, Lawrence—Mediphase Venture Partners
Miller, Matt—Walden Venture Capital
Miller, Michael—Allied Capital Corporation
Miller, Michael—CIVC Partners LP (FKA: Continental Illinois Venture Corp.)
Miller, Michael—Centerfield Capital Partners
Miller, Michael—Comspace Development LLC
Miller, Michael—Perseus LLC
Miller, Norvell—Southeast Interactive Technology Funds
Miller, Piotr—AVALLON Sp. z o.o.
Miller, Rainer—SHS Gesellschaft fuer Beteiligungsmanagement mbH
Miller, Randy—Endeavour Capital
Miller, Robert—MidOcean Partners
Miller, Rudy—Miller Capital Corporation
Miller, Seth—DBL Investors (AKA: Double Bottom Line Venture Capital)
Miller, Steven—Origin Ventures, LLC
Miller, Tony—Lemhi Ventures
Miller-Jones, Charles—Cinven, Ltd.
Millet, David—Gemini Investors
Millet, Jean-Pierre—Carlyle Group, The
Millhouse, David—MillhouseIAG
Milligan, David—Bay City Capital LLC
Milligan, Todd—Private Advisors LLC
Millman, Robert—MPM Capital (FKA: MPM Asset Management LLC)
Mills, Alastair—Gresham LLP
Mills, Charles—Lincolnshire Management, Inc.
Mills, Christopher—Undisclosed Firm
Mills, Daniel—Northwater capital Management
Mills, David—Willis Stein & Partners
Mills, Geoffrey—Brown Brothers Harriman & Company (AKA: BBH)
Mills, Jeffrey—Dorset Capital
Mills, Jeffrey—Probitas Partners, Inc.
Mills, Jeffrey—Weston Presidio (FKA: Weston Presidio Capital Management)
Mills, Jim—VantagePoint Venture Partners
Mills, John—GSC Partners (FKA: Greenwich Street Capital Partners)
Mills, Karen—Solera Capital, LLC
Mills, Kojo—Shanduka Fund Mangers (Pty) Ltd.
Mills, Mark—Digital Power Capital, LLC
Mills, Peter—@Ventures
Mills, Steven—DCA Partners, Inc.
Mills, Timothy—Sanderling Ventures
Mills, Timothy—Tenex Greenhouse Ventures
Milne, David—CVC Capital Partners (Europe), Ltd.
Milne, David—SV Life Sciences Advisers
Milne, George—Radius Ventures LLC
Milne, Neil—Abris Capital Partners
Miltenberger, William—Independent Bankers Capital Funds
Mims, Cory—ICV Capital Partners LLC
Min, David—Steamboat Ventures
Min, James—Montgomery & Co. (FKA: Digital Coast Partners)
Min, Ji—Citi Venture Capital International
Min, So-June—.406 Ventures (AKA: Point 406 Ventures)
Mina, Alessandro—Sverica International
Minami, Rio—Carlyle Group, The
Minars, Michael—Quadrangle Group LLC
Mine, Hidetoshi—Ridgeway Capital Partners, Ltd. (FKA:OPE Partners Ltd.)
Mine, Masahiro—Arise Capital Partners, Inc.
Mineiro, Duarte—Espirito Santo (ES) Ventures - Sociedade de Capital de Risco
Miner, Allen—SunBridge Partners
Miner, Dennis—Morgan Creek Capital Management LLC
Miner, John—Altien Ventures LLC
Miner, John—Pivotal Investments LLC
Minerva, Daniel—Alumni Capital Network
Minevielle, Dominique—Champagne Ardenne Croissance
Ming, Cui—China Capital Management Company, Ltd.
Ming, Jenny—Advent International
Ming, Yeh—SVB Capital
Mingyan, Li—Bohai Sea Region Venture Capital Management Company, Ltd.
Minihan, Kenneth—Paladin Capital Management LLC
Minnick, James—Lovell Minnick Partners LLC
Minnick, Mary—Lion Capital (FKA: Hicks Muse (Europe))
Minno, Derek—Wilshire Private Markets
Minocherhomjee, Arda—Chicago Growth Partners (William Blair Capital Partners)
Minoda, Shusaku—Kohlberg, Kravis, Roberts & Company, L.P.
Minor, Jonathan—Investcorp Bank B.S.C.
Minshall, Cathy—De Novo Ventures
Mintah, Nathan—Kingdom Zephyr Africa Management (AKA: KZAM)
Minter, Alison—North Castle Partners
Minton, Greg—Archer Capital
Mintz, Louis—J.F. Lehman & Company
Mion, Gianni—Orlando Capital Management GmbH
Mir, Abrar—NBD Sana Capital
Mirabelli, Christopher—HealthCare Ventures LLC
Miran Khan, Aman—BPE Unternehmensbeteiligungen GmbH
Miranda, Antonio—Littlejohn & Company LLC
Miranda, Gonzalo—Austral Capital
Miranda, Stan—Partners Capital Investment Group, LLC
Mirani, Hemal—CVC Asia Pacific, Ltd.
Mirani, Hemal—CVC Capital Partners (Europe), Ltd.
Mirchandani, Satin—Impact Venture Partners
Miron, Claude—BMO Capital Corporation
Miron, Claude—Business Development Bank of Canada
Miron, Claude—InVivo Ventures
Mirow, Thomas—European Bank for Reconstruction and Development
Mirra, Anthony—Court Square Capital Partners
Mirza, Muzzafar—Odyssey Investment Partners, LLC
Miscoll, Douglas—Newlight Associates
Misfeldt, Naheed Ismaili—Aberdare Ventures
Mish-Vered, Tal—Gmul Investment Company, Ltd.
Mishima, Tetsuya—Watervein Partners Co., Ltd.
Mishkin, Max—Water Street Healthcare Partners
Misholi, Boaz—YL Ventures GP, Ltd.
Mishra, Sunil—Adams Street Partners LLC
Mishra, Sunil—CCMP Capital Advisors LLC
Mishra, Sunil—New Mountain Capital LLC

Misso, Jerome—Balderton Capital (FKA: Benchmark Capital Europe)

Mistry, Dharmash—Balderton Capital (FKA: Benchmark Capital Europe)

Mistry, Minesh—General Atlantic LLC

Mistry, Samir—Jina Ventures, Inc.

Mital, Neeraj—Evercore Partners

Mitard, Thomas—H.I.G. Capital LLC

Mitchell, Andrew—North East Finance

Mitchell, Anne—Fidelity Ventures

Mitchell, Anne—Volition Capital

Mitchell, Christopher—Spectrum Equity Investors

Mitchell, Daniel—Sequel Venture Partners

Mitchell, David—Transportation Resource Partners (TRP) (FKA: Penske Capital)

Mitchell, George—Bank of Scotland Corporate

Mitchell, Ivar—Andlinger & Company, Inc.

Mitchell, John—Audax Group

Mitchell, Kate—Scale Venture Partners

Mitchell, Lee—Thoma Bravo LLC

Mitchell, Lee—Thoma Cressey Bravo

Mitchell, Mark—Safeguard Scientifics, Inc.

Mitchell, Matthew—Heritage Partners

Mitchell, Maureen—Highland Capital Management, L.P.

Mitchell, Steven—Argonaut Private Equity

Mitchell, Stuart—Ironbridge Capital Pty., Ltd.

Mitchell, Timothy—Ziff Brothers Investments

Mitgang, Michael—Rigel Associates LLC

Mitjavile, Regis—IFE Mezzanine

Mitri, Kerim—SHUAA Partners

Mitsakos, Nicholas—Monitor Venture Management, L.L.C.

Mitsuda, Hideo—Polaris Principal Finance Co., Ltd.

Mitsui, Maki—Carlyle Group, The

Mittal, Alok—Canaan Partners

Mittal, Deepak—Edelweiss Capital, Ltd.

Mittal, Nishant—General Atlantic LLC

Mittelberg, Andreas—BGM Beteiligungsgesellschaft KS Ravensburg

Mitushin, Nikolay—ABRT Venture Fund

Miu, Thomas—Daiwa PI Partners Co., Ltd.

Miura-Ko, Ann—Floodgate Fund, L.P.

Mix, Harald—Altor Equity Partners AB

Mixer, David—Columbia Capital LLC

Mixer, David—Point Judith Capital

Mixon, Malachi—Resilience Capital Partners LLC

Miyake, Suguru—Japan Private Equity Co., Ltd

Miyamoto, Kazunori—Arise Capital Partners, Inc.

Miyamoto, Yuji—Fund Creation Co., Ltd.

Miyasaki, Alan—Blackstone Group, L.P.

Miyasato, Leigh-Ann—Manoa Venture Partners

Miyashita, Shinji—CrossBridge Venture Partners

Miyazaki, Tadashi—Mizuho Capital Partners Co., Ltd.

Miyoshi, Yasuyuki—Longreach Group, Ltd., The

Mize, Christopher—GCP Capital Partners

Mizeur, Mike—Companion Capital Management, Inc.

Mizukami, Kei—CVC Asia Pacific, Ltd.

Mizukami, Kei—CVC Capital Partners (Europe), Ltd.

Mizukawa, Atsuhiko—STB Investment Corporation

Mizuno, Hiromichi—Coller Capital

Mizushima, Tadashi—Daiwa Quantum Capital, Ltd.

Mlavsky, Ed—Gemini Israel Funds, Ltd.

Mnaymneh, Sami—H.I.G. Capital LLC

Moalemzadeh, Shary—Carlyle Group, The

Moalmi, Faris—HBG Holdings, Ltd.

Moatti, Olivier—Abenex Capital (FKA: ABN AMRO Capital France)

Mobbs, Jeremy—Innvotec, Ltd.

Mocarski, Thadeus—Key Venture Partners

Mock, Lawrence—Navigation Capital Partners

Mock, Ronald—Ontario Teachers' Pension Plan

Mockett, Tim—Climate Change Capital, Ltd.

Model, Brian—Stonehenge Capital Company

Modersitzki, Blake—Pelion Venture Partners

Modesitt, Brian—Vestar Capital Partners, Inc.

Modi, Nilesh—Milestone Religare Investment Advisors Pvt., Ltd.

Modi, Sangeeta—Aureos Capital, Ltd.

Modica, Mark—Avansis Ventures, LLC

Modig, Charlotta—Volvo Technology Transfer AB

Mody, Rahul—GCP Capital Partners

Moehrle, Christina—Star Ventures Management GmbH & Co. KG

Moelchert, Louis—Private Advisors LLC

Moeller, George—Robeco Private Equity

Moeller, Thomas—BioMedPartners

Moens, Marc—Pentech Ventures, LLP

Moerel, Wouter—AlpInvest Partners N.V.

Moerschel, Greg—Beecken, Petty & Company LLC

Moeschel, Helga—INTRO-Verwaltungs GmbH

Moessner, Juergen—Global Capital Finance

Moffat, Kimberly—Sterling Partners

Mogk, Peter—Huron Capital Partners LLC

Mogoroase, Cristina—Axxess Capital Partners S.A. (FKA: Enterprise Capital)

Mogull, Marc—Doughty Hanson & Co., Ltd.

Mohammadioun, Said—TechOperators LLC

Mohammed, Idris—Development Partners International

Mohan Menon, A.—Zeus Inframanagement Pvt, Ltd.

Mohan, Kevin—Summit Partners

Mohan, Ravi—Shasta Ventures Management LLC

Mohan, Venkat—Norwest Venture Partners

Mohaupt, Jorg—Continuum Group, Ltd. (AKA: Continuum Advisory, Ltd.)

Mohr, Claudio—affentranger associates (FKA: Ultreia Capital, Ltd.)

Mohren, Stephan—Wellington Partners Venture Capital GmbH

Moinet, Edouard—Cathay Capital Private Equity SAS

Moitra, Shamik—Aditya Birla Capital Advisors Pvt., Ltd.

Moje, Anja—Beaufort Capital GmbH

Mojela, Louisa—Wipprivate Equity

Mok, Martin—EQT Funds management Limited

Mok, Peter—KLM Capital Management, Inc.

Mok, Weng-Sun—Affinity Equity Partners

Mol, Bert—AAC Capital Partners

Molcho, Avi—Forbion Capital Partners

Moldow, Charles—Foundation Capital

Molefe, Popo—Lereko Invesments Property, Ltd.

Molenaar, Boudewijn—Gilde Buy Out Partners

Molenaar, Boudewijn—Gilde Investment Management B.V.

Moley, Andrew—Lightspeed Venture Partners (FKA: Weiss, Peck & Greer)

Moley, Dick—Storm Ventures LLC

Molin, Jean-Pierre—IFE Mezzanine

Molina, Jose Luis—Altamar Private Equity

Molinaro, Samuel—Progress Investment Management Company

Moliner, Jose Tomas—iNova Capital SCR SA

Molins Gil, Joaquin—Active Capital Partners S.L.

Moll, David—Infield Capital

Mollatt, Andreas—Teknoinvest AS

Moller, Christopher—Devon Park Bioventures

Moller, Merete Lundbye—Sunstone Capital A/S

Moller, Peter—FSN Capital Partners AS

Mollman, Chad—Ascent Equity Capital (FKA: Pinnacle Equity Capital)

Mollof, Wladimir—ACG Private Equity (FKA: Altium Capital Gestion)

Molloy, Richard—Gordon River Capital

Molner, Phillip—Primus Capital Funds

Moloney, Damian—Industry Funds Management

Molyneux, Robert—Imperial Capital Corporation

Momoi, Kunio—Meiji Capital Co., Ltd.

Momsen, Robert—MedVenture Associates

Monaghan, Art—Granite Equity Partners

Monahan, David—Colony Capital LLC

Monahan, Lee—Harren Equity Partners

Monarca, Daniele—Abacus Invest S.C.A. SICAR

Monath, Thomas—Kleiner Perkins Caufield & Byers

Moncrief, L. Ray—Southern Appalachian Management Company LLC

Mondre, Greg—Silver Lake Sumeru

Monego, Philip—Allegis Capital (AKA: Media Technology Ventures)

Money-Kyrle, Nicholas—Steadfast Capital GmbH (FKA: BHF Private Equity GmbH)

Monis, Marco—21 Centrale Partners

Monis, Marco—21 Partners SpA

Moniz, Michael—Paladin Capital Management LLC

Monk, Robert—Allied Capital Corporation

Monmousseau, Stephane—Pragma Capital

Monnier, Edward—Corridor Capital, LLC

Monribot, Mathias—Petit Poucet Participation

Monroe, Kevin—VCFA Group

Monsalve, Sergio—Norwest Venture Partners

Monsky, John—Oak Hill Capital Management, Inc.

Monster, Robert—Monster Venture Partners

Montagu, Rupert—Greenspring Associates, Inc.

Montana, Gabriel—One Earth Capital LLC

Montanari, Claudio—Sanpaolo IMI Private Equity SpA

Montano, Chris—Seraphima Ventures

Montanus, Gerard—Atlas Venture, Ltd.

Monte-Sano, Alex—Octane Capital Management

Monteleone, Michael—Point Lookout Capital Partners, L.P.

Montezemolo, Luca—Undisclosed Firm

Montgomery, George—Montgomery & Co. (FKA: Digital Coast Partners)

Montgomery, H. DuBose—Menlo Ventures

Montgomery, James—Montgomery & Co. (FKA: Digital Coast Partners)

Montgomery, Jeffrey—GMT Communications Partners LLP

Montgomery, Mark—Initium Capital LLC

Montgomery, Michael—Montgomery & Co. (FKA: Digital Coast Partners)

Montgomery, Ralph—Houlihan, Lokey, Howard & Zukin

Montgomery, Richard—VCE Capital

Monthye, Troy—UIB Capital, Inc.

Montoya, David—SeaView Capital Advisors, LLC
Moochhala, Murtaza—Citi Venture Capital International
Moock, Hans—Equita Management GmbH
Moody, Steve—Calvert Funds
Moody, Steve—Calvert Social Venture Partners, L.P.
Moody, Trevor—Frazier Healthcare and Technology Ventures
Moody, William—Castle Creek Capital LLC
Moon, Byung hak—Korea Venture Investment Corporation
Moon, Greg—SoftBank Ventures Korea, Inc.
Moon, John—Morgan Stanley Private Equity
Moon, Michael—Calera Capital (FKA: Fremont Partners)
Moonly, Scott—Brookstone Capital, Inc.
Moonly, Scott—Johnson & Johnson Development Corporation
Moons, Raf—Fortis Private Equity NV/SA (FKA: VIV NV)
Moor, Markus—Emerald Technology Ventures AG
Moore Haynes, Hollie—Silver Lake Sumeru
Moore, Alan—Red Oak Capital
Moore, Blake—UBS Capital Corporation
Moore, Charles—Nobska Ventures
Moore, Chris—Redpoint Ventures
Moore, Church—Kelso & Company
Moore, Craig—American Capital, Ltd.
Moore, Dan—Longstreet Partners, LLC
Moore, Darla—Goff Moore Strategic Partners
Moore, Dennis—Odyssey Investment Partners, LLC
Moore, Duncan—East West Capital Partners Pte, Ltd.
Moore, Geoffrey—Mohr Davidow Ventures
Moore, Gordon—Cinven, Ltd.
Moore, Hazel—FirstVentures
Moore, Jeffrey—MP Healthcare Venture Management, Inc.
Moore, John—3i (US)
Moore, John—Robin Hood Ventures
Moore, Joseph—DesignWorks Investments
Moore, Kenneth—First Reserve Corporation
Moore, Laura—Nobska Ventures
Moore, Michael—Maverick Capital Ltd.
Moore, Ryan—GrandBanks Capital
Moore, Simon—Carlyle Group, The
Moore, Stephen—Motorola Ventures
Moore, W. Merrette—IDEA Fund Partners
Moores, Bill—Oaktree Capital Management LLC
Moores, Rob—Bridgepoint Capital, Ltd.
Moorhead, Alex—Tandem Expansion Fund, Inc.
Moorhead, Rodman—Warburg Pincus LLC
Moorin, Jay—ProQuest Investments
Moorse, Dan—Thayer Hidden Creek
Moortgat, Katherine—Mohr Davidow Ventures
Moose, Lisa—Third Security LLC
Moosholzer, Josef—TVM Capital GmbH
Moot, Alex—Seaflower Ventures
Moragne, John—Trident Capital
Morales Cortes, Juan Carlos—European Capital Financial Services Ltd.
Morali-Efinowicz, Monika—Advent International
Moraly, Dana—Clearstone Venture Partners
Moran, Garrett—Blackstone Group, L.P.
Moran, James—North Bridge Venture Partners
Moran, Jason—Thomas Weisel Partners Group, Inc.
Moran, Kathleen—Greenbriar Equity Group LLC
Moran, Matt—Anglo Irish Capital Partners Limited
Moran, Michael—Brockway Moran & Partners, Inc.
Moran, Michael—Linsalata Capital Partners
Moran, Peter—DCM
Moran, Richard—Trivest Partners, L.P.
Moran, Robert—Allco Equity Partners Management Pty Ltd.
Morand, Patrick—SWMF Life Science Venture Fund, L.P.
Morandi, Nik—Pantheon Ventures, Ltd.
Morck, Anders—Bure Equity
Mordehachvili, Paulo—Axxon Group
More, Anand—Bain Capital
More, Bob—Frazier Healthcare and Technology Ventures
Moreau, Olivier—Orium SAS
Moreau, Richard—Harvest Partners LLC
Moreland, Ira—ICV Capital Partners LLC
Morelli, Vincenzo—TPG Capital
Moreno, Michael—Atlantic-Pacific Capital, Inc.
Morff, Robert—Hatteras Venture Partners (FKA:Catalysta Partners)
Morfitt, Brian—Frazier Healthcare and Technology Ventures
Morgan, Alan—MMC Ventures, Ltd.
Morgan, Allen—Mayfield Fund
Morgan, Eric—National City Equity Partners, Inc.
Morgan, Frank—Coller Capital
Morgan, George—Ridgemont Equity Partners
Morgan, Howard—Branford Castle, Inc.
Morgan, Howard—First Round Capital
Morgan, Howard—idealab!
Morgan, Jeremy—New Mountain Capital LLC
Morgan, John—Highland Capital Management, L.P.
Morgan, John—Pantheon Ventures, Ltd.
Morgan, Jonathan—Long Point Capital Inc.
Morgan, Michael—Caltius Equity Partners
Morgan, Richard—Amphion Capital Management, LLC (FKA: Wolfensohn Associates)
Morgan, Terry—Capstone Capital Partners LLC
Morgan, Thomas—New Mountain Capital LLC
Morgenfeld, Todd—Silver Lake Sumeru
Morgenstein, Morris—Capital Resource Co. of Connecticut
Morgenstern, Marc—C&T Access Ventures
Morgenthal, Lawrence—Bank of America Capital Advisors (BACA)
Morgenthaler, David—Morgenthaler Ventures
Morgenthaler, Gary—Morgenthaler Ventures
Morgenthau, Anthony—Morgenthau Venture Partners, LLC
Mori, Ikuo—Daiwa Securities SMBC Principal Investments Co., Ltd.
Mori, Takeshi—Zenshin Capital Management
Moriarty, Michael—IndexAtlas Group
Moritz, J. Kenneth—Stonewood Capital Management, Inc.
Moritz, Michael—Sequoia Capital
Morjaria, Raj—Aureos Capital, Ltd.
Morkved, Jorgen—Verdane Capital (FKA: Four Seasons Venture Capital AS)
Morley, Andrew—Montis Capital, LLC
Morley, Candida—LDC (FKA: Lloyds TSB Development Capital, Ltd.)
Morningstar, John—Castle Harlan, Inc.
Morningstar, John—Wellspring Capital Management LLC
Moro, Paolo—Synergo SGR S.p.A.
Morrill, Nicholas—Rutland Fund Management, Ltd. (AKA: Rutland Partners LLP)
Morris, Ben—Signet Healthcare Partners (FKA: Sanders Morris Harris)
Morris, Blake—CHB Capital Partners
Morris, Bobby—Boxwood Capital Partners, LLC
Morris, Brett—Neo Technology Ventures Pty, Ltd.
Morris, Charles (Chip)—Integral Capital Partners
Morris, Erik—Roark Capital Group
Morris, Frederic—Brook Venture Partners LLC
Morris, Jeffrey—NeoMed Management AS
Morris, John—GKM Ventures
Morris, John—HarbourVest Partners LLC
Morris, Lester—Mesirow Private Equity Investments, Inc.
Morris, Mark—Blue Point Capital Partners (FKA: Key Equity Capital)
Morris, Mark—Morgan Creek Capital Management LLC
Morris, Michael—Creation Capital LLC
Morris, Nigel—Columbia Capital LLC
Morris, Peter—New Enterprise Associates, Inc.
Morris, Robert—Y Combinator
Morrison, Alastair—Standard Chartered Private Equity, Ltd.
Morrison, D. Neal—Pamlico Capital
Morrison, Don—OMERS Private Equity
Morrison, Jay—Rising Tide Fund
Morrison, John—Goldner Hawn Johnson & Morrison, Inc.
Morrison, Leslie—Invest Northern Ireland
Morrison, Paul—Republic Financial Corporation
Morrison, Sean—Maxam Capital Corp.
Morrison, Tucker—Headwaters Merchant Bank
Morriss, Nicholas—EMAlternatives LLC
Morrissette, Mark—North Atlantic Capital Corporation
Morrissey, Michael—Inverness Graham Investments
Morrissey, Todd—LLR Partners, Inc.
Morrone, Jonathan—Wall Street Venture Capital
Morrow, William—Ground Swell Equity Partners
Morse, Monica—Cargill Ventures
Morse, Richard—GCP Capital Partners
Morse, Robert—Oak Hill Capital Management, Inc.
Morse, Thomas—Liberty Venture Partners, Inc.
Morteani, Arne—ETF Manager LLP
Mortensen, Mikael—SLS Invest AB
Morton, Ian—Crimson
Morz, Siegfried—Capexit Beteiligungsmanagement AG
Mosca, Franco—IDeA Capital Funds Sgr SpA
Moseley, Allen—Noro-Moseley Partners
Moseley, Charles—Noro-Moseley Partners
Moseley, Frederick—LLM Capital Partners LLC
Moseley, Harry—Blackstone Group, L.P.
Moser, Andrew—Kairos Capital Partners
Moser, Carlo—Investitori Associati SpA
Moser, Johann—Austria Wirtschaftsservice Gesellschaft mbH
Moser, Kent—Blackstone Group, L.P.
Moser, Thomas—PONTIS Capital GmbH
Moses, Oliver—MTS Health Partners, L.P.
Moshir, Kevin—Moshir Venture Partners

Moshir, Sean—Moshir Venture Partners
Moskowitz, Cliff—Tailwind Capital Partners
Moskowitz, Jason—Merit Capital Partners (FKA:William Blair Mezzanine)
Moskowitz, Robert—Shamrock Holdings, Inc.
Mosley, I. Sigmund—Armada Venture Group LLC
Mosley, I. Sigmund—Imlay Investments
Mosoiu, Razvan—Mackenzie Capital srl
Moss, Edwin—Arcturus Capital
Moss, Edwin—Lincolnshire Management, Inc.
Moss, Jeffrey—Sterling Partners
Moss, Malcolm—Beringea LLC
Moss, Sylvia—Blackstone Group, L.P.
Mostyn-Williams, Stephen—CapVest Management Ltd
Moszer, David—FriedbergMilstein, LLC
Motley, Joel—Delany Capital Management Corporation (DCM)
Mott, David—New Enterprise Associates, Inc.
Mott, Edward—Oxford Capital Partners
Mott, Ted—Oxford Capital Partners
Motte, Alexandre—AXA Private Equity
Motte, Olivier—Turenne Capital SA
Motulsky, John—Stonehill Capital Management
Motzfeldt, Christian—Vaekstfonden (AKA: Danish Growth Fund, The)
Moua, Chong—American Capital, Ltd.
Moua, Chong—Boathouse Capital
Moue, Hidemi—Japan Industrial Partners, Inc.
Mougenot, Gilles—Argos Soditic SA
Mould, John—Hermes Private Equity Management, Ltd.
Mould, John—New Star Asset Management
Moulin, Andre—SORIDEC
Moulton, Eben—Seacoast Capital
Mountain, Cliff—Accent Capital
Moura, Andre—New Mountain Capital LLC
Moussalem, Nadra—Colony Capital LLC
Mowinckel, John—Investindustrial Partners, Ltd.
Mowlem, Michael—LGV Capital, Ltd. (FKA: Legal & General Ventures, Ltd.)
Moxon, Paul—AAC Capital Partners
Moy, Jennifer—Dawntreader Ventures
Moya, Josep Maria—Delta Partners FZ LLC
Moye, Andrew—AAC Capital Partners
Moynihan, Chester—Allegro Private Equity Pty, Ltd.
Moyo, Nkosana—Actis Capital LLP
Moyo, Nkosana—Batanai Capital Finance
Moyo, Rute—Shanduka Fund Mangers (Pty) Ltd.
Moyses, Christiano—FIR Capital Partners, Ltd.
Mpofu, Ndaba—Batanai Capital Finance
Mraz, Paul—Point Judith Capital
Mrnjavac, Ljubo—Rosengard Invest AB
Mrozek, Therese—Weston Presidio (FKA: Weston Presidio Capital Management)
Mruck, Chris—Advent International
Mtonga, Daudi—Venture Partners Botswana
Mucci, Achille—INTERBANCA SpA
Much, Paul—Houlihan, Lokey, Howard & Zukin
Mudd, Daniel—Fortress Investment Group LLC
Mudge, Jeffrey—Shoreview Industries
Muehlenbeck, Frank—firstVentury GmbH
Muelder, Philip—Permira Advisers LLP
Mueller, Christoph—Shaw Kwei & Partners
Mueller, Claus-Georg—mic AG
Mueller, Jason—Saw Mill Capital, LLC
Mueller, John—CapitalWorks LLC
Mueller, Kurt—Target Partners GmbH
Muenchbach, Martin—Bellevue Asset Management AG
Muffler, Juerg—Fabrel Lotos (AKA: Fabrel AG)
Muftuler, Omer—Odien Group
Mugford, Kristin—Bain Capital
Mugnai, Andrea—PM & Partners SpA
Muhtadie, Fayez—Stone Point Capital LLC
Muijrers, Joep—Life Sciences Partners BV
Muir, Craig—Third Rock Ventures LLC
Muir, Jeffrey—Fulcrum Ventures
Muirhead, Sandy—Phoenix Equity Partners (FKA: DLJ European Private Equity)
Mukherjee, Anjan—Blackstone Group, L.P.
Mukohira, Tak—MP Healthcare Venture Management, Inc.
Mukouhara, Michitaka—Mitsubishi UFJ Capital Co., Ltd.
Mulder, Geert-Jan—Forbion Capital Partners
Mulderry, Andrew—Alta Communications
Mulderry, Dan—Paul Capital Partners
Mulderry, Daniel—Paul Capital Partners
Mulet, Juan—Axon Capital
Mulhern, George—Highway 12 Ventures
Mullaney, Patrick—Cabot Properties, Inc.
Mullen, David—HSBC Capital (Canada)
Mullen, Fergal—Highland Capital Partners LLC
Mullen, Mike—JMH Capital
Mullen, Terrence—Arsenal Capital Partners
Muller, Hans-Ulrich—Partners Group AG
Muller, Luc—Otto Capital Partners
Muller, Stefan—ARC China, Inc.
Muller, Wolfgang—LGT Capital Partners AG
Mullett, Connor—Updata Partners
Mulliez, Jerome—Creadev SAS
Mulligan, Gregory—Bay Capital Advisors, LLC
Mulligan, Kate—Advance Asset Management, Ltd.
Mulligan, William—Primus Capital Funds
Mullin, M. Hadley—TSG Consumer Partners
Mullins, Paul—Permira Advisers LLP
Mulloy, Corey—Highland Capital Partners LLC
Mulloy, Jennifer—TA Associates, Inc.
Mulrow, William—Paladin Capital Management LLC
Multani, Arneek—Trident Capital
Mulvaney, Brian—Headwaters Merchant Bank
Mulvey, Boyd—Create Partners Ltd
Mulye, Vishakha—ICICI Venture Funds Management Co., Pvt. Ltd. (FKA: TDICI)
Mumford, Hugh—Acuity Capital LLP (FKA: Electra Partners LLP)
Mumford, John—Crosspoint Venture Partners
Mumma, Mitchell—Intersouth Partners
Munafo, Christian—Thomas Weisel Partners Group, Inc.
Munch-Thore, Alex—Kistefos Venture Capital AS
Munchmeyer, Hans Hermann—Mulligan BioCapital AG
Mundassery, Appu—H.I.G. Capital LLC
Mundassery, Appu—Highland Capital Management, L.P.
Mundheim, Peter—Stone Point Capital LLC
Mundie, Don—Delta Capital Management LLC
Mundkur, Yatin—Artiman Ventures
Mundt, Jason—Siguler Guff & Company
Mundt, Kevin—Vestar Capital Partners, Inc.
Mundy, Justin—Climate Change Capital, Ltd.
Muniz, Mary Theresa—C.M. Capital Corporation
Munk, Anthony—Onex Corporation
Munnell, Thomas—C.W. Downer & Company (FKA: Downer & Company)
Munnich, Walter—American Capital, Ltd.
Munnich, Walter—European Capital Financial Services Ltd.
Munoz, Rafael—MCH Private Equity SA
Munro, Brad—GrowthWorks
Munro, Rod—Vendages
Munro, Simon—Lime Rock Partners LLC
Munson, Peter—Cardinal Equity Partners (FKA: Cardinal Ventures)
Munsters, Roderick—Robeco Private Equity
Munthe, Gert W.—Herkules Capital AS
Munton, Dick—Cinven, Ltd.
Muoto, Martin—Accretive LLC (FKA: Accretive Technology Partners LLC)
Murad, Alexander—Firm Factory Network
Murakami, Teru—University of Tokyo Edge Capital Co., Ltd., The (AKA: UTEC)
Murane, Peter—Brand Journey Capital LP
Murchison, J. Hardy—First Reserve Corporation
Murdoch, Britton—Strattech Partners LLC
Murdock, Jerry—Insight Venture Partners
Murphree, Dennis—Murphree Venture Partners
Murphy, Barbara—Carlyle Group, The
Murphy, Brian—NewSpring Capital
Murphy, Brian—Portfolio Advisors LLC
Murphy, Brian—Solera Capital, LLC
Murphy, George—Taraval Associates LLC
Murphy, Gerry—Blackstone Group, L.P.
Murphy, Gordon—Auda Private Equity LLC
Murphy, Jacqui—Tech Capital Partners
Murphy, John—Investec Wentworth Private Equity Pty., Ltd.
Murphy, John—Murphy & Partners, L.P.
Murphy, Jonathan—Portfolio Advisors LLC
Murphy, Kate—Horsley Bridge Partners
Murphy, Kathy—Trinity Ventures
Murphy, Kevin—Encore Consumer Capital LLC
Murphy, Kevin—Pacific Alliance Capital Group
Murphy, Kevin—Silverfern Group, Inc., The
Murphy, Leland—Trellis Partners
Murphy, Matthew—Kleiner Perkins Caufield & Byers
Murphy, Neil—CBPE Capital, LLP (AKA: Close Brothers Private Equity, Ltd.)
Murphy, Owen—ACT Venture Capital, Ltd.
Murphy, Paul—Sentinel Capital Partners
Murphy, Ronald—Makaira Venture Partners
Murphy, Ryan—Stephens Group, Inc.
Murphy, Scott—Advantage Capital Partners
Murphy, Sharon—WP Global Partners Inc.
Murphy, Thomas—General Atlantic LLC
Murphy, Timothy—Octane Capital Management
Murray, Andrew—ITU Ventures
Murray, Arthur—Union Capital Corporation
Murray, Campbell—Novartis Venture Fund (FKA: Novartis Corp.)
Murray, Dave—Southern Capitol Ventures
Murray, Fulton—Hunt BioVentures
Murray, James—Bridgepoint Capital, Ltd.
Murray, James—Court Square Ventures, LLC
Murray, John—Technology Venture Partners Pty Ltd.
Murray, Jonathan—Early Stage Partners, L.P.

Ndiaye, Papa Madiaw—Advanced Finance & Investment Group LLC (AKA: AFIG)
Neal, Jeffrey—Horizon Capital
Neal, Stephen—Cooley Godward LLP
Nealy, Larry—Axiom Equity Partners
Neary, James—Warburg Pincus LLC
Neath, Martin—Adams Capital Management, Inc.
Nebel, Simon—Aravis SA
Nebenzahl, Charles—CS Capital Partners LLC
Nebgen, Georg—NGN Capital LLC
Neblett, Glenn—Capital Southwest Corporation
Nedeau, Nicholas—Lincolnshire Management, Inc.
Nedelec, Jean-Paul—Oaktree Capital Management LLC
Nedungadi, Ajit—TA Associates, Inc.
Nedwed, Peter—PONTIS Capital GmbH
Nee, Kevin—Wilshire Private Markets
Needham, George—Needham Asset Management
Needleman, Philip—Prospect Venture Partners (FKA: Prospect Management LLC)
Neeley, Tad—Gemini Partners, Inc.
Neels, Guido—Essex Woodlands Health Ventures
Neermann, Jorg—DVC Deutsche Venture Capital
Neermann, Jorg—Life Sciences Partners BV
Nef, Robert—Swiss Re Private Equity Advisers
Neff, P. Sherrill—Quaker BioVentures, Inc.
Negus, Kevin—CampVentures
Negus, Russell—Abacus Private Equity (ASA: Abacus Capital Corporation)
Neidhart, Jim—Crossroads Capital Partners, LLC
Neighbours, David—Waud Capital Partners LLC
Neighoff, Robert—American Capital, Ltd.
Neild, W. Carter—OrbiMed Advisors LLC
Neilson, Fergus—DIF Capital Partners, Ltd.
Neiman, Seth—Crosspoint Venture Partners
Neimark, Jason—Sun Capital Partners, Inc.
Neis, John—American Capital, Ltd.
Neis, John—Venture Investors LLC
Nelles, Norbert—Odewald & Compagnie GmbH
Nelsen, Robert—ARCH Venture Partners
Nelson, Amy—SCF Partners
Nelson, Andrea—Spell Capital Partners LLC
Nelson, Anna—Wakefield Group
Nelson, Carl—Thayer Hidden Creek
Nelson, David—Divergent Capital Partners (FKA: Bluefire Innovation)
Nelson, Hakan—Oresund-Healthcare A/S
Nelson, James—Integra Ventures
Nelson, John—Brown Brothers Harriman & Company (AKA: BBH)
Nelson, John—HarbourVest Partners LLC
Nelson, John—Shepherd Ventures
Nelson, Jonathan—Providence Equity Partners LLC
Nelson, Michael—Redleaf Group, Inc
Nelson, Michael—Wind Point Partners
Nelson, Mitchell—Asia Pacific Ventures
Nelson, Steve—Wakefield Group
Nelson, Thomas—Wakefield Group
Nelson, Timothy—Saw Mill Capital, LLC
Nelson, Travis—Pacific Partners
Nemeskal, David—Fidelity Equity Partners
Nemeth, Wayne—Sprout Group
Nemirovsky, Ofer—HarbourVest Partners LLC
Nenadovic, Daniel—Comvest Investment Partners
Neofytou, Neofytos—First Elements Ventures, Ltd. (FKA: SFS Corporate Analysis)
Neporent, Mark—Cerberus Capital Management, L.P.
Nergaard, Birger—Verdane Capital (FKA: Four Seasons Venture Capital AS)
Nesbitt, William—Good Energies, Inc.
Neske, Martina—ACA Equity-Partners GmbH
Ness, Oliver—Abacus Private Equity (ASA: Abacus Capital Corporation)
Nessi, Claudio—NeoMed Management AS
Netjes, David—Kohlberg, Kravis, Roberts & Company, L.P.
Netravali, Arun—Omni Capital Group LLC
Nettles, Cory—Generation Growth Capital, Inc.
Neubauer, David—Atherton Venture Partners, LLC
Neubeck, Peter—TVM Capital GmbH
Neuenschwander, Rhett—Huntsman Gay Global Capital LLC
Neuenschwander, Rhett—Sorenson Capital Partners
Neugarten, Ilan—Dor Ventures Management SA
Neuger, Win—AIG Capital Partners
Neuger, Win—PineBridge Investments
Neuhaus, Gottfried—Neuhaus Partners GmbH
Neuhauser, Horst—"schilling" Unternehmensbeteiligung GmbH
Neuman, Joshua—Irving Place Capital
Neumann, Ingeborg—PEPPERMINT. Financial Partners (FKA schroder + partner)
Neumann, Jan-Daniel—Brockhaus Private Equity GmbH
Neumann, Mark—Nobska Ventures
Neumann, Martin—Creathor Venture Management GmbH
Neumann, Steven—KRG Capital Partners LLC
Neundorfer, Paul—Blue Point Capital Partners (FKA: Key Equity Capital)
Neustaetter, Thomas—JK&B Capital
Neuwirth, Daniel—Quad Ventures
Nevatia, Vishal—India Value Fund Advisors Private Ltd. (FKA: GW Capital)
Neveu, Brigitte—Cobalt Capital SAS
Nevin, Andrew—Merrill Lynch Capital Partners
New, Jason—Blackstone Group, L.P.
Newbold, Gregory—Torch Hill Partners
Newbold, Robert—Graham Partners, Inc.
Newburger, Martin—KSL Capital Partners
Newby, Tom—Montgomery & Co. (FKA: Digital Coast Partners)
Newcom, Jennings—Lovell Minnick Partners LLC
Newcomb, T.R.—General Atlantic LLC
Newell, Carla—Technology Crossover Ventures
Newell, Carol—Renewal Partners
Newell, Dan—McGowan Capital Group
Newell, Tom—Cascadia Capital LLC
Newhall, C. Ashton—Greenspring Associates, Inc.
Newhall, Charles—New Enterprise Associates, Inc.
Newhouse, Douglas—Sterling Investment Partners
Newman, Andrew—Low Carbon Accelerator
Newman, Arthur—Blackstone Group, L.P.
Newman, Barry—NeoCarta Ventures, Inc.
Newman, Bruce—Entrepreneur Partners, L.P.
Newman, Dan—Sofinnova Partners
Newman, David—Ridgelift Ventures
Newman, Harold—Neuberger Berman LLC
Newman, Harris—TZP Group LLC
Newman, Henry—Solstice Capital
Newman, Kenneth—Vexiom Equity Partners, L.P.
Newman, Kevin—Atlantic-Pacific Capital, Inc.
Newman, Simon—JP Capital Partners, LLC
Newman, Victoria—Virgin Green Fund
Newman, William—Northwest Technology Ventures
Newmark, Gregg—American Capital, Ltd.
Newmark, Tammy—EcoEnterprises Fund
Newnam, Todd—Carlyle Group, The
Newsam, John—NGEN Partners LLC (FKA: NextGen Partners LLC)
Newsome, Michael—Zachary Scott & Co.
Newton, Jeffrey—Gemini Investors
Newton, Jeremy—National Endowment for Science, Technology & the Arts NESTA
Newton, Matthew—Columbia Capital LLC
Newton, Ray—Evercore Partners
Ng, Ben—SAIF Partners
Ng, Chee We—Arsenal Capital Partners
Ng, Chee Yuen—SEDCO Direct Investment Group
Ng, Doris—AIF Capital Pvt, Ltd.
Ng, Edmond Chi-Man—Axiom Asia Private Capital
Ng, Francis L.F.—SEAVI Advent Corporation, Ltd.
Ng, Judith—Ingenious Haus Group
Ng, Kimberly—Thomas Weisel Partners Group, Inc.
Ng, Lak-Chuan—Affinity Equity Partners
Ng, Maisy—Add Partners, Ltd.
Ng, Michael—Gemplus SCA
Ng, Philip—FEO Ventures Pte., Ltd.
Ng, Thomas—GGV Capital
Ng, Wing-Fai—Primus Pacific Partners
Ng, Yi Pin—GGV Capital
Ngo, A. Catherine—Startup Capital Ventures L.P.
Ngqula, K—Industrial Development Corporation of South Africa Ltd (IDC)
Ngu Ewodo, Jude—BayTech Venture Capital Beratungs GmbH
Nguyen, Daniel—Ares Management, Inc.
Nguyen, David—Court Square Capital Partners
Nguyen, Franck—AXA Private Equity
Nguyen, Hoang Bao—IDG Ventures Vietnam
Nguyen, Louis—Saigon Asset Management
Nguyen, My Le—Francisco Partners
Nguyen, Philippe—Investors In Private Equity (AKA : IPE)
Nguyen, Thi Thu Lam—Templeton Asset Management, Ltd.
Nguyen, Trung Ha—Vietnam Pioneer Partners
Nguyen, Tung Kim—Indochina Capital Management
Ni, Chris—AsiaVest Partners, TCW/YFY Ltd. (FKA: TCW/YFY Investment)
Nibarger, Michael—Evergreen Pacific Partners LLC
Nibi, Theresa—Bunker Hill Capital
Nicholai, Marco—Finlombarda Gestioni SGR SpA
Nicholls, Jamie—Forstmann Little & Company
Nichols, Alan—Blue Horizon Equity
Nichols, Carl—Outlook Ventures (FKA: iMinds, Interactive Minds)
Nichols, Carol—Texas Women Ventures Fund
Nichols, Curt—Intel Capital
Nichols, Matthew—Highland Capital Partners LLC
Nichols, Phil—Ontario Teachers' Pension Plan
Nichols, Rob—Tasman Capital Partners
Nicholson, Christopher—Compass Capital Fund Management LLC
Nicholson, Christopher—Vector Capital
Nickel, Timothy—ABRY Partners LLC
Nickelberry, Kevin—Investcorp Bank B.S.C.

Nickels, Wolfgang—WestLB AG Equity Investments (AKA: Westdeutsche Landesbank)
Nickerson, Sam—Investor Growth Capital AB
Nicklin, F. Oliver—First Analysis Corporation
Nickoll, Ben—Gleacher & Co.
Nickse, Jay—Adler & Co.
Nicod, Alain—Venture Incubator AG (AKA: VI Partners AG)
Nicolas, Amedee—Naxicap Partners SA
Nicolay, Stefaan—ITP-Management N.V.
Nicum, Pinal—Adams Street Partners LLC
Niedel, James—New Leaf Venture Partners LLC
Niederhofer, Maximilian—Atlas Venture, Ltd.
Niednagel, Jonathan—Momentum Venture Management LLC
Nieh, Peter—Lightspeed Venture Partners (FKA: Weiss, Peck & Greer)
Niehaus, Hans-Jurgen—WestLB AG Equity Investments (AKA: Westdeutsche Landesbank)
Niehaus, Joseph—Housatonic Partners
Niehaus, Matthew—Battery Ventures, L.P.
Nielsen, Clark—Darby Overseas Investments, Ltd.
Nielsen, Jack—Novo A/S
Nielsen, Jan—Blackstone Group, L.P.
Nielsen, Jesper Wadum—Odin Equity Partners
Nielsen, Jimmy Fussing—Sunstone Capital A/S
Nielsen, Kirk—Versant Ventures
Nielson, Kren—NBD Sana Capital
Nielson, William—Wall Street Venture Capital
Niemann, Matthew—Houlihan, Lokey, Howard & Zukin
Niers, Edwin—Bregal Investments
Nieto, Juan Jose—Arcano Capital
Nietzer, Peter G—German Capital GmbH
Nieuwenburg, Kristiaan—IK Investment Partners, Ltd.
Nieuwoudt, Stacy—Crosslink Capital
Nighan Jr., William—Incubic Venture Capital
Nihalani, Suresh—Finaventures
Nii, Bradley—American Capital, Ltd.
Niiva, Eero—MB Funds (AKA: MB Rahastot Oy)
Nikitinas, Andrius—UAB Lignum Cordis
Nikkel, Mike—Global Infrastructure Partners
Nikolay, Joern—General Atlantic LLC
Nikou, Cyrus—Revolution Capital Group LLC
Niland, Michael—Woodside Capital Partners
Niles, Kimberley—North Atlantic Capital Corporation
Nilforoushan, Keyvan—NextStage SAS
Nilsen, Jorgen Andre—TeleVenture Management AS (FKA: Telenor Venture AS)
Nilsson, Henrik—Nordic Biotech Advisors APS
Nilsson, Ludvig—Jade Alternative Investment Advisors
Nilsson, Martin—Morgan Stanley Private Equity
Nilsson, Martin—Spinn Investment AB
Nimetz, Matthew—General Atlantic LLC
Nimmo, William—Halpern, Denny & Company
Nims, Melissa—LINX Partners
Nir, Arik—Athlone Global Security, Inc.
Nir, Elka—Giza Venture Capital (FKA: Giza Investment Management)
Nir, Ronen—Carmel Ventures
Niranjan, J—CLSA Capital Partners (AKA: Credit Lyonnais Securities Asia)
Nisar, Faisal—Baker Capital Corp.
Nishimuta, Isao—Ridgeway Capital Partners, Ltd. (FKA:OPE Partners Ltd.)
Niss, Thomas—Darby Overseas Investments, Ltd.
Nissenbaum, Scott—Novitas Capital (FKA: PA Early Stage Partners)
Nistal Murillo, Rosario—Axis ParticIpaCiones Empresariales SGECR SA
Niv, Eyal—Giza Venture Capital (FKA: Giza Investment Management)
Niwa, Norimitsu—CVC Asia Pacific, Ltd.
Niwa, Norimitsu—CVC Capital Partners (Europe), Ltd.
Nixon, Jim—Beacon Partners, Inc.
Niziol, Robert—Penton Consulting Sp. K. (AKA: Penton Partners)
Niznik, Mark—LINX Partners
Noack, Robert—Aequitas Capital Management, Inc.
Noard, Troy—Frontenac Company
Nobre, Lise—Butler Capital Partners SA
Nobre, Lise—PAI Partners (FKA: PAI Management)
Nochomovitz, Les—Hargan Ventures, Inc.
Noe-Nordberg, Markus—Pamplona Capital Management LLP
Noel, Georges—Fortis Private Equity NV/SA (FKA: VIV NV)
Noell, Charles—JMI Equity
Noguchi, Masayuki—MKS Partners, Ltd. (FKA: Schroder Ventures K.K.)
Noh, Jisoo—Hamilton Lane Advisors, Inc.
Noh, Jong Yoon—Boston Investment Company, Ltd.
Nohra, Guy—Alta Partners
Noir, Jean-Yves—Nem Partners (AKA: Natexis Equity Management)
Noiret, Franck—CDC Innovation SAS (FKA: CDC IXIS Innovation)
Nokes, Humphrey—GATX European Technology Ventures
Nolan, Gerry—Orlando Venture Capital Inc.
Nolan, Ian—3i Group PLC
Nolan, Joseph—GTCR Golder Rauner LLC
Nolan, Leo—Wall Street Venture Capital
Nolan, Peter—Leonard Green & Partners
Nolan, Robert—BMO Capital Corporation
Nolan, Robert—Halyard Partners
Nolan, Rosemary—Hawkesbridge Private Equity
Nolff, Gregory—ACI Capital Co., LLC
Nollmann, Walter—Alumni Capital Network
Nomura, Yoshi—Conduit Ventures Limited
Nonomiya, Hiroshi—RHJ International Japan
Noonan, Leslie—Summit Partners
Noonan, Tighe—4D Global Energy Advisors
Nooner, Jackie—Oaktree Capital Management LLC
Noorani, Mehrdad—Global Infrastructure Partners
Nora, PJ—KCA Partners, Ltd.
Nord, Asgeir—Selvaag Invest AS
Nordan, Cary—Triangle Capital Corporation
Nordan, Matthew—Venrock Associates
Nordberg, Per—Fouriertransform AB
Nordbotten, Arnstein—Verdane Capital (FKA: Four Seasons Venture Capital AS)
Nordemann, Gerhard H.—Gilde Equity Management Benelux B.V.
Nordlander, Eva—SamInvest Mitt AB
Nordlander, Per—Verdane Capital (FKA: Four Seasons Venture Capital AS)
Nordlander, Rune—Forsta Entreprenorsfonden i Norden AB
Norhagen, Per-Henrik—ForetagsByggarna AB (AKA: Business Builders)
Norman, Geoff—Stafford Timberland, ltd.
Norment, Phil—Platinum Equity LLC
Norris, Jack—SK Capital Partners
Norris, Nickie—Heritage Partners
Norsig, George—Monitor Venture Management, LLC
North, Kerry—Stephens Group, Inc.
Northington, Ryan—Meridian Venture Partners (MVP)
Norton, James—Pfingsten Partners, L.P.
Nosal, Miroslav—PPF Investments, Ltd.
Noseda, Francesco—Wizard Partners Srl
Nosek, Luke—Founders Fund, The
Nossaman, Gregory—BB&T Capital Markets
Notaras, Paul—Staenberg Venture Partners (FKA: Staenberg Private Capital)
Notario Romero, Esperanza—Inverjaen S.C.R. SA
Noth, Pascal—Palamon Capital Partners (FKA: Amphion Capital Partners)
Notter, Peter—Madison Capital Funding LLC (AKA: Madison Capital)
Notz, Peter—Drum Capital Management
Nour-Omid, Bahram—Shelter Capital Partners LLC
Nourse, Richard—novusmodus LLP
Nouss, James—Oakwood Medical Investors
Nova, Daniel—Highland Capital Partners LLC
Novak, David—Clayton, Dubilier & Rice, Inc.
Novak, E. Rogers—Novak Biddle Venture Partners, L.P.
Novak, Jay—Houlihan, Lokey, Howard & Zukin
Novak, John—Paine & Partners LLC
Novak, John—Swander Pace Capital
November, Pete—Pacific Community Ventures (FKA: SVCV)
Novogratz, Jacqueline—Acumen Fund
Novotny, Carl—Venture Capital Fund of New England, The
Nowaczyk, John—Milestone Partners
Nowak, David—Westerkirk Capital, Inc.
Nowak, Kevin—MFC Capital Funding, Inc.
Nowak, Michael—Yorkville Advisors LLC
Noyelle, Donatien—Azulis Capital (FKA:Banexi Capital Partenaires)
Noyola, Pedro—NAFTA Fund of Mexico, LP
Nozad, Pejman—AmidZad, LLC
Nsouli, Nadim—Lago Partners Ltd
Nsouli, Nadim—Providence Equity Partners LLC
Ntsele, Ndaba—Pamodzi Investment Holdings
Nuber, Toby—Headwaters Merchant Bank
Nugent, F. Michael—Obsidian Finance Group LLC
Nugent, Jack—Argosy Capital
Nugent, Kevin—SCF Partners
Numata, Kengo—Mizuho Capital Company, Ltd.
Nundwe, Basil—Aureos Capital, Ltd.
Nunez, F.Ray—American River Ventures
Nunez, Ramon—MCH Private Equity SA
Nunn, Jake—New Enterprise Associates, Inc.
Nunnelly, Mark—Bain Capital
Nusbaum, Gary—Palladium Equity Partners LLC
Nussrallah, Steve—Value Plus Ventures
Nyberg, Fredrik—BioVeda Capital Private, Ltd.
Nye, Benjamin—Bain Capital
Nye, Bob—JMI Equity
Nye, Gordon—Prism VentureWorks
Nye, J. Benjamin—Bain Capital Ventures
Nygren, Jan—EuroUs Ventures
Nygren, Jonas—Provider Venture Partners AB (FKA: IT Provider Advisor 1 AB)

Nykin, Ilya—Prolog Ventures LLC
Nyman, Tom—Pod Venture Partners Inc.
O'Brian, Martin—Bank of Scotland Venture Capital (FKA: ICC Venture Capital)
O'Brien, Christopher—Investcorp Bank B.S.C.
O'Brien, Christopher—Wynnchurch Capital, Ltd.
O'Brien, Dana—Paul Capital Partners
O'Brien, Dennis—Gryphon Investors, Inc.
O'Brien, Eric—Lightspeed Venture Partners (FKA: Weiss, Peck & Greer)
O'Brien, Gordon—American Capital, Ltd.
O'Brien, Kevin—CCMP Capital Advisors LLC
O'Brien, Kevin—Twin Haven Capital Partners
O'Brien, Mike—Gresham LLP
O'Brien, Patrick—ADM Capital
O'Brien, Robert—CID Capital
O'Connell, Alan—Seroba BioVentures Limited
O'Connell, Alan—Seroba Kernel Life Sciences, Ltd. (AKA: Seroba Kernel)
O'Connell, Daniel—NeuroVentures Capital
O'Connell, Dennis—Dolphin Equity Partners
O'Connell, Frank—Wall Street Venture Capital
O'Connell, Jim—Safeguard Scientifics, Inc.
O'Connell, Timothy—Archbrook Capital Management LLC
O'Connor, Brian—Canaccord Genuity
O'Connor, Brian—Vestar Capital Partners, Inc.
O'Connor, Conor—Enterprise Equity Venture Capital Group
O'Connor, Diane—Headwaters Merchant Bank
O'Connor, Donald—Tully & Holland, Inc. (FKA: Ulin & Holland, Inc.)
O'Connor, James—MVC Capital (FKA: meVC)
O'Connor, John—Fort Washington Capital Partners Group
O'Connor, Sean—New York Business Development Corporation
O'Dell, Bradley—Silver Oak Management
O'Dell, Michael—New Enterprise Associates, Inc.
O'Donnell, Christopher—Trillium Group LLC
O'Donnell, Hugh—Crescent Private Capital, L.P.
O'Donnell, James—Bush O'Donnell Capital Partners
O'Donnell, James—Capital For Business, Inc.
O'Donnell, James—First Capital Group Management Co. LLC (AKA: FCG)
O'Donnell, John—Montlake Capital
O'Donnell, Michael—LGV Capital, Ltd. (FKA: Legal & General Ventures, Ltd.)
O'Donnell, Niall—RiverVest Venture Partners
O'Donnell, R. Timothy—Jefferson Capital Partners, Ltd.
O'Donoghue, Tom—CRG Partners
O'Driscoll, Pat—Terra Firma Capital Partners, Ltd.
O'Driscoll, Rory—Scale Venture Partners
O'Farrell, John—Andreessen Horowitz
O'Farrell, John—Venture Capital Partners Pty., Ltd.
O'Flaherty, Kevin—Pamplona Capital Management LLP
O'Gara, B. Timothy—Lazard Capital Partners
O'Grady, Standish—Granite Ventures LLC
O'Hara, James—TSG Consumer Partners
O'Hara, Michael—One Equity Partners (FKA: Banc One Venture Partners)
O'Hara, Seamus—Seroba BioVentures Limited
O'Hara, Seamus—Seroba Kernel Life Sciences, Ltd. (AKA: Seroba Kernel)
O'Hara, Walter—Allen & Company
O'Keefe, Daniel—Technology Crossover Ventures
O'Keefe, Kenneth—Beecken, Petty & Company LLC
O'Keefe, Kenny—Vestar Capital Partners, Inc.
O'Keefe, Patrick—Excellere Capital Management
O'Keeffe, Graham—Atlas Venture, Ltd.
O'Keeffe, Timothy—First Reserve Corporation
O'Kelly, Conor—NCB Ventures, Ltd.
O'Leary, Brendan—Prism VentureWorks
O'Leary, Ciaran—Earlybird Venture Capital GmbH & Co. KG
O'Leary, Mary Helen—Sternhill Partners
O'Leary, Neil—ION Equity, Ltd.
O'Leary, Rich—Lacuna, LLC
O'Mahony, Daniel—Seroba Kernel Life Sciences, Ltd. (AKA: Seroba Kernel)
O'Malley, Brian—Battery Ventures, L.P.
O'Malley, Denis—Partners Group AG
O'Malley, John—WestLB Mellon Asset Management (USA) LLC
O'Malley, Mike—Inflection Point Ventures
O'Malley, Patty—Physic Ventures
O'Meara, Charles—Ziegler HealthVest Management LLC
O'Molony, Kearnon—Blackstone Group, L.P.
O'Neal, E. Stanley—Merrill Lynch Capital Partners
O'Neil, Bevin—Avista Capital Holdings, L.P.
O'Neill, Grover—Meriwether Capital
O'Neill, J. Brian—Merion Investment Partners, L.P.
O'Neill, John—Graphite Capital (FKA: F&C Ventures, Ltd.)
O'Neill, John—Midven, Ltd. (AKA: Midlands Venture Fund Managers, Ltd.)
O'Neill, Joseph—Arcadia Management, LLC (AKA: Arcadia Partners)
O'Neill, Stephen—PCGI LLC (AKA: PCG International)
O'Neill, Stephen—Pacific Corporate Group
O'Reilly, Cameron—Bayard Group (AKA: Landis+Gyr Holdings)
O'Riordain, Fearghal—Scottish Equity Partners
O'Rourke, Robert—PPM America Capital Partners LLC
O'Shea, Donald—Custer Capital, Inc.
O'Sullivan, Colm—PAI Partners (FKA: PAI Management)
O'Sullivan, John—ACT Venture Capital, Ltd.
O'Sullivan, John—Delta Partners, Ltd.
O'Sullivan, Robert—Comvest Investment Partners
O'Toole, Terence—Tinicum Capital Partners
Oakland, Simon—Alchemy Partners LLP
Obegi, Melissa—Oaktree Capital Management LLC
Obenchain, Tiffany—Lake Capital Partners, Inc.
Obenshain, Suzanne—Castanea Partners
Ober, Kevin—Divergent Ventures
Oberbeck, Christian—Saratoga Partners, LP
Oberfield, Eric—Capvent AG
Oberg, Soren—Thomas H. Lee Partners (AKA: TH Lee Partners)
Oberholtzer, Greg—WP Global Partners Inc.
Oberholtzer, William—High Street Capital
Oberman, Micha—Kinrot Technology Ventures
Obermiller, Gary—Goldner Hawn Johnson & Morrison, Inc.
Obershaw, Elizabeth—Horsley Bridge Partners
Oblak, Geoffrey—Ascent Venture Partners
Obuch, Robert—Palomar Ventures
Occena, Samuel—Aureos Capital, Ltd.
Occhiogrosso, Neill—Highland Capital Partners LLC
Occhiogrosso, Neill—Investor Growth Capital, Inc.
Occhipinti, John—Woodside Fund
Occhipinti, Vincent—Woodside Fund
Och, Daniel—Och-Ziff Capital Management Group
Ochs, Patrick—Blackstone Group, L.P.
Ocko, Julia—HarbourVest Partners LLC
Oddi, David—Goode Partners LLC
Odefey, Andreas M.—BPE Unternehmensbeteiligungen GmbH
Odeh, Ismail—Global Investment House
Oden, David—Haynes and Boone LLC
Oder, Troy—Golub Capital
Odewald, Jens—Odewald & Compagnie GmbH
Odlander, Bjorn—Odlander, Fredrikson & Co. AB (AKA: HealthCap)
Odom, David—Arsenal Venture Partners
Odrich, Michael—Lehman Brothers, Inc.
Odugbesan, Lekan—Kingdom Zephyr Africa Management (AKA: KZAM)
Odunsi, Bolaji—Stirling Square Capital Partners
Oei, Ting Pau—L Capital Partners
Oemcke, Mark—Pacific Corporate Group
Oertel, Gerald—ECM Equity Capital Management GmbH
Oettmeier, Brett—WindSail Ventures LLC
Ofer, Abraham—Oaktree Capital Management LLC
Offenberg, Alan—Compass Group International LLC, The
Offenhauser, Peter—Stone Arch Capital LLC
Offermann, Peter—HT Capital Advisors LLC
Oftedal, Ole—Permira Advisers LLP
Ogawa, Ryoichi—Polaris Principal Finance Co., Ltd.
Ogden, William—Union Capital Corporation
Ogenstam, Bjorn—Stiftelsen Industrifonden
Ogenstam, Bjorn—Svenskt Rekonstruktionskapital AB
Oglesby, William—Blackstone Group, L.P.
Ogtrop, Robert-Jan—CVC Capital Partners (Europe), Ltd.
Ogunlesi, Adebayo—Global Infrastructure Partners
Ogur, Scott—Scimitar Global Ventures
Ogura, Hidemasa—Mizuho Capital Company, Ltd.
Ogut, Bilge—Warburg Pincus LLC
Oh, Duk-Hwan—IDG Ventures Korea
Oh, Kwanghee—Ilshin Investment Co., Ltd. (AKA:Ilshin Venture Capital)
Oh, Tae Sung—Premier Venture Partners LLC
Ohana, Bella—Infinity Venture Capital Fund (AKA: Israel Infinity Fund)
Ohana, Laurent—Parkview Ventures LLC
Ohgishi, Takayuki—Tokio Marine Capital Company, Ltd.
Ohldin, Gabriella—InnovationsKapital
Ohlsson, Jan—Accent Equity Partners AB
Ohman, Gustav—IK Investment Partners, Ltd.
Ohmeroluoma, Ritva—Nordia Management Oy
Ohmura, Nobuaki—Daiwa Securities SMBC Principal Investments Co., Ltd.
Ohrstrom, Wright—G.L. Ohrstrom & Co., Inc. (AKA: GLO & Co.)
Ohta, Yoshiharu—Minato Mirai Capital Co., Ltd.
Oinino, Jeremy—CAP ISF SA
Okajima, Ichiro—DoCoMo Capital

Okamoto, Yukio—Pacifica Fund
Oken, Glenn—Mangrove Equity Partners LLC
Oken, Marc—Falfurrias Capital Partners
Oksanen, Petri—Francisco Partners
Okun, Robert—Synergy Partners
Okuno, Kei—CITIC Capital Partners, Ltd.
Olafsson, Skuli Valberg—Thule Investments
Olaguibel, Inigo—Qualitas Equity Partners
Olah, Laszlo—Mezzanine Management Finanz- und Unternehmensberatungs GmbH
Olaso-Yohn, Mariano—Altamar Private Equity
Olausson, Lennart—Start Invest AB
Olbort, Martin—PINOVA Capital GmbH
Olden, Niall—Kernel Capital Partners
Olden, Niall—Seroba Kernel Life Sciences, Ltd. (AKA: Seroba Kernel)
Oldroyd, Graham—Bridgepoint Capital, Ltd.
Olexy, Mark—Atlantic-Pacific Capital, Inc.
Olhoeft, Mark—Seabury Venture Partners
Olin, Mary Louise—Ridgewood Capital Management, LLC
Oliva, Adele—Apax Partners Worldwide
Oliva, Adele—Quaker BioVentures, Inc.
Oliver, Brian—Aequitas Capital Management, Inc.
Oliver, Darry—Edison Venture Fund
Oliver, John—TPG Capital
Oliver, Roland—Monumental Venture Partners LLC
Oliver, Roland—NAC Ventures, LLC
Olivier, Albert—CDC Entreprises SAS
Olivier, Bernard—SORIDEC
Olivier, Edmund—Oxford Bioscience Partners
Olivier, Francois—Czura Thornton
Olivier, Ned—VenturEast (FKA: APIDC Venture Capital Limited)
Olivier, Pierre—Acces Capital QuEbec
Olivier, Serge—Acces Capital QuEbec
Olkkola, Ed—Teakwood Capital, L.P.
Ollier, Michele—Index Ventures
Ollila, Harri—VNT Management Oy
Ollwerther, Robert—Avenue Capital Group
Olmedillo, Hector—Small Business Guarantee and Finance Corporation
Olof Larson, Lars—AB Traction
Olofsson, Susanne—Ekonord Invest AB
Olsen, Christopher—Sequoia Capital
Olsen, Erik—Ferd Venture
Olsen, Erik—Herkules Capital AS
Olsen, Henrik—ETF Manager LLP
Olsen, Henrik—GE Commercial Finance - Equity
Olsen, Lee—BlueCar Partners
Olson, Mattias—Procuritas Partners KB
Olsson, Dan Sten—Stena Adactum AB
Olsson, Mikael—Amplico Kapital AB
Olsson, Morgan—Nordic Capital (AKA: NC Advisory)
Olveira, Fernando—General Atlantic LLC
Omar Abdulla, Abdul Rahman—Invest AD
Omdal, Sven Petter—Cinclus AS
Omid, Uri—Gmul Investment Company, Ltd.
Omidyar, Pam—Omidyar Network
Ommen, Gordon—Capitaline Advisors, LLC
Omstead, Dan—Hambrecht & Quist Capital Management (H&Q) LLC
Onan, Chris—Appian Ventures
Oncken, Peter—INTRO-Verwaltungs GmbH
Ong, Andrew—TCIB Investment Co., Ltd.
Ong, Peng—GSR Ventures
Ong, Phui Fatt—Pica (M) Corporation Berhad
Onishi, Toshihiko—Daiwa Securities SMBC Principal Investments Co., Ltd.
Onn, Shai—Shaked Global Group Ltd.
Ono, R. Dana—VIMAC Ventures LLC (FKA: VIMAC LLC)
Ono, Shinzo—Ant Capital Partners Co., Ltd.
Onopchenko, John—Synergy Life Science Partners
Onopchenko, Laura—TechFarm Ventures (AKA:TechFund Capital)
Onsi, Douglas—HealthCare Ventures LLC
Onuma, Ataru—Ant Capital Partners Co., Ltd.
Ookita, Tomoyoshi—KSP (Kanagawa Science Park)
Oota, Yoshimi—Minato Mirai Capital Co., Ltd.
Opalski, Stefan—Skypoint Capital Corporation
Opdendyk, Terry—ONSET Ventures
Oporto, Michael—Investor Growth Capital AB
Oporto, Michael—Investor Growth Capital, Inc.
Oppenheimer, Rodolfo—Prosperitas Capital Partners
Oravkin, Jozef—Penta Investments, Ltd.
Orbach, Michael—Cascadia Capital LLC
Orban, M. Michel—RRE Ventures LLC
Ord, John—BV-Cornerstone Ventures, L.P.
Ordoqui, Ruben—Prosperitas Capital Partners
Oren, Timothy—Pacifica Fund
Oreschnick, Bob—3i Group PLC
Orfao, David—General Catalyst Partners (FKA: General Catalyst Group LLC)
Orgill, Jim—Business Development Bank of Canada
Origenes, Peter—BD Ventures (AKA: Becton, Dickinson & Co.)
Orlandella, David—Enhanced Capital Partners, LLC
Orlando, Jim—OMERS Private Equity
Orlin, Paul—CF Advisors, LLC
Orlow, Seth—Easton Hunt Capital Partners, L.P.
Ormond, Henry—Leeds Equity Partners
Ormond, Henry—Quadrangle Group LLC
Oron, Yifat—Vertex Management Israel (AKA: Vertex Venture Capital)
Oron, Yifat—Vertex Venture Capital
Oronsky, Arnold—InterWest Partners
Orr, Lawrence—Trinity Ventures
Orr, R. Wilson—SSM Partners
Orsak, Michael—Worldview Technology Partners
Ortale, W. Patrick—Richland Ventures
Ortberg, Todd—Coral Group LLC
Ortenzio, Robert—Select Capital Ventures
Ortenzio, Rocco—Select Capital Ventures
Ortez, Timothy—Drum Capital Management
Orthwein, Peter—Spring Capital Partners (FKA: Spring Capital Investors LLC)
Ortiz, Ana Lei—Hamilton Lane Advisors, Inc.
Ortiz, Rafael—Palladium Equity Partners LLC
Ortiz-Duran, Edison—MerchantBansa S.A.
Orum, Nicholas—Gryphon Investors, Inc.
Ory-Lavollee, Laure—AGF Private Equity
Osako, Yoshihiro—Tokio Marine Capital Company, Ltd.
Osborn, Richard—Second City Capital Partners
Osborn, William—Massachusetts Green Energy Fund
Osborne, Stanley de—Kelso & Company
Osburn, Todd—Greyrock Capital Group
Oshman, Ilya—Pfizer Venture Investments
Osifo, Osaze—Travant Capital Partners
Osinga, Johannes—NoorderHuys Participaties BV
Osler, Andrew—GFI Energy Ventures
Osmundson, Aaron—Headwaters Merchant Bank
Osnoss, Joe—Silver Lake Sumeru
Osorio, George—Conduit Capital Partners, LLC
Osorio, Jose Luiz—Jardim Botanico Partners (FKA: Araujo Fontes Consultoria)
Ospalik, Rob—Baird Capital Partners
Osseiran, Salah—Fairford Holdings Scandinavia AB (AKA: Fairford Holdings)
Ossentjuk, Tako—Plain Vanilla Investments BV
Ossmark, Andreas—Scope Capital Advisory AB
Oster, Wolfgang—PolyTechnos Venture-Partners GmbH
Osterberg, Klementina—Holdingbolaget vid Goteborgs universitet AB
Osterrieth, Robert—Rho Capital Partners, Inc.
Osthaus, Anne—IKB Private Equity GmbH
Ostro, Marc—Devon Park Bioventures
Ostrover, Douglas—Blackstone Group, L.P.
Osund, Anders—Investor Growth Capital AB
Osund, Anders—Investor Growth Capital, Inc.
Oswal, Motilal—Motilal Oswal Private Equity Advisors Pvt., Ltd.
Oswald, Brian—GSC Partners (FKA: Greenwich Street Capital Partners)
Oswald, Brian—Prospect Street Ventures
Otani, Toshiya—TransLink Capital
Otawa, Mitsuru—Mizuho Capital Partners Co., Ltd.
Ott, Alex—JVP
Otte, Daryl—Montefiore, LLC
Ottenwaelter, Benoit—Societe Generale Capital Partenaires SAS
Otterling, Hans—Northzone Ventures AS (FKA: Venture Partners AS)
Otterson, John—SVB Capital
Oudea, Frederic—Societe Generale Capital Partenaires SAS
Oursel, Maximilien—SEEFT Management SAS
Ousseimi, Mohamed—Gefinor Ventures
Outerbridge, Amanda—HarbourVest Partners LLC
Outland, James—New Capital Partners
Ouwendijk, Hans—fr2 Capital B.V.
Ovadia, Arie—Shamrock Holdings, Inc.
Overbay, John—Court Square Capital Partners
Overbeck, Gernot—EquiVest GmbH & Co
Overmyer, Craig—Hopewell Ventures
Owayda, Solomon—Siguler Guff & Company
Owen, Brian—Masthead Venture Partners
Owen, Daniel—HO2 Partners
Owen, Douglas—Petra Capital Partners, LLC
Owen, Dustin—Northern Plains Capital, Ltd.
Owen, Richard—Yellowstone Capital, Inc.
Owens, Jessica—Kleiner Perkins Caufield & Byers
Owens, Willaim—Aetos Capital LLC
Owens, William—Stonehenge Capital Company
Owers, Paul—Actis Capital LLP
Oweson, Frederik—Scope Capital Advisory AB
Owsley, Henry—Bacchus Capital Management LLC
Owsley, Jonathan—Catterton Partners
Oxaal, John—Sevin Rosen Funds
Oxley, Ian—Silverfleet Capital (FKA: PPM Capital Partners)
Oyama, Shigeaki—Wendel
Oyama, Tatsuya—Fund Creation Co., Ltd.
Oyer, Philip—MedVenture Associates

Ozaki, Kazunori—Ant Capital Partners Co., Ltd.
Ozaki, Kazunori—TransLink Capital
Ozgen, A. Murat—Is Private Equity Investment Trust
Ozimska, Anna—Krokus Private Equity Sp. z o.o.
Ozin, Stephen—Acuity Capital LLP (FKA: Electra Partners LLP)
P. Mantzounis, Demetrios—Alpha Ventures SA
Paananen, Jokke—Intera Equity Partners Oy
Paardenkooper, Patrick—NIBC Principal Investments (FKA: Parnib Holding NV)
Paasche, Michael—Providence Equity Partners LLC
Paasi, Martin—Amanda Capital Oyj
Pacala, Mark—Essex Woodlands Health Ventures
Pace, Christopher—Siguler Guff & Company
Pace, Christopher—WestLB Mellon Asset Management (USA) LLC
Pace, Daniel—Merrill Lynch Capital Partners
Pace, David—Unicorn Investment Bank B.S.C.
Pace, Linda—Carlyle Group, The
Pacha, Robert—Evercore Partners
Pacitti, Christopher—Austin Ventures, L.P.
Packard, Warren—DFJ Athena
Packard, Warren—Draper Fisher Jurvetson
Pade, William—Oak Hill Capital Management, Inc.
Padnos, Cynthia—Illuminate Ventures
Padval, Umesh—Bessemer Venture Partners
Paez, Juan Fernando—Conduit Capital Partners, LLC
Paff, Andrew—Headwaters Merchant Bank
Paffen, De Heer Tom—Capital-C Ventures B.V.
Paganoni, Roberto—LGT Capital Partners AG
Pagar, Gary—Cappello Capital Corp.
Page Nelson, Liza—Investor Growth Capital AB
Page Nelson, Liza—Investor Growth Capital, Inc.
Page, Andrew—Foresight Group
Page, Joseph—Gores Group LLC, The
Page, Marcia—Varde Partners, Inc.
Page, Mary—KLM Capital Management, Inc.
Page, Neil—RMB Private Equity
Page, Neville—Wilshire Private Markets
Pagel, Eric—Tennenbaum Capital Partners LLC
Pagliuca, Stephen—Bain Capital
Pagnotta, Isabelle—Arcapita, Inc.
Pahima, Eyal—ProSeed Venture Capital Fund
Pai, Jeng-Ming—China Venture Management, Inc.
Pai, PM—New Enterprise Associates, Inc.
Pai, Rajesh—Global Environment Fund Management Corporation
Paiement, Constance—BlueStream Ventures
Paik, Seunggwon—Partners Venture Capital Co., Ltd.
Paine, Robert—GSC Partners (FKA: Greenwich Street Capital Partners)
Paine, W.Dexter—Paine & Partners LLC
Painter, Michael—Plexus Capital LLC (FKA: Plexus Fund)
Paisley, Thomas—Industrial Opportunity Partners, LLC
Paiva, William—Chisholm Private Capital Partners, LC
Paiva, William—Sevin Rosen Funds
Pajarin, Elena—Diana Capital SGECR SA
Pajarola, Sandra—Partners Group AG
Pak-Poy, Fiona—Innovation Capital Associates Pty, Ltd.
Pakianathan, Deepa—Delphi Ventures
Pakman, David—Venrock Associates
Palastanga, Tina—Global Leisure Partners LLP
Palavatana, Chittinan—Thai Strategic Capital Management Co., Ltd.
Palazzo, Royce—Axiom Equity Partners
Palcheck, Tony—Motorola Ventures
Paldus, Barbara—Skymoon Ventures
Palefsky, Howard—Montreux Equity Partners
Palexas, Zaharias—Parthenon Trust SA
Palfrey, John—RSS Investors
Palhon, Jean-Marc—OTC Asset Management
Palin, Adam—Global Private Equity PLC
Pallota, Joseph—Comvest Investment Partners
Palmer, Adam—Carlyle Group, The
Palmer, John—Hanover Partners, Inc
Palmer, Raquel—KPS Capital Partners, L.P.
Palmer, Robert—CMS Companies
Palmer, Shirley—Synova Capital LLP
Palmer, Thomas—AH Ventures (AKA: Adams Harkness & Hill Technology Ventures)
Palmer, Thomas—Gazelle TechVentures
Palmer, Tim—Charlesbank Capital Partners LLC
Palmisano, Robert—SV Life Sciences Advisers
Palmisano, Samuel—IBM Corporation
Palmquist, Jonas—Scope Capital Advisory AB
Palmroth, Jussi—VNT Management Oy
Palter, Gilbert—EdgeStone Capital Partners, Inc.
Paluck, Robert—CenterPoint Venture Partners
Palumbo, Keith—Audax Group
Palumbo, Rob—Accel-KKR LLC
Pamplona, Eduardo—Decisao Gestao Financeira (AKA: DGF Investimentos)
Pan, Alex—GSR Ventures
Pan, Gordon—Baird Capital Partners
Pan, Richard—Stripes Group
Panaccio, Frank—Fidelity Ventures
Panaccio, Michael—Starfish Ventures Pty., Ltd.
Panandiker, Vibhav—J.P. Morgan Partners (FKA: Chase Capital Partners)
Pancrazi, Jacques—Qualium Investissement
Pande, Tarun—Kubera Partners, LLC
Pandey, Shantanu—Jacob Ballas Capital India Pvt, Ltd. (AKA:JBC)
Pandhare, Sandesh—Istithmar World Capital
Pandit, Kunal—Avista Capital Holdings, L.P.
Pandit, Ranjit—General Atlantic LLC
Pandole, Darius—New Silk Route Partners LLC
Panem, Sandra—Cross Atlantic Partners, Inc.
Panero, Hugh—New Enterprise Associates, Inc.
Panfilo, Francesco—AAC Capital Partners
Panfilo, Francesco—PM & Partners SpA
Pangia, Robert—Ivy Capital Partners
Panoff, Brian—Granite Ventures LLC
Panos, Alexander—TSG Consumer Partners
Panos, Ernie—Hercules Technology Growth Capital, Inc.
Pansing, Daniel—Merit Capital Partners (FKA:William Blair Mezzanine)
Pant, Sangam—Evercore Partners
Panton, David—Caribbean Equity Partners Limited
Panton, David—Navigation Capital Partners
Panton, David—Navigation Capital Partners (AKA: NCP)
Panturu, Sorin—Mackenzie Capital srl
Pantuso, Anthony—NeoCarta Ventures, Inc.
Pantuso, Lee—NeoCarta Ventures, Inc.
Panzo, Andrew—NewSpring Capital
Pao, Ellen—Kleiner Perkins Caufield & Byers
Paolilo, Douglas—Blackstone Group, L.P.
Papageorgiou, Yannis—CDP Capital - Technology Ventures (FKA: CDP Sofinov)
Papantonis, Nicholas—Alliance Technology Ventures
Papazian, Charles—Great Hill Equity Partners LLC
Pape, Florian—Orlando Capital Management GmbH
Paperin, Stewart—Steve Norris Partners
Papetti, Alessandro—Clessidra Capital
Papiernik, Antoine—Sofinnova Partners
Pappalardo, Vincent—Dresner Partners (FKA: Dresner Capital Resources, Inc.)
Pappas, Andrew—MFC Capital Funding, Inc.
Pappas, Arthur—Pappas Ventures
Pappas, Milton—EuclidSR Partners
Pappas, Tracy—Synergy Life Science Partners
Pappendick, Ted—Bain Capital
Paquin, Antoine—Rho Capital Partners, Inc.
Paquin, Jacques—Baird Capital Partners Europe
Paracchi, Pierluigi—Axon Capital
Paradis, Laura—Octane Capital Management
Parapatits, Harald—HANNOVER Finanz Austria GmbH
Parasuram, Hemanth—Virgo Capital
Pardi, Robert—Evolvence Capital
Pardo, Mario—Carlyle Group, The
Pardoe, Richard—Chevron Technology Ventures
Parekh, Deven—Insight Venture Partners
Parekh, Mehool—eIndia Venture Management
Parekh, Raj—Advent Venture Partners LLP
Parekh, Raj—Redwood Venture Partners
Parekh, Vijay—Temasek Holdings Pvt., Ltd.
Parfet, Donald—Apjohn Ventures, LLC
Parfuss, Gero—Gruenderfonds GmbH & Co KEG
Parham, Iain—CVC Capital Partners (Europe), Ltd.
Parier, Christophe—Activa Capital SAS
Parija, Kartik—Zephyr Management, L.P.
Parikh, Nilesh—Blue Wolf Capital Management LLC
Parikh, Tuhin—Blackstone Group, L.P.
Parikh, Viral—Blackstone Group, L.P.
Parilla, Mike—Maranon Capital, L.P.
Pariso, Christina—Sterling Partners
Parisot, Tristan—European Capital Financial Services Ltd.
Park, Brandon—Pacific Corporate Group
Park, Chris—JC Asia Alpha Private Equity
Park, Felix—Gryphon Investors, Inc.
Park, Hoon—KTB Securities Co., Ltd. (FKA: KTB Network Co., Ltd.)
Park, Howard—Global Innovation Partners LLC
Park, Hyung Tae—Sovik Venture Capital Company, Ltd.
Park, Hyung Tae—Tong Yang Venture Capital Corporation
Park, Jay—BlackRock Private Equity Partners
Park, Jeong Seo—Korea Venture Investment Corporation
Park, Jeong Seo—M-Venture Investment, Inc. (FKA: Shinyoung Venture Capital)
Park, Jonghyuk—MVP Capital Company, Ltd.
Park, Juntae—Hanwha Venture Capital Corporation
Park, Kiho—LB Investment, Inc.
Park, Mansoon—Mirae Asset Venture Investment Co., Ltd. (FKA:Korean Dream)
Park, Michele—Clarus Ventures

Peck, Donald—Actis Capital LLP
Peck, Drew—Crimson
Peck, Michael—Open Prairie Ventures
Pecoux, Olivier—Paris Orleans (Francarep SA)
Pedersen, Allan Bach—Polaris Management A/S
Pedersen, Debra—Carlyle Group, The
Pedersen, Kim—Nordea Private Equity
Pedersen, Lars—Redpoint Ventures
Pedersen, Peder—ComTech Invest A/S (FKA: AHEAD Enterprise SA)
Pederson, Steven—Sherpa Partners LLC
Pedley, Matt—AllianceBernstein L.P. (FKA: Alliance Capital Management)
Pedrero, Anne—Cargill Ventures
Pedriks, Markus—7 L Capital Partners
Peechu, Sundeep—Felicis Ventures
Peek, Diane—GKM Newport Generation Funds
Peek, Jeffrey—CIT Group Inc.
Peel, Doug—Kilmer Capital Partners
Peele, Ron—Time Warner Investments (FKA: AOL Time Warner Ventures)
Peeler, D. Randolph—Berkshire Partners LLC
Peeters, Jos—Capricorn Venture Partners N.V.
Pei, Gang—Shenzhen Right-Sun Investment Company, Ltd.
Peinado, George—Madison Dearborn Partners LLC
Peix, Andrew—Serent Capital LLC
Pekala, Andrea—Carlyle Group, The
Pekkarinen, Erkki—Bio Fund Management Oy
Pelaez, Toni—UIB Capital, Inc.
Peleg, Lior—Maayan Ventures
Pelisek, David—Baird Capital Partners
Pelkonen, Arno—Taito Capital Partners Oy
Pellegrini, Lorenzo—Care Capital, LLC
Pelletier, Mark—American Capital, Ltd.
Pelligrono, Francis—Fin'Active
Pelly, Richard—European Investment Fund (AKA: EIF)
Pelowski, Kenneth—Pinnacle Ventures
Peltier, Philippe—Auriga Partners S.A.
Peltola, Juha—Pohjola Capital Partners Oy
Pelton, Scott—GrowthWorks
Peluchiwski, Bill—Houlihan, Lokey, Howard & Zukin
Pelusi, James—Axia Capital
Pelzer, Joern—PINOVA Capital GmbH
Pemberton, Brandon—Meridian Capital (FKA: Olympic Capital Partners, LLC)
Pemberton, Gerard—Caribbean Development Capital, Ltd. (AKA: DEVCAP)
Pena, Isabel—MBF Healthcare Partners L.P.
Penarrocha, Luis—Inversiones Ibersuizas S.A.
Pendenza, Paolo—BS Private Equity SpA (FKA: B&S Private Equity Group)
Penfold, Robert—Prudential Capital Group
Peng, Bingming—Development Principles Group, Ltd.
Peng, Henry—Industrial Bank of Taiwan
Peng, Peter—WI Harper Group
Peng, Sean—WI Harper Group
Peng, Teh Kok—GIC Special Investments Pte, Ltd.
Penhale, John—Canadian Imperial Bank of Commerce (AKA: CIBC)
Peninon, Dominique—Access Capital Partners
Penman, Gordon—Venture Capital Fund of New England, The
Penn, Kevin—ACI Capital Co., LLC
Penn, Thomas—Meridian Venture Partners (MVP)
Penn, Thomas—Penn Venture Partners, LP
Pennell, Keith—DFW Capital Partners (AKA:DeMuth, Folger & Wetherill)
Pennell, Thomas—Pennell Venture Partners
Penner, Greg—DT Capital Partners
Penner, Greg—Madrone Capital Partners
Pennycook, Carol—Davies Ward Phillips & Vineberg
Penske, Roger—Transportation Resource Partners (TRP) (FKA: Penske Capital)
Pentecost, Edward—National City Equity Partners, Inc.
Pentikainen, Ilkka—Pohjola Capital Partners Oy
Pentimonti, E. Kenneth—Paladin Capital Management LLC
Pentland, Jeff—Northleaf Capital Partners
Penzias, Arno—New Enterprise Associates, Inc.
Peperstraete, Bernard—NGN Capital LLC
Pepper, Douglas—InterWest Partners
Peppet, Russel—Park Avenue Equity Partners, L.P.
Percival, Philip—Syntegra Capital, Ltd.
Pereira, Carlton—Tano Capital LLC
Pereira, Carol—Opus Capital
Perekhojev, Alexei—Renova Capital Advisors
Perel, Gabriel—Odin Investments
Peres, Chemi—Pitango Venture Capital (FKA:Polaris Venture Capital Israel)
Perez Barnes, Cesar—Southern Cross Group (AKA: SCG)
Perez Benayas, Rafael—AC Desarrollo SGECR SA
Perez Jimenez, Miguel Angel—Inverjaen S.C.R. SA
Perez, David—Palladium Equity Partners LLC
Perez, Gil—Gilo Ventures
Perez, Jeff—Third Security LLC
Perez, Patrick—BNP Paribas Private Equity SAS
Perez, Raul—Oakwood Medical Investors
Perez, Sergio—Qualitas Equity Partners
Perez-Montes, Antonio—ECM-Bulgarian Post-Privatisation Fund
Perez-Seoane, Carlos Prado—Espiga Capital Gestion SCR SA
Perezcano, Luis—NAFTA Fund of Mexico, LP
Perille, Robert—Shamrock Holdings, Inc.
Periou, Claude—Proparco
Perkal, Richard—Irving Place Capital
Perkins, Georgeanne—Fisher Lynch Capital
Perkins, Gretchen—Long Point Capital Inc.
Perkins, H. Donald—Zon Capital Partners
Perkins, Sonja—Menlo Ventures
Perkins, Stephen—Crosslink Capital
Perkins, Stephen—Leapfrog Ventures
Perkins, Tony—DFJ Frontier
Perkins, Tracy—Greyrock Capital Group
Perkins, William—Small Ventures USA, L.P.
Perl, Jonathan—Boulder Ventures, Ltd.
Perlis, Michael—SoftBank Capital
Perlman, Doug—Accrue Sports and Entertainment Partners LLC
Perlman, Ezra—Francisco Partners
Perlman, Jeffrey—LNK Partners
Perlmutter, Aaron—Levine Leichtman Capital Partners, Inc.
Perlmutter, Tom—Behrman Capital
Perlo, Maria Cristina—Finpiemonte SpA
Peroncini, Stefano—Axon Capital
Peroni, Renato—Investitori Associati SpA
Perony, Gilles—Azulis Capital (FKA:Banexi Capital Partenaires)
Perper, Scott—Pamlico Capital
Perrachon, John—Lincolnshire Management, Inc.
Perreau de Pinnick, Carlos—Simbiosis Venture Capital S.L.
Perreault, Justin—Commonwealth Capital Ventures
Perricelli, Scott—LLR Partners, Inc.
Perricone, Antonio—BS Private Equity SpA (FKA: B&S Private Equity Group)
Perriello, Christopher—AlpInvest Partners N.V.
Perriquet, Stephane—21 Centrale Partners
Perriquet, Stephane—21 Partners SpA
Perron, Larry—Skypoint Capital Corporation
Perry, Christopher—CIVC Partners LP (FKA: Continental Illinois Venture Corp.)
Perry, Ed—Murphree Venture Partners
Perry, Jack—Scottish Enterprise
Perry, James—Madison Dearborn Partners LLC
Perry, Kay—Paperboy Ventures, LLC
Perry, Lloyd—Argan Capital (FKA: BA Capital Partners Europe, BACPE)
Perry, Mark—New Enterprise Associates, Inc.
Perry, Stephen—Linsalata Capital Partners
Perry, Xander—Anthem Capital Management
Persky, Michael—Alerion Partners
Persson, Finn—PNP Venture Capital AB
Persson, Magnus—Odlander, Fredrikson & Co. AB (AKA: HealthCap)
Persson, Staffan—ITP Invest AB (AKA: I Teknisk Partner Invest AB)
Persson, Staffan—Rite Internet Ventures AB
Pertsovsky, Alexander—Renaissance Capital
Pertuz, Brett—Bruckmann, Rosser, Sherrill & Co.
Peru, Sebastien—21 Centrale Partners
Peruri, Sang—J&W Seligman & Company
Perutz, Mark—DBL Investors (AKA: Double Bottom Line Venture Capital)
Peskoff, Johnathan—NextPoint Partners, L.P.
Pesnani, Amyn—Clayton, Dubilier & Rice, Inc.
Petering, Andrew—Wolseley Private Equity
Peterman, Matjaz—KD Group
Peters, Joseph—Avenue Capital Group
Peters, Nicholas—Tricor Pacific Capital, Inc.
Peters, Richard—Transportation Resource Partners (TRP) (FKA: Penske Capital)
Petersen, Allen—Draupnir LLC
Petersen, Bernd—Odin Equity Partners
Petersen, Gabriel—Blackstone Group, L.P.
Petersen, Hans-Peter—MBG Schleswig-Holstein GmbH
Petersen, Klaus—Park Square Capital, LLP
Petersen, Michael—Cross Equity Partners AG
Petersen, Ron—Longbow Capital
Petersen, Timothy—Arboretum Ventures
Peterson, Barry—Northcreek Mezzanine
Peterson, Clifford—Gateway City Capital, Inc.
Peterson, Dan—JCP Capital LLC
Peterson, Dan—SEB Venture Capital
Peterson, Erik—Aureos Capital, Ltd.
Peterson, Hunter—Trinity Hunt Partners
Peterson, Joel—JCP Capital LLC
Peterson, Paul—Wind Point Partners
Peterson, Steven—Brass Ring Capital, Inc.
Peterson, Thomas—El Dorado Ventures
Peterson, Trent—Catalyst Investment Managers Pty, Ltd.

Pivato, Ugo—BS Private Equity SpA (FKA: B&S Private Equity Group)
Pixler, Bruce—HarbourVest Partners LLC
Pizarro, Peter—Small Business Guarantee and Finance Corporation
Pizette, Michael—Crystal Capital
Pizzani, Paul—Cartesian Capital Group, LLC
Plain, Hank—Morgenthaler Ventures
Plaisted, Don—Draper Investment Company
Plakopitas, Angelos—Global Finance SA
Plamondon, Jean—AGF Private Equity
Plantevin, Michel—Bain Capital
Plass, Eduardo—Opus Electra & Partners
Platnick, Joseph—iGlobe Treasury Management, Ltd.
Platonow, Serge—Colony Capital LLC
Platshon, Mark—VantagePoint Venture Partners
Plattfaut, Eberhard—Wellington Partners Venture Capital GmbH
Plattus, Seth—Cerberus Capital Management, L.P.
Plavin, Stephen—CT Investment Management Co. (AKA: Capital Trust)
Playfair, John—First Associates Investments, Inc.
Pleskonjic, Dragan—Eagle Ventures
Plessis-Belair, Michel—Power Corporation of Canada
Pliner, Michael—Jerusalem Global Ventures
Ploix, Helene—Pechel Industries
Plotkin, Daniel—Ofer Hi-Tech
Plotkin, Serge—Opus Capital
Plourde, Jean-Maurice—Centre QuEbEcois de valorisation des biotechnologies (CQVB)
Plouvier, Hubert—Fin.Co
Plum, John—Cavalry Investments LLC
Plume, Stephen—RB Webber & Company
Plummer, William—Milestone Capital Management, Ltd.
Plumridge, David—Hawkesbridge Private Equity
Plumridge, Scott—Halifax Group, The
Pluta, John—Hancock Capital Management LLC
Pluvinet, Gerard—21 Partners SpA
Poch, Gerald—FirstMark Capital LLC
Pocius, Karolis—GILD Bankers (FKA: LHV Ventures)
Poddar, Anoop—Energy Ventures AS
Podlesak, Dennis—Domain Associates LLC
Podziewski, Arkaduisz—Innova Capital
Poe, Michael—Corsair Capital LLC
Poensgen, Tobias—Momentum Capital Limited
Poerink, John Jonge—Circle Peak Capital LLC (AKA: CPC)
Poettinger, Harald—HYPO-Unternehmensbeteiligungen AG
Poff, Mark—Swander Pace Capital
Poffenberger, James—MCM Capital Partners, LP
Poffenroth, Barry—SpringBank TechVentures
Poggioli, Philippe—Access Capital Partners
Pohren, Gene—PCGI LLC (AKA: PCG International)
Pohren, Gene—Pacific Corporate Group
Poiares Baptista, Joao Paulo—Burrill & Company
Poindexter, Victoria—Shattuck Hammond Partners
Poirier, Francois—SEEFT Management SAS
Pokorny, Brian—Baseline Ventures LLC
Polack, Axel—TVM Capital GmbH
Polak, Keith—Versa Capital Management (FKA: Chrysalis Capital Partners)
Polak, Patrick—Newion Investments B.V.
Polak, Yaron—Genesis Partners
Poldoja, Priit—Alta Capital
Poler, Dwight—Bain Capital
Poletti, Philippe—AXA Private Equity
Poletti, Robert—Levine Leichtman Capital Partners, Inc.
Polimino, Peter—Avalon Equity Partners
Poliner, Randall—Antares Capital Corporation
Polis, Jared—TechStars
Politi, Santo—Spark Capital
Poll, Thomas—ECO Unternehmensbeteiligungs-AG
Pollack, Bruce—Centre Partners Management LLC
Pollack, Bruce—Palisades Ventures (FKA: Centre Palisades Ventures)
Pollack, Gregg—Dresner Partners (FKA: Dresner Capital Resources, Inc.)
Pollack, Kenneth—American Capital, Ltd.
Pollack, Kimberly—Levine Leichtman Capital Partners, Inc.
Pollard, Patrick—BlueStar Ventures L.P.
Pollard, Patrick—Red Barn Investments LLC
Polli, Rolando—Ambienta SGR S.p.A.
Pollock, Sam—Brookfield Asset Management
Pollock, Scott—B4 Ventures
Polmann, Berry—Adveq Management AG
Polny, Jacob—TPG Capital
Polo, David—Diana Capital SGECR SA
Polodna, Duane—World Investments, Inc.
Poltack, David—TVM Capital GmbH
Pommerening, Christopher—Active Capital Partners S.L.
Pommier, Dominique—Active Capital Asia, Ltd.
Pompan, Bruce—Cappello Capital Corp.
Pompidou, Thomas—Crescent Point Group
Pomponio, Louis—Blackstone Group, L.P.
Pomroy, Neal—DLJ Merchant Banking Partners
Ponteri, Joseph—TMB Industries Investments
Pontet, Francois—Siparex Group SAS
Pontillo, Franco—Plataforma Capital Partners
Pontin, Johan—Pod Venture Partners Inc.
Ponuick, Blake—Moventis Capital, Inc. (FKA:Online Innovation, Inc.)
Pool, Philip—Willis Stein & Partners
Poole, Scott—Ridgemont Equity Partners
Poole, Walker—Ridgemont Equity Partners
Poon, Cathina—Darby Overseas Investments, Ltd.
Poor, David—Parkmead Group PLC, The (FKA: Interregnum PLC)
Popa-Radu, Emma—Advent International
Pope, Christopher—Parkway Capital Investors LLC
Pope, Rory—Advent International
Poplawski, Jay—Canal Partners LLC
Popov, Alexander—Oaktree Capital Management LLC
Popovich, Alexander—Versa Capital Management (FKA: Chrysalis Capital Partners)
Poppel, Ariel—Infinity Venture Capital Fund (AKA: Israel Infinity Fund)
Popper, Caroline—BCM Technologies, Inc.
Popper, Karla—CCMP Capital Advisors LLC
Poptia, Zaheed—Signal Hill Equity Partners, Inc.
Popusoi, Victor—NCH Capital, Inc.
Porell, Robert—Gefinor Ventures
Porndhithi, Artapong—Lombard Investments, Inc.
Porras, Luis—Monterrey Capital Partners
Porteous, Will—RRE Ventures LLC
Porter, Barry—Clarity Partners
Porter, Craig—Ancor Capital Partners
Porter, David—Apposite Capital LLP
Porter, Jack—Ethanol Capital Management, LLC
Porter, Kelly—ZAP Ventures
Porter, Tim—Madrona Venture Group
Portner, Mark—Shorenstein Company LLC
Portnoy, Bram—Old City Partners, LLC (OCP)
Porzio, Claudio—Vertis SGR SpA
Poseidon, Lee—JumpStart, Inc.
Posner, Henry—Hawthorne Group
Posner, Louis—Dutchess Advisors LLC
Posnick, David—Blackstone Group, L.P.
Posselt, J. Wolfgang—Aurelia Private Equity GmbH
Poston, Edwin—TrueBridge Capital Partners
Potamianos, Phokion—Francisco Partners
Potanin, Vladimir—Interros Holding
Pothier, Robert—EPIC Ventures
Potter, Cheryl—Permira Advisers LLP
Potter, Henry—Alpha Associates AG
Potter, Matthew—Delphi Ventures
Potter, Scott—San Francisco Equity Partners
Potthof, Ingo—smac partners GmbH
Potts, Katie—Herald Investment Management Ltd (HIML)
Pouladdej, Parham—CRG Capital
Pouladdej, Parham—CRG Partners
Pouletty, Philippe—Truffle Venture SAS
Poulos, James—Maryland Technology Development Corporation
Poulsen, Stig—Danfoss Ventures A/S
Poupee, Francois—AtriA Capital Partenaires
Pouschine, John—Pouschine Cook Capital Management, LLC
Poux-Guillaume, Gregoire—CVC Capital Partners (Europe), Ltd.
Powell, Charles—Haynes and Boone LLC
Powell, Earl—Trivest Partners, L.P.
Powell, Earl—Westshore Capital Partners
Powell, John—Integral Capital Partners
Powell, Keith—Longbow Capital
Powell, Michael—Sofinnova Ventures
Powell, Richard—AP Capital Partners
Power, David—Fidelity Ventures
Powers, Averill—Celtic Pharma Management, LP
Powers, Averill—Celtic Therapeutics Management, L.L.L.P.
Powers, Edward—BAML Capital Access Funds
Powers, Joe—DesignWorks Investments
Powers, Laurie—Crown Capital Partners Inc.
Powers, Linda—Toucan Capital
Powis, Deb—Cobalt Capital, Inc.
Prabhakar, Arati—U.S. Venture Partners
Prabhu, Krish—Mobility Ventures
Prado, Antonio Henrique—Plataforma Capital Partners
Prado, Dennis—Main Street Capital Holdings LLC
Prado, Gerald—Main Street Capital Holdings LLC
Prado, Ricardo—Sterling Partners
Praeger, Robin—Versant Ventures
Prahl, Peder—Triton Partners
Prais, David—Pembridge Partners LLP
Prakash, Arun—Virgo Capital
Prakke, Frits—Alchemy Partners LLP
Prang, Joseph—Mentor Capital Group

Prasad, Dhruv—Thomas H. Lee Partners (AKA: TH Lee Partners)
Prasad, N.K.—Pathfinder Investment Co., Ltd.
Prasad, Pulak—Nalanda Capital Pte, Ltd.
Prasad, S.Vishwanatha—Caspian Advisors Pvt. Ltd.
Prasetya, Sigit—CVC Asia Pacific, Ltd.
Prasetya, Sigit—CVC Capital Partners (Europe), Ltd.
Prata, Gregory—Gotham Private Equity Partners, L.P.
Prather, Jason—MFC Capital Funding, Inc.
Pratt, Richard—Meridian Capital (FKA: Olympic Capital Partners, LLC)
Praznuik, Ken—Manitoba Capital Fund
Preaux, Guy—Sambrinvest S.A.
Preissier, Jim—Panthera Capital Group
Prelz, Massimo—GMT Communications Partners LLP
Prend, David—Rockport Capital Partners
Prendergast, Daniel—Atlantic-Pacific Capital, Inc.
Prendergast, Daniel—Blackstone Group, L.P.
Prentice, Geoffrey—Atomico Ventures
Presnal, Jeff—CCG Venture Partners, LLC
Presser, Mitchell—Paine & Partners LLC
Presser, Stephen—Monomoy Capital Partners, LLC
Presser-Velder, Soren—Investcorp Bank B.S.C.
Pressler, Townes—Lime Rock Partners LLC
Pressman, Jason—Shasta Ventures Management LLC
Preston, Charles—Harris Preston & Partners, LLC
Preston, Heather—TPG Growth
Preston, Mark—WHEB Ventures, Ltd.
Preston, Robert—Epi-V LLP
Pretlow, Joseph—Bain Capital
Pretlow, Joseph—JP Capital Partners, LLC
Pretolani, Mauro—TLcom Capital LLP
Pretorius, Rudolf—Treacle Venture Partners
Price, Kent—Parker Price Venture Capital Inc.(FKA: Allegro Capital, Inc)
Price, Matthew—Nth Power
Price, Paul—Prudential Capital Group
Price, Philip—PHD Equity Partners LLP
Price, Roger—Innovation Capital Associates Pty, Ltd.
Price, Steven—American Capital, Ltd.
Price, Steven—Centerbridge Partners
Price, William—TPG Capital
Priddy, Robert—Comvest Investment Partners
Priebe, Christopher—Hamilton Lane Advisors, Inc.
Prier, Diane—American Capital, Ltd.
Priestley, Bill—LGV Capital, Ltd. (FKA: Legal & General Ventures, Ltd.)
Prieto, Dave—Headwaters Merchant Bank
Prihti, Aki—Inveni Capital
Prince, Gingee—Enhanced Capital Partners, LLC
Prins, Marius—Participation Company East Netherlands NV (AKA : PPM Oost)
Prior, John—Needham Asset Management
Pritchard, Gary—Palamon Capital Partners (FKA: Amphion Capital Partners)
Pritzker, J.B.—New World Ventures
Procheus, Lars—Firm Factory Network
Proctor, Steven—Henderson Equity Partners (AKA: Henderson Private Capital)
Proemm, Philipp—Climate Solutions Management GmbH
Prokop, Kevin—Questor Management Company LLC
Prokop, Kevin—RockBridge Equity Partners LLC
Prokopich, Lori—Cassels Brock Lawyers
Pronczuk, Dariusz—Enterprise Investors Sp z oo
Pronk, Nikolai R.D.—Gilde Buy Out Partners
Propper de Callejon, Diana—Expansion Capital Partners LLC
Prostko, E. Richard—VantagePoint Venture Partners
Protard, Olivier—Seventure Partners SA (FKA: SPEF Venture)
Protard, Olivier—Sofinnova Partners
Protash, Eugene—Allen & Company
Prough, Jeffrey—Concentric Equity Partners, L.P.
Proujansky, Philip—Cayuga Venture Fund
Proven, John—GrowthWorks
Provera, Nino Tronchetti—Ambienta SGR S.p.A.
Prsa, Joseph—Mariner Financial, Ltd. (AKA: Mariner Brand Capital, Ltd.)
Prudencio, Rodrigo—Nth Power
Pruett, Shelby—Gryffindor Capital Partners LLC
Prusnek, Brian—Climate Change Capital, Ltd.
Pruss, Paul—Silverfleet Capital (FKA: PPM Capital Partners)
Pruthi, Vineet—Lincolnshire Management, Inc.
Pruzan, Robert—Centerview Partners Holdings LLC
Pruzansky, Mark—Undisclosed Firm
Pryce, Tim—Terra Firma Capital Partners, Ltd.
Pryke, Phillip—Co-Investor Capital Partners Pty., Ltd.
Pryma, Thomas—AEA Investors LP
Pryor, Brian—Media Venture Partners
Pryor, Dan—Carlyle Group, The
Prytula, Richard—TechnoCap, Inc.
Pu, Allen—Navigation Capital Partners (AKA: NCP)
Pu, James—Simon Murray and Associates
Puchniak, Robert—Richardson Capital Limited
Pucillo, Tony—Corinthian Capital Group LLC
Puech, Jean-Francois—Siparex Group SAS
Puelinckx, Kristoff—Delta Partners FZ LLC
Puertas, Juan—GED Group
Pugatch, Michael—HarbourVest Partners LLC
Puglisi, Michael—Blackstone Group, L.P.
Puhakka, Hannu—MB Funds (AKA: MB Rahastot Oy)
Puig, Marian—Suma Capital
Pujol, Jerome—Rothschild Gestion
Pujol, Juan—JHP Enterprises LLC
Pulges, Virapan—H&Q Asia Pacific
Pullman, Patrick—Pacesetter Capital Group (FKA: MESBIC Ventures Holding Co.)
Pun, Patrick—Monster Venture Partners
Punch, Justin—Archer Capital
Pundak-Mintz, Adi—Gemini Israel Funds, Ltd.
Punnoose, Manu—Subhkam Ventures
Puonti, Kalevi—Helmet Business Mentors Oy
Pupin, Antoine—21 Centrale Partners
Pupin, Antoine—21 Partners SpA
Pupo, Alex Luis—Aztec Equity Partners, LLC
Purcell, Gregory—Arbor Private Investment Company, LLC
Purcell, Jack—Ridgemont Equity Partners
Purcell, Sandy—Houlihan, Lokey, Howard & Zukin
Purcell, Tim—J.P. Morgan Capital Corporation
Purcell, Tim—Linzor Capital Partners, L.P.
Purdy, Todd—Leonard Green & Partners
Puri, Dennis—Crosslink Capital
Purkar, Prashant—ICICI Venture Funds Management Co., Pvt. Ltd. (FKA: TDICI)
Purkayastha, Dev—Timeline Ventures LLC
Purkert, Gert—EVP Capital Management AG
Puro, Nicholas—Edelson Technology Partners
Purse, Charles—Blackstone Group, L.P.
Purslow, Christian—MidOcean Partners
Purushotham, Arvind—Menlo Ventures
Pusey, Greg—Livingston Capital, Ltd.
Putnam, Mitch—32 Degrees Capital
Putnam, Travis—Navitas Capital
Putney, Mark—TAT Capital Partners Ltd
Pyett, Nicholas—Camelot Ventures
Pyne, Russell—Atrium Capital
Qadir, Kamran—Jahangir Siddiqui Group (AKA: JS Group)
Qi, Jue—Pride Investments Group, Ltd., The
Qi, Li—TeChina Investment Management Ltd
Qian, Bill—Wuhan Huagong Venture Capital Co., Ltd.
Qian, Charles—Gold Stone Investment, Ltd.
Qian, Jin—Comway Capital Limited
Qiu, Cynthia—WI Harper Group
Qiu, David—Hony Capital Ltd.
Qiu, Guohua—Sichuan Shizhi Investment Co., Ltd.
Qiu, Liping—Milestone Capital Management, Ltd.
Qiu, Shufang—MTM Capital Partners
Qiu, Zhizhong—DragonTech Ventures Management, Ltd.
Qu, Jianzhong—CSV Capital Partners (FKA: China Seed Ventures)
Qu, Summer Xiaopeng—Northern Light Venture Capital
Qu, Xiang Jun—Xi'an Prutention Investment & Development Co., Ltd.
Quade, Bruce—Catalyst Capital Managment
Quadros, Paul—Tenex Greenhouse Ventures
Quagliaroli, Jim—Spectrum Equity Investors
Quamme, Steven—Blackstreet Capital Management (FKA: MMP Capital Advisors)
Quarta, Roberto—Clayton, Dubilier & Rice, Inc.
Quartieri, Ferdinando Grimaldi—Bain Capital
Quasha, Alan—Vanterra Capital, Ltd.
Quattrocchi, Massimo—Clubinvest Private Equity
Quazi, Jullia—Shattuck Hammond Partners
Qubbai, Muhannad—Gulf Capital
Queally, Paul—Welsh, Carson, Anderson & Stowe
Queen, Michael—3i Group PLC
Quek, Cher Teck—New Horizon Capital
Quella, James—Blackstone Group, L.P.
Queveau, Philippe—CITA Gestion SA
Quigley, John—YL Ventures GP, Ltd.
Quigley, Matthew—Blackstone Group, L.P.
Quigley, William—Clearstone Venture Partners
Quinlivan, David—Saints Ventures
Quinn, David—Pinpoint Ventures
Quinn, Larry—Atlantic Bridge
Quinn, Michael—Innovation Capital Associates Pty, Ltd.
Quinn, Michael—Shattuck Hammond Partners
Quinn, William—Natural Gas Partners (NGP)
Quinn, William—Versa Capital Management (FKA: Chrysalis Capital Partners)
Quint, Susanne—Halder Holdings BV
Quintana, Mario—Pegasus Venture Capital
Quinty, Herve—Groupe Sofimac
Quon, David—Orchard First Source

Quy, Roger—Technology Partners
R. Jones, Boyd—Fitch crown Venture Capital Management (Shenzhen) Co., Ltd.
Raab, Yitzhak—KCPS Israel Private Equity Partners
Raaby Bronden, Christian—ATP Private Equity Partners
Raanan, Gil—Sequoia Capital
Raatz, Stan—Warburg Pincus LLC
Rabini, Johannes—Triginta Capital Partners GmbH (FKA: Avida Equity Partners)
Rachesky, Mark—MHR Capital Partners
Rachleff, Andrew—Benchmark Capital
Rachwalski, John—Oak Hill Capital Management, Inc.
Racich, Nicholas—BIG Capital, SA
Radberg, Jan—Nordea Private Equity
Radchenko, Andrew—NCH Capital, Inc.
Radecki, Joseph—Headwaters Merchant Bank
Rader, J. Mitchell—BrightPath Capital, Inc.
Rader, Stephen—Clarity Partners
Radhakrishnan, Ram—East West Capital Partners Pte, Ltd.
Radis, Craig—PPM America Capital Partners LLC
Radley, Gordon—Allegis Capital (AKA: Media Technology Ventures)
Radosevich, H.Ray—Verge
Radoshitzky, Limor—Star Ventures Management GmbH & Co. KG
Radwanski, Witold—Krokus Private Equity Sp. z o.o.
Radzik, Mark—Granite Creek Partners
Rael, Lillian—Flywheel Ventures
Rafanelli, Paolo—Fidi Toscana SpA
Raffa, Joseph—Adams Capital Management, Inc.
Raffel, David—Brass Ring Capital, Inc.
Raffel, Wes—Advanced Technology Ventures
Rafferty, Richard—Haynes and Boone LLC
Raffini, George—HSBC Pte Equity (Asia), Ltd. (FKA: HSBC Private Equity Mgt.)
Raffle, Tim—ECI Partners LLP
Rafuse, Brady—Columbia Capital LLC
Ragab, Karim—Citadel Capital S.A.E.
Ragatz, Erik—Hellman & Friedman LLC
Raghavan, Harsha—Candover Investments PLC
Raghavan, N.S.—Nadathur Holdings and Investments Pvt., Ltd.
Raghavan, Rangarajan—Investcorp Bank B.S.C.
Raghavan, Sharat—Ericsson Venture Partners
Raghavendran, Ramanan—Kubera Partners, LLC
Raghavendran, Ramanan—TH Lee Putnam Ventures, L.P.
Ragio, Tony—Capvest Venture Fund (FKA: Virgin Ventures Fund LP)
Ragnarsson, Jonas—EQT Funds management Limited
Rahe, Eric—Capital Z Investment Partners (FKA: Union Square Partners)
Rahe, Eric—Clayton, Dubilier & Rice, Inc.
Rahim, Basil—MerchantBridge & Co., Ltd.
Rahmn, Jonas—KTH-Chalmers Capital KB
Rahumaa, Indrek—Alta Capital
Rai, Atual Kumar—IFCI Venture Capital Funds, Ltd. (FKA: Risk Capital & Tech.)
Rai, Rajesh—New Markets Venture Partners (AKA: New Markets Growth Fund)
Rai, Raul—General Atlantic LLC
Rai, Sumit—Riverside Partners
Raibaut, Patrick—Debaeque Venture Capital
Raich, Steven—Littlejohn & Company LLC
Raicher, Serge—Pantheon Ventures, Ltd.
Raid, Jaak—Alta Capital
Raidma, Pirje—GILD Bankers (FKA: LHV Ventures)
Raiff, Thierry—Euromezzanine Conseil (AKA: Euromezzanine Gestion)
Raimondi, Jill—Housatonic Partners
Raimondo, Gina—Point Judith Capital
Raina, Vikrant—Boston Ventures Management, Inc.
Rainey, Donald—Grotech Ventures
Rainville, Todd—Ampersand Ventures
Raisurana, Rahul—Standard Chartered Private Equity, Ltd.
Raith, James—Gleacher & Co.
Raj, Prem Mohan—ISIS Equity Partners PLC
Raja, Saad—Draper Fisher Jurvetson ePlanet Ventures, L.P.
Rajab, Mufeed—Investcorp Bank B.S.C.
Rajago, Sundaram—Starwood Capital Group
Rajagopal, Sundaram—Starwood Capital Group
Rajagopalan, Sreevatsan—Investcorp Bank B.S.C.
Rajagopalan, Supraj—Cinven, Ltd.
Rajamani, Vijay—Wasserstein Ventures (FKA: Wasserstein & Co.)
Rajan, AST—Aquarius Investment Advisors Pte., Ltd.
Rajan, Hari—Corsair Capital LLC
Rajaraman, Anand—Cambrian Ventures
Rajaratnam, Raj—New Silk Route Partners LLC
Rajee, R—Canbank Venture Capital Fund Limited
Rajevich, Ilaria—Alice Ventures Srl
Rajkumar, Raj—Symphony Asia Holdings Pte. Ltd.
Rajpurohit, David—Stanford Investment Group
Raju, Champ—PPM America Capital Partners LLC
Raju, Vikram—IDFC Capital (Singapore) Pte, Ltd.
Rakavy, Yuval—BRM Capital
Raker, Geoffrey—Tailwind Capital Partners
Raker, Geoffrey—Thomas Weisel Partners Group, Inc.
Raker, Jill—Greenbriar Equity Group LLC
Rallet, Jean-Michel—MBO Partenaires
Rallo, Eduardo—Pacific Community Ventures (FKA: SVCV)
Ralls, Rawleigh—Lacuna, LLC
Ralph, Jon—Freeman Spogli & Co.
Ralph, Randal—Northwestern Mutual Capital
Ralston, Craig—Cascade Investment Group
Ramachandaran, Anuradha—VenturEast (FKA: APIDC Venture Capital Limited)
Ramakrishna, K.V.—Kotak Investment Advisors, Ltd. (AKA: KPEG)
Ramati, Roy—Aviv Venture Capital (FKA: Fantine Group, The)
Rambaud, Bertrand—Siparex Group SAS
Ramberg, Bradley—idealab!
Ramdeen, Gerald—Millennium Equity
Ramdev, Raghav—ChrysCapital Management Company
Ramesh, A.—VenturEast (FKA: APIDC Venture Capital Limited)
Ramich, J. Michael—Frontier Capital LLC
Ramirez, Juan Luis—Inversiones Ibersuizas S.A.
Ramirez, Santiago—CVC Capital Partners (Europe), Ltd.
Ramljak, Ante—Quaestus Private Equity, Ltd.
Ramnath, Renuka—Multiples Alternate Asset Management
Ramnauth, Satyam—Aureos Capital, Ltd.
Ramoisy, Christophe—Pragma Capital
Ramos, Vicente Miguel—Constitution Capital Partners, LLC
Ramos, Vicente Miguel—SL Capital Partners LLP
Ramos-Fuentenebro, Miguel—Blackstone Group, L.P.
Ramsauer, Richard G.—VTC Partners GmbH
Ramsay, Brian—Littlejohn & Company LLC
Ramsay, David—Care Capital, LLC
Ramsay, Michael—New Enterprise Associates, Inc.
Ramsay, Mike—Carlyle Group, The
Ramsay, Thomas—EQT Funds management Limited
Ramsey, Charles—JMI Equity
Ramsin, Hakan—Provider Venture Partners AB (FKA: IT Provider Advisor 1 AB)
Ranasinghe, Cheryl—Aureos Capital, Ltd.
Rand, Amanda—Spinnaker Trust
Rand, Kenneth—Agility Capital LLC
Rand, Lee—Sun Mountain Capital
Rand, Len—Granite Ventures LLC
Rand, Michael—GB Merchant Partners, LLC (FKA: GB Palladin Capital LLC)
Rand, Michael—WindSail Ventures LLC
Rand, William—Vostok Gas, Ltd. (FKA: Vostok Nafta Investment)
Randall, Chris—MFC Capital Funding, Inc.
Randall, Leigh—TopSpin Partners
Randall, Mike—LRG Capital Group (FKA: Baystar Capital, LLC)
Randall, Roderick—Vesbridge Partners, LLC
Randazzo, Chris—Brook Street Investments LLC
Randolph, Gregory—GCP Capital Partners
Ranera, Roberto—3i Group PLC
Raney, Scott—Redpoint Ventures
Rangam, Bir—Al'yans ROSNO Upravleniye Aktivami, OAO
Ranganath, V.R.—Sandalwood Capital Partners
Ranganath, V.R.—Solar Venture Partners
Ranganathan, Natarajan—Helion Venture Partners
Rangaswami, Madhavan—Sand Hill Group, LLC
Ranger, Michael—Diamond Castle Holdings LLC
Ranger, Rheal—Borealis Infrastructure Management, Inc.
Rangnekar, Aseem—ICICI Venture Funds Management Co., Pvt. Ltd. (FKA: TDICI)
Ranson, Michael—Blue Wolf Capital Management LLC
Rantanen, Jacqueline—Hamilton Lane Advisors, Inc.
Ranzetta, Theresia—Accel Partners
Rao, Ganesh—Thomas H. Lee Partners (AKA: TH Lee Partners)
Rao, Kiran—Grove Street Advisors LLC
Rao, Raj—Global Infrastructure Partners
Rao, Tirumala—Jacob Ballas Capital India Pvt, Ltd. (AKA:JBC)
Rao, Zeena—ICV Capital Partners LLC
Raouf, Firas—OpenView Venture Partners
Rapeport, Willian—Column Group, The
Rapoport, Borris—FTV Capital (FKA: FTVentures)
Rapp, Eric-Alan—Sunstone Capital A/S
Rappaport, Andrew—August Capital Management
Rapport, Michael—Perseus LLC

Rasche, Thom—Earlybird Venture Capital GmbH & Co. KG
Raschle, Bruno—Adveq Management AG
Rashdan, Waleed—Tadhamon Capital BSC
Rashotte, Tom—TD Capital Group, Ltd.
Rasmussen, Adam—Granite Capital Partners
Rasmussen, Erik—Safeguard Scientifics, Inc.
Rasmussen, Jesper Frydensberg—Dansk Kapitalanlaeg Aktieselskab
Rastetter, William—Venrock Associates
Rastrick, John—Phoenix Equity Partners (FKA: DLJ European Private Equity)
Rathinam, G—Actis Capital LLP
Rathman, Lincoln—Vistech Corp.
Ratnayaka, Kshanika—Washington Technology Partners, Inc. (AKA: WTP)
Ratoff, Steven—ProQuest Investments
Ratsepp, Andres—Alta Capital
Rattee, Helen—Coburn Ventures, LLC
Rattle, Philip—August Equity LLP
Rattner, Jonathan—Atrium Capital
Rattner, Steven—DLJ Merchant Banking Partners
Ratzan, Brian—Vestar Capital Partners, Inc.
Raucci, Robert—Newlight Associates
Rauch, Liliana—Conduit Capital Partners, LLC
Rauh, James—JLL Partners (FKA: Joseph, Littlejohn & Levy, Inc.)
Rauschenbusch, Alec—Grazia Equity GmbH
Rauschenbusch, Erich—Grazia Equity GmbH
Rauvola, Bridget—Morgenthaler Ventures
Raventos, Francesc—Catalana D'Iniciatives CR SA
Ravich, Jess—Caltius Equity Partners
Ravindran, Sanuj—Radius Ventures LLC
Ravindran, V.—Paracor Capital Advisors Pvt., Ltd.
Rawie, Damon—Advantage Capital Partners
Rawji, Irfhan—Birch Hill Equity Partners Management, Inc.
Rawlings, Michael—CIC Partners, L.P. (FKA: Cardinal Investment Company, Inc.)
Ray, Brent—Harbert Venture Partners
Ray, Christopher—Natural Gas Partners (NGP)
Ray, Daniel—JatoTech Management LLC
Ray, Russell—HLM Venture Partners
Ray, Thomas—Carlyle Group, The
Raygorodetsky, Philip—Black Diamond Capital Management, LLC
Raygorodetsky, Philip—GSC Partners (FKA: Greenwich Street Capital Partners)
Raymond, Colin—Natural Gas Partners (NGP)
Raynard, Robert—Industry Ventures
Raynard, Robert—Walden Venture Capital
Rayne, Robert—Derwent London PLC
Rays, Cedric—Cognetas LLP
Raythatha, Jigar—Red Abbey Venture Partners, LLC
Razak, Affeiz Abdul—Malaysian Technology Development Corp Sdn Bhd
Razak, Dato Nazir—CIMB Private Equity Sdn Bhd
Razaq, Masood—NBD Sana Capital
Raziano, Robert—Stonebridge Partners
Razzano, Dante—Investindustrial Partners, Ltd.
Razzouk, Assaad—Sindicatum Carbon Capital, Ltd.
Rea, Steven—ATEL Ventures, Inc.
Read, Graham—Pantheon Ventures, Ltd.
Read, J. Leighton—Alloy Ventures
Read, Jim—MML Capital Partners
Read, Steve—Climate Change Capital, Ltd.
Read, Susan—TechnoCap, Inc.
Read, William—Lakeview Equity Partners, LLC
Reade, K. Deane—Bangert Dawes Reade Davis & Thom
Reagh, John—WRF Capital
Reale, Steve—Levensohn Venture Partners LLC (FKA: Levensohn Capital Mgmt)
Reardon, John—J.P. Morgan Partners (FKA: Chase Capital Partners)
Reardon, Thomas—WestView Capital Partners
Rebar, Thomas—SCP Private Equity Partners
Rebello, James—Growth Capital Partners, L.P.
Recanati, Leon—GlenRock Israel, Ltd.
Recanati, Leon—NGN Capital LLC
Recchia, Luiz—Stratus Banco de Negocios
Rechav, Geva—Concord Ventures (FKA: Nitzanim)
Rechtman, Marcos—AIG Capital Investments do Brasil S.A.
Redding, Douglas—VIMAC Ventures LLC (FKA: VIMAC LLC)
Reddy, Pratap—Draper Fisher Jurvetson ePlanet Ventures, L.P.
Reddy, R. Venkatram—Caspian Advisors Pvt. Ltd.
Reddy, Rachan—IDG Ventures Vietnam
Reddy, Sandeep—Peepul Capital LLC
Reddy, Ven—Annex Venture Management, LLC
Redelfs, Richard—Foundation Capital
Redman, Mark—OMERS Private Equity
Redmon, Todd—American Capital, Ltd.
Redmond, Ben—Risk Capital Partners, Ltd.
Redmond, Nathan—Rustic Canyon Partners
Reed, Amanda—Palomar Ventures
Reed, Dominic—United Financial Group Asset Management (AKA: UFG)
Reed, Douglas—Hatteras Venture Partners (FKA:Catalysta Partners)
Reed, Jeffrey—Pantheon Ventures, Ltd.
Reed, Kimberly—American Capital, Ltd.
Reed, Matthew—CCMP Capital Advisors LLC
Reed, Paul—Montlake Capital
Reed, Phillip—Highway 12 Ventures
Reed, Ron—Seneca Partners, Inc.
Reed, Rusty—Great Pacific Capital, LLC
Reed, Scott—BankCap Partners
Rees, Robert—Startup Capital Ventures L.P.
Rees, Stephen—Atila Ventures
Rees-Jones, Hywel—Actis Capital LLP
Rees-Jones, Hywel—CDC Group PLC (FKA: Commonwealth Development Corporation)
Reese, Luke—Winona Capital Management
Reeve, N. Dan—Horsley Bridge Partners
Reeve, Patrick—Albion Ventures LLP (FKA: Close Venture Management)
Reeves, Lisa—Vista Ventures
Reeves, William—DFJ Esprit
Reffreger, Juan—Blue Equity, LLC
Regan, Brian—Welsh, Carson, Anderson & Stowe
Regan, Joseph—GrowthWorks
Regan, Kathy—Radius Ventures LLC
Regev, Guy—Shaked Global Group Ltd.
Regnery, George—Bedford Funding
Regulla, Suneel—Indo-Nordic Private Equity AS
Rehberg, Harald—Sachsen LB Corporate Finance Holding GmbH
Rehm, George—firstVentury GmbH
Rehman, Aamir—Fajr Capital Ltd
Rehman, Omer—HYPO-Unternehmensbeteiligungen AG
Reich, Marc—Ironwood Capital (AKA: Ironwood Capital Advisors LLC)
Reich, Markus—3i Group PLC
Reich, Markus—Cross Equity Partners AG
Reich, Tobias—One Equity Partners (FKA: Banc One Venture Partners)
Reichardt, Sarah—Crown Capital Corporation
Reichenbach, George—Braemar Energy Ventures
Reichenberger, Wolfgang—inventages venture capital S.A.
Reicher, Andrew—Actis Capital LLP
Reichert, Bill—Garage Technology Ventures LLC (FKA: Garage.com)
Reichert, Hunter—Mangrove Equity Partners LLC
Reichmann, Phillip—ReichmannHauer Capital Partners
Reichmayr, Ernst—Andlinger & Company, Inc.
Reicin, Glenn—Skyline Ventures
Reid, Keith—GKA Bayete
Reid, Mike—Frog Capital, Ltd.
Reid, Robert—Blackstone Group, L.P.
Reid, Ronan—Fourth Level Ventures (AKA : 4th Level Ventures)
Reidencach, Peter—Industrial Growth Partners
Reidy, Brendan—Trident Capital
Reidy, Stephen—EuclidSR Partners
Reijula, Peter—American Capital, Ltd.
Reiland, Kathleen—Evercore Partners
Reilly, Andrew—Accretive Exit Capital Partners LLC
Reilly, Cameron—Black Canyon Capital
Reilly, Philip—Third Rock Ventures LLC
Reilly, Robert—C.W. Downer & Company (FKA: Downer & Company)
Reilly, Scott—Golub Capital
Reilly, Scott—Peninsula Capital Partners LLC
Reilly, Scott—Superior Capital Partners
Reily, Kevin—Rosewood Capital, L.P.
Rein, Harry—Foundation Medical Partners
Reineman, Jay—Visa Inc. (FKA: Visa International)
Reinemo, Rikke Tobiasson—Herkules Capital AS
Reinholdt, Steen Louis—IVS A/S (AKA: Internet Ventures Scandinavia A/S)
Reiniger, Peter—European Bank for Reconstruction and Development
Reinisch, Peter—Global Life Science Ventures GmbH
Reinsdorf, Michael—Mercantile Capital Group (MCG)
Reinseth, Bjorn Erik—Ferd Venture
Reinseth, Bjorn Erik—Herkules Capital AS
Reis, Norbert—Carlyle Group, The
Reiser, William—Murphree Venture Partners
Reisler, Bill—Consumer Growth Partners
Reisman, Sam—Rose Corporation, The
Reisner, Daniel—Sterling Partners
Reisner, Hunter—ACI Capital Co., LLC
Reisner, Hunter—Citigroup Private Equity
Reisner, Rick—Andrew W. Byrd & Co. LLC
Reiss, Stanley—Matrix Partners
Reitberger, Christian—Wellington Partners Venture Capital GmbH
Reiten, Narve—Reiten & Co Strategic Investments AS
Reiter, Allon—Giza Venture Capital (FKA: Giza Investment Management)

Rodrigues, Ross—Odyssey Investment Partners, LLC
Rodriguez Segovia, Javier—Axis ParticIpaCiones Empresariales SGECR SA
Rodriguez Simon, Ivelisse—Avante Mezzanine Partners
Rodriguez, Antonio—Matrix Partners
Rodriguez, Frank—JLL Partners (FKA: Joseph, Littlejohn & Levy, Inc.)
Rodriguez, Harold—GCP Capital Partners
Rodriguez, Ricardo—Southern Cross Group (AKA: SCG)
Rodriguez-Fraile, Gonzalo—Prax Capital
Rodseth, Pal—Ferd Venture
Rodzevik, Paul—Jordan Company, The
Roe, Jason—Kenda Capital BV
Roe, Wayne—DFJ InCube Ventures
Roeder, Douglas—Delphi Ventures
Roeder, Richard—Aurora Capital Group (FKA: Aurora Capital Partners)
Roeder, Richard—Vance Street Capital LLC
Roehrs, Carsten—Haspa BGM
Roellig, Charles—Century Park Capital Partners
Roenick, Russ—Transom Capital Group
Roeper, Robert—VIMAC Ventures LLC (FKA: VIMAC LLC)
Roeper, Robert—Wave Equity Partners
Roepers, Jack—New Enterprise East Investments (AKA: NEEI)
Roesch, Philippe—Auda Private Equity LLC
Roessler, Luciane—Trenwith Securities LLC
Roetman, Edward—Adirondack Venture Fund, The
Roex, Erwin—Coller Capital
Roffler, Roland—Partners Group AG
Rogan, James—Path4 Ventures, LLC
Rogan, Paul—Challenger International Ltd.
Rogero, David—Cressey & Company, L.P.
Rogero, David—Thoma Cressey Bravo
Rogers, Alex—HarbourVest Partners LLC
Rogers, Bill—Halifax Group, The
Rogers, Bruce—KRG Capital Partners LLC
Rogers, Christopher—Shattuck Hammond Partners
Rogers, Jef—Gryphon Investors, Inc.
Rogers, Jesse—Altamont Capital Partners
Rogers, John—Gryphon Investors, Inc.
Rogers, Kyle—Keating Investments LLC
Rogers, Robert—Vista Equity Partners
Rogers, Sarah—Glynn Capital Management
Rogerson, Simon—Octopus Asset Management, Ltd.
Rogerson, Steve—Scsi Capital
Rogoff, Eric—Falcon Investment Advisors LLC
Rogowski, Olaf—Findos Investor GmbH
Rohall, Douglas—Ampersand Ventures
Rohall, Douglas—JMH Capital
Rohr, George—NCH Capital, Inc.
Rohrsheim, Victoria—Propel Investments
Roine, Pekka—Prime Technology Ventures NV
Roithner, Friedrich—Unternehmens Invest AG
Roitman, Wesley—Romspen Investment Corporation
Rojas, Javier—Kennet Venture Partners, Ltd. (FKA: Kennet Capital, Ltd.)
Rokosh, Norm—TriWest Capital Management Corporation
Roland, Gilles—Fin'Active
Roland, Kjell—Norfund
Rolfs, Theodore—Red Top Capital LLC (FKA: Crimson Capital Company)
Rolfs, Thomas—Red Top Capital LLC (FKA: Crimson Capital Company)
Roll, Penni—Allied Capital Corporation
Rolland, J. Michael—Borealis Infrastructure Management, Inc.
Rollins, Vinton—Shattuck Hammond Partners
Rollwagen, John—Quatris Fund
Rolo, Miguel—Novabase Capital
Rolph, Colin—Tall Oaks Capital Partners LLC
Romani, Enrique Lucas—Nordkapp Gestion S.G.I.I.C., S.A.
Romanos, Guillermo—Iame Capital Riesgo SGECR SA
Romans, Andrew—Georgetown Venture Partners (AKA: GVP)
Rombeau, Suzanne—Paul Capital Partners
Rome, Brett—North Hill Ventures
Romer, Max—Quadriga Capital
Romic, Joseph—American Capital, Ltd.
Ron, Hadar—Israel Healthcare Ventures
Ron, Yossi—Mofet B-Yehuda Technological and Business Incubator
Ronc, Michel—Demeter Partners S.A.
Rond, Patrick—Key Principal Partners LLC (AKA: KPP)
Ronen, Osnat—Viola Private Equity
Ronfeldt, Carsten—Danske Private Equity A/S
Rong, He—Guangdong Technology Venture Capital Group., Ltd
Ronje, Torben—InnoVenture A/S
Ronn, Harald—Alpha Group
Ronningen, Gudmund—Borea AS
Rook, Frederick—Capital Z Investment Partners (FKA: Union Square Partners)
Roon, Chris—Mentor Capital Group
Rooney, Philip—Internet Capital Group
Roongta, Prateek—India Value Fund Advisors Private Ltd. (FKA: GW Capital)
Roos, Axel—Pod Venture Partners Inc.
Roos, Christo—Ethos Private Equity
Rooseboom, Laura—Start Green Venture Capital
Root, Jonathan—U.S. Venture Partners
Ropert, Jean Michel—Wendel
Roques, Bernard-Louis—Truffle Venture SAS
Roriston, Robert—Lindsay Goldberg LLC (FKA: Lindsay Goldberg & Bessemer GP)
Rortveit, Jon—EuroUs Ventures
Rosa, Katherine—J.P. Morgan Asset Management
Rosa, Wilson—Advent International
Rosas, Roy—Berkshire Partners LLC
Rosberg, Jenny—Skandia Innovation AB
Rosberg, Ulf—Nordic Capital (AKA: NC Advisory)
Rosborough, Bradley—Headwaters Merchant Bank
Rosch, Thomas—InterWest Partners
Rose, Alex—Crestview Partners L.P. (FKA: Crestview, LLC)
Rose, David—Rose Tech Ventures, LLC
Rose, Jay—JLL Partners (FKA: Joseph, Littlejohn & Levy, Inc.)
Rose, John—Alpha Capital Partners, Ltd.
Rose, John—CapGen Financial Group
Rose, John—Rolls Royce Corporate Venture
Rose, Peter—Blackstone Group, L.P.
Rose, Porter—Azalea Capital LLC
Rose, Stuart—Tully & Holland, Inc. (FKA: Ulin & Holland, Inc.)
Rose, Wolfgang—BV Capital (FKA: Bertelsmann Ventures, LP)
Roselle, Arthur—Pamlico Capital
Roseman, Loren—Monomoy Capital Partners, LLC
Rosemary, Ripley—NGEN Partners LLC (FKA: NextGen Partners LLC)
Rosen, Alexander—IDG Ventures SF
Rosen, Andrew—HM Capital Partners LLC
Rosen, Daniel—Highland Capital Partners LLC
Rosen, David—Pacific Community Ventures (FKA: SVCV)
Rosen, Eric—MSD Capital L.P.
Rosen, Jonathan—TDR Capital LLP
Rosen, Mark—Charlesbank Capital Partners LLC
Rosen, Michael—Pamplona Capital Management LLP
Rosen, Modi—Magma Venture Partners
Rosen, Rick—H.I.G. Capital LLC
Rosenbaum, Mark—Aurora Capital Group (FKA: Aurora Capital Partners)
Rosenbaum, Robert—Nobska Ventures
Rosenberg, Daniel—Sterling Partners
Rosenberg, Jason—Sterling Partners
Rosenberg, John—Technology Crossover Ventures
Rosenberg, Robert—FFR Capital Partners
Rosenberg, Robert—New Venture Partners LLC
Rosenberg, Sheli—Forstmann Little & Company
Rosenberg, Teddy—CIBC Capital Partners
Rosenberry, Kenton—MTS Health Partners, L.P.
Rosenbloom, Keith—Comvest Investment Partners
Rosenblum, Bruce—Carlyle Group, The
Rosenboim, Yaron—Concord Ventures (FKA: Nitzanim)
Rosenfeld, Arie—Dor Ventures Management SA
Rosenfeld, Eric—Capybara Ventures LLC
Rosenfeld, Eric—DFJ Frontier
Rosenfelt, Michael—Impact Venture Partners
Rosenlew, Michael—IK Investment Partners, Ltd.
Rosenstein, David—General Atlantic LLC
Rosenthal, Jeffrey—Imperial Capital Corporation
Rosenzweig, Arthur—Research Partners, Ltd.
Rosenzweig, Eric—Stone Point Capital LLC
Rosenzweig, William—Physic Ventures
Roser, Christopher—Roser Ventures LLC
Roser, James—Roser Ventures LLC
Roshko, Peter—Boulder Ventures, Ltd.
Roshwalb, Gur—Venrock Associates
Rosich, Mitchell—Athenian Venture Partners
Roslyn, Marshall—Revolution Learning
Rosmus, Roger—Aberdeen Gould
Ross, Cathy—Oasis Capital Partners LLC
Ross, Daniel—Evercore Partners
Ross, Edward—Fidus Capital
Ross, Eric—Avenue Capital Group
Ross, Harry—Aweida Capital Management LLP
Ross, Heather—LRG Capital Group (FKA: Baystar Capital, LLC)
Ross, Howard—LLR Partners, Inc.
Ross, Ian—Concentric Equity Partners, L.P.
Ross, Lawrence—Lime Rock Partners LLC
Ross, Michael—Babson Capital Management LLC
Ross, Michael—SV Life Sciences Advisers
Ross, Michael—Schroder Ventures Life Sciences

Ross, Nina—Mithra Group, LLC
Ross, Timothy—Liberty Partners
Ross, Wilbur—W.L. Ross & Co. LLC
Rossbach, Peter—Impax Asset Management
Rosselli, Michael—Yorkville Advisors LLC
Rosser, Harold—Bruckmann, Rosser, Sherrill & Co.
Rossetter, Stephen—Centripetal Capital Partners, Inc.
Rossetti, Paul—American Securities Capital Partners LLC
Rossi, Alexander—Latin Idea Ventures, LLC
Rossignol, Charles-Henri—Cavipar SASU
Rossignol, Jacques—21 Centrale Partners
Rossignol, Jacques—21 Partners SpA
Rossolatos, George—TorQuest Partners, Inc.
Rossow, Alfred—Tully & Holland, Inc. (FKA: Ulin & Holland, Inc.)
Rosston, Steven—Glynn Capital Management
Rostrup, Jorgen—Norsk Hydro ASA (AKA: Norsk Hydro Technology Ventures)
Roszak, Matthew—SilkRoad Equity, LLC
Rotberg, Joseph—Lee Equity Partners
Rotgin, Michael—Shelter Capital Partners LLC
Roth, David—Carlyle Group, The
Roth, Greg—Hercules Technology Growth Capital, Inc.
Roth, John—Freeman Spogli & Co.
Roth, Jonathan—Cascadia Capital LLC
Roth, Marsha—Angelo, Gordon & Company
Roth, Millard—Corporate Growth Assistance, Ltd.
Roth, Werner—Foo Brains&Capital, The
Rothblum, Maydan—Sigma Capital Partners, LLC
Rothe, Joachim—Life Sciences Partners BV
Rothfus, Eric—Guggenheim Venture Partners LLC
Rothman, Matt—Hemisphere Capital LLC
Rothman, Matthew—EuclidSR Partners
Rothman, Steven—Primus Capital Funds
Rothrock, Ray—Venrock Associates
Rothschild, Douglas—Ritchie Capital
Rothschild, James—Monument Capital Group LLC
Rothschild, Shannon—Heron Capital LLC
Rothstein, Alain—Vicente Capital Partners
Rothstein, Bruce—RBC Capital Partners/RBC Technology Ventures
Rothstein, Charles—Beringea LLC
Rothwell, Doug—Detroit Renaissance
Rotner, Philip—Massachusetts Institute of Technology
Rottenberg, Jason—Arsenal Venture Partners
Rottenberg, Jason—OnPoint Technologies
Rottier, Peter—Summit Partners
Rottner, Thomas—Platina Partners LLP
Roubinowitz, Emmanuel—Fondinvest Capital (Grp. Caisse de Depots)
Roubinowitz, Emmanuel—Saints Ventures
Roucaud, Yves—iXEN Partners
Rountree, Ashley—C.W. Downer & Company (FKA: Downer & Company)
Rouse, Joe—iNovia Capital
Rousseau, Anne—ARCIS Finance SA
Rousseau, Henri-Paul—CDP Capital - Technology Ventures (FKA: CDP Sofinov)
Rousseau, John—New England Partners
Rousseau, John—Nexus Medical Partners
Roussel, Jean-Remy—CVC Capital Partners (Europe), Ltd.
Rousset, Bruno—Evolem SA
Rousset, Vanessa—Evolem SA
Routhier, Dina—MTDC (Massachusetts Technology Development Corp.)
Roux, Andre—Ethos Private Equity
Roux, Bertrand—Auxitex
Rouzier, Eric—Clayton, Dubilier & Rice, Inc.
Rovere, Silvia—Virtus Capital Partners
Rovero, Maria—Finpiemonte SpA
Roversi, Mauro—Ambienta SGR S.p.A.
Rovine, Joshua—Blackstone Group, L.P.
Rovinski, Benjamin—Lumira Capital Corporation.
Rovner, Michael—Austin Ventures, L.P.
Row, Dennis—Endeavour Capital, Ltd.
Rowan, Marc—Apollo Management
Rowan, Michel—Azulis Capital (FKA:Banexi Capital Partenaires)
Rowbotham, Tom—Vesbridge Partners, LLC
Rowe, Alan—Crown Capital Partners Inc.
Rowe, Joshua—Hawkesbridge Private Equity
Rowe, Kevin—Lake Capital Partners, Inc.
Rowe, Mark—Partners Group AG
Rowe, Simon—Swicorp Capital Partners
Rowe, Timothy—New Atlantic Ventures
Rowghani, Mood—Summit Partners
Rowland, Gene—Pacific Horizon Ventures LLC
Rowlands, Chris—3i Group PLC
Rowlands, Lindsay—incite.Capital Management Pty, Ltd.
Rowlands, Simon—Cinven, Ltd.
Rowntree, David—Tricor Pacific Capital, Inc.
Rowohlt, Jens—Sal. Oppenheim Private Equity Partners
Roy, Aki von—inventages venture capital S.A.
Roy, Ashok—Daiwa Quantum Capital, Ltd.
Roy, Colin—GCP Capital Partners
Roy, Henri—Societe Generale de Financement du Quebec (SGF)
Roy, Noah—Greenbriar Equity Group LLC
Royce, Elliot—Allianz Capital Partners GmbH
Royce, Elliot—AlpInvest Partners N.V.
Royer, Stephen—Shamrock Holdings, Inc.
Rozelle, Kacy—St. Cloud Capital, LLC
Rozengarten, Kobi—JVP
Rozenstraten, Bert-Jan—AAC Capital Partners
Rozental, Nelson—GP Investimentos
Ruatti, Jean Louis—Agro Invest SAS
Ruaudel, Jean-Yves—Bretagne Participations
Rubahn, Thomas—Steadfast Capital GmbH (FKA: BHF Private Equity GmbH)
Rubel, Michael—RFE Investment Partners
Rubeli, Christoph—Partners Group AG
Rubenstein, Barry—Wheatley Partners
Rubenstein, David—Carlyle Group, The
Rubenstein, Gordon—Pacific Partners
Rubin, Bryan—Constellation Ventures (AKA: Constellation Growth Capital)
Rubin, Daniel—Alloy Ventures
Rubin, Jamie—One Equity Partners (FKA: Banc One Venture Partners)
Rubin, Marco—NAC Ventures, LLC
Rubino, Cameron—Crystal Internet Venture Fund, L.P.
Rubino, Louis—Zurich Alternative Asset Management, LLC (ZAAM)
Rubinoff, Gary—Summerhill Venture Partners
Rubinov, Leon—Sterling Partners
Rubins, Matthew—M/C Venture Partners
Rubinstein, Andrew—Paul Capital Partners
Rubio, Manuel—Columbia Equity Partners
Ruby, Lucien—Private Equity Investors, Inc.
Ruch, Joshua—Rho Capital Partners, Inc.
Rudat, William—American Capital, Ltd.
Rudd, Edward—Longbow Capital
Rudd, Nigel—Longbow Capital
Rudd, Tracey—Hampshire Equity Partners (FKA: ING Equity Partners)
Ruddock, Greg—Ironbridge Capital Pty., Ltd.
Rudengren, Pia—Investor Growth Capital AB
Ruder, Brian—Permira Advisers LLP
Ruder, Christopher—Portfolio Advisors LLC
Ruderman, Frank—Tenex Greenhouse Ventures
Rudin, Murray—Riordan, Lewis & Haden
Rudisch, Doug—Bain Capital
Rudnick, Seth—Canaan Partners
Rudolf, Joachim—HBM BioVentures AG (FKA: HBM Partners AG)
Rudolph, Barry—Presidio Investors LLC
Rudolph, Richard—Bradford Equities Management LLC
Rue, Travis—Headwaters Merchant Bank
Ruebel, Felix—Bax Capital Advisors AG
Rueckel, Wallace—Questor Management Company LLC
Rued, Scott—Thayer Hidden Creek
Ruediger, Gerd—MBG Schleswig-Holstein GmbH
Ruehl, Bruce—Gleacher & Co.
Ruehne, Klaus—ATP Private Equity Partners
Rueter, Andreas—Grazia Equity GmbH
Ruff, Jack—Royal Palm Capital Partners, LLP
Rufini, Rossano—Synergo SGR S.p.A.
Ruger, Jared—Bertram Capital
Rughwani, Ashish—Dominus Capital, L.P.
Rugland, Jank Erik—HitecVision AS
Ruigrok, Niels—NIBC Principal Investments (FKA: Parnib Holding NV)
Ruijs, Maarten—CVC Asia Pacific, Ltd.
Ruiz, Abdon—Miradero Capital Partners, Inc.
Ruiz, Fernando—American Capital, Ltd.
Ruiz, Gerardo—Carlyle Group, The
Rule, Rob—MTI Partners, Ltd.
Rullman, Charles—Freeman Spogli & Co.
Rumilly, Matt—Clearview Capital LLC
Runco, Jason—BlackEagle Partners (FKA: Centurion Capital Partners)
Rundgren, Anders—Scope Capital Advisory AB
Runkle, Matthew—ArcLight Capital
Runnells, John—Vertical Group, The
Runnquist, Kristofer—AAC Capital Partners
Rupan, Monica—Pantheon Ventures, Ltd.
Rupani, Jai—India Value Fund Advisors Private Ltd. (FKA: GW Capital)
Ruppersberg, J.Peter—Seed GmbH
Rush, Andrew—Diamond Castle Holdings LLC
Rusiecki, Michal—Enterprise Investors Sp z oo
Russ, Joel—Audax Group
Russell, Chris—Veronis Suhler Stevenson (FKA: Veronis, Suhler & Associates)
Russell, Daniel—Allied Capital Corporation
Russell, Devon—Madison Capital Funding LLC (AKA: Madison Capital)
Russell, Erin—Vestar Capital Partners, Inc.

Russell, Frederick—Virginia Capital
Russell, Jay—DDJ Capital Management, LLC
Russell, Jonathan—3i Group PLC
Russell, Steven—iNetworks, LLC
Russick, Joseph—Blackstone Group, L.P.
Russo, Lorenzo—Vision Capital LLP
Russo, Vito—Meriturn Partners LLC
Rust, Anthony—GKM Newport Generation Funds
Rust, Christopher—U.S. Venture Partners
Rustgi, Atul—Accolade Capital Management
Rutberg, Bryan—Rutberg & Company, LLC
Ruth, Chip—Marquette Venture Partners
Rutherford, James—3i Group PLC
Rutherford, Jan—Scottish Equity Partners
Rutherford, John—Parthenon Capital LLC
Rutherfurd, Lewis—Inter-Asia Venture Management
Rutland, Peter—Advent International
Rutland, Peter—CVC Capital Partners (Europe), Ltd.
Rutledge, Rob—Genstar Capital LLC
Rutledge, Robyn Lawrie—TSG Consumer Partners
Ruttenberg, Eric—Tinicum Capital Partners
Ruzdak, Kresimir—Nexus Private Equity Partneri d.o.o.
Ryan, Charles—Almaz Capital Partners
Ryan, Cornelius—Oxford Bioscience Partners
Ryan, Daniel—Spring Bay Companies, The (AKA: Spring Bay Ventures)
Ryan, David—Green Spark Ventures LLC
Ryan, Frank—Banc of America Securities LLC
Ryan, Gavin—KD Group
Ryan, John—J.P. Morgan Partners (FKA: Chase Capital Partners)
Ryan, John—ONSET Ventures
Ryan, Neil—Tullis Health Investors (FKA: Tullis-Dickerson & Co., Inc.)
Ryan, Pat—SV Life Sciences Advisers
Ryczek, Edward—MFC Capital Funding, Inc.
Ryde, Magnus—Quan Ventures
Ryland, Kyle—Silver Lake Sumeru
Rytkonen, Kari—MB Funds (AKA: MB Rahastot Oy)
Ryutaro, Aida—MKS Partners, Ltd. (FKA: Schroder Ventures K.K.)
Saalfield, James—Still River Fund, The
Saaranen, Jarmo—VNT Management Oy
Saba, Aladdin—Beltone Private Equity
Sabad, Shondell—Peak Capital Group LLC
Sabaini, Patricio—GE Commercial Finance - Equity
Saban, Haim—Saban Ventures
Sabau, Hernan—NAFTA Fund of Mexico, LP
Sabben-Clare, Matthew—Cinven, Ltd.
Saberi, Nina—Castile Ventures
Sabet, Bijan—Spark Capital
Sabet, Lori—Carlyle Group, The
Sabharwal, Sunil—GE Commercial Finance - Equity
Sabin, Ralph—Pacific Venture Group
Sabo, Elias—Compass Group International LLC, The
Sabo, Paul—Crosslink Capital
Sabol, Damir—Eagle Ventures
Sabre, John—Mount Yale Asset Management
Sachar, Laura—StarVest Partners, L.P.
Sacher, William—Oaktree Capital Management LLC
Sachs, Bruce—Charles River Ventures
Sachs, Daniel—Proventus AB
Sachs, Ian—TowerBrook Capital Partners L.P.
Sachs, Karol—Towarzystwo Inwestcyji Spoteczno-Ekonomicznych SA (TISE)
Sachs, Kylie A.D.—Ascend Venture Group LLC
Sachse, Dirk—Frankfurt CapitalPartners AG (AKA: FCP)
Sachwitz, Kirsten—CSI (FKA: Virginia Community Development Loan Fund)
Sacks, Marc—Mesirow Private Equity Investments, Inc.
Sadaranganey, Neil—Bay Partners
Sadayasu, Alan—GE Commercial Finance - Equity
Saddi, Karim—TowerBrook Capital Partners L.P.
Sadeghi, Mani—Capital Z Investment Partners (FKA: Union Square Partners)
Sadeghi, Mani—Equifin Capital Partners
Sadeharju, Vesa—VNT Management Oy
Sadek, Karim—Citadel Capital S.A.E.
Sadek, Zachary—Parthenon Capital LLC
Sadger, Haim—Sequoia Capital
Sadrian, Justin—Warburg Pincus LLC
Saeed, Ahmed—NextCom Ventures
Saeed, Mohammad—Tadhamon Capital BSC
Saenz, Pierre—Impala Capital Partners (FKA; Suala Capital Advisors)
Saetre, Ola—HitecVision AS
Saevarsson, Sigurdur—Thule Investments
Safaii, David—Windspeed Ventures
Safer, Pennina—Medica Venture Partners
Safrai, Yair—Concord Ventures (FKA: Nitzanim)
Sagabraaten, Jon-Atle—IT Fornebu Inkubator AS
Sagar, Akanksha—3 Degrees Asset Management Pte., Ltd.
Sage, Hansjoerg—GIMV N.V.
Sager, Edward—Mentor Capital Partners
Sagiryan, Igor—Renaissance Capital
Sagmeister, Bernhard—Austria Wirtschaftsservice Gesellschaft mbH
Sahai, Rishi—Infinity Venture Capital
Sahashi, Kazuya—Asset Managers Holding Company, Ltd.
Sahay, Praveen—VIMAC Ventures LLC (FKA: VIMAC LLC)
Sahay, Praveen—Wave Equity Partners
Sahin, Kitty—Watermill Group, The
Said, Rafic—Blackstone Group, L.P.
Sain, Sameer—Everstone Capital
Saint-Jacques, Louis—ID Capital
Saiontz, Marc—American Securities Capital Partners LLC
Saito, Katsuhiko—CrossBridge Venture Partners
Sakagami, Takumi—Ridgeway Capital Partners, Ltd. (FKA:OPE Partners Ltd.)
Sakai, Hiroshi—IGNITE Group, The (AKA: Ignite Associates, LLC)
Sakai, Hirosuke—China New Enterprise Investment (AKA: CNEI)
Sakai, Stan—Defta Partners
Sakamoto, Koji—Fund Creation Co., Ltd.
Sakoda, Jon—New Enterprise Associates, Inc.
Saks, Peeter—Baltcap
Sakurai, Ayumi—MKS Partners, Ltd. (FKA: Schroder Ventures K.K.)
Sakurai, Ayumi—Valiant Partners Co. Ltd.
Sakurai, Hideaki—J-Star Co., Ltd.
Saladi, Mahesh—First Atlantic Capital, Ltd.
Salam, Ahmad—Dar Capital (UK), Ltd.
Salamat, Khaled—HBG Holdings, Ltd.
Salame, Kamil—CVC Asia Pacific, Ltd.
Salame, Kamil—CVC Capital Partners (Europe), Ltd.
Salamon, Michael—Birch Hill Equity Partners Management, Inc.
Salapa, Vasile—Oltenia Financial Investment Cy
Salata, Jean Eric—BPEP International
Salaverria, Julia—Ysios Capital Partners
Salazar i Canalda, Miquel—ICF Capital
Saldutti, Joseph—Gridiron Capital LLC
Salehizadeh, Bijan—Highland Capital Partners LLC
Salem, Luis Fernando—BPE Investimentos
Salem, Paul—Providence Equity Partners LLC
Salembier, Andy—Accolade Capital Management
Sales, Chris—Cabot Square Capital, Ltd.
Salesny, Petra—Alpha Associates AG
Saleur, Regis—CEA Valorisation SA
Salewski, Anthony—Genstar Capital LLC
Salice, Thomas—SFW Capital Partners, LLC
Salim, David—Swiss Life Private Equity Partners Ltd
Salim, Michael—Brazos Private Equity Partners LLC
Salinger, Jeffrey—Stuart Mill Capital, Inc.
Sallaberry, Paul—JAFCO Ventures
Salleh, Husni—Malaysian Venture Capital Management (MAVCAP)
Sallick, A. Peter—Design Investors LLC
Sallmard, Julien—Invus Group Ltd., The
Salmon, Steve—Latterell Venture Partners
Salon, Jonathan—Bedford Funding
Salonen, Petri—Aura Capital Oy
Salonoja, Pekka—Nexit Ventures Oy
Salty, Samer—Zouk Ventures, Ltd.
Saltzman, Richard—Colony Capital LLC
Saluja, Vishal—J&W Seligman & Company
Salvato, Luca—Coller Capital
Salvatore, Louis—Blackstone Group, L.P.
Salyer, Stephen—Atlantic-Pacific Capital, Inc.
Salyer, Stephen—Probitas Partners, Inc.
Salyers, Kyle—Clarian Health Ventures, Inc.
Sama, Alok—Baer Capital Partners, Ltd.
Samberg, Arthur—Twin Haven Capital Partners
Sambonet, Sergio—3i Group PLC
Samek, Edward—Carlyle Group, The
Samengo-Turner, Anthony—GCP Capital Partners
Sammartino, Sabina—Paul Capital Partners
Sammut, Stephen—Burrill & Company
Sampath, Dilip—Panasonic Ventures
Samper, J.Phillip—Gabriel Venture Partners
Sampson, Mark—Vintage Capital Partners
Sampson, Nicholas—Vexiom Equity Partners, L.P.
Samson, Jerome—Seventure Partners SA (FKA: SPEF Venture)
Samson, Louis—Platinum Equity LLC
Samson, Serafin—Affinity Capital Management
Samson, Wil—Coronis Medical Ventures
Samuel, David—Birch Hill Equity Partners Management, Inc.
Samuel, David—Mosaic Venture Partners
Samuel, Jeremy—Anacacia Capital
Samuels, Ami—Poalim Capital Markets Technologies Ltd
Samuels, Camille—Versant Ventures
Samuelsson, Lennart—Stiftelsen Industrifonden
Samuelsson, Per—Odlander, Fredrikson & Co. AB (AKA: HealthCap)
Samura, Reijiro—Ant Capital Partners Co., Ltd.
Samwer, Alexander—European Founders Fund GmbH

Samwer, Marc—European Founders Fund GmbH
Samwer, Oliver—European Founders Fund GmbH
Sanan, Puneet—MVC Capital (FKA: meVC)
Sancheti, Sanjeeve—SREI Venture Capital Ltd. (FKA: SREI Global Asset Mgt.)
Sanchez Rael, Kim—Flywheel Ventures
Sanchez-Asiain, Inigo—Inversiones Ibersuizas S.A.
Sand, Jakob—Capital+ A/S
Sand, Ole—Global Environment Fund Management Corporation
Sandach, Limor—7 Health Ventures
Sandach, Limor—Evergreen Venture Partners
Sandahl, Patrick—TeleVenture Management AS (FKA: Telenor Venture AS)
Sandal, Ejvind—Oresund-Healthcare A/S
Sandejas, Jose—Narra Venture Capital
Sandejas, Paco—Narra Venture Capital
Sandell, Scott—New Enterprise Associates, Inc.
Sanders, Lewis—AllianceBernstein L.P. (FKA: Alliance Capital Management)
Sanders, Martin—Charter Life Sciences
Sanders, Ronald—Colony Capital LLC
Sandersen, Erik—Selvaag Invest AS
Sanderson, Philip—IDG Ventures SF
Sandham, Andrew—Abingworth Management, Ltd.
Sandler, Neil—Symphony Capital LLC
Sandlund, Ulf—Initium AB
Sandoski, Aaron—Norwich Ventures
Sandoval, Daniel—Diana Capital SGECR SA
Sands, David—National City Equity Partners, Inc.
Sands, Fred—Vintage Capital Partners
Sands, Gregory—Sutter Hill Ventures
Sands, Jeff—GCP Capital Partners
Sandu, Neculai—Axxess Capital Partners S.A. (FKA: Enterprise Capital)
Sandys, Peter—Seroba BioVentures Limited
Sandys, Peter—Seroba Kernel Life Sciences, Ltd. (AKA: Seroba Kernel)
Sanfeliu, Josep Ll.—Ysios Capital Partners
Sanford, Matt—H.I.G. Capital LLC
Sanford, P. Craig—Westshore Capital Partners
Sangalis, Stephen—Progress Equity Partners, Ltd.
Sanger, Jim—ABS Ventures
Sanger, Philip—TEXO Ventures
Sangermano, Nick—Hudson Capital Management, L.P.
Sangster, Ray—MTI Partners, Ltd.
Sankaran, Deepa—Darby Overseas Investments, Ltd.
Sankey, N. Darius—Zone Ventures
Sanner, Dan—Alpine Investors, L.P.
Sans Huecas, Luis—Iame Capital Riesgo SGECR SA
Sant, Lex—Persimmon Tree Capital, L.P.
Santa Maria, Chris—Alpine Investors, L.P.
Santasalo, Hannu—Accent Equity Partners AB
Santeri Makal, Pekka—3TS Capital Partners, Ltd.
Santinelli, Paul—North Bridge Venture Partners
Santino, Jo—Indufin
Santisteban, Cipriano—Palmfund Management LLC
Santomero, Camillo—TMB Industries Investments
Santoro, Charles—Sterling Investment Partners
Santos Silva, Artur—BPI Private Equity
Santos, Lamberto—AB Capital & Investment Corporation
Saraceni, Diana—360 Capital Management SA (AKA: 360 Capital Partners)
Sarafa, Martin—Century Park Capital Partners
Sarag, Ziv—Resilience Capital Partners LLC
Saraiya Multani, Saloni—Hellman & Friedman LLC
Saran, Michael—Odien Group
Sarasa, Jose Angel—BPEP International
Sardar, Dali—DTA Capital
Sargeant, Winslow—Venture Investors LLC
Sargent, Joseph—Tennant Capital Partners LLC
Sargent, Kevin—Brown Gibbons Lang & Company LLC
Sargent, Robert—Tennant Capital Partners LLC
Sargent, Thomas—Tennant Capital Partners LLC
Sarie, Albane—Naxicap Partners SA
Sarin, Anil—Bessemer Venture Partners
Sarin, Tony—Hamilton Bradshaw
Sarjoo, Euclid—RBC Capital Partners/RBC Technology Ventures
Sarkar, Neel—Centennial Ventures
Sarkis, Walid—Bain Capital
Sarkis, Ziad Joseph—PAI Partners (FKA: PAI Management)
Sarkozy, Olivier—Carlyle Group, The
Sarlo, George—Walden Venture Capital
Sarner, Michael—American Capital, Ltd.
Sarnoff, Stuart—Avenue Capital Group
Sarraut, Jean-Philippe—iGlobe Partners, Ltd.
Sarria, Ignacio—Arcano Capital
Sarullo, Vincent—Odyssey Investment Partners, LLC
Sarup, Amit—Milestone Religare Investment Advisors Pvt., Ltd.
Sasaki, Brion—MASA Life Science Ventures, L.P. (AKA: MLSV)
Sasaki, Daniel—Hemisphere Capital LLC
Sasaki, Koji—Tokio Marine Capital Company, Ltd.
Sasaki, Yoshiki—Japan Asia Investment Company, Ltd. (AKA: JAIC)
Sasanuma, Taisuke—Advantage Partners LLP
Sasikumar, P.C.—Paracor Capital Advisors Pvt., Ltd.
Sasnauskas, Kestutis—East Capital Private Equity AB
Sassolas, Sebastien—Odyssee Venture
Sasson, Eric—Carlyle Group, The
Sasson, Ori—Primera Capital
Sasson, Sharam—Primera Capital
Sathaye, Shirish—Matrix Partners
Satnick, Matthew—Odyssey Investment Partners, LLC
Sato, Akio—Sun Capital Partners Japan K.K.
Sato, Mikio—Ant Capital Partners Co., Ltd.
Satterfield, Mike—Yaletown Venture Partners, Inc.
Sattin, Fabio Lorenzo—Private Equity Partners SpA
Satzberg, Michael—Sun Capital Partners, Inc.
Saudi, Adel—Tuareg Capital, Ltd.
Saul, N. Grant—Hamilton Lane Advisors, Inc.
Saul, Shai—Tamir Fishman Ventures
Saulnier, Monique—Sofinnova Partners
Saunders, Glen—Triodos International Fund Management BV
Saunders, Thomas—Goode Partners LLC
Saurel, Zita—Hellman & Friedman LLC
Sauter, Dominik—EGS Beteiligungen AG
Sautter, Thilo—Investcorp Bank B.S.C.
Sauve, Thomas—T Squared Partners LLC
Sava, Guy—H & S Capital (AKA: Heidrick & Struggles Capital)
Savage, Colin—Worldview Technology Partners
Savage, George—Spring Ridge Ventures
Savage, Graham—Callisto Capital
Savage, James—Longworth Venture Partners, L.P.
Savage, Thomas—Spire Capital
Savage, Tige—Time Warner Investments (FKA: AOL Time Warner Ventures)
Saval, Arturo—Nexxus Capital, S.C.
Savani, Vishal—Jina Ventures, Inc.
Savarese, John—Montreux Equity Partners
Savellano, Ann—Francisco Partners
Savelsberg, Rene—SET Venture Partners
Saverio Carpinelli, Francesco—MPS VENTURE Societa di Gestione del Risparmio SpA
Saviane, Roberto—Wise SRG S.p.A. (AKA: Wisequity)
Saviano, Joseph—Baker Capital Corp.
Savig, Joe—Accel-KKR LLC
Savignol, Robert—M/C Venture Partners
Savoie, Bob—Pinnacle Ventures
Savov, Emil—McLean Watson Capital Inc.
Sawaf, Omar—Yellowstone Capital, Inc.
Sawamura, Nobukazu—CAS Capital, Inc.
Sawhney, Rahul—Z Capital Partners LLC
Sawhney, Vikrant—Blackstone Group, L.P.
Sawyer, Edward—Edgewater Capital Group, Inc.
Sawyer, Kenneth—Saints Ventures
Sawyer, Philip—Helix Ventures
Sawyer, Thomas—Shattuck Hammond Partners
Saxena, Anil—Religare Enterprises, Ltd.
Saxena, Parag—Vedanta Capital
Say, Mustafa E.—AccessTurkey Private Equity
Saya, Frank—Axiom Equity Partners
Sayama, Nobuo—Unison Capital, Inc.
Sayle, Robert—Thoma Cressey Bravo
Sayre, James—Cargill Ventures
Sazhinov, Georgy—Marshall Capital Partners
Scandariato, Anthony—Apollo Real Estate Advisors
Scanlan, Daniel—Peninsula Capital Partners LLC
Scanlan, David—Silverhawk Capital Partners LLC
Scanlon, Catherine—Global Equity Capital LLC
Scannapieco, Dario—European Investment Bank, The (AKA: EIB)
Scarff, Steve—Pantheon Ventures, Ltd.
Scarlatti, Paolo—Orlando Capital Management GmbH
Scarpa, Carmen—Tudor Ventures
Scarpa, Rudy—Pantheon Ventures, Ltd.
Scarpis, Stefano—Alto Partners SGR SpA
Scaturro, Philip—Allen & Company
Scee, Austin—H.I.G. Capital LLC
Scerbo, John—Catterton Partners
Schaafsma, Gerald—Anthem Capital Management
Schaar, William—Horizon Partners, Ltd.
Schachenhofer, Evi—HARDT GROUP Capital Partners Limited
Schacht, Henry—Warburg Pincus LLC
Schad, Michael—Coller Capital
Schade, Karl—Presidio Investors LLC
Schaechter, Robert—Euro Capital Partners
Schaefer, Cary—Fidus Capital
Schaefer, Chris—Thomas Weisel Partners Group, Inc.
Schaefer, Curt—TPH Partners LLC
Schaefer, James—UBS Capital Corporation
Schaefer, Neil—GenNx360 Capital Partners

Schaeffer, Sherri—Delaware Innovation Fund (AKA: DIF)
Schaeli, Stephan—Partners Group AG
Schaepe, Christopher—Lightspeed Venture Partners (FKA: Weiss, Peck & Greer)
Schafer, Lee—BlueFire Partners Capital Markets
Schafer, Marc—BBE Business Development AB
Schaffer, Mark—Shamrock Holdings, Inc.
Schafler, R. Scott—Cortec Group, Inc.
Schaller, Timothy—New Enterprise Associates, Inc.
Schapiro, Benjamin—QuestMark Partners, L.P.
Schapiro, Ian—GFI Energy Ventures
Schapiro, Ken—Condor Capital Management, Inc.
Schappert, Keith—Credit Suisse Asset Management
Schar, Dwight—Red Zone Capital Partners
Scharfenberger, Joseph—Bear Growth Capital Partners
Schattner, Michael—Onondaga Venture Capital Fund, Inc.
Schauerman, Thomas—Norwest Equity Partners
Schauman, Kristina—D. Carnegie & Co AB
Sche, Schui—WI Harper Group
Schechter, Jeffrey—Sterling Partners
Schecter, Sam—Rosemont Investment Partners LLC
Scheer, David—Scheer & Company
Scheetz, Ned—Aphelion Capital, LLC
Scheffler, Wolfgang—Freudenberg Venture Capital GmbH
Scheidegger, Alfred—Nextech Venture AG
Schein, Jeremy—Corsair Capital LLC
Scheinrock, Jeff—GKM Newport Generation Funds
Schelbert, Mark—Shackleton Equity Partners LLC
Schelde, Pelle—Inventure Capital A/S
Schell, Richard—ONSET Ventures
Schell, Tony—Escalate Capital
Schenck, Moritz Freiherr—Baird Capital Partners Europe
Schenk, Leo—Synergia Capital Partners B.V.
Schenker, Daniel—Swicorp Capital Partners
Scherago, Nina—Investment Fund for Foundations
Scherbakovsky, Alex—3i Group PLC
Scherl, Zev—NewSpring Capital
Scherrer, Doug—General Atlantic LLC
Scherrer, Matthew—Thompson Street Capital Partners
Scherzer, Mitch—Silverfern Group, Inc., The
Schettini, Eric—Viveris Management S.A.S.
Scheurer, John—Allied Capital Corporation
Schiano, Dominick—DLJ Merchant Banking Partners
Schiano, Dominick—Questor Management Company LLC
Schiavello, Rose—Hastings Private Equity
Schiavo, Chris—Battery Ventures, L.P.
Schiciano, Kenneth—TA Associates, Inc.
Schick, Bruno—Cinven, Ltd.
Schick, Lou—NewWorld Capital Group LLC
Schickedanz, Sean—Clean Pacific Ventures
Schiefer, Peter—M2 Capital Management AG
Schieman, Susan—Blue Chip Venture Company
Schieman, Susan—Isabella Capital LLC
Schiendl, Petra—HARDT GROUP Capital Partners Limited
Schier, Robert—inventages venture capital S.A.
Schiermbock, Chris—Apollo Real Estate Advisors
Schiff, Andrew—Aisling Capital
Schiff, Frank—MidOcean Partners
Schiff, Jay—Prospect Street Ventures
Schiff, Peter—Northwood Ventures
Schifter, Soren—Novo A/S
Schifter, Trudi—iGlobe Partners, Ltd.
Schilberg, Barbara—BioAdvance
Schiller, Christian—Cascadia Capital LLC
Schiller, Karl—Austria Wirtschaftsservice Gesellschaft mbH
Schiller, Shai—Concord Ventures (FKA: Nitzanim)
Schilling, Debra—Aspen Ventures
Schilling, Debra—Olympus Capital Partners
Schilling, Lonnie—Worldview Technology Partners
Schilling, Mathias—BV Capital (FKA: Bertelsmann Ventures, LP)
Schilling, Ronald—Mi3 Venture Partners
Schillinger, Douglas—DW Healthcare Partners
Schimmler, Martin—Blackstone Group, L.P.
Schindler, Walter—SAIL Venture Partners
Schirmers, Bernhard—SHS Gesellschaft fuer Beteiligungsmanagement mbH
Schlaack, Paul—Blackstone Group, L.P.
Schlachter, Robert—LGT Capital Partners AG
Schlanger, Richard—Palm Beach Capital Partners
Schlegell, John E. von—Endeavour Capital
Schlein, Philip—U.S. Venture Partners
Schlein, Ted—Kleiner Perkins Caufield & Byers
Schlenker, Andreas—Partech International
Schlenker, Steven—DN Capital, Ltd. (FKA: Digital Networks Global Ventures)
Schlenzig, Moritz—Mesa Capital Partners
Schlesinger, Thomas—Beecken, Petty & Company LLC
Schley, Daniel—Dolphin Capital Group, LLC
Schlick, Erich—Wellington Partners Venture Capital GmbH
Schliebs, Charles—iNetworks, LLC
Schlitzer, Guido—High-Tech Gruenderfonds Management GmbH
Schlossareck, Steve—Quicksilver Ventures (FKA: QTV Capital)
Schlosstein, Ralph—Evercore Partners
Schlueter, William—Ropart Group
Schmeding, Carsten—Equity Partners GmbH
Schmeelk, Richard—CAI Capital Management Company
Schmelig, Karlheinz—Creathor Venture Management GmbH
Schmelter, Jay—RiverVest Venture Partners
Schmickle, Michael—Palm Beach Capital Partners
Schmid, Bernhard—DVC Deutsche Venture Capital
Schmidly, Jason—Carousel Capital Partners
Schmidt, Andreas—Sal. Oppenheim Private Equity Partners
Schmidt, Bob—Fletcher Spaght Associates
Schmidt, Daniel—Sal. Oppenheim Private Equity Partners
Schmidt, Gerald—Cordova Ventures (FKA:Cordova Capital)
Schmidt, Jean-Bernard—Sofinnova Partners
Schmidt, Pierre—Althera Capital
Schmidt, Randall—Lemhi Ventures
Schmidt, Volker—Riverside Company
Schmidt, Will—Advent International
Schmidt-Foerger, Berthold—AFINUM Management GmbH
Schmidt-Gothan, Hanno—Perusa Partners GmbH
Schmitt, George—TeleSoft Partners
Schmitt, Paul—Novitas Capital (FKA: PA Early Stage Partners)
Schmitt, Thomas—Augur Capital Group
Schmitz, Frank—Blackstone Group, L.P.
Schmitz, Hans-Jurgen—ECOS Beteiligungsmanagement GmbH
Schmitz, Hans-Jurgen—Mangrove Capital Partners SA
Schmitz, Michael—American Capital, Ltd.
Schmitz, Tony—Pine Street Capital Partners LLC
Schmuck, David—GE Antares Capital Corporation
Schnabel, Hansjorg—Equita Management GmbH
Schnabel, John—Falcon Investment Advisors LLC
Schnadig, David—Cortec Group, Inc.
Schnakenberg, Ben—High Road Capital Partners
Schnall, Richard—Clayton, Dubilier & Rice, Inc.
Schnatz, Oliver—ACA Equity-Partners GmbH
Schneer, George—Horizon Ventures
Schneider, Anton—Nordwind Capital GmbH
Schneider, David—Main Street Resources (FKA: Colt Capital Group)
Schneider, Edward—Quan Ventures
Schneider, Frank—KSH Capital Partners AG (FKA: UEG Beteiligungs AG)
Schneider, Geoff—Emerge Venture Capital (AKA: Emerge VC)
Schneider, Markus—GCP Capital Partners
Schneider, Richard—Easton Hunt Capital Partners, L.P.
Schneider, Steve—ITU Ventures
Schneider, Steven—Newbridge Capital, Ltd.
Schneider, Steven—TPG Capital
Schneider, Steven—Warburg Pincus LLC
Schneider, Toni—True Ventures
Schneiderman, Arthur—Global Catalyst Partners
Schneiorr, John—Allen & Company
Schnel, Jonah—ITU Ventures
Schnell, David—Prospect Venture Partners (FKA: Prospect Management LLC)
Schnettler, Thomas—Piper Jaffray Private Capital LLC
Schnettler, Thomas—Piper Jaffray Ventures
Schnipper, Edward—CMEA Capital
Schnoes, Holger—Advent International
Schock, Paul—Bluestem Capital Partners
Schocken, Joseph—Broadmark Capital Corp.
Schoder, Robert—Blackstone Group, L.P.
Schoen, Scott—Thomas H. Lee Partners (AKA: TH Lee Partners)
Schoendorf, Nancy—Mohr Davidow Ventures
Schoenfeld, Mark—Carlyle Group, The
Schoenknecht, Oliver—Odewald & Compagnie GmbH
Schoenthal, Andrew—Harvest Partners LLC
Schoenwetter, Lewis—H.I.G. Capital LLC
Schoeter, Johannes—China New Enterprise Investment (AKA: CNEI)
Schoff, Robert—Scorpion Capital Partners, L.P.
Schoffstall, Martin—Schoffstall Ventures
Schoffstall, Marvin—Schoffstall Ventures
Schofield, Jon—PHD Equity Partners LLP
Scholes, C. Patrick—Morgan Keegan Merchant Banking
Scholl, David—Athenian Venture Partners

Scholl, Thomas—Novak Biddle Venture Partners, L.P.
Scholnick, Dan—Trinity Ventures
Scholze, Jennifer—SAP Ventures
Schonberger, Stuart—CDH China Management Co., Ltd.
Schoneman, Debbra—Piper Jaffray Ventures
Schonharting, Florian—Nordic Biotech Advisors APS
Schopin, Michael—WHI Capital Partners
Schorr, Herbert—Allegis Capital (AKA: Media Technology Ventures)
Schorr, Paul—Blackstone Group, L.P.
Schottler, Jeffrey—Headwaters Merchant Bank
Schou, Carsten—SEED Capital Denmark K/S
Schoultz, Mikael—Platina Partners LLP
Schraith, Jim—DFJ Frontier
Schreck, Hans—TVM Capital GmbH
Schreiber, Alain—ProQuest Investments
Schreiber, Charles—Brown Brothers Harriman & Company (AKA: BBH)
Schreiber, Douglas—Bain Capital
Schreiber, Gottfried—von Braun & Schreiber Private Equity Partners GmbH
Schreiber, Richard—Cavipar SASU
Schreiber, Ronald—SoftBank Capital
Schreurs, Martijn—Gilde Buy Out Partners
Schrier, Douglas—Rembrandt Venture Partners
Schrimpff, Robert—novusmodus LLP
Schrock, Jeff—Monster Venture Partners
Schroder, David—InvestAmerica Venture Group, Inc.
Schroder, James—Montgomery & Co. (FKA: Digital Coast Partners)
Schroder, Paul—Capital-C Ventures B.V.
Schroeck, Maximilian—Cipio Partners
Schroeder, Christoph—TVM Capital GmbH
Schroeder, Joachim—BayBG Bayerische Beteiligungsgesellschaft mbH
Schroeder, Luke—Gryphon Investors, Inc.
Schroeder, Lutz—Sigma Capital Management
Schroeder, Philipp—Active Capital Partners S.L.
Schroeder, Reese—Motorola Ventures
Schroeter, Hinako—Biofrontier Partners, Inc.
Schroll, Josef—"schilling" Unternehmensbeteiligung GmbH
Schroter, Lutz—Saarlandische Wagnisfinanzierungsgesellschaft mbH (AKA SWG)
Schubauer, James—Westbury Partners
Schubert, Christoph—EquiVest GmbH & Co
Schubert, Felix von—Zouk Ventures, Ltd.
Schuch, Philip—Atlas Holdings FRM LLC
Schuck, Wolfgang—Maple Partners Financial Group, Inc.
Schuder, Ray—El Dorado Ventures
Schuehsler, Helmut—TVM Capital GmbH
Schuele, Al—Sevin Rosen Funds
Schueppert, Stenning—Eos Partners, L.P.
Schuetz, Thomas—OrbiMed Advisors LLC
Schug, Christoph—AdCapital AG
Schuh, Michael—Foundation Capital
Schuhardt, Frank—DVC Deutsche Venture Capital
Schule, Lisa—Global Environment Fund Management Corporation
Schule, Lisa—Perseus LLC
Schulhof, Jonathan—Global Technology Investment (GTI)
Schulhof, Michael—Global Technology Investment (GTI)
Schull, Joseph—Warburg Pincus LLC
Schulman, Bruce—Natural Gas Partners (NGP)
Schult, Robert—VMG Equity Partners
Schulte, David—Kaiser Permanente Ventures
Schulte, Peter—CM Equity Partners (FKA; Lynx Investment Management, L.P.)
Schultz, Daniel—Draper Fisher Jurvetson Gotham Venture Partners
Schultz, Eric—Braemar Energy Ventures
Schultz, Howard—Maveron LLC
Schultz, Randall—Versa Capital Management (FKA: Chrysalis Capital Partners)
Schultz, Richard—Morgan Stanley Private Equity
Schultz, Richard—Morgan Stanley Venture Partners (AKA: MSDW)
Schultze, George—Schultze Asset Management LLC
Schultze, Jan-Gisbert—Acton Capital Partners GmbH
Schulz, Mark—Fontinalis Partners LLC
Schulz, Michael H—Sigma Capital Management
Schulz, Robert—Health Enterprise Partners (AKA: HEP Fund)
Schulze, Andreas—BioMedPartners
Schumacher, Matt—Boxwood Capital Partners, LLC
Schumacher, Patrick—Blackstone Group, L.P.
Schumann, Oliver—Glenalta Capital LLP
Schuppan, David—Cressey & Company, L.P.
Schuppan, David—Thoma Cressey Bravo
Schurink, Titus—Holland Private Equity B.V.
Schuster, Michael—Carlyle Group, The
Schuster, Steffen—TVM Capital GmbH
Schuster, Stephan—Ventacc Beteiligungs- und Beratungs GmbH
Schuster, Stewart—Novus Ventures
Schut, Hans—Triodos International Fund Management BV
Schutte, Christian—HighTech Private Equity GmbH
Schutz, Jeffrey—Centennial Ventures
Schuurmans, Pierre—Birch Hill Equity Partners Management, Inc.
Schwab, Bertrand—Patron Capital, Ltd.
Schwab, David—Sierra Ventures
Schwab, Martin—Pamplona Capital Management LLP
Schwab, Michael—Big Sky Partners
Schwab, Michael—Greenhouse Capital Partners
Schwab, Nelson—Carousel Capital Partners
Schwabe, Robert—Forum Capital Partners
Schwaber, Glen—Israel Cleantech Ventures
Schwager, Gary—Griffon Venture Partners
Schwager, Reto—Partners Group AG
Schwarck, Charles—CVC Capital Partners (Europe), Ltd.
Schwart, Bob—Energy Ventures AS
Schwartz, Alan—First Reserve Corporation
Schwartz, Alan—Yarra Capital Partners
Schwartz, Alvin—Sigma Capital Corp.
Schwartz, Aron—Fenway Partners, Inc.
Schwartz, Bela—Riverside Company
Schwartz, Brian—H.I.G. Capital LLC
Schwartz, Brian—Vestar Capital Partners, Inc.
Schwartz, Gerald—Onex Corporation
Schwartz, Jeffrey—Bain Capital
Schwartz, Jeffrey—Bain Capital Ventures
Schwartz, Jon—Crosslink Capital
Schwartz, Jonathan—Sun Microsystems, Inc.
Schwartz, Jonathan—Wizard Partners Srl
Schwartz, Kevin—Paine & Partners LLC
Schwartz, Mark—New Silk Route Partners LLC
Schwartz, Michael—JLL Partners (FKA: Joseph, Littlejohn & Levy, Inc.)
Schwartz, Ron—UBS Capital Markets
Schwartz, Samuel—Comcast Interactive Capital
Schwartz, Scott—CIVC Partners LP (FKA: Continental Illinois Venture Corp.)
Schwartz, Sheryl—Teachers Insurance & Annuity Association College Retirement
Schwartz, Steven—Prudent Capital
Schwarz, Hans Jorg—Sachsen LB Corporate Finance Holding GmbH
Schwarz, Ryan—Carlyle Group, The
Schwarz, Tom—Erasmus MC
Schwarz, Tom—Life Sciences Partners BV
Schwarzer, Fred—Charter Life Sciences
Schwed, Gustavo—Providence Equity Partners LLC
Schweda, Uwe—DPE Deutsche Private Equity GmbH (AKA: Parcom Deutsche PE)
Schwegler, Christoph—affentranger associates (FKA: Ultreia Capital, Ltd.)
Schwegler, Georg—T-Venture Holding GmbH
Schweikhardt, Alexander—HARDT GROUP Capital Partners Limited
Schwen, Steve—Split Rock Partners LLC
Schwen, Steve—St. Paul Venture Capital, Inc.
Schwendimann, Werner—Aralon AG
Schwenke, J.—Business Partners
Schwerdtle, Wolfgang—MidOcean Partners
Schwerin, Samuel—Millennium Technology Ventures
Schwertner, Ray—Capital Southwest Corporation
Schwinger, Steven—Snow Phipps Group LLC (FKA: SPG Partners, LLC)
Schwyn, Andreas—Panda Capital Asia, Ltd.
Scibetta, Tom—Blackstone Group, L.P.
Scifres, Donald—SDL Ventures, LLC
Scoggins, Christopher—Sequel Venture Partners
Scola, Nick—Capital Resource Partners
Scolan, Francois—Innovacom SA
Scollans, Brendan—Avista Capital Holdings, L.P.
Scolnick, Edward—Clarus Ventures
Scopa, James—MPM Capital (FKA: MPM Asset Management LLC)
Scopelliti, David—GarMark Partners
Scott, Alex—Pantheon Ventures, Ltd.
Scott, Bruce—NBC Capital Pty., Ltd.
Scott, Charles—Imprimatur Capital, Ltd.
Scott, Donald—Blackstone Group, L.P.
Scott, Erik—Palladium Equity Partners LLC
Scott, Hugh—Commonfund Realty
Scott, John—Harbert Venture Partners
Scott, K. Dunlop—Columbia Partners LLC
Scott, Kevin—3i (US)
Scott, Michael—Platinum Equity LLC
Scott, Michael—Sorenson Capital Partners
Scott, Michael—Talisman Capital
Scott, Nigel—Climate Change Capital, Ltd.
Scott, Paul—Windward Ventures
Scott, Richard—PineBridge Investments
Scott, Steven—Penta Capital LLP (FKA: Penta Capital Partners, Ltd.)
Scott, Thomas—Triton Pacific Capital Partners LLC
Scott, Valerie—Swander Pace Capital

Scotto, Anthony—Roark Capital Group
Scoular, Mark—Maven Capital Management LLC
Scouler, Brian—Dunedin Capital Partners, Ltd. (FKA: Dunedin Ventures, Ltd.)
Scowcroft, John—Cross Creek Capital, an affiliate of Wasatch Advisors
Scragg, Neil—Gresham LLP
Scull, John—Southern Cross Venture Partners
Sculley, John—Rho Capital Partners, Inc.
Scully, Thomas—Welsh, Carson, Anderson & Stowe
Scully, William—Apollo Real Estate Advisors
Seabrook, J.Connor—Alliance Technology Ventures
Seabrooke, Christopher—Sabvest, Ltd.
Seah, Kian Wee—UOB Venture Management Pte, Ltd.
Seah, Ronald—AIG Investment Corporation, (Asia) Ltd.
Sealy, Joe—Greater Pacific Capital LLP
Seaman, Bradley—Tricor Pacific Capital, Inc.
Searcy, Connor—Insight Equity Holdings LLC
Searle, Susan—Imperial Innovations (AKA: Imperial College Innovations)
Sears, Peter—Quaker BioVentures, Inc.
Seaver, Christopher—CLSA Capital Partners (AKA: Credit Lyonnais Securities Asia)
Seawell, A. Brooke—New Enterprise Associates, Inc.
Seawell, Brooke—Formative Ventures
Sebastian, Roberto—Marsman-Drysdale Corporation
Sebastian, Sean—Birchmere Ventures
Sebastian, Terry—Lake Pacific Partners, LLC
Sebba, Yoav—Ofer Hi-Tech
Sebek, Gary—2x Consumer Products Growth Partners LP
Sebel, Benjamin—CHAMP Private Equity Pty Ltd.
Secretain- Guibout, Britta—UFG Private Equity SAS
Seden, T. Lynne—J.P. Morgan Capital Corporation
Seeber, Jon—Updata Partners
Seegopaul, Purnesh—Pangaea Ventures
Seegull, Fran—Funk Ventures, Inc.
Seehaus, Frank—Acton Capital Partners GmbH
Seehaus, Frank—Burda Digital Ventures GmbH
Seelendfreund, Deena—VCFA Group
Seelig, Jonathan—Globespan Capital Partners
Seeman, Cooper—Abacus Private Equity (ASA: Abacus Capital Corporation)
Seers, Phillip—Phoenix Equity Partners (FKA: DLJ European Private Equity)
Seese, Patrick—Headwaters Merchant Bank
Seewald, Richard—Alpha Associates AG
Sefrioui, Rachid—Finaventures
Segal, Anat—Xenia Venture Capital
Segal, Brent—Axon Capital
Segal, Malcolm—NIB-MDM Fund Managers (Pty) Ltd
Segal, Rick—JLA Ventures (FKA: J.L. Albright Venture Partners)
Segal, Steven—J.W. Childs Associates
Segall, Gregory—Versa Capital Management (FKA: Chrysalis Capital Partners)
Segel, Robert—Park Street Capital LLC
Seger, Andrew—Frontenac Company
Segerborg, Katarina—Innovationsbron AB
Segerborg, Katarina—Iteksa Venture AB
Segev-Gal, Rona—Pitango Venture Capital (FKA:Polaris Venture Capital Israel)
Seggewiss, Herbert—Aheim Capital GmbH (FKA: Buchanan Capital Partners GmbH)
Seghezzi, Graziano—Sofinnova Partners
Segrest, Michael—Silver Creek Ventures
Segui Casas, Luis—Miura Private Equity SGECR, S.A.
Sehgal, Sanjay—East West Capital Partners Pte, Ltd.
Seibel, Amy—BIA Digital Partners, L.P.
Seibert, Michael—Stone Canyon Venture Partners (SCVP)
Seibold, Wolfgang—Earlybird Venture Capital GmbH & Co. KG
Seid, Jacob—Lightspeed Venture Partners (FKA: Weiss, Peck & Greer)
Seidelmann, Scott—Ericsson Venture Partners
Seidenberg, Beth—Kleiner Perkins Caufield & Byers
Seidenberg, Peter—MVC Capital (FKA: meVC)
Seidler, Peter—Seidler Equity Partners
Seidler, Robert—Seidler Equity Partners
Seidman, Jeffrey—Harbert Management Corporation
Seifert, William—Prism VentureWorks
Seiffer, Jonathan—Leonard Green & Partners
Seitz, Tasha—JK&B Capital
Sejiny, Ayman—Unicorn Investment Bank B.S.C.
Sekhar, Giri—FA Technology Ventures
Sekhon, Tex—Markpoint Venture Partners
Sekine, Kanako—Troika Capital Partners
Sekula, Christopher—Cambria Group, The
Sela, Yossi—Gemini Israel Funds, Ltd.
Selassie, Sengal—Cowen Capital Partners LLC (FKA: SG Capital Partners LLC)
Selati, Robin—Madison Dearborn Partners LLC
Selby, Norman—Perseus LLC
Selby, Sunil—Trellis Capital Corporation
Selchow, Thilo von—WHEB Ventures, Ltd.
Selden, William—Sterling Investment Partners
Selkirk, Rod—Bridgepoint Development Capital
Sell, Charles—Andrew W. Byrd & Co. LLC
Sellers, Colleen—Deutsche Banc Alex Brown (FKA: Bankers Trust New York Corp)
Sellers, Ian—Permira Advisers LLP
Sellers, Patrick—LDC (FKA: Lloyds TSB Development Capital, Ltd.)
Sellers, Scott—Encore Consumer Capital LLC
Sellery, Alan—Ironbridge Equity Partners
Selman, Cenzig—Arsenal Capital Partners
Selman, Sanford—Asia West, LLC
Selmonosky, Daniel—One Equity Partners (FKA: Banc One Venture Partners)
Selnick, Jesse—Blackstone Group, L.P.
Seltzer, Robert—Care Capital, LLC
Selwood, Ryan—CPP Investment Board
Selzer, Kenneth—Finistere Ventures LLC
Semelmacher, Paula—Goode Partners LLC
Semenzato, Michele—Wise SRG S.p.A. (AKA: Wisequity)
Semerci, Osman—Duet Capital
Semler, Gregory—Pivotal Investments LLC
Semmel, David—Kettle Partners
Semmens, Guy—Argos Soditic SA
Semmler, Marcos—Demeter Partners S.A.
Sen, Bidyut—Omni Capital Group LLC
Sen, Ranjen—Advent International
Senan, Amar—Saints Ventures
Senapati, Santosh—AIG Investment Corporation, (Asia) Ltd.
Senderov, Yevgeny—Alfa Capital Partners
Senequier, Dominique—AXA Private Equity
Senft, Roderick—Tricor Pacific Capital, Inc.
Seng, Lim Yew—3V SourceOne Capital Pte, Ltd.
Seng, Teo Eu—DBS Private Equity
Seng, Ulrich—ViewPoint Capital Partners GmbH
Sengsuwan, Michel—Colony Capital LLC
Senior, Enrique—Allen & Company
Senkler, Robert—Advantus Capital Management, Inc.
Senkut, Aydin—Felicis Ventures
Senneff, John—Thompson Street Capital Partners
Senor, Daniel—Rosemont Solebury Capital Management LLC
Sentilhes, Gregoire—NextStage SAS
Senyei, Andrew—Enterprise Partners Venture Capital
Seol, Kyungseok—Mirae Asset Venture Investment Co., Ltd. (FKA:Korean Dream)
Sequeira, Neil—General Catalyst Partners (FKA: General Catalyst Group LLC)
Serebrisky, Diego—Advent International
Serena di Lapigio, Ottavio—Lincolnshire Management, Inc.
Seretan, Wendy—Stone Canyon Venture Partners (SCVP)
Serfaty, Dan—Agregator Gestion SAS
Serkal, Abdul Aziz—M'Sharie LLC
Sermon, Charles—Nomura Phase4 Ventures, Ltd.
Serobe, Gloria—Wipprivate Equity
Serra, Jaime—NAFTA Fund of Mexico, LP
Serrato, Ruben—TEL Venture Capital, Inc.
Serrure, Piet—NIBC Principal Investments (FKA: Parnib Holding NV)
Serry, Mostafa—Nile Capital
Sertoglu, Cem—iLab Holding AS
Seshadri, A.N.—Nalanda Capital Pte, Ltd.
Seshadri, Singari—Parkview Ventures LLC
Sessions, Andrew—Thomas Weisel Partners Group, Inc.
Sessions, Benjamin—Global Environment Fund Management Corporation
Sestili, Paul—Sand Hill Capital
Seth, Rohit—Duchossois Technology Partners LLC (DTEC)
Sethi, Sudhir—IDG Ventures India
Seton-Rogers, Sean—PROfounders Capital
Sett, Vivek—New Silk Route Partners LLC
Settle, Dana—Greycroft Partners
Settle, Dana—VSP Capital (FKA: Venture Strategy Partners)
Settman, Peter—Firm Factory Network
Seu, David—STB Investment Corporation
Seung, John—Li & Fung Investments
Seungwoo, Kevin Choi—Skylake Incuvest & Company
Sevigny, Johanne—Entrepia Ventures, Inc.
Sevin, Philippe—Syntegra Capital, Ltd.
Sevinga, Ieko—F. van Lanschot Participaties BV
Sewell, George—Lion Capital (FKA: Hicks Muse (Europe))
Sewing, Peter—Triton Partners
Sexton, Theresa—Claritas Capital LLC
Seynave, Leon—Mitiska
Sgobbo, Rocco—AIG Capital Partners
Sha, Ye—Chengwei Ventures

Shabecoff, Peter—Atlantic Street Capital Management, LLC
Shachak, Yossi—SCP Private Equity Partners
Shachar, Erez—Evergreen Venture Partners
Shackelton, Sarah—Abingworth Management, Ltd.
Shadman, Ali—JK&B Capital
Shafer, Matt—Vision Capital LLP
Shaffer, Leslie—Caris, Ltd.
Shaffer, Michael—Brown Gibbons Lang & Company LLC
Shafrir, Haim—China Israel Value Capital (AKA: CIVC)
Shagory, Peter—Baird Venture Partners
Shagrin, Lawrence—Brockway Moran & Partners, Inc.
Shah, Ajay—Silver Lake Sumeru
Shah, Ameesh—Tennenbaum Capital Partners LLC
Shah, Amit—Artiman Ventures
Shah, Baiju—BioEnterprise
Shah, Bipin—INC3 Ventures, LLC
Shah, Deep—Francisco Partners
Shah, Dhiren—GCP Capital Partners
Shah, Neil—EonTech Ventures (FKA: Triton Ventures)
Shah, Nimesh—Cutlass Capital
Shah, Nimesh—Domain Associates LLC
Shah, Nirav—HM Capital Partners LLC
Shah, Niren—Norwest Venture Partners
Shah, Parag—Hercules Technology Growth Capital, Inc.
Shah, Pradyut—Behrman Capital
Shah, Prashant—Hummer Winblad Venture Partners
Shah, Pratik—Thomas, McNerney & Partners LLC
Shah, Rahul—IL&FS Investment Managers Ltd (FKA: IL&FS Venture Corp)
Shah, Ranjit—Gaja Capital Partners
Shah, Rashesh—Edelweiss Capital, Ltd.
Shah, Shimi—Synergis Technologies, Ltd.
Shah, Suken—Huntsman Gay Global Capital LLC
Shah, Suken—Prospect Partners LLC
Shah, Yogesh—Scsi Capital
Shahaf, Moshe—Vertex Management Israel (AKA: Vertex Venture Capital)
Shahaf, Moshe—Vertex Venture Capital
Shahbaz, Shahzad—QInvest LLC
Shahdadpuri, Deepak—Baer Capital Partners, Ltd.
Shahor, Ran—Star Ventures Management GmbH & Co. KG
Shahryar, Humayun—Rasmala Partners, Ltd.
Shaia, John—Saw Mill Capital, LLC
Shaikh, Abdul Hafeez—New Silk Route Partners LLC
Shainski, Rina—Carmel Ventures
Shairman, Lee—Blackstone Group, L.P.
Shaked, Ohad—Shaked Global Group Ltd.
Shalev, Eddy—Genesis Partners
Sham, Simon—Darby Asia Investors, Ltd.
Sham, Simon—Darby Overseas Investments, Ltd.
Shamapant, Venu—Austin Ventures, L.P.
Shan, Weijian—Newbridge Capital, Ltd.
Shan, Weijian—Pacific Alliance Capital Group
Shan, Xiangshuang—China Science & Merchants Capital Management Co., Ltd.
Shanahan, Keven—Argosy Capital
Shanahan, Michael—Egan-Managed Capital
Shanahan, Thomas—Needham Asset Management
Shanahan, Timothy—Water Tower Capital LLC
Shane, Anne—BioCrossroads, Inc.
Shanfield, Robert—Landmark Partners, Inc.
Shang, Alexander—Global Emerging Markets
Shang, Mark—Serent Capital LLC
Shang, Xuanyu—Cybernaut (China) Capital Management
Shankland, Graeme—Bank of Scotland Corporate
Shanmugam, Sivaprakash Siva —Headwaters Merchant Bank
Shannon, Glenn—Shorenstein Company LLC
Shannon, James—Private Advisors LLC
Shannon, Mary—Masthead Venture Partners
Shannon, Michael—KSL Capital Partners
Shannon, Peter—Firelake Capital Management
Shannon, Rick—CORE Partners, Inc.
Shannon, Tim—Canaan Partners
Shansby, J. Gary—TSG Consumer Partners
Shao, Bo—Matrix Partners
Shao, Nicholas—Carlyle Group, The
Shao, Rocky—ChinaEquity Group, Inc.
Shao, Yang Dong—Chengwei Ventures
Shaoul, Edward—Headwaters Merchant Bank
Shaper, Peter—Genesis Park Ventures
Shapero, Rich—Crosspoint Venture Partners
Shapiro, Bennett—PureTech Ventures
Shapiro, David—Marquette Capital Partners
Shapiro, Jackie—MVC Capital (FKA: meVC)
Shapiro, James—Kearny Venture Partners
Shapiro, Jonathan—Ropart Group
Shapiro, Marvin—Veronis Suhler Stevenson (FKA: Veronis, Suhler & Associates)
Shapiro, Neil—GF Capital Management & Advisors LLC
Shapiro, Philip—Synova Capital LLP
Shapiro, Stephen—Clayton, Dubilier & Rice, Inc.
Shapiro, Steve—Galen Associates
Sharara, Mohamed—Gulf Capital
Shareef, Dara—Glenmont Partners, LLC
Sharer, Kevin—Amgen, Inc.
Shariar, Mark—Voobon Ventures, Inc.
Sharif, Nazar—Oaktree Capital Management LLC
Shariff, Viq—Rizvi Traverse Management, LLC
Sharma, Amitvikram—Milestone Religare Investment Advisors Pvt., Ltd.
Sharma, Nishant—General Atlantic LLC
Sharma, Rajiv—BTS Investment Advisors, Ltd.
Sharma, Ray—Extreme Venture Partners, Inc.
Sharma, Sanjeev—GVFL Limited (FKA: Gujarat Venture Finance Limited)
Sharma, Sunish—General Atlantic LLC
Sharma, Sunny—OrbiMed Advisors LLC
Sharma, Tarun—New Enterprise Associates, Inc.
Sharma, Vishal—Tuscan Ventures Pvt., Ltd.
Sharon, Zachary—Symphony Capital LLC
Sharp, Bob—American Capital, Ltd.
Sharp, Robert—MidOcean Partners
Sharp, Roger—Co-Investor Capital Partners Pty., Ltd.
Sharpe, J. Louis—AEA Investors LP
Sharpe, Jim—Lux Capital
Shasha, Tsachy—Docor International B.V.
Shattenkirk, Patrick—Vestar Capital Partners, Inc.
Shattuck, Barbara—Shattuck Hammond Partners
Shavit, Gilad—KCPS Israel Private Equity Partners
Shaw, Benjamin—Marwyn Investment Management, LLP
Shaw, Charles—First Atlantic Capital, Ltd.
Shaw, Gordon—BPEP International
Shaw, John—Jefferies Group, Inc.
Shaw, Kyle—Shaw Kwei & Partners
Shaw, Leslie—Sun Mountain Capital
Shaw, Leslie—Vance Street Capital LLC
Shaw, Matt—Sunrock Ventures, Inc.
Shaw, Philip—Invesco Private Capital
Shaw, Robert—Arete Corporation
Shaw, Robert—Silicon Valley Innovation Capital (SVIC)
Shaw, Roman—DT Capital Partners
Shaw, Roman—DragonTech Ventures Management, Ltd.
Shaw, Vicki—Here Be Dragons (HBD) Mgt Services (AKA:HBD Venture Capital)
Shawki, Hazem—EFG-Hermes Private Equity
Shawver, Robert—New Enterprise Associates, Inc.
Shay, Izhar—Canaan Partners
Shayer, Fernando—Tarpon Investment Group
Shea, Stephen—Signature Capital LLC
Shea, W. Andrew—GenNx360 Capital Partners
Shear, Barry—GE Antares Capital Corporation
Shearburn, John—Warburg Pincus LLC
Shearer, W. Gregory—Channel Medical Partners
Shechter, Doron—Gmul Investment Company, Ltd.
Shechter, Zvi—Giza Venture Capital (FKA: Giza Investment Management)
Sheedy, John—Latitude Partners
Sheehan, Andy—Sutter Hill Ventures
Sheehan, Chris—CommonAngels
Sheehan, John—Equis Capital Partners
Sheehan, Patrick—ETF Manager LLP
Sheehan, William—Ironside Capital Group (FKA:Ironside Ventures LLC)
Sheehy, Timothy—Bunker Hill Capital
Sheeline, Kip—Levensohn Venture Partners LLC (FKA: Levensohn Capital Mgmt)
Sheeline, Kip—Summit Accelerator Fund
Sheeren, Christopher—Huron Capital Partners LLC
Sheets, Bryon—Paul Capital Partners
Sheffer, David—Monitor Clipper Partners LLC
Sheffery, Michael—OrbiMed Advisors LLC
Sheft, Robert—Roark Capital Group
Sheftel, Bradley—Valor Equity Partners
Sheiner, Andrew—Onex Corporation
Sheldon, Ronald—Advent International
Sheldon, S. Douglas—ESP Equity Partners LLC
Shelem, Avner—Ascend Technology Ventures
Shell, Lori—Frontier Capital LLC
Shelton, Charles—Nancy Creek Capital
Shelton, Theresa—KRG Capital Partners LLC
Shen, Bill—Encore Consumer Capital LLC
Shen, Christopher—Essex Woodlands Health Ventures
Shen, Frank—Cnstar Capital Pte., Ltd
Shen, Jennifer—AlpInvest Partners N.V.
Shen, Laura—Headway Capital Partners LLP
Shen, Lin—Milestone Capital Management, Ltd.
Shen, Robert—H&Q Asia Pacific
Shepard, Jay—Sofinnova Ventures
Shepard, Michael—Heron Capital LLC
Shepherd, Jay—ClearLight Partners LLC
Shepherd, Pam—Greenmont Capital Partners
Shepherd, T. Nathanael—TSG Equity Partners, L.L.C.

Shepler, Robert—Telegraph Hill Partners (AKA: THP)
Sher, Dani—Anchorage Capital Partners
Sherblom, James—Seaflower Ventures
Sherer, Paul—GKM Ventures
Sherer, Paul—Osprey Ventures, L.P.
Sheridan, Robert—Ridgemont Equity Partners
Sheriff, Alan—Rosemont Solebury Capital Management LLC
Sherman, Jonathan—Imperial Capital Corporation
Sherman, Lana—Rose Corporation, The
Sherman, Mark—Battery Ventures, L.P.
Sherman, Michael—Chrysalix Energy
Sherman, Michael—Elm Street Ventures
Sherman, Richard—SCP Private Equity Partners
Sherman, Robert—Boston Millennia Partners
Sherman, Sebastian—Borealis Infrastructure Management, Inc.
Sherrill, Stephen—Bruckmann, Rosser, Sherrill & Co.
Sherwin, Elton—Ridgewood Capital Management, LLC
Sherwood, Charles—Permira Advisers LLP
Sherwood, Ned—ZS Fund L.P.
Sheshol, Robert—Kilcullen Kapital Partners
Sheshuryak, Sergey—Adams Street Partners LLC
Sheth, Brian—Vista Equity Partners
Shetty, R.B.—Karnataka Information Technology Venture Capital Fund
Shevlet, James—Carlyle Group, The
Shevlin, James—American Capital, Ltd.
Shewmaker, Bruce—MVC Capital (FKA: meVC)
Shi, Lan—Cybernaut (China) Capital Management
Shi, Yi—Lilly Asian Ventures
Shi-min, Zhang—Shenzhen Careall Capital Investment Co., Ltd. Kangwo
Shibasaki, Kenji—Asset Managers Holding Company, Ltd.
Shibata, Hidetosi—MKS Partners, Ltd. (FKA: Schroder Ventures K.K.)
Shibuya, Seiji—Yamaguchi Capital Co., Ltd
Shick, Lee—PrimePartners Asset Management Pte, Ltd.
Shields, David—Accede Capital
Shields, John—Abingworth Management, Ltd.
Shields, John—Boston Capital Ventures
Shields, Robert—Questor Management Company LLC
Shields, Thomas—Woodside Fund
Shiferaw, Bethlehem—ONCAP Investment Partners
Shiftan, Andrew—Brooks, Houghton & Company, Inc.
Shigemura, Eisuke—Tokio Marine Capital Company, Ltd.
Shih, Ben—JAFCO Ventures
Shih, Irene—Pac-Link Management Corporation
Shih, Stan—iD Innovation, Inc.
Shikata, Osamu—Shikata Venture Fund
Shiland, Jay—MTS Health Partners, L.P.
Shiller, Robert—Romspen Investment Corporation
Shilling, Ken—Vanguard Ventures
Shillito, James—Fenway Partners, Inc.
Shim, Youn Kyu—Darby Overseas Investments, Ltd.
Shimamura, Yoshihide—Daiwa Corporate Investment Co., Ltd.
Shimer, Daniel—Teakwood Capital, L.P.
Shimoura, Kazutaka—Orix Capital Corporation
Shimp, John—Ridgemont Equity Partners
Shin, Bong Kyun—Darby Overseas Investments, Ltd.
Shin, Hugh—STIC Investments, Inc.
Shin, Jason—Vogo Investment
Shin, Jee—ProQuest Investments
Shin, Jin-Ho—KTB Securities Co., Ltd. (FKA: KTB Network Co., Ltd.)
Shin, Jongkyu—HST Venture Capital
Shin, Kicheon—Atinum Investment Co., Ltd.
Shin, Mark—Newton Technology Partners (NTP)
Shin, Michael—American Capital, Ltd.
Shinada, Koichi—Oak Capital Corporation
Shine, Timothy—Commonfund Realty
Shinoura, Yuichi—Iyogin Capital Co., Ltd.
Shintani, Daisuke—Valiant Partners Co. Ltd.
Shiong, Wayne—WI Harper Group
Shipley, Richard—Shiprock Capital LLC
Shipman, Christopher—Catalyst Investors
Shipp, Terrance—Merit Capital Partners (FKA:William Blair Mezzanine)
Shirai, Takehiro—Information Technology Farm Corporation (AKA: IT Farm)
Shiralagi, Kumar—NEA-IndoUS Capital Advisors Pvt. Ltd.
Shirhattikar, Gautam—Prospect Street Ventures
Shisler, Bradley—Willis Stein & Partners
Shles, Julian—J.P. Morgan Asset Management
Shlesinger, Joe—Callisto Capital
Shoan, Harj—Morgan Stanley Private Equity
Shoch, John—Alloy Ventures
Shockley, Dan—Lake Capital Partners, Inc.
Shockley, Ryan—First Reserve Corporation
Shoeb, Tarek—One Equity Partners (FKA: Banc One Venture Partners)
Shoemaker, John—Milestone Partners
Shoemaker, Peter—Wedbush Capital Partners
Shoemaker, Raleigh—Berkshire Partners LLC
Shofet, Jonathan—NB Alternatives - Fund of Funds
Shoham, Amnon—Cedar Fund
Shoham, Yair—Genesis Partners
Shomron, Gur—Stage One Ventures
Shong, Hugo—IDG Technology Venture Investment, Inc.
Shook, Charles—Morgan Keegan Merchant Banking
Shore, Graham—Shore Capital, Ltd.
Shorenstein, Douglas—Shorenstein Company LLC
Shorin, James—Horizon Holdings, LLC
Shorrock, Mark—Low Carbon Accelerator
Short, Don—CORE Partners, Inc.
Shorthouse, Dominic—Englefield Capital
Shortsleeve, Brian—General Catalyst Partners (FKA: General Catalyst Group LLC)
Shoshan, Yuri—Pitango Venture Capital (FKA:Polaris Venture Capital Israel)
Shotland, David—CIBC Capital Partners
Shove, Greg—Kohlberg Ventures LLC
Showalter, Carl—Opus Capital
Shpantzer, Isaac—Concord Ventures (FKA: Nitzanim)
Shpindler, Liora—China Israel Value Capital (AKA: CIVC)
Shrestha, Abhaya—Behrman Capital
Shridhar, N—Everstone Capital
Shriner, Rick—Woodside Fund
Shriram, Ram—Sherpalo Ventures
Shrivastava, Anil—Vestar Capital Partners, Inc.
Shrivastava, Anubha—CDC Group PLC (FKA: Commonwealth Development Corporation)
Shrivastava, Rupam—Draper Fisher Jurvetson ePlanet Ventures, L.P.
Shroff, Kunal—ChrysCapital Management Company
Shroff, Zubeen—Galen Associates
Shroyer, Christopher—InDecatur Ventures LLC
Shu, Ming—Henderson Equity Partners (AKA: Henderson Private Capital)
Shuang, Ronald—Balloch China Fund, The
Shuart, Rick—Caltius Mezzanine
Shuart, Rick—Industrial Renaissance Inc.
Shuchman, Salem—Entrepreneur Partners, L.P.
Shuda, Scott—BlueLine Partners LLC
Shufro, Mark—Greyrock Capital Group
Shuiwen, Zhou—NewMargin Ventures
Shukla, Amita—New Enterprise Associates, Inc.
Shulkin, Jonathan—Valor Equity Partners
Shulman, John—Allied Capital Corporation
Shulman, Zachary—Cayuga Venture Fund
Shumadine, Anne—Signature Financial Managment, Inc.
Shuman, Stanley—Allen & Company
Shuping-Russell, Sallie—BlackRock Private Equity Partners
Shure, Randl—CapVest Management Ltd
Shurtleff, Robert—Divergent Ventures
Shuwall, Meredith—Investment Fund for Foundations
Siadat, Barry—SK Capital Partners
Sibony, Armand—Convergent Capital SAS
Sica, Frank—Tailwind Capital Partners
Sicard, Gilles—Cerea Gestion SAS
Sicard, Yves—iNovia Capital
Sichel, Olivier—Sofinnova Partners
Sicoli, Richard—Westbury Partners
Sidana, Ashmeet—Foundation Capital
Siddiqi, Naveed—Nomura Phase4 Ventures, Ltd.
Siddique, Waqar Hassan—Abraaj Capital
Siddiqui, Kashif—EFG-Hermes Private Equity
Sideropoulos, Lester—CT Holdings
Sidhu, Gurmit—Abundance Venture Capital
Sidler, Jean-Francois—Synapsis Associates
Sidler, Patrick—M2 Capital Management AG
Sidwell, David—Morgan Stanley Private Equity
Sieber, Erich—Direct Capital Private Equity
Sieber, Erich—inventages venture capital S.A.
Siefke, Michael—Bain Capital
Siegal, Jeffrey—Metalmark Capital LLC
Siegel, Amanda—Quadrangle Group LLC
Siegel, Bernie—KSL Capital Partners
Siegel, Harold—Highland Capital Management, L.P.
Siegel, Harvey—GSC Partners (FKA: Greenwich Street Capital Partners)
Siegel, John—Columbia Capital LLC
Siegel, Mark—Menlo Ventures
Siegel, Phillip—Austin Ventures, L.P.
Siegel, Steven—KSL Capital Partners
Siegel, Sue—Mohr Davidow Ventures
Siegel, Susan—Affymetrix, Inc.
Siegel, Tom—Shepherd Ventures
Siegelman, Russell—Kleiner Perkins Caufield & Byers
Sieh, Stephen—Evercore Partners

Sieler, Miguel—Truffle Venture SAS
Sienna, Lee—Ontario Teachers' Pension Plan
Sieranski, Edward—Regionalne Fundusze Inwestycji Sp. z o.o.
Sietses, Dick—Residex BV
Sievert, Christian—Segulah Advisor AB
Sievert, Joerg—SAP Ventures
Siew, Lim Tiang—CIMB Private Equity Sdn Bhd
Siewert, Patrick—Carlyle Group, The
Sigalow, Ian—Greycroft Partners
Sigda, Neal—SigmaBleyzer
Sigel, Anthony—Kilmer Capital Partners
Sigl, Susan—Seapoint Ventures
Sigler, Mary Ann—Platinum Equity LLC
Sigmond, Steve—BlueStream Ventures
Signorelli, Michael—Origo Partners PLC
Signoret, Carlos—Hispania Capital Partners (HCP)
Siguler, George—Siguler Guff & Company
Sikand, Davinder—Aureos Capital, Ltd.
Sikkens, Han—Summit Partners
Siklos, Eugene—Canterbury Park Capital
Sikorski, Thomas—First Reserve Corporation
Silber, Allan—Counsel Corporation
Silberdick, Norman—Cornestone Capital Partners
Silbert, Ben—Avista Capital Holdings, L.P.
Siletto, Joseph—Bio Equity Risk Management LLC
Silgardo, Mark—IL&FS Investment Managers Ltd (FKA: IL&FS Venture Corp)
Sillman, Eric—Aperture Venture Partners, LLC
Silva Ricciardi, Antonio—Espirito Santo Capital - Sociedade de Capital de Risco SA
Silver, Andrew—Houlihan, Lokey, Howard & Zukin
Silver, Benjamin—Babson Capital Management LLC
Silvera, David—Rosemont Investment Partners LLC
Silverberg, Brad—Ignition Partners (FKA: Ignition Corporation)
Silverman, David—3i (US)
Silverman, Henry—Apollo Management
Silverman, Jeremy—Frontenac Company
Silverman, Lauren—Novartis Venture Fund (FKA: Novartis Corp.)
Silverman, Mark—Catamount Ventures, L.P.
Silverman, Meg—Advent Venture Partners LLP
Silvershatz, Avishai—Infinity Venture Capital Fund (AKA: Israel Infinity Fund)
Silverstein, Jonathan—OrbiMed Advisors LLC
Silvestri, Joseph—Court Square Capital Partners
Silvey, Jerome—Starwood Capital Group
Sim, Boon—Credit Suisse Private Equity
Sim, Edward—Dawntreader Ventures
Simatos, Michael—Investcorp Bank B.S.C.
Simler, Dominik—Investcorp Bank B.S.C.
Simm, Ian—Impax Asset Management
Simmons, Brian—Code, Hennessy & Simmons LLC
Simmons, J. Frederick—Freeman Spogli & Co.
Simmons, John—JC Simmons & Associates
Simmons, L.—SCF Partners
Simmons, Molly—Tonka Bay Equity Partners
Simmons, N.John—Quantum Capital Partners
Simmons, Walker—Pamlico Capital
Simon, Andreas—Capvis Equity Partners AG
Simon, Daniel—Wedbush Capital Partners
Simon, David—Littlejohn & Company LLC
Simon, Dennis—Crossroads Capital Partners, LLC
Simon, Henry—SV Life Sciences Advisers
Simon, John—General Catalyst Partners (FKA: General Catalyst Group LLC)
Simon, Lawrence—Clearview Capital LLC
Simon, Martin—Rose Corporation, The
Simon, Nicholas—Clarus Ventures
Simon, Rafael—VantagePoint Venture Partners
Simon, Robert—Bradford Equities Management LLC
Simoni, Catherine—Carlyle Group, The
Simoni, Richard—Asset Management Company Venture Capital
Simonneau, Emmanuel—SIGMA Gestion SA
Simons, James—Split Rock Partners LLC
Simons, James—St. Paul Venture Capital, Inc.
Simons, John—Corporate Fuel Partners
Simonsen, Lennart—CapMan Plc
Simonson, Tom—Meritage Funds
Simonsson, Kjell—Karolinska Investment Management AB
Simoudis, Evangelos—Trident Capital
Simpkins, Neil—Blackstone Group, L.P.
Simpson, Carl—Coronis Medical Ventures
Simpson, Thomas—Northwest Venture Associates, Inc.(FKA:Spokane Capital Mgmt)
Sims, Edgar—Nancy Creek Capital
Sims, Tim—Pacific Equity Partners
Sinadski, Slava—Alfa Capital Partners
Sinard, Jean-Claude—Hydro-Quebec CapiTech Inc.
Sinatra, John—Veronis Suhler Stevenson (FKA: Veronis, Suhler & Associates)
Sinclair, Andrew—Abingworth Management, Ltd.
Sinclair, David—Lux Capital
Sinclair, Peter—Leapfrog Ventures
Sindi, Nabil Ali—Crescent Point Group
Sinding, Christian—EQT Funds management Limited
Sindwani, Deepak—Comcast Interactive Capital
Sinfield-Hain, Craig—Investcorp Bank B.S.C.
Singer, Carl—Fundamental Management Corporation
Singer, David—Maverick Capital Ltd.
Singer, John—Advent International
Singer, Lori—Delta Capital Management (AKA:Delta Private Equity Partners)
Singer, Marc—BEV Capital (FKA: Brand Equity Ventures)
Singer, Marc—Osage Partners, LLC
Singer, Maria—Blackstone Group, L.P.
Singh, Ajeet—Unitas Capital Pte, Ltd.
Singh, Alok—New Mountain Capital LLC
Singh, Devinjit—Carlyle Group, The
Singh, Praneet—Siguler Guff & Company
Singh, Raj—Redwood Venture Partners
Singh, Ravi—Sycamore Ventures Pte, Ltd.
Singh, Shailendra Jit—Sequoia Capital India (FKA: WestBridge Capital Partners)
Singh, Shailesh—2i Capital Asset Management Company, Ltd.
Singh, T.Raj—Parkview Ventures LLC
Singh, Tom—Zouk Ventures, Ltd.
Singhal, Rajesh—Milestone Religare Investment Advisors Pvt., Ltd.
Singhal, Sandeep—Nexus Venture Partners
Singhal, Sandeep—Sequoia Capital India (FKA: WestBridge Capital Partners)
Singhal, Sanjiv—BanyanTree Finance Pvt. Ltd.
Singleton, Lincoln—Evercore Partners
Sinha, Bipul—Blumberg Capital Ventures
Sinha, Bipul—Lightspeed Venture Partners (FKA: Weiss, Peck & Greer)
Sinha, Jit—JMI Equity
Sinha, Padmanabh—Temasek Holdings Pvt., Ltd.
Sinik, John—TowerBrook Capital Partners L.P.
Siniscalco, Claudio—HarbourVest Partners LLC
Sinnenberg, John—Key Principal Partners LLC (AKA: KPP)
Sinno, Mustafa—Evolvence Capital
Siow, Rose—RimAsia Capital Partners
Sipahimalani, Rohit—Temasek Holdings Pvt., Ltd.
Siponmaa, Ari—Aura Capital Oy
Sipp, Sebastian—GMT Communications Partners LLP
Sippl, Roger—Sippl Macdonald Ventures
Sirett, Tom—Langholm Capital LLP
Sirois, Charles—Propulsion Ventures, Inc.
Sironi, Francesco—BS Private Equity SpA (FKA: B&S Private Equity Group)
Sissel, Greg—Platte River Ventures
Sisteron, Yves—GRP Partners
Sithian, Vikram—Beekman Group LLC, The
Siu, Christine—Thomas, McNerney & Partners LLC
Siugzda, Sarunas—Askembla Asset Management AB
Sivanithy, Dushy—Pantheon Ventures, Ltd.
Siwawa, Anthony—Venture Partners Botswana
Sjoerdsma, Jelle—Dynamic Equity, Ltd.
Sjogren, Anders—Vita Nova Ventures AB
Sjogren, Johan—CVC Capital Partners (Europe), Ltd.
Sjostrom, Linda—BankInvest Group A/S
Sjostrom, Thomas—SEB Venture Capital
Skaff, Daniel—Sienna Ventures (FKA: Sienna Holdings Inc.)
Skaff, Michael—Seneca Partners, Inc.
Skagseth, Erlend—Sarsia Innovation AS
Skagseth, Erlend—Sarsia Seed Management AS
Skajem, John—Kaupthing Bank hf.
Skapinker, Mark—Brightspark Ventures
Skarback, Marcus—TeknoSeed AB
Skare, Leif Andre—Energy Ventures AS
Skaterschikov, Sergey—IndexAtlas Group
Skatoff, David—GCP Capital Partners
Skattum, Dag—TPG Capital
Skeete Tatum, Lisa—Cardinal Partners
Skegro, Borislav—Quaestus Private Equity, Ltd.
Skelton, James—Crossroads Capital Partners, LLC
Skibiel, Andreas—York Street Capital Partners LLC
Skillen, Lynn—Sun Capital Partners, Inc.
Skillins, Eric—CFI Capital
Skinner, Peter—Apax Partners Worldwide
Skinner, Robert—Agility Capital LLC
Skinner, Spencer—Active Private Equity Advisory LLP
Skjervold, Herbjorn—ProVenture AS
Skoglund, Martin—Scandinavian Financial Management AB
Skok, David—Matrix Partners
Skok, Michael—North Bridge Venture Partners
Skok, Natasha—Tallwood Venture Capital
Skoler, Steven—Friend Skoler & Co., L.L.C.
Skolnick, Craig—CAI Capital Management Company
Skott, Allen—Vista Capital LLC (FKA: AO Capital Corp.)
Skrenta, Stephen—Blackstone Group, L.P.

Skrzynski, Joseph—CHAMP Private Equity Pty Ltd.
Skrzypek, Gunther—Augur Capital Group
Skvortsov, Serguei—Troika Capital Partners
Skyrius, Sarunas—GILD Bankers (FKA: LHV Ventures)
Slade, Dominic—Alchemy Partners LLP
Slade, Ed—Quest Capital, Inc.
Slade, Michael—Second Avenue Partners
Slagel, Dean—Esperante BV
Slater, Bob—Alcatel-Lucent Ventures
Slater, Iain—CBPE Capital, LLP (AKA: Close Brothers Private Equity, Ltd.)
Slatter, Ben—Rutland Fund Management, Ltd. (AKA: Rutland Partners LLP)
Slattery, Domhnal—Claret Capital, Ltd.
Slattery, John—Vertical Group, The
Slauer, Chris—Markpoint Venture Partners
Slavet, James—Greylock Partners
Slavin, Bill—ARC Financial Corporation
Slawson, Michael—Alliance Technology Ventures
Sledzik, Jim—Energy Ventures AS
Sleeper, Nathan—Clayton, Dubilier & Rice, Inc.
Sleigh, Stephen—P.A.G. Capital Partners
Sletting, Lauge—Nordea Private Equity
Slipper, James—Gresham LLP
Slitz, John—Osprey Ventures, L.P.
Sloan, H. Bradley—Parthenon Capital LLC
Sloboda, E.J.—Wicks Group of Companies LLC, The
Slootweg, Sander—Forbion Capital Partners
Sloutski, Niklas—Accent Equity Partners AB
Slutzkin, Craig—New Leaf Venture Partners LLC
Slye, Jack—Sterling Partners
Slykhous, Stewart—Tucker Partners
Smaby, Gary—Quatris Fund
Small, Elaine—Paul Capital Partners
Small, Michael—Park Square Capital, LLP
Small, Robert—Berkshire Partners LLC
Smallbone, Tim—Inflexion plc (AKA: Inflexion Private Equity)
Smaller, Daniel—Algebra Capital
Smardon, Dave—Nibiru Capital
Smart, Christopher—Acacia Capital Partners
Smart, Christopher—Akara, Ltd. (DBA: IDG Ventures Europe)
Smart, Michael—Cordova, Smart & Williams, LLC
Smart, Shawn—HealthRight Partners
Smartt, David—Venquest Capital Partners
Smeltzer, James—Cardinal Equity Partners (FKA: Cardinal Ventures)
Smereczynski, Daniel—First Analysis Corporation
Smets, Julien—Fortis Private Equity NV/SA (FKA: VIV NV)
Smidt, Jorgen—Sunstone Capital A/S
Smiggen, Michael—Tonka Bay Equity Partners
Smiley, Stephen—Hunt Private Equity Group, Inc. (FKA: Hunt Financial Corp.)
Smit, Marlou L.—Undisclosed Firm
Smith Thorne, Heather—Thoma Cressey Bravo
Smith, Adrian—Ignition Partners (FKA: Ignition Corporation)
Smith, Alastair—Finsbury Life Sciences Investment Trust
Smith, Amanda D.H.—Design Investors LLC
Smith, Amanda—Waterman Capital Ltd
Smith, Andrew—Sciens Capital Partners (FKA: Zilkha Venture Partners)
Smith, Archie—SightLine Partners
Smith, Brian—Dominion Ventures, Inc.
Smith, Brian—Montauk TriGuard Management, Inc.
Smith, Brian—Peninsula Ventures
Smith, Brian—S3 Ventures
Smith, Brien—NB Alternatives - Fund of Funds
Smith, Brigitte—GBS Venture Partners, Ltd.
Smith, Brook—Ancor Capital Partners
Smith, Bryan—Gazelle TechVentures
Smith, Candace—MicroVest Capital Management LLC
Smith, Cheryl—Signal Lake
Smith, Christopher—GarMark Partners
Smith, Daniel—Blackstone Group, L.P.
Smith, David—Bay Hills Capital (FKA: Mansbridge Capital Management)
Smith, David—Glenalta Capital LLP
Smith, David—Pine Street Capital Partners LLC
Smith, David—Unigestion SA
Smith, Deborah—Investcorp Bank B.S.C.
Smith, Derek—UBS Capital Corporation
Smith, Douglas—Prospect Partners LLC
Smith, Dustin—American Capital, Ltd.
Smith, Eamon—TCS Capital LLC
Smith, Everett—NewWorld Capital Group LLC
Smith, Gary—Encore Consumer Capital LLC
Smith, Geoffrey—Ascent Biomedical Ventures
Smith, Greg—Corning Innovation Ventures
Smith, Gregory—SciVentures Investments Pty., Ltd.
Smith, H. Dabney—Dogwood Equity
Smith, Howard—First Analysis Corporation
Smith, Howard—SeventySix Capital
Smith, Hugh—Alta Berkeley Venture Partners
Smith, Ian—Aquiline Capital Partners
Smith, Ian—Reed Elsevier Ventures
Smith, J. Albert—Blackstone Group, L.P.
Smith, JB—Equity 11, Ltd.
Smith, Jan—Funk Ventures, Inc.
Smith, Jason—Lime Rock Partners LLC
Smith, Jason—Peak Capital Group LLC
Smith, Jed—Catamount Ventures, L.P.
Smith, Jim—Mohr Davidow Ventures
Smith, John—Vexiom Equity Partners, L.P.
Smith, Julian—Imperial Innovations (AKA: Imperial College Innovations)
Smith, Karl—Frank Russell Capital
Smith, Kathleen—New World Ventures
Smith, Kevin—H & S Capital (AKA: Heidrick & Struggles Capital)
Smith, Kevin—Silverfern Group, Inc., The
Smith, Kevin—UBS Capital Corporation
Smith, Lisa—Unilever Ventures, Ltd. (AKA: Unilever NV)
Smith, Mark—JumpStart, Inc.
Smith, Matthew—Odeon Capital Partners, L.P.
Smith, Michael—Ares Management, Inc.
Smith, Michael—Emerald Hill Capital Partners, Ltd.
Smith, Michael—Ranch Capital LLC
Smith, Nancy—ARC Financial Corporation
Smith, Peter—5280 Partners
Smith, Philip—Stone Canyon Venture Partners (SCVP)
Smith, Raymond—Arlington Capital Partners
Smith, Renny—Staley Capital Management LLC
Smith, Richard—Allegra Partners (FKA: Lawrence, Smith & Horey)
Smith, Richard—Century Capital Management, Inc.
Smith, Richard—One Earth Capital LLC
Smith, Rick—Crosscut Ventures
Smith, Rick—One Equity Partners (FKA: Banc One Venture Partners)
Smith, Robb—Nevada Ventures
Smith, Robert—C3 Capital LLC
Smith, Robert—Castanea Partners
Smith, Robert—GCP Capital Partners
Smith, Robert—JMI Equity
Smith, Robert—Petra Capital Partners, LLC
Smith, Rowan—Shanduka Fund Mangers (Pty) Ltd.
Smith, Sean—Pamlico Capital
Smith, Stanley—Syncom Management Co. Inc.
Smith, Stephen—Banyan Capital Advisors LLC
Smith, Stephen—JS Group
Smith, Stephen—Masthead Venture Partners
Smith, Steve—RSS Investors
Smith, Steven—GE Commercial Finance - Equity
Smith, T. Otey—RLJ Equity Partners LLC
Smith, Teresa—Walden International
Smith, Terry—SFW Capital Partners, LLC
Smith, Thomas—Lombard Investments, Inc.
Smith, Thomas—Mason Wells Private Equity (FKA: M&I Ventures)
Smith, Thomas—Mid-Atlantic Venture Funds (FKA: NEPA Management Corp.)
Smith, Timothy—Houlihan, Lokey, Howard & Zukin
Smith, Tom—Smith Defieux Capital Partners
Smith, Warren—TH Lee Putnam Ventures, L.P.
Smith, Wayne—Bush O'Donnell Capital Partners
Smith, Willaim—Houlihan, Lokey, Howard & Zukin
Smith-MacKenzie, Helen—Peregrine Ventures, LP
Smits, Jelto—Prime Technology Ventures NV
Smitshoek, Roy—Moneta Capital Partners, Ltd.
Smolens, Donna—Portfolio Advisors LLC
Smoley, David—Lovett Miller & Co. Incorporated
Smoot, Timothy—Meridian Management Group, Inc. (AKA: MMG)
Smulders, Patrick—MST Capital, Ltd.
Smulders, Patrick—TowerBrook Capital Partners L.P.
Smyth, Derek—EdgeStone Capital Partners, Inc.
Snape, Edwin—Nexus Medical Partners
Snare, Philip—Blue Water Capital LLC
Snarelid, Pelle—Forsta Entreprenorsfonden i Norden AB
Sneddon, David—Scottish Equity Partners
Snellenbarger, Reid—Houlihan, Lokey, Howard & Zukin
Sneyers, Tycho—LGT Capital Partners AG
Snider, Bill—Emerging Technology Partners, LLC
Snook, John—CBPE Capital, LLP (AKA: Close Brothers Private Equity, Ltd.)
Snow, Alex—Evolution Group (FKA: EVC Christows PLC)
Snow, Ian—Snow Phipps Group LLC (FKA: SPG Partners, LLC)
Snowdy, Stephen—MB Venture Partners, LLC
Snyder, Brett—Nicolet Capital Partners LLC
Snyder, Darren—Prairie Capital
Snyder, James—Hammond Kennedy Whitney & Co
Snyder, Jon—Arboretum Ventures
Snyder, William—CRG Partners
Snyderman, Ralph—New Enterprise Associates, Inc.
Snyman, Fanie—GKA Bayete

So, Andy—Avant Capital Group, Inc.
So, Jason—SAIF Partners
So, Raymond—Vogo Investment
Soames, Jeremy—GSC Partners (FKA: Greenwich Street Capital Partners)
Soane, Mark—Appian Ventures
Soanes, Darren—Borealis Infrastructure Management, Inc.
Sobecki, Christopher—Invus Group Ltd., The
Sobel, Richard—Alfa Capital Partners
Sobel, Robert—Brahman Management, LLC
Sobieski, Ian—Band of Angels
Sobiloff, Peter—Insight Venture Partners
Socas, James—Updata Partners
Socha, Kenneth—Perseus LLC
Socolof, Stephen—New Venture Partners LLC
Soden, John—Thomas Weisel Partners Group, Inc.
Soder, Bjorn—Parklane Capital Beteiligungsberatung GmbH
Soderberg, Bo—Nordic Capital (AKA: NC Advisory)
Soderberg, Ricard—Active Capital Partners S.L.
Soderberg, Sten—MedCap AB (FKA: New Science Svenska AB)
Soderling, Stephen—Tonka Bay Equity Partners
Sodhani, Arvind—Intel Capital
Sodi, Marco—Veronis Suhler Stevenson (FKA: Veronis, Suhler & Associates)
Soeda, Amy—Corsair Capital LLC
Soghikian, Shahan—J.P. Morgan Partners (FKA: Chase Capital Partners)
Soghikian, Shahan—Panorama Capital
Sohail, Faysal—CMEA Capital
Soheborn, Bill—Trust Company of the West (AKA: TCW/Crescent)
Sohn, Albert—Credit Suisse Private Equity
Sohn, Jon—Climate Change Capital, Ltd.
Soignet, Steven—Arcus Ventures Management LLC
Soignet, Steven—Cross Atlantic Partners, Inc.
Soileau, Stephen—TGF Management Corp (FKA:Texas Growth Fund)
Soinski, Jeffrey—Galen Associates
Sokol, Marc—JK&B Capital
Sokoloff, Jonathan—Leonard Green & Partners
Solan, Mike—Mercantile Capital Group (MCG)
Solibieda, Markus—Baigo Capital GmbH
Solich, Geoff—SB Energy Partners
Solich, Mitchell—SB Energy Partners
Soliz, Angela—First Analysis Corporation
Solo, David—UBS Capital Corporation
Solomon, Curt—New York Business Development Corporation
Solomon, Gary—Baird Capital Partners Europe
Solomon, Glenn—GGV Capital
Solomon, Harold—Seraphim Partners
Solomon, Michael—Leonard Green & Partners
Solomon, Stephen—Cutlass Capital
Solomon, Steve—Accrue Sports and Entertainment Partners LLC
Solomon, Steven—CT Holdings
Solomons, Alton—Sanlam Private Equity
Solon, Mark—Highway 12 Ventures
Solorzano, Luis—Advent International
Solotar, Joan—Banc of America Securities LLC
Solotar, Joan—Blackstone Group, L.P.
Solow, Todd—Norwest Equity Partners
Solvik, Peter—Sigma Partners
Solway, Gary—Bennett Jones
Somaia, Bejul—Lightspeed Venture Partners (FKA: Weiss, Peck & Greer)
Soman, Meb—Actis Capital LLP
Somberg, Debra—Maveron LLC
Somers, Nicholas—SV Investment Partners (FKA: Schroder Ventures US)
Somerville, Lorne—CVC Capital Partners (Europe), Ltd.
Sommerseth, Kjell E.—Kistefos Venture Capital AS
Somol, Mark—NeoCarta Ventures, Inc.
Son, Masayoshi—SOFTBANK China Venture Capital
Sonalier, Thierry—Montefiore Investment
Sondag, Eric—GTCR Golder Rauner LLC
Sonderlyng, Peter—EVO Holding A/S (AKA: EVO Management A/S)
Song, Alan—SOFTBANK China Venture Capital
Song, Eugene—W Capital Partners
Song, Eunkang—MVP Capital Company, Ltd.
Song, Hyuk Jin—Premier Venture Partners LLC
Song, Injun—IMM Private Equity, Inc.
Song, Jaehwan—Next Venture Investment
Song, Joonyong—Blackstone Group, L.P.
Song, Jungsoon—Tube Investment, Inc.
Song, Ken—Venrock Associates
Song, Ki Han—Shinwon Venture Capital (a.k.a. Shinyon Venture Capital)
Song, Madeline—Siemens Venture Capital GmbH
Song, Michael—Rustic Canyon Partners
Song, Ng Kok—GIC Special Investments Pte, Ltd.
Song, Paul—Millennium Ark Investment Co., Ltd.
Song, Sang—Unitas Capital Pte, Ltd.
Soni, Amit—General Atlantic LLC
Soni, Robert—Matrix Partners
Soni, Suresh—Global Technology Investment (GTI)
Sonshine, Daniel—TorQuest Partners, Inc.
Sonsini, Peter—New Enterprise Associates, Inc.
Sonstegard, Jeannie—Varde Partners, Inc.
Sontag, Frederick—Spring Bay Companies, The (AKA: Spring Bay Ventures)
Soo Boon, Koh—iGlobe Treasury Management, Ltd.
Soo, Yar-Ping—Adams Street Partners LLC
Sooch, Mina—Apjohn Ventures, LLC
Soong, Jacky—Pacific Alliance Capital Group
Soong, Tai-Sen—CDIB BioScience Venture Management
Soontornwat, Sumalee—Thai Strategic Capital Management Co., Ltd.
Sopp, David—Kamylon Capital LLC
Soref, Ezer—Giza Venture Capital (FKA: Giza Investment Management)
Sorensen, E. Per—Vistech Corp.
Sorensen, Joshua—Leeds Equity Partners
Sorenson, Luke—Sorenson Capital Partners
Sorrel, Lawrence—Tailwind Capital Partners
Sorrel, Lawrence—Thomas Weisel Partners Group, Inc.
Sorrells, Christopher—Natural Gas Partners (NGP)
Sorriqueta, Javier Herrero—MCH Private Equity SA
Sorsdahl, Dag—Borea AS
Sorum, Rune—TeleVenture Management AS (FKA: Telenor Venture AS)
Sorzon, Eli—Xenia Venture Capital
Sosa, Bertrand—MPower Ventures, L.P.
Soskin, Lance—Hargan Ventures, Inc.
Sotirhos, Michael—Atlantic-Pacific Capital, Inc.
Soto, Manuel—Mercapital Servicios Financieros
Soto, Rita—Crossbow Ventures
Soto, Tom—Craton Equity Partners
Sotoloff, Peter—Blackstone Group, L.P.
Sotomayor, Raul—Southern Cross Group (AKA: SCG)
Souaid, Karim—GrowthGate Capital Corporation
Soudry, Dan—IK Investment Partners, Ltd.
Soule, Edgar—Audax Group
Soule, Erin—American Capital, Ltd.
Souleles, Thomas—Madison Dearborn Partners LLC
Soulignac, Charles—Fondinvest Capital (Grp. Caisse de Depots)
Sourthez, Philippe—UFG Private Equity SAS
Southern, James—Pacific Lake Partners
Southwell, Paul—AAC Capital Partners
Souto, Flavio Silva—Latin America Equity Partners (FKA: LAEP)
Souza, Marcio—BPEP International
Sovik, Atle—Verdane Capital (FKA: Four Seasons Venture Capital AS)
Sowelem, Mostafa—Citadel Capital S.A.E.
Sowerby, Mark—Blue Sky Private Equity
Sowul, Christian—Vista Equity Partners
Soyoye, Babatunde—Helios Investment Partners LLP
Spaeth, Jason—Varde Partners, Inc.
Spaght, Peary—Fletcher Spaght Associates
Spahn, Stephen—Quad Ventures
Spaht, P. Holden—Thoma Cressey Bravo
Spain, Kevin—Emergence Capital Partners LLC
Spalding, Richard—Kearny Venture Partners
Spalding, Richard—Thomas Weisel Partners Group, Inc.
Spalter, Jonathan—Pantheon Ventures, Ltd.
Spangberg, Per—Biolin Medical AB
Spangler, Mark—Spangler Ventures, LLC
Spark, Frances—MVC Capital (FKA: meVC)
Sparrow, Richard—Scottish Equity Partners
Spasov, Peter—Marlin Equity Partners, LLC
Spass, Robert—Capital Z Investment Partners (FKA: Union Square Partners)
Spatscheck, Reinhilde—SHS Gesellschaft fuer Beteiligungsmanagement mbH
Spell, William—Spell Capital Partners LLC
Spence, Adam—American Capital, Ltd.
Spence, Michael—Oak Hill Venture Partners (OHVP)
Spence, Stuart—Ariya Capital Group, Ltd.
Spencer, Bradley—Black Canyon Capital
Spencer, David—Emerald Hill Capital Partners, Ltd.
Spencer, David—Texas Intrepid Ventures
Spencer, Donald—Siguler Guff & Company
Spencer, Edson—Affinity Capital Management
Spencer, James—Morgan Creek Capital Management LLC
Spencer, Jeb—TVC Capital, LLC (FKA: TVC Ventures LLC)
Spencer, Richard—Kamylon Capital LLC
Spencer, Tim—Archer Capital
Spencer, Timothy—Thompson Street Capital Partners
Spender, Geoff—General Enterprise Management Services Ltd (AKA: GEMS)
Spens, Jacob—GCP Capital Partners

Steffek, Cory—Altira Group LLC

Steffelin, Edward—GSC Partners (FKA: Greenwich Street Capital Partners)

Steffens, Jorge—DML Invista

Steg, Jean-Michel—Blackstone Group, L.P.

Stegaras, Peter—Paron Ventures AB

Stegimen, Greg—Forstmann Little & Company

Steil, Justin—Evercore Partners

Stein, Avy—Willis Stein & Partners

Stein, Bruce—Shamrock Holdings, Inc.

Stein, Elliot—Commonwealth Capital Partners LP

Stein, Jeffrey—Sofinnova Ventures

Stein, Jonathan—Cortec Group, Inc.

Stein, Josh—Draper Fisher Jurvetson

Stein, Peter—Hunt Capital Group

Stein, Peter—Trinity Hunt Partners

Stein, Robert—Argantis GmbH

Stein, William—Blackstone Group, L.P.

Steinarsson, Skarphedinn—Baugur-ID

Steinbacher, Uwe—Brockhaus Private Equity GmbH

Steinberg, Howard—RBC Capital Partners/RBC Technology Ventures

Steinberg, Matthias—Summit Partners

Steiner, Cindy—EuroUs Ventures

Steiner, Donald—Webster Capital Management, L.L.C.

Steiner, Eugen—Odlander, Fredrikson & Co. AB (AKA: HealthCap)

Steiner, Michael—Medicis AG

Steiner, Perry—Arlington Capital Partners

Steinglass, David—American Capital, Ltd.

Steinman, Richard—GCP Capital Partners

Steinmann, Andreas—Frankfurt CapitalPartners AG (AKA: FCP)

Steinmann, Martin—Vesbridge Partners, LLC

Steinmetz, Michael—Clarus Ventures

Steinmetz, William—BlueStar Ventures L.P.

Steinour, Stephen—CrossHarbor Capital Partners LLC

Stel, Alfred—NoorderHuys Participaties BV

Stellakis, Pavlos—NBGI Private Equity

Stelzer, Norbert—Ingenium Capital GmbH & Co KG

Stemberg, Thomas—Highland Capital Partners LLC

Stemler, M. Todd—Caltius Mezzanine

Stenbaek, Claus—Keyhaven Capital Partners, Ltd.

Stenberg, Olle—Chalmers Innovation

Stencel, Daniel—Pegasus Capital Advisors, L.P.

Stento, Gregory—HarbourVest Partners LLC

Stenzler, Ehren B.—Continuum Group, Ltd. (AKA: Continuum Advisory, Ltd.)

Stephansen, Patrick—Glastad Invest AS

Stephens, Anita—Opportunity Capital Partners

Stephens, John—EMAlternatives LLC

Stephens, John—Vestar Capital Partners, Inc.

Stephens, Warren—Stephens Group, Inc.

Stephenson, Andrea—Adams Capital Management, Inc.

Stephenson, Thomas—Murphree Venture Partners

Stephenson, Thomas—Sequoia Capital

Stephenson, Thomas—Verge

Sterling, Howard—Sands Brothers & Co., Ltd.

Sterling, O. James—Aleutian Capital Partners LLC

Stern, Adam—American Capital, Ltd.

Stern, Daniel H.—Reservoir Capital Group

Stern, David—Clearstone Venture Partners

Stern, Jeffrey—Forum Capital Partners

Stern, Marc—TCW Capital

Stern, Paul—Arlington Capital Partners

Stern, Paul—Golub Capital

Stern, Roger—Coronis Medical Ventures

Stern, Ron—Shamrock Holdings, Inc.

Sternberg, Menachem—Eagle Trading Systems, Inc.

Sternberg, Nick—Creo Capital Partners, LLC

Sterne, Richard—Lightyear Capital LLC

Sterner, Hakan—Holdingbolaget vid Goteborgs universitet AB

Sternheimer, Philip—Hellman & Friedman LLC

Stetson, Charles—Private Equity Investors, Inc.

Steuart, John—Claremont Creek Ventures

Steuerman, Andrew—Golub Capital

Stevenin, Frederic—PAI Partners (FKA: PAI Management)

Stevens, Bruce—GrowthPath Capital, LLC (FKA: Tangram Partners, Inc.)

Stevens, Brynne—Coburn Ventures, LLC

Stevens, Dominic—Challenger International Ltd.

Stevens, James—MSD Capital L.P.

Stevens, Kelly—Cabot Properties, Inc.

Stevens, Kenneth—Leopard Capital, Ltd.

Stevens, Mark—Cabot Properties, Inc.

Stevens, Scott—Pamlico Capital

Stevens, Todd—EPIC Ventures

Stevens, William—Birch Hill Equity Partners Management, Inc.

Stevenson, Andrew—E-Synergy

Stevenson, Gary—MB Venture Partners, LLC

Stevenson, James—ABS Capital Partners

Stevenson, Jeffrey—Veronis Suhler Stevenson (FKA: Veronis, Suhler & Associates)

Stevenson, Larry—Callisto Capital

Stevenson, Sharon—Okapi Venture Capital LLC

Stewart, Diana—American Capital, Ltd.

Stewart, Donald—Spire Capital

Stewart, Edward Jack—Venture Capital Fund of New England, The

Stewart, Guthrie—EdgeStone Capital Partners, Inc.

Stewart, Hugh—Shackleton Ventures, Ltd.

Stewart, John—McLean Watson Capital Inc.

Stewart, Lucinda—OVP Venture Partners

Stewart, Michael—Carlyle Group, The

Stewart, Quentin—Terra Firma Capital Partners, Ltd.

Stewart, Robert—Spring Capital Partners (FKA: Spring Capital Investors LLC)

Stewart, Steve—Unitas Capital Pte. Ltd.

Stewart, Victoria—Abingworth Management, Ltd.

Stewart, William—CSV Capital Partners (FKA: China Seed Ventures)

Stewart, William—Nassau Capital LLC

Stewart, William—Sand Hill Capital

Steyer, Thomas—Hellman & Friedman LLC

Steyn, Howard—Catterton Partners

Stiassny, Kurt—Buy-Out Central Europe

Stickells, Stephen—Boston Millennia Partners

Stiefler, Jeffrey—Emergence Capital Partners LLC

Stienes, David—LLR Partners, Inc.

Stienstra, H.N.F.—Mercurius Beleggingsmaatschappij B.V.

Still, George—Norwest Venture Partners

Stillman, Jon—High Peaks Venture Partners, LLC

Stillman, Lawrence—First New England Capital, L.P.

Stillstrom, Bengt—AB Traction

Stilman, Randy—Hamilton Lane Advisors, Inc.

Stimson, Keith—Gryphon Investors, Inc.

Stinton, Dale—Second Century Ventures LLC

Stirling, Alex—Carlyle Group, The

Stitt, David—Banyan Capital Partners

Stjernfeldt, Carl—Castile Ventures

Stjernholm, Helena—IK Investment Partners, Ltd.

Stobo, John—ABS Capital Partners

Stocchetti, John—Ritchie Capital

Stock, Simon—Lion Capital Advisers Ltd (FKA: Lion Capital Partners Plc)

Stockner, Werner—S-Partner Kapital AG

Stockton, John—Mayfield Fund

Stoddard, Thomas—Blackstone Group, L.P.

Stoddart, James—Undisclosed Firm

Stoeckle, Greg—Invesco Private Capital

Stoesser, Nils—Candover Investments PLC

Stoffman, Assif—Ofer Hi-Tech

Stolar, Frederic—Sagard SAS

Stolberg, E. Theodore—Stolberg Equity Partners LLC

Stoleson, Mark—Legatum Capital

Stoll, Peter—Blackstone Group, L.P.

Stolle, Bryan—Mohr Davidow Ventures

Stoller, Christian—Invision Private Equity AG

Stolper, Charles—Watermill Group, The

Stone, Brent—ABRY Partners LLC

Stone, Christopher—EPIC Ventures

Stone, James—Imperial Capital, LLC

Stone, Jared—Northgate Capital Group

Stone, Lorra—IDG Ventures SF

Stone, Mark—Gores Group LLC, The

Stone, Paul—5AM Ventures

Stone, Richard—Sunrise Financial Group, Inc.

Stone, Sheldon—Oaktree Capital Management LLC

Stoneberg, David—NB Alternatives - Fund of Funds

Stoneburn, Michelle—Quadrangle Group LLC

Stonehouse, Frederick—Unicorn Investment Bank B.S.C.

Stoner, Elizabeth—MPM Capital (FKA: MPM Asset Management LLC)

Stoner, Tom—Econergy International Corporation

Storebaug, Roar—Pantheon Ventures, Ltd.

Storey, Mark—Alcuin Capital

Stork, Carl—Wyndcrest Holdings, LLC

Story, John—Catalyst Investment Managers Pty. Ltd.

Stott, David—Wind Point Partners

Stott, Peter—GCP Capital Partners

Stott, Tony—Midven, Ltd. (AKA: Midlands Venture Fund Managers, Ltd.)

Stout, C. Morris—Swander Pace Capital

Stowe, Kathleen—SV Investment Partners (FKA: Schroder Ventures US)

Stowe, Richard—Health Enterprise Partners (AKA: HEP Fund)

Stradtner, James—Century Capital Management, Inc.

Straface, Nancy—Bessemer Venture Partners

Strafehl, Richard—Meridius Capital

Strahan, Randy—Mohr Davidow Ventures

Strain, Christian—Summit Partners

Strain, Hilary—Alta Partners

Strait, Richard—Northwestern Mutual Capital

Strand Nielsen, Frode—FSN Capital Partners AS

Strandberg, Goran—Novestra AB

Strandberg, Goran—Verdane Capital (FKA: Four Seasons Venture Capital AS)

Strandberg, Steven—WestBridge Ventures LLC
Strasberg, Jeffrey—Ridgewood Capital Management, LLC
Straser, Erik—Mohr Davidow Ventures
Strashna, Oksana—Horizon Capital
Strassberg, Matthew—Mid Europa Partners
Strasser, Martin—AEA Investors LP
Strasser, Scott—GB Merchant Partners, LLC (FKA: GB Palladin Capital LLC)
Strather, Herbert—Park High Apartments
Stratonova, Maria—MTM Capital Partners
Stratton, Oliver—Candover Investments PLC
Stratton, Ryan—Huntsman Gay Global Capital LLC
Straub, Paul—Claremont Creek Ventures
Straume, Rolf—Norvestor Equity AS (FKA: Norsk Vekst Forvaltning AS)
Strauss, Robert—Insight Equity Holdings LLC
Strawbridge, James—Worldview Technology Partners
Stray, Bjorn—Northzone Ventures AS (FKA: Venture Partners AS)
Streator, James—Thomas Weisel Partners Group, Inc.
Street, Kevin—Darwin Private Equity LLP
Stretch, Aidan—Broadmark Capital Corp.
Strid, Carina—Ratos AB
Strife, Jason—Bison Capital Asset Management LLC
Strisofsky, Pamela—TL Ventures
Strobeck, Mark—S.R. One, Ltd.
Strobel, Marc—CVC Capital Partners (Europe), Ltd.
Stroeer, Dirk—Media Ventures GmbH
Strohband, Sven—Mohr Davidow Ventures
Strohm, David—Greylock Partners
Strohmayer, Johannes—Euro Capital Partners
Strohmayr, Leopold—Invest Unternehmensbeteiligungs AG
Strohmenger, Rainer—Wellington Partners Venture Capital GmbH
Strom, Anders—Rite Internet Ventures AB
Strom, Bernee D.—NextPoint Partners, L.P.
Strom, John—Haddington Ventures, LLC
Stromberg, Daniel—GESD Capital Partners, LLC
Stromholm, Fredrik—Altor Equity Partners AB
Strong, Frank—Trillium Group LLC
Strothman, Peter—Water Street Healthcare Partners
Stroud, Eric—Hoak & Co.
Strouse, Mimi—Warburg Pincus LLC
Strum, Derek—Clayton, Dubilier & Rice, Inc.
Strumingher, Neil—Integral Capital Partners
Strumskis, Arvydas—Scandinavian Baltic Development, Ltd.
Strutz, Wolfgang—MBMV Mecklenburg-Vorpommern mbH
Stuart, Michael—Stephens Group, Inc.
Stuart, William—Portal Capital LLC
Stubblefield, Richard—Lighthouse Capital Partners
Stubitz, Steven—American Capital, Ltd.
Stubler, Michael—Draper Triangle Ventures
Stuchberry, Richard—First Associates Investments, Inc.
Stuck, Bart—Signal Lake
Stuckey, Robert—Carlyle Group, The
Studdard, John—Linsalata Capital Partners
Student, James—Presidio Investors LLC
Studzinski, John—Blackstone Group, L.P.
Stuecheli, Gregory—Highland Capital Management, L.P.
Stulberger, Adam—Tailwind Capital Partners
Stulberger, Adam—Thomas Weisel Partners Group, Inc.
Stull, Andrew—Houlihan, Lokey, Howard & Zukin
Stull, Steven—Advantage Capital Partners
Stump, Jeffrey—Andreessen Horowitz
Stumpel, Bob—Result Venture Knowledge International
Stumpf, Anton—RECAP Management GmbH
Stuntz, Mayo—Pilot Group LLC
Sturgill, Jerry—Headwaters Merchant Bank
Sturgis, Fred—H.I.G. Capital LLC
Sturiale, Nick—JAFCO Ventures
Sturiale, Nick—Sevin Rosen Funds
Su, David—Matrix Partners
Su, Weichou—Hina Capital Partners
Suarez, Joaquin—Nmas1 Private Equity (FKA: Nmas1 Electra Capital Privado)
Suarez, Jose—Investor Growth Capital AB
Suarez, Jose—Investor Growth Capital, Inc.
Sube, Fadwa—Seventure Partners SA (FKA: SPEF Venture)
Subhedar, Sanjay—Storm Ventures LLC
Subramani, Ramesh—New Leaf Venture Partners LLC
Subramaniam, Guhan—IL&FS Investment Managers Ltd (FKA: IL&FS Venture Corp)
Subramaniam, Rajesh—Walden International
Subramaniam, Somu—New Science Ventures, LLC
Subramanian, Biswajit—Providence Equity Partners LLC
Subramanian, K. Ganapathy—JumpStartUp Fund Advisors Pvt. Ltd.
Subramanian, N—BPEP International
Subramanian, Vivek—Avigo Capital Partners
Subramanya, S.N.—Hexagram Investment Advisors Pvt, Ltd.
Subramanya, S.V.—Bessemer Venture Partners
Subramanya, SN—Aquarius Investment Advisors Pte., Ltd.
Such, Craig—Lake Street Capital LLC
Sud, Atul—Strategic Capital Corporation
Sudduth, Drew—Growth Capital Partners, L.P.
Sudhakar, Shilpa—Caspian Advisors Pvt. Ltd.
Suel, Patrick—Panasonic Ventures
Sufrin, Zachary—Atlas Holdings FRM LLC
Sugarman, Mark—MHS Capital Management, LLC
Sugaya, Tsunesaburo—JAFCO Ventures
Sugden, Christopher—Edison Venture Fund
Sugimoto, Nick—Honda Strategic Venturing (HSV)
Sugimoto, Tomoya—Longreach Group, Ltd., The
Sugita, Shigeki—New Business Investment Co., Ltd.
Suh, Alexander—California Technology Ventures LLC
Suh, Alexander—Jacobs Capital Group, LLC
Suh, Bum Seok—Benex Investment, Inc.
Suh, Don—Skylake Incuvest & Company
Suh, Eugene—J.P. Morgan Partners (FKA: Chase Capital Partners)
Suh, Haksoo—Daesung Private Equity, Inc.
Suhler, John—Veronis Suhler Stevenson (FKA: Veronis, Suhler & Associates)
Suhrcke, Pierre—DN Capital, Ltd. (FKA: Digital Networks Global Ventures)
Suit, Dickson—Ironwood Capital (AKA: Ironwood Capital Advisors LLC)
Sujan, Suvir—Nexus Venture Partners
Sujoy, Nicolas—Advent International
Sulaski, David C.—Brown Gibbons Lang & Company LLC
Sulger, Justin—AnaCap Financial Partners LLP
Suliman, Fawzia—First South Investment Managers
Sullens, Stephens—Blackstone Group, L.P.
Sullivan, Ben—Lazard Capital Partners
Sullivan, Bill—Apax Partners Worldwide
Sullivan, Brian—Paul Capital Partners
Sullivan, Chris—Blackstone Group, L.P.
Sullivan, Christopher—MVC Capital (FKA: meVC)
Sullivan, Graham—American Industrial Partners
Sullivan, Greg—Chrysalix Energy
Sullivan, Gregory—Friend Skoler & Co., L.L.C.
Sullivan, Jeanne—StarVest Partners, L.P.
Sullivan, Jerry—Adams Capital Management, Inc.
Sullivan, John—CapGen Financial Group
Sullivan, John—Foundation Medical Partners
Sullivan, Kevin—Riverside Partners
Sullivan, Kevin—Thompson Street Capital Partners
Sullivan, Lara—Paul Capital Partners
Sullivan, Matthew—Peachtree Equity Partners
Sullivan, Michael—Forest Hill Partners LLC
Sullivan, Patrick—Manoa Venture Partners
Sullivan, Peter—Lombard Investments, Inc.
Sullivan, Sean—Aetos Capital LLC
Sullivan, Sean—Brown Gibbons Lang & Company LLC
Sullivan, Stephen—Skyline Ventures
Sullivan, Timothy—Madison Dearborn Partners LLC
Sully, Jesse—Greenstone Partners Private Capital Pty, Ltd.
Sultan, Fabien—AtriA Capital Partenaires
Sum, Charles—Redleaf Group, Inc
Sumers, Gary—Blackstone Group, L.P.
Sumitani, Taro—Vestar Capital Partners, Inc.
Summer, Gordon—firstVentury GmbH
Summerhayes, Mark—RMB Capital Partners, Ltd.
Summerscale, Zak—Babson Capital Europe
Sumner, John—CRG Partners
Sumner, Martin—Carlyle Group, The
Sun, Anthony—Aisling Capital
Sun, Daniel—Hina Capital Partners
Sun, Dayi—Jade Alternative Investment Advisors
Sun, Henry—Pacific Enterprise Capital, LLC
Sun, Hongwei—Richlink International Capital Co., Ltd.
Sun, Kang—WI Harper Group
Sun, Nelson—Valor Equity Partners
Sun, Qiang Chang—Warburg Pincus LLC
Sun, Ray—Applied Ventures, LLC
Sun, Shih-Wei—UMC Capital
Sun, Wenhai—GGV Capital
Sun, Yi—Horsley Bridge Partners
Sundar, S.G. Shyam—IDFC Private Equity
Sundberg, Asa—Provider Venture Partners AB (FKA: IT Provider Advisor 1 AB)
Sundby, Christian—Huvudkontoret i Kristinehamn AB
Sunderji, Amand—Adveq Management AG
Sundlun, Stuart—Global Emerging Markets
Sundstrom, Mirja—MB Funds (AKA: MB Rahastot Oy)
Sundstrom, Vilhelm—Axcel Industriinvestor AS
Sung, David—H.I.G. Capital LLC

Sung, Ki Hong—Korea Venture Investment Corporation
Sung, Woonki—Darby Overseas Investments, Ltd.
Sunouchi, Shinji—Vestar Capital Partners, Inc.
Suri, Monish—Prime Technology Ventures NV
Surma, Karl E.—"schilling" Unternehmensbeteiligung GmbH
Sury, Sharath—Valence Capital Management, LP
Susanto, Hendrik—Global Technology Investment (GTI)
Susi, Andres—Martinson Trigon Venture Partners AS
Suslak, Neil—Braemar Energy Ventures
Sussane, Kure—Vaekstfonden (AKA: Danish Growth Fund, The)
Sussman, Philip—Channel Group LLC, The (TCG)
Sussner, Heiner—Miramar Venture Partners
Suster, Mark—GRP Partners
Sutherland, Jason—Brazos Private Equity Partners LLC
Sutherland, Nikola—Duke Street Capital
Sutherland, Nikola—Park Square Capital, LLP
Sutka, J. Michael—Lazard Capital Partners
Sutter, Martin—Essex Woodlands Health Ventures
Sutter, William—Hopewell Ventures
Suttin, Adam—J.W. Childs Associates
Sutton, Dana—Plymouth Venture Partners
Sutton, Matthew—Lionheart Ventures
Sutton, Ralph—Thomas Weisel Partners Group, Inc.
Suurmunne, Vesa—Nordic Mezzanine Advisers Ltd
Suutarinen, Matti—Sponsor Capital Oy
Suykens, Jan—Sofinim NV
Suzuki, David—Worldview Technology Partners
Suzuki, Ryota—Japan Industrial Partners, Inc.
Suzuki, Takao—Yasuda Enterprise Development Co., Ltd.(FKA: Nippon Ent.Dev)
Svalstedt, Martin—Stena Adactum AB
Svardstrom, Jakob—KTH-Chalmers Capital KB
Svennilson, Peter—Column Group, The
Svensson, Jan—Investment AB Latour
Svoboda, John—Svoboda Capital Partners (FKA: Svoboda, Collins LLC)
Svrluga, Bradley—Berkshires Capital Investors
Svrluga, Bradley—High Peaks Venture Partners, LLC
Swai, Richard—Southern Africa Enterprise Development Fund, The (SAEDF)
Swain, Robert—Investment Fund for Foundations
Swaminathan, Guhan—Virgo Capital
Swan, Kevin—Water Street Healthcare Partners
Swani, Sanjay—Welsh, Carson, Anderson & Stowe
Swanson, David—Compass Group International LLC, The
Swanson, David—GE Antares Capital Corporation
Swanson, Mark—Lane Five Ventures LLC (FKA: Swan Holdings LLC)
Swanson, Paul—Legend Partners, The
Swartling, Karl—Investor Growth Capital, Inc.
Swartwood, Thayer—ABS Ventures
Swartz, Eric—Roswell Capital Partners, LLC
Swartz, James—Accel Partners
Swartzman, Steven—C3 Capital LLC
Sweemer, Jonathan—Nassau Capital LLC
Sweeney, Chris—Water Street Healthcare Partners
Sweeney, Joan—Allied Capital Corporation
Sweeney, Michael—Goldner Hawn Johnson & Morrison, Inc.
Sweeney, Michael—InterWest Partners
Sweeney, Ryan—Accel Partners
Sweeney, Susan—Ironwood Capital (AKA: Ironwood Capital Advisors LLC)
Sweeney, Thecla—Birch Hill Equity Partners Management, Inc.
Sweeney, Tom—Garage Technology Ventures Canada
Sweet, Andrew—Rhone Capital LLC
Sweet, David—Sutter Hill Ventures
Sweet, Scott—Lombard Investments, Inc.
Sweet, Tony—Derwent London PLC
Sweet-Escott, Tom—Exponent Private Equity LLP (FKA: Square Capital Management)
Sweetser, Adrienne—General Catalyst Partners (FKA: General Catalyst Group LLC)
Swenson, David—SSM Partners
Swenson, Ingrid—Bertram Capital
Swenson, Jeff—Thomas H. Lee Partners (AKA: TH Lee Partners)
Swift, Jane—Arcadia Management, LLC (AKA: Arcadia Partners)
Swildens, Hans—Industry Ventures
Swimmer, Erik—Sun Capital Partners, Inc.
Swimmer, Ted—Fidus Capital
Swirski, George—Abris Capital Partners
Switzer, Scott—FirstMark Capital LLC
Sy, Alice—Small Business Guarantee and Finance Corporation
Syder, Tim—Acuity Capital LLP (FKA: Electra Partners LLP)
Sydow, Jason—QuestMark Partners, L.P.
Sykes, Toby—Essex Woodlands Health Ventures
Sykes, Trey—Inverness Graham Investments
Sylven, Claes-Goran—Hakon Invest AB (FKA: ICA Forbundet Invest)
Sylvia, John—Aqua International Partners, LP
Symon, Warren—Newbury Partners LLC
Symondson, David—Acuity Capital LLP (FKA: Electra Partners LLP)
Syrrist, Dag—Vision Capital Management
Sywolski, Robert—JMI Equity
Szajda, Marcin—Brooke Private Equity Associates
Szczepanski, Przemek—Syntaxis Capital
Szczurek, Thomas—American Capital, Ltd.
Sze, David—Greylock Partners
Sze, Jerry—Sycamore Ventures Pte, Ltd.
Szerenyi, Laszlo—Genesis Campus, L.P.
Szeto, Michael—W.R. Hambrecht & Co., LLC
Szigethy, Andrea—Morgan Creek Capital Management LLC
Szigeti, Mihaly—Crosslink Capital
Szlavik, Peter—Eagle Ventures
Szlezinger, Leon—Jefferies Group, Inc.
Szoke, Istvan—Advent International
Szoke, Istvan—CVC Capital Partners (Europe), Ltd.
Szonyi, Andrew—First Nations Equity, Inc.
Szwaikowski, Michael—CapitalSource Holdings, Inc.
Ta, Lynn—DragonTech Ventures Management, Ltd.
Ta-Ngoc, Luc—Invus Group Ltd., The
Tabacinic, Moris—NCH Capital, Inc.
Tabbara, Marwan—Stratum W.L.L.
Taber, Clark—Capital International Research, Inc.
Taber, Gregory—Linsalata Capital Partners
Taber, Mark—Great Hill Equity Partners LLC
Tabet, Karim—Providence Equity Partners LLC
Tabladini, Marco—Impresa e Finanza SGR
Tabors, David—Battery Ventures, L.P.
Tada, Mitsunaga—Ridgeway Capital Partners, Ltd. (FKA:OPE Partners Ltd.)
Tadikonda, Madhu—Accretive LLC (FKA: Accretive Technology Partners LLC)
Tadler, Richard—TA Associates, Inc.
Tadler, Steven—Advent International
Taetle, Alan—Noro-Moseley Partners
Taft, Peter—Morgenthaler Ventures
Tagaya, Osamu—Angel Capital Network
Tagliaferri, Mark—Global Innovation Partners LLC
Tagt, Anders—Doughty Hanson & Co., Ltd.
Tahan, David—York Street Capital Partners LLC
Tai, Augustus—Trinity Ventures
Tai, Janet C.C.—AsiaVest Partners, TCW/YFY Ltd. (FKA: TCW/YFY Investment)
Tai, Kenneth—InveStar Capital, Inc.
Tai, William—Charles River Ventures
Taiber, Werner—WestLB AG Equity Investments (AKA: Westdeutsche Landesbank)
Taillieu, Denis—Canterbury Park Capital
Tainiter, Andrew—Global Innovation Partners LLC
Takacs, Peter—Austria Wirtschaftsservice Gesellschaft mbH
Takagi, Akihiro—IGNITE Group, The (AKA: Ignite Associates, LLC)
Takagi, Akira—Valiant Partners Co. Ltd.
Takahashi, Akio—Daiwa Securities SMBC Principal Investments Co., Ltd.
Takahashi, Daisuke—Pacific Rim Ventures Company, Ltd.
Takahashi, Hirohide—Resona Capital Co., Ltd.
Takahashi, Shinya—Arise Capital Partners, Inc.
Takamori, Kotaro—ORIX Asia Limited
Takano, Naoto—Mizuho Capital Company, Ltd.
Takashi, Yoshida—Okasan Venture Capital Co., Ltd.
Takashima, Fumito—JAFCO Investment [FKA: Nomura/JAFCO Investment (Asia), Ltd.]
Takashima, Tatsuyoshi—Dentsu.com, Inc.
Takashina, Tadashi—Ant Capital Partners Co., Ltd.
Takatsuki, Daisuke—Carlyle Group, The
Takeda, Goro—Sofinnova Ventures
Takei, Hiroyasu—Oak Capital Corporation
Takei, Yuji—Advantage Partners LLP
Takemoto, Naohiro—JBF Partners
Takke, Christina—Forbion Capital Partners
Talarico, Gary—Sun Capital Partners, Inc.
Talbot, Robert—Propulsion Ventures, Inc.
Tall, Spencer—Allegis Capital (AKA: Media Technology Ventures)
Tallarida, Steven—Makaira Venture Partners
Tallering, Kenneth—Industrial Opportunity Partners, LLC
Talmor, Yair—L Capital Partners
Talon, Christophe—Green Recovery
Talone, Joao—Magnum Capital Industrial Partners
Tam, Benson—Fidelity Growth Partners Asia
Tam, John—Accretive LLC (FKA: Accretive Technology Partners LLC)
Tamakoshi, Go—CVC Capital Partners (Europe), Ltd.
Tamashunas, Robert—Seaport Capital, LLC
Tamba, Toshihito—Itochu Corporation
Tambourin, Pierre—Genopole 1er Jour (AKA: G1J)
Tambunting, Jesus—Plantersbank Venture Capital Corporation

Tamer, Tony—H.I.G. Capital LLC
Tamir, Eldad—Tamir Fishman Ventures
Tamm, Rain—GILD Bankers (FKA: LHV Ventures)
Tan, Alvin—American Capital, Ltd.
Tan, Angela—Crest Capital Partners
Tan, Arthur—Narra Venture Capital
Tan, Bien Kiat—Newbridge Capital, Ltd.
Tan, Boon Wah—Sembawang Capital Pte., Ltd.
Tan, Cheng Gay—Juniper Capital Ventures Pte, Ltd.
Tan, Christopher—FTV Capital (FKA: FTVentures)
Tan, Damian—Vickers Venture Partners
Tan, David—Crest Capital Partners
Tan, Edmund—CMIA Capital Partners (AKA: CM Investment Advisers Pte Ltd.)
Tan, Eric—CID Group, The
Tan, Finian—Vickers Venture Partners
Tan, Frankie Siew Teck—iGlobe Partners, Ltd.
Tan, Glendon—Crest Capital Partners
Tan, Jason—Summit Partners
Tan, Joan—DBS Private Equity
Tan, Jui—BlueRun Ventures
Tan, Keng Boon—SEAVI Advent Corporation, Ltd.
Tan, Khai—Advent International
Tan, Khai—Bridgepoint Capital, Ltd.
Tan, Kim Seng—3V SourceOne Capital Pte, Ltd.
Tan, Kim Seng—Tembusu Partners Pte., Ltd.
Tan, Kim Song—Frontier Investment & Development Partners
Tan, Kim—SpringHill Management Sdn Bhd (FKA: Ikatan Menawan Sdn Bhd)
Tan, Kong Cheng—DTA Capital
Tan, Nang Yong—P.T. Pama Ventura Indonesia
Tan, Olivia—Axiom Asia Private Capital
Tan, Peter—SkyVen Asset Management Pte, Ltd.
Tan, Shiong—Blackstone Group, L.P.
Tan, Sunny—BioVeda Capital Private, Ltd.
Tan, Terence—Infotech Pacific Ventures L.P. (FKA: Infotech Ventures Co.)
Tan, Tommy—TC Capital Pte., Ltd.
Tan, Wan That—Aventures Capital Management Pte Ltd.
Tan, Wen—Squadron Capital Advisors, Ltd.
Tan, Wun Qing—Shenzhen OFC Investment Management, Ltd.
Tan, Zhi—Northern Light Venture Capital
Tanaka, Mitsuharu—Daiwa Securities SMBC Principal Investments Co., Ltd.
Tanaka, Susumu—Worldview Technology Partners
Tanamli, Sharif—HT Capital Advisors LLC
Tananbaum, James—Prospect Venture Partners (FKA: Prospect Management LLC)
Tanczos, Peter—Euroventures Capital Kft.
Tandon, Nandini—Lumira Capital Corporation.
Taneja, Hemant—General Catalyst Partners (FKA: General Catalyst Group LLC)
Tanen, Paul—Allied Capital Corporation
Tang, BoBo—Pride Investments Group, Ltd., The
Tang, Chen—Tallwood Venture Capital
Tang, Donald—CITIC Securities International Partners, Ltd.
Tang, Frank—FountainVest Partners (Asia), Ltd.
Tang, Hamilton—Simon Murray and Associates
Tang, Jennifer—Avenue Capital Group
Tang, Jo—AIG Investment Corporation, (Asia) Ltd.
Tang, Kainan—Hina Capital Partners
Tang, Kay Hua—Centurion Investment Management
Tang, Minyi—Pac-Link Management Corporation
Tang, Miranda—CLSA Capital Partners (AKA: Credit Lyonnais Securities Asia)
Tang, Samuel—Montauk TriGuard Management, Inc.
Tangen, Darren—Colony Capital LLC
Tango, Jo—Kepha Partners
Tanguy, Patrick—Wendel
Tani, Ayako—Ant Capital Partners Co., Ltd.
Tani, Muhammad—Exploit Technologies Pte, Ltd.
Tanimoto, Toru—Ant Capital Partners Co., Ltd.
Tankersley, G. Jackson—Meritage Funds
Tanner, Chris—Henderson Equity Partners (AKA: Henderson Private Capital)
Tanner, William—Athenian Venture Partners
Tanner, William—Reservoir Venture Partners
Tanous, Joe—eFund, LLC
Tansey, Casey—U.S. Venture Partners
Tansey, Greg—Riverlake Partners LLC
Tanzi, Stefano—21 Centrale Partners
Tanzi, Stefano—21 Partners SpA
Tao, Feng—NewMargin Ventures
Tao, Jack—Fortune Venture Investment Group (AKA:Fortune Consulting)
Tao, Tao—ChinaVest, Ltd.
Tarabakin, Dmytro—Dragon Capital
Taradash, Kathleen—Northgate Capital Group
Taragin, Bruce—Blumberg Capital Ventures
Taranto, Harri—Symphony Capital LLC
Tardif, Jean Paul—ID Capital
Tardio, Stephen—HT Capital Advisors LLC
Tarini, Mark—ArcLight Capital
Tarjanne, Artturi—Nexit Ventures Oy
Tarlowe, Jeff—Pharma Capital Ventures (AKA: PCV)
Tarr, Bernard—Kinetic Ventures LLC
Tartaglia, Louis—Third Rock Ventures LLC
Tashima, Katsuhiro—Fund Creation Co., Ltd.
Taslitz, Steven—Sterling Partners
Tataroglu, Ahmet—NBK Capital, Ltd.
Tatum, Alexander—Constitution Capital Partners, LLC
Taub, Andrew—Catterton Partners
Tauber, Jan—Genesis Capital, s.r.o.
Taubman, Steven—VCFA Group
Taunt, Nigel—Impax Asset Management
Tauzin, Thomas—BlueCar Partners
Tavel, Olivier—Vinci Capital
Tavridis, Stathis—Incubation For Growth
Tawfik, Raouf—Citadel Capital S.A.E.
Tay, Choon Chong—Vertex Management Pte, Ltd. (AKA: Vertex Venture Holdings)
Tay, KC—Fortune Venture Investment Group (AKA:Fortune Consulting)
Tay, Ronnie—Infocomm Investments Pte., Ltd. (FKA: NCB Holdings Pte Ltd)
Tayeh, David—Investcorp Bank B.S.C.
Taylor, Alan—GB Merchant Partners, LLC (FKA: GB Palladin Capital LLC)
Taylor, Allison—Invico Capital Corporation
Taylor, Barry—Warburg Pincus LLC
Taylor, Brian—Hall Capital Partners LLC (FKA: Offit Hall Capital Mgmt)
Taylor, Bruce—Cortec Group, Inc.
Taylor, Cindy—SCF Partners
Taylor, Craig—Alloy Ventures
Taylor, Gary—Counsel Corporation
Taylor, George—Thomas H. Lee Partners (AKA: TH Lee Partners)
Taylor, Gregory—Blue Chip Venture Company
Taylor, Harry—TA Associates, Inc.
Taylor, Jim—Avrio Ventures Management Corp.
Taylor, Jo—3i Group PLC
Taylor, Joseph—Allied Capital Corporation
Taylor, Keith—Carlyle Group, The
Taylor, Lance—Legacy Venture
Taylor, Lawrence—Pfingsten Partners, L.P.
Taylor, Martin—Vista Equity Partners
Taylor, Matt—Foresight Group
Taylor, Matthew—Lombard Investments, Inc.
Taylor, Meg—Independent Bankers Capital Funds
Taylor, Michael—HarbourVest Partners LLC
Taylor, Mike—Pacific Corporate Group
Taylor, Neil—Bradford Equities Management LLC
Taylor, Peter—Duke Street Capital
Taylor, R. Eugene—North American Financial Holdings, Inc.
Taylor, Robb—Granite Capital Partners
Taylor, Robert—Advent International
Taylor, Robert—Centinela Capital Partners LLC
Taylor, Rowan—Oak Hill Capital Management, Inc.
Taylor, Scott—CPP Investment Board
Taylor, Thomas—Sun Capital Partners, Inc.
Taylor, William—Mountaineer Capital, L.P.
Taylor-Smith, Ralph—Battelle Ventures
Teaford, Jonathan—Wyndcrest Holdings, LLC
Teagle, Scott—Headwaters Merchant Bank
Teague, Teresa—Banc of America Securities LLC
Teasdale, Nick—Advent Venture Partners LLP
Tecce, Frederick—Cross Atlantic Capital Partners
Tedeschi, Theodore—Accretive Exit Capital Partners LLC
Tedesko, Jennifer—Atlantic-Pacific Capital, Inc.
Tedford, Alastair—Albion Investors, LLC (FKA: Albion Alliance, LLC)
Teeger, John—Founders Equity, Inc.
Teele, Brett—Venrock Associates
Teetsel, Wayne—Stonehill Capital Management
Teeven, Jeffrey—Consumer Growth Partners
Tefft, E. Lyndon—Commonfund Capital, Inc. (FKA: Common Fund)
Tegan, Jennifer—Cayuga Venture Fund
Teillon, Geoffrey—Pouschine Cook Capital Management, LLC
Teilman, Andreas—Verdane Capital (FKA: Four Seasons Venture Capital AS)
Teinturier, Cyrille—Butler Capital Partners SA
Teixeira Favaro, Felipe—Performa Investimentos
Teixeira, Pedro Paulo—TMG Capital Partners Ltd.
Teja, Salim—Brightspark Ventures
Tejera, Carlos—Gala Capital Partners (AKA: GCP)
Tek Kuang, Cheah—Malaysian Ventures Management Incorporated Sdn Bhd
Televantos, John—Arsenal Capital Partners
Telidevara, Subba Rao—Actis Capital LLP
Temperton, Ian—Climate Change Capital, Ltd.
Temple, Christopher—Friend Skoler & Co., L.L.C.
Temple, Jeff—P.A.G. Capital Partners
Temple, Stephen—Asia Mezzanine Capital Advisers, Ltd.
Templeton, Ian—Acorn Capital Partners
Templeton, Troy—Trivest Partners, L.P.
Temuru, Lucinda—Stonehenge Capital Company
Ten Cate, Jan—NoorderHuys Participaties BV
TenBroek, James—Wind Point Partners

Tiberini, Antonio—Aravis SA
Tice, William—Blackstone Group, L.P.
Tichenor, Timothy—Barnard Associates, Inc.
Ticknor, Samuel—Corporate Fuel Partners
Tidbury, Hugh—GCP Capital Partners
Tidwell, Brandon—Canopy Group
Tidwell, Ken—Carlyle Group, The
Tidwell, Kevin—Global Environment Fund Management Corporation
Tiefenbacher, Christoph—ARCADIA Beteiligungen Bensel Tiefenbacher & Co GmbH
Tierney, Matthew—Aperture Venture Partners, LLC
Tierney, Paul—Aperture Venture Partners, LLC
Tiers, Pierre—IPO (Institut de Participations de L'Ouest)
Tietmann, Andreas—Intelligent Venture Capital Management GmbH
Tigay, Eytan—Lazard Capital Partners
Tighe, Kenneth—India Venture Partners
Tikautz, Heidemarie—RECAP Management GmbH
Tikker, Blair—KRG Capital Partners LLC
Tilbury, Mike—Graphite Capital (FKA: F&C Ventures, Ltd.)
Tilenius, Eric—Maveron LLC
Tilenius, Eric—Tilenius Investments (FKA: Tilenius Ventures)
Tili, Marco—Gepafin SpA
Till, Michael—Actis Capital LLP
Tilley, Josh—Morgan Creek Capital Management LLC
Tilley, Mike—Challenger International Ltd.
Tillier, Dennis—Sambrinvest S.A.
Tilson, John—Brown Gibbons Lang & Company LLC
Tilton, Lynn—Patriarch Partners LLC
Timashev, Ratmir—ABRT Venture Fund
Timken, Alexander—Global Emerging Markets
Timlin, Joe—GrowthWorks
Timmer, Marcel—LogiSpring Management Company S.a.r.l.
Timmermans, Willem—Magellan Capital Partners, Ltd.
Timmins, Rick—G-51 Capital LLC
Timmis, Gerald—ValStone Partners LLC
Timoll, Garth A.L.—Paul Capital Partners
Timor, Emanuel—Vertex Management Israel (AKA: Vertex Venture Capital)
Timor, Emanuel—Vertex Venture Capital
Timsit, Thierry—Astorg Partners SAS (FKA : Suez Capital Partenaires)
Tinelli, Davide—FONDACO Societa di Gestione Risparmio SpA
Ting, Gary—Cnstar Capital Pte., Ltd
Ting, Lee—W.R. Hambrecht & Co., LLC
Ting, Simon—BOC International Holdings, Ltd.
Tinkelenberg, Arthur—Ascent Biomedical Ventures
Tinker, John—Diamond Point Capital Management
Tinsley, Tom—General Atlantic LLC
Tipper, Gary—Zeus Private Equity
Tipping, Stephen—Condor Capital Management, Inc.
Tippit, Carl—Peppertree Capital Management, Inc.
Tirabassi, Salvatore—M/C Venture Partners
Tirkkonen, Timo—Inventure Oy
Tirrell, Matthew—NGEN Partners LLC (FKA: NextGen Partners LLC)
Tirta, Arip—Hercules Technology Growth Capital, Inc.
Tis, Eric—Gores Group LLC, The
Tisdale, Andrew—Providence Equity Partners LLC
Tison, Francois—360 Capital Management SA (AKA: 360 Capital Partners)
Tison, Francois—Net Partners
Titi, Fani—Tiso Group
Titley, Mitch—Gresham LLP
Titolo, Vincent—EuroUs Ventures
Tittiger, Gottfried—Industrial Growth Partners
Titus, M. David—Windward Ventures
Tiwari, Adrian—Saffar Capital, Ltd.
Tiwari, Amit—Invesco Private Capital
Tjahjono, Bagus—BT Venture Fund Management, LLC
Tjan, Anthony—Cue Ball Group, LLC, The
Tliss-Davie, Alison—Macquarie Shinhan Infrastructure Management Co., Ltd.
To, Kilin—Sycamore Ventures Pte, Ltd.
Toader, Daniela—Axxess Capital Partners S.A. (FKA: Enterprise Capital)
Tobias, Andrea—Brandon Capital Partners
Tobias, Martin—Ignition Partners (FKA: Ignition Corporation)
Tobin, Hannah—HarbourVest Partners LLC
Tobin, Rob—ABS Capital Partners
Tobin, Scott—Battery Ventures, L.P.
Toby, Elias—Dancap Private Equity Inc.
Tochner, Ira—Yucaipa Companies LLC, The
Todd, James—Industrial Opportunity Partners, LLC
Todd, James—Wolseley Private Equity
Todd, John—Maven Capital Management LLC
Todd, Michael—Element Partners
Todd, Robert—Red Rock Ventures
Toennesen, Erik—Skagerak Venture Capital AS
Tofte Hansen, Thomas—Nordic Venture Partners (FKA: Danske Venture Partners)
Toh, Keith—Francisco Partners
Tojner, Michael—Buy-Out Central Europe
Tolbert, Steven—Nogales Investors Management, LLC
Tolk, Jeffrey—3 Degrees Asset Management Pte., Ltd.
Tolkoff, M. Joshua—Ironwood Capital (AKA: Ironwood Capital Advisors LLC)
Tolley, David—Blackstone Group, L.P.
Tolmie, David—Bolder Capital LLC
Tolmie, David—Edgewater Funds, The
Tolvanen, Kari—Sitra
Tom, Kevin—Wedbush Capital Partners
Tom, Shonn—GESD Capital Partners, LLC
Tomai, William—Centre Partners Management LLC
Tomas, Perez—Inverjaen S.C.R. SA
Tomaschu, Andrea—Riello Investimenti SpA
Tomasdottir, Halla—Audur Capital
Tomasi, Adam—Alta Partners
Tombas, Enrique—Suma Capital
Tomei, Joseph—Capital Z Investment Partners (FKA: Union Square Partners)
Tomei, Joseph—Equifin Capital Partners
Tomes, John—Hilco Equity Management, LLC
Tomioka, Takaomi—Carlyle Group, The
Tomkinson, Robert—DFJ Athena
Tomlin, Stephen—Avalon Ventures
Tomlinson, Audrey—New York Business Development Corporation
Tompkins, Ben—Eden Ventures (UK), Ltd.
Tompkins, Craig—Pfingsten Partners, L.P.
Toms, Rob—Smedvig Capital, Ltd. (FKA: Peder Smedvig Capital Ltd)
Tones, Michael—BC Brandenburg Capital GmbH
Tong, Boning—MetLife Investments Asia, Ltd.
Tong, Bryant—Nth Power
Tong, Lucene—CSV Capital Partners (FKA: China Seed Ventures)
Tong, Richard—Ignition Capital
Tong, Richard—Ignition Partners (FKA: Ignition Corporation)
Tong, Richard—Qiming Venture Partners
Tong, Sean—Providence Equity Partners LLC
Tonn, Jens—Vestar Capital Partners, Inc.
Tonnesen, Lars—LD Invest A/S
Tonooka, Shinichiro—DoCoMo Capital
Tonsgaard, Amanda—Langholm Capital LLP
Tonussi, Domenico—Finint & Partners SpA
Toolan, Brian—Crystal Ridge Partners, LLC
Toomey, John—HarbourVest Partners LLC
Toon, Paul—Generis Capital Partners
Toon, Paul—Innoven Partenaires S.A.
Toone, Curtis—Sorenson Capital Partners
Toor, Yasser—TSG Consumer Partners
Tooth, Mathew—Blackstone Group, L.P.
Topfer, Alan—Castletop Capital
Topfer, Morton—Castletop Capital
Topfer, Peter—S-Siegerlandfonds 1 GmbH & Co.
Topfer, Richard—Castletop Capital
Topham, David—Huntsman Gay Global Capital LLC
Toporek, Michael—Brookstone Partners
Topper, James—Frazier Healthcare and Technology Ventures
Tor, Teo Ek—PrimePartners Asset Management Pte, Ltd.
Tordjman, Rafaele—Sofinnova Partners
Toren, Gadi—Partech International
Torgerson, Erik—Norwest Equity Partners
Tornquist, Peter—CVC Capital Partners (Europe), Ltd.
Toro, Christian—American Capital, Ltd.
Torre de Silva, Jose Antonio—CVC Capital Partners (Europe), Ltd.
Torres, Juan—Advent International
Torres, S. Edward—Lilly Ventures (FKA: e.Lilly Ventures)
Torsater, Bertil—Start Invest AB
Torsen, Hans Olav—ProVenture AS
Torti, Frank—New Enterprise Associates, Inc.
Tortorelli, Tony—Apollo Management
Toscani, Luca—Avant Capital Group, Inc.
Toseroni, Marco—Alcedo SGR SpA
Totah, Raymond—Argos Soditic SA
Totah, Sami—Viola Private Equity
Toth, Donna—Atlantic-Pacific Capital, Inc.
Toth, Johann—EK Mittelstandsfinanzierungs AG
Toth, Louis—Comcast Interactive Capital
Totia, Sever—Edison Venture Fund
Tottrup, Peter—SEED Capital Denmark K/S
Totty, Matthew—Redwood Capital, Inc.
Toubia, Adil—GCC Energy Fund, The
Touborg, Margaret—Design Investors LLC
Toulouse, Christian—SEEFT Management SAS
Toups, W. Anthony—Advantage Capital Partners
Touvelle, Steven—Northcreek Mezzanine
Tower, Frank—Gold Hill Capital Management LLC

Tyapin, Alexander—Baring Vostok Capital Partners
Tybur, Jim—Trinity Ventures
Tydeman, Natalie—GMT Communications Partners LLP
Tye, Steve—C&B Capital
Tyler, Aaron—Lighthouse Capital Partners
Tyree, James—Mesirow Private Equity Investments, Inc.
Tyrell, Jack—Richland Ventures
Tyrrell, Gary—Woodside Fund
Tyrrell, Michael—Venrock Associates
Tyrrell, Thomas—Glengary LLC
Tysdal, Tyler—Brand Journey Capital LP
Tysoe, Ronald—Legend Partners, The
Tzeng, John—Harbinger Venture Management
Tzeng, Joseph—Crystal Internet Venture Fund, L.P.
U Prichard, David—Red Abbey Venture Partners, LLC
Uberla, Jorg—ETF Manager LLP
Uchida, Kenji—SunBridge Partners
Uchikata, Junitsu—JAFCO Investment [FKA: Nomura/JAFCO Investment (Asia), Ltd.]
Uchiyama, Akiyoshi—Asia Private Equity Capital (FKA: MediBIC Alliance)
Udall, Paul—Climate Change Capital, Ltd.
Udhas, Pradeep—Greater Pacific Capital LLP
Ueda, Kenichi—Ant Capital Partners Co., Ltd.
Ueda, Kenzi—Iwakaze Capital, Inc.
Ueda, Teruaki—Daiwa Securities SMBC Principal Investments Co., Ltd.
Ueno, Masatoshi—Yasuda Enterprise Development Co., Ltd.(FKA: Nippon Ent.Dev)
Uga, Shiniji—Ridgeway Capital Partners, Ltd. (FKA:OPE Partners Ltd.)
Ugale, Ravi—Crossbow Ventures
Ughetta, William—Long Point Capital Inc.
Ugras, N.George—Adams Capital Management, Inc.
Uhlemann, Dirk—Target Partners GmbH
Uhlemann, Juergen—JCMB Beteiligungs GmbH
Uhlemann, Marcel—JCMB Beteiligungs GmbH
Uhlman, Thomas—New Venture Partners LLC
Uhrin, John—Harbert Management Corporation
Uhrin, John—Harbert Venture Partners
Ukeles, Meir—Israel Cleantech Ventures
Ulate, Jose—Aureos Capital, Ltd.
Ulecia, Javier—Bullnet Capital SCR SA
Ulevitch, Richard—5AM Ventures
Ullah, Salman—Merus Capital Investment
Ullman, Chris—Carlyle Group, The
Ulrich, Robert—Vanguard Ventures
Umanto, Hanjaya—Aureos Capital, Ltd.
Umbach, Andreas—Bayard Group (AKA: Landis+Gyr Holdings)
Umeda, Mochio—Pacifica Fund
Umedaly, Mossadiq—Wellington Partners Venture Capital GmbH
Umlah, James—Crocus Investment Fund
Underdown, Brian—Lumira Capital Corporation.
Underdown, Brian—MedTech Partners, Inc.
Underhill, Robert—Shorenstein Company LLC
Underwood, John—Pfingsten Partners, L.P.
Ungar, Regina—Platinum-Neurone Ventures
Unger, David—Avalon Equity Partners
Unger, Howard—Saw Mill Capital, LLC
Ungerer, Scott—EnerTech Capital
Ungermann, Ralph—CSV Capital Partners (FKA: China Seed Ventures)
Ungermann, Ralph—CSV Capital Partners (FKA: China Seed Ventures)
Unkan, Tugba—Li & Fung Investments
Unneland, Trond—Chevron Technology Ventures
Unrein, Lawrence—J.P. Morgan Asset Management
Unruh, James—Alerion Capital Group
Unruh, Jeffrey—Alerion Capital Group
Unser, Matthias—Sal. Oppenheim Private Equity Partners
Unterganschnigg, Gerhard—Andlinger & Company, Inc.
Unterman, Thomas—Rustic Canyon Partners
Unwin, Ashley—Terra Firma Capital Partners, Ltd.
Uotila, Mika—Sentica Partners Oy
Ural skaya, Ol ga—Al'yans ROSNO Upravleniye Aktivami, OAO
Urban, George—Harren Equity Partners
Urban, Konstantin—Holtzbrinck Ventures GmbH
Urbina, Lee—Accent Capital
Urech, Alan—Stoney River Capital Partners LLC
Uribe, Angel—Southern Cross Group (AKA: SCG)
Uribe, Juan—Invus Group Ltd., The
Urquhart, Jamie—Pond Venture Partners
Urquhart, Jodie—J.W. Childs Associates
Urruti, Eric—Corning Innovation Ventures
Urry, James—Court Square Capital Partners
Ursprung, Tobias—Capvis Equity Partners AG
Usami, Isao—Tokyo Small & Medium Business Investment & Consultation Co.
Usami, Yasushi—Tokio Marine Capital Company, Ltd.
Usher, Mark—Wellington Financial LP
Ushio, Misti—Harris & Harris Group, Inc.
Usifer, Doug—Headwaters Merchant Bank
Utay, Marc—Clarion Capital Partners LLC
Utendahl, John—Praesidian Capital, LLC
Utsugi, Shigeru—Sun Capital Partners Japan K.K.
Uzumeri, Erol—Searchlight Capital Partners LLC
Vacchiano, Cesar—Iame Capital Riesgo SGECR SA
Vacchino, Paolo—Abacus Invest S.C.A. SICAR
Vachet, Claude—Multiple Capital, Inc.
Vadapalas, Joseph—Nexos Capital Partners
Vaddi, Gopi—Columbia Capital LLC
Vaden, Erich—Generation Capital Partners
Vago, Derek—ACP Capital, Ltd.
Vahabzadeh, Alex—BV-Cornerstone Ventures, L.P.
Vahk, Tonno—GILD Bankers (FKA: LHV Ventures)
Vaid, Rahul—Pacesetter Capital Group (FKA: MES-BIC Ventures Holding Co.)
Vaidya, Mahesh—GF Private Equity Group, LLC
Vainio, Petri—Essex Woodlands Health Ventures
Vaksvik, J. Frode—Convexa Capital AS
Val Ferreira, Rui—DRIVE Sociedade de Capital de Risco, SA
Valdenaire, Olivier—Endeavour Vision SA
Valdes, Antoine—Alto Invest
Valdez Mingramm, Rafael—SinoLatin Capital
Vale, Brad—Johnson & Johnson Development Corporation
Vale, Christopher—Rexiter Capital Management Ltd.
Valenti, Alan—Roser Ventures LLC
Valentin, Benoit—Cinven, Ltd.
Valentine, Donald—Sequoia Capital
Valenty, Jeffrey—FlatWorld Capital LLC
Valeri, Andrea—Blackstone Group, L.P.
Valet, Didier—Societe Generale Capital Partenaires SAS
Valianos, Chris—Cordova Ventures (FKA:Cordova Capital)
Valimaa, Kalle—Miraimon Oy
Valis, Tom—Celtic House Venture Partners
Valkin, Adam—Arts Alliance Advisors
Valle, Victorio—Iame Capital Riesgo SGECR SA
Vallee, Jacques—Astrolabe Ventures
Vallee, Jacques—Astrolabe Ventures
Vallee, Jacques—SBV Venture Partners
Vallee, Jacques—Siparex Group SAS
Vallee, Luc—CDP Capital - Technology Ventures (FKA: CDP Sofinov)
Vallen, Audrey—Panorama Capital
Valler, Yaron—Giza Venture Capital (FKA: Giza Investment Management)
Valler, Yaron—Hasso Plattner Ventures Management GmbH
Vallis, Chip—Covington Capital Corporation (FKA: C.I. Covington Fund)
Valtos, William—ICCP Venture Partners, Inc.
Valvasori, Franco—Alcedo SGR SpA
Van Alkemade, Floris—Solid Capital BV
Van Barlingen, Harrold—Thuja Capital B.V.
Van Barneveld, Jaap—Newion Investments B.V.
Van Beaver, Stephen—Pilot House Ventures Group, LLC
Van Berckel, Hugo—CVC Capital Partners (Europe), Ltd.
Van Beuren, Gregory—BB&T Capital Markets
Van Bladel, Sigrid—New Enterprise Associates, Inc.
Van Bon, Andreas—bmp AG
Van Cuylenberg, Peter—Crescendo Venture Management LLC
Van Degna, Robert—Nautic Partners LLC
Van Delden, Tim—Holland Private Equity B.V.
Van Den Berg, Marc—VantagePoint Venture Partners
Van Den Bosch, Fred—Wellington Partners Venture Capital GmbH
Van Den Hoek, Henk—Indofin
Van Der Burg, E.J.—NIBC Principal Investments (FKA: Parnib Holding NV)
Van Der Have, Frits—Life Sciences Partners BV
Van Der Mersbrugghe, Guy—Orium SAS
Van Deventer, John—Cabot Square Capital, Ltd.
Van Deventer, Sander—Forbion Capital Partners
Van Dijk, Ed—Nimbus
Van Doesburg, Stef—Greenfield Capital Partners
Van Driessche, Rogier—Delta Partners FZ LLC
Van Droogenbroeck, Eric—Sofindev Management N.V.
Van Duijvenvoorde, Erik—American Capital, Ltd.
Van Dussen, Jason—Golub Capital
Van Dyck, Carlo—QiFund
Van Dyke, J.W.—Vista Capital LLC (FKA: AO Capital Corp.)
Van Eesteren, William—Wilshire Private Markets
Van Gessel, Zoran—Bencis Capital Partners
Van Goethem, Robert—Permira Advisers LLP
Van Golstein Brouwers, Marilou—Triodos International Fund Management BV
Van Gorp, Jasper—Gilde Healthcare Partners B.V.
Van Griethuysen, Hans—Charlemagne Capital (UK) Limited

Versaw, Jennifer—Relativity Capital LLC
Verschelde, Patrick—CVC Capital Partners (Europe), Ltd.
Versino, Adriana—AF Mezzanine SGRpA
Verster, Braam—Palamon Capital Partners (FKA: Amphion Capital Partners)
Vertiz, Antonio—BPEP International
Vervoort, Maarten—AlpInvest Partners N.V.
Vescovo, Victor—Insight Equity Holdings LLC
Vesely, Jon—Code, Hennessy & Simmons LLC
Vesseur, Jan—Life Sciences Partners BV
Vest, Frank—Catterton Partners
Vestergaard-Poulsen, Soren—CVC Capital Partners (Europe), Ltd.
Vettel, Matthew—Great Hill Equity Partners LLC
Vettivetpillai, Sivendran—Aureos Capital, Ltd.
Vettivetpillai, Sivendran—Aureos Capital, Ltd.
Veyssiere, Frederic—Innovacom SA
Viberti, Marco—Management & Capitali SpA
Vicary, Scott—Global Environment Fund Management Corporation
Vickers, Phil—Infinity Asset Management LLP
Victor, Jonathan—Balmoral Advisors LLC
Victor, Roger—Montlake Capital
Vidal, Dominique—Index Ventures
Vidal, Philippe—SNVB Participations
Videt, Pote—Lombard Investments, Inc.
Vidrevich, Simon—IndexAtlas Group
Vieider, Karl—Invest Equity Management Consulting GmbH
Viet-Jacobsen, Denis—Altor Equity Partners AB
Vig, Rajneesh—Tennenbaum Capital Partners LLC
Vigano, Paul—J.H. Whitney & Co. LLC
Vigil, Fernando—Bain Capital
Vigil, Fernando—Bain Capital Ventures
Vigliotta, Thomas—Quadrangle Group LLC
Vignola, Eric—Beacon Partners, Inc.
Vignola, Leonard—Beacon Partners, Inc.
Vigoda, Robert—Catalyst Health and Technology Partners LLC
Viguier, Fabrice—Global Emerging Markets
Vijayakar, Sameer—Churchill Equity, Inc.
Vijums, Judith—Thayer Hidden Creek
Vik, Jostein—Viking Venture Management AS
Vila, Fernando—Prax Capital
Villa, Sebastian—Southern Cross Group (AKA: SCG)
Villabo, Malvin—Leiv Eiriksson Nyfotek AS (FKA: Sakorn Midt Norge)
Villalba, Felix—Pacesetter Capital Group (FKA: MESBIC Ventures Holding Co.)
Villecroze, Stephane—Demeter Partners S.A.
Villers, Ned—Water Street Healthcare Partners
Villhard, Peter—Thompson Street Capital Partners
Villon, Bertrand—Investcorp Bank B.S.C.
Vincent, Jeffrey—Grey Mountain Partners
Vincent, Roger—Founders Equity, Inc.
Vincent, Trey—Riverside Company
Vineburg, Stephen—CVC Capital Partners (Europe), Ltd.
Viner, Les—Torys LLP
Vinet, Anne-Sophie—Phillimore Investissement
Vinish, Lorne—SOCO
Vink, Eric-Jan B.—Gilde Buy Out Partners
Vinton, Fred—Opus Electra & Partners
Viola, Carlo—Sanpaolo IMI Private Equity SpA
Virani, Moez—Mohr Davidow Ventures
Virtanen, Visa—Midinvest Management Oy
Viscogliosi, Anthony—Viscogliosi Bros LLC
Viscogliosi, John—Viscogliosi Bros LLC
Viscogliosi, Marc—Viscogliosi Bros LLC
Vish, Ravi—WestLB Mellon Asset Management (USA) LLC
Visioni, Mario—Alto Partners SGR SpA
Visioni, Paolo—Investitori Associati SpA
Viso, Nemesio—Stonehenge Capital Company
Visser, Jacques—Algebra Capital
Visser, Mark—Behrman Capital
Visser, Peter—Egeria B.V.
Vissichelli, Steve—Knightsbridge Management, L.L.C.
Viswanathan, Aruna—Aegis Capital Group LLC
Viswanathan, Ravi—New Enterprise Associates, Inc.
Vitale, Raffaele—PAI Partners (FKA: PAI Management)
Vitangcol, Alvin—Capital Midwest Fund, L.P.
Vitkauskas, Rytis—Summit Partners
Vitullo, Nicole—Domain Associates LLC
Vitus, Andy—Scale Venture Partners
Vivian, Stephen—Prism Capital
Vlayen, Frank—Waterland Private Equity Investments B.V.
Vo, Phong—BIDV Vietnam Partners Investment Management Co. (AKA: BVIM)
Voeks, Robert—Private Advisors LLC
Vogel, Dale—Montlake Capital
Vogel, David—Velocity Equity Partners LLC
Vogel, Jeffrey—Court Square Capital Partners
Vogel, Jeffrey—Velocity Equity Partners LLC
Vogelbaum, Martin—Rho Capital Partners, Inc.
Vogler, Andreas—BioMedical Innovations, Ltd.
Vogler, Jorn-Marc—H.I.G. Capital LLC
Vogt, Hans-Peter—VenGrow Corporate Finance AG
Vogt, Michael—Frankfurt CapitalPartners AG (AKA: FCP)
Vogt, Nils—Sarsia Innovation AS
Vohlmuth, Ivan—Royalton Partners
Vohra, Neeraj—Washington Technology Partners, Inc. (AKA: WTP)
Voigt, Greg—Adlevo Capital Managers LLC
Voison, Jean-Marie—Undisclosed Firm
Vold, Henning—Norvestor Equity AS (FKA: Norsk Vekst Forvaltning AS)
Volio, Jorge—Volio Capital, S.A.
Volk, David—Castle Creek Capital LLC
Volk, Kimberly—Spinnaker Trust
Vollebregt, Erik—Kenda Capital BV
Vollman, Michael—Axiom Equity Partners
Volpe, Louis—Kodiak Venture Partners
Volpi, Michelangelo—Index Ventures
Volpi, Mike—Index Ventures
Volpi, Nicola—Permira Advisers LLP
Voltolina, Giovanna—Cognetas LLP
Volyanskaya, Natasha—American Capital, Ltd.
Volz, Gabriele—WealthCap Initiatoren GmbH
Von Arnswaldt, Wolf Christian—Hamilton Lane Advisors, Inc.
Von Bassewitz, Jan Graf—Sal. Oppenheim Private Equity Partners
Von Bismarck, Johannes—Veronis Suhler Stevenson (FKA: Veronis, Suhler & Associates)
Von Blottnitz, Andreas—BV Capital (FKA: Bertelsmann Ventures, LP)
Von Braun, Emmeram—von Braun & Schreiber Private Equity Partners GmbH
Von Burg, Philip—Monomoy Capital Partners, LLC
Von Cramm, Egbert Freiherr—Sal. Oppenheim Private Equity Partners
Von Cramm, Egbert—Sal. Oppenheim Private Equity Partners
Von Deylen, Jeffrey—Savvis, Inc. (FKA: Savvis Communications)
Von Euw, Mikael—BioMedical Innovations, Ltd.
Von Finckenstein, Robert—American Capital, Ltd.
Von Finckenstein, Robert—European Capital Financial Services Ltd.
Von Fischer, Scott—Prudential Capital Group
Von Frankenberg, Alexander—High-Tech Gruenderfonds Management GmbH
Von Freyberg, Berthold—Target Partners GmbH
Von Hofsten, Erland—Huvudkontoret i Kristinehamn AB
Von Hugo, Christopher—One Equity Partners (FKA: Banc One Venture Partners)
Von Joest, August—Odewald & Compagnie GmbH
Von Kreuter, James—Headwaters Merchant Bank
Von Lehe, Peter—NB Alternatives - Fund of Funds
Von Lehe, Peter—Swiss Re Private Equity Advisers
Von Meibom, Hans-Dieter—One Equity Partners (FKA: Banc One Venture Partners)
Von Moeller, Krischan—Paragon Partners GmbH
Von Oppen, Christian—Triginta Capital Partners GmbH (FKA: Avida Equity Partners)
Von Peter, Johann-Melchior—One Equity Partners (FKA: Banc One Venture Partners)
Von Preyss, Daniel—Impax Asset Management
Von Ribbentrop, Joachim—Odewald & Compagnie GmbH
Von Roy, Aki—Direct Capital Private Equity
Von Schroeter, Carlo—WestView Capital Partners
Von Simson, Justin—HgCapital
Von Stroh, Eric—Long Point Capital Inc.
Von Summer, Alexander—Metamorphic Ventures, LLC (FKA: Gersh Venture Partners)
Von Weissenfluh, Hans—Fabrel Lotos (AKA: Fabrel AG)
Von Zelowitz, Per—Nordic Venture Partners (FKA: Danske Venture Partners)
Von Zuben, Max—Wicks Group of Companies LLC, The
Von der Goltz, Alexander—Boston Capital Ventures
Von der Goltz, Johan—Boston Capital Ventures
Von der Goltz, Johan—Brooke Private Equity Associates
Von der Osten, Dinnies—Acceres Beteiligungsmanagement GmbH & Co KG
Vonderhaar III, Bernard—Highland Capital Management, L.P.
Vora, Rupa—IDFC Private Equity
Vorhoff, Robbert—General Atlantic LLC
Vorlicek, Martha—HarbourVest Partners LLC
Vorndran, Helmut—VENTIZZ Capital Partners Advisory AG
Vorster, Paul—Inspired Evolution Investment Management
Voss, Christian—Atlantic-Pacific Capital, Inc.
Voss, Scott—HarbourVest Partners LLC
Voss, William—Lake Pacific Partners, LLC

Vota, John—HillStreet Capital, Inc.
Votron, Jean-Paul—Fortis Private Equity NV/SA (FKA: VIV NV)
Voute, Jan Reinier—CVC Capital Partners (Europe), Ltd.
Vovokes, Mary—Penn Venture Partners, LP
Vrdoljak, Ivan—Eagle Ventures
Vreeman, Hans—Eagle Venture Partners
Vrionis, John—Lightspeed Venture Partners (FKA: Weiss, Peck & Greer)
Vromen, Frits—Mercurius Beleggingsmaatschappij B.V.
Vu, Le T. T.—BIDV Vietnam Partners Investment Management Co. (AKA: BVIM)
Vuorela, Panu—Pohjola Capital Partners Oy
Vuursteen, Gijsbert—CVC Capital Partners (Europe), Ltd.
Vyas, Devendra—SREI Venture Capital Ltd. (FKA: SREI Global Asset Mgt.)
Vyas, Vinnie—Crossover Advisors Pvt., Ltd. (FKA: Meta Crossover Advisors)
Vynerib, David—Sigma Capital Partners, LLC
Vyshlova, Anna—Renaissance Capital
Wabnegger, Stephan—PONTIS Capital GmbH
Wacaster, Steven—Pegasus Capital Advisors, L.P.
Wachsmuth, Marc—Capital-e
Wachter, David—W Capital Partners
Wachtman, Jim—SV Life Sciences Advisers
Wack, Patrick—Rho Capital Partners, Inc.
Wada, Kei—Arise Capital Partners, Inc.
Waddell, John—Archangel Informal Investments Limited
Wade, Hugh—Madison Capital Funding LLC (AKA: Madison Capital)
Wade, James—M/C Venture Partners
Wadsworth, Chris—Ceyuan Ventures Management, LLC
Wadsworth, Eliot—Housatonic Partners
Wadsworth, Robert—HarbourVest Partners LLC
Waeckerle, Mirko—Deutsche Effecten- und Wechsel-Beteiligungsgesellschaft AG
Waga, Kazimierz—AKJ Investments SA
Wagar, James—Northern Lights Ventures, LLC
Wagenberg, Lawrence—Wheatley Partners
Wagener, Carlos—HSBC Private Equity Latin America
Wagener, Friedrich—Beteiligungsgesellschaft fur die deutsche Wirtschaft mbH
Wages, Robert—Castle Harlan, Inc.
Wagner, Alyse—Leonard Green & Partners
Wagner, Andrew—GSC Partners (FKA: Greenwich Street Capital Partners)
Wagner, Andrew—Silver Lake Sumeru
Wagner, Ira—European Capital Financial Services Ltd.
Wagner, J. Peter—Accel Partners
Wagner, Jack—HarbourVest Partners LLC
Wagner, John—Granite Hall Partners (FKA: Sports Venture Partners, LLC)
Wagner, Karen—Ysios Capital Partners
Wagner, Lucian—EuroUs Ventures
Wagner, Markus—gcp gamma capital partners Beratungs- & Beteiligungs AG
Wagner, Robert—Imperial Capital, LLC
Wagner, Roland C—Investitions- und Strukturbank Rheinland-Pfalz (ISB) GmbH
Wagner, Trina—CNET
Wagstaff, Philip—New Star Asset Management
Wahl, Frederick—Gleacher & Co.
Wahl, Jurgen—gcp gamma capital partners Beratungs- & Beteiligungs AG
Wahl, Michael—Halder Holdings BV
Wahlback, Magnus—Maxus Capital AB
Wahlen, Edwin—CGW Southeast Partners (AKA: Cravey, Green, & Wahlen)
Wahr, Dennis—RiverVest Venture Partners
Wahrhaftig, David—Kelso & Company
Waite, Andrew—SCF Partners
Waite, Charles—OVP Venture Partners
Waite, Steven—Accuitive Medical Ventures
Waitz, Laura—Blackstone Group, L.P.
Wakabayashi, Takuro—Advanced Science and Technology Enterprise Corporation
Wakefield, David—Shoreview Industries
Wakefield, Edward—GCP Capital Partners
Wakeman, Fred—Advent International
Wakimizu, Junichiro—Daiwa Corporate Investment Co., Ltd.
Walbom, Lynette—Keystone National Group LLC
Walchek, Scott—Draper Fisher Jurvetson ePlanet Ventures, L.P.
Wald, Hiroshi—Austral Capital
Wald, Ryan—Gores Group LLC, The
Waldeier, Janet—TGF Management Corp (FKA:Texas Growth Fund)
Waldman, Kevin—Veronis Suhler Stevenson (FKA: Veronis, Suhler & Associates)
Waldner, Gunter—AlpInvest Partners N.V.
Waldo, Adam—Silver Oak Management
Waldvogel, Christian—Vinci Capital
Walecka, John—Brentwood Venture Capital
Walecka, John—Redpoint Ventures
Walfish, Marc—Merit Capital Partners (FKA:William Blair Mezzanine)
Walia, Amit—Highland Capital Management, L.P.
Walji, Karim—Redwood Venture Partners
Walka, Martin—HANNOVER Finanz Austria GmbH
Walker, Charles—J.P. Morgan H&Q (FKA: Chase H&Q)
Walker, Chet—Forsyth Capital Investors LLC
Walker, Christopher—HarbourVest Partners LLC
Walker, Clete—Aegis Capital Group LLC
Walker, Clinton—Clarity Partners
Walker, Darrell—Ignition Capital
Walker, Donald—Arbor Partners LLC
Walker, Donald—Blue Chip Venture Company
Walker, Jeffrey—J.P. Morgan Partners (FKA: Chase Capital Partners)
Walker, Jim—Callisto Capital
Walker, Paul—New Enterprise Associates, Inc.
Walker, Robert—Sierra Ventures
Walker, Stephen—Walker Ventures SBIC (AKA: Walker Ventures)
Walker, Thomas—J.P. Morgan Partners (FKA: Chase Capital Partners)
Walkinshaw, Michael—Chrysalix Energy
Wall, Brian—Platinum Equity LLC
Wall, Kevin—Craton Equity Partners
Wall, Kevin—Shelter Capital Partners LLC
Wall, Shelly—Morgan Stanley Venture Partners (AKA: MSDW)
Wall, Terrence—DaneVest Tech Fund Advisors
Wall, Thomas—Kelso & Company
Wallace, Ben—Azalea Capital LLC
Wallace, Brian—Access Venture Partners
Wallace, Chris—Second City Capital Partners
Wallace, George—SV Life Sciences Advisers
Wallace, Jonathan—WWC Capital Group LLC
Wallace, Joseph—Houlihan, Lokey, Howard & Zukin
Wallace, Peter—Blackstone Group, L.P.
Wallace, Wayne—Mutual Capital Partners
Waller, Paul—3i Group PLC
Walley, Noah—Investor Growth Capital AB
Walley, Noah—Investor Growth Capital, Inc.
Wallis, Chris—Doughty Hanson & Co., Ltd.
Wallis, Ian—MML Capital Partners
Wallis, Sandra—Weathergage Venture Capital
Walls, David—Highland Capital Management, L.P.
Walls, Stephen—Next Wave Partners LLP
Walrod, David—Bridgescale Partners
Walsh, Brian—Nth Power
Walsh, Colin—Crescent Capital (NI) Ltd
Walsh, David—One Equity Partners (FKA: Banc One Venture Partners)
Walsh, Dennis—Blackstone Group, L.P.
Walsh, James—Broadmark Capital Corp.
Walsh, James—TCIB Investment Co., Ltd.
Walsh, Kevin—Horizon Technology Finance Management LLC
Walsh, Michael—Gridiron Capital LLC
Walsh, Robert—Evercore Partners
Walsh, Robert—Symmetric Capital LLC
Walsh, Timothy—CCMP Capital Advisors LLC
Walsh, Timothy—J.P. Morgan Partners (FKA: Chase Capital Partners)
Walsh, William—Portfolio Advisors LLC
Walt, Bertie—GKA Bayete
Walter, Christopher—Ascent Venture Partners
Walter, Jochen—BayTech Venture Capital Beratungs GmbH
Walter, Matthew—Talisman Capital
Walters, Brad—Academy Funds
Walters, Eric—Englefield Capital
Walters, Jeff—LaSalle Capital Group, Inc.
Walters, Kenneth—Emigrant Capital
Walters, Logan—SCF Partners
Walters, Scott—Palomar Ventures
Walton, Alan—Oxford Bioscience Partners
Walton, Derek—American Capital, Ltd.
Walton, O.B.—MAF of Mississippi, Inc.
Walton, Roger—Castile Ventures
Walton, William—Allied Capital Corporation
Walzer, Yoav—Medica Venture Partners
Wambold, Ali—Lazard Capital Partners
Wan, Joseph—Cinven, Ltd.
Wan, Kum Tho—Vertex Management Pte, Ltd. (AKA: Vertex Venture Holdings)
Wan, Mark—Three Arch Partners
Wand, Michael—Carlyle Group, The
Wandoff, Richard—Brockway Moran & Partners, Inc.
Wang, Alice—Revolution Learning
Wang, Arthur—Development Principles Group, Ltd.
Wang, Arthur—Pacific Venture Partners
Wang, Chao—ChinaEquity Group, Inc.
Wang, Chester—Acorn Campus Ventures
Wang, Conrad—Three Arch Partners
Wang, Daizong—3i Group PLC
Wang, David—WI Harper Group

Wang, Edwin—Accretive Exit Capital Partners LLC
Wang, Edwin—Zero Stage Capital Co., Inc.
Wang, Frances—China Renaissance Capital Investment
Wang, Fred—Trinity Ventures
Wang, Gloria—Whitesun Equity Partners
Wang, Gongquan—IDG Technology Venture Investment, Inc.
Wang, Guo—Tripod Capital International, Ltd.
Wang, Hans—CVC Asia Pacific, Ltd.
Wang, Hans—CVC Capital Partners (Europe), Ltd.
Wang, Hetty—Apax Partners Worldwide
Wang, James—Pacific Venture Partners
Wang, Jessica—Pac-Link Management Corporation
Wang, Jia Fen—GGV Capital
Wang, Jiansheng—Actis Capital LLP
Wang, Jonas—Sycamore Ventures Pte, Ltd.
Wang, Jonathan—OrbiMed Advisors LLC
Wang, Jun—AsiaTech Internet Group (ATIG) (FKA: AsiaTech Ventures)
Wang, Ken—Power Capital Co., Ltd.
Wang, Laure—Asia Alternatives Management LLC
Wang, Le-Chun—Pac-Link Management Corporation
Wang, Lucas—WI Harper Group
Wang, Lynn—Centenium-Pinetree China Private Equity
Wang, Neng-guang—Legend Capital
Wang, Paul—Pacific Venture Partners
Wang, Peijun—Shanghai Venture Capital Co., Ltd.
Wang, Philip—Fortune Venture Investment Group (AKA:Fortune Consulting)
Wang, Piau-Voon—Adams Street Partners LLC
Wang, Pingao—Shanghai Venture Capital Co., Ltd.
Wang, Qi—Development Principles Group, Ltd.
Wang, Qin—LB Investment, Inc.
Wang, Rex—Daiwa Quantum Capital, Ltd.
Wang, Sean—DragonTech Ventures Management, Ltd.
Wang, Sha—Cybernaut (China) Capital Management
Wang, Shaojun—Beijing Capital Investment Co., Ltd.
Wang, Sing—TPG Capital
Wang, Sona—Ceres Venture Fund
Wang, T.G.—Crimson
Wang, Tony—Centenium-Pinetree China Private Equity
Wang, Warren—Avant Capital Group, Inc.
Wang, Xiaomei—Shanghai Huile Investment & Management Co., Ltd.
Wang, Xin—Investor Growth Capital AB
Wang, Xin—Investor Growth Capital, Inc.
Wang, Xiping—Eos Asia Investments, Ltd. (FKA: JCAR Funds, Ltd.)
Wang, Yanhui—Eastern Link Capital
Wang, Yen—TCIB Investment Co., Ltd.
Wang, Ying—Northern Light Venture Capital
Wang, Yong—Shenzhen Green Pine Capital Partners Co., Ltd.
Wang, Yulong—DaLian KaiDa Venture Capital Co., Ltd.
Wangerin, William—One Equity Partners (FKA: Banc One Venture Partners)
Wanner, Katherine—Adams Street Partners LLC
Wanshou, Li—Shenzhen Capital Group Co., Ltd.
Wanske, Bruno—PRICOA Capital Group, Ltd.
Ward, Bob—DFJ Frontier
Ward, Bob—Kaiser Permanente Ventures
Ward, Carter—ArcLight Capital
Ward, David—MTI Partners, Ltd.
Ward, David—Salix Ventures
Ward, Gary—Gresham LLP
Ward, Jeffrey—MedEquity Investors LLC
Ward, John—Key Venture Partners
Ward, Justin—Bridgepoint Development Capital
Ward, Lawrence—ClearLight Partners LLC
Ward, Michael—Bain Capital
Ward, Michael—Nobska Ventures
Ward, Michael—QuestMark Partners, L.P.
Ward, Nathan—Palm Beach Capital Partners
Ward, Paul—Pantheon Ventures, Ltd.
Ward, Robert—Capybara Ventures LLC
Ward, Robert—Meritech Capital Partners
Ward, Sean—Blue Point Capital Partners (FKA: Key Equity Capital)
Warden, Charles—Versant Ventures
Wardlaw, William—Freeman Spogli & Co.
Wardman-Browne, Stuart—AMWIN Management Pty., Ltd.
Wardrop, Brian—Arx Equity Partners
Wargo, J. David—New Mountain Capital LLC
Warmbold, Benita—Northwater capital Management
Warms, Ellen—IBM Corporation
Warn, Kai—IK Investment Partners, Ltd.
Warner, DeVer—Saugatuck Capital Company
Warner, John—CCMP Capital Advisors LLC
Warner, Stephen—Crossbow Ventures
Warner, Steve—Baird Capital Partners
Warner, Steve—GE Commercial Finance - Equity
Warnken-Brill, John—Vista Equity Partners
Warnock, David—Camden Partners, Inc. (FKA: Cahill, Warnock & Co. LLC)
Warnock, Greg—Mercato Partners
Warnock, Todd—RoundTable Health Care Partners
Warrell, Geoffrey—Gatehouse Ventures, L.P.
Warren, Anthony—Adams Capital Management, Inc.
Warren, Kenneth—Littlejohn & Company LLC
Warren, Lisa—Research Partners, Ltd.
Warren, Tracy—Battelle Ventures
Warren, W. Scott—Milestone Partners
Warrick, Vincent—Thompson Street Capital Partners
Warriner, Don—Headwaters Merchant Bank
Waryn, Richard—Centurion Capital Ltd
Waryn, Richard—Centurion Capital Ltd (FKA: Finartis Private Equity, Ltd.)
Wash, Darryl—Ascend Venture Group LLC
Washing, Thomas—Sequel Venture Partners
Washington, Alex—Wind Point Partners
Washington, Kirk—Yaletown Venture Partners, Inc.
Waslin, Craig—Adams Street Partners LLC
Waslin, Craig—PPM America Capital Partners LLC
Wasmayr, Bernhard—Investitions- und Strukturbank Rheinland-Pfalz (ISB) GmbH
Wasserman, David—Clayton, Dubilier & Rice, Inc.
Wasserman, Thomas—Constellation Ventures (AKA: Constellation Growth Capital)
Wasserstein, Kevin—Versant Ventures
Watanabe, Akihito—Nomura Research & Advisory Co., Ltd.
Watanabe, Akira—Tokyo Small & Medium Business Investment & Consultation Co.
Watanabe, August—Twilight Venture Partners
Watanabe, Gwendolyn—Lava Management, LLC
Watanabe, Hideo—Daiwa Securities SMBC Principal Investments Co., Ltd.
Watanabe, Hiroshi—Gogin Capital Company, Ltd., The
Watanabe, Junichi—MP Healthcare Venture Management, Inc.
Watanabe, Kouhei—Itochu Corporation
Watanabe, Mikifumi—AXA Investment Managers
Watanabe, Nao—Ridgeway Capital Partners, Ltd. (FKA:OPE Partners Ltd.)
Watanabe, Yasuharu—Worldview Technology Partners
Watchmaker, Linda—CORAL Ventures Management, Inc.
Watchmaker, Linda—Coral Group LLC
Waterhouse, Daniel—Wellington Partners Venture Capital GmbH
Waterman, David—DeltaPoint Capital Management LLC
Waterson, Tim—Gold Hill Capital Management LLC
Wathen, David—Questor Management Company LLC
Watkins, Dan—DFJ Mercury
Watkins, Jay—De Novo Ventures
Watkins, John—M/C Venture Partners
Watkins, Stephen—Arcturus Capital
Watkins, Timothy—Valor Equity Partners
Watkins, Todd—Houlihan, Lokey, Howard & Zukin
Watkinson, Sam—August Equity LLP
Watson, Christopher—Aquiline Capital Partners
Watson, Doug—Shell Internet Ventures
Watson, J. Derek—Windjammer Capital Investors (FKA:Pacific Mezzanine Inv.)
Watson, J.W.Henry—BlackEagle Partners (FKA: Centurion Capital Partners)
Watson, James—Burrill & Company
Watson, James—CMEA Capital
Watson, Tony—Hermes Private Equity Management, Ltd.
Watt, Fred—CVC Capital Partners (Europe), Ltd.
Watt, James—Concentric Equity Partners, L.P.
Watts, Andrew—Oaktree Capital Management LLC
Watts, Claudius—Carlyle Group, The
Watts, Colin—TLcom Capital LLP
Watts, Jeff—Frank Russell Capital
Watts, Mark—Marwyn Investment Management, LLP
Watts, Mark—PHD Equity Partners LLP
Watts, Robert—Nancy Creek Capital
Waud, Reeve—Waud Capital Partners LLC
Waugh, Brad—Point Judith Capital
Waugh, Stuart—Northleaf Capital Partners
Waugh, Stuart—TD Capital Group, Ltd.
Waxman, Albert—Psilos Group Managers LLC
Waxman, David—Equip Ventures LLC
Waye, Thom—Sigma Capital Partners, LLC
Weatherby, Lance—Advanced Technology Development Center
Weatherly, Bobby—CapSource Fund, L.P.
Weatherman, Elizabeth—Warburg Pincus LLC
Weathersby, William—Nexus Group LLC
Weatherston, Kevin—CORE Partners, Inc.
Weaver, Allen—Prudential Capital Group
Weaver, Graham—Alpine Investors, L.P.
Weaver, Ned—Alpine Investors, L.P.
Webb, Brad—Claremont Creek Ventures
Webb, David—SFW Capital Partners, LLC

Webb, David—Wilshire Private Markets
Webb, Doug—QinetiQ Ventures Ltd
Webb, Jeffrey—Industrial Growth Partners
Webb, Timothy—Inflection Point Ventures
Webb, Wendy Markus—Tennenbaum Capital Partners LLC
Webber, David—Stonehenge Capital Company
Webber, Jeffrey—RB Webber & Company
Weber, Burkhard—CBPE Capital, LLP (AKA: Close Brothers Private Equity, Ltd.)
Weber, Eckard—Domain Associates LLC
Weber, Eugene—Weber Capital Management LLC
Weber, John—Court Square Capital Partners
Weber, Klaus—Deutsche Beteiligungs AG
Weber, Martin—Holtzbrinck Ventures GmbH
Weber, Pascale—TrustCapital Partners NV
Weber, Sonnfried—BayBG Bayerische Beteiligungsgesellschaft mbH
Weber, Sven—SVB Capital
Weber, Thomas—LGT Capital Partners AG
Weber, Tony—Natural Gas Partners (NGP)
Webster, Robert—Twin Haven Capital Partners
Webster, Thomas—Vintage Capital Partners
Wechsler, John—Equinox Capital, Inc.
Wecken, Gerlach—Next Wave Funds
Weckstein, Brad—New Mountain Capital LLC
Weckwerth, Martin—Permira Advisers LLP
Wedbush, Eric—Wedbush Capital Partners
Weddrien, Olivier—DZ Equity Partner GmbH
Wedegaertner, Christoph—Cipio Partners
Wedel, Michael—B12 Capital Partners LLC
Wedell, Christian—Copan, Inc
Wedner, Marcus—CIVC Partners LP (FKA: Continental Illinois Venture Corp.)
Wee, Caroline—BPEP International
Wee, Ericson—AB Capital & Investment Corporation
Wee, Jeremy—Blackstone Group, L.P.
Weeden, Charles—Inclusive Ventures, LLC
Weene, Adam—Saban Ventures
Weerasekera, Nissanka—Aureos Capital, Ltd.
Weglicki, Timothy—ABS Capital Partners
Wegter, Mark—Life Sciences Partners BV
Weguelin, John—European Islamic Investment Bank Plc
Wei, Eric—Gilbert Global Equity Capital, L.L.C.
Wei, Eric—RimAsia Capital Partners
Wei, James—Worldview Technology Partners
Wei, Lidong—Huinong Capital
Wei, Wang—Infinity Venture Capital Fund (AKA: Israel Infinity Fund)
Wei, Yuan—NewMargin Ventures
Wei, Zhou—Jade Alternative Investment Advisors
Weidenmiller, Ryan—SIG Asia Investments, LLLP
Weidner, James—Atlantic-Pacific Capital, Inc.
Weigang, Ye—NewMargin Ventures
Weigman, Albert—HLM Venture Partners
Weiguo, Zhao—Ceyuan Ventures Management, LLC
Weil, Burton—Venture Associates Partners LLC
Weiland, Armin—German Capital GmbH
Weimer, Carolyn—Carlyle Group, The
Weinbach, Lawrence—Yankee Hill Capital Management LLC
Weinbach, Peter—Yankee Hill Capital Management LLC
Weinberg, Andrew—Lindsay Goldberg LLC (FKA: Lindsay Goldberg & Bessemer GP)
Weinberg, Barry—CW Group, Inc.
Weinberg, Martin—Canterbury Park Capital
Weinberg, Michael—FriedbergMilstein, LLC
Weinberg, Richard—Pegasus Capital Advisors, L.P.
Weinberg, Serge—Weinberg Capital Partners SAS
Weincken, Kim—NorthCap Partners ApS
Weiner, Michael—Apollo Real Estate Advisors
Weingarten, Ian—Gores Group LLC, The
Weingarten, Michael—Signal Lake
Weingarten, Tim—Worldview Technology Partners
Weinhardt, John—American Capital, Ltd.
Weinhoff, Gregory—CHL Medical Partners
Weinman, Barry—Allegis Capital (AKA: Media Technology Ventures)
Weinmann, Michael—Capital Royalty Partners
Weinstein, Allan—Lincolnshire Management, Inc.
Weinstein, Gary—Providence Equity Partners LLC
Weinstein, Meir—Giza Venture Capital (FKA: Giza Investment Management)
Weinstein, Paul—Azure Capital Partners
Weinstein, Steven—Novartis Venture Fund (FKA: Novartis Corp.)
Weintraut, Neil—Nueva Ventures
Weintraut, Neil—Palo Alto Venture Partners
Weinzierl, John—Natural Gas Partners (NGP)
Weiping, Jiang—China Israel Value Capital (AKA: CIVC)
Weiping, Jiang—Shenzhen Capital Group Co., Ltd.
Weirich, Jochen—Partners Group AG
Weis, Seth—Stockwell Capital LLC
Weise, Christoph—Quadriga Capital
Weisel, Thomas—Thomas Weisel Partners Group, Inc.
Weisenfeld, Andrew—MTS Health Partners, L.P.
Weiser, Marc—RPM Ventures (FKA: Waypoint Ventures)
Weiskam, Andreas—SAP Ventures
Weisman, Amy—Sterling Investment Partners
Weisman, Howard—ESP Equity Partners LLC
Weisman, Wayne—SCP Private Equity Partners
Weiss, Chad—JOG Capital
Weiss, Daniel—Angeleno Group, LLC
Weiss, Daniel—MFC Capital Funding, Inc.
Weiss, Eric—Stripes Group
Weiss, Gary—Blue Hill Partners LLC
Weiss, Harold—Swiss Re Private Equity Advisers
Weiss, Jason—Terrapin Partners LLC
Weiss, Jeffrey—Point Judith Capital
Weiss, Joanne—NewSchools Venture Fund
Weiss, Joel—Jerusalem Global Ventures
Weiss, Linda—Oaktree Capital Management LLC
Weiss, Marc—Partners Group AG
Weiss, Paul—Venture Investors LLC
Weiss, Randy—Triathlon Medical Ventures LLC
Weiss, Shai—Virgin Green Fund
Weiss, Warren—Foundation Capital
Weisschaedel, Gerhard—Invision Private Equity AG
Weisskoff, Robert—Beacon Bioventures
Weissman, Carl—OVP Venture Partners
Weissman, Ronald—Apax Partners Worldwide
Weissmann, Eric—Kachi Partners
Weithman, Tom—CIT GAP Funds
Weitzberg, Toni—Nordic Capital (AKA: NC Advisory)
Weklar, Edward—Arlington Capital Partners
Wekselblatt, Joe—Angelo, Gordon & Company
Welborn, Steve—Wynnchurch Capital, Ltd.
Weld, Daniel—Madrona Venture Group
Welde, Joar—Viking Venture Management AS
Weldon, Guy—Bridgepoint Capital, Ltd.
Weldon, Kent—Thomas H. Lee Partners (AKA: TH Lee Partners)
Weldon, Norman—Partisan Management Group
Weldon, Thomas—Accuitive Medical Ventures
Welgs, Lee—Rosetta Capital Corporation
Weller, Andrew—Industrial Opportunity Partners, LLC
Weller, Harold—New Enterprise Associates, Inc.
Weller, R. Jason—Willis Stein & Partners
Welles, Timothy—Pine Street Capital Partners LLC
Wells, Chris—Infiniti Capital Limited
Wells, Norman—SFW Capital Partners, LLC
Wells, Richard—Insight Venture Partners
Wells, Tracey—MidOcean Partners
Welp, David—Morgan Creek Capital Management LLC
Welsh, David—Adams Street Partners LLC
Weltman, Robert—Genstar Capital LLC
Welton, Stephen—J.P. Morgan Partners (FKA: Chase Capital Partners)
Welzel, Michael—EquiVest GmbH & Co
Wen, Aaron—Orchid Asia Group Management, Ltd.
Wen, Bo—Balloch China Fund, The
Wen, Zhimin—San Shan Capital Partners
Wencki, Marek—MCI Management
Wendel, Peter—Forsta Entreprenorsfonden i Norden AB
Wendell, Michel—Nexit Ventures Oy
Wendell, Peter—Sierra Ventures
Wendelstadt, Florian—General Atlantic LLC
Wendt, Johannes—Bain Capital
Wendt, Johannes—Golding Capital Partners GmbH
Weng, David—TCW Capital Ventures LLC (AKA: TCW Holdings LLC)
Weng, Jerry—Ivy Capital
Wenger, Albert—Union Square Ventures
Wenger, Jurg—Partners Group AG
Wenneberg, Trond E.—NorgesInvestor Management AS
Wennmachers, Margit—Andreessen Horowitz
Wenstrup, David—Warburg Pincus LLC
Wentworth, Robert—Platinum Equity LLC
Wenzel, Daniel—Mountain Super Angel AG
Werlin, Jason—TA Associates, Inc.
Werme, Peter—Forsta Entreprenorsfonden i Norden AB
Werndl, Manfred—Salzburger Unternehmensbeteiligungsgesellschaft m.b.H.
Werner, Harold—HealthCare Ventures LLC
Werner, Scott—Accretive LLC (FKA: Accretive Technology Partners LLC)
Wertheim, Harvey—Harvest Partners LLC
Wertheimer, Samuel—OrbiMed Advisors LLC
Wertheimer, Stephen—W Capital Partners
Wertz, Boris—W Media Ventures
Werwaiss, John A.W.—Lindsay Goldberg LLC (FKA: Lindsay Goldberg & Bessemer GP)
Wesner, Blaine—Austin Ventures, L.P.
Wessel-As, Stein—Anchor Capital Management Ltd
Wesselink, Pieter—Export Venture Capital Corporation (Pty) Ltd.
Wesson, Bruce—Galen Associates
Wesson, Stephen—Auda Private Equity LLC

West, Bob—Thomas Weisel Partners Group, Inc.
West, Casey—SSM Partners
West, Dick—Midwest Venture Alliance
West, Dobson—Spell Capital Partners LLC
West, Thomas—Brown Gibbons Lang & Company LLC
West, William—Pacific Venture Group
Westbrook, D.Kirk—Invencor, Inc.
Wester, Forest—Trivest Partners, L.P.
Westerkamp, George—AlpInvest Partners N.V.
Westerlind, Victor—Rockport Capital Partners
Westerling, Austin—Charles River Ventures
Westervelt, William—Ashby Point Capital
Westley, Charlotte—Pantheon Ventures, Ltd.
Weston, Dennis—Fluke Venture Partners
Weston, Jamie—Wicks Group of Companies LLC, The
Weston, Mark—Cognetas LLP
Weston, R.Patrick—Azalea Capital LLC
Weston, Richard—Emerging ISV Capital Partners
Westphal, Christoph—S.R. One, Ltd.
Westreich, Glenn—Haynes and Boone LLC
Westwater, John—Nomura Phase4 Ventures, Ltd.
Westwood, Matt—Wilshire Private Markets
Wetherbee, Jeffrey—Glenmont Partners, LLC
Wetherell, David—GBP Capital (AKA: Greenwich Biotech Partners)
Wetterman, Terry—Atlantic-Pacific Capital, Inc.
Wettstein, Urs—BioMedical Innovations, Ltd.
Whalen, Christopher—Harvest Partners LLC
Whalen, Kristian—Vestar Capital Partners, Inc.
Whaley, John—Norwest Mezzanine Partners
Wheaton, Calbraith—ABS Capital Partners
Wheeler, Adam—Babson Capital Management LLC
Wheeler, Kurt—Clarus Ventures
Wheeler, Patrick—Adirondack Venture Fund, The
Wheeler, Thomas—Core Capital Partners
Whelan, Edward—Berkshire Partners LLC
Whelan, J.P.—Kern Whelan Capital, LLC
Whelan, Matthew—Brentwood Associates
Whiley, Gareth—Silverfleet Capital (FKA: PPM Capital Partners)
Whims, James—TechFund Capital
Whims, Jim—Techfund Capital Europe Management SAS
Whitaker, Raymond—EuclidSR Partners
Whitaker, Raymond—S.R. One, Ltd.
White, Adrian—Hermes Private Equity Management, Ltd.
White, Anthony—Climate Change Capital, Ltd.
White, Brandon—Charlesbank Capital Partners LLC
White, Dayle—GKA Bayete
White, Gregory—Thomas H. Lee Partners (AKA: TH Lee Partners)
White, Gregory—Thomas Weisel Partners Group, Inc.
White, Herman—CrossBridge Venture Partners
White, James—Sutter Hill Ventures
White, Jeff—Trestle Ventures
White, John—E-Synergy
White, John—Next Capital Pty., Ltd.
White, Michael—EnerCap Capital Partners
White, Morty—Wynnchurch Capital, Ltd.
White, Patrick—American Capital, Ltd.
White, Peter—CIT Group Inc.
White, Richard—CIBC Wood Gundy Capital
White, Robert—Bain Capital
White, Robert—Lazard Capital Partners
White, Sean—Spire Capital
White, Timothy—Blackstone Group, L.P.
Whitehouse, Jonathan—Coates Myer & Co. Pty Ltd.
Whitelaw, Granger—BlueCar Partners
Whiteley, Angus—Solon Ventures, Ltd.
Whiteman, Adrian—Infiniti Capital Limited
Whiteman, Raymond—Carlyle Group, The
Whiting, Richard—DynaFund Ventures LLC
Whitlock, Steven—Path4 Ventures, LLC
Whitman, Andrew—2x Consumer Products Growth Partners LP
Whitman, Anne—Longroad Asset Management
Whitman, Douglas—Whitman Capital, LLC
Whitman, John—Sycamore Ventures Pte, Ltd.
Whitman, Michael—Blackstone Group, L.P.
Whitman, Michael—Citigroup Private Equity
Whitmeyer, Bud—Research Triangle Ventures (RTV)
Whitmire, Jason—Earlybird Venture Capital GmbH & Co. KG
Whitnack, Bryan—Synapsis Associates
Whitney, Benson—Gideon Hixon Fund
Whitney, Kenneth—Blackstone Group, L.P.
Whitney, Richard—New Enterprise Associates, Inc.
Whitt, Jason—VantagePoint Venture Partners
Whittaker, Curt—New Energy Capital Corporation
Whittington, Patricia—Obsidian Finance Group LLC
Whittle, Jonathan—Darby Overseas Investments, Ltd.
Whittle, Jonathan—Darby Technology Ventures Group (AKA: DTV)
Whittle, Kevin—Sovereign Capital LLP (FKA:Sovereign Capital, Ltd.)
Whorton, David—Tugboat Ventures
Wiberg, Bill—Advanced Technology Ventures
Wick, Tyler—Ticonderoga Capital, Inc. (FKA: Dillon Read Venture Capital)
Wick, William—EuroUs Ventures
Wick, William—Vision Capital Management
Wickenkamp, Rolf—CAM Private Equity Consulting & Verwaltungs - GmbH
Wickenkamp, Rolf—Sal. Oppenheim Private Equity Partners
Wicker, Damion—J.P. Morgan Partners (FKA: Chase Capital Partners)
Wicker, Damion—Panorama Capital
Wickham, Marc—Ventures West Management, Inc.
Wicki, Andreas—HBM BioVentures AG (FKA: HBM Partners AG)
Wickramasuriya, Chanaka—Aureos Capital, Ltd.
Widder, Kenneth—Latterell Venture Partners
Widder, Kenneth—Windamere Venture Partners, LLC
Widing, Christian—Borevind AB
Widner, Melissa—Seapoint Ventures
Widroe, Greg—Media Venture Partners
Wiebe, Charles—BIA Digital Partners, L.P.
Wieclawski, Robert—AVALLON Sp. z o.o.
Wieczorek, John—Axiom Venture Partners, L.P.
Wieczorek, John—CCP Equity Partners
Wiedmer, Alexander—Iris Capital Management (FKA: Part'Com Management S.A.)
Wieduwilt, Marcel—Partners Group AG
Wiegand, Andrew—Superior Capital Partners
Wiegman, Bert—Langholm Capital LLP
Wieland, Kim—Allen & Company
Wiemker, Hans Jurgen—Equita Management GmbH
Wien, Per Anders—Reiten & Co Strategic Investments AS
Wienbar, Sharon—Scale Venture Partners
Wiener, Bret—H.I.G. Capital LLC
Wiener, Ron—Venture Mechanics, LLC
Wiese, Hanns-Peter—Global Life Science Ventures GmbH
Wiesen, Eric—RRE Ventures LLC
Wiesinger, Christian—Siemens Technology Accelerator (STA)
Wieslander, Johan—Deseven Catalyst Group AB
Wietlisbach, Urs—Partners Group AG
Wietrzyk, Robert—Lead Equities GmbH
Wiggins, Stephen—Essex Woodlands Health Ventures
Wigginton, Jeffrey—Strength Capital Partners
Wigglesworth, Ken—Rising Tide Fund
Wiggs, Peter—Archer Capital
Wigh, Jorgen—Konceptkapital AB
Wightman, Bradley—Nautic Partners LLC
Wignall, Mark—Matrix Private Equity Partners LLP
Wijeyeratne, Harin—Investcorp Bank B.S.C.
Wijnand, Hubertusn. N—Undisclosed Firm
Wijono, Rizal—SHK Fund Management, Ltd.
Wikart, Andrea—Venture Partners AG
Wikse, Hans—Procuritas Partners KB
Wikstrom, Tommy—AAC Capital Partners
Wilcove, Brian—Sofinnova Ventures
Wilcoxson, William—Axiom Venture Partners, L.P.
Wild, Daniel—TIBURON Partners AG
Wildauer, Bradford—Apollo Real Estate Advisors
Wilde, Andreas—Sal. Oppenheim Private Equity Partners
Wilde, Peter—Providence Equity Partners LLC
Wilder, Hugh—GE Antares Capital Corporation
Wildern, William—Resilience Capital Partners LLC
Wildhaber, Frances—BioMedPartners
Wildig, Simon—CBPE Capital, LLP (AKA: Close Brothers Private Equity, Ltd.)
Wildmoser, Christian—CVC Capital Partners (Europe), Ltd.
Wilds, David—First Avenue Partners, L.P.
Wildstein, Amy—Boldcap Ventures LLC
Wilenius, Willie—Result Venture Knowledge International
Wilens, Noel—First Atlantic Capital, Ltd.
Wiley, Joseph—Birch Hill Equity Partners Management, Inc.
Wilhelm, David—Adena Ventures
Wilhelm, David—Hopewell Ventures
Wilhelm, Robert—Van den Ende & Deitmers B.V.
Wilhelmer, Manfred—Undisclosed Firm
Wilhelmsen, Jens A.—Anchor Capital Management Ltd
Wilk, Mark—Wellington Financial LP
Wilke, Chuck—Meridian Capital (FKA: Olympic Capital Partners, LLC)
Wilke, Tiffany—Phenomenelle Angels Management
Wilkening, Benjamin—Mint Capital, Ltd.
Wilkerson, Kathleen—Next Frontier Capital
Wilkerson, L. John—Galen Associates
Wilkey, Brent—Aqua Alta NV/SA
Wilkins, Andrew—Atlantic Street Capital Management, LLC

Wittman, Marlene—Aquitaine Investment Advisors, Ltd.
Witzofsky, William—Capital For Business, Inc.
Wizel, Neil—First Reserve Corporation
Wobker, Bernard—BayTech Venture Capital Beratungs GmbH
Wodak, Martin—Horizonte Venture Management GmbH
Woeber, Andrew—GCP Capital Partners
Woehrl, Hans Rudolf—INTRO-Verwaltungs GmbH
Wohrer, Francois—CBPE Capital, LLP (AKA: Close Brothers Private Equity, Ltd.)
Woiteshek, Edward—Hellman & Friedman LLC
Woiwode, Tom—Versant Ventures
Wojcik, Marlene—Bain Capital
Wojtal, Dedee—Phenomenelle Angels Management
Wolf, Bryan—Intel Capital
Wolf, Eric—Bow River Capital Partners
Wolf, Jeffrey—Sunrock Ventures, Inc.
Wolf, Jochen—BWK GmbH Unternehmensbeteiligungsgesellschaft
Wolf, Lex—Beekman Group LLC, The
Wolf, Paul—Century Park Capital Partners
Wolf, Richard—Wall Street Technology Partners
Wolf, Scott—Prospect Venture Partners (FKA: Prospect Management LLC)
Wolf, Werner—TVM Capital GmbH
Wolf-Powers, Josh—Blue Wolf Capital Management LLC
Wolfe, Allan—Pelion Venture Partners
Wolfe, Brad—Sante Ventures
Wolfe, Daniel—Alfa Capital Partners
Wolfe, David—Brand Journey Capital LP
Wolfe, Howard—New Venture Partners
Wolfe, James—Red River Ventures
Wolfe, Josh—Lux Capital
Wolfe, Paul—Ritchie Capital
Wolfe, Robert—Northwest Venture Associates, Inc.(FKA:Spokane Capital Mgmt)
Wolfe, Stephen—Vector Capital
Wolfers, Peter—FirstVentures
Wolff, Neil—VantagePoint Venture Partners
Wolff, Susan—GBS Venture Partners, Ltd.
Wolfington, J. Eustace—Liberty Capital Management Corporation
Wolfle, Michael—Wellington Partners Venture Capital GmbH
Wolfman, Alexander—Avenue Capital Group
Wolfram, Tyler—Oak Hill Capital Management, Inc.
Wolfrum, Ulrich—VTC Partners GmbH
Wolfson, Gene—Catalyst Investors
Wolfson, Mark—Oak Hill Capital Management, Inc.
Wolfson, Rob—H.I.G. Capital LLC
Wolkon, Shari—Thomas H. Lee Partners (AKA: TH Lee Partners)
Wollaeger, Timothy—Sanderling Ventures
Wollak, Nicholas—Axxon Group
Woloson, Bradford—JMI Equity
Woloson, Todd—Greenmont Capital Partners
Wolstenholme, Iain—Gresham LLP
Womsley, Robert—Citigroup Private Equity
Womsley, Robert—Water Street Healthcare Partners
Won, Dae Ro—KTB Ventures
Wong, Alexander—D. E. Shaw Group, The
Wong, Bob—NewSmith Asset Management LLP
Wong, Cathy—Ridgewood Capital Management, LLC
Wong, Chi Tsung—Juniper Capital Ventures Pte, Ltd.
Wong, Daniel—Anchorage Capital Partners
Wong, David—Darby Overseas Investments, Ltd.
Wong, Erik—Pantheon Ventures, Ltd.
Wong, Eugene—Sirius Venture Consulting Pte, Ltd.
Wong, Felix—FCP Investors
Wong, Fred—InveStar Capital, Inc.
Wong, Gilbert—Bull Capital Partners Ltd.
Wong, Helen—GGV Capital
Wong, Helen—QED Global, Ltd.
Wong, Henry—Diamond TechVentures
Wong, Henry—Draper Fisher Jurvetson ePlanet Ventures, L.P.
Wong, Henry—Garage Technology Ventures LLC (FKA: Garage.com)
Wong, Hing—Walden International
Wong, Ken—SHK Fund Management, Ltd.
Wong, Kenny—SBI E2-Capital Asia Holdings, Ltd.
Wong, Laca—Shattuck Hammond Partners
Wong, Lawrence—Auda Private Equity LLC
Wong, Lily—Pantheon Ventures, Ltd.
Wong, Lisa—Pantheon Ventures, Ltd.
Wong, Louis S.K.—Inter-Asia Venture Management
Wong, Michael—Leonard Green & Partners
Wong, Phillip—AsiaTech Internet Group (ATIG) (FKA: AsiaTech Ventures)
Wong, Rebecca—Global Private Equity PLC
Wong, Richard—Accel Partners
Wong, Simon—Telesystem-Argo Global Capital
Wong, Su-Ming—CHAMP Ventures Pty Ltd.
Wong, Todd—GE Commercial Finance - Equity
Wong, Tze Kai—Banyan Ventures Sdn Bhd
Wonnacott, Larry—Symmetry Investment Advisors, Inc.
Woo, Adrian—Transpac Capital Pte, Ltd.
Woo, Charles—Pasadena Capital Partners
Woo, Teresa—AsiaTech Internet Group (ATIG) (FKA: AsiaTech Ventures)
Woo, William—TSG Equity Partners, L.L.C.
Wood, Alastair—Symphony Capital LLC
Wood, Anne—Spinnaker Trust
Wood, Bryan—Alta Berkeley Venture Partners
Wood, Christopher—Riverside Management Group
Wood, Daniel—Mesa Verde Venture Partners
Wood, David—Kirtland Capital Partners
Wood, Donald—Draper Fisher Jurvetson
Wood, Donald—Vanguard Ventures
Wood, Joel—Delta Capital Management LLC
Wood, Marcus—Cinven, Ltd.
Wood, Pam—Parallax Capital Partners LLC
Wood, Thomas—Elm Street Ventures
Wood, Tim—Modern Africa Fund Managers
Woodall, Mark—Climate Change Capital, Ltd.
Woodard, John—Vestar Capital Partners, Inc.
Woodburn, William—Global Infrastructure Partners
Woodbury, Paul—Henderson Equity Partners (AKA: Henderson Private Capital)
Woodford, Gregory—BB&T Capital Markets
Woodley, Ryan—Polaris Venture Partners
Woodman, Rob—Sofinnova Partners
Woods, Joseph—Navigation Capital Partners (AKA: NCP)
Woods, Willie—ICV Capital Partners LLC
Woodson, Wade—Sigma Partners
Woodward, David—Socius Capital Group LLC
Woodward, Marc—Neo Technology Ventures Pty, Ltd.
Woodward, Tim—Nth Power
Woodward, William—Anthem Venture Partners
Woodworth, Alfred—Echelon Ventures LLC
Woodworth, John—Providence Equity Partners LLC
Woody, James—Latterell Venture Partners
Woody, Ken—Innova Memphis, Inc.
Wooldridge, Zach—Elm Creek Partners
Woolley, Geoffrey—EPIC Ventures
Woolley, Kristin—Abingworth Management, Ltd.
Woolsey, R. James—VantagePoint Venture Partners
Wootton, Steven—Renaissance Capital
Working, Mark—Zachary Scott & Co.
Wormley, Paul—Hadley Capital
Worms, Vincent—Partech International
Wormsley, Alistar—Vision Capital LLP
Worner, Gerald—EVP Capital Management AG
Worning, Niels—Polaris Management A/S
Worrell, Dan—Tennenbaum Capital Partners LLC
Worrell, David—Monterey Venture Partners, LLC
Worsley, Todd—CIBC Capital Partners
Worth, W. Andrew—Fidus Capital
Worthy, Ford—Pappas Ventures
Worzman, Steven—NGEN Partners LLC (FKA: NextGen Partners LLC)
Woseth, Rob—Water Tower Capital LLC
Wottrich, Richard—Dresner Partners (FKA: Dresner Capital Resources, Inc.)
Wouterse, Alexander—H2 Equity Partners BV
Wriedt, Oliver—Providence Equity Partners LLC
Wriedt, Oliver—Sciens Capital Partners (FKA: Zilkha Venture Partners)
Wright, Alexander—GSC Partners (FKA: Greenwich Street Capital Partners)
Wright, Andrew—Dubai International Capital LLC
Wright, Jason—Apax Partners Worldwide
Wright, John—Silver Lake Sumeru
Wright, Lee—Diamond Castle Holdings LLC
Wright, Mark—Blue Chip Venture Company
Wright, Nigel—Onex Corporation
Wright, Rob—Pantheon Ventures, Ltd.
Wright, Roger—Nibiru Capital
Wright, Stephen—STAR Capital Partners, Ltd.
Wright, Steven—Aequitas Capital Management, Inc.
Wright, Thomas—Hawthorne Group
Wright, Thomas—Rosetta Capital Corporation
Wright, Thomas—Rosetta Capital Corporation
Wright, Tim—GrandBanks Capital
Wright, Tim—Vision Capital LLP
Wright, Timothy—Capital Z Investment Partners (FKA: Union Square Partners)
Wrigley, Graham—Permira Advisers LLP
Wrubel, Lee—Foundation Medical Partners
Wu, Ben—Wedbush Capital Partners
Wu, Charles—Charlesbank Capital Partners LLC
Wu, Ching—Morgenthaler Ventures
Wu, Davisson—Avant Capital Group, Inc.
Wu, Hajie—Lunar Capital Management, Ltd.
Wu, Jeff—Behrman Capital
Wu, Jerry—Taishin Management and Consulting Co., Ltd.
Wu, Jian—Regal Investment
Wu, John—Northern Light Venture Capital
Wu, Kelvin—AID Partners Capital, Ltd.
Wu, Lucian—Paul Capital Partners

Wu, Marianne—Mohr Davidow Ventures
Wu, Max—InveStar Capital, Inc.
Wu, Michael Ming-Yih—3V SourceOne Capital Pte, Ltd.
Wu, Michael—Chart Venture Partners
Wu, Neil—Pac-Link Management Corporation
Wu, Scott—Blue Horizon Equity
Wu, Shangzhi—CDH China Management Co., Ltd.
Wu, Sonny—GSR Ventures
Wu, Steve—Aureos Capital, Ltd.
Wu, Suzie—Pacific Venture Partners
Wu, Vivian—TA Associates, Inc.
Wu, Wei—ShenZhen CDF-Capital Co., Ltd.
Wu, William—Hina Capital Partners
Wu, Xu—Beijing Tianyi Huirong Investment Management Co., Ltd.
Wu, Yibing—CITIC Private Equity Funds Management Co., Ltd.
Wuisan, Dennis—Kendall Court Capital Partners, Ltd.
Wunderlich, Hans-Dieter—Wunderlich & Partner Wirtschaftsberatung fur den Mittelstand
Wuoristo, Jussi—Vitruvian Partners LLP
Wurzer, David—Connecticut Innovations, Inc.
Wyant, John—Blue Chip Venture Company
Wyant, Margaret H.—Isabella Capital LLC
Wyard, Brett—Carlyle Group, The
Wyatt, Gordon—Accuitive Medical Ventures
Wyles, David—GCP Capital Partners
Wyles, Toby—Vitruvian Partners LLP
Wylie, Alex—Thomas Weisel Partners Group, Inc.
Wylie, Cay—Ridgemont Equity Partners
Wylie, Rob—WHEB Ventures, Ltd.
Wyly, Evan—Maverick Capital Ltd.
Wymbs, Robert—Platinum Equity LLC
Wyncoll, Oliver—Langholm Capital LLP
Wynn, Peter—Amadeus Capital Partners, Ltd.
Wynperle, William—Shamrock Holdings, Inc.
Wyse, Roger—Burrill & Company
Wysocki, Marcin—Tar Heel
Wyss, Ralph—Gilde Buy Out Partners
Wyss, Ralph—Gilde Investment Management B.V.
Xavier, Asish—Johnson & Johnson Development Corporation
Xavier, Bernard—Formative Ventures
Xia, Charles—Ivy Capital
Xia, Dong—New Enterprise Associates, Inc.
Xiang, Liang—Guangdong Technology Venture Capital Group., Ltd
Xiangti, Zhao—Tripod Capital International, Ltd.
Xiangyu, Ouyang—Legend Capital
Xiao, Bing—Shenzhen Fortune Venture Capital Co., Ltd.
Xiao, Feng—Carlyle Group, The
Xiao, Margaret—Shenzhen Fortune Venture Capital Co., Ltd.
Xie, Zhigang—Huinong Capital
Ximing, Zhao—Wuhan Good Insight Venturing Investment Co., Ltd.
Xin, Eric—CITIC Capital Partners, Ltd.
Xitian, Wang—Jilin Huizheng Investment Co.
Xu, Alex—ChinaVest, Ltd.
Xu, David—Mingly Capital
Xu, Eric—SAIF Partners
Xu, Hang—SAIF Partners
Xu, Hanjie—Zhejiang Zheshang Venture Capital Management Co., Ltd.
Xu, James—Power Capital Co., Ltd.
Xu, Jayee—Vector Capital
Xu, Ken—Gobi Partners, Inc.
Xu, Michael—Prax Capital
Xu, Rebecca—Asia Alternatives Management LLC
Xu, Vincent—Vickers Venture Partners
Xu, Zheng—Sequoia Capital
Xue, Thomas—Spring Capital Asia, Ltd.
Yaakub, Encick Nor Idzam—Musharaka Venture Management Sdn Bhd
Yabe, Yoshikazu—MU Hands-on Capital Ltd. (FKA:Tsubasa Hands-On Capital, Ltd)
Yablunsky, Robert—SCP Private Equity Partners
Yachini, Ron—Genesis Partners
Yadav, Rahul—Citi Venture Capital International
Yadegardjam, Farsim—EVP Capital Management AG
Yager, Steven—Gores Group LLC, The
Yagi, Kaori—Polaris Principal Finance Co., Ltd.
Yagi, Seiichi—Mizuho Capital Company, Ltd.
Yagjian, Marc—Origin Partners
Yahav, Oren Monhite—Pacific Corporate Group
Yakobovich, Elisheva—Vertex Management Israel (AKA: Vertex Venture Capital)
Yakobovich, Elisheva—Vertex Venture Capital
Yakovlev, Gleb—Da Vinci Capital Management
Yam, Ben—SAIF Partners
Yama, Arthur—Aquitaine Investment Advisors, Ltd.
Yamada, Hiroshi—JAFCO Co., Ltd. (FKA: Japan Associated Finance Co. Ltd.)
Yamada, Kazuhiro—Carlyle Group, The
Yamada, Keith—CIVC Partners LP (FKA: Continental Illinois Venture Corp.)
Yamada, Masami—Biofrontier Partners, Inc.
Yamada, Shinjiro—Nippon Monozukuri Capital Co., Ltd.
Yamada, Yusuke—JAFCO Co., Ltd. (FKA: Japan Associated Finance Co. Ltd.)
Yamagami, Takaharu—CrossBridge Venture Partners
Yamaguchi, Mike—TEL Venture Capital, Inc.
Yamaguchi, Satoshi—Information Technology Farm Corporation (AKA: IT Farm)
Yamaguchi, Takashi—Daiwa Securities SMBC Principal Investments Co., Ltd.
Yamakawa, Taketo—Kohlberg, Kravis, Roberts & Company, L.P.
Yamamoto, Naoki—ITX International Holdings, Inc.
Yamamoto, Osamu—Unison Capital, Inc.
Yamamoto, Ted—University of Tokyo Edge Capital Co., Ltd., The (AKA: UTEC)
Yamane, Masaki—Daiwa Securities SMBC Principal Investments Co., Ltd.
Yamani, Hassan—Crescent Point Group
Yamashita, Jun—Daiwa Quantum Capital, Ltd.
Yamashita, Kevin—Bertram Capital
Yan, Andy—SAIF Partners
Yanagi, Tad—TA Associates, Inc.
Yanar, Marco—CAM Private Equity Consulting & Verwaltungs - GmbH
Yanar, Marco—Sal. Oppenheim Private Equity Partners
Yanatos, Evelyn—Investcorp Bank B.S.C.
Yanez, Maggie—Marquette Capital Partners
Yang Ho, Byeon—Vogo Investment
Yang, Ben—Pacific Venture Partners
Yang, Bing—Beijing Bingyuan Venture Capital Co., Ltd.
Yang, Chris—Grove Street Advisors LLC
Yang, Daniel—SAIF Partners
Yang, Edward—BPEP International
Yang, Eileen—Crimson Capital China
Yang, Fei—Guangdong Pacific Technology Venture Co., Ltd.
Yang, Fei—IDG Technology Venture Investment, Inc.
Yang, Geoffrey—Redpoint Ventures
Yang, George—iD Innovation, Inc.
Yang, Helen—American Capital, Ltd.
Yang, Hong-Ru—Gold Stone Investment, Ltd.
Yang, Hong-Ru—Tsing Capital
Yang, Jack—Highland Capital Management, L.P.
Yang, Jackie—TransLink Capital
Yang, Janet—Novak Biddle Venture Partners, L.P.
Yang, Jung-kyoo—Draper Fisher Jurvetson ePlanet Ventures, L.P.
Yang, Junyuan—Shenzhen Right-Sun Investment Company, Ltd.
Yang, Kemin—Power Capital Co., Ltd.
Yang, Kwang-sun—Aju IB Invesment Co., Ltd.
Yang, Lei—VantagePoint Venture Partners
Yang, Mei-Ni—Hamilton Lane Advisors, Inc.
Yang, Michael—Comcast Interactive Capital
Yang, Nam Sik—KB Investment Co., Ltd. (FKA: Kookmin Investment Company)
Yang, Nick—Draper Fisher Jurvetson ePlanet Ventures, L.P.
Yang, Raymond—Navi Capital
Yang, Richard—STIC Investments, Inc.
Yang, Robert—Blackstone Group, L.P.
Yang, Shengde—London Asia Capital Plc (FKA: netvest.com Plc)
Yang, Shih-Chien—GSIM Corporation (AKA: Global Strategic Investment Mgmt.)
Yang, Steven—Adveq Management AG
Yang, Sybil—Crystal Internet Venture Fund, L.P.
Yang, Wolfgang—VCChina, Ltd.
Yang, Xia—Legend Capital
Yang, Xiang-Dong—Carlyle Group, The
Yang, Xiaohua—Shanghai Dingjia Ventures Co., Ltd.
Yang, Yongku—KTIC Global Investment Advisory Co., Ltd.
Yang, Zhi—BioVeda Capital Private, Ltd.
Yano, Hiroaki—IGNITE Group, The (AKA: Ignite Associates, LLC)
Yanowitch, Richard—Emergence Capital Partners LLC
Yao Wei Min, Henry—SEAVI Advent Corporation, Ltd.
Yao, Elaine—Shattuck Hammond Partners
Yao, James—AsiaTech Internet Group (ATIG) (FKA: AsiaTech Ventures)
Yao, Jeff Jie-Ping—Prax Capital
Yao, Max—Ivy Capital
Yao, Mei—Sentient Group, The
Yap, Eddie—OSK Ventures International Bhd (AKA: OSK Ventures Equities)
Yap, Tony—Catalyst Investment Managers Pty, Ltd.
Yaphe, Scott—ABS Ventures
Yarbrough, Benjamin—Merit Capital Partners (FKA:William Blair Mezzanine)
Yarbrough, Stuart—CrossHill Financial Group, Inc

Yarel, Adi—Magma Venture Partners
Yariv, Amnon—Arcturus Capital
Yarnell, David—BEV Capital (FKA: Brand Equity Ventures)
Yashiro, Masamoto—Ripplewood Holdings LLC
Yassa, Samer—EFG-Hermes Private Equity
Yastine, Barbara—Credit Suisse Private Equity
Yasuda, Akihiko—Asia Alternatives Management LLC
Yasuda, Jeffrey—Redwood Venture Partners
Yasui, Shinji—Investor Growth Capital AB
Yasui, Shinji—Investor Growth Capital, Inc.
Yasunaga, Ken—Entrepia Ventures, Inc.
Yasuoka, Masayuki—Newbridge Capital, Ltd.
Yates, Byrren—GMG Capital Partners (FKA: GMS Capital Partners)
Yates, James—IK Investment Partners, Ltd.
Yates, Peter—Allco Equity Partners Management Pty Ltd.
Yates, Philip—Great Hill Equity Partners LLC
Yates, Roger—Henderson Equity Partners (AKA: Henderson Private Capital)
Yau, Paul—Compass Technology Partners
Yau, Shane—HSBC Pte Equity (Asia), Ltd. (FKA: HSBC Private Equity Mgt.)
Yawney, Paola—Tricor Pacific Capital, Inc.
Yaworsky, Darren—BMO Capital Corporation
Ye, Alice—Dragonvest Partners
Ye, Ming—Holding Venture Capital, Ltd.
Ye, Young—Jordan Company, The
Yearwood, Pat—Delta Capital Management LLC
Yee, Calvin—Pangaea Ventures
Yee, Clara—Keynote Ventures (FKA: Dali, Hook Partners)
Yee, Clara—Rembrandt Venture Partners
Yee, Doris—iGlobe Partners, Ltd.
Yee, Doris—iGlobe Treasury Management, Ltd.
Yee, Kenneth—Cappello Capital Corp.
Yeh, Don D.C.—AsiaVest Partners, TCW/YFY Ltd. (FKA: TCW/YFY Investment)
Yeh, Huoy-Ming—SmartForest Ventures
Yeh, Kuantai—Highland Capital Partners LLC
Yeh, Lung—Enspire Capital Pte Ltd.
Yek Meng, Wong—Tembusu Ventures Pte., Ltd.
Yellurkar, Devdutt—Charles River Ventures
Yen, Earl—CSV Capital Partners (FKA: China Seed Ventures)
Yen, Gan Chee—Temasek Holdings Pvt., Ltd.
Yen, Tuff—Seraph Group
Yeo, Marvin—Frontier Investment & Development Partners
Yeo, Yongdong—Darwin Venture Capital Co., Ltd.
Yeoham, Paul—Progress Equity Partners, Ltd.
Yeomans, Jan—3M Corporation
Yeon, Alex—Muhan Investment Co. (FKA: TeraSource Venture Capital Co.)
Yepez, J. Alberto—Trident Capital
Yeshaya, Avner Ben—Odin Investments
Yett, Paul—Hamilton Lane Advisors, Inc.
Yeung, Amy—Sprout Group
Yeung, David—AIG Investment Corporation, (Asia) Ltd.
Yeung, David—PineBridge Investments
Yeung, Stephen—Asia Mezzanine Capital Advisers, Ltd.
Yi, Hee-Jin—ValStone Partners LLC
Yi, Myung—American Capital, Ltd.
Yi, Wang—Ceyuan Ventures Management, LLC
Yi-Dar, Teo—SEAVI Advent Corporation, Ltd.
Yie, Charles—Ampersand Ventures
Yim, Simon—Longreach Group, Ltd., The
Yin, Kevin—GSR Ventures
Ying, Alan—Chrysalis Ventures
Ying, Alex—Carlyle Group, The
Ying, Wenlu—Jiangsu High-Tech Investment Group (AKA: Govtor Capital)
Yip, Eric—Asset Managers Holding Company, Ltd.
Yip, Tommy Y.—Emerald Hill Capital Partners, Ltd.
Yli-Tainio, Risto—Nexit Ventures Oy
Ylimartino, Arto—Head Industrial Partner Oy
Yoffe, Amir—CIC Partners, L.P. (FKA: Cardinal Investment Company, Inc.)
Yokell, Abe—Rockport Capital Partners
Yokota, Akira—Itochu Corporation
Yoldi, Jose Maria—SODENA - Sociedad de Desarrollo de Navarra
Yona, Hanan—Jerusalem Capital (AKA: JCP)
Yonce, Clifford—Siguler Guff & Company
Yoneyama, Tomoko—J-Seed Ventures, Inc.
Yong, Soo Ping—Walden International
Yong, Yaw-Nam—Qleap Accelerators, Ltd.
Yong, Yoon Jung—Korea Venture Investment Corporation
Yong, Zhang—Qiming Venture Partners
Yongkai, Zhou—NewMargin Ventures
Yongo, Eddie—GoEast Ventures, Ltd.
Yontef, Barry—Penfund Partners, Inc.
Yoo, Eugene—Globespan Capital Partners
Yook, Jay—OpenGate Capital
Yoon, Charles—Monitor Clipper Partners LLC
Yoon, David—FriedbergMilstein, LLC
Yoon, GunSoo—LB Investment, Inc.
Yoon, Hyo hwan—Korea Venture Investment Corporation
Yoon, KC—Avant Capital Group, Inc.
Yoon, Kwan—BlueRun Ventures
Yoon, Sung—KTB Ventures
Yoong, Sim—Kaizen Private Equity
York, David—Paul Capital Partners
York, Gwill—Lighthouse Capital Partners
York, Monty—GenNx360 Capital Partners
Yort, Monty—GenNx360 Capital Partners
Yort, W. Montague—SV Investment Partners (FKA: Schroder Ventures US)
Yosef-Or, Tomer—ABRY Partners LLC
Yoshida, Takashi—Fund Creation Co., Ltd.
Yoshidome, Shin—Daiwa Securities SMBC Principal Investments Co., Ltd.
Yoshimura, Kazumi—Mitsubishi International Corp.
Yoshinaga, Chika—Sofinnova Partners
Yoshinaga, Chika—Sofinnova Partners
Yoshioka, Shuji—Ant Capital Partners Co., Ltd.
Yoshizaki, Koichiro—MKS Partners, Ltd. (FKA: Schroder Ventures K.K.)
Yoshizawa, Masamichi—Longreach Group, Ltd., The
Young Syrrist, Anne—Convexa Capital AS
Young, Allison—American Capital, Ltd.
Young, Christopher—New England Partners
Young, David—Bregal Investments
Young, David—CCP Equity Partners
Young, Donald—Sciens Capital Partners (FKA: Zilkha Venture Partners)
Young, Donna—Tallwood Venture Capital
Young, Eric—Canaan Partners
Young, Eric—J.F. Lehman & Company
Young, Frank—Essex Woodlands Health Ventures
Young, Frank—Sverica International
Young, J. Steven—Huntsman Gay Global Capital LLC
Young, James—5AM Ventures
Young, Jason—Vanterra Capital, Ltd.
Young, Jeremy—Warburg Pincus LLC
Young, John—OMERS Private Equity
Young, Ken—CVC Capital Partners (Europe), Ltd.
Young, Matt—Mangrove Equity Partners LLC
Young, Matt—Platinum Equity LLC
Young, Phillip—U.S. Venture Partners
Young, Richard—Manchester Technology Fund Ltd, The
Young, Robert—Darwin Ventures LLC
Young, Robert—Mirador Capital
Young, Roderick—Three Arch Partners
Young, Steve—Sorenson Capital Partners
Young, T. Michael—CapStreet Group LLC, The (FKA: Summit Capital Group)
Young, Theodore—Irving Place Capital
Young, William—Clarus Ventures
Young, William—Monitor Clipper Partners LLC
Youngblood, Eric—ACP Capital, Ltd.
Younger, William—Sutter Hill Ventures
Youngkin, Glenn—Carlyle Group, The
Youngren, Bryce—Polaris Venture Partners
Yount, Donald—Mid-Atlantic Venture Funds (FKA: NEPA Management Corp.)
Youssef, Khaled—International Sicar
Youstra, Bill—Kohlberg Ventures LLC
Yu, Andy—Centenium-Pinetree China Private Equity
Yu, Ben—CITIC Capital Partners, Ltd.
Yu, Ben—Sierra Ventures
Yu, Bruce—GGV Capital
Yu, Chen—Vivo Ventures
Yu, Gideon—Khosla Ventures
Yu, Intack—Asia Culture Technology Investment Co., Ltd.
Yu, Jianming—New Horizon Capital
Yu, JooDong—SAIF Partners
Yu, Manfred—CAI Capital Management Company
Yu, Michael—iD Innovation, Inc.
Yu, Michelle—TCIB Investment Co., Ltd.
Yu, Peter—Cartesian Capital Group, LLC
Yu, Qian—Fidelity Growth Partners Asia
Yu, Sungwoon—SoftBank Ventures Korea, Inc.
Yu, TieCheng—Dojane Capital
Yu, Wang—Raystone Capital, Ltd.
Yu, Wiliam—Cansbridge Capital Corporation
Yu, Xiaoyang—China New Enterprise Investment (AKA: CNEI)
Yu, Zhihua—Hina Capital Partners
Yuan, Brian—Unisun (Beijing) Investment Co., Ltd.
Yuan, David—Redpoint Ventures
Yuan, David—Technology Crossover Ventures
Yuan, Fang—Matrix Partners
Yuan, Huaizhong—Blue Oak Venture Capital Co., Ltd.
Yuan, Jayson—Francisco Partners
Yuan, Shirley—SAIF Partners
Yudkoff, Royce—ABRY Partners LLC
Yue, Stan—Genesis Capital Consulting & Management, Ltd.

Zhou, Ning—Infotech Pacific Ventures L.P. (FKA: Infotech Ventures Co.)
Zhou, Quan—IDG Technology Venture Investment, Inc.
Zhou, Robert Shuhua—Northern Light Venture Capital
Zhou, Tony—Shanghai Amara Equity Investment Management Co., Ltd.
Zhou, Wei—Jade Alternative Investment Advisors
Zhou, Zheng—China Mining United Fund
Zhu, Allen—GSR Ventures
Zhu, Ching—Novitas Capital (FKA: PA Early Stage Partners)
Zhu, Daming—DT Capital Partners
Zhu, Dennis—Oaktree Capital Management LLC
Zhu, Guo Xian—Shenzhen ZhongAn Venture Capital Co., Ltd. (AKA: ZA Capital)
Zhu, Guo Ying—Zhejiang University Venture Capital Co., Ltd.
Zhu, Jian Huan—JAFCO Investment (Hong Kong), Ltd.
Zhu, Jian Huan—JAFCO Investment [FKA: Nomura/JAFCO Investment (Asia), Ltd.]
Zhu, Li-nan—Legend Capital
Zhu, Min—Cybernaut (China) Capital Management
Zhu, Pei Feng—Fair Value Investment (AKA: Shanghai Anyi Investment)
Zhu, Shuyun—Eos Asia Investments, Ltd. (FKA: JCAR Funds, Ltd.)
Zhu, Victor—Hina Capital Partners
Zhu, Wenbo—GSC Partners (FKA: Greenwich Street Capital Partners)
Zhu, Wendy—AlpInvest Partners N.V.
Zhu, Yunlai—China International Capital Corporation, Ltd.
Zhuang, David—Eos Asia Investments, Ltd. (FKA: JCAR Funds, Ltd.)
Zhuang, Steve—M-Venture Investment, Inc. (FKA: Shinyoung Venture Capital)
Zhung, Haitong—LB Investment, Inc.
Zhuo, Fu Min—Vertex Management Pte, Ltd. (AKA: Vertex Venture Holdings)
Zhuo, Fumin—GGV Capital
Zide, Stephen—Bain Capital
Zidlicky, Peter—Atlantic-Pacific Capital, Inc.
Ziebelman, Peter—Palo Alto Venture Partners
Ziebold, W. Townsend—Wasserstein Ventures (FKA: Wasserstein & Co.)
Ziegler, Ryan—Edison Venture Fund
Ziegler, Wolfgang—Findos Investor GmbH
Ziehm, Kirk—Seneca Partners, Inc.
Zielinski, Robert—Riordan, Lewis & Haden
Ziering, Mark—Genesis Partners
Zieserl, Robert—KB Partners LLC
Ziff, Stephen—Coller Capital
Zigrossi, Rosemary—Ontario Teachers' Pension Plan
Zihal, Michael—New York Business Development Corporation
Zikatanov, Nikola—NCH Capital, Inc.
Zilberman, David—Comcast Interactive Capital
Zilka, Yahal—Magma Venture Partners
Zillmer, Matthias—Baird Capital Partners Europe
Zilly, Pamela—Blackstone Group, L.P.
Zimbalist, Jonathan—Eureka Growth Capital
Zimits, Eric—Granite Ventures LLC
Zimmer, Mary—RBC Dain Rauscher
Zimmerer, Yimin—Walden International
Zimmerman, Brian—OpenView Venture Partners
Zimmerman, Harlan—Capital Z Investment Partners (FKA: Union Square Partners)
Zimmerman, Larry—Piper Jaffray Ventures
Zimmerman, Michael—Technology Venture Partners Pty Ltd.
Zimmerman, Rosanne—Warburg Pincus LLC
Zimmermann, Jens Yahya—New Silk Route Partners LLC
Zink, Jeppe—Amadeus Capital Partners, Ltd.
Zinterhofer, Eric—Searchlight Capital Partners LLC
Ziobro, Catherine—Carlyle Group, The
Ziolkowski, Andrew—IN Partners LLC (AKA: Midpoint)
Zipkin, Ilan—Prospect Venture Partners (FKA: Prospect Management LLC)
Zipp, Bob—Amicus Capital, LLC
Zissis, Peter—Birch Hill Equity Partners Management, Inc.
Zisson, Alex—Thomas, McNerney & Partners LLC
Ziv, Udi—Giza Venture Capital (FKA: Giza Investment Management)
Zmijeski, Casey—Fifth Street Capital LLC
Znaimer, Sam—Ventures West Management, Inc.
Zobel de Ayala, Jaime Augusto—Narra Venture Capital
Zocco, Giuseppe—Index Ventures
Zoellner, Scott—AEA Investors LP
Zoellner, Werner—Seed GmbH
Zohar, Daphne—PureTech Ventures
Zohar, Yishai—PureTech Ventures
Zoll, Joe—Liberty Capital Management Corporation
Zollo, Steve—Platinum Equity LLC
Zondi, Gcina—Imbewu Capital Partners
Zong, Peimin—Sinowisdom Investment Management Co., Ltd.
Zong, Sherry—Hina Capital Partners
Zoralioglu, Selahattin—Pamplona Capital Management LLP
Zorner, Paul—Finistere Ventures LLC
Zou, Terence—3V SourceOne Capital Pte, Ltd.
Zrebiec, J. L.—Clayton, Dubilier & Rice, Inc.
Zu bi, Fawaz—Accelerator Management Company B.S.C
Zuaiter, Abbas—Soros Strategic Partners
Zuberi, Bilal—General Catalyst Partners (FKA: General Catalyst Group LLC)
Zucchet, Steven—Borealis Infrastructure Management, Inc.
Zucchini, Juan Pablo—Advent International
Zucco, James—Blue Rock Capital
Zucco, James—Omni Capital Group LLC
Zuckerwise, Penny—Boldcap Ventures LLC
Zuehlsdorff, Peter—DIH Deutsche Industrie-Holding GmbH
Zug, D. Brooks—HarbourVest Partners LLC
Zug, David—HarbourVest Partners LLC
Zuga, Matt—Red Abbey Venture Partners, LLC
Zukin, James—Houlihan, Lokey, Howard & Zukin
Zulfiqar, Kamran—Investcorp Bank B.S.C.
Zulli, Joseph—Nautic Partners LLC
Zupan, Thomas—Riverlake Partners LLC
Zupon, Michael—Carlyle Group, The
Zur, Ari—Brockway Moran & Partners, Inc.
Zurita, Miguel—Mercapital Servicios Financieros
Zurlo, Paul—Bain Capital Ventures
Zvan, Barbara—Ontario Teachers' Pension Plan
Zwemstra, Charly—Main Corporate Finance
Zwemstra, Charly—NIBC Principal Investments (FKA: Parnib Holding NV)
Zweng, Paul—Palo Alto Investors
Zweyer, Heinz—L-EigenkapitalAgentur
Zych, Douglas—Jordan Company, The
Zylman, Adam—SCF Partners